Stanley Gibbons

SIMPLIFIED CATALOGUE

Stamps
of the
World

2003
Edition

An illustrated and priced four-volume guide to the postage stamps of the whole world, excluding changes of paper, perforation, shade and watermark

VOLUME 1

COUNTRIES A–D

STANLEY GIBBONS LTD
London and Ringwood

**By Appointment to
Her Majesty the Queen
Stanley Gibbons Limited
London
Philatelists**

68th Edition

**Published in Great Britain by
Stanley Gibbons Ltd**
Publications Editorial, Sal Offices and Distribution Centre
Parksi hurch Road,
R ire BH24 3SH
25 472363

9-536-0

ons Simplified Stamp
, renamed Stamps of the
in two (1982-88), three
volumes as Stanley Gibbons
tamps of the World.
November 2002

S.G. Item No. 2881 (03)

Printed in Great Britain by Bemrose Security Printing, London & Derby

Stanley Gibbons
SIMPLIFIED CATALOGUE
Stamps of the World

This popular catalogue is a straightforward listing of the stamps that have been issued everywhere in the world since the very first–Great Britain's famous Penny Black in 1840.

This edition, in which both the text and the illustrations have been captured electronically, is arranged completely alphabetically in a four-volume format. Volume 1 (Countries A–D), Volume 2 (Countries E–J), Volume 3 (Countries K–R) and Volume 4 (Countries S–Z).

Readers are reminded that the Catalogue Supplements, published in each issue of **Gibbons Stamp Monthly**, can be used to update the listings in **Stamps of the World** as well as our twenty-two part standard catalogue. To make the supplement even more useful the Type numbers given to the illustrations are the same in the Stamps of the World as in the standard catalogues. The first Catalogue Supplement to this Volume appeared in the September 2002 issue of **Gibbons Stamp Monthly**.

Gibbons Stamp Monthly can be obtained through newsagents or on postal subscription from Stanley Gibbons Publications, Parkside, Christchurch Road, Ringwood, Hants BH24 3SH.

The catalogue has many important features:

- As an indication of current values virtually every stamp is priced. Thousands of alterations have been made since the last edition.

- By being set out on a simplified basis that excludes changes of paper, perforation, shade, watermark, gum or printer's and date imprints it is particularly easy to use. (For its exact scope see "Information for users" pages following.)

- The thousands of illustrations and helpful descriptions of stamp designs make it of maximum appeal to collectors with thematic interests.

- Its catalogue numbers are the world-recognised Stanley Gibbons numbers throughout.

- Helpful introductory notes for the collector are included, backed by much historical, geographical and currency information.

- A very detailed index gives instant location of countries in this volume, and a crossreference to those included in the other volumes.

Over 1,609 stamps and 553 new illustrations have been added to the listings in this volume. This year's four-volume edition contained over 389,940 stamps and 94,640 illustrations.

The listings in this edition are based on the standard catalogues: Part 1, Commonwealth & British Empire Stamps 1840–1952 (formerly Part 1), Part 2 (Austria & Hungary) (6th edition), Part 3 (Balkans) (4th edition), Part 4 (Benelux) (4th edition), Part 5 (Czechoslovakia & Poland) (5th edition), Part 6 (France) (5th edition), Part 7 (Germany) (6th edition), Part 8 (Italy & Switzerland) (5th edition), Part 9 (Portugal & Spain) (4th edition), Part 10 (Russia) (5th edition), Part 11 (Scandinavia) (5th edition), Part 12 (Africa since Independence A-E) (2nd edition), Part 13 (Africa since Independence F-M) (1st edition), Part 14 (Africa since Independence N-Z) (1st edition), Part 15 (Central America) (2nd edition), Part 16 (Central Asia) (3rd edition), Part 17 (China) (6th edition), Part 18 (Japan & Korea) (4th edition), Part 19 (Middle East) (5th edition), Part 20 (South America) (3rd edition), Part 21 (South-East Asia) (3rd edition) and Part 22 (United States) (5th edition).

This edition includes major repricing for all Western Europe countries in addition to the changes for Germany Part 7 and Scandinavia Part 11. Prices for Azerbaijan; Bosnia and Herzegovina, Bohemia and Moravia, Congo Democratic Republic (from 1997) and thematic issues for Burundi, Congo (Kinshasa), Portugese Colonies, have also been revised for this volume.

Acknowledgements

A wide-ranging revision of prices for Western European countries has been undertaken for this edition with the intention that the catalogue should be more accurate to reflect the market for foreign issues.

Many dealers in both Great Britain and overseas have participated in this scheme by supplying copies of their retail price lists on which the research has been based.

We would like to acknowledge the assistance of the following for this edition:

ALMAZ CO
of Brooklyn, U.S.A.

AMATEUR COLLECTOR LTD, THE
of London, England

E. ANGELOPOULOS
of Thessaloniki, Greece

AVION THEMATICS
of Nottingham, England

J BAREFOOT LTD
of York, England

BELGIAN PHILATELIC SPECIALISTS INC
of Larchmont, U.S.A.

Sir CHARLES BLOMEFIELD
of Chipping Camden, England

T. BRAY
of Shipley, West Yorks, England

CENTRAL PHILATELIQUE
of Brussels, Belgium

JEAN-PIERRE DELMONTE
of Paris, France

EUROPEAN & FOREIGN STAMPS
of Pontypridd, Wales

FILATELIA LLACH SL
of Barcelona, Spain

FILATELIA RIVA RENO
of Bologna, Italy

FILATELIA TORI
of Barcelona, Spain

FORMOSA STAMP COMPANY, THE
of Koahsiung, Taiwan

FORSTAMPS
of Battle, England

ANTHONY GRAINGER
of Leeds, England

HOLMGREN STAMPS
of Bollnas, Sweden

INDIGO
of Orewa, New Zealand

ALEC JACQUES
of Selby, England

M. JANKOWSKI
of Warsaw, Poland

D.J.M. KERR
of Earlston, England

H. M. NIELSEN
of Vejle, Denmark

LEO BARESCH LTD
of Hassocks, England

LORIEN STAMPS
of Chesterfield, England

MANDARIN TRADING CO
of Alhambra, U.S.A.

MICHAEL ROGERS INC
of Winter Park, U.S.A.

PHILATELIC SUPPLIES
of Letchworth, England

PHIL-INDEX
of Eastbourne, England

PHILTRADE A/S
of Copenhagen, Denmark

PITTERI SA
of Chiasso, Switzerland

KEVIN RIGLER
of Shifnal, England

ROLF GUMMESSON AB
of Stockholm, Sweden

R. D. TOLSON
of Undercliffe, England

R. G. SHELLEY
of Hove, England

JAY SMITH
of Snow Camp, U.S.A.

R. SCHNEIDER
of Belleville, U.S.A.

ROBSTINE STAMPS
of Hampshire, England

SANGUINETTI S.A.S.
of Milan, Italy

SOUTHERN MAIL
of Eastbourne, England

STAMP CENTER
of Reykjavik, Iceland

SUMMIT STAMPS
of Storrington, England

REX WHITE
of Winchester, England

Western European countries will now be repriced each year in Stamps of the World and where there is no up-to-date specialised foreign volume in a country these will be the new Stanley Gibbons prices.

It is hoped that this improved pricing scheme will be extended to other foreign countries and thematic issues as information is consolidated.

Information for users

Aim

The aim of this catalogue is to provide a straightforward illustrated and priced guide to the postage stamps of the whole world to help you to enjoy the greatest hobby of the present day.

Arrangement

The catalogue lists countries in alphabetical order and there is a complete index at the end of each volume. For ease of reference country names are also printed at the head of each page.

Within each country, postage stamps are listed first. They are followed by separate sections for such other categories as postage due stamps, parcel post stamps, express stamps, official stamps, etc.

All catalogue lists are set out according to dates of issue of the stamps, starting from the earliest and working through to the most recent.

Scope of the Catalogue

The *Simplified Catalogue of Stamps of the World* contains listings of postage stamps only. Apart from the ordinary definitive, commemorative and air-mail stamps of each country – which appear first in each list – there are sections for the following where appropriate:

> postage due stamps
> parcel post stamps
> official stamps
> express and special delivery stamps
> charity and compulsory tax stamps
> newspaper and journal stamps
> printed matter stamps
> registration stamps
> acknowledgement of receipt stamps
> late fee and too late stamps
> military post stamps
> recorded message stamps
> personal delivery stamps

We receive numerous enquiries from collectors about other items which do not fall within the categories set out above and which consequently do not appear in the catalogue lists. It may be helpful, therefore, to summarise the other kinds of stamp that exist but which we deliberately exclude from this postage stamp catalogue.

We do *not* list the following:

Fiscal or revenue stamps: stamps used solely in collecting taxes or fees for non-postal purposes. Examples would be stamps which pay a tax on a receipt, represent the stamp duty on a contract or frank a customs document. Common inscriptions found include: Documentary, Proprietary, Inter. Revenue, Contract Note.

Local stamps: postage stamps whose validity and use are limited in area, say to a single town or city, though in some cases they provided, with official sanction, services in parts of countries not covered by the respective government.

Local carriage labels and Private local issues: many labels exist ostensibly to cover the cost of ferrying mail from one of Great Britain's offshore islands to the nearest mainland post office. They are not recognised as valid for national or international mail. Examples: Calf of Man, Davaar, Herm, Lundy, Pabay, Stroma. Items from some other places have only the status of tourist souvenir labels.

Telegraph stamps: stamps intended solely for the prepayment of telegraphic communication.

Bogus or "phantom" stamps: labels from mythical places or non-existent administrations. Examples in the classical period were Sedang, Counani, Clipperton Island and in modern times Thomond and Monte Bello Islands. Numerous labels have also appeared since the War from dissident groups as propaganda for their claims and without authority from the home governments. Common examples are labels for "Free Albania", "Free Rumania" and "Free Croatia" and numerous issues for Nagaland, Indonesia and the South Moluccas ("Republik Maluku Selatan").

Railway letter fee stamps: special stamps issued by railway companies for the conveyance of letters by rail. Example: Talyllyn Railway. Similar services are now offered by some bus companies and the labels they issue likewise do not qualify for inclusion in the catalogue.

Perfins ("perforated initials"): numerous postage stamps may be found with initial letters or designs punctured through them by tiny holes. These are applied by private and public concerns as a precaution against theft and do not qualify for separate mention.

Information for users

Labels: innumerable items exist resembling stamps but – as they do not prepay postage – they are classified as labels. The commonest categories are:

- propaganda and publicity labels: designed to further a cause or campaign;
- exhibition labels: particularly souvenirs from philatelic events;
- testing labels: stamp-size labels used in testing stamp-vending machines;
- Post Office training school stamps: British stamps overprinted with two thick vertical bars or SCHOOL SPECIMEN are produced by the Post Office for training purposes;
- seals and stickers: numerous charities produce stamp-like labels, particularly at Christmas and Easter, as a means of raising funds and these have no postal validity.

Cut-outs: items of postal stationary, such as envelopes, cards and wrappers, often have stamps impressed or imprinted on them. They may usually be cut out and affixed to envelopes, etc., for postal use if desired, but such items are not listed in this catalogue.

Collectors wanting further information about exact definitions are referred to *Philatelic Terms Illustrated*, published by Stanley Gibbons and containing many illustrations in colour (new edition in preparation).

There is also a priced listing of the postal fiscals of Great Britain in our *Commonwealth & British Empire Stamps 1840–1952 (formerly Part 1)* Catalogue and in Volume 1 of the *Great Britain Specialised* Catalogue (5th and later editions).

Catalogue Numbers

Stanley Gibbons catalogue numbers are recognised universally and any individual stamp can be identified by quoting the catalogue number (the one at the left of the column) prefixed by the name of the country and the letters "S.G.". Do not confuse the catalogue number with the type numbers which refer to illustrations.

Prices

Prices in the left-hand column are for unused stamps and those in the right-hand column for used. Prices are given in pence and pounds:
100 pence (p) 1 pound (£1).

Prices are shown as follows:
10 means 10p (10 pence);
1.75 means £1.75 (1 pound and 75 pence);
For £100 and above, prices are in whole pounds.

Our prices are for stamps in fine average condition, and in issues where condition varies we may ask more for the superb and less for the sub-standard.

The minimum catalogue price quoted is 10p. For individual stamps prices between 10p and 45p are provided as a guide for catalogue users. The lowest price charged for individual stamps purchased from Stanley Gibbons is 50p.

The prices quoted are generally for the cheapest variety of stamps but it is worth noting that differences of watermark, perforation, or other details, outside the scope of this catalogue, may often increase the value of the stamp.

Prices quoted for mint issues are for single examples. Those in se-tenant pairs, strips, blocks or sheets may be worth more.

Where prices are not given in either column it is either because the stamps are not known to exist in that particular condition, or, more usually, because there is no reliable information as to value.

All prices are subject to change without prior notice and we give no guarantee to supply all stamps priced. Prices quoted for albums, publications, etc. advertised in this catalogue are also subject to change without prior notice.

Due to different production methods it is sometimes possible for new editions of Parts 2 to 22 to appear showing revised prices which are not included in that year's *Stamps of the World*.

Unused Stamps

In the case of stamps from *Great Britain* and the *Commonwealth*, prices for unused stamps of Queen Victoria to King George V are for lightly hinged examples; unused prices of King Edward VIII to Queen Elizabeth II issues are for unmounted mint. The prices of unused Foreign stamps are for lightly hinged examples for those issued before 1946, thereafter for examples unmounted mint.

Used Stamps

Prices for used stamps generally refer to postally used examples, though for certain issues they are for cancelled-to-order.

Information for users

Guarantee

All stamps supplied by us are guaranteed originals in the following terms:

If not as described, and returned by the purchaser, we undertake to refund the price paid to us in the original transaction. If any stamp is certified as genuine by the Expert Committee of the Royal Philatelic Society, London, or by B.P.A. Expertising Ltd., the purchaser shall not be entitled to make any claim against us for any error, omission or mistake in such certificate.

Consumers' statutory rights are not affected by the above guarantee.

Currency

At the beginning of each country brief details give the currencies in which the values of the stamps are expressed. The dates, where given, are those of the earliest stamp issues in the particular currency. Where the currency is obvious, e.g. where the colony has the same currency as the mother country, no details are given.

Illustrations

Illustrations of any surcharges and overprints which are shown and not described are actual size; stamp illustrations are reduced to $\frac{3}{4}$ linear, *unless otherwise stated*.

"Key-Types"

A number of standard designs occur so frequently in the stamps of the French, German, Portuguese and Spanish colonies that it would be a waste of space to repeat them. Instead these are all illustrated on page xiv together with the descriptive names and letters by which they are referred to in the lists.

Type Numbers

These are the bold figures found below each illustration. References to "Type 6", for example, in the lists of a country should therefore be understood to refer to the illustration below which the number **"6"** appears. These type numbers are also given in the second column of figures alongside each list of stamps, thus indicating clearly the design of each stamp. In the case of Key-Types – see above – letters take the place of the type numbers.

Where an issue comprises stamps of similar design, represented in this catalogue by one illustration, the corresponding type numbers should be taken as indicating this general design.

Where there are blanks in the type number column it means that the type of the corresponding stamps is that shown by the last number above in the type column of the same issue.

A dash (–) in the type column means that no illustration of the stamp is shown.

Where type numbers refer to stamps of another country, e.g. where stamps of one country are overprinted for use in another, this is always made clear in the text.

Stamp Designs

Brief descriptions of the subjects of the stamp designs are given either below or beside the illustrations, at the foot of the list of the issue concerned, or in the actual lists. Where a particular subject, e.g. the portrait of a well-known monarch, recurs frequently the description is not repeated, nor are obvious designs described.

Generally, the unillustrated designs are in the same shape and size as the one illustrated, except where otherwise indicated.

Surcharges and Overprints

Surcharges and overprints are usually described in the headings to the issues concerned. Where the actual wording of a surcharge or overprint is given it is shown in bold type.

Some stamps are described as being "Surcharged in words", e.g. **TWO CENTS**, and others "Surcharged in figures and words", e.g. **20 CENTS**, although of course many surcharges are in foreign languages and combinations of words and figures are numerous. There are often bars, etc., obliterating old values or inscriptions but in general these are only mentioned where it is necessary to avoid confusion.

No attention is paid in this catalogue to colours of overprints and surcharges so that stamps with the same overprints in different colours are not listed separately.

Numbers in brackets after the descriptions of overprinted or surcharged stamps are the catalogue numbers of the unoverprinted stamps.

Note – the words "inscribed" or "inscription" always refer to wording incorporated in the design of a stamp and not surcharges or overprints.

Coloured Papers

Where stamps are printed on coloured paper the description is given as e.g. "4 c. black on blue" – a stamp printed in black on blue paper. No attention is paid in this catalogue to difference in the texture of paper, e.g. laid, wove.

Information for users

Watermarks

Stamps having different watermarks, but otherwise the same, are not listed separately. No reference is therefore made to watermarks in this volume.

Stamp Colours

Colour names are only required for the identification of stamps, therefore they have been made as simple as possible. Thus "scarlet", "vermilion", "carmine" are all usually called red. Qualifying colour names have been introduced only where necessary for the sake of clearness.

Where stamps are printed in two or more colours the central portion of the design is in the first colour given, unless otherwise stated.

Perforations

All stamps are perforated unless otherwise stated. No distinction is made between the various gauges of perforation but early stamp issues which exist both imperforate and perforated are usually listed separately.

Where a heading states "Imperf. or perf". or "Perf. or rouletted" this does not necessarily mean that all values of the issue are found in both conditions.

Dates of Issue

The date given at the head of each issue is that of the appearance of the earliest stamp in the series. As stamps of the same design or issue are usually grouped together a list of King George VI stamps, for example, headed "1938" may include stamps issued from 1938 to the end of the reign.

Se-tenant Pairs

Many modern issues are printed in sheets containing different designs or face values. Such pairs, blocks, strips or sheets are described as being "se-tenant" and they are outside the scope of this catalogue, although reference to them may occur in instances where they form a composite design.

Miniature Sheets

These are outside the scope of this catalogue but are listed in all other Stanley Gibbons catalogues.

"Appendix" Countries

We regret that, since 1968, it has been necessary to establish an Appendix (at the end of each country as appropriate) to which numerous stamps have had to be consigned. Several countries imagine that by issuing huge quantities of unnecessary stamps they will have a ready source of income from stamp collectors – and particularly from the less-experienced ones. Stanley Gibbons refuse to encourage this exploitation of the hobby and we do not stock the stamps concerned.

Two kinds of stamp are therefore given the briefest of mentions in the Appendix, purely for the sake of record. Administrations issuing stamps greatly in excess of true postal needs have the offending issues placed there. Likewise it contains stamps which have not fulfilled all the normal conditions for full catalogue listing.

These conditions are that the stamps must be issued by a legitimate postal authority, recognised by the government concerned, and are adhesives, valid for proper postal use in the class of service for which they are inscribed. Stamps, with the exception of such categories as postage dues and officials, must be available to the general public at face value with no artificial restrictions being imposed on their distribution.

The publishers of this catalogue have observed, with concern, the proliferation of 'artificial' stamp-issuing territories. On several occasions this has resulted in separately inscribed issues for various component parts of otherwise united states or territories.

Stanley Gibbons Publications have decided that where such circumstances occur, they will not, in the future, list these items in the SG catalogue without first satisfying themselves that the stamps represent a genuine political, historical or postal division within the country concerned. Any such issues which do not fulfil this stipulation will be recorded in the Catalogue Appendix only.

Stamps in the Appendix are kept under review in the light of any newly acquired information about them. If we are satisfied that a stamp qualifies for proper listing in the body of the catalogue it is moved there.

"Undesirable Issues"

The rules governing many competitive exhibitions – including the Melville Competition – are set by the Federation Internationale de Philatelie and stipulate a downgrading of marks for stamps classed as "undesirable issues".

This catalogue can be taken as a guide to status. All stamps in the main listings and Addenda are acceptable. Stamps in the Appendix should not be entered for competition as these are the "undesirable issues".

Information for users

Particular care is advised with Aden Protectorate States, Ajman, Bhutan, Chad, Fujeira, Khor Fakkan, Manama, Ras al Khaima, Sharjah, Umm al Qiwain and Yemen. Totally bogus stamps exist (as explained in Appendix notes) and these are to be avoided also for competition. As distinct from "undesirable stamps" certain categories are not covered in this catalogue purely by reason of its scope (see page viii). Consult the particular competition rules to see if such are admissable even though not listed by us.

Where to Look for More Detailed Listings

The present work deliberately omits details of paper, perforation, shade and watermark. But as you become more absorbed in stamp collecting and wish to get greater enjoyment from the hobby you may well want to study these matters.

All the information you require about any particular postage stamp will be found in the main Stanley Gibbons Catalogues.

Commonwealth countries before 1952 are covered by the Commonwealth & British Empire Stamps 1840–1952 (formerly Part 1) published annually.

For foreign countries you can easily find which catalogue to consult by looking at the country headings in the present book.

To the right of each country name are code letters specifying which volume of our main catalogues contains that country's listing.

The code letters are as follows:

Pt. 2   Part 2
Pt. 3   Part 3 etc.

(See page xiii for complete list of Parts.)

So, for example, if you want to know more about Chinese stamps than is contained in the Simplified Catalogue of Stamps of the World the reference to

CHINA   Pt. 17

guides you to the Gibbons Part 17 (China) Catalogue listing for the details you require.

New editions of Parts 2 to 22 appear at irregular intervals.

Correspondence

Whilst we welcome information and suggestions we must ask correspondents to include the cost of postage for the return of any stamps submitted plus registration where appropriate. Letters should be addressed to The Catalogue Editor at Ringwood.

Where information is solicited purely for the benefit of the enquirer we regret we cannot undertake to reply unless stamps or reply coupons are sent to cover the postage.

Identification of Stamps

We regret we do not give opinions as to the genuineness of stamps, nor do we identify stamps or number them by our Catalogue.

Users of this catalogue are referred to our companion booklet entitled Stamp Collecting – How to Identify Stamps. It explains how to look up stamps in this catalogue, contains a full checklist of stamp inscriptions and gives help in dealing with unfamiliar scripts.

Stanley Gibbons would like to complement your collection

At Stanley Gibbons we offer a range of services which are designed to complement your collection.

Our modern stamp shop, the largest in Europe, together with our rare stamp department has one of the most comprehensive stocks of Great Britain in the world, so whether you are a beginner or an experienced philatelist you are certain to find something to suit your special requirements.

Alternatively through our Mail Order services you can control the growth of your collection from the comfort of your own home. Our Postal Sales Department regularly sends out mailings of Special Offers. We can also help with your wants list—so why not ask us for those elusive items?

Why not take advantage of the many services we have to offer? Visit our premises in the Strand or, for more information, write to the appropriate address on page x.

The Stanley Gibbons Group Addresses

Stanley Gibbons Limited, Stanley Gibbons Auctions

339 Strand, London WC2R 0LX
Telephone 020 7836 8444, Fax 020 7836 7342,
E-mail: enquires@stanleygibbons.co.uk
Internet: www.stanleygibbons.com for all departments.

Auction Room and Specialist Stamp Departments.

Open Monday–Friday 9.30 a.m. to 5 p.m.
Shop. Open Monday–Friday 9 a.m. to 5.30 p.m. and Saturday 9.30 a.m. to 5.30 p.m.

Fraser's

(a division of Stanley Gibbons Ltd)

399 Strand, London WC2R 0LX
Autographs, photographs, letters and documents

Telephone 020 7836 8444, Fax 020 7836 7342,
E-mail: info@frasersautographs.co.uk
Internet: www.frasersautographs.com

Monday–Friday 9 a.m. to 5.30 p.m. and Saturday 10 a.m. to 4 p.m.

Stanley Gibbons Publications

Parkside, Christchurch Road, Ringwood, Hants BH24 3SH.
Telephone 01425 472363 (24 hour answer phone service), Fax 01425 470247,
E-mail: info@stanley gibbons.co.uk

Publications Mail Order. FREEPHONE 0800 611622
Monday–Friday 8.30 a.m. to 5 p.m.

Stanley Gibbons Publications Overseas Representation

Stanley Gibbons Publications are represented overseas by the following sole distributors (*), distributors (**) or licensees (***).

Australia
Lighthouse Philatelic (Aust.) Pty. Ltd.*
Locked Bag 5900 Botany DC, New South Wales, 2019 Australia.

Stanley Gibbons (Australia) Pty. Ltd.***
Level 6, 36 Clarence Street, Sydney, New South Wales 2000, Australia.

Belgium and Luxembourg**
Davo c/o Philac, Rue du Midi 48, Bruxelles, 1000 Belgium.

Canada*
Lighthouse Publications (Canada) Ltd., 255 Duke Street, Montreal Quebec, Canada H3C 2M2.

Denmark**
Samlerforum/Davo,
Ostergade 3,
DK 7470 Karup, Denmark.

Finland**
Davo c/o Kapylan Merkkiky Pohjolankatu 1 00610 Helsinki, Finland.

France*
Davo France (Casteilla), 10, Rue Leon Foucault, 78184 St. Quentin Yvelines Cesex, France.

Hong Kong**
Po-on Stamp Service, GPO Box 2498, Hong Kong.

Israel**
Capital Stamps, P.O. Box 3769, Jerusalem 91036, Israel.

Italy*
Ernesto Marini Srl,
Via Struppa 300, I-16165,
Genova GE, Italy.

Japan**
Japan Philatelic Co. Ltd.,
P.O. Box 2, Suginami-Minami, Tokyo, Japan.

Netherlands*
Davo Publications, P.O. Box 411, 7400 AK Deventer, Netherlands.

New Zealand***
Mowbray Collectables.
P.O. Box 80, Wellington, New Zealand.

Norway**
Davo Norge A/S, P.O. Box 738 Sentrum, N-0105, Oslo, Norway.

Singapore**
Stamp Inc Collectibles Pte Ltd.,
10 Ubi Cresent, #01-43 Ubi Tech Park, Singapore 408564.

Sweden*
Chr Winther Soerensen AB, Box 43, S-310 Knaered, Sweden.

Switzerland**
Phila Service, Burgstrasse 160, CH 4125, Riehen, Switzerland.

Abbreviations

Anniv.	denotes	Anniversary
Assn.	,,	Association
Bis.	,,	Bistre
Bl.	,,	Blue
Bldg.	,,	Building
Blk.	,,	Black
Br.	,,	British or Bridge
Brn.	,,	Brown
B.W.I.	,,	British West Indies
C.A.R.I.F.T.A.	,,	Caribbean Free Trade Area
Cent.	,,	Centenary
Chest.	,,	Chestnut
Choc.	,,	Chocolate
Clar.	,,	Claret
Coll.	,,	College
Commem.	,,	Commemoration
Conf.	,,	Conference
Diag.	,,	Diagonally
E.C.A.F.E.	,,	Economic Commission for Asia and Far East
Emer.	,,	Emerald
E.P.T. Conference	,,	European Postal and Telecommunications Conference
Exn.		Exhibition
F.A.O.	,,	Food and Agriculture Organization
Fig.	,,	Figure
G.A.T.T.	,,	General Agreement on Tariffs and Trade
G.B.	,,	Great Britain
Gen.	,,	General
Govt.	,,	Government
Grn.	,,	Green
Horiz.	,,	Horizontal
H.Q.	,,	Headquarters
Imperf.	,,	Imperforate
Inaug.	,,	Inauguration
Ind.	,,	Indigo
Inscr.	,,	Inscribed or inscription
Int.	,,	International
I.A.T.A.	,,	International Air Transport Association
I.C.A.O.	,,	International Civil Aviation Organization
I.C.Y.	,,	International Co-operation Year
I.G.Y.	,,	International Geophysical Year
I.L.O.	,,	International Labour Office (or later, Organization)
I.M.C.O.	,,	Inter-Governmental Maritime Consultative Organization
I.T.U.	,,	International Telecommunication Union
Is.	,,	Islands
Lav.	,,	Lavender
Mar.	,,	Maroon
mm.	,,	Millimetres
Mult.	,,	Multicoloured

Mve.	denotes	Mauve
Nat.	,,	National
N.A.T.O.	,,	North Atlantic Treaty Organization
O.D.E.C.A.	,,	Organization of Central American States
Ol.	,,	Olive
Optd.	,,	Overprinted
Orge. or oran.	,,	Orange
P.A.T.A.	,,	Pacific Area Travel Association
Perf.	,,	Perforated
Post.	,,	Postage
Pres.	,,	President
P.U.	,,	Postal Union
Pur.	,,	Purple
R.	,,	River
R.S.A.	,,	Republic of South Africa
Roul.	,,	Rouletted
Sep.	,,	Sepia
S.E.A.T.O.	,,	South East Asia Treaty Organization
Surch.	,,	Surcharged
T.	,,	Type
T.U.C.	,,	Trades Union Congress
Turq.	,,	Turquoise
Ultram.	,,	Ultramarine
U.N.E.S.C.O.	,,	United Nations Educational, Scientific Cultural Organization
U.N.I.C.E.F.	,,	United Nations Children's Fund
U.N.O.	,,	United Nations Organization
U.N.R.W.A.	,,	United Nations Relief and Works Agency for Palestine Refugees in the Near East
U.N.T.E.A.	,,	United Nations Temporary Executive Authority
U.N.R.R.A.	,,	United Nations Relief and Rehabilitation Administration
U.P.U.	,,	Universal Postal Union
Verm.	,,	Vermilion
Vert.	,,	Vertical
Vio.	,,	Violet
W.F.T.U.	,,	World Federation of Trade Unions
W.H.O.	,,	World Health Organization
Yell.	,,	Yellow

Arabic Numerals

As in the case of European figures, the details of the Arabic numerals vary in different stamp designs, but they should be readily recognised with the aid of this illustration:

٠	١	٢	٣	٤
0	1	2	3	4

٥	٦	٧	٨	٩
5	6	7	8	9

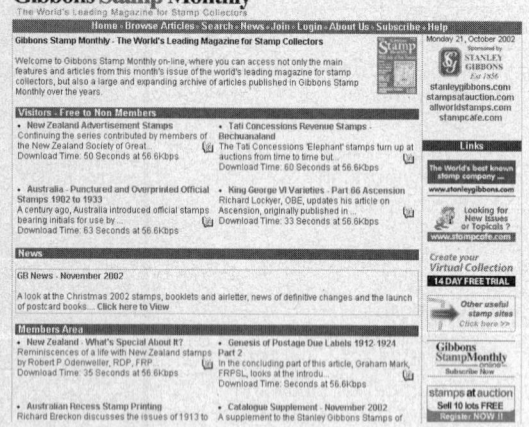
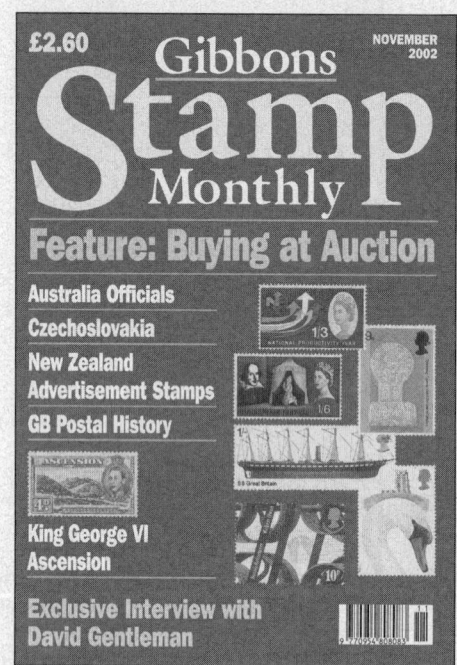

Stanley Gibbons Stamp Catalogue
Complete List of Parts

1   Commonwealth & British Empire Stamps 1840–1952 (formerly Part 1) (Annual)

Foreign Countries

2   Austria & Hungary (6th edition, 2002)
Austria · U.N. (Vienna) · Hungary

3   Balkans (4th edition, 1998)
Albania · Bosnia & Herzegovina · Bulgaria · Croatia · Greece & Islands · Macedonia · Rumania · Slovenia · Yugoslavia

4   Benelux (4th edition, 1993)
Belgium & Colonies · Luxembourg · Netherlands & Colonies

5   Czechoslovakia & Poland (5th edition, 1994)
Czechoslovakia · Czech Republic · Slovakia · Poland

6   France (5th edition, 2001)
France · Colonies · Post Offices · Andorra · Monaco

7   Germany (6th edition, 2002)
Germany · States · Colonies · Post Offices

8   Italy & Switzerland (5th edition, 1997)
Italy & Colonies · Liechtenstein · San Marino · Switzerland · U.N. (Geneva) · Vatican City

9   Portugal & Spain (4th edition, 1996)
Andorra · Portugal & Colonies · Spain & Colonies

10   Russia (5th edition, 1999)
Russia · Armenia · Azerbaijan · Belarus · Estonia · Georgia · Kazakhstan · Kyrgyzstan · Latvia · Lithuania · Moldova · Tajikistan · Turkmenistan · Ukraine · Uzbekistan · Mongolia

11   Scandinavia (5th edition, 2001)
Aland Islands · Denmark · Faroe Islands · Finland · Greenland · Iceland · Norway · Sweden

12   Africa since Independence A-E (2nd edition, 1983)
Algeria · Angola · Benin · Burundi · Cameroun · Cape Verdi · Central African Republic · Chad · Comoro Islands · Congo · Djibouti · Equatorial Guinea · Ethiopia

13   Africa since Independence F-M (1st edition, 1981)
Gabon · Guinea · Guinea-Bissau · Ivory Coast · Liberia · Libya · Malagasy Republic · Mali · Mauritania · Morocco · Mozambique

14   Africa since Independence N-Z (1st edition, 1981)
Niger Republic · Rwanda · St. Thomas & Prince · Senegal · Somalia · Sudan · Togo · Tunisia · Upper Volta · Zaire

15   Central America (2nd edition, 1984)
Costa Rica · Cuba · Dominican Republic · El Salvador · Guatemala · Haiti · Honduras · Mexico · Nicaragua · Panama

16   Central Asia (3rd edition, 1992)
Afghanistan · Iran · Turkey

17   China (6th edition, 1998)
China · Taiwan · Tibet · Foreign P.O.s · Hong Kong · Macao

18   Japan & Korea (4th edition, 1997)
Japan · Korean Empire · South Korea · North Korea

19   Middle East (5th edition, 1996)
Bahrain · Egypt · Iraq · Israel · Jordan · Kuwait · Lebanon · Oman · Qatar · Saudi Arabia · Syria · U.A.E. · Yemen

20   South America (3rd edition, 1989)
Argentina · Bolivia · Brazil · Chile · Colombia · Ecuador · Paraguay · Peru · Surinam · Uruguay · Venezuela

21   South-East Asia (3rd edition, 1995)
Bhutan · Burma · Indonesia · Kampuchea · Laos · Nepal · Philippines · Thailand · Vietnam

22   United States (5th edition, 2000)
U.S. & Possessions · Marshall Islands · Micronesia · Palau · U.N. (New York, Geneva, Vienna)

Thematic Catalogues

Stanley Gibbons Catalogues for use with **Stamps of the World.**
Collect Aircraft on Stamps (out of print)
Collect Birds on Stamps (new edition in preparation)
Collect Chess on Stamps (2nd edition, 1999)
Collect Fish on Stamps (1st edition, 1999)
Collect Fungi on Stamps (2nd edition, 1997)
Collect Motor Vehicles on Stamps (in preparation)
Collect Railways on Stamps (3rd edition, 1999)
Collect Shells on Stamps (1st edition, 1995)
Collect Ships on Stamps (3rd edition, 2001)

Key-Types

(see note on page vii)

French Group

A. "Blanc."

B. "Mouchon."

C "Merson."

D. "Tablet."

E.

F.

G.

H.

"International Colonial Exhibition."

I. "Faidherbe."

J. "Palms."

K. "Balay."

L. "Natives."

M. "Figure."

German Group

N. "Yacht."

O. "Yacht."

Spanish Group

X. "Alfonso XII."

Y. "Baby."

Z. "Curly Head"

Portuguese Group

P. "Crown."

Q. "Embossed."

R. "Figures."

S. "Carlos."

T. "Manoel."

U. "Ceres."

V. "Newspaper."

W. "Due."

STANLEY GIBBONS SIMPLIFIED CATALOGUE OF STAMPS OF THE WORLD—VOLUME 1 COUNTRIES A–D

ABU DHABI — Pt. 19

The largest of the Trucial States in the Persian Gulf. Treaty relations with Great Britain expired on 31 December 1966, when Abu Dhabi took over the postal services. On 18 July 1971, seven of the Gulf sheikhdoms, including Abu Dhabi, agreed to form the State of the United Arab Emirates. The federation came into being on 1 August 1972.

1964. 100 naye paise = 1 rupee.
1966. 1,000 fils = 1 dinar.

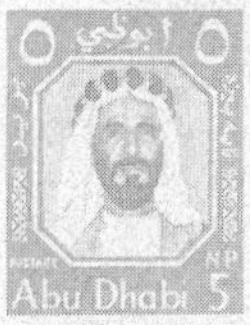

1 Shaikh Shakhbut bin Sultan

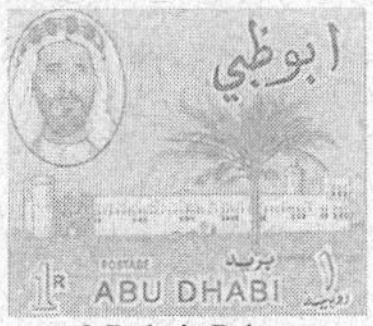

3 Ruler's Palace

1964.

1	1	5n.p. green	1·50	2·25
2		15n.p. brown	2·00	1·50
3		20n.p. blue	2·25	1·50
4		30n.p. orange	3·25	1·50
5	–	40n.p. violet	3·25	70
6	–	50n.p. bistre	4·00	2·50
7	–	75n.p. black	4·00	3·75
8	3	1r. green	4·00	1·25
9		2r. black	7·50	3·25
10	–	5r. red	17·00	10·00
11	–	10r. blue	23·00	14·00

DESIGNS: As Type **1**: 40 to 75n.p. Mountain gazelle; As Type **3**: 5, 10r. Oil rig and camels.

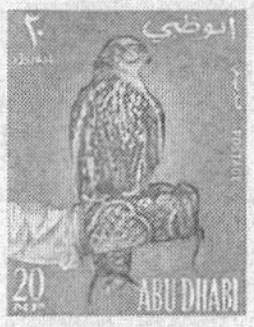

5 Saker Falcon

1965. Falconry.

12	5	20n.p. brown and blue	10·00	1·75
13	–	40n.p. brown and blue	13·00	2·75
14	–	2r. sepia and turquoise	22·00	13·00

DESIGNS: 40n.p., 2r. Other types of Saker falcon on gloved hand.

1966. Nos. 1/11 surch in new currency ("Fils" only on Nos. 5/7) and ruler's portrait obliterated with bars.

15	1	5f. on 5n.p. green	8·00	5·50
16		15f. on 15n.p. brown	8·00	6·00
17		20f. on 20n.p. blue	10·00	8·00
18		30f. on 30n.p. orange	9·00	14·00
19	–	40f. on 40n.p. violet	13·00	1·00
20	–	50f. on 50n.p. bistre	22·00	23·00
21	–	75f. on 75n.p. black	22·00	23·00
22	3	100f. on 1r. green	16·00	3·50
23		200f. on 2r. black	18·00	13·00
24	–	500f. on 5r. red	30·00	38·00
25	–	1d. on 10r. blue	40·00	65·00

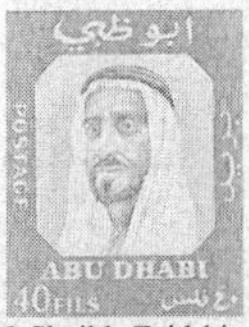

9 Shaikh Zaid bin Sultan al Nahayyan

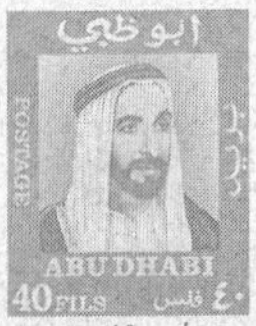

10

1967.

26	–	5f. red and green	20	15
27	–	15f. red and brown	30	10
28	–	20f. red and blue	50	15
29	–	35f. red and violet	60	20
30	9	40f. green	80	20
38	10	40f. green	1·10	85
31	9	50f. brown	1·00	25
39	10	50f. brown	1·40	60
32	9	60f. blue	1·10	30
40	10	60f. blue	2·40	85
33	9	100f. red	1·75	40
41	10	100f. red	6·50	1·60
34	–	125f. brown and green	3·50	1·40
35	–	200f. brown and blue	15·00	3·00
36	–	500f. violet and orange	11·00	5·50
37	–	1d. blue and green	20·00	10·00

DESIGNS—As Types **9/10**—VERT: 5f. to 35f. National flag. HORIZ: (47 × 27 mm); 125f. Mountain gazelle; 200f. Lanner falcon; 500f., 1d. Palace. Each with portrait of Ruler.

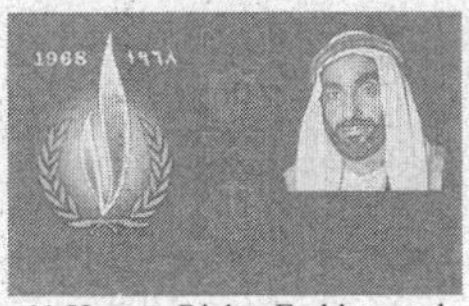

11 Human Rights Emblem and Shaikh Zaid

1968. Human Rights Year.

42	11	35f. multicoloured	1·25	50
43		60f. multicoloured	2·00	60
44		150f. multicoloured	3·75	1·40

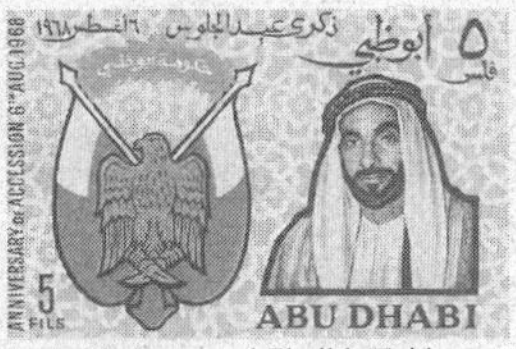

12 Arms and Shaikh Zaid

1968. Anniv of Shaikh Zaid's Accession.

45	12	5f. multicoloured	1·25	20
46		10f. multicoloured	1·25	20
47		100f. multicoloured	3·50	1·25
48		125f. multicoloured	5·00	1·90

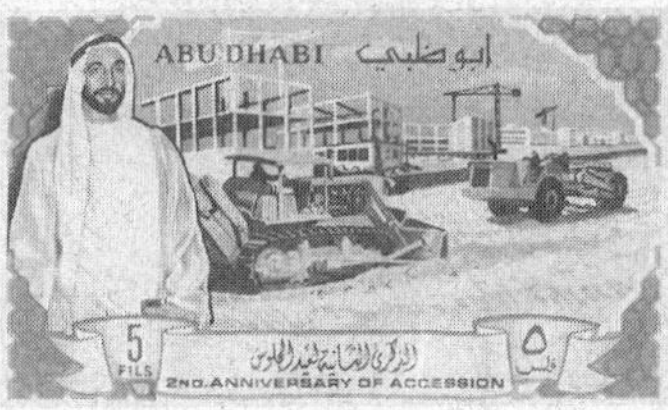

13 New Construction

1968. 2nd Anniv of Shaikh's Accession. "Progress in Abu Dhabi". Multicoloured.

49		5f. Type **13**	55	20
50		10f. Airport buildings (46½ × 34 mm)	1·25	50
51		35f. Shaikh Zaid, bridge and Northern goshawk (59 × 34 mm)	9·50	2·75

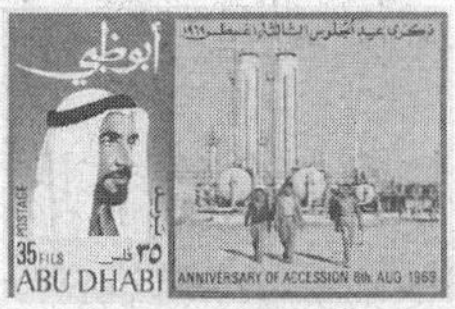

14 Petroleum Installations

1969. 3rd Anniv of Shaikh's Accession. Petroleum Industry. Multicoloured.

52		35f. Type **14**	75	30
53		60f. Marine drilling platform	3·25	95
54		125f. Separator platform, Zakum field	4·50	1·50
55		200f. Tank farm	5·00	2·25

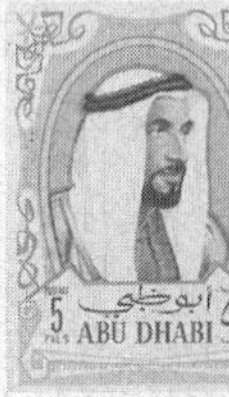

15 Shaikh Zaid

1970.

56	–	5f. multicoloured	30	15
57	15	10f. multicoloured	40	15
58	–	25f. multicoloured	75	15
59	15	35f. multicoloured	1·00	15
60		50f. multicoloured	1·50	25
61	–	60f. multicoloured	1·60	30
62	15	70f. multicoloured	2·50	45
63	–	90f. multicoloured	3·25	75
64	–	125f. multicoloured	4·50	1·25
65	–	150f. multicoloured	5·50	1·50
66	–	500f. multicoloured	20·00	8·00
67	–	1d. multicoloured	35·00	13·00

DESIGNS: Nos. 56, 58, 61 and 63 as Type **15**, but frames changed, and smaller country name; 125f. Arab stallion; 150f. Mountain gazelle; 500f. Fort Jahili; 1d. Great Mosque.

No. 67 has face value in Arabic only.

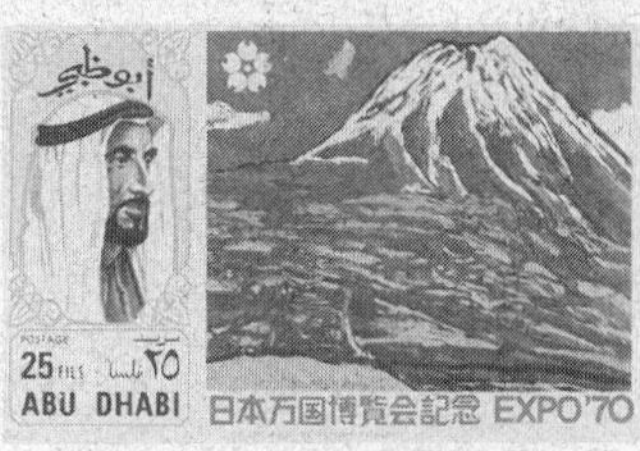

17 Shaikh Zaid and "Mt. Fuji" (T. Hayashi)

1970. "Expo 70" World Fair, Osaka, Japan.

68	17	25f. multicoloured	1·00	30
69		35f. multicoloured	1·25	30
70		60f. multicoloured	2·00	1·25

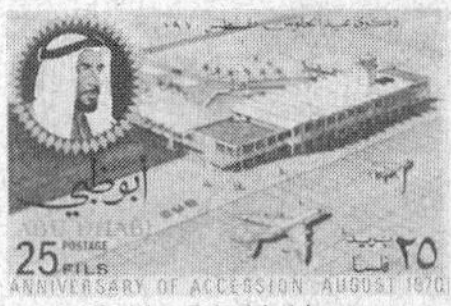

18 Abu Dhabi Airport

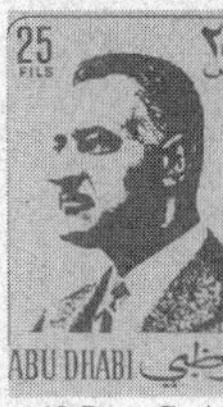

19 Pres. G. A. Nasser

1970. 40th Anniv of Shaikh's Accession. Completion of Abu Dhabi Airport. Mult.

71		25f. Type **18**	1·75	40
72		60f. Airport entrance	3·00	95
73		150f. Aerial view of Abu Dhabi (vert)	7·00	3·25

1971. Gamal Nasser (President of Egypt) Commemoration.

74	19	25f. black on pink	1·60	60
75		35f. black on lilac	2·25	80

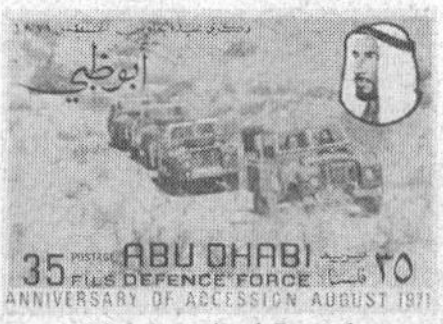

20 Motorized Patrol

1971. 5th Anniv of Shaikh's Accession. Defence Force. Multicoloured.

76		35f. Type **20**	2·50	80
77		60f. Patrol-boat "Baniyas"	3·75	1·25
78		125f. Armoured car	7·00	1·75
79		150f. Hawker Hunter FGA.76 jet fighters	9·00	2·75

1971. No. 60 surch.

80	15	5f. on 50f. multicoloured	48·00	40·00

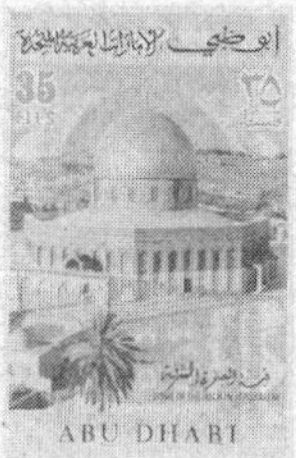

22 Dome of the Rock

1972. Dome of the Rock, Jerusalem. Multicoloured.

81		35f. Type **22**	6·25	2·25
82		60f. Mosque entrance	9·50	3·00
83		125f. Mosque dome	17·00	6·75

1972. Provisional Issue. Nos. 56/67 optd **UAE** and arabic inscr.

84	–	5f. multicoloured	1·00	1·00
85	15	10f. multicoloured	1·00	60
86	–	25f. multicoloured	1·50	1·50
87	15	35f. multicoloured	2·25	1·75
88		50f. multicoloured	3·50	3·50
89	–	60f. multicoloured	4·00	4·00
90	15	70f. multicoloured	5·00	5·00
91	–	90f. multicoloured	7·00	7·00
92	–	125f. multicoloured	22·00	22·00
93	–	150f. multicoloured	30·00	30·00
94	–	500f. multicoloured	70·00	70·00
95	–	1d. multicoloured	£130	£130

For later issues see **UNITED ARAB EMIRATES**.

ADEN — Pt. 1

Peninsula on southern coast of Arabia. Formerly part of the Indian Empire. A Crown Colony from 1 April 1937 to 18 January 1963, when Aden joined the South Arabian Federation, whose stamps it then used.

1937. 16 annas = 1 rupee.
1951. 100 cents = 1 shilling.

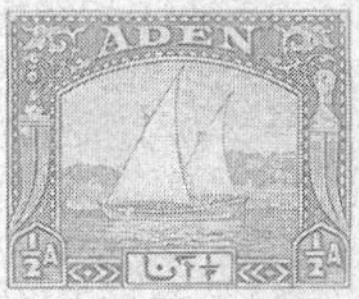

1 Dhow

1937.

1	1	½a. green	3·75	1·50
2		9p. green	3·75	1·75
3		1a. brown	3·75	70
4		2a. red	3·75	2·00
5		2½a. blue	3·75	80
6		3a. red	9·00	6·50
7		3½a. blue	7·50	2·50
8		8a. purple	22·00	5·50
9		1r. brown	32·00	6·00
10		2r. yellow	48·00	16·00
11		5r. purple	90·00	65·00
12		10r. olive	£275	£325

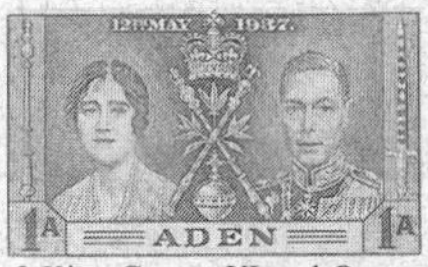

2 King George VI and Queen Elizabeth

1937. Coronation.

13	2	1a. brown	65	80
14		2½a. blue	75	1·40
15		3½a. blue	1·00	2·50

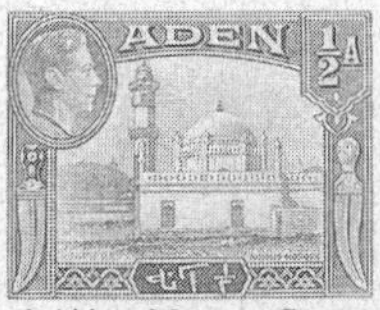

3 Aidrus Mosque, Crater

1939.

16	3	½a. green	50	60
17	–	¾a. brown	1·25	1·25
18	–	1a. blue	20	40
19	–	1½a. red	55	60
20	3	2a. brown	20	25
21	–	2½a. blue	40	30
22	–	3a. brown and red	60	25
23	–	8a. orange	55	40
23a	–	14a. brown and blue	2·50	1·00
24	–	1r. green	2·25	2·00
25	–	2r. blue and mauve	4·75	2·25
26	–	5r. brown and olive	11·00	8·00
27	–	10r. brown and violet	30·00	11·00

DESIGNS: ¾a., 5r. Adenese Camel Corps; 1a., 2r. Harbour; 1½a., 1r. Adenese dhow; 2½, 8a. Mukalla; 3, 14a., 10r. "Capture of Aden, 1839" (Capt. Rundle).

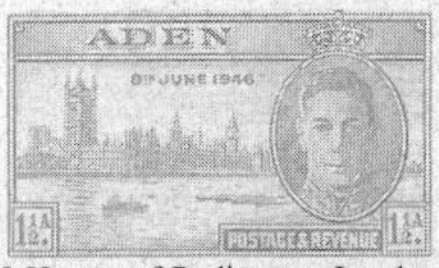

9 Houses of Parliament, London

1946. Victory.

28	9	1½a. red	15	1·00
29		2½a. blue	15	30

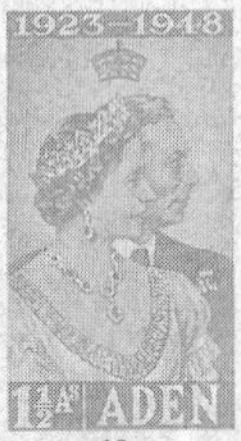

10

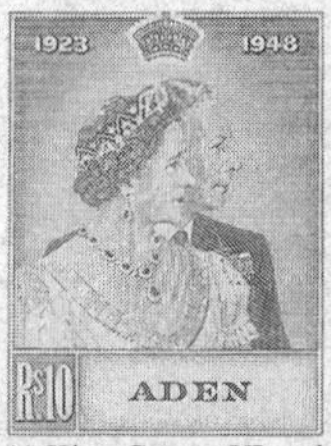

11 King George VI and Queen Elizabeth

1949. Royal Silver Wedding.

30 10 1½a. red 40 1·00
31 11 10r. purple 27·00 32·00

1949. 75th Anniv of U.P.U. As T **20/23** of Antigua surch with new values.

32 2½a. on 20c. blue 50 1·50
33 3a. on 30c. red 1·75 1·50
34 8a. on 50c. orange 1·10 1·50
35 1r. on 1s. blue 1·60 2·75

1951. Stamps of 1939 surch in cents or shillings.

36 5c. on 1a. blue 15 40
37 10c. on 2a. brown 15 45
38 15c. on 2½a. blue 20 1·25
39 20c. on 3a. brown and red 30 40
40 30c. on 8a. orange 30 65
41 50c. on 8a. orange 30 35
42 70c. on 14a. brown and blue 2·00 1·50
43 1s. on 1r. green 35 30
44 2s. on 2r. blue and mauve 7·50 2·75
45 5s. on 5r. brown and olive 16·00 9·50
46 10s. on 10r. brown and violet 24·00 11·00

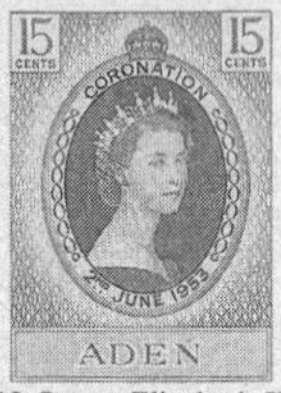
13 Queen Elizabeth II

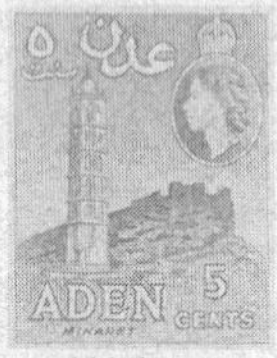
14 Minaret

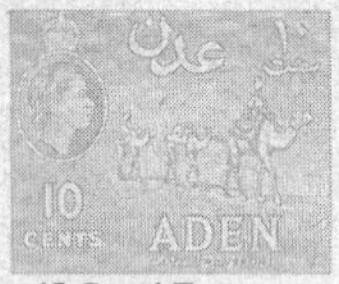
15 Camel Transport

1953. Coronation.

47 13 15c. black and green 70 1·25

1953.

48 14 5c. green 20 10
49a 5c. turquoise 10 70
50 15 10c. orange 40 10
51 10c. red 10 30
52 – 15c. turquoise 1·25 60
79 – 15c. grey 30 3·50
80 – 25c. red 30 40
56 – 35c. blue 2·50 2·00
58 – 50c. blue 20 10
60 – 70c. grey 20 10
61a – 70c. black 90 20
62 – 1s. brown and violet 30 10
63 – 1s. black and violet 1·50 10
64 – 1s.25 blue and black 2·25 60
65 – 2s. brown and red 1·25 50
66 – 2s. black and red 8·50 50
67 – 5s. brown and blue 1·50 1·00
68 – 5s. black and blue 5·00 1·25
69 – 10s. brown and green 1·75 8·00
70 – 10s. black and bronze 13·00 1·75
71 – 20s. brown and lilac 6·50 10·00
72 – 20s. black and lilac 40·00 14·00

DESIGNS—HORIZ: 15c. Crater; 25c. Mosque; 1s. Dhow building; 20s. (38 × 27 mm); Aden in 1572. VERT: 35c. Dhow; 50c. Map; 70c. Salt works; 1s.25, Colony's badge; 2s. Aden Protectorate Levy; 5s. Crater Pass; 10s. Tribesmen.

1954. Royal Visit. As No. 62 but inscr "ROYAL VISIT 1954".

73 1s. sepia and violet 30 55

1959. Revised Constitution. Optd **REVISED CONSTITUTION 1959** (in Arabic on No. 74).

74 15c. green (No. 53) 30 2·00
75 1s.25 blue and black (No. 64) 1·00 1·00

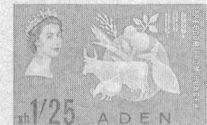

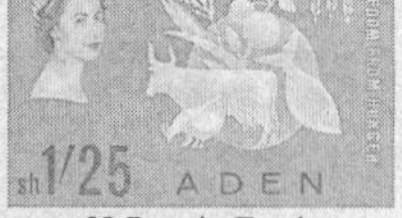
28 Protein Foods

1963. Freedom from Hunger.

76 28 1s.25 green 1·25 1·75

For later issues see **SOUTH ARABIAN FEDERATION**.

AFGHANISTAN Pt. 16

An independent country in Asia, to N.W. of Pakistan. Now a republic, the country was formerly ruled by monarchs from 1747 to 1973.

1871. 60 paisa = 12 shahi = 6 sanar = 3 abasi = 2 kran = 1 rupee.
1920. 60 paisa = 2 kran = 1 rupee.
1926. 100 poul (pul) = 1 afghani (rupee).

The issues from 1860 to 1892 (Types **1** to **16**) are difficult to classify because the values of each set are expressed in native script and are generally all printed in the same colour. As it is not possible to list these in an intelligible simplified form we would refer users to the detailed list in the Stanley Gibbons Part 16 (Central Asia) Catalogue.

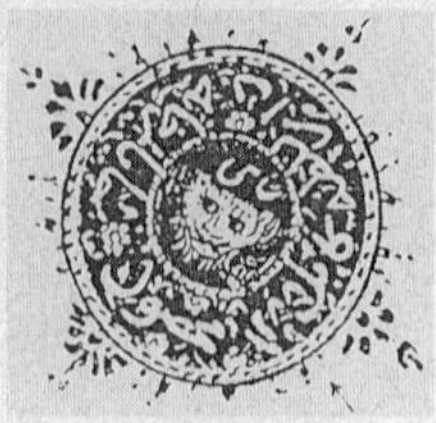
1

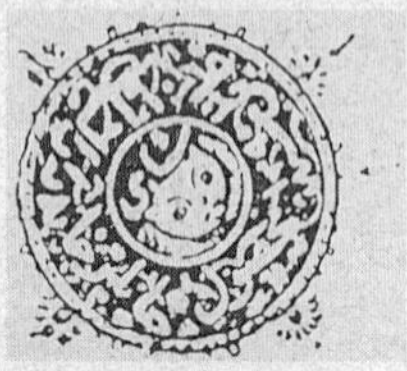
4

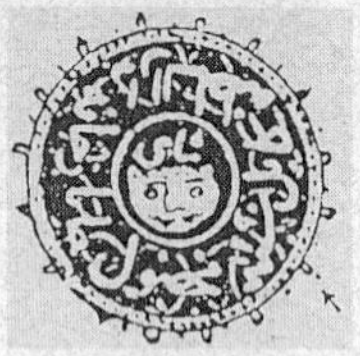
5

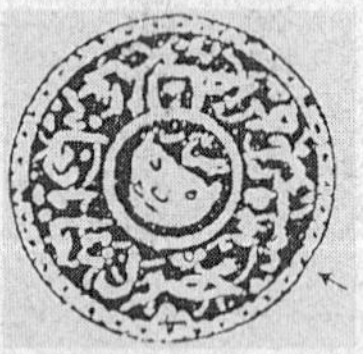
6

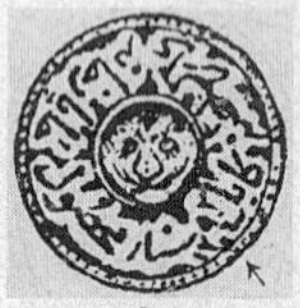
8

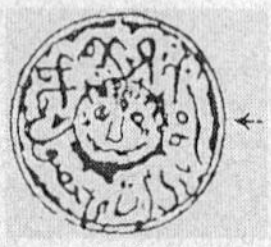
10

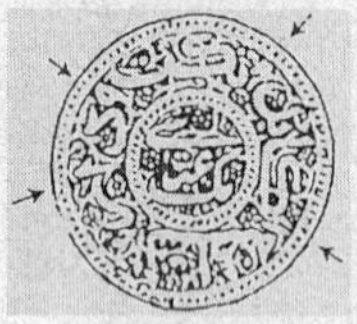
12

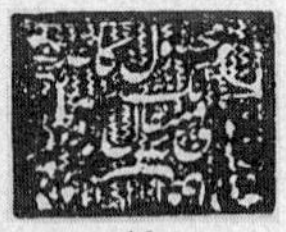
16

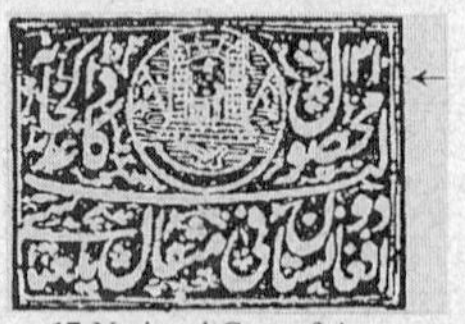
17 National Coat of Arms

1893. Dated "1310".

147 17 1a. black on green 2·75 2·75
148 1a. black on red 3·00 2·75
149a 1a. black on purple 3·25 3·00
150 1a. black on yellow 3·00 2·75
151 1a. black on orange 3·75 2·50
152 1a. black on blue 5·00 4·25

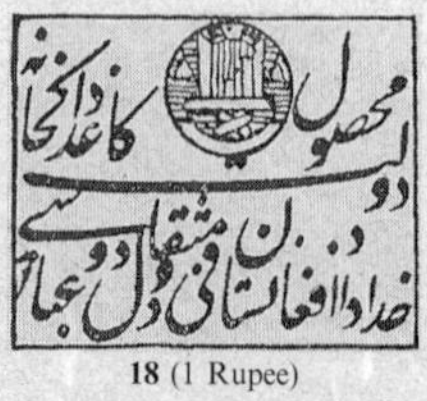
18 (1 Rupee)

1894. Undated.

153 18 2a. black on green 10·00 6·00
154 1r. black on green 12·00 7·50

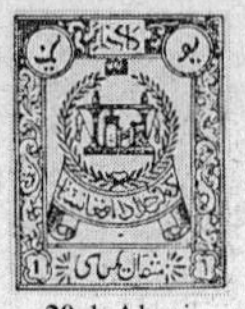
20 1 Abasi

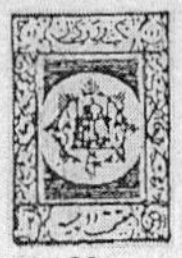
23

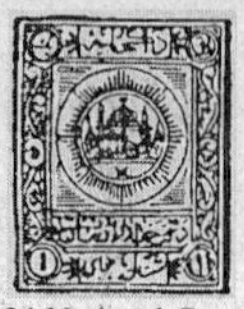
24 National Coat of Arms

1907. Imperf, roul or perf.

156a 20 1a. green 10·00 8·50
157 – 2a. blue 5·50 5·50
158 – 1r. green 7·50 9·00

The 2a. and 1r. are in similar designs.

1909. Perf.

165 23 2 paisa brown 2·50 3·50
166 24 1a. blue 4·50 1·50
168 1a. red 90 80
169 – 2a. green 2·25 2·00
170a – 2a. bistre 1·50 2·25
171 – 1r. brown 4·00 4·25
172 – 1r. olive 5·50 5·50

The frames of the 2a. and 1r. differ from Type **24**.

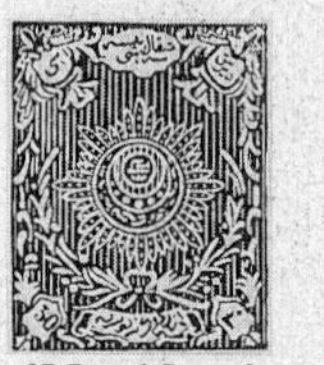
27 Royal Star of Order of Independence

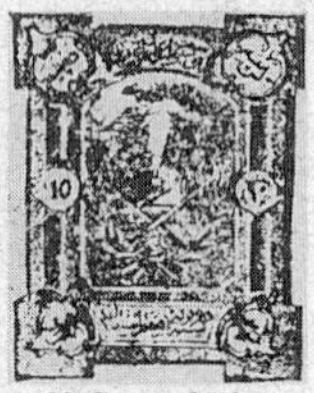
29 Crest of King Amanullah

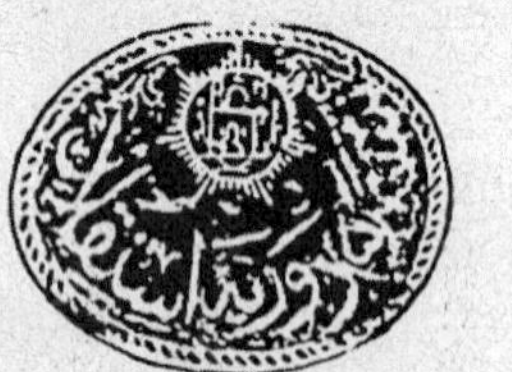
(28)

1920. 1st Anniv of End of War of Independence. Size 39 × 47 mm.

173 27 10p. red 22·00 22·00
174 20p. purple 40·00 42·00
175 30p. green 80·00 85·00

1921. Size 23 × 29 mm.

177 27 10p. red 75 75
178 20p. purple 1·50 1·50
180b 30p. green 2·50 2·25

1923. 5th Independence Day. Optd with T **28**.

181 27 10p. red 35·00 35·00
181a 20p. brown 40·00 40·00
182 30p. green 45·00 45·00

1924. 6th Independence Day.

183 29 10p. brown (24 × 32 mm) 30·00 30·00

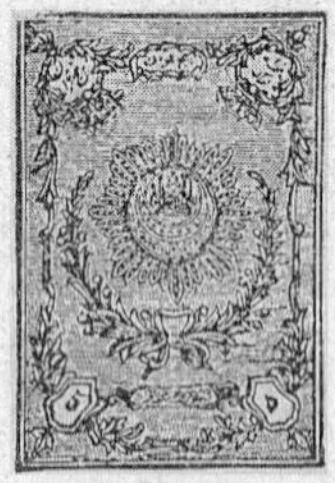
29a

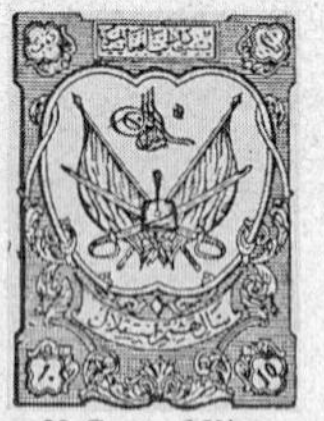
30 Crest of King Amanullah

1924.

183b 29a 5k. blue 30·00 35·00
183c 5r. mauve 14·00 20·00

1925. 7th Independence Day.

184 29 10p. brown (29 × 37 mm) 30·00 28·00

1926. 7th Anniv of Independence.

185 29 10p. blue (26 × 33 mm) 5·50 7·50

1927. 8th Anniv of Independence.

186 30 10p. mauve 10·00 9·00

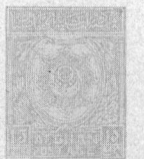

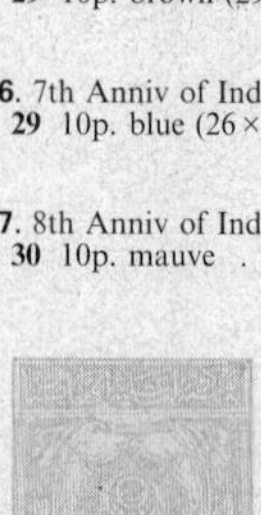
31

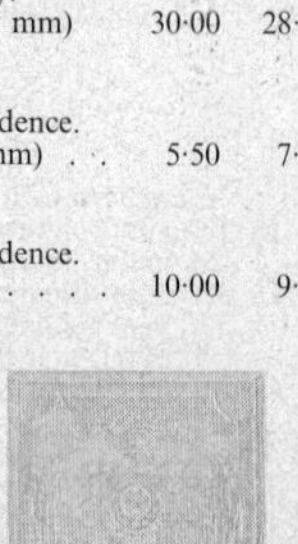
32

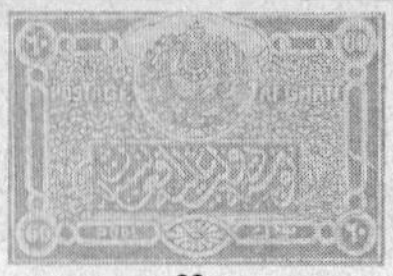
33

Types **31/3**, **36/37** and **41**, National Seal.

1927. Perf or imperf.

188 31 15p. red 85 75
189 32 30p. green 1·40 85
190 33 60p. blue 2·25 2·00

See also Nos. 207/13.

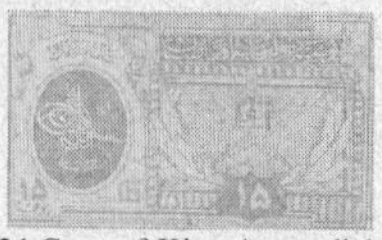
34 Crest of King Amanullah

1928. 9th Anniv of Independence.

191 34 15p. red 3·50 3·25

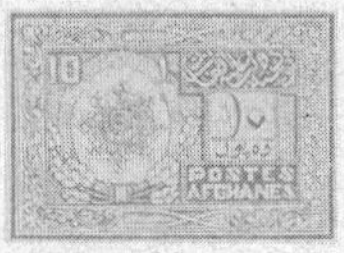
36

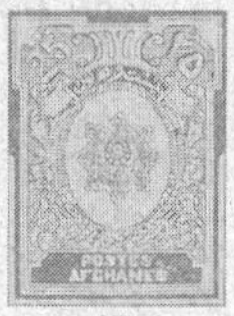
37

1928.

193 36 10p. green 85 65
194 37 25p. red 1·00 75
195 – 40p. blue 1·25 95
196 – 50p. red 1·75 95

The frames of the 40 and 50p. differ from Type **37**. See also Nos. 207/13.

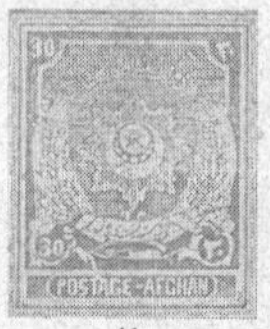
41

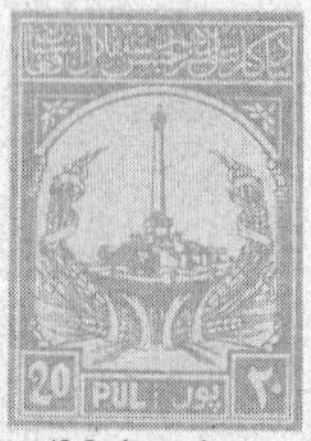
42 Independence Memorial

1929.

207 36 10p. brown 1·75 1·25
208 31 15p. blue 1·75 1·10
209 37 25p. blue 1·75 1·10
210 41 30p. green 2·25 1·25
211 – 40p. red 2·50 1·50
212 – 50p. blue 2·50 2·00
213 33 60p. black 2·75 2·00

1931. 13th Independence Day.

214 42 20p. red 3·25 2·25

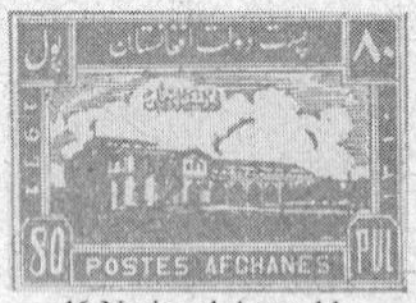
46 National Assembly Building

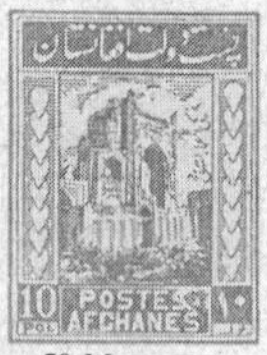
50 Mosque at Balkh

1932. Inauguration of National Council.

215 – 40p. brown (31 × 24 mm) 65 65
216 – 60p. violet (29 × 26 mm) 95 85
217 46 80p. red 1·25 1·00
218 – 1a. black (24 × 27 mm) 10·00 9·00
219 – 2a. blue (36 × 25 mm) 4·50 4·25
220 – 3a. green (36 × 24 mm) 5·00 4·00

DESIGNS: Nos. 215/16, 218/19, Council Chamber; 3a. National Assembly Building (different).

1932.

221 50 10p. brown 50 30
222 – 15p. brown 40 35
223 – 20p. red 60 25
224 – 25p. green 75 25
225 – 30p. red 75 25
226 – 40p. orange 90 45
227 – 50p. blue 1·40 1·40
228 – 60p. blue 1·25 1·00
229 – 80p. violet 2·25 2·00
230 – 1a. blue 4·25 80
231 – 2a. purple 4·50 2·50
232 – 3a. red 5·50 3·25

DESIGNS—32 × 23 mm: 15p. Kabul Fortress; 20, 25p. Parliament House, Darul Funun, Kabul; 40p. Memorial Pillar of Knowledge and Ignorance, Kabul; 1a. Ruins at Balkh; 2a. Minarets at Herat. 32 × 16 mm: 30p. Arch of Paghman. 23 × 32 mm: 60p. Minaret at Herat. 23 × 25 mm: 30p. Arch at Qalai Bust, near Kandahar; 50p. Independence Memorial, Kabul. 16 × 32 mm: 3a. Great Buddha at Bamian.

See also Nos. 237/51.

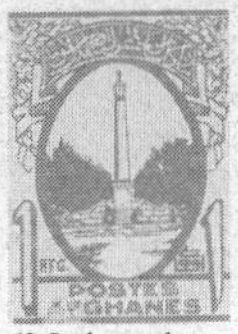
62 Independence Memorial

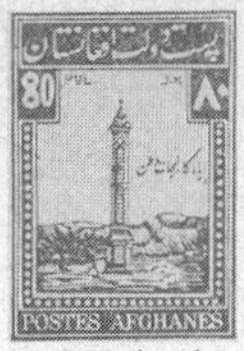
63 National Liberation Monument, Kabul

1932. 14th Independence Day.

233	62	1a. red	5·50	3·75

1932. Commemorative Issue.

234	63	80p. red	2·75	2·00

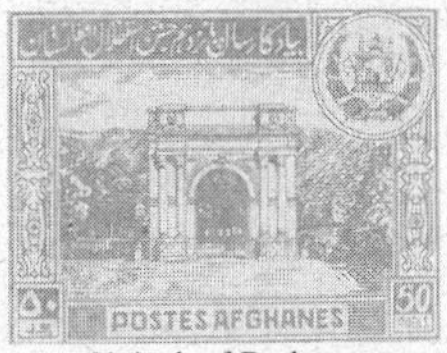
64 Arch of Paghman

1933. 15th Independence Day.

235	64	50p. blue	2·75	2·00

65 Independence Memorial

1934. 16th Independence Day.

236	65	50p. green	3·25	2·75

1934. As Nos. 219/20 and 221/30, but colours changed and new values.

237	50	10p. violet	25	15
238	–	15p. green	40	15
239	–	20p. mauve	45	15
240	–	25p. red	50	25
241	–	30p. orange	60	30
242	–	40p. black	65	35
243	–	45p. blue	2·00	1·50
244	–	45p. red	45	25
245	–	50p. red	75	25
246	–	60p. violet	80	45
247	–	75p. red	3·00	2·25
248	–	75p. blue	1·00	80
248b	–	80p. brown	1·50	85
249	–	1a. mauve	2·25	2·00
250	–	2a. grey	4·25	3·00
251	–	3a. blue	4·50	3·50

DESIGNS (new values)—34 × 23 mm: 45p. Royal Palace, Kabul. 20 × 34 mm: 75p. Hunters Canyon Pass, Hindu Kush.

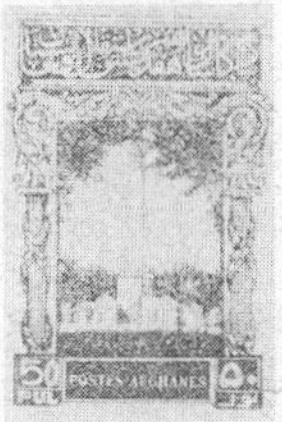
68 Independence Memorial

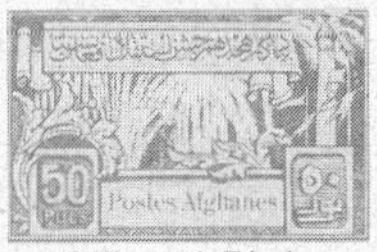
69 Firework Display

1935. 17th Independence Day.

252	68	50p. blue	3·25	2·75

1936. 18th Independence Day.

253	69	50p. mauve	3·50	2·75

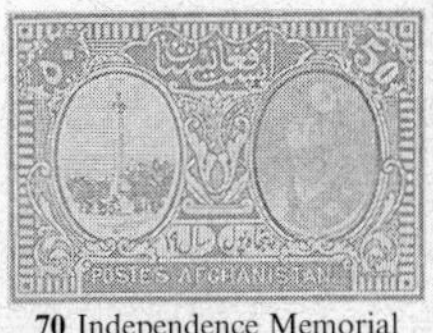
70 Independence Memorial and Mohamed Nadir Shah

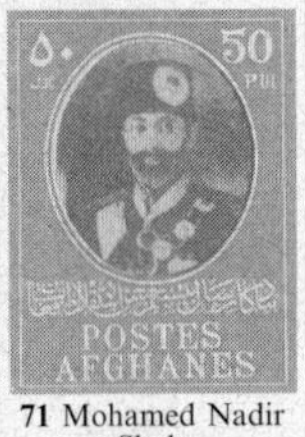
71 Mohamed Nadir Shah

1937. 19th Independence Day. Perf or imperf.

254	70	50p. brown and violet	2·50	2·25

1938. 20th Independence Day. Perf or imperf.

255	71	50p. brown and blue	2·25	2·25

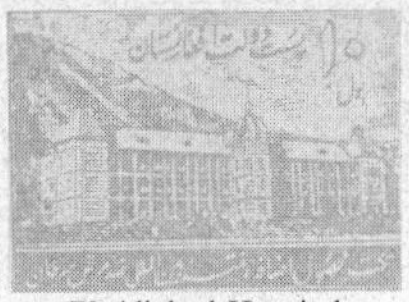
72 Aliabad Hospital

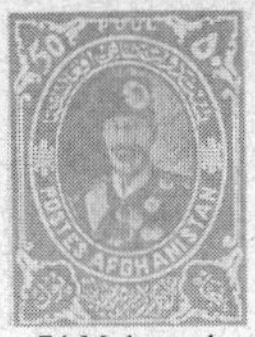
74 Mohamed Nadir Shah

1938. Obligatory Tax. Int Anti-cancer Fund.

256	72	10p. green	3·25	5·00
257	–	15p. blue	3·25	5·00

DESIGN—44 × 28 mm: 15p. Pierre and Marie Curie.

1939. 21st Independence Day.

258	74	50p. red	2·25	1·50

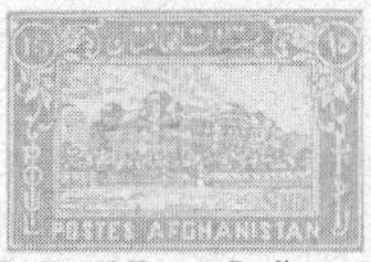
76 Darul Funun Parliament House, Kabul

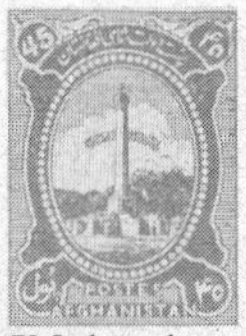
79 Independence Memorial

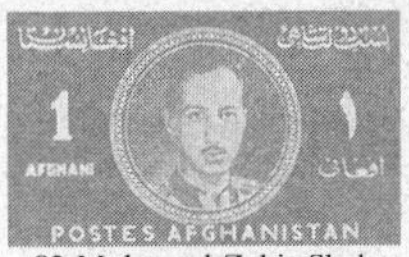
82 Mohamed Zahir Shah

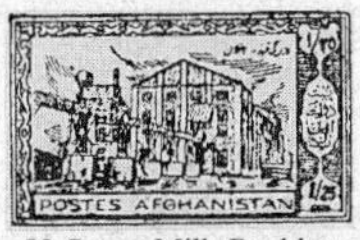
83 Sugar Mill, Baghlan

1939.

259	76	10p. purple (36½ × 24 mm)	25	20
260		15p. green (34 × 21 mm)	35	20
261		20p. purple (34 × 22½ mm)	40	25
262	–	25p. red	45	30
263	–	25p. green	30	25
264	–	30p. orange	40	25
265	–	35p. orange	1·00	65
266	–	40p. grey	80	45
267	79	45p. red	80	40
268		50p. orange	60	25
269		60p. violet	75	25
270	–	70p. violet	1·50	65
271	–	70p. purple	1·50	65
272	–	75p. blue	2·25	75
273	–	75p. purple	1·75	1·90
274	–	75p. red	2·50	2·50
275	–	80p. brown	1·50	80
276	82	1a. purple	1·50	75
277	–	1a. purple	1·50	80
278d	83	1a.25 blue	1·60	70
279a	–	2a. red	2·25	1·00
280	–	3a. blue	3·50	1·60

DESIGNS—31 × 19 mm: 25, 30p. Royal Palace, Kabul. 30 × 18 mm: 40p. Royal Palace, Kabul. 30 × 21 mm: 70p. Ruins at Qalai Bust, near Kandahar. 35½ × 21½ mm: 75p. Independence Memorial and Mohamed Nadir Shah. 34½ × 21 mm: 80p. As 75p. 35 × 20 mm: 1a. (No. 277), 2a. Mohamed Zahir Shah; 3a. As Type 82 but head turned more to left. 19 × 31 mm: 35p. Minarets at Herat.

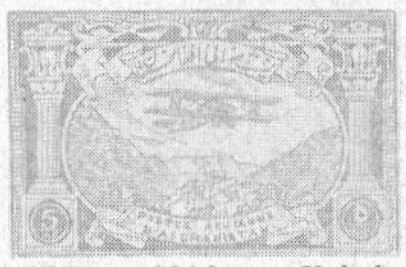
85 Potez 25A2 over Kabul

1939. Air.

280a	85	5a. orange	3·50	4·50
280b		10a. blue	3·75	4·50
280c		20a. green	6·50	7·50

See also Nos. 300/2.

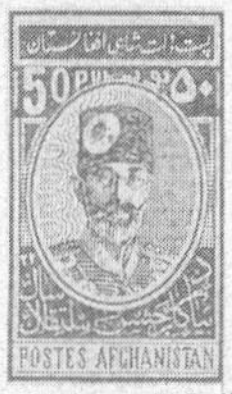
86 Mohamed Nadir Shah

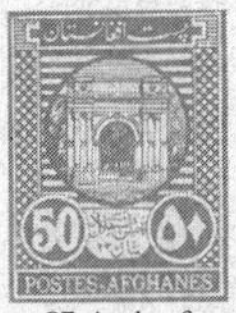
87 Arch of Paghman

1940. 22nd Independence Day.

281	86	50p. green	2·25	1·50

1941. 23rd Independence Day.

282	–	15p. green	6·00	3·75
283	87	50p. brown	1·75	1·50

DESIGN: (19 × 29½ mm): 15p. Independence Memorial.

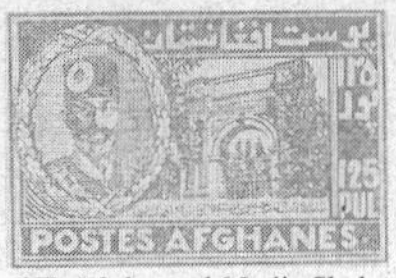
87b Mohamed Nadir Shah and Arch of Paghman

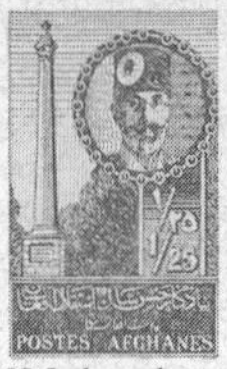
88 Independence Memorial and Mohamed Nadir Shah

1942. 24th Independence Day.

284	–	35p. green	4·25	3·75
285	87b	125p. blue	2·75	2·25

DESIGN—VERT: 35p. Independence Memorial in medallion.

1943. 25th Independence Day.

286	–	35p. red	12·00	9·50
287	88	1a.25 blue	2·50	2·25

DESIGN—HORIZ: 35p. Independence Memorial seen through archway and Mohamed Nadir Shah in oval frame.

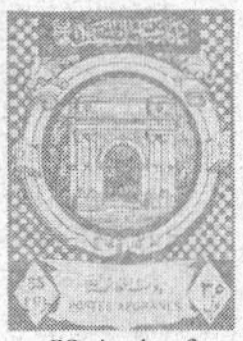
89 Arch of Paghman

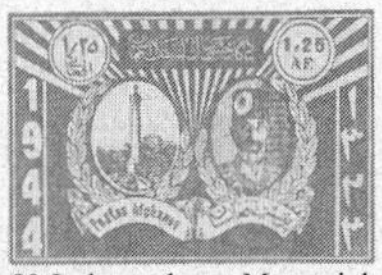
90 Independence Memorial and Mohamed Nadir Shah

1944. 26th Independence Day.

288	89	35p. red	1·25	75
289	90	1a.25 blue	2·25	2·00

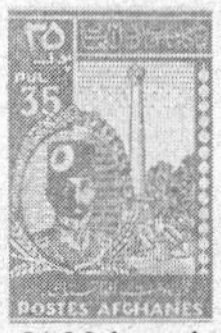
91 Mohamed Nadir Shah and Independence Memorial

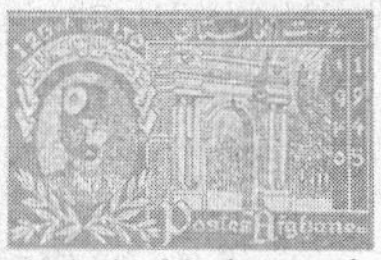
92 Arch of Paghman and Mohamed Nadir Shah

1945. 27th Independence Day.

290	91	35p. red	2·25	75
291	92	1a.25 blue	3·75	2·00

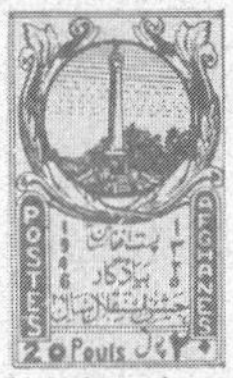
93 Independence Memorial

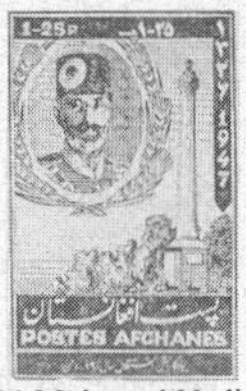
94 Mohamed Nadir Shah and Independence Memorial

1946. 28th Independence Day. Dated "1946".

292	–	15p. green	1·25	75
293	93	20p. mauve	2·00	85
294	–	125p. blue	3·25	2·00

DESIGNS—HORIZ: 15p. Mohamed Zahir Shah. VERT: 125p. Mohamed Nadir Shah.

1947. 29th Independence Day. Dated "1947".

295	–	15p. green	1·00	60
296	–	35p. mauve	1·25	75
297	94	125p. blue	3·25	2·00

DESIGNS—HORIZ: 15p. Mohamed Zahir Shah and ruins of Kandahar Fort; 35p. Mohamed Zahir Shah and Arch of Paghman.

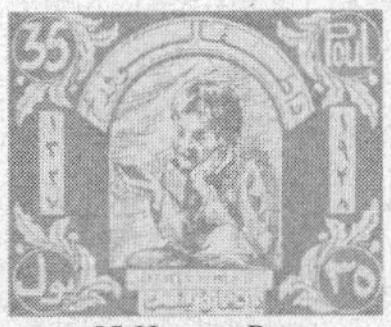
95 Hungry Boy

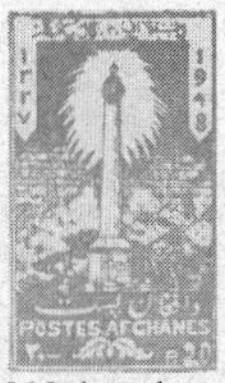
96 Independence Memorial

1948. Child Welfare Fund.

298	95	35p. green	5·00	4·25
299	–	125p. blue	5·00	4·25

DESIGN—26 × 33½ mm: 125p. Hungry boy in vert frame.

See also No. 307.

1948. Air. As T 85 but colours changed.

300	85	5a. green	25·00	25·00
301		10a. orange	25·00	25·00
302		20a. blue	25·00	25·00

1948. 30th Independence Day. Dated "1948".

303	–	15p. green	75	35
304	96	20p. mauve	1·00	40
305	–	125p. blue	2·00	1·00

DESIGNS—VERT: 15p. Arch of Paghman. HORIZ: 125p. Mohamed Nadir Shah.

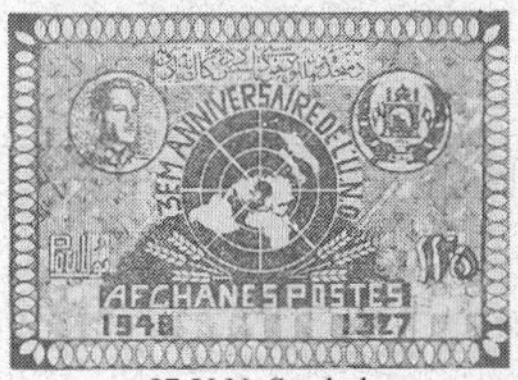
97 U.N. Symbol

1948. 3rd Anniv of U.N.O.

306	97	1a.25 blue	11·00	9·00

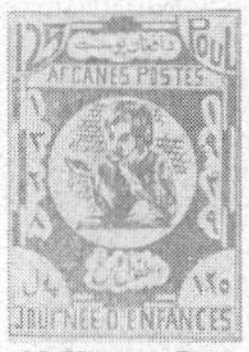
98 Hungry Boy

99 Victory Monument

1949. Obligatory Tax. Child Welfare Fund.

307	–	35p. orange	3·25	1·75
308	98	125p. blue	3·25	1·75

DESIGN—HORIZ: 35p. As Type 98 but 29 × 22½ mm.

1949. 31st Independence Day. Dated "1949" (Nos. 310/11).

309	99	25p. green	80	40
310	–	35p. mauve	1·00	45
311	–	1a.25 blue	2·25	1·25

DESIGNS—HORIZ: 35p. Mohamed Zahir Shah and ruins of Kandahar Fort; 1a.25, Independence Memorial and Mohamed Nadir Shah.

100 Arch of Paghman

1949. Obligatory Tax. 4th Anniv of U.N.O.

312	100	125p. green	16·00	10·00

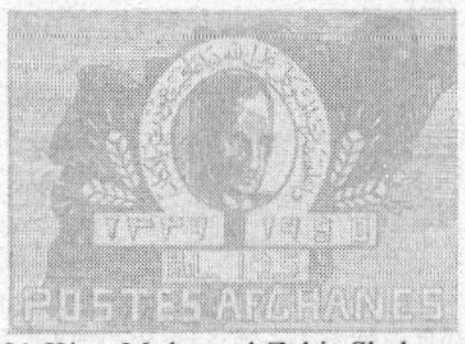
101 King Mohamed Zahir Shah and Map of Afghanistan

1950. Obligatory Tax. Return of King Mohamed Zahir Shah from Visit to Europe.

313	101	125p. green	3·75	1·50

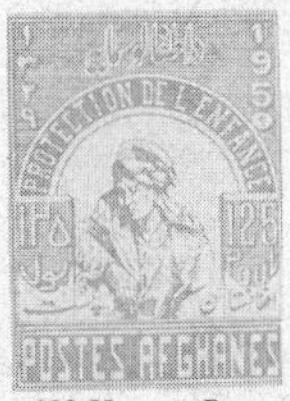
102 Hungry Boy

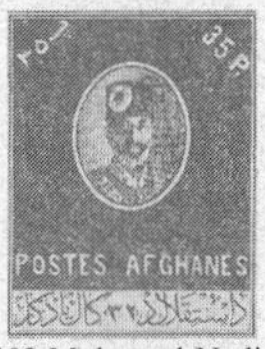
103 Mohamed Nadir Shah

1950. Obligatory Tax. Child Welfare Fund.

314	102	125p. green	4·50	2·50

1950. 32nd Independence Day.

315	103	35p. brown	70	45
316		125p. blue	2·25	75

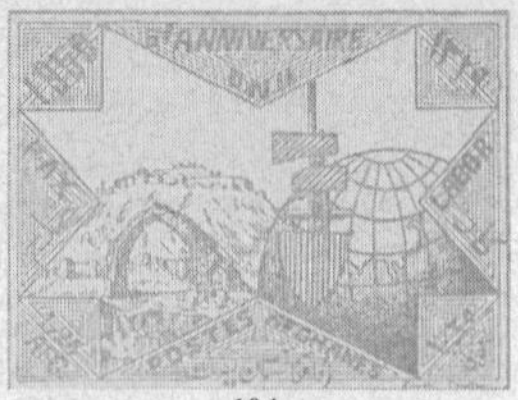
104

1950. Obligatory Tax. 5th Anniv of U.N.O.
317 **104** 1a.25 blue . . . . 7·50 4·50

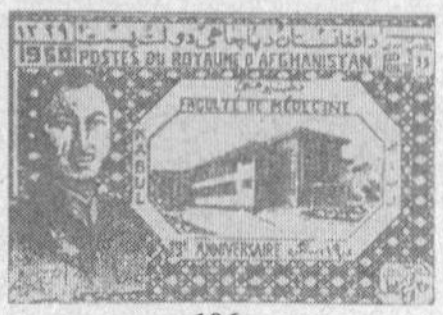
106

1950. 19th Anniv of Faculty of Medicine, Kabul.
318 **106** 35p. green (postage) . . . 1·25 75
319 – 1a.25 blue . . . . 4·25 2·25
320 **106** 35p. red (obligatory tax) 1·25 60
321 – 1a.25 black . . . . 8·50 2·75
DESIGN: Nos. 319 and 321, Sanatorium. Nos. 318 and 320 measure 38½ × 25½ mm and Nos. 319 and 321, 45 × 30 mm.

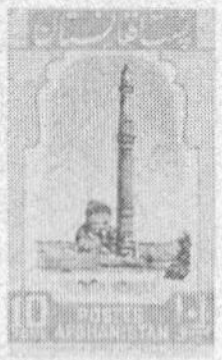
107 Minaret at Herat

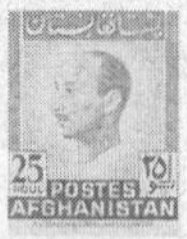
109 Mohamed Zahir Shah

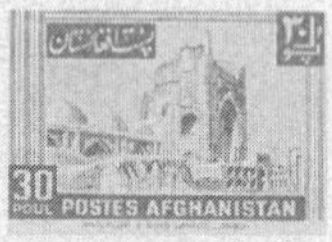
110 Mosque at Balkh

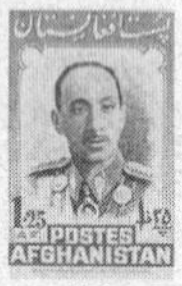
118

1951.
322 **107** 10p. brown and yellow . . 25 20
323 15p. brown and blue . . . 40 20
324 – 20p. black . . . . 8·00 4·25
325 **109** 25p. green 40 15
326 **110** 30p. red 45 20
327 **109** 35p. violet 50 20
328 – 40p. brown 55 20
329 – 45p. blue 55 20
330 – 50p. black . . . . 1·50 25
331 – 60p. black . . . . 1·25 25
332 – 70p. black, red and green 60 25
333 – 75p. red . . . . 1·00 40
334 – 80p. black and red . . . 1·75 75
335 – 1a. violet and green . . . 1·25 60
336 **118** 125p. black and purple . . 1·40 75
337 2a. blue . . . . 2·25 70
338 3a. blue and black . . . . 4·25 1·00
DESIGNS—19 × 29 mm: 20p. Buddha of Bamian; 45p. Maiwand Victory Monument; 60p. Victory Towers, Ghazni. 22 × 28 mm: 75, 80p., 1a. Mohamed Zahir Shah. 28 × 19 mm: 40p. Ruins at Qalai Bust; 70p. Flag. 30 × 19 mm: 50p. View of Kandahar.
See also Nos. 425/425k.

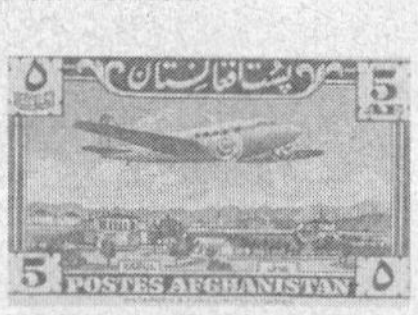
119 Douglas DC-3 over Kabul

1951. Air.
339 **119** 5a. red . . . . 3·50 75
339a 5a. green . . . . 1·60 55
340 10a. grey . . . . 8·00 1·60
341 20a. blue . . . . 12·00 2·75
See also Nos. 415a/b.

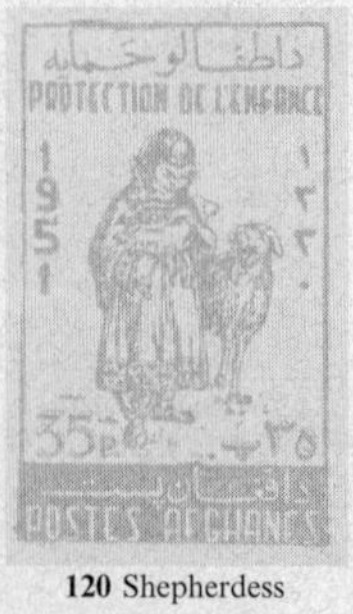
120 Shepherdess

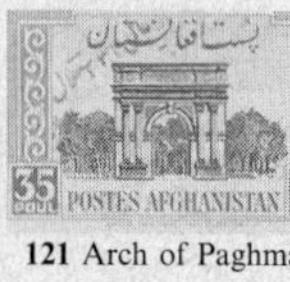
121 Arch of Paghman

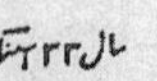
(122)

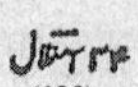
(123)

1951. Obligatory Tax. Child Welfare Fund.
342 **120** 35p. green . . . . 1·50 95
343 – 125p. blue . . . . 1·50 95
DESIGN—34½ × 44 mm: 125p. Young shepherd.

1951. 33rd Independence Day. Optd with T **122**.
344 **121** 35p. black and green . . 1·10 60
345 – 125p. blue . . . . 2·75 1·25
DESIGN (34 × 18½ mm): 125p. Mohamed Nadir Shah and Independence Memorial.
See also Nos. 360/1b and 418/19.

IMPERF STAMPS. From 1951 many issues were made available imperf from limited printings.

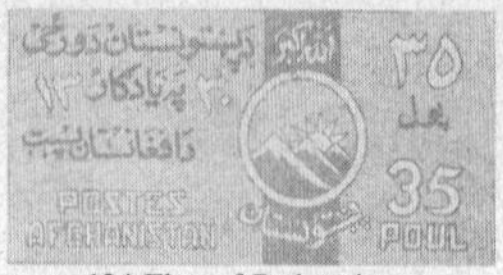
124 Flag of Pashtunistan

1951. Obligatory Tax. Pashtunistan Day.
346 **124** 35p. brown . . . . 1·75 1·00
347 – 125p. blue . . . . 3·25 2·25
DESIGN—42½ × 21½ mm: 125p. Afridi tribesman.

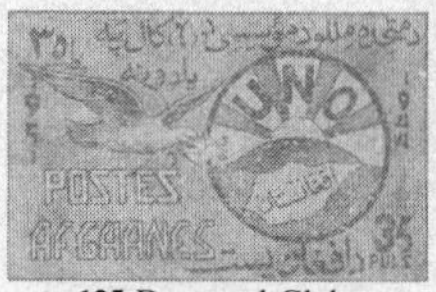
125 Dove and Globe

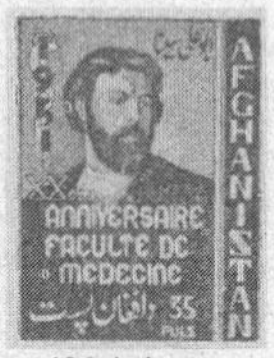
126 Avicenna (physician)

1951. Obligatory Tax. United Nations Day.
348 **125** 35p. mauve . . . . 1·00 50
349 – 125p. blue . . . . 2·50 2·00
DESIGN—VERT: 125p. Dove and globe.

1951. Obligatory Tax. 20th Anniv of Faculty of Medicine.
350 **126** 35p. mauve . . . . 3·00 1·25
351 125p. blue . . . . 1·00 3·25

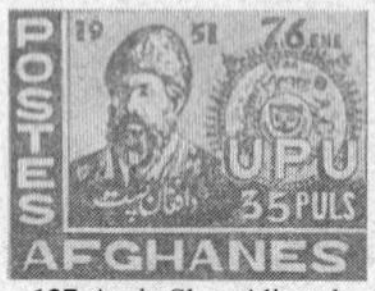
127 Amir Sher Ali and First Stamp

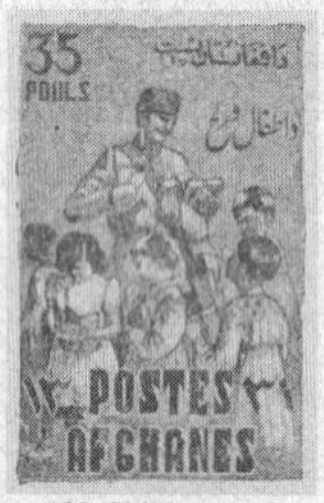
128 Children and Postman

1951. Obligatory Tax. 76th Anniv of U.P.U.
352 **127** 35p. brown 75 50
353 – 35p. mauve 75 50
354 **127** 125p. blue . . . . 1·25 75
355 – 125p. blue . . . . 1·25 75
DESIGN: Nos. 353 and 355, Mohamed Zahir Shah and first stamp.

1952. Obligatory Tax. Child Welfare Fund.
356 **128** 35p. brown 75 60
357 – 125p. violet . . . . . . 1·50 85
DESIGN—HORIZ: 125p. Girl dancing (33 × 23 mm).

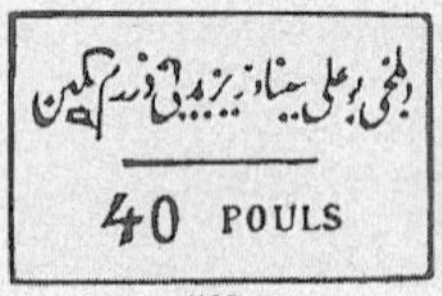

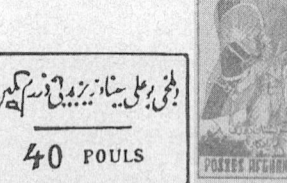

(129)

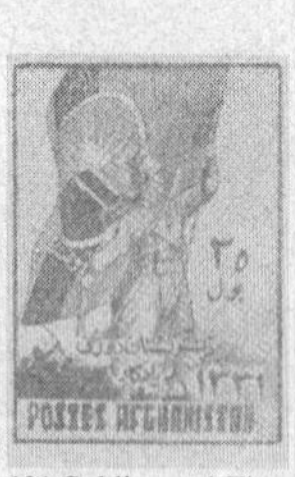
131 Soldier and Flag of Pashtunistan

1952. Obligatory Tax. Birth Millenary of Avicenna (physician and philosopher). (a) Surch with T **129**.
358 **110** 40p. on 30p. red . . . . 3·50 2·50

(b) Surch **MILLIEME ANNIVERSAIRE DE BOALI SINAI BALKI 125 POULS** in frame.
359 **110** 125p. on 30p. red . . . . 4·50 2·75

1952. 34th Independence Day. As Nos. 344/5. (a) Optd with T **123**.
360 35p. black and green . . . . 3·25 2·25
361 125p. blue . . . . 3·25 2·25

(b) Without opt.
361a 35p. black and green . . . . 1·50 65
361b 125p. blue . . . . 3·25 1·25

1952. Obligatory Tax. Pashtunistan Day.
362 **131** 35p. red 65 55
363 125p. blue . . . . 1·10 1·10

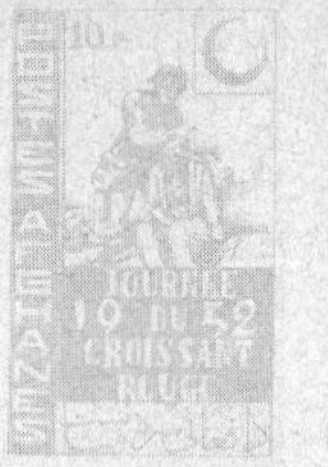
132 Orderly and Wounded Soldier

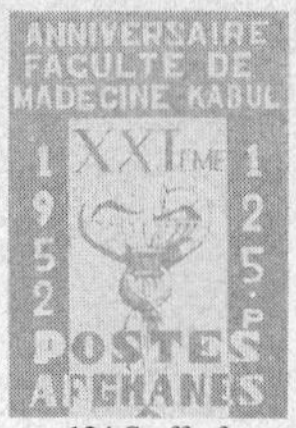
134 Staff of Aesculapius

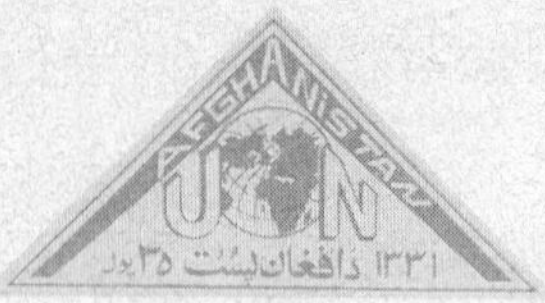
133

1952. Obligatory Tax. Red Crescent Day.
364 **132** 10p. green 50 40

1952. Obligatory Tax. United Nations Day.
365 **133** 35p. red 75 50
366 125p. turquoise . . . . . 1·75 1·25

1952. Obligatory Tax. 21st Anniv of Faculty of Medicine.
367 **134** 35p. brown 80 50
368 125p. blue . . . . 2·25 1·50

135 Stretcher Bearers and Wounded

1953. Obligatory Tax. Red Crescent Day.
369 **135** 10p. green and brown . . 70 70
370 – 10p. brown and orange 70 70
DESIGN: No. 370, Wounded soldier, orderly and eagle.

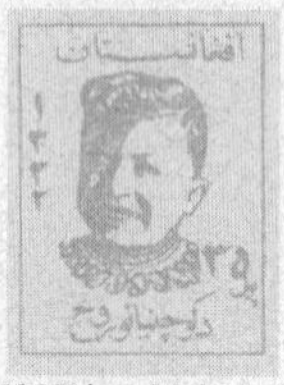
136 Prince Mohamed Nadir

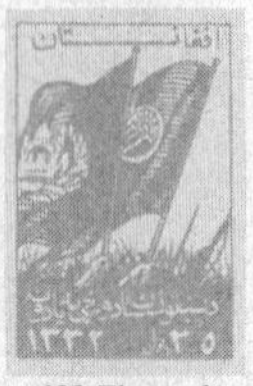
138 Flags of Afghanistan and Pashtunistan

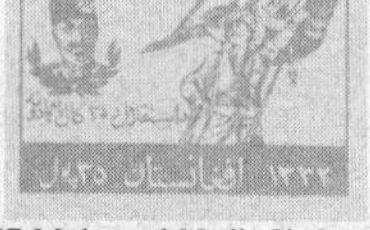
137 Mohamed Nadir Shah and Flag-bearer

1953. Obligatory Tax. Children's Day.
371 **136** 35p. orange 40 25
372 125p. blue 85 60

1953. 35th Year of Independence. Inscr "1953".
373 **137** 35p. green 40 35
374 – 125p. violet . . . . . . 1·10 65
DESIGN—VERT: 125p. Independence Memorial and Mohamed Nadir Shah.

1953. Obligatory Tax. Pashtunistan Day. Inscr "1953".
375 **138** 35p. red 40 20
376 – 125p. blue 85 55
DESIGN—HORIZ: 125p. Badge of Pashtunistan (26 × 20 mm).

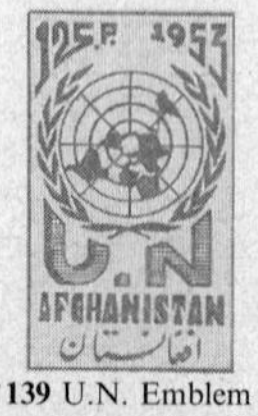
139 U.N. Emblem

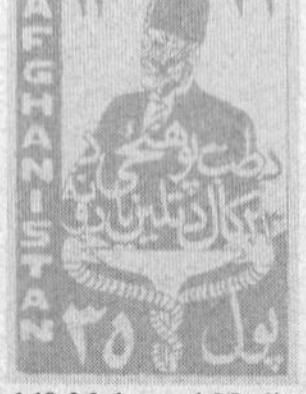
140 Mohamed Nadir Shah

1953. Obligatory Tax. United Nations Day.
377 **139** 35p. mauve 85 75
378 125p. blue . . . . 2·00 1·25

1953. Obligatory Tax. 22nd Anniv of Faculty of Medicine.
379 **140** 35p. orange . . . . . . 1·25 1·25
380 – 125p. blue . . . . 2·50 2·75
DESIGN: 125p. As Type **140** but inscribed "1953" and with French inscription.
No. 379 was wrongly inscribed "23rd" in Arabic (the extreme right-hand figure in the second row of the inscription) and No. 380 was wrongly inscr "XXIII" and had the words "ANNIVERSAIRE" and "MEDECINE" wrongly spelt "ANNIVERAIRE" and "MADECINE". These mistakes were subsequently corrected but the corrected stamps are much rarer than the original issue.

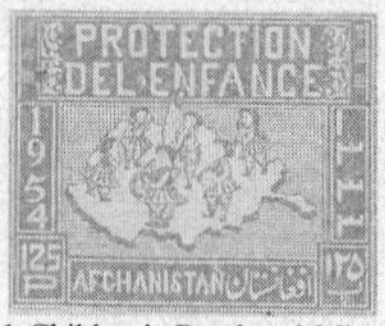
141 Children's Band and Map of Afghanistan

1954. Obligatory Tax. Child Welfare Fund.
381 **141** 35p. violet 50 25
382 125p. blue . . . . 1·50 1·00

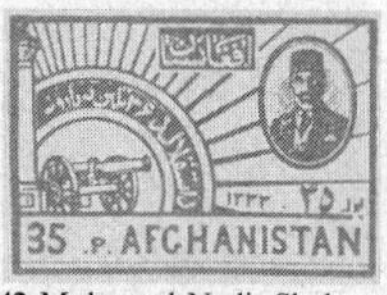
142 Mohamed Nadir Shah and Cannon

1954. 36th Independence Day.
383 **142** 35p. red 75 50
384 125p. blue . . . . 2·25 1·00

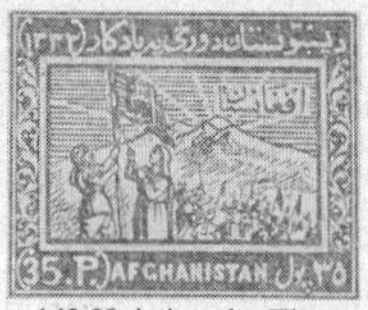
143 Hoisting the Flag

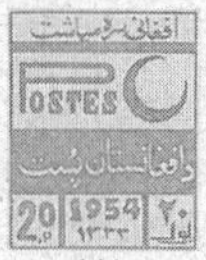
144

1954. Obligatory Tax. Pashtunistan Day.
385 **143** 35p. orange 75 50
386 125p. blue . . . . 2·00 1·10

1954. Red Crescent Day.
387 **144** 20p. red and blue 75 30

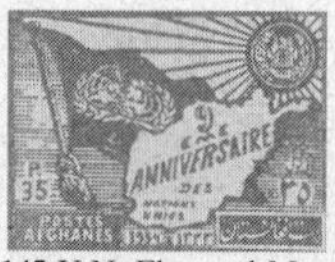
145 U.N. Flag and Map

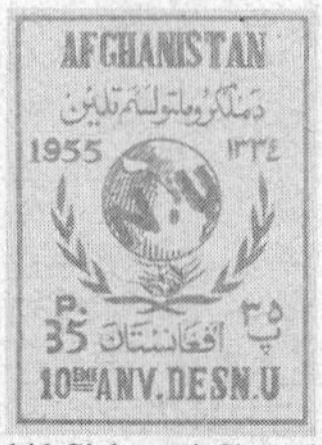
146 Globe and Clasped Hands

1954. United Nations Day and 9th Anniv of U.N.O.
388 **145** 35p. red . . . . 1·25 1·25
389 125p. blue . . . . 3·25 3·25

1955. 10th Anniv of Signing of U.N. Charter.
390 **146** 35p. green 75 50
391 – 125p. blue . . . . 1·75 1·00
DESIGN—28½ × 36 mm. 125p. U.N. emblem and flags.
See also Nos. 403/4.

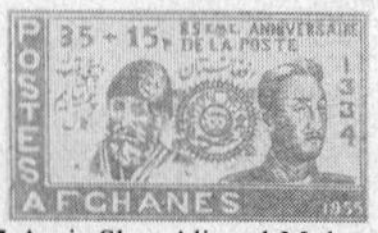
147 Amir Sher Ali and Mohamed Zahir Shah

1955. 85th Anniv of Postal Service.
392 **147** 35p.+15p. red . . . . . 1·25 55
393 125p.+25p. grey . . . . . 2·00 1·00

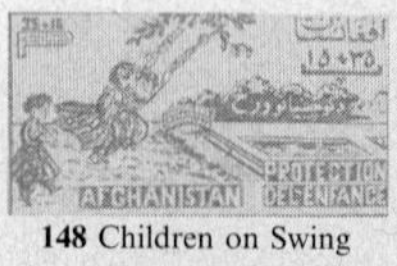
148 Children on Swing

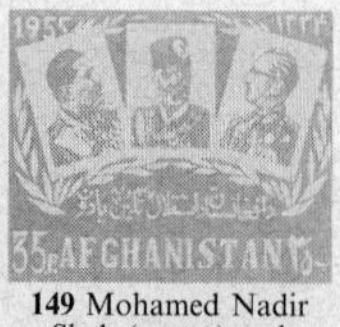
149 Mohamed Nadir Shah (centre) and brothers

1955. Child Welfare Fund.
394 148 35p.+15p. green . . . . . 1·00 60
395 125p.+25p. violet . . . . 2·00 1·10

1955. 37th Year of Independence.
396 149 35p. blue 70 45
397 35p. mauve 70 45
398 – 125p. violet . . . . 1·50 1·00
399 – 125p. purple . . . . . . 1·50 1·00
DESIGN: 125p. Mohamed Zahir Shah and battle scene.

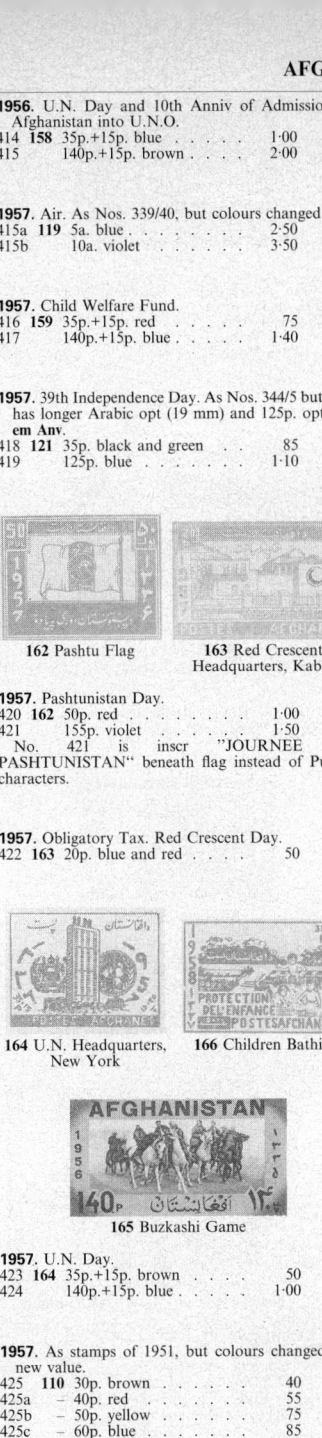

150   151 Red Crescent

1955. Obligatory Tax. Pashtunistan Day.
400 150 35p. brown 60 30
401 125p. green . . . . . . 1·75 50

1955. Obligatory Tax. Red Crescent Day.
402 151 20p. red and grey 40 40

152 U.N. Flag   153 Child on Slide

1955. Obligatory Tax. 10th Anniv of United Nations.
403 152 35p. brown 90 60
404 125p. blue . . . . . 1·75 1·10

1956. Children's Day.
405 153 35p.+15p. blue 60 40
406 140p.+15p. brown . . . 1·90 85

154 Independence   155 Exhibition Building
Memorial and
Mohamed Nadir
Shah

1956. 38th Year of Independence.
407 154 35p. green 60 35
408 140p. blue . . . . . . 2·40 95

1956. International Exhibition, Kabul.
409 155 50p. brown 75 35
410 50p. blue 75 35

156 Pashtun Square,   157 Mohamed Zahir
Kabul   Shah and Crescent

1956. Pashtunistan Day.
411 156 35p.+15p. violet 40 25
412 140p.+15p. brown . . . 1·00 70

1956. Obligatory Tax. Red Crescent Day.
413 157 20p. green and red . . . 55 25

158 Globe and Sun   159 Children on See-saw

1956. U.N. Day and 10th Anniv of Admission of Afghanistan into U.N.O.
414 158 35p.+15p. blue . . . . . 1·00 95
415 140p.+15p. brown . . . . 2·00 1·75

1957. Air. As Nos. 339/40, but colours changed.
415a 119 5a. blue . . . . 2·50 60
415b 10a. violet . . . . . . 3·50 1·25

1957. Child Welfare Fund.
416 159 35p.+15p. red 75 55
417 140p.+15p. blue . . . . 1·40 1·25

1957. 39th Independence Day. As Nos. 344/5 but 35p. has longer Arabic opt (19 mm) and 125p. optd **39 em Anv**.
418 121 35p. black and green . . . 85 45
419 125p. blue . . . . . . 1·10 85

162 Pashtu Flag   163 Red Crescent
Headquarters, Kabul

1957. Pashtunistan Day.
420 162 50p. red . . . . 1·00 60
421 155p. violet . . . . . . 1·50 1·10
No. 421 is inscr "JOURNEE DU PASHTUNISTAN" beneath flag instead of Pushtu characters.

1957. Obligatory Tax. Red Crescent Day.
422 163 20p. blue and red 50 25

164 U.N. Headquarters,   166 Children Bathing
New York

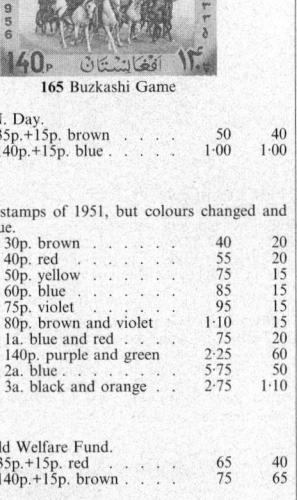

165 Buzkashi Game

1957. U.N. Day.
423 164 35p.+15p. brown 50 40
424 140p.+15p. blue . . . . 1·00 1·00

1957. As stamps of 1951, but colours changed and new value.
425 110 30p. brown 40 20
425a – 40p. red 55 20
425b – 50p. yellow 75 15
425c – 60p. blue 85 15
425d – 75p. violet 95 15
425e – 80p. brown and violet . . 1·10 15
425f – 1a. blue and red . . . 75 20
425g 165 140p. purple and green 2·25 60
425k 118 2a. blue . . . . . 5·75 50
425h 3a. black and orange . . 2·75 1·10

1958. Child Welfare Fund.
426 166 35p.+15p. red 65 40
427 140p.+15p. brown . . . 75 65

167 Mohamed Nadir Shah and
Old Soldier

1958. 40th Independence Day.
428 167 35p. green 45 25
429 140p. brown . . . . . . 1·10 85

168 Exhibition Buildings

1958. International Exhibition, Kabul.
430 168 35p. green 40 25
431 140p. red . . . . 1·10 65

169   170 President Bayar

1958. Pashtunistan Day.
432 169 35p.+15p. turquoise . . . 40 25
433 140p.+15p. brown . . . 1·10 65

1958. Visit of Turkish President.
434 170 50p. blue 45 25
435 100p. brown 75 35

171 Red Crescent and Map of
Afghanistan

1958. Obligatory Tax. Red Crescent Day.
436 171 25p. red and green . . . 35 15

172

1958. "Atoms for Peace".
437 172 50p. blue 50 40
438 100p. purple 85 65

173 Flags of U.N.   174 U.N.E.S.C.O.
and Afghanistan   Headquarters, Paris

1958. U.N. Day.
439 173 50p. multicoloured . . . 75 75
440 100p. multicoloured . . . 1·50 1·25

1958. Inauguration of U.N.E.S.C.O. Headquarters Building, Paris.
441 174 50p. green 75 65
442 100p. brown 75 75

175 Globe and Torch

1958. 10th Anniv of Declaration of Human Rights.
443 175 50p. mauve 40 40
444 100p. purple 60 70

176 Tug-of-War

1959. Child Welfare Fund.
445 176 35p.+15p. purple 45 40
446 165p.+15p. mauve . . . 1·25 60

177 Mohamed Nadir Shah and
Flags

1959. 41st Independence Day.
447 177 35p. red 50 40
448 165p. violet . . . . . 1·25 60

178 Tribal Dance

1959. Pashtunistan Day.
449 178 35p.+15p. green 40 25
450 165p.+15p. orange . . . 1·00 65

179 Badge-sellers   180 Horseman

1959. Obligatory Tax. Red Crescent Day.
451 179 25p. red and violet . . . 35 15

1959. United Nations Day.
452 180 35p.+15p. orange . . . 30 25
453 165p.+15p. green . . . 65 45

181 "Uprooted   182 Buzkashi Game
Tree"

183 Buzkashi Game

1960. World Refugee Year.
454 181 50p. orange 15 10
455 165p. blue 35 25

1960.
456 182 25p. pink 50 20
457 25p. violet 50 20
458 25p. olive 60 15
459 50p. turquoise . . . . 1·25 50
460 50p. blue . . . . . . 1·25 15
460a 50p. orange 40 15
461 183 100p. olive 65 25
462 150p. orange 55 25
463 175p. brown . . . . . 2·50 50
464 2a. green . . . . . . 1·25 85

184 Children receiving Ball

1960. Child Welfare Fund.
465 184 75p.+25p. blue 50 30
466 175p.+25p. green 80 40

185 Douglas DC-6 over
Mountains

1960. Air.
467 185 75p. violet 65 25
468 125p. blue 75 35
469 5a. olive . . . . . . 1·75 60

186 Independence   188 Insecticide Sprayer
Monument, Kabul

187

1960. 42nd Independence Day.
470 **186** 50p. blue 40 25
471 　　175p. mauve . . . . 1·10 35

1960. Pashtunistan Day.
472 **187** 50p.+50p. red 50 25
473 　　175p.+50p. blue . . . . . 1·25 95

1960. Anti-Malaria Campaign Day.
474 **188** 50p.+50p. orange . . . . 1·25 1·25
475 　　175p.+50p. brown . . . . . 2·75 1·60

189 Mohamed Zahir Shah

1960. King's 46th Birthday.
476 **189** 50p. brown 60 50
477 　　150p. red . . . . 1·60 45

190 Ambulance

1960. Red Crescent Day.
478 **190** 50p.+50p. violet & red . . 75 55
479 　　175p.+50p. blue & red . . 1·90 1·10

191 Teacher with Globe and
Children

1960. Literacy Campaign.
480 **191** 50p. mauve 45 35
481 　　100p. green . . . . 1·10 45

192 Globe and Flags　　195 Mir Wais Nika
　　　　　　　　　　　　　(patriot)

1960. U.N. Day.
482 **192** 50p. purple 30 30
483 　　175p. blue . . . . 1·00 65

1960. Olympic Games, Rome. Optd **1960** in figures
and in Arabic and Olympic Rings.
484 **183** 175p. brown . . . . . . 1·50 1·75

1960. World Refugee Year. Nos. 454/5 surch
+ 25 Ps.
485 **181** 50p.+25p. orange . . . . 1·25 1·75
486 　　165p.+25p. blue . . . . . 1·25 1·75

1960. Mir Wais Nika Commemoration.
487 **195** 50p. mauve 65 40
488 　　175p. blue . . . . 1·10 55

The very numerous issues of Afghanistan which we
do not list appeared between 21 April 1961 and
15 March 1964 (both dates inclusive), and were made
available to the philatelic trade by an agency acting
under the authority of a contract granted by the
Afghanistan Government.

It later became evident that token supplies were
only placed on sale in Kabul for a few hours and some
of these sets contained stamps of very low
denominations for which there was no possible postal
use.

When the contract for the production of these
stamps expired in 1963 it was not renewed and the
Afghanistan Government set up a Philatelic Advisory
Board to formulate stamp policy. The issues from
No. 489 onwards were made in usable denominations
and placed on sale without restriction in Afghanistan
and distributed to the trade by the Philatelic
Department of the G.P.O. in Kabul.

Issues not listed here will be found recorded in the
Appendix at the end of this country. It is believed that
some of the higher values from the agency sets were
utilised for postage in late 1979.

196 Band Amir Lake

1961.
489 **196** 3a. blue 45 25
490 　　10a. purple . . . . 1·25 1·00

197 Independence　　198 Tribesmen
Memorial

1963. 45th Independence Day.
491 **197** 25p. green 25 20
492 　　50p. orange 25 20
493 　　150p. mauve 45 25

1963. Pashtunistan Day.
494 **198** 25p. violet 20 20
495 　　50p. blue 25 20
496 　　150p. brown 55 35

199 Assembly Building

1963. National Assembly.
497 **199** 25p. brown 15 15
498 　　50p. red 20 20
499 　　75p. brown 25 20
500 　　100p. olive 25 15
501 　　125p. lilac 30 20

200 Balkh Gate　　201 Kemal Ataturk

1963.
502 **200** 3a. brown 95 25

1963. 25th Death Anniv of Kemal Ataturk.
503 **201** 1a. blue 15 20
504 　　3a. violet 60 40

202 Mohamed Zahir　　203 Afghan Stamp of
Shah　　　　　　　　1878

1963. King's 49th Birthday.
505 **202** 25p. green 20 20
506 　　50p. grey 25 20
507 　　75p. red 25 20
508 　　100p. brown 35 20

1964. "Philately". Stamp Day.
509 **203** 1a.25 black, green & gold . . 25 20
510 　　5a. black, red and gold . . 45 35

204 Kabul International Airport

1964. Air. Inaug of Kabul Int Airport.
511 **204** 10a. green and purple . . . 25
512 　　20a. purple and green . . 1·10 40
513 　　50a. turquoise and blue . 2·50 1·00

205 Kandahar International
Airport

1964. Air. Inauguration of Kandahar Int Airport.
514 **205** 7a.75 brown 65 40
515 　　9a.25 blue 85 75
516 　　10a.50 green . . . . . . 1·10 90
517 　　13a.75 red . . . . 1·25 90

206 Unisphere and Flags　　207 "Flame of
　　　　　　　　　　　　　　Freedom"

1964. New York World's Fair.
518 **206** 6a. black, red and green . . 25 20

1964. 1st U.N. Human Rights Seminar, Kabul.
519 **207** 3a.75 multicoloured . . . 25 15

208 Snow Leopard

1964. Afghan Wildlife.
520 **208** 25p. blue and yellow . . . 55 15
521 　　50p. green and red . . . 60 15
522 　　75p. purple and blue . . . 60 15
523 　　5a. brown and green . . . 75 20
ANIMALS—VERT: 50p. Ibex. HORIZ: 75p. Argali;
5a. Yak.

209 Herat　　210 Hurdling

1964. Tourist Publicity. Inscr "1964".
524 **209** 25p. brown and blue . . . 20 15
525 　　75p. blue and ochre . . . 25 15
526 　　3a. black, red and green . 40 25
DESIGNS—VERT: 75p. Tomb of Gowhar Shad,
Herat. HORIZ: 3a. Map and flag.

1964. Olympic Games, Tokyo.
527 **210** 25p. sepia, red and bistre . 15 10
528 　　1a. sepia, red and blue . . 15 10
529 　　3a.75 sepia, red and green . 40 25
530 　　5a. sepia, red and brown . 50 25
DESIGNS—VERT: 1a. Diving. HORIZ: 3a.75,
Wrestling; 5a. Football.

211 Afghan Flag　　212 Pashtu Flag

1964. 46th Independence Day.
531 **211** 25p. multicoloured 20 15
532 　　75p. multicoloured . . . 25 15
On the above the Pushtu inscription "33rd
Anniversary" is blocked out in gold.

1964. Pashtunistan Day.
533 **212** 100p. multicoloured . . . 20 15

213 Mohamed Zahir　　214 "Blood
Shah　　　　　　　　Transfusion"

1964. King's 50th Birthday.
534 **213** 1a.25 green and gold . . . 25 20
535 　　3a.75 red and gold . . . 40 35
536 　　50a. black and gold . . . 2·75 2·00

1964. Red Crescent Day.
537 **214** 1a.+50p. red and black . . 20 15

215 Badges of Afghanistan and
U.N.

1964. U.N. Day.
538 **215** 5a. blue, black and gold . . 20 15

216 Doves with Necklace　　217 M. Jami

1964. Women's Day.
539 **216** 25p. blue, green and pink . . 15 15
540 　　75p. blue, green & lt blue . 15 15
541 　　1a. blue, green and silver . 25 10

1964. 550th Birth Anniv of Mowlana Jami (poet).
542 **217** 1a.50 cream, green & blk . 1·00 85

218 Scaly-bellied Green　　220 "The Red City"
Woodpecker

1965. Birds. Multicoloured.
543 　　1a.25 Type **218** . . . . . . 2·25 50
544 　　3a.75 Lanceolated jay (vert) . 4·50 1·25
545 　　5a. Himalayan monal
　　　　pheasant (vert) . . . . . 5·25 2·40

219 I.T.U. Emblem and Symbols

1965. Centenary of I.T.U.
546 **219** 5a. black, red and blue . . 50 25

1965. Tourist Publicity. Inscr "1965". Mult.
547 　　1a. Type **220** 25 10
548 　　3a.75 Bami Yan (valley and
　　　　mountains) 35 20
549 　　5a. Band-E-Amir (lake and
　　　　mountains) 55 25

221 I.C.Y. Emblem

1965. International Co-operation Year.
550 **221** 5a. multicoloured 40 35

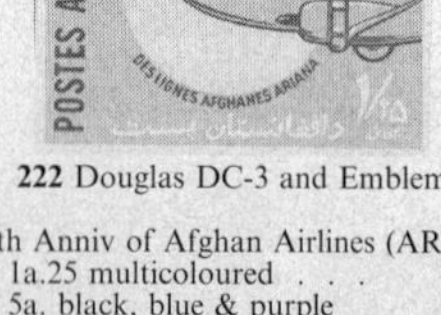

222 Douglas DC-3 and Emblem

1965. 10th Anniv of Afghan Airlines (ARIANA).
551 **222** 1a.25 multicoloured . . . 30 10
552 　　5a. black, blue & purple . . 85 20
553 　　10a. multicoloured . . . 1·50 50
DESIGNS: 5a. Convair CV 240; 10a. Douglas
DC-6A.

223 Mohamed Nadir Shah

224 Pashtu Flag

1965. 47th Independence Day.
554 **223** 1a. brown, black & green ... 40 10

1965. Pashtunistan Day.
555 **224** 1a. multicoloured 35 10

225 Promulgation of New Constitution

1965. New Constitution.
556 **225** 1a.50 black and green .. 30 15

226 Mohamed Zahir Shah

227 First Aid Post

1965. King's 51st Birthday.
557 **226** 1a.25 brown, blue & pink ... 25 10
558 6a. indigo, purple & blue ... 35 30
See also Nos. 579/80, 606/7 and 637/8.

1965. Red Crescent Day.
559 **227** 1a.50+50 brn, grn & red ... 20 15

228 U.N. and Afghan Flags

1965. U.N. Day.
560 **228** 5a. multicoloured 20 20

229 Fat-tailed Gecko

1966. Reptiles. Multicoloured.
561 3a. Type **229** 40 20
562 4a. "Agama caucasica" (lizard) 55 20
563 8a. "Testudo horsfieldi" (tortoise) 70 35

230 Cotton

231 Footballer

1966. Agriculture Day. Multicoloured.
564 1a. Type **230** 20 10
565 5a. Silkworm moth (caterpillar) 40 20
566 7a. Oxen 45 30

1966. World Cup Football Championship, England.
567 **231** 2a. black and red ... 25 15
568 6a. black and blue ... 50 25
569 12a. black and brown ... 1·00 50

232 Independence Memorial

1966. Independence Day.
570 **232** 1a. multicoloured 15 10
571 3a. multicoloured 30 15

233 Pashtu Flag

1966. Pashtunistan Day.
572 **233** 1a. blue 25 10

234 Founding Members

1966. Red Crescent Day.
573 **234** 2a.+1a. green and red ... 25 10
574 5a.+1a. brown & mve ... 45 15

235 Map of Afghanistan

1966. Tourist Publicity. Multicoloured.
575 2a. Type **235** 20 10
576 4a. Bagh-i-Bala, former Palace of Abdur Rahman ... 40 20
577 8a. Tomb of Abdur Rahman, Kabul 55 40

1966. King's 52nd Birthday. Portrait similar to T **226** but with position of inscr changed. Dated "1966".
579 1a. green 25 10
580 5a. brown 35 15

236 Mohamed Zahir Shah and U.N. Emblem

1966. U.N. Day. Inscr "20TH ANNIVERSAIRE DES REFUGIES".
581 **236** 5a. green, brown & emer ... 35 15
582 10a. red, green & yellow ... 70 25

237 Children Dancing

1966. Child Welfare Day.
583 **237** 1a.+1a. red and green ... 20 10
584 3a.+2a. brown & yell ... 40 20
585 7a.+3a. green & purple ... 65 40

238 Construction of Power Station

239 U.N.E.S.C.O. Emblem

1967. Afghan Industrial Development. Mult.
586 2a. Type **238** 20 10
587 5a. Handwoven carpet (vert) ... 25 15
588 8a. Cement works 35 20

1967. 20th Anniv (1966) of U.N.E.S.C.O.
589 **239** 2a. multicoloured ... 25 15
590 6a. multicoloured ... 40 20
591 12a. multicoloured ... 85 20

240 I.T.Y. Emblem

241 Inoculation

1967. International Tourist Year.
592 **240** 2a. black, blue and yellow 10 10
593 6a. black, blue and brown 35 20
DESIGN: 6a. I.T.Y. emblem on map of Afghanistan.

1967. Anti-tuberculosis Campaign.
595 **241** 2a.+1a. black & yellow ... 15 10
596 5a.+2a. brown & pink ... 35 25

242 Hydroelectric Power Station, Dorunta

243 Rhesus Macaque

1967. Development of Electricity for Agriculture.
597 **242** 1a. lilac and green 10 10
598 6a. turquoise and brown ... 30 20
599 8a. blue and purple ... 35 25
DESIGNS—VERT: 6a. Dam. HORIZ: 8a. Reservoir, Jalalabad.

1967. Wildlife.
600 **243** 2a. blue and buff 30 10
601 6a. sepia and green ... 55 25
602 12a. brown and blue ... 85 50
ANIMALS—HORIZ: 6a. Striped hyena; 12a. Goitred gazelles.

244 "Saving the Guns at Maiwand" (after R. Caton Woodville)

1967. Independence Day.
603 **244** 1a. brown and red ... 20 10
604 2a. brown and mauve ... 30 15

245 Pashtu Dancers

1967. Pashtunistan Day.
605 **245** 2a. violet and purple ... 25 10

1967. King's 53rd Birthday. Portrait similar to T **226** but with position of inscr changed. Dated "1967".
606 2a. brown 15 10
607 8a. blue 50 25

246 Red Crescent

247 U.N. Emblem and Fireworks

1967. Red Crescent Day.
608 **246** 3a.+1a. red, blk & ol ... 15 10
609 5a.+1a. red, blk & blue ... 25 15

1967. U.N. Day.
610 **247** 10a. multicoloured ... 45 25

248 Wrestling

249 Said Jamal-ud-Din Afghan

1967. Olympic Games, Mexico City.
611 **248** 4a. purple and green ... 25 10
612 6a. brown and red ... 40 15
DESIGN: 6a. Wrestling throw.

1967. 70th Death Anniv of Said Afghan.
614 **249** 1a. purple 10 10
615 5a. brown 35 15

250 Bronze Vase

251 W.H.O. Emblem

1967. Archaeological Treasures (11th–12th century Ghasnavide era).
616 **250** 3a. brown and green ... 25 10
617 7a. green and yellow ... 45 20
DESIGN: 7a. Bronze jar.

1968. 20th Anniv of W.H.O.
619 **251** 2a. blue and bistre ... 15 10
620 7a. blue and red 25 15

252 Karakul Sheep

1968. Agricultural Day.
621 **252** 1a. black and yellow ... 10 10
622 6a. brown, black and blue ... 40 15
623 12a. brown, sepia & blue ... 55· 25

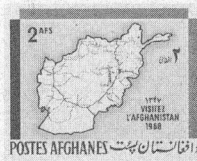
253 Map of Afghanistan

1968. Tourist Publicity. Multicoloured.
624 2a. Type **253** 20 10
625 3a. Victory Tower, Ghazni (21 × 31 mm) 25 10
626 16a. Mausoleum, Ghazni (21 × 31 mm) 65 35

254 Queen Humaira

255 Cinereous Vulture

1968. Mothers' Day.
627 **254** 2a.+2a. brown 15 15
628 7a.+2a. green 50 35

1968. Wild Birds. Multicoloured.
629 1a. Type **255** ...... 1·00 40
630 6a. Eagle owl ...... 2·25 1·10
631 7a. Greater flamingos ... 3·25 1·25

256 "Pig-sticking"

1968. Olympic Games, Mexico. Multicoloured.
632 2a. Olympic flame and rings (21 × 31 mm) 15 10
633 8a. Type **256** 35 20
634 12a. Buzkashi game 50 30

257 Flowers on Gun-carriage

1968. Independence Day.
635 **257** 6a. multicoloured 25 15

258 Pashtu Flag

259 Red Crescent

1968. Pashtunistan Day.
636 258 3a. multicoloured 20 10

1968. King's 54th Birthday. Portrait similar to T **226** but differently arranged and in smaller size (21 × 31 mm).
637 2a. blue 20 10
638 8a. brown 30 25

1968. Red Crescent Day.
639 259 4a.+1a. multicoloured . . . 30 20

260 Human Rights Emblem
261 Maolala Djalalodine Balkhi

1968. U.N. Day and Human Rights Year.
640 260 1a. brown, bistre & green 10 10
641 2a. black, bistre & violet 15 10
642 6a. violet, bistre & purple 35 15

1968. 695th Death Anniv of Maolala Djalalodine Balkhi (historian).
644 261 4a. mauve and green . . . 20 10

262 Temple Painting
263 I.L.O. Emblem

1969. Archaeological Treasures (Bagram era).
645 262 1a. red, yellow and green 25 10
646 — 3a. purple and violet . . . 45 20
DESIGN: 3a. Carved vessel.

1969. 50th Anniv of I.L.O.
648 263 5a. black and yellow . . . 25 15
649 8a. black and blue 45 20

264 Red Cross Emblems
266 Mother and Child

1969. 50th Anniv of League of Red Cross Societies.
650 264 3a.+1a. multicoloured . . 45 20
651 5a.+1a. multicoloured . . 65 20
On Nos. 650/1 the commemorative inscr in English and Pushtu for the 50th anniv of the League of Red Cross Societies has been obliterated by gold bars.

1969. Mothers' Day.
654 266 1a.+1a. brown & yell . . 20 20
655 4a.+1a. violet & mve . . 40 40

267 Road Map of Afghanistan
268 Bust (Hadda era)

1969. Tourist Publicity. Badakshan and Pamir Region. Multicoloured.
657 2a. Type **267** 25 10
658 4a. Pamir landscape 25 15
659 7a. Mountain mule transport 45 25

1969. Archaeological Discoveries. Multicoloured.
661 10a. Type **268** 10 10
662 5a. Vase and jug (Bagram period) 40 15
663 10a. Statuette (Bagram period) 65 20

269 Mohamed Zahir Shah and Queen Humaira
270 Map and Rising Sun

1969. Independence Day.
664 269 5a. red, blue and gold . . 40 15
665 10a. green, purple & gold 55 25

1969. Pashtunistan Day.
666 270 2a. red and blue 25 10

271 Mohamed Zahir Shah
272 Red Crescent

1969. King's 55th Birthday.
667 271 2a. multicoloured 20 10
668 6a. multicoloured 45 15

1969. Red Crescent Day.
669 272 6a.+1a. multicoloured . . 60 20

273 U.N. Emblem, Afghan Arms and Flag

1969. United Nations Day.
670 273 5a. multicoloured 25 15

274 I.T.U. Emblem
275 Indian Crested Porcupine

1969. World Telecommunications Day.
671 274 6a. multicoloured 20 15
672 12a. multicoloured 40 25

1969. Wild Animals. Multicoloured.
673 1a. Type **275** 20 10
674 3a. Wild boar 45 10
675 8a. Bactrian red deer 65 15

276 Footprint on the Moon
277 "Cancer the Crab"

1969. 1st Man on the Moon.
676 276 1a. multicoloured 10 10
677 3a. multicoloured 15 10
678 6a. multicoloured 20 15
679 10a. multicoloured 35 30

1970. W.H.O. "Fight Cancer" Day.
680 277 2a. red, dp green & green 15 10
681 6a. red, deep blue & blue 25 20

278 Mirza Bedel
279 I.E.Y. Emblem

1970. 250th Death Anniv of Mirza Abdul Quader Bedel (poet).
682 278 5a. multicoloured 30 10

1970. International Education Year.
683 279 1a. black 10 10
684 6a. red 25 10
685 12a. green 50 25

280 Mother and Child
281 U.N. Emblem, Scales and Satellite

1970. Mothers' Day.
686 280 6a. multicoloured 25 20

1970. 25th Anniv of United Nations.
687 281 4a. blue, dp blue & yellow 15 15
688 6a. blue, deep blue & red 25 15

282 Map of Afghanistan with Location of Sites
283 Common Quail

1970. Tourist Publicity. Inscr "1970". Mult.
689 282 2a. black, green and blue 20 10
690 — 3a. multicoloured 25 10
691 — 7a. multicoloured 55 15
DESIGNS (36 × 26 mm): 3a. Lakeside mosque, Kabul; 7a. Arch of Paghman.

1970. Wild Birds. Multicoloured.
692 2a. Type **283** . . . . 1·40 50
693 4a. Golden eagle . . . . . . 2·75 80
694 6a. Common pheasant . . . 3·25 1·25

284 Shah Reviewing Troops

1970. Independence Day.
695 284 8a. multicoloured 35 35

285 Group of Pashtus

1970. Pashtunistan Day.
696 285 2a. blue and red 35 10

286 Mohamed Zahir Shah
287 Red Crescent Emblems

1970. King's 56th Birthday.
697 286 3a. violet and green . . . 15 10
698 7a. purple and blue . . . 55 15

1970. Red Crescent Day.
699 287 2a. black, red and gold 15 10

288 U.N. Emblem and Plaque

1970. United Nations Day.
700 288 1a. multicoloured 10 10
701 5a. multicoloured 15 25

289 Afghan Stamps of 1871

1970. Centenary of First Afghan Stamps.
702 289 1a. black, blue & orange 20 10
703 4a. black, yellow & blue 25 15
704 12a. black, blue and lilac 45 25

290 Global Emblem

1971. World Telecommunications Day.
705 290 12a. multicoloured . . . 50 25

291 "Callimorpha principalis"
292 Lower half of old Kushan Statue

1971. Butterflies and Moths. Multicoloured.
706 1a. Type **291** 30 10
707 3a. "Epizygaenella afghana" 45 10
708 5a. "Parnassius autocrator" 75 15

1971. U.N.E.S.C.O. Kushan Seminar.
709 292 6a. violet and yellow . . 35 15
710 10a. purple and blue . . . 55 20

293 Independence Memorial

1971. Independence Day.
711 293 7a. multicoloured 40 15
712 9a. multicoloured 55 20

294 Pashtunistan Square, Kabul

1971. Pashtunistan Day.
713 294 5a. purple 35 15

295 Mohamed Zahir Shah and Kabul Airport

1971. Air. Multicoloured.
714 50a. Type **295** . . . . . . 3·25 3·00
715 100a. King, airline emblem
and Boeing 727 airplane . . 3·50 2·50

296 Mohamed Zahir Shah
297 Map, Nurse and Patients

1971. King's 57th Birthday.
716 **296** 9a. multicoloured 40 25
717 17a. multicoloured . . . 75 35

1971. Red Crescent Day.
718 **297** 8a. multicoloured 40 15

298 Emblem of Racial Equality Year
299 Human Heart

1971. United Nations Day.
719 **298** 24a. blue . . . . 1·25 50

1972. World Health Day and World Heart Month.
720 **299** 9a. multicoloured 35 20
721 12a. multicoloured 45 25

300 "Tulipa lanata"
301 Buddha of Hadda

1972. Afghan Flora and Fauna. Multicoloured.
722 7a. Type **300** 60 60
723 10a. Chukar partridge (horiz) 3·75 1·40
724 12a. Lynx (horiz) . . . . 1·25 1·00
725 18a. "Allium stipitatum" . . 1·25 1·10

1972. Tourist Publicity.
726 **301** 3a. blue and brown . . . 25 15
727 — 7a. green and red 40 20
728 — 9a. purple and green . . 50 25
DESIGNS: 7a. Greco-Bactrian seal; 250 B.C.; 9a. Greek temple, Ai-Khanum, 3rd–2nd century B.C.

302 King with Queen Humaira at Independence Parade

1972. Independence Day.
729 **302** 25a. multicoloured . . . . 1·50 1·25

303 Wrestling

1972. Olympic Games, Munich. Various Wrestling Holds as T **303**.
730 4a. multicoloured 25 10
731 8a. multicoloured 40 20
732 10a. multicoloured 55 25
733 19a. multicoloured 75 30
734 21a. multicoloured 95 30

304 Pathan and Mountain View
305 Mohamed Zahir Shah

1972. Pashtunistan Day.
736 **304** 5a. multicoloured 40 10

1972. King's 58th Birthday.
737 **305** 5a. blue, black and gold . . 50 15
738 14a. brown, black & gold . . 90 35

306 Ruined Town and Refugees

1972. Red Crescent Day.
739 **306** 7a. black, red and blue . . 50 15

307 E.C.A.F.E. Emblem

1972. U.N. Day. 25th Anniv of U.N. Economic Commission for Asia and the Far East.
740 **307** 12a. black and blue . . . 45 25

308 Ceramics

1973. Afghan Handicrafts. Multicoloured.
741 7a. Type **308** 40 25
742 9a. Embroidered coat (vert) 55 25
743 12a. Coffee set (vert) . . . 65 35
744 16a. Decorated boxes 90 35

309 W.M.O. and Afghan Emblems

1973. Cent of World Meteorological Organization.
746 **309** 7a. green and mauve . . . 50 15
747 14a. red and blue . . . . 1·00 30

310 Emblems and Harvester

1973. 10th Anniv of World Food Programme.
748 **310** 14a.+7a. purple & blue . . 1·00 1·00

311 Al-Biruni
312 Association Emblem

1973. Birth Millenary of Abu-al Rayhan al-Biruni (mathematician and philosopher).
749 **311** 10a. multicoloured 60 30

1973. Family Planning Week.
750 **312** 9a. purple and orange . . 60 20

313 Himalayan Monal Pheasant

1973. Birds. Multicoloured.
751 8a. Type **313** . . . . 2·25 2·00
752 9a. Great crested grebe . . . 2·75 2·25
753 12a. Himalayan snowcock . . . 3·25 3·00

314 Buzkashi Game

1973. Tourism.
754 **314** 8a. black 40 15

315 Firework Display

1973. Independence Day.
755 **315** 12a. multicoloured . . . 55 25

316 Landscape and Flag

1973. Pashtunistan Day.
756 **316** 9a. multicoloured 60 20

317 Red Crescent

1973. Red Crescent.
757 **317** 10a. multicoloured 85 25

318 Kemal Ataturk

1973. 50th Anniv of Turkish Republic.
758 **318** 1a. blue 25 10
759 7a. brown 80 15

319 Human Rights Flame

1973. 25th Anniv of Declaration of Human Rights.
760 **319** 12a. blue, black and silver 40 25

320 Asiatic Black Bears

1974. Wild Animals. Multicoloured.
761 5a. Type **320** 35 10
762 7a. Afghan hound 55 20
763 10a. Goitred gazelle 70 25
764 12a. Leopard 90 30

321 "Workers"

1974. Labour Day.
766 **321** 9a. multicoloured 35 15

322 Arch of Paghman and Independence Memorial

1974. Independence Day.
767 **322** 4a. multicoloured 40 10
768 11a. multicoloured 50 20

323 Arms of Afghanistan and Hands clasping Seedling

1974. 1st Anniv of Republic. Multicoloured.
769 4a. Type **323** 40 10
770 5a. Republican flag
(36 × 26 mm) 50 15
771 7a. Gen. Mohammed Daoud
(26 × 36 mm) 65 15
772 15a. Soldiers and arms . . . 1·00 25

324 Lesser Spotted Eagle

1974. Afghan Birds. Multicoloured.
774 1a. Type **324** . . . . 1·25 40
775 6a. White-fronted goose,
ruddy shelduck and greylag
goose . . . . 2·75 70
776 11a. Black crane and
common coots . . . . 4·25 1·10

325 Flags of Pashtunistan and Afghanistan

1974. Pashtunistan Day.
777 325 5a. multicoloured   20   15

326 Republic's Coat of Arms

1974.
778 326 100p. green   65   25

327 Pres. Daoud   328 Arms and Centenary Years

1974.
779 327 10a. multicoloured . . .   35   20
780   16a. multicoloured . . .   1·00   40
781   19a. multicoloured . . .   65   40
782   21a. multicoloured . . .   75   35
783   22a. multicoloured . . .   1·25   50
784   30a. multicoloured . . .   1·50   50

1974. Centenary of U.P.U.
785 328 7a. green, black and gold   20   10

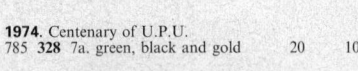

329 "UN" and U.N. Emblem   330 Pres. Daoud

1974. United Nations Day.
786 329 5a. blue and ultramarine   35   10

1975.
787 330 50a. multicoloured . . .   1·50   85
788   100a. multicoloured . . .   3·00   1·60

331 Minaret, Jam

1975. South Asia Tourist Year. Multicoloured.
789 331 7a. Type 331   30   15
790   14a. "Griffon and Lady" (2nd century) . . .   55   30
791   15a. Head of Buddha (4th–5th century) . . .   65   30

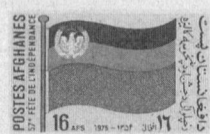

332 Afghan Flag

1975. Independence Day.
793 332 16a. multicoloured . . .   70   25

333 Rejoicing Crowd

1975. 2nd Anniv of Revolution.
794 333 9a. multicoloured . . .   45   15
795   12a. multicoloured . . .   65   20

334 I.W.Y. Emblem   335 Rising Sun and Flag

1975. International Women's Year.
796 334 9a. black, blue and purple   50   15

1975. Pashtunistan Day.
797 335 10a. multicoloured . . .   40   15

336 Wazir M. Akbar Khan   337 Independence Monument and Arms

1976. 130th Death Anniv of Akbar Khan (resistance leader).
798 336 15a. multicoloured . . .   50   25

1976. Independence Day.
799 337 22a. multicoloured . . .   60   30

338 Pres. Daoud raising Flag   339 Mountain

1976. 3rd Anniv of Republic.
800 338 30a. multicoloured . . .   85   50

1976. Pashtunistan Day.
801 339 16a. multicoloured . . .   50   30

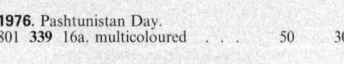

340 Arms

1976.
802   – 25p. salmon   40   25
803 340 50p. green   50   15
804   1a. blue   50   10
DESIGN: 25p. As Type 340 but with Arms on left and inscription differently arranged.

341 Flag and Monuments on Open Book

1977. Independence Day.
805 341 20a. multicoloured . . .   45   30

342 Presidential Address

1977. Election of First President and New Constitution. Multicoloured.
806   7a. President Daoud and Election (45 × 27 mm) . .   40   10
807   8a. Type 342   45   10
808   10a. Inaugural ceremony . .   65   15
809   18a. Promulgation of new constitution (45 × 27 mm)   85   30

343 Medal   344 Crowd with Afghan Flag

1977. 80th Death Anniv of Sayed Jamaluddin (Afghan reformer).
811 343 12a. black, blue & gold   40   20

1977. Republic Day.
812 344 22a. multicoloured . . .   65   35

345 Dancers around Fountain   346 Dome of the Rock

1977. Pashtunistan Day.
813 345 30a. multicoloured . . .   90   50

1977. Palestinian Welfare.
814 346 12a.+3a. black, gold and pink . . . .   2·00   60

347 Arms and Carrier Pigeon

1977.
815 347 1a. blue and black . . .   50   15

348 President Daoud acknowledging Crowd

1978. 1st Anniv of Presidential Election.
816 348 20a. multicoloured . . .   75   40

349 U.P.U. Emblem on Map of Afghanistan

1978. 50th Anniv of Admission to U.P.U.
817 349 10a. gold, green & black   40   15

350 Transmitting Aerial and Early Telephone

1978. 50th Anniv of Admission to I.T.U.
818 350 8a. multicoloured   35   10

351 Red Crescent, Red Cross and Red Lion Emblems

1978. Red Crescent.
819 351 3a. black   40   15

352 Arms

1978.
820 352 1a. red and gold   45   15
821   4a. red and gold   75   10

353 Ruin, Qalai Bust

1978. Independence Day. Multicoloured.
822   16a. Buddha, Bamian . . .   75   25
823   22a. Type 353   85   40
824   30a. Women in national costume . . . .   1·50   75

 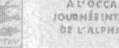

354 Afghans with Flag   355 Crest and Symbols of the Five Senses

1978. Pashtunistan Day.
825 354 7a. red and blue   50   15

1978. International Literacy Day.
826 355 20a. red   85   35

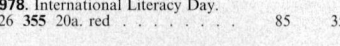

356 Flag

1978. "The Mail is in the Service of the People".
827 356 8a. red, gold and brown   60   15
828   9a. red, gold and brown   90   15

357 Martyr   358 President Mohammed Taraki

1978. "The People's Democratic Party Honours its Martyrs".
829 357 18a. green 95 30

1978. 14th Anniv of People's Democratic Party.
830 358 12a. multicoloured . . . 85 10

359 Emancipated Woman

1979. Women's Day.
831 359 14a. blue and red 85 40

360 Farmers planting Tree

1979. Farmers' Day.
832 360 1a. multicoloured 45 15

361 Map and Census Taking

1979. 1st Complete Population Census.
833 361 3a. black, blue and red . . 50 15

362 Pres. Taraki reading "Khalq"

1979. 1st Publication of "Khalq" (party newspaper).
834 362 2a. multicoloured 55 15

363 Pres. Taraki and   364 Pres. Taraki
Tank

1979. 1st Anniv of Sawr Revolution (1st issue).
835 363 50p. multicoloured . . . 60 15

1979. 1st Anniv of Sawr Revolution (2nd issue). Multicoloured.
836   4a. Type 364 . . . . 40 10
837   5a. Revolutionary H.Q. and Tank Monument, Kabul (47 × 32 mm) 55 10
838   6a. Command room, Revolutionary H.Q. (vert) 65 15
839   12a. House where first Khalq Party Congress was held (vert) 90 25

372 Woman with   374 Healthy Non-smoker
Baby, Dove and   and Prematurely Aged
Rifle   Smoker

365 Carpenter and Blacksmith

1979. Workers' Solidarity.
840 365 10a. multicoloured 85 15

366 Children on Map of Afghanistan

1979. International Year of the Child.
841 366 16a. multicoloured . . . . 1·50 65

367 Revolutionaries   368 Afghans and
and Kabul   Flag
Monuments

1979. Independence Day.
842 367 30a. multicoloured . . . 1·25 65

1979. Pashtunistan Day.
843 368 9a. multicoloured 75 15

369 U.P.U. Emblem and Arms on Map

1979. Stamp Day.
844 369 15a. multicoloured . . . 60 20

370 Headstone and Tomb

1979. Martyrs' Day.
845 370 22a. multicoloured . . . 1·60 45

371 Doves around Globe

1979.
845a 371 2a. blue and red 85 15

373 Farmers receiving Land Grants

1980. International Women's Day.
846 372 8a. multicoloured . . . . 1·10 25

1980. Farmers' Day.
847 373 2a. multicoloured . . . . 1·75 65

1980. World Health Day. Anti-smoking Campaign.
848 374 5a. multicoloured . . . . 1·50 60

375 "Lenin speaking from Tribune"

1980. 110th Birth Anniv of Lenin.
849 375 12a. multicoloured . . . 2·50 75

376 Crowd and Clenched Fist

1980. 2nd Anniv of Sawr Revolution.
850 376 1a. multicoloured 65 15

377 Quarry Worker and Blacksmith

1980. Workers' Solidarity.
851 377 9a. multicoloured 45 15

378 Football   379 Soldiers attacking
Fortress

1980. Olympic Games, Moscow. Mult.
852   3a. Type 378 . . . . . . 60 15
853   6a. Wrestling 65 15
854   9a. Pigsticking 75 15
855   10a. Buzkashi 85 20

1980. Independence Day.
856 379 3a. multicoloured 60 15

380 Pashtus with Flag

1980. Pashtunistan Day.
857 380 25a. multicoloured . . . 1·00 35

381 Post Office

1980. World U.P.U. Day.
858 381 20a. multicoloured . . . 85 35

382 Buzkashi

1980.
859 382 50a. multicoloured . . . 1·60 1·10
860   100a. multicoloured . . . 3·00 1·25

383 Arabic "H", Medina Mosque and Kaaba

1981. 1400th Anniv of Hegira.
861 383 13a.+2a. multicoloured . . 1·50 25

384 Mother and Child with Dove and Globe

1981. International Women's Day.
862 384 15a. multicoloured . . . 95 25

385 Ox Plough, Tractor and Planting Trees

1981. Farmers' Day.
863 385 1a. multicoloured 80 20

386 Urial   387 Crowd and Afghan
Arms

1981. Protected Wildlife.
864 386 12a. multicoloured . . . 75 50

1981. 3rd Anniv of Sawr Revolution.
865 387 50p. brown 55 10

388 Road Workers   389 Red Crescent enclosing
in Ravine   Scenes of Disaster and
Medical Aid

1981. Workers' Day.
866 388 10a. multicoloured . . . 65 20

1981. Red Crescent Day.
867 389 1a.+4a. multicoloured . . 50 60

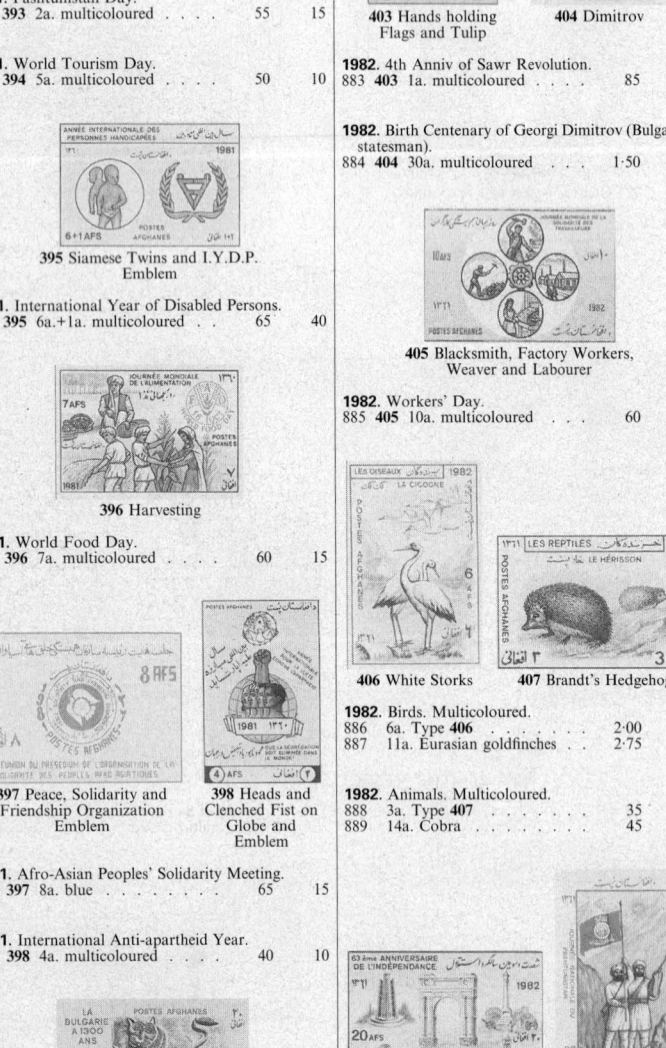

390 Satellite Receiving Station **391** Map enclosing playing Children

1981. World Telecommunications Day.
868 390 9a. multicoloured 50 15

1981. International Children's Day.
869 391 15a. multicoloured . . . 65 30

392 Afghans and Monument

1981. Independence Day.
870 392 4a. multicoloured 65 15

393 Pashtus around Flag **394** Terracotta Horseman

1981. Pashtunistan Day.
871 393 2a. multicoloured 55 15

1981. World Tourism Day.
872 394 5a. multicoloured 50 10

395 Siamese Twins and I.Y.D.P. Emblem

1981. International Year of Disabled Persons.
873 395 6a.+1a. multicoloured . . 65 40

396 Harvesting

1981. World Food Day.
874 396 7a. multicoloured 60 15

397 Peace, Solidarity and Friendship Organization Emblem **398** Heads and Clenched Fist on Globe and Emblem

1981. Afro-Asian Peoples' Solidarity Meeting.
875 397 8a. blue 65 15

1981. International Anti-apartheid Year.
876 398 4a. multicoloured 40 10

399 Lion (bas-relief at Stara Zagora)

1981. 1300th Anniv of Bulgarian State.
877 399 20a. stone, purple and red 1·10 40

---

400 Mother rocking Cradle

1982. Women's Day.
878 400 6a. multicoloured . . . 45 10

401 Farmers **402** Judas Tree

1982. Farmers' Day.
879 401 4a. multicoloured 50 10

1982. Plants. Multicoloured.
880 3a, Type **402** 25 10
881 4a. Hollyhock 50 10
882 16a. Rhubarb 95 30

403 Hands holding Flags and Tulip **404** Dimitrov

1982. 4th Anniv of Sawr Revolution.
883 403 1a. multicoloured . . . 85 15

1982. Birth Centenary of Georgi Dimitrov (Bulgarian statesman).
884 404 30a. multicoloured . . . 1·50 60

405 Blacksmith, Factory Workers, Weaver and Labourer

1982. Workers' Day.
885 405 10a. multicoloured . . . 60 20

406 White Storks **407** Brandt's Hedgehog

1982. Birds. Multicoloured.
886 6a. Type **406** . . . . . . 2·00 65
887 11a. Eurasian goldfinches . . 2·75 85

1982. Animals. Multicoloured.
888 3a. Type **407** 35 15
889 14a. Cobra 45 25

408 National Monuments **409** Pashtus and Flag

1982. Independence Day.
890 408 20a. multicoloured . . . 85 40

1982. Pashtunistan Day.
891 409 32a. multicoloured . . . 1·60 55

410 Tourists

1982. World Tourism Day.
892 410 9a. multicoloured . . . 55 20

411 Postman delivering Letter, Post Office and U.P.U. Emblem

1982. World U.P.U. Day.
893 411 4a. multicoloured . . . 60 20

412 Family eating Meal **413** U.N. Emblem illuminating Globe

1982. World Food Day.
894 412 9a. multicoloured . . . 85 20

1982. 37th Anniv of United Nations.
895 413 15a. multicoloured . . . 80 30

414 Earth Satellite Station

1982. I.T.U. Delegates' Conference, Nairobi.
896 414 8a. multicoloured 55 15

415 Dr. Robert Koch **416** Hand holding Torch, Globe and Scales

1982. Centenary of Discovery of Tubercle Bacillus.
897 415 7a. black, brown & pink . 40 25

1982. 34th Anniv of Declaration of Human Rights.
898 416 5a. multicoloured 30 15

417 Lions

1982. Wild Animals. Multicoloured.
899 2a. Type **417** 20 10
900 7a. Asiatic wild asses . . . 40 25
901 12a. Sable (vert) 85 35

418 Woman releasing Dove **419** Mir Alicher-e-Nawai (poet)

1983. International Women's Day.
902 418 3a. multicoloured . . . 20 10

1983. "Mir Alicher-e-Nawai and his Times" Study Decade.
903 419 22a. multicoloured . . . 65 25

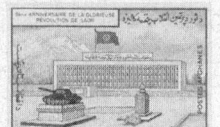

420 Distributing Land Ownership Documents

1983. Farmers' Day.
904 420 10a. multicoloured . . . 50 20

421 Revolution Monument

1983. 5th Anniv of Sawr Revolution.
905 421 15a. multicoloured . . . 45 20

422 World Map and Hands holding Cogwheel

1983. Labour Day.
906 422 20a. multicoloured . . . 55 20

423 Broadcasting Studio, Dish Aerial, Satellites and Television

1983. World Communications Year. Multicoloured.
907 4a. Type **423** 25 10
908 11a. Telecommunications headquarters 45 15

424 Hands holding Child **425** Arms and Map of Afghanistan

1983. International Children's Day.
909 424 25a. multicoloured . . . 60 25

1983. 2nd Anniv of National Fatherland Front.
910 425 1a. multicoloured 25 10

426 Apollo **427** Racial Segregation

1983. Butterflies. Multicoloured.
911 9a. Type **426** 35 25
912 13a. Swallowtail 85 45
913 21a. Small tortoiseshell (horiz) . . . . . . 1·00 55

1983. Anti-apartheid Campaign.
914 427 10a. multicoloured . . . 35 15

428 National Monuments   429 Pashtus with Flag

1983. Independence Day.
915 428 6a. multicoloured 30 10

1983. Pashtunistan Day.
916 429 3a. multicoloured 30 10

430 Afghan riding Camel

1983. World Tourism Day.
917 430 5a. multicoloured 25 10
918 – 7a. brown and black 35 15
919 – 12a. multicoloured . . . 45 15
920 – 16a. multicoloured . . . 65 15
DESIGNS—VERT: 7a. Stone carving. 16a. Carved stele. HORIZ: 12a. Three statuettes.

431 Winter Landscape

1983. Multicoloured.
921 50a. Type 431 . . . . . . 1·40 25
922 100a. Woman with camel . . 2·75 30

432 "Communications"

1983. World Communications Year. Mult.
923 14a. Type 432 . . . . . . 55 15
924 15a. Ministry of
     Communications, Kabul   55 15

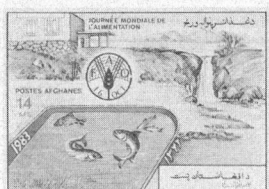

433 Fish Breeding

1983. World Food Day.
925 433 14a. multicoloured 80 15

434 Football

1983. Sports. Multicoloured.
926 1a. Type 434 . . . . . . 10 10
927 18a. Boxing 50 15
928 21a. Wrestling 65 15

435 Jewellery

1983. Handicrafts. Multicoloured.
929 2a. Type 435 . . . . . . 15 10
930 8a. Polished stoneware . . 25 10
931 9a. Furniture 45 10
932 30a. Leather goods 95 15

436 Map, Sun, Scales and Torch

1983. 35th Anniv of Declaration of Human Rights.
933 436 20a. multicoloured . . . 65 15

437 Polytechnic Buildings and Emblem

1983. 20th Anniv of Kabul Polytechnic.
934 437 30a. multicoloured . . . 95 20

438 Ice Skating   439 Dove, Woman and Globe

1984. Winter Olympic Games, Sarajevo. Mult.
935 5a. Type 438 . . . . . . 20 10
936 9a. Skiing 25 10
937 11a. Speed skating 35 10
938 15a. Ice hockey 45 10
939 18a. Biathlon 50 10
940 20a. Ski jumping 55 10
941 22a. Bobsleigh 65 15

1984. International Women's Day.
942 439 4a. multicoloured 10 10

440 Ploughing with Tractor

1984. Farmers' Day. Multicoloured.
943 2a. Type 440 . . . . . . 10 10
944 4a. Digging irrigation channel 15 10
945 7a. Saddling donkey by
     water-mill 15 10
946 9a. Harvesting wheat . . . 20 10
947 15a. Building haystack . . . 30 10
948 18a. Showing cattle 40 10
949 20a. Ploughing with oxen and
     sowing seed 45 10

441 "Luna I"

1984. World Aviation and Space Navigation Day.
Multicoloured.
950 5a. Type 441 . . . . . 15 10
951 8a. "Luna II" 25 10
952 11a. "Luna III" 35 10
953 17a. "Apollo XI" 40 10
954 22a. "Soyuz VI" 55 15
955 28a. "Soyuz VII" 55 15
956 34a. "Soyuz VI", "VII" and
     "VIII" 75 15

442 Flags, Soldier and Workers   443 Hunting Dog

1984. 6th Anniv of Sawr Revolution.
958 442 3a. multicoloured 30 10

1984. Animals. Multicoloured.
959 1a. Type 443 . . . . . . 10 10
960 2a. Argali 20 10

961 6a. Przewalski's horse (horiz) 45 10
962 8a. Wild boar 60 10
963 17a. Snow leopard (horiz) . . 1·25 15
964 19a. Tiger (horiz) . . . . 1·75 20
965 22a. Indian elephant . . . 2·25 25

444 Postal Messenger

1984. 19th U.P.U. Congress, Hamburg. Mult.
966 25a. Type 444 . . . . . . 75 15
967 35a. Post rider . . . . . 1·10 20
968 40a. Bird with letter . . . . 1·40 20

445 Antonov AN-2

1984. 40th Anniv of Ariana Airline. Mult.
970 1a. Type 445 . . . . . . 10 10
971 4a. Ilyushin Il-12 . . . . 15 10
972 9a. Tupolev Tu-104A . . . 45 10
973 10a. Ilyushin Il-18 . . . . 70 10
974 13a. Yakovlev Yak-42 . . . 85 10
975 17a. Tupolev Tu-154 . . . 1·10 15
976 21a. Ilyushin Il-86 . . . 1·25 15

446 Ettore Bugatti and Bugatti "43"

1984. Motor Cars. Multicolored.
977 2a. Type 446 . . . . . . 10 10
978 5a. Henry Ford and Ford
     "A", 1903 . . . . . 15 10
979 8a. Rene Panhard and 1899
     model 25 10
980 11a. Gottlieb Daimler and
     Daimler "DB 18", 1935 . . 30 10
981 12a. Karl Benz and Benz
     "Victoris", 1893 . . . 40 10
982 15a. Armand Peugeot and
     Peugeot "Vis-a-vis", 1892 45 10
983 22a. Louis Chevrolet and
     Chevrolet sedan, 1925 . . 55 10

447 Open Book showing Monuments and Fortress

1984. Independence Day.
984 447 6a. multicoloured 30 10

448 Truck on Mountain Road and Pashtunistan Badge

1984. Pashtunistan Day.
985 448 3a. multicoloured 25 10

449 Arch at Qalai Bust   450 Pine Cone

1984. World Tourism Day. Multicoloured.
986 1a. Type 449 . . . . . . 10 10
987 4a. Ornamented belt . . . 10 10
988 5a. Kabul monuments . . . 15 10
989 9a. Statuette (vert) 20 10
990 15a. Buffalo riders in snow . . 45 10
991 19a. Camel in ornate
     caparison 60 10
992 21a. Buzkashi players . . . 65 10

1984. World Food Day. Multicoloured.
993 2a. Type 450 . . . . . . 10 10

994 4a. Walnuts 20 10
995 6a. Pomegranate 25 10
996 9a. Apples 35 10
997 13a. Cherries 45 10
998 15a. Grapes 55 10
999 26a. Pears 85 10

451 Globe and Emblem

1985. 20th Anniv (1984) of Peoples' Democratic Party.
1000 451 25a. multicoloured . . . 85 10

452 Cattle   453 Map and Geologist

1985. Farmers' Day. Multicoloured.
1001 1a. Type 452 . . . . . . 10 10
1002 3a. Mare and foal 15 10
1003 7a. Galloping horse . . . 25 10
1004 9a. Grey horse (vert) . . . 30 10
1005 15a. Karakul sheep and
     sheepskins 45 10
1006 16a. Herder watching over
     cattle and sheep . . . 65 10
1007 25a. Family with pack
     camels 85 10

1985. Geologists' Day.
1008 453 4a. multicoloured . . . 25 10

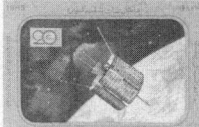

454 Satellite

1985. 20th Anniv of "Intelsat" Communications Satellite. Multicoloured.
1009 6a. Type 454 . . . . . . 45 10
1010 9a. "Intelsat III" 55 10
1011 10a. Rocket launch (vert) . . 75 10

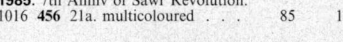

455 "Visitors for Lenin" (V. Serov)   456 Revolutionaries with Flags

1985. 115th Birth Anniv of Lenin. Multicoloured.
1012 10a. Type 455 . . . . . . 50 10
1013 15a. "With Lenin" (detail,
     V. Serov) 65 10
1014 25a. Lenin and Red Army
     fighters 85 10

1985. 7th Anniv of Sawr Revolution.
1016 456 21a. multicoloured . . . 85 10

457 Olympic Stadium and Moscow Skyline

1985. 12th World Youth and Students' Festival, Moscow. Multicoloured.
1017 7a. Type 457 . . . . . . 20 10
1018 12a. Festival emblem . . . 40 10
1019 13a. Moscow Kremlin . . . 45 10
1020 18a. Doll 60 10

458 Soviet Memorial, Berlin-Treptow, and Tank before Reichstag

1985. 40th Anniv of End of World War II. Multicoloured.
1021 6a. Type **458** 45 10
1022 9a. "Mother Homeland" war memorial, Volgograd, and fireworks over Moscow Kremlin 60 10
1023 10a. Cecilienhof Castle, Potsdam, and flags of United Kingdom, U.S.S.R. and U.S.A. . . . 75 10

459 Weighing Baby **460** Purple Blewit

1985. U.N.I.C.E.F. Child Survival Campaign. Mult.
1024 1a. Type **459** 10 10
1025 2a. Vaccinating child . . . 15 10
1026 4a. Breast-feeding baby . . 25 10
1027 5a. Mother and child . . . 25 10

1985. Fungi. Multicoloured.
1028 3a. Type **460** 15 10
1029 4a. Flaky-stemmed witches' mushroom 25 15
1030 7a. The blusher 35 20
1031 11a. Brown birch bolete . . 50 35
1032 12a. Common ink cap . . . 60 35
1033 18a. "Hypholoma sp." . . . 85 40
1034 20a. "Boletus aurantiacus" . . 90 40

461 Emblems

1985. United Nations Decade for Women.
1035 **461** 10a. multicoloured . . . 50 10

462 Evening Primrose

1985. "Argentina "85" International Stamp Exhibition, Buenos Aires. Flowers. Multicoloured.
1036 2a. Type **462** 10 10
1037 4a. Cockspur coral tree . . 15 10
1038 8a. "Tillandsia aeranthos" 25 10
1039 13a. Periwinkle 40 10
1040 18a. Marvel-of-Peru 60 10
1041 25a. "Cypella herbertii" . . 85 10
1042 30a. "Clytostoma callistegioides" . . . . . 1·00 10

463 Building

1985. Independence Day.
1044 **463** 33a. multicoloured . . . 1·40 15

464 Dancers in Pashtunistan Square, Kabul

1985. Pashtunistan Day.
1045 **464** 25a. multicoloured . . . 1·10 10

465 Guldara Stupa

1985. 10th Anniv of World Tourism Organization. Multicoloured.
1046 1a. Type **465** 10 10
1047 2a. Mirwais tomb (vert) . . 10 10
1048 10a. Buddha of Bamian (vert) 35 10
1049 13a. No Gumbad mosque (vert) 50 10
1050 14a. Pule Kheshti mosque 55 10
1051 15a. Arch at Qalai Bust . . 60 10
1052 20a. Ghazni minaret (vert) 85 10

466 Boxing

1985. Sport. Multicoloured.
1053 1a. Type **466** 10 10
1054 2a. Volleyball 15 10
1055 3a. Football (vert) 40 10
1056 12a. Buzkashi 45 10
1057 14a. Weightlifting 55 10
1058 18a. Wrestling 55 10
1059 25a. Pigsticking 75 10

467 Fruit Stall

1985. World Food Day.
1060 **467** 25a. multicoloured . . . 75 10

468 Flags and U.N. Building, New York **469** Black-billed Magpie

1985. 40th Anniv of United Nations Organization.
1061 **468** 22a. multicoloured . . . 75 10

1985. Birds. Multicoloured.
1062 2a. Type **469** 15 10
1063 4a. Green woodpecker . . . 75 35
1064 8a. Common pheasants . . 80 35
1065 13a. Bluethroat, Eurasian goldfinch and hoopoe . . 1·25 65
1066 18a. Peregrine falcons . . . 1·50 75
1067 25a. Red-legged partridge 2·10 1·10
1068 30a. Eastern white pelicans (horiz) . . . . 2·75 1·25

470 Leopard and Cubs

1985. World Wildlife Fund. The Leopard. Mult.
1070 2a. Type **470** 10 10
1071 9a. Head of leopard 35 10
1072 11a. Leopard 55 10
1073 15a. Leopard cub 85 10

471 Triumph "650" and Big Ben Tower

1985. Motor Cycles. Multicoloured.
1074 2a. Type **471** 10 10
1075 4a. Motobecane and Eiffel Tower, Paris 15 10
1076 8a. Motor cycle and Don Quixote monument, Madrid 25 10
1077 13a. Honda and Mt. Fuji, Japan 40 10
1078 18a. Jawa and Old Town Hall clock, Prague . . . 50 10
1079 25a. Motor cycle and T.V. Tower, Berlin 70 10
1080 30a. Motor cycle and Colosseum, Rome 85 10

472 Crowd with Flags

1986. 21st Anniv of Peoples' Democratic Party.
1082 **472** 2a. multicoloured . . . 25 10

473 Lenin writing

1986. 27th Soviet Communist Party Congress, Moscow.
1083 **473** 25a. multicoloured . . . 70 10

474 "Vostok 1"

1986. 25th Anniv of First Manned Space Flight. Multicoloured.
1084 3a. Type **474** 10 10
1085 7a. Russian Cosmonaut Medal (vert) 25 10
1086 9a. Launch of "Vostok 1" (vert) 30 10
1087 11a. Yuri Gagarin (first man in space) (vert) 45 10
1088 13a. Cosmonauts reading newspaper 45 10
1089 15a. Yuri Gagarin and Sergei Pavlovich Korolev (rocket designer) 55 10
1090 17a. Valentina Tereshkova (first woman in space) (vert) 65 10

475 Footballers **476** Lenin

1986. World Cup Football Championship, Mexico.
1091 **475** 3a. multicoloured . . . 10 10
1092 – 4a. multicoloured (horiz) 15 10
1093 – 7a. multicoloured (horiz) 25 10
1094 – 11a. multicoloured . . . 45 10
1095 – 12a. mult (horiz) 45 10
1096 – 18a. multicoloured . . . 65 10
1097 – 20a. multicoloured . . . 75 10
DESIGNS: 4a. to 20a. Various footballing scenes.

1986. 116th Birth Anniv of Lenin.
1099 **476** 16a. multicoloured . . . 60 10

477 Delegates voting

1986. 1st Anniv of Supreme Council Meeting of Tribal Leaders.
1100 **477** 3a. brown, red and blue 25 10

478 Flags and Crowd **479** Worker with Cogwheel and Globe

1986. 8th Anniv of Sawr Revolution.
1101 **478** 8a. multicoloured . . . 30 10

1986. Labour Day.
1102 **479** 5a. multicoloured . . . 25 10

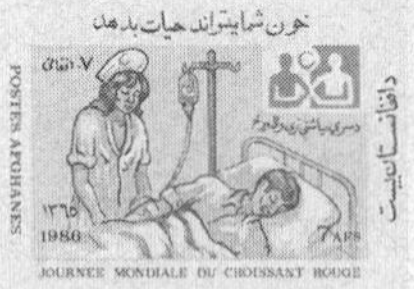

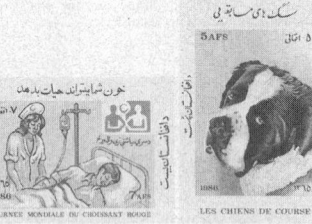

480 Patient receiving Blood Transfusion **481** St. Bernard

1986. International Red Cross/Crescent Day.
1103 **480** 7a. multicoloured . . . 45 10

1986. Pedigree Dogs. Multicoloured.
1104 5a. Type **481** 20 10
1105 7a. Rough collie 25 10
1106 8a. Spaniel 35 10
1107 9a. Long-haired dachshund 35 10
1108 11a. German shepherd . . . 45 10
1109 15a. Bulldog 60 10
1110 20a. Afghan hound 85 10

482 Tiger Barb **483** Mother and Children

1986. Fishes. Multicoloured.
1111 5a. Type **482** 25 15
1112 7a. Mbuna 45 15
1113 8a. Clown loach 55 15
1114 9a. Lisa 65 15
1115 11a. Figure-eight pufferfish 80 15
1116 15a. Six-barred distichodus 1·10 15
1117 20a. Sail-finned molly . . . 1·40 15

1986. World Children's Day. Multicoloured.
1118 1a. Type **483** 10 10
1119 3a. Woman holding boy and emblem 15 10
1120 9a. Circle of children on map (horiz) 30 10

484 Italian Birkenhead Locomotive

1986. 19th-century Railway Locomotives. Mult.
1121 4a. Type **484** 40 10
1122 5a. Norris locomotive . . . 60 10
1123 6a. Stephenson "Patentee" type locomotive 70 10
1124 7a. Bridges Adams locomotive 90 10
1125 8a. Ansoldo locomotive . . . 1·10 10
1126 9a. Locomotive "St. David" 1·50 10
1127 11a. Jones & Potts locomotive . . . . 2·00 15

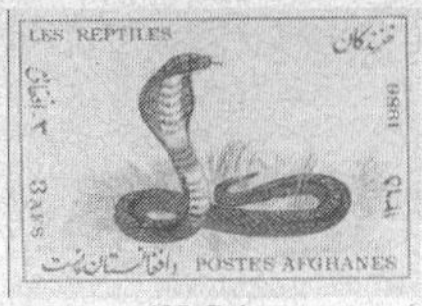

485 Cobra

1986. Animals. Multicoloured.

1128	3a. Type **485**	10	10
1129	4a. Lizards (vert)	10	10
1130	5a. Praying mantis	15	10
1131	8a. Beetle (vert)	20	15
1132	9a. Spider	25	20
1133	10a. Snake	25	20
1134	11a. Scorpions	25	20

Nos. 1130/2 and 1134 are wrongly inscr "Les Reptiles".

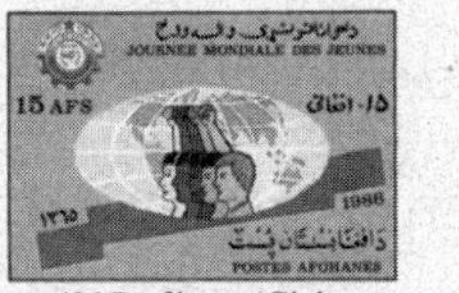

486 Profiles on Globe

1986. World Youth Day.
1135 **486** 15a. multicoloured . . . 90 65

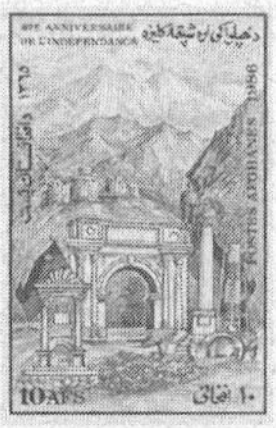

487 National Monuments

1986. Independence Day.
1136 **487** 10a. multicoloured . . . 40 10

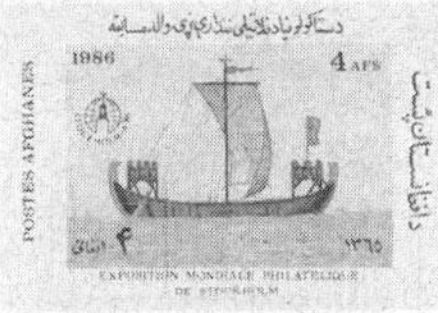

488 11th-century Ship

1986. "Stockholmia 86" International Stamp Exhibition. Sailing Ships. Multicoloured.

1137	4a. Type **488**	40	25
1138	5a. Roman galley	55	25
1139	6a. English royal kogge	85	25
1140	7a. Early dhow	90	25
1141	8a. Nao	1·00	25
1142	9a. Ancient Egyptian ship	1·10	25
1143	11a. Medieval galeasse	1·10	25

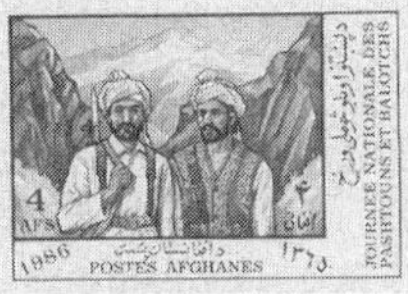

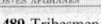

489 Tribesmen

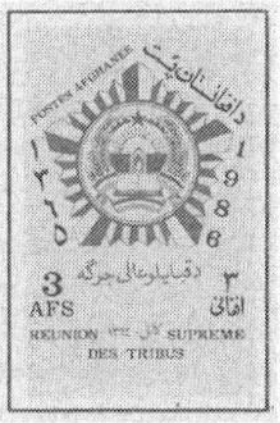

490 State Arms

1986. Pashtunistan Day.
1145 **489** 4a. multicoloured . . . 25 10

1986. Supreme Council Meeting of Tribal Leaders.
1146 **490** 3a. gold, blue and black 25 10

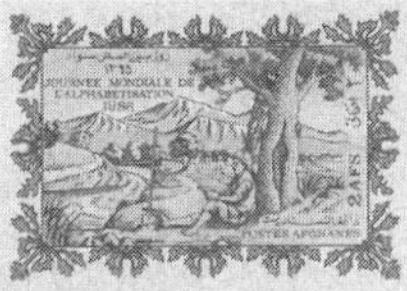

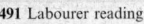

491 Labourer reading

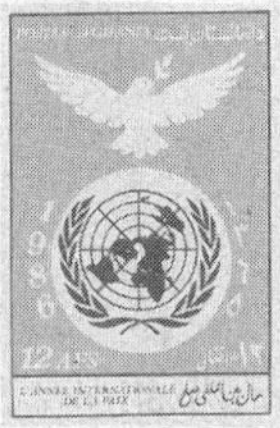

492 Dove and U.N. Emblem

1986. World Literacy Day.
1147 **491** 2a. multicoloured . . . 20 10

1986. International Peace Year.
1148 **492** 12a. black and blue . . . 40 10

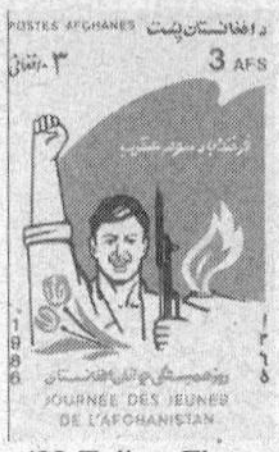

493 Tulips, Flame and Man with Rifle

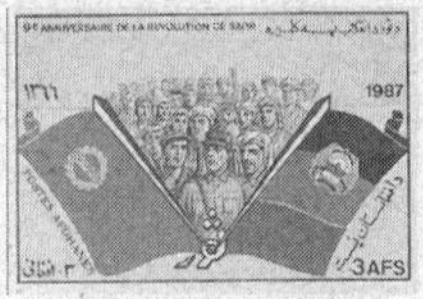

494 Crowd and Flags

1986. Afghanistan Youth Day.
1149 **493** 3a. red and black . . . 25 10

1987. 9th Anniv of Sawr Revolution.
1150 **494** 3a. multicoloured . . . 25 10

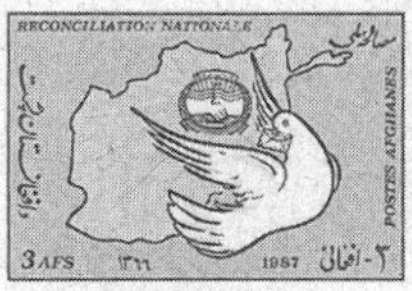

495 Map and Dove

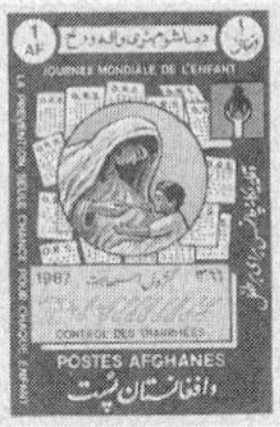

496 Oral Rehydration

1987. National Reconciliation.
1151 **495** 3a. multicoloured . . . 25 10

1987. International Children's Day. Multicoloured.

1152	1a. Type **496**	10	10
1153	5a. Weighing babies	15	10
1154	9a. Vaccinating babies	25	10

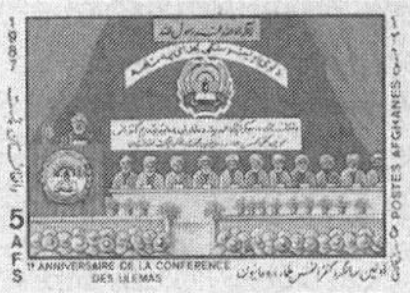

497 Conference Delegates

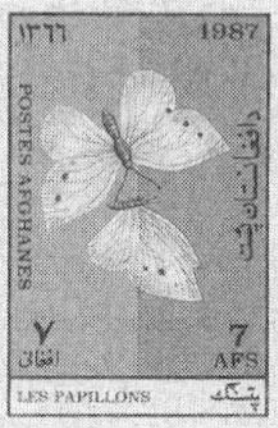

498 "Pieris sp."

1987. 1st Anniv of Tribal Conference.
1155 **497** 5a. multicoloured . . . 25 10

1987. Butterflies and Moths. Multicoloured.

1156	7a. Type **498**	30	20
1157	9a. Brimstone and unidentified butterfly	35	20
1158	10a. Garden tiger moth (horiz)	40	25
1159	12a. "Parnassius sp."	45	25
1160	15a. Butterfly (unidentified) (horiz)	60	40
1161	22a. Butterfly (unidentified) (horiz)	65	40
1162	25a. Butterfly (unidentified)	75	45

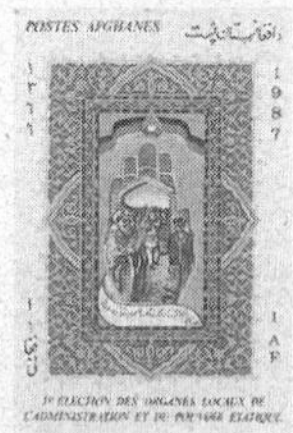

499 People on Hand

1987. 1st Local Government Elections.
1163 **499** 1a. multicoloured . . . 20 10

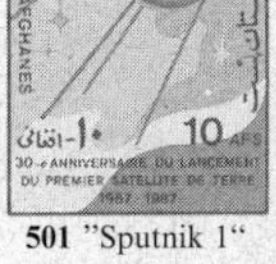

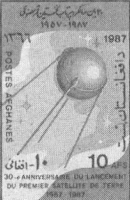

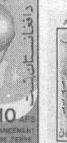

501 "Sputnik 1"

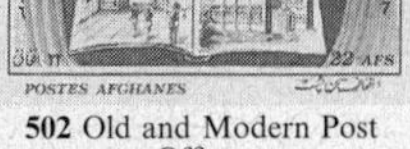

502 Old and Modern Post Offices

1987. 30th Anniv of Launch of "Sputnik 1" (first artificial satellite). Multicoloured.

1165	10a. Type **501**	35	10
1166	15a. Rocket launch	45	10
1167	25a. "Soyuz"–"Salyut" space complex	65	10

1987. World U.P.U. Day.
1168 **502** 22a. multicoloured . . . 75 10

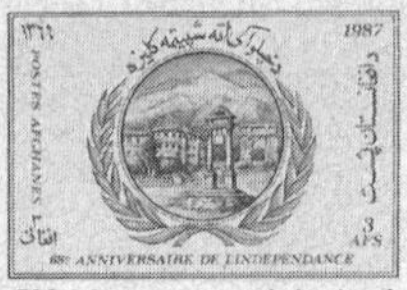

503 Monument and Arch of Paghman

1987. Independence Day.
1169 **503** 3a. multicoloured . . . 20 10

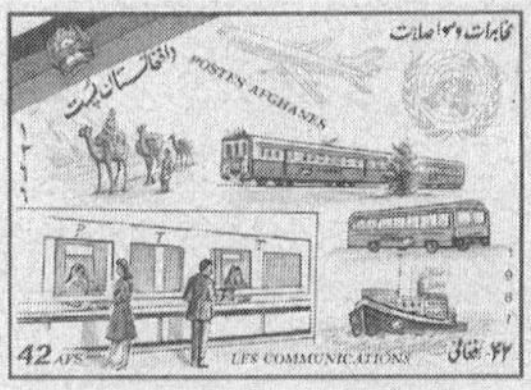

504 "Communications"

1987. United Nations Day.
1170 **504** 42a. multicoloured . . . 3·75 75

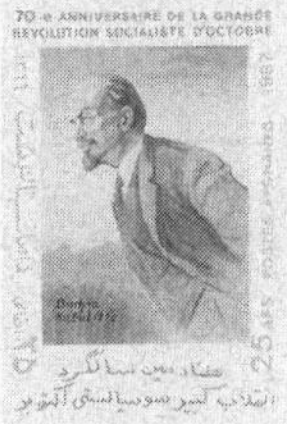

505 Lenin

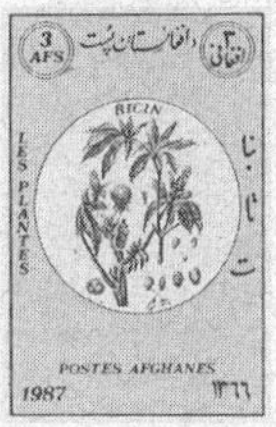

506 Castor Oil Plant

1987. 70th Anniv of Russian Revolution.
1171 **505** 25a. multicoloured . . . 95 10

1987. Plants. Multicoloured.

1172	3a. Type **506**	15	10
1173	6a. Liquorice	30	10
1174	9a. Camomile	40	10
1175	14a. Thorn apple	60	10
1176	18a. Chicory	80	10

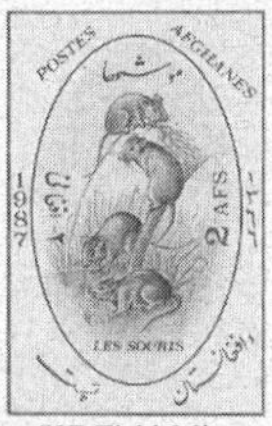

507 Field Mice

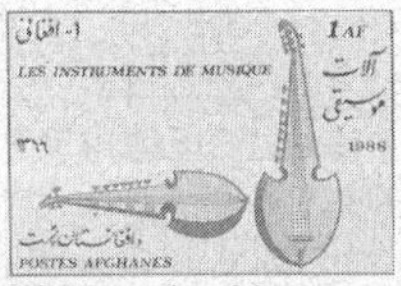

508 Four-stringed Instrument

1987. Mice. Multicoloured.

1177	2a. Type **507**	15	10
1178	4a. Brown and white mice (horiz)	20	10
1179	8a. Ginger mice (horiz)	25	10
1180	16a. Black mice (horiz)	45	10
1181	20a. Spotted and ginger mice (horiz)	55	10

1988. Musical Instruments. Multicoloured.

1182	1a. Type **508**	10	10
1183	3a. Drums	15	10
1184	5a. Two-stringed instruments with two pegs	20	10
1185	15a. Two-stringed instrument with ten pegs	45	10
1186	18a. Two-stringed instruments with fourteen or ten pegs	60	10
1187	25a. Four-stringed bowed instruments	85	10
1188	33a. Two-stringed bowed instruments	1·25	10

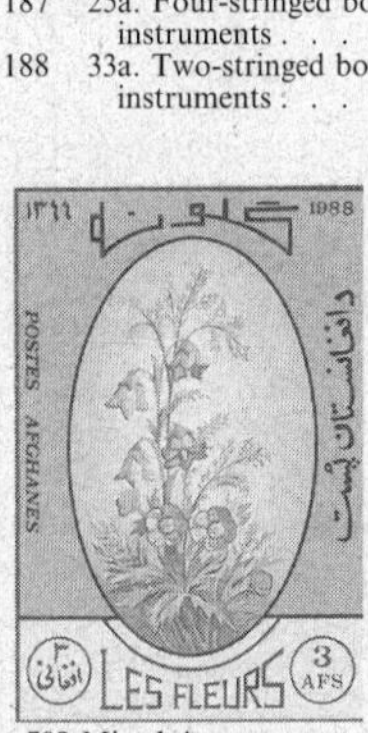

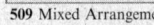

509 Mixed Arrangement

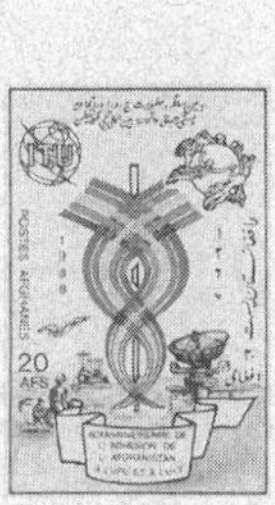

510 Emblems and Means of Communication

1988. Flowers. Multicoloured.

1189	3a. Type **509**	15	10
1190	5a. Tulips (horiz)	20	10
1191	7a. Mallows	25	10
1192	9a. Small mauve flowers	35	10
1193	12a. Marguerites	50	10
1194	15a. White flowers	65	10
1195	24a. Red and blue flowers (horiz)	1·00	10

1988. 60th Anniv of Membership of U.P.U. and I.T.U.
1196 **510** 20a. multicoloured . . . 65 10

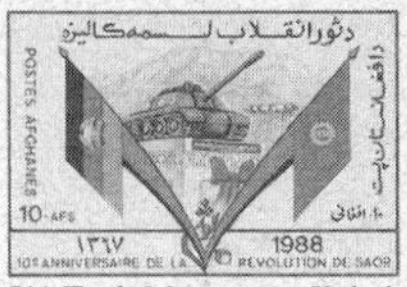

511 Tank Monument, Kabul, and Flags

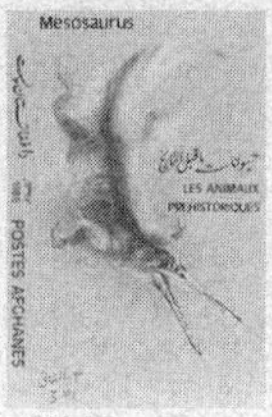

512 Mesosaurus

1988. 10th Anniv of Sawr Revolution.
1197 **511** 10a. multicoloured . . . 40 10

1988. Prehistoric Animals. Multicoloured.

1198	3a. Type **512**	15	10
1199	5a. Styracosaurus (horiz)	25	10
1200	10a. Uintatherium (horiz)	45	10
1201	15a. Protoceratops (horiz)	65	10
1202	20a. Stegosaurus (horiz)	85	10
1203	25a. Ceratosaurus	1·10	10
1204	30a. Moa ("Dinornis maximus")	2·00	1·25

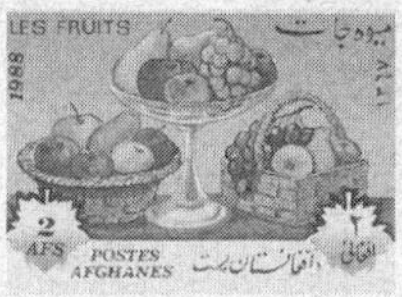

513 Baskets and Bowl of Fruit

1988. Fruit. Multicoloured

1205	2a. Type **513**	10	10
1206	4a. Baskets of fruit	15	10
1207	7a. Large basket of fruit	25	10
1208	8a. Bunch of grapes on branch (vert)	25	10
1209	16a. Buying fruit from market stall	45	10
1210	22a. Arranging fruit on market stall	65	10
1211	25a. Stallholder weighing fruit (vert)	80	10

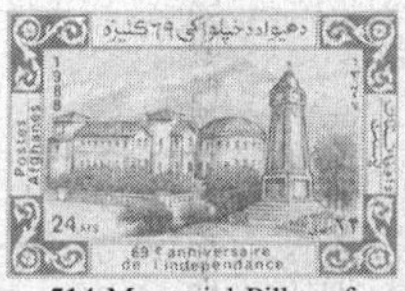

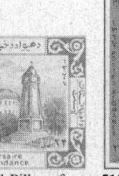

514 Memorial Pillar of Knowledge and Ignorance, Kabul

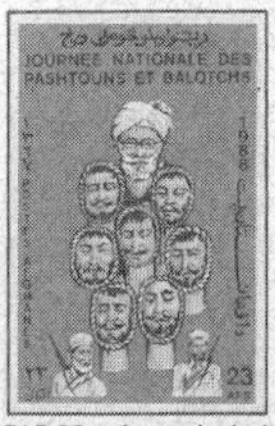

515 Heads encircled with Rope

1988. Independence Day.
1212 **514** 24a. multicoloured . . . 90 10

1988. Pashtunistan Day.
1213 **515** 23a. multicoloured . . . 80 10

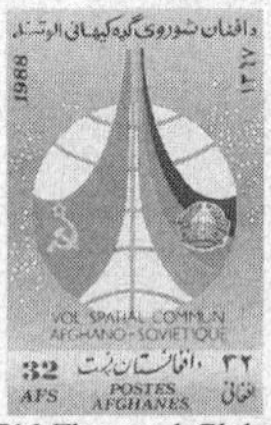

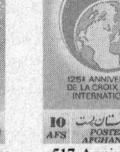

516 Flags and Globe

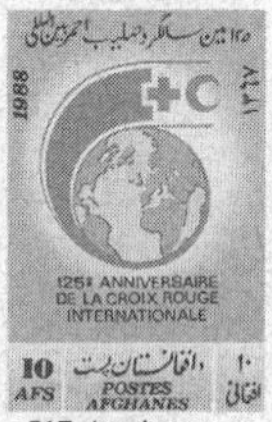

517 Anniversary Emblem

1988. Afghan–Soviet Space Flight.
1214 **516** 32a. multicoloured . . . 90 10

1988. 125th Anniv of International Red Cross.
1215 **517** 10a. multicoloured . . . 50 10

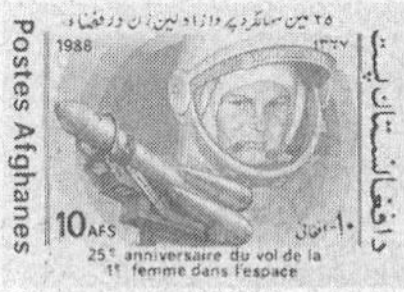

518 Rocket and V. Tereshkova

1988. 25th Anniv of First Woman Cosmonaut Valentina Tereshkova's Space Flight. Mult.

1216	10a. Type **518**	80	20
1217	15a. Bird, globe and rocket (vert)	65	10
1218	25a. "Vostok 6" and globe	90	10

519 Decorated Metal Vessels   **520** Indian Flag and Nehru

1988. Traditional Crafts. Multicoloured.
1219	2a. Type **519**	10	10
1220	4a. Pottery	15	10
1221	5a. Clothing (vert)	20	10
1222	9a. Carpets	25	10
1223	15a. Bags	45	10
1224	23a. Jewellery	65	10
1225	50a. Furniture	1·25	10

1988. Birth Centenary of Jawaharlal Nehru (Indian statesman).
1226	**520** 40a. multicoloured	1·50	25

521 Emeralds   **522** Ice Skating

1988. Gemstones. Multicoloured.
1227	13a. Type **521**	60	15
1228	37a. Lapis lazuli	1·40	25
1229	40a. Rubies	1·75	25

1988. Winter Olympic Games, Calgary. Mult.
1230	2a. Type **522**	10	10
1231	5a. Slalom	20	10
1232	9a. Two-man bobsleigh	35	10
1233	22a. Biathlon	65	10
1234	37a. Speed skating	1·40	20

523 Old City

1988. International Campaign for Preservation of Old Sana'a, Yemen.
1236	**523** 32a. multicoloured	90	10

524 Emblem

1989. 2nd Anniv of Move for Nat Reconciliation.
1237	**524** 4a. multicoloured	20	10

525 Bishop and Game from "The Three Ages of Man" (attr. Estienne Porchier)

1989. Chess. Multicoloured.
1238	2a. Type **525**	10	10
1239	3a. Faience queen and 14th-century drawing of Margrave Otto IV of Brandenburg and his wife playing chess	20	10
1240	4a. French king and game	25	10
1241	7a. King and game	35	10
1242	16a. Knight and game	55	10
1243	24a. Arabian knight and "Great Chess"	85	10
1244	45a. Bishop and teaching of game	1·40	15

Nos. 1240/4 show illustrations from King Alfonso X's "Book of Chess, Dice and Tablings".

526 "The Old Jew"   **527** Euphrates Jerboa

1989. Picasso Paintings. Multicoloured.
1245	4a. Type **526**	25	10
1246	6a. "The Two Harlequins"	25	10
1247	8a. "Portrait of Ambrouse Vollar"	25	10
1248	22a. "Majorcan Woman"	65	10
1249	35a. "Acrobat on Ball"	1·25	15

1989. Animals. Multicoloured.
1251	3a. Type **527**	20	10
1252	4a. Asiatic wild ass	25	10
1253	14a. Lynx	60	10
1254	35a. Lammergeier	2·40	1·40
1255	44a. Markhor	1·50	20

528 Bomb breaking, Dove and Woman holding Wheat   **529** Cattle

1989. International Women's Day (1988).
1257	**528** 8a. multicoloured	25	10

1989. Farmers' Day. Multicoloured.
1258	1a. Type **529**	10	10
1259	2a. Ploughing with oxen and tractors	10	10
1260	3a. Picking cotton	10	10

530 Dish Aerial

1989. World Meteorology Day. Multicoloured.
1261	27a. Type **530**	1·00	15
1262	32a. World Meteorological Organization emblem and state arms	1·25	15
1263	40a. Data-collecting equipment (vert)	1·50	15

531 Rejoicing Crowd

1989. 11th Anniv of Sawr Revolution.
1264	**531** 20a. multicoloured	75	10

532 Outdoor Class   **533** Eiffel Tower and Arc de Triomphe

1989. Teachers' Day.
1265	**532** 42a. multicoloured	1·50	15

1989. Bicentenary of French Revolution.
1266	**533** 25a. multicoloured	90	15

534 Transmission Mast

1989. 10th Anniv of Asia-Pacific Telecommunity.
1267	3a. Type **534**	10	10
1268	27a. Dish aerial	1·00	15

535 National Monuments   **536** Pashtu

1989. Independence Day.
1269	**535** 25a. multicoloured	90	15

1989. Pashtunistan Day.
1270	**536** 3a. multicoloured	10	10

537 White Spoonbill   **539** Mosque

538 Duchs, 1910

1989. Birds, Multicoloured.
1271	3a. Type **537**	15	15
1272	5a. Purple swamphen	35	15
1273	10a. Eurasian bittern (horiz)	60	25
1274	15a. Eastern white pelican	80	35
1275	20a. Red-crested pochard	1·10	40
1276	25a. Mute swan	1·40	50
1277	30a. Great cormorant (horiz)	1·60	60

1989. Vintage Cars. Multicoloured.
1278	5a. Type **538**	20	10
1279	10a. Ford, 1911	35	10
1280	20a. Renault, 1911	75	10
1281	25a. Russo-Balte, 1911	90	15
1282	30a. Fiat, 1926	1·00	15

1989. Multicoloured.
1283	1a. Type **539**	
1284	2a. Minaret, Jam	
1285	3a. Buzkashi (horiz)	
1286	4a. Airplane over Hindu Kush (horiz)	

NEWSPAPER STAMPS

N 35

1928.
N192	N 35	2p. blue	3·50	4·50

1929.
N205	N 35	2p. red	25	45

N 43

1932.
N215	N 43	2p. red	40	60
N216		2p. black	25	65
N217		2p. green	25	75
N219		2p. red	45	75

N 75 Coat-of-Arms

N259	N 75	2p. green	15	55
N260		2p. mauve (no gum)	15	75

1969. As Type N **75**, but larger and with different Pushtu inscr.
N652		100p. green	15	20
N653		150p. brown	15	20

OFFICIAL STAMPS

O 27   **O 86**

1909.
O173	O 27	(–) red	1·10	1·10

1939. Design 22½ × 28 mm.
O281	O 86	15p. green	85	75
O282		30p. brown	1·25	1·25
O283		45p. red	1·00	1·00
O284		1a. mauve	1·60	1·50

1954. Design 24½ × 31 mm.
O285b	O 86	50p. red	1·00	60

1965. Design 24 × 30½ mm.
O287	O 86	50p. pink	1·25	60

PARCEL POST STAMPS

P 27

1909.
P173	P 27	3s. brown	1·00	1·50
P174		3s. green	1·50	2·50
P175		1k. green	1·50	2·50
P176		1k. red	1·50	2·25
P177		1r. orange	2·75	2·75
P178		1r. grey	20·00	
P179		1r. brown	1·50	1·50
P180		2r. red	2·75	2·75
P181		2r. blue	5·00	5·50

P 28 Old Habibia College, Kabul

1921.
P182	P 28	10p. brown	3·50	4·50
P183		15p. brown	4·50	5·50
P184		30p. purple	8·50	5·50
P185		1r. blue	10·00	10·00

1923. 5th Independence Day. Optd with T **28.**
P186	P 28	10p. brown	60·00	
P187		15p. brown	65·00	
P188		30p. purple	£110	

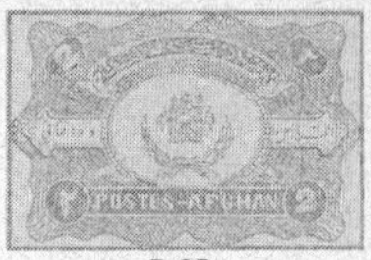

P 35

P 36

1928.

P192	P 35	2a. orange	5·50	4·25
P193	P 36	3a. green	10·00	10·00

1930.

P214	P 35	2a. green	6·50	6·50
P215	P 36	3a. brown	8·50	10·00

REGISTRATION STAMP

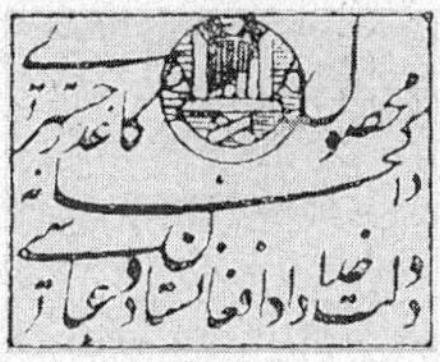
R 19

1894. Undated.

R155	R 19	2a. black on green	8·00	7·00

APPENDIX

The following stamps have either been issued in excess of postal needs or have not been available to the public in reasonable quantities at face value. Such stamps may later be given full listing if there is evidence of regular postal use.

1961.

Agriculture Day. Fauna and Flora. 2, 2, 5, 10, 15, 25, 50, 100, 150, 175p.

Child Welfare. Sports and Games. 2, 2, 5, 10, 15, 25, 50, 100, 150, 175p.

U.N.I.C.E.F. Surch on 1961 Child Welfare issue. 2+25, 2+25, 5+25, 10+25, 15p.+25p.

Women's Day. 50, 175p.

Independence Day. Mohamed Nadir Shah. 50, 175p.

International Exhibition, Kabul. 50, 175p. Pashtunistan Day. 50, 175p.

National Assembly. 50, 175p.

Anti-malaria Campaign. 50, 175p.

King's 47th Birthday. 50, 175p.

Red Crescent Day. Fruits. 2, 2, 5, 10, 15, 25, 50, 100, 150, 175p.

Afghan Red Crescent Fund. 1961 Red Crescent Day issue surch 2+25, 2+25, 5+25, 10+25, 15p.+25p.

United Nations Day. 1, 2, 3, 4, 50, 75, 175p.

Teachers' Day. Flowers and Educational Scenes. 2, 2, 5, 10, 15, 25, 50, 100, 150, 175p.

U.N.E.S.C.O. 1961 Teachers' Day issue surch 2+25, 2+25, 5+25, 10+25, 15p.+25p.

1962.

15th Anniv (1961) of U.N.E.S.C.O. 2, 2, 5, 10, 15, 25, 50, 75, 100p.

Ahmed Shah Baba. 50, 75, 100p.

Agriculture Day. Animals and Products. 2, 2, 5, 10, 15, 25, 50, 75, 100, 125p.

Independence Day. Marching Athletes. 25, 50, 150p.

Women's Day. Postage 25, 50p.; Air 100, 175p.

Pashtunistan Day. 25, 50, 150p.

Malaria Eradication. 2, 2, 5, 10, 15, 25, 50, 75, 100, 150, 175p.

National Assembly. 25, 50, 75, 100, 125p.

4th Asian Games, Djakarta, Indonesia. Postage 1, 2, 3, 4, 5p.; Air 25, 50, 75, 100, 150, 175p.

Children's Day. Sports and Produce. Postage 1, 2, 3, 4, 5p.; Air 75, 150, 200p.

King's 48th Birthday. 25, 50, 75, 100p.

Red Crescent Day. Fruits and Flowers. Postage 1, 2, 3, 4, 5p.; Air 25, 50, 100p.

Boy Scouts' Day. Postage 1, 2, 3, 4p.; Air 25, 50, 75, 100p.

1st Anniv of Hammarskjold's Death. Surch on 1961 U.N.E.S.C.O. issue. 2+20, 2+20, 5+20, 10+20, 15+20, 25+20, 50+20, 75+20, 100p.+20p.

United Nations Day. Postage 1, 2, 3, 4, 5p.; Air 75, 100, 125p.

Teachers' Day. Sport and Flowers. Postage 1, 2, 3, 4, 5p.; Air 100, 150p.

World Meteorological Day. 50, 100p.

1963.

Famous Afghans Pantheon, Kabul. 50, 75, 100p.

Agriculture Day. Sheep and Silkworms. Postage 1, 2, 3, 4, 5p.; Air 100, 150, 200p.

Freedom from Hunger. Postage 2, 3, 300p.; Air 500p.

Malaria Eradication Fund. 1962 Malaria Eradication issue surch 2+15, 2+15, 5+15, 10+15, 15+15, 25+15, 50+15, 75+15, 100+15, 150+15, 175p.+15p.

World Meteorological Day. Postage 1, 2, 3, 4, 5p.; Air 200, 300, 400, 500p.

"GANEFO" Athletic Games, Djakarta, Indonesia. Postage 2, 3, 4, 5, 10p., 9a.; Air 300, 500p.

Red Cross Centenary Postage 2, 3, 4, 5, 10p.; Air 100, 200p., 4, 6a.

Nubian Monuments Preservation. Postage 100, 200, 500p.; Air 5a., 7a.50.

1964.

Women's Day (1963). 2, 3, 4, 5, 10p.

Afghan Boy Scouts and Girl Guides. Postage 2, 3, 4, 5, 10p.; Air 2, 2, 2a.50, 3, 4, 5, 12a.

Child Welfare Day (1963). Sports and Games. Postage 2, 3, 4, 5, 10p.; Air 200, 300p.

Afghan Red Crescent Society. Postage 100, 200p.; Air 5a., 7a.50.

Teachers' Day (1963). Flowers. Postage 2, 3, 4, 5, 10p.; Air 3a., 3a.50.

United Nations Day (1963). Postage 2, 3, 4, 5, 10p.; Air 100p., 2, 3a.

15th Anniv of Human Rights Declaration. Surch on 1964 United Nations Day issue. Postage 2+50, 3+50, 4+50, 5+50, 10p.+50p.; Air 100p.+50p., 2a.+50p., 3a.+50p.

U.N.I.C.E.F. (dated 1963). Postage 100, 200p.; Air 5a. 7a.50.

Malaria Eradication (dated 1963). Postage 2, 3, 4, 5p., 10p. on 4p.; Air 2, 10a.

AITUTAKI Pt. 1

Island in the South Pacific.

1903. 12 pence = 1 shilling;
20 shillings = 1 pound.
1967. 100 cents = 1 dollar.

A. NEW ZEALAND DEPENDENCY.

The British Government, who had exercised a protectorate over the Cook Islands group since the 1880s, handed the islands, including Aitutaki, to New Zealand administration in 1901. Cook Islands stamps were used from 1932 to 1972.

1903. Pictorial stamps of New Zealand surch **AITUTAKI.** and value in native language.

1	23	½d. green	4·50	6·50
2	42	1d. red	4·75	5·50
4	26	2½d. blue	11·00	12·00
5	28	3d. brown	18·00	15·00
6	31	6d. red	30·00	25·00
7	34	1s. red	55·00	85·00

1911. King Edward VII stamps of New Zealand surch **AITUTAKI.** and value in native language.

9	51	½d. green	1·00	3·00
10	53	1d. red	3·00	9·50
11	51	6d. red	45·00	95·00
12		1s. red	55·00	£140

1916. King George V stamps of New Zealand surch **AITUTAKI.** and value in native language.

13a	62	6d. red	7·50	27·00
14		1s. red	24·00	90·00

1917. King George V stamps of New Zealand optd **AITUTAKI.**

19	62	½d. green	1·00	5·50
20	53	1d. red	3·50	25·00
21	62	1½d. grey	3·75	30·00
22		1½d. brown	80	7·00
15a		2½d. blue	1·75	15·00
16a		3d. brown	1·50	22·00
17a		6d. red	4·75	21·00
18a		1s. red	12·00	32·00

1920. As 1920 pictorial stamps of Cook Islands but inscr "AITUTAKI".

30	½d. black and green	2·00	11·00
31	1d. black and red	6·00	6·50
26	1½d. black and brown	6·00	12·00
32	2½d. black and blue	7·50	50·00
27	3d. black and blue	2·50	14·00
28	6d. brown and grey	5·50	14·00
29	1s. black and purple	9·50	16·00

B. PART OF COOK ISLANDS

On 9 August 1972. Aitutaki became a Port of Entry into the Cook Islands. Whilst remaining part of the Cook Islands, Aitutaki has a separate postal service.

1972. Nos. 227/8, 230, 233/4, 238, 240/1, 243 and 244 of Cook Islands optd **Aitutaki**.

33	79	½c. multicoloured	30	80
34	–	1c. multicoloured	70	1·40
35	–	2½c. multicoloured	2·25	7·00
36	–	4c. multicoloured	70	85
37	–	5c. multicoloured	2·50	7·50
38	–	10c. multicoloured	2·50	5·50
39	–	20c. multicoloured	3·00	1·00
40	–	25c. multicoloured	70	1·00
41	–	50c. multicoloured	2·75	2·75
42	–	$1 multicoloured	4·00	5·50

1972. Christmas. Nos. 406/8 of Cook Islands optd **Aitutaki**.

43	130	1c. multicoloured	10	10
44	–	5c. multicoloured	15	15
45	–	10c. multicoloured	15	25

1972. Royal Silver Wedding. As Nos. 413 and 415 of Cook Islands, but inscr "COOK ISLANDS Aitutaki".

46	131	5c. black and silver	3·50	2·75
47	–	15c. black and silver	1·50	1·50

1972. No. 245 of Cook Islands optd **AITUTAKI**.

48	$2 multicoloured	50	75

1972. Nos. 227/8, 230, 233, 234, 238, 240, 241, 243 and 244 of Cook Islands optd **AITUTAKI** within ornamental oval.

49	79	½c. multicoloured	15	10
50	–	1c. multicoloured	15	10
51	–	2½c. multicoloured	20	10
52	–	4c. multicoloured	25	15
53	–	5c. multicoloured	25	15
54	–	10c. multicoloured	35	25
55	–	20c. multicoloured	1·25	50
56	–	25c. multicoloured	50	55
57	–	50c. multicoloured	75	90
58	–	$1 multicoloured	1·25	1·75

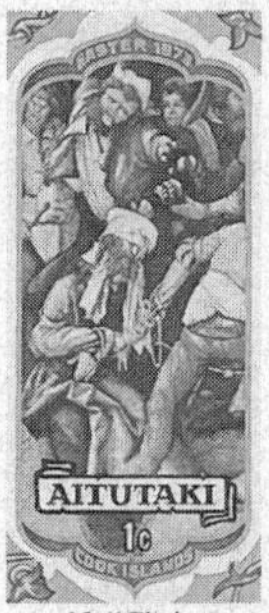

13 "Christ Mocked" (Grunewald)

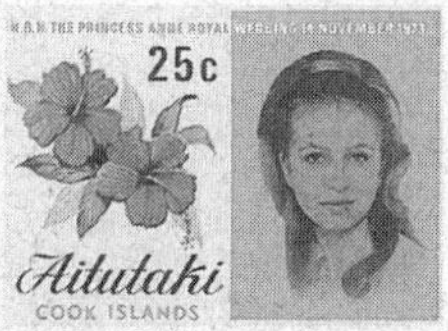

16 Red Hibiscus and Princess Anne

1973. Easter. Multicoloured.

59	1c. Type **13**	15	10
60	1c. "St. Veronica" (Van der Weyden)	15	10
61	1c. "The Crucified Christ with Virgin Mary, Saints and Angels" (Raphael)	15	10
62	1c. "Resurrection" (Piero della Francesca)	15	10
63	5c. "The Last Supper" (Master of Amiens)	20	15
64	5c. "Condemnation" (Holbein)	20	15
65	5c. "Christ on the Cross" (Rubens)	20	15
66	5c. "Resurrection" (El Greco)	20	15
67	10c. "Disrobing of Christ" (El Greco)	25	15
68	10c. "St. Veronica" (Van Oostsanen)	25	15
69	10c. "Christ on the Cross" (Rubens)	25	15
70	10c. "Resurrection" (Bouts)	25	15

1973. Silver Wedding Coinage. Nos. 417/23 of Cook Islands optd **AITUTAKI**.

71	132	1c. black, red and gold	10	10
72	–	2c. black, blue and gold	10	10
73	–	5c. black, green and silver	15	10
74	–	10c. black, blue and silver	20	10
75	–	20c. black, green and silver	30	15
76	–	50c. black, red and silver	50	30
77	–	$1 black, blue and silver	70	45

1973. 10th Anniv of Treaty Banning Nuclear Testing. Nos. 236, 238, 240 and 243 of Cook Islands optd **AITUTAKI** within ornamental oval and **TENTH ANNIVERSARY CESSATION OF NUCLEAR TESTING TREATY**.

78	8c. multicoloured	15	15
79	10c. multicoloured	15	15
80	20c. multicoloured	30	20
81	50c. multicoloured	70	50

1973. Royal Wedding. Multicoloured.

82	25c. Type **16**	25	10
83	30c. Capt. Mark Phillips and blue hibiscus	25	10

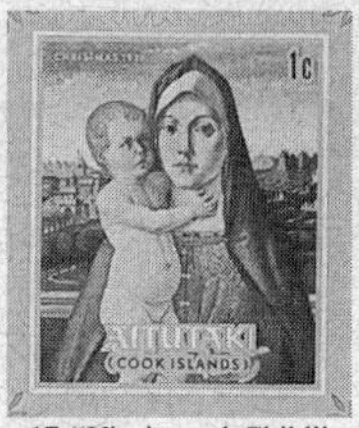

17 "Virgin and Child" (Montagna)

1973. Christmas. "Virgin and Child" paintings by artists listed below. Multicoloured.

85	1c. Type **17**	10	10
86	1c. Crivelli	10	10
87	1c. Van Dyck	10	10
88	1c. Perugino	10	10
89	5c. Veronese (child at shoulder)	25	10
90	5c. Veronese (child on lap)	25	10
91	5c. Cima	25	10
92	5c. Memling	25	10
93	10c. Memling	25	10
94	10c. Del Colle	25	10
95	10c. Raphael	25	10
96	10c. Lotto	25	10

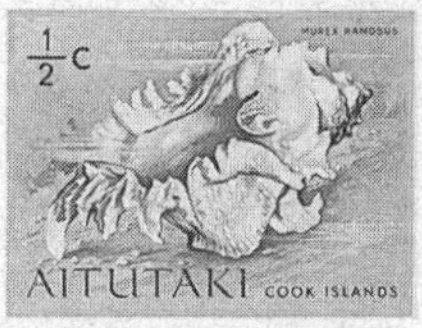

18 Rose-branch Murex

1974. Sea Shells. Multicoloured.

97	½c. Type **18**	90	80
98	1c. New Caledonia nautilus	90	80
99	2c. Common or major harp	90	80
100	3c. Striped bonnet	90	80
101	4c. Mole cowrie	90	80
102	5c. Pontifical mitre	90	80
103	8c. Trumpet triton	90	80
104	10c. Venus comb murex	90	80
105	20c. Red-mouth olive	1·25	80
106	25c. Ruddy frog shell	1·25	80
107	60c. Widest pacific conch	3·50	1·25
108	$1 Maple-leaf triton or winged frog shell	2·50	1·40
109	$2 Queen Elizabeth II and Marlin-spike auger	6·00	9·00
110	$5 Queen Elizabeth II and Tiger cowrie	27·00	10·00

The $2 and $5 are larger, 53 × 25 mm.

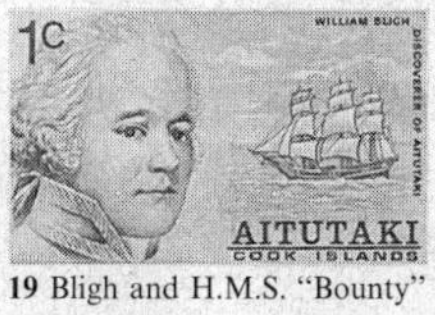

19 Bligh and H.M.S. "Bounty"

1974. William Bligh's Discovery of Aitutaki. Multicoloured

114	1c. Type **19**	40	40
115	1c. H.M.S. "Bounty"	40	40
116	5c. Bligh, and H.M.S. "Bounty" at Aitutaki	80	80
117	5c. Aitutaki chart of 1856	80	80
118	8c. Captain Cook and H.M.S. "Resolution"	1·10	70
119	8c. Map of Aitutaki and inset location map	1·10	70

See also Nos. 123/8.

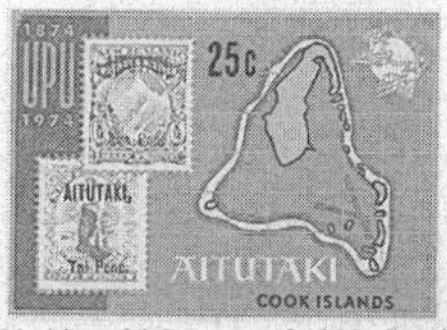

20 Aitutaki Stamps of 1903, Sand Map

1974. Centenary of U.P.U. Multicoloured.

120	25c. Type **20**	65	50
121	50c. Stamps of 1903 and 1920, and map	85	75

1974. Air. As Nos. 114/119 in larger size (46 × 26 mm), additionally inscr "AIR MAIL".

123	10c. Type **19**	60	55
124	10c. H.M.S. "Bounty"	60	55
125	25c. Bligh, and H.M.S. "Bounty" at Aitutaki	70	65
126	25c. Aitutaki chart of 1856	70	65
127	30c. Captain Cook and H.M.S. "Resolution"	80	70
128	30c. Map of Aitutaki and inset location map	80	70

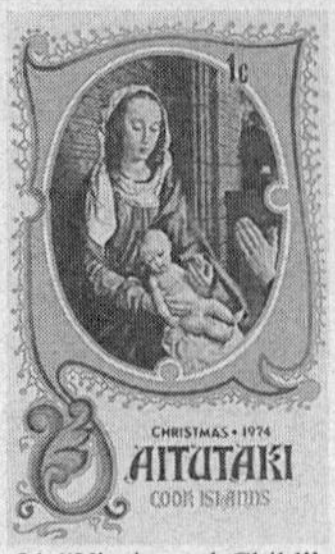

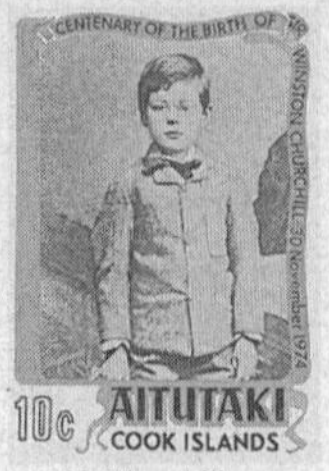

21 "Virgin and Child" (Hugo van der Goes) **22** Churchill as Schoolboy

1974. Christmas. "Virgin and Child" paintings by artists named. Multicoloured.
129 1c. Type **21** 10 10
130 5c. Bellini 10 15
131 8c. Gerard David 10 15
132 10c. Antonello da Messina 10 15
133 25c. Joos van Cleve 20 25
134 30c. Master of the Life of St. Catherine 20 25

1974. Birth Centenary of Sir Winston Churchill. Multicoloured.
136 10c. Type **22** 20 25
137 25c. Churchill as young man 25 40
138 30c. Churchill with troops . . 25 45
139 50c. Churchill painting . . . 30 60
140 $1 Giving "V" sign 40 75

1974. Children's Christmas Fund. Nos. 129/34 surch.
142 **21** 1c.+1c. multicoloured . . . 10 10
143 – 5c.+1c. multicoloured . . . 10 10
144 – 8c.+1c. multicoloured . . . 10 10
145 – 10c.+1c. multicoloured . . 10 10
146 – 25c.+1c. multicoloured . . 20 20
147 – 30c.+1c. multicoloured . . 20 20

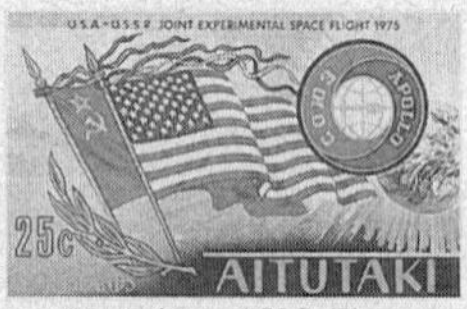

24 Soviet and U.S. Flags

1975. "Apollo–Soyuz" Space Project. Mult.
148 25c. Type **24** 30 20
149 50c. Daedalus with space capsule 40 30

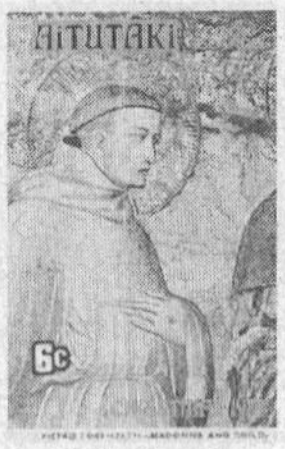

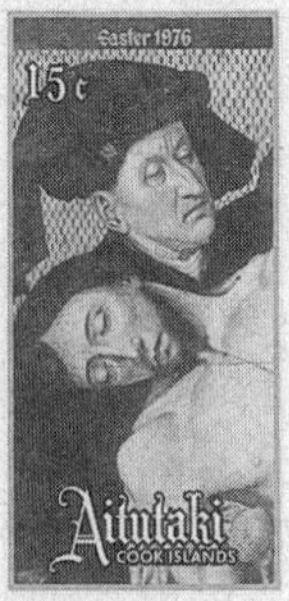

25 St. Francis **26** "The Descent" (detail, 15th-century Flemish School)

1975. Christmas. Multicoloured.
151 6c. Type **25** 10 10
152 6c. Madonna and Child . . . 10 10
153 6c. St. John 10 10
154 7c. King and donkey 10 10
155 7c. Madonna, Child and King 10 10
156 7c. Kings with gifts 10 10
157 15c. Madonna and Child . . 15 15
158 15c. St. Onufrius 15 15
159 15c. John the Baptist 15 15
160 20c. Shepherd and cattle . . 20 15
161 20c. Madonna and Child . . 20 15
162 20c. Shepherds 20 15
Stamps of the same value were printed together, se-tenant, each strip forming a composite design of a complete painting as follows: Nos. 151/3, "Madonna and Child with Saints Francis and John" (Lorenzetti); 154/6, "Adoration of the Kings" (Van der Weyden); 157/9, "Madonna and Child Enthroneth with Saints Onufrius and John the Baptist" (Montagna); 160/2, "Adoration of the Shepherds" (Reni).

1975. Children's Christmas Fund. Nos. 151/62 surch.
164 **25** 6c.+1c. multicoloured . . . 10 10
165 – 6c.+1c. multicoloured . . . 10 10
166 – 6c.+1c. multicoloured . . . 10 10
167 – 7c.+1c. multicoloured . . . 10 10
168 – 7c.+1c. multicoloured . . . 10 10
169 – 7c.+1c. multicoloured . . . 10 10
170 – 15c.+1c. multicoloured . . 15 15
171 – 15c.+1c. multicoloured . . 15 15
172 – 15c.+1c. multicoloured . . 15 15
173 – 20c.+1c. multicoloured . . 20 20
174 – 20c.+1c. multicoloured . . 20 20
175 – 20c.+1c. multicoloured . . 20 20

1976. Easter. Multicoloured.
176 15c. Type **26** 15 10
177 30c. "The Descent" (detail) 20 15
178 35c. "The Descent" (detail) 25 20

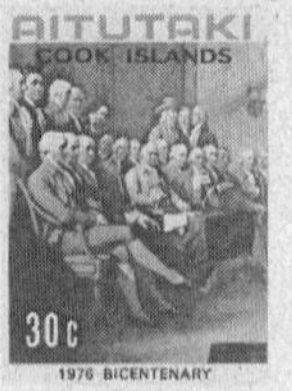

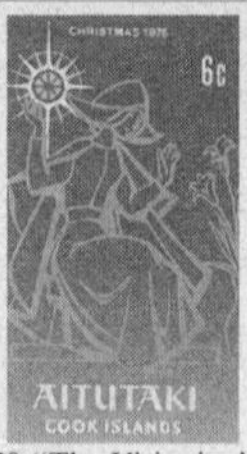

27 Left Detail **30** "The Visitation"

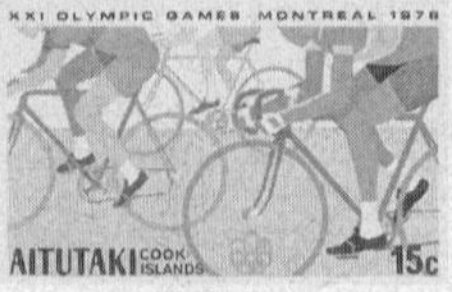

28 Cycling

1976. Bicentenary of American Revolution. Paintings by John Turnbull.
180 **27** 30c. multicoloured 25 10
181 – 30c. multicoloured 25 10
182 – 30c. multicoloured 25 10
183 – 35c. multicoloured 25 15
184 – 35c. multicoloured 25 15
185 – 35c. multicoloured 25 15
186 – 50c. multicoloured 25 15
187 – 50c. multicoloured 25 15
188 – 50c. multicoloured 25 15
PAINTINGS: Nos. 180/2, "The Declaration of Independence"; 183/5, "The Surrender of Lord Cornwallis at Yorktown"; 186/8, "The Resignation of General Washington".
Stamps of the same value were printed together, se-tenant, each strip forming a composite design of the whole painting.

1976. Olympic Games, Montreal. Multicoloured.
190 15c. Type **28** 50 15
191 35c. Sailing 45 20
192 60c. Hockey 80 25
193 70c. Sprinting 70 30

1976. Royal Visit to the U.S.A. Nos. 190/3 optd **ROYAL VISIT JULY 1976.**
195 **28** 15c. multicoloured 50 15
196 – 35c. multicoloured 45 25
197 – 60c. multicoloured 80 40
198 – 70c. multicoloured 70 45

1976. Christmas.
200 **30** 6c. gold and green 10 10
201 – 6c. gold and green 10 10
202 – 7c. gold and purple 10 10
203 – 7c. gold and purple 10 10
204 – 15c. gold and blue 10 10
205 – 15c. gold and blue 10 10
206 – 20c. gold and violet . . . 15 15
207 – 20c. gold and violet . . . 15 15
DESIGNS: No. 201, Angel; 202, Angel; 203, Shepherds; 204, Joseph; 205, Mary and the Child; 206, Wise Man; 207, Two Wise Men.
Stamps of the same value were printed together, se-tenant, each pair forming a composite design.

1976. Children's Christmas Fund. Nos. 200/7 surch.
209 **30** 6c.+1c. gold and green . . 10 10
210 – 6c.+1c. gold and green . . 10 10
211 – 7c.+1c. gold and purple . . 10 10
212 – 7c.+1c. gold and purple . . 10 10
213 – 15c.+1c. gold and blue . . 15 15
214 – 15c.+1c. gold and blue . . 15 15
215 – 20c.+1c. gold and violet . . 15 15
216 – 20c.+1c. gold and violet . . 15 15

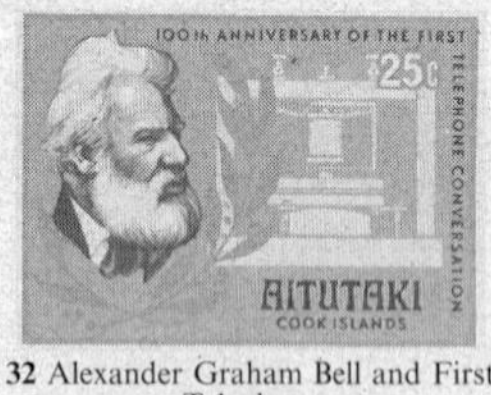

32 Alexander Graham Bell and First Telephone

1977. Centenary (1976) of Telephone.
218 **32** 25c. black, gold and red . . 20 15
219 – 70c. black, gold and lilac 40 40
DESIGN: 70c. Satellite and Earth station.

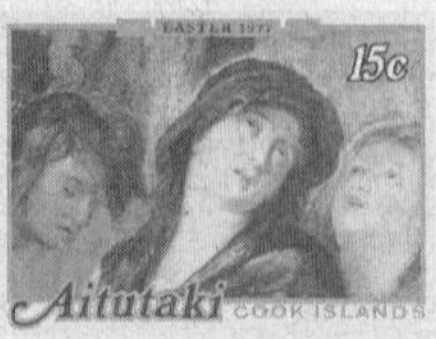

33 "Christ on the Cross" (detail)

1977. Easter. 400th Birth Anniv of Rubens. Mult.
221 15c. Type **33** 45 15
222 20c. "Lamentation for Christ" 60 20
223 35c. "Christ with Straw" . . 75 25

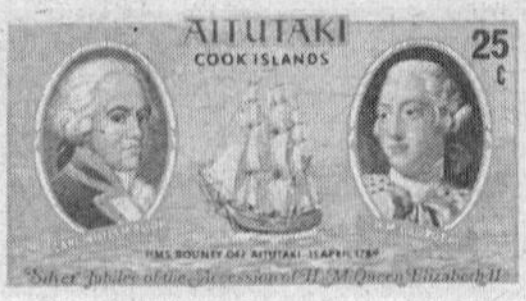

34 Captain Bligh, George III and H.M.S. "Bounty"

1977. Silver Jubilee. Multicoloured.
225 25c. Type **34** 35 35
226 35c. Rev. Williams, George IV and Aitutaki Church . . 40 40
227 50c. Union Jack, Queen Victoria and island map . . 45 45
228 $1 Balcony scene, 1953 . . . 50 50

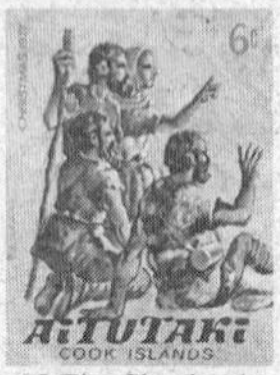

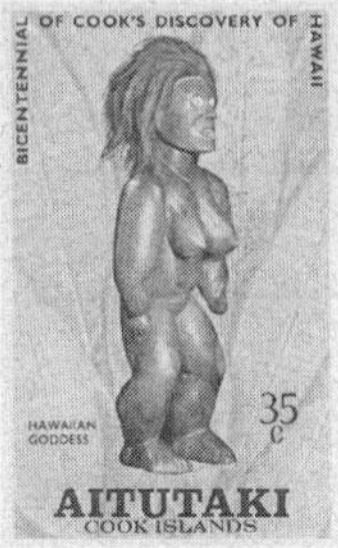

35 The Shepherds **37** Hawaiian Goddess

1977. Christmas. Multicoloured
230 6c. Type **35** 10 10
231 6c. Angel 10 10
232 7c. Mary, Jesus and ox . . . 10 10
233 7c. Joseph and donkey . . . 10 10
234 15c. Three Kings 10 10
235 15c. Virgin and Child 10 10
236 20c. Joseph 10 10
237 20c. Mary and Jesus on donkey 10 10
Stamps of the same value were printed together, se-tenant, forming composite designs.

1977. Children's Christmas Fund. Nos. 230/7 surch **+1c.**
239 6c.+1c. Type **35** 10 10
240 6c.+1c. Angel 10 10
241 7c.+1c. Mary, Jesus and ox 10 10
242 7c.+1c. Joseph and donkey 10 10
243 15c.+1c. Three Kings 15 10
244 15c.+1c. Virgin and Child . . 15 10
245 20c.+1c. Joseph 15 10
246 20c.+1c. Mary and Jesus on donkey 15 10

1978. Bicentenary of Discovery of Hawaii. Mult.
248 35c. Type **37** 35 25
249 50c. Figurehead of H.M.S. "Resolution" (horiz) . . . 60 40
250 $1 Hawaiian temple figure . . 70 70

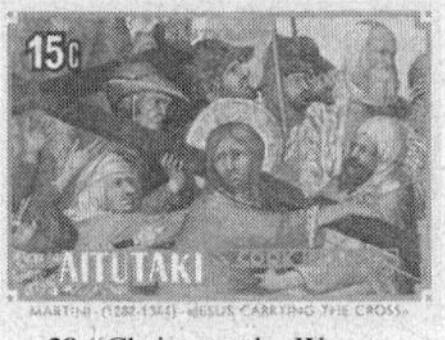

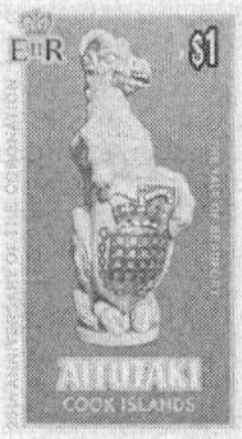

38 "Christ on the Way to Calvary" (Martini) **39** The Yale of Beaufort

1978. Easter. Paintings from the Louvre, Paris. Mult.
252 15c. Type **38** 15 10
253 20c. "Pieta of Avignon" (E. Quarton) 20 10
254 35c. "The Pilgrims at Emmaus" (Rembrandt) . . 25 10

1978. 25th Anniv of Coronation. Multicoloured.
257 $1 Type **39** 30 50
258 $1 Queen Elizabeth II . . . 30 50
259 $1 Aitutaki ancestral statue 30 50

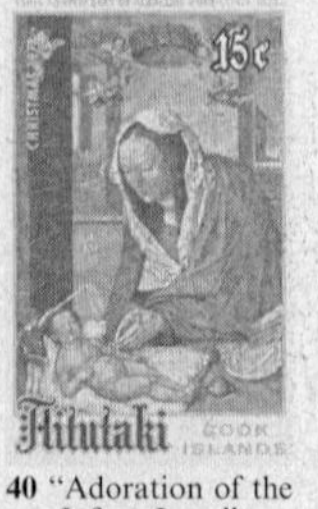

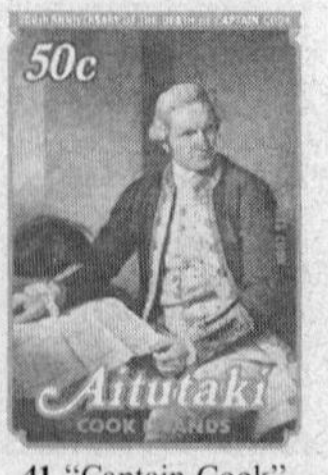

40 "Adoration of the Infant Jesus" **41** "Captain Cook" (Nathaniel Dance)

1978. Christmas. 450th Death Anniv of Durer. Multicoloured.
261 15c. Type **40** 35 15
262 17c. "The Madonna with Child" 40 15
263 30c. "The Madonna with the Iris" 55 20
264 35c. "The Madonna of the Siskin" 60 25

1979. Death Bicent of Captain Cook. Mult.
266 50c. Type **41** . . . . 1·00 80
267 75c. "H.M.S. 'Resolution' and 'Adventure' at Matavai Bay," Tahiti (W. Hodges) . . . . 1·75 95

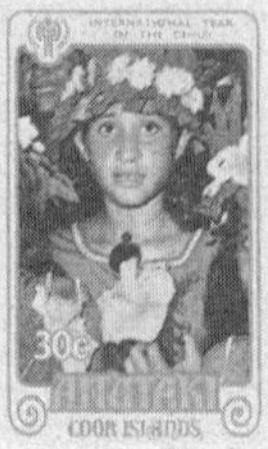

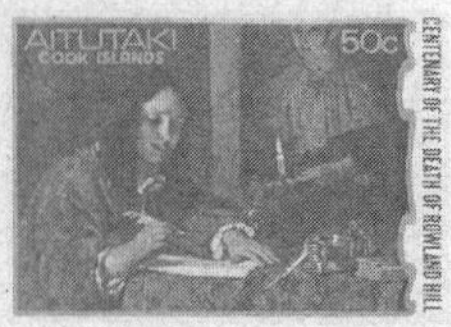

42 Girl with Flowers **43** "Man writing a Letter" (painting by Gabriel Metsu)

1979. International Year of the Child. Multicoloured.
269 30c. Type **42** 15 15
270 35c. Boy playing guitar . . . 20 20
271 65c. Children in canoe . . . 30 30

1979. Death Centenary of Sir Rowland Hill. Multicoloured.
273 50c. Type **43** 45 45
274 50c. Sir Rowland Hill with Penny Black, 1903 ½d. and 1911 1d. stamps 45 45
275 50c. "Girl in Blue reading a Letter" (Jan Vermeer) . . 45 45
276 65c. "Woman writing a Letter" (Gerard Terborch) 50 50
277 65c. Sir Rowland Hill, with Penny Black, 1903 3d. and 1920 ½d. stamps 50 50
278 65c. "Lady reading a Letter" (Jan Vermeer) 50 50

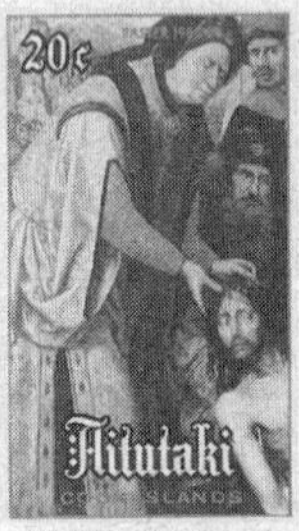

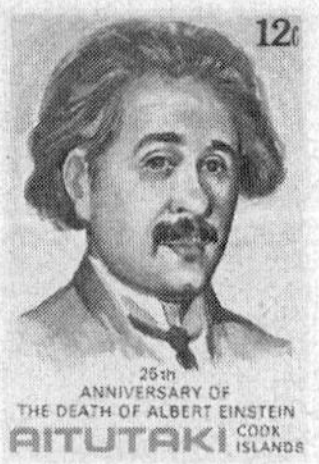

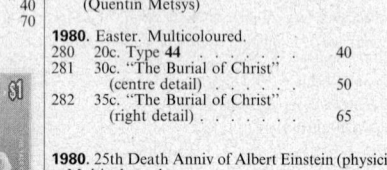

44 "The Burial of Christ" (left detail) (Quentin Metsys) **45** Einstein as a Young Man

1980. Easter. Multicoloured.
280 20c. Type **44** 40 25
281 30c. "The Burial of Christ" (centre detail) 50 35
282 35c. "The Burial of Christ" (right detail) 65 45

1980. 25th Death Anniv of Albert Einstein (physicist). Multicoloured.
284 12c. Type **45** 50 50
285 12c. Atom and "$E=mc^2$" equation 50 50
286 15c. Einstein in middle-age 55 55
287 15c. Cross over nuclear explosion (Test Ban Treaty, 1963) 55 55
288 20c. Einstein as an old man 65 65
289 20c. Hand preventing atomic explosion 65 65

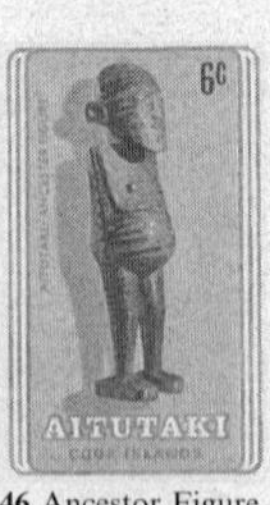

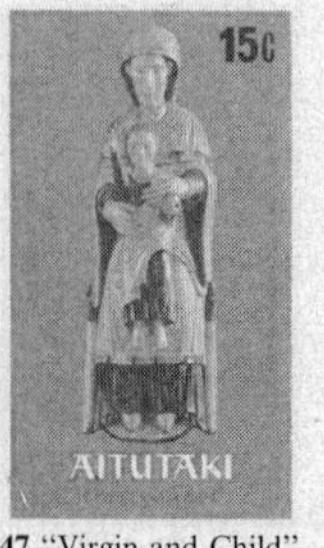

46 Ancestor Figure, Aitutaki **47** "Virgin and Child" (13th century)

1980. 3rd South Pacific Festival of Arts. Mult.
291 6c. Type **46** 10 10
292 6c. Staff god image, Rarotonga 10 10
293 6c. Trade adze, Mangaia . . 10 10
294 6c. Carved image of Tangaroa, Rarotonga . . . 10 10
295 12c. Wooden image Aitutaki 10 10
296 12c. Hand club, Rarotonga 10 10
297 12c. Carved mace "god", Mangaia 10 10
298 12c. Fisherman's god, Rarotonga 10 10
299 15c. Ti'i image, Aitutaki . . 15 15
300 15c. Fisherman's god, Rarotonga (different) . . . 15 15

301	15c. Carved mace "god", Cook Islands	15	15
302	15c. Carved image of Tangaroa, Rarotonga (different)	15	15
303	20c. Chief's headdress, Aitutaki	15	15
304	20c. Carved mace "god", Cook Islands (different)	15	15
305	20c. Staff god image, Rarotonga (different)	15	15
306	20c. Carved image of Tangaroa, Rarotonga (different)	15	15

1980. Christmas. Sculptures of "The Virgin and Child". Multicoloured.

308	15c. Type **47**	20	15
309	20c. 14th century	20	15
310	25c. 15th century	20	15
311	35c. 15th century (different)	30	20

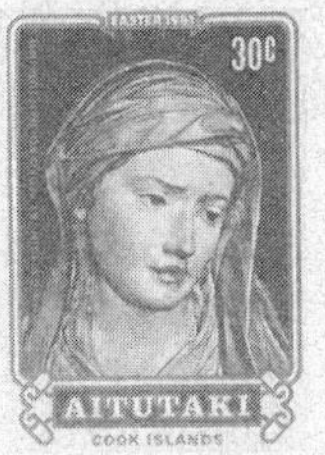
48 "Mourning Virgin"

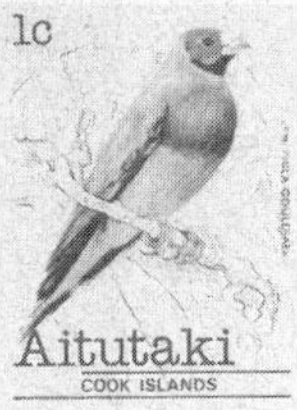
49 Gouldian Finch

1981. Easter. Details of Sculpture "Burial of Christ" by Pedro Roldan.

313	**48** 30c. gold and green	25	25
314	– 40c. gold and lilac	30	30
315	– 50c. gold and blue	30	30

DESIGNS: 40c. "Christ"; 50c. "Saint John".

1981. Birds (1st series). Multicoloured.

317	1c. Type **49**	45	30
318	1c. Common starling	45	30
319	2c. Golden whistler	50	30
320	2c. Scarlet robin	50	30
321	3c. Rufous fantail	60	30
322	3c. Peregrine falcon	60	30
323	4c. Java sparrow	70	30
324	4c. Barn owl	70	30
325	5c. Tahitian lory	70	30
326	5c. White-breasted wood swallow	70	30
327	6c. Purple swamphen	70	30
328	6c. Feral rock pigeon	70	30
329	10c. Chestnut-breasted mannikin	90	30
330	10c. Zebra dove	90	30
331	12c. Reef heron	1·00	40
332	12c. Common mynah	1·00	40
333	15c. Whimbrel (horiz)	1·25	40
334	15c. Black-browed albatross (horiz)	1·25	40
335	20c. Pacific golden plover (horiz)	1·50	55
336	20c. White tern (horiz)	1·50	55
337	25c. Pacific black duck (horiz)	1·75	70
338	25c. Brown booby (horiz)	1·75	70
339	30c. Great frigate bird (horiz)	2·00	85
340	30c. Pintail (horiz)	2·00	85
341	35c. Long-billed reed warbler	2·25	1·00
342	35c. Pomarine skua	2·25	1·00
343	40c. Buff-banded rail	2·75	1·25
344	40c. Spotted triller	2·75	1·25
345	50c. Royal albatross	3·00	1·50
346	50c. Stephen's lory	3·00	1·50
347	70c. Red-headed parrot-finch	5·50	3·00
348	70c. Orange dove	5·50	3·00
349	$1 Blue-headed flycatcher	5·50	3·75
350	$2 Red-bellied flycatcher	6·50	8·00
351	$4 Red munia	11·00	14·00
352	$5 Flat-billed kingfisher	12·00	16·00

See also Nos. 475/94.

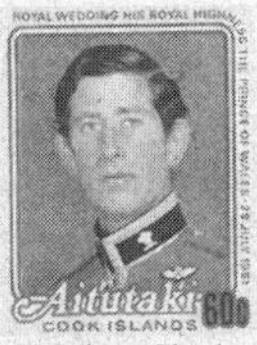
50 Prince Charles

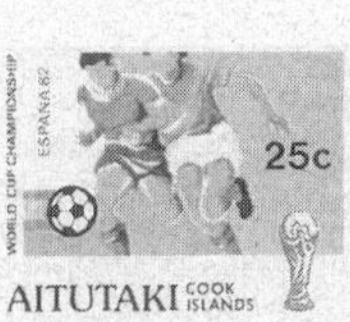
52 Footballers

1981. Royal Wedding. Multicoloured.

391	60c. Type **50**	30	40
392	80c. Lady Diana Spencer	40	55
393	$1.40 Prince Charles and Lady Diana (87 × 70 mm)	60	80

1981. International Year for Disabled Persons. Nos. 391/3 surch **+5c.**

394	60c.+5c. Type **50**	60	90
395	80c.+5c. Lady Diana Spencer	70	1·10
396	$1.40+5c. Prince Charles and Lady Diana	90	1·60

1981. World Cup Football Championship, Spain (1982). Football Scenes. Multicoloured.

397	12c. Ball to left of stamp	50	35
398	12c. Ball to right	50	35
399	15c. Ball to right	55	40
400	15c. Ball to left	55	40
401	20c. Ball to left	55	50
402	20c. Ball to right	55	50
403	25c. Type **52**	60	55
404	25c. "ESPANA 82" inscription	60	55

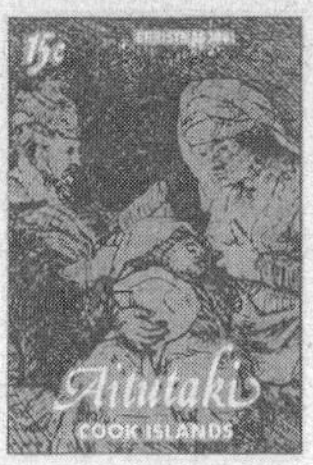
53 "The Holy Family"

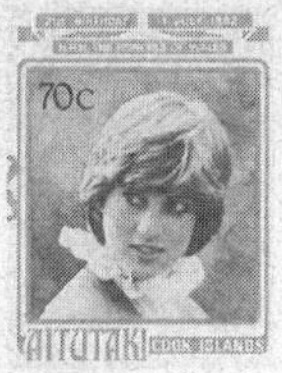
54 Princess of Wales

1981. Christmas. Etchings by Rembrandt.

406	**53** 15c. brown and gold	45	45
407	– 30c. brown and gold	70	70
408	– 40c. brown and gold	95	95
409	– 50c. brown and gold	1·25	1·25

DESIGNS—VERT: 30c. "Virgin with Child". HORIZ: 40c. "Adoration of the Shepherds"; 50c. "The Holy Family".

1982. 21st Birthday of Princess of Wales. Mult.

411	70c. Type **54**	1·75	60
412	$1 Prince and Princess of Wales	1·75	75
413	$2 Princess Diana (different)	3·00	1·50

1982. Birth of Prince William of Wales (1st issue). Nos. 391/3 optd.

415	60c. Type **50**	90	70
416	60c. Type **50**	90	70
417	80c. Lady Diana Spencer	1·10	80
418	80c. Lady Diana Spencer	1·10	80
419	$1.40 Prince Charles and Lady Diana	1·25	1·00
420	$1.40 Prince Charles and Lady Diana	1·25	1·00

OPTS: Nos. 415, 417 and 419, **21 JUNE 1982. PRINCE WILLIAM OF WALES**. Nos. 416, 418 and 420, **COMMEMORATING THE ROYAL BIRTH**.

1982. Birth of Prince William of Wales (2nd issue). As Nos. 411/13 but inscr "ROYAL BIRTH 21 JUNE 1982 PRINCE WILLIAM OF WALES".

421	70c. Type **54**	70	60
422	$1 Prince and Princess of Wales	80	75
423	$2 Princess Diana (different)	1·60	1·50

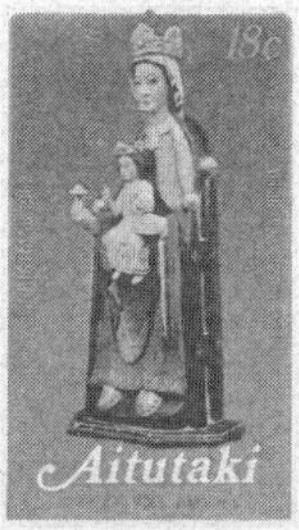
56 "Virgin and Child" (12th-century sculpture)

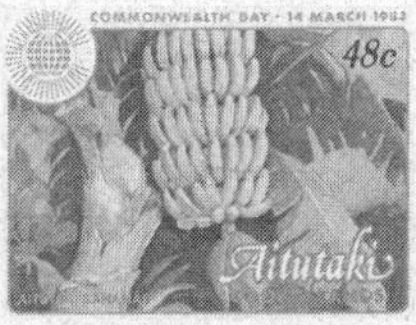
57 Aitutaki Bananas

1982. Christmas. Religious Sculptures. Multicoloured.

425	18c. Type **56**	60	60
426	36c. "Virgin and Child" (12th-century)	75	75
427	48c. "Virgin and Child" (13th-century)	90	90
428	60c. "Virgin and Child" (15th-century)	1·25	1·25

1983. Commonwealth Day. Multicoloured.

430	48c. Type **57**	1·00	50
431	48c. Ancient Ti'i image	1·00	50
432	48c. Tourist canoeing	1·00	50
433	48c. Captain William Bligh and chart	1·00	50

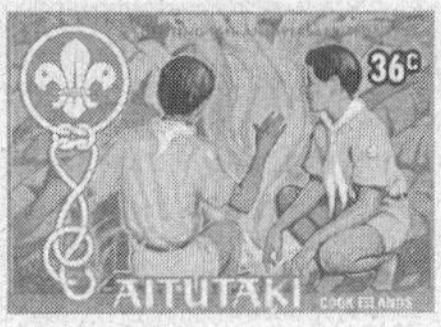
58 Scouts around Campfire

1983. 75th Anniv of Boy Scout Movement. Mult.

434	36c. Type **58**	65	65
435	48c. Scout saluting	75	75
436	60c. Scouts hiking	80	80

1983. 15th World Scout Jamboree, Alberta, Canada. Nos. 434/6 optd **15TH WORLD SCOUT JAMBOREE**.

438	36c. Type **58**	80	45
439	48c. Scout saluting	1·00	55
440	60c. Scouts hiking	1·25	75

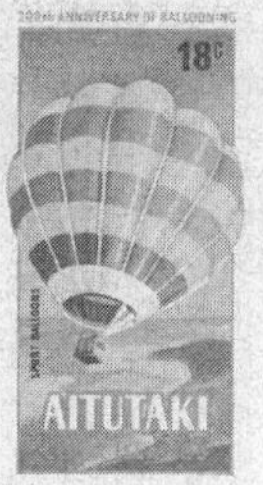
60 Modern Sport Balloon

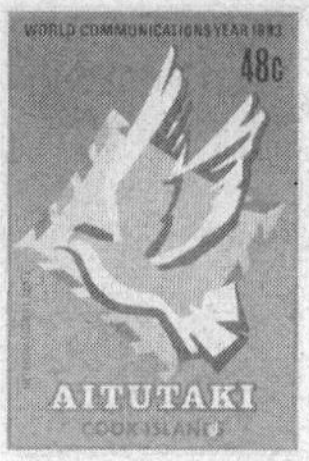
63 International Mail

1983. Bicentenary of Manned Flight.

442	**60** 18c. multicoloured	55	30
443	– 36c. multicoloured	75	50
444	– 48c. multicoloured	90	60
445	– 60c. multicoloured	1·00	80

DESIGNS: 36c. to 60c. Showing different modern sports balloons.

1983. Various stamps surch (a) Nos. 335/48 and 352.

447	18c. on 20c. Pacific golden plover	2·50	1·00
448	18c. on 20c. White tern	2·50	1·00
449	36c. on 25c. Pacific black duck	3·50	1·25
450	36c. on 25c. Brown booby	3·50	1·25
451	36c. on 30c. Great frigate bird	3·50	1·25
452	36c. on 30c. Pintail	3·50	1·25
453	36c. on 35c. Long-billed reed warbler	3·50	1·25
454	36c. on 35c. Pomarine skua	3·50	1·25
455	48c. on 40c. Buff-banded rail	4·00	1·25
456	48c. on 40c. Spotted triller	4·00	1·25
457	48c. on 50c. Royal albatross	4·00	1·25
458	48c. on 50c. Stephen's lory	4·00	1·25
459	72c. on 70c. Red-headed parrot finch	7·00	2·50
460	72c. on 70c. Orange dove	7·00	2·50
461	$5.60 on $5 Flat-billed kingfisher (vert)	20·00	10·00
	(b) Nos. 392/3 and 412/3.		
462	96c. on 80c. Lady Diana Spencer	3·00	2·50
463	96c. on $1 Prince and Princess of Wales	2·75	2·00
464	$1.20 on $1.40 Prince Charles and Lady Diana	3·00	2·50
465	$1.20 on $2 Princess Diana	2·75	2·00

1983. World Communications Year. Multicoloured.

466	48c. Type **63**	65	50
467	60c. Telecommunications	95	70
468	96c. Space satellite	1·40	1·00

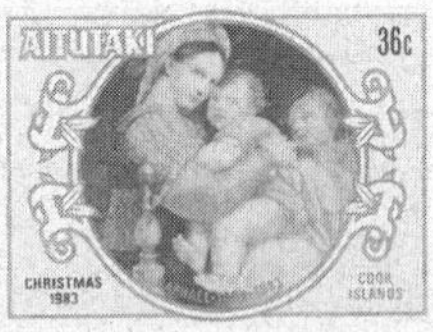
64 "Madonna of the Chair"

1983. Christmas. 500th Birth Anniv of Raphael. Multicoloured.

470	36c. Type **64**	75	40
471	48c. "The Alba Madonna"	90	50
472	60c. "Conestabile Madonna"	1·25	70

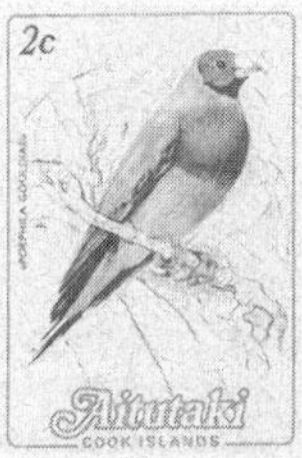
65 Gouldian Finch

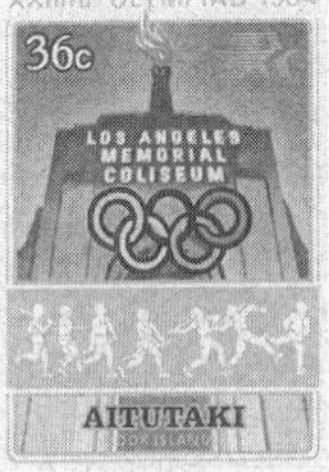
66 Javelin throwing

1984. Birds (2nd series). Multicoloured.

475	2c. Type **65**	1·75	1·00
476	3c. Common starling	1·75	1·00
477	5c. Scarlet robin	1·75	1·10
478	10c. Golden whistler	2·25	1·10
479	12c. Rufous fantail	2·25	1·10
480	18c. Peregrine falcon	2·25	1·50
481	24c. Barn owl	2·25	1·50
482	30c. Java sparrow	2·25	1·50
483	36c. White-breasted wood swallow	2·25	1·50
484	48c. Tahitian lory	2·25	1·50
485	50c. Feral rock pigeon	2·50	2·00
486	60c. Purple swamphen	2·50	2·00
487	72c. Zebra dove	3·00	2·00
488	96c. Chestnut-breasted mannikin	3·00	2·00
489	$1.20 Common mynah	3·00	2·75
490	$2.10 Reef heron	4·00	3·75
491	$3 Blue-headed flycatcher	6·50	6·00
492	$4.20 Red-bellied flycatcher	3·75	7·50
493	$5.60 Red munia	4·50	8·00
494	$9.60 Flat-billed kingfisher	7·50	11·00

1984. Olympic Games. Los Angeles. Multicoloured.

495	36c. Type **66**	35	35
496	48c. Shot-putting	40	45
497	60c. Hurdling	45	55
498	$2 Basketball	1·75	1·50

DESIGNS: 48c. to $2, show Memorial Coliseum and various events.

1984. Olympic Gold Medal Winners. Nos. 495/8 optd.

500	36c. Type **66** (optd **Javelin Throw Tessa Sanderson Great Britain**)	35	35
501	48c. Shot-putting (optd **Shot Put Claudia Losch Germany**)	40	45
502	60c. Hurdling (optd **Heptathlon Glynis Nunn Australia**)	45	55
503	$2 Basketball (optd **Team Basketball United States**)	1·10	1·50

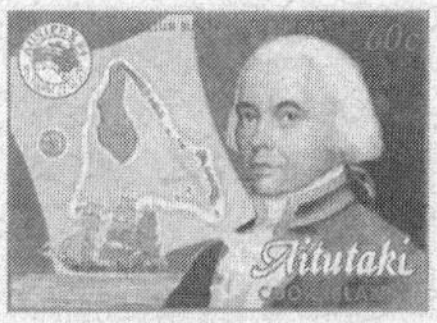
67 Captain William Bligh and Chart

1984. "Ausipex" International Stamp Exhibition, Melbourne. Multicoloured.

504	60c. Type **67**	3·75	3·25
505	96c. H.M.S. "Bounty" and map	3·75	3·50
506	$1.40 Aitutaki stamps of 1974, 1979 and 1981 with map	3·75	3·50

1984. Birth of Prince Henry (1st issue). No. 391 optd **15-9-84 Birth Prince Henry** and surch also.

508	$3 on 60c. Type **50**	2·25	3·25

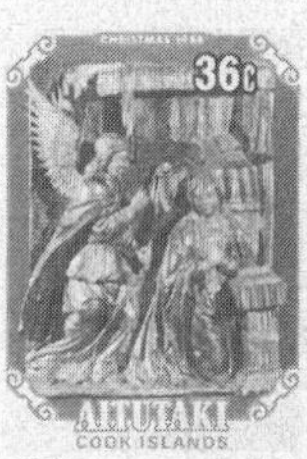
69 The Annunciation

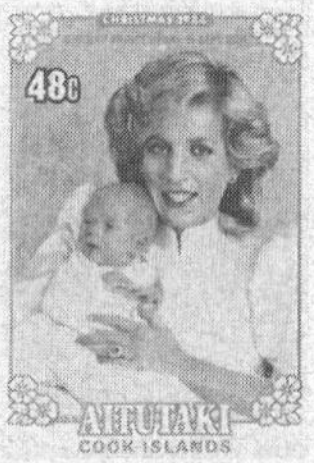
70 Princess Diana with Prince Henry

1984. Christmas. Details from Altarpiece, St Paul's Church, Palencia, Spain. Multicoloured.

509	36c. Type **69**	30	35
510	48c. The Nativity	40	45
511	60c. The Epiphany	45	50
512	96c. The Flight into Egypt	75	80

1984. Birth of Prince Henry (2nd issue). Mult.

514	48c. Type **70**	2·25	1·75
515	60c. Prince William with Prince Henry	2·25	1·75
516	$2.10 Prince and Princess of Wales with children	3·25	3·50

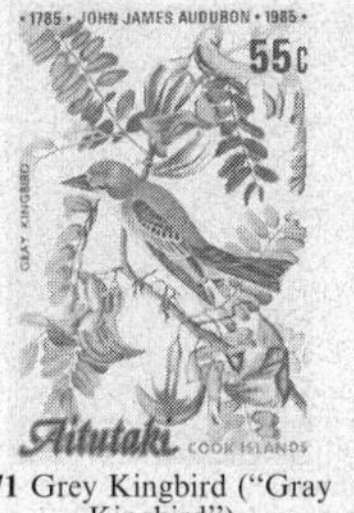
71 Grey Kingbird ("Gray Kingbird")

1985. Birth Bicentenary of John J. Audubon (ornithologist). Designs showing original paintings. Multicoloured.

518	55c. Type **71**	1·10	1·10
519	65c. Bohemian waxwing	1·25	1·25
520	75c. Summer tanager	1·40	1·40
521	95c. Common cardinal ("Cardinal")	1·50	1·50
522	$1.15 White-winged crossbill	1·90	1·90

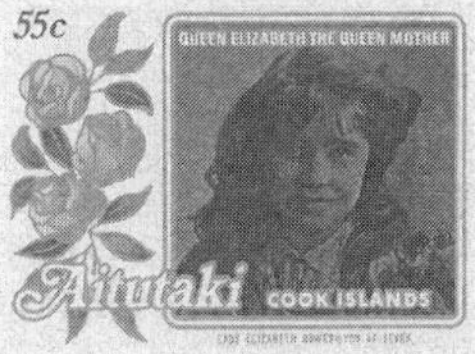
72 The Queen Mother, aged Seven

1985. Life and Times of Queen Elizabeth the Queen Mother. Multicoloured.

523	55c. Type **72**	45	50
524	65c. Engagement photograph, 1922	50	55
525	75c. With young Princess Elizabeth	60	65
526	$1.30 With baby Prince Charles	1·00	1·10

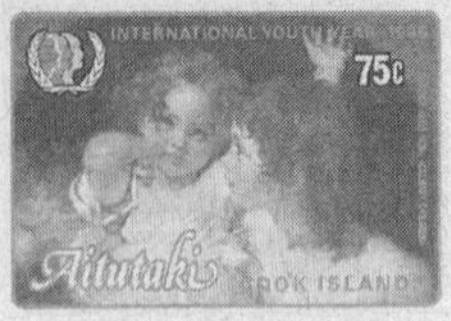

73 "The Calmady Children" (T. Lawrence)

1985. International Youth Year. Multicoloured.

528 75c. Type **73** . . . . 2·75 2·50
529 90c. "Madame Charpentier's Children" (Renoir) . . . . 2·75 2·75
530 $1.40 "Young Girls at Piano" (Renoir) . . . . 3·50 3·75

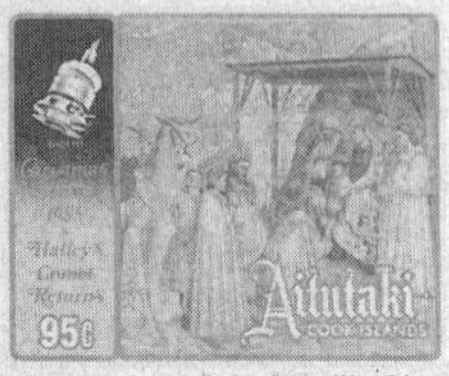

74 "Adoration of the Magi" (Giotto) and "Giotto" Spacecraft

1985. Christmas. Appearance of Halley's Comet (1st issue). Multicoloured.

532 95c. Type **74** . . . . 1·50 1·50
533 95c. As Type **74** but showing "Planet A" spacecraft . . . 1·50 1·50
534 $1.15 Type **74** . . . . 1·50 1·50
535 $1.15 As No. 533 . . . . . . 1·50 1·50

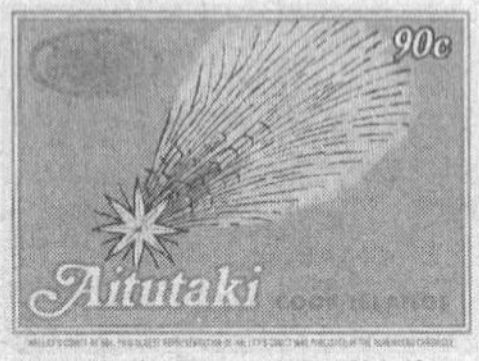

75 Halley's Comet A.D. 684 (from "Nuremberg Chronicle")

1986. Appearance of Halley's Comet (2nd issue). Multicoloured.

537 90c. Type **75** 90 90
538 $1.25 Halley's Comet, 1066 (from Bayeux Tapestry) . . 1·10 1·10
539 $1.75 Halley's Comet, 1456 (from "Lucerne Chronicles") . . . . 1·50 1·50

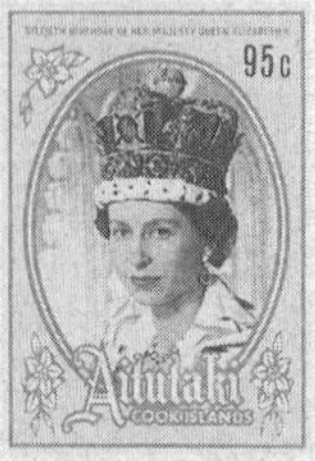

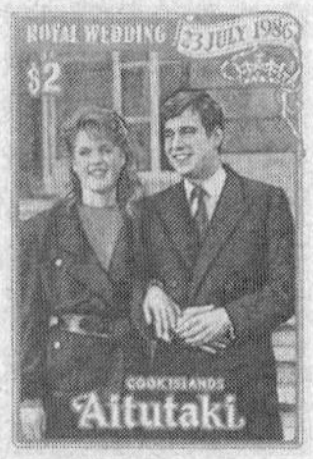

76 Queen Elizabeth II on Coronation Day (from photo by Cecil Beaton)

78 Prince Andrew and Miss Sarah Ferguson

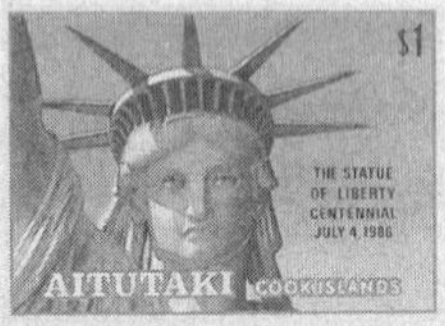

77 Head of Statue of Liberty

1986. 60th Birthday of Queen Elizabeth II.

542 **76** 95c. multicoloured . . . . 1·75 1·75

1986. Centenary of Statue of Liberty. Mult.

544 $1 Type **77** . . . . 1·25 1·25
545 $2.75 Statue of Liberty at sunset . . . . 2·75 2·75

1986. Royal Wedding.

547 **78** $2 multicoloured . . . . . 2·00 2·00

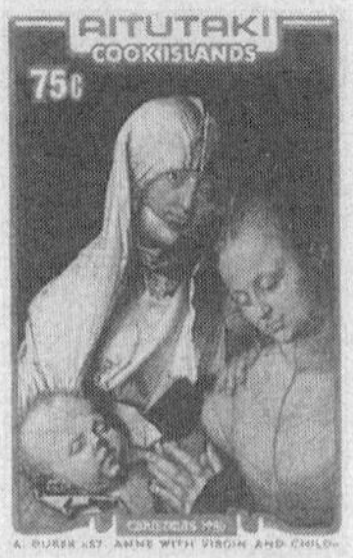

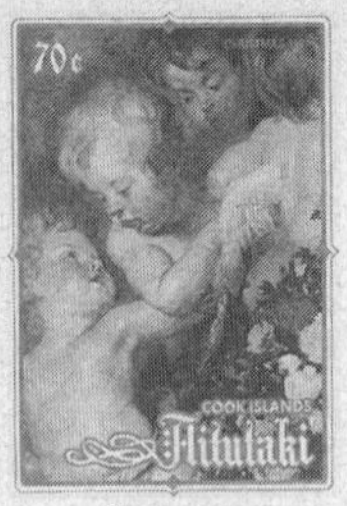

79 "St. Anne with Virgin and Child"

83 Angels

1986. Christmas. Paintings by Durer. Multicoloured.

551 75c. Type **79** . . . . 1·25 1·25
552 $1.35 "Virgin and Child" . . 1·75 1·75
553 $1.95 "The Adoration of the Magi" . . . . 2·25 2·25
554 $2.75 "Madonna of the Rosary" . . . . 3·00 3·00

1986. Visit of Pope John Paul II to South Pacific. Nos. 551/4 optd **NOVEMBER 21-24 1986 FIRST VISIT TO SOUTH PACIFIC** and surch also.

556 75c.+10c. Type **79** . . . . . 2·75 2·50
557 $1.35+10c. "Virgin and Child" . . . . 3·25 3·00
558 $1.95+10c. "The Adoration of the Magi" . . . . 4·00 3·50
559 $2.75+10c. "Madonna of the Rosary" . . . . 5·00 5·00

1987. Hurricane Relief Fund. Nos. 544/5, 547, 551/4 and 556/9 surch **HURRICANE RELIEF +50c**.

561 75c.+50c. Type **79** . . . . . 2·75 2·75
562 75c.+10c.+50c. Type **79** . . 3·50 3·50
563 $1+50c. Type **77** . . . . . . 3·00 3·00
564 $1.35+50c. "Virgin and Child" (Durer) . . . . . . 3·25 3·25
565 $1.35+10c.+50c. "Virgin and Child" (Durer) . . . . . . 4·00 4·00
566 $1.95+50c. "The Adoration of the Magi" (Durer) . . . 4·00 4·00
567 $1.95+10c.+50c. "The Adoration of the Magi" (Durer) . . . . 4·50 4·50
568 $2+50c. Type **78** . . . . . 4·00 4·00
569 $2.75+50c. Statue of Liberty at sunset . . . . 4·50 4·50
570 $2.75+50c. "Madonna of the Rosary" (Durer) . . . . . 4·50 4·50
571 $2.75+10c.+50c. "Madonna of the Rosary" (Durer) . . 5·50 5·50

1987. Royal Ruby Wedding. Nos. 391/3 surch **2.50 Royal Wedding 40th Anniv**.

572 $2.50 on 60c. Type **50** . . . 2·00 2·50
573 $2.50 on 80c. Lady Diana Spencer . . . . 2·00 2·50
574 $2.50 on $1.40 Prince Charles and Lady Diana (87 × 70 mm) . . . . . . 2·00 2·50

1987. Christmas. Details of angels from "Virgin with Garland" by Rubens.

575 **83** 70c. multicoloured . . . . 2·00 2·00
576 – 85c. multicoloured . . . . 2·00 2·00
577 – $1.50 multicoloured . . . 2·25 2·25
578 – $1.85 multicoloured . . . 3·25 3·25

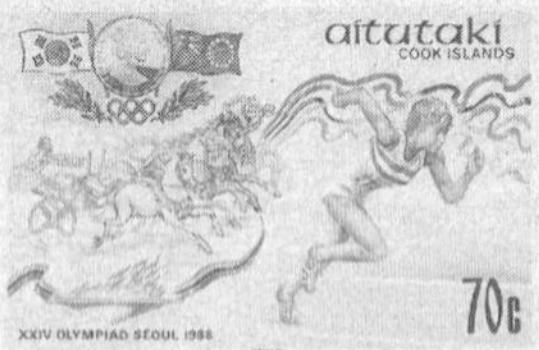

84 Chariot Racing and Athletics

1988. Olympic Games, Seoul. Ancient and modern Olympic sports. Multicoloured.

581 70c. Type **84** . . . . 2·00 2·00
582 85c. Greek runners and football . . . . 2·25 2·25
583 95c. Greek wrestling and handball . . . . 2·25 2·25
584 $1.40 Greek hoplites and tennis . . . . 3·00 3·00

1988. Olympic Medal Winners, Los Angeles. Nos. 581/4 optd.

586 70c. Type **84** (optd **FLORENCE GRIFFITH JOYNER UNITED STATES 100 M AND 200 M**) . . . . 1·75 1·75
587 85c. Greek runners and football (optd **GELINDO BORDIN ITALY MARATHON**) . . . . . 1·75 1·75
588 95c. Greek wrestling and handball (optd **HITOSHI SAITO JAPAN JUDO**) . . 1·75 1·75
589 $1.40 Greek hoplites and tennis (optd **STEFFI GRAF WEST GERMANY WOMEN'S TENNIS**) . . 3·75 3·75

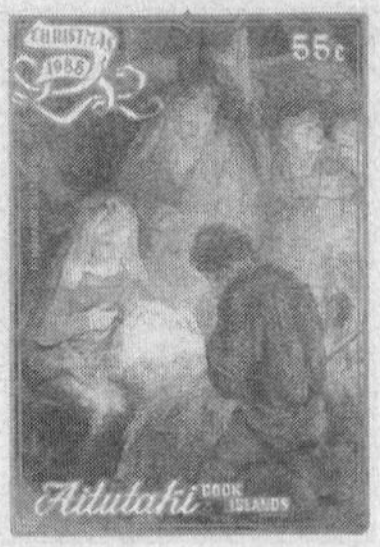

85 "Adoration of the Shepherds" (detail)

1988. Christmas. Paintings by Rembrandt. Mult.

590 55c. Type **85** . . . . 1·75 1·75
591 70c. "The Holy Family" . . 2·00 2·00
592 85c. "Presentation in the Temple" . . . . 2·25 2·25
593 95c. "The Holy Family" (different) . . . . 2·25 2·25
594 $1.15 "Presentation in the Temple" (different) . . . . 2·50 2·50

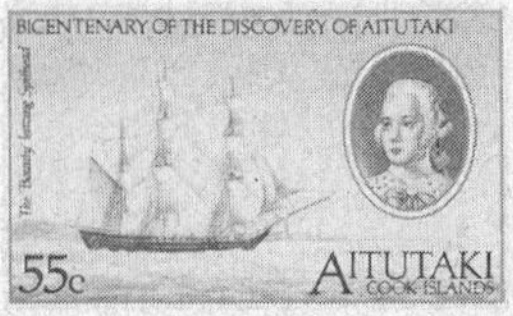

86 H.M.S. "Bounty" leaving Spithead and King George III

1989. Bicentenary of Discovery of Aitutaki by Captain Bligh. Multicoloured.

596 55c. Type **86** . . . . 1·75 1·75
597 65c. Breadfruit plants . . . . 2·00 2·00
598 75c. Old chart showing Aitutaki and Captain Bligh 2·25 2·25
599 95c. Native outrigger and H.M.S. "Bounty" off Aitutaki . . . . 2·50 2·50
600 $1.65 Fletcher Christian confronting Bligh . . . . 3·00 3·00

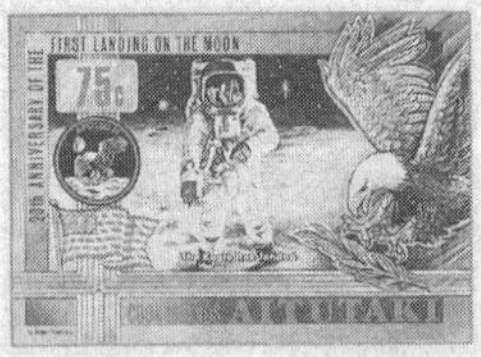

87 "Apollo 11" Astronaut on Moon

1989. 20th Anniv of First Manned Landing on Moon. Multicoloured.

602 75c. Type **87** . . . . 2·25 2·00
603 $1.15 Conducting experiment on Moon . . . . 2·75 2·50
604 $1.80 Astronaut on Moon carrying equipment . . . . 3·50 3·50

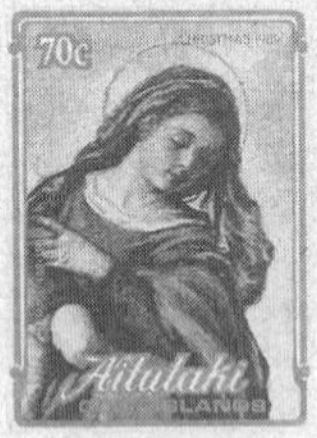

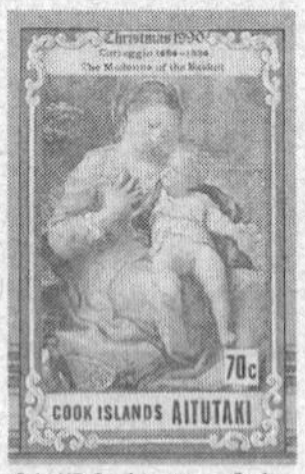

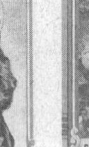

88 Virgin Mary

91 "Madonna of the Basket" (Correggio)

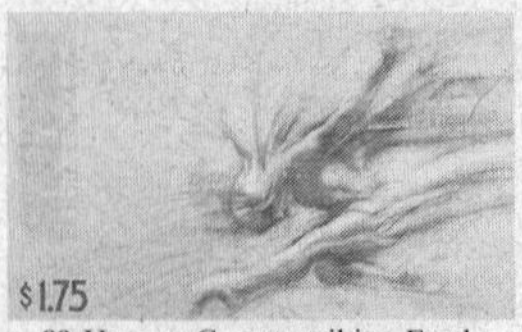

89 Human Comet striking Earth

1989. Christmas. Details from "Virgin in the Glory" by Titian. Multicoloured.

606 70c. Type **88** . . . . . . 2·00 2·00
607 85c. Christ Child . . . . . 2·50 2·50
608 95c. Angel . . . . 2·75 2·75
609 $1.25 Cherubs . . . . 3·25 3·25

1990. Protection of the Environment. Mult.

611 $1.75 Type **89** . . . . 2·25 2·25
612 $1.75 Comet's tail . . . . . 2·25 2·25

Nos. 611/12 were printed together, se-tenant, forming a composite design.

1990. Christmas. Religious Paintings. Mult.

615 70c. Type **91** . . . . 1·50 1·50
616 85c. "Virgin and Child" (Morando) . . . . 1·60 1·60
617 95c. "Adoration of the Child" (Tiepolo) . . . . . 1·75 1·75
618 $1.75 "Mystic Marriage of St. Catherine" (Memling) . . 2·50 2·75

1990. "Birdpex '90" Stamp Exhibition, Christchurch, New Zealand. Nos. 349/50 optd **Birdpex '90** and bird's head.

620 $1 Blue-headed flycatcher . . 3·75 3·75
621 $2 Red-bellied flycatcher . . 4·75 4·75

1991. 65th Birthday of Queen Elizabeth II. No. 352 optd **COMMEMORATING 65th BIRTHDAY OF H.M. QUEEN ELIZABETH II**.

622 $5 Flat-billed kingfisher . . . 9·50 10·00

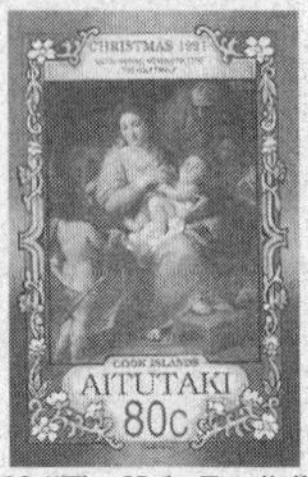

93 "The Holy Family" (A. Mengs)

1991. Christmas. Religious Paintings. Mult.

623 80c. Type **93** . . . . 1·50 1·50
624 90c. "Virgin and the Child" (Lippi) . . . . 1·60 1·60
625 $1.05 "Virgin and Child" (A. Durer) . . . . 1·75 1·75
626 $1.75 "Adoration of the Shepherds" (G. de la Tour) 2·50 2·75

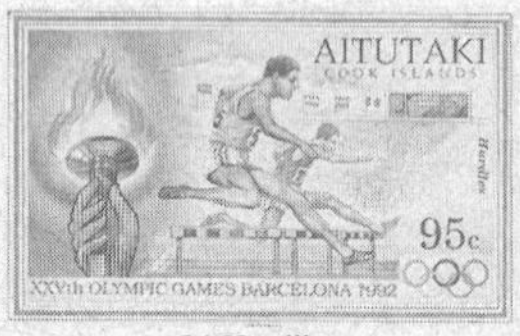

94 Hurdling

1992. Olympic Games, Barcelona. Mult.

628 95c. Type **94** . . . . 1·75 1·50
629 $1.25 Weightlifting . . . . . 2·00 1·75
630 $1.50 Judo . . . . 2·50 2·25
631 $1.95 Football . . . . 2·75 2·75

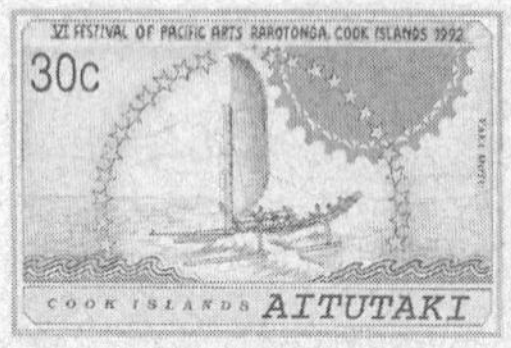

95 Vaka Motu Canoe

1992. 6th Festival of Pacific Arts, Rarotonga. Sailing Canoes. Multicoloured.

632 30c. Type **95** 65 65
633 50c. Hamatafua 80 80
634 95c. Alia Kalia Ndrua . . . 1·50 1·50
635 $1.75 Hokule'a Hawaiian . . 2·25 2·50
636 $1.95 Tuamotu Pahi . . . . 2·50 2·75

1992. Royal Visit by Prince Edward. Nos. 632/6 optd **ROYAL VISIT**.

637 30c. Type **95** 75 75
638 50c. Hamatafua . . . . . . 1·00 1·00
639 95c. Alia Kalia Ndrua . . . 1·75 1·75
640 $1.75 Hokule'a Hawaiian . . 2·50 2·75
641 $1.95 Tuamotu Pahi . . . . 2·50 2·75

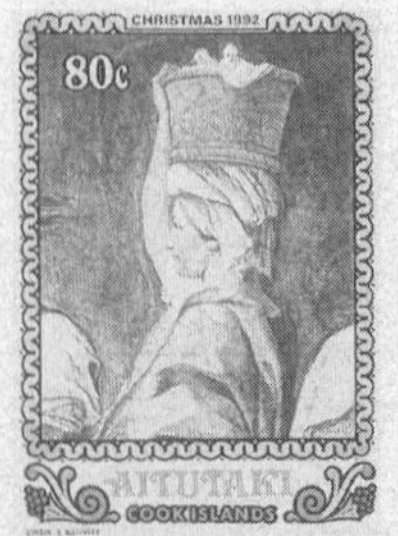

96 "Virgin's Nativity" (detail) (Reni)

1992. Christmas. Different details from "Virgin's Nativity" by Guido Reni.

642 **96** 80c. multicoloured . . . . 1·40 1·40
643 – 90c. multicoloured . . . . 1·60 1·60
644 – $1.05 multicoloured . . . 1·75 1·75
645 – $1.75 multicoloured . . . 2·50 2·75

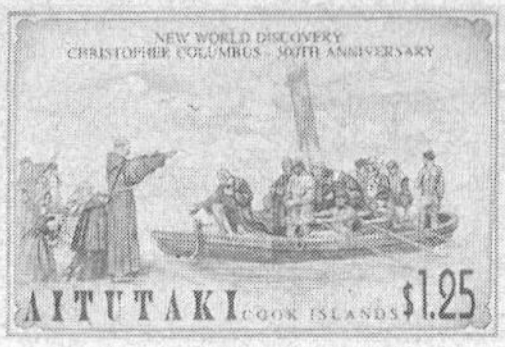

97 The Departure from Palos

1992. 500th Anniv of Discovery of America by Columbus. Multicoloured.

647 $1.25 Type **97** . . . . 2·25 2·50
648 $1.75 Map of voyages . . . 2·75 3·00
649 $1.95 Columbus and crew in New World . . . . 3·25 3·50

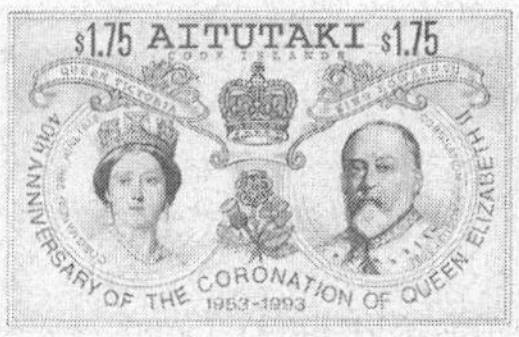

98 Queen Victoria and King Edward VII

1993. 40th Anniv of Coronation. Mult.

650 $1.75 Type **98** . . . . 3·00 2·75
651 $1.75 King George V and King George VI . . . . . 3·00 2·75
652 $1.75 Queen Elizabeth II in 1953 and 1986 . . . . . . 3·00 2·75

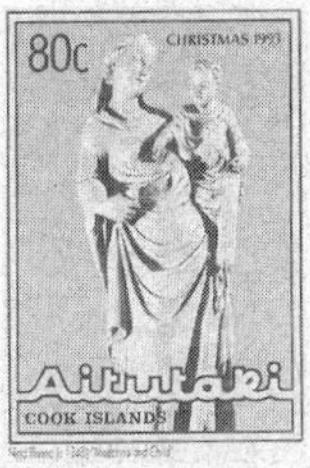

99 "Madonna and Child" (Nino Pisano)

1993. Christmas. Religious Sculptures. Mult.

653 80c. Type **99** 90 90
654 90c. "Virgin on Rosebush" (Luca della Robbia) . . . 1·00 1·00
655 $1.15 "Virgin with Child and St. John" (Juan Francisco Rustici) . . . . 1·40 1·40
656 $1.95 "Virgin with Child" (Miguel Angel) . . . . . 2·25 2·25
657 $3 "Madonna and Child" (Jacopo della Quercia) (32 × 47 mm) . . . . . . 3·25 3·75

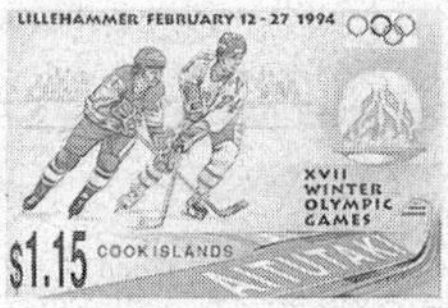

100 Ice Hockey

1994. Winter Olympic Games, Lillehammer. Multicoloured.

658 $1.15 Type **100** . . . . . . 3·00 2·75
659 $1.15 Ski-jumping . . . . . 3·00 2·75
660 $1.15 Cross-country skiing 3·00 2·75

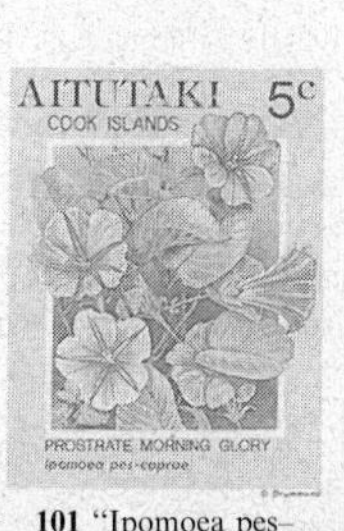

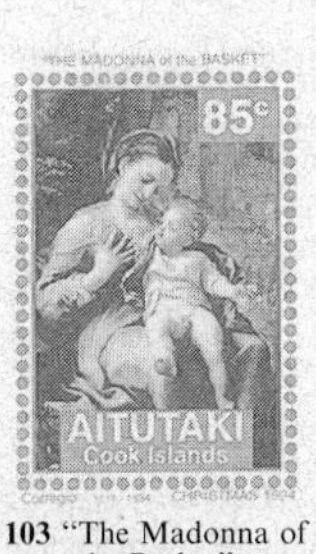

101 "Ipomoea pes-caprae" **103** "The Madonna of the Basket" (Correggio)

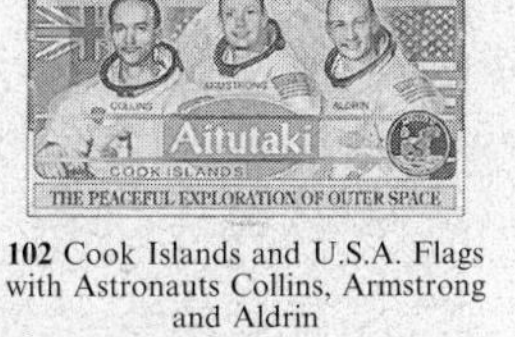

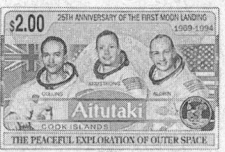

102 Cook Islands and U.S.A. Flags with Astronauts Collins, Armstrong and Aldrin

1994. Flowers. Multicoloured.

661 5c. Type **101** 10 10
662 10c. "Plumeria alba" 10 10
663 15c. "Hibiscus rosa-sinensis" 10 15
664 20c. "Allamanda cathartica" 10 15
665 25c. "Delonix regia" 15 20
666 30c. "Gardenia taitensis" . . 15 20
667 50c. "Plumeria rubra" . . . 30 35
668 80c. "Ipomoea littoralis" . . 45 50
669 85c. "Hibiscus tiliaceus" . . 50 55
670 90c. "Erythrina variegata" . . 50 55
671 $1 "Solandra nitida" 55 60
672 $2 "Cordia subcordata" . . . 1·10 1·25
673 $3 "Hibiscus rosa-sinensis" (different) (34x47mm) . . . 1·75 1·90
674 $5 As $3 (34x47mm) . . . . 2·75 3·00
675 $8 As $3 (34x47mm) . . . . 4·50 4·75

Nos. 671/5 include a portrait of Queen Elizabeth II at top right.

1994. 25th Anniv of First Manned Moon Landing. Multicoloured.

676 $2 Type **102** . . . . 6·00 6·00
677 $2 "Apollo 11" re-entering atmosphere and landing in sea . . . . 6·00 6·00

1994. Christmas. Religious Paintings. Mult.

678 85c. Type **103** . . . . 1·00 1·10
679 85c. "The Virgin and Child with Saints" (Memling) . . 1·00 1·10
680 85c. "The Virgin and Child with Flowers" (Dolci) . . . 1·00 1·10
681 85c. "The Virgin and Child with Angels" (Bergognone) 1·00 1·10
682 90c. "Adoration of the Kings" (Dosso) . . . . . 1·00 1·10
683 90c. "The Virgin and Child" (Bellini) . . . . 1·00 1·10
684 90c. "The Virgin and Child" (Schiavone) . . . . 1·00 1·10
685 90c. "Adoration of the Kings" (Dolci) . . . . . . 1·00 1·10

No. 678 is inscribed "Corregio" in error.

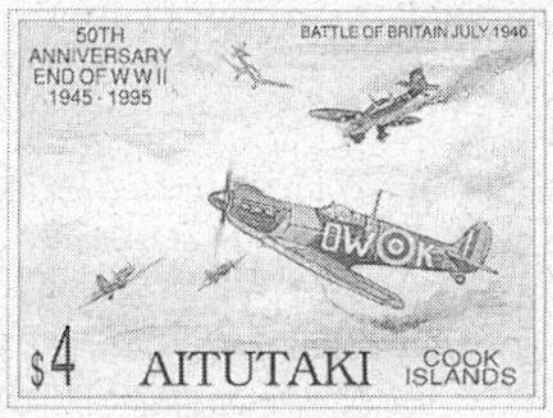

104 Battle of Britain

1995. 50th Anniv of End of Second World War. Multicoloured.

686 $4 Type **104** . . . . 7·50 7·50
687 $4 Battle of Midway . . . . 7·50 7·50

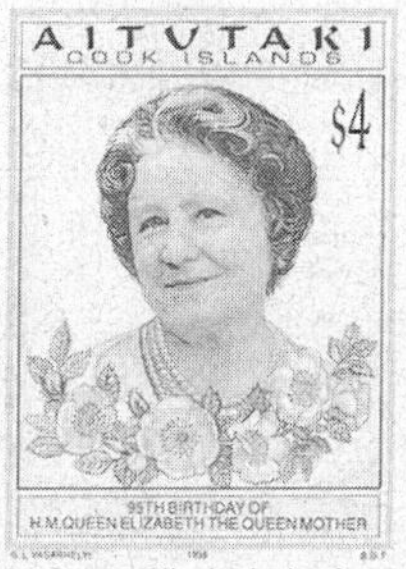

105 Queen Elizabeth the Queen Mother

1995. 95th Birthday of Queen Elizabeth the Queen Mother.

688 **105** $4 multicoloured . . . . 7·00 7·50

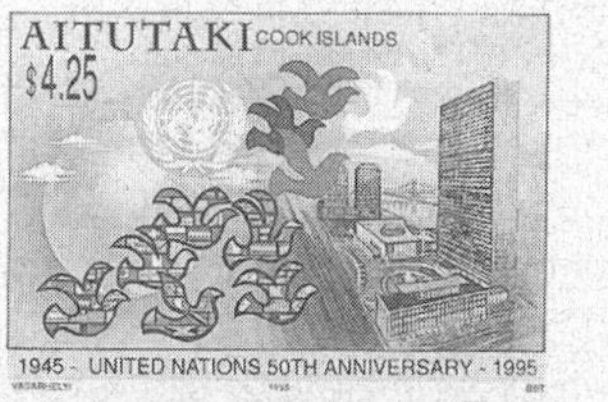

106 Globe, Doves, United Nations Emblem and Headquarters

1995. 50th Anniv of United Nations.

689 **106** $4.25 multicoloured . . . 5·50 6·50

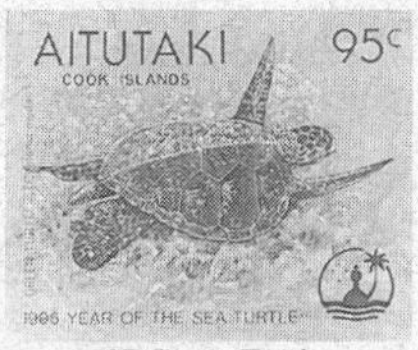

107 Green Turtle

1995. Year of the Sea Turtle. Multicoloured.

690 95c. Type **107** . . . . 1·75 1·75
691 $1.15 Leatherback turtle . . . 2·00 2·00
692 $1.50 Olive Ridley turtle . . . 2·25 2·25
693 $1.75 Loggerhead turtle . . . 2·50 2·50

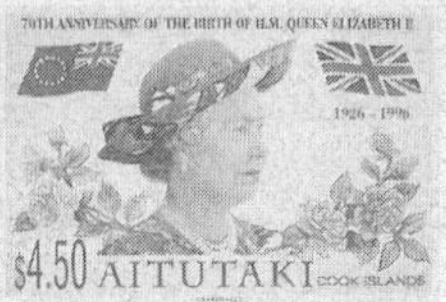

108 Queen Elizabeth II

1996. 70th Birthday of Queen Elizabeth II.

694 **108** $4.50 multicoloured . . . 7·50 8·00

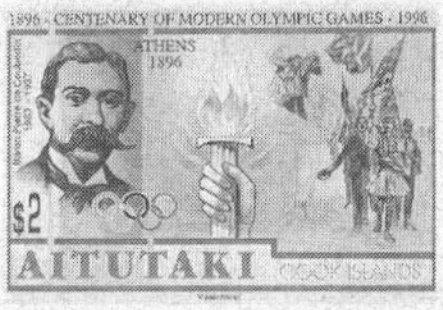

109 Baron Pierre de Coubertin, Torch and Opening of 1896 Olympic Games

1996. Centenary of Modern Olympic Games. Multicoloured.

695 $2 Type **109** . . . . 4·00 4·00
696 $2 Athletes and American flag, 1996 . . . . 4·00 4·00

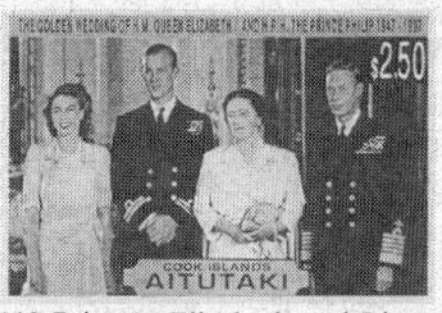

110 Princess Elizabeth and Lieut. Philip Mountbatten with King George VI and Queen Elizabeth, 1947

1997. Golden Wedding of Queen Elizabeth and Prince Philip.

697 **110** $2.50 multicoloured . . . 3·50 3·25

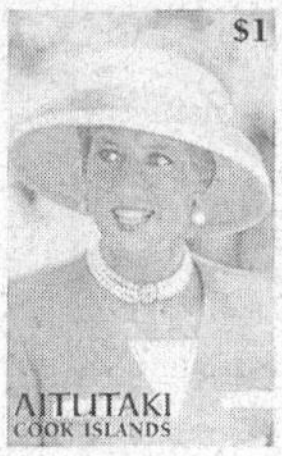

111 Diana, Princess of Wales

1998. Diana, Princess of Wales Commemoration.

699 **111** $1 multicoloured . . . . 1·00 1·00

1999. New Millennium. Nos. 632/6 optd **KIA ORANA THIRD MILLENNIUM**.

702 30c. Type **95** 50 50
703 50c. Hamatafua 60 60
704 95c. Alia Kalia Ndrua . . . 85 85
705 $1.75 Hokule'a Hawaiian . . 1·40 1·40
706 $1.95 Tuamotu Pahi . . . . 1·60 1·60

2000. Queen Elizabeth the Queen Mother's 100th Birthday. As T **277** of Cook Islands.

707 $3 blue and brown . . . . . 2·50 2·50
708 $3 multicoloured . . . . . . 2·50 2·50
709 $3 multicoloured . . . . . . 2·50 2·50
710 $3 green and brown . . . . 2·50 2·50

DESIGNS: No. 707, Queen Mother in evening dress and tiara; 708, Queen Mother in evening dress standing by table; 709, Queen Mother in Garter robes; 710, King George VI and Queen Elizabeth.

2000. Olympic Games, Sydney. As T **278** of Cook Islands. Multicoloured.

712 $2 Ancient Greek wrestlers 1·75 1·90
713 $2 Modern wrestlers . . . . 1·75 1·90
714 $2 Ancient Greek boxer . . . 1·75 1·90
715 $2 Modern boxers . . . . . 1·75 1·90

OFFICIAL STAMPS

1978. Nos. 98/105, 107/10 and 227/8 optd **O.H.M.S.** or surch also.

O 1 1c. multicoloured 90 10
O 2 2c. multicoloured . . . . . 1·00 10
O 3 3c. multicoloured . . . . . 1·00 10
O 4 4c. multicoloured . . . . . 1·00 10
O 5 5c. multicoloured . . . . . 1·00 10
O 6 8c. multicoloured . . . . . 1·25 10
O 7 10c. multicoloured . . . . 1·50 15
O 8 15c. on 60c. multicoloured 2·75 20
O 9 18c. on 60c. multicoloured 2·75 20
O10 20c. multicoloured . . . . 2·75 20
O11 50c. multicoloured . . . . 1·00 55
O12 62c. multicoloured . . . . 10·00 70
O13 $1 multicoloured (No. 108) 10·00 80
O14 $2 multicoloured . . . . . 9·00 75
O15 $4 on $1 mult (No. 228) . . 1·75 75
O16 $5 multicoloured . . . . . 11·00 1·25

1985. Nos. 351/2, 430/3, 475 and 477/94 optd **O.H.M.S.** or surch also.

O17 2c. Type **65** 70 70
O18 5c. Scarlet robin 80 80
O19 10c. Golden whistler . . . . 1·00 1·00
O20 12c. Rufous fantail . . . . . 1·10 1·10
O21 18c. Peregrine falcon . . . . 2·00 1·50
O22 20c. on 24 c Barn owl . . . 2·00 1·50
O23 30c. Java sparrow . . . . . 1·25 1·00
O24 40c. on 36c. White-breasted wood swallow . . . . . 1·50 1·00
O25 50c. Feral rock pigeon . . . 1·50 1·00
O26 55c. on 48c. Tahitian lory . . 1·50 1·00
O27 60c. Purple swamphen . . . 1·75 1·25
O28 65c. on 72c. Zebra dove . . 1·75 1·25
O38 75c. on 48c. Type **57** . . . 1·00 1·00
O39 75c. on 48c. Ancient Ti'i image . . . . 1·00 1·00
O40 75c. on 48c. Tourist canoeing . . . . 1·00 1·00
O41 75c. on 48c. Captain William Bligh and chart . . . . . 1·00 1·00
O29 80c. on 96c. Chestnut-breasted mannikin . . . . 1·75 1·25
O30 $1.20 Common mynah . . . 2·50 1·75
O31 $2.10 Reef heron . . . . . 3·50 3·00
O32 $3 Blue-headed flycatcher . . 5·00 5·00
O33 $4.20 Red-bellied flycatcher 6·50 6·50
O34 $5.60 Red munia . . . . . 7·50 7·50
O35 $9.60 Flat-billed kingfisher 11·00 11·00
O36 $14 on $4 Red munia (35 × 48 mm) . . . . . . 14·00 14·00
O37 $18 on $5 Flat-billed kingfisher (35 × 48 mm) . . 16·00 16·00

AJMAN Pt. 19

One of the Trucial States in the Persian Gulf. On 18 July 1971, seven Gulf sheikhdoms, including Ajman, formed the State of the United Arab Emirates. The federation became effective on 1 August 1972.

1964. 100 naye paise = 1 rupee.
1967. 100 dirhams = 1 riyal.

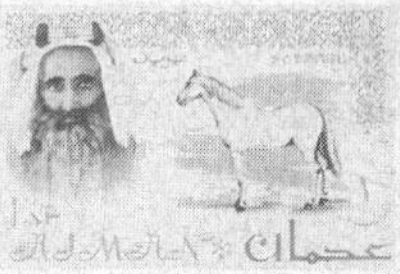

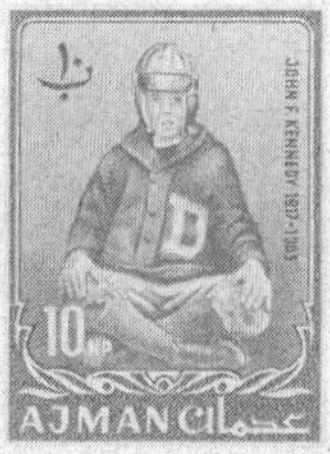

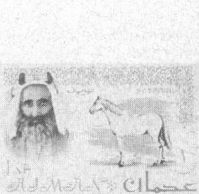

1 Shaikh Rashid bin Humaid al Naimi and Arab Stallion **2** Kennedy in Football Kit

1964. Multicoloured. (a) Size $34\frac{1}{2} \times 23$ mm.

1 1n.p. Type **1** 15 15
2 2n.p. Regal angelfish 15 15
3 3n.p. Dromedary 15 15
4 4n.p. Yellow-banded angelfish 15 15
5 5n.p. Tortoise 15 15
6 10n.p. Jewel cichlid 25 15
7 15n.p. White stork 40 15
8 20n.p. Black-headed gulls . . . 40 15
9 30n.p. Lanner falcon 40 15

(b) Size $42\frac{1}{2} \times 27$ mm.

10 40n.p. Type **1** 20 20
11 50n.p. Regal angelfish . . . 25 20
12 70n.p. Dromedary 25 25
13 1r. Yellow-banded angelfish 50 30
14 1r.50 Tortoise 50 50
15 2r. Jewel cichlid . . . . . . 1·25 75

(c) Size 53 × 34 mm.

16 3r. White stork . . . . 1·25 25
17 5r. Black-headed gulls . . . 1·60 1·50
18 10r. Lanner falcon . . . . . 3·50 1·75

1964. Pres. Kennedy Commem. Perf or imperf.

19 **2** 10n.p. purple and green . . . 15 15
20 – 15n.p. violet and turquoise 15 15
21 – 50n.p. blue and brown . . . 20 20
22 – 1r. turquoise and sepia . . . 35 35
23 – 2r. olive and purple . . . 75 65
24 – 3r. brown and green . . . . 1·25 95
25 – 5r. brown and violet . . . . 2·25 2·10
26 – 10r. brown and blue . . . . 5·00 3·75

DESIGNS—Various pictures of Kennedy: 15n.p. Diving; 50n.p. As naval officer; 1r. Sailing with Mrs. Kennedy; 2r. With Mrs. Eleanor Roosevelt; 3r. With wife and child; 5r. With colleagues; 10r. Full-face portrait.

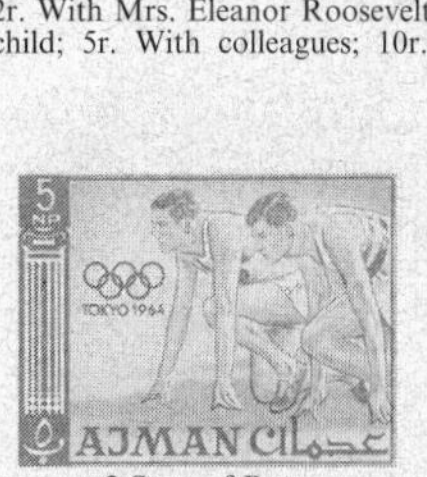

3 Start of Race

1965. Olympic Games, Tokyo. Perf or imperf.

27 **3** 5n.p. slate, brown & mauve 15 15
28 – 10n.p. red, bronze and blue 15 15
29 **3** 15n.p. brown, violet & green 15 15
30 – 25n.p. black, blue and red . 15 15
31 – 50n.p. slate, purple and blue 20 20
32 – 1r. blue, green and purple . . 70 35
33 – 1r.50 purple, violet and green 75 50
34 – 2r. blue, purple and ochre . . 1·25 90
35 – 3r. violet, brown and red . . 2·25 1·40
36 – 5r. purple, green and yellow 2·50 2·10

DESIGNS: 10n.p., 1r.50, Boxing; 25n.p., 2r. Judo; 50n.p., 5r. Gymnastics; 1, 3r. Sailing.

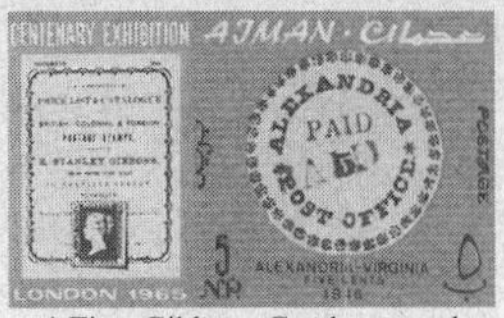

4 First Gibbons Catalogue and Alexandria (U.S.) 5c. Postmaster's Stamp

1965. Stanley Gibbons Catalogue Centenary Exhibition, London. Multicoloured.

37	5n.p. Type **4**	15	15
38	10n.p. Austria (6k.) scarlet "Mercury" newspaper stamp	15	15
39	15n.p. British Guiana "One Cent", 1856	15	15
40	25n.p. Canada "Twelvepence Black", 1851	15	15
41	50n.p. Hawaii "Missionary" 2c., 1851	25	25
42	1r. Mauritius "Post Office" 2d. blue, 1847	40	40
43	3r. Switzerland "Double Geneva" 5c.+5c., 1843	1·40	1·25
44	5r. Tuscany 3 lire, 1860	2·75	2·10

The 5, 15 and 50n.p. and 3r. also include the First Gibbons Catalogue and the others, the Gibbons "Elizabethan" Catalogue.

1965. Pan Arab Games, Cairo. Perf or imperf. Nos. 29, 31 and 33/5 optd. (a) Optd **PAN ARAB GAMES CAIRO 1965**.

45	3	15n.p. brown, violet & green	15	15
46	–	50n.p. slate, purple and blue	25	25
47	–	1r.50 purple, violet & green	90	90
48	–	2r. blue, red and ochre	1·25	1·25
49	–	3r. violet, brown and blue	2·00	2·00

(b) Optd as Nos. 45/9 but equivalent in Arabic.

50	3	15n.p. brown, violet & green	15	15
51	–	50n.p. slate, purple and blue	25	25
52	–	1r.50 purple, violet and green	90	90
53	–	2r. blue, red and ochre	1·25	1·25
54	–	3r. violet, brown and blue	2·00	2·00

1965. Air. Designs similar to Nos. 1/9, but inscr "AIR MAIL". Mult. (a) Size 42½ × 25½ mm.

55	15n.p. Type **1**	15	15
56	25n.p. Regal angelfish	15	15
57	35n.p. Dromedary	20	15
58	50n.p. Yellow-banded angelfish	25	15
59	75n.p. Tortoise	40	20
60	1r. Jewel cichlid	75	25

(b) Size 53 × 34 mm.

61	2r. White stork	1·10	30
62	3r. Black-headed gull	1·60	30
63	5r. Lanner falcon	3·25	50

1966. Stamp Cent Exn, Cairo. Nos. 38/9 and 41/3 optd **STAMP CENTENARY EXHIBITION CAIRO, JANUARY 1966** and pyramid motif.

73	10n.p. multicoloured	15	15
74	15n.p. multicoloured	15	15
75	50n.p. multicoloured	25	25
76	1r. multicoloured	65	65
77	3r. multicoloured	1·75	1·75

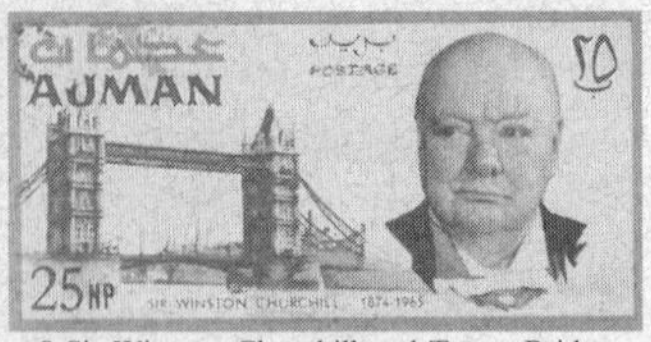

8 Sir Winston Churchill and Tower Bridge

1966. Churchill Commemoration. Each design includes portrait of Churchill. Multicoloured.

79	25n.p. Type **8**	15	15
80	50n.p. Buckingham Palace	25	15
81	75n.p. Blenheim Palace	40	20
82	1r. British Museum	50	25
83	2r. St. Paul's Cathedral in wartime	1·00	40
84	3r. National Gallery and St. Martin in the Fields Church	1·50	60
85	5r. Westminster Abbey	2·50	90
86	7r.50 Houses of Parliament at night	3·75	1·60

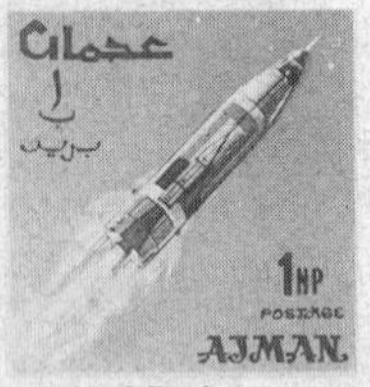

9 Rocket

1966. Space Achievements. Multicoloured. (a) Postage. Size as T **9**.

88	1n.p. Type **9**	15	15
89	3n.p. Capsule	15	15
90	5n.p. Astronaut entering capsule in space	15	15
91	10n.p. Astronaut outside capsule in space	15	15
92	15n.p. Astronauts and globe	15	15
93	25n.p. Astronaut in space	25	15

(b) Air. Size 38 × 38 mm.

95	50n.p. As Type **9**	25	15
96	1r. Astronauts and globe	40	20
97	3r. Astronaut outside capsule in space	1·25	40
98	5r. Capsule	3·25	90

1967. Various issues with currency names changed by overprinting in **Dh.** or **Riyals**. (a) Postage. Nos. 1/18 (1964 Definitives).

99	1d. on 1n.p.	15	15
100	2d. on 2n.p.	15	15
101	3d. on 3n.p.	15	15
102	4d. on 4n.p.	15	15
103	5d. on 5n.p.	15	15
104	10d. on 10n.p.	15	15
105	15d. on 15n.p.	1·25	15
106	20d. on 20n.p.	1·25	15
107	30d. on 30n.p.	1·25	15
108	40d. on 40n.p.	20	15
109	50d. on 50n.p.	30	15
110	70d. on 70n.p.	40	25
111	1r. on 1r.	65	25
112	1r.50 on 1r.50	65	30
113	2r. on 2r.	1·50	65
114	3r. on 3r.	1·50	70
115	5r. on 5r.	2·50	1·25
116	10r. on 10r.	7·50	2·75

(b) Air. Nos. 55/63 (Airmails).

117	15d. on 15n.p.	15	15
118	25d. on 25n.p.	20	15
119	35d. on 35n.p.	25	15
120	50d. on 50n.p.	30	15
121	75d. on 75n.p.	45	25
122	1r. on 1r.	65	50
123	2r. on 2r.	1·25	70
124	3r. on 3r.	2·50	1·25
125	5r. on 5r.	3·50	2·40

NEW CURRENCY SURCHARGES. Nos. 19/44 and 79/98 are known surch in new currency (dirhams and riyals), in limited quantities, but there is some doubt as to whether they were in use locally.

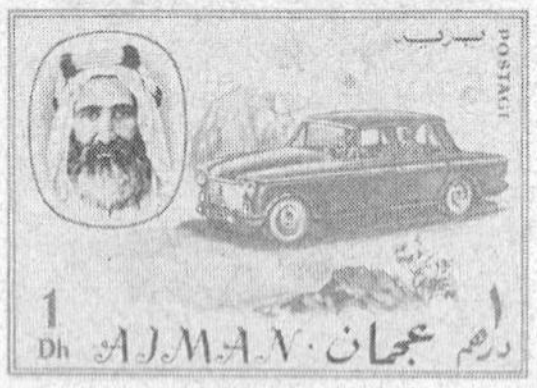

11 Motor-car

1967. Transport.

135	11	1d. brown & blk (postage)	15	15
136	–	2d. blue and brown	15	15
137	–	3d. mauve and black	15	15
138	–	4d. blue and brown	15	15
139	–	5d. green and black	30	15
140	–	15d. blue and brown	50	15
141	–	30d. brown and black	25	15
142	–	50d. black and brown	50	15
143	–	70d. violet and black	65	15
144	11	1r. green and brown (air)	40	15
145	–	2r. mauve and black	1·00	25
146	–	3r. black and brown	1·60	40
147	–	5r. brown and black	2·25	1·00
148	–	10r. blue and brown	6·75	1·50

DESIGNS: 2d., 2r. Motor coach; 3d., 3r. Motor cyclist; 4d., 5r. Boeing 707 airliner; 5d., 10r. "Brasil" (liner); 15d. "Yankee" (sail training and cruise ship); 30d. Cameleer; 50 d Arab horse; 70d. Sikorsky S-58 helicopter.

OFFICIAL STAMPS

1965. Designs similar to Nos. 1/9, additionally inscr "ON STATE'S SERVICE". Multicoloured. (i) Postage. Size 43 × 26 mm.

O64	25n.p. Type **1**	15	15
O65	40n.p. Regal angelfish	20	15
O66	50n.p. Dromedary	20	15
O67	75n.p. Yellow-banded angelfish	55	25
O68	1r. Tortoise	85	40

(ii) Air. (a) Size 43 × 26 mm.

O69	75n.p. Jewel cichlid	50	15

(b) Size 53 × 34 mm.

O70	2r. White stork	1·25	35
O71	3r. Black-headed gulls	1·75	50
O72	5r. Lanner falcon	5·50	1·25

1967. Nos. O64/72 with currency names changed by overprinting in **Dh.** or **Riyals**.

O126	25d. on 25n.p.	15	15
O127	40d. on 40n.p.	20	15
O128	50d. on 50n.p.	20	15
O129	75d. on 75n.p. (No. O67)	55	45
O130	75d. on 75n.p. (No. O69)	55	45
O131	1r. on 1r.	60	60
O132	2r. on 2r.	6·00	3·00
O133	3r. on 3r.	11·00	4·50
O134	5r. on 5r.	17·00	8·50

For later issues see **UNITED ARAB EMIRATES**.

APPENDIX

From June 1967 very many stamp issues were made by a succession of agencies which had been awarded contracts by the Ruler, sometimes two agencies operating at the same time. Several contradictory statements were made as to the validity of some of these issues which appeared 1967–72 and for this reason they are only listed in abbreviated form.

1967.

50th Birth Anniv of President J. F. Kennedy. Air 10, 20, 40, 70d., 1r.50, 2, 3, 5r.

Paintings. Postage. Arab Paintings 1, 2, 3, 4, 5, 30, 70d.; Air. Asian Paintings 1, 2, 3, 5r.; Indian Painting 10r.

Tales from "The Arabian Nights". Postage 1, 2, 3, 10, 30, 50, 70d.; Air 90d., 1, 2, 3r.

World Scout Jamboree, Idaho. Postage 30, 70d., 1r.; Air 2, 3, 4r.

Olympic Games, Mexico (1968). Postage 35, 65, 75d., 1r.; Air 1r.25, 2, 3, 4r.

Winter Olympic Games, Grenoble (1968). Postage 5, 35, 60, 75d.; Air 1, 1r.25, 2, 3r.

Pres. J. F. Kennedy Memorial. Die-stamped on gold foil. Air 10r.

Paintings by Renoir and Terbrugghen. Air 35, 65d., 1, 2r. × 3.

1968.

Paintings by Velasquez. Air 1r. × 2, 2r. × 2.

Winter Olympic Games, Grenoble. Die-stamped on gold foil. Air 7r.

Paintings from Famous Galleries. Air 1r. × 4, 2r. × 6.

Costumes. Air 30d. × 2, 70d. × 2, 1r. × 2, 2r. × 2.

Olympic Games, Mexico. Postage 1r. × 4; Air 2r. × 4.

Satellites and Spacecraft. Air 30d. × 2, 70d. × 2, 1r. × 2, 2r. × 2, 3r. × 2.

Paintings. Hunting Dogs. Air 2r. × 6.

Paintings. Adam and Eve. Air 2r. × 4.

Human Rights Year. Kennedy Brothers and Martin Luther King. Air 1r. × 3, 2r. × 3.

Kennedy Brothers Memorial. Postage 2r.; Air 5r.

Sports Champions. Inter-Milano Football Club. Postage 5, 10, 15, 20, 25d.; Air 10r.

Sports Champions. Famous Footballers. Postage 15, 20, 50, 75d., 1r.; Air 10r.

Cats. Postage 1, 2, 3d.; Air 2, 3r.

Olympic Games, Mexico. Die-stamped on gold foil. 5r.

5th Death Anniv of Pres. J. F. Kennedy. On gold foil. Air 10r.

Paintings of the Madonna. Air 30, 70d., 1, 2, 3r.

Space Exploration. Postage 5, 10, 15, 20, 25d.; Air 15r.

Olympic Games, Mexico. Gold Medals. Postage 2r. × 4; Air 5r. × 4.

Christmas. Air 5r.

1969.

Sports Champions. Cyclists. Postage 1, 2, 5, 10, 15, 20d.; Air 12r.

Sports Champions. German Footballers. Postage 5, 10, 15, 20, 25d.; Air 10r.

Sports Champions. Motor-racing Drivers. Postage 1, 5, 10, 15, 25d.; Air 10r.

Motor-racing Cars. Postage 1, 5, 10, 15, 25d.; Air 10r.

Sports Champions. Boxers. Postage 5, 10, 15, 20d.; Air 10r.

Sports Champions. Baseball Players. Postage 1, 2, 5, 10, 15d.; Air 10r.

Birds. Air 1r. × 11.

Roses. 1r. × 6.

Wild Animals. Air 1r. × 6.

Paintings. Italian Old Masters. 5, 10, 15, 20d., 10r.

Paintings. Famous Composers. Air 5, 10, 25d., 10r.

Paintings. French Artists. 1r. × 4.

Paintings. Nudes. Air 2r. × 4.

Three Kings Mosaic. Air 1r. × 2, 3r. × 2.

Kennedy Brothers. Air 2, 3, 10r.

Olympic Games, Mexico. Gold Medal Winners. Postage 1, 2d., 10r.; Air 10d., 5, 10r.

Paintings of the Madonna. Postage 10d.; Air 10r.

Space Flight of "Apollo 9". Optd on 1968 Space Exploration issue. Air 15r.

Space Flight of "Apollo 10". Optd on 1968 Space Exploration issue. Air 15r.

1st Death Anniv of Gagarin. Optd on 1968 Space Exploration issue. 5d.

2nd Death Anniv of Edward White. Optd on 1968 Space Exploration issue. 10d.

1st Death Anniv of Robert Kennedy. Optd on 1969 Kennedy Brothers issue. Air 2r.

European Football Championship. Optd on 1968 Famous Footballers issue. Air 10r.

Olympic Games, Munich (1972). Optd on 1969 Mexico Gold Medal Winners issue. Air 10d., 5, 10r.

Moon Landing of "Apollo 11". Air 1, 2, 5r.

Moon Landing of "Apollo 11". Circular designs on gold or silver foil. Air 3r. × 3, 5r. × 3, 10r. × 14.

Paintings. Christmas. Postage 1, 2, 3, 4, 5, 15d.; Air 2, 3r.

1970.

"Apollo" Space Flights. Postage 1, 2, 4, 5, 10d.; Air 3, 5r.

Birth Bicentenary of Napoleon Bonaparte. Die-stamped on gold foil. Air 20r.

Paintings. Easter. Postage 5, 10, 12, 30, 50, 70d.; Air 1, 2r.

Moon Landing. Die-stamped on gold foil. Air 20r.

Paintings by Michelangelo. Postage 1, 2, 4, 5, 8, 10d.; Air 3, 5r.

World Cup Football Championship, Mexico. Air 25, 50, 75d., 1, 2, 3r.

"Expo 70" World Fair, Osaka, Japan. Japanese Paintings. Postage 1, 2, 3, 4, 5, 10, 15d.; Air 1, 5r.

Birth Bicent Napoleon Bonaparte. Postage 1, 2, 4, 5, 10d.; Air 3, 5r.

Paintings. Old Masters. Postage 1, 2, 5, 6, 10d.; Air 1, 2, 3r.

Space Flight of "Apollo 13". Air 50, 75, 80d., 1, 2, 3r.

World Cup Football Championship, Mexico. Die-stamped on gold foil. Air 20r.

Olympic Games, 1960-1972. Postage 15, 30, 50, 70d.; Air 2, 5r.

"Expo 70" World Fair, Osaka, Japan. Pavilions. Postage 1, 2, 3, 4, 10, 15d.; Air 1, 3r.

Brazil's Victory in World Cup Football Championship. Optd on 1970 World Football Cup issue. Air 25, 50, 75d., 1, 2, 3r.

"Gemini" and "Apollo" Space Flights. Postage 1, 2, 3, 4, 5, 6, 8, 10, 12, 15, 20, 25, 30, 35, 40, 50d.; Air 1, 1r.50, 2, 3r.

Vintage and Veteran Cars. Postage 1, 2, 4, 5, 8, 10d.; Air 2, 3r.

Pres. D. Eisenhower Commem. Postage 30, 50, 70d.; Air 1, 2, 3r.

Paintings by Ingres. Air 25, 30, 35, 50, 70, 85d., 1, 2r.

500th Birth Anniv (1971) of Albrecht Durer. Air 25, 30, 35, 50, 70, 85d., 1, 2r.

Christmas Paintings. Air 25, 30, 35, 50, 70, 85d., 1, 2r.

Winter Olympic Games, Sapporo, Japan (1972). Die-stamped on gold foil. Air 20r.

Meeting of Eisenhower and De Gaulle, 1942. Die-stamped on gold foil. Air 20r.

General De Gaulle Commem. Air 25, 50, 75d., 1, 2, 3r.

Winter Olympic Games, Sapporo, Japan (1972). Sports. Postage 1, 2, 5, 10d.; Air 3, 5r.

J. Rindt, World Formula 1 Motor-racing Champion. Die-stamped on gold foil. Air 20r.

1971.

"Philatokyo" Stamp Exhibition, Tokyo. Japanese Paintings. Air 25, 30, 35, 50, 70, 85d., 1, 2r.

Mars Space Project. Air 50, 75, 80d., 1, 2, 3r.

Napoleonic Military Uniforms. Postage 5, 10, 15, 20, 25, 30d.; Air 2, 3r.

Olympic Games, Munich (1972). Sports. Postage 10, 15, 25, 30, 40d.; Air 1, 2, 3r.

Paintings by Modern Artists. Air 25, 30, 35, 50, 70, 85d., 1, 2r.

Paintings by Famous Artists. Air 25, 30, 35, 50, 70, 85d., 1, 2r.

25th Anniv of United Nations. Optd on 1971 Modern Artists issue. Air 25, 30, 35, 50, 70, 85d., 1, 2r.

Olympic Games, Munich (1972). Sports. Postage 1, 2, 3, 4, 5, 6, 8, 10, 12, 15, 20, 25, 30, 35, 40, 50d.; Air 1, 1r.50, 2, 3r.

Butterflies. Air 25, 30, 35, 50, 70, 85d., 1, 2r.

Space Flight of "Apollo 14". Postage 15, 25, 50, 60, 70d.; Air 5r.

Winter Olympic Games, 1924-1968. Postage 30, 40, 50, 75d., 1r.; Air 2r.

Signs of the Zodiac. 1, 2, 5, 10, 12, 15, 25, 30, 35, 45, 50, 60d.

Famous Men. Air 65, 70, 75, 80, 85, 90d., 1, 1r.25, 1r.50, 2, 2r.50, 3r.

Death Bicent of Beethoven. 20, 30, 40, 60d., 1r.50, 2r.

Dr. Albert Schweitzer Commem. 20, 30, 40, 60d., 1r.50, 2r.

Tropical Birds. Postage 1, 2, 3, 4, 5, 10d.; Air 2, 3r.

Paintings by French Artists. Postage 1, 2, 3, 4, 5, 10d.; Air 2, 3r.

Paintings by Modern Artists. Postage 1, 2, 3, 4, 5, 10d.; Air 2, 3r.

Paintings by Degas. Postage 1, 2, 3, 4, 5, 10d.; Air 2, 3r.

Paintings by Titian. Postage 1, 2, 3, 4, 5, 10d.; Air 2, 3r.

Paintings by Renoir. Postage 1, 2, 3, 4, 5, 10d.; Air 2, 3r.

Space Flight of "Apollo 15". Postage 25, 40, 50, 60d., 1r.; Air 6r.

"Philatokyo" Stamp Exhibition, Tokyo. Stamps. Postage 10, 15, 20, 30, 35, 50, 60, 80d.; Air 1, 2r.

Tropical Birds. Postage 1, 2, 3, 5, 7, 10, 12, 15, 20, 25, 30, 40d.; Air 50, 80d., 1, 3r.

Paintings depicting Venus. Postage 1, 2, 3, 4, 5, 10d.; Air 2, 3r.

13th World Scout Jamboree, Asagiri, Japan. Scouts. Postage 1, 2, 3, 5, 7, 10, 12, 15, 20, 25, 30, 35, 40, 50, 65, 80d.; Air 1, 1r.25, 1r.50, 2r.

Lions International Clubs. Optd on 1971 Famous Paintings issue. Air 25, 30, 35, 50, 70, 85d., 1, 2r.

13th World Scout Jamboree, Asagiri, Japan. Japanese Paintings. Postage 20, 30, 40, 60, 75d.; Air 3r.

25th Anniv of U.N.I.C.E.F. Optd on 1971 Scout Jamboree (paintings) issue. Postage 20, 30, 40, 60, 75d.; Air 3r.

Christmas 1971. (1st series. Plain frames). Portraits of Popes. Postage 1, 2, 3, 4, 5, 10d.; Air 2, 3r.

Modern Cars. Postage 10, 15, 25, 40, 50d.; Air 3r.

Olympic Games, Munich (1972). Show-jumping. Embossed on gold foil. Air 20r.

Exploration of Outer Space. Postage 15, 25, 50, 60, 70d.; Air 5r.

Royal Visit of Queen Elizabeth II to Japan. Postage 1, 2, 3, 4, 5, 10d.; Air 2, 3r.

Meeting of Pres. Nixon and Emperor Hirohito of Japan in Alaska. Design as 3r. value of 1970 Eisenhower issue but value changed and optd with commemorative inscr. Air 5r. (silver opt), 5r. (gold opt).

"Apollo" Astronants. Postage 5, 20, 35, 40, 50d.; Air 1, 2, 3r.

Discoverers of the Universe. Astronomers and Space Scientists. Postage 5, 10, 15, 20, 25, 30d.; Air 2, 5r.

"ANPHILEX 71" Stamp Exn, New York. Air 2r.50.

Christmas 1971. Portraits of Popes (2nd series. Ornamental frames). Postage 1, 2, 3, 4, 5, 10d.; Air 2, 3r.

Royal Silver Wedding of Queen Elizabeth II and Prince Philip (1972). Air 1, 2, 3r.

Space Flight of "Apollo 16". Postage 20, 30, 40, 50, 60d.; Air 3, 4r.

Fairy Tales. "Baron Munchhausen" Stories. Postage 1, 2, 4, 5, 10d.; Air 3r.

World Fair, Philadelphia (1976). Paintings. Postage 25, 50, 75d.; Air 5r.

Fairy Tales. Stories of the Brothers Grimm. Postage 1, 2, 4, 5, 10d.; Air 3r.

European Tour of Emperor Hirohito of Japan. Postage 1, 2, 4, 5, 10d.; Air 6r.

13th World Scout Jamboree, Asagiri, Japan. Postage 5, 10, 15, 20, 25d.; Air 5r.

Winter Olympic Games, Sapporo, Japan (1972). Postage 5, 10, 15, 20, 25d.; Air 5r.

Olympic Games, Munich (1972). Postage 5, 10, 15, 20, 25d.; Air 5r.

"Japanese Life". Postage 10d. × 4, 20d. × 4, 30d. × 4, 40d. × 4, 50d. × 4; Air 3r. × 4.

Space Flight of "Apollo 15". Postage 5, 10, 15, 20, 25, 50d.; Air 1, 2, 3, 5r.

"Soyuz 11" Disaster. Air 50d., 1r., 1r.50.

"The Future in Space". Postage 5, 10, 15, 20, 25, 50d.

2500th Anniv of Persian Empire. Postage 10, 20, 30, 40, 50d., Air 3r.

Cats. Postage 10, 15, 20, 25d.; Air 50d., 1r.

50th Anniv of Tutankhamun Tomb Discovery. Postage 1, 2, 3, 4, 5, 6, 7, 8, 9, 10, 11, 12, 13, 14, 15, 16d.; Air 1r. × 4.

400th Birth Anniv of Johannes Kepler (astronomer). Postage 50d.; Air 5r.

Famous Men. Air. 1r. × 5.

1972.

150th Death Anniv of Napoleon Bonaparte (1971). Postage 10, 20, 30, 40d.; Air 1, 2, 3, 4r.

1st Death Anniv of General de Gaulle. Postage 10, 20, 30, 40d.; Air 1, 2, 3, 4r.

Wild Animals (1st series). Postage 5, 10, 15, 20, 25, 30, 35, 40d.

Tropical Fishes. Postage 5, 10, 15, 20, 25d.; Air 50, 75d., 1r.

Famous Musicians. Postage 5d. × 3, 10d. × 3, 15d. × 3, 20d. × 3, 25d. × 3, 30d. × 3, 35d. × 3, 40d. × 3.

Easter. Postage 5, 10, 15, 20, 25d.; Air 5r.

Wild Animals (2nd series). Postage 5, 10, 15, 20, 25d.; Air 5r.

"Tour de France" Cycle Race. Postage 5, 10, 15, 20, 25, 30, 35, 40, 45, 50, 55d.; Air 60, 65, 70, 75, 80, 85, 90, 95d., 1r.

Many other issues were released between 1 September 1971 and 1 August 1972, but their authenticity has been denied by the Ajman Postmaster-General. Certain issues of 1967–69 exist overprinted to commemorate other events but the Postmaster General states that these are unofficial.

Ajman joined the United Arab Emirates on 1 August 1972 and the Ministry of Communications assumed responsibility for the postal services. Further stamps inscribed "Ajman" issued after that date were released without authority and had no validity.

ALAND ISLANDS Pt. 11

Aland is an autonomous province of Finland. From 1984 separate stamps were issued for the area although stamps of Finland could also still be used there. On 1 January 1993 Aland assumed control of its own postal service and Finnish stamps ceased to be valid there.

1984. 100 pennia = 1 markka.
2002. 100 cents = 1 euro.

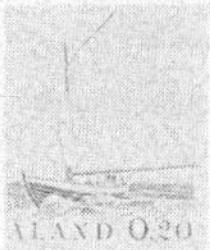
1 Fishing Boat

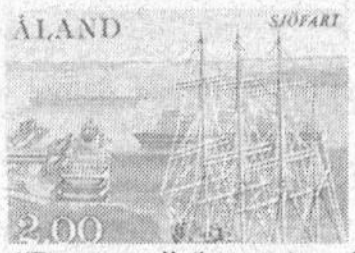
2 "Pommern" (barque) and Car Ferries, Mariehamn West Harbour

1984.

1	1	10p. mauve	10	10
2		20p. green	10	10
3		50p. green	10	15
4	–	1m. green	35	35
5	1	1m.10 blue	30	35
6		1m.20 black	35	40
7		1m.30 green	35	35
8	–	1m.40 multicoloured	70	70
9a	–	1m.50 multicoloured	45	50
10	–	1m.90 multicoloured	60	70
12	–	3m. blue, green and black	80	95
14	–	10m. black, chestnut & brn	2·10	2·25
15	–	13m. multicoloured	3·50	4·00

DESIGNS—20 × 29 mm: 1m.50, Midsummer pole, Storby village. 21 × 31 mm: 13m. Rug, 1793. 26 × 32 mm: 3m. Map of Aland Islands. 30 × 20 mm: 1m. Farjsund Bridge. 31 × 21 mm: 1m.40, Aland flag; 1m.90, Mariehamn Town Hall. 32 × 26 mm: 10m. Seal of Aland showing St. Olaf (patron saint).

1984. 50th Anniv of Society of Shipowners.

16	2	2m. multicoloured	85	1·40

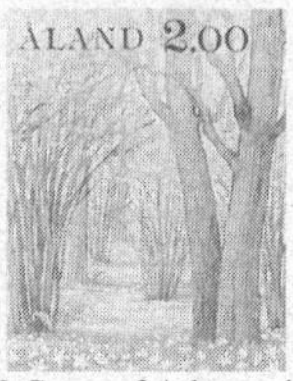
3 Grove of Ashes and Hazels

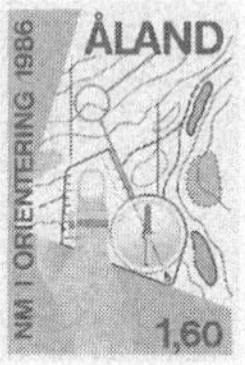
4 Map, Compass and Measuring Instrument

1985. Aland Scenes. Multicoloured.

17	2m. Type **3**	80	65
18	5m. Kokar Church and shore (horiz)	1·25	1·25
19	8m. Windmill and farm (horiz)	2·00	2·00

1986. Nordic Orienteering Championships, Aland.

20	4	1m.60 multicoloured	85	1·00

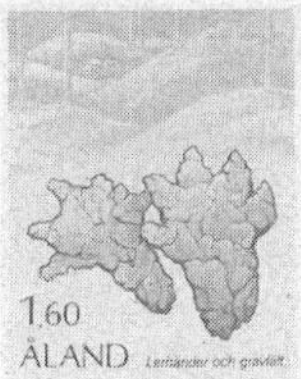
5 Clay Hands and Burial Mounds, Skamkulla

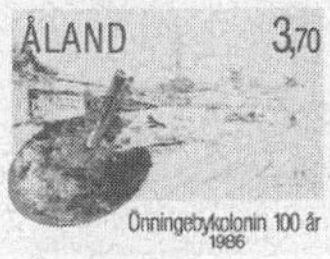
6 "Onnigeby" (drawing, Victor Westerholm)

1986. Archaeology. Multicoloured.

21	1m.60 Type **5**	1·00	60
22	2m.20 Bronze staff from Finby and Apostles	70	65
23	20m. Monument at ancient court site, Saltvik, and court in session (horiz)	5·25	5·00

1986. Centenary of Onnigeby Artists' Colony.

24	6	3m.70 multicoloured	95	1·25

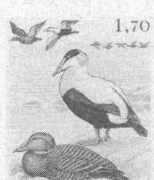

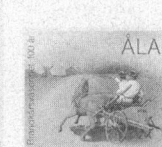

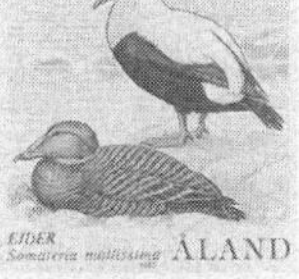
7 Eiders

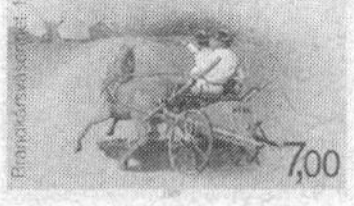
8 Firemen in Horse-drawn Cart

1987. Birds. Multicoloured.

25	1m.70 Type **7**	4·00	4·75
26	2m.30 Tufted ducks	2·00	1·60
27	12m. Velvet scoters	3·00	4·00

1987. Centenary of Mariehamn Fire Brigade.

28	8	7m. multicoloured	3·50	4·75

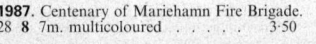

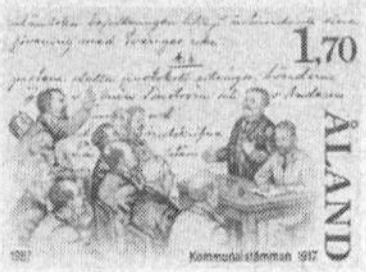
9 Meeting and Item 3 of Report

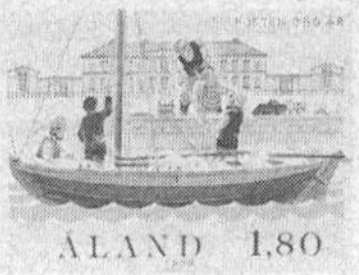
10 Loading Mail Barrels at Eckero

1987. 70th Anniv of Aland Municipalities Meeting, Finstrom.

29	9	1m.70 multicoloured	65	80

1988. 350th Anniv of Postal Service in Aland.

30	10	1m.80 multicoloured	45	1·25

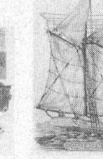

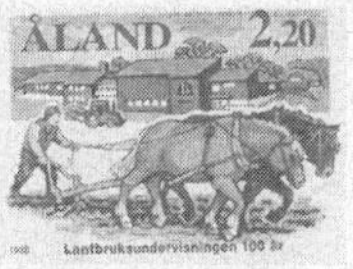
11 Ploughing with Horses

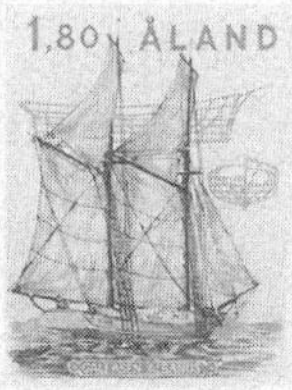
12 Baltic Galleass "Albanus"

1988. Centenary of Agricultural Education in Aland.

31	11	2m.20 multicoloured	95	1·40

1988. Sailing Ships. Multicoloured.

32	1m.80 Type **12**	1·10	1·25
33	2m.40 Schooner "Ingrid" (horiz)	2·00	2·10
34	11m. Barque "Pamir" (horiz)	4·00	5·00

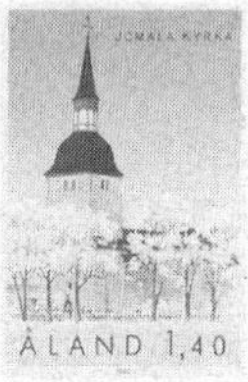
13 St. Olaf's Church, Jomala

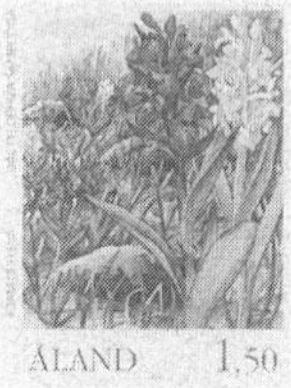
14 Elder-flowered Orchid

1988.

35	13	1m.40 multicoloured	70	85

1989. Orchids. Multicoloured.

36	1m.50 Type **14**	1·25	1·25
37	2m.50 Narrow-leaved helleborine	1·40	1·40
38	14m. Lady's slipper	5·75	6·75

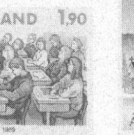

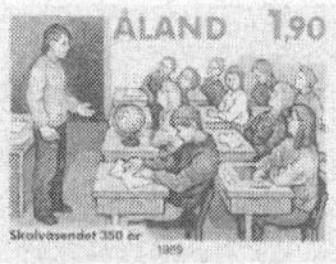
15 Teacher and Pupils

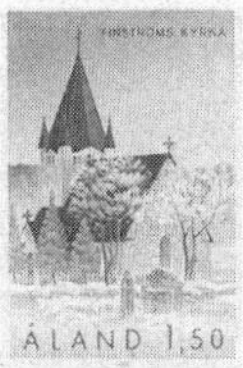
16 St. Michael's Church, Finstrom

1989. 350th Anniv of First Aland School, Saltvik.

39	15	1m.90 multicoloured	50	85

1989.

40	16	1m.50 multicoloured	70	85

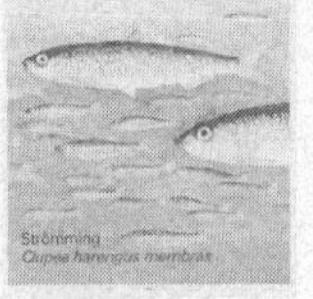
17 Baltic Herring

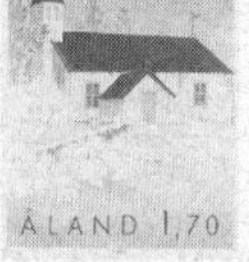
18 St. Andrew's Church, Lumparland

1990. Fishes. Multicoloured.

41	1m.50 Type **17**	60	65
42	2m. Northern pike	80	70
43	2m.70 European flounder	1·10	1·00

1990.

44	18	1m.70 multicoloured	60	70

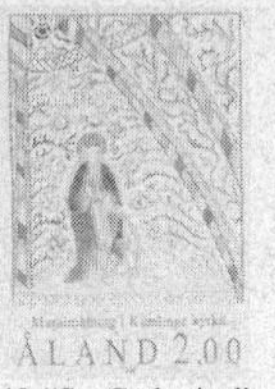
19 "St. Catherine" (fresco, St. Anna's Church, Kumlinge)

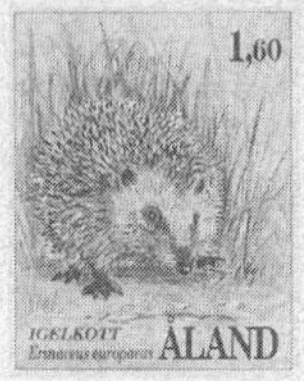
20 West European Hedgehog

1990.

45	19	2m. multicoloured	65	70

1991. Mammals. Multicoloured.

46	1m.60 Type **20**	70	65
47	2m.10 Eurasian red squirrel	85	70
48	2m.90 Roe deer	1·10	1·10

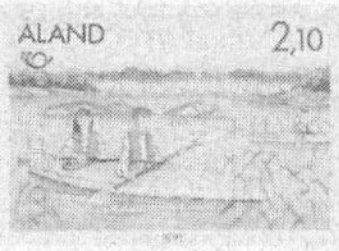
22 Canoeing

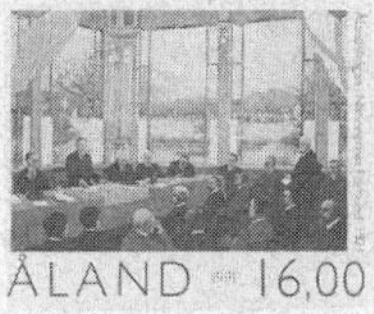
23 "League of Nations Meeting, Geneva, 1921" (print by F. Rackwitz)

1991. Nordic Countries' Postal Co-operation. Tourism. Multicoloured.

50	2m.10 Type **22**	65	70
51	2m.90 Cycling	85	1·00

1991. 70th Anniv of Aland Autonomy.

52	23	16m. multicoloured	4·25	4·75

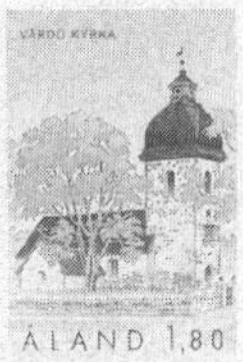
24 St. Mathias's Church, Vardo

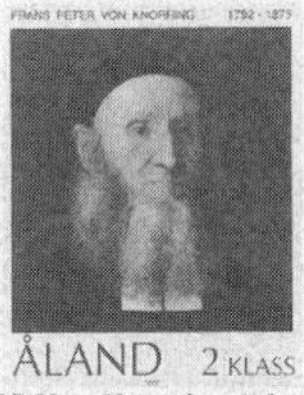
25 Von Knorring (after Karl Jansson)

1991.

53	24	1m.80 multicoloured	60	70

1992. Birth Bicentenary of Rev. Frans Peter von Knorring (social reformer).

54	25	2 klass (1m.60) mult	65	65

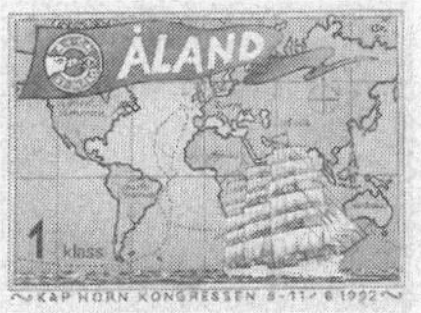
26 Barque "Herzogen Cecilie" and Wheat Transport Route Map

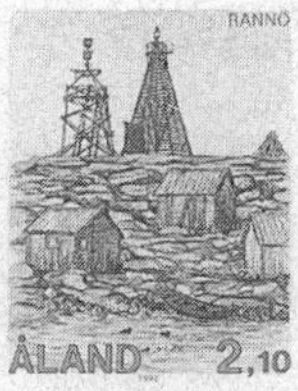
27 Ranno Lighthouse

1992. 48th International Association of Cape Horners Congress, Mariehamn.

55	26	1 klass (2m.10) mult	80	85

1992. Lighthouses. Multicoloured.

56	2m.10 Type **27**	1·75	1·50
57	2m.10 Salskar	1·75	1·10
58	2m.10 Lagskar	1·75	1·10
59	2m.10 Market	1·75	1·10

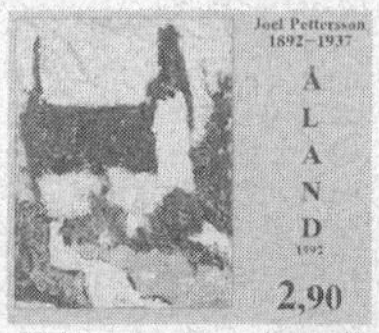
28 "Lemland Landscape"

1992. Birth Cent of Joel Pettersson (painter). Mult.

60	2m.90 Type **28**	80	95
61	16m. "Self-portrait"	3·50	5·00

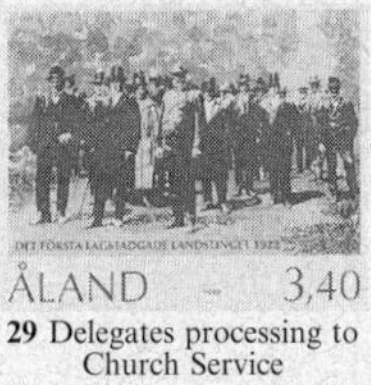
29 Delegates processing to Church Service

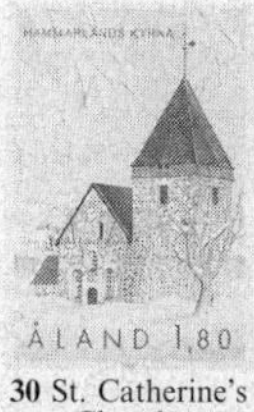
30 St. Catherine's Church, Hammarland

1992. 70th Anniv of First Aland Provincial Parliament.
62   29   3m.40 multicoloured . . . .   1·00   1·10

1992.
63   30   1m.80 multicoloured . . .   50   65

31 Arms   **32** Fiddler

1993. Postal Autonomy.
64   31   1m.60 multicoloured   60   65

1993. Nordic Countries' Postal Co-operation. Tourism. Exhibits from Jan Karlsgarden Open-air Museum.
66   32   2m. red, pink and black . .   65   65
67   –   2m.30 blue, black and azure   80   70
DESIGN—HORIZ: 2m.30, Boat-house.

33 Saltvik Woman   **34** Boulder Field, Dano Gamlan

1993. Costumes. Multicoloured.
68   1m.90 Type **33**   50   65
69   3m.50 Eckero and Brando women and Mariehamn couple . . . . . .   1·10   1·25
70   17m. Finstrom couple . . . .   5·00   5·00

1993. Aland Geology. Multicoloured.
71   10p. Type **34**   10   10
72   1m.60 Drumlin (hillock), Markusbole   60   60
73   2m. Diabase dyke, Sottunga   2·00   2·00
74   2m.30 Pitcher of Kallskar . .   65   85
75   2m.70 Pillow lava, Kumlinge   80   70
76   2m.90 Red Cow (islet), Lumpurn   95   95
77   3m.40 Erratic boulder, Torsskar, Kokar Osterbygge (horiz) . . . . . .   1·40   1·40
78   6m. Folded gneiss . . . .   1·60   1·60
79   7m. Pothole, Bano Foglo (horiz) . . . . . .   3·00   3·25

35 Mary Magdalene Church, Sottunga   **37** Glanville's Fritillary ("Melitaea cinxia")

1993.
80   35   1m.80 multicoloured . . .   65   60

1994. Butterflies. Multicoloured.
81   2m.30 Type **37**   70   80
82   2m.30 "Quercusia querqus" . .   70   80
83   2m.30 Clouded apollo ("Parnassius mnemosyne")   70   80
84   2m.30 "Hesperia comma" . .   70   80

38 Genetic Diagram   **39** Comb Ceramic and Pitted Ware Pottery

1994. Europa. Medical Discoveries. Multicoloured.
85   2m.30 Type **38** (discovery of Von Willebrand's disease (hereditary blood disorder))   1·40   1·40
86   2m.90 Molecular diagram (purification of heparin by Erik Jorpes) . . . .   1·10   1·40

1994. The Stone Age.
87   39   2m.40 brown   65   85
88   –   2m.80 blue . . . . .   1·00   1·10
89   –   18m. green . . . . .   7·00   7·00
DESIGNS—VERT: 2m.80, Stone tools. HORIZ:

18m. Canoe and tent by river (reconstruction of Stone-age village, Langbergsoda).

40 St. John the Baptist's Church, Sund   **42** "Skuta" (Cargo Sailing Boat)

1994.
90   40   2m. multicoloured   65   70

1995. Cargo Sailing Ships. Multicoloured.
91   2m.30 Type **42**   65   65
92   2m.30 "Sump" (well-boat) . .   65   65
93   2m.30 "Storbat" (farm boat) . .   65   65
94   2m.30 "Jakt"   65   65

43 National Colours and E.U. Emblem   **44** Doves and Cliffs

1995. Admission of Aland Islands to European Union.
95   43   2m.90 multicoloured   95   1·00

1995. Europa. Peace and Freedom. Multicoloured.
96   2m.80 Type **44** . . . . . .   1·00   1·00
97   2m.90 Dove, night sky and island . . . . . .   1·00   1·00

45 Golf   **46** Racing Dinghies

1995. Nordic Countries' Postal Co-operation. Tourism. With service indicator. Multicoloured.
98   2 klass (2m.) Type **45**   60   80
99   1 klass (2m.30) Sport fishing   80   85

1995. Optimist World Dinghy Championships, Mariehamn.
100   46   3m.40 multicoloured . . .   1·10   1·25

47 St. George's Church, Geta   **48** "St. Olaf" (Wooden Carving from Sund Church)

1995.
101   47   2m. multicoloured   65   65

1995. Birth Millenary of St. Olaf.
102   48   4m.30 multicoloured . . .   1·25   1·40

49 Fish holding Flag in Mouth ("Greetings from Aland")   **50** Landing on Branch

1996. Greetings Stamps. With service indicator. Multicoloured.
103   1 klass Type **49**   80   70
104   1 klass Bird holding flower in beak ("Congratulations")   80   70

1996. Endangered Species. The Eagle Owl. Multicoloured.
105   2m.40 Type **50**   70   80
106   2m.40 Perched on branch . .   70   80

107   2m.40 Adult owl   70   80
108   2m.40 Juvenile owl   70   80
Nos. 105/6 form a composite design.

51 Sally Salminen (novelist)

1996. Europa. Famous Women. Multicoloured.
109   2m.80 Type **51** . . . . . .   1·00   1·00
110   2m.90 Fanny Sundstrom (politician) . . . . .   1·10   1·25

52 Choir   **53** "Haircut"

1996. "Aland 96" Song and Music Festival, Mariehamn.
111   52   2m.40 multicoloured . . .   85   80

1996. 150th Birth Anniv of Karl Jansson (painter).
112   53   18m. multicoloured . . . .   4·75   5·75

54 "Trilobita asaphus"   **55** Brando Church

1996. Fossils. Multicoloured.
113   40p. Type **54**   10   15
114   9m. "Gastropoda euomophalus" . . . . . .   4·50   3·50

1996.
115   55   2m. multicoloured . . .   50   70

56 Giant Isopod ("Saduria entomon") and Opossum Shrimp ("Mysis relicta")   **57** Coltsfoot ("Tussilago farfara")

1997. Marine Survivors from the Ice Age. Multicoloured.
116   30p. Type **56**   10   10
117   2m.40 Four-horned sculpin ("Myotocephalus quadricornis")   75   80
118   4m.30 Ringed seal ("Phoca hispida botrica") . . . .   1·75   1·75

1997. Spring Flowers. Multicoloured.
119   2m.40 Type **57**   60   75
120   2m.40 Blue anemone ("Hepatica nobilis") . . .   60   75
121   2m.40 Wood anemone ("Anemone nemorosa") . . .   60   75
122   2m.40 Yellow anemone ("Anemone ranunculoides") . . .   60   75

58 Floorball   **59** The Devil's Dance

1997. 1st Women's Floorball World Championship, Mariehamn and Godby.
123   58   3m.40 multicoloured . . .   90   95

1997. Europa. Tales and Legends.
124   59   2m.90 multicoloured . . .   80   90

60 Kastelholm Castle and Arms

1997. 600th Anniv of Kalmar Union between Sweden, Denmark and Norway.
125   60   2m.40 multicoloured . . .   90   75

62 "Thornbury" (freighter)   **63** St George's Church, Mariehamn

1997. Steam Freighters. Multicoloured.
127   2m.80 Type **62**   95   90
128   3m.50 "Osmo" (freighter) . . .   1·75   1·50

1997. 70th Anniv of Mariehamn Church.
129   63   1m.90 multicoloured . . .   60   60

64 Man harvesting Apples

1998. Horticulture. Multicoloured.
130   2m. Type **64**   70   60
131   2m.40 Woman harvesting cucumbers   70   75

65 Boy on Moped   **66** Midsummer Celebrations

1998. Youth Activities. Multicoloured.
132   2m.40 Type **65**   70   70
133   2m.40 Laptop computer . . .   70   70
134   2m.40 CD disk and headphones   70   70
135   2m.40 Step aerobics   70   70

1998. Europa. National Festivals.
136   66   4m.20 multicoloured . . .   1·10   1·25

67 "Isabella" (ferry)

1998. Nordic Countries' Postal Co-operation. Shipping.
137   67   2m.40 multicoloured . . .   75   75

68 Waves breaking

1998. International Year of the Ocean.
138   68   6m.30 multicoloured . . .   2·25   2·25

69 Players

1998. Association of Tennis Professionals Senior Tour, Mariehamn. Self-adhesive.
139   69   2m.40 multicoloured . . .   70   70

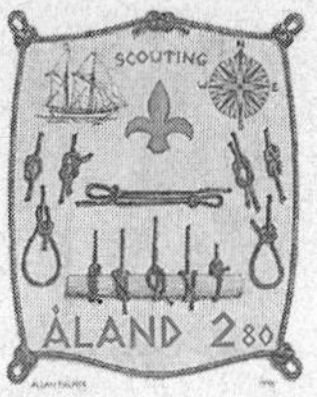

70 Schooner, Compass Rose and Knots

1998. Ninth International Sea Scout Camp, Bomarsund Fortress, Aland.
140 **70** 2m.80 multicoloured . . . 80 90

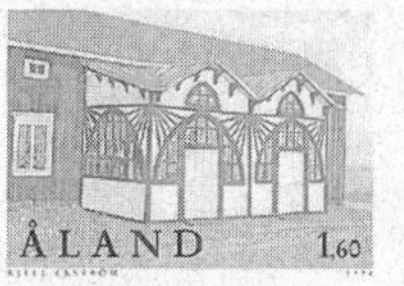

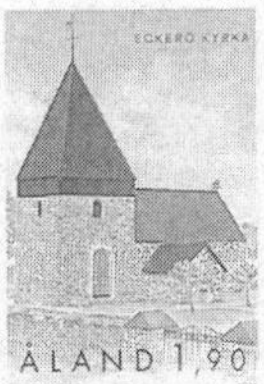

71 Seffers Homestead, Onningeby
72 Eckero Church

1998. Traditional Porches. Multicoloured.
141 1m.60 Type **71** 50 55
142 2m. Labbas homestead, Storby 55 60
143 2m.90 Abras homestead, Bjorko 75 90

1998.
144 **72** 1m.90 multicoloured . . . 60 70

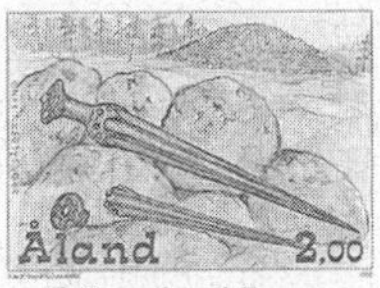

73 Sword and Dagger

1999. Bronze Age Relics. Multicoloured.
145 2m. Type **73** 60 70
146 2m.20 "Ship" tumulus (vert) 60 75

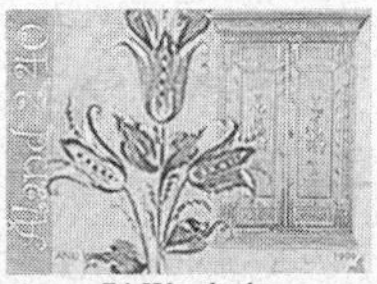
74 Wardrobe

1999. Folk Art. Decorated Furniture. Mult.
147 2m.40 Type **74** 70 75
148 2m.40 Distaff 70 75
149 2m.40 Chest 70 75
150 2m.40 Spinning wheel 70 75

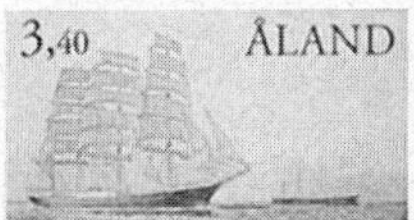

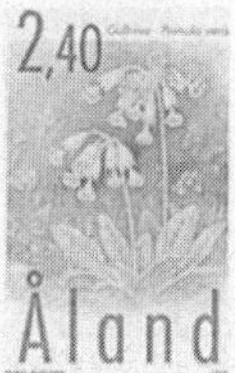

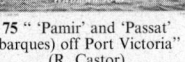

75 " 'Pamir' and 'Passat' (barques) off Port Victoria" (R. Castor)
76 Cowslip

1999. 50th Anniv of Rounding of Cape Horn by "Pamir" on Last Wheat-carrying Voyage.
151 **75** 3m.40 multicoloured . . . 1·00 1·10

1999. Provincial Plant of Aland. Self-adhesive.
152 **76** 2m.40 multicoloured . . . 75 80

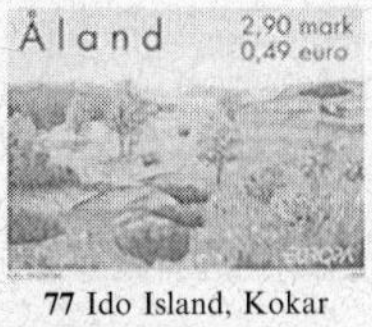

77 Ido Island, Kokar

1999. Europa. Parks and Gardens.
153 **77** 2m.90 multicoloured . . . 80 90
No. 153 is denominated both in markkas and in euros.

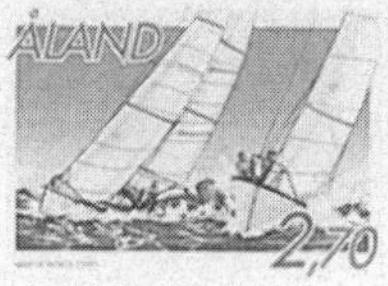

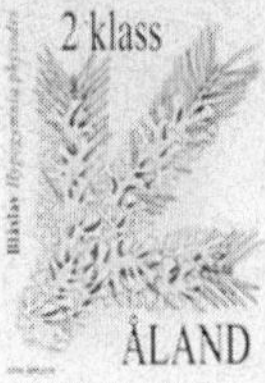

78 Racing Yachts
79 Puffed Shield Lichen ("Hypogymnia physodes")

1999. Sailing
154 **78** 2m.70 multicoloured . . . 75 80

1999. Lichens. With service indicator. Mult.
155 2 klass (2m.) Type **79** 70 70
156 1 klass (2m.40) Common orange lichen ("Xanthoria parietina") 85 85

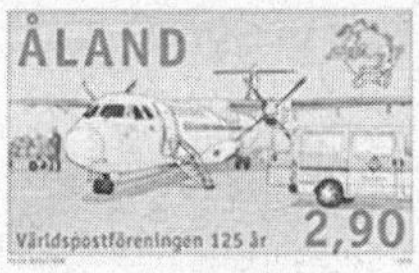

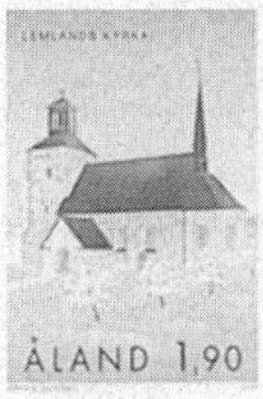

80 Loading Mail Plane
81 St. Bridget's Church, Lemland

1999. 125th Anniv of Universal Postal Union
157 **80** 2m.90 multicoloured . . . 85 85

1999.
158 **81** 1m.90 multicoloured . . . 60 60

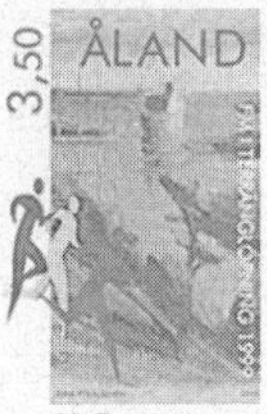

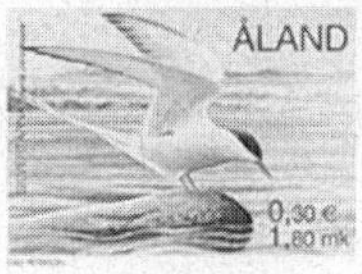

82 Runners
83 Arctic Tern (*Sterna paradisaea*)

1999. Finnish Cross-country Championships, Mariehamn.
159 **82** 3m.50 multicoloured . . . 1·00 1·00

DENOMINATION. From No. 162 Aland Islands stamps are denominated both in markkas and in euros. As no cash for the latter is in circulation, the catalogue continues to use the markka value.

2000. Sea Birds. Multicoloured.
162 1m.80 Type **83** 45 50
164 2m.20 Common gull (*Larus canus*) (vert) 85 80
166 2m.60 Great black-backed gull (*Larus marinus*) . . . 80 85

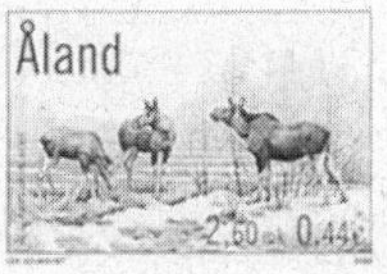

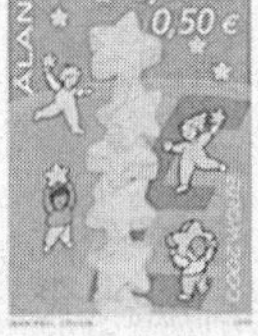

85 Elk
86 "Building Europe"

2000. The Elk (*Alces alces*). Multicoloured.
172 2m.60 Type **85** 55 75
173 2m.60 With young 55 75
174 2m.60 Beside lake 55 75
175 2m.60 In snow 55 75

2000. Europa.
176 **86** 3m. multicoloured 65 85

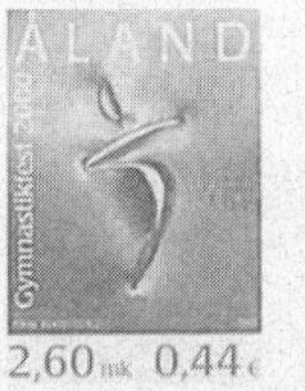

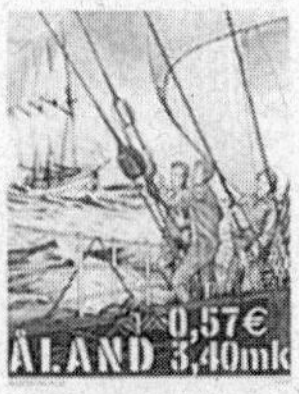

87 Gymnast
88 Crew and *Linden* (schooner)

2000. Finno-Swedish Gymnastics Association Exhibition, Mariehamn. Self-adhesive.
177 **87** 2m.60 multicoloured . . . 55 75

2000. Visit by *Cutty Sark* Tall Ships' Race Competitors to Mariehamn.
178 **88** 3m.40 multicoloured . . . 75 75

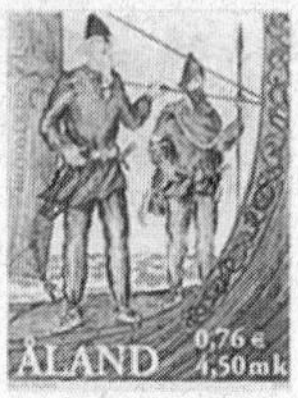

89 Lange on prow of Longship

2000. Death Millenary of Hlodver Lange the Viking.
179 **89** 4m.50 multicoloured . . . 1·00 1·00

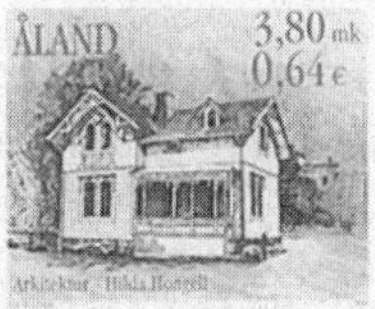

90 Wooden Ornamented Swiss-style House, Mariehamn

2000. 48th Death Anniv of Hilda Hongell (architect). Multicoloured.
180 3m.80 Type **90** 80 80
181 10m. House with central front entrance, Mariehamn 2·10 2·10

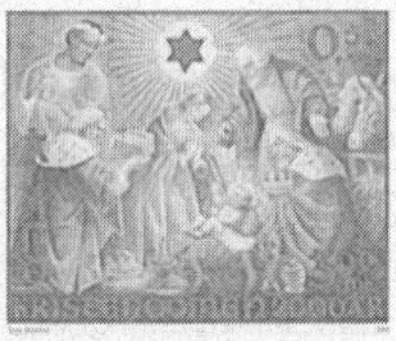
91 The Nativity

2000. 2000 Years of Christianity.
182 **91** 3m. multicoloured 65 65

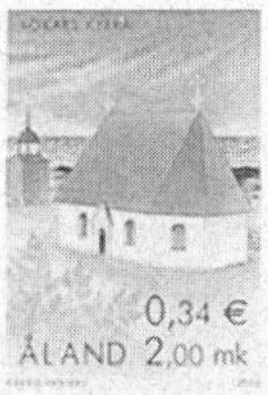

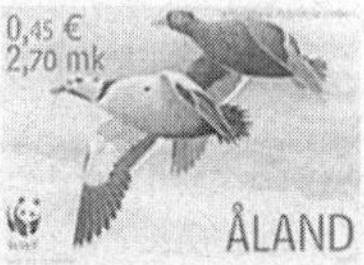

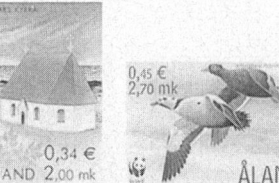

92 Kokar Church
93 Steller's Eider in Flight

2000.
183 **92** 2m. multicoloured 45 45

2001. Endangered Species. The Steller's Eider (*Polysticta stelleri*). Multicoloured.
184 2m.70 Type **93** 60 60
185 2m.70 Duck and drake . . . 60 60
186 2m.70 Duck and drake swimming 60 60
187 2m.70 Drake 60 60

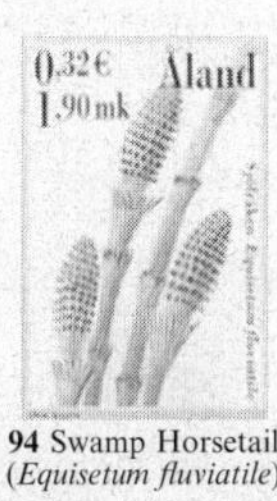

94 Swamp Horsetail (*Equisetum fluviatile*)

2001. Plants. Multicoloured.
188 1m.90 Type **94** 40 40
189 2m.80 Stiff clubmoss (*Lycopodium annotinum*) . . 60 60
190 3m.50 Polypody (*Polybodium vulgare*) 75 75

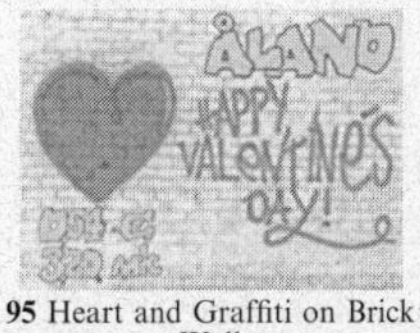

95 Heart and Graffiti on Brick Wall

2001. St. Valentine's Day.
200 **95** 3m.20 multicoloured . . . 70 70

96 Fisherman and Fish

2001. Europa. Water Resources.
201 **96** 3m.20 multicoloured . . . 70 70

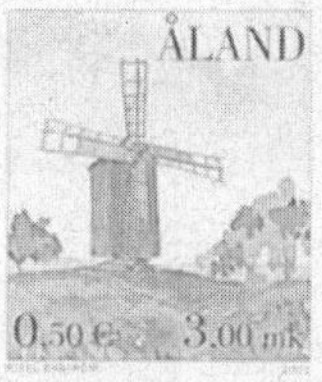

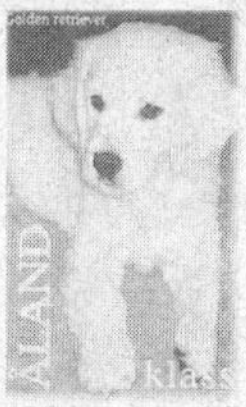

97 Archipelago Windmill
98 Golden Retriever

2001. Windmills. Multicoloured.
202 3m. Type **97** 65 65
203 7m. Timbered windmill (horiz) . . . . 1·50 1·50
204 20m. Nest windmill (horiz) 4·25 4·25

2001. Puppies. Multicoloured.
205 2 klass (2m.30) Type **98** . . . 40 40
206 1 klass (2m.70) Wire-haired dachshund 55 55

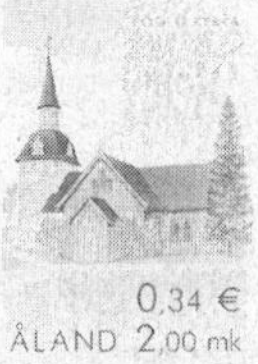

99 Foglo Church

2001.
207 **99** 2m. multicoloured 45 45

ALAOUITES Pt. 19

A coastal district of Syria, placed under French mandate in 1920. Became the Republic of Latakia in 1930. Incorporated with Syria in 1937.

100 centimes = 1 piastre.

1925. Stamps of France surch **ALAOUITES** and value in French and Arabic.
1 **11** 0p.10 on 2c. purple . . . . 1·75 4·25
2 **18** 0p.25 on 5c. orange . . . . 2·25 3·50
3 **15** 0p.75 on 15c. green . . . . 3·00 4·50
4 **18** 1p. on 20c. brown . . . . . 2·25 3·50
5 1p.25 on 25c. blue . . . . . 2·25 2·50
6 1p.50 on 30c. red . . . . . 9·00 11·00
7 2p. on 35c. violet . . . . . 80 4·00
8 **13** 2p. on 40c. red and blue . . 3·50 5·25
9 2p. on 45c. green and blue 8·00 12·00
10 3p. on 60c. violet and blue 2·50 6·75
11 **15** 3p. on 60c. violet . . . . . 10·50 11·00
12 4p. on 85c. red . . . . . . 1·60 3·25
13 **13** 5p. on 1f. red and yellow . . 4·00 8·75
14 10p. on 2f. orange & grn . . 4·50 10·00
15 25p. on 5f. blue and buff . . 8·50 8·00

1925. "Pasteur" issue of France surch **ALAOUITES** and value in French and Arabic.
16 **30** 0p.50 on 10c. green . . . . 1·75 3·50
17 0p.75 on 15c. green . . . . 1·50 3·50
18 1p.50 on 30c. red . . . . . 1·25 4·00
19 2p. on 45c. red . . . . . . 2·25 4·25
20 2p.50 on 50c. blue . . . . . 3·00 4·50
21 4p. on 75c. blue . . . . . . 2·25 5·50

1925. Air. Stamps of France optd **ALAOUITES Avion** and value in French and Arabic.
22 **13** 2p. on 40c. red and blue . . 6·25 11·00
23 3p. on 60c. violet and blue 7·25 18·00
24 5p. on 1f. red and yellow . . 6·25 10·50
25 10p. on 2f. orange & green 6·00 10·00

1925. Pictorial stamps of Syria (1925) optd **ALAOUITES** in French and Arabic.
26 0p.10 violet . . . . 45 3·00
27 0p.25 black . . . . 70 3·00
28 0p.50 green . . . . 75 1·75
29 0p.75 red . . . . 95 3·00
30 1p. purple . . . . 95 2·25
31 1p.25 green . . . . 1·75 2·25
32 1p.50 pink . . . . 95 2·25
33 2p. brown . . . . 1·75 3·75
34 2p.50 blue . . . . 1·75 3·75
35 3p. brown . . . . 95 2·50
36 5p. violet . . . . 1·75 2·75
37 10p. purple . . . . 1·90 3·00
38 25p. blue . . . . 2·50 6·75

1925. Air. Nos. 33 and 35/37 optd **AVION** in French and Arabic.
40 2p. brown . . . . 1·10 4·00
41 3p. brown . . . . 1·00 3·75

| 42 | 5p. violet | 1·10 | 4·00 |
| 43 | 10p. purple | 1·10 | 4·00 |

1926. Air. Air stamps of Syria with airplane overprint optd **ALAOUITES** in French and Arabic.

44	2p. brown	2·00	5·25
45	3p. brown	2·00	5·25
46	5p. violet	2·00	5·25
47	10p. purple	2·00	5·25

See also Nos. 59/60 and 63.

1926. Pictorial stamps of 1925 surcharged.

53	05 on 0p.10 violet	25	3·00
54	2p. on 1p.25 green	8·00	7·00
48	3p.50 on 0p.75 red	1·00	2·25
49	4p. on 0p.25 black	85	2·25
56	4p.50 on 0p.75 red	2·50	3·75
50	4p.50 on 2p.50 blue	1·25	2·25
57	7p.50 on 2p.50 blue	2·50	1·90
51	12p. on 1p.25 green	2·75	3·25
58	15p. on 25p. blue	7·25	6·25
52	20p. on 1p.25 green	2·75	4·25

1929. Air. (a) Pictorial stamps of Syria optd with airplane and **ALAOUITES** in French and Arabic.

59	0p.50 green	2·00	4·25
60	1p. purple	4·50	9·00
61	25p. blue	22·00	30·00

(b) Nos. 54 and 58 of Alaouites optd with airplane.

| 62 | 2p. on 1p.25 green | 2·75 | 5·00 |
| 63 | 15p. on 25p. blue | 19·00 | 25·00 |

POSTAGE DUE STAMPS

1925. Postage Due stamps of France surch **ALAOUITES** and value in French and Arabic.

D26	D 11	0p.50 on 10c. brown	2·10	4·75
D27		1p. on 20c. green	2·10	5·00
D28		2p. on 30c. red	2·10	5·00
D29		3p. on 50c. purple	2·10	5·25
D30		5p. on 1f. pur on yell	2·10	5·00

1925. Postage Due stamps of Syria (Nos. D192/6) optd **ALAOUITES** in French and Arabic.

D44	0p.50 brown on yellow	75	3·25
D45	1p. red on red	75	3·50
D46	2p. black on blue	1·25	4·00
D47	3p. brown on red	1·25	4·75
D48	5p. black on green	2·40	5·00

For later issues see **LATAKIA.**

ALBANIA   Pt. 3

Albania, formerly part of the Turkish Empire, was declared independent on 28 November 1912, and this was recognized by Turkey in the treaty of 30 May 1913. After chaotic conditions during and after the First World War a republic was established in 1925. Three years later the country became a kingdom. From 7 April 1939 until December 1944, Albania was occupied, firstly by the Italians and then by the Germans. Following liberation a republic was set up in 1946.

    1913. 40 paras = 1 piastre or grosch.
    1913. 100 qint = 1 franc.
    1947. 100 qint = 1 lek.

1913. Various types of Turkey optd with double-headed eagle and **SHQIPENIA.**

3	**28**	2pa. green (No. 271)	£225	£200
4		5pa. brown (No. 261)	£225	£200
2	**25**	10pa. green (No. 252)	£350	£300
5	**28**	10pa. green (No. 262)	£190	£130
12		10pa. green (No. 289)	£375	£375
11		10pa. on 20pa. red (No.	£600	£600
6		20pa. red (No. 263)	£180	£110
13		20pa. red (No. 290)	£400	£350
7		1pi. blue (No. 264)	£130	£120
14a		1pi. blue (No. 291)	£900	£900
15		1pi. blk on red (No. D288)	£1500	£1500
8		2pi. black (No. 265)	£250	£200
14b		2pi. black (No. 292)		
1	**25**	2½pi. brown (No. 239)	£450	£350
9	**28**	5pi. purple (No. 267)	£700	£600
10		10pi. red (No. 268)	£2500	£2500

3

2

1913.

16	**2**	10pa. violet	8·00	6·00
17		20pa. red and grey	10·00	8·00
18		1g. grey	10·00	10·00
19		2g. blue and violet	12·00	9·50
20		5g. violet and blue	15·00	12·00
21		10g. blue and violet	15·00	12·00

3   4 Skanderbeg (after
                      Heinz Kautsch)

1913. Independence Anniv.

22	**3**	10pa. black and green	2·75	1·75
23		20pa. black and red	3·00	2·75
24		30pa. black and violet	3·50	2·75
25		1g. black and blue	5·00	3·50
26		2g. black	8·00	6·00

1913.

27	**4**	2q. brown and yellow	1·00	1·00
28		5q. green and yellow	1·00	1·00
29		10q. red	1·10	1·10
30		25q. blue	1·25	1·25
31		50q. mauve and red	5·00	4·00
32		1f. brown	8·00	8·00

1914. Arrival of Prince William of Wied. Optd **7 Mars 1461 RROFTE MBRETI 1914.**

33	**4**	2q. brown and yellow	22·00	18·00
34		5q. green and yellow	22·00	18·00
35		10q. red and rose	22·00	18·00
36		25q. blue	22·00	18·00
37		50q. mauve and rose	22·00	18·00
38		1f. brown	22·00	18·00

1914. Surch.

40	**4**	5pa. on 2q. brown & yellow	1·75	1·75
41		10pa. on 5q. green & yellow	1·75	1·75
42		20pa. on 10q. red	2·25	1·75
43		1g. on 25q. blue	2·75	2·50
44		2g. on 50q. mauve and red	3·50	3·50
45		5g. on 1f. brown	15·00	10·00

1914. Valona Provisional Issue. Optd **POSTE D'ALBANIE** and Turkish inscr in circle with star in centre.

45a	**4**	2q. brown and yellow	£150	£150
45b		5q. green and yellow		
45c		10q. red and rose	8·50	8·50
45d		25q. blue	8·50	8·50
45e		50q. mauve and red	8·50	8·50
45f		1f. brown	£475	
45g		5pa. on 2q. brown & yellow	25·00	25·00
45h		10pa. on 5q. green & yellow	50·00	50·00
45i		20pa. on 10q. red and rose	13·00	13·00
45j		1gr. on 25q. blue	7·50	7·50
45k		2gr. on 50q. mauve and red	13·00	13·00
45l		5gr. on 1f. brown	18·00	18·00

11   12

1917. Inscribed "SHQIPERIE KORCE VETQEVERITARE" or "REPUBLIKA KORCE SHQIPETARE" or "QARKU-POSTES-I-KORCES".

75	**11**	1c. brown and green	2·00	4·00
76		2c. brown and green	2·00	4·00
77		3c. grey and green	2·00	4·00
78		5c. green and black	2·75	2·50
79		10c. red and black	2·75	2·50
72		25c. blue and black	9·00	6·25
80		50c. purple and black	5·00	4·50
81		1f. brown and black	16·00	15·00

1918. No. 78 surch **QARKUI KORCES 25 CTS.**

| 81a | 25c. on 5c. green and black | 60·00 | 48·00 |

1919. Fiscal stamps used by the Austrians in Albania. Handstamped with control.

83	**12**	(2)q. on 2h. brown	5·50	5·50
84		05q. on 16h. green	5·50	5·50
85		10q. on 8h. red	5·50	5·50
86		20q. on 64h. blue	5·50	5·50
87a		50q. on 33h. violet	5·50	5·50
88		1f. on 1.28k. brown on blue	8·00	8·00

Three sets may be made of this issue according to whether the handstamped control is a date, a curved comet or a comet with straight tail.

1919. No. 43 optd **SHKODER 1919.**

| 103 | **4** | 1g. on 25q. blue | 8·00 | 8·00 |

1919. Fiscal stamps surch **POSTAT SHQIPTARE** and new value.

104	**12**	05q. on 2h. brown	4·50	4·50
111		10q. on 8h. red	4·50	4·50
112		15q. on 8h. red	4·50	4·50
113		20q. on 16h. green	4·50	4·50
113b		25q. on 64h. blue	4·50	4·50
107		25q. on 64h. blue	4·50	4·50
108		50q. on 32h. violet	4·50	4·50
113c		50q. on 32h. violet	10·00	10·00
113d		1f. on 96h. orange	6·00	6·00
113e		2f. on 160h. violet	8·50	8·50

17 Prince William I   19 Skanderbeg

1920. Optd with double-headed eagle and **SHKORDA** or surch also.

114	**17**	1q. grey	21·00	40·00
115		2q. on 10q. red	3·50	6·25
116		5q. on 10q. red	3·50	6·25
117		10q. red	3·25	6·25
118		20q. brown	12·00	22·00
119		25q. blue	£140	£275
120		25q. on 10q. red	3·50	7·00
121		50q. violet	17·00	32·00
122		50q. on 10q. red	3·50	7·00

1920. Optd with posthorn.

123	**19**	2q. orange	5·00	6·25
124		5q. green	6·75	11·00
125		10q. red	13·50	22·00
126		25q. blue	26·00	22·00
127		50q. green	5·00	7·50
128		1f. mauve	5·00	7·50

Stamps as Type **19** also exist optd **BESA** meaning "Loyalty".

1922. No. 123 surch with value in frame.

| 143 | **19** | 1q. on 2q. orange | 3·50 | 2·00 |

24

1922. Views.

144	**24**	2q. orange (Gjinokaster)	80	1·75
145		5q. green (Kanina)	50	75
146		10q. red (Berat)	50	75
147		25q. blue (Veziri Bridge)	50	75
148		50q. green (Rozafat Fortress, Shkoder)	60	75
149		1f. lilac (Korce)	1·10	1·25
150		2f. green (Durres)	2·75	4·00

1924. Opening of National Assembly. Optd **TIRANE KALLNUER 1924** in frame with **Mbledhje Kushtetuese** above.

151	**24**	2q. orange	4·75	8·00
152		5q. green	4·75	8·00
153		10q. red	4·75	8·00
154		25q. blue	4·75	8·00
155		50q. green	4·75	8·00

1924. No. 144 surch with value and bars.

| 156 | **24** | 1 on 2q. orange | 2·50 | 3·75 |

1924. Red Cross. (a) Surch with small red cross and premium.

157		5q.+5q. green	7·50	7·50
158		10q.+5q. red	7·50	7·50
159		25q.+5q. blue	7·50	7·50
160		50q.+5q. green	7·50	7·50

(b) Nos. 157/60 with further surch of large red cross and premium.

161	**24**	5q.+5q.+5q. green	7·50	7·50
162		10q.+5q.+5q. red	7·50	7·50
163		25q.+5q.+5q. blue	7·50	7·50
164		50q.+5q.+5q. green	7·50	7·50

1925. Return of Government to Capital in 1924. Optd **Triumf' i legalitetit 24 Dhetuer 1924.**

164a	**24**	1 on 2q. orange (No. 156)	2·50	3·25
165		2q. orange	2·50	3·25
166		5q. green	2·50	3·25
167		10q. red	2·50	3·25
168		25q. blue	2·50	3·25
169		50q. green	2·50	3·25
170		1f. lilac	2·50	3·25

1925. Proclamation of Republic. Optd **Republika Shqiptare 21 Kallnduer 1925.**

171	**24**	1 on 2q. orange (No. 156)	2·50	3·25
172		2q. orange	2·50	3·25
173		5q. green	2·50	3·25
174		10q. red	2·50	3·25
175		25q. blue	2·50	3·25
176		50q. green	2·50	3·25
177		1f. lilac	2·50	3·25

1925. Optd **Republika Shqiptare.**

178	**24**	1 on 2q. orange (No. 156)	65	85
179		2q. orange	65	85
180		5q. green	65	85
181		10q. red	65	85
182		25q. blue	65	85
183		50q. green	65	85
184		1f. lilac	2·75	3·75
185		2f. green	2·75	3·75

POSTA AERORE

32

1925. Air.

186	**32**	5q. green	3·25	3·25
187		10q. red	3·50	3·50
188		25q. blue	3·50	3·50
189		50q. green	5·00	5·00
190		1f. black and red	8·25	8·25
191		2f. violet and olive	11·00	11·00
192		3f. green and brown	19·00	19·00

33 Pres. Ahmed   34
Zogu, later King
Zog I

1925.

193	**33**	1q. yellow	15	10
194		2q. brown	15	10
195		5q. green	15	10
196		10q. red	15	10
197		15q. brown	75	75
198		25q. blue	15	10
199		50q. green	75	75
200	**34**	1f. blue and red	1·25	1·25
201		2f. orange and green	1·75	1·25
202		3f. violet	3·50	3·00
203		5f. black and violet	4·25	4·75

1927. Air. Optd **Rep. Shqiptare.**

204	**32**	5q. green	10·00	10·00
205		10q. red	10·00	10·00
206		25q. blue	8·50	8·50
207		50q. green	8·00	8·00
208		1f. black and violet	8·00	8·00
209		2f. violet and olive	9·75	9·75
210		3f. green and brown	17·00	17·00

1927. Optd **A.Z.** and wreath.

211	**33**	1q. yellow	50	65
212		2q. brown	20	25
213		5q. green	1·10	35
214		10q. red	20	20
215		15q. brown	6·00	7·00
216		25q. blue	50	25
217		50q. green	50	25
218	**34**	1f. blue and red	50	25
219		2f. orange and green	75	50
220		3f. violet and brown	1·10	1·00
221		5f. black and violet	1·75	2·00

1928. Inauguration of Vlore (Valona)-Brindisi Air Service. Optd **REP. SHQYPTARE Fluturim' i I-ar Vlone-Brindisi 21.IV.1928.**

222	**32**	5q. green	9·25	11·50
223		10q. red	9·25	11·50
224		25q. blue	9·25	9·50
225		50q. green	10·50	14·50
226		1f. black and violet	95·00	£110
227		2f. violet and olive	£100	£110
228		3f. green and brown	£100	£120

1928. Surch in figures and bars.

| 229 | **33** | 1 on 10q. red (No. 214) | 50 | 40 |
| 230 | | 5 on 25q. blue (No. 216) | 50 | 40 |

39 Pres. Ahmed   40
Zogu, later King
Zog I

1928. National Assembly. Optd **Kujtim i Mbledhjes Kushtetuese 25.8.28.**

231	**39**	1q. brown	3·50	4·25
232		2q. grey	3·50	4·25
233		5q. green	3·50	4·25
234		10q. red	3·50	4·25
235		15q. brown	9·00	14·00
236		25q. blue	4·25	3·75
237		50q. lilac	6·75	5·00
238	**40**	1f. black and blue	4·25	3·75

1928. Accession of King Zog I. Optd **Mbretnia-Shqiptare Zog I 1.IX.1928.**

239	**39**	1q. brown	8·50	13·00
240		2q. grey	8·50	13·00
241		5q. green	6·50	11·00
242		10q. red	6·00	6·25
243		15q. brown	6·00	7·50
244		25q. blue	6·00	7·50
245		50q. lilac	6·75	8·75
246	**40**	1f. black and blue	8·25	15·00
247		2f. black and green	8·25	11·00

1928. Optd **Mbretnia-Shqiptare** only.

248	**39**	1q. brown	50	50
249		2q. grey	45	35
250		5q. green	2·50	50
251		10q. red	50	35
252		15q. brown	10·00	12·00
253		25q. blue	50	35
254		50q. lilac	75	35
255	**40**	1f. black and blue	1·50	1·90
256		2f. black and green	1·50	2·10

257		3f. olive and red	4·00	2·75
258		5f. black and violet	5·25	7·50

1929. Surch **Mbr. Shqiptare** and new value.

259	33	1 on 50q. green	25	40
260		5 on 25q. blue	30	40
261		15 on 10q. red	50	70

1929. King Zog's 35th Birthday. Optd **RROFT-MBRETI 8.X.1929**.

262	33	1q. yellow	4·50	6·75
263		2q. brown	4·50	6·75
264		5q. green	4·50	6·75
265		10q. red	4·50	6·75
266		25q. blue	4·50	6·75
267		50q. green	5·00	8·00
268	34	1f. blue and red	8·00	12·00
269		2f. orange and green	8·50	12·50

1929. Air. Optd **Mbr. Shqiptare**.

270	32	5q. green	8·00	12·00
271		10q. red	8·00	12·00
272		25q. blue	15·00	12·50
273		50q. green	45·00	60·00
274		1f. black and violet	£250	£325
275		2f. violet and olive	£275	£350
276		3f. green and brown	£500	£550

49 Lake Butrinto

50 King Zog I

1930. 2nd Anniv of Accession of King Zog I.

277	49	1q. grey	15	20
278		2q. red	15	20
279	50	5q. green	15	15
280		10q. red	25	30
281		15q. brown	25	30
282		25q. blue	20	30
283	49	50q. green	40	45
284	–	1f. violet	85	60
285	–	2f. blue	1·00	60
286	–	3f. green	2·50	95
287	–	5f. brown	3·25	2·50

DESIGNS—VERT: 1, 2f. Ahmed Zog Bridge, River Mati. HORIZ: 3, 5f. Ruins of Zogu Castle.

53 Junkers F-13 (over Tirana)

1930. Air. T **53** and similar view.

288	53	5q. green	2·10	2·10
289		15q. red	2·10	2·10
290		20q. blue	2·10	2·10
291		50q. olive	3·75	3·75
292	–	1f. blue	6·25	6·25
293	–	2f. brown	21·00	21·00
294	–	3f. violet	24·00	24·00

1931. Air. Optd **TIRANE-ROME 6 KORRIK 1931**.

295	53	5q. green	9·00	9·00
296		15q. red	9·00	9·00
297		20q. blue	9·00	9·00
298		50q. olive	9·00	9·00
299	–	1f. blue	50·00	50·00
300	–	2f. brown	50·00	50·00
301	–	3f. violet	50·00	50·00

1934. 10th Anniv of Revolution. Optd **1924-24 Dhetuer-1934**.

302	49	1q. grey	2·00	3·50
303		2q. orange	2·00	3·50
304	50	5q. green	2·00	3·50
305		10q. red	2·00	3·50
306		15q. brown	2·00	3·50
307		25q. blue	3·00	3·75
308	49	50q. turquoise	3·00	3·75
309	–	1f. violet (No. 284)	4·00	7·50
310	–	2f. blue (No. 285)	8·00	13·00
311	–	3f. green (No. 286)	14·00	18·00

56 Horse and Flag of Skanderbeg

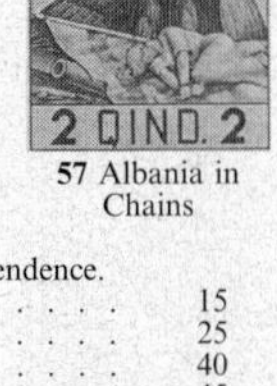

57 Albania in Chains

1937. 25th Anniv of Independence.

312	56	1q. violet	15	15
313	57	2q. brown	25	20
314	–	5q. green	40	20
315	56	10q. olive	45	50
316	57	15q. red	60	45
317	–	25q. blue	1·25	1·50
318	56	50q. green	1·75	2·00
319	57	1f. violet	5·00	5·25
320	–	2f. brown	8·00	8·50

DESIGN: 5, 25q., 2f. As Type **57**, but eagle with opened wings (Liberated Albania).

58 Countess Geraldine Apponyi and King Zog

1938. Royal Wedding.

321	58	1q. purple	20	20
322		2q. brown	20	20
323		5q. green	20	25
324		10q. olive	50	50
325		15q. red	50	50
326		25q. blue	65	85
327		50q. green	3·50	2·75
328		1f. violet	4·75	3·75

59 National Emblems

60 King Zog

1938. 10th Anniv of Accession.

329	–	1q. purple	15	35
330	59	2q. red	25	35
331	–	5q. green	35	40
332	60	10q. brown	65	1·00
333	–	15q. red	65	1·00
334	60	25q. blue	85	1·10
335	59	50q. black	5·00	3·75
336	60	1f. green	7·50	5·50

DESIGN: 1, 5, 15q. As Type **60**, but Queen Geraldine's portrait.

ITALIAN OCCUPATION

1939. Optd **Mbledhja Kushtetuese 12-IV-1939 XVII**.

(a) Postage.

337	49	1q. grey	35	35
338		2q. red	35	35
339	50	5q. green	30	30
340		10q. red	30	30
341		15q. brown	70	75
342		25q. blue	80	95
343	49	50q. turquoise	1·00	1·25
344	–	1f. violet (No. 284)	2·00	2·75
345	–	2f. blue (No. 285)	2·25	3·00
346	–	3f. green	5·00	7·50
347	–	5f. brown	6·75	8·50

(b) Air. Optd as Nos. 337/47 or surch also.

348	53	5q. green	4·25	3·75
349		15q. red	3·00	3·75
350		20q. on 50q. olive	7·25	7·25

62 Gheg

64 Broken Columns, Botrint

63 King Victor Emmanuel

65 King and Fiat G18V on Tirana–Rome Service

1939.

351	62	1q. blue (postage)	40	25
352	–	2q. brown	30	10
353	–	3q. brown	30	10
354	–	5q. green	40	10
355	63	10q. brown	40	15
356		15q. red	50	15
357		25q. blue	50	25
358		30q. violet	80	60
359	–	50q. violet	1·10	60
360	–	65q. red	2·25	2·50
361	–	1f. green	2·50	1·50
362	–	2f. red	6·50	8·00
363	64	3f. black	10·00	14·50
364	–	5f. purple	12·00	18·00
365	65	20q. brown (air)	45·00	10·50

DESIGNS—SMALL: 2q. Tosk man; 3q. Gheg woman; 5, 65q. Profile of King Victor Emmanuel; 50q. Tosk woman. LARGE: 1f. Kruje Fortress; 2f. Bridge over River Kiri at Mes; 5f. Amphitheatre ruins, Berat.

66 Sheep Farming

67 King Victor Emmanuel

1940. Air.

366	66	5q. green	1·25	1·25
367	–	15q. red	1·75	1·60
368	–	20q. blue	4·00	2·40
369	–	50q. brown	4·50	4·75
370	–	1f. green	6·00	6·00
371	–	2f. black	13·50	14·00
372	–	3f. purple	55·00	24·00

DESIGNS: Savoia Marchetti S.M.75 airplane and—HORIZ: 20q. King of Italy and Durres harbour; 1f. Bridge over River Kiri at Mes. VERT: 15q. Aerial map; 50q. Girl and valley; 2f. Archway and wall, Durres; 3f. Women in North Eprius.

1942. 3rd Anniv of Italian Occupation.

373	67	5q. green	60	75
374		10q. brown	60	75
375		15q. red	75	1·25
376		25q. blue	75	1·25
377		65q. brown	1·75	2·00
378		1f. green	1·75	2·00
379		2f. purple	1·75	2·50

1942. No. 352 surch **1 QIND**.

380		1q. on 2q. brown	85	1·50

69

1943. Anti-tuberculosis Fund.

381	69	5q. + 5q. green	50	85
382		10q. + 10q. brown	50	85
383		15q. + 10q. red	50	85
384		25q. + 15q. blue	1·00	1·60
385		30q. + 20q. violet	1·00	1·60
386		50q. + 25q. orange	1·00	1·60
387		65q. + 30q. grey	1·25	2·10
388		1f. + 40q. brown	1·75	3·00

GERMAN OCCUPATION

1943. Postage stamps of 1939 optd **14 Shtator 1943** or surch also.

389	–	1q. on 3q. brn (No. 353)	1·00	3·00
390	–	2q. brown (No. 352)	1·00	3·00
391	–	3q. brown (No. 353)	1·00	3·00
392	–	5q. green (No. 354)	1·00	3·00
393	63	10q. brown	1·00	3·00
394	–	15q. red (No. 356)	1·00	3·00
395	–	25q. blue (No. 357)	1·00	3·00
396	–	30q. violet (No. 358)	1·00	3·00
397	–	50q. on 65q. brn (No. 360)	1·25	6·00
398	–	65q. red (No. 360)	1·25	6·00
399	–	1f. green (No. 361)	6·00	18·00
400	–	2f. red (No. 362)	10·00	70·00
401	64	3f. black	50·00	£225

71 War Refugees

(**73**)

1944. War Refugees' Relief Fund.

402	71	5q. + 5q. green	2·50	12·00
403		10q. + 5q. brown	2·50	12·00
404		15q. + 5q. red	2·50	12·00
405		25q. + 10q. blue	2·50	12·00
406		1f. + 50q. green	2·50	12·00
407		2f. + 1f. violet	2·50	12·00
408		3f. + 1f.50 orange	2·50	12·00

INDEPENDENT STATE

1945. Nos. 353/8 and 360/2 surch **QEVERIJA DEMOKRAT. E SHQIPERISE 22-X-1944** and value.

409		30q. on 3q. brown	4·25	5·00
410		40q. on 5q. green	4·25	5·00
411		50q. on 10q. brown	4·25	5·00
412		60q. on 15q. red	4·25	5·00
413		80q. on 25q. blue	4·25	5·00
414		1f. on 30q. violet	4·25	5·00
415		2f. on 65q. brown	4·25	5·00
416		3f. on 1f. green	4·25	5·00
417		5f. on 2f. red	4·25	5·00

1945. 2nd Anniv of Formation of People's Army. Surch as T **73**.

418	49	30q. on 1q. grey	2·50	3·75
419		60q. on 1q. grey	2·50	3·75
420		80q. on 1q. grey	2·75	3·75
421		1f. on 1q. grey	6·00	7·50
422		2f. on 2q. red	7·50	8·75
423		3f. on 50q. green	13·50	16·00
424	–	5f. on 2f. blue (No. 285)	20·00	25·00

1945. Red Cross Fund. Surch with Red Cross, **JAVA E K.K. SHQIPTAR 4-11 MAJ 1945** and value.

425	69	30q.+15q. on 5q.+5q. green	5·00	6·50
426		50q.+25q. on 10q.+10q. brown	5·00	6·50
427		1f.+50q. on 15q.+10q. red	14·00	16·00
428		2f.+1f. on 25q.+15q. blue	20·00	22·00

75 Labinot

77 Globe, Dove and Olive Branch

1945.

429	75	20q. green	50	85
430		30q. orange	75	1·25
431	–	40q. brown	75	1·25
432	–	60q. red	1·00	1·75
433	–	1f. red	2·00	3·75
434	–	3f. blue	12·00	15·00

DESIGNS: 40, 60q. Bridge at Berat; 1f., 3f. Permet landscape.

1946. Constitutional Assembly. Optd **ASAMBLEJA KUSHTETUESE 10 KALLNUER 1946**.

435	75	20q. green	1·25	1·25
436		30q. orange	1·75	1·75
437	–	40q. brown (No. 431)	2·00	2·00
438	–	60q. red (No. 432)	3·50	3·50
439	–	1f. red (No. 433)	12·00	12·00
440	–	3f. blue (No. 434)	20·00	20·00

PEOPLE'S REPUBLIC

1946. Int Women's Congress. Perf or imperf.

441	77	20q. mauve and red	85	85
442		40q. lilac and red	1·25	1·25
443		50q. violet and red	1·75	1·75
444		1f. blue and red	4·25	4·25
445		2f. blue and red	6·25	6·25

1946. Proclamation of Albanian People's Republic. Optd **REPUBLIKA POPULLORE E SHQIPERISE**.

446	75	20q. green	1·40	1·40
447		30q. orange	1·60	1·60
448	–	40q. brown (No. 431)	2·75	2·75
449	–	60q. red (No. 432)	5·50	5·50
450	–	1f. red (No. 433)	12·00	12·00
451	–	3f. blue (No. 434)	22·00	22·00

1946. Albanian Red Cross Congress. Surch **KONGRESI K.K.SH. 24-25-11-46** and premium.

452	75	20q.+10q. green	20·00	20·00
453		30q.+15q. orange	20·00	20·00
454	–	40q.+20q. brown	20·00	20·00
455	–	60q.+30q. red	20·00	20·00
456	–	1f.+50q. red	20·00	20·00
457	–	3f.+1f.50 blue	20·00	20·00

79 Athletes

80 Qemal Stafa

1946. Balkan Games.

458	79	1q. black	14·00	11·50
459		2q. green	14·00	11·50
460		5q. brown	14·00	11·50
461		10q. red	14·00	11·50
462		20q. blue	14·00	11·50
463		40q. lilac	16·00	11·50
464		1f. orange	32·00	30·00

1947. 5th Death Anniv of Qemal Stafa (Communist activist).

465	80	20q. dp brown & brown	9·00	9·00
466		28q. deep blue and blue	9·00	9·00
467		40q. dp brown & brown	9·00	9·00

81 Railway Construction

1947. Construction of Durres–Elbasan Railway.

468	81	1q. black and drab	5·00	1·25
469		4q. deep green and green	5·00	1·25
470		10q. black & brown	5·25	1·60
471		15q. red and rose	5·25	1·60
472		20q. black and blue	12·00	1·75
473		28q. deep blue and blue	17·00	2·25
474		40q. red and purple	32·00	2·50
475		68q. dp brown & brown	40·00	22·00

82 Partisans

83 Enver Hoxha and Vasil Shanto

1947. 4th Anniv of Formation of People's Army. Inscr "1943–1947".
476 **82** 16q. brown . . . . 4·50 4·50
477 **83** 20q. brown . . . . 4·50 4·50
478 – 28q. blue . . . . 4·50 4·50
479 – 40q. brown and mauve . . 4·50 4·50
DESIGNS—HORIZ: 28q. Infantry column. VERT: 40q. Portrait of Vojo Kushi.

84 Ruined Conference Building

1947. 5th Anniv of Peza Conference.
480 **84** 2l. purple and mauve . . . 6·00 4·00
481 2l.50 deep blue and blue 6·00 4·00

85 War Invalids

86 Peasants

1947. 1st Congress of War Invalids.
482 **85** 1l. red . . . . 10·00 10·00

1947. Agrarian Reform. Inscr "REFORMA AGRARE".
483 **86** 1l.50 purple . . . . . . 7·50 6·50
484 – 2l. brown . . . . 7·50 6·50
485 – 2l.50 blue . . . . 7·50 6·50
486 – 3l. red . . . . 7·50 6·50
DESIGNS—HORIZ: 2l. Banquet; 2l.50, Peasants rejoicing. VERT: 3l. Soldier being chaired.

87 Burning Village

1947. 3rd Anniv of Liberation. Inscr "29-XI-1944–1947".
487 **87** 1l.50 red . . . . 3·75 3·75
488 – 2l.50 purple . . . . . . 3·75 3·75
489 – 5l. blue . . . . 8·00 6·00
490 – 8l. mauve . . . . 12·00 8·00
491 – 12l. brown . . . . 20·00 14·00
DESIGNS: 2l.50, Riflemen; 5l. Machine-gunners; 8l. Mounted soldier; 12l. Infantry column.

1948. Nos. 429/34 surch **Lek** and value.
492 **75** 0l.50 on 30q. orange . . . 35 35
493 1l. on 20q. green 90 90
494 – 2l.50 on 60q. red . . . . 2·50 2·25
495 – 3l. on 1f. red . . . . . 3·00 3·00
496 – 5l. on 3f. blue . . . . . 6·00 5·50
497 – 12l. on 40q. brown . . . . 15·00 12·50

88 Railway Construction

1948. Construction of Durres–Tirana Railway.
498 **88** 0l.50 red . . . . 2·50 1·00
499 1l. green . . . . 2·75 1·10
500 1l.50 red . . . . 4·25 1·10
501 2l.50 brown . . . . 5·25 2·00
502 5l. blue . . . . 10·00 2·75
503 8l. orange . . . . 16·00 4·75
504 12l. purple . . . . 20·00 8·00
505 20l. black . . . . 40·00 18·00

89 Parade of Infantrymen

90 Labourer, Globe and Flag

1948. 5th Anniv of People's Army.
506 **89** 2l.50 brown . . . . 3·00 2·50
507 5l. blue . . . . 5·00 4·50
508 – 8l. slate (Troops in action) 8·00 6·00

1949. Labour Day.
509 **90** 2l.50 brown . . . . 1·00 1·00
510 5l. blue . . . . 2·25 2·25
511 8l. purple . . . . 4·00 4·00

91 Soldier and Map

92 Albanian and Kremlin Tower

1949. 6th Anniv of People's Army.
512 **91** 2l.50 brown . . . . 1·10 1·10
513 5l. blue . . . . 2·25 2·25
514 8l. orange . . . . 4·00 4·00

1949. Albanian–Soviet Amity.
515 **92** 2l.50 brown . . . . 1·25 1·50
516 5l. blue . . . . 3·00 3·25

93 Gen. Enver Hoxha

94 Soldier and Flag

1949.
517 **93** 0l.50 purple 25 10
518 1l. green 30 10
519 1l.50 red 40 10
520 2l.50 brown 65 10
521 5l. blue . . . . 1·60 25
522 8l. purple . . . . 3·00 1·75
523 12l. purple . . . . 10·50 3·00
524 20l. slate . . . . 12·50 4·00

1949. 5th Anniv of Liberation.
525 **94** 2l.50 brown 70 70
526 – 3l. red . . . . 1·75 1·90
527 **94** 5l. violet . . . . 2·50 2·75
528 – 8l. black . . . . 5·25 5·50
DESIGN—HORIZ: 3, 8l. Street fighting.

96 Joseph Stalin

1949. Stalin's 70th Birthday.
529 **96** 2l.50 brown . . . . 1·00 1·25
530 5l. blue . . . . 1·90 2·50
531 8l. lake . . . . 4·25 5·50

97

98 Sami Frasheri

1950. 75th Anniv of U.P.U.
532 **97** 5l. blue . . . . 2·75 4·00
533 8l. purple . . . . 5·00 5·75
534 12l. black . . . . 9·00 10·00

1950. Literary Jubilee. Inscr "1950-JUBILEU I SHKRIMTAREVE TE RILINDJES".
535 **98** 2l. green . . . . 1·10 85
536 – 2l.50 brown . . . . 1·50 1·40
537 – 3l. red . . . . 1·75 2·00
538 – 5l. blue . . . . 3·00 3·00
PORTRAITS: 2l.50, A. Zako (Cajupi); 3l. Naim Frasheri; 5l. K. Kristoforidhi.

99 Vuno-Himare

100 Stafa and Shanto

1950. Air.
539 **99** 0l.50 black 90 90
540 – 1l. purple 90 90
541 – 2l. blue . . . . 1·60 1·60
542 **99** 5l. green . . . . 5·50 5·50
543 – 10l. blue . . . . 12·00 12·00
544 – 20l. violet . . . . 20·00 20·00
DESIGNS: Douglas DC-3 airplane over—1, 10l. Rozafat Shkodor; 2, 20l. Keshtjelle-Butrinto.

1950. Albanian Patriots.
545 – 2l. green . . . . 1·25 1·25
546 – 2l.50 violet . . . . 1·50 1·50
547 – 3l. red . . . . 2·50 2·25
548 – 5l. blue . . . . 3·00 2·50
549 **100** 8l. brown . . . . 8·00 7·25
PORTRAITS: 2l. Ahmet Haxhia, Hydajet Lezha, Naim Gjylbegu, Ndoc Mazi and Ndoc Deda; 2l.50, Asim Zeneli, Ali Demi, Kajo Karafili, Dervish Hakali and Asim Vokshi; 3l. Ataz Shehu, Baba Faja, Zoja Cure, Mustafa Matohiti and Gjok Doci; 5l. Perlat Rexhepi, Bako, Vojo Kushi, Reshit Collaku and Misto Mame.

101 Arms and Flags

102 Skanderbeg

1951. 5th Anniv of Republic.
550 **101** 2l.50 red . . . . 1·50 1·60
551 5l. blue . . . . 3·75 3·75
552 8l. black . . . . 5·50 5·75

1951. 483rd Death Anniv of Skanderbeg (patriot).
553 **102** 2l.50 brown . . . . . . 1·50 1·40
554 5l. violet . . . . 3·00 3·25
555 8l. bistre . . . . 4·75 4·75

103 Gen. Enver Hoxha and Assembly

104 Child and Globe

1951. 7th Anniv of Permet Congress.
556 **103** 2l.50 brown 90 90
557 3l. red . . . . 1·10 1·10
558 5l. blue . . . . 2·00 2·00
559 8l. mauve . . . . 3·75 3·75

1951. International Children's Day.
560 **104** 2l. green . . . . 1·50 1·10
561 – 2l.50 brown . . . . . . 1·75 1·50
562 – 3l. red . . . . 2·50 1·75
563 **104** 5l. blue . . . . 3·50 2·40
DESIGN—HORIZ: 2l.50, 3l. Nurse weighing baby.

105 Enver Hoxha and Meeting-house

106 Young Partisans

1951. 10th Anniv of Albanian Communists.
564 **105** 2l.50 brown 55 55
565 3l. red 65 65
566 5l. blue . . . . 1·00 1·00
567 8l. black . . . . 2·25 2·25

1951. 10th Anniv of Albanian Young Communists' Union. Inscr "1941–1951".
568 **106** 2l.50 brown 75 90
569 – 5l. blue . . . . 4·75 2·75
570 – 8l. red . . . . 3·50 3·50
DESIGNS: Schoolgirl, railway, tractor and factories; 8l. Miniature portraits of Stafa, Spiru, Mame and Kondi.

1952. Air. Surch in figures.
571 – 0.50l. on 2l. blue (No. 541) £160 £130
572 **99** 0.50l. on 5l. green . . . . 35·00 25·00
573 2l.50 on 5l. green £250 £140
574 – 2l.50 on 10l. blue (No. 543) 35·00 25·00

108 Factory

1953.
575 **108** 0l.50 brown 75 10
576 – 1l. green 75 10
577 – 2l.50 sepia . . . . . . 1·60 20
578 – 3l. red . . . . 2·00 35
579 – 5l. blue . . . . 3·75 90
580 – 8l. olive . . . . 4·00 1·10
581 – 12l. purple . . . . . . 5·50 1·40
582 – 20l. blue . . . . 12·50 3·25
DESIGNS—HORIZ: 1l. Canal; 2l.50, Girl and cotton mill; 3l. Girl and sugar factory; 5l. Film studio; 8l. Girl and textile machinery; 20l. Dam. VERT: 12l. Pylon and hydroelectric station.

109 Soldiers and Flags

1954. 10th Anniv of Liberation.
583 **109** 0l.50 lilac 15 15
584 1l. green 65 15
585 2l.50 brown . . . . . . 1·10 70
586 3l. red . . . . 2·00 85
587 5l. blue . . . . 2·75 1·25
588 8l. purple . . . . 5·25 3·50

110 First Albanian School

111

1956. 70th Anniv of Albanian Schools.
589 **110** 2l. purple 30 20
590 – 2l.50 green 85 30
591 – 5l. blue . . . . 1·60 1·25
592 **110** 10l. turquoise . . . . . . 4·25 3·50
DESIGN: 2l.50, 5l. Portraits of P. Sotiri, P. N. Luarasi and N. Naci.

1957. 15th Anniv of Albanian Workers' Party.
593 **111** 2l.50 brown 75 20
594 – 5l. blue . . . . 1·50 65
595 – 8l. purple . . . . 3·25 2·25
DESIGNS: 5l. Party headquarters, Tirana; 8l. Marx and Lenin.

112 Congress Emblem

1957. 4th World Trade Unions Congress, Leipzig.
596 **112** 2l.50 purple 50 20
597 3l. red 75 50
598 5l. blue . . . . 1·25 85
599 8l. green . . . . 3·50 2·25

113 Lenin and Cruiser "Aurora"

114 Raising the Flag

1957. 40th Anniv of Russian Revolution.
600 **113** 2l.50 brown . . . . . . 1·25 55
601 5l. blue . . . . 2·10 1·60
602 8l. black . . . . 3·60 2·25

1957. 45th Anniv of Proclamation of Independence.
603 **114** 1l.50 purple 75 30
604 2l.50 brown . . . . . . 1·10 75
605 5l. blue . . . . 3·00 1·40
606 8l. green . . . . 4·25 2·75

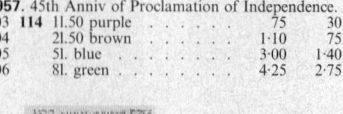

115 N. Veqilharxhi

116 L. Gurakuqi

1958. 160th Birth Anniv of Veqilharxhi (patriot).

607	**115**	2l.50 brown	80	30
608		5l. blue	1·50	60
609		8l. purple	3·25	1·50

1958. Removal of Ashes of Gurakuqi (patriot).

610	**116**	1l.50 green	20	20
611		2l.50 brown	75	60
612		5l. blue	1·10	75
613		8l. sepia	3·00	1·10

117 Freedom Fighters — **118** Soldiers in Action

1958. 50th Anniv of Battle of Mashkullore.

614	**117**	2l.50 ochre	60	20
615	–	3l. green	80	20
616	**117**	5l. blue	1·25	75
617	–	8l. brown	2·50	1·50

DESIGN: 3, 8l. Tree and buildings.

1958. 15th Anniv of Albanian People's Army.

618	**118**	1l.50 green	20	15
619	–	2l.50 brown	60	25
620	**118**	8l. red	1·60	1·40
621	–	11l. blue	2·40	2·25

DESIGN: 2l.50, 11l. Tank-driver, sailor, infantryman and tanks.

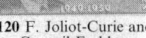

119 Bust of Apollo and Butrinto Amphitheatre — **120** F. Joliot-Curie and Council Emblem

1959. Cultural Monuments Week.

622	**119**	2l.50 brown	75	25
623		6l.50 green	3·00	1·40
624		11l. blue	4·25	2·50

1959. 10th Anniv of World Peace Council.

625	**120**	1l.50 red	2·25	80
626		2l.50 violet	5·00	2·00
627		11l. blue	10·50	6·00

121 Basketball — **122** Soldier

1959. 1st National Spartacist Games.

628	**121**	1l.50 violet	75	35
629	–	2l.50 green	1·10	35
630	–	5l. red	1·75	1·40
631	–	11l. blue	6·25	3·75

DESIGNS: 2l.50, Football; 5l. Running; 11l. Runners with torches.

1959. 15th Anniv of Liberation.

632	**122**	1l.50 red	50	25
633	–	2l.50 brown	1·40	40
634	–	3l. green	1·60	50
635	–	6l.50 red	3·25	4·50

DESIGNS: 2l.50, Security guard. 3l. Harvester; 6l.50, Laboratory workers.

123 Mother and Child — **124**

1959. 10th Anniv of Declaration of Human Rights.

636	**123**	5l. blue	7·25	2·00

1960. 50th Anniv of International Women's Day.

637	**124**	2l.50 brown	1·00	55
638		11l. red	4·00	1·40

125 Congress Building — **126** A. Moisiu — **127** Lenin

1960. 40th Anniv of Lushnje Congress.

639	**125**	2l.50 brown	55	25
640		7l.50 blue	1·50	80

1960. 80th Birth Anniv of Alexandre Moisiu (actor).

641	**126**	3l. brown	65	45
642		11l. green	2·25	80

1960. 90th Birth Anniv of Lenin.

643	**127**	4l. turquoise	1·75	35
644		11l. red	5·50	1·25

128 Vaso Pasha — **129** Frontier Guard — **130** Family with Policeman

1960. 80th Anniv of Albanian Alphabet Study Association.

645	**128**	1l. olive	30	20
646	–	1l.50 brown	85	25
647	–	6l.50 blue	1·75	85
648	–	11l. red	4·25	1·60

DESIGNS: 1l.50, Jani Vreto; 6l.50, Sami Frasheri; 11l. Association statutes.

1960. 15th Anniv of Frontier Force.

649	**129**	1l.50 red	50	30
650		11l. blue	3·00	1·40

1960. 15th Anniv of People's Police.

651	**130**	1l.50 green	55	25
652		8l.50 brown	3·00	1·25

131 Normal School, Elbasan — **132** Soldier and Cannon

1960. 50th Anniv of Normal School, Elbasan.

653	**131**	5l. green	2·50	1·40
654		6l.50 purple	2·50	1·40

1960. 40th Anniv of Battle of Vlore.

655	**132**	1l.50 brown	75	25
656		2l.50 purple	1·10	40
657		5l. blue	2·50	90

133 Tirana Clock Tower, Kremlin and Tupolev Tu-104A Jetliner — **134** Federation Emblem

1960. 2nd Anniv of Tirana–Moscow Jet Air Service.

658	**133**	1l. brown	1·00	75
659		7l.50 blue	3·75	1·50
660		11l.50 grey	6·00	3·00

1960. 15th Anniv of World Democratic Youth Federation.

661	**134**	1l.50 blue	25	15
662		8l.50 red	1·40	55

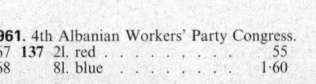

135 Ali Kelmendi — **136** Flags of Albania and Russia, and Clasped Hands — **137** Marx and Lenin

1960. 60th Birth Anniv of Kelmendi (Communist).

663	**135**	1l.50 olive	55	20
664		11l. purple	1·40	85

1961. 15th Anniv of Albanian-Soviet Friendship Society.

665	**136**	2l. violet	55	20
666		8l. purple	1·75	75

1961. 4th Albanian Workers' Party Congress.

667	**137**	2l. red	55	20
668		8l. blue	1·60	80

138 Malsi e Madhe (Shkoder) Costume — **139** European Otter

1961. Provincial Costumes.

669	**138**	1l. black	75	20
670	–	1l.50 purple	1·10	25
671	–	6l.50 blue	3·75	1·10
672	–	11l. red	7·25	2·40

COSTUMES: 1l.50, Malsi e Madhe (Shkoder) (female); 6l.50, Lume; 11l. Mirdite.

1961. Albanian Fauna.

673	**139**	2l.50 blue	4·00	1·00
674	–	6l.50 green (Eurasian badger)	8·00	2·50
675	–	11l. brown (Brown bear)	13·50	5·00

140 Dalmatian Pelicans — **141** Cyclamen

1961. Albanian Birds.

676	**140**	1l.50 red on pink	3·50	60
677	–	7l.50 violet on blue	5·75	1·60
678	–	11l. brown on pink	8·75	2·00

BIRDS: 7l.50, Grey heron; 11l. Little egret.

1961. Albanian Flowers.

679	**141**	1l.50 purple and blue	2·50	50
680	–	8l. orange and purple	5·00	2·00
681	–	11l. red and green	8·00	2·50

FLOWERS: 8l. Forsythia; 11l. Lily.

142 M. G. Nikolla — **143** Lenin and Marx on Flag

1961. 50th Birth Anniv of Nikolla (poet).

682	**142**	0l.50 brown	40	30
683		8l.50 green	2·00	1·40

1961. 20th Anniv of Albanian Workers' Party.

684	**143**	2l.50 red	90	25
685		7l.50 purple	2·00	90

144 — **145** Yuri Gagarin and "Vostok 1"

1961. 20th Anniv of Albanian Young Communists' Union.

686	**144**	2l.50 blue	90	25
687		7l.50 mauve	1·60	1·00

1962. World's First Manned Space Flight. (a) Postage.

688	**145**	0l.50 blue	90	15
689		4l. purple	3·75	90
690		11l. green	9·00	3·00

(b) Air. Optd **POSTA AJRORE**.

691	**145**	0l.50 blue on cream	35·00	35·00
692		4l. purple on cream	35·00	35·00
693		11l. green on cream	35·00	35·00

147 P. N. Luarasi — **148** Campaign Emblem

1962. 50th Death Anniv of Petro N. Luarasi (patriot).

694	**147**	0l.50 blue	75	15
695		8l.50 brown	3·00	75

IMPERF STAMPS. Many Albanian stamps from No. 696 onwards exist imperf and/or in different colours from limited printings.

1962. Malaria Eradication.

696	**148**	1l.50 green	15	10
697		2l.50 red	20	10
698		10l. purple	1·10	65
699		11l. blue	1·60	90

149 Camomile — **150** Throwing the Javelin

1962. Medicinal Plants.

700	**149**	0l.50 yellow, green & blue	35	20
701	–	8l. green, yellow and grey	1·60	1·00
702	–	11l.50 violet, grn & ochre	2·75	1·25

PLANTS: 8l. Silver linden; 11l.50, Sage.

1962. Olympic Games, Tokyo, 1964 (1st issue). Inscr as in T **102**.

703	–	0l.50 black and blue	20	15
704	–	2l.50 sepia and brown	70	15
705	–	3l. black and blue	90	20
706	**150**	9l. purple and red	2·50	75
707	–	10l. black and olive	2·75	1·00

DESIGNS—VERT: 0l.50, Diving; 2l.50, Pole-vaulting; 10l. Putting the shot. HORIZ: 3l. Olympic flame.

See also Nos. 754/8, 818/21 and 842/51.

151 "Sputnik 1" in Orbit — **152** Footballer and Ball in Net

1962. Cosmic Flights.

708	**151**	0l.50 yellow and violet	60	20
709	–	1l. sepia and green	85	25
710	–	1l.50 yellow and red	1·40	35
711	–	20l. blue and purple	9·00	3·00

DESIGNS: 1l. Dog "Laika" and "Sputnik 2"; 1l.50, Artificial satellite and Sun; 20l. "Lunik 3" photographing Moon.

1962. World Cup Football Championship, Chile.

712	**152**	1l. violet and orange	20	15
713	–	2l.50 blue and green	1·00	20
714	**152**	6l.50 purple and brown	2·00	25
715	–	15l. purple and green	2·75	70

DESIGN: 2l.50, 15l. As Type **152** but globe in place of ball in net.

153 "Europa" and Albanian Maps — **154** Dardhe Woman

1962. Tourist Publicity.

716	**153**	0l.50 red, yellow & green	30	30
717	–	1l. red, purple and blue	1·40	1·40
718	–	2l.50 red, purple and blue	8·00	8·00
719	**153**	11l. red, yellow and grey	16·00	16·00

DESIGN: 1, 2l.50, Statue and map.

1962. Costumes of Albania's Southern Region.

720	**154**	0l.50 red, purple and blue	25	10
721	–	1l. brown and buff	30	15
722	–	2l.50 black, violet & grn	1·40	40
723	–	14l. red, brown and green	4·25	1·60

COSTUMES: 1l. Devoll man; 2l.50, Lunxheri woman; 14l. Gjirokaster man.

155 Chamois — **156** Golden Eagle

1962. Albanian Animals.

724	**155**	0l.50 purple and green	50	15
725	–	1l. black and yellow	1·40	30
726	–	1l.50 black and brown	2·00	35
727	–	15l. brown and green	20·00	3·75

ANIMALS—HORIZ. 1l. Lynx; 1l.50, Wild boar. VERT: 15l. Roe deer.

1962. 50th Anniv of Independence.
728 **156** 1l. brown and red 40 35
729 – 3l. black and brown . . . 1·75 75
730 – 16l. black and mauve . . 4·75 1·90
DESIGNS: 3l. I. Qemali; 16l. "RPSH" and golden eagle.

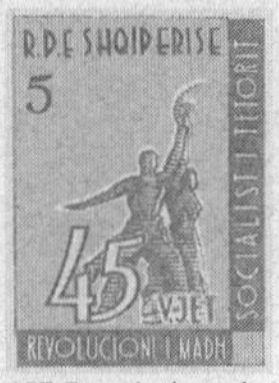
157 Revolutionaries

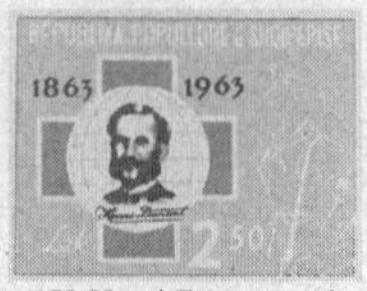
158 Henri Dunant and Globe

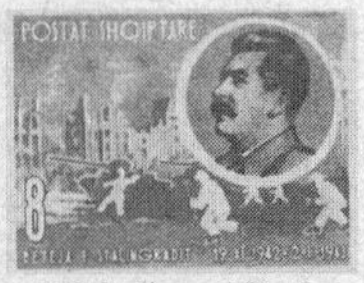
159 Stalin and Battle

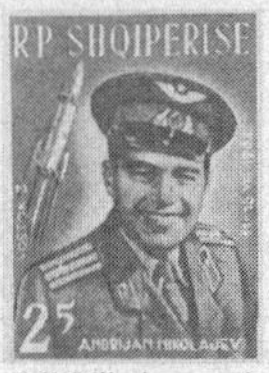
160 Nikolaev and "Vostok 3"

1963. 45th Anniv of October Revolution.
731 **157** 5l. violet and yellow . . . 1·10 55
732 – 10l. black and red . . . . 2·25 1·25
DESIGN: 10l. Statue of Lenin.

1963. Red Cross Centenary. Cross in red.
733 **158** 1l.50 black and red . . . 65 20
734 2l.50 black, red and blue 85 40
735 6l. black, red and green 1·60 90
736 10l. black, red and yellow 3·50 1·75

1963. 20th Anniv of Battle of Stalingrad.
737 **159** 8l. black & grn (postage) 9·00 2·50
738 – 7l. red and green (air) . . 9·00 2·00
DESIGN: 7l. "Lenin" flag, map, tanks, etc.

1963. 1st "Team" Manned Space Flights.
739 **160** 2l.50 brown and blue . . 75 30
740 – 7l.50 black and blue . . . 1·75 1·00
741 – 20l. brown and violet . . 6·00 2·75
DESIGNS—HORIZ: 7l.50, Globe, "Vostok 3" and "Vostok 4". VERT: 20l. P. Popovic and "Vostok 4".

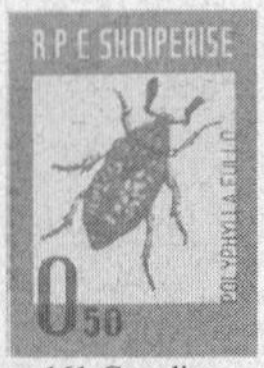
161 Crawling Cockchafer

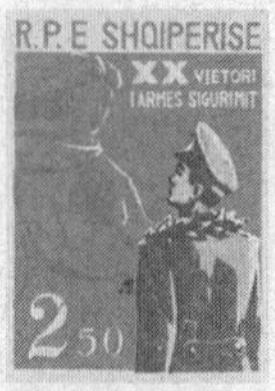
162 Policeman and Allegorical Figure

1963. Insects.
742 **161** 0l.50 brown and green . . 75 30
743 – 1l. brown and blue . . . 1·50 75
744 – 8l. purple and red . . . . 6·50 1·75
745 – 10l. black and yellow . . 8·00 3·25
INSECTS: 1l.50, Stagbeetle; 8l. "Procerus gigas" (ground beetle); 10l. "Cicindela albanica" (tiger beetle).

1963. 20th Anniv of Albanian Security Police.
746 **162** 2l.50 black, purple & red 90 50
747 7l.50 black, lake and red 3·25 80

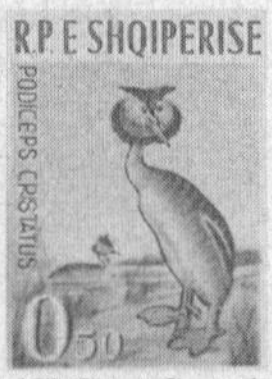
163 Great Crested Grebe

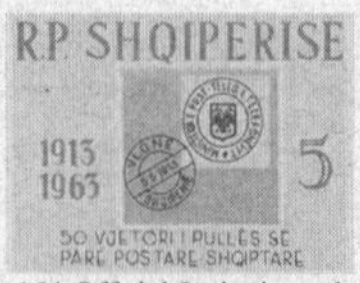
164 Official Insignia and Postmark of 1913

1963. Birds. Multicoloured.
748 0l.50 Type **163** 80 25
749 3l. Golden eagle . . . . . . 2·00 30
750 6l.50 Grey partridge . . . . 3·25 1·10
751 11l. Western capercaillie . . . 6·75 1·75

1963. 50th Anniv of First Albanian Stamps.
752 **164** 5l. multicoloured . . . . 1·90 90
753 – 10l. green, black and red . 3·50 1·60
DESIGN: 10l. Albanian stamps of 1913, 1937 and 1962.

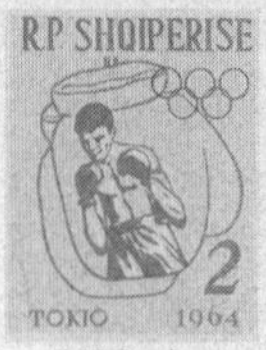
165 Boxing

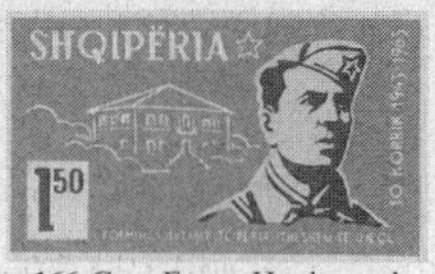
166 Gen. Enver Hoxha and Labinoti Council Building

1963. Olympic Games, Tokyo (1964) (2nd issue).
754 **165** 2l. green, red and yellow 65 65
755 – 3l. brown, blue & orange 85 25
756 – 5l. purple, brown and blue . . . . 1·25 35
757 – 6l. black, grey and green 1·75 90
758 – 9l. blue and brown . . . 3·50 1·40
SPORTS: 3l. Basketball; 5l. Volleyball; 6l. Cycling; 9l. Gymnastics.

1963. 20th Anniv of Albanian People's Army.
759 **166** 1l.50 yellow, black & red 40 20
760 – 2l.50 bistre, brown & blue 1·00 30
761 – 5l. black, drab & turq . . 1·90 90
762 – 6l. blue, buff and brown 2·75 1·40
DESIGNS: 2l.50, Soldier with weapons; 5l. Soldier attacking; 6l. Peacetime soldier.

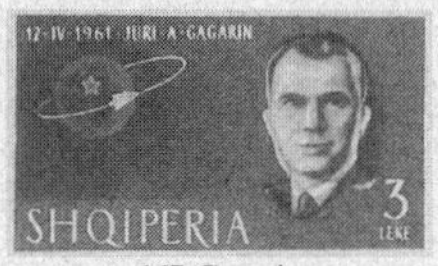
167 Gagarin

1963. Soviet Cosmonauts. Portraits in yellow and brown.
763 **167** 3l. violet . . . . 1·00 20
764 – 5l. blue . . . . 1·40 40
765 – 7l. violet and grey . . . . 2·25 65
766 – 11l. blue and purple . . . 3·75 1·00
767 – 14l. blue and turquoise . . 4·75 1·40
768 – 20l. blue . . . . 7·25 3·50
COSMONAUTS: 5l. Titov; 7l. Nikolaev; 11l. Popovich; 14l. Bykovsky; 20l. Valentina Tereshkova.

168 Volleyball (Rumania)

1963. European Sports Events, 1963.
769 **168** 2l. red, black and olive . . 85 20
770 – 3l. bistre, black and red 85 30
771 – 5l. orange, black & green 1·25 65
772 – 7l. green, black and pink 1·90 85
773 – 8l. red, black and blue . . 3·50 1·10
SPORTS: 3l. Weightlifting (Sweden); 5l. Football (European Cup); 7l. Boxing (Russia); 8l. Ladies' Rowing (Russia).

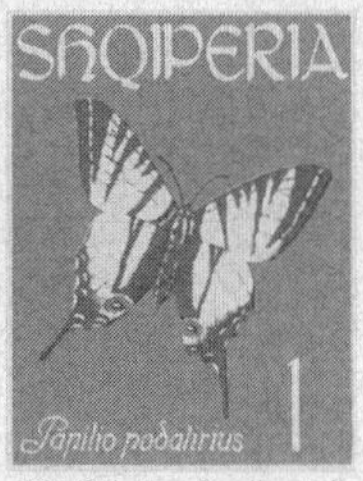
169 Celadon Swallowtail

1963. Butterflies and Moths.
774 **169** 1l. black, yellow and red 75 25
775 – 2l. black, red and blue . . 90 30
776 – 4l. black, yellow & purple 2·00 85
777 – 5l. multicoloured . . . . 2·75 75
778 – 8l. black, red and brown 4·75 1·60
779 – 10l. orange, brown & blue 6·25 2·25
DESIGNS: 2l. Jersey tiger moth; 4l. Brimstone; 5l. Death's-head hawk moth; 8l. Orange tip; 10l. Peacock.

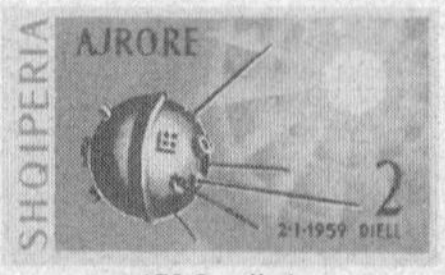
170 Lunik 1

1963. Air. Cosmic Flights.
780 **170** 2l. olive, yellow & orange 40 25
781 – 3l. multicoloured . . . . 1·00 25
782 – 5l. olive, yellow & purple 1·60 65
783 – 8l. red, yellow and violet 2·50 1·10
784 – 12l. red, orange and blue 4·50 3·50
DESIGNS: 3l. Lunik 2; 5l. Lunik 3; 8l. Venus 1; 12l. Mars 1.

171 Food Processing Works

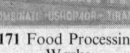

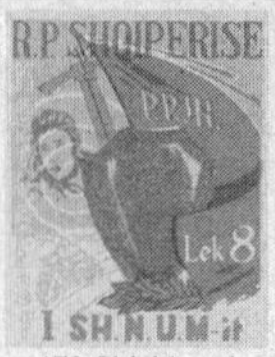
172 Shield and Banner

1963. Industrial Buildings.
785 **171** 2l.50 red on pink 90 20
786 – 20l. green on green . . . 4·75 1·25
787 – 30l. purple on blue . . . 7·50 1·90
788 – 50l. bistre on cream . . . 9·50 3·50
DESIGNS—VERT: 20l. Naphtha refinery; 30l. Fruit-bottling plant. HORIZ: 50l. Copper-processing works.

1963. 1st Army and Defence Aid Assn Congress.
789 **172** 2l. multicoloured 70 25
790 8l. multicoloured . . . . 2·00 1·40

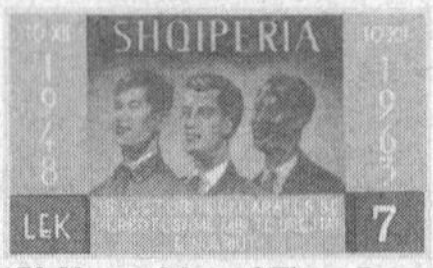
173 Young Men of Three Races

1963. 15th Anniv of Declaration of Human Rights.
791 **173** 3l. black and ochre . . . 65 55
792 5l. blue and ochre . . . 1·40 85
793 7l. violet and ochre . . . 2·25 1·40

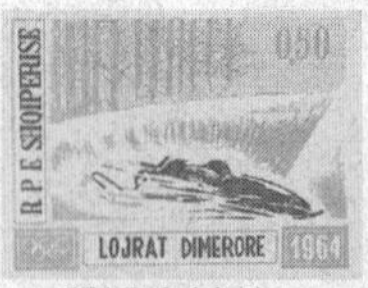
174 Bobsleighing

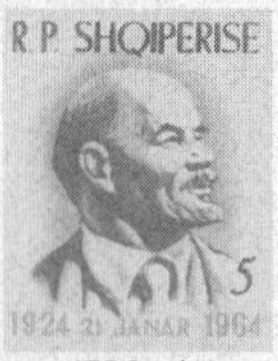
175 Lenin

1963. Winter Olympic Games, Innsbruck. Inscr "1964".
794 **174** 0l.50 black and blue . . . 20 20
795 – 2l.50 black, red and grey 90 25
796 – 6l.50 black, yellow & grey 1·75 35
797 – 12l.50 red, black & green 3·50 1·60
DESIGNS—VERT: 2l.50, Skiing; 12l.50, Figure-skating. HORIZ: 6l.50, Ice-hockey.

1964. 40th Death Anniv of Lenin.
798 **175** 5l. olive and bistre . . . 1·10 35
799 10l. olive and bistre . . . 1·50 85

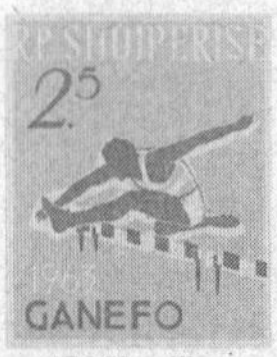
176 Hurdling

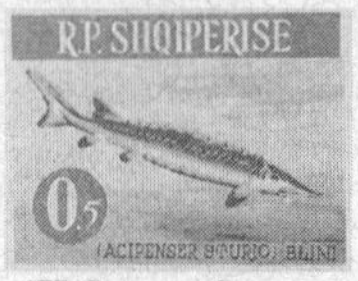
177 Common Sturgeon

1964. "GANEFO" Games, Djakarta (1963).
800 **176** 2l.50 blue and lilac . . . 85 25
801 – 3l. brown and green . . . 1·25 30
802 – 6l.50 red and blue . . . 1·60 40
803 – 8l. ochre and blue . . . . 2·50 90
SPORTS—HORIZ: 3l. Running; 6l.50, Rifle-shooting. VERT: 8l. Basketball.

1964. Fishes. Multicoloured.
804 0l.50 Type **177** 30 10
805 1l. Gilthead seabream 75 20
806 1l.50 Flat-headed grey mullet 1·00 30
807 2l.50 Common carp . . . . 1·50 50
808 6l.50 Atlantic mackerel . . . 3·00 1·25
809 10l. Lake Ochrid salmon . . 5·00 2·00

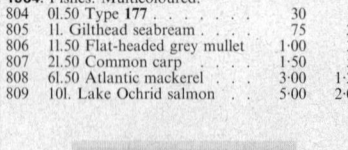

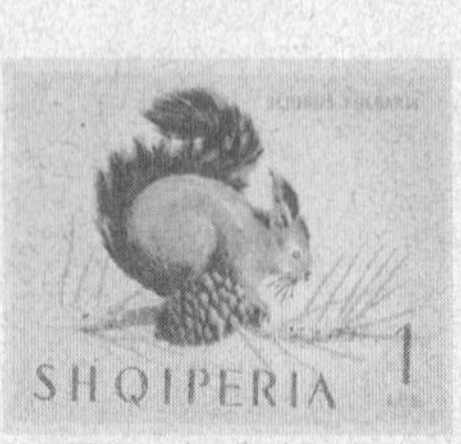
178 Eurasian Red Squirrel

1964. Forest Animals. Multicoloured.
810 1l. Type **178** 30 20
811 1l.50 Beech marten 50 25
812 2l. Red fox 70 30
813 2l.50 East European hedgehog 80 30
814 3l. Brown hare . . . . 1·00 70
815 5l. Golden jackal . . . . . 1·75 70
816 7l. Wild cat . . . . 3·00 90
817 8l. Wolf . . . . 4·50 1·10

179 Lighting Olympic Torch

1964. Olympic Games, Tokyo (3rd issue). Inscr "DREJT TOKIOS".
818 **179** 3l. yellow, buff and green 30 15
819 – 5l. blue, violet and red . . 65 25
820 – 7l. lt blue, blue & yellow 90 30
821 – 10l. multicoloured . . . . 1·25 85
DESIGNS: 5l. Torch and globes; 7l. Olympic flag and Mt. Fuji; 10l. Olympic Stadium, Tokyo.

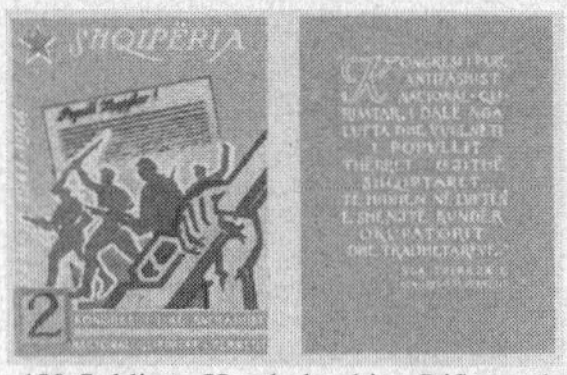
180 Soldiers, Hand clutching Rifle, and Inscription

1964. 20th Anniv of Permet Congress.
822 **180** 2l. sepia, red and orange 75 50
823 – 5l. multicoloured . . . . 2·00 1·50
824 – 8l. sepia, red and brown 3·50 3·00
DESIGNS (each with different inscription at right): 5l. Albanian Arms; 8l. Gen. Enver Hoxha.

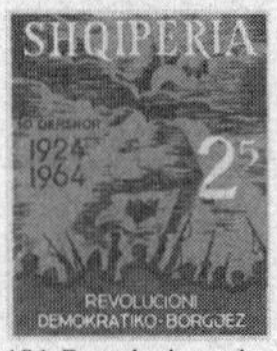
181 Revolutionaries with Flag

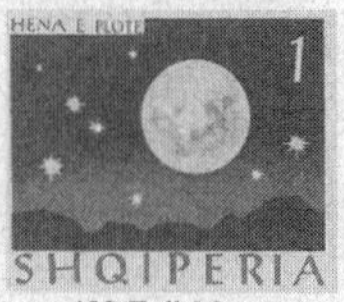
183 Full Moon

1964. 40th Anniv of Revolution.
825 **181** 2l.50 black and red . . . 25 20
826 7l.50 black and mauve . . 1·00 45

1964. "Verso Tokyo" Stamp Exhibition, Rimini (Italy). Optd **Rimini 25-VI-64**.
827 10l. blue, violet, orange and black (No. 821) . . . . . 7·25 7·25

1964. Moon's Phases.
828 **183** 1l. yellow and violet . . . 30 15
829 – 5l. yellow and blue . . . 1·10 65
830 – 8l. yellow and blue . . . 1·75 85
831 – 11l. yellow and green . . 4·25 1·25
PHASES: 5l. Waxing Moon; 8l. Half-Moon; 11l. Waning Moon.

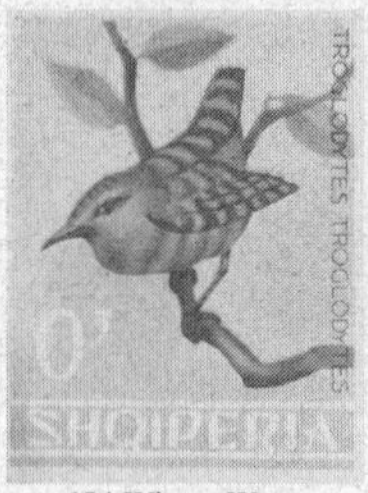
184 Winter Wren

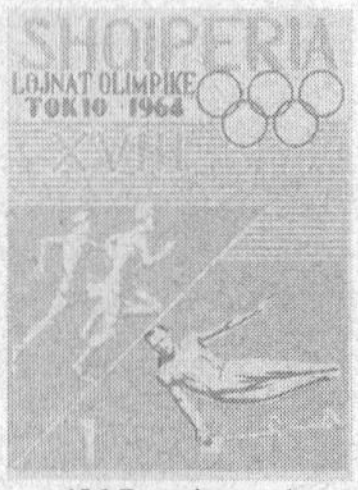
186 Running and Gymnastics

1964. Albanian Birds. Multicoloured.
832 0l.50 Type **184** 35 25
833 1l. Penduline tit 60 30
834 2l.50 Green woodpecker . . . 85 40
835 3l. Common treecreeper . . . 1·25 40
836 4l. Eurasian nuthatch . . . . 1·40 60
837 5l. Great tit . . . . 1·75 60
838 6l. Eurasian goldfinch . . . . 2·00 60
839 18l. Golden oriole . . . . . 4·75 2·10

1964. Air. Riccione "Space" Exhibition. Optd **Riccione 23-8-1964**.
840 **170** 2l. olive, yellow & orange 10·50 10·50
841 – 8l. red, yellow and violet (No.783) . . . . 25·00 25·00

1964. Olympic Games, Tokyo.
842 **186** 1l. red, blue and green . . 20 15
843 – 2l. brown, blue and violet 25 20
844 – 3l. brown, violet and olive 35 20
845 – 4l. olive, turquoise & blue 50 25
846 – 5l. turquoise, purple & red 85 65
847 – 6l. ultram, lt blue & orge 1·00 75
848 – 7l. green, orange and blue 1·40 90
849 – 8l. grey, green and yellow 1·40 1·10
850 – 9l. lt blue, yellow & purple . . . . 1·40 1·25
851 – 10l. brown, green & turq 1·90 1·60
SPORTS: 2l. Weightlifting and judo; 3l. Horse-jumping and cycling; 4l. Football and water-polo; 5l. Wrestling and boxing; 6l. Various sports and hockey;

7l. Swimming and yachting; 8l. Basketball and volleyball; 9l. Rowing and canoeing; 10l. Fencing and pistol-shooting.

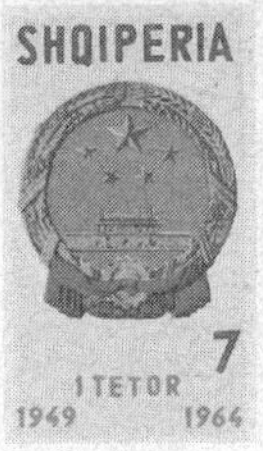
187 Chinese Republican Emblem

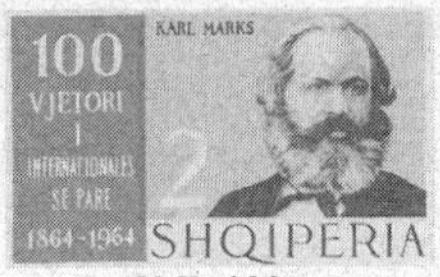
188 Karl Marx

1964. 15th Anniv of Chinese People's Republic. Inscr "I TETOR 1949 1964.".

852	187	7l. red, black and yellow	1·60	85
853	–	8l. black, red and yellow	2·75	1·25

DESIGN—HORIZ: 8l. Mao Tse-tung.

1964. Centenary of "First International".

854	188	2l. black, red and lavender	90	20
855	–	5l. slate	2·40	75
856	–	8l. black, red and buff	4·00	1·25

DESIGNS: 5l. St. Martin's Hall, London; 8l. F. Engels.

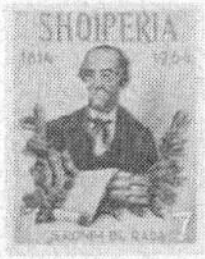
189 J. de Rada

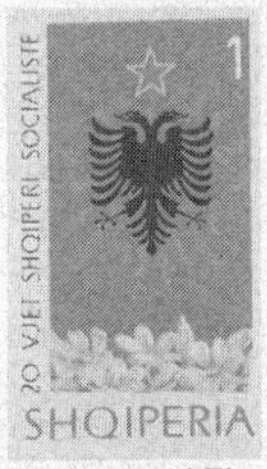
190 Arms and Flag

1964. 150th Birth Anniv of Jeronim de Rada (poet).

857	189	7l. green	1·60	65
858		8l. violet	2·50	1·10

1964. 20th Anniv of Liberation.

859	190	1l. multicoloured	20	20
860	–	2l. blue, red and yellow	65	20
861	–	3l. brown, red and yellow	1·00	65
862	–	4l. green, red and yellow	1·40	85
863	–	10l. black, red and blue	3·50	1·60

DESIGNS—HORIZ: 2l. Industrial scene; 3l. Agricultural scene. 4l. Laboratory worker. VERT: 10l. Hands holding Constitution, hammer and sickle.

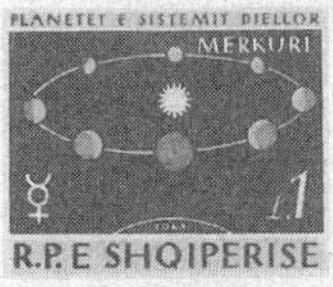
191 Mercury

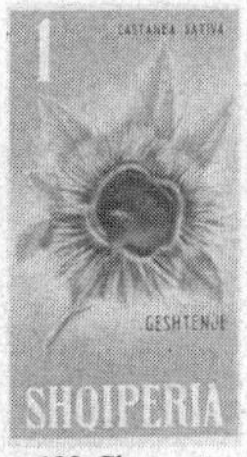
192 Chestnut

1964. Solar System Planets. Multicoloured.

864	1l. Type 191	25	20
865	2l. Venus	45	25
866	3l. Earth	70	30
867	4l. Mars	85	35
868	5l. Jupiter	1·10	40
869	6l. Saturn	1·60	50
870	7l. Uranus	1·90	65
871	8l. Neptune	2·00	1·25
872	9l. Pluto	2·10	1·60

1965. Winter Fruits. Multicoloured.

873	1l. Type 192	25	15
874	2l. Medlars	35	20
875	3l. Persimmon	75	25
876	4l. Pomegranate	95	35
877	5l. Quince	1·60	40
878	10l. Orange	2·75	1·10

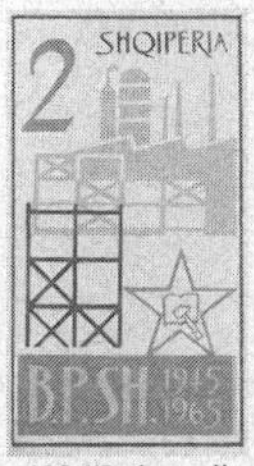
193 "Industry"

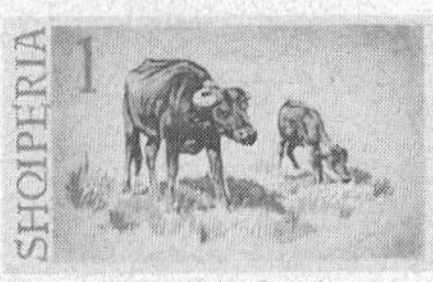
194 Buffalo Grazing

1965. 20th Anniv of Albanian Trade Unions. Inscr "B.P.S.H. 1945–1965".

879	193	2l. red, pink and black	3·50	3·00
880	–	5l. black, grey and ochre	7·00	6·00
881	–	8l. blue, lt blue & black	8·50	6·50

DESIGNS: 5l. Set square, book and dividers ("Technocracy"); 8l. Hotel, trees and sunshade ("Tourism").

1965. Water Buffaloes.

882	194	1l. multicoloured	50	15
883	–	2l. multicoloured	1·10	20
884	–	3l. multicoloured	1·90	30
885	–	7l. multicoloured	4·50	1·10
886	–	12l. multicoloured	8·00	2·50

DESIGNS: 2l. to 12l. As Type 194, showing different views of buffalo.

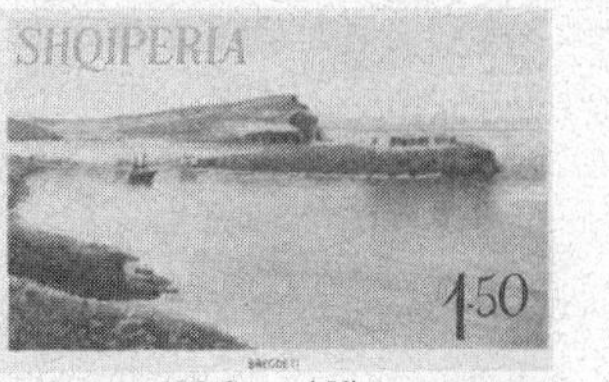
195 Coastal View

1965. Albanian Scenery. Multicoloured.

887	1l.50 Type 195	1·60	80
888	2l.50 Mountain forest	2·75	1·10
889	3l. Lugina Peak (vert)	3·50	1·40
890	4l. White River, Thethi (vert)	4·25	1·90
891	5l. Dry Mountain	5·25	2·50
892	9l. Lake of Flowers, Lure	12·00	4·50

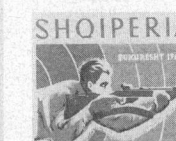

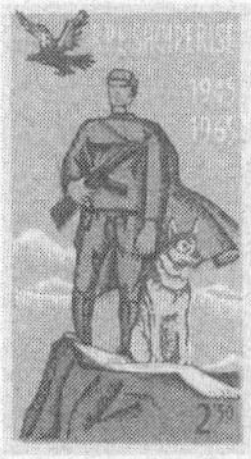
196 Frontier Guard

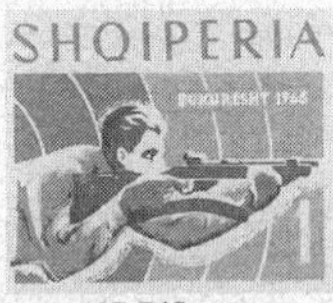
197 Rifleman

1965. 20th Anniv of Frontier Force.

893	196	2l.50 multicoloured	1·40	85
894		12l.50 multicoloured	8·00	3·50

1965. European Shooting Championships, Bucharest.

895	197	1l. purple, red and violet	20	15
896	–	2l. purple, ultram & blue	65	20
897	–	3l. red and pink	85	30
898	–	4l. multicoloured	1·25	30
899	–	15l. multicoloured	5·00	95

DESIGNS: 2, 15l. Rifle-shooting (different); 3l. "Target" map; 4l. Pistol-shooting.

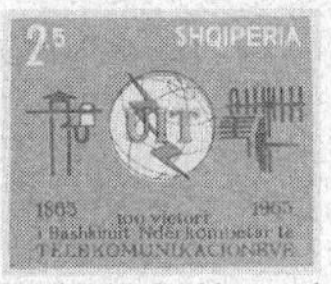
198 I.T.U. Emblem and Symbols

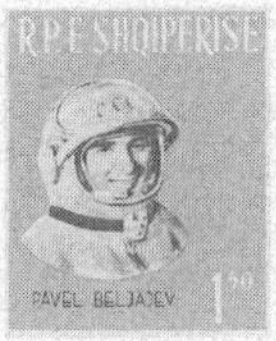
199 Belyaev

1965. Centenary of I.T.U.

900	198	2l.50 mauve, black & grn	1·60	20
901		12l.50 blue, black & violet	6·00	1·40

1965. Space Flight of "Voskhod 2".

902	199	1l.50 brown and blue	20	10
903	–	2l. blue, ultram & lilac	30	15
904	–	6l.50 brown and mauve	1·25	35
905	–	20l. yellow, black & blue	4·50	1·25

DESIGNS: 2l. "Voskhod 2"; 6l.50, Leonov; 20l. Leonov in space.

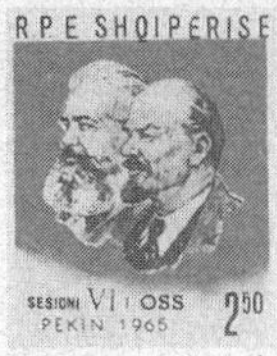
200 Marx and Lenin

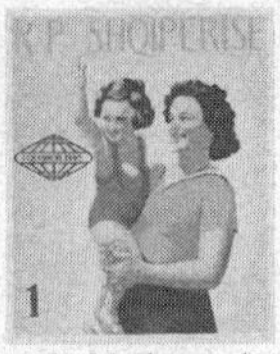
201 Mother and Child

1965. Postal Ministers' Congress, Peking.

907	200	2l.50 sepia, red & yellow	75	30
908		7l.50 green, red & yellow	3·25	1·25

1965. International Children's Day. Multicoloured.

909	1l. Type 201	25	15
910	2l. Children planting tree	45	20
911	3l. Children and construction toy (horiz)	75	20
912	4l. Child on beach	90	30
913	15l. Child reading book	4·25	1·75

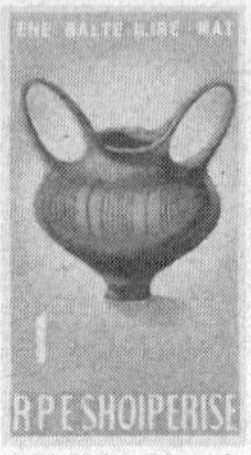
202 Wine Vessel

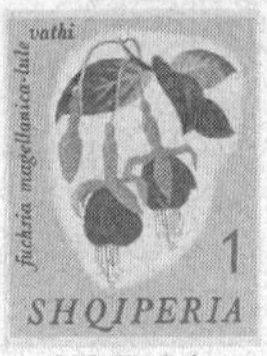
203 Fuchsia

1965. Albanian Antiquities. Multicoloured.

914	1l. Type 202	20	10
915	2l. Helmet and shield	40	15
916	3l. Mosaic of animal (horiz)	85	25
917	4l. Statuette of man	1·60	30
918	15l. Statuette of headless and limbless man	4·25	1·60

1965. Albanian Flowers. Multicoloured.

919	1l. Type 203	25	15
920	2l. Cyclamen	75	20
921	3l. Lilies	1·10	25
922	3l.50 Iris	1·40	25
923	4l. Dahlia	1·60	35
924	4l.50 Hydrangea	1·75	35
925	5l. Rose	2·00	70
926	7l. Tulips	2·75	90

(currency revaluation 10 (old) leks = 1 (new) lek.)

1965. Surch.

927	5q. on 30l. (No. 787)	20	20
928	15q. on 30l. (No. 787)	45	20
929	25q. on 50l. (No. 788)	65	25
930	80q. on 50l. (No. 788)	2·10	90
931	1l.10 on 20l. (No. 786)	3·25	1·10
932	2l. on 20l. (No. 786)	6·25	2·10

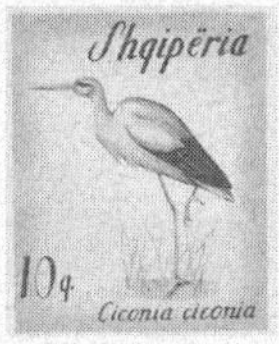
205 White Stork

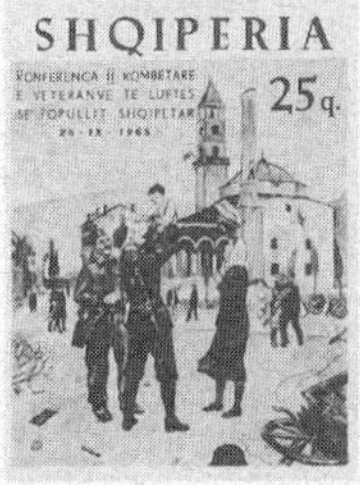
206 "War Veterans" (after painting by B. Sejdini)

1965. Migratory Birds. Multicoloured.

933	10q. Type 205	35	35
934	20q. European cuckoo	65	35
935	30q. Hoopoe	1·10	50
936	40q. European bee-eater	1·75	60
937	50q. European nightjar	2·00	70
938	1l.50 Common quail	6·00	2·00

1965. War Veterans Conference.

939	206	25q. brown and black	3·25	85
940		65q. blue and black	7·25	1·75
941		1l.10 black	10·00	2·50

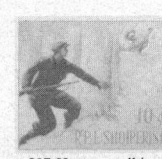

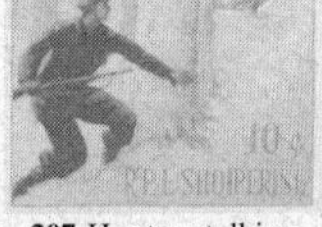
207 Hunter stalking Western Capercaillie

208 "Nerium oleander"

1965. Hunting.

942	207	10q. multicoloured	85	25
943	–	20q. brown, sepia & grn	85	25
944	–	30q. multicoloured	1·90	80
945	–	40q. purple and green	2·25	90
946	–	50q. brown, blue & black	2·00	55
947	–	1l. brown, bistre & green	4·25	1·00

DESIGNS: 20q. Shooting roe deer; 30q. Common pheasant; 40q. Shooting mallard; 50q. Dogs chasing wild boar; 1l. Hunter and brown hare.

1965. Mountain Flowers. Multicoloured.

948	10q. Type 208	30	20
949	20q. "Myosotis alpestris"	40	20
950	30q. "Dianthus glacialis"	65	30
951	40q. "Nymphaea alba"	1·25	40
952	50q. "Lotus corniculatus"	1·60	50
953	1l. "Papaver rhoeas"	3·75	1·60

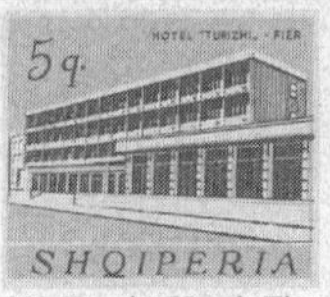
209 Tourist Hotel, Fier

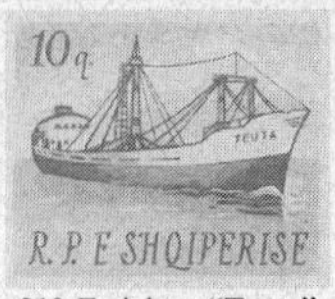
210 Freighter "Teuta"

1965. Public Buildings.

954	209	5q. black and blue	10	10
955	–	10q. black and buff	15	10
956	–	15q. black and green	20	10
957	–	25q. black and violet	75	15
958	–	65q. black and brown	1·25	35
959	–	80q. black and green	1·50	45
960	–	1l.10 black and purple	2·25	50
961	–	1l.60 black and blue	3·00	1·25
962	–	2l. black and pink	4·25	1·40
963	–	3l. black and grey	8·00	2·40

BUILDINGS: 10q. Peshkopi Hotel; 15q. Sanatorium, Tirana; 25q. "House of Rest", Pogradec; 65q. Partisans Sports Palace, Tirana; 80q. "House of Rest", Dajti Mountain; 1l.10. Palace of Culture, Tirana; 1l.60, Adriatic Hotel, Durres; 2l. Migjeni Theatre, Shkoder; 3l. "A. Moisiu" Cultural Palace, Durres.

1965. Evolution of Albanian Ships.

964	210	10q. green and light green	40	20
965	–	20q. bistre and green	55	20
966	–	30q. ultramarine and blue	75	35
967	–	40q. violet and light violet	1·00	45
968	–	50q. red and rose	2·10	55
969	–	1l. brown and ochre	4·25	1·00

DESIGNS: 20q. Punt; 30q. 19th-century sailing ship; 40q. 18th-century brig; 50q. Freighter "Vlora"; 1l. Illyrian galliots.

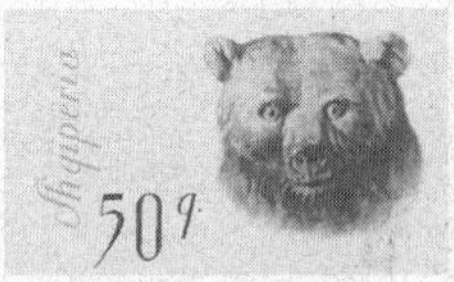
211 Head of Brown Bear

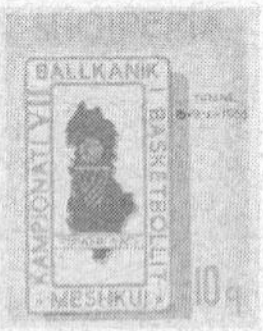
212 Championships Emblem

1965. Brown Bears. Different Bear designs as T 211.

970	–	10q. brown and buff	30	15
971	–	20q. brown and buff	75	20
972	–	30q. brown, red and buff	1·00	35
973	–	35q. brown and buff	1·25	40
974	–	40q. brown and buff	1·60	45
975	211	50q. brown and buff	2·50	50
976	–	55q. brown and buff	3·50	85
977	–	60q. brown, red and buff	5·00	2·75

The 10q. to 40q. are vert.

1965. 7th Balkan Basketball Championships, Tirana. Multicoloured.

978	10q. Type 212	20	10
979	20q. Competing players	40	15
980	30q. Clearing ball	85	20
981	50q. Attempted goal	2·10	25
982	1l.40 Medal and ribbon	4·25	1·00

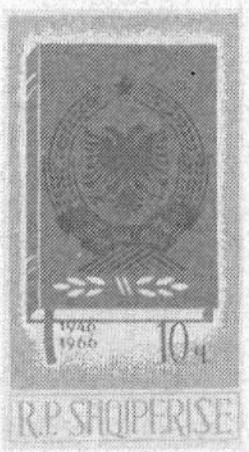
213 Arms on Book

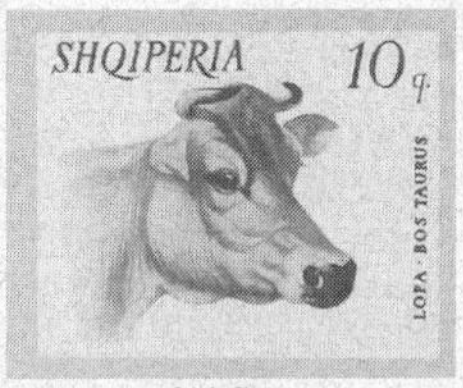
214 Cow

1966. 20th Anniv of Albanian People's Republic.

983	213	10q. gold, red and brown	15	10
984	–	20q. gold, blue & ultram	20	15
985	–	30q. gold, yellow & brown	75	20
986	–	60q. gold, lt grn & green	1·40	65
987	–	80q. gold, red and brown	2·25	75

DESIGNS (Arms and): 20q. Chimney stacks; 30q. Ear of corn; 60q. Hammer, sickle and open book; 80q. Industrial plant.

1966. Domestic Animals. Animals in natural colours; inscr in black: frame colours given.

988	214	10q. turquoise	30	20
989	–	20q. green	85	25
990	–	30q. blue	1·25	30
991	–	35q. lavender	1·40	35
992	–	40q. pink	1·75	35
993	–	50q. yellow	2·00	40
994	–	55q. blue	2·25	70
995	–	60q. yellow	4·50	95

ANIMALS—HORIZ. 20q. Pig; 30q. Sheep; 35q. Goat; 40q. Dog. VERT: 50q. Cat; 55q. Horse; 60q. Ass.

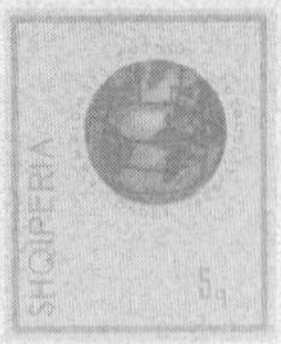

215 Football

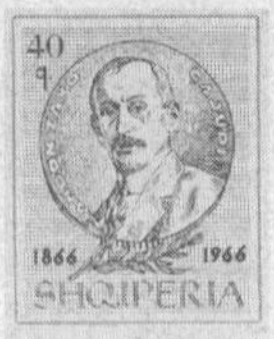

216 A. Z. Cajupi

1966. World Cup Football Championships (1st series).

996	**215**	5q. orange grey & buff	15	10
997	–	10q. multicoloured . . .	20	10
998	–	15q. blue, yellow & buff	25	15
999	–	20q. multicoloured . . .	35	20
1000	–	25q. sepia, red and buff	45	20
1001	–	30q. brown, green & buff	50	30
1002	–	35q. green, blue and buff	85	30
1003	–	40q. brown red and buff	90	35
1004	–	50q. multicoloured . . .	1·00	65
1005	–	70q. multicoloured . . .	1·40	90

DESIGNS—Footballer and map showing: 10q. Montevideo (1930); 15q. Rome (1934); 20q. Paris (1938); 25q. Rio de Janeiro (1950); 30q. Berne (1954); 35q. Stockholm (1958); 40q. Santiago (1962); 50q. London (1966); 70q. World Cup and football.

See also Nos. 1035/42.

1966. Birth Centenary of Andon Cajupi (poet).

1006	**216**	40q. indigo and blue . .	1·10	55
1007		1l.10 bronze and green	2·50	1·10

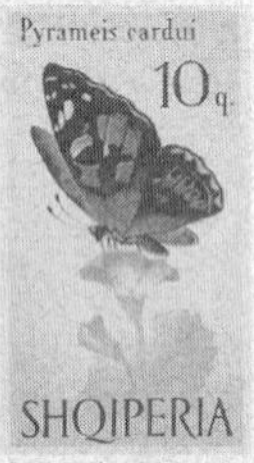

217 Painted Lady

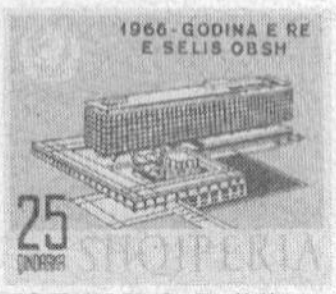

218 W.H.O. Building

1966. Butterflies and Dragonflies. Multicoloured.

1008		10q. Type **217**	35	20
1009		20q. "Calopteryx virgo" . .	50	20
1010		30q. Pale clouded yellow . .	70	20
1011		35q. Banded agrion	85	25
1012		40q. Banded agrion (different)	1·10	30
1013		50q. Swallowtail	1·50	40
1014		55q. Danube clouded yellow	2·00	50
1015		60q. Hungarian glider . . .	5·00	1·25

The 20, 35 and 40q. are dragonflies, remainder are butterflies.

1966. Inaug of W.H.O. Headquarters, Geneva.

1016	**218**	25q. black and blue . .	45	15
1017	–	35q. blue and orange . .	1·25	20
1018	–	60q. red, blue and green	1·60	35
1019	–	80q. blue, yellow & brn	2·75	65

DESIGNS—VERT: 35q. Ambulance and patient; 60q. Nurse and mother weighing baby. HORIZ: 80q. Medical equipment.

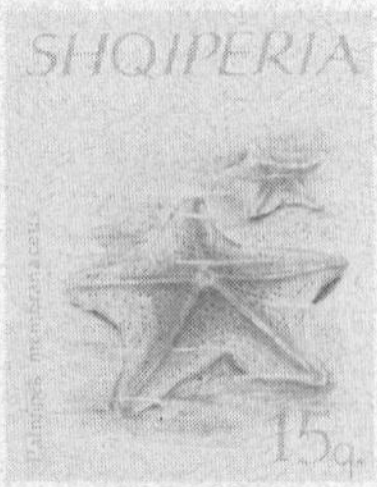

219 Leaf Star

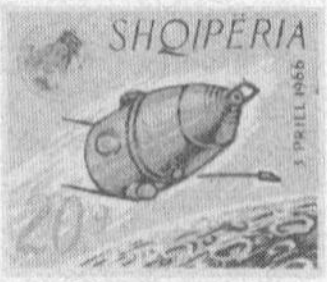

220 "Luna 10"

1966. "Starfish". Multicoloured.

1020		15q. Type **219**	30	15
1021		25q. Spiny Star	50	20
1022		35q. Brittle Star	1·10	25
1023		45q. Sea Star	1·60	30
1024		50q. Blood Star	1·75	40
1025		60q. Sea Cucumber	2·25	40
1026		70q. Sea Urchin	4·00	1·75

1966. "Luna 10". Launching.

1027	**220**	20q. multicoloured . . .	70	20
1028	–	30q. multicoloured . . .	90	25
1029	**220**	70q. multicoloured . . .	1·75	35
1030	–	80q. multicoloured . . .	3·50	1·00

DESIGN: 30, 80q. Earth, Moon and trajectory of "Luna 10".

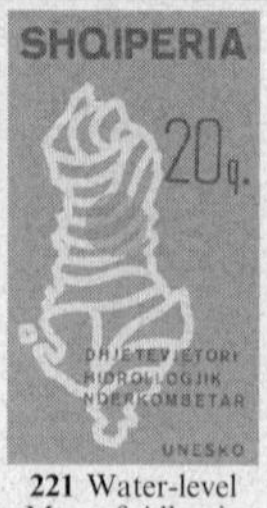

221 Water-level Map of Albania

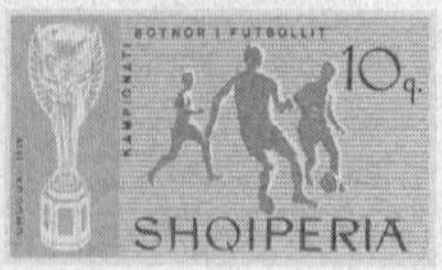

222 Footballers (Uruguay, 1930)

1966. International Hydrological Decade.

1031	**221**	20q. black, orge & red	50	20
1032	–	30q. multicoloured . . .	1·00	25
1033	–	70q. black and violet . .	2·10	40
1034	–	80q. multicoloured . . .	2·75	1·25

DESIGNS: 30q. Water scale and fields; 70q. Turbine and electricity pylon; 80q. Hydrological decade emblem.

1966. World Cup Football Championship (2nd series). Inscriptions and values in black.

1035	**222**	10q. purple and ochre	20	10
1036	–	20q. olive and blue . . .	30	15
1037	–	30q. slate and red . . .	75	15
1038	–	35q. red and blue . . .	85	20
1039	–	40q. brown and green . .	1·00	20
1040	–	50q. green and brown . .	1·25	50
1041	–	55q. green and mauve	1·25	95
1042	–	60q. ochre and red . . .	2·50	1·40

DESIGNS—Various footballers representing World Cup winners: 20q. Italy, 1934; 30q. Italy, 1938; 35q. Uruguay, 1950; 40q. West Germany, 1954; 50q. Brazil, 1958; 55q. Brazil, 1962; 60q. Football and names of 16 finalists in 1966 Championship.

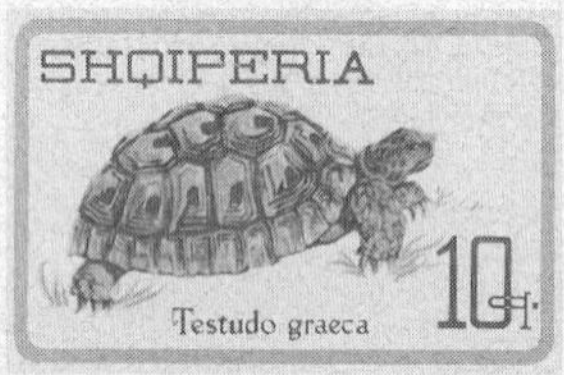

223 Tortoise

1966. Reptiles. Multicoloured.

1043		10q. Type **223**	20	15
1044		15q. Grass snake	30	20
1045		25q. Swamp tortoise	45	25
1046		30q. Lizard	55	30
1047		35q. Salamander	70	35
1048		45q. Green lizard	1·25	40
1049		50q. Slow-worm	1·25	75
1050		90q. Sand viper	3·25	1·40

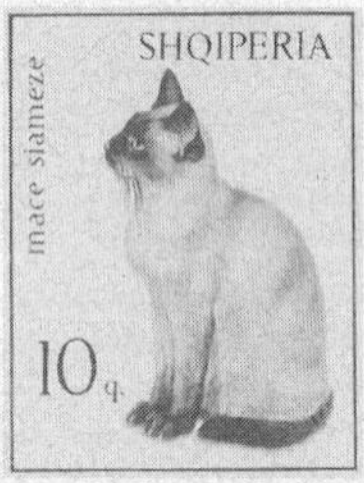

224 Siamese Cat

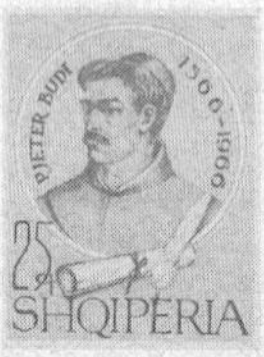

225 P. Budi (writer)

1966. Cats. Multicoloured.

1051		10q. Type **224**	25	15
1052		15q. Tabby	30	20
1053		25q. Kitten	90	30
1054		45q. Persian	1·75	40
1055		60q. Persian	2·25	90
1056		65q. Persian	2·50	1·00
1057		80q. Persian	3·25	1·25

Nos. 1053/7 are horiz.

1966. 400th Birth Anniv of P. Budi.

1058	**225**	25q. bronze and flesh . .	40	25
1059		1l.75 purple and green	3·25	1·90

226 U.N.E.S.C.O. Emblem

1966. 20th Anniv of U.N.E.S.C.O. Multicoloured.

1060		5q. Type **226**	20	15
1061		15q. Tulip and open book	35	20
1062		25q. Albanian dancers . . .	95	25
1063		1l.55 Jug and base of column	4·75	1·60

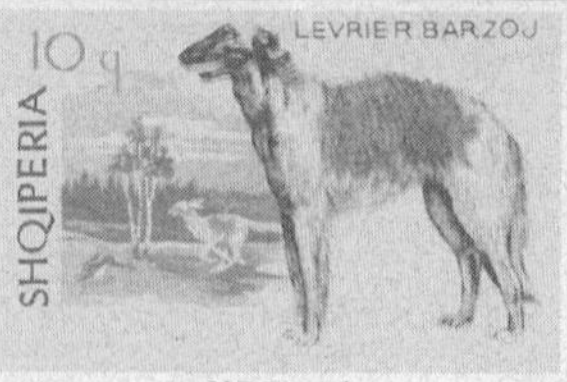

227 Borzoi

1966. Dogs. Multicoloured.

1064		10q. Type **227**	40	15
1065		15q. Kuvasz	50	20
1066		25q. Setter	1·25	25
1067		45q. Cocker spaniel	1·90	85
1068		60q. Bulldog	2·00	1·00
1069		65q. St. Bernard	2·75	1·10
1070		80q. Dachshund	3·50	1·60

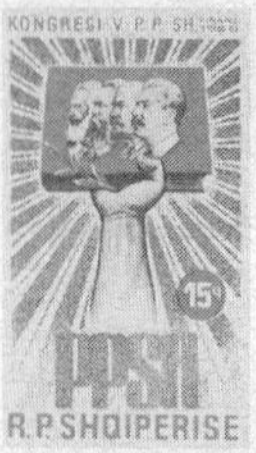

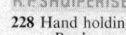

228 Hand holding Book

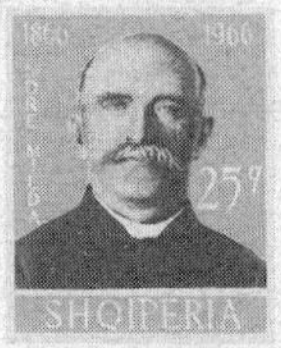

229 Ndre Mjeda (poet)

1966. 5th Workers Party Congress, Tirana. Multicoloured.

1071		15q. Type **228**	40	15
1072		25q. Emblems of agriculture and industry	85	15
1073		65q. Hammer and sickle, wheat and industrial skyline	1·90	35
1074		95q. Hands holding banner on bayonet and implements	3·25	65

1966. Birth Centenary of Ndre Mjeda.

1075	**229**	25q. brown and blue . .	65	20
1076		1l.75 brown and green	3·75	1·40

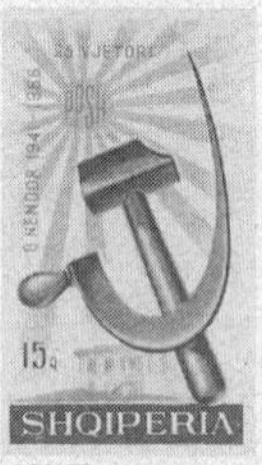

230 Hammer and Sickle

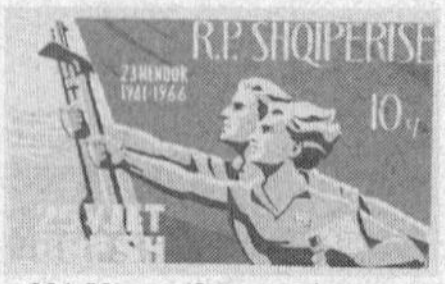

231 Young Communists and Banner

1966. 25th Anniv of Albanian Young Communists' Union. Multicoloured.

1077		15q. Type **230**	35	10
1078		25q. Soldier leading attack	75	10
1079		65q. Industrial worker . . .	1·60	30
1080		95q. Agricultural and industrial vista	2·75	55

1966. 25th Anniv of Young Communists' Union. Multicoloured.

1081		5q. Manifesto (vert)	10	10
1082		10q. Type **231**	20	10
1083		1l.85 Partisans and banner (vert)	3·25	1·10

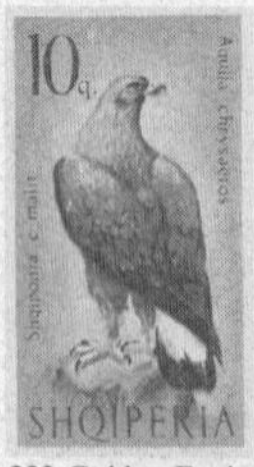

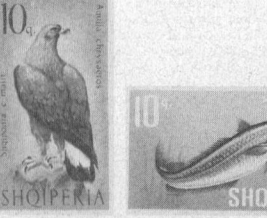

232 Golden Eagle

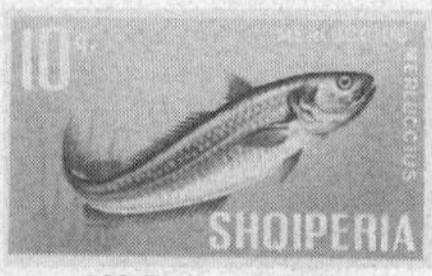

233 European Hake

1966. Birds of Prey. Multicoloured,

1084		10q. Type **232**	75	25
1085		15q. White-tailed sea eagle	1·10	40
1086		25q. Griffon vulture	1·90	90
1087		40q. Northern sparrow hawk	2·75	1·10
1088		50q. Osprey	3·50	1·40
1089		70q. Egyptian vulture . . .	4·75	2·00
1090		90q. Common kestrel . . .	5·25	2·75

1967. Fishes. Multicoloured.

1091		10q. Type **233**	30	15
1092		15q. Striped red mullet . . .	45	15
1093		25q. Opali	1·00	20
1094		40q. Atlantic wolffish . . .	1·25	30
1095		65q. Lumpsucker	1·60	70
1096		80q. Swordfish	2·50	80
1097		1l.15 Short-spined sea-scorpion	2·75	1·40

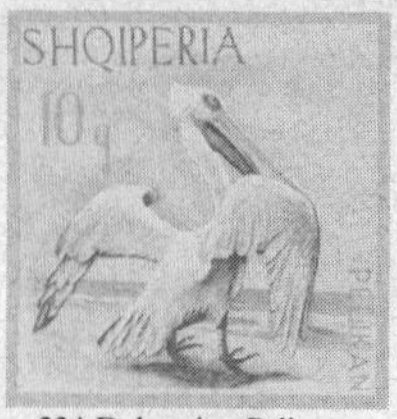

234 Dalmatian Pelicans

1967. Dalmatian Pelicans. Multicoloured.

1098		10q. Type **234**	35	25
1099		15q. Three pelicans	75	35
1100		25q. Pelican and chicks at nest	2·00	55
1101		50q. Pelicans "taking off" and airborne	4·25	70
1102		2l. Pelican "yawning" . . .	11·00	3·50

235 "Camellia williamsi"

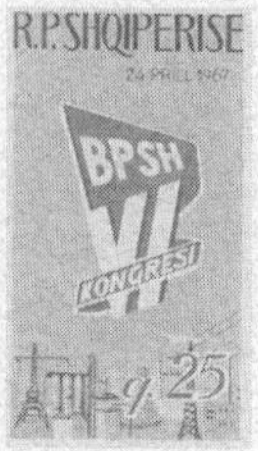

236 Congress Emblem

1967. Flowers. Multicoloured.

1103		5q. Type **235**	20	10
1104		10q. "Chrysanthemum indicum"	25	15
1105		15q. "Althaea rosea" . . .	30	15
1106		25q. "Abutilon striatum" . .	90	20
1107		35q. "Paeonia chinensis" . .	1·25	20
1108		65q. "Gladiolus gandavensis"	2·00	40
1109		80q. "Freesia hybrida" . . .	2·50	65
1110		1l.15 "Dianthus caryophyllus"	2·75	1·75

1967. 6th Trade Unions Congress, Tirana.

1111	**236**	25q. red, sepia and lilac	90	15
1112		1l.75 red, green and grey	4·00	1·60

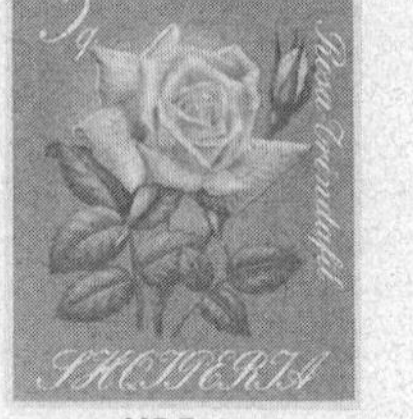

237 Rose

1967. Roses. Designs as T **237**.

1113	**237**	5q. multicoloured . . .	25	10
1114	–	10q. multicoloured . . .	55	10
1115	–	15q. multicoloured . . .	70	15
1116	–	25q. multicoloured . . .	85	15
1117	–	35q. multicoloured . . .	1·00	25
1118	–	65q. multicoloured . . .	1·50	40
1119	–	80q. multicoloured . . .	1·90	50
1120	–	1l.65 multicoloured . . .	4·50	1·25

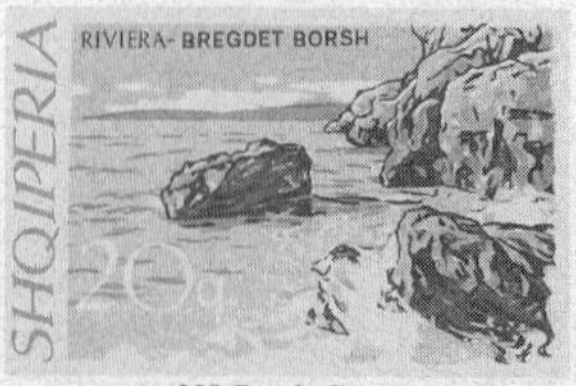

238 Borsh Coast

1967. Albanian Riviera. Multicoloured.

1121		15q. Butrinti (vert)	40	20
1122		20q. Type **238**	50	20
1123		25q. Piqeras village	90	30
1124		45q. Coastal view	1·40	30
1125		50q. Himara coast	1·60	40
1126		65q. Fishing boat, Saranda	2·25	55
1127		80q. Dhermi	2·50	1·00
1128		1l. Sunset at sea (vert) . . .	4·25	1·60

239 Fawn

1967. Roe Deer. Multicoloured.
1129	15q. Type **239**	50	15
1130	20q. Head of buck (vert)	50	20
1131	25q. Head of doe (vert)	95	20
1132	30q. Doe and fawn	95	25
1133	35q. Doe and new-born fawn	1·40	30
1134	40q. Young buck (vert)	1·40	35
1135	65q. Buck and doe (vert)	2·75	1·00
1136	70q. Running deer	3·50	1·40

240 Costumes of Malesia e Madhe Region   **241 Battle Scene and Newspaper**

1967. National Costumes. Multicoloured.
1137	15q. Type **240**	35	15
1138	20q. Zadrima	45	20
1139	25q. Kukesi	55	20
1140	45q. Dardhe	70	35
1141	50q. Myzeqe	75	70
1142	65q. Tirana	1·40	85
1143	80q. Dropulli	1·75	1·00
1144	1l. Laberise	2·25	1·25

1967. 25 Years of the Albanian Popular Press. Mult.
1145	25q. Type **241**	70	20
1146	75q. Newspapers and printery	1·90	50
1147	2l. Workers with newspaper	4·25	1·60

242 University, Torch and Open Book   **243 Soldiers and Flag**

1967. 10th Anniv of Tirana University.
1148	**242** 25q. multicoloured	45	30
1149	1l.75 multicoloured	2·75	1·10

1967. 25th Anniv of Albanian Democratic Front. Multicoloured.
1150	15q. Type **243**	25	15
1151	65q. Pick, rifle and flag	1·00	25
1152	1l.20 Torch and open book	1·90	75

244 Grey Rabbits

1967. Rabbit-breeding. Multicoloured.
1153	15q. Type **244**	20	10
1154	20q. Black and white rabbit (vert)	30	15
1155	25q. Brown hare	75	15
1156	35q. Brown rabbits	1·10	20
1157	40q. Common rabbits	1·40	20
1158	50q. Grey rabbit (vert)	1·75	65
1159	65q. Head of white rabbit (vert)	2·50	85
1160	1l. White rabbit	3·50	1·25

245 "Shkoder Wedding" (detail, Kole Idromeno)

1967. Albanian Paintings.
1161	**245** 15q. multicoloured	55	10
1162	– 20q. multicoloured	80	10
1163	– 25q. multicoloured	1·10	10
1164	– 45q. multicoloured	2·25	10
1165	– 50q. multicoloured	2·40	15
1166	– 65q. multicoloured	3·25	55
1167	– 80q. multicoloured	4·25	80
1168	– 1l. multicoloured	7·25	1·10

DESIGNS—VERT: 20q. "Head of the Prophet David" (detail, 16th-century fresco); 45q. Ancient mosaic head (from Durres); 50q. Detail, 16th-century icon (30×51 mm); 1l. "Our Sister" (K. Idromeno). HORIZ (51×30 mm): 25q. "Commandos of the Hakmarrja Battalion" (S. Shijaku); 65q. "Co-operative" (farm women, Z. Shoshi); 80q. "Street in Korce" (V. Mio).

246 Lenin and Stalin

1967. 50th Anniv of October Revolution. Mult.
1169	15q. Type **246**	20	15
1170	25q. Lenin with soldiers	65	15
1171	50q. Lenin addressing meeting	1·10	25
1172	1l.10 Revolutionaries	2·75	70

The 25q. and 50q. are vert.

247 Common Turkey   **248 First Aid**

1967. Domestic Fowl. Multicoloured.
1173	15q. Type **247**	20	10
1174	20q. Goose	50	10
1175	25q. Hen	75	15
1176	45q. Cockerel	1·25	20
1177	50q. Helmeted guineafowl	1·40	50
1178	65q. Greylag goose (horiz)	1·90	65
1179	80q. Mallard (horiz)	2·50	85
1180	1l. Chicks (horiz)	3·50	1·25

1967. 6th Red Cross Congress, Tirana. Mult.
1181	15q.+5q. Type **248**	1·00	65
1182	25q.+5q. Stretcher case	1·90	1·00
1183	65q.+25q. Heart patient	5·00	3·50
1184	80q.+40q. Nurse holding child	8·75	5·25

249 Arms of Skanderbeg   **250 Winter Olympic Emblem**

1967. 500th Death Anniv of Castriota Skanderbeg (patriot) (1st issue). Multicoloured.
1185	10q. Type **249**	20	10
1186	15q. Skanderbeg	20	15
1187	25q. Helmet and sword	50	15
1188	30q. Kruja Castle	65	20
1189	35q. Petrela Castle	75	25
1190	65q. Berati Castle	1·40	30
1191	80q. Meeting of chiefs	1·75	65
1192	90q. Battle of Albulena	1·90	2·25

See also Nos. 1200/7.

1967. Winter Olympic Games, Grenoble. Mult.
1193	15q. Type **250**	15	10
1194	25q. Ice hockey	20	15
1195	30q. Figure skating	25	15
1196	50q. Skiing (slalom)	40	20
1197	80q. Skiing (downhill)	70	30
1198	1l. Ski jumping	1·60	40

251 Skanderbeg Memorial, Tirana

1968. 500th Death Anniv of Castriota Skanderbeg (2nd issue). Multicoloured.
1200	10q. Type **251**	25	10
1201	15q. Skanderbeg portrait	30	15
1202	25q. Skanderbeg portrait (different)	90	15
1203	30q. Equestrian statue, Kruja	1·10	20
1204	35q. Skanderbeg and mountains	1·40	20
1205	65q. Bust of Skanderbeg	2·50	20
1206	80q. Title page of biography	2·75	85
1207	90q. "Skanderbeg battling with the Turks" (painting)	3·50	1·25

The 35q. and 90q. are horiz.

252 Alpine Dianthus

1968. Flowers. Multicoloured.
1208	15q. Type **252**	20	10
1209	20q. Chinese dianthus	25	15
1210	25q. Pink carnation	30	15
1211	50q. Red carnation and bud	85	20
1212	80q. Two red carnations	1·40	50
1213	1l.10 Yellow carnations	1·90	85

253 Ear of Wheat and Electricity Pylon

1968. 5th Agricultural Co-operative Congress. Mult.
1214	25q. Type **253**	40	15
1215	65q. Tractor (horiz)	1·25	45
1216	1l.10 Cow	1·90	40

254 Long-horned Goat

1968. Goats. Multicoloured.
1217	15q. Zane female	20	10
1218	20q. Kid	20	10
1219	25q. Long-haired capore	30	15
1220	30q. Black goat at rest	35	15
1221	40q. Kids dancing	75	20
1222	50q. Red and piebald goats	90	20
1223	80q. Long-haired ankara	1·60	30
1224	1l.40 Type **254**	2·75	85

The 15q., 20q. and 25q. are vert.

255 Zef Jubani   **256 Doctor using Stethoscope**

1968. 150th Birth Anniv of Zef Jubani (patriot).
1225	**255** 25q. brown and yellow	20	15
1226	1l.75 blue, black & vio	2·75	65

1968. 20th Anniv of W.H.O.
1227	**256** 25q. red and green	35	10
1228	– 65q. black, blue & yellow	75	20
1229	– 1l.10 brown and black	1·25	35

DESIGNS—HORIZ: 65q. Hospital and microscope. VERT: 1l.10, Mother feeding child.

257 Servicewoman

1968. 25th Anniv of Albanian Women's Union.
1230	**257** 15q. red and orange	25	15
1231	– 25q. turquoise and green	35	20
1232	– 60q. brown and ochre	1·00	30
1233	– 1l. violet and light violet	1·75	55

DESIGNS: 25q. Teacher; 60q. Farm-girl; 1l. Factory-worker.

258 Karl Marx

1968. 150th Birth Anniv of Karl Marx. Mult.
1234	15q. Type **258**	40	20
1235	25q. Marx addressing students	85	20
1236	65q. "Das Kapital", "Communist Manifesto" and marchers	1·60	65
1237	95q. Karl Marx	3·50	85

259 Heliopsis

1968. Flowers. Multicoloured.
1238	15q. Type **259**	10	10
1239	20q. Red flax	15	10
1240	25q. Orchid	20	10
1241	30q. Gloxinia	30	15
1242	40q. Orange lily	50	15
1243	80q. Hippeastrum	1·40	25
1244	1l.40 Purple magnolia	2·75	90

260 A. Frasheri and Torch

1968. 90th Anniv of Prizren Defence League.
1245	**260** 25q. black and green	40	15
1246	– 40q. multicoloured	95	20
1247	– 85q. multicoloured	1·60	40

DESIGNS: 40q. League headquarters; 85q. Frasheri's manifesto and partisans.

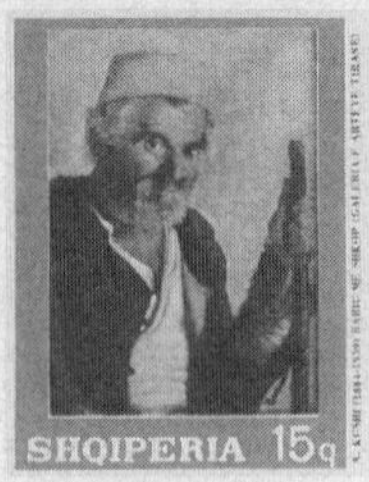

261 "Shepherd" (A. Kushi)

1968. Paintings in Tirana Gallery. Multicoloured.

1248	15q. Type **261**	15	10
1249	20q. "Tirana" (V. Mio) (horiz)	20	10
1250	25q. "Highlander" (G. Madhi)	25	15
1251	40q. "Refugees" (A. Buza)	75	15
1252	80q. "Partisans at Shahin Matrakut" (S. Xega)	1·40	50
1253	1l.50 "Old Man" (S. Papadhimitri)	2·75	1·00
1254	1l.70 "Shkoder Gate" (S. Rrota)	3·50	1·25

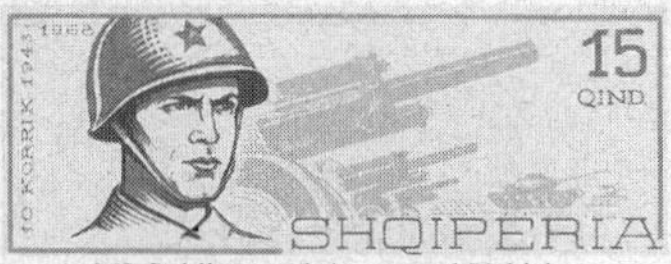

262 Soldiers and Armoured Vehicles

1968. 25th Anniv of People's Army. Multicoloured.

1256	15q. Type **262**	35	15
1257	25q. Sailor and naval craft	1·25	30
1258	65q. Pilot and Ilyushin Il-28 and Mikoyan Gurevich MiG-17 aircraft (vert)	2·50	85
1259	95q. Soldier and patriots	3·75	1·25

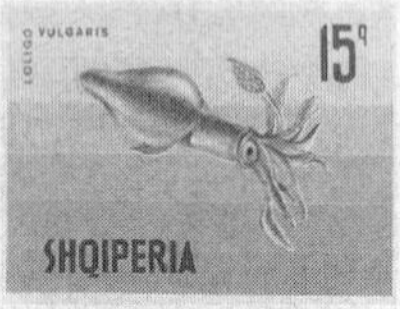

263 Common Squid

1968. Marine Fauna. Multicoloured.

1260	15q. Type **263**	25	10
1261	20q. Common lobster	20	10
1262	25q. Common northern whelk	65	15
1263	50q. Edible crab	1·00	40
1264	70q. Spiny lobster	1·40	65
1265	80q. Common green crab	1·75	85
1266	90q. Norwegian lobster	1·90	1·40

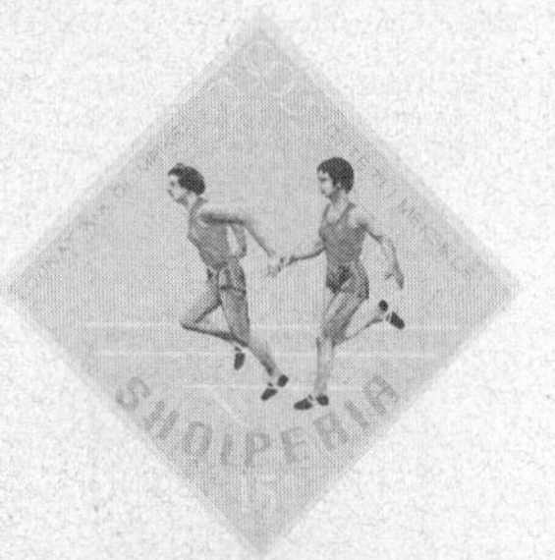

264 Relay-racing

1968. Olympic Games, Mexico. Multicoloured.

1267	15q. Type **264**	15	10
1268	20q. Running	20	10
1269	25q. Throwing the discus	25	10
1270	30q. Horse-jumping	30	15
1271	40q. High-jumping	35	15
1272	50q. Hurdling	40	20
1273	80q. Football	80	30
1274	1l.40 High diving	1·75	85

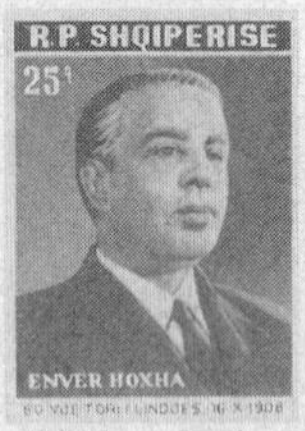

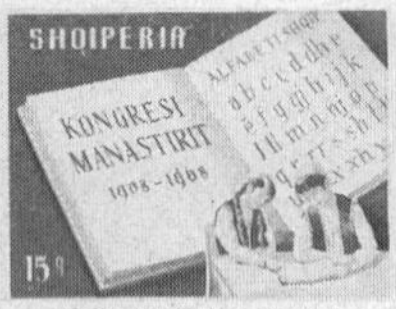

265 Enver Hoxha (Party Secretary)

266 Alphabet Book

1968. Enver Hoxha's 60th Birthday.

1276	**265** 25q. blue	35	25
1277	35q. purple	85	30
1278	80q. violet	1·75	90
1279	1l.10 brown	1·90	1·40

1968. 60th Anniv of Monastir Language Congress.

1281	**266** 15q. lake and green	65	15
1282	85q. brown and green	3·25	55

267 Bohemian Waxwing

1968. Birds. Multicoloured.

1283	15q. Type **267**	55	20
1284	20q. Rose-coloured starling	75	20
1285	25q. River kingfishers	1·10	30
1286	50q. Long-tailed tit	1·60	75
1287	80q. Wallcreeper	3·25	90
1288	1l.10 Bearded reedling	4·00	1·40

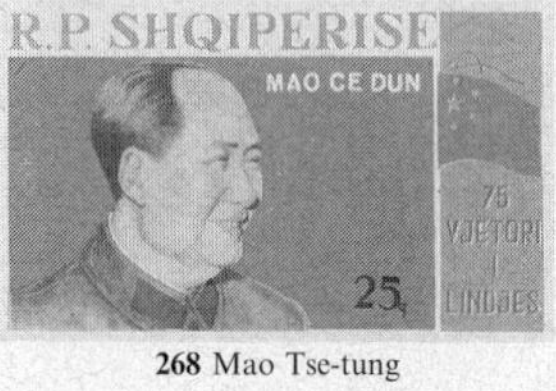

268 Mao Tse-tung

1968. Mao Tse-tung's 75th Birthday.

1289	**268** 25q. black, red and gold	85	30
1290	1l.75 black, red and gold	4·25	1·75

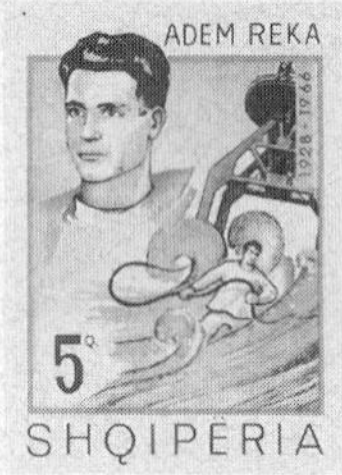

269 Adem Reka (dock foreman)

1969. Contemporary Heroes. Multicoloured.

1291	5q. Type **269**	10	10
1292	10q. Pjeter Lleshi (telegraph linesman)	15	10
1293	15q. M. Shehu and M. Kepi (fire victims)	20	15
1294	25q. Shkurte Vata (railway worker)	2·25	35
1295	65q. Agron Elezi (earthquake victim)	95	25
1296	80q. Ismet Bruca (schoolteacher)	1·25	40
1297	1l.30 Fuat Cela (blind Co-op leader)	1·90	50

270 Meteorological Equipment

1969. 20th Anniv of Albanian Hydro-meteorology. Multicoloured.

1298	15q. Type **270**	65	20
1299	25q. "Arrow" indicator	1·00	25
1300	1l.60 Meteorological balloon and isobar map	4·75	1·50

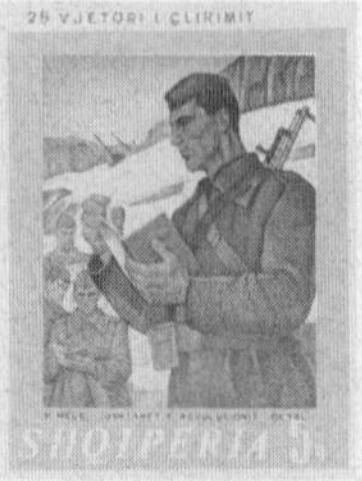

271 "Student Revolutionaries" (P. Mele)

1969. Albanian Paintings since 1944. Mult.

1301	5q. Type **271**	15	10
1302	25q. "Partisans 1914" (F. Haxhiu)	20	10
1303	65q. "Steel Mill" (C. Ceka)	75	15
1304	80q. "Reconstruction" (V. Kilica)	85	30
1305	1l.10 "Harvest" (N. Jonuzi)	1·40	35
1306	1l.15 "Seaside Terraces" (S. Kaceli)	1·75	1·00

SIZES: The 25q., 80q., 1l.10 and 1l.15 are 50×30 mm. Nos. 1302/6 are horiz.

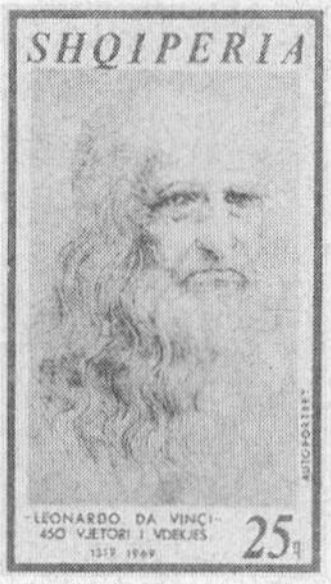

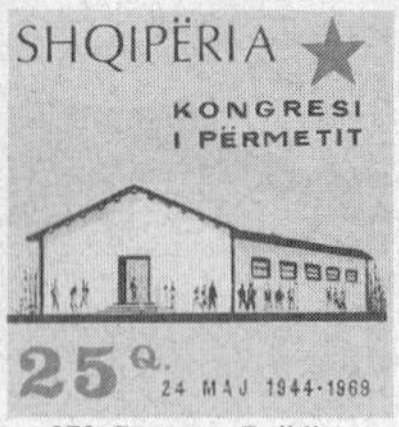

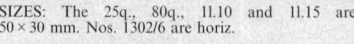

272 "Self-portrait"

273 Congress Building

1969. 450th Death Anniv of Leonardo da Vinci.

1308	**272** 25q. agate, brown & gold	30	15
1309	– 35q. agate, brown & gold	65	20
1310	– 40q. agate, brown & gold	85	20
1311	– 1l. multicoloured	1·90	85
1312	– 2l. agate, brown & gold	3·75	1·75

DESIGNS—VERT: 35q. "Lilies"; 1l. "Portrait of Beatrice"; 2l. "Portrait of a Lady". HORIZ: 40q. Design for "Helicopter".

1969. 25th Anniv of Permet Congress. Mult.

1314	25q. Type **273**	35	25
1315	2l.25 Two partisans	4·25	2·75

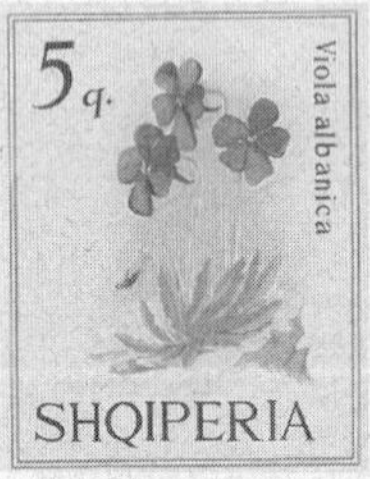

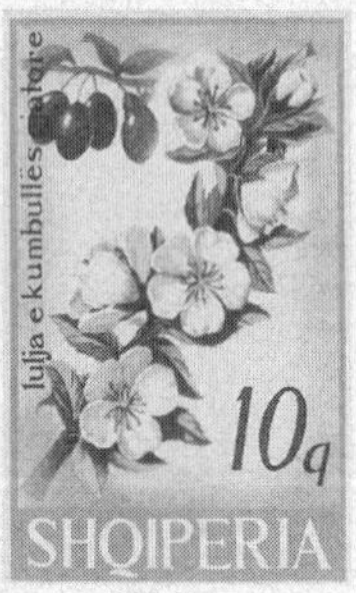

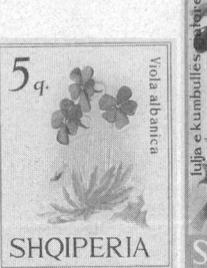

274 "Viola albanica"

275 Plum

1969. Flowers. Viola Family. Multicoloured.

1317	5q. Type **274**	10	10
1318	10q. "Viola hortensis"	15	10
1319	15q. "Viola heterophylla"	20	15
1320	20q. "Viola hortensis" (different)	25	20
1321	25q. "Viola odorata"	35	20
1322	80q. "Viola hortensis" (different)	1·25	85
1323	1l.95 "Viola hortensis" (different)	2·25	1·75

1969. Fruit Trees. Blossom and Fruit. Mult.

1324	10q. Type **275**	15	20
1325	15q. Lemon	15	15
1326	25q. Pomegranate	50	15
1327	50q. Cherry	1·00	20
1328	80q. Apricot	1·75	85
1329	1l.20 Apple	2·75	1·40

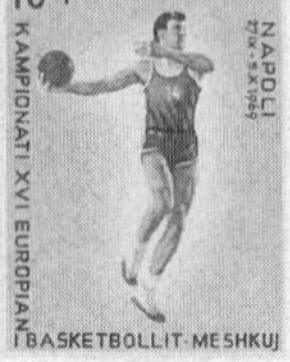

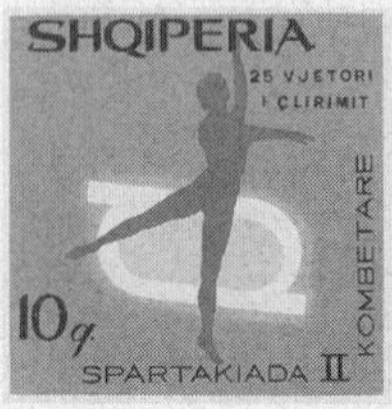

276 Throwing the Ball

277 Gymnastics

1969. 16th European Basketball Championships, Naples. Multicoloured.

1330	10q. Type **276**	20	10
1331	15q. Trying for goal	20	10
1332	25q. Ball and net (horiz)	35	15
1333	80q. Scoring a goal	1·10	25
1334	2l.20 Intercepting a pass	2·75	1·00

1969. National Spartakiad. Multicoloured.

1335	5q. Pickaxe, rifle, flag and stadium	15	10
1336	10q. Type **277**	15	10
1337	15q. Running	20	10
1338	20q. Pistol-shooting	25	15
1339	25q. Swimmer on starting block	30	15
1340	80q. Cycling	1·00	25
1341	95q. Football	1·25	45

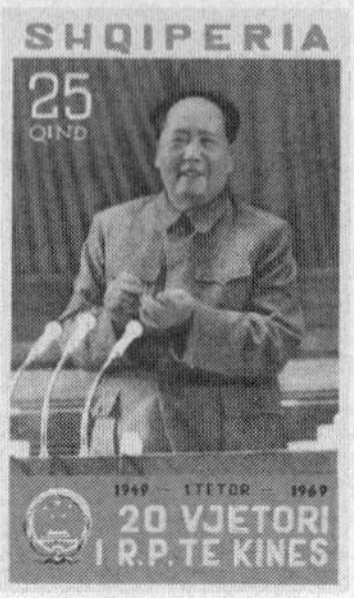

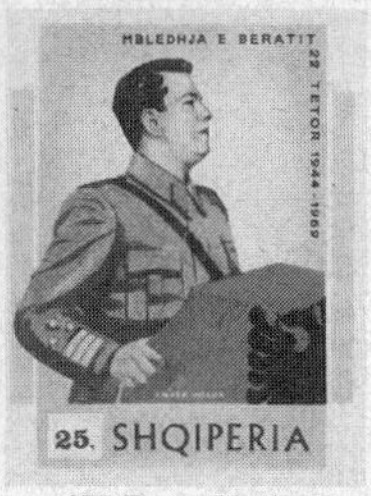

278 Mao Tse-tung

279 Enver Hoxha

1969. 20th Anniv of Chinese People's Republic. Multicoloured

1342	25q. Type **278**	1·25	50
1343	85q. Steel ladle and control room (horiz)	4·00	1·25
1344	1l.40 Rejoicing crowd	6·00	2·25

1969. 25th Anniv of 2nd National Liberation Council Meeting, Berat. Multicoloured.

1345	25q. Type **279**	25	15
1346	80q. Star and Constitution	85	20
1347	1l.45 Freedom-fighters	1·60	40

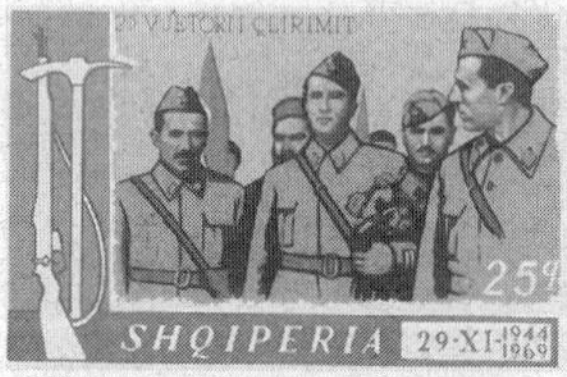

280 Entry of Provisional Government, Tirana

1969. 25th Anniv of Liberation. Multicoloured.

1348	25q. Type **280**	20	10
1349	30q. Oil refinery	35	10
1350	35q. Combine harvester	75	15
1351	45q. Hydrolectric power station	1·10	15
1352	55q. Soldier and partisans	1·60	65
1353	1l.10 People rejoicing	2·75	1·25

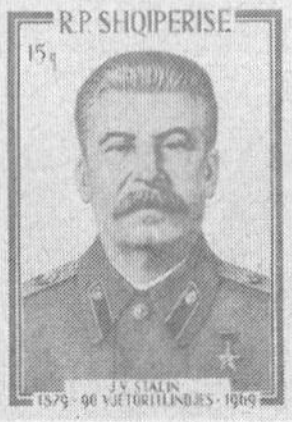

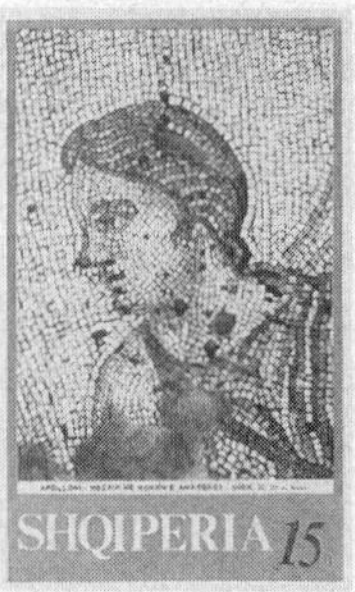

281 Stalin

282 Head of Woman

1969. 90th Birth Anniv of Joseph Stalin.

1354	**281** 15q. lilac	15	10
1355	25q. blue	20	15
1356	1l. brown	1·10	30
1357	1l.10 blue	1·25	35

1969. Mosaics. (1st series). Multicoloured.

1358	15q. Type **282**	15	10
1359	25q. Floor pattern	20	10
1360	80q. Bird and tree	85	20
1361	1l.10 Diamond floor pattern	1·10	30
1362	1l.20 Corn in oval pattern	1·60	35

Nos. 1359/61 are horiz.

See also Nos. 1391/6, 1564/70 and 1657/62.

283 Manifesto and Congress Building   **285** "Lilium cernum"

284 "25" and Workers

1970. 50th Anniv of Lushnje Congress.
1363 **283** 25q. black, red and grey . . 30 20
1364 – 11.25 black, yell & grn 1·90 85
DESIGN: 11.25, Lushnje postmark of 1920.

1970. 25th Anniv of Albanian Trade Unions.
1365 **284** 25q. multicoloured . . . 30 15
1366 11.75 multicoloured . . . 1·90 90

1970. Lilies. Multicoloured.
1367 5q. Type **285** 25 10
1368 15q. "Lilium candidum" . . 40 10
1369 25q. "Lilium regale" . . 70 20
1370 80q. "Lilium martagon" . . 1·75 30
1371 11.10 "Lilium tigrinum" . . 2·25 75
1372 11.15 "Lilium albanicum" . 2·50 90
Nos. 1370/2 are horiz.

286 Lenin

1970. Birth Cent of Lenin. Each blk, silver & red.
1373 5q. Type **286** 10 10
1374 15q. Lenin making speech 15 15
1375 25q. As worker . . . 20 15
1376 95q. As revolutionary . . 95 35
1377 11.10 Saluting . . . . . 1·40 40
Nos. 1374/6 are horiz.

287 Frontier Guard

1970. 25th Anniv of Frontier Force.
1378 **287** 25q. multicoloured . . . 50 10
1379 11.25 multicoloured . . 2·00 75

288 Jules Rimet Cup

1970. World Cup Football Championship, Mexico. Multicoloured.
1380 5q. Type **288** 10 10
1381 10q. Aztec Stadium 15 10
1382 15q. Three footballers . . 20 10
1383 25q. Heading goal 25 15
1384 65q. Two footballers . . 40 20
1385 80q. Two footballers . . 1·00 25
1386 2l. Two footballers . . 2·50 45

289 New U.P.U. Headquarters Building

1970. New U.P.U. Headquarters Building, Berne.
1388 **289** 25q. blue, black & lt
blue 20 15
1389 11.10 pink, black & orge 1·25 35
1390 11.15 turq, blk & grn . . 1·40 45

290 Birds and Grapes

1970. Mosaics (2nd series). Multicoloured.
1391 5q. Type **290** 15 10
1392 10q. Waterfowl 20 10
1393 20q. Pheasant and tree
stump 20 10
1394 25q. Bird and leaves 30 15
1395 65q. Fish 90 25
1396 21.25 Peacock (vert) . . . 2·25 85

291 Harvesters and Dancers   **292** Partisans going into Battle

1970. 25th Anniv of Agrarian Reform.
1397 **291** 15q. lilac and black . . . 20 10
1398 – 25q. blue and black . . 25 10
1399 – 80q. brown and black . . 85 20
1400 – 11.30 brown and black 1·25 35
DESIGNS: 25q. Ploughed fields and open-air conference; 80q. Cattle and newspapers; 11.30, Combine-harvester and official visit.

1970. 50th Anniv of Battle of Vlore.
1401 **292** 15q. brown, orge &
black 20 10
1402 – 25q. brown, yell & black 30 15
1403 – 11.60 myrtle, grn & blk 1·40 85
DESIGNS: 25q. Victory parade; 11.60, Partisans.

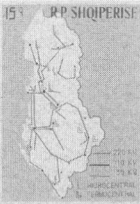

293 "The Harvesters" (I. Sulovari)   **294** Electrification Map

1970. 25th Anniv of Liberation. Prize-winning Paintings. Multicoloured.
1404 5q. Type **293** 10 10
1405 15q. "Return of the
Partisan" (D. Trebicka) 15 10
1406 25q. "The Miners"
(N. Zajmi) 20 10
1407 65q. "Instructing the
Partisans" (H. Nallbani) 35 20
1408 95q. "Making Plans"
(V. Kilica) . . . 85 50
1409 2l. "The Machinist"
(Z. Shoshi) . . . 2·50 90
The 15q. and 2l. are vert.

1970. Rural Electrification Completion. Mult.
1411 15q. Type **294** 20 10
1412 25q. Lamp and graph . . . 25 15
1413 80q. Erecting power lines . . 85 20
1414 11.10 Uses of electricity . . 1·40 50

295 Engels   **296** Beethoven's Birthplace

295a Tractor Factory, Tirana

1970. 150th Birth Anniv of Friedrich Engels.
1415 **295** 25q. blue and bistre . . 25 15
1416 – 11.10 purple and bistre 1·25 55
1417 – 11.15 olive and bistre 1·25 70
DESIGNS: 11.10, Engels as a young man; 11.15, Engels making speech.

1971. Industry. Multicoloured.
1417a 10q. Type **295a** . . . . £130 75·00
1417b 15q. Fertiliser factory, Fier £130 75·00
1417c 20q. Superphosphate
factory, Lac (vert) . . . £130 75·00
1417d 25q. Cement factory,
Elbasan . . . . £130 75·00

1970. Birth Bicentenary of Beethoven.
1418 **296** 5q. violet and gold . . 20 10
1419 – 15q. purple and silver . . 20 20
1420 – 25q. green and gold . . 50 20
1421 – 65q. purple and silver . . 1·00 50
1422 – 11.10 blue and gold . . 1·50 50
1423 – 11.80 black and silver . . 3·00 1·00
DESIGNS—VERT: Beethoven: 15q. In silhouette; 25q. As young man; 65q. Full-face; 11.10, Profile. HORIZ: 11.80, Stage performance of "Fidelio".

297 Republican Emblem

1971. 25th Anniv of Republic.
1424 **297** 15q. multicoloured . . . 10 10
1425 – 25q. multicoloured . . . 15 10
1426 – 80q. black, gold & green 90 15
1427 – 11.30 black, gold & brn 1·25 65
DESIGNS: 25q. Proclamation; 80q. Enver Hoxha; 11.30, Patriots.

298 "Storming the Barricades"

1971. Centenary of Paris Commune.
1428 – 25q. blue and deep blue 40 10
1429 – 50q. green and grey . . 50 20
1430 **298** 65q. chestnut and brown 80 20
1431 – 11.10 lilac and violet . . 1·50 80
DESIGNS—VERT: 25q. "La Marseillaise"; 50q. Women Communards. HORIZ: 11.10, Firing squad.

299 "Conflict of Race"   **300** Tulip

1971. Racial Equality Year.
1432 **299** 5q. black and brown . . 20 15
1433 – 11.10 black and red . . . 85 25
1434 – 11.15 black and red . . . 95 30
DESIGNS—VERT: 11.10, Heads of three races; 11.15, Freedom fighters.

1971. Hybrid Tulips.
1435 **300** 5q. multicoloured . . . 15 10
1436 – 10q. multicoloured . . . 15 10
1437 – 15q. multicoloured . . . 20 10
1438 – 20q. multicoloured . . . 20 10
1439 – 25q. multicoloured . . . 55 15
1440 – 80q. multicoloured . . . 1·40 20

1441 – 1l. multicoloured . . . 1·90 65
1442 – 11.45 multicoloured . . . 3·50 1·40
DESIGNS: 10q. to 11.45, Different varieties of tulips.

301 "Postrider"   **302** Globe and Satellite (1970)

1971. 500th Birth Anniv of Albrecht Durer (painter and engraver).
1443 **301** 10q. black and green . . . 15 10
1444 – 15q. black and blue . . 30 10
1445 – 25q. black and blue . . 50 15
1446 – 45q. black and purple . . 85 15
1447 – 65q. multicoloured . . . 1·25 25
1448 – 21.40 multicoloured . . . 3·25 1·00
DESIGNS—VERT: 15q. "Three Peasants"; 25q. "Peasant Dancers"; 45q. "The Bagpiper". HORIZ: 65q. "View of Kalchreut"; 21.40, "View of Trient".

1971. Chinese Space Achievements. Multicoloured.
1450 60q. Type **302** 75 20
1451 11.20 Public Building, Tirana 1·25 30
1452 21.20 Globe and satellite
(1971) . . . . . . 2·50 40
The date on No. 1451 refers to the passage of Chinese satellite over Tirana.

303 Mao Tse-tung

1971. 50th Anniv of Chinese Communist Party. Multicoloured.
1454 25q. Type **303** 70 20
1455 11.05 Party Birthplace
(horiz) . . . . . . 1·75 70
1456 11.20 Chinese celebrations
(horiz) . . . . . . 2·50 1·00

304 Crested Tit

1971. Birds. Multicoloured.
1457 5q. Type **304** 25 20
1458 10q. European serin 30 20
1459 15q. Linnet 40 20
1460 25q. Firecrest 60 20
1461 45q. Rock thrush 90 25
1462 60q. Blue tit . . . . . . 1·40 60
1463 21.40 Chaffinch . . . . . 5·25 4·00

305 Running

1971. Olympic Games (1972). (1st issue). Mult.
1464 5q. Type **305** 10 10
1465 10q. Hurdling 15 10
1466 15q. Canoeing 15 10
1467 25q. Gymnastics 25 15
1468 80q. Fencing 55 25
1469 11.05 Football . . . . . 1·10 25
1470 31.60 Diving . . . . . 4·00 1·10
See also Nos. 1522/29.

306 Workers with Banner　　**307** "XXX" and Red Flag

1971. 6th Workers' Party Congress. Multicoloured.
1472	25q. Type **306**		25	15
1473	11.05 Congress hall		1·40	95
1474	11.20 "VI", flag, star and rifle (vert)		1·75	1·25

1971. 30th Anniv of Albanian Workers' Party. Multicoloured.
1475	15q. Workers and industry (horiz)		2·50	15
1476	80q. Type **307**		1·00	75
1477	11.55 Enver Hoxha and flags (horiz)		2·00	1·75

308 "Young Man" (R. Kuci)

1971. Albanian Paintings. Multicoloured.
1478	5q. Type **308**		10	10
1479	15q. "Building Construction" (M. Fushekati)		15	10
1480	25q. "Partisan" (D. Jukniu)		20	10
1481	80q. "Fighter Pilots" (S. Kristo) (horiz)		1·00	20
1482	11.20 "Girl Messenger" (A. Sadikaj) (horiz)		1·40	65
1483	11.55 "Medieval Warriors" (S. Kamberi) (horiz)		2·00	1·25

309 Emblems and Flags

1971. 30th Anniv of Albanian Young Communists' Union.
1485	**309** 15q. multicoloured		15	10
1486	11.35 multicoloured		1·60	80

310 Village Girls

1971. Albanian Ballet "Halili and Hajria". Mult.
1487	5q. Type **310**		15	10
1488	10q. Parting of Halili and Hajria		20	10
1489	15q. Hajria before Sultan Suleiman		20	10
1490	50q. Hajria's marriage		85	20
1491	80q. Execution of Halili		1·25	65
1492	11.40 Hajria killing her husband		2·25	1·25

311 Rifle-shooting (Biathlon)

1972. Winter Olympic Games, Sapporo, Japan. Multicoloured.
1493	5q. Type **311**		10	10
1494	10q. Tobogganing		15	10
1495	15q. Ice-hockey		15	10
1496	20q. Bobsleighing		20	10
1497	50q. Speed skating		30	20
1498	11. Slalom skiing		1·10	30
1499	21. Ski jumping		2·00	95

312 Wild Strawberries

1972. Wild Fruits, Multicoloured.
1501	5q. Type **312**		15	10
1502	10q. Blackberries		15	10
1503	15q. Hazelnuts		20	10
1504	20q. Walnuts		25	15
1505	25q. Strawberry-tree fruit		30	15
1506	30q. Dogwood berries		45	20
1507	21.40 Rowanberries		2·50	1·10

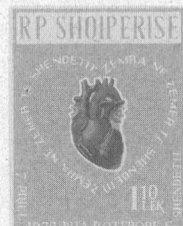

313 Human Heart　　**314** Congress Delegates

1972. World Health Day. Multicoloured.
1508	11.10 Type **313**		1·10	30
1509	11.20 Treatment of cardiac patient		1·25	75

1972. 7th Albanian Trade Unions Congress. Mult.
1510	25q. Type **314**		30	20
1511	21.05 Congress Hall		1·90	1·00

315 Memorial Flame

1972. 30th Anniv of Martyrs' Day, and Death of Qemal Stafa.
1512	**315** 15q. multicoloured		20	10
1513	25q. black, orge & grey		25	15
1514	11.90 black and ochre		1·90	35

DESIGNS—VERT: 25q. "Spirit of Defiance" (statue). HORIZ: 11.90, Qemal Stafa.

316 "Camellia japonica Kamelie"

1972. Camellias.
1515	**316** 5q. multicoloured		15	10
1516	10q. multicoloured		20	10
1517	15q. multicoloured		20	10
1518	25q. multicoloured		25	10
1519	45q. multicoloured		40	15
1520	50q. multicoloured		50	20
1521	21.50 multicoloured		3·50	2·25

DESIGNS: Nos. 1516/21, Various camellias as Type 316.

317 High Jumping

1972. Olympic Games, Munich (2nd issue). Mult.
1522	5q. Type **317**		10	10
1523	10q. Running		10	10
1524	15q. Putting the shot		15	10
1525	20q. Cycling		15	10
1526	25q. Pole-vaulting		20	10
1527	50q. Hurdling		35	15
1528	75q. Hockey		65	25
1529	21. Swimming		90	75

318 Articulated bus

1972. Modern Transport. Multicoloured.
1531	15q. Type **318**		15	10
1532	25q. Czechoslovakian Class T699 diesel locomotive		2·00	15
1533	80q. Freighter "Tirana"		1·40	30
1534	11.05 Motor-car		80	25
1535	11.20 Container lorry		1·25	50

319 "Trial of Strength"

1972. 1st Nat Festival of Traditional Games. Mult.
1536	5q. Type **319**		10	10
1537	10q. Pick-a-back ball game		15	10
1538	15q. Leaping game		15	10
1539	25q. Rope game		20	10
1540	90q. Leap-frog		65	20
1541	21. Women's throwing game		1·60	75

320 Newspaper "Mastheads"

1972. 30th Anniv of Press Day.
1542	**320** 15q. black and blue		20	10
1543	25q. green, red & black		25	15
1544	11.90 black and mauve		1·90	95

DESIGNS: 25q. Printing-press and partisan; 11.90, Workers with newspaper.

321 Location Map and Commemorative Plaque

1972. 30th Anniv of Peza Conference. Mult.
1545	15q. Type **321**		30	20
1546	25q. Partisans with flag		45	30
1547	11.90 Conference Memorial		2·00	1·25

322 "Partisans Conference" (S. Capo)

1972. Albanian Paintings. Multicoloured.
1548	5q. Type **322**		10	10
1549	10q. "Head of Woman" (I. Lulani) (vert)		15	10
1550	15q. "Communists" (L. Shkreli) (vert)		15	10
1551	20q. "Nendorit, 1941" (S. Shijaku) (vert)		20	10
1552	50q. "Farm Woman" (Z. Shoshi) (vert)		65	20
1553	11. "Landscape" (D. Trebicka)		1·25	50
1554	21. "Girls with Bicycles" (V. Kilica)		2·50	1·25

323 Congress Emblem　　**324** Lenin

1972. 6th Congress of Young Communists' Union.
1556	**323** 25q. gold, red and silver		30	15
1557	21.05 multicoloured		2·00	1·00

DESIGN: 21.05, Young worker and banner.

1972. 55th Anniv of Russian October Revolution. Multicoloured.
1558	11.10 multicoloured		1·25	65
1559	**324** 11.20 red, blk & pink		1·25	75

DESIGN: 11.10, Hammer and Sickle.

325 Albanian Soldiers

1972. 60th Anniv of Independence.
1560	**325** 15q. blue, red and black		15	15
1561	25q. black, red & yellow		25	20
1562	65q. multicoloured		45	20
1563	11.25 black and red		1·00	75

DESIGNS—VERT: 25q. Ismail Qemali; 11.25, Albanian double-eagle emblem. HORIZ: 65q. Proclamation of Independence, 1912.

326 Cockerel (mosaic)

1972. Ancient Mosaics from Apolloni and Butrint (3rd series). Multicoloured.
1564	5q. Type **326**		10	10
1565	10q. Bird (vert)		15	10
1566	15q. Partridges (vert)		20	10
1567	25q. Warrior's leg		25	15
1568	45q. Nude on dolphin (vert)		35	20
1569	50q. Fish (vert)		40	20
1570	21.50 Warrior's head		3·25	1·75

327 Nicolas Copernicus

1973. 500th Birth Anniv of Copernicus. Mult.
1571	5q. Type **327**		10	10
1572	10q. Copernicus and signatures		15	10
1573	25q. Engraved portrait		20	15
1574	80q. Copernicus at desk		1·00	25
1575	11.20 Copernicus and planets		1·60	65
1576	11.60 Planetary diagram		1·90	85

328 Policeman and Industrial Scene

1973. 30th Anniv of State Security Police.
1577 **328** 25q. black, blue & lt
blue 30 20
1578 – 11.80 multicoloured . . . 1·90 1·40
DESIGN: 11.80, Prisoner under escort.

329/30 Cactus Flowers

1973. Cacti. As T **329/30**.
1579 **329** 10q. multicoloured . . . 10 10
1580 **330** 15q. multicoloured . . . 15 10
1581 – 20q. multicoloured . . . 20 10
1582 – 25q. multicoloured . . . 20 10
1583 – 30q. multicoloured . . . 4·50 1·75
1584 – 65q. multicoloured . . . 85 50
1585 – 80q. multicoloured . . . 1·00 25
1586 – 2l. multicoloured . . . 1·90 85
Nos. 1579/86 were issued together se-tenant within the sheet and in alternate formats as Types **329/30**.

331 Common Tern

1973. Sea Birds. Multicoloured.
1587 5q. Type **331** 25 20
1588 15q. White-winged black
tern 35 25
1589 25q. Black-headed gull . . . 40 25
1590 45q. Great black-headed gull 75 45
1591 80q. Slender-billed gull . . . 1·40 80
1592 21.40 Sandwich tern . . . . 3·50 2·10

332 Postmark of 1913, and Letters

1973. 60th Anniv of First Albanian Stamps. Mult.
1593 25q. Type **332** . . . . . . 1·00 35
1594 11.80 Postman and
postmarks . . . . 4·00 1·50

333 Albanian Woman

1973. 7th Albanian Women's Congress.
1595 **333** 25q. red and pink . . . 25 15
1596 – 11.80 black, orge & yell 1·75 1·40
DESIGN: 11.80, Albanian female workers.

334 "Creation of the General Staff"
(G. Madhi)

1973. 30th Anniv of Albanian People's Army. Mult.
1597 25q. Type **334** . . . . . . 12·00 5·00
1598 40q. "August 1949"
(sculpture by Sh. Haderi)
(vert) . . . . 12·00 5·00
1599 60q. "Generation after
Generation" (Statue by H.
Dule) (vert) . . . . . . 12·00 5·00
1600 80q. "Defend Revolutionary
Victories" (M. Fushekati) 12·00 5·00

335 "Electrification" (S. Hysa)

1973. Albanian Paintings. Multicoloured.
1601 5q. Type **335** 10 10
1602 10q. "Textile Worker"
(E. Nallbani) (vert) . . . 15 10
1603 15q. "Gymnastics Class"
(M. Fushekati) 15 10
1604 50q. "Aviator" (F. Stamo)
(vert) 65 15
1605 80q. "Downfall of Fascism"
(A. Lakuriqi) 90 20
1606 11.20 "Koci Bako"
(demonstrators (P. Mele))
(vert) . . . . 1·40 25
1607 11.30 "Peasant Girl"
(Z. Shoshi) (vert) . . . . 1·75 30

336 "Mary Magdalene"

338 Weightlifting

337 Goalkeeper with Ball

1973. 400th Birth Anniv of Caravaggio. Paintings.
Multicoloured.
1609 5q. Type **336** 10 10
1610 10q. "The Guitar Player"
(horiz) 15 10
1611 15q. Self-portrait 20 10
1612 50q. "Boy carrying Fruit" 65 20
1613 80q. "Basket of Fruit"
(horiz) 90 25
1614 11.20 "Narcissus" . . . . 1·40 65
1615 11.30 "Boy peeling Apple" 2·25 90

1973. World Cup Football Championship, Munich
(1974) (1st issue). Multicoloured.
1617 **337** 5q. multicoloured . . . 10 10
1618 – 10q. multicoloured . . . 15 10
1619 – 15q. multicoloured . . . 15 10
1620 – 20q. multicoloured . . . 20 10
1621 – 25q. multicoloured . . . 25 15
1622 – 90q. multicoloured . . . 1·40 20
1623 – 11.20 multicoloured . . 1·90 30
1624 – 11.25 multicoloured . . 1·90 85
DESIGNS: Nos. 1618/24 are similar to Type **337**,
showing goalkeepers saving goals.
See also Nos. 1663/70.

1973. World Weightlifting Championships, Havana,
Cuba.
1626 **338** 5q. multicoloured . . . 10 10
1627 – 10q. multicoloured . . . 15 10
1628 – 25q. multicoloured . . . 20 10
1629 – 90q. multicoloured . . . 90 25
1630 – 11.20 mult (horiz) . . . 1·10 35
1631 – 11.60 mult (horiz) . . . 1·60 40
DESIGNS: Nos. 1627/31 are similar to Type **338**,
showing various lifts.

339 Ballet Scene

340 Mao Tse-tung

1973. "Albanian Life and Work". Multicoloured.
1632 5q. Cement Works, Kavaje 10 10
1633 10q. "Ali Kelmendi" lorry
factory (horiz) 15 10
1634 15q. Type **339** 20 10
1635 20q. Combine-harvester
(horiz) 25 15
1636 25q. "Telecommunications" 25 15
1637 35q. Skier and hotel, Dajt
(horiz) 35 15
1638 60q. Llogora holiday village
(horiz) 50 20
1639 80q. Lake scene 65 25
1640 1l. Textile mill (horiz) . . 50 20
1641 11.20 Furnacemen (horiz) . . 80 25
1642 21.40 Welder and pipeline
(horiz) . . . . 2·00 50
1643 3l. Skanderbeg Statue,
Tirana . . . . 2·75 65
1644 5l. Roman arches, Durres 4·25 1·75

1973. 80th Birth Anniv of Mao Tse-tung. Mult.
1645 85q. Type **340** . . . . . . 1·00 20
1646 11.20 Mao Tse-tung at
parade . . . . 1·75 85

341 "Horse's Head" (Gericault)

1974. 150th Death Anniv of Jean-Louis Gericault
(French painter).
1647 **341** 10q. multicoloured . . . 15 10
1648 – 15q. multicoloured . . . 15 10
1649 – 20q. black and gold . . . 20 10
1650 – 25q. black, lilac and gold 25 15
1651 – 11.20 multicoloured . . 1·60 30
1652 – 21.20 multicoloured . . 3·50 1·25
DESIGNS—VERT: 15q. "Male Model" (Gericault);
20q. "Man and Dog"; 25q. "Head of a Negro"; 11.20,
Self-portrait. HORIZ: 21.20, "Battle of the Giants".

342 "Lenin with Crew of the 'Aurora'"
(D. Trebicka)

1974. 50th Death Anniv of Lenin. Multicoloured.
1654 25q. Type **342** 25 15
1655 60q. "Lenin" (P. Mele)
(vert) . . . . 1·00 20
1656 11.20 "Lenin" (seated)
(V. Kilica) (vert) . . . . 2·00 1·25

343 Duck

1974. Ancient Mosaics from Butrint, Pogradec and
Apolloni (4th series). Multicoloured.
1657 5q. Duck (different) 10 10
1658 10q. Bird and flower 15 10
1659 15q. Ornamental basket and
grapes 15 10
1660 25q. Type **343** 20 10
1661 40q. Donkey and cockerel 35 20
1662 21.50 Dragon . . . . . . 2·75 1·10

344 Shooting at Goal

1974. World Cup Football Championships, Munich
(2nd issue).
1663 **344** 10q. multicoloured . . . 15 10
1664 – 15q. multicoloured . . . 15 10
1665 – 20q. multicoloured . . . 20 10
1666 – 25q. multicoloured . . . 25 10
1667 – 40q. multicoloured . . . 35 15
1668 – 80q. multicoloured . . . 1·00 25
1669 – 1l. multicoloured . . . . 1·25 25
1670 – 11.20 multicoloured . . 1·60 45
DESIGNS: Nos. 1664/70, Players in action similar to
Type **344**.

345 Memorial and   346 "Solanum dulcamara"
Arms

1974. 30th Anniv of Permet Congress. Mult.
1672 25q. Type **345** 20 15
1673 11.80 Enver Hoxha and text 1·40 40

1974. Useful Plants. Multicoloured.
1674 10q. Type **346** 15 10
1675 15q. "Arbutus uva-ursi"
(vert) 15 10
1676 20q. "Convallaria majalis"
(vert) 15 10
1677 25q. "Colchicum
autumnale" (vert) . . . 20 10
1678 40q. "Borago officinalis" . . 75 20
1679 80q. "Saponaria officinalis" 1·40 25
1680 21.20 "Gentiana lutea" . . . 3·50 1·40

347 Revolutionaries

1974. 50th Anniv of 1924 Revolution.
1681 **347** 25q. mauve, black & red 20 15
1682 – 11.80 multicoloured . . . 1·25 40
DESIGN—VERT: 11.80, Prominent revolutionaries.

348 Redwing

1974. Song Birds. Multicoloured.
1683 10q. Type **348** 20 20
1684 15q. European robin 20 20
1685 20q. Western greenfinch . . 20 20
1686 25q. Northern bullfinch
(vert) 45 20
1687 40q. Hawfinch (vert) 55 20
1688 80q. Blackcap (vert) . . . . 1·25 60
1689 21.20 Nightingale (vert) . . 3·00 1·90

349 Globe and Post Office
Emblem

1974. Centenary of Universal Postal Union.
Multicoloured.
1690 **349** 85q. multicoloured . . . 1·00 50
1691 – 11.20 green, lilac & violet 1·50 75
DESIGN: 11.20, U.P.U. emblem.

350 "Widows" (Sali Shijaku)

1974. Albanian Paintings. Multicoloured.
1693	10q. Type **350**		10	10
1694	15q. "Road Construction" (Danish Jukniu)		20	10
1695	20q. "Fulfilling the Plans" (Clirim Ceka)		25	10
1696	25q. "The Call to Action" (Spiro Kristo)		30	20
1697	40q. "The Winter Battle" (Sabaudin Xhaferi)		40	20
1698	80q. "Three Comrades" (Clirim Ceka)		80	50
1699	1l. "Step by Step, Aid the Partisans" (Guri Madhi)		1·00	60
1700	1l.20 "At the War Memorial" (Kleo Nini)		1·25	70

Nos. 1694, 1696 and 1698 are vert designs.

351 Chinese Festivities

1974. 25th Anniv of Chinese People's Republic. Multicoloured.
1702	**351** 85q. multicoloured		85	25
1703	– 1l.20 black, red and gold		1·25	30

DESIGN—VERT: 1l.20, Mao Tse-tung.

352 Volleyball   **353** Berat

1974. National Spartakiad. Multicoloured.
1704	10q. Type **352**		10	10
1705	15q. Hurdling		10	10
1706	20q. Hoop exercises		15	10
1707	25q. Stadium parade		15	10
1708	40q. Weightlifting		20	10
1709	80q. Wrestling		40	20
1710	1l. Rifle shooting		75	25
1711	1l.20 Football		85	25

1974. 30th Anniv of 2nd Berat Liberal Council Meeting.
1712	**353** 25q. red and black		20	15
1713	– 80q. yellow, brown & blk		75	20
1714	– 1l. purple and black		1·10	50

DESIGNS—HORIZ: 80q. "Liberation" frieze. VERT: 1l. Council members walking to meeting.

354 Security Guards patrolling Industrial Plant

1974. 30th Anniv of Liberation. Multicoloured.
1715	25q. Type **354**		15	10
1716	35q. Chemical industry		20	10
1717	50q. Agricultural produce		30	15
1718	80q. Cultural activities		40	20
1719	1l. Scientific technology		80	25
1720	1l.20 Railway construction		2·50	50

355 Head of Artemis   **356** Clasped hands

1974. Archaeological Discoveries. Multicoloured.
1722	**355** 10q. black, mauve & sil		10	10
1723	– 15q. black, green & silver		15	10
1724	– 20q. black, buff & silver		15	10
1725	– 25q. black, mauve & sil		20	10
1726	– 40q. multicoloured		20	10
1727	– 80q. black, blue & silver		70	20
1728	– 1l. black, green & silver		90	20
1729	– 1l.20 black, sepia & sil		1·75	75

DESIGNS: 15q. Statue of Zeus; 20q. Statue of Poseidon; 25q. Illyrian helmet; 40q. Greek amphora; 80q. Bust of Agrippa; 1l. Bust of Demosthenes; 1l.20, Bust of Bilia.

1975. 30th Anniv of Albanian Trade Unions. Mult.
1731	25q. Type **356**		20	15
1732	1l.80 Workers with arms raised (horiz)		1·25	50

357 "Cichorium intybus"

1975. Albanian Flowers. Multicoloured.
1733	5q. Type **357**		10	10
1734	10q. "Sempervivum montanum"		10	10
1735	15q. "Aquilegia alpina"		10	10
1736	20q. "Anemone hortensis"		15	10
1737	25q. "Hibiscus trionum"		15	10
1738	30q. "Gentiana kochiana"		20	10
1739	35q. "Lavatera arborea"		20	10
1740	2l.70 "Iris graminea"		1·90	70

358 Head of Jesus (detail, Doni Tondo)

1975. 500th Birth Anniv of Michelangelo. Mult.
1741	**358** 5q. multicoloured		10	10
1742	– 10q. brown, grey & gold		10	10
1743	– 15q. brown, grey & gold		15	10
1744	– 20q. sepia, grey and gold		20	10
1745	– 25q. multicoloured		20	10
1746	– 30q. brown, grey & gold		20	10
1747	– 1l.20 brn, grey & gold		85	30
1748	– 3l.90 multicoloured		2·50	1·00

DESIGNS: 10q. "The Heroic Captive"; 15q. "Head of Dawn"; 20q. "Awakening Giant" (detail); 25q. "Cumaenian Sybil" (detail, Sistine chapel); 30q. "Lorenzo di Medici"; 1l.20, Head and shoulders of "David"; 3l.90, "Delphic Sybil" (detail, Sistine chapel).

359 Horseman

1975. "Albanian Transport of the Past". Mult.
1750	5q. Type **359**		10	10
1751	10q. Horse and cart		15	10
1752	15q. Ferry		40	15
1753	20q. Barque		40	15
1754	25q. Horse-drawn cab		30	15
1755	3l.35 Early motor-car		2·75	85

360 Frontier Guard

1975. 30th Anniv of Frontier Force. Mult.
1756	25q. Type **360**		20	15
1757	1l.80 Guards patrolling industrial plant		1·75	90

361 Patriot affixing Anti-fascist Placard

1975. 30th Anniv of "Victory over Fascism". Mult.
1758	25q. Type **361**		15	10
1759	60q. Partisans in battle		30	10
1760	1l.20 Patriot defeating Nazi soldier		1·25	55

362 European Wigeon

1975. Albanian Wildfowl. Multicoloured.
1761	5q. Type **362**		20	20
1762	10q. Red-crested pochard		20	20
1763	15q. White-fronted goose		20	20
1764	20q. Pintail		20	20
1765	25q. Red-breasted merganser		20	20
1766	30q. Eider		35	20
1767	35q. Whooper swans		45	20
1768	2l.70 Common shoveler		2·75	1·40

363 "Shyqyri Kanapari" (Musa Qarri)

1975. Albanian Paintings. People's Art Exhibition, Tirana. Multicoloured.
1769	5q. Type **363**		10	10
1770	10q. "Sea Rescue" (Agim Faja)		10	10
1771	15q. "28 November 1912" (Petri Ceno) (horiz)		10	10
1772	20q. "Workers' Meeting" (Sali Shijaka)		15	10
1773	25q. "Shota Galica" (Ismail Lulani)		15	10
1774	30q. "Victorious Fighters" (Nestor Jonuzi)		20	15
1775	80q. "Partisan Comrades" (Vilson Halimi)		65	30
1776	2l.25 "Republic Day Celebration" (Fatmir Haxhiu) (horiz)		1·60	1·25

364 Farmer with Declaration of Reform

1975. 30th Anniv of Agrarian Reform. Mult.
1778	15q. Type **364**		15	15
1779	2l. Agricultural scene		1·40	75

365 Dead Man's Fingers   **366** Cycling

1975. Marine Corals. Multicoloured.
1780	5q. Type **365**		10	10
1781	10q. "Paramuricea chamaeleon"		15	10
1782	20q. Red Coral		15	10
1783	25q. Tube Coral or Sea Fan		30	15
1784	3l.70 "Cladocora cespitosa"		4·25	1·75

1975. Olympic Games, Montreal (1976). Mult.
1785	5q. Type **366**		10	10
1786	10q. Canoeing		10	10
1787	15q. Handball		15	10
1788	20q. Basketball		15	10
1789	25q. Water-polo		20	10
1790	30q. Hockey		20	10
1791	1l.20 Pole vaulting		85	25
1792	2l.05 Fencing		1·40	35

367 Power Lines leading to Village

1975. 5th Anniv of Electrification of Albanian Countryside. Multicoloured.
1794	**367** 15q. multicoloured		15	15
1795	– 25q. violet, red and lilac		20	15
1796	– 80q. black, turq & green		85	20
1797	– 85q. buff, brn & ochre		1·25	85

DESIGNS: 25q. High power insulators; 80q. Dam and power station; 85q. T.V. pylons and emblems of agriculture and industry.

368 Berat

1975. Air. Tourist Resorts. Multicoloured.
1798	20q. Type **368**		25	15
1799	40q. Gjirokaster		40	20
1800	60q. Sarande		70	30
1801	90q. Durres		90	40
1802	1l.20 Krujae		1·25	50
1803	2l.40 Boga		2·40	1·00
1804	4l.05 Tirana		3·50	1·75

369 Child, Rabbit and Bear planting Saplings

1975. Children's Tales. Multicoloured.

1805	5q. Type **369**	10	10
1806	10q. Mrs. Fox and cub	10	10
1807	15q. Ducks in school	15	10
1808	20q. Bears building	15	10
1809	25q. Animals watching television	20	10
1810	30q. Animals with log and electric light bulbs	20	10
1811	35q. Ants with spade and guitar	35	15
1812	2l.70 Boy and girl with sheep and dog	1·90	85

370 Arms and Rejoicing Crowd

1976. 30th Anniv of Albanian People's Republic. Multicoloured.

1813	25q. Type **370**	20	15
1814	1l.90 Folk-dancers	1·40	40

371 Ice Hockey

1976. Winter Olympic Games, Innsbruck. Mult.

1815	5q. Type **371**	10	10
1816	10q. Speed skating	15	10
1817	15q. Rifle shooting (biathlon)	20	10
1818	50q. Ski jumping	30	15
1819	1l.20 Skiing (slalom)	90	25
1820	2l.30 Bobsleighing	1·90	45

372 "Colchicum autumnale"

1976. Medicinal Plants. Multicoloured.

1822	5q. Type **372**	10	10
1823	10q. "Atropa belladonna"	15	10
1824	15q. "Gentiana lutea"	15	10
1825	20q. "Aesculus hippocastanum"	15	10
1826	70q. "Polystichum filix"	35	20
1827	80q. "Althaea officinalis"	55	20
1828	2l.30 "Datura stamonium"	2·25	1·00

373 Wooden Bowl and Spoon

1976. Ethnographical Studies Conference, Tirana. Albanian Artifacts. Multicoloured.

1829	10q. Type **373**	10	10
1830	15q. Flask (vert)	15	10
1831	20q. Ornamental handles (vert)	20	10
1832	25q. Pistol and dagger	25	10
1833	80q. Hand-woven rug (vert)	70	20
1834	1l.20 Filigree buckle and earrings	1·00	25
1835	1l.40 Jugs with handles (vert)	1·25	85

374 "Founding the Co-operatives" (Zef Shoshi)

1976. Albanian Paintings. Multicoloured.

1836	5q. Type **374**	10	10
1837	10q. "Going to Work" (Agim Zajmi) (vert)	10	10
1838	25q. "Listening to Broadcast" (Vilson Kilica)	15	10
1839	40q. "Female Welder" (Sabaudin Xhaferi) (vert)	25	10
1840	50q. "Steel Workers" (Isuf Sulovari) (vert)	35	15
1841	1l.20 "1942 Revolt" (Lec Shkreli) (vert)	90	25
1842	1l.60 "Returning from Work" (Agron Dine)	1·25	35

375 Demonstrators attacking Police

376 Party Flag, Industry and Agriculture

1976. 35th Anniv of Hoxha's Anti-fascist Demonstration. Multicoloured.

1844	25q. Type **375**	20	15
1845	1l.90 Crowd with flag	1·40	55

1976. 7th Workers' Party Congress. Multicoloured.

1846	25q. Type **376**	1·75	45
1847	1l.20 Hand holding Party symbols, and flag	85	30

377 Communist Advance

1976. 35th Anniv of Workers' Party. Mult.

1848	15q. Type **377**	20	10
1849	25q. Hands holding emblems and revolutionary army	20	10
1850	80q. "Reconstruction"	40	20
1851	1l.20 "Heavy Industry and Agriculture"	95	30
1852	1l.70 "The Arts" (ballet)	1·40	40

378 Young Communist

1976. 35th Anniv of Young Communists' Union. Multicoloured.

1853	80q. Type **378**	1·90	45
1854	1l.25 Young Communists in action	90	40

379 Ballet Dancers

1976. Albanian Ballet "Cuca e Malexe".

1855	**379** 10q. multicoloured	10	10
1856	– 15q. multicoloured	15	10
1857	– 20q. multicoloured	20	10
1858	– 25q. multicoloured	25	10
1859	– 80q. multicoloured	45	20
1860	– 1l.20 multicoloured	70	25
1861	– 1l.40 multicoloured	85	30

DESIGNS: 15q. to 1l.40, Various ballet scenes.

380 Bashtoves Castle

381 Skanderbeg's Shield and Spear

1976. Albanian Castles.

1863	**380** 10q. black and blue	10	10
1864	– 15q. black and green	10	10
1865	– 20q. black and grey	20	15
1866	– 25q. black and ochre	30	20
1867	– 80q. black, pink and red	90	50
1868	– 1l.20 black and blue	1·25	80
1869	– 1l.40 black, red & pink	1·75	90

DESIGNS: 15q. Gjirokaster; 20q. All Pash Tepelenes; 25q. Petreles; 80q. Berat; 1l.20, Durres; 1l.40, Krujes.

1977. Crest and Arms of Skanderbeg's Army. Mult.

1870	15q. Type **381**	1·25	70
1871	80q. Helmet, sword and scabbard	4·00	2·50
1872	1l. Halberd, spear, bow and arrows	6·00	3·00

382 Ilya Oiqi

383 Polyvinyl-chloride Plant, Vlore

1977. Albanian Heroes. Multicoloured.

1873	5q. Type **382**	10	10
1874	10q. Ilia Dashi	20	10
1875	25q. Fran Ndue Ivanaj	75	30
1876	80q. Zeliha Allmetaj	1·25	35
1877	1l. Ylli Zaimi	1·50	50
1878	1l.90 Isuf Plloci	2·50	80

1977. 6th Five-year Plan. Multicoloured.

1879	15q. Type **383**	25	20
1880	25q. Naphtha plant, Ballsh	40	25
1881	65q. Hydroelectric station, Fjerzes	80	50
1882	1l. Metallurgical combinate, Elbasan	1·60	80

384 Shote Galica

385 Crowd and Martyrs' Monument, Tirana

1977. 50th Death Anniv of Shote Galica (Communist partisan).

1883	**384** 80q. red and pink	80	40
1884	– 1l.25 grey and blue	1·50	75

DESIGN: 1l.25, Shote Galica and father.

1977. 35th Anniv of Martyrs' Day. Multicoloured.

1885	25q. Type **385**	40	25
1886	80q. Clenched fist and Albanian flag	1·00	40
1887	1l.20 Bust of Qemal Stafa	1·75	70

386 Doctor calling at Village House

387 Workers outside Factory

1977. "Socialist Transformation of the Villages". Multicoloured.

1888	5q. Type **386**	10	10
1889	10q. Cowherd with cattle	15	10
1890	20q. Harvesting	20	20
1891	80q. Modern village	1·00	40
1892	2l.95 Tractor and greenhouse	3·50	70

1977. 8th Trade Unions Congress. Multicoloured.

1893	25q. Type **387**	25	20
1894	1l.80 Three workers with flags	1·50	80

388 Advancing Soldiers

389 Two Girls with Handkerchiefs

1977. "All the People are Soldiers". Multicoloured.

1895	15q. Type **388**	20	10
1896	25q. Enver Hoxha and marching soldiers	25	10
1897	80q. Soldiers and workers	75	25
1898	1l. The Armed Forces	1·00	35
1899	1l.90 Marching soldiers and workers	2·00	40

1977. National Costume Dances (1st series). Mult.

1900	5q. Type **389**	15	10
1901	10q. Two male dancers	15	10
1902	15q. Man and woman in kerchief dance	15	15
1903	25q. Two male dancers (different)	20	15
1904	80q. Two women dancers with kerchiefs	55	25
1905	1l.20 "Elbow dance"	85	30
1906	1l.55 Two women with kerchiefs (different)	1·10	50

See also Nos. 1932/6 and 1991/5.

390 Armed Worker with Book

391 "Beni Ecen Vet"

1977. New Constitution.

1908	**390** 25q. gold, red and black	25	15
1909	– 1l.20 gold, red and black	1·10	35

DESIGN: 1l.20, Industrial and agricultural symbols and hand with book.

1977. Albanian Films.

1910	**391** 10q. green and grey	20	10
1911	– 15q. multicoloured	30	10
1912	– 25q. green, black & grey	40	20
1913	– 80q. multicoloured	1·00	50
1914	– 1l.20 brown and grey	1·50	60
1915	– 1l.60 multicoloured	2·50	90

DESIGNS: 15q. "Rruge te Bardha"; 25q. "Rrugicat qe Kerkonin Diell"; 80q. "Ne Fillim te Veres"; 1l.20, "Lulekuqet Mbi Mure"; 1l.60, "Zonja nga Qyteti".

392 Rejoicing Crowd and Independence Memorial, Tirana

393 "Farm Workers"

1977. 65th Anniv of Independence. Multicoloured.

1916	15q. Type **392**	15	15
1917	25q. Independence leaders marching in Tirana	25	15
1918	1l.65 Albanians dancing under national flag	1·25	45

1977. Paintings by V. Mio. Multicoloured.

1919	5q. Type **393**	10	10
1920	10q. "Landscape in the Snow"	10	10
1921	15q. "Sheep under a Walnut Tree, Springtime"	15	10
1922	25q. "Street in Korce"	25	10
1923	80q. "Riders in the Mountains"	65	20
1924	1l. "Boats by the Seashore"	85	25
1925	1l.75 "Tractors Ploughing"	1·10	30

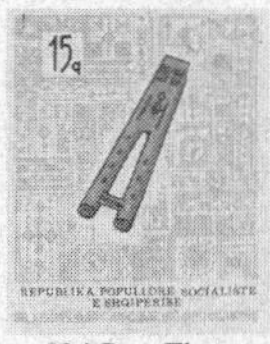

394 Pan Flute

395 "Tractor Drivers" (D. Trebicka)

1978. Folk Music Instruments.

1927	**394** 15q. red, black and green	30	15
1928	– 25q. yellow, black & vio	60	25
1929	– 80q. red, black and blue	1·50	40
1930	– 1l.20 yellow, blk & blue	3·00	60
1931	– 1l.70 lilac, black & grn	5·00	1·25

DESIGNS: 25q. Single-string goat's head fiddle; 80q. Trumpet; 1l.20, Drum; 1l.70, Bagpipes.

1978. National Costume Dances (2nd series). As T **389**. Multicoloured.

1932	5q. Girl dancers with scarves	10	10
1933	25q. Male dancers	20	15
1934	80q. Kneeling dancers	40	20
1935	1l. Female dancers	70	25
1936	2l.30 Male dancers with linked arms	1·75	50

1978. Paintings of the Working Class. Mult.

1937	25q. Type **395**	15	10
1938	80q. "Steeplejack" (S. Kristo)	30	20
1939	85q. "A Point in the Discussion" (S. Milori)	35	20
1940	90q. "Oil Rig Crew" (A. Cini) (vert)	45	20
1941	1l.60 "Metal Workers" (R. Karanxha)	75	30

396 Boy and Girl

1978. International Children's Day. Multicoloured.

1943	5q. Type **396**	10	10
1944	10q. Boy and girl with pickaxe and rifle	15	10
1945	25q. Children dancing	25	20
1946	1l.80 Classroom scene	2·00	45

397 Woman with Pickaxe and Rifle

1978. 8th Women's Union Congress.

1947 **397**	25q. red and gold	30	10
1948 –	1l.95 red and gold	2·50	75

DESIGN: 1l.95, Peasant, Militia Guard and industrial installation.

398 Battle of Mostar Bridge

399 Guerillas and Flag

1978. Centenary of the League of Prizren.

1949 **398**	10q. multicoloured	15	10
1950 –	25q. multicoloured	20	15
1951 –	80q. multicoloured	45	20
1952 –	1l.20 blue, black & vio	75	30
1953 –	1l.65 multicoloured	1·00	40
1954 –	2l.60 lt grn, blk & grn	1·60	60

DESIGNS: 25q. Spirit of Skanderbeg; 80q. Albanians marching under national flag; 1l.20, Riflemen; 1l.65, Abdyl Frasheri (founder); 2l.60, League Headquarters, Prizren.

1978. 35th Anniv of People's Army.

1956	5q. Type **399**	35	15
1957	25q. Men of armed forces (horiz)	75	30
1958	1l.90 Men of armed forces, civil guards and Young Pioneers	4·00	1·50

1978. International Fair, Riccione. No. 1832 surch **3.30L. RICCIONE 78 26.8.78.**

1959	3l.30 on 25q. multicoloured	10·00	3·25

401 Man with Target Rifle

402 Kerchief Dance

1978. 32nd National Shooting Championships.

1960 **401**	25q. black and yellow	20	15
1961 –	80q. black and orange	40	20
1962 –	95q. black and red	50	25
1963 –	2l.40 black and red	1·75	50

DESIGNS—VERT: 80q. Woman with machine carbine; 2l.40, Pistol shooting. HORIZ: 95q. Shooting from prone position.

1978. National Folklore Festival, Gjirokaster. Mult.

1964	10q. Type **402**	10	10
1965	15q. Musicians	15	10
1966	25q. Fiddle player	20	15
1967	80q. Singers	45	20
1968	1l.20 Sabre dance	80	25
1969	1l.90 Girl dancers	1·40	35

403 Enver Hoxha (after V. Kilica)

404 Woman with Wheatsheaf

1978. Enver Hoxha's 70th Birthday.

1970 **403**	80q. multicoloured	65	20
1971	1l.20 multicoloured	90	25
1972	2l.40 multicoloured	1·40	65

1978. Agriculture and Stock Raising. Multicoloured.

1974	15q. Type **404**	30	20
1975	25q. Woman with boxes of fruit	40	30
1976	80q. Shepherd and flock	1·25	60
1977	2l.60 Dairymaid and cattle	4·00	2·00

405 Pupils entering School

406 Dora D'Istria

1978.

1978 **405**	5q. brown, lt brn & gold	15	10
1979 –	10q. blue, lt bl & gold	20	10
1980 –	15q. violet, lilac and gold	30	15
1981 –	20q. brown, drab & gold	45	20
1982 –	25q. red, pink and gold	55	25
1983 –	60q. green, lt grn & gold	1·75	45
1984 –	80q. blue, lt blue & gold	2·50	55
1985 –	1l.20 magenta, mauve and gold	3·50	90
1986 –	1l.60 blue, lt blue & gold	12·00	1·40
1987 –	2l.40 grn, lt grn & gold	6·00	2·10
1988 –	3l. blue, lt blue & gold	7·50	3·75

DESIGNS: 10q. Telephone, letters, telegraph wires and switchboard operators; 15q. Pouring molten iron; 20q. Dancers, musical instruments, book and artist's materials; 25q. Newspapers, radio, television and broadcasting tower; 60q. Assistant in clothes shop; 80q. Militiamen and women, tanks, ships, aircraft and radar equipment; 1l.20, Industrial complex and symbols of industry; 1l.60, Train and lorry; 2l.40, Workers hoeing fields, cattle and girl holding wheat sheaf; 3l. Microscope and nurse holding up baby.

1979. 150th Birth Anniv of Dora D'Istria (pioneer of women's rights).

1989 **406**	80q. green and black	85	20
1990 –	1l.10 grey and black	1·25	1·00

DESIGN: 1l.10, Full-face portrait.

1979. National Costume Dances (3rd series). As T **389**. Multicoloured.

1991	15q. Girl dancers with scarves	15	10
1992	25q. Male dancers	20	10
1993	80q. Girl dancers with scarves (different)	50	25
1994	1l.20 Male dancers with pistols	80	40
1995	1l.40 Female dancers with linked arms	1·25	45

407 Stone-built Galleried House

408 Aleksander Moissi

1979. Traditional Albanian Houses (1st series). Multicoloured.

1996	15q. Type **407**	15	10
1997	25q. Tower house (vert)	20	10
1998	80q. House with wooden galleries	85	25
1999	1l.20 Galleried tower house (vert)	1·25	40
2000	1l.40 Three-storied fortified house (vert)	1·75	65

See also Nos. 2116/19.

1979. Birth Centenary of Aleksander Moissi (actor).

2002 **408**	80q. green, black & gold	65	20
2003 –	1l.10 brown, blk & gold	1·00	25

DESIGN: 1l.10, Aleksander Moissi (different).

409 Vasil Shanto

1979. Anti-fascist Heroes (1st series). Multicoloured.

2004	15q. Type **409**	25	10
2005	25q. Qemal Stafa	30	15
2006	60q. Type **409**	80	20
2007	90q. As 25q.	1·25	60

See also Nos. 2052/5, 2090/3, 2126/9, 2167/70, 2221/4, 2274/7 and 2313/5.

410 Soldier, Crowd and Coat of Arms

1979. 35th Anniv of Permet Congress. Mult.

2008	25q. Soldier, factories and wheat	40	20
2009	1l.65 Type **410**	2·00	1·00

411 Albanian Flag

1979. 5th Albanian Democratic Front Congress.

2010 **411**	25q. multicoloured	40	20
2011	1l.65 multicoloured	2·00	1·00

412 "Ne Stervitje" (Arben Basha)

1979. Paintings. Multicoloured.

2012	15q. Type **412**	10	10
2013	25q. "Shtigje Lufte" (Ismail Lulani)	20	10
2014	80q. "Agim me Fitore" (Myrteza Fushekati)	75	25
2015	1l.20 "Gjithe Populli ushtare" (Muhamet Deliu)	1·10	35
2016	1l.40 "Zjarret Ndezur Mbajme" (Jorgji Gjikopulli)	1·40	85

413 Athletes round Party Flag

414 Founder-president

1979. 35th Anniv of Liberation Spartakiad. Mult.

2018	15q. Type **413**	10	10
2019	25q. Shooting	20	10
2020	80q. Girl gymnast	65	25
2021	1l.10 Football	90	35
2022	1l.40 High jump	1·10	35

1979. Centenary of Albanian Literary Society.

2023 –	25q. black, brown & gold	20	15
2024 **414**	80q. black, brown & gold	45	20
2025 –	1l.20 black, blue & gold	70	30
2026 –	1l.55 black, vio & gold	95	40

DESIGNS: 25q. Foundation document and seal of 1880; 1l.20, Headquarters building, 1979; 1l.55, Headquarters building, 1879.

415 Congress Building

1979. 35th Anniv of Berat Congress. Multicoloured.

2028	25q. Arms and congress document	80	50
2029	1l.65 Type **415**	3·00	2·00

416 Workers and Industrial Complex

417 Joseph Stalin

1979. 35th Anniv of Liberation. Multicoloured.

2030	25q. Type **416**	20	10
2031	80q. Wheat and hand grasping hammer and pickaxe	45	25
2032	1l.20 Open book, star and musical instrument	60	30
2033	1l.55 Open book, compasses and gear wheel	1·00	45

1979. Birth Centenary of Joseph Stalin.

2034 **417**	80q. blue and red	40	25
2035 –	1l.10 blue and red	85	40

DESIGN: 1l.10, Stalin and Enver Hoxha.

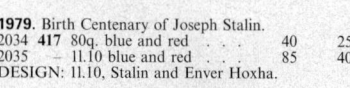

418 Fireplace and Pottery, Korce

1980. Interiors (1st series). Multicoloured.

2036	25q. Type **418**	20	20
2037	80q. Carved bed alcove and weapons, Shkoder	50	40
2038	1l.20 Cooking hearth and carved chair, Mirdite	1·10	85
2039	1l.35 Turkish-style chimney, dagger and embroidered jacket, Gjirokaster	1·40	90

See also Nos. 2075/8.

419 Lacework

420 Aleksander Xhuvani

1980. Handicrafts. Multicoloured.

2040	25q. Pipe and flask	20	20
2041	80q. Leather handbags	55	35
2042	1l.20 Carved eagle and embroidered rug	75	60
2043	1l.35 Type **419**	95	65

1980. Birth Centenary of Dr. Aleksander Xhuvani.

2044 **420**	80q. blue, grey and black	1·00	50
2045	1l. brown, grey and black	1·50	1·00

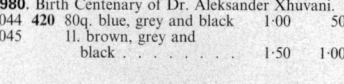

421 Insurrectionists

1980. 70th Anniv of Kosovo Insurrection.

2046 **421**	80q. black and red	1·00	50
2047 –	1l. black and red	1·50	1·00

DESIGN: 1l. Battle scene.

422 "Soldiers and Workers helping Stricken Population" (D. Jukniu and L. Lulani)

1980. 1979 Earthquake Relief.
| 2048 | 422 | 80q. multicoloured | 1·00 | 50 |
| 2049 | | 11. multicoloured | 1·50 | 1·00 |

423 Lenin

1980. 110th Birth Anniv of Lenin.
| 2050 | 423 | 80q. grey, red and pink | 1·00 | 50 |
| 2051 | | 11. multicoloured | 1·50 | 1·00 |

424 Misto Mame and Ali Demi

1980. Anti-fascist Heroes (2nd series). Mult.
2052	25q. Type 424		25	10
2053	80q. Sadik Staveleci, Vojo Kushi and Xhoxhi Martini		60	30
2054	11.20 Bule Naipi and Persefoni Kokedhima		90	60
2055	11.35 Ndoc Deda, Hydajet Lezha, Naim Gjylbegu, Ndoc Mazi and Ahmet Haxhia		1·00	70

425 "Mirela"

1980. Children's Tales. Multicoloured.
2056	15q. Type 425		10	10
2057	25q. "Shkarravina"		20	15
2058	80q. "Ariu Artist"		45	40
2059	21.40 "Pika e Ujit"		2·25	1·40

426 "The Enver Hoxha Tractor Combine" (S. Shijaku and M. Fushekati)

1980. Paintings from Gallery of Figurative Arts, Tirana. Multicoloured.
2060	25q. Type 426		20	15
2061	80q. "The Welder" (Harilla Dhima)		50	35
2062	11.20 "Steel Erector (Petro Kokushta)		70	65
2063	11.35 "Harvest Festival" (Pandeli Lena)		80	75

427 Decorated Door (Pergamen miniature)

1980. Art of the Middle Ages. Each black and gold.
2065	25q. Type 427		15	10
2066	80q. Bird (relief)		45	25
2067	11.20 Crowned lion (relief)		75	65
2068	11.35 Pheasant (relief)		80	75

428 Divjaka

1980. National Parks. Multicoloured.
2069	80q. Type 428		45	30
2070	11.20 Lura		1·00	75
2071	11.60 Thethi		1·75	1·00

429 Flag, Arms and rejoicing Albanians

1981. 35th Anniv of Albanian People's Republic. Multicoloured.
| 2073 | 80q. Type 429 | | 75 | 30 |
| 2074 | 11. Crowd and flags outside People's Party headquarters | | 75 | 45 |

1981. Interiors (2nd series). Multicoloured.
2075	25q. As T 418		20	15
2076	80q. Sleeping mats and spirit keg, Labara		45	30
2077	11.20 Fireplace and covered dish mat		1·00	50
2078	11.35 Interior and embroidered jacket, Dibres		1·25	65

430 Wooden Cot

1981. Folk Art. Multicoloured.
2079	25q. Type 430		20	15
2080	80q. Bucket and flask		60	30
2081	11.20 Embroidered slippers		70	40
2082	11.35 Jugs		80	85

431 Footballers

1981. World Cup Football Championship Eliminating Rounds. Multicoloured.
2083	25q. Type 431		1·25	60
2084	80q. Tackle		3·75	1·75
2085	11.20 Player kicking ball		5·25	2·25
2086	11.35 Goalkeeper saving goal		6·25	2·75

432 Rifleman **433** Acrobats

1981. Cent of Battle of Shtimje. Each purple & red.
| 2087 | 80q. Type 432 | | 65 | 35 |
| 2088 | 11. Albanian with sabre | | 80 | 50 |

1981. Anti-fascist Heroes (3rd series). As T 424. Multicoloured.
2090	25q. Perlat Rexhepi and Branko Kadia		20	15
2091	80q. Xheladin Beqiri and Hajdah Dushi		50	35
2092	11.20 Koci Bako, Vasil Laci and Mujo Ulqinaku		85	55
2093	11.35 Mine Peza and Zoja Cure		95	70

1981. Children's Circus.
2094	— 15q. black, green & stone		15	10
2095	— 25q. black, blue and grey		20	15
2096	433 80q. black, mve & pink		45	35
2097	— 21.40 black, orge & yell		1·60	1·40
DESIGNS: 15q. Monocyclists. 25q. Human pyramid; 21.40, Acrobats spinning from marquee pole.

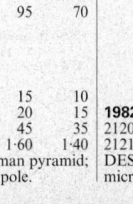

434 "Rallying to the Flag, December 1911" (A. Zajmi)

1981. Paintings. Multicoloured.
2098	25q. "Allies" (Sh. Hysa) (horiz)		20	15
2099	80q. "Azem Galica breaking the Ring of Turks" (A. Buza) (horiz)		50	30
2100	11.20 Type 434		70	45
2101	11.35 "My Flag is my Heart" (L. Cefa)		1·10	90

435 Weightlifting

1981. Albanian Participation in Inter Sports. Mult.
2103	25q. Rifle shooting		15	10
2104	80q. Type 435		45	30
2105	11.20 Volleyball		65	45
2106	11.35 Football		1·00	70

436 Flag and Hands holding Pickaxe and Rifle **437** Industrial and Agricultural Symbols

1981. 8th Workers' Party Congress.
| 2107 | 436 80q. red, brown & black | | 55 | 35 |
| 2108 | — 11. red and black | | 70 | 50 |
DESIGN: 11. Party flag, hammer and sickle.

1981. 40th Anniv of Workers' Party. Mult.
| 2109 | 80q. Type 437 | | 2·00 | 45 |
| 2110 | 21.80 Albanian flag and hand holding pickaxe and rifle | | 2·00 | 1·25 |

438 Pickaxe, Rifle and Young Communists Flag **439** F. S. Noli

1981. 40th Anniv of Young Communists' Union. Multicoloured.
| 2112 | 80q. Type 438 | | 1·25 | 40 |
| 2113 | 11. Workers' Party flag and Young Communists emblem | | 2·00 | 85 |

1981. Birth Centenary of F. S. Noli (author).
| 2114 | 439 80q. green and gold | | 75 | 35 |
| 2115 | — 11.10 brown and gold | | 90 | 45 |

1982. Traditional Albanian Houses (2nd series). As T 407, but vert. Multicoloured.
2116	25q. House in Bulqize		25	15
2117	80q. House in Kosovo		80	50
2118	11.20 House in Bicaj		1·10	75
2119	11.55 House in Mat		1·50	1·00

440 Map, Globe and Bacillus

1982. Centenary of Discovery of Tubercle Bacillus.
| 2120 | 440 80q. multicoloured | | 1·75 | 80 |
| 2121 | — 11.10 brown & dp brown | | 3·00 | 1·50 |
DESIGN: 11.10, Robert Koch (discoverer); microscope and bacillus.

441 "Prizren Castle" (G. Madhi)

1982. Paintings of Kosovo. Multicoloured.
2122	25q. Type 441		25	20
2123	80q. "House of the Albanian League, Prizren" (K. Buza) (horiz)		75	60
2124	11.20 "Mountain Gorge, Rogove" (K. Buza)		1·25	75
2125	11.55 "Street of the Hadhji, Zekes" (G. Madhi)		1·75	1·00

1982. Anti-fascist Heroes (4th series). As T 424. Multicoloured.
2126	25q. Hibe Palikuqi and Liri Gero		20	15
2127	80q. Mihal Duri and Kojo Karafili		60	40
2128	11.20 Fato Dudumi, Margarita Tutulani and Shejnaze Juka		80	50
2129	11.55 Memo Meto and Gjok Doci		1·10	75

442 Factories and Workers

1982. 9th Trade Unions Congress. Multicoloured.
| 2130 | 80q. Type 442 | | 1·50 | 75 |
| 2131 | 11.10 Congress emblem | | 2·00 | 1·00 |

443 Ship in Harbour

1982. Children's Paintings. Multicoloured.
2132	15q. Type 443		25	15
2133	80q. Forest camp		75	45
2134	11.20 House		90	70
2135	11.65 House and garden		1·50	80

444 "Village Festival" (Danish Jukniu)

1982. Paintings from Gallery of Figurative Arts, Tirana. Multicoloured.
2136	25q. Type 444		25	15
2137	80q. "The Hydroelectric Station Builders" (Ali Miruku)		60	40
2138	11.20 "Steel Workers" (Clirim Ceka)		1·00	60
2139	11.55 "Oil Drillers" (Pandeli Lena)		1·25	85

445 "Voice of the People" (party newspaper) **446** Heroes of Peza Monument

1982. 40th Anniv of Popular Press. Multicoloured.
2141 80q. Type **445** . . . . . . 65·00 65·00
2142 1l.10 Hand duplicator producing first edition of "Voice of the People" . . 65·00 65·00

1982. 40th Anniv of Democratic Front. Mult.
2143 80q. Type **446** . . . . . . 2·50 1·50
2144 1l.10 Peza Conference building and marchers with flag . . . . 3·75 2·00

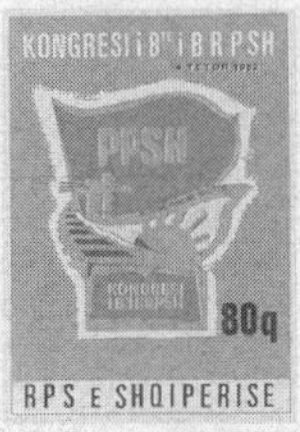

447 Congress Emblem

1982. 8th Young Communists' Union Congress.
2145 **447** 80q. multicoloured . . . 3·00 1·50
2146 1l.10 multicoloured . . . 4·50 2·25

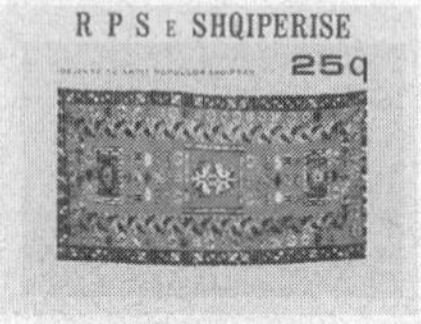

448 Tapestry

1982. Handicrafts. Multicoloured.
2147 25q. Type **448** 25 15
2148 80q. Bags (vert) 60 40
2149 1l.20 Butter churns 85 55
2150 1l.55 Jug (vert) . . . . . . 1·25 1·10

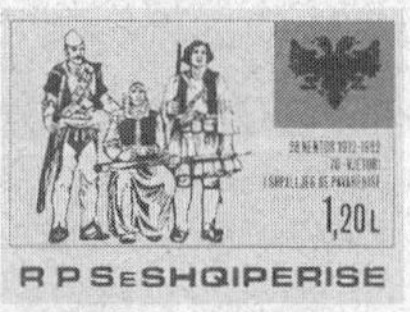

449 Freedom Fighters

1982. 70th Anniv of Independence.
2151 **449** 20q. deep red, red & blk 20 15
2152 – 1l.20 black, grn & red 85 60
2153 – 2l.40 brown, buff and red . . . . 1·90 1·50
DESIGNS: 20q. Ismail Qemali (patriot) and crowd around building; 2l.40, Six freedom fighters (58 × 55 mm).

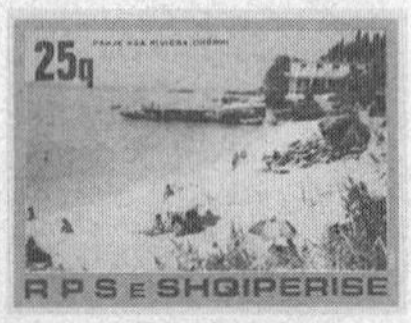

450 Dhermi

1982. Coastal Views. Multicoloured.
2155 25q. Type **450** 20 15
2156 80q. Sarande 55 35
2157 1l.20 Ksamil 85 55
2158 1l.55 Lukove . . . . 1·10 1·00

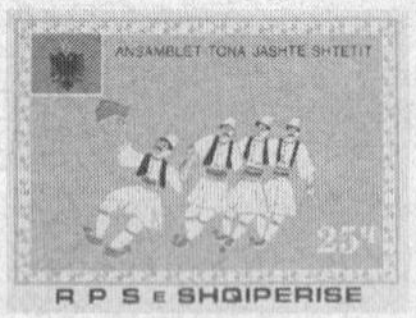

451 Male Dancers

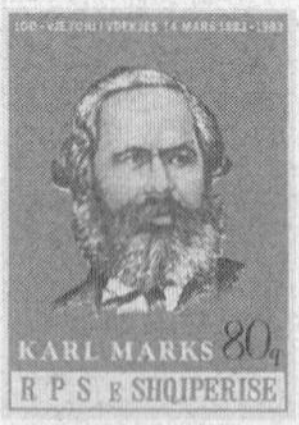

452 Karl Marx

1983. Folk Dance Assemblies Abroad. Mult.
2159 25q. Type **451** 15 10
2160 80q. Male dancers and drummer 50 30
2161 1l.20 Musicians 70 40
2162 1l.55 Group of female dancers . . . . 1·00 90

1983. Death Centenary of Karl Marx.
2163 **452** 80q. multicoloured . . . 1·00 50
2164 1l.10 multicoloured . . . 1·25 60

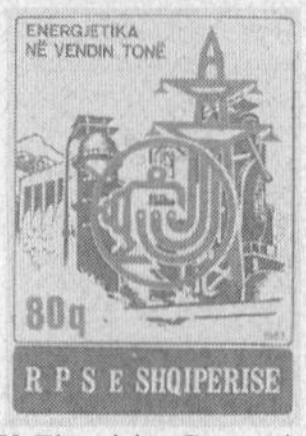

453 Electricity Generation

1983. Energy Development.
2165 **453** 80q. blue and orange . . 55 35
2166 – 1l.10 mauve and green 90 55
DESIGN: 1l.10, Gas and oil production.

1983. Anti-fascist Heroes (5th series). As T **424**. Multicoloured.
2167 25q. Asim Zeneli and Nazmi Rushiti 20 15
2168 80q. Shyqyri Ishmi, Shyqyri Alimerko and Myzafer Asqeriu 55 35
2169 1l.20 Qybra Sokoli, Qeriba Derri and Ylbere Bilibashi 90 55
2170 1l.55 Themo Vasi and Abaz Shehu . . . . 1·25 75

454 Congress Emblem

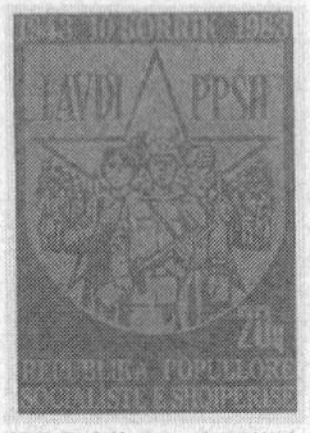

456 Soldier and Militia

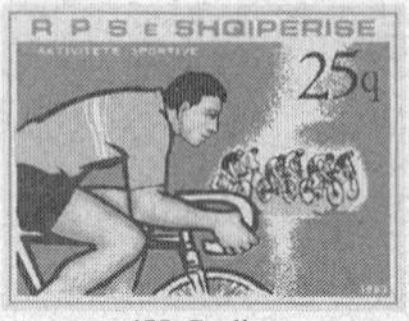

455 Cycling

1983. 9th Women's Union Congress.
2171 **454** 80q. multicoloured . . . 60 50
2172 1l.10 multicoloured . . . 70 60

1983. Sport and Leisure. Multicoloured.
2173 25q. Type **455** 25 15
2174 80q. Chess . . . . 1·00 50
2175 1l.20 Gymnastics . . . . . 1·25 70
2176 1l.55 Wrestling . . . . . . 1·40 80

1983. 40th Anniv of People's Army.
2177 **456** 20q. gold and red . . . 20 15
2178 – 1l.20 gold and red . . . 85 50
2179 – 2l.40 gold and brown . . 1·75 1·40
DESIGNS: 1l.20, Soldier; 2l.40 Factory guard.

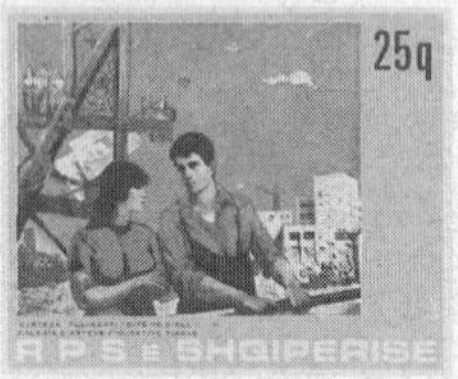

457 "Sunny Day" (Myrteza Fushekati)

1983. Paintings from Gallery of Figurative Arts, Tirana. Multicoloured.
2180 25q. Type **457** 20 15
2181 80q. "Morning Gossip" (Niko Progri) 55 40
2182 1l.20 "29th November, 1944" (Harilla Dhimo) . . 85 50
2183 1l.55 "Demolition" (Pandi Mele) . . . . 1·10 70

1983. National Folklore Festival, Gjirokaster. As T **402**. Multicoloured.
2185 25q. Sword dance 25 15
2186 80q. Kerchief dance 75 45
2187 1l.20 Musicians . . . . . . 1·10 70
2188 1l.55 Women dancers with garlands . . . . 1·25 85

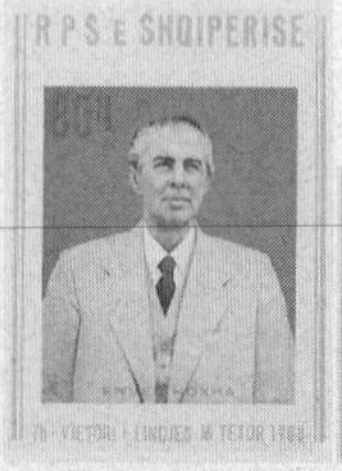

458 Enver Hoxha

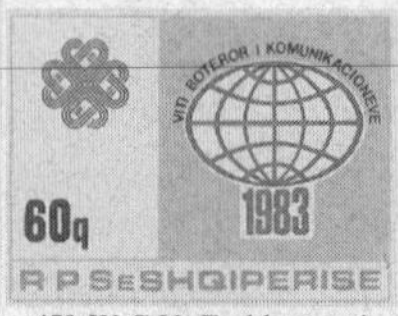

459 W.C.Y. Emblem and Globe

1983. 75th Birthday of Enver Hoxha.
2189 **458** 80q. multicoloured . . . 45 35
2190 1l.20 multicoloured . . . 75 50
2191 1l.80 multicoloured . . . 1·40 85

1983. World Communications Year.
2193 **459** 60q. multicoloured . . . 40 25
2194 1l.20 blue, orange & blk 65 45

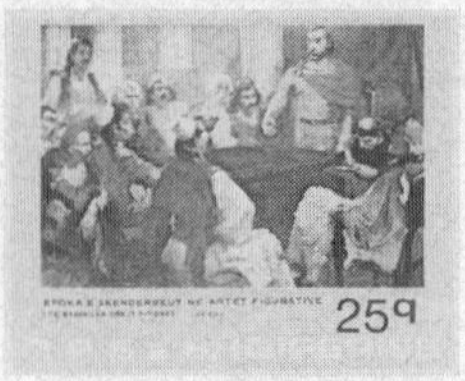

460 "Combine to Triumph" (J. Keraj)

1983. Skanderbeg Epoch in Art. Multicoloured.
2195 25q. Type **460** 20 15
2196 80q. "The Heroic Resistance at Krujes" (N. Bakalli) . . 60 35
2197 1l.20 "United we are Unconquerable by our Enemies" (N. Progri) . . 90 55
2198 1l.55 "Assembly at Lezhe" (B. Ahmeti) . . . . . . 1·25 70

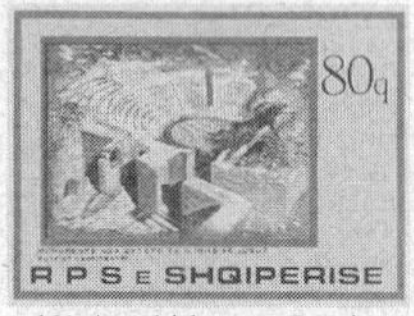

461 Amphitheatre, Butrint (Buthrotum)

1983. Graeco-Roman Remains in Illyria. Mult.
2200 80q. Type **461** . . . . . . 1·00 75
2201 1l.20 Colonnade, Apoloni Cesma (Apollonium) . . . 1·50 90
2202 1l.80 Vaulted gallery of amphitheatre, Dyrrah (Epidamnus) . . . . . . 1·90 1·25

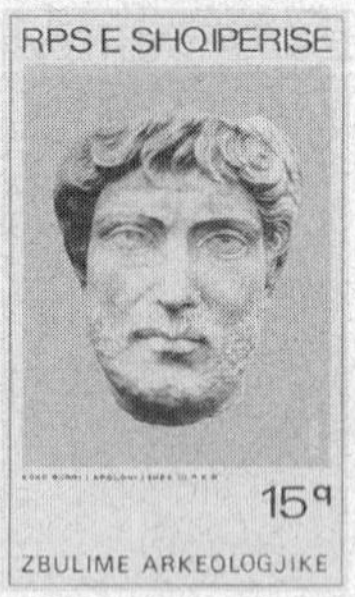

462 Man's Head from Apoloni

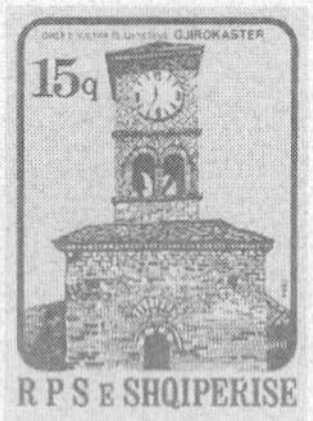

463 Clock Tower, Gjirokaster

1984. Archaeological Discoveries (1st series). Mult.
2203 15q. Type **462** 20 15
2204 25q. Tombstone from Korce 25 15
2205 80q. Woman's head from Apoloni 55 35
2206 1l.10 Child's head from Tren 85 65
2207 1l.20 Man's head from Dyrrah 90 70
2208 2l.20 Bronze statuette of Eros from Dyrrah . . . . 1·75 1·25
See also Nos. 2258/61.

1984. Clock Towers.
2209 **463** 15q. purple 20 15
2210 – 25q. brown 25 15
2211 – 80q. violet 55 35
2212 – 1l.10 red 85 65
2213 – 1l.20 green 90 70
2214 – 2l.20 brown . . . . . . 1·75 1·25
DESIGNS: 25q. Kavaje; 80q. Elbasan; 1l.10, Tirana; 1l.20, Peqin; 2l.20, Kruje.

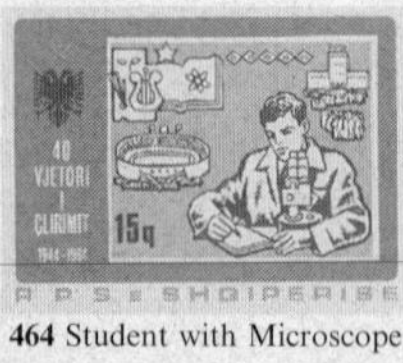

464 Student with Microscope

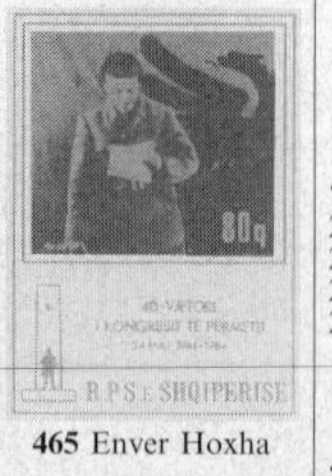

465 Enver Hoxha

1984. 40th Anniv of Liberation (1st issue). Mult.
2215 15q. Type **464** 20 15
2216 25q. Soldier with flag . . . 25 15
2217 80q. Schoolchildren 65 35
2218 1l.10 Soldier, ships, airplanes and weapons . . 95 65
2219 1l.20 Workers with flag . . 1·10 75
2220 2l.20 Armed guards on patrol . . . . 4·00 1·75
See also Nos. 2255/6.

1984. Anti-fascist Heroes (6th series). As T **424**. Multicoloured.
2221 15q. Manush Alimani, Mustafa Matohiti and Kastriot Muco 15 10
2222 25q. Zaho Koka, Reshit Collaku and Maliq Muco 20 15
2223 1l.20 Lefter Talo, Tom Kola and Fuat Babani 85 55
2224 2l.20 Myslysm Shyri, Dervish Hekali and Skender Caci . . . . . . 1·75 1·25

1984. 40th Anniv of Permet Congress.
2225 **465** 80q. brown, orge & red 1·50 80
2226 – 1l.10 black, yell & lilac 1·75 1·25
DESIGN: 1l.10, Resistance fighter (detail of monument).

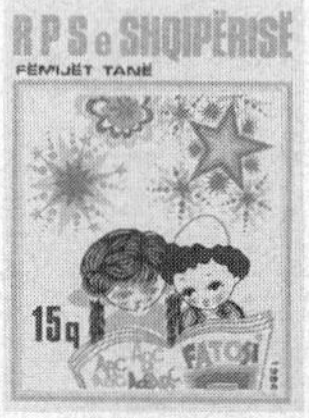

466 Children reading Comic

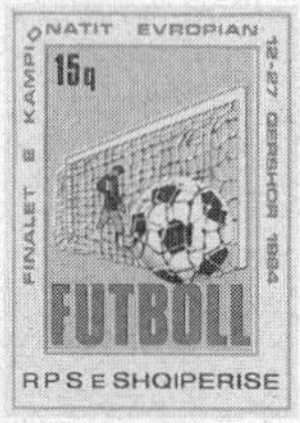

467 Football in Goal

1984. Children. Multicoloured.
2227 15q. Type **466** 20 15
2228 25q. Children with toys . . 25 20
2229 60q. Children gardening and rainbow 55 35
2230 2l.80 Children flying kite bearing Albanian arms . . 2·25 1·75

1984. European Football Championship Finals. Multicoloured.
2231 15q. Type **467** 40 20
2232 25q. Referee and football . . 60 30
2233 1l.20 Football and map of Europe . . . . 1·25 60
2234 2l.20 Football and pitch . . 3·50 1·75

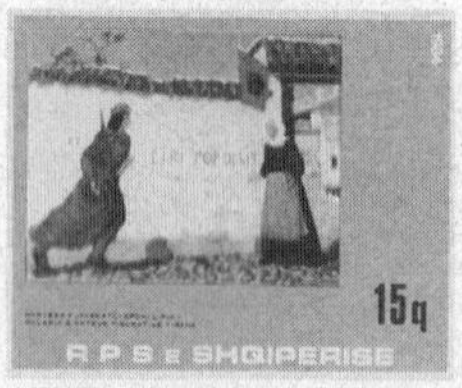

468 "Freedom is Here" (Myrteza Fushekati)

1984. Paintings from Gallery of Figurative Arts, Tirana. Multicoloured.
2235 15q. Type **468** 20 15
2236 25q. "Morning" (Zamir Mati) (vert) 25 15
2237 80q. "My Darling" (Agim Zajmi) (vert) 70 40
2238 2l.60 "For the Partisans" (Arben Basha) . . . . . 2·00 1·75

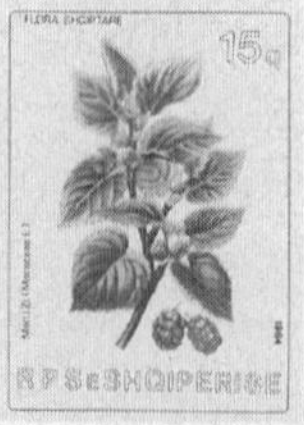

469 Mulberry

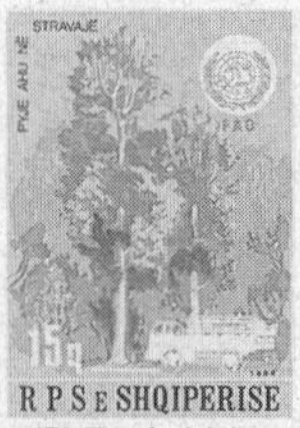

471 Truck driving through Forest

1984. Flowers. Multicoloured.
2240 15q. Type **469** 25 15
2241 25q. Plantain 65 15
2242 1l.20 Hypericum . . . . . 3·25 1·10
2243 2l.20 Edelweiss . . . . . . 6·25 2·50

1984. Forestry. Multicoloured.
2245 15q. Type **471** 40 25
2246 25q. Transporting logs on overhead cable 75 40
2247 1l.20 Sawmill in forest . . 2·25 75
2248 2l.20 Lumberjack sawing down trees . . . . 3·00 1·60

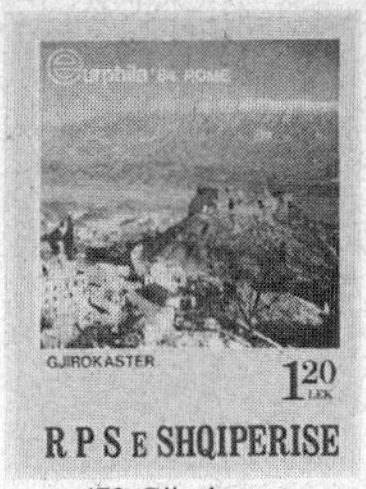

472 Gjirokaster

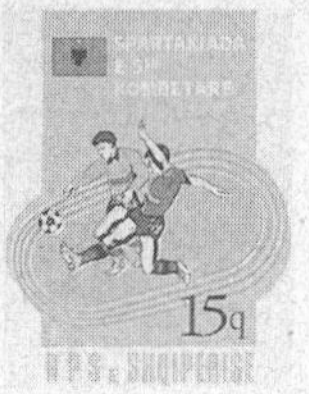

473 Football

1984. "Eurphila '84" Int Stamp Exn, Rome.
2249 **472** 1l.20 multicoloured . . . 1·10 90

1984. 5th National Spartakiad. Multicoloured.
2250 15q. Type **473** 20 15
2251 25q. Running 25 15
2252 80q. Weightlifting 65 35
2253 2l.20 Pistol shooting . . . . 1·75 1·40

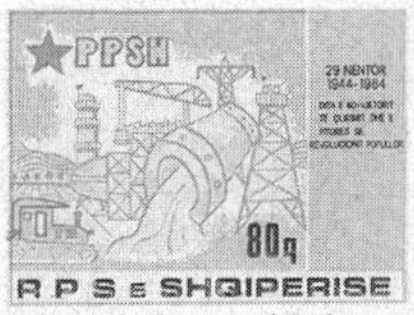

474 Agriculture and Industry

1984. 40th Anniv of Liberation (2nd issue). Mult.
2255 80q. Type **474** 80 40
2256 1l.10 Soldiers and flag . . . 1·25 60

1985. Archaeological Discoveries (2nd series). As T **462**, showing Illyrian finds. Multicoloured.
2258 15q. Pot 25 15
2259 80q. Terracotta head of woman 65 35
2260 1l.20 Terracotta bust of Aphrodite . . . . 1·00 65
2261 1l.70 Bronze statuette of Nike . . . . 1·75 1·25

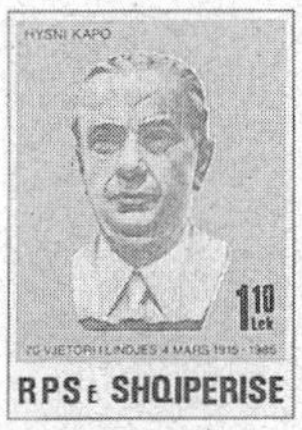

476 Kapo (bust)

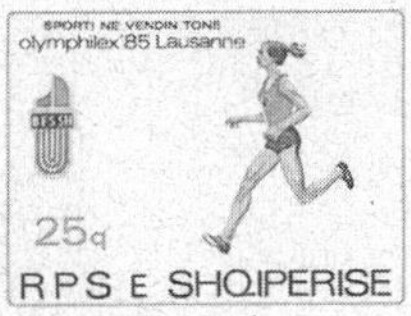

477 Running

1985. 70th Birthday of Hysni Kapo (politician).
2262 **476** 90q. black and red . . . 90 60
2263 1l.10 black and blue . . 1·25 75

1985. "Olymphilex '85" Olympic Stamps Exhibition, Lausanne. Multicoloured.
2264 25q. Type **477** 25 15
2265 60q. Weightlifting 50 25
2266 1l.20 Football . . . . . . 1·10 65
2267 1l.50 Pistol shooting . . . . 1·60 1·10

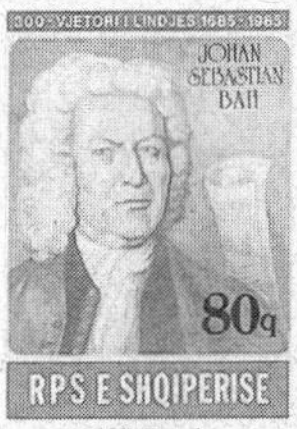

478 Bach

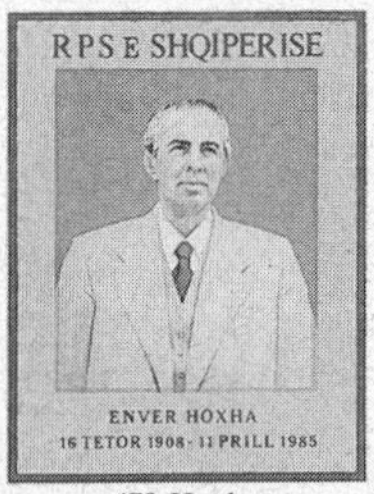

479 Hoxha

1985. 300th Birth Anniv of Johann Sebastian Bach (composer).
2268 **478** 80q. orange, brn & blk 6·50 4·50
2269 – 1l.20 blue, dp blue & blk 7·50 5·50
DESIGN—1l.20, Bach's birthplace, Eisenach.

1985. Enver Hoxha Commemoration.
2270 **479** 80q. multicoloured . . . 1·00 80

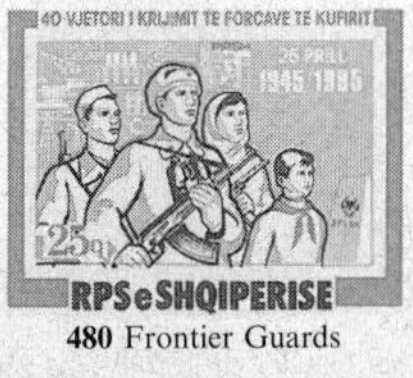

480 Frontier Guards

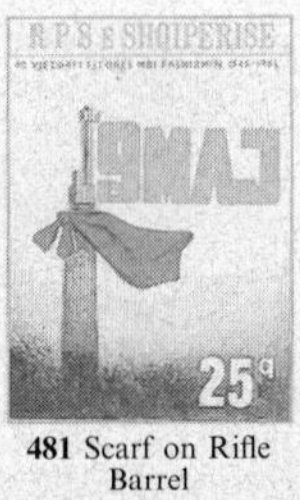

481 Scarf on Rifle Barrel

1985. 40th Anniv of Frontier Force. Multicoloured.
2272 25q. Type **480** 75 50
2273 80q. Frontier guard . . . . 1·75 1·00

1985. Anti-fascist Heroes (7th series). As T **424**. Multicoloured.
2274 25q. Mitro Xhani, Nimete Progonati and Kozma Nushi 40 25
2275 40q. Ajet Xhindoli, Mustafa Kacaci and Estref Caka 60 40
2276 60q. Celo Sinani, Llambro Andoni and Meleo Gosnishti 80 50
2277 1l.20 Thodhori Mastora, Fejzi Micoli and Hysen Cino . . . . 1·50 1·00

1985. 40th Anniv of V.E. (Victory in Europe) Day. Multicoloured.
2278 25q. Type **481** 75 50
2279 80q. Crumpled swastika and hand holding rifle butt . . 1·75 1·00

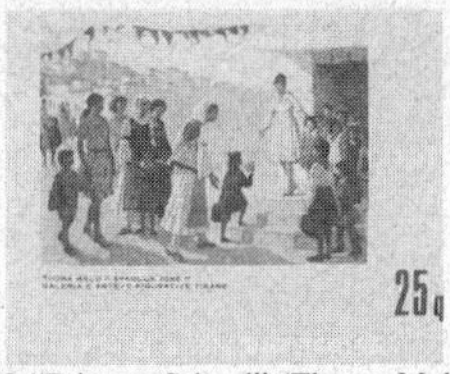

482 "Primary School" (Thoma Malo)

1985. Paintings from Gallery of Figurative Arts, Tirana. Multicoloured.
2280 25q. Type **482** 25 15
2281 80q. "Heroes and Mother" (Hysen Devolli) (vert) . . 90 35
2282 90q. "Mother writing" (Angjelin Dodmasej) (vert) 1·00 70
2283 1l.20 "Women off to Work" (Ksenofen Dilo) . . . . . 1·40 70

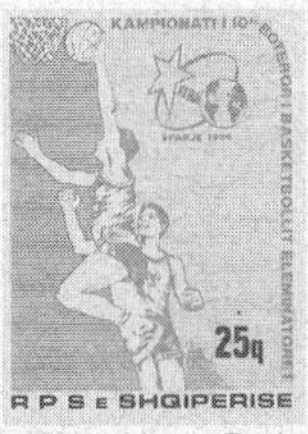

483 Scoring a Goal

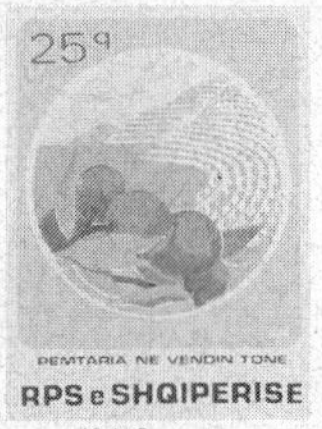

484 Oranges

1985. 10th World Basketball Championship, Spain.
2285 **483** 25q. blue and black . . 25 15
2286 – 80q. green and black . . 65 35
2287 – 1l.20 violet and black . . 1·00 70
2288 – 1l.60 red and black . . . 1·60 1·10
DESIGNS: 80q. Player running with ball; 1l.20, Defending goal; 1l.60, Defender capturing ball.

1985. Fruit Trees. Multicoloured.
2289 25q. Type **484** . . . . . . 1·50 55
2290 80q. Plums . . . . 2·25 80
2291 1l.20 Apples . . . . 3·25 1·50
2292 1l.60 Cherries . . . . . . 6·50 2·75

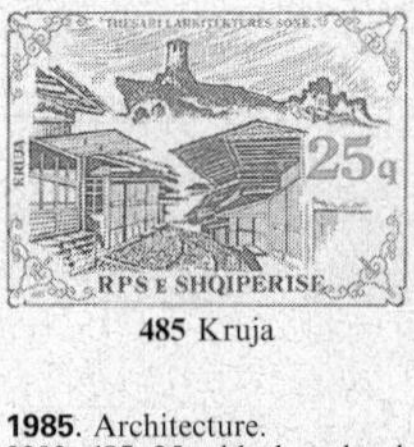

485 Kruja

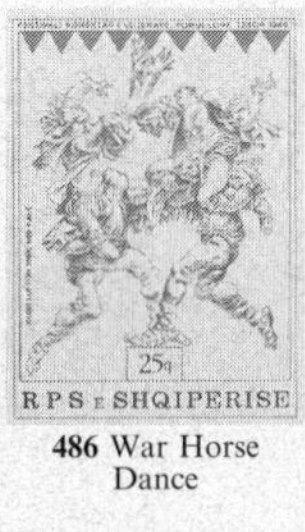

486 War Horse Dance

1985. Architecture.
2293 **485** 25q. black and red . . . 25 15
2294 – 80q. black, grey & brown . . . . 1·25 35
2295 – 1l.20 black, brown & bl 1·75 65
2296 – 1l.60 black, brown & red 2·50 1·10
DESIGNS: 80q. Gjirokastra; 1l.20, Berat; 1l.60, Shkoder.

1985. National Folklore Festival. Dances.
2297 **486** 25q. brown, red & black 25 15
2298 – 80q. brown, red & black 65 35
2299 – 1l.20 brown, red & blk 1·00 65
2300 – 1l.60 brown, red & blk 1·60 1·10
DESIGNS: 80q. Pillow dance; 1l.20, Ladies' kerchief dance; 1l.60, Men's one-legged pair dance.

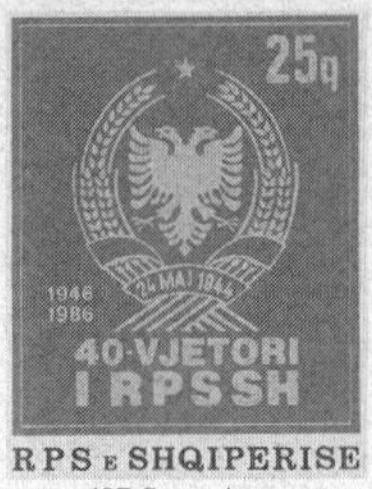

487 State Arms

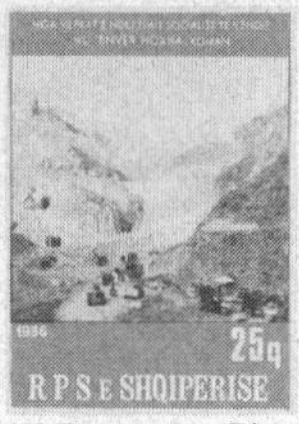

488 Dam across River Drin

1986. 40th Anniv of Albanian People's Republic.
2302 **487** 25q. gold, red and black 60 40
2303 – 80q. multicoloured . . . 1·50 80
DESIGN: 80q. "Comrade Hoxha announcing the News to the People" (Vilson Kilica) and arms.

1986. Enver Hoxha Hydroelectric Power Station. Multicoloured.
2304 25q. Type **488** . . . . . . 2·50 1·00
2305 80q. Control building . . . 5·50 3·00

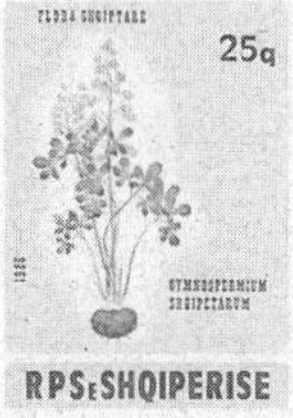

489 "Gymnospermium shqipetarum"

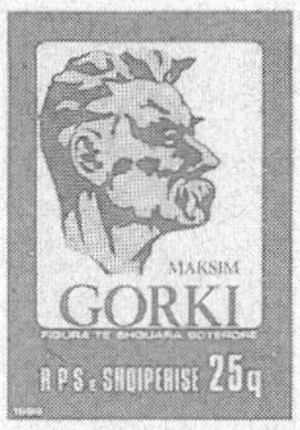

490 Maksim Gorky (writer)

1986. Flowers. Multicoloured.
2306 25q. Type **489** 60 40
2307 1l.20 "Leucojum valentinum" . . . . . . 3·00 1·50

1986. Anniversaries.
2308 **490** 25q. brown 25 15
2309 – 80q. violet . . . . . . 1·25 65
2310 – 1l.20 green . . . . . . 2·50 2·00
2311 – 2l.40 purple . . . . . . 4·25 2·75
DESIGNS: 25q. Type **490** (50th death anniv); 80q. Andre Ampere (physicist and mathematician, 150th death anniv); 1l.20, James Watt (inventor, 250th birth); 2l.40, Franz Liszt (composer, death cent).

1986. Anti-fascist Heroes (8th series). As T **424**. Multicoloured.
2313 25q. Ramiz Aranitasi, Inajete Dumi and Laze Nuro Ferraj 80 60
2314 80q. Dine Kalenja, Kozma Naska, Met Hasa and Fahri Raalbani . . . . . 2·00 1·00
2315 1l.20 Hiqmet Buzi, Bajram Tusha, Mumin Selami and Hajredin Bylyshi . . . . 3·00 2·00

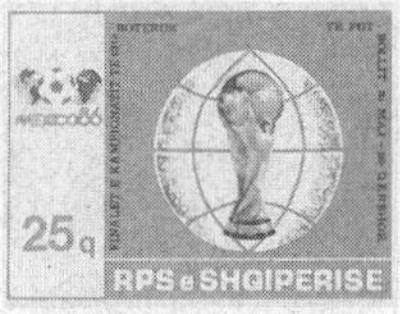

491 Trophy on Globe

1986. World Cup Football Championship, Mexico. Multicoloured.
2316 25q. Type **491** 30 20
2317 1l.20 Goalkeeper's hands and ball . . . . 1·25 1·00

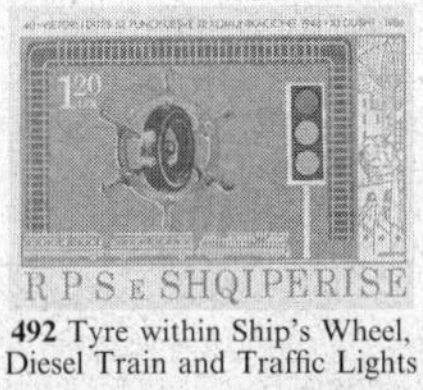

492 Tyre within Ship's Wheel, Diesel Train and Traffic Lights

1986. 40th Anniv of Transport Workers' Day.
2319 **492** 1l.20 multicoloured . . . 4·25 1·25

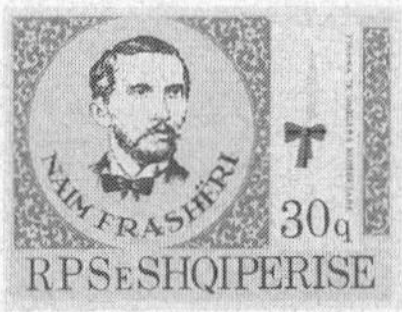

493 Naim Frasheri (poet)

1986. Anniversaries. Multicoloured.
2320 30q. Type **493** (140th birth anniv) 50 15
2321 60q. Ndre Mjeda (poet, 120th birth anniv) . . . . 1·00 65
2322 90q. Petro Nini Luarasi (jounalist, 75th death anniv) . . . . 1·50 1·00
2323 1l. Andon Zaka Cajupi (poet, 120th birth anniv) 1·60 1·10
2324 1l.20 Millosh Gjergj Nikolla (Migjeni) (revolutionary writer, 75th birth anniv) 2·00 1·40
2325 2l.60 Urani Rumbo (women's education pioneer, 50th death anniv) 4·25 2·75

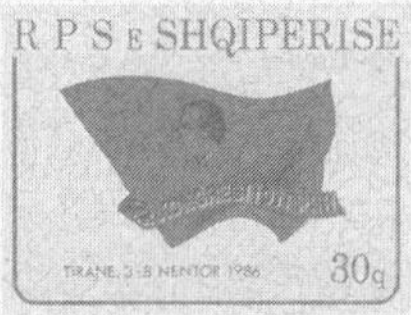

494 Congress Emblem

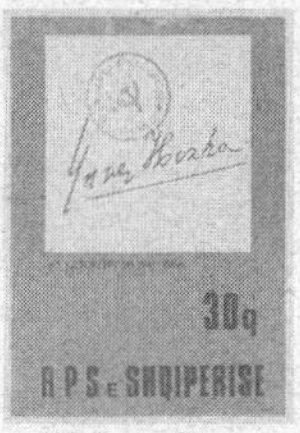

495 Party Stamp and Enver Hoxha's Signature

1986. 9th Workers' Party Congress, Tirana.
2326 **494** 30q. multicoloured . . . 5·75 4·25

1986. 45th Anniv of Workers' Party.
2327 **495** 30q. red, grey and gold 1·10 55
2328 – 1l.20 red, orange & gold 4·75 2·40
DESIGNS: 1l.20, Profiles of Marx, Engels, Lenin and Stalin and Tirana house where Party was founded.

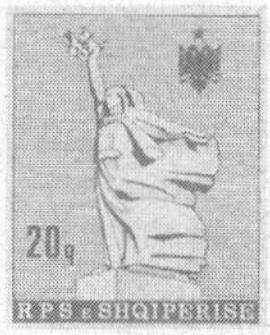

496 "Mother Albania"

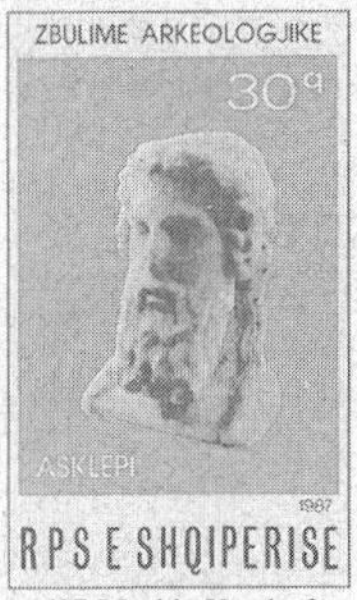

497 Marble Head of Aesculapius

1986.
2329 **496** 10q. blue 10 10
2330 20q. red 10 10
2331 30q. red 10 10
2332 50q. brown 20 15
2333 60q. green 25 15
2334 80q. red 30 20
2335 90q. blue 35 25
2336 1l.20 green 45 30
2337 1l.60 purple 60 40
2338 2l.20 green 85 55
2339 3l. brown . . . . 1·10 75
2340 6l. yellow . . . . 2·25 1·50

1987. Archaeological Discoveries. Multicoloured.
2341 30q. Type **497** 45 30
2342 80q. Terracotta figure of Aphrodite . . . . 1·10 75
2343 1l. Bronze figure of Pan . . 1·40 95
2344 1l.20 Limestone head of Jupiter . . . . 1·75 1·10

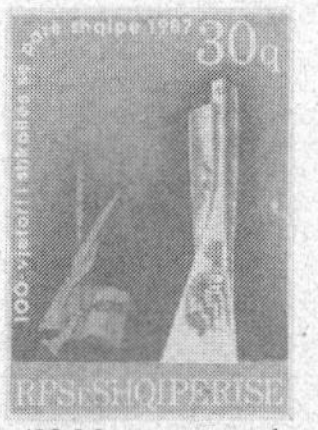

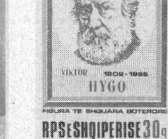

498 Monument and Centenary Emblem

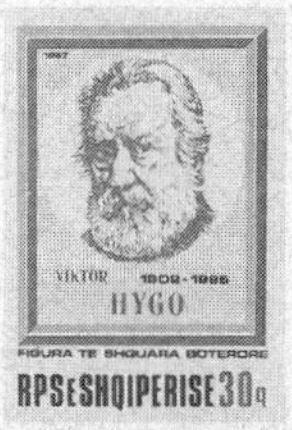

499 Victor Hugo (writer, 185th birth anniv)

1987. Centenary of First Albanian School.
2345 **498** 30q. brown, lt brn & yell 30 20
2346 – 80q. multicoloured . . . 80 55
2347 – 1l.20 multicoloured . . . 1·25 85
DESIGNS: 80q. First school building; 1l.20, Woman soldier running, girl reading book and boy doing woodwork.

1987. Anniversaries.
2348 **499** 30q. vio, lavender & blk 30 20
2349 – 80q. brown, lt brn & blk 80 60
2350 – 90q. dp blue, blue & blk 90 65
2351 – 1l.30 dp grn, grn & brn 1·25 90
DESIGNS: 80q. Galileo Galilei (astronomer, 345th death); 90q. Charles Darwin (naturalist, 105th death); 1l.30. Miguel de Cervantes Saavedra (writer, 440th birth).

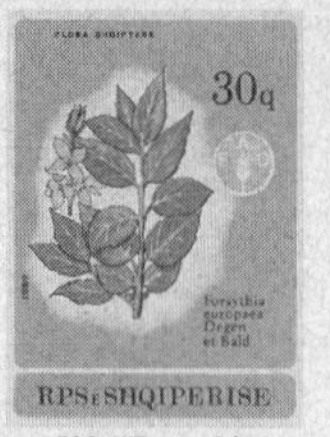

500 "Forsythia europaea"

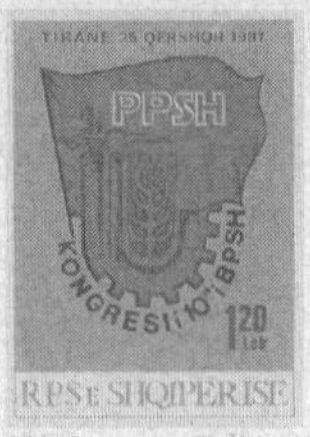

501 Congress Emblem

1987. Flowers. Multicoloured.
2352 30q. Type **500** 30 20
2353 90q. "Moltkia doerfleri" . . 90 60
2354 2l.10 "Wulfenia baldacii" . . 2·10 1·40

1987. 10th Trade Unions Congress, Tirana.
2355 **501** 1l.20 dp red, red & gold 3·00 2·00

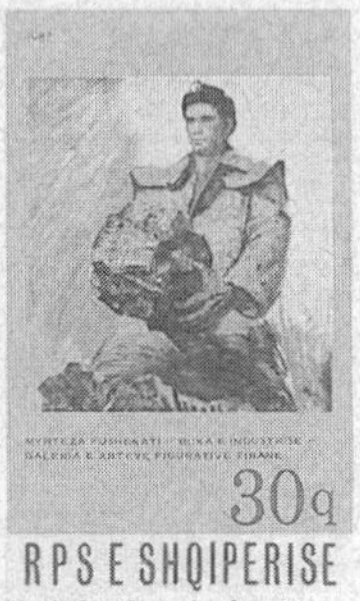

502 "The Bread of Industry" (Myrteza Fushekati)

1987. Paintings from Gallery of Figurative Arts, Tirana. Multicoloured.
2356 30q. Type **502** 25 20
2357 80q. "Partisan Gift" (Skender Kokobobo) . . 65 50
2358 1l. "Sowers" (Bujar Asllani) (horiz) 80 60
2359 1l.20 "At the Foundry" (Clirim Ceka) (horiz) . . 90 75

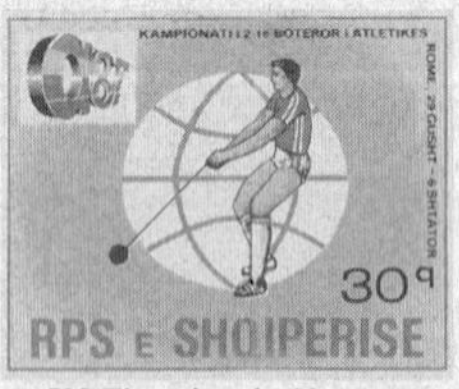

503 Throwing the Hammer

1987. World Light Athletics Championships, Rome. Multicoloured.
2360 30q. Type **503** 25 20
2361 90q. Running 75 55
2362 1l.10 Putting the shot . . . 95 70

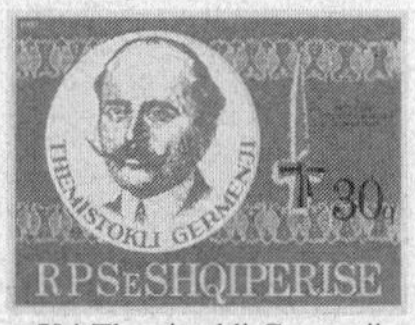

504 Themistokli Germenji (revolutionary, 70th death)

1987. Anniversaries.
2364 **504** 30q. brown, red & black 35 25
2365 – 80q. red, scarlet & black 1·00 65
2366 – 90q. violet, red and black . . . . 1·10 75
2367 – 1l.30 green, red & black 1·60 1·10
DESIGNS: 80q. Bajram Curri (organizer of Albanian League, 125th birth); 90q. Aleks Stavre Drenova (poet, 40th death); 1l.30, Gjerasim Qiriazi (educational pioneer, 126th birth).

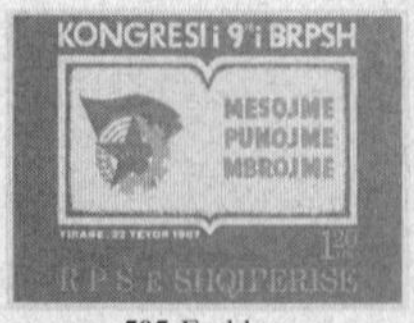

505 Emblem

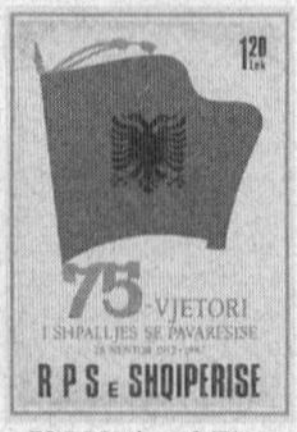

506 National Flag

1987. 9th Young Communists' Union Congress, Tirana.
2368 **505** 1l.20 multicoloured . . . 4·00 2·75

1987. 75th Anniv of Independence.
2369 **506** 1l.20 multicoloured . . . 4·00 2·75

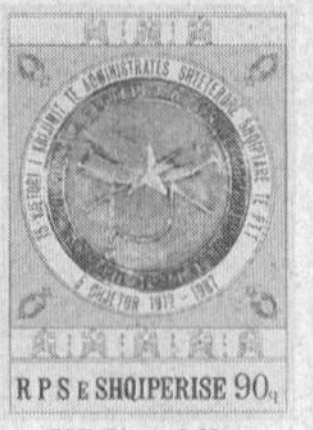

507 Post Office Emblem

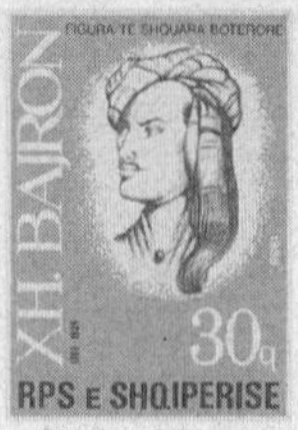

508 Lord Byron (writer, bicentenary)

1987. 75th Anniv of Albanian Postal Administration. Multicoloured.
2370 90q. Type **507** . . . . . . 6·00 4·00
2371 1l.20 National emblem on bronze medallion . . . . 8·50 5·75

1988. Birth Anniversaries.
2372 **508** 30q. black and orange 2·75 2·25
2373 – 1l.20 black and mauve 10·50 8·50
DESIGN: 1l.20, Eugene Delacroix (painter, 190th anniv.).

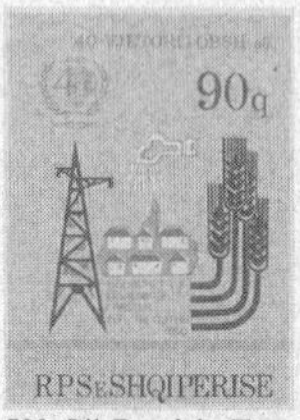

509 Oil Derrick, Tap, Houses and Wheat Ears

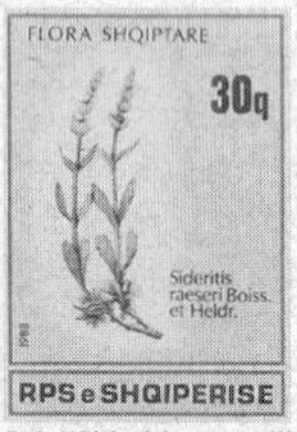

510 "Sideritis raeseri"

1988. 40th Anniv of W.H.O.
2374 **509** 90q. multicoloured . . . 17·00 14·00
2375 1l.20 multicoloured . . . 23·00 19·00

1988. Flowers. Multicoloured.
2376 30q. Type **510** . . . . . . 2·25 1·75
2377 90q. "Lunaria telekiana" . . 6·75 5·50
2378 2l.10 "Sanguisorba albanica" . . . . 16·00 13·00

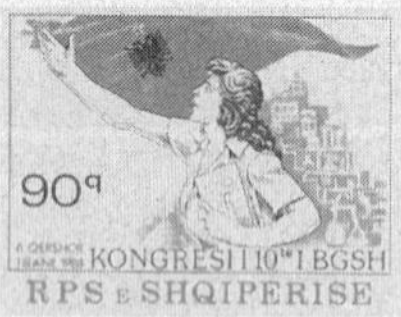

511 Flag and Woman with Book

1988. 10th Women's Union Congress, Tirana.
2379 **511** 90q. black, red & orange 7·00 6·00

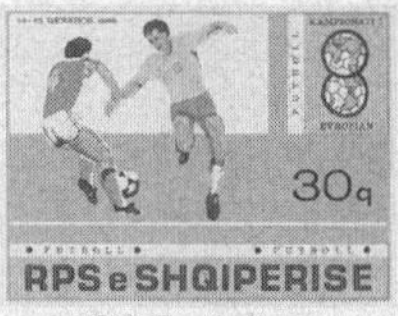

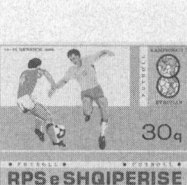

512 Footballers

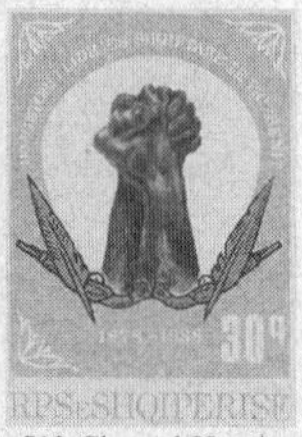

513 Clasped Hands

1988. 8th European Football Championship, West Germany. Multicoloured.
2380 30q. Type **512** 65 50
2381 80q. Players jumping for ball . . . . 1·75 1·25
2382 1l.20 Tackling . . . . . . 2·50 1·90

1988. 110th Anniv of League of Prizren. Mult.
2384 30q. Type **513** . . . . . . 6·50 6·50
2385 1l.20 League Headquarters, Prizren . . . . 27·00 27·00

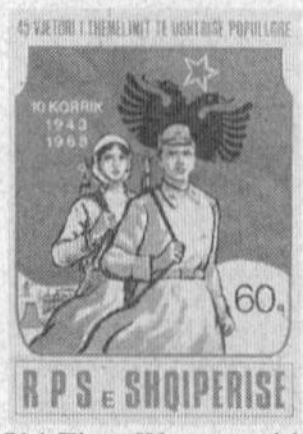

514 Flag, Woman with Rifle and Soldier

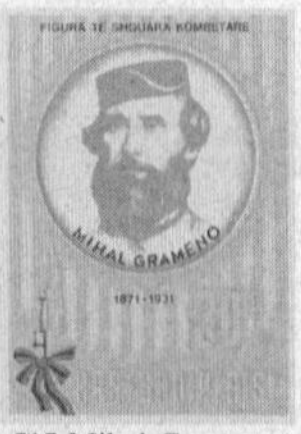

515 Mihal Grameno (writer)

1988. 45th Anniv of People's Army. Multicoloured.
2386 60q. Type **514** . . . . . . 15·00 15·00
2387 90q. Army monument, partisans and Labinot house . . . . 23·00 23·00

1988. Multicoloured.
2388 30q. Type **515** . . . . . . 5·50 5·50
2389 90q. Bajo Topulli (revolutionary) . . . . . 16·00 16·00
2390 1l. Murat Toptani (sculptor and poet) . . . . 18·00 18·00
2391 1l.20 Jul Variboba (poet) . . 22·00 22·00

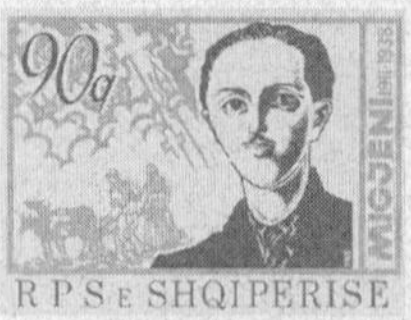

516 Migjeni

1988. 50th Death Anniv of Millosh Gjergj Nikolla (Migjeni) (writer).
2392 **516** 90q. silver and brown . . 6·75 6·00

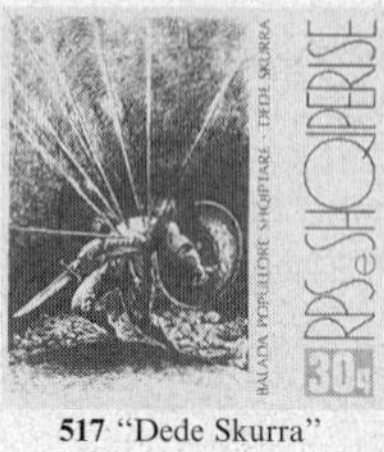

517 "Dede Skurra"

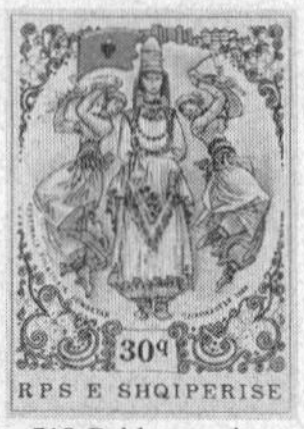

518 Bride wearing Fezzes, Mirdita

1988. Ballads. Each black and grey.
2393 30q. Type **517** . . . . . . 5·00 5·00
2394 90q. "Young Omer" . . . . 15·00 15·00
2395 1l.20 "Gjergj Elez Alia" . . 19·00 19·00

1988. National Folklore Festival, Gjirokaster. Wedding Customs. Multicoloured.
2396 30q. Type **518** . . . . . . 9·00 9·00
2397 1l.20 Pan Dance, Gjirokaster . . . . 35·00 35·00

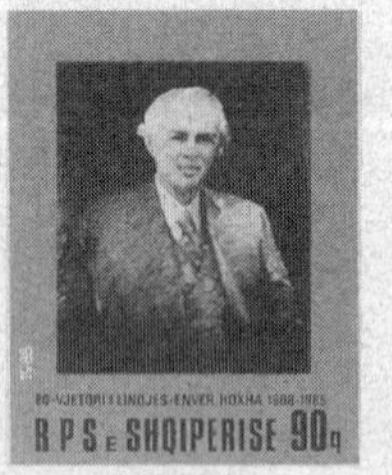

519 Hoxha

1988. 80th Birth Anniv of Enver Hoxha. Mult.
2398 90q. Type **519** . . . . . . 3·00 3·00
2399 1l.20 Enver Hoxha Museum (horiz) . . . . 4·00 4·00

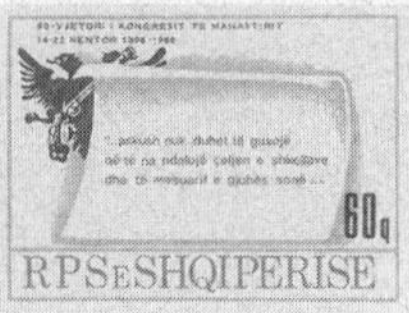

520 Detail of Congress Document

1988. 80th Anniv of Monastir Language Congress. Multicoloured.
2400 60q. Type **520** . . . . . . 12·50 12·50
2401 90q. Alphabet book and Congress building . . . . 16·00 16·00

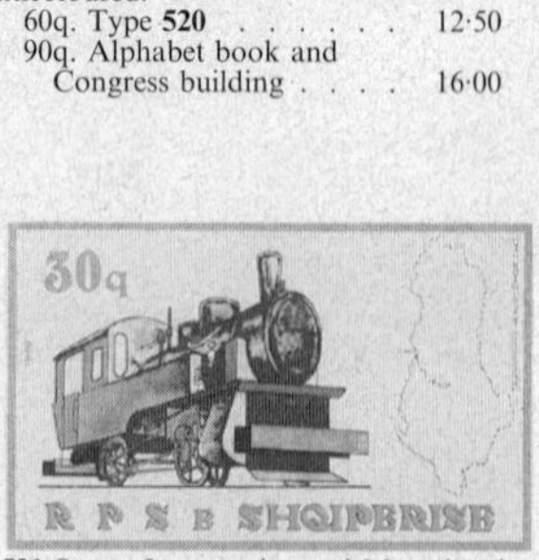

521 Steam Locomotive and Map showing 1947 Railway line

1989. Railway Locomotives. Multicoloured.
2402 30q. Type **521** 40 10
2403 90q. Polish steam locomotive and map of 1949 network . . . . . . 1·25 35
2404 1l.20 Diesel locomotive and 1978 network . . . . . . 1·60 45
2405 1l.80 Diesel locomotive and 1985 network . . . . . . 2·40 70
2406 2l.40 Czechoslovakian diesel-electric locomotive and 1988 network . . . . 3·25 90

522 Entrance to Two-storey Tomb

1989. Archaeological Discoveries in Illyria.
2407 **522** 30q. black, brown & grey 15 10
2408 – 90q. black and green . . 50 35
2409 – 2l.10 multicoloured . . . 1·10 75
DESIGNS: 90q. Buckle showing battle scene; 2l.10, Earring depicting head.

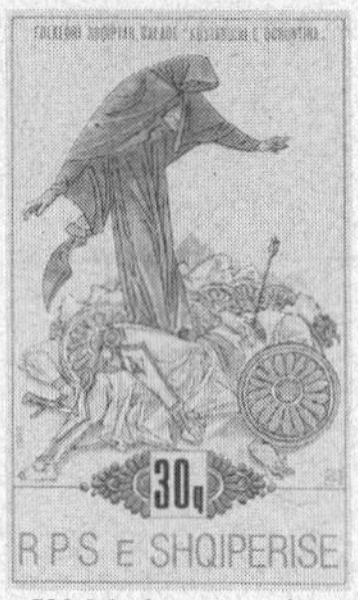

523 Mother mourning Son

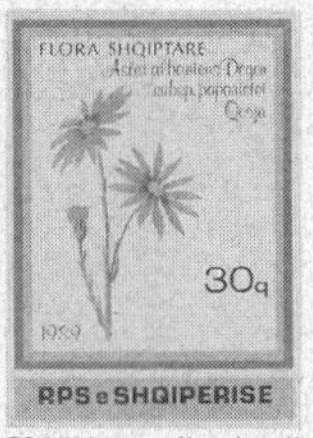

524 "Aster albanicus"

1989. "Kostandini and Doruntina" (folk tale). Mult.
2410 30q. Type **523** 15 10
2411 80q. Mother weeping over tomb and son rising from dead 45 30
2412 1l. Son and his sister on horseback 55 35
2413 1l.20 Mother and daughter reunited 65 45

1989. Flowers. Multicoloured.
2414 30q. Type **524** 15 10
2415 90q. "Orchis paparisti" . . 50 35
2416 2l.10 "Orchis albanica" . . 1·10 75

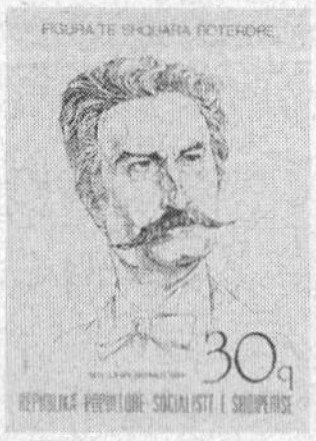

525 Johann Strauss (composer, 90th death anniv)

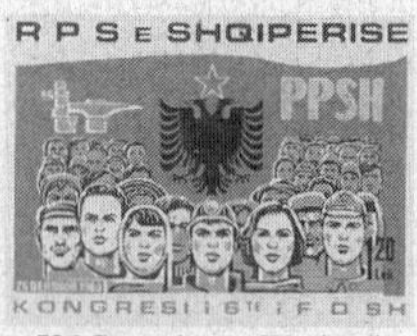

526 State Arms, Workers' Party Flag and Crowd

1989. Anniversaries. Each brown and gold.
2417 30q. Type **525** 15 10
2418 80q. Marie Curie (physicist, 55th death anniv) 45 30
2419 1l. Federico Garcia Lorca (writer, 53rd death anniv) 55 35
2420 1l.20 Albert Einstein (physicist, 110th birth anniv) 65 45

1989. 6th Albanian Democratic Front Congress, Tirana.
2421 **526** 1l.20 multicoloured . . . 5·00 4·00

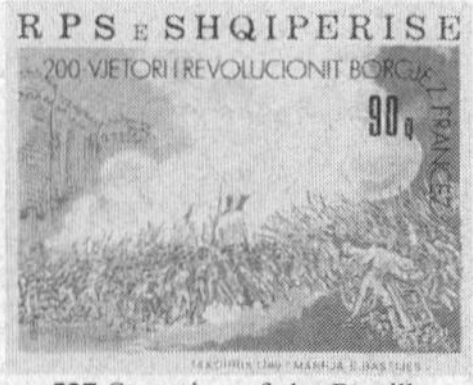

527 Storming of the Bastille

1989. Bicentenary of French Revolution. Mult.
2422 90q. Type **527** 40 30
2423 1l.20 Monument 55 40

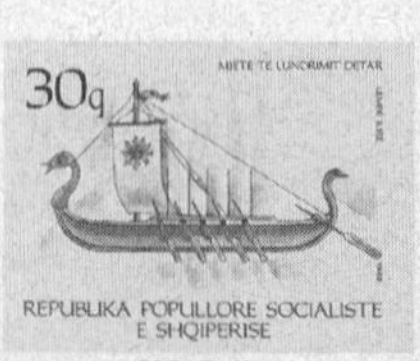

528 Galley

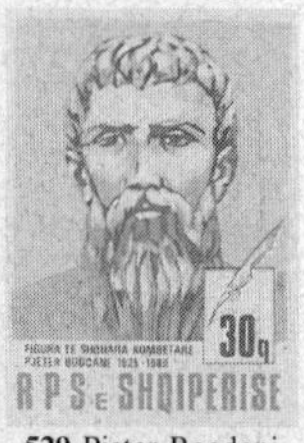

529 Pjeter Bogdani (writer, 300th anniv)

1989. Ships.
2424 **528** 30q. green and black . . 30 15

2425	– 80q. blue and black . .	75	35
2426	– 90q. blue and black . .	95	45
2427	– 11.30 lilac and black . .	1·25	60

DESIGNS: 80q. Kogge; 90q. Schooner; 11.30, "Tirana" (freighter).

1989. Death Anniversaries. Multicoloured.

2428	30q. Type 529	20	15
2429	80q. Gavril Dara (writer, centenary)	50	35
2430	90q. Thimi Mitko (writer, centenary (1990)) . . .	60	40
2431	11.30 Kole Idromeno (painter, 50th anniv) . . .	85	55

530 Engels, Marx and Marchers   531 Gymnastics

1989. 125th Anniv of "First International". Mult.

2432	90q. Type 530	40	30
2433	11.20 Factories, marchers and worker with pickaxe and rifle	55	40

1989. 6th National Spartakiad.

2434	531 30q. black, orange & red	15	10
2435	– 80q. black, lt grn & grn	40	25
2436	– 11. black, blue & dp blue	50	35
2437	– 11.20 black, pur & red	55	35

DESIGNS: 80q. Football; 11. Cycling; 11.20, Running.

532 Soldier   533 Chamois

1989. 45th Anniv of Liberation. Multicoloured.

2438	30q. Type 532	15	10
2439	80q. Date	35	25
2440	11. State arms	45	30
2441	11.20 Young couple . . .	50	35

1990. Endangered Animals. The Chamois. Mult.

2442	10q. Type 533	10	10
2443	30q. Mother and young . .	25	20
2444	80q. Chamois keeping lookout	65	50
2445	90q. Head of chamois . . .	70	55

534 Eagle Mask

1990. Masks. Multicoloured.

2446	30q. Type 534	10	10
2447	90q. Sheep	35	25
2448	11.20 Goat	50	35
2449	11.80 Stork	70	45

535 Caesar's Mushroom

1990. Fungi. Multicoloured.

2450	30q. Type 535	30	15
2451	90q. Parasol mushroom . .	85	40
2452	11.20 Cep	1·10	50
2453	11.80 "Clathrus cancelatus"	1·60	80

536 Engraving Die

1990. 150th Anniv of the Penny Black. Mult.

2454	90q. Type 536	50	40
2455	11.20 Mounted postal messenger	65	55
2456	11.80 Mail coach passengers reading letters	95	80

537 Mascot and Flags

1990. World Cup Football Championship, Italy. Multicoloured.

2457	30q. Type 537	15	10
2458	90q. Mascot running . . .	40	25
2459	11.20 Mascot preparing to kick ball	55	35

538 Young Van Gogh and Paintings

1990. Death Centenary of Vincent van Gogh (painter). Multicoloured.

2461	30q. Type 538	15	10
2462	90q. Van Gogh and woman in field	40	25
2463	21.10 Van Gogh in asylum	90	60

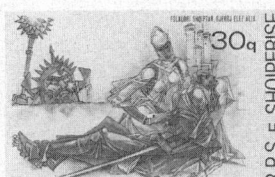

539 Gjergj Elez Alia lying wounded

1990. Gjergj Elez Alia (folk hero). Multicoloured.

2465	30q. Type 539	15	10
2466	90q. Alia being helped onto horse	40	25
2467	11.20 Alia fighting Bajloz .	50	35
2468	11.80 Alia on horseback and severed head of Bajloz . .	75	50

 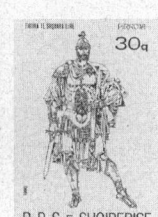

540 Mosque   541 Pirroja

1990. 2400th Anniv of Berat. Multicoloured.

2469	30q. Type 540	10	10
2470	90q. Triadha's Church . .	30	20
2471	11.20 River	40	25
2472	11.80 Onufri (artist) . . .	60	40
2473	21.40 Nikolla	80	55

1990. Illyrian Heroes. Each black.

2474	30q. Type 541	10	10
2475	90q. Teuta	30	20
2476	11.20 Bato	40	25
2477	11.80 Bardhyli	65	45

542 School and "Globe" of Books   543 "Albanian Horsemen" (Eugene Delacroix)

1990. International Literacy Year.

2478	542 90q. multicoloured . . .	30	20
2479	11.20 multicoloured . . .	40	25

1990. Albanians in Art. Multicoloured.

2480	30q. Type 543	15	10
2481	11.20 "Albanian Woman" (Camille Corot) . . .	50	40
2482	11.80 "Skanderbeg" (anon)	75	55

544 Boletini   545 Armorial Eagle

1991. 75th Death Anniv of Isa Boletini (revolutionary). Multicoloured.

2483	90q. Type 544	20	15
2484	11.20 Boletini and flag . . .	30	25

1991. 800th Anniv (1990) of Founding of Arberi State.

2485	545 90q. multicoloured . . .	20	15
2486	11.20 multicoloured . . .	30	25

546 "Woman reading"   547 "Cistus albanicus"

1991. 150th Birth Anniv of Pierre Auguste Renoir (artist). Multicoloured.

2487	30q. Type 546	15	10
2488	90q. "The Swing"	50	40
2489	11.20 "The Boat Club" (horiz)	85	50
2490	11.80 Still life (detail) (horiz)	95	70

1991. Flowers. Multicoloured.

2492	30q. Type 547	15	10
2493	90q. "Trifolium pilczii" . . .	35	25
2494	11.80 "Lilium albanicum" . .	75	55

548 Rozafa breastfeeding Child   549 Mozart conducting

1991. Imprisonment of Rozafa (folk tale). Mult.

2495	30q. Type 548	10	10
2496	90q. The three brothers talking to old man . . .	30	25
2497	11.20 Building of walls around Rozafa	40	30
2498	11.80 Figures symbolizing water flowing between stones	60	45

1991. Death Bicentenary of Wolfgang Amadeus Mozart (composer). Multicoloured.

2499	90q. Type 549	30	25
2500	11.20 Mozart and score . .	45	35
2501	11.80 Mozart composing . .	65	50

550 Vitus Bering

1992. Explorers. Multicoloured.

2503	30q. Type 550	10	10
2504	90q. Christopher Columbus and his flagship "Santa Maria"	50	25
2505	11.80 Ferdinand Magellan and his flagship "Vitoria"	90	50

551 Otto Lilienthal's Biplane Glider, 1896

1992. Aircraft.

2506	551 30q. black, red and blue	10	10
2507	– 80q. multicoloured . . .	25	20
2508	– 90q. multicoloured . . .	30	25
2509	– 11.20 multicoloured . . .	40	30
2510	– 11.80 multicoloured . . .	55	40
2511	– 21.40 black, grey & mve	75	55

DESIGNS: 80q. Clement Ader's "Avion III", 1897; 90q. Wright Brothers' Type A, 1903; 11.20, Concorde supersonic jetliner; 11.80, Tupolev Tu-144 jetliner (wrongly inscr "114"); 21.40, Dornier Do-31E (wrongly inscr "Dernier").

552 Ski Jumping

1992. Winter Olympic Games, Albertville. Mult.

2512	30q. Type 552	10	10
2513	90q. Skiing	30	25
2514	11.20 Ice skating (pairs) . .	40	30
2515	11.80 Luge	60	45

553 "Europe" and Doves

1992. Admission of Albania to European Security and Co-operation Conference at Foreign Ministers' Meeting, Berlin. Multicoloured.

2516	90q. Type 553	30	25
2517	11.20 Members' flags and map of Europe	45	35

554 Envelopes and Emblem

1992. Admission of Albania to E.P.T. Conference. Multicoloured.

2518	90q. Type 554	30	25
2519	11.20 Emblem and tape reels	45	35

555 Everlasting Flame

1992. National Martyrs' Day. Multicoloured.
2520 90q. Type **555** 25 20
2521 4l.10 Poppies (horiz) . . . . 1·10 85

556 Pictograms

1992. European Football Championship, Sweden.
2522 **556** 30q. light green & green . 10 10
2523 — 90q. red and blue 35 25
2524 — 10l.80 ochre and brown . 4·00 3·00
DESIGNS: 90q., 10l.80, Different pictograms.

557 Lawn Tennis

1992. Olympic Games, Barcelona. Multicoloured.
2526 30q. Type **557** 10 10
2527 90q. Baseball 35 25
2528 11.80 Table tennis 75 55

558 Map and Doves

1992. European Unity.
2530 **558** 11.20 multicoloured . . . 35 25

559 Native Pony

1992. Horses. Multicoloured.
2531 30q. Type **559** 10 10
2532 90q. Hungarian nonius . . . 25 20
2533 11.20 Arab (vert) 35 25
2534 10l.60 Haflinger (vert) . . . 3·25 2·40

560 Map of Americas, Columbus
and Ships

1992. Europa. 500th Anniv of Discovery of America
by Columbus. Multicoloured.
2535 60q. Type **560** 60 20
2536 31.20 Map of Americas and
Columbus meeting
Amerindians . . . . 1·10 1·85

561 Mother Teresa   562 Pope John Paul II
and Child

1992. Mother Teresa (Agnes Gonxhe Bojaxhi)
(founder of Missionaries of Charity).
2538 **561** 40q. red 10 10
2539 60q. brown 10 10
2540 1l. violet 10 10
2541 1l.80 grey 10 10
2542 2l. red 15 10
2543 2l.40 green 15 10
2544 3l.20 blue 20 15
2545 5l. violet 25 20
2546 5l.60 purple 35 25
2547 7l.20 green 45 35
2548 10l. orange 55 40
2549 18l. orange 85 65
2550 20l. purple 30 25
2551 25l. green . . . . . . 1·00 75
2552 60l. green 85 65

1993. Papal Visit.
2555 **562** 16l. multicoloured . . . 95 70

1993. Nos. 2329/32 and 2335 surch **POSTA
SHQIPTARE** and new value.
2556 **496** 3l. on 10q. blue 25 20
2557 6l.50 on 20q. red 50 35
2558 13l. on 30q. red . . . . 1·00 1·75
2559 20l. on 90q. blue . . . . 1·50 1·10
2560 30l. on 50q. brown . . . 2·25 1·75

564 Lef Nosi (first Postal   565 "Life Weighs
Minister)   Heavily on Man"
(A. Zajmi)

1993. 80th Anniv of First Albanian Stamps.
2561 **564** 6l.50 brown and green . 35 25

1993. Europa. Contemporary Art. Multicoloured.
2562 3l. Type **565** 30 25
2563 7l. "The Green Star"
(E. Hila) (horiz) 70 55

566 Running

1993. Mediterranean Games, Agde and Roussillon
(Languedoc), France. Multicoloured.
2565 3l. Type **566** 20 15
2566 16l. Canoeing . . . . . . 1·10 85
2567 21l. Cycling . . . . 1·40 1·10

567 Bardhi   568 Mascot and Flags
around Stadium

1993. 350th Death Anniv of Frang Bardhi (scholar).
2569 **567** 6l.50 brown and stone . 45 35

1994. World Cup Football Championship, U.S.A.
Multicoloured.
2571 42l. Type **568** 50 40
2572 68l. Mascot kicking ball . . 80 60

569 Gjovalin Gjadri   571 Richard Wagner
(construction engineer)

570 Emblem and Benz

1994. Europa. Discoveries and Inventions.
2573 **569** 50l. dp brn, ches & brn . 70 55
2574 — 100l. dp brn, ches & brn 1·75 1·25
DESIGN: 100l. Karl Ritter von Ghega (railway
engineer).

1995. 150th Birth Anniv (1994) of Karl Benz
(engineer). Multicoloured.
2576 5l. Type **570** 10 10
2577 10l. Modern Mercedes
motor-car 20 15
2578 60l. First four-wheel Benz
motor-car, 1886 . . . . 1·00 75
2579 125l. Pre-war Mercedes
touring car . . . . 2·10 1·60

1995. Composers. Each brown and gold.
2580 3l. Type **571** 10 10
2581 6l.50 Edvard Grieg 10 10
2582 11l. Charles Gounod . . . 20 15
2583 20l. Pyotr Tchaikovsky . . 35 25

572 Intersections

1995. 50th Anniv (1994) of Liberation.
2584 **572** 50l. black and red . . . 75 55

573 Ali Pasha

1995. 250th Birth Anniv (1994) of Ali Pasha of
Tepelene (Pasha of Janina, 1788–1820).
2585 **573** 60l. black, yellow & brn 95 70

574 Veskopoja, 1744   577 Hands holding
(left half)   Olive Branch

576 Palace of Europe, Strasbourg

1995. 250th Anniv (1994) of Veskopoja Academy.
Multicoloured.
2587 42l. Type **574** 60 45
2588 68l. Veskopoja, 1744 (right
half) . . . . 1·00 75

Nos. 2587/8 were issued together, se-tenant,
forming a composite design.

1995. Admission of Albania to Council of Europe.
Multicoloured.
2590 25l. Type **576** 30 25
2591 85l. State arms and map of
Europe . . . . 1·40 1·10

1995. Europa. Peace and Freedom. Multicoloured.
2592 50l. Type **577** 80 60
2593 100l. Dove flying over hands 1·60 1·25

578 Mice sitting around Table and
Stork with Fox

1995. 300th Death Anniv of Jean de La Fontaine
(writer). Multicoloured.
2595 2l. Type **578** 10 10
2596 3l. Stork with foxes around
table 10 10
2597 25l. Frogs under tree . . . 45 35

579 Bee on Flower   580 Fridtjof Nansen

1995. The Honey Bee. Multicoloured.
2599 5l. Type **579** 10 10
2600 10l. Bee and honeycomb . . 20 15
2601 25l. Bee on comb 45 35

1995. Polar Explorers. Multicoloured.
2602 25l. Type **580** 55 45
2603 25l. James Cook 55 45
2604 25l. Roald Amundsen . . . 55 45
2605 25l. Robert Scott 55 45
Nos. 2602/5 were issued together, se-tenant,
forming a composite design.

581 Flags outside U.N. Building,
New York

1995. 50th Anniv of U.N.O. Multicoloured.
2606 2l. Type **581** 10 10
2607 100l. Flags flying to right
outside U.N. building,
New York . . . . 1·60 1·25

582 Male Chorus   583 "Poet"

1995. National Folklore Festival, Berat. Mult.
2608 18l. Type **582** 10 10
2609 50l. Female participant . . . 85 65

1995. Jan Kukuzeli (11th-century poet, musician and
teacher). Abstract representations of Kukuzeli.
Multicoloured.
2610 18l. Type **583** 30 25
2611 20l. "Musician" 35 25

584 Church and   585 Paul Eluard
Preacher, Berat Kruje

1995. 20th Anniv of World Tourism Organization. Multicoloured.

2613	18l. Type **584**	30	25
2614	20l. Street, Shkoder	35	25
2615	42l. Buildings, Gjirokaster	70	35

1995. Poets' Birth Centenaries. Multicoloured.

2616	25l. Type **585**	35	25
2617	50l. Sergei Yessenin	75	55

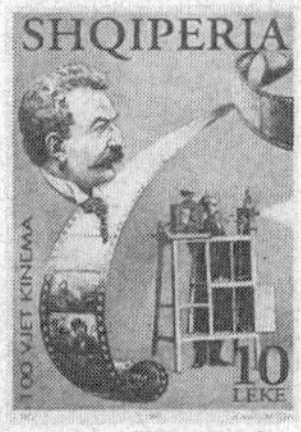

586 Louis, Film Reel and Projector

1995. Centenary of Motion Pictures. Lumiere Brothers (developers of cine camera). Mult.

2618	10l. Type **586**	25	20
2619	85l. Auguste, film reel and cinema audience	1·50	40

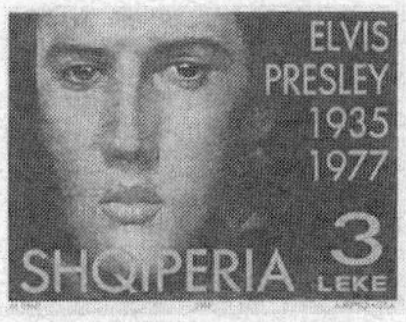

587 Presley

1995. 60th Birth Anniv of Elvis Presley (entertainer). Multicoloured.

2620	3l. Type **587**	10	10
2621	60l. Presley (different)	1·00	75

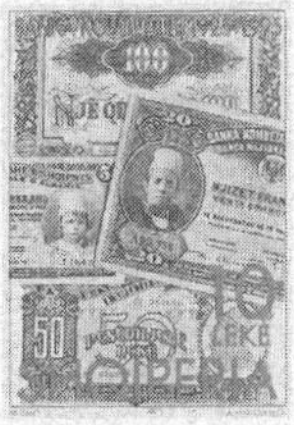

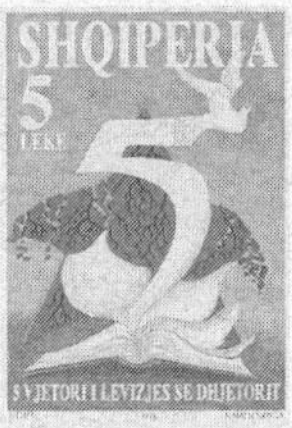

588 Banknotes of 1925 **589** "5", Crumbling Star, Open Book and Peace Dove

1995. 70th Anniv of Albanian National Bank. Mult.

2622	10l. Type **588**	20	15
2623	25l. Modern banknotes	45	35

1995. 5th Anniv of Democratic Movement. Mult.

2624	5l. Type **589**	10	10
2625	50l. Woman planting tree	85	65

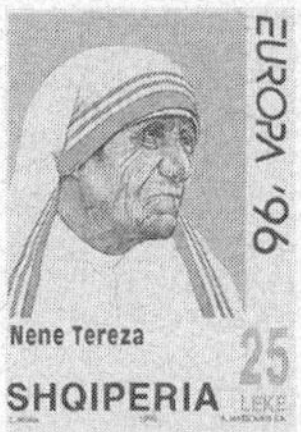

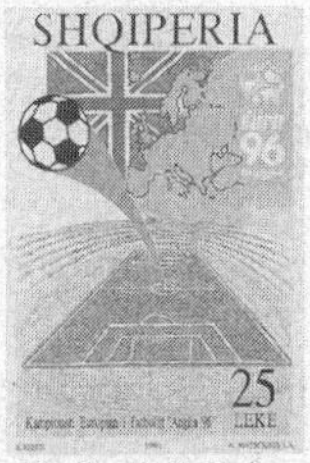

590 Mother Teresa **591** Football, Union Flag, Map of Europe and Stadium

1996. Europa. Famous Women. Mother Teresa (founder of Missionaries of Charity).

2626	**590**	25l. multicoloured	45	35
2627		100l. multicoloured	1·75	1·25

1996. European Football Championship, England. Multicoloured.

2629	25l. Type **591**	65	35
2630	100l. Map of Europe, ball and player	1·75	1·25

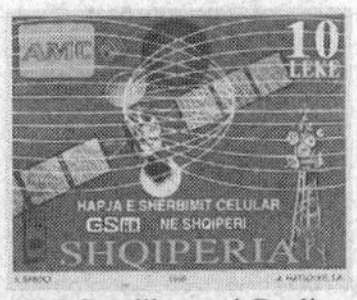

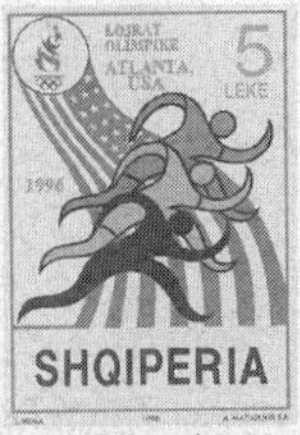

592 Satellite and Radio Mast **593** Running

1996. Inaug of Cellular Telephone Network. Mult.

2631	10l. Type **592**	20	10
2632	60l. User, lorry, container ship and mobile telephone (vert)	1·75	75

1996. Olympic Games, Atlanta, U.S.A. Mult.

2633	5l. Type **593**	10	10
2634	25l. Throwing the hammer	45	35
2635	60l. Long jumping	1·00	75

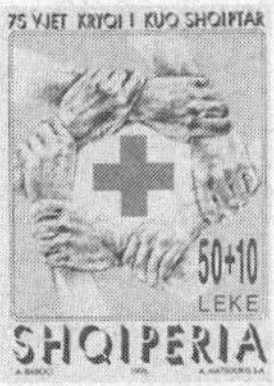

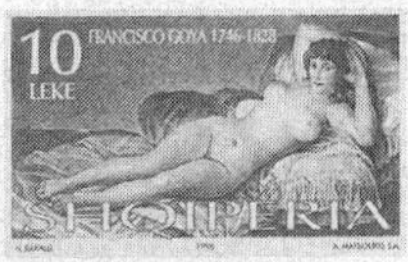

594 Linked Hands **596** "The Naked Maja"

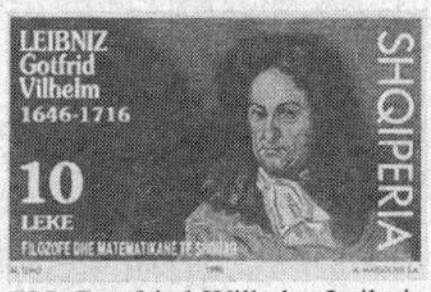

595 Gottfried Wilhelm Leibniz (350th)

1996. 75th Anniv of Albanian Red Cross.

2637	**594**	50l.+10l. mult	1·00	1·00

1996. Philosopher-mathematicians' Birth Annivs. Multicoloured.

2638	10l. Type **595**	20	10
2639	85l. Rene Descartes (400th)	1·50	1·10

1996. 250th Birth Anniv of Francisco de Goya (artist). Multicoloured.

2640	10l. Type **596**	20	10
2641	60l. "Dona Isabel Cobos de Porcel"	1·00	75

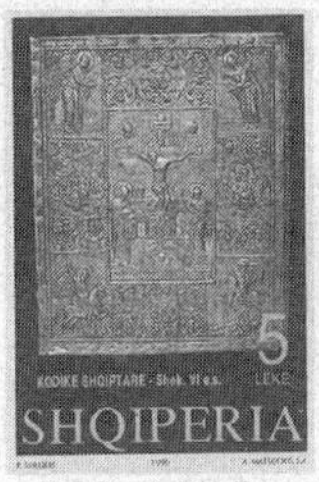

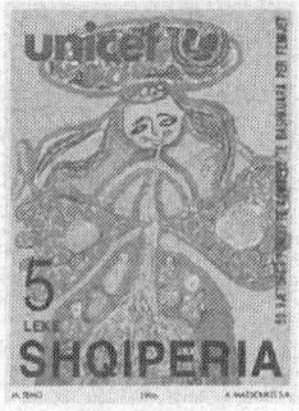

597 Book Binding **598** Princess

1996. Christian Art Exhibition. Multicoloured.

2643	5l. Type **597**	10	10
2644	25l. Book clasp showing crucifixion	45	35
2645	85l. Book binding (different)	1·50	1·10

1996. 50th Anniv of U.N.I.C.E.F. Children's Paintings. Multicoloured.

2646	5l. Type **598**	10	10
2647	10l. Woman	20	15
2648	25l. Sea life	45	35
2649	50l. Harbour	85	65

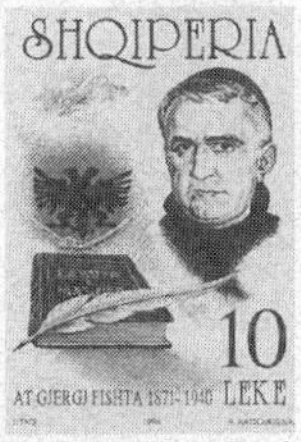

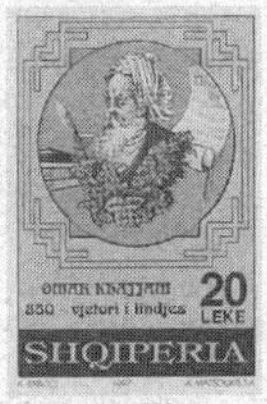

599 State Arms, Book and Fishta **600** Omar Khayyam and Writing Materials

1996. 125th Birth Anniv of Gjergj Fishta (writer and politician). Multicoloured.

2650	10l. Type **599**	20	15
2651	60l. Battle scene and Fishta	1·00	75

1997. 950th Birth Anniv of Omar Khayyam (astronomer and poet). Multicoloured.

2652	20l. Type **600**	35	25
2653	50l. Omar Khayyam and symbols of astronomy	85	65

Nos. 2652/3 are inscribed "850" in error.

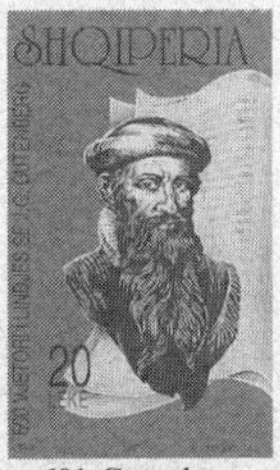

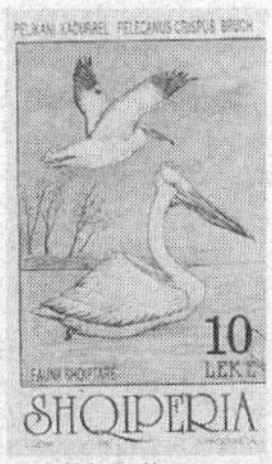

601 Gutenberg **602** Pelicans

1997. 600th Birth Anniv of Johannes Gutenberg (printer). Multicoloured.

2654	20l. Type **601**	40	25
2655	60l. Printing press	1·00	75

Nos. 2654/5 were issued together, se-tenant, forming a composite design.

1997. The Dalmatian Pelican. Multicoloured.

2656	10l. Type **602**	20	15
2657	80l. Pelicans on shore and in flight	1·40	45

Nos. 2656/7 were issued together, se-tenant, forming a composite design.

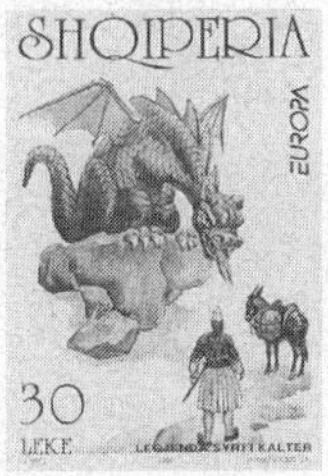

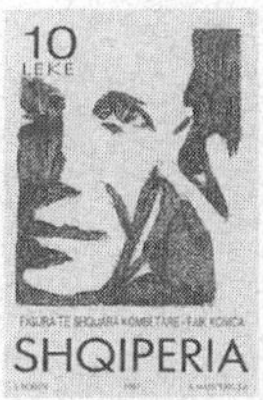

603 Dragon **604** Konica

1997. Europa. Tales and Legends. "The Blue Pool". Multicoloured.

2658	30l. Type **603**	50	40
2659	100l. Dragon drinking from pool	1·75	1·25

1997. 55th Death Anniv of Faik Konica (writer and politician).

2660	**604**	10l. brown and black	20	15
2661		25l. blue and black	45	35

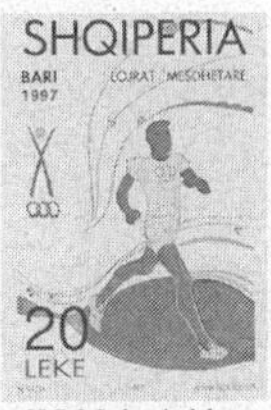

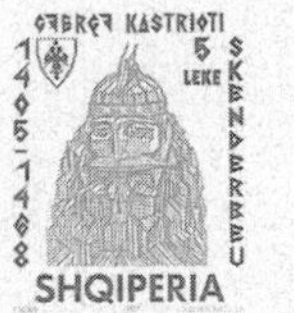

605 Male Athlete **606** Skanderbeg

1997. Mediterranean Games, Bari. Multicoloured.

2663	20l. Type **605**	35	25
2664	30l. Female athlete and rowers	50	40

1997.

2666	**606**	5l. red and brown	10	10
2667		10l. green and olive	10	10
2668		20l. green and deep green	20	15
2669		25l. mauve and purple	25	20
2670		30l. violet and lilac	30	25
2671		50l. grey and black	50	40
2672		60l. lt brown & brown	60	45
2673		80l. lt brown & brown	80	60
2674		100l. red and lake	1·00	75
2675		110l. blue and deep blue	1·10	85

1997. Mother Teresa (founder of Missionaries of Charity) Commemoration. No. 2627 optd **HOMAZH 1910–1997**.

2676	**590**	100l. multicoloured	1·00	75

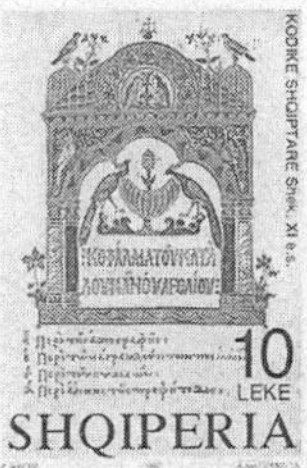

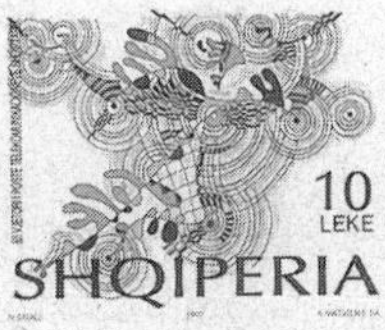

608 Codex Aureus (11th century) **609** Twin-headed Eagle (postal emblem)

1997. Codices (1st series). Multicoloured.

2677	10l. Type **608**	10	10
2678	25l. Codex Purpureus Beratinus (7th century) showing mountain and scribe	25	20
2679	60l. Codex Purpureus Beratinus showing church and scribe	60	45

See also Nos. 2712/14.

1997. 85th Anniv of Albanian Postal Service.

2680	**609**	10l. multicoloured	10	10
2681		30l. multicoloured	30	25

The 30l. differs from Type **609** in minor parts of the design.

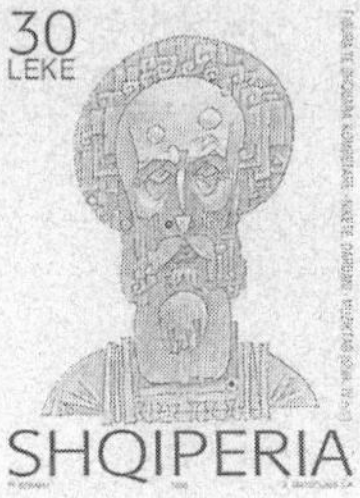

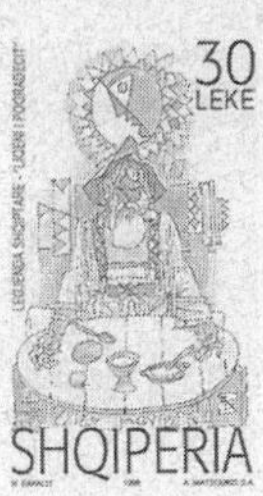

610 Nikete of Ramesiana **611** Man sitting at Table

1998. Nikete Dardani, Bishop of Ramesiana (philosopher and composer).

2682	**610**	30l. multicoloured	25	20
2683		100l. multicoloured	85	65

There are minor differences of design between the two values.

1998. Legend of Pogradeci Lake. Multicoloured.

2684	30l. Type **611**	25	20
2685	50l. The Three Graces	40	30
2686	60l. Women drawing water	50	40
2687	80l. Man of ice	70	55

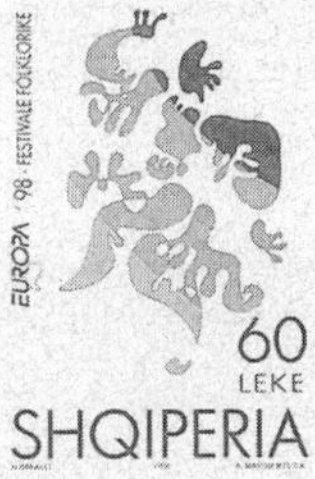

612 Stylized Dancers

1998. Europa. National Festivals. Multicoloured.

2688	60l. Type **612**	50	40
2689	100l. Female dancer	85	65

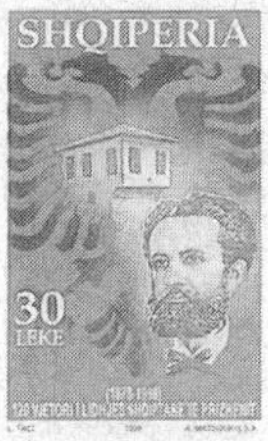

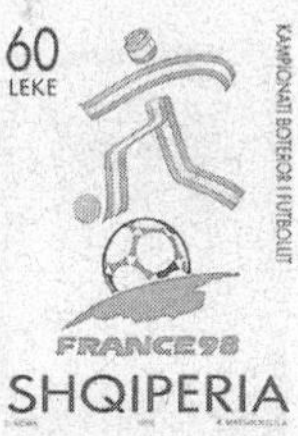

613 Abdyl Frasheri (founder) **614** Player with Ball

1998. 120th Anniv of League of Prizren. Mult.

2691	30l. Type **613**	25	15
2692	50l. Sulejman Vokshi and partisan	40	30
2693	60l. Iljaz Pashe Dibra and crossed rifles	50	35
2694	80l. Ymer Prizreni and partisans	70	50

1998. World Cup Football Championship, France. Multicoloured.

2695	60l. Type **614**	50	35
2696	100l. Player with ball (different)	85	65

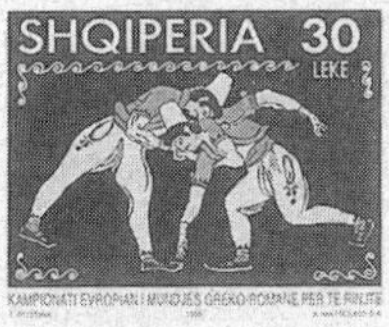

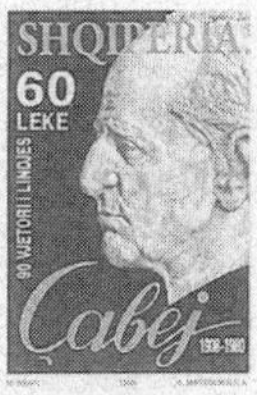

615 Wrestlers in National Costume **616** Cacej

1998. European Junior Wrestling Championship. Multicoloured.

2698	30l. Type **615**	25	15
2699	60l. Ancient Greek wrestlers	25	15

1998. 90th Birth Anniv of Eqerem Cabej (linguist).

2700	**616**	60l. black and yellow	25	15
2701		80l. yellow, black & red	70	50

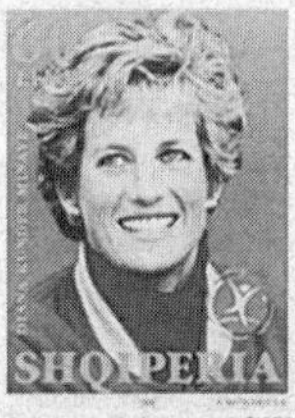

617 Diana, Princess of Wales

1998. Diana, Princess of Wales Commemoration. Multicoloured.
2702 60l. Type **617** 55 30
2703 100l. With Mother Teresa 90 45

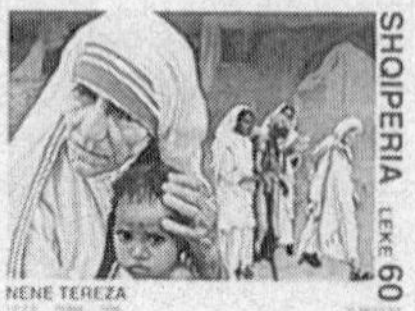

618 Mother Teresa holding Child

1998. Mother Teresa (founder of Missionaries of Charity) Commemoration. Multicoloured.
2704 60l. Type **618** 55 30
2705 100l. Mother Teresa (vert) 90 45

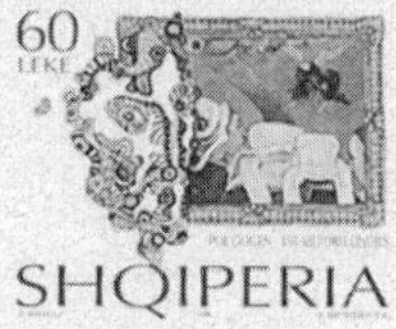

619 Detail of Painting

1998. 150th Birth Anniv of Paul Gauguin (artist). Multicoloured.
2706 60l. Type **619** 55 30
2707 80l. "Women of Tahiti" . . 70 35

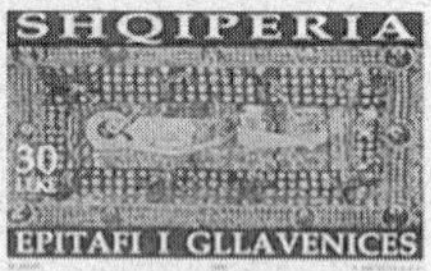

620 Epitaph

1998. 625th Anniv of Epitaph of Gllavenica (embroidery of dead Christ). Multicoloured.
2709 30l. Type **620** 25 10
2710 80l. Close-up of upper body 70 35

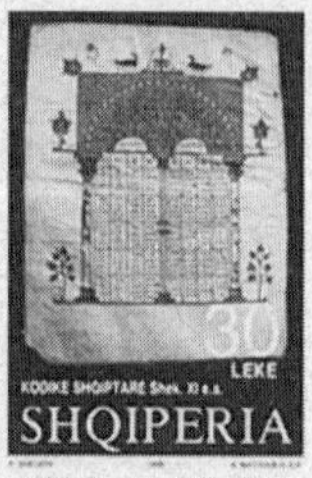

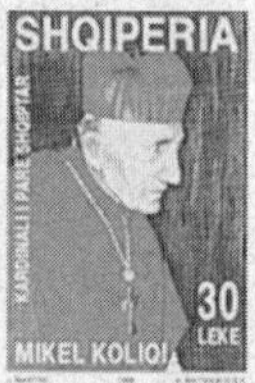

621 Page of Codex **623** Koliqi

1998. Codices (2nd series). 11th-century Manuscripts. Multicoloured.
2712 30l. Type **621** 25 10
2713 50l. Front cover of manuscript 45 20
2714 80l. Page showing mosque 70 35

1998. 1st Death Anniv of Cardinal Mikel Koliqi (first Albanian Cardinal). Multicoloured.
2716 30l. Type **623** 25 15
2717 100l. Koliqi (different) . . . 90 45

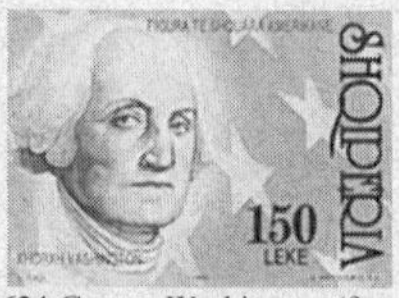

624 George Washington (first President, 1789–97)

1999. American Anniversaries. Multicoloured.
2718 150l. Type **624** (death bicentenary) . . . . . . 1·40 70
2719 150l. Abraham Lincoln (President 1861–65, 190th birth anniv) . . . . . . 1·40 70
2720 150l. Martin Luther King Jr. (civil rights campaigner, 70th birth anniv) . . . . 1·40 70

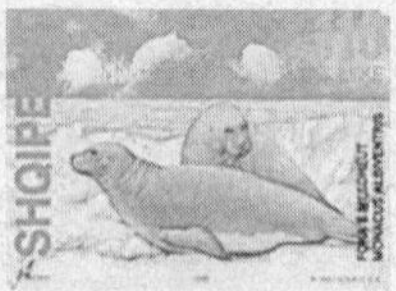

625 Monk Seals

1999. The Monk Seal. Multicoloured.
2721 110l. Type **625** . . . . 1·00 50
2722 110l. Two seals (both facing left) . . . . 1·00 50
2723 150l. As No. 2722 but both facing right . . . . 1·40 70
2724 150l. As Type **625** but seal at back facing left and seal at front facing right 1·40 70

Nos. 2721/4 were issued together, se-tenant, forming a composite design.

1999. 50th Anniv of Council of Europe. No. 2590 surch **150 LEKE** and emblem.
2725 **576** 150l. on 25l. mult . . . 1·40 70

1999. "iBRA '99" International Stamp Exhibition, Nuremberg, Germany. No. 2496 surch **150 LEKE** in black (new value) and multicoloured (emblem).
2726 150l. on 90q. multicoloured 1·40 70

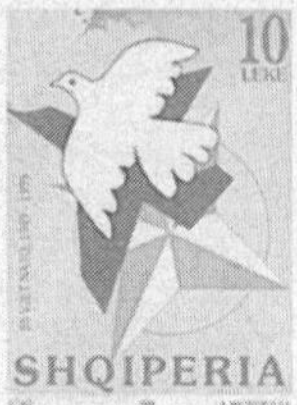

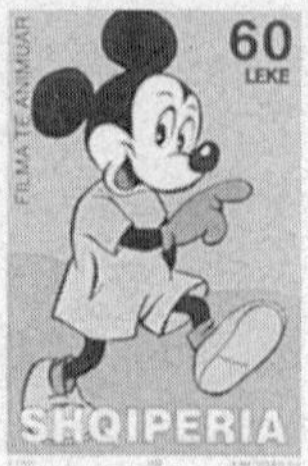

628 Dove, Airplane and NATO Emblem **629** Mickey Mouse

1999. 50th Anniv of North Atlantic Treaty Organization.
2727 **628** 10l. multicoloured . . . 10 10
2728 100l. multicoloured . . . 90 45

1999. Mickey Mouse (cartoon film character). Multicoloured.
2730 60l. Type **629** 55 30
2731 80l. Mickey writing letter . . 70 35
2732 110l. Mickey thinking . . . 1·00 50
2733 150l. Wearing black and red jumper . . . . 1·40 70

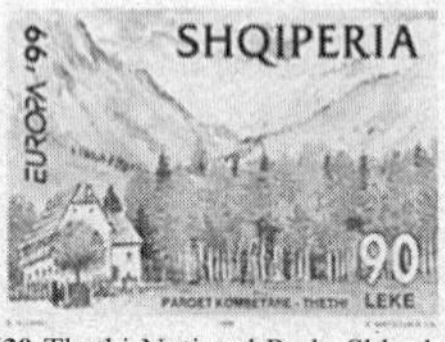

630 Thethi National Park, Shkoder

1999. Europa. Parks and Gardens. Multicoloured.
2734 90l. Type **630** 80 40
2735 310l. Lura National Park, Dibra . . . . 2·75 1·40

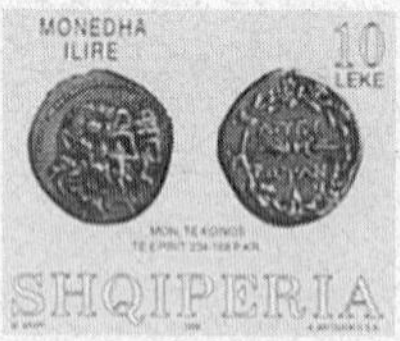

631 Coin

1999. Illyrian Coins. Multicoloured.
2737 10l. Type **631** 10 10
2738 20l. Coins from Labeateve, Bylisi and Scutari 20 10
2739 200l. Coins of King Monuni 1·75 90

1999. "Philexfrance 99" International Stamp Exhibition, Paris. No. 2512 surch with new value and Exhibition logo.
2741 **552** 150l. on 30q. mult . . . 1·40 70

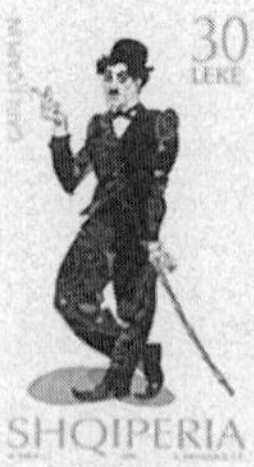

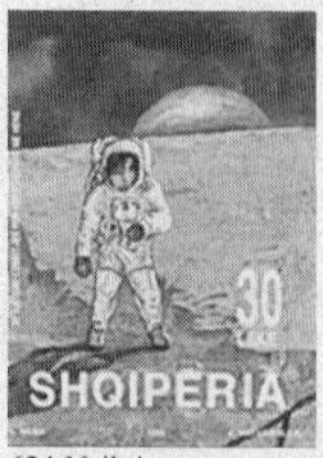

633 Chaplin **634** Neil Armstrong on Moon

1999. 110th Birth Anniv of Charlie Chaplin (film actor and director). Multicoloured.
2742 30l. Type **633** 25 10
2743 50l. Raising hat 45 25
2744 250l. Dancing . . . . 2·25 1·10

1999. 30th Anniv of First Manned Moon Landing. Multicoloured.
2745 30l. Type **634** 25 10
2746 150l. Lunar module . . . . 1·40 70
2747 300l. Astronaut and American flag . . . . . 2·75 1·40

Nos. 2745/7 were issued together, se-tenant, forming a composite design.

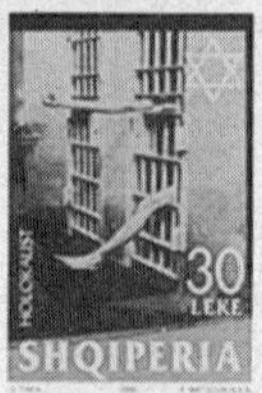

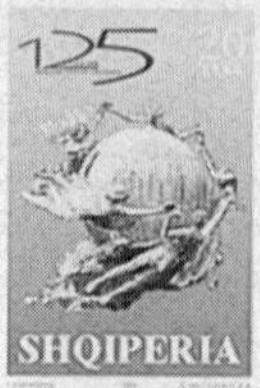

635 Prisoner behind Bars **636** Emblem

1999. The Nazi Holocaust.
2749 **635** 30l. multicoloured . . . 25 10
2750 150l. black and yellow 1·40 70

1999. 125th Anniv of Universal Postal Union.
2751 **636** 20l. multicoloured . . . 20 10
2752 60l. multicoloured . . . 55 30

1999. "China 1999" International Stamp Exhibition, Peking. No. 2497 surch **150 LEKE.**
2753 150l. on 11.20 multicoloured 1·40 70

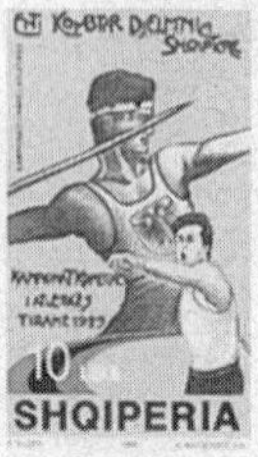

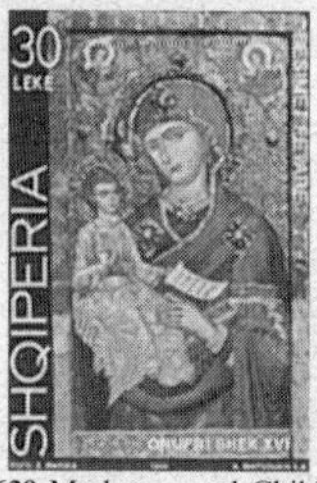

638 Javelin **639** Madonna and Child

1999. 70th Anniv of National Athletic Championships. Multicoloured.
2754 10l. Type **638** 10 10
2755 20l. Discus 20 10
2756 200l. Running . . . . . . 1·90 85

1999. Icons by Onufri Shek (artist). Multicoloured.
2757 30l. Type **639** 25 10
2758 300l. The Resurrection . . . 2·75 1·40

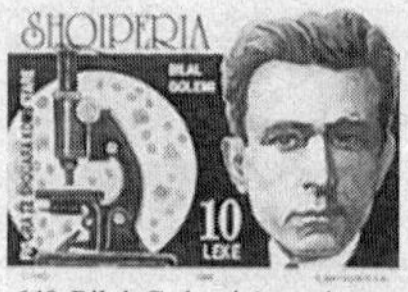

640 Bilal Golemi (veterinary surgeon)

1999. Birth Anniversaries. Multicoloured.
2759 10l. Type **640** (centenary) . . 10 10
2760 20l. Azem Galica (revolutionary) (centenary) 20 10
2761 50l. Viktor Eftimiu (writer) (centenary) 45 20
2762 300l. Lasgush Poradeci (poet) (centenary (2000)) 2·75 1·40

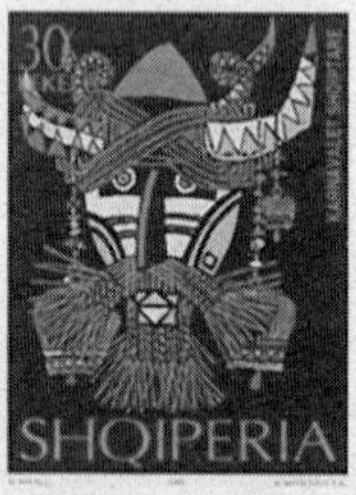

641 Carnival Mask

1999. Carnivals. Multicoloured.
2763 30l. Type **641** 25 10
2764 300l. Turkey mask . . . . 2·75 1·40

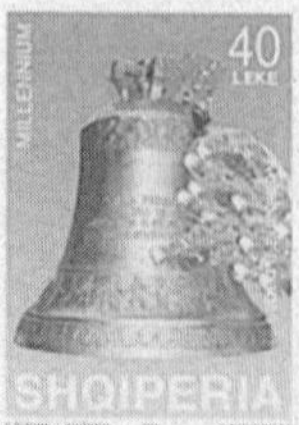

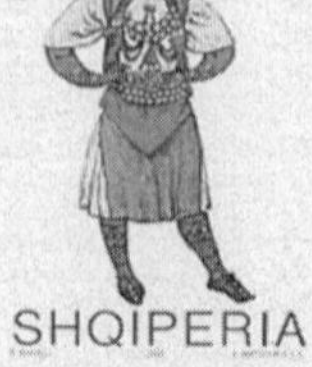

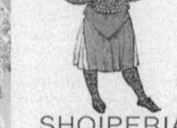

642 Bell and Flowers **643** Woman's Costume, Librazhdi

2000. New Millennium. The Peace Bell. Mult.
2765 40l. Type **642** 35 15
2766 90l. Bell and flowers (different) 80 40

2000. Regional Costumes. Multicoloured.
2767 5l. Type **643** 10 10
2768 10l. Woman's costume, Malesia E Madhe 10 10
2769 15l. Man's costume, Malesia E Madhe 15 10
2770 20l. Man's costume, Tropoje 20 10
2771 30l. Man's costume, Dumrea 30 15
2772 35l. Man's costume, Tirana 30 15
2773 40l. Woman's costume, Tirana 35 15
2774 45l. Woman's costume, Arbereshe 40 20
2775 50l. Man's costume, Gjirokastra 45 25
2776 55l. Woman's costume, Lunxheri 50 25
2777 70l. Woman's costume, Cameria 65 30
2778 90l. Man's costume, Laberia 80 40

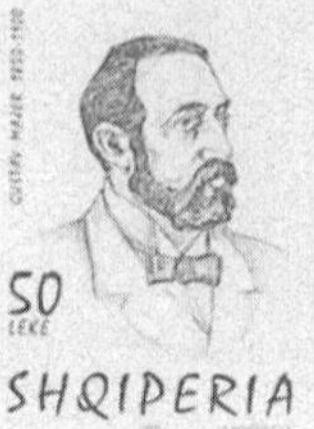

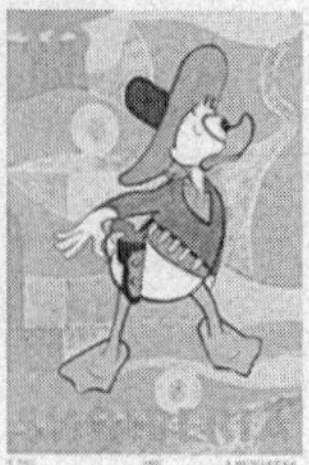

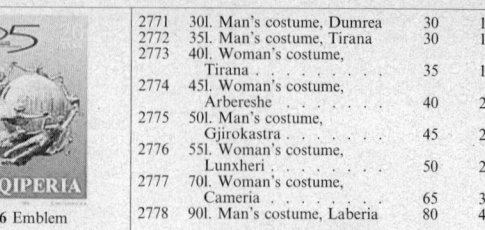

644 Majer **645** Donald Duck

2000. 150th Birth Anniv of Gustav Majer (etymologist).
2779 **644** 50l. green 45 25
2780 130l. red . . . . 1·25 65

2000. Donald and Daisy Duck (cartoon film characters). Multicoloured.
2781 10l. Type **645** 10 10
2782 30l. Donald Duck 30 15
2783 90l. Daisy Duck 80 40
2784 250l. Donald Duck . . . . 2·25 1·10

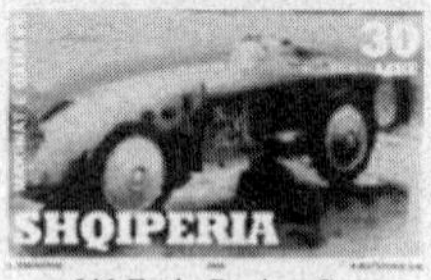

646 Early Racing Car

2000. Motor Racing. Multicoloured.
2785 30l. Type **646** 30 15
2786 30l. Two-man racing car . . 30 15
2787 30l. Racing car with wire nose 30 15
2788 30l. Racing car with solid wheels 30 15
2789 30l. Car No. 1 . . . . . . 30 15
2790 30l. Car No. 2 . . . . . . 30 15
2791 30l. White Formula 1 racing car (facing left) 30 15
2792 30l. Blue Formula 1 racing car 30 15
2793 30l. Red Formula 1 racing car 30 15
2794 30l. White Formula 1 racing car (front view) 30 15

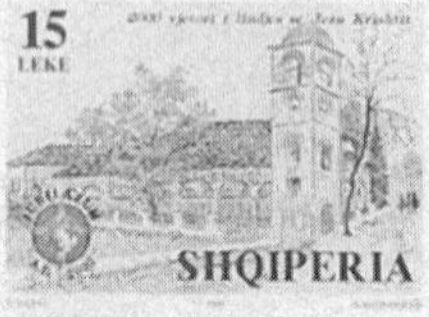

647 Ristoz of Mborja Church, Korca

2000. Birth Bimillenary of Jesus Christ. Mult.
2795 15l. Type **647** 15 10
2796 40l. St. Kolli Church, Voskopoja 35 15
2797 90l. Church of Flori and Lauri, Kosovo 80 40

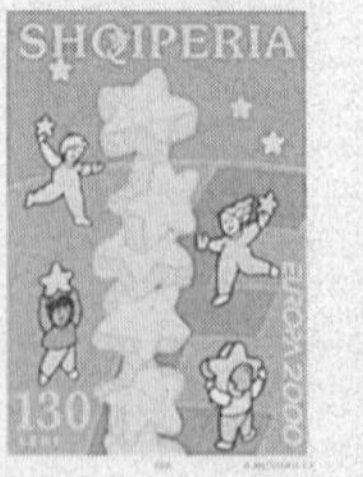

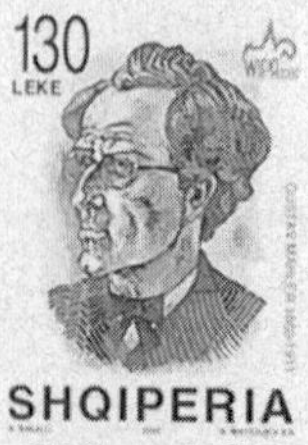

648 "Building Europe" **650** Gustav Mahler (composer) (40th death anniv)

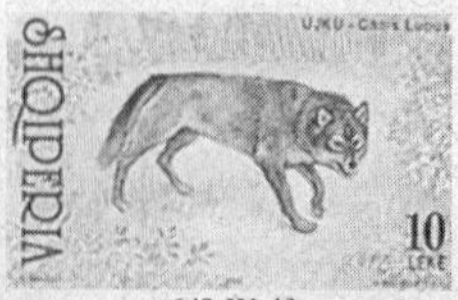

649 Wolf

2000. Europa.
2799 **648** 130l. multicoloured . . . 1·25 60

2000. Animals. Multicoloured.
2801 10l. Type **649** 10 10
2802 40l. Brown bear 35 15

2803 90l. Wild boar 80 40
2804 220l. Red fox . . . . 2·00 1·00

2000. "WIPA 2000" International Stamp Exhibition, Vienna.
2805 **650** 130l. multicoloured . . . 1·25 1·00

651 Footballer saving Ball

2000. European Football Championship, Belgium and The Netherlands. Multicoloured.
2806 10l. Type **651** 10 10
2807 120l. Footballer heading ball 1·10 55

652 Musicans

2000. Paintings by Picasso. Multicoloured.
2809 30l. Type **652** 30 15
2810 40l. Abstract face 35 15
2811 250l. Two women running
   along beach . . . . . . 2·25 1·10

653 Basketball   **655** "Self-portrait"
                      (Picasso)

654 *LZ-1* (first Zeppelin airship) over Lake Constance, Friedrichshafen (first flight)

2000. Olympic Games, Sydney. Multicoloured.
2813 10l. Type **653** 10 10
2814 40l. Football 40 20
2815 90l. Athletics 85 45
2816 250l. Cycling . . . . 2·40 1·25

2000. Centenary of First Zeppelin Flight. Airship Development. Multicoloured.
2817 15l. Type **654** 15 10
2818 30l. Santos-Dumont airship
   Ballon No. 5 and Eiffel
   Tower C attempted round
   trip from St. Cloud via
   Eiffel Tower, 1901) . . . 30 15
2819 300l. Beardmore airship
   R-34 over New York (first
   double crossing of
   Atlantic) . . . . 2·75 1·25

2000. "Espana 2000" World Stamp Exhibition, Madrid.
2821 **655** 130l. multicoloured . . . 1·25 65

656 Yellow Gentian   **658** Mother holding
(*Gentiana lutea*)   Child

657 Naim Frasheri (poet) and Landscape

2000. Medicinal Plants. Multicoloured.
2822 50l. Type **656** 50 25
2823 70l. Cross-leaved gentian
   (*Gentiana cruciata*) . . . 65 35

2000. Personalities. Multicoloured.
2824 30l. Type **657** 20 15
2825 50l. Bajram Curri
   (revolutionary) and
   landscape 50 25
Nos. 2824/5 were issued together, se-tenant, forming a composite design.

2000. 50th Anniv of United Nations High Commission for Refugees. Multicoloured.
2826 50l. Type **658** 50 25
2827 90l. Mother breastfeeding
   child 85 40

659 Dede Ahmed Myftar   **661** Southern
Ahmataj   Magnolia (*Magnolia
                              gandiflora*)

2001. Religious Leaders. Multicoloured.
2828 90l. Type **65** 85 45
2829 90l. Dede Sali Njazi 85 45

2001. "For Kosovo". Nos. 2592/3 surch **PER KOSOVEN** and new value.
2830 80l.+10l. on 50l.
   multicoloured 85 45
2831 130l.+20l. on 100l.
   multicoloured . . . . . 1·40 70

2001. Regional Costumes (2nd series). As T **643**. Multicoloured.
2832 20l. Man's costume, Tropoje 20 10
2833 20l. Woman's costume,
   Lume 20 10
2834 20l. Woman's costume,
   Mirdite 20 10
2835 20l. Man's costume, Lume 20 10
2836 20l. Woman's costume,
   Zadrime 20 10
2837 20l. Woman's costume,
   Shpati 20 10
2838 20l. Man's costume, Kruje 20 10
2839 20l. Woman's costume,
   Macukulli 20 10
2840 20l. Woman's costume,
   Dardhe 20 10
2841 20l. Man's costume, Lushnje 20 10
2842 20l. Woman's costume,
   Dropulli 20 10
2843 20l. Woman's costume,
   Shmili 20 10

2001. Scented Flowers. Multicoloured.
2844 10l. Type **661** 10 10
2845 20l. Virginia rose (*Rosa
   virginiana*) 20 10
2846 90l. *Dianthus barbatus* . . . 85 45
2847 140l. Lilac (*Syringa vulgaris*) 1·25 65

662 Goofy in Shorts

2001. Goofy (cartoon film character). Multicoloured.
2848 20l. Type **662** 20 10
2849 50l. Goofy in blue hat . . . 50 25
2850 90l. Goofy in red trousers 85 45
2851 140l. Goofy in purple
   waistcoat . . . . . . 1·25 65

663 Vincenzo Bellini

2001. Composers' Anniversaries. Multicoloured.
2852 90l. Type **663** (birth
   centenary) 85 45
2853 90l. Guiseppe Verdi (death
   centenary) 85 45

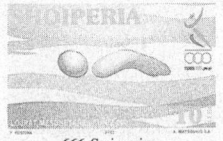

664 Cliffs and Stream

2001. Europa. Water Resources. Multicoloured.
2855 40l. Type **664** 40 20
2856 110l. Waterfall . . . . . . 1·10 55
2857 200l. Lake . . . . 1·90 95

665 Horse

2001. Domestic Animals. Multicoloured.
2859 10l. Type **665** 10 10
2860 15l. Donkey 15 10
2861 80l. Siamese cat 75 40
2862 90l. Dog 85 45

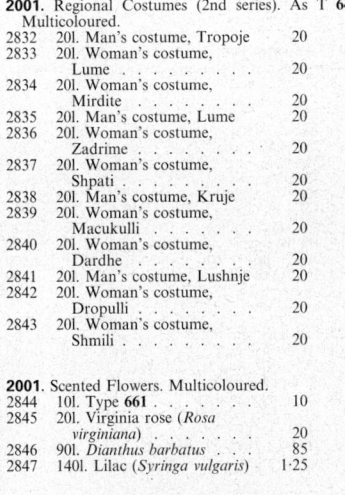

666 Swimming

2001. Mediterranean Games, Tunis. Multicoloured.
2864 10l. Type **666** 10 10
2865 90l. Athletics 85 45
2866 140l. Cycling . . . . 1·40 70

667 *Eole* (first powered take-off by Clement Ader, 1890)

2001. Aviation History. Multicoloured.
2868 40l. Type **667** 40 20
2869 40l. *Bleriot XI* (first powered
   crossing of English
   channel by Louis Bleriot,
   1909) 40 20
2870 40l. *Spirit of St. Louis* (first
   solo non-stop crossing of
   North Atlantic from Paris
   to New York by Charles
   Lindbergh, 1927) . . . 40 20
2871 40l. First flight to Tirana,
   1925 . . . . 40 20
2872 40l. Antonov AH-10 (first
   flight, 1956) 40 20
2873 40l. Concorde (first flight,
   1969) 40 20
2874 40l. Concorde (first
   commercial flight, 1970) 40 20
2875 40l. Space shuttle *Colombia*
   (first flight, 1981) 40 20

668 Tabakeve   **669** Dimitri of
                      Arber

2001. Old Bridges.
2876 **668** 10l. multicoloured . . . 10 10
2877 – 20l. multicoloured . . 20 10
2878 – 40l. multicoloured . . 40 20
2879 – 90l. black 85 45
DESIGNS: 20l. Kamares; 40l. Golikut; 90l. Mesit. 49 × 22 mm-21.50, Tabakeve.

2001. Arms.
2881 20l. Type **669** 20 10
2882 45l. Balsha pricipality . . . 45 25
2883 50l. Muzaka family 50 25
2884 90l. George Castriot
   (Skanderbeg) 85 45

ITALIAN OCCUPATION

E **67** King Victor Emmanuel

1940.
E373 E **67** 25q. violet . . . . . . 2·00 2·50
E374   50q. red . . . . . . 4·00 6·25
No. E374 is inscr "POSTAT EXPRES".

1943. Optd **14 Shtator 1943**.
E402 E **67** 25q. violet . . . . . 16·00 25·00

POSTAGE DUE STAMPS

1914. Optd **TAKSE** through large letter T.
D33 **4** 2q. brown and yellow . . 6·00 2·00
D34   5q. green and yellow . . 6·00 3·75
D35   10q. red and pink . . . . 8·00 2·25
D36   25q. blue . . . . 10·00 2·50
D37   50q. mauve and red . . . 11·00 4·50

1914. Nos. 40/4 optd **TAKSE**.
D46 **4** 10pa. on 5q. green & yell 2·75 2·50
D47   20pa. on 10q. red and pink 2·75 2·50
D48   1g. on 25q. blue . . . . 2·75 2·50
D49   2g. on 50q. mauve and red 2·75 2·50

1919. Fiscal stamps optd **TAXE**.
D89 **12** 4q. on 4h. pink . . . . . 6·75 6·75
D90   10q. on 10k. red on grn 6·75 6·75
D91   20q. on 2k. orge on lilac 6·75 6·75
D92   50q. on 5k. brown on yell 6·75 6·75

D **20** Fortress   D **22**   D **35**
of Shkoder

1920. Optd with posthorn.
D129 D **20** 4q. olive 75 75
D130   10q. red . . . . . . 1·50 4·75
D131   20q. brown . . . . . 1·50 2·00
D132   50q. black . . . . . 1·50 4·75

1922.
D141 D **22** 4q. black on red . . 85 1·75
D142   10q. black on red . . 85 1·75
D143   20q. black on red . . 85 1·75
D144   50q. black on red . . 85 1·75

1922. Optd **Republika Shiqiptare**.
D186 D **22** 4q. black on red . . 1·25 1·90
D187   10q. black on red . . 1·25 1·90
D188   20q. black on red . . 1·25 1·90
D189   50q. black on red . . 1·25 1·90

1925.
D204 D **35** 10q. blue 45 75
D205   20q. green 50 75
D206   30q. brown . . . . . 75 2·00
D207   50q. dark brown . . . 1·25 2·75

D **53** Arms of   D **67**
Albania

1930.
D288 D **53** 10q. blue . . . . . 5·00 6·50
D289   20q. red . . . . . . 1·50 2·00
D290   30q. violet . . . . . 1·50 2·00
D291   50q. green . . . . . 1·50 2·00

1936. Optd **Takse**.
D312 **50** 10q. red . . . . . . 8·50 11·50

1940.
D373 D **67** 4q. red . . . . . . 20·00 25·00
D374   10q. violet . . . . . 20·00 25·00
D375   20q. brown . . . . . 20·00 25·00
D376   30q. blue . . . . . . 20·00 25·00
D377   50q. red . . . . . . 20·00 25·00

ALEXANDRETTA   Pt. 6

The territory of Alexandretta. Autonomous under French control from 1923 to September 1938.

1938. 100 centiemes = 1 piastre.

1938. Stamps of Syria of 1930/1 optd **Sandjak d'Alexandrette** (Nos. 1, 4, 7 and 11) or **SANDJAK D'ALEXANDRETTE** (others), Nos. 7 and 11 surch also.
1 0p.10 purple . . . . 1·75 2·00
2 0p.20 red . . . . 1·75 2·25
3 0p.50 violet . . . . 1·75 2·00
4 0p.75 red . . . . 1·75 2·25

5		1p. brown	1·75	2·25
6		2p. violet	2·00	2·50
7		2p.50 on 4p. orange	2·25	2·75
8		3p. green	2·75	3·25
9		4p. orange	2·75	3·00
10		6p. black	3·00	3·50
11		12p.50 on 15p. red (No. 267)	4·75	5·75
12		25p. purple	9·25	10·50

1938. Air. Stamps of Syria of 1937 (Nos. 322 etc) optd **SANDJAK D'ALEXANDRETTE**.

13		½p. violet	2·00	2·50
14		1p. black	2·00	2·50
15		2p. green	3·00	3·50
16		3p. blue	3·50	4·00
17		5p. mauve	7·75	9·50
18		10p. brown	8·00	10·00
19		15p. brown	8·50	11·00
20		25p. blue	13·00	14·50

1938. Death of Kemal Ataturk. Nos. 4, 5, 7, 9 and 11 optd **10-11-1938** in frame.

27		0p.75 red	26·00	45·00
28		1p. brown	16·00	35·00
29		2p.50 on 4p. orange	12·50	12·50
30		4p. orange	11·00	13·50
31		12p.50 on 15p. red	40·00	50·00

POSTAGE DUE STAMPS

1938. Postage Due stamps of Syria of 1925 optd **SANDJAK D'ALEXANDRETTE**.

D21	D 20	0p.50 brown on yellow	1·75	2·75
D22		1p. purple on pink	1·75	3·00
D23		2p. black on blue	2·75	3·25
D24		3p. black on red	3·00	5·00
D25		5p. black on green	4·75	5·00
D26		8p. black on blue	3·25	5·50

ALEXANDRIA Pt. 6

Issues of the French P.O. in this Egyptian port. The French Post Offices in Egypt closed on 31 March 1931.

1899. 100 centimes = 1 franc.
1921. 10 milliemes = 1 piastre.

1899. Stamps of France optd **ALEXANDRIE**.

1	10	1c. black on blue	1·25	1·10
2		2c. brown on yellow	1·75	2·50
3		3c. grey	1·40	2·25
4		4c. brown on grey	1·10	2·50
5		5c. green	2·25	2·25
7		10c. black on lilac	5·50	7·25
9		15c. blue	6·25	4·25
10		20c. red on green	7·50	7·00
11		25c. black on red	5·50	55
12		30c. brown	5·75	7·00
13		40c. red on yellow	9·75	10·00
15		50c. red	19·00	12·50
16		1f. olive	12·00	14·00
17		2f. brown on blue	70·00	75·00
18		5f. mauve on lilac	95·00	85·00

1902. "Blanc", "Mouchon" and "Merson" key-types, inscr "ALEXANDRIE".

19	A	1c. grey	1·40	1·00
20		2c. purple	45	1·50
21		3c. red	55	1·00
22		4c. brown	35	1·00
24		5c. green	1·25	70
25	B	10c. red	2·75	75
26		15c. red	3·00	1·75
27		15c. orange	85	2·00
28		20c. brown	3·25	1·25
29		25c. blue	2·00	10
30		30c. mauve	4·25	3·25
31	C	40c. red and blue	2·75	2·25
32		50c. brown and lilac	5·50	55
33		1f. red and green	9·25	1·25
34		2f. lilac and buff	13·00	4·50
35		5f. blue and buff	17·00	10·50

1915. Red Cross. Surch **5c** and Red Cross.

36	B	10c. + 5c. red	20	2·75

1921. Surch thus, **15 Mill.**, in one line (without bars).

37	A	2m. on 5c. green	3·00	6·00
38		3m. on 3c. red	6·00	7·50
39	B	4m. on 10c. red	4·00	5·00
40	A	5m. on 1c. grey	7·25	7·50
41		5m. on 4c. brown	6·75	7·75
42	B	6m. on 15c. orange	2·50	4·50
43		8m. on 20c. brown	4·00	5·25
44		10m. on 25c. blue	1·75	3·75
45		12m. on 30c. mauve	11·50	12·50
46	A	15m. on 2c. purple	6·00	3·25
47	C	15m. on 40c. red and blue	12·00	12·50
48		15m. on 50c. brown & lilac	6·00	10·00
49		30m. on 1f. red and green	£120	£100
50		60m. on 2f. lilac and buff	£140	£140
51		150m. on 5f. blue and buff	£225	£225

1921. Surch thus, **15 MILLIEMES**, in two lines (without bars).

53	A	1m. on 1c. grey	2·50	3·50
54		2m. on 5c. green	1·75	3·25
55	B	4m. on 10c. red	3·00	4·25
65		4m. on 10c. green	2·25	3·25
56	A	5m. on 3c. orange	4·25	6·50
57	B	6m. on 15c. orange	2·25	3·50
58		8m. on 20c. brown	1·75	3·00
59		10m. on 25c. blue	1·90	2·25
60		10m. on 30c. mauve	4·25	4·25
61	C	15m. on 50c. brown & lilac	3·75	4·50
66	B	15m. on 50c. blue	2·50	2·50
62	C	30m. on 1f. red and green	3·25	3·00
63		60m. on 2f. lilac and buff	£1400	£1500
67		60m. on 2f. red and green	9·75	9·75
64		150m. on 5f. blue and buff	11·00	10·00

1925. Surch in milliemes with bars over old value.

68	A	1m. on 1c. grey	15	3·00
69		2m. on 5c. orange	20	2·75
70		2m. on 5c. green	2·50	3·50
71	B	4m. on 10c. green	20	3·25
72	A	5m. on 3c. red	80	2·50
73	B	6m. on 15c. orange	55	3·25
74		8m. on 20c. brown	20	3·25
75		10m. on 25c. blue	35	1·90
76		15m. on 50c. blue	1·75	1·75
77	C	30m. on 1f. red and green	1·10	55
78		60m. on 2f. red and green	2·75	4·75
79		150m. on 5f. blue and buff	3·75	5·50

1927. Altered key-types, inscr "Mm" below value.

80	A	3m. orange	2·00	3·25
81	B	15m. blue	2·25	1·40
82		20m. mauve	4·00	5·00
83	C	50m. red and green	9·25	7·50
84		100m. blue and yellow	11·50	10·50
85		250m. green and red	17·00	17·00

1927. Sinking Fund. As No. 81, colour changed, surch **+ 5 Mm Caisse d'Amortissement**.

86	B	15m.+5m. orange	3·25	5·00
87		15m.+5m. red	4·50	5·00
88		15m.+5m. brown	7·50	10·00
89		15m.+5m. lilac	12·00	16·00

POSTAGE DUE STAMPS

1922. Postage Due Stamps of France surch in milliemes.

D65	D 11	2m. on 5c. blue	1·10	4·25
D66		4m. on 10c. brown	2·25	4·25
D67		10m. on 30c. red	2·00	4·50
D68		15m. on 50c. purple	1·50	4·75
D69		30m. on 1f. pur on yell	1·25	6·25

D 10

1928.

D90	D 10	1m. grey	1·40	3·50
D91		2m. blue	2·75	3·50
D92		4m. pink	2·75	3·75
D93		5m. olive	2·75	3·25
D94		10m. red	3·00	3·75
D95		20m. purple	3·00	3·50
D96		30m. green	5·75	6·25
D97		40m. lilac	5·00	6·25

This set was issued for use in both Alexandria and Port Said.

ALGERIA Pt. 6; Pt. 12

French territory in N. Africa. Stamps of France were used in Algeria from July 1958 until 3 July 1962, when the country achieved independence following a referendum.

1924. 100 centimes = 1 franc.
1964. 100 centimes = 1 dinar.

1924. Stamps of France optd **ALGERIE**.

1	11	½c. on 1c. grey	35	1·75
2		1c. grey	65	2·25
3		2c. red	10	2·50
4		3c. red	40	2·25
5		4c. brown	65	2·50
6	18	5c. orange	95	75
7	11	5c. green	10	10
8	30	10c. green	1·40	1·25
9	18	10c. green	10	75
10	15	15c. green	1·50	1·40
11	30	15c. green	85	2·00
12	18	15c. brown	1·50	1·10
13		20c. brown	1·50	65
14		25c. blue	10	10
15	30	30c. red	75	70
16	18	30c. blue	10	10
17		30c. red*	30	90
18		35c. violet	1·25	1·50
19	13	40c. red and blue	1·60	1·75
20	18	40c. olive	1·25	1·90
21	13	45c. green and blue	1·25	2·25
22	30	45c. red	40	85
23		50c. blue	1·50	85
24	15	60c. violet	1·10	65
25		65c. red	25	60
26	30	75c. blue	25	45
27	15	80c. red	70	70
28		85c. red	35	50
29	13	1f. red and green	1·75	55
30	18	1f.05 red	55	1·75
31	13	2f. red and green	2·00	3·25
32		3f. violet and blue	2·00	3·00
33		5f. blue and yellow	8·00	8·50

*No. 17 was only issued pre-cancelled and the price in the unused column is for stamps with full gum.

3 Street in the Casbah

4 Mosque of Sidi Abderahman

5 Grand Mosque

6 Bay of Algiers

1926.

34	3	1c. green	40	1·25
35		2c. purple	30	1·50
36		3c. orange	10	1·40
37		5c. green	25	10
38		10c. mauve	35	10
39	4	15c. brown	10	10
40		20c. green	10	10
41		20c. red	1·40	10
43		25c. green	95	75
45		25c. blue	45	30
46		30c. blue	80	1·40
47		30c. green	1·25	40
48		35c. violet	1·25	3·25
49		40c. green	10	10
50	5	45c. purple	15	10
51		50c. blue	2·25	15
53		50c. red	1·10	10
54		60c. green	20	90
55		65c. brown	1·50	1·60
56	3	65c. blue	1·10	10
57	5	75c. red	10	20
58		75c. blue	2·50	10
59		80c. orange	35	2·10
60		90c. red	1·75	2·50
61	6	1f. purple and green	80	10
62	5	1f.05 brown	35	1·90
63		1f.10 mauve	3·50	6·00
64	6	1f.25 ultramarine and blue	1·00	3·50
65		1f.50 ultramarine and blue	70	10
66		2f. brown and green	1·40	35
67		3f. red and mauve	3·25	1·50
68		5f. mauve and red	3·75	3·00
69		10f. red and brown	48·00	32·00
70		20f. green and violet	8·00	9·00

1926. Surch ½ **centime**.

71	3	½c. on 1c. olive	10	1·75

1927. Wounded Soldiers of Moroccan War Charity Issue. Surch with star and crescent and premium.

72	3	5c.+5c. green	95	3·25
73		10c.+10c. mauve	90	3·25
74	4	15c.+15c. brown	90	3·25
75		20c.+20c. red	90	3·25
76		25c.+25c. green	80	3·25
77		30c.+30c. blue	1·10	3·25
78		35c.+35c. violet	55	3·25
79		40c.+40c. olive	80	3·25
80	5	50c.+50c. blue	85	3·75
81		80c.+80c. orange	85	3·75
82	6	1f.+1f. purple and green	1·25	3·75
83		2f.+2f. brown and green	22·00	40·00
84		5f.+5f. mauve and red	35·00	55·00

1927. Surch in figures.

85	4	10 on 35c. violet	10	90
86		25 on 30c. blue	65	10
87		30 on 25c. green	15	10
88	5	65 on 60c. green	60	1·25
89		90 on 80c. orange	20	20
90		1f.10 on 1f.05 brown	10	15
91	6	1f.50 on 1f.25 ultramarine and blue	1·25	90

1927. Surch **5c.**

92	11	5c. on 4c. brown (No. 5)	45	1·75

11 Railway Terminus, Oran

1930. Centenary of French Occupation.

93	11	5c.+5c. orange	9·00	14·50
94	–	10c.+10c. olive	8·00	14·00
95	–	15c.+15c. brown	6·25	13·50
96	–	25c.+25c. grey	6·00	13·50
97	–	30c.+30c. red	5·75	14·00
98	–	40c.+40c. green	5·25	14·00
99	–	50c.+50c. blue	5·25	14·00
100	–	75c.+75c. purple	5·00	13·50
101	–	1f.+1f. orange	5·50	13·50
102	–	1f.50+1f.50 blue	5·75	13·50
103	–	2f.+2f. red	5·25	13·50
104	–	3f.+3f. green	5·75	13·50
105	–	5f.+5f. red and green	10·50	35·00

DESIGNS—HORIZ: 10c. Constantine; 15c. Admiralty, Algiers; 25c. Algiers; 30c. Ruins of Timgad; 40c. Ruins of Djemila. VERT: 50c. Ruins of Djemila; 75c. Tlemcen; 1f. Ghardaia; 1f.50, Tolga; 2f. Tuaregs; 3f. Native quarter, Algiers; 5f. Mosque, Algiers.

12 Bay of Algiers, after painting by Verecque

1930. N. African International Philatelic Exn.

106	12	10f.+10f. brown	24·00	30·00

15 Admiralty and Penon Lighthouse, Algiers

1936.

107	A	1c. blue	35	1·10
108	F	2c. purple	10	90
109	B	3c. green	65	1·50
110	C	5c. mauve	10	10
111	15	10c. green	70	65
112	D	15c. red	15	10
113	G	20c. green	20	10
114	E	25c. purple	2·00	20
115	C	30c. green	35	10
116	D	40c. purple	50	20
117	G	45c. blue	1·25	3·25
118	15	50c. red	2·25	10
119	A	65c. brown	6·25	8·25
120		65c. red	2·25	35
121		70c. brown	80	85
122	F	75c. slate	50	15
124	B	90c. red	85	1·50
125	E	1f. brown	30	10
126	15	1f.25 violet	1·90	60
127		1f.25 red	40	1·40
128	F	1f.50 blue	2·25	85
129		1f.50 red	3·50	3·50
130	C	1f.75 orange	95	70
131	B	2f. purple	40	10
132	A	2f.25 green	16·00	24·00
133	E	2f.25 blue	1·50	1·60
134	C	2f.50 blue	1·75	2·25
135	G	3f. mauve	55	25
136	E	3f.50 blue	2·25	2·75
137	15	5f. slate	1·25	1·50
138	F	10f. orange	75	2·00
139	D	20f. blue	1·90	3·00

DESIGNS—HORIZ: A, In the Sahara; B, Arc de Triomphe, Lambese; C, Ghardaia, Mzab; D, Marabouts, Touggourt; E, El Kebir Mosque, Algiers. VERT: F, Colomb Bechar-Oued; G, Cemetery, Tlemcen.

17 Exhibition Pavilion

18 Constantine in 1837

1937. Paris International Exhibition.

140	17	40c. green	40	30
141		50c. red	40	50
142		1f.50 blue	60	1·00
143		1f.75 black	95	1·25

1937. Centenary of Capture of Constantine.

144	18	65c. red	80	20
145		1f. brown	2·75	65
146		1f.75 blue	35	95
147		2f.15 purple	25	40

19 Ruins of Roman Villa

1938. Centenary of Philippeville.

148	19	30c. green	1·75	2·00
149		65c. blue	75	55
150		75c. purple	1·60	3·25
151		3f. red	3·75	2·50
152		5f. brown	4·25	5·00

1938. 20th Anniv of Armistice Day. No. 132 surch **1918 - 11 Nov. - 1938 0.65 + 0.35**.

153		65c.+35c. on 2f.25 green	1·00	3·75

1938. Surch **0,25**.

154	15	25c. on 50c. red	25	10

22 Caillie, Lavigerie and Duveyrier

1939. Sahara Pioneers' Monument Fund.
155 **22** 30c.+20c. green . . . . . . 2·50 3·75
156 90c.+60c. red . . . . . . 1·10 3·25
157 2f.25+75c. blue . . . . . 8·50 2·00
158 5f.+5f. black . . . . . . 14·50 45·00

23 "Extavia" (freighter) in Algiers Harbour

1939. New York World's Fair.
159 **23** 20c. green . . . . 1·60 3·50
160 40c. purple . . . . 1·75 3·50
161 90c. brown . . . . 2·25 75
162 1f.25 red . . . . 6·00 6·50
163 2f.25 blue . . . . 2·25 2·40

1939. Surch with new values and bars or cross.
173 **3** 50c. on 65c. blue 30 10
173c B 90c.+60c. red (No. 124) . . 20 10
164 **3** 1f. on 90c. red 40 10

25 Algerian Soldiers

26 Algiers

1940. Soldiers' Dependants' Relief Fund. Surch **+** and premium.
166 **25** 1f.+1f. blue . . . . 2·25 3·00
167 1f.+2f. red . . . . 1·90 3·50
168 1f.+4f. green . . . . . . 2·00 3·75
169 1f.+9f. brown . . . . . . 2·25 4·25

1941.
170 **26** 30c. blue . . . . 75 1·25
171 70c. brown 15 10
172 1f. red 15 10

28 Marshal Petain

1941.
174 **28** 1f. blue . . . . 40 1·10

1941. National Relief Fund. As No. 174, but surch **+4 f** and colour changed.
175 1f.+4f. black . . . . 1·25 2·50

1942. National Relief Fund. Surch **SECOURS NATIONAL +4f.**
176 1f.+4f. blue (No. 174) . . . . 70 3·00

1942. Various altered types. (a) As T **26**, but without "RF".
177 **26** 30c. blue . . . . 20 2·75
(b) As T **5**, but without "REPUBLIQUE FRANCAISE".
178 **5** 40c. grey . . . . 25 3·00
179 50c. red . . . . 35 1·40
(c) As No. 129 but without "RF".
180 F 1f.50 red . . . . 1·10 65

32 Arms of Oran

34 Marshal Petain

1942. Coats-of-Arms.
190 A 10c. lilac . . . . 1·00 2·25
191 **32** 30c. green . . . . 1·00 3·00
181 B 40c. violet . . . . 45 2·75
192 40c. lilac . . . . 1·75 2·25
182 **32** 60c. red . . . . 1·40 1·60
194 B 70c. blue . . . . 1·25 2·25
195 A 80c. green . . . . 75 1·90
183 B 1f.20 green . . . . 1·10 2·00
184 A 1f.50 red 15 30
198 **32** 2f. blue 20 95
186 B 2f.40 red . . . . 1·25 1·00
187 A 3f. blue 20 45
188 B 4f. blue . . . . 1·00 1·10
201 **32** 4f.50 purple 80 10
189 5f. green . . . . 1·00 1·40
ARMS: A, Algiers; B, Constantine.

1943.
202 **34** 1f.50 red . . . . 15 2·50

35 "La Marseillaise"

36 Allegory of Victory

1943.
203 **35** 1f.50 red . . . . 80 2·25
204 **36** 1f.50 blue 20 60

1943. Surch **2f.**
205 **32** 2f. on 5f. orange 15 90

38 Summer Palace, Algiers

39 Mother and Children

1943.
206 **38** 15f. grey . . . . 1·10 1·90
207 20f. green . . . . 1·50 1·90
208 50f. red . . . . 90 1·50
209 100f. blue . . . . 3·00 2·75
210 200f. brown . . . . 3·50 2·75

1943. Prisoners-of-war Relief Fund.
211 **39** 50c.+4f.50 pink . . . . . 60 3·50
212 1f.50+8f.50 green . . . . . 30 3·50
213 3f.+12f. blue . . . . . . 30 3·50
214 5f.+15f. brown . . . . . . 55 3·50

40 "Marianne"

41 Gallic Cock

1944.
215 **40** 10c. grey 15 75
216 30c. lilac 15 65
217 50c. red 10 15
218 80c. green . . . . 25 1·00
219 1f.20 lilac . . . . 40 1·75
220 1f.50 blue 10 10
221 2f.40 red 10 35
222 3f. violet 15 15
223 4f.50 black 25 10

1944.
224 **41** 40c. red . . . . 30 2·75
225 1f. green 15 20
226 2f. red 15 15
227 2f. brown 40 90
228 4f. blue . . . . 1·60 10
229 10f. black . . . . 1·10 2·25

1944. Surch **0f.30.**
230 **4** 0f.30 on 15c. brown 25 60
No. 230 was only issued pre-cancelled and the price in the unused column is for stamps with full gum.

1945. Types of France optd **ALGERIE.**
247 **239** 10c. black and blue . . . 10 2·75
231 **217** 40c. mauve 20 75
232 50c. blue 15 10
248 – 50c. brown, yellow and red (No. 973) 65 60
233 **218** 60c. blue 50 70
236 **136** 80c. green . . . . 1·00 1·25
237 1f. blue 80 10
234 **218** 1f. red 70 25
238 **136** 1f.20 violet . . . . . . 55 2·50
235 **218** 1f.50 lilac . . . . 70 1·50
239 **136** 2f. brown 20 10
242 **219** 2f. green 85 10
240 **136** 2f.40 red . . . . 70 1·75
241 3f. orange 55 95
243 **219** 3f. red 35 10
244 4f.50 blue . . . . 1·75 40
245 5f. green 10 25
246 10f. blue . . . . 1·75 1·25

1945. Airmen and Dependants Fund. As No. 742 of France (bombers) optd **RF ALGERIE.**
249 **169** 1f.50+3f.50 blue . . . . . 1·50 3·00

1945. Postal Employees War Victims' Fund. As No. 949 of France overprinted **ALGERIE.**
250 **223** 4f.+6f. brown . . . . . . 55 3·00

1945. Stamp Day. As No. 955 of France (Louis XI) optd **ALGERIE.**
251 **228** 2f.+3f. purple . . . . . . 1·25 2·50

1946. No. 184 surch **0f50 RF.**
252 50c. on 1f.50 red 15 30

1946. Type of France optd **ALGERIE** and surch **2F.**
253 **136** 2f. on 1f.50 brown . . . 15 10

46 Potez 56 over Algiers

1946. Air.
254 **46** 5f. red 35 50
255 10f. blue 20 10
256 15f. green 65 35
257a 20f. brown 70 10
258 25f. violet 70 20
259 40f. black . . . . 1·25 1·40

1946. Stamp Day. As No. 975 of France (De la Varane), optd **ALGERIE.**
260 **241** 3f.+2f. red . . . . 90 3·75

47 Children at Spring

49 Arms of Constantine

1946. Charity. Inscr as in T **47**.
261 **47** 3f.+17f. green . . . . . . 1·75 4·00
262 4f.+21f. red . . . . 1·25 3·75
263 8f.+27f. purple . . . . . 3·00 9·50
264 10f.+35f. blue . . . . . . 1·75 4·00
DESIGNS—VERT: 4f. Boy gazing skywards; 8f. Laurel-crowned head. HORIZ: 10f. Soldier looking at Algerian coast.

1947. Air. Surch **-10%.**
265 **46** "-10%" on 5f. red 20 55

1947. Stamp Day. As No. 1008 of France (Louvois), optd **ALGERIE.**
266 **253** 4f.50+5f.50 blue . . . . . 35 3·25

1947. Various Arms.
267 **49** 10c. green and red . . . . 10 1·75
268 A 50c. black and orange . . 10 10
269 B 1f. blue and yellow . . . 10 10
270 **49** 1f.30 black and blue . . . 75 3·00
271 A 1f.50 violet and yellow . . 10 10
272 B 2f. black and green 10 10
273 **49** 2f.50 black and red 90 70
274 A 3f. red and green 10 65
275 B 3f.50 green and purple . . 45 10
276 **49** 4f. brown and green . . . 10 10
277 A 4f.50 blue and red 10 10
278 5f. black and blue 10 10
279 B 6f. brown and red 20 10
280 8f. brown and blue 15 10
281 **49** 10f. pink and brown . . . 25 10
282 A 15f. black and red . . . . 1·75 10
ARMS: A, Algiers; B, Oran. See also Nos. 364/8 and 381/3.

1947. Air. 7th Anniv of Gen. de Gaulle's Call to Arms. Surch with Lorraine Cross and **18 Juin 1940 + 10 Fr.**
283 **46** 10f.+10f. blue . . . . . . 2·50 3·50

1947. Resistance Movement. Type of France surch **ALGERIE+10f.**
284 **261** 5f.+10f. grey . . . . . . 1·25 3·25

1948. Stamp Day. Type of France (Arago) optd **ALGERIE.**
285 **267** 6f.+4f. green . . . . . . 1·25 3·75

1948. Air. 8th Anniv of Gen. de Gaulle's Call to Arms. Surch with Lorraine Cross and **18 JUIN 1940 + 10 Fr.**
286 **46** 5f.+10f. red . . . . 2·50 3·50

1948. General Leclerc Memorial. Type of France surch **ALGERIE + 4f.**
287 **270** 6f.+4f. red . . . . 1·40 3·50

57 Battleship "Richelieu"

58 White Storks over Minaret

1949. Naval Welfare Fund.
288 **57** 10f.+15f. blue . . . . . . 5·25 12·50
289 – 18f.+22f. red . . . . . . 8·75 12·50
DESIGN: 18f. Aircraft-carrier "Arromanches".

1949. Air.
290 **58** 50f. green . . . . 4·00 1·10
291 – 100f. brown . . . . 2·25 40
292 **58** 200f. red . . . . 11·00 3·75
293 – 500f. blue . . . . 29·00 28·00
DESIGN—HORIZ: 100, 500f. Dewoitine D-338 trimotor airplane over valley dwellings.

1949. Stamp Day. As No. 1054 of France (Choiseul) optd **ALGERIE.**
294 **278** 15f.+5f. mauve . . . . . 45 4·50

60 French Colonials

61 Statue of Duke of Orleans

1949. 75th Anniv of U.P.U.
295 **60** 5f. green . . . . 1·60 3·75
296 15f. red . . . . 1·00 3·75
297 25f. blue . . . . 3·25 9·25

1949. Air. 25th Anniv of First Algerian Postage Stamp.
298 **61** 15f.+20f. brown . . . . . 5·75 10·00

62 Grapes

63 Foreign Legionary

1950.
299 **62** 20f. purple, green & dp pur 85 65
300 – 25f. brown, green & black 1·75 55
301 – 40f. orange, green & brown 2·75 2·50
DESIGNS: 25f. Dates; 40f. Oranges and lemons.

1950. Stamp Day. As No. 1091 of France (Postman), optd **ALGERIE.**
302 **292** 12f.+3f. brown . . . . . 1·60 4·50

1950. Foreign Legion Welfare Fund.
303 **63** 15f.+5f. green . . . . . . 85 4·50

64 R. P. de Foucauld and Gen. Laperrine

1950. 50th Anniv of French in the Sahara (25f.) and Unveiling of Monument to Abd-el-Kader (40f.).
304 **64** 25f.+5f. black and green 5·00 9·25
305 – 40f.+10f. dp brown & brn 4·75 9·25
DESIGN: 40f. Emir Abd-el-Kader and Marshal Bugeaud.

65 Col. C. d'Ornano

1951. Col. d'Ornano Monument Fund.
306 **65** 15f.+5f. purple, brn blk . . 1·25 3·75

1951. Stamp Day. As No. 1107 of France (Travelling Post Office sorting van), optd **ALGERIE.**
307 **300** 12f.+3f. brown . . . . . 3·00 4·25

66 Apollo of Cherchel

67 Algerian War Memorial

1952.

308 **66** 10f. sepia 20 25
309 – 12f. brown 35 10
310 – 15f. blue 20 10
311 – 18f. red 40 30
312 – 20f. green 45 15
313 **66** 30f. blue 50 30
STATUES: 12, 18f. Isis of Cherchel; 15, 20f. Boy and eagle.

1952. Stamp Day. As No. 1140 of France (Mail Coach), optd **ALGERIE**.
314 **319** 12f.+3f. blue . . . . . . 2·25 4·75

1952. African Army Commemoration.
315 **67** 12f. green . . . . 85 2·25

68 Medaille Militaire

69 Fossil ("Berbericeras sekikensis")

1952. Military Medal Centenary.
316 **68** 15f.+5f. brown, yell & grn 2·50 4·75

1952. 19th Int Geological Convention, Algiers.
317 **69** 15f. red . . . . 2·50 5·00
318 – 30f. blue . . . . 1·50 3·25
DESIGN: 30f. Phonolite Dyke, Hoggar.

1952. 10th Anniv of Battle of Bir-Hakeim. As No. 1146 of France surch **ALGERIE+5 F**.
319 **325** 30f.+5f. blue . . . . . . 3·00 4·75

72 Bou-Nara

73 Members of Corps and Camel

1952. Red Cross Fund.
320 – 8f.+2f. red and blue . . . 1·75 4·50
321 **72** 12f.+3f. red . . . . 2·75 6·75
DESIGN: 8f. El-Oued and map of Algeria.

1952. 50th Anniv of Sahara Corps.
322 **73** 12f. brown . . . . 2·00 3·00

1953. Stamp Day. As No. 1161 of France (Count D'Argenson), optd **ALGERIE**.
323 **334** 12f.+3f. violet . . . . . 1·25 4·25

74 "Victory" of Cirta

75 E. Millon

1954. Army Welfare Fund.
324 **74** 15f.+5f. brown and sepia 70 3·25

1954. Military Health Service.
325 **75** 25f. sepia and green . . . 95 30
326 – 40f. red and brown 90 25
327 – 50f. indigo and blue . . . 1·25 25
DOCTORS—VERT: 40f. F. Maillot. HORIZ: 50f. A. Laveran.

1954. Stamp Day. As No. 1202 of France (Lavalette), optd **ALGERIE**.
328 **346** 12f.+3f. red . . . . . . 90 3·75

76 French and Algerian Soldiers

77 Foreign Legionary

1954. Old Soldiers' Welfare Fund.
329 **76** 15f.+5f. sepia . . . . . . 1·60 3·00

1954. Foreign Legion Welfare Fund.
330 **77** 15f.+5f. green . . . . . . 2·75 4·75

78

79 Darguinah Hydroelectric Station

80 Courtyard of Bardo Museum

1954. 3rd International Congress of Mediterranean Citrus Fruit Culture.
331 **78** 15f. blue and indigo . . . 1·25 3·75

1954. 10th Anniv of Liberation. As No. 1204 of France ("D-Day") optd **ALGERIE**.
332 **348** 15f. red . . . . 75 2·25

1954. Inauguration of River Agrioun Hydroelectric Installations.
333 **79** 15f. purple . . . . 1·60 3·75

1954.

334 **80** 10f. brown & light brown 15 10
335 12f. orange and brown (I) 85 10
336 12f. orange and brown (II) 25 60
337 15f. blue and light blue . . 55 20
338 18f. carmine and red . . . 30 45
339 20f. green and light green 25 1·10
340 25f. lilac and mauve . . . 30 10
12f. "POSTES" and "ALGERIE" in orange (I) or in white (II).

1954. 150th Anniv of Presentation of First Legion of Honour. As No. 1223 of France, optd **ALGERIE**.
341 **356** 12f. green . . . . 50 3·00

81 Red Cross Nurses

82 St. Augustine

1954. Red Cross Fund. Cross in red.
342 **81** 12f.+3f. blue . . . . . . 3·75 6·25
343 – 15f.+5f. violet . . . . . . 5·50 7·75
DESIGN: 15f. J.H. Dunant and Djemila ruins.

1954. 1600th Birth Anniv of St. Augustine.
344 **82** 15f. brown . . . . 1·50 3·00

83 Earthquake Victims and Ruins

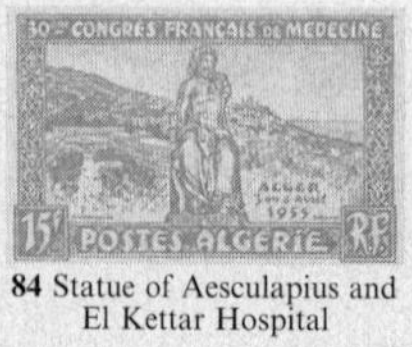
84 Statue of Aesculapius and El Kettar Hospital

1954. Orleansville Earthquake Relief Fund. Inscr as in T **83**.
345 **83** 12f.+4f. brown . . . . . 1·90 4·75
346 15f.+5f. blue . . . . . 2·00 4·75
347 – 18f.+6f. mauve . . . . 2·25 4·75
348 – 20f.+7f. violet . . . . . 2·50 4·75
349 – 25f.+8f. lake . . . . . . 2·75 5·25
350 – 30f.+10f. turquoise . . . 2·50 5·75
DESIGNS—HORIZ: 18, 20f. Red Cross workers. 25, 30f. Stretcher-bearers.

1955. Stamp Day. As No. 1245 of France (Balloon Post), optd **ALGERIE**.
351 **364** 12f.+3f. blue . . . . . . 1·10 4·00

1955. 30th French Medical Congress.
352 **84** 15f. red . . . . 45 1·00

85 Ruins of Tipasa

86 Widows and Children

1955. Bimillenary of Tipasa.
353 **85** 50f. brown 50 20

1955. 50th Anniv of Rotary International. As No. 1235 of France optd **ALGERIE**.
354 **361** 30f. blue . . . . 90 2·00

1955. As Nos. 1238 and 1238b of France ("France") inscr "ALGERIE".
355 **362** 15f. red 15 10
356 20f. blue . . . . 90 1·50

1955. War Victims' Welfare Fund.
357 **86** 15f.+5f. indigo and blue . . 1·90 2·75

87 Grand Kabylie

88

1955.

358 **87** 100f. indigo and blue . . . 2·25 30

1956. Anti-cancer Fund.
359 **88** 15f.+5f. brown . . . . . . 1·90 3·25

1956. Stamp Day. As No. 1279 of France ("Francis of Taxis"), optd **ALGERIE**.
360 **383** 12f.+3f. red . . . . . . 1·10 3·50

89 Foreign Legion Retirement Home, Sidi Bel Abbes

1956. Foreign Legion Welfare Fund.
361 **89** 15f.+5f. green . . . . . . 1·90 4·25

90 Marshal Franchet d'Esperey (after J. Ebstein)

1956. Birth Cent of Marshal Franchet d'Esperey.
362 **90** 15f. indigo and blue . . . 2·50 3·50

91 Marshal Leclerc and Memorial

1956. Marshal Leclerc Commemoration
363 **91** 15f. brown and sepia . . . 40 3·25

1956. Various arms as T **49**.
364 1f. green and red 25 70
365 3f. blue and green . . . . 50 2·10
366 5f. blue and yellow 20 60
367 6f. green and red . . . . . 50 2·50
368 12f. blue and red . . . . . 90 3·25
DESIGNS: 1f. Bone; 3f. Mostaganem; 5f. Tlemcen; 6f. Algiers; 12f. Orleansville.

92 Oran

1956.

369 **92** 30f. purple . . . . 1·40 10
370 35f. red . . . . 2·00 3·50

1957. Stamp Day. As No. 1322 of France ("Felucca") optd **ALGERIE**.
371 **403** 12f.+3f. purple . . . . . 2·50 3·75

93 Electric Train Crossing Viaduct

1957. Electrification of Bone-Tebessa Railway Line.
372 **93** 40f. turquoise and green 1·75 20

94 Fennec Fox

1957. Red Cross Fund. Cross in red.
373 **94** 12f.+3f. brown . . . . . . 4·50 12·50
374 – 15f.+5f. sepia (White storks) . . . . 6·00 12·00

1957. 17th Anniv of Gen. de Gaulle's Call to Arms. Surch **18 JUIN 1940 + 5F**.
375 **91** 15f.+5f. red and carmine 1·10 4·00

96 Beni Bahdel Barrage, Tlemcen

97 "Horseman Crossing Ford" (after Delacroix)

1957. Air.
376 **96** 200f. red . . . . 6·00 8·00

1957. Army Welfare Fund. Inscr "OEUVRES SOCIALES DE L'ARMEE".
377 **97** 15f.+5f. red . . . . 6·00 12·50
378 – 20f.+5f. green . . . . . . 5·25 12·50
379 – 35f.+10f. blue . . . . . . 5·50 12·50
DESIGNS—HORIZ: 20f. "Lakeside View" (after Fromentin). VERT: 35f. "Arab Dancer" (after Chasseriau).

1958. Stamp Day. As No. 1375 of France (Rural Postal Service), optd **ALGERIE**.
380 **421** 15f.+5f. brown . . . . . 1·75 3·75

1958. Arms. As T **49** but inscr "REPUBLIQUE FRANCAISE" instead of "RF" at foot.
381 2f. red and blue . . . . . 75 3·25
382 6f. green and red . . . . . 32·00 42·00
383 10f. purple and green . . . . 85 3·00
ARMS: 2f. Tizi-Ouzou; 6f. Algiers; 10f. Setif.

99 "Strelitzia Reginae"

100

1958. Algerian Child Welfare Fund.
384 **99** 20f.+5f. orge, vio & grn . . 4·00 5·25

1958. Marshal de Lattre Foundation.
385 **100** 20f.+5f. red, grn & bl . . 3·75 4·25

INDEPENDENT STATE

1962. Stamps of France optd **EA** and with bars obliterating "REPUBLIQUE FRANCAISE".
386 **344** 10c. green 70 35
387 **463** 25c. grey and red 45 20
393 – 45c. violet, purple and sepia (No. 1463) . . . 5·00 4·00

394 – 50c. pur & grn (No. 1464) 5·00 4·00
395 – 1f. brown, blue and myrtle (No. 1549) . . . 2·25 1·10

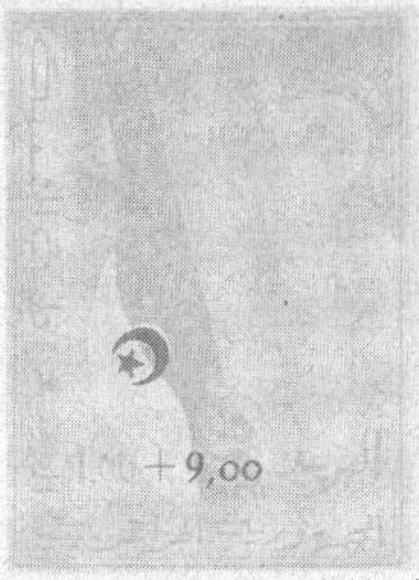

103a Maps of Africa and Algeria

1962. War Orphans' Fund.
395a **103a** 1f.+9f. green, black and red . . £325

1962. As pictorial types of France but inscr "REPUBLIQUE ALGERIENNE".
396 – 5c. turquoise, grn & brn 15 10
397 **438** 10c. blue and sepia . . . 20 10
398 – 25c. red, slate & brown 45 10
399 – 95c. blue, buff and sepia 2·75 80
400 – 1f. sepia and green . . . 1·90 1·40
DESIGNS—VERT: 5c. Kerrata Gorges; 25c. Tlemcen Mosque; 95c. Oil derrick and pipeline at Hassi-Massaoud, Sahara. HORIZ: 1f. Medea.

104 Flag, Rifle and Olive Branch — **105** Campaign Emblem and Globe

1963. "Return of Peace". Flag in green and red. Inscription and background colours given.
401 **104** 5c. bistre 15 10
402 10c. blue 20 10
403 25c. red . . . . 1·90 10
404 95c. violet . . . . 1·40 65
405 – 1f. green . . . . 1·25 30
406 – 2f. brown . . . . 3·00 65
407 – 5f. purple . . . . 5·50 2·50
408 – 10f. black . . . . 20·00 12·00
DESIGN: 1f. to 10f. As Type **104** but with dove and broken chain added.

1963. Freedom from Hunger.
409 **105** 25c. yellow, green and red 40 20

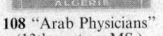

106 Clasped Hands — **107** Map and Emblems

1963. National Solidarity Fund.
410 **106** 50c.+20c. red, grn & blk 1·10 55

1963. 1st Anniv of Independence.
411 **107** 25c. multicoloured 50 20

108 "Arab Physicians" (13th-century MS.) — **109** Branch of Orange Tree

1963. 2nd Arab Physicians Union Congress.
412 **108** 25c. brown, green & bistre 1·60 45

1963.
413 **109** 8c. orange and bronze* 10 10
414 20c. orange and green* 15 10
415 40c. orange & turq* . . . 45 20
416 55c. orange and green* 80 45
*These stamps were only issued pre-cancelled, the unused prices being for stamps with full gum.

110 "Constitution" — **111** "Freedom Fighters"

1963. Promulgation of Constitution.
417 **110** 25c. red, green and sepia 55 25

1963. 9th Anniv of Revolution.
418 **111** 25c. red, green and brown 55 20

112 Centenary Emblem — **113** Globe and Scales of Justice

1963. Red Cross Centenary.
419 **112** 25c. blue, red and yellow 80 55

1963. 15th Anniv of Declaration of Human Rights.
420 **113** 25c. black and blue . . . 60 20

114 Labourers — **115** Map of Africa and Flags

1964. Labour Day.
421 **114** 50c. multicoloured . . . . 1·10 35

1964. 1st Anniv of Africa Day, and African Unity Charter.
422 **115** 45c. red, orange and blue 80 30

116 Tractors — **117** Rameses II in War Chariot, Abu Simbel

1964.
423 **116** 5c. purple 10 10
424 – 10c. brown 10 10
425 – 12c. green 45 15
426 – 15c. blue 35 15
427 – 20c. yellow 35 10
428 **116** 25c. red 45 10
429 – 30c. violet 40 10
430 – 45c. lake 55 20
431 – 50c. blue 55 10
432 – 65c. orange 65 15
433 **116** 85c. green . . . . 1·10 20
434 – 95c. red . . . . 1·40 20
DESIGNS: 10, 30, 65c. Apprentices; 12, 15, 45c. Research scientist; 20, 50, 95c. Draughtsman and bricklayer.

1964. Nubian Monuments Preservation.
435 **117** 20c. purple, red and blue 80 35
436 – 30c. ochre, turq & red . . 90 45
DESIGN: 30c. Heads of Rameses II.

118 Hertzian-wave Radio Transmitting Pylon — **119** Fair Emblems

1964. Inauguration of Algiers–Annaba Radio-Telephone Service.
437 **118** 85c. black, blue & brown 1·60 55

1964. Algiers Fair.
438 **119** 30c. blue, yellow and red 40 15

120 Gas Plant — **121** Planting Trees

1964. Inaug of Natural Gas Plant at Arzew.
439 **120** 25c. blue, yellow & violet 65 45

1964. Reafforestation Campaign.
440 **121** 25c. green, red and yellow 40 20

122 Children — **123** Mehariste Saddle

1964. Children's Charter.
441 **122** 15c. blue, green and red 40 20

1965. Saharan Handicrafts.
442 **123** 20c. multicoloured 45 20

124 Books Aflame — **125** I.C.Y. Emblem

1965. Reconstitution of Algiers University Library.
443 **124** 20c.+5c. red, blk & grn 45 30

1965. International Co-operation Year.
444 **125** 30c. black, green and red 80 35
445 60c. black, green and blue 1·10 40

126 I.T.U. Emblem and Symbols

1965. Centenary of I.T.U.
446 **126** 60c. violet, ochre & green 80 40
447 95c. brown, ochre & lake 1·10 45

127 Musicians playing Rebbah and Lute

1965. Mohamed Racim's Miniatures (1st series). Multicoloured.
448 30c. Type **127** . . . . 1·40 55
449 60c. Musicians playing derbouka and tarr . . . . 1·90 85
450 5d. Algerian princess and sand gazelle . . . . 11·00 6·75
See also Nos. 471/3.

128 Cattle

1966. Rock-paintings of Tassili-N-Ajjer (1st series).
451 **128** 1d. brown, ochre & purple . . . . 4·00 2·25
452 – 1d. multicoloured . . . . 4·00 2·25
453 – 2d. dp brown, buff & brn 8·25 4·00
454 – 3d. multicoloured . . . . 9·00 5·00
DESIGNS—VERT: No. 452, Peuhl shepherd; 454, Peuhl girls. HORIZ: No. 453, Ostriches.
See also Nos. 474/7.

129 Pottery — **130** Meteorological Instruments

1966. Grand Kahylie Handicrafts.
455 **129** 40c. brown, sepia and blue 40 20
456 – 50c. orange, green & bl 55 30
457 – 70c. black, red and blue 1·10 45
DESIGNS—HORIZ: 50c. Weaving. VERT: 70c. Jewellery.

1966. World Meteorological Day.
458 **130** 1d. purple, green and blue 1·10 40

131 Open Book, Cogwheel and Ear of Corn — **132** W.H.O. Building

1966. Literacy Campaign.
459 **131** 30c. black and ochre . . . 35 20
460 – 60c. red, black and grey 55 30
DESIGN: 60c. Open primer, cogwheel and ear of corn.

1966. Inaug of W.H.O. Headquarters, Geneva.
461 **132** 30c. turq, grn & brn . . . 40 30
462 60c. slate, blue and brown 70 35

133 Mohammedan Scout Emblem and Banner — **134** Soldiers and Battle Casualty

1966. 30th Anniv of Algerian Mohammedan Scouts, and 7th Arab Scout Jamboree, Jedaid (Tripoli). Multicoloured.
463 30c. Type **133** 45 30
464 1d. Jamboree emblem . . . . 1·40 55

1966. Freedom Fighters' Day.
465 **134** 30c.+10c. mult 80 55
466 95c.+10c. mult . . . . . 1·40 1·10

135 Massacre Victims — **136** Emir Abd-el-Kader

1966. Deir Yassin Massacre (1948).
467 **135** 30c. black and red 45 20

1966. Return of Emir Abd-el-Kader's Remains.
468 **136** 30c. multicoloured 20 10
469 95c. multicoloured 90 35
See also Nos. 498/502.

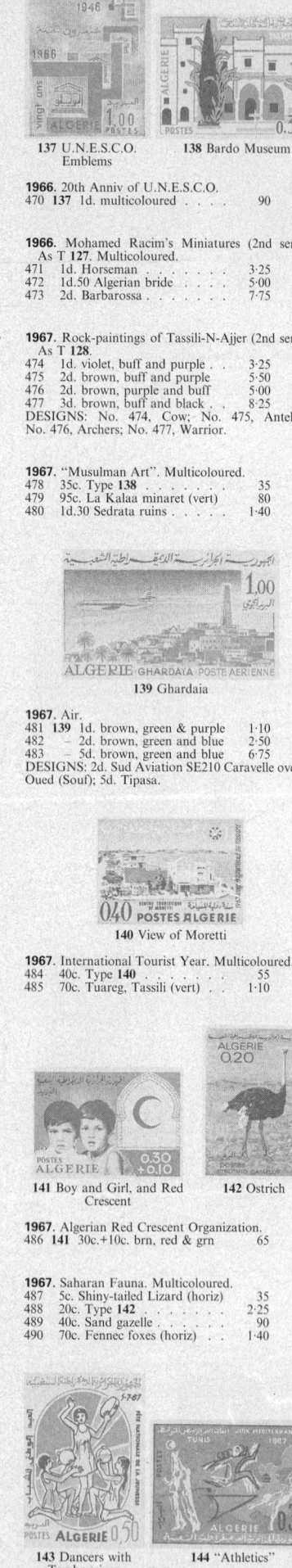

137 U.N.E.S.C.O. Emblems   138 Bardo Museum

1966. 20th Anniv of U.N.E.S.C.O.
470 137 1d. multicoloured 90   35

1966. Mohamed Racim's Miniatures (2nd series). As T 127. Multicoloured.
471   1d. Horseman . . . . 3·25   1·10
472   1d.50 Algerian bride . . . . 5·00   1·60
473   2d. Barbarossa . . . . 7·75   2·75

1967. Rock-paintings of Tassili-N-Ajjer (2nd series). As T 128.
474   1d. violet, buff and purple . . 3·25   1·60
475   2d. brown, buff and purple . 5·50   3·25
476   2d. brown, purple and buff . 5·00   2·75
477   3d. brown, buff and black . . 8·25   4·50
DESIGNS: No. 474, Cow; No. 475, Antelope; No. 476, Archers; No. 477, Warrior.

1967. "Musulman Art". Multicoloured.
478   35c. Type 138 35   15
479   95c. La Kalaa minaret (vert)   80   40
480   1d.30 Sedrata ruins . . . . . 1·40   55

139 Ghardaia

1967. Air.
481 139 1d. brown, green & purple   1·10   45
482   – 2d. brown, green and blue   2·50   1·25
483   – 5d. brown, green and blue   6·75   2·75
DESIGNS: 2d. Sud Aviation SE210 Caravelle over El Oued (Souf); 5d. Tipasa.

140 View of Moretti

1967. International Tourist Year. Multicoloured.
484 140 40c. Type 140 55   35
485   70c. Tuareg, Tassili (vert) . . 1·10   45

141 Boy and Girl, and Red Crescent   142 Ostrich

1967. Algerian Red Crescent Organization.
486 141 30c.+10c. brn, red & grn   65   40

1967. Saharan Fauna. Multicoloured.
487   5c. Shiny-tailed Lizard (horiz)   35   30
488   20c. Type 142 . . . . 2·25   75
489   40c. Sand gazelle 90   45
490   70c. Fennec foxes (horiz) . . 1·40   80

143 Dancers with Tambourines   144 "Athletics"

1967. National Youth Festival.
491 143 50c. black, yellow & blue   80   35

1967. 5th Mediterranean Games, Tunis.
492 144 30c. black, blue and red . . 50   30

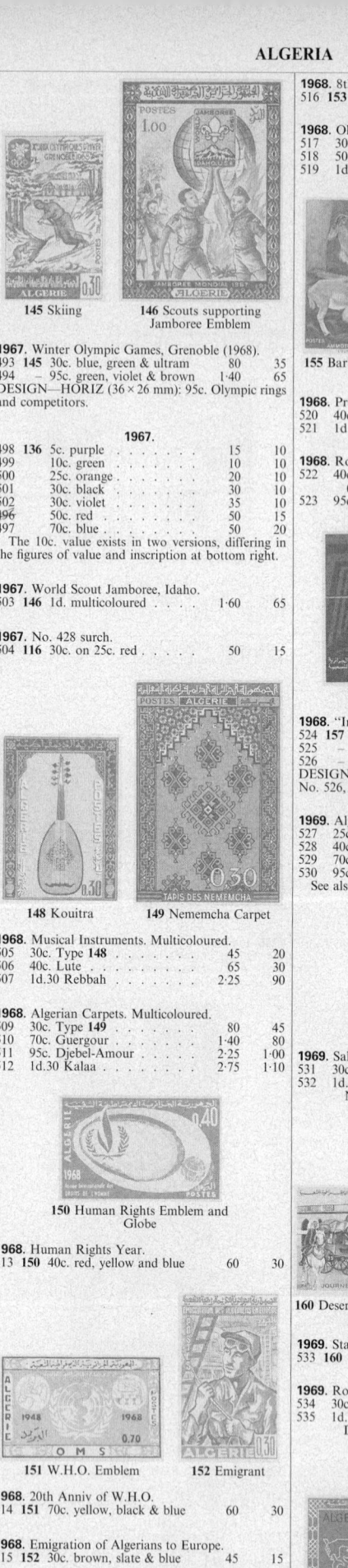

145 Skiing   146 Scouts supporting Jamboree Emblem

1967. Winter Olympic Games, Grenoble (1968).
493 145 30c. blue, green & ultram   80   35
494   – 95c. green, violet & brown   1·40   65
DESIGN—HORIZ (36 × 26 mm): 95c. Olympic rings and competitors.

1967.
498 136 5c. purple 15   10
499   10c. green 10   10
500   25c. orange 20   10
501   30c. black 30   10
502   30c. violet 35   10
496   50c. red 50   15
497   70c. blue 50   20
   The 10c. value exists in two versions, differing in the figures of value and inscription at bottom right.

1967. World Scout Jamboree, Idaho.
503 146 1d. multicoloured . . . . 1·60   65

1967. No. 428 surch.
504 116 30c. on 25c. red 50   15

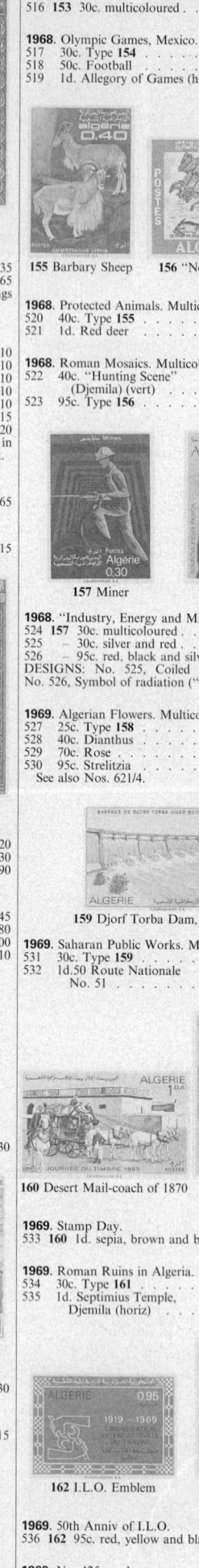

148 Kouitra   149 Nememcha Carpet

1968. Musical Instruments. Multicoloured.
505   30c. Type 148 45   20
506   40c. Lute 65   30
507   1d.30 Rebbah . . . . 2·25   90

1968. Algerian Carpets. Multicoloured.
509   30c. Type 149 80   45
510   70c. Guergour . . . . . . 1·40   80
511   95c. Djebel-Amour . . . . 2·25   1·00
512   1d.30 Kalaa . . . . 2·75   1·10

150 Human Rights Emblem and Globe

1968. Human Rights Year.
513 150 40c. red, yellow and blue   60   30

151 W.H.O. Emblem   152 Emigrant

1968. 20th Anniv of W.H.O.
514 151 70c. yellow, black & blue   60   30

1968. Emigration of Algerians to Europe.
515 152 30c. brown, slate & blue   45   15

153 Scouts holding Jamboree Emblem   154 Torch and Athletes

1968. 8th Arab Scouts Jamboree, Algiers.
516 153 30c. multicoloured 55   20

1968. Olympic Games, Mexico. Multicoloured.
517   30c. Type 154 50   35
518   50c. Football 85   40
519   1d. Allegory of Games (horiz)   1·40   80

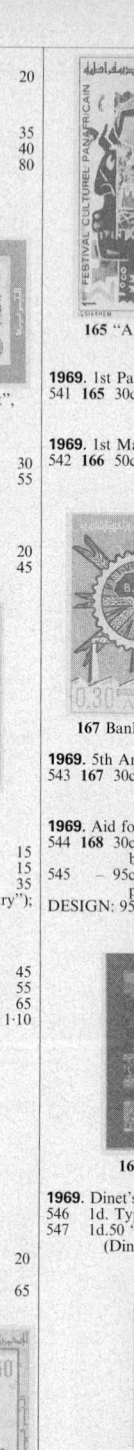

155 Barbary Sheep   156 "Neptune's Chariot", Timgad

1968. Protected Animals. Multicoloured.
520   40c. Type 155 65   30
521   1d. Red deer . . . . 1·60   55

1968. Roman Mosaics. Multicoloured.
522   40c. "Hunting Scene" (Djemila) (vert) 50   20
523   95c. Type 156 . . . . 1·10   45

157 Miner   158 Opuntia

1968. "Industry, Energy and Mines".
524 157 30c. multicoloured 40   15
525   – 30c. silver and red 40   15
526   – 95c. red, black and silver   1·10   35
DESIGNS: No. 525, Coiled spring ("Industry"); No. 526, Symbol of radiation ("Energy").

1969. Algerian Flowers. Multicoloured.
527   25c. Type 158 55   45
528   40c. Dianthus 85   55
529   70c. Rose . . . . 1·40   65
530   95c. Strelitzia . . . . 2·25   1·10
   See also Nos. 621/4.

159 Djorf Torba Dam, Oued Guir

1969. Saharan Public Works. Multicoloured.
531   30c. Type 159 45   20
532   1d.50 Route Nationale No. 51 . . . . 1·60   65

160 Desert Mail-coach of 1870   161 The Capitol, Timgad

1969. Stamp Day.
533 160 1d. sepia, brown and blue   1·40   55

1969. Roman Ruins in Algeria. Multicoloured.
534   30c. Type 161 45   15
535   1d. Septimius Temple, Djemila (horiz) . . . . . 1·10   40

162 I.L.O. Emblem   164 Carved Bookcase

1969. 50th Anniv of I.L.O.
536 162 95c. red, yellow and black   1·00   40

1969. No. 425 surch.
537   20c. on 12c. green 35   10

1969. Handicrafts. Multicoloured.
538   30c. Type 164 40   20
539   60c. Copper tray 60   30
540   1d. Arab saddle . . . . . . 1·25   50

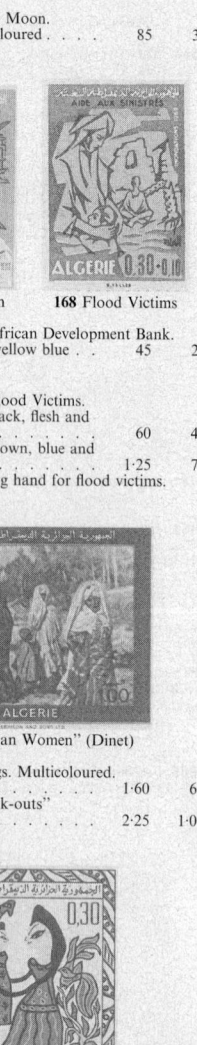

165 "Africa" Head   166 Astronauts on Moon

1969. 1st Pan-African Cultural Festival, Algiers.
541 165 30c. multicoloured 35   20

1969. 1st Man on the Moon.
542 166 50c. multicoloured 85   35

167 Bank Emblem   168 Flood Victims

1969. 5th Anniv of African Development Bank.
543 167 30c. black, yellow blue . . 45   20

1969. Aid for 1969 Flood Victims.
544 168 30c.+10c. black, flesh and blue 60   40
545   – 95c.+25c. brown, blue and purple . . . . 1·25   70
DESIGN: 95c. Helping hand for flood victims.

169 "Algerian Women" (Dinet)

1969. Dinet's Paintings. Multicoloured.
546   1d. Type 169 . . . . 1·60   65
547   1d.50 "The Look-outs" (Dinet) . . . . 2·25   1·00

170 "Mother and Child"

1969. "Protection of Mother and Child".
548 170 30c. multicoloured 50   30

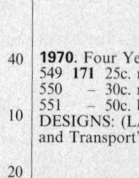

171 "Agriculture"   172 Postal Deliveries by Donkey and Mail Van

1970. Four Year Plan.
549 171 25c. multicoloured 20   15
550   – 30c. multicoloured . . . . 1·75   15
551   – 50c. black and purple . . . 45   20
DESIGNS: (LARGER, 49 × 23 mm): 30c. "Industry and Transport"; 50c. "Industry" (abstract).

1970. Stamp Day.
552 172 30c. multicoloured 45   20

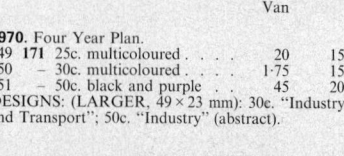

173 Royal Prawn   174 Oranges

1970. Marine Life. Multicoloured.
553	30c. Type 173	45	20
554	40c. Noble pen (mollusc) . .	75	35
555	75c. Neptune's basket . . .	1·10	45
556	1d. Red coral	1·60	65

1970. "Expo 70" World Fair, Osaka, Japan. Multicoloured.
557	30c. Type 174	55	20
558	60c. Algerian Pavilion . . .	55	35
559	70c. Bunches of grapes . . .	1·10	45

175 Olives and Bottle of Olive-oil

1970. World Olive-oil Year.
560	**175** 1d. multicoloured	1·40	65

176 New U.P.U. H.Q. Building

1970. Inaug of New U.P.U. Headquarters Building.
561	**176** 75c. multicoloured	60	30

177 Crossed Muskets

1970. Algerian 18th-century Weapons. Mult.
562	40c. Type **177**	85	45
563	75c. Sabre (vert)	1·10	65
564	1d. Pistol	1·60	90

178 Arab League Flag, Arms and Map   179 Lenin

1970. 25th Anniv of Arab League.
565	**178** 30c. multicoloured	45	15

1970. Birth Centenary of Lenin.
566	**179** 30c. bistre and ochre . .	1·10	30

180 Exhibition Palace

1970. 7th International Algiers Fair.
567	**180** 60c. green	55	35

181 I.E.Y. and Education Emblems

1970. International Education Year. Mult.
568	30c. Type **181**	35	15
569	3d. Illuminated Koran (30 × 41 mm)	2·40	1·40

182 Great Mosque, Tlemcen

1970. Mosques.
570	**182** 30c. multicoloured	30	15
571	— 40c. brown and bistre . .	45	15
572	— 1d. multicoloured	85	30
DESIGNS—VERT: 40c. Ketchaoua Mosque, Algiers; 1d. Sidi-Okba Mosque.

183 "Fine Arts"

1970. Algerian Fine Arts.
573	**183** 1d. orange, grn & lt grn	90	35

184 G.P.O., Algiers   186 "Racial Equality"

185 Hurdling

1971. Stamp Day.
574	**184** 30c. multicoloured	65	30

1971. 6th Mediterranean Games, Izmir (Turkey).
575	**185** 20c. grey and blue . . .	35	15
576	— 40c. grey and green . . .	50	30
577	— 75c. grey and brown . .	85	40
DESIGNS—VERT: 40c. Gymnastics; 75c. Basketball.

1971. Racial Equality Year.
578	**186** 60c. multicoloured	60	30

187 Symbols of Learning, and Students

1971. Inaug of Technological Institutes.
579	**187** 70c. multicoloured	65	20

188 Red Crescent Banner

1971. Red Crescent Day.
580	**188** 30c.+10c. red and green	55	35

189 Casbah, Algiers

1971. Air.
581	**189** 2d. multicoloured . . .	1·90	85
582	— 3d. violet and black . .	2·75	1·40
583	— 4d. multicoloured . . .	3·25	1·60
DESIGNS: 3d. Port of Oran; 4d. Rhumel Gorges.

190 Aures Costume   191 U.N.I.C.E.F. Emblem, Tree and Animals

1971. Regional Costumes (1st series). Multicoloured.
584	50c. Type **190**	90	45
585	70c. Oran	1·00	65
586	80c. Algiers	1·25	80
587	90c. Djebel-Amour	1·60	90
See also Nos. 610/13 and 659/62.

1971. 25th Anniv of U.N.I.C.E.F.
588	**191** 60c. multicoloured	60	35

192 Lion of St. Mark's

1971. U.N.E.S.C.O. "Save Venice" Campaign. Mult.
589	80c. Type **192**	90	45
590	1d. 15 Bridge of Sighs . . .	1·60	80

193 Cycling   194 Book and Bookmark

1972. Olympic Games, Munich. Multicoloured.
591	25c. Type **193**	35	15
592	40c. Throwing the javelin (vert)	40	20
593	60c. Wrestling (vert)	65	40
594	1d. Gymnastics (vert) . . .	1·10	

1972. International Book Year.
595	**194** 1d.15 red, black and brown	70	40

195 Algerian Postmen   196 Jasmine

1972. Stamp Day.
596	**195** 40c. multicoloured	45	15

1972. Flowers. Multicoloured.
597	50c. Type **196**	50	30
598	60c. Violets	55	35
599	1d.15 Tuberose	1·40	50

197 Olympic Stadium   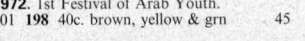198 Festival Emblem

1972. Inaug of Cheraga Olympic Stadium.
600	**197** 50c. green, brown & violet	55	30

1972. 1st Festival of Arab Youth.
601	**198** 40c. brown, yellow & grn	45	15

199 Rejoicing Algerians   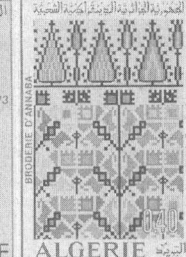201 Child posting Letter

1972. 10th Anniv of Independence.
602	**199** 1d. multicoloured	95	50

1972. Regional Costumes (2nd series). As T **190**. Multicoloured.
610	50c. Hoggar	1·10	55
611	60c. Kabylie	1·10	55
612	70c. Mzab	1·40	80
613	90c. Tlemcen	1·60	90

1973. Stamp Day.
614	**201** 40c. multicoloured	35	15

202 Ho-Chi-Minh and Map   203 Annaba Embroidery

1973. "Homage to the Vietnamese People".
615	**202** 40c. multicoloured	60	30

1973. Algerian Embroidery. Multicoloured.
616	40c. Type **203**	50	30
617	60c. Algiers embroidery . . .	70	40
618	80c. Constantine embroidery	1·00	50

204 "Food Cultivation"   206 O.A.U. Emblem

1973. 10th Anniv of World Food Programme.
619	**204** 1d.15 multicoloured . . .	65	30

205 Serviceman and Flag

1973. National Service.
620	**205** 40c. multicoloured	45	15

1973. Algerian Flowers. As T **158**. Multicoloured.
621	30c. Type **158**	45	20
622	40c. As No. 529	55	35
623	1d. As No. 528	1·25	55
624	1d.15 As No. 530	1·60	65

1973. 10th Anniv of Organization of African Unity.
625	**206** 40c. multicoloured	45	20

207 Peasant Family

1973. Agrarian Revolution.
626	**207** 40c. multicoloured	50	20

 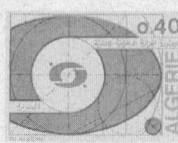

208 Scout Badge on Map   **209** P.T.T. Symbol

1973. 24th World Scouting Congress, Nairobi, Kenya.
627 **208** 80c. mauve   60   30

1973. Inauguration of New P.T.T. Symbol.
628 **209** 40c. orange and blue . .   45   15

210 Conference Emblem   **211** "Skikda Harbour"

1973. 4th Summit Conference of Non-Aligned Countries, Algiers.
629 **210** 40c. multicoloured   35   15
630   80c. multicoloured   60   20

1973. Opening of Skikda Port.
631 **211** 80c. multicoloured   60   30

212 Young Workers   **213** Arms of Algiers

1973. Volontariat Students' Volunteer Service.
632 **212** 40c. multicoloured   45   20

1973. Millenary of Algiers.
633 **213** 2d. multicoloured . . . .   2·25   1·10

214 "Protected Infant"

1974. Anti-TB Campaign.
634 **214** 80c. multicoloured   60   30

215 Industrial Scene

1974. Four Year Plan.
635 **215** 80c. multicoloured   65   35

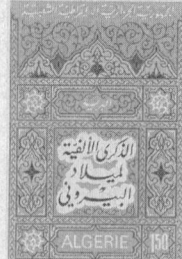

216 Arabesque Motif

1974. Birth Millenary of Abu-al Rayhan al-Biruni (mathematician and philosopher).
636 **216** 1d.50 multicoloured . . .   1·60   1·10

217 Map and Arrows   **218** Upraised Weapon and Fist

1974. Meeting of Maghreb Committee for Co-ordination of Posts and Telecommunications, Tunis.
637 **217** 40c. multicoloured   45   20

1974. Solidarity with South African People's Campaign.
638 **218** 80c. black and red   55   20

219 Algerian Family

1974. Homage to Algerian Mothers.
639 **219** 85c. multicoloured   55   20

220 Urban Scene

1974. Children's Drawings. Multicoloured.
640 **220** 70c. Type **220**   60   15
641   80c. Agricultural scene . . .   70   30
642   90c. Tractor and sunrise . .   90   45
Nos. 641/2 are size 49 × 33 mm.

1974. "Floralies 1974" Flower Show, Algiers. Nos. 623/4 optd **FLORALIES 1974**.
643   1d. multicoloured . . . . .   1·25   65
644   1d.15 multicoloured . . . .   1·60   1·00

222 Automatic Stamp-vending Machine   **223** U.P.U. Emblem on Globe

1974. Stamp Day.
645 **222** 80c. multicoloured   55   20

1974. Centenary of U.P.U.
646 **223** 80c. multicoloured   60   30

224 Revolutionaries

1974. 20th Anniv of Revolution. Multicoloured.
647   40c. Type **224**   35   20
648   70c. Armed soldiers (vert) . .   45   20
649   95c. Raising the flag (vert) . .   70   20
650   1d. Algerians looking to Independence   95   30

225 "Towards the Horizon"   **226** Ewer

1974. "Horizon 1980".
651 **225** 95c. red, brown & black . .   60   30

1974. Algerian 17th-century Brassware. Mult.
652 **226** 50c. Type **226**   40   20
653   60c. Coffee pot   45   30
654   95c. Sugar basin   65   40
655   1d. Bath vessel   95   50

1975. No. 622 surch.
656   50c. on 40c. multicoloured . .   1·10   45

228 Games Emblem

1975. 7th Mediterranean Games (1st issue).
657 **228** 50c. violet, green & yellow   40   15
658   1d. orange, violet & blue   70   20
See also Nos. 671/5.

1975. Regional Costumes (3rd series). As T **190**. Multicoloured.
659   1d. Algiers . . . .   1·10   60
660   1d. The Hoggar . . . . . .   1·10   60
661   1d. Oran . . . .   1·10   60
662   1d. Tlemcen . . . .   1·10   60

229 Labour Emblems

1975. 10th Anniv of Arab Labour Organization.
663 **229** 50c. brown   45   10

230 Transfusion

1975. Blood Collection and Transfusion Service.
664 **230** 50c. multicoloured   55   30

231 El Kantara Post Office   **232** Policeman and Oil Rig on Map of Algeria

1975. Stamp Day.
665 **231** 50c. multicoloured   45   15

1975. Police Day.
666 **232** 50c. multicoloured   45   20

233 Ground Receiving Aerial

1975. Satellite Telecommunications. Mult.
667 **233** 50c. Type **233**   40   15
668   1d. Map of receiving sites . .   65   20
669   1d.20 Main and subsidiary ground stations   85   30

234 Revolutionary with Flag   **235** Swimming

1975. 20th Anniv of "Skikda" Revolution.
670 **234** 1d. multicoloured   60   30

1975. 7th Mediterranean Games, Algiers (2nd issue). Multicoloured.
671   25c. Type **235**   15   10
672   50c. Wrestling   30   15
673   70c. Football (vert)   50   20
674   1d. Athletics (vert)   65   30
675   1d.20 Handball (vert)   85   45

236 "Setif-Guelma-Kherrata"   **237** Map of the Maghreb and A.P.U. Emblem

1975. 30th Anniv of Setif, Guelma and Kherrata Massacres (1st issue).
677 **236** 5c. black and orange . . .   10   10
678   10c. black and green . . .   10   10
679   25c. black and blue . . .   15   10
680   30c. black and brown . . .   20   10
681   50c. black and green . . .   30   10
682   70c. black and red . . .   40   15
683   1d. black and red   60   30
See also No. 698.

1975. 10th Arab Postal Union Congress, Algiers.
684 **237** 1d. multicoloured   60   30

238 Mosaic, Palace of the Bey, Constantine

1975. Historic Buildings.
685 **238** 1d. multicoloured   85   35
686   2d. multicoloured . . . . .   1·60   80
687   2d.50 black and brown . .   2·25   1·10
DESIGNS—VERT: 2d. Medersa Sidi-Boumedienne Oratory, Tlemcen. HORIZ: 2d.50, Palace of the Dey, Algiers.

239 University Building   **240** Red-billed Fire Finch

1975. Millenary of Al-Azhar University, Cairo.
688 **239** 2d. multicoloured . . . . 1·60 65

1976. Algerian Birds (1st series). Multicoloured.
689 50c. Type **240** . . . . . 1·25 60
690 1d.40 Black-headed bush
shrike (horiz) . . . . 2·00 1·00
691 2d. Blue-tit . . . . . 2·40 1·10
692 2d.50 Black-bellied sandgrouse (horiz) . . . . 2·75 1·50
See also Nos. 722/5.

241 Early and Modern Telephones
242 Map and Angolan Flag

1976. Telephone Centenary.
693 **241** 1d.40 multicoloured . . . 85 40

1976. "Solidarity with Republic of Angola".
694 **242** 50c. multicoloured 45 15

243 Child on Map
244 Postman

1976. Solidarity with People of Western Sahara.
695 **243** 50c. multicoloured 45 20

1976. Stamp Day.
696 **244** 1d.40 multicoloured . . . 85 35

245 People, Microscope and Slide
246 "Setif-Guelma-Kherrata"

1976. Campaign Against Tuberculosis.
697 **245** 50c. multicoloured 45 15

1976. 30th Anniv of Setif, Guelma and Kherrata
Massacres (2nd issue).
698 **246** 50c. yellow and blue . . . 45 10

247 Ram's Head and Landscape
248 Algerians holding Torch

1976. Sheep Raising.
699 **247** 50c. multicoloured 45 20

1976. National Charter.
700 **248** 50c. multicoloured 50 15

249 Flag and Map
250 Map of Africa

1976. Solidarity with the Palestinian People.
701 **249** 50c. multicoloured 50 15

1976. 2nd Pan-African Commercial Fair, Algiers.
702 **250** 2d. multicoloured . . . 1·40 50

251 Blind Man making Brushes
253 Soldiers planting Seedlings

252 Open Book

1976. Rehabilitation of the Blind. Multicoloured.
703 1d.20 Type **251** 80 35
704 1d.40 "The Blind Man"
(E. Dinet) (horiz) . . 1·10 50

1976. The Constitution.
705 **252** 2d. multicoloured . . . . 1·40 55

1976. Protection against Saharan Encroachment.
706 **253** 1d.40 multicoloured . . . 1·10 45

254 Arabic Inscription

1976. Election of President Boumedienne.
707 **254** 2d. multicoloured . . . 1·40 55

255 Map of Telephone Centres
256 "Pyramid" of Heads

1977. Inauguration of Automatic Telephone Dialling
System.
708 **255** 40c. multicoloured 35 15

1977. 2nd General Population and Housing Census.
709 **256** 60c. on 50c. mult 45 15

257 Museum Building
258 El Kantara Gorges

1977. Sahara Museum, Ouargla.
710 **257** 60c. multicoloured 55 35

1977.
711 **258** 20c. green and cream . . . 1·10 45
712 60c. mauve and cream . . . 1·60 45
713 1d. brown and cream . . . 6·00 50

259 Assembly in Session

1977. National Assembly.
714 **259** 2d. multicoloured . . . . 1·10 45

260 Soldiers with Flag
261 Soldier with Flag

1977. Solidarity with People of Zimbabwe.
715 **260** 2d. multicoloured . . . . 1·10 45

1977. Solidarity with People of Namibia.
716 **261** 3d. multicoloured . . . 1·75 65

262 "Winter"

1977. Roman Mosaics. "The Seasons". Mult.
717 1d.20 Type **262** . . . . . 1·25 65
718 1d.40 "Autumn" . . . . . 1·35 65
719 2d. "Summer" . . . . . 1·75 1·10
720 3d. "Spring" . . . . . 2·40 1·40

1977. Algerian Birds (2nd series). As T **240**.
Multicoloured.
722 60c. Tristram's warbler . . . 1·10 60
723 1d.40 Moussier's redstart
(horiz) . . . . . 1·50 75
724 2d. Temminck's horned lark
(horiz) . . . . . 2·25 1·10
725 3d. Hoopoe . . . . . 3·50 1·60

263 Horseman
264 Ribbon and Games Emblem

1977. "The Cavaliers" (performing horsemen).
Multicoloured.
726 2d. Type **263** . . . . . 1·60 65
727 5d. Three horsemen (horiz) . 3·75 1·60

1977. 3rd African Games, Algiers (1978) (1st issue).
Multicoloured.
728 60c. Type **264** 45 20
729 1d.40 Symbolic design and
emblem . . . . . 1·10 45
See also Nos. 740/4.

265 Tessala el Merdja

1977. Socialist Agricultural Villages.
730 **265** 1d.40 multicoloured . . . 85 35

266 12th-century Almohad Dirham

1977. Ancient Coins. Multicolored.
731 60c. Type **266** 45 30
732 1d.40 12th-century Alomhad
dinar . . . . . 1·00 40
733 2d. 11th-century Almorarid
dinar . . . . . 1·40 70

267 Cherry ("Cerasus avium")
269 Children with Traffic Signs opposing Car

1978. Fruit Tree Blossom. Multicoloured.
734 60c. Type **267** 45 20
735 1d.20 "Persica vulgaris"
(peach) 80 55
736 1d.30 "Amygdalus
communis" (almond) . . 80 55
737 1d.40 "Malus communis"
(crab apple) . . . . 1·10 65

1978. Surch.
738 **236** 60c. on 50c. black & grn 55 15

1978. Road Safety for Children.
739 **269** 60c. multicoloured 50 20

270 Boxing and Map of Africa

1978. 3rd African Games, Algiers (2nd issue).
Multicoloured.
740 40c. Sports emblems and
volleyball (horiz) . . . 20 10
741 60c. Olympic rings and table
tennis symbol . . . 35 15
742 1d.20 Basketball symbol
(horiz) 70 30
743 1d.30 Hammerthrowing
symbol 70 40
744 1d.40 Type **270** 90 40

271 Patient returning to Family

1978. Anti-tuberculosis Campaign.
745 **271** 60c. multicoloured 50 20

272 Ka'aba, Mecca

1978. Pilgrimage to Mecca.
746 **272** 60c. multicoloured . . . 50 10

273 Road-building   **274** Triangular Brooch

1978. African Unity Road.
747 **273** 60c. multicoloured   50   15

1978. Jewellery (1st series). Multicoloured.
748   1d.20 Type **274**   90   45
749   1d.35 Circular brooch . . . .   1·10   55
750   1d.40 Anklet . . . .   1·40   65
    See also Nos. 780/2 and 833/5.

275 President Houari   **276** Books and Hands holding
Boumedienne   Torch

1979. President Boumedienne Commem (1st issue).
751 **275** 60c. brown, red & turq   45   20
    See also No. 753.

1979. National Liberation Front Party Congress.
752 **276** 60c. multicoloured   40   15

277 President Houari Boumedienne

1979. President Boumedienne Commem (2nd issue).
753 **277** 1d.40 multicoloured . . .   95   40

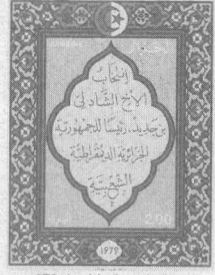

278 Arabic Inscription   **279** White Storks

1979. Election of President Chadli Bendjedid.
754 **278** 2d. multicoloured . . . .   1·25   35

1979. Air.
755 **279** 10d. blue, black and red   6·00   2·00

280 Ben Badis   **281** Globe within
Telephone Dial

1979. 90th Birth Anniv of Sheikh Abdelhamid Ben
    Badis (journalist and education pioneer).
756 **280** 60c. multicoloured   40   15

1979. "Telecom 79" Exhibition. Multicoloured.
757   1d.20 Type **281**   70   20
758   1d.40 Sound waves   90   35

282 Children dancing on
Globe

1979. International Year of the Child. Mult.
759   60c. Picking Dates   40   10
760   1d.40 Type **282** (vert)   85   35

283 Kabylie   **284** Fighting for the
Nuthatch   Revolution and
             Construction work

1979.
761 **283** 1d.40 multicoloured . . .   3·00   1·25

1979. 25th Anniv of Revolution. Multicoloured.
762   1d.40 Type **284**   80   20
763   3d. Algerians with flag . . .   1·75   65

285 Arabic Inscription

1979. 1400th Anniv of Hegira.
764 **285** 3d. gold, turquoise & blue   1·60   65

286 Return of Dionysus   **287** Books
(right detail)

1980. Dionysus Mosaic, Setif. Multicoloured.
765   1d.20 Type **286**   80   35
766   1d.35 Centre detail   90   45
767   1d.40 Left detail . . . . . .   1·00   65
    Nos. 765/7 were issued together, se-tenant, forming
a composite design.

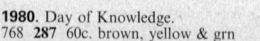

1980. Day of Knowledge.
768 **287** 60c. brown, yellow & grn   40   10

288 Five Year Plan   **289** Olympic Flame

1980. Extraordinary Congress of National Liberation
    Front Party.
769 **288** 60c. multicoloured   40   15

1980. Olympic Games, Moscow. Multicoloured.
770   50c. Type **289**   35   10
771   1d.40 Olympic sports (horiz)   80   30

290 Figures supporting O.P.E.C.
Emblem

1980. 20th Anniv of Organization of Petroleum
    Exporting Countries.
772 **290** 60c. green, blue and red   40   10
773   – 1d.40 green and blue   95   35
DESIGN: 1d.40, O.P.E.C. emblem on world map.

291 Aures

1980. World Tourism Conference, Manila. Mult.
774   50c. Type **291**   35   15
775   1d. El Oued   65   20
776   1d.40 Tassili   90   35
777   2d. Algiers . . . .   1·40   50

292 Ibn Sina

1980. Birth Millenary of Ibn Sina (Avicenna)
    (philosopher).
778 **292** 3d. multicoloured . . . .   1·60   65

293 Earthquake Devastation

1980. El Asnam Earthquake Relief.
779 **293** 3d. multicoloured . . . .   1·60   45

1980. Jewellery (2nd series). As T **274**. Mult.
780   60c. Necklace   45   20
781   1d.40 Earrings and bracelet   80   45
782   2d. Diadem (horiz) . . . .   1·25   55

294 Emblem

1981. Five Year Plan.
783 **294** 60c. multicoloured   35   10

295 Basket-worker

1981. Traditional Arts. Multicoloured.
784   40c. Type **295**   20   10
785   60c. Spinning   35   15
786   1d. Copper-smith   55   20
787   1d.40 Jeweller   80   35

296 Cedar "Cedrus atlantica"

1981. World Tree Day. Multicoloured.
788   60c. Type **296**   35   10
789   1d.40 Cypress "Cupressus
    dupreziana"   80   35

297 Mohamed Bachir el   **298** Children and
Ibrahimi   Blackboard (Basic
             Schooling)

1981. Day of Knowledge.
790 **297** 60c. multicoloured   35   10
791 **298** 60c. multicoloured   35   10

299 Archer, Dog and Internal
Organs

1981. 12th Int Hydatidological Congress, Algiers.
792 **299** 2d. multicoloured . . . .   1·40   45

300 Dish Aerial and   **301** "Disabled"
Caduceus

1981. World Telecommunications Day.
793 **300** 1d.40 multicoloured   80   20

1981. International Year of Disabled People.
794 **301** 1d.20 blue, red & orange   65   15
795   – 1d.40 multicoloured   80   15
DESIGN: 1d.40, Disabled people and hand holding
flower.

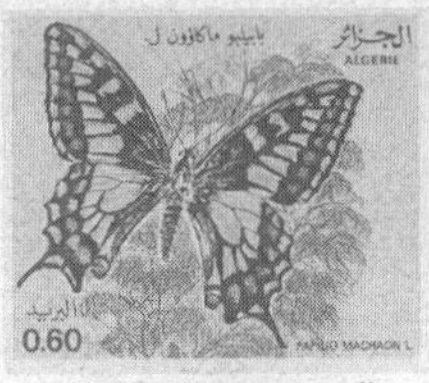

302 "Papilio machaon"

1981. Butterflies. Multicoloured.
796 60c. Type **302** 45 15
797 1d.20 "Rhodocera rhamni gonepteryx rhamni" . . . 80 35
798 1d.40 "Charaxes jasius" . . . 1·00 50
799 2d. "Papilio podalirius" . . . 1·40 65

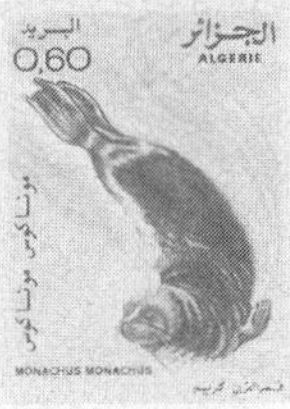

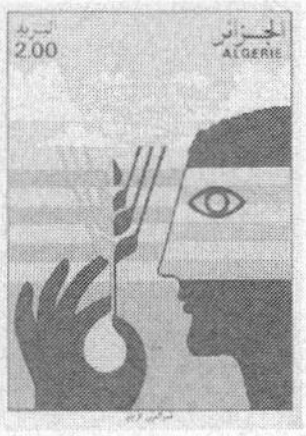

303 Mediterranean Monk Seal

304 Man holding Ear of Wheat

1981. Nature Protection. Multicoloured.
800 60c. Type **303** 55 35
801 1d.40 Barbary ape . . . . . 1·10 80

1981. World Food Day.
802 **304** 2d. multicoloured . . . . 1·00 40

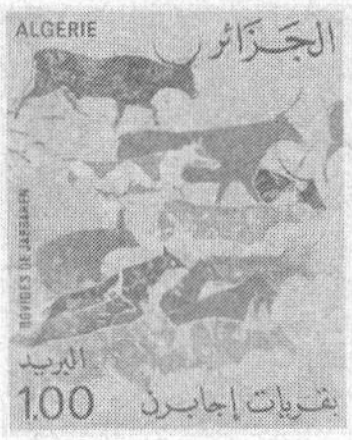

305 Cattle, Jabbaren

1981. Cave Paintings. Multicoloured.
803 60c. Mouflon, Tan Zoumaitek 35 15
804 1d. Type **305** 55 20
805 1d.60 Cattle, Iherir (horiz) . . 80 35
806 2d. One-horned bull, Jabbaren (horiz) . . . . . 1·10 40

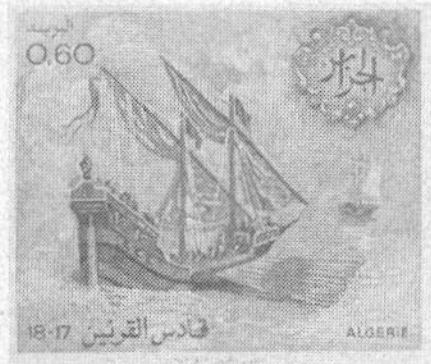

306 Galley

1981. Algerian Ships of 17th and 18th Centuries. Multicoloured.
807 60c. Type **306** 60 25
808 1d.60 Xebec . . . . 1·50 45

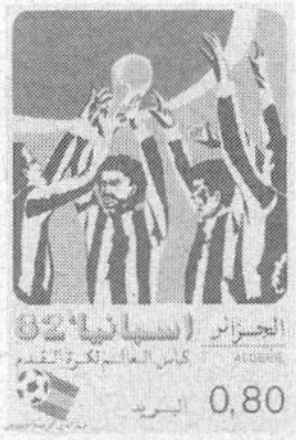

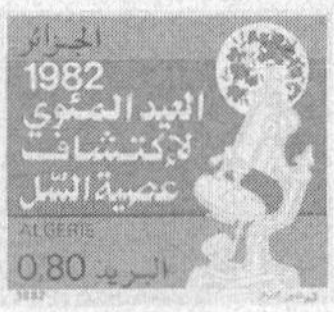

307 Footballers with Cup

308 Microscope

1982. World Cup Football Championship, Spain. Multicoloured.
809 80c. Type **307** 45 15
810 2d.80 Footballers and ball (horiz) . . . . 1·40 50

1982. Centenary of Discovery of Tubercle Bacillus.
811 **308** 80c. blue, lt blue & orge 45 15

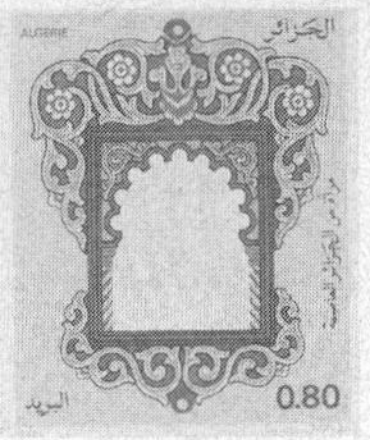

309 Mirror

1982. Popular Traditional Arts. Multicoloured.
812 80c. Type **309** 45 15
813 2d. Whatnot . . . . 1·00 40
814 2d.40 Chest (48 × 32 mm) . . 1·40 55

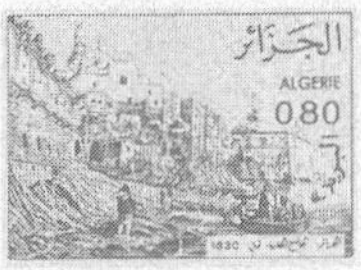

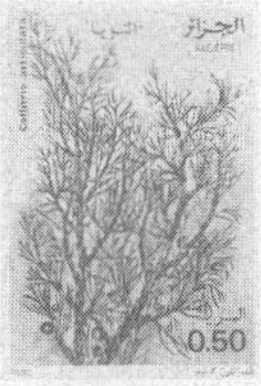

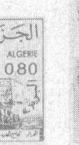

310 New Mosque, Algiers

311 "Callitris articulata"

1982. Views of Algeria before 1830 (1st series). Size 32 × 22 mm.
815 **310** 80c. brown 35 15
816 – 2d.40 violet 90 45
817 – 3d. green . . . . 1·25 55
DESIGNS: 2d.40, Sidi Boumedienne Mosque, Tlemcen; 3d. Garden of Dey, Algiers.
See also Nos. 859/62, 873/5, 880/2, 999/1001, 1054/6 and 1075/86.

1982. Medicinal Plants. Multicoloured.
818 50c. Type **311** 30 10
819 80c. "Artemisia herba-alba" 40 15
820 1d. "Ricinus communis" . . 55 20
821 2d.40 "Thymus fontanesii" 1·25 50

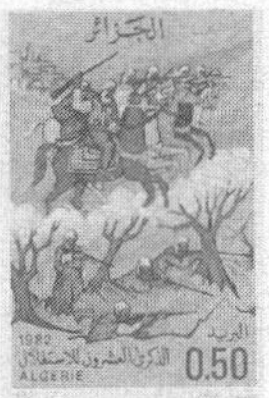

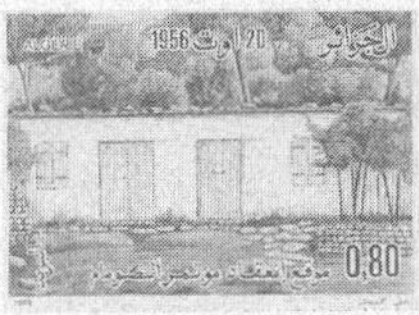

312 Independence Fighter

313 Congress House

1982. 20th Anniv of Independence. Mult.
822 50c. Type **312** 30 10
823 80c. Modern soldiers 40 15
824 2d. Algerians and symbols of prosperity . . . . 1·00 45

1982. Soumman Congress.
826 **313** 80c. multicoloured 45 10

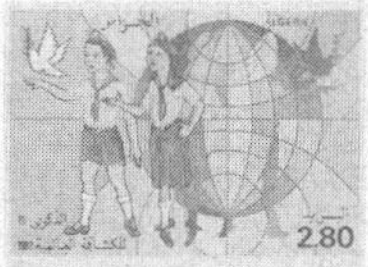

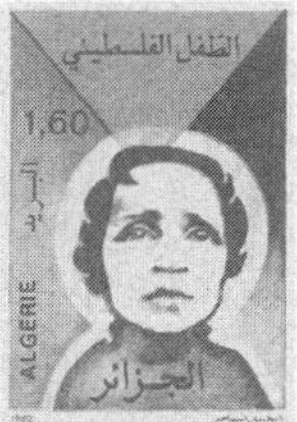

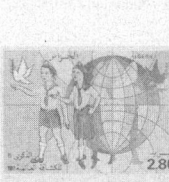

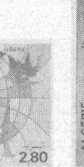

314 Scout and Guide releasing Dove

315 Child

1982. 75th Anniv of Boy Scout Movement.
827 **314** 2d.80 multicoloured . . . 1·40 45

1982. Palestinian Children.
828 **315** 1d.60 multicoloured . . . 80 20

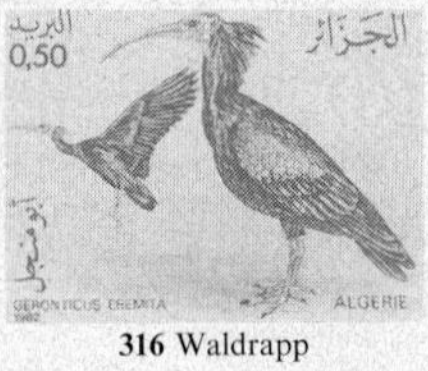

316 Waldrapp

1982. Nature Protection. Multicoloured.
829 50c. Type **316** 60 50
830 80c. Houbara bustard (vert) 75 75
831 2d. Tawny eagle . . . . . . 2·10 1·40
832 2d.40 Lammergeier (vert) . . 2·75 1·50

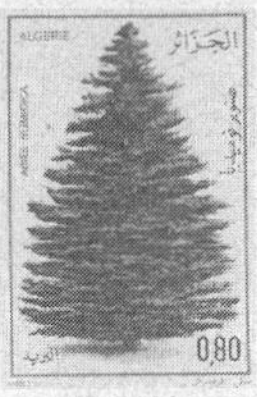

317 Mirror

318 "Abies numidica"

1983. Silver Work.
833 **317** 50c. silver, black and red 20 10
834 – 1d. multicoloured 45 30
835 – 2d. silver, black, & purple 90 45
DESIGNS—VERT. 1d. Perfume flasks. HORIZ: 2d. Belt buckle.

1983. World Tree Day. Multicoloured.
836 80c. Type **318** 40 15
837 2d.80 "Acacia raddiana" . . 1·50 55

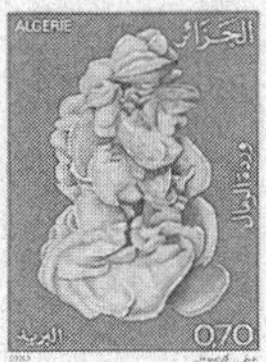

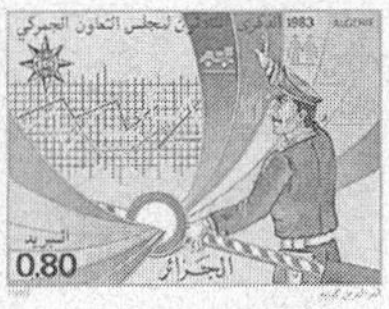

319 Mineral

320 Customs Officer

1983. Mineral Resources.
838 **319** 70c. multicoloured 55 20
839 80c. multicoloured 55 30
840 1d.20 mult (horiz) 85 55
841 2d.40 mult (horiz) . . . . 1·60 90

1983. 30th Anniv of Customs Co-operation Council.
842 **320** 80c. multicoloured 55 20

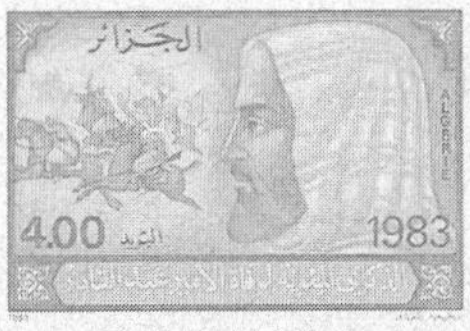

321 Emir Abdelkader

1983. Death Centenary of Emir Abdelkader.
843 **321** 4d. multicoloured . . . . 1·75 70

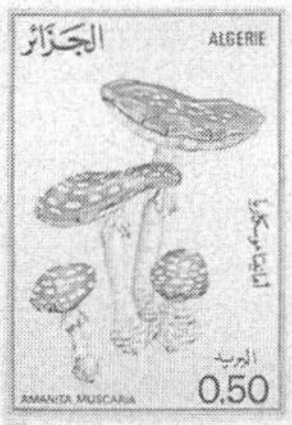

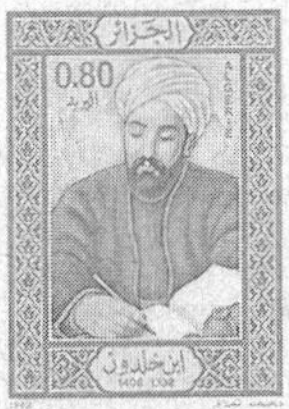

322 Fly Agaric

323 Ibn Khaldoun

1983. Mushrooms. Multicoloured.
844 50c. Type **322** 65 25
845 80c. Death cap 95 50
846 1d.40 "Pleurotus eryngii" . . 2·10 75
847 2d.80 "Terfezia leonis" . . . 3·50 1·50

1983. Ibn Khaldoun Commemoration.
848 **323** 80c. multicoloured 55 20

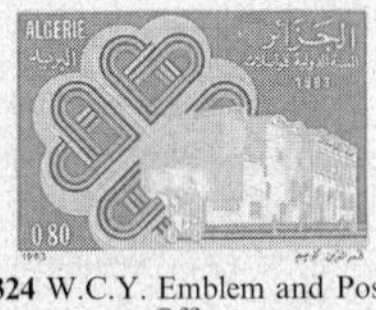

324 W.C.Y. Emblem and Post Office

1983. World Communications Year. Mult.
849 80c. Type **324** 45 15
850 2d.40 W.C.Y. emblem and telephone switch box . . . 1·10 40

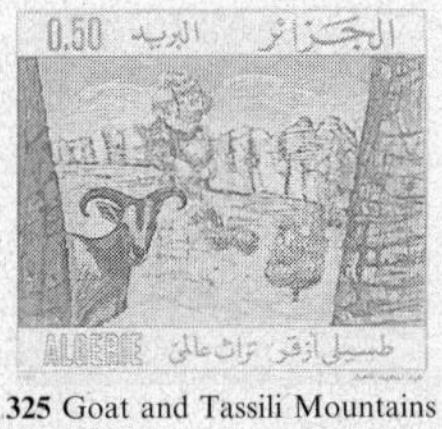

325 Goat and Tassili Mountains

1983. Tassili World Patrimony. Multicoloured.
851 50c. Type **325** 30 10
852 80c. Touaregs 40 15
853 2d.40 Rock paintings . . . . 1·10 40
854 2d.80 Rock formation . . . 1·40 55

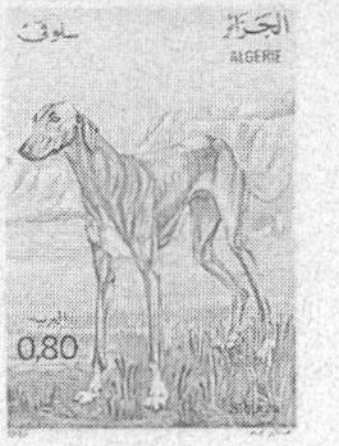

326 Sloughi

1983. Sloughi. Multicoloured.
855 80c. Type **326** 55 20
856 2d.40 Sloughi . . . . 1·40 65

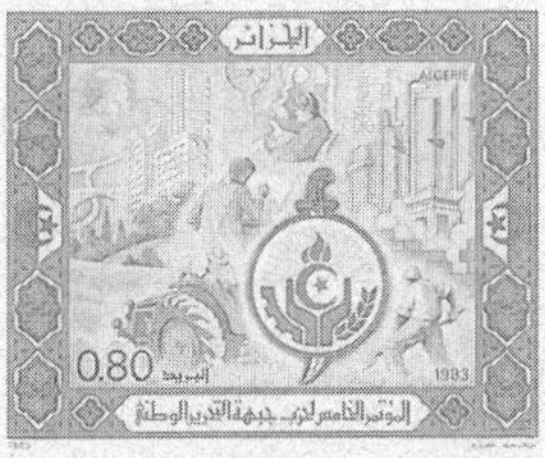

327 Symbols of Economic Progress

1983. 5th National Liberation Front Party Congress.
857 **327** 80c. multicoloured 55 30

1984. Views of Algeria before 1830 (2nd series). As T **310**.
859 10c. blue 10 10
860 1d. purple 40 15
861 2d. blue 80 35
862 4d. red . . . . 1·60 55
DESIGNS: 10c. Oran; 1d. Sidi Abderahmane Mosque, Et Taalibi; 2d. Bejaia; 4d. Constantine.

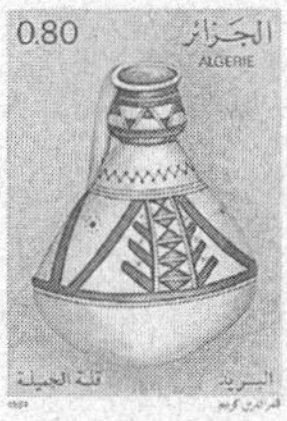

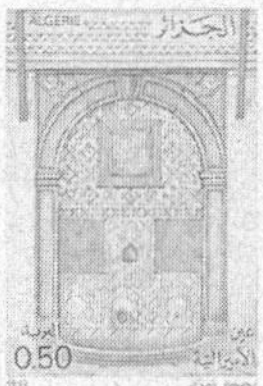

328 Jug

329 Fountain

1984. Pottery. Multicoloured.
863 80c. Type **328** 40 20
864 1d. Dish (horiz) 50 20
865 2d. Lamp . . . . 1·00 45
866 2d.40 Jug (horiz) . . . . . . 1·25 55

1984. Fountains of Old Algiers.
867 **329** 50c. multicoloured 20 15
868 – 80c. multicoloured 40 20
869 – 2d.40 multicoloured . . . 1·00 55
DESIGNS: 80c., 2d.40, Different fountains.

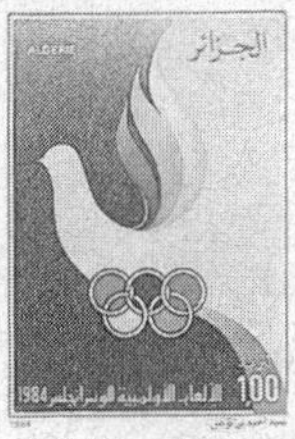

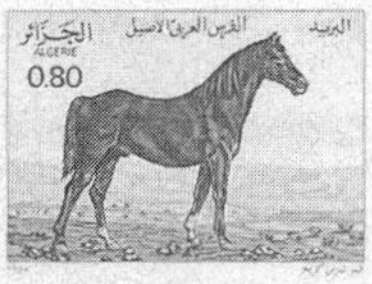

330 Dove, Flames and Olympic Rings

331 Stallion

1984. Olympic Games, Los Angeles.
870 **330** 1d. multicoloured 60 30

1984. Horses. Multicoloured.
871 80c. Type **331** 45 35
872 2d.40 Mare . . . . 1·40 80

1984. Views of Algeria before 1830 (3rd series). As T **310**.
873 5c. purple 10 10
874 20c. blue 10 10
875 70c. violet 30 15
DESIGNS: 5c. Mustapha Pacha; 20c. Bab Azzoun; 70c. Mostaganem.

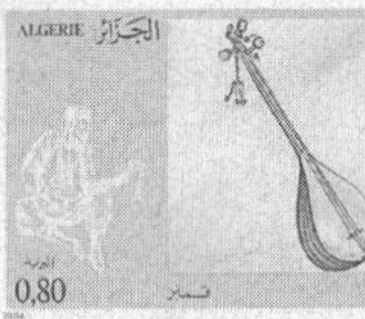

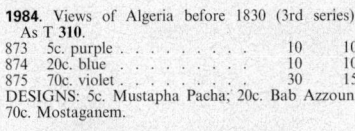

332 Lute

1984. Musical Instruments. Multicoloured.
876 80c. Type **332** 45 20
877 1d. Drum 55 20

878 2d.40 One-stringed instrument 1·25 55
879 2d.80 Bagpipes . . . . 1·40 65

1984. Views of Algeria before 1830 (4th series). As T **310**.
880 30c. red and black 15 10
881 40c. black 20 10
882 50c. brown 30 10
DESIGNS: 30c. Algiers from Admiralty; 40c. Kolea; 50c. Algiers from aqueduct.

333 Partisans in Mountains and Flag

1984. 30th Anniv of Revolution.
883 **333** 80c. multicoloured 55 20

334 Map of M'Zab Valley

1984. M'Zab Valley. Multicoloured.
885 80c. Type **334** 45 10
886 2d.40 M'Zab town . . . . . 1·25 45

335 Coffee Pot **336** Blue-finned Tuna

1985. Ornamental Tableware.
887 **335** 80c. black, silver & yellow 35 20
888 – 2d. black, silver and green 90 45
889 – 2d.40 black, silver & pink 1·25 55
DESIGNS—HORIZ: 2d. Bowl. VERT: 2d.40, Lidded jar.

1985. Fishes. Multicoloured.
890 50c. Type **336** 45 20
891 80c. Gilthead seabream . . 70 25
892 2d.40 Dusky grouper . . . 2·00 90
893 2d.80 Smooth hound . . . 2·40 1·10

337 Birds in Flight and Emblem

1985. National Games.
894 **337** 80c. multicoloured 50 15

338 Stylized Trees **339** Algiers Casbah

1985. Environmental Protection. Multicoloured.
895 80c. Type **338** 40 15
896 1d.40 Stylized waves 70 20

1985.
897 **339** 20c. blue and cream 10 10
898 80c. green and cream 45 10
899 2d.40 brown and cream 1·25 10

340 Dove within "40" **341** Figures linking arms and Emblem

1985. 40th Anniv of U.N.O.
900 **340** 1d. multicoloured 60 20

1985. 1st National Youth Festival.
901 **341** 80c. multicoloured 50 15

342 Figures linking arms on Globe and Dove **343** O.P.E.C. Emblem

1985. International Youth Year. Multicoloured.
902 80c. Type **342** 45 15
903 1d.40 Doves making globe with laurels 65 20

1985. 25th Anniv of Organization of Petroleum Exporting Countries.
904 **343** 80c. multicoloured 50 20

344 Mother and Children **345** Chetaibi Bay

1985. Family Planning. Multicoloured.
905 80c. Type **344** 40 15
906 1d.40 Doctor weighing baby 65 20
907 1d.70 Mother breast-feeding baby 85 30

1985. Tourist Sites.
908 **345** 80c. blue, green & brown 35 15
909 – 2d. brown, green & blue 1·00 30
910 – 2d.40 brown, green & bl 1·10 40
DESIGNS—VERT: 2d. El Meniaa. HORIZ: 2d.40, Bou Noura.

346 "Palm Grove" **347** Line Pattern

1985. Paintings by N. Dinet. Multicoloured.
911 2d. Type **346** . . . . 1·10 55
912 3d. "Palm Grove" (different) 1·60 85

1985. Weavings. Multicoloured.
913 80c. Type **347** 50 35
914 1d.40 Diamond pattern . . 90 50
915 2d.40 Patterned horizontal stripes . . . . 1·40 85
916 2d.80 Vertical and horizontal stripes . . . . 1·90 1·40

348 "Felis margarita"  **349** Oral Vaccination

1986. Wild Cats. Multicoloured.
917 80c. Type **348** 45 35
918 1d. Caracal 55 45
919 2d. Wild cat . . . . . . 1·25 90
920 2d.40 Serval (vert) . . . . 1·60 1·10

1986. U.N.E.S.C.O. Child Survival Campaign. Mult.
921 80c. Type **349** 45 20
922 1d.40 Sun behind mother and baby 90 35
923 1d.70 Children playing . . . 1·10 55

350 Industrial Skyline, Clasped Hands and Emblem **351** Books and Crowd

1986. 30th Anniv of Algerian General Workers' Union.
924 **350** 2d. multicoloured . . . . 1·10 45

1986. National Charter.
925 **351** 4d. multicoloured . . . . 2·25 1·00

352 Emblem on Book and Drawing Instruments **353** Children playing

1986. Disabled Persons' Day.
926 **352** 80c. multicoloured 50 20

1986. Anti-tuberculosis Campaign.
927 **353** 80c. multicoloured . . . 55 30

354 Sombrero on Football **355** Courtyard with Fountain

1986. World Cup Football Championship, Mexico. Multicoloured.
928 2d. Type **354** . . . . 1·00 40
929 2d.40 Players and ball . . . . 1·25 45

1986. Traditional Dwellings. Multicoloured.
930 80c. Type **355** 45 20
931 2d.40 Courtyard with two beds of shrubs . . . . . . 1·40 70
932 3d. Courtyard with plants in tall pot . . . . 1·75 1·00

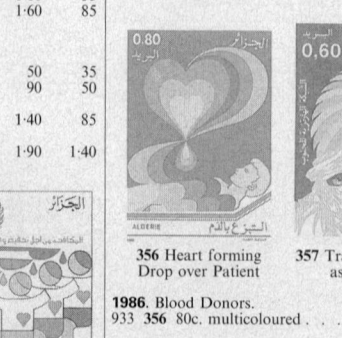
356 Heart forming Drop over Patient **357** Transmission Mast as Palm Tree

1986. Blood Donors.
933 **356** 80c. multicoloured 90 30

1986. Opening of Hertzian Wave Communications (Southern District).
934 **357** 60c. multicoloured 35 15

358 Studded Gate

1986. Mosque Gateways. Multicoloured.
935 2d. Type **358** . . . . 1·00 45
936 2d.40 Ornate gateway . . . . 1·25 65

359 Dove

1986. International Peace Year.
937 **359** 2d.40 multicoloured . . . 1·25 45

360 Girl dancing **361** "Narcissus tazetta"

1986. Folk Dances. Multicoloured.
938 80c. Type **360** 45 20
939 2d.40 Woman with purple dress dancing . . . . . . 1·25 55
940 2d.80 Veiled sword dancer . . 1·25 55

1986. Flowers. Multicoloured.
941 80c. Type **361** 45 20
942 1d.40 "Iris unguicularis" . . 80 45
943 2d.40 "Capparis spinosa" . . 1·10 65
944 2d.80 "Gladiolus segetum" . . 1·40 90

362 "Algerian Family" **363** Earrings

1987. Paintings by Mohammed Issiakhem in National Museum. Multicoloured.
945 2d. Type **362** . . . . 1·10 55
946 5d. "Man and Books" . . . . 2·50 1·60

1987. Jewellery from Aures. Multicoloured.
947 1d. Type **363** 45 30
948 1d.80 Bangles 80 45
949 2d.90 Brooches . . . . . . 1·25 85
950 3d.30 Necklace (horiz) . . . . 1·40 95

364 Boy and Girl

1987. Rock Carvings. Multicoloured.
951 1d. Type **364** 55 35
952 2d.90 Goat . . . . 1·40 1·10
953 3d.30 Animals . . . . . . 1·60 1·10

365 Baby holding Syringe "Umbrella"   366 Workers and Circles

1987. African Vaccination Year.
954 365 1d. multicoloured   45   20

1987. Voluntary Service.
955 366 1d. multicoloured   45   20

367 People and Buildings

1987. 3rd General Population Census.
956 367 1d. multicoloured   45   20

368 1962 War Orphans Fund Stamps and Magnifying Glass

1987. 25th Anniv of Independent Algeria Stamps.
957 368 1d.80 multicoloured . . .   80   50

369 Hand holding Torch   370 Actors in Spotlight

1987. 25th Anniv of Independence. Multicoloured.
958 369 1d. multicoloured   45   20

1987. Amateur Theatre Festival, Mostaganem. Multicoloured.
960 1d. Type 370   40   15
961 1d.80 Theatre   70   40

371 Discus Thrower   372 Greater Flamingo

1987. Mediterranean Games, Lattaquie. Mult.
962 1d. Type 371   40   15
963 2d.90 Tennis player (vert) . .   1·10   50
964 3d.30 Footballer . . . . . .   1·40   65

1987. Birds. Multicoloured.
965 1d. Type 372   45   35
966 1d.80 Purple swamphen . .   90   75
967 2d.50 Black-shouldered kite   1·75   95
968 2d.90 Red kite . . . . . .   1·90   1·25

373 Reservoir   374 Map, Transmitter and Radio Waves

1987. Agriculture. Multicoloured.
969 1d. Type 373   45   15
970 1d. Forestry (36×28 mm) . .   45   15
971 1d. Foodstuffs (25×37 mm)   45   15
972 1d. Erecting hedge against desert (25×37 mm)   45   15

1987. African Telecommunications Day.
973 374 1d. multicoloured   45   20

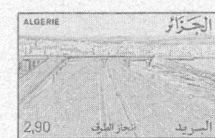

375 Motorway

1987. Transport. Multicoloured.
974 2d.90 Type 375 . . . . . .   1·10   45
975 3d.30 Diesel locomotive and passenger train . . . . . .   2·75   1·10

376 Houari Boumedienne University, Algiers

1987. Universities. Multicoloured.
976 1d. Type 376   40   15
977 2d.50 Oran University . . .   90   35
978 2d.90 Constantine University   1·10   45
979 3d.30 Emir Abdelkader University, Constantine (vert) . . . . . .   1·40   55

377 Wheat, Sun and Farmer ploughing with Oxen   378 Emblem as Sun above Factories

1988. 10th Anniv of International Agricultural Development Fund.
980 377 1d. multicoloured   40   20

1988. Autonomy of State-owned Utilities.
981 378 1d. multicoloured   40   20

379 Woman's Face and Emblem   380 Globe, Flag, Wood Pigeon and Scout Salute

1988. International Women's Day.
982 379 1d. multicoloured   40   20

1988. 75th Anniv of Arab Scouting.
983 380 2d. multicoloured . . .   80   35

381 Bau-Hanifia   382 Running

1988. Spas. Multicoloured.
984 1d. Type 381   40   15
985 2d.90 Chellala . . . . . .   1·10   45
986 3d.30 Righa-Ain Tolba . . . .   1·25   50

1988. Olympic Games, Seoul.
987 382 2d.90 multicoloured . . .   1·00   45

383 Pencil and Globe   384 Barbary Ape

1988. International Literacy Day.
988 383 2d.90 multicoloured . . .   1·00   45

1988. Endangered Animals. Barbary Ape. Mult.
989 50c. Type 384   20   10
990 90c. Ape family   35   15
991 1d. Ape's head and shoulders (vert)   40   20
992 1d.80 Ape in tree (vert) . . .   70   35

385 Family Group   386 Different Races raising Fists

1988. 40th Anniv of W.H.O.
993 385 2d.90 multicoloured . . .   1·00   45

1988. Anti-apartheid Campaign.
994 386 2d.50 multicoloured . . .   85   35

387 Emblem   388 Man irrigating Fields

1988. 6th National Liberation Front Party Congress.
995 387 1d. multicoloured   40   15

1988. Agriculture. Multicoloured.
996 1d. Type 388   40   15
997 1d. Fields, cattle and man picking fruit   40   15

389 Constantine   390 Courtyard

1989.
998 389 1d. deep green and green   30   10

1989. Views of Algeria before 1830 (5th series). As T 310.
999 2d.50 green   70   35
1000 2d.90 green   80   15
1001 5d. brown and black . . .   2·00   70
DESIGNS: 2d.50, Bay; 2d.90, Harbour; 5d. View of harbour through archway.

1989. National Achievements. Multicoloured.
1002 1d. Type 390   35   20
1003 1d. Flats (housing)   35   20
1004 1d. Gateway, Timimoun (tourism)   35   20
1005 1d. Dish aerial and telephones (communications)   35   20

391 Oran Es Senia Airport

1989. Airports. Multicoloured.
1006 2d.90 Type 391   85   35
1007 3d.30 Tebessa airport . . .   95   45
1008 5d. Tamanrasset airport (vert) . . . .   1·60   90

392 Irrigation   393 Soldiers at Various Tasks

1989. Development of South. Multicoloured.
1009 1d. Type 392   30   15
1010 1d.80 Ouargla secondary school   50   30
1011 2d.50 Gas complex, Hassi R'mel (vert)   70   35

1989. 20th Anniv of National Service.
1012 393 2d. multicoloured . . .   1·50   75

394 Locusts and Crop Spraying

1989. Anti-locusts Campaign.
1013 394 1d. multicoloured   30   15

395 Mother and Baby

1989. International Children's Day.
1014 395 1d.+30c. mult   40   30

396 Moon

1989. 20th Anniv of First Manned Landing on Moon. Multicoloured.
1015 2d.90 Type 396   85   35
1016 4d. Astronaut on moon . . .   1·10   55

397 Globe and Emblem

1989. Centenary of Interparliamentary Union.
1017 397 2d.90 mauve, brn & gold   85   30

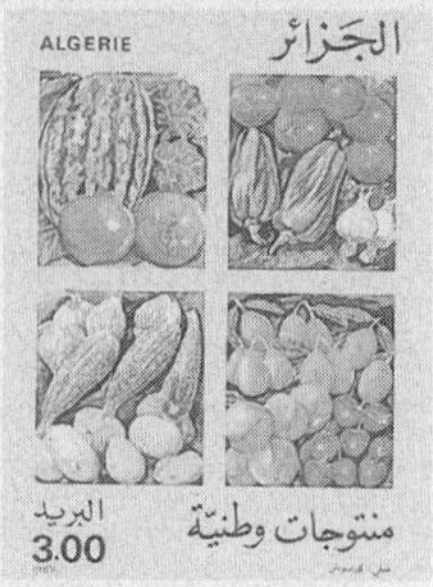
398 Fruits and Vegetables

1989. National Production.
1018 **398** 2d. multicoloured . . . 55 35
1019 – 3d. multicoloured . . . 85 50
1020 – 5d. multicoloured . . . 1·40 85
DESIGNS: 3, 5d. Various fruits and vegetables.

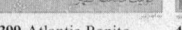

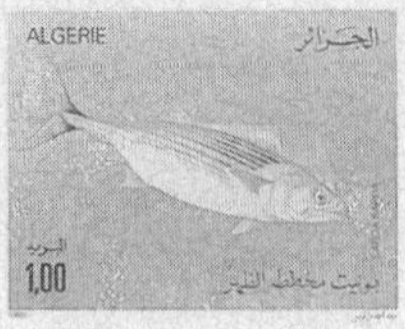
399 Atlantic Bonito

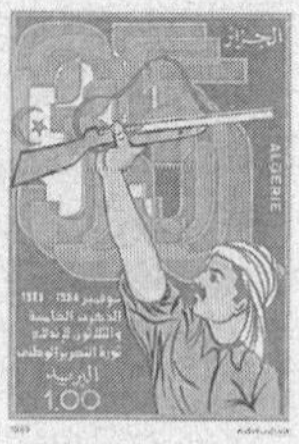
400 "35" and Soldier with Rifle

1989. Fishes. Multicoloured.
1021 1d. Type **399** 45 15
1022 1d.80 John dory 95 30
1023 2d.90 Red seabream . . . . 1·40 45
1024 3d.30 Swordfish . . . . . . 1·60 55

1989. 35th Anniv of Revolution.
1025 **400** 1d. multicoloured . . . 30 10

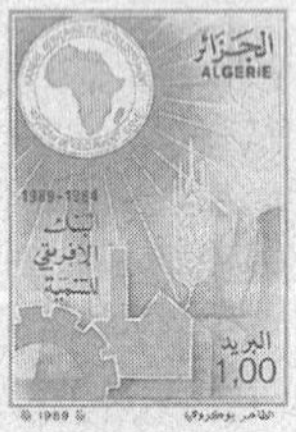
401 Bank Emblem Cogwheel, Factory and Wheat

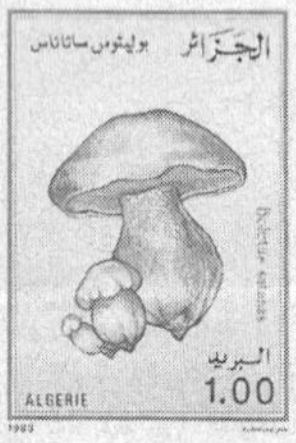
402 Satan's Mushroom

1989. 25th Anniv of African Development Bank.
1026 **401** 1d. multicoloured . . . 30 15

1989. Fungi. Multicoloured.
1027 1d. Type **402** 60 20
1028 1d.80 Yellow stainer . . . . 1·10 40
1029 2d.90 Parasol mushroom . . 1·75 60
1030 3d.30 Saffron milk cap . . . 1·90 70

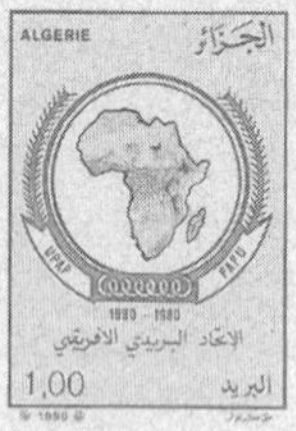
403 Emblem

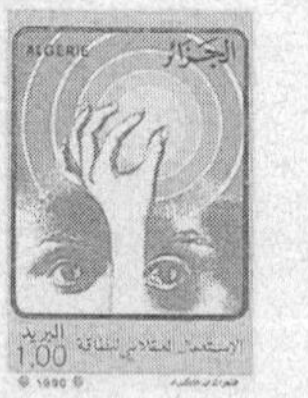
404 Sun, Arm and Face

1990. 10th Anniv of Pan-African Postal Union.
1031 **403** 1d. multicoloured . . . 30 15

1990. Rational Use of Energy.
1032 **404** 1d. multicoloured . . . 30 15

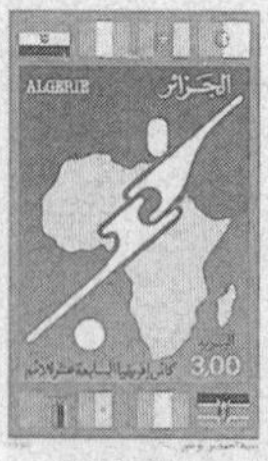
405 Emblem

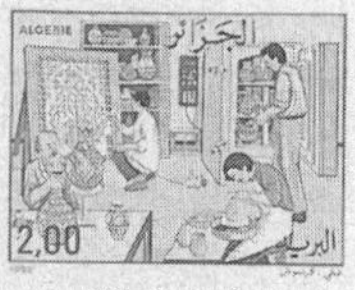
406 Ceramics

1990. African Nations Cup Football Championship.
1033 **405** 3d. multicoloured . . . 85 40

1990. Industries. Multicoloured.
1034 2d. Type **406** 55 30
1035 2d.90 Car maintenance . . . 85 35
1036 3d.30 Fishing . . . . 1·75 45

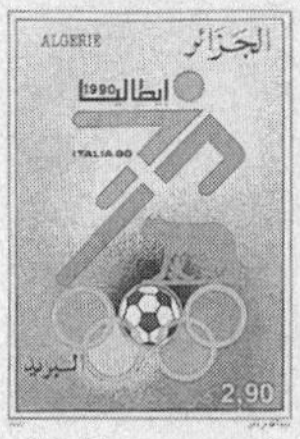
407 Pictogram and Olympic Rings

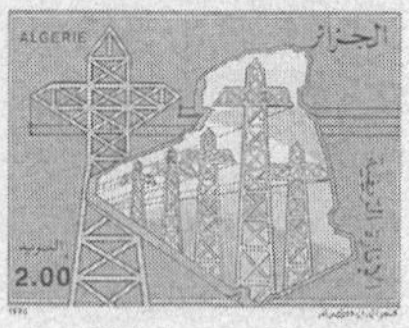
408 Pylons on Map

1990. World Cup Football Championship, Italy. Multicoloured.
1037 2d.90 Type **407** 85 35
1038 5d. Trophy, ball and flag . . 1·40 65

1990. Rural Electrification.
1039 **408** 2d. multicoloured . . . 55 20

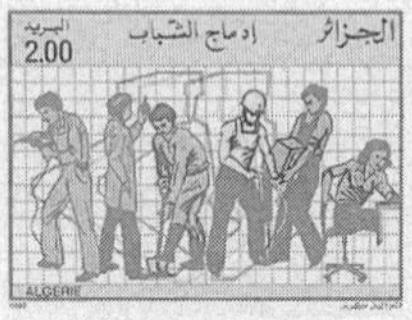
409 Young Workers

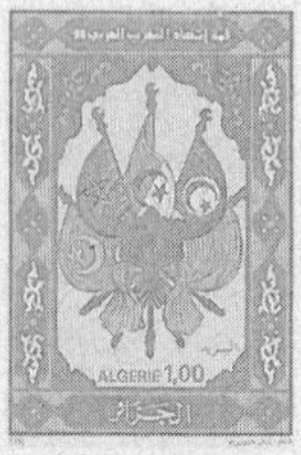
410 Members Flags

1990. Youth. Multicoloured.
1040 2d. Type **409** 55 20
1041 3d. Youth in crowd (vert) 85 30

1990. Arab Maghreb Union Summit Conference.
1042 **410** 1d. multicoloured . . . 30 15

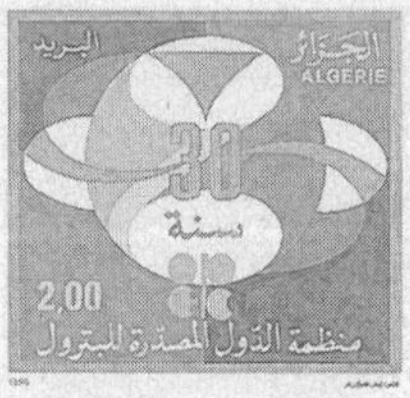
411 Anniversary Emblem

1990. 30th Anniv of O.P.E.C.
1043 **411** 2d. multicoloured . . . 50 20

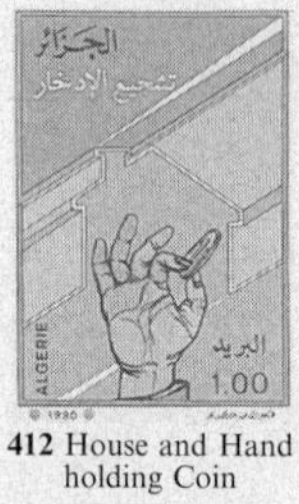
412 House and Hand holding Coin

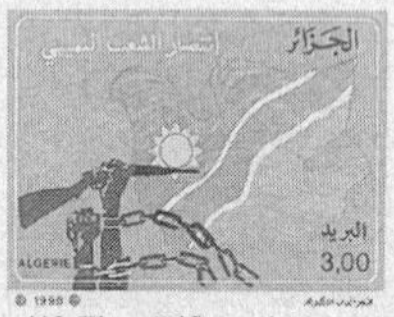
413 Flag, Rifle and Hands with Broken Manacles

1990. Savings Day.
1044 **412** 1d. multicoloured . . . 20 10

1990. Namibian Independence.
1045 **413** 3d. multicoloured . . . 60 15

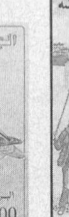

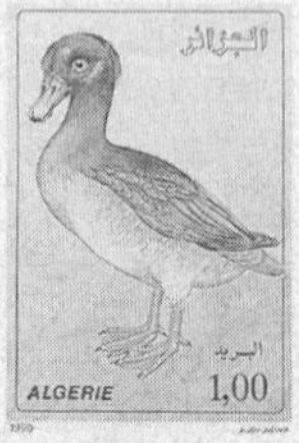
414 Duck

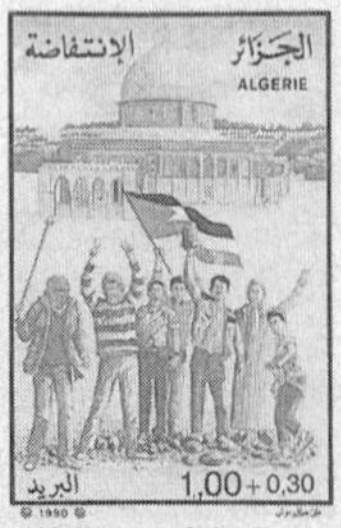
415 Dome of the Rock and Palestinians

1990. Domestic Animals. Multicoloured.
1046 1d. Type **414** 20 10
1047 2d. Hare (horiz) 45 20
1048 2d.90 Common turkey . . . 65 35
1049 3d.30 Red junglefowl (horiz) 90 55

1990. Palestinian "Intifada" Movement.
1050 **415** 1d.+30c. mult 35 20

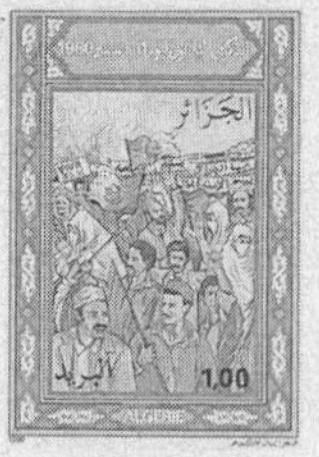
416 Crowd with Banners

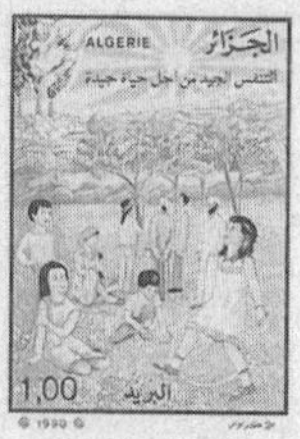
417 Families in Countryside

1990. 30th Anniv of 11 December 1960 Demonstration.
1051 **416** 1d. multicoloured . . . 20 10

1990. Campaign against Respiratory Diseases.
1052 **417** 1d. multicoloured . . . 20 10

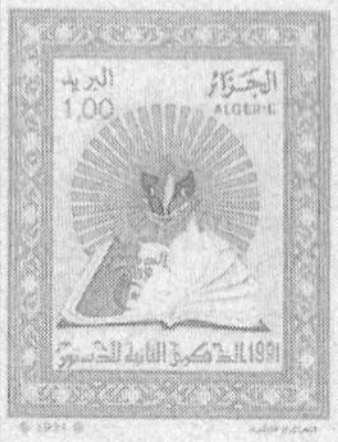
418 Sunburst, Torch and Open Book

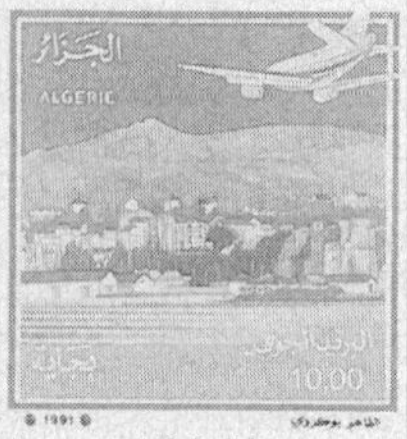
419 Bejaia

1991. 2nd Anniv of Constitution.
1053 **418** 1d. multicoloured . . . 20 10

1991. Views of Algeria before 1830 (6th series). As T **310**.
1054 1d.50 red 35 10
1055 4d.20 green 90 35
DESIGNS: 1d.50, Kolea; 4d.20, Constantine.

1991. Air. Multicoloured.
1056 10d. Type **419** . . . . . . 1·90 85
1057 20d. Annaba . . . . 4·00 1·90

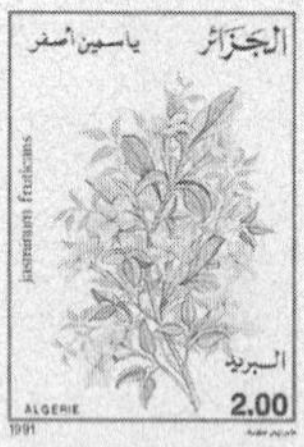
420 "Jasminum fruticans"

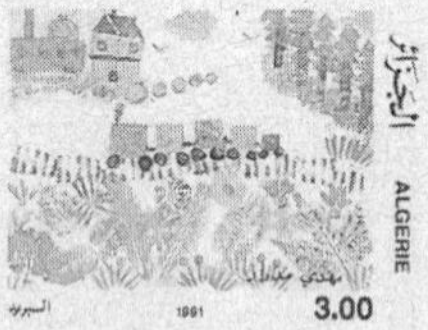
421 "Trip to the Country" (Mehdi Medrar)

1991. Flowers. Multicoloured.
1058 2d. Type **420** 45 20
1059 4d. "Dianthus crinitus" . . 90 35
1060 5d. "Cyclamen africanum" 1·10 55

1991. Children's Drawings. Multicoloured.
1061 3d. Type **421** . . . . 3·50 1·75
1062 4d. "Children playing" (Ouidad Bounab) 90 35

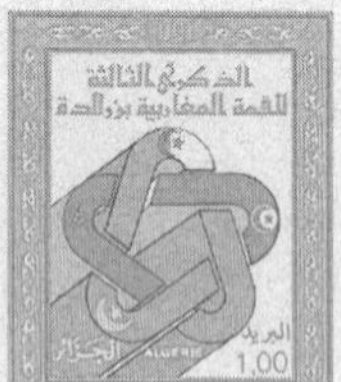
422 Emblem

1991. 3rd Anniv of Arab Maghreb Union Summit Conference, Zeralda.
1063 **422** 1d. multicoloured . . . 20 10

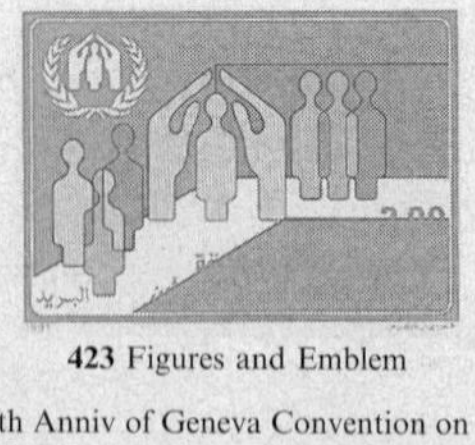
423 Figures and Emblem

1991. 40th Anniv of Geneva Convention on Status of Refugees.
1064 **423** 3d. multicoloured . . . 65 20

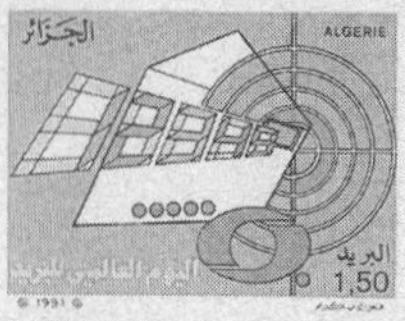
424 Coded Letter and Target

1991. World Post Day (1065) and "Telecom 91" International Telecommunications Exhibition, Geneva (1066). Multicoloured.
1065 1d.50 Type **424** 35 15
1066 4d.20 Exhibition and I.T.U. emblems (vert) 95 35

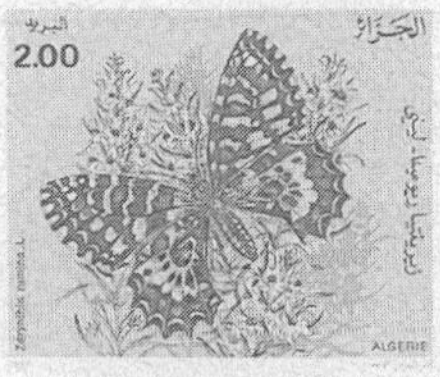
425 Spanish Festoon

1991. Butterflies. Multicoloured.
1067 2d. Type **425** 20 15
1068 4d. "Melitaea didyma" . . . 45 30
1069 6d. Red admiral 65 45
1070 7d. Large tortoiseshell . . . 90 65

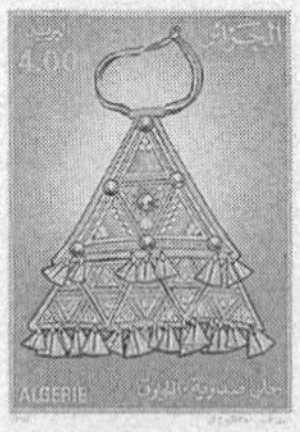
426 Chest Ornament

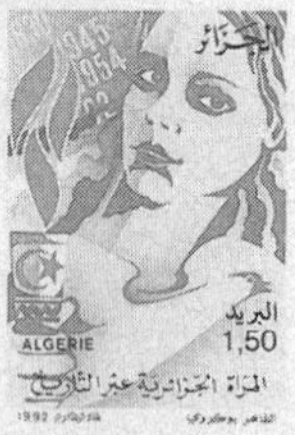
427 Woman

1991. Silver Jewellery from South Algeria. Mult.
1071 3d. Necklaces 35 20
1072 4d. Type **426** 45 30
1073 5d. Enamelled ornament . . 55 45
1074 7d. Bangles (horiz) 90 70

1992. Views of Algeria before 1830. As previous issues and new values. Size 30½ × 21 mm.
1075 5c. purple 10 10
1076 10c. blue 10 10
1077 20c. blue 10 10
1078 30c. red and black 20 10
1079 50c. brown 10 10
1080 70c. lilac 10 10
1081 80c. brown 10 10
1082 1d. brown 10 10
1083 2d. blue 10 10
1084 3d. green 20 10
1085 4d. red 25 10
1086 6d.20 blue 70 20
1087 7d.50 red 85 20
DESIGNS: 5c., 6d.20, As No. 873; 10c., 7d.50, As No. 859; 20c. As No. 1000; 30c. As No. 1001; 50c. As No. 882; 70c. As No. 875; 80c. Type **310**; 1d. As No. 860; 2d. As No. 861; 3d. As No. 817; 4d. As No. 1055.

1992. International Women's Day.
1095 **427** 1d.50 multicoloured . . 20 10

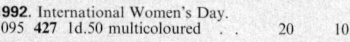

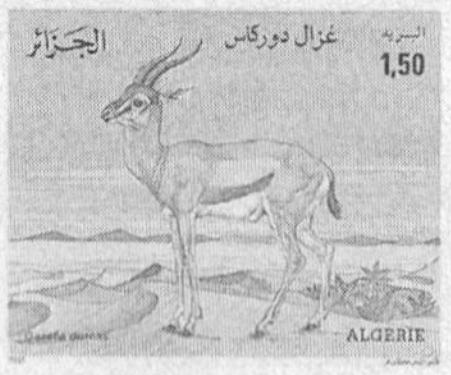
428 Dorcas Gazelle

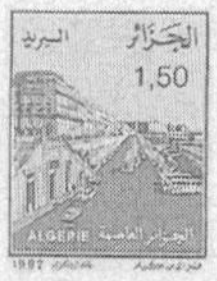
429 Algiers

1992. Gazelles. Multicoloured.
1096 1d.50 Type **428** 15 10
1097 6d.20 Edmi gazelle 70 45
1098 8d.60 Addra gazelle 95 55

1992.
1099 **429** 1d.50 brown & lt brown 15 10
1132 2d. blue 10 10
1147 3d. blue 10 10

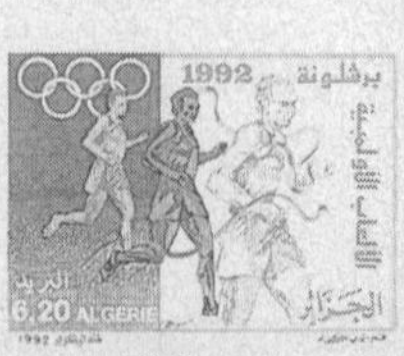
430 Runners

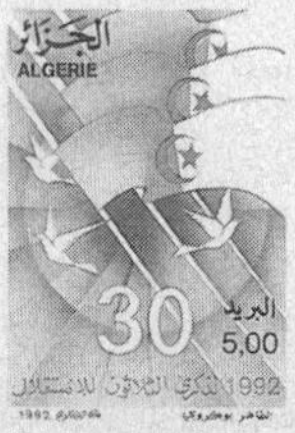
431 Doves and Flags

1992. Olympic Games, Barcelona.
1100 **430** 6d.20 multicoloured . .   70   30

1992. 30th Anniv of Independence.
1101 **431** 5d. green, red and black   55   20

432 "Ajuga iva"   **433 Computerized Post Office Equipment**

1992. Medicinal Plants. Multicoloured.
1102 1d.50 Type **432**   15   10
1103 5d.10 Buckthorn   55   30
1104 6d.20 Milk thistle   70   35
1105 8d.60 French lavender . . .   1·00   50

1992. World Post Day. Modernization of Postal Service.
1106 **433** 1d.50 multicoloured   15   10

434 Boudiaf

1992. Mohammed Boudiaf (chairman of Committee of State) Commemoration.
1107 **434** 2d. multicoloured . . .   20   15
1108 8d.60 multicoloured   95   55

435 2nd-century B.C. Numidian Coin

1992. Coinage. Multicoloured.
1109 1d.50 Type **435**   15   10
1110 2d. 14th-century Zianide dinar   20   15
1111 5d.10 11th-century Almoravid dinar   55   20
1112 6d.20 19th-century Emir Abd-el-Kader coin . . .   70   35

436 Short-snouted Seahorse   **437 Algiers Door Knocker**

1992. Marine Animals. Multicoloured.
1113 1d.50 Type **436**   20   10
1114 2d.70 Loggerhead turtle . .   35   15
1115 6d.20 Mediterranean moray .   90   35
1116 7d.50 Lobster   85   50

1993. Door Knockers. Multicoloured.
1117 2d. Type **437**   10   10
1118 5d.60 Constantine   30   15
1119 8d.60 Tlemcen   50   25

438 Medlar Blossom

1993. Fruit-tree Blossom. Multicoloured.
1120 4d.50 Type **438**   25   10
1121 8d.60 Quince (vert)   50   25
1122 11d. Apricot (vert)   60   30

439 Patrol Boat, Emblem and Flag   **440 Grain Storage Jar**

1993. 20th Anniv of Coastguard Service.
1123 **439** 2d. multicoloured . . .   20   10

1993. Traditional Utensils. Multicoloured.
1124 2d. Type **440**   10   10
1125 5d.60 Grindstone   30   15
1126 8d.60 Oil-press   50   25

441 Mauretanian Royal Mausoleum, Tipaza   **442 Jijelienne Coast**

1993. Mausoleums. Multicoloured.
1127 8d.60 Type **441**   50   25
1128 12d. Royal Mausoleum, El Khroub   65   30

1993. Air.
1129 **442** 50d. green, brown & blue . . . .   2·75   1·25

443 Annaba   **444 Chameleon**

1993. Ports. Multicoloured.
1130 2d. Type **443**   15   10
1131 8d.60 Arzew   95   25

1993. Reptiles. Multicoloured.
1133 2d. Type **444**   10   10
1134 8d.60 Desert monitor (horiz)   50   25

445 Tipaza   **446 Map, Processing Plant and Uses of Hydrocarbons**

1993. Tourism. Multicoloured.
1135 2d. Type **445**   10   10
1136 8d.60 Kerzaz   25   10

1993. 30th Anniv of Sonatrach (National Society for Transformation and Commercialization of Hydrocarbons).
1137 **446** 2d. multicoloured . . .   10   10

447 Dove, Flag and "18"   **448 Crown of Statue of Liberty, Football, U.S. Flag and Trophy**

1994. National Chahid Day.
1138 **447** 2d. multicoloured . . .   10   10

1994. World Cup Football Championship, U.S.A.
1139 **448** 8d.60 multicoloured . . .   25   10

449 Monkey Orchid   **450 Hoggar Script on Stone**

1994. Orchids. Multicoloured.
1140 5d.60 Type **449**   15   10
1141 8d.60 "Orphrys lutea"   25   10
1142 11d. Bee orchid   35   15

1994. Ancient Communication. Multicoloured.
1143 3d. Type **450**   10   10
1144 10d. Abizar stele   30   15

451 Flags and Olympic Rings   **452 Figures and City on Globe**

1994. Cent of International Olympic Committee.
1145 **451** 12d. multicoloured . . .   35   15

1994. World Population Day.
1146 **452** 3d. multicoloured . . .   10   10

453 Sandstone   **454 Brooches**

1994. Minerals. Multicoloured.
1148 3d. Type **453**   10   10
1149 5d. Cipolin   15   10
1150 10d. Turitella shells in chalk   25   15

1994. Saharan Silver Jewellery. Multicoloured.
1151 3d. Type **454**   10   10
1152 5d. Belt (horiz)   15   10
1153 12d. Bracelets (horiz) . . .   30   15

455 Soldiers   **456 Ladybirds on Leaves**

1994. 40th Anniv of Revolution.
1154 **455** 3d. multicoloured . . .   10   10

1994. Insects. Multicoloured.
1155 3d. Type **456**   10   10
1156 12d. Beetle ("Buprestidae") on plant   30   15

457 Virus and Family

1994. World Anti-AIDS Campaign Day.
1157 **457** 3d. black, blue & mauve   10   10

458 Algiers   **459 Southern Algeria**

1994. Regional Dances. Multicoloured.
1158 3d. Type **458**   10   10
1159 10d. Constantine   25   15
1160 12d. Alaoui   30   15

1995. 20th Anniv of World Tourism Organization.
1161 **459** 3d. multicoloured . . .   10   10

460 Honey Bee on Comb   **461 Dahlia**

1995. Bee-keeping. Multicoloured.
1162 3d. Type **460**   10   10
1163 13d. Bee on flower (horiz) .   35   20

1995. Flowers. Multicoloured.
1164 3d. Type **461**   10   10
1165 10d. Zinnias   25   15
1166 13d. Lilac   35   20

462 Circular Design   **463 Doves, Graves, Victims and Soldiers**

1995. Stucco Work from Sedrata (4th century after Hegira).
1167 **462** 3d. brown   10   10
1168 – 4d. green   10   10
1169 – 5d. brown   15   10
DESIGNS—4d. Circular design within square; 5d. Stylized flowers.

1995. 50th Anniv of End of Second World War. Multicoloured.
1170 **463** 3d. multicoloured . . .   10   10

464 Water Pollution   **465 Players and Anniversary Emblem**

1995. Environmental Protection. Multicoloured.
1172 3d. Type **464**   10   10
1173 13d. Air pollution   35   20

1995. Centenary of Volleyball.
1174 **465** 3d. multicoloured . . .   10   10

466 Map and Pylon   **467 Children and Schoolbag Contents**

1995. Electrification.
1175 **466** 3d. multicoloured . . .   10   10

1995. National Solidarity.
1176 **467** 3d.+50c. mult   10   10

468 Doves and Anniversary Emblem

469 Pitcher from Lakhdaria

1995. 50th Anniv of U.N.O.
1177 **468** 13d. multicoloured . . .   30   15

1995. Traditional Pottery.
1178 **469** 10d. brown   20   10
1179 – 20d. brown   45   25
1180 – 21d. brown   45   25
1181 – 30d. brown   65   35
DESIGNS: 20d. Water jug (Aokas); 21d. Jar (Larbaa nath Iraten); 30d. Jar (Ouadhia).

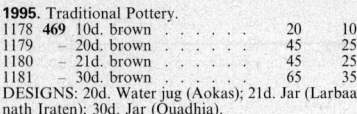

470 Common Shelduck

1995. Water Birds. Multicoloured.
1182 **470** 3d. Type **470**   10   10
1183 5d. Common snipe   10   10

471 Doves flying over Javelin Thrower and Olympic Rings

1996. Centenary of Modern Olympic Games and Olympic Games, Atlanta.
1184 **471** 20d. multicoloured . . .   45   25

472 Fringed Bag   **473** Pasteur Institute

1996. Handicrafts. Leather Bags. Multicoloured.
1185 **472** 5d. Type **472**   10   10
1186 16d. Shoulder bag with handle (vert)   35   20

1996. Centenary (1994) of Algerian Pasteur Institute.
1187 **473** 5d. multicoloured . . .   10   10

474 Arabic Script and Computer

1996. Scientific and Technical Education Day. Multicoloured.
1188 **474** 5d. Type **474**   10   10
1189 16d. Dove, fountain pen and symbols (vert)   35   20
1190 23d. Pencil, pen, dividers and satellite over Earth on pages of open book (vert)   50   25

475 Iron Ore, Djebel Quenza

1996. Minerals. Multicoloured.
1191 10d. Type **475**   20   10
1192 20d. Gold, Tirek-Amesmessa   45   25

476 "Pandoriana pandora"

1996. Butterflies. Multicoloured.
1193 **476** 5d. Type **476**   10   10
1194 10d. "Coenonympha pamphilus"   20   10
1195 20d. Painted lady   45   25
1196 23d. Marbled white   50   25

477 Globe, Drug Addict and Drugs

1996. World Anti-drugs Day.
1197 **477** 5d. multicoloured . . .   10   10

478 "Woman with Pigeons"

1996. Paintings by Ismail Samsom. Multicoloured.
1198 20d. Type **478**   40   20
1199 30d. "Interrogation"   60   30

479 Paramedic holding Child (Medical Aid)

480 Children, Syringe and Pens

1996. Civil Defence. Multicoloured.
1200 **479** 5d. Type **479**   10   10
1201 23d. Globe resting in cupped hands (natural disaster prevention) (vert)   45   25

1996. 50th Anniv of U.N.I.C.E.F. Multicoloured.
1202 **480** 5d. Type **480**   10   10
1203 10d. Family holding pencil, key, syringe and flower   20   10

481 Dar Hassan Pacha

482 Minbar Inscription, Nedroma Mosque

1996. Algiers Courtyards. Multicoloured.
1204 **481** 5d. Type **481**   10   10
1205 10d. Dar Kedaoudj el Amia   20   10
1206 20d. Palais des Rais   40   20
1207 30d. Villa Abdellatif   60   30

1997. Mosque Carvings. Multicoloured.
1208 **482** 5d. Type **482**   10   10
1209 23d. Doors, Ketchaoua Mosque, Algiers   45   25

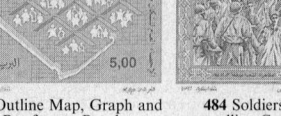

483 Outline Map, Graph and Roofs over People

484 Soldiers controlling Crowd with Flags

1997. 4th General Population and Housing Census.
1210 **483** 5d. multicoloured   10   10

1997. 35th Anniv of Oargla Protest.
1211 **484** 5d. multicoloured . . .   10   10

485 Doves above Crowd with Flags

1997. 35th Anniv of Victory Day.
1212 **485** 5d. multicoloured . . .   10   10

486 "Ficaria verna"

1997. Flowers. Multicoloured.
1213 **486** 5d. Type **486**   10   10
1214 16d. Honeysuckle   35   20
1215 23d. Common poppy   45   25

487 "No Smoking" Sign on Map

488 Crowd and Map

1997. World No Smoking Day.
1216 **487** 5d. multicoloured . . .   10   10

1997. Legislative Elections.
1217 **488** 5d. multicoloured . . .   10   10

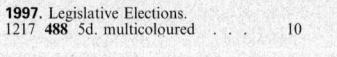

489 "Buthus occitanus"

1997. Scorpions. Multicoloured.
1218 **489** 5d. Type **489**   10   10
1219 10d. "Androctonus australis"   20   10

491 Zakaria

1997. 20th Death Anniv of Moufdi Zakaria (poet).
1222 **491** 5d. multicoloured   10   10

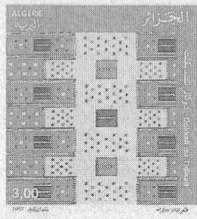

492 Dokkali Design, Tidikelt

1997. Textiles. Multicoloured.
1223 3d. Type **492**   10   10
1224 5d. Tellis design, Aures . . .   10   10
1225 10d. Bou Taleb design, M'Sila   20   10
1226 20d. Ddil design, Ait-Hichem   40   20

493 Map, Emblem and Rainbow

1997. 25th Anniv of Pan-Arab Security Forces Organization.
1227 **493** 5d. multicoloured . . .   10   10

494 Packages and Express Mail Service Emblem

1997. World Post Day.
1228 **494** 5d. multicoloured   10   10

495 Rising Sun on Map

1997. Local Elections.
1229 **495** 5d. multicoloured . . .   10   10

496 Tenes Lighthouse

1997. Lighthouses. Multicoloured.
1230 5d. Type **496**   10   10
1231 10d. Cap Caxine, Algiers (vert)   20   10

490 Crowd with Flags

497 Mail Plane

1997. 35th Anniv of Independence.
1220 **490** 5d. multicoloured . . .   10   10

1997. 1st Anniv of Aeropostale.
1232 **497** 5d. multicoloured   10   10

498 Variable Scallop

1997. Sea Shells. Multicoloured.
1233	5d. Type **498**	10	10
1234	10d. "Bolinus brandaris"	20	10
1235	20d. "Hinia reticulata" (vert)	40	20

499 National Flag and Columned Facade   **500** Flag, Ballot Box, Constitution and People

1997. Inauguration of Council of the Nation (upper parliamentary chamber).
| 1236 | **499** 5d. multicoloured | 10 | 10 |

1997. Completion of Government Reform. Mult.
1237	5d. Type **500** (presidential election)	10	10
1238	5d. Constitution and torch (constitution referendum)	10	10
1239	5d. Ballot box and voting papers (elections to National Assembly (lower chamber of Parliament))	10	10
1240	5d. Flag, sun and rose (local elections)	10	10
1241	5d. Flag and Parliament (elections to National Council (upper chamber))	10	10

Nos. 1237/41 were issued together, se-tenant, forming a composite design.

501 Exhibition Emblem

1998. "Expo '98" World's Fair, Lisbon.
| 1242 | **501** 5d. multicoloured | 10 | 10 |

502 Aerial Bombardment

1998. 40th Anniv of Bombing of Sakiet Sidi Youcef.
| 1244 | **502** 5d. multicoloured | 10 | 10 |

503 Archives Building

1998. National Archives.
| 1245 | **503** 5d. multicoloured | 10 | 10 |

504 Lalla Fadhma N'Soumeur

1998. International Women's Day.
| 1246 | **504** 5d. multicoloured | 10 | 10 |

505 Players and Eiffel Tower   **506** View from Land

1998. World Cup Football Championship, France.
| 1247 | **505** 24d. multicoloured | 50 | 25 |

1998. Algiers Kasbah. Multicoloured.
1248	5d. Type **506**	10	10
1249	10d. Street	20	10
1250	24d. View from sea (horiz)	50	25

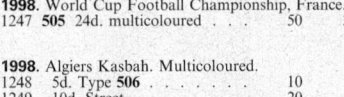

507 Crescent and Flag

1998. Red Crescent.
| 1251 | **507** 5d.+1d. red, green and black | 10 | 10 |

508 Battle Scene

1998. 150th Anniv of Insurrection of the Zaatcha.
| 1252 | **508** 5d. multicoloured | 10 | 10 |

509 Parent and Child and Hand holding Rose   **510** "Tourism and the Environment"

1998. International Children's Day. National Solidarity. Multicoloured.
| 1253 | 5d.+1d. Type **509** | 10 | 10 |
| 1254 | 5d.+1d. Children encircling emblem (horiz) | 10 | 10 |

1998. Tourism. Multicoloured.
1255	5d. Type **510**	10	10
1256	10d. Young tourists and methods of transportation (horiz)	10	10
1257	24d. Taghit (horiz)	50	25

511 Map of North Africa and Arabia

1998. Arab Post Day.
| 1258 | **511** 5d. multicoloured | 10 | 10 |

512 Interpol and Algerian Police Force Emblems

1998. 75th Anniv of Interpol.
| 1259 | **512** 5d. multicoloured | 10 | 10 |

513 Provisional Government and State Flag

1998. 40th Anniv of Creation of Provisional Government of Algerian Republic.
| 1260 | **513** 5d. multicoloured | 10 | 10 |

514 Arrows leading from Algeria around the World

1998. National Diplomacy Day.
| 1261 | **514** 5d. multicoloured | 10 | 10 |

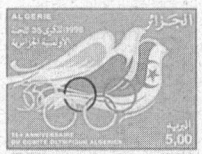

515 Dove and Olympic Rings

1998. 35th Anniv of Algerian Olympic Committee.
| 1262 | **515** 5d. multicoloured | 10 | 10 |

516 Osprey

1998. Birds. Multicoloured.
1263	5d. Type **516**	10	10
1264	10d. Audouin's gull	20	10
1265	24d. Shag (vert)	45	25
1266	30d. Common cormorant (vert)	55	30

517 Anniversary Emblem and Profiles   **518** Comb

1998. 50th Anniv of Universal Declaration of Human Rights. Multicoloured.
| 1267 | 5d. Type **517** | 10 | 10 |
| 1268 | 24d. Anniversary emblem, dove and people | 45 | 25 |

1999. Spinning and Weaving Implements. Mult.
1269	5d. Type **518**	10	10
1270	10d. Carding (horiz)	20	10
1271	20d. Spindle	35	20
1272	24d. Loom	45	25

519 Dove, Torch, Flag and Soldiers

1999. National Chahid Day.
| 1273 | **519** 5d. multicoloured | 10 | 10 |

520 Pear

1999. Fruit Trees. Multicoloured.
1274	5d. Type **520**	10	10
1275	10d. Plum	20	10
1276	24d. Orange (vert)	45	25

521 Calligraphy   **522** 14th-century Ceramic Mosaic, Tlemcen

1999. Presidential Election.
| 1277 | **521** 5d. multicoloured | 10 | 10 |

1999. Crafts. Multicoloured.
1278	5d. Type **522**	10	10
1279	10d. 11th-century ceramic mosaic, Kalaa des Beni Hammad	20	10
1280	20d. Cradle (horiz)	35	20
1281	24d. Table with raised rim (horiz)	45	25

523 Pictograms on Map of Africa and South African Flag   **524** Gneiss

1999. 7th African Games, Johannesburg. Mult.
| 1282 | 5d. Type **523** | 10 | 10 |
| 1283 | 10d. Pictograms of athletes and South African flag (horiz) | 20 | 10 |

1999. Minerals. Multicoloured.
1284	5d. Type **524**	10	10
1285	20d. Granite	35	20
1286	24d. Sericite schist	45	25

525 Emblem   **526** Family and Map of Africa

1999. Organization of African Unity Summit, Algiers.
| 1287 | **525** 5d. multicoloured | 10 | 10 |

527 Emblem and Police Officers

1999. 40th Anniv of Organization of African Unity Convention on Refugees.
| 1288 | **526** 5d. multicoloured | 10 | 10 |

1999. Police Day.
| 1289 | **527** 5d. multicoloured | 10 | 10 |

528 Linked Hands and "2000"

1999. International Year of Culture and Peace.
1290 **528** 5d. multicoloured 10 10

529 Dentex Seabream

1999. Fishes. Multicoloured.
1291   5d. Type **529** 10 10
1292   10d. Striped red mullet . . . 15 10
1293   20d. Pink dentex 35 20
1294   24d. White seabream 40 20

530 Rainbow

1999. Referendum.
1295 **530** 5d. multicoloured 10 10

531 Emblem and Rainbow

1999. 125th Anniv of Universal Postal Union. Mult.
1296   5d. Type **531** 10 10
1297   5d. Globe, satellite and
     stamps 10 10

532 Woman's Face

1999. Rural Women's Day.
1298 **532** 5d. multicoloured 10 10

533 Partisans and   **534** Chaoui
Helicopters

1999. 45th Anniv of Revolution. Multicoloured.
1299   5d. Type **533** 10 10
1300   5d. Partisans and fires . . . 10 10
    Nos. 1299/300 were issued together, se-tenant,
forming a composite design.

1999. Folk Dances. Multicoloured.
1301   5d. Type **534** 10 10
1302   10d. Targuie 15 10
1303   24d. M'zab 40 20

535 Doves   **536** Chaffinches

2000. New Millennium. Mult. Self-adhesive.
1304   5d. Type **535** (peace) . . . 10 10
1305   5d. Plants and tree
     (environment) 10 10
1306   5d. Umbrella over ears of
     grain (food security) . . . 10 10
1307   5d. Wind farm (new energy
     sources) 10 10
1308   5d. Globe and ballot box
     (democracy) 10 10
1309   5d. Microscope (health) . . . 10 10
1310   5d. Cargo ship at quayside
     (commerce) 10 10
1311   5d. Space satellite, dish
     aerial, jet plane and train
     (communications) 10 10
1312   5d. Astronaut and lunar
     buggy on Moon (space) . . 10 10
1313   5d. Film cave paintings,
     mandolin and music notes
     (culture) 10 10
1314   5d. Outline of dove (peace) . 10 10
1315   5d. Hand above flora and
     fauna (environment) . . . 10 10
1316   5d. Space satellites,
     computer and printed
     circuits forming maps of
     Europe and Africa
     (communications) 10 10
1317   5d. Sun, clouds, flame and
     water (new energy
     sources) 10 10
1318   5d. Hand holding seedling
     (food security) 10 10
1319   5d. Staff of Aesculapius and
     heart (health) 10 10
1320   5d. Arrows around globe
     (communication) 10 10
1321   5d. Cave paintings, book,
     painting and violin
     (culture) 10 10
1322   5d. Parthenon and envelopes
     (democracy) 10 10
1323   5d. Space satellite, solar
     system, space shuttle and
     astronaut (space) 10 10

2000. Birds. Multicoloured.
1324   5d. Type **536** 10 10
1325   5d. Canary (horiz) 10 10
1326   10d. Bullfinch (horiz) 15 10
1327   24d. Goldfinch 40 20

537 Emblem

2000. "EXPO 2000" World's Fair, Hanover.
1328 **537** 5d. multicoloured 10 10

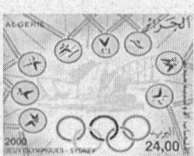

538 Sydney Opera House and
Sports Pictograms

2000. Olympic Games, Sydney.
1329 **538** 24d. multicoloured 40 20

539 Emblem   **540** Crowd, Linked
Hands and White
Doves

2000. Telethon 2000 (fundraising event).
1330 **539** 5d. multicoloured 10 10

2000. "Concorde Civile". Multicoloured.
1331   5d. Type **540** 10 10
1332   10d. Hands releasing doves
     (horiz) 15 10
1333   20d. Flag, doves and hands
     forming heart (horiz) . . 35 20
1334   24d. Doves and clasped
     hands above flowers . . . 40 20

541 Building

2000. National Library.
1335 **541** 5d. multicoloured 10 10

542 Hand holding Blood
Droplet

2000. Blood Donation Campaign.
1336 **542** 5d. multicoloured 10 10

543 Lock

2000. Touareg Cultural Heritage. Multicoloured.
1337   5d. Type **543** 10 10
1338   10d. Lock (vert) 20 10

544 Mohamed Racim (artist)

2000. Personalities. Multicoloured.
1339   10d. Type **544** 20 10
1340   10d. Mohammed Dib
     (writer) 20 10
1341   10d. Mustapha Kateb
     (theatre director) 20 10
1342   10d. Ali Maachi (musician) . . 20 10

545 Cock-chafer   **546** Jug

2000. Insects. Multicoloured.
1343   5d. Type **545** 10 10
1344   5d. Carpet beetle 10 10
1345   10d. Drugstore beetle 20 10
1346   24d. Carabus 45 25

2000. Roman Artefacts, Tipasa. Multicoloured.
1347   5d. Type **546** 10 10
1348   10d. Vase 20 10
1349   24d. Jug 45 25

547 *Limodorum abortivum*

2000. Orchids. Multicoloured.
1350   5d. Type **547** 10 10
1351   10d. *Orchis papilionacea* . . . 20 10
1352   24d. *Orchis provincialis* . . . 45 25

548 Greylag Goose (*Anser anser*)

2001. Waterfowl. Multicoloured.
1353   5d. Type **548** 10 10
1354   5d. Avocet (*Recurvirostra
     avosetta*) (vert) 10 10
1355   10d. Eurasian bittern
     (*Botaurus stellaris*) (vert) 20 10
1356   24d. Curlew (*Numenius
     arquata*) 45 25

549 Painted Table   **550** Forest, Belezma
National Park, Batna

2001. Traditional Crafts. Multicoloured.
1357   5d. Type **549** 10 10
1358   10d. Decorated shelf (horiz) . 20 10
1359   24d. Ornate mirror 45 25

2001. National Parks. Multicoloured.
1360   5d. Type **550** 10 10
1361   10d. Headland, Gouraya
     National Park, Bejaia
     (horiz) 20 10
1362   20d. Forest and mountains,
     Theneit el Had National
     Park, Tissemsilt (horiz) . 35 20
1363   24d. El Tarf National Park . . 45 25

551 St. Augustine as Child
(statue)

2001. St. Augustine of Hippo Conference, Algiers and
Annaba. Multicoloured.
1364   5d. Type **551** 10 10
1365   24d. 4th-century Christian
     mosaic (43 × 31 mm) . . . 45 25

552 Obverse and Reverse of Ryal
Boudjou, 1830

2001. Coins. Multicoloured.
1366   5d. Type **552** 10 10
1367   10d. Obverse and reverse of
     Double Boudjou, 1826 . . 20 10
1368   24d. Obverse and reverse of
     Ryal Drahem, 1771 . . . 45 25

553 Emblem and Scouts

2001. National Scouts' Day.
1369 **553** 5d. multicoloured 10 10

554 Child throwing   **555** Asthma Sufferer
Stones

2001. Intifida.

1370	554	5d. multicoloured	10	10

2001. National Asthma Day.

1371	556	5d. multicoloured	10	10

556 Hopscotch

2001. Children's Games. Multicoloured.

1372	5d. Type **556**	10	10
1373	5d. Jacks	10	10
1374	5d. Spinning top	10	10
1375	5d. Marbles	10	10

POSTAGE DUE STAMPS

1926. As Postage Due stamps of France, but inscr "ALGERIE".

D 34	D 11	5c. blue	10	2·75
D 35		10c. brown	10	95
D 36		20c. olive	85	2·75
D 37		25c. red	95	3·25
D 38		30c. red	10	20
D 39		45c. green	2·00	3·25
D 40		50c. purple	10	20
D 41		60c. green	2·00	4·50
D 42		1f. red on yellow	40	90
D249		1f.50 lilac	1·75	3·00
D 43		2f. mauve	35	1·10
D250		2f. blue	2·50	3·00
D 44		3f. blue	50	1·25
D251		5f. red	1·75	3·00
D252		5f. green	3·00	3·00

1926. As Postage Due stamps of France, but inscr "ALGERIE".

D45	D 19	1c. olive	20	2·75
D46		10c. violet	85	1·25
D47		30c. bistre	70	30
D48		60c. red	1·10	25
D49		1f. violet	7·75	2·10
D50		2f. blue	10·50	2·50

1927. Nos. D36, D39 and D37 surch.

D92	D 11	60 on 20c. olive	1·25	45
D93		2f. on 45c. green	1·90	4·25
D94		3f. on 25c. red	1·10	3·50

1927. Nos. D45/8 surch.

D95	D 19	10c. on 30c. bistre	3·25	6·50
D96		1f. on 1c. olive	1·50	2·50
D97		1f. on 60c. red	18·00	15
D98		2f. on 10c. violet	7·25	23·00

1942. As 1926 issue, but without "RF".

D181	D 11	30c. red	1·90	2·75
D182		2f. mauve	2·25	2·75

1944. No. 208 surch **TAXE P. C. V. DOUANE 20Fr.**

D230	38	20f. on 50f. red	2·00	3·00

1944. Surch **T 0.50**.

D231	4	50c. on 20c. green	1·10	2·75

1947. Postage Due Stamps of France optd **ALGERIE**.

D283	10c. brown (No. D985)	10	3·00
D284	30c. purple (No. D986)	10	2·50

D 53

1947.

D285	D 53	20c. red	20	3·00
D286		60c. blue	45	2·75
D287		1f. brown	10	2·75
D288		1f.50 olive	1·00	3·50
D289		2f. red	20	2·25
D290		3f. violet	40	2·50
D291		5f. blue	35	1·00
D292		6f. black	40	1·75
D293		10f. purple	1·10	80
D294		15f. myrtle	2·00	3·25
D295		20f. green	1·40	95
D296		30f. red	3·00	3·25
D297		50f. black	3·75	4·00
D298		100f. blue	14·50	10·50

INDEPENDENT STATE

1962. Postage Due stamps of France optd **EA** and with bar obliterating "REPUBLIQUE FRANCAISE".

D391	D 457	5c. mauve	11·00	11·00
D392		10c. red	11·00	11·00
D393		20c. brown	11·00	11·00
D394		50c. green	22·00	22·00
D395		1f. green	45·00	45·00

The above also exist with larger overprint applied with handstamps.

D 107 Scales of Justice

D 200 Ears of Corn

1963.

D411	D 107	5c. red and olive	10	10
D412		10c. olive and red	10	10
D413		20c. blue and black	35	20
D414		50c. brown and green	80	55
D415		1f. violet and orange	1·40	1·25

1968. No. D415 surch.

D508	D 107	60c. on 1f. vio & orge	55	40

1972.

D603	D 200	10c. brown	10	10
D604		20c. brown	10	10
D605		40c. orange	20	10
D606		50c. blue	20	10
D607		80c. brown	45	20
D608		1d. green	55	35
D609		2d. blue	1·10	65
D610		3d. violet	15	10
D611		4d. purple	20	10

ALLENSTEIN Pt. 7

A district of E. Prussia retained by Germany as the result of a plebiscite in 1920. Stamps issued during the plebiscite period.

100 pfennig = 1 mark.

1920. Stamps of Germany inscr "DEUTSCHES REICH" optd **PLEBISCITE OLSZTYN ALLENSTEIN**.

1	17	5pf. green	15	15
2		10pf. red	15	15
3	24	15pf. violet	15	15
4		15pf. purple	6·00	7·00
5	17	20pf. blue	15	15
6		30pf. black & orge on buff	30	30
7		40pf. black and red	15	20
8		50pf. black & pur on buff	15	20
9		75pf. black and green	20	20
10	18	1m. red	60	90
11		1m.25 green	65	90
12		1m.50 brown	65	90
13b	20	2m.50 red	1·10	3·25
14	21	3m. black	1·60	2·10

1920. Stamps of Germany inscr "DEUTSCHES REICH" optd **TRAITE DE VERSAILLES** etc. in oval.

15	17	5pf. green	20	25
16		10pf. red	20	25
17	24	15pf. violet	20	40
18		15pf. purple	26·00	22·00
19	17	20pf. blue	20	40
20		30pf. black & orge on buff	25	25
21		40pf. black and red	25	25
22		50pf. black & pur on buff	20	20
23		75pf. black and green	20	20
24	18	1m. red	65	50
25		1m.25 green	80	65
26		1m.50 brown	80	65
27	20	2m.50 red	1·10	1·90
28	21	3m. black	1·25	3·25

ALSACE AND LORRAINE Pt. 7

Stamps used in parts of France occupied by the German army in the war of 1870–71, and afterwards temporarily in the annexed provinces of Alsace and Lorraine.

100 pfennig = 1 mark.

1

1870.

1	1	1c. green	42·00	80·00
3		2c. brown	65·00	£100
5		4c. grey	55·00	85·00
8		5c. green	42·00	6·75
10		10c. brown	32·00	8·25
14		20c. blue	48·00	8·25
16		25c. brown	85·00	65·00

For 1940 issues see separate lists for Alsace and Lorraine under German Occupations.

ALWAR Pt. 1

A state of Rajputana, N. India. Now uses Indian stamps.

12 pies = 1 anna; 16 annas = 1 rupee

1 Native Dagger

1877. Roul or perf.

1c	1	¼a. blue	3·75	1·00
5		¼a. green	3·25	2·25
2c		1a. brown	2·25	1·00

ANDORRA Pt. 6; Pt. 9

An independent state in the Pyrenees under the joint suzerainty of France and Spain.

FRENCH POST OFFICES

1931. 100 centimes = 1 franc.
2002. 100 cents = 1 euro.

1931. Stamps of France optd **ANDORRE**.

F 1	11	½c. on 1c. grey	60	1·75
F 2		1c. grey	60	1·25
F 3		2c. red	60	3·00
F 4		3c. orange	65	3·00
F 5		5c. green	90	3·00
F 6		10c. lilac	2·50	3·75
F 7	18	15c. brown	5·75	5·50
F 8		20c. mauve	9·50	9·00
F 9		25c. brown	6·00	6·00
F10		30c. green	9·00	10·50
F11		40c. blue	11·00	10·50
F12	15	45c. violet	12·00	11·50
F13		50c. red	7·00	8·00
F14		65c. green	17·00	16·00
F15		75c. mauve	20·00	21·00
F16	18	90c. red	24·00	26·00
F17	15	1f. blue	28·00	22·00
F18	18	1f.50 blue	32·00	35·00
F19	13	2f. red and green	29·00	32·00
F20		3f. mauve and red	75·00	£100
F21		5f. blue and buff	£120	£140
F22		10f. green and red	£225	£275
F23		20f. mauve and green	£275	£300

F 3 Our Lady's Chapel, Meritxell

F 5 St. Michael's Church, Engolasters

1932.

F24	F 3	1c. slate	40	2·50
F25		2c. violet	1·00	2·25
F26		3c. brown	80	2·50
F27		5c. green	60	2·50
F28	A	10c. lilac	1·75	3·00
F29	F 3	15c. red	3·25	3·00
F30	A	20c. mauve	9·75	8·25
F31	F 5	25c. brown	5·50	6·50
F32	A	25c. brown	12·00	22·00
F33		30c. green	2·75	1·90
F34		40c. blue	9·50	11·00
F35		40c. brown	1·60	3·00
F36		45c. red	13·50	15·00
F37		45c. green	4·50	5·25
F38	F 5	50c. mauve	13·00	13·00
F39	A	50c. violet	4·00	8·00
F40		50c. green	1·60	4·25
F41		55c. violet	18·00	17·00
F42		60c. brown	1·60	3·00
F43	F 5	65c. green	35·00	40·00
F44	A	65c. blue	13·50	12·00
F45		70c. red	1·60	4·25
F46	F 5	75c. violet	6·75	6·00
F47	A	75c. blue	3·25	6·25
F48		80c. green	22·00	22·00
F49	B	80c. green	1·25	2·50
F50		90c. red	9·00	7·50
F51		90c. green	5·00	6·00
F52		1f. green	19·00	15·00
F53		1f. red	23·00	22·00
F54		1f. blue	1·10	2·75
F55		1f. 20 violet	1·40	2·75
F56	F 3	1f. 25 mauve	42·00	42·00
F57		1f.25 red	5·75	8·00
F58	B	1f.30 brown	1·40	2·75
F59	C	1f.50 blue	21·00	23·00
F60	B	1f.50 red	1·40	2·75
F61		1f.75 violet	95·00	85·00
F62		1f.75 blue	40·00	40·00
F63		2f. mauve	9·00	8·25
F64	F 3	2f. red	1·40	3·50
F65		2f. green	1·40	2·75
F66		2f.15 violet	50·00	55·00
F67		2f.25 blue	8·00	8·00
F68		2f.40 red	1·75	2·75
F69		2f.50 black	8·50	8·00
F70		2f.50 blue	1·75	2·40
F71	B	3f. brown	11·00	9·25
F72	F 3	3f. brown	1·75	2·75
F73		4f. blue	1·75	2·50
F74		4f.50 violet	1·40	1·75
F75	C	5f. brown	2·00	2·75
F76		10f. violet	2·25	3·00
F78		15f. blue	1·40	3·00
F79		20f. red	2·00	1·75
F81	A	50f. blue	3·00	3·75

DESIGNS—HORIZ: A, St. Anthony's Bridge; C, Andorra la Vella. VERT: B, Valley of Sant Julia.

1935. No. F38 surch **20c**.

F82	F 5	20c. on 50c. purple	15·00	22·00

F 9

F 13 Andorra la Vella

F 10

F 14 Councillor Jaume Bonell

1936.

F83	F 9	1c. black	50	2·50
F84		2c. blue	35	2·25
F85		3c. brown	65	2·50
F86		5c. red	25	2·25
F87		10c. blue	20	2·50
F88		15c. mauve	3·25	1·40
F89		20c. green	50	2·50
F90		30c. red	45	2·75
F91		30c. black	1·60	2·50
F92		35c. green	55·00	60·00
F93		40c. brown	1·25	2·50
F94		50c. green	1·25	2·50
F95		60c. blue	2·00	2·50
F96		70c. violet	1·25	2·50

1944.

F 97	F 10	10c. violet	10	2·25
F 98		30c. red	35	2·00
F 99		40c. blue	60	2·25
F100		50c. red	25	2·50
F101		60c. black	25	2·25
F102		70c. mauve	30	2·50
F103		80c. green	10	2·50
F104		1f. blue	90	2·50
F105	D	1f. purple	30	2·50
F106		1f.20 blue	15	2·50
F107		1f.50 red	15	2·50
F108		2f. green	15	2·50
F109	E	2f.40 red	25	2·25
F110		2f.50 red	3·00	4·50
F111		3f. brown	50	2·25
F112	D	3f. red	6·00	4·75
F113	E	4f. blue	35	2·50
F114		4f. green	55	3·00
F115	D	4f. brown	1·60	4·25
F116	E	4f.50 brown	25	2·50
F117	F 13	4f.50 blue	6·00	3·00
F118		5f. blue	60	2·50
F119		5f. green	1·25	2·75
F120	E	5f. green	2·75	2·10
F121		5f. violet	8·50	4·75
F122	F 13	6f. red	50	2·25
F123		6f. purple	30	2·50
F124	E	6f. green	5·50	4·00
F125	F 13	8f. blue	1·40	3·25
F126	E	8f. brown	1·00	2·75
F127	F 13	10f. green	50	2·25
F128		10f. blue	1·50	1·75
F129		12f. red	90	2·75
F130		12f. green	1·25	3·00
F131	F 14	15f. purple	1·75	2·75
F132	F 13	15f. red	1·40	2·50
F133		15f. brown	9·50	2·25
F134	F 14	18f. blue	2·50	1·90
F135	F 13	18f. red	19·00	12·00
F136	F 14	20f. blue	1·40	2·75
F137		20f. violet	2·75	4·00
F138		25f. red	3·00	4·25
F139		25f. blue	1·25	1·25
F140		30f. blue	27·00	15·00
F141		40f. green	3·25	2·75
F142		50f. brown	1·25	3·25

DESIGNS—HORIZ: D, Church of St. John of Caselles; E, House of the Valleys.

F 15 Chamois and Pyrenees

F 16 Les Escaldes

1950. Air.

F143	F 15	100f. blue	60·00	60·00

1955.

F144	F 16	1f. blue (postage)	15	2·25
F145		2f. green	30	2·25
F146		3f. red	75	2·00
F147		5f. brown	80	1·75
F148	–	6f. green	2·00	2·25
F149	–	8f. red	2·00	2·75
F150	–	10f. violet	2·00	2·25
F151	–	12f. blue	2·25	2·25

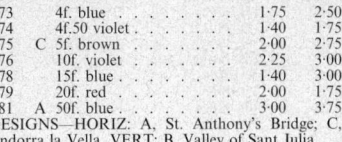

F152 – 15f. red . . . . 2·50 2·50
F153 – 18f. blue . . . . 1·75 3·25
F154 – 20f. violet . . . . . . 2·10 1·75
F155 – 25f. brown . . . . . . 3·00 3·50
F156 – 30f. blue . . . . 30·00 26·00
F157 – 35f. blue . . . . 10·50 13·50
F158 – 40f. green . . . . . . 38·00 38·00
F159 – 50f. red . . . . 3·25 4·00
F160 – 65f. violet . . . . . . 8·00 16·00
F161 – 70f. brown . . . . . . 5·50 8·00
F162 – 75f. blue . . . . 55·00 45·00

F163 – 100f. green (air) . . . 8·75 10·50
F164 – 200f. red . . . . 14·50 15·00
F165 – 500f. blue . . . . . . 90·00 60·00
DESIGNS—VERT: 15f. to 25f. Gothic cross, Andorra la Vella; 100f. to 500f. East Valira River. HORIZ: 6f. to 12f. Santa Coloma Church; 30f. to 75f. Les Bons village.

New currency. 100 (old) francs = 1 (new) franc.

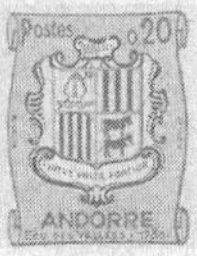
F 21

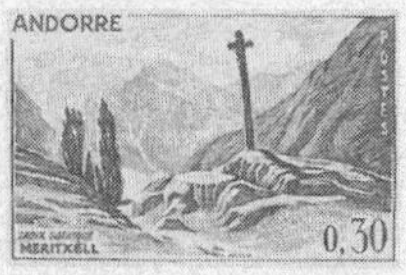
F 22 Gothic Cross, Meritxell

1961.
F166 F 21 1c. grey, blue and slate (postage) . . . 10 1·60
F167 2c. lt orge, blk & orge 80 1·60
F168 5c. lt grn, blk & grn 40 1·60
F169 10c. pink, blk & red 40 55
F170a 12c. yell, pur & grn 1·10 2·25
F171 15c. lt bl, blk & bl . . 40 1·60
F172 18c. pink, blk & mve 1·60 2·25
F173 20c. lt yell, brn & yell 60 55
F174 F 22 25c. blue, vio & grn 1·00 1·00
F175 30c. pur, red & grn 1·00 70
F175a 40c. green and brown 1·60 1·75
F176 45c. blue, ind & grn 17·00 15·00
F176a 45c. brown, bl & vio 1·40 2·00
F177 50c. multicoloured . . 2·00 1·25
F177a 60c. brown & chestnut 1·75 2·00
F178 65c. olive, bl & brn 16·00 15·00
F179 85c. multicoloured . . 16·00 15·00
F179a 90c. green, bl & brn 1·10 2·50
F180 1f. blue, brn & turq 1·60 1·25
F181 – 2f. grn, red & pur (air) . . . . 2·00 2·00
F182 – 3f. purple, bl & grn 3·25 2·25
F183 – 5f. orange, pur & red 3·00 4·75
F184 – 10f. green and blue . . 8·50 10·00
DESIGNS—As Type F 22: 60c. to 1f. Engolasters Lake; 2f. to 10f. Incles Valley.

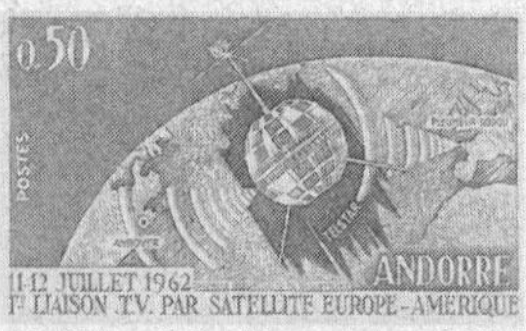
F 23 "Telstar" Satellite and part of Globe

1962. 1st Trans-Atlantic TV Satellite Link.
F185 F 23 50c. violet and blue . . 1·50 1·40

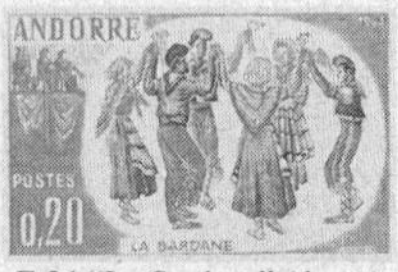
F 24 "La Sardane" (dance)

1963. Andorran History (1st issue).
F186 F 24 20c. purple, mve & grn 3·25 5·00
F187 – 50c. red and green . . 7·25 10·00
F188 – 1f. green, blue & brn 11·00 11·00
DESIGNS—LARGER (48½ × 27 mm): 50c. Charlemagne crossing Andorra. (48 × 27 mm): 1f. Foundation of Andorra by Louis le Debonnaire.
See also Nos. F190/1.

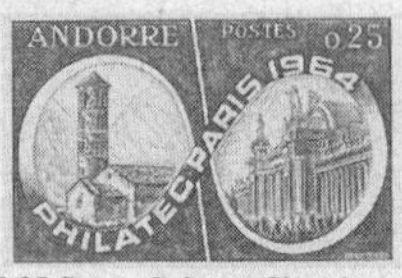
F 25 Santa Coloma Church and Grand Palais, Paris

1964. "PHILATEC 1964" International Stamp Exhibition, Paris.
F189 F 25 25c. green, pur & brn 1·50 1·60

1964. Andorran History (2nd issue). As Nos. F187/8, inscribed "1964".
F190 60c. green, chestnut & brown . . . . 13·50 22·00
F191 1f. blue, sepia and brown 13·50 22·00
DESIGNS (48½ × 27 mm): 60c. "Napoleon re-establishes the Andorran Statute, 1806"; 1f. "Confirmation of the Co-government, 1288".

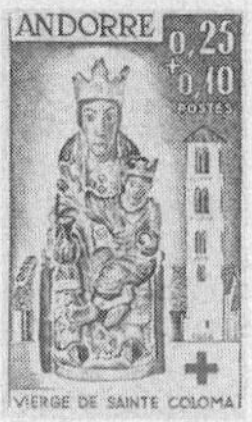
F 26 Virgin of Santa Coloma

F 27 "Syncom", Morse Key and Pleumeur-Bodou centre

1964. Red Cross Fund.
F192 F 26 25c. + 10c. red, green and blue . . . . . 20·00 20·00

1965. Centenary of I.T.U.
F193 F 27 60c. violet, blue and red . . . . 4·75 4·50

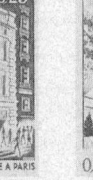

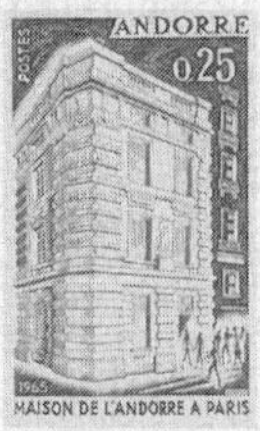
F 28 Andorra House, Paris

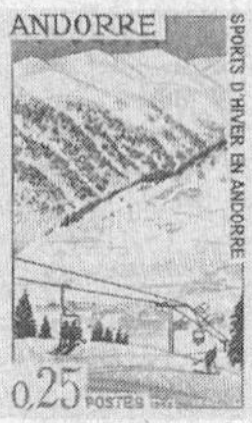
F 29 Chair-lift

1965. Opening of Andorra House, Paris.
F194 F 28 25c. brown, olive & bl 90 90

1966. Winter Sports.
F195 F 29 25c. green, purple & bl 1·40 2·25
F196 – 40c. brown, blue & red 1·75 2·75
DESIGN—HORIZ: 40c. Ski-lift.

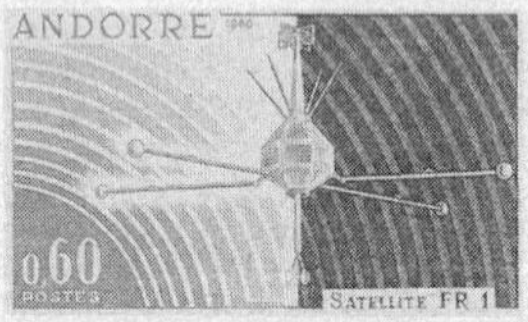
F 30 Satellite "FR 1"

1966. Launching of Satellite "FR 1".
F197 F 30 60c. blue, emer & grn 1·75 1·60

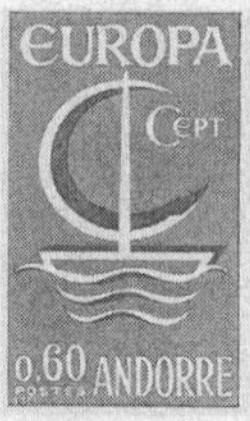
F 31 Europa "Ship"

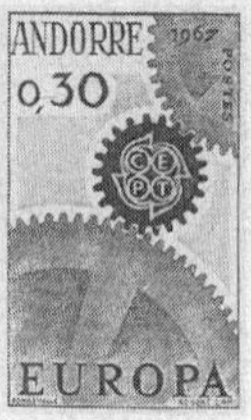
F 32 Cogwheels

1966. Europa.
F198 F 31 60c. brown . . . . . . 3·25 5·75

1967. Europa.
F199 F 32 30c. indigo and blue 4·75 2·75
F200 60c. red and purple . . 9·50 4·75

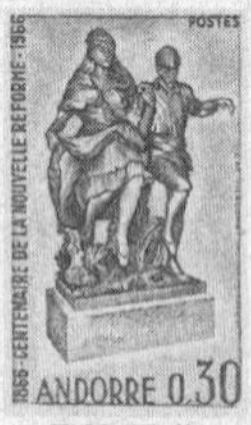
F 33 "Folk Dancers" (statue)

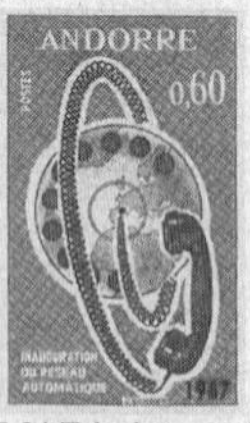
F 34 Telephone and Dial

1967. Centenary (1966) of New Reform.
F201 F 33 30c. green, olive & slate 1·10 90

1967. Inaug of Automatic Telephone Service.
F202 F 34 60c. black, violet & red 1·75 2·75

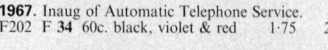

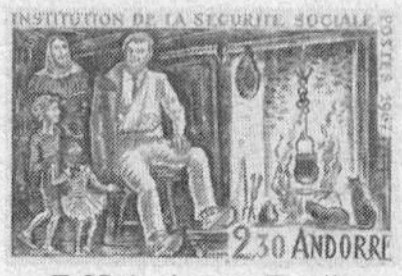
F 35 Andorran Family

1967. Institution of Social Security.
F203 F 35 2f.30 brown & purple 8·00 7·25

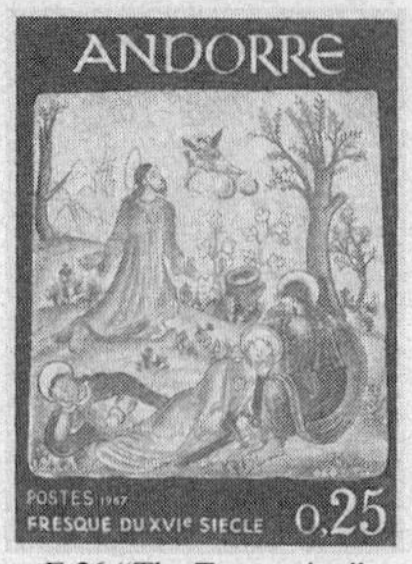
F 36 "The Temptation"

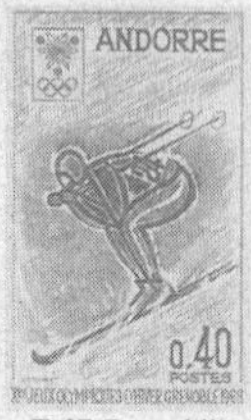
F 37 Downhill Skiing

1967. 16th-century Frescoes in House of the Valleys (1st series).
F204 F 36 25c. red and black . . 1·10 2·00
F205 – 30c. purple and violet 90 2·25
F206 – 60c. blue and indigo 1·25 2·75
FRESCOES: 30c. "The Kiss of Judas"; 60c. "The Descent from the Cross".
See also Nos. F210/12.

1968. Winter Olympic Games, Grenoble.
F207 F 37 40c. purple, orge & red 1·25 1·00

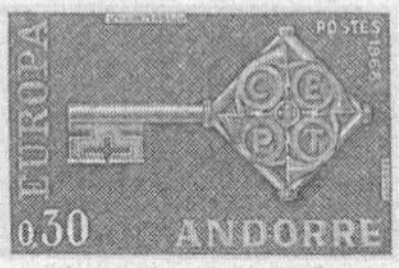
F 38 Europa "Key"

1968. Europa.
F208 F 38 30c. blue and slate . . 9·75 6·00
F209 60c. violet & brown . . 14·50 8·75

1968. 16th-century Frescoes in House of the Valleys (2nd series). Designs as Type F 36.
F210 25c. deep green and green 60 55
F211 30c. purple and brown . . . 70 70
F212 60c. brown and red . . . . 1·25 1·50
FRESCOES: 25c. "The Beating of Christ"; 30c. "Christ Helped by the Cyrenians"; 60c. "The Death of Christ".

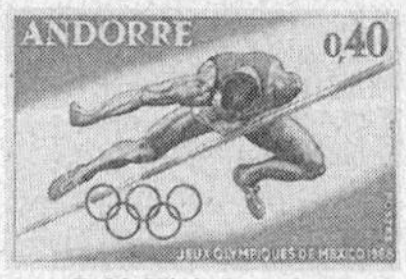
F 39 High Jumping

1968. Olympic Games, Mexico.
F213 F 39 40c. brown and blue 1·25 1·10

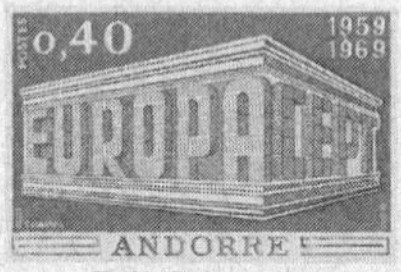
F 40 Colonnade

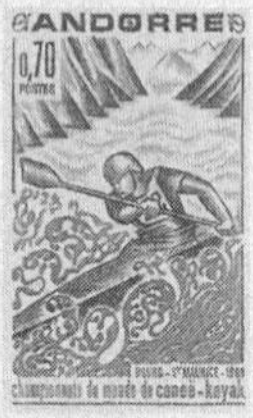
F 41 Canoeing

1969. Europa.
F214 F 40 40c. grey, blue and red 12·00 5·75
F215 70c. red, green and blue . . . . 17·00 9·50

1969. World Kayak-Canoeing Championships, Bourg-St. Maurice.
F216 F 41 70c. dp blue, bl & grn 2·00 3·25

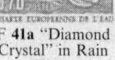

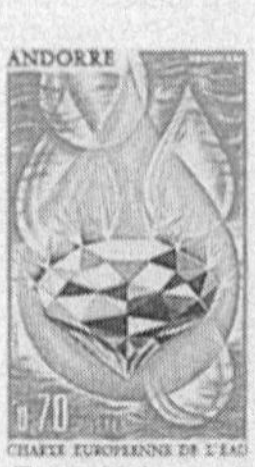
F 41a "Diamond Crystal" in Rain Drop

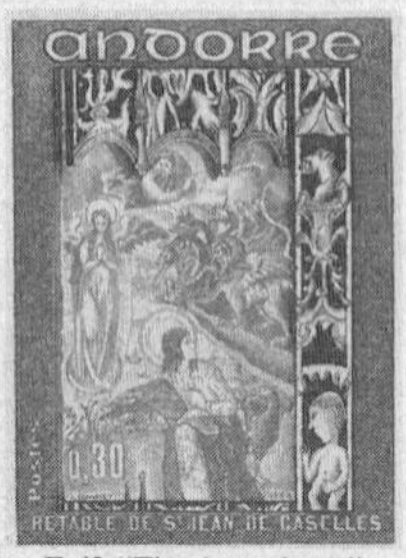
F 42 "The Apocalypse"

1969. European Water Charter.
F217 F 41a 70c. black, bl & ultram . . . . . . 4·50 6·50

1969. Altar-screen, Church of St. John of Caselles (1st series). "The Revelation of St. John".
F218 F 42 30c. red, violet & brn 1·10 2·25
F219 – 40c. bistre, brn & grey 1·90 2·50
F220 – 70c. purple, lake & red 1·75 2·75
DESIGNS: 40c. Angel "clothed with cloud with face as the sun, and feet as pillars of fire" (Rev. 10); 70c. Christ with sword and stars, and seven candlesticks.
See also Nos. F225/7, F233/5 and F240/2.

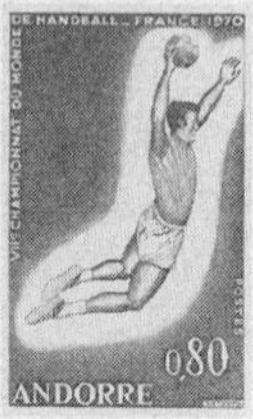
F 43 Handball Player

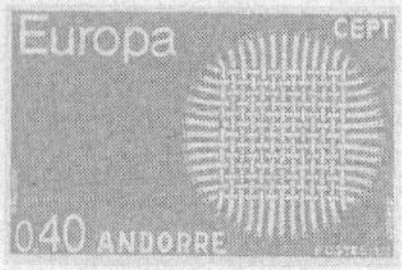
F 44 "Flaming Sun"

1970. 7th World Handball Championships, France.
F221 F 43 80c. blue, brn & dp bl 2·25 3·75

1970. Europa.
F222 F 44 40c. orange . . . . . 9·50 5·00
F223 80c. violet . . . . . . 16·00 9·00

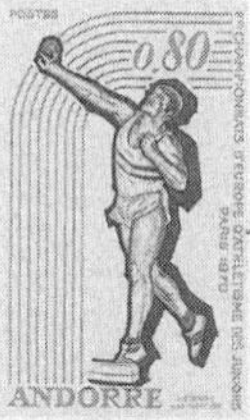
F 45 Putting the Shot

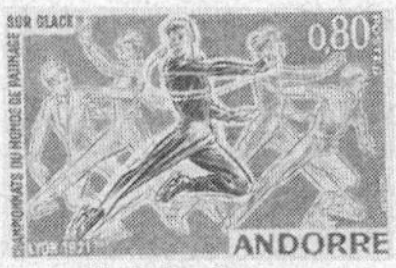
F 46 Ice Skaters

1970. 1st European Junior Athletic Championships, Paris.
F224 F 45 80c. purple and blue 2·40 2·25

1970. Altar-screen, Church of St. John of Caselles (2nd series). Designs as Type F 42.
F225 30c. violet, brown and red 1·25 2·25
F226 40c. green and violet . . . 90 3·25
F227 80c. red, blue and green . . 2·25 3·25
DESIGNS: 30c. Angel with keys and padlock; 40c. Angel with pillar; 80c. St. John being boiled in cauldron of oil.

1971. World Ice Skating Championships, Lyon.
F228 F 46 80c. violet, pur & red 1·90 2·00

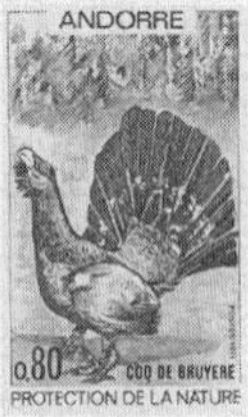
F 47 Western Capercaillie

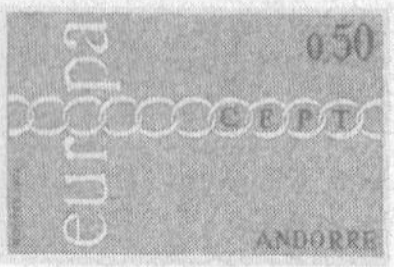
F 48 Europa Chain

1971. Nature Protection.
F229 F 47 80c. multicoloured . . 4·00 3·25
F230 – 80c. brown, green & bl 2·75 3·50
DESIGN: No. F230, Brown bear.

1971. Europa.
F231 F 48 50c. red . . . . 9·50 5·00
F232 80c. green . . . . . . 16·00 8·75

1971. Altar-screen, Church of St. John of Caselles (3rd series). As Type F 42.
F233 30c. green, brown and myrtle . . . . 1·10 2·25
F234 50c. brown, orange and lake 1·40 2·50
F235 90c. blue, purple and brown 2·00 3·25
DESIGNS: 30c. St. John in temple at Ephesus; 50c. St. John with cup of poison; 90c. St. John disputing with pagan philosophers.

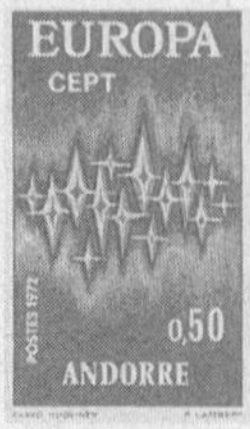
F 49 "Communications"

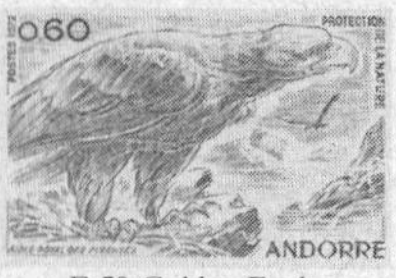
F 50 Golden Eagle

1972. Europa.
F236 F 49 50c. multicoloured . . 11·00 5·25
F237 90c. multicoloured . . 17·00 8·00

1972. Nature Protection.
F238 F 50 60c. olive, green & pur 4·00 4·00

F 51 Rifle-shooting   F 52 General De Gaulle

1972. Olympic Games, Munich.
F239 F 51 1f. purple . . . . . . 2·50 3·75

1972. Altar-screen, Church of St. John of Caselles (4th series). As Type F 42.
F240 30c. purple, grey and green 90 2·25
F241 50c. grey and blue . . . . 1·25 2·50
F242 90c. green and blue . . . . 1·75 3·25
DESIGNS: 30c. St. John in discussion with bishop; 50c. St. John healing a cripple; 90c. Angel with spear.

1972. 5th Anniv of Gen. De Gaulle's Visit to Andorra.
F243 F 52 50c. blue . . . . . . 2·50 3·25
F244 — 90c. red . . . . 3·25 3·50
DESIGN: 90c. Gen. De Gaulle in Andorra la Vella, 1967.
  See also Nos. F434/5.

F 53 Europa "Posthorn"

1973. Europa.
F245 F 53 50c. multicoloured . . 9·50 6·00
F246 90c. multicoloured . . 16·00 9·75

F 54 "Virgin of Canolich"   F 55 Lily
(wood carving)

1973. Andorran Art.
F247 F 54 1f. lilac, blue and drab 2·10 2·10

1973. Pyrenean Flowers (1st series). Multicoloured.
F248 30c. Type F 55 . . . . . . 1·10 1·75
F249 50c. Columbine . . . . . 2·00 2·25
F250 90c. Wild pinks . . . . . . 1·50 2·25
  See also Nos. F253/5 and F264/6.

F 56 Blue Tit   F 57 "The Virgin of
("Mesange Bleue")   Pal"

1973. Nature Protection. Birds. Multicoloured.
F251 90c. Type F 56 . . . . . . 2·75 3·25
F252 1f. Lesser spotted
    woodpecker ("Pic
    Epeichette") . . . . . 2·75 3·25
  See also Nos. F259/60.

1974. Pyrenean Wild Flowers (2nd series). As Type F 55. Multicoloured.
F253 45c. Iris . . . . 60 1·75
F254 65c. Tobacco Plant . . . . . 75 1·75
F255 90c. Narcissus . . . . . . 1·50 2·25

1974. Europa. Church Sculptures. Mult.
F256 50c. Type F 57 . . . . . 14·50 7·00
F257 90c. "The Virgin of Santa
    Coloma" . . . . . . 22·00 10·00

F 58 Arms of Andorra   F 59 Letters crossing
Globe

1974. Meeting of Co-Princes, Cahors.
F258 F 58 1f. blue, violet & orge 1·50 2·75

1974. Nature Protection. Birds. As Type F 56. Multicoloured.
F259 60c. Citril finch ("Venturon
    Montagnard") . . . . . 3·00 2·50
F260 80c. Northern bullfinch
    ("Boureuil") . . . . . . 3·00 2·00

1974. Centenary of U.P.U.
F261 F 59 1f.20 red, grey & brn 1·25 1·40

F 60 "Calvary"

1975. Europa. Paintings from La Cortinada Church. Multicoloured.
F262 80c. Type F 60 . . . . . . 10·50 5·75
F263 1f.20 "Coronation of St.
    Martin" (horiz) . . . . . 14·50 8·75

1975. Pyrenean Flowers (3rd series). As Type F 55.
F264 60c. multicoloured . . . . 70 1·75
F265 80c. multicoloured . . . . 1·25 1·25
F266 1f.20 yellow, red and green 1·00 2·00
DESIGNS: 60c. Gentian; 80c. Anemone; 1f.20, Colchicum.

F 61 "Arphila" Motif

1975. "Arphila 75" International Stamp Exhibition, Paris.
F267 F 61 2f. red, green and blue 1·75 1·75

F 62 Pres. Pompidou   F 63 "La Pubilla"
(Co-prince of   and Emblem
Andorra)

1976. President Pompidou of France Commem.
F268 F 62 80c. black and violet 85 85

1976. International Women's Year.
F269 F 63 1f.20 black, pur & bl 1·25 1·25

F 64 Skier   F 65 Telephone
and Satellite

1976. Winter Olympic Games, Innsbruck.
F270 F 64 1f.20 black, green & bl 1·25 1·25

1976. Telephone Centenary.
F271 F 65 1f. green, black and red 95 1·10

F 66 Catalan Forge

1976. Europa.
F272 F 66 80c. brown, blue & grn 2·40 1·50
F273 — 1f.20 red, green & blk 3·50 2·40
DESIGN: 1f.20, Andorran folk-weaving.

F 67 Thomas   F 68 Ball-trap (clay
Jefferson   pigeon) Shooting

1976. Bicentenary of American Revolution.
F274 F 67 1f.20 dp grn, brn & grn 1·10 1·10

1976. Olympic Games, Montreal.
F275 F 68 2f. brown, violet & grn 1·50 1·40

F 69 New Chapel

1976. New Chapel of Our Lady, Meritxell.
F276 F 69 1f. green, purple & brn 95 95

F 70 Apollo   F 71 Stoat

1976. Nature Protection. Butterflies. Mult.
F277 80c. Type F 70 . . . . . . 2·50 3·25
F278 1f.40 Camberwell beauty . . 2·25 3·00

1977. Nature Protection.
F279 F 71 1f. grey, black & blue 1·40 2·50

F 72 Church of St.   F 73 Book and
John of Caselles   Flowers

1977. Europa.
F280 F 72 1f. purple, green & bl 5·50 2·25
F281 — 1f.40 indigo, grn & bl 9·00 3·50
DESIGN: 1f.40, St. Vicens Chateau.

1977. 1st Anniv of Institute of Andorran Studies.
F282 F 73 80c. brown, green & bl 90 85

F 74 St. Roma

1977. Reredos, St. Roma's Chapel, Les Bons.
F283 F 74 2f. multicoloured . . . 2·25 2·50

F 75 General Council   F 76 Eurasian Red
Assembly Hall   Squirrel

1977. Andorran Institutions.
F284 F 75 1f.10 red, blue & brn 1·25 1·25
F285 — 2f. brown and red . . 1·25 1·25
DESIGN—VERT. 2f. Don Guillem d'Areny Plandolit.

1978. Nature Protection.
F286 F 76 1f. brown, grn & olive 1·60 1·75

F 77 Escalls Bridge   F 78 Church at Pal

1978. 700th Anniv of Parity Treaties (1st issue).
F287 F 77 80c. green, brown & bl 60 60
  See also No. F292.

1978. Europa.
F288 F 78 1f. brown, green & red 5·00 2·25
F289 — 1f.40 brown, bl & red 8·75 3·50
DESIGN: 1f.40, Charlemagne's House.

F 79 "Virgin of Sispony"

1978. Andorran Art.
F290 F 79 2f. multicoloured . . . 1·25 1·25

F 80 Tribunal Meeting

1978. Tribunal of Visura.
F291 F 80 1f.20 multicoloured . . 85 70

F 81 Treaty Text

1978. 700th Anniv of Parity Treaties (2nd issue).
F292   F **81**   1f.50 brown, grn & red   1·00   2·00

F **82** Chamois   F **83** Rock Ptarmigans ("Perdiu Blanca")

1978. Nature Protection.
F293   F **82**   1f. brown, lt brn & bl   1·10   1·60

1979. Nature Protection.
F294   F **83**   1f.20 multicoloured   . .   1·40   2·00

F **84** Early 20th Century Postman and Church of St. John of Caselles   F **85** Wall painting, Church of St. Cerni, Nagol

1979. Europa.
F295   F **84**   1f.20 black, brn & grn   1·25   1·25
F296   —   1f.70 brown, grn & mve   . . . . . .   1·90   1·90
DESIGN: 1f.70, Old French Post Office, Andorra.

1979. Pre-Romanesque Art.
F297   F **85**   2f. green, pink & brown   . . . . . .   1·75   2·00
See also No. F309.

F **86** Boy with Sheep   F **87** Co-princes Monument (Luigiteruggi)

1979. International Year of the Child.
F298   F **86**   1f.70 multicoloured   . .   85   1·75

1979. Co-princes Monument.
F299   F **87**   2f. dp green, grn & red   1·75   2·00

F **88** Judo   F **89** Cal Pal, La Cortinada

1979. World Judo Championships, Paris.
F300   F **88**   1f.30 black, dp bl & bl   1·25   1·75

1980.
F301   F **89**   1f.10 brown, bl & grn   65   1·75

F **90** Cross-country Skiing   F **91** Charlemagne

1980. Winter Olympics, Lake Placid.
F302   F **90**   1f.80 ultram, bl & red   1·25   1·25

1980. Europa.
F303   F **91**   1f.30 brn, chest & red   60   65
F304   —   1f.80 green and brown   95   95
DESIGN: 1f.80, Napoleon I.

F **93** Dog's-tooth Violet   F **94** Cyclists

1980. Nature Protection. Multicoloured.
F306   1f.10 Type F **93**   40   1·60
F305   1f.30 Pyrenean lily   40   1·60

1980. World Cycling Championships.
F307   F **94**   1f.20 violet, mve & brn   60   55

F **95** House of the Valleys

1980. 400th Anniv of Restoration of House of the Valleys (meeting place of Andorran General Council).
F308   F **95**   1f.40 brown, vio & grn   70   1·60

1980. Pre-Romanesque Art. As Type F **85**. Mult.
F309   2f. Angel (wall painting, Church of St. Cerni, Nagol) (horiz)   80   2·25

F **97** Shepherds' Huts, Mereig

1981. Architecture.
F310   F **97**   1f.40 brown and blue   80   1·75

F **98** Bear Dance (Emcamp Carnival)   F **99** Bonelli's Warbler

1981. Europa.
F311   F **98**   1f.40 black, green & bl   70   1·75
F312   —   2f. black, blue and red   65   2·00
DESIGN: 2f. El Contrapas (dance).

1981. Nature Protection. Birds. Multicoloured.
F313   1f.20 Type F **99**   60   1·75
F314   1f.40 Wallcreeper   65   1·75

F **100** Fencing

1981. World Fencing Championships, Clermont-Ferrand.
F315   F **100**   2f. blue and black   . .   65   1·75

F **101** Chasuble of St. Martin (miniature)

1981. Art.
F316   F **101**   3f. multicoloured   . .   1·25   2·50

F **102** Fountain, Sant Julia de Loria   F **103** Symbolic Disabled

1981. International Decade of Drinking Water.
F317   F **102**   1f.60 blue and brown   50   1·75

1981. International Year of Disabled Persons.
F318   F **103**   2f.30 blue, red & grn   60   1·75

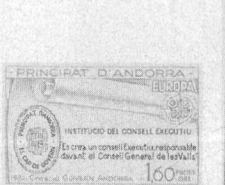

F **104** Scroll and Badge (creation of Andorran Executive Council, 1981)   F **105** Footballer running to right

1982. Europa.
F319   F **104**   1f.60 blue, brn & orge   85   75
F320   —   2f.30 blue, blk & orge   1·25   1·40
DESIGN: 2f.30, Hat and cloak (creation of Land Council, 1419).

1982. World Cup Football Championship, Spain.
F321   F **105**   1f.60 brown and red   1·75   1·75
F322   —   2f.60 brown and red   3·75   3·75
DESIGN: 2f.60, Footballer running to left.

F **107** Wall Painting, La Cortinada Church

1982. Romanesque Art.
F324   F **107**   3f. multicoloured   . .   80   2·25

F **108** Wild Cat   F **109** Dr. Robert Koch

1982. Nature Protection.
F325   F **108**   1f.80 blk, grn & grey   1·10   1·75
F326   —   2f.60 brown & green   1·25   1·75
DESIGN: 2f.60, Scots Pine.

1982. Centenary of Discovery of Tubercle Bacillus.
F327   F **109**   2f.10 lilac   . . .   1·10   1·75

F **110** St. Thomas Aquinas   F **111** Montgolfier and Charles Balloons over Tuileries, Paris

1982. St. Thomas Aquinas Commemoration.
F328   F **110**   2f. deep brown, brown and grey   . . . . .   1·00   1·75

1983. Bicentenary of Manned Flight.
F329   F **111**   2f. green, red & brown   80   1·75

F **112** Silver Birch

1983. Nature Protection.
F330   F **112**   1f. red, brown & green   . . . . .   1·10   1·50
F331   —   1f.50 green, bl & brn   65   1·75
DESIGN: 1f.50, Brown trout.

F **113** Mountain Cheesery

1983. Europa.
F332   F **113**   1f. purple and violet   75   1·75
F333   —   2f.60 red, mve & pur   90   2·25
DESIGN: 2f.60, Catalan forge.

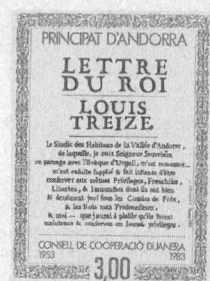

F **114** Royal Edict of Louis XIII

1983. 30th Anniv of Customs Co-operation Council.
F334   F **114**   3f. black and slate   . .   1·25   1·40

F **115** Early Coat of Arms

1983. Inscr "POSTES".

F335	F **115**	5c. green and red . .	60	1·40
F336		10c. dp green & green	60	1·40
F337		20c. violet and mauve	60	40
F338		30c. purple and violet	30	1·40
F339		40c. blue & ultram .	60	1·40
F340		50c. black and red .	65	1·40
F341		1f. lake and red . .	70	1·40
F342		1f.90 green	1·25	2·25
F343		2f. red and brown .	1·00	55
F344		2f.10 green	1·00	55
F345		2f.20 red	40	1·75
F346		2f.30 red	90	1·75
F347		3f. green and mauve	1·50	2·25
F348		4f. orange and brown	1·60	2·75
F349		5f. brown and red .	1·50	2·25
F350		10f. red and brown	2·50	2·75
F351		15f. green & dp green	3·50	4·25
F352		20f. blue and brown	4·00	4·00

For design as Type F **115** but inscribed "LA POSTE" see Nos. F446/9.

F 116 Wall Painting, La
Cortinada Church

F 117 Plandolit
House

1983. Romanesque Art.
F354 F **116** 4f. multicoloured . . 1·50 1·50

1983.
F355 F **117** 1f.60 brown & green 50 1·75

F 118 Snowflakes and Olympic
Torch

1984. Winter Olympic Games, Sarajevo.
F356 F **118** 2f.80 red, blue & grn 1·00 2·00

F 119 Pyrenees and Council of
Europe Emblem

1984. Work Community of Pyrenees Region.
F357 F **119** 3f. blue and brown . . 1·00 2·25

F 120 Bridge

1984. Europa.
F358 F **120** 2f. green . . . . . . 1·50 1·25
F359 2f.80 red . . . . . . 2·10 1·90

F 121 Sweet Chestnut

1984. Nature Protection.
F360 F **121** 1f.70 grn, brn & pur 55 1·75
F361 – 2f.10 green & brown 70 1·75
DESIGN: 2f.10, Walnut.

F 122 Centre Members

1984. Pyrenean Cultures Centre, Andorra.
F362 F **122** 3f. blue, orange & red 90 2·00

F 123 "St. George" (detail of fresco,
Church of St. Cerni, Nagol)

1984. Pre-Romanesque Art.
F363 F **123** 5f. multicoloured . . 1·50 2·75

F 124 Sant Julia Valley

F 125 Title Page of
"Le Val
d'Andorre" (comic
opera)

1985.
F364 F **124** 2f. green, olive & brn 75 2·00

1985. Europa.
F365 F **125** 2f.10 green . . . . . 1·75 1·40
F366 – 3f. brown & dp brown 2·40 2·00
DESIGN: 3f. Musical instruments within frame.

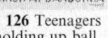

F 126 Teenagers
holding up ball

F 127 Mallard

1985. International Youth Year.
F367 F **126** 3f. red and brown . . 70 2·00

1985. Nature Protection. Multicoloured.
F368 1f.80 Type F **127** . . . . . 85 2·00
F369 2f.20 Eurasian goldfinch . . 90 2·00

F 128 St. Cerni and Angel (fresco,
Church of St. Cerni, Nagol)

1985. Pre-Romanesque Art.
F370 F **128** 5f. multicoloured . . 1·40 2·75

F 130 1979 Europa Stamp

1986. Inauguration of Postal Museum.
F381 F **130** 2f.20 brown & green 60 1·75

F 131 Ansalonga

F 132 Players

1986. Europa.
F382 F **131** 2f.20 black and blue 1·50 1·25
F383 – 3f.20 black and green 2·40 1·90
DESIGN: 3f.20, Pyrenean chamois.

1986. World Cup Football Championship, Mexico.
F384 F **132** 3f. green, blk & dp
grn . . . . . . 1·25 3·50

F 133 Angonella Lakes

1986.
F385 F **133** 2f.20 multicoloured 85 2·75

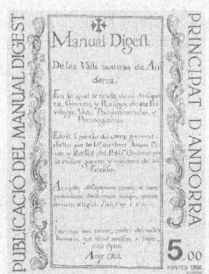

F 134 Title Page of "Manual
Digest", 1748

1986. "Manual Digest".
F386 F **134** 5f. black, grn & brn 1·75 2·75

F 135 Dove with Twig

F 136 St. Vincent's
Chapel, Enclar

1986. International Peace Year.
F387 F **135** 1f.90 blue and indigo 1·10 1·75

1986.
F388 F **136** 1f.90 brn, blk & grn 75 1·75

F 137 Arms

F 138 Meritxell Chapel

1987. Visit of French Co-prince (French president).
F389 F **137** 2f.20 multicoloured 1·75 2·00

1987. Europa.
F390 F **138** 2f.20 purple and red 1·75 1·60
F391 – 3f.40 violet and blue 2·75 2·25
DESIGN: 3f.40, Ordino.

F 139 Ransol

F 140 Horse

1987.
F392 F **139** 1f.90 multicoloured 90 2·00

1987. Nature Protection. Multicoloured.
F393 1f.90 Type F **140** . . . . 1·40 1·75
F394 2f.20 Isabel (moth) . . . . 1·25 1·75

F 141 Arualsu (fresco, La Cortinada
Church)

1987. Romanesque Art.
F395 F **141** 5f. multicoloured . . 1·40 2·75

F 142 Walker with Map by
Signpost

1987. Walking.
F396 F **142** 2f. pur, grn & dp grn 65 1·75

F 143 Key

F 144 Arms

1987. La Cortinada Church Key.
F397 F **143** 3f. multicoloured . . 1·25 1·25

1988.
F398 F **144** 2f.20 red . . . . . . 65 1·75
F399 2f.30 red . . . . . . 95 1·75
F400 2f.50 red . . . . . . 95 1·75
F401 2f.80 red . . . . . . 95 1·75
Nos. F400/1 are inscribed "LA POSTE".

F 145 Bronze Boot
and Mountains

F 146 Players

1988. Archaeology.
F407 F **145** 3f. multicoloured . . 1·25 1·25

1988. Rugby.
F408 F **146** 2f.20 blk, yell & grn 70 2·00

F 147 Enclar Aerial

F 148 Les Escaldes
Hot Spring

1988. Europa. Transport and Communications. Each
green, brown and blue.
F409 2f.20 Type F **147** . . . . 2·10 2·10
F410 3f.60 Hand pointing to map
on screen (tourist
information) . . . . . . 3·00 2·50

1988.
F411 F **148** 2f.20 blue, brn & grn 70 2·00

F 149 Ansalonga Pass

F 150 Pyrenean
Shepherd Dog

1988.
F412 F **149** 2f. blue, green & olive 55 1·75

1988. Nature Protection. Multicoloured.
F413 2f. Type F **150** . . . . . 1·25 1·75
F414 2f.20 Hare . . . . 1·40 1·75

F 151 Fresco, Andorra La Vella Church

1988. Romanesque Art.
F415 F **151** 5f. multicoloured . . 1·40 2·75

F **152** Birds   F **153** Pal

1989. Bicentenary of French Revolution.
F416 F **152** 2f.20 violet, blk & red   1·00   1·75

1989.
F417 F **153** 2f.20 violet and blue   55   1·75

F **154** The Strong Horse

1989. Europa. Children's Games. Each brown and cream.
F418   2f.20 Type F **154** . . . . .   1·50   1·50
F419   3f.60 The Handkerchief . .   2·10   1·90

F **155** Wounded Soldiers   F **156** Archaeological
                                 Find and St.
                                 Vincent's Chapel,
                                 Enclar

1989. 125th Anniv of International Red Cross.
F420 F **155** 3f.60 brn, blk & red   1·25   2·25

1989. Archaeology.
F421 F **156** 3f. multicoloured . .   1·00   2·25

F **157** Wild Boar

1989. Nature Protection.
F422 F **157** 2f.20 blk, grn & brn   1·10   1·75
F423   – 3f.60 blk, grn & dp
                 grn . . . .   1·40   2·25
DESIGN: 3f.60, Palmate newt.

F **158** Retable of St. Michael de la
Mosquera, Encamp

1989.
F424 F **158** 5f. multicoloured . .   2·00   2·75

F **159** La Margineda Bridge

1990.
F425 F **159** 2f.30 blue, brn & turq   55   1·75

F **160** Llorts Iron Ore Mines

1990.
F426 F **160** 3f.20 multicoloured   80   2·00

F **161** Exterior of Old Post Office,
Andorra La Vella

1990. Europa. Post Office Buildings.
F427 F **161** 2f.30 red and black   1·75   1·40
F428   – 3f.20 violet and red   2·75   1·40
DESIGN: 3f.20, Interior of modern post office.

F **162** Censer, St. Roma's   F **163** Wild Roses
Chapel, Les Bons

1990.
F429 F **162** 3f. multicoloured . .   80   2·00

1990. Nature Protection. Multicoloured.
F430   2f.30 Type F **163**   80   1·75
F431   3f.20 Otter (horiz) . . . .   1·25   2·00

F **164** Tobacco-drying Sheds, Les
Bons

1990.
F432 F **164** 2f.30 yell, blk & red   55   1·75

F **165** Part of Mural from Santa
Coloma Church

1990.
F433 F **165** 5f. multicoloured . .   1·75   2·50

1990. Birth Centenary of Charles de Gaulle (French statesman). As Nos. F243/4 but values and inscriptions changed.
F434 F **52** 2f.30 blue . . . . . .   1·75   1·75
F435   3f.20 red . . . .   2·00   2·00

F **166** Coin from St. Eulalia's
Church, Encamp

1990.
F436 F **166** 3f.20 multicoloured   70   2·00

F **167** Chapel of Sant Roma   F **168** Emblem
Dels Vilars   and Track

1991.
F437 F **167** 2f.50 blue, blk & grn   75   1·75

1991. 4th European Small States Games.
F438 F **168** 2f.50 multicoloured   80   1·75

F **169** Television   F **170** Bottles
Satellite

1991. Europa. Europe in Space. Multicoloured.
F439   2f.50 Type F **169** . . . . .   1·75   1·50
F440   3f.50 Globe, telescope and
                 eye (horiz) . . . .   2·75   2·00

1991. Artefacts from Tomb of St. Vincent of Enclar.
F441 F **170** 3f.20 multicoloured   80   1·00

F **171** Sheep

1991. Nature Protection.
F442 F **171** 2f.50 brown, bl & blk   1·40   1·75
F443   – 3f.50 brn, mve & blk   1·50   1·75
DESIGN: 3f.50, Pyrenean cow.

F **172** Players

1991. World Petanque Championship, Engordany.
F444 F **172** 2f.50 blk, bistre & red   1·10   1·10

F **173** Mozart, Quartet and Organ
Pipes

1991. Death Bicentenary of Wolfgang Amadeus Mozart (composer).
F445 F **173** 3f.40 blue, blk & turq   1·75   2·00

1991. As Type F **115** but inscr "LA POSTE".
F446 F **115** 2f.20 green   85   1·60
F447   2f.40 green   85   1·75
F448   2f.50 red   85   1·75
F449   2f.70 green   70   1·75
F450   2f.80 red   85   1·75
F451   3f. red   70   1·90

F **174** "Virgin of the Remedy   F **175** Slalom
of Sant Julia and Sant
Germa"

1991.
F455 F **174** 5f. multicoloured . .   1·00   2·10

1992. Winter Olympic Games, Albertville. Mult.
F456   2f.50 Type F **175**   80   80
F457   3f.40 Figure skating . . . .   1·25   1·25

F **176** St. Andrew's Church, Arinsal

1992.
F458 F **176** 2f.50 black and buff   60   90

F **177** Navigation Instrument   F **178** Canoeing
and Columbus's Fleet

1992. Europa. 500th Anniv of Discovery of America by Columbus. Multicoloured.
F459   2f.50 Type F **177** . . . .   2·75   1·90
F460   3f.40 Fleet, Columbus and
                 Amerindians . . . . . .   4·25   3·00

1992. Olympic Games, Barcelona. Multicoloured.
F461   2f.50 Type F **178**   80   80
F462   3f.40 Shooting . . . .   1·25   1·25

F **179** Globe   F **180** "Martyrdom of St.
Flowers   Eulalia" (altarpiece, St.
                     Eulalia's Church, Encamp)

1992. Nature Protection. Multicoloured.
F463   2f.50 Type F **179**   60   90
F464   3f.40 Griffon vulture ("El
                 Voltor") (horiz) . . . .   1·25   1·25

1992.
F465 F **180** 4f. multicoloured . .   90   1·40

F **181** "Ordino Arcalis 91" (Mauro
Staccioli)

1992. Modern Sculpture. Multicoloured.
F466   5f. Type F **181** . . . . .   1·90   1·90
F467   5f. "Storm in a Teacup"
                 (Dennis Oppenheim)
                 (horiz) . . . .   1·90   1·90

F **182** Grau Roig   F **183** "Estructures
                         Autogeneradores" (Jorge du
                         Bon)

1993. Ski Resorts. Multicoloured.
F468   2f.50 Type F **182** . . . .   1·00   1·00
F469   2f.50 Ordino . . . . . .   1·00   1·00
F470   2f.50 Soldeu el Tarter . . . .   1·00   1·00
F471   3f.40 Pal . . . .   1·00   1·00
F472   3f.40 Arinsal . . . .   1·00   1·00

1993. Europa. Contemporary Art.
F473 F **183** 2f.50 dp bl, bl & vio   65   1·00
F474   3f.40 multicoloured   80   1·25
DESIGN—HORIZ: 3f.40, "Fisicromia per Andorra" (Carlos Cruz-Diez).

F 184 Common Blue   F 185 Cyclist

1993. Nature Protection. Butterflies. Multicoloured.
F475   2f.50 Type F 184   70   1·00
F476   4f.20 "Nymphalidae" . . .   1·10   1·50

1993. Tour de France Cycling Road Race.
F477   F 185   2f.50 multicoloured   70   1·00

F 186 Smiling Hands

1993. 10th Anniv of Andorran School.
F478   F 186   2f.80 multicoloured   80   1·10

F 187 "A Pagan Place" (Michael Warren)

1993. Modern Sculpture.
F479   F 187   5f. black and blue . .   2·10   1·75
F480   – 5f. multicoloured . .   2·10   1·75
DESIGN: No. F480, "Pep, Lu, Canolic, Ton, Meritxell, Roma, Anna, Pau, Carles, Eugenia,...and Others" (Erik Dietman).

F 188 Cross-country Skiing   F 189 Constitution Monument

1994. Winter Olympic Games, Lillehammer, Norway.
F481   F 188   3f.70 multicoloured   1·10   1·25

1994. 1st Anniv of New Constitution.
F482   F 189   2f.80 multicoloured   80   85
F483   – 3f.70 blk, yell & mve   1·10   1·40
DESIGN: 3f.70, Stone tablet.

F 190 AIDS Virus

1994. Europa. Discoveries and Inventions. Mult.
F484   2f.80 Type F 190   80   80
F485   3f.70 Radio mast . . . . .   1·10   1·10

F 191 Competitors' Flags and Football   F 192 Horse Riding

1994. World Cup Football Championship, U.S.A.
F486   F 191   3f.70 multicoloured   1·10   1·25

1994. Tourist Activities. Multicoloured.
F487   2f.80 Type F 192   90   90
F488   2f.80 Mountain biking . . .   90   90

F489   2f.80 Climbing   90   90
F490   2f.80 Fishing   90   90

F 193 Scarce Swallowtail   F 194 "26 10 93"

1994. Nature Protection. Butterflies. Multicoloured.
F491   2f.80 Type F 193 . . . . .   1·25   1·25
F492   4f.40 Small tortoiseshell . .   1·75   1·75

1994. Meeting of Co-princes.
F493   F 194   2f.80 multicoloured   90   1·00

F 195 Emblem   F 196 Globe, Goal and Player

1995. European Nature Conservation Year.
F494   F 195   2f.80 multicoloured   90   1·00

1995. 3rd World Cup Rugby Championship, South Africa.
F495   F 196   2f.80 multicoloured   90   1·00

F 197 Dove and Olive Twig ("Peace")

1995. Europa. Peace and Freedom. Multicoloured.
F496   2f.80 Type F 197 . . . . .   1·10   1·10
F497   3f.70 Flock of doves ("Freedom") . . . . . .   1·25   1·25

F 198 Emblem

1995. 15th Anniv of Caritas Andorrana (welfare organization).
F498   F 198   2f.80 multicoloured   90   75

F 199 Caldea Thermal Baths, Les Escaldes-Engordany

1995.
F499   F 199   2f.80 multicoloured   90   75

F 200 National Auditorium, Ordino

1995.
F500   F 200   3f.70 black and buff   1·25   1·00

F 201 "Virgin of Meritxell"

1995.
F501   F 201   4f.40 multicoloured   1·25   1·50

F 202 Brimstone   F 203 National Flag over U.N. Emblem

1995. Nature Protection. Butterflies. Multicoloured.
F502   2f.80 Type F 202 . . . . .   1·10   1·10
F503   3f.70 Marbled white (horiz)   1·75   1·50

1995. 50th Anniv of U.N.O. Multicoloured.
F504   2f.80 Type F 203   95   1·00
F505   3f.70 Anniversary emblem over flag . . . .   1·25   1·25

F 204 National Flag and Palace of Europe, Strasbourg

1995. Admission of Andorra to Council of Europe.
F506   F 204   2f.80 multicoloured   95   1·00

F 205 Emblem   F 206 Basketball

1996. 4th Borrufa Trophy Skiing Competition.
F507   F 205   2f.80 multicoloured   95   1·00

1996.
F508   F 206   3f.70 red, blk & yell   1·25   1·25

F 207 Children

1996. 25th Anniv of Our Lady of Meritxell Special School.
F509   F 207   2f.80 multicoloured   95   1·00

F 208 European Robin

1996. Nature Protection. Multicoloured.
F510   3f. Type F 208 . . . . .   1·10   1·10
F511   3f.80 Great tit . . . . . .   1·40   1·40

F 209 Cross, St. James's Church, Engordany   F 210 Ermessenda de Castellbo

1996. Religious Objects. Multicoloured.
F512   3f. Type F 209   80   95
F513   3f.80 Censer, St. Eulalia's Church, Encamp (horiz)   1·00   1·25

1996. Europa. Famous Women.
F514   F 210   3f. multicoloured . .   1·25   1·25

F 211 Chessmen   F 212 Canillo

1996. Chess.
F515   F 211   4f.50 red, black & bl   1·50   1·60

1996. No value expressed. Self-adhesive.
F516   F 212   (3f.) multicoloured . .   1·10   1·10

F 213 Cycling, Running and Throwing the Javelin

1996. Olympic Games, Atlanta.
F517   F 213   3f. multicoloured . . .   1·10   1·10

F 214 Singers

1996. 5th Anniv of National Youth Choir.
F518   F 214   3f. multicoloured . . .   1·10   1·10

F 215 Man and Boy with Animals

1996. Livestock Fair.
F519   F 215   3f. yellow, red & black . . . .   1·10   1·10

 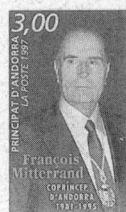

F 216 St. Roma's Chapel, Les Bons   F 217 Mitterrand

1996. Churches. Multicoloured.
F520   6f.70 Type F 216 . . . . .   2·10   2·10
F521   6f.70 Santa Coloma . . . .   2·10   2·10

1997. Francois Mitterrand (President of France and Co-prince of Andorra, 1981–95) Commemoration.
F522   F 217   3f. multicoloured . .   1·00   1·00

F 218 Parish Emblem   F 219 Volleyball

1997. Parish of Encamp. No value expressed. Self-adhesive.
F523   F 218   (3f.) blue . . . . . .   1·10   1·10

1997.
F524   F 219   3f. multicoloured . . .   1·00   1·00

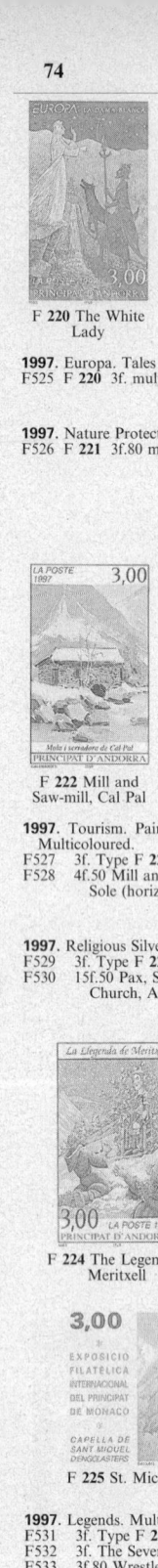

F **220** The White Lady   F **221** Swallow approaching Nest

1997. Europa. Tales and Legends.
F525 F **220** 3f. multicoloured . .   1·00   1·00

1997. Nature Protection.
F526 F **221** 3f.80 multicoloured   1·25   1·25

F **222** Mill and   F **223** Monstrance, St. Iscle
Saw-mill, Cal Pal   and St. Victoria's Church

1997. Tourism. Paintings by Francesc Galobardes. Multicoloured.
F527   3f. Type F **222** . . . . . .   1·00   95
F528   4f.50 Mill and farmhouse, Sole (horiz) . . . . . .   1·50   1·50

1997. Religious Silver Work. Multicoloured.
F529   3f. Type F **223** . . . .   1·25   1·25
F530   15f.50 Pax, St. Peter's Church, Aixirivall . . .   5·00   5·00

F **224** The Legend of   F **226** Harlequin
Meritxell   juggling Candles

F **225** St. Michael's Chapel, Engolasters

1997. Legends. Multicoloured.
F531   3f. Type F **224** . . .   1·00   1·00
F532   3f. The Seven-armed Cross   1·00   1·00
F533   3f.80 Wrestlers (The Fountain of Esmelicat)   1·25   1·25

1997. International Stamp Exn, Monaco.
F534 F **225** 3f. multicoloured . .   1·00   1·00

1998. Birthday Greetings Stamp.
F535 F **226** 3f. multicoloured . .   1·00   1·00

F **227** Super Giant   F **228** Arms of
Slalom   Ordino

1997. Winter Olympic Games, Nagano, Japan.
F536 F **227** 4f.40 multicoloured   1·00   1·00

1998. No value expressed. Self-adhesive.
F537 F **228** (3f.) multicoloured . .   1·00   1·00

F **229** Altarpiece and Vila Church

1998.
F538 F **229** 4f.50 multicoloured   1·50   1·25

F **230** Emblem and Cogwheels

1998. 20th Anniv of Rotary Int in Andorra.
F539 F **230** 3f. multicoloured   95   95

F **231** Chaffinch and Berries   F **232** Players

1998. Nature Protection.
F540 F **231** 3f.80 multicoloured   1·10   1·10

1998. World Cup Football Championship, France.
F541 F **232** 3f. multicoloured   95   95

F **233** Treble Score and Stylized Orchestra

1998. Europa. National Festivals. Music Festival.
F542 F **233** 3f. multicoloured   95   1·10

F **234** River

1998. "Expo '98" World's Fair, Lisbon, Portugal.
F543 F **234** 5f. multicoloured . .   1·50   1·50

F **235** Chalice   F **237** Andorra, 1717

1998. Chalice from the House of the Valleys.
F544 F **235** 4f.50 multicoloured   95   95

1998. French Victory in World Cup Football Championship. No. F541 optd **FINAL FRANCA/ BRASIL 3-0.**
F545 F **232** 3f. multicoloured . .   65   65

1998. Relief Maps. Multicoloured.
F546   3f. Type F **237**   65   65
F547   15f.50 Andorra, 1777 (horiz) . . . . . .   3·25   3·25

F **238** Museum

1998. Inauguration of Postal Museum.
F548 F **238** 3f. multicoloured . .   65   65

F **239** Front Page of First   F **240** Arms of
Edition   La Massana

1998. 250th Anniv of "Manual Digest".
F549 F **239** 3f.80 multicoloured   80   80

1999. No value expressed. Self-adhesive.
F550 F **240** (3f.) multicoloured . .   65   65

F **241** House and Recycling Bins

1999. "Green World". Recycling of Waste.
F551 F **241** 5f. multicoloured . .   1·00   1·00

F **242** Vall de Sorteny (½-size illustration)

1999. Europa. Parks and Gardens.
F552 F **242** 3f. multicoloured . .   60   60

F **243** Council Emblem and Seat, Strasbourg

1999. 50th Anniv of Council of Europe.
F553 F **243** 3f.80 multicoloured   75   75

F **244** "The First   F **245** Footballer and
Mail Coach"   Flags

1999.
F554 F **244** 2f.70 multicoloured   55   55

1999. Andorra–France Qualifying Match for European Nations Football Championship.
F555 F **245** 4f.50 multicoloured   90   90

F **246** St. Michael's Church, Engolasters, and Emblem

1999. "Philexfrance 99" International Stamp Exhibition, Paris, France.
F556 F **246** 3f. multicoloured . .   60   60

F **247** Winter Scene

1999. Paintings of Pal by Francesc Galobardes. Multicoloured.
F557   3f. Type F **247**   60   60
F558   Summer scene (horiz) . .   60   60

F **248** Emblem and "50"

1999. 50th Anniv of International Photographic Art Federation.
F559 F **248** 4f.40 multicoloured   85   85

F **249** Rull House, Sispony

1999.
F560 F **249** 15f.50 multicoloured   3·00   3·00

F **250** Chest with Six Locks

1999.
F561 F **250** 6f.70 multicoloured   1·25   1·25

F **251** Angels

1999. Christmas.
F562 F **251** 3f. multicoloured . .   60   60

F **252** Revellers   F **253** Arms of
        La Vella

2000. New Millennium.
F563 F **252** 3f. multicoloured . .   60   60

2000. No value expressed. Self-adhesive.
F564 F **253** (3f.) multicoloured . .   55   55

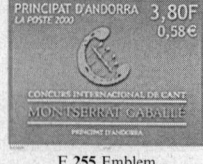

F **254** Snow   F **255** Emblem
Boarder

2000.
F565 F **254** 4f.50 blue, brown and black   80   80

2000. Montserrat Caballe International Opera Competition, Saint Julia de Loria.
F566 F **255** 3f.80 yellow and blue   70   70

F **256** *Campanula*   F **257** "Building
cochleariifolia   Europe"

2000.
F567 F **256** 2f.70 multicoloured   50   50

2000. Europa.
F568 F **257** 3f. multicoloured . .   55   55

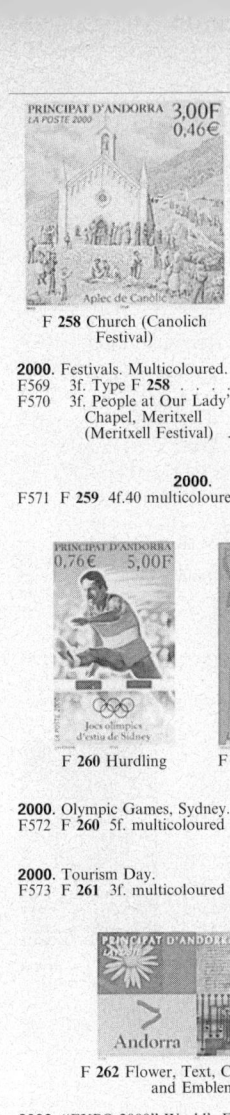

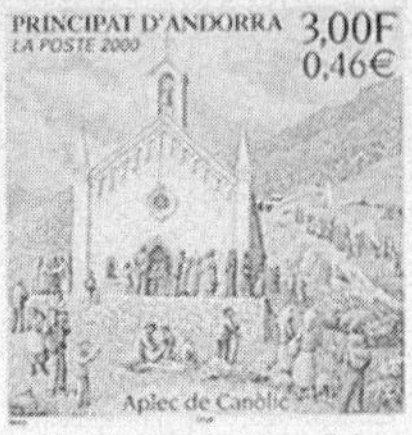
F **258** Church (Canolich Festival)

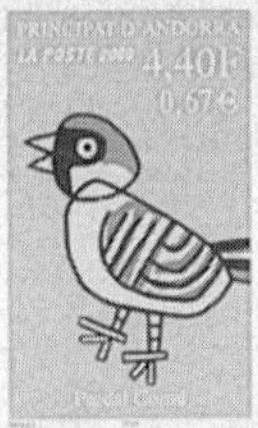
F **259** Sparrow

2000. Festivals. Multicoloured.

F569	3f. Type F **258**	55	55
F570	3f. People at Our Lady's Chapel, Meritxell (Meritxell Festival)	55	55

2000.

F571	F **259** 4f.40 multicoloured	80	80

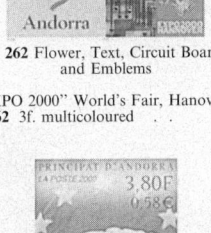

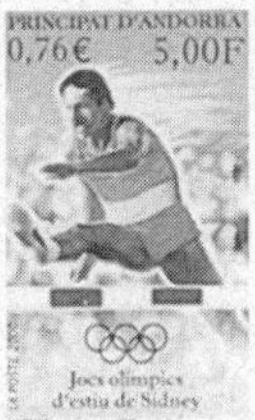
F **260** Hurdling

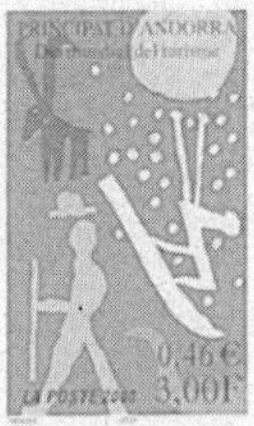
F **261** Goat, Skier and Walker

2000. Olympic Games, Sydney.

F572	F **260** 5f. multicoloured	1·10	1·10

2000. Tourism Day.

F573	F **261** 3f. multicoloured	75	75

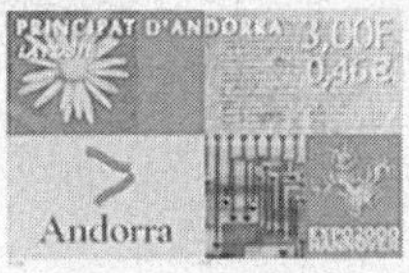
F **262** Flower, Text, Circuit Board and Emblems

2000. "EXPO 2000" World's Fair, Hanover.

F574	F **262** 3f. multicoloured	75	75

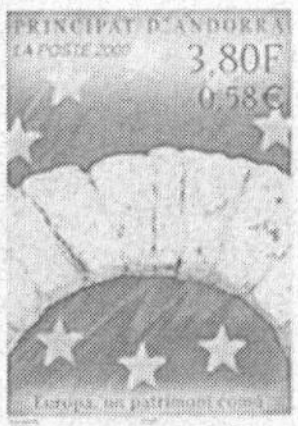
F **263** Stone Arch and Flag

2000. European Community.

F575	F **263** 3f.80 multicoloured	85	85

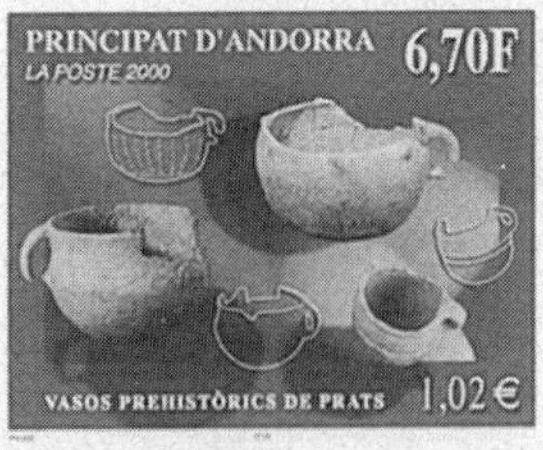
F **264** Pottery

2000. Prehistoric Pottery.

F576	F **264** 6f.70 multicoloured	1·60	1·60

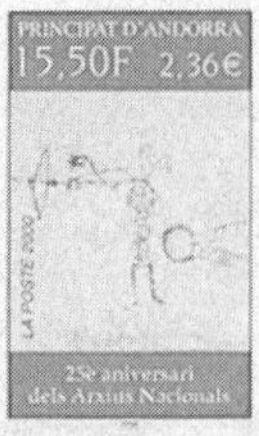
F **265** Drawing

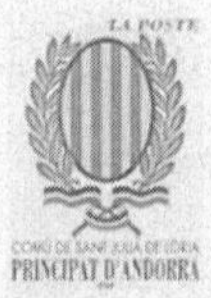
F **266** Arms of Saint Julia de Loria

2000. 25th Anniv of National Archives.

F577	F **265** 15f.50 multicoloured	3·25	3·25

2001. No value expressed. Self-adhesive.

F578	F **266** (3f.) multicoloured	75	75

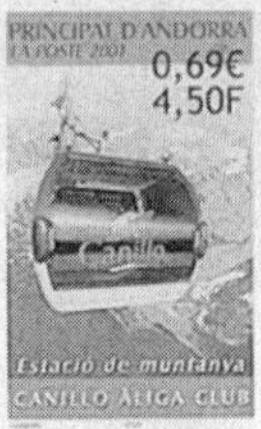
F **267** Ski Lift

2001. Canillo Aliga Club.

F579	F **267** 4f.50 multicoloured	1·10	1·10

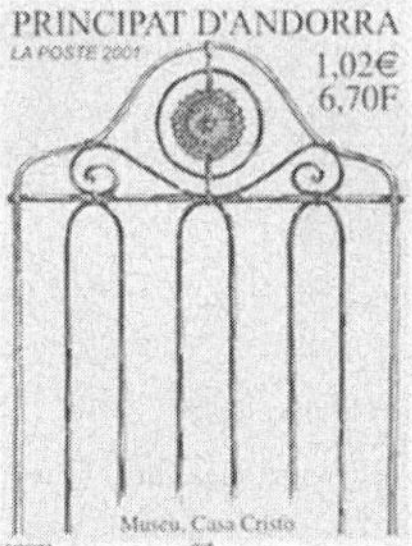
F **268** Decorative Metalwork

2001. Casa Cristo Museum.

F580	F **268** 6f.70 multicoloured	1·60	1·60

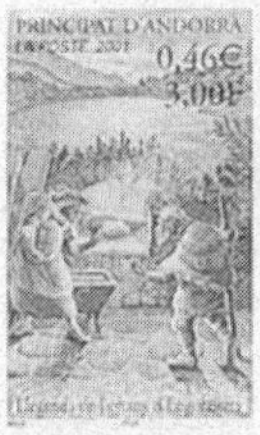
F **269** Legend of Lake Engolasters

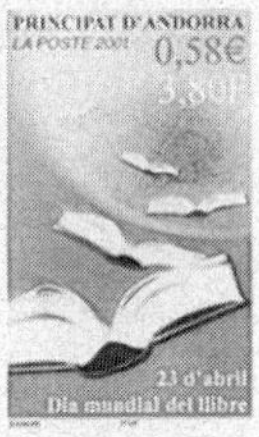
F **270** Globe and Books

2001. Legends. Multicoloured.

F581	3f. Type F **269**	75	75
F582	3f. Lords before King (foundation of Andorra)	75	75

2001. World Book Day.

F583	F **270** 3f.80 multicoloured	85	85

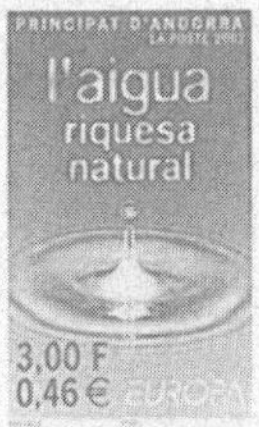
F **271** Water Splash

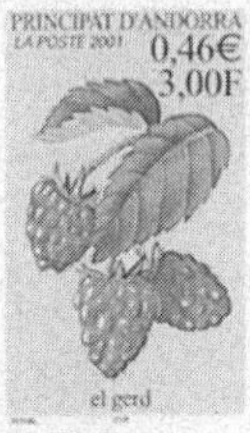
F **272** Raspberry

2001. Europa. Water Resources.

F584	F **271** 3f. multicoloured	75	75

2001. Multicoloured.

F585	3f. Type F **272**	75	75
F586	4f.40 Jay (horiz)	1·10	1·10

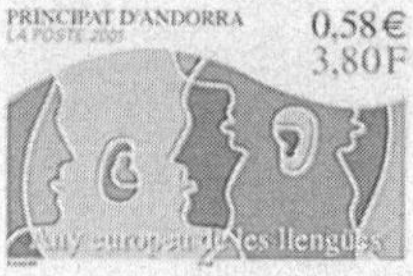
F **273** Profiles talking

2001. European Year of Languages.

F587	F **273** 3f.80 multicoloured	95	95

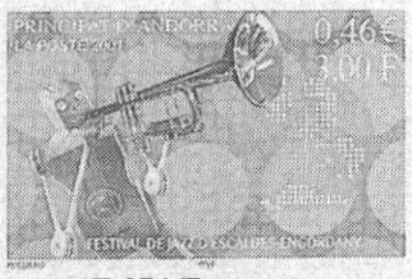
F **274** Trumpeter

2001. Jazz Festival, Escaldes-Engordany.

F588	F **274** 3f. multicoloured	55	55

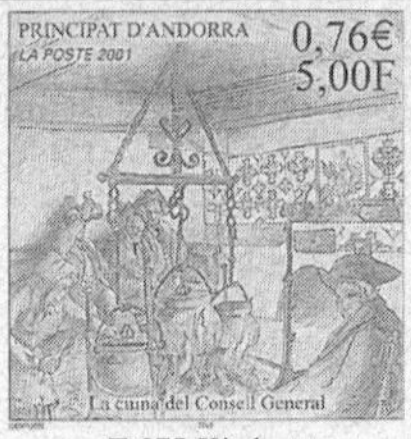
F **275** Kitchen

2001.

F589	F **275** 5f. multicoloured	95	95

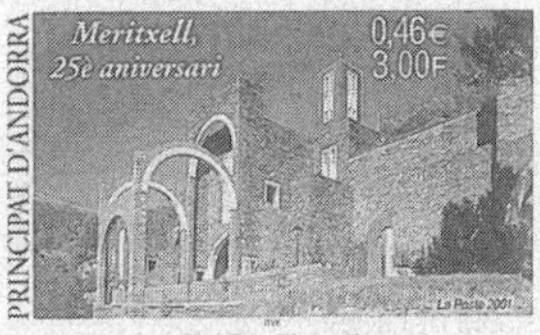
F **276** Chapel

2001. 25th Anniv of Chapel of Our Lady, Meritxell.

F590	F **276** 3f. multicoloured	55	55

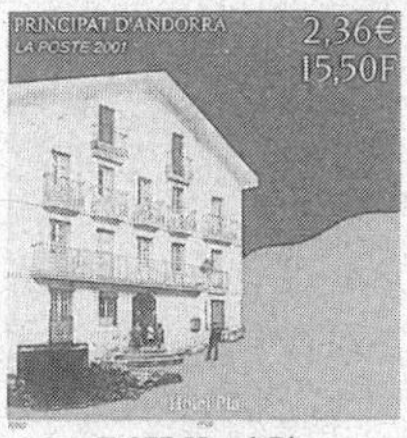
F **277** Hotel Pla

2001.

F591	F **277** 15f. 50 black, violet and green	3·25	3·25

POSTAGE DUE STAMPS

1931. Postage Due stamps of France optd **ANDORRE**.

FD24	D **11** 5c. blue	90	2·75
FD25	10c. brown	80	2·75
FD26	30c. red	65	2·75
FD27	50c. purple	1·00	2·75
FD28	60c. green	22·00	20·00
FD29	1f. brown on yellow	1·00	3·00
FD30	2f. mauve	11·00	10·00
FD31	3f. mauve	1·50	4·00

1931. Postage Due stamps of France optd **ANDORRE**.

FD32	D **43** 1c. green	55	3·75
FD33	10c. red	4·00	9·50
FD34	60c. red	20·00	35·00
FD35	1f. green	70·00	85·00
FD36	1f.20 on 2f. blue	50·00	£100
FD37	2f. brown	£130	£140
FD38	5f. on 1f. purple	60·00	£100

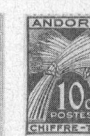

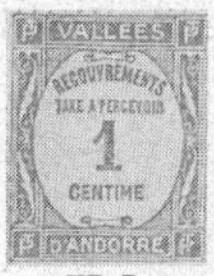
FD **7**

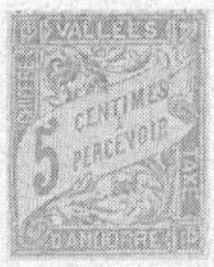
FD **10**

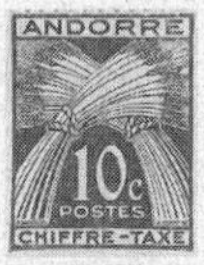
FD **11** Wheat Sheaves

1935.

FD82	FD **7** 1c. green	1·40	4·25

1937.

FD 97	FD **10** 5c. blue	5·50	12·00
FD 98	10c. brown	3·25	12·00
FD 99	2f. mauve	7·75	8·75
FD100	5f. orange	14·50	18·00

1943.

FD101a	FD **11** 10c. brown	1·00	2·75
FD102	30c. mauve	2·50	3·00
FD103	50c. green	1·00	3·00
FD104	1f. blue	2·50	2·75
FD105	1f.50 red	5·25	6·25
FD106	2f. blue	2·50	3·00
FD107	3f. red	2·75	3·75
FD108	4f. violet	3·25	4·25
FD109	5f. mauve	4·75	5·75
FD110	10f. orange	5·25	5·75
FD111	20f. brown	4·25	3·00

1946. As Type FD **11**, but inscr "TIMBRE-TAXE".

FD143	10c. brown	25	2·75
FD144	1f. blue	1·00	2·75
FD145	2f. blue	80	2·75
FD146	3f. brown	1·75	4·00
FD147	4f. violet	2·25	4·50
FD148	5f. red	1·25	3·75
FD149	10f. orange	2·00	5·00
FD150	20f. brown	6·00	12·00
FD151	50f. green	30·00	35·00
FD152	100f. green	£100	£110

1961. As Nos. FD143/52 but new values and colours.

FD185	5c. red	3·00	5·00
FD186	10c. orange	6·00	10·00
FD187	20c. brown	15·00	15·00
FD188	50c. green	23·00	25·00

1964. Designs as Nos. D1650/6 of France, but inscr "ANDORRE".

FD192	5c. red, green and purple	40	1·60
FD193	10c. blue, green and purple	60	1·60
FD194	15c. red, green and brown	1·10	1·60
FD195	20c. purple, green & turq	65	1·75
FD196	30c. blue, green and brown	70	45
FD197	40c. yellow, red and green	1·10	55
FD198	50c. red, green and blue	1·25	55

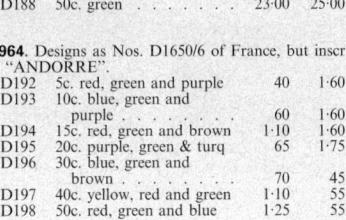

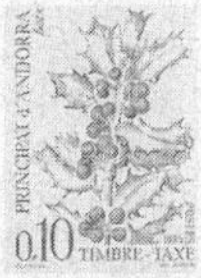
FD **129** Holly Berries

1985. Fruits.

FD371	FD **129** 10c. red and green	80	1·40
FD372	– 20c. brown & blue	80	1·40
FD373	– 30c. green and red	80	1·40
FD374	– 40c. brown & blk	85	1·40
FD375	– 50c. olive & violet	90	1·40
FD376	– 1f. green and blue	1·00	1·60
FD377	– 2f. red and brown	1·25	1·75
FD378	– 3f. purple & green	1·60	2·00
FD379	– 4f. olive and blue	1·75	2·50
FD380	– 5f. olive and red	2·25	3·00

DESIGNS: 20c. Wild plum; 30c. Raspberry; 40c. Dogberry; 50c. Blackberry; 1f. Juniper; 2f. Rose hip; 3f. Elder; 4f. Bilberry; 5f. Strawberry.

SPANISH POST OFFICES

1928. 100 centimos = 1 peseta.
2002. 100 cents = 1 euro.

1928. Stamps of Spain optd **CORREOS ANDORRA**.

1	**68** 2c. green	45	60
2	5c. red	75	2·00
3	10c. green	1·25	2·75
5	15c. blue	1·60	1·90
6	20c. violet	1·60	1·90
7	25c. red	2·75	3·00
8	30c. brown	9·25	12·00
9	40c. blue	11·00	12·00
10	50c. orange	12·00	14·00
11	**69** 1p. grey	15·00	19·00
12	4p. red	90·00	£110
13	10p. brown	£120	£130

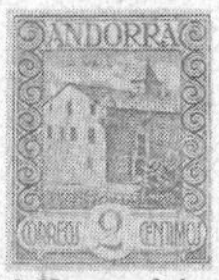
2 House of the Valleys

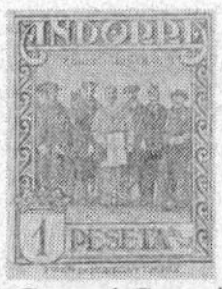
3 General Council of Andorra

1929.

14	**2** 2c. green	1·00	1·00
26	2c. brown	1·00	1·00
15	– 5c. purple	2·00	2·25
27	– 5c. brown	1·25	1·25
16	– 10c. green	2·00	2·25
17	– 15c. blue	2·75	2·50
30	– 15c. green	3·50	3·50
18	– 20c. violet	2·50	3·25
33	– 25c. red	1·50	1·50
20	**2** 30c. brown	70·00	70·00
34	30c. red	1·50	2·00
21	– 40c. blue	4·50	4·50
36	**2** 45c. red	1·00	1·00
22	– 50c. orange	4·50	4·50
38	**2** 60c. blue	3·00	3·00
23	**3** 1p. slate	12·00	16·00
39	4p. purple	45·00	45·00
40	10p. brown	45·00	45·00

DESIGNS: 5, 40c. Church of St. John of Caselles; 10, 20, 50c. Sant Julia de Loria; 15, 25c. Santa Coloma Church.

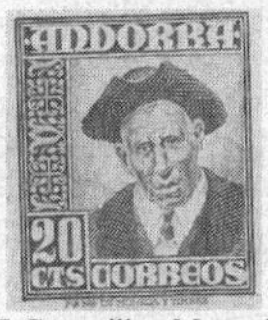
7 Councillor Manuel Areny Bons

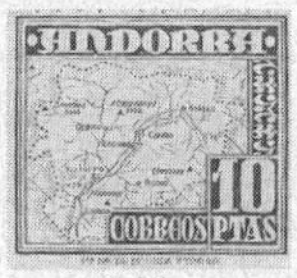
11 Map

1948.

41	F 2c. olive	50	1·00
42	5c. orange	50	1·00
43	10c. blue	50	1·00
44	**7** 20c. purple	4·50	3·25
45	25c. orange	4·50	1·75
46	G 30c. green	12·00	4·00
47	H 50c. green	16·00	7·00
48	I 75c. blue	14·00	8·00
49	H 90c. purple	2·00	3·00
50	I 1p. red	14·00	4·00
51	G 1p.35 violet	7·00	7·50
52	**11** 4p. blue	11·00	12·00
53	10p. brown	20·00	13·00

DESIGNS—VERT: F. Edelweiss; G. Arms; H. Market Place, Ordino; I. Shrine near Meritxell Chapel.

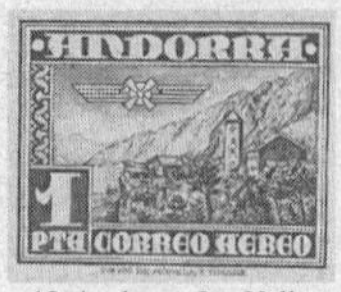

12 Andorra La Vella

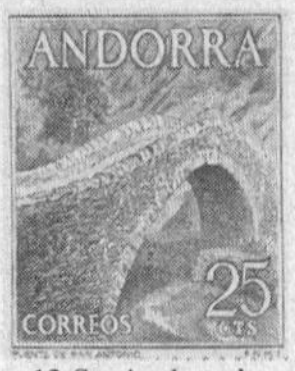

13 St. Anthony's Bridge

1951. Air.
54 **12** 1p. brown . . . . 18·00 13·50

1963.
55 **13** 25c. brown and black . . . 20 20
56 – 70c. black and green 25 35
57 – 1p. lilac and grey 30 55
58 – 2p. violet and lilac 50 75
59 – 2p.50 deep red and purple 35 90
60 – 3p. slate and black . . . . 75 1·10
61 – 5p. purple and brown . . . 2·10 2·00
62 – 6p. red and brown . . . . 2·75 2·25
DESIGNS—VERT: 70c. Anyos meadows (wrongly inscr "AYNOS"); 1p. Canillo; 2p. Santa Coloma Church; 2p.50, Arms; 6p. Virgin of Meritxell. HORIZ: 3p. Andorra la Vella; 5p. Ordino.

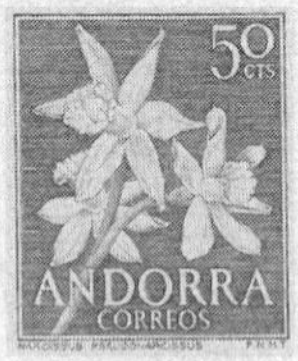

14 Daffodills

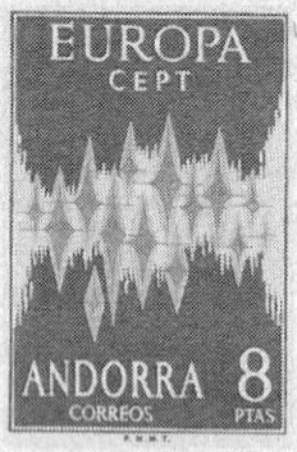

15 "Communications"

1966. Pyrenean Flowers.
63 **14** 50c. blue and slate 10 45
64 – 1p. purple and brown . . . 1·25 85
65 – 5p. blue and green . . . . 2·00 2·00
66 – 10p. slate and violet . . . . 1·00 1·60
DESIGNS: 1p. Carnation; 5p. Narcissus; 10p. Anemone (wrongly inscr "HELEBORUS CONI").

1972. Europa.
67 **15** 8p. multicoloured . . . . . £100 85·00

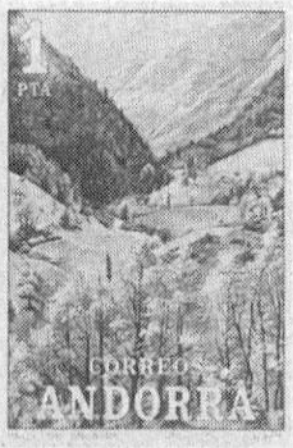

16 Encamp Valley

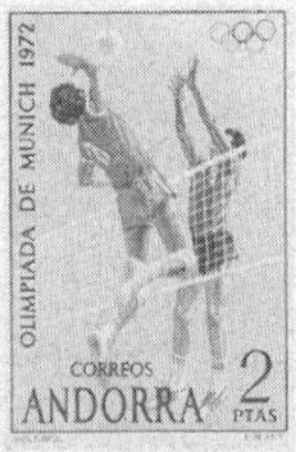

17 Volleyball

1972. Tourist Views. Multicoloured.
68 1p. Type **16** 50 55
69 1p.50 La Massana 60 55
70 2p. Skis and snowscape, Pas de la Casa . . . . 1·25 1·10
71 5p. Lake Pessons (horiz) . . . 1·50 1·10

1972. Olympic Games, Munich. Multicoloured.
72 2p. Type **17** 35 35
73 5p. Swimming (horiz) 45 55

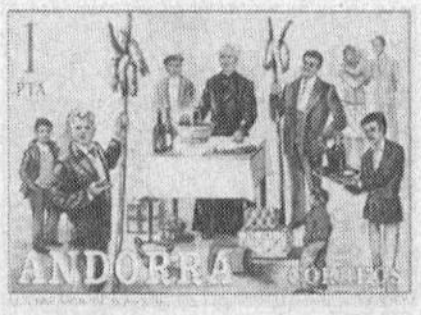

18 St. Anthony's Auction

1972. Andorran Customs. Multicoloured.
74 1p. Type **18** 20 25
75 1p.50 "Les Caramelles" (choir) 25 25
76 2p. Nativity play (Christmas) 25 35
77 5p. Giant cigar (vert) 70 55
78 8p. Carved shrine, Meritxell (vert) 90 75
79 15p. "La Marratxa" (dance) 1·60 1·50

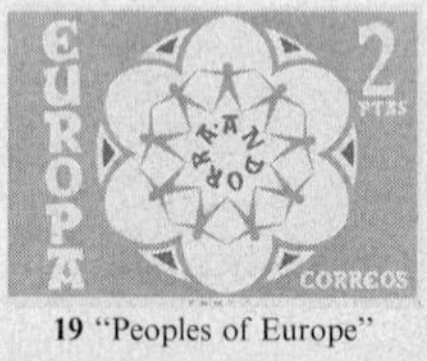

19 "Peoples of Europe"

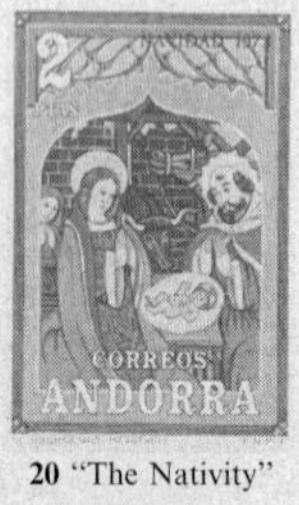

20 "The Nativity"

1973. Europa.
80 **19** 2p. black, red and blue . . 25 35
81 – 8p. red, brown and black . . 75 80
DESIGN: 8p. Europa "Posthorn".

1973. Christmas. Frescoes from Meritxell Chapel. Multicoloured.
82 2p. Type **20** 25 35
83 5p. "Adoration of the Kings" 70 1·10

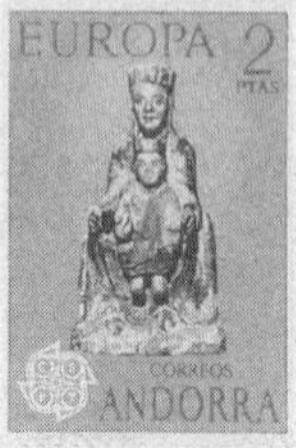

21 "Virgin of Ordino"

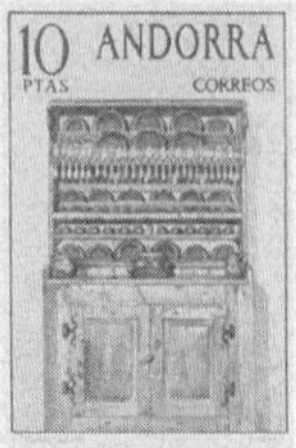

22 Oak Cupboard and Shelves

1974. Europa. Sculptures. Multicoloured.
84 2p. Type **21** . . . . 1·50 1·40
85 8p. Cross . . . . 2·50 2·75

1974. Arts and Crafts. Multicoloured.
86 10p. Type **22** . . . . 2·00 2·25
87 25p. Crown of the Virgin of the Roses . . . . 3·00 3·25

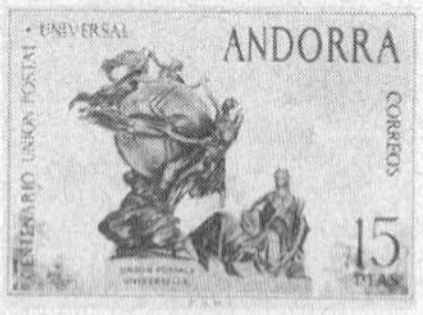

23 U.P.U. Monument, Berne

1974. Centenary of Universal Postal Union.
88 **23** 15p. multicoloured . . . . 1·40 1·60

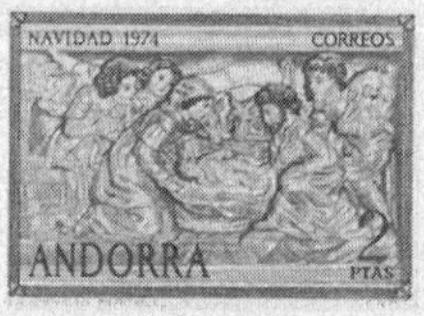

24 "The Nativity"

1974. Christmas. Carvings from Meritxell Chapel. Multicoloured.
89 2p. Type **24** . . . . 75 1·00
90 5p. "Adoration of the Kings" 1·60 1·25

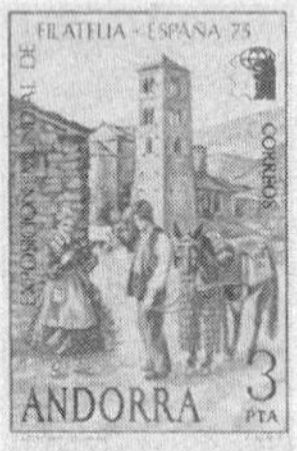

25 19th-century Postman and Church of St. John of Caselles

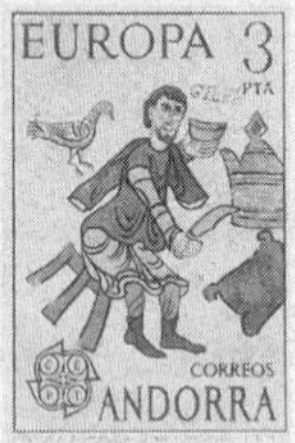

26 "Peasant with Knife"

1975. "Espana 75" Int Stamp Exhibition, Madrid.
91 **25** 3p. multicoloured 30 45

1975. Europa. 12th-century Romanesque Paintings from La Cortinada Church. Multicoloured.
92 3p. Type **26** . . . . 1·40 1·60
93 12p. "Christ" . . . . 2·50 3·25

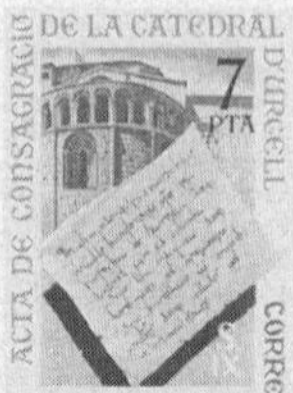

27 Cathedral and Consecration Text

1975. 1100th Anniv of Consecration of Urgel Cathedral.
94 **27** 7p. multicoloured . . . . . 1·25 1·25

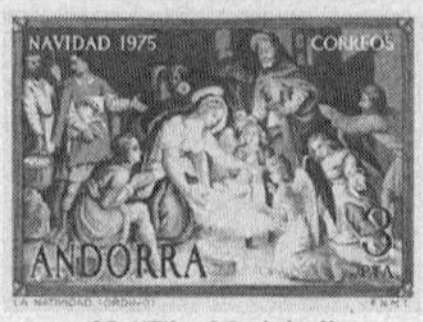

28 "The Nativity"

1975. Christmas. Paintings from La Cortinada Church. Multicoloured.
95 3p. Type **28** 35 40
96 7p. "Adoration of The Kings" 50 70

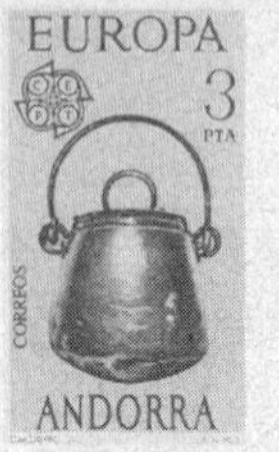

29 Copper Cauldron

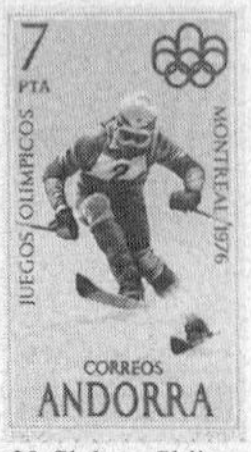

30 Slalom Skiing

1976. Europa. Multicoloured.
97 3p. Type **29** 25 45
98 12p. Wooden marriage chest (horiz) 90 90

1976. Olympic Games, Montreal. Multicoloured.
99 7p. Type **30** 25 40
100 15p. Canoeing (horiz) 65 85

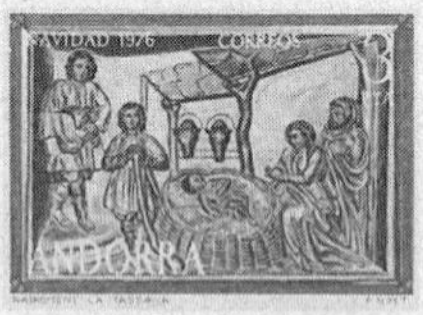

31 "The Nativity"

1976. Christmas. Carvings from La Massana Church. Multicoloured.
101 3p. Type **31** 10 20
102 25p. "Adoration of the Kings" . . . . 65 1·10

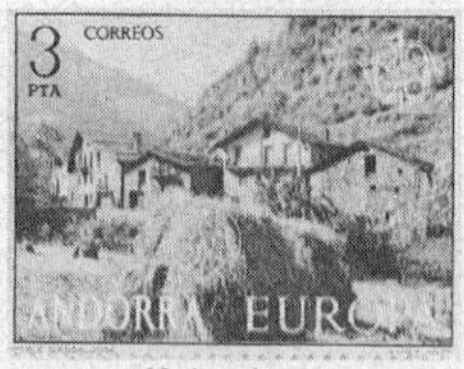

32 Ansalonga

1977. Europa. Multicoloured.
103 3p. Type **32** 20 30
104 12p. Xuclar 60 75

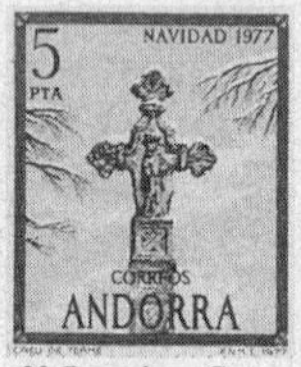

33 Boundary Cross

1977. Christmas. Multicoloured.
105 5p. Type **33** 25 35
106 12p. St. Michael's Church, Engolasters . . . . 65 1·00

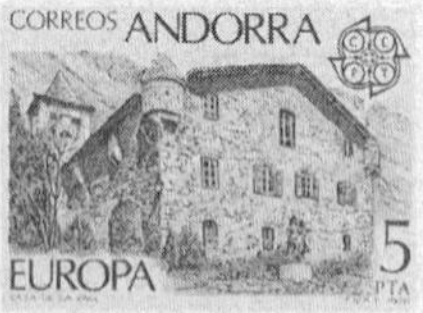

35 House of the Valleys

1978. Europa. Multicoloured.
108 5p. Type **35** 20 30
109 12p. Church of St. John of Caselles 50 70

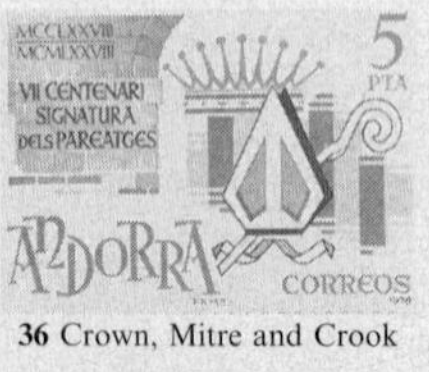

36 Crown, Mitre and Crook

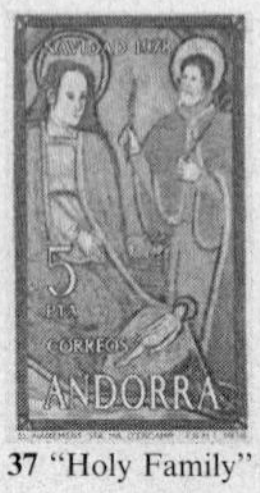

37 "Holy Family"

1978. 700th Anniv of Parity Treaties.
110 **36** 5p. multicoloured 40 55

1978. Christmas. Frescoes in St. Mary's Church, Encamp. Multicoloured.
111 5p. Type **37** 15 25
112 25p. "Adoration of the Kings" 45 55

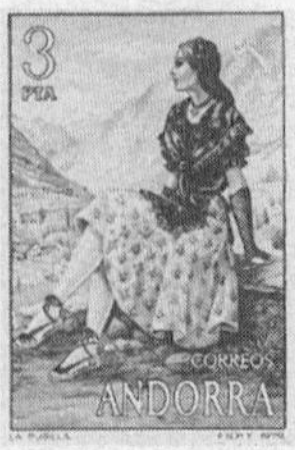

38 Young Woman's Costume

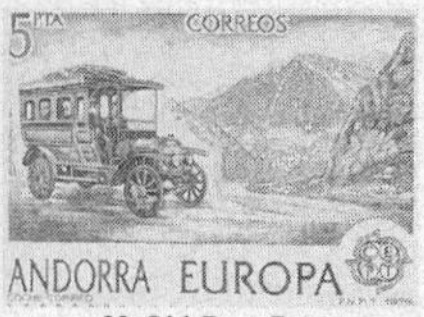

39 Old Post Bus

1979. Local Costumes. Multicoloured.
113 3p. Type **38** 15 15
114 5p. Young man's costume . . 15 25
115 12p. Newly-weds 30 35

1979. Europa.
116 **39** 5p. green & blue on yellow 25 25
117 – 12p. lilac and red on yellow 65 70
DESIGN: 12p. Pre-stamp letters.

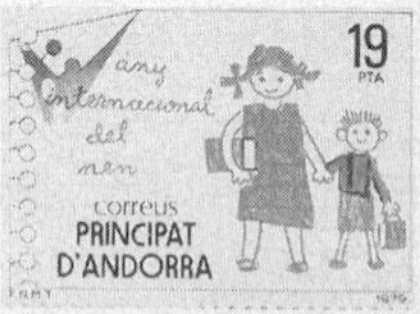

40 Drawing of Boy and Girl

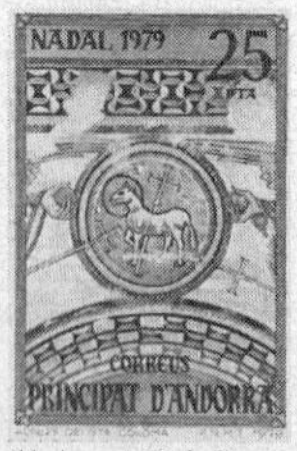

41 Agnus Dei, Santa Coloma Church

1979. International Year of the Child.
118 **40** 19p. blue, red and black 40 55

1979. Christmas. Multicoloured.
119 **41** 8p. Santa Coloma Church 20 25
120 25p. Type **41** 40 55

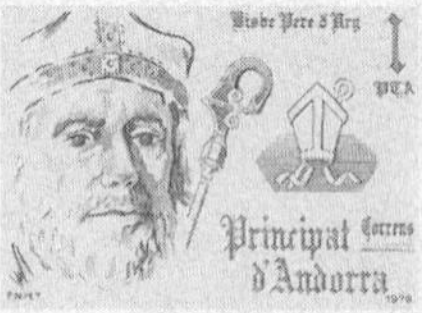

42 Pere d'Urg

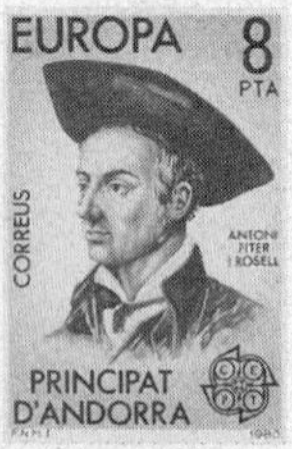

43 Antoni Fiter i Rosell

1979. Bishops of Urgel, Co-princes of Andorra (1st series).
121 **42** 1p. blue and brown 10 10
122 – 5p. red and violet 10 20
123 – 13p. brown and green . . . 20 35
DESIGNS: 5p. Joseph Caixal; 13p. Joan Benlloch.
See also Nos. 137/8, 171, 182 and 189.

1980. Europa.
124 **43** 8p. brown, ochre and green 20 25
125 – 19p. black, green & dp grn 50 55
DESIGN: 19p. Francesc Cairat i Freixes.

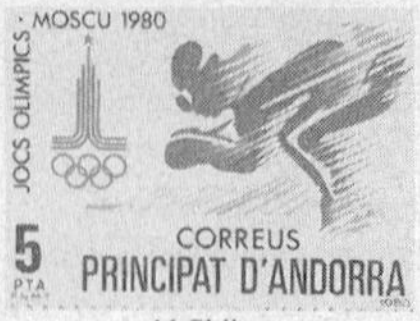

44 Skiing

1980. Olympic Games, Moscow.
126 **44** 5p. turquoise, red and blk 10 25
127 – 8p. multicoloured 10 25
128 – 50p. multicoloured 50 80
DESIGNS: 8p. Boxing; 50p. Shooting.

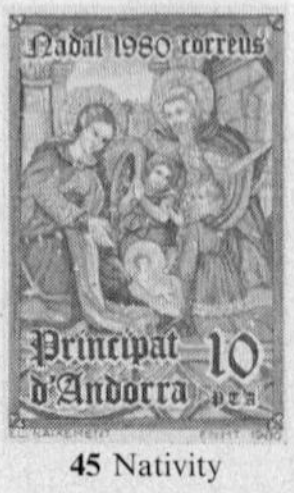

45 Nativity

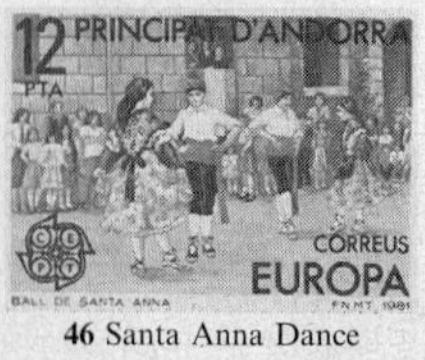

46 Santa Anna Dance

1980. Christmas. Multicoloured.
129   10p. Type **45**   15   25
130   22p. Epiphany   25   55

1981. Europa. Multicoloured.
131   12p. Type **46**   25   50
132   30p. Festival of the Virgin of
         Canolich   55   55

47 Militia Members

1981. 50th Anniv of People's Militia.
133 **47** 30p. green, grey and black   40   80

48 Handicapped Child learning to Write

1981. International Year of Disabled Persons.
134 **48** 50p. multicoloured   70   1·00

49 "The Nativity"   **50** Arms of Andorra

1981. Christmas. Carvings from Encamp Church. Multicoloured.
135   12p. Type **49**   20   35
136   30p. "The Adoration" . . .   40   50

1981. Bishops of Urgel, Co-princes of Andorra (2nd series). As T **42**.
137   7p. purple and blue   15   25
138   20p. brown and green   25   55
DESIGNS: 7p. Salvador Casanas; 20p. Josep de Boltas.

1982. With "PTA" under figure of value.
139 **50** 1p. mauve   10   10
140   3p. brown   10   10
141   7p. red   15   10
142   12p. red   15   25
143   15p. blue   25   25
144   20p. green   25   25
145   30p. red   30   20
146   50p. green (25 × 31 mm) .   90   55
147   100p. blue (25 × 31 mm) .   2·10   1·00
See also Nos. 203/6.

51 The New Reforms, 1866

1982. Europa. Multicoloured.
154   14p. Type **51**   35   35
155   33p. Reform of the
         Institutions, 1981   55   70

52 Footballers

1982. World Cup Football Championship, Spain. Multicoloured.
156   14p. Type **52**   65   65
157   33p. Tackle . . . .   1·40   1·40

53 Arms and 1929 1p. stamp

1982. National Stamp Exhibition.
158 **53** 14p. black and green . . .   40   55

54 Spanish and French   **55** "Virgin and Child"
Permanent Delegations   (statue from Andorra
Buildings   la Vella Parish Church)

1982. Anniversaries.
159 **54** 9p. brown and blue . . .   15   20
160   – 23p. blue and brown . . .   25   45
161   – 33p. black and green . . .   40   55
DESIGNS—VERT: 9p. Type **54** (centenary of Permanent Delegations); 23p. "St. Francis feeding the Birds" (after Ciambue) (800th birth anniv of St. Francis of Assisi); 33p. Title page of "Relacio sobre la Vall de Andorra" (birth centenary of Tomas Junoy (writer)).

1982. Christmas. Multicoloured.
162   14p. Type **55**   20   20
163   33p. Children beating log
         with sticks   40   55

56 Building Romanesque   **57** "Lactarius
Church   sanguifluus"

1983. Europa.
164 **56** 16p. green, purple & black   30   25
165   – 38p. brown, blue and black   60   90
DESIGN: 38p. 16th-century water mill.

1983. Nature Protection.
166 **57** 16p. multicoloured   65   65

58 Ballot Box on Map and
Government Building

1983. 50th Anniv of Universal Suffrage in Andorra.
167 **58** 10p. multicoloured   20   35

59 Mgr. Cinto Verdaguer   **60** Jaume Sansa
                                      Nequi

1983. Centenary of Mgr. Cinto Verdaguer's Visit.
168 **59** 50p. multicoloured   70   90

1983. Air. Jaume Sansa Nequi (Verger-Episcopal) Commemoration.
169 **60** 20p. deep brown & brown   30   45

61 Wall Painting, Church of
San Cerni, Nagol

1983. Christmas.
170 **61** 16p. multicoloured   30   35

1983. Bishops of Urgel, Co-princes of Andorra (3rd series). As T **42**.
171   26p. brown and red   40   45
DESIGN: 26p. Joan Laguarda.

62 Ski Jumping

1984. Winter Olympic Games, Sarajevo.
172 **62** 16p. multicoloured   30   45

63 Exhibition and F.I.P. Emblems

1984. "Espana 84" Int Stamp Exhibition, Madrid.
173 **63** 26p. multicoloured   40   45

64 Bridge

1984. Europa.
174 **64** 16p. brown   40   40
175   – 38p. blue   60   60

65 Hurdling

1984. Olympic Games, Los Angeles.
176 **65** 40p. multicoloured   60   80

66 Common Morel

1984. Nature Protection.
177 **66** 11p. multicoloured . . . .   5·00   5·00

67 Pencil, Brush   **68** The Holy Family (wood
and Pen   carvings)

1984. Pyrenean Cultures Centre, Andorra.
178 **67** 20p. multicoloured   30   35

1984. Christmas.
179 **68** 17p. multicoloured   30   35

69 Mossen Enric Marfany and Score

1985. Europa.
180 **69** 18p. green, purple & brown   35   35
181   – 45p. brown and green   75   70
DESIGN: 45p. Musician with viola (fresco detail, La Cortinada Church).

1985. Air. Bishops of Urgel, Co-princes of Andorra (4th series). As T **42**.
182   20p. brown and ochre   30   35
DESIGN: 20p. Ramon Iglesias.

70 Beefsteak Morel   **71** Pal

1985. Nature Protection.
183 **70** 30p. multicoloured   70   70

1985.
184 **71** 17p. deep blue and blue . .   30   35

72 Angels (St. Bartholomew's Chapel)

1985. Christmas.
185 **72** 17p. multicoloured   30   35

73 Scotch Bonnet   **74** Sun, Rainbow,
                               Lighthouse and Fish

1986. Nature Protection.
186 **73** 30p. multicoloured   70   70

1986. Europa. Each blue, red and green.
187   17p. Type **74**   30   45
188   45p. Sun and trees on rocks   90   90

1986. Bishops of Urgel, Co-princes of Andorra (5th series). As T **42**.
189   35p. blue and brown   65   65
DESIGN: 35p. Justi Guitart.

75 Bell of St. Roma's   **76** Arms
Chapel, Les Bons

1986. Christmas.
190 **75** 19p. multicoloured   35   35

1987. Meeting of Co-princes.
191 **76** 48p. multicoloured   70   65

77 Interior of Chapel   **79** Cep

1987. Europa. Meritxell Chapel.
192   **77**   19p. brown and blue   35   45
193   – 48p. blue and brown . . .   95   90
DESIGN: 48p. Exterior of Chapel.

1987. Nature Protection.
195   **79**   100p. multicoloured . . .   1·75   1·75

80 Extract from "Doctrina Pueril" by Ramon Llull

1987. Christmas.
196   **80**   20p. multicoloured   30   35

81 Copper Lance Heads

1988. Archaeology.
197   **81**   50p. multicoloured   70   80

82 Early 20th-century Trader and Pack Mules   **83** Pyrenean Mountain Dog

1988. Europa. Communications. Each blue and red.
198   20p. Ancient road, Les Bons   40   35
199   45p. Type **82**   80   80

1988. Nature Protection.
200   **83**   20p. multicoloured . . .   70   70

84 Commemorative Coin   **86** Leap-frog

85 Church of St. John of Caselles

1988. 700th Anniv of Second Parity Treaty.
201   **84**   20p. black, grey and brown   35   35

1988. Christmas.
202   **85**   20p. multicoloured   30   35

1988. As T **50** but without "PTA" under figure of value.
203   20p. green   20   25
204   50p. green (25 × 31 mm) . . .   60   45
205   100p. blue (25 × 31 mm) . . .   1·50   90
206   500p. brown (25 × 31 mm) . . .   6·50   6·75

1989. Europa. Children's Games. Multicoloured.
210   20p. Type **86**   45   70
211   45p. Girl trying to pull child from grip of other children (horiz) . . .   1·00   1·40

87 St. Roma's Chapel, Les Bons

1989.
212   **87**   50p. black, green and blue   70   70

88 Anniversary Emblem   **89** "Virgin Mary" (detail of altarpiece, Les Escaldes Church)

1989. 125th Anniv of International Red Cross.
213   **88**   20p. multicoloured   40   55

1989. Christmas.
214   **89**   20p. multicoloured   35   45

90 Old French and Spanish Post Offices, Andorra La Vella

1990. Europa. Post Office Buildings. Multicoloured.
215   20p. Type **90**   35   35
216   50p. Modern Spanish post office, Andorra La Vella (vert)   85   60

91 "Gomphidius rutilus"

1990. Nature Protection.
217   **91**   45p. multicoloured   80   80

92 Plandolit House   **93** Angel, La Massana Church

1990.
218   **92**   20p. brown and yellow . .   35   35

1990. Christmas.
219   **93**   25p. brown, stone and red   35   45

94 Throwing the Discus

1991. European Small States' Games. Multicoloured.
220   25p. Type **94**   40   55
221   45p. High jumping and running   60   65

95 "Olympus 1" Satellite   **96** Parasol Mushroom

1991. Europa. Europe in Space. Multicoloured.
222   25p. Type **95**   40   55
223   55p. Close-up of "Olympus l" telecommunications satellite (horiz)   80   90

1991. Nature Protection.
224   **96**   45p. multicoloured   80   80

97 "Virgin of the Three Hands" (detail of triptych in Meritxell Chapel by Maria Assumpta Ortado i Maimo)   **98** Woman fetching Water from Public Tap

1991. Christmas.
225   **97**   25p. multicoloured   40   45

1992.
226   **98**   25p. multicoloured   40   45

99 "Santa Maria"   **100** White-water Canoeing

1992. Europa. 500th Anniv of Discovery of America by Columbus.
227   **99**   27p. multicoloured . . .   45   50
228   – 45p. brown, red and orange   75   75
DESIGN—HORIZ: 45p. Engraving of King Ferdinand from map sent by Columbus to Ferdinand and Queen Isabella the Catholic.

1992. Olympic Games, Barcelona.
229   **100**   27p. multicoloured . . .   35   45

101 Benz "Velo", 1894   **102** "Nativity" (Fra Angelico)

1992. National Motor Car Museum, Encamp.
230   **101**   27p. multicoloured . . .   35   45

1992. Christmas.
231   **102**   27p. multicoloured . . .   35   45

103 Chanterelle

1993. Nature Protection.
232   **103**   28p. multicoloured . . .   40   40

104 "Upstream" (J. A. Morrison)

1993. Europa. Contemporary Art. Multicoloured.
233   28p. Type **104**   45   50
234   45p. "Ritme" (Angel Calvente) (vert) . . .   65   65

105 Society Emblem on National Colours   **106** Illuminated "P" (Galceran de Vilanova Missal)

1993. 25th Anniv of Andorran Arts and Letters Circle.
235   **105**   28p. multicoloured . . .   35   45

1993. Christmas.
236   **106**   28p. multicoloured . . .   35   45

108 Sir Alexander Fleming and Penicillin

1994. Europa. Discoveries.
238   **108**   29p. multicoloured . . .   50   50
239   – 55p. blue and black . . .   80   85
DESIGN: 55p. Test tube and AIDS virus.

109 "Hygrophorus gliocyclus"   **110** "Madonna and Child" (anon)

1994. Nature Protection.
240   **109**   29p. multicoloured . . .   40   40

1994. Christmas.
241   **110**   29p. multicoloured . . .   40   40

111 Madriu Valley (south)

1995. European Nature Conservation Year. Mult.
242   30p. Type **111**   50   50
243   60p. Madriu Valley (north)   85   95

112 Sun, Dove and Barbed Wire   **113** "Flight into Egypt" (altarpiece, St. Mark and St. Mary Church, Encamp)

1995. Europa. Peace and Freedom.
244   **112**   60p. green, orange & blk   80   90

1995. Christmas.
245   **113**   30p. multicoloured . . .   40   45

114 Palace of Europe, Strasbourg

1995. Admission of Andorra to Council of Europe.
246   **114**   30p. multicoloured . . .   40   45

115 "Ramaria aurea"

1996. Nature Protection. Multicoloured.
247   30p. Type **115**   45   50
248   60p. Black truffles   85   95

116 Isabelle Sandy (writer)

1996. Europa. Famous Women.
249 **116** 60p. multicoloured . . . 90 1·00

117 Old Iron

1996. International Museums Day.
250 **117** 60p. multicoloured . . . 85 95

118 "The Annunciation" (altarpiece, St. Eulalia's Church, Encamp)

1996. Christmas.
251 **118** 30p. multicoloured . . . 40 45

119 Drais Velocipede, 1818

1997. Bicycle Museum (1st series). Multicoloured.
252   32p. Type **119** 40 45
253   65p. Michaux velocipede, 1861 . . . . . . 90 85
See also Nos. 258/9 and 264/5.

120 The Bear and The Smugglers   **121** Dove and Cultural Symbols

1997. Europa. Tales and Legends.
254 **120** 65p. multicoloured . . . 90 90

1997. National U.N.E.S.C.O. Commission.
255 **121** 32p. multicoloured . . . 45 50

122 Catalan Crib Figure

1997. Christmas.
256 **122** 32p. multicoloured . . . 45 50

123 Giant Slalom

1998. Winter Olympic Games, Nagano, Japan.
257 **123** 35p. multicoloured . . . 45 50

1998. Bicycle Museum (2nd series). As T **119.** Multicoloured
258   35p. Kangaroo bicycle, Great Britain, 1878 . . . . . . 45 50
259   70p. The Swallow, France, 1889 . . . . . . 90 1·00

124 Harlequins of Canillo

1998. Europa. National Festivals.
260 **124** 70p. multicoloured . . . 90 90

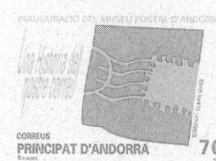

125 Front Page of First Edition and Landscape

1998. 250th Anniv of "Manual Digest".
261 **125** 35p. multicoloured . . . 45 50

126 Emblem

1998. Inauguration of Postal Museum.
262 **126** 70p. violet and yellow . . 90 1·00

127 St. Lucia Fair

1998. Christmas.
263 **127** 35p. multicoloured . . . 45 50

1999. Bicycle Museum (3rd series). As T **119.** Multicoloured.
264   35p. Salvo tricycle, 1878 (vert) 45 50
265   70p. Rudge tricycle, Coventry, England . . . . 90 1·00

128 Mules

1999. Postal History.
266 **128** 35p. black and brown . . . 45 50

129 Palace of Human Rights, Strasbourg

1999. 50th Anniv of Council of Europe.
267 **129** 35p. multicoloured . . . 45 50

130 Vall d'Incles National Park, Canillo

1999. Europa. Parks and Gardens.
268 **130** 70p. multicoloured . . . 90 1·00

131 Rull House, Sispony

1999.
269 **131** 35p. multicoloured . . . 45 50

132 Angel (detail of altarpiece, St. Serni's Church, Canillo)   **133** Santa Coloma Church

1999. Christmas.
270 **132** 35p. brown and light brown . . . 45 50

1999. European Heritage.
271 **133** 35p. multicoloured . . . 45 50

134 "Building Europe"

2000. Europa.
272 **134** 70p. multicoloured . . . 90 1·00

135 Angonella Lakes, Ordino

2000.
273 **135** 35p. multicoloured . . . 40 40

136 Casa Lacruz

2000. 131st Birth Anniv of Josep Cadafalch (architect).
274 **136** 35p. multicoloured . . . 40 40

137 Dinner Service   **138** Hurdling

2000. D'Areny-Plandolit Museum.
275 **137** 70p. multicoloured . . . 85 85

2000. Olympic Games, Sydney.
276 **138** 70p. multicoloured . . . 85 85

139 United Nations Headquarters, Strasbourg

2000. 50th Anniv of United Nations Declaration of Human Rights.
277 **139** 70p. multicoloured . . . 85 85

140 Gradual, St. Roma, Les Bons   **141** "Quadre de les Animes" (Joan Casanovas)

2000. 25th Anniv of the National Archives.
278 **140** 35p. multicoloured . . . 40 40

2000. Christmas.
279 **141** 35p. multicoloured . . . 40 40

142 Rec del Sola

2001. Natural Heritage.
280 **142** 40p. multicoloured . . . 30 30

143 Roc del Metge (thermal spring), Escaldes-Engordany

2001. Europa. Water Resources.
281 **143** 75p. muticoloured . . . 55 55

144 Casa Palau, Sant   **145** Part of Sanctuary, Julia de Loria Meritxell

2001.
282 **144** 75p. multicoloured . . . 55 55

2001. 25th Anniv of Chapel of Our Lady, Meritxell.
283 **145** 40p. multicoloured . . . 30 30

146 Building

2001. 10th Anniv of National Auditorium, Ordino.
284 **146** 75p. multicoloured . . . 55 55

EXPRESS LETTER STAMPS

1928. Express Letter stamp of Spain optd **CORREOS ANDORRA.**
E15 E **53** 20c. red . . . . 38·00 42·00

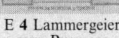

E 4 Lammergeier over Pyrenees

E 12 Eurasian Red Squirrel (after Durer) and Arms

1929.
E41 E 4 20c. red . . . . 6·50 6·00

1949.
E54 E 12 25c. red . . . . 4·00 5·50

ANGOLA Pt. 9; Pt. 12

Republic of Southern Africa. Independent of Portugal since 11 November 1975.

1870. 1000 reis = 1 milreis.
1913. 100 centavos = 1 escudo.
1932. 100 centavos = 1 angolar.
1954. 100 centavos = 1 escudo.
1977. 100 lweis = 1 kwanza.

1870. "Crown" key-type inscr "ANGOLA".
7 P 5r. black 1·00 95
17 10r. yellow 8·75 4·25
31 10r. green 2·75 1·25
9 20r. bistre 1·50 95
26 20r. red 4·75 3·50
10 25r. red 5·25 2·40
27 25r. purple 3·75 1·25
19b 40r. blue 80·00 48·00
33 40r. yellow 2·75 2·00
12 50r. green 20·00 7·50
30 50r. blue 12·00 1·25
21a 100r. lilac 1·40 95
22 200r. orange 1·75 1·10
23a 300r. brown 1·90 1·50

1886. "Embossed" key-type inscr "PROVINCIA DE ANGOLA".
35 Q 5r. black 4·25 2·40
36 10r. green 4·25 2·40
37 20r. red 6·50 4·50
39 25r. mauve 4·50 1·00
40 40r. brown 5·00 2·50
41 50r. blue 5·75 1·40
42 100r. brown 7·50 3·50
43 200r. violet 10·50 4·75
44 300r. orange 10·50 4·75

1894. "Figures" key-type inscr "ANGOLA".
49 R 5r. orange 85 40
62 10r. mauve 1·60 55
63 15r. brown 1·60 95
54 20r. lavender 1·90 1·10
74 25r. green 1·00 75
66 50r. blue 2·00 95
67 75r. red 4·25 2·25
68 80r. green 4·00 3·00
69 100r. brown on buff 4·25 3·00
70 150r. red on rose 7·50 5·00
77 200r. blue on blue 7·50 5·75
78 300r. blue on brown 7·50 5·75

1894. No. N51 with circular surch **CORREIOS DE ANGOLA 25 REIS.**
79b V 25r. on 2½r. brown 27·00 25·00

1898. "King Carlos" key-type inscr "ANGOLA".
80 S 2½r. grey 20 20
81 5r. orange 20 20
82 10r. green 20 20
83 15r. brown 1·10 55
142 15r. green 45 40
84 20r. lilac 25 20
85 25r. green 65 25
143 25r. red 30 10
86 50r. blue 95 35
144 50r. brown 2·25 1·10
145 65r. blue 3·00 2·75
87 75r. red 3·00 1·40
146 75r. purple 1·00 70
88 80r. mauve 3·00 1·40
89 100r. blue on blue 60 40
147 115r. brown on pink 3·00 2·75
148 130r. brown on yellow 3·00 2·75
90 150r. brown on buff 3·00 2·25
91 200r. purple on pink 1·75 60
92 300r. blue on pink 2·00 1·75
149 400r. blue on yellow 2·00 1·60
93 500r. black on blue 2·25 1·75
94 700r. mauve on yellow 9·50 6·75

1902. "Embossed", "Figures" and "Newspaper" key-types of Angola surch.
98 R 65r. on 5r. orange 3·00 2·25
100 65r. on 10r. mauve 2·25 1·60
102 65r. on 20r. violet 4·00 2·25
104 65r. on 25r. green 2·25 1·75
95 Q 65r. on 40r. brown 3·50 2·10
96 65r. on 300r. orange 3·50 2·10
106 115r. on 10r. green 4·00 2·00
109 R 115r. on 80r. green 4·50 3·50
111 115r. on 100r. brn on buff 3·75 2·10
113 115r. on 150r. red on rose 5·50 4·25
108 Q 115r. on 200r. violet 4·00 1·90
120 R 130r. on 15r. brown 2·25 1·50
116 Q 130r. on 50r. blue 4·25 3·00
124 R 130r. on 75r. red 3·25 1·75
118 Q 130r. on 100r. brown 2·75 1·90
126 R 130r. on 300r. blue on brn 7·50 4·75
136 V 400r. on 2½r. brown 55 50
127 Q 400r. on 5r. black 6·25 5·25
128 400r. on 20r. red 25·00 16·00
130 400r. on 25r. mauve 6·25 3·25
131 R 400r. on 50r. pale blue 2·75 2·00
133 400r. on 200r. blue on blue 3·50 2·40

1902. "King Carlos" key-type of Angola optd **PROVISORIO.**
138 S 15r. brown 80 45
139 25r. green 65 30
140 50r. blue 1·40 70
141 75r. red 2·00 1·50

1905. No. 145 surch **50 REIS** and bar.
150 S 50r. on 65r. blue 1·25 75

1911. "King Carlos" key-type optd **REPUBLICA.**
151 S 2½r. grey 20 15
152 5r. orange 20 15
153 10r. green 20 15
154 15r. green 20 15
155 20r. lilac 20 15
156 25r. red 20 15
157 50r. brown 75 55
232 50r. blue (No. 140) 75 45
224 75r. purple 45 30
234 75r. red (No. 141) 1·50 1·10
225 100r. blue on blue 95 95
160 115r. brown on pink 75 45
161 130r. brown on yellow 75 45
226 200r. purple on pink 85 45
163 400r. blue on yellow 1·00 50
164 500r. black on blue 1·10 50
165 700r. mauve on yellow 1·40 65

1912. "King Manoel" key-type inscr "ANGOLA" optd **REPUBLICA.**
166 T 2½r. lilac 20 20
167 5r. black 20 20
168 10r. green 20 20
169 20r. red 20 20
170 25r. brown 20 20
171 50r. blue 45 35
172 75r. brown 50 45
173 100r. brown on green 1·00 65
174 200r. green on pink 1·00 70
175 300r. black on blue 1·00 70

1912. "King Carlos" key-type of Angola optd **REPUBLICA** and surch.
176 S 2½ on 15r. green 1·50 1·00
177 5 on 15r. green 1·25 90
178 10 on 15r. green 1·25 80
179 25 on 75r. red (No. 141) 22·00 15·00
180 25 on 75r. purple 1·60 1·25

1913. Surch **REPUBLICA ANGOLA** and value in figures on "Vasco da Gama" issues of (a) Portuguese Colonies.
181 ¼c. on 2½r. green 45 35
182 ½c. on 5r. red 45 35
183 1c. on 10r. purple 45 35
184 2½c. on 25r. green 45 35
185 5c. on 50r. blue 45 35
186 7½c. on 75r. brown 1·90 1·60
187 10c. on 100r. brown 80 55
188 15c. on 150r. bistre 65 55

(b) Macao.
189 ¼c. on ½a. green 75 65
190 ½c. on 1a. red 75 65
191 1c. on 2a. purple 65 50
192 2½c. on 4a. green 55 45
193 5c. on 8a. blue 55 45
194 7½c. on 12a. brown 1·90 1·10
195 10c. on 16a. brown 1·10 65
196 15c. on 24a. bistre 85 65

(c) Timor.
197 ¼c. on ½a. green 75 65
198 ½c. on 1a. red 75 65
199 1c. on 2a. purple 65 50
200 2½c. on 4a. green 55 40
201 5c. on 8a. blue 55 50
202 7½c. on 12a. brown 1·90 1·10
203 10c. on 16a. brown 1·00 65
204 15c. on 24a. bistre 90 65

1914. "Ceres" key-type inscr "ANGOLA".
296 U ¼c. olive 10 10
297 ½c. black 10 10
298 1c. green 10 10
299 1½c. brown 10 10
300 2c. red 10 10
301 2c. grey 15 15
281 2½c. violet 10 10
303 3c. orange 10 10
304 4c. red 10 10
305 4½c. grey 10 10
284a 5c. blue 10 10
307 6c. mauve 10 10
308 7c. blue 10 10
309 7½c. brown 10 10
288 8c. grey 10 10
311 10c. brown 10 10
312 12c. brown 15 15
313 12c. green 15 10
291 15c. purple 15 10
314 15c. pink 10 10
315 20c. green 35 25
316 24c. blue 40 35
317 25c. brown 40 35
217 30c. brown on green 1·10 75
318 30c. green 15 10
218 40c. brown on pink 1·10 75
319 40c. blue 40 15
219 50c. orange on pink 3·50 2·50
320 50c. purple 35 15
321 60c. blue 40 25
322 60c. red 25·00 20·00
322a 80c. pink 55 25
220 1e. green on blue 2·10 1·50
323 1e. red 50 25
325 1e. blue 1·00 55
326 2e. purple 1·10 65
327 5e. brown 4·00 3·25
328 10e. pink 11·00 8·00
329 20e. green 32·00 25·00

1914. Provisional stamps of 1902 optd **REPUBLICA.**
233 S 50r. on 65r. blue 1·50 1·40
256 Q 115r. on 10r. green 80 60
258 R 115r. on 80r. green 65 60
261 115r. on 100r. brn on buff 55 45
263 115r. on 150r. red on rose 85 60
266 Q 115r. on 200r. violet 60 40
267 R 130r. on 15r. brown 55 40
246 Q 130r. on 50r. blue 6·50 6·50
269 R 130r. on 75r. red 1·10 55
273 Q 130r. on 100r. brown 45 40
274 R 130r. on 300r. blue on brn 45 40
254 V 400r. on 2½r. brown 25 20

1919. Stamps of 1911, 1912 or 1914 surch.
332 S ½c. on 75r. purple 55 45
331 T ½c. on 75r. brown 35 30
336 1c. on 50r. blue 65 60
335 S 2½c. on 100r. blue on blue 65 30
334 2½c. on 100r. brown on grn 65 55
337 4c. on 130r. brown on yell 65 55
339 U $04 on 15c. purple 45 45
340 $04 on 15c. pink 7·50
341 T $00.5 on 75r. brown 50 45
342 U $00.5 on 7½c. brown 65 55

1925. Nos. 136 and 133 surch **Republica 40 C.**
345 V 40c. on 400r. on 2½r. brn 25 25
343 R 40c. on 400r. on 200r. blue on blue 25 25

1931. "Ceres" key-type of Angola surch.
347 U 50c. on 60c. red 55 55
348 70c. on 80c. pink 1·40 85
349 70c. on 1e. blue 1·10 85
350 1e.40 on 2e. purple 90 55

17 Ceres

1932.
351 17 1c. brown 10 10
352 5c. sepia 10 10
353 10c. mauve 10 10
354 15c. black 10 10
355 20c. grey 10 10
356 30c. green 10 10
357 35c. green 3·00 1·25
358 40c. red 15 10
359 45c. blue 45 40
360 50c. brown 15 10
361 60c. olive 30 15
362 70c. brown 30 15
363 80c. green 20 10
364 85c. red 1·50 85
365 1a. red 35 10
366 1a.40 blue 3·00 1·50
367 1a.75 blue 5·75 1·60
368 2a. mauve 1·25 15
369 5a. green 2·40 50
370 10a. brown 5·75 95
371 20a. orange 14·00 1·90

1934. Surch.
380 17 5c. on 80c. green (A) 25 10
419 5c. on 80c. green (B) 30 25
413 10c. on 45c. blue 65 55
381 10c. on 80c. green 45 20
414 15c. on 45c. blue 65 55
382 15c. on 80c. green 65 25
415 20c. on 85c. red 65 55
374 30c. on 1a.40 blue 1·00 85
416 35c. on 85c. red 65 55
417 50c. on 1a.40 blue 65 55
418 60c. on 1a. red 3·25 3·00
375 70c. on 2a. mauve 1·25 95
376 80c. on 5a. green 2·10 1·00
(A) surch **0,05 Cent.** in one line; (B) surch **5 CENTAVOS** in two lines.

1935. "Due" key-type surch **CORREIOS** and new value.
377 W 5c. on 6c. brown 85 65
378 30c. on 50c. grey 85 65
379 40c. on 50c. grey 85 65

22 Vasco da Gama

27 Airplane over Globe

1938. Name and value in black.
383 22 1c. olive (postage) 10 10
384 5c. brown 10 10
385 10c. red 10 10
386 15c. purple 10 10
387 20c. grey 10 10
388 – 30c. purple 15 10
389 – 35c. green 20 15
390 – 40c. brown 10 10
391 – 50c. mauve 10 10
392 – 60c. black 25 15
393 – 70c. violet 25 15
394 – 80c. orange 25 15
395 – 1a. red 25 15
396 – 1a.75 blue 70 30
397 – 2a. red 1·00 30
398 – 5a. olive 3·50 30
399 – 10a. blue 8·00 45
400 – 20a. brown 14·00 90
401 27 10c. red (air) 20 15
402 20c. violet 20 15
403 50c. orange 20 15
404 1a. blue 20 15
405 2a. red 30 15
406 3a. green 65 20
407 5a. brown 1·75 25
408 9a. red 2·40 70
409 10a. mauve 3·25 80
DESIGNS: 30c. to 50c. Mousinho de Albuquerque; 60c. to 1a. "Fomento" (symbolizing Progress); 1a.75, 2, 5a. Prince Henry the Navigator; 10, 20a. Afonso de Albuquerque.

28 Portuguese Colonial Column

31 Arms of Angola

1938. President's Colonial Tour.
410 28 80c. green 1·10 85
411 1a.75 blue 8·00 1·90
412 20a. brown 19·00 10·50

1945. Nos. 394/6 surch.
420 5c. on 80c. orange 50 30
421 50c. on 1a. red 50 30
422 50c. on 1a.75 blue 50 30

1947. Air.
423a 31 1a. brown 4·00 1·50
423b 2a. green 4·00 1·50
423c 3a. orange 4·25 1·50
423d 3a.50 orange 8·25 1·75
423e 5a. green 45·00 4·50
423f 6a. pink 45·00 7·50
423g 9a. red £130 80·00
423h 10a. green £120 30·00
423i 20a. blue £120 30·00
423j 50a. black £190 90·00
423k 100a. yellow £350 £250

32 Sao Miguel Fortress, Luanda

33 Our Lady of Fatima

1948. Tercentenary of Restoration of Angola. Inscr "Tricentenario da Restauracao de Angola 1648–1948".
424 32 5c. violet 10 10
425 – 10c. brown 30 15
426 – 30c. green 10 10
427 – 50c. purple 10 10
428 – 1a. red 25 10
429 – 1a.75 blue 50 10
430 – 2a. green 50 10
431 – 5a. black 1·75 30
432 – 10a. mauve 3·75 55
433 – 20a. blue 8·00 1·10
DESIGNS—HORIZ: 10c. Our Lady of Nazareth Hermitage, Luanda; 1a. Surrender of Luanda; 5a. Inscribed Rocks of Yelala; 20a. Massangano Fortress. VERT (portraits): 30c. Don John IV; 50c. Salvador Correia de Sa Benevides; 1a.75, Dioga Cao; 7a. Manuel Cerveira Pereira; 10a. Paulo Dias de Novais.

1948. Honouring Our Lady of Fatima.
434 33 50c. red 1·25 1·00
435 3a. blue 3·25 2·00
436 6a. orange 13·50 5·00
437 9a. red 27·00 6·50

35 River Chiumbe

36 Pedras Negras

1949.
438 35 20c. blue 30 15
439 36 40c. brown 30 10
440 – 50c. red 30 10
441 – 2a.50 blue 1·60 30
442 – 3a.50 grey 1·60 1·40
443 – 15a. green 13·50 1·40
444 – 50a. green 75·00 4·75
DESIGNS—As T 35: 50c. Luanda; 2a.50, Bandeira; 3a.50, Mocamedes; 50a. Braganza Falls. 31 × 26 mm: 15a. River Cubal.

37 Aircraft and Globe

38 "Tentativa Feliz"

1949. Air.

445	**37**	1a. orange	30	10
446		2a. brown	65	10
447		3a. mauve	90	10
448		6a. green	2·00	50
449		9a. purple	2·75	1·10

1949. Centenary of Founding of Mocamedes.

450	**38**	1a. purple	5·25	60
451		4a. green	13·50	1·60

39 Letter and Globe

40 Reproduction of "Crown" key-type

1949. 75th Anniv of U.P.U.

452	**39**	4a. green	6·00	2·40

1950. Philatelic Exhibition and 80th Anniv of First Angolan Stamp.

453	**40**	50a. green	95	30
454		1a. red	95	45
455		4a. black	3·25	1·25

41 Bells and Dove

42 Angels holding Candelabra

1950. Holy Year.

456	**41**	1a. violet	65	10
457	**42**	4a. black	3·00	55

43 Dark Chanting Goshawk

44 Our Lady of Fatima

1951. Birds. Multicoloured.

458		5c. Type **43**	20	10
459		10c. Racquet-tailed roller	20	10
460		15c. Bateleur	30	10
461		20c. European bee eater	35	25
462		50c. Giant kingfisher	35	10
463		1a. Anchieta's barbet	35	10
464		1a.50 African open-bill stork	50	15
465		2a. Southern ground hornbill	1·75	15
466		2a.50 African skimmer	70	15
467		3a. Shikra	50	15
468		3a.50 Senham's bustard	70	15
469		4a. African golden oriole	80	15
470		4a.50 Magpie shrike	80	15
471		5a. Red-shouldered glossy starling	3·50	35
472		6a. Sharp-tailed glossy starling	4·75	90
473		7a. Fan-tailed whydah	5·25	1·25
474		10a. Half-collared kingfisher	20·00	1·40
475		12a.50 White-crowned shrike	5·75	2·00
476		15a. White-winged starling	5·25	2·00
477		20a. Southern yellow-billed hornbill	50·00	4·75
478		25a. Violet starling	16·00	4·00
479		30a. Sulphur-breasted bush shrike	16·00	4·75
480		40a. Secretary bird	26·00	6·75
481		50a. Peach-faced lovebird	60·00	14·50

The 10, 15 and 20c., 2a.50, 3a., 4a.50, 12a.50 and 30a. are horiz, the remainder vert.

1951. Termination of Holy Year.

482	**44**	4a. orange	1·90	1·00

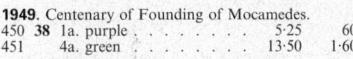

45 Laboratory

46 The Sacred Face

1952. 1st Tropical Medicine Congress, Lisbon.

483	**45**	1a. grey and blue	60	25

1952. Missionary Art Exhibition.

484	**46**	10c. blue and flesh	15	15
485		50c. green and stone	40	15
486		2a. purple and flesh	2·00	30

47 Leopard

48 Stamp of 1853 and Colonial Arms

1953. Angolan Fauna. Multicoloured.

487		5c. Type **47**	15	15
488		10c. Sable antelope (vert)	25	20
489		20c. African elephant (vert)	25	20
490		30c. Eland (vert)	25	20
491		40c. Crocodile	25	20
492		50c. Impala (vert)	25	20
493		1a. Mountain zebra (vert)	50	20
494		1a.50 Sitatunga (vert)	25	20
495		2a. Black rhinoceros	75	20
496		2a.30 Gemsbok (vert)	50	20
497		2a.50 Lion (vert)	75	20
498		3a. African buffalo	65	20
499		3a.50 Springbok (vert)	65	20
500		4a. Blue wildebeest (vert)	15·00	25
501		5a. Hartebeest (vert)	1·25	20
502		7a. Warthog (vert)	1·60	25
503		10a. Waterbuck (vert)	2·10	25
504		12a.50 Hippopotamus (vert)	7·00	1·60
505		15a. Greater kudu (vert)	7·00	1·60
506		20a. Giraffe (vert)	9·50	1·10

1953. Portuguese Stamp Centenary.

507	**48**	50c. multicoloured	65	45

49 Father M. da Nobrega and Sao Paulo

50 Route of President's Tour

1954. 4th Centenary of Sao Paulo.

508	**49**	1e. black and buff	40	20

1954. Presidential Visit.

509	**50**	35c. multicoloured	15	10
510		4e.50 multicoloured	1·00	45

51 Map of Angola

52 Col. A. de Paiva

1955. Map mult. Angola territory in colour given.

511	**51**	5c. white	20	15
512		20c. salmon	20	15
513		50c. blue	20	15
514		1e. orange	20	15
515		2e.30 yellow	90	30
516		4e. blue	1·75	15
517		10e. green	2·10	15
518		20e. white	3·00	1·10

1956. Birth Centenary of De Paiva.

519	**52**	1e. black, blue and orange	25	20

53 Quela Chief

54 Father J. M. Antunes

1957. Natives. Multicoloured.

520		5c. Type **53**	15	15
521		10c. Andulo flute player	15	15
522		15c. Dembos man and woman	15	15
523		20c. Quissama dancer (male)	15	15
524		30c. Quibala family	15	15
525		40c. Bocolo dancer (female)	15	15
526		50c. Quissama woman	15	15
527		80c. Cuanhama woman	20	15
528		1e.50 Luanda widow	1·60	15
529		2e.50 Bocolo dancer (male)	1·60	15
530		4e. Muquixe man	80	15
531		10e. Cabinda chief	1·40	30

1957. Birth Centenary of Father Antunes.

532	**54**	1e. multicoloured	55	30

55 Exhibition Emblem, Globe and Arms

1958. Brussels International Exhibition.

533	**55**	1e.50 multicoloured	45	40

56 "Securidaca longipedunculata"

57 Native Doctor and Patient

1958. 6th Int Tropical Medicine Congress.

534	**56**	2e.50 multicoloured	1·50	90

1958. 75th Anniv of Maria Pia Hospital, Luanda.

535	**57**	1e. brown, black and blue	30	20
536	–	1e.50 multicoloured	80	40
537	–	2e.50 multicoloured	1·50	75

DESIGNS: 1e.50, 17th-century doctor and patient; 2e.50, Present-day doctor, orderly and patients.

58 Welwitschia (plant)

59 Old Map of West Africa

1959. Centenary of Discovery of Welwitschia.

538	**58**	1e.50 multicoloured	70	30
539	–	2e.50 multicoloured	1·00	40
540	–	5e. multicoloured	1·60	40
541	–	10e. multicoloured	5·00	1·25

DESIGNS: 2e.50, 5, 10e. Various types of Welwitschia ("Welwitschia mirabilis").

1960. 500th Death Anniv of Prince Henry the Navigator.

542	**59**	2e.50 multicoloured	40	20

60 "Agriculture" (distribution of seeds)

61

1960. 10th Anniv of African Technical Co-operation Commission.

543	**60**	2e.50 multicoloured	50	20

1961. Angolan Women. As T **61**. Portraits multicoloured; background colours given.

544		10c. green	10	10
545		15c. blue	10	10
546		30c. yellow	10	10
547		40c. grey	10	10
548		60c. brown	10	10
549		1e.50 turquoise	10	10
550		2e. lilac	75	10
551		2e.50 lemon	75	10
552		3e. pink	2·75	20
553		4e. olive	1·40	20
554		5e. blue	90	20
555		7e.50 yellow	1·25	60
556		10e. buff	90	45
557		15e. brown	1·40	60
558		25e. red	1·90	90
559		50e. grey	4·25	1·90

62 Weightlifting

1962. Sports. Multicoloured.

560		50c. Flying	15	15
561		1e. Rowing	80	15
562		1e.50 Water polo	55	20
563		2e.50 Throwing the hammer	70	20
564		4e.50 High jumping	55	40
565		15e. Type **62**	1·40	1·00

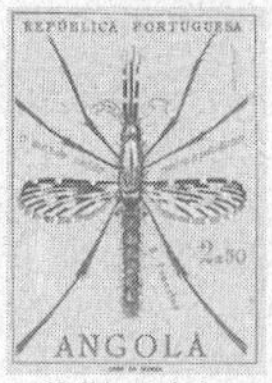

63 "Anopheles funestus" (mosquito)

64 Gen. Norton de Matos (statue)

1962. Malaria Eradication.

566	**63**	2e.50 multicoloured	1·00	55

1962. 50th Anniv of Nova Lisboa.

567	**64**	2e.50 multicoloured	40	20

65 Red Locusts

1963. 15th Anniv of Int Locust Eradication Service.

568	**65**	2e.50 multicoloured	65	30

66 Arms of St. Paul of the Assumption, Luanda

67 Rear-Admiral A. Tomas

1963. Angolan Civic Arms (1st series). Mult.

569		5c. Type **66**	15	15
570		10c. Massangano	15	15
571		30c. Muxima	15	15
572		50c. Carmona	15	15
573		1e. Salazar	45	15
574		1e.50 Malanje	90	15
575		2e. Henry of Carvalho	45	15
576		2e.50 Mocamedes	2·50	40
577		3e. Novo Redondo	65	15
578		3e.50 St. Salvador (Congo)	75	15
579		5e. Luso	65	25
580		7e.50 St. Philip (Benguela)	90	75
581		10e. Lobito	1·00	65
582		12e.50 Gabela	1·25	1·00
583		15e. Sa da Bandeira	1·25	1·00
584		17e.50 Silva Porto	2·00	1·75
585		20e. Nova Lisboa	2·00	1·60
586		22e.50 Cabinda	2·00	1·75
587		30e. Serpa Pinto	2·50	2·25

See also Nos. 589/610.

1963. Presidential Visit.

588	**67**	2e.50 multicoloured	40	15

68 Arms of Sanza-Pombo

69 Map of Africa, Boeing 707 and Lockheed Super Constellation Airliners

1963. Angolan Civic Arms (2nd series). Mult.

589		15c. Type **68**	10	10
590		20c. St. Antonio do Zaire	10	10
591		25c. Ambriz	10	10
592		40c. Ambrizete	10	10
593		50c. Catete	10	10
594		70c. Quibaxe	10	10
595		1e. Maquela do Zombo	15	10

596	1e.20 Bembe	10	10
597	1e.50 Caxito	50	10
598	1e.80 Dondo	25	20
599	2e.50 Damba	1·75	10
600	4e. Cuimba	35	15
601	6e.50 Negage	35	30
602	7e. Quitexe	60	40
603	8e. Mucaba	60	50
604	9e. 31 de Janeiro	85	75
605	11e. Novo Caipemba	1·00	85
606	14e. Songo	1·10	1·00
607	17e. Quimbele	1·25	1·10
608	25e. Noqui	1·50	1·10
609	35e. Santa Cruz	2·10	1·75
610	50e. General Freire	2·75	1·50

1963. 10th Anniv of T.A.P. Airline.
611 **69** 1e. multicoloured 40 20

70 Bandeira Cathedral
71 Dr. A. T. de Sousa

1963. Angolan Churches. Multicoloured.

612	10c. Type **70**	10	10
613	20c. Landana	10	10
614	30c. Luanda (Cathedral)	10	10
615	40c. Gabela	10	10
616	50c. St. Martin, Bay of Tigers (Chapel)	10	10
617	1e. Melange (Cathedral)	15	10
618	1e.50 St. Peter, Chibia	15	10
619	2e. Benguela	20	10
620	2e.50 Jesus, Luanda	25	10
621	3e. Camabatela	30	15
622	3e.50 Cabinda Mission	40	15
623	4e. Vila Folgares	40	25
624	4e.50 Arrabida, Lobito	50	25
625	5e. Cabinda	55	30
626	7e.50 Cacuso, Malange	85	50
627	10e. Lubanga Mission	1·10	50
628	12e.50 Huila Mission	1·25	70
629	15e. Island Cape, Luanda	1·50	50

The 1e., 2e., 3e., 4e., 4e.50, 7e.50, 12e.50 and 15e. are horiz, the rest vert.

1964. Centenary of National Overseas Bank.
630 **71** 2e.50 multicoloured 55 25

72 Arms and Palace of Commerce, Luanda
73 I.T.U. Emblem and St. Gabriel

1964. Cent of Luanda Commercial Association.
631 **72** 1e. multicoloured 20 15

1965. Centenary of I.T.U.
632 **73** 2e.50 multicoloured . . . 80 40

74 Boeing 707 over Petroleum Refinery
75 Fokker F.27 Friendship over Luanda Airport

1965. Air. Multicoloured.

633	1e.50 Type **74**	85	10
634	2e.50 Cambabe Dam	80	10
635	3e. Salazar Dam	1·10	10
636	4e. Captain Trofilo Duarte Dam	1·10	15
637	4e.50 Creveiro Lopes Dam	80	15
638	5e. Cuango Dam	80	20
639	6e. Quanza Bridge	1·25	30
640	7e. Captain Trofilo Duarte Railway Bridge	2·75	40
641	8e.50 Dr. Oliveira Salazar Bridge	2·25	70
642	12e.50 Captain Silva Carvalho Railway Bridge	3·25	1·00

Nos. 634/42 are horiz and each design includes a Boeing 707 airliner overhead.

1965. 25th Anniv of Direccao dos Transportes Aereos (Angolan airline).
643 **75** 2e.50 multicoloured 25 15

76 Arquebusier, 1539
77 St. Paul's Hospital, Luanda, and Sarmento Rodrigues Commercial and Industrial School

1966. Portuguese Military Uniforms. Mult.

644	50c. Type **76**	10	10
645	1e. Arquebusier, 1640	10	10
646	1e.50 Infantry officer, 1777	15	10
647	2e. Infantry standard-bearer, 1777	20	10
648	2e.50 Infantryman, 1777	20	10
649	3e. Cavalry officer, 1783	25	10
650	4e. Trooper, 1783	30	15
651	4e.50 Infantry officer, 1807	40	20
652	5e. Infantryman, 1807	50	20
653	6e. Cavalry officer, 1807	70	20
654	8e. Trooper, 1807	1·00	30
655	9e. Infantryman, 1873	1·00	45

1966. 40th Anniv of National Revolution.
656 **77** 1e. multicoloured 20 15

78 Emblem of Brotherhood
79 Mendes Barata and Cruiser "Don Carlos I"

1966. Centenary of Brotherhood of the Holy Spirit.
657 **78** 1e. multicoloured 15 15

1967. Centenary of Military Naval Assn. Mult.

658	1e. Type **79**	70	35
659	2e.50 Augusto de Castilho and sail/steam corvette "Mindelo"	85	40

80 Basilica of Fatima
81 17th-century Map and M. C. Pereira (founder)

1967. 50th Anniv of Fatima Apparitions.
660 **80** 50c. multicoloured 15 10

1967. 350th Anniv of Benguela.
661 **81** 50c. multicoloured 15 10

82 Town Hall, Uige-Carmona
83 "The Three Orders"

1967. 50th Anniv of Uige-Carmona.
662 **82** 1e. multicoloured 15 10

1967. Portuguese Civil and Military Orders. Mult.

663	50c. Type **83**	10	10
664	1e. "Tower and Sword"	10	10
665	1e.50 "Avis"	10	10
666	2e. "Christ"	10	10
667	2e.50 "St. James of the Sword"	10	10
668	3e. "Empire"	20	10
669	4e. "Prince Henry"	25	15
670	5e. "Benemerencia"	30	25
671	10e. "Public Instruction"	60	25
672	20e. "Agricultural and Industrial Merit"	1·25	70

84 Belmonte Castle
85 Francisco Inocencio de Souza Countinho

1968. 500th Birth Anniv of Pedro Cabral (explorer). Multicoloured.

673	50c. Our Lady of Hope	15	15
674	1e. Type **84**	20	15
675	1e.50 St. Jeronimo's hermitage	25	15
676	2e.50 Cabral's fleet	70	15

The 50c., 1e.50 and 2e.50 are vert.

1969. Bicent of Novo Redondo (Angolan city).
677 **85** 2e. multicoloured 25 15

86 Gunboat "Loge" and Admiral Coutinho
87 Compass

1969. Birth Centenary of Admiral Gago Coutinho.
678 **86** 2e.50 multicoloured 60 20

1969. 500th Birth Anniv of Vasco da Gama (explorer).
679 **87** 1e. multicoloured 15 10

88 L. A. Rebello de Silva
89 Gate of Jeronimos

1969. Cent of Overseas Administrative Reforms.
680 **88** 1e.50 multicoloured 15 10

1969. 500th Birth Anniv of King Manoel I.
681 **89** 3e. multicoloured 20 15

90 "Angolasaurus bocagei"
91 Marshal Carmona

1970. Fossils and Minerals. Multicoloured.

682	50c. Type **90**	35	15
683	1e. Ferro-meteorite	35	15
684	1e.50 Dioptase	55	35
685	2e. "Gondwanidium validium"	55	35
686	2e.50 Diamonds	55	35
687	3e. Estromatolitos	55	35
688	3e.50 Giant-toothed shark ("Procarcharodon megalodon")	1·25	55
689	4e. Dwarf lungfish ("Microceratodus angolensis")	1·25	55
690	4e.50 Muscovite (mica)	90	55
691	5e. Barytes	90	55
692	6e. "Nostoceras helicinum"	1·60	75
693	10e. "Rotula orbiculus angolensis"	1·75	1·00

1970. Birth Centenary of Marshal Carmona.
694 **91** 2e.50 multicoloured 25 15

92 Cotton-picking

1970. Centenary of Malanje Municipality.
695 **92** 2e.50 multicoloured 30 20

93 Mail Steamers "Infante Dom Henrique" and "Principe Perfeito" and 1870 5r. Stamp
94 Map and Emblems

1970. Stamp Centenary. Multicoloured.

696	1e.50 Type **93** (postage)	50	25
697	4e.50 Beyer-Garratt steam locomotive and 25r. stamp of 1870	1·75	1·75
698	2e.50 Fokker F.27 Friendship and Boeing 707 mail planes and 10r. stamp of 1870 (air)	50	25

1971. 5th Regional Soil and Foundation Engineering Conference, Luanda.
700 **94** 2e.50 multicoloured 20 15

96 16th-century Galleon at Mouth of Congo
97 Sailing Yachts

1972. 400th Anniv of Camoens' "The Lusiads" (epic poem).
704 **96** 1e. multicoloured 50 15

1972. Olympic Games, Munich.
705 **97** 50c. multicoloured 30 15

98 Fairey IIID Seaplane "Santa Cruz" near Fernando de Noronha

1972. 50th Anniv of 1st Flight Lisbon–Rio de Janeiro.
706 **98** 1e. multicoloured 20 15

99 W.M.O. Emblem

1974. Centenary of W.M.O.
707 **99** 1e. multicoloured 20 15

100 Dish Aerials

1974. Inauguration of Satellite Communications Station Network.
708 **100** 2e. multicoloured 25 20

101 Doris Harp

1974. Sea Shells. Multicoloured.

709	25c. Type **101**	10	10
710	30c. West African murex	10	10
711	50c. Scaly-ridged venus	10	10
712	70c. Filose latirus	10	10
713	1e. "Cymbium cisium"	15	10
714	1e.50 West African helmet	15	10
715	2e. Rat cowrie	15	10
716	2e.50 Butterfly cone	25	10
717	3e. Bubonian conch	25	15
718	3e.50 "Tympanotonus fuscatus"	30	15
719	4e. Great ribbed cockle	30	15
720	5e. Lightning moon	40	15
721	6e. Lion's-paw scallop	45	20
722	7e. Giant tun	60	15

723	10e. Rugose donax	80	30
724	25e. Smith's distorsio	2·25	90
725	30e. "Olivancilaria		
	acuminata"	2·25	1·00
726	35e. Giant hairy melongena	2·75	1·25
727	40e. Wavy-leaved turrid . .	3·50	1·40
728	50e. American sundial . . .	4·50	1·75

1974. Youth Philately. No. 511 optd **1974**
FILATELIA JUVENIL.

729	**51** 5c. multicoloured	2·00	2·25

103 Arm with Rifle and Star   104 Diquiche-ua-Puheue Mask

1975. Independence.

730	**103** 1e.50 multicoloured	10	10

1975. Angolan Masks. Multicoloured.

731	50c. Type **104**	10	10
732	3e. Bui ou Congolo mask . .	15	10

105 Workers   107 Pres. Agostinho Neto

1976. Workers' Day.

733	**105** 1e. multicoloured	10	10

1976. Stamp Day. Optd **DIA DO SELO 15 Junho
1976 REP. POPULAR DE.**

734	**51** 10e. multicoloured	1·50	1·25

1976. 1st Anniv of Independence.

735	**107** 50c. black and grey . . .	10	10
736	2e. purple and grey . . .	10	10
737	3e. blue and grey . . .	10	10
738	5e. brown and buff . . .	15	10
739	10e. brown and drab . . .	25	10

1976. St. Silvestre Games. Optd **S Silvestre Rep.
Popular de.**

741	**62** 15e. multicoloured	55	35

1977. Nos. 518, 724/5 and 728 optd **REPUBLICA
POPULAR DE.**

742	20e. Type **51**	3·50	3·50
743	25e. "Cymatium trigonum"	60	15
744	30e. "Olivancilaria		
	acuminata"	75	25
745	50e. "Solarium granulatum"	1·25	40

111 Child receiving Vaccine   112 Map of Africa and Flag

1977. Polio Vaccination Campaign.

746	**111** 2k.50 blue and black . . .	10	10

1977. MPLA Congress.

747	**112** 6k. multicoloured	20	15

113 Human Rights Flame   114 Emblem

1979. 30th Anniv of Declaration of Human Rights.

748	**113** 2k.50 yellow, red & black	15	10

1979. International Anti-apartheid Year.

749	**114** 1k. multicoloured	10	10

 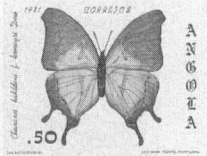

115 Child raising Arms to Light   117 Pres. Agostinho Neto

1980. International Year of the Child (1979).

750	**115** 3k.50 multicoloured . . .	15	10

1980. Nos. 697/8 optd **REPUBLICA POPULAR DE.**

751	4e.50 multicoloured (postage)	2·75	1·75
752	2e.50 multicoloured (air) . .	15	10

1980. National Heroes Day. Multicoloured.

753	4k.50 Type **117**	15	10
754	50k. Pres. Neto with		
	machine-gun	1·25	70

118 Arms and Workers   119 "The Liberated Angolan" (A. Vaz de Carvalho)

1980. "Popular Power".

755	**118** 40k. blue and black	1·00	55

1980. 5th Anniv of Independence.

756	**119** 5k.50 multicoloured	15	10

120 Running   121 Millet

1980. Olympic Games, Moscow.

757	**120** 9k. pink and red	20	10
758	– 12k. light blue and blue	30	10

DESIGN: 12k. Swimming.

1980. Angolan Produce. Multicoloured.

759	50l. Type **121**	10	10
760	5k. Coffee	15	10
761	7k.50 Sunflower	20	10
762	13k.50 Cotton	30	15
763	14k. Petroleum	30	15
764	16k. Diamonds	35	20

1981. Nos. 708, 713/16 and 718/27 with
"REPUBLICA PORTUGUESA" inscr obliterated.
(a) Dish aerials.

765	**100** 2e. multicoloured	10	10

(b) Sea Shells. Multicoloured.

766	1e. "Cymbium cisium" . . .	10	10
767	1e.50 West African helmet . .	15	10
768	2e. Rat cowrie	20	10
769	2e.50 Butterfly cone	25	10
770	3e.50 "Tympanotonus		
	fuscatus"	30	10
771	4e. Great ribbed cockle . .	35	15
772	5e. Lightning moon	40	15
773	6e. Lion's-paw scallop . .	45	20
774	7e. Giant tun	50	20
775	10e. Rugose donax	70	25
776	25e. Smith's distorsio . . .	1·75	30
777	30e. "Olivancilaria		
	acuminata"	1·90	65
778	35e. Giant hairy melongena	2·40	90
779	40e. Wavy-leaved turrid . . .	3·00	1·00

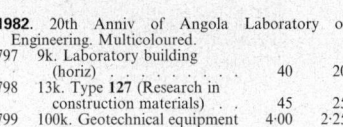

1981. 5th Anniv of Soweto Riots in South Africa.

780	**122** 4k.50 black, red & silver	20	15

123 Basketball and Volleyball

1981. 2nd Central African Games. Mult.

781	50l. Cycling and Tennis . . .	10	10
782	5k. Judo and Boxing	20	15
783	6k. Type **123**	25	15
784	10k. Handball and football . .	40	20

124 Statuette   125 "Charaxes kahldeni f. homeyri"

1981. "Turipex 81".

785	**124** 9k. multicoloured	40	20

1982. Butterflies. Multicoloured.

787	50l. Type **125**	10	10
788	1k. "Abantis gambesiaca" . .	10	10
789	5k. "Catacroptera cloanthe"	25	30
790	9k. "Myrina ficedula" (vert)	60	25
791	10k. "Colotis danae"	60	25
792	15k. "Acraea acrita bella" . .	80	30
793	100k. "Precis hierta cebrese"	5·25	2·40

126 "Silence of Night"   127 Worker and Building

1982. 5th Anniv of Admission to United Nations.
Multicoloured.

794	5k.50 Type **126**	25	15
795	7k.50 "Cotton Fields" . . .	35	15

1982. 20th Anniv of Angola Laboratory of
Engineering. Multicoloured.

797	9k. Laboratory building		
	(horiz)	40	20
798	13k. Type **127** (Research in		
	construction materials) . .	45	25
799	100k. Geotechnical equipment	4·00	2·25

128 "Albizzia versicolor"

1983. Flowers (1st series). Multicoloured.

800	5k. "Dichrostachys		
	glomerata"	25	10
801	12k. "Amblygonocarpus		
	obtusangulus"	45	20
802	50k. Type **128**	2·00	1·10

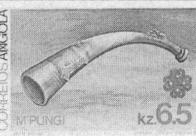

129 Angolan Woman and Emblem

1983. 1st Angolan Women's Organization Congress.

803	**129** 20k. multicoloured	80	25

130 M'pungi (horn)

1983. World Communications Year. Mult.

804	6k.50 Type **130**	25	20
805	12k. Mondu (drum)	50	45

131 Spear breaking Chain around South Africa

1983. 30th Anniv of Organization of African Unity.

806	**131** 6k.50 multicoloured . . .	30	25

132 "Antestiopsis lineaticollis intricata"

1983. "Brasiliana 83" International Stamp Exn, Rio
de Janeiro. Harmful Insects. Mult.

807	4k.50 Type **132**	25	15
808	6k.50 "Stephanoderes		
	hampei"	35	25
809	10k. "Zonocerus variegatus"	60	45

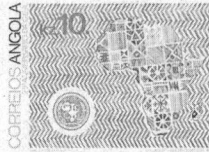

133 Map of Africa and E.C.A. Emblem

1983. 25th Anniv of Economic Commission for
Africa.

810	**133** 10k. multicoloured	45	40

134 Collecting Mail   136 Dove

135 "Parasa karschi"

1983. 185th Anniv of Postal Service. Multicoloured.

811	50l. Type **134**	10	10
812	3k.50 Unloading mail from		
	aircraft (horiz)	20	15
813	5k. Sorting mail (horiz) . .	35	25
814	15k. Posting letter	85	80
815	30k. Collecting mail from		
	private box (horiz)	1·75	1·50

1984. Moths. Multicoloured.

817	50l. Type **135**	10	10
818	1k. "Diaphone angolensis" . .	10	10
819	3k.50 "Choeropais jucunda" . .	30	15
820	6k.50 "Hespagarista rendalli"	50	35
821	15k. "Euchromia guineensis"	95	80
822	17k.50 "Mazuca roseistriga" . .	1·10	95
823	20k. "Utetheisa callima" . .	1·40	1·25

1984. 1st National Union of Angolan Workers
Congress.

824	**136** 30k. multicoloured	1·75	1·50

137 Flag and Agostinho Neto

1984. 5th National Heroes Day. Multicoloured.
825 10k.50 Type **137** 50 45
826 36k.50 Flag and Agostinho Neto (different) . . . . . 1·60 1·50

138 Southern Ground Hornbill

1984. Birds. Multicoloured.
827 10k.50 Type **138** 90 90
828 14k. Palm-nut vulture . . . . 1·25 1·25
829 16k. Goliath heron . . . . . . 1·50 1·50
830 19k.50 Eastern white pelican 1·75 1·75
831 22k. African spoonbill . . . 2·00 2·00
832 26k. South African crowned crane . . . . 2·40 2·40

139 Greater Kudu

1984. Mammals. Multicoloured.
833 1k. Type **139** 10 10
834 4k. Springbok 25 15
835 5k. Chimpanzee 30 25
836 10k. African buffalo 55 50
837 15k. Sable antelope 80 65
838 20k. Aardvark . . . . 1·25 1·10
839 25k. Spotted hyena . . . . . 1·50 1·25

140 Sao Pedro da Barra Fortress

1985. Monuments. Multicoloured.
840 5k. Type **140** 25 20
841 12k.50 Nova Oerias ruins . . 60 55
842 18k. Antiga cathedral ruins, M'Banza Kongo 80 75
843 26k. Massangano fortress . . 1·25 1·10
844 39k. Escravatura museum . . 1·75 1·60

141 Flags on World Map **142** Flags and "XXV"

1985. 5th Anniv of Southern Africa Development Co-ordination Conference. Multicoloured.
845 1k. Type **141** 10 10
846 11k. Offshore drilling . . . . 1·25 50
847 57k. Conference session . . . 2·50 2·40

1985. 25th Anniv of National Union of Angolan Workers.
848 **142** 77k. multicoloured . . . 3·50 3·25

143 "Lonchocarpas sericeus"

1985. Medicinal Plants. Multicoloured.
849 1k. Type **143** 10 10
850 4k. "Gossypium sp." 20 15
851 11k. Senna 50 45
852 25k.50 "Gloriosa superba" 1·10 1·00
853 55k. "Cochlospermum angolensis" . . . . 2·50 2·40

144 Map of Angola as Dove and Conference Emblem

1984. Ministerial Conference of Non-aligned Countries, Luanda.
854 **144** 35k. multicoloured . . . 1·60 1·50

145 Dove and U.N. Emblem

1985. 40th Anniv of U.N.O.
855 **145** 12k.50 multicoloured . . 60 55

146 Cement Works

1985. 10th Anniv of Independence. Multicoloured.
856 50l. Type **146** 10 10
857 5k. Timber yard 20 15
858 7k. Quartz 30 25
859 10k. Iron works 50 45

147 Emblem, Open Book, Soldier, Farmer and Factory

1985. 2nd MPLA Congress.
861 **147** 20k. multicoloured . . . 90 85

148 Runner on Track

1985. 30th Anniv of Demostenes de Almeida Clington Races. Multicoloured.
862 50l. Type **148** 10 10
863 5k. Two runners on road . . 20 15
864 6k.50 Three runners on road 30 25
865 10k. Two runners on track 50 45

149 Map, Stadium and Players **150** Crowd

1986. World Cup Football Championship, Mexico.
866 **149** 50l. multicoloured . . . 10 10
867 – 3k.50 multicoloured . . . 15 15
868 – 5k. multicoloured 30 25
869 – 7k. multicoloured 35 30
870 – 10k. multicoloured . . . 50 45
871 – 18k. multicoloured . . . 85 70
DESIGNS: 3k.50 to 18k. Different footballers.

1986. 25th Anniv of Armed Independence Movement.
872 **150** 15k. multicoloured . . . 75 70

151 Soviet Space Project

1985. 25th Anniv of First Man in Space. Mult.
873 50l. Type **151** 10 10
874 1k. "Voskhod 1" 10 10
875 5k. Cosmonaut on space walk 20 15
876 10k. Moon vehicle 50 45
877 13k. "Soyuz"–"Apollo" link-up 60 55

152 National Flag and U.N. Emblem **153** People at Work

1986. 10th Anniv of Angolan Membership of U.N.O.
878 **152** 22k. multicoloured . . . 1·00 90

1986. 30th Anniv of Popular Movement for the Liberation of Angola. Multicoloured.
879 5k. Type **153** 20 15
880 5k. Emblem and people (29 × 36 mm) 20 15
881 5k. Soldiers fighting 20 15
Nos. 879/81 were printed together, se-tenant, forming a composite design.

154 Lecturer and Students (Faculty of Engineering) **155** Ouioca

1986. 10th Anniv of Agostinho Neto University. Multicoloured.
882 50l. Type **154** 10 10
883 7k. Students and Judges (Faculty of Law) 30 25
884 10k. Students using microscopes and surgeons operating (Faculty of Medicine) 50 45

1987. Traditional Hairstyles. Multicoloured.
885 1k. Type **155** 10 10
886 1k.50 Luanda 10 10
887 5k. Humbe 20 15
888 7k. Muila 35 25
889 20k. Muila (different) 80 70
890 30k. Lunda, Dilolo . . . . . 1·25 1·00

156 "Lenin in the Smolny Institute" (detail, Serov) **157** Pambala Beach

1987. 70th Anniv of Russian Revolution.
891 **156** 15k. multicoloured . . . 60 25

1987. Scenic Spots. Multicoloured.
892 50l. Type **157** 10 10
893 1k.50 Quedas do Dala (waterfalls) 10 10
894 3k.50 Black Feet Rocks, Pungo Adongo (vert) . . . 15 10
895 5k. Cuango River valley . . 20 15
896 10k. Luanda shore (vert) . . 40 35
897 20k. Serra da Leba road . . 80 75

158 Emblem **159** Dancers

1988. 2nd Angolan Women's Organization Congress. Multicoloured.
898 2k. Type **158** 10 10
899 10k. Women engaged in various pursuits 40 35

1988. 10th Anniv of Vitoria Carnival. Mult.
900 5k. Type **159** 15 10
901 10k. Revellers 40 35

160 Augusto N'Gangula (child revolutionary)

1989. Pioneers. Multicoloured.
902 12k. Type **160** (20th death anniv) 50 45
903 15k. Pioneers (25th anniv (1988) of Agostinho Neto Pioneers Organization) . . 60 55

161 Luanda 1st August Sports Club (1979–81)

1989. 10th National Football League Championship. Championship Winners. Multicoloured.
904 5k. Type **161** 15 15
905 5k. Luanda Petro Atletico (1982, 1984, 1986–88) . . . 15 15
906 5k. Benguela 1st May Sports Club (1983, 1985) 15 15

162 Watering Cabbages

1990. 10th Anniv (1987) of International Fund for Agricultural Development.
907 **162** 10k. multicoloured . . . 35 30

163 19th-century Middle-class Houses, Luanda

1990. Historical Buildings. Multicoloured.
908 1k. Type **163** 10 10
909 2k. Cidade Alta railway station, Luanda . . . . . 1·75 30
910 5k. National Anthropology Museum 20 15
911 15k. Palace of Ana Joaquina dos Santos 55 50
912 23k. Iron Palace 80 75
913 36k. Meteorological observatory (vert) . . . . 1·25 1·10
914 50k. Governor's palace . . . 1·75 1·60

164 "General Machado" and Route Map

1990. Benguela (915) and Luanda Railways. Mult.
915 5k. Type **164** 45 30

916	12k. Beyer-Garratt steam locomotive (facing left) . .	80	75
917	12k. Beyer-Garratt steam locomotive (facing right)	80	75
918	14k. Mikado steam locomotive	1·25	95

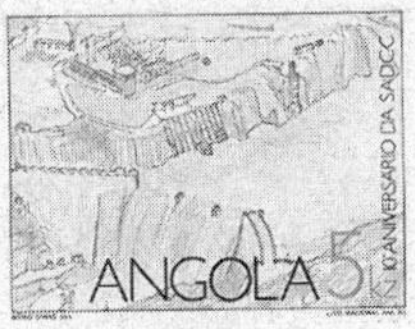

165 Hydroelectric Production

1990. 10th Anniv of Southern Africa Development Co-ordinating Conference. Multicoloured.

920	5k. Type **165**	20	15
921	9k. Oil industry	90	30

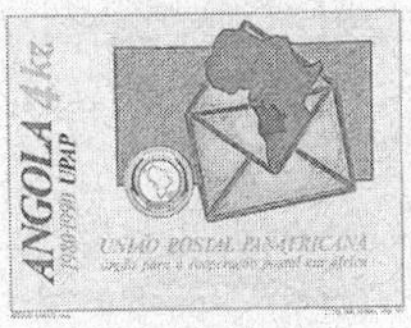

166 Map in Envelope

1990. 10th Anniv of Pan-African Postal Union. Multicoloured.

922	4k. Type **166**	15	10
923	10k. Map consisting of stamps and envelopes . . .	35	30

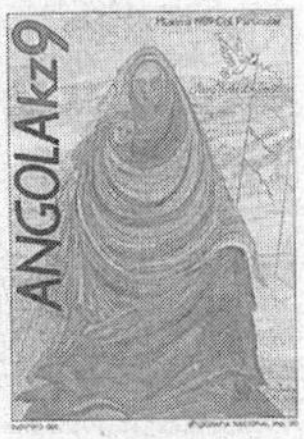

167 "Muxima"

1990. "Stamp World London 90" International Stamp Exn. Paintings by Raul Indipwo. Mult.

924	6k. "Three Graces" (horiz)	20	15
925	9k. Type **167**	30	25

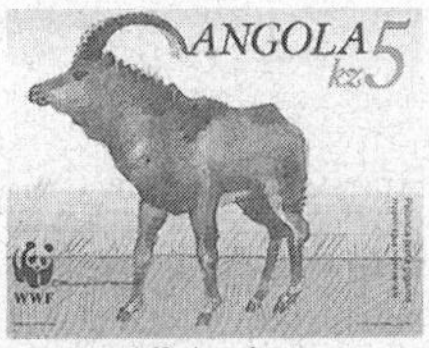

168 Antelope

1990. Protected Animals. Sable Antelope. Mult.

926	5k. Type **168**	2·40	1·90
927	5k. Male and female	2·40	1·90
928	5k. Female	2·40	1·90
929	5k. Female and young . . .	2·40	1·90

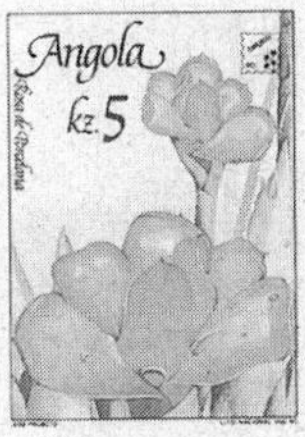

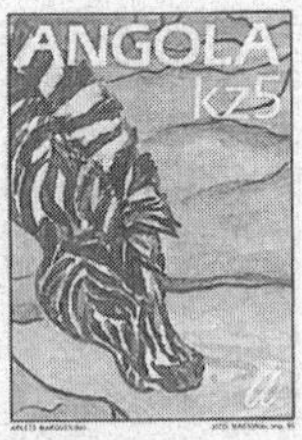

169 Porcelain Rose **170** Zebra Drinking

1990. "Belgica 90" International Stamp Exhibition, Brussels. Flowers. Multicoloured.

930	5k. Type **169**	20	15
931	8k. Indian carnation	30	25
932	10k. Allamanda	35	30

1990. International Literacy Year. Multicoloured.

934	5k. Type **170**	20	15
935	5k. Butterfly	20	15
936	5k. Horse's head	20	15

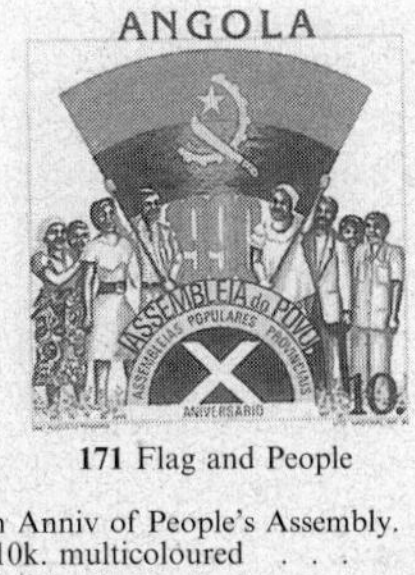

171 Flag and People

1990. 10th Anniv of People's Assembly.

938	**171**	10k. multicoloured . . .	35	30

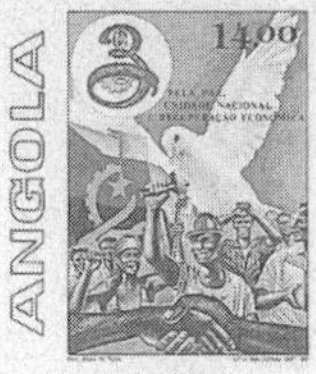

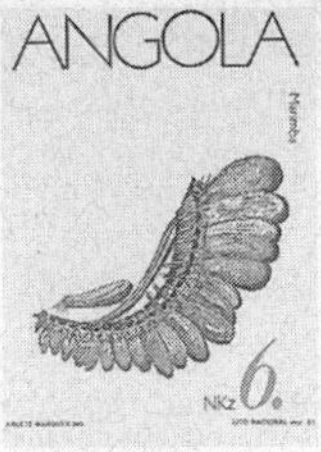

172 Dove, Flag and Workers **174** Marimba

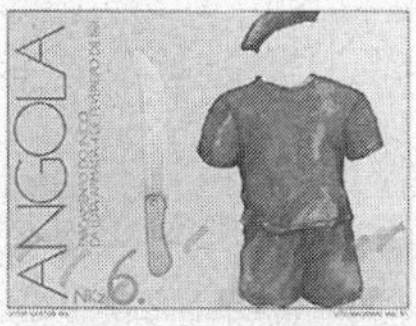

173 Uniform, 1961

1990. 3rd Popular Movement for the Liberation of Angola-Labour Party Congress.

939	**172**	14k. multicoloured . . .	50	45

1991. 30th Anniv of Armed Independence Movement. Freedom Fighters' Uniforms. Mult.

940	6k. Type **173**	20	15
941	6k. Pau N'Dulo, 1962–63 . .	20	15
942	6k. Military uniform, 1968	20	15
943	6k. Military uniform from 1972	20	15

1991. Musical Instruments. Multicoloured.

944	6k. Type **174**	10	10
945	6k. Ngoma ya Mucupela (double-ended drum) . . .	10	10
946	6k. Ngoma la Txina (floor-standing drum)	10	10
947	6k. Kissange	10	10

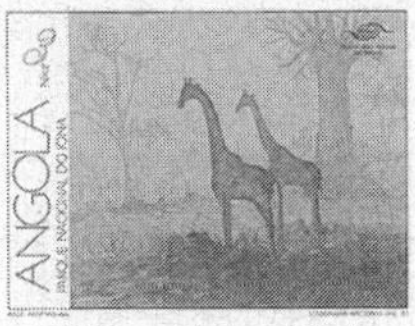

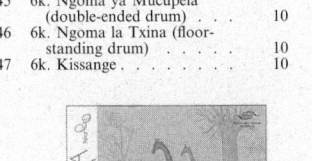

175 Iona National Park

1991. African Tourism Year. Multicoloured.

948	3k. Type **175**	10	10
949	7k. Kalandula Falls	10	10
950	35k. Lobito Bay	70	30
951	60k. "Welwitschia mirabilis"	65	55

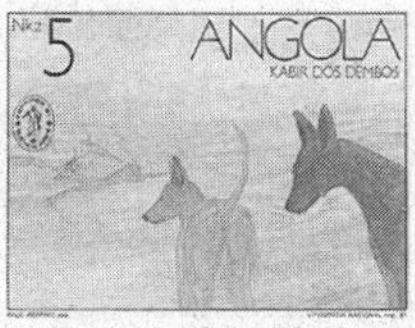

176 Kabir of the Dembos

1991. "Espamer '91" Spain–Latin America Stamp Exhibition, Buenos Aires. Dogs. Multicoloured.

953	5k. Type **176**	10	10
954	7k. Ombua	20	10
955	11k. Kabir massongo	15	10
956	12k. Kawa tchowe	15	10

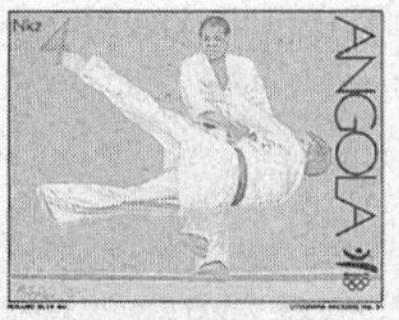

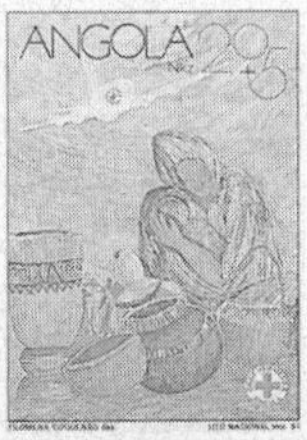

177 Judo **178** Mother and Child

1991. Olympic Games, Barcelona (1992) (1st issue). Multicoloured.

957	4k. Type **177**	10	10
958	6k. Yachting	10	10
959	10k. Marathon	15	10
960	100k. Swimming	1·10	95

1991. 13th Anniv of Angolan Red Cross. Mult.

961	20k.+5k. Type **178**	30	20
962	40k.+5k. Zebra and foal . .	50	40

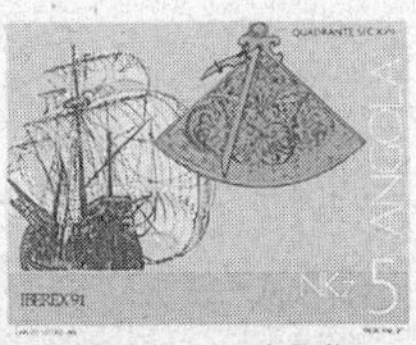

179 Quadrant and Galleon

1991. "Iberex '91" Stamp Exhibition. Navigational Instruments. Multicoloured.

963	5k. Type **179**	15	10
964	15k. Astrolabe and caravel	30	10
965	20k. Cross-staff and caravel	50	20
966	50k. Navigation chart by Fran-cisco Rodrigues and galleon	1·50	60

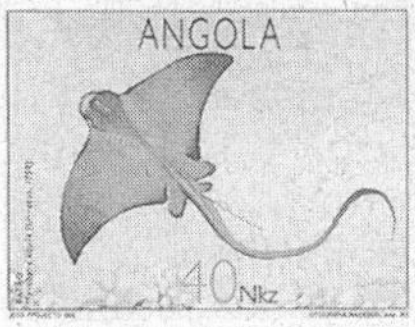

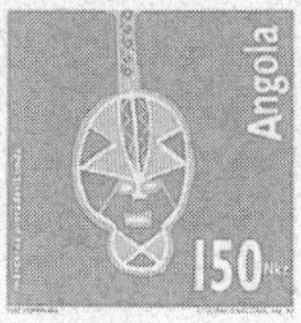

180 Common Eagle Ray **181** Mukixi wa Mbwesu Mask

1992. Rays. Multicoloured.

967	40k. Type **180**	35	25
968	50k. Spotted eagle ray . . .	40	35
969	66k. Manta ray	55	40
970	80k. Brown ray	65	50

1992. Quioca Painted Masks (1st series).

972	–	60k. orange and brown	15	10
973	–	100k. black, verm & red	25	20
974	**181**	150k. pink and orange . .	35	30
975	–	250k. red and brown . .	60	50

DESIGNS: 60k. Kalelwa mask; 100k. Mikixe wa Kino mask; 250k. Cikunza mask.

See also Nos. 1006/7 and 1021/4.

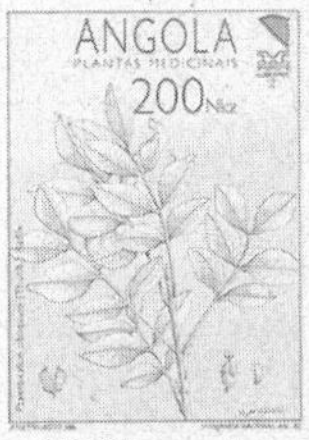

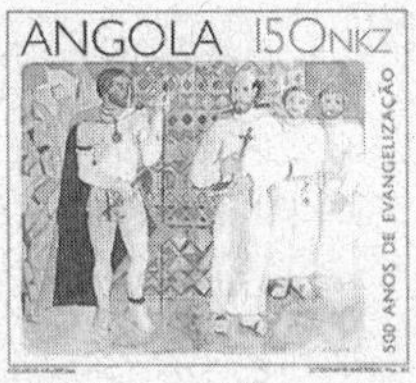

182 "Ptaeroxylon obliquum" **183** King and Missionaries

1992. "Lubrapex 92" Brazilian–Portuguese Stamp Exhibition, Lisbon. Medicinal Plants. Each brown, stone and deep brown.

976	200k. Type **182**	45	35
977	300k. "Spondias mombin"	70	55
978	500k. "Parinari curatellifolia"	1·25	1·00
979	600k. "Cochlospermum angolense"	1·40	1·10

1992. 500th Anniv (1991) of Baptism of First Angolans. Multicoloured.

980	150k. Type **183**	35	30
981	420k. Ruins of M'Banza Congo Church	1·00	80
982	470k. Muxima Church . . .	1·10	90
983	500k. Cross superimposed on children's faces	1·25	1·00

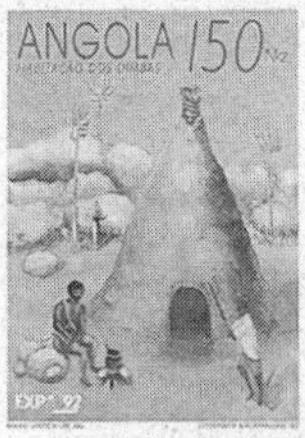

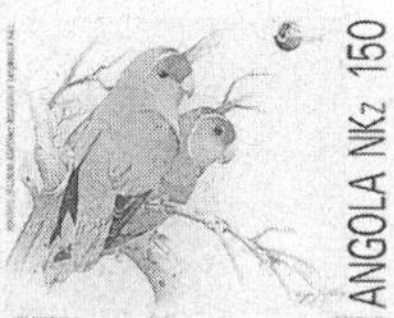

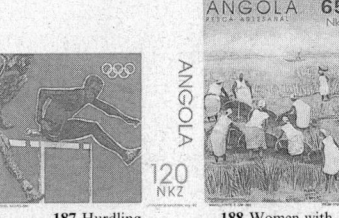

184 Dimba House **185** Lovebirds

1992. "Expo '92" World's Fair, Seville. Traditional Houses. Multicoloured.

984	150k. Type **184**	35	30
985	330k. Cokwe house	80	65
986	360k. Mbali house	85	70
987	420k. Ambwela house . . .	1·00	80
988	500k. House of the Upper Zambezi	1·25	1·00

1992. Nature Protection. Peach-faced Lovebirds. Multicoloured.

989	150k. Type **185**	35	30
990	200k. Birds feeding	45	35
991	250k. Bird in hand	60	50
992	300k. Bird on perch	70	55

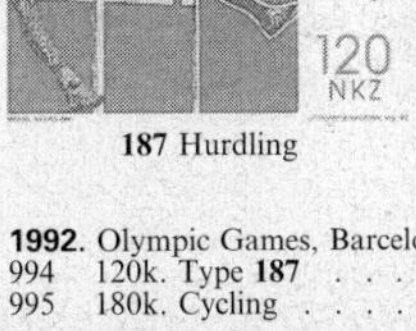

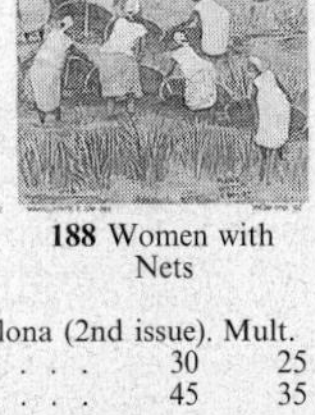

187 Hurdling **188** Women with Nets

1992. Olympic Games, Barcelona (2nd issue). Mult.

994	120k. Type **187**	30	25
995	180k. Cycling	45	35
996	240k. Roller hockey	55	45
997	360k. Basketball	85	70

1992. Fishing. Multicoloured.

998	65k. Type **188**	20	10
999	90k. Fishermen pulling in nets	30	15
1000	100k. Fishermen checking traps	35	20
1001	120k. Fishing canoes . . .	30	25

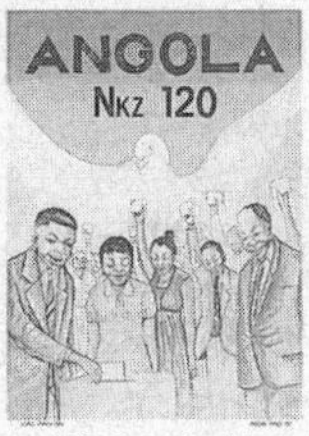

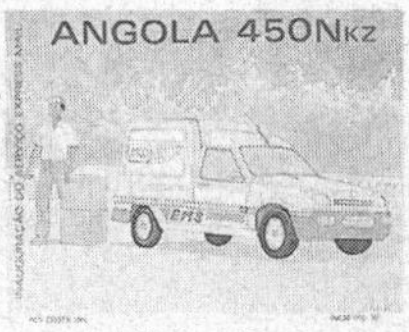

190 Crowd with Ballot Papers around Ballot Box **191** Post Van

1992. 1st Free Elections. Multicoloured.

1003	120k. Type **190**	30	25
1004	150k. Doves, map, people and ballot box	35	30
1005	200k. Dove, crowd and ballot box	45	35

1992. Quioca Painted Masks (2nd series). As T **181**.

1006	72k. brown, black and yellow	15	10
1007	80k. red, black and brown	20	15
1008	120k. pink, black and red	30	25
1009	210k. black and yellow . . .	50	40

DESIGNS: 72k. Cihongo mask; 80k. Mbwasu mask; 120k. Cinhanga mask; 210k. Kalewa mask.

1992. Introduction of Express Mail Service in Angola. Multicoloured.

1010	450k. Type **191**	55	45
1011	550k. Boeing 707 airplane	65	50

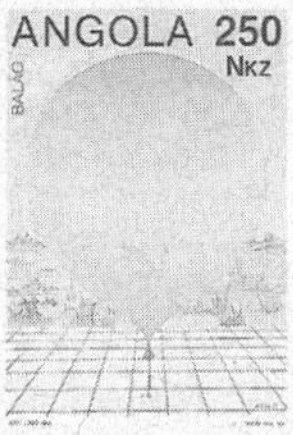

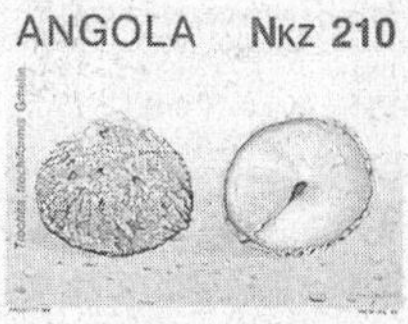

192 Weather Balloon **193** Rayed Hat

1993. World Meteorology Day. Meteorological Instruments. Multicoloured.

1012	250k. Type **192**	10	10
1013	470k. Actinometer	10	10
1014	500k. Rain-gauge	10	10

1993. Molluscs. Multicoloured.

1015	210k. Type **193**	10	10
1016	330k. Bubonian conch . . .	15	10
1017	400k. African pelican's foot	15	10
1018	500k. White spindle	20	15

1993. Quioca Art (1st series). As T **181**.

1021	72k. grey, red and brown	10	10
1022	210k. pink and brown . . .	10	10
1023	420k. black, brn & orge . .	10	10
1024	600k. black, red and brown	10	10

DESIGNS: 72k. Men with vehicles; 210k. Rider on antelope; 420k. Bird-plane; 600k. Carrying "soba".

See also Nos. 1038/41 and 1050/3.

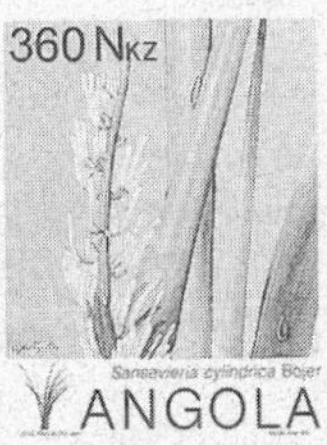

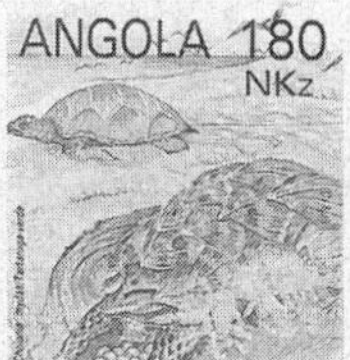

195 "Sansevieria cylindrica" **196** Atlantic Hawksbill Turtle laying Eggs and Green Turtle

1993. Cacti and Succulents. Multicoloured.

1025	360k. Type **195**	10	10
1026	400k. Milk-bush	10	10
1027	500k. Indian fig	10	10
1028	600k. "Dracaena aubryana"	10	10

1993. Sea Turtles. Multicoloured.

1029	180k. Type **196**	10	10
1030	450k. Head of Atlantic hawksbill turtle and newly hatched turtles	10	10
1031	550k. Leather-back turtle . .	10	10
1032	630k. Loggerhead turtles . .	15	10

Nos. 1029/32 were issued together, se-tenant, forming a composite design.

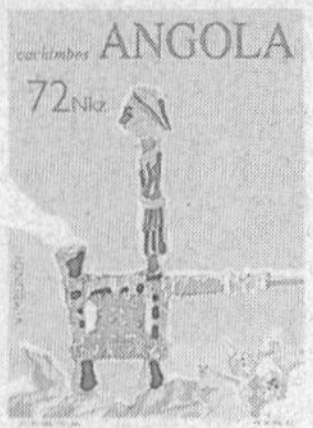

198 Vimbundi Pipe

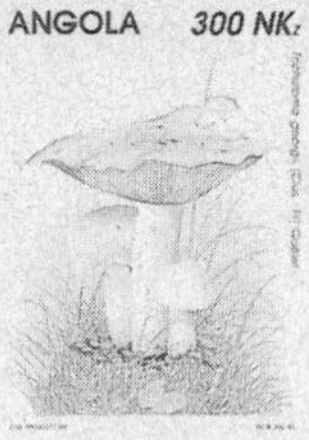

199 St. George's Mushroom

1993. Tobacco Pipes. Multicoloured.
1034 72k. Type **198** 10 10
1035 200k. Vimbundi pipe (different) 10 10
1036 420k. Mutopa calabash water pipe 10 10
1037 600k. Pexi carved-head pipe 10 10

1993. Quioca Art (2nd series). As T **181**.
1038 300k. brown and orange . . 10 10
1039 600k. red and brown . . . 10 10
1040 800k. black, orange & dp orge 15 10
1041 1000k. orange and brown 20 15
DESIGNS: 300k. Leopard and dog; 600k. Rabbits; 800k. Birds; 1000k. Birds and cockerel.

1993. Fungi. Multicoloured.
1042 300k. Type **199** 55 15
1043 500k. Death cap 90 30
1044 600k. "Amanita vaginata" 1·10 35
1045 1000k. Parasol mushroom 1·90 60

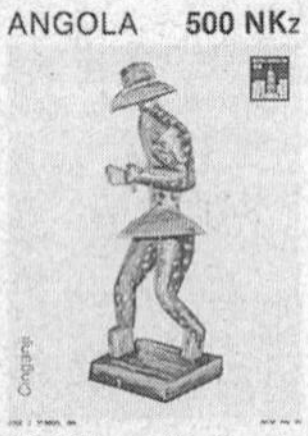

200 "Cinganji" (figurine of dancer, Bie province)

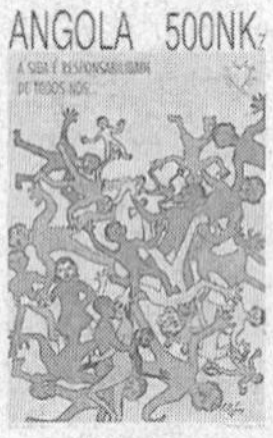

201 Orgy

1994. National Culture Day. "Hong Kong '94" International Stamp Exhibition. Multicoloured.
1046 500k. Type **200** 10 10
1047 1000k. Chief's staff with carved woman's head (Bie province) 20 15
1048 1200k. Statuette of traveller riding ox (Huambo province) 25 20
1049 2200k. Corn pestle (Ovimbundu) 45 35

1994. Quioca Art (3rd series). As T **181**.
1050 500k. multicoloured 10 10
1051 2000k. red and brown . . . 40 30
1052 2500k. red and brown . . . 50 40
1053 3000k. carmine and red . . 60 50
DESIGNS: 500k. Bird on plant; 2000k. Plant with roots; 2500k. Plant; 3000k. Fern.

1994. AIDS Awareness Campaign. Multicoloured.
1054 500k. Type **201** 10 10
1055 1000k. Masked figure using infected syringe passing box of condoms to young couple 10 10
1056 3000k. Victims 20 15

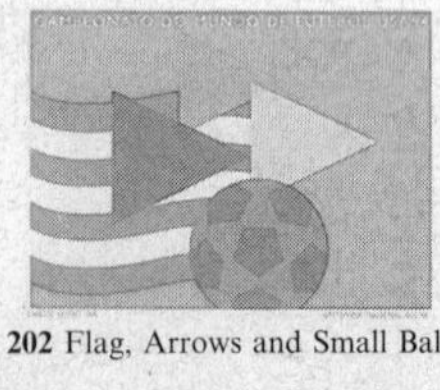

202 Flag, Arrows and Small Ball

1994. World Cup Football Championship, U.S.A. Multicoloured.
1057 500k. Type **202** 10 10
1058 700k. Flag, four arrows and large ball 10 10
1059 2200k. Flag, goal net and ball 10 10
1060 2500k. Flag, ball and boot 10 10

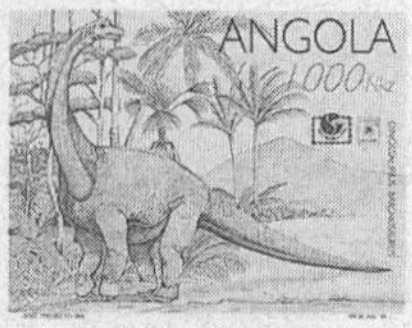

203 Brachiosaurus

1994. "Philakorea 1994" International and "Singpex '94" Stamp Exhibitions. Dinosaurs. Multicoloured.
1061 1000k. Type **203** 10 10
1062 3000k. Spinosaurus 10 10
1063 5000k. Ouranosaurus . . . 10 10
1064 10000k. Lesothosaurus . . . 15 10

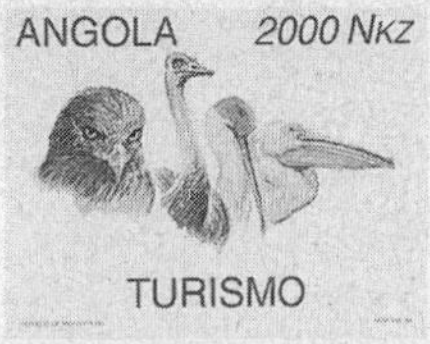

204 Brown Snake Eagle, Ostrich, Yellow-billed Stork and Pink-backed Pelican

1994. Tourism. Multicoloured.
1066 2000k. Type **204** 10 10
1067 4000k. Animals 10 10
1068 8000k. Women 10 10
1069 10000k. Men 10 10

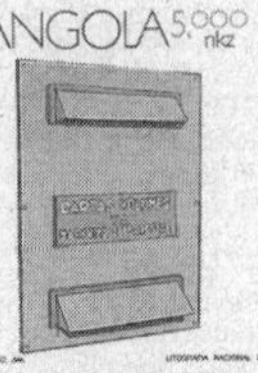

205 Dual-service Wall-mounted Post Box

1994. Post Boxes. Multicoloured.
1070 5000k. Type **205** 10 10
1071 7500k. Wall-mounted philatelic post box 10 10
1072 10000k. Free-standing post box 10 10
1073 21000k. Multiple service wall-mounted post box . . 25 15

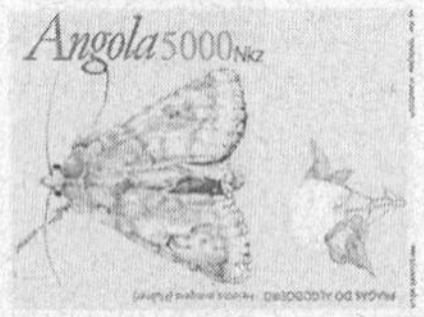

206 "Heliothis armigera" (moth)

1994. Insects. Multicoloured.
1074 5000k. Type **206** 10 10
1075 6000k. "Bemisia tabasi" . . 10 10
1076 10000k. "Dysdercus sp." (bug) 10 10
1077 27000k. "Spodoptera exigua" (moth) 25 15

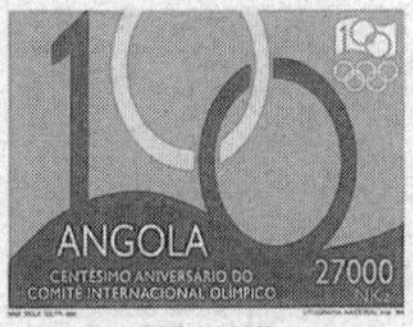

207 "100"

1994. Cent of International Olympic Committee.
1078 **207** 27000k. red, yell & blk 25 20

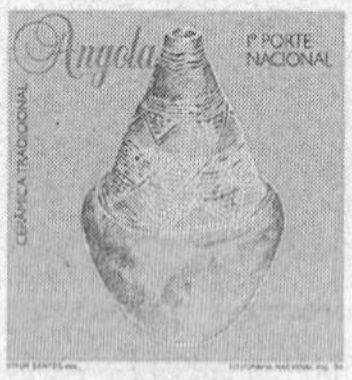

208 Pot

1995. Traditional Ceramics. With service indicator. Multicoloured. (a) INLAND POSTAGE. Inscr "PORTE NACIONAL".
1079 (1°) Type **208** 10 10
1080 (2°) Pot with figure of woman on lid 10 10

(b) INTERNATIONAL POSTAGE. Inscr "PORTE INTERNACIONAL".
1081 (1°) Pot with man's head on lid 20 15
1082 (2°) Duck-shaped pot . . . 25 20

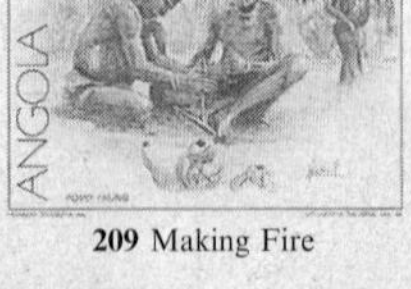

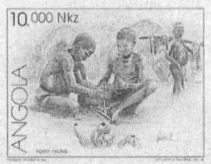

209 Making Fire

1995. The !Kung (Khoisan tribe). Multicoloured.
1083 10000k. Type **209** 10 10
1084 15000k. Tipping darts with poison 15 10
1085 20000k. Smoking 20 15
1086 25000k. Hunting 20 15
1087 28000k. Women and children 25 20
1088 30000k. Painting animals on walls 25 20

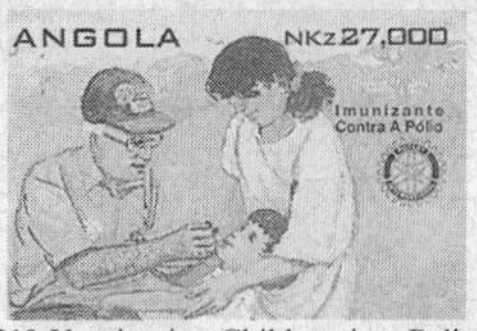

210 Vaccinating Child against Polio

1995. 90th Anniv of Rotary International. Multicoloured. (a) Inscr in Portuguese.
1089 27000k. Type **210** 15 10
1090 27000k. Examining baby . . 15 10
1091 27000k. Giving child vaccination 15 10

(b) Inscr in English.
1092 27000k. Type **210** 15 10
1093 27000k. As No. 1090 . . . 15 10
1094 27000k. As No. 1091 . . . 15 10
Nos. 1089/91 and 1092/4 respectively were issued together, se-tenant, forming composite designs.

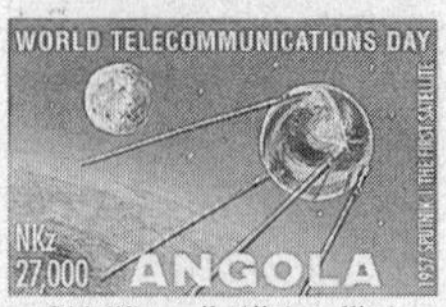

211 "Sputnik 1" (satellite)

1995. World Telecommunications Day. Mult.
1096 27000k. Type **211** 15 10
1097 27000k. "Intelsat" satellite and space shuttle 15 10

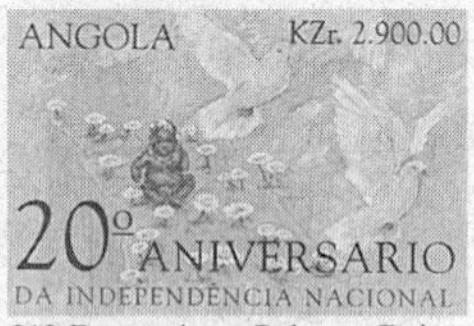

212 Doves above Baby on Daisy-covered Map

1995. 20th Anniv of Independence.
1099 **212** 2900k. multicoloured . . 65 50

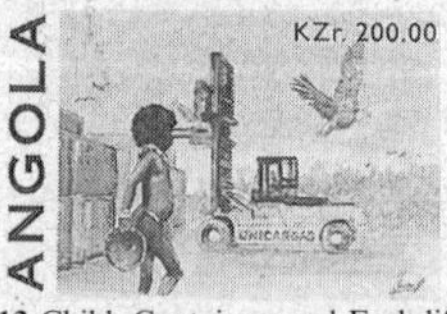

213 Child, Containers and Fork-lift Truck

1996. Goods Transportation. Multicoloured.
1100 200k. Type **213** 10 10
1101 1265k. Sailing boats and "Mount Cameroon" (ferry) 25 25
1102 2583k. Fork-lift trucks loading and unloading "Mount Cameroon" (ferry) 90 50
1103 2583k. Lorry 60 50

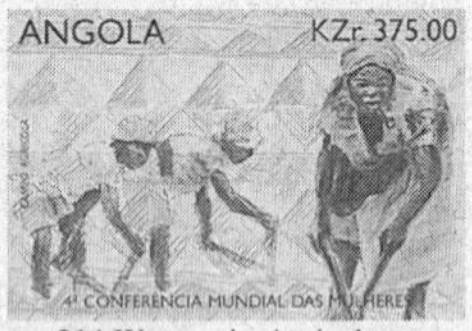

214 Women in Agriculture

1996. 4th World Conference on Women, Peking (1995). Multicoloured.
1105 375k. Type **214** 10 10
1106 1106k. Women in education 25 20
1107 1265k. Women in business 30 25
1108 2900k. Dimba servant girl (vert) 65 50

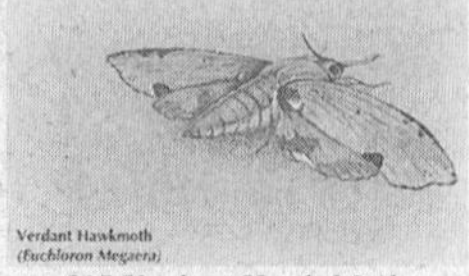

215 Verdant Hawk Moth

1996. Flora and Fauna. Multicoloured.
1110 1500k. Type **215** 10 10
1111 1500k. Honey buzzard ("Western Honey Buzzard") 10 10
1112 1500k. Bateleur 10 10
1113 1500k. Common kestrel . . 10 10
1114 4400k. Water lily 20 15
1115 4400k. Red-crested turaco 20 15
1116 4400k. Giraffe 20 15
1117 4400k. African elephant . . 20 15
1118 5100k. Panther toad 20 15
1119 5100k. Hippopotamus . . . 20 15
1120 5100k. Cattle egret 20 15
1121 5100k. Lion 20 15
1122 6000k. African hunting ("wild") dog 25 20
1123 6000k. Helmeted turtle . . . 25 20
1124 6000k. African pygmy goose 25 20
1125 6000k. Egyptian plover . . 25 20
Nos. 1111/13, 1115/17, 1119/21 and 1123/5 respectively were issued together, se-tenant, forming composite designs.

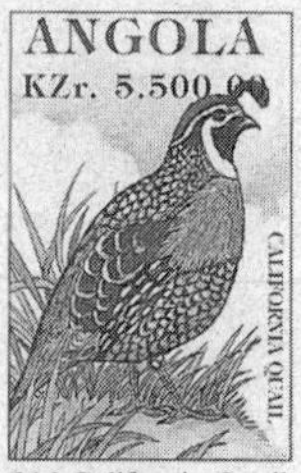

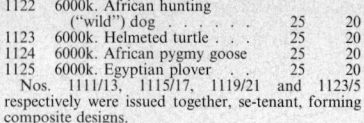

216 California Quail

1997. Birds. Multicoloured.
1127 5500k. Type **216** 20 15
1128 5500k. Greater prairie chicken 20 15
1129 5500k. Painted quail 20 15
1130 5500k. Golden pheasant . . 20 15
1131 5500k. Roulroul partridge 20 15
1132 5500k. Ceylon spurfowl ("sourfowl") 20 15
1133 5500k. Himalayan snowcock 20 15
1134 5500k. Temminck's ("Temmincks") tragopan 20 15
1135 5500k. Lady Amherst's pheasant 20 15
1136 5500k. Great curassow . . . 20 15
1137 5500k. Red-legged partridge 20 15
1138 5500k. Impeyan pheasant 20 15
1139 5500k. Anna's hummingbird 20 15
1140 5500k. Blue-throated hummingbird 20 15
1141 5500k. Broad-tailed hummingbird 20 15
1142 5500k. Costa's hummingbird 20 15
1143 5500k. White-eared hummingbird 20 15
1144 5500k. Calliope hummingbird 20 15
1145 5500k. Violet-crowned hummingbird 20 15
1146 5500k. Rufous hummingbird 20 15
1147 5500k. Crimson topaz . . . 20 15
1148 5500k. Broad-billed hummingbird 20 15
1149 5500k. Frilled coquette . . . 20 15
1150 5500k. Ruby-throated hummingbird 20 15

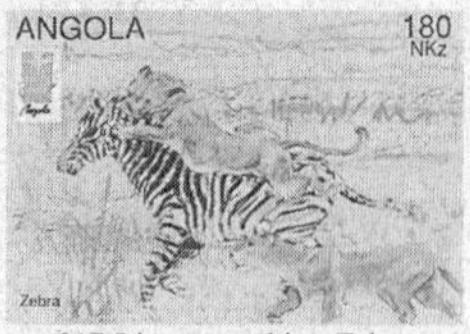

217 Lions attacking Zebra

1996. African Wildlife. Multicoloured.
1152 180k. Type **217** 10 10
1153 180k. Lions watching zebras 10 10
1154 180k. African hunting dogs attacking gnu 10 10
1155 180k. Pack of hunting dogs chasing herd of gnu . . 10 10
1156 450k. Lions stalking isolated zebra 10 10
1157 450k. Male lion 10 10
1158 450k. Hunting dogs surrounding gnu 10 10
1159 450k. Close-up of African hunting dog 10 10
1160 550k. Cheetah 10 10
1161 550k. Cheetah chasing springbok 10 10
1162 550k. Leopard 10 10
1163 550k. Leopard stalking oryx 10 10
1164 630k. Cheetah running beside herd of springbok 10 10
1165 630k. Cheetah overpowering springbok 10 10
1166 630k. Leopard approaching oryx 10 10
1167 630k. Leopard leaping at oryx 10 10
Nos. 1152/67 were issued together, se-tenant, in sheetlets with each horizontal strip forming a composite design of lions, cheetah, hunting dogs or leopard attacking prey.

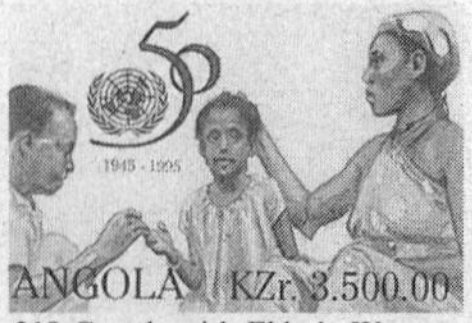

218 Couple with Elderly Woman

1996. 50th Anniv of U.N.O. Multicoloured.
1168 3500k. Type **218** 15 10
1169 3500k. Children at water pump 15 10

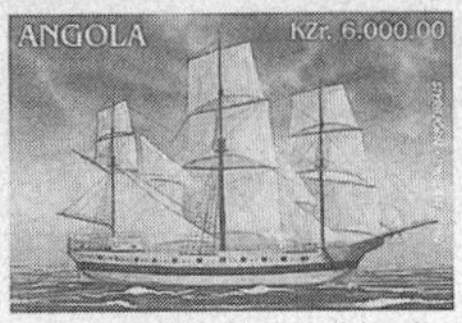
ANGOLA
KZr. 6.000.00

219 "Styrbjorn" (Swedish sail warship), 1789

1996. Ships. Multicoloured.

1171	6000k. Type **219**	35	20
1172	6000k. U.S.S. "Constellation" (United States frigate), 1797	35	20
1173	6000k. "Taureau" (French torpedo-boat), 1865	35	20
1174	6000k. French bomb ketch	35	20
1175	6000k. "Sardegna" (Italian battleship), 1881	35	20
1176	6000k. H.M.S. "Glasgow" (frigate), 1867	35	20
1177	6000k. U.S.S. "Essex" (frigate), 1812	35	20
1178	6000k. H.M.S. "Inflexible" (battleship), 1881	35	20
1179	6000k. H.M.S. "Minotaur" (ironclad), 1863	35	20
1180	6000k. "Napoleon" (French steam ship of the line), 1854	35	20
1181	6000k. "Sophia Amalia" (Danish galleon), 1650	35	20
1182	6000k. "Massena" (French battleship), 1887	35	20

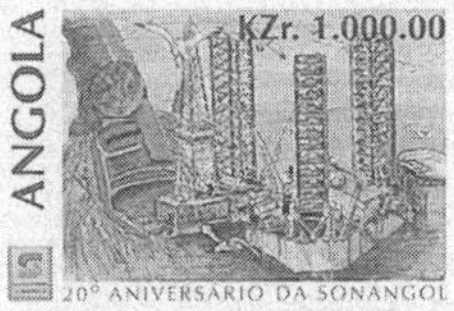
ANGOLA
KZr. 1.000.00
20° ANIVERSARIO DA SONANGOL

220 Mask and Drilling Platform

1996. 20th Anniv of Sonangol. Multicoloured.

1184	1000k. Type **220**	30	10
1185	1000k. Storage tanks and mask of woman's face	10	10
1186	2500k. Mask with beard and gas bottles	10	10
1187	5000k. Refuelling airplane and mask of monkey's face	20	15

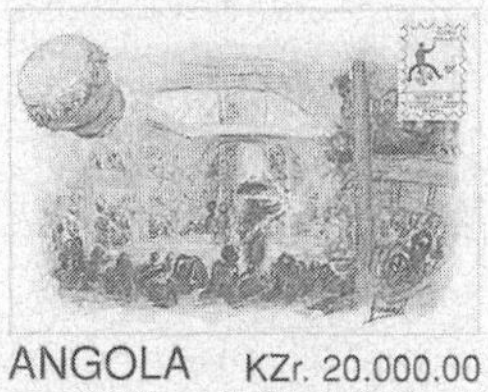
ANGOLA KZr. 20.000.00

221 Slaves in Ship's Hold

1996. "Brapex 96" National Stamp Exhibition, Recife, Brazil. Multicoloured.

1188	20000k. Type **221**	10	10
1189	20000k. Ship capsizing	20	10
1190	30000k. Boats punting out to ship	30	15
1191	30000k. Inspection of slaves	20	15

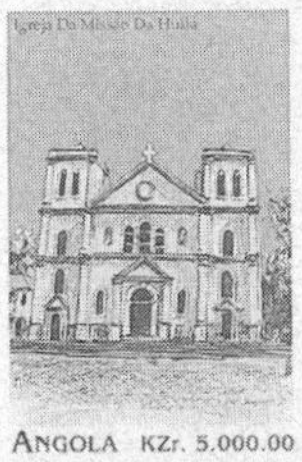
ANGOLA KZr. 5.000.00

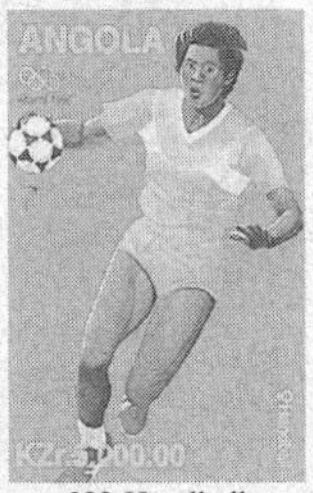
ANGOLA

222 Mission Church, Huila 223 Handball

1996. Churches. Multicoloured.

1193	5000k. Type **222**	10	10
1194	10000k. Church of Our Lady, PoPulo	10	10
1195	10000k. Church of Our Lady, Nazare	10	10
1196	25000k. St. Adriao's Church	10	10

1996. Olympic Games, Atlanta, U.S.A. Mult.

1197	5000k. Type **223**	10	10
1198	10000k. Swimming (horiz)	10	10
1199	25000k. Athletics	10	10
1200	35000k. Shooting (horiz)	15	10

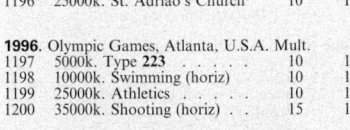

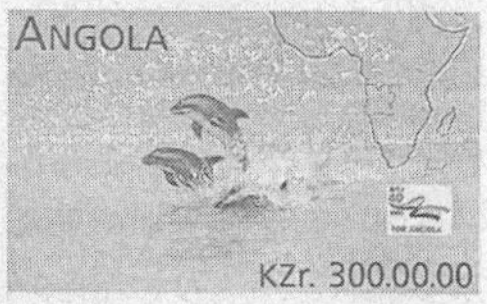
ANGOLA
KZr. 300.00.00

224 Dolphins, and Angola on Map of Africa

1996. 40th Anniv of Popular Movement for the Liberation of Angola (MPLA).

1202	**224** 30000k. multicoloured	15	10

The face value of No. 1202 is wrongly inscr as "300.00.00".

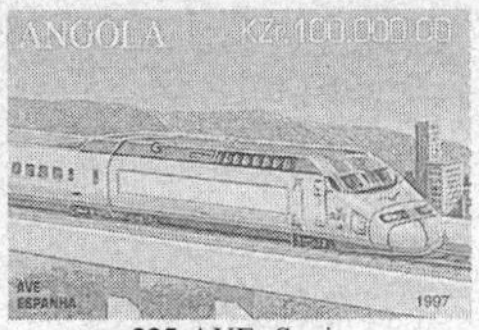
ANGOLA
KZr. 100.000.00
1997

225 AVE, Spain

1997. Trains. Multicoloured.

1203	100000k. Type **225**	60	50
1204	100000k. "Hikari", Japan	60	50
1205	100000k. "Warbonnet" diesel locomotives, U.S.A.	60	50
1206	100000k. "Deltic" diesel locomotive, Great Britain	60	50
1207	100000k. "Eurostar", France and Great Britain	60	50
1208	100000k. ETR 450, Italy	60	50
1209	140000k. Class E1300 diesel locomotive, Morocco	85	70
1210	140000k. ICE, Germany	85	70
1211	140000k. Class X2000, Sweden	85	70
1212	140000k. TGV, France	85	70
1213	250000k. Steam locomotive	1·10	90
1214	250000k. Garratt steam locomotive	1·10	90
1215	250000k. General Electric electric locomotive	1·10	90

Nos. 1203/8 were issued together, se-tenant, forming a composite design.

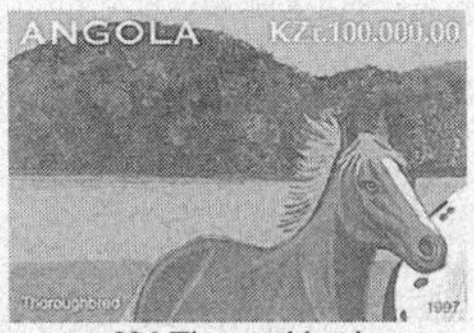
ANGOLA
KZr.100.000.00
Thoroughbred
1997

226 Thoroughbred

1997. Horses. Multicoloured.

1217	100000k. Type **226**	45	35
1218	100000k. Palomino and Appaloosa	45	35
1219	100000k. Grey and white Arabs	45	35
1220	100000k. Arab colt	45	35
1221	100000k. Thoroughbred colt	45	35
1222	100000k. Mustang (with hind quarters of another mustang)	45	35
1223	100000k. Head of mustang and hind quarters of Furioso	45	35
1224	100000k. Head and shoulders of Furioso	45	35
1225	120000k. Thoroughbred	55	45
1226	120000k. Arab and palomino	55	45
1227	120000k. Arab and Chincoteague	55	45
1228	120000k. Pintos	55	45
1229	120000k. Przewalski's Horse	55	45
1230	120000k. Thoroughbred colt	55	45
1231	120000k. Arabs	55	45
1232	120000k. New Forest pony	55	45
1233	140000k. Selle Francais	65	50
1234	140000k. Fjord	65	50
1235	140000k. Percheron	65	50
1236	140000k. Italian heavy draught horse	65	50
1237	140000k. Shagya Arab	65	50
1238	140000k. Avelignese	65	50
1239	140000k. Czechoslovakian warmblood	65	50
1240	140000k. New Forest pony	65	50

Stamps of the same value were issued together, se-tenant, Nos. 1217/24 and 1225/32 respectively forming composite designs.

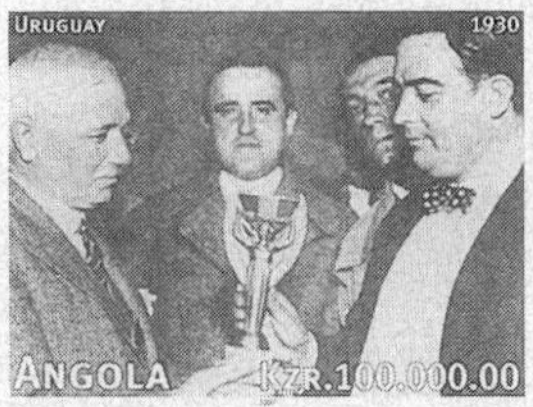
URUGUAY
1930
ANGOLA
KZr.100.000.00

227 Jules Rimet Trophy (Uruguay, 1930)

1997. World Cup Football Championship, France.

1241	**227** 100000k. black	45	35
1242	– 100000k. black	45	35
1243	– 100000k. multicoloured	45	35
1244	– 100000k. multicoloured	45	35
1245	– 100000k. black	45	35
1246	– 100000k. multicoloured	45	35
1247	– 100000k. black	45	35
1248	– 100000k. black	45	35
1249	– 100000k. multicoloured	45	35
1250	– 100000k. multicoloured	45	35
1251	– 100000k. black	45	35

DESIGNS—Victory celebrations: No. 1240, Germany (1954); 1241, Brazil (1970); 1242, Maradona holding trophy (Argentina, 1986); 1243, Brazil (1994). Official team photographs: 1244, Germany (1954); 1245, Uruguay (1958); 1246, Italy (1938); 1247, Brazil (1962); 1248, Brazil (1970); 1249, Uruguay (1930).

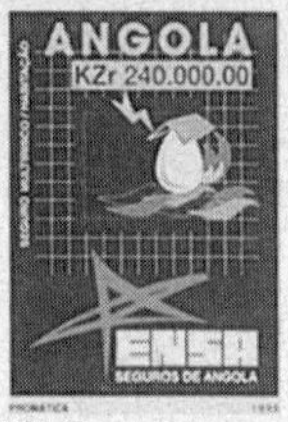
ANGOLA
KZr 240.000.00
ENSA
SEGUROS DE ANGOLA

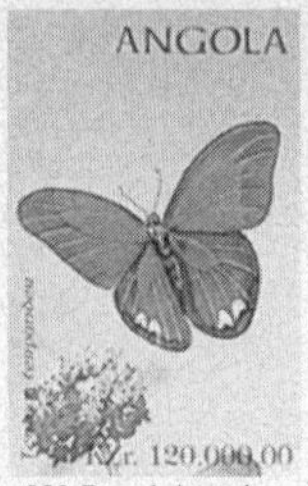
ANGOLA

228 House Insurance 230 Royal Assyrian ("Terinos terpander")

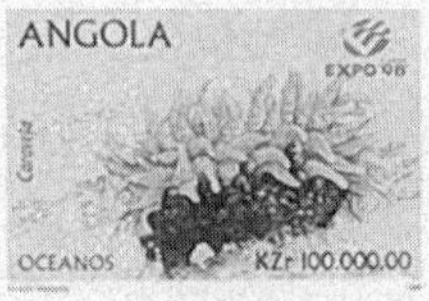
ANGOLA
EXPO 98
OCEANOS
KZr 100.000.00

229 Coral

1998. 20th Anniv of ENSA Insurance. Mult.

1254	240000k. Type **228**	1·10	90
1255	240000k. Forklift truck carrying egg (industrial risks)	1·10	90
1256	240000k. Egg on cross (personal accidents)	1·10	90
1257	240000k. Egg on waves (pleasure boating)	1·10	90

1998. "Expo '98" World's Fair, Lisbon, Portugal. Multicoloured.

1259	100000k. Type **229**	45	35
1260	100000k. Sea urchin	45	35
1261	100000k. Seahorses	45	35
1262	100000k. Sea anemone	45	35
1263	240000k. Sea slug	1·10	90
1264	240000k. Finger coral	1·10	90

1998. Butterflies. Multicoloured.

1265	120000k. Type **230**	55	45
1266	120000k. Wanderer ("Bematistes aganice")	55	45
1267	120000k. Great orange-tip ("Hebomoia glaucippe")	55	45
1268	120000k. Alfalfa butterfly ("Colias eurytheme")	55	45
1269	120000k. Red-banded perelite ("Pereute leucodrosime")	55	45
1270	120000k. Large copper ("Lycaena dispar")	55	45
1271	120000k. Malachite ("Metamorpha stelenes")	55	45
1272	120000k. Tiger swallowtail ("Papilio glaucus")	55	45
1273	120000k. Monarch ("Danaus plexippus")	55	45
1274	120000k. Grecian shoemaker ("Catonephele numili")	55	45
1275	120000k. Silver-studded blue ("Plebejus argus")	55	45
1276	120000k. Common eggfly ("Hypolimnas bolina")	55	45
1277	120000k. Brazilian dynastor ("Dynastor napolean") (horiz)	55	45
1278	120000k. Saturn butterfly ("Zeuxidia amethystus") (horiz)	55	45
1279	120000k. Pipevine swallowtail ("Battus philenor") (horiz)	55	45
1280	120000k. Orange-barred sulphur ("Phoebis philea") (horiz)	55	45
1281	120000k. African monarch ("Danaus chrysippus") (horiz)	55	45
1282	120000k. Green-underside blue ("Glaucopsyche alexis") (horiz)	55	45

Nos. 1265/70, 1271/6 and 1277/82 respectively were issued together, se-tenant, forming composite designs.

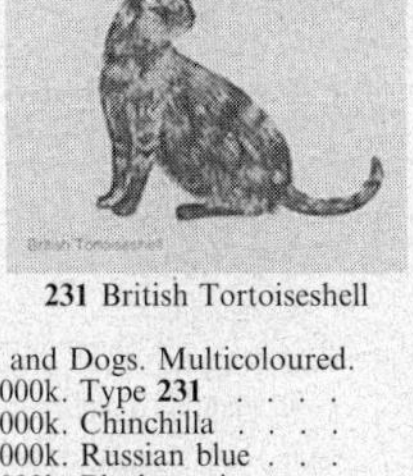
Angola

231 British Tortoiseshell

1998. Cats and Dogs. Multicoloured.

1284	140000k. Type **231**	65	55
1285	140000k. Chinchilla	65	55
1286	140000k. Russian blue	65	55
1287	140000k. Black persian (longhair) (wrongly inscribed "Longhiar")	65	55
1288	140000k. British red tabby	65	55
1289	140000k. Birman	65	55
1290	140000k. West Highland white terrier	65	55
1291	140000k. Red setter	65	55
1292	140000k. Dachshund	65	55
1293	140000k. St. John water-dog	65	55
1294	140000k. Shetland sheep-dog	65	55
1295	140000k. Dalmatian	65	55

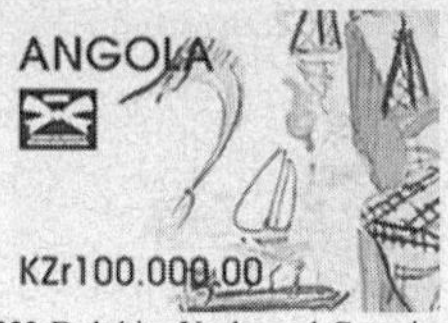
ANGOLA
KZr100.000.00

232 Dolphin, Yacht and Container Ship

1998. 1st Anniv of Government of Unity and National Reconciliation. Multicoloured.

1297	100000k. Type **232**	45	35
1298	100000k. Yacht, dolphin and container ship (different)	45	35
1299	100000k. Yacht, container ship and railway line	45	35
1300	100000k. Coastline and electricity pylons	45	35
1301	200000k. Grapes, goat and railway	95	75
1302	200000k. Village	95	75
1303	200000k. Tractor, grapes and railway	95	75
1304	200000k. Coal train	95	75
1305	200000k. Railway line with branch and pylons	95	75
1306	200000k. Elephant and tip of tree	95	75
1307	200000k. Edge of coastline with pylon	95	75
1308	200000k. Tree trunk and coastline	95	75

Nos. 1297/1308 were issued together, se-tenant, forming a composite design.

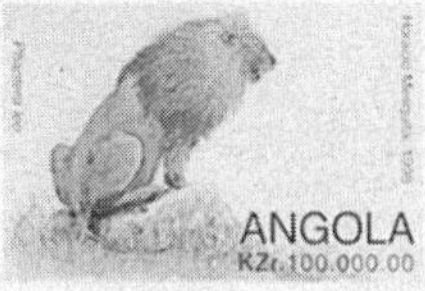
ANGOLA
KZr.100.000.00

234 Lion

1998. Animals of the Grande Porte. Multicoloured.

1310	100000k. Type **234**	45	35
1311	100000k. Hippopotamus ("Hippopotamus amphibius")	45	35
1312	100000k. African elephant ("Loxodonta africana")	45	35
1313	100000k. Giraffe ("Giraffa campelopardalis")	45	35
1314	220000k. African buffalo ("Synceros caffer")	1·00	80
1315	220000k. Gorilla ("Gorilla gorilla")	1·00	80
1316	220000k. White rhinoceros ("Ceratotherium simum")	1·00	80
1317	220000k. Gemsbok ("Oryx gazella")	1·00	80

There are errors in the Latin inscriptions.

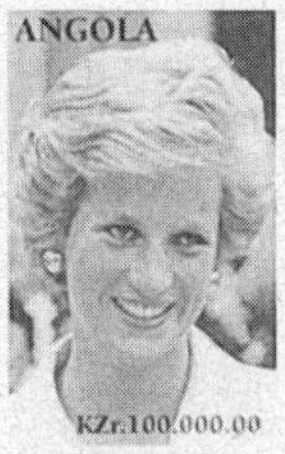
ANGOLA
KZr.100.000.00

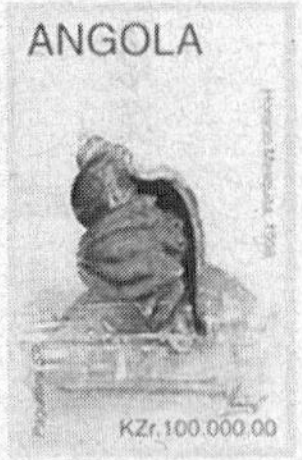
ANGOLA
KZr.100.000.00

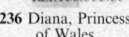

236 Diana, Princess of Wales 237 "Pagurites sp."

1998. Diana, Princess of Wales Commemoration. Multicoloured.

1319	100000k. Type **236**	45	35
1320	100000k. Wearing white balldress	45	35
1321	100000k. Holding handbag	45	35
1322	100000k. Wearing black evening dress	45	35
1323	100000k. Holding bouquet (white jacket)	45	35
1324	100000k. Wearing pearl necklace (looking down)	45	35
1325	100000k. Wearing pearl necklace (head raised)	45	35
1326	100000k. Speaking, wearing green velvet jacket	45	35
1327	100000k. Wearing sunglasses	45	35
1328	100000k. Wearing black jacket and white blouse	45	35
1329	100000k. Wearing green blouse	45	35
1330	100000k. Holding flowers (black jacket)	45	35
1331	150000k. With young girl amputee	70	55
1332	150000k. With two amputees	70	55
1333	150000k. Walking through minefield	70	55

1998. International Year of the Ocean. Mult.

1335	100000k. Type **237**	45	35
1336	100000k. "Callinectes marginatus" (crab)	45	35
1337	100000k. "Thais forbesi"	45	35
1338	100000k. "Ostrea tulipa"	45	35
1339	100000k. "Balanus amphitrite"	45	35
1340	100000k. "Uca tangeri"	45	35
1341	170000k. "Littorina angulifera"	80	65

1342	170000k. Great hairy melongena ("Semifusus morio")	80	65
1343	170000k. "Thais coronata"	80	65
1344	170000k. "Cerithium atratum" on red branch	80	65
1345	170000k. "Ostrea tulipa" (different)	80	65
1346	170000k. "Cerithium atratum" on green branch	80	65

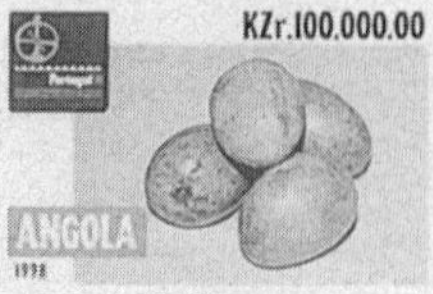

238 Mangos

1998. "Portugal 98" International Stamp Exhibition, Lisbon. Fruit and Vegetables. Multicoloured.

1348	100000k. Type **238**	45	35
1349	100000k. Guava	45	35
1350	120000k. Chillies	55	45
1351	120000k. Sweet corn	55	45
1352	140000k. Sliced bananas	65	55
1353	140000k. Avocadoes	65	55

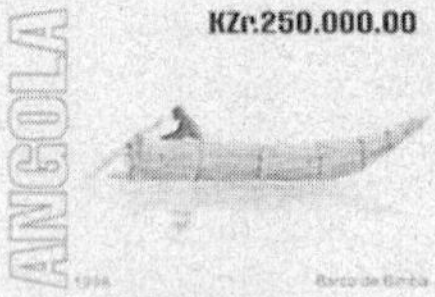

239 Bimba Canoe

1998. Canoes. Multicoloured.

1354	250000k. Type **239**	1·10	90
1355	250000k. Sailing canoe, Ndongo	1·10	90
1356	250000k. Building canoes in Ndongo	1·10	90

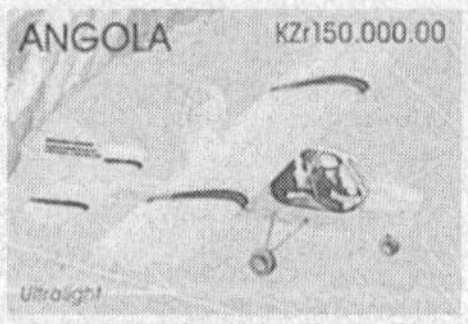

241 Ultralight Plane

1998. Aircraft. Multicoloured.

1358	150000k. Type **241**	70	55
1359	150000k. Gyroplane	70	55
1360	150000k. Business jet	70	55
1361	150000k. Convertible plane	70	55
1362	150000k. Chuterplane	70	55
1363	150000k. Twin-rotor craft	70	55
1364	150000k. Skycrane	70	55
1365	150000k. British Aerospace/ Aerospatiale Concorde Supersonic airliner	70	55
1366	150000k. Flying boat	70	55
1367	200000k. Boeing 737-100	70	55
1368	200000k. Ilyushin Il-62M	70	55
1369	250000k. Pedal-powered plane	70	55
1370	250000k. Sail plane	70	55
1371	250000k. Aerobatic plane	70	55
1372	250000k. Hang-gliding	70	55
1373	250000k. Balloon	70	55
1374	250000k. Glidercraft	70	55
1375	250000k. Model airplane	70	55
1376	250000k. Air racing	70	55
1377	250000k. Solar-celled plane	70	55

Nos. 1358/66 and 1369/77 respectively were issued together, se-tenant, forming composite designs.

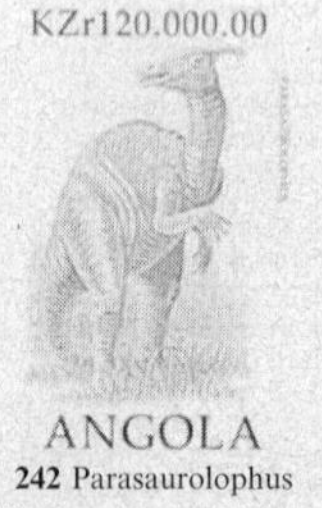

242 Parasaurolophus

1998. Prehistoric Animals. Multicoloured.

1379	120000k. Type **242**	55	45
1380	120000k. Elaphosaurus	55	45
1381	120000k. Iguanodon	55	45
1382	120000k. Maiasaura	55	45
1383	120000k. Brontosaurus	55	45
1384	120000k. Plateosaurus	55	45
1385	120000k. Brachiosaurus	55	45
1386	120000k. Anatosaurus	55	45
1387	120000k. Tyrannosaurus rex	55	45
1388	120000k. Carnotaurus	55	45
1389	120000k. Corythosaurus	55	45
1390	120000k. Stegosaurus	55	45
1391	120000k. Iguanodon (different)	55	45
1392	120000k. Hadrosaurus (horiz)	55	45
1393	120000k. Ouranosaurus (horiz)	55	45
1394	120000k. Hypsilophodon (horiz)	55	45
1395	120000k. Brachiosaurus (horiz)	55	45
1396	120000k. Shunosaurus (horiz)	55	45
1397	120000k. Amargasaurus (horiz)	55	45
1398	120000k. Tuojiangosaurus (horiz)	55	45
1399	120000k. Monoclonius	55	45
1400	120000k. Struthiosaurus (horiz)	55	45

APPENDIX

1995.

90th Anniv of Rotary International (on gold foil). 81000k.

CHARITY TAX STAMPS

Used on certain days of the year as an additional tax on internal letters. If one was not used in addition to normal postage, postage due stamps were used to collect the deficiency and the fine.

1925. Marquis de Pombal Commemorative stamps of Portugal but inscr "ANGOLA".

C343	C **73**	15c. violet	30	25
C344	–	15c. violet	30	25
C345	C **75**	15c. violet	30	25

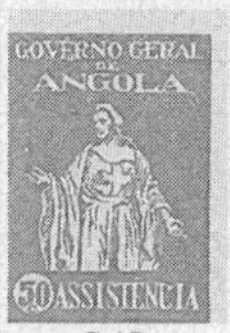

C **15**

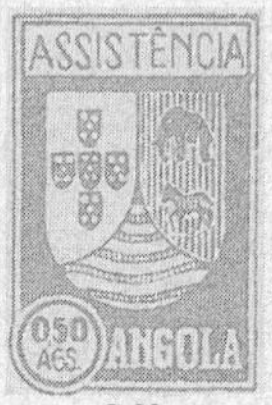

C **29**

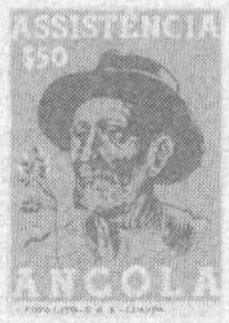

C **52** Old Man

1929.

C347	C **15**	50c. blue	1·60	60

1939. No gum.

C413	C **29**	50c. green	1·25	10
C414		1a. red	1·60	70

1955. Heads in brown.

C646	C **52**	50c. orange	15	10
C647	–	1e. red (Boy)	15	10
C648	–	1e.50 green (Girl)	15	10
C522	–	2e.50 blue (Old woman)	50	30

1957. Surch.

C535	C **52**	10c. on 50c. orange	20	15
C534		30c. on 50c. orange	20	15

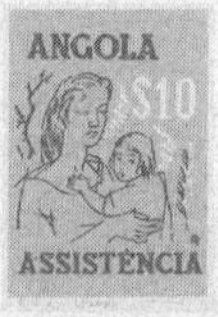

C **58** Mother and Child

C **75** "Full Employment"

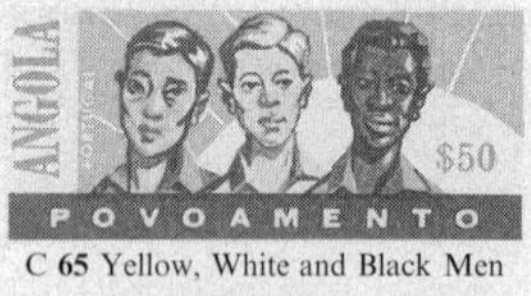

C **65** Yellow, White and Black Men

1959.

C538	C **58**	10c. black and orange	15	15
C539	–	30c. black and slate	15	15

DESIGN: 30c. Boy and girl.

1962. Provincial Settlement Committee.

C568	C **65**	50c. multicoloured	20	10
C569		1e. multicoloured	40	20

1965. Provincial Settlement Committee.

C643	C **75**	50c. multicoloured	15	10
C644		1e. multicoloured	15	10
C645		2e. multicoloured	20	15

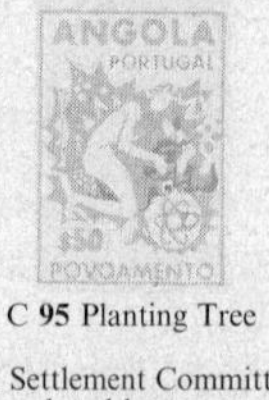

C **95** Planting Tree

1972. Provincial Settlement Committee.

C701	C **95**	50c. red and brown	15	15
C702	–	1e. black and green	15	15
C703	–	2e. black and brown	15	15

DESIGNS: 1e. Agricultural workers; 2e. Corncobs and flowers.

NEWSPAPER STAMP

1893. "Newspaper" key-type inscr "ANGOLA".

N51	V	2½r. brown	95	55

POSTAGE DUE STAMPS

1904. "Due" key-type inscr "ANGOLA".

D150	W	5r. green	15	15
D151		10r. grey	15	15
D152		20r. brown	25	20
D153		30r. orange	25	20
D154		50r. brown	30	20
D155		60r. brown	2·75	1·50
D156		100r. mauve	95	75
D157		130r. blue	95	85
D158		200r. red	3·25	1·50
D159		500r. lilac	3·00	1·50

See also Nos. D343/52.

1911. Nos. D150/9 optd **REPUBLICA**.

D166	W	5r. green	15	10
D167		10r. grey	15	10
D168		20r. brown	15	10
D169		30r. orange	20	10
D170		50r. brown	20	15
D171		60r. brown	50	30
D172		100r. mauve	50	30
D173		130r. blue	50	35
D174		200r. red	50	35
D175		500r. lilac	65	40

1921. Values in new currency.

D343	W	½c. green	10	10
D344		1c. grey	10	10
D345		2c. brown	10	10
D346		3c. orange	10	10
D347		5c. brown	10	10
D348		6c. brown	10	10
D349		10c. mauve	10	10
D350		13c. blue	20	20
D351		20c. red	20	20
D352		50c. grey	20	20

1925. Marquis de Pombal stamps of Angola, as Nos. C343/5, optd **MULTA**.

D353	C **73**	30c. violet	25	25
D354	–	30c. violet	25	25
D355	C **75**	30c. violet	25	25

1949. Surch **PORTEADO** and value.

D438	**17**	10c. on 20c. grey	25	25
D439		20c. on 30c. green	25	25
D440		30c. on 50c. brown	25	25
D441		40c. on 1a. red	50	50
D442		50c. on 2a. mauve	75	75
D443		1a. on 5a. green	85	85

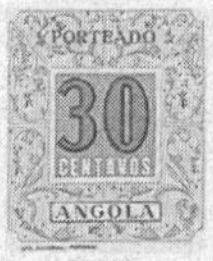

D **45**

1952. Numerals in red, name in black.

D483	D **45**	10c. brown and olive	15	15
D484		30c. green and blue	15	15
D485		50c. brown & lt brn	15	15
D486		1a. blue, green & orge	15	15
D487		2a. brown and red	20	20
D488		5a. brown and blue	30	30

ANGRA Pt. 9

A district of the Azores, which used the stamps of the Azores except from 1892 to 1905.

1000 reis = 1 milreis.

1892. As T **4** of Funchal, inscr "ANGRA".

16	5r. yellow	2·25	1·40
5	10r. mauve	2·50	1·40
6	15r. brown	2·75	2·10
7	20r. violet	2·75	2·10
8	25r. green	3·50	55
9	50r. blue	5·75	3·25
10	75r. red	6·75	4·00
11	80r. green	8·00	7·75
24	100r. brown on yellow	29·00	11·00
13	150r. red on rose	40·00	32·00
14	200r. blue on blue	40·00	32·00
15	300r. blue on brown	40·00	32·00

1897. "King Carlos" key-type inscr "ANGRA".

28	S	2½r. grey	55	40
29		5r. red	55	40
30		10r. green	55	40
31		15r. brown	6·75	3·75
43		15r. green	60	45
32		20r. lilac	1·40	1·00
33		25r. green	2·10	1·00
44		25r. red	85	45
34		50r. blue	3·75	1·25
46		65r. blue	1·00	45
35		75r. red	2·50	1·25
47		75r. brown on yellow	9·75	8·50
36		80r. mauve	1·10	95
37		100r. blue on blue	2·00	1·25
48		115r. red on pink	2·00	1·60
49		130r. brown on cream	2·00	1·60
38		150r. brown on yellow	2·00	1·25
50		180r. grey on pink	2·25	2·10
39		200r. purple on pink	4·00	2·75
40		300r. blue on pink	5·75	4·50
41		500r. black on blue	13·00	10·50

ANGUILLA Pt. 1

St. Christopher, Nevis and Anguilla were granted Associated Statehood on 27 February 1967, but following a referendum Anguilla declared her independence and the St. Christopher authorities withdrew. On 7 July 1969, the Anguilla post office was officially recognised by the Government of St. Christopher, Nevis and Anguilla and normal postal communications via St. Christopher were resumed.

By the Anguilla Act of 27 July 1971, the island was restored to direct British control.

100 cents = 1 West Indian dollar.

1967. Nos. 129/44 of St. Kitts-Nevis optd **Independent Anguilla** and bar.

1	–	½c. sepia and blue	30·00	22·00
2	**33**	1c. multicoloured	32·00	7·00
3	–	2c. multicoloured	32·00	1·50
4	–	3c. multicoloured	32·00	4·50
5	–	4c. multicoloured	32·00	5·50
6	–	5c. multicoloured	£120	20·00
7	–	6c. multicoloured	60·00	9·00
8	–	10c. multicoloured	32·00	6·50
9	–	15c. multicoloured	70·00	11·00
10	–	20c. multicoloured	£110	13·00
11	–	25c. multicoloured	£100	23·00
12	–	50c. multicoloured	£2000	£450
13	–	60c. multicoloured	£2500	£850
14	–	$1 yellow and blue	£1800	£400
15	–	$2.50 multicoloured	£1600	£300
16	–	$5 multicoloured	£1600	£300

Owing to the limited stocks available for overprinting, the sale of the stamps were personally controlled by the Postmaster and no orders from the trade were accepted.

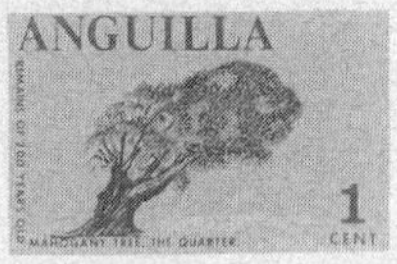

2 Mahogany Tree, The Quarter

1967.

17	**2**	1c. green, brown and orange	10	85
18	–	2c. turquoise and black	10	85
19	–	3c. black and green	10	10
20	–	4c. blue and black	10	10
21	–	5c. multicoloured	10	10
22	–	6c. red and black	10	10
23	–	10c. multicoloured	15	10
24	–	15c. multicoloured	1·40	20
25	–	20c. multicoloured	1·25	1·50
26	–	25c. multicoloured	60	20
27	–	40c. green, blue and black	1·00	25
28	–	60c. multicoloured	3·75	3·75
29	–	$1 multicoloured	1·75	3·25
30	–	$2.50 multicoloured	2·00	4·25
31	–	$5 multicoloured	3·00	4·25

DESIGNS: 2c. Sombrero Lighthouse; 3c. St. Mary's Church; 4c. Valley Police Station; 5c. Old Plantation House, Mt. Fortune; 6c. Valley Post Office; 10c. Methodist Church, West End; 15c. Wall Blake Airport; 20c. Beech A90 King Air aircraft over Sandy Ground; 25c. Island harbour; 40c. Map of Anguilla; 60c. Hermit crab and starfish; $1, Hibiscus; $2.50, Local scene; $5, Spiny lobster.

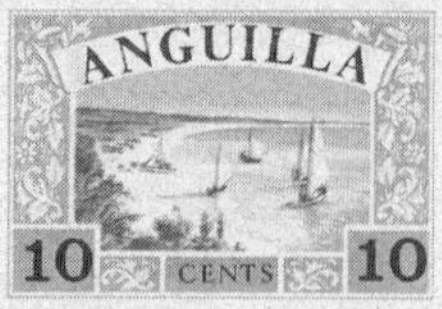

17 Yachts in Lagoon

1968. Anguillan Ships. Multicoloured.

32	10c. Type **17**	30	10
33	15c. Boat on beach	35	10
34	25c. Schooner "Warspite"	50	15
35	40c. Schooner "Atlantic Star"	60	20

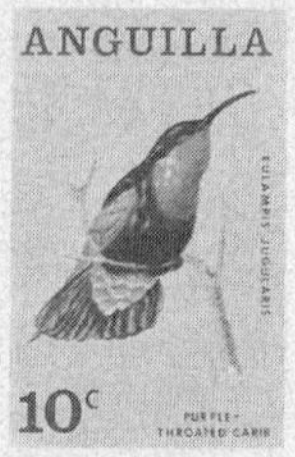

18 Purple-throated Carib

1968. Anguillan Birds. Multicoloured.

36	10c. Type **18**	85	15
37	15c. Bananaquit	1·10	20
38	25c. Black-necked stilt (horiz)	1·40	20
39	40c. Royal tern (horiz)	1·60	30

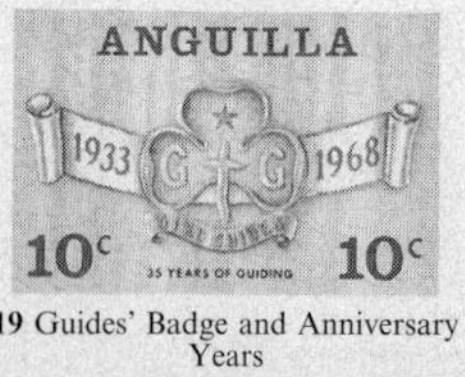

19 Guides' Badge and Anniversary Years

1968. 35th Anniv of Anguillan Girl Guides. Mult.

40	10c. Type **19**	10	10
41	15c. Badge and silhouettes of guides (vert)	15	10
42	25c. Guides' badge and Headquarters	20	15
43	40c. Association and proficiency badges (vert)	25	15

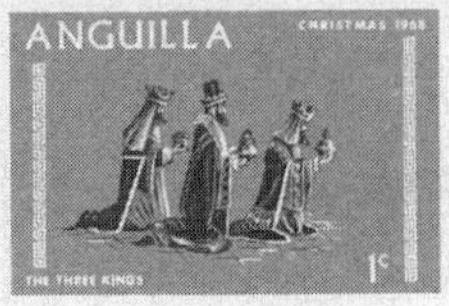

20 The Three Kings

1968. Christmas.

44	**20**	1c. black and red	10	10
45	–	10c. black and blue	10	10
46	–	15c. black and brown	15	10
47	–	40c. black and blue	15	10
48	–	50c. black and green	20	15

DESIGNS—VERT: 10c. The Wise Men; 15c. Holy Family and manger. HORIZ: 40c. The Shepherds; 50c. Holy Family and donkey.

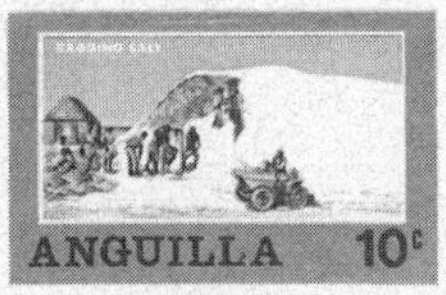

21 Bagging Salt

1969. Anguillan Salt Industry. Multicoloured.

49	10c. Type **21**	25	10
50	15c. Packing salt	30	10
51	40c. Salt pond	35	10
52	50c. Loading salt	35	10

1969. Expiration of Interim Agreement on Status of Anguilla. Nos. 19/22, 24 and 26/7 optd **INDEPENDENCE JANUARY 1969**.

52a	3c. black and green	10	20
52b	4c. blue and black	10	20
52c	5c. multicoloured	10	20
52d	6c. red and black	10	20
52e	15c. multicoloured	90	30
52f	25c. multicoloured	80	30
52g	40c. green, blue and black	1·00	40

The remaining values of the 1967 series. Nos. 17/31 also come with this overprint but these are outside the scope of this catalogue

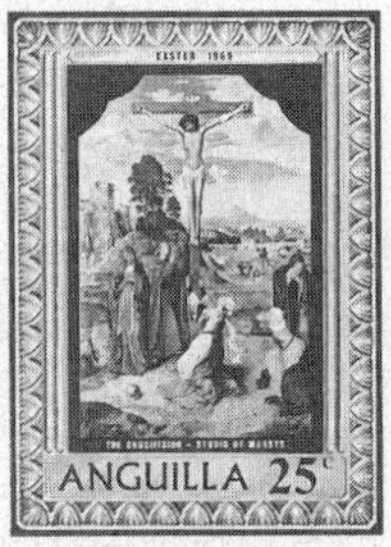

22 "The Crucifixion" (Studio of Massys)

1969. Easter Commemoration. Multicoloured.

53	25c. Type **22**	25	15
54	40c. "The Last Supper" (ascribed to Roberti)	35	15

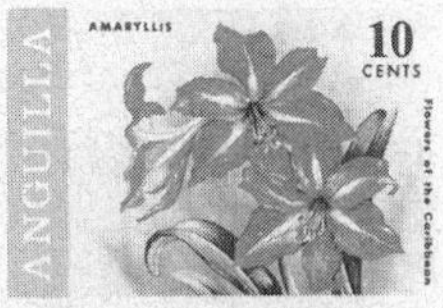

23 Amaryllis

1969. Flowers of the Caribbean. Multicoloured.

55	10c. Type **23**	20	20
56	15c. Bougainvillea	25	25
57	40c. Hibiscus	50	50
58	50c. "Cattleya" orchid	1·50	1·25

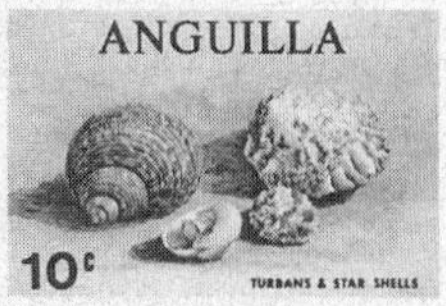

24 Superb Gaza, Channelled Turban, Chestnut Turban and Carved Star Shell

1969. Sea Shells. Multicoloured.

59	10c. Type **24**	20	20
60	15c. American thorny oysters	20	20
61	40c. Scotch, royal and smooth scotch bonnets	30	30
62	50c. Atlantic trumpet triton	40	30

1969. Christmas. Nos. 17 and 25/8 optd with different seasonal emblems.

63	1c. green, brown and orange	10	10
64	20c. multicoloured	20	10
65	25c. multicoloured	20	10
66	40c. green, blue and black	25	15
67	60c. multicoloured	40	20

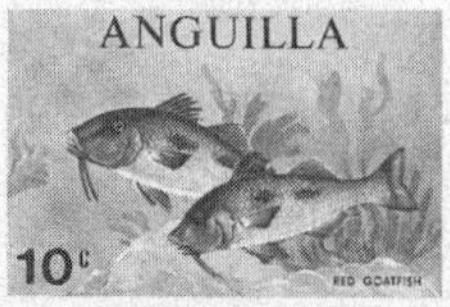

30 Spotted Goatfish

1969. Fishes. Multicoloured.

68	10c. Type **30**	30	15
69	15c. Blue-striped grunt	45	15
70	40c. Nassau grouper	55	20
71	50c. Banded butterflyfish	65	20

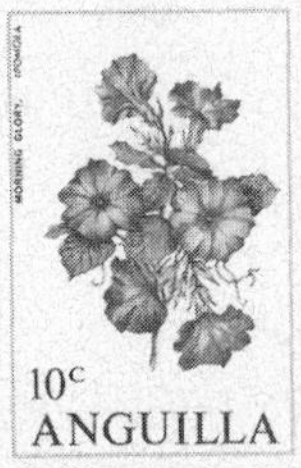

31 "Morning Glory"

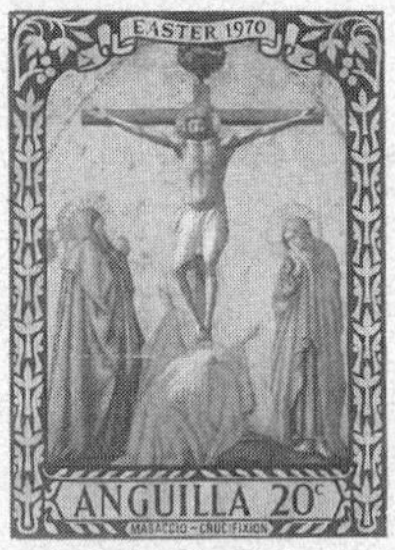

32 "The Crucifixion" (Masaccio)

1970. Flowers. Multicoloured.

72	10c. Type **31**	30	10
73	15c. Blue petrea	45	10
74	40c. Hibiscus	70	20
75	50c. "Flame Tree"	80	25

1970. Easter. Multicoloured.

76	10c. "The Ascent to Calvary" (Tiepolo) (horiz)	15	10
77	20c. Type **32**	20	10
78	40c. "Deposition" (Rosso Fiorentino)	25	15
79	60c. "The Ascent to Calvary" (Murillo) (horiz)	25	15

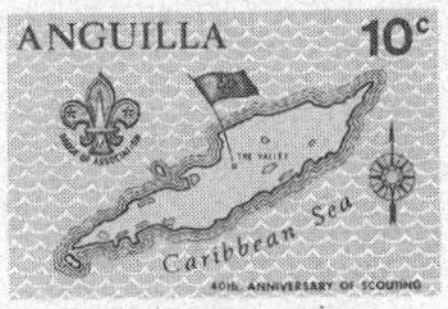

33 Scout Badge and Map

1970. 40th Anniv of Scouting in Anguilla. Multicoloured.

80	10c. Type **33**	15	15
81	15c. Scout camp, and cubs practising first aid	20	20
82	40c. Monkey bridge	25	30
83	50c. Scout H.Q. building and Lord Baden-Powell	35	30

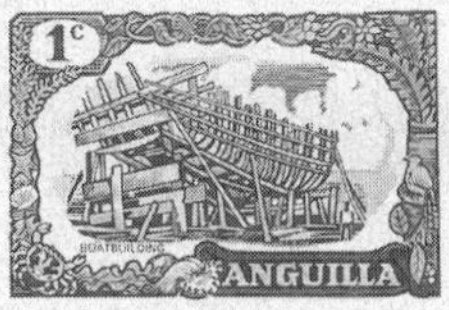

34 Boatbuilding

1970. Multicoloured.

84	1c. Type **34**	30	40
85	2c. Road construction	30	40
86	3c. Quay, Blowing Point	30	20
87	4c. Broadcaster, Radio Anguilla	30	50
88	5c. Cottage Hospital extension	40	50
89	6c. Valley Secondary School	30	50
90	10c. Hotel extension	30	30
91	15c. Sandy Ground	30	30
92	20c. Supermarket and cinema	55	30
93	25c. Bananas and mangoes	35	80
94	40c. Wall Blake Airport	2·75	2·75
95	60c. Sandy Ground jetty	65	3·00
96	$1 Administration buildings	1·25	1·40
97	$2.50 Livestock	1·50	3·75
98	$5 Sandy Hill Bay	2·75	3·75

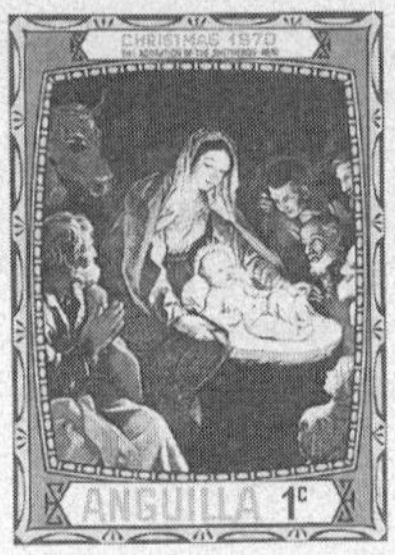

35 "The Adoration of the Shepherds" (Reni)

1970. Christmas. Multicoloured.

99	1c. Type **35**	10	10
100	20c. "The Virgin and Child" (Gozzoli)	30	20
101	25c. "Mystic Nativity" (detail, Botticelli)	30	20
102	40c. "The Santa Margherita Madonna" (detail, Mazzola)	40	25
103	50c. "The Adoration of the Magi" (detail, Tiepolo)	40	25

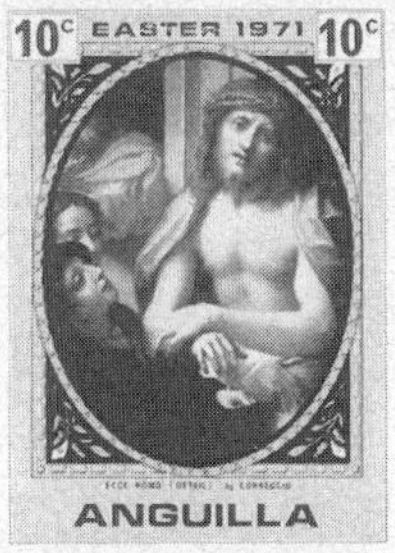

36 "Ecce Homo" (detail, Correggio)

1971. Easter. Paintings. Multicoloured.

104	10c. Type **36**	25	10
105	15c. "Christ appearing to St Peter" (detail, Carracci)	25	10
106	40c. "Angels weeping over the Dead Christ" (detail, Guercino) (horiz)	30	10
107	50c. "The Supper at Emmaus" (detail, Caravaggio) (horiz)	30	15

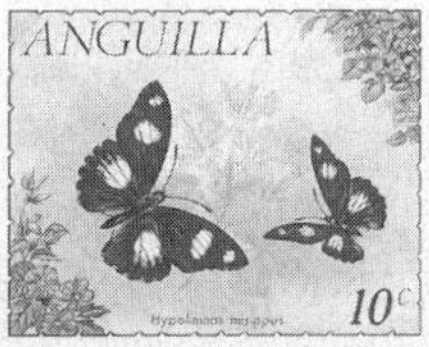

37 "Hypolimnas misippus"

1971. Butterflies. Multicoloured.

108	10c. Type **37**	1·60	70
109	15c. "Junonia evarete"	1·60	80
110	40c. "Agraulis vanillae"	2·00	1·25
111	50c. "Danaus plexippus"	2·00	1·50

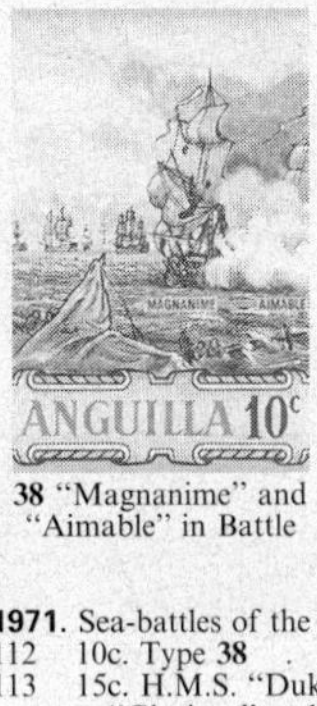

38 "Magnanime" and "Aimable" in Battle

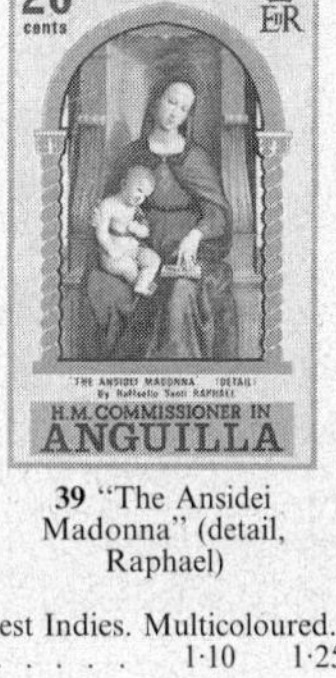

39 "The Ansidei Madonna" (detail, Raphael)

1971. Sea-battles of the West Indies. Multicoloured.

112	10c. Type **38**	1·10	1·25
113	15c. H.M.S. "Duke", "Glorieux" and H.M.S. "Agamemnon"	1·25	1·40
114	25c. H.M.S. "Formidable" and H.M.S. "Namur" against "Ville de Paris"	1·50	1·60
115	40c. H.M.S. "Canada"	1·60	1·75
116	50c. H.M.S. "St. Albans" and wreck of "Hector"	1·75	1·90

Nos. 112/116 were issued together, se-tenant, forming a composite design.

1971. Christmas. Multicoloured.

117	20c. Type **39**	25	30
118	25c. "Mystic Nativity" (detail, Botticelli)	25	30
119	40c. "Adoration of the Shepherds" (detail, ascr to Murillo)	30	40
120	50c. "The Madonna of the Iris" (detail, ascr to Durer)	35	45

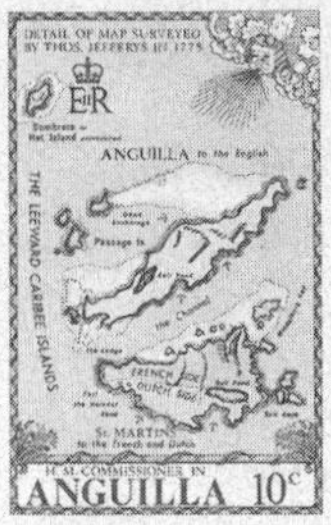

40 Map of Anguilla and St. Martin by Thomas Jefferys, 1775

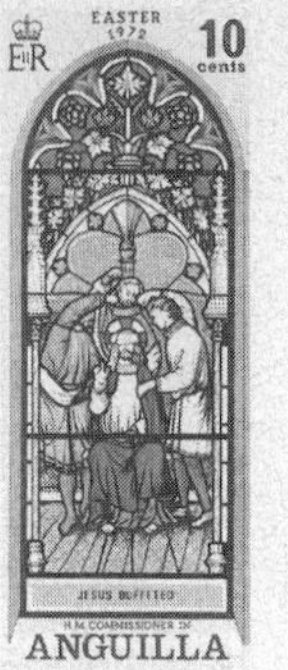

41 "Jesus Buffeted"

1972. Caribbean Maps depicting Anguilla. Multicoloured.

121	10c. Type **40**	25	10
122	15c. Samuel Fahlberg's Map, 1814	35	15
123	40c. Thomas Jefferys' Map, 1775 (horiz)	50	25
124	50c. Captain E. Barnett's Map, 1847 (horiz)	60	25

1972. Easter. Multicoloured.

125	10c. Type **41**	25	25
126	15c. "The Way of Sorrows"	30	30
127	25c. "The Crucifixion"	30	30
128	40c. "Descent from the Cross"	35	35
129	50c. "The Burial"	40	40

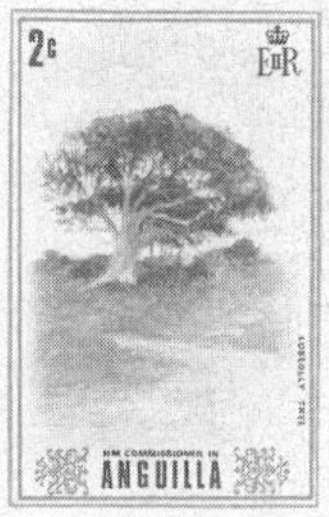

42 Loblolly Tree

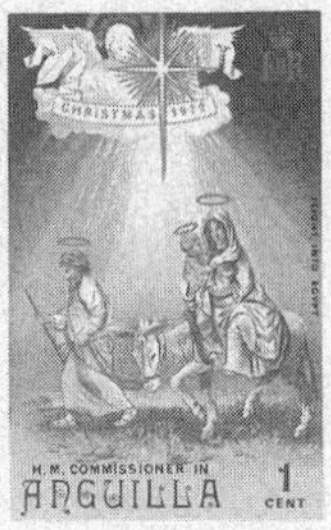

44 Flight into Egypt

1972. Multicoloured.

130	1c. Spear fishing	10	40
131	2c. Type **42**	10	40
132	3c. Sandy Ground	10	40
133	4c. Ferry at Blowing Point	1·50	20
134	5c. Agriculture	15	80
135	6c. St. Mary's Church	25	20
136	10c. St. Gerard's Church	25	40
137	15c. Cottage hospital extension	25	30
138	20c. Public library	30	35
139	25c. Sunset at Blowing Point	40	1·75
140	40c. Boat building	4·50	1·50
141	60c. Hibiscus	4·00	3·50
142	$1 Magnificent frigate bird ("Man-o'-War")	8·50	7·50
143	$2.50 Frangipani	6·00	9·00
144	$5 Brown pelican	15·00	16·00
144a	$10 Green-back turtle	15·00	18·00

1972. Royal Silver Wedding. As T **52** of Ascension, but with Schooner and Common dolphin in background.

145	25c. green	50	75
146	40c. brown	50	75

1972. Christmas. Multicoloured.

147	1c. Type **44**	10	10
148	20c. Star of Bethlehem	20	20
149	25c. Holy Family	20	20
150	40c. Arrival of the Magi	20	25
151	50c. Adoration of the Magi	25	25

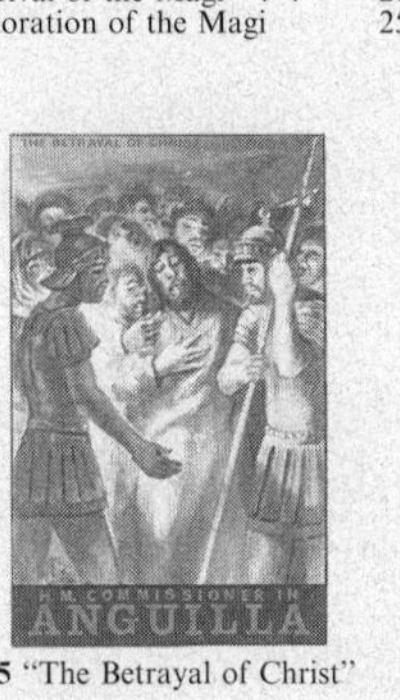

45 "The Betrayal of Christ"

1973. Easter. Multicoloured.

152	1c. Type **45**	10	10
153	10c. "The Man of Sorrows"	10	10
154	20c. "Christ bearing the Cross"	10	15
155	25c. "The Crucifixion"	15	15
156	40c. "The Descent from the Cross"	15	15
157	50c. "The Resurrection"	15	20

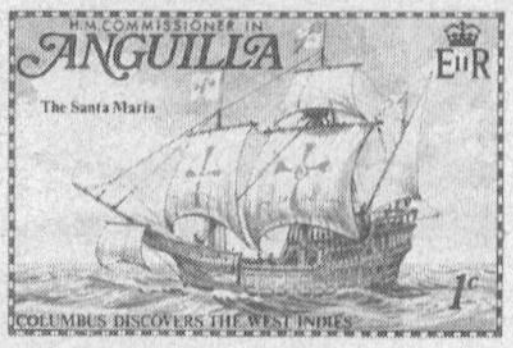

46 "Santa Maria"

1973. Columbus Discovers the West Indies. Multicoloured.
159 1c. Type **46** 10 10
160 20c. Early map . . . . . 1·50 1·25
161 40c. Map of voyages . . . . 1·60 1·40
162 70c. Sighting land . . . . 1·90 1·75
163 $1.20 Landing of Columbus 2·50 2·25

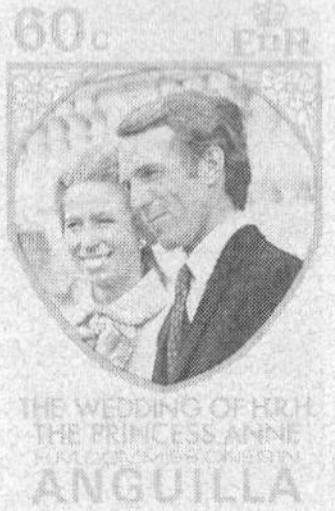

47 Princess Anne and Captain Mark Phillips

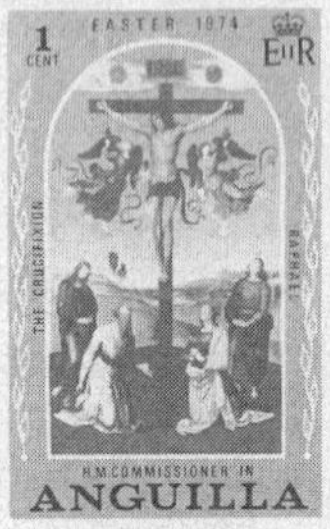

49 "The Crucifixion" (Raphael)

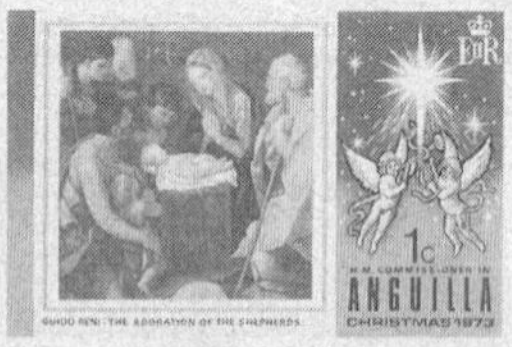

48 "The Adoration of the Shepherds" (Reni)

1973. Royal Wedding. Multicoloured. Background colours given.
165 **47** 60c. green 20 15
166 $1.20 mauve 30 15

1973. Christmas. Multicoloured.
167 1c. Type **48** 10 10
168 10c. "The Madonna and Child with Saints Jerome and Dominic" (Filippino Lippi) 10 10
169 20c. "The Nativity" (Master of Brunswick) 15 15
170 25c. "Madonna of the Meadow" (Bellini) . . . 15 15
171 40c. "Virgin and Child" (Cima) 20 20
172 50c. "Adoration of the Kings" (Geertgen) 20 20

1974. Easter. Details of Raphael's "Crucifixion".
174 **49** 1c. multicoloured 10 10
175 – 15c. multicoloured 10 10
176 – 20c. multicoloured 15 15
177 – 25c. multicoloured 15 15
178 – 40c. multicoloured 15 15
179 – $1 multicoloured 20 25

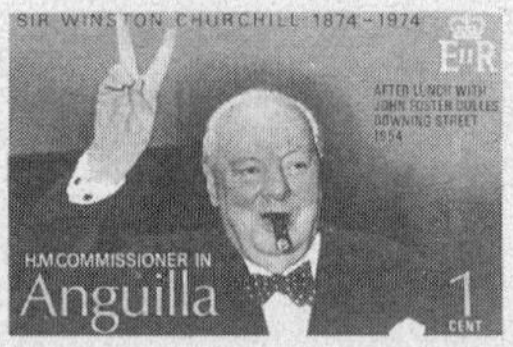

50 Churchill Making "Victory" Sign

1974. Birth Centenary of Sir Winston Churchill. Multicoloured.
181 1c. Type **50** 10 10
182 20c. Churchill with Roosevelt 20 20
183 25c. Wartime broadcast . . . 20 20
184 40c. Birthplace, Blenheim Palace 30 30
185 60c. Churchill's statue . . . 30 35
186 $1.20 Country residence, Chartwell 45 55

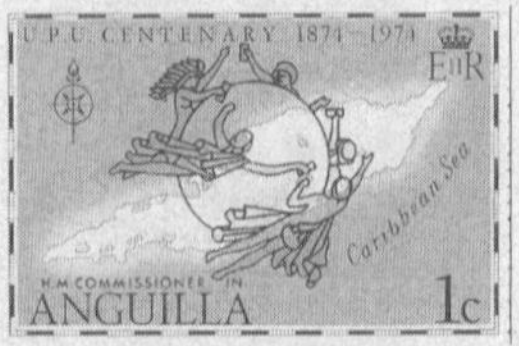

51 U.P.U. Emblem

1974. Centenary of U.P.U.
188 **51** 1c. black and blue 10 10
189 20c. black and orange . . 15 15
190 25c. black and yellow . . 15 15
191 40c. black and mauve . . 20 25
192 60c. black and green . . 30 40
193 $1.20 black and blue . . 50 60

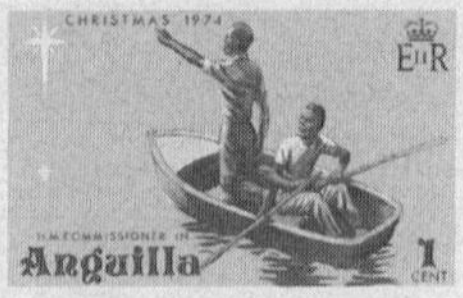

52 Anguillan pointing to Star

1974. Christmas. Multicoloured.
195 1c. Type **52** 10 10
196 20c. Child in Manger 10 20
197 25c. King's offering 10 20
198 40c. Star over map of Anguilla 15 20
199 60c. Family looking at star 15 20
200 $1.20 Angels of Peace 20 30

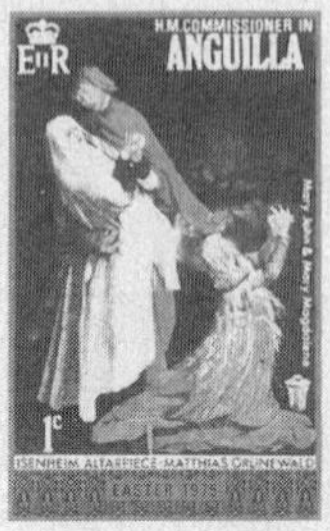

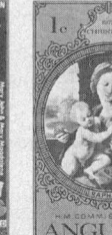

53 "Mary, John and Mary Magdalene" (Matthias Grunewald)

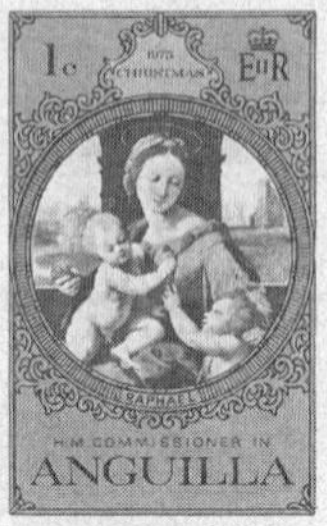

55 "Madonna, Child and the Infant John the Baptist" (Raphael)

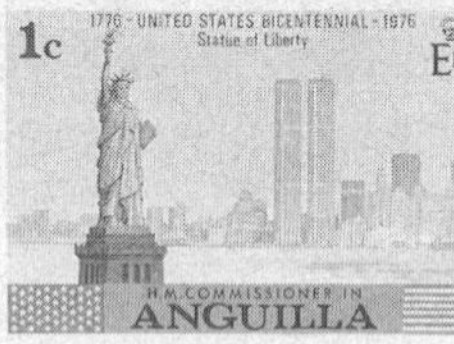

54 Statue of Liberty

1975. Easter. Details from Isenheim Altarpiece, Colmar Museum. Multicoloured.
202 1c. Type **53** 10 10
203 10c. "The Crucifixion" . . . 15 15
204 15c. "St. John the Baptist" 15 15
205 20c. "St. Sebastian and Angels" 15 20
206 $1 "The Entombment" (horiz) 20 35
207 $1.50 "St. Anthony the Hermit" 25 45

1975. Bicentenary of American Revolution. Mult.
209 1c. Type **54** 10 10
210 10c. The Capitol 20 10
211 15c. "Congress voting for Independence" (Pine and Savage) 30 15
212 20c. Washington and map . . 30 15
213 $1 Boston Tea Party 45 40
214 $1.50 Bicentenary logo . . . 50 60

1975. Christmas. "Madonna and Child" paintings by artists named. Multicoloured.
216 1c. Type **55** 10 10
217 10c. Cima 15 15
218 15c. Dolci 20 15
219 20c. Durer 20 20
220 $1 Bellini 35 25
221 $1.50 Botticelli 45 35

1976. New Constitution. Nos. 130 etc optd **NEW CONSTITUTION 1976** or surch also.
223 1c. Spear fishing 30 40
224 2c. on 1c. Spear fishing . . . 30 40
225 2c. Type **42** . . . . 6·00 1·75
226 3c. on 40c. Boat building . . 75 70
227 4c. Ferry at Blowing Point 1·00 1·00
228 5c. on 40c. Boat building . . 30 50
229 6c. St. Mary's Church . . . 30 50
230 10c. on 20c. Public library . . 30 50
231 10c. St. Gerard's Church . . 6·00 4·50
232 15c. Cottage Hospital extension 30 90
233 20c. Public library 30 50
234 25c. Sunset at Blowing Point 30 50
235 40c. Boat building . . . . . 1·00 70
236 60c. Hibiscus 70 70
237 $1 Magnificent frigate bird 6·00 2·25
238 $2.50 Frangipani . . . . . 2·25 2·25
239 $5 Brown pelican . . . . . 7·50 7·00
240 $10 Green-back turtle . . . . 3·00 6·00

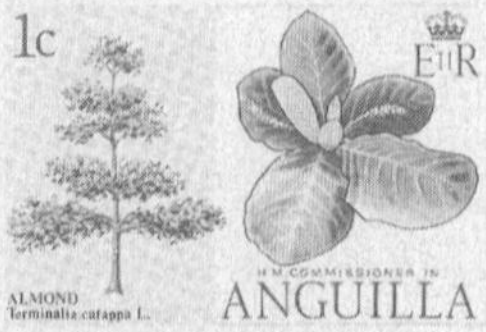

57 Almond

1976. Flowering Trees. Multicoloured.
241 1c. Type **57** 10 10
242 10c. Autograph 20 20
243 15c. Calabash 20 20
244 20c. Cordia 20 20
245 $1 Papaya 30 45
246 $1.50 Flamboyant 35 55

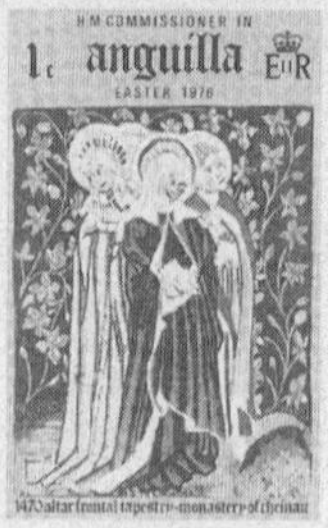

58 The Three Marys

1976. Easter. Showing portions of the Altar Frontal Tapestry, Rheinau. Multicoloured.
248 1c. Type **58** 10 10
249 10c. The Crucifixion 10 10
250 15c. Two Soldiers 15 15
251 20c. The Annunciation . . . 15 15
252 $1 The complete tapestry (horiz) 65 65
253 $1.50 The Risen Christ . . . 80 80

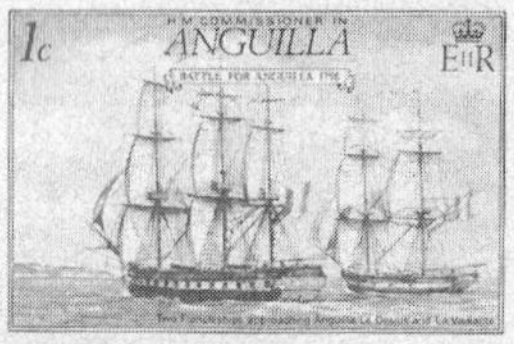

59 French Ships approaching Anguilla

1976. Bicentenary of Battle of Anguilla. Mult.
255 1c. Type **59** 10 10
256 3c. "Margaret" (sloop) leaving Anguilla . . . . . 1·25 35
257 15c. Capture of "Le Desius" 1·50 55
258 25c. "La Vaillante" forced aground . . . . 1·50 80
259 $1 H.M.S. "Lapwing" . . . 2·00 1·25
260 $1.50 "Le Desius" burning 2·25 1·75

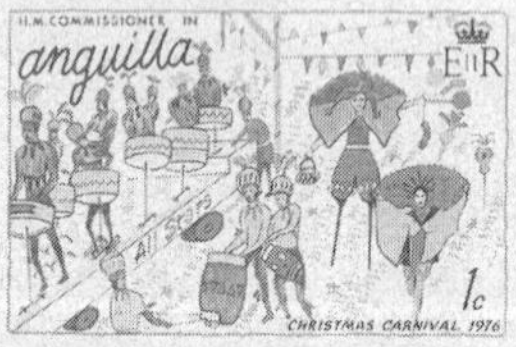

60 "Christmas Carnival" (A. Richardson)

1976. Christmas. Children's Paintings. Multicoloured.
262 1c. Type **60** 10 10
263 3c. "Dreams of Christmas Gifts" (J. Connor) 10 10
264 15c. "Carolling" (P. Richardson) 15 15
265 25c. "Candle-light Procession" (A. Mussington) 20 20
266 $1 "Going to Church" (B. Franklin) 30 30
267 $1.50 "Coming Home for Christmas" (E. Gumbs) . . 40 40

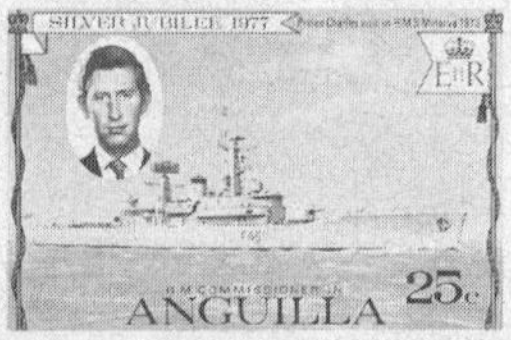

61 Prince Charles and H.M.S. "Minerva" (frigate)

1977. Silver Jubilee. Multicoloured.
269 25c. Type **61** 15 10
270 40c. Prince Philip landing by launch at Road Bay, 1964 15 10
271 $1.20 Coronation scene . . . 20 20
272 $2.50 Coronation regalia and map of Anguilla 25 30

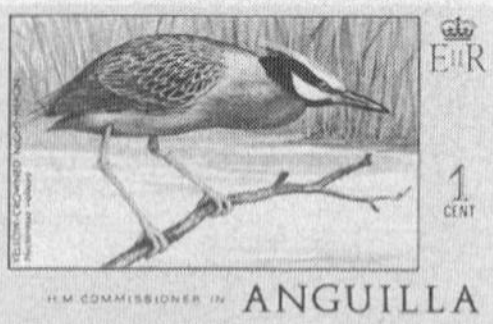

62 Yellow-crowned Night Heron

1977. Multicoloured.
274 1c. Type **62** . . . . 30 1·00
275 2c. Great barracuda . . . . 30 1·40
276 3c. Queen or pink conch . . 1·75 2·50
277 4c. Spanish bayonet (flower) 40 30
278 5c. Honeycomb trunkfish . . 1·50 30
279 6c. Cable and Wireless building 30 30
280 10c. American kestrel ("American Sparrow Hawk") . . . . 4·50 2·25
281 15c. Ground orchid . . . . 2·75 1·75
282 20c. Stop-light parrotfish . . 3·00 75
283 22c. Lobster fishing boat . . 45 60
284 35c. Boat race . . . . 1·40 70
285 50c. Sea bean 90 50
286 $1 Sandy Island 60 50
287 $2.50 Manchineel . . . . . 1·00 1·00
288 $5 Ground lizard . . . . . 2·00 1·75
289 $10 Red-billed tropic bird . . 9·00 4·25

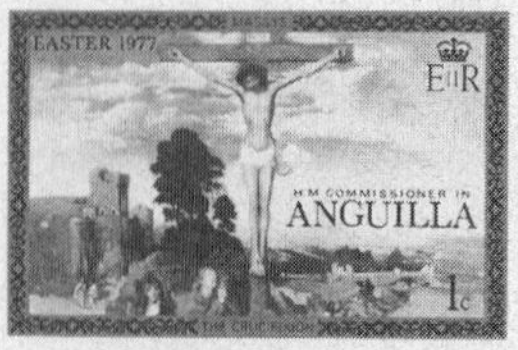

63 "The Crucifixion" (Massys)

1977. Easter. Paintings by Castagno ($1.50) or Ugolino (others). Multicoloured.
291 1c. Type **63** 10 10
292 3c. "The Betrayal" 10 10
293 22c. "The Way to Calvary" 20 20
294 30c. "The Deposition" . . . 25 25
295 $1 "The Resurrection" . . . 50 50
296 $1.50 "The Crucifixion" . . . 65 65

1977. Royal Visit. Nos. 269/72 optd **ROYAL VISIT TO WEST INDIES**.
298 25c. Type **61** 10 10
299 40c. Prince Philip landing at Road Bay, 1964 . . . . . 10 15
300 $1.20 Coronation scene . . . 20 25
301 $1.50 Coronation regalia and map of Anguilla 25 35

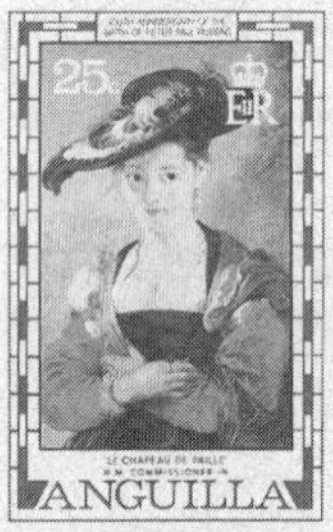

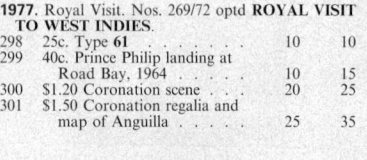

65 "Le Chapeau de Paille"

1977. 400th Birth Anniv of Rubens. Multicoloured.
303 25c. Type **65** 15 15
304 40c. "Helene Fourment and her Two Children" 20 25
305 $1.20 "Rubens and his Wife" 60 65
306 $2.50 "Marchesa Brigida Spinola-Doria" 75 95

1977. Christmas. Nos. 262/7 with old date blocked out and additionally inscr "1977", some also surch.
308 1c. Type **60** 10 10
309 5c. on 3c. "Dreams of Christmas Gifts" 10 10
310 12c. on 15c. "Carolling" . . 15 15
311 18c. on 25c. "Candle-light Procession" 20 20
312 $1 "Going to Church" . . . 45 45
313 $2.50 on $1.50 "Coming Home for Christmas" . . . 90 90

1978. Easter. Nos. 303/6 optd **EASTER 1978**.
315 25c. Type **65** 15 20
316 40c. "Helene Fourment with her Two Children" 15 20
317 $1.20 "Rubens and his Wife" 35 40
318 $2.50 "Marchesa Brigida Spinola-Doria" 45 60

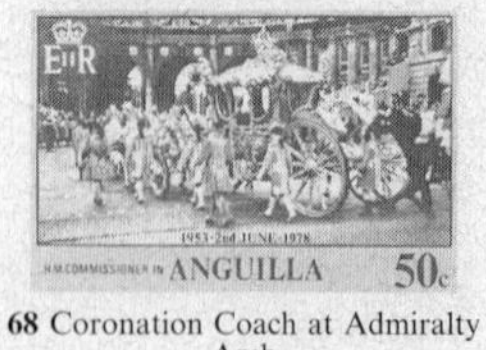

68 Coronation Coach at Admiralty Arch

1978. 25th Anniv of Coronation. Multicoloured.
320 22c. Buckingham Palace . . . 10 10
321 50c. Type **68** 15 10
322 $1.50 Balcony scene 15 15
323 $2.50 Royal coat of arms . . 25 25

1978. Anniversaries. Nos. 283/4 and 287 optd **VALLEY SECONDARY SCHOOL 1953–1978** and Nos. 285/6 and 288 optd **ROAD METHODIST CHURCH 1878–1978**, or surch also.
325 22c. Lobster fishing boat . . 20 15
326 35c. Boat race 30 20
327 50c. Sea bean 30 30
328 $1 Sandy Island 35 40
329 $1.20 on $5 Ground lizard . . 40 45
330 $1.50 on $2.50 Manchineel . . 45 55

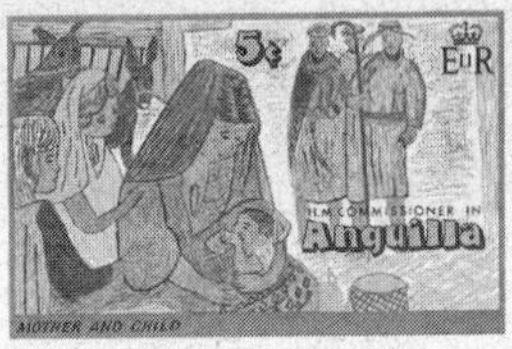

71 Mother and Child

1978. Christmas. Children's Paintings. Multicoloured.

331	5c. Type **71**	10	10
332	12c. Christmas masquerade	15	10
333	18c. Christmas dinner	15	10
334	22c. Serenading	15	10
335	$1 Child in manger	45	20
336	$2.50 Family going to church	90	40

1979. International Year of the Child. As Nos. 331/6, but additionally inscr "1979 INTERNATIONAL YEAR OF THE CHILD" and emblem. Borders in different colours.

338	5c. Type **71**	10	10
339	12c. Christmas masquerade	10	10
340	18c. Christmas dinner	10	10
341	22c. Serenading	10	10
342	$1 Child in manger	30	30
343	$2.50 Family going to church	50	50

1979. Nos. 274/7 and 279/80 surch.

345	12c. on 2c. Great barracuda	50	50
346	14c. on 4c. Spanish bayonet	40	50
347	18c. on 3c. Queen conch	80	55
348	25c. on 6c. Cable and Wireless building	55	50
349	38c. on 10c. American kestrel	2·50	70
350	40c. on 1c. Type **62**	2·50	70

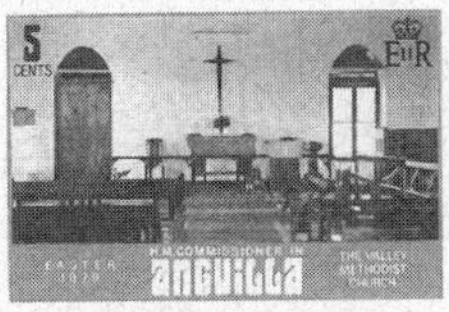

73 Valley Methodist Church

1979. Easter. Church Interiors. Multicoloured.

351	5c. Type **73**	10	10
352	12c. St. Mary's Anglican Church, The Valley	10	10
353	18c. St. Gerard's Roman Catholic Church, The Valley	15	15
354	22c. Road Methodist Church	15	15
355	$1.50 St. Augustine's Anglican Church, East End	60	60
356	$2.50 West End Methodist Church	75	75

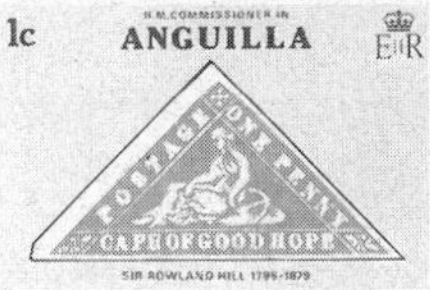

74 Cape of Good Hope 1d. "Woodblock" of 1881

1979. Death Centenary of Sir Rowland Hill. Multicoloured.

358	1c. Type **74**	10	10
359	1c. U.S.A. "inverted Jenny" of 1918	10	10
360	22c. Penny Black ("V.R." Official)	15	15
361	35c. Germany 2m, "Graf Zeppelin" of 1928	20	20
362	$1.50 U.S.A. $5 "Columbus" of 1893	40	60
363	$2.50 Great Britain £5 orange of 1882	60	95

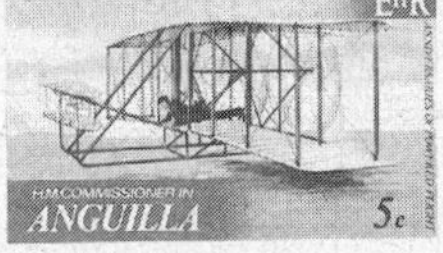

75 Wright "Flyer I" (1st powered Flight, 1903)

1979. History of Powered Fight. Multicoloured.

365	5c. Type **75**	15	10
366	12c. Louis Bleriot at Dover after Channel crossing, 1909	20	10
367	18c. Vickers FB-27 Vimy (1st non-stop crossing of Atlantic, 1919)	25	15
368	22c. Ryan NYP Special "Spirit of St Louis" (1st solo Atlantic flight by Charles Lindbergh, 1927)	25	20
369	$1.50 Airship LZ 127 "Graf Zeppelin", 1928	60	60
370	$2.50 Concorde, 1979	2·50	90

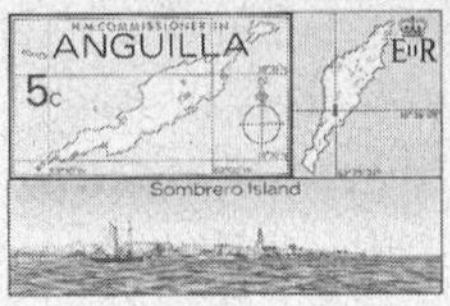

76 Sombrero Island

1979. Outer Islands. Multicoloured.

372	5c. Type **76**	10	10
373	12c. Anguillita Island	10	10
374	18c. Sandy Island	15	15
375	25c. Prickly Pear Cays	15	15
376	$1 Dog Island	30	40
377	$2.50 Scrub Island	50	70

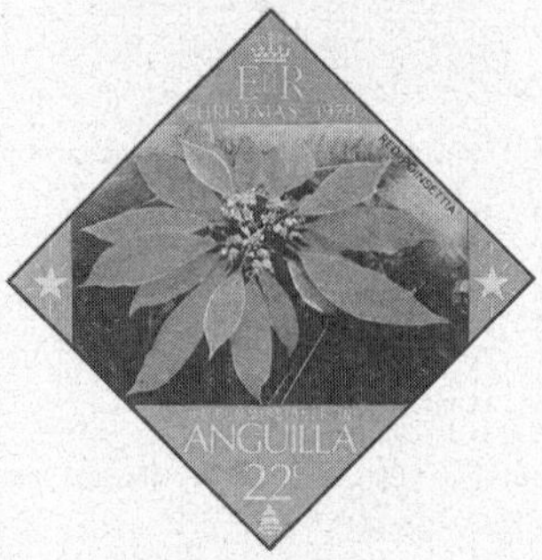

77 Red Poinsettia

1979. Christmas. Multicoloured.

379	22c. Type **77**	15	20
380	35c. Kalanchoe	20	30
381	$1.50 Cream poinsettia	40	50
382	$2.50 White poinsettia	60	70

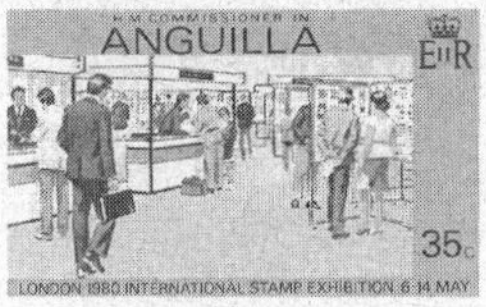

78 Exhibition Scene

1979. "London 1980" International Stamp Exhibition (1st issue). Multicoloured.

384	35c. Type **78**	15	20
385	50c. Earls Court Exhibition Centre	15	25
386	$1.50 Penny Black and Two-penny Blue stamps	25	60
387	$2.50 Exhibition Logo	45	95

See also Nos. 407/9.

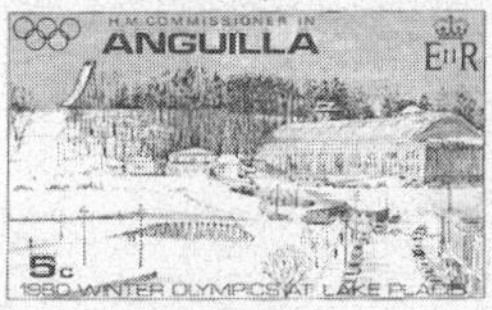

79 Games Site

1980. Winter Olympic Games, Lake Placid, U.S.A. Multicoloured.

389	5c. Type **79**	10	10
390	18c. Ice hockey	20	10
391	35c. Ice skating	20	20
392	50c. Bobsleighing	20	20
393	$1 Skiing	20	35
394	$2.50 Luge-tobogganing	40	80

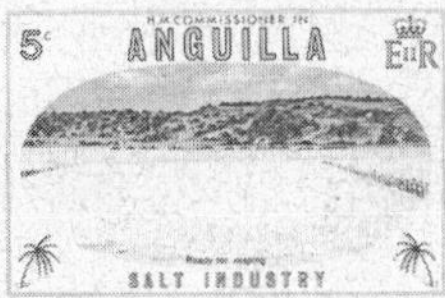

80 Salt ready for "Reaping"

1980. Salt Industry. Multicoloured.

396	5c. Type **80**	10	10
397	12c. Tallying salt	10	10
398	18c. Unloading salt flats	15	15
399	22c. Salt storage heap	15	15
400	$1 Salt for bagging and grinding	30	40
401	$2.50 Loading salt for export	50	70

1980. Anniversaries. Nos. 280, 282 and 287/8 optd **50th Anniversary Scouting 1980** (10c., $2.50) or **75th Anniversary Rotary 1980** (others).

403	10c. American kestrel	1·75	15
404	20c. Stop-light parrotfish	1·00	20
405	$2.50 Manchineel	1·75	1·25
406	$5 Ground lizard	2·50	1·90

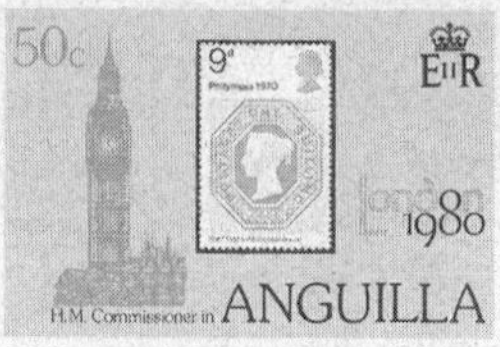

83 Palace of Westminster and Great Britain 1970 9d. "Philympia" Commemoration

1980. "London 1980" International Stamp Exhibition (2nd issue). Multicoloured.

407	50c. Type **83**	55	65
408	$1.50 City Hall, Toronto and "Capex 1978" stamp of Canada	85	1·00
409	$2.50 Statue of Liberty and 1976 "Interphil" stamp of U.S.A	1·10	1·40

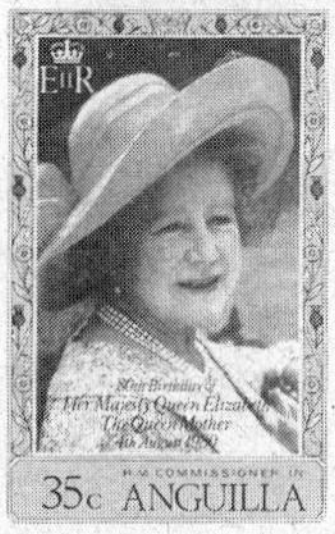

84 Queen Elizabeth the Queen Mother

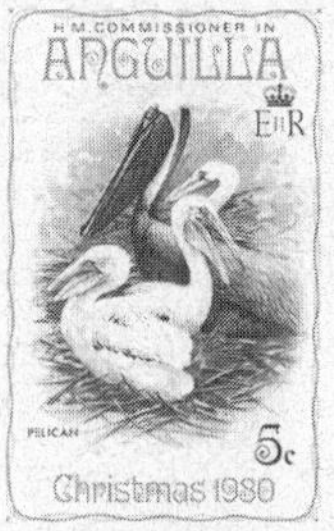

85 Brown Pelicans ("Pelican")

1980. 80th Birthday of The Queen Mother.

411	**84**	35c. multicoloured	70	40
412		50c. multicoloured	85	50
413		$1.50 multicoloured	1·50	1·25
414		$3 multicoloured	2·25	2·00

1980. Christmas. Birds. Multicoloured.

416	5c. Type **85**	30	10
417	22c. Great blue heron ("Great Grey Heron")	75	20
418	$1.50 Barn swallow ("Swallow")	1·75	60
419	$3 Ruby-throated hummingbird ("Hummingbird")	2·25	1·40

1980. Separation from St. Kitts. Nos. 274, 277, 280/9, 334 and 418/19 optd **SEPARATION 1980** or surch also.

421	1c. Type **62**	15	70
422b	2c. on 4c. Spanish bayonet	15	70
423	5c. on 15c. Ground orchid	70	70
424	5c. on $1.50 Barn swallow	70	70
425	5c. on $3 Ruby-throated hummingbird	70	70
426	10c. American kestrel	1·00	70
427	12c. on $1 Sandy Island	20	70
428	14c. on $2.50 Manchineel	20	70
429	15c. Ground orchid	80	70
430	18c. on $5 Ground lizard	25	70
431	20c. Stop-light parrotfish	25	70
432	22c. Lobster fishing boat	25	70
433	25c. on 15c. Ground orchid	80	75
434	35c. Boat race	30	75
435	38c. on 22c. Serenading	30	75
436	40c. on 1c. Type **62**	30	75
437	50c. Sea bean	35	85
438	$1 Sandy Island	50	1·00
439	$2.50 Manchineel	1·00	2·75
440	$5 Ground lizard	2·25	3·75
441	$10 Red-billed tropic bird	5·00	6·00
442	$10 on 6c. Cable and Wireless Building	5·00	6·00

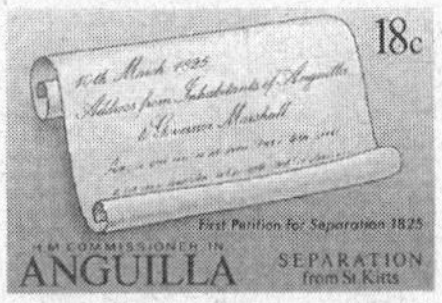

87 First Petition for Separation, 1825

1980. Separation from St. Kitts. Multicoloured.

443	18c. Type **87**	10	10
444	22c. Referendum ballot paper, 1967	15	10
445	35c. Airport blockade, 1967	15	15
446	50c. Anguillan flag	20	20
447	$1 Separation celebration, 1980	30	35

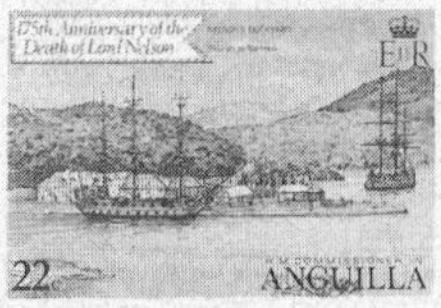

88 "Nelson's Dockyard" (R. Granger Barrett)

1981. 175th Death Anniv of Lord Nelson. Mult.

449	22c. Type **88**	1·40	40
450	35c. "Ships in which Nelson Served" (Nicholas Pocock)	1·60	60
451	50c. "H.M.S. Victory" (Monamy Swaine)	1·90	85
452	$3 "Battle of Trafalgar" (Clarkson Stanfield)	2·50	3·00

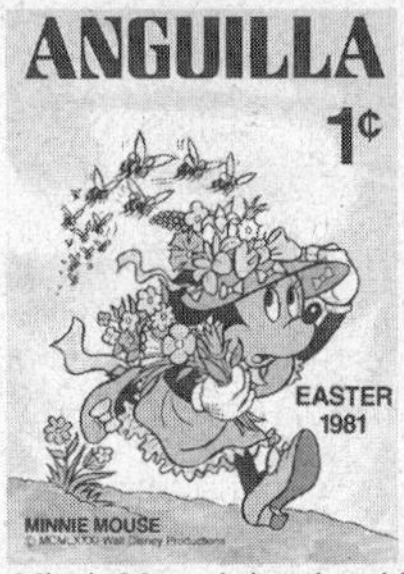

89 Minnie Mouse being chased by Bees

1981. Easter. Walt Disney Cartoon Characters. Multicoloured.

454	1c. Type **89**	10	10
455	2c. Pluto laughing at Mickey Mouse	10	10
456	3c. Minnie Mouse tying ribbon round Pluto's neck	10	10
457	5c. Minnie Mouse confronted by love-struck bird who fancies her bonnet	10	10
458	7c. Dewey and Huey admiring themselves in mirror	10	10
459	9c. Horace Horsecollar and Clarabelle Cow out for a stroll	10	10
460	10c. Daisy Duck with hat full of Easter eggs	10	10
461	$2 Goofy unwrapping Easter hat	1·40	1·40
462	$3 Donald Duck in his Easter finery	1·60	1·60

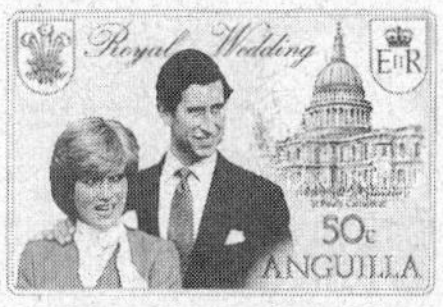

90 Prince Charles, Lady Diana Spencer and St. Paul's Cathedral

1981. Royal Wedding. Multicoloured.

464	50c. Type **90**	15	20
465	$2.50 Althorp	30	50
466	$3 Windsor Castle	35	60

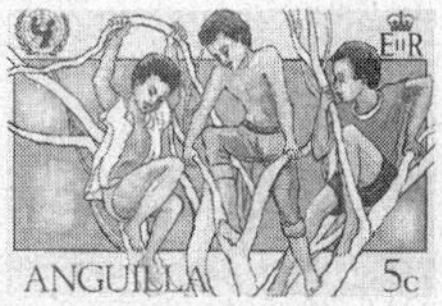

91 Children playing in Tree

1981. 35th Anniv of U.N.I.C.E.F. Multicoloured.

470	5c. Type **91**	20	30
471	10c. Children playing by pool	20	30
472	15c. Children playing musical instruments	20	30
473	$3 Children playing with pets	2·50	3·00

1981. Christmas. Designs as T **89** showing scenes from Walt Disney's cartoon film "The Night before Christmas".

475	1c. multicoloured	10	10
476	2c. multicoloured	10	10
477	3c. multicoloured	10	10
478	5c. multicoloured	15	10
479	7c. multicoloured	15	10
480	10c. multicoloured	15	10
481	12c. multicoloured	15	10
482	$2 multicoloured	3·75	1·25
483	$3 multicoloured	3·75	1·60

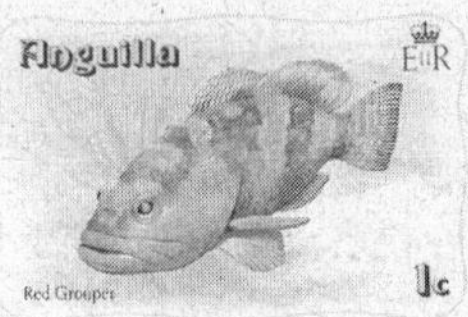

92 Red Grouper

1982. Multicoloured.

485	1c. Type **92**	15	80
486	5c. Ferry service, Blowing Point	30	80
487	10c. Island dinghies	20	60
488	15c. Majorettes	20	60
489	20c. Launching boat, Sandy Hill	40	60
490	25c. Corals	1·50	60
491	30c. Little Bay cliffs	30	75
492	35c. Fountain Cave interior	1·50	80
493	40c. Sunset over Sandy Island	30	75
494	45c. Landing at Sombrero	50	80
495	60c. Seine fishing	3·25	3·00
496	75c. Boat race at sunset, Sandy Ground	1·00	1·75

497 $1 Bagging lobster at Island Harbour 2·25 1·75
498 $5 Brown pelicans 16·00 12·00
499 $7.50 Hibiscus 11·00 14·00
500 $10 Queen triggerfish 16·00 15·00

1982. No. 494 surch **50c**.
501 50c. on 45c. Landing at Sombrero 50 35

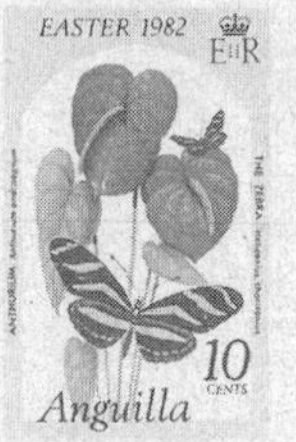

94 Anthurium and "Heliconius charithonia"

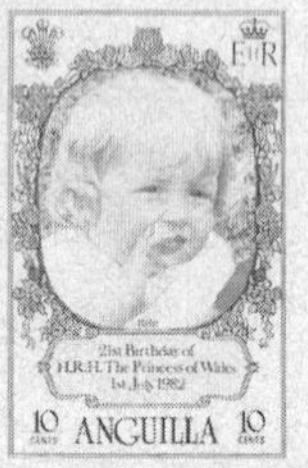

95 Lady Diana Spencer in 1961

1982. Easter. Flowers and Butterflies. Multicoloured.
502 10c. Type **94** 75 10
503 35c. Bird of paradise and "Junonia evarete" 1·40 40
504 75c. Allamanda and "Danaus plexippus" 1·60 70
505 $3 Orchid tree and "Biblis hyperia" 2·75 2·25

1982. 21st Birthday of Princess of Wales. Mult.
507 10c. Type **95** 40 20
508 30c. Lady Diana Spencer in 1968 1·00 25
509 40c. Lady Diana in 1970 50 30
510 60c. Lady Diana in 1974 55 35
511 $2 Lady Diana in 1981 80 1·10
512 $3 Lady Diana in 1981 (different) 4·00 1·40

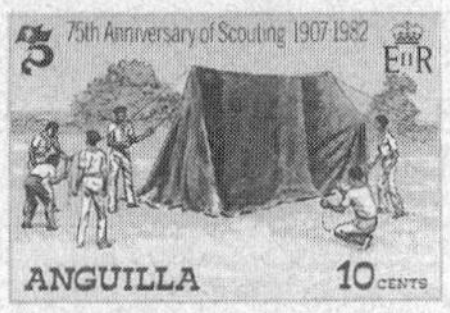

96 Pitching Tent

1982. 75th Anniv of Boy Scout Movement. Multicoloured.
515 10c. Type **96** 45 20
516 35c. Scout band 85 50
517 75c. Yachting 1·25 90
518 $3 On parade 3·00 2·75

1982. World Cup Football Championship, Spain. Horiz designs as T **89** showing scenes from Walt Disney's cartoon film "Bedknobs and Broomsticks".
520 1c. multicoloured 10 10
521 3c. multicoloured 10 10
522 4c. multicoloured 10 10
523 5c. multicoloured 10 10
524 7c. multicoloured 10 10
525 9c. multicoloured 10 10
526 10c. multicoloured 10 10
527 $2.50 multicoloured 2·25 1·75
528 $3 multicoloured 2·25 2·00

1982. Commonwealth Games, Brisbane. Nos. 487, 495/6 and 498 optd **COMMONWEALTH GAMES 1982**
530 10c. Island dinghies 15 25
531 60c. Seine fishing 45 60
532 75c. Boat race at sunset, Sandy Ground 60 80
533 $5 Brown pelicans 3·25 3·75

1982. Birth Cent of A. A. Milne (author). As T **89**.
534 1c. multicoloured 20 15
535 2c. multicoloured 20 15
536 3c. multicoloured 20 15
537 5c. multicoloured 30 15
538 7c. multicoloured 30 25
539 10c. multicoloured 30 15
540 12c. multicoloured 45 20
541 20c. multicoloured 60 25
542 $5 multicoloured 6·50 7·50
DESIGNS—HORIZ: 1c. to $5 Scenes from various "Winnie the Pooh" stories.

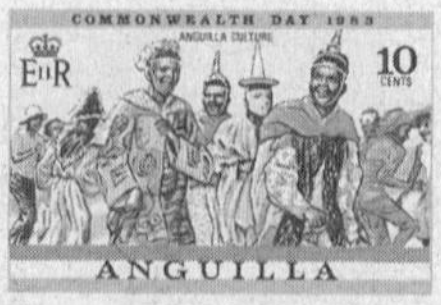

98 Culture

1983. Commonwealth Day. Multicoloured.
544 10c. Type **98** 10 15
545 35c. Anguilla and British flags 30 30
546 75c. Economic co-operation 60 80
547 $2.50 Salt industry (salt pond) 3·75 4·25

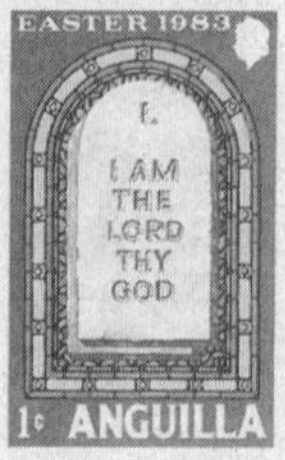

99 "I am the Lord Thy God"

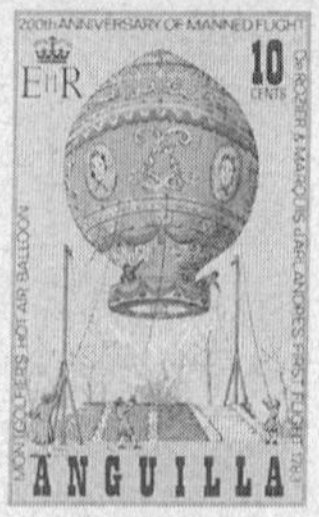

101 Montgolfier Hot Air Balloon, 1783

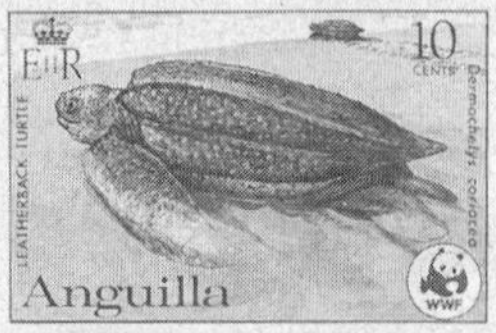

100 Leatherback Turtle

1983. Easter. The Ten Commandments. Mult.
549 1c. Type **99** 10 10
550 2c. "Thou shalt not make any graven image" 10 10
551 3c. "Thou shalt not take My Name in vain" 10 10
552 10c. "Remember the Sabbath Day" 20 10
553 35c. "Honour thy father and mother" 45 20
554 60c. "Thou shalt not kill" 80 40
555 75c. "Thou shalt not commit adultery" 90 50
556 $2 "Thou shalt not steal" 2·25 1·50
557 $2.50 "Thou shalt not bear false witness" 2·50 1·50
558 $5 "Thou shalt not covet" 3·75 2·75

1983. Endangered Species. Turtles. Multicoloured.
560 10c. Type **100** 2·75 80
561 35c. Hawksbill turtle 5·00 1·25
562 75c. Green turtle 6·00 3·00
563 $1 Loggerhead turtle 7·00 7·00

1983. Bicentenary of Manned Flight. Multicoloured.
565 10c. Type **101** 50 50
566 60c. Blanchard and Jefferies crossing English Channel by balloon, 1785 1·25 85
567 $1 Henri Giffard's steam-powered dirigible airship, 1852 1·75 1·25
568 $2.50 Otto Lillienthal and biplane glider, 1890–96 2·50 2·50

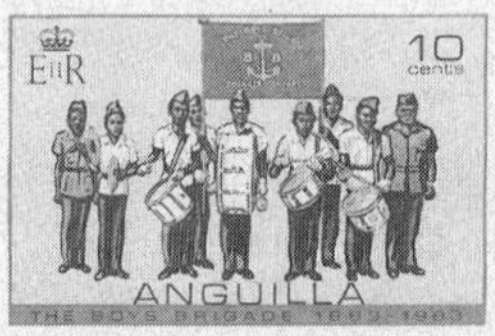

102 Boys' Brigade Band and Flag

1983. Centenary of Boys' Brigade. Multicoloured.
570 10c. Type **102** 50 15
571 $5 Brigade members marching 3·50 2·75

1983. 150th Anniv of Abolition of Slavery (1st issue). Nos. 487, 493 and 497/8 optd **150TH ANNIVERSARY ABOLITION OF SLAVERY ACT**.
573 10c. Island dinghies 20 10
574 40c. Sunset over Sandy Island 30 25
575 $1 Bagging lobster at Island Harbour 70 50
576 $5 Brown pelicans 6·00 2·75
See also Nos. 616/23.

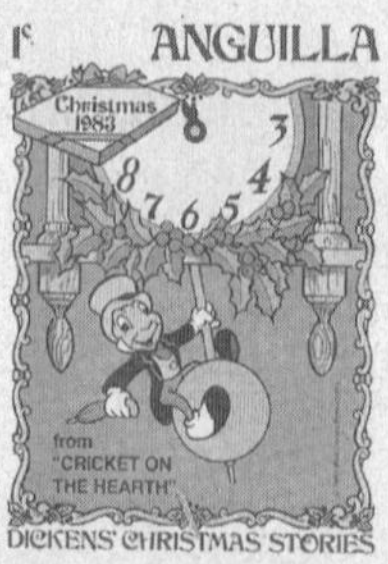

104 Jiminy on Clock ("Cricket on the Hearth")

1983. Christmas. Walt Disney Cartoon Characters. Multicoloured.
577 1c. Type **104** 10 10
578 2c. Jiminy with fiddle ("Cricket on the Hearth") 10 10
579 3c. Jiminy among toys ("Cricket on the Hearth") 10 10
580 4c. Mickey as Bob Cratchit ("A Christmas Carol") 10 10
581 5c. Donald Duck as Scrooge ("A Christmas Carol") 10 10
582 6c. Mini and Goofy in "The Chimes" 10 10
583 10c. Goofy sees an imp appearing from bells ("The Chimes") 10 10
584 $2 Donald Duck as Mr. Pickwick ("The Pickwick Papers") 3·25 2·75
585 $3 Disney characters as Pickwickians ("The Pickwick Papers") 3·75 2·25

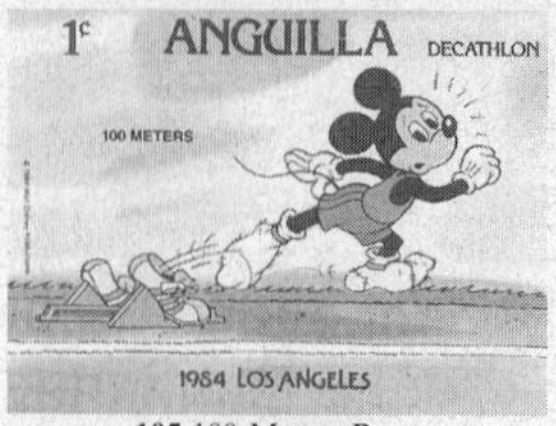

105 100 Metres Race

1984. Olympic Games, Los Angeles. Multicoloured. (A) Inscr "1984 Los Angeles".
587A 1c. Type **105** 10 10
588A 2c. Long jumping 10 10
589A 3c. Shot-putting 10 10
590A 4c. High jumping 10 10
591A 5c. 400 metres race 10 10
592A 6c. Hurdling 10 10
593A 10c. Discus-throwing 10 10
594A $1 Pole-vaulting 3·25 3·75
595A $4 Javelin-throwing 6·00 3·50

(B) Inscr "1984 Olympics Los Angeles" and Olympic emblem.
587B 1c. Type **105** 10 10
588B 2c. Long jumping 10 10
589B 3c. Shot-putting 10 10
590B 4c. High jumping 10 10
591B 5c. 400 metres race 10 10
592B 6c. Hurdling 10 10
593B 10c. Discus-throwing 10 10
594B $1 Pole-vaulting 3·75 3·00
595B $4 Javelin-throwing 7·50 8·50

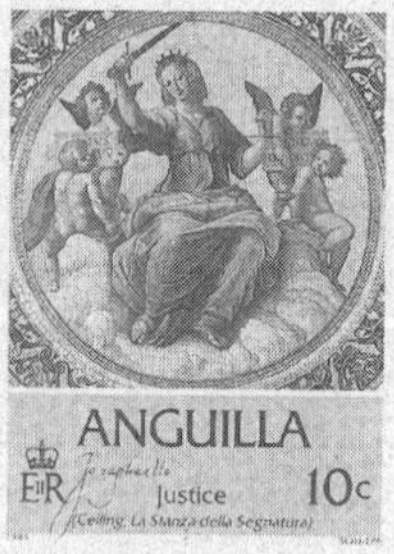

106 "Justice"

1984. Easter. Multicoloured.
597 10c. Type **106** 15 10
598 25c. "Poetry" 20 20
599 35c. "Philosophy" 30 30
600 40c. "Theology" 30 30
601 $1 "Abraham and Paul" 85 95
602 $2 "Moses and Matthew" 1·60 2·25
603 $3 "John and David" 2·25 3·00
604 $4 "Peter and Adam" 2·50 3·00
Nos. 597/604 show details from "La Stanza della Segnatura" by Raphael.

1984. Nos. 485, 491, 498/500 surch.
606 25c. on $7.50 Hibiscus 65 35
607 35c. on 30c. Little Bay cliffs 50 40
608 60c. on 1c. Type **92** 55 45
609 $2.50 on $5 Brown pelicans 3·00 1·50
610 $2.50 on $10 Queen triggerfish 1·75 1·50

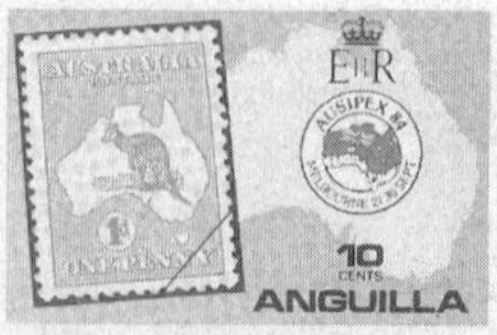

108 1913 1d. Kangaroo Stamp

1984. "Ausipex 84" International Stamp Exhibition. Multicoloured.
611 10c. Type **108** 40 30
612 75c. 1914 6d. Laughing Kookaburra 1·25 1·00
613 $1 1932 2d. Sydney Harbour Bridge 1·75 1·40
614 $2.50 1938 10s. King George VI 2·25 2·50

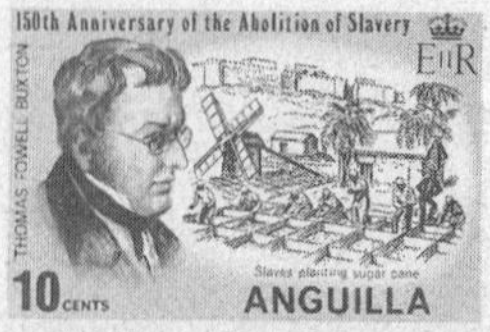

109 Thomas Fowell Buxton

1984. 150th Anniv of Abolition of Slavery (2nd issue). Multicoloured.
616 10c. Type **109** 10 10
617 25c. Abraham Lincoln 25 25
618 35c. Henri Christophe 35 35
619 60c. Thomas Clarkson 50 50
620 75c. William Wilberforce 60 60
621 $1 Olaudah Equiano 70 70
622 $2.50 General Charles Gordon 1·60 1·60
623 $5 Granville Sharp 3·00 3·00

1984. Universal Postal Union Congress, Hamburg. Nos. 486/7 and 498 optd **U.P.U. CONGRESS HAMBURG 1984** or surch also (No 626).
625 5c. Ferry service, Blowing Point 30 10
626 20c. on 10c. Island dinghies 30 15
627 $5 Brown pelicans 5·50 3·50

1984. Birth of Prince Henry. Nos. 507/12 optd **PRINCE HENRY BIRTH 15.9.84.**
628 10c. Type **95** 20 10
629 30c. Lady Diana Spencer in 1968 40 25
630 40c. Lady Diana in 1970 25 30
631 60c. Lady Diana in 1974 40 45
632 $2 Lady Diana in 1981 1·00 1·25
633 $3 Lady Diana in 1981 (different) 1·50 1·75

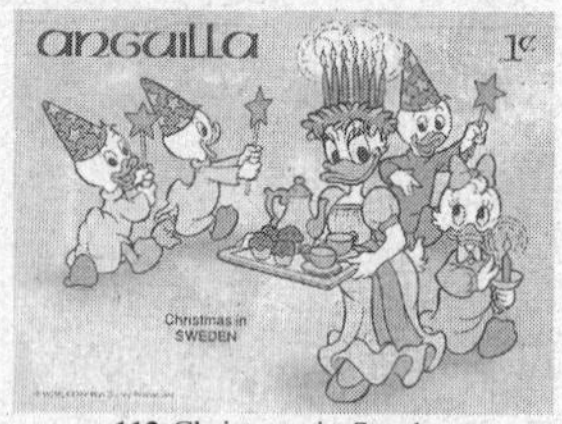

112 Christmas in Sweden

1984. Christmas. Walt Disney Cartoon Characters. National Scenes. Multicoloured.
636 1c. Type **112** 10 10
637 2c. Italy 10 10
638 3c. Holland 10 10
639 4c. Mexico 10 10
640 5c. Spain 10 10
641 10c. Disneyland, U.S.A. 10 10
642 $1 Japan 3·00 2·00
643 $2 Anguilla 4·00 4·50
644 $4 Germany 6·50 7·50

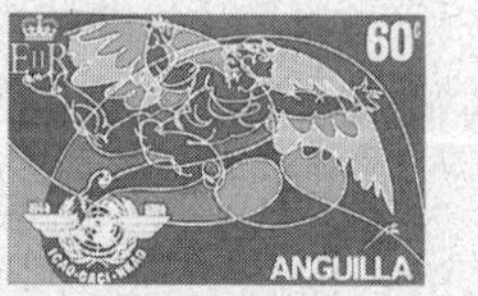

113 Icarus in Flight

1984. 40th Anniv of International Civil Aviation Authority. Multicoloured.
646 60c. Type **113** 60 75
647 75c. "Solar Princess" (abstract) 80 90
648 $2.50 I.C.A.O. emblem (vert) 2·25 3·00

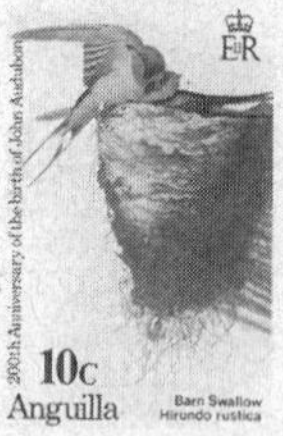

114 Barn Swallow

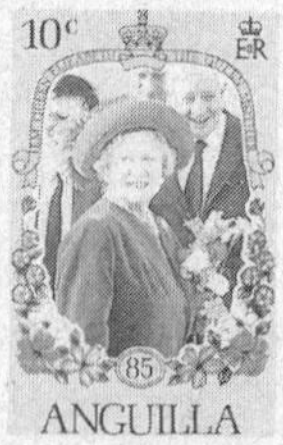

115 The Queen Mother visiting King's College Hospital, London

1985. Birth Bicentenary of John J. Audubon (ornithologist). Multicoloured.
650 10c. Type **114** 80 65
651 60c. American wood stork ("Woodstork") 1·50 1·25
652 75c. Roseate tern 1·50 1·25
653 $5 Osprey 4·50 5·00

1985. Life and Times of Queen Elizabeth the Queen Mother. Multicoloured.
655 10c. Type **115** 10 10
656 $2 The Queen Mother inspecting Royal Marine Volunteer Cadets, Deal 80 1·25
657 $3 The Queen Mother outside Clarence House 1·10 1·50

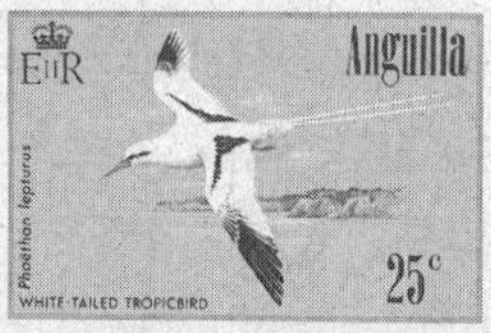

116 White-tailed Tropic Bird

1985. Birds. Multicoloured.
659 5c. Brown pelican 1·75 1·75
660 10c. Mourning dove ("Turtle Dove") 1·75 1·75

661 15c. Magnificent frigate bird (inscr "Man-o-War") . . 1·75 1·75
662 20c. Antillean crested hummingbird . . . . . . 1·75 1·75
663 25c. Type **116** . . . . . . 1·75 1·75
664 30c. Caribbean elaenia . . . 1·75 1·75
665 35c. Black-whiskered vireo 7·50 5·00
665a 35c. Lesser Antillean bullfinch . . . . 1·75 1·75
666 40c. Yellow-crowned night heron . . . . 1·75 1·75
667 45c. Pearly-eyed thrasher . . 1·75 1·75
668 50c. Laughing gull . . . . 1·75 1·75
669 65c. Brown booby . . . . . 1·75 1·75
670 80c. Grey kingbird . . . . 2·25 3·00
671 $1 Audubon's shearwater 2·25 3·00
672 $1.35 Roseate tern . . . . 1·75 3·00
673 $2.50 Bananaquit . . . . . 5·50 7·00
674 $5 Belted kingfisher . . . . 4·25 8·00
675 $10 Green-backed heron ("Green Heron") . . . . 7·00 10·00

1985. 75th Anniv of Girl Guide Movement. Nos. 486, 491, 496 and 498 optd **GIRL GUIDES 75TH ANNIVERSARY 1910–1985** and anniversary emblem.
676 5c. Ferry service, Blowing Point 30 30
677 30c. Little Bay cliffs 40 35
678 75c. Boat race at sunset, Sandy Ground 60 85
679 $5 Brown pelicans . . . . . 7·00 7·50

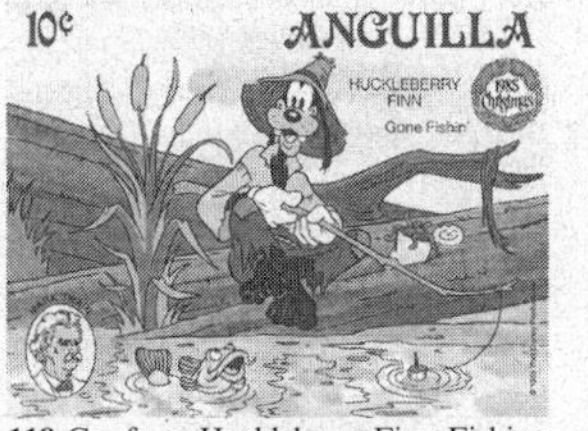

118 Goofy as Huckleberry Finn Fishing

1985. 150th Birth Anniv of Mark Twain (author). Walt Disney cartoon characters in scenes from "Huckleberry Finn". Multicoloured.
680 10c. Type **118** 55 20
681 60c. Pete as Pap surprising Huck . . . . 1·75 85
682 $1 "Multiplication tables" . . 2·25 1·25
683 $3 The Duke reciting Shakespeare . . . . 3·50 4·00

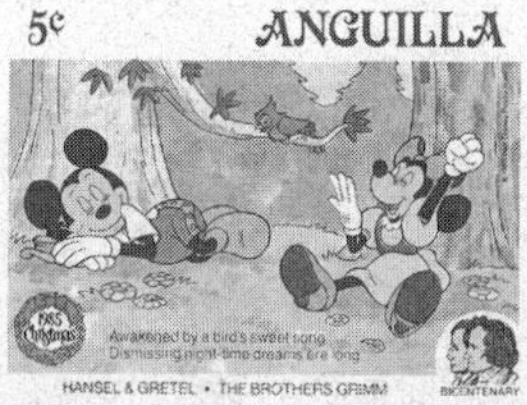

119 Hansel and Gretel (Mickey and Minnie Mouse) awakening in Forest

1985. Birth Bicentenaries of Grimm Brothers (folklorists). Designs showing Walt Disney cartoon characters in scenes from "Hansel and Gretel". Multicoloured.
685 5c. Type **119** 40 40
686 50c. Hansel and Gretel find the gingerbread house . . 1·25 45
687 90c. Hansel and Gretel meeting the Witch . . . . 1·75 1·00
688 $4 Hansel and Gretel captured by the Witch . . 3·25 4·25

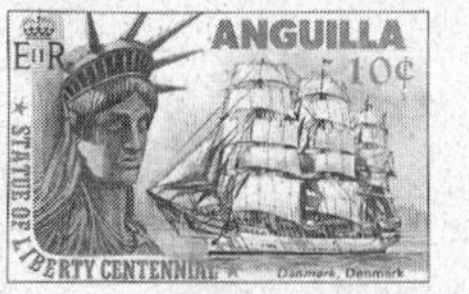

120 Statue of Liberty and "Danmark" (Denmark)

1985. Centenary of the Statue of Liberty (1986). The Statue of Liberty and Cadet ships.
690 10c. Type **120** 65 65
691 20c. "Eagle" (U.S.A.) 85 85
692 60c. "Amerigo Vespucci" (Italy) . . . . 1·25 1·50
693 75c. "Sir Winston Churchill" (Great Britain) . . . . . 1·25 1·00
694 $2 "Nippon Maru" (Japan) 1·25 2·75
695 $2.50 "Gorch Fock" (West Germany) . . . . 1·50 2·75

1985. 80th Anniv of Rotary (10, 35c.) and International Youth Year (others). Nos. 487, 491 and 497 optd or surch **80TH ANNIVERSARY ROTARY 1985** and emblem (10, 35c.) or **INTERNATIONAL YOUTH YEAR** and emblem ($1, $5).
697 10c. Island dinghies 25 15
698 35c. on 30c. Little Bay cliffs 55 30
699 $1 Bagging lobster at Island Harbour . . . . 1·25 80
700 $5 on 30c. Little Bay cliffs . . 4·00 4·00

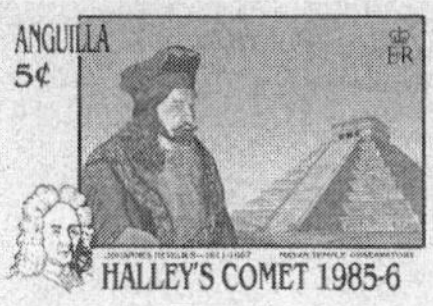

123 Johannes Hevelius (astronomer) and Mayan Temple Observatory

1986. Appearance of Halley's Comet. Multicoloured.
701 5c. Type **123** 35 35
702 10c. "Viking Lander" space vehicle on Mars, 1976 . . 35 35
703 60c. Comet in 1664 (from "Theatri Cosmicum", 1668) 1·00 85
704 $4 Comet over Mississippi riverboat, 1835 (150th birth anniv of Mark Twain) . . 3·75 3·75

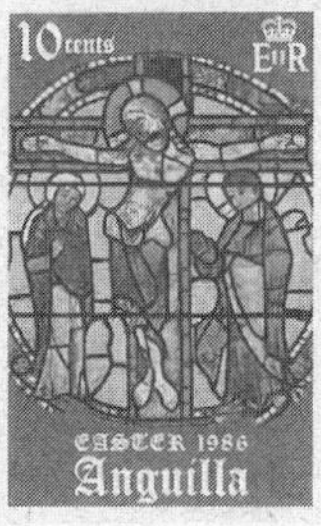

124 "The Crucifixion"

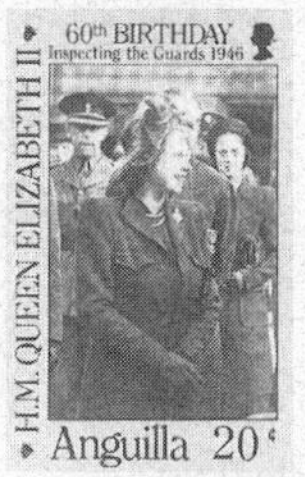

125 Princess Elizabeth inspecting Guards, 1946

1986. Easter.
706 **124** 10c. multicoloured 20 20
707 – 25c. multicoloured 35 35
708 – 45c. multicoloured 65 65
709 – $4 multicoloured . . . . 3·25 3·75
DESIGNS: 25c. to $4 Different stained glass windows from Chartres Cathedral.

1986. 60th Birthday of Queen Elizabeth II.
711 **125** 20c. black and yellow . . 40 20
712 – $2 multicoloured . . . . 1·75 1·50
713 – $3 multicoloured . . . . 1·75 1·75
DESIGNS: $2 Queen at Garter ceremony; $3 At Trooping the Colour.

1986. "Ameripex" International Stamp Exhibition, Chicago. Nos. 659, 667, 671, 673 and 675 optd **AMERIPEX 1986**.
715 5c. Brown pelican 60 75
716 45c. Pearly-eyed thrasher . . 1·25 45
717 $1 Audubon's shearwater . . 2·00 1·10
718 $2.50 Bananaquit . . . . . 2·75 3·00
719 $10 Green-backed heron . . 6·50 8·50

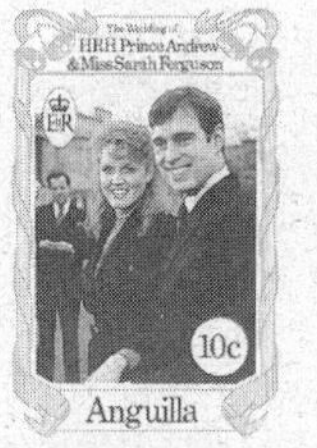

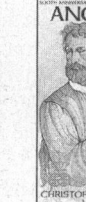

127 Prince Andrew and Miss Sarah Ferguson

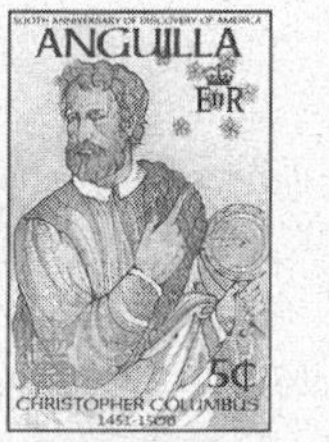

130 Christopher Columbus with Astrolabe

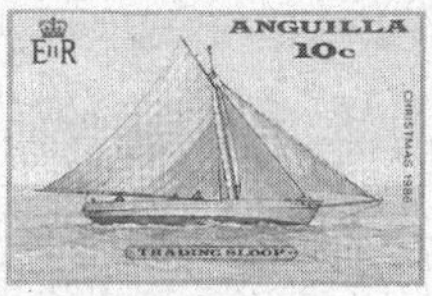

129 Trading Sloop

1986. Royal Wedding. Multicoloured.
720 10c. Type **127** 30 15
721 35c. Prince Andrew 60 35
722 $2 Miss Sarah Ferguson . . 1·75 1·50
723 $3 Prince Andrew and Miss Sarah Ferguson (diffferent) 2·25 2·00

1986. International Peace Year. Nos. 616/23 optd **INTERNATIONAL YEAR OF PEACE**.
725 10c. Type **109** 40 30
726 25c. Abraham Lincoln . . . 65 45
727 35c. Henri Christophe . . . 80 55
728 60c. Thomas Clarkson . . . 1·25 80
729 75c. William Wilberforce . . 1·25 90
730 $1 Olaudah Equiano . . . . 1·25 1·00
731 $2.50 General Gordon . . . 2·25 3·00
732 $5 Granville Sharp . . . . . 3·25 4·00

1986. Christmas. Ships. Multicoloured.
734 10c. Type **129** . . . . 1·25 60
735 45c. "Lady Rodney" (cargo liner) . . . . 2·25 1·10
736 80c. "West Derby" (19th-century sailing ship) . . . 3·25 2·50
737 $3 "Warspite" (local sloop) 5·50 7·00

1986. 500th Anniv (1992) of Discovery of America by Columbus (1st issue). Multicoloured.
739 5c. Type **130** 60 60
740 10c. Columbus on board ship 1·00 60
741 35c. "Santa Maria" . . . . 2·00 1·10
742 80c. King Ferdinand and Queen Isabella of Spain (horiz) . . . . 1·50 1·75
743 $4 Caribbean Indians smoking tobacco (horiz) . . 3·25 5·00
See also Nos. 902/5.

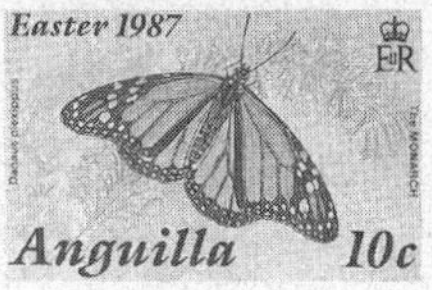

131 "Danaus plexippus"

1987. Easter. Butterflies. Multicoloured.
745 10c. Type **131** . . . . 1·25 60
746 80c. "Anartia jatrophae" . . 3·25 2·50
747 $1 "Heliconius charithonia" 3·50 2·50
748 $2 "Junonia evarete" . . . . 5·50 7·00

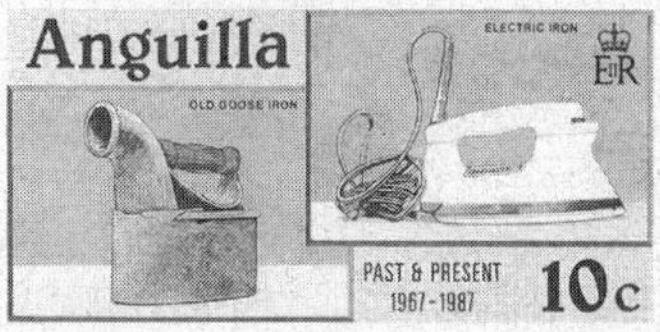

132 Old Goose Iron and Modern Electric Iron

1987. 20th Anniv of Separation from St. Kitts-Nevis. Multicoloured.
750 10c. Type **132** 40 40
751 35c. Old East End School and Albena Lake-Hodge Comprehensive College . . 45 45
752 45c. Past and present markets 50 50
753 80c. Previous sailing ferry and new motor ferry, Blowing Point . . . . . . 1·00 70
754 $1 Original mobile office and new telephone exchange . . 1·00 85
755 $2 Open-air meeting, Burrowes Park and House of Assembly in session . . 1·25 2·25

1987. "Capex '87" International Stamp Exhibition, Toronto. Nos. 665a, 667, 670 and 675 optd **CAPEX'87**.
757 35c. Lesser Antillean bullfinch . . . . 1·25 70
758 45c. Pearly-eyed thrasher . . 1·25 70
759 80c. Grey kingbird . . . . . 2·25 1·25
760 $10 Green-backed heron . . 8·00 10·00

1987. 20th Anniv of Independence. Nos. 659, 661/4 and 665a/75 optd **20 YEARS OF PROGRESS 1967–1987**, No. 762 surch also.
761 5c. Brown pelican . . . . . 1·75 1·75
762 10c. on 15c. Magnificent frigate bird . . . . 1·75 1·75
763 15c. Magnificent frigate bird 2·00 2·00
764 20c. Antillean crested hummingbird . . . . . . 2·00 2·00
765 25c. Type **116** . . . . 2·00 2·00
766 30c. Caribbean elaenia . . . 2·00 2·00
767 35c. Lesser Antillean bullfinch . . . . 2·00 2·00
768 40c. Yellow-crowned night heron . . . . 2·00 2·00
769 45c. Pearly-eyed thrasher . . 2·00 2·00
770 50c. Laughing gull . . . . . 2·00 2·00
771 65c. Brown booby . . . . . 2·25 2·50
772 80c. Grey kingbird . . . . . 2·25 2·50
773 $1 Audubon's shearwater . . 2·25 2·50
774 $1.35 Roseate tern . . . . . 2·75 3·00
775 $2.50 Bananaquit . . . . . 3·00 4·00
776 $5 Belted kingfisher . . . . 4·25 6·50
777 $10 Green-backed heron . . 6·00 8·50

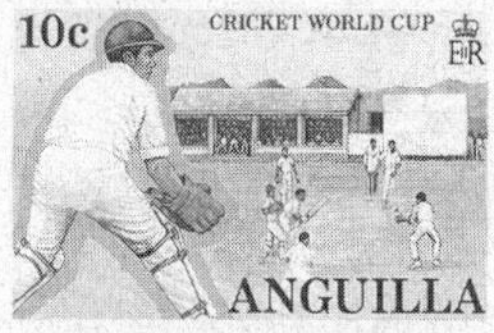

135 Wicket Keeper and Game in Progress

1987. Cricket World Cup. Multicoloured.
778 10c. Type **135** . . . . 1·25 70
779 35c. Batsman and local Anguilla team . . . . . . 1·75 70
780 45c. Batsman and game in progress . . . . 1·75 75
781 $2.50 Bowler and game in progress . . . . 3·75 5·50

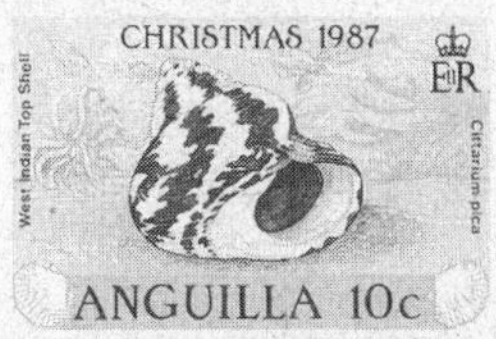

136 West Indian Top Shell

1987. Christmas. Sea Shells and Crabs. Mult.
783 10c. Type **136** . . . . 1·25 55
784 35c. Ghost crab . . . . . . 1·75 60
785 50c. Spiny Caribbean vase . . 2·50 1·40
786 $2 Great land crab . . . . . 4·00 6·00

1987. Royal Ruby Wedding. Nos. 665a, 671/2 and 675 optd **40TH WEDDING ANNIVERSARY H.M. QUEEN ELIZABETH II H.R.H. THE DUKE OF EDINBURGH**.
788 35c. Lesser Antillean bullfinch 75 40
789 $1 Audubon's shearwater . . 1·40 80
790 $1.35 Roseate tern . . . . . 1·60 90
791 $10 Green-backed heron . . 6·00 8·50

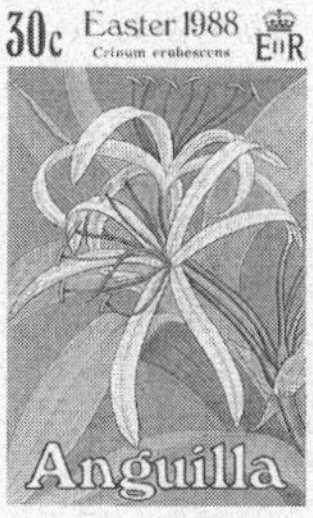

138 "Crinum erubescens"

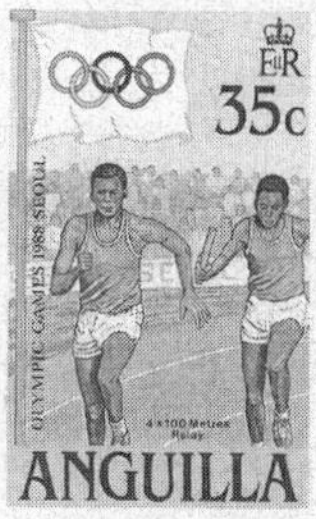

139 Relay Racing

1988. Easter. Lilies. Multicoloured.
792 30c. Type **138** 50 25
793 45c. Spider lily 60 25
794 $1 "Crinum macowanii" . . 1·50 85
795 $2.50 Day lily . . . . 1·75 3·00

1988. Olympic Games, Seoul. Multicoloured.
797 35c. Type **139** 45 30
798 45c. Windsurfing 55 45
799 50c. Tennis . . . . 1·50 1·10
800 80c. Basketball . . . . 3·50 2·75

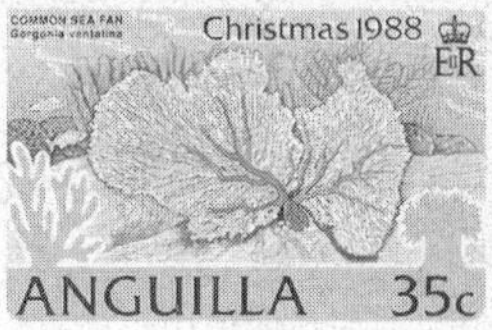

140 Common Sea Fan

1988. Christmas. Marine Life. Multicoloured.
802 35c. Type **140** 75 30
803 80c. Coral crab . . . . . . 1·25 70
804 $1 Grooved brain coral . . . 1·60 1·00
805 $1.60 Queen triggerfish . . . 2·00 3·00

1988. Visit of Princess Alexandra. Nos. 665a, 670/1 and 673 optd **H.R.H. PRINCESS ALEXANDRA'S VISIT NOVEMBER 1988**.
807 35c. Lesser Antillean bullfinch . . . . 1·50 60
808 80c. Grey kingbird . . . . . 2·00 1·40
809 $1 Audubon's shearwater . . 2·00 1·60
810 $2.50 Bananaquit . . . . . 3·50 4·25

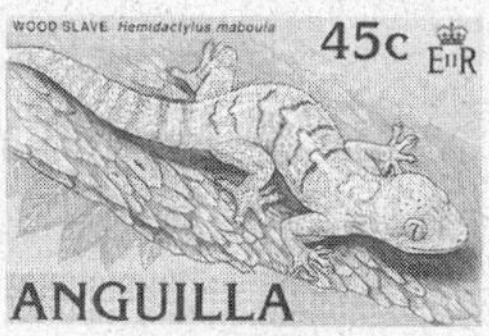

142 Wood Slave

1989. Lizards. Multicoloured.
811 45c. Type **142** 85 50
812 80c. Slippery back . . . . . 1·40 85
813 $2.50 "Iguana delicatissima" 3·00 4·00

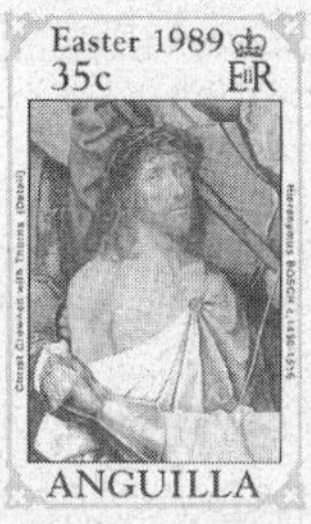

143 "Christ Crowned with Thorns" (detail) (Bosch)

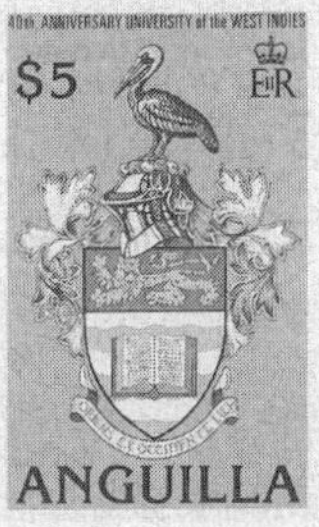

144 University Arms

1989. Easter. Religious Paintings. Multicoloured.
815 35c. Type **143** 45 20
816 80c. "Christ bearing the Cross" (detail) (Gerard David) 75 55

817	$1 "The Deposition" (detail) (Gerard David)	80	60
818	$1.60 "Pieta" (detail) (Rogier van der Weyden)	1·25	2·00

1989. 40th Anniv of University of the West Indies.

820	144 $5 multicoloured	3·00	3·50

1989. 20th Anniv of First Manned Landing on Moon. Nos. 670/2 and 674 optd **20TH ANNIVERSARY MOON LANDING.**

821	80c. Grey kingbird	1·50	90
822	$1 Audubon's shearwater	1·50	1·00
823	$1.35 Roseate tern	1·60	1·60
824	$5 Belted kingfisher	5·00	6·50

146 Lone Star (house), 1930

1989. Christmas. Historic Houses. Multicoloured.

825	5c. Type **146**	25	50
826	35c. Whitehouse, 1906	65	45
827	45c. Hodges House	75	50
828	80c. Warden's Place	1·25	1·40

147 Bigeye ("Blear Eye")

1990. Fishes. Multicoloured.

830B	5c. Type **147**	60	75
831B	10c. Long-spined squirrelfish ("Redman")	60	75
832A	15c. Stop-light parrotfish ("Speckletail")	60	60
833A	25c. Blue-striped grunt	70	80
834A	30c. Yellow jack	70	80
835B	35c. Red hind	75	75
836A	40c. Spotted goatfish	90	80
837A	45c. Queen triggerfish ("Old wife")	90	60
838A	50c. Coney ("Butter fish")	90	80
839A	65c. Smooth trunkfish ("Shell fish")	1·00	80
840A	80c. Yellow-tailed snapper	1·25	90
841A	$1 Banded butterflyfish ("Katy")	1·25	1·00
842A	$1.35 Nassau grouper	1·50	1·50
843A	$2.50 Blue tang ("Doctor fish")	2·25	3·00
844A	$5 Queen angelfish	3·00	4·50
845A	$10 Great barracuda	4·75	7·00

148 The Last Supper

149 G.B. 1840 Penny Black

1990. Easter. Multicoloured.

846	25c. Type **148**	75	30
847	45c. The Trial	75	30
848	$1.35 The Crucifixion	2·00	2·00
849	$2.50 The Empty Tomb	2·50	3·75

1990. "Stamp World London 90" International Stamp Exhibition. Multicoloured.

851	25c. Type **149**	60	25
852	50c. G.B. 1840 Twopenny Blue	1·00	50
853	$1.50 Cape of Good Hope 1861 1d. "woodblock" (horiz)	2·00	2·25
854	$2.50 G.B. 1882 £5 (horiz)	2·50	3·00

1990. Anniversaries and Events. Nos. 841/4 optd.

856	$1 Banded butterflyfish (optd **EXPO '90**)	1·50	1·00
857	$1.35 Nassau grouper (optd **1990 INTERNATIONAL LITERACY YEAR**)	1·60	1·25
858	$2.50 Blue tang (optd **WORLD CUP FOOTBALL CHAMPIONSHIPS 1990**)	3·75	4·00
859	$5 Queen angelfish (optd **90TH BIRTHDAY H.M. THE QUEEN MOTHER**)	6·00	6·50

151 Mermaid Flag

1990. Island Flags. Multicoloured.

860	50c. Type **151**	1·00	50
861	80c. New Anguilla official flag	1·50	1·00
862	$1 Three Dolphins flag	1·60	1·10
863	$5 Governor's official flag	4·25	6·50

152 Laughing Gulls

1990. Christmas. Sea Birds. Multicoloured.

864	10c. Type **152**	60	50
865	35c. Brown booby	1·00	50
866	$1.50 Bridled tern	2·00	2·00
867	$3.50 Brown pelican	3·25	4·25

1991. Easter. Nos. 846/9 optd **1991.**

869	35c. Type **148**	75	50
870	45c. The Trial	85	50
871	$1.35 The Crucifixion	1·75	1·75
872	$2.50 The Empty Tomb	3·00	4·75

154 Angel

155 Angels with Palm Branches outside St. Gerard's Church

1991. Christmas.

874	**154** 5c. violet, brown & black	50	60
875	– 35c. multicoloured	1·25	55
876	– 80c. multicoloured	2·25	2·00
877	– $1 multicoloured	2·25	2·00

DESIGNS—VERT: 35c. Father Christmas. HORIZ: 80c. Church and house; $1 Palm trees at night.

1992. Easter. Multicoloured.

879	30c. Type **155**	75	25
880	45c. Angels singing outside Methodist Church	85	35
881	80c. Village (horiz)	1·50	90
882	$1 Congregation going to St. Mary's Church	1·50	1·00
883	$5 Dinghy regatta (horiz)	4·50	6·50

1992. No. 834 surch **$1.60.**

884	$1.60 on 30c. Yellow jack	1·75	1·75

157 Anguillan Flags

1992. 25th Anniv of Separation from St. Kitts-Nevis. Multicoloured.

885	80c. Type **157**	1·50	1·00
886	$1 Present official seal	1·50	1·25
887	$1.60 Anguillan flags at airport	2·75	2·75
888	$2 Royal Commissioner's official seal	2·75	3·00

158 Dinghy Race

1992. Sailing Dinghy Racing.

890	**158** 20c. multicoloured	85	65
891	– 35c. multicoloured	1·10	60
892	– 45c. multicoloured	1·25	60
893	– 80c. multicoloured	2·00	2·75
894	– 80c. black and blue	2·00	2·75
895	– $1 multicoloured	2·00	2·25

DESIGNS—VERT: 35c. Stylized poster; 80c. (No. 893) "Blue Bird" in race; 80c. (No. 894) Construction drawings of "Blue Bird" by Douglas Pyle; $1 Stylized poster (different). HORIZ: 45c. Dinghies on beach.

159 Mucka Jumbie on Stilts

1992. Christmas. Local Traditions. Mult.

897	20c. Type **159**	45	30
898	70c. Masqueraders	1·00	50
899	$1.05 Baking in old style oven	1·25	85
900	$2.40 Collecting presents from Christmas tree	2·25	3·00

160 Columbus landing in New World

1992. 500th Anniv of Discovery of America by Columbus (2nd issue).

902	**160** 80c. multicoloured	1·75	1·25
903	– $1 black and brown	1·75	1·25
904	– $2 multicoloured	2·75	3·25
905	– $3 multicoloured	3·25	4·00

DESIGNS—VERT: $1 Christopher Columbus. HORIZ: $2 Fleet of Columbus; $3 "Pinta".

161 "Kite Flying" (Kyle Brooks)

163 Lord Great Chamberlain presenting Spurs of Charity to Queen

162 Salt Picking

1993. Easter. Children's Paintings. Mult.

907	20c. Type **161**	85	50
908	45c. "Clifftop Village Service" (Kara Connor)	1·25	50
909	80c. "Morning Devotion on Sombrero" (Junior Carty)	2·00	1·40
910	$1.50 "Hill Top Church Service" (Leana Harris)	2·75	4·00

1993. Traditional Industries. Mult.

912	20c. Type **162**	1·75	80
913	80c. Tobacco growing	1·75	1·00
914	$1 Cotton picking	1·75	1·00
915	$2 Harvesting sugar cane	2·75	4·00

1993. 40th Anniv of Coronation. Mult.

917	80c. Type **163**	1·15	70
918	$1 The Benediction	1·40	80
919	$2 Queen Elizabeth II in Coronation robes	2·00	2·25
920	$3 St. Edward's Crown	2·50	3·25

164 Carnival Pan Player

1993. Anguilla Carnival. Multicoloured.

922	20c. Type **164**	50	40
923	45c. Revellers dressed as pirates	75	40
924	80c. Revellers dressed as stars	1·25	75
925	$1 Mas dancing	1·25	80
926	$2 Masked couple	2·25	3·25
927	$3 Revellers dressed as commandos	2·75	3·50

165 Mucka Jumbies Carnival Characters

167 Princess Alexandra, 1988

166 Travelling Branch Mail Van at Sandy Ground

1993. Christmas. Multicoloured.

929	20c. Type **165**	55	50
930	35c. Local carol singers	75	50
931	45c. Christmas home baking	85	50
932	$3 Decorating Christmas tree	3·25	4·50

1994. Delivering the Mail. Multicoloured.

934	20c. Type **166**	90	60
935	45c. "Betsy R" (mail schooner) at The Forest (vert)	1·50	60
936	80c. Mail van at old Post Office	2·00	1·40
937	$1 Jeep on beach, Island Harbour (vert)	2·00	1·40
938	$4 New Post Office	4·00	5·50

1994. Royal Visitors. Multicoloured.

939	45c. Type **167**	85	60
940	50c. Princess Alice, 1960	90	60
941	80c. Prince Philip, 1993	1·50	1·00
942	$1 Prince Charles, 1973	1·75	1·25
943	$2 Queen Elizabeth II, 1994	2·25	3·50

168 "The Crucifixion"

170 "The Nativity" (Gustave Dore)

169 Cameroun Player and Pontiac Silverdome, Detroit

1994. Easter. Stained-glass Windows. Multicoloured.

945	20c. Type **168**	40	40
946	45c. "The Empty Tomb"	55	45
947	80c. "The Resurrection"	90	90
948	$3 "Risen Christ with Disciples"	2·75	4·00

1994. World Cup Football Championship, U.S.A. Multicoloured.

949	20c. Type **169**	45	30
950	70c. Argentine player and Foxboro Stadium, Boston	85	65
951	$1.80 Italian player and RFK Memorial Stadium, Washington	1·75	2·25
952	$2.40 German player and Soldier Field, Chicago	2·00	3·00

1994. Christmas. Religious Paintings. Multicoloured.

954	20c. Type **170**	45	40
955	30c. "The Wise Men guided by the Star" (Dore)	60	40
956	35c. "The Annunciation" (Dore)	65	40
957	45c. "Adoration of the Shepherds" (detail) (Poussin)	75	45
958	$2.40 "The Flight into Egypt" (Dore)	2·00	3·25

171 Pair of Zenaida Doves

1995. Easter. Zenaida Doves. Multicoloured.
959	20c. Type **171**	50	40
960	45c. Dove on branch	75	50
961	50c. Guarding nest	80	55
962	$5 With chicks	5·50	7·00

172 Trygve Lie (first Secretary-General)
and General Assembly

1995. 50th Anniv of United Nations. Multicoloured.
963	20c. Type **172**	30	30
964	80c. Flag and building showing "50"	60	65
965	$1 Dag Hammarskjold and U. Thant (former Secretary-Generals) and U.N. Charter	70	75
966	$5 U.N. Building (vert)	4·00	6·00

173 Anniversary Emblem and Map of
Anguilla

1995. 25th Anniv of Caribbean Development Bank. Multicoloured.
967	45c. Type **173**	1·50	1·75
968	$5 Bank building and launches	3·00	4·00

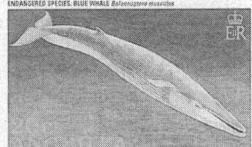

174 Blue Whale

1995. Endangered Species. Whales. Multicoloured.
969	20c. Type **174**	1·50	70
970	45c. Right whale (vert)	1·75	60
971	$1 Sperm whale	2·25	1·50
972	$5 Humpback whale	6·50	8·50

175 Palm Tree

1995. Christmas. Multicoloured.
973	10c. Type **175**	50	50
974	25c. Balloons and fishes	70	50
975	45c. Shells	90	50
976	$5 Fishes in shape of Christmas tree	7·00	8·50

176 Deep Water Gorgonia   177 Running

1996. Corals. Multicoloured.
977	20c. Type **176**	1·00	70
978	80c. Common sea fan	2·00	1·00
979	$5 Venus sea fern	6·50	7·50

1996. Olympic Games, Atlanta. Multicoloured.
980	20c. Type **177**	65	50
981	80c. Javelin throwing and wheelchair basketball	1·75	1·00

982	$1 High jumping and hurdles	1·25	1·00
983	$3.50 Olympic rings and torch with Greek and American flags	3·50	4·00

178 Siege of Sandy Hill Fort

1996. Bicentenary of the Battle for Anguilla. Multicoloured.
984	60c. Type **178**	75	75
985	75c. French troops destroying church (horiz)	80	75
986	$1.50 Naval battle (horiz)	1·75	2·00
987	$4 French troops landing at Rendezvous Bay	2·75	4·25

179 Gooseberry

1997. Fruit. Multicoloured.
988	10c. Type **179**	10	10
989	20c. West Indian cherry	10	15
990	40c. Tamarind	20	25
991	50c. Pomme-surette	25	30
992	60c. Sea almond	30	35
993	75c. Sea grape	40	45
994	80c. Banana	40	45
995	$1 Genip	50	55
996	$1.10 Coco plum	60	65
997	$1.25 Pope	65	70
998	$1.50 Pawpaw	80	85
999	$2 Sugar apple	1·00	1·10
1000	$3 Soursop	1·50	1·60
1001	$4 Pomegranate	2·00	2·10
1002	$5 Cashew	2·50	2·75
1003	$10 Mango	5·00	5·25

180 West Indian Iguanas hatching

1997. Endangered Species. West Indian Iguanas. Multicoloured.
1004	20c. Type **180**	1·25	1·10
1005	50c. On rock	1·40	1·25
1006	75c. On branch	1·50	1·40
1007	$3 Head of West Indian iguana	2·25	3·00

181 "Juluca, Rainbow Deity"

1997. Ancient Stone Carvings from Fountain Cavern. Multicoloured.
1008	30c. Type **181**	45	35
1009	$1.25 "Lizard with front legs extended"	90	90
1010	$2.25 "Chief"	1·60	2·25
1011	$2.75 "Jocahu, the Creator"	2·00	2·75

182 Diana, Princess of Wales

1998. Diana, Princess of Wales Commemoration. Multicoloured.
1012	15c. Type **182**	1·00	1·25
1013	$1 Wearing yellow blouse	1·75	1·60
1014	$1.90 Wearing tiara	1·90	2·00
1015	$2.25 Wearing blue short-sleeved Red Cross blouse	2·00	2·50

183 "Treasure Island" (Valarie Alix)

1998. International Arts Festival. Multicoloured.
1016	15c. Type **183**	45	40
1017	30c. "Posing in the Light" (Melsadis Fleming) (vert)	50	40
1018	$1 "Pescadores de Anguilla" (Juan Garcia) (vert)	80	80
1019	$1.50 "Fresh Catch" (Verna Hart)	1·00	1·60
1020	$1.90 "The Bell Tower of St. Mary's" (Ricky Racardo Edwards) (vert)	1·25	1·75

184 Roasting Corn-cobs on Fire

1998. Christmas. "Hidden Beauty of Anguilla". Children's Paintings. Multicoloured.
1021	15c. Type **184**	35	30
1022	$1 Fresh fruit and market stallholder	80	50
1023	$1.50 Underwater scene	1·00	1·25
1024	$3 Cacti and view of sea	1·60	2·50

185 University of West Indies Centre,
Anguilla

1998. 50th Anniv of University of West Indies. Multicoloured.
1025	$1.50 Type **185**	80	85
1026	$1.90 Man with torch and University arms	1·10	1·40

186 Sopwith Camel and Bristol F2B
Fighters

1998. 80th Anniv of Royal Air Force. Multicoloured.
1027	30c. Type **186**	50	40
1028	$1 Supermarine Spitfire Mk II and Hawker Hurricane Mk I	1·00	80
1029	$1.50 Avro Lancaster	1·40	1·40
1030	$1.90 Panavia Tornado F3 and Harrier GR7	1·50	2·00

187 Saturn 5 Rocket and "Apollo 11"
Command Module

1999. 30th Anniv of First Manned Landing on Moon. Multicoloured.
1031	30c. Type **187**	55	33
1032	$1 Astronaut Edwin Aldrin, Lunar Module "Eagle" and first footprint on Moon	1·00	70
1033	$1.50 Lunar Module leaving Moon's surface	1·00	1·00
1034	$1.90 Recovery of Command Module	1·40	2·00

188 Albena Lake   189 Library and Resource
Hodge   Centre

1999. Anguillan Heroes and Heroines (1st series). Each black, green and cream.
1035	30c. Type **188**	40	30
1036	$1 Collins O. Hodge	80	65
1037	$1.50 Edwin Wallace Rey	1·00	1·25
1038	$1.90 Walter G. Hodge	1·25	2·00

1999. Modern Architecture. Multicoloured.
1039	30c. Type **189**	30	30
1040	65c. Parliamentary building and Court House	50	50
1041	$1 Caribbean Commercial Bank	70	70
1042	$1.50 Police Headquarters	1·00	1·00
1043	$1.90 Post Office	1·10	1·50

190 Beach Barbeque and Fireworks

1999. Christmas and New Millennium. Mult.
1044	30c. Type **190**	25	20
1045	$1 Musicians around globe	60	50
1046	$1.50 Family at Christmas dinner	90	90
1047	$1.90 Celebrations around decorated shrub	1·00	1·50

191 Shoal Bay (East)

2000. Beaches. Multicoloured.
1048	15c. Type **191**	30	30
1049	30c. Maundys Bay	35	30
1050	$1 Rendezvous Bay	75	50
1051	$1.50 Meads Bay	1·00	1·00
1052	$1.90 Little Bay	1·25	1·50
1053	$2 Sandy Ground	1·25	1·50

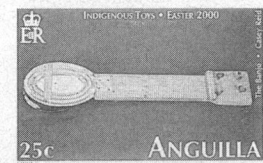

192 Toy Banjo (Casey Reid)

2000. Easter. Indigenous Toys. Multicoloured.
1055	25c. Type **192**	40	30
1056	30c. Spinning top (Johniela Harrigan)	40	30
1057	$1.50 Catapult (Akeem Rogers)	1·10	1·10
1058	$1.90 Roller (Melisa Mussington)	1·40	1·50
1059	$2.50 Killy Ban (trap) (Casey Reid)	1·75	2·00

193 Lanville Harrigan

2000. West Indies Cricket Tour and 100th Test Match at Lord's. Multicoloured.
1061	$2 Type **193**	1·75	1·75
1062	$4 Cardigan Connor	2·75	3·25

194 Prince William and Royal Family
after Trooping the Colour

2000. 18th Birthday of Prince William. Mult.
1065	30c. Type **194**	50	35
1066	$1 Prince and Princess of Wales with sons	1·00	60
1067	$1.90 With Prince Charles and Prince Harry	1·50	1·60
1068	$2.25 Skiing with father and brother	1·75	1·90

195 Queen Elizabeth the Queen Mother and Prince William

2000. 100th Birthday of Queen Elizabeth the Queen Mother. Showing different portraits. Multicoloured.

1070		30c. Type **195**	50	35
1071		$1.50 Island scene	1·25	1·00
1072		$1.90 Clarence House	1·40	1·60
1073		$5 Castle of Mey	3·00	3·50

196 "Anguilla Montage" (Weme Caster)

2000. International Arts Festival. Multicoloured.

1074		15c. Type **196**	30	30
1075		30c. "Serenity" (Damien Carty)	35	30
1076		65c. "Inter Island Cargo" (Paula Walden)	55	45
1077		$1.50 "Rainbow City where Spirits find Form" (Fiona Percy)	1·25	1·25
1078		$1.90 "Sailing Silver Seas" (Valerie Carpenter)	1·40	1·75

197 Dried Flower Arrangement

2000. Christmas. Flower and Garden Show.

1080	**197**	15c. multicoloured	25	25
1081	–	25c. multicoloured	30	25
1082	–	30c. multicoloured	30	25
1083	–	$1 multicoloured	75	60
1084	–	$1.50 multicoloured	1·25	1·50
1085	–	$1.90 multicoloured	1·50	1·75

DESIGNS: 25c. to $1.90, Different floral arrangements.

198 Winning Primary School Football Team (Bank Sponsorship)

2000. 15th Anniv of National Bank of Anguilla. Multicoloured.

1086		30c. Type **198**	30	25
1087		$1 *De-Chan* (yacht) (Bank sponsorship) (vert)	70	60
1088		$1.50 Bank crest (vert)	1·25	1·50
1089		$1.90 New Bank Headquarters	1·50	1·75

199 Ebenezer Methodist Church in 19th Century

2000. 170th Anniv of Ebenezer Methodist Church.

1090	**199**	30c. brown and black	30	20
1091	–	$1.90 multicoloured	1·50	1·75

DESIGN: $1.90, Church in 2000.

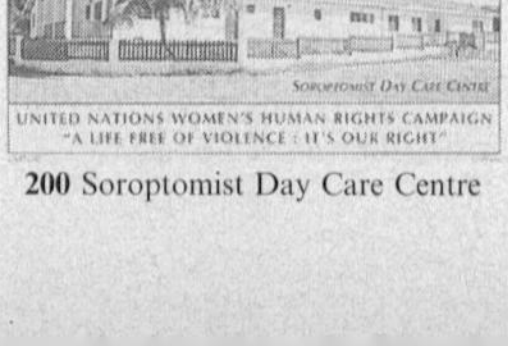

200 Soroptomist Day Care Centre

2001. United Nations Women's Human Rights Campaign. Multicoloured.

1092		25c. Type **200**	30	20
1093		30c. Britannia Idalia Gumbs (Anguillan politician) (vert)	30	20
1094		$2.25 "Caribbean Woman II" (Leisel Renee Jobity) (vert)	1·60	2·00

201 John Paul Jones and U.S.S. *Ranger* (frigate)

2001. 225th Anniv of American War of Independence. Multicoloured.

1095		30c. Type **201**	15	20
1096		$1 George Washington and Battle of Yorktown	50	55
1097		$1.50 Thomas Jefferson and submission of Declaration of Independence to Congress	80	85
1098		$1.90 John Adams and the signing of the Treaty of Paris	95	1·00

202 Bahama Pintail

2001. Anguillian Birds. Multicoloured.

1099		30c. Type **202**	15	20
1100		$1 Black-faced grassquit (vert)	50	55
1101		$1.50 Common noddy	80	85
1102		$2 Black-necked stilt (vert)	1·00	1·10
1103		$3 Kentish plover ("Snowy Plover")	1·50	1·60

203 "Children encircling Globe" (Urska Golob)

2001. U.N. Year of Dialogue among Civilisations.

1105	**203**	$1.90 multicoloured	95	1·00

204 Triangle

2001. Christmas. Indigenous Musical Instruments. Multicoloured.

1106		15c. Type **204**	10	10
1107		25c. Maracas	15	20
1108		30c. Guiro (vert)	15	20
1109		$1.50 Marimba	80	85
1110		$1.90 Tambu (hand drum) (vert)	95	1·00
1111		$2.50 Bass pan	1·25	1·40

205 Sombrero Lighthouse, 1962

2002. Commissioning of New Sombrero Lighthouse. Multicoloured.

1113		30c. Type **205**	15	20
1114		$1.50 Old and new lighthouses (horiz)	80	85
1115		$1.90 New, fully-automated lighthouse, 2001	95	1·00

ANJOUAN Pt. 6

One of the Comoro Is. between Madagascar and the East coast of Africa. Used stamps of Madagascar from 1914 and became part of the Comoro Islands in 1950.

100 centimes = 1 franc.

1892. "Tablet" key-type inscr "SULTANAT D'ANJOUAN".

1	D	1c. black on blue	1·00	1·75
2		2c. brown on buff	2·00	2·00
3		4c. brown on grey	2·25	2·25
4		5c. green on green	4·00	3·75
5		10c. black on lilac	4·00	4·00
14		10c. red	11·50	13·50
6		15c. blue	4·25	5·00
15		15c. grey	7·25	9·00
7		20c. red on green	5·00	6·25
8		25c. black on pink	6·00	6·25
16		25c. blue	9·00	11·00
9		30c. brown on grey	14·50	12·50
17		35c. black on yellow	5·50	5·50
10		40c. red on yellow	19·00	18·00
18		45c. black on green	75·00	65·00
11		50c. red on pink	21·00	22·00
19		50c. brown on blue	15·00	17·00
12		75c. brown on orange	29·00	24·00
13		1f. green	65·00	60·00

1912. Surch in figures.

20	D	05 on 2c. brown on buff	2·50	3·00
21		05 on 4c. brown on grey	1·25	2·50
22		05 on 15c. blue	1·25	2·50
23		05 on 20c. red on green	1·50	3·00
24		05 on 25c. black on pink	1·10	2·50
25		05 on 30c. brown on grey	2·25	2·75
26		10 on 40c. red on yellow	1·25	2·25
27		10 on 45c. black on green	95	1·75
28		10 on 50c. red on pink	2·25	4·75
29		10 on 75c. brown on orange	2·25	3·50
30		10 on 1f. green	3·25	3·75

ANNAM AND TONGKING Pt. 6

Later part of Indo-China and now included in Vietnam.

100 centimes = 1 franc.

1888. Stamps of French Colonies, "Commerce" type, surch **A & T** and value in figures.

1	J	1 on 2c. brown on yellow	38·00	32·00
2		1 on 4c. lilac on grey	32·00	25·00
3		5 on 10c. black on lilac	38·00	28·00

ANTIGUA Pt. 1

One of the Leeward Islands, Br. W. Indies. Used general issues for Leeward Islands, concurrently with Antiguan stamps until 1 July 1956. Ministerial Government introduced on 1 January 1960. Achieved Associated Statehood on 3 March 1967 and Independence within the Commonwealth on 1 November 1981.

Nos. 718/21 and 733 onwards are inscribed "Antigua and Barbuda".

1862. 12 pence = 1 shilling;
20 shillings = 1 pound.
1951. 100 cents = 1 West Indian dollar.

1

3

1862.

5	**1**	1d. mauve	£130	48·00
25		1d. red	1·75	2·75
29		6d. green	60·00	£120

1879.

21	**3**	½d. green	2·50	12·00
22		2½d. brown	£160	55·00
27		2½d. blue	6·00	11·00
23		4d. blue	£275	15·00
28		4d. brown	2·00	2·75
30		1s. mauve	£160	£120

4

5

8

1903.

31	**4**	½d. black and green	3·75	6·50
41		½d. green	2·75	4·50
32		1d. black and red	6·50	1·25
43		1d. red	6·00	2·25
45		2d. purple and brown	4·75	28·00
34		2½d. black and blue	9·00	15·00
46		2½d. blue	12·00	15·00
47		3d. green and brown	6·50	19·00
48		6d. purple and black	7·50	48·00
49		1s. blue and purple	15·00	70·00
50		2s. green and violet	75·00	85·00
39		2s.6d. black and purple	17·00	55·00
40	**5**	5s. green and violet	70·00	95·00

1913. Head of King George V.

51	**5**	5s. green and violet	70·00	£110

1916. Optd **WAR STAMP.**

52	**4**	½d. green	1·25	2·50
54		1½d. orange	1·50	2·50

1921.

62	**8**	½d. green	2·25	50
63		1d. red	2·00	50
64		1d. violet	3·50	1·50
67		1½d. orange	3·00	7·00
68		1½d. red	4·25	1·75
69		1½d. brown	3·00	60
70		2d. grey	2·50	75
72		2½d. yellow	2·50	17·00
73		2½d. blue	4·25	5·50
74		3d. purple on yellow	4·50	8·50
56		4d. black and red on yellow	2·25	5·50
75		6d. purple	3·25	6·50
57		1s. black on green	4·25	9·00
58		2s. purple and blue on blue	13·00	19·00
78		2s.6d. black and red on blue	24·00	28·00
79		3s. green and violet	28·00	90·00
80		4s. black and red	48·00	65·00
60		5s. green and red on yellow	8·50	50·00
61		£1 purple and black on red	£170	£275

9 Old Dockyard, English Harbour

10 Government House, St. John's

1932. Tercentenary. Designs with medallion portrait of King George V.

81	**9**	½d. green	2·75	7·00
82	–	1d. red	3·25	6·50
83	–	1½d. brown	3·25	4·75
84	**10**	2d. grey	4·25	17·00
85		2½d. blue	4·25	8·50
86		3d. orange	4·25	12·00
87	–	6d. violet	15·00	12·00
88	–	1s. olive	19·00	27·00
89	–	2s.6d. purple	40·00	55·00
90	–	5s. black and brown	85·00	£110

DESIGNS—HORIZ: 6d. to 2s.6d. Nelson's "Victory"; 5s. Sir Thomas Warner's "Conception".

13 Windsor Castle

1935. Silver Jubilee.

91	**13**	1d. blue and red	2·00	2·50
92		1½d. blue and grey	2·75	55
93		2½d. brown and blue	6·50	1·25
94		1s. grey and purple	8·50	12·00

1937. Coronation. As T **2** of Aden.

95		1d. red	50	1·00
96		1½d. brown	60	1·00
97		2½d. blue	1·25	1·75

15 English Harbour

16 Nelson's Dockyard

1938.

98	**15**	½d. green	40	1·25
99	**16**	1d. red	2·75	2·00
100a		1½d. brown	2·25	1·75
101	**15**	2d. grey	50	50
102	**16**	2½d. blue	80	80
103	–	3d. orange	75	1·00

104	– 6d. violet	2·75	1·25
105	– 1s. black and brown	3·25	1·50
106a	– 2s.6d. purple	22·00	9·00
107	– 5s. olive	14·00	7·50
108	**16** 10s. mauve	16·00	26·00
109	– £1 green	25·00	38·00

DESIGNS—HORIZ: 3d., 2s.6d., £1, Fort James.
VERT: 6d., 1s., 5s. St. John's Harbour.

1946. Victory. As T **9** of Aden.

| 110 | 1½d. brown | 20 | 10 |
| 111 | 3d. orange | 20 | 30 |

1949. Silver Wedding. As T **10/11** of Aden.

| 112 | 2½d. blue | 40 | 1·50 |
| 113 | 5s. green | 8·50 | 7·00 |

20 Hermes, Globe and Forms of Transport

21 Hemispheres, Jet-powered Vickers Viking Airliner and Steamer

22 Hermes and Globe

23 U.P.U. Monument

1949. 75th Anniv of U.P.U.

114	**20** 2½d. blue	40	50
115	**21** 3d. orange	1·50	2·00
116	**22** 6d. purple	45	1·25
117	**23** 1s. brown	45	75

24 Arms of University   **25** Princess Alice

1951. Inauguration of B.W.I. University College.

| 118 | **24** 3c. black and brown | 45 | 50 |
| 119 | **25** 12c. black and violet | 65 | 80 |

1953. Coronation. As T **13** of Aden.

| 120 | 2c. black and green | 30 | 75 |

27 Martello Tower

1953. Designs as 1938 issues but with portrait of Queen Elizabeth II as in T **27**.

120a	– ½c. brown	30	30
121	**15** 1c. grey	30	70
122	**16** 2c. green	30	10
123	– 3c. black and yellow	40	20
153	**15** 4c. red	30	50
154	**16** 5c. black and lilac	20	10
155	– 6c. yellow	60	30
156	**27** 8c. blue	30	20
157	– 12c. violet	40	20
124	– 24c. black and brown	2·50	15
130	**27** 48c. purple and blue	7·00	2·75
131	– 60c. purple	7·50	80

132	– $1.20 olive	2·25	70
133	**16** $2.40 purple	11·00	12·00
134	– $4.80 slate	15·00	24·00

DESIGNS—HORIZ: ½, 6, 60c., $4.80, Fort James.
VERT: 12, 24c., $1.20, St John's Harbour.

28 Federation Map

1958. Inaug of British Caribbean Federation.

135	**28** 3c. green	1·00	30
136	– 6c. blue	1·40	2·75
137	– 12c. red	1·60	75

1960. New Constitution. Nos. 123 and 157 optd
**COMMEMORATION   ANTIGUA
CONSTITUTION.**

| 138 | **16** 3c. black and yellow | 15 | 15 |
| 139 | – 12c. violet | 15 | 15 |

30 Nelson's Dockyard and Admiral Nelson

1961. Restoration of Nelson's Dockyard.

| 140 | **30** 20c. purple and brown | 90 | 1·25 |
| 141 | – 30c. green and blue | 1·10 | 1·50 |

31 Stamp of 1862 and R.M.S.P. "Solent I" at English Harbour

1962. Stamp Centenary.

142	**31** 3c. purple and green	60	10
143	– 10c. blue and green	70	10
144	– 12c. sepia and green	80	10
145	– 50c. brown and green	1·50	1·75

1963. Freedom from Hunger. As T **28** of Aden.

| 146 | 12c. green | 15 | 15 |

33 Red Cross Emblem

1963. Centenary of Red Cross.

| 147 | **33** 3c. red and black | 40 | 75 |
| 148 | – 12c. red and blue | 60 | 1·25 |

34 Shakespeare and Memorial Theatre, Stratford-upon-Avon

1964. 400th Birth Anniv of Shakespeare.

| 164 | **34** 12c. brown | 30 | 10 |

1965. No. 157 surch **15c.**

| 165 | 15c. on 12c. violet | 10 | 10 |

36 I.T.U. Emblem

1965. Centenary of I.T.U.

| 166 | **36** 2c. blue and red | 25 | 15 |
| 167 | – 50c. yellow and blue | 75 | 80 |

37 I.C.Y. Emblem

1965. International Co-operation Year.

| 168 | **37** 4c. purple and turquoise | 20 | 10 |
| 169 | – 15c. green and lavender | 30 | 20 |

38 Sir Winston Churchill, and St. Paul's Cathedral in Wartime

1966. Churchill Commemoration. Designs in black, red and gold with background in colours given.

170	**38** ½c. blue	10	1·75
171	– 4c. green	40	10
172	– 25c. brown	1·10	45
173	– 35c. violet	1·10	55

39 Queen Elizabeth II and Duke of Edinburgh

1966. Royal Visit.

| 174 | **39** 6c. black and blue | 1·25 | 1·10 |
| 175 | – 15c. black and mauve | 1·25 | 1·40 |

40 Footballer's Legs, Ball and Jules Rimet Cup

1966. World Cup Football Championship.

| 176 | **40** 6c. multicoloured | 20 | 50 |
| 177 | – 35c. multicoloured | 60 | 25 |

41 W.H.O. Building

1966. Inaug of W.H.O. Headquarters, Geneva.

| 178 | **41** 2c. black, green and blue | 20 | 25 |
| 179 | – 15c. black, purple & brn | 80 | 25 |

42 Nelson's Dockyard

1966.

180	**42** ½c. green and blue	10	40
181	– 1c. purple and mauve	10	30
182	– 2c. blue and orange	10	20
183a	– 3c. red and black	15	15
184a	– 4c. violet and brown	15	15
185	– 5c. blue and green	10	10
186	– 6c. orange and purple	30	10
187	– 10c. green and red	15	10
188a	– 15c. brown and blue	55	10
189	– 25c. blue and brown	35	20
190a	– 35c. mauve and brown	60	1·00
191a	– 50c. green and black	70	2·25
192	– 75c. blue and ultramarine	1·50	2·50
193b	– $1 mauve and green	1·25	5·00
194	– $2.50 black and mauve	3·50	6·50
195	– $5 green and violet	6·00	6·50

DESIGNS: 1c. Old Post Office, St John's; 2c. Health Centre; 3c. Teachers' Training College; 4c. Martello Tower, Barbuda; 5c. Ruins of Officers' Quarters, Shirley Heights; 6c. Government House, Barbuda; 10c. Princess Margaret School; 15c. Air terminal building; 25c. General Post Office; 35c. Clarence House; 50c. Government House, St. John's; 75c. Administration building; $1 Court-house, St. John's; $2.50, Magistrates' Court; $5 St. John's Cathedral.

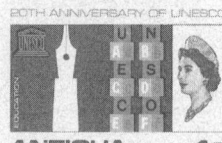

54 "Education"

55 "Science"

56 "Culture"

1966. 20th Anniv of U.N.E.S.C.O.

196	**54** 4c. violet, yellow & orange	15	10
197	**55** 25c. yellow, violet and olive	35	10
198	**56** $1 black, purple and orange	80	2·25

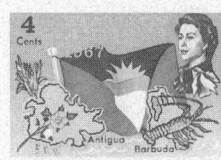

57 State Flag and Maps

1967. Statehood. Multicoloured.

199	4c. Type **57**	10	10
200	15c. State Flag	10	20
201	25c. Premier's Office and State Flag	10	25
202	35c. As 15c.	15	25

60 Gilbert Memorial Church

1967. Attainment of Autonomy by the Methodist Church.

203	**60** 4c. black and red	10	10
204	– 25c. black and green	15	15
205	– 35c. black and blue	15	15

DESIGNS: 25c. Nathaniel Gilbert's House; 35c. Caribbean and Central American map.

63 Coat of Arms   **66** Tracking Station

1967. 300th Anniv of Treaty of Breda and Grant of New Arms.

| 206 | **63** 15c. multicoloured | 15 | 10 |
| 207 | – 35c. multicoloured | 15 | 10 |

64 "Susan Constant" (settlers' ship)

1967. 300th Anniv of Barbuda Settlement.

208	**64** 4c. blue	30	10
209	– 6c. purple	30	1·25
210	**64** 25c. green	40	20
211	– 35c. black	40	25

DESIGN: 6, 35c. Blaeu's Map of 1665.

1968. N.A.S.A. Apollo Project. Inauguration of Dow Hill Tracking Station.

212	**66** 4c. blue, yellow and black	10	10
213	– 15c. blue, yellow and black	20	10
214	– 25c. blue, yellow and black	20	10
215	– 50c. blue, yellow and black	30	40

DESIGNS: 15c. Antenna and spacecraft taking off; 25c. Spacecraft approaching Moon; 50c. Re-entry of space capsule.

70 Limbo-dancing

1968. Tourism. Multicoloured.
216 ½c. Type **70** 10 20
217 15c. Water-skier and bathers 30 10
218 25c. Yachts and beach 40 10
219 35c. Underwater swimming 40 10
220 50c. Type **70** 60 1·10

74 Old Harbour in 1768

1968. Opening of St. John's Deep Water Harbour.
221 **74** 2c. blue and red 10 40
222 – 15c. green and sepia 35 10
223 – 25c. yellow and blue 40 10
224 – 35c. salmon and emerald 50 10
225 **74** $1 black 90 2·00
DESIGNS: 15c. Old harbour in 1829; 25c. Freighter and chart of new harbour; 35c. New harbour.

78 Parliament Buildings

1969. Tercentenary of Parliament. Multicoloured.
226 4c. Type **78** 10 10
227 15c. Antigua Mace and bearer 20 10
228 25c. House of Representative's Room 20 10
229 50c. Coat of arms and Seal of Antigua 30 1·60

82 Freight Transport

1969. 1st Anniv of Caribbean Free Trade Area.
230 **82** 4c. black and purple 10 10
231 15c. black and blue 20 30
232 – 25c. brown, black & ochre 25 30
233 – 35c. chocolate, blk & brn 25 30
DESIGN—VERT: 25, 35c. Crate of cargo.

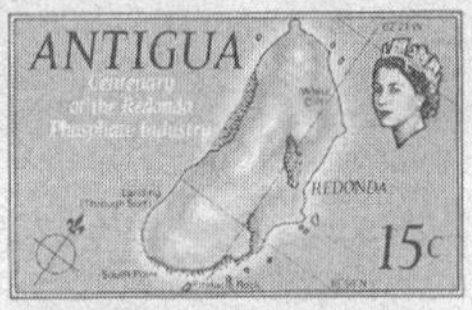

84 Island of Redonda (Chart)

1969. Centenary of Redonda Phosphate Industry. Multicoloured.
249 15c. Type **84** 20 10
250 25c. View of Redonda from the sea 20 10
251 50c. Type **84** 45 75

86 "The Adoration of the Magi" (Marcillat)

1969. Christmas. Stained Glass Windows. Mult.
252 6c. Type **86** 10 10
253 10c. "The Nativity" (unknown German artist, 15th century) 10 10
254 35c. Type **86** 25 10
255 50c. As 10c. 50 40

1970. Surch **20c** and bars.
256 20c. on 25c. (No. 189) 10 10

89 Coat of Arms **90** Sikorsky S-38 Flying Boat

1970. Coil Stamps.
257A **89** 5c. blue 10 10
258A 10c. green 10 15
259A 25c. red 20 25

1970. 40th Anniv of Antiguan Air Services. Multicoloured.
260 5c. Type **90** 50 10
261 20c. Dornier Do-X flying boat 1·00 10
262 35c. Hawker Siddeley H.S.748 1·25 10
263 50c. Douglas C-124C Globemaster II 1·25 1·50
264 75c. Vickers Super VC-10 1·50 2·00

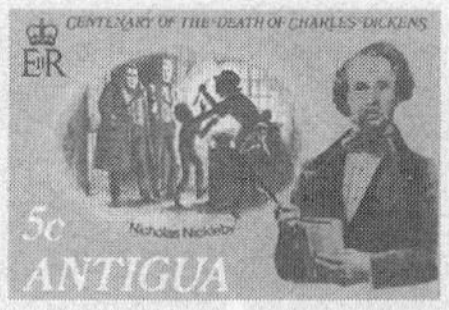

91 Dickens and Scene from "Nicholas Nickleby"

1970. Death Centenary of Charles Dickens.
265 **91** 5c. bistre, sepia and black 10 10
266 – 20c. turq, sepia & blk 20 10
267 – 35c. blue, sepia and black 30 10
268 – $1 red, sepia and black 75 70
DESIGNS: All stamps show Dickens and scene from: 20c. "Pickwick Papers"; 35c. "Oliver Twist"; $1 "David Copperfield".

92 Carib Indian and War Canoe

1970. Multicoloured.
323 ½c. Type **92** 20 50
270 1c. Columbus and "Nina" 30 1·25
271 2c. Sir Thomas Warner's emblem and "Concepcion" 40 2·00
325 3c. Viscount Hood and H.M.S. "Barfleur" 35 1·25
273 4c. Sir George Rodney and H.M.S. "Formidable" 40 2·00
274 5c. Nelson and H.M.S. "Boreas" 50 40
275 6c. William IV and H.M.S. "Pegasus" 70 2·50
276 10c. "Blackbeard" and pirate ketch 80 20
277 15c. Collingwood and H.M.S. "Pelican" 4·00 1·00
278 20c. Nelson and H.M.S. "Victory" 1·25 40
279 25c. "Solent I" (paddle-steamer) 1·25 40
280 35c. George V (when Prince George) and H.M.S. "Canada" (screw corvette) 1·75 80
281 50c. H.M.S. "Renown" (battle cruiser) 4·00 3·75
331 75c. "Federal Maple" (freighter) 7·50 3·00
332 $1 "Sol Quest" (yacht) and class emblem 3·00 1·75
333 $2.50 H.M.S. "London" (destroyer) 2·75 6·50
285 $5 "Pathfinder" (tug) 4·00 6·00

93 "The Small Passion" (detail) (Durer) **94** 4th King's Own Regiment, 1759

1970. Christmas.
286 **93** 3c. black and blue 10 10
287 – 10c. purple and pink 10 10
288 **93** 35c. black and red 30 10
289 – 50c. black and lilac 45 50
DESIGN: 10, 50c. "Adoration of the Magi" (detail)(Durer).

1970. Military Uniforms (1st series). Mult.
290 ½c. Type **94** 10 10
291 10c. 4th West India Regiment, 1804 50 10
292 20c. 60th Regiment, The Royal American, 1809 75 10
293 35c. 93rd Regiment, Sutherland Highlanders, 1826–34 1·00 10
294 75c. 3rd West India Regiment, 1851 1·75 2·00
See also Nos. 303/7, 313/17, 353/7 and 380/4.

95 Market Woman casting Vote **96** "The Last Supper"

1971. 20th Anniv of Adult Suffrage.
296 **95** 5c. brown 10 10
297 – 20c. olive 10 10
298 – 35c. purple 10 10
299 – 50c. blue 15 30
DESIGNS: People voting: 20c. Executive; 35c. Housewife; 50c. Artisan.

1971. Easter. Works by Durer.
300 **96** 5c. black grey and red 10 10
301 – 35c. black, grey and violet 10 10
302 – 75c. black, grey and gold 20 30
DESIGNS: 35c. "The Crucifixion"; 75c. "The Resurrection".

1971. Military Uniforms (2nd series). As T **94**. Multicoloured.
303 ½c. Private, 12th Regiment, The Suffolk (1704) 10 10
304 10c. Grenadier, 38th Regiment, South Staffordshire (1751) 35 10
305 20c. Light Company, 5th Regiment, Royal Northumberland Fusiliers (1778) 50 10
306 35c. Private, 48th Regiment, The Northamptonshire (1793) 60 10
307 75c. Private, 15th Regiment, East Yorks (1805) 1·00 3·00

97 "Madonna and Child" (detail, Veronese)

1971. Christmas. Multicoloured.
309 3c. Type **97** 10 10
310 5c. "Adoration of the Shepherds" (detail, Veronese) 10 10
311 35c. Type **97** 25 10
312 50c. As 5c. 40 30

1972. Military Uniforms (3rd series). As T **94**. Multicoloured.
313 ½c. Battalion Company Officer, 25th Foot, 1815 10 10
314 10c. Sergeant, 14th Foot, 1837 85 10
315 20c. Private, 67th Foot, 1853 1·60 15
316 35c. Officer, Royal Artillery, 1854 1·90 20
317 75c. Private, 29th Foot, 1870 2·25 4·00

98 Reticulated Cowrie Helmet

1972. Shells. Multicoloured.
319 3c. Type **98** 50 10
320 5c. Measled cowrie 50 10
321 35c. West Indian fighting conch 1·40 15
322 50c. Hawk-wing conch 1·60 3·00

99 St. John's Cathedral, Side View

1972. Christmas and 125th Anniv of St. John's Cathedral. Multicoloured.
335 35c. Type **99** 20 10
336 50c. Cathedral interior 25 25
337 75c. St. John's Cathedral 30 60

1972. Royal Silver Wedding. As T **52** of Ascension, but with floral background.
339 20c. blue 15 15
340 35c. blue 15 15

101 Batsman and Map

1972. 50th Anniv of Rising Sun Cricket Club. Multicoloured.
341 5c. Type **101** 55 15
342 35c. Batsman and wicket-keeper 65 10
343 $1 Club badge 1·00 2·25

102 Yacht and Map **103** "Episcopal Coat of Arms"

1972. Inauguration of Antigua and Barbuda Tourist Office in New York. Multicoloured.
345 35c. Type **102** 15 10
346 50c. Yachts 20 15
347 75c. St. John's G.P.O. 25 25
348 $1 Statue of Liberty 25 25

1973. Easter. Multicoloured.
350 **103** 5c. Type **103** 10 10
351 – 35c. "The Crucifixion" 15 10
352 – 75c. "Arms of 1st Bishop of Antigua" 25 30
Nos. 350/2 show different stained-glass windows from St. John's Cathedral.

1973. Military Uniforms (4th series). As T **94**. Multicoloured.
353 ½c. Private, Zachariah Tiffin's Regiment of Foot 1701 10 10
354 10c. Private, 63rd Regiment of Foot, 1759 40 10
355 20c. Light Company Officer, 35th Regiment of Foot, 1828 50 15
356 35c. Private, 2nd West India Regiment, 1853 65 15
357 75c. Sergeant, 49th Regiment, 1858 1·00 1·25

104 Butterfly Costumes

1973. Carnival. Multicoloured.
359 5c. Type **104** 10 10
360 20c. Carnival street scene 15 10
361 35c. Carnival troupe 20 10
362 75c. Carnival Queen 30 30

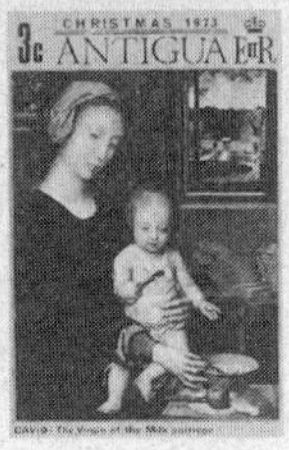

105 "Virgin of the Milk Porridge" (Gerard David)

1973. Christmas. Multicoloured.

364	3c. Type **105**	10	10
365	5c. "Adoration of the Magi" (Stomer)	10	10
366	20c. "The Granducal Madonna" (Raphael)	15	10
367	35c. "Nativity with God the Father and Holy Ghost" (Battista)	20	10
368	$1 "Madonna and Child" (Murillo)	40	60

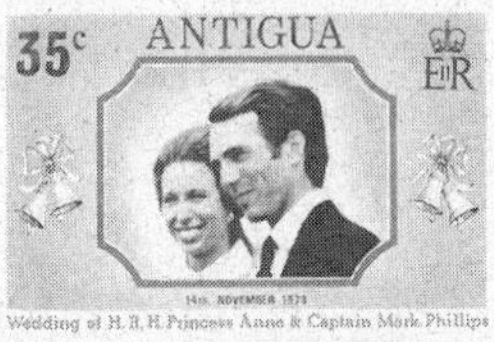

106 Princess Anne and Captain Mark Phillips

1973. Royal Wedding.

370 **106**	35c. multicoloured	10	10
371 –	$2 multicoloured	25	25

The $2 is as Type **106** but has a different border.

1973. Nos. 370/1 optd **HONEYMOON VISIT DECEMBER 16TH 1973.**

373 **106**	35c. multicoloured	15	10
374 –	$2 multicoloured	30	30

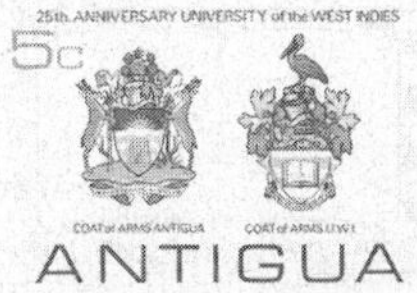

108 Coat of Arms of Antigua and University

1974. 25th Anniv of University of West Indies. Multicoloured.

376	5c. Type **108**	10	10
377	20c. Extra-mural art	15	10
378	35c. Antigua campus	20	10
379	75c. Antigua chancellor	25	35

1974. Military Uniforms (5th series). As T **94**. Multicoloured.

380	½c. Officer, 59th Foot, 1797	10	10
381	10c. Gunner, Royal Artillery, 1800	35	10
382	20c. Private, 1st West India Regiment, 1830	50	10
383	35c. Officer, 92nd Foot, 1843	60	10
384	75c. Private, 23rd Foot, 1846	75	2·25

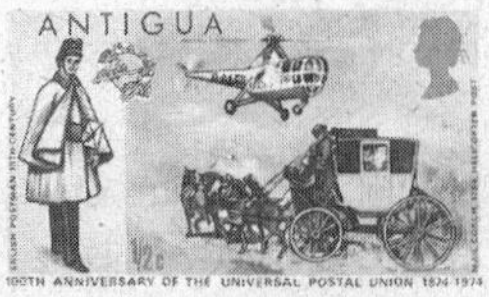

109 English Postman, Mailcoach and Westland Dragonfly Helicopter

1974. Centenary of U.P.U. Multicoloured.

386	½c. Type **109**	10	10
387	1c. Bellman, mail steamer "Orinoco" and satellite	10	10
388	2c. Train guard, post-bus and hydrofoil	10	10
389	5c. Swiss messenger, Wells Fargo coach and Concorde	60	30
390	20c. Postilion, Japanese postmen and carrier pigeon	35	10
391	35c. Antiguan postman, Sikorsky S-88 flying boat and tracking station	45	15
392	$1 Medieval courier, American express train and Boeing 747-100	1·75	2·00

On the ½c. English is spelt "Enlish" and on the 2c. Postal is spelt "Fostal".

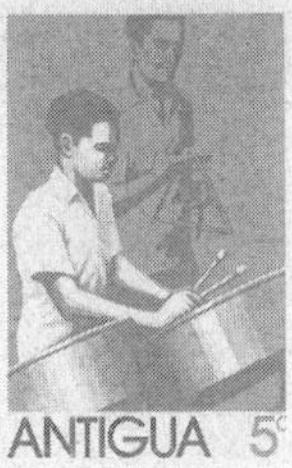

110 Traditional Player

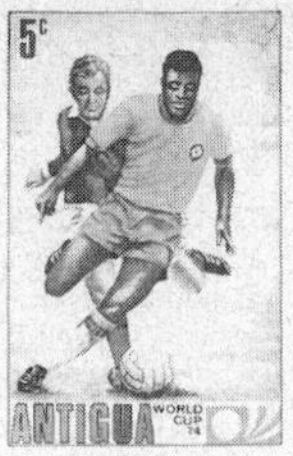

111 Footballers

1974. Antiguan Steel Bands.

394 **110**	5c. dp red, red and black	10	10
395 –	20c. brown, lt brn & blk	10	10
396 –	35c. lt green, green & blk	10	10
397 –	75c. blue, dp blue & blk	20	85

DESIGNS—HORIZ: 20c. Traditional band; 35c. Modern band. VERT: 75c. Modern player.

1974. World Cup Football Championships.

399 **111**	5c. multicoloured	10	10
400 –	35c. multicoloured	15	10
401 –	75c. multicoloured	30	30
402 –	$1 multicoloured	35	40

Nos. 400/2 show various footballing designs similar to Type **111**.

1974. Earthquake Relief Fund. Nos. 400/2 and 397 optd or surch **EARTHQUAKE RELIEF**.

404	35c. multicoloured	20	10
405	75c. multicoloured	30	25
406	$1 multicoloured	40	30
407	$5 on 75c. deep blue, blue and black	1·25	2·00

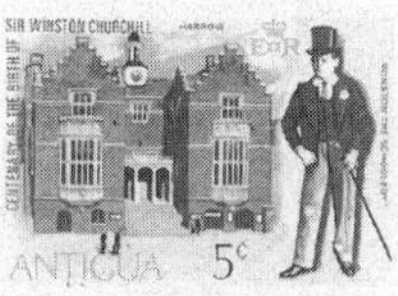

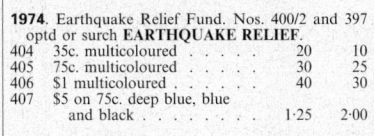

113 Churchill as Schoolboy and School College Building, Harrow

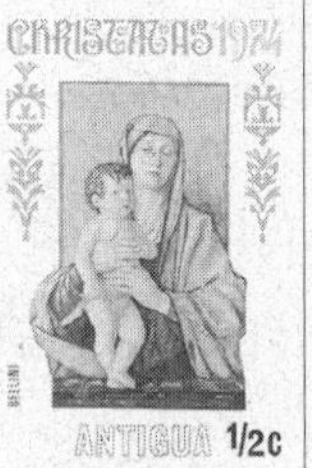

114 "Madonna of the Trees" (Bellini)

1974. Birth Centenary of Sir Winston Churchill. Multicoloured.

408	5c. Type **113**	15	10
409	35c. Churchill and St. Paul's Cathedral	20	10
410	75c. Coat of arms and catafalque	25	55
411	$1 Churchill, "reward" notice and South African escape route	40	90

1974. Christmas. "Madonna and Child" paintings by named artists. Multicoloured.

413	½c. Type **114**	10	10
414	1c. Raphael	10	10
415	2c. Van der Weyden	10	10
416	3c. Giorgione	10	10
417	5c. Mantegna	10	10
418	20c. Vivarini	20	10
419	35c. Montagna	30	10
420	75c. Lorenzo Costa	55	1·10

1975. Nos. 390/2 and 331 surch.

422	50c. on 20c. multicoloured	1·25	2·00
423	$2.50 on 35c. multicoloured	2·00	5·50
424	$5 on $1 multicoloured	6·00	7·00
425	$10 on 75c. multicoloured	4·00	7·50

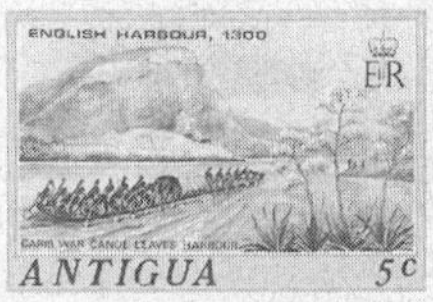

116 Carib War Canoe, English Harbour, 1300

1975. Nelson's Dockyard. Multicoloured.

427	5c. Type **116**	20	10
428	15c. Ship of the line, English Harbour, 1770	80	15
429	35c. H.M.S "Boreas" at anchor, and Lord Nelson, 1787	1·25	15
430	50c. Yachts during "Sailing Week", 1974	1·25	1·50
431	$1 Yacht Anchorage, Old Dockyard, 1970	1·50	2·25

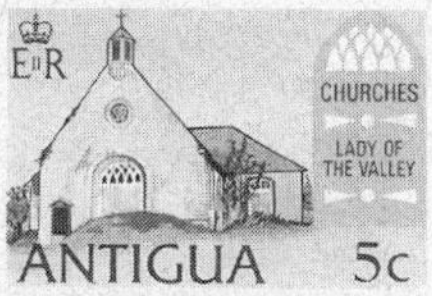

117 Lady of the Valley Church

1975. Antiguan Churches. Multicoloured.

433	5c. Type **117**	10	10
434	20c. Gilbert Memorial	10	10
435	35c. Grace Hill Moravian	15	10
436	50c. St. Phillips	20	20
437	$1 Ebenezer Methodist	35	50

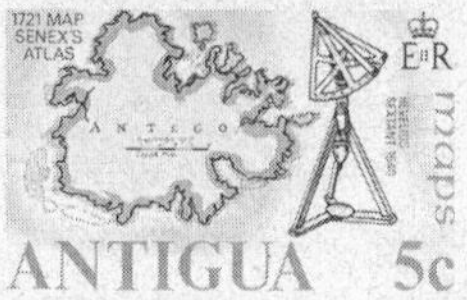

118 Map of 1721 and Sextant of 1640

1975. Maps of Antigua. Multicoloured.

439	5c. Type **118**	30	15
440	20c. Map of 1775 and galleon	55	15
441	35c. Maps of 1775 and 1955	70	15
442	$1 1973 maps of Antigua and English Harbour	1·40	2·00

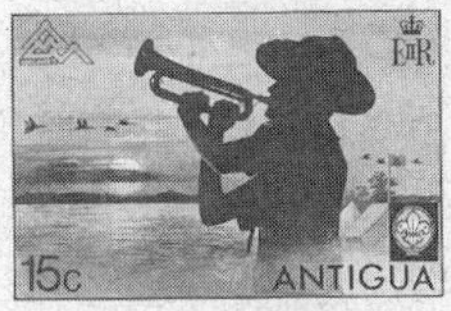

119 Scout Bugler

1975. World Scout Jamboree, Norway. Mult.

444	15c. Type **119**	25	15
445	20c. Scouts in camp	30	15
446	35c. "Lord Baden-Powell" (D. Jagger)	50	20
447	$2 Scout dancers from Dahomey	1·50	2·00

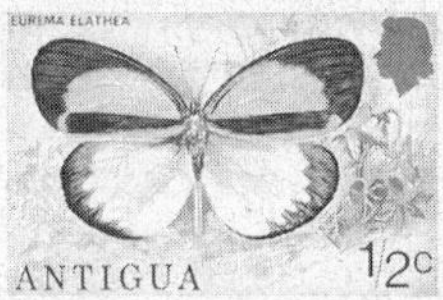

120 "Eurema elathea"

1975. Butterflies. Multicoloured.

449	½c. Type **120**	10	10
450	1c. "Danaus plexippus"	10	10
451	2c. "Phoebis philea"	10	10
452	5c. "Hypolimnas misippus"	20	10
453	20c. "Eurema proterpia"	75	60
454	35c. "Battus polydamas"	1·40	90
455	$2 "Cynthia cardui"	4·00	8·00

No. 452 is incorrectly captioned "Marpesia petreus thetys".

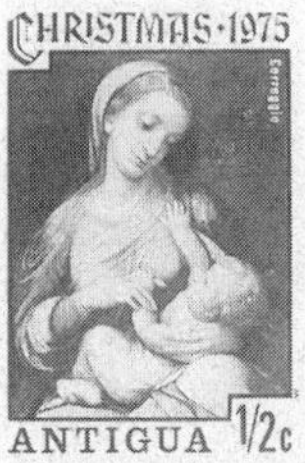

121 "Madonna and Child" (Correggio)

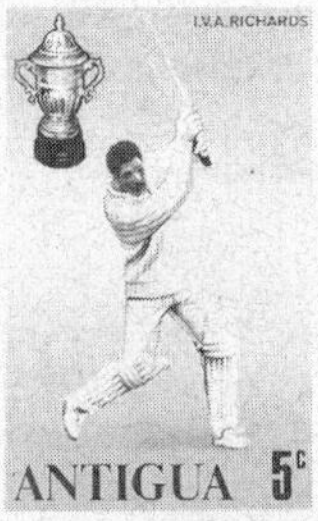

122 Vivian Richards

1975. Christmas. "Madonna and Child" paintings by artists named. Multicoloured.

457	½c. Type **121**	10	10
458	1c. El Greco	10	10
459	2c. Durer	10	10
460	3c. Antonello	10	10
461	5c. Bellini	10	10
462	10c. Durer (different)	10	10
463	35c. Bellini (different)	40	10
464	$2 Durer (different again)	1·00	1·00

1975. World Cricket Cup Winners. Multicoloured.

466	5c. Type **122**	1·25	20
467	35c. Andy Roberts	2·25	60
468	$2 West Indies team (horiz)	4·25	8·00

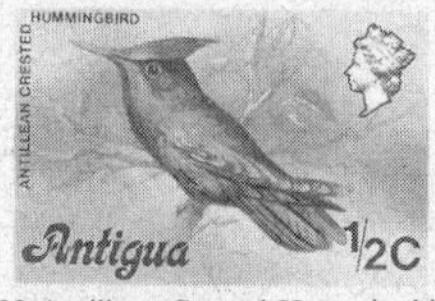

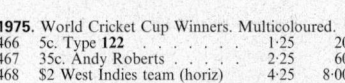

123 Antillean Crested Hummingbird

1976. Multicoloured.

469A	½c. Type **123**	40	50
470A	1c. Imperial amazon ("Imperial Parrot")	80	50
471A	2c. Zenaida dove	80	50
472A	3c. Loggerhead kingbird	80	60
473A	4c. Red-necked pigeon	80	1·00
474A	5c. Rufous-throated solitaire	1·75	10
475A	6c. Orchid tree	30	1·00
476A	10c. Bougainvillea	30	10
477A	15c. Geiger tree	35	10
478A	20c. Flamboyant	35	35
479A	25c. Hibiscus	40	15
480A	35c. Flame of the wood	40	40
481A	50c. Cannon at Fort James	55	60
482A	75c. Premier's Office	60	1·00
483A	$1 Potworks Dam	75	1·00
484A	$2.50 Diamond irrigation scheme (44 × 28 mm)	1·00	4·25
485B	$5 Government House (44 × 28 mm)	1·50	7·00
486A	$10 Coolidge International Airport (44 × 28 mm)	3·50	6·50

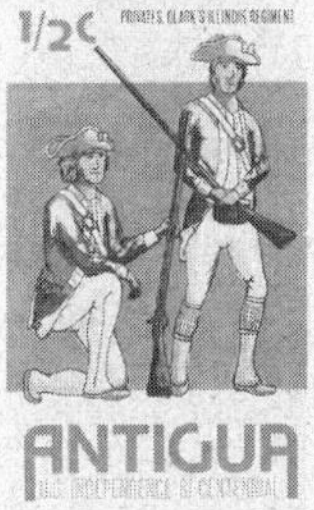

124 Privates, Clark's Illinois Regiment

1976. Bicentenary of American Revolution. Mult.

487	½c. Type **124**	10	10
488	1c. Rifleman, Pennsylvania Militia	10	10
489	2c. Powder horn	10	10
490	5c. Water bottle	10	10
491	35c. American flags	50	10
492	$1 "Montgomery" (American brig)	1·25	40
493	$5 "Ranger" (privateer sloop)	2·00	2·25

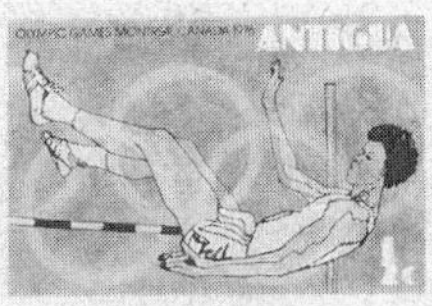

125 High Jump

1976. Olympic Games, Montreal.

495 **125**	½c. brown, yellow & black	10	10
496 –	1c. violet, blue and black	10	10
497 –	2c. green and black	10	10
498 –	15c. blue and black	15	10
499 –	30c. brown, yell & blk	20	15
500 –	$1 orange, red and black	40	40
501 –	$2 red and black	60	80

DESIGNS: 1c. Boxing; 2c. Pole vault; 15c. Swimming; 30c. Running; $1 Cycling; $2 Shot put.

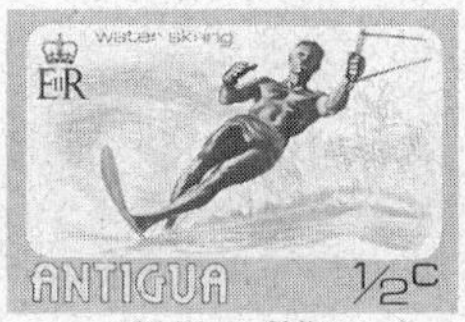

126 Water Skiing

1976. Water Sports. Multicoloured.

503	½c. Type **126**	10	10
504	1c. Sailing	10	10
505	2c. Snorkeling	10	10
506	20c. Deep sea fishing	50	10
507	50c. Scuba diving	75	35
508	$2 Swimming	1·25	1·25

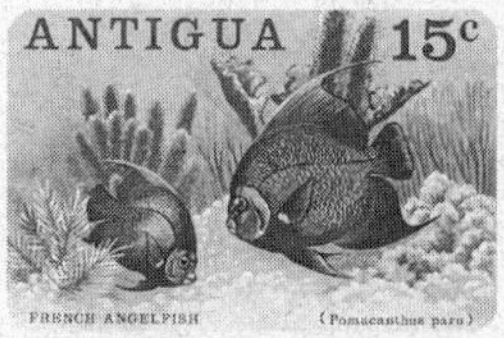

127 French Angelfish

1976. Fishes. Multicoloured.

510	15c. Type **127**	50	15
511	30c. Yellow-finned grouper	75	30
512	50c. Yellow-tailed snapper	95	50
513	90c. Shy hamlet	1·25	80

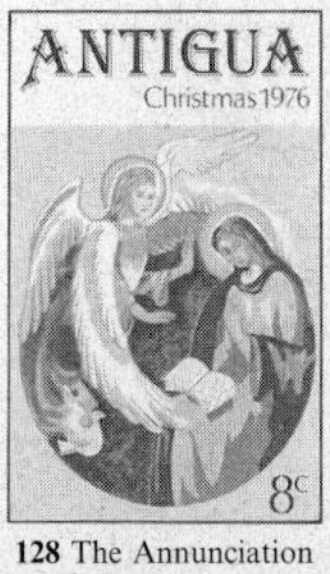

128 The Annunciation

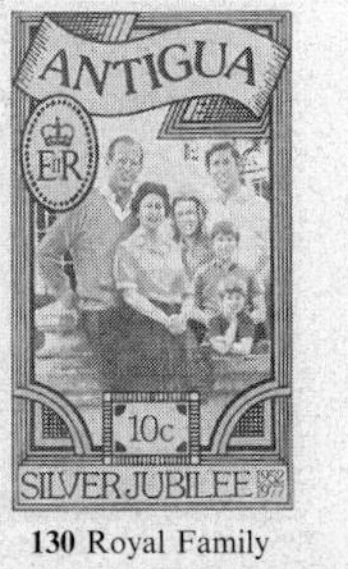

130 Royal Family

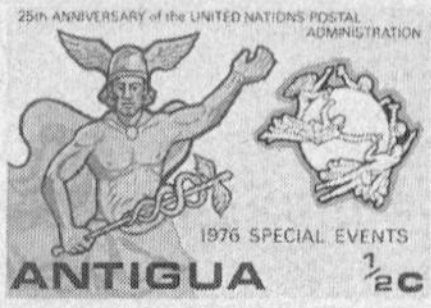

129 Mercury and U.P.U. Emblem

1976. Christmas. Multicoloured.

514	8c. Type **128**	10	10
515	10c. The Holy Family	10	10
516	15c. The Magi	10	10
517	50c. The Shepherds	20	25
518	$1 Epiphany scene	30	50

1976. Special Events, 1976. Multicoloured.

519	½c. Type **129**	10	10
520	1c. Alfred Nobel	10	10
521	10c. Space satellite	30	10
522	50c. Viv Richards and Andy Roberts	3·50	1·75
523	$1 Bell and telephones	1·00	2·00
524	$2 Yacht "Freelance"	2·25	4·00

1977. Silver Jubilee. Multicoloured. (a) Perf.

526	10c. Type **130**	10	10
527	30c. Royal Visit, 1966	10	10
528	50c. The Queen enthroned	15	15
529	90c. The Queen after Coronation	15	25
530	$2.50 Queen and Prince Charles	30	55
	(b) Roul × imperf. Self-adhesive.		
532	50c. As 90c.	35	60
533	$5 The Queen and Prince Philip	2·00	3·50

Nos. 532/3 come from booklets.

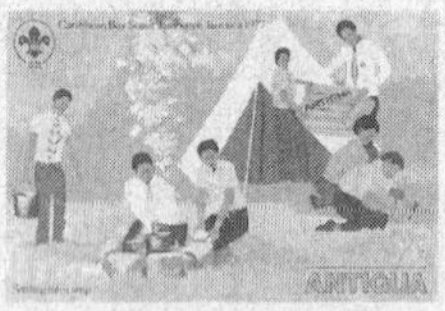

131 Making Camp

1977. Caribbean Scout Jamboree, Jamaica. Mult.

534	½c. Type **131**	10	10
535	1c. Hiking	10	10
536	2c. Rock-climbing	10	10
537	10c. Cutting logs	15	10
538	30c. Map and sign reading	40	10
539	50c. First aid	65	25
540	$2 Rafting	1·75	2·50

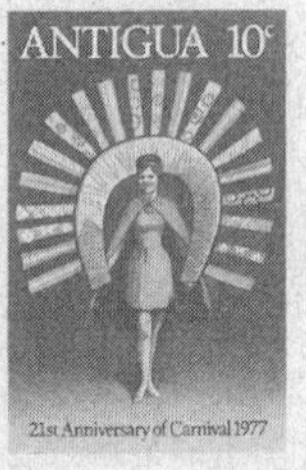

132 Carnival Costume

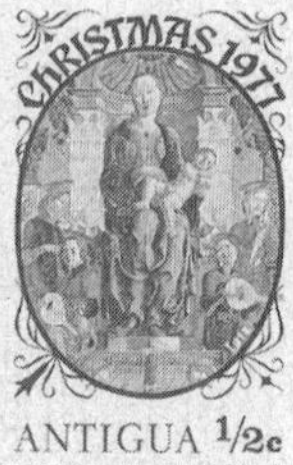

134 "Virgin and Child Enthroned" (Tura)

1977. 21st Anniv of Carnival. Multicoloured.

542	10c. Type **132**	10	10
543	30c. Carnival Queen	20	10
544	50c. Butterfly costume	25	15
545	90c. Queen of the band	35	25
546	$1 Calypso King and Queen	35	30

1977. Royal Visit. Nos. 526/30 optd **ROYAL VISIT 28TH OCTOBER 1977**.

548	10c. Type **130**	10	10
549	30c. Royal Visit, 1966	15	10
550	50c. The Queen enthroned	20	10
551	90c. The Queen after Coronation	30	20
552	$2.50 Queen and Prince Charles	50	35

1977. Christmas. Paintings by artists listed. Mult.

554	½c. Type **134**	10	10
555	1c. Crivelli	10	10
556	2c. Lotto	10	10
557	8c. Pontormo	15	10
558	10c. Tura (different)	15	10
559	25c. Lotto (different)	30	10
560	$2 Crivelli (different)	85	60

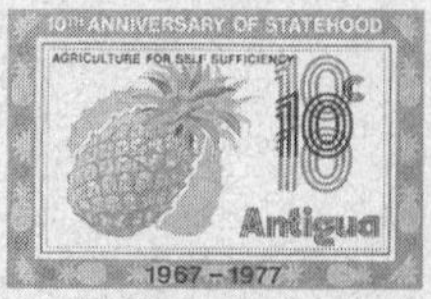

135 Pineapple

1977. 10th Anniv of Statehood. Multicoloured.

562	10c. Type **135**	10	10
563	15c. State flag	10	10
564	50c. Police band	2·00	80
565	90c. Premier V. C. Bird	55	80
566	$2 State Coat of Arms	90	1·60

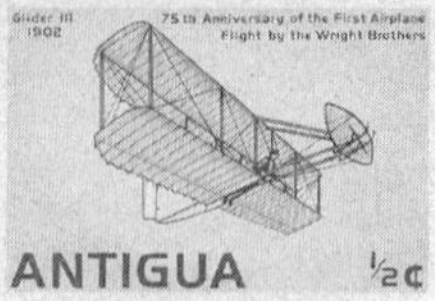

136 Wright Glider III, 1902

1978. 75th Anniv of Powered Flight. Mult.

568	½c. Type **136**	10	10
569	1c. Wright Flyer I, 1903	10	10
570	2c. Launch system and engine	10	10
571	10c. Orville Wright (vert)	30	10
572	50c. Wright Flyer III, 1905	60	15
573	90c. Wilbur Wright (vert)	80	30
574	$2 Wright Type B, 1910	1·00	80

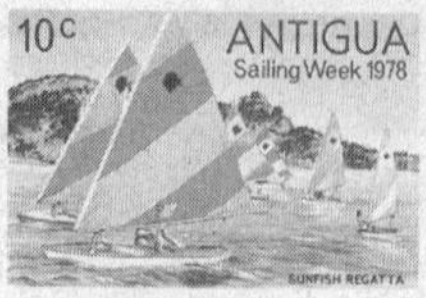

137 Sunfish Regatta

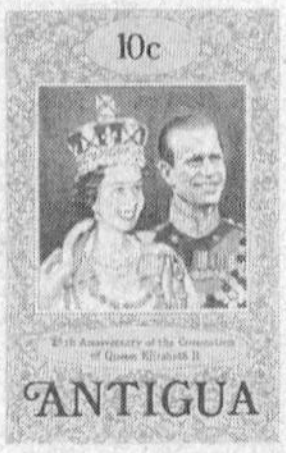

138 Queen Elizabeth and Prince Philip

1978. Sailing Week. Multicoloured.

576	10c. Type **137**	20	10
577	50c. Fishing and work boat race	35	20
578	90c. Curtain Bluff race	60	35
579	$2 Power boat rally	1·10	1·25

1978. 25th Anniv of Coronation. Mult. (a) Perf.

581	10c. Type **138**	10	10
582	30c. Crowning	10	10
583	50c. Coronation procession	15	10
584	90c. Queen seated in St. Edward's Chair	20	15
585	$2.50 Queen wearing Imperial State Crown	40	40
	(b) Roul × imperf. Self-adhesive. Horiz designs as Type **138**.		
587	25c. Glass Coach	15	30
588	50c. Irish State Coach	25	50
589	$5 Coronation Coach	1·75	3·00

Nos. 587/9 come from booklets.

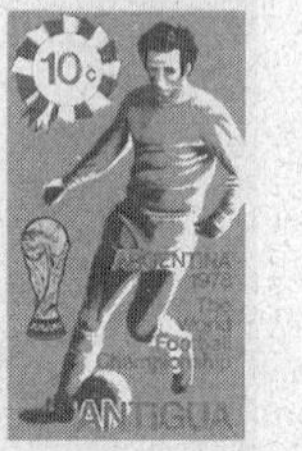

140 Player running with Ball

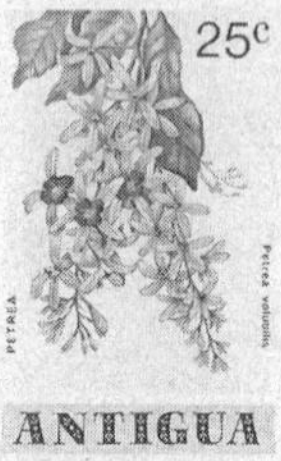

141 Petrea

1978. World Cup Football Championship, Argentina. Multicoloured.

590	10c. Type **140**	15	10
591	15c. Players in front of goal	15	10
592	$3 Referee and player	2·00	1·75

1978. Flowers. Multicoloured.

594	25c. Type **141**	25	10
595	50c. Sunflower	35	20
596	90c. Frangipani	60	30
597	$2 Passion flower	1·25	1·10

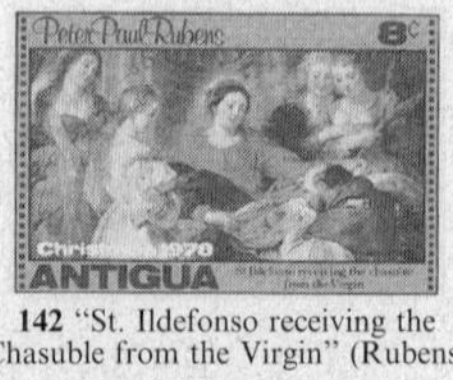

142 "St. Ildefonso receiving the Chasuble from the Virgin" (Rubens)

1978. Christmas. Multicoloured.

599	8c. Type **142**	10	10
600	25c. "The Flight of St. Barbara" (Rubens)	20	10
601	$2 "Madonna and Child, with St. Joseph, John the Baptist and Donor"	65	55

The painting shown on No. 601 is incorrectly attributed to Rubens on the stamp. The artist was Sebastiano del Piombo.

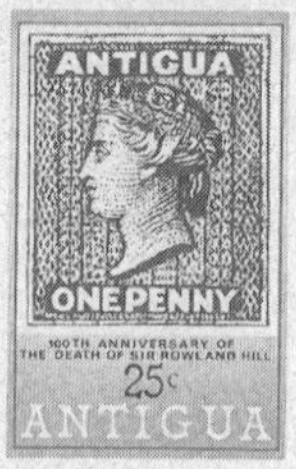

143 1d. Stamp of 1863

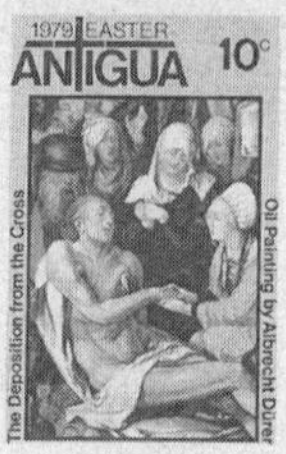

144 "The Deposition from the Cross" (painting)

1979. Death Centenary of Sir Rowland Hill. Mult.

603	25c. Type **143**	10	10
604	50c. 1840 Penny Black	20	15
605	$1 Mail coach and woman posting letter, c. 1840	30	20
606	$2 Modern transport	1·10	60

1979. Easter. Works by Durer.

608 **144**	10c. multicoloured	10	10
609 –	50c. multicoloured	35	20
610 –	$4 black, mauve and yellow	1·00	90

DESIGNS: 50c. "Christ on the Cross–The Passion" (wood engraving); $4 "Man of Sorrows with Hands Raised" (wood engraving).

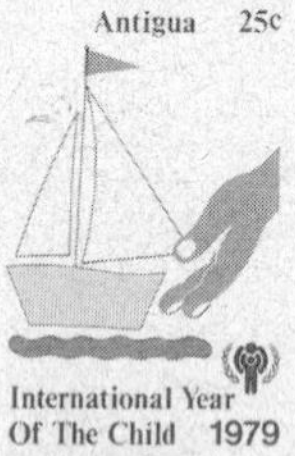

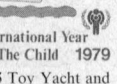

145 Toy Yacht and Child's Hand

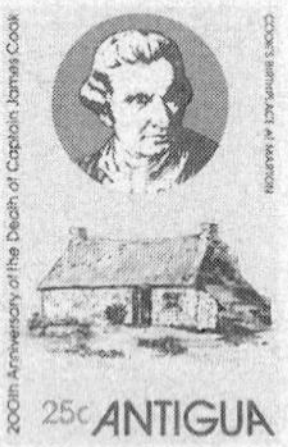

147 Cook's Birthplace, Marton

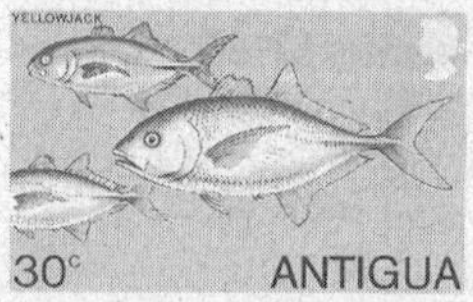

146 Yellow Jack

1979. International Year of the Child. Mult.

612	25c. Type **145**	10	10
613	50c. Rocket	25	15
614	90c. Car	40	25
615	$2 Toy train	1·00	90

Nos. 612/15 also show the hands of children of different races.

1979. Fishes. Multicoloured.

617	30c. Type **146**	40	15
618	50c. Blue-finned tuna	50	25
619	90c. Sailfish	75	40
620	$3 Wahoo	2·25	1·75

1979. Death Bicentenary of Captain Cook. Mult.

622	25c. Type **147**	55	25
623	50c. H.M.S. "Endeavour"	75	60
624	90c. Marine chronometer	75	80
625	$3 Landing at Botany Bay	1·60	2·75

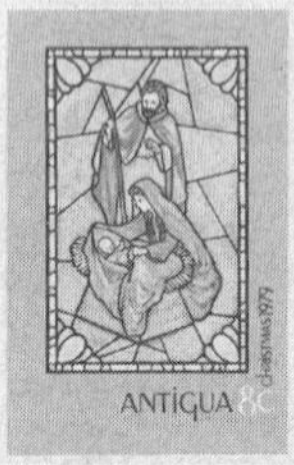

148 The Holy Family

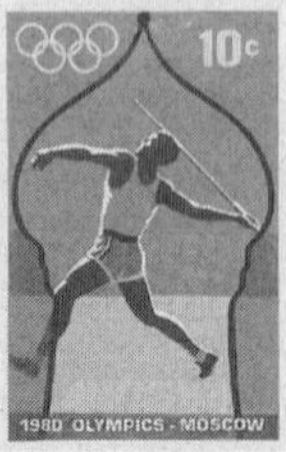

149 Javelin Throwing

1979. Christmas. Multicoloured.

627	8c. Type **148**	10	10
628	25c. Virgin and Child on ass	15	10
629	50c. Shepherd and star	25	35
630	$4 Wise Men with gifts	85	2·25

1980. Olympic Games, Moscow. Multicoloured.

632	10c. Type **149**	20	10
633	25c. Running	20	10
634	$1 Pole vault	50	50
635	$2 Hurdles	70	1·75

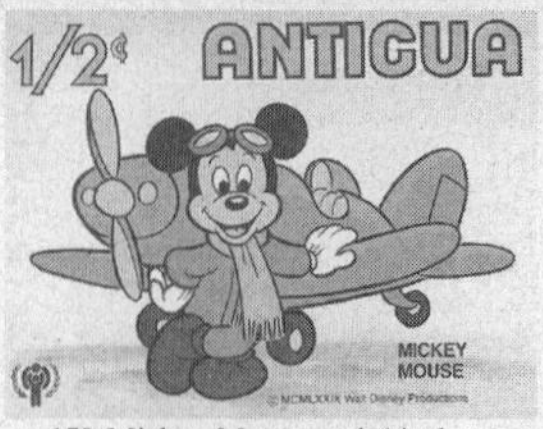

150 Mickey Mouse and Airplane

1980. International Year of the Child. Walt Disney Cartoon Characters. Multicoloured.

637	½c. Type **150**	10	10
638	1c. Donald Duck driving car (vert)	10	10
639	2c. Goofy driving taxi	10	10
640	3c. Mickey and Minnie Mouse on motorcycle	10	10
641	4c. Huey, Dewey and Louie on a bicycle for three	10	10
642	5c. Grandma Duck and truck of roosters	10	10
643	10c. Mickey Mouse in jeep (vert)	10	10
644	$1 Chip and Dale in yacht	1·75	2·00
645	$4 Donald Duck riding toy train (vert)	3·75	6·00

1980. "London 1980" International Stamp Exhibition. Nos. 603/6 optd **LONDON 1980**.

647	25c. Type **143**	25	15
648	50c. Penny Black	35	35
649	$1 Stage-coach and woman posting letter, c. 1840	60	70
650	$2 Modern mail transport	3·25	3·00

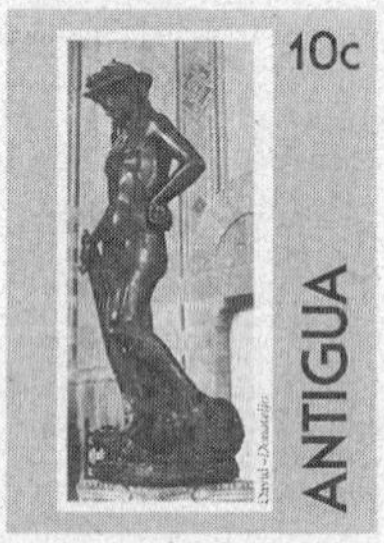

152 "David" (statue, Donatello)

1980. Famous Works of Art. Multicoloured.

651	10c. Type **152**	10	10
652	30c. "The Birth of Venus" (painting, Botticelli) (horiz)	30	15
653	50c. "Reclining Couple" (sarcophagus), Cerveteri (horiz)	40	40
654	90c. "The Garden of Earthly Delights" (painting by Bosch) (horiz)	55	65
655	$1 "Portinari Altarpiece" (painting, van der Goes) (horiz)	65	75
656	$4 "Eleanora of Toledo and her Son, Giovanni de'Medici" (painting, Bronzino)	1·75	3·00

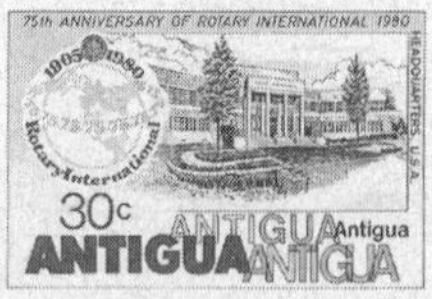

153 Anniversary Emblem and Headquarters, U.S.A.

1980. 75th Anniv of Rotary International. Mult.

658	30c. Type **153**	30	30
659	50c. Rotary anniversary emblem and Antigua Rotary Club banner	40	50
660	90c. Map of Antigua and Rotary emblem	60	70
661	$3 Paul P. Harris (founder) and Rotary emblem	2·00	3·25

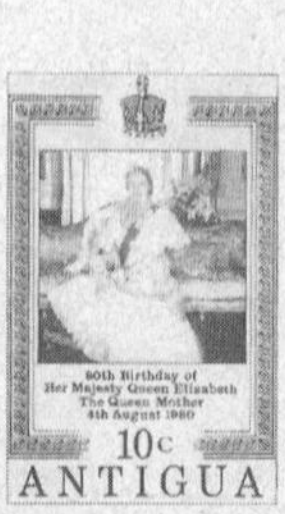

154 Queen Elizabeth the Queen Mother

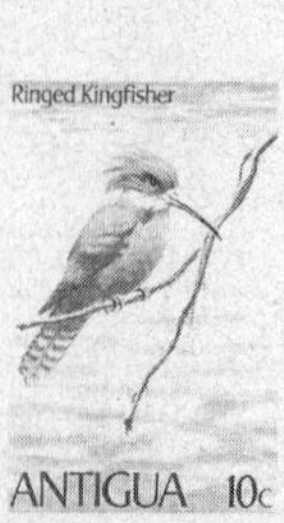

155 Ringed Kingfisher

1980. 80th Birthday of The Queen Mother.

663 **154**	10c. multicoloured	40	10
664	$2.50 multicoloured	1·50	1·75

1980. Birds. Multicoloured.

666	10c. Type **155**	70	25
667	30c. Plain pigeon	1·00	50

| 668 | $1 Green-throated carib | 1·50 | 1·75 |
| 669 | $2 Black-necked stilt | 2·00 | 3·50 |

1980. Christmas. Walt Disney's "Sleeping Beauty". As T 150. Multicoloured.

671	½c. The Bad Fairy with her raven	10	10
672	1c. The good fairies	10	10
673	2c. Aurora	10	10
674	4c. Aurora pricks her finger	10	10
675	8c. The prince	10	10
676	10c. The prince fights the dragon	15	10
677	25c. The prince awakens Aurora with a kiss	20	20
678	$2 The prince and Aurora's betrothal	2·25	2·25
679	$2.50 The prince and princess	2·50	2·50

156 Diesel Locomotive No. 15

1981. Sugar Cane Railway Locomotives. Mult.

681	25c. Type 156	15	15
682	50c. Narrow-gauge steam locomotive	30	30
683	90c. Diesel locomotives Nos. 1 and 10	55	60
684	$3 Steam locomotive hauling sugar cane	2·00	2·25

1981. Independence. Nos. 475/6 and 478/86 optd "INDEPENDENCE 1981".

686B	6c. Orchid tree	10	10
687B	10c. Bougainvillea	10	10
688B	20c. Flamboyant	10	10
689B	25c. Hibiscus	15	15
690B	35c. Flame of the wood	20	20
691B	50c. Cannon at Fort James	35	35
692B	75c. Premier's Office	40	40
693B	$1 Potworks Dam	55	55
694B	$2.50 Irrigation scheme, Diamond Estate	1·00	1·25
695B	$5 Government House	1·75	2·50
696B	$10 Coolidge International Airport	3·50	5·00

158 "Pipes of Pan"

1981. Birth Centenary of Picasso. Multicoloured.

697	10c. Type 158	10	10
698	50c. "Seated Harlequin"	30	30
699	90c. "Paulo as Harlequin"	55	55
700	$4 "Mother and Child"	2·00	2·00

159 Prince Charles and Lady Diana Spencer

160 Prince of Wales at Investiture, 1969

1981. Royal Wedding (1st issue). Multicoloured.

702	25c. Type 159	10	10
703	50c. Glamis Castle	10	10
704	$4 Prince Charles skiing	80	80

1981. Royal Wedding (2nd issue). Multicoloured. Roul × imperf. Self-adhesive.

706	25c. Type 160	15	25
707	25c. Prince Charles as baby, 1948	15	25
708	$1 Prince Charles at R.A.F. College, Cranwell, 1971	25	50
709	$1 Prince Charles attending Hill House School, 1956	25	50
710	$2 Prince Charles and Lady Diana Spencer	50	75
711	$2 Prince Charles at Trinity College, 1967	50	75
712	$5 Prince Charles and Lady Diana (different)	1·00	1·50

161 Irene Joshua (founder)

1981. 50th Anniv of Antigua Girl Guide Movement. Multicoloured.

713	10c. Type 161	15	10
714	50c. Campfire sing-song	45	35
715	90c. Sailing	75	65
716	$2.50 Animal tending	1·75	2·00

162 Antigua and Barbuda Coat of Arms

163 "Holy Night" (Jacques Stella)

1981. Independence. Multicoloured.

718	10c. Type 162	25	10
719	50c. Pineapple, with Antigua and Barbuda flag and map	75	30
720	90c. Prime Minister Vere Bird	55	55
721	$2.50 St. John's Cathedral (38 × 25 mm)	1·50	3·25

1981. Christmas. Paintings. Multicoloured.

723	8c. Type 163	15	10
724	30c. "Mary with Child" (Julius Schnorr von Carolfeld)	40	15
725	$1 "Virgin and Child" (Alonso Cano)	75	90
726	$3 "Virgin and Child" (Lorenzo di Credi)	1·10	3·75

164 Swimming

1981. International Year of Disabled People. Sports for the Disabled. Multicoloured.

728	10c. Type 164	10	10
729	50c. Discus-throwing	20	30
730	90c. Archery	40	55
731	$2 Baseball	1·00	1·40

165 Scene from Football Match

1982. World Cup Football Championship, Spain.

733	165 10c. multicoloured	30	10
734	– 50c. multicoloured	60	35
735	– 90c. multicoloured	1·10	70
736	– $4 multicoloured	3·50	3·50

DESIGNS: 50c. to $4 Scenes from various matches.

166 Airbus Industrie A300

167 Cordia

1982. Coolidge International Airport. Mult.

738	10c. Type 166	10	10
739	50c. Hawker-Siddeley H.S.748	30	30
740	90c. De Havilland D.H.C.6 Twin Otter	60	60
741	$2.50 Britten Norman Islander	1·75	1·75

1982. Death Centenary of Charles Darwin. Fauna and Flora. Multicoloured.

743	10c. Type 167	25	10
744	50c. Small Indian mongoose (horiz)	55	40
745	90c. Corallita	85	75
746	$2 Mexican bulldog bat (horiz)	2·25	3·25

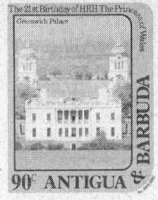

168 Queen's House, Greenwich

1982. 21st Birthday of Princess of Wales. Mult.

748	90c. Type 168	45	45
749	$1 Prince and Princess of Wales	50	50
750	$4 Princess Diana	2·00	2·00

170 Boy Scouts decorating Streets for Independence Parade

1982. 75th Anniv of Boy Scout Movement. Multicoloured.

752	10c. Type 170	25	10
753	50c. Boy Scout giving helping hand during street parade	60	40
754	90c. Boy Scouts attending H.R.H. Princess Margaret at Independence Ceremony	1·00	75
755	$2.20 Cub Scout giving directions to tourists	1·90	2·75

1982. Birth of Prince William of Wales. Nos. 748/50 optd ROYAL BABY 21.6.82.

757	90c. Type 168	45	45
758	$1 Prince and Princess of Wales	50	50
759	$4 Princess Diana	2·00	1·50

172 Roosevelt in 1940

1982. Birth Centenary of Franklin D. Roosevelt. (Nos. 761, 763 and 765/6) and 250th Birth Anniv of George Washington (others). Multicoloured.

761	10c. Type 172	20	10
762	25c. Washington as blacksmith	45	15
763	45c. Churchill, Roosevelt and Stalin at Yalta Conference	1·00	40
764	60c. Washington crossing the Delaware (vert)	1·00	40
765	$1 "Roosevelt Special" train (vert)	1·25	90
766	$3 Portrait of Roosevelt (vert)	1·40	2·40

173 "Annunciation"

1982. Christmas. Religious Paintings by Raphael. Multicoloured.

769	10c. Type 173	10	10
770	30c. "Adoration of the Magi"	15	15
771	$1 "Presentation at the Temple"	50	50
772	$4 "Coronation of the Virgin"	2·10	2·25

174 Tritons and Dolphins

1983. 500th Birth Anniv of Raphael. Details from "Galatea" Fresco. Multicoloured.

| 774 | 45c. Type 174 | 20 | 25 |
| 775 | 50c. Sea nymph carried off by Triton | 25 | 30 |

| 776 | 60c. Winged angel steering dolphins (horiz) | 30 | 35 |
| 777 | $4 Cupids shooting arrows (horiz) | 1·60 | 2·00 |

175 Pineapple Produce

1983. Commonwealth Day. Multicoloured.

779	25c. Type 175	15	15
780	45c. Carnival	20	25
781	60c. Tourism	30	35
782	$3 Airport	1·00	1·50

176 T.V. Satellite Coverage of Royal Wedding

1983. World Communications Year. Multicoloured.

783	15c. Type 176	40	20
784	50c. Police communications	2·25	1·50
785	60c. House-to-train telephone call	2·25	1·50
786	$3 Satellite earth station with planets Jupiter and Saturn	4·75	5·00

177 Bottle-nosed Dolphin

1983. Whales. Multicoloured.

788	15c. Type 177	85	20
789	50c. Fin whale	1·75	1·25
790	60c. Bowhead whale	2·00	1·25
791	$3 Spectacled porpoise	3·75	4·25

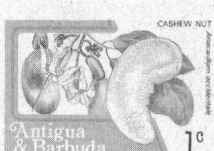

178 Cashew Nut

1983. Fruits and Flowers. Multicoloured.

793	1c. Type 178	15	60
794	2c. Passion fruit	15	60
795	3c. Mango	15	60
796	5c. Grapefruit	20	50
797a	10c. Pawpaw	30	20
798	15c. Breadfruit	75	20
799	20c. Coconut	50	20
800a	25c. Oleander	75	20
801	30c. Banana	60	40
802a	40c. Pineapple	75	30
803a	45c. Cordia	85	40
804	50c. Cassia	90	60
805	60c. Poui	1·75	1·00
806a	$1 Frangipani	2·25	1·50
807a	$2 Flamboyant	3·75	4·00
808	$2.50 Lemon	4·50	5·50
809	$5 Linum vitae	7·00	11·00
810	$10 National flag and coat of arms	11·00	16·00

179 Dornier Do-X Flying Boat

1983. Bicentenary of Manned Flight. Mult.

811	30c. Type 179	75	30
812	50c. Supermarine S.6B seaplane	90	60
813	60c. Curtiss F-9C Sparrowhawk biplane and airship U.S.S. "Akron"	1·00	85
814	$4 Hot-air balloon "Pro Juventute"	3·00	5·00

Antigua & Barbuda · Christmas · 1983
10c
Raphael: Sibyls and Angels (detail)

180 "Sibyls and Angels" (detail) (Raphael)

1983. Christmas. 500th Birth Anniv of Raphael.
816 **180** 10c. multicoloured 30 20
817 – 30c. multicoloured 65 35
818 – $1 multicoloured . . . . 1·50 1·25
819 – $4 multicoloured . . . . 3·00 5·00
DESIGNS—HORIZ: 10c. to $4, Different details from "Sibyls and Angels".

Methodist Church Anniversary
JOHN WESLEY
Founder of Methodism
15c
ANTIGUA & BARBUDA

ANTIGUA & BARBUDA 25¢

181 John Wesley (founder) **182** Discus

1983. Bicentenary of Methodist Church (1984). Multicoloured.
821 15c. Type **181** 25 15
822 50c. Nathaniel Gilbert (founder in Antigua) . . . 70 50
823 60c. St. John Methodist Church steeple 75 65
824 $3 Ebenezer Methodist Church, St. John's . . . . 2·00 4·00

1984. Olympic Games, Los Angeles. Multicoloured.
825 25c. Type **182** 20 15
826 50c. Gymnastics 35 30
827 90c. Hurdling 65 70
828 $3 Cycling . . . . 2·50 3·50

45c
ANTIGUA
BARBUDA
BOOKER VANGUARD

183 "Booker Vanguard" (freighter)

1984. Ships. Multicoloured.
830 45c. Type **183** . . . . 1·00 55
831 50c. S.S. "Canberra" (liner) 1·25 80
832 60c. Yachts . . . . 1·50 1·00
833 $4 "Fairwind" (cargo liner) 3·00 7·00

Antigua & Barbuda 15c
19th U.P.U. CONGRESS

10c
ANTIGUA & BARBUDA

184 Chenille **187** Abraham Lincoln

1984. Universal Postal Union Congress, Hamburg. Multicoloured.
835 15c. Type **184** 40 15
836 50c. Shell flower 80 70
837 60c. Anthurium . . . . . . 85 1·10
838 $3 Angels trumpet . . . . . 2·75 6·50

1984. Various stamps surch. (a) Nos. 702/4.
840 $2 on 25c. Type **159** . . . . 2·50 2·50
841 $2 on 50c. Glamis Castle . . 2·50 2·50
842 $2 on $4 Prince Charles skiing . . . . 2·50 2·50

(b) Nos. 748/50.
844 $2 on 90c. Type **168** . . . . 2·00 2·00
845 $2 on $1 Prince and Princess of Wales . . . . 2·00 2·00
846 $2 on $4 Princess Diana . . 2·00 2·00

(c) Nos. 757/9.
848 $2 on 90c. Type **168** . . . . 2·00 2·00
849 $2 on $1 Prince and Princess of Wales . . . . 2·00 2·00
850 $2 on $4 Princess Diana . . 2·00 2·00

(d) Nos. 779/82.
852 $2 on 25c. Type **175** . . . . 2·50 1·25
853 $2 on 45c. Carnival . . . . 2·50 1·25
854 $2 on 60c. Tourism . . . . . 2·50 1·25
855 $2 on $3 Airport . . . . . . 2·50 1·25

1984. Presidents of the United States of America. Multicoloured.
856 10c. Type **187** 15 10
857 20c. Harry S. Truman . . . 20 15
858 30c. Dwight D. Eisenhower 30 25
859 40c. Ronald W. Reagan . . . 50 30
860 90c. Gettysburg Address, 1863 . . . . 90 75
861 $1.10 Formation of N.A.T.O.,1949 . . . . . . 1·25 1·25
862 $1.50 Eisenhower during the war . . . . 1·60 1·75
863 $2 Reagan and Caribbean Basin Initiative . . . . . 1·75 2·00

ANTIGUA & BARBUDA 40c
150th ANNIVERSARY of the ABOLITION of SLAVERY

188 View of Moravian Mission

1984. 150th Anniv of Abolition of Slavery. Multicoloured.
864 40c. Type **188** 80 50
865 50c. Antigua Courthouse, 1823 . . . . 90 65
866 60c. Planting sugar-cane, Monks Hill 95 75
867 $3 Boiling house, Delaps' estate . . . . 4·00 5·00

Rufous-sided Towhee
40c
Antigua & Barbuda

$1
GRASS SKIING

189 Rufous-sided Towhee **190** Grass-skiing

1984. Songbirds. Multicoloured.
869 40c. Type **189** . . . . 1·25 85
870 50c. Parula warbler . . . . . 1·40 1·10
871 60c. House wren . . . . . . 1·50 1·50
872 $2 Ruby-crowned kinglet . . 2·00 3·75
873 $3 Common flicker ("Yellow-shafted Flicker") . . . . . 2·75 5·00

1984. "Ausipex" International Stamp Exhibition, Melbourne. Australian Sports. Multicoloured.
875 $1 Type **190** . . . . 1·25 1·50
876 $5 Australian football . . . 3·75 5·50

450th ANNIVERSARY of the DEATH of CORREGGIO
Antigua 25c & Barbuda

150th ANNIVERSARY of the BIRTH of EDGAR DEGAS
ANTIGUA & BARBUDA 15c

191 "The Virgin and Infant with Angels and Cherubs" **192** "The Blue Dancers"

1984. 450th Death Anniv of Correggio (painter). Multicoloured.
878 25c. Type **191** 40 20
879 60c. "The Four Saints" . . . 80 50
880 90c. "St. Catherine" . . . . 1·10 90
881 $3 "The Campori Madonna" 2·25 4·25

1984. 150th Birth Anniv of Edgar Degas (painter). Multicoloured.
883 15c. Type **192** 35 15
884 50c. "The Pink Dancers" . . 80 60
885 70c. "Two Dancers" . . . . 1·10 85
886 $4 "Dancers at the Bar" . . 2·50 4·75

ANTIGUA & BARBUDA
60¢
WINSTON CHURCHILL

ANTIGUA & BARBUDA
1c
CARIBBEAN CRUISE HOLIDAY
CHRISTMAS 1984

193 Sir Winston Churchill **194** Donald Duck fishing

1984. Famous People. Multicoloured.
888 60c. Type **193** . . . . 1·10 1·50
889 60c. Mahatma Gandhi . . . 1·10 1·50
890 60c. John F. Kennedy . . . 1·10 1·50
891 60c. Mao Tse-tung . . . . . 1·10 1·50
892 $1 Churchill with General De Gaulle, Paris, 1944 (horiz) 1·25 1·75
893 $1 Gandhi leaving London by train, 1931 (horiz) . . . 1·25 1·75
894 $1 Kennedy with Chancellor Adenauer and Mayor Brandt, Berlin, 1963 (horiz) 1·25 1·75
895 $1 Mao Tse-tung with Lin Piao, Peking, 1969 (horiz) 1·25 1·75

1984. Christmas. 50th Birthday of Donald Duck. Walt Disney Cartoon Characters. Multicoloured.
897 1c. Type **194** 10 10
898 2c. Donald Duck lying on beach 10 10
899 3c. Donald Duck and nephews with fishing rods and fishes 10 10
900 4c. Donald Duck and nephews in boat 10 10
901 5c. Wearing diving masks . . 10 10
902 10c. In deckchairs reading books 10 10
903 $1 With toy shark's fin . . . 2·25 1·25
904 $2 In sailing boat . . . . . 2·50 3·00
905 $5 Attempting to propel boat 5·50 6·00

ANTIGUA & BARBUDA
THE STATUE OF LIBERTY CENTENNIAL JULY 4, 1986
25¢

195 Torch from Statue in Madison Square Park, 1885

1985. Centenary (1986) of Statue of Liberty. Mult.
907 25c. Type **195** 20 20
908 30c. Statue of Liberty and scaffolding ("Restoration and Renewal") (vert) . . . 20 20
909 50c. Frederic Bartholdi (sculptor) supervising construction, 1876 . . . . 30 30
910 90c. Close-up of statue . . . 60 65
911 $1 Statue and cadet ship ("Operation Sail", 1976) (vert) . . . . 1·40 1·25
912 $3 Dedication ceremony, 1886 . . . . 1·75 2·75

ANTIGUA & BARBUDA 15c

196 Arawak Pot Sherd and Indians making Clay Utensils

1985. Native American Artefacts. Multicoloured.
914 15c. Type **196** 15 10
915 50c. Arawak body design and Arawak Indians tattooing 30 40
916 60c. Head of the god "Yocahu" and Indians harvesting manioc 40 50
917 $3 Carib war club and Carib Indians going into battle 1·25 2·50

ANTIGUA & BARBUDA
10c
TRIUMPH 2HP JAP 1903

197 Triumph 2hp "Jap", 1903

1985. Centenary of the Motorcycle. Multicoloured.
919 10c. Type **197** 65 15
920 30c. "Indian Arrow", 1949 1·10 40
921 60c. BMW "R100RS", 1976 1·60 1·25
922 $4 Harley-Davidson "Model II", 1916 . . . . 5·50 7·50

90c
Antigua & Barbuda
200th Anniversary of the birth of John Audubon

198 Slavonian Grebe ("Horned Grebe")

1985. Birth Bicentenary of John J. Audubon (ornithologist) (1st issue). Multicoloured. Designs showing original paintings.
924 90c. Type **198** . . . . 1·75 1·25
925 $1 British storm petrel ("Least Petrel") . . . . . 2·00 1·25
926 $1.50 Great blue heron . . 2·50 3·25
927 $3 Double-crested cormorant 3·75 6·50
See also Nos. 990/3.

25c
ANTIGUA & BARBUDA

199 "Anaea cyanea"

1985. Butterflies. Multicoloured.
929 25c. Type **199** . . . . 1·00 30
930 60c. "Leodonta dysoni" . . . 2·25 1·25
931 90c. "Junea doraete" . . . . 2·75 1·50
932 $4 "Prepona pylene" . . . . 7·50 10·50

ANTIGUA & BARBUDA 30c
Cessna 172
40th Anniversary of the International Civil Aviation Organization

200 Cessna 172D Skyhawk

1985. 40th Anniv of International Civil Aviation Organization. Multicoloured.
934 30c. Type **200** . . . . 1·25 30
935 90c. Fokker D.VII . . . . . 2·75 1·25
936 $1.50 SPAD VII . . . . . . 3·75 3·25
937 $3 Boeing 747-100 . . . . . 5·50 7·50

850TH ANNIVERSARY OF THE BIRTH OF MAIMONIDES
$2
ANTIGUA AND BARBUDA

$1
85
ANTIGUA BARBUDA

201 Maimonides **203** The Queen Mother attending Church

ANTIGUA & BARBUDA 25c
FARMING

202 Young Farmers with Produce

1985. 850th Birth Anniv of Maimonides (physician, philosopher and scholar).
939 **201** $2 green . . . . 4·00 3·25

1985. International Youth Year. Multicoloured.
941 25c. Type **202** 20 20
942 50c. Hotel management trainees 35 40
943 60c. Girls with goat and boys with football ("Environment") 80 70
944 $3 Windsurfing ("Leisure") 2·50 4·50

1985. Life and Times of Queen Elizabeth the Queen Mother. Multicoloured.
946 $1 Type **203** 45 60
947 $1.50 Watching children playing in London garden 60 85
948 $2.50 The Queen Mother in 1979 . . . . 90 1·40
Stamps as Nos. 946/8, but with face values of 90c., $1 and $3 exist from additional sheetlets with changed background colours.

ANTIGUA & BARBUDA
15¢

Antigua & Barbuda
300th Birth Anniversary of Johann Sebastian Bach
Bass Trombone
25¢

204 Magnificent Frigate Bird **206** Bass Trombone

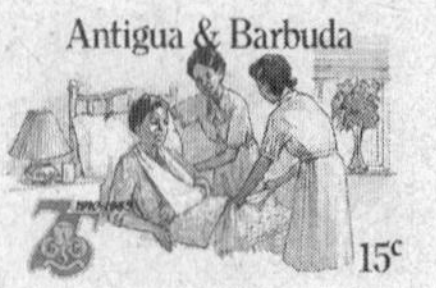
Antigua & Barbuda
15c

205 Girl Guides Nursing

1985. Marine Life. Multicoloured.
950 15c. Type **204** . . . . 1·00 30
951 45c. Brain coral . . . . . . 2·00 95
952 60c. Cushion star . . . . . 2·25 1·75
953 $3 Spotted moray . . . . . 7·00 9·00

1985. 75th Anniv of Girl Guide Movement. Multicoloured.
955 15c. Type **205** 75 20
956 45c. Open-air Girl Guide meeting . . . . 1·40 60
957 60c. Lord and Lady Baden-Powell . . . . 1·75 90
958 $3 Girl Guides gathering flowers . . . . 4·25 4·50

1985. 300th Birth Anniv of Johann Sebastian Bach (composer). Multicoloured.
960 25c. Type **206** . . . . 1·40 55

961 50c. English horn . . . . . 1·75 1·10
962 $1 Violino piccolo . . . . . 3·25 1·75
963 $3 Bass rackett . . . . . . 6·00 7·00

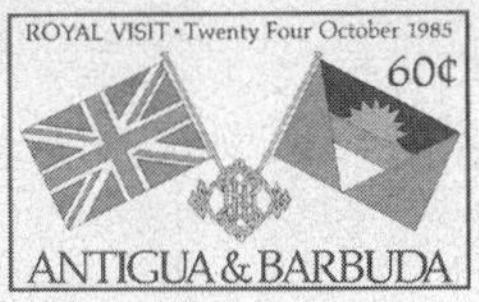

207 Flags of Great Britain and Antigua

1985. Royal Visit. Multicoloured.
965 60c. Type **207** . . . . 1·00 65
966 $1 Queen Elizabeth II (vert) 1·50 1·25
967 $4 Royal Yacht "Britannia" 3·25 6·00

1985. 150th Birth Anniv of Mark Twain (author). As T **118** of Anguilla showing Walt Disney cartoon characters in scenes from "Roughing It". Multicoloured.
969 25c. Donald Duck and Mickey Mouse meeting Indians 85 20
970 50c. Mickey Mouse, Donald Duck and Goofy canoeing 1·25 55
971 $1.10 Goofy as Pony Express rider . . . . 2·00 1·75
972 $1.50 Donald Duck and Goofy hunting buffalo . . 2·50 3·00
973 $2 Mickey Mouse and silver mine . . . . 3·00 4·00

1985. Birth Bicentenaries of Grimm Brothers (folklorists). As T **119** of Anguilla showing Walt Disney cartoon characters in scenes from "Spindle, Shuttle and Needle". Multicoloured.
975 30c. The Prince (Mickey Mouse) searches for a bride 90 40
976 60c. The Prince finds the Orphan Girl (Minnie Mouse) . . . . 1·25 80
977 70c. The Spindle finds the Prince . . . . 1·60 1·10
978 $1 The Needle tidies the Girl's house . . . . 2·00 1·75
979 $3 The Prince proposes . . . 4·25 6·00

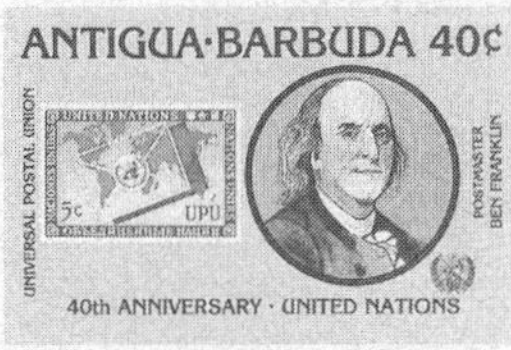

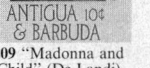

208 Benjamin Franklin and U.N. (New York) 1953 U.P.U. 5c. Stamp

1985. 40th Anniv of United Nations Organization. Multicoloured.
981 40c. Type **208** . . . . 1·00 70
982 $1 George Washington Carver (agricultural chemist) and 1982 Nature Conservation 28c. stamp 2·00 2·00
983 $3 Charles Lindbergh (aviator) and 1978 I.C.A.O. 25c. stamp . . . . . . 4·75 7·00
Nos. 981/3 each include a United Nations (New York) stamp design.

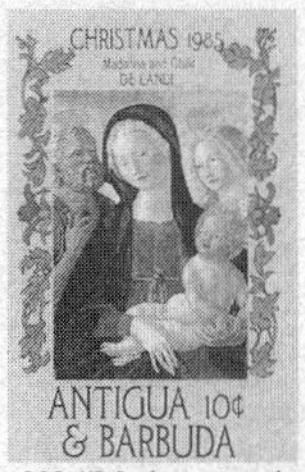

209 "Madonna and Child" (De Landi)

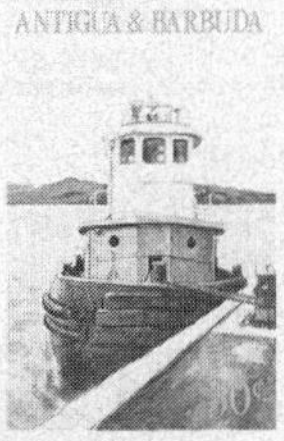

211 Tug

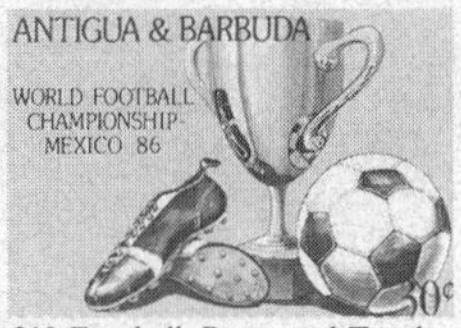

210 Football, Boots and Trophy

1985. Christmas. Religious Paintings. Mult.
985 10c. Type **209** 30 15
986 25c. "Madonna and Child" (Berlinghiero) 55 25
987 60c. "The Nativity" (Fra Angelico) 70 60
988 $4 "Presentation in the Temple" (Giovanni di Paolo) . . . . 1·75 4·25

1986. Birth Bicentenary of John J. Audubon (ornithologist) (2nd issue). As T **198** showing original paintings. Multicoloured.
990 60c. Mallard . . . . 2·25 1·50
991 90c. North American black duck ("Dusky Duck") . . 2·75 2·00
992 $1.50 Pintail ("Common Pintail") . . . . 3·50 4·50
993 $3 American wigeon ("Wigeon") . . . . 4·75 6·50

1986. World Cup Football Championship, Mexico. Multicoloured.
995 30c. Type **210** . . . . 1·50 40
996 60c. Goalkeeper (vert) . . . 2·00 85
997 $1 Referee blowing whistle (vert) . . . . 2·50 1·75
998 $4 Ball in net . . . . 6·50 9·00

1986. Appearance of Halley's Comet (1st issue). As T **123** of Anguilla. Multicoloured.
1000 5c. Edmond Halley and Old Greenwich Observatory 30 20
1001 10c. Messerschmitt Me 163B Komet (fighter aircraft), 1944 . . . . 30 15
1002 60c. Montezuma (Aztec emperor) and Comet in 1517 (from "Historias de las Indias de Neuva Espana") . . . . 1·50 70
1003 $4 Pocahontas saving Capt. John Smith and Comet in 1607 . . . . 4·50 5·50
See also Nos. 1047/50.

1986. 60th Birthday of Queen Elizabeth II. As T **125** of Anguilla.
1005 60c. black and yellow . . . 30 35
1006 $1 multicoloured 50 55
1007 $4 multicoloured . . . . . 1·40 1·90
DESIGNS: 60c. Wedding photograph, 1947; $1 Queen at Trooping the Colour; $4 In Scotland.

1986. Local Boats. Multicoloured.
1009 30c. Type **211** 25 20
1010 60c. Game fishing boat . . 45 35
1011 $1 Yacht 75 60
1012 $4 Lugger with auxiliary sail 2·50 3·25

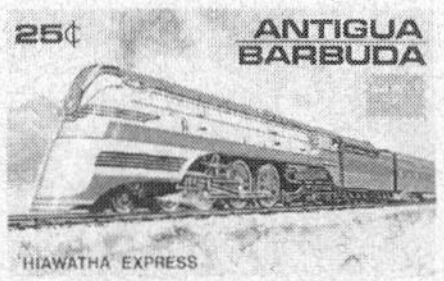

212 "Hiawatha" express

1986. "Ameripex '86" International Stamp Exhibition, Chicago. Famous American Trains. Multicoloured.
1014 25c. Type **212** . . . . . . 1·00 40
1015 50c. "Grand Canyon" express . . . . 1·25 75
1016 $1 "Powhattan Arrow" express . . . . 1·50 1·75
1017 $3 "Empire State" express 3·00 6·50

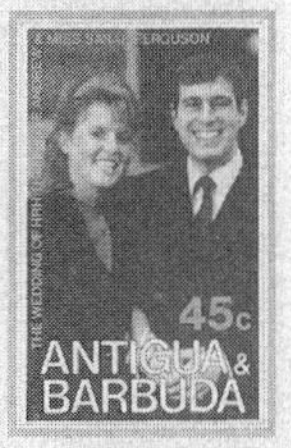

213 Prince Andrew and Miss Sarah Ferguson

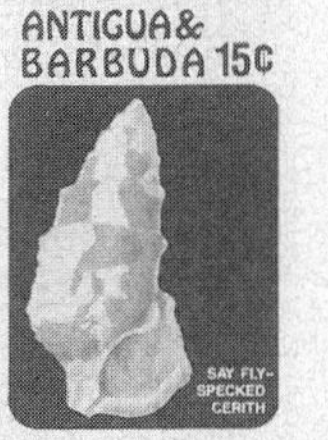

214 Fly-specked Cerith

1986. Royal Wedding. Multicoloured.
1019 45c. Type **213** 55 35
1020 60c. Prince Andrew 65 45
1021 $4 Prince Andrew with Prince Philip . . . . . . 2·50 3·50

1986. Sea Shells. Multicoloured.
1023 15c. Type **214** 75 50
1024 45c. Smooth Scotch bonnet 1·75 1·25
1025 60c. West Indian crown conch . . . . 2·00 2·00
1026 $3 Ciboney murex . . . . . 6·50 10·00

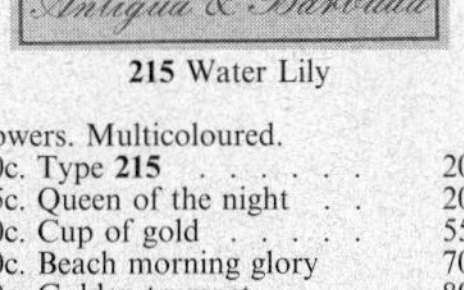

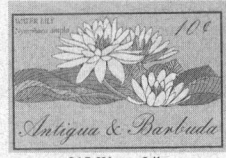

215 Water Lily

1986. Flowers. Multicoloured.
1028 10c. Type **215** 20 15
1029 15c. Queen of the night . . 20 15
1030 50c. Cup of gold 55 55
1031 60c. Beach morning glory 70 70
1032 70c. Golden trumpet 80 80
1033 $1 Air plant . . . . 90 1·10
1034 $4 Purple wreath . . . . . 1·75 3·00
1035 $4 Zephyr lily . . . . . . 2·00 3·75

1986. World Cup Football Championship Winners, Mexico. Nos. 995/8 optd **WINNERS Argentina 3 W.Germany 2**.
1037 30c. Type **210** . . . . . . 1·00 40
1038 60c. Goalkeeper (vert) . . . 1·50 75
1039 $1 Referee blowing whistle (vert) . . . . 2·00 1·10
1040 $4 Ball in net . . . . 5·00 4·50

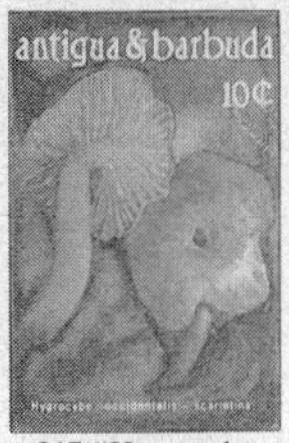

217 "Hygrocybe occidentalis var. scarletina"

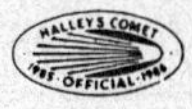

(218)

1986. Mushrooms. Multicoloured.
1042 10c. Type **217** 30 25
1043 50c. "Trogia buccinalis" . . 70 55
1044 $1 "Collybia subpruinosa" 1·25 1·25
1045 $4 "Leucocoprinus brebissonii" . . . . . . 3·00 4·50

1986. Appearance of Halley's Comet (2nd issue). Nos. 1000/3 optd with T **218**.
1047 5c. Edmond Halley and Old Greenwich Observatory 15 10
1048 10c. Messerschmitt Me 163B Komet (fighter aircraft), 1944 . . . . 20 10
1049 60c. Montezuma (Aztec emperor) and Comet in 1517 (from "Historias de las Indias de Neuva Espana") . . . . 1·00 65
1050 $4 Pocahontas saving Capt. John Smith and Comet in 1607 . . . . 4·50 4·00

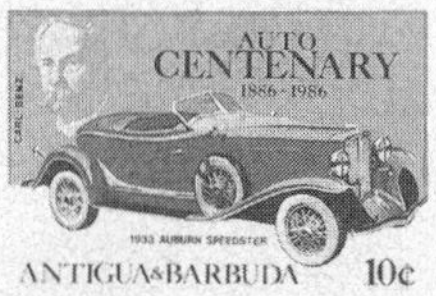

219 Auburn "Speedster" (1933)

1986. Centenary of First Benz Motor Car. Mult.
1052 10c. Type **219** 15 10
1053 15c. Mercury "Sable" (1986) 20 10
1054 50c. Cadillac (1959) 55 30
1055 60c. Studebaker (1950) . . . 70 45
1056 70c. Lagonda "V-12" (1939) 80 55
1057 $1 Adler "Standard" (1930) 1·10 75
1058 $3 DKW (1956) . . . . . . 2·50 2·50
1059 $4 Mercedes "500K" (1936) 3·00 3·00

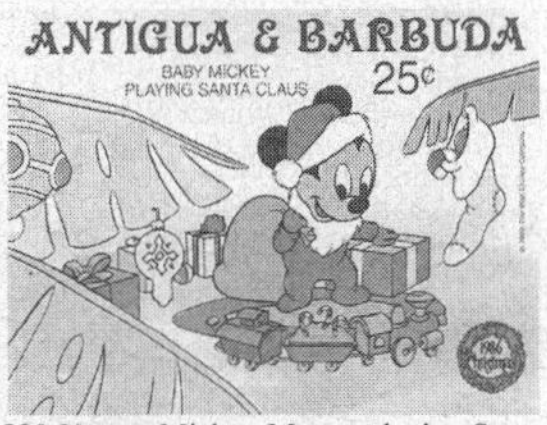

220 Young Mickey Mouse playing Santa Claus

1986. Christmas. Designs showing Walt Disney cartoon characters as babies. Multicoloured.
1061 25c. Type **220** 60 35
1062 30c. Mickey and Minnie Mouse building snowman 70 40
1063 40c. Aunt Matilda and Goofy baking 75 45
1064 60c. Goofy and Pluto . . . 1·00 85
1065 70c. Pluto, Donald and Daisy Duck carol singing 1·10 1·00
1066 $1.50 Donald Duck, Mickey Mouse and Pluto stringing popcorn . . . . 1·75 2·50
1067 $3 Grandma Duck and Minnie Mouse . . . . . 3·00 4·50
1068 $4 Donald Duck and Pete 3·25 4·50

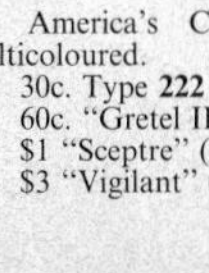

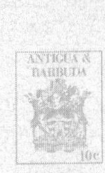

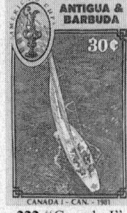

221 Arms of Antigua

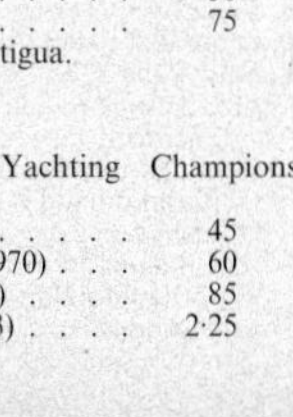

222 "Canada I" (1981)

1986.
1070 **221** 10c. blue 50 50
1071 – 25c. red 75 75
DESIGN: 25c. Flag of Antigua.

1987. America's Cup Yachting Championship. Multicoloured.
1072 30c. Type **222** 45 20
1073 60c. "Gretel II" (1970) . . . 60 50
1074 $1 "Sceptre" (1958) . . . . 85 1·00
1075 $3 "Vigilant" (1893) . . . . 2·25 3·00

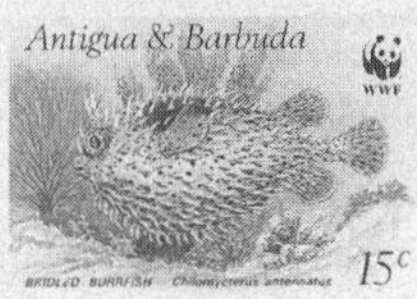

223 Bridled Burrfish

1987. Marine Life. Multicoloured.
1077 15c. Type **223** . . . . . . 2·50 50
1078 30c. Common noddy ("Brown Noddy") . . . . 4·50 60
1079 40c. Nassau grouper . . . . 3·00 70
1080 50c. Laughing gull . . . . 5·50 1·50
1081 60c. French angelfish . . . 3·50 1·50
1082 $1 Porkfish . . . . 3·50 1·75
1083 $2 Royal tern . . . . 7·50 6·00
1084 $3 Sooty tern . . . . 7·50 8·00
Nos. 1078, 1080 and 1083/4 are without the World Wildlife Fund logo shown on Type **223**.

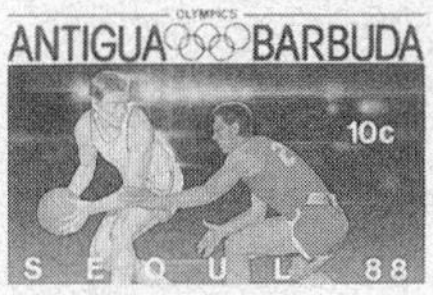

224 Handball

1987. Olympic Games, Seoul (1988) (1st issue). Multicoloured.
1086 10c. Type **224** 60 10
1087 60c. Fencing 85 35
1088 $1 Gymnastics . . . . . . 1·25 75
1089 $3 Football . . . . 2·50 4·00
See also Nos. 1222/5.

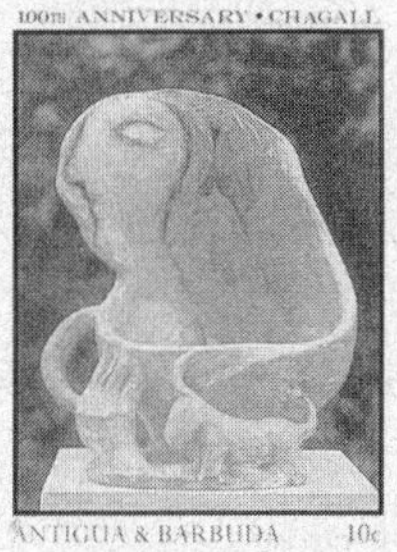

225 "The Profile"

1987. Birth Centenary of Marc Chagall (artist). Multicoloured.
1091 10c. Type **225** 30 15
1092 30c. "Portrait of the Artist's Sister" 45 30
1093 40c. "Bride with Fan" . . . 50 40
1094 60c. "David in Profile" . . 55 45
1095 90c. "Fiancee with Bouquet" 75 60
1096 $1 "Self Portrait with Brushes" 75 65
1097 $3 "The Walk" . . . . . . 1·75 2·25
1098 $4 "Three Candles" . . . . 2·00 2·50

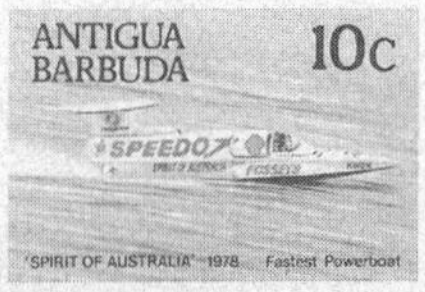

226 "Spirit of Australia" (fastest powerboat), 1978

1987. Milestones of Transportation. Multicoloured.
1100 10c. Type **226** 60 30
1101 15c. Werner von Siemens's electric locomotive, 1879 80 40
1102 30c. U.S.S. "Triton" (first submerged circum-navigation), 1960 . . . . 80 45
1103 50c. Trevithick's steam carriage (first passenger-carrying vehicle), 1801 . . 1·00 60
1104 60c. U.S.S. "New Jersey" (battleship), 1942 . . . . 1·00 70
1105 70c. Draisaine bicycle, 1818 1·00 80
1106 90c. "United States" (liner) (holder of Blue Riband), 1952 . . . . 1·00 1·00
1107 $1.50 Cierva C.4 (first autogyro), 1923 . . . . . 1·40 2·25
1108 $2 Curtiss NC-4 flying boat (first transatlantic flight), 1919 . . . . 1·50 2·50
1109 $3 "Queen Elizabeth 2" (liner), 1969 . . . . . . 2·50 3·50

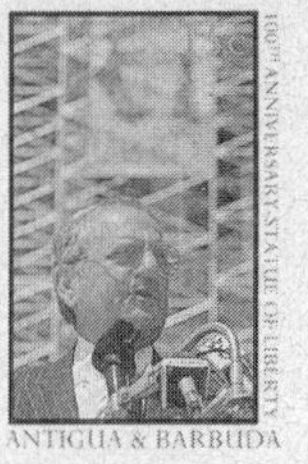
ANTIGUA & BARBUDA

227 Lee Iacocca at Unveiling of Restored Statue

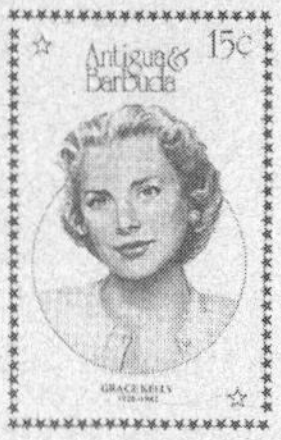
Antigua & Barbuda 15c

228 Grace Kelly

1987. Centenary of Statue of Liberty (1986) (2nd issue). Multicoloured.

1110	15c. Type **227**	15	15
1111	30c. Statue at sunset (side view)	20	20
1112	45c. Aerial view of head	30	30
1113	50c. Lee Iacocca and torch	35	35
1114	60c. Workmen inside head of Statue (horiz)	35	35
1115	90c. Restoration work (horiz)	50	50
1116	$1 Head of Statue	55	55
1117	$2 Statue at sunset (front view)	1·00	1·25
1118	$3 Inspecting restoration work (horiz)	1·25	1·75
1119	$5 Statue at night	2·00	3·00

1987. Entertainers. Multicoloured.

1120	15c. Type **228**	90	40
1121	30c. Marilyn Monroe	2·25	80
1122	45c. Orson Welles	90	60
1123	50c. Judy Garland	90	65
1124	60c. John Lennon	3·75	1·25
1125	$1 Rock Hudson	1·40	1·10
1126	$2 John Wayne	2·50	2·00
1127	$3 Elvis Presley	7·50	4·50

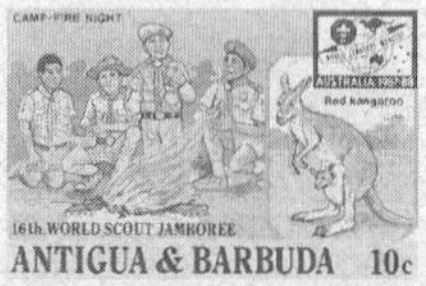
16th WORLD SCOUT JAMBOREE
ANTIGUA & BARBUDA 10c

229 Scouts around Camp Fire and Red Kangaroo

1987. 16th World Scout Jamboree, Australia. Mult.

1128	10c. Type **229**	65	20
1129	60c. Scouts canoeing and blue-winged kookaburra	1·25	80
1130	$1 Scouts on assault course and ring-tailed rock wallaby	1·00	85
1131	$3 Field kitchen and koala	1·50	4·25

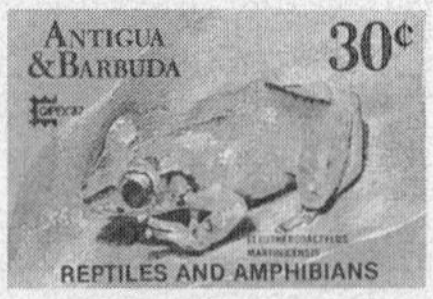
ANTIGUA & BARBUDA 30c
REPTILES AND AMPHIBIANS

230 Whistling Frog

1987. "Capex '87" International Stamp Exhibition, Toronto. Reptiles and Amphibians. Mult.

1133	30c. Type **230**	55	20
1134	60c. Croaking lizard	75	40
1135	$1 Antiguan anole	1·00	70
1136	$3 Red-footed tortoise	2·00	3·00

1987. 10th Death Anniv of Elvis Presley (entertainer). No. 1127 optd **10th ANNIVERSARY 16th AUGUST 1987**.

1138	$3 Elvis Presley	6·00	3·75

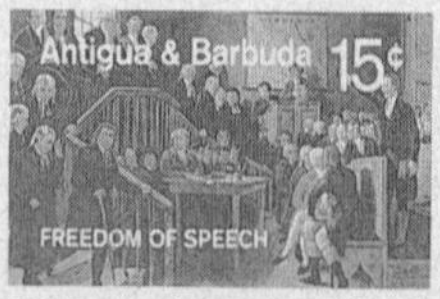
Antigua & Barbuda 15c
FREEDOM OF SPEECH

232 House of Burgesses, Virginia ("Freedom of Speech")

1987. Bicentenary of U.S. Constitution. Mult.

1139	15c. Type **232**	10	10
1140	45c. State Seal, Connecticut	20	25
1141	60c. State Seal, Delaware	25	35
1142	$4 Governor Morris (Pennsylvania delegate) (vert)	1·75	2·25

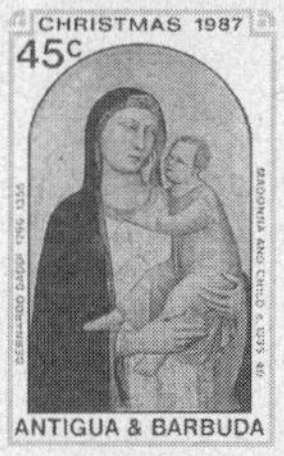
CHRISTMAS 1987
45c
ANTIGUA & BARBUDA

233 "Madonna and Child" (Bernardo Daddi)

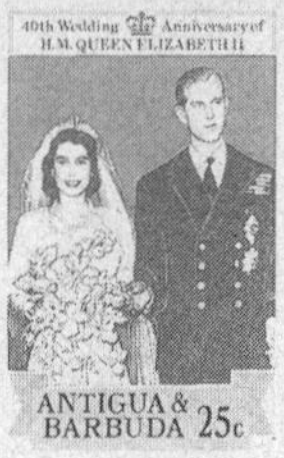
ANTIGUA & BARBUDA 25c

234 Wedding Photograph, 1947

1987. Christmas. Religious Paintings. Mult.

1144	45c. Type **233**	50	15
1145	60c. St. Joseph (detail, "The Nativity" (Sano di Pietro))	65	30
1146	$1 Virgin Mary (detail, "The Nativity" (Sano di Pietro))	85	55
1147	$4 "Music-making Angel" (Melozzo da Forli)	2·25	3·50

1988. Royal Ruby Wedding.

1149	**234** 25c. brown, black and blue	25	15
1150	– 60c. multicoloured	50	40
1151	– $2 brown, black and green	1·00	1·10
1152	– $3 multicoloured	2·75	1·60

DESIGNS: 60c. Queen Elizabeth II; $2 Princess Elizabeth and Prince Philip with Prince Charles at his christening, 1948; $3 Queen Elizabeth (from photo by Tim Graham), 1980.

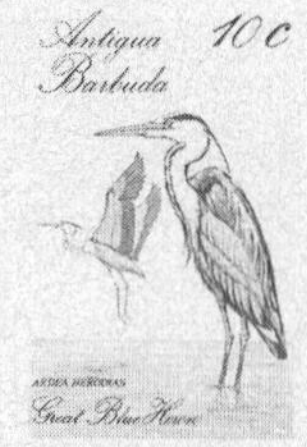
Antigua 10c
Barbuda
Great Blue Heron

235 Great Blue Heron

1988. Birds of Antigua. Multicoloured.

1154	10c. Type **235**	45	50
1155	15c. Ringed kingfisher (horiz)	50	40
1156	50c. Bananaquit (horiz)	90	50
1157	60c. American purple gallinule ("Purple Gallinule") (horiz)	90	50
1158	70c. Blue-hooded euphonia (horiz)	1·00	55
1159	$1 Brown-throated conure ("Caribbean Parakeet")	1·25	75
1160	$3 Troupial (horiz)	2·50	3·50
1161	$4 Purple-throated carib ("Hummingbird") (horiz)	2·50	3·50

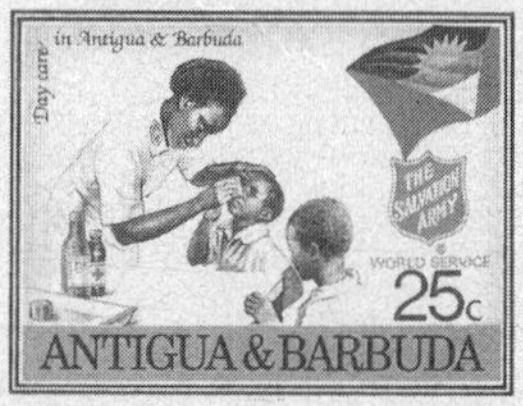
Day care in Antigua & Barbuda
25c
ANTIGUA & BARBUDA

236 First Aid at Daycare Centre, Antigua

1988. Salvation Army's Community Service. Multicoloured.

1163	25c. Type **236**	80	65
1164	30c. Giving penicillin injection, Indonesia	80	65
1165	40c. Children at daycare centre, Bolivia	90	75
1166	45c. Rehabilitation of the handicapped, India	90	75
1167	50c. Training blind man, Kenya	1·00	1·25
1168	60c. Weighing baby, Ghana	1·00	1·25
1169	$1 Training typist, Zambia	1·40	1·75
1170	$2 Emergency food kitchen, Sri Lanka	2·00	3·50

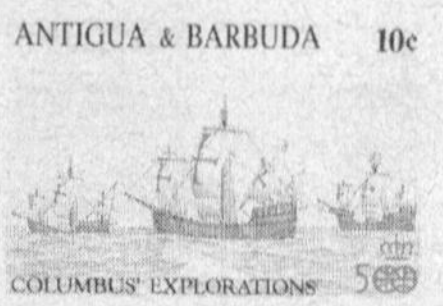
ANTIGUA & BARBUDA 10c
COLUMBUS' EXPLORATIONS

237 Columbus's Second Fleet, 1493

1988. 500th Anniv (1992) of Discovery of America by Columbus (1st issue). Multicoloured.

1172	10c. Type **237**	60	40
1173	30c. Painos Indian village and fleet	60	45
1174	45c. "Santa Mariagalante" (flagship) and Painos village	70	45
1175	60c. Painos Indians offering Columbus fruit and vegetables	70	50
1176	90c. Painos Indian and Columbus with scarlet macaw	1·25	1·00
1177	$1 Columbus landing on island	1·25	1·00
1178	$3 Spanish soldier and fleet	2·25	3·00
1179	$4 Fleet under sail	2·50	3·00

See also Nos. 1267/70, 1360/7, 1503/10, 1654/9 and 1670/1.

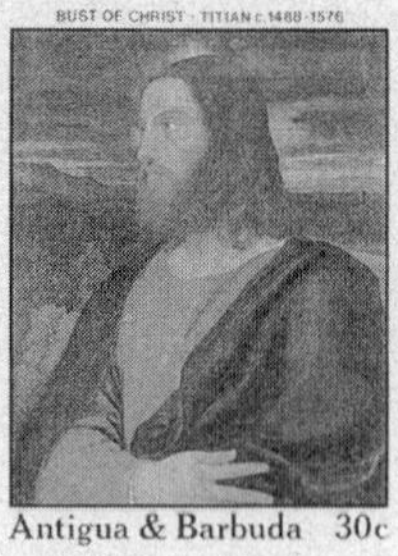
BUST OF CHRIST · TITIAN c.1488-1576
Antigua & Barbuda 30c

238 "Bust of Christ"

1988. Easter. 500th Birth Anniv of Titian (artist). Multicoloured.

1181	30c. Type **238**	40	20
1182	40c. "Scourging of Christ"	45	25
1183	45c. "Madonna in Glory with Saints"	45	25
1184	50c. "The Averoldi Polyptych" (detail)	45	35
1185	$1 "Christ Crowned with Thorns"	70	55
1186	$2 "Christ Mocked"	1·10	1·25
1187	$3 "Christ and Simon of Cyrene"	1·50	1·75
1188	$4 "Crucifixion with Virgin and Saints"	1·75	2·25

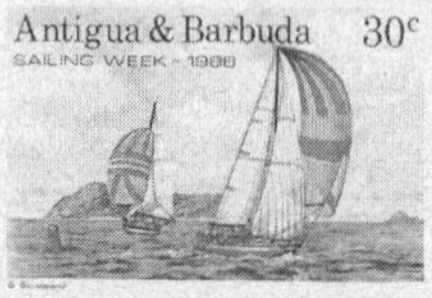
Antigua & Barbuda 30c
SAILING WEEK - 1988

239 Two Yachts rounding Buoy

1988. Sailing Week. Multicoloured.

1190	30c. Type **239**	35	20
1191	60c. Three yachts	50	40
1192	$1 British yacht under way	60	55
1193	$3 Three yachts (different)	1·10	2·50

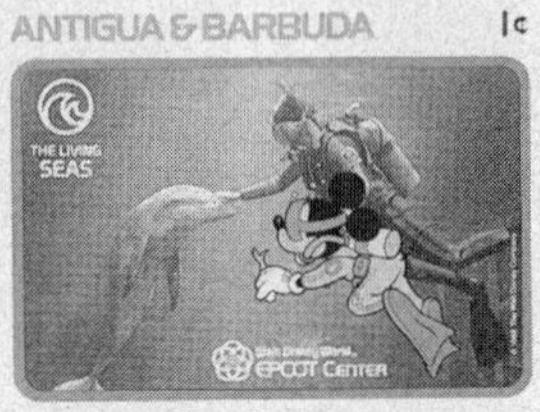
ANTIGUA & BARBUDA 1c
THE LIVING SEAS
EPCOT CENTER

240 Mickey Mouse and Diver with Porpoise

1988. Disney EPCOT Centre, Orlando, Florida. Designs showing cartoon characters and exhibits. Multicoloured.

1195	1c. Type **240**	10	10
1196	2c. Goofy and Mickey Mouse with futuristic car (vert)	10	10
1197	3c. Mickey Mouse and Goofy as Atlas (vert)	10	10
1198	4c. Mickey Mouse and "Eda-phosaurus" (prehistoric reptile)	10	10
1199	5c. Mickey Mouse at Journey into Imagination exhibit	10	10
1200	10c. Mickey Mouse collecting vegetables (vert)	15	10
1201	25c. Type **240**	45	25
1202	30c. As 2c.	45	25
1203	40c. As 3c.	55	30
1204	60c. As 4c.	75	50
1205	70c. As 5c.	85	60
1206	$1.50 As 10c.	1·75	1·75
1207	$3 Goofy and Mickey Mouse with robot (vert)	2·25	2·50
1208	$4 Mickey Mouse and Clarabelle at Horizons exhibit	2·25	2·50

1988. Stamp Exhibitions. Nos. 1083/4 optd.

1210	$2 Royal tern (optd **Praga '88**, Prague)	3·25	2·25
1211	$3 Sooty tern (optd **INDEPENDENCE 40**, Israel)	3·25	3·00

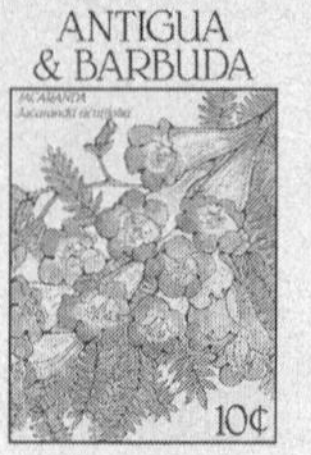
ANTIGUA & BARBUDA
10¢

242 Jacaranda

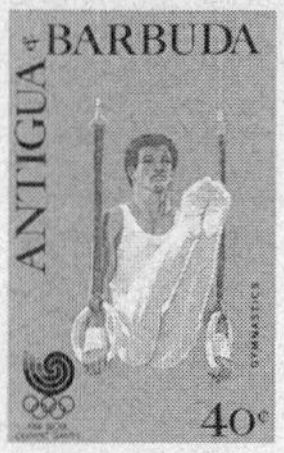
ANTIGUA BARBUDA
40c

243 Gymnastics

1988. Flowering Trees. Multicoloured.

1213	10c. Type **242**	30	20
1214	30c. Cordia	40	20
1215	50c. Orchid tree	60	40
1216	90c. Flamboyant	70	50
1217	$1 African tulip tree	75	55
1218	$2 Potato tree	1·40	1·60
1219	$3 Crepe myrtle	1·60	2·00
1220	$4 Pitch apple	1·75	2·75

1988. Olympic Games, Seoul (2nd issue). Mult.

1222	40c. Type **243**	30	25
1223	60c. Weightlifting	40	30
1224	$1 Water polo (horiz)	80	50
1225	$3 Boxing (horiz)	1·50	2·25

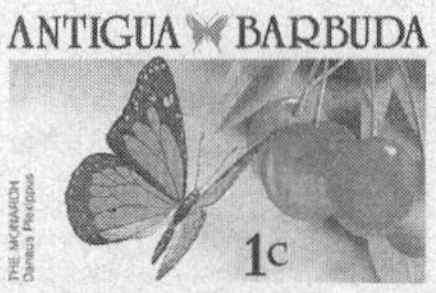
ANTIGUA BARBUDA
1c

244 "Danaus plexippus"

1988. Caribbean Butterflies. Multicoloured.

1227	1c. Type **244**	40	50
1228	2c. "Greta diaphanus"	50	60
1229	3c. "Calisto archebates"	50	60
1230	5c. "Hamadryas feronia"	60	60
1231	10c. "Mestra dorcas"	75	30
1232	15c. "Hypolimnas misippus"	1·00	30
1233	20c. "Dione juno"	1·10	30
1234	25c. "Heliconius charithonia"	1·10	30
1235	30c. "Eurema pyro"	1·10	30
1236	40c. "Papilio androgeus"	1·10	30
1237	45c. "Anteos maerula"	1·10	30
1238	50c. "Aphrissa orbis"	1·25	45
1239	60c. "Astraptes xagua"	1·40	60
1240	$1 "Heliopetes arsalte"	1·75	1·00
1241	$2 "Polites baracoa"	2·75	3·50
1242	$2.50 "Phocides pigmalion"	3·25	4·50
1243	$5 "Prepona amphitoe"	5·00	6·50
1244	$10 "Oarisma nanus"	7·00	9·50
1244a	$20 "Parides lycimenes"	14·00	16·00

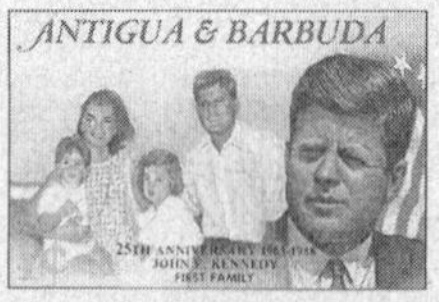
ANTIGUA & BARBUDA

245 President Kennedy and Family

1988. 25th Death Anniv of John F. Kennedy (American statesman). Multicoloured.

1245	1c. Type **245**	10	10
1246	2c. Kennedy commanding "PT109"	10	10
1247	3c. Funeral cortege	10	10
1248	4c. In motorcade, Mexico City	10	10
1249	30c. As 1c.	35	15
1250	60c. As 4c.	60	40
1251	$1 As 3c.	75	75
1252	$4 As 2c.	2·25	3·25

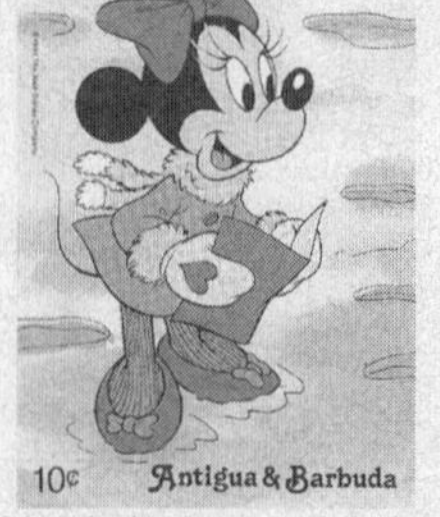
10c Antigua & Barbuda

246 Minnie Mouse carol singing

1988. Christmas. "Mickey's Christmas Chorale". Design showing Walt Disney cartoon characters. Multicoloured.

1254	10c. Type **246**	30	30
1255	25c. Pluto	45	45
1256	30c. Mickey Mouse playing ukelele	45	45
1257	70c. Donald Duck and nephew	80	80
1258	$1 Mordie and Ferdie carol singing	80	1·00
1259	$1 Goofy carol singing	80	1·00
1260	$1 Chip n'Dale sliding off roof	80	1·00
1261	$1 Two of Donald Duck's nephews at window	80	1·00
1262	$1 As 10c.	80	1·00

1263 $1 As 25c. .... 80 1·00
1264 $1 As 30c. .... 80 1·00
1265 $1 As 70c. .... 80 1·00
Nos. 1258/65 were printed together, se-tenant, forming a composite design.

247 Arawak Warriors

1989. 500th Anniv of Discovery of America by Columbus (1992) (2nd issue). Pre-Columbian Arawak Society. Multicoloured.
1267 $1.50 Type **247** ...... 1·10 1·40
1268 $1.50 Whip dancers ... 1·10 1·40
1269 $1.50 Whip dancers and chief with pineapple ... 1·10 1·40
1270 $1.50 Family and camp fire ... 1·10 1·40
Nos. 1267/70 were printed together, se-tenant, forming a composite design.

248 De Havilland Comet 4 Airliner

1989. 50th Anniv of First Jet Flight. Mult.
1272 10c. Type **248** 70 45
1273 30c. Messerschmitt Me 262 fighter .... 1·25 45
1274 40c. Boeing 707 airliner . 1·25 45
1275 60c. Canadair CL-13 Sabre (inscr "F-86") fighter . 1·50 55
1276 $1 Lockheed F-104 Starfighters .... 1·75 90
1277 $2 McDonnell Douglas DC-10 airliner .... 2·50 2·50
1278 $3 Boeing 747-300/400 airliner .... 2·75 4·00
1279 $4 McDonnell Douglas F-4 Phantom II fighter ... 2·75 4·00

249 "Festivale"

1989. Caribbean Cruise Ships. Multicoloured.
1281 25c. Type **249** ...... 1·00 40
1282 45c. "Southward" .... 1·25 40
1283 50c. "Sagafjord" .... 1·25 40
1284 60c. "Daphne" ..... 1·25 50
1285 75c. "Cunard Countess" . 1·40 1·10
1286 90c. "Song of America" . 1·50 1·10
1287 $3 "Island Princess" .. 3·00 4·50
1288 $4 "Galileo" ...... 3·00 4·50

250 "Fish swimming by Duck half-submerged in Stream"

1989. Japanese Art. Paintings by Hiroshige. Mult.
1290 25c. Type **250** 80 30
1291 45c. "Crane and Wave" .. 1·00 40
1292 50c. "Sparrows and Morning Glories" .... 1·10 40
1293 60c. "Crested Blackbird and Flowering Cherry" ... 1·25 50
1294 $1 "Great Knot sitting among Water Grass" .. 1·50 70
1295 $2 "Goose on a Bank of Water" .... 2·25 2·25
1296 $3 "Black Paradise Flycatcher and Blossoms" . 2·75 2·75
1297 $4 "Sleepy Owl perched on a Pine Branch" ... 2·75 2·75

251 Mickey and Minnie Mouse in Helicopter over River Seine

1989. "Philexfrance 89" International Stamp Exhibition, Paris. Walt Disney cartoon characters in Paris. Multicoloured.
1299 1c. Type **251** 10 10
1300 2c. Goofy and Mickey Mouse passing Arc de Triomphe 10 10
1301 3c. Mickey Mouse painting picture of Notre Dame ... 10 10
1302 4c. Mickey and Minnie Mouse with Pluto leaving Metro station 10 10
1303 5c. Minnie Mouse as model in fashion show 10 10
1304 10c. Daisy Duck, Minnie Mouse and Clarabelle as Folies Bergere dancers . 10 10
1305 $5 Mickey and Minnie Mouse shopping in street market .... 6·50 6·50
1306 $6 Mickey and Minnie Mouse, Jose Carioca and Donald Duck at pavement cafe .... 6·50 6·50

252 Goalkeeper

1989. World Cup Football Championship, Italy (1990). Multicoloured.
1308 15c. Type **252** 85 30
1309 25c. Goalkeeper moving towards ball 90 30
1310 $1 Goalkeeper reaching for ball .... 2·00 1·25
1311 $4 Goalkeeper saving goal 3·50 5·00

253 "Mycena pura"

1989. Fungi. Multicoloured.
1313 10c. Type **253** 75 50
1314 25c. "Psathyrella tuberculata" (vert) .... 1·10 40
1315 50c. "Psilocybe cubensis" .. 1·50 60
1316 60c. "Leptonia caeruleocapitata" (vert) . 1·50 70
1317 75c. "Xeromphalina tenuipes" (vert) .... 1·75 1·10
1318 $1 "Chlorophyllum molybdites" (vert) ... 1·75 1·25
1319 $3 "Marasmius haematocephalus" .... 2·75 3·75
1320 $4 "Cantharellus cinnabarinus" ...... 2·75 3·75

254 Desmarest's Hutia

1989. Local Fauna. Multicoloured.
1322 25c. Type **254** 80 50
1323 45c. Caribbean monk seal . 2·50 1·00
1324 80c. Mustache bat (vert) . 1·50 1·00
1325 $4 American manatee (vert) 3·50 5·50

255 Goofy and Old Printing Press

258 Launch of "Apollo II"

256 Mickey Mouse and Donald Duck with Camden and Amboy Locomotive "John Bull", 1831

1989. "American Philately". Walt Disney cartoon characters with stamps and the logo of the American Philatelic Society. Multicoloured.
1327 1c. Type **255** 10 10
1328 2c. Donald Duck cancelling first day cover for Mickey Mouse 10 10
1329 3c. Donald Duck's nephews reading recruiting poster for Pony Express riders 10 10
1330 4c. Morty and Ferdie as early radio broadcasters . 10 10
1331 5c. Donald Duck and water buffalo watching television 10 10
1332 10c. Donald Duck with stamp album 10 10
1333 $4 Daisy Duck with computer system .... 4·00 5·00
1334 $6 Donald's nephews with stereo radio, trumpet and guitar .... 5·00 6·00

1989. "World Stamp Expo '89" International Stamp Exhibition, Washington. Walt Disney cartoon characters and locomotives. Mult.
1336 25c. Type **256** 75 50
1337 45c. Mickey Mouse and friends with "Atlantic", 1832 .... 90 50
1338 50c. Mickey Mouse and Goofy with "William Crooks", 1861 .... 90 50
1339 60c. Mickey Mouse and Goofy with "Minnetonka", 1869 ... 90 65
1340 $1 Chip n'Dale with "Thatcher Perkins", 1863 1·00 75
1341 $2 Mickey and Minnie Mouse with "Pioneer", 1848 .... 1·75 2·25
1342 $3 Mickey Mouse and Donald Duck with cog railway locomotive "Peppersass", 1869 ... 2·00 3·00
1343 $4 Mickey Mouse with Huey, Dewey and Louie aboard N.Y. World's Fair "Gimbels Flyer", 1939 . 2·25 3·00

1989. 20th Anniv of First Manned Landing on Moon. Multicoloured.
1346 10c. Type **258** 50 30
1347 45c. Aldrin on Moon ... 1·25 30
1348 $1 Module "Eagle" over Moon (horiz) ..... 1·75 1·10
1349 $4 Recovery of "Apollo II" crew after splashdown (horiz) .... 2·75 5·00

259 "The Small Cowper Madonna" (Raphael)
260 Star-eyed Hermit Crab

1989. Christmas. Paintings by Raphael and Giotto. Multicoloured.
1351 10c. Type **259** 30 15
1352 25c. "Madonna of the Goldfinch" (Raphael) . 45 20
1353 30c. "The Alba Madonna" (Raphael) 45 20
1354 50c. Saint (detail, "Bologna Altarpiece") (Giotto) .. 65 30
1355 60c. Angel (detail, "Bologna Altarpiece") (Giotto) . 70 35

1356 70c. Angel slaying serpent (detail, "Bologna Altarpiece") (Giotto) ... 80 40
1357 $4 Evangelist (detail, "Bologna Altarpiece") (Giotto) .... 3·00 4·25
1358 $5 "Madonna of Foligno" (detail) (Raphael) .... 3·00 4·25

1990. 500th Anniv (1992) of Discovery of America by Columbus (3rd issue). New World Natural History–Marine Life. Multicoloured.
1360 10c. Type **260** 45 20
1361 20c. Spiny lobster 65 25
1362 25c. Magnificent banded fanworm 65 25
1363 45c. Cannonball jellyfish . 80 40
1364 60c. Red-spiny sea star .. 1·00 60
1365 $2 Peppermint shrimp .. 2·00 2·50
1366 $3 Coral crab ...... 2·25 3·50
1367 $4 Branching fire coral . 2·25 3·50

261 "Vanilla mexicana"
262 Queen Victoria and Queen Elizabeth II

1990. "Expo '90" International Garden and Greenery Exhibition, Osaka. Orchids. Multicoloured.
1369 15c. Type **261** 75 50
1370 45c. "Epidendrum ibaguense" ...... 1·10 50
1371 50c. "Epidendrum secundum" ...... 1·25 55
1372 60c. "Maxillaria conferta" . 1·40 55
1373 $1 "Oncidium altissimum" 1·50 1·00
1374 $2 "Spiranthes lanceolata" 2·00 2·50
1375 $3 "Tonopsis utricularioides" ..... 2·25 3·50
1376 $5 "Epidendrum nocturnum" ...... 3·25 4·50

1990. 150th Anniv of the Penny Black.
1378 **262** 45c. green 85 40
1379 — 60c. mauve .... 1·00 65
1380 — $5 blue ..... 3·50 5·50
DESIGNS: 60c., $5 As Type **262**, but with different backgrounds.

263 "Britannia" (mail paddle-steamer), 1840

1990. "Stamp World London '90" International Stamp Exhibition.
1382 **263** 50c. green and red ... 85 35
1383 — 75c. brown and red ... 1·10 90
1384 — $4 blue and red ... 3·75 5·50
DESIGNS: 75c. Travelling Post Office sorting van, 1892; $4 Short S.23 Empire "C" Class flying boat "Centaurus", 1938.

264 Flamefish

1990. Reef Fishes. Multicoloured.
1386 10c. Type **264** 65 55
1387 15c. Coney 80 55
1388 50c. Long-spined squirrelfish 1·25 60
1389 60c. Sergeant major ... 1·25 60
1390 $1 Yellow-tailed snapper . 1·50 85
1391 $2 Rock beauty .... 2·25 2·75
1392 $3 Spanish hogfish ... 2·75 3·75
1393 $4 Striped parrotfish .... 2·75 3·75

265 "Voyager 2" passing Saturn
266 Queen Mother in Evening Dress

1990. Achievement in Space. Multicoloured.
1395 45c. Type **265** 75 75
1396 45c. "Pioneer 11" photographing Saturn ... 75 75

106 ANTIGUA

1397	45c. Astronaut in transporter	75	75
1398	45c. Space shuttle "Columbia"	75	75
1399	45c. "Apollo 10" command module on parachutes	75	75
1400	45c. "Skylab" space station	75	75
1401	45c. Astronaut Edward White in space	75	75
1402	45c. "Apollo" spacecraft on joint mission	75	75
1403	45c. "Soyuz" spacecraft on joint mission	75	75
1404	45c. "Mariner 1" passing Venus	75	75
1405	45c. "Gemini 4" capsule	75	75
1406	45c. "Sputnik 1"	75	75
1407	45c. Hubble space telescope	75	75
1408	45c. North American X-15 rocket plane	75	75
1409	45c. Bell XS-1 airplane	75	75
1410	45c. "Apollo 17" astronaut and lunar rock formation	75	75
1411	45c. Lunar Rover	75	75
1412	45c. "Apollo 14" lunar module	75	75
1413	45c. Astronaut Buzz Aldrin on Moon	75	75
1414	45c. Soviet "Lunokhod" lunar vehicle	75	75

1990. 90th Birthday of Queen Elizabeth the Queen Mother.

1415	**266** 15c. multicoloured	55	20
1416	– 35c. multicoloured	75	25
1417	– 75c. multicoloured	1·00	85
1418	– $3 multicoloured	2·50	3·50

DESIGNS: Nos. 1416/18, Recent photographs of the Queen Mother.

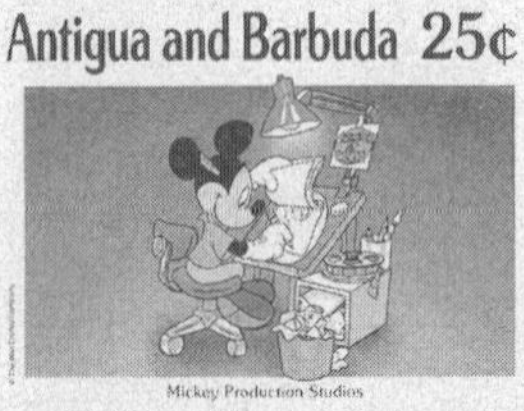
Antigua and Barbuda 25¢
Mickey Production Studios

267 Mickey Mouse as Animator

1990. Mickey Mouse in Hollywood. Walt Disney cartoon characters. Multicoloured.

1420	25c. Type **267**	60	25
1421	45c. Minnie Mouse learning lines while being dressed	80	25
1422	50c. Mickey Mouse with clapper board	90	30
1423	60c. Daisy Duck making-up Mickey Mouse	1·00	35
1424	$1 Clarabelle Cow as Cleopatra	1·25	70
1425	$2 Mickey Mouse directing Goofy and Donald Duck	1·75	2·25
1426	$3 Mickey Mouse directing Goofy as birdman	2·25	3·00
1427	$4 Donald Duck and Mickey Mouse editing film	2·25	3·00

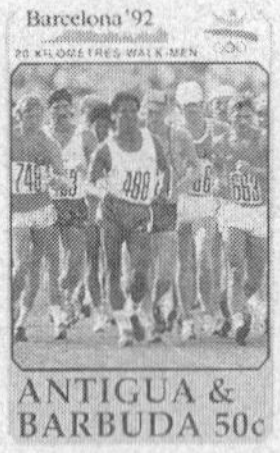
Barcelona'92
ANTIGUA &
BARBUDA 50c

268 Men's 20 Kilometres Walk

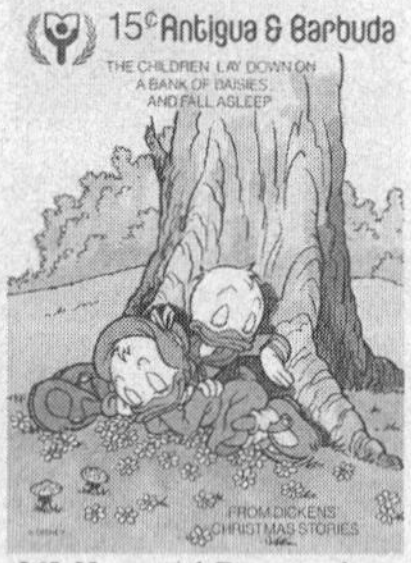
15c Antigua & Barbuda
THE CHILDREN LAY DOWN ON A BANK OF DAISIES AND FALL ASLEEP

269 Huey and Dewey asleep ("Christmas Stories")

1990. Olympic Games, Barcelona (1992) (1st issue). Multicoloured.

1429	50c. Type **268**	75	40
1430	75c. Triple jump	1·00	75
1431	$1 Men's 10,000 metres	1·25	85
1432	$5 Javelin	3·50	5·50

See also Nos. 1553/60 and 1609/16.

1990. International Literacy Year. Walt Disney cartoon characters illustrating works by Charles Dickens. Multicoloured.

1434	15c. Type **269**	65	35
1435	45c. Donald Duck as Poor Jo looking at grave ("Bleak House")	1·00	45
1436	50c. Dewey as Oliver asking for more ("Oliver Twist")	1·10	50
1437	60c. Daisy Duck as The Marchioness ("Old Curiosity Shop")	1·25	55
1438	$1 Little Nell giving nosegay to her grandfather ("Little Nell")	1·40	85
1439	$2 Scrooge McDuck as Mr. Pickwick ("Pickwick Papers")	2·00	2·25
1440	$3 Minnie Mouse as Florence and Mickey Mouse as Paul ("Dombey and Son")	2·25	3·25
1441	$5 Minnie Mouse as Jenny Wren ("Our Mutual Friend")	2·75	4·25

1990. World Cup Football Championship Winners, Italy. Nos. 1308/11 optd **Winners West Germany 1 Argentina 0**.

1443	15c. Type **252**	75	40
1444	25c. Goalkeeper moving towards ball	75	40
1445	$1 Goalkeeper reaching for ball	1·75	1·60
1446	$4 Goalkeeper saving goal	3·75	5·50

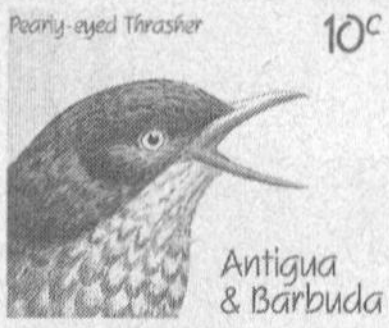
Pearly-eyed Thrasher
10c
Antigua
& Barbuda

271 Pearly-eyed Thrasher

1990. Birds. Multicoloured.

1448	10c. Type **271**	45	30
1449	25c. Purple-throated carib	45	35
1450	50c. Common yellowthroat	50	40
1451	60c. American kestrel	1·00	70
1452	$1 Yellow-bellied sapsucker	1·00	80
1453	$2 American purple gallinule ("Purple Gallinule")	2·00	2·25
1454	$3 Yellow-crowned night heron	2·10	2·75
1455	$4 Blue-hooded euphonia	2·10	2·75

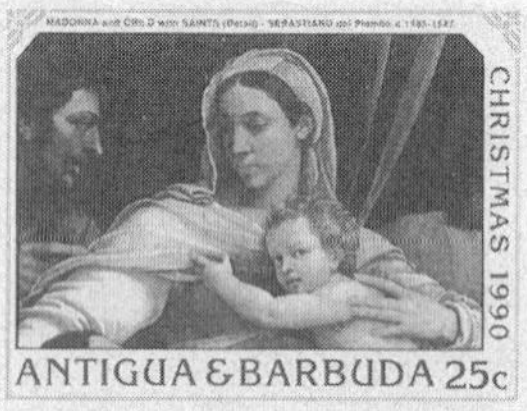
CHRISTMAS 1990
ANTIGUA & BARBUDA 25c

272 "Madonna and Child with Saints" (detail, Sebastiano del Piombo)

1990. Christmas. Paintings by Renaissance Masters. Multicoloured.

1457	25c. Type **272**	60	30
1458	30c. "Virgin and Child with Angels" (detail, Grunewald) (vert)	70	30
1459	40c. "The Holy Family and a Shepherd" (detail, Titian)	80	30
1460	60c. "Virgin and Child" (detail, Lippi) (vert)	1·00	40
1461	$1 "Jesus, St. John and Two Angels" (Rubens)	1·25	70
1462	$2 "Adoration of the Shepherds" (detail, Vincenzo Catena)	1·75	2·00
1463	$4 "Adoration of the Magi" (detail, Giorgione)	2·75	3·75
1464	$5 "Virgin and Child adored by Warrior" (detail, Vincenzo Catena)	2·75	3·75

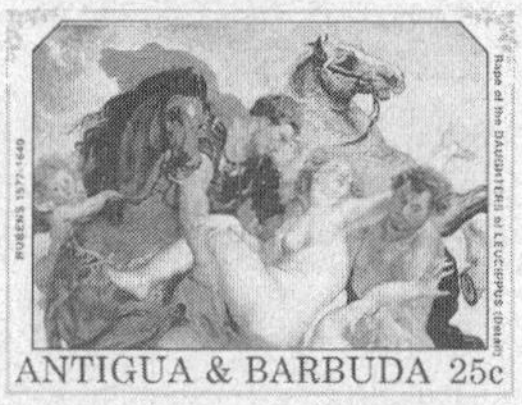
ANTIGUA & BARBUDA 25c

273 "Rape of the Daughters of Leucippus" (detail)

1991. 350th Death Anniv of Rubens. Mult.

1466	25c. Type **273**	75	40
1467	45c. "Bacchanal" (detail)	1·00	45
1468	50c. "Rape of the Sabine Women" (detail)	1·10	50
1469	60c. "Battle of the Amazons" (detail)	1·25	65
1470	$1 "Rape of the Sabine Women" (different detail)	1·50	1·00
1471	$2 "Bacchanal" (different detail)	2·00	2·25
1472	$3 "Rape of the Sabine Women" (different detail)	2·50	3·50
1473	$4 "Bacchanal" (different detail)	2·50	3·50

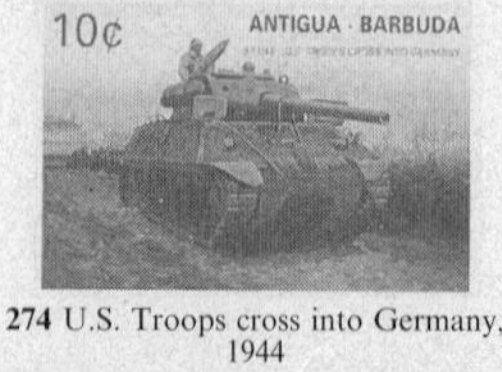
10¢
ANTIGUA · BARBUDA

274 U.S. Troops cross into Germany, 1944

1991. 50th Anniv of Second World War. Mult.

1475	10c. Type **274**	80	55
1476	15c. Axis surrender in North Africa, 1943	90	40
1477	25c. U.S. tanks invade Kwalajalein, 1944	90	40
1478	45c. Roosevelt and Churchill meet at Casablanca, 1943	1·75	70
1479	50c. Marshal Badoglio, Prime Minister of Italian anti-fascist government, 1943	1·00	70
1480	$1 Lord Mountbatten, Supreme Allied Commander South-east Asia, 1943	2·25	1·25
1481	$2 Greek victory at Koritza, 1940	2·00	2·50
1482	$4 Anglo-Soviet mutual assistance pact, 1941	2·50	3·50
1483	$5 Operation Torch landings, 1942	2·50	3·50

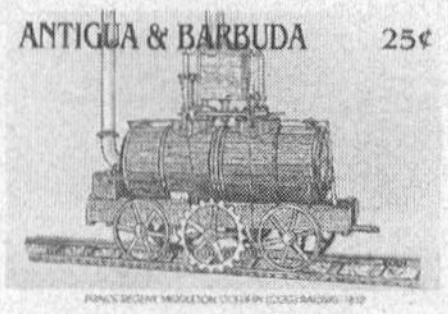
ANTIGUA & BARBUDA 25¢

275 Locomotive "Prince Regent", Middleton Colliery, 1812

1991. Cog Railways. Multicoloured.

1485	25c. Type **275**	1·00	55
1486	30c. Snowdon Mountain Railway	1·00	55
1487	40c. First railcar at Hell Gate, Manitou Pike's Peak Railway, U.S.A	1·10	65
1488	60c. P.N.K.A. rack railway, Java	1·40	70
1489	$1 Green Mountain Railway, Maine, 1883	1·75	1·00
1490	$2 Rack locomotive "Pike's Peak", 1891	2·50	2·75
1491	$4 Vitznau–Rigi Railway, Switzerland, and Mt. Rigi hotel local post stamp	3·25	4·25
1492	$5 Leopoldina Railway, Brazil	3·25	4·25

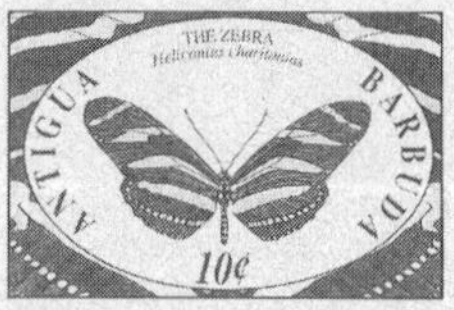
THE ZEBRA
ANTIGUA
BARBUDA
10¢

276 "Heliconius charithonia"

1991. Butterflies. Multicoloured.

1494	10c. Type **276**	65	50
1495	35c. "Marpesia petreus"	1·10	50
1496	50c. "Anartia amathea"	1·25	60
1497	75c. "Siproeta stelenes"	1·50	1·00
1498	$1 "Battus polydamas"	1·75	1·10
1499	$2 "Historis odius"	2·25	2·75
1500	$4 "Hypolimnas misippus"	3·25	4·25
1501	$5 "Hamadryas feronia"	3·25	4·25

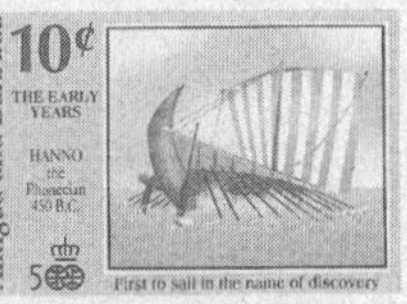
10¢
Antigua and Barbuda
THE EARLY YEARS
HANNO
First to sail in the name of discovery

277 Hanno the Phoenician, 450 B.C.

1991. 500th Anniv (1992) of Discovery of America by Columbus (4th issue). History of Exploration.

1503	10c. Type **277**	60	40
1504	15c. Pytheas the Greek, 325 B.C.	70	40
1505	45c. Erik the Red discovering Greenland, 985 A.D.	1·00	50
1506	60c. Leif Eriksson reaching Vinland, 1000 A.D.	1·25	60
1507	$1 Scylax the Greek in the Indian Ocean, 518 A.D.	1·50	85
1508	$2 Marco Polo sailing to the Orient, 1259 A.D.	2·00	2·50
1509	$4 Ship of Queen Hatshepsut of Egypt, 1493 B.C.	2·75	2·75
1510	$5 St. Brendan's coracle, 500 A.D.	2·75	2·75

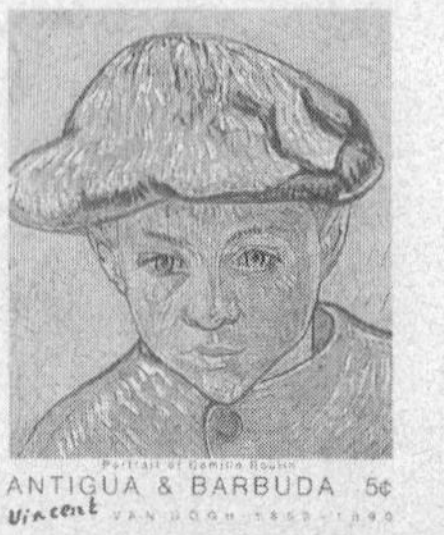
ANTIGUA & BARBUDA 5¢
Vincent

278 "Camille Roulin" (Van Gogh)

1991. Death Centenary (1990) of Vincent van Gogh (artist). Multicoloured.

1512	5c. Type **278**	50	60
1513	10c. "Armand Roulin"	50	50
1514	15c. "Young Peasant Woman with Straw Hat sitting in the Wheat"	65	50
1515	25c. "Adeline Ravoux"	75	50
1516	30c. "The Schoolboy"	75	50
1517	40c. "Doctor Gachet"	85	50
1518	50c. "Portrait of a Man"	90	50
1519	75c. "Two Children"	1·40	70
1520	$2 "The Postman Joseph Roulin"	2·25	2·50
1521	$3 "The Seated Zouave"	2·75	3·50
1522	$4 "L'Arlesienne"	3·00	3·75
1523	$5 "Self-Portrait, November/December 1888"	3·25	4·00

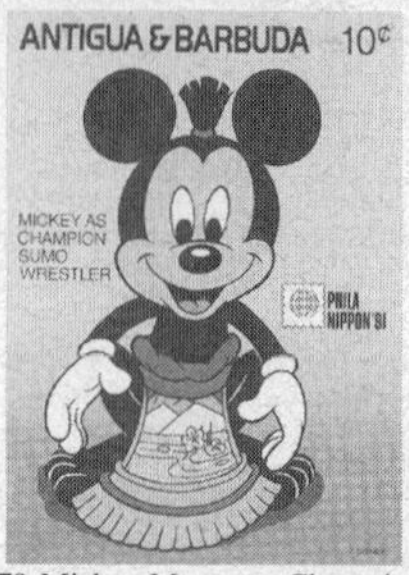
ANTIGUA & BARBUDA 10¢
MICKEY AS CHAMPION SUMO WRESTLER
PHILA NIPPON '91

279 Mickey Mouse as Champion Sumo Wrestler

1991. "Philanippon '91" International Stamp Exhibition, Tokyo. Walt Disney cartoon characters participating in martial arts. Multicoloured.

1525	10c. Type **279**	60	20
1526	15c. Goofy using the tonfa (horiz)	75	25
1527	45c. Donald Duck as a Ninja (horiz)	1·25	50
1528	60c. Mickey armed for Kung fu	1·60	65
1529	$1 Goofy with Kendo sword	2·00	1·25
1530	$2 Mickey and Donald demonstrating Aikido (horiz)	2·50	2·50
1531	$4 Mickey and Donald in Judo bout (horiz)	3·25	4·50
1532	$5 Mickey performing Yabusame (mounted archery)	3·25	4·50

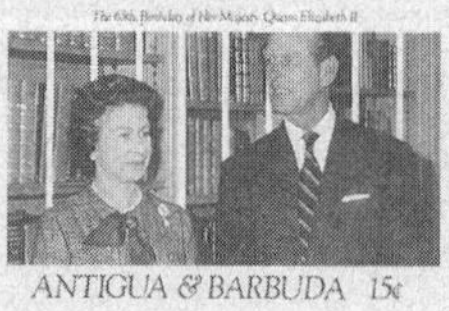
ANTIGUA & BARBUDA 15¢

280 Queen Elizabeth and Prince Philip in 1976

1991. 65th Birthday of Queen Elizabeth II. Multicoloured.

1534	15c. Type **280**	30	10
1535	20c. The Queen and Prince Philip in Portugal, 1985	30	10
1536	$2 Queen Elizabeth II	1·50	1·50
1537	$4 The Queen and Prince Philip at Ascot, 1986	2·75	3·25

1991. 10th Wedding Anniv of Prince and Princess of Wales. As T **280**. Multicoloured.

1539	10c. Prince and Princess of Wales at party, 1986	40	10
1540	40c. Separate portraits of Prince, Princess and sons	80	25
1541	$1 Prince Henry and Prince William	1·10	70
1542	$5 Princess Diana in Australia and Prince Charles in Hungary	4·25	4·50

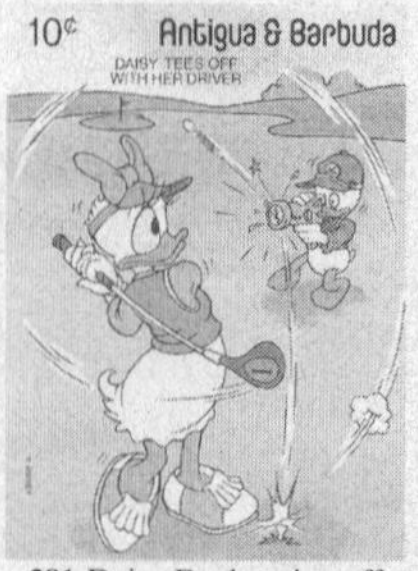
10¢ Antigua & Barbuda
DAISY TEES OFF WITH HER DRIVER

281 Daisy Duck teeing-off

1991. Golf. Walt Disney cartoon characters. Mult.

1544	10c. Type **281**	70	50
1545	15c. Goofy playing ball from under trees	75	50
1546	45c. Mickey Mouse playing deflected shot	1·25	50
1547	60c. Mickey hacking divot out of fairway	1·50	65
1548	$1 Donald Duck playing ball out of pond	1·75	1·10
1549	$2 Minnie Mouse hitting ball over pond	2·50	2·75
1550	$4 Donald in a bunker	3·25	4·00
1551	$5 Goofy trying snooker shot into hole	3·25	4·00

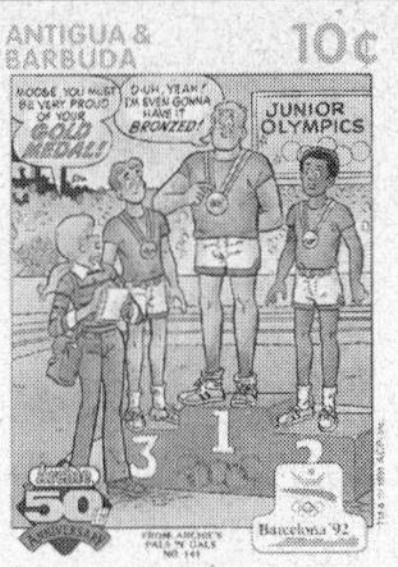
ANTIGUA & BARBUDA
10¢
JUNIOR OLYMPICS
Barcelona '92

282 Moose receiving Gold Medal

1991. 50th Anniv of Archie Comics, and Olympic Games, Barcelona (1992) (2nd issue). Multicoloured.

1553	10c. Type **282**	55	40
1554	25c. Archie playing polo on a motorcycle (horiz)	85	40
1555	40c. Archie and Betty at fencing class	1·10	45
1556	60c. Archie joining girls' volleyball team	1·40	65
1557	$1 Archie with tennis ball in his mouth	1·75	1·10
1558	$2 Archie running marathon	2·50	3·00
1559	$4 Archie judging women's gymnastics (horiz)	3·75	4·50
1560	$5 Archie watching the cheer-leaders	3·75	4·50

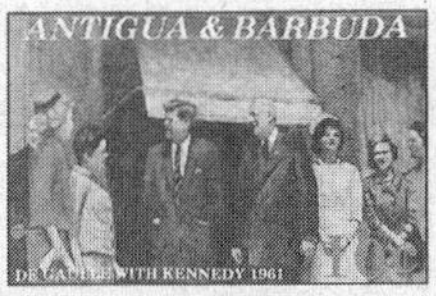
ANTIGUA & BARBUDA
DE GAULLE WITH KENNEDY 1961

283 Presidents De Gaulle and Kennedy, 1961

1991. Birth Centenary of Charles de Gaulle (French statesman). Multicoloured.

1562	10c. Type **283**	70	40
1563	15c. General De Gaulle with President Roosevelt, 1945 (vert)	70	40
1564	45c. President De Gaulle with Chancellor Adenauer, 1962 (vert)	1·10	40
1565	60c. De Gaulle at Arc de Triomphe, Liberation of Paris, 1944 (vert)	1·25	65
1566	$1 General De Gaulle crossing the Rhine, 1945	1·50	1·10
1567	$2 General De Gaulle in Algiers, 1944	2·25	2·75
1568	$4 Presidents De Gaulle and Eisenhower, 1960	3·00	4·00
1569	$5 De Gaulle returning from Germany, 1968 (vert)	3·00	4·00

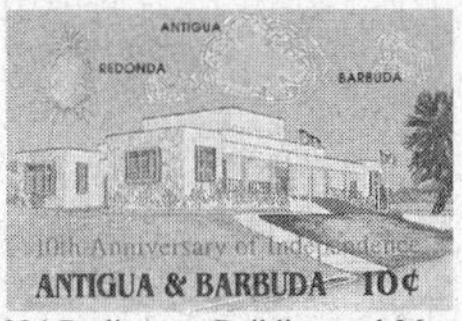
ANTIGUA & BARBUDA 10¢

284 Parliament Building and Map

1991. 10th Anniv of Independence.

1571	**284** 10c. multicoloured	75	50

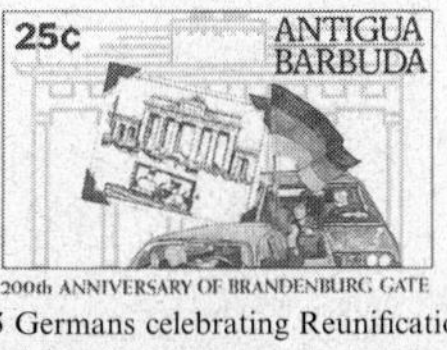
25¢
ANTIGUA BARBUDA
200th ANNIVERSARY OF BRANDENBURG GATE

285 Germans celebrating Reunification

1991. Anniversaries and Events. Multicoloured.

1573	25c. Type **285**	30	30
1574	75c. Cubs erecting tent	50	50
1575	$1.50 "Don Giovanni" and Mozart	3·00	2·25
1576	$2 Chariot driver and Gate at night	1·10	1·75
1577	$2 Lord Baden-Powell and members of 3rd Antigua Methodist cub pack (vert)	2·50	2·25
1578	$2 Lilienthal's signature and glider "Flugzeug Nr. 5"	2·75	2·25
1579	$2.50 Driver in Class P36 steam locomotive (vert)	3·50	3·00
1580	$3 Statues from podium	1·75	2·50
1581	$3.50 Cubs and camp fire	1·90	2·50
1582	$4 St. Peter's Cathedral, Salzburg	5·00	5·00

ANNIVERSARIES AND EVENTS: Nos. 1573, 1576, 1580, Bicentenary of Brandenburg Gate, Germany; 1574, 1577, 1581, 17th World Scout Jamboree, Korea; 1575, 1582, Death bicentenary of Mozart (composer); 1578, Centenary of Otto Lilienthal's gliding experiments; 1579, Centenary of Trans-Siberian Railway.

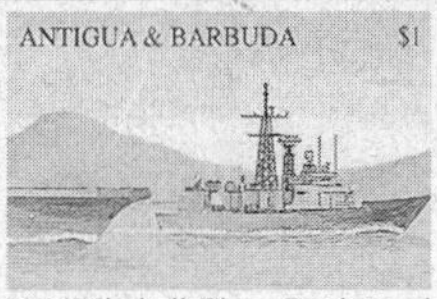
ANTIGUA & BARBUDA $1

286 "Nimitz" Class Carrier and "Ticonderoga" Class Cruiser

1991. 50th Anniv of Japanese Attack on Pearl Harbor. Multicoloured.

1585	$1 Type **286**	1·50	1·50
1586	$1 Tourist launch	1·50	1·50
1587	$1 U.S.S. "Arizona" memorial	1·50	1·50
1588	$1 Wreaths on water and aircraft	1·50	1·50
1589	$1 White tern	1·50	1·50
1590	$1 Mitsubishi A6M Zero-Sen fighters over Pearl City	1·50	1·50
1591	$1 Mitsubishi A6M Zero-Sen fighters attacking	1·50	1·50
1592	$1 Battleship Row in flames	1·50	1·50
1593	$1 U.S.S. "Nevada" (battleship) underway	1·50	1·50
1594	$1 Mitsubishi A6M Zero-Sen fighters returning to carriers	1·50	1·50

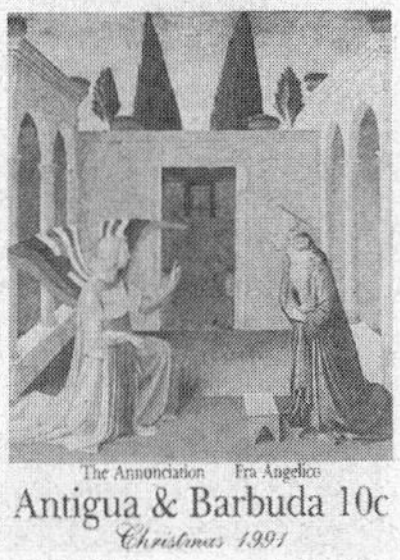
The Annunciation Fra Angelico
Antigua & Barbuda 10c
Christmas 1991

287 "The Annunciation"

1991. Christmas. Religious Paintings by Fra Angelico. Multicoloured.

1595	10c. Type **287**	40	30
1596	30c. "Nativity"	65	30
1597	40c. "Adoration of the Magi"	75	30
1598	60c. "Presentation in the Temple"	1·00	45
1599	$1 "Circumcision"	1·25	65
1600	$3 "Flight into Egypt"	2·50	3·25
1601	$4 "Massacre of the Innocents"	2·50	3·50
1602	$5 "Christ teaching in the Temple"	2·50	3·50

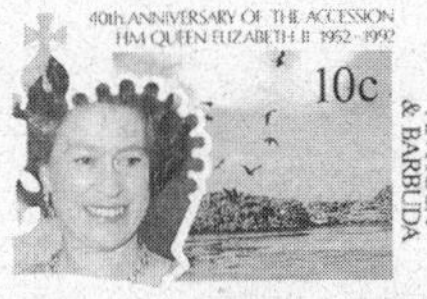
40th ANNIVERSARY OF THE ACCESSION
HM QUEEN ELIZABETH II 1952-1992
10c
ANTIGUA & BARBUDA

288 Queen Elizabeth II and Bird Sanctuary

1992. 40th Anniv of Queen Elizabeth II's Accession. Multicoloured.

1604	10c. Type **288**	75	40
1605	30c. Nelson's Dockyard	90	40
1606	$1 Ruins on Shirley Heights	1·00	70
1607	$5 Beach and palm trees	2·75	3·75

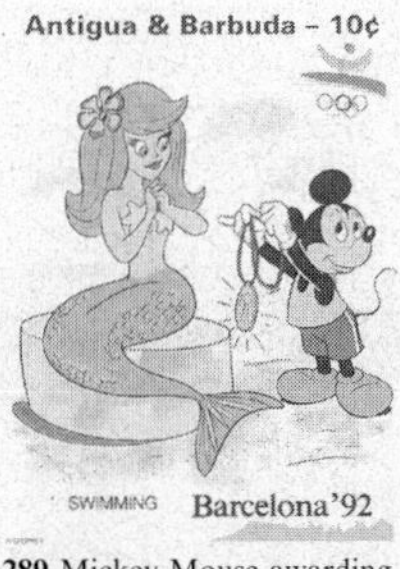
Antigua & Barbuda – 10¢
SWIMMING
Barcelona'92

289 Mickey Mouse awarding Swimming Gold Medal to Mermaid

1992. Olympic Games, Barcelona (3rd issue). Walt Disney cartoon characters. Multicoloured.

1609	10c. Type **289**	40	30
1610	15c. Huey, Dewey and Louie with kayak	50	30
1611	30c. Donald Duck and Uncle Scrooge in yacht	65	35
1612	50c. Donald and horse playing water polo	85	50
1613	$1 Big Pete weightlifting	1·25	85
1614	$2 Donald and Goofy fencing	1·75	1·75
1615	$4 Mickey and Donald playing volleyball	2·50	3·00
1616	$5 Goofy vaulting	2·50	3·00

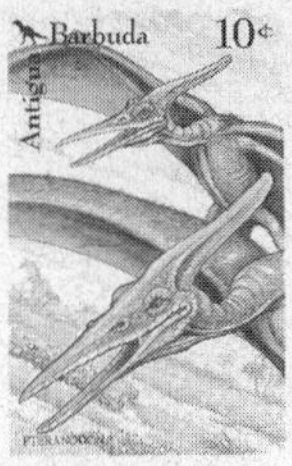
Antigua Barbuda 10¢
PTERANODON

290 Pteranodon

1992. Prehistoric Animals. Mult.

1618	10c. Type **290**	65	40
1619	15c. Brachiosaurus	65	40
1620	30c. Tyrannosaurus Rex	85	40
1621	50c. Parasaurolophus	1·00	50
1622	$1 Deinonychus (horiz)	1·50	1·00
1623	$2 Triceratops (horiz)	2·00	2·00
1624	$4 Protoceratops hatching (horiz)	2·25	2·75
1625	$5 Stegosaurus (horiz)	2·25	2·75

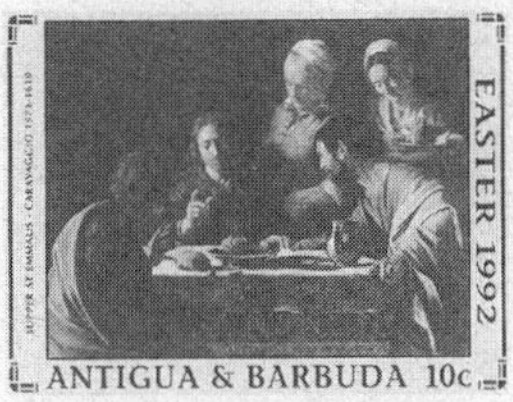
EASTER 1992
ANTIGUA & BARBUDA 10c

291 "Supper at Emmaus" (Caravaggio)

1992. Easter. Religious Paintings. Multicoloured.

1627	10c. Type **291**	35	25
1628	15c. "The Vision of St. Peter" (Zurbaran)	45	25
1629	30c. "Christ driving the Money-changers from the Temple" (Tiepolo)	65	40
1630	40c. "Martyrdom of St. Bartholomew" (detail) (Ribera)	75	50
1631	$1 "Christ driving the Money-changers from the Temple" (detail) (Tiepolo)	1·25	1·00
1632	$2 "Crucifixion" (detail) (Altdorfer)	2·25	2·50
1633	$4 "The Deposition" (detail) (Fra Angelico)	3·00	3·75
1634	$5 "The Deposition" (different detail) (Fra Angelico)	3·00	3·75

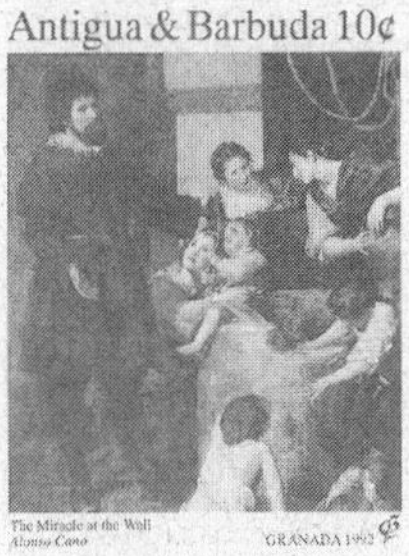
Antigua & Barbuda 10¢

292 "The Miracle at the Well" (Alonso Cano)

1992. "Granada '92" International Stamp Exhibition, Spain. Spanish Paintings. Multicoloured.

1636	10c. Type **292**	40	30
1637	15c. "The Poet Luis de Goingora y Argote" (Velazquez)	50	30
1638	30c. "The Painter Francisco Goya" (Vincente Lopez Portana)	65	40
1639	40c. "Maria de las Nieves Michaela Fourdinier" (Luis Paret y Alcazar)	75	50
1640	$1 "Carlos III eating before his Court" (Alcazar) (horiz)	1·25	1·00
1641	$2 "Rain Shower in Granada" (Antonio Munoz Degrain) (horiz)	2·00	2·50
1642	$4 "Sarah Bernhardt" (Santiago Rusinol i Prats)	3·00	3·75
1643	$5 "The Hermitage Garden" (Joaquim Mir Trinxet)	3·00	3·75

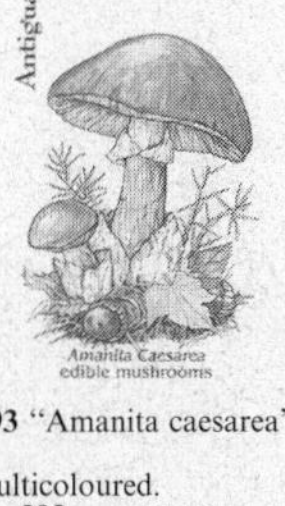
Antigua & Barbuda 10¢
Amanita Caesarea
edible mushrooms

293 "Amanita caesarea"

1992. Fungi. Multicoloured.

1645	10c. Type **293**	70	40
1646	15c. "Collybia fusipes"	85	40
1647	30c. "Boletus aereus"	1·25	40
1648	40c. "Laccaria amethystina"	1·25	50
1649	$1 "Russula virescens"	2·00	1·25
1650	$2 "Tricholoma equestre" ("Tricholoma auratum")	2·75	2·75
1651	$4 "Calocybe gambosa"	3·50	3·75
1652	$5 "Lentinus tigrinus" ("Panus tigrinus")	3·50	3·75

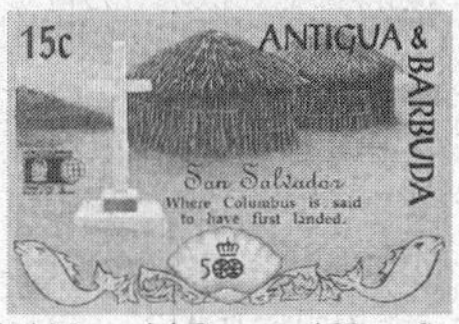
15c
ANTIGUA & BARBUDA
San Salvador

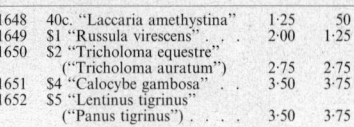

294 Memorial Cross and Huts, San Salvador

1992. 500th Anniv of Discovery of America by Columbus (5th issue). World Columbian Stamp "Expo '92", Chicago. Multicoloured.

1654	15c. Type **294**	30	20
1655	30c. Martin Pinzon with telescope	45	25
1656	40c. Christopher Columbus	55	35
1657	$1 "Pinta"	2·00	1·00
1658	$2 "Nina"	2·25	2·50
1659	$4 "Santa Maria"	3·00	4·50

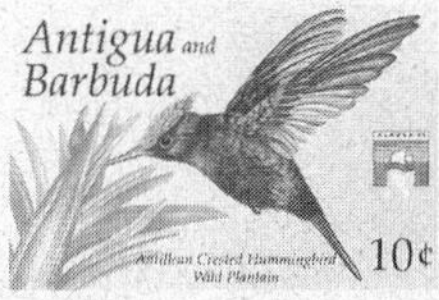
Antigua and Barbuda
10¢

295 Antillean Crested Hummingbird and Wild Plantain

1992. "Genova '92" International Thematic Stamp Exhibition. Hummingbirds and Plants. Multicoloured.

1661	10c. Type **295**	35	50
1662	25c. Green mango and parrot's plantain	50	40
1663	45c. Purple-throated carib and lobster claws	70	45
1664	60c. Antillean mango and coral plant	80	55
1665	$1 Vervain hummingbird and cardinal's guard	1·10	85
1666	$2 Rufous-breasted hermit and heliconia	1·75	2·00
1667	$4 Blue-headed hummingbird and red ginger	3·00	3·25
1668	$5 Green-throated carib and ornamental banana	3·00	3·25

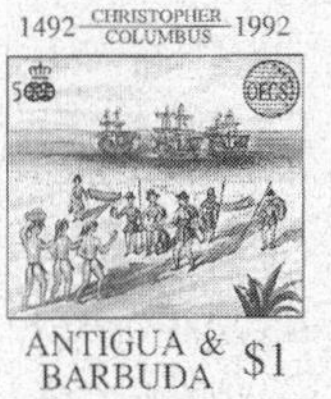
1492 CHRISTOPHER COLUMBUS 1992
ANTIGUA & BARBUDA $1

296 Columbus meeting Amerindians

1992. 500th Anniv of Discovery of America by Columbus (6th issue). Organization of East Caribbean States. Multicoloured.

1670	$1 Type **296**	85	65
1671	$2 Ships approaching island	1·40	1·60

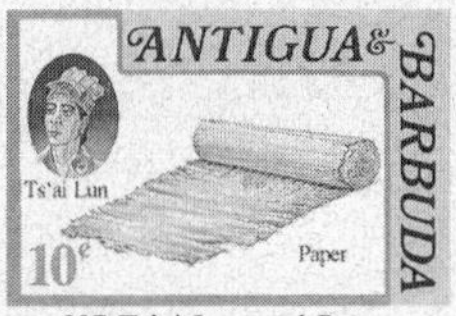
ANTIGUA & BARBUDA
Ts'ai Lun
Paper
10¢

297 Ts'ai Lun and Paper

1992. Inventors and Inventions. Mult.

1672	10c. Type **297**	25	25
1673	25c. Igor Sikorsky and "Bolshoi Baltiskii" (first four-engined airplane)	75	40
1674	30c. Alexander Graham Bell and early telephone	55	45
1675	40c. Johannes Gutenberg and early printing press	55	45
1676	60c. James Watt and stationary steam engine	2·00	1·00
1677	$1 Anton van Leeuwenhoek and early microscope	1·25	1·10
1678	$4 Louis Braille and hands reading braille	3·75	4·50
1679	$5 Galileo and telescope	3·75	4·50

108 ANTIGUA

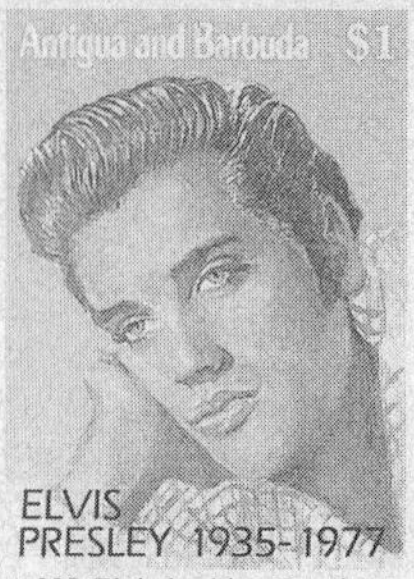
Antigua and Barbuda $1
ELVIS
PRESLEY 1935-1977

298 Elvis looking Pensive

1992. 15th Death Anniv of Elvis Presley. Mult.

1681	$1 Type **298**	1·25	1·00
1682	$1 Wearing black and yellow striped shirt	1·25	1·00
1683	$1 Singing into microphone	1·25	1·00
1684	$1 Wearing wide-brimmed hat	1·25	1·00
1685	$1 With microphone in right hand	1·25	1·00
1686	$1 In Army uniform	1·25	1·00
1687	$1 Wearing pink shirt	1·25	1·00
1688	$1 In yellow shirt	1·25	1·00
1689	$1 In jacket and bow tie	1·25	1·00

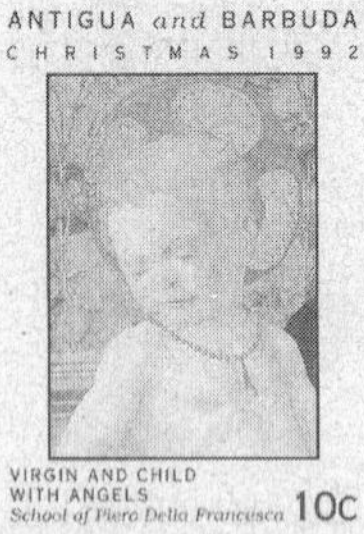
ANTIGUA and BARBUDA
CHRISTMAS 1992
VIRGIN AND CHILD WITH ANGELS
10c

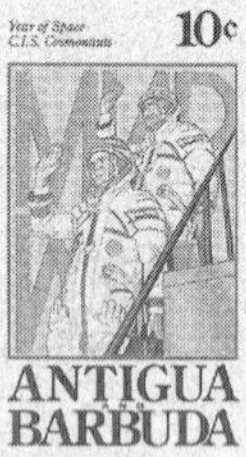
10c
ANTIGUA
BARBUDA

300 "Virgin and Child with Angels" (detail) (School of Piero della Francesca) **301** Russian Cosmonauts

1992. Christmas. Details of the Holy Child from various paintings. Multicoloured.

1691	10c. Type **300**	50	20
1692	25c. "Madonna degli Alberelli" (Giovanni Bellini)	75	20
1693	30c. "Madonna and Child with St. Anthony Abbot and St. Sigismund" (Neroccio)	80	30
1694	40c. "Madonna and the Grand Duke" (Raphael)	90	30
1695	60c. "The Nativity" (Georges de la Tour)	1·25	60
1696	$1 "Holy Family" (Jacob Jordaens)	1·50	1·00
1697	$4 "Madonna and Child Enthroned" (Magaritone)	3·50	4·75
1698	$5 "Madonna and Child on a Curved Throne" (Byzantine school)	3·50	4·75

1992. Anniversaries and Events. Mult.

1700	10c. Type **301**	60	50
1701	40c. "Graf Zeppelin" (airship), 1929	1·25	65
1702	45c. Bishop Daniel Davis	50	40
1703	75c. Konrad Adenauer making speech	65	65
1704	$1 Bus Mosbacher and "Weatherly" (yacht)	1·25	1·00
1705	$1.50 Rain forest	1·40	1·25
1706	$2 Tiger	3·75	3·00
1707	$2 National flag, plant and emblem (horiz)	2·50	2·00
1708	$2 Members of Community Players company (horiz)	1·75	2·00
1709	$2.25 Women carrying pots	1·75	2·25
1710	$3 Lions Club emblem	2·25	2·50
1711	$4 Chinese rocket on launch tower	2·50	3·00
1712	$4 West German and N.A.T.O. flags	2·50	3·00
1713	$6 Hugo Eckener (airship pioneer)	3·25	3·75

ANNIVERSARIES AND EVENTS: Nos. 1700, 1711, International Space Year; 1701, 1713, 75th death anniv of Count Ferdinand von Zeppelin; 1702, 150th anniv of Anglican Diocese of North-eastern Caribbean and Aruba; 1703, 1712, 25th death anniv of Konrad Adenauer (German statesman); 1704, Americas Cup yachting championship; 1705/6, Earth Summit '92, Rio; 1707, 50th anniv of Inter-American Institute for Agricultural Co-operation; 1708, 40th anniv of Cultural Development; 1709, United Nations World Health Organization Projects; 1710, 75th anniv of International Association of Lions Clubs.

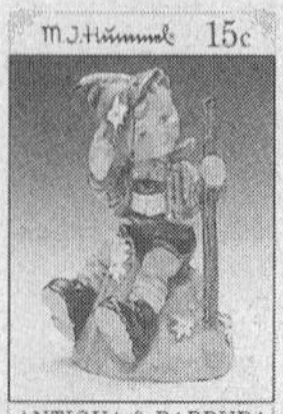
15c
ANTIGUA & BARBUDA

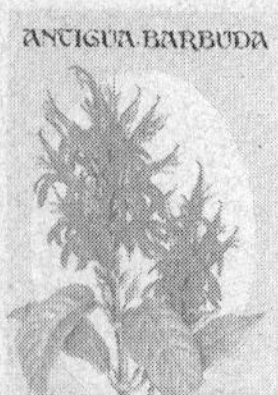
ANTIGUA BARBUDA
15c

302 Boy Hiker resting **304** Cardinal's Guard

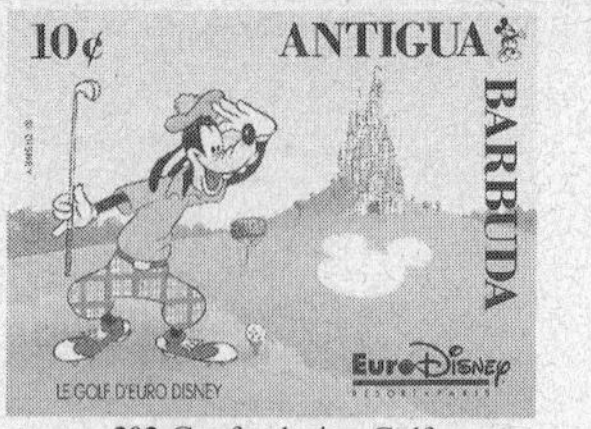
10¢ ANTIGUA
BARBUDA

303 Goofy playing Golf

1993. Hummel Figurines. Multicoloured.

1715	15c. Type **302**	35	15
1716	30c. Girl sitting on fence	55	25
1717	40c. Boy hunter	65	35
1718	50c. Boy with umbrella	75	45
1719	$1 Hikers at signpost	1·25	75
1720	$2 Boy hiker with pack and stick	1·75	2·25
1721	$4 Girl with young child and goat	2·75	3·50
1722	$5 Boy whistling	2·75	3·50

1993. Opening of Euro-Disney Resort, Paris. Multicoloured.

1724	10c. Type **303**	60	30
1725	25c. Chip and Dale at Davy Crockett's campground	80	30
1726	30c. Donald Duck at the Cheyenne Hotel	80	35
1727	40c. Goofy at the Santa Fe Hotel	85	35
1728	$1 Mickey and Minnie Mouse at the New York Hotel	1·60	1·00
1729	$2 Mickey, Minnie and Goofy in car	2·25	2·25
1730	$4 Goofy at Pirates of the Caribbean	3·25	4·25
1731	$5 Donald at Adventureland	3·25	4·25

1993. Flowers. Multicoloured.

1733	15c. Type **304**	75	30
1734	25c. Giant granadilla	85	30
1735	30c. Spider flower	85	35
1736	40c. Gold vine	90	35
1737	$1 Frangipani	1·50	1·00
1738	$2 Bougainvillea	2·00	2·25
1739	$4 Yellow oleander	3·00	3·75
1740	$5 Spicy jatropha	3·00	3·75

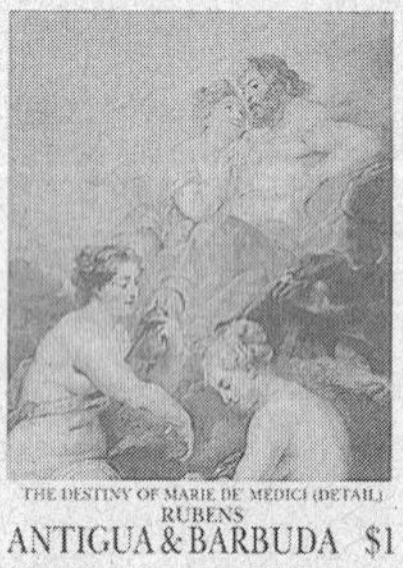
ANTIGUA & BARBUDA $1

305 "The Destiny of Marie de' Medici" (upper detail)

1993. Bicentenary of the Louvre, Paris. Paintings by Peter Paul Rubens. Multicoloured.

1742	$1 Type **305**	80	80
1743	$1 "The Birth of Marie de' Medici"	80	80
1744	$1 "The Education of Marie de' Medici"	80	80
1745	$1 "The Destiny of Marie de' Medici" (lower detail)	80	80
1746	$1 "Henry VI receiving the Portrait of Marie"	80	80
1747	$1 "The Meeting of the King and Marie at Lyons"	80	80
1748	$1 "The Marriage by Proxy"	80	80
1749	$1 "The Birth of Louis XIII"	80	80
1750	$1 "The Capture of Juliers"	80	80
1751	$1 "The Exchange of the Princesses"	80	80
1752	$1 "The Regency"	80	80
1753	$1 "The Majority of Louis XIII"	80	80
1754	$1 "The Flight from Blois"	80	80
1755	$1 "The Treaty of Angouleme"	80	80
1756	$1 "The Peace of Angers"	80	80
1757	$1 "The Reconciliation of Louis and Marie de' Medici"	80	80

Nos. 1742/57 depict details from "The Story of Marie de' Medici".

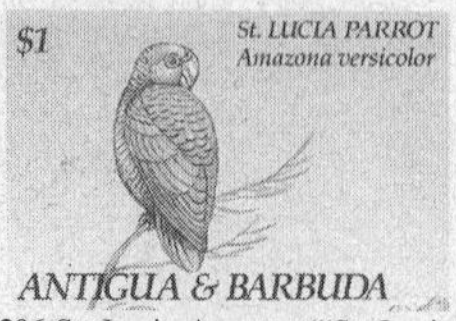
$1
St. LUCIA PARROT
Amazona versicolor
ANTIGUA & BARBUDA

306 St. Lucia Amazon ("St, Lucia Parrot")

1993. Endangered Species. Multicoloured.

1759	$1 Type **306**	90	90
1760	$1 Cahow	90	90
1761	$1 Swallow-tailed kite	90	90
1762	$1 Everglade kite ("Everglades Kite")	90	90
1763	$1 Imperial amazon ("Imperial Parrot")	90	90
1764	$1 Humpback whale	90	90
1765	$1 Plain pigeon ("Puerto Rican Plain Pigeon")	90	90
1766	$1 St. Vincent amazon ("St. Vincent Parrot")	90	90
1767	$1 Puerto Rican amazon ("Puerto Rican Parrot")	90	90
1768	$1 Leatherback turtle	90	90
1769	$1 American crocodile	90	90
1770	$1 Hawksbill turtle	90	90

Nos. 1759/70 were printed together, se-tenant, with the background forming a composite design.

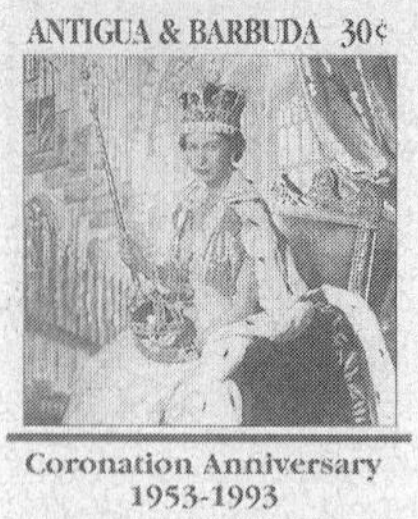
ANTIGUA & BARBUDA 30¢
Coronation Anniversary
1953-1993

307 Queen Elizabeth II at Coronation (photograph by Cecil Beaton)

1993. 40th Anniv of Coronation (1st issue).

1772	**307**	30c. multicoloured	50	50
1773	–	40c. multicoloured	60	60
1774	–	$2 blue and black	1·50	1·75
1775	–	$4 multicoloured	1·90	2·00

DESIGNS: 40c. Queen Elizabeth the Queen Mother's Crown, 1937; $2 Procession of heralds; $4 Queen Elizabeth II and Prince Edward.

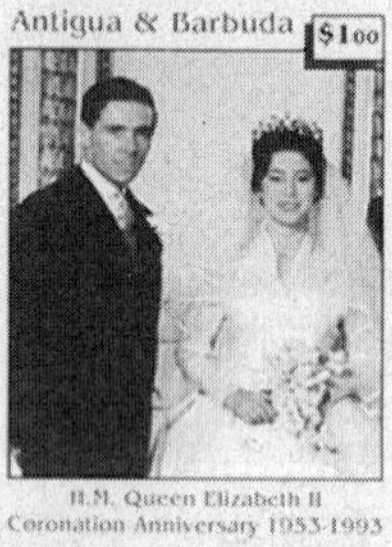
Antigua & Barbuda $1.00
H.M. Queen Elizabeth II
Coronation Anniversary 1953-1993

308 Princess Margaret and Antony Armstrong-Jones

1993. 40th Anniv of Coronation (2nd issue).

1777/1808	$1 × 32 either grey and black or multicoloured	22·00	24·00

DESIGNS: Various views as Type **308** from each decade of the reign.

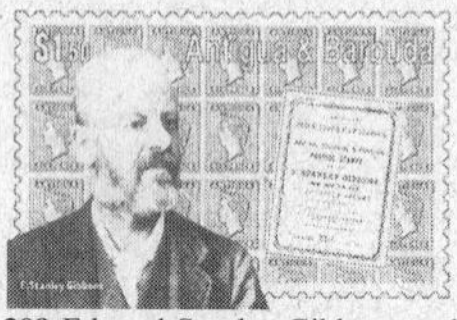

309 Edward Stanley Gibbons and Catalogue of 1865

1993. Famous Professional Philatelists (1st series).

1809	**309**	$1.50 brown, black & grn	1·25	1·25
1810	–	$1.50 multicoloured	1·25	1·25
1811	–	$1.50 multicoloured	1·25	1·25
1812	–	$1.50 multicoloured	1·25	1·25
1813	–	$1.50 multicoloured	1·25	1·25
1814	–	$1.50 multicoloured	1·25	1·25

DESIGNS: No. 1810, Theodore Champion and France 1849 1f. stamp; 1811, J. Walter Scott and U.S.A. 1918 24c. "Inverted Jenny" error; 1812, Hugo Michel and Bavaria 1849 1k. stamp; 1813, Alberto and Giulio Bolaffi with Sardinia 1851 5c. stamp; 1814, Richard Borek and Brunswick 1865 1gr. stamp.

See also No. 1957.

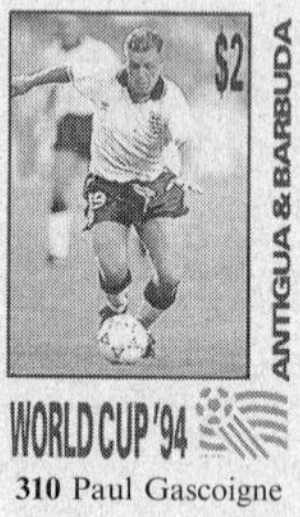
$2
ANTIGUA & BARBUDA
WORLD CUP '94

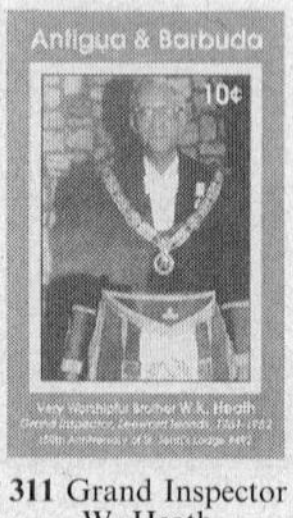
Antigua & Barbuda
10c

310 Paul Gascoigne **311** Grand Inspector W. Heath

1993. World Cup Football Championship, U.S.A. (1st issue). English Players. Multicoloured.

1816	$2 Type **310**	1·50	1·40
1817	$2 David Platt	1·50	1·40
1818	$2 Martin Peters	1·50	1·40
1819	$2 John Barnes	1·50	1·40
1820	$2 Gary Lineker	1·50	1·40
1821	$2 Geoff Hurst	1·50	1·40
1822	$2 Bobby Charlton	1·50	1·40
1823	$2 Bryan Robson	1·50	1·40
1824	$2 Bobby Moore	1·50	1·40
1825	$2 Nobby Stiles	1·50	1·40
1826	$2 Gordon Banks	1·50	1·40
1827	$2 Peter Shilton	1·50	1·40

See also Nos. 2039/44.

1993. Anniversaries and Events. Mult.

1829	10c. Type **311**	1·25	70
1830	15c. Rodnina and Oulanov (U.S.S.R.) (pairs figure skating) (horiz)	60	30
1831	30c. Present Masonic Hall, St. John's (horiz)	1·50	70
1832	30c. Willy Brandt with Helmut Schmidt and George Leber (horiz)	40	30
1833	30c. "Cat and Bird" (Picasso) (horiz)	50	40
1834	40c. Previous Masonic Hall, St. John's (horiz)	1·50	70
1835	40c. "Fish on a Newspaper" (Picasso) (horiz)	50	40
1836	40c. Early astronomical equipment	50	40
1837	40c. Prince Naruhito and engagement photographs (horiz)	50	40
1838	60c. Grand Inspector J. Jeffery	1·75	85
1839	$1 "Woman combing her Hair" (W. Slewinski) (horiz)	80	1·00
1840	$3 Masako Owada and engagement photographs (horiz)	2·00	2·25
1841	$3 "Artist's Wife with Cat" (Konrad Kryzanowski) (horiz)	2·00	2·25
1842	$4 Willy Brandt and protest march (horiz)	2·25	2·75
1843	$4 Galaxy	2·25	2·75
1844	$5 Alberto Tomba (Italy) (giant slalom) (horiz)	2·25	2·75
1845	$5 "Dying Bull" (Picasso) (horiz)	2·25	2·75
1846	$5 Pres. Clinton and family (horiz)	2·25	2·75

ANNIVERSARIES AND EVENTS: Nos. 1829, 1831, 1834, 1838, 150th anniv of St. John's Masonic Lodge No. 492; 1830, 1844, Winter Olympic Games '94, Lillehammer; 1832, 1842, 80th birth anniv of Willy Brandt (German politician); 1833, 1835, 1845, 20th death anniv of Picasso (artist); 1836, 1843, 450th death anniv of Copernicus (astronomer); 1837, 1840, Marriage of Crown Prince Naruhito of Japan; 1839, 1841, "Polska '93" International Stamp Exhibition, Poznan; 1846 Inauguration of U.S. President William Clinton.

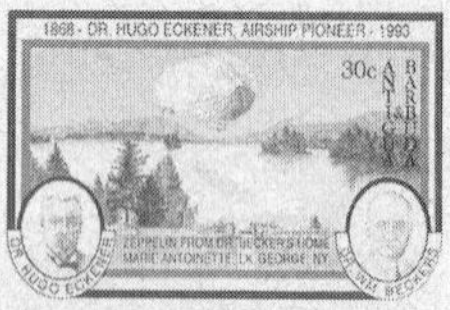
1868 - DR. HUGO ECKENER, AIRSHIP PIONEER - 1990
30c

312 Hugo Eckener and Dr. W. Beckers with Airship "Graf Zeppelin" over Lake George, New York

1993. Aviation Anniversaries. Multicoloured.

1848	30c. Type **312**	1·00	70
1849	40c. Chicago World's Fair from "Graf Zeppelin"	1·00	1·00
1850	40c. Gloster Whittle E.28/39, 1941	1·00	1·00
1851	40c. George Washington writing balloon mail letter (vert)	1·00	1·00
1852	$4 Pres. Wilson and Curtiss JN-4 Jenny	3·75	4·00
1853	$5 Airship "Hindenburg" over Ebbets Field baseball stadium, 1937	3·75	4·00
1854	$5 Gloster Meteor in dogfight	3·75	4·00

ANNIVERSARIES: Nos. 1848/9, 1853, 125th birth anniv of Hugo Eckener (airship commander); 1850, 1854, 75th anniv of Royal Air Force; 1851/2, Bicentenary of first airmail flight.

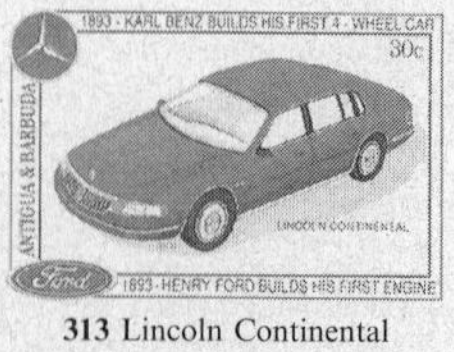
1893 - KARL BENZ BUILDS HIS FIRST 4 - WHEEL CAR
30c
ANTIGUA & BARBUDA
1893 - HENRY FORD BUILDS HIS FIRST ENGINE

313 Lincoln Continental

1993. Centenaries of Henry Ford's First Petrol Engine (Nos. 1856, 1858), and Karl Benz's First Four-wheeled Car (others). Multicoloured.

1856	30c. Type **313**	1·00	75
1857	40c. Mercedes racing car, 1914	1·00	75
1858	$4 Ford "GT40", 1966	4·00	4·50
1859	$5 Mercedes Benz "gull-wing" coupe, 1954	4·00	4·50

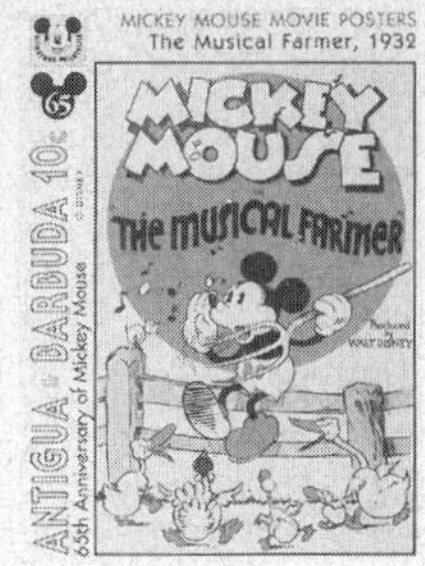

314 "The Musical Farmer", 1932

1993. Mickey Mouse Film Posters. Mult.

1861	10c. Type **314**	60	30
1862	15c. "Little Whirlwind", 1941	70	35
1863	30c. "Pluto's Dream House", 1940	80	40
1864	40c. "Gulliver Mickey", 1934	80	40
1865	50c. "Alpine Climbers", 1936	80	45
1866	$1 "Mr. Mouse Takes a Trip", 1940	1·25	80
1867	$2 "The Nifty Nineties", 1941	1·75	2·00
1868	$4 "Mickey Down Under", 1948	2·50	3·50
1869	$5 "The Pointer", 1939	2·50	3·50

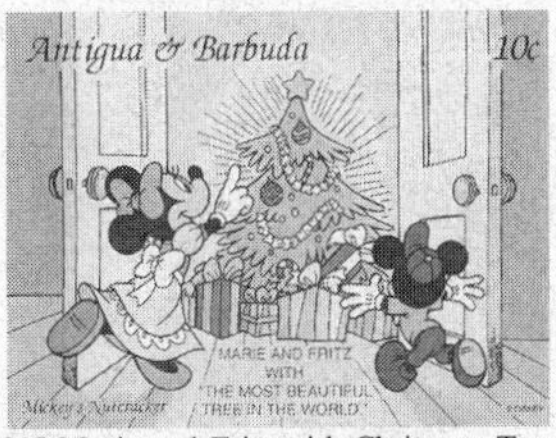

315 Marie and Fritz with Christmas Tree

1993. Christmas. Mickey's Nutcracker. Walt Disney cartoon characters in scenes from "The Nutcracker". Multicoloured.

1871	10c. Type **315**	65	40
1872	15c. Marie receives Nutcracker from Godfather Drosselmeir	70	40
1873	20c. Fritz breaks Nutcracker	70	40
1874	30c. Nutcracker with sword	80	40
1875	40c. Nutcracker and Marie in the snow	85	40
1876	50c. Marie and the Prince meet Sugar Plum Fairy	90	60
1877	60c. Marie and Prince in Crystal Hall	90	60
1878	$3 Huey, Dewey and Louie as Cossack dancers	2·75	3·50
1879	$6 Mother Ginger and her puppets	4·00	6·00

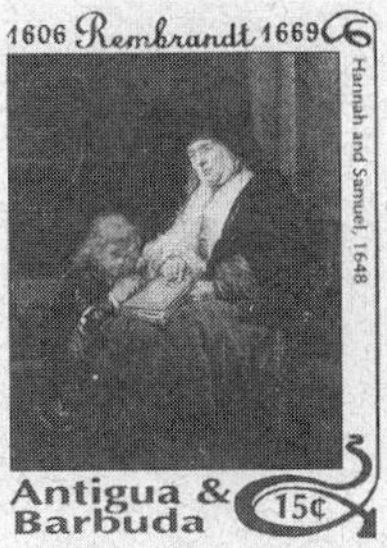

316 "Hannah and Samuel" (Rembrandt)

1993. Famous Paintings by Rembrandt and Matisse. Multicoloured.

1881	15c. Type **316**	30	30
1882	15c. "Guitarist" (Matisse)	30	30
1883	30c. "The Jewish Bride" (Rembrandt)	40	30
1884	40c. "Jacob wrestling with the Angel" (Rembrandt)	50	30
1885	60c. "Interior with a Goldfish Bowl" (Matisse)	70	50
1886	$1 "Mlle Yvonne Landsberg" (Matisse)	1·00	80
1887	$4 "The Toboggan" (Matisse)	2·75	3·50
1888	$5 "Moses with the Tablets of the Law" (Rembrandt)	2·75	3·50

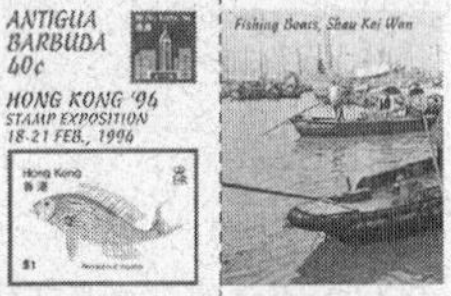

317 Hong Kong 1981 $1 Golden Threadfin Bream Stamp and Sampans, Shau Kei Wan

1994. "Hong Kong '94" International Stamp Exhibition (1st issue). Multicoloured.

1890	40c. Type **317**	65	65
1891	40c. Antigua 1990 $2 Rock beauty stamp and sampans, Shau Kei Wan	50	55

Nos. 1890/1 were printed together, se-tenant, forming a composite design.

See also Nos. 1892/7 and 1898/1905.

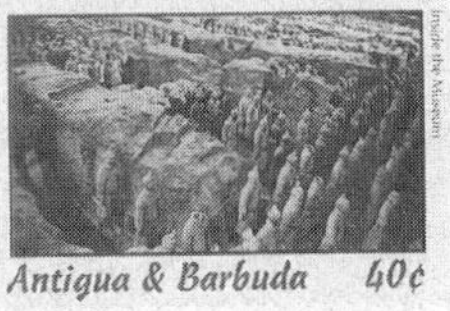

318 Terracotta Warriors

1994. "Hong Kong '94" International Stamp Exhibition (2nd issue). Qin Dynasty Terracotta Figures. Multicoloured.

1892	40c. Type **318**	55	55
1893	40c. Cavalryman and horse	55	55
1894	40c. Warriors in armour	55	55
1895	40c. Painted bronze chariot and team	55	55
1896	40c. Pekingese dog	55	55
1897	40c. Warriors with horses	55	55

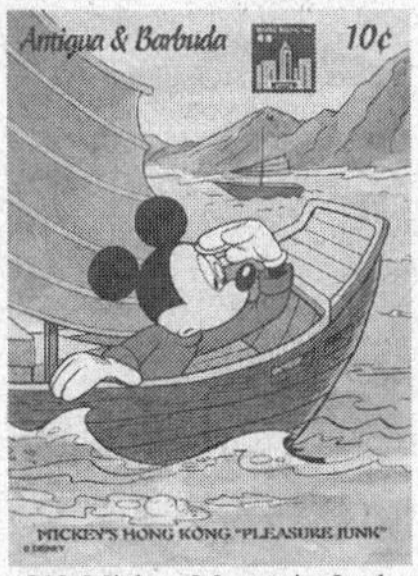

319 Mickey Mouse in Junk

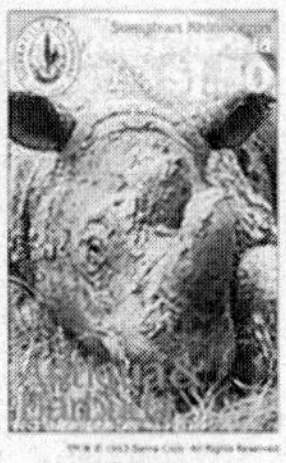

320 Sumatran Rhinoceros lying down

1994. "Hong Kong '94" International Stamp Exhibition (3rd issue). Walt Disney cartoon characters. Multicoloured.

1898	10c. Type **319**	60	30
1899	15c. Minnie Mouse as mandarin	65	35
1900	30c. Donald and Daisy Duck on houseboat	80	45
1901	50c. Mickey holding bird in cage	95	60
1902	$1 Pluto and ornamental dog	1·60	1·00
1903	$2 Minnie and Daisy celebrating Bun Festival	2·25	2·50
1904	$4 Goofy making noodles	3·00	4·00
1905	$5 Goofy pulling Mickey in rickshaw	3·00	4·00

1994. Centenary (1992) of Sierra Club (environmental protection society). Endangered Species. Multicoloured.

1907	$1.50 Type **320**	1·25	1·25
1908	$1.50 Sumatran rhinoceros feeding	1·25	1·25
1909	$1.50 Ring-tailed lemur on ground	1·25	1·25
1910	$1.50 Ring-tailed lemur on branch	1·25	1·25
1911	$1.50 Red-fronted brown lemur on branch	1·25	1·25
1912	$1.50 Head of red-fronted brown lemur	1·25	1·25
1913	$1.50 Head of red-fronted brown lemur in front of trunk	1·25	1·25
1914	$1.50 Sierra Club Centennial emblem	1·25	1·25
1915	$1.50 Head of Bactrian camel	1·25	1·25
1916	$1.50 Bactrian camel	1·25	1·25
1917	$1.50 African elephant drinking	1·25	1·25
1918	$1.50 Head of African elephant	1·25	1·25
1919	$1.50 Leopard sitting upright	1·25	1·25
1920	$1.50 Leopard in grass (emblem at right)	1·25	1·25
1921	$1.50 Leopard in grass (emblem at left)	1·25	1·25

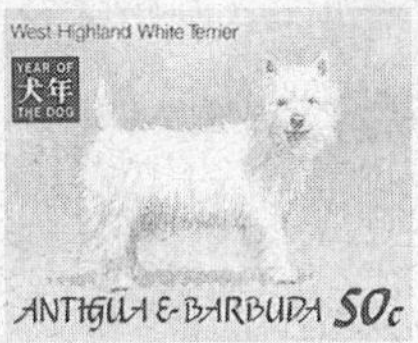

321 West Highland White Terrier

1994. Dogs of the World. Chinese New Year ("Year of the Dog"). Multicoloured.

1923	50c. Type **321**	60	60
1924	50c. Beagle	60	60
1925	50c. Scottish terrier	60	60
1926	50c. Pekingese	60	60
1927	50c. Dachshund	60	60
1928	50c. Yorkshire terrier	60	60
1929	50c. Pomeranian	60	60
1930	50c. Poodle	60	60
1931	50c. Shetland sheepdog	60	60
1932	50c. Pug	60	60
1933	50c. Shih Tzu	60	60
1934	50c. Chihuahua	60	60
1935	75c. Mastiff	60	60
1936	75c. Border collie	60	60
1937	75c. Samoyed	60	60
1938	75c. Airedale terrier	60	60
1939	75c. English setter	60	60
1940	75c. Rough collie	60	60
1941	75c. Newfoundland	60	60
1942	75c. Weimarana	60	60
1943	75c. English springer spaniel	60	60
1944	75c. Dalmatian	60	60
1945	75c. Boxer	60	60
1946	75c. Old English sheepdog	60	60

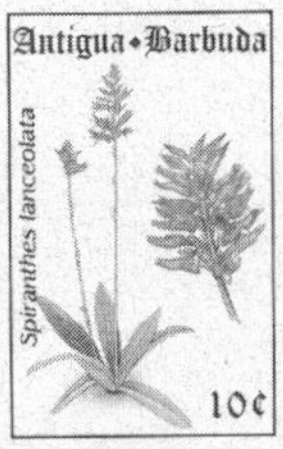

322 "Spiranthes lanceolata"

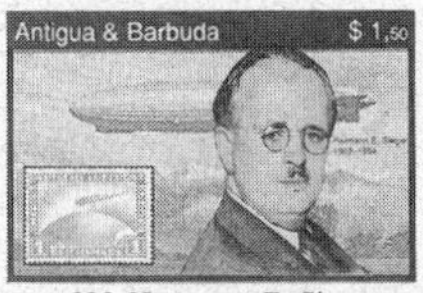

323 Hermann E. Sieger, Germany 1931 1m. Zeppelin Stamp and Airship LZ-127 "Graf Zeppelin"

1994. Orchids. Multicoloured.

1948	10c. Type **322**	55	50
1949	20c. "Ionopsis utricularioides"	75	50
1950	30c. "Tetramicra canaliculata"	85	50
1951	50c. "Oncidium picturatum"	1·00	65
1952	$1 "Epidendrum difforme"	1·50	90
1953	$2 "Epidendrum ciliare"	2·00	2·25
1954	$4 "Epidendrum ibaguense"	2·75	3·50
1955	$5 "Epidendrum nocturnum"	2·75	3·50

1994. Famous Professional Philatelists (2nd series).

1957	**323** $1.50 multicoloured	1·60	1·60

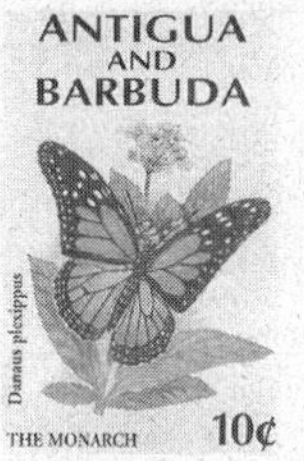

324 "Danaus plexippus"

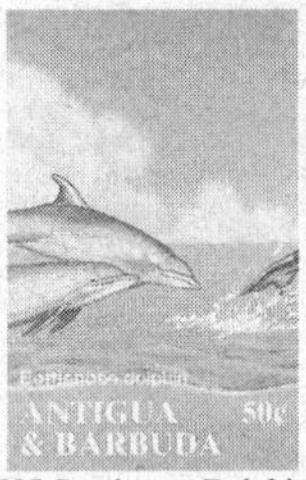

325 Bottlenose Dolphin

1994. Butterflies. Multicoloured.

1958	10c. Type **324**	60	60
1959	15c. "Appias drusilla"	75	35
1960	30c. "Eurema lisa"	90	50
1961	40c. "Anaea troglodyta"	90	60
1962	$1 "Urbanus proteus"	1·40	90
1963	$2 "Junonia evarete"	2·00	2·25
1964	$4 "Battus polydamas"	2·75	3·50
1965	$5 "Heliconius charitonia"	2·75	3·50

No. 1959 is inscribed "Appisa drusilla" and No. 1965 "Heliconius charitonius", both in error.

1994. Marine Life. Multicoloured.

1967	50c. Type **325**	65	65
1968	50c. Killer whale	65	65
1969	50c. Spinner dolphin	65	65
1970	50c. Oceanic sunfish	65	65
1971	50c. Caribbean reef shark and short fin pilot whale	65	65
1972	50c. Copper-banded butterflyfish	65	65
1973	50c. Mosaic moray	65	65
1974	50c. Clown triggerfish	65	65
1975	50c. Red lobster	65	65

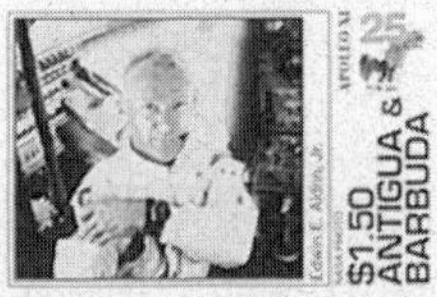

326 Edwin Aldrin (astronaut)

1994. 25th Anniv of First Manned Moon Landing. Multicoloured.

1977	$1.50 Type **326**	1·50	1·50
1978	$1.50 First lunar footprint	1·50	1·50
1979	$1.50 Neil Armstrong (astronaut)	1·50	1·50
1980	$1.50 Aldrin stepping onto Moon	1·50	1·50
1981	$1.50 Aldrin and equipment	1·50	1·50
1982	$1.50 Aldrin and U.S.A. flag	1·50	1·50
1983	$1.50 Aldrin at Tranquility Base	1·50	1·50
1984	$1.50 Moon plaque	1·50	1·50
1985	$1.50 "Eagle" leaving Moon	1·50	1·50
1986	$1.50 Command module in lunar orbit	1·50	1·50
1987	$1.50 First day cover of U.S.A. 1969 10c. First Man on Moon stamp	1·50	1·50
1988	$1.50 Pres. Nixon and astronauts	1·50	1·50

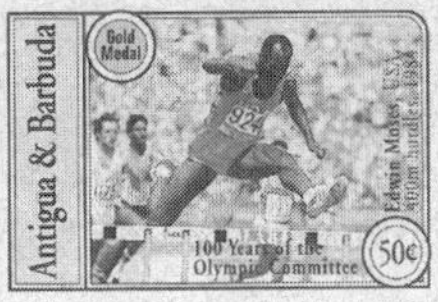

327 Edwin Moses (U.S.A.) (400m hurdles, 1984)

1994. Centenary of International Olympic Committee. Gold Medal Winners. Multicoloured.

1990	50c. Type **327**	40	30
1991	$1.50 Steffi Graf (Germany) (tennis, 1988)	1·50	1·50

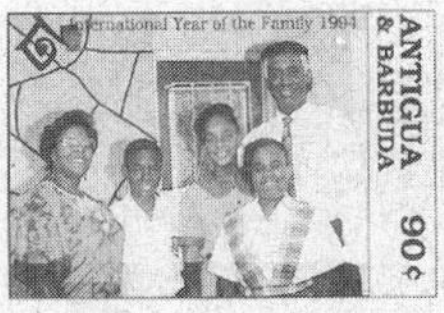

328 Antiguan Family

1994. International Year of the Family.

1993	**328** 90c. multicoloured	60	60

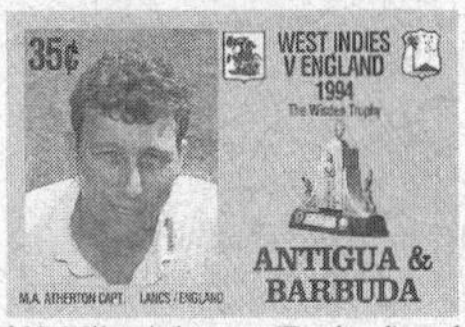

329 Mike Atherton (England) and Wisden Trophy

1994. Centenary (1995) of First English Cricket Tour to the West Indies. Multicoloured.

1994	35c. Type **329**	75	50
1995	75c. Viv Richards (West Indies) (vert)	1·25	80
1996	$1.20 Richie Richardson (West Indies) and Wisden Trophy	1·50	2·00

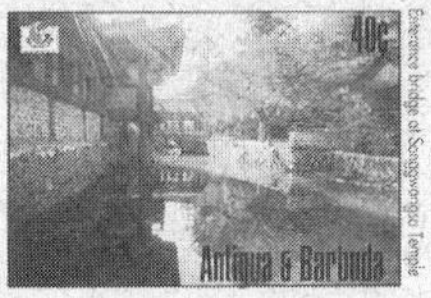

330 Entrance Bridge, Songgwangsa Temple

1994. "Philakorea '94" International Stamp Exhibition, Seoul. Multicoloured.

1998	40c. Type **330**	40	40
1999	75c. Long-necked bottle	60	60
2000	75c. Punch'ong ware jar with floral decoration	60	60
2001	75c. Punch'ong ware jar with blue dragon pattern	60	60
2002	75c. Ewer in shape of bamboo shoot	60	60
2003	75c. Punch'ong ware green jar	60	60
2004	75c. Pear-shaped bottle	60	60
2005	75c. Porcelain jar with brown dragon pattern	60	60
2006	75c. Porcelain jar with floral pattern	60	60
2007	90c. Song-op Folk Village, Cheju	60	60
2008	$3 Port Sogwipo	1·75	2·25

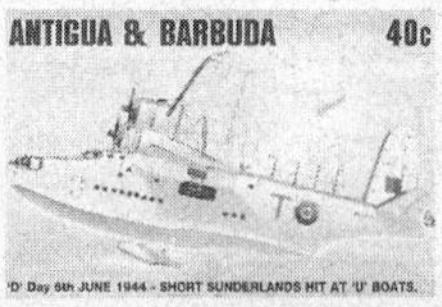

331 Short S.25 Sunderland (flying boat)

1994. 50th Anniv of D-Day. Multicoloured.

2010	40c. Type **331**	80	40
2011	$2 Lockheed P-38 Lightning fighters attacking train	2·00	2·25
2012	$3 Martin B-26 Marauder bombers	2·50	3·00

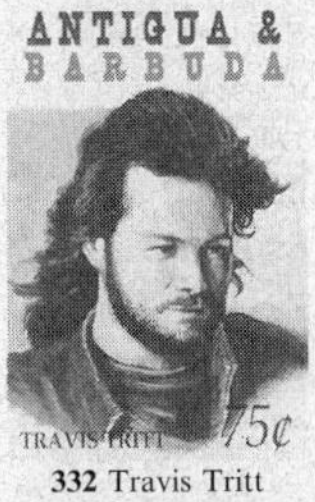

332 Travis Tritt

1994. Stars of Country and Western Music. Multicoloured.

2014	75c. Type **332**	60	60
2015	75c. Dwight Yoakam	60	60
2016	75c. Billy Ray Cyrus	60	60
2017	75c. Alan Jackson	60	60
2018	75c. Garth Brooks	60	60
2019	75c. Vince Gill	60	60
2020	75c. Clint Black	60	60
2021	75c. Eddie Rabbit	60	60
2022	75c. Patsy Cline	60	60
2023	75c. Tanya Tucker	60	60
2024	75c. Dolly Parton	60	60
2025	75c. Anne Murray	60	60
2026	75c. Tammy Wynette	60	60
2027	75c. Loretta Lynn	60	60
2028	75c. Reba McEntire	60	60
2029	75c. Skeeter Davis	60	60
2030	75c. Hank Snow	60	60
2031	75c. Gene Autry	60	60
2032	75c. Jimmie Rodgers	60	60
2033	75c. Ernest Tubb	60	60
2034	75c. Eddy Arnold	60	60
2035	75c. Willie Nelson	60	60
2036	75c. Johnny Cash	60	60
2037	75c. George Jones	60	60

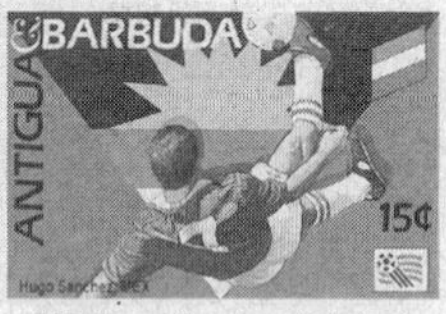

333 Hugo Sanchez (Mexico)

1994. World Cup Football Championship, U.S.A. (2nd issue). Multicoloured.

2039	15c. Type **333**	65	30
2040	35c. Jurgen Klinsmann (Germany)	1·00	45
2041	65c. Antiguan player	1·25	55
2042	$1.20 Cobi Jones (U.S.A.)	1·75	1·40
2043	$4 Roberto Baggio (Italy)	3·00	3·75
2044	$5 Bwalya Kalusha (Zambia)	3·00	3·75

No. 2040 is inscribed "Klinsman" in error.

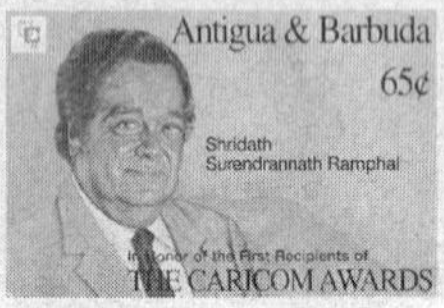

334 Sir Shridath Ramphal

1994. 1st Recipients of Order of the Caribbean Community. Multicoloured.

2046	65c. Type **334**	50	40
2047	90c. William Demas	65	60
2048	$1.20 Derek Walcott	1·50	1·50

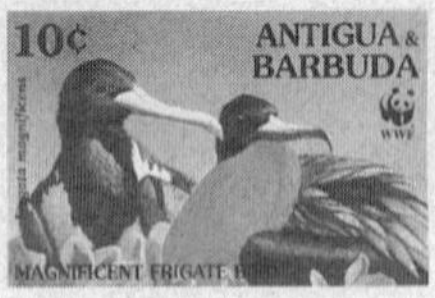

335 Pair of Magnificent Frigate Birds

1994. Birds. Multicoloured.

2049	10c. Type **335**	45	45
2050	15c. Bridled quail dove	50	40
2051	30c. Magnificent frigate bird chick hatching	70	70
2052	40c. Purple-throated carib (vert)	70	70
2053	$1 Male magnificent frigate bird in courtship display (vert)	1·00	1·00
2054	$1 Broad-winged hawk (vert)	1·00	1·00
2055	$3 Young magnificent frigate bird	2·00	2·75
2056	$4 Yellow warbler	2·00	2·75

Nos. 2049, 2051, 2053 and 2055 also show the W.W.F. Panda emblem.

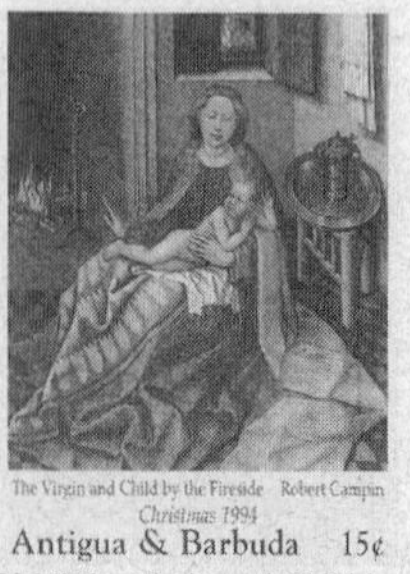

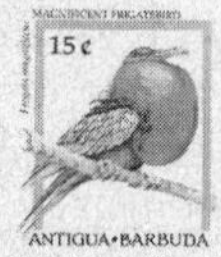

336 "The Virgin and Child by the Fireside" (Robert Campin)

337 Magnificent Frigate Bird

1994. Christmas. Religious Paintings. Multicoloured.

2058	15c. Type **336**	60	30
2059	35c. "The Reading Madonna" (Giorgione)	85	30
2060	40c. "Madonna and Child" (Giovanni Bellini)	90	30
2061	45c. "The Litta Madonna" (Da Vinci)	90	30
2062	65c. "The Virgin and Child under the Apple Tree" (Lucas Cranach the Elder)	1·25	55
2063	75c. "Madonna and Child" (Master of the Female Half-lengths)	1·40	70
2064	$1.20 "An Allegory of the Church" (Alessandro Allori)	1·75	1·50
2065	$5 "Madonna and Child wreathed with Flowers" (Jacob Jordaens)	3·25	4·00

1995. Birds. Multicoloured.

2067	15c. Type **337**	10	10
2068	25c. Blue-hooded euphonia	15	20
2069	35c. Eastern meadowlark ("Meadowlark")	20	25
2070	40c. Red-billed tropic bird	20	25
2071	45c. Greater flamingo	25	30
2072	60c. Yellow-faced grassquit	30	35
2073	65c. Yellow-billed cuckoo	35	40
2074	70c. Purple-throated carib	35	40
2075	75c. Bananaquit	40	45
2076	90c. Painted bunting	45	50
2077	$1.20 Red-legged honeycreeper	60	65
2078	$2 Northern jacana ("Jacana")	1·00	1·10
2079	$5 Greater Antillean bullfinch	2·50	2·75
2080	$10 Caribbean elaenia	5·00	5·25
2081	$20 Brown trembler ("Trembler")	10·00	10·50

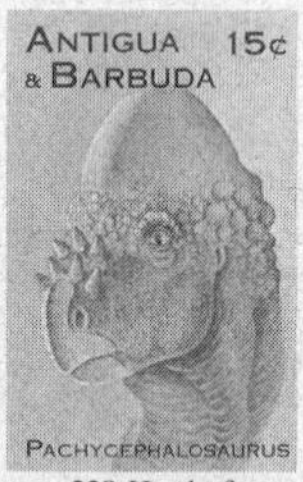

338 Head of Pachycephalosaurus

1995. Prehistoric Animals. Multicoloured.

2082	15c. Type **338**	50	50
2083	20c. Head of afrovenator	50	50
2084	65c. Centrosaurus	70	70
2085	75c. Kronosaurus (horiz)	70	70
2086	75c. Ichthyosaurus (horiz)	70	70
2087	75c. Plesiosaurus (horiz)	70	70
2088	75c. Archelon (horiz)	70	70
2089	75c. Pair of tyrannosaurus (horiz)	70	70
2090	75c. Tyrannosaurus (horiz)	70	70
2091	75c. Parasaurolophus (horiz)	70	70
2092	75c. Pair of parasaurolophus (horiz)	70	70
2093	75c. Oviraptor (horiz)	70	70
2094	75c. Protoceratops with eggs (horiz)	70	70
2095	75c. Pteranodon and protoceratops (horiz)	70	70
2096	75c. Pair of protoceratops (horiz)	70	70
2097	90c. Pentaceratops drinking	90	90
2098	$1.20 Head of tarbosaurus	1·10	1·10
2099	$5 Head of styracosaurus	3·00	3·50

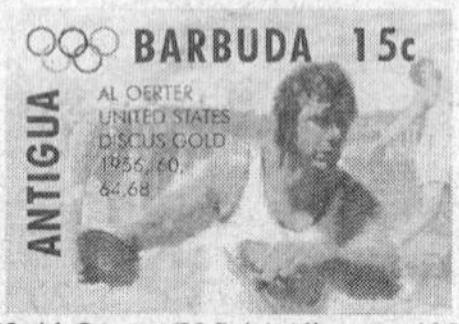

339 Al Oerter (U.S.A.) (discus – 1956, 1960, 1964, 1968)

1995. Olympic Games, Atlanta (1996). Previous Gold Medal Winners (1st issue). Multicoloured.

2101	15c. Type **339**	40	30
2102	20c. Greg Louganis (U.S.A.) (diving – 1984, 1988)	40	30
2103	65c. Naim Suleymanoglu (Turkey) (weightlifting – 1988)	65	50
2104	90c. Louise Ritter (U.S.A.) (high jump – 1988)	80	70
2105	$1.20 Nadia Comaneci (Rumania) (gymnastics – 1976)	1·40	1·10
2106	$5 Olga Bondarenko (Russia) (10,000 metres – 1988)	3·00	4·50

No. 2106 is inscribed "BOLDARENKO" in error.

See also Nos. 2302/23.

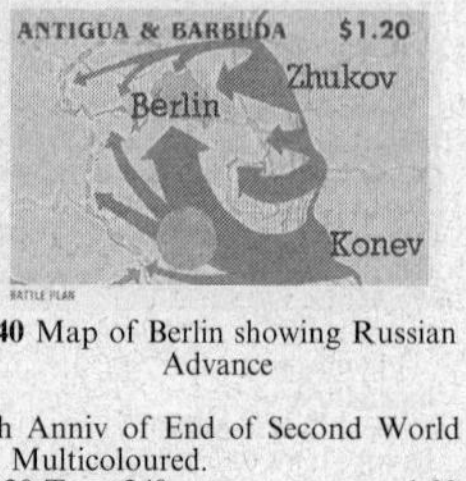

340 Map of Berlin showing Russian Advance

1995. 50th Anniv of End of Second World War in Europe. Multicoloured.

2108	$1.20 Type **340**	1·00	1·00
2109	$1.20 Russian tank and infantry	1·00	1·00
2110	$1.20 Street fighting in Berlin	1·00	1·00
2111	$1.20 German tank exploding	1·00	1·00
2112	$1.20 Russian air raid	1·00	1·00
2113	$1.20 German troops surrendering	1·00	1·00
2114	$1.20 Hoisting the Soviet flag on the Reichstag	1·00	1·00
2115	$1.20 Captured German standards	1·00	1·00

See also Nos. 2132/7.

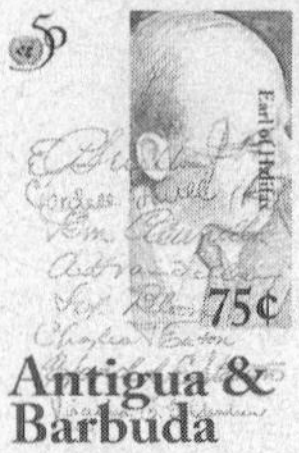

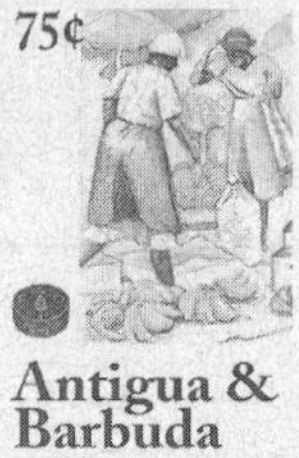

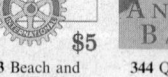

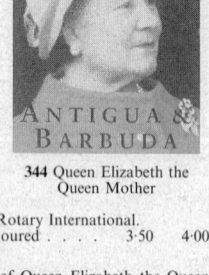

341 Signatures and Earl of Halifax

342 Woman buying Produce from Market

1995. 50th Anniv of United Nations. Multicoloured.

2117	75c. Type **341**	60	70
2118	90c. Virginia Gildersleeve	60	70
2119	$1.20 Harold Stassen	60	70

Nos. 2117/19 were printed together, se-tenant, forming a composite design.

1995. 50th Anniv of F.A.O. Multicoloured.

2121	75c. Type **342**	60	70
2122	90c. Women shopping	60	70
2123	$1.20 Women talking	60	70

Nos. 2121/3 were printed together, se-tenant, forming a composite design.

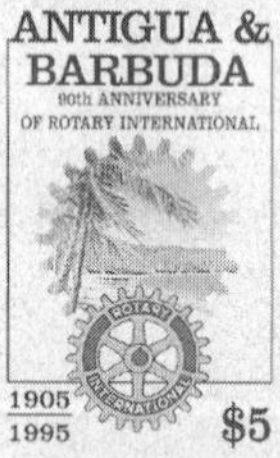

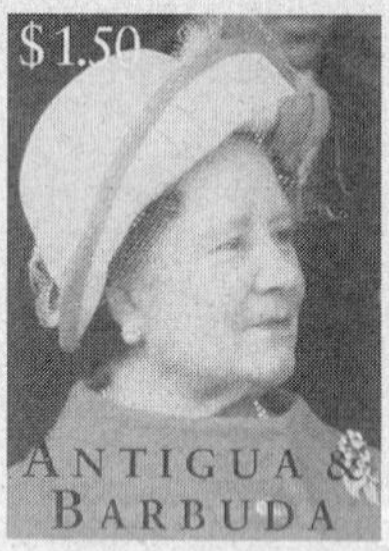

343 Beach and Rotary Emblem

344 Queen Elizabeth the Queen Mother

1995. 90th Anniv of Rotary International.

2125	**343** $5 multicoloured	3·50	4·00

1995. 95th Birthday of Queen Elizabeth the Queen Mother.

2127	– $1.50 brown, light brown and black	1·40	1·40
2128	**344** $1.50 multicoloured	1·40	1·40
2129	– $1.50 multicoloured	1·40	1·40
2130	– $1.50 multicoloured	1·40	1·40

DESIGNS: No. 2127, Queen Elizabeth the Queen Mother (pastel drawing); 2129, At desk (oil painting); 2130, Wearing green dress.

1995. 50th Anniv of End of Second World War in the Pacific. As T **340**. Multicoloured.

2132	$1.20 Gen. Chang Kai-Shek and Chinese guerrillas	95	1·00
2133	$1.20 Gen. Douglas MacArthur and beach landing	95	1·00
2134	$1.20 Gen. Claire Chennault and U.S. fighter aircraft	95	1·00
2135	$1.20 Brig. Orde Wingate and supply drop	95	1·00
2136	$1.20 Gen. Joseph Stilwell and U.S. supply plane	95	1·00
2137	$1.20 Field-Marshal Bill Slim and loading cow into plane	95	1·00

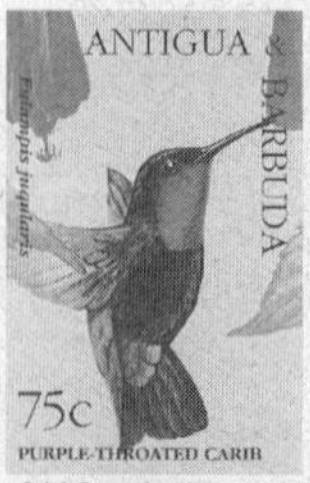

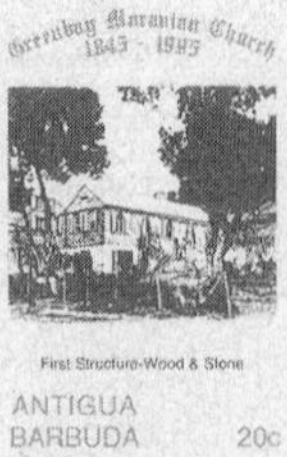

346 Purple-throated Carib

347 Original Church, 1845

1995. Birds. Multicoloured.

2140	75c. Type **346**	80	80
2141	75c. Antillean crested hummingbird	80	80
2142	75c. Bananaquit	80	80
2143	75c. Mangrove cuckoo	80	80
2144	75c. Troupial	80	80
2145	75c. Green-throated carib	80	80
2146	75c. Yellow warbler	80	80
2147	75c. Blue-hooded euphonia	80	80
2148	75c. Scaly-breasted thrasher	80	80
2149	75c. Burrowing owl	80	80
2150	75c. Carib grackle	80	80
2151	75c. Adelaide's warbler	80	80
2152	75c. Ring-necked duck	80	80
2153	75c. Ruddy duck	80	80
2154	75c. Green-winged teal	80	80
2155	75c. Wood duck	80	80
2156	75c. Hooded merganser	80	80
2157	75c. Lesser scaup	80	80
2158	75c. Black-billed whistling duck ("West Indian Tree Duck")	80	80
2159	75c. Fulvous whistling duck	80	80
2160	75c. Bahama pintail	80	80
2161	75c. Shoveler	80	80
2162	75c. Masked duck	80	80
2163	75c. American wigeon	80	80

Nos. 2140/51 and 2152/63 respectively were printed together, se-tenant, forming composite designs.

1995. 150th Anniv of Greenbay Moravian Church. Multicoloured.

2165	20c. Type **347**	45	30
2166	60c. Church in 1967	70	40
2167	75c. Present church	80	50
2168	90c. Revd. John Buckley (first minister of African descent)	1·00	60
2169	$1.20 Bishop John Ephraim Knight (longest-serving minister)	1·25	1·25
2170	$2 As 75c.	2·00	2·50

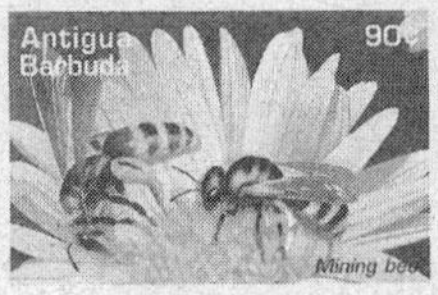

348 Mining Bees

1995. Bees. Multicoloured.

2172	90c. Type **348**	90	70
2173	$1.20 Solitary bee	1·25	90
2174	$1.65 Leaf-cutter bee	1·75	1·75
2175	$1.75 Honey bees	1·75	1·75

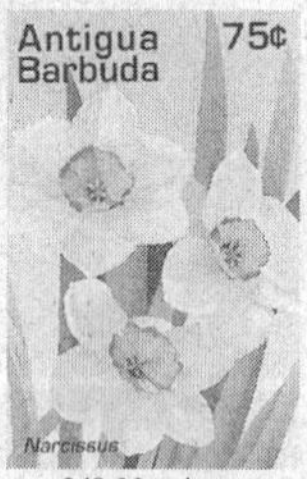

349 Narcissus

1995. Flowers. Multicoloured.

2177	75c. Type **349**	65	65
2178	75c. Camellia	65	65
2179	75c. Iris	65	65
2180	75c. Tulip	65	65
2181	75c. Poppy	65	65
2182	75c. Peony	65	65
2183	75c. Magnolia	65	65
2184	75c. Oriental lily	65	65
2185	75c. Rose	65	65
2186	75c. Pansy	65	65
2187	75c. Hydrangea	65	65
2188	75c. Azaleas	65	65

No. 2186 is inscribed "Pansie" in error.

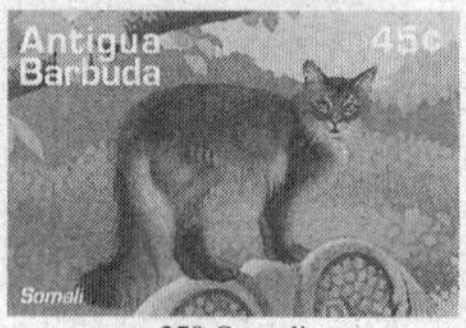

350 Somali

1995. Cats. Multicoloured.

2190	45c. Type **350**	55	55
2191	45c. Persian and butterflies	55	55
2192	45c. Devon rex	55	55
2193	45c. Turkish angora	55	55
2194	45c. Himalayan	55	55
2195	45c. Maine coon	55	55
2196	45c. Ginger non-pedigree	55	55
2197	45c. American wirehair	55	55
2198	45c. British shorthair	55	55
2199	45c. American curl	55	55
2200	45c. Black non-pedigree and butterfly	55	55
2201	45c. Birman	55	55

Nos. 2190/2201 were printed together, se-tenant, forming a composite design.

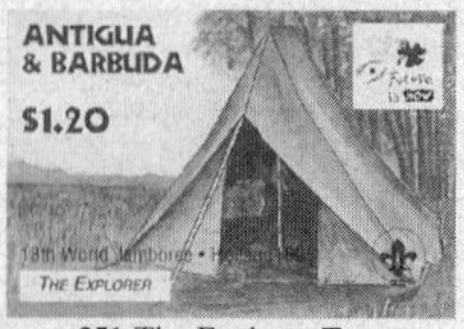

351 The Explorer Tent

1995. 18th World Scout Jamboree, Netherlands. Tents. Multicoloured.

2203	$1.20 Type **351**	1·25	1·25
2204	$1.20 Camper tent	1·25	1·25
2205	$1.20 Wall tent	1·25	1·25
2206	$1.20 Trail tarp	1·25	1·25

| 2207 | $1.20 Miner's tent | 1·25 | 1·25 |
| 2208 | $1.20 Voyager tent | 1·25 | 1·25 |

352 Trans-Gabon Diesel-electric Train

1995. Trains of the World. Multicoloured.

2210	35c. Type 352	75	65
2211	65c. Canadian Pacific diesel-electric locomotive	1·00	90
2212	75c. Santa Fe Railway diesel-electric locomotive, U.S.A.	1·25	1·00
2213	90c. High Speed Train, Great Britain	1·25	1·00
2214	$1.20 TGV express train, France	1·25	1·25
2215	$1.20 Diesel-electric locomotive, Australia	1·25	1·25
2216	$1.20 Pendolino "ETR 450" electric train, Italy	1·25	1·25
2217	$1.20 Diesel-electric locomotive, Thailand	1·25	1·25
2218	$1.20 Pennsylvania Railroad Type K4 steam locomotive, U.S.A.	1·25	1·25
2219	$1.20 Beyer-Garratt steam locomotive, East African Railways	1·25	1·25
2220	$1.20 Natal Government steam locomotive	1·25	1·25
2221	$1.20 Rail gun, American Civil War	1·25	1·25
2222	$1.20 Locomotive "Lion" (red livery), Great Britain	1·25	1·25
2223	$1.20 William Hedley's "Puffing Billy" (green livery), Great Britain	1·25	1·25
2224	$6 Amtrak high speed diesel locomotive, U.S.A.	3·00	3·50

353 Dag Hammarskjold (1961 Peace)

1995. Cent of Nobel Prize Trust Fund. Mult.

2226	$1 Type 353	90	90
2227	$1 Georg Wittig (1979 Chemistry)	90	90
2228	$1 Wilhelm Ostwald (1909 Chemistry)	90	90
2229	$1 Robert Koch (1905 Medicine)	90	90
2230	$1 Karl Ziegler (1963 Chemistry)	90	90
2231	$1 Alexander Fleming (1945 Medicine)	90	90
2232	$1 Hermann Staudinger (1953 Chemistry)	90	90
2233	$1 Manfred Eigen (1967 Chemistry)	90	90
2234	$1 Arno Penzias (1978 Physics)	90	90
2235	$1 Shmuel Agnon (1966 Literature)	90	90
2236	$1 Rudyard Kipling (1907 Literature)	90	90
2237	$1 Aleksandr Solzhenitsyn (1970 Literature)	90	90
2238	$1 Jack Steinberger (1988 Physics)	90	90
2239	$1 Andrei Sakharov (1975 Peace)	90	90
2240	$1 Otto Stern (1943 Physics)	90	90
2241	$1 John Steinbeck (1962 Literature)	90	90
2242	$1 Nadine Gordimer (1991 Literature)	90	90
2243	$1 William Faulkner (1949 Literature)	90	90

354 Elvis Presley

1995. 60th Birth Anniv of Elvis Presley. Mult.

2245	$1 Type 354	90	75
2246	$1 Holding microphone in right hand	90	75
2247	$1 In blue shirt and with neck of guitar	90	75
2248	$1 Wearing blue shirt and smiling	90	75
2249	$1 On wedding day	90	75
2250	$1 In army uniform	90	75
2251	$1 Wearing red shirt	90	75

| 2252 | $1 Wearing white shirt | 90 | 75 |
| 2253 | $1 In white shirt with microphone | 90 | 75 |

355 John Lennon and Signature   357 "Rest on the Flight into Egypt" (Paolo Veronese)

1995. 15th Death Anniv of John Lennon (entertainer). Multicoloured.

2255	45c. Type 355	50	50
2256	50c. In beard and spectacles	50	50
2257	65c. Wearing sunglasses	55	55
2258	75c. In cap with heart badge	65	65

1995. Hurricane Relief. Nos. 2203/8 optd **"Hurricane Relief".**

2260	$1.20 Type 351	1·00	1·00
2261	$1.20 Camper tent	1·00	1·00
2262	$1.20 Wall tent	1·00	1·00
2263	$1.20 Trail tarp	1·00	1·00
2264	$1.20 Miner's tent	1·00	1·00
2265	$1.20 Voyager tent	1·00	1·00

1995. Christmas. Religious Paintings. Multicoloured.

2267	15c. Type 357	30	30
2268	35c. "Madonna and Child" (Van Dyck)	40	40
2269	65c. "Sacred Conversation Piece" (Veronese)	60	50
2270	75c. "Vision of St. Anthony" (Van Dyck)	70	60
2271	90c. "Virgin and Child" (Van Eyck)	80	65
2272	$6 "The Immaculate Conception" (Giovanni Tiepolo)	3·00	4·00

358 "Hygrophoropsis aurantiaca"   360 Florence Griffith Joyner (U.S.A.) (Gold – track, 1988)

359 H.M.S. "Resolution" (Cook)

1996. Fungi. Multicoloured.

2274	75c. Type 358	40	45
2275	75c. "Hygrophorus bakerensis"	40	45
2276	75c. "Hygrophorus conicus"	40	45
2277	75c. "Hygrophorus miniatus" ("Hygrocybe miniata")	40	45
2278	75c. "Suillus brevipes"	40	45
2279	75c. "Suillus luteus"	40	45
2280	75c. "Suillus granulatus"	40	45
2281	75c. "Suillus caerulescens"	40	45

1996. Sailing Ships. Multicoloured.

2283	15c. Type 359	10	15
2284	25c. "Mayflower" (Pilgrim Fathers)	15	20
2285	45c. "Santa Maria" (Columbus)	25	30
2286	75c. "Aemilia" (Dutch galleon)	40	45
2287	75c. "Sovereign of the Seas" (English galleon)	40	45
2288	90c. H.M.S. "Victory" (Nelson)	45	50
2289	$1.20 As No. 2286	60	65
2290	$1.20 As No. 2287	60	65
2291	$1.20 "Royal Louis" (French galleon)	60	65
2292	$1.20 H.M.S. "Royal George" (ship of the line)	60	65
2293	$1.20 "Le Protecteur" (French frigate)	60	65
2294	$1.20 As No. 2288	60	65
2295	$1.50 As No. 2285	80	85
2296	$1.50 "Vitoria" (Magellan)	80	85
2297	$1.50 "Golden Hind" (Drake)	80	85
2298	$1.50 As No. 2284	80	85

| 2299 | $1.50 "Griffin" (La Salle) | 80 | 85 |
| 2300 | $1.50 Type 359 | 80 | 85 |

1996. Olympic Games, Atlanta. Previous Medal Winners (2nd issue). Multicoloured.

2302	65c. Type 360	35	40
2303	75c. Olympic Stadium, Seoul (1988) (horiz)	40	45
2304	90c. Allison Jolly and Lynne Jewell (U.S.A.) (Gold – yachting, 1988) (horiz)	45	50
2305	90c. Wolfgang Nordwig (Germany) (Gold – pole vaulting, 1972)	45	50
2306	90c. Shirley Strong (Great Britain) (Silver – 100 metres hurdles, 1984)	45	50
2307	90c. Sergei Bubka (Russia) (Gold – pole vault, 1988)	45	50
2308	90c. Filbert Bayi (Tanzania) (Silver – 3000 metres steeplechase, 1980)	45	50
2309	90c. Victor Saneyev (Russia) (Gold – triple jump, 1968, 1972, 1976)	45	50
2310	90c. Silke Renk (Germany) (Gold – javelin, 1992)	45	50
2311	90c. Daley Thompson (Great Britain) (Gold – decathlon, 1980, 1984)	45	50
2312	90c. Robert Richards (U.S.A.) (Gold – pole vault, 1952, 1956)	45	50
2313	90c. Parry O'Brien (U.S.A.) (Gold – shot put, 1952, 1956)	45	50
2314	90c. Ingrid Kramer (Germany) (Gold – women's platform diving, 1960)	45	50
2315	90c. Kelly McCormick (U.S.A.) (Silver – women's springboard diving, 1984)	45	50
2316	90c. Gary Tobian (U.S.A.) (Gold – men's springboard diving, 1960)	45	50
2317	90c. Greg Louganis (U.S.A.) (Gold – men's diving, 1984 and 1988)	45	50
2318	90c. Michelle Mitchell (U.S.A.) (Silver – women's platform diving, 1984 and 1988)	45	50
2319	90c. Zhou Jihong (China) (Gold – women's platform diving, 1984)	45	50
2320	90c. Wendy Wyland (U.S.A.) (Bronze – women's platform diving, 1984)	45	50
2321	90c. Xu Yanmei (China) (Gold – women's platform diving, 1988)	45	50
2322	90c. Fu Mingxia (China) (Gold – women's platform diving, 1992)	45	50
2323	$1.20 2000 metre tandem cycle race (horiz)	60	65

Nos. 2305/13 and 2314/22 respectively were printed together, se-tenant, with the background forming a composite design.

361 Black Skimmer

1996. Sea Birds. Multicoloured.

2325	75c. Type 361	40	45
2326	75c. Black-capped petrel	40	45
2327	75c. Sooty tern	40	45
2328	75c. Royal tern	40	45
2329	75c. Pomarine skua ("Pomarine Jaegger")	40	45
2330	75c. White-tailed tropic bird	40	45
2331	75c. Northern gannet	40	45
2332	75c. Laughing gull	40	45

362 Mickey and Goofy on Elephant ("Around the World in Eighty Days")

1996. Novels of Jules Verne. Walt Disney cartoon characters in scenes from the books. Multicoloured.

2334	1c. Type 362	10	10
2335	2c. Mickey, Donald and Goofy entering cave ("A Journey to the Centre of the Earth")	10	10
2336	5c. Mickey and Minnie driving postcart ("Michel Strogoff")	15	15
2337	10c. Mickey, Donald and Goofy in space rocket ("From the Earth to the Moon")	20	15
2338	15c. Mickey and Goofy in balloon ("Five Weeks in a Balloon")	20	15

2339	20c. Mickey and Goofy in China ("Around the World in Eighty Days")	20	15
2340	$1 Mickey, Goofy and Pluto on island ("The Mysterious Island")	1·25	85
2341	$2 Mickey, Pluto, Goofy and Donald on Moon ("From the Earth to the Moon")	1·75	1·75
2342	$3 Mickey being lifted by bird ("Captain Grant's Children")	2·25	2·50
2343	$5 Mickey with seal and squid ("Twenty Thousand Leagues Under the Sea")	3·25	3·75

363 Bruce Lee

1996. "CHINA '96" 9th Asian International Stamp Exhibition, Peking. Bruce Lee (actor). Multicoloured.

2345	75c. Type 363	40	45
2346	75c. Bruce Lee in white shirt and red tie	40	45
2347	75c. In plaid jacket and tie	40	45
2348	75c. In mask and uniform	40	45
2349	75c. Bare-chested	40	45
2350	75c. In mandarin jacket	40	45
2351	75c. In brown jumper	40	45
2352	75c. In fawn shirt	40	45
2353	75c. Shouting	40	45

364 Queen Elizabeth II

1996. 70th Birthday of Queen Elizabeth II. Multicoloured.

2355	$2 Type 364	1·00	1·10
2356	$2 With bouquet	1·00	1·10
2357	$2 In Garter robes	1·00	1·10

365 Ancient Egyptian Cavalryman

1996. Cavalry through the Ages. Multicoloured.

2359	60c. Type 365	30	35
2360	60c. 13th-century English knight	30	35
2361	60c. 16th-century Spanish lancer	30	35
2362	60c. 18th-century Chinese cavalryman	30	35

366 Girl in Red Sari   367 Tomb of Zachariah and "Verbascum sinuatum"

1996. 50th Anniv of U.N.I.C.E.F. Multicoloured.

2364	75c. Type 366	40	45
2365	90c. South American mother and child	45	50
2366	$1.20 Nurse with child	60	65

1996. 3000th Anniv of Jerusalem. Multicoloured.

2368	75c. Type 367	40	45
2369	90c. Pool of Siloam and "Hyacinthus orientalis"	45	50
2370	$1.20 Hurva Synagogue and "Ranunculus asiaticus"	60	65

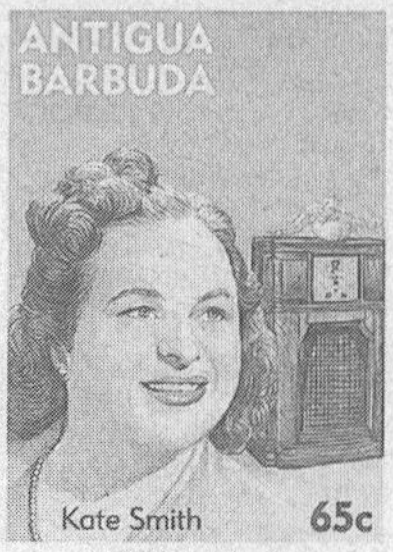

368 Kate Smith

1996. Cent of Radio. Entertainers. Mult.
2372 65c. Type **368** 35 40
2373 75c. Dinah Shore 40 45
2374 90c. Rudy Vallee 45 50
2375 $1.20 Bing Crosby 60 65

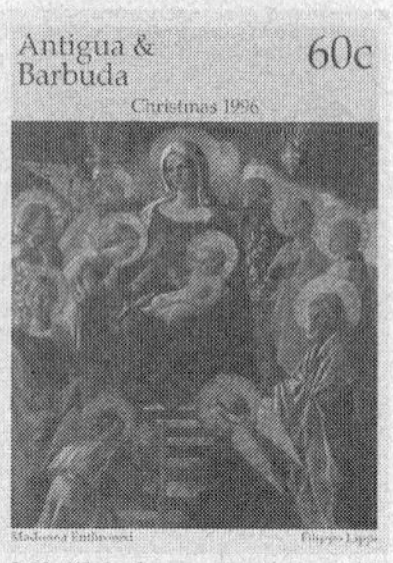

369 "Madonna Enthroned"

1996. Christmas. Religious Paintings by Filippo Lippi. Multicoloured.
2377 60c. Type **369** 30 35
2378 90c. "Adoration of the Child and Saints" 45 50
2379 $1 "The Annunciation" 50 55
2380 $1.20 "Birth of the Virgin" 60 65
2381 $1.60 "Adoration of the Child" 80 85
2382 $1.75 "Madonna and Child" 90 95

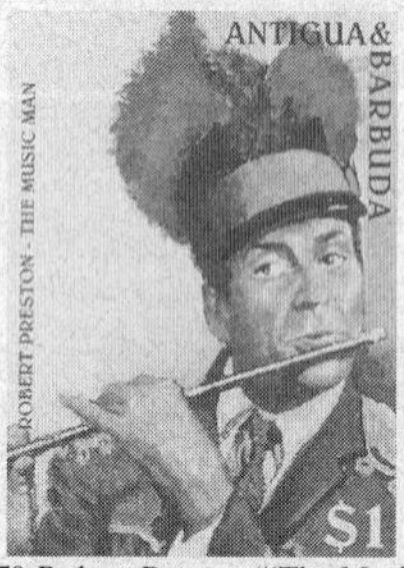

370 Robert Preston ("The Music Man")

1997. Broadway Musical Stars. Multicoloured.
2384 $1 Type **370** 50 55
2385 $1 Michael Crawford ("Phantom of the Opera") 50 55
2386 $1 Zero Mostel ("Fiddler on the Roof") 50 55
2387 $1 Patti Lupone ("Evita") 50 55
2388 $1 Raul Julia ("Threepenny Opera") 50 55
2389 $1 Mary Martin ("South Pacific") 50 55
2390 $1 Carol Channing ("Hello Dolly") 50 55
2391 $1 Yul Brynner ("The King and I") 50 55
2392 $1 Julie Andrews ("My Fair Lady") 50 55

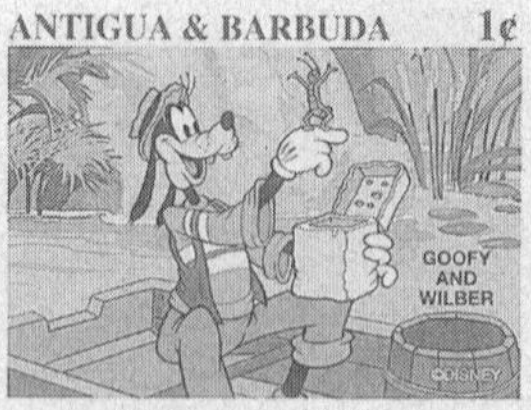

371 Goofy and Wilbur

1997. Walt Disney Cartoon Characters. Mult.
2394 1c. Type **371** 10 10
2395 2c. Donald and Goofy in boxing ring 10 10
2396 5c. Donald, Panchito and Jose Carioca 10 10
2397 10c. Mickey and Goofy playing chess 20 15
2398 15c. Chip and Dale with acorns 20 15
2399 20c. Pluto and Mickey 20 15
2400 $1 Daisy and Minnie eating ice-cream 90 75
2401 $2 Daisy and Minnie at dressing table 1·50 1·75
2402 $3 Gus Goose and Donald 2·00 2·50

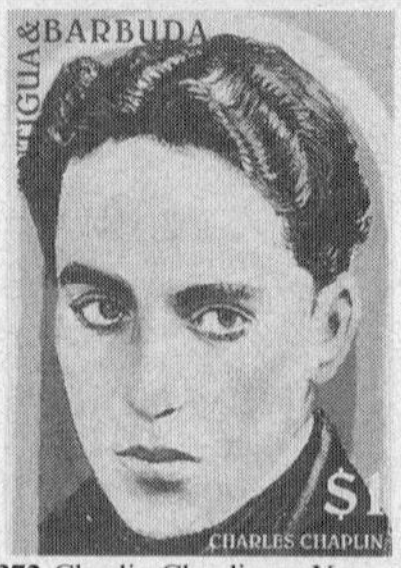

372 Charlie Chaplin as Young Man

1997. 20th Death Anniv of Charlie Chaplin (film star). Multicoloured.
2404 $1 Type **372** 50 55
2405 $1 Pulling face 50 55
2406 $1 Looking over shoulder 50 55
2407 $1 In cap 50 55
2408 $1 In front of star 50 55
2409 $1 In "The Great Dictator" 50 55
2410 $1 With movie camera and megaphone 50 55
2411 $1 Standing in front of camera lens 50 55
2412 $1 Putting on make-up 50 55
Nos. 2404/12 were printed together, se-tenant, with the backgrounds forming a composite design.

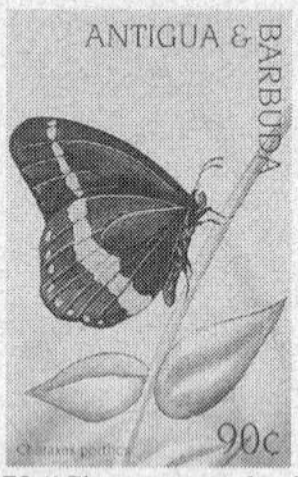

373 "Charaxes porthos"

1997. Butterflies. Multicoloured.
2414 90c. Type **373** 45 50
2415 $1.10 "Charaxes protoclea protoclea" 60 65
2416 $1.10 "Byblia ilithyia" 60 65
2417 $1.10 Black-headed bush shrike ("Tchagra") (bird) 60 65
2418 $1.10 "Charaxes nobilis" 60 65
2419 $1.10 "Pseudacraea boisduvali trimeni" 60 65
2420 $1.10 "Charaxes smaragdalis" 60 65
2421 $1.10 "Charaxes lasti" 60 65
2422 $1.10 "Pseudacrea poggei" 60 65
2423 $1.10 "Graphium colonna" 60 65
2424 $1.10 Carmine bee eater (bird) 60 65
2425 $1.10 "Pseudacraea eurytus" 60 65
2426 $1.10 "Hypolimnas monteironis" 60 65
2427 $1.10 "Charaxes anticlea" 60 65
2428 $1.10 "Graphium leonidas" 60 65
2429 $1.10 "Graphium illyris" 60 65
2430 $1.10 "Nephronia argia" 60 65
2431 $1.10 "Graphium policenes" 60 65
2432 $1.10 "Papilio dardanus" 60 65
2433 $1.20 "Aethiopana honorius" 60 65
2434 $1.60 "Charaxes hadrianus" 80 85
2435 $1.75 "Precis westermanni" 90 95
Nos. 2415/23 and 2424/32 respectively were printed together, se-tenant, with the backgrounds forming a composite design.
No. 2430 is inscribed "Nepheronia argia" in error.

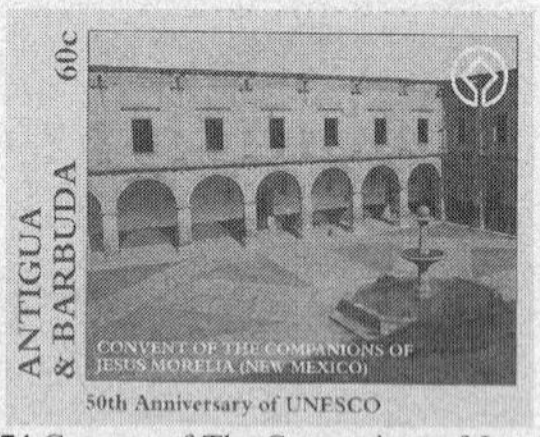

374 Convent of The Companions of Jesus, Morelia, Mexico

1997. 50th Anniv of U.N.E.S.C.O. Multicoloured.
2437 60c. Type **374** 30 35
2438 90c. Fortress at San Lorenzo, Panama (vert) 45 50
2439 $1 Canaima National Park, Venezuela (vert) 50 55
2440 $1.10 Aerial view of church with tower, Guanajuato, Mexico (vert) 60 65
2441 $1.10 Church facade, Guanajuato, Mexico (vert) 60 65
2442 $1.10 Aerial view of churches with domes, Guanajuato, Mexico (vert) 60 65
2443 $1.10 Jesuit Missions of the Chiquitos, Bolivia (vert) 60 65
2444 $1.10 Huascaran National Park, Peru (vert) 60 65
2445 $1.10 Jesuit Missions of La Santisima, Paraguay (vert) 60 65
2446 $1.10 Cartagena, Colombia (vert) 60 65
2447 $1.10 Fortification, Havana, Cuba (vert) 60 65
2448 $1.20 As No. 2444 (vert) 60 65
2449 $1.60 Church of San Fransisco, Guatemala (vert) 80 85
2450 $1.65 Tikal National Park, Guatemala 85 90
2451 $1.65 Rio Platano Reserve, Honduras 85 90
2452 $1.65 Ruins of Copan, Honduras 85 90
2453 $1.65 Antigua ruins, Guatemala 85 90
2454 $1.65 Teotihuacan, Mexico 85 90
2455 $1.75 Santo Domingo, Dominican Republic (vert) 90 95
No. 2446 is inscribed "Columbia" in error.

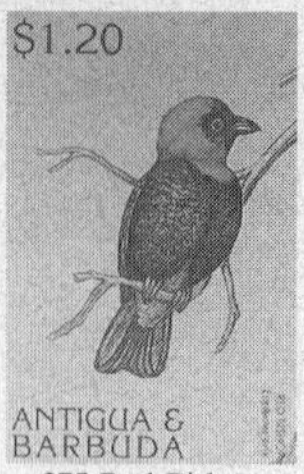

375 Red Bishop

1997. Endangered Species. Multicoloured.
2457 $1.20 Type **375** 60 65
2458 $1.20 Yellow baboon 60 65
2459 $1.20 Superb starling 60 65
2460 $1.20 Ratel 60 65
2461 $1.20 Hunting dog 60 65
2462 $1.20 Serval 60 65
2463 $1.65 Okapi 85 90
2464 $1.65 Giant forest squirrel 85 90
2465 $1.65 Lesser masked weaver 85 90
2466 $1.65 Small-spotted genet 85 90
2467 $1.65 Yellow-billed stork 85 90
2468 $1.65 Red-headed agama 85 90
Nos. 2457/62 and 2463/8 respectively were printed together, se-tenant, with the backgrounds forming composite designs.

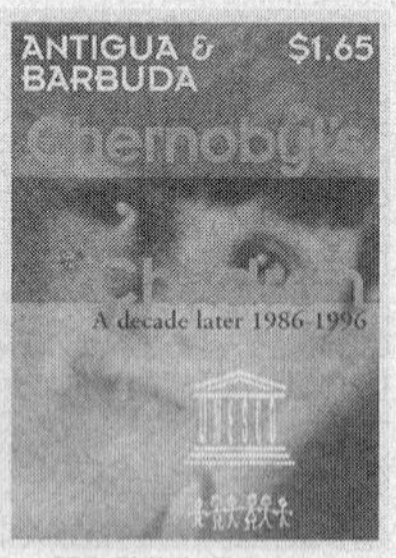

376 Child's Face and U.N.E.S.C.O. Emblem

1997. 10th Anniv of Chernobyl Nuclear Disaster. Multicoloured.
2470 $1.65 Type **376** 85 90
2471 $2 As Type **376**, but inscr "CHABAD'S CHILDREN OF CHERNOBYL" at foot 1·00 1·10

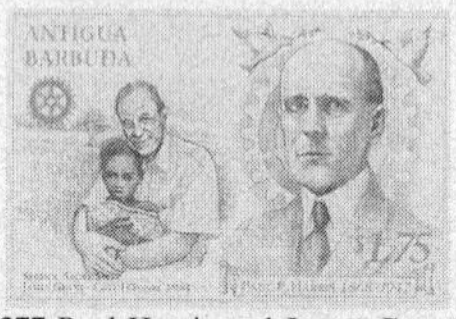

377 Paul Harris and James Grant

1997. 50th Death Anniv of Paul Harris (founder of Rotary International).
2472 **377** $1.75 multicoloured 90 95

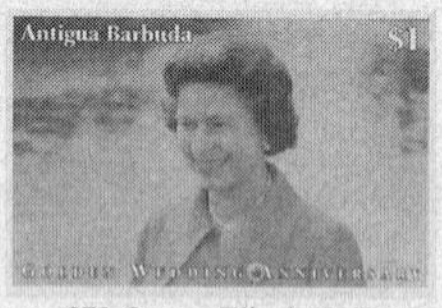

378 Queen Elizabeth II

1997. Golden Wedding of Queen Elizabeth and Prince Philip. Multicoloured.
2474 $1 Type **378** 50 55
2475 $1 Royal coat of arms 50 55
2476 $1 Queen Elizabeth and Prince Philip at reception 50 55
2477 $1 Queen Elizabeth and Prince Philip in landau 50 55
2478 $1 Balmoral 50 55
2479 $1 Prince Philip 50 55

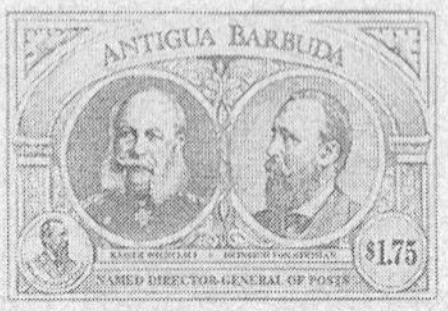

379 Kaiser Wilhelm I and Heinrich von Stephan

1997. "Pacific '97" International Stamp Exhibition, San Francisco. Death Centenary of Heinrich von Stephan (founder of the U.P.U.).
2481 **379** $1.75 blue 90 95
2482 – $1.75 brown 90 95
2483 – $1.75 mauve 90 95
DESIGNS: No. 2482, Von Stephan and Mercury; 2483, Carrier pigeon and loft.
No. 2483 is inscribed "PIDGEON" in error.

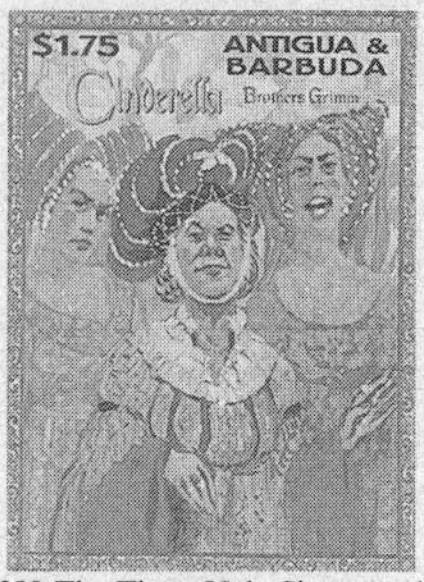

380 The Three Ugly Sisters and their Mother

1997. 175th Anniv of Brothers Grimm's Third Collection of Fairy Tales. Cinderella. Multicoloured.
2485 $1.75 Type **380** 90 95
2486 $1.75 Cinderella and her Fairy Godmother 90 95
2487 $1.75 Cinderella and the Prince 90 95

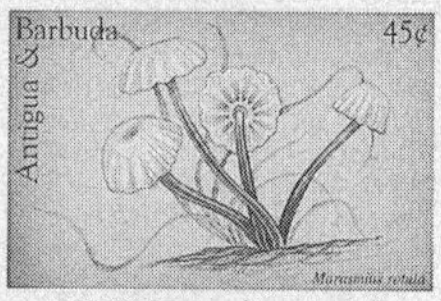

381 "Marasmius rotula"

1997. Fungi. Multicoloured.
2489 45c. Type **381** 25 30
2490 65c. "Cantharellus cibarius" 35 40
2491 70c. "Lepiota cristata" 35 40
2492 90c. "Auricularia mesenteric" 45 50
2493 $1 "Pholiota alnicola" 50 55
2494 $1.65 "Leccinum aurantiacum" 85 90
2495 $1.75 "Entoloma serrulatum" 90 95
2496 $1.75 "Panaeolus sphinctrinus" 90 95
2497 $1.75 "Volvariella bombycina" 90 95
2498 $1.75 "Conocybe percincta" 90 95
2499 $1.75 "Pluteus cervinus" 90 95
2500 $1.75 "Russula foetens" 90 95

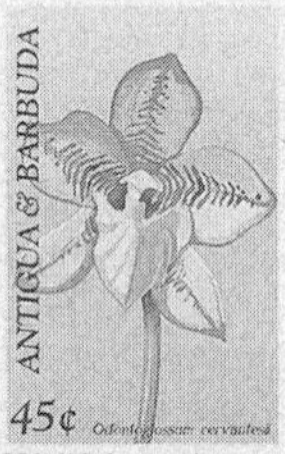

382 "Odontoglossum cervantesii"

1997. Orchids of the World. Multicoloured.
2502 45c. Type **382** 25 30
2503 65c. "Phalaenopsis" Medford Star 35 40
2504 75c. "Vanda Motes" Resplendent 40 45
2505 90c. "Odontonia" Debutante 45 50
2506 $1 "Iwanagaara" Apple Blossom 50 55
2507 $1.65 "Cattleya" Sophia Martin 85 90
2508 $1.65 Dogface Butterfly 85 90
2509 $1.65 "Laeliocattleya" Mini Purple 85 90
2510 $1.65 "Cymbidium" Showgirl 85 90
2511 $1.65 "Brassolaeliocattleya" Dorothy Bertsch 85 90
2512 $1.65 "Disa Blackii" 85 90
2513 $1.65 "Paphiopedilum leeanum" 85 90
2514 $1.65 "Paphiopedilum macranthum" 85 90
2515 $1.65 "Brassocattleya" Angel Lace 85 90
2516 $1.65 "Saphrolae liocattleya" Precious Stones 85 90
2517 $1.65 Orange Theope Butterfly 85 90
2518 $1.65 "Promenaea xanthina" 85 90
2519 $1.65 "Lycasle macrobulbon" 85 90
2520 $1.65 "Amestella philippinensis" 85 90
2521 $1.65 "Masdevallia" Machu Picchu 85 90
2522 $1.65 "Phalaenopsis" Zuma Urchin 85 90
2523 $2 "Dendrobium victoria-reginae" 1·00 1·10

Nos. 2507/14 and 2515/22 respectively were printed together, se-tenant, with the backgrounds forming composite designs.

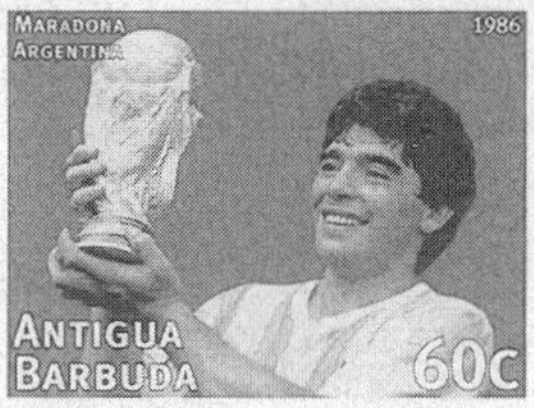

383 Maradona holding World Cup Trophy, 1986

1997. World Cup Football Championship, France (1998).

2525	**383** 60c. multicoloured	30	35
2526	– 75c. brown	40	45
2527	– 90c. multicoloured	45	50
2528	– $1 brown	50	55
2529	– $1 brown	50	55
2530	– $1 brown	50	55
2531	– $1 black	50	55
2532	– $1 brown	50	55
2533	– $1 brown	50	55
2534	– $1 brown	50	55
2535	– $1 brown	50	55
2536	– $1.20 multicoloured	60	65
2537	– $1.65 multicoloured	85	90
2538	– $1.75 multicoloured	90	95

DESIGNS—HORIZ: No. 2526, Fritzwalter, West Germany, 1954; 2527, Zoff, Italy, 1982; 2536, Moore, England, 1966; 2537, Alberto, Brazil, 1970; 2538, Matthaus, West Germany, 1990. VERT: No. 2528, Ademir, Brazil, 1950; 2529, Eusebio, Portugal, 1966; 2530, Fontaine, France, 1958; 2531, Schillaci, Italy, 1990; 2532, Leonidas, Brazil, 1938; 2533, Stabile, Argentina, 1930; 2534, Nejedly, Czechoslovakia, 1934; 2535, Muller, West Germany, 1970.

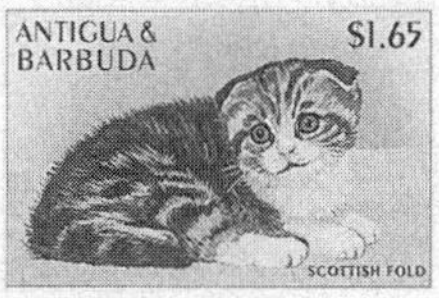

384 Scottish Fold Kitten

1997. Cats and Dogs. Multicoloured.

2540	$1.65 Type **384**	85	90
2541	$1.65 Japanese bobtail	85	90
2542	$1.65 Tabby manx	85	90
2543	$1.65 Bicolor American shorthair	85	90
2544	$1.65 Sorrel Abyssinian	85	90
2545	$1.65 Himalayan blue point	85	90
2546	$1.65 Dachshund	85	90
2547	$1.65 Staffordshire terrier	85	90
2548	$1.65 Shar-pei	85	90
2549	$1.65 Beagle	85	90
2550	$1.65 Norfolk terrier	85	90
2551	$1.65 Golden retriever	85	90

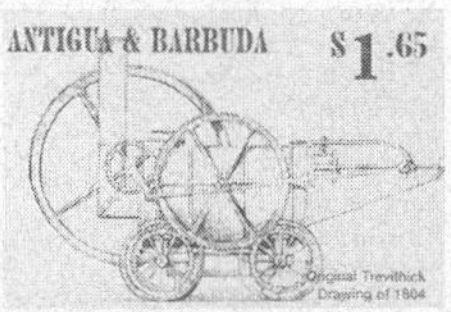

385 Original Drawing by Trevithick, 1803

1997. Railway Locomotives of the World. Multicoloured.

2553	$1.65 Type **385**	85	90
2554	$1.65 William Hedley's "Puffing Billy", (1813–14)	85	90
2555	$1.65 Crampton locomotive of French Nord Railway, 1858	85	90
2556	$1.65 Lawrence Machine Shop locomotive, U.S.A., 1860	85	90
2557	$1.65 Natchez and Hamburg Railway steam locomotive "Mississippi", U.S.A., 1834	85	90
2558	$1.65 Bury "Coppernob" locomotive, Furness Railway, 1846	85	90
2559	$1.65 David Joy's "Jenny Lind", 1847	85	90
2560	$1.65 Schenectady Atlantic locomotive, U.S.A., 1899	85	90
2561	$1.65 Kitsons Class 1800 tank locomotive, Japan, 1881	85	90
2562	$1.65 Pennsylvania Railroad express frieght	85	90
2563	$1.65 Karl Golsdorf's 4 cylinder locomotive, Austria	85	90
2564	$1.65 Series "E" locomotive, Russia, 1930	85	90

No. 2554 is dated "1860" in error.

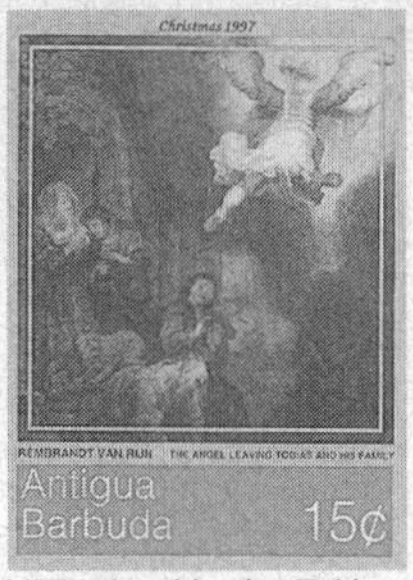

386 "The Angel leaving Tobias and his Family" (Rembrandt)

1997. Christmas. Religious Paintings. Multicoloured.

2566	15c. Type **386**	10	15
2567	25c. "The Resurrection" (Martin Knoller)	15	20
2568	60c. "Astronomy" (Raphael)	30	35
2569	75c. "Music-making Angel" (Melozzo da Forli)	40	45
2570	90c. "Amor" (Parmigianino)	45	50
2571	$1.20 "Madonna and Child with Saints" (Rosso Fiorentino)	60	65

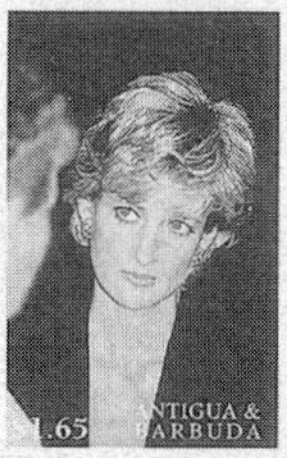

387 Diana, Princess of Wales

1998. Diana, Princess of Wales Commemoration. Multicoloured (except Nos. 2574 and 2581/2).

2573	$1.65 Type **387**	85	90
2574	$1.65 Wearing hoop earrings (red and black)	85	90
2575	$1.65 Carrying bouquet	85	90
2576	$1.65 Wearing floral hat	85	90
2577	$1.65 With Prince Harry	85	90
2578	$1.65 Wearing white jacket	85	90
2579	$1.65 In kitchen	85	90
2580	$1.65 Wearing black and white dress	85	90
2581	$1.65 Wearing hat (brown and black)	85	90
2582	$1.65 Wearing floral print dress (brown and black)	85	90
2583	$1.65 Dancing with John Travolta	85	90
2584	$1.65 Wearing white hat and jacket	85	90

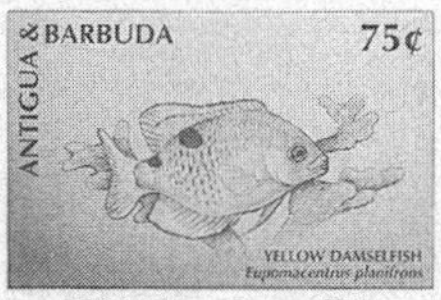

388 Yellow Damselfish

1998. Fishes. Multicoloured.

2586	75c. Type **388**	40	45
2587	90c. Barred hamlet	45	50
2588	$1 Yellow-tailed damselfish ("Jewelfish")	50	55
2589	$1.20 Blue-headed wrasse	60	65
2590	$1.50 Queen angelfish	80	85
2591	$1.65 Jackknife-fish	85	90
2592	$1.65 Spot-finned hogfish	85	90
2593	$1.65 Sergeant major	85	90
2594	$1.65 Neon goby	85	90
2595	$1.65 Jawfish	85	90
2596	$1.65 Flamefish	85	90
2597	$1.65 Rock beauty	85	90
2598	$1.65 Yellow-tailed snapper	85	90
2599	$1.65 Creole wrasse	85	90
2600	$1.65 Slender filefish	85	90
2601	$1.65 Long-spined squirrelfish	85	90
2602	$1.65 Royal gramma ("Fairy Basslet")	85	90
2603	$1.75 Queen triggerfish	90	95

Nos. 2591/6 and 2597/2602 respectively were printed together, se-tenant, with the backgrounds forming composite designs.

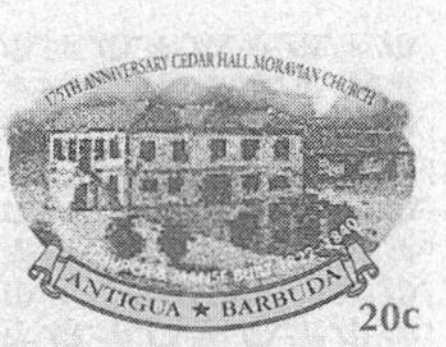

389 First Church and Manse, 1822–40

1998. 175th Anniv of Cedar Hall Moravian Church. Multicoloured.

2605	20c. Type **389**	10	15
2606	45c. Cedar Hall School, 1840	25	30
2607	75c. Hugh A. King, minister 1945–53	40	45
2608	90c. Present Church building	45	50
2609	$1.20 Water tank, 1822	60	65
2610	$2 Former Manse, demolished 1978	1·00	1·10

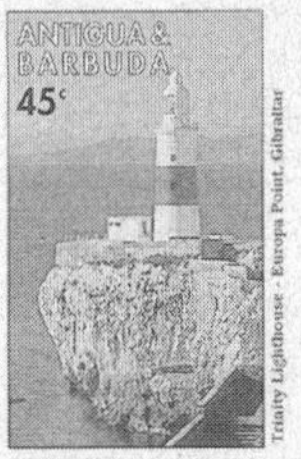

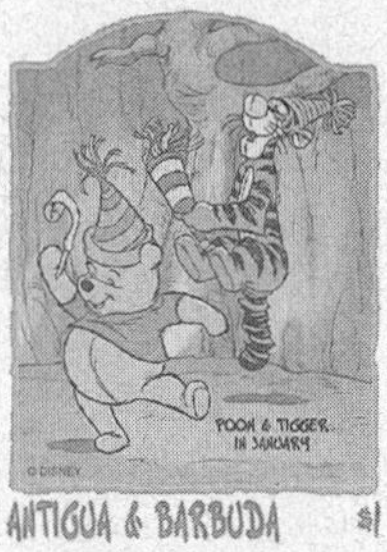

390 Europa Point Lighthouse, Gibraltar

391 Pooh and Tigger (January)

1998. Lighthouses of the World. Multicoloured.

2612	45c. Type **390**	25	30
2613	65c. Tierra del Fuego, Argentina (horiz)	35	40
2614	75c. Point Loma, California, U.S.A. (horiz)	40	45
2615	90c. Groenpoint, Cape Town, South Africa	45	50
2616	$1 Youghal, Cork, Ireland	50	55
2617	$1.20 Launceston, Tasmania, Australia	60	65
2618	$1.65 Point Abino, Ontario, Canada (horiz)	85	90
2619	$1.75 Great Inagua, Bahamas	90	95

No. 2613 is inscribed "Terra Del Fuego" in error.

1998. Through the Year with Winnie the Pooh. Multicoloured.

2621	$1 Type **391**	70	70
2622	$1 Pooh and Piglet indoors (February)	70	70
2623	$1 Piglet hang-gliding with scarf (March)	70	70
2624	$1 Tigger, Pooh and Piglet on pond (April)	70	70
2625	$1 Kanga and Roo with posy of flowers (May)	70	70
2626	$1 Pooh on balloon and Owl (June)	70	70
2627	$1 Pooh, Eeyore, Tigger and Piglet gazing at stars (July)	70	70
2628	$1 Pooh and Piglet by stream (August)	70	70
2629	$1 Christopher Robin going to school (September)	70	70
2630	$1 Eeyore in fallen leaves (October)	70	70
2631	$1 Pooh and Rabbit gathering pumpkins (November)	70	70
2632	$1 Pooh and Piglet skiing (December)	70	70

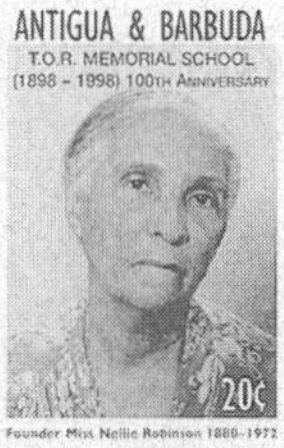

392 Miss Nellie Robinson (founder)

1998. Centenary of Thomas Oliver Robinson Memorial School.

2634	**392** 20c. green and black	10	15
2635	– 45c. multicoloured	25	30
2636	– 65c. green and black	35	40
2637	– 75c. multicoloured	40	45
2638	– 90c. multicoloured	45	50
2639	– $1.20 brown, green and black	60	65

DESIGNS—HORIZ: 45c. School photo, 1985; 65c. Former school building, 1930–49; 75c. Children with Mrs. Natalie Hurst (present headmistress); $1.20 Present school building, 1950. VERT: 90c. Miss Ina Loving (former teacher).

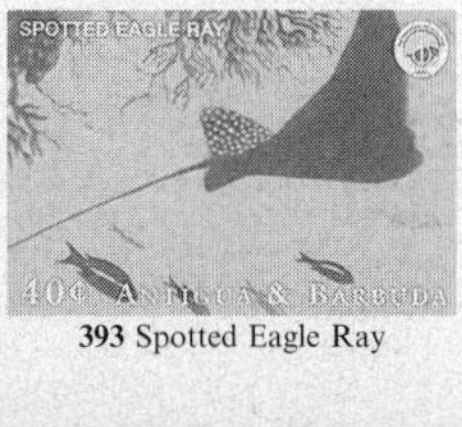

393 Spotted Eagle Ray

1998. International Year of the Ocean. Multicoloured.

2641/65	40c. × 25 Type **393**; Manta ray; Hawksbill turtle; Jellyfish; Queen angelfish; Octopus; Emperor angelfish; Regal angelfish; Porkfish; Racoon butterflyfish; Atlantic barracuda; Sea horse; Nautilus; Trumpetfish; White tip shark; Sunken Spanish galleon; Black-tip shark; Long-nosed butterflyfish; Green moray eel; Captain Nemo; Treasure chest; Hammerhead shark; Divers; Lionfish; Clownfish		
2666/77	75c. × 12 Maroon-tailed conure; Cocoi heron; Common tern; Rainbow lorikeet; Saddleback butterflyfish; Goatfish and cat shark; Blue shark and stingray; Majestic snapper; Nassau grouper; Black-cap gramma and blue tang; Stingrays; Stingrays and giant starfish		
2641/77	Set of 37	9·75	10·00

Nos. 2641/65 and 2666/77 respectively were printed together, se-tenant, with the backgrounds forming composite designs.

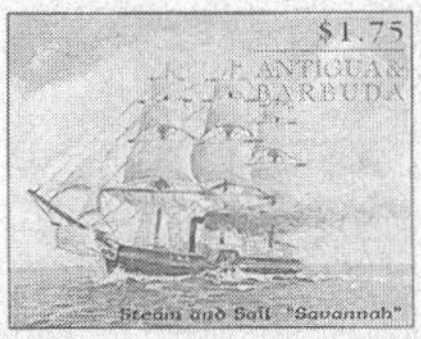

394 "Savannah" (paddle-steamer)

1998. Ships of the World. Multicoloured.

2679	$1.75 Type **394**	90	95
2680	$1.75 Viking longship	90	95
2681	$1.75 Greek galley	90	95
2682	$1.75 Sailing clipper	90	95
2683	$1.75 Dhow	90	95
2684	$1.75 Fishing catboat	90	95

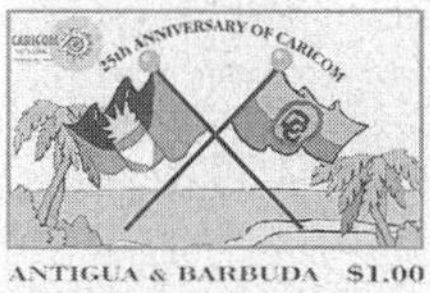

395 Flags of Antigua and CARICOM

1998. 25th Anniv of Caribbean Community.

2686	**395** $1 multicoloured	50	55

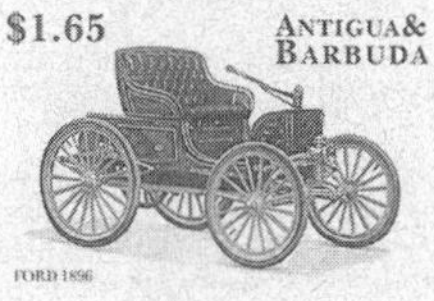

396 Ford, 1896

1998. Classic Cars. Multicoloured.

2687	$1.65 Type **396**	85	90
2688	$1.65 Ford A, 1903	85	90
2689	$1.65 Ford T, 1928	85	90
2690	$1.65 Ford T, 1922	85	90
2691	$1.65 Ford Blackhawk, 1929	85	90
2692	$1.65 Ford Sedan, 1934	85	90
2693	$1.65 Torpedo, 1911	85	90
2694	$1.65 Mercedes 22, 1913	85	90
2695	$1.65 Rover, 1920	85	90
2696	$1.65 Mercedes-Benz, 1956	85	90
2697	$1.65 Packard V-12, 1934	85	90
2698	$1.65 Opel, 1924	85	90

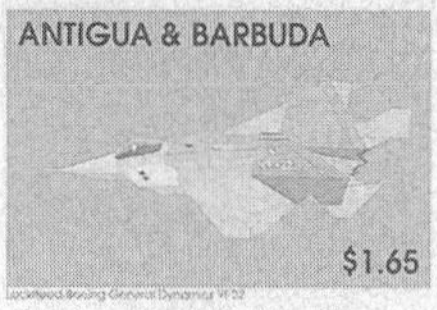

397 Lockheed-Boeing General Dynamics Yf-22

1998. Modern Aircraft. Multicoloured.

2700	$1.65 Type **397**	85	90
2701	$1.65 Dassault-Breguet Rafale BO 1	85	90
2702	$1.65 MiG 29	85	90
2703	$1.65 Dassault-Breguet Mirage 2000D	85	90
2704	$1.65 Rockwell B-1B "Lancer"	85	90
2705	$1.65 McDonnell-Douglas C-17A	85	90
2706	$1.65 Space Shuttle	85	90
2707	$1.65 SAAB "Grippen"	85	90

2708	$1.65 Eurofighter EF-2000	85	90
2709	$1.65 Sukhoi SU 27	85	90
2710	$1.65 Northrop B-2	85	90
2711	$1.65 Lockheed F-117		
	"Nighthawk"	85	90

398 Karl Benz
(internal-combustion
engine)

399 Stylised Americas

1998. Millennium Series. Famous People of the Twentieth Century. Inventors. Multicoloured.

2713	$1 Type **398**	50	55
2714	$1 Early Benz car and Mercedes-Benz racing car (53 × 38 mm)	50	55
2715	$1 Atom bomb mushroom cloud (53 × 38 mm) . . .	50	55
2716	$1 Albert Einstein (theory of relativity)	50	55
2717	$1 Leopold Godowsky Jr. and Leopold Damrosch Mannes (Kodachrome film)	50	55
2718	$1 Camera and transparencies (53 × 38 mm)	50	55
2719	$1 Heinkel He 178 (first turbo jet plane) (53 × 38 mm)	50	55
2720	$1 Dr. Hans Pabst von Ohain (jet turbine engine)	50	55
2721	$1 Rudolf Diesel (diesel engine)	50	55
2722	$1 Early Diesel engine and forms of transport (53 × 38 mm)	50	55
2723	$1 Zeppelin airship (53 × 38 mm)	50	55
2724	$1 Count Ferdinand von Zeppelin (airship pioneer)	50	55
2725	$1 Wilhelm Conrad Rontgen (X-rays)	50	55
2726	$1 X-ray of hand (53 × 38 mm)	50	55
2727	$1 Launch of Saturn rocket (53 × 38 mm)	50	55
2728	$1 Wernher von Braun (rocket research) . . .	50	55

No. 2713 is inscribed "CARL BENZ" in error.

1998. 50th Anniv of Organization of American States.

2730	**399** $1 multicoloured	50	55

400 "Figures on the Seashore"

1998. 25th Death Anniv of Pablo Picasso (painter). Multicoloured.

2731	$1.20 Type **400**	60	65
2732	$1.65 "Three Figures under a Tree" (vert)	85	90
2733	$1.75 "Two Women running on the Beach"	90	95

401 Dino 246 GT-GTS

1998. Birth Centenary of Enzo Ferrari (car manufacturer). Multicoloured.

2735	$1.75 Type **401**	1·40	1·40
2736	$1.75 Front view of Dino 246 GT-GTS	1·40	1·40
2737	$1.75 365 GT4 BB	1·40	1·40

402 Scout Handshake

1998. 19th World Scout Jamboree, Chile. Multicoloured.

2739	90c. Type **402**	45	50
2740	$1 Scouts hiking	50	55
2741	$1.20 Scout salute	60	65

403 Mahatma Gandhi

405 Diana, Princess of Wales

404 McDonnell Douglas Phantom F-GR1

1998. 50th Death Anniv of Mahatma Gandhi. Multicoloured.

2743	90c. Type **403**	45	50
2744	$1 Gandhi seated	50	55
2745	$1.20 As young man . . .	60	65
2746	$1.65 At primary school in Rajkot, aged 7	85	90

1998. 80th Anniv of Royal Air Force. Multicoloured.

2748	$1.75 Type **404**	90	95
2749	$1.75 Two Sepecat Jaguar GR1As	90	95
2750	$1.75 Panavia Tornado F3	90	95
2751	$1.75 McDonnell Douglas Phantom F-GR2	90	95

1998. 1st Death Anniv of Diana, Princess of Wales.

2753	**405** $1.20 multicoloured . .	60	65

406 Brown Pelican

1998. Sea Birds of the World. Multicoloured.

2754	15c. Type **406**	10	15
2755	25c. Dunlin	15	20
2756	45c. Atlantic puffin . . .	25	30
2757	75c. King eider	40	45
2758	75c. Inca tern	40	45
2759	75c. Little auk ("Dovekie")	40	45
2760	75c. Ross's gull	40	45
2761	75c. Common noddy ("Brown Noddy") . . .	40	45
2762	75c. Marbled murrelet . .	40	45
2763	75c. Northern gannet . .	40	45
2764	75c. Razorbill	40	45
2765	75c. Long-tailed skua ("Long-tailed Jaegar") . .	40	45
2766	75c. Black guillemot . . .	40	45
2767	75c. Whimbrel	40	45
2768	75c. Oystercatcher . . .	40	45
2769	90c. Pied cormorant . . .	45	50

Nos. 2757/68 were printed together, se-tenant, with the backgrounds forming a composite design.
No. 2760 is inscribed "ROSS' BULL" in error.

407 Border Collie

1998. Christmas. Dogs. Multicoloured.

2771	15c. Type **407**	10	15
2772	25c. Dalmatian	15	20
2773	65c. Weimaraner	35	40
2774	75c. Scottish terrier . . .	40	45
2775	90c. Long-haired dachshund	45	50
2776	$1.20 Golden retriever . .	60	65
2777	$2 Pekingese	1·00	1·10

408 Mickey Mouse Sailing

1999. 70th Birthday of Mickey Mouse. Walt Disney characters participating in water sports. Multicoloured.

2779	$1 Type **408**	75	75
2780	$1 Mickey and Goofy sailing	75	75
2781	$1 Goofy windsurfing . .	75	75
2782	$1 Mickey sailing and seagull	75	75
2783	$1 Goofy sailing	75	75
2784	$1 Mickey windsurfing . .	75	75
2785	$1 Goofy running with surfboard	75	75
2786	$1 Mickey surfing	75	75
2787	$1 Donald Duck holding surfboard	75	75
2788	$1 Donald on surfboard (face value at right) . . .	75	75
2789	$1 Minnie Mouse surfing in green shorts	75	75
2790	$1 Goofy surfing	75	75
2791	$1 Goofy in purple shorts waterskiing	75	75
2792	$1 Mickey waterskiing . .	75	75
2793	$1 Goofy waterskiing with Mickey	75	75
2794	$1 Donald on surfboard (face value at left) . . .	75	75
2795	$1 Goofy in yellow shorts waterskiing	75	75
2796	$1 Minnie in pink shorts surfing	75	75

409 Hell's Gate Steel Orchestra, 1996

1999. 50th Anniv of Hell's Gate Steel Orchestra. Multicoloured.

2798	20c. Type **409**	10	15
2799	60c. Orchestra members, New York, 1992 . . .	30	35
2800	75c. Orchestra members with steel drums, 1950 .	40	45
2801	90c. Eustace Henry, 1964 .	45	50
2802	$1.20 Alston Henry playing double tenor	60	65

410 Tulips

411 Elle Macpherson

1999. Flowers. Multicoloured.

2804	60c. Type **410**	30	35
2805	75c. Fuschia	40	45
2806	90c. Morning glory (horiz)	45	50
2807	90c. Geranium (horiz) . .	45	50
2808	90c. Blue hibiscus (horiz) .	45	50
2809	90c. Marigolds (horiz) . .	45	50
2810	90c. Sunflower (horiz) . .	45	50
2811	90c. Impatiens (horiz) . .	45	50
2812	90c. Petunia (horiz) . . .	45	50
2813	90c. Pansy (horiz) . . .	45	50
2814	90c. Saucer magnolia (horiz)	45	50
2815	$1 Primrose (horiz) . . .	50	55
2816	$1 Bleeding heart (horiz) .	50	55
2817	$1 Pink dogwood (horiz) .	50	55
2818	$1 Peony (horiz)	50	55
2819	$1 Rose (horiz)	50	55
2820	$1 Hellebores (horiz) . .	50	55
2821	$1 Lily (horiz)	50	55
2822	$1 Violet (horiz)	50	55
2823	$1 Cherry blossom (horiz)	50	55
2824	$1 Calla lily (horiz) . . .	50	55
2825	$1.65 Sweet pea	85	90

Nos. 2806/14 and 2815/23 respectively were each printed together, se-tenant, forming composite designs

1999. "Australia '99" International Stamp Exhibition, Melbourne (1st issue). Elle Macpherson (model). Multicoloured.

2827	$1.20 Type **411**	60	65
2828	$1.20 Lying on couch . . .	60	65
2829	$1.20 In swimsuit	60	65
2830	$1.20 Looking over shoulder	60	65
2831	$1.20 Wearing cream shirt .	60	65
2832	$1.20 Wearing stetson . .	60	65
2833	$1.20 Wearing black T-shirt	60	65
2834	$1.20 Holding tree branch	60	65

See also Nos. 2875/92.

412 "Luna 2" Moon Probe

413 John Glenn entering "Mercury" Capsule, 1962

1999. Satellites and Spacecraft. Multicoloured.

2835	$1.65 Type **412**	85	90
2836	$1.65 "Mariner 2" space probe	85	90
2837	$1.65 "Giotto" space probe	85	90
2838	$1.65 Rosat satellite . . .	85	90
2839	$1.65 International Ultraviolet Explorer . .	85	90
2840	$1.65 "Ulysses" space probe	85	90
2841	$1.65 "Mariner 10" space probe	85	90
2842	$1.65 "Luna 9" Moon probe	85	90
2843	$1.65 Advanced X-ray Astrophysics Facility . .	85	90
2844	$1.65 "Magellan" space probe	85	90
2845	$1.65 "Pioneer – Venus 2" space probe	85	90
2846	$1.65 Infra-red Astronomy Satellite	85	90

Nos. 2835/40 and 2841/46 repectively were each printed together, se-tenant, with the backgrounds forming composite designs.

1999. John Glenn's Return to Space. Multicoloured.

2848	$1.75 Type **413**	90	95
2849	$1.75 Glenn in "Mercury" mission spacesuit . . .	90	95
2850	$1.75 Fitting helmet for "Mercury" mission . . .	90	95
2851	$1.75 Outside pressure chamber	90	95

414 Brachiosaurus

1999. Prehistoric Animals. Multicoloured.

2852	65c. Type **414**	35	40
2853	75c. Oviraptor (vert) . . .	40	45
2854	$1 Homotherium	50	55
2855	$1.20 Macrauchenia (vert)	60	65
2856	$1.65 Struthiomimus . . .	85	90
2857	$1.65 Corythosaurus . . .	85	90
2858	$1.65 Dsungaripterus . . .	85	90
2859	$1.65 Compsognathus . . .	85	90
2860	$1.65 Prosaurolophus . . .	85	90
2861	$1.65 Montanoceratops . .	85	90
2862	$1.65 Stegosaurus	85	90
2863	$1.65 Deinonychus	85	90
2864	$1.65 Ouranosaurus . . .	85	90
2865	$1.65 Leptictidium	85	90
2866	$1.65 Ictitherium	85	90
2867	$1.65 Plesictis	85	90
2868	$1.65 Hemicyon	85	90
2869	$1.65 Diacodexis	85	90
2870	$1.65 Stylinodon	85	90
2871	$1.65 Kanuites	85	90
2872	$1.65 Chriacus	85	90
2873	$1.65 Argyrolagus	85	90

Nos. 2856/64 and 2865/73 respectively were each printed together, se-tenant, with the backgrounds forming composite designs.

415 Two White Kittens

1999. "Australia '99" International Stamp Exhibition, Melbourne (2nd issue). Cats. Mult.

2875	35c. Type **415**	20	25
2876	45c. Kitten with string . .	25	30
2877	60c. Two kittens under blanket	30	35
2878	75c. Two kittens in basket .	40	45
2879	90c. Kitten with ball . . .	45	50
2880	$1 White kitten	50	55
2881	$1.65 Two kittens playing .	85	90
2882	$1.65 Black and white kitten	85	90
2883	$1.65 Black kitten and sleeping cream kitten .	85	90
2884	$1.65 White kitten with green string	85	90
2885	$1.65 Two sleeping kittens	85	90
2886	$1.65 White kitten with black tip to tail . . .	85	90

2887 $1.65 Kitten with red string 85 90
2888 $1.65 Two long-haired kittens 85 90
2889 $1.65 Ginger kitten 85 90
2890 $1.65 Kitten playing with mouse 85 90
2891 $1.65 Kitten asleep on blue cushion 85 90
2892 $1.65 Tabby kitten 85 90

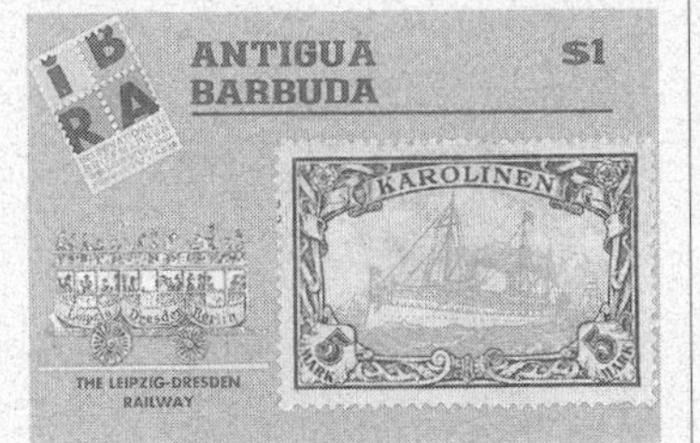

416 Early Leipzig–Dresden Railway Carriage and Caroline Islands 1901 Yacht Type 5m. Stamp

1999. "iBRA '99" International Stamp Exhibition, Nuremberg. Multicoloured.
2894 $1 Type **416** 50 55
2895 $1.20 Golsdorf steam locomotive and Caroline Islands 1901 Yacht type 1m. 60 65
2896 $1.65 Early Leipzig–Dresden Railway carriage and Caroline Islands 1899 20pf. optd on Germany 85 90
2897 $1.90 Golsdorf steam locomotive and Caroline Islands 1901 Yacht type 5pf. and 20pf. 95 1·00

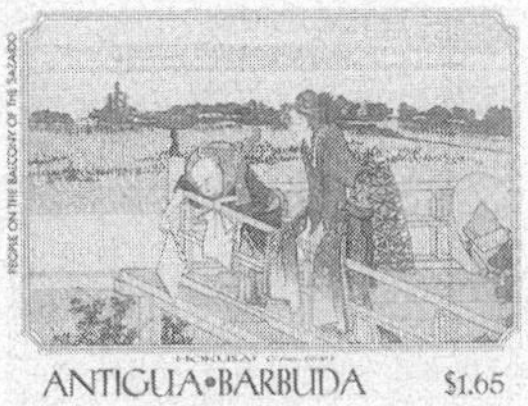

417 "People on Balcony of Sazaido" (Hokusai)

1999. 150th Death Anniv of Katsushika Hokusai (Japanese artist). Multicoloured.
2899 $1.65 Type **417** 85 90
2900 $1.65 "Nakahara in Sagami Province" 85 90
2901 $1.65 "Defensive Positions" (two wrestlers) 85 90
2902 $1.65 "Defensive Positions" (three wrestlers) 85 90
2903 $1.65 "Mount Fuji in Clear Weather" 85 90
2904 $1.65 "Nihonbashi in Edo" 85 90
2905 $1.65 "Asakusa Honganji" 85 90
2906 $1.65 "Dawn at Isawa in Kai Province" 85 90
2907 $1.65 "Samurai with Bow and Arrow" (with arrows on ground) 85 90
2908 $1.65 "Samurai with Bow and Arrow" (trees in background) 85 90
2909 $1.65 "Kajikazawa in Kai Province" 85 90
2910 $1.65 "A Great Wave" 85 90

No. 2903 is inscribed "MOUNT FUGI" in error.

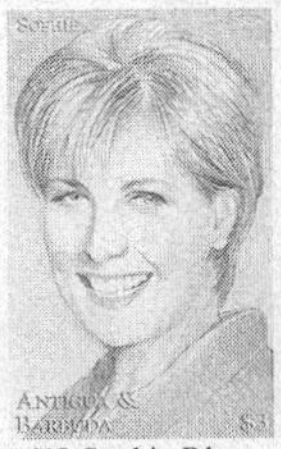

418 Sophie Rhys-Jones

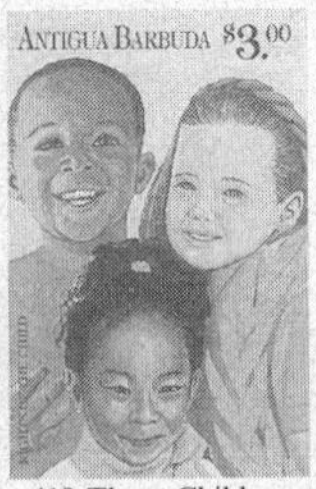

419 Three Children

1999. Royal Wedding. Multicoloured.
2912 $3 Type **418** 1·50 1·60
2913 $3 Sophie and Prince Edward 1·50 1·60
2914 $3 Prince Edward 1·50 1·60

1999. 10th Anniv of United Nations Rights of the Child Convention. Multicoloured.
2916 $3 Type **419** 1·50 1·60
2917 $3 Adult hand holding child's hand 1·50 1·60
2918 $3 Dove and U.N. Headquarters 1·50 1·60

Nos. 2916/18 were printed together, se-tenant, forming a composite design.

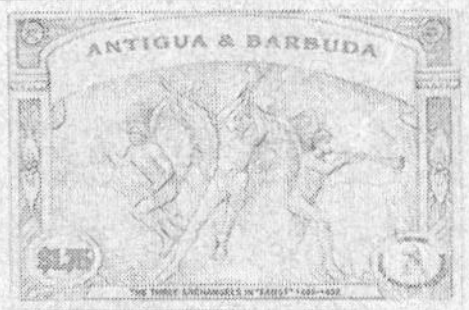

421 Three Archangels from "Faust"

1999. 250th Birth Anniv of Johann von Goethe (German writer).
2921 **421** $1.75 purple, mauve and black 90 95
2922 – $1.75 blue, violet and black 90 95
2923 – $1.75 green and black 90 95

DESIGNS: No. 2922, Von Goethe and Von Schiller; 2923, Faust reclining with spirits.

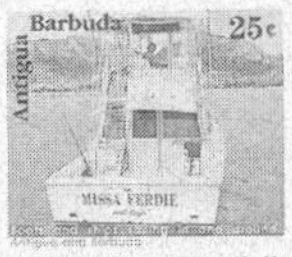

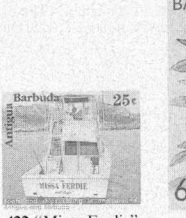

422 "Missa Ferdie" (fishing launch)

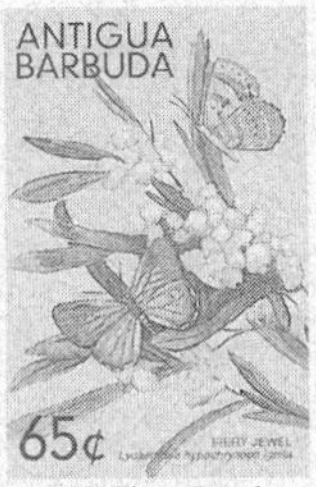

423 Fiery Jewel

1999. Local Ships and Boats. Multicoloured.
2925 25c. Type **422** 15 20
2926 45c. Yachts in 32nd Annual Antigua International Sailing Week 25 30
2927 60c. "Jolly Roger" (tourist ship) 30 35
2928 90c. "Freewinds" (cruise liner) (10th anniv of first visit) 45 50
2929 $1.20 "Monarch of the Seas" (cruise liner) 60 65

1999. Butterflies. Multicoloured.
2931 65c. Type **423** 35 40
2932 75c. Hewitson's blue hairstreak 40 45
2933 $1 California dog face (horiz) 50 55
2934 $1 Small copper (horiz) 50 55
2935 $1 Zebra swallowtail (horiz) 50 55
2936 $1 White "M" hairstreak (horiz) 50 55
2937 $1 Old world swallowtail (horiz) 50 55
2938 $1 Buckeye (horiz) 50 55
2939 $1 Apollo (horiz) 50 55
2940 $1 Sonoran blue (horiz) 50 55
2941 $1 Purple emperor (horiz) 50 55
2942 $1.20 Scarce bamboo page (horiz) 60 65
2943 $1.65 Paris peacock (horiz) 85 90

Nos. 2933/41 were printed together, se-tenant, forming a composite design.

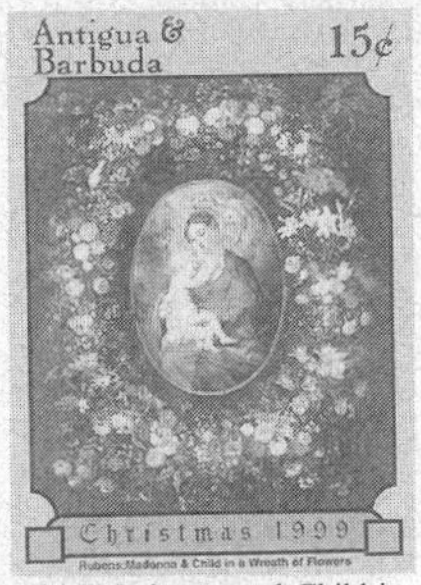

424 "Madonna and Child in Wreath of Flowers" (Rubens)

1999. Christmas. Religious Paintings.
2945 **424** 15c. multicoloured 10 15
2946 – 25c. black, stone & yellow 15 20
2947 – 45c. multicoloured 25 30
2948 – 60c. multicoloured 30 35
2949 – $2 multicoloured 1·00 1·10
2950 – $4 black, stone & yell 2·00 2·10

DESIGNS: 25c. "Shroud of Christ held by Two Angels" (Durer); 45c. "Madonna and Child enthroned between Two Saints" (Raphael); 60c. "Holy Family with Lamb" (Raphael); $2 "The Transfiguration" (Raphael); $4 "Three Putti holding Coat of Arms (Durer).

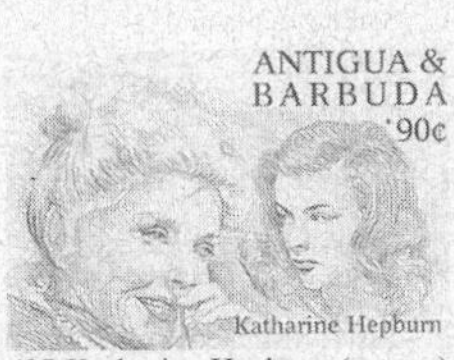

425 Katharine Hepburn (actress)

2000. Senior Celebrities of the 20th Century. Mult.
2952 90c. Type **425** 45 50
2953 90c. Martha Graham (dancer) 45 50
2954 90c. Eubie Blake (jazz pianist) 45 50
2955 90c. Agatha Christie (novelist) 45 50
2956 90c. Eudora Welty (American novelist) 45 50
2957 90c. Helen Hayes (actress) 45 50
2958 90c. Vladimir Horowitz (concert pianist) 45 50
2959 90c. Katharine Graham (newspaper publisher) 45 50
2960 90c. Pablo Casals (cellist) 45 50
2961 90c. Pete Seeger (folk singer) 45 50
2962 90c. Andres Segovia (guitarist) 45 50
2963 90c. Frank Lloyd Wright (architect) 45 50

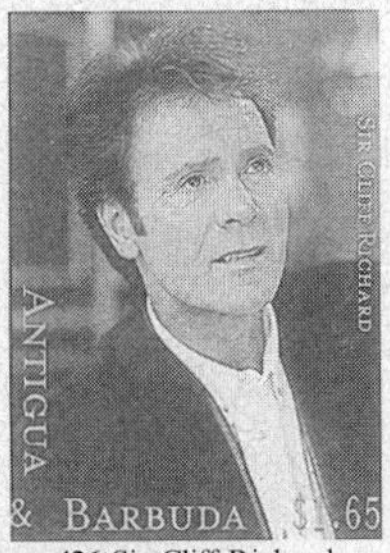

426 Sir Cliff Richard

2000. 60th Birthday of Sir Cliff Richard (entertainer).
2964 **426** $1.65 multicoloured 85 90

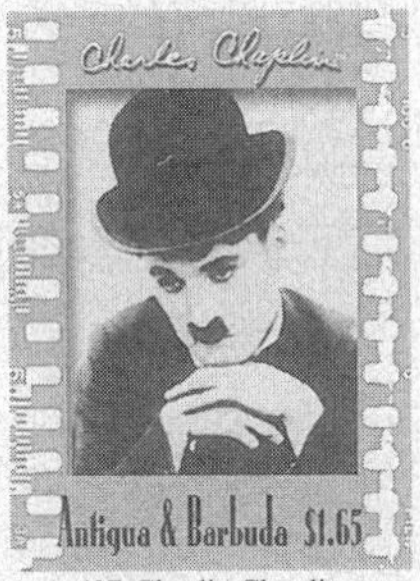

427 Charlie Chaplin

2000. Charlie Chaplin (actor and director) Commemoration. Designs showing film scenes. Mult.
2965 $1.65 Standing in street (*Modern Times*) 85 90
2966 $1.65 Hugging man (*The Gold Rush*) 85 90
2967 $1.65 Type **427** 85 90
2968 $1.65 Wielding tools (*Modern Times*) 85 90
2969 $1.65 With hands on hips (*The Gold Rush*) 85 90
2970 $1.65 Wearing cape (*The Gold Rush*) 85 90

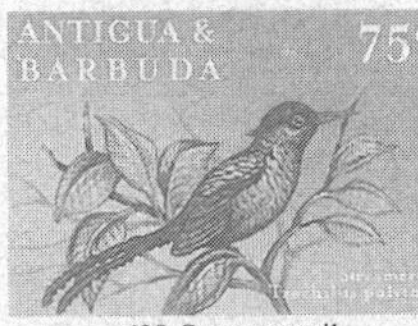

428 Streamertail

2000. "The Stamp Show 2000" International Stamp Exhibition, London. Birds of the Caribbean. Mult.
2971 75c. Type **428** 40 45
2972 90c. Yellow-bellied sapsucker 45 50
2973 $1.20 Rufous-tailed jacamar 60 65
2974 $1.20 Scarlet macaw 60 65
2975 $1.20 Yellow-crowned ("fronted") amazon 60 65
2976 $1.20 Golden conure ("Queen-of-Bavaria") 60 65
2977 $1.20 Nanday conure 60 65
2978 $1.20 Jamaican tody 60 65
2979 $1.20 Smooth-billed ani 60 65
2980 $1.20 Puerto Rican woodpecker 60 65
2981 $1.20 Ruby-throated hummingbird 60 65
2982 $1.20 Scaly-breasted ground dove 60 65
2983 $1.20 American wood stork 60 65
2984 $1.20 Saffron finch 60 65
2985 $1.20 Green-backed heron 60 65
2986 $1.20 Lovely cotinga 60 65
2987 $1.20 St. Vincent amazon ("Parrot") 60 65
2988 $1.20 Cuban grassquit 60 65
2989 $1.20 Red-winged blackbird 60 65
2990 $2 Spectacled owl 1·00 1·10

Nos. 2974/81 and 2982/9 were each printed together, se-tenant, with the backgrounds forming composite designs.

No. 2981 is inscribed "Arhilochus colubria" in error.

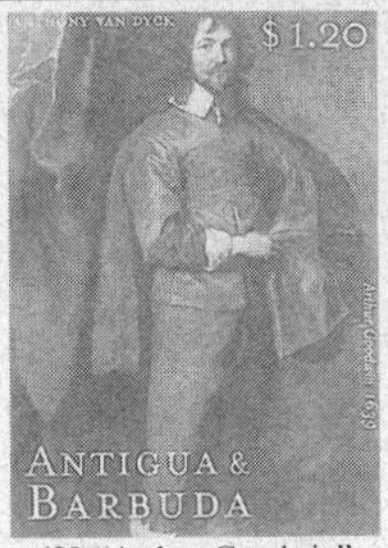

429 "Arthur Goodwin"

2000. 400th Birth Anniv of Sir Anthony Van Dyck (Flemish painter). Multicoloured.
2992 $1.20 Type **429** 60 65
2993 $1.20 "Sir Thomas Wharton" 60 65
2994 $1.20 "Mary Villiers, Daughter of Duke of Buckingham" 60 65
2995 $1.20 "Christina Bruce, Countess of Devonshire" 60 65
2996 $1.20 "James Hamilton, Duke of Hamilton" 60 65
2997 $1.20 "Henry Danvers, Earl of Danby" 60 65
2998 $1.20 "Marie de Raet, Wife of Philippe le Roy" 60 65
2999 $1.20 "Jacomo de Cachiopin" 60 65
3000 $1.20 "Princess Henrietta of Lorraine attended by a Page" 60 65
3001 $1.20 "Portrait of a Man" 60 65
3002 $1.20 "Portrait of a Woman" 60 65
3003 $1.20 "Philippe le Roy, Seigneur de Ravels" 60 65
3004 $1.20 "Charles I in State Robes" 60 65
3005 $1.20 "Queen Henrietta Maria" (in white dress) 60 65
3006 $1.20 "Queen Henrietta Maria with Sir Jeffrey Hudson" 60 65
3007 $1.20 "Charles I in Armour" 60 65
3008 $1.20 "Queen Henrietta Maria in Profile facing right" 60 65
3009 $1.20 "Queen Henrietta Maria" (in black dress) 60 65

No. 2994 is inscribed "Mary Villers", No. 3002 "Portrait of a Women", No. 3005 "Henrieta Maria", all in error.

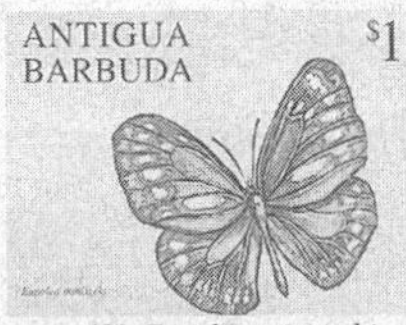

430 *Eupolea miniszeki*

2000. Butterflies. Multicoloured.
3011 $1.65 Type **430** 85 90
3012 $1.65 *Heliconius doris* 85 90
3013 $1.65 *Evenus coronata* 85 90
3014 $1.65 *Papilio anchisiades* 85 90
3015 $1.65 *Syrmatia dorilas* 85 90
3016 $1.65 *Morpho patroclus* 85 90
3017 $1.65 *Mesosemia loruhama* 85 90
3018 $1.65 *Bia actorion* 85 90
3019 $1.65 *Anteos clorinde* 85 90
3020 $1.65 *Menander menande* 85 90
3021 $1.65 *Catasticta manco* 85 90
3022 $1.65 *Urania leilus* 85 90
3023 $1.65 *Theope eudocia* (vert) 85 90
3024 $1.65 *Uranus sloanus* (vert) 85 90
3025 $1.65 *Helicopis cupido* (vert) 85 90
3026 $1.65 *Papilio velovis* (vert) 85 90
3027 $1.65 *Graphium androcles* (vert) 85 90
3028 $1.65 *Mesene phareus* (vert) 85 90

Nos. 3011/16, 3017/22 and 3023/8 were each printed together, se-tenant, with the backgrounds forming composite designs.

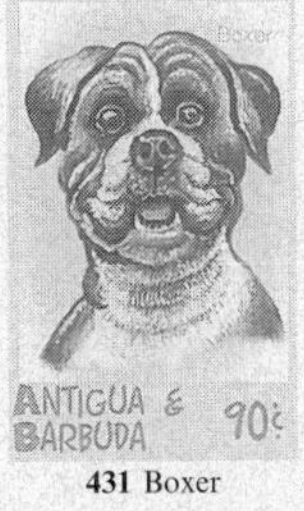

431 Boxer

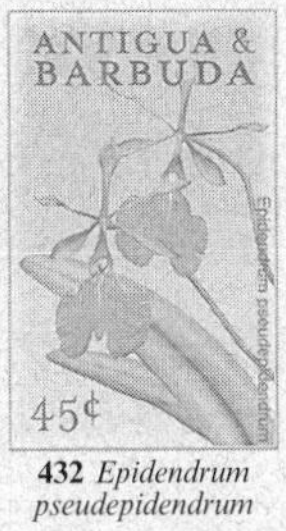

432 *Epidendrum pseudepidendrum*

2000. Cats and Dogs. Multicoloured.
3030 90c. Type **431** 45 50
3031 $1 Alaskan malamute 50 55
3032 $1.65 Bearded collie 85 90
3033 $1.65 Cardigan Welsh corgi 85 90
3034 $1.65 Saluki (red) 85 90
3035 $1.65 Basset hound 85 90
3036 $1.65 White standard poodle 85 90
3037 $1.65 Boston terrier 85 90
3038 $1.65 Long-haired blue and white cat (horiz) 85 90
3039 $1.65 Snow shoe (horiz) 85 90
3040 $1.65 Persian (horiz) 85 90

3041 $1.65 Chocolate lynx point (horiz) 85 90
3042 $1.65 Brown and white sphynx (horiz) 85 90
3043 $1.65 White tortoiseshell (horiz) 85 90
3044 $2 Wirehaired pointer . . . 1·00 1·10
3045 $4 Saluki (black) . . . . . 2·00 2·25

2000. Flowers of the Caribbean. Multicoloured.
3047 45c. Type **432** 25 30
3048 65c. *Odontoglossum cervantesii* 35 40
3049 75c. *Cattleya dowiana* . . . 40 45
3050 90c. *Beloperone guttata* . . . 45 50
3051 $1 *Colliandra haematocephala* 50 55
3052 $1.20 *Brassavola nodosa* . . 60 65
3053 $1.65 *Pseudocalymna alliaceum* 85 90
3054 $1.65 *Datura candida* . . . 85 90
3055 $1.65 *Ipomoea tuberosa* . . 85 90
3056 $1.65 *Allamanda cathartica* 85 90
3057 $1.65 *Aspasia epidendroides* 85 90
3058 $1.65 *Maxillaria cucullata* 85 90
3059 $1.65 *Anthurium andreanum* 85 90
3060 $1.65 *Doxantha unguiscati* 85 90
3061 $1.65 *Hibiscus rosa-sinensis* 85 90
3062 $1.65 *Canna indica* 85 90
3063 $1.65 *Heliconius umilis* . . . 85 90
3064 $1.65 *Strelitzia reginae* . . . 85 90
3065 $1.65 *Masdevallia coccinea* 85 90
3066 $1.65 *Paphinia cristata* . . . 85 90
3067 $1.65 *Vanilla planifolia* . . . 85 90
3068 $1.65 *Cattleya forbesii* . . . 85 90
3069 $1.65 *Lycaste skinneri* . . . 85 90
3070 $1.65 *Cattleya percivaliana* 85 90
No. 3061 is inscribed "rosa-senensis" in error.

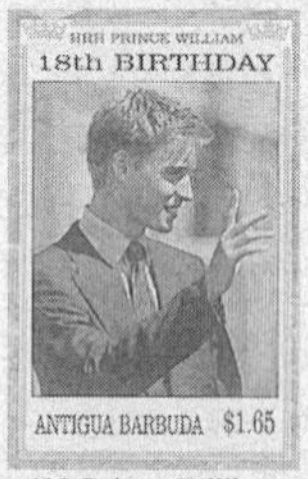

433 Prince William

2000. 18th Birthday of Prince William. Multicoloured.
3072 $1.65 Prince William waving 85 90
3073 $1.65 Wearing Eton school uniform 85 90
3074 $1.65 Wearing grey suit . . 85 90
3075 $1.65 Type **433** 85 90

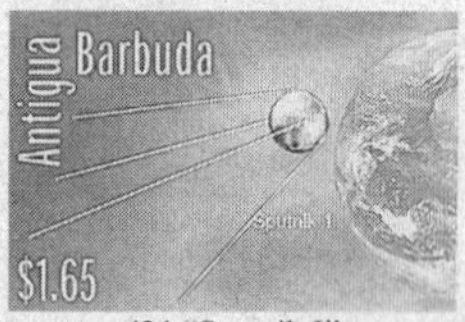

434 "Sputnik I"

2000. "EXPO 2000" World Stamp Exhibition, Anaheim, U.S.A. Space Satellites. Multicoloured.
3077 $1.65 Type **434** 85 90
3078 $1.65 "Explorer I" 85 90
3079 $1.65 "Mars Express" . . . 85 90
3080 $1.65 "Lunik I Solnik" . . 85 90
3081 $1.65 "Ranger 7" 85 90
3082 $1.65 "Mariner 4" 85 90
3083 $1.65 "Mariner 10" 85 90
3084 $1.65 "Soho" 85 90
3085 $1.65 "Mariner 2" 85 90
3086 $1.65 "Giotto" 85 90
3087 $1.65 "Exosat" 85 90
3088 $1.65 "Pioneer Venus" . . . 85 90
Nos. 3077/82 and 3083/8 were each printed together, se-tenant, with the backgrounds forming composite designs.

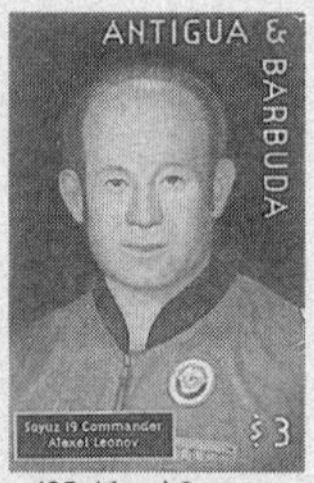

435 Alexei Leonov (Commander of "Soyuz 19")

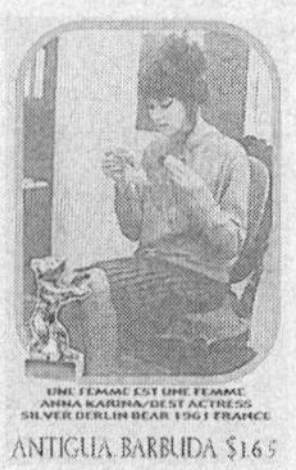

436 Anna Karina in *Une Femme est Une Femme*, 1961

2000. 25th Anniv of "Apollo–Soyuz" Joint Project. Multicoloured.
3090 $3 Type **435** . . . . 1·50 1·60
3091 $3 "Soyuz 19" . . . . 1·50 1·60
3092 $3 Valeri Kubasov ("Soyuz 19" engineer) . . . . . . 1·50 1·60

2000. 50th Anniv of Berlin Film Festival. Designs showing actors, directors and film scenes. Mult.
3094 $1.65 Type **436** 85 90
3095 $1.65 *Carmen Jones*, 1955 85 90
3096 $1.65 *Die Ratten*, 1955 . . . 85 90
3097 $1.65 *Die Vier im Jeep*, 1951 85 90
3098 $1.65 Sidney Poitier in *Lilies of the Field*, 1963 . . . . 85 90
3099 $1.65 *Invitation to the Dance*, 1956 . . . . . . 85 90
No. 3096 is inscribed "GOLDER BERLIN BEAR" and shows the award date "1966" in error.

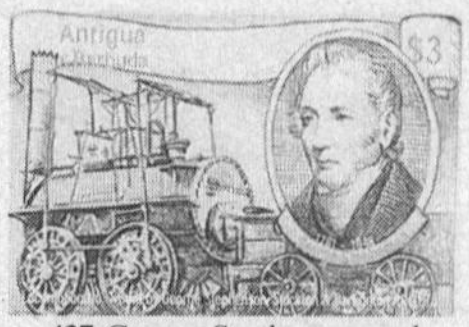

437 George Stephenson and *Locomotion No. 1*, 1825

2000. 175th Anniv of Stockton and Darlington Line (first public railway). Multicoloured.
3101 $3 Type **437** . . . . 1·50 1·60
3102 $3 Camden and Amboy Railroad locomotive *John Bull*, 1831 . . . . 1·50 1·60

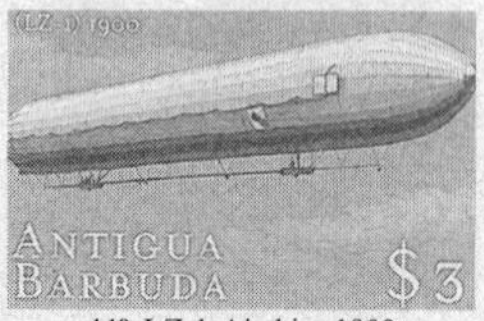

440 LZ-1 Airship, 1900

2000. Centenary of First Zeppelin Flight.
3105 **440** $3 brown, black and blue . . . . 1·50 1·60
3106 – $3 brown, black and blue . . . . 1·50 1·60
3107 – $3 multicoloured . . . . 1·50 1·60
DESIGNS: No. 3106, LZ-2, 1906; 3107, LZ-3, 1906.
Nos. 3105/7 were printed together, se-tenant, with the backgrounds forming a composite design.

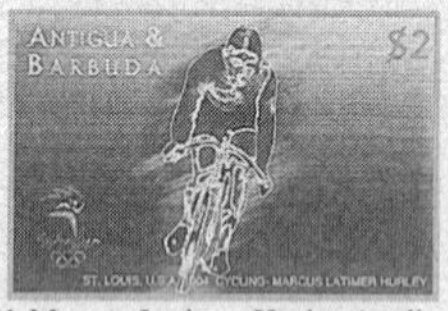

441 Marcus Latimer Hurley (cycling), St. Louis (1904)

2000. Olympic Games, Sydney. Multicoloured.
3109 $2 Type **441** . . . . 1·00 1·10
3110 $2 Diving . . . . 1·00 1·10
3111 $2 Flaminio Stadium, Rome (1960) and Italian flag . . 1·00 1·10
3112 $2 Ancient Greek javelin thrower . . . . 1·00 1·10

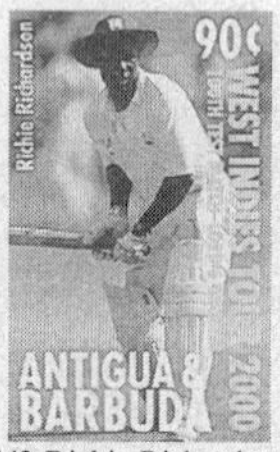

442 Richie Richardson

2000. West Indies Cricket Tour and 100th Test Match at Lord's. Multicoloured.
3113 90c. Type **442** 45 50
3114 $5 Viv Richards . . . . . 2·50 2·75
No. 3114 is inscribed "Viv Richard" in error.

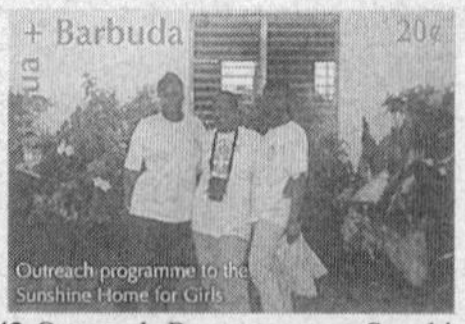

443 Outreach Programme at Sunshine Home for Girls

2000. Girls Brigade. Multicoloured.
3116 20c. Type **443** 10 15
3117 60c. Ullida Rawlins Gill (International Vice President) (vert) 30 35
3118 75c. Officers and girls . . . 40 45
3119 90c. Girl with flag (vert) . . 45 50
3120 $1.20 Members of 8th Antigua Company with flag (vert) 60 65

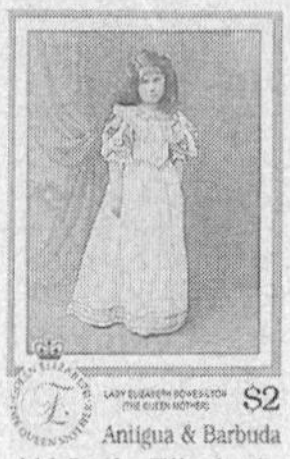

444 Lady Elizabeth Bowes-Lyon as Young Girl

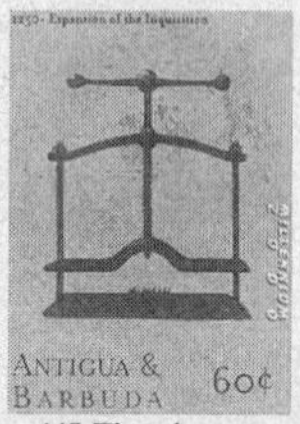

445 Thumbscrew (Expansion of Inquisition, 1250)

2000. "Queen Elizabeth the Queen Mother's Century".
3122 **444** $2 multicoloured . . . . 1·00 1·10
3123 – $2 black and gold . . . 1·00 1·10
3124 – $2 black and gold . . . 1·00 1·10
3125 – $2 multicoloured . . . . 1·00 1·10
DESIGNS: No. 3123, Queen Elizabeth in 1940; 3124, Queen Mother with Princess Anne, 1951; 3125, Queen Mother in Canada, 1989.

2000. New Millennium. People and Events of Thirteenth Century (1250–1300). Multicoloured (except No. 3127).
3127 60c. Type **445** (black and red) 30 35
3128 60c. Chartres Cathedral (completed, 1260) 30 35
3129 60c. Donor's sculpture, Naumberg (completed, 1260) 30 35
3130 60c. Delegates (Simon de Montfort's Parliament, 1261) 30 35
3131 60c. "Maesta" (Cimabue) (painted 1270) 30 35
3132 60c. Marco Polo (departure from Venice, 1271) . . . 30 35
3133 60c. "Divine Wind" (Kamikaze wind saves Japan from invasion, 1274) 30 35
3134 60c. St. Thomas Aquinas (died 1274) 30 35
3135 60c. Arezzo Cathedral (completed 1277) 35 35
3136 60c. Margrethe ("The Maid of Norway") (crowned Queen of Scotland, 1286) 30 35
3137 60c. Jewish refugees (Expulsion of Jews from England, 1290) 30 35
3138 60c. Muslim horseman (capture of Acre, 1291) 30 35
3139 60c. Moshe de Leon (compiles *The Zohar*, 1291) 30 35
3140 60c. Knights in combat (German Civil War, 1292–98) 30 35
3141 60c. Kublai Khan (died 1294) 30 35
3142 60c. Dante (writes *La Vita Nuova*, 1295) (59 × 39 mm) 30 35
3143 60c. "Autumn Colours on Quiao and Hua Mountains" (Zhan Mengfu) (painted 1296) 30 35

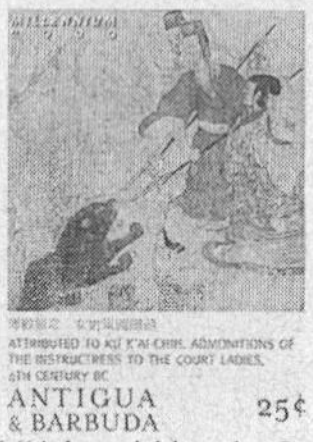

446 "Admonishing the Court Ladies" (after Ku K'ai-Chih)

2000. New Millennium. Two Thousand Years of Chinese Paintings. Multicoloured.
3144 25c. Type **446** 15 20
3145 25c. Ink on silk drawing from Zhan Jadashan . . . 15 20
3146 25c. Ink and colour on silk drawing from Mawangdui Tomb 15 20
3147 25c. "Scholars collating Texts" (attr Yang Zihua) 15 20
3148 25c. "Spring Outing" (attr Zhan Ziqian) 15 20
3149 25c. "Portrait of the Emperors" (attr Yen Liben) 15 20
3150 25c. "Sailing Boats and Riverside Mansion" (attr Li Sixun) 15 20
3151 25c. "Two Horses and Groom" (Han Kan) . . . 15 20
3152 25c. "King's Portrait" (attr Wu Daozi) 15 20
3153 25c. "Court Ladies wearing Flowered Headdresses" (attr Zhou Fang) 15 20
3154 25c. "Distant Mountain Forest" (mountain) (Juran) 15 20
3155 25c. "Mount Kuanglu" (Jiang Hao) 15 20
3156 25c. "Pheasant and Small Birds" (Huang Jucai) . . 15 20
3157 25c. "Deer among Red Maples" (anon) 15 20
3158 25c. "Distant Mountain Forest" (river and fields) (Juran) 15 20
3159 25c. "Literary Gathering" (Han Huang) (57 × 39 mm) 15 20
3160 25c. "Birds and Insects" (Huang Quan) 15 20
No. 3148 is inscribed "SPRINTING", No. 3150 "MASION" and No. 3153 "HEADRESSES", all in error.

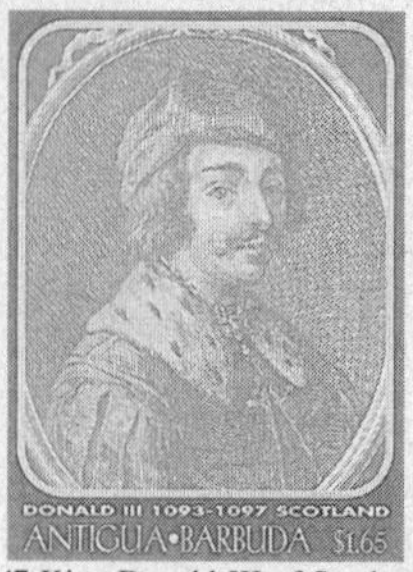

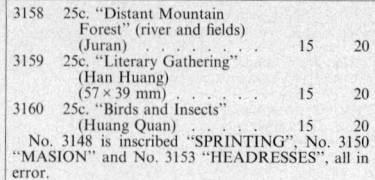

447 King Donald III of Scotland

2000. Monarchs of the Millennium.
3161 **447** $1.65 black, stone and brown 85 90
3162 – $1.65 black, stone and brown 85 90
3163 – $1.65 black, stone and brown 85 90
3164 – $1.65 black, stone and brown 85 90
3165 – $1.65 black, stone and brown 85 90
3166 – $1.65 black, stone and brown 85 90
3167 – $1.65 multicoloured . . 85 90
3168 – $1.65 multicoloured . . 85 90
3169 – $1.65 multicoloured . . 85 90
3170 – $1.65 multicoloured . . 85 90
3171 – $1.65 multicoloured . . 85 90
3172 – $1.65 multicoloured . . 85 90
DESIGNS: No. 3162, King Duncan I of Scotland; 3163, King Duncan II of Scotland; 3164, King Macbeth of Scotland; 3165, King Malcolm III of Scotland; 3166, King Edgar of Scotland; 3167, King Charles I of England and Scotland; 3168, King Charles II of England and Scotland; 3169, Prince Charles Edward Stuart ("The Young Pretender"); 3170, King James II of England and VII of Scotland; 3171, King James II of Scotland; 3172, King James III of Scotland.
No. 3169 is inscribed "George III 1760–1820 Great Britain" in error.

2000. Popes of the Millennium. As T **447**. Each black, yellow and green.
3174 $1.65 Alexander VI (bare-headed) 85 90
3175 $1.65 Benedict XIII 85 90
3176 $1.65 Boniface IX 85 90
3177 $1.65 Alexander VI (wearing cap) 85 90
3178 $1.65 Clement VIII 85 90
3179 $1.65 Clement VI 85 90
3180 $1.65 John Paul II 85 80
3181 $1.65 Benedict XV 85 90
3182 $1.65 John XXIII 85 90
3183 $1.65 Pius XI 95 90
3184 $1.65 Pius XII 85 90
3185 $1.65 Paul VI 85 90
No. 3181 is inscribed "BENIDICT XV" in error.

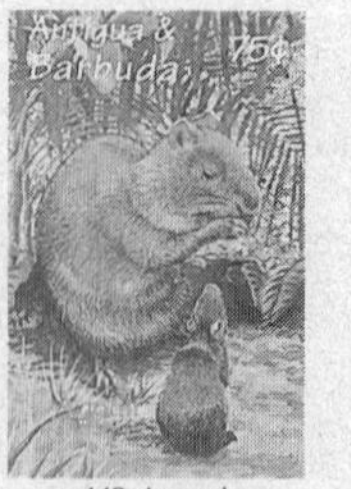

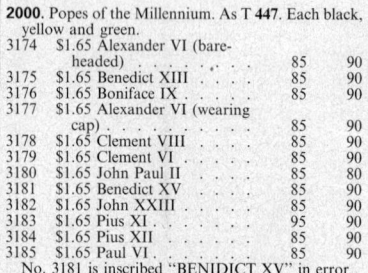

448 Agouti

2000. Fauna of the Rain Forest. Multicoloured.
3187 75c. Type **448** 40 45
3188 90c. Capybara 45 50
3189 $1.20 Basilisk lizard 60 65
3190 $1.65 Green violetear . . . 85 90
3191 $1.65 Harpy eagle 85 90
3192 $1.65 Three-toed sloth . . . 85 90
3193 $1.65 White uakari monkey 85 90
3194 $1.65 Anteater 85 90
3195 $1.65 Coati 85 90
3196 $1.75 Red-eyed tree frog . . 90 95
3197 $1.75 Black spider monkey 90 95
3198 $1.75 Emerald toucanet . . 90 95
3199 $1.75 Kinkajou 90 95
3200 $1.75 Spectacled bear . . . 90 95
3201 $1.75 Tapir 90 95
3202 $2 Heliconid butterfly . . 1·00 1·10
Nos. 3190/5 and 3196/201 were printed together, se-tenant, forming composite designs.

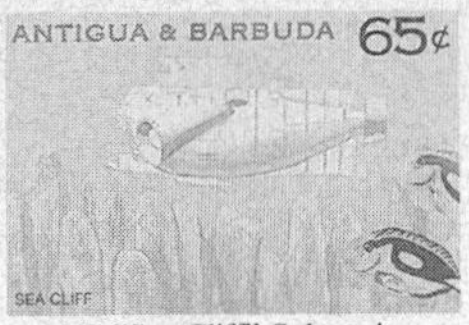
ANTIGUA & BARBUDA 65¢
SEA CLIFF

449 "Sea Cliff" Submarine

2000. Submarines. Multicoloured.

3204 65c. Type **449** 35 40
3205 75c. "Beaver Mark IV" . . 40 45
3206 90c. "Reef Ranger" 45 50
3207 $1 "Cubmarine" 50 55
3208 $1.20 "Alvin" 60 65
3209 $2 H.M.S. *Revenge* . . . 1·00 1·10
3210 $2 *Walrus*, Netherlands . . 1·00 1·10
3211 $2 U.S.S. *Los Angeles* . . . 1·00 1·10
3212 $2 *Daphne*, France . . . . 1·00 1·10
3213 $2 U.S.S. *Ohio* . . . . . . 1·00 1·10
3214 $2 U.S.S. *Skipjack* . . . . 1·00 1·10
3215 $3 "Argus", Russia . . . . 1·50 1·60

Nos. 3209/14 were printed together, se-tenant, with the backgrounds forming a composite design.

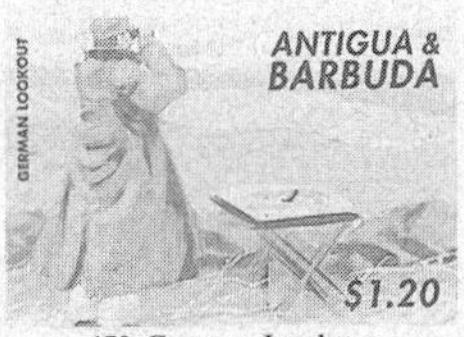
ANTIGUA & BARBUDA
GERMAN LOOKOUT
$1.20

450 German Lookout

2000. 60th Anniv of Battle of Britain. Multicoloured (except No. 3222).

3217 $1.20 Type **450** 60 65
3218 $1.20 Children's evacuation train 60 65
3219 $1.20 Evacuating hospital patients 60 65
3220 $1.20 Hawker Hurricane (fighter) 60 65
3221 $1.20 Rescue team 60 65
3222 $1.20 Churchill cartoon (black) 60 65
3223 $1.20 King George VI and Queen Elizabeth inspecting bomb damage 60 65
3224 $1.20 Barrage balloon above Tower Bridge 60 65
3225 $1.20 Bristol Blenheim (bomber) 60 65
3226 $1.20 Prime Minister Winston Churchill 60 65
3227 $1.20 Bristol Blenheim and barrage balloons 60 65
3228 $1.20 Heinkel (fighter) . . . 60 65
3229 $1.20 Supermarine Spitfire (fighter) 60 65
3230 $1.20 German rescue launch 60 65
3231 $1.20 Messerschmitt 109 (fighter) 60 65
3232 $1.20 R.A.F. rescue launch 60 65

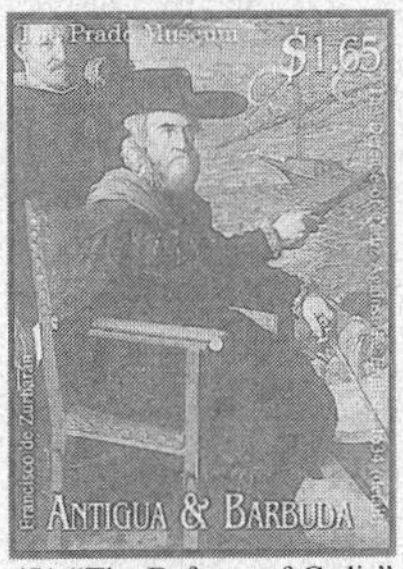
Prado Museum
$1.65
ANTIGUA & BARBUDA

451 "The Defence of Cadiz" (Zurbaran)

2000. "Espana 2000" International Stamp Exhibition, Madrid. Paintings from the Prado Museum. Mult.

3234 $1.65 Type **451** 85 90
3235 $1.65 "The Defence of Cadiz" (General and galleys) 85 90
3236 $1.65 "The Defence of Cadiz" (officers) 85 90
3237 $1.65 "Vulcan's Forge" (Vulcan) (Velazquez) . . . 85 90
3238 $1.65 "Vulcan's Forge" (working metal) 85 90
3239 $1.65 "Vulcan's Forge" (workers with hammers) 85 90
3240 $1.65 "Family Portrait" (three men) (Adriaen Key) 85 90
3241 $1.65 "Family Portrait" (one man) 85 90
3242 $1.65 "Family Portrait" (three women) 85 90
3243 $1.65 "The Devotion of Rudolf I" (horseman with lantern) (Rubens and Jan Wildens) 85 90
3244 $1.65 "The Devotion of Rudolf I" (priest on horseback) 85 90
3245 $1.65 "The Devotion of Rudolf I" (huntsman) . . 85 80
3246 $1.65 "The Concert" (lute player) (Vincente Gonzalez) 85 90
3247 $1.65 "The Concert" (lady with fan) 85 90
3248 $1.65 "The Concert" (two gentlemen) 85 90
3249 $1.65 "The Adoration of the Magi" (Wise Man) (Juan Maino) 85 90
3250 $1.65 "The Adoration of the Magi" (two Wise Men) 85 90
3251 $1.65 "The Adoration of the Magi" (Holy Family) . . 85 90

Nos. 3246/8 are inscribed "Gonzlez" with No. 3248 additionally inscribed "Francisco Rizi", all in error.

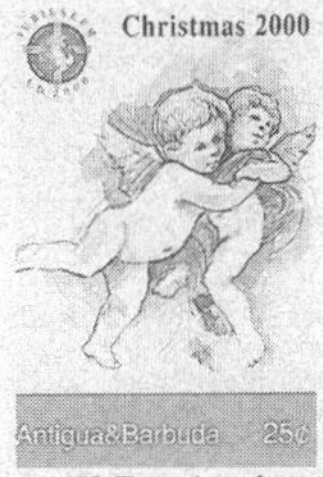
Christmas 2000
Antigua&Barbuda 25¢

452 Two Angels

2000. Christmas and Holy Year. Multicoloured.

3253 25c. Type **452** 15 20
3254 45c. Heads of two angels looking down 25 30
3255 90c. Heads of two angels, one looking up 45 50
3256 $1.75 Type **452** 90 95
3257 $1.75 As 45c. 90 95
3258 $1.75 As 90c. 90 95
3259 $1.75 As $5 . . . . 90 95
3260 $5 Two angels with drapery 2·50 2·75

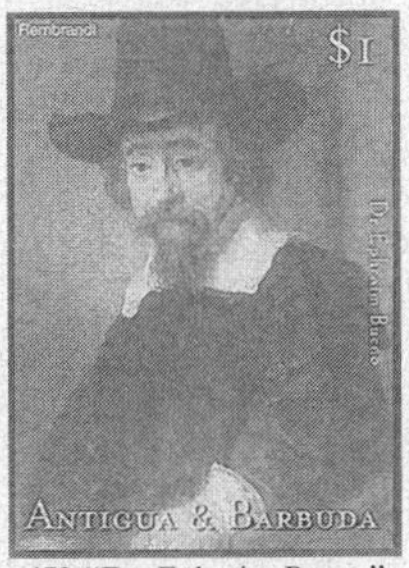
Rembrandt
$1
ANTIGUA & BARBUDA

453 "Dr. Ephraim Bueno" (Rembrandt)

2000. Bicentenary of Rijksmuseum, Amsterdam. Dutch Paintings. Multicoloured.

3262 $1 Type **453** 50 55
3263 $1 "Woman writing a Letter" (Frans van Meris de Oude) 50 55
3264 $1 "Mary Magdalen" (Jan van Scorel) 50 55
3265 $1 "Anna Coddle" (Maerten van Heemskerck) 50 55
3266 $1 "Cleopatra's Banquet" (Gerard Lairesse) 50 55
3267 $1 "Titus in Friar's Habit" (Rembrandt) 50 55
3268 $1.20 "Saskia" (Rembrandt) 60 65
3269 $1.20 "In the Month of July" (Paul Joseph Constantin Gabriel) . . . 60 65
3270 $1.20 "Maria Trip" (Rembrandt) 60 65
3271 $1.20 "Still Life with Flowers" (Jan van Huysum) 60 65
3272 $1.20 "Haesje van Cleyburgh" (Rembrandt) 60 65
3273 $1.20 "Girl in a White Kimono" (George Hendrick Breitner) . . . 60 65
3274 $1.65 "Man and Woman at a Spinning Wheel" (Pieter Pietersz) 85 90
3275 $1.65 "Self-portrait" (Rembrandt) 85 90
3276 $1.65 "Jeremiah lamenting the Destruction of Jerusalem" (Rembrandt) 85 90
3277 $1.65 "The Jewish Bride" (Rembrandt) 85 90
3278 $1.65 "Anna accused by Tobit of stealing a Kid" (Rembrandt) 85 90
3279 $1.65 "The Prophetess Anna" (Rembrandt) . . . 85 90

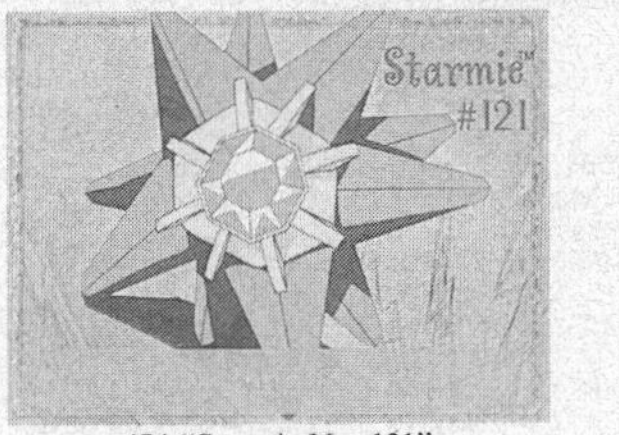
Starmie
#121

454 "Starmie No. 121"

2000. Characters from "Pokemon" (children's cartoon series). Multicoloured.

3281 $1.75 Type **454** 90 95
3282 $1.75 "Misty" 90 95
3283 $1.75 "Brock" 90 95
3284 $1.75 "Geodude No. 74" . . 90 95
3285 $1.75 "Krabby No. 98" . . 90 95
3286 $1.75 "Ash" 90 95

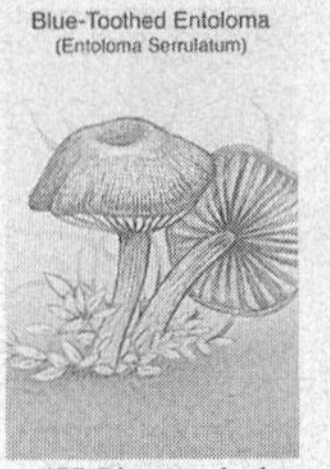
Blue-Toothed Entoloma
(Entoloma Serrulatum)

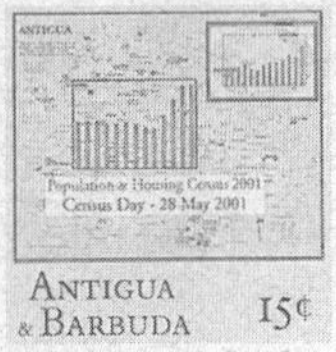
ANTIGUA
& BARBUDA 15¢

455 Blue-toothed Entoloma **456** Map and Graphs

2001. "Hong Kong 2001" Stamp Exhibition. Tropical Fungi. Multicoloured.

3288 25c. Type **455** 15 20
3289 90c. Common morel 45 50
3290 $1 Red cage fungus 50 55
3291 $1.65 Copper trumpet . . . 85 90
3292 $1.65 Field mushroom ("Meadow Mushroom") 85 90
3293 $1.65 Green gill ("Green-gilled Parasol") 85 90
3294 $1.65 The panther 85 90
3295 $1.65 Death cap 85 90
3296 $1.65 Royal boletus ("King Bolete") 85 90
3297 $1.65 Lilac fairy helmet ("Lilac Bonnet") 85 90
3298 $1.65 Silky volvar 85 90
3299 $1.65 Agrocybe mushroom ("Poplar Field Cap") . . 85 90
3300 $1.65 Saint George's mushroom 85 90
3301 $1.65 Red-stemmed tough shank 85 90
3302 $1.65 Fly agaric 85 90
3303 $1.75 Common fawn agaric ("Fawn Shield-Cap") . . 90 95

Nos. 3291/6 and 3297/302 were each printed together, se-tenant, with the backgrounds forming composite designs.

2001. Population and Housing Census.

3305 **456** 15c. multicoloured . . . 10 15
3306 – 25c. multicoloured . . . 15 20
3307 – 65c. multicoloured . . . 35 40
3308 – 90c. multicoloured . . . 45 50

DESIGNS: 25c. to 90c. Map and different form of graph.

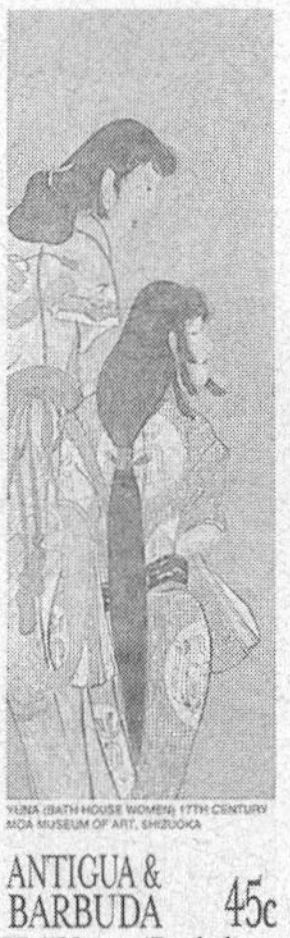
ANTIGUA &
BARBUDA 45c

457 "Yuna (Bath-house Women)" (detail)

2001. "PHILANIPPON 2001" International Stamp Exhibition, Tokyo. Traditional Japanese Paintings. Multicoloured.

3310 45c. Type **457** 25 30
3311 60c. "Yuna (Bath-house Women)" (different detail) 30 35
3312 65c. "Yuna (Bath-house Women)" (different detail) 35 40
3313 75c. "The Hikone Screen" (detail) 40 45
3314 $1 "The Hikone Screen" (different detail) 50 55
3315 $1.20 "The Hikone Screen" (different detail) 60 65
3316 $1.65 Galleon and Dutch merchants with horse . . 85 90
3317 $1.65 Galleon and merchants with tiger . . . 85 90
3318 $1.65 Merchants unpacking goods 85 90
3319 $1.65 Merchants with parasol and horse 85 90
3320 $1.65 Women packing food 85 90
3321 $1.65 Picnic under the cherry tree 85 90
3322 $1.65 Palanquins and resting bearers 85 90
3323 $1.65 Women dancing . . . 85 90
3324 $1.65 Three samurai 85 90
3325 $1.65 One samurai 85 90

Nos. 3316/19 ("The Namban Screen" by Kano Nizen) and Nos. 3320/5 ("Merry-making under the Cherry Blossoms" by Kano Naganobu) were each printed together, se-tenant, with both sheetlets forming the entire painting.

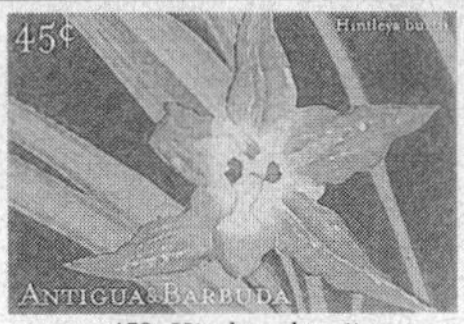
45¢
ANTIGUA&BARBUDA

459 *Hintleya burtii*

2001. Caribbean Orchids. Multicoloured.

3328 45c. Type **459** 25 30
3329 75c. *Neomoovea irrovata* . . 40 45
3330 90c. *Comparettia speciosa* . . 45 50
3331 $1 *Cyprepedium crapeanum* 50 55
3332 $1.20 *Trichoceuos muralis* (vert) 60 65
3333 $1.20 *Dracula rampira* (vert) 60 65
3334 $1.20 *Psychopsis papilio* (vert) 60 65
3335 $1.20 *Lycaste clenningiana* (vert) 60 65
3336 $1.20 *Telipogon nevuosus* (vert) 60 65
3337 $1.20 *Masclecallia ayahbacana* (vert) 60 65
3338 $1.65 *Cattleya dowiana* (vert) 85 90
3339 $1.65 *Dendiobium cruentum* (vert) 85 90
3340 $1.65 *Bulbophyllum lobb* (vert) 85 90
3341 $1.65 *Chysis laevis* (vert) . . 85 90
3342 $1.65 *Ancistrochilus rothschildicanus* (vert) . . 85 90
3343 $1.65 *Angraecun sororium* (vert) 85 90
3344 $1.65 *Rhyncholaelia glanca* (vert) 85 90
3345 $1.65 *Oncidium barbatum* (vert) 85 90
3346 $1.65 *Phaius tankervillege* (vert) 85 90
3347 $1.65 *Ghies brechtiana* (vert) 85 90
3348 $1.65 *Angraecum leonis* (vert) 85 90
3349 $1.65 *Cycnoches loddigesti* (vert) 85 90

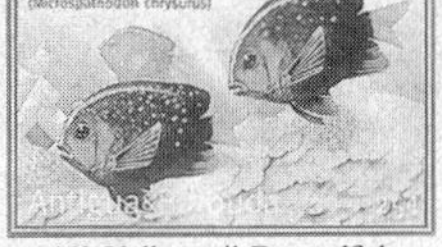

460 Yellowtail Damselfish

2001. Tropical Marine Life. Multicoloured.

3351 25c. Type **460** 15 20
3352 45c. Indigo hamlet 25 30
3353 65c. Great white shark . . . 35 40
3354 90c. Bottle-nose dolphin . . 45 50
3355 90c. Palette surgeonfish . . 45 50
3356 $1 Octopus 50 55
3357 $1.20 Common dolphin . . 60 65
3358 $1.20 Franklin's gull 60 65
3359 $1.20 Rock beauty 60 65
3360 $1.20 Bicoloured angelfish 60 65
3361 $1.20 Beaugregory 60 65
3362 $1.20 Banded butterflyfish 60 65
3363 $1.20 Common tern 60 65
3364 $1.20 Flying fish 60 65
3365 $1.20 Queen angelfish . . . 60 65
3366 $1.20 Blue-striped grunt . . 60 65
3367 $1.20 Porkfish 60 65
3368 $1.20 Blue tang 60 65
3369 $1.65 Red-footed booby . . 85 90
3370 $1.65 Bottle-nose dolphin 85 90
3371 $1.65 Hawksbill turtle . . . 85 90
3372 $1.65 Monk seal 85 90
3373 $1.65 Great white shark (inscr "Bull Shark") . . . 85 90
3374 $1.65 Lemon shark 85 90
3375 $1.65 Dugong 85 90
3376 $1.65 White-tailed tropicbird 85 90
3377 $1.65 Bull shark 85 90
3378 $1.65 Manta ray 85 90
3379 $1.65 Green turtle 85 90
3380 $1.65 Spanish grunt 85 90

Nos. 3357/62, 3363/8, 3369/74 and 3375/80 were each printed together, se-tenant, the backgrounds forming composite designs.

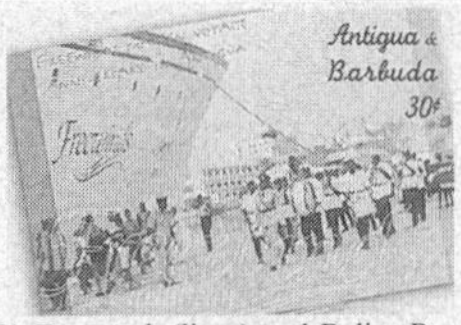
Antigua &
Barbuda
30¢

461 *Freewinds* (liner) and Police Band, Antigua

2001. Work of *Freewinds* (Church of Scientology flagship) in Caribbean. Multicoloured.

3382 30c. Type **461** 15 20
3383 45c. At anchor off St. Barthelemy 25 30
3384 75c. At sunset 40 45
3385 90c. Off Bonaire 45 50
3386 $1.50 *Freewinds* anchored off Bequia 80 90

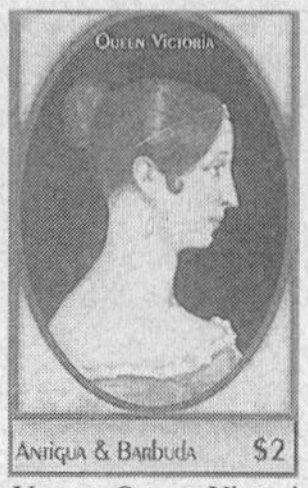

462 Young Queen Victoria in Blue Dress

2001. Death Centenary of Queen Victoria. Multicoloured.

3388	$2 Type **462**	1·00	1·10
3389	$2 Queen Victoria wearing red head-dress	1·00	1·10
3390	$2 Queen Victoria with jewelled hair ornament	1·00	1·10
3391	$2 Queen Victoria, after Chalon, in brooch	1·00	1·10

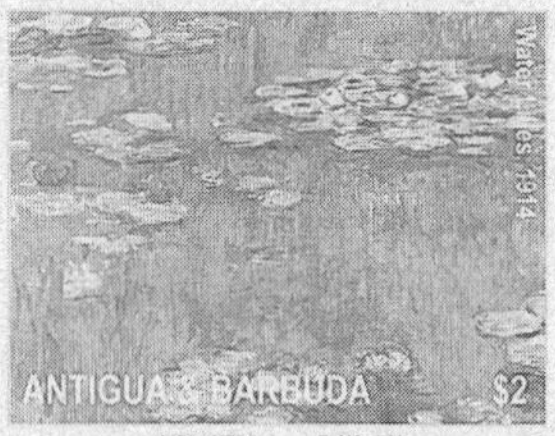

463 "Water Lilies"

2001. 75th Death Anniv of Claude-Oscar Monet (French painter). Multicoloured.

3393	$2 Type **463**	1·00	1·10
3394	$2 "Rose Portals, Giverny"	1·00	1·10
3395	$2 "Water Lily Pond, Harmony in Green"	1·00	1·10
3396	$2 "Artist's Garden, Irises"	1·00	1·10

No. 3396 is inscribed "Artists's" in error.

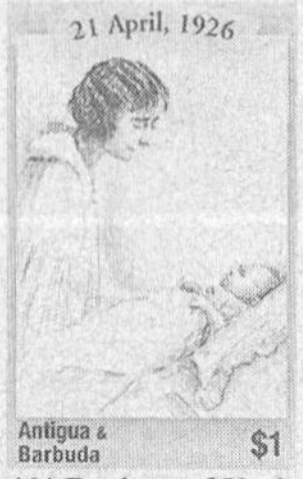

464 Duchess of York with Baby Princess Elizabeth (1926)

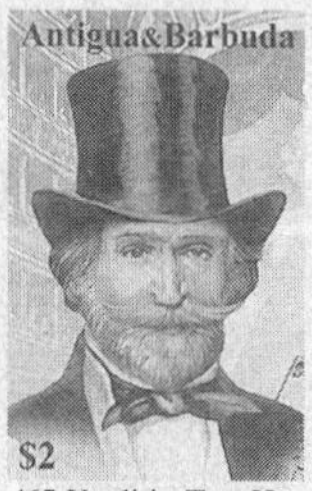

465 Verdi in Top Hat

2001. 75th Birthday of Queen Elizabeth II. Multicoloured.

3398	$1 Type **464**	50	55
3399	$1 Queen in Coronation robes (1953)	50	55
3400	$1 Young Princess Elizabeth (1938)	50	55
3401	$1 Queen Elizabeth in Garter robes (1956)	50	55
3402	$1 Princess Elizabeth with pony (1939)	50	55
3403	$1 Queen Elizabeth in red dress and pearls (1985)	50	55

2001. Death Centenary of Giuseppe Verdi (Italian composer). Multicoloured.

3405	$2 Type **465**	1·00	1·10
3406	$2 Don Carlos and part of opera score	1·00	1·10
3407	$2 Conductor and score for *Aida*	1·00	1·10
3408	$2 Musicians and score for *Rigoletto*	1·00	1·10

Nos. 3405/8 were printed together, se-tenant, the backgrounds forming a composite design.

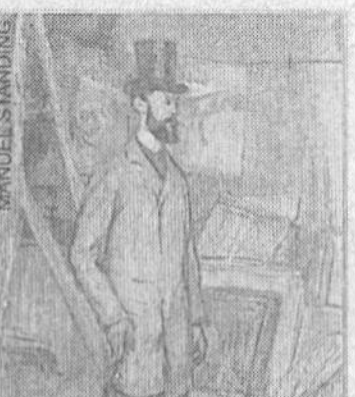

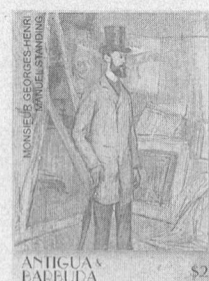

466 "Georges-Henri Manuel"

2001. Death Centenary of Henri de Toulouse-Lautrec (French painter). Multicoloured.

3410	$2 Type **466**	1·00	1·10
3411	$2 "Louis Pascal"	1·00	1·10
3412	$2 "Romain Coolus"	1·00	1·10
3413	$2 "Monsieur Fourcade"	1·00	1·10

No 3412 is inscribed "ROMAN" in error.

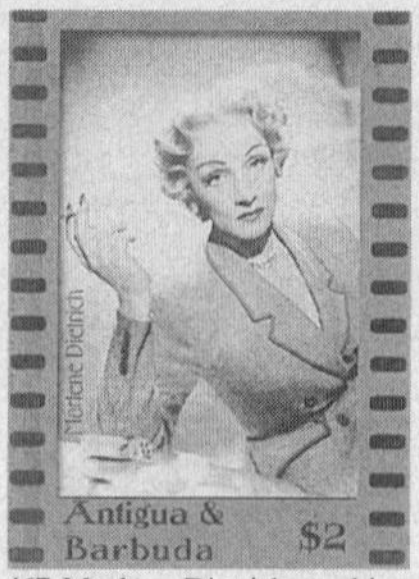

467 Marlene Dietrich smoking

2001. Birth Centenary of Marlene Dietrich (actress and singer).

3415	**467** $2 black, purple and red	1·00	1·10
3416	– $2 black, purple and red	1·00	1·10
3417	– $2 multicoloured	1·00	1·10
3418	– $2 black, purple and red	1·00	1·10

DESIGNS: No. 3416, Marlene Dietrich, in evening gown, sitting on settee; 3417, In black dress; 3418, Sitting on piano.

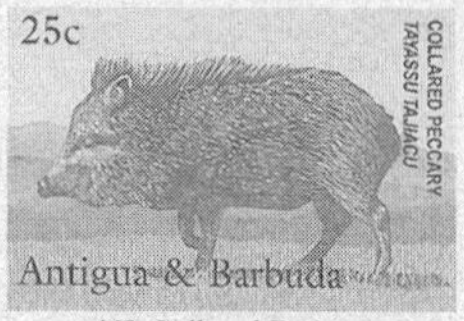

468 Collared Peccary

2001. Vanishing Fauna of the Caribbean. Multicoloured.

3419	25c. Type **468**	15	20
3420	30c. Baird's tapir	15	20
3421	45c. Agouti	25	30
3422	75c. Bananaquit	40	45
3423	90c. Six-banded armadillo	45	50
3424	$1 Roseate spoonbill	50	55
3425	$1.80 Mouse opossum	90	95
3426	$1.80 Magnificent black frigate bird	90	95
3427	$1.80 Northern jacana	90	95
3428	$1.80 Painted bunting	90	95
3429	$1.80 Haitian solenodon	90	95
3430	$1.80 St. Lucia iguana	90	95
3431	$2.50 West Indian iguana	1·25	1·40
3432	$2.50 Scarlet macaw	1·25	1·40
3433	$2.50 Cotton-topped tamarin	1·25	1·40
3434	$2.50 Kinkajou	1·25	1·40

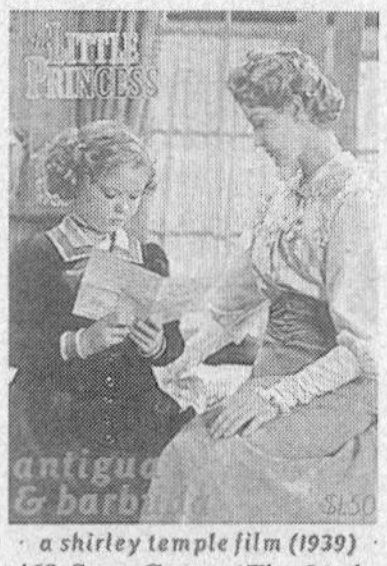

469 Sara Crewe (*The Little Princess*) reading a Letter

2001. Shirley Temple Films. Multicoloured. Showing film scenes. (a) *The Little Princess*. Multicoloured.

3436	$1.50 Type **469**	80	85
3437	$1.50 Sara in pink dressing gown	80	85
3438	$1.50 Sara cuddling doll	80	85
3439	$1.50 Sara as Princess on throne	80	85
3440	$1.50 Sara talking to man in frock coat	80	85
3441	$1.50 Sara blowing out candles	80	85
3442	$1.80 Sara with Father (horiz)	90	95
3443	$1.80 Sara scrubbing floor (horiz)	90	95
3444	$1.80 Sara and friend with Headmistress (horiz)	90	95
3445	$1.80 Sara with Queen Victoria (horiz)	90	95

(b) *Baby, Take a Bow.*

3447	$1.65 Shirley in dancing class (horiz)	85	90
3448	$1.65 Shirley cuddling Father (horiz)	85	90
3449	$1.65 Shirley at bedtime with parents (horiz)	85	90
3450	$1.65 Shirley in yellow dress with Father (horiz)	85	90
3451	$1.65 Shirley and Father at Christmas party (horiz)	85	90
3452	$1.65 Shirley and gangster looking in cradle (horiz)	85	90
3453	$1.65 Shirley in spotted dress	85	90
3454	$1.65 Shirley on steps with gangster	85	90
3455	$1.65 Shirley with gangster holding gun	85	90
3456	$1.65 Shirley with Mother	85	90

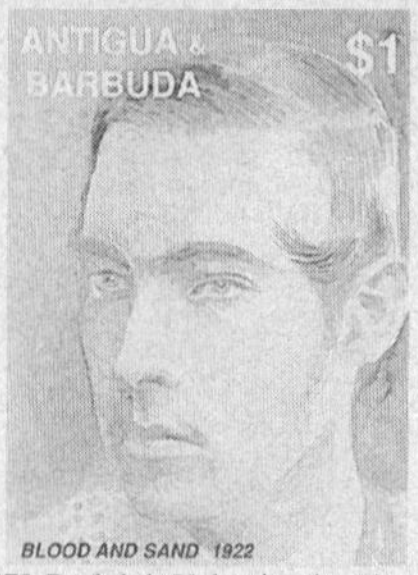

470 Rudolph Valentino in *Blood and Sand*, 1922

2001. 75th Death Anniv of Rudolph Valentino (Italian film actor).

3458	**470** $1 brown and black	50	55
3459	– $1 lilac and black	50	55
3460	– $1 brown and black	50	55
3461	– $1 brown and black	50	55
3462	– $1 red and black	50	55
3463	– $1 lilac and black	50	55
3464	– $1 multicoloured	50	55
3465	– $1 multicoloured	50	55
3466	– $1 multicoloured	50	55
3467	– $1 multicoloured	50	55
3468	– $1 multicoloured	50	55
3469	– $1 multicoloured	50	55

DESIGNS: No. 3459, In *Eyes of Youth* with Clara Kimbal Young, 1919; 3460, In *All Night Long* with Carmel Meyers, 1918; 3461, Valentino in 1926; 3462, In *Camille* with Alla Nazimova, 1921; 3463, In *Cobra* with Nita Naldi, 1925; 3464, In *The Son of the Sheik* with Vilma Banky, 1926; 3465, In *The Young Rajah*, 1922; 3466, In *The Eagle* with Vilma Banky, 1925; 3467, In *The Sheik* with Agnes Ayres, 1921; 3468, In *A Sainted Devil*, 1924; 3469, In *Monsieur Beaucaire*, 1924.

Nos. 3464 and 3466 are inscribed "BLANKY" and No. 3467 "AYERS", all in error.

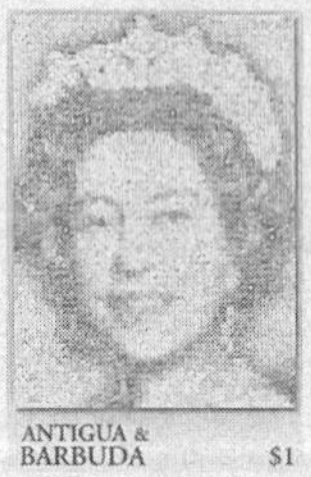

471 Queen Elizabeth

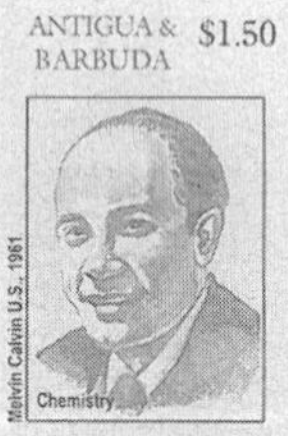

472 Melvin Calvin, 1961

2001. Golden Jubilee (1st issue).

3471	**471** $1 multicoloured	50	55

No. 3471 was printed in sheetlets of 8, containing two vertical rows of four, separated by a large illustrated central gutter. Both the stamp and the illustration on the central gutter are made up of a collage of miniature flower photographs.

See also Nos. 3535/8.

2001. Centenary of Nobel Prizes. Chemistry Winners. Multicoloured.

3472	$1.50 Type **472**	80	85
3473	$1.50 Linus Pauling, 1954	80	85
3474	$1.50 Vincent du Vigneaud, 1955	80	85
3475	$1.50 Richard Synge, 1952	80	85
3476	$1.50 Archer Martin, 1952	80	85
3477	$1.50 Alfred Werner, 1913	80	85
3478	$1.50 Robert Curl Jr., 1996	80	85
3479	$1.50 Alan Heeger, 2000	80	85
3480	$1.50 Michael Smith, 1993	80	85
3481	$1.50 Sidney Altman, 1989	80	85
3482	$1.50 Elias Corey, 1990	80	85
3483	$1.50 William Giauque, 1949	80	85

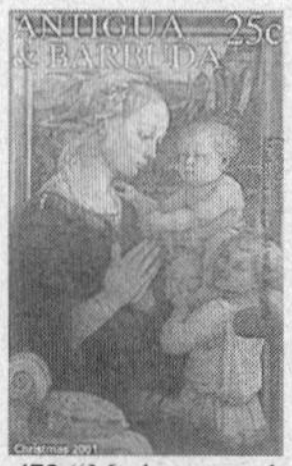

473 "Madonna and Child with Angels" (Filippo Lippi)

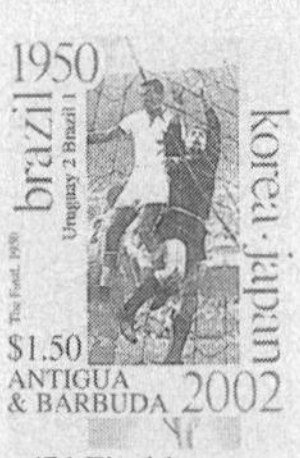

474 Final between Uruguay and Brazil, Brazil 1950

2001. Christmas. Italian Religious Paintings. Multicoloured.

3485	25c. Type **473**	15	20
3486	45c. "Madonna of Corneto Tarquinia" (Lippi)	25	30
3487	50c. "Madonna and Child" (Domenico Ghirlandaio)	30	35
3488	75c. "Madonna and Child" (Lippi)	40	45
3489	$4 "Madonna Delceppo" (Lippi)	2·00	2·10

2001. World Cup Football Championship, Japan and Korea (2002). Multicoloured.

3491	$1.50 Type **474**	80	85
3492	$1.50 Ferenc Puskas (Hungary), Switzerland 1954	80	85
3493	$1.50 Raymond Kopa (France), Sweden 1958	80	85
3494	$1.50 Mauro (Brazil), Chile 1962	80	85
3495	$1.50 Gordon Banks (England), England 1966	80	85
3496	$1.50 Pele (Brazil), Mexico 1970	80	85
3497	$1.50 Daniel Passarella (Argentina), Argentina 1978	80	85
3498	$1.50 Karl-Heinz Rummenigge (Germany), Spain 1982	80	85
3499	$1.50 World Cup Trophy, Mexico 1986	80	85
3500	$1.50 Diego Maradona (Argentina), Italy 1990	80	85
3501	$1.50 Roger Milla (Cameroun), U.S.A. 1994	80	85
3502	$1.50 Zinedine Zidane (France), France 1998	80	85

No. 3500 is inscribed "Deigo" in error.

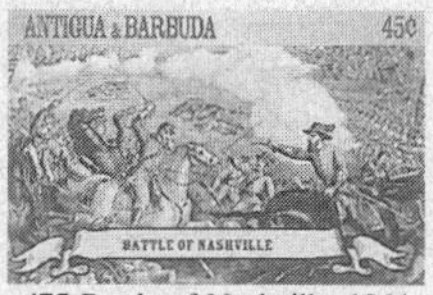

475 Battle of Nashville, 1864

2002. American Civil War. Multicoloured.

3504	45c. Type **475**	25	30
3505	45c. Capture of Atlanta, 1864	25	30
3506	45c. Battle of Spotsylvania, 1864	25	30
3507	45c. Battle of The Wilderness, 1864	25	30
3508	45c. Battle of Chickamauga Creek, 1863	25	30
3509	45c. Battle of Gettysburg, 1863	25	30
3510	45c. Lee and Jackson at Chancellorsville, 1863	25	30
3511	45c. Battle of Fredericksburg, 1862	25	30
3512	45c. Battle of Antietam, 1862	25	30
3513	45c. Second Battle of Bull Run, 1862	25	30
3514	45c. Battle of Five Forks, 1865	25	30
3515	45c. Seven Days' Battles, 1862	25	30
3516	45c. First Battle of Bull Run, 1861	25	30
3517	45c. Battle of Shiloh, 1862	25	30
3518	45c. Battle of Seven Pines, 1862	25	30
3519	45c. Bombardment of Fort Sumter, 1861	25	30
3520	45c. Battle of Chattanooga, 1863	25	30
3521	45c. Grant and Lee at Appomattox, 1865	25	30
3522	50c. General Ulysses S. Grant (vert)	30	35
3523	50c. President Abraham Lincoln (vert)	30	35
3524	50c. President Jefferson Davis (vert)	30	35
3525	50c. General Robert E. Lee (vert)	30	35
3526	50c. General George Custer (vert)	30	35
3527	50c. Admiral Andrew Hull Foote (vert)	30	35
3528	50c. General "Stonewall" Jackson (vert)	30	35
3529	50c. General Jeb Stuart (vert)	30	35
3530	50c. General George Meade (vert)	30	35
3531	50c. General Philip Sheridan (vert)	30	35
3532	50c. General James Longstreet (vert)	30	35
3533	50c. General John Mosby (vert)	30	35

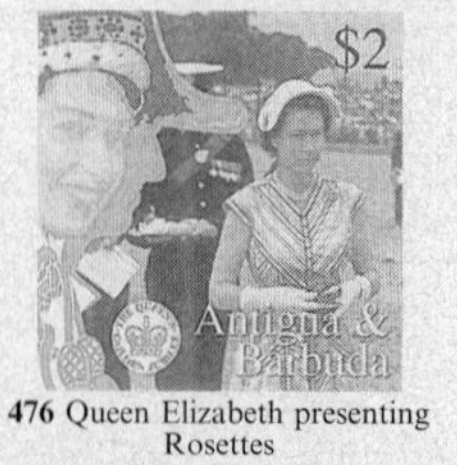

476 Queen Elizabeth presenting Rosettes

2002. Golden Jubilee (2nd issue). Multicoloured.

3535	$2 Type **476**	1·00	1·10
3536	$2 Queen Elizabeth at garden party	1·00	1·10
3537	$2 Queen Elizabeth in evening dress	1·00	1·10
3538	$2 Queen Elizabeth in cream coat	1·00	1·10

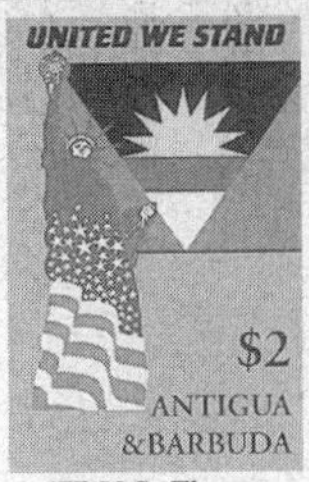
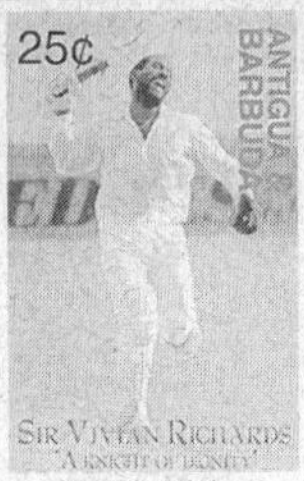

477 U.S. Flag as Statue of Liberty and Antigua & Barbuda Flag

478 Sir Vivian Richards waving Bat

2002. "United We Stand". Support for Victims of 11 September 2001 Terrorist Attacks.

3540	477	$2 multicoloured	1·00	1·10

2002. 50th Birthday of Sir Vivian Richards (West Indian cricketer). Multicoloured.

3541	25c. Type **478**	15	20
3542	30c. Sir Vivian Richards receiving presentation from Antigua Cricket Association	15	20
3543	50c. Sir Vivian Richards wearing sash	30	35
3544	75c. Sir Vivian Richards batting	40	45
3545	$1.50 Sir Vivian Richards and Lady Richards	80	85
3546	$1.80 Sir Vivian Richards with enlarged action photograph of himself	90	95

ANTIOQUIA Pt. 20

One of the states of the Granadine Confederation.
A department of Colombia from 1886, now uses Colombian stamps.

100 centavos = 1 peso.

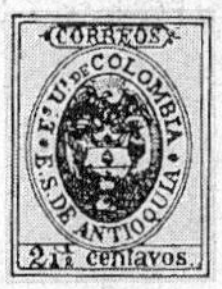
1

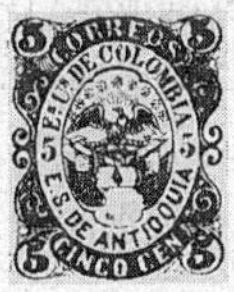
5

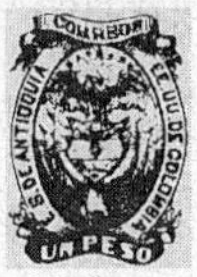
6

1868. Various arms designs. Imperf.

1	1	2½c. blue	£450	£225
2	–	5c. green	£350	£200
3	–	10c. lilac	£850	£385
4	–	1p. red	£300	£185

1869. Various frames. Imperf.

5	5	2½c. blue	2·50	2·00
6		5c. green	3·25	3·00
8		10c. mauve	4·00	2·00
9		20c. brown	4·50	3·00
10	6	1p. red	7·50	7·50

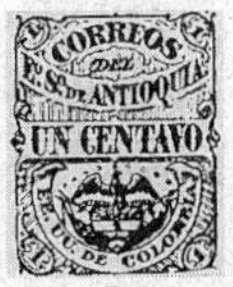
7

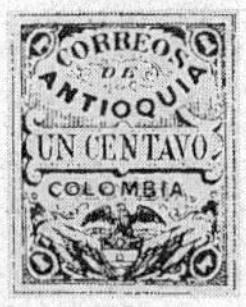
15

1873. Arms designs inscr "E.S." (or "Eo. So." or "Estado Soberano") "de Antioquia". Imperf.

11	7	1c. green	2·00	1·50
12	–	5c. green	2·50	1·60
13	–	10c. mauve	16·00	12·00
14	–	20c. brown	4·00	2·50
15	–	50c. blue	1·00	80
16	–	1p. red	2·50	2·50
17	–	2p. black on yellow	5·00	5·00
18	–	5p. black on red	25·00	20·00

The 5p. is larger (25½ × 31½ mm).

1875. Imperf.

20	15	1c. black on green	60	60
43		1c. mauve	1·00	1·00
21		1c. black	60	60
52		1c. green	1·00	1·00
22	–	2½c. blue (Arms)	80	80
23	–	5c. green ("Liberty")	6·00	5·00
25	–	10c. mauve (J. Berrio)	8·00	7·00

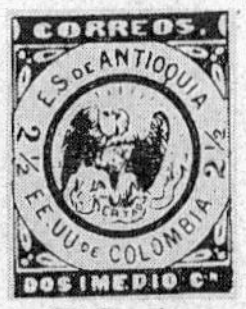
20 Condor

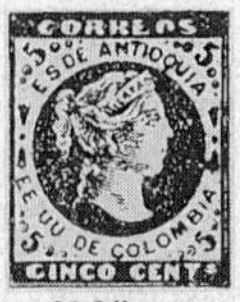
21 Liberty

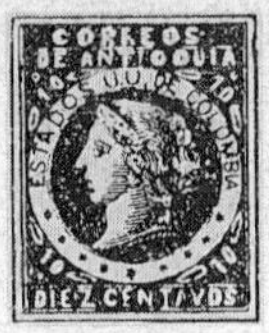
23 Liberty

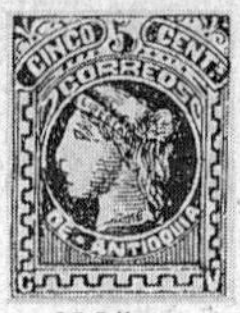
25 Liberty

1879. Imperf.

30	20	2½c. blue	3·00	3·00
38		2½c. green	80	1·00
45		2½c. black on buff	3·00	3·00
39	21	5c. green	85	1·00
40		5c. violet	1·75	1·00
32	–	10c. violet (Arms)	£250	£200
36	23	10c. violet	50·00	16·00
41		10c. red	1·00	1·00
42	21	20c. brown	1·25	1·25

1883. Various frames. Head of Liberty to left. Imperf.

53	25	5c. brown	4·00	2·00
47		5c. yellow	3·00	2·50
48		5c. green	55·00	40·00
49		10c. green	2·00	2·00
50		10c. mauve	3·50	3·50
55		10c. blue	4·00	3·50
51		20c. blue	2·50	2·50

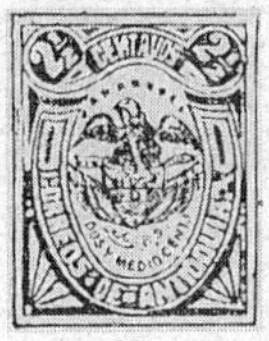
28

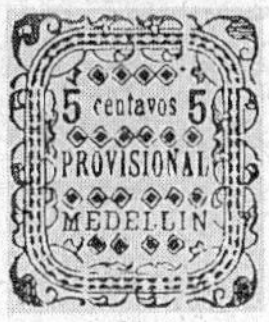

31

1886. Imperf.

57	28	1c. green on pink	50	50
65		1c. red on lilac	30	30
58		2½c. black on orange	35	40
66		2½c. mauve on pink	50	40
59		5c. blue on buff	2·00	75
67		5c. red on green	2·25	2·25
68		5c. lake on buff	1·00	80
60		10c. red on buff	1·00	60
69		10c. brown on green	1·00	80
61		20c. purple on buff	1·00	60
62		50c. yellow on buff	2·00	2·00
63		1p. yellow on green	4·00	4·00
64		2p. green on lilac	4·00	4·00

1888. Various sizes and frames. Inscr "MEDELLIN". Imperf.

70	31	2½c. black on yellow	15·00	12·00
71		2½c. red on white	2·50	2·50
72		5c. black on yellow	2·00	2·00
73		5c. red on orange	1·75	1·75

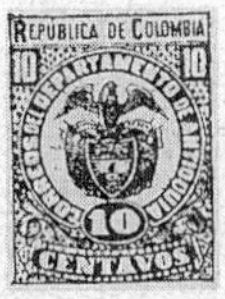
34

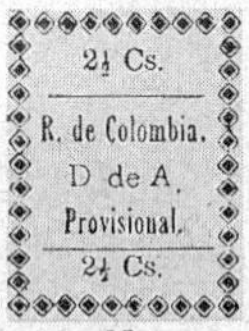

35

1889. Arms in various frames.

74	34	1c. black on red	10	10
75		2½c. black on blue	20	15
76		5c. black on yellow	45	25
77		10c. black on green	50	40
95		10c. brown	25	25
78		20c. blue	1·00	1·00
79		50c. brown	2·00	2·00
80		50c. green	1·75	1·75
81		1p. red	1·00	1·00
82		2p. black on mauve	7·50	6·00
83		5p. black on red	10·00	7·50

1890. Perf.

84	35	2½c. black on buff	1·00	1·00
85		5c. black on yellow	1·00	1·00
86		10c. black on buff	4·75	4·75
87		10c. black on red	5·00	5·00
88		20c. black on yellow	5·00	5·00

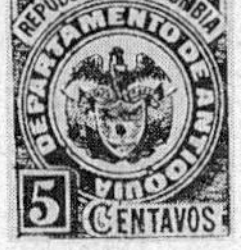
36

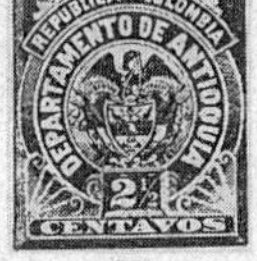
37

1892.

89	36	1c. brown on buff	50	40
90		1c. blue	20	20
91		2½c. violet on lilac	30	30
92		2½c. green	30	30
93		5c. black	80	60
94		5c. red	20	20

1896.

96	37	2c. grey	40	40
107		2c. red	25	40
97		2½c. brown	40	40
108		2½c. blue	25	40
98		3c. red	50	50
109		3c. olive	25	40
99		5c. green	25	20
110		5c. yellow	20	30
100		10c. lilac	45	45
111		10c. brown	50	60
101		20c. brown	70	70
112		20c. blue	75	1·00
102		50c. sepia	90	90
113		50c. red	1·00	1·40
103		1p. black and blue	10·00	10·00
114		1p. black and red	10·00	10·00
104		2p. black and orange	40·00	40·00
115		2p. black and green	35·00	35·00
105		5p. black and mauve	50·00	50·00

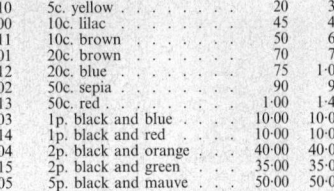

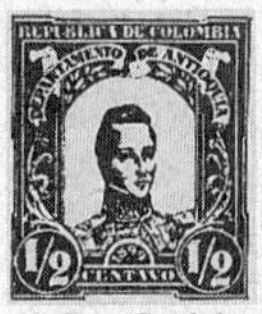
39 Gen. Cordoba

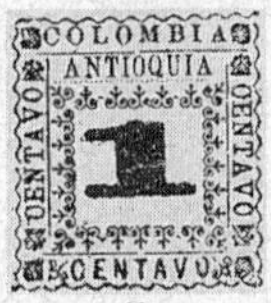
43

1899.

118	39	½c. blue	10	10
119		1c. blue	10	10
120		2c. black	10	10
121		3c. red	10	10
122		4c. brown	10	10
123		5c. green	10	10
124		10c. red	10	10
125		20c. violet	10	10
126		50c. yellow	10	10
127		1p. green	10	15
128		2p. green	10	20

1901. Various frames.

132	43	1c. red	10	15
133		1c. brown	25	25
134		1c. blue	25	25

Nos. 132 and 134 also exist with "CENTAVO" inside the rectangle below figure "1".

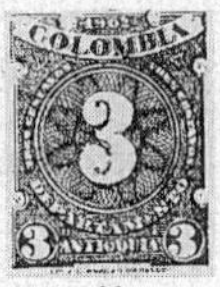
46

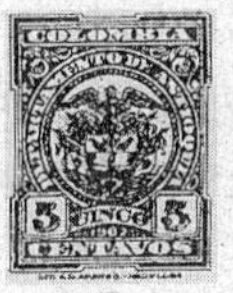
47

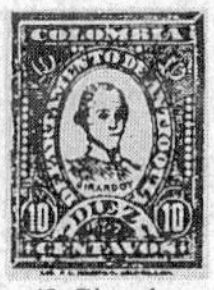
48 Girardot

1902.

138	46	1c. red	10	10
139		1c. blue	10	10
140		2c. blue	10	10
141		2c. violet	10	10
142		3c. green	10	10
143		4c. purple	10	10
144	47	5c. red	10	10
145		10c. mauve	10	10
147		20c. green	15	15
148		30c. red	15	10
149	48	40c. blue	15	10
150		50c. brown on yellow	20	20
152	–	1p. black and violet	40	45
153	–	2p. black and red	40	45
154	–	5p. black and blue	50	55

DESIGN: 1p. to 5p. Dr. J. Felix de Restrepo.
No. 145 also exists with smaller head.

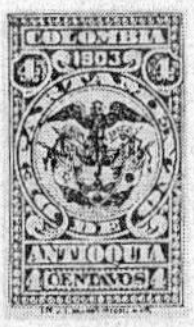
54

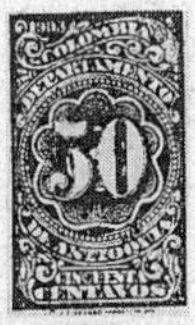
55

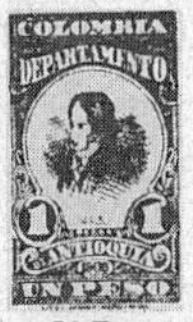
56 Zea

1903.

159	54	4c. brown	10	10
160		5c. blue	10	10
161	55	10c. yellow	10	10
162		20c. lilac	10	10
163		30c. brown	30	30
164		40c. green	30	30
165		50c. red	10	15
166	56	1p. green	25	20
167		2p. mauve (Rovira)	25	20
168		3p. blue (La Pola)	30	30
169		4p. red (Restrepo)	50	30
170		5p. brown (Madrid)	50	40
171		10p. red (Corral)	2·25	2·25

ACKNOWLEDGEMENT OF RECEIPT STAMPS

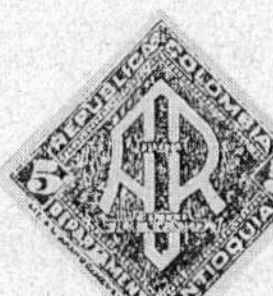
AR 53

1902.

AR157	AR 53	5c. black on red	30	20
AR158		5c. green	10	10

REGISTRATION STAMPS

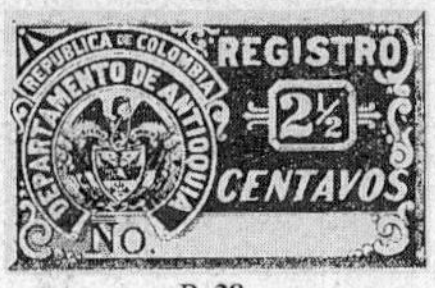
R 38

1896.

R106	R 38	2½c. pink	50	50
R117		2½c. blue	60	60

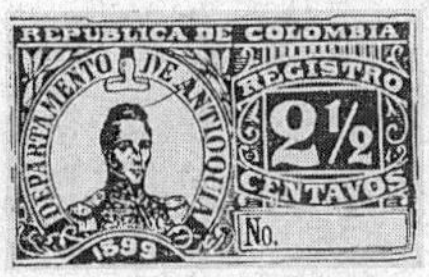
R 41 Gen. Cordoba

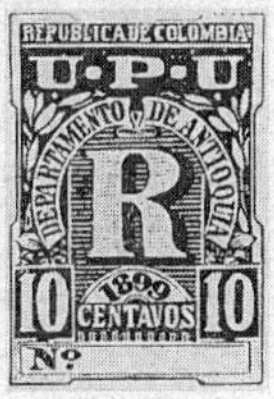
R 42

1899.

R130	R 41	2½c. blue	10	10
R131	R 42	10c. red	10	10

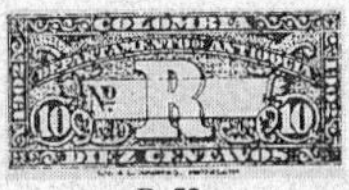
R 52

1902.

R156	R 52	10c. violet on green	10	10

TOO LATE STAMPS

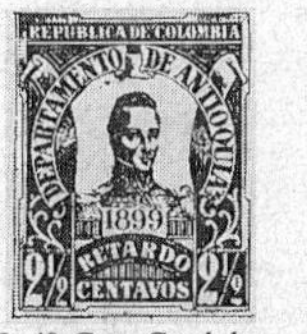
L 40 Gen. Cordoba

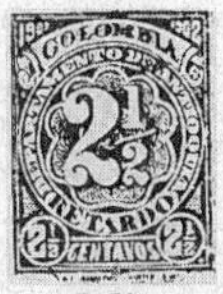
L 51

1899.

L129	L 40	2½c. green	10	10

1901. As T **43**, but inscr "RETARDO" at sides.

L137a	2½c. purple	60	60

1902.

L155	L 51	2½c. lilac	10	10

ARBE Pt. 8

During the period of D'Annunzio's Italian Regency of Carnaro (Fiume), separate issues were made for Arbe (now Rab).

100 centesimi = 1 lira.

1920. No. 148, etc of Fiume optd **ARBE**.

1	5c. green	2·50	2·50
2	10c. red	4·50	4·50
3	20c. brown	7·50	7·50
4	25c. blue	7·50	7·50
5	50c. on 20c. brown	7·50	7·50
6	55c. on 5c. green	7·50	7·50

EXPRESS LETTER STAMPS

1920. Nos. E163/4 of Fiume optd **ARBE**.

E7	30c. on 20c. brown	42·00	35·00
E8	50c. on 5c. green	32·00	35·00

ARGENTINE REPUBLIC Pt. 20

A republic in the S.E. of S. America formerly part of the Spanish Empire.

1858. 100 centavos = 1 peso.
1985. 100 centavos = 1 austral.
1992. 100 centavos = 1 peso.

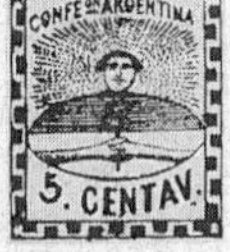
1 Argentine Confederation

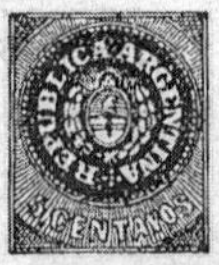
3 Argentine Confederation

1858. Imperf.

1	1	5c. red	1·60	9·50
2		10c. green	2·25	55·00
3		15c. blue	16·00	£140

1862. Imperf.

10	3	5c. red	20·00	24·00
8		10c. green	£160	75·00
9		15c. blue	£325	£250

5 Rivadavia

6 Rivadavia

1864. Imperf.

24	5	5c. red	£250	65·00
14	6	10c. green	£1700	£1000
15	5	15c. blue	£8000	£3500

1864. Perf.

16	5	5c. red	35·00	14·00
17	6	10c. green	80·00	35·00
18	5	15c. blue	£160	75·00

9 Rivadavia

10 Gen. Belgrano

11 Gen. San Martin

1867. Perf.

28	9	5c. red	12·00	75
29	10	10c. green	35·00	5·00
30a	11	15c. blue	50·00	15·00

12 Balcarce

22 Sarsfield

24 Lopez

1873. Portraits. Perf.

31	12	1c. violet	4·00	2·25
32	–	4c. brown (Moreno)	5·50	45
33	–	30c. orange (Alvear)	£120	17·00
34	–	60c. black (Posadas)	£120	5·50
35	–	90c. blue (Saavedra)	28·00	2·50

1877. Surch with large figure of value.

37	9	1 on 5c. red	55·00	17·00
38		2 on 5c. red	£110	70·00
39	10	8 on 10c. green	£140	35·00

1876. Roul.

36	9	5c. red	£170	70·00
40		8c. lake	28·00	30
41	10	16c. green	9·00	1·25
42	22	20c. blue	9·50	3·50
43	11	24c. blue	19·00	3·50

1877. Perf.

46	24	2c. green	4·75	1·00
44	9	8c. lake	4·75	15
45	11	24c. blue	8·50	50
47	–	25c. lake (Alvear)	25·00	7·00

1882. Surch **1/2 (PROVISORIO)**.

51	9	½ on 5c. red	1·00	90

29

33

1882.

52	29	½c. brown	1·60	90
55		1c. red	4·00	1·25
54		12c. blue	65·00	10·00

1884. Surch **1884** and value in figures or words.

90	9	½c. on 5c. red	3·00	2·25
92	11	½c. on 15c. blue	2·25	1·75
94		1c. on 15c. blue	7·00	5·50
100	9	4c. on 5c. red	10·00	6·00

1884.

101	33	½c. brown	1·00	50
102		1c. red	6·00	50
103		12c. blue	28·00	1·40

34 Urquiza

45 Mitre

1888. Portrait types, inscr "CORREOS ARGENTINOS".

108	34	½c. blue	55	50
110	–	2c. green (Lopez)	10·00	7·00
111	–	3c. green (Celman)	1·90	70
113	–	5c. red (Rivadavia)	9·00	65
114	–	6c. red (Sarmiento)	24·00	16·00
115	–	10c. brown (Avellaneda)	16·00	1·25
116	–	15c. orange (San Martin)	16·00	1·75
117a	–	20c. green (Roca)	13·00	1·40
118	–	25c. violet (Belgrano)	16·00	1·75
119	–	30c. brown (Dorrego)	24·00	2·75
120a	–	40c. grey (Moreno)	24·00	3·25
121	45	50c. blue	85·00	9·00

60 Paz

51 Rivadavia

1888. Portrait types, inscr "CORREOS Y TELEGRAFOS" except No. 126.

137	60	¼c. green	10	15
122	–	½c. blue (Urquiza)	30	15
123	–	1c. brown (Sarsfield)	95	20
125	–	2c. violet (Derqui)	95	15
126	–	3c. green (Celman)	2·25	45
127	51	5c. red	3·00	20
129	–	6c. blue (Sarmiento)	1·60	60
130	–	10c. brown (Avellaneda)	1·90	30
131	–	12c. blue (Alberti)	4·75	1·25
132	–	40c. grey (Moreno)	4·50	90
133	–	50c. orange (Mitre)	4·50	90
134	–	60c. black (Posadas)	17·00	3·00

1890. No. 131 surch **1/4** and bars.

135		¼ on 12c. blue	40	35

52 Rivadavia

63 La Madrid

61 Rivadavia

1890.

128a	52	5c. red	2·25	15

1891. Portraits.

139	–	1p. blue (San Martin)	45·00	6·50
140	63	5p. blue	£225	24·00
141	–	20p. green (G. Brown)	£325	70·00

1891.

138	61	8c. red	1·40	25

65 Rivadavia

66 Belgrano

67 San Martin

1892.

142	65	½c. blue	20	15
143		1c. brown	40	15
144		2c. green	25	15
145		3c. orange	70	15
146		5c. red	70	15
147	66	10c. red	5·50	15
148		12c. blue	2·75	15
149		16c. slate	6·50	60
150		24c. sepia	11·00	60
257		30c. orange	8·00	50
151		50c. green	10·00	50
188		80c. lilac	12·00	50
152a	67	1p. red	10·00	80
190		1p.20 black	9·50	4·00
153		2p. green	17·00	8·00
154		5p. blue	42·00	3·00

70 Fleet of Columbus

71 "Liberty" and Shield

1892. 4th Centenary of Discovery of America by Columbus.

219	70	2c. blue	12·50	4·50
220		5c. blue	26·00	5·00

1899.

221	71	½c. brown	15	15
222		1c. green	10	10
223		2c. grey	10	10
224		3c. orange	95	15
225		4c. yellow	1·75	15
226		5c. red	10	10
227		6c. black	1·10	20
228		10c. green	1·75	15
229a		12c. blue	1·10	30
230		12c. green	1·10	30
231		15c. blue	3·00	15
232		16c. orange	8·50	4·25
233		20c. red	2·25	15
234		24c. purple	4·00	80
235		30c. red	4·25	20
237		50c. blue	5·50	15
238		1p. black and blue	16·00	80
239		5p. black and orange	65·00	11·00
240		10p. black and green	60·00	11·00
241		20p. black and red	£225	32·00

The peso values are larger (19 × 32 mm).

73 Port Rosario

74 Gen. San Martin

1902. Completion of Port Rosario Docks.

290	73	5c. blue	80	2·00

1908.

291	74	½c. violet	15	10
292		1c. brown	20	10
293		2c. brown	60	10
294		3c. green	75	35
295		4c. mauve	1·50	35
296		5c. red	35	10
297		6c. green	85	25
298		10c. green	1·75	10
299		12c. brown	45	40
300		12c. blue	1·40	10
301		15c. green	1·90	90
302		20c. blue	1·40	10
303		24c. red	3·75	70
304		30c. red	6·00	70
305		50c. black	5·50	45
306		1p. red and blue	13·00	1·90

The 1p. is larger (21½ × 27 mm) with portrait at upper left.

76 Pyramid of May

80 Saavedra

78 Azcuenaga and Alberti

1910. Cent of Deposition of the Spanish Viceroy.

366	76	½c. blue and grey	40	10
367	–	1c. black and green	40	10
368	–	2c. black and green	30	10
369	78	3c. green	85	10
370	–	4c. green and blue	85	15
371	80	5c. red	70	10
372	–	10c. black and brown	2·00	15
373	–	12c. blue	1·60	25
374	–	20c. black and green	3·75	40
375	–	24c. blue and brown	2·00	1·00
376	–	30c. black and lilac	2·00	75
377	–	50c. black and red	5·00	1·00
378	–	1p. blue	12·00	3·50
379	–	5p. purple and orange	80·00	35·00
380	–	10p. black and orange	£100	75·00
381	–	20p. black and blue	£170	£100

DESIGNS—VERT: 50c. Crowds on 25 May 1810; 10p. Centenary Monument; 20p. San Martin. HORIZ: 1c. Pena and Vieytes; 2c. Meeting at Pena's house; 4c. Fort of the Viceroys, Buenos Aires; 10c. Distribution of cockades; 12c. Congress Building; 20c. Castelli and Matheu; 24c. First National Council; 30c. Belgrano and Larrea; 1p. Moreno and Paso; 5p. "Oath of the Junta".

90 Sarmiento

91 Ploughman

1911. Birth Centenary of Pres. Sarmiento.

382	90	5c. black and brown	70	40

1911.

383	91	5c. red	40	15
384		12c. blue	4·50	20

92 Ploughman

94

1911.

395	92	½c. violet	20	20
396		1c. brown	20	15
397		2c. brown	40	15
398		3c. green	50	20
399		4c. purple	40	20
400		5c. red	20	15
401		10c. green	60	15
402		12c. blue	1·60	15
403		20c. blue	5·00	1·25
404		24c. brown	3·75	20
405		30c. red	2·00	70
406		50c. black	6·00	70
408	94	1p. red and blue	7·00	1·10
409		5p. green and grey	22·00	7·00
410		10p. blue and violet	85·00	10·00
411		20p. red and blue	£200	70·00

95 Dr. F. N. Laprida

97 San Martin

96 Declaration of Independence

1916. Centenary of Independence.

417	95	½c. violet	20	15
418		1c. brown	25	15
419		2c. brown	20	15
420		3c. green	50	15
421		4c. purple	75	15
422	96	5c. red	35	15
423		10c. green	1·60	15
424	97	12c. blue	75	15
425		20c. blue	1·25	15
426		24c. red	2·00	85
427		30c. red	2·00	40
428		50c. black	3·75	50
429		1p. red and blue	11·00	4·50
430		5p. green and grey	£130	45·00
431		10p. blue and violet	£130	85·00
432		20p. red and grey	£190	75·00

98 San Martin

100 Dr. Juan Pujol

1917.

433	98	½c. violet	20	15
434		1c. buff	20	15
435		2c. brown	20	15
436		3c. green	70	15
454		4c. purple	30	15
455		5c. red	15	15
456		10c. green	1·75	15
457	–	12c. blue	1·40	15
458	–	20c. blue	1·75	15
459	–	24c. red	5·00	2·25
460	–	30c. red	5·00	70
461	–	50c. black	4·50	70
445	–	1p. red and blue	4·50	20
446	–	5p. green and grey	19·00	3·50
447	–	10p. blue and violet	45·00	11·00
448	–	20p. red and grey	81·00	17·00

The 12c. to 20p. values are larger (21 × 27 mm).

1918. Birth Centenary of Juan Pujol, 1st P.M.G. of Argentina.

449	100	5c. grey and bistre	80	30

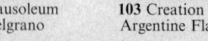

102 Mausoleum of Belgrano

103 Creation of Argentine Flag

1920. Death Centenary of Gen. Manuel Belgrano.
478	102	2c. red	50	15
479	103	5c. blue and red	50	15
480	–	12c. blue and green	1·00	75

DESIGN—VERT: 12c. Gen. Belgrano.

| 106 General Urquiza | 107 General Mitre |  108 |

1920. Gen. Urquiza's Victory at Cepada.
| 488 | 106 | 5c. blue | 30 | 10 |

1921. Birth Centenary of Gen. Mitre.
| 490 | 107 | 2c. brown | 35 | 10 |
| 491 | | 5c. blue | 35 | 10 |

1921. 1st Pan-American Postal Congress.
492	108	3c. lilac	1·50	65
493		5c. blue	2·00	20
494		10c. brown	2·50	90
495		12c. red	4·50	1·90

1921. As T 108, but smaller. Inscr "BUENOS AIRES AGOSTO DE 1921".
| 496 | | 5c. red | 2·25 | 25 |

1921. As No. 496, but inscr "REPUBLICA ARGENTINA" at foot.
| 511 | | 5c. red | 1·75 | 25 |

| 112 |  114 B. Rivadavia |

1923. With or without stop below "c".
513	112	½c. purple	15	15
530		1c. brown	15	15
515		2c. brown	35	15
532		3c. green	15	15
533		4c. red	50	15
518		5c. red	15	15
535		10c. green	35	15
520		12c. blue	45	15
537		20c. blue	85	15
538		24c. brown	2·00	1·00
539		25c. violet	1·00	15
540		30c. red	2·00	15
541		50c. black	2·00	15
542		1p. red and blue	2·25	15
543		5p. green and lilac	17·00	70
544		10p. blue and red	38·00	3·75
545		20p. lake and slate	55·00	8·50

The peso values are larger (21 × 27 mm).

1926. Rivadavia Centenary.
| 546 | 114 | 5c. red | 50 | 15 |

| 115 Rivadavia |  116 San Martin |

| 117 G.P.O., 1926 | 118 G.P.O., 1826 |

1926. Postal Centenary.
547	115	3c. green	15	15
548	116	5c. red	10	15
549	117	12c. blue	1·00	20
550	118	25c. brown	1·75	15

| 120 Biplane and Globe | 122 |

1928. Air.
558	120	5c. red	1·75	50
559		10c. blue	2·75	85
560		15c. brown	2·50	90
561	120	18c. violet	4·25	3·25
562		20c. blue	2·75	90

563		24c. blue	4·25	3·00
564	122	25c. violet	4·25	1·40
565		30c. red	5·50	1·00
566		35c. red	4·25	1·25
567a	120	36c. brown	3·25	1·40
568		50c. black	4·50	65
569		54c. brown	4·25	2·10
570		72c. green	5·50	2·10
571	122	90c. purple	10·00	1·90
572		1p. red and blue	12·00	70
573		1p.08 blue and red	17·00	4·75
574		1p.26 green and violet	23·00	9·00
575		1p.80 red and blue	23·00	9·00
576		3p.60 blue and grey	48·00	21·00

DESIGNS—VERT: 15, 20, 24, 54, 72c. Yellow-headed Caracara over sea. HORIZ: 35, 50c., 1p.26, 1p.80, 3p.60, Andean Condor on mountain top.

| 124 Arms of Argentina and Brazil | 125 Torch illuminating New World |

1928. Centenary of Peace with Brazil.
| 577 | 124 | 5c. red | 1·00 | 35 |
| 578 | | 12c. blue | 1·60 | 70 |

1929. "Day of the Race" issue.
579	125	2c. brown	85	20
580		5c. red	95	15
581		12c. blue	2·25	75

DESIGNS: 5c. Symbolical figures, Spain and Argentina; 12c. American offering laurels to Columbus.

'ZEPPELIN' 1º VUELO 1930
(128)

1930. Air. "Zeppelin" Europe–Pan-America Flight. Optd with T 128.
587		20c. blue (No. 562)	10·50	5·50
588		50c. black (No. 568)	18·00	8·50
589	122	90c. purple	9·00	6·50
584		1p. red and blue	20·00	13·00
585		1p.80 (No. 575)	60·00	32·00
586		3p.60 (No. 576)	£170	95·00

| 129 Soldier and Civilian Insurgents | 130 The Victorious March, 6 September 30 |

1930. Revolution of 6 September 1930.
592	129	½c. violet	20	15
611	130	½c. mauve	15	10
593	129	1c. green	25	15
612	130	1c. black	1·00	40
594		2c. lilac	35	15
595	129	3c. green	50	25
613	130	3c. green	50	25
596	129	4c. violet	40	25
614	130	4c. lake	40	20
597	129	5c. red	20	15
615	130	5c. red	15	10
598	129	10c. black	85	35
616	130	10c. green	1·00	25
599		12c. blue	85	25
600		20c. buff	85	25
601	130	24c. brown	3·25	1·50
602		25c. green	4·25	1·50
603		30c. violet	6·00	2·00
604		50c. black	9·00	2·75
605		1p. red and blue	17·00	10·00
606		2p. orange and black	30·00	10·00
607		5p. black and green	90·00	40·00
608		10p. blue and lake	£120	50·00
609		20p. blue and green	£325	£120
610		50p. violet and green	£900	£650

1931. 1st Anniv of 1930 Revolution. Optd 6 Septembre 1930 - 1931.
617	112	3c. green (postage)	25	25
618		10c. green	70	70
619		30c. red	3·75	3·75
620		50c. black	3·75	3·75
621		1p. red and blue	4·25	3·75
623	130	2p. orange and black	15·00	8·50
622	112	5p. green and lilac	75·00	23·00
624	129	18c. violet (air)	2·25	1·75
625		72c. green (No. 570)	21·00	13·00
626	122	90c. purple	16·00	12·00
627		1p.80 red & bl (No. 575)	40·00	30·00
628		3p.60 bl & grey (No. 576)	60·00	45·00

1932. Zeppelin Air stamps. Optd GRAF ZEPPELIN 1932.
629	120	5c. red	2·50	1·60
630		18c. violet	12·00	7·50
631	122	90c. purple	35·00	20·00

| 134 Refrigerating Plant |  135 Port La Plata |

1932. 6th International Refrigerating Congress.
632	134	3c. green	50	25
633		10c. red	1·25	15
634		12c. blue	3·50	1·40

1933. 50th Anniv of La Plata City.
635	135	3c. brown and green	1·00	25
636		10c. purple and orange	60	20
637		15c. blue	4·00	2·00
638		20c. brown and lilac	2·00	1·00
639		30c. red and green	16·00	6·00

DESIGNS: 10c. President J. A. Roca; 15c. Municipal buildings; 20c. La Plata Cathedral; 30c. Dr. D. Rocha.

| 139 Christ of the Andes | 141 "Liberty" with Arms of Brazil and Argentina |

1934. 32nd Int Eucharistic Congress, Buenos Aires.
| 640 | 139 | 10c. red | 85 | 25 |
| 641 | | 15c. blue | 1·60 | 55 |

DESIGN—HORIZ: 15c. Buenos Aires Cathedral.

1935. Visit of President Vargas of Brazil. Inscr "MAYO DE 1935".
| 642 | 141 | 10c. red | 85 | 25 |
| 643 | | 15c. blue | 1·60 | 55 |

DESIGN: 15c. Clasped hands and flags.

| 143 D. F. Sarmiento | 146 Prize Bull | 151 With Boundary Lines |

1935. Portraits.
644		½c. purple (Belgrano)	15	10
645		1c. brown (Type 143)	15	10
646		2c. brown (Urquiza)	15	10
647		3c. green (San Martin)	15	10
653b		5c. brown (Moreno)	60	10
650		6c. green (Alberdi)	15	10
653d		10c. red (Rivadavia)	25	10
651		12c. purple (Mitre)	10	10
708		15c. grey (Martin Guemes)	80	10
652		20c. blue (Juan Martin Guemes)	80	10
653		20c. blue (Martin Guemes)	80	10

See also Nos. 671 etc.

1936. Production and Industry.
676	146	15c. blue	60	15
677a		20c. blue (19½ × 26 mm)	15	15
755		20c. blue (22 × 33 mm)	1·50	15
656		25c. red and pink	40	15
757		30c. brown and yellow	40	15
658		40c. purple and mauve	35	15
659		50c. red and salmon	25	15
660	151	1p. blue and brown	19·00	75
760		1p. blue and brown	3·00	15
661		2p. blue and purple	85	15
662		5p. green and blue	11·50	75
763		10p. black and purple	11·50	1·60
764		20p. brown and blue	11·00	1·60

DESIGNS—VERT: 25c. Ploughman; 50c. Oil well; 1p. (No. 760) as Type 151 but without country boundaries; 5p. Iguazu Falls; 10p. Grapes; 20p. Cotton plant. HORIZ: 30c. Patagonian ram; 40c. Sugar cane and factory; 2p. Fruit products.

| 157 | 158 Pres. Sarmiento |

1936. Pan-American Peace Conference.
| 665 | 157 | 10c. red | 50 | 15 |

1938. President's 50th Death Anniv.
| 666 | 158 | 3c. green | 40 | 40 |
| 667 | | 5c. red | 40 | 40 |

| 668 | | 15c. blue | 75 | 40 |
| 669 | | 50c. orange | 2·25 | 80 |

| 159 "Presidente Sarmiento" | 160 Allegory of the Post |

1939. Last Voyage of Cadet Ship "Presidente Sarmiento".
| 670 | 159 | 5c. green | 85 | 10 |

1939. Portraits as T 143.
671		2½c. black	15	10
672		3c. grey (San Martin)	40	10
672a		3c. grey (Moreno)	15	10
673		4c. green	10	10
894		5c. brown (16½ × 22½ mm)	10	10
674		8c. orange	10	10
678		10c. purple	15	10
675		12c. red	10	10
895		20c. lilac (21 × 27 mm)	20	10
895b		20c. lilac (19½ × 25½ mm)	15	10

PORTRAITS: 2½c. L. Braille; 4c. G. Brown; 5c. Jose Hernandez; 8c. N. Avellaneda; 10c. B. Rivadavia; 12c. B. Mitre; 20c. G. Brown.

1939. 11th U.P.U. Congress, Buenos Aires.
679	160	5c. red	15	10
680		15c. grey	40	25
681		20c. blue	40	10
682		25c. green	85	35
683		50c. brown	2·25	80
684		1p. purple	4·50	1·75
685		2p. mauve	20·00	11·50
686		5p. violet	46·00	23·00

DESIGNS—VERT: 20c. Seal of Argentina; 1p. Symbols of postal communications; 2p. Argentina, "Land of Promise" from a pioneer painting. HORIZ: 15c. G.P.O.; 25c. Iguazu Falls; 50c. Mt. Bonete; 5p. Lake Frias.

| 165 Working-class Family and New Home | 167 North and South America |

1939. 1st Pan-American Housing Congress.
| 687 | 165 | 5c. green | 20 | 10 |

1940. 50th Anniv of Pan-American Union.
| 688 | 167 | 15c. blue | 35 | 10 |

169 Airplane and Envelope

1940. Air.
689	169	30c. orange	7·00	10
690		50c. brown	9·50	15
691	169	1p. red	3·50	10
692		1p.25 green	80	10
693	169	2p.50 blue	2·75	40

DESIGNS—VERT: 50c. "Mercury"; 1p.25, Douglas DC-2 in clouds.

172 Gen. French, Col. Beruti and Rosette of the "Legion de Patricios"

1941. 131st Anniv of Rising against Spain.
| 694 | 172 | 5c. blue | 40 | 10 |

| 173 Marco M. de Avellaneda | 174 Statue of Gen. J. A. Roca |

1941. Death Centenary of Avellaneda (patriot).
695 173 5c. blue 40   10

1941. Dedication of Statue of Gen. Roca.
696 174 5c. green 40   10

175 Pellegrini (founder) and National Bank
176 Gen. Juan Lavalle

1941. 50th Anniv of National Bank.
697 175 5c. lake 40   10

1941. Death Centenary of Gen. Lavalle.
698 176 5c. blue 40   10

177 New P.O. Savings Bank
178 Jose Manuel Estrada

1942. Inauguration of P.O. Savings Bank.
699 177 1c. green 40   10

1942. Birth Centenary of Estrada (patriot).
700 178 5c. purple 50   10

180 G.P.O., Buenos Aires
181 Proposed Columbus Lighthouse

1942. Postage and Express Stamps.
717 180 35c. blue . . . . 5·50   15
746 180 35c. blue . . . . 1·10   15
No. 717 is inscr "PALACIO CENTRAL DE CORREOS Y TELEGRAFOS" and No. 746 "PALACIO CENTRAL DE CORREOS Y TELECOMUNICACIONES".

1942. 450th Anniv of Discovery of America by Columbus.
721 181 15c. blue . . . . 4·00   15

182 Dr. Paz (founder of "La Prensa")
183 Flag of Argentina and Books
184 Arms of Argentina

1942. Birth Centenary of Dr. Jose C. Paz.
722 182 5c. blue 40   15

1943. 1st National Book Fair.
723 183 5c. blue 20   15

1943. Revolution of 4 June 1943.
724 184 5c. red 20   15
725   15c. green 60   15
726   20c. blue (larger) 80   15

185 National Independence House
186 Head of Liberty, Money-box and Laurels

1943. Restoration of Tucuman Museum.
727 185 5c. green 35   15

1943. 1st Savings Bank Conference.
728 186 5c. brown 40   10

187 Buenos Aires in 1800

1944. Export Day.
729 187 5c. black 40   10

188 Postal Union of the Americas and Spain
189 Alexander Graham Bell
191 Liner, Warship and Yacht

1944. Postmen's Benefit Fund. Inscr "PRO-CARTERO".
730   – 3c.+2c. black and violet . 1·10   1·10
731 188 5c.+5c. black and red . . 85   20
732 189 10c.+5c. black and orge . 1·10   35
733   – 25c.+15c. black and brn . 2·40   75
734   – 1p.+50c. black and green 10·00   7·75
DESIGNS: 3c. Samuel Morse; 25c. Rowland Hill; 1p. Columbus landing in America.

1944. Naval Week.
735 191 5c. blue 75   10

192 Argentina
193 Arms of Argentina

1944. San Juan Earthquake Relief Fund.
736 192 5c.+10c. black & olive . . 60   50
737   5c.+50c. black and red . . 3·50   1·10
738   5c.+1p. black & orange . 7·00   5·50
739   5c.+20p. black & blue . . 28·00   23·00

1944. 1st Anniv of Revolution of 4 June 1943.
740 193 5c. blue 40   15

194 Archangel Gabriel
195 Cross of Palermo
196 Allegory of Savings

1944. 4th National Eucharistic Congress.
741 194 3c. green 50   15
742 195 5c. red 50   15

1944. 20th Anniv of Universal Savings Day.
743 196 5c. black 40   15

197 Reservists

1944. Reservists' Day.
744 197 5c. blue 40   15

198 Bernardino Rivadavia
199 Rivadavia's Mausoleum

1945. Rivadavia's Death Centenary.
770 198 3c. green 15   15
771   – 5c. red 15   15
772 199 20c. blue 15   15
DESIGN—As Type 198: 5c. Rivadavia and Scales of Justice.

200 San Martin
201 Monument to Andes Army, Mendoza

1945.
773 200 5c. red 10   10

1946. "Homage to the Unknown Soldier of Independence".
776 201 5c. purple 15   15

202 Pres. Roosevelt
203 "Affirmation"

1946. 1st Death Anniv of Pres. Franklin Roosevelt.
777 202 5c. grey 10   10

1946. Installation of Pres. Juan Peron.
778 203 5c. blue 15   15

204 Airplane over Iguazu Falls

1946. Air.
779 204 15c. red 15   10
780   – 25c. green 20   10
DESIGN: 25c. Airplane over Andes.

205 "Flight"

1946. Aviation Week.
781 205 15c. green on green . . . 55   10
782   – 60c. purple on buff . . . 55   15
DESIGN: 60c. Hand upholding globe.

207 "Argentina and Populace"

1946. 1st Anniv of Peron's Defeat of Counter-revolution.
783 207 5c. mauve 20   10
784   10c. green 30   10
785   15c. blue 60   25
786   50c. brown 60   40
787   1p. red . . . . 1·25   1·10

208 Money-box and Map
209 Industry

1946. Annual Savings Day.
788 208 30c. red 35   10

1946. Industrial Exhibition.
789 209 5c. purple 10   10

210 Argentine–Brazil International Bridge
211 South Pole

1947. Opening of Bridge between Argentina and Brazil.
790 210 5c. green 25   25

1947. 43rd Anniv of 1st Argentine Antarctic Mail.
791 211 5c. violet 60   15
792   20c. red . . . . 1·25   15

212 "Justice"
213 Icarus Falling

1947. 1st Anniv of Col. Juan Peron's Presidency.
793 212 5c. purple and buff . . . 10   10

1947. "Week of the Wing".
794 213 15c. purple 15   10

214 "Presidente Sarmiento"
215 Cervantes and "Don Quixote"

1947. 50th Anniv of Launching of Cadet Ship "Presidente Sarmiento".
795 214 5c. blue 50   10

1947. 400th Birth Anniv of Cervantes.
796 215 5c. green 10   10

216 Gen. San Martin and Urn

1947. Arrival from Spain of Ashes of Gen. San Martin's Parents.
797 216 5c. green 10   10

217 Young Crusaders
218 Statue of Araucarian Indian

1947. Educational Crusade for Universal Peace.
798 217 5c. green 10   10
799   20c. brown 30   10

1948. American Indian Day.
801 218 25c. brown 25   10

219 Phrygian Cap and Sprig of Wheat
220 "Stop"

1948. 5th Anniv of Anti-isolationist Revolution of 4 June 1943.
802 219 5c. blue 10   10

1948. Safety First Campaign.
803 220 5c. yellow and brown . . . 15   10

221 Posthorn and Oak Leaves

222 Argentine Farmers

1948. Bicent of Postal Service in Rio de la Plata.
804 221 5c. mauve 15 15

1948. Agriculture Day.
805 222 10c. brown 15 15

223 "Liberty and Plenty"

225 Statue of Atlas

226 Map, Globe and Compasses

1948. Re-election of President Peron.
806 223 25c. red 15 15

1948. Air. 4th Meeting of Pan-American Cartographers.
807 225 45c. brown 35 10
808 226 70c. green 65 15

227 Winged Railway Wheel

1949. 1st Anniv of Nationalization of Argentine Railways.
809 227 10c. blue 25 10

228 Head of Liberty

1949. Constitution Day.
810 228 1p. purple and red . . . 80 15

229 Trophy and Target

230 "Intercommunication"

1949. Air. International Shooting Championship.
811 229 75c. brown 65 15

1949. 75th Anniv of U.P.U.
812 230 25c. green and olive . . 20 15

231 San Martin

233 Stamp Designer

232 San Martin at Boulogne

1950. San Martin's Death Cent. Dated "1850 1950".
813 – 10c. purple and blue . . . 15 10
814 231 20c. brown and red . . . 15 10
815 232 25c. brown . . . 15 10
816 – 50c. blue and green . . . 40 10
817 – 75c. green and brown . . 40 10
818 – 1p. green . . . . 1·00 20
819 – 2p. purple 85 35
DESIGNS—As Type 231: 10, 50, 75c. Portraits of San Martin; 2p. San Martin Mausoleum. As Type 232: 1p. House where San Martin died.

1950. Int Philatelic Exhibition, Buenos Aires.
820 233 10c.+10c. violet (postage) 15 15
821 – 45c.+45c. blue (air) . . . 40 25
822 – 70c.+70c. brown . . . 60 40
823 – 1p.+1p. red . . . . 1·75 1·60
824 – 2p.50+2p.50 olive . . . 9·50 7·00
825 – 5p.+5p. green . . . 11·00 8·50
DESIGNS: 45c. Engraver; 70c. Proofing; 1p. Printer; 2p.50, Woman reading letter; 5p. San Martin.

234 S. America and Antarctic

235 Douglas DC-3 and Andean Condor

1951.
826 234 1p. blue and brown . . . 50 15

1951. Air. 10th Anniv of State Airlines.
827 235 20c. olive 30 20

236 Pegasus and Steam Locomotive

1951. Five-year Plan.
828 236 5c. brown (postage) . . . 15 15
829 – 25c. green 45 10
830 – 40c. purple 40 15
831 – 20c. blue (air) 25 15
DESIGNS—HORIZ: 25c. "President Peron" (liner) and common dolphin. VERT: 20c. Douglas DC-4 and Andean condor; 40c. Head of Mercury and telephone.

237 Woman Voter and "Argentina"

238 "Piety"

1951. Women's Suffrage in Argentina.
832 237 10c. purple 10 10

1951. Air. Eva Peron Foundation Fund.
833 238 2p.45+7p.55 olive . . . . 20·00 13·50

239 Eva Peron

240 Eva Peron

1952. (a) Size 20 × 26 mm.
834 239 1c. brown 10 10
835 – 5c. grey 10 10
836 – 10c. red 10 10
837 – 20c. red 10 10
838 – 25c. green 10 10
839 – 40c. purple 15 10
841 – 45c. blue 25 10
840 – 50c. bistre 25 10
(b) Size 22 × 33 mm. Without inscr "EVA PERON".
842 240 1p. brown 35 10
843 – 1p.50 green . . . . 1·75 10
844 – 2p. red 50 10
845 – 3p. blue 85 15
(c) Size 22 × 33 mm. Inscr "EVA PERON".
846 240 1p. brown 35 10
847 – 1p.50 green . . . . 1·10 10
848 – 2p. red . . . . 1·25 10
849 – 3p. blue . . . . 1·75 45
(d) Size 30½ × 40 mm. Inscr "EVA PERON".
850 240 1p. brown . . . . 1·75 40
851 239 10p. red . . . . 4·75 1·40
852 240 20p. green . . . . 8·00 3·25
853 239 50p. blue . . . . 14·00 7·75

241 Indian Funeral Urn

242 Rescue Ship "Uruguay"

1953. 4th Centenary of Santiago del Estero.
854 241 50c. green 15 10

1953. 50th Anniv of Rescue of the "Antarctic".
855 242 50c. blue . . . . 1·25 40

243 Planting Flag in S. Orkneys

244 "Telegraphs"

1954. 50th Anniv of Argentine P.O. in South Orkneys.
856 243 1p.45 blue 85 40

1954. International Telecommunications Conference. Symbolical designs inscr as in T 244.
857 244 1p.50 purple 40 15
858 – 3p. blue . . . . 1·10 25
859 – 5p. red . . . . 1·60 35
DESIGNS—VERT: 3p. "Radio". HORIZ: 5p. "Television".

245 Pediment, Buenos Aires Stock Exchange

246 Eva Peron

1954. Centenary of Argentine Stock Exchange.
860 245 1p. green 30 10

1954. 2nd Death Anniv of Eva Peron.
861 246 3p. red . . . . 1·60 20

247 San Martin

249 Wheat

250 Mt. Fitz Roy

248 "Prosperity"

1954.
862 247 20c. red 10 10
863 – 40c. red 30 10
868 – 50c. blue (33 × 22 mm) 60 10
869 – 50c. blue (32 × 21 mm) 70 10
870 249 80c. brown 25 10
871 – 1p. brown 30 10
872 – 1p.50 blue 25 10
873 – 2p. red 35 10
874 – 3p. purple 35 10
875a – 5p. green . . . . 6·25 10
876 – 10p. green and grey 6·25 10
877 250 20p. violet . . . . 9·25 40
1018 – 22p. blue . . . . 1·40 10
878 – 50p. indigo and blue
(30½ × 40½ mm) . . 80
1023 – 50p. blue (29½ × 40 mm) 6·25 40
1287 – 50p. blue
(22½ × 32½ mm) . . 1·00 10
DESIGNS—As Type 249: HORIZ: 50c. Port of Buenos Aires; 1p. Cattle; 2p. Eva Peron Foundation; 3p. El Nihuil Dam. As Type 250: VERT: 1p.50, 22p. Industrial Plant; 5p. Iguazu Falls; 50p. San Martin. HORIZ: 10p. Humahuaca Ravine.
For 43p. in the design of the 1p.50 and 22p. see No. 1021.
For 65c. in same design see No. 1313.

1954. Centenary of Argentine Corn Exchange.
867 248 1p.50 grey 65 10

251 Clasped Hands and Congress Emblem

252 Father and Son with Model Airplane

1955. Productivity and Social Welfare Congress.
879 251 3p. brown 90 10

1955. 25th Anniv of Commercial Air Services.
880 252 1p.50 grey 80 10

253 "Liberation"

254 Forces Emblem

1955. Anti-Peronist Revolution of 16 Sept. 1955.
881 253 1p.50 olive 20 10

1955. Armed Forces Commemoration.
882 254 3p. blue 35 10

255 Gen. Urquiza (after J. M. Blanes)

256 Detail from "Antiope" (Correggio)

1956. 104th Anniv of Battle of Caseros.
883 255 1p.50 green 25   10

1956. Infantile Paralysis Relief Fund.
884 256 20c.+30c. grey 20   10

257 Coin and Die   258 Corrientes Stamp of 1856

259 Dr. J. G. Pujol   260 Cotton, Chaco

1956. 75th Anniv of National Mint.
885 257 2p. brown and sepia . . . 20   10

1956. Centenary of 1st Argentine Stamps.
886 258 40c. blue and green . . . 15   10
887   2p.40 mauve and brown . . 20   10
888 259 4p.40 blue 50   15
The 40c. shows a 1r. stamp of 1856.

1956. New Provinces.
889   — 50c. blue 10   10
890 260 1p. lake 20   10
891   — 1p.50 green 30   10
DESIGNS—HORIZ: 50c. Lumbering, La Pampa. VERT: 1p.50, Mate tea plant, Misiones.

261 "Liberty"   262 Detail from "Virgin of the Rocks" (Leonardo)

1956. 1st Anniv of Revolution.
892 261 2p.40 mauve 25   10

1956. Air. Infantile Paralysis Victims, Gratitude for Help.
893 262 1p. purple 30   10

264 Esteban Echeverria (writer)   265 F. Ameghino (anthropologist)

266 Roque Saenz Pena (statesman)   267 Franklin

1956.
896 264 2p. purple 20   10
897 265 2p.40 brown 30   10
898 266 4p.40 green 45   10

1956. 250th Birth Anniv of Benjamin Franklin.
899 267 40c. blue 25   10

268 "Hercules" (sail frigate)   269 Admiral G. Brown

1957. Death Cent of Admiral Guillermo Brown.
900 268 40c. blue (postage) . . . 50   10
901   — 2p.40 green 40   10
902   — 60c. grey (air) 75   10
903   — 1p. mauve 20   10
904 269 2p. brown 25   10
DESIGNS—HORIZ: 60c. "Zefiro" and "Nancy" (sail warships) at Battle of Montevideo; 1p. L. Rosales and T. Espora. VERT: 2p.40, Admiral Brown in later years.

270 Church of Santo Domingo   271 Map of the Americas and Badge of Buenos Aires

1957. 150th Anniv of Defence of Buenos Aires.
905 270 40c. green 10   10

1957. Air. Inter-American Economic Conference.
906 271 2p. purple 35   10

272 "La Portena", 1857   273 Globe, Flag and Compass Rose

1957. Centenary of Argentine Railways.
907 272 40c. sepia (postage) . . . 45   10
908   — 60c. grey (air) 45   10
DESIGN: 60c. Diesel locomotive.

1957. Air. Int Tourist Congress, Buenos Aires.
909 273 1p. brown 15   10
910   — 2p. turquoise 20   10
DESIGN: 2p. Symbolic key of tourism.

274 Head of Liberty   275

1957. Reform Convention.
911 274 40c. red 10   10

1957. Air. International Correspondence Week.
912 275 1p. blue 15   10

276 "Wealth in Oil"   277 La Plata Museum

1957. 50th Anniv of Argentine Oil Industry.
913 276 40c. blue 15   10

1958. 75th Anniv of Founding of La Plata.
914 277 40c. black 15   10

278 Health Emblem and Flower

1958. Air. Child Welfare.
915 278 1p.+50c. red 20   20

279 Stamp of 1858 and River Ferry   280 Stamp of 1858

1958. Centenary of Argentine Confederation Stamps and Philatelic Exhibition, Buenos Aires.
916 279 40c.+20c. purple and green (postage) . . . 45   20
917   — 2p.40+1p.20 blue and black 40   25
918   — 4p.40+2p.20 pur & bl . . 60   40
919 280 1p.+50c. blue and olive (air) 40   35
920   2p.+1p. violet and red . . 55   45
921   3p.+1p.50 brown & grn 60   55
922   5p.+2p.50 red and olive 1·00   85
923   10p.+5p. sepia & olive . . 1·50   1·40
DESIGNS—HORIZ: 2p.40, Magnifier, stamp album and stamp of 1858; 4p.40, P.O. building of 1858.

281 Steam Locomotive and Arms of Argentina and Bolivia   282 Douglas DC-6 over Map of Argentine-Bolivian Frontier

1958. Argentine–Bolivian Friendship. (a) Inauguration of Yacuiba–Santa Cruz Railway.
924 281 40c. red and slate . . . 35   10

(b) Exchange of Presidential Visits.
925 282 1p. brown 15   10

283 "Liberty and Flag"   284 Farman H.F.20 Biplane

1958. Transfer of Presidential Mandate. Head of "Liberty" in grey; inscr black; flag yellow and blue; background colours given.
926 283 40c. buff 10   10
927   — 1p. salmon 15   10
928   — 2p. green 25   10

1958. 50th Anniv of Argentine Aero Club.
929 284 2p. brown 20   10

285 National Flag Monument, Rosario   286 Map of Antarctica

1958. 1st Anniv of Inauguration of National Flag Monument.
930 285 40c. grey and blue 10   10

1958. International Geophysical Year.
931 286 40c. black and red . . 50   10

287 Confederation Stamp and "The Santa Fe Mail" (after J. L. Palliere)

1958. Cent of Argentine Confederation Stamps.
932   — 40c. grn & blue (postage) 15   10
933   — 80c. blue & yellow (air) 40   10
934 287 1p. blue and orange . . 20   10
DESIGNS: 40c. First local Cordoba 5c. stamp of 1858 and mail coach; 80c. Buenos Aires Type 1 of 1858 and "View of Buenos Aires" (after Deroy).

288 Aerial view of Flooded Town

1958. Flood Disaster Relief Fund. Inscr as in T 288.
935 288 40c.+20c. brn (postage) 15   10
936   — 1p.+50c. plum (air) . . 20   10
937   — 5p.+2p.50 blue 50   20
DESIGNS—HORIZ: 1p. Different aerial view of flooded town; 5p. Motor truck in flood water and garage.

289 Child receiving Blood   290 U.N. Emblem and "Dying Captive" (after Michelangelo)

1958. Leukaemia Relief Campaign.
938 289 1p.+50c. red and black . . 15   10

1959. 10th Anniv of Declaration of Human Rights.
939 290 40c. grey and brown . . . 10   10

291 Hawker Siddeley Comet 4

1959. Air. Inauguration of Comet Jet Airliners by Argentine National Airlines.
940 291 5p. black and green . . . 35   10

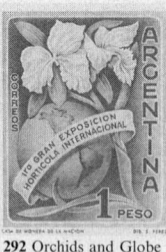

292 Orchids and Globe   293 Pope Pius XII

1959. 1st Int Horticultural Exn, Buenos Aires.
941 292 1p. purple 15   10

1959. Pope Pius XII Commemoration.
942 293 1p. black and yellow . . 15   10
PORTRAITS: 1p. Claude Bernard; 1p.50, Ivan P. Pavlov.

294 William Harvey

1959. 21st International Physiological Science Congress. Medical Scientists.
943 294 50c. green 10   10
944   — 1p. red 15   10
945   — 1p.50 brown 20   10

295 Creole Horse

296 Tierra del Fuego

1959.
946 – 10c. green 10 10
947 – 20c. purple 10 10
948 – 50c. ochre 10 10
950 295 1p. red 10 10
1016 – 1p. brown 10 10
1027 – 1p. brown 10 10
1035 – 2p. red 35 10
951 – 3p. blue 10 10
1036 – 4p. red 40 10
952 296 5p. brown 25 10
1037 – 8p. red 25 10
1286 – 10p. brown 50 10
1038 – 10p. red 70 10
1017 – 12p. purple 90 10
954 – 20p. green . . . . . . 2·40 10
1039 – 20p. red 30 10
1019 – 23p. green . . . . . . 4·00 10
1020 – 25p. lilac . . . . . . 1·25 10
1021 – 43p. lake . . . . . . 5·50 10
1022 – 45p. brown . . . . . . 3·25 10
1025 – 100p. blue . . . . . . 6·25 20
1026 – 300p. violet . . . . . 3·25 10
1032 – 500p. green . . . . . 1·60 30
1290 – 1000p. blue . . . . . 4·50 90

DESIGNS—As Type 295—HORIZ: 10c. Spectacled caiman; 20c. Llama; 50c. Puma. VERT: 2, 4, 8, 10p. (No 1038), 20p. (No. 1039) San Martin. As Type 296—HORIZ: 3p. Zapata Hill, Catamarca; 300p. Mar del Plata (40 × 29½ mm). VERT: 1p. (No. 1016) Sunflowers; 1p. (No. 1027) Sunflower (22 × 32 mm); 10p. (No. 1286) Inca Bridge, Mendoza; 12, 23, 25p. Red quebracho tree; 20p. (No. 954) Lake Nahuel Huapi; 43, 45p. Industrial plant (30 × 39½ mm); 100p. Ski-jumper; 500p. Red deer (stag); 1,000p. Leaping salmon.

For these designs with face values in revalued currency, see Nos. 1300 etc.

298 Runner

299

1959. 3rd Pan-American Games, Chicago. Designs embody torch emblem. Centres and torch in black.
955 298 20c.+10c. green (postage) 10 10
956 – 50c.+20c. yellow 15 15
957 – 1p.+50c. purple 15 15
958 – 2p.+1p. blue (air) 30 15
959 – 3p.+1p.50 olive 45 30

DESIGNS—VERT: 50c. Basketball; 1p. Boxing. HORIZ: 2p. Rowing; 3p. High-diving.

1959. Red Cross Hygiene Campaign.
960 299 1p. red, blue and black 10 10

300 Child with Toys

1959. Mothers' Day.
961 300 1p. red and black 10 10

301 Buenos Aires 1p. stamp of 1859

1959. Stamp Day.
962 301 1p. blue and grey 10 10

302 B. Mitre and J. J. de Urquiza

303 Andean Condor

1959. Centenary of Pact of San Jose de Flores.
963 302 1p. plum 10 10

1960. Child Welfare. Birds.
964 303 20c.+10c. blue (postage) 70 15
965 – 50c.+20c. violet 70 15
966 – 1p.+50c. brown . . . . . 1·00 25
967 – 2p.+1p. mauve (air) . . . 70 30
968 – 3p.+1p.50 green 70 50

BIRDS: 50c. Fork-tailed flycatcher; 1p. Magellanic woodpecker; 2p. Red-winged tinamou; 3p. Greater rhea.

304 "Uprooted Tree"

305 Abraham Lincoln

1960. World Refugee Year.
969 304 1p. red and brown . . . 10 10
970 4p.20 purple and green . . 15 10

1960. 150th Birth Anniv of Abraham Lincoln.
972 305 5p. blue 25 15

306 Saavedra and Chapter Hall, Buenos Aires

307 Dr. L. Drago

1960. 150th Anniv of May Revolution.
973 306 1p. purple (postage) . . . 10 10
974 – 2p. green 10 10
975 – 4p.20 green and grey . . 20 10
976 – 10p.70 blue and slate . . 40 15
977 – 1p.80 brown (air) 10 10
978 – 5p. purple and brown . . 30 10

DESIGNS—Chapter Hall and: 1p.80, Moreno; 2p. Paso; 4p.20, Alberti and Azcuenaga; 5p. Belgrano and Castelli; 10p.70, Larrea and Matheu.

1960. Birth Centenary of Drago.
980 307 4p.20 brown 15 10

308 "Five Provinces"

309 "Market Place 1810" (Buenos Aires)

1960. Air. New Argentine Provinces.
981 308 1p.80 blue and red . . . 10 10

1960. Air. Inter-American Philatelic Exhibition, Buenos Aires ("EFIMAYO") and 150th Anniv of Revolution. Inscr "EFIMAYO 1960".
982 309 2p.+1p. lake 15 10
983 – 6p.+3p. grey 35 20
984 – 10p.70+5p.30 blue 60 35
985 – 20p.+10p. turquoise . . . 75 60

DESIGNS: 6p. "The Water Carrier"; 10p.70, "The Landing Place"; 20p. "The Fort".

310 J. B. Alberdi

311 Seibo (Argentine National Flower)

1960. 150th Birth Anniv of J. B. Alberdi (statesman).
986 310 1p. green 10 10

1960. Air. Chilean Earthquake Relief Fund. Inscr "AYUDA CHILE".
987 311 6p.+3p. red 30 25
988 – 10p.70+5p.30 red 40 35

DESIGN: 10p.70, Copihue (Chilean national flower).

312 Map of Argentina

313 Galleon

1960. Census.
989 312 5p. lilac 40 10

1960. 8th Spanish-American P.U. Congress.
990 313 1p. green (postage) . . . 40 10
991 5p. brown 85 20
992 1p.80 purple (air) 40 10
993 10p.70 turquoise . . . . 1·10 30

1960. Air. U.N. Day. Nos. 982/5 optd **DIA DE LAS NACIONES UNIDAS 24 DE OCTUBRE**.
994 309 2p.+1p. red 20 15
995 – 6p.+3p. black 25 25
996 – 10p.70+5p.30 blue 50 40
997 – 20p.+10p. turquoise . . . 70 65

315 Blessed Virgin of Lujan

316 Jacaranda

1960. 1st Inter-American Marian Congress.
998 315 1p. blue 10 10

1960. International Thematic Stamp Exhibition ("TEMEX"). Inscr "TEMEX-61".
999 316 50c.+50c. blue 10 10
1000 – 1p.+1p. turquoise . . . 10 10
1001 – 3p.+3p. brown 30 20
1002 – 5p.+5p. brown 50 30

FLOWERS: 1p. Passion flowers; 3p. Hibiscus; 5p. Black lapacho.

317 Argentine Scout Badge

318 "Shipment of Cereals" (after B. Q. Martin)

1961. International Scout (Patrol) Camp.
1003 317 1p. red and black . . . 15 10

1961. Export Campaign.
1004 318 1p. brown 15 10

319 Emperor Penguin and Chick

320 "America"

1961. Child Welfare. Inscr "PRO-INFANCIA".
1005 – 4p.20+2p.10 brown (postage) . . . . . . 1·00 75
1006 319 1p.80+90c. black (air) . . 60 50

DESIGN: 4p.20, Blue-eyed cormorant.

1961. 150th Anniv of Battle of San Nicolas.
1007 320 2p. black 55 10

321 Dr. M. Moreno

322 Emperor Trajan

1961. 150th Death Anniv of Dr. M. Moreno.
1008 321 2p. blue 15 10

1961. Visit of President of Italy.
1009 322 2p. green 15 10

1961. Americas Day. Nos. 999/1002 optd **14 DE ABRIL DE LAS AMERICAS**.
1010 316 50c.+50c. blue 10 10
1011 – 1p.+1p. turquoise . . . 15 10
1012 – 3p.+3p. brown 20 20
1013 – 5p.+5p. brown 40 35

324 Tagore

325 San Martin Monument, Madrid

1961. Birth Centenary of Rabindranath Tagore (Indian poet).
1014 324 2p. violet on green . . . 20 10

1961. Inaug of Spanish San Martin Monument.
1015 325 1p. black 15 10

331a Gen. Belgrano (after monument by Rocha, Buenos Aires)

1961. Gen. Manuel Belgrano Commemoration.
1034 331a 2p. blue 15 10

333 Antarctic Scene

1961. 10th Anniv of San Martin Antarctic Base.
1044 333 2p. black 50 10

334 Conquistador and Sword

335 Sarmiento Statue (Rodin)

1961. 4th Centenary of Jujuy City.
1045 334 2p. red and black . . . 15 10

1961. 150th Birth Anniv of Sarmiento.
1046 335 2p. violet 15 10

336 Cordoba Cathedral

343 15c. Stamp of 1862

1961. "Argentina 62" International Philatelic Exn.
1047 336 2p.+2p. purple (postage) 20 15
1048 – 3p.+3p. green 30 15
1049 – 10p.+10p. blue 85 50
1059 343 6p.50+6p.50 blue and turquoise (air) 40 30

DESIGNS—HORIZ: 10p. Buenos Aires Cathedral. VERT: 3p. As Type 343 but showing 10c. value and different inscr.

337

338 "The Flight into Egypt" (after Ana Maria Moncalvo)

1961. World Town-planning Day.
1052 **337** 2p. blue and yellow . . . 15 10

1961. Child Welfare.
1053 **338** 2p.+1p. brown & lilac 15 10
1054 10p.+5p. pur & mauve 50 15

339 Belgrano Statue (C. Belleuse)

340 Mounted Grenadier

1962. 150th Anniv of National Flag.
1055 **339** 2p. blue 15 10

1962. 150th Anniv of Gen. San Martin's Mounted Grenadiers.
1056 **340** 2p. red 15 10

341 Mosquito and Emblem

342 Lujan Basilica

1962. Malaria Eradication.
1057 **341** 2p. black and red . . . 10 10

1962. 75th Anniv of Coronation of the Holy Virgin of Lujan.
1058 **342** 2p. black and brown . . 10 10

344 Juan Jufre (founder)

345 U.N.E.S.C.O. Emblem

1962. 400th Anniv of San Juan.
1060 **344** 2p. blue 10 10

1962. Air. 15th Anniv of U.N.E.S.C.O.
1061 **345** 13p. brown and ochre 30 15

346 "Flight"

347 Juan Vucetich (fingerprints pioneer)

1962. 50th Anniv of Argentine Air Force.
1062 **346** 2p. blue, black & purple 15 10

1962. Vucetich Commem.
1063 **347** 2p. green 15 10

348 19th-century Mail Coach

350 U.P.A.E. Emblem

1962. Air. Postman's Day.
1064 **348** 5p.60 black and drab . . 15 10

1962. Air. Surch **AEREO** and value.
1065 **296** 5p.60 on 5p. brown . . 30 15
1066 18p. on 5p. brn on grn 1·00 20

1962. Air. 50th Anniv of Postal Union of Latin America.
1067 **350** 5p.60 blue 10 10

351 Pres. Sarmiento

352 Chalk-browed Mockingbird

1962.
1073 **351** 2p. green 45 10
1069 – 4p. red 60 10
1075 – 6p. red . . . . 1·40 10
1071 – 6p. brown 10 10
1072 – 90p. bistre . . . . . . 2·00 15
PORTRAITS: 4, 6p. Jose Hernandez; 90p. G. Brown.

1962. Child Welfare.
1076 **352** 4p.+2p. sepia, turquoise and brown . . . . . 1·25 75
1077 – 12p.+6p. brown, yellow and slate . . . . . . 2·00 1·25
DESIGN—VERT: 12p. Rufous-collared sparrow.
See also Nos. 1101/2, 1124/5, 1165/6, 1191/2, 1214/15, 1264/5, 1293/4, 1394/5, 1415/16 and 1441/2.

353 Skylark 3 Glider

354 "20 de Febrero" Monument, Salta

1963. Air. 9th World Gliding Championships, Junin.
1078 **353** 5p.60 black and blue . . 20 10
1079 – 11p. black, red and blue 40 10
DESIGN: 11p. Super Albatross glider.

1963. 150th Anniv of Battle of Salta.
1080 **354** 2p. green 15 10

355 Cogwheels

356 National College

1963. 75th Anniv of Argentine Industrial Union.
1081 **355** 4p. red and grey 10 10

1963. Centenary of National College, Buenos Aires.
1082 **356** 4p. black and buff . . . 10 10

357 Child drinking Milk

358 "Flight"

1963. Freedom from Hunger.
1083 **357** 4p. ochre, black and red 15 10

1963. Air. (a) As T **358**.
1084 **358** 5p.60 green, mve & pur 35 10
1085 7p. black & yellow (I) 45 10
1086 7p. black & yellow (II) 4·25 75
1087 11p. purple, green & blk 45 15
1088 18p. blue, red and mauve 1·10 25
1089 21p. grey, red and brown 1·50 35
Two types of 7p. I, "ARGENTINA" reads down, and II, "ARGENTINA" reads up as in Type **358**.

(b) As T **358** but inscr "REPUBLICA ARGENTINA" reading down.
1147 12p. lake and brown . . . . 1·50 15
1148 15p. blue and red . . . . . 1·50 15
1291 26p. ochre 25 15
1150 27p.50 green and black . . 2·25 30
1151 30p.50 brown and blue . . . 2·25 35
1292 40p. lilac . . . . 2·25 15
1153 68p. green . . . . 2·75 25
1154 78p. blue 55 35
See also Nos. 1374/80 in revalued currency.

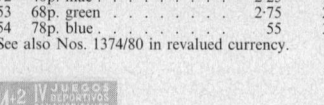

359 Football

360 Frigate "La Argentina" (after Bouchard)

1963. 4th Pan-American Games, Sao Paulo.
1090 **359** 4p.+2p. green, black and pink (postage) 20 10
1091 – 12p.+6p. purple, black and salmon 30 25
1092 – 11p.+5p. red, black and green (air) 35 25
DESIGNS: 11p. Cycling; 12p. Show-jumping.

1963. Navy Day.
1093 **360** 4p. blue 80 10

361 Assembly House and Seal

1963. 150th Anniv of 1813 Assembly.
1094 **361** 4p. black and blue . . . 15 10

362 Battle Scene

1963. 150th Anniv of Battle of San Lorenzo.
1095 **362** 4p. black & green on grn 20 10

363 Queen Nefertari (bas-relief)

1963. U.N.E.S.C.O. Campaign for Preservation of Nubian Monuments.
1096 **363** 4p. black, green & buff 25 10

364 Government House

365 "Science"

1963. Presidential Installation.
1097 **364** 5p. brown and pink . . 15 10

1963. 10th Latin-American Neurosurgery Congress.
1098 **365** 4p. blue, black & brown 20 10

366 Blackboards

367 F. de las Carreras (President of Supreme Court)

1963. "Alliance for Progress".
1099 **366** 5p. red, black and blue 15 10

1963. Centenary of Judicial Power.
1100 **367** 5p. green 15 10

1963. Child Welfare. As T **352**. Mult.
1101 4p.+2p. Vermilion flycatcher (postage) 35 25
1102 11p.+5p. Great kiskadee (air) 75 75

368 Kemal Ataturk

369 "Payador" (after Castagnino)

1963. 25th Death Anniv of Kemal Ataturk.
1103 **368** 12p. grey 30 10

1964. 4th National Folklore Festival.
1104 **369** 4p. black, blue & ultram 15 10

370 Map of Antarctic Islands

1964. Antarctic Claims Issue.
1105 **370** 2p. bl & ochre (postage) 80 30
1106 – 4p. bistre and blue . . . 1·25 35
1107 – 18p. bl & bistre (air) . . 2·25 55
DESIGNS—VERT: (30 × 39½ mm): 4p. Map of Argentina and Antarctica. HORIZ: (as Type **291**): 18p. Map of "Islas Malvinas" (Falkland Islands).

371 Jorge Newbery in Airplane

1964. 50th Death Anniv of Jorge Newbery (aviator).
1108 **371** 4p. green 15 10

372 Pres. Kennedy

373 Father Brochero

1964. President Kennedy Memorial Issue.
1109 **372** 4p. blue and mauve . . 15 10

1964. 50th Death Anniv of Father J. G. Brochero.
1110 **373** 4p. brown 15 10

374 U.P.U. Monument, Berne

375 Soldier of the Patricios Regiment

1964. Air. 15th U.P.U. Congress, Vienna.
1111 **374** 18p. purple and red . . 50 20

1964. Army Day.
1112 **375** 4p. multicoloured . . . 50 15
See also Nos. 1135, 1170, 1201, 1223, 1246, 1343, 1363, 1399, 1450, 1515, 1564, 1641 and 1678.

376 Pope John XXIII

377 Olympic Stadium

1964. Pope John Commemoration
1113 376 4p. black and orange ... 20 10

1964. Olympic Games, Tokyo.
1114 377 4p.+2p. brown, yellow
and red (postage) 15 15
1115 – 12p.+6p. black & green 30 30
1116 – 11p.+5p. blk & bl (air) 40 40
DESIGNS—VERT: 11p. Sailing; 12p. Fencing.

378 University Arms   379 Olympic Flame
and Crutch

1964. 350th Anniv of Cordoba University.
1117 378 4p. yellow, blue & black 15 10

1964. Air. Invalids Olympic Games, Tokyo.
1118 379 18p.+9p. multicoloured 35 45

380 "The Discovery of   381 Pigeons and
America" (Florentine   U.N. Headquarters
woodcut)

1964. Air. "Columbus Day" (or "Day of the Race").
1119 380 13p. black and drab .. 35 15

1964. United Nations Day.
1120 381 4p. ultramarine and blue 15 10

382 J. V. Gonzalez   383 Gen. J. Roca
(medallion)

1964. Birth Centenary of J. V. Gonzalez.
1121 382 4p. red 15 10

1964. 50th Death Anniv of General Julio Roca.
1122 383 4p. blue 15 10

384 "Market-place,   385 Icebreaker "General
Montserrat Square"   San Martin" and Bearded
(after C. Morel)   Penguin

1964. "Argentine Painters".
1123 384 4p. sepia 25 10

1964. Child Welfare. As T 352. Multicoloured.
1124 4p.+2p. Red-crested cardinal
(postage) 65 35
1125 18p.+9p. Chilean swallow
(air) .... 1·25 80

1965. "National Territory of Tierra del Fuego,
Antarctic and South Atlantic Isles".
1126 – 2p. purple (postage) ... 50 10
1127 385 4p. blue ...... 2·00 40
1128 – 11p. red (air) 85 15
DESIGNS: 2p. General Belgrano Base (inscr "BASE
DE EJERCITO" etc); 11p. Teniente Matienzo Joint
Antarctic Base (inscr "BASE CONJUNTA" etc).

1965. Air. First Rio Plata Philatelists' Day. Optd
**PRIMERAS JORNADAS FILATELICAS
RIOPLATENSES.**
1129 358 7p. black & yellow (II) 15 15

387 Young Saver   388 I.T.U. Emblem

1965. 50th Anniv of National Postal Savings Bank.
1130 387 4p. black and red ... 10 10

1965. Air. Centenary of I.T.U.
1131 388 18p. multicoloured ... 40 15

389 I.Q.S.Y. Emblem   390 Soldier of the
"Pueyrredon Hussars"

1965. Int Quiet Sun Year and Space Research.
1132 389 4p. black, orange and
blue (postage) 15 10
1133 – 18p. red (air) 55 20
1134 – 50p. blue 80 35
DESIGNS—VERT: 18p. Rocket launching. HORIZ:
50p. Earth, trajectories and space phenomena (both
inscr "INVESTIGACIONES ESPACIALES").

1965. Army Day (29 May).
1135 390 8p. multicoloured ... 70 15
See also Nos. 1170, 1201, 1223, 1246, 1343, 1363,
1399, 1450, 1515, 1564 and 1641.

391 Ricardo   392 H. Yrigoyen
Guiraldes   (statesman)

1965. Argentine Writers (1st series). Each brown.
1136 8p. Type 391 .... 35 10
1137 8p. E. Larreta 35 10
1138 8p. L. Lugones 35 10
1139 8p. R. J. Payro 35 10
1140 8p. R. Rojas 35 10
See also Nos 1174/8.

1965. Hipolito Yrigoyen Commemoration
1141 392 8p. black and red ... 15 10

393 "Children looking through a
Window"

1965. International Mental Health Seminar.
1142 393 8p. black and brown ... 15 10

394 Ancient Map and Funeral   395 Mgr. Dr. J.
Urn   Cagliero

1965. 400th Anniv of San Miguel de Tucuman.
1143 394 8p. multicoloured ... 15 10

1965. Cagliero Commemoration.
1144 395 8p. violet 15 10

396 Dante (statue in   397 Sail Merchantman
Church of the Holy   "Mimosa"
Cross, Florence)

1965. 700th Birth Anniv of Dante.
1145 396 8p. blue 15 10

1965. Centenary of Welsh Colonisation of Chubut
and Foundation of Rawson.
1146 397 8p. black and red ... 65 20

398 Police Emblem on Map of
Buenos Aires

1965. Federal Police Day.
1155 398 8p. red 15 10

399 Schoolchildren

1965. 81st Anniv of Law 1420 (Public Education).
1156 399 8p. black and green ... 15 10

400 St. Francis's   401 R. Dario
Church, Catamarca   (Nicaraguan poet)

1965. Brother Mamerto Esquiu Commemoration.
1157 400 8p. brown and yellow .. 15 10

1965. 50th Death Anniv of Ruben Dario.
1158 401 15p. violet on grey ... 15 10

402 "The Orange-seller" (detail)

1966. Prilidiano Pueyrredon's Paintings. Designs
show details from the original works, each green.
1159 8p. Type 402 ...... 55 45
1160 8p. "A Halt at the Village
Grocer's Shop" 55 45
1161 8p. "San Fernando
Landscape" 75 45
1162 8p. "Bathing Horses on the
Banks of the River Plate" 55 45

403 Rocket "Centaur" and   404 Dr. Sun Yat-sen
Antarctic Map

1966. Air. Rocket Launches in Antarctica.
1163 403 27p.50 red, black & blue 65 25

1966. Birth Centenary of Dr. Sun Yat-sen.
1164 404 8p. brown 45 25

1966. Child Welfare. As T 352, inscr
"R. ARGENTINA". Multicoloured.
1165 8p.+4p. Southern lapwing
(postage) ...... 1·00 55
1166 27p.50+12p.50 Rufous
hornero (air) ...... 1·25 85

406 "Human Races"

1966. Inaug of W.H.O. Headquarters, Geneva.
1168 406 8p. black and brown ... 15 10

407 Magellan Gull

1966. Air. 50th Anniv of Naval Aviation School,
Puerto Militar.
1169 407 12p. multicoloured ... 40 25

1966. Army Day (29 May). As T 390.
1170 8p. multicoloured 65 15
DESIGN: 8p. Militiaman of Guemes's "Infernals".

408 Arms of Argentina

1966. Air. "Argentina '66" Philatelic Exhibition,
Buenos Aires.
1171 408 10p.+10p. multicoloured 1·50 1·10

410 "Charity" Emblem

1966. Argentine Charities.
1173 410 10p. blue, black & green 25 15

1966. Argentine Writers (2nd series). Portraits
as T 391. Each green.
1174 10p. H. Ascasubi 40 10
1175 10p. Estanislao del Campo 40 10
1176 10p. M. Cane 40 10
1177 10p. Lucio V. Lopez 40 10
1178 10p. R. Obligado 40 10

411 Anchor

1966. 25th Anniv of Argentine Mercantile Marine.
1179 411 4p. multicoloured ... 25 15

412 L. Agote   413 Map and Flags of the
American States

1966. Argentine Scientists. Each violet.
1180 10p. Type 412 .... 40 10
1181 10p. J. B. Ambrosetti 40 10
1182 10p. M. I. Lillo 40 10
1183 10p. F. P. Moreno 40 10
1184 10p. F. J. Muniz 40 10

1966. 7th American Armies Conf, Buenos Aires.
1185 413 10p. multicoloured ... 15 10

414 Bank Facade   **415** La Salle Statue and College

1966. 75th Anniv of Argentine National Bank.
1186 **414** 10p. green 10   10

1966. 75th Anniv of La Salle College, Buenos Aires.
1187 **415** 10p. black and brown . . 10   10

416 Antarctic Map with Expedition Route   **417** Gen. J. M. de Pueyrredon

1966. Argentine South Pole Expedition, 1965–66.
1188 **416** 10p. multicoloured . . . 80   50

1966. Gen. J. M. de Pueyrredon Commemoration
1189 **417** 10p. red 10   10

418 Gen. J. G. de Las Heras   **419** Ancient Pot

1966. Gen. Juan G. de Las Heras Commemoration.
1190 **418** 10p. black 10   10

1967. Child Welfare. As T **352**, inscr "R. ARGENTINA". Multicoloured.
1191   10p.+5p. Scarlet-headed blackbird (horiz) (postage)   80   60
1192   15p.+7p. Blue and yellow tanager (air) . . . . . . 1·25   90

1967. 20th Anniv of U.N.E.S.C.O.
1193 **419** 10p. multicoloured . . . 15   10

420 "The Meal" (after F. Fader)

1967. Fernando Fader (painter).
1194 **420** 10p. brown 15   10

421 Juana Azurduy de Padilla   **422** Schooner "Invencible"

1967. Famous Argentine Women. Each sepia.
1195   6p. Type **421** 30   10
1196   6p. J. M. Gorriti 30   10
1197   6p. C. Grierson 30   10
1198   6p. J. P. Manson 30   10
1199   6p. A. Storni 30   10

1967. Navy Day.
1200 **422** 20p. multicoloured . . . 1·25   20

1967. Army Day (29 May). As T **390**.
1201   20p. multicoloured . . . 75   15
DESIGN: 20p. Soldier of the Arribenos Regiment.

424 Suitcase and Dove   **425** PADELAI Emblem and Sun

1967. International Tourist Year.
1203 **424** 20p. multicoloured . . . 15   10

1967. 75th Anniv of PADELAI (Argentine Children's Welfare Association).
1204 **425** 20p. multicoloured . . . 15   10

426 Teodoro Fels's Bleriot XI   **427** Ferreyra's Oxwagon and Skyscrapers

1967. Air. 50th Anniv of 1st Argentine–Uruguay Airmail Flight.
1205 **426** 26p. brown, olive & blue   30   10

1967. Centenary of Villa Maria.
1206 **427** 20p. multicoloured . . . 15   10

428 "General San Martin" (from statue by M. P. Nunez de Ibarra)   **429** Interior of Museum

1967. 150th Anniv of Battle of Chacabuco.
1207 **428** 20p. brown and yellow   45   15
1208   — 40p. blue 70   15
DESIGN—(48 × 31 mm)—HORIZ: 40p. "Battle of Chacabuco" (from painting by P. Subercaseaux).

1967. 10th Anniv of Government House Museum.
1209 **429** 20p. blue 15   10

430 Pedro Zanni and "Provincia de Buenos Aires"

1967. Aeronautics Week.
1210 **430** 20p. multicoloured . . . 15   10

431 Cadet Ship "General Brown" (from painting by E. Biggeri)   **432** Ovidio Lagos and Front Page of "La Capital" (newspaper)

1967. "Temex 67" Stamp Exhibition and 95th Anniv of Naval Military School.
1211 **431** 20p. multicoloured . . . 1·00   20

1967. Centenary of "La Capital".
1212 **432** 20p. brown 15   10

433 St. Barbara (from altar-painting, Segovia, Spain)   **434** "Sivori's Wife"

1967. Artillery Day (4 Dec).
1213 **433** 20p. red 15   10

1967. Child Welfare. Bird designs as T **352**. Multicoloured.
1214   20p.+10p. Amazon kingfisher (postage) . . . 75   40
1215   26p.+13p. Toco toucan (air)   1·00   60

1968. 50th Death Anniv of Eduardo Sivori (painter).
1216 **434** 20p. green 15   10

435 "Almirante Brown" Scientific Station   **436** Man in Wheelchair

1968. "Antarctic Territories".
1217   — 6p. multicoloured . . . 60   15
1218 **435** 20p. multicoloured . . . 85   20
1219   — 40p. multicoloured . . . 1·10   55
DESIGNS—VERT (22½ × 32 mm): 6p. Map of Antarctic radio-postal stations. HORIZ (as Type **435**): 40p. Aircraft over South Pole ("Trans-Polar Round Flight").

1968. Rehabilitation Day for the Handicapped.
1220 **436** 20p. black and green . . 20   10

437 "St. Gabriel" (detail from "The Annunciation" by Leonardo da Vinci)   **438** Children and W.H.O. Emblem

1968. St. Gabriel (patron saint of army communications).
1221 **437** 20p. mauve 15   10

1968. 20th Anniv of W.H.O.
1222 **438** 20p. blue and red . . . 15   10

1968. Army Day (29 May). As T **390**.
1223   20p. multicoloured . . . 85   15
DESIGN: 20p. Iriarte's artilleryman.

439 Full-rigged Cadet Ship "Libertad" (E. Biggeri)

1968. Navy Day.
1224 **439** 20p. multicoloured . . . 65   15

440 G. Rawson and Hospital

1968. Centenary of Guillermo Rawson Hospital.
1225 **440** 6p. bistre 15   10

441 Vito Dumas and "Legh II"

1968. Air. Vito Dumas' World Voyage in Yacht "Legh II".
1226 **441** 68p. multicoloured . . . 60   20

442 Children crossing "Zebra"

1968. Road Safety.
1227 **442** 20p. multicoloured . . . 20   10

443 "O'Higgins greeting San Martin" (P. Subercaseaux)

1968. 150th Anniv of Battle of the Maipu.
1228 **443** 40p. blue 55   20

444 Dr. O. Magnasco (lawyer)   **445** "The Sea" (E. Gomez)

446 "Grandmother's Birthday" (P. Lynch)

1968. Magnasco Commemoration.
1229 **444** 20p. brown 20   10

1968. Children's Stamp Design Competition.
1230 **445** 20p. multicoloured . . . 20   15
1231 **446** 20p. multicoloured . . . 20   15

447 Mar del Plata at Night   **448** Mounted Gendarme

1968. 4th Plenary Assembly of Int Telegraph and Telephone Consultative Committee, Mar del Plata.
1232 **447** 20p. black, yellow and blue (postage) 25   15
1233   — 40p. black, mauve and blue (air) 35   15
1234   — 68p. multicoloured . . . 50   25
DESIGNS (as Type **447**): 40p. South America in Assembly hemisphere. (Larger, 40 × 30 mm): 68p. Assembly emblem.

1968. National Gendarmerie.
1235 **448** 20p. multicoloured . . . 30   10

449 Coastguard Cutter "Lynch" **450** A. de Anchorena and "Pampero"

1968. National Maritime Prefecture (Coastguard).
1236 **449** 20p. black, grey and blue 65 10

1968. Aeronautics Week.
1237 **450** 20p. multicoloured . . . 30 10

451 St. Martin of Tours (A. Guido) **452** Bank Emblem

1968. St. Martin of Tours (patron saint of Buenos Aires).
1238 **451** 20p. brown and lilac . . 15 10

1968. Municipal Bank of Buenos Aires.
1239 **452** 20p. black, green & yell 15 10

453 Anniversary and A.L.P.I. Emblems

1968. 25th Anniv of "Fight Against Polio Association" (A.L.P.I.).
1240 **453** 20p. green and red . . . 20 10

454 "My Grandmother's Birthday" (Patricia Lynch)

1968. 1st "Solidarity" Philatelic Exn, Buenos Aires.
1241 **454** 40p.+20p. multicoloured 75 30

455 "The Potter Woman" (Ramon Gomez Cornet) **456** Emblem of State Coalfields

1968. Cent. of Whitcomb Gallery, Buenos Aires.
1242 **455** 20p. red 15 10

1968. Coal and Steel Industries. Multicoloured.
1243 20p. Type **456** 15 10
1244 20p. Ladle and emblem of Military Steel-manufacturing Agency ("FM") 15 10

457 Illustration from Schmidl's book "Journey to the River Plate and Paraguay"

1969. Ulrich Schmidl Commemoration.
1245 **457** 20p. yellow, red & black 15 10

1969. Army Day (29 May). As T **390**.
1246 20p. Sapper, Buenos Aires Army, 1856 . . . . . . 70 15

459 Sail Frigate "Hercules"

1969. Navy Day.
1247 **459** 20p. multicoloured . . . 1·00 20

460 "Freedom and Equality" (from poster by S. Zagorski) **461** I.L.O. Emblem within Honeycomb

1969. Human Rights Year.
1254 **460** 20p. black and yellow . . 15 10

1969. 50th Anniv of I.L.O.
1255 **461** 20p. multicoloured . . . 15 10

462 P. N. Arata (biologist) **463** Dish Aerial and Satellite

1969. Argentine Scientists.
1256 **462** 6p. brown on yellow . . 35 15
1257 – 6p. brown on yellow . . 35 15
1258 – 6p. brown on yellow . . 35 15
1259 – 6p. brown on yellow . . 35 15
1260 – 6p. brown on yellow . . 35 15
PORTRAITS: No. 1257, M. Fernandez (zoologist); No. 1258, A. P. Gallardo (biologist); No. 1259, C. M. Hicken (botanist); No. 1260, E. L. Holmberg (botanist).

1969. Satellite Communications.
1261 **463** 20p. blk & yell (postage) 25 15
1262 – 40p. blue (air) 55 20
DESIGN—HORIZ: 40p. Earth station and dish aerial.

464 Nieuport 28 and Route Map

1969. 50th Anniv of 1st Argentine Airmail Service.
1263 **464** 20p. multicoloured . . . 20 10

1969. Child Welfare. As T **352**, inscr "R. ARGENTINA". Multicoloured.
1264 20p.+10p. White-faced whistling duck (postage) 1·00 45
1265 26p.+13p. Lineated woodpecker (air) . . . . 1·00 45

465 College Entrance **466** General Pacheco (from painting by R. Guidice)

1969. Centenary of Argentine Military College.
1266 **465** 20p. multicoloured . . . 15 10

1969. Death Centenary of General Angel Pacheco.
1267 **466** 20p. green 15 10

467 Bartolome Mitre and Logotypes of "La Nacion" **468** J. Aguirre

1969. Centenary of Newspapers "La Nacion" and "La Prensa".
1268 **467** 20p. black, emer & grn 50 15
1269 – 20p. black orange & yell 50 15
DESIGN: No. 1269 "The Lantern" (masthead) and logotypes of "La Prensa".

1969. Argentine Musicians.
1270 **468** 6p. green and blue . . . 65 15
1271 – 6p. green and blue . . . 65 15
1272 – 6p. green and blue . . . 65 15
1273 – 6p. green and blue . . . 65 15
1274 – 6p. green and blue . . . 65 15
MUSICIANS: No. 1271, F. Boero; No. 1272, C. Gaito; No. 1273, C. L. Buchardo; No. 1274, A. Williams.

469 Hydro-electric Project on Rivers Limay and Neuquen

1969. National Development Projects. Mult.
1275 6p. Type **469** (postage) . . . 50 10
1276 20p. Parana–Santa Fe river tunnel 60 15
1277 26p. Atomic power plant, Atucha (air) . . . . . . 1·00 40

470 Lieut. B. Matienzo and Nieuport 28 Biplane

1969. Aeronautics Week.
1278 **470** 20p. multicoloured . . . 50 10

471 Capital "L" and Lions Emblem

1969. 50th Anniv of Lions International.
1279 **471** 20p. olive, orge & green 50 10

472 "Madonna and Child" (after R. Soldi)

1969. Christmas.
1280 **472** 20p. multicoloured . . . 55 15

1970. Child Welfare. As T **352**, but differently arranged and inscr "REPUBLICA ARGENTINA". Multicoloured.
1293 20c.+10c. Slender-tailed woodstar (postage) . . . 85 55
1294 40c.+20c. Chilean flamingo (air) 90 70
See also Nos. 1394/5, 1415/16 and 1441/2.

474 "General Belgrano" (lithograph by Gericault)

1970. Birth Bicent of General Manuel Belgrano.
1295 **474** 20c. brown 45 15
1296 – 50c. black, flesh & blue 80 25
DESIGN—HORIZ (56 × 15 mm): 50c. "Monument to the Flag" (bas-relief by Jose Fioravanti).

475 Early Fire Engine

1970. Air. Centenary of Buenos Aires Fire Brigade.
1297 **475** 40c. multicoloured . . . 60 10

476 Naval Schooner "Juliet", 1814

1970. Navy Day.
1298 **476** 20c. multicoloured . . . 1·25 20

477 San Jose Palace **478** General Belgrano

1970. President Justo de Urquiza Commemoration.
1299 **477** 20c. multicoloured . . . 15 10

1970. Revalued currency. Previous designs with values in centavos and pesos as T **478**. Inscr "REPUBLICA ARGENTINA" or "ARGENTINA".

1300		1c. green (No. 1016) . .	15	10
1301	–	3c. red (No. 951) . . .	15	10
1302	**296**	5c. blue	15	10
1303	**478**	6c. blue	15	10
1304		8c. green	15	10
1305	–	10c. brown (No. 1286)*	45	10
1306	–	10c. red (No. 1286) . .	1·25	10
1307	–	10c. brown (No. 1286)*	55	10
1308	**478**	10c. brown	20	10
1309	–	25c. brown	40	10
1310	**478**	30c. purple	10	10
1311	–	50c. red	80	10
1312	**478**	60c. yellow	10	10
1313	–	65c. brown (No. 878)	85	10
1314	–	70c. blue	10	10
1315	–	90c. green (No. 878) . .	2·00	10
1316a	–	1p. brown (as No. 1027, but 23 × 29 mm)	40	10
1317	–	1p.15 blue (No. 1072)	80	10
1318	–	1p.20 orange (No. 878)	80	10
1319	–	1p.20 red	35	10
1320	–	1p.80 brn (as No. 1072)	30	10
1321	**478**	1p.80 blue	20	10
1322	–	2p. brown	20	10
1323	–	2p.70 bl (as No. 878)	25	10
1323a	**478**	3p. grey	15	10
1392	–	4p.50 green (as No. 1288) (G. Brown)	40	10
1325	–	5p. green (as No. 1032)	95	10
1326	–	6p. red	25	10
1327	–	6p. green	25	10
1328	–	7p.50 grn (as No. 878)	85	10
1329	–	10p. blue (as No. 1033)	1·25	10
1329a	–	12p. green	25	10
1329b	–	12p. red	25	10
1330	–	13p.50 red (as No. 1288)	1·00	10
1331	–	13p.50 red (as No. 1072 but larger, 16 × 24 mm)	40	10
1332	–	15p. red	25	10
1333	–	15p. blue	25	10
1334	–	20p. red	40	10
1335	–	22p.50 blue (as No. 878) (22 × 32½ mm) . . .	1·00	10
1393	–	22p.50 blue (as No. 878) (26 × 39 mm)	40	10

1336	– 30p. red		40	10
1337	478 40p. green		70	15
1338	– 40p. red		40	10
1339	478 60p. blue		80	20
1340	– 70p. blue		1·00	20
1340a	478 90p. green		55	30
1340b	– 100p. red		55	25
1340c	– 110p. red		35	15
1340d	– 120p. red		40	20
1340e	– 130p. red		40	25

DESIGNS—VERT (as Type 478): 25, 50, 70c., 1p.20, 2, 6, 12, 15p. (No. 1332), 20, 30, 40p. (No. 1338), 100, 110, 120, 130p. General Jose de San Martin; 15p. (No. 1333), 70p. Guillermo Brown.

*No. 1307 differs from Nos. 1305/6 in being without imprint. It also has "CORREOS" at top right.

482 Wireless Set of 1920 and Radio "Waves"

1970. 50th Anniv of Argentine Radio Broadcasting.
1341 **482** 20c. multicoloured . . . 15 10

483 Emblem of Education Year

485 "United Nations"

1970. Air. International Education Year.
1342 **483** 68c. black and blue . . . 30 15

1970. Military Uniforms. As T **390**. Multicoloured.
1343   20c. Military courier, 1879   75   25

1970. 150th Anniv of Peruvian Liberation.
1344 **484** 26c. multicoloured . . . 1·40 20

484 "Liberation Fleet leaving Valparaiso" (A. Abel)

1970. 25th Anniv of U.N.
1345 **485** 20c. multicoloured . . . 15 10

486 Cordoba Cathedral

1970. 400th Anniv of Tucuman Diocese.
1346 **486** 50c. blk & grey (postage)   85   10
1347   – 40c. multicoloured (air)   85   20
DESIGN—HORIZ: 40c. Chapel, Sumampa.

487 Planetarium

1970. Air. Buenos Aires Planetarium.
1348 **487** 40c. multicoloured . . . 40 15

488 "Liberty" and Mint Building

1970. 25th Anniv of State Mint Building, Buenos Aires.
1349 **488** 20c. black, green & gold   15   10

489 "The Manger" (H. G. Gutierrez) (½-size illustration)

1970. Christmas.
1350 **489** 20c. multicoloured . . . 25 10

490 Jorge Newbery and Morane Saulnier Type L Airplane

1970. Air. Aeronautics Week.
1351 **490** 26c. multicoloured . . . 40 15

491 St. John Bosco and College Building

1970. Salesian Mission in Patagonia.
1352 **491** 20c. black and green . . 15 10

492 "Planting the Flag"

1971. 5th Anniv of Argentine Expedition to the South Pole.
1353 **492** 20c. multicoloured . . . 1·25 35

493 Dorado (½-size illustration)

1971. Child Welfare. Fishes. Multicoloured.
1354   20c.+10c. Type **493**
         (postage) 65   45
1355   40c.+20c. River Plate pejerry
         (air) 55   35

494 Einstein and Scanners   **495** E. I. Alippi

1971. Electronics in Postal Development.
1356 **494** 25c. multicoloured . . . 30 10

1971. Argentine Actors and Actresses. Each black and brown.
1357   15c. Type **495** 40 10
1358   15c. J. A. Casaberta 40 10
1359   15c. R. Casaux 40 10
1360   15c. Angelina Pagano 40 10
1361   15c. F. Parravicini 40 10

496 Federation Emblem

1971. Inter-American Regional Meeting of International Roads Federation.
1362 **496** 25c. black and blue . . . 15 10

1971. Army Day. As T **390**.
1363   25c. multicoloured . . . . 1·00 15
DESIGN: 25c. Artilleryman of 1826.

1971. Navy Day. As T **476**.
1364   25c. multicoloured . . . 1·75 20
DESIGN: Sloop "Carmen".

498 "General Guemes" (L. Gigli)

1971. 150th Death Anniv of General M. de Guemes. Multicoloured.
1365   25c. Type **498** 55 20
1366   25c. "Death of Guemes"
         (A. Alice) (84 × 29 mm)   55   20

499 Order of the Peruvian Sun

1971. 150th Anniv of Peruvian Independence.
1367 **499** 31c. yellow, black & red   40   10

500 Stylized Tulip   **501** Dr. A. Saenz (founder) (after Jose Gut)

1971. 3rd Int and 8th Nat Horticultural Exhibition.
1368 **500** 25c. multicoloured . . . 25 15

1971. 150th Anniv of Buenos Aires University.
1369 **501** 25c. multicoloured . . . 20 15

502 Arsenal Emblem

1971. 30th Anniv of Fabricaciones Militares (Arsenals).
1370 **502** 25c. multicoloured . . . 20 15

503 Road Transport

1971. Nationalized Industries.
1371 **503** 25c. mult (postage) . . . 35 10
1372   – 65c. multicoloured . . . 90 35
1373   – 31c. yell, blk & red (air)   45   25
DESIGNS: 31c. Refinery and formula ("Petrochemicals"); 65c. Tree and paper roll ("Paper and Cellulose").

1971. Air. Revalued currency. Face values in centavos.
1374 **358** 45c. brown . . . 2·50 15
1375   68c. red . . . 30 15

1376a	70c. blue . . .	1·60	15
1377	90c. green . . .	1·75	15
1378	1p.70 blue . . .	55	10
1379	1p.95 green . . .	55	15
1380	2p.65 purple . . .	55	15

504 Constellation and Telescope

1971. Centenary of Cordoba Observatory.
1381 **504** 25c. multicoloured . . . 25 15

505 Capt. D. L. Candelaria and Morane Saulnier Type P Airplane

1971. 25th Aeronautics and Space Week.
1382 **505** 25c. multicoloured . . . 40 10

506 "Stamps" (Mariette Lydis)   **507** "Christ in Majesty" (tapestry by Butler)

1971. 2nd Charity Stamp Exhibition.
1383 **506** 1p.+50c. multicoloured   35   35

1971. Christmas.
1384 **507** 25c. multicoloured . . . 20 10

1972. Child Welfare. As T **352**, but differently arranged and inscr "REPUBLICA ARGENTINA".
1394   25c.+10c. Saffron finch
         (vert) 90   40
1395   65c.+30c. Rufous-bellied
         thrush (horiz) . . . 1·10   50

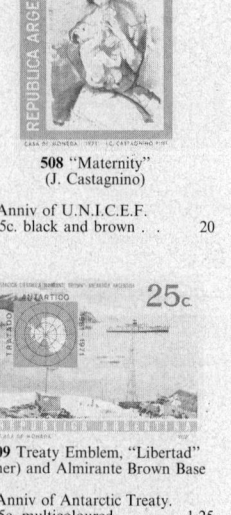

508 "Maternity" (J. Castagnino)

1972. 25th Anniv of U.N.I.C.E.F.
1396 **508** 25c. black and brown . . 20 15

509 Treaty Emblem, "Libertad" (liner) and Almirante Brown Base

1972. 10th Anniv of Antarctic Treaty.
1397 **509** 25c. multicoloured . . . 1·25 20

510 Postman's Mail Pouch

1972. Bicentenary of 1st Buenos Aires Postman.
1398 **510** 25c. multicoloured . . . 15 10

1972. Army Day. As T **390**. Multicoloured.
1399 25c. Sergeant of Negro and
Mulatto Battalion
(1806–7) 65 15

1972. Navy Day. As T **476**. Multicoloured.
1400 25c. Brigantine "Santisima
Trinidad" . . . . 1·40 20

512 Sonic Balloon   **513** Oil Pump

1972. National Meteorological Service.
1401 **512** 25c. multicoloured . . . 25 15

1972. 50th Anniv of State Oilfields (Y.P.F.).
1402 **513** 45c. black, blue & gold 80 10

514 Forest Centre

1972. 7th World Forestry Congress, Buenos Aires.
1403 **514** 25c. black, blue & lt bl 45 10

515 Arms and Cadet Ship "Presidente Sarmiento"

1972. Centenary of Naval School.
1404 **515** 25c. multicoloured . . . 1·25 20

516 Baron A. de   **517** Bartolome Mitre
Marchi, Balloon and
Voisin "Boxkite"

1972. Aeronautics Week.
1405 **516** 25c. multicoloured . . . 40 10

1972. 150th Birth Anniv of General Bartolome Mitre.
1406 **517** 25c. blue 20 10

518 Heart and Flower   **519** "Martin Fierro"
(J. C. Castignino)

1972. World Health Day.
1407 **518** 90c. blk, violet & blue 45 15

1972. Int Book Year and Cent of "Martin Fierro"
(poem by Jose Hernandez). Multicoloured.
1408 **519** Type **519** 25 15
1409 90c. "Spirit of the Gaucho"
(V. Forte) 50 20

520 Iguazu Falls

1972. American Tourist Year.
1410 **520** 45c. multicoloured . . . 30 10

521 "Wise Man on   **522** Cockerel Emblem
Horseback" (18th-
century wood-carving)

1972. Christmas.
1411 **521** 50c. multicoloured . . . 40 10

1973. 150th Anniv of Federal Police Force.
1412 **522** 50c. multicoloured . . . 20 10

523 Bank Emblem   **525** Presidential Chair
and First Coin

524 Douglas DC-3 Aircraft and Polar
Map

1973. 150th Anniv of Provincial Bank of Buenos
Aires.
1413 **523** 50c. multicoloured . . . 15 10

1973. 10th Anniv of 1st Argentine Flight to South
Pole.
1414 **524** 50c. multicoloured . . . 90 20

1973. Child Welfare. As T **473**, but differently
arranged and inscr "R. ARGENTINA". Mult.
1415 50c.+25c. Crested screamer
(vert) 85 50
1416 90c.+45c. Saffron-cowled
blackbird (horiz) . . . . 1·25 75

1973. Presidential Inauguration
1417 **525** 50c. multicoloured . . . 20 10

526 San Martin and Bolivar

1973. San Martin's Farewell to People of Peru.
Multicoloured.
1418 50c. Type **526** 25 15
1419 50c. "San Martin" (after Gil
de Castro) (vert) 25 15

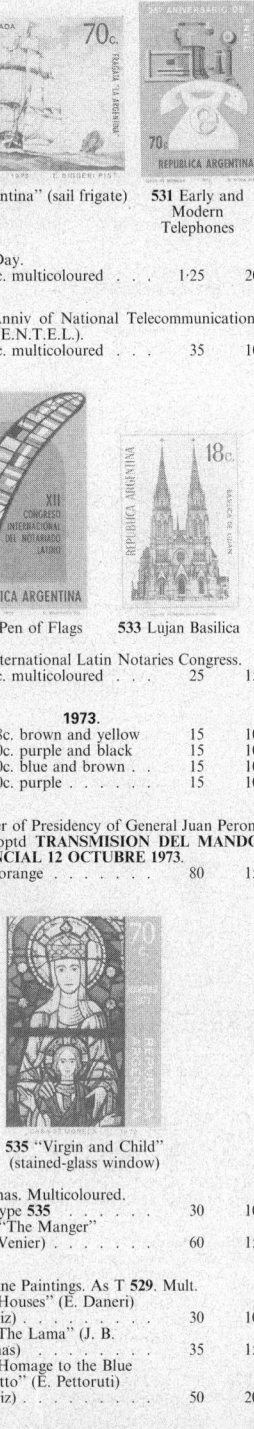

527 "Eva Peron – Eternally with her
People"

1973. Eva Peron Commemoration.
1420 **527** 70c. multicoloured . . . 20 15

528 "House of Viceroy Sobremonte" (H. de
Virgilio)

1973. 4th Centenary of Cordoba.
1421 **528** 50c. multicoloured . . . 20 10

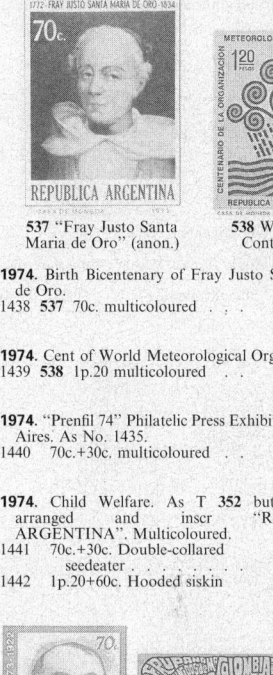

529 "Woman" (L. Spilimbergo)

1973. Philatelists' Day. Argentine Paintings. Mult.
1422 15c.+15c. "Nature Study"
(A. Guttero) (horiz) . . . 50 10
1423 70c. Type **529** 80 15
1424 90c.+90c. "Nude" (M. C.
Victorica) (horiz) 85 70
See also Nos. 1434/6 and 1440.

530 "La Argentina" (sail frigate)   **531** Early and
Modern
Telephones

1973. Navy Day.
1425 **530** 70c. multicoloured . . . 1·25 20

1973. 25th Anniv of National Telecommunications
Enterprise (E.N.T.E.L.).
1426 **531** 70c. multicoloured . . . 35 10

532 Quill Pen of Flags   **533** Lujan Basilica

1973. 12th International Latin Notaries Congress.
1427 **532** 70c. multicoloured . . . 25 15

1973.
1428 **533** 18c. brown and yellow 15 10
1429 50c. purple and black 15 10
1429a 50c. blue and brown . 15 10
1430 50c. purple 15 10

1973. Transfer of Presidency of General Juan Peron.
No. 1318 optd **TRANSMISION DEL MANDO**
PRESIDENCIAL 12 OCTUBRE 1973.
1431 1p.20 orange 80 15

535 "Virgin and Child"
(stained-glass window)

1973. Christmas. Multicoloured.
1432 70c. Type **535** 30 10
1433 1p.20 "The Manger"
(B. Venier) 60 15

1974. Argentine Paintings. As T **529**. Mult.
1434 50c. "Houses" (E. Daneri)
(horiz) 30 10
1435 70c. "The Lama" (J. B.
Planas) 35 15
1436 90c. "Homage to the Blue
Grotto" (E. Pettoruti)
(horiz) 50 20

536 View of Mar del Plata

1974. Centenary of Mar del Plata.
1437 **536** 70c. multicoloured . . . 30 10

537 "Fray Justo Santa   **538** Weather
Maria de Oro" (anon.)   Contrasts

1974. Birth Bicentenary of Fray Justo Santa Maria
de Oro.
1438 **537** 70c. multicoloured . . . 20 10

1974. Cent of World Meteorological Organization.
1439 **538** 1p.20 multicoloured . . 40 10

1974. "Prenfil 74" Philatelic Press Exhibition, Buenos
Aires. As No. 1435.
1440 70c.+30c. multicoloured . . 20 20

1974. Child Welfare. As T **352** but differently
arranged and inscr "REPUBLICA
ARGENTINA". Multicoloured.
1441 70c.+30c. Double-collared
seedeater 65 45
1442 1p.20+60c. Hooded siskin 1·10 65

539 B. Roldan   **540** O.E.A. Member Countries

1974. Birth Centenary of Belisario Roldan (writer).
1443 **539** 70c. brown and blue . . 10 10

1974. 25th Anniv of Organization of American
States' Charter.
1444 **540** 1p.38 multicoloured . . 15 10

541 Posthorn Emblem

1974. Creation of State Posts and
Telecommunications Enterprise (E.N.C.O.T.E.L.).
1445 **541** 1p.20 blue, black & gold 40 10

542 Flags of Member   **543** El Chocon Hydro-
Countries   electric Complex

1974. 6th Meeting of River Plate Countries' Foreign
Ministers.
1446 **542** 1p.38 multicoloured . . 15 15

1974. Nationalized Industries. Multicoloured.
1447 70c. Type **543** 35 10
1448 1p.20 Blast furnace, Somisa
steel mills 55 25
1449 4p.50 General Belgrano
Bridge (61 × 25 mm) . . 2·75 60

1974. Army Day. As T **390**. Multicoloured.
1450 1p.20 Mounted Grenadier 70 15
See also Nos. 1515 and 1564.

544 A. Mascias and Bleriot XI

1974. Air Force Day.
1451 544 1p.20 multicoloured . . 75 15

545 Brigantine "Belgrano"

1974. 150th Anniv of San Martin's Departure into Exile.
1452 545 1p.20 multicoloured . . 1·25 20

546 San Francisco Convent, Santa Fe

1974. 400th Anniv of Santa Fe.
1453 546 1p.20 multicoloured . . 45 10

547 Symbolic Posthorn

1974. Centenary of U.P.U.
1454 547 2p.65 multicoloured . . 70 10

549 Congress Building, Buenos Aires

1974.
1456 549 30p. purple and yellow 1·50 10

550 Boy examining Stamp

1974. International Year of Youth Philately.
1457 550 1p.70 black and yellow 40 10

551 "Christmas in Peace" (V. Campanella)

1974. Christmas. Multicoloured.
1458 1p.20 Type 551 . . . . 35 10
1459 2p.65 "St. Anne and the Virgin Mary" 40 15

552 "Space Monsters" (R. Forner)

1975. Contemporary Argentine Paintings. Mult.
1460 2p.70 Type 552 . . . . . 80 15
1461 4p.50 "Sleep" (E. Centurion) . . . . . 1·50 25

553 Cathedral and Weaver, Catamarca (Illustration reduced. Actual size 83 × 29 mm)

1975. Tourist Views (1st series). Multicoloured.
1462 1p.20 Type 553 . . . . . . 25 15
1463 1p.20 Street scene and carved pulpit, Jujuy 25 15
1464 1p.20 Monastery and tree-felling, Salta 25 15
1465 1p.20 Dam and vase, Santiago del Estero . . . 25 15
1466 1p.20 Colombres Museum and farm cart, Tucuman 25 15
See also Nos. 1491/3.

554 "We're Vaccinated Now" (M. L. Alonso)   555 "Don Quixote" (Zuloaga)

1975. Children's Vaccination Campaign.
1467 554 2p. multicoloured . . . 50 15

1975. Air. "Espana 75" International Stamp Exhibition, Madrid.
1468 555 2p.75 black, yell & red 60 15

556 Hugo S. Acuna and South Orkneys Base (Illustration reduced. Actual size 83 × 29 mm)

1975. Antarctic Pioneers. Multicoloured.
1469 2p. Type 556 . . . . . . 45 10
1470 2p. Francisco P. Moreno and Quetrihue Peninsula 45 10
1471 2p. Capt. Carlos M. Moyano and Cerra Torre, Santa Cruz 45 10
1472 2p. Lt. Col. Luis Piedra Buena and naval cutter "Luisito" in the Antarctic 1·40 25
1473 2p. Ensign Jose M. Sobral and "Snow Hill" House 45 10

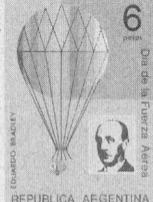

557 Valley of the Moon, San Juan Province   559 Eduardo Bradley and Balloon

1975.
1474 557 50p. multicoloured . . . 1·75 10
1474a 300p. multicoloured . . . 2·10 40
1474b – 500p. multicoloured . . 4·25 85
1474c – 1000p. multicoloured . . 3·75 1·00
DESIGNS—HORIZ: 500p. Admiral Brown Antarctic Station; 1000p. San Francisco Church, Salta.

1975. Air. Surch.
1475 358 9p.20 on 5p.60 green, mauve and purple . . 90 10
1476 19p.70 on 5p.60 green, mauve and purple . . 1·10 20
1477 100p. on 5p.60 green, mauve and purple . . 2·75 40

1975. Air Force Day.
1478 559 6p. multicoloured . . . 60 15

560 Sail Frigate "25 de Mayo"

1975. Navy Day.
1479 560 6p. multicoloured . . . 90 20

561 "Oath of the 33 Orientales on the Beach of La Agraciada" (J. Blanes)

1975. 150th Anniv of Uruguayan Independence.
1480 561 6p. multicoloured . . . 30 15

1975. Air. Surch. **REVALORIZADO** and value.
1481 358 9p.20 on 5p.60 green, mauve and purple . . 85 15
1482 19p.70 on 5p.60 green, mauve and purple . . 1·00 30

563 Flame Emblem

1975. 30th Anniv of Pres. Peron's Seizure of Power.
1483 563 6p. multicoloured . . . 35 15

1975. Surch **REVALORIZADO** and value.
1484 533 5p. on 18c. brown & yell 45 10

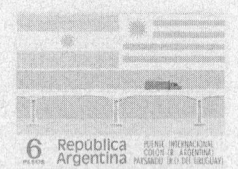

565 Bridge and Flags of Argentina and Uruguay

1975. "International Bridge" between Colon (Argentina) and Paysandu (Uruguay).
1485 565 6p. multicoloured . . . 50 15

566 Posthorn Emblem   568 "The Nativity" (stained-glass window)

1975. Introduction of Postal Codes.
1486 566 10p. on 20c. yellow, black and green . . . 35 10

1975. Nos. 951 and 1288 surch **REVALORIZADO** and value.
1487 6c. on 3p. blue 15 10
1488 30c. on 90p. bistre . . . 15 10

1975. Christmas.
1489 568 6p. multicoloured . . . 30 15

569 Stylized Nurse and Child   570 "Numeral"

1975. Centenary of Children's Hospital.
1490 569 6p. multicoloured . . . 35 10

1975. Tourist Views (2nd series). As T 553. Mult.
1491 6p. Mounted patrol and oil rig, Chubut 55 15
1492 6p. Glacier and sheep-shearing, Santa Cruz 55 15
1493 6p. Lake Lapataia, Tierra del Fuego, and Antarctic scene 55 15

1976.
1494 570 12c. grey and black . . . 10 10
1495 50c. slate and green . . 10 10
1496 1p. red and black . . . 10 10
1497 4p. blue and black . . . 15 10
1498 5p. yellow and black . . 15 10
1499 6p. brown and black . . 15 10
1500 10p. grey and violet . . 20 10
1501 27p. green and black . . 55 10
1502 30p. blue and black . . . 75 10
1503 45p. yellow and black . . 75 10
1504 50p. green and black . . 75 10
1505 100p. green and red . . . 1·10 10

571 Airliner in Flight

1976. 25th Anniv of "Aerolineas Argentinas".
1513 571 30p. multicoloured . . . 90 15

572 Sail Frigate "Heroina" and Map of Malvinas

1976. Argentine Claims to Falkland Islands (Malvinas).
1514 572 6p. multicoloured 85 20

1976. Army Day. As T 390. Multicoloured.
1515 12p. Infantryman of Conde's 7th Regiment 50 15

573 Louis Braille   574 Plush-crested Jay

1976. Louis Braille (inventor of characters for the Blind) Commemoration.
1516 573 19p.70 blue 30 15

1976. Argentine Philately. Multicoloured.
1517 7p.+3p.50 Type 574 . . . . 60 35
1518 13p.+6p.50 Yellow-collared macaw 80 35
1519 20p.+10p. "Begonia micranthera" 65 40
1520 40p.+20p. "Echinopsis shaferi" (teasel) 90 55

575 Schooner "Rio de la Plata"

1976. Navy Day.
1521 575 12p. multicoloured . . . 1·00 20

576 Dr. Bernardo Houssay (Medicine)

1976. Argentine Nobel Prize Winners.
1522 576 10p. black, orge & grey 30 10
1523 – 15p. black, yell & grey 35 15
1524 – 20p. black, brn & grey 50 25
DESIGNS: 15p. Dr. Luis Leloir (chemistry); 20p. Dr. Carlos Lamas (peace).

577 Bridge and Ship

1976. "International Bridge" between Unzue (Argentina) and Fray Bentos (Uruguay).
1525 **577** 12p. multicoloured . . . 30 10

578 Cooling Tower and Pipelines

1976. General Mosconi Petrochemical Project.
1526 **578** 28p. multicoloured . . . 45 15

579 Teodoro Fels and Bleriot XI

1976. Air Force Day.
1527 **579** 15p. multicoloured . . . 40 10

580 "Nativity" (E. Chiapetto)

1976. Christmas.
1528 **580** 20p. multicoloured . . . 50 10

581 Dr. D. Velez Sarsfield   582 Conference
(statesman)   Emblem

1977. Death Cent (1975) of Dr. D. V. Sarsfield.
1529 **581** 50p. brown and red . . . 60 15

1977. United Nations Water Conference.
1530 **582** 70p. multicoloured . . . 45 25

583 "The Visit" (Horacio Butler)

1977. Plastic Arts. Multicoloured.
1531 50p. Type **583** 50 15
1532 70p. "Consecration" (M. P. Caride) (vert) 70 25

584 World Cup Emblem   585 City of La Plata
                                              Museum

1977. World Cup Football Championship, Argentina. Multicoloured.
1533 30p. Type **584** 50 15
1534 70p. Stadium and flags (vert) 65 30

1977.
1535 **585** 5p. black and brown   10 10
1536 – 10p. black and blue . . 10 10
1538 – 20p. black and yellow   10 10
1539 – 40p. black and blue . . 20 10
1540 – 50p. black and yellow   40 10
1541 – 50p. black and brown   25 10
1542 – 100p. black and pink   35 10
1543 – 100p. black and orange   10 10
1544 – 100p. black and green   10 10
1545 – 200p. black and blue   25 20
1546 – 280p. black and lilac   4·50 15
1547b – 300p. black and yellow   85 10
1548 – 480p. black and yellow   80 20
1549b – 500p. black and green   60 15
1550 – 520p. black and orange   90 20
1551 – 800p. black and purple   1·10 25
1552a – 1000p. black and gold   1·60 35
1553 – 1000p. black and yellow   1·25 35
1554 – 2000p. multicoloured   1·00 35
DESIGNS—HORIZ: 10p. House of Independence, Tucuman; 20p. Type **585**; 50p. (No. 1541), Cabildo, Buenos Aires; 100p. (Nos. 1542/3), Columbus Theatre, Buenos Aires; 280p., 300p. Rio Grande Museum Chapel, Tierra del Fuego; 480p., 520p., 800p. San Ignacio Mission Church ruins; 500p. Candonga Chapel; 1000p. General Post Office, Buenos Aires (No. 1552 39×29 mm, No. 1553 32×21 mm); 2000p. Civic Centre, Bariloche. VERT: 40p. Cabildo, Salta; 50p. (No. 1540), Cabildo, Buenos Aires; 200p. Monument to the Flag, Rosario.

586 Morse Key and Satellite

1977. "Argentine Philately". Multicoloured.
1560 10p.+5p. Type **586** . . . 25 15
1561 20p.+10p. Old and modern mail vans 45 25
1562 60p.+30p. Old and modern ships . . . . . . 1·25 75
1563 70p.+35p. SPAD XIII and Boeing 707 aircraft . . . 85 60

1977. Army Day. As T **390**. Multicoloured.
1564 30p. Trooper of 16th Lancers 50 15

587 Schooner "Sarandi"

1977. Navy Day.
1565 **587** 30p. multicoloured . . . 1·25 20

1977. 150th Anniv of Uruguay Post Office. As No. 1325 but colour changed. Surch **100 PESOS 150 ANIV. DEL CORREO NACIONAL DEL URUGUAY.**
1566 100p. on 5p. brown 90 40

1977. "Argentina '77" Exhibition. As No. 1474c, but inscr "EXPOSICION ARGENTINA '77".
1567 160p.+80p. multicoloured . . 1·60 1·25

589 Admiral Guillermo Brown

1977. Birth Bicent of Admiral Guillermo Brown.
1568 **589** 30p. multicoloured . . . 40 15

590 Civic Centre, Santa Rosa (La Pampa)

1977. Provinces of the Argentine. Multicoloured.
1569 30p. Type **590** 40 20
1570 30p. Sierra de la Ventana (Buenos Aires) 40 20

1571 30p. Skiers at Chapelco, San Martin de los Andes (Neuquen) 40 20
1572 30p. Lake Fonck (Rio Negro) 40 20

591 Savoia S.16 ter Flying Boat over Rio de la Plata

1977. Air Force and 1926 Buenos Aires–New York Flight Commemoration.
1573 **591** 40p. multicoloured . . . 35 15

592 Jet Fighter Outline

1977. 50th Anniv of Military Aviation Factory.
1574 **592** 30p. blue, pale blue & blk 30 10

593 "The Adoration of the Kings" (stained-glass window, Holy Sacrament Basilica, Buenos Aires)

1977. Christmas.
1575 **593** 100p. multicoloured . . 75 20

595 World Cup Emblem

1978. World Cup Football Championship, Argentina.
1577 **595** 200p. green and blue . . 55 20

596 Rosario

1978. World Cup Football Championship (3rd issue). Match Sites. Multicoloured.
1578 50p. Type **596** 20 15
1579 100p. Cordoba 40 15
1580 150p. Mendoza 50 15
1581 200p. Mar del Plata 50 25
1582 300p. Buenos Aires . . . . 2·00 75

597 Children and Institute Emblem

1978. 50th Anniv of Inter-American Children's Institute.
1583 **597** 100p. multicoloured . . 40 15

598 "The Working Day"   600 Hooded Siskin
(B. Quinquela Martin)

1978. Argentine Art. Multicoloured.
1584 100p. Type **598** 65 15
1585 100p. "Bust of an Unknown Woman" (Orlando Pierri) 2·00 75

599 Players from Argentina, Hungary, France and Italy (Group One)

1978. World Cup Football Championship (4th issue).
1586 **599** 100p. multicoloured . . 35 10
1587 – 200p. multicoloured . . 40 15
1588 – 300p. multicoloured . . 65 20
1589 – 400p. multicoloured . . 1·00 30
DESIGNS: 200p. Group Two players; 300p. Group Three players; 400p. Group Four players.

1978. Inter-American Philatelic Exhibition. Mult.
1591 50p.+50p. Type **600** . . . 1·75 1·50
1592 100p.+100p. Double-collared seedeater . . . . . . 2·00 2·00
1593 150p.+150p. Saffron-cowled blackbird . . . . . 2·50 2·10
1594 200p.+200p. Vermilion flycatcher . . . . . . 2·75 2·40
1595 500p.+500p. Great kiskadee 7·00 5·75

601 Young Tree with Support

1978. Technical Co-operation among Developing Countries Conference, Buenos Aires.
1596 **601** 100p. multicoloured . . . 30 15

603 Bank Emblems of 1878 and 1978

1978. Centenary of Bank of Buenos Aires.
1598 **603** 100p. multicoloured . . . 30 15

604 General Manuel Savio and Steel Production

1978. 30th Death Anniv of General Manuel Savio (director of military manufacturing).
1599 **604** 100p. multicoloured . . . 30 15

605 San Martin   606 Numeral

1978. Birth Bicentenary of Gen. San Martin.
1600	605	2000p. green	. . . . .	3·25	30
1600a		10000p. blue	. . . . .	3·00	35

1978.
1601	606	150p. blue and light blue	40	20
1602		180p. blue and light blue	40	10
1603		200p. blue and light blue	30	15

607 Chessboard, Pawn and Queen   608 Argentine Flag supporting Globe

1978. 23rd Chess Olympiad, Buenos Aires.
1604	607	200p. multicoloured	. .	2·00	65

1978. 12th Int Cancer Congress, Buenos Aires.
1605	608	200p. multicoloured	. .	80	20

609 "Correct Franking"

1978. Postal Publicity.
1606	609	20p. blue	. . . .	15	10
1607		– 30p. green	. . . .	15	10
1608		– 50p. red	. . . .	25	10

DESIGN—VERT: 30p. "Collect postage stamps".
HORIZ: 50p. "Indicate the correct post code".

610 Push-pull Tug

1978. 20th Anniv of Argentine River Fleet. Mult.
1609		100p. Type 610	. . .	40	15
1610		200p. Tug "Legador"	. . .	90	25
1611		300p. Tug "Rio Parana Mini"	. . .	95	30
1612		400p. River passenger ship "Ciudad de Parana"	. .	1·25	25

611 Bahia Blanca and Arms

1978. 150th Anniv of Bahia Blanca.
1613	611	200p. multicoloured	. .	45	15

612 "To Spain" (Arturo Dresco)

1978. Visit of King and Queen of Spain.
1614	612	300p. multicoloured	. .	1·75	25

613 Stained-glass Window, San Isidro Cathedral, Buenos Aires

1978. Christmas.
1615	613	200p. multicoloured	. .	60	15

614 "Chacabuco Slope" (Pedro Subercaseaux)

1978. Birth Bicent of General Jose de San Martin.
1616		500p. Type 614	. . . .	1·25	35
1617		1000p. "The Embrace of Maipo" (Pedro Subercaseaux) (vert)	. . .	2·25	50

615 San Martin Stamp of 1877 and U.P.U. Emblem

1979. Cent of Argentine Membership of U.P.U.
1618	615	200p. blue, black & brn	35	15

616 Mariano Moreno (revolutionary)

1979. Celebrities.
1619	616	200p. yellow, blk & red	45	15
1620		– 200p. blue, blk & dp bl	45	15

DESIGNS: No. 1620, Adolfo Alsina (statesman).

617 "Still Life" (Ernesto de la Carcova)

1979. Argentine Paintings. Multicoloured.
1621		200p. Type 617	. . . .	60	15
1622		300p. "The Washer-woman" (F. Brughetti)	. . . .	80	20

618 Balcarce Antenna and Radio Waves

1979. 3rd Inter-American Telecommunications Conference.
1623	618	200p. multicoloured	. .	35	15

619 Rosette   620 Olives

1979.
1624	619	240p. blue and brown	35	10
1625		260p. blue and black	35	10
1626		290p. blue and brown	40	10
1627		310p. blue and purple	45	10
1628		350p. blue and red	60	15
1629		450p. blue and ultram	55	15
1630		600p. blue and green	50	20
1631		700p. blue and black	50	20
1632		800p. blue and orange	45	10
1632a		1100p. blue and grey	65	10
1632b		1500p. blue and black	40	10
1632c		1700p. blue and green	50	10

1979. Agricultural Products. Multicoloured.
1633		100p. Type 620	. . . .	25	10
1634		200p. Tea	. . . . .	50	25
1635		300p. Sorghum	. . . .	65	40
1636		400p. Flax	. . . . .	1·00	55

621 "75" and Symbol

1979. 75th Anniv of Argentine Automobile Club.
1637	621	200p. multicoloured	. .	35	15

622 Laurel Leaves and Army Emblem

1979. Naming of Village Subteniente Berdina, Tucuman.
1638	622	200p. multicoloured	. .	30	15

623 Wheat Exchange and Emblem

1979. 125th Anniv of Wheat Exchange, Buenos Aires.
1639	623	200p. blue, gold & black	30	15

624 "Uruguay" (sail/steam gunboat)

1979. Navy Day.
1640	624	250p. multicoloured	. .	1·00	20

1979. Army Day. As T 390. Multicoloured.
1641		200p. Trooper of Mounted Chasseurs, 1817	. . . .	1·00	20

625 "Comodoro Rivadavia" (hydrographic survey ship)

1979. Naval Hydrographic Service.
1642	625	250p. multicoloured	. .	1·00	20

626 Tree and Man Symbol

1979. Ecology Day.
1643	626	250p. multicoloured	. .	55	15

627 SPAD XIII and Vicente Almandos

1979. Air Force Day.
1644	627	250p. multicoloured	. .	80	20

628 "Military Occupation of Rio Negro by Gen. Julio A. Roca's Expedition" (detail, J. M. Blanes)

1979. Centenary of Conquest of the Desert.
1645	628	250p. multicoloured	. .	70	20

629 Caravel "Magdalena"

1979. "Buenos Aires '80" International Stamp Exhibition. Multicoloured.
1646		400p.+400p. Type 629	. .	2·50	2·10
1647		500p.+500p. Three-masted sailing ship	. .	8·50	4·50
1648		600p.+600p. Corvette "Descubierta"	. .	8·00	6·75
1649		1500p.+1500p. Yacht "Fortuna"	. . . .	17·00	8·75

630 Rowland Hill   631 Francisco de Viedma y Narvaez Monument (A. Funes and J. Agosta)

1979. Death Centenary of Sir Rowland Hill.
1650	630	300p. black, grey & red	45	20

1979. Bicentenary of Founding of Viedma and Carmen de Patagones Towns.
1651	631	300p. multicoloured	. .	45	20

632 Pope Paul VI   633 Molinas Church

1979. Election of Pope John Paul I.
1652	632	500p. black	. . . . .	80	35
1653		– 500p. black	. . . . .	80	35

DESIGN: No. 1653, Pope John Paul I.

1979. Churches. Multicoloured.
1654		100p.+50p. Purmamarca Church	. . . .	30	15
1655		200p.+100p. Type 633	. .	45	20
1656		300p.+150p. Animana Church	. . . .	50	35
1657		400p.+200p. San Jose de Lules Church	. . . .	75	50

1979. 75th Anniv of Rosario Philatelic Society. No. 1545 optd **75 ANIV. SOCIEDAD FILATELICA DE ROSARIO**.
1658		200p. blue and black	. . .	70	20

635 Children's Faces, and Sun on Map of Argentina

1979. Resettlement Policy.
1659 **635** 300p. yellow, black & bl   50   20

636 Stained-glass Window, Salta Cathedral

1979. Christmas.
1660 **636** 300p. multicoloured   . .   55   20

637 Institute Emblem

1979. Centenary of Military Geographical Institute.
1661 **637** 300p. multicoloured   . .   70   20

638 General Mosconi and Oil Rig

1979. Birth Centenary of General Enrique Mosconi.
1662 **638** 1000p. blue and black   1·75   50

640 Rotary Emblem and Globe

1979. 75th Anniv of Rotary International.
1664 **640** 300p. multicoloured   . .   1·00   25

641 Girl with Ruddy Ground Doves   642 Guillermo Brown

1979. International Year of the Child.
1665 **641** 500p. brown, blue & blk   90   40
1666   – 1000p. multicoloured   1·25   30
DESIGN: 1000p. "Family".

1980.
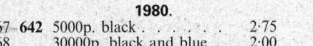
1667 **642** 5000p. black   . . . . . .   2·75   20
1668   – 30000p. black and blue   2·00   50

643 I.T.U. Emblem and Microphone

1980. Regional Administrative Conference on Broadcasting, Buenos Aires.
1669 **643** 500p. blue, gold & ultram   80   30

644 Organization of American States Emblem

1980. Day of the Americas.
1670 **644** 500p. multicoloured   . .   50   20

645 Angel

1980. Centenary of Argentinian Red Cross.
1671 **645** 500p. multicoloured   . .   60   20

646 Salto Grande Hydro-electric Complex

1980. National Development Projects. Mult.
1672   300p. Type **646**   90   35
1673   300p. Zarate-Brazo Largo bridge   90   35
1674   300p. Dish aerials, Balcarce   50   20

647 Hipolito Bouchard and Sail Frigate "La Argentina"

1980. Navy Day.
1675 **647** 500p. multicoloured   . .   1·25   30

648 "Villarino" and Woodcut of San Martin Theodore by Gericault

1980. Centenary of Return of General Jose de San Martin's Remains.
1676 **648** 500p. multicoloured   . .   1·25   30

649 "Gazeta de Buenos-Ayres" and Signature of Dr. Mariano Moreno (first editor)

1980. Journalists' Day.
1677 **649** 500p. multicoloured   . .   60   20

651 Soldier feeding Dove

1980. Army Day.
1679 **651** 500p. green, blk & gold   60   30

652 Lt. Gen. Aramburu

1980. 10th Death Anniv of Lt. Gen. Pedro Eugenio Aramburu.
1680 **652** 500p. yellow and black   50   20

653 Gen. Juan Gregorio de Las Heras

1980. National Heroes.
1681 **653** 500p. stone and black . .   60   20
1682   – 500p. yellow, blk & pur   60   20
1683   – 500p. mauve and black   60   20
DESIGNS: No. 1682, Bernardino Rivadavia; No. 1683, Brigadier-General Jose Matias Zapiola.

654 University of La Plata

1980. 75th Anniv of La Plata University.
1684 **654** 500p. multicoloured   . .   60   20

655 Major Francisco de Arteaga and Avro 504K

1980. Air Force Day.
1685 **655** 500p. multicoloured   . .   75   20

656 Flag and "Pencil" Figure   658 Congress Emblem

1980. National Census.
1686 **656** 500p. black and blue . .   1·25   20

1980. National Marian Congress, Mendoza.
1688 **658** 700p. multicoloured   . .   50   15

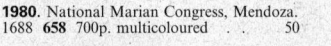

659 Heart pierced by Cigarette   661 Radio Antenna and Call Sign

1980. Anti-smoking Campaign.
1689 **659** 700p. multicoloured   . .   60   20

1980. Radio Amateurs.
1691 **661** 700p. blue, black & green   50   15

662 Academy Emblem   663 Commemorative Medallion

1980. 50th Anniv of Technical Military Academy.
1692 **662** 700p. multicoloured . .   50   15

1980. Christmas. 150th Anniv of Appearance of Holy Virgin to St. Catherine Laboure.
1693 **663** 700p. multicoloured . .   50   15

664 Plan of Lujan Cathedral and Outline of Virgin   665 Simon Bolivar

1980. Christmas. 350th Anniv of Appearance of Holy Virgin at Lujan.
1694 **664** 700p. green and brown   50   15

1980. 150th Death Anniv of Simon Bolivar.
1695 **665** 700p. multicoloured   . .   50   15

666 Football and Flags of Competing Nations

1981. Gold Cup Football Competition, Montevideo.
1696 **666** 1000p. multicoloured . .   85   20

667 "Lujan Landscape" (Marcos Tiglio)

1981. Paintings. Multicoloured.
1697   1000p. Type **667**   70   20
1698   1000p. "Effect of Light on Lines" (Miguel Angel Vidal)   70   20

668 Congress Emblem

1981. International Congress on Medicine and Sciences applied to Sport.
1699 **668** 1000p. blue, brown & blk   45   15

669 Esperanza Army Base, Antarctica

1981. 20th Anniv of Antarctic Treaty. Mult.
1700 1000p. Type **669** . . . . . 1·50 50
1701 2000p. Map of
        Vicecomodoro Marambio
        Island and De Havilland
        Twin Otter airplane
        (59½ × 25 mm) . . . . . 2·00 80
1702 2000p. Icebreaker
        "Almirante Irizar" . . . 3·00 95

670 Military Club

1981. Centenary of Military Club. Multicoloured.
1703 1000p. Type **670** 60 20
1704 2000p. Blunderbusses . . . 80 25

671 "Minuet" (Carlos E. Pellegrini)

1981. "Espamer '81" International Stamp Exhibition,
Buenos Aires (1st issue).
1705 **671** 500p.+250p. purple, gold
        and brown 60 45
1706 – 700p.+350p. green, gold
        and brown 80 70
1707 – 800p.+400p. brown, gold
        and deep brown . . . 1·00 80
1708 – 1000p.+500p. mult . . . 1·25 1·10
DESIGNS: 700p. "La Media Cana" (Carlos Morel);
800p. "Cielito" (Carlos E. Pellegrini); 1000p. "El
Gato" (Juan Leon Palliere).
See also Nos. 1719 and 1720/1.

672 Juan A. Alvarez de
Arenales

1981. Celebrities' Anniversaries.
1709 **672** 1000p. black, yell & brn 70 20
1710 – 1000p. blk, pink & lilac 70 20
1711 – 1000p. black, pale green
        and green 70 20
DESIGNS: No. 1709, Type **672** (patriot, 150th death
anniv); No. 1710, Felix G. Frias (writer and politician,
death centenary); No. 1711, Jose E. Uriburu
(statesman, 150th birth centenary).

1981. 50th Anniv of Bahia Blanca Philatelic and
Numismatic Society. No. 1553 optd **50 ANIV DE
LA ASOCIACION FILATELICA Y
NUMISMATICA DE BAHIA BLANCA.**
1712 1000p. black and yellow . . 1·60 65

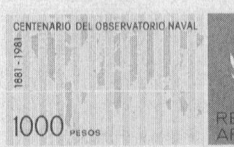 

674 World Map divided into Time Zones and Sun

1981. Centenary of Naval Observatory.
1713 **674** 1000p. multicoloured . . 55 30

675 "St. Cayetano" (detail, stained-
glass window, San Cayetano Basilica)

1981. 500th Death Anniv of St. Cayetano (founder
of Teatino Order).
1714 **675** 1000p. multicoloured . . 45 20

676 Pablo Castaibert and Bleriot XI

1981. Air Force Day.
1715 **676** 1000p. multicoloured . . 75 20

677 First Argentine Blast Furnace,
Sierra de Palpala

1981. 22nd Latin American Steel-makers Congress,
Buenos Aires.
1716 **677** 1000p. multicoloured . . 45 20

678 Emblem of National   **679** Sperm Whale
Directorate for Special   and Map of
Education   Argentina and
                                Antarctica

1981. International Year of Disabled People.
1717 **678** 1000p. multicoloured . . 50 20

1981. Campaign against Indiscriminate Whaling.
1718 **679** 1000p. multicoloured . . 2·25 25

680 "Espamer 81" Emblem and
15th-century Caravel

1981. "Espamer 81" International Stamp Exhibition,
Buenos Aires (2nd issue).
1719 **680** 1300p. pink, brn & blk 95 20

681 "San Martín at the   **682** Argentine Army
Battle of Bailen"   Emblem
(equestrian statuette)

1981. "Espamer 81" International Stamp Exhibition,
Buenos Aires (3rd issue).
1720 **681** 1000p. multicoloured . . 20 15
1721 – 1500p. multicoloured . . 60 15

1981. Argentine Army. 175th Anniv of Infantry
Regiment No. 1 "Patricios". Multicoloured.
1722 1500p. Type **682** 55 20
1723 1500p. "Patricios" badge . . 55 20

1981. Philatelic Services Course, Postal Union of the
Americas and Spain Technical Training School,
Buenos Aires. Optd **CURSO SUPERIOR DE
ORGANIZACION DE SERVICIOS
FILATELICOS-UPAE-BUENOS AIRES-1981.**
1724 680 1300p. pink, brn & blk . 1·10 20

685 "Patacon" (one peso piece)

1981. Centenary of First Argentine Coins.
1726 **685** 2000p. silver, blk & pur 55 15
1727 – 3000p. gold, black & bl 70 20
DESIGN: 3000p. Argentine oro (five pesos piece).

686 Stained-glass Window,
Church of Our Lady of Mercy,
Tucuman

1981. Christmas.
1728 **686** 1500p. multicoloured . . 75 20

687 "Drive Carefully"   **688** Francisco Luis
                              Bernardez

1981. Road Safety. Multicoloured.
1729 1000p. "Observe traffic
        lights" . . . . 1·40 20
1730 2000p. Type **687** 90 25
1731 3000p. Zebra Crossing
        ("Cross at the white
        lines") (horiz) . . . . 1·00 35
1732 4000p. Headlights ("Don't
        dazzle") (horiz) . . . 1·25 45

1982. Authors. Multicoloured.
1733 1000p. Type **688** . . . . . 1·25 20
1734 2000p. Lucio V. Mansilla . 85 25
1735 3000p. Conrado Nale Roxlo . 1·10 35
1736 4000p. Victoria Ocampo . . 1·25 45

689 Emblem   **690** Dr. Robert Koch

1982. 22nd American Air Force Commanders
Conference, Buenos Aires.
1737 **689** 2000p. multicoloured . . 85 25

1982. 25th World Tuberculosis Conf, Buenos Aires.
1738 **690** 2000p. brown, red & blk 60 25

691 Pre-Columbian Artwork and
Signature of Hernando de Lerma
(founder)

1982. 400th Anniv of Salta City.
1739 **691** 2000p. green, blk & gold 80 20

1982. Argentine Invasion of the Falkland Islands.
Optd **LAS MALVINAS SON ARGENTINAS**.
1741 619 1700p. blue and green . 60 20

693 "Poseidon with Trophies of War" (sculpture)
and Naval Centre Arms

1982. Centenary of Naval Centre.
1742 **693** 2000p. multicoloured . . 90 25

694 "Chorisia   **695** Juan C. Sanchez
speciosa"

1982. Flowers. Multicoloured.
1743 200p. "Zinnia peruviana" 10 10
1744 300p. "Ipomoea purpurea" 10 10
1745 400p. "Tillandsia aeranthos" 10 10
1746 500p. Type **694** 10 10
1747 800p. "Oncidium bifolium" . 10 10
1748 1000p. "Erythrina crista-
        galli" 10 10
1749 2000p. "Jacaranda
        mimosifolia" 15 10
1750 3000p. "Bauhinia
        candicans" 50 10
1751 5000p. "Tecoma stans" . . 60 10
1752 10000p. "Tabebuia ipe" . . 90 15
1753 20000p. "Passiflora
        coerulea" . . . . . 1·00 20
1754 30000p. "Aristolochia
        littoralis" . . . . . 1·25 30
1755 50000p. "Oxalis
        enneaphylla" . . . . . 2·40 40

1982. 10th Death Anniv of Lt. Gen. Juan C. Sanchez.
1761 **695** 5000p. multicoloured . . 80 25

696 Don Luis Verne (first
Commander)

1982. 153rd Anniv of Political and Military
Command for the Malvinas.
1762 **696** 5000p. black and brown 1·25 50
1763 – 5000p. light bl, blk & bl 90 35
DESIGN (82 × 28 mm): No. 1763, Map of the South
Atlantic Islands.

697 Pope John Paul II   **698** San Martin

1982. Papal Visit.
1764 **697** 5000p. multicoloured . . 1·00 55

1982.
1765 **698** 50000p. brown and red 4·00 50

699 "The Organ Player"   **700** "Gen. de Sombras"
(detail, Aldo Severi)   (Sylvia Sieburger)

1982. Paintings. Multicoloured.
1766 2000p. Type **699** 65 20
1767 3000p. "Flowers" (Santiago
        Cogorno) 70 25

1982. "Argentine Philately". Tapestries. Mult.
1768 1000p.+500p. Type **700** . . . 20 15
1769 2000p.+1000p.
        "Interpretation of a
        Rectangle" (Silke Haupt) 30 20

1770 3000p.+1500p. "Canal"
      (detail, Beatriz Bongliani)
      (horiz) . . . . 1·10 40
1771 4000p.+2000p. "Pueblito de
      Tilcara" (Tana Sachs)
      (horiz) 75 55

701 Petrol Pump and   704 Map of Africa
    Sugar Cane   showing Namibia

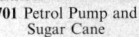

703 Belt Buckle with Argentine Scout
    Emblem

1982. Alconafta (petrol-alcohol mixture) Campaign.
1772 **701** 2000p. multicoloured . . 40 10

1982. 50th Anniv of Tucuman Philatelic Society.
No. 1751 optd **50 ANIVERSARIO SOCIEDAD
FILATELICA DE TUCUMAN.**
1773 5000p. multicoloured . . . 1·60 90

1982. 75th Anniv of Boy Scout Movement.
1774 **703** 5000p. multicoloured . . 1·00 25

1982. Namibia Day.
1775 **704** 5000p. multicoloured . . 55 15

705 Rio Tercero Nuclear Power
    Station

1982. Atomic Energy. Multicoloured.
1776 2000p. Type **705** 40 10
1777 2000p. Control room of Rio
      Tercero power station . . 40 10

706 Our Lady of Itati,   707 "Sidereal Tension"
    Corrientes   (M. A. Agatiello)

1982. Churches and Cathedrals of the North-east
Provinces.
1778 **706** 2000p. green and black 50 15
1779 –   3000p. grey and purple 60 15
1780 –   5000p. blue and purple 80 20
1781 –   10000p. brown and black 1·25 40
DESIGNS—VERT: 3000p. Resistencia Cathedral,
Chaco. HORIZ: 5000p. Formosa Cathedral; 10000p.
Ruins of San Ignacio, Misiones.

1982. Art. Multicoloured.
1782 2000p. Type **707** 60 20
1783 3000p. "Sugerencia II"
      (E. MacEntyre) 70 20
1784 5000p. "Storm" (Carlos
      Silva) . . . . 1·00 25

708 Games Emblem and Santa Fe
    Bridge

1982. 2nd "Southern Cross" Games, Rosario and
Santa Fe.
1785 **708** 2000p. blue and black 45 10

709 Volleyball

1982. 10th Men's Volleyball World Championship.
1786 **709** 2000p. multicoloured . . 30 10
1787 –   5000p. multicoloured . . 60 20

710 Road Signs

1982. 50th Anniv of National Roads Administration.
1788 **710** 5000p. multicoloured . . 60 20

711 Monument to the Army of the
    Andes

1982. Centenary of "Los Andes" Newspaper.
1789 **711** 5000p. multicoloured . . 50 20

712 La Plata Cathedral   714 Dr. Carlos Pellegrini
                             (founder) (after J.
                             Sorolla y Bastida)

713 First Oil Rig

1982. Centenary of La Plata. Multicoloured.
1790 5000p. Type **712** 50 20
1791 5000p. Municipal Palace . . 50 20

1982. 75th Anniv of Discovery of Oil in Comodoro
Rivadavia.
1793 **713** 5000p. multicoloured . . 50 25

1982. Cent of Buenos Aires Jockey Club. Mult.
1794 5000p. Jockey Club emblem 55 20
1795 5000p. Type **714** 55 20

715 Cross of St. Damian,   716 "St. Vincent de
    Assisi   Paul" (stained-glass
                                window, Our Lady of
                                the Miraculous Medal,
                                Buenos Aires)

1982. 800th Birth Anniv of St. Francis of Assisi.
1796 **715** 5000p. multicoloured . . 1·00 20

1982. Christmas.
1797 **716** 3000p. multicoloured . . 1·40 40

717 Pedro B. Palacios

1982. Authors. Each red and green.
1798 1000p. Type **717** 15 10
1799 2000p. Leopoldo Marechal 20 10
1800 3000p. Delfina Bunge de
      Galvez 25 10
1801 4000p. Manuel Galvez . . 50 15
1802 5000p. Evaristo Carriego 65 15

718 Argentine Flag and Map of South
    Atlantic Islands (½-size illustration)

1983. 1st Anniv of Argentine Invasion of Falkland
Islands.
1803 **718** 20000p. multicoloured 95 35

719 Sitram (automatic message
    transmission service) Emblem

1983. Information Technology. Multicoloured.
1804 5000p. Type **719** . . . . 1·00 20
1805 5000p. Red Arpac (data
      communications system)
      emblem . . . . 1·00 20

720 Naval League Emblem

1983. Navy Day. 50th Anniv of Naval League.
1806 **720** 5000p. multicoloured . . 50 15

721 Allegorical Figure (Victor
    Rebuffo)

1983. 25th Anniv of National Arts Fund.
1807 **721** 5000p. multicoloured . . 45 15

722 Golden Saloon

1983. 75th Anniv of Columbus Theatre, Buenos
Aires. Multicoloured.
1808 5000p. Type **722** 70 15
1809 10000p. Stage curtain . . 90 20

(Currency reform. 10000 (old) pesos = 1 (new)
peso.)

723 Marbles

1983. Argentine Philately. Children's Games (1st
series). Multicoloured.
1810 20c.+10c. Type **723** 15 10
1811 30c.+15c. Skipping 30 15
1812 50c.+25c. Hopscotch 40 25
1813 1p.+50c. Boy with kite . . 60 40
1814 2p.+1p. Boy with spinning
      top 70 55
See also Nos. 1870/4.

724 Maned Wolf

1983. Protected Animals (1st series). Mult.
1815 1p. Type **724** 35 10
1816 1p.50 Pampas deer 55 15
1817 2p. Giant anteater 60 15
1818 2p.50 Jaguar 75 25
See also Nos 1883/87.

1983. Flowers. As T **694** but inscr in new currency.
Multicoloured.
1819 5c. Type **694** 40 10
1820 10c. "Erythrina crista-galli" 10 10
1821 20c. "Jacaranda
      mimosifolia" 10 10
1822 30c. "Bauhinia candicans" 35 10
1823 40c. "Eichhornia crassipes" 10 10
1824 50c. "Tecoma stans" . . . 10 10
1825 1p. "Tabebuia ipe" 10 10
1826 1p.80 "Mutisia retusa" . . 15 10
1827 2p. "Passiflora coerulea" . 20 10
1828 3p. "Aristolochia littoralis" 30 10
1829 5p. "Oxalis enneaphylla" . 50 10
1830 10p. "Alstroemeria
      aurantiaca" 40 10
1831 20p. "Ipomoea purpurea" 40 10
1832 30p. "Embothrium
      coccineum" 40 15
1833 50p. "Tillandsia aeranthos" 45 15
1834 100p. "Oncidium bifolium" 65 15
1835 300p. "Cassia carnaval" . 1·60 45

725 "Founding of City of
    Catamarca" (detail, Luis
    Varela Lezana)

1983. 300th Anniv of San Fernando del Valle de
Catamarca.
1836 **725** 1p. multicoloured . . . 30 10

726 Brother Mamerto   727 Bolivar (painting
    Esquiu   by Herrera Toro after
                           engraving by C.
                           Turner)

1983. Death Centenary of Brother Mamerto Esquiu, Bishop of Cordoba.
1837 **726** 1p. black, red and grey   30   10

1983. Birth Bicentenary of Simon Bolivar.
1838 **727** 1p. multicoloured . . .   30   10
1839 – 2p. red and black . .   60   15
DESIGN: 2p. Bolivar (engraving by Kepper).

728 San Martin   **729** Gen. Toribio de Luzuriaga

1983.
1840 **728** 10p. green and black . .   2·50   45
1841 – 20p. blue and black . .   90   40
1842 **728** 50p. brown and blue . .   2·00   45
1843 – 200p. black and blue . .   1·25   45
1844 – 500p. blue and brown .   1·75   25
DESIGNS: 20p., 500p. Guillermo Brown; 200p. Manuel Belgrano.

1983. Birth Bicentenary (1982) of Gen. Toribio de Luzuriaga.
1845 **729** 1p. multicoloured . . .   30   10

730 Grand Bourg House, Buenos Aires

1983. 50th Anniv of Sanmartinian National Institute.
1846 **730** 2p. brown and black . .   55   15

731 Dove and Rotary Emblem

1983. Rotary International South American Regional Conference, Buenos Aires.
1847 **731** 1p. multicoloured . . .   55   20

732 Running Track and Games Emblem

1983. 9th Pan-American Games, Venezuela.
1848 **732** 1p. red, green & black   35   15
1849 – 2p. multicoloured . . .   60   25
DESIGN: 2p. Games emblem.

733 W.C.Y. Emblem   **734** "The Squash Peddler" (Antonio Berni)

1983. World Communications Year (1st issue).
1850 **733** 2p. multicoloured . . .   55   20
See also Nos. 1853/6 and 1857.

1983. Argentine Paintings. Multicoloured.
1851   1p. Type **734**   35   10
1852   2p. "Figure in Yellow" (Luis Seoane)   55   20

735 Ox-drawn Wagon   **736** "Central Post Office, Buenos Aires" (Lola Frexas)

1983. World Communications Year (2nd issue). Mail Transport. Multicoloured.
1853   1p. Type **735**   45   10
1854   2p. Horse-drawn mail cart   50   15
1855   4p. Locomotive "La Portena" . . . .   1·25   50
1856   5p. Tram . . . .   1·25   50

1983. World Communications Year (3rd issue).
1857 **736** 2p. multicoloured . . .   35   15

737 Rockhopper Penguin   **738** Coin of 1813

1983. Fauna and Pioneers of Southern Argentina. Multicoloured.
1858a   2p. Type **737**   40   15
1858b   2p. Wandering albatross   40   15
1858c   2p. Black-browed albatross   40   15
1858d   2p. Macaroni penguin .   40   15
1858e   2p. Luis Piedra Buena (after Juan R. Mezzadra)   40   15
1858f   2p. Carlos Maria Moyano (after Mezzadra) . . .   40   15
1858g   2p. Luis Py (after Mezzadra)   40   15
1858h   2p. Augusto Lasserre (after Horacio Alvarez Boero)   40   15
1858i   2p. Light-mantled sooty albatross   40   15
1858j   2p. Leopard seal   40   15
1858k   2p. Crabeater seal . . .   40   15
1858l   2p. Weddell seal   40   15

1983. Transfer of Presidency.
1859 **738** 2p. silver, black and blue   35   15

739 "Christmas Manger" (tapestry by Silke)

1983. Christmas. Multicoloured.
1860   2p. Type **739**   35   15
1861   3p. Stained-glass window, San Carlos de Bariloche Church   55   20

740 Printing Cylinder and Newspaper

1984. Centenary of "El Dia" Newspaper.
1862 **740** 4p. multicoloured . . .   40   15

741 Compass Rose

1984. "Espana 84" (Madrid) and "Argentina 85" (Buenos Aires) International Stamp Exhibitions (1st issue). Multicoloured.
1863   5p.+2p.50 Type **741** . . .   50   15

1864   5p.+2p.50 Arms of Spain and Argentine Republic   50   15
1865   5p.+2p.50 Arms of Christopher Columbus . .   50   15
1866   5p.+2p.50 "Nina" . . . . .   1·25   45
1867   5p.+2p.50 "Pinta" . . . .   1·25   45
1868   5p.+2p.50 "Santa Maria"   1·25   45
See also Nos. 1906/10, 1917/18 and 1920/4.

742 College

1984. Centenary of Alejandro Carbo Teacher Training College, Cordoba.
1869 **742** 10p. multicoloured . . .   40   15

1984. Argentine Philately. Children's Games (2nd series). As T **723**. Multicoloured.
1870   2p.+1p. Blind man's buff .   20   15
1871   3p.+1p.50 Girls throwing hoop   30   25
1872   4p.+2p. Leap frog   40   35
1873   5p.+2p.50 Boy rolling hoop   55   45
1874   6p.+3p. Ball and stick . .   60   55

743 Rowing and Basketball

1984. Olympic Games, Los Angeles. Mult.
1875   5p. Type **743**   25   15
1876   5p. Weightlifting and discus   25   15
1877   10p. Cycling and swimming   45   20
1878   10p. Pole vault and fencing   45   20

744 Wheat

1984. Food Supplies. Multicoloured.
1879   10p. Type **744** (18th F.A.O. Latin American Regional Conference, Buenos Aires)   40   20
1880   10p. Sunflowers (World Food Day)   40   20
1881   10p. Maize (3rd National Maize Congress, Pergamino)   40   20

745 Stock Exchange

1984. Centenary of Rosario Stock Exchange.
1882 **745** 10p. multicoloured . . .   40   20

1984. Protected Animals (2nd series). As T **724**. Multicoloured.
1883   20p. Brazilian merganser .   65   20
1884   20p. Black-fronted piping guan   65   20
1885   20p. Hooded grebes . . .   65   20
1886   20p. Vicunas   65   20
1887   20p. Chilean guemal . . .   65   20

746 Festival Emblem

1984. 1st Latin American Theatre Festival, Cordoba.
1888 **746** 20p. multicoloured . . .   25   15

747 "Apostles' Communion" (detail, Fra Angelico)

1984. 50th Anniv of Buenos Aires International Eucharist Congress.
1889 **747** 20p. multicoloured . . .   25   15

748 Antonio Oneto and Railway Station (Puerto Deseado)

1984. City Centenaries. Multicoloured.
1890   20p. Type **748**   75   25
1891   20p. 19th-century view and sail/steam corvette "Parana" (Ushuaia) . . .   1·25   35

749 Glacier

1984. World Heritage Site. Los Glaciares National Park. Multicoloured.
1892   20p. Glacier (different) . . .   30   10
1893   30p. Type **749**   40   15

1984. 50th Anniv of Buenos Aires Philatelic Centre. No. 1830 optd **1934–50° ANIVERSARIO-1984 CENTRO FILATELICO BUENOS-AIRES**.
1894   10p. multicoloured   20   15

751 "Jesus and the Star" (Diego Aguero)

1984. Christmas. Multicoloured.
1895   20p. Type **751**   30   15
1896   30p. "The Three Kings" (Leandro Ruiz)   40   15
1897   50p. "The Holy Family" (Maria Castillo) (vert) . .   60   20

752 "Sheds (La Boca)" (Marcos Borio)   **753** Angel J. Carranza (historian, 150th)

1984. Argentine Paintings. Multicoloured.
1898   20p. Type **752**   30   20
1899   20p. "View of the Zoo" (Fermin Eguia) (horiz) . .   35   20
1900   20p. "Floodlit Congress Building" (Francisco Travieso)   30   20

1985. Birth Anniversaries.
1901 **753** 10p. deep blue & blue   40   10
1902 – 20p. deep brown & brn   40   10
1903 – 30p. deep blue & blue   45   15
1904 – 40p. black and green .   70   15
DESIGNS: 20p. Estanislao del Campo (poet, 150th); 30p. Jose Hernandez (journalist, 150th); 40p. Vicente Lopez y Planes (President of Argentine Confederation 1827–28, birth bicent).

754 Guemes and "Infernal" (soldier)

1985. Birth Bicentenary of General Martin Miguel de Guemes (Independence hero).
1905 **754** 30p. multicoloured . . . 30 15

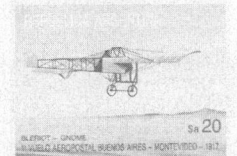

755 Teodoro Fels's Bleriot XI Gnome

1985. "Argentina '85" International Stamp Exhibition, Buenos Aires (2nd issue). First Airmail Flights. Multicoloured.
1906 20p. Type **755** (Buenos Aires–Montevideo, 1917) 30 10
1907 40p. Junkers F-13L (Cordoba–Villa Dolores, 1925) 50 15
1908 60p. Saint-Exupery's Latecoere 25 (first Bahia Blanca-Comodoro Rivadavia, 1929) 75 20
1909 80p. "Graf Zeppelin" airship (Argentina-Germany, 1934) 1·10 45
1910 100p. Consolidated PBY-5A Catalina amphibian (to Argentine Antarctic, 1952) 1·25 60

756 Central Bank

1985. 50th Anniv of Central Bank, Buenos Aires.
1911 **756** 80p. multicoloured . . . 40 20

757 Jose A. Ferreyra and "Munequitas Portenas"

1985. Argentine Film Directors. Multicoloured.
1912 100p. Type **757** 45 25
1913 100p. Leopoldo Torre Nilsson and "Martin Fierro" 45 25

758 "Carlos Gardel" (Hermenegildo Sabat)

1985. 50th Death Anniv of Carlos Gardel (entertainer). Multicoloured.
1914 200p. Type **758** 65 25
1915 200p. "Carlos Gardel" (Carlos Alonso) 65 25
1916 200p. "Carlos Gardel" (Aldo Severi and Martiniano Arce) 65 25

759 "The Arrival" (Pedro Figari)

1985. "Argentina '85" International Stamp Exhibition (3rd issue). Multicoloured.
1917 20c. Type **759** 65 25
1918 30c. "Mail Coach Square" (detail, Cesareo B. de Quiros) 75 25

760 Cover of 1917 Teodoro Fels Flight

1985. "Argentina '85" International Stamp Exhibition (4th issue). Multicoloured.
1920 10c. Type **760** 40 15
1921 10c. Cover of 1925 Cordoba–Villa Dolores flight 40 15
1922 10c. Cover of 1929 Saint-Exupery flight 40 15
1923 10c. Cover of 1934 "Graf Zeppelin" flight 40 15
1924 10c. Cover of 1952 Antarctic flight 40 15

1985. Flowers. As T **694** but with currency expressed as "A". Multicoloured.
1930 ¼c. "Oxalis enneaphylla" 40 10
1931 1c. "Alstroemeria aurantiaca" 10 10
1932 2c. "Ipomoea purpurea" 10 10
1933 3c. "Embothrium coccineum" 10 10
1934a 5c. "Tillandsia aeranthos" 10 10
1927 8½c. "Erythrina crista-galli" 25 10
1935a 10c. "Oncidium bifolium" 40 10
1936a 20c. "Chorisia speciosa" 35 10
1937 30c. "Cassia carnaval" 40 10
1938 50c. "Zinnnia peruviana" 65 10
1941 1a. "Begonia micranthera var. Hieronymi" 80 10
1941a 2a. "Bauhinia candicans" 10 10
1942 5a. "Gymnocalyciun bruchii" 10 10
1942a 10a. "Eichhornia crassipes" 10 10
1942b 20a. "Mutisia retusa" 10 10
1942c 50a. Passion flower 10 10
1943 100a. "Alstroemeria aurantiaca" 10 10
1943a 300a. "Ipomoea purpurea" 10 10
1943b 500a. "Embothrium coccineum" 10 10
1943c 1000a. "Aristolochia littoralis" 20 10
1943d 5000a. "Erythrina crista-galli" 1·25 10
1943e 10000a. "Jacaranda mimosifolia" 4·00 55
No. 1927 is 15 × 23 mm, the remainder 22 × 32 mm.

761 "Woman with Bird" (Juan del Prete)   **762** Musical Bow

1985. Argentine Paintings. Multicoloured.
1944 20c. Type **761** 75 30
1945 30c. "Illuminated Fruits" (Fortunato Lacamera) . . 75 30

1985. Traditional Musical Instruments. Mult.
1946 20c. Type **762** 60 20
1947 20c. Long flute with drum accompaniment 60 20
1948 20c. Frame drum 60 20
1949 20c. Pan's flute 60 20
1950 20c. Jew's harp 60 20

763 Juan Bautista Alberdi (writer)

1985. Anniversaries.
1951 10c. Type **763** (death centenary (1984)) 25 15
1952 20c. Nicolas Avellaneda (President 1874–80, death centenary) 50 25
1953 30c. Brother Luis Beltran (Independence hero, birth bicentenary (1984)) 75 25
1954 40c. Ricardo Levene (historian) (birth centenary) 90 25

764 Roller Skaters

1985. International Youth Year.
1955 **764** 20c. black and blue . . . 60 20
1956 – 30c. multicoloured . . . 65 30
DESIGN: 30c. "Disappointment".

765 "Rothschildia jacobaeae"

1985. Argentine Philately. Butterflies.
1958 5c.+2c. Type **765** 35 10
1959 10c.+5c. "Heliconius erato phyllis" 55 20
1960 20c.+10c. "Precis evarete hilaris" . . . . 1·10 40
1961 25c.+13c. "Cyanopepla pretiosa" . . . . 1·40 55
1962 40c.+20c. "Papilio androgeus" . . . . 1·75 90

766 Forclaz Windmill (Entre Rios)   **768** "Birth of Our Lord" (Carlos Cortes)

767 Hand holding White Stick

1985. Tourism. Argentine Provinces. Mult.
1963 10c. Type **766** 40 10
1964 10c. Sierra de la Ventana (Buenos Aires) 40 10
1965 10c. Potrero de los Funes artificial lake (San Luis) 40 10
1966 10c. Church belfry (North-west Argentina) 40 10
1967 10c. Magellanic penguins, Punta Tombo (Chubut) 1·00 30
1968 10c. Sea of Mirrors (Cordoba) 40 10

1985. National Campaign for the Prevention of Blindness.
1969 **767** 10c. multicoloured . . 40 10

1985. Christmas. Multicoloured.
1970 10c. Type **768** 30 15
1971 20c. "Christmas" (Hector Viola) 80 25

769 Rio Gallegos Cathedral

1985. Centenary of Rio Gallegos.
1972 **769** 10c. multicoloured . . . 50 10

770 Grape Harvesting

1986. 50th Anniv of Grape Harvest Nat Festival.
1973 **770** 10c. multicoloured . . . 40 10

771 House of Valentin Alsina (Italian Period)

1986. Buenos Aires Architecture, 1880–1930. Mult.
1974 20c. Type **771** 55 20
1975 20c. 1441 Calle Cerrito (French period) 55 20
1976 20c. Customs House (Academic period) (horiz) 55 20
1977 20c. House, Avenido de Mayo (Art Nouveau) . . 55 20
1978 20c. Isaac Fernandez Blanco Museum (National Restoration period) (horiz) 55 20

772 Jubany Base   **773** "Foundation of Nereid" (detail, Lola Mora)

1986. Argentine Antarctic Research. Mult.
1979 10c. Type **772** 60 20
1980 10c. Kerguelen fur seal . . . 60 20
1981 10c. Southern sealion . . . 60 20
1982 10c. General Belgrano Base . 60 20
1983 10c. Pintado petrel . . . . 1·00 40
1984 10c. Black-browed albatross . 1·00 40
1985 10c. King penguin . . . . 1·00 40
1986 10c. Giant petrel . . . . 1·00 40
1987 10c. Hugo Alberto Acuna (explorer) 60 20
1988 10c. Magellanic penguin . . 1·00 40
1989 10c. Magellan snipe . . . 1·00 40
1990 10c. Capt. Augustin Servando del Castillo (explorer) 60 20

1986. Sculpture. Multicoloured.
1991 20c. Type **773** 85 25
1992 30c. "Work Song" (detail, Rogelio Yrurtia) . . . . 1·25 40

774 Dr. Alicia Moreau de Justo (suffragist, d. 1986)   **775** Dr. Francisco Narciso Laprida

1986. Anniversaries.
1993 **774** 10c. black, yellow & brn 30 10
1994 – 10c. black, turq & blue 30 10
1995 – 30c. black, red & mauve 65 30
DESIGNS: No. 1994, Dr. Emilio Ravignani (historian, birth centenary); 1995, Indira Gandhi (Prime Minister of India, 1st death anniv).

1986. Birth Bicentenaries of Independence Heroes. Each brown, yellow and black.
1996 20c. Type **775** 50 45
1997 20c. Brig. Gen. Estanislao Lopez 50 45
1998 20c. Gen. Francisco Ramirez 50 45

776 Namuncura   **777** Drawing by Nazarena Pastor

1986. Birth Centenary of Ceferino Namuncura (first Indian seminary student).
1999 **776** 20c. multicoloured . . . 25 15

1986. Argentine Philately. Children's Drawings. Multicoloured.
2000　5c.+2c. Type **777** 15 15
2001　10c.+5c. Girl and boy holding flowers and balloon (Tatiana Valleistein) (horiz) 20 20
2002　20c.+10c. Boy and girl (Juan Manel Flores) 70 70
2003　25c.+13c. Town and waterfront (Marcelo E. Pezzuto) (horiz) 85 85
2004　40c.+20c. Village (Esteban Diehl) (horiz) . . . . . 1·00 1·00

1986. No. 1825 surch A0,10.
2005　10c. on 1p. "Tabebuia ipe" 65 30

779 Argentine Team (value top left)

1986. Argentina, World Cup Football Championship (Mexico) Winners. Multicoloured.
2006　75c. Type **779** . . . . . 1·10 1·10
2007　75c. Argentine team (value top right) . . . . . . 1·10 1·10
2008　75c. Argentine team (value bottom left) . . . . . . 1·10 1·10
2009　75c. Argentine team (value bottom right) . . . . 1·10 1·10
2010　75c. Player shooting for goal 1·10 1·10
2011　75c. Player tackling and goalkeeper on ground . . . 1·10 1·10
2012　75c. Player number 11 . . . 1·10 1·10
2013　75c. Player number 7 . . . 1·10 1·10
2014　75c. Crowd and Argentina player . . . . 1·10 1·10
2015　75c. West German player . . 1·10 1·10
2016　75c. Goalkeeper on ground . 1·10 1·10
2017　75c. Footballers' legs . . . 1·10 1·10
2018　75c. Hand holding World Cup trophy . . . . . . 1·10 1·10
2019　75c. Raised arm and crowded stadium . . . . 1·10 1·10
2020　75c. People with flags and cameras . . . . 1·10 1·10
2021　75c. Player's body and crowd . . . . 1·10 1·10
Nos. 2006/13 were printed together se-tenant in a sheetlet of eight stamps arranged in two blocks, each block forming a composite design. Nos. 2014/21 were similarly arranged in a second sheetlet.

780 Municipal Building

1986. Centenary of San Francisco City.
2022 **780** 20c. multicoloured . . . 50 20

781 Old Railway Station

1986. Centenary of Trelew City.
2023 **781** 20c. multicoloured . . . 1·00 45

782 Emblem and Colours

1986. Mutualism Day.
2024 **782** 20c. multicoloured . . . 25 15

783 "Primitive Retable" (Aniko Szabo)

1986. Christmas. Multicoloured.
2025　20c. Type **783** 50 10
2026　30c. "Everybody's Tree" (Franca Delacqua) . . . 60 15

784 St. Rosa of Lima　**785** Municipal Building

1986. 400th Birth Anniv of St. Rosa de Lima.
2027 **784** 50c. multicoloured . . . 80 20

1986. Anniversaries. Multicoloured.
2028　20c. Type **785** (bicentenary of Rio Cuarto city) . . . 40 10
2029　20c. Palace of Justice, Cordoba (50th anniv) . . . 40 10

786 Marine Biology

1987. 25th Anniv of Antarctic Treaty. Mult.
2030　20c. Type **786** 80 20
2031　30c. Study of native birds . 1·75 30

787 Emblem

1987. Centenary of National Mortgage Bank.
2033 **787** 20c. yellow, brown & blk 20 15

788 Stylized Pine Trees

1987. Argentine Co-operative Movement.
2034 **788** 20c. multicoloured . . . 20 15

789 Pope

1987. 2nd Visit of Pope John Paul II.
2035 **789** 20c. blue and red . . . 40 10
2036　－ 80c. brown and green . . 1·00 55
DESIGN: 80c. Pope in robes with Crucifix.

790 Flag forming "PAZ" (peace)

1987. International Peace Year.
2038 **790** 20c. blue, dp blue & blk 45 15
2039　－ 30c. multicoloured 55 20
DESIGN: 30c. "Pigeon" (sculpture, Victor Kaniuka).

791 "Polo Players" (Alejandro Moy)　**792** "Supplicant" (Museum of Natural Sciences, La Plata)

1987. World Polo Championships, Palermo.
2040 **791** 20c. multicoloured . . . 80 15

1987. 14th International Museums Council General Conference, Buenos Aires. Multicoloured.
2041　25c. Conference emblem . . 45 15
2042　25c. Shield of Potosi (National History Museum, Buenos Aires) 45 15
2043　25c. Statue of St. Bartholomew (Enrique Larreta Spanish Art Museum, Buenos Aires) 45 15
2044　25c. Cudgel with animal design (Patagonia Museum, San Carlos de Bariloche) 45 15
2045　25c. Type **792** 45 15
2046　25c. Grate from Argentine Confederation House (Entre Rios Historical Museum, Parana) 45 15
2047　25c. Statue of St. Joseph (Northern Historical Museum, Salta) 45 15
2048　25c. Funeral urn (Provincial Archaeological Museum, Santiago del Estero) . . . 45 15

793 Pillar Box　**794** Spotted Metynis ("Metynnis maculatus")

1987. No value expressed. (a) Inscr "C" and "TARIFA INTERNA/HASTA 10 GRAMOS".
2049 **793** (18c.) red, black & yell . 1·25 15
(b) Inscr "C" and "TARIFA INTERNA/DE 11 A 20 GRAMOS".
2050 **793** (33c.) black, yell & grn . 1·60 15

1987. Argentine Philately. River Fishes. Mult.
2051　10c.+5c. Type **794** 35 10
2052　10c.+5c. Black-finned pearlfish ("Cynolebias nigripinnis") 35 10
2053　10c.+5c. Solar's leporinus ("Leporinus solarii") . . 35 10
2054　10c.+5c. Red-flanked bloodfin ("Aphyocharax rathbuni") 35 10
2055　10c.+5c. Bronze catfish ("Corydoras aeneus") . . 35 10
2056　10c.+5c. Giant hatchetfish ("Thoracocharax securis") 35 10
2057　10c.+5c. Black-striped pearlfish ("Cynolebias melanotaenia") 35 10
2058　10c.+5c. Chanchito cichlid ("Cichlasoma facetum") . 35 10
2059　20c.+10c. Silver tetra ("Tetragonopterus argente") 65 25
2060　20c.+10c. Buenos Aires tetra ("Hemigrammus caudovittatus") 65 25
2061　20c.+10c. Two-spotted astyanax ("Astyanax bimaculatus") 65 25
2062　20c.+10c. Black widow tetra ("Gymnocorymbus ternetzi") 65 25
2063　20c.+10c. Trahira ("Hoplias malabaricus") 65 25
2064　20c.+10c. Blue-finned tetra ("Aphyocharax rubripinnis") 65 25
2065　20c.+10c. Agassiz's dwarf cichlid ("Apistogramma agassizi") 65 25
2066　20c.+10c. Fanning pyrrhulina ("Pyrrhulina rachoviana") 65 25

796 Jorge Luis Borges (writer)

1987. Anniversaries. Multicoloured.
2068　20c. Type **796** (1st death anniv) 25 10
2069　30c. Armando Discepolo, (dramatist and theatre director, birth cent) . . . 40 15
2070　50c. Dr Carlos Alberto Pueyrredon (historian, birth centenary) 65 20

797 Drawing by Leonardo da Vinci

1987. "The Post, a Medium for Communication and Prevention of Addictions".
2071 **797** 30c. multicoloured . . . 40 15

798 "The Sower" (Julio Vanzo)

1987. 75th Anniv of Argentine Farmers' Union.
2072 **798** 30c. multicoloured . . . 40 15

799 Basketball　**800** Col. Maj. Ignacio Alvarez Thomas

1987. 10th Pan-American Games, Indianapolis. Multicoloured.
2073　20c. Type **799** 40 10
2074　30c. Rowing 45 15
2075　50c. Dinghies 65 15

1987. Anniversaries. Multicoloured.
2076　25c. Type **800** (birth bicent) 35 10
2077　25c. Col. Manuel Dorrego (birth bicentenary) 35 10
2078　50c. 18th-century Spanish map of Falkland Islands (death bicentenary of Jacinto de Altolaguirre, governor of Islands) (horiz) 60 20
2079　50c. "Signing the Accord" (Rafael del Villar) (50th anniv of House of Accord Museum, San Nicolas) (horiz) 60 20

801 Children as Nurse and Mother

1987. U.N.I.C.E.F. Child Vaccination Campaign.
2080 **801** 30c. multicoloured . . . 40 15

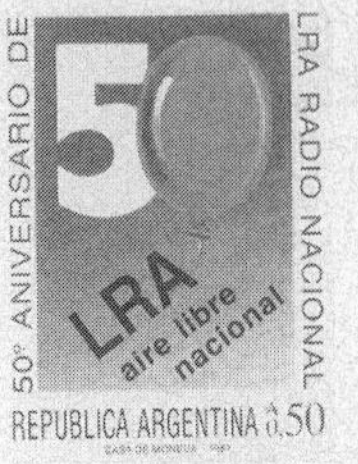

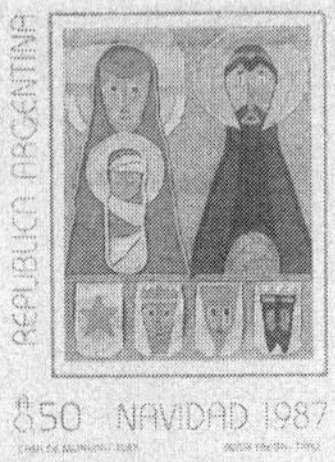

802 Balloon **803** "Nativity" (tapestry, Alisia Frega)

1987. Anniversaries. Multicoloured.

2081 50c. Type **802** (50th anniv of LRA National Radio) . . 40 20
2082 50c. Celendonio Galvan Moreno (first editor) (50th anniv of "Postas Argentinas" magazine) . . 40 20
2083 1a. Dr. Jose Marco del Pont (founder) (centenary of Argentine Philatelic Society) 60 25

1987. Christmas. Multicoloured.

2084 50c. Type **803** 35 25
2085 1a. Doves and flowers (tapestry, Silvina Trigos) 45 25

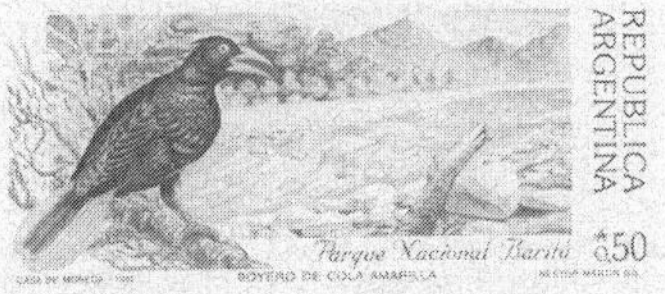

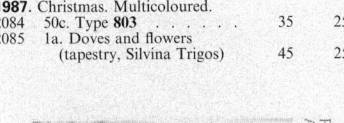

804 Crested Oropendola, Baritu National Park

1987. National Parks (1st series). Multicoloured.

2086 50c. Type **804** . . . . . . 1·00 40
2087 50c. Otter, Nahuel Huapi National Park 65 30
2088 50c. Night monkey, Rio Pilcomayo National Park 65 30
2089 50c. Kelp goose, Tierra del Fuego National Park . . 1·00 40
2090 50c. Alligator, Iguazu National Park 65 30

See also Nos. 2150/4, 2222/6 and 2295/9.

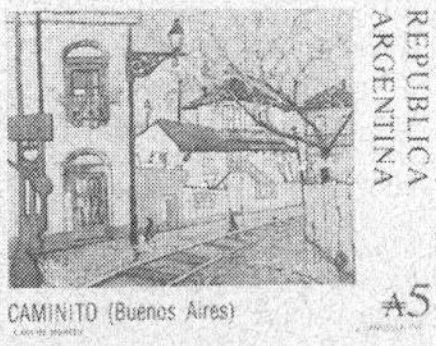

805 "Caminito" (Jose Canella)

1988. Historical and Tourist Sites. Multicoloured.

2090a 3a. "Purmamarca" (Nestor Martin) (33 × 22 mm) . . 60 20
2091 5a. Type **805** . . . . . . 1·75 30
2092 10a. "Old Almacen" (Jose Canella) (A) . . . . . . 3·25 1·50
2092a 10a. "Old Almacen" (Jose Canella) (B) . . . . . . 1·00 45
2095 20a. "Ushuaia" (Nestor Martin) (vert) . . . . . 2·75 1·10
2099 50a. Type **805** 75 10

10a. A. Inscr "Viejo Almacen". B. Inscr "El Viejo Almacen".

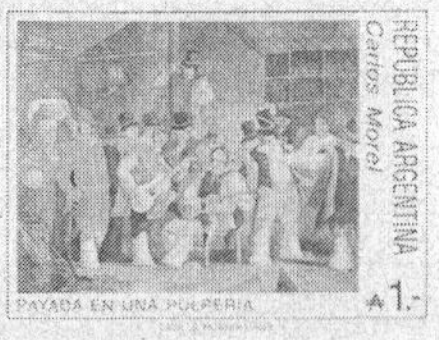

806 "Minstrel singing in a Grocer's Shop" (Carlos Morel)

1988. Argentine Paintings. Multicoloured.

2105 1a. Type **806** 50 15
2106 1a. "Curuzu" (detail, Candido Lopez) 50 15

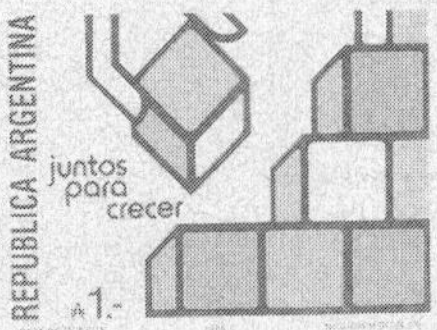

807 Hand arranging Coloured Cubes

1988. Argentine–Brazil Economic Co-operation.

2107 **807** 1a. multicoloured . . . 45 15

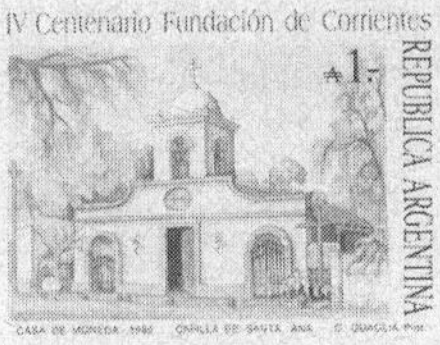

808 St. Anne's Chapel, Corrientes

1988. 400th Annivs of Corrientes and Alta Gracia. Multicoloured.

2108 1a. Type **808** 45 15
2109 1a. Alta Gracia church . . . 45 15

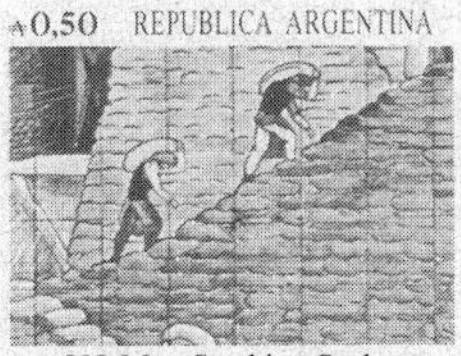

809 Men Stacking Sacks

1988. Labour Day. Details of mural "Cereals" (Nueve de Julio station, Buenos Aires underground railway). Multicoloured.

2110 50c. Type **809** 70 70
2111 50c. Sacks 70 70
2112 50c. Men unloading lorry 70 70
2113 50c. Horse and cart 70 70

Nos. 2110/13 were printed together, se-tenant, forming a composite design.

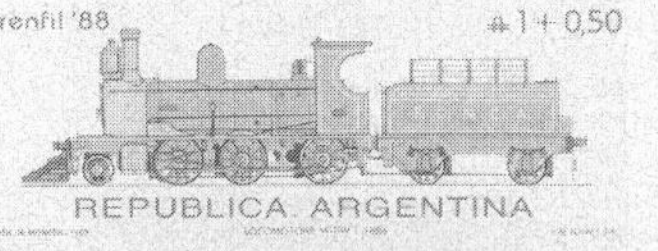

810 Steam Locomotive "Yatay" and Tender, 1888 (½-size illustration)

1988. "Prenfil '88" Philatelic Literature Exhibition, Buenos Aires (1st issue). Railways. Multicoloured.

2114 1a.+50c. Type **810** 35 35
2115 1a.+50c. Electric passenger coach, 1914 . . . . . . 35 35
2116 1a.+50c. Type B-15 locomotive and tender, 1942 35 35
2117 1a.+50c. Type GT-22 diesel locomotive, 1988 . . . . 35 35

See also Nos. 2134/7.

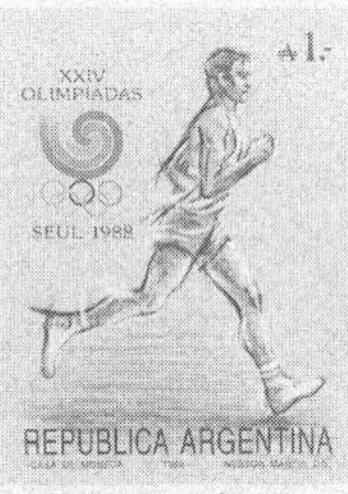

811 Running

1988. Olympic Games, Seoul. Multicoloured.

2118 1a. Type **811** 35 10
2119 2a. Football 45 15
2120 3a. Hockey 55 20
2121 4a. Tennis 65 35

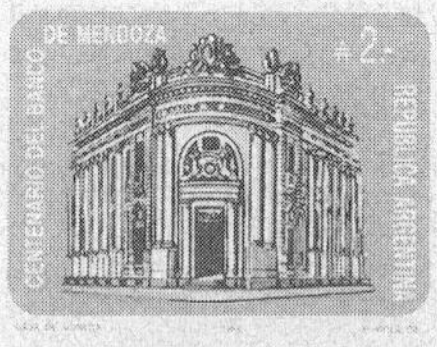

812 Bank Facade

1988. Centenary of Bank of Mendoza.

2122 **812** 2a. multicoloured . . . 20 15

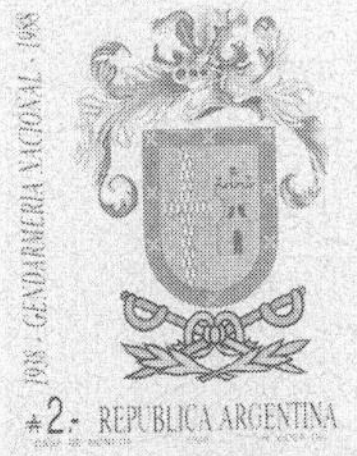

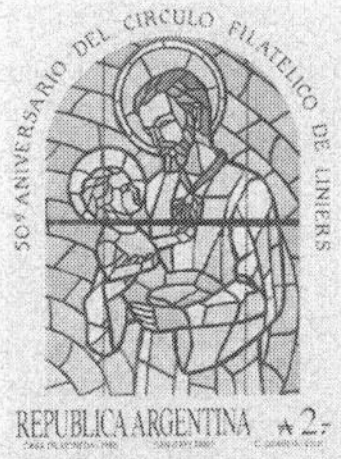

813 Arms of Guemes and National Guard Emblem **814** "St. Cayetano (patron saint of workers)" (C. Quaglia)

1988. 50th Anniv of National Guard.

2123 **813** 2a. multicoloured . . . 20 15

1988. Philatelic Anniversaries and Events. Mult.

2124 2a. Type **814** (50th anniv of Liniers (Buenos Aires) Philatelic Circle) 45 15
2125 3a. "Our Lady of Carmen (patron saint of Cuyo)" (window, Carlos Quaglia) (50th anniv of West Argentina Philatelic Society) 60 20

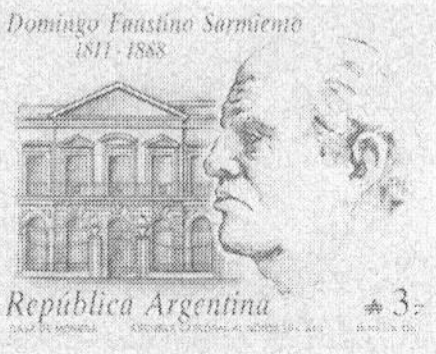

815 Sarmiento (after Mario Chierico) and Cathedral of the North School

1988. Death Centenary of Domingo Faustino Sarmiento (President, 1868–74).

2127 **815** 3a. multicoloured . . . 35 20

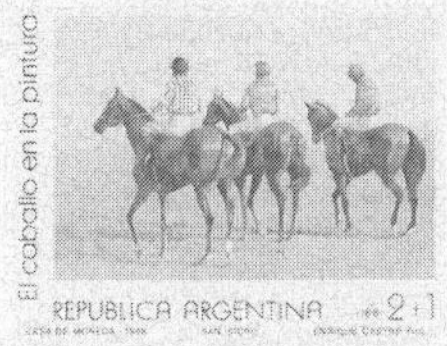

816 "San Isidro" (Enrique Castro)

1988. Horse Paintings. Multicoloured.

2128 2a.+1a. Type **816** 60 60
2129 2a.+1a. "Waiting" (Gustavo Solari) 60 60
2130 2a.+1a. "Beside the Pond" (F. Romero Carranza) . . 60 60
2131 2a.+1a. "Mare and Colt" (Enrique Castro) 60 60
2132 2a.+1a. "Under the Tail" (Enrique Castro) 60 60

1988. 21st International Urological Society Congress. No. 2091 optd **XXI CONGRESO DE LA SOCIEDAD INTERNACIONAL DE UROLOGIA SIU 88**.

2133 **805** 5a. multicoloured . . . 2·00 1·50

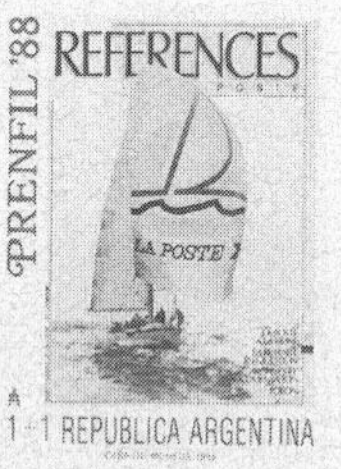

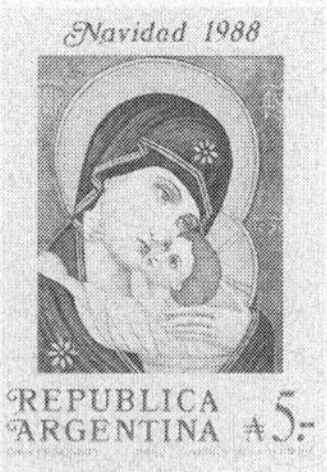

818 Cover of "References de la Poste" **821** "Virgin of Tenderness"

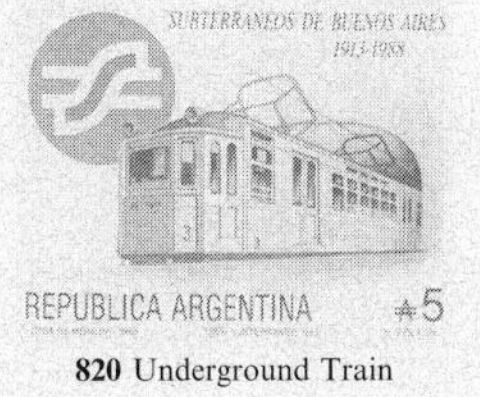

820 Underground Train

1988. "Prenfil '88" Philatelic Literature Exhibition, Buenos Aires (2nd issue). Designs showing magazine covers. Multicoloured.

2134 1a.+1a. Type **818** 60 30
2135 1a.+1a. "Cronaca Filatelica" 55 20
2136 1a.+1a. "Co Fi" 75 35
2137 2a.+2a. "Postas Argentinas" 55 20

1988. 75th Anniv of Buenos Aires Underground Railway.

2139 **820** 5a. multicoloured . . . 1·25 75

1988. Christmas. Virgins in Ucrania Cathedral, Buenos Aires. Multicoloured.

2140 5a. Type **821** 60 40
2141 5a. "Virgin of Protection" 60 40

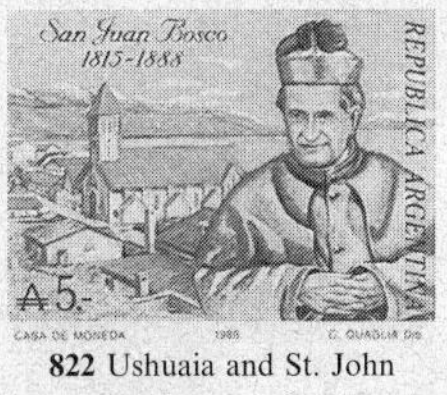

822 Ushuaia and St. John

1989. Death Centenary (1988) of St. John Bosco (founder of Salesian Brothers).

2142 **822** 5a. multicoloured . . . 35 10

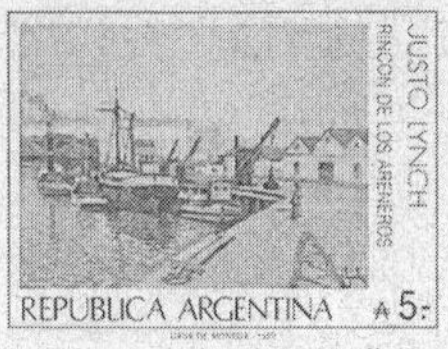

823 "Rincon de los Areneros" (Justo Lynch)

1989. Paintings. Multicoloured.

2143 5a. Type **823** 35 10
2144 5a. "Blancos" (Fernando Fader) 35 10

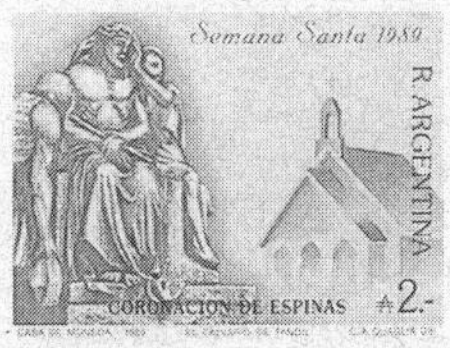

824 "Crowning with Thorns" and Church of Our Lady of Carmen, Tandil

1989. Holy Week. Multicoloured.

2145 2a. Type **824** 15 10
2146 2a. "Jesus of Nazareth" and Buenos Aires Cathedral 15 10
2147 3a. "Our Lady of Sorrows" and Humahuaca Church, Jujuy 15 10
2148 3a. "Jesus Meets His Mother" (statue) and La Quebrada Church, San Luis 15 10

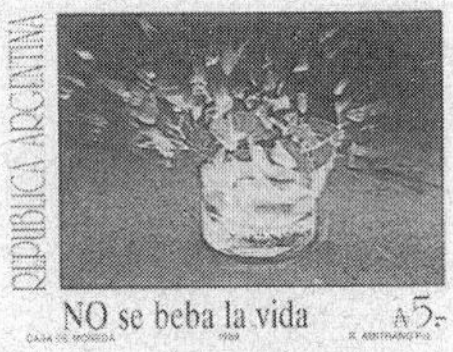

825 Shattering Drinking Glass

1989. Anti-alcoholism Campaign.

2149 **825** 5a. multicoloured . . . 25 10

1989. National Parks (2nd series). As T **804**. Mult.

2150 5a. Crested gallito ("Gallito Capeton"), Lihue Calel National Park 75 20
2151 5a. Lizard, El Palmar National Park 50 20
2152 5a. Tapirs, Calilegua National Park 60 20
2153 5a. Howler monkey, Chaco National Park 65 20
2154 5a. Magellanic woodpecker ("Carpintero Negro Patagonico"), Los Glaciares National Park 75 20

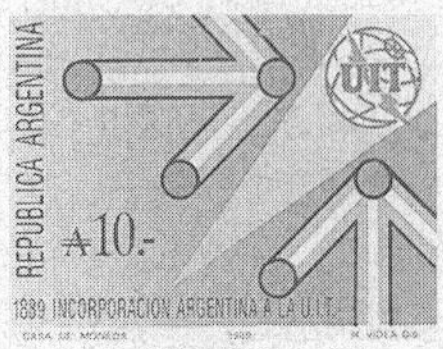

826 Emblem

1989. Cent of Argentine Membership of I.T.U.

2155 **826** 10a. multicoloured . . . 40 10

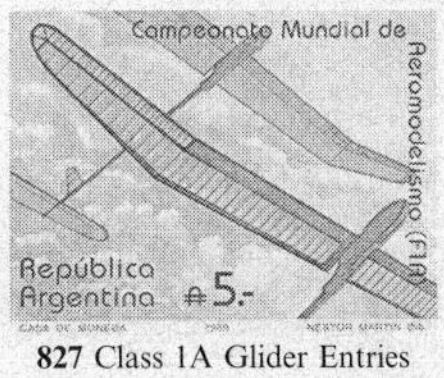

827 Class 1A Glider Entries

1989. World Model Airplane Championships, La Cruz-Embals-Cordoba. Multicoloured.

2156 5a. Type **827** 35 10
2157 5a. Class 1B rubber-powered entries 35 10
2158 10a. Class 1C petrol-engined entries 35 10

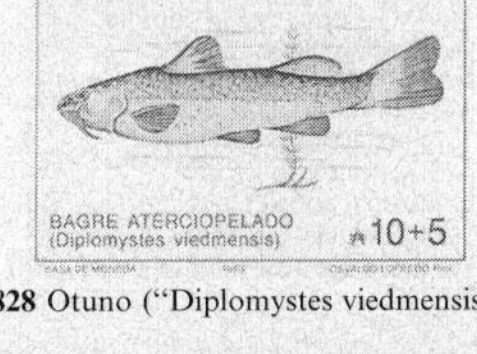

828 Otuno ("Diplomystes viedmensis")

1989. Argentine Philately. Fishes. Multicoloured.
2159   10a.+5a. Type **828**   30   25
2160   10a.+5a. Striped galaxiid
     ("Haplochiton taeniatus")   30   25
2161   10a.+5a. Creole perch
     ("Jenyns percichthys
     tucha")   30   25
2162   10a.+5a. River Plate
     galaxiid ("Galaxias
     platei")   30   25
2163   10a.+5a. Brown trout
     ("Salmo fario")   30   25

829 "All Men are Born Free and
Equal"

1989. Bicentenary of French Revolution.
2164 **829** 10a. red, blue and black   35   10
2165   – 15a. black, red and blue   35   10
DESIGN: 15a. "Marianne" (Gandon) and French flag.

830 "Weser" (steamer)

1989. Immigration. Multicoloured.
2167   150a. Type **830**   90   35
2168   200a. Immigrants' hostel . .   40   35

831 "Republic" (bronze bust)

1989. Transference of Presidency. Unissued stamp surch as in T **831**.
2170 **831** 300a. on 50a. mult . . .   60   55

832 Arms of Columbus and Title
Page of "Book of Privileges"

1989. "Espamer '90" Spain–Latin America Stamp Exhibition. Chronicles of Discovery. Each yellow, black and red.
2171   100a.+50a. Type **832** . . .   30   30
2172   150a.+50a. Illustration from
     "New Chronicle and
     Good Government"
     (Guaman Poma de Ayala)   40   40
2173   200a.+100a. Illustration
     from "Discovery and
     Conquest of Peru" (Pedro
     de Cieza de Leon) . . .   60   60
2174   250a.+100a. Illustration
     from "A Journey to the
     River Plate" (Ulrico
     Schmidl)   70   70

833 Fr. Guillermo Furlong and Title
Page of "Los Jesuitas"

1989. Birth Anniversaries.
2175 **833** 150a. black, light green
     and green (centenary)   30   25
2176   – 150a. black, buff and
     brown (centenary) . .   30   25
2177   – 200a. black, light blue
     and blue (bicentenary)   40   35
DESIGNS: No. 2176, Dr. Gregorio Alvarez

(physician) and title page of "Canto A Chos Mala"; 2177, Brigadier Gen. Enrique Martinez and "Battle of Maipu" (detail of lithograph, Theodore Gericault).

834 Wooden Mask from   **835** "Policewoman with
Atajo   Children" (Diego
                         Molinari)

1989. America. Pre-Columbian Artefacts. Mult.
2178   200a. Type **834**   65   35
2179   300a. Urn from Punta de
     Balastro   85   55

1989. Federal Police Week. Winning entries in a schools' painting competition.
2180   100a. Type **835**   20   15
2181   100a. "Traffic policeman"
     (Carlos Alberto Sarago)   20   15
2182   150a. "Adults and child by
     traffic lights" (Roxana
     Andrea Osuna)   30   25
2183   150a. "Policeman and child
     stopping traffic at
     crossing" (Pablo Javier
     Quaglia)   30   25

836 "Dream of Christmas" (Maria
Carballido)

1989. Christmas. Multicoloured.
2184   200a. Type **836**   40   35
2185   200a. "Cradle Song for
     Baby Jesus" (Gato Frias)   40   35
2186   300a. "Christ of the Hills"
     (statue, Chipo Cespedes)
     (vert)   85   55

837 "Battle of Vuelta de Obligado" (Ulde Todo)

1989.
2187 **837** 300a. multicoloured . .   1·25   45

838 Port Building   **839** Aconcagua Peak and
                             Los Horcones Lagoon

1990. Cent of Buenos Aires Port. Multicoloured.
2188   200a. Type **838** . . . . .   1·50   75
2189   200a. Crane and bows of
     container and sailing ships   1·50   75
2190   200a. Lorry on quay and
     ships in dock . . . .   1·50   75
2191   200a. Van and building . .   1·50   75
Nos. 2188/91 were printed together, se-tenant, forming a composite design.

1990. Aconcagua International Fair. Mult.
2192   500a. Type **839**   60   35
2193   500a. Aconcagua Peak and
     Los Horcones Lagoon
     (right-hand detail) . . .   60   35
Nos. 2192/3 were printed together, se-tenant, forming a composite design.

840 "75" and Girl with Savings Box

1990. 75th Anniv of National Savings and Insurance Fund.
2194 **840** 1000a. multicoloured . .   20   15

841 Footballer in Striped Shirt

1990. World Cup Football Championship, Italy. Multicoloured.
2195   2500a. Type **841** . . . .   1·25   1·00
2196   2500a. Upper body of foot-
     baller in blue shirt . .   1·25   1·00
2197   2500a. Ball and footballers'
     legs . . . .   1·25   1·00
2198   2500a. Lower body of foot-
     baller . . . .   1·25   1·00
Nos. 2195/8 were printed together, se-tenant, forming a composite design.

842 Flowers

1990. Anti-drugs Campaign.
2199 **842** 2000a. multicoloured . .   85   30

843 School Emblem and Pellegrini

1990. Centenary of Carlos Pellegrini Commercial High School.
2200 **843** 2000a. multicoloured . .   65   30

844 "Calleida suturalis"   **847** Players

845 Letters and Globe

1990. Argentine Philately. Insects. Multicoloured.
2201   1000a.+500a. Type **844** . .   60   35
2202   1000a.+500a. "Adalia
     bipunctata"   60   35
2203   1000a.+500a. "Hippodamia
     convergens"   60   35
2204   1000a.+500a. "Nabis
     punctipennis"   60   35
2205   1000a.+500a. "Podisus
     nigrispinus"   60   35

1990. International Literacy Year.
2206 **845** 2000a. multicoloured . .   85   30

1990. World Basketball Championship. Mult.
2208 **847** 2000a. multicoloured . .   85   30

848 Junkers Ju 52/3m

1990. Air. 50th Anniv of LADE (airline). Mult.
2210   2500a. Type **848** . . . . .   1·25   45
2211   2500a. Grumman SA-16
     Albatross flying boat . .   1·25   45
2212   2500a. Fokker Friendship . .   1·25   45
2213   2500a. Fokker Fellowship . .   1·25   45

849 Arms of West Indies Maritime
Post

1990. 14th Postal Union of the Americas and Spain Congress, Buenos Aires.
2214 **849** 3000a. brown & black   85   50
2215   – 3000a. multicoloured . .   1·50   75
2216   – 3000a. multicoloured . .   1·50   75
2217   – 3000a. multicoloured . .   1·25   50
DESIGNS: No. 2215, Sailing packet and despatch boat; 2216, "Rio Carcarana" (cargo liner); 2217, Boeing 707 airplane.

851 "Hamelia erecta" and Iguazu
Falls

1990. America. Natural World. Multicoloured.
2219   3000a. Type **851** . . . . .   1·50   45
2220   3000a. Sea cow, Puerto
     Deseado . . . .   1·50   45

852 U.P.U. Emblem on "Stamp"

1990. World Post Day.
2221 **852** 3000a. multicoloured . .   95   45

1990. National Parks (3rd series). As T **804**. Mult.
2222   3000a. Anteater, El Rey
     National Park . . . .   1·25   45
2223   3000a. Black-necked swans
     ("Cisne de Cuello
     Negro"), Laguna Blanca
     National Park . . . .   2·00   70
2224   3000a. Black-chested
     buzzard eagle ("Aguila
     Mora"), Lanin National
     Park . . . .   2·00   70
2225   3000a. Armadillo, Perito
     Moreno National Park .   1·25   45
2226   3000a. Pudu, Puelo National
     Park . . . .   1·25   45

853 Hands (after Michelangelo) and
Army Emblem

1990. Cent of Salvation Army in Argentina (2227) and Nat University of the Littoral (2228). Mult.
2227   3000a. Type **853** . . . . .   1·10   50
2228   3000a. University building
     and emblem . . . . .   1·10   50

854 Archangel   **856** "Landscape" (Pio
Gabriel   Collivadino)

1990. Christmas. Stained-glass windows by Carlos Quaglia from Church of Immaculate Conception, Villaguay. Multicoloured.

2229	3000a. Dove's wing and hand	85	50
2230	3000a. Dove and Mary	85	50
2231	3000a. Type **854**	85	50
2232	3000a. Lower half of Mary and open book	85	50
2233	3000a. Joseph	85	50
2234	3000a. Star, shepherds and head of Mary	85	50
2235	3000a. Manger	85	50
2236	3000a. Baby Jesus in Mary's arms	85	50
2237	3000a. Joseph with two doves and Mary	85	50
2238	3000a. Simeon	85	50
2239	3000a. Lower halves of Joseph and Mary	85	50
2240	3000a. Lower half of Simeon and altar	85	50

Nos. 2229/32, 2233/6 and 2237/40 were printed together in se-tenant sheetlets of four stamps, each sheetlet forming a composite design of stained glass windows entitled "Incarnation of Son of God", "The Birth of Christ" and "Presentation of Jesus in the Temple".

1991. Paintings. Multicoloured.

2242	4000a. Type **856**	90	45
2243	4000a. "Weeping Willows" (Atilio Malinverno) (horiz)	90	45

858 Rosas   **860** "Hernan, the Pirate" (Jose Salinas)

1991. Return of Remains of Brig. Gen. Juan Manuel de Rosas.

2245	**858** 4000a. multicoloured	80	35

1991. Comic Strips. Each black and blue.

2247	4000a. Type **860**	1·40	70
2248	4000a. "Don Fulgencio" (Lino Palacio)	1·40	70
2249	4000a. "Tablas Medicas de Salerno" (Oscar Conti)	1·40	70
2250	4000a. "Buenos Aires en Camiseta" (Alejandro del Prado)	1·40	70
2251	4000a. "Girls!" (Jose Divito)	1·40	70
2252	4000a. "Langostino" (Eduardo Ferro)	1·40	70
2253	4000a. "Mafalda" (Joaquin Lavado)	1·40	70
2254	4000a. "Mort Cinder" (Alberto Breccia)	1·40	70

861 "Flags" (Maria Augustina Ferreyra)

1991. 700th Anniv of Swiss Confederation.

2255	**861** 4000a. multicoloured	80	30

862 Divine Child Mayor

1991. 400th Anniv of La Rioja City.

2256	**862** 4000a. multicoloured	80	30

863 Eduardo Bradley, Angel Zuloaga and Balloon "Eduardo Newbery"

1991. 75th Anniv of Crossing of Andes by Balloon.

2257	**863** 4000a. multicoloured	90	35

864 "Vitoria" (Magellan's galleon)

1991. America. Voyages of Discovery. Mult.

2258	4000a. Type **864**	1·25	40
2259	4000a. Juan Diaz de Solis's fleet	1·25	40

865 "Virgin of the Valley, Catamarca" (top half)

1991. Christmas. Stained-glass Windows from Church of Our Lady of Lourdes, Santos Lugares, Buenos Aires. Multicoloured.

2260	4000a. Type **865**	1·10	40
2261	4000a. "Virgin of the Valley" (bottom half)	1·10	40
2262	4000a. Church and "Virgin of the Rosary of the Miracle, Cordoba" (top half)	1·10	40
2263	4000a. "Virgin of the Rosary of the Miracle" (bottom half)	1·10	40

Nos. 2260/3 were issued together, se-tenant, Nos. 2260/1 and 2262/3 forming composite designs.

866 Enrique Pestalozzi (editor) and Masthead

1991. Centenaries. Multicoloured.

2264	4000a. Type **866** ("Argentinisches Tageblatt" (1989))	85	40
2265	4000a. Leandro Alem (founder) and flags (Radical Civic Union)	85	40
2266	4000a. Marksman (Argentine Shooting Federation)	85	40
2267	4000a. Dr. Nicasio Etchepareborda (first professor) and emblem (Buenos Aires Faculty of Odontology)	85	40
2268	4000a. Dalmiro Huergo and emblem (Graduate School of Economics)	85	40

867 Gen. Juan Lavalle and Medal

1991. Anniversaries. Multicoloured.

2269	4000a. Type **867** (150th death anniv)	85	40
2270	4000a. Gen. Jose Maria Paz and Battle of Ituzaingo medal (birth bicentenary)	85	40
2271	4000a. Dr. Marco Avellaneda and opening words of "Ode to the 25th May" (politician and writer, 150th death anniv)	85	40
2272	4000a. William Henry Hudson and title page of "Far Away and Long Ago" (writer, 150th birth anniv)	85	40

868 "Castor" (rocket)

1991. "Iberoprenfil '92" Iberia–Latin America Philatelic Literature Exhibition, Buenos Aires (1st issue). Multicoloured.

2273	4000a.+4000a. Type **868**	2·00	1·00
2274	4000a.+4000a. "Lusat-1" satellite	2·00	1·00

See also Nos. 2313/14 and 2325/8.

869 Guiana Crested Eagle ("Morphnu guianensis")   **871** Golden Tops

1991. Birds. Multicoloured.

2275	4000a. Type **869**	1·50	1·00
2276	4000a. Green-winged macaw ("Ara chloroptera")	1·50	1·00
2277	4000a. Lesser rhea ("Pterocnemia pennata")	1·50	1·00

1992. Fungi.

2279	10c. Type **871**	50	10
2280	25c. Common ink cap	70	20
2281	38c. Type **871**	1·75	25
2282	48c. As 25c.	1·75	30
2283	50c. Granulated boletus	1·75	30
2284	51c. Common morel	1·75	40
2285	61c. Fly agaric	2·25	45
2286	68c. Lawyer's wig	2·25	40
2289	1p. As 61c.	3·00	40
2290	1p.25 As 50c.	3·25	40
2293	2p. As 51c.	6·50	60

For redrawn, smaller, designs see Nos. 2365/77.

1992. National Parks (4th series). As T **804**. Multicoloured.

2295	38c. Chucao tapaculo ("Chucao"), Los Alerces National Park	1·25	85
2296	38c. Opossum, Los Arrayanes National Park	1·00	40
2297	38c. Giant armadillo, Formosa Nature Reserve	1·00	40
2298	38c. Cavy, Petrified Forests Natural Monument	1·00	40
2299	38c. James's flamingo ("Parina chica"), Laguna de los Pozuelos Natural Monument	1·25	85

872 Soldier and Truck

1992. National Heroes Commem. Multicoloured.

2300	38c. Type **872**	75	40
2301	38c. "General Belgrano" (cruiser)	90	40
2302	38c. FMA Pucara fighter	90	40

873 "Carnotaurus sastrei"   **874** "Tileforo Areco"

1992. Dinosaurs. Multicoloured.

2303	38c.+38c. Type **873**	2·25	1·25
2304	38c.+38c. "Amargasaurus cazaui"	2·25	1·25

1992. Birth Centenary (1991) of Florencio Molina Campios (painter). Multicoloured.

2305	38c. Type **874**	1·10	45
2306	38c. "In the Shade" (horiz)	1·10	45

876 General Lucio N. Mansilla and "San Martin" (frigate)

1992. Birth Anniversaries. Multicoloured.

2308	38c. Type **876** (bicentenary)	1·10	50
2309	38c. Jose Manuel Estrada (historian, 150th)	85	40
2310	38c. General Jose I. Garmendia (150th)	85	40

877 Hearts as Flowers

1992. Anti-drugs Campaign.

2311	**877** 38c. multicoloured	85	40

878 Steam Pump Fire Engine and Calaza

1992. 140th Birth Anniv of Col. Jose Calaza (founder of fire service).

2312	**878** 38c. multicoloured	1·10	50

879 "The Party"

1992. "Iberoprenfil '92" Iberia–Latin America Philatelic Literature Exhibition, Buenos Aires (2nd issue). Paintings by Raul Soldi. Multicoloured.

2313	76c.+76c. Type **879**	3·50	1·75
2314	76c.+76c. "Church of St. Anne of Glew"	3·50	1·75

880 Columbus, European Symbols and "Santa Maria"

1992. America. 500th Anniv of Discovery of America by Columbus. Multicoloured.

2315	38c. Type **880**	1·25	40
2316	38c. American symbols and Columbus	1·25	40

1992. 50th Anniv of Neuquen and Rio Negro Philatelic Centre. Unissued stamp as T **871** optd **50°** **ANIVERSARIO CENTRO FILATELICO DE NEUQUEN Y RIO NEGRO**. Multicoloured.

2317	1p.77 Verdigris agaric	4·50	2·50

 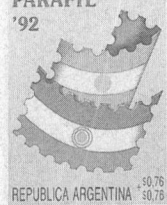
882 "God Pays You"   **883** Flags of Paraguay and Argentina as Stamps

1992. Argentine Films. Advertising posters. Mult.

2318	38c. Type **882**	1·00	40
2319	38c. "The Turbid Waters"	1·00	40
2320	38c. "Un Guapo del 900"	1·00	40

2321	38c. "The Truce"	1·00	40
2322	38c. "The Official Version"	1·00	40

1992. "Parafil '92" Paraguay–Argentina Stamp Exhibition, Buenos Aires.

2323	**883**	76c.+76c. mult	3·00	1·50

884 Angel and Baby Jesus   885 Punta Mogotes Lighthouse

1992. Christmas.

2324	**884**	38c. multicoloured	1·00	40

1992. "Iberoprenfil '92" Iberia–Latin America Philatelic Literature Exhibition, Buenos Aires (3rd issue). Lighthouses. Multicoloured.

2325	38c. Type **885**		1·00	50
2326	38c. Rio Negro		1·00	50
2327	38c. San Antonio		1·00	50
2328	38c. Cabo Blanco		1·00	50

886 Campaign Emblem   887 "Sac-B" Research Satellite

1992. Anti-AIDS Campaign.

2329	**886**	10c. black, red and blue	80	15
2330	–	26c. multicoloured	1·60	25

DESIGN: 26c. AIDS cloud over house of life.

1992. International Space Year.

2331	**887**	38c. multicoloured	80	40

889 Footballers and Emblem

1993. Centenary of Argentine Football Assn.

2333	**889**	38c. multicoloured	1·25	60

890 Arquebusier and Arms of Francisco de Arganaras (founder)   892 Order of San Martin

1993. 400th Anniv of Jujuy.

2334	**890**	38c. multicoloured	1·00	40

1993. Anniversaries. Multicoloured.

2336	38c. Type **892** (50th anniv)		85	45
2337	38c. Entrance to and emblem of National History Academy (centenary)		85	45

893 Flag-bearer and Arms of Gendarmerie   895 Snowy Egret ("Egretta thula")

894 Luis Candelaria and Morane Saulnier Type P Monoplane

1993. National Heroes Commemoration. Mult.

2338	38c. Type **893**	1·00	40
2339	38c. "Rio Iguazu" (coastguard corvette)	1·00	40

1993. 75th Anniv of First Flight over the Andes.

2340	**894**	38c. multicoloured	1·25	40

1993. Paintings of Birds by Axel Amuchastegui. Multicoloured.

2341	38c.+38c. Type **895**	1·60	1·60
2342	38c.+38c. Scarlet-headed blackbird ("Amblyramphus holosericeus")	1·60	1·60
2343	38c.+38c. Red-crested cardinal ("Paroaria coronata")	1·60	1·60
2344	38c.+38c. Amazon kingfisher ("Chloroceryle amazona")	1·60	1·60

896 "Coming Home" (Adriana Zaefferer)

1993. Paintings. Multicoloured.

2345	38c. Type **896**	90	40
2346	38c. "The Old House" (Norberto Russo)	90	40

897 Pato

1993. 40th Anniv of Declaration of Pato as National Sport.

2347	**897**	1p. multicoloured	2·40	65

898 Segurola's Pacara ("Enterolobium contortisiliquum")

1993. Old Trees in Buenos Aires. Multicoloured.

2348	75c. Type **898** (Puan and Baldomero Fernandez Moreno Streets)	1·25	40
2349	75c. Pueyrredon's carob tree ("Prosopis alba") (Pueyrredon Square)	1·25	40
2350	1p.50 Alvear's coral tree ("Erythrina falcata") (Lavalle Square)	2·50	80
2351	1p.50 Avellaneda's magnolia ("Magnolia grandiflora") (Adolfo Berro Avenue)	2·50	80

899 Southern Right Whale

1993. America. Endangered Animals. Mult.

2352	50c. Type **899**	1·25	55
2353	75c. Commerson's dolphin	1·75	80

900 Star, Leaf and Bell (Christmas)

1993. Christmas and New Year. Festive Symbols. Multicoloured.

2354	75c. Type **900**	1·25	40
2355	75c. Leaf, sun and moon (New Year)	1·25	40
2356	75c. Leaf and fir tree (Christmas)	1·25	40
2357	75c. Fish and moon (New Year)	1·25	40

Nos. 2354/7 were issued together, se-tenant, forming a composite design.

901 Cave Painting

1993. Cave of Hands, Santa Cruz.

2358	**901**	1p. multicoloured	2·00	40

902 Emblem

1994. New Argentine Post Emblem.

2359	**902**	75c. multicoloured	1·25	40

903 Brazil Player   904 Golden Tops

1994. World Cup Football Championship, U.S.A. (1st issue). Multicoloured.

2360	25c. German player	30	20
2361	50c. Type **903**	90	45
2362	75c. Argentine player	1·40	50
2363	1p. Italian player	1·90	75

See also Nos. 2380/3.

1994. Fungi. Multicoloured.

2365	10c. Type **904**	20	10
2366	25c. Common ink cap	55	20
2369	50c. Granulated boletus	1·25	50
2374	1p. Fly agaric	2·75	1·10
2377	2p. Common morel	5·25	2·25

905 Argentine Player with Ball (Matias Taylor)

1994. World Cup Football Championship, U.S.A. (2nd issue). Winning entries in children's competition. Multicoloured.

2380	75c. Type **905**	1·40	50
2381	75c. Tackle (Torcuato Santiago Gonzalez Agote)	1·40	50
2382	75c. Players (Julian Lisenberg) (horiz)	1·40	50
2383	75c. Match scene (Maria Paula Palma) (horiz)	1·40	50

906 Black-throated Finch

1994. Animals of the Falkland Islands (Islas Malvinas). Multicoloured.

2384	25c. Type **906**	55	40
2385	50c. Gentoo penguins	1·10	75
2386	75c. Falkland Islands flightless steamer ducks	1·60	1·10
2387	1p. Southern elephant-seal	1·75	60

907 Town Arms

1994. Anniversaries. Multicoloured.

2388	75c. Type **907** (400th anniv of San Luis)	1·25	50
2389	75c. Arms (3rd anniv of provincial status of Tierra del Fuego, Antarctica and South Atlantic Islands)	1·25	50

908 Ladislao Jose Biro

1994. Inventors. Multicoloured.

2390	75c. Type **908** (ball-point pen)	1·25	50
2391	75c. Raul Pateras de Pescara (helicopter)	1·25	50
2392	75c. Quirino Cristiani (animated films)	1·25	50
2393	75c. Enrique Finochietto (surgical instruments)	1·25	50

909 Star, Purple Bauble and Bell

1994. U.N.I.C.E.F. Children's Fund in Argentina. Multicoloured.

2394	50c. Type **909**	85	45
2395	75c. Bell, red bauble and star	1·25	50

910 Children holding Globe (Ivana Mirna de Caro)

1994. "Care of the Planet". Children's Painting Competition. Multicoloured.

2396	25c. Type **910**	30	20
2397	25c. Girl polishing sunbeam and boy tending tree (Elena Tsouprik)	30	20
2398	50c. Children of all races around globe (Estefania Navarro) (horiz)	60	45
2399	50c. Globe as house (Maria Belen Gidoni) (horiz)	60	45

911 Star and Angel (The Annunciation)

1994. Christmas. Multicoloured.
2400 50c. Type **911** 60 45
2401 75c. Madonna and Child
(Nativity) . . . . 1·25 50

912 Running

1995. 12th Pan-American Games, Mar del Plata. Multicoloured.
2402 75c. Type **912** . . . . . . 1·25 45
2403 75c. Cycling . . . . . . 1·25 45
2404 75c. Diving . . . . . . 1·25 45
2405 1p.25 Football (vert) . . . . 2·00 60
2406 1p.25 Gymnastics (vert) . . . 2·00 60

913 Postal Emblem

1995. Self-adhesive.
2407 **913** 25c. yellow, blue & black 3·75 50
2408 75c. yellow, blue & black 1·25 50

914 National Congress Building and "The Republic Triumphant" (statue, detail)

1995. New Constitution, August 1994.
2409 **914** 75c. multicoloured . . . 1·25 40

915 Letters and Disk

1995. 21st International Book Fair.
2410 **915** 75c. multicoloured . . . 1·25 50

916 Bay-winged Cowbird

1995. Birds. Multicoloured.
2412 5p. Hooded siskin . . . . . 10·50 7·50
2413 9p.40 Type **916** . . . . . 21·00 15·00
2414 10p. Rufous-collared
sparrow . . . . 20·00 13·50

917 Clouds seen through Atrium

1995. Centenary of Argentine Engineers' Centre, Buenos Aires.
2420 **917** 75c. multicoloured . . . 1·25 45

920 Jose Marti

1995. Revolutionaries' Anniversaries. Mult.
2423 1p. Type **920** (death cent) 1·60 45
2424 1p. Antonio de Sucre (birth
bicentenary) . . . . . . 1·60 45

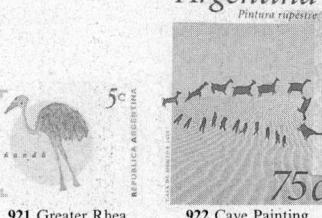

921 Greater Rhea   **922** Cave Painting
(Patagonia)

1995. Birds. Multicoloured.
2425 5c. Type **921** 15 10
2425a 10c. Giant wood rail
("ipecae") 15 10
2426 25c. Penguin 45 20
2427 50c. Toco toucan 85 45
2428 75c. Andean condor . . . 1·40 75
2429 1p. Barn owl . . . . . . 1·75 1·00
2430 2p. Olivaceous cormorant . 3·50 2·00
2431 2p.75 Cayenne plover . . . 5·00 2·75
2432 3p.25 Lapwing . . . . . 4·00 3·00

1995. Animals. As T **921**. Multicoloured.
2436 25c. Alligator 30 20
2437 50c. Red fox 60 45
2438 75c. Anteater . . . . . . 1·25 75
2439 75c. Vicuna . . . . . . 1·25 75
2440 75c. Sperm whale . . . . 1·25 75

1995. Archaeology. Multicoloured.
2441 75c. Type **922** . . . . . 1·25 40
2442 75c. Stone mask (Tafi
culture, Tucuman) . . . . 1·25 40
2443 75c. Anthropomorphic vase
(Catamarca) . . . . . . 1·25 40
2444 75c. Woven cloth (North
Patagonia) . . . . 1·25 40

923 Peron

1995. Birth Centenary of Juan Peron (President, 1946–55 and 1973–74).
2445 **923** 75c. blue and bistre . . . 1·25 40

924 Postal Emblem on Sunflower

1995.
2446 **924** 75c. multicoloured . . . 1·25 40

926 Christmas Tree

1995. Christmas. Multicoloured.
2448 75c. Type **926** . . . . . 1·25 40
2449 75c. "1996" . . . . . . 1·25 40
2450 75c. Glasses of champagne 1·25 40
2451 75c. Present . . . . . . 1·25 40
2452 75c. Type **926** . . . . . 1·25 40

927 "Les 400 Coups" (dir. Francois Truffaut)

1995. Centenary of Motion Pictures. Each black, grey and orange.
2453 75c. "Battleship Potemkin"
(dir. Sergei Eisenstein) . . 1·25 40
2454 75c. "Casablanca" (dir.
Michael Curtiz) . . . . 1·25 40
2455 75c. "Bicycle Thieves" (dir.
Vittorio de Sica) . . . . 1·25 40
2456 75c. Charlie Chaplin in
"Limelight" . . . . . . 1·25 40
2457 75c. Type **927** . . . . . 1·25 40
2458 75c. "Chronicle of an Only
Child" (dir. Leonardo
Favio) . . . . 1·25 40

928 Horse-drawn Mail Coach

1995. America (1994). Postal Transport. Mult.
2459 75c. Type **928** . . . . . 1·25 40
2460 75c. Early postal van . . . 1·25 40

929 Dirigible Airship

1995. The Sky. Multicoloured.
2461 25c. Type **929** 55 20
2462 25c. Kite 55 20
2463 25c. Hot-air balloon . . . 55 20
2464 50c. Balloons 85 45
2465 50c. Paper airplane . . . 85 45
2466 75c. Airplane . . . . . 1·25 45
2467 75c. Helicopter . . . . . 1·25 45
2468 75c. Parachute . . . . . 1·25 45

930 Ancient Greek and Modern Runners

1996. Multicoloured. (a) Centenary of Modern Olympic Games. Horiz designs.
2471 75c. Type **930** . . . . . 1·25 35
2472 1p. "The Discus Thrower"
(ancient Greek statue,
Miron) and modern
thrower . . . . 1·60 50

(b) Olympic Games. Vert designs.
2473 75c. Torch bearer (Buenos
Aires, 2004) . . . . . 1·25 35
2474 1p. Rowing (Atlanta, 1996) 1·60 50

931 Francisco Muniz (founder of Academy of Medicine and Public Hygiene Council)

1996. Physicians' Anniversaries. Multicoloured.
2475 50c. Type **931** (birth
bicentenary (1995)) . . . 85 45
2476 50c. Ricardo Gutierrez
(founder of Children's
Hospital and co-founder
of periodical "La Patria
Argentina", death
centenary) 85 45
2477 50c. Ignacio Pirovano (death
centenary (1995)) . . . 85 45
2478 50c. Esteban Maradona
(birth centenary (1995)
and first death anniv) . . 85 45

932 Mosaic Map of Jerusalem (left-hand detail)

1996. 3000th Anniv of Jerusalem. Multicoloured.
2479 75c. Type **932** . . . . . 1·25 40
2480 75c. Map (right-hand detail) 1·25 40
Nos. 2479/80 were issued together, se-tenant, forming a composite design.

933 Capybaras

1996. America. Endangered Species. Mult.
2481 75c. Type **933** . . . . . 1·50 45
2482 75c. Guanacos . . . . . 1·50 45

934 Ramon Franco's Seaplane "Plus Ultra"

1996. "Aerofila '96" Latin American Airmail Exhibition. Aircraft. Multicoloured.
2483 25c.+25c. Type **934** . . . 1·25 60
2484 25c.+25c. Alberto Santos-
Dumont's biplane "14
bis" . . . . 1·25 60
2485 50c.+50c. Charles
Lindbergh's "Spirit of St.
Louis" . . . . 2·50 1·25
2486 50c.+50c. Eduardo Olivero's
biplane "Buenos Aires" 2·50 1·25

1996. As Nos. 2407/8. Self-adhesive. Imperf.
2486a **913** 25c. yellow and blue . . 3·75 50
2486b 75c. yellow and blue . . 1·25 70

935 Mountain Peahen, Diamante National Park

1996. National Parks. Multicoloured.
2487 75c. Type **935** . . . . . 1·25 45
2488 75c. Mountain viscacha, El
Leoncito Nature Reserve 1·60 70
2489 75c. Marsh deer, Otamendi
Nature Reserve . . . . 1·25 45
2490 75c. Parrot, San Antonio
Nature Reserve . . . . 1·60 70

936 Dragon

1996. Murals from Buenos Aires Underground Railway. Multicoloured.
2491 1p.+50c. Type **936** . . . 3·00 1·75
2492 1p.50+1p. Bird . . . . . 5·00 2·50

937 "San Antonio" (tank landing ship)

1996. Cent of Port Belgrano Naval Base. Mult.
2493 25c. Type **937** 65 20
2494 50c. "Rosales" (corvette) . 1·25 45

2495	75c. "Hercules" (destroyer)	1·75	70
2496	1p. "25 de Mayo" (aircraft carrier)	2·50	1·00

938 Decorative Panel

1996. Carousel. Multicoloured.

2497	25c. Type **938**	55	20
2498	25c. Child on horse	55	20
2499	25c. Carousel	55	20
2500	50c. Fairground horses	85	20
2501	50c. Child in airplane	85	20
2502	50c. Pig	85	20
2503	75c. Child in car	1·25	45

939 Head Post Office, Buenos Aires   **940** "Adoration of the Wise Men" (Gladys Rinaldi)

1996. Size 24½ × 34½ mm. Self-adhesive. Imperf.

2504	**939** 75c. multicoloured	90	70

See also Nos. 2537/8.

1996. Christmas. Tapestries. Multicoloured.

2505	75c. Type **940**	1·25	45
2506	1p. Abstract (Norma Bonet de Maekawa) (horiz)	1·60	70

941 Melchior Base

1996. Argentinian Presence in Antarctic. Mult.

2507	75c. Type **941**	1·40	45
2508	1p.25 "Irizar" (ice-breaker)	2·75	70

942 "Vahine no te Miti" (Gauguin)

1996. Cent of National Gallery of Fine Arts. Mult.

2509	75c. Type **942**	1·25	45
2510	1p. "The Nymph surprised" (Edouard Manet)	1·60	65
2511	1p. "Figure of Woman" (Amedeo Modigliani)	1·60	65
2512	1p.25 "Woman lying down" (Pablo Picasso) (horiz)	2·00	75

943 Granite Mining, Cordoba

1997. Mining Industry. Multicoloured.

2513	75c. Type **943**	1·25	45
2514	1p.25 Borax mining, Salta	2·00	65

944 "They amuse Themselves in Dancing" (Raul Soldi)

1997. America (1996). National Costume.

2515	**944** 75c. multicoloured	1·25	45

945 Arms, Sabre and Shako

1997. Centenary of Repatriation of General San Martin's Sabre.

2516	**945** 75c. multicoloured	1·25	45

946 Match Scene

1997. 29th World Rugby Youth Championship, Argentina.

2517	**946** 75c. multicoloured	1·25	45

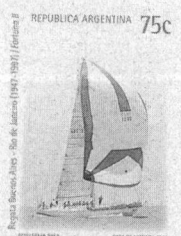

947 "Fortuna" (yacht)

1997. 50th Anniv of Buenos Aires to Rio de Janeiro Regatta.

2518	**947** 75c. multicoloured	90	30

948 Ceres Design, France (1849–52)

1997. "Mevifil '97" First Int Exn of Philatelic Audio-visual and Computer Systems. Mult.

2519	50c.+50c. Type **948**	1·60	1·25
2520	50c.+50c. Queen Isabella II design, Spain (1851)	1·60	1·25
2521	50c.+50c. Rivadavia design, Argentine Republic (1864)	1·60	1·25
2522	50c.+50c. Paddle-steamer design, Buenos Aires (1858)	1·60	1·25

Nos. 2519/22 were issued together, se-tenant, with the centre of the block forming the composite design of an eye.

949 Museum

1997. Centenary of National History Museum, Buenos Aires.

2523	**949** 75c. multicoloured	1·25	45

950 Seal and Oak Leaf   **951** Carcano (after Dolores Capdevila)

1997. Centenary of La Plata National University.

2524	**950** 75c. multicoloured	1·25	45

1997. 50th Death Anniv (1996) of Ramon Carcano (postal reformer).

2525	**951** 75c. multicoloured	1·25	45

952 Cabo Virgenes Lighthouse

1997. Lighthouses. Multicoloured.

2526	75c. Type **952**	1·25	45
2527	75c. Isla Pinguino	1·25	45
2528	75c. San Juan de Salvamento	1·25	45
2529	75c. Punta Delgada	1·25	45

953 Condor and Olympic Rings

1997. Inclusion of Buenos Aires in Final Selection Round for 2004 Olympic Games.

2530	**953** 75c. multicoloured	1·25	45

954 Lacroze Company Suburban Service, 1912

1997. Centenary of First Electric Tramway in Buenos Aires. Illustrations from "History of the Tram" by Marcelo Mayorga. Multicoloured.

2531	75c. Type **954**	1·40	70
2532	75c. Lacroze Company urban service, 1907	1·40	70
2533	75c. Anglo Argentina Company tramcar, 1930	1·40	70
2534	75c. City of Buenos Aires Transport Corporation tramcar, 1942	1·40	70
2535	75c. Fabricaciones Militares tramcar, 1956	1·40	70
2536	75c. Electricos de Sur Company tramcar, 1908	1·40	70

Nos. 2531/6 were issued together, se-tenant, showing a composite design of a tram in a city street.

1997. As No. 2504 but size 23 × 35 mm. Self-adhesive. Imperf.

2537	**939** 25c. multicoloured	70	20
2538	75c. multicoloured	1·40	20

955 Monument (by Mauricio Molina)

1997. Inauguration of Monument to Joaquin Gonzalez (politician) at La Rioja.

2539	**955** 75c. multicoloured	1·25	45

956 Alberto Ginastera (after Carlos Nine)

1997. Composers. Multicoloured.

2540	75c. Type **956**	1·25	45
2541	75c. Astor Piazzolla (after Carlos Alonso)	1·25	45
2542	75c. Anibal Troilo (after Hermenegildo Sabat)	1·25	45
2543	75c. Atahualpa Yupanqui (after Luis Scafati)	1·25	45

957 "Tren a las Nubes", Salta

1997. Trains. Multicoloured.

2544	50c.+50c. Type **957**	1·60	80
2545	50c.+50c. Preserved steam locomotive, Buenos Aires	1·60	80
2546	50c.+50c. Patagonian express "La Trochita" Rio Negro–Chubut	1·60	80
2547	50c.+50c. Austral Fueguino Railway locomotive No. 2, Tierra del Fuego	1·60	80

958 Eva Peron (after Raul Manteola)

1997. 50th Anniv of Women's Suffrage.

2548	**958** 75c. pink and grey	1·25	45

959 Jorge Luis Borges and Maze

1997. Writers. Multicoloured.

2549	1p. Type **959**	1·60	50
2550	1p. Julio Cortazar and hopscotch grid	1·60	50

961 Members' Flags and Southern Cross

1997. Mercosur (South American Common Market).

2552	**961** 75c. multicoloured	1·25	45

962 "Presidente Sarmiento" (Hugo Leban)

1997. Centenary of Launch of "Presidente Sarmiento" (cadet ship).
2553 **962** 75c. multicoloured . . . 2·00 55

963 Guevara

1997. 30th Death Anniv of Ernesto "Che" Guevara (revolutionary).
2555 **963** 75c. brown, red & black 1·25 45

964 Vicuna (Julian Chiapparo)

1997. "Draw an Ecostamp" Children's Competition Winners. Multicoloured.
2556 50c. Type **964** 80 20
2557 50c. Vicuna (Leandro Lopez Portal) 80 20
2558 75c. Seal (Andres Lloren) (horiz) . . . . 1·25 45
2559 75c. Ashy-headed goose (Jose Saccone) (horiz) . . 1·25 45

965 "Nativity" (Mary Jose)

1997. Christmas. Tapestries of the Nativity. Designs by artists named. Mult. (a) Size 45 × 34 mm.
2560 75c. Type **965** . . . . 1·25 45

(b) Size 44 × 27 mm. Self-adhesive. Imperf.
2561 25c. Elena Aguilar 40 20
2562 25c. Silvia Pettachi 40 20
2563 50c. Ana Escobar 80 20
2564 50c. Alejandra Martinez . . 80 20
2565 75c. As No. 2560 but with inscriptions differently arranged . . . . . . 1·25 45
2566 75c. Nidia Martinez . . . . 1·25 45

966 Mother Teresa

1997. Mother Teresa (founder of the Missionaries of Charity) Commemoration.
2567 **966** 75c. multicoloured . . 1·25 45

967 Houssay

1998. 50th Anniv (1997) of Award to Bernardo Houssay of Nobel Prize for Medicine and Physiology.
2568 **967** 75c. multicoloured . . . 90 70

968 Mountaineers

1998. Cent of First Ascent of Mt. Aconcagua.
2569 **968** 1p.25 multicoloured . . . 1·25 1·00

969 San Martin de los Andes and Lake Lacar

1998. Centenary of San Martin de los Andes.
2570 **969** 75c. multicoloured . . . 90 70

970 Grenadier Monument (Juan Carlos Ferraro)

1998. Declaration as National Historical Monument of Palermo Barracks of General San Martin Horse Grenadiers. Multicoloured.
2571 75c. Type **970** 90 70
2572 75c. Sevres urn with portrait of San Martin 90 70
2573 75c. Regiment coat of arms 90 70
2574 75c. Main facade of barracks 90 70

971 Globe and Baby

1998. Protection of Ozone Layer.
2575 **971** 75c. multicoloured . . . 90 70

972 Postman, 1920

1998. America. The Postman. Multicoloured.
2576 75c. Type **972** 90 70
2577 75c. Postman, 1998 . . . . 90 70

973 "El Reino del Reves"

1998. Stories by Maria Elena Walsh. Illustrations by Eduardo and Ricardo Fuhrmann. Multicoloured. Self-adhesive.
2578 75c. Type **973** 90 70
2579 75c. "Zoo Loco" 90 70
2580 75c. "Dailan Kifki" 90 70
2581 75c. "Manuelita" 90 70

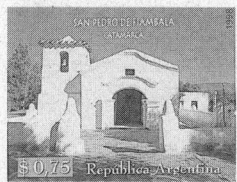

974 St Peter's, Fiambala, Catamarca

1998. Historic Chapels. Multicoloured.
2582 75c. Type **974** 90 70
2583 75c. Huacalera, Jujuy . . . 90 70
2584 75c. St. Dominic's, La Rioja 90 70
2585 75c. Tumbaya, Jujuy . . . 90 70

975 Raised Hands

1998. White Helmets (volunteer humanitarian workers).
2586 **975** 1p. multicoloured . . . 1·25 1·00

976 Argentine Player

1998. World Cup Football Championship, France. Multicoloured.
2587 75c. Type **976** 90 70
2588 75c. Croatian player 90 70
2589 75c. Jamaican player . . . 90 70
2590 75c. Japanese player . . . 90 70

977 Typewriter, Camera, Pen, Computer and Satellite

1998. Journalism Day.
2591 **977** 75c. multicoloured . . . 90 70

978 Corrientes 1860 3c. Stamps and Postal Emblem

1998. 250th Anniv of Establishment of Regular Postal Service in Rio de la Plata (Spanish dominion in South America). Multicoloured.
2592 75c. Type **978** 90 70
2593 75c. Buenos Aires Post Office and pillar box . . . 90 70

979 Jesuit Ruins, San Ignacio Mini

1998. Mercosur Missions.
2594 **979** 75c. multicoloured . . . 90 70

980 Aberdeen Angus

1998. Cattle. Multicoloured.
2595 25c. Type **980** 30 20
2596 25c. Brahman 30 20
2597 50c. Hereford 60 45
2598 50c. Criolla 60 45
2599 75c. Holando-Argentina . . 90 70
2600 75c. Shorthorn 90 70

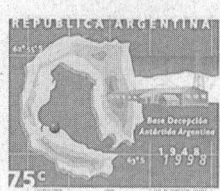

981 Map and Base

1998. 50th Anniv of Decepcion Antarctic Base.
2601 **981** 75c. multicoloured . . . 90 70

982 Anniversary Emblem

1998. 50th Anniv of State of Israel.
2602 **982** 75c. multicoloured . . . 90 70

983 Bridge in Japanese Garden, Buenos Aires

1998. Cent of Argentina–Japan Friendship Treaty.
2603 **983** 75c. multicoloured . . . 90 70

984 Facade and clock

1998. 70th Anniv of Head Post Office, Buenos Aires. Multicoloured.
2604 75c. Type **984** 90 70
2605 75c. Capital and bench . . . 90 70

985 Patoruzu   **986** Heart with Arms
(Quinterno)   holding Baby

1998. Comic Strip Characters. Multicoloured.
2606 75c. Type **985**   90   70
2607 75c. Matias (Sendra)   90   70
2608 75c. Clemente (Caloi) . . .   90   70
2609 75c. El Eternauta
        (Oesterheld Solano Lopez)   90   70
2610 75c. Loco Chavez (Trillo
        Altuna)   90   70
2611 75c. Inodoro Pereyra
        (Fontanarrosa)   90   70
2612 75c. Tia Vicenta (Landru)   90   70
2613 75c. Gaturro (Nik)   90   70

1998. 220th Anniv of Dr. Pedro de Elizalde
Children's Hospital.
2614 **986** 75c. multicoloured . . .   90   70

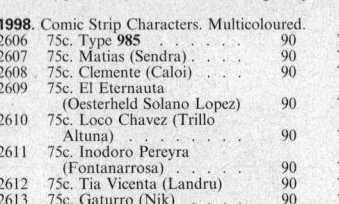

987 Post Banner and Pennant, 1785,
and Arms of Maritime Post

1998. "Espamer '98" Iberian–Latin American Stamp
Exhibition, Buenos Aires. Mult. Self-adhesive.
2615 25c. Type **987**   30   20
2616 75c. Mail brigantine . . . .   1·25   70
2617 75c.+75c. Mail brigantine
        (different) . . . . . .   2·50   1·75
2618 1p.25+1p.25 Mail brig . .   4·25   3·00

988 Passport and Wallenberg

1998. Raoul Wallenberg (Swedish diplomat in
Hungary who helped Jews escape, 1944–45)
Commemoration.
2619 **988** 75c. multicoloured . . .   90   70

989 Aguada Culture Bird

1998. 50th Anniv of Organization of American
States.
2620 **989** 75c. multicoloured . . .   90   70

990 Eoraptor

1998. Prehistoric Animals. Multicoloured.
2621 75c. Type **990**   90   70
2622 75c. Gasparinisaura   90   70
2623 75c. Giganotosaurus   90   70
2624 75c. Patagosaurus   90   70
Nos. 2621/4 were issued together, se-tenant,
forming a composite design.

991 Child as Angel, Stars   **993** Postman
and Score

1998. Christmas.
2625 **991** 75c. multicoloured . . .   90   70

1998. Centenary of "El Liberal" (newspaper).
2626 **992** 75c. multicoloured . . .   90   70

992 Juan Figueroa (founder) and
First Issue

1998. Postmen. Size 25 × 35 mm. Multicoloured. Self-
adhesive.
2627 25c. Type **993**   30   20
2628 75c. Modern postman   90   70
For 75c. in reduced size see No. 2640.

1998. Birds. As T **921**. Multicoloured. Self-adhesive.
2629 60c. Hummingbird   75   60

994 Child (painting, Francisco Ramirez)

1998. 50th Anniv of Universal Declaration of Human
Rights.
2635 **994** 75c. multicoloured . . .   90   70

995 Enrique Julio (founder) and
Newspaper Offices

1998. Cent of "La Nueva Provincia" (newspaper).
2636 **995** 75c. multicoloured . . .   90   70

996 "Haggadah" of Pessah (exhibit)
and Carving on Cathedral

1998. Permanent Exhibition commemorating
Holocaust Victims, Buenos Aires Cathedral.
2637 **996** 75c. multicoloured . . .   90   70

1999. Postmen. Size 21 × 27 mm. Mult. Self-adhesive.
2638 15c. Type **993**   30   20
2639 50c. Postman, 1950   60   45
2640 75c. As No. 2628   90   70

997 Oil-smeared Penguin

1999. International Year of the Ocean. Mult.
2641 50c. Type **997**   60   45
2642 75c. Dolphins (horiz) . . .   90   70

998 Buildings and Draughtsman's
Instruments

1999. National Arts Fund.
2643 **998** 75c. multicoloured . . .   90   70

999 Computer and Book

1999. 25th Book Fair, Buenos Aires. Multicoloured.
2644 75c. Type **999** 90   70
2645 75c. Obelisk, compact disk
        case and readers   90   70
Nos. 2644/5 were issued together, se-tenant,
forming a composite design.

1000 Rugby Balls and Player

1999. Centenary of Argentine Rugby Union.
2646 **1000** 75c. multicoloured . . . 90   70

1001 Glass, La Giralda   **1002** Pierre de Coubertin,
                                   1924 Olympic Gold Medal
                                   and Olympic Rings

1999. Cafes. Multicoloured. Self-adhesive.
2648 25c. Type **1001**   30   20
2649 75c. Two glasses, Cafe
        Homero Manzi   90   70
2650 75c. Hatstand, Confiteria
        Ideal   90   70
2651 1p.25 Cup and saucer, Cafe
        Tortoni . . . .   1·50   1·00

1999. 75th Anniv of Argentine Olympic Committee.
2652 **1002** 75c. multicoloured . . . 90   70

1003 Enrico Caruso (Italian tenor)

1999. Opera. Multicoloured.
2653 75c. Type **1003** (125th birth
        anniv and centenary of
        American debut)   90   70
2654 75c. Singer and musical
        instruments   90   70
2655 75c. Buenos Aires Opera
        House   90   70
2656 75c. Scene from "El
        Matrero" (Felipe Boero)   90   70

1004 Rosario Vera Penaloza
(educationist)

1999. America (1998). Famous Women, Mult.
2659 75c. Type **1004**   90   70
2660 75c. Julieta Lanteri
        (women's rights
        campaigner)   90   70

1006 Local Road Network

1999. Bulk Mailing Stamps. Mult. Self-adhesive.
2662 35c. Type **1006**   40   30
2663 40c. Town plan   50   40
2664 50c. Regional map   60   45

1007 Carrier Pigeon

1999.
2665 **1007** 75c. multicoloured . . . 90   70

1008 Boxer

1999. Dogs. Multicoloured.
2666 25c. Type **1008**   20   20
2667 25c. Old English sheepdog   30   20
2668 50c. Welsh collie   60   45
2669 50c. St. Bernard   60   45
2670 75c. German shepherd . . .   90   70
2671 75c. Siberian husky   90   70

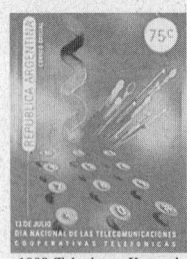

1009 Telephone Keypad

1999. National Telecommunications Day.
2672 **1009** 75c. multicoloured . . . 90   70

1010 College Gates

1999. 150th Anniv of Justo Jose de Urquiza College,
Concepcion del Uruguay.
2673 **1010** 75c. multicoloured . . .   90   70

1011 Krause (engineer) and Industrial Instruments

1999. Centenary of Technical School No. 1 Otto Krause.
2674 **1011** 75c. multicoloured . . . 90 70

1012 Nativity

1999. Bethlehem 2000.
2675 **1012** 75c. blue, gold and red 90 70

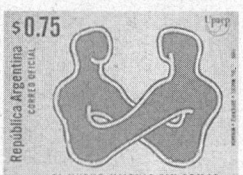

1013 Brotherhood among Men

1999. America. A New Millennium without Arms. Multicoloured.
2676 75c. Type **1013** 90 70
2677 75c. Liberty Tree (vert) . . 90 70

1014 Coypu ("Myocastor coypus"), Mburucuya National Park

1999. National Parks. Multicoloured.
2678 50c. Type **1014** 60 50
2679 50c. Andean condor, Quebrada de los Condoritos National Park 60 50
2680 50c. Vicuna, San Guillermo National Park 60 50
2681 75c. Puma, Sierra de las Quijadas National Park 90 70
2682 75c. Argentine grey fox ("Dusicyon griseus"), Talampaya National Park 90 70

1015 Map of the Americas, Road Network and Wickerwork

1999. 40th Anniv of Inter-American Development Bank.
2683 **1015** 75c. multicoloured . . . 90 70

1016 "Evidencias VI" (Carlos Gallardo)

1999. 125th Anniv of Universal Postal Union.
2684 **1016** 1p.50 multicoloured . . . 1·75 1·40

1017 "Fournier" and Map

1999. 50th Anniv of Sinking of the "Fournier" (minesweeper) in Antarctica.
2685 **1017** 75c. multicoloured . . . 90 70

1018 "Nothofagus pumillio"

1999. Trees (1st series). Multicoloured.
2686 75c. Type **1018** 90 70
2687 75c. "Prosopis caldenia" . . 90 70
2688 75c. "Schinopsis balansae" 90 70
2689 75c. "Cordia trichotoma" 90 70
Nos. 2686/9 were issued together, se-tenant, forming a composite design.

1019 Latecoere 25 Mailplane

1999. 50th Anniv of World Record for Consecutive Parachute Jumps. Multicoloured.
2690 75c. Type **1019** 90 70
2691 75c. Parachutists 90 70

1021 Boca Juniors Club Supporters

1999. Football. Multicoloured. (a) Size 42 × 33 mm.
2693 75c. Type **1021** 90 70
2694 75c. River Plate Club supporters 90 70

(b) Size 37 × 34 mm (1p.50) or 37 × 27 mm (others)
(i) Boca Juniors
2695 25c. Two players and ball 30 25
2696 50c. Club badge 60 50
2697 50c. Players hugging . . . 60 50
2698 75c. Supporters and balloons 90 70
2699 75c. Club banner 90 70
2700 75c. Players 90 70
2701 1p.50 Player making high kick 1·75 1·40

(ii) River Plate
2702 25c. Stadium 30 25
2703 50c. Players arriving on pitch 60 50
2704 50c. Supporters waving flags 60 50
2705 50c. Club badge 90 70
2706 75c. Trophy 90 70
2707 75c. Supporters with banner 90 70
2708 1p.50 Player preparing to kick ball . . . . . . 1·75 1·40
Nos. 2695/708 are self-adhesive.

1022 Planisphere of Central South America (Pierre Descelliers, 1546)

1999. Maps. Multicoloured.
2709 25c.+25c. Type **1022** 60 60
2710 50c.+50c. 17th-century map of estuary of the River Plate (Claes Voogt) . . . 1·25 1·25

2711 50c.+50c. Buenos Aires (Military Geographical Institute, 1910) . . . . . 1·25 1·25
2712 75c.+75c. Mouth of Riachuelo river and Buenos Aires harbour (satellite picture, 1999) . . 1·75 1·75

1023 Valdivielso and St. Peter's Cathedral, Rome

1999. Canonization of Hector Valdivielso Saez (Brother of the Christian Schools).
2713 **1023** 75c. multicoloured . . . 90 70

1024 "San Francisco Xavier" (brig)

1999. Bicentenary of Manuel Belgrano Naval Academy.
2714 **1024** 75c. multicoloured . . . 90 70

1026 Holy Family

1999. Christmas. Multicoloured.
2716 25c. Wise Man (29 × 29 mm) 30 25
2717 25c. Bell (29 × 29 mm) . . . 30 25
2718 50c. Two kings and camels (39 × 29 mm) 60 50
2719 50c. Holly leaf (39 × 29 mm) 60 50
2720 75c. Angel with star (39 × 30 mm) 90 70
2721 75c. Star (29 × 30 mm) . . . 90 70
2722 75c. Nativity (39 × 29 mm) 90 70
2723 75c. Tree decorations (29 × 29 mm) 90 70
2724 75c. Type **1026** 90 70

1027 Grape on Vine

2000. Wine Making. Multicoloured.
2725 25c. Type **1027** 35 30
2726 25c. Glass and bottle of wine 35 30
2727 50c. Wine bottles 70 55
2728 50c. Cork screw and cork 70 55

1028 Mathematical Symbol and "2000"

2000. International Mathematics Year.
2729 **1028** 75c. multicoloured . . . 1·00 80

1029 White-fronted Dove

2000. Doves and Pigeon. Mult. Self-adhesive.
2730 75c. Type **1029** . . . . . 1·00 80
2731 75c. Picazuro pigeon (Columba picazuro) . . . 1·00 80

2732 75c. Picui dove (Columbina picni) . . . . 1·00 80
2733 75c. Eared dove (Fenaida auriculata) . . . . . . 1·00 80

1031 Open Book (CONABIP Library)

2000. Libraries. Multicoloured.
2735 25c. Type **1031** 35 35
2736 50c. Building facade (Jujuy library) 70 55
2737 75c. Hands and braille book (Argentine Library for the Blind) . . . . 1·00 80
2738 $1 Open book and building (National Library) . . . 2·10 1·60
No. 2737 has an inscription in braille across the stamp.

1032 Caravel, Compass Rose and Letter

2000. 500th Anniv of the Discovery of Brazil. Multicoloured.
2739 25c. Type **1032** 35 30
2740 75c. Pedro Alvares Cabral (discoverer) and map of South America . . . . . 1·00 80

1033 Lieutenant General Luis Maria Campos (founder)

2000. Centenary of the Higher Military Academy.
2741 **1033** 75c. multicoloured . . . 1·00 80

1035 Convention Emblem

2000. 91st Rotary International Convention, Buenos Aires.
2743 **1035** 75c. multicoloured . . . 1·00 80

1036 Futuristic Houses and Emblems (Rocio Casado)

2000. "Stampin' the Future". Winning Entries in Children's International Painting Competition. Mult.
2744 25c. Type **1036** 35 30
2745 50c. Sea and clouds (Carolina Cacerez) (vert) 70 55
2746 75c. Flower (Valeria A. Pizarro) . . . . . . 1·00 80
2747 $1 Flying cars (Cristina Ayala Castro) (vert) . . . 1·40 1·10

1037 Ribbon

2000. America. AIDS Awareness. Multicoloured.
2748   75c. Type **1037** . . . . . .   1·00   80
2749   75c. Arms circling faces .   1·00   80

1038 Potez 25 Biplane

2000. Birth Centenary of Antoine de Saint-Exupery (novelist and pilot). Multicoloured.
2750   25c. Type **1038**   35   30
2751   50c. Late 28   70   55

1039 Potez 25 Biplane

2000. "Aerofila 2000" Mercosur Air Philately Exhibition, Buenos Aires. Multicoloured.
2752   25c. As Type **1039**   35   30
2753   25c. Antoine de Saint-
         Exupery (novelist and
         pilot) (29 × 29 mm) .   35   30
2754   50c. Late 28   70   55
2755   50c. Henri Guillaumet,
         Almonacid and Jean
         Mermoz (aviation
         pioneers) (29 × 29 mm) .   70   55
2756   50c. Map of South America
         and tail of Late 25
         (39 × 39 mm)   70   55
2757 $1 Late 25 and cover
         (39 × 29 mm) . . . . .   1·40   1·10

1040 Illia

2000. Birth Centenary of Arturo U. Illia (President, 1963–66).
2758   **1040** 75c. multicoloured . . .   1·00   80

 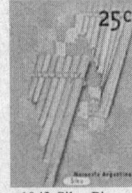

1041 San Martin   **1042** Siku Pipes

2000. 150th Death Anniv of General Jose de San Martin.
2759   **1041** 75c. multicoloured . . .   1·00   80

2000. Argentine Culture. Multicoloured.
2760   10c. Ceremonial axe   15   10
2761   25c. Type **1042**   35   30
2762   50c. Andean loom   70   55
2763   60c. Pampeana poncho . .   80   60
2764   75c. Funeral mask . . . . .   1·00   80
2765 $1 Basket . . . . . .   1·40   1·10
2766 $2 Kultun ritual drum . .   2·75   2·25
2767 $3.25 Ceremonial tiger mask   4·50   3·50
2768 $5 Funeral urn . . . . .   7·00   5·50
2770 $9.40 Suri ceremonial
         costume . . . . . .   13·00   10·00

1043 Sarsfield, Signature and Cordoba Province Arms

2000. Birth Bicentenary of Dalmacio Velez Sarsfield (lawyer).
2775   **1043** 75c. multicoloured . . .   1·00   80

1044 Windsurfing

2000. Olympic Games, Sydney. Multicoloured.
2776   75c. Type **1044** . . . . . .   1·00   80
2777   75c. Hockey . . . . . .   1·00   80
2778   75c. Volleyball . . . . .   1·00   80
2779   75c. High jump and pole
         vault . . . . . .   1·00   80

1045 Argentine Petiso

2000. "Espana 2000" International Stamp Exhibition, Madrid. Horses. Multicoloured.
2780   25c. Type **1045**   35   30
2781   25c. Carriage horse   35   30
2782   50c. Peruvian horse   70   55
2783   50c. Criolla   70   55
2784   75c. Saddle horse . . . .   1·00   80
2785   75c. Polo horse . . . . .   1·00   80

1046 Man on Bicycle and Las Nereidas Fountain

2000. Transportation. Multicoloured.
2787   25c.+25c. Type **1046**   70   55
2788   50c.+50c. *Graf Zeppelin* over
         Buenos Aires . . .   1·25   1·00
2789   50c.+50c. *Ganz* (diesel
         locomotive) . . . .   1·40   1·10
2790   75c.+75c. Tram . . . .   2·10   1·75

1047 Nuclear Reactor

2000. 50th Anniv of National Commission for Atomic Energy.
2791   **1047** 75c. multicoloured . . .   1·00   80

1048 "Filete" (left-hand detail)

2000. Fileteado (painting genre) (Nos. 2792/3) and Tango (dance) (Nos. 2794/5). Multicoloured.
2792   75c. Type **1048** . . . . .   1·00   80
2793   75c. "Filete" (right-hand
         detail) (Brunetti brothers)   1·00   80
2794   75c. Tango orchestra . . . .   1·00   80
2795   75c. Couple dancing . . . .   1·00   80

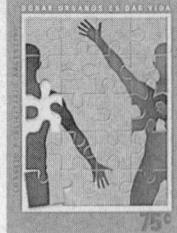

1049 Human Bodies on Jigsaw

2000. 40th Anniv of Organ Donation Publicity Campaign.
2796   **1049** 75c. multicoloured . . .   1·00   60

1050 "Birth of Jesus" (stained glass window, Sanctuary of Our Lady of the Rosary, New Pompeii)

2000. Christmas.
2797   **1050** 75c. multicoloured . . .   1·00   60

1051 *Commelina erecta*

2000. Medicinal Plants. Multicoloured.
2798   75c. Type **1051** . . . . . .   1·00   60
2799   75c. *Senna corymbosa* . . .   1·00   60
2800   75c. *Mirabilis jalapa* . . . .   1·00   60
2801   75c. *Eugenia uniflora* . . . .   1·00   60

1052 Human-shaped Vessel, Cienaga

2000. Traditional Crafts. Multicoloured.
2802   75c. Type **1052** . . . . .   1·00   60
2803   75c. Painted human-shaped
         vase, Vaquerias . . . .   1·00   60
2804   75c. Animal-shaped vessel,
         Condorhuasi . . . . .   1·00   60
2805   75c. Human-shaped vase,
         Candelaria . . . . .   1·00   60

1053 "U. P." Unidad Postal

2001. Postal Agents' Stamps. Multicoloured, background colours given. Self-adhesive gum.
2806   **1053** 10c. turquoise   15   10
2807   25c. green   35   20
2808   60c. yellow   80   45
2809   75c. red . . . . . .   1·00   60
2810 $1 blue . . . . . .   1·40   80
2811 $3 red . . . . . .   4·00   2·40
2812 $3.25 yellow . . . . .   4·50   2·75
2813 $5.50 mauve . . . . .   7·50   4·50
Nos. 2806/13 were issued for use by Postal Agents as opposed to branches of the Argentine Post Office.

1054 *Megatherium americanum* ("Megaterio")

2001. Cainozoic Mammals. Multicoloured.
2820   75c. Type **1054**   80   45
2821   75c. *Doedicurus clavcaudatus*
         ("Gliptodonte")   80   45
2822   75c. *Macrauchenia
         patachonica*
         ("Macrauqueria")   80   45
2823   75c. *Toxodon platensis*
         ("Toxodonte")   80   45

1055 Map, South Polar Skua and San Martin Base

2001. 50th Anniv of San Martín and Brown Antarctic Bases. Multicoloured.
2824   75c. Type **1055**   80   45
2825   75c. Blue-eyed cormorant,
         map and Brown Base . . .   80   45

1056 Bees on Clover Flower

2001. Apiculture. Multicoloured.
2826   75c. Type **1056**   80   45
2827   75c. Bees on honeycomb . . .   80   45
2828   75c. Bees and bee-keeper
         attending hives   80   45
2829   75c. Jar of honey and
         swizzle   80   45
Nos. 2826/9 were issued together, se-tenant, forming a composite design.

1058 Dornier Do-j Wal Flying Boat *Plus Ultra* and Route Map

2001. 75th Anniv of Major Ramon Franco's Flight from Spain to Argentina.
2831   **1058** 75c. multicoloured . . .   80   45

1059 Horse's Bridle Fittings

2001. Silver Work. Each blue, silver and black.
2832   75c. Type **1059**   80   45
2833   75c. Stirrups   80   45
2834   75c. Spurs   80   45
2835   75c. Rastra (gaucho belt
         decoration)   80   45

1061 Goalkeeper catching Ball

2001. Under 20's World Youth Football Championship, Argentine Republic. Multicoloured.

2837	75c. Type **1061**	80	45
2838	75c. Player kicking ball . .	80	45

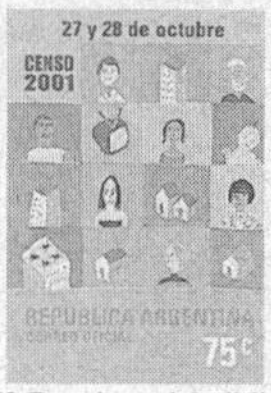

1062 People and Buildings

2001. National Census.

2839	**1062**	75c. multicoloured . . .	80	45

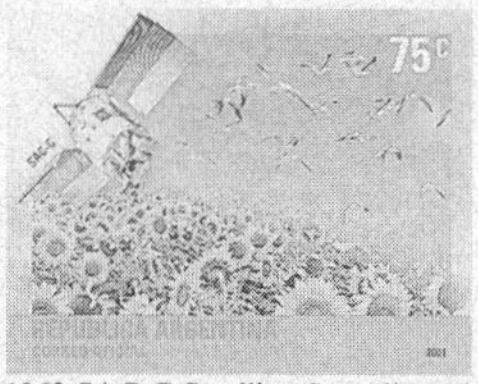

1063 SAC-C Satellite, Seagulls and Sunflowers

2001. Environmental Protection. Satellite Tracking Project.

2840	**1063**	75c. multicoloured . . .	80	45

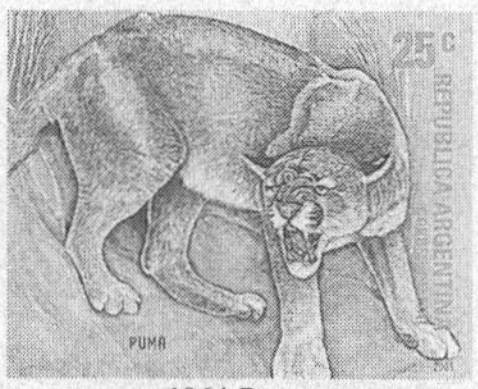

1064 Puma

2001. Wild Cats. Multicoloured.

2841	25c. Type **1064**	35	20
2842	25c. Jaguar	35	20
2843	50c. Jaguarundi	70	50
2844	50c. Ocelot	70	50
2845	75c. Geoffroy's Cat	80	45
2846	75c. Kodkod	80	45

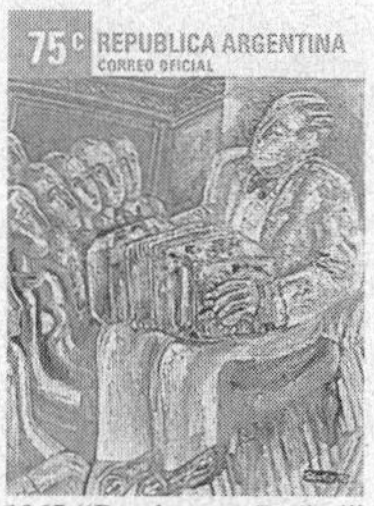

1065 "Bandoneon Recital" (painting, Aldo Severi)

2001.

2847	**1065**	75c. multicoloured . . .	80	45

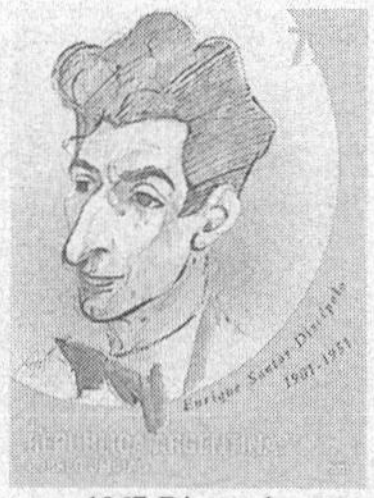
1067 Discepolo

2001. Birth Centenary of Enriques Santos Discepolo (actor and lyric writer).

2849	**1067**	75c. multicoloured . . .	80	45

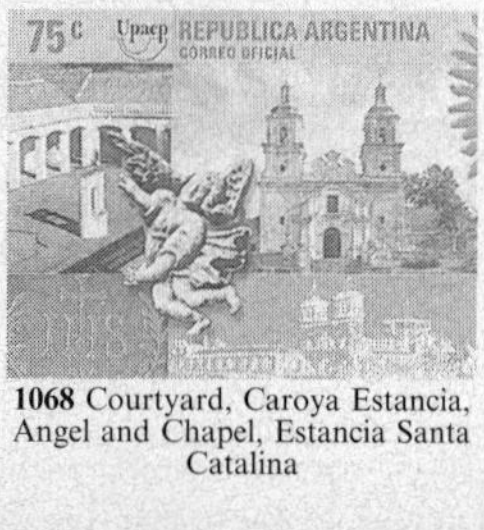

1068 Courtyard, Caroya Estancia, Angel and Chapel, Estancia Santa Catalina

2001. U.N.E.S.C.O World Heritage Sites. Multicoloured.

2850	75c. Type **1068**	80	45
2851	75c. Emblem and chapel, Estancia La Candelaria, dome of Estancia Alta Gracia and belfry, Estancia Jesus Maria . .	80	45

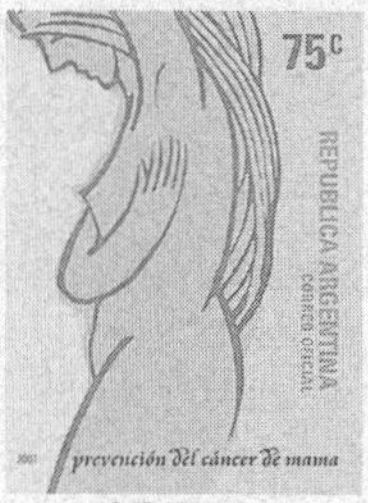

1069 Woman

2001. Breast Cancer Awareness.

2852	**1069**	75c. multicoloured . . .	80	45

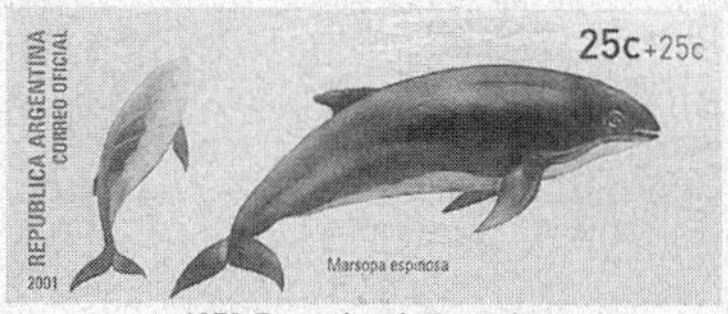

1070 Burmeister's Porpoise

2001. Marine Mammals. Multicoloured.

2853	25c.+25c. Type **1070**	70	70
2854	50c.+50c. La Plata River dolphin	1·40	1·40
2855	50c.+50c. Minke whale . . .	1·40	1·40
2856	75c.+75c. Humpback whale	2·10	2·10

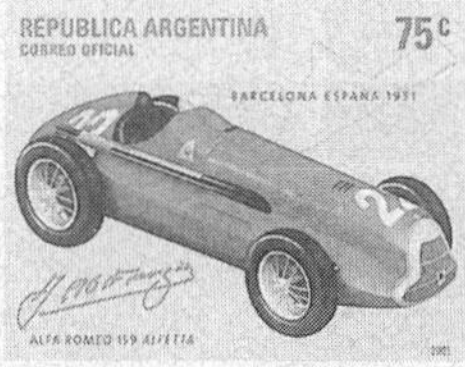

1071 Alfa Romeo 159 Alfetta, Spain 1951

2001. Formula 1 Racing Cars driven by Juan Manuel Fangio. Multicoloured.

2857	75c. Type **1071**	1·00	60
2858	75c. Mercedes Benz W 196, France, 1954	1·00	60
2859	75c. Lancia-Ferrari D50, Monaco, 1956	1·00	60
2860	75c. Maserati 250 F, Germany, 1957	1·00	60

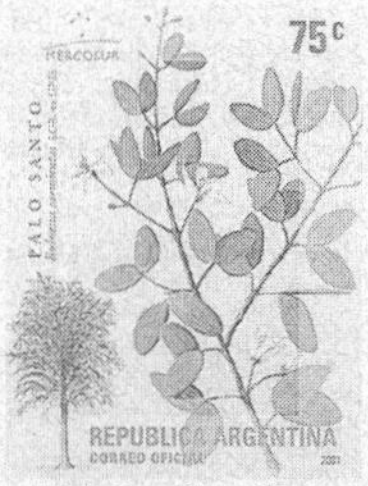

1072 Palo Santo Tree

2001. Mercosur (South American Common Market).

2861	**1072**	75c. multicoloured . . .	1·00	60

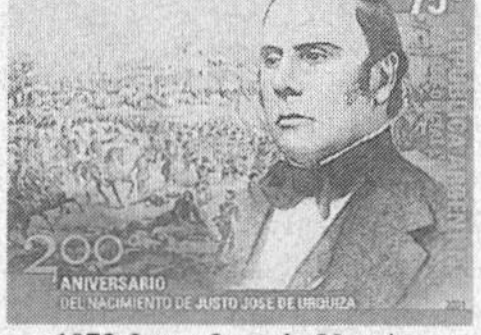

1073 Justo Jose de Urquiza

2001. Birth Anniversaries. Multicoloured.

2862	75c. Type **1073** (politician) (bicentenary)	1·00	60
2863	75c. Roque Saenz Pena (President 1910—14) (150th anniv)	1·00	60

EXPRESS SERVICE MAIL

E **999** Express Service Emblem

1999. Self-adhesive.

E2644	E **999**	8p.75 blue and silver	12·00	9·50
E2645	–	17p.50 blue and gold	24·00	19·00

DESIGN: 24-hour service emblem.

No. E2644 was for express service mail and No. E2645 for use on 24-hour express service mail.

OFFICIAL STAMPS

1884. Optd **OFICIAL**.

O66	**33**	½c. brown	8·00	6·00
O69		1c. red	45	15
O70	**24**	2c. green	45	15
O71	–	4c. brown (No. 32) . . .	45	15
O72	**9**	8c. red	45	15
O73	**10**	10c. green	42·00	22·00
O76	**33**	12c. blue	70	60
O77	**10**	16c. green	1·90	75
O78	**22**	20c. blue	8·00	6·00
O79	**11**	24c. blue (roul)	1·40	85
O80		24c. blue (perf)	1·25	70
O81	–	25c. red (No. 47)	9·50	6·50
O82	–	30c. orange (No. 33) . . .	17·00	12·00
O83	–	60c. black (No. 34) . . .	12·00	7·50
O84	–	90c. blue (No. 35)	8·50	6·50

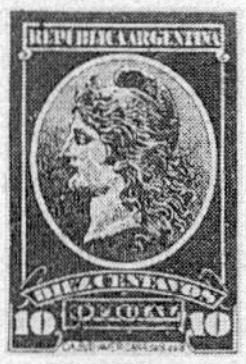

O 73

1901.

O275	O **73**	1c. grey	25	10
O276		2c. brown	35	15
O277		5c. red	45	15
O278		10c. green	50	15
O279		30c. blue	3·50	85
O280		50c. orange	1·90	65

1938. (a) Optd **SERVICIO OFICIAL** in two lines.

O668	**143**	1c. brown (No. 645) . .	10	10
O669	–	2c. brown (No. 646) . .	10	10
O670	–	3c. green (No. 647) . .	10	10
O679	–	3c. grey (No. 672) . . .	10	10
O771	–	3c. grey (No. 751) . . .	3·00	1·25
O671	–	5c. brown (No. 653b) . .	10	10
O782	**200**	5c. red (No. 773) . . .	10	10
O667	–	10c. red (No. 653d) . . .	10	10
O773	–	10c. purple (No. 678) . .	10	10
O681	**146**	15c. blue (No. 676) . .	10	10
O774	–	15c. grey (No. 708) . .	10	10
O683	**146**	20c. blue (19½ × 26 mm)	50	10
O872	**247**	20c. red	10	10
O813	–	25c. (No. 673)	10	10
O674	–	40c. (No. 658)	10	10
O675	–	50c. (No. 659)	10	10
O676	**152**	1p. (No. 760)	10	10
O827	**234**	1p. (No. 826)	35	10
O778	–	2p. (No. 661)	10	10
O779	–	5p. (No. 662)	15	10
O780	–	10p. (No. 763)	25	10
O781	–	20p. (No. 764)	80	20

(b) Optd **SERVICIO OFICIAL** in one line.

O897	–	20c. lilac (No. 895) . . .	15	10

1953. Eva Peron stamps optd **SERVICIO OFICIAL**.

O854	**239**	5c. grey	10	10
O855		10c. red	10	10
O856		20c. red	10	10
O857		25c. green	10	10
O858		40c. purple	10	10
O859		45c. blue	15	10
O860		50c. bistre	10	10
O862	**240**	1p. brown (No. 846) . .	10	10
O863		1p.50 green (No. 847)	25	10
O864		2p. red (No. 848) . . .	20	10
O865		3p. blue (No. 849) . . .	45	15
O866		5p. brown	70	40
O867	**239**	10p. red	4·00	3·00
O868	**240**	20p. green	32·00	20·00

1955. Stamps of 1954 optd **SERVICIO OFICIAL** in one line.

O869	**247**	20c. red	10	10
O870		40c. red	10	10
O880	–	1p. brown (No. 871) . .	10	10
O882	–	3p. purple (No. 874) . .	10	10
O883	–	5p. green (No. 875) . .	30	10
O884	–	10p. green and grey (No. 876)	40	10
O886	**250**	20p. violet	75	15

1955. Various stamps optd. (a) Optd **S. OFICIAL**.

O 896	–	5c. brown (No. 894)	10	10
O 955	–	10c. green (No. 946)	10	10
O 956	–	20c. purple (No. 947)	10	10
O 879	–	50c. blue (No. 868) . .	20	10
O 957	–	50c. ochre (No. 948)	10	10
O1034	–	1p. brn (No. 1016) . .	10	10
O 899	**264**	2p. purple	10	10
O1050	–	2p. red (No. 1035) . .	10	10
O 959	–	3p. blue (No. 951) . .	15	10
O1051	–	4p. red (No. 1036) . .	15	10
O 961	**296**	5p. brown	20	10
O1052	–	8p. red (No. 1037) . .	15	10
O 962	–	10p. brown (No. 1286)	15	10
O1053	–	10p. red (No. 1038) . .	15	10
O1036	–	12p. dull purple (No. 1028)	40	10
O 964	–	20p. green (No. 954)	50	10
O1055	–	20p. red (No. 1039) . .	20	10
O1037	–	22p. blue (No. 1018)	50	10
O1038	–	23p. green (No. 1019)	95	10
O1039	–	25p. lilac (No. 1020)	50	10
O1040	–	43p. lake (No. 1021)	1·40	65
O1041	–	45p. brn (No. 1022) . .	1·40	65
O1042	–	50p. blue (No. 1023)	2·40	95
O1043	–	50p. blue (No. 1287)	3·25	95
O1045	–	100p. blue (No. 1289)	1·60	65
O1046	–	300p. violet (No. 1026)	4·75	2·25

(b) Optd **SERVICIO OFICIAL**.

O 900	**265**	2p.40 brown	20	10
O 958	–	3p. blue (No. 951) . .	15	10
O 901	**266**	4p.40 green	25	10
O 960	**296**	5p. brown	20	10
O 887	–	50p. ind & bl (No. 878)	1·60	65
O1049	–	500p. grn (No. 1032)	7·75	3·75

For lists of stamps optd **M.A.**, **M.G.**, **M.H.**, **M.I.**, **M.J.I.**, **M.M.**, **M.O.P.** or **M.R.C.** for use in ministerial offices see the Stanley Gibbons Catalogue Part 20 (South America).

1963. Nos. 1068, etc., optd **S. OFICIAL**.

O1076	**351**	2p. green	20	10
O1080	–	4p. red (No. 1069) . .	15	10
O1081	–	6p. red (No. 1070) . .	25	10
O1078	–	90p. bistre (No. 1288)	4·00	2·00

RECORDED MESSAGE STAMPS

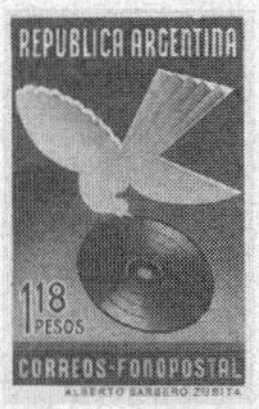

RM **166** Winged Messenger

1939. Various symbolic designs inscr "CORREOS FONOPOSTAL".

RM688	RM **166**	1p.18 blue . . .	16·00	8·00
RM689	–	1p.32 blue . . .	16·00	8·00
RM690	–	1p.50 brown . .	48·00	24·00

DESIGNS—VERT: 1p.32, Head of Liberty and National Arms. HORIZ: 1p.50, Record and winged letter.

TELEGRAPH STAMPS USED FOR POSTAGE

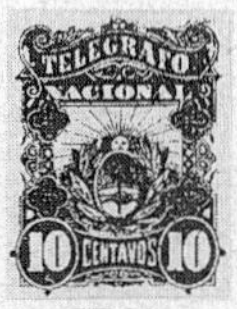

PT 34

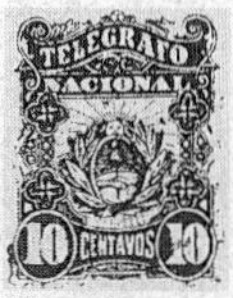

PT 35 (Sun closer to "NACIONAL")

1887.

PT104	PT **34**	10c. red	50	10
PT105	PT **35**	10c. red	50	10
PT106	PT **34**	40c. blue	60	10
PT107	PT **35**	40c. blue	60	15

ARMENIA — Pt. 10

Formerly part of Transcaucasian Russia. Temporarily independent after the Russian revolution of 1917. From 12 March 1922, Armenia, Azerbaijan and Georgia formed the Transcaucasian Federation. Issues for the federation were superseded by those of the Soviet Union in 1924.

With the dissolution of the Soviet Union in 1991 Armenia once again became independent.

NOTE. Only one price is given for Nos. 3/245, which applies to unused or cancelled to order. Postally used copies are worth more.

All the overprints and surcharges were handstamped and consequently were applied upright or inverted indiscriminately, some occurring only inverted.

1919. 100 kopeks = 1 rouble.
1994. 100 luna = 1 dram.

NATIONAL REPUBLIC

28 May 1918 to 2 December 1920 and 18 February to 2 April 1921.

1919. Arms type of Russia and unissued Postal Savings Bank stamp (No. 6) surch. Imperf or perf.

(a) Surch thus **k. 60 k** with or without stops.

3	**22**	60k. on 1k. orange	40
6	–	60k. on 1k. red on buff	10·00

(b) Surch in figures only.

7	**22**	60k. on 1k. orange	30·00
8		120k. on 1k. orange	30·00

 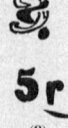

     (6)   (8)

1919. Stamps of Russia optd as T **6** in various sizes, with or without frame. Imperf or perf. (a) Arms types.

53B	22	1k. orange		13·00
54B		2k. green		50
55B		3k. red		50
11B	23	4k. red		25
12B	22	5k. red		25
13B	23	10k. blue		40
14B	22	10k. on 7k. blue		30
15B	10	15k. blue and purple		35
16B	14	20k. red and blue		30
17	10	25k. mauve and green		60
45B		35k. green and purple		50
19B	14	50k. green and purple		20
30B	22	60k. on 1k. orange (No. 3)		50
31B	10	70k. orange and brown		30
32B	15	1r. orange and brown		50
33B	11	3r.50 green and brown		1·00
23B	20	5r. green and blue		1·40
62	11	7r. yellow and black		25·00
24B		7r. pink and green		2·50
52B	20	10r. grey, red and yellow		3·00

    (b) Romanov type.

63B	4k. red (No. 129)		2·00

   (c) Unissued Postal Savings Bank stamp.

64A	1k. red on buff		3·50

1920. Stamps of Russia surch as T **8** in various types and sizes. Imperf or perf. (a) Arms types.

94B	22	1r. on 60k. on 1k. orange (No. 3)	80
65B		1r. orange	50
66B		3r. on 3k. red	50
67B		3r. on 4k. red	6·00
97B		5r. on 2k. green	60
69B	23	5r. on 4k. red	1·00
70B	22	5r. on 5k. red	50
71B		5r. on 7k. blue	1·00
72B	23	5r. on 10k. blue	40
73B	22	5r. on 10 on 7k. blue	90
74B	10	5r. on 14k. red and blue	2·25
75B		5r. on 15k. blue and purple	75
76B	14	5r. on 20k. red and blue	1·25
76aB	10	5r. on 20 on 14k. red and blue	7·00
77B		5r. on 25k. mauve and green	7·00
111B	22	5r. on 3 r .on 5k. red	7·50
78B	10	10r. on 25k. mauve and green	1·00
79B		10r. on 35k. green and purple	65
80B	14	10r. on 50k. green and purple	1·00
80aB	9	25r. on 1k. orange	35·00
80bB		25r. on 3k. red	35·00
80cB		25r. on 5k. purple	35·00
80dB	22	25r. on 10 on 7k. blue	35·00
80eB	10	25r. on 15k. blue and purple	35·00
81B	14	25r. on 20k. red and blue	4·00
82B	10	25r. on 25k. mauve and green	4·00
83B		25r. on 35k. green and purple	3·50
84B	14	25r. on 50k. green and purple	3·50
85B	10	25r. on 70k. orange and brown	4·00
104aB	9	50r. on 1k. orange	32·00
104bB		50r. on 3k. red	32·00
85bB	10	50r. on 4k. red	38·00
104cB	14	50r. on 5k. purple	32·00
85cB	10	50r. on 15k. blue and purple	38·00
85dB	14	50r. on 20k. red and blue	38·00
85eB	10	50r. on 35k. green & purple	38·00
85fB	14	50r. on 50k. green & purple	20·00
105B	10	50r. on 70k. orange and brown	4·50
106B	15	50r. on 1or. orange and brown	1·10
107B		100r. on 1r. orange and brown	6·50
108B	11	100r. on 3r.50 green and brown	4·50
88B	20	100r. on 5r. green and blue	5·00
89B	11	100r. on 7r. yellow and black	20·00
90B		100r. on 7r. pink and green	6·75
93B	20	100r. on 10r. grey, red and yellow	6·00

    (b) Romanov issue of 1913.

112	1r. on 1k. orange	7·00
113	1r. on 3k. red	5·00
114	5r. on 4k. red	3·50
115	5r. on 10 on 7k. brown	3·50
116	5r. on 14k. green	22·00
117	5r. on 20 on 14k. green	5·00
118	25r. on 4k. red	5·00
118a	100r. on 1k. orange	50·00
119	100r. on 2k. green	50·00
120	100r. on 3r. violet	55·00

  (c) War Charity issues of 1914 and 1915.

121	15	25r. on 1k. green and red on yellow	38·00
122		25r. on 3k. green and red on rose	30·00
123		50r. on 7k. green and brown on buff	24·00
124		50r. on 10k. brown and blue	24·00
125		100r. on 1k. green and red on yellow	24·00
126		100r. on 1k. grey and brown	24·00
127		100r. on 3k. green and red on rose	24·00
128		100r. on 7k. green and brown on buff	24·00
129		100r. on 10k. brown and blue	24·00

1920. Arms types of Russia optd as T **6** in various sizes with or without frame, and surch as T **8** or with value only in various types and sizes. Imperf or perf.

155B	22	1r. on 60k. on 1k. orange (No. 3)	1·10
156A		3r. on 3k. red	1·50
157A		5r. on 2k. green	90
141A	23	5r. on 4k. red	3·00
158A	22	5r. on 5k. red	2·75
142A	23	5r. on 10 on 7k. blue	3·00
143A	22	5r. on 15k. blue & pur	1·25
144A	10	5r. on 15k. blue & pur	1·25
145A	14	5r. on 20k. red and blue	1·25

132B	10	10r. on 15k. blue & pur	7·50
145aB	14	10r. on 20k. red & blue	9·00
146A	10	10r. on 25k. mauve and green	1·25
147B		10r. on 35k. green and purple	1·00
148A	14	10r. on 50k. green and purple	2·50
159A	10	10r. on 70k. orange and brown	8·75
163A	22	10r. on 5r. red	18·00
164A	10	10r. on 5r. on 25k. mauve and green	20·00
165A		10r. on 5r. on 35k. green and purple	6·50
138A		25r. on 70k. orange and brown	5·00
161B	15	50r. on 1r. orange and brown	1·75
135B	11	100r. on 3r.50 green and brown	1·75
151A	20	100r. on 5r. green & bl	6·00
136A	11	100r. on 7r. pink and green	5·00
154aA	20	100r. on 10r. grey, red and yellow	8·00
166A		100r. on 25r. on 5r. green and blue	18·00

1920. Stamps of Russia optd as T **6** in various sizes, with or without frame and surch **10.** Perf. (a) Arms types.

168	14	10 on 20k. red and blue	18·00
169	10	10 on 25k. mauve and green	18·00
170		10 on 35k. green and purple	12·00
171	14	10 on 50k. green and purple	14·00

    (b) Romanov type.

172	10 on 4k. red (No. 129)		30·00

1920. Stamps of Russia optd with monogram as in T **8** in various types and sizes and surch **10.** Imperf or perf. (a) Arms types.

173	23	10 on 4k. red	30·00
174	22	10 on 5k. red	30·00
175	10	10 on 15k. blue & purple	30·00
176	14	10 on 20k. red and blue	28·00
176a	10	10 on 20 on 14k. red and blue	14·00
177		10 on 25k. mauve & green	14·00
178		10 on 35k. green & purple	14·00
179	14	10 on 50k. green & purple	14·00

    (b) Romanov type.

181	10 on 4k. red (No. 129)		38·00

   11   **12** Mt. Ararat

Stamps in Types **11, 12** and a similar horizontal type showing a woman spinning were printed in Paris to the order of the Armenian National Government, but were not issued in Armenia as the Bolshevists had assumed control. (Price 10p. each).

SOVIET REPUBLIC

2 December 1920 to 18 February 1921 and 2 April 1921 to 12 March 1922.

    (13)

1921. Arms types of Russia surch with T **13.** Perf.

182	15	5000r. on 1r. orange and brown	5·00
183	11	5000r. on 3r.50 grn & brn	5·00
184	20	5000r. on 5r. green & blue	5·00
185	11	5000r. on 7r. pink and green	5·00
186	20	5000r. on 10r. grey, red & yellow	5·00

  14 Common   **16** Village Scene
    Crane

1922. Unissued stamps surch in gold kopeks. Imperf.

187	14	1 on 250r. red	13·50
188		1 on 250r. slate	21·00
189	16	2 on 500r. red	4·50
190		3 on 500r. slate	1·00
191		4 on 1000r. red	2·75
192		4 on 1000r. slate	6·00
193		5 on 2000r. slate	24·00
194		10 on 2000r. red	24·00
195		15 on 5000r. red	12·00
196		15 on 5000r. slate	3·00

DESIGNS (sizes in mm): 1000r. Woman at well (17 × 26); 2000r. Erivan railway station (35 × 24½); 5000r. Horseman and Mt. Ararat (39½ × 24½).

 17 Soviet Emblems    **18** Wall Sculpture at Ani

       19 Mt. Aragatz

1922. Unissued stamps as T **17/19** surch in gold kopeks in figures. Imperf or perf.

210	17	1 on 1r. green	3·00
198	18	2 on 2r. slate	7·50
212		3 on 3r. red	12·00
213		4 on 25r. green	2·50
201		5 on 50r. red	3·00
215		10 on 100r. orange	4·00
203		15 on 250r. blue	2·00
204a	19	20 on 500r. purple	2·50
205		35 on 20,000r. red	18·00
206a		50 on 25,000r. green	28·00
209		50r. on 25,000r. blue	4·00

DESIGNS (sizes in mm): 3r. (29 × 22) and 250r. (21 × 35) Soviet emblems; 25r. (30 × 22½); 100r. (34½ × 23) and 20,000r. (43 × 27) Mythological sculptures, Ani. 50r. (25½ × 37). Armenian soldier; 25,000r. (45½ × 27½) Mt. Ararat.
  The above and other values were not officially issued without the surcharges.

TRANSCAUCASIAN FEDERATION ISSUES FOR ARMENIA

1923. As T **19**, etc., surch in gold kopeks in figures. Imperf or perf.

219		1 on 250r. blue	3·00
217	19	2 on 500r. purple	3·00
218		3 on 20000r. lake	8·50

 26 Mt. Ararat and   **28** Ploughing
 Soviet Emblems

1923. Unissued stamps in various designs as T **26/28** surch in Transcaucasian roubles in figures. Perf.

227	26	10,000r. on 50r. green and red	1·50
228		15,000r. on 300r. blue and buff	1·50
229		25,000r. on 400r. blue and buff	1·50
240B		30,000r. on 500r. violet and lilac	1·50
231		50,000r. on 1000r. blue	1·50
232		75,000r. on 3000r. black and green	1·75
233		100,000r. on 2000r. black and grey	2·00
243		200,000r. on 4000r. black and brn	1·00
235		300,000r. on 5000r. black and red	2·75
245	28	500,000r. on 10,000r. black and red	1·25

DESIGNS (sizes in mm): 300r. (26 × 35) Star over Mt. Ararat; 400r. (26 × 34½) Crane (bird); 1000r. (19 × 25) Peasant in print; 2000r. (26 × 31) Human-headed bird from old bas-relief; 3000r. (26½ × 36) Sower; 4000r. (26 × 31½) Star and dragon; 5000r. (26 × 32) Blacksmith.

INDEPENDENT REPUBLIC

  31 Mount Ararat and National
     Colours

1992. Independence Day.

246	31	20k. multicoloured	15 15
247		2r. multicoloured	90 90
248		5r. multicoloured	2·10 2·10

  32 Dish Aerial and World Map

1992. Inauguration of International Direct-dial Telephone System.

250	32	50k. multicoloured	1·25 1·25

 33 Ancient Greek   **34** National Flag
   Wrestling

1992. Olympic Games, Barcelona. Multicoloured.

251		40k. Type 33	10 10
252		3r.60 Boxing	30 30
253		5r. Weightlifting	35 35
254		12r. Gymnastics (ring exercises)	75 75

1992.

255	34	20k. multicoloured (postage)	10 10
256		1r. black	10 10
257		3r. brown	25 25
258		3r. brown	10 10
259		5r. black	40 40
260		20r. grey	25 25
261		2r. blue (air)	35 35

DESIGNS: 1r. Goddess Waroubini statuette from Orgov radio-optical telescope; 2r. Zvartnots Airport, Yerevan; 3r. (No. 257) Goddess Anahit; 3r. (No. 258) Runic inscription Karmir-Blour; 5r. U.P.U. Monument, Berne, Switzerland; 20r. Silver cup from Karashamb.
  See also Nos. 275/82.

 36 Engraved 10th-   **37** Garni Canyon
 century Tombstone,
 Makenis

1993. Armenian Cultural History. Multicoloured.

263		40k. Type 36	10 10
264		80k. Illuminated page from Gospel of 1295	15 15
265		3r.60 13th-century bas-relief, Gandzasar	60 60
266		5r. "Glorious Mother of God" (18th-century painting, H. Hovnatanian)	1·00 1·00

1993. Landscapes. Multicoloured.

268		40k. Type 37	10 10
269		80k. Shaki Falls, Zangezur	10 10
270		3r.60 River Arpa gorge, Vike	25 25
271		5r. Lake Sevan (horiz)	40 40
272		12r. Mount Ararat (horiz)	90 90

 38 Temple of Garni   **39** Reliquary for Arm
                of St. Thaddeus (17th
                century)

1993. "YEREVAN '93" International Stamp Exn.

273	38	10r. red, black and brown	35 35

1994. As T **34** but new currency.

275		10l. agate and brown	10 10
277		50l. deep brown and brown	10 10
280		10d. brown and grey	25 25
282		25d. gold and red	75 75

DESIGNS: 10l. Shivini, Sun God (Karmir-Blour); 50l. Tayshaba, God of the Elements (Karmir-Blour); 10d. Khaldi, Supreme God (Karmir-Blour); 25d. National arms.

1994. Treasures of Etchmiadzin (seat of Armenian church). Multicoloured.

286		3d. Descent from the Cross (9th-century wooden panel)	10 10

287 5d. Gilded silver reliquary of
　　Holy Cross of Khotakerats
　　(1300) . . . . 10　10
288 12d. Cross with St. Karapet's
　　right hand (14th century) 20　20
289 30d. Type **39** . . . . . 65　65
290 50d. Gilded silver chrism
　　vessel (1815) . . . . . . 90　90

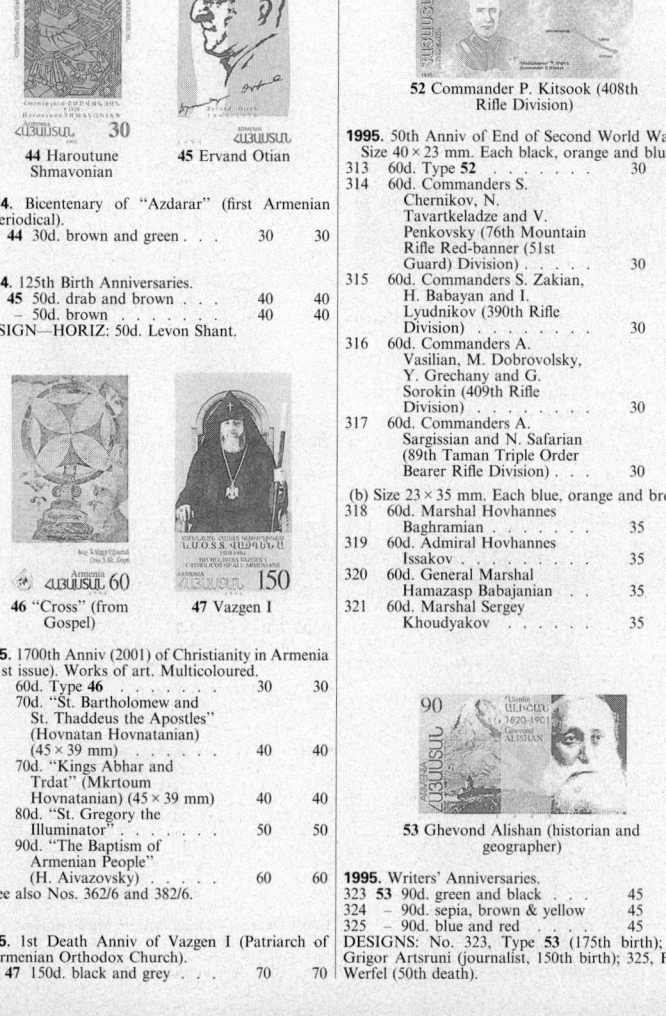

40　　　**40**
(40)　　　(41)

1994. Stamp Exhibitions, Yerevan. (a) "Armenia '94"
National Exn. No. 273 surch with T **40**.
291 **38** 40d. on 10r. red, blk & brn　1·00　1·00
　(b) "Armenia–Argentina" Exhibition. No. 273 surch
with T **41**.
292 **38** 40d. on 10r. red, blk & brn　1·00　1·00

42 Cancelled Stamps of 1919　**43** Stadium and
　　　　　　　　　　　Arms of National
　　　　　　　　　　　Committee

1994. 75th Anniv of First Stamp Issue.
293 **42** 16d. multicoloured . . . . 30　30

1994. Olympic Committees. Multicoloured.
294 30d. Type **43** . . . . . . 15　15
295 40d. Olympic rings (centenary
　　of Int Olympic Committee) 20　20

44 Haroutune　**45** Ervand Otian
　Shmavonian

1994. Bicentenary of "Azdarar" (first Armenian
periodical).
296 **44** 30d. brown and green . . 30　30

1994. 125th Birth Anniversaries.
297 **45** 50d. drab and brown . . 40　40
298 – 50d. brown . . . . . . 40　40
DESIGN—HORIZ: 50d. Levon Shant.

46 "Cross" (from　**47** Vazgen I
　Gospel)

1995. 1700th Anniv (2001) of Christianity in Armenia
(1st issue). Works of art. Multicoloured.
299 60d. Type **46** . . . . . . 30　30
300 70d. "St. Bartholomew and
　　St. Thaddeus the Apostles"
　　(Hovnatan Hovnatanian)
　　(45 × 39 mm) . . . . . . 40　40
301 70d. "Kings Abhar and
　　Trdat" (Mkrtoum
　　Hovnatanian) (45 × 39 mm) 40　40
302 80d. "St. Gregory the
　　Illuminator" . . . . . . 50　50
303 90d. "The Baptism of
　　Armenian People"
　　(H. Aivazovsky) . . . . 60　60
　See also Nos. 362/6 and 382/6.

1995. 1st Death Anniv of Vazgen I (Patriarch of
Armenian Orthodox Church).
305 **47** 150d. black and grey . . 70　70

48 Black-polished　**49** Red Kite and Oak
　　Pottery

1995. Museum Artefacts (1st series). Multicoloured.
306 30d. Type **48** . . . . . . 10　10
307 60d. Silver horn . . . . . 20　20
308 130d. Gohar carpet . . . . 50　50
　See also Nos. 332/4.

1995. Birds and Trees. Multicoloured.
309 40d. Type **49** . . . . . . 60　60
310 60d. Golden eagle and
　　juniper . . . . 80　80

50 Workers building "Honeycomb"
　　Map

1995. Hyastan All-Armenian Fund.
311 **50** 90d. multicoloured . . . . 40　40

51 Rainbows around U.N. Emblem

1995. 50th Anniv of U.N.O.
312 **51** 90d. multicoloured . . . . 40　40

52 Commander P. Kitsook (408th
　　Rifle Division)

1995. 50th Anniv of End of Second World War. (a)
Size 40 × 23 mm. Each black, orange and blue.
313 60d. Type **52** . . . . . . 30　30
314 60d. Commanders S.
　　Chernikov, N.
　　Tavartkeladze and V.
　　Penkovsky (76th Mountain
　　Rifle Red-banner (51st
　　Guard) Division) . . . . 30　30
315 60d. Commanders S. Zakian,
　　H. Babayan and I.
　　Lyudnikov (390th Rifle
　　Division) . . . . 30　30
316 60d. Commanders A.
　　Vasilian, M. Dobrovolsky,
　　Y. Grechany and G.
　　Sorokin (409th Rifle
　　Division) . . . . 30　30
317 60d. Commanders A.
　　Sargissian and N. Safarian
　　(89th Taman Triple Order
　　Bearer Rifle Division) . . . 30　30
　(b) Size 23 × 35 mm. Each blue, orange and brown.
318 60d. Marshal Hovhannes
　　Baghramian . . . . . . 35　35
319 60d. Admiral Hovhannes
　　Issakov . . . . 35　35
320 60d. General Marshal
　　Hamazasp Babajanian . . 35　35
321 60d. Marshal Sergey
　　Khoudyakov . . . . . . 35　35

53 Ghevond Alishan (historian and
　　geographer)

1995. Writers' Anniversaries.
323 **53** 90d. green and black . . 45　45
324 – 90d. sepia, brown & yellow 45　45
325 – 90d. blue and red . . . . 45　45
DESIGNS: No. 323, Type **53** (175th birth); 324,
Grigor Artsruni (journalist, 150th birth); 325, Franz
Werfel (50th death).

54 Sports and Concert Complex　**55** Katsian and
　　　　　　　　　　　　Spectators
　　　　　　　　　　　watching Flight

1995. Yerevan.
326 – 60d. black and orange . . 20　20
327 – 80d. black and pink . . . 25　25
328 **54** 90d. black and buff . . . 30　30
329 – 100d. black and buff . . . 35　35
330 – 120d. black and pink . . . 45　45
DESIGNS—As T **54**: 60d. Brandy distillery and wine
cellars; 80d. Abovian Street; 400d. Panoramic view of
Yerevan. 60 × 23 mm: 100d. Baghramian Avenue;
120d. Republic Square.

1995. Museum Artefacts (2nd series). As T **48**. Mult.
332 40d. Four-wheeled carriages
　　(horiz) . . . . 10　10
333 60d. Bronze model of solar
　　system . . . . 20　20
334 90d. Tombstone from
　　Loriberd . . . . 35　35

1995. Air. 86th Anniv of Artiom Katsian's 1909
World Record for Range and Altitude.
335 **55** 90d. ochre, brown and blue 50　50

(56)　　　**57** Griboedov

1996. No. 275 surch as T **56**.
336 40d. on 10l. agate and brown 50　50
337 100d. on 10l. agate and
　　brown . . . . 1·40　1·40
338 150d. on 10l. agate and
　　brown . . . . 1·90　1·90
339 200d. on 10l. agate and
　　brown . . . . 2·50　2·50

1996. Birth Bicentenary of Aleksandr Griboedov
(historian).
340 **57** 90d. stone, brown and red　35　35

58 Hayrik Khrimian (patriarch of
　　Armenian Orthodox Church, 175th
　　birth anniv (1995))

1996. Anniversaries.
341 **58** 90d. blue & brn (postage)　35　35
342 – 90d. multicoloured . . . . 35　35
343 – 90d. grey, blue & red (air)　35　35
DESIGNS—HORIZ: No. 342, Lazar Serebryakov
(Admiral of the Fleet, and 19th-century Russian
warships, birth bicentenary (1995)). VERT: No. 343,
Nelson Stepanian (Second World War pilot, 50th
death anniv (1994)).

59 Opening Frame from First
　　Armenian Film

1996. Centenary of Motion Pictures.
344 **59** 60d. black, grey and blue　50　75

60 Angel and Red　**61** Wild Goats
　Cross

1996. 75th Anniv of Armenian Red Cross Society.
345 **60** 60d. multicoloured . . . . 30　30

1996. Mammals. Multicoloured.
346 40d. Type **61** . . . . . . 25　25
347 60d. Leopards . . . . . . 30　30

62 Nansen and "Fram"

1996. Centenary of Return of Fridtjof Nansen's
Arctic Expedition.
348 **62** 90d. multicoloured . . . . 40　40

63 Cycling　**64** Torch Bearer

1996. Olympic Games, Atlanta. Multicoloured.
349 40d. Type **63** . . . . . . 20　20
350 60d. Triple jumping . . . . 30　30
351 90d. Wrestling . . . . . . 40　40
　Nos. 349/51 were issued together, se-tenant, the
backgrounds forming a composite design showing
ancient Greek athletes.

1996. Centenary of Modern Olympic Games.
352 **64** 90d. multicoloured . . . . 30　30

65 Genrikh Kasparian　**66** Tigran Petrosian
（first prize winner, "Chess　（World chess
in USSR" competition,　champion, 1963–69)
1939）　　　　　　and Tigran
　　　　　　　　　Petrosian Chess
　　　　　　　　　House, Yerevan

1996. 32nd Chess Olympiad, Yerevan. Designs
showing positions from previous games. Mult.
353 40d. Type **65** . . . . . . 40　40
354 40d. Tigran Petrosian v.
　　Mikhail Botvinnik (World
　　Championship, Moscow,
　　1963) . . . . 40　40
355 40d. Gary Kasparov v.
　　Anatoly Karpov (World
　　Championship, Leningrad,
　　1986) . . . . 40　40
356 40d. Olympiad emblem . . 40　40

1996.
357 **66** 90d. multicoloured . . . . 50　50

67 Goats

1996. The Wild Goat. Multicoloured.
358 70d. Type **67** . . . . . . 30　30
359 100d. Lone female . . . . 40　40
360 130d. Lone male . . . . . 50　50
361 350d. Heads of male and
　　female . . . . 1·40　1·40

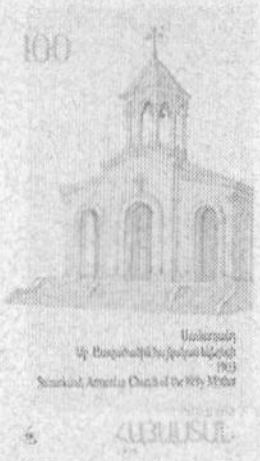

68 Church of the Holy Mother, Samarkand, Uzbekistan

1997. 1700th Anniv (2001) of Christianity in Armenia (2nd issue). Armenian Apostolic Overseas Churches. Multicoloured.

362	100d. Type **68**	35	35
363	100d. Church of the Holy Mother, Kishinev, Moldova	35	35
364	100d. St. Hripsime's Church, Yalta, Ukraine	35	35
365	100d. St. Catherine's Church, St. Petersburg, Russia	35	35
366	100d. Church, Lvov, Ukraine	35	35

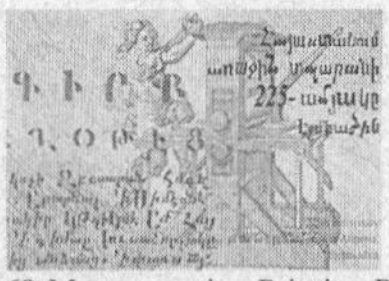

69 Man operating Printing Press

1997. 225th Anniv of First Printing Press in Armenia.

368 **69** 70d. multicoloured 35 35

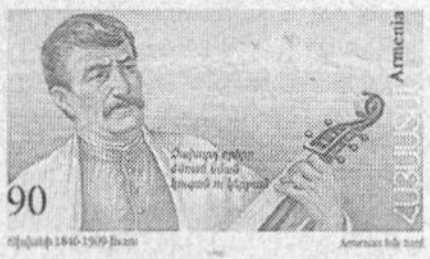

70 Jivani and Mount Ararat

1997. 150th Birth Anniv of Jivani (folk singer).

369 **70** 90d. multicoloured 35 35

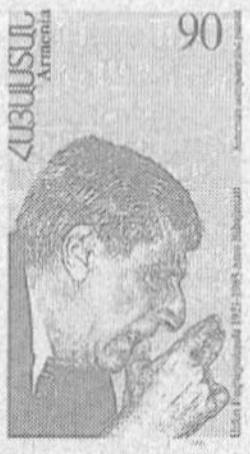

71 Babajanian and Score of "Heroic Ballad"

1997. 75th Birth Anniv (1996) of Arno Babajanian (composer and pianist).

370 **71** 90d. black, lilac & purple 35 35

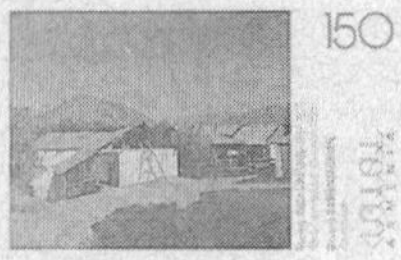

72 Countryside (Gevorg Bashinjaghian)

1997. Paintings in National Gallery of Armenia (1st series). Multicoloured.

371	150d. Type **72**	50	50
372	150d. "One of My Dreams" (Eghishe Tadevossian)	50	50
373	150d. "Portrait of Natalia Tehumian" (Hakob Hovnatanian) (vert)	50	50
374	150d. "Salome" (Vardges Sureniants) (vert)	50	50

See also Nos. 390/2.

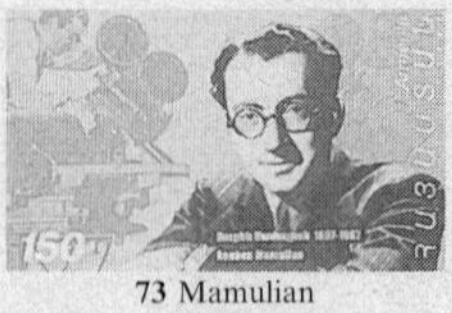

73 Mamulian

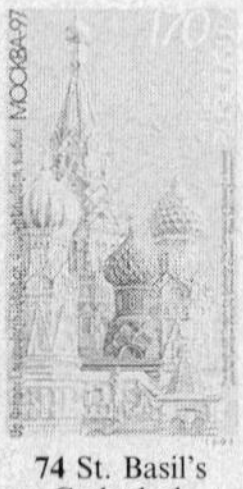

74 St. Basil's Cathedral, Moscow

1997. Birth Centenary of Rouben Mamulian (film director).

375 **73** 150d. multicoloured . . . 45 45

1997. "Moscow 97" Int Stamp Exhibition.

376 **74** 170d. multicoloured . . . 55 55

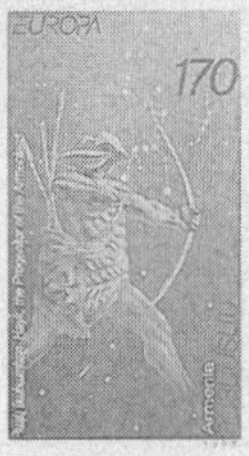

75 Hayk and Bel

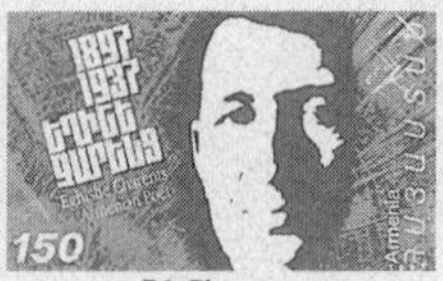

76 Charents

1997. Europa. Tales and Legends. Multicoloured.

377	170d. Type **75**	55	55
378	250d. The Song of Vahagn	75	75

1997. Birth Centenary of Eghishe Charents (poet).

379 **76** 150d. brown and red . . . 45 45

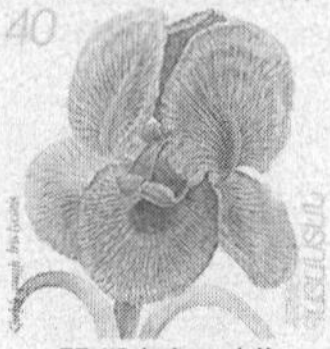

77 "Iris lycotis"

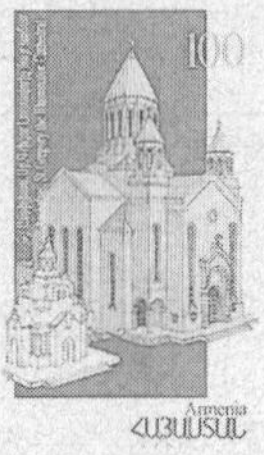

78 St. Gregory the Illuminator Cathedral, Anthelias, Libya

1997. Irises. Multicoloured.

380	40d. Type **77**	15	15
381	170d. "Iris elegantissima"	55	55

1997. 1700th Anniv (2001) of Christianity in Armenia (3rd issue). Armenian Overseas Educational Centres. Multicoloured.

382	100d. Type **78**	30	30
383	100d. St. Khach Armenian Church, Nakhijevan, Rostov-on-Don	30	30
384	100d. St. James's Monastery, Jerusalem (horiz)	30	30
385	100d. Nercissian School, Tblisi, Georgia (60 × 21 mm)	30	30
386	100d. San Lazzaro Mekhitarian Congregation, Venice (horiz)	30	30

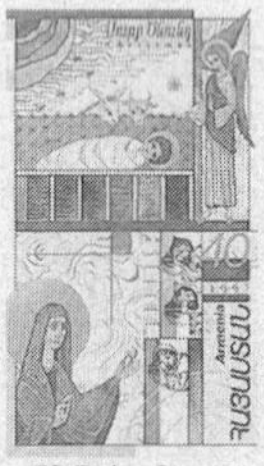

79 Baby Jesus, Angel and Mary

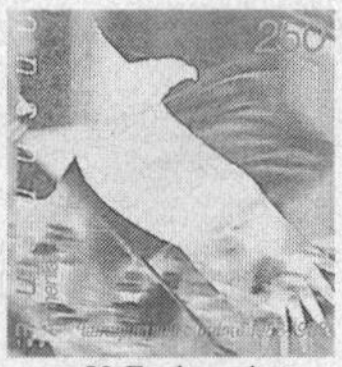

80 Eagle and Demonstrator with Flag

1997. Christmas.

388 **79** 40d. multicoloured 15 15

1998. 10th Anniv of Karabakh Movement.

389 **80** 250d. multicoloured . . . 75 75

1998. Paintings in National Gallery of Armenia (2nd series). As T **72**. Multicoloured.

390	150d. "Family. Generations" (Yervand Kochar) (vert)	45	45
391	150d. "Tartar Women's Dance" (Alexander Bazhbeouk-Melikian)	45	45
392	150d. "Spring in Our Yard" (Haroutiun Kalents) (vert)	45	45

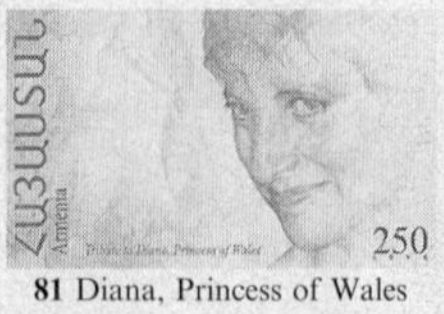

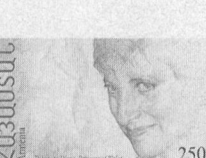

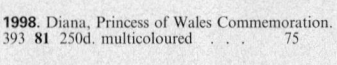

81 Diana, Princess of Wales

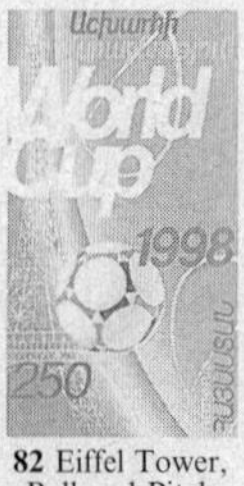

82 Eiffel Tower, Ball and Pitch

1998. Diana, Princess of Wales Commemoration.

393 **81** 250d. multicoloured . . . 75 75

1998. World Cup Football Championship, France.

394 **82** 250d. multicoloured . . . 75 75

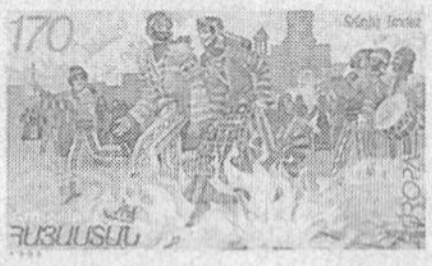

83 Couple leaping through Flames (Trndez)

1998. Europa. National Festivals. Multicoloured.

395	170d. Type **83**	55	55
396	250d. Girls in traditional costume (Ascension)	75	75

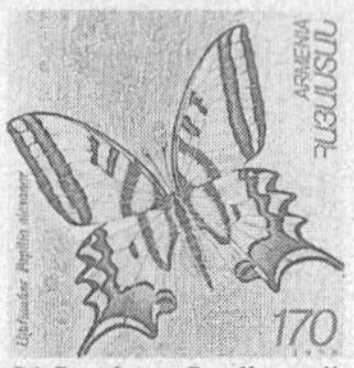

84 Southern Swallowtail

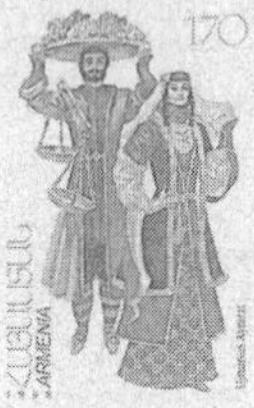

85 Ayrarat Couple

1998. Insects. Multicoloured.

397	170d. Type **84**	55	55
398	250d. "Rethera komarovi" (moth)	75	75

1998. Traditional Costumes (1st series). Mult.

399	170d. Type **85**	55	55
400	250d. Vaspurakan family	75	75

See also Nos. 408/9.

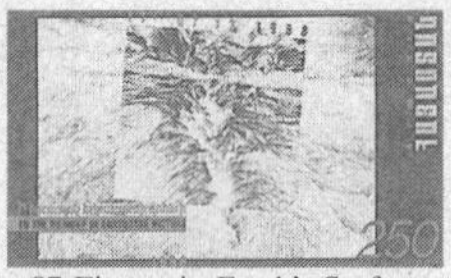

87 Fissure in Earth's Surface

1998. 10th Anniv of Armenian Earthquake.

402 **87** 250d. black, red and lilac 75 75

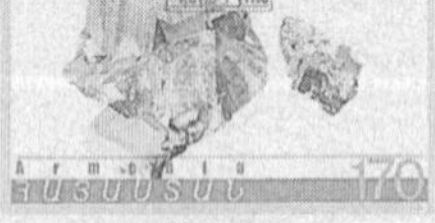

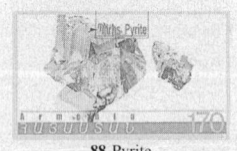

88 Pyrite

1998. Minerals. Multicoloured.

403	170d. Type **88**	55	55
404	250d. Agate	75	75

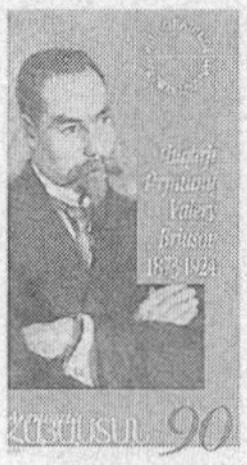

89 Briusov

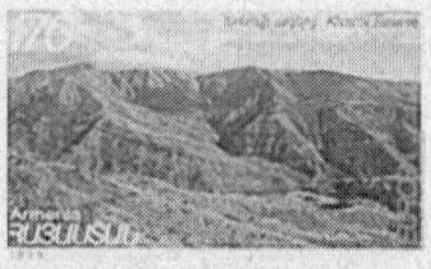

91 Khosrov Reserve

1998. 125th Birth Anniv of Valery Briusov (Russian translator of Armenian works).

405 **89** 90d. multicoloured 35 35

1999. Traditional Costumes (2nd series). As T **85**.

408	170d. Mother and child from Karin	40	40
409	250d. Zangezour couple	60	60

1999. Europa. Parks and Gardens. Multicoloured.

410	170d. Type **91**	40	40
411	250d. Dilijan Reserve	60	60

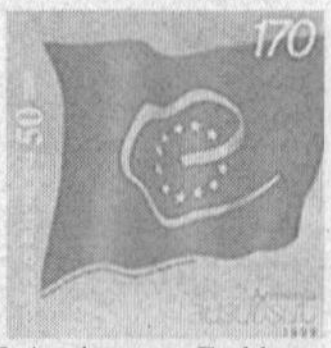

92 Anniversary Emblem on Flag

1999. 50th Anniv of Council of Europe.

412 **92** 170d. multicoloured . . . 40 40

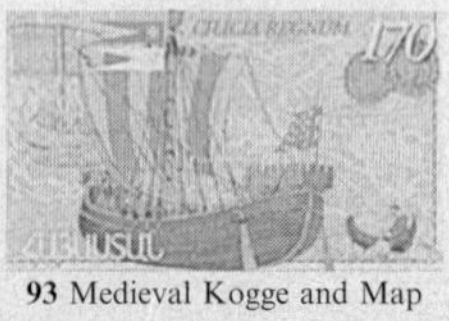

93 Medieval Kogge and Map

1999. Ships of the Armenian Kingdom of Cilicia (11–14th centuries). Multicoloured.

413	170d. Type **93**	40	40
414	250d. Medieval single-masted sailing ships	60	60
415	250d. As No. 414 but with emblem of "Philexfrance 99" International Stamp Exhibition, Paris, France, in lower right corner	60	60

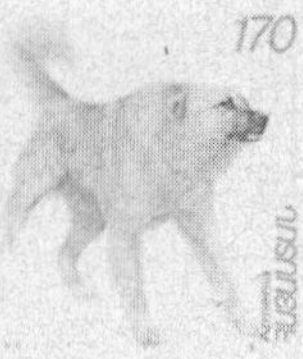

94 Armenian Gampr

1999. Domestic Pets. Multicoloured.

416	170d. Type **94**	40	40
417	250d. Turkish van cat	60	60
418	250d. As No. 417 but with emblem of "China 1999" International Stamp Exhibition, Peking, China, in lower right corner	60	60

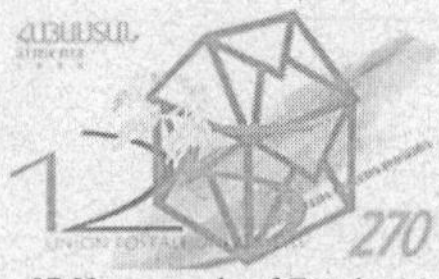

97 House made of Envelopes

1999. 125th Anniv of Universal Postal Union.

421 **97** 270d. multicoloured . . . 65 65

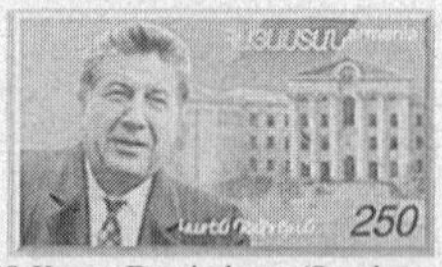

98 Karen Demirchyan (Speaker of the National Assembly)

2000. Commemoration of Victims of Attack on National Assembly. Multicoloured.

422	250d. Type **98**	60	60
423	250d. Vazgen Sargsyan (Prime Minister)	60	60

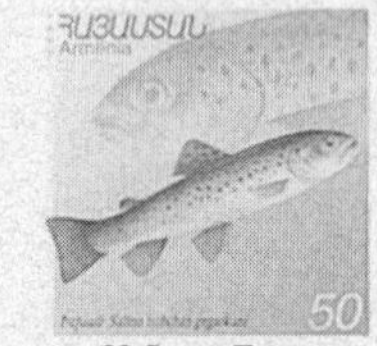

99 Sevan Trout

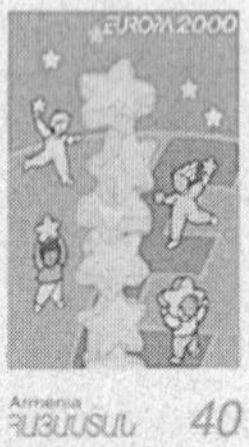

101 "Building Europe"

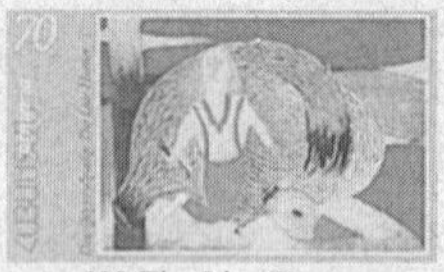

100 The Liar Hunter

2000. Fishes. Multicoloured.

425	50d. Type **99**	10	10
426	270d. Sevan barbel	70	70

2000. National Fairy Tales. Multicoloured.

427	70d. Type **100**	15	15
428	130d. The King and the Peddler	30	30

2000. Europa.

429	**101**	40d. multicoloured	10	10
430		500d. multicoloured	1·25	1·25

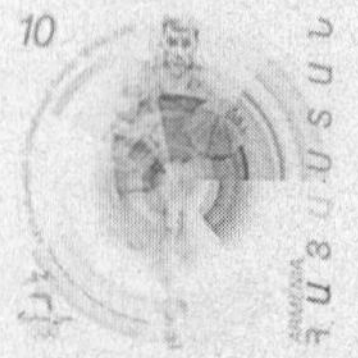

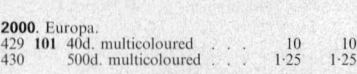

103 Basketball

2000. Olympic Games, Sydney. Multicoloured.

432	10d. Type **103**	10	10
433	30d. Tennis	10	10
434	500d. Weightlifting	1·25	1·25

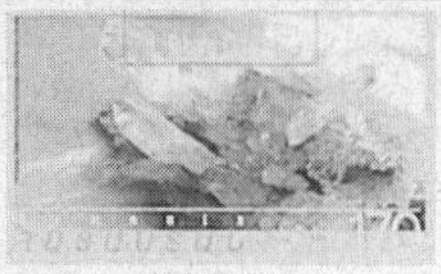

104 Quartz

2000. Minerals. Multicoloured.
435 170d. Type **104** 40 40
436 250d. Molybdenite 60 60

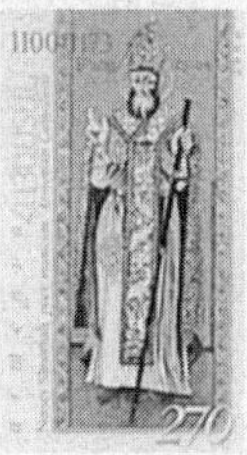

105 Shnorhali

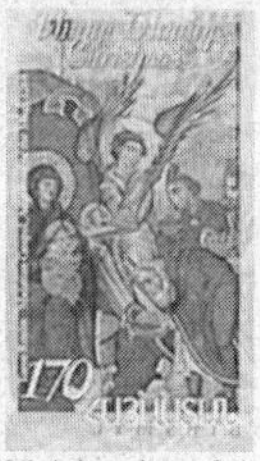

106 Adoration of the Magi

2000. 900th Birth Anniv of Nerses Shnorhali (writer and musician).
437 **105** 270d. multicoloured . . . 70 70

2000. Christmas.
438 **106** 170d. multicoloured . . . 40 40

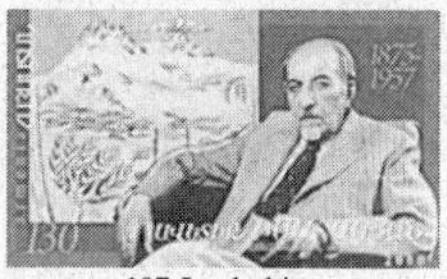

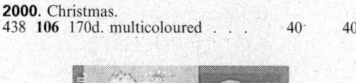

107 Issahakian

2000. 125th Birth Anniv of Avetik Issahakian (poet).
439 **107** 130d. multicoloured . . . 30 30

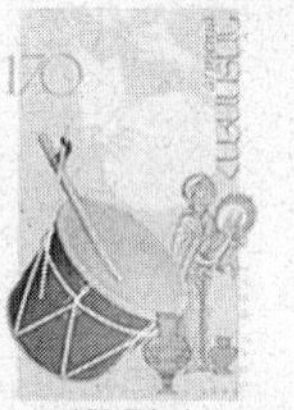

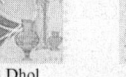

108 Dhol

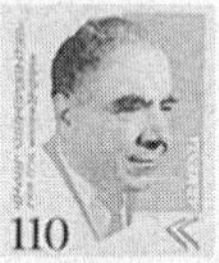

109 Viktor Hambartsoumian (astrophysicist)

2000. Musical Instruments. Multicoloured.
440 170d. Type **108** 40 40
441 250d. Duduk (wind instrument) 60 60

2000. New Millennium. Famous Armenians. Mult.
442 110d. Type **109** 25 25
443 110d. Abraham Alikhanov (physicist) 25 25
444 110d. Andranik Iossifan (electrical engineer) 25 25
445 110d. Sargis Saltikov (metallurgist) 25 25
446 110d. Samval Kochariants (electrical engineer) 25 25
447 110d. Artem Mikoyan (aircraft designer) 25 25
448 110d. Norayr Sisisakian (biochemist) 25 25
449 110d. Ivan Knunyants (chemist) 25 25
450 110d. Nikoghayos Yenikolopian (physical chemist) 25 25
451 110d. Nikoghayos Adonts (historian) 25 25
452 110d. Manouk Abeghian (folklore scholar) 25 25
453 110d. Hovhannes Toumanian (poet) 25 25
454 110d. Hrachya Ajarian (linguist) 25 25
455 110d. Gevorg Emin (poet) . . 25 25
456 110d. Yervand Lalayan (anthropologist) 25 25
457 110d. Daniel Varoujan (poet) 25 25
458 110d. Paruyr Sevak (poet) . . 25 25
459 110d. William Saroyan (dramatist and novelist) . . 25 25
460 110d. Hamo Beknazarian (film director) 25 25
461 110d. Alexandre Tamanian (architect) 25 25
462 110d. Vahram Papazian (actor) 25 25
463 110d. Vasil Tahirov (viticulturist) 25 25
464 110d. Leonid Yengibarian (mime artist) 25 25
465 110d. Haykanoush Danielian (singer) 25 25
466 110d. Sergo Hambartsoumian (weight lifter) 25 25
467 110d. Hrant Shahinian (gymnast) 25 25
468 110d. Toros Toramanian (architect) 25 25
469 110d. Komitas (composer) . . 25 25
470 110d. Aram Khachatourian (composer) 25 25
471 110d. Martiros Sarian (artist) 25 25
472 110d. Avet Terterian (composer) 25 25
473 110d. Alexandre Spendiarian (composer) 25 25
474 110d. Arshile Gorky (artist) 25 25
475 110d. Minas Avetissian (artist) 25 25
476 110d. (Levon Orbeli physiologist) 25 25
477 110d. Hripsimeh Simonian (ceramics artist) 25 25

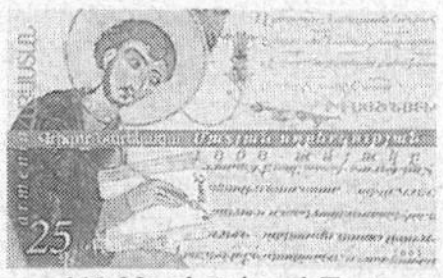

111 Narekatsi and Text

2001. Millenary of A Record of Lamentations by Grigor Narekatsi.
479 **111** 25d. multicoloured . . . 10 10

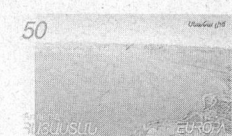

112 Lake Sevan

2001. Europa. Water Resources. Multicoloured.
480 50d. Type **112** 10 10
481 500d. Spandarian Reservoir 1·25 1·25

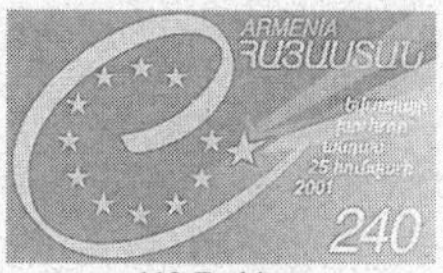

113 Emblem

2001. Armenian Membership of Council of Europe.
482 **113** 240d. multicoloured . . . 55 55

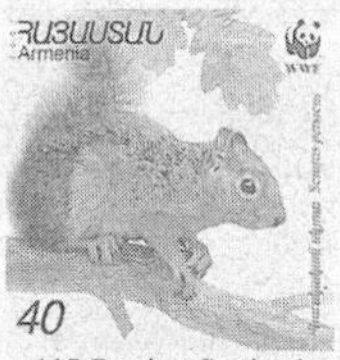

115 Persian Squirrel

2001. Endangered Species. Persian Squirrel (*Sciurus persicus*). Multicoloured.
484 40d. Type **115** 10 10
485 50d. Adult sitting on branch with young in tree hole . . 10 10
486 80d. Head of squirrel 20 20
487 120d. On ground 30 30

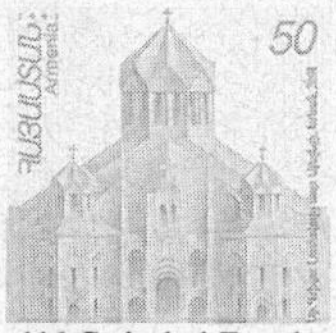

116 Cathedral Facade

2001. 1700th Anniv of Christianity in Armenia (7th issue). St. Gregory the Illuminator Cathedral, Yerevan. Multicoloured.
488 50d. Type **116** 10 10
489 205d. Interior elevation of Cathedral (44 × 30 mm) . . 50 50
490 240d. Exterior elevation of Cathedral (44 × 30 mm) . . 55 55

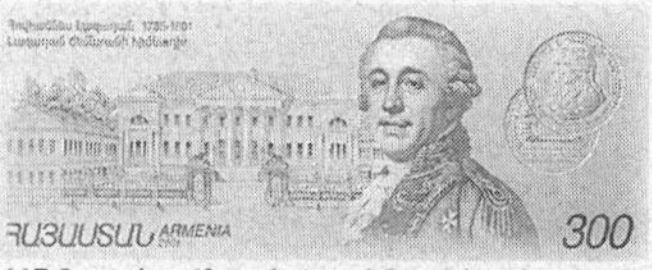

117 Lazarian (founder) and Lazarian Academy, Moscow

2001. Death Bicentenary of Hovhannes Lazarian.
491 **117** 300d. multicoloured . . . 75 75

2001. Traditional Costumes (3rd series). As T **85**. Multicoloured.
492 50d. Javakhch couple 10 10
493 250d. Artzakh couple 60 60

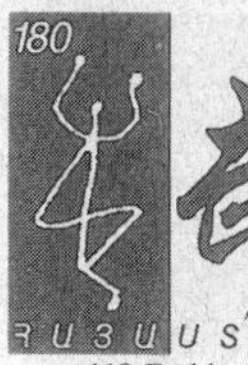

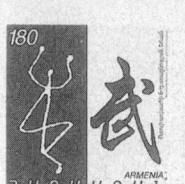

118 Emblem

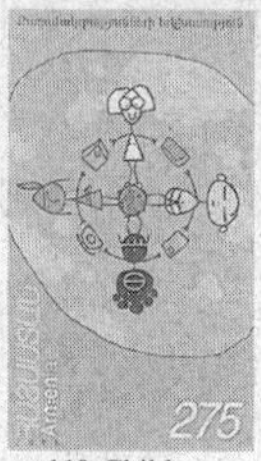

119 Children encircling Globe

2001. 6th World Wushu Championships, Yerevan.
494 **118** 180d. black 40 40

2001. United Nations Year of Dialogue among Civilizations.
495 **119** 275d. multicoloured . . . 65 65

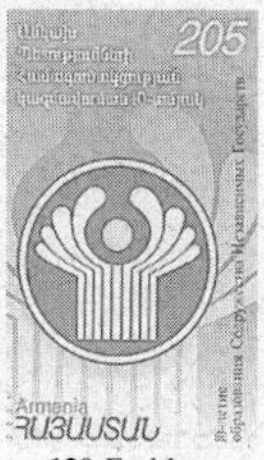

120 Emblem

2001. 10th Anniv of Commonwealth of Independent States.
496 **120** 205d. multicoloured . . . 50 50

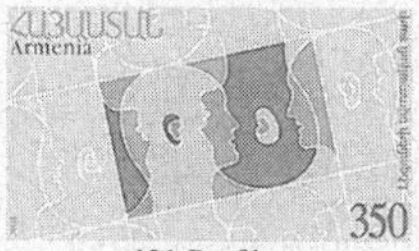

121 Profiles

2001. European Year of Languages.
497 **121** 350d. multicoloured . . . 85 85

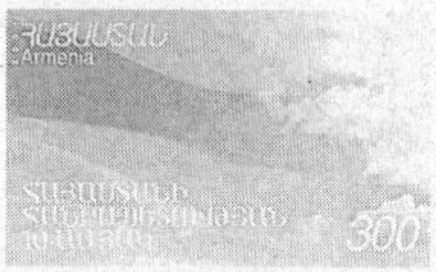

122 Flag

2001. 10th Anniv of Independence.
498 **122** 300d. multicoloured . . . 70 70

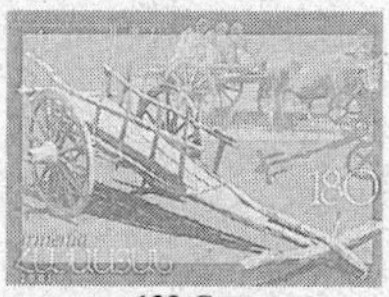

123 Cart

2001. Transport. Multicoloured.
499 180d. Type **123** 40 40
500 205d. Phaeton 50 50

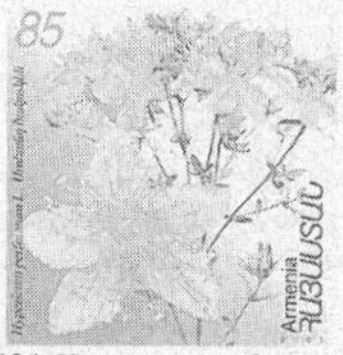

124 *Hypericum perforatum*

2001. Medicinal Plants. Multicoloured.
501 85d. Type **124** 20 20
502 205d. *Thymus serpyllum* . . . 50 50

ARUBA Pt. 4

An island in the Caribbean, formerly part of Netherlands Antilles. In 1986 became an autonomous country within the Kingdom of the Netherlands.

100 cents = 1 gulden.

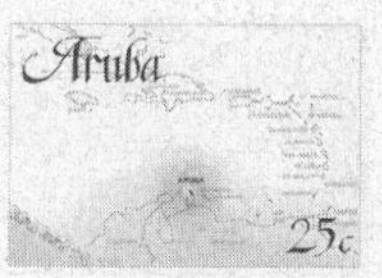

1 Map

1986. New Constitution.
1 **1** 25c. yellow, blue and black . . 25 20
2 – 45c. multicoloured 50 40
3 – 55c. black, grey and red . . . 70 70
4 – 100c. multicoloured . . . . . 1·10 1·10
DESIGNS—VERT: 45c. Aruban arms; 55c. National anthem. HORIZ: 100c. Aruban flag.

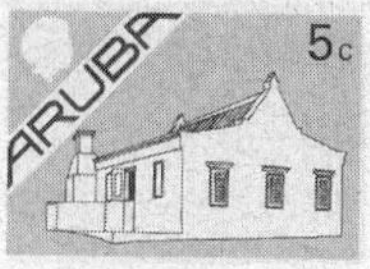

2 House

1986.
5 **2** 5c. black and yellow 10 10
6 – 15c. black and blue 15 10
7 – 20c. black and grey 15 15
8 – 25c. black and violet 25 15
9 – 30c. black and red 90 35
10 – 35c. black and bistre 40 30
12 – 45c. black and blue 55 35
14 – 55c. black and grey 50 45
15 – 60c. black and blue 65 50
16 – 65c. black and blue 70 55
18 – 75c. black and brown 70 65
20 – 85c. black and orange . . . 75 70
21 – 90c. black and green 80 75
22 – 100c. black and brown . . . 90 85
23 – 150c. black and green . . . . 1·50 1·10
24 – 250c. black and green . . . . 2·50 2·10
DESIGNS: 15c. Clock tower; 20c. Container crane; 25c. Lighthouse; 30c. Snake; 35c. Burrowing owl; 45c. Caribbean vase (shell); 55c. Frog; 60c. Water-skier; 65c. Fisherman casting net; 75c. Hurdy-gurdy; 85c. Pot; 90, 250c. Different cacti; 100c. Maize; 150c. Watapana Tree.

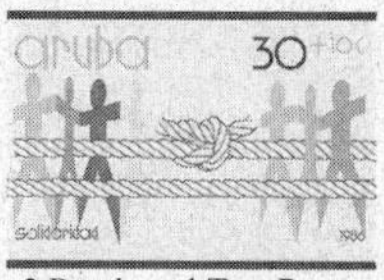

3 People and Two Ropes

1986. "Solidarity". Multicoloured.
25 30c.+10c. Type **3** 45 45
26 35c.+15c. People and three ropes 55 55
27 60c.+25c. People and one rope 90 90

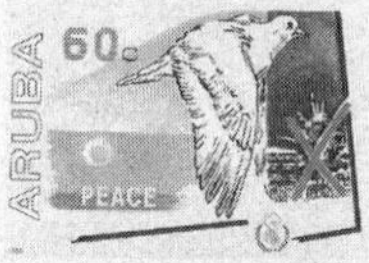

4 Dove between Scenes of Peace and War

1986. International Peace Year. Multicoloured.
28 60c. Type **4** 60 60
29 100c. Doves flying over broken barbed wire . . . . 1·00 1·00

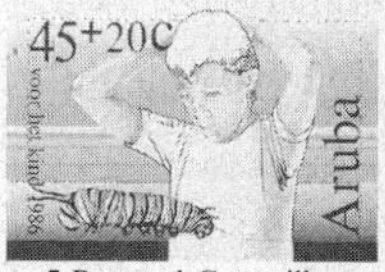

5 Boy and Caterpillar

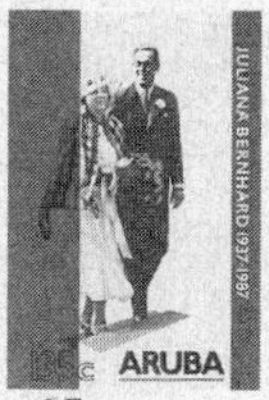

6 Engagement Picture

1986. Child Welfare. Multicoloured.
30 45c.+20c. Type **5** 65 65
31 70c.+25c. Boy and shell . . . 1·00 1·00
32 100c.+40c. Girl and butterfly 1·40 1·40

1987. Golden Wedding of Princess Juliana and Prince Bernhard.
33 **6** 135c. orange, black and gold 1·10 1·10

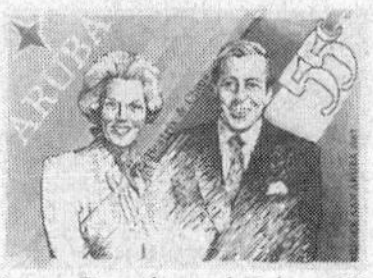

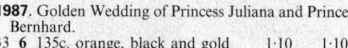

7 Queen Beatrix and Prince Claus

1987. Royal Visit. Multicoloured.
34 55c. Type **7** 45 45
35 60c. Prince Willem-Alexander 50 50

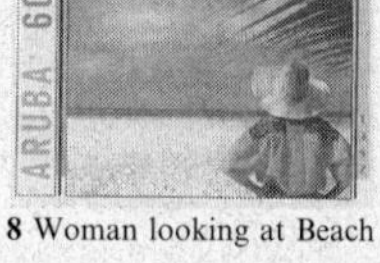

8 Woman looking at Beach

1987. Tourism. Multicoloured.
36 60c. Type **8** 50 40
37 100c. Woman looking at desert landscape 90 85

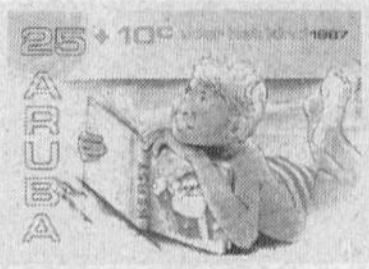

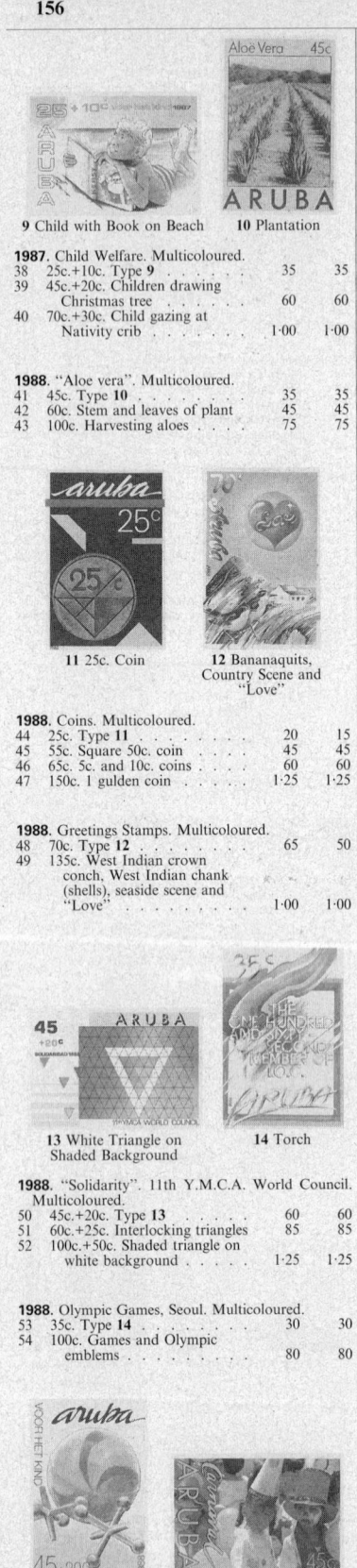

9 Child with Book on Beach

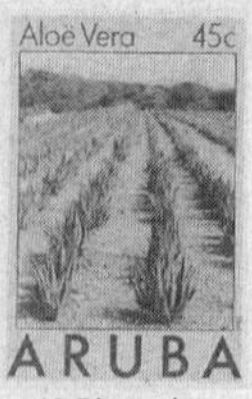

10 Plantation

1987. Child Welfare. Multicoloured.
38 25c.+10c. Type **9** 35 35
39 45c.+20c. Children drawing Christmas tree 60 60
40 70c.+30c. Child gazing at Nativity crib . . . . 1·00 1·00

1988. "Aloe vera". Multicoloured.
41 45c. Type **10** 35 35
42 60c. Stem and leaves of plant 45 45
43 100c. Harvesting aloes 75 75

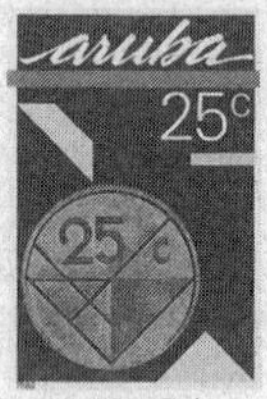

11 25c. Coin

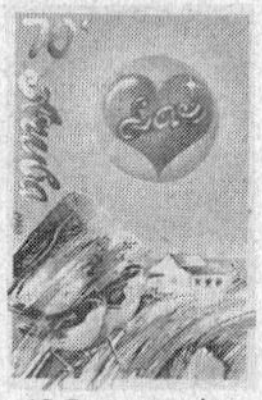

12 Bananaquits, Country Scene and "Love"

1988. Coins. Multicoloured.
44 25c. Type **11** 20 15
45 55c. Square 50c. coin 45 45
46 65c. 5c. and 10c. coins 60 60
47 150c. 1 gulden coin . . . . . . 1·25 1·25

1988. Greetings Stamps. Multicoloured.
48 70c. Type **12** 65 50
49 135c. West Indian crown conch, West Indian chank (shells), seaside scene and "Love" . . . . 1·00 1·00

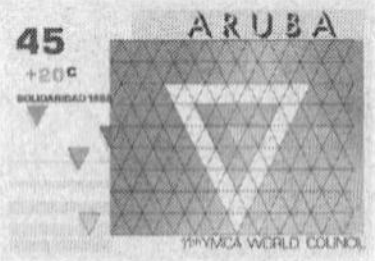

13 White Triangle on Shaded Background

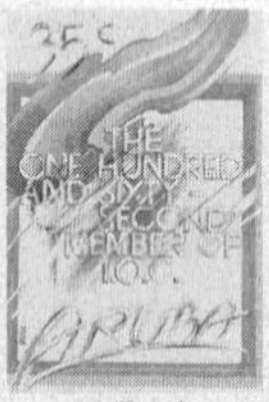

14 Torch

1988. "Solidarity". 11th Y.M.C.A. World Council. Multicoloured.
50 45c.+20c. Type **13** 60 60
51 60c.+25c. Interlocking triangles 85 85
52 100c.+50c. Shaded triangle on white background . . . . . 1·25 1·25

1988. Olympic Games, Seoul. Multicoloured.
53 35c. Type **14** 30 30
54 100c. Games and Olympic emblems 80 80

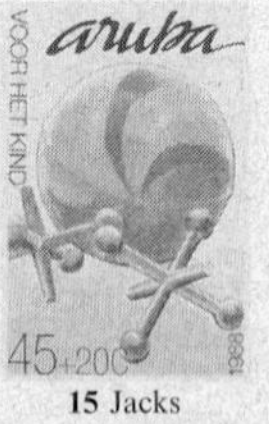

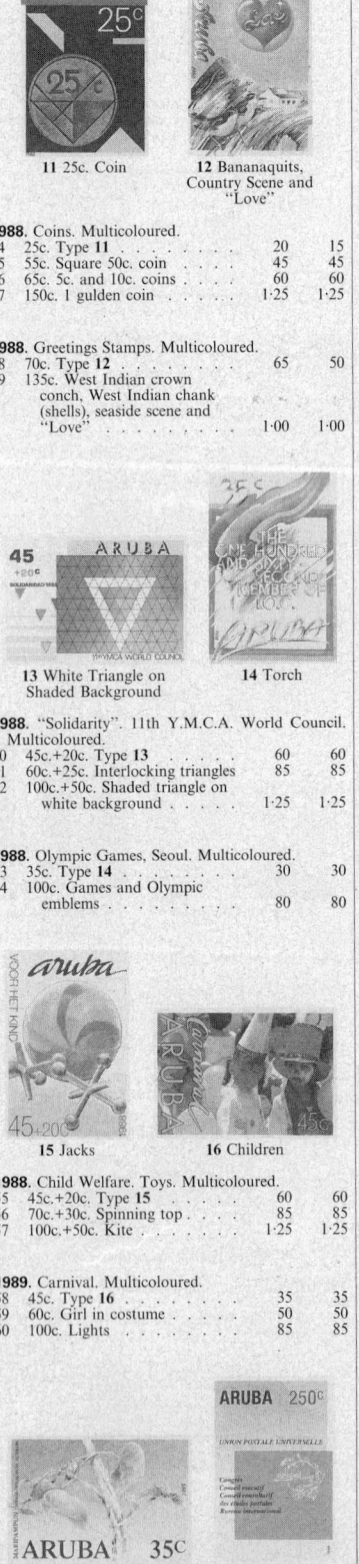

15 Jacks

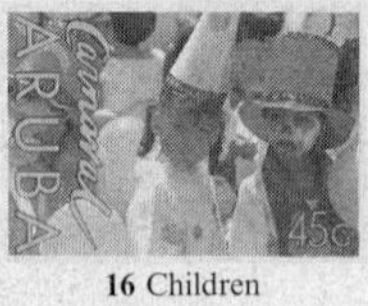

16 Children

1988. Child Welfare. Toys. Multicoloured.
55 45c.+20c. Type **15** 60 60
56 70c.+30c. Spinning top 85 85
57 100c.+50c. Kite . . . . 1·25 1·25

1989. Carnival. Multicoloured.
58 45c. Type **16** 35 35
59 60c. Girl in costume 50 50
60 100c. Lights 85 85

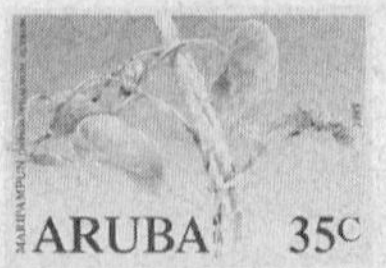

17 Maripampun

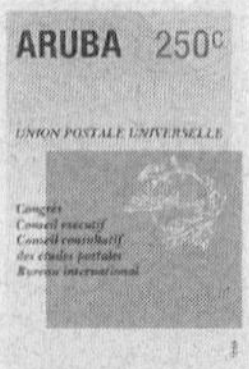

18 Emblem

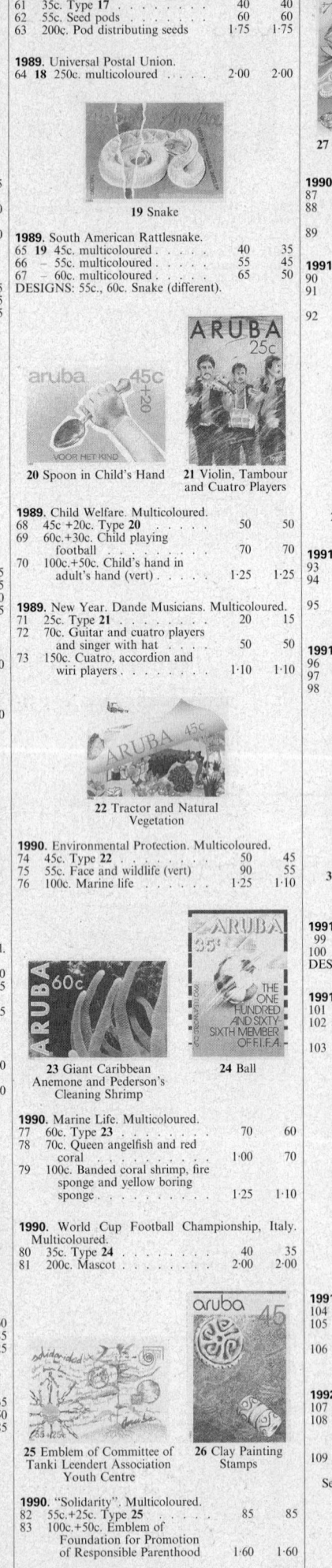

1989. Maripampun. Multicoloured.
61 35c. Type **17** 40 40
62 55c. Seed pods 60 60
63 200c. Pod distributing seeds 1·75 1·75

1989. Universal Postal Union.
64 **18** 250c. multicoloured . . . . 2·00 2·00

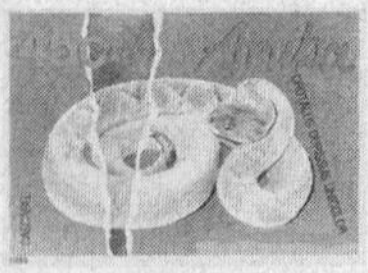

19 Snake

1989. South American Rattlesnake.
65 **19** 45c. multicoloured 40 35
66 – 55c. multicoloured 55 45
67 – 60c. multicoloured 65 50
DESIGNS: 55c., 60c. Snake (different).

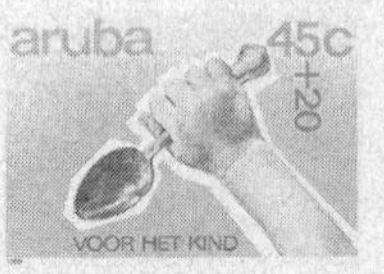

20 Spoon in Child's Hand

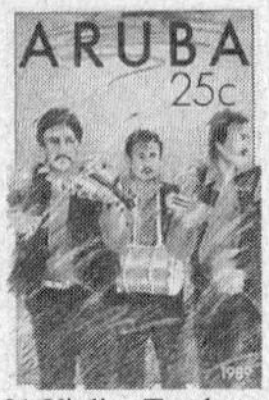

21 Violin, Tambour and Cuatro Players

1989. Child Welfare. Multicoloured.
68 45c +20c. Type **20** 50 50
69 60c.+30c. Child playing football 70 70
70 100c.+50c. Child's hand in adult's hand (vert) . . . . . 1·25 1·25

1989. New Year. Dande Musicians. Multicoloured.
71 25c. Type **21** 20 15
72 70c. Guitar and cuatro players and singer with hat 50 50
73 150c. Cuatro, accordion and wiri players . . . . 1·10 1·10

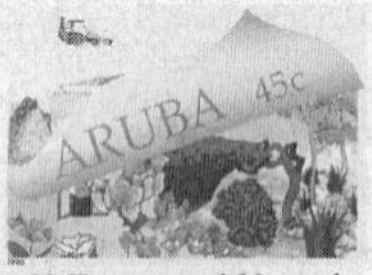

22 Tractor and Natural Vegetation

1990. Environmental Protection. Multicoloured.
74 45c. Type **22** 50 45
75 55c. Face and wildlife (vert) 90 55
76 100c. Marine life . . . . 1·25 1·10

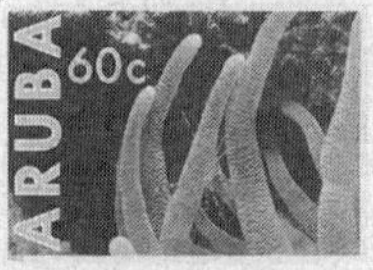

23 Giant Caribbean Anemone and Pederson's Cleaning Shrimp

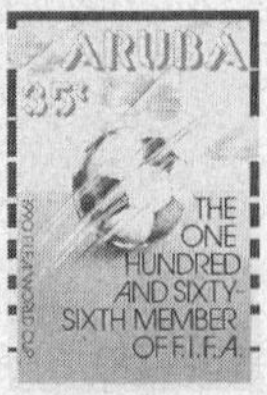

24 Ball

1990. Marine Life. Multicoloured.
77 60c. Type **23** 70 60
78 70c. Queen angelfish and red coral . . . . 1·00 70
79 100c. Banded coral shrimp, fire sponge and yellow boring sponge . . . . 1·25 1·10

1990. World Cup Football Championship, Italy. Multicoloured.
80 35c. Type **24** 40 35
81 200c. Mascot . . . . 2·00 2·00

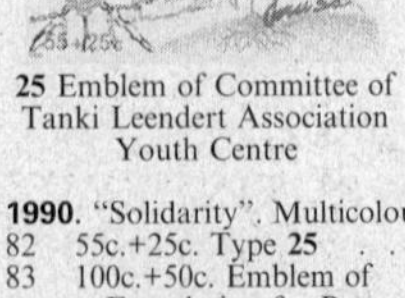

25 Emblem of Committee of Tanki Leendert Association Youth Centre

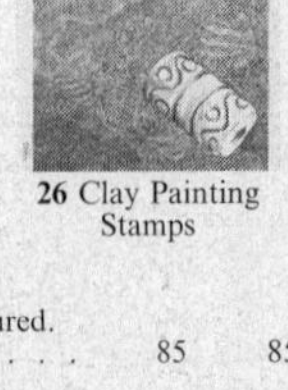

26 Clay Painting Stamps

1990. "Solidarity". Multicoloured.
82 55c.+25c. Type **25** 85 85
83 100c.+50c. Emblem of Foundation for Promotion of Responsible Parenthood 1·60 1·60

1990. Archaeology. Multicoloured.
84 45c. Type **26** 50 45
85 60c. Stone figure 70 60
86 100c. Dabajuroid-style jar . . 1·25 1·10

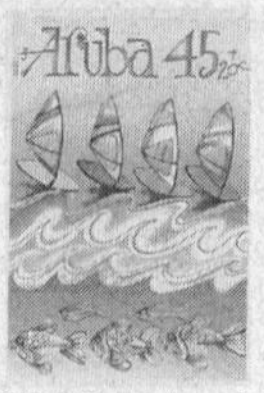

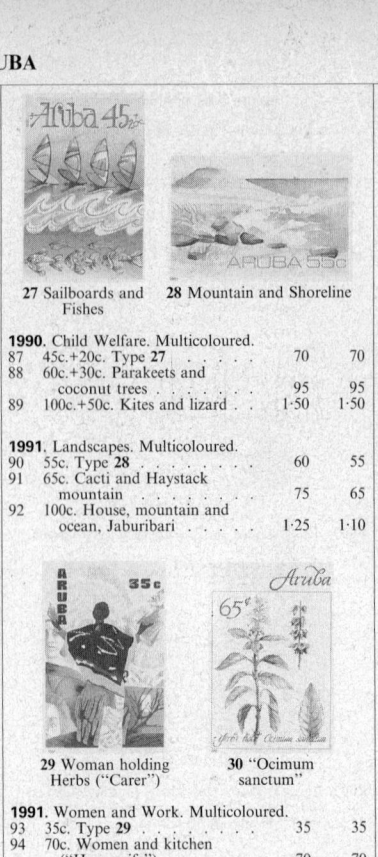

27 Sailboards and Fishes

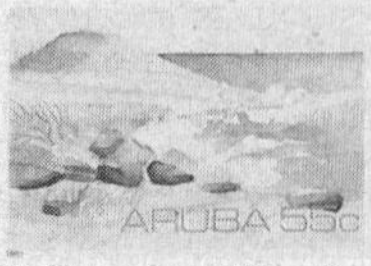

28 Mountain and Shoreline

1990. Child Welfare. Multicoloured.
87 45c.+20c. Type **27** 70 70
88 60c.+30c. Parakeets and coconut trees 95 95
89 100c.+50c. Kites and lizard . . 1·50 1·50

1991. Landscapes. Multicoloured.
90 55c. Type **28** 60 55
91 65c. Cacti and Haystack mountain 75 65
92 100c. House, mountain and ocean, Jaburibari . . . . . 1·25 1·10

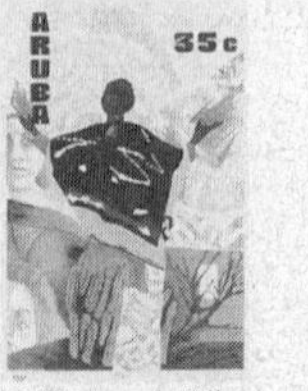

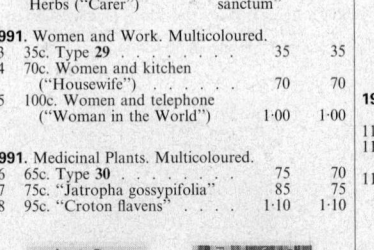

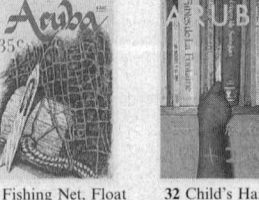

29 Woman holding Herbs ("Carer")

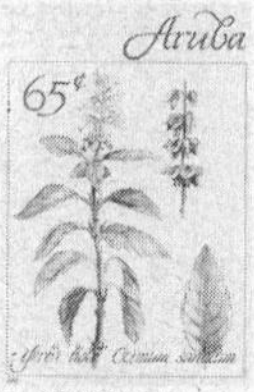

30 "Ocimum sanctum"

1991. Women and Work. Multicoloured.
93 35c. Type **29** 35 35
94 70c. Women and kitchen ("Housewife") 70 70
95 100c. Women and telephone ("Woman in the World") 1·00 1·00

1991. Medicinal Plants. Multicoloured.
96 65c. Type **30** 75 70
97 75c. "Jatropha gossypifolia" 85 75
98 95c. "Croton flavens" . . . . 1·10 1·10

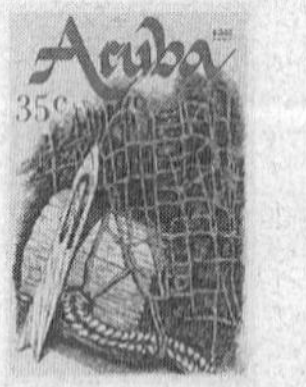

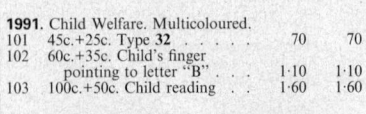

31 Fishing Net, Float and Needle

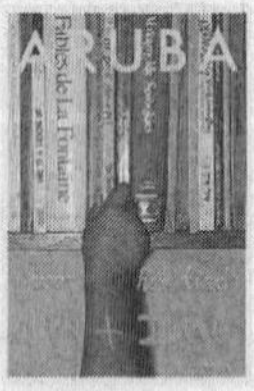

32 Child's Hand taking Book from Shelf

1991. Traditional Crafts.
99 **31** 35c. black, ultram & blue 35 35
100 – 250c. black, lilac & purple 2·50 2·50
DESIGNS: 250c. Hat, straw and hat-block.

1991. Child Welfare. Multicoloured.
101 45c.+25c. Type **32** 70 70
102 60c.+35c. Child's finger pointing to letter "B" . . . 1·10 1·10
103 100c.+50c. Child reading . . 1·60 1·60

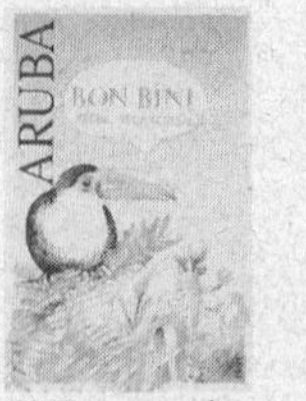

33 Toucan saying "Welcome"

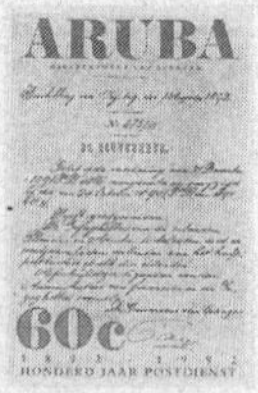

34 Government Decree of 1892 establishing first Aruban Post Office

1991. Tourism. Multicoloured.
104 35c. Type **33** 55 35
105 70c. Aruban youth welcoming tourist 70 70
106 100c. Windmill and Bubali swamp . . . . 1·00 1·00

1992. Centenary of Postal Service (1st issue). Mult.
107 60c. Type **34** 50 50
108 75c. Lt.-Governor's building (mail service office, 1892–1908) (horiz) 60 60
109 80c. Present Oranjestad P.O. (horiz) 70 70
See also Nos. 117/19.

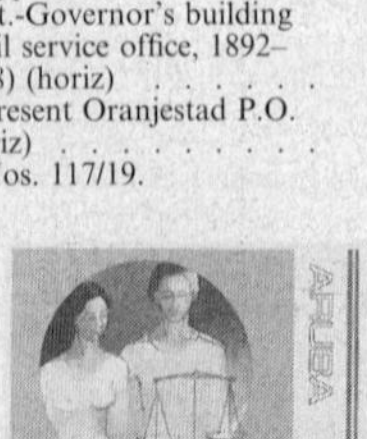

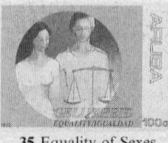

35 Equality of Sexes

1992. Equality. Multicoloured.
110 100c. Type **35** 85 85
111 100c. People of different races (equality of nations) . . . 85 85

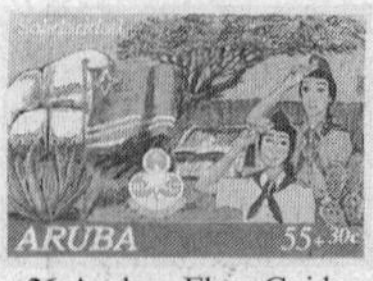

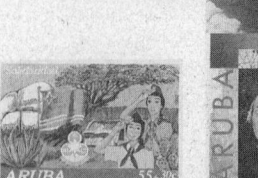

36 Aruban Flag, Guide Emblem and Girl Guides

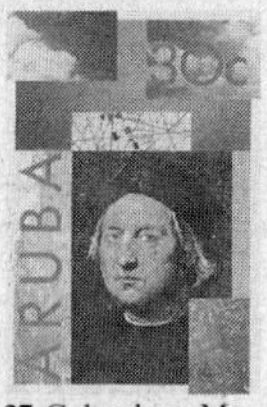

37 Columbus, Map and Clouds

1992. "Solidarity". Multicoloured.
112 55c.+30c. Type **36** 75 75
113 100c.+50c. Open hand with Cancer Fund emblem . . . 1·25 1·25

1992. 500th Anniv of Discovery of America by Columbus. Multicoloured.
114 30c. Type **37** 25 25
115 40c. Caravel (from navigation chart, 1525) 45 30
116 50c. Indians, queen conch shell and 1540 map 50 40

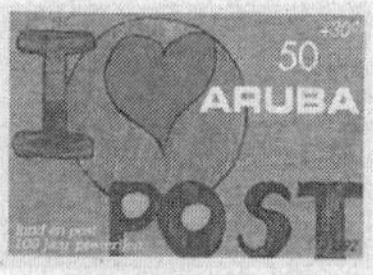

38 "I Love Post" (Jelissa Boekhoudt)

1992. Child Welfare. Centenary of Postal Service (2nd issue). Children's Drawings. Multicoloured.
117 50c.+30c. Type **38** 60 60
118 70c.+35c. Airplane dropping letters (Marianne Fingal) 80 80
119 100c.+50c. Pigeon carrying letter in beak (Minorenti Jacobs) (vert) . . . . . . 1·10 1·10

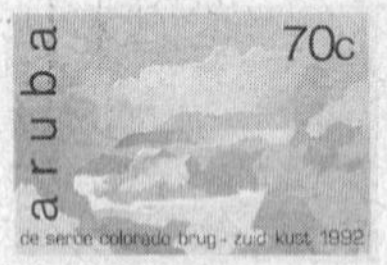

39 Seroe Colorado Bridge

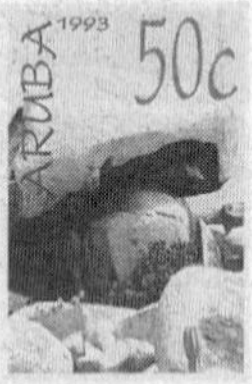

41 Rocks at Ayo

1992. Natural Bridges. Multicoloured.
120 70c. Type **39** 55 55
121 80c. Natural Bridge 60 60

1993. Rock Formations. Multicoloured.
123 50c. Type **41** 40 40
124 60c. Casibari 45 45
125 100c. Ayo (different) 75 75

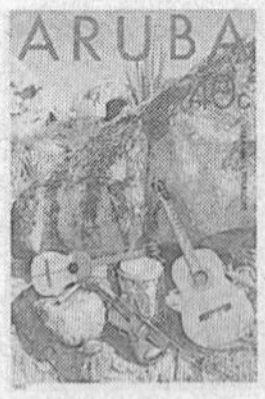

42 Traditional Instruments

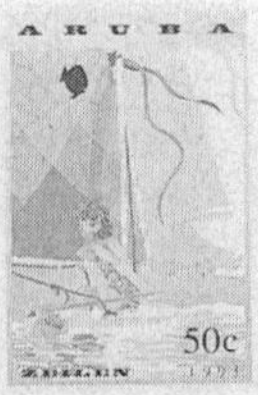

43 Sailfish dinghy

1993. Cock's Burial (part of St. John's Feast celebrations). Multicoloured.
126 40c. Type **42** 30 30
127 70c. "Cock's Burial" (painting, Leo Kuiperi) . . 50 50
128 80c. Verses of song, yellow flag, and calabashes . . . 60 60

1993. Sports. Multicoloured.
129 50c. Type **43** 60 60
130 65c. Land sailing 50 50
131 75c. Sailboard 80 80

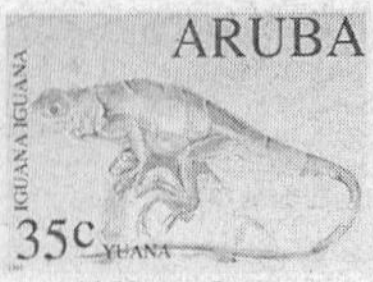

44 Young Iguana

1993. The Iguana. Multicoloured.
132 35c. Type **44** 25 25
133 60c. Young adult 45 45
134 100c. Adult (vert) 75 75

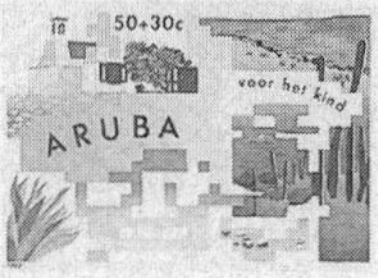

45 Aruban House, Landscape and Cacti

1993. Child Welfare. Multicoloured.

135	50c.+30c. Type **45**	60	60
136	75c.+40c. Face, bridge and sea (vert)	85	85
137	100c.+50c. Bridge, buildings and landscape	1·10	1·10

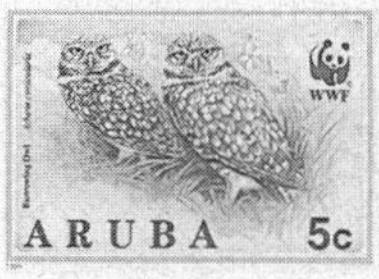

46 Owls

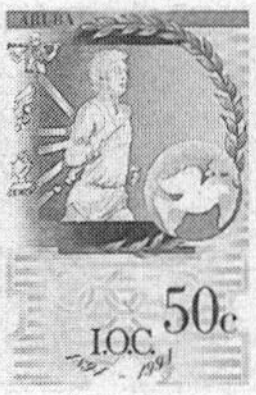

47 Athlete

1994. The Burrowing Owl. Multicoloured.

138	5c. Type **46**	20	20
139	10c. Pair with young	20	20
140	35c. Owl with locust in claw (vert)	65	70
141	40c. Owl (vert)	70	70

1994. Centenary of Int Olympic Committee. Mult.

142	50c. Type **47**	35	35
143	90c. Baron Pierre de Coubertin (founder)	60	60

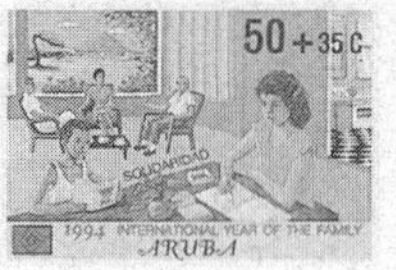

48 Family in House

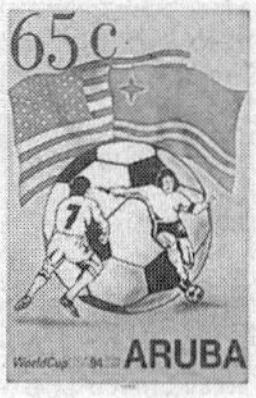

49 Flags of U.S.A. and Aruba, Ball and Players

1994. "Solidarity". Int Year of The Family. Mult.

144	50c.+35c. Type **48**	60	60
145	100c.+50c. Family outside house	1·00	1·00

1994. World Cup Football Championship, U.S.A. Multicoloured.

146	65c. Type **49**	45	45
147	150c. Mascot	1·00	1·00

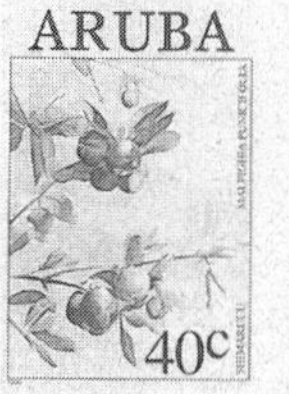

50 West Indian Cherry

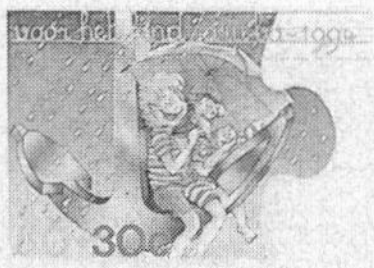

51 Children with Umbrella sitting on Anchor (shelter and security)

1994. Wild Fruits. Multicoloured.

148	40c. Type **50**	30	30
149	70c. Geiger tree	50	50
150	85c. "Pithecellobium unguis-cati"	60	60
151	150c. Sea grape	1·00	1·00

1994. Child Welfare. Influence of the Family. Mult.

152	50c.+30c. Type **51**	55	55
153	80c.+35c. Children in smiling sun (warmth of nurturing home)	80	80
154	100c.+50c. Child flying on owl (wisdom guiding the child)	1·00	1·00

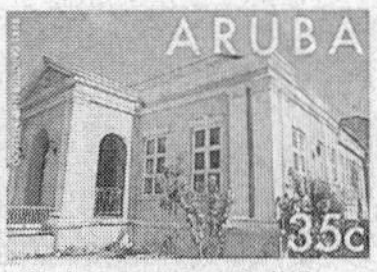

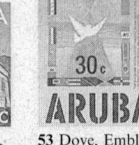

52 Government Building, 1888

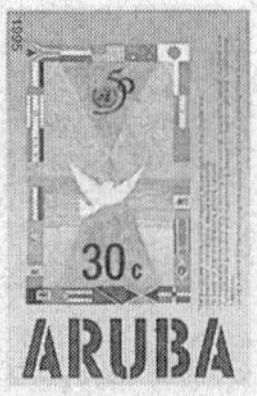

53 Dove, Emblem and Flags

1995. Historic Buildings. Multicoloured.

155	35c. Type **52**	25	25
156	60c. Ecury Residence, 1929 (vert)	40	40
157	100c. Protestant Church, 1846 (vert)	70	70

1995. 50th Anniv of U.N.O. Multicoloured.

158	30c. Type **53**	20	20
159	200c. Emblem, flags, globe and doves	1·40	1·40

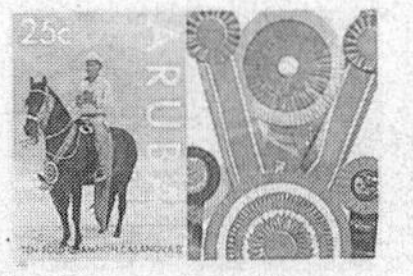

54 Casanova II and Rosettes

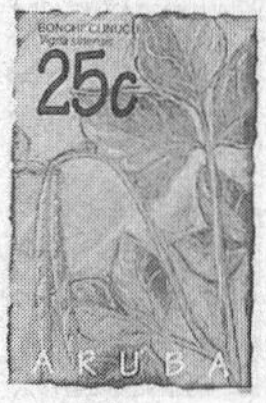

55 Cowpea

1995. Interpaso Horses. Multicoloured.

160	25c. Type **54**	20	20
161	75c. Horse performing Paso Fino	55	55
162	80c. Horse performing Figure 8 (vert)	60	60
163	90c. Girl on horseback (vert)	65	65

1995. Vegetables. Multicoloured.

164	25c. Type **55**	20	20
165	50c. Apple cucumber	35	35
166	70c. Okra	50	50
167	85c. Pumpkin	60	60

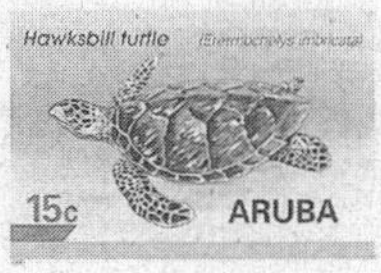

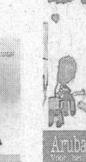

56 Hawksbill Turtle

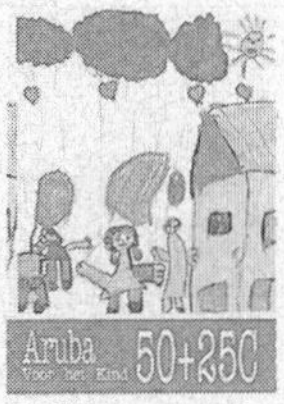

57 Children holding Balloons outside House (Christina Trejo)

1995. Turtles. Multicoloured.

168	15c. Type **56**	10	10
169	50c. Green turtle	35	35
170	95c. Loggerhead turtle	70	70
171	100c. Leatherback turtle	70	70

1995. Child Welfare. Children's Drawings. Mult.

172	50c.+25c. Type **57**	55	55
173	70c.+35c. Children at seaside (Julysses Tromp)	75	75
174	100c.+50c. Children and adults gardening (Ronald Tromp)	1·10	1·10

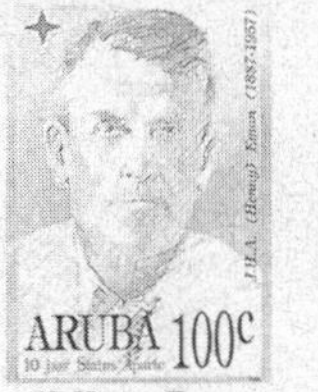

58 Henry Eman

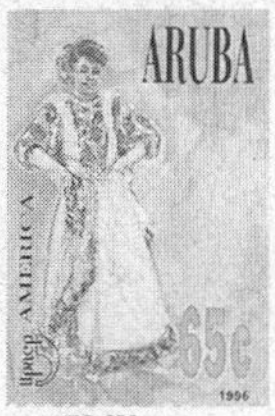

59 Woman

1996. 10th Anniv of Internal Autonomy. Politicians. Multicoloured.

175	100c. Type **58**	70	70
176	100c. Juancho Irausquin	70	70
177	100c. Shon Eman	70	70
178	100c. Betico Croes	70	70

1996. America. Traditional Costumes. Mult.

179	65c. Type **59**	45	45
180	70c. Man	50	50
181	100c. Couple dancing (horiz)	70	70

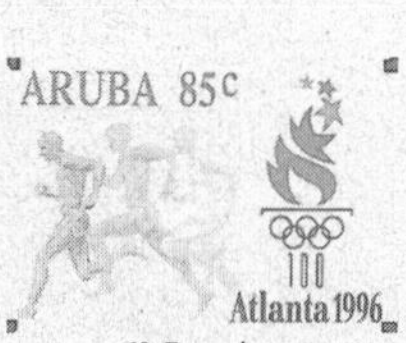

60 Running

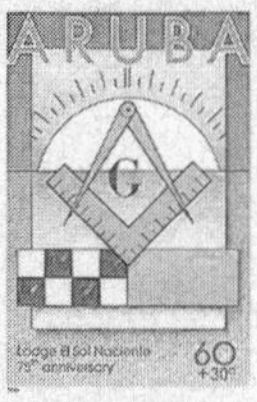

61 Mathematical Instruments, "G" and Rising Sun

1996. Olympic Games, Atlanta. Multicoloured.

182	85c. Type **60**	60	60
183	130c. Cycling	90	90

1996. "Solidarity". 75th Anniv of Freemasons' Lodge El Sol Naciente. Multicoloured.

184	60c.+30c. Type **61**	65	65
185	100c.+50c. Globes on top of columns and doorway	1·00	1·00

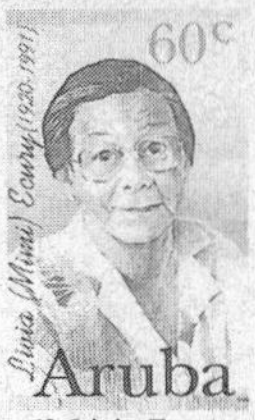

62 Livia Ecury (teacher and nurse)

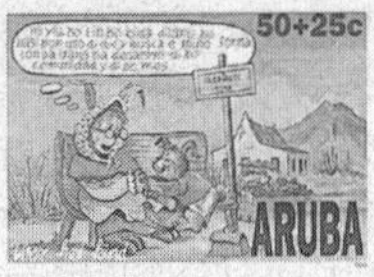

63 Rabbits at Bus-stop

1996. Anniversaries. Multicoloured.

186	60c. Type **62** (5th death)	40	40
187	60c. Laura Wernet-Paskel (teacher and politician, 85th birth)	40	40
188	60c. Lolita Euson (poet, 2nd death)	40	40

1996. Child Welfare. Comic Strips. Multicoloured.

189	50c.+25c. Type **63**	50	50
190	70c.+35c. Young owl on way to school with mother	75	75
191	100c.+50c. Boy flying kite with friend	1·00	1·00

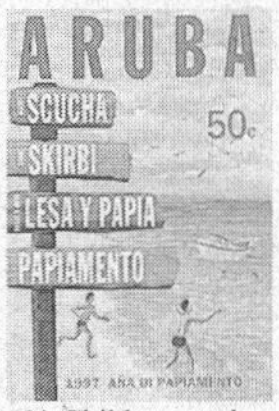

64 Children at the Seaside and Words on Signpost

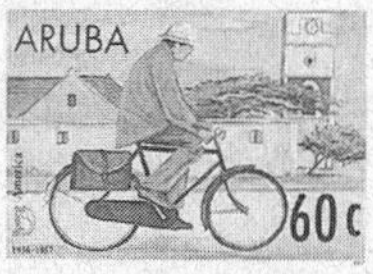

65 Postman on Bicycle, 1936–57

1997. "Year of Papiamento" (Creole language). Multicoloured.

192	50c. Type **64**	55	55
193	140c. Sunrise over ocean	95	95

1997. America. The Postman. Multicoloured.

194	60c. Type **65**	40	40
195	70c. Postman delivering package by jeep, 1957–88	45	45
196	80c. Postman delivering letter from motor scooter, 1995	55	55

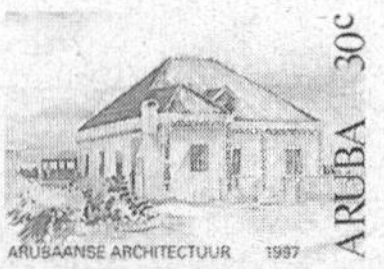

66 Decorated Cunucu House

1997. Aruban Architecture. Multicoloured.

197	30c. Type **66**	20	20
198	65c. Bannistered steps	45	45
199	100c. Arends Building (vert)	65	65

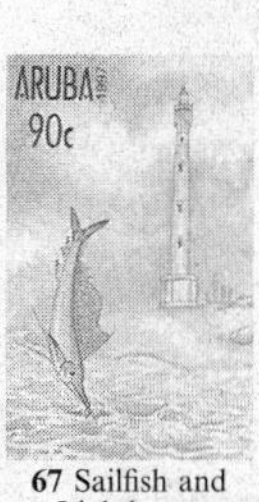

67 Sailfish and Lighthouse

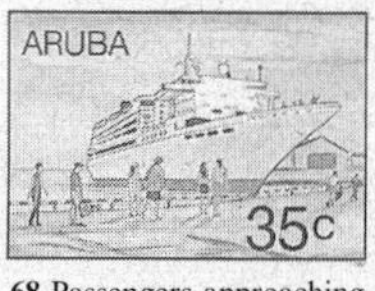

68 Passengers approaching Cruise Liner

1997. "Pacific 97" International Stamp Exhibition, San Francisco. Multicoloured.

200	90c. Type **67**	60	60
201	90c. Windswept trees and dolphin	60	60
202	90c. Iguana on rock and cacti	60	60
203	90c. Rock beauty, yellow-tailed snapper, soldierfishes and one dolphin	60	60
204	90c. Two dolphins and yellow-tailed snapper	60	60
205	90c. Owl on shore, turtle, four-eyed butterflyfish and pufferfish	60	60
206	90c. Stingray, rock beauty, angelfishes, squirrelfish and coral reef	60	60
207	90c. Diver and stern of shipwreck	90	90
208	90c. Shipwreck, reef, stop-light parrotfish, blue angelfish, great barracuda and four-eyed butterflyfish	90	90

Nos. 200/8 were issued together, se-tenant, forming a composite design.

1997. Cruise Tourism. Multicoloured.

209	35c. Type **68**	40	40
210	50c. Passengers disembarking	60	60
211	150c. Cruise liner at sea and launch at shore	1·75	1·75

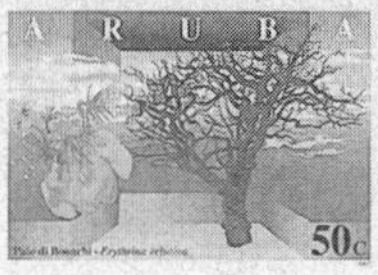

69 Coral Tree

1997. Trees. Multicoloured.

212	50c. Type **69**	35	35
213	60c. "Cordia dentata"	40	40
214	70c. "Tabebuia billbergii"	45	45
215	130c. "Lignum vitae"	85	85

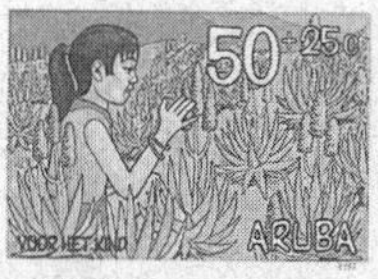

70 Girl among Aloes

1997. Child Welfare. Child and Nature. Mult.

216	50c.+25c. Type **70**	50	50
217	70c.+35c. Boy and butterfly (vert)	70	70
218	100c.+50c. Girl swimming underwater by coral reef	1·00	1·00

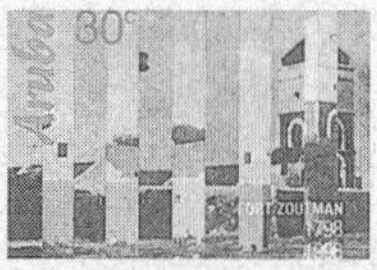

71 Fort Zoutman

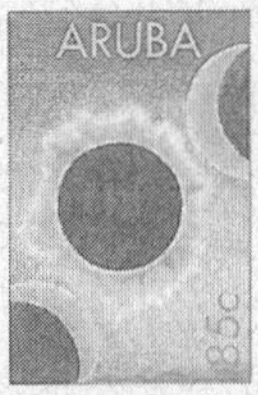

72 Stages of Eclipse

1998. Bicentenary of Fort Zoutman.

219 **71**	30c. multicoloured	20	20
220	250c. multicoloured	1·75	1·75

Each design consists of alternating strips in brown tones or black and white. When the 250c. is laid on top of the 30c., the brown strips form a composite design of the fort in its early years and the black and white strips a composite design of the fort after 1929, when various alterations were made.

1998. Total Solar Eclipse. Multicoloured.

221	85c. Type **72**	55	55
222	100c. Globe showing path of eclipse and map of Aruba plotting duration of total darkness	65	65

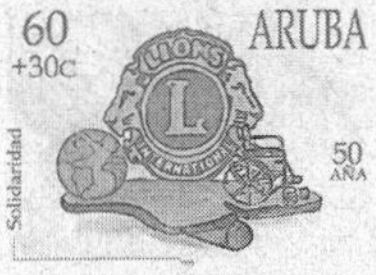

73 Globe, Emblem and Wheelchair balanced on Map of Aruba

1998. "Solidarity" Anniversaries. Multicoloured.

223	60c.+30c. Type **73** (50th anniv of Lions Club of Aruba)	60	60
224	100c.+50c. Boy reading, emblem and grandmother in rocking chair (60th anniv of Rotary Club of Aruba)	1·00	1·00

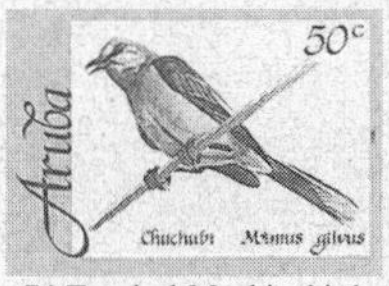

74 Tropical Mockingbird

1998. Birds. Multicoloured.

225	50c. Type **74**	35	35
226	60c. American kestrel (vert)	40	40
227	70c. Troupial (vert)	45	45
228	150c. Bananaquit	1·00	1·00

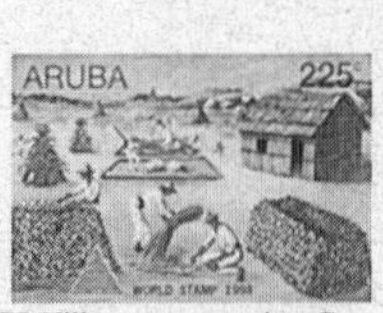

75 Villagers processing Corn

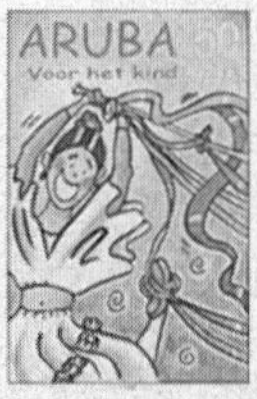

76 Ribbon Dance

1998. World Stamp Day.
229　75　225c. multicoloured . . . .　1·50　1·50

1998. Child Welfare. Multicoloured.
230　50c.+25c. Type **76** . . . . .　50　50
231　80c.+40c. Boy playing cuarta
　　　(four-string guitar)　　　80　80
232　100c. + 50c. Basketball . . .　1·00　1·00

77 Two Donkeys

1999. The Donkey. Multicoloured.
233　40c. Type **77** . . . .　25　25
234　65c. Two adults and foal . .　45　45
235　100c. Adult and foal . . . .　70　70

78 "Opuntia wentiana"　　**79** Creole Dog

1999. Cacti. Multicoloured.
236　50c. Type **78** . . . . . .　35　35
237　60c. "Lemaireocereus griseus"　40　40
238　70c. "Cephalocereus
　　　lanuginosus" . . . . . .　45　45
239　75c. "Cephalocereus
　　　lanuginosus" (different) . .　50　50

1999. Creole Dogs ("Canis familiaris"). Mult.
240　40c. Type **79** . . . . . .　25　25
241　60c. White dog on rock . .　40　40
242　80c. Dog sitting by sea . .　55　55
243　165c. Black and tan dog . .　1·10　1·10

80 Indian Cave Drawings and Antique Map

1999. 500 Years of Cultural Diversity. Mult.
244　150c. Type **80** . . . . .　1·00　1·00
245　175c. Indian cave drawings
　　　and carnival headdress . .　1·25　1·25

81 Public Library and Children

1999. 50th Anniv of Public Library Service. Mult.
247　70c. Type **81** . . . . . .　45　45
248　100c. Library, Santa Cruz . .　70　70

82 Boy with Fisherman　**83** Three Wise Men

1999. Child Welfare. Multicoloured.
249　60c.+30c. Type **82** . . . . .　70　70
250　80c.+40c. Man reading to
　　　children . . . .　90　90
251　100c.+50c. Woman with child
　　　(vert) . . . .　1·10　1·10

1999. Christmas. Multicoloured. Self-adhesive.
252　40c. Type **83** . . . . . .　30　30
253　70c. Shepherds . . . . . .　55　55
254　100c. Holy Family . . . . .　1·10　1·10

84 Norops lineatus

2000. Reptiles. Multicoloured.
255　40c. Type **84** . . . . . .　30　30
256　60c. Common iguana . . .　45　45
257　75c. Annulated snake . . .　60　60
258　150c. Racerunner . . . . .　1·10　1·10

85 Flags

2000. America. AIDS Awareness. Multicoloured.
259　75c. Type **85** . . . . . .　60　60
260　175c. Ribbon on globe (vert)　1·40　1·40

86 Bank Facade

2000. Anniversaries. Multicoloured.
261　150c. Type **86** (75th anniv of
　　　Aruba Bank) . . . . .　1·10　1·10
262　165c. Chapel (250th anniv of
　　　Alto Vista Chapel) . . . .　1·25　1·25

87 Guadirikiri Cave

2000. Aspects of Aruba. Multicoloured.
263　15c. West Indian top shell . . .　10　10
264　25c. Type **87** . . . . . .　20　20
265　35c. Mud-house (vert) . . .　30　30
267　55c. Cacti . . . .　20　40
269　85c. Hooiberg . . . . . .　65　65
271　100c. Gold smelter, Balashi
　　　(vert) . . . .　75　75
272　250c. Rock crystal . . . .　1·90　1·90
275　500c. Conchi . . . . . .　3·75　3·75

88 Children at Beach Playground

2000. "Solidarity". Multicoloured.
280　75c.+35c. Type **88** . . . . .　80　80
281　100c.+50c. Children building
　　　sandcastles . . . . . .　1·10　1·10

89 "Solar Energy" (Nikki Johanna Teresia Willems)

2000. Child Welfare. "Stampin' the Future". Winning
Entries in Children's International Painting
Competition. Multicoloured.
282　60c.+30c. Type **89** . . . . .　70　70
283　80c.+40c. "Environmental
　　　Protection" (Samantha
　　　Jeanne Tromp) . . . .　90　90
284　100c.+50c. "Future Vehicles"
　　　(Jennifer Huntington) . . .　1·10　1·10

90 Cat

2001. Domestic Animals. Multicoloured.
285　5c. Type **90** . . . . . .　10　10
286　30c. Tortoise . . . . . .　20　20
287　50c. Rabbit . . . . . .　40　40
288　200c. Parakeet . . . . .　1·50　1·50

91 Shaman preparing for Sun Ceremony

2001. 40 Years of Mascaruba (amateur theatre
group). Depicting scenes from *Macuarima* (play).
Mult.
289　60c. Type **91** . . . . . .　45　45
290　150c. Love scene between
　　　Guadarikiri and Blanco . .　1·10　1·10

92 Ford Crown Victoria Leatherback, 1930

2001. Motor Cars. Multicoloured.
291　25c. Type **92** . . . . . .　20　20
292　40c. Citroen Comerciale, 1933　30　30
293　70c. Plymouth Pick-up, 1948　55　55
294　75c. Ford Edsel, 1959 . . .　60　60

93 Rock Drawings

2001. Universal Postal Union. United Nations Year
of Dialogue among Civilizations.
295　**93**　175c. multicoloured . . .　1·40　1·40

EXPRESS MAIL SERVICE

E **40** Globe, Planets and Aruban Arms

1993.
E122　E **40**　200c. multicoloured . .　1·50　1·50

ASCENSION　　　　　　　Pt. 1

An island in South Atlantic. A dependency of St.
Helena.

　　1922.　12 pence = 1 shilling;
　　　　　20 shillings = 1 pound.
　　1971.　100 pence = 1 pound.

1922. Stamps of St. Helena of 1912 optd
ASCENSION
1　½d. black and green . . . . .　4·50　15·00
2　1d. green . . . .　4·50　14·00
3　1½d. red . . . .　15·00　48·00
4　2d. black and slate . . . .　15·00　13·00
5　3d. blue . . . .　13·00　17·00
6　8d. black and purple . . . .　26·00　48·00
9　1s. black on green . . . .　28·00　48·00
7　2s. black and blue on blue . .　85·00　£120
8　3s. black and violet . . . . .　£120　£160

2 Badge of St. Helena

1924.
10　**2**　½d. black . . . . . .　3·50　13·00
11　1d. black and green . . .　5·50　7·50
12　1½d. red . . . .　7·50　26·00
13　2d. black and grey . . .　13·00　7·00
14　3d. blue . . . .　8·00　13·00
15　4d. black on yellow . . .　48·00　80·00
15d　5d. purple and green . . .　10·00　20·00
16　6d. black and purple . . .　48·00　90·00
17　8d. black and violet . . .　15·00　42·00
18　1s. black and brown . . .　20·00　50·00
19　2s. black and blue on blue .　55·00　85·00
20　3s. black on blue . . . .　80·00　90·00

3 Georgetown　　**4** Ascension Island

1934. Medallion portrait of King George V (except
1s.)
21　**3**　½d. black and violet . . .　90　80
22　1d. black and green . . .　1·75　1·25
23　1½d. black and red . . .　1·75　2·25
24　**4**　2d. black and orange . . . .　1·75　2·50
25　–　3d. black and blue . . . .　1·75　1·50
26　–　5d. black and blue . . . .　2·25　3·25
27　**4**　8d. black and brown . . . .　4·25　4·75
28　–　1s. black and red . . . .　18·00　6·50
29　**4**　2s.6d. black and purple . .　45·00　32·00
30　–　5s. black and brown . . .　45·00　55·00
DESIGNS—HORIZ: 1½d. The Pier; 3d. Long Beach;
5d. Three Sisters; 1s. Sooty tern ("Wideawake Fair");
5s. Green mountain.

1935. Silver Jubilee. As T **13** of Antigua.
31　1½d. blue and red . . . .　3·50　7·00
32　2d. blue and grey . . .　11·00　23·00
33　5d. green and blue . . .　17·00　24·00
34　1s. grey and purple . . .　23·00　27·00

1937. Coronation. As T **2** of Aden.
35　1d. green . . . .　50　80
36　2d. orange . . . . . .　1·00　40
37　3d. blue . . . .　1·00　50

10 The Pier

1938.
38b　A　½d. black and violet . . .　70　1·75
39　B　1d. black and green . . .　40·00　8·00
39b　　1d. black and orange . . .　45　60
39d　C　1d. black and green . . .　60　50
40b　**10**　1½d. black and red . . .　85　80
40d　　1½d. black and pink . . .　55　80
41a　B　2d. black and orange . . .　80　40
41c　　2d. black and red . . .　1·00　85
42　D　3d. black and blue . . .　£100　27·00
42b　　3d. black and grey . . .　70　80
42d　B　4d. black and blue . . .　4·50　3·00
43　C　6d. black and blue . . .　9·00　4·50
44a　A　1s. black and brown . . .　4·75　2·00
45　**10**　2s.6d. black and red . . .　42·00　9·50
46a　D　5s. black and brown . . .　38·00　27·00
47a　C　10s. black and purple . . .　45·00　55·00
DESIGNS: A, Georgetown; B, Green Mountain; C,
Three Sisters; D, Long Beach.

1946. Victory. As T **9** of Aden.
48　2d. orange . . . . . .　40　50
49　4d. blue . . . .　40　30

1948. Silver Wedding. As T **10/11** of Aden.
50　3d. black . . . .　30
51　10s. mauve . . . . . .　45·00　40·00

1949. U.P.U. As T **20/23** of Antigua.
52　3d. red . . . .　1·00　1·25
53　4d. blue . . . .　3·50　1·25
54　6d. olive . . . .　2·00　2·75
55　1s. black . . . .　2·00　1·50

1953. Coronation. As T **13** of Aden.
56　3d. black and grey . . . .　1·00　1·50

15 Water Catchment

1956.
57　**15**　½d. black and brown . . . .　10　50
58　–　1d. black and mauve . . .　2·25　70
59　–　1½d. black and orange . . .　50　70
60　–　2d. black and red . . . .　2·00　1·00
61　–　2½d. black and brown . .　1·00　1·50
62　–　3d. black and blue . . .　3·25　1·25
63　–　4d. black and turquoise .　1·25　1·75
64　–　6d. black and blue . . .　1·25　1·50
65　–　7d. black and olive . . .　1·25　1·00
66　–　1s. black and red . . .　1·00　90
67　–　2s.6d. black and purple .　27·00　6·50
68　–　5s. black and green . . .　35·00　17·00
69　–　10s. black and purple . .　48·00　35·00
DESIGNS: 1d. Map of Ascension; 1½d. Georgetown;
2d. Map showing Atlantic cables; 2½d. Mountain
road; 3d. White-tailed tropic bird ("Boatswain Bird");
4d. Yellow-finned tuna; 6d. Rollers on seashore; 7d.
Turtles; 1s. Land crab; 2s.6d. Sooty tern
("Wideawake"); 5s. Perfect Crater; 10s. View of
Ascension from north-west.

28 Brown Booby

1963. Birds. Multicoloured.
70　1d. Type **28** . . . . . .　90　30
71　1½d. White-capped noddy
　　　("Black Noddy") . . .　1·25　60
72　2d. White tern ("Fairy Tern")　1·25　30
73　3d. Red-billed tropic bird .　1·25　30
74　4½d. Common noddy ("Brown
　　　Noddy") . . . . . .　1·25　30
75　6d. Sooty tern ("Wideawake
　　　Tern") . . . .　1·25　30
76　7d. Ascension frigate bird
　　　("Frigate bird") . . .　1·25　30

77 10d. Blue-faced booby ("White Booby") . . . . 1·25 30
78 1s. White-tailed tropic bird ("Yellow-billed Tropicbird") 1·25 30
79 1s.6d. Red-billed tropic bird 4·50 1·75
80 2s.6d. Madeiran storm petrel 7·00 9·00
81 5s. Red-footed booby (brown phase) . . . . 7·00 8·00
82 10s. Ascension frigate birds ("Frigate birds") . . . . . 13·00 9·00
83 £1 Red-footed booby (white phase) . . . . 20·00 11·00

1963. Freedom from Hunger. As T **28** of Aden.
84 1s.6d. red 75 40

1963. Centenary of Red Cross. As T **33** of Antigua.
85 3d. red and black . . . . . . 2·00 1·25
86 1s.6d. red and blue . . . . . 4·00 2·25

1965. Centenary of I.T.U. As T **36** of Antigua.
87 3d. mauve and violet 50 65
88 6d. turquoise and brown . . . 75 65

1965. I.C.Y. As T **37** of Antigua.
89 1d. purple and turquoise . . . 40 60
90 6d. green and lavender 60 90

1966. Churchill Commemoration. As T **38** of Antigua.
91 1d. blue 50 75
92 3d. green . . . . 2·75 1·25
93 6d. brown . . . . 3·50 1·50
94 1s.6d. violet . . . . 4·50 2·00

1966. World Cup Football Championship. As T **40** of Antigua.
95 3d. multicoloured . . . . . . 1·25 60
96 6d. multicoloured . . . . . . 1·50 80

1966. Inauguration of W.H.O. Headquarters, Geneva. As T **41** of Antigua.
97 3d. black, green and blue . . . 1·75 1·00
98 1s.6d. black, purple and ochre 4·25 2·00

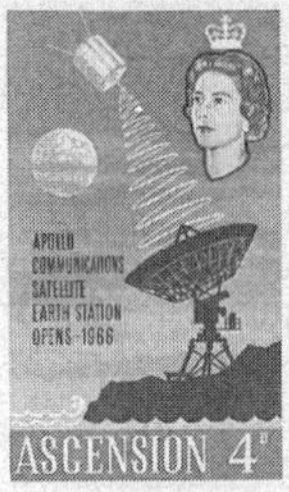

42 Satellite Station

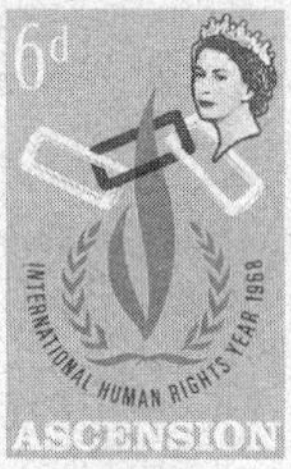

44 Human Rights Emblem and Chain Links

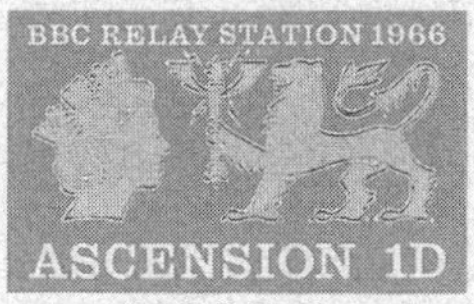

43 B.B.C. Emblem

1966. Opening of Apollo Communication Satellite Earth Station.
99 **42** 4d. black and violet . . . 15 20
100 8d. black and green . . . 15 20
101 1s.3d. black and brown . . 20 25
102 2s.6d. black and blue . . . 25 35

1966. Opening of B.B.C. Relay Station.
103 **43** 1d. gold and blue 10 20
104 3d. gold and green 15 25
105 6d. gold and violet 15 25
106 1s.6d. gold and red 15 25

1967. 20th Anniv of U.N.E.S.C.O. As T **54/56** of Antigua.
107 3d. multicoloured . . . . . 2·00 1·25
108 6d. yellow, violet and olive 2·75 1·75
109 1s.6d. black, purple and orange . . . . 4·50 2·25

1968. Human Rights Year.
110 **44** 6d. orange, red and black 25 25
111 1s.6d. blue, red and black 35 35
112 2s.6d. green, red and black 40 40

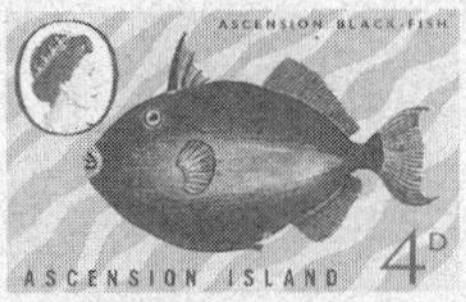

45 Black Durgon ("Ascension Black-Fish")

1968. Fishes (1st series).
113 **45** 4d. black, grey and blue . . 30 40
114 – 8d. multicoloured 35 70
115 – 1s.9d. multicoloured . . . 40 80
116 – 2s.3d. multicoloured . . . 40 85
DESIGNS: 8d. Scribbled filefish ("Leather-jacket"); 1s.9d. Yellow-finned tuna; 2s.3d. Short-finned mako.
See also Nos. 117/20 and 126/9.

1969. Fishes (2nd series). As T **45**. Multicoloured.
117 4d. Sailfish 75 90
118 6d. White seabream ("Old wife") . . . . 1·00 1·25
119 1s.6d. Yellowtail . . . . . . 1·50 2·50
120 2s.11d. Rock hind ("Jack") 2·00 3·00

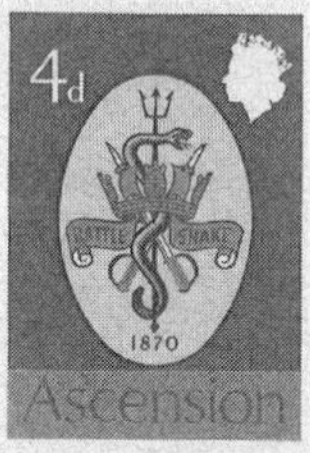

46 H.M.S. "Rattlesnake"

1969. Royal Navy Crests (1st series).
121 **46** 4d. multicoloured 60 30
122 – 9d. multicoloured 75 35
123 – 1s.9d. blue and gold . . . 1·10 45
124 – 2s.3d. multicoloured . . . 1·25 55
DESIGNS: 9d. H.M.S. "Weston"; 1s.9d. H.M.S. "Undaunted"; 2s.3d. H.M.S. "Eagle".
See also Nos. 130/3, 149/52, 154/7 and 166/9.

1970. Fishes (3rd series). As T **45**. Multicoloured.
126 4d. Wahoo . . . . 4·50 2·75
127w 9d. Ascension jack ("Coalfish") . . . . 3·00 1·25
128 1s.9d. Pompouno dolphin 5·50 3·50
129w 2s.3d. Squirrelfish ("Soldier") . . . . 5·50 3·50

1970. Royal Navy Crests (2nd series). As T **46**. Multicoloured.
130 4d. H.M.S. "Penelope" . . . 1·00 1·00
131 9d. H.M.S. "Carlisle" . . . . 1·25 1·50
132 1s.6d. H.M.S. "Amphion" . . 1·75 2·00
133 2s.6d. H.M.S. "Magpie" . . 1·75 2·00

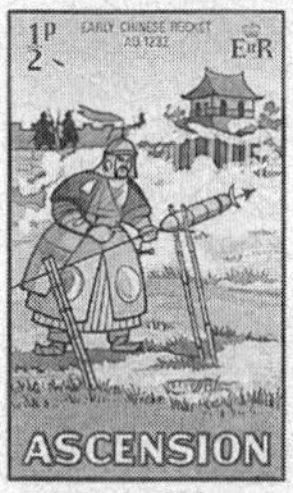

50 Early Chinese Rocket

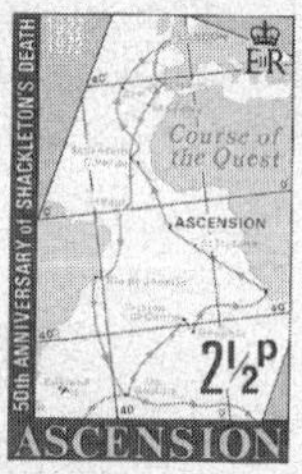

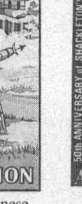

51 Course of the "Quest"

1971. Decimal Currency. Evolution of Space Travel. Multicoloured.
135 ½p. Type **50** 15 20
136 1p. Medieval Arab astronomers 20 20
137 1½p. Tycho Brahe's observatory, quadrant and supernova 30 30
138 2p. Galileo, Moon and telescope 40 30
139 2½p. Isaac Newton, instruments and apple . . 1·00 70
140 3½p. Harrison's chronometer and H.M.S. "Deptford" (frigate), 1735 . . . . . . 2·00 70
141 4½p. Space rocket taking off 1·25 70
142 5p. World's largest telescope, Palomar . . . . 1·00 70
143 7½p. World's largest radio telescope, Jodrell Bank . . 4·00 1·60
144 10p. "Mariner VII" and Mars . . . . 3·50 1·75
145 12½p. "Sputnik II" and Space dog, Laika . . . . . . 5·00 2·00
146 25p. Walking in Space . . . 6·00 2·25
147 50p. "Apollo XI" crew on Moon . . . . 5·00 2·50
148 £1 Future Space Research station . . . . 5·00 4·50
Nos. 137/40, 142/5 and 147/8 are horiz.

1971. Royal Navy Crests (3rd series). As T **46**. Mult.
149 2p. H.M.S. "Phoenix" . . . 1·00 30
150 4p. H.M.S. "Milford" . . . 1·25 55
151 9p. H.M.S. "Pelican" . . . 1·50 80
152 15p. H.M.S. "Oberon" . . . 1·50 1·00

1972. Royal Navy Crests (4th series). As T **46**. Mult.
154 1½p. H.M.S. "Lowestoft" . . 50 50
155 3p. H.M.S. "Auckland" . . . 55 75
156 6p. H.M.S. "Nigeria" . . . 60 1·25
157 17½p. H.M.S. "Bermuda" . . 90 2·50

1972. 50th Anniv of Shackleton's Death. Mult.
159 2½p. Type **51** 40 60
160 4p. Shackleton and "Quest" (horiz) 50 60
161 7½p. Shackleton's cabin and "Quest" (horiz) 55 65
162 11p. Shackleton statue and memorial 55 80

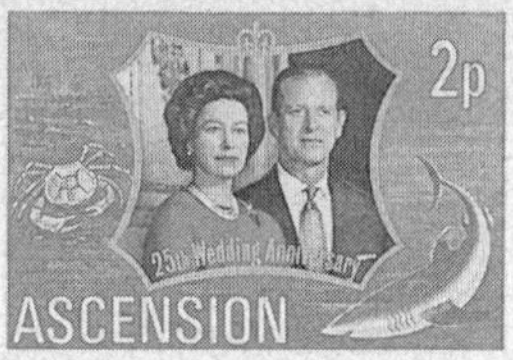

52 Land Crab and Short-finned Mako

1972. Royal Silver Wedding. Multicoloured.
164 **52** 2p. violet 15 10
165 16p. red 35 30

1973. Royal Naval Crests (5th series). As T **46**. Multicoloured.
166 2p. H.M.S. "Birmingham" 2·00 1·25
167 4p. H.M.S. "Cardiff" . . . . 2·25 1·25
168 9p. H.M.S. "Penzance" . . . 3·00 1·50
169 13p. H.M.S. "Rochester" . . 3·25 1·50

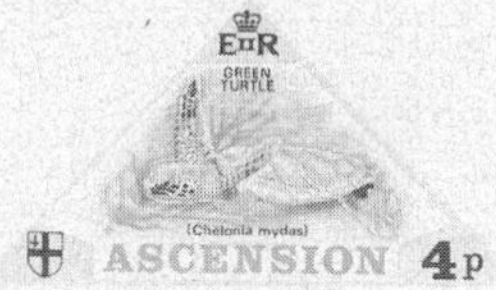

53 Green Turtle

1973. Turtles. Multicoloured.
171 4p. Type **53** . . . . 2·75 1·25
172 9p. Loggerhead turtle . . . . 3·00 1·50
173 12p. Hawksbill turtle . . . . 3·25 1·75

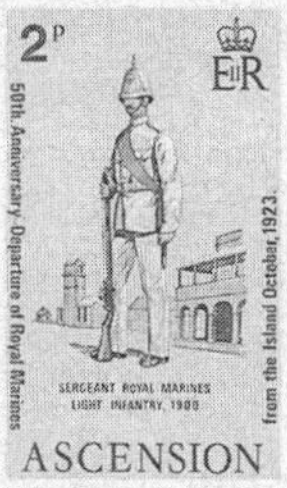

54 Sergeant, R.M. Light Infantry, 1900

1973. 50th Anniv of Departure of Royal Marines from Ascension. Multicoloured.
174 2p. Type **54** . . . . 1·50 1·25
175 6p. R.M. Private, 1816 . . . 2·25 1·75
176 12p. R.M. Light Infantry Officer, 1880 . . . . . . 2·50 2·25
177 20p. R.M. Artillery Colour Sergeant, 1910 . . . . . 3·00 2·50

1973. Royal Wedding. As T **47** of Anguilla. Multicoloured. Background colours given.
178 2p. brown 15 10
179 18p. green . . . .

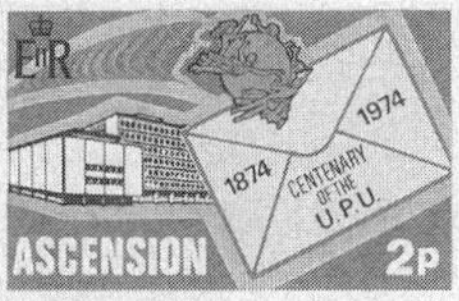

55 Letter and H.Q., Berne

1974. Centenary of Universal Postal Union. Mult.
180 2p. Type **55** 25 30
181 9p. Hermes and U.P.U. monument 40 45

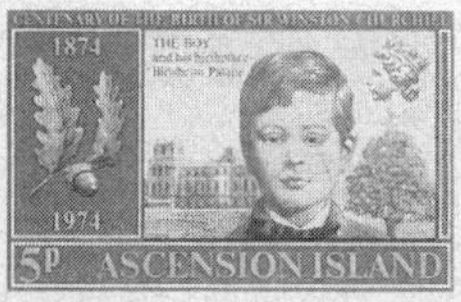

56 Churchill as a Boy, and Birthplace, Blenheim Palace

1974. Birth Centenary of Sir Winston Churchill. Multicoloured.
182 5p. Type **56** 25 35
183 25p. Churchill as statesman, and U.N. Building 40 75

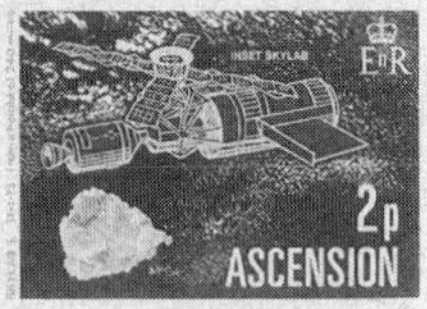

57 "Skylab 3" and Photograph of Ascension

1975. Space Satellites. Multicoloured.
185 2p. Type **57** 30 30
186 18p. "Skylab 4" Command module and photograph . . 35 40

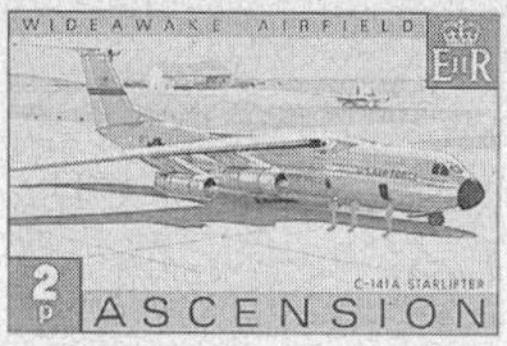

58 U.S.A.F. Lockheed C-141A Starlifter

1975. Wideawake Airfield. Multicoloured.
187 2p. Type **58** . . . . 1·00 65
188 5p. R.A.F. Lockheed C-130 Hercules . . . . 1·25 85
189 9p. Vickers Super VC-10 . . 1·25 1·40
190 24p. U.S.A.F. Lockheed C-5A Galaxy . . . . . . 2·00 3·00

1975. "Apollo-Soyuz" Space Link. Nos. 141 and 145/6 optd **APOLLO-SOYUZ LINK 1975**.
192 4½p. multicoloured 15 20
193 12½p. multicoloured 20 25
194 25p. multicoloured 30 40

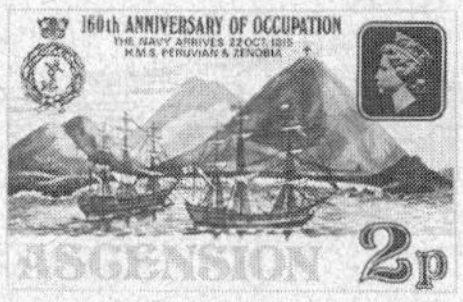

60 Arrival of Royal Navy, 1815

1975. 160th Anniv of Occupation. Multicoloured.
195 2p. Type **60** 25 25
196 5p. Water supply, Dampiers Drip 30 40
197 9p. First landing, 1815 . . . 35 60
198 15p. The garden on Green Mountain 45 85

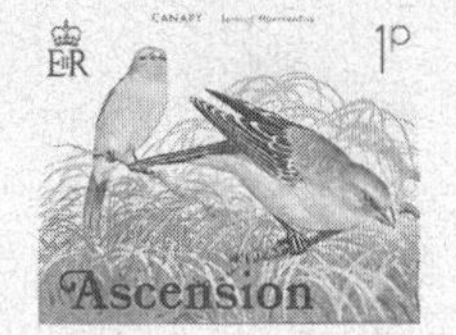

61 Yellow Canaries ("Canary")

1976. Multicoloured.
199 1p. Type **61** . . . . 40 1·50
200 2p. White tern ("Fairy Tern") (vert) . . . . 45 1·50
201 3p. Common waxbill ("Waxbill") . . . . 45 1·50
202 4p. White-capped noddy ("Black Noddy") (vert) . . 50 1·50
203 5p. Common noddy ("Brown Noddy") . . . . 70 1·50
204 6p. Common mynah . . . . 70 1·50
205 7p. Madeiran storm petrel (vert) . . . . 70 1·50
206 8p. Sooty tern . . . . 70 1·50
207 9p. Blue-faced booby ("White Booby") (vert) . . . . . 70 1·50
208 10p. Red-footed booby . . . 70 1·50
209 15p. Red-necked spur fowl ("Red-throated Francolin") (vert) . . . . 85 1·50
210 18p. Brown booby (vert) . . 85 1·50
211 25p. Red-billed tropic bird ("Red-billed Bo'sun Bird") 90 1·50
212 50p. White-tailed tropic bird ("Yellow-billed Tropic Bird") . . . . 1·50 2·25
213 £1 Ascension frigate-bird (vert) . . . . 1·75 2·75
214 £2 Boatswain Bird Island Sanctuary (50 × 38 mm) . . 3·00 5·50

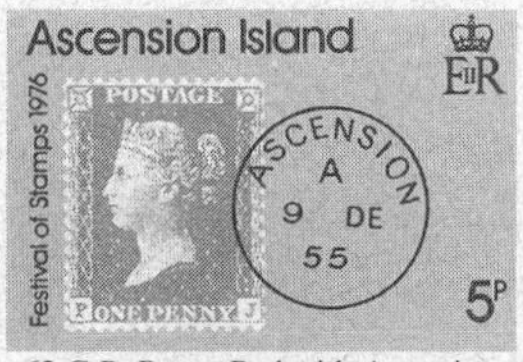

63 G.B. Penny Red with Ascension Postmark

1976. Festival of Stamps, London.
215 **63** 5p. red, black and brown 20 15
216 – 9p. green, black and brown 20 20
217 – 25p. multicoloured 30 45
DESIGNS—VERT: 9p. ½d. stamp of 1922. HORIZ: 25p. "Southampton Castle" (liner).

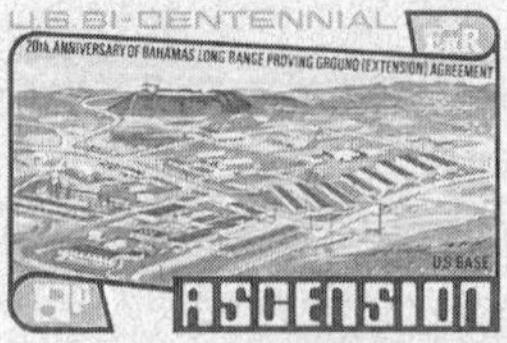

64 U.S. Base, Ascension

1976. Bicentenary of American Revolution. Multicoloured.

219	8p. Type **64**	30	40
220	9p. NASA Station at Devils Ashpit	30	45
221	25p. "Viking" landing on Mars	40	80

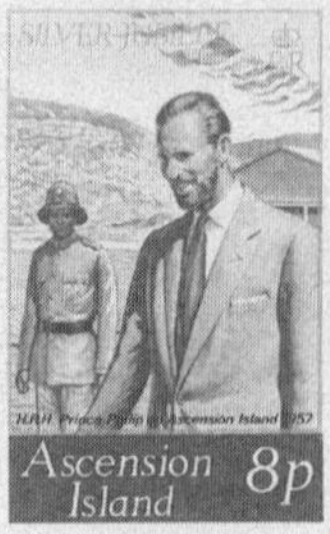

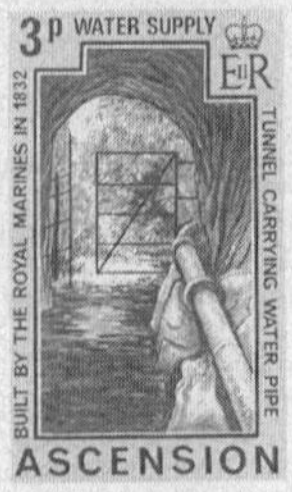

65 Visit of Prince Philip, 1957 **66** Tunnel carrying Water Pipe

1977. Silver Jubilee. Multicoloured.

222	8p. Type **65**	15	15
223	12p. Coronation Coach leaving Buckingham Palace (horiz)	20	20
224	25p. Coronation Coach (horiz)	35	40

1977. Water Supplies. Multicoloured.

225	3p. Type **66**	15	15
226	5p. Breakneck Valley wells	20	20
227	12p. Break tank (horiz)	35	35
228	25p. Water catchment (horiz)	55	65

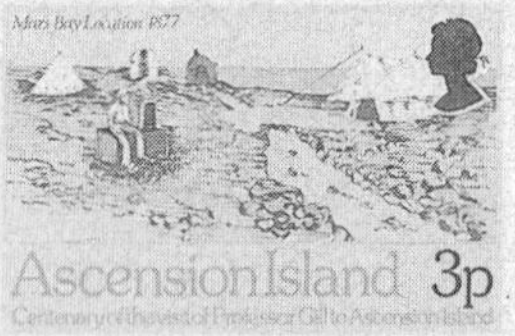

67 Mars Bay Location, 1877

1977. Centenary of Visit of Professor Gill (astronomer). Multicoloured.

229	3p. Type **67**	15	20
230	8p. Instrument sites, Mars Bay	20	25
231	12p. Sir David and Lady Gill	30	40
232	25p. Maps of Ascension	60	70

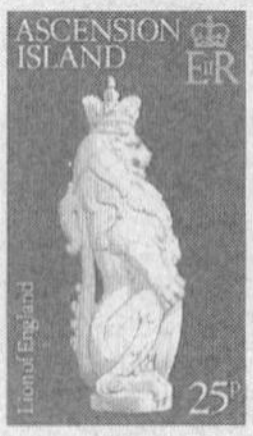

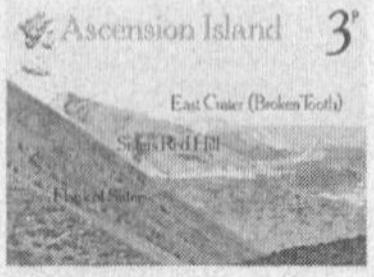

68 Lion of England **70** Flank of Sisters, Sisters' Red Hill and East Crater

1978. 25th Anniv of Coronation.

233 **68**	25p. yellow, brown and silver	35	50
234 –	25p. multicoloured	35	50
235 –	25p. yellow, brown and silver	35	50

DESIGNS: No 234, Queen Elizabeth II; No 235, Green turtle.

1978. Ascension Island Volcanic Rock Formations. Multicoloured.

236	3p. Type **70**	15	20
237	5p. Holland's Crater (Hollow Tooth)	20	30
238	12p. Street Crater, Lower Valley Crater and Bear's Back	25	40
239	15p. Butt Crater, Weather Post and Green Mountain	30	45
240	25p. Flank of Sisters, Thistle Hill and Two Boats Village	35	50

Nos. 236/40 were issued as a se-tenant strip within the sheet, forming a composite design.

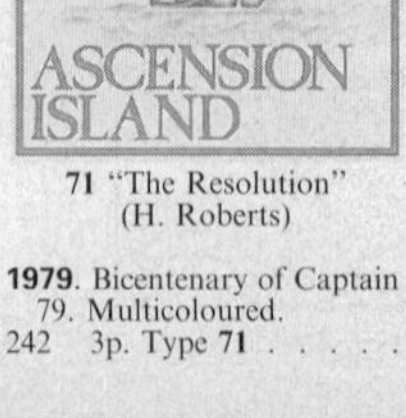

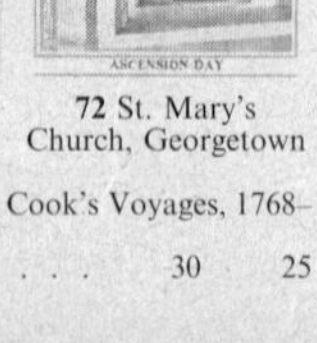

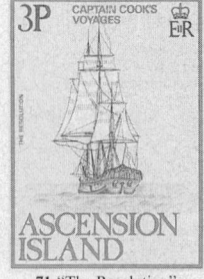

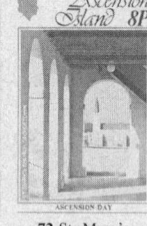

71 "The Resolution" (H. Roberts) **72** St. Mary's Church, Georgetown

1979. Bicentenary of Captain Cook's Voyages, 1768–79. Multicoloured.

242	3p. Type **71**	30	25
243	8p. Cook's chronometer	30	40
244	12p. Green turtle	35	50
245	25p. Flaxman/Wedgwood medallion of Cook	40	70

1979. Ascension Day. Muticoloured.

246	8p. Type **72**	15	20
247	12p. Map of Ascension	20	30
248	50p. "The Ascension" (painting by Rembrandt)	55	90

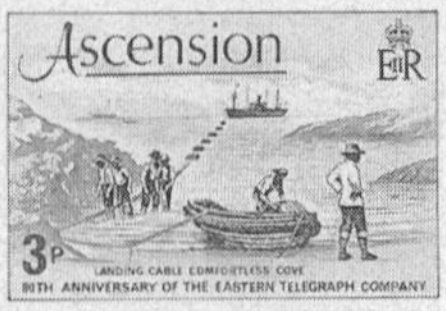

73 Landing Cable, Comfortless Cove

1979. 80th Anniv of Eastern Telegraph Company's Arrival on Ascension.

249 **73**	3p. black and red	15	10
250 –	8p. black and green	20	20
251 –	12p. black and yellow	25	25
252 –	15p. black and violet	25	35
253 –	25p. black and brown	35	50

DESIGNS—HORIZ: 8p. C.S. "Anglia"; 15p. C.S. "Seine"; 25p. Cable and Wireless earth station. VERT: 12p. Map of Atlantic cable network.

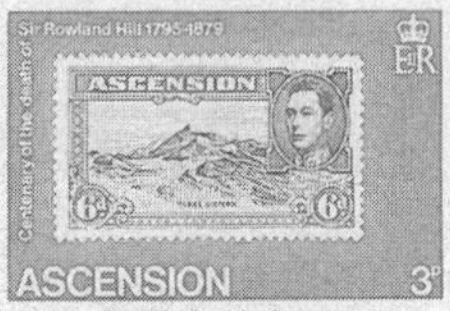

74 1938 6d. Stamp

1979. Death Centenary of Sir Rowland Hill.

254 **74**	3p. black and blue	15	10
255 –	8p. black, green and pale green	15	20
256 –	12p. black, blue and pale blue	20	25
257 –	50p. black and red	60	90

DESIGNS—HORIZ: 8p. 1956 5s. definitive. VERT: 12p. 1924 3s. stamp; 50p. Sir Rowland Hill.

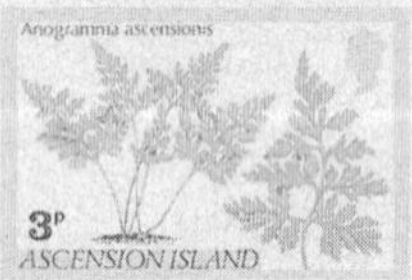

75 "Anogramma ascensionis"

1980. Ferns and Grasses. Multicoloured.

258	3p. Type **75**	10	10
259	6p. "Xiphopteris ascensionense"	15	15
260	8p. "Sporobolus caespitosus"	15	15
261	12p. "Sporobolus durus" (vert)	15	25
262	18p. "Dryopteris ascensionis" (vert)	20	35
263	24p. "Marattia purpurascens" (vert)	30	50

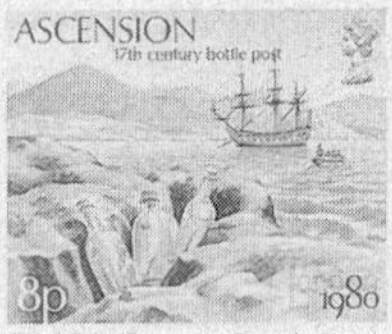

76 17th-Century Bottle Post

1980. "London 1980" International Stamp Exhibition. Multicoloured.

264	8p. Type **76**	15	20
265	12p. 19th-century chance calling ship	20	25
266	15p. "Garth Castle" (regular mail service from 1863)	20	30
267	50p. "St. Helena" (mail services, 1980)	60	90

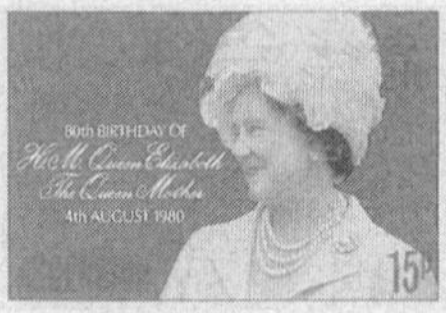

77 H.M. Queen Elizabeth the Queen Mother

1980. 80th Birthday of The Queen Mother.

269 **77**	15p. multicoloured	40	40

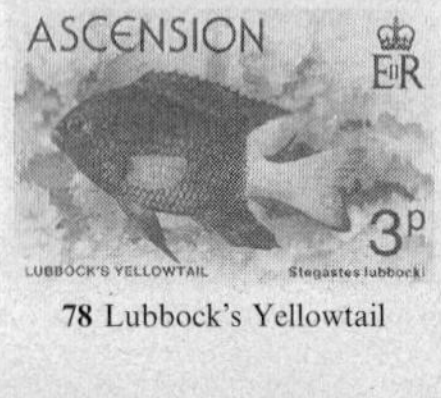

78 Lubbock's Yellowtail

1980. Fishes. Multicoloured.

270	3p. Type **78**	30	15
271	10p. Resplendent angelfish	40	25
272	25p. Bicoloured butterflyfish	50	50
273	40p. Marmalade razorfish	60	65

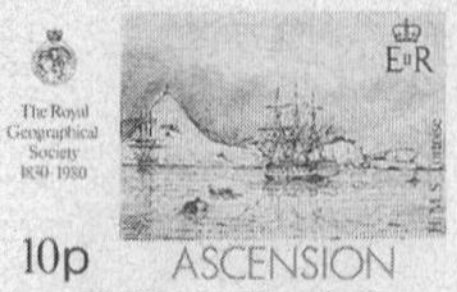

79 H.M.S. "Tortoise"

1980. 150th Anniv of Royal Geographical Society. Multicoloured.

274	10p. Type **79**	20	40
275	15p. "Wideawake Fair"	30	45
276	60p. Mid-Atlantic Ridge (38 × 48 mm)	65	1·25

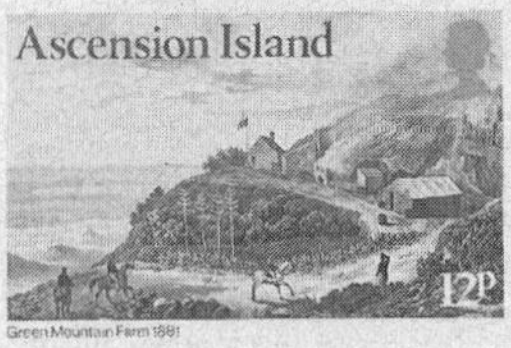

80 Green Mountain Farm, 1881

1981. Green Mountain Farm. Multicoloured.

277	12p. Type **80**	15	35
278	15p. Two Boats, 1881	20	40
279	20p. Green Mountain and Two Boats, 1981	25	50
280	30p. Green Mountain Farm, 1981	35	70

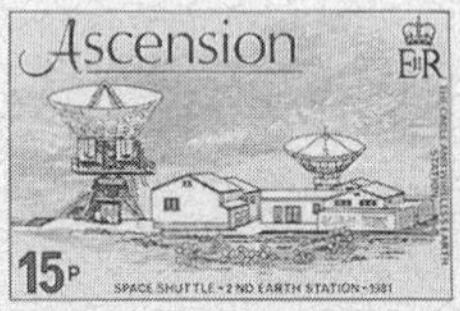

81 Cable and Wireless Earth Station

1981. "Space Shuttle" Mission and Opening of 2nd Earth Station.

281 **81**	15p. black, blue and pale blue	30	35

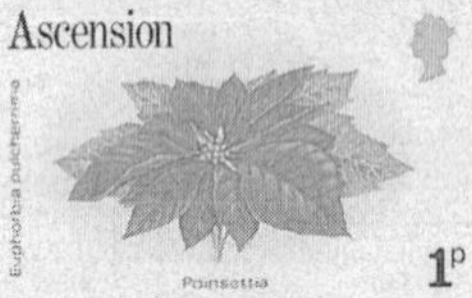

82 Poinsettia

83 Solanum

1981. Flowers. Multicoloured.

282A	1p. Type **82**	70	70
283B	2p. Clustered wax flower	50	75
284B	3p. Kolanchoe (vert)	50	75
285A	4p. Yellow pops	80	75
286A	5p. Camels foot creeper	80	75
287A	8p. White oleander	80	80
288B	10p. Ascension lily (vert)	45	75
289A	12p. Coral plant (vert)	1·50	85
290B	15p. Yellow allamanda	50	75
291B	20p. Ascension euphorbia	1·00	75
292A	30p. Flame of the forest (vert)	1·25	1·25
293A	40p. Bougainvillea "King Leopold"	1·25	2·00
294A	50p. Type **83**	1·25	2·50
295B	£1 Ladies petticoat	2·00	2·75
296A	£2 Red hibiscus	3·75	5·50

Nos. 294/6 are as Type **83**.

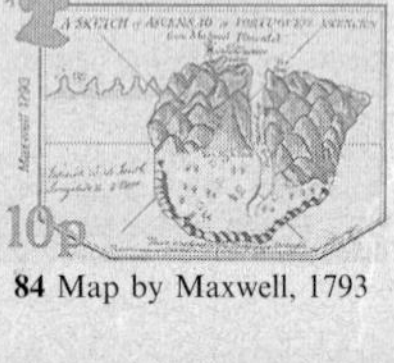

84 Map by Maxwell, 1793

1981. Early Maps of Ascension.

297 **84**	10p. black, gold and blue	25	35
298 –	12p. black, gold and green	25	35
299 –	15p. black, gold and stone	25	35
300 –	40p. black, gold and yellow	55	70

DESIGNS: 12p. Maxwell, 1793 (different); 15p. Ekeberg and Chapman, 1811; 40p. Campbell, 1819.

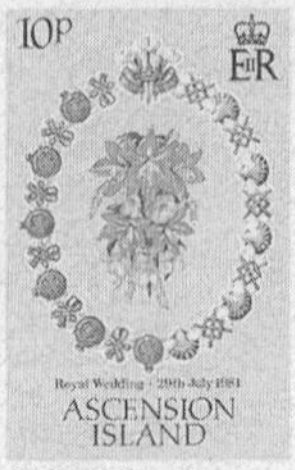

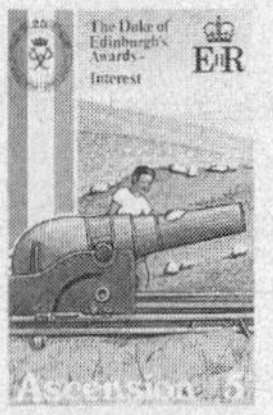

85 Wedding Bouquet from Ascension **87** "Interest"

1981. Royal Wedding. Multicoloured.

302	10p. Type **85**	15	15
303	15p. Prince Charles in Fleet Air Arm flying kit	30	25
304	50p. Prince Charles and Lady Diana Spencer	65	75

1981. 25th Anniv of Duke of Edinburgh Award Scheme. Multicoloured.

305	5p. Type **87**	15	15
306	10p. "Physical activities"	15	15
307	15p. "Service"	20	20
308	40p. Duke of Edinburgh	45	45

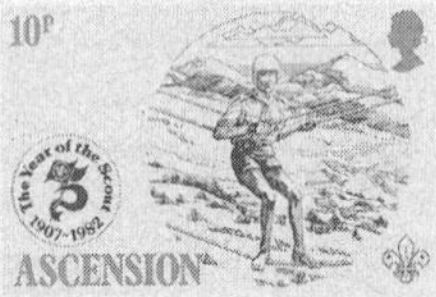

88 Scout crossing Rope Bridge

1982. 75th Anniv of Boy Scout Movement.

309 **88**	10p. black, blue and light blue	15	35
310 –	15p. black, brown and yellow	20	50
311 –	25p. black, mve & lt mve	30	60
312 –	40p. black, red and orange	50	85

DESIGNS: 15p. 1st Ascension Scout Group flag; 25p. Scouts learning to use radio; 40p. Lord Baden-Powell.

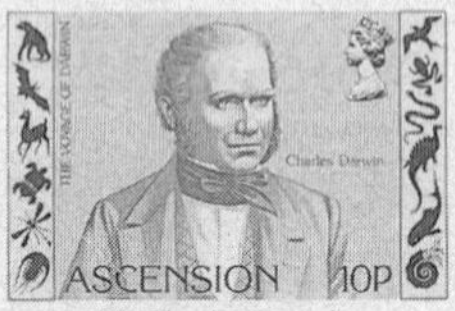

89 Charles Darwin

1982. 150th Anniv of Charles Darwin's Voyage. Multicoloured.

314	10p. Type **89**	25	40
315	12p. Darwin's pistols	30	50
316	15p. Rock crab	35	55
317	40p. H.M.S. "Beagle"	75	95

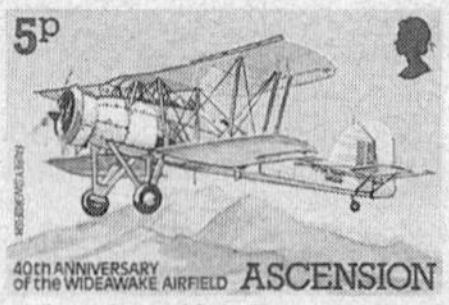

90 Fairey Swordfish Torpedo Bomber

1982. 40th Anniv of Wideawake Airfield. Multicoloured.

318	5p. Type **90**	1·00	35
319	10p. North American B-25C Mitchell	1·25	40
320	15p. Boeing EC-135N Aria	1·50	55
321	50p. Lockheed C-130 Hercules	2·25	1·10

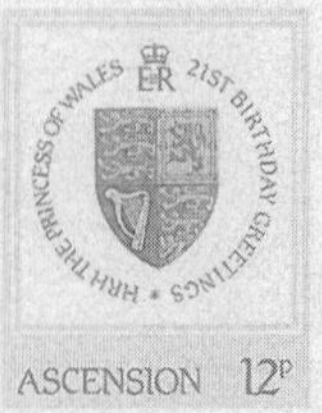

91 Ascension Coat of Arms

1982. 21st Birthday of Princess of Wales. Mult.

322	12p. Type **91**	25	25
323	15p. Lady Diana Spencer in Music Room, Buckingham Palace	25	25

324 25p. Bride and Earl Spencer leaving Clarence House . . 40 40
325 50p. Formal portrait 75 75

1982. Commonwealth Games, Brisbane. Nos. 290/1 optd **1st PARTICIPATION COMMONWEALTH GAMES 1982.**
326 15p. Yellow allamanda . . . 30 40
327 20p. Ascension euphorbia . . 40 45

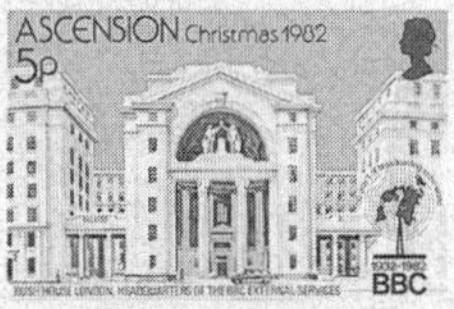

94 Bush House, London

1982. Christmas. 50th Anniv of B.B.C. External Broadcasting. Multicoloured.
328 5p. Type **94** 15 20
329 10p. Atlantic relay station . . 20 30
330 25p. Lord Reith, first Director-General 30 60
331 40p. King George V making his first Christmas broadcast, 1932 . . . . . 45 75

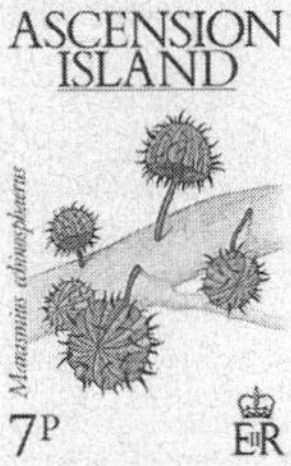

95 "Marasmius echinosphaerus"

1983. Fungi. Multicoloured.
332 7p. Type **95** 45 30
333 12p. "Chlorophyllum molybdites" 60 45
334 15p. "Leucocoprinus cepaestripes" 70 50
335 20p. "Lycoperdon marginatum" 80 65
336 50p. "Marasmiellus distantifolius" . . . . . . 1·25 1·25

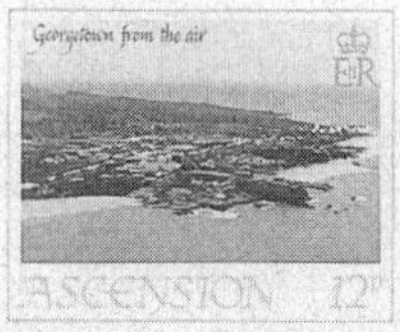

96 Aerial View of Georgetown

1983. Island Views (1st series). Multicoloured.
337 12p. Type **96** 15 25
338 15p. Green Mountain farm 15 25
339 20p. Boatswain Bird Island 25 40
340 60p. Telemetry Hill by night 60 80
See also Nos. 367/70.

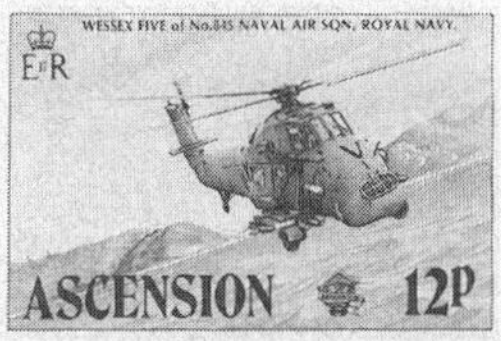

97 Westland Wessex 5 Helicopter of No. 845 Naval Air Squadron

1983. Bicentenary of Manned Flight. British Military Aircraft. Multicoloured.
341 12p. Type **97** 60 65
342 15p. Avro Vulcan B.2 of No. 44 Squadron 70 75
343 20p. Hawker Siddeley Nimrod M.R.2P of No. 20 Squadron 75 85
344 60p. Handey Page Victor K2 of No. 55 Squadron . . . 1·25 2·00

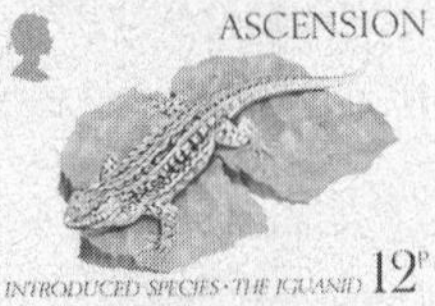

98 Iguanid

1983. Introduced Species. Multicoloured.
345 12p. Type **98** 30 30
346 15p. Common rabbit 35 35
347 20p. Cat 45 45
348 60p. Donkey . . . . 1·10 1·40

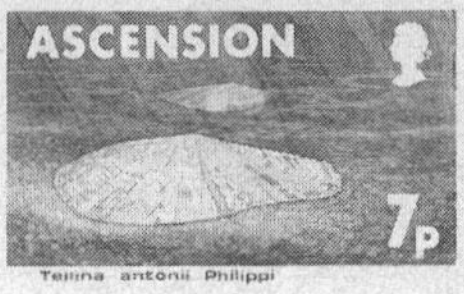

99 Speckled Tellin

1983. Sea Shells. Multicoloured.
349 7p. Type **99** 15 20
350 12p. Lion's paw scallop . . . 20 30
351 15p. Lurid cowrie 20 35
352 20p. Ascension nerite 25 45
353 50p. Miniature melo . . . . 55 1·10

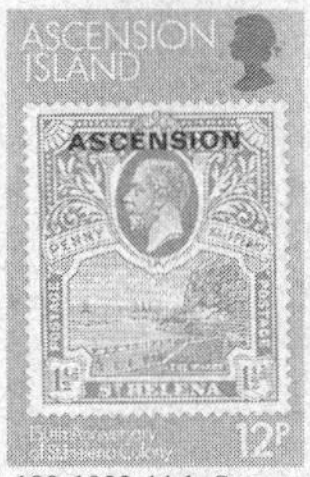

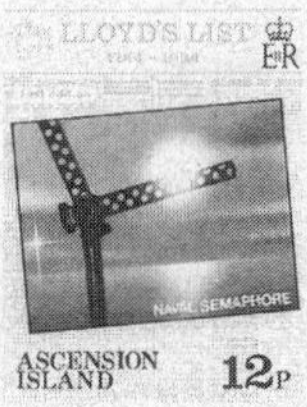

100 1922 1½d. Stamp **102** Naval Semaphore

1984. 150th Anniv of St. Helena as a British Colony. Multicoloured.
354 12p. Type **100** 30 45
355 15p. 1922 2d. stamp 35 50
356 20p. 1922 8d. stamp 35 55
357 60p. 1922 1s. stamp . . . . 75 1·40

1984. 250th Anniv of "Lloyd's List" (newspaper). Multicoloured.
359 12p. Type **102** 40 30
360 15p. "Southampton Castle" (liner) 40 35
361 20p. Pier head 45 45
362 70p. "Dane" (screw steamer) 1·00 1·50

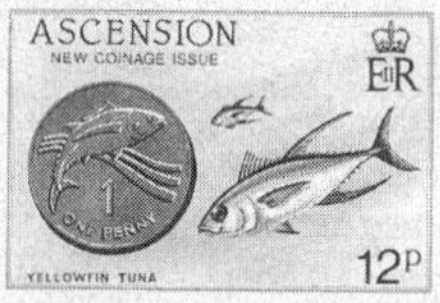

103 Penny Coin and Yellow-finned Tuna

1984. New Coinage. Multicoloured.
363 12p. Type **103** 45 35
364 15p. Twopenny coin and donkey 50 40
365 20p. Fifty pence coin and green turtle 60 50
366 70p. Pound coin and sooty tern . . . . 1·00 1·75

1984. Island Views (2nd series). As T **96**. Mult.
367 12p. The Devil's Riding-school 20 30
368 15p. St. Mary's Church . . . 25 35
369 20p. Two Boats Village . . . 25 45
370 70p. Ascension from the sea 80 1·50

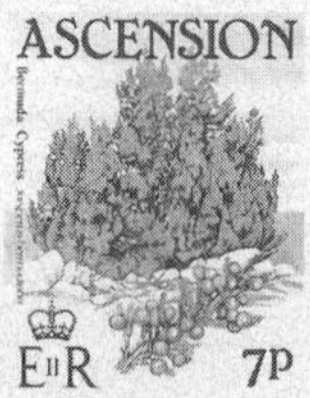

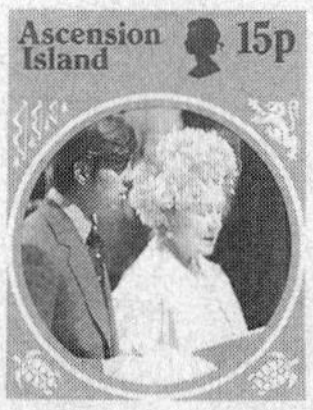

104 Bermuda Cypress **105** The Queen Mother with Prince Andrew at Silver Jubilee Service

1985. Trees. Multicoloured.
371 7p. Type **104** 35 20
372 12p. Norfolk Island pine . . 40 30
373 15p. Screwpine 40 35
374 20p. Eucalyptus 45 45
375 65p. Spore tree . . . . . . 1·00 1·40

1985. Life and Times of Queen Elizabeth the Queen Mother. Multicoloured.
376 12p. With the Duke of York at Balmoral, 1924 . . . . 25 35
377 15p. Type **105** 25 40
378 20p. The Queen Mother at Ascot 30 55
379 70p. With Prince Henry at his christening (from photo by Lord Snowdon) . . . . . 80 1·75

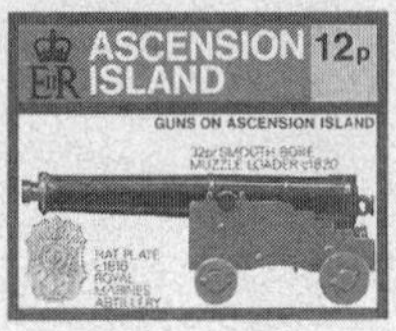

106 32 Pdr. Smooth Bore Muzzle-loader, c. 1820, and Royal Marine Artillery Hat Plate, c. 1816

1985. Guns on Ascension Island. Multicoloured.
381 12p. Type **106** 60 90
382 15p. 7 inch rifled muzzle-loader, c. 1866, and Royal Cypher on barrel . . . . . 70 1·00
383 20p. 7 pdr rifled muzzle-loader, c. 1877, and Royal Artillery Badge . . . . . 70 1·25
384 70p. 5.5 inch gun, 1941, and crest from H.M.S. "Hood" 1·75 3·50

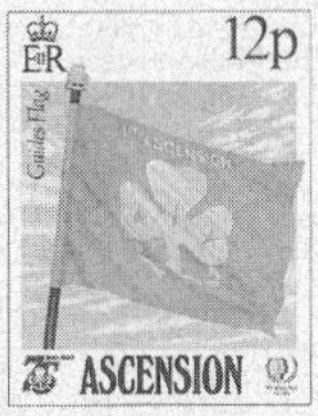

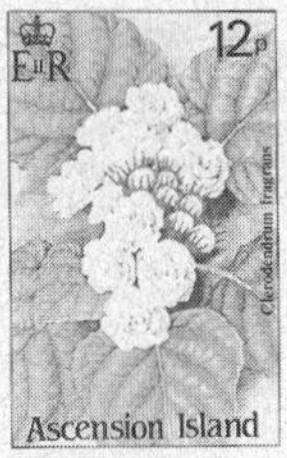

107 Guide Flag **108** "Clerodendrum fragrans"

1985. 75th Anniv of Girl Guide Movement and International Youth Year. Multicoloured.
385 12p. Type **107** 60 70
386 15p. Practising first aid . . . 65 80
387 20p. Camping 70 90
388 70p. Lady Baden-Powell . . 2·00 2·50

1985. Wild Flowers. Multicoloured.
389 12p. Type **108** 35 75
390 15p. Shell ginger 40 90
391 20p. Cape daisy 45 90
392 70p. Ginger lily . . . . . . 1·00 2·50

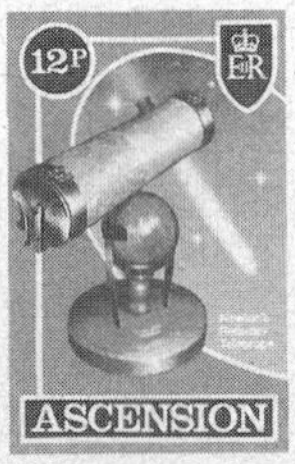

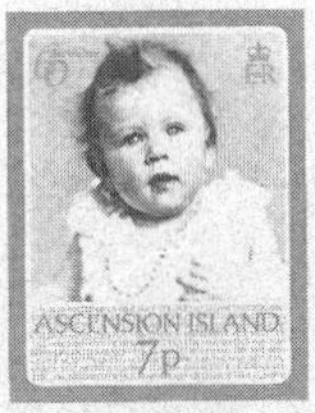

109 Newton's Reflector Telescope **110** Princess Elizabeth in 1926

1986. Appearance of Halley's Comet. Mult.
393 12p. Type **109** . . . . 60 1·10
394 15p. Edmond Halley and Old Greenwich Observatory . . 70 1·25
395 20p. Short's Gregorian telescope and comet, 1759 75 1·25
396 70p. Ascension satellite tracking station and ICE spacecraft . . . . 2·00 3·50

1986. 60th Birthday of Queen Elizabeth II. Mult.
397 7p. Type **110** 15 25
398 15p. Queen making Christmas broadcast, 1952 20 40
399 20p. At Garter ceremony, Windsor Castle, 1983 . . . 25 50
400 35p. In Auckland, New Zealand, 1981 . . . . . 35 80
401 £1 At Crown Agents' Head Office, London, 1983 . . .

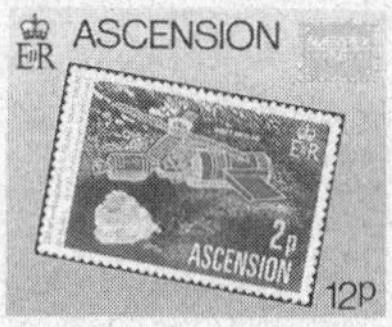

111 1975 Space Satellites 2p. Stamp

1986. "Ameripex '86" International Stamp Exhibition, Chicago. Designs showing previous Ascension stamps. Multicoloured.
402 12p. Type **111** 40 60
403 15p. 1980 "London 1980" International Stamp Exhibition 50p. 45 70
404 20p. 1976 Bicentenary of American Revolution 8p. 55 90
405 70p. 1982 40th anniv of Wideawake Airfield 10p. 1·25 2·00

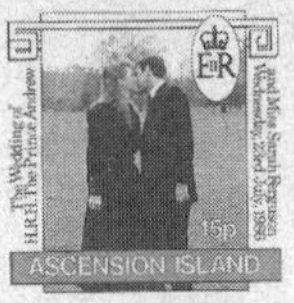

112 Prince Andrew and Miss Sarah Ferguson

1986. Royal Wedding. Multicoloured.
407 15p. Type **112** 25 35
408 35p. Prince Andrew aboard H.M.S. "Brazen" 50 75

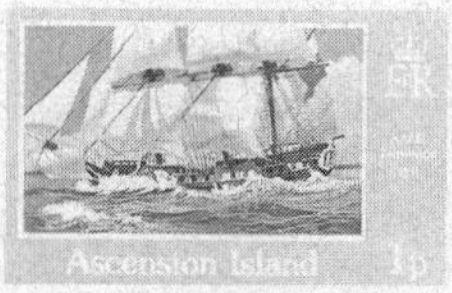

113 H.M.S. "Ganymede" (c. 1811)

1986. Ships of the Royal Navy. Multicoloured.
409 1p. Type **113** . . . . 55 1·50
410 2p. H.M.S. "Kangaroo" (c. 1811) . . . . 60 1·50
411 4p. H.M.S. "Trinculo" (c. 1811) . . . . 60 1·50
412 5p. H.M.S. "Daring" (c. 1811) . . . . 60 1·50
413 9p. H.M.S. "Thais" (c. 1811) 70 1·50
414 10p. H.M.S. "Pheasant" (1819) . . . . 70 1·50
415 15p. H.M.S. "Myrmidon" (1819) . . . . 80 1·75
416 18p. H.M.S. "Atholl" (1825) 90 1·75
417 20p. H.M.S. "Medina" (1830) 90 1·75
418 25p. H.M.S. "Saracen" (1840) . . . . 1·00 2·00
419 30p. H.M.S. "Hydra" (c. 1845) . . . . 1·00 2·00
420 50p. H.M.S. "Sealark" (1849) 1·25 2·50
421 70p. H.M.S. "Rattlesnake" (1868) . . . . 1·75 3·00
422 £1 H.M.S. "Penelope" (1889) 2·40 3·75
423 £2 H.M.S. "Monarch" (1897) 5·00 6·50

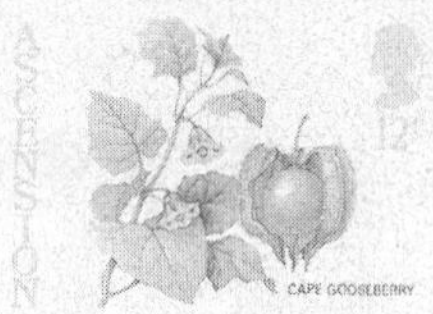

114 Cape Gooseberry

1987. Edible Bush Fruits. Multicoloured.
424 12p. Type **114** 65 90
425 15p. Prickly pear . . . . . . 75 1·00
426 20p. Guava . . . . 85 1·10
427 70p. Loquat . . . . 1·50 2·75

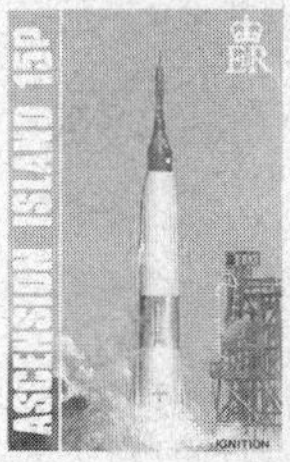

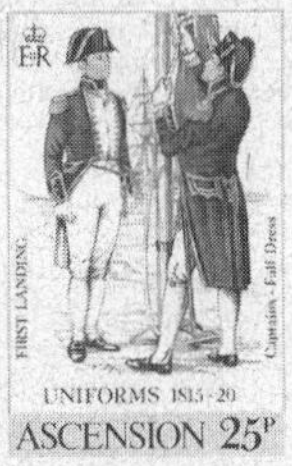

115 Ignition of Rocket Motors **116** Captains in Full Dress raising Red Ensign

1987. 25th Anniv of First American Manned Earth Orbit. Multicoloured.
428 15p. Type **115** 55 75
429 18p. Lift-off 60 80
430 25p. Re-entry 75 95
431 £1 Splashdown . . . . . . 2·50 3·25

1987. 19th-century Uniforms (1st series). Royal Navy, 1815–20. Multicoloured.
433 25p. Type **116** 50 60
434 25p. Surgeon and seamen . . 50 60
435 25p. Seaman with water-carrying donkey 50 60
436 25p. Midshipman and gun . . 50 60
437 25p. Commander in undress uniform surveying 50 60
See also Nos. 478/82.

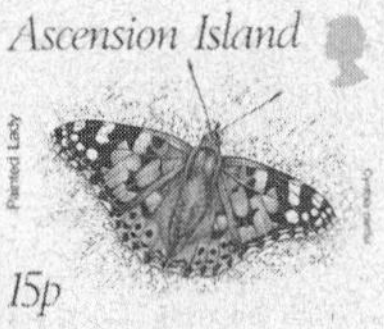

117 "Cynthia cardui"

1987. Insects (1st series). Multicoloured.
438 15p. Type **117** 65 65
439 18p. "Danaus chrysippus" . . 70 75
440 25p. "Hypolimnas misippus" 85 85
441 £1 "Lampides boeticus" . . . 2·25 2·50
See also Nos. 452/5 and 483/6.

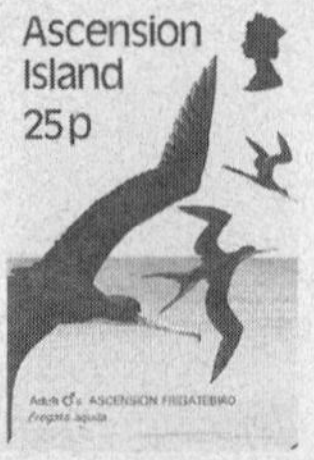

118 Male Ascension Frigate Birds

1987. Sea Birds (1st series). Multicoloured.
442 25p. Type **118** 1·60 1·90
443 25p. Juvenile Ascension frigate bird, brown booby and blue-faced boobies 1·60 1·90
444 25p. Male Ascension frigate bird and blue-faced boobies 1·60 1·90
445 25p. Female Ascension frigate bird 1·60 1·90
446 25p. Adult male feeding juvenile Ascension frigate bird 1·60 1·90
Nos. 442/6 were printed together, se-tenant, forming a composite design.
See also Nos. 469/73.

1987. Royal Ruby Wedding. Nos. 397/401 optd **40TH WEDDING ANNIVERSARY**.
447 7p. Type **110** 15 15
448 15p. Queen making Christmas broadcast, 1952 25 30
449 20p. At Garter ceremony, Windsor Castle, 1983 30 40
450 35p. In Auckland, New Zealand, 1981 50 60
451 £1 At Crown Agents' Head Office, London, 1983 1·25 1·40

1988. Insects (2nd series). As T **117**. Multicoloured.
452 15p. "Gryllus bimaculatus" (field cricket) 50 50
453 18p. "Ruspolia differeus" (bush cricket) 55 55
454 25p. "Chilomenus lunata" (ladybird) 70 70
455 £1 "Diachrysia orichalcea" (moth) 2·25 2·25

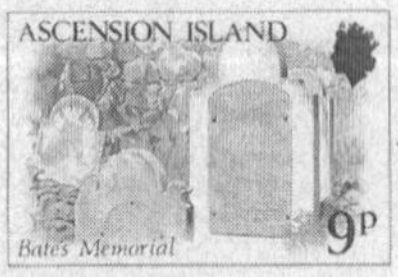

120 Bate's Memorial, St. Mary's Church

1988. 150th Death Anniv of Captain William Bate (garrison commander, 1828–38). Multicoloured.
456 9p. Type **120** 35 35
457 15p. Commodore's Cottage 45 45
458 18p. North East Cottage 50 50
459 25p. Map of Ascension 70 70
460 70p. Captain Bate and marines 1·75 1·75

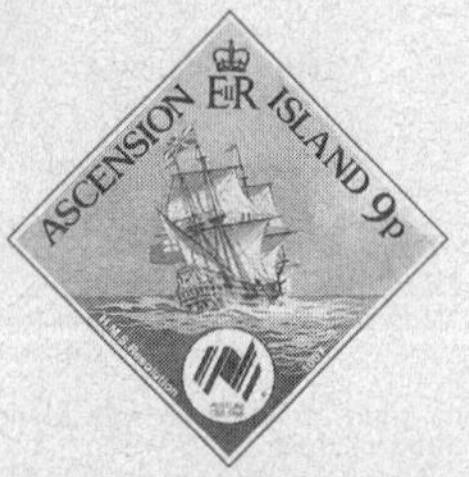

121 H.M.S. "Resolution" (ship of the line), 1667

1988. Bicentenary of Australian Settlement. Ships of the Royal Navy. Multicoloured.
461 9p. Type **121** 1·00 45
462 18p. H.M.S. "Resolution" (Captain Cook), 1772 1·50 70
463 25p. H.M.S. "Resolution" (battleship), 1892 1·50 85
464 65p. H.M.S. "Resolution" (battleship), 1916 2·50 1·50

1988. "Sydpex '88" National Stamp Exhibition, Sydney. Nos. 461/4 optd **SYDPEX 88 30.7.88 - 7.8.88**.
465 9p. Type **121** 50 40
466 18p. H.M.S. "Resolution" (Captain Cook), 1772 75 60
467 25p. H.M.S. "Resolution" (battleship), 1892 85 70
468 65p. H.M.S. "Resolution" (battleship), 1916 1·60 1·40

1988. Sea Birds (2nd series). Sooty Tern. As T **118**. Multicoloured.
469 25p. Pair displaying 1·60 1·60
470 25p. Turning egg 1·60 1·60
471 25p. Incubating egg 1·60 1·60
472 25p. Feeding chick 1·60 1·60
473 25p. Immature sooty tern 1·60 1·60
Nos. 469/73 were printed together, se-tenant, forming a composite design of a nesting colony.

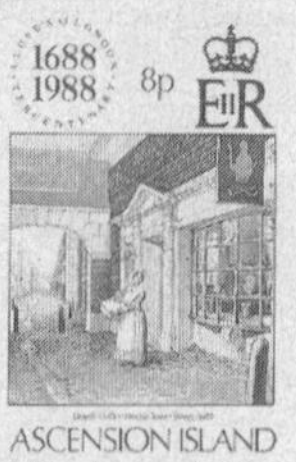

123 Lloyd's Coffee House, London, 1688

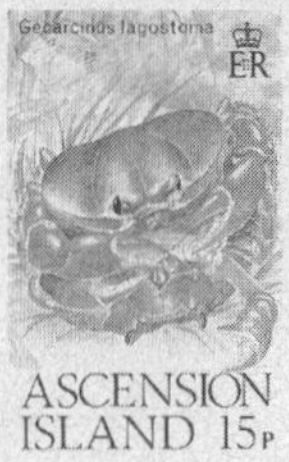

124 Two Land Crabs

1988. 300th Anniv of Lloyd's of London. Mult.
474 8p. Type **123** 25 35
475 18p. "Alert IV" (cable ship) (horiz) 65 70
476 25p. Satellite recovery in space (horiz) 80 90
477 65p. "Good Hope Castle" (cargo liner) on fire off Ascension, 1973 1·75 2·00

1988. 19th-century Uniforms (2nd series). Royal Marines 1821–34. As T **116**. Multicoloured.
478 25p. Marines landing on Ascension, 1821 1·10 1·60
479 25p. Officer and Marine at semaphore station, 1829 1·10 1·60
480 25p. Sergeant and Marine at Octagonal Tank, 1831 1·10 1·60
481 25p. Officers at water pipe tunnel, 1833 1·10 1·60
482 25p. Officer supervising construction of barracks, 1834 1·10 1·60

1989. Insects (3rd series). As T **117**. Mult.
483 15p. "Trichoptilus wahlbergi" (moth) 75 50
484 18p. "Lucilia sericata" (fly) 80 55
485 25p. "Alceis ornatus" (weevil) 1·10 70
486 £1 "Polistes fuscatus" (wasp) 3·00 2·40

1989. Ascension Land Crabs. Multicoloured.
487 15p. Type **124** 40 45
488 18p. Crab with claws raised 45 50
489 25p. Crab on rock 60 70
490 £1 Crab in surf 2·25 2·50

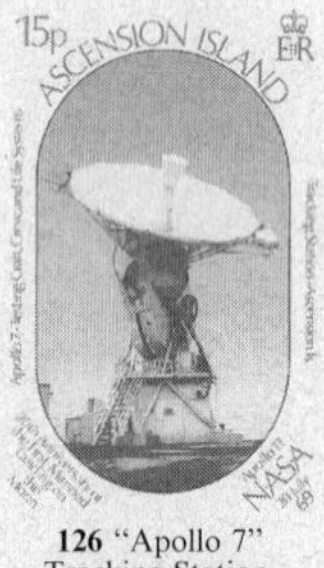

126 "Apollo 7" Tracking Station, Ascension

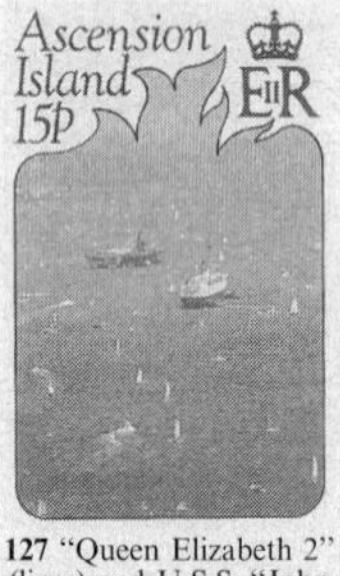

127 "Queen Elizabeth 2" (liner) and U.S.S. "John F. Kennedy" (aircraft carrier) in New York Harbour

1989. 20th Anniv of First Manned Landing on Moon. Multicoloured.
493 15p. Type **126** 65 45
494 18p. Launch of "Apollo 7" (30 × 30 mm) 70 50
495 25p. "Apollo 7" emblem (30 × 30 mm) 90 70
496 70p. "Apollo 7" jettisoning expended Saturn rocket 1·75 1·75

1989. "Philexfrance 89" International Stamp Exhibition, Paris, and "World Stamp Expo '89", Washington. Designs showing Statue of Liberty and Centenary celebrations. Mult.
498 15p. Type **127** 35 35
499 15p. Cleaning statue 35 35
500 15p. Statue of Liberty 35 35
501 15p. Crown of statue 35 35
502 15p. Warships and New York skyline 35 35
503 15p. "Jean de Vienne" (French destroyer) and skyscrapers 35 35

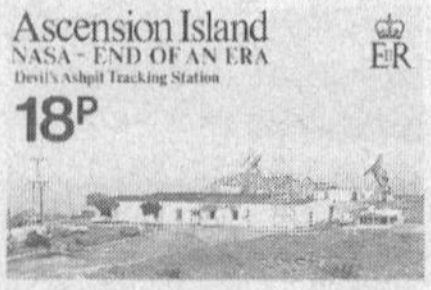

128 Devil's Ashpit Tracking Station

1989. Closure of Devil's Ashpit Tracking Station, Ascension. Multicoloured.
504 18p. Type **128** 80 50
505 25p. Launch of shuttle "Atlantis" 80 55

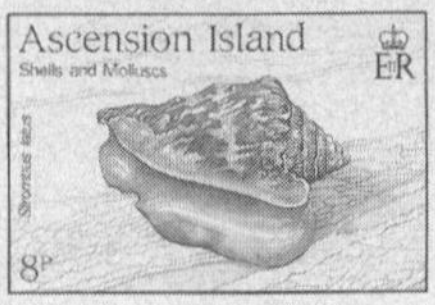

129 Bubonian Conch

1989. Sea Shells. Multicoloured.
506 8p. Type **129** 40 30
507 18p. Giant tun 70 50
508 25p. Doris loup 90 65
509 £1 Atlantic trumpet triton 2·75 2·50

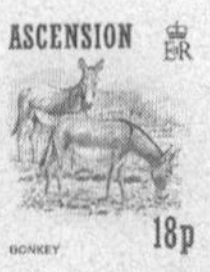

130 Donkeys

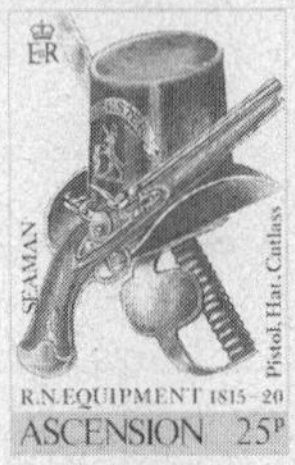

131 Seaman's Pistol, Hat and Cutlass

1989. Ascension Wildlife. Multicoloured.
510 18p. Type **130** 45 60
511 25p. Green turtle 60 75

1990. Royal Navy Equipment, 1815–20. Mult.
512 25p. Type **131** 70 70
513 25p. Midshipman's belt plate, button, sword and hat 70 70
514 25p. Surgeon's hat, sword and instrument chest 70 70
515 25p. Captain's hat, telescope and sword 70 70
516 25p. Admiral's epaulette, megaphone, hat and pocket 70 70
See also Nos. 541/5.

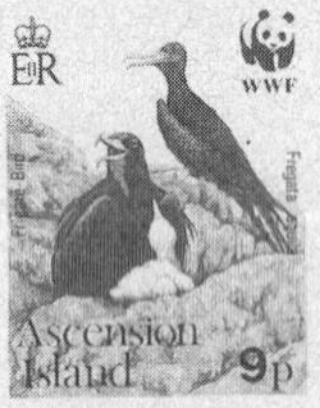

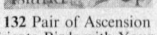

132 Pair of Ascension Frigate Birds with Young

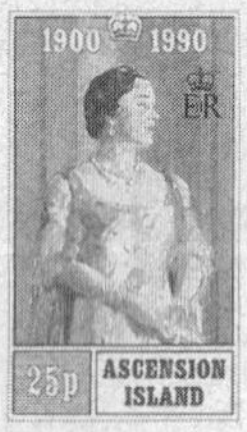

134 "Queen Elizabeth, 1940" (Sir Gerald Kelly)

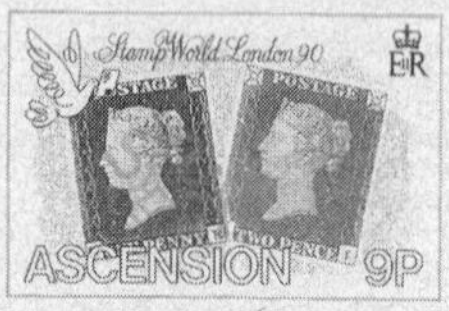

133 Penny Black and Twopence Blue

1990. Endangered Species. Ascension Frigate Bird. Multicoloured.
517 9p. Type **132** 1·50 1·00
518 10p. Fledgeling 1·50 1·00
519 11p. Adult male in flight 1·50 1·00
520 15p. Female and immature birds in flight 1·75 1·25

1990. "Stamp World London 90" International Stamp Exhibition. Multicoloured.
521 9p. Type **133** 50 40
522 18p. Ascension postmarks used on G.B. stamps 70 60
523 25p. Unloading mail at Wideawake Airfield 95 85
524 £1 Mail van and Main Post Office 2·25 2·75

1990. 90th Birthday of Queen Elizabeth the Queen Mother.
525 **134** 25p. multicoloured 75 75
526 – £1 black and lilac 2·25 2·25
DESIGN—29 × 37mm: £1 King George VI and Queen Elizabeth with Bren-gun carrier.

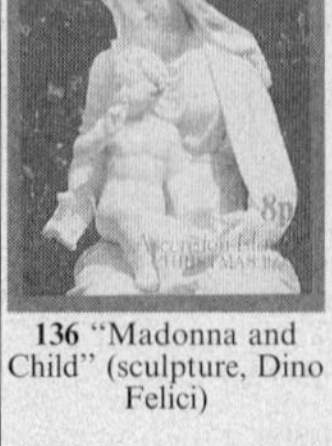

136 "Madonna and Child" (sculpture, Dino Felici)

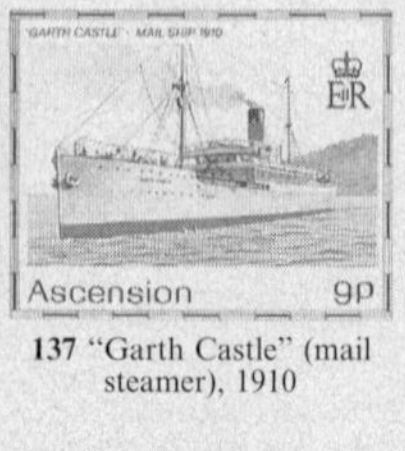

137 "Garth Castle" (mail steamer), 1910

1990. Christmas. Works of Art. Multicoloured.
527 8p. Type **136** 70 70
528 18p. "Madonna and Child" (anon) 1·25 1·25
529 25p. "Madonna and Child with St. John" (Johann Gebhard) 1·75 1·75
530 65p. "Madonna and Child" (Giacomo Gritti) 3·00 4·00

1990. Maiden Voyage of "St. Helena II". Mult.
531 9p. Type **137** 90 75
532 18p. "St. Helena I" during Falkland Islands campaign, 1982 1·25 1·25
533 25p. Launch of "St. Helena II" 1·75 1·75
534 70p. Duke of York launching "St. Helena II" 3·00 4·00

1991. 175th Anniv of Occupation. Nos. 418, 420 and 422 optd **BRITISH FOR 175 YEARS**.
536 25p. H.M.S. "Saracen" (1840) 1·75 2·00
537 50p. H.M.S. "Sealark" (1849) 2·25 2·75
538 £1 H.M.S. "Penelope" (1889) 3·25 4·25

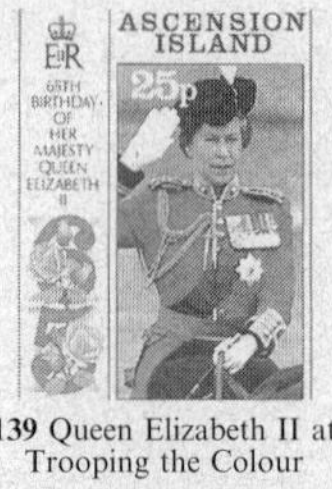

139 Queen Elizabeth II at Trooping the Colour

1991. 65th Birthday of Queen Elizabeth II and 70th Birthday of Prince Philip. Multicoloured.
539 25p. Type **139** 1·00 1·40
540 25p. Prince Philip in naval uniform 1·00 1·40

1991. Royal Marines Equipment, 1821–1844. As T **131**. Multicoloured.
541 25p. Officer's shako, epaulettes, belt plate and button 1·10 1·50
542 25p. Officer's cap, sword, epaulettes and belt plate 1·10 1·50
543 25p. Drum major's shako and staff 1·10 1·50
544 25p. Sergeant's shako, chevrons, belt plate and canteen 1·10 1·50
545 25p. Drummer's shako and side-drum 1·10 1·50

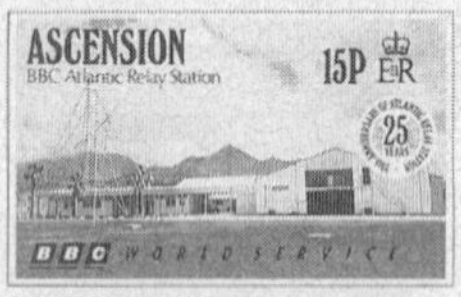

140 B.B.C. World Service Relay Station

1991. 25th Anniv of B.B.C. Atlantic Relay Station. Multicoloured.
546 15p. Type **140** 90 1·10
547 18p. Transmitters at English Bay 1·00 1·25
548 25p. Satellite receiving station (vert) 1·25 1·40
549 70p. Antenna support tower (vert) 2·50 3·50

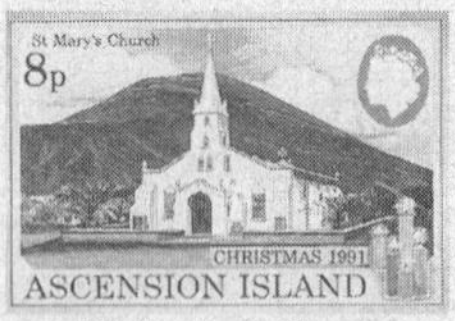

141 St. Mary's Church

1991. Christmas. Ascension Churches. Mult.
550 8p. Type **141** 55 55
551 18p. Interior of St. Mary's Church 1·00 1·00
552 25p. Our Lady of Ascension Grotto 1·25 1·25
553 65p. Interior of Our Lady of Ascension Grotto 2·75 4·50

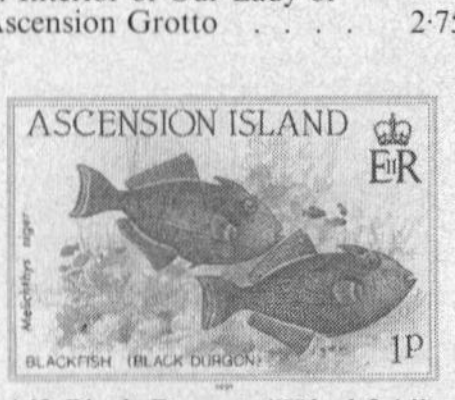

142 Black Durgon ("Blackfish")

1991. Fishes. Multicoloured.
554 1p. Type **142** 60 60
555 2p. Sergeant major ("Five finger") 70 60
556 4p. Resplendent angelfish 80 70
557 5p. Derbio ("Silver fish") 80 70
558 9p. Spotted scorpionfish ("Gurnard") 1·00 80
559 10p. St. Helena parrotfish ("Blue dad") 1·00 80
560 15p. St. Helena butterflyfish ("Cunning fish") 1·25 1·00

561 18p. Rock hind ("Grouper") 1·25 1·00
562 20p. Spotted moray 1·25 1·25
563 25p. Squirrelfish ("Hardback soldierfish") 1·25 1·25
564 30p. Blue marlin 1·25 1·40
565 50p. Wahoo 1·75 2·00
566 70p. Yellow-finned tuna 2·25 2·75
567 £1 Blue shark 2·75 3·50
568 £2.50 Bottlenose dolphin 6·00 7·00

143 Holland's Crater

1992. 40th Anniv of Queen Elizabeth II's Accession. Multicoloured.
569 9p. Type **143** 30 30
570 15p. Green Mountain 50 50
571 18p. Boatswain Bird Island 60 60
572 25p. Three portraits of Queen Elizabeth 80 80
573 70p. Queen Elizabeth II 2·00 2·00
The portraits shown on the 25p. are repeated from the three lower values of the set.

144 Compass Rose and "Eye of the Wind" (cadet brig)

1992. 500th Anniv of Discovery of America by Columbus and Re-enactment Voyages. Mult.
574 9p. Type **144** 85 70
575 18p. Map of re-enactment voyages and "Soren Larsen" (cadet brigantine) 1·40 1·00
576 25p. "Santa Maria", "Pinta" and "Nina" 1·75 1·25
577 70p. Columbus and "Santa Maria" 3·25 2·75

145 Control Tower, Wideawake Airfield. **146** Hawker Siddeley Nimrod

1992. 50th Anniv of Wideawake Airfield. Multicoloured.
578 15p. Type **145** 65 65
579 18p. Nose hangar 70 70
580 25p. Site preparation by U.S. Army engineers 90 90
581 70p. Laying fuel pipeline 2·25 2·25

1992. 10th Anniv of Liberation of Falkland Islands. Aircraft. Multicoloured.
582 15p. Type **146** 1·25 1·25
583 18p. Vickers VC-10 landing at Ascension 1·25 1·25
584 25p. Westland Wessex HU Mk 5 helicopter lifting supplies 1·75 1·50
585 65p. Avro Vulcan B.2 over Ascension 3·00 3·75

147 "Christmas in Great Britain and Ascension"

1992. Christmas. Children's Paintings. Mult.
587 8p. Type **147** 80 80
588 18p. "Santa Claus riding turtle" 1·25 1·25
589 25p. "Nativity" 1·50 1·50
590 65p. "Nativity with rabbit" 2·75 4·25

148 Male Canary Singing

1993. Yellow Canary. Multicoloured.
591 15p. Type **148** 75 70
592 18p. Adult male and female 85 80
593 25p. Young birds calling for food 95 95
594 70p. Adults and young birds on the wing 2·50 3·50

149 Sopwith Snipe

1993. 75th Anniv of Royal Air Force. Multicoloured.
595 20p. Type **149** 1·50 1·25
596 25p. Supermarine Southampton 1·50 1·25
597 30p. Avro Type 652 Anson 1·60 1·40
598 70p. Vickers-Armstrong Wellington 2·75 3·50

150 Map of South Atlantic Cable

1993. 25th Anniv of South Atlantic Cable Company. Multicoloured.
600 20p. Type **150** 80 80
601 25p. "Sir Eric Sharpe" laying cable 90 90
602 30p. Map of Ascension 1·00 1·00
603 70p. "Sir Eric Sharpe" (cable ship) off Ascension 2·25 2·50

151 Lanatana Camara

1993. Local Flowers. Multicoloured.
604 20p. Type **151** 1·00 70
605 25p. Moonflower 1·10 75
606 30p. Hibiscus 1·10 85
607 70p. Frangipani 2·50 2·25

152 Posting Christmas Card to Ascension **153** Ichthyosaurus

1993. Christmas. Multicoloured.
608 12p. Type **152** 45 45
609 20p. Loading mail onto R.A.F. Lockheed TriStar at Brize Norton 75 55
610 25p. TriStar over South Atlantic 85 65
611 30p. Unloading mail at Wideawake Airfield 1·10 75
612 65p. Receiving card and Georgetown Post Office 1·60 2·00

1994. Prehistoric Aquatic Reptiles. Mult.
614 12p. Type **153** 70 80
615 20p. Metriorhynchus 85 90
616 25p. Mosasaurus 90 1·00
617 30p. Elasmosaurus 90 1·10
618 65p. Plesiosaurus 1·75 2·50

1994. "Hong Kong '94" International Stamp Exhibition. Nos. 614/18 optd HONG KONG '94 and emblem.
619 12p. Type **153** 85 1·25
620 20p. Metriorhynchus 1·10 1·25
621 25p. Mosasaurus 1·10 1·40
622 30p. Elasmosaurus 1·25 1·40
623 65p. Plesiosaurus 2·25 3·00

155 Young Green Turtles heading towards Sea

1994. Green Turtles. Multicoloured.
624 20p. Type **155** 1·50 1·50

156 "Yorkshireman" (tug)

1994. Civilian Ships used in Liberation of Falkland Islands, 1982. Multicoloured.
625 25p. Turtle digging nest 1·60 1·60
626 30p. Turtle leaving sea 1·75 1·75
627 65p. Turtle swimming 2·75 3·50
629 20p. Type **156** 1·50 1·50
630 25p. "St. Helena I" (minesweeper support ship) 1·60 1·60
631 30p. "British Esk" (tanker) 1·75 1·75
632 65p. "Uganda" (hospital ship) 2·75 3·50

157 Sooty Tern Chick

1994. Sooty Tern. Multicoloured.
633 20p. Type **157** 90 1·25
634 25p. Juvenile bird 95 1·25
635 30p. Brooding adult 1·10 1·40
636 65p. Adult male performing courting display 1·75 2·50

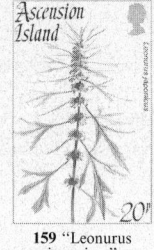

158 Donkey Mare with Foal **159** "Leonurus japonicus"

1994. Christmas. Donkeys. Multicoloured.
638 12p. Type **158** 90 70
639 20p. Juvenile 1·25 1·00
640 25p. Foal 1·25 1·10
641 30p. Adult and cattle egrets 1·40 1·25
642 65p. Adult 2·50 3·25

1995. Flowers. Multicoloured.
643 20p. Type **159** 1·75 1·75
644 25p. "Catharanthus roseus" (horiz) 1·75 1·75
645 30p. "Mirabilis jalapa" 2·00 2·00
646 65p. "Asclepias curassavica" (horiz) 2·75 3·50

160 Two Boats and Green Mountain

1995. Late 19th-century Scenes. Each in cinnamon and brown.
647 12p. Type **160** 50 60
648 20p. Island Stewards' Store 70 70
649 25p. Navy headquarters and barracks 90 90
650 30p. Police office 1·75 1·75
651 65p. Pierhead 2·00 2·75

161 5.5-inch Coastal Battery

1995. 50th Anniv of End of Second World War. Multicoloured.
652 20p. Type **161** 1·00 1·25
653 25p. Fairey Swordfish aircraft 1·25 1·50
654 30p. H.M.S. "Dorsetshire" (cruiser) 1·50 1·75
655 65p. H.M.S. "Devonshire" (cruiser) 2·50 3·50

162 Male and Female "Lampides boeticus"

1995. Butterflies. Multicoloured.
657 20p. Type **162** 1·00 75
658 25p. "Vanessa cardui" 1·10 80
659 30p. Male "Hypolimnas misippus" 1·25 85
660 65p. "Danaus chrysippus" 2·25 2·00

163 "Santa Claus on Boat" (Phillip Stephens)

1995. Christmas. Children's Drawings. Multicoloured.
662 12p. Type **163** 75 75
663 20p. "Santa sitting on Wall" (Kelly Lemon) 1·00 1·00
664 25p. "Santa in Chimney" (Mario Anthony) 1·10 1·10
665 30p. "Santa riding Dolphin" (Verena Benjamin) 1·25 1·25
666 65p. "Santa in Sleigh over Ascension" (Tom Butler) 2·25 3·00

164 "Cypraea lurida oceanica"

1996. Molluscs. Multicoloured.
667 12p. Type **164** 1·50 1·25
668 25p. "Cypraea spurca sanctaehelenae" 1·75 1·50
669 30p. "Harpa doris" 1·75 1·50
670 65p. "Umbraculum umbraculum" 2·25 2·00
Nos. 667/70 were printed together, se-tenant, forming a composite design.

165 Queen Elizabeth II and St. Mary's Church

1996. 70th Birthday of Queen Elizabeth II. Mult.
671 20p. Type **165** 55 60
672 25p. The Residency 60 60
673 30p. The Roman Catholic Grotto 70 70
674 65p. The Exiles' Club 1·75 1·75

166 American Army Jeep

1996. "CAPEX '96" International Stamp Exhibition, Toronto. Island Transport. Multicoloured.
675 20p. Type **166** 75 75
676 25p. Citroen 7.5hp two-seater car, 1924 80 80
677 30p. Austin ten tourer car, 1930 90 90
678 65p. Series 1 Land Rover 1·75 1·75

167 Madeiran Storm Petrel　　　**168** Pylons

1996. Birds and their Young. Multicoloured.
679	1p. Type **167**	10	10
680	2p. Red-billed tropic bird	10	10
681	4p. Common mynah	10	10
682	5p. House sparrow	10	15
683	7p. Common waxbill	15	20
684	10p. White tern	20	25
685	12p. Bare-throated francolin	25	30
686	15p. Common noddy	30	35
687	20p. Yellow canary	40	45
688	25p. Lesser noddy	50	55
689	30p. Red-footed booby	60	65
690	40p. White-tailed tropic bird	80	85
691	65p. Brown booby	1·25	1·40
692	£1 Blue-faced booby	2·00	2·10
693	£2 Sooty tern	4·00	4·25
694	£3 Ascension frigate bird	6·00	6·25

See also Nos. 726/7.

1996. 30th Anniv of B.B.C. Atlantic Relay Station. Multicoloured.
695	20p. Type **168**	65	65
696	25p. Pylons (different)	70	70
697	30p. Pylons and station buildings	80	80
698	65p. Dish aerial, pylon and beach	1·75	1·75

169 Santa Claus on Dish Aerial

1996. Christmas. Santa Claus. Multicoloured.
699	12p. Type **169**	35	35
700	20p. Playing golf	65	65
701	25p. In deck chair	65	65
702	30p. On top of aircraft	75	75
703	65p. On funnel of "St. Helena II" (mail ship)	1·75	2·00

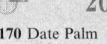

170 Date Palm　　　**171** Red Ensign and "Maersk Ascension" (tanker)

1997. "Hong Kong '97" International Stamp Exhibition. Trees. Multicoloured.
704	20p. Type **170**	55	55
705	25p. Mauritius hemp	65	65
706	30p. Norfolk Island pine	75	75
707	65p. Dwarf palm	1·50	1·60

1997. Flags. Multicoloured.
709	12p. Type **171**	45	45
710	25p. R.A.F. flag and Tristar airliner	75	75
711	30p. N.A.S.A. emblem and Space Shuttle "Atlantis" landing	85	85
712	65p. White Ensign and H.M.S. "Northumberland" (frigate)	1·60	1·60

172 "Solanum sodomaeum"

1997. Wild Herbs. Multicoloured.
713	30p. Type **172**	90	1·00
714	30p. "Ageratum conyzoides"	90	1·00
715	30p. "Leonurus sibiricus"	90	1·00
716	30p. "Cerastium vulgatum"	90	1·00
717	30p. "Commelina diffusa"	90	1·00

Nos. 713/17 are printed together, se-tenant, with the backgrounds forming a composite design.

173 Queen Elizabeth II

1997. Golden Wedding of Queen Elizabeth and Prince Philip. Multicoloured.
719	20p. Type **173**	90	1·00
720	20p. Prince Philip on horseback	90	1·00
721	25p. Queen Elizabeth with polo pony	1·00	1·25
722	25p. Prince Philip in Montserrat	1·00	1·25
723	30p. Queen Elizabeth and Prince Philip	1·25	1·25
724	30p. Prince William and Prince Harry on horseback	1·25	1·25

Nos. 719/20, 721/2 and 723/4 respectively were printed together, se-tenant, with the backgrounds forming composite designs.

1997. Birds and their Young. As Nos. 683 and 687, but smaller, size 20 × 24 mm. Multicoloured.
726	15p. Common waxbill	30	35
727	35p. Yellow canary	70	75

174 Black Marlin

1997. Gamefish. Multicoloured.
728	12p. Type **174**	40	40
729	20p. Atlantic sailfish	65	65
730	25p. Swordfish	75	75
731	30p. Wahoo	85	85
732	£1 Yellowfin tuna	2·25	2·25

175 Interior of St. Mary's Church　　　**176** "Cactoblastis cactorum" (caterpillar and moth)

1997. Christmas. Multicoloured.
733	15p. Type **175**	45	45
734	35p. Falklands memorial window showing Virgin and child	85	85
735	40p. Falklands memorial window showing Archangel	95	1·10
736	50p. Pair of stained glass windows	1·25	1·40

1998. Biological Control using Insects. Mult.
737	15p. Type **176**	70	70
738	35p. "Teleonemia scrupulosa" (lace-bug)	1·10	1·10
739	40p. "Neltumius arizonensis" (beetle)	1·25	1·25
740	50p. "Algarobius prosopis" (beetle)	1·25	1·25

178 Fairey Fawn

1998. 80th Anniv of Royal Air Force. Mult.
742	15p. Type **178**	65	65
743	35p. Vickers Vernon	1·25	1·25
744	40p. Supermarine Spitfire F.22	1·40	1·40
745	50p. Bristol Britannia C.2	1·60	1·60

179 Barn Swallow　　　**180** Cricket

1998. Migratory Birds. Multicoloured.
747	15p. Type **179**	60	60
748	25p. House martin	80	85
749	35p. Cattle egret	1·00	1·10
750	40p. Common swift	1·00	1·25
751	50p. Allen's gallinule	1·10	1·40

1998. Sporting Activities. Multicoloured.
752	15p. Type **180**	1·25	75
753	35p. Golf	1·75	1·25
754	40p. Football	1·50	1·25
755	50p. Shooting	1·50	1·25

181 Children in Nativity Play

1998. Christmas. Multicoloured.
756	15p. Type **181**	75	75
757	35p. Santa Claus arriving on Ascension	1·25	1·25
758	40p. Santa Claus on carnival float	1·25	1·25
759	50p. Carol singers	1·25	1·25

182 Curtiss C-46 Commando

1999. Aircraft. Multicoloured.
760	15p. Type **182**	75	80
761	35p. Douglas C-47 Dakota	1·25	1·50
762	40p. Douglas C-54 Skymaster	1·25	1·50
763	50p. Consolidated Liberator Mk. V	1·25	1·50

183 "Glengorm Castle" (mail ship), 1929

1999. "Australia '99" World Stamp Exhibition, Melbourne. Ships. Multicoloured.
765	15p. Type **183**	75	75
766	35p. "Gloucester Castle" (mail ship), 1930	1·25	1·25
767	40p. "Durham Castle" (mail ship), 1930	1·25	1·25
768	50p. "Garth Castle" (mail ship), 1930	1·25	1·25

184 Pair of White Terns ("Fairy Terns")

1999. Endangered Species. White Tern ("Fairy Tern"). Multicoloured.
770	10p. Type **184**	30	30
771	10p. On branch	30	30
772	10p. Adult and fledgeling	30	30
773	10p. In flight	30	30

185 Prince Edward and Miss Sophie Rhys-Jones　　　**186** Command and Service Modules

1999. Royal Wedding. Multicoloured.
774	50p. Type **185**	1·25	1·25
775	£1 Engagement photograph	2·25	2·25

1999. 30th Anniv of First Manned Landing on Moon. Multicoloured.
776	15p. Type **186**	75	75
777	35p. Moon from "Apollo 11"	1·25	1·25
778	40p. Devil's Ashpit Tracking Station and command module	1·25	1·25
779	50p. Lunar module leaving Moon	1·25	1·25

187 King George VI, Queen Elizabeth and Prime Minister Winston Churchill, 1940

1999. "Queen Elizabeth the Queen Mother's Century". Multicoloured.
781	15p. Type **187**	75	75
782	35p. With Prince Charles at Coronation, 1953	1·25	1·25
783	40p. On her 88th Birthday, 1988	1·25	1·25
784	50p. With Guards' drummers, 1988	1·25	1·25

188 Babies with Toys

1999. Christmas. Multicoloured.
786	15p. Type **188**	75	75
787	35p. Children dressed as clowns	1·25	1·25
788	40p. Getting ready for bed	1·25	1·25
789	50p. Children dressed as pirates	1·25	1·25

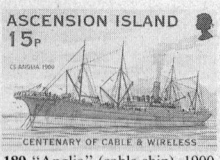

189 "Anglia" (cable ship), 1900

1999. Centenary of Cable & Wireless Communications plc on Ascension.
790	**189**	15p. black, brown and bistre	75	75
791		35p. black, brown and bistre	1·25	1·25
792		40p. multicoloured	1·25	1·25
793		50p. black, brown and bistre	1·40	1·40

DESIGNS: 35p. "Cambria" (cable ship), 1910; 40p. Cable network map; 50p. "Colonia" (cable ship), 1910.

190 Baby Turtles

2000. Turtle Project on Ascension. Multicoloured.
795	15p. Type **190**	75	75
796	35p. Turtle on beach	1·25	1·25
797	40p. Turtle with tracking device	1·25	1·25
798	50p. Turtle heading for sea	1·40	1·40

191 Prince William as Toddler, 1983

2000. 18th Birthday of Prince William. Multicoloured.

801	15p. Type **191**	75	75
802	35p. Prince William in 1994	1·25	1·25
803	40p. Skiing at Klosters, Switzerland (horiz)	1·25	1·25
804	50p. Prince William in 1997 (horiz)	1·40	1·40

192 Royal Marine and Early Fort, 1815

2000. Forts. Multicoloured

806	15p. Type **192**	75	75
807	35p. Army officer and Fort Thornton, 1817	1·25	1·25
808	40p. Soldier and Fort Hayes, 1860	1·25	1·25
809	50p. Naval lieutenant and Fort Bedford, 1940	1·40	1·40

193 Ships and Dockside Crane ("I saw Three Ships")

2000. Christmas. Carols. Multicoloured.

810	15p. Type **193**	55	55
811	25p. Choir and musicians on beach ("Silent Night")	75	75
812	40p. Donkeys and church ("Away in a Manger")	1·25	1·25
813	90p. Carol singers outside church ("Hark the Herald Angels Sing")	2·25	2·50

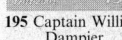

195 Captain William Dampier

196 Alfonso de Albuquerque

2001. Centenary of Wreck of the *Roebuck*. Mult.

815	15p. Type **195**	70	70
816	35p. Construction drawing (horiz)	1·10	1·10
817	40p. Cave dwelling at Dampier's Drip (horiz)	1·10	1·10
818	50p. Map of Ascension	1·25	1·25

2001. 500th Anniv of the Discovery of Ascension Island. Multicoloured.

819	15p. Type **196**	70	70
820	35p. Portuguese caravel	1·10	1·10
821	40p. Cantino map	1·10	1·10
822	50p. Rear Admiral Sir George Cockburn	1·25	1·25

197 Great Britain 1d. Stamp used on Ascension, 1855

2001. Death Centenary of Queen Victoria. Mult.

823	15p. Type **197**	30	35
824	25p. Navy church parade, 1901 (horiz)	50	55
825	35p. H.M.S. *Phoebe* (cruiser) (horiz)	70	75
826	40p. The Red Lion, 1863 (horiz)	80	85
827	50p. "Queen Victoria"	1·00	1·10
828	65p. Sir Joseph Hooker (botanist)	1·25	1·40

198 Islander Hostel

2001. "BELGICA 2001" International Stamp Exhibition, Brussels. Tourism. Multicoloured.

830	35p. Type **198**	70	75
831	35p. The Residency	70	75
832	40p. The Red Lion	80	85
833	40p. Turtle Ponds	80	85

199 Female Ascension Frigate Bird

2001. Birdlife World Bird Festival. Ascension Frigate Birds. Multicoloured.

834	15p. Type **199**	30	35
835	35p. Fledgeling	70	75
836	40p. Male bird in flight (horiz)	80	85
837	50p. Male bird with pouch inflated (horiz)	1·00	1·10

200 Princess Elizabeth and Dog

2002. Golden Jubilee.

839	**200** 15p. agate, mauve and gold	30	35
840	– 35p. multicoloured	70	75
841	– 40p. multicoloured	80	85
842	– 50p. multicoloured	1·00	1·10

DESIGNS: 35p. Queen Elizabeth wearing tiara, 1978; 40p Princess Elizabeth, 1946; 50p. Queen Elizabeth visiting Henley-on-Thames, 1998.

POSTAGE DUE STAMPS

D 1 Outline Map of Ascension

1986.

D1	**D 1** 1p. deep brown and brown	15	20
D2	2p. brown and orange	15	20
D3	5p. brown and orange	15	20
D4	7p. black and violet	20	30
D5	10p. black and blue	25	35
D6	25p. black and green	65	75

AUSTRALIA Pt. 1

An island continent to the S.E. of Asia. A Commonwealth consisting of the states of New S. Wales, Queensland, S. Australia, Tasmania, Victoria and W. Australia.

1913. 12 pence = 1 shilling;
20 shillings = 1 pound.
1966. 100 cents = 1 dollar.

1 Eastern Grey Kangaroo

3

1913.

1	**1** ½d. green	6·00	3·25
2	1d. red	8·50	1·00
35	2d. grey	25·00	6·50
36	2½d. blue	23·00	10·00
37	3d. green	28·00	4·50
6	4d. orange	50·00	22·00
8	5d. brown	40·00	32·00
38	6d. blue	55·00	7·50
73	6d. brown	24·00	1·75
133	9d. violet	28·00	1·25
40	1s. green	35·00	3·75
41	2s. brown	£150	12·00
134	2s. purple	5·00	60
135	5s. grey and yellow	£120	12·00
136	10s. grey and pink	£250	£100
15	£1 brown and blue	£1000	£1100
137	£1 grey	£425	£160
138	£2 black and pink	£1600	£325

1913.

20	**3** ½d. green	3·75	1·00
94	½d. orange	2·25	1·40
17	1d. red	2·50	4·50
57	1d. violet	6·00	1·50
125	1d. green	1·75	20
59a	1½d. brown	6·50	60
61	1½d. green	4·00	80
77	1½d. red	2·25	40
62	2d. orange	15·00	1·00
127	2d. red	1·75	10
98	2d. brown	8·00	9·00
128	3d. blue	18·00	1·25
22	4d. orange	27·00	2·50
64	4d. violet	13·00	15·00
65	4d. blue	48·00	8·50
129	4d. green	18·00	1·25
92	4½d. violet	18·00	3·75
130	5d. brown	15·00	20
131	1s.4d. blue	50·00	3·50

4 Laughing Kookaburra

8 Parliament House, Canberra

1913.

19	**4** 6d. purple	65·00	38·00

1927. Opening of Parliament House.

105	**8** 1½d. red	50	50

1928. National Stamp Exhibition, Melbourne.

106	**4** 3d. blue	4·25	4·75

9 De Havilland Hercules and Pastoral Scene

10 Black Swan

1929. Air.

115	**9** 3d. green	10·00	4·00

1929. Centenary of Western Australia.

116	**10** 1½d. red	1·25	1·60

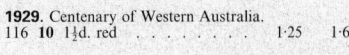

11 "Capt. Chas Sturt" (J. H. Crossland)

13 The "Southern Cross" above Hemispheres

1930. Centenary of Sturt's Exploration of River Murray.

117	**11** 1½d. red	1·00	1·00
118	3d. blue	3·25	6·50

1930. Surch in words.

119	**3** 2d. on 1½d. red	1·50	75
120	5d. on 4½d. violet	6·00	8·50

1931. Kingsford Smith's Flights.

121	**13** 2d. red (postage)	1·00	1·00
122	3d. blue	4·50	5·00
123	6d. purple (air)	6·50	12·00

1931. Air. As T **13** but inscr "AIR MAIL SERVICE".

139	6d. brown	16·00	12·00

1931. Air. No. 139 optd **O S**.

139a	6d. brown	35·00	50·00

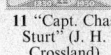

17 Superb Lyrebird

18 Sydney Harbour Bridge

1932.

140	**17** 1s. green	42·00	2·00

1932. Opening of Sydney Harbour Bridge.

144	**18** 2d. red	2·00	1·40
142	3d. blue	4·25	7·00
143	5s. green	£375	£180

19 Laughing Kookaburra

20 Melbourne and River Yarra

1932.

146	**19** 6d. red	25·00	55

1934. Centenary of Victoria.

147	**20** 2d. red	2·50	1·75
148	3d. blue	5·00	5·50
149	1s. black	48·00	20·00

21 Merino Ram

22 Hermes

1934. Death Centenary of Capt. John Macarthur (founder of Australian sheep-farming).

150	**21** 2d. red	4·25	1·50
151	3d. blue	10·00	9·50
152	9d. purple	38·00	42·00

1934.

153b	**22** 1s.6d. purple	2·50	1·40

23 Cenotaph, Whitehall

24 King George V on "Anzac"

1935. 20th. Anniv of Gallipoli Landing.

154	**23** 2d. red	80	30
155	1s. black	42·00	38·00

1935. Silver Jubilee.

156	**24** 2d. red	1·50	30
157	3d. blue	5·00	7·50
158	2s. violet	27·00	40·00

25 Amphitrite and Telephone Cable

26 Site of Adelaide, 1836; Old Gum Tree, Glenelg; King William Street, Adelaide

1936. Opening of Submarine Telephone Cable to Tasmania.

159	**25** 2d. red	75	50
160	3d. blue	2·75	2·75

1936. Centenary of South Australia.

161	**26** 2d. red	1·25	40
162	3d. blue	4·00	3·50
163	1s. green	10·00	8·50

27 Wallaroo

28 Queen Elizabeth

29 King George VI

30 King VI

31 King George VI

33 Merino Ram

38 Queen Elizabeth

40 King George VI and Queen Elizabeth

1937.

228	**27**	½d. orange	20	10
165	**28**	1d. green	60	20
180	–	1d. green	3·00	20
181	–	1d. purple	1·50	20
182	**29**	1½d. purple	4·00	7·50
183		1½d. green	1·00	1·00
167	**30**	2d. red	60	10
184	–	2d. red	3·00	10
185	**30**	2d. purple	50	1·00
186	**31**	3d. blue	45·00	2·75
187		3d. brown	40	10
188	–	4d. green	1·00	10
189	**33**	5d. purple	50	1·50
190a	–	6d. brown	1·75	10
191	–	9d. brown	1·00	20
192	–	1s. green	1·25	10
175	**31**	1s.4d. mauve	1·50	1·50
176a	**38**	5s. purple	3·50	2·25
177	–	10s. purple	38·00	13·00
178	**40**	£1 slate	60·00	30·00

DESIGNS—As Type **28**: 4d. Koala; 6d. Kookaburra; 1s. Lyrebird. As Type **33**: 9d. Platypus. As Type **38**: 10s. King George VI.

Nos. 180 and 184 are as Types **28** and **30** but with completely shaded background.

41 Governor Phillip at Sydney Cove (J. Alcott)

42 A.I.F. and Nurse

1937. 150th Anniv of New South Wales.

193	**41**	2d. red	2·25	20
194		3d. blue	6·00	2·25
195		9d. purple	16·00	10·00

1940. Australian Imperial Forces.

196	**42**	1d. green	1·75	1·75
197		2d. red	1·75	60
198		3d. blue	12·00	8·00
199		6d. purple	22·00	14·00

1941. Surch with figures and bars.

200	**30**	2½d. on 2d. red	60	60
201	**31**	3½d. on 3d. blue	75	1·75
202	**33**	5½d. on 5d. purple	3·50	4·25

46a Queen Elizabeth

47 King George VI

48 King George VI

49 King George VI

50 Emu

1942.

203	**46a**	1d. purple	80	10
204		1½d. green	80	10
205	**47**	2d. purple	65	85
206	**48**	2½d. red	30	10
207	**49**	3½d. blue	60	40
208	**50**	5½d. grey	65	10

52 Duke and Duchess of Gloucester

53 Star and Wreath

1945. Royal Visit.

209	**52**	2½d. red	10	10
210		3½d. blue	15	70
211		5½d. grey	20	70

1946. Victory. Inscr "PEACE 1945".

213	**53**	2½d. red	10	10
214	–	3½d. blue	25	75
215	–	5½d. green	30	50

DESIGNS—HORIZ: 3½d. Flag and dove. VERT: 5½d. Angel.

56 Sir Thomas Mitchell and Queensland

1946. Centenary of Mitchell's Central Queensland Exploration.

216	**56**	2½d. red	10	10
217		3½d. blue	35	1·00
218		1s. green	35	45

57 Lt. John Shortland, R.N.

58 Steel Foundry

1947. 150th Anniv of City of Newcastle.

219	**57**	2½d. lake	10	10
220	**58**	3½d. blue	40	80
221	–	5½d. green	40	45

DESIGNS—As Type **58**: HORIZ: 5½d. Coal carrier cranes.

60 Queen Elizabeth II when Princess

1947. Wedding of Princess Elizabeth.

222a	**60**	1d. purple	10	10

61 Hereford Bull

61a Hermes and Globe

62 Aboriginal Art

62a Commonwealth Coat of Arms

1948.

223	**61**	1s.3d. brown	1·75	1·10
223a	**61a**	1s.6d. brown	70	10
224	**62**	2s. brown	2·00	10
224a	**62a**	5s. red	2·75	10
224b		10s. purple	14·00	70
224c		£1 blue	30·00	3·50
224d		£2 green	80·00	14·00

63 William J. Farrer

64 Ferdinand von Mueller

1948. W. J. Farrer (wheat research) Commem.

225	**63**	2½d. red	10	10

1948. Sir Ferdinand von Mueller (botanist) Commemoration.

226	**64**	2½d. red	10	10

65 Boy Scout

66 "Henry Lawson" (Sir Lionel Lindsay)

1948. Pan-Pacific Scout Jamboree, Wonga Park.

227	**65**	2½d. lake	10	10

For 3½d. value dates "1952–53", see No. 254.

1949. Henry Lawson (poet) Commemoration.

231	**66**	2½d. purple	15	10

67 Mounted Postman and Convair CV 240 Aircraft

68 John, Lord Forrest of Bunbury

1949. 75th Anniv of U.P.U.

232	**67**	3½d. blue	30	50

1949. John, Lord Forrest (explorer and politician) Commemoration.

233	**68**	2½d. red	15	10

69 Queen Elizabeth

70 King George VI

81 King George VI

80 King George VI

71 Aborigine

82 King George VI

1950.

236	**69**	1½d. green	40	20
237		2d. green	15	10
234	**70**	2½d. red	10	10
237c		2½d. brown	15	20
235		3d. red	15	10
237d		3d. green	15	10
247	**81**	3½d. purple	10	10
248		4½d. red	15	80
249		6½d. brown	15	60
250		6½d. green	10	15
251	**80**	7½d. blue	15	45
238	**71**	8½d. brown	15	60
252	**82**	1s.0½d. blue	60	30
253	**71**	2s.6d. brown (21 × 25½ mm)	1·50	35

72 Reproduction of First Stamp of N.S.W.

73 Reproduction of First Stamp of Victoria

1950. Centenary of Australian States Stamps.

239	**72**	2½d. purple	25	10
240	**73**	2½d. purple	25	10

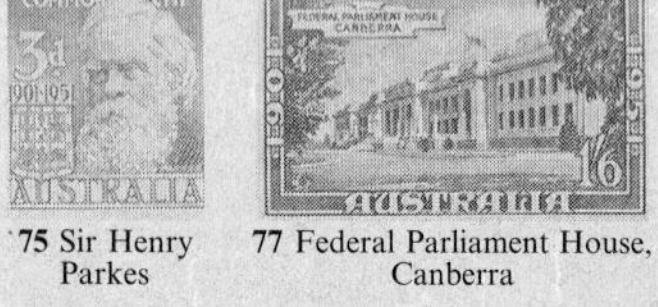

75 Sir Henry Parkes

77 Federal Parliament House, Canberra

1951. 50th Anniv of Commonwealth. Inscr as in T **75** and **77**.

241	**75**	3d. lake	30	10
242	–	3d. lake	30	10
243	–	5½d. blue	20	2·00
244	**77**	1s.6d. brown	35	50

DESIGNS—As Type **70**: No. 242, Sir Edmund Barton. As Type **77**: No. 243, Opening first Federal Parliament.

78 E. H. Hargraves

79 C. J. Latrobe

1951. Centenaries. Discovery of Gold in Australia and of Responsible Government in Victoria.

245	**78**	3d. purple	30	10
246	**79**	3d. purple	30	10

1952. Pan-Pacific Scout Jamboree, Greystanes. As T **65** but dated "1952–53".

254	**65**	3½d. lake	10	10

83 Butter

86 Queen Elizabeth II

1953. Food Production. Inscr "PRODUCE FOOD!".

255	**83**	3d. green	30	10
256	–	3d. green (Wheat)	30	10
257	–	3d. green (Beef)	30	10
258	**83**	3½d. red	30	10
259	–	3½d. red (Wheat)	30	10
260	–	3½d. red (Beef)	30	10

1953.

261	**86**	1d. purple	15	15
261a		2½d. blue	20	15
262		3d. green	20	10
263		3½d. red	20	10
263a		6½d. orange	1·75	50

87 Queen Elizabeth II

88 Young Farmers and Calf

1953. Coronation.

264	**87**	3½d. red	40	10
265		7½d. violet	75	1·10
266		2s. turquoise	2·50	1·10

1953. 25th Anniv of Australian Young Farmers' Clubs.

267	**88**	3½d. brown and green	10	10

89 Lt.-Gov. D. Collins

90 Lt.-Gov. W. Paterson

91 Sullivan Cove, Hobart, 1804

92 Stamp of 1853

1953. 150th Anniv of Settlement in Tasmania.

268	**89**	3½d. purple	30	10
269	**90**	3½d. purple	30	10
270	**91**	2s. green	1·25	2·75

1953. 1st Centenary of Tasmania Postage Stamps.

271	**92**	3d. red	10	40

93 Queen Elizabeth II and Duke of Edinburgh

94 Queen Elizabeth II — **95** "Telegraphic Communications"

1954. Royal Visit.

272	**93**	3½d. red	20	10
273	**94**	7½d. purple	30	1·25
274	**93**	2s. green	60	65

1954. Centenary of Telegraph.

275	**95**	3½d. brown	10	10

96 Red Cross and Globe — **97** Mute Swan

1954. 40th Anniv of Australian Red Cross Society.

276	**96**	3½d. blue and red	10	10

1954. Centenary of Western Australian Stamps.

277	**97**	3½d. black	20	10

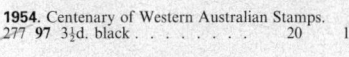

98 Locomotives of 1854 and 1954

1954. Centenary of Australian Railways.

278	**98**	3½d. purple	30	10

99 Territory Badge — **100** Olympic Games Symbol

1954. Australian Antarctic Research.

279	**99**	3½d. black	15	10

1954. Olympic Games Propaganda.

280	**100**	2s. blue	70	80
280a		2s. green	1·75	1·75

101 Rotary Symbol, Globe and Flags — **103** American Memorial, Canberra

1955. 50th Anniv of Rotary International.

281	**101**	3½d. red	10	10

1955. Australian–American Friendship.

283	**103**	3½d. blue	10	10

101a Queen Elizabeth II — **102** Queen Elizabeth II

1955.

282a	**101a**	4d. lake	20	10
282b		7½d. violet	60	1·25
282c		10d. blue	60	75
282	**102**	1s.0½d. blue	1·50	75
282d		1s.7d. brown	1·50	30

104 Cobb & Co. Coach (from etching by Sir Lionel Lindsay)

1955. Mail-coach Pioneers Commemoration.

284	**104**	3½d. sepia	25	10
285		2s. brown	50	1·40

105 Y.M.C.A. Emblem and Map of the World

1955. World Centenary of Y.M.C.A.

286	**105**	3½d. green and red	10	10

106 Florence Nightingale and Young Nurse — **107** Queen Victoria

1955. Nursing Profession Commemoration.

287	**106**	3½d. lilac	10	10

1955. Centenary of South Australian Postage Stamps.

288	**107**	3½d. green	10	10

108 Badges of N.S.W., Victoria and Tasmania

1956. Centenary of Responsible Government in N.S.W., Victoria and Tasmania.

289	**108**	3½d. lake	10	10

109 Arms of Melbourne — **110** Olympic Torch and Symbol

111 Collins Street, Melbourne

1956. Olympic Games, Melbourne.

290	**109**	4d. red	25	10
291	**110**	7½d. blue	50	1·25
292	**111**	1s. multicoloured	60	30
293	–	2s. multicoloured	85	1·25

DESIGN—As Type **111**: 2s. Melbourne across River Yarra.

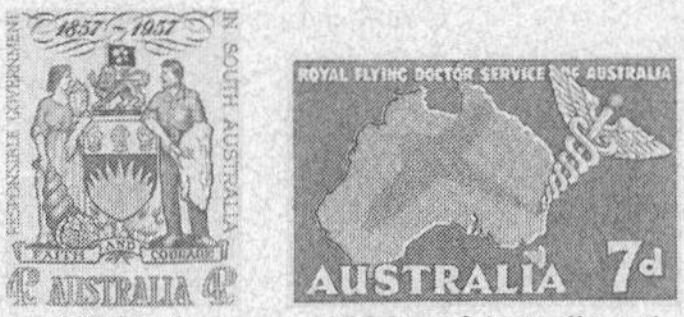

115 South Australia Coat of Arms — **116** Map of Australia and Caduceus

1957. Centenary of Responsible Government in South Australia.

296	**115**	4d. brown	10	10

1957. Royal Flying Doctor Service of Australia.

297	**116**	7d. blue	15	10

117 "The Spirit of Christmas" (after Sir Joshua Reynolds)

1957. Christmas.

298	**117**	3½d. red	10	20
299		4d. purple	10	10

118 Lockheed Super Constellation Airliner

1958. Inaug of Australian "Round-the-World" Air Service.

301	**118**	2s. blue	75	1·00

119 Hall of Memory, Sailor and Airman

1958.

302	**119**	5½d. lake	40	30
303	–	5½d. lake	40	30

No. 303 shows a soldier and servicewoman instead of the sailor and airman.

120 Sir Charles Kingsford Smith and the "Southern Cross" — **122** The Nativity

121 Silver Mine, Broken Hill

1958. 30th Anniv of 1st Air Crossing of the Tasman Sea.

304	**120**	8d. blue	60	1·00

1958. 75th Anniv of Founding of Broken Hill.

305	**121**	4d. brown	30	10

1958. Christmas Issue.

306	**122**	3½d. red	20	10
307		4d. violet	20	10

124 Queen Elizabeth II — **126** Queen Elizabeth II

127 Queen Elizabeth II — **128** Queen Elizabeth II — **129** Queen Elizabeth II

1959.

308	–	1d. purple	10	10
309	**124**	2d. brown	50	20
311	**126**	3d. turquoise	15	10
312	**127**	3½d. green	15	15
313	**128**	4d. red	1·75	10
314	**129**	5d. blue	90	10

No. 308 shows a head and shoulders portrait as in Type **128** and is vert.

131 Numbat — **137** Christmas Bells

142 Aboriginal Stockman

1959.

316	**131**	6d. brown	2·00	10
317	–	8d. red	75	10
318	–	9d. sepia	1·75	55
319	–	11d. blue	1·25	15
320	–	1s. green	3·00	40
321	–	1s.2d. purple	1·25	15
322	**137**	1s.6d. red on yellow	2·00	80
323	–	2s. blue	70	10
324	–	2s.3d. green on yellow	1·00	10
324a	–	2s.3d. green	4·00	1·50
325	–	2s.5d. brown on yellow	5·00	75
326	–	3s. red	1·00	20
327	**142**	5s. brown	22·00	1·25

DESIGNS—As Type **131**: VERT: 8d. Tiger Cat; 9d. Eastern grey kangaroo; 11d. Common rabbit bandicoot; 1s. Platypus. HORIZ: 1s.2d. Thylacine. As Type **137**: 2s. Flannel flower; 2s.3d. Wattle; 2s.5d. Banksia (plant); 3s. Waratah.

143 Postmaster Isaac Nichols boarding the Brig "Experiment"

1959. 150th Anniv of Australian P.O.

331	**143**	4d. slate	15	10

144 Parliament House, Brisbane, and Arms of Queensland — **145** "The Approach of the Magi"

1959. Centenary of Queensland Self-Government.

332	**144**	4d. lilac and green	10	10

1959. Christmas.

333	**145**	5d. violet	10	10

146 Girl Guide and Lord Baden-Powell — **147** "The Overlanders" (after Sir Daryl Lindsay)

1960. 50th Anniv of Girl Guide Movement.

334	**146**	5d. blue	30	15

1960. Centenary of Northern Territory Exploration.

335	**147**	5d. mauve	30	15

148 "Archer" and Melbourne Cup — **149** Queen Victoria

1960. 100th Melbourne Cup Race Commemoration.

336	**148**	5d. sepia	20	10

1960. Centenary of Queensland Stamps.

337	**149**	5d. green	25	10

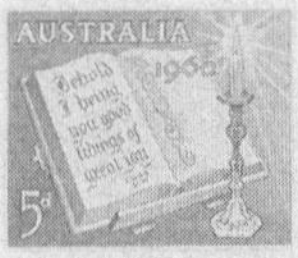

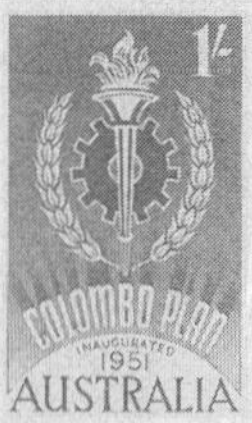

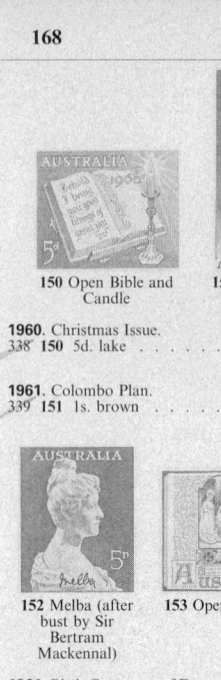

150 Open Bible and Candle — **151** Colombo Plan Bureau Emblem

1960. Christmas Issue.
338 **150** 5d. lake 10 10

1961. Colombo Plan.
339 **151** 1s. brown 10 10

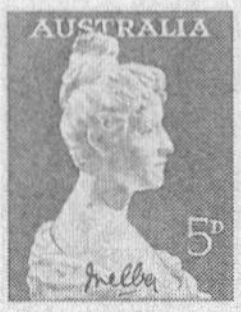

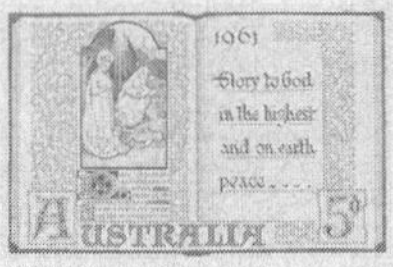

152 Melba (after bust by Sir Bertram Mackennal) — **153** Open Prayer Book and Text

1961. Birth Centenary of Dame Nellie Melba (singer).
340 **152** 5d. blue 30 15

1961. Christmas Issue.
341 **153** 5d. brown 10 10

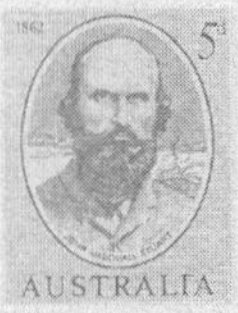

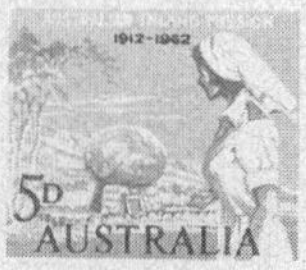

154 J. M. Stuart — **155** Flynn's Grave and Nursing Sister

1962. Centenary of Stuart's South to North Crossing of Australia.
342 **154** 5d. red 15 10

1962. 50th Anniv of Australian Inland Mission.
343 **155** 5d. multicoloured 30 15

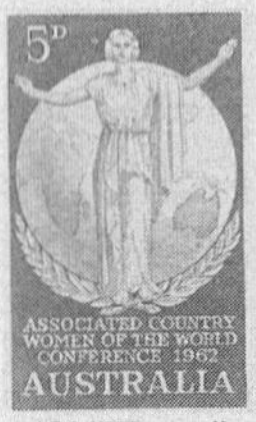

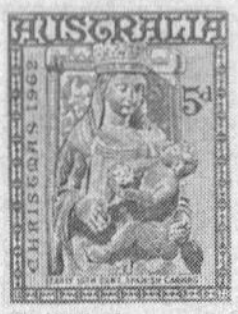

156 "Woman" — **157** "Madonna and Child"

1962. "Associated Country Women of the World" Conference, Melbourne.
344 **156** 5d. green 10 10

1962. Christmas.
345 **157** 5d. violet 15 10

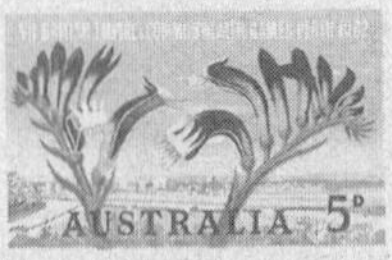

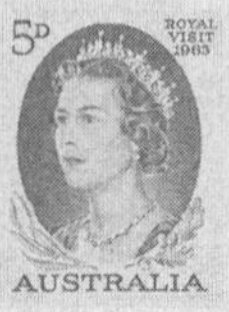

158 Perth and Kangaroo Paw (plant) — **160** Queen Elizabeth II

1962. British Empire and Commonwealth Games, Perth. Multicoloured.
346 5d. Type **158** 40 10
347 2s.3d. Arms of Perth and running track . . . . . . 2·00 2·75

1963. Royal Visit.
348 **160** 5d. green 35 10
349 – 2s.3d. lake . . . . 1·50 3·00
DESIGN: 2s.3d. Queen Elizabeth II and Duke of Edinburgh.

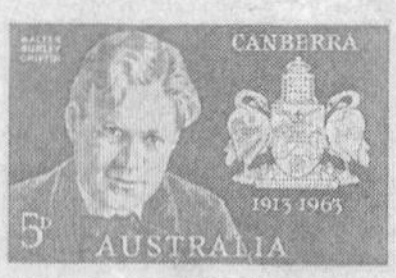

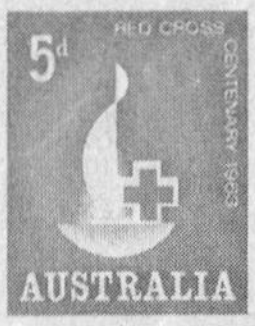

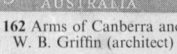

162 Arms of Canberra and W. B. Griffin (architect) — **163** Centenary Emblem

1963. 50th Anniv of Canberra.
350 **162** 5d. green 15 10

1963. Centenary of Red Cross.
351 **163** 5d. red, grey and blue . . 40 10

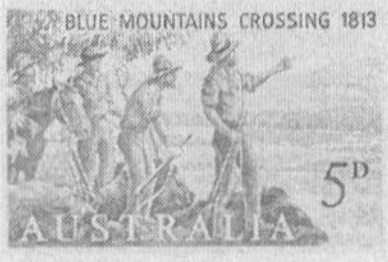

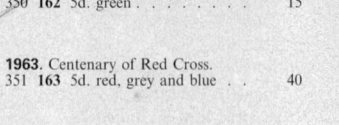

164 Blaxland, Lawson and Wentworth on Mount York

1963. 150th Anniv of First Crossing of Blue Mountains.
352 **164** 5d. blue 15 10

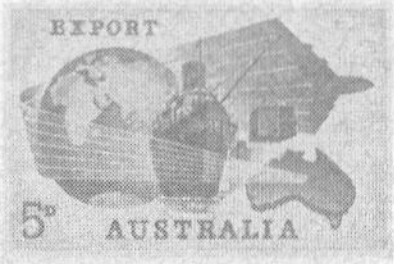

165 "Export"

1963. Export Campaign.
353 **165** 5d. red 10 10

1963. As T **160** but smaller $17\frac{1}{2}\times21\frac{1}{2}$ mm "5D" at top right replacing "ROYAL VISIT 1963" and oak leaves omitted.
354 5d. green 65 10
354c 5d. red 55 10

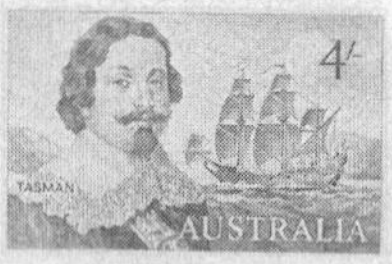

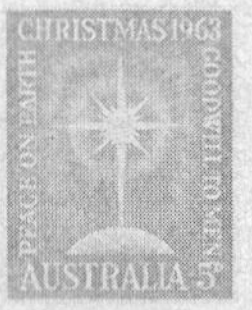

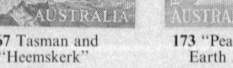

167 Tasman and "Heemskerk" — **173** "Peace on Earth ..."

1963. Navigators.
355 **167** 4s. blue . . . . 3·00 55
356 – 5s. brown . . . . 3·25 1·50
357 – 7s.6d. olive . . . . . . 19·00 16·00
358 – 10s. purple . . . . . . 25·00 4·50
359 – £1 violet . . . . 30·00 16·00
360 – £2 sepia . . . . 55·00 75·00
DESIGNS—As Type **167**: 7s.6d. Captain Cook; 10s. Flinders and "Investigator". $20\frac{1}{2}\times5\frac{1}{2}$ mm: 5s. Dampier and "Roebuck"; £1 Bass and "Tom Thumb" (whale boat); £2 Admiral King and "Mermaid" (survey cutter).

1963. Christmas.
361 **173** 5d. blue 10 10

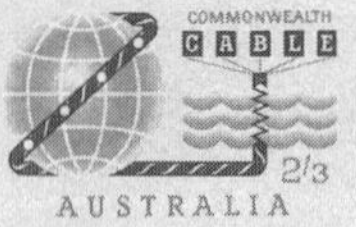

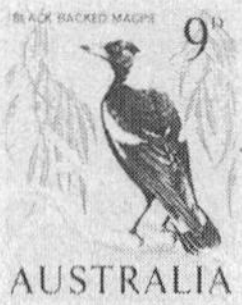

174 "Commonwealth Cable" — **176** Black-backed Magpie

1963. Opening of COMPAC (Trans-Pacific Telephone Cable).
362 **174** 2s.3d. multicoloured . . . 1·25 2·75

1964. Birds.
363 – 6d. multicoloured 80 25
364 **176** 9d. black, grey and green 1·00 2·75
365 – 1s.6d. multicoloured . . . 75 1·40
366 – 2s. yellow, black and pink 1·40 50
367 – 2s.5d. multicoloured . . . 1·75 3·50
368 – 2s.6d. multicoloured . . . 3·00 3·75
369 – 3s. multicoloured . . . . 3·00 1·75
BIRDS—HORIZ: 6d. Yellow-tailed thornbill; 2s.6d. Scarlet robin. VERT: 1s.6d. Galah (cockatoo); 2s. Golden whistler (Thickhead); 2s.5d. Blue wren; 3s. Straw-necked ibis.

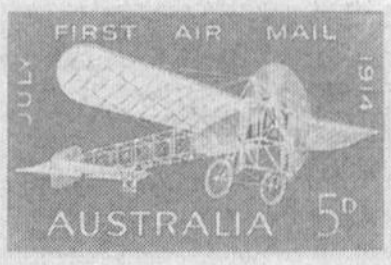

182 Bleriot XI Aircraft (type flown by M. Guillaux, 1914)

1964. 50th Anniv of 1st Australian Airmail Flight.
370 **182** 5d. green 30 10
371 2s.3d. red . . . . 1·75 2·75

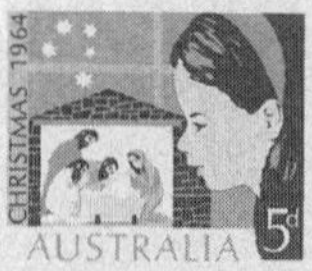

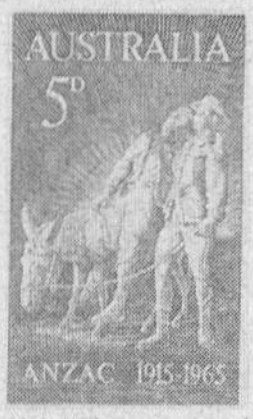

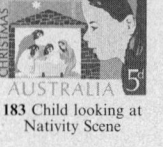

183 Child looking at Nativity Scene — **184** "Simpson and his Donkey"

1964. Christmas.
372 **183** 5d. red, blue, buff and black 10 10

1965. 50th Anniv of Gallipoli Landing.
373 **184** 5d. brown 65 10
374 8d. blue . . . . 1·00 2·50
375 2s.3d. purple . . . . . . 1·75 2·50

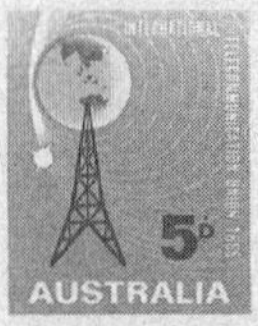

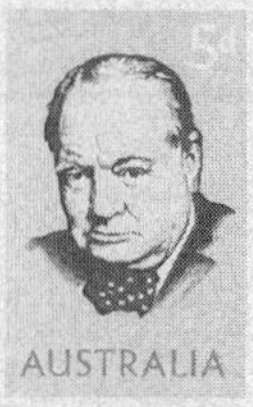

185 "Telecommunications" — **186** Sir Winston Churchill

1965. Centenary of I.T.U.
376 **185** 5d. black, brown and blue 40 10

1965. Churchill Commemoration.
377 **186** 5d. multicoloured 15 10

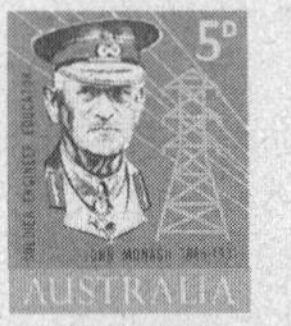

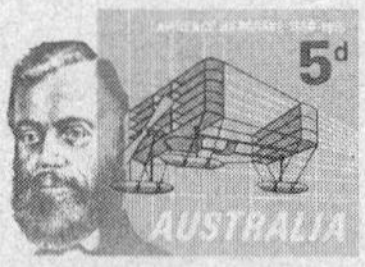

187 General Monash — **188** Hargrave and "Multiplane" Seaplane (1902)

1965. Birth Centenary of General Sir John Monash (engineer and soldier).
378 **187** 5d. multicoloured 15 10

1965. 50th Death Anniv of Lawrence Hargrave (aviation pioneer).
379 **188** 5d. multicoloured 15 10

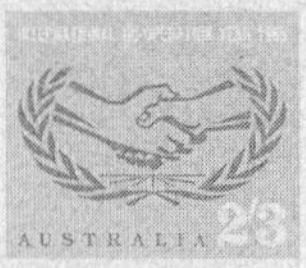

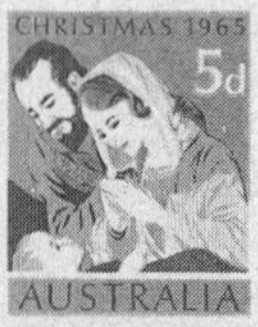

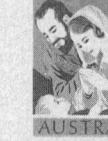

189 I.C.Y. Emblem — **190** "Nativity Scene"

1965. International Co-operation Year.
380 **189** 2s.3d. green and blue . . 65 1·50

1965. Christmas.
381 **190** 5d. multicoloured 15 10

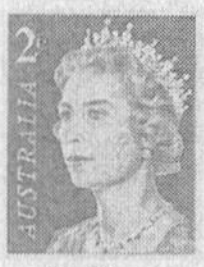

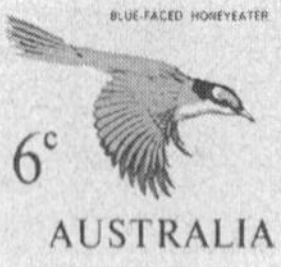

191 Queen Elizabeth II — **192** Blue-faced Honeyeater

1966. Decimal currency. As earlier issues but with values in cents and dollars as in T **191/2**. Also some new designs.
382 **191** 1c. brown 25 10
383 2c. green 70 10
384 3c. green 70 10
404 3c. black, pink and green 45 80
385 4c. red 20 10
405 4c. black, brown and red 35 50
405a 5c. black, brown and blue 40 10
386 – 5c. multicoloured (as 363) 25 10
386c **191** 5c. blue 70 10
387 **192** 6c. multicoloured 80 55
387a **191** 6c. orange 55 10
388 – 7c. multicoloured 60 10
388a **191** 7c. purple 70 10
389 – 8c. multicoloured 60 75
390 – 9c. multicoloured 60 20
391 – 10c. multicoloured . . . 60 10
392 – 13c. multicoloured . . . 1·75 25
393 – 15c. multicoloured (as 365) . . . . 1·50 1·25
394 – 20c. yellow, black and pink (as 366) . . . . 3·00 15
395 – 24c. multicoloured . . . . 65 1·25
396 – 25c. multicoloured (as 368) . . . . 3·75 30
397 – 30c. multicoloured (as 369) . . . . 10·00 1·00
398 **167** 40c. blue . . . . 4·00 10
399 – 50c. brown (as 356) . . 5·00 10
400 – 75c. olive (as 357) . . . 1·00 1·00
401 – \$1 purple (as 358) . . . 1·75 20
402 – \$2 violet (as 359) . . . . 7·50 1·00
403 – \$4 brown (as 360) . . . 5·50 6·50
DESIGNS—VERT: 7c. White-tailed Dascyllus ("Humbug fish"); 8c. Copper-banded butterflyfish ("Coral fish"); 9c. Hermit crab; 10c. Orange clownfish ("Anemone fish"); 13c. Red-necked avocet. HORIZ: 24c. Azure kingfisher.

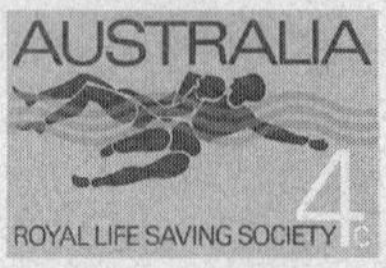

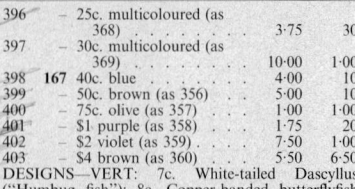

200 "Saving Life"

1966. 75th Anniv of Royal Life Saving Society.
406 **200** 4c. black, lt bl & bl . . . 15 10

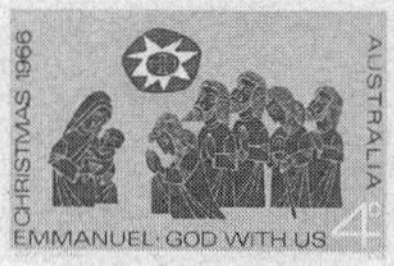

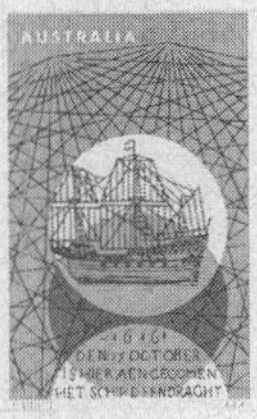

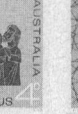

201 "Adoration of the Shepherds" — **202** "Eendracht"

1966. Christmas.
407 **201** 4c. black and olive . . . 10 10

1966. 350th Anniv of Dirk Hartog's Landing in Australia.
408 **202** 4c. multicoloured 10 10

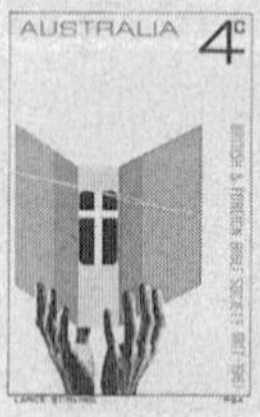

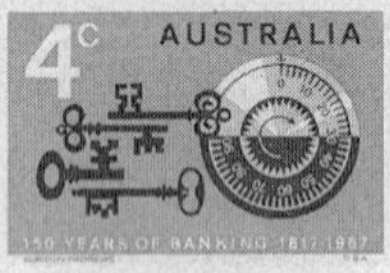

203 Open Bible — **204** Ancient Keys and Modern Lock

1967. 150th Anniv of British and Foreign Bible Society in Australia.
409 **203** 4c. multicoloured 10 10

1967. 150th Anniv of Australian Banking.
410 **204** 4c. black, blue and green 10 10

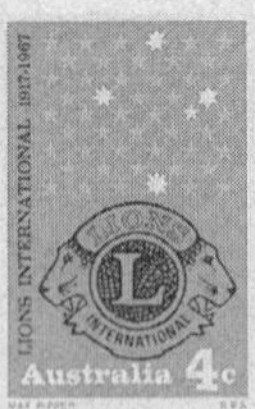

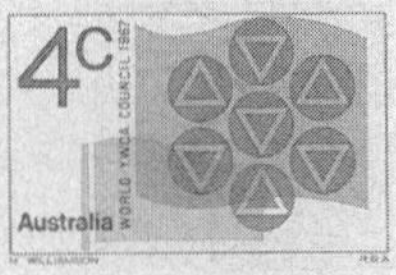

205 Lions Badge and 50 Stars — **206** Y.W.C.A. Emblem

1967. 50th Anniv of Lions International.
411 **205** 4c. black, gold and blue 10 10

1967. World Y.W.C.A. Council Meeting, Monash University, Melbourne.
412 **206** 4c. multicoloured 10 10

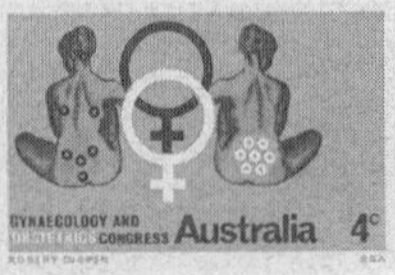

207 Anatomical Figures

1967. 5th World Gynaecology and Obstetrics Congress, Sydney.
413 **207** 4c. black, blue and violet 10 10

1967. No. 385 surch.
414 **191** 5c. on 4c. red 35 10

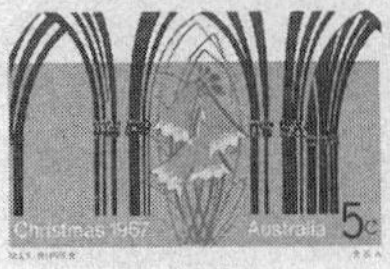

209 Christmas Bells and Gothic Arches

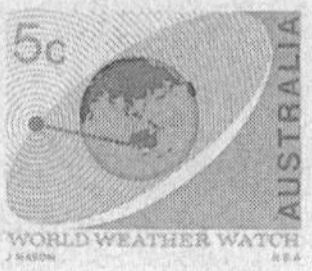

211 Satellite in Orbit

1967. Christmas. Multicoloured.

415 5c. Type **209** 20 10
416 25c. Religious symbols (vert) 1·00 1·75

1968. World Weather Watch. Multicoloured.

417 5c. Type **211** 30 10
418 20c. World weather map . . 1·10 2·75

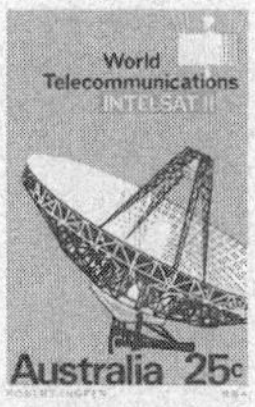

213 Radar Antenna

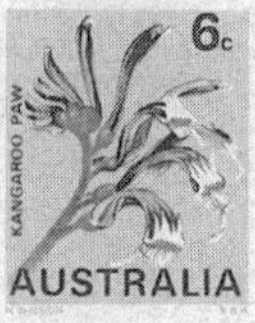

214 Kangaroo Paw (Western Australia)

1968. World Telecommunications via Intelsat II.

419 **213** 25c. blue, black and green 1·25 2·50

1968. State Floral Emblems. Multicoloured.

420 6c. Type **214** . . . . 45 1·25
421 13c. Pink Heath (Victoria) . . 50 60
422 15c. Tasmanian Blue Gum (Tasmania) 70 20
423 20c. Sturt's Desert Pea (South Australia) . . . . 2·00 60
424 25c. Cooktown Orchid (Queensland) . . . . . . 1·40 60
425 30c. Waratah (New South Wales) 50 10

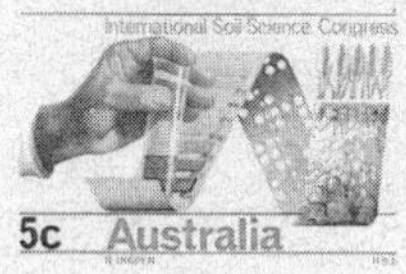

220 Soil Sample Analysis

1968. International Soil Science Congress and World Medical Association Assembly. Mult.

426 5c. Type **220** 10 10
427 5c. Rubber-gloved hands, syringe and head of Hippocrates 10 10

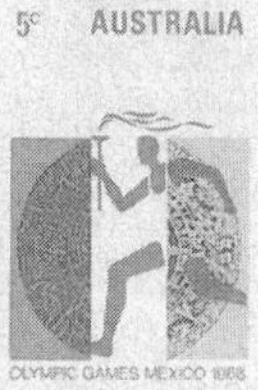

222 Athlete carrying Torch and Sunstone Symbol

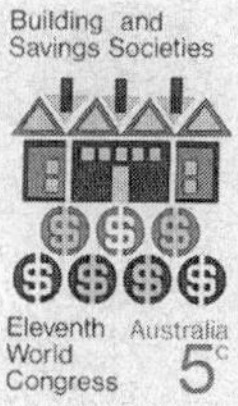

224 Houses and Dollar Signs

1968. Olympic Games, Mexico City. Mult.

428 5c. Type **222** 30 10
429 25c. Sunstone symbol and Mexican flag . . . . 40 1·50

1968. Building and Savings Societies Congress.

430 **224** 5c. multicoloured 10 40

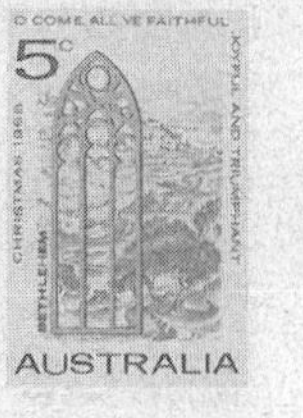

225 Church Window and View of Bethlehem

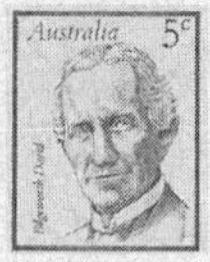

226 Edgeworth David (geologist)

1968. Christmas.

431 **225** 5c. multicoloured 10 10

1968. Famous Australians (1st series).

432 **226** 5c. green on myrtle . . . 35 20
433 – 5c. black on blue 35 20
434 – 5c. brown on buff 35 20
435 – 5c. violet on lilac 35 20

DESIGNS: No. 433, A. B. Paterson (poet); No. 434, Albert Namatjira (artist); No. 435, Caroline Chrisholm (social worker).

Nos. 432/5 were only issued in booklets and exist with one or two sides imperf.

See also Nos. 446/9, 479/82, 505/8, 537/40, 590/5, 602/7 and 637/40.

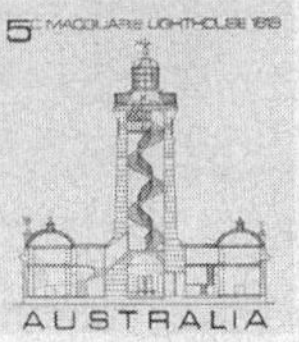

230 Macquarie Lighthouse

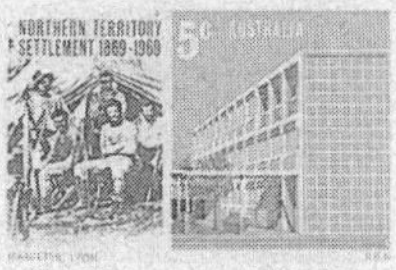

231 Pioneers and Modern Building, Darwin

1968. 150th Anniv of Macquarie Lighthouse.

436 **230** 5c. black and yellow . . . 30 50

1969. Centenary of Northern Territory Settlement.

437 **231** 5c. brown, olive and ochre 10 10

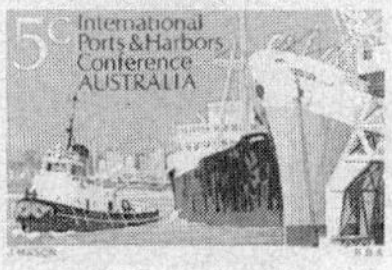

232 Melbourne Harbour

1969. 6th Biennial Conference of International Association of Ports and Harbours, Melbourne.

438 **232** 5c. multicoloured 15 10

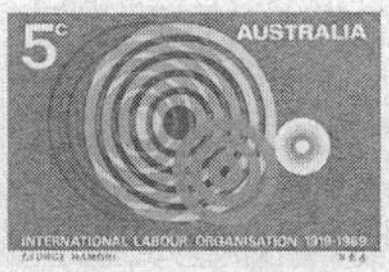

233 Concentric Circles (symbolizing Management, Labour and Government)

1969. 50th Anniv of I.L.O.

439 **233** 5c. multicoloured 15 10

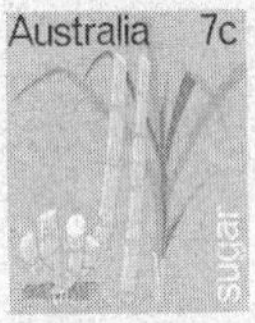

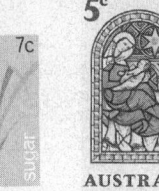

234 Sugar Cane

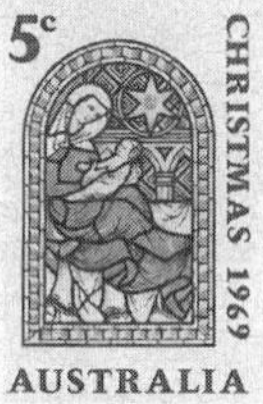

238 "The Nativity" (stained glass window)

1969. Primary Industries. Multicoloured.

440 7c. Type **234** . . . . 60 1·25
441 15c. Timber . . . . 1·00 2·50
442 20c. Wheat 35 60
443 25c. Wool . . . . 60 1·50

1969. Christmas. Multicoloured.

444 5c. Type **238** 20 10
445 25c. "Tree of Life", Christ in crib and Christmas Star (abstract) . . . . 1·00 2·00

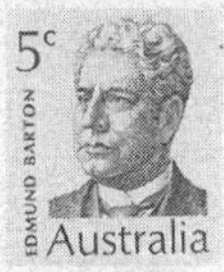

240 Edmund Barton

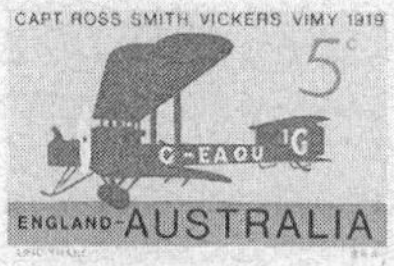

244 Capt. Ross Smith's Vickers Vimy, 1919

1969. Famous Australians (2nd series). Prime Ministers.

446 **240** 5c. black on green 40 20
447 – 5c. black on green 40 20
448 – 5c. black on green 40 20
449 – 5c. black on green 40 20

DESIGNS: No. 447, Alfred Deakin; No. 448, J. C. Watson; No. 449, G. H. Reid.

Nos. 446/9 were only issued in booklets and only exist with one or two adjacent sides imperf.

1969. 50th Anniv of 1st England–Australia Flight.

450 **244** 5c. multicoloured 15 10
451 – 5c. red, black and green . . 15 10
452 – 5c. multicoloured 15 10

DESIGNS: No. 451, Lt. H. Fysh and Lt. P. McGinness on 1919 survey with Ford car; No. 452, Capt. Wrigley and Sgt. Murphy in Royal Aircraft Factory B.E.2E taking off to meet the Smiths.

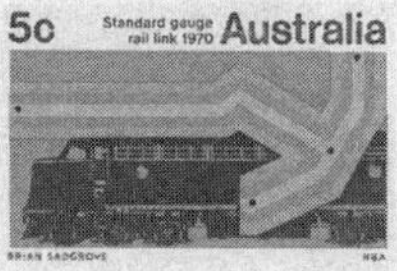

247 Symbolic Track and Diesel Locomotive

1970. Sydney–Perth Standard Gauge Railway Link.

453 **247** 5c. multicoloured 15 10

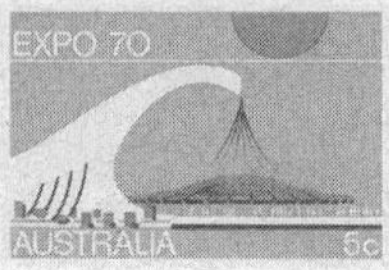

248 Australian Pavilion, Osaka

1970. World Fair, Osaka.

454 **248** 5c. multicoloured 15 10
455 – 20c. red and black 35 65

DESIGN: 20c., "Southern Cross" and "from the Country of the south with warm feelings" (message).

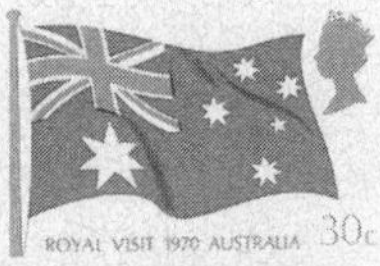

251 Australian Flag

1970. Royal Visit.

456 – 5c. black and ochre . . . 35 15
457 **251** 30c. multicoloured . . . . 1·25 2·50

DESIGN: 5c. Queen Elizabeth II and Duke of Edinburgh.

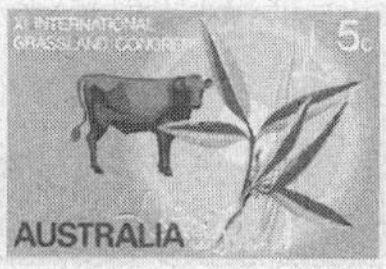

252 Lucerne Plant, Bull and Sun

1970. 11th International Grasslands Congress, Queensland.

458 **252** 5c. multicoloured 10 50

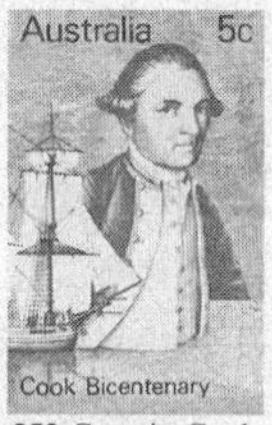

253 Captain Cook and H.M.S. "Endeavour"

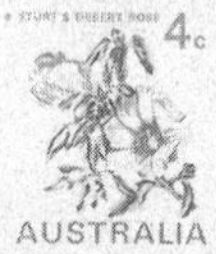

259 Sturt's Desert Rose

1970. Bicentenary of Captain Cook's Discovery of Australia's East Coast. Multicoloured.

459 5c. Type **253** 25 10
460 5c. Sextant and H.M.S. "Endeavour" 25 10
461 5c. Landing at Botany Bay 25 10
462 5c. Charting and exploring 25 10
463 5c. Claiming possession . . . 25 10
464 30c. Captain Cook, H.M.S. "Endeavour", sextant, aborigines and kangaroo (63 × 30 mm) . . . . . . 1·00 2·50

Nos. 459/63 were issued together, se-tenant in horizontal strips of five, forming a composite design.

1970. Coil Stamps. Multicoloured.

465a 2c. Type **259** 40 20
466 4c. Type **259** . . . . 70 1·25
467 5c. Golden wattle 20 10
468 6c. Type **259** . . . . 1·25 1·00
468b 7c. Sturt's desert pea . . . 40 40
468d 10c. As 7c. 40 40

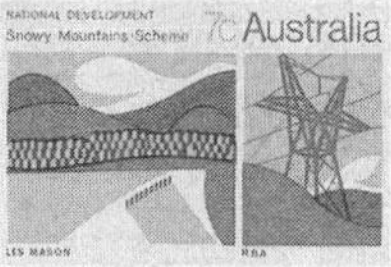

264 Snowy Mountains Scheme

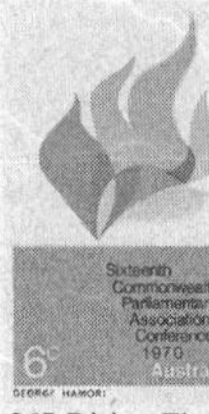

265 Rising Flames

1970. National Development (1st series). Mult.

469 7c. Type **264** 20 80
470 8c. Ord River scheme 10 15
471 9c. Bauxite to aluminium . . 15 15
472 10c. Oil and natural gas . . . 30 10

See also Nos. 541/4.

1970. 16th Commonwealth Parliamentary Association Conference, Canberra.

473 **265** 6c. multicoloured 10 10

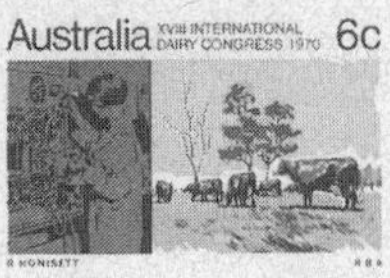

266 Milk Analysis and Dairy Herd

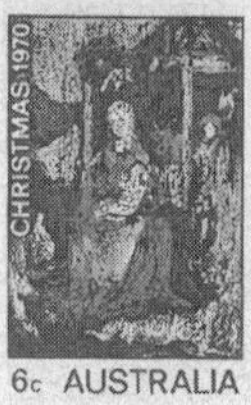

267 "The Nativity"

1970. 18th International Dairy Congress, Sydney.

474 **266** 6c. multicoloured 10 10

1970. Christmas.

475 **267** 6c. multicoloured 10 10

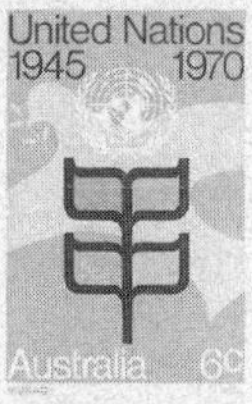

268 U.N. "Plant" and Dove of Peace

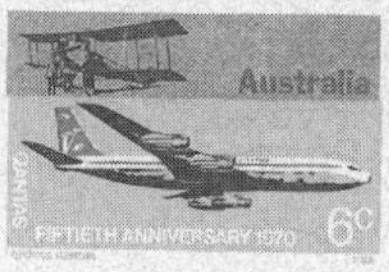

269 Boeing 707 and Avro 504

1970. 25th Anniv of United Nations.

476 **268** 6c. multicoloured 15 10

1970. 50th Anniv of QANTAS Airline.

477 **269** 6c. multicoloured 30 10
478 – 30c. multicoloured . . . . 70 1·50

DESIGN: 30c. Avro 504 and Boeing 707.

1970. Famous Australians (3rd series). As T **226**.

479 6c. blue 65 20
480 6c. black on brown 65 20
481 6c. purple on pink 65 20
482 6c. red on pink 65 20

DESIGNS: No. 479, The Duigan brothers (pioneer aviators); 480, Lachlan Macquarie (Governor of New South Wales); 481, Adam Lindsay Gordon (poet); 482, E. J. Eyre (explorer).

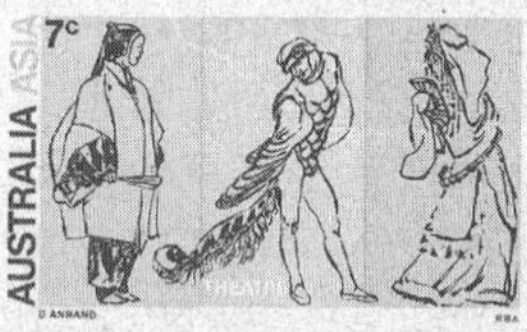

271 "Theatre"

1971. "Australia–Asia". 28th International Congress of Orientalists, Canberra. Multicoloured.

483 7c. Type **271** 45 60
484 15c. "Music" . . . . 70 1·00
485 20c. "Sea Craft" 65 90

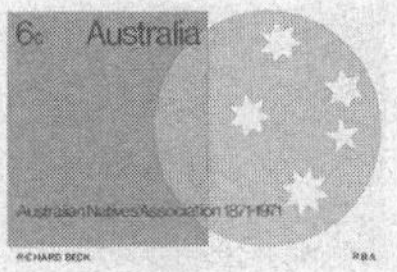

272 The Southern Cross

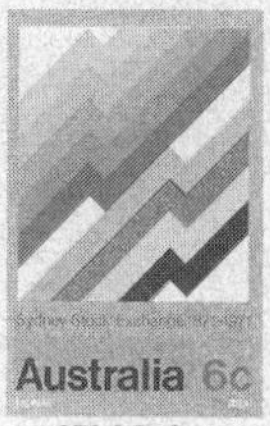

273 Market "Graph"

1971. Centenary of Australian Natives' Association.

486 **272** 6c. black, red and blue . . 10 10

1971. Centenary of Sydney Stock Exchange.

487 **273** 6c. multicoloured 10 10

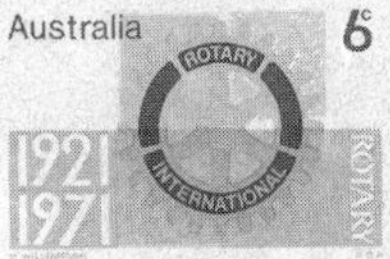

274 Rotary Emblem

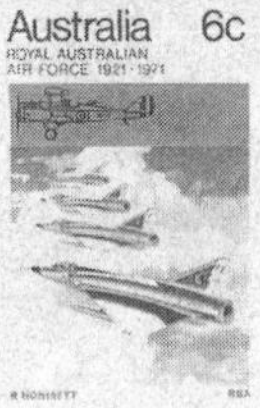

275 Dassault Mirage Jets and De Havilland D.H.9A Biplane

1971. 50th Anniv of Rotary International in Australia.

488 **274** 6c. multicoloured 15 10

1971. 50th Anniv of R.A.A.F.

489 **275** 6c. multicoloured 40 10

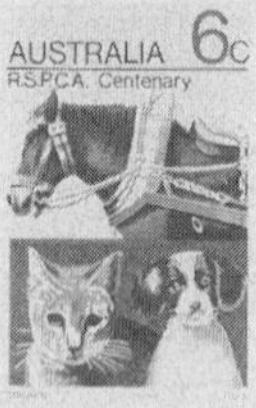

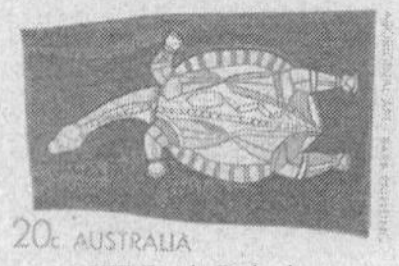

276 Draught-horse, Cat and Dog

277 Bark Painting

1971. Animals. Multicoloured.

490 6c. Type **276** 20 10
491 12c. Vet and lamb ("Animal Science") 45 20
492 18c. Red Kangaroo ("Fauna Conservation") 80 35
493 24c. Guide-dog ("Animals Aid to Man") . . . . . . 80 1·40

The 6c. commemorates the Centenary of the Australian R.S.P.C.A.

1971. Aboriginal Art. Multicoloured.

494 20c. Type **277** 20 20
495 25c. Body decoration 20 55
496 30c. Cave painting (vert) . . 40 20
497 35c. Grave posts (vert) . . . 30 15

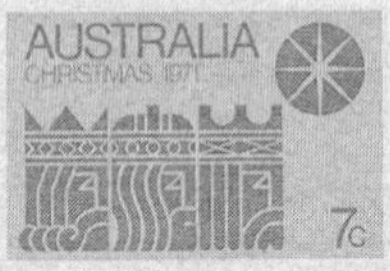

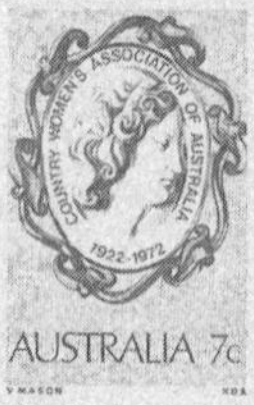

278 The Three Kings and the Star

280 Cameo Brooch

1971. Christmas. Colours of star and colour of "AUSTRALIA" given.

498 **278** 7c. blue, mauve and brown 50 15
499 7c. mauve, brown and white 50 15
500 7c. mauve, white and black . . . . 3·25 80
501 7c. black, green and black 50 15
502 7c. lilac, green and mauve 50 15
503 7c. black, brown and white 50 15
504 7c. blue, mauve and green 14·00 2·25

1972. Famous Australians. (4th series). As T **240**. Prime Ministers.

505 7c. blue 30 20
506 7c. blue 30 20
507 7c. red 30 20
508 7c. red 30 20

DESIGNS: No. 505, Andrew Fisher; No. 506, W. M. Hughes; No. 507, Joseph Cook; No. 508, S. M. Bruce.

1972. 50th Anniv of Country Women's Association.

509 **280** 7c. multicoloured 20 10

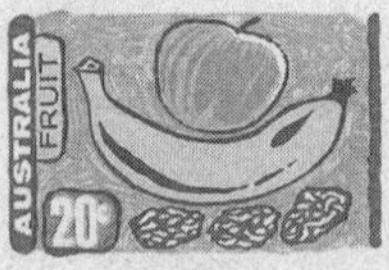

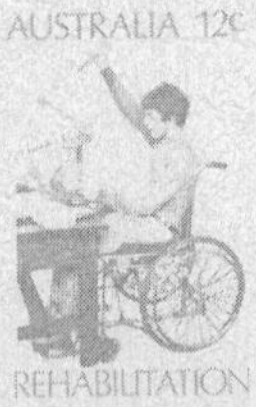

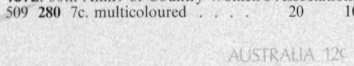

281 Fruit

282 Worker in Wheelchair

1972. Primary Industries. Multicoloured.

510 20c. Type **281** . . . . 1·00 2·50
511 25c. Rice . . . . 1·00 4·00
512 30c. Fish . . . . 1·00 1·00
513 35c. Beef . . . . 2·25 75

1972. Rehabilitation of the Disabled.

514 **282** 12c. brown and green . . 10 10
515 – 18c. green and orange . . 85 35
516 – 24c. blue and brown . . . 15 10

DESIGNS—HORIZ: 18c. Patient and teacher. VERT: 24c. Boy playing with ball.

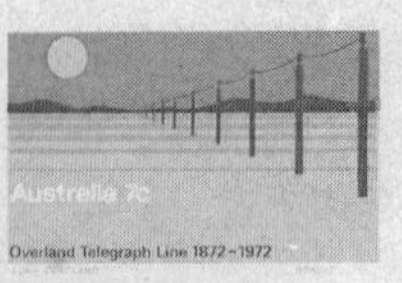

283 Telegraph Line

284 Athletics

1972. Centenary of Overland Telegraph Line.

517 **283** 7c. multicoloured 15 15

1972. Olympic Games, Munich. Multicoloured.

518 7c. Type **284** 20 25
519 7c. Rowing 20 25
520 7c. Swimming 20 25
521 35c. Equestrian . . . . . 1·25 3·50

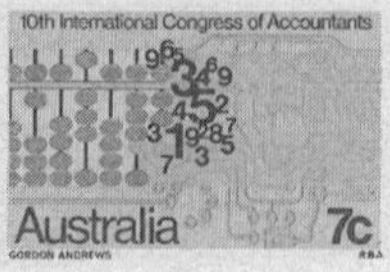

285 Numerals and Computer Circuit

1972. 10th Int Congress of Accountants, Sydney.

522 **285** 7c. multicoloured 15 15

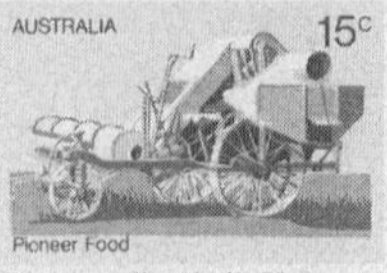

286 Australian-built Harvester

1972. Pioneer Life. Multicoloured.

523 5c. Pioneer family (vert) . . . 10 10
524 10c. Water-pump (vert) . . . 20 10
525 15c. Type **286** 15 10
526 40c. House 15 30
527 50c. Stage-coach 35 20
528 60c. Morse key (vert) 30 80
529 80c. "Gem" (paddle-steamer) 30 80

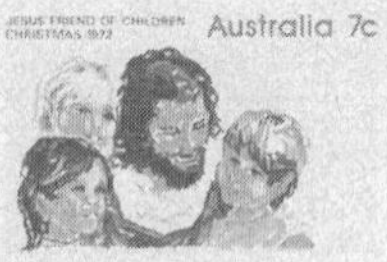

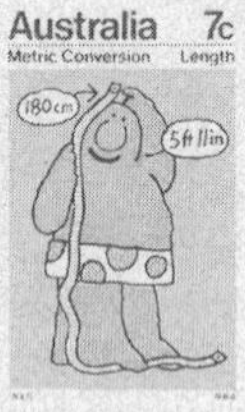

287 Jesus with Children

288 "Length"

1972. Christmas. Multicoloured.

530 7c. Type **287** 30 10
531 35c. Dove and spectrum motif (vert) . . . . 2·75 5·00

1973. Metric Conversion. Multicoloured.

532 7c. Type **288** 40 50
533 7c. "Volume" 40 50
534 7c. "Mass" 40 50
535 7c. "Temperature" (horiz) . . 40 50

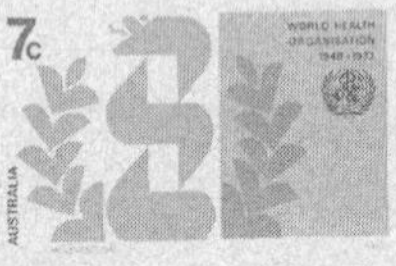

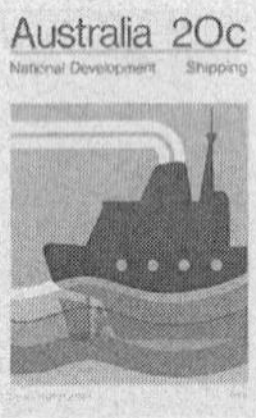

289 Caduceus and Laurel Wreath

291 Shipping

1973. 25th Anniv of World Health Organization.

536 **289** 7c. multicoloured 30 15

1973. Famous Australians (5th series). As T **226**.

537 7c. brown and black 35 45
538 7c. lilac and black 35 45
539 7c. brown and black 35 45
540 7c. lilac and black 35 45

PORTRAITS: No. 537, William Wentworth (statesman and explorer); No. 538, Isaac Issacs (1st Australian-born Governor-General); No. 539, Mary Gilmore (writer); No. 540, Marcus Clarke (author).

1973. National Development (2nd series). Mult.

541 20c. Type **291** . . . . . . 1·50 2·75
542 25c. Iron ore and steel . . . 1·50 2·75
543 30c. Beef roads . . . . . . 1·50 2·75
544 35c. Mapping . . . . 2·00 2·75

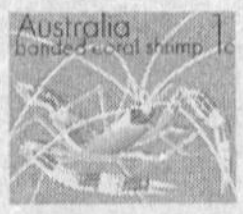

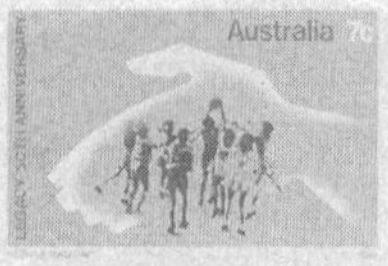

292 Banded Coral Shrimp

293 Children at Play

1973. Marine Life and Gemstones. Multicoloured.

545 1c. Type **292** 10 10
546 2c. Fiddler crab 10 10
547 3c. Coral crab 10 10
548 4c. Mauve stinger 20 55
549 6c. Chrysoprase (vert) . . . 20 20
550 7c. Agate (vert) 30 10
551 8c. Opal (vert) 30 10
552 9c. Rhodonite (vert) 60 15
552a 10c. Star sapphire (vert) . . 60 10

1973. 50th Anniv of Legacy (welfare organization).

553 **293** 7c. brown, red and green 30 10

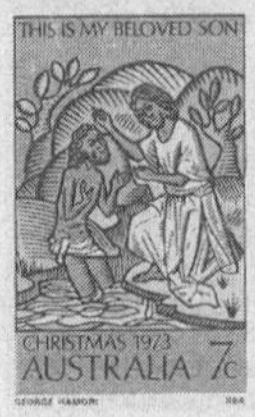

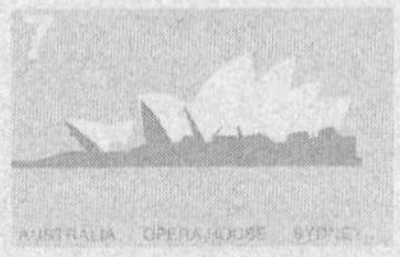

294 John baptizing Jesus

295 Sydney Opera House

1973. Christmas. Multicoloured.

554 7c. Type **294** 35 10
555 30c. The Good Shepherd . . 1·75 2·00

1973. Architecture.

556 **295** 7c. blue and pale blue . . 30 15
557 – 10c. ochre and brown . . 60 70
558 – 40c. grey, brown and black . . . . 1·00 2·25
559 – 50c. multicoloured . . . . 1·00 2·50

DESIGNS—HORIZ: 10c. Buchanan's Hotel, Townsville; 40c. Como House, Melbourne. VERT: 50c. St. James's Church, Sydney.

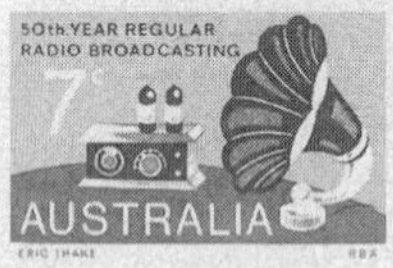

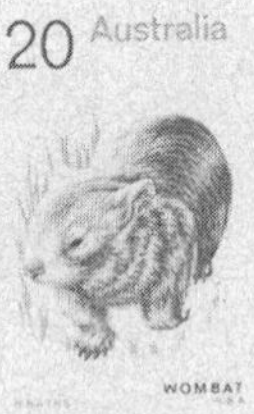

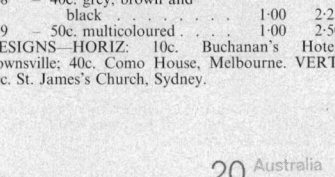

296 Wireless Receiver and Speaker

297 Common Wombat

1973. 50th Anniv of Regular Radio Broadcasting.

560 **296** 7c. blue, red and black . . 15 10

1974. Animals. Multicoloured.

561 20c. Type **297** 25 10
562 25c. Short-nosed echidna (inscr "Spiny Anteater") 60 60
563 30c. Brush-tailed possum . . 40 15
564 75c. Pygmy (inscr "Feather-tailed") glider 80 85

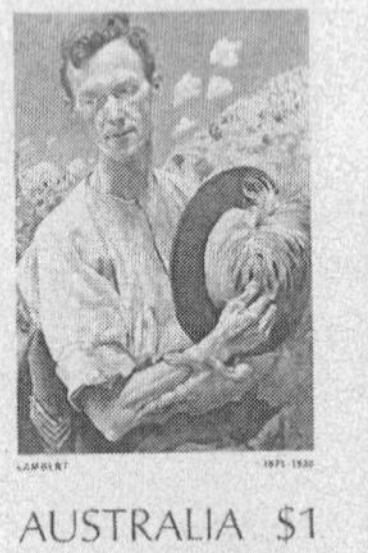

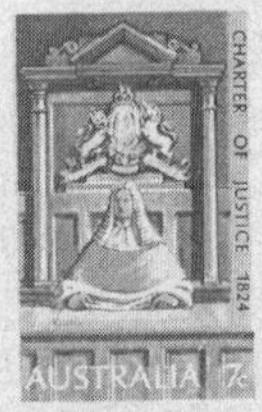

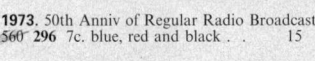

298 "Sergeant of Light Horse" (G. Lambert)

299 Supreme Court Judge

1974. Australian Paintings. Multicoloured.

565 $1 Type **298** . . . . 1·00 10
566 $2 "Red Gums of the Far North" (H. Heysen) . . . 1·50 25
566a $4 "Shearing the Rams" (Tom Roberts) . . . . . 2·25 2·25
567 $5 "McMahon's Point" (Sir Arthur Streeton) . . . . 6·00 2·25
567a $10 "Coming South" (Tom Roberts) . . . . 7·50 3·50

The $2 and $4 are horiz.

1974. 150th Anniv of Australia's Third Charter of Justice.

568 **299** 7c. multicoloured 20 10

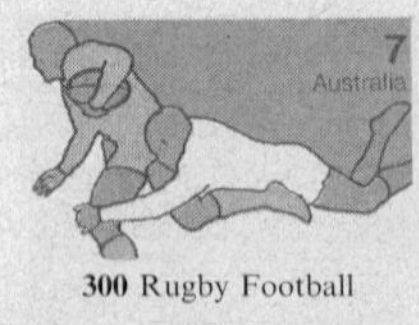

300 Rugby Football

1974. Non-Olympic Sports. Multicoloured.

569 7c. Type **300** 40 40
570 7c. Bowls 40 40
571 7c. Australian football (vert) 40 40
572 7c. Cricket (vert) 40 40
573 7c. Golf (vert) 40 40
574 7c. Surfing (vert) 40 40
575 7c. Tennis (vert) 40 40

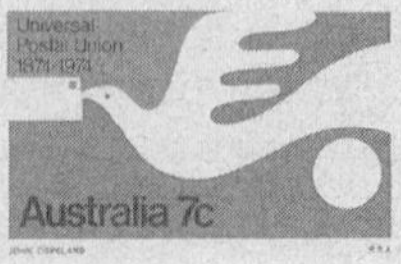

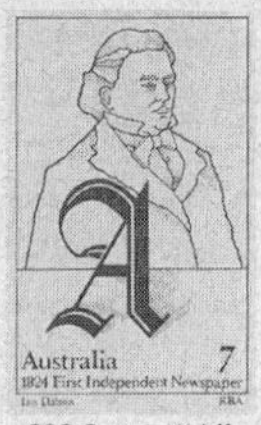

301 "Transport of Mails"

302 Letter "A" and W. C. Wentworth (co-founder)

1974. Centenary of U.P.U. Multicoloured.

576 7c. Type **301** 40 20
577 30c. Three-part version of T **301** (vert) . . . . . 85 1·90

1974. 150th Anniv of First Independent Newspaper, "The Australian".

578 **302** 7c. black and brown . . . 40 40

1974. No. 551 surch.

579 9c. on 8c. multicoloured . . . 15 15

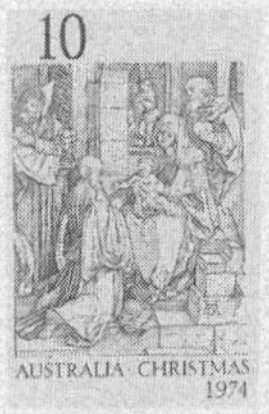

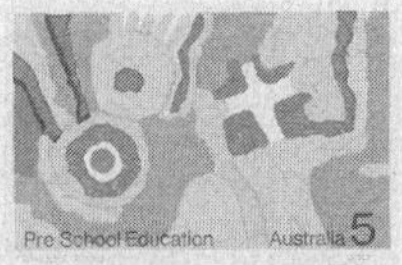

304 "The Adoration of the Magi"

305 "Pre-school Education"

1974. Christmas. Woodcuts by Durer.

580 **304** 10c. black on cream . . . 25 10
581 – 35c. black on cream . . . 80 1·00

DESIGN: 35c. "The Flight into Egypt".

1974. Education in Australia. Multicoloured.

582 5c. Type **305** 25 40
583 11c. "Correspondence Schools" 25 30
584 15c. "Science Education" . . 40 40
585 60c. "Advanced Education" (vert) . . . . 50 1·75

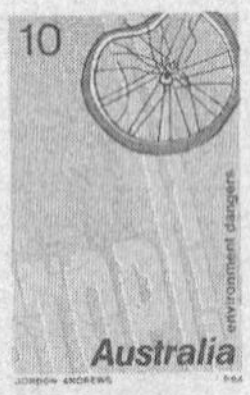

306 "Road Safety"

307 Australian Women's Year Emblem

1975. Environment Dangers. Multicoloured.

586 10c. Type **306** 50 50
587 10c. "Pollution" (horiz) . . . 50 50
588 10c. "Bush Fires" (horiz) . . 50 50

1975. International Women's Year.

589 **307** 10c. blue, green and violet 20 15

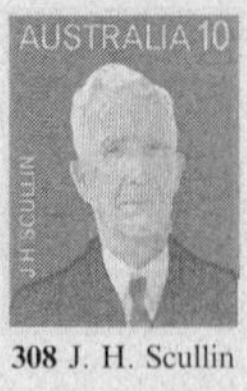

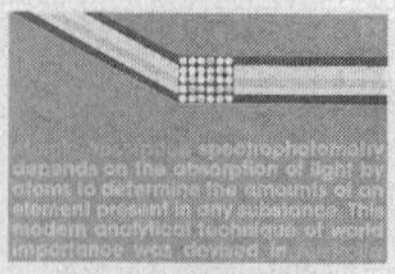

308 J. H. Scullin

309 Atomic Absorption Spectrophotometry

1975. Famous Australians (6th series). Prime Ministers. Multicoloured.

590 10c. Type **308** 25 35
591 10c. J. A. Lyons 25 35
592 10c. Earle Page 25 35
593 10c. Arthur Fadden 25 35
594 10c. John Curtin 25 35
595 10c. J. B. Chifley 25 35

1975. Scientific Development. Multicoloured.

596 11c. Type **309** 60 50
597 24c. Radio astronomy . . . 1·00 1·50
598 33c. Immunology . . . . . 1·00 1·50
599 48c. Oceanography . . . . 1·25 2·75

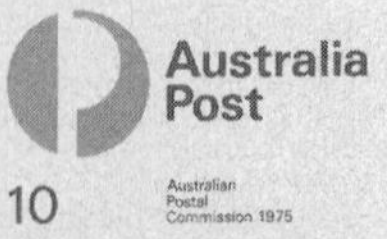

310 Logo of Australian Postal Commission

1975. Inauguration of Australian Postal and Telecommunications Commissions.

600	**310**	10c. black, red and grey	25	10
601		— 10c. black, orange and grey	25	10

DESIGN: No. 601, Logo of Australian Telecommunications Commission.

600/601 ALSO 15×14

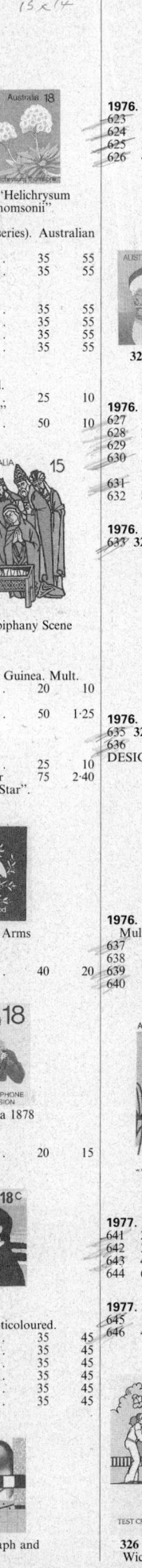

311 Edith Cowan   **312** "Helichrysum thomsonii".

1975. Famous Australians (7th series). Australian
Women. Multicoloured.

602	10c. Type **311**	35	55
603	10c. Louisa Lawson	35	55
604	10c. "Henry Richardson" (pen name of Ethel Richardson)	35	55
605	10c. Catherine Spence	35	55
606a	10c. Constance Stone	35	55
607	10c. Truganini	35	55

1975. Wild Flowers. Multicoloured.

608	18c. Type **312**	25	10
609	45c. "Callistemon teretifolius" (horiz)	50	10

313 "Tambaran" House and Sydney Opera House   **314** Epiphany Scene

1975. Independence of Papua New Guinea. Mult.

610	18c. Type **313**	20	10
611	25c. "Freedom" (bird in flight) (horiz)	50	1·25

1975. Christmas.

612	**314** 15c. multicoloured	25	10
613	— 45c. violet, blue and silver	75	2·40

DESIGN—HORIZ: 45c. "Shining Star".

315 Australian Coat of Arms

1976. 75th Anniv of Nationhood.

614	**315** 18c. multicoloured	40	20

316 Telephone-user, circa 1878

1976. Centenary of Telephone.

615	**316** 18c. multicoloured	20	15

317 John Oxley

1976. 19th Century Explorers. Multicoloured.

616	18c. Type **317**	35	45
617	18c. Hume and Hovell	35	45
618	18c. John Forrest	35	45
619	18c. Ernest Giles	35	45
620	18c. William Gosse	35	45
621	18c. Peter Warburton	35	45

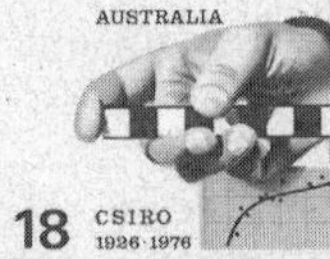

318 Measuring Stick, Graph and Computer Tape

1976. 50th Anniv of Commonwealth Scientific and
Industrial Research Organization.

622	**318**	18c. multicoloured	20	15

319 Football

1976. Olympic Games, Montreal. Multicoloured.

623	18c. Type **319**	20	20
624	18c. Gymnastics (vert)	20	20
625	25c. Diving (vert)	35	80
626	40c. Cycling	90	1·25

320 Richmond Bridge, Tasmania    **321** Blamire Young (designer of first Australian stamp)

1976. Australian Scenes. Multicoloured.

627	5c. Type **320**	20	10
628	25c. Broken Bay, N.S.W	65	20
629	35c. Wittenoom Gorge, W.A	45	20
630	50c. Mt. Buffalo, Victoria (vert)	90	30
631	70c. Barrier Reef	1·25	1·25
632	85c. Ayers Rock, N.T	1·25	1·75

1976. National Stamp Week.

633	**321**	18c. multicoloured	15	15

322 "Virgin and Child" (detail, Simone Contarini)

1976. Christmas.

635	**322** 15c. mauve and blue	20	10
636	— 45c. multicoloured	50	90

DESIGN: 45c. Toy koala bear and decorations.

323 John Gould

1976. Famous Australians. (8th series). Scientists.
Multicoloured.

637	18c. Type **323**	35	50
638	18c. Thomas Laby	35	50
639	18c. Sir Baldwin Spencer	35	50
640	18c. Griffith Taylor	35	50

324 "Music"    **325** Queen Elizabeth II

1977. Performing Arts. Multicoloured.

641	20c. Type **324**	20	25
642	30c. Drama	25	35
643	40c. Dance	35	40
644	60c. Opera	1·00	1·75

1977. Silver Jubilee. Multicoloured.

645	18c. Type **325**	20	10
646	45c. The Queen and Duke of Edinburgh	50	80

326 Fielder and Wicket Keeper    **327** Parliament House

1977. Centenary of Australia-England Test Cricket.

647	18c. Type **326**	50	65
648	18c. Umpire and batsman	50	65
649	18c. Fielders	50	65
650	18c. Batsman and umpire	50	65
651	18c. Bowler and fielder	50	65
652	45c. Batsman facing bowler	65	1·50

1977. 50th Anniv of Opening of Parliament House,
Canberra.

653	**327**	18c. multicoloured	15	10

328 Trade Union Workers    **329** Surfing Santa

1977. 50th Anniv of Australian Council of Trade
Unions.

654	**328**	18c. multicoloured	15	10

1977. Christmas. Multicoloured.

655	15c. Type **329**	25	10
656	45c. Madonna and Child	75	1·25

330 National Flag

1978. Australia Day.

657	**330**	18c. multicoloured	20	15

331 Harry Hawker and Sopwith Atlantic

1978. Early Australian Aviators. Multicoloured.

658	18c. Type **331**	40	50
659	18c. Bert Hinkler and Avro Type 581 Avian	40	50
660	18c. Sir Charles Kingsford Smith and "Southern Cross"	40	50
661	18c. Charles Ulm and "Southern Cross"	40	50

332 Piper PA-31 Navajo landing at Station Airstrip

1978. 50th Anniv of Royal Flying Doctor Service.

663	**332**	18c. multicoloured	20	15

333 Illawarra Flame Tree    **334** Sturt's Desert Rose and Map

1978. Trees. Multicoloured.

664	18c. Type **333**	20	15
665	25c. Ghost gum	35	1·10
666	40c. Grass tree	45	1·75
667	45c. Cootamundra wattle	45	70

1978. Establishment of State Government for the
Northern Territory.

668	**334**	18c. multicoloured	20	15

335 Hooded Plover    **336** 1928 3d. National Stamp Exhibition Commemorative

1978. Birds (1st series). Multicoloured.

669	1c. Spotted-sided ("Zebra") finch	10	20
670	2c. Crimson finch	10	20
671	5c. Type **335**	50	10
672	15c. Forest kingfisher (vert)	20	20
673	20c. Australian dabchick ("Little Grebe")	70	10
674	20c. Yellow robin ("Eastern Yellow Robin")	40	10
675	22c. White-tailed kingfisher (22 × 29 mm)	30	10
676	25c. Masked ("Spur-wing") plover	90	70
677	30c. Pied oystercatcher	1·00	25
678	40c. Variegated ("Lovely") wren (vert)	30	45
679	50c. Flame robin (vert)	70	50
680	55c. Comb-crested jacana ("Lotus-Bird")	1·25	60

See also Nos. 734/40.

1978. 50th Anniv of National Stamp Week, and
National Stamp Exhibition.

694	**336**	20c. multicoloured	15	15

337 "The Madonna and the Child" (after van Eyck)    **338** "Tulloch"

1978. Christmas. Multicoloured.

696	15c. Type **337**	30	10
697	25c. "The Virgin and Child" (Marmion)	45	55
698	55c. "The Holy Family" (del Vaga)	70	90

1978. Horse-racing. Multicoloured.

699	20c. Type **338**	30	10
700	35c. "Bernborough" (vert)	45	85
701	50c. "Phar Lap" (vert)	60	1·25
702	55c. "Peter Pan"	60	1·10

339 Raising the Flag, Sydney Cove, 26 January 1788    **340** "Canberra" (paddle-steamer)

1979. Australia Day.

703	**339**	20c. multicoloured	15	15

1979. Ferries and Murray River Steamers. Mult.

704	20c. Type **340**	35	10
705	35c. "Lady Denman"	60	1·00
706	50c. "Murray River Queen" (paddle-steamer)	80	1·40
707	55c. "Curl Curl" (hydrofoil)	90	1·25

341 Port Campbell, Victoria

1979. National Parks. Multicoloured.

708	20c. Type **341**	25	25
709	20c. Uluru, Northern Territory	25	25
710	20c. Royal, New South Wales	25	25
711	20c. Flinders Ranges, South Australia	25	25
712	20c. Nambung, Western Australia	25	25

713	20c. Girraween, Queensland (vert)	25	25
714	20c. Mount Field, Tasmania (vert)	25	25

342 "Double Fairlie" Type Locomotive, Western Australia

1979. Steam Railways. Multicoloured.

715	20c. Type **342**	30	10
716	35c. Locomotive, Puffing Billy Line, Victoria	60	70
717	50c. Locomotive, Pichi Richi Line, South Australia	70	1·50
718	55c. Locomotive, Zig Zag Railway, New South Wales	80	1·40

343 Symbolic Swan

1979. 150th Anniv of Western Australia.

719	**343** 20c. multicoloured	15	15

344 Children playing on Slide **345** Letters and Parcels

1979. International Year of the Child.

720	**344** 20c. multicoloured	15	10

1979. Christmas. Multicoloured.

721	15c. "Christ's Nativity" (Eastern European icon)	15	10
722	25c. Type **345**	25	65
723	55c. "Madonna and Child" (Buglioni)	40	80

346 Fly-fishing **347** Matthew Flinders

1979. Fishing.

724	**346** 20c. multicoloured	20	10
725	— 35c. blue and violet	35	70
726	— 50c. multicoloured	40	90
727	— 55c. multicoloured	45	85

DESIGNS: 35c. Spinning; 50c. Deep sea game-fishing; 55c. Surf-fishing.

1980. Australia Day.

728	**347** 20c. multicoloured	20	10

348 Dingo

1980. Dogs. Multicoloured.

729	20c. Type **348**	35	10
730	25c. Border collie	35	40
731	35c. Australian terrier	40	70
732	50c. Australian cattle dog	70	1·50
733	55c. Australian kelpie	70	1·25

1980. Birds (2nd series). As T **335**. Multicoloured.

734	10c. Golden-shouldered parrot (vert)	50	10
734b	18c. Spotted catbird (vert)	50	1·25
735	28c. Australian bee eater ("Rainbow Bird") (vert)	50	20
736	35c. Regent bower bird (vert)	35	10
737	45c. Masked wood swallow	40	10
738	60c. Australian king parrot ("King Parrot") (vert)	50	15
739	80c. Rainbow pitta	1·00	75
740	$1 Black-backed magpie ("Western Magpie") (vert)	1·00	10

349 Queen Elizabeth II **350** "Once a jolly Swagman camp'd by a Billabong"

1980. Birthday of Queen Elizabeth II.

741	**349** 22c. multicoloured	30	20

1980. Folklore. "Waltzing Matilda". Multicoloured.

742	22c. Type **350**	30	20
743	22c. "And he sang as he shoved that jumbuck in his tuckerbag"	30	20
744	22c. "Up rode the squatter mounted on his thoroughbred"	30	20
745	22c. "Down came the troopers one, two, three"	30	20
746	22c. "And his ghost may be heard as you pass by that billabong"	30	20

351 High Court Building, Canberra **352** Salvation Army

1980. Opening of High Court Building.

747	**351** 22c. multicoloured	20	20

1980. Community Welfare. Multicoloured.

748	22c. Type **352**	40	40
749	22c. St. Vincent de Paul Society (vert)	40	40
750	22c. Meals on Wheels (vert)	40	40
751	22c. "Life. Be in it"	40	40

353 Postbox, c. 1900 **354** "Holy Family" (painting, Prospero Fontana)

1980. National Stamp Week. Multicoloured.

752	22c. Type **353**	30	20
753	22c. Postman, facing left	30	20
754	22c. Mail van	30	20
755	22c. Postman, facing right	30	20
756	22c. Postman and postbox	30	20

1980. Christmas. Multicoloured.

758	15c. "The Virgin Enthroned" (Justin O'Brien) (detail)	15	10
759	28c. Type **354**	25	40
760	60c. "Madonna and Child" (sculpture by School of M. Zuern)	50	1·10

355 Commonwealth Aircraft Factory Wackett, 1941

1980. Australian Aircraft. Multicoloured.

761	22c. Type **355**	30	10
762	40c. Commonwealth Aircraft Factory Winjeel, 1955	50	75
763	45c. Commonwealth Aircraft Factory Boomerang, 1944	50	85
764	60c. Government Aircraft Factory Nomad, 1975	65	1·40

356 Flag in shape of Australia

1981. Australia Day.

765	**356** 22c. multicoloured	20	20

357 Caricature of Darby Munro (jockey) **358** 1931 Kingsford Smith's Flights 6d. Commemorative

1981. Sporting Personalities. Caricatures. Mult.

766	22c. Type **357**	25	10
767	35c. Victor Trumper (cricket)	55	60
768	55c. Sir Norman Brookes (tennis)	60	1·00
769	60c. Walter Lindrum (billiards)	60	1·25

1981. 50th Anniversary of Official Australia-U.K. Airmail Service.

770	**358** 22c. lilac, red and blue	20	10
771	— 60c. lilac, red and blue	60	90

DESIGN—HORIZ: 60c. As T **358**, but format changed.

359 Apex Emblem and Map of Australia

1981. 50th Anniv of Apex (young men's service club).

772	**359** 22c. multicoloured	20	20

360 Queen's Personal Standard for Australia **361** "Licence Inspected"

1981. Birthday of Queen Elizabeth II.

773	**360** 22c. multicoloured	20	20

1981. Gold Rush Era. Sketches by S. T. Gill. Mult.

774	22c. Type **361**	20	25
775	22c. "Puddling"	20	25
776	22c. "Quality of washing stuff"	20	25
777	22c. "On route to deposit gold"	20	25

362 "On the Wallaby Track" (Fred McCubbin)

1981. Paintings. Multicoloured.

778	$2 Type **362**	1·50	30
779	$5 "A Holiday at Mentone, 1888" (Charles Conder)	4·75	1·25

363 Thylacine **363a** Blue Mountain Tree Frog

363b "Papilio ulysses" (butterfly)

1981. Wildlife. Multicoloured.

781	1c. Lace monitor	10	20
782	3c. Corroboree frog	10	10
783	4c. Regent skipper (butterfly) (vert)	55	70
784	5c. Queensland hairy-nosed wombat (vert)	10	10
785	10c. Cairns birdwing (butterfly) (vert)	60	10
786	15c. Eastern snake-necked tortoise	80	60
787	20c. MacLeay's swallowtail (butterfly) (vert)	80	35
788	24c. Type **363**	45	10
789	25c. Common rabbit-bandicoot (inscr "Greater Bilby") (vert)	40	70
790	27c. Type **363a**	1·00	20
791	27c. Type **363b**	1·00	30
792	30c. Bridle nail-tailed wallaby (vert)	70	15
792a	30c. Chlorinda hairstreak (butterfly) (vert)	1·00	20
793	35c. Blue tiger (butterfly) (vert)	1·00	15
794	40c. Smooth knob-tailed gecko	45	10
795	45c. Big greasy (butterfly) (vert)	1·00	15
796	50c. Leadbeater's possum	50	10
797	55c. Stick-nest rat (vert)	50	30
798	60c. Wood white (butterfly) (vert)	1·10	30
799	65c. Yellow-faced whip snake	1·50	1·00
800	70c. Crucifix toad	65	1·25
801	75c. Eastern water dragon	1·25	70
802	80c. Amaryllis azure (butterfly) (vert)	1·40	1·75
803	85c. Centralian blue-tongued lizard	1·10	1·25
804	90c. Freshwater crocodile	1·60	1·25
805	95c. Thorny devil	1·25	1·75
806	$1 Sword-grass brown (butterfly) (vert)	1·40	30

364 Prince Charles and Lady Diana Spencer **365** "Cortinarius cinnabarinus"

1981. Royal Wedding.

821	**364** 24c. multicoloured	20	10
822	60c. multicoloured	55	1·00

1981. Australian Fungi. Multicoloured.

823	24c. Type **365**	25	10
824	35c. "Coprinus comatus"	45	1·10
825	55c. "Armillaria luteobubalina"	60	1·25
826	60c. "Cortinarius austro-venetus"	70	1·40

366 Disabled People playing Basketball **367** "Christmas Bush for His Adorning"

1981. International Year for Disabled Persons.

827	**366** 24c. multicoloured	20	20

1981. Christmas. Scenes and Verses from Carols by W. James and J. Wheeler. Multicoloured.

828	18c. Type **367**	25	10
829	30c. "The Silver Stars are in the Sky"	35	25
830	60c. "Noeltime"	60	85

368 Globe depicting Australia **369** "Ragamuffin" ocean racing yacht

1981. Commonwealth Heads of Government Meeting, Melbourne.

831	**368** 24c. black, blue and gold	20	10
832	60c. black, blue and silver	65	75

1981. Yachts. Multicoloured.

833	24c. Type **369**	25	10
834	35c. "Sharpie"	40	55
835	55c. "12 Metre"	55	1·00
836	60c. "Sabot"	80	1·25

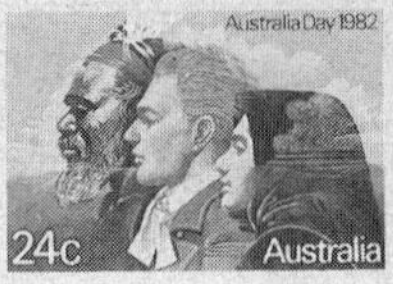

370 Aborigine, Governor Phillip (founder of N.S.W., 1788) and Post World War II Migrant

1982. Australia Day. "Three Great Waves of Migration".
837 **370** 24c. multicoloured 35 25

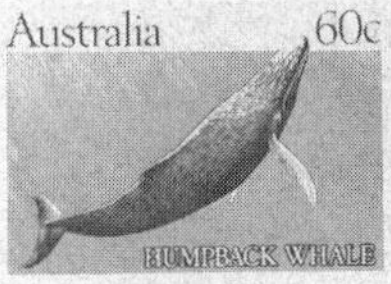

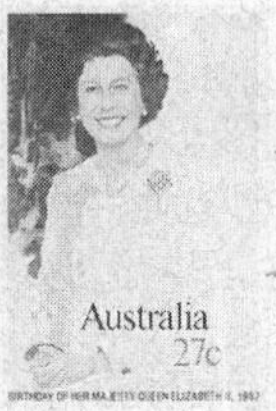

371 Humpback Whale **372** Queen Elizabeth II

1982. Whales. Multicoloured.
838 24c. Sperm whale 30 10
839 35c. Black (inscr "Southern") right whale (vert) 40 60
840 55c. Blue whale (vert) . . . . 60 1·50
841 60c. Type **371** . . . . 70 1·50

1982. Birthday of Queen Elizabeth II.
842 **372** 27c. multicoloured 35 15

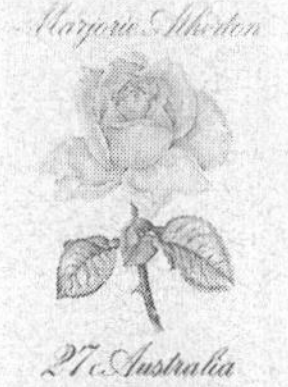

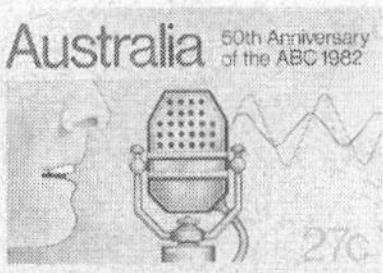

373 "Marjorie Atherton" **374** Radio Announcer and 1930-style Microphone

1982. Roses. Multicoloured.
843 27c. Type **373** 30 15
844 40c. "Imp" 50 60
845 65c. "Minnie Watson" . . . 1·00 1·75
846 75c. "Satellite" . . . . 1·00 1·25

1982. 50th Anniv of ABC (Australian Broadcasting Commission). Multicoloured.
847 27c. Type **374** 40 65
848 27c. ABC logo 40 65

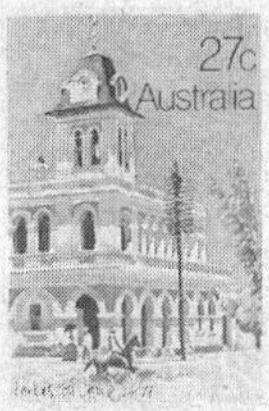

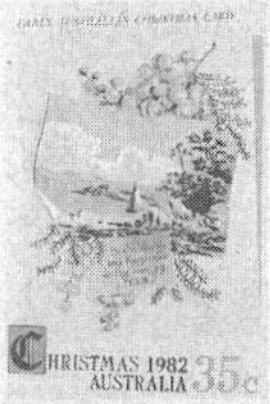

375 Forbes Post Office **376** Early Australian Christmas Card

1982. Historic Australian Post Offices. Multicoloured.
849 27c. Type **375** 40 40
850 27c. Flemington Post Office 40 40
851 27c. Rockhampton Post Office 40 40
852 27c. Kingston S. E. Post Office (horiz) 40 40
853 27c. York Post Office (horiz) 40 40
854 27c. Launceston Post Office 40 40
855 27c. Old Post and Telegraph Station, Alice Springs (horiz) 40 40

1982. Christmas. Multicoloured.
856 21c. Bushman's Hotel with Cobb's coach arriving (horiz) 25 10
857 35c. Type **376** 40 60
858 75c. Little girl offering Christmas pudding to swagman . . . . 60 1·40

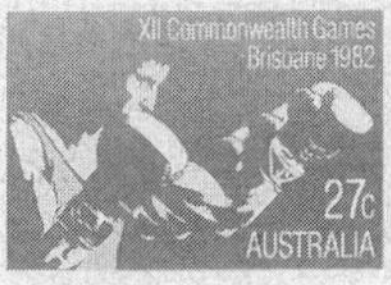

377 Boxing

1982. Commonwealth Games, Brisbane.
859 **377** 27c. stone, yellow and red 25 25
860 – 27c. yellow, stone and green 25 25
861 – 27c. stone, yellow and brown 25 25
862 – 75c. multicoloured . . . . 60 1·00

DESIGNS: No. 860, Archery; No. 861, Weight-lifting; No. 862, Pole-vaulting.

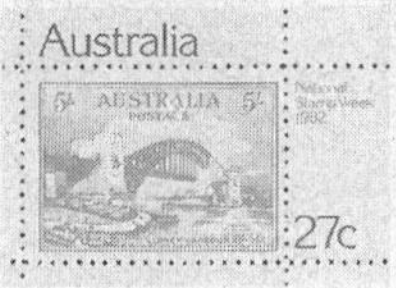

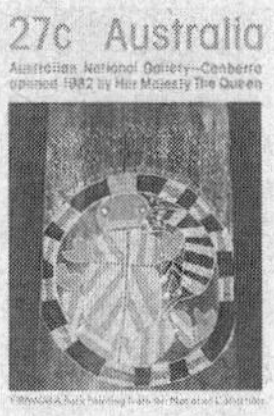

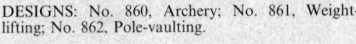

378 Sydney Harbour Bridge 5s. Stamp of 1932 **379** "Yirawala" Bark Painting

1982. National Stamp Week.
864 **378** 27c. multicoloured 35 30

1982. Opening of Australian National Gallery.
865 **379** 27c. multicoloured 30 25

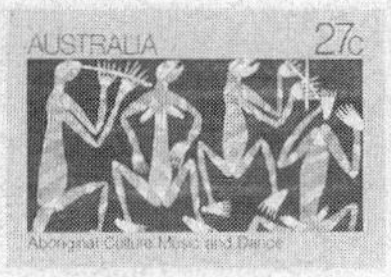

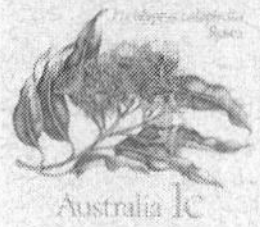

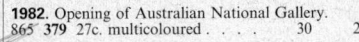

380 Mimi Spirits Dancing **381** "Eucalyptus calophylla" "Rosea"

1982. Aboriginal Culture. Music and Dance.
866 **380** 27c. multicoloured 20 10
867 – 40c. multicoloured 30 60
868 – 65c. multicoloured . . . . 45 1·00
869 – 75c. multicoloured . . . . 50 1·00

DESIGN: 40c. to 75c. Aboriginal bark paintings of Mimi Spirits.

1982. Eucalyptus Flowers. Multicoloured.
870 1c. Type **381** 10 30
871 2c. "Eucalyptus casia" . . . 10 30
872 3c. "Eucalyptus ficifolia" . . 1·25 1·75
873 10c. "Eucalyptus globulus" 1·25 1·75
874 27c. "Eucalyptus forrestiana" 30 40

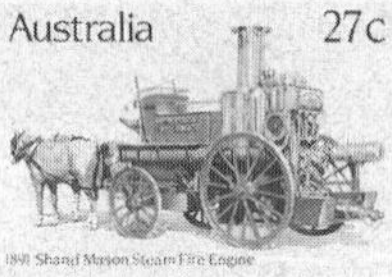

382 Shand Mason Steam Fire Engine, 1891

1983. Historic Fire Engines. Multicoloured.
875 27c. Type **382** 35 10
876 40c. Hotchkiss fire engine, 1914 . . . . 45 75
877 65c. Ahrens-Fox PS2 fire engine, 1929 . . . . 70 1·50
878 75c. Merryweather manual fire appliance, 1851 . . . . 70 1·40

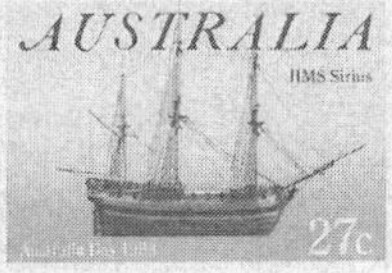

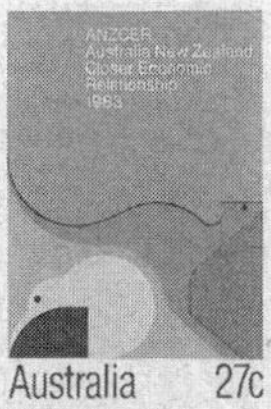

383 H.M.S. "Sirius" **384** Stylised Kangaroo and Kiwi

1983. Australia Day. Multicoloured.
879 27c. Type **383** 40 65
880 27c. H.M.S. "Supply" . . . 40 65

1983. Closer Economic Relationship Agreement with New Zealand.
881 **384** 27c. multicoloured 30 30

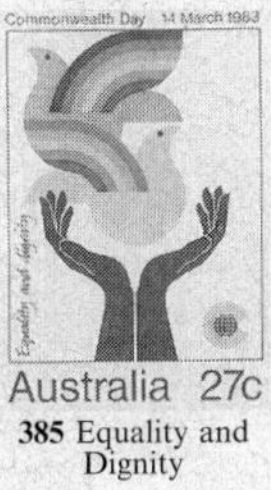

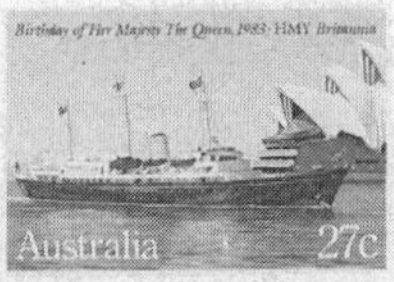

385 Equality and Dignity **386** R.Y. "Britannia" passing Sydney Opera House

1983. Commonwealth Day. Multicoloured.
882 27c. Type **385** 20 25
883 27c. Liberty and Freedom . . 20 25
884 27c. Social Justice and Co-operation 20 25
885 75c. Peace and Harmony . . 50 1·50

1983. Birthday of Queen Elizabeth II.
886 **386** 27c. multicoloured 45 30

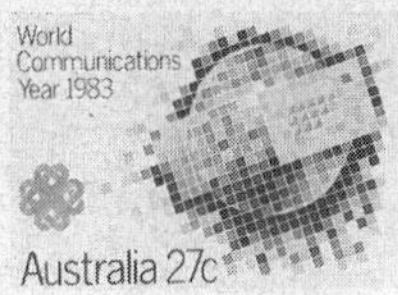

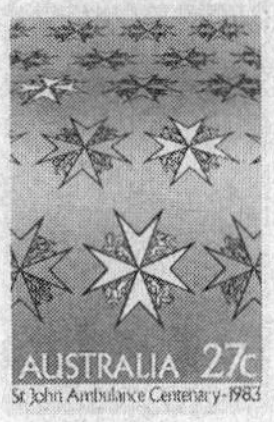

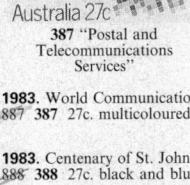

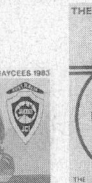

387 "Postal and Telecommunications Services" **388** Badge of the Order of St. John

1983. World Communications Year.
887 **387** 27c. multicoloured 30 30

1983. Centenary of St. John Ambulance in Australia.
888 **388** 27c. black and blue . . . 35 30

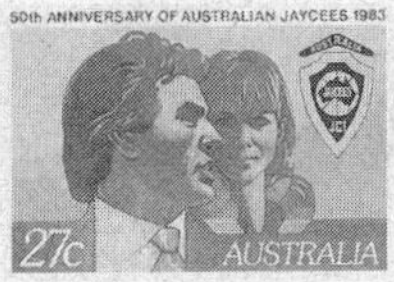

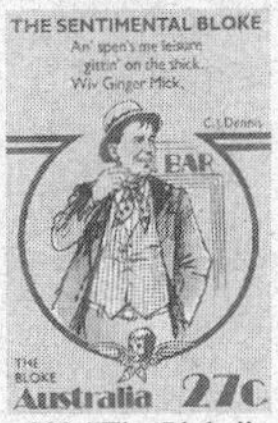

389 Jaycee Members and Badge **390** "The Bloke"

1983. 50th Anniv of Australian Jaycees.
889 **389** 27c. multicoloured 30 30

1983. Folklore. "The Sentimental Bloke" (humorous poem by C. J. Dennis). Multicoloured.
890 27c. Type **390** 40 50
891 27c. "Doreen—The Intro" . . 40 50
892 27c. "The Stror' at Coot" . . 40 50
893 27c. "Hitched" 40 50
894 27c. "The Mooch o' Life" . . 40 50

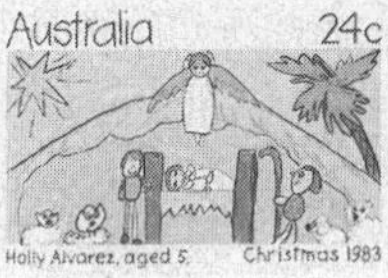

391 Nativity Scene

1983. Christmas. Children's Paintings. Mult.
895 24c. Type **391** 20 10
896 35c. Kookaburra 35 45
897 85c. Father Christmas in sleigh over beach . . . . . 90 1·40

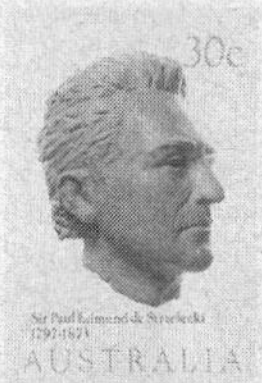

392 Sir Paul Edmund de Strzelecki

1983. Explorers of Australia. Multicoloured.
898 30c. Type **392** 35 40
899 30c. Ludwig Leichhardt . . . 35 40
900 30c. William John Wills and Robert O'Hara Burke . . 35 40
901 30c. Alexander Forrest . . . 35 40

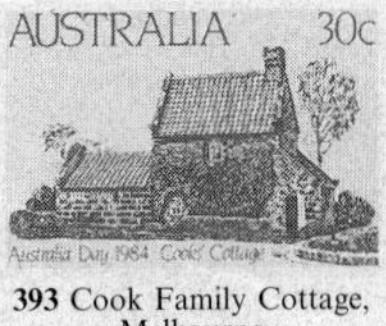

393 Cook Family Cottage, Melbourne

1984. Australia Day.
902 **393** 30c. black and stone . . . 30 35

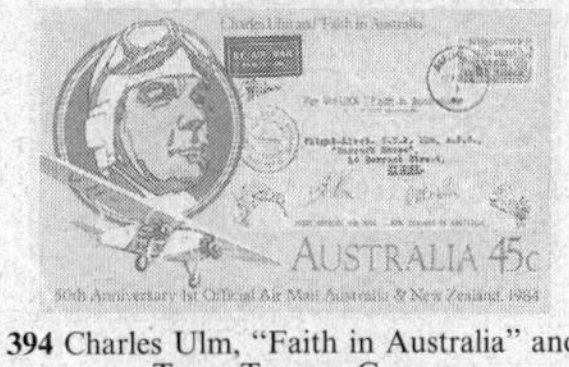

394 Charles Ulm, "Faith in Australia" and Trans-Tasman Cover

1984. 50th Anniv of First Official Airmail Flights. New Zealand–Australia and Australia–Papua New Guinea. Multicoloured.
903 45c. Type **394** . . . . 1·00 1·40
904 45c. As Type **394** but showing flown cover to Papua New Guinea . . . . 1·00 1·40

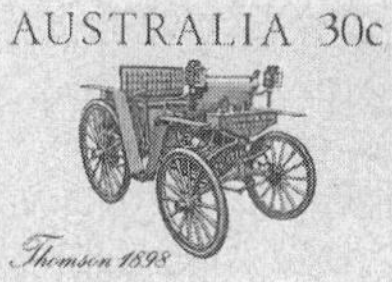

395 Thomson "Steamer", 1898

1984. Veteran and Vintage Cars. Multicoloured.
905 30c. Type **395** 50 60
906 30c. Tarrant, 1906 . . . . . 50 60
907 30c. Gordon & Co "Australian Six", 1919 . . 50 60
908 30c. Summit, 1923 . . . . . 50 60
909 30c. Chic, 1924 . . . . . . 50 60

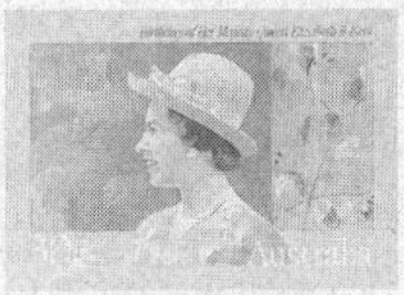

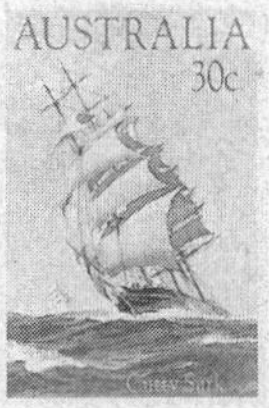

396 Queen Elizabeth II **397** "Cutty Sark"

1984. Birthday of Queen Elizabeth II.
910 **396** 30c. multicoloured 30 35

1984. Clipper Ships. Multicoloured.
911 30c. Type **397** 35 25
912 45c. "Orient" (horiz) 50 80
913 75c. "Sobraon" (horiz) . . . 70 1·75
914 85c. "Thermopylae" . . . . 70 1·50

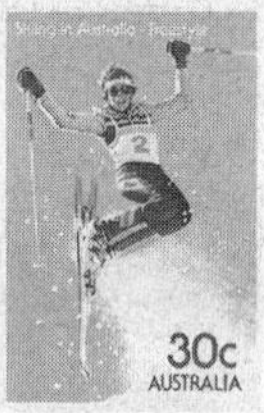

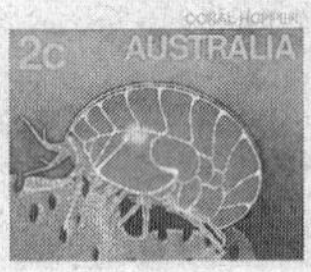

398 Freestyle **399** Coral Hopper

1984. Skiing. Multicoloured.
915 30c. Type **398** 40 45
916 30c. Downhill racer 40 45
917 30c. Slalom (horiz) 40 45
918 30c. Nordic (horiz) 40 45

1984. Marine Life. Multicoloured.
919 2c. Type **399** 10 30
920 3c. Jimble 20 30
921 5c. Tasselled frogfish ("Anglerfish") 15 10
922 10c. Rough stonefish 50 20
923 20c. Red handfish 65 40
924 25c. Orange-lipped cowrie . . 45 40
925 30c. Choat's wrasse 45 40
926 33c. Leafy seadragon 65 10
927 40c. Red velvetfish . . . . . 85 1·25
928 45c. Textile or cloth of gold cone . . . . 1·00 50
929 50c. Clown surgeonfish . . . 80 50
930 55c. Bennet's nudibranch . . 80 50
931 60c. Zebra lionfish . . . . . 1·00 70
932 65c. Banded stingray . . . . 1·25 1·50
933 70c. Southern blue-ringed octopus . . . . 1·25 1·50
934 80c. Pineconefish ("Pineapple fish") . . . . 1·25 1·25
935 85c. Royal angelfish 90 70
936 90c. Crab-eyed goby . . . . 1·60 75
937 $1 Crown of thorns starfish 1·50 80

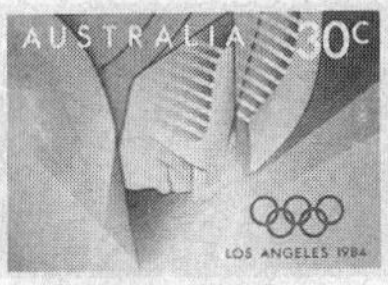

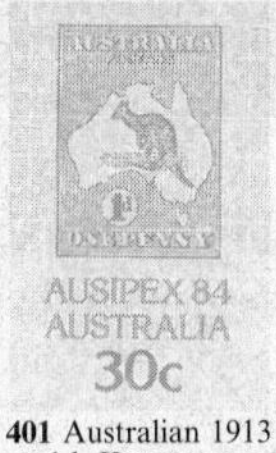

400 Before the Event **401** Australian 1913 1d. Kangaroo Stamp

1984. Olympic Games, Los Angeles. Multicoloured.
941 30c. Type **400** 40 40
942 30c. During the event 40 40
943 30c. After the event (vert) . . 40 40

1984. "Ausipex '84" International Stamp Exhibition, Melbourne.
944 **401** 30c. multicoloured 35 30

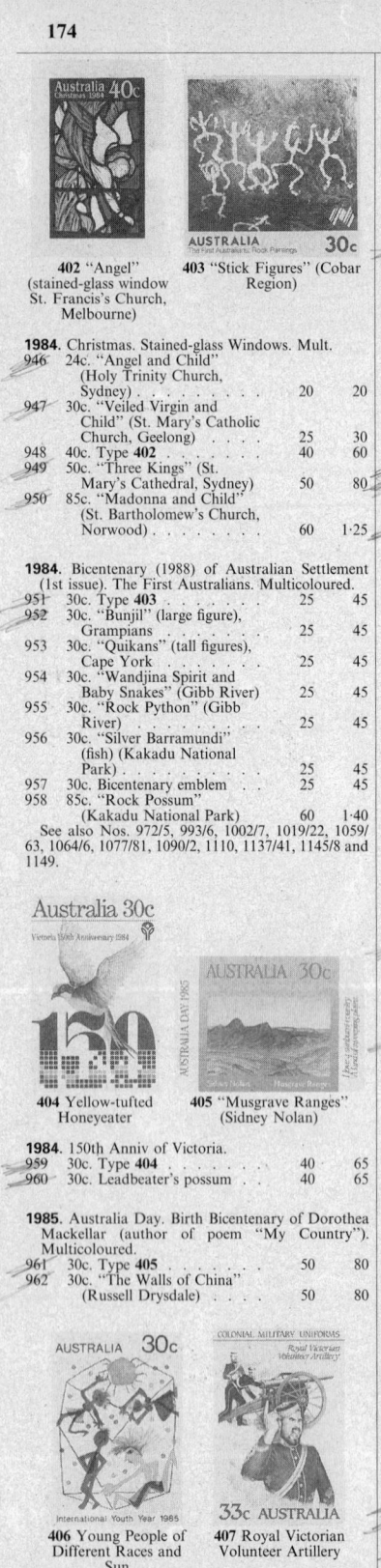

402 "Angel"
(stained-glass window
St. Francis's Church,
Melbourne)

403 "Stick Figures" (Cobar
Region)

1984. Christmas. Stained-glass Windows. Mult.

946	24c. "Angel and Child" (Holy Trinity Church, Sydney)	20	20
947	30c. "Veiled Virgin and Child" (St. Mary's Catholic Church, Geelong)	25	30
948	40c. Type **402**	40	60
949	50c. "Three Kings" (St. Mary's Cathedral, Sydney)	50	80
950	85c. "Madonna and Child" (St. Bartholomew's Church, Norwood)	60	1·25

1984. Bicentenary (1988) of Australian Settlement (1st issue). The First Australians. Multicoloured.

951	30c. Type **403**	25	45
952	30c. "Bunjil" (large figure), Grampians	25	45
953	30c. "Quikans" (tall figures), Cape York	25	45
954	30c. "Wandjina Spirit and Baby Snakes" (Gibb River)	25	45
955	30c. "Rock Python" (Gibb River)	25	45
956	30c. "Silver Barramundi" (fish) (Kakadu National Park)	25	45
957	30c. Bicentenary emblem	25	45
958	85c. "Rock Possum" (Kakadu National Park)	60	1·40

See also Nos. 972/5, 993/6, 1002/7, 1019/22, 1059/63, 1064/6, 1077/81, 1090/2, 1110, 1137/41, 1145/8 and 1149.

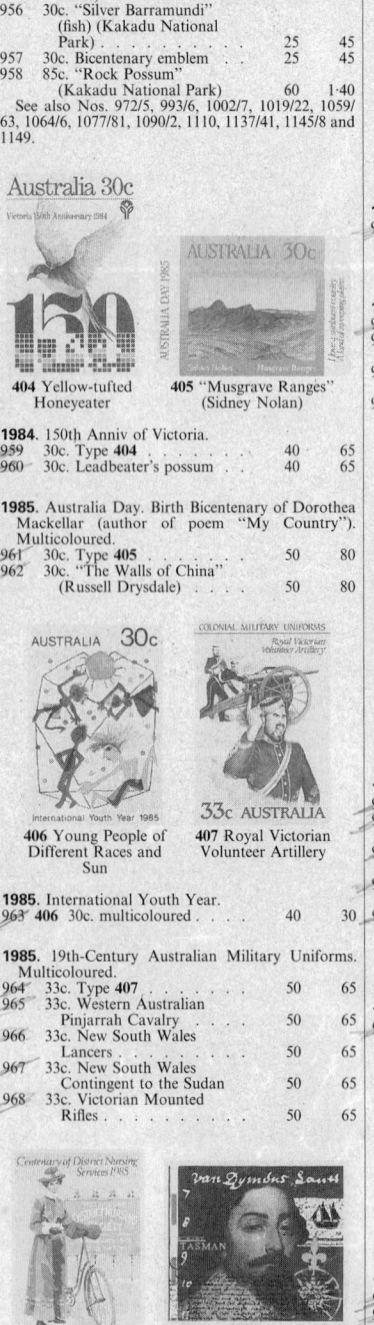

404 Yellow-tufted
Honeyeater

405 "Musgrave Ranges"
(Sidney Nolan)

1984. 150th Anniv of Victoria.

959	30c. Type **404**	40	65
960	30c. Leadbeater's possum	40	65

1985. Australia Day. Birth Bicentenary of Dorothea Mackellar (author of poem "My Country"). Multicoloured.

961	30c. Type **405**	50	80
962	30c. "The Walls of China" (Russell Drysdale)	50	80

406 Young People of
Different Races and
Sun

407 Royal Victorian
Volunteer Artillery

1985. International Youth Year.

963	**406** 30c. multicoloured	40	30

1985. 19th-Century Australian Military Uniforms. Multicoloured.

964	33c. Type **407**	50	65
965	33c. Western Australian Pinjarrah Cavalry	50	65
966	33c. New South Wales Lancers	50	65
967	33c. New South Wales Contingent to the Sudan	50	65
968	33c. Victorian Mounted Rifles	50	65

408 District Nurse of
early 1900s

410 Abel Tasman and
Journal Entry

409 Sulphur-crested Cockatoos

1985. Centenary of District Nursing Services.

969	**408** 33c. multicoloured	45	35

1985. Multicoloured, background colour given.

970	**409** 1c. flesh	1·50	2·25
971	33c. turquoise	45	55

1985. Bicentenary (1988) of Australian Settlement (2nd issue). Navigators. Multicoloured.

972	33c. Type **410**	45	35
973	33c. Dirk Hartog's "Eendracht" (detail, Aert Anthonisz)	45	35
974	33c. "William Dampier" (detail, T. Murray)	45	35
975	90c. Globe and hand with extract from Dampier's journal	1·00	2·25

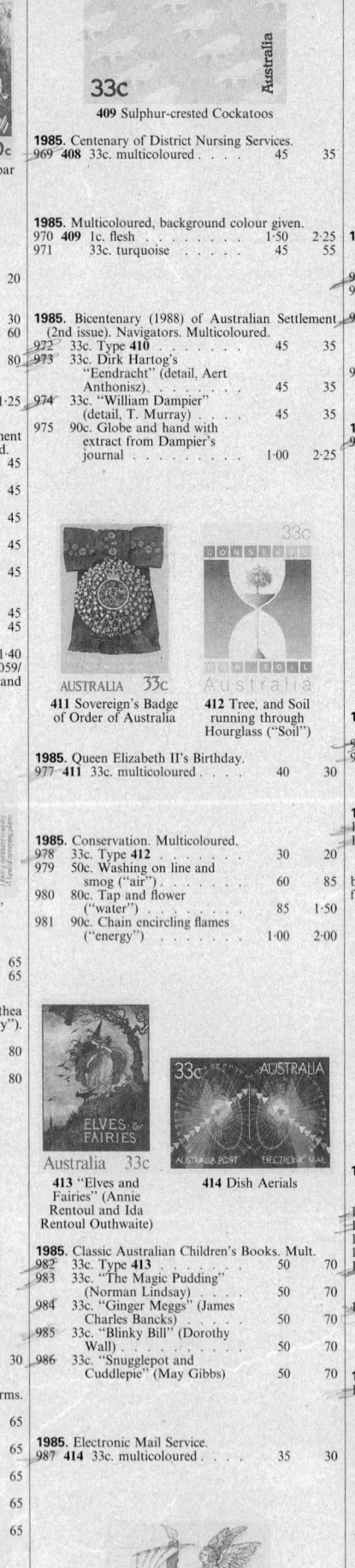

411 Sovereign's Badge
of Order of Australia

412 Tree, and Soil
running through
Hourglass ("Soil")

1985. Queen Elizabeth II's Birthday.

977	**411** 33c. multicoloured	40	30

1985. Conservation. Multicoloured.

978	33c. Type **412**	30	20
979	50c. Washing on line and smog ("air")	60	85
980	80c. Tap and flower ("water")	85	1·50
981	90c. Chain encircling flames ("energy")	1·00	2·00

413 "Elves and
Fairies" (Annie
Rentoul and Ida
Rentoul Outhwaite)

414 Dish Aerials

1985. Classic Australian Children's Books. Mult.

982	33c. Type **413**	50	70
983	33c. "The Magic Pudding" (Norman Lindsay)	50	70
984	33c. "Ginger Meggs" (James Charles Bancks)	50	70
985	33c. "Blinky Bill" (Dorothy Wall)	50	70
986	33c. "Snugglepot and Cuddlepie" (May Gibbs)	50	70

1985. Electronic Mail Service.

987	**414** 33c. multicoloured	35	30

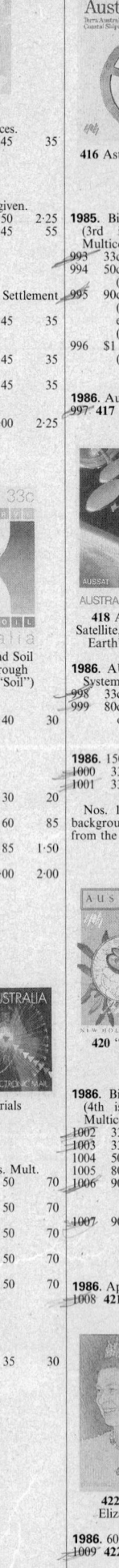

415 Angel in Sailing Ship

1985. Christmas. Multicoloured.

988	27c. Angel with holly wings	25	15
989	33c. Angel with bells	30	15
990	45c. Type **415**	40	30
991	55c. Angel with star	50	65
992	90c. Angel with Christmas tree bauble	75	1·50

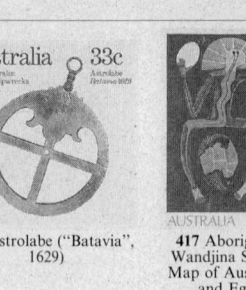
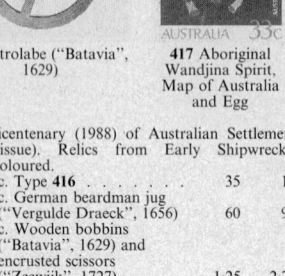

416 Astrolabe ("Batavia",
1629)

417 Aboriginal
Wandjina Spirit,
Map of Australia
and Egg

1985. Bicentenary (1988) of Australian Settlement (3rd issue). Relics from Early Shipwrecks. Multicoloured.

993	33c. Type **416**	35	15
994	50c. German beardman jug ("Vergulde Draeck", 1656)	60	90
995	90c. Wooden bobbins ("Batavia", 1629) and encrusted scissors ("Zeewijk", 1727)	1·25	2·75
996	$1 Silver and brass buckle ("Zeewijk", 1727)	1·25	2·25

1986. Australia Day.

997	**417** 33c. multicoloured	40	30

418 AUSSAT
Satellite, Moon and
Earth's Surface

419 H.M.S. "Buffalo"

1986. AUSSAT National Communications Satellite System. Multicoloured.

998	33c. Type **418**	40	15
999	80c. AUSSAT satellite in orbit	1·00	2·25

1986. 150th Anniv of South Australia. Mult.

1000	33c. Type **419**	70	1·00
1001	33c. "City Sign" sculpture (Otto Hajek), Adelaide	70	1·00

Nos. 1000/1 were printed together se-tenant, the background of each horiz pair showing an extract from the colony's Letters Patent of 1836.

420 "Banksia serrata"

421 Radio Telescope,
Parkes, and Diagram
of Comet's Orbit

1986. Bicentenary (1988) of Australian Settlement (4th issue). Cook's Voyage to New Holland. Multicoloured.

1002	33c. Type **420**	60	35
1003	33c. "Hibiscus meraukensis"	60	35
1004	50c. "Dillenia alata"	90	1·10
1005	80c. "Correa reflexa"	1·75	2·50
1006	90c. "Joseph Banks" (botanist) (Reynolds) and Banks with Dr. Solander	2·25	2·25
1007	90c. "Sydney Parkinson" (self-portrait) and Parkinson drawing	2·25	2·25

1986. Appearance of Halley's Comet.

1008	**421** 33c. multicoloured	50	35

422 Queen
Elizabeth II

423 Brumbies (wild horses)

1986. 60th Birthday of Queen Elizabeth.

1009	**422** 33c. multicoloured	45	35

1986. Australian Horses. Multicoloured.

1010	33c. Type **423**	60	15
1011	80c. Mustering	1·50	2·25
1012	90c. Show-jumping	1·50	2·50
1013	$1 Child on pony	1·75	2·25

424 "The Old
Shearer stands"

425 "King George III"
(A. Ramsay) and Convicts

1986. Folklore. Scenes and Verses from the Folksong "Click go the Shears". Multicoloured.

1014	33c. Type **424**	55	80
1015	33c. "The ringer looks around"	55	80
1016	33c. "The boss of the board"	55	80
1017	33c. "The tar-boy is there"	55	80
1018	33c. "Shearing is all over"	55	80

Nos. 1014/18 were printed together, se-tenant, forming a composite design.

1986. Bicentenary (1988) of Australian Settlement (5th issue). Convict Settlement in New South Wales. Multicoloured.

1019	33c. Type **425**	80	50
1020	33c. "Lord Sydney" (Gilbert Stuart) and convicts	80	50
1021	33c. "Captain Arthur Phillip" (F. Wheatley) and ship	80	50
1022	$1 "Captain John Hunter" (W. B. Bennett) and aborigines	3·25	5·00

426 Red Kangaroo

427 Royal Bluebell

1986. Australian Wildlife (1st series). Mult.

1023	36c. Type **426**	60	80
1024	36c. Emu	60	80
1025	36c. Koala	60	80
1026	36c. Laughing kookaburra ("Kookaburra")	60	80
1027	36c. Platypus	60	80

See also Nos. 1072/6.

1986. Alpine Wildflowers. Multicoloured.

1028	3c. Type **427**	50	60
1029	5c. Alpine marsh marigold	1·75	2·75
1030	25c. Mount Buffalo sunray	1·75	2·75
1031	36c. Silver snow daisy	45	30

428 Pink Enamel
Orchid

429 "Australia II"
crossing Finishing
Line

1986. Native Orchids. Multicoloured.

1032	36c. Type **428**	70	20
1033	55c. "Dendrobium nindii"	1·25	1·00
1034	90c. Duck orchid	2·00	3·25
1035	$1 Queen of Sheba orchid	2·00	2·25

1986. Australian Victory in America's Cup, 1983. Multicoloured.

1036	36c. Type **429**	75	75
1037	36c. Boxing kangaroo flag of winning syndicate	75	75
1038	36c. America's Cup trophy	75	75

430 Dove with Olive
Branch and Sun

431 Mary and Joseph

1986. International Peace Year.
1039 430 36c. multicoloured . . . 65 40

1986. Christmas. Scenes from children's nativity play. Multicoloured.
1040 30c. Type **431** 40 30
1041 36c. Three Wise Men
      leaving gifts 50 45
1042 60c. Angels (horiz) . . . . 90 1·50

432 Australian Flag on Printed Circuit Board **433** Aerial View of Yacht

1987. Australia Day. Multicoloured.
1044 36c. Type **432** 55 65
1045 36c. "Australian Made"
      Campaign logos 55 65

1987. America's Cup Yachting Championship. Multicoloured.
1046 36c. Type **433** 40 20
1047 55c. Two yachts tacking . . 90 1·00
1048 90c. Two yachts beating . . 1·40 2·25
1049 $1 Two yachts under full
      sail . . . . 1·50 1·75

434 Grapes and Melons **435** Livestock

1987. Australian Fruit. Multicoloured.
1050 36c. Type **434** 40 20
1051 65c. Tropical and sub-
      tropical fruits . . . . . 1·00 1·25
1052 90c. Citrus fruit, apples and
      pears . . . . 1·40 2·25
1053 $1 Stone and berry fruits . . 1·40 1·60

1987. Agricultural Shows. Multicoloured.
1054 36c. Type **435** 60 20
1055 65c. Produce . . . . . . 1·25 1·75
1056 90c. Sideshows . . . . . 1·75 2·40
1057 $1 Competitions . . . . . 1·90 2·40

436 Queen Elizabeth in Australia, 1986

1987. Queen Elizabeth II's Birthday.
1058 **436** 36c. multicoloured . . . 55 50

437 Convicts on Quay **438** "At the Station"

1987. Bicentenary (1988) of Australian Settlement (6th issue). Departure of the First Fleet. Multicoloured.
1059 36c. Type **437** 80 95
1060 36c. Royal Marines officer
      and wife 80 95
1061 36c. Sailors loading supplies . 80 95
1062 36c. Officers being ferried to
      ships 80 95
1063 36c. Fleet in English
      Channel 80 95
      See also Nos. 1064/6, 1077/81 and 1090/2.

1987. Bicentenary (1988) of Australian Settlement (7th issue). First Fleet at Tenerife. As T **437**. Multicoloured.
1064 36c. Ferrying supplies, Santa
      Cruz 70 90
1065 36c. Canary Islands
      fishermen and departing
      fleet 70 90
1066 $1 Fleet arriving at Tenerife . 1·75 2·00

Nos. 1064/5 were printed together, se-tenant, forming a composite design.

1987. Folklore. Scenes and Verses from Poem "The Man from Snowy River". Multicoloured.
1067 36c. Type **438** 70 90
1068 36c. "Mountain bred" . . . 70 90
1069 36c. "That terrible descent" . 70 90
1070 36c. "At their heels" 70 90
1071 36c. "Brought them back" . . 70 90

Nos. 1067/71 were printed together, se-tenant, forming a composite background design of mountain scenery.

1987. Australian Wildlife (2nd series). As T **426**. Multicoloured.
1072 37c. Common brushtail
      possum 55 70
1073 37c. Sulphur-crested
      cockatoo ("Cockatoo") . . 55 70
1074 37c. Common wombat . . . 55 70
1075 37c. Crimson rosella
      ("Rosella") 55 70
1076 37c. Echidna 55 70

1987. Bicentenary (1988) of Australian Settlement (8th issue). First Fleet at Rio de Janeiro. As T **437**. Multicoloured.
1077 37c. Sperm whale and fleet . 80 90
1078 37c. Brazilian coast 80 90
1079 37c. British officers in
      market 80 90
1080 37c. Religious procession . . 80 90
1081 37c. Fleet leaving Rio . . . 80 90

Nos. 1077/81 were printed together, se-tenant, forming a composite design.

439 Bionic Ear **440** Catching Crayfish

1987. Australian Achievements in Technology. Mult.
1082 37c. Type **439** 40 35
1083 53c. Microchips 75 60
1084 63c. Robotics 85 70
1085 68c. Ceramics 95 75

1987. "Aussie Kids". Multicoloured.
1086 37c. Type **440** 40 35
1087 55c. Playing cat's cradle . . 75 75
1088 90c. Young football
      supporters . . . . . . 1·25 1·75
1089 $1 Children with kangaroo . 1·25 1·50

1987. Bicentenary (1988) of Australian Settlement (9th issue). First Fleet at Cape of Good Hope. As T **437**. Multicoloured.
1090 37c. Marine checking list of
      livestock 65 90
1091 37c. Loading livestock . . . 65 90
1092 $1 First Fleet at Cape Town . 1·50 2·00

Nos. 1090/1 were printed together, se-tenant, forming a composite design.

441 Detail of Spearthrower, Western Australia

1987. Aboriginal Crafts. Multicoloured.
1093 3c. Type **441** . . . . . 1·10 1·50
1094 15c. Shield pattern, New
      South Wales . . . . . . 4·00 4·75
1095 37c. Basket weave,
      Queensland . . . . . . 1·10 1·50
1096 37c. Bowl design, Central
      Australia . . . . 90 1·25
1097 37c. Belt pattern, Northern
      Territory . . . . 1·10 1·50

442 Grandmother and Granddaughters with Candles **443** Koala with Stockman's Hat and Eagle dressed as Uncle Sam

1987. Christmas. Designs showing carol singing by candlelight. Multicoloured.
1098 30c. Type **442** 50 65
1099 30c. Father and daughters . . 50 65
1100 30c. Four children 50 65
1101 30c. Family 50 65
1102 30c. Six teenagers 50 65
1103 37c. Choir (horiz) 50 65
1104 63c. Father and two
      children (horiz) . . . . . 85 1·25

1988. Bicentenary of Australian Settlement (10th issue). Arrival of First Fleet. As T **437**. Mult.
1105 37c. Aborigines watching
      arrival of Fleet, Botany
      Bay 65 90
1106 37c. Aborigine family and
      anchored ships 65 90
1107 37c. Fleet arriving at Sydney
      Cove 65 90
1108 37c. Ship's boat 65 90
1109 37c. Raising the flag, Sydney
      Cove, 26 January 1788 . . 65 90

Nos. 1105/9 were printed together, se-tenant, forming a composite design.

1988. Bicentenary of Australian Settlement (11th issue). Joint issue with U.S.A.
1110 **443** 37c. multicoloured . . . 60 35

444 "Religion" (A. Horner) **445** "Government House, Sydney, 1790" (George Raper)

1988. "Living Together". Designs showing cartoons. Multicoloured (except 30c.).
1111 1c. Type **444** 50 40
1112 2c. "Industry"
      (P. Nicholson) 50 40
1113 3c. "Local Government"
      (A. Collette) 50 40
1114 4c. "Trade Unions" (Liz
      Honey) 10 20
1115 5c. "Parliament" (Bronwyn
      Halls) 50 50
1116 10c. "Transport" (Meg
      Williams) 30 40
1117 15c. "Sport" (G. Cook) . . . 70 50
1118 20c. "Commerce"
      (M. Atcherson) 70 60
1119 25c. "Housing" (C. Smith) . 45 40
1120 30c. "Welfare"
      (R. Tandberg) (black
      and lilac) 55 60
1121 37c. "Postal Services"
      (P. Viska) 60 50
1121b 39c. "Tourism"
      (J. Spooner) 60 50
1122 40c. "Recreation"
      (R. Harvey) 70 70
1123 45c. "Health" (Jenny
      Coopes) 70 70
1124 50c. "Mining"
      (G. Haddon) 70 50
1125 53c. "Primary Industry"
      (S. Leahy) . . . . 1·75 1·50
1126 55c. "Education" (Victoria
      Roberts) . . . . 1·50 75
1127 60c. "Armed Forces"
      (B. Green) . . . . 1·50 70
1128 63c. "Police" (J. Russell) . . 2·00 1·10
1129 65c. "Telecommunications"
      (B. Petty) . . . . 1·50 1·50
1130 68c. "The Media"
      (A. Langoulant) . . . . 2·00 2·25
1131 70c. "Science and
      Technology" (J. Hook) . . 1·75 1·00
1132 75c. "Visual Arts"
      (G. Dazeley) . . . . . . 1·00 1·00
1133 80c. "Performing Arts"
      (A. Stitt) . . . . 1·25 1·00
1134 90c. "Banking"
      (S. Billington) . . . . . 1·50 1·00
1135 95c. "Law" (C. Aslanis) . . 1·00 1·25
1136 $1 "Rescue and
      Emergency" (M. Leunig) . 1·10 1·00

1988. Bicentenary of Australian Settlement (12th issue). "The Early Years, 1788–1809". Mult.
1137 37c. Type **445** 60 85
1138 37c. "Government Farm,
      Parramatta, 1791" ("The
      Port Jackson Painter") . . 60 85
1139 37c. "Parramatta Road,
      1796" (attr Thomas
      Watling) 60 85
1140 37c. "View of Sydney Cove,
      c. 1800" (detail) (Edward
      Dayes) 60 85
1141 37c. "Sydney Hospital,
      1803", (detail) (George
      William Evans) 60 85

Nos. 1137/41 were printed together, se-tenant, forming a composite background design from the painting "View of Sydney from the East Side of the Cove, c. 1808" by John Eyre.

446 Queen Elizabeth II (from photo by Tim Graham)

1988. Queen Elizabeth II's Birthday.
1142 **446** 37c. multicoloured . . . 50 40

447 Expo '88 Logo

1988. "Expo '88" World Fair, Brisbane.
1143 **447** 37c. multicoloured 50 40

448 New Parliament House

1988. Opening of New Parliament House, Canberra.
1144 **448** 37c. multicoloured . . . 50 40

449 Early Settler and Sailing Clipper

1988. Bicentenary of Australian Settlement (13th issue). Multicoloured.
1145 37c. Type **449** . . . . . 75 1·00
1146 37c. Queen Elizabeth II with
      British and Australian
      Parliament Buildings . . . 75 1·00
1147 $1 W. G. Grace (cricketer)
      and tennis racquet . . . 1·50 2·25
1148 $1 Shakespeare, John
      Lennon (entertainer) and
      Sydney Opera House . . 1·50 2·25

Stamps in similar designs were also issued by Great Britain.

450 Kiwi and Koala at Campfire

1988. Bicentenary of Australian Settlement (14th issue).
1149 **450** 37c. multicoloured . . . 65 40

A stamp in a similar design was also issued by New Zealand.

451 "Bush Potato Country" (Turkey Tolsen Tjupurrula and David Corby Tjapaltjarri)

1988. Art of the Desert. Aboriginal Paintings from Central Australia. Multicoloured.
1150 37c. Type **451** 30 30
1151 55c. "Courtship Rejected"
      (Limpi Puntungka
      Tjapangati) 55 60
1152 90c. "Medicine Story" (artist
      unknown) . . . . 75 2·10
1153 $1 "Ancestor Dreaming"
      (Tim Leura Tjapaltjarri) . 80 1·40

452 Basketball

1988. Olympic Games, Seoul. Multicoloured.
1154	37c. Type **452**	50	40
1155	65c. Athlete crossing finish line	60	1·25
1156	$1 Gymnast with hoop	85	1·75

453 Rod and Mace

1988. 34th Commonwealth Parliamentary Conference, Canberra.
1157	**453** 37c. multicoloured	50	60

454 Necklace by Peter Tully

1988. Australian Crafts. Multicoloured.
1158	2c. Type **454**	3·50	4·50
1159	5c. Vase by Colin Levy	3·50	4·50
1160	39c. Teapot by Frank Bauer	50	35

455 Pinnacles Desert

1988. Panorama of Australia. Multicoloured.
1161	39c. Type **455**	40	40
1162	55c. Flooded landscape, Arnhem Land	70	80
1163	65c. Twelve Apostles, Victoria	80	1·60
1164	70c. Mountain Ash wood	90	1·60

456 "The Nativity" (Danielle Hush)

1988. Christmas. Multicoloured.
1165	32c. Type **456**	50	35
1166	39c. "Koala as Father Christmas" (Kylie Courtney)	55	40
1167	63c. "Christmas Cockatoo" (Benjamin Stevenson)	1·10	1·40

457 Sir Henry Parkes   **458** Bowls

1989. Australia Day. Centenary of Federation Speech by Sir Henry Parkes (N.S.W. Prime Minister).
1168	**457** 37c. multicoloured	45	40

1989. Sports. Multicoloured.
1169	1c. Type **458**	10	10
1170	2c. Tenpin-bowling	10	10
1171	3c. Australian football	30	30
1172	5c. Kayaking and canoeing	15	10
1174	10c. Sailboarding	15	15
1176	20c. Tennis	20	25
1179	39c. Fishing	45	40
1180	41c. Cycling	60	1·35
1181	43c. Skateboarding	50	40
1184	55c. Kite-flying	40	45
1186	65c. Rock-climbing	70	60
1187	70c. Cricket	1·00	80
1188	75c. Netball	55	70
1189	80c. Squash	60	65
1190	85c. Diving	1·75	80
1191	90c. Soccer	1·75	80
1192	$1 Fun-run	1·00	95
1193	$1.10 Golf	1·25	90
1194	$1.20 Hang-gliding	2·50	1·10

459 Merino

1989. Sheep in Australia. Multicoloured.
1195	39c. Type **459**	70	45
1196	39c. Poll Dorset	70	45
1197	85c. Polwarth	1·40	2·00
1198	$1 Corriedale	1·40	1·50

460 Adelaide Botanic Garden

1989. Botanic Gardens. Multicoloured.
1199	$2 Noroo, New South Wales	1·50	40
1200	$5 Mawarra, Victoria	4·25	60
1201	$10 Type **460**	7·50	1·25
1201a	$20 "A View of the Artist's House and Garden in Mills Plains, Van Diemen's Land" (John Glover)	15·00	8·00

461 "Queen Elizabeth II" (sculpture, John Dowie)   **462** Arrival of Immigrant Ship, 1830s

1989. Queen Elizabeth II's Birthday.
1202	**461** 39c. multicoloured	55	50

1989. Colonial Development (1st issue). Pastoral Era 1810–1850. Multicoloured.
1203	39c. Type **462**	55	55
1204	39c. Pioneer cottage and wool dray	55	55
1205	39c. Squatter's homestead	55	55
1206	39c. Shepherd with flock (from Joseph Lycett's "Views of Australia")	55	55
1207	39c. Explorer in desert (after watercolour by Edward Frome)	55	55

See also Nos. 1254/8 and 1264/8.

463 Gladys Moncrieff and Roy Rene   **464** "Impression" (Tom Roberts)

1989. Australian Stage and Screen Personalities. Multicoloured.
1208	39c. Type **463**	45	40
1209	85c. Charles Chauvel and Chips Rafferty	1·25	1·75
1210	$1 Nellie Stewart and J. C. Williamson	1·25	1·10
1211	$1.10 Lottie Lyell and Raymond Longford	1·25	1·50

1989. Australian Impressionist Paintings. Mult.
1212	41c. Type **464**	45	50
1213	41c. "Impression for Golden Summer" (Sir Arthur Streeton)	45	50
1214	41c. "All on a Summer's Day" (Charles Conder) (vert)	45	50
1215	41c. "Petit Dejeuner" (Frederick McCubbin)	45	50

465 Freeways

1989. The Urban Environment.
1216	**465** 41c. black, purple and green	65	1·00
1217	– 41c. black, purple and mauve	65	1·00
1218	– 41c. black, purple and blue	65	1·00

DESIGNS: No. 1217, City buildings, Melbourne; No. 1218, Commuter train at platform.

466 Hikers outside Youth Hostel

1989. 50th Anniv of Australian Youth Hostels.
1219	**466** 41c. multicoloured	55	50

467 Horse Tram, Adelaide, 1878

1989. Historic Trams. Multicoloured.
1220	41c. Type **467**	60	60
1221	41c. Steam tram, Sydney, 1884	60	60
1222	41c. Cable tram, Melbourne, 1886	60	60
1223	41c. Double-deck electric tram, Hobart, 1893	60	60
1224	41c. Combination electric tram, Brisbane, 1901	60	60

468 "Annunciation" (15th-century Book of Hours)   **469** Radio Waves and Globe

1989. Christmas. Illuminated Manuscripts. Multicoloured.
1225	36c. Type **468**	40	20
1226	41c. "Annunciation to the Shepherds" (Wharncliffe Book of Hours, c. 1475)	50	25
1227	80c. "Adoration of the Magi" (15th-century Parisian Book of Hours)	1·25	1·75

1989. 50th Anniv of Radio Australia.
1228	**469** 41c. multicoloured	55	50

470 Golden Wattle   **471** Australian Wildflowers

1990. Australia Day.
1229	**470** 41c. multicoloured	55	50

1990. Greetings Stamps.
1230	**471** 41c. multicoloured	65	65
1231	43c. multicoloured	50	50

472 Dr. Constance Stone (first Australian woman doctor), Modern Doctor and Nurses

1990. Centenary of Women in Medical Practice.
1232	**472** 41c. multicoloured	50	45

473 Greater Glider   **474** "Stop Smoking"

1990. Animals of the High Country. Multicoloured.
1233	41c. Type **473**	60	45
1234	65c. Tiger cat ("Spotted-tailed Quoll")	90	1·25
1235	70c. Mountain pygmy-possum	95	1·25
1236	80c. Brush-tailed rock-wallaby	1·10	1·25

1990. Community Health. Multicoloured.
1237	41c. Type **474**	55	55
1238	41c. "Drinking and driving don't mix"	55	55
1239	41c. "No junk food, please"	55	55
1240	41c. "Guess who's just had a check up?"	55	55

475 Soldiers from Two World Wars   **476** Queen at Australian Ballet Gala Performance, London, 1988

1990. "The Anzac Tradition". Multicoloured.
1241	41c. Type **475**	50	40
1242	41c. Fighter pilots and munitions worker	50	40
1243	65c. Veterans and Anzac Day parade	85	90
1244	$1 Casualty evacuation, Vietnam, and disabled veteran	1·25	1·40
1245	$1.10 Letters from home and returning troopships	1·40	1·50

1990. Queen Elizabeth II's Birthday.
1246	**476** 41c. multicoloured	65	45

477 New South Wales 1861 5s. Stamp

1990. 150th Anniv of the Penny Black. Designs showing stamps. Multicoloured.
1247	41c. Type **477**	60	75
1248	41c. South Australia 1855 unissued 1s.	60	75
1249	41c. Tasmania 1853 4d.	60	75
1250	41c. Victoria 1867 5s.	60	75
1251	41c. Queensland 1897 unissued 6d.	60	75
1252	41c. Western Australia 1855 4d. with inverted frame	60	75

478 Gold Miners on Way to Diggings

1990. Colonial Development (2nd issue). Gold Fever. Multicoloured.
1254	41c. Type **478**	80	85
1255	41c. Mining camp	80	85
1256	41c. Panning and washing for gold	80	85
1257	41c. Gold Commissioner's tent	80	85
1258	41c. Moving gold under escort	80	85

479 Glaciology Research

1990. Australian–Soviet Scientific Co-operation in Antarctica. Multicoloured.
1261 41c. Type **479** 65 40
1262 $1.10 Krill (marine biology research) . . . . 1·60 1·50
Stamps in similar designs were also issued by Russia.

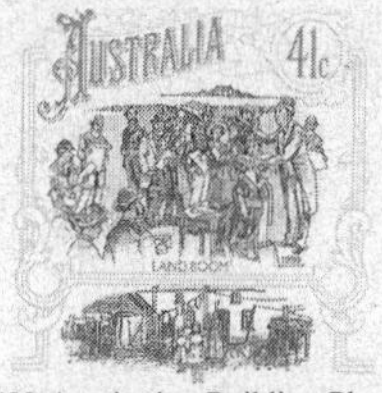

480 Auctioning Building Plots

1990. Colonial Development (3rd series). Boomtime. Multicoloured.
1264 41c. Type **480** 55 55
1265 41c. Colonial mansion . . . 55 55
1266 41c. Stock exchange 55 55
1267 41c. Fashionable society . . 55 55
1268 41c. Factories 55 55

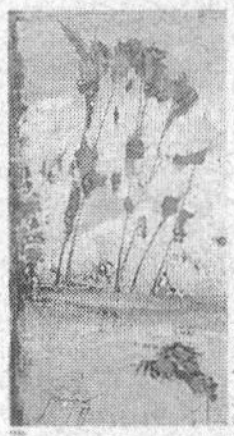

481 "Salmon Gums" (Robert Juniper)

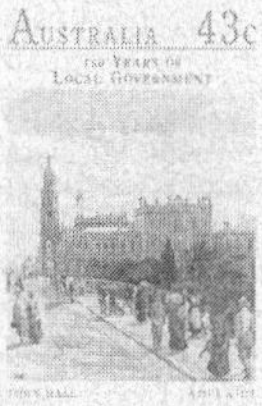

482 "Adelaide Town Hall" (Edmund Gouldsmith)

1990. "Heidelberg and Heritage" Art Exhibition. Multicoloured.
1269 28c. Type **481** . . . . . . 2·25 2·75
1270 43c. "The Blue Dress" (Brian Dunlop) 40 45

1990. 150th Anniv of Local Government.
1271 **482** 43c. multicoloured . . . 75 50

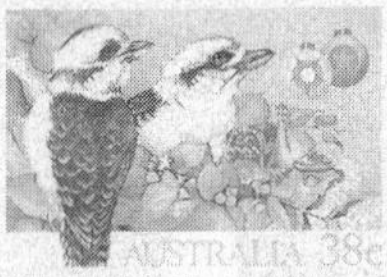

483 Laughing Kookaburras and Gifts

1990. Christmas. Multicoloured.
1272 38c. Type **483** 50 25
1273 43c. Baby Jesus with koalas and wallaby (vert) 50 25
1274 80c. Possum on Christmas tree . . . . 1·50 2·50

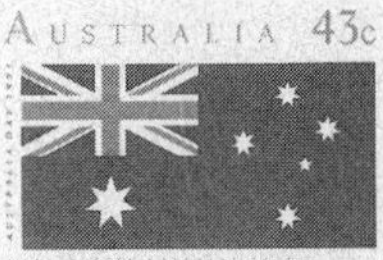

484 National Flag

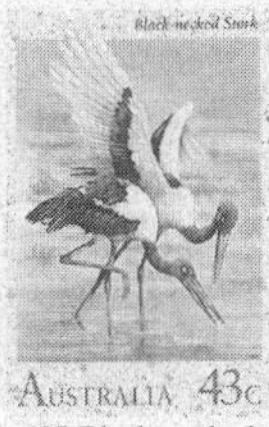

485 Black-necked Stork

1991. Australia Day. 90th Anniv of Australian Flag.
1275 **484** 43c. blue, red and grey 50 40
1276 – 90c. multicoloured . . . 1·10 1·25
1277 – $1 multicoloured . . . . 1·25 1·40
1278 – $1.20 red, blue and grey 1·60 1·75
DESIGNS: 90c. Royal Australian Navy ensign; $1 Royal Australian Air Force standard; $1.20, Australian merchant marine ensign.

1991. Waterbirds. Multicoloured.
1279 43c. Type **485** 75 40
1280 43c. Black swan (horiz) . . 75 40
1281 85c. Cereopsis goose ("Cape Barren") . . . . 1·75 2·25
1282 $1 Chestnut-breasted teal ("Chestnut Teal") (horiz) 1·90 1·75

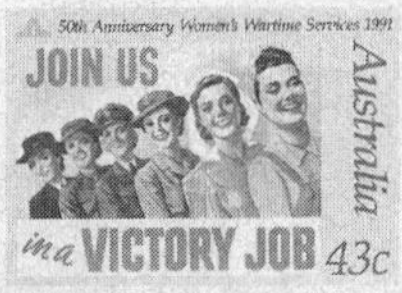

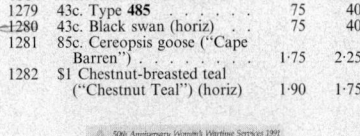

486 Recruitment Poster (Women's Services)

1991. Anzac Day. 50th Anniversaries.
1283 **486** 43c. multicoloured . . . 60 40
1284 – 43c. black, green & brn 60 40
1285 – $1.20 multicoloured . . 2·25 2·00

DESIGNS: 43c. (No. 1284) Patrol (Defence of Tobruk); $1.20, "V-P Day Canberra" (Harold Abbot) (Australian War Memorial).

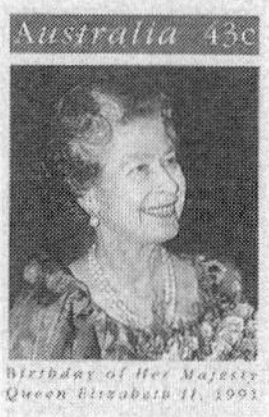

487 Queen Elizabeth at Royal Albert Hall, London

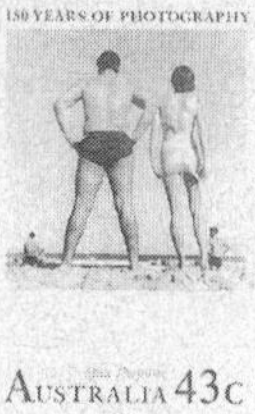

489 "Bondi" (Max Dupain)

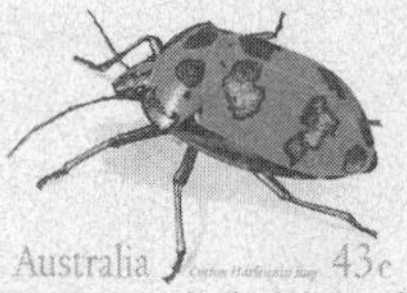

488 "Tectocoris diophthalmus" (bug)

1991. Queen Elizabeth II's Birthday.
1286 **487** multicoloured 80 50

1991. Insects. Multicoloured.
1287 43c. Type **488** 75 45
1288 43c. "Cizara ardeniae" (hawk moth) 75 45
1289 80c. "Petasida ephippigera" (grasshopper) . . . . . . 2·00 2·00
1290 $1 "Castiarina producta" (beetle) . . . . 2·00 1·50

1991. 150 Years of Photography in Australia.
1291 **489** 43c. black, brown and blue 75 65
1292 – 43c. black, green & brn 75 65
1293 – 70c. black, green & brn 1·25 1·10
1294 – $1.20 black, brown & green . . . . 1·75 1·50
DESIGNS: No. 1292, "Gears for the Mining Industry, Vickers Ruwolt, Melbourne" (Wolfgang Sievers): 1293, "The Wheel of Youth" (Harold Cazneaux): 1294, "Teacup Ballet" (Olive Cotton).

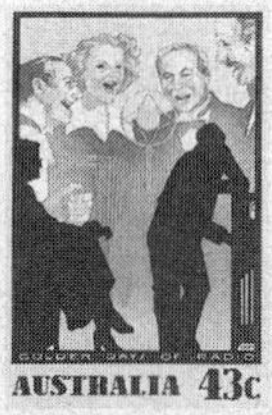

490 Singing Group

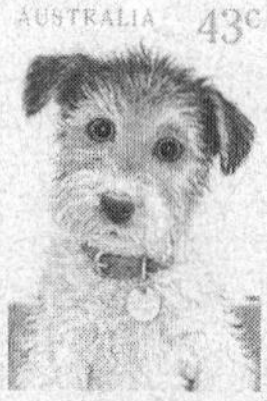

491 Puppy

1991. Australian Radio Broadcasting. Designs showing listeners and scenes from radio programmes. Multicoloured.
1295 43c. Type **490** 60 45
1296 43c. "Blue Hills" serial . . . 60 45
1297 85c. "The Quiz Kids" . . . 1·25 1·25
1298 $1 "Argonauts' Club" children's programme . . 1·50 1·40

1991. Domestic Pets. Multicoloured.
1299 43c. Type **491** 70 45
1300 43c. Kitten 70 45
1301 70c. Pony . . . . 1·40 2·25
1302 $1 Sulphur-crested cockatoo 1·90 1·50

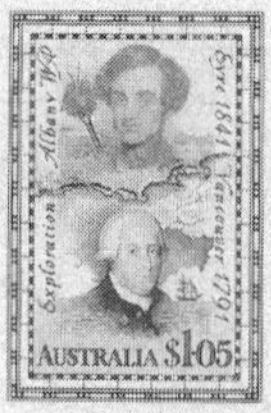

492 George Vancouver (1791) and Edward Eyre (1841)

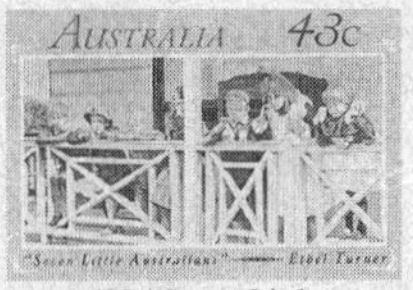

493 "Seven Little Australians" (Ethel Turner)

1991. Exploration of Western Australia.
1303 **492** $1.05 multicoloured . . 1·00 1·10

1991. Australian Writers of the 1890s. Multicoloured.
1305 43c. Type **493** 50 45
1306 75c. "On Our Selection" (Steele Rudd) . . . . . . 80 1·00
1307 $1 "Clancy of the Overflow" (poem, A. B. Paterson) (vert) . . . . 1·10 1·00
1308 $1.20 "The Drover's Wife" (short story, Henry Lawson) (vert) . . . . . 1·25 1·60

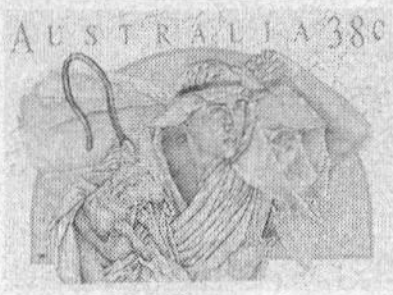

494 Shepherd

1991. Christmas. Multicoloured.
1309 38c. Type **494** 40 25
1310 43c. Infant Jesus 45 25
1311 90c. Wise Man . . . . . . 1·50 1·50

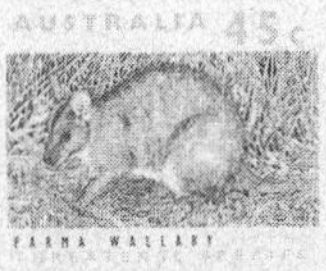

495 Parma Wallaby

1992. Threatened Species. Multicoloured.
1312 45c. Type **495** 65 60
1313 45c. Ghost bat 65 60
1314 45c. Long-tailed dunnart . . 65 60
1315 45c. Little pygmy-possum 65 60
1316 45c. Dusky hopping-mouse 65 60
1317 45c. Squirrel glider 65 60

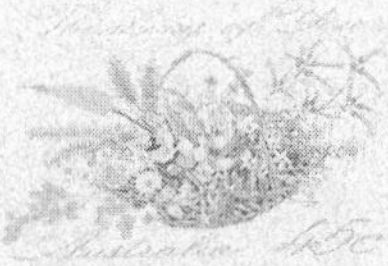
496 Basket of Wild Flowers

1992. Greetings Stamp.
1318 **496** 45c. multicoloured . . . 50 50

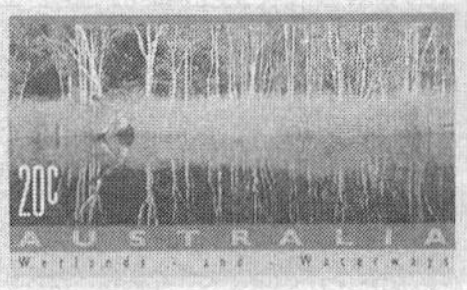

497 Noosa River, Queensland

1992. Wetlands and Waterways. Multicoloured.
1319 20c. Type **497** . . . . . . 1·75 2·00
1320 45c. Lake Eildon, Victoria 40 45

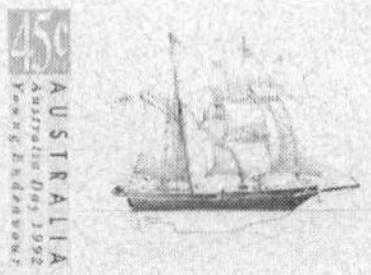

498 "Young Endeavour" (brigantine)

1992. Australia Day. Sailing Ships. Multicoloured.
1333 45c. Type **498** 80 50
1334 45c. "Britannia" (yacht) (vert) 80 50
1335 $1.05 "Akarana" (cutter) (vert) . . . . 1·75 2·75
1336 $1.20 "John Louis" (pearling lugger) . . . . 2·00 2·00

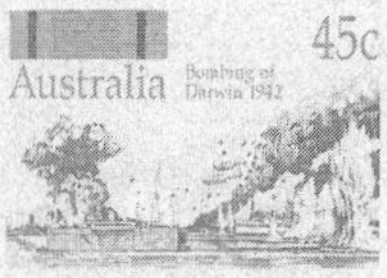

499 Bombing of Darwin

1992. 50th Anniv of Second World War Battles. Multicoloured.
1338 45c. Type **499** 70 45
1339 75c. Anti-aircraft gun and fighters, Milne Bay . . . 1·25 1·25
1340 75c. Infantry on Kokoda Trail . . . . 1·25 1·25
1341 $1.05 H.M.A.S. "Australia" (cruiser) and U.S.S. "Yorktown" (aircraft carrier), Coral Sea . . . . 1·50 1·50
1342 $1.20 Australians advancing, El Alamein . . . . 1·75 1·60

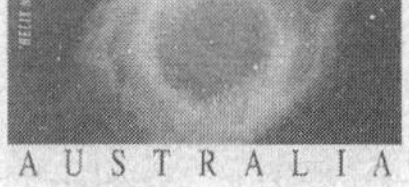

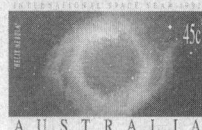

500 "Helix Nebula"

1992. International Space Year. Multicoloured.
1343 45c. Type **500** 60 45
1344 $1.05 "The Pleiades" . . . 1·50 1·25
1345 $1.20 "Spiral Galaxy, NGC 2997" . . . . 1·75 1·50

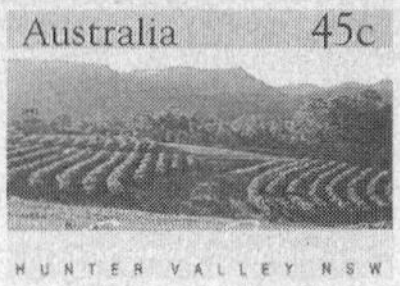

501 Hunter Valley, New South Wales

1992. Vineyard Regions. Multicoloured.
1347 45c. Type **501** 60 65
1348 45c. North-east Victoria . . 60 65
1349 45c. Barossa Valley, South Australia 60 65
1350 45c. Coonawarra, South Australia 60 65
1351 45c. Margaret River, Western Australia 60 65

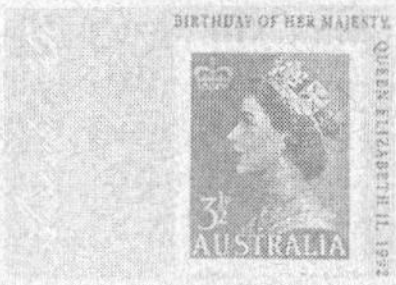

502 3½d. Stamp of 1953

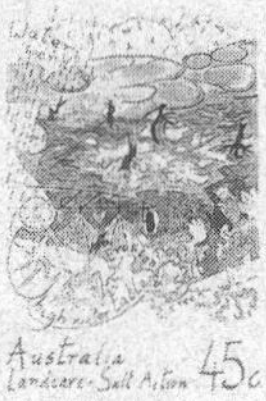

503 Salt Action

1992. Queen Elizabeth II's Birthday.
1352 **502** 45c. multicoloured . . . 70 50

1992. Land Conservation. Multicoloured.
1353 45c. Type **503** . . . . . . 85 1·00
1354 45c. Farm planning . . . . 85 1·00
1355 45c. Erosion control . . . . 85 1·00
1356 45c. Tree planting . . . . . 85 1·00
1357 45c. Dune care . . . . . . 85 1·00

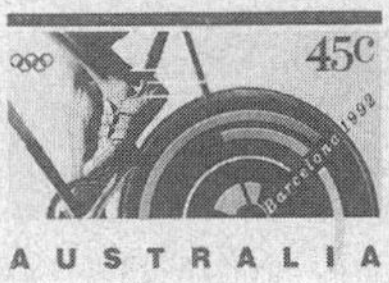

504 Cycling

1992. Olympic Games and Paralympic Games (No. 1359), Barcelona. Multicoloured.
1358 45c. Type **504** 60 45
1359 $1.20 High jumping . . . . 1·50 1·60
1360 $1.20 Weightlifting . . . . 1·50 1·60

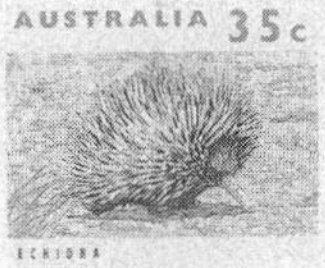

505 Echidna

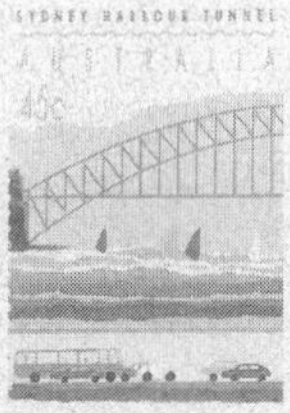

506 Sydney Harbour Tunnel (value at left)

1992. Australian Wildlife (1st series). Multicoloured.
1361 30c. Saltwater crocodile . . 25 20
1362 35c. Type **505** 50 20
1363 40c. Platypus . . . . . . 1·00 25
1364 50c. Koala 60 35
1365 60c. Common bushtail possum 70 75
1366 70c. Laughing kookaburra ("Kookaburra") . . . . 1·50 1·00
1367 85c. Australian pelican ("Pelican") 65 70
1368a 90c. Eastern grey kangaroo 1·25 1·00
1369 95c. Common wombat . . 1·00 1·60
1370a $1.20 Major Mitchell's cockatoo ("Pink Cockatoo") . . . . . . 1·25 1·10
1371 $1.35 Emu . . . . 1·00 1·50
See also Nos. 1453/8.

1992. Opening of Sydney Harbour Tunnel. Mult.
1375b 45c. Type **506** . . . . . . 1·75 1·75
1376b 45c. Sydney Harbour Tunnel (value at right) 1·75 1·75
Nos. 1375/6 were printed together, se-tenant, forming a composite design.

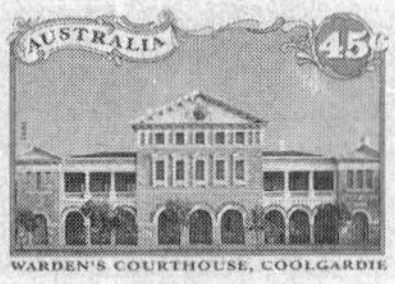

507 Warden's Courthouse, Coolgardie

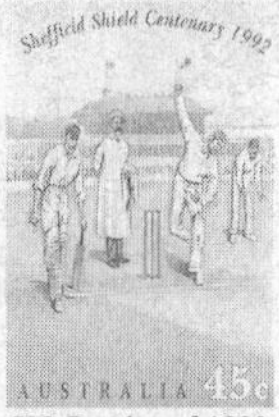

508 Bowler of 1892

1992. Centenary of Discovery of Gold at Coolgardie and Kalgoorlie. Multicoloured.
1377 45c. Type **507** 70 45
1378 45c. Post Office, Kalgoorlie 70 45

1379 $1.05 York Hotel, Kalgoorlie ... 1·60 1·60
1380 $1.20 Town Hall, Kalgoorlie ... 1·90 1·90

1992. Centenary of Sheffield Shield Cricket Tournament. Multicoloured.
1381 45c. Type 508 ... 85 50
1382 $1.20 Batsman and wicket-keeper ... 1·90 2·50

509 Children's Nativity Play

1992. Christmas. Multicoloured.
1383 40c. Type 509 ... 55 25
1384 45c. Child waking on Christmas Day ... 60 25
1385 $1 Children carol singing ... 1·90 2·00

510 "Ghost Gum, Central Australia" (Namatjira)

1993. Australia Day. Paintings by Albert Namatjira. Multicoloured.
1386 45c. Type 510 ... 75 1·25
1387 45c. "Across the Plain to Mount Giles" ... 75 1·25

511 "Wild Onion Dreaming" (Pauline Nakamarra Woods)

1993. "Dreamings". Paintings by Aboriginal Artists. Multicoloured.
1388 45c. Type 511 ... 60 30
1389 75c. "Yam Plants" (Jack Wunuwun) (vert) ... 1·10 95
1390 85c. "Goose Egg Hunt" (George Milpurrurru) (vert) ... 1·25 1·40
1391 $1 "Kalumpiwarra-Ngulalintji" (Rover Thomas) ... 1·40 1·40

512 Uluru (Ayers Rock) National Park

1993. World Heritage Sites (1st series). Multicoloured.
1392 45c. Type 512 ... 70 30
1393 85c. Rain forest, Fraser Island ... 1·75 1·60
1394 95c. Beach, Shark Bay ... 1·75 1·60
1395 $2 Waterfall, Kakadu ... 2·25 2·25
See also Nos. 1582/5.

513 Queen Elizabeth II on Royal Visit, 1992
514 H.M.A.S. "Sydney" (cruiser, launched 1934) in Action

1993. Queen Elizabeth II's Birthday.
1396 513 45c. multicoloured ... 70 60

1993. Second World War Naval Vessels. Mult.
1397 45c. Type 514 ... 80 45
1398 85c. H.M.A.S. "Bathurst" (mine-sweeper) ... 1·60 1·75
1399 $1.05 H.M.A.S. "Arunta" (destroyer) ... 1·75 2·75
1400 $1.20 "Centaur" (hospital ship) and tug ... 2·00 2·75

515 "Work in the Home"
516 "Centenary Special", Tasmania, 1971

1993. Working Life in the 1890s. Mult.
1401 45c. Type 515 ... 55 50
1402 45c. "Work in the Cities" ... 55 50
1403 $1 "Work in the Country" ... 1·10 1·10
1404 $1.20 Trade Union banner ... 1·50 2·00

1993. Australian Trains. Multicoloured.
1405 45c. Type 516 ... 65 75
1406 45c. "Spirit of Progress", Victoria ... 65 75
1407 45c. "Western Endeavour", Western Australia, 1970 ... 65 75
1408 45c. "Silver City Comet", New South Wales ... 65 75
1409 45c. Cairns-Kuranda tourist train, Queensland ... 65 75
1410 45c. "The Ghan", Northern Territory ... 65 75
Nos. 1405/10 also come self-adhesive.

517 "Black Cockatoo Feather" (Fiona Foley)
518 Conference Emblem

1993. International Year of Indigenous Peoples. Aboriginal Art. Multicoloured
1417 45c. Type 517 ... 55 30
1418 75c. "Ngarrgooroon Country" (Hector Jandany) (horiz) ... 1·10 1·50
1419 $1 "Ngak Ngak" (Ginger Riley Munduwalawala) (horiz) ... 1·25 1·60
1420 $1.05 "Untitled" (Robert Cole) ... 1·50 2·50

1993. Inter-Parliamentary Union Conference and 50th Anniv of Women in Federal Parliament. Multicoloured.
1421 45c. Type 518 ... 1·00 1·40
1422 45c. Dame Enid Lyons and Senator Dorothy Tangney ... 1·00 1·40

519 Ornithocheirus
520 "Goodwill"

1993. Prehistoric Animals. Multicoloured.
1423 45c. Type 519 ... 60 50
1424 45c. Leaellynasaura (25×30 mm) ... 60 50
1425 45c. Timimus (26×33 mm) ... 60 50
1426 45c. Allosaurus (26×33 mm) ... 60 50
1427 75c. Muttaburrasaurus (30×50 mm) ... 1·00 90
1428 $1.05 Minmi (50×30 mm) ... 1·50 1·50
Nos. 1423/4 also come self-adhesive.

1993. Christmas. Multicoloured.
1432 40c. Type 520 ... 50 25
1433 45c. "Joy" ... 55 25
1434 $1 "Peace" ... 1·90 2·00

521 "Shoalhaven River Bank—Dawn" (Arthur Boyd)

1994. Australia Day. Landscape Paintings. Mult.
1435 45c. Type 521 ... 60 30
1436 85c. "Wimmera" (Sir Sidney Nolan) ... 1·40 1·40
1437 $1.05 "Lagoon, Wimmera" (Nolan) ... 1·60 1·60
1438 $2 "White Cockatoos with Flame Trees" (Boyd) (vert) ... 2·50 2·75

522 Teaching Lifesaving Techniques

1994. Centenary of Organized Life Saving in Australia. Multicoloured.
1439 45c. Type 522 ... 60 45
1440 45c. Lifeguard on watch ... 60 45
1441 95c. Lifeguard team ... 1·25 1·40
1442 $1.20 Lifeguards on surf boards ... 1·60 1·75
Nos. 1439/40 also come self-adhesive.

523 Rose
524 Bridge and National Flags

1994. Greetings Stamps. Flower photographs by Lariane Fonseca. Multicoloured.
1445 45c. Type 523 ... 40 45
1446 45c. Tulips ... 40 45
1447 45c. Poppies ... 40 45

1994. Opening of Friendship Bridge between Thailand and Laos.
1448 524 95c. multicoloured ... 1·25 1·40

525 "Queen Elizabeth II" (Sir William Dargie)
526 "Family in Field" (Bobbie-Lea Blackmore)

1994. Queen Elizabeth II's Birthday.
1449 525 45c. multicoloured ... 70 70

1994. International Year of the Family. Children's Paintings. Multicoloured.
1450 45c. Type 526 ... 55 30
1451 75c. "Family on Beach" (Kathryn Teoh) ... 1·00 1·25
1452 $1 "Family around Fire" (Maree McCarthy) ... 1·25 1·50

1994. Australian Wildlife (2nd series). As T 505. Multicoloured. Ordinary or self-adhesive gum.
1453 45c. Kangaroo ... 75 55
1454 45c. Female kangaroo with young ... 75 55
1455 45c. Two kangaroos ... 75 55
1456 45c. Family of koalas on branch ... 75 55
1457 45c. Koala on ground ... 75 55
1458 45c. Koala asleep in tree ... 75 55

527 Suffragettes

1994. Centenary of Women's Emancipation in South Australia.
1465 527 45c. multicoloured ... 60 60

528 Bunyip from Aboriginal Legend

1994. The Bunyip (mythological monster). Mult.
1466 45c. Type 528 ... 70 70
1467 45c. Nature spirit bunyip ... 70 70
1468 90c. "The Bunyip of Berkeley's Creek" (book illustration) ... 1·75 1·75
1469 $1.35 Bunyip as natural history ... 2·25 2·25

529 "Robert Menzies" (Sir Ivor Hele)
530 Lawrence Hargrave and Box Kites

1994. Wartime Prime Ministers. Multicoloured.
1470 45c. Type 529 ... 85 90
1471 45c. "Arthur Fadden" (William Dargie) ... 85 90
1472 45c. "John Curtin" (Anthony Dattilo-Rubbo) ... 85 90
1473 45c. "Francis Forde" (Joshua Smith) ... 85 90
1474 45c. "Joseph Chifley" (A. D. Colquhoun) ... 85 90

1994. Aviation Pioneers.
1475 530 45c. brown, green and cinnamon ... 70 50
1476 – 45c. brown, red and lilac ... 70 50
1477 – $1.35 brown, violet and blue ... 2·25 3·00
1478 – $1.80 brown, deep green and green ... 2·50 3·25
DESIGNS: No. 1476, Ross and Keith Smith with Vickers Vimy (first England–Australia flight); 1477, Ivor McIntyre, Stanley Goble and Fairey IIID seaplane (first aerial circumnavigation of Australia); 1478, Freda Thompson and De Havilland Moth Major "Christopher Robin" (first Australian woman to fly solo from England to Australia).

531 Scarlet Macaw
532 "Madonna and Child" (detail)

1994. Australian Zoos. Endangered Species. Mult.
1479 45c. Type 531 ... 65 55
1480 45c. Cheetah (25×30 mm) ... 65 55
1481 45c. Orang-utan (26×37 mm) ... 65 55
1482 45c. Fijian crested iguana (26×37 mm) ... 65 55
1483 $1 Asian elephants (49×28 mm) ... 1·75 1·60
Nos. 1479/80 also come self-adhesive.

1994. Christmas. "The Adoration of the Magi" by Giovanni Toscani. Multicoloured.
1487 40c. Type 532 ... 60 25
1488 45c. "Wise Man and Horse" (detail) (horiz) ... 60 25
1489 $1 "Wise Man and St. Joseph" (detail) (horiz) ... 1·50 1·40
1490 $1.80 Complete painting (49×29 mm) ... 2·00 2·75

533 Yachts outside Sydney Harbour
534 Symbolic Kangaroo

1994. 50th Sydney to Hobart Yacht Race. Mult.
1491 45c. Type 533 ... 80 70
1492 45c. Yachts passing Tasmania coastline ... 80 70
Nos. 1491/92 also come self-adhesive.

1994. Self-adhesive. Automatic Cash Machine Stamps.
1495 534 45c. gold, emerald and green ... 50 50
1496 45c. gold, green and blue ... 50 50
1497 45c. gold, green and lilac ... 50 50
1498 45c. gold, emerald and green ... 50 50
1499 45c. gold, emerald and green ... 50 50
1500 45c. gold, green and pink ... 50 50
1501 45c. gold, green and red ... 50 50
1502 45c. gold, green and brown ... 50 50

535 "Back Verandah" (Russell Drysdale)

1995. Australia Day. Paintings. Multicoloured.
1503 45c. Type **535** 50 45
1504 45c. "Skull Springs
Country" (Guy Grey-
Smith) 50 45
1505 $1.05 "Outcamp" (Robert
Juniper) . . . . . . 1·40 1·50
1506 $1.20 "Kite Flying" (Ian
Fairweather) . . . . . 1·50 1·50

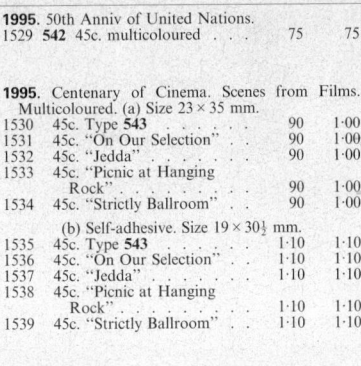

536 Red Heart and **537** "Endeavour" Replica at
Rose Sea

1995. St. Valentine's Day. Multicoloured.
1507 45c. Type **536** 55 55
1508 45c. Gold and red heart
with rose 55 55
1509 45c. Gold heart and roses 85 85

1995. Completion of "Endeavour" Replica. Mult.
1510 45c. Type **537** . . . . . 1·25 1·25
1511 45c. "Captain Cook's
Endeavour" (detail)
(Oswald Brett) . . . . 1·25 1·25

538 Coalport Plate and Bracket
Clock, Old Government House,
Parramatta

1995. 50th Anniv of Australian National Trusts.
1514 **538** 45c. blue and brown . . 45 45
1515 – 45c. green and brown . . 45 45
1516 – $1 red and brown . . . 1·00 95
1517 – $2 green and blue . . . 1·90 1·90
DESIGNS: No. 1515, Steiner doll and Italian-style
chair, Ayers House, Adelaide; 1516, "Advance
Australia" teapot and parian-ware statuette, Victoria;
1517, Silver bowl and china urn, Old Observatory,
Perth.

539 Light Opal (hologram)

1995. Opals. Mulitcoloured.
1518 $1.20 Type **539** . . . . . 2·25 1·25
1519 $2.50 Black opal (hologram) 3·75 3·75

540 Queen Elizabeth **541** Sir Edward
II at Gala Concert, Dunlop and P.O.W.
1992 Association Badge

1995. Queen Elizabeth II's Birthday.
1520 **540** 45c. multicoloured . . . 65 75

1995. Australian Second World War Heroes (1st
series). Mult. Ordinary or self-adhesive gum.
1521 45c. Type **541** 60 60
1522 45c. Mrs. Jessie Vasey and
War Widows' Guild
badge 60 60
1523 45c. Sgt. Tom Derrick and
Victoria Cross 60 60
1524 45c. Flt. Sgt. Rawdon
Middleton and Victoria
Cross 60 60
See also Nos. 1545/8.

542 Children and Globe of **543** "The Story of
Flags the Kelly Gang"

1995. 50th Anniv of United Nations.
1529 **542** 45c. multicoloured . . . 75 75

1995. Centenary of Cinema. Scenes from Films.
Multicoloured. (a) Size 23 × 35 mm.
1530 45c. Type **543** . . . . . 90 1·00
1531 45c. "On Our Selection" . . 90 1·00
1532 45c. "Jedda" . . . . . . 90 1·00
1533 45c. "Picnic at Hanging
Rock" . . . . . . 90 1·00
1534 45c. "Strictly Ballroom" . . 90 1·00
(b) Self-adhesive. Size 19 × 30½ mm.
1535 45c. Type **543** . . . . . 1·10 1·10
1536 45c. "On Our Selection" . . 1·10 1·10
1537 45c. "Jedda" . . . . . . 1·10 1·10
1538 45c. "Picnic at Hanging
Rock" . . . . . . 1·10 1·10
1539 45c. "Strictly Ballroom" . . 1·10 1·10

544 Man in **545** Koala with Cub
Wheelchair flying
Kite

1995. People with Disabilities. Multicoloured.
1540 45c. Type **544** 90 75
1541 45c. Blind woman playing
violin 90 75

1995. 50th Anniv of Peace in the Pacific. Designs as
1946 Victory Commemoration (Nos. 213/15)
redrawn with new face values.
1542 **53** 45c. red 75 60
1543 – 45c. green 75 60
1544 – $1.50 blue . . . . . . 1·90 2·25
DESIGNS—VERT: No. 1543, Angel. HORIZ:
No. 1544, Flag and dove.

1995. Australian Second World War Heroes (2nd
series). As T **541**. Multicoloured.
1545 45c. Sister Ellen Savage and
George Medal 75 75
1546 45c. Chief Petty Officer
Percy Collins and
Distinguished Service
Medal and Bar . . . 75 75
1547 45c. Lt.-Comm. Leon
Goldsworthy and George
Cross 75 75
1548 45c. Warrant Officer Len
Waters and R.A.A.F.
wings 75 75

1995. Australia–China Joint Issue. Endangered
Species. Multicoloured.
1549 45c. Type **545** . . . . . 70 1·00
1550 45c. Giant panda with cubs 70 1·00

546 Father Joseph Slattery,
Thomas Lyle and Walter Filmer
(Radiology)

1995. Medical Scientists. Multicoloured.
1552 45c. Type **546** 80 90
1553 45c. Dame Jean Macnamara
and Sir Macfarlane
Burnet (viruses) 80 90
1554 45c. Fred Hollows
(ophthalmology) (vert) . . 80 60
1555 $2.50 Sir Howard Florey
(antibiotics) (vert) . . . 4·25 5·00

547 Flatback Turtle **548** "Madonna and
Child"

1995. Marine Life. Multicoloured. Ordinary or self-
adhesive gum.
1556 45c. Type **547** 55 55
1557 45c. Flame angelfish and
nudibranch 55 55
1558 45c. Potato grouper
("Potato cod") and hump-
headed wrasse ("Maori
wrasse") 55 55
1559 45c. Giant trevally . . . 55 55

1560 45c. Black marlin 55 55
1561 45c. Mako and tiger sharks 55 55

1995. Christmas. Stained-glass Windows from Our
Lady Help of Christians Church, Melbourne.
Multicoloured.
1569 40c. Type **548** 60 25
1570 45c. "Angel carrying the
Gloria banner" 60 25
1571 $1 "Rejoicing Angels" . . 1·75 2·25
No. 1569 also comes self-adhesive.

549 "West Australian Banksia"
(Margaret Preston)

1996. Australia Day. Paintings. Multicoloured.
1573 45c. Type **549** 60 30
1574 85c. "The Babe is Wise"
(Lina Bryans) . . . . 1·40 1·50
1575 $1 "The Bridge in Curve"
(Grace Cossington Smith)
(horiz) . . . . . . 1·50 1·50
1576 $1.20 "Beach Umbrellas"
(Vida Lahey) (horiz) . . . 1·75 2·50

550 Gold Heart and Rose

1996. St. Valentine's Day.
1577 **550** 45c. multicoloured . . . 50 50

551 Bristol Type 156 Beaufighter
and Curtiss P-40E Kittyhawk I

1996. Military Aviation. Multicoloured.
1578 45c. Type **551** 75 90
1579 45c. Hawker Sea Fury and
Fairey Firefly 75 90
1580 45c. Bell Kiowa helicopters 75 90
1581 45c. Government Aircraft
Factory Hornets . . . 75 90

552 Tasmanian Wilderness

1996. World Heritage Sites (2nd series). Mult.
1582 45c. Type **552** 50 45
1583 75c. Willandra Lakes . . . 90 90
1584 95c. Naracoorte Fossil Cave 1·25 1·25
1585 $1 Lord Howe Island . . . 1·50 1·60

553 Australian Spotted **555** North Melbourne
Cuscus Players

554 Head of Queen Elizabeth II

1996. Australia–Indonesia Joint Issue. Mult.
1586 45c. Type **553** 70 80
1587 45c. Indonesian bear cuscus 70 80

1996. Queen Elizabeth II's Birthday.
1589 **554** 45c. multicoloured . . . 65 55

1996. Centenary of Australian Football League.
Players from different teams. Multicoloured.
Ordinary or self-adhesive gum.
1590 45c. Type **555** 60 65
1591 45c. Brisbane (red and
yellow shirt) 60 65
1592 45c. Sydney (red and white
shirt) 60 65
1593 45c. Carlton (black shirt
with white emblem) . . 60 65
1594 45c. Adelaide (black, red
and yellow shirt) . . . 60 65
1595 45c. Fitzroy (yellow, red and
blue shirt) 60 65
1596 45c. Richmond (black shirt
with yellow diagonal
stripe) 60 65
1597 45c. St. Kilda (red, white
and black shirt) . . . 60 65
1598 45c. Melbourne (black shirt
with red top) 60 65
1599 45c. Collingwood (black and
white vertical striped
shirt) 60 65
1600 45c. Fremantle (green, red,
white and blue shirt) . . 60 65
1601 45c. Footscray (blue, white
and red shirt) 60 65
1602 45c. West Coast (deep blue
shirt with yellow stripes) 60 65
1603 45c. Essendon (black shirt
with red stripe) . . . 60 65
1604 45c. Geelong (black and
white horizontal striped
shirt) 60 65
1605 45c. Hawthorn (black and
yellow vertical striped
shirt) 60 65

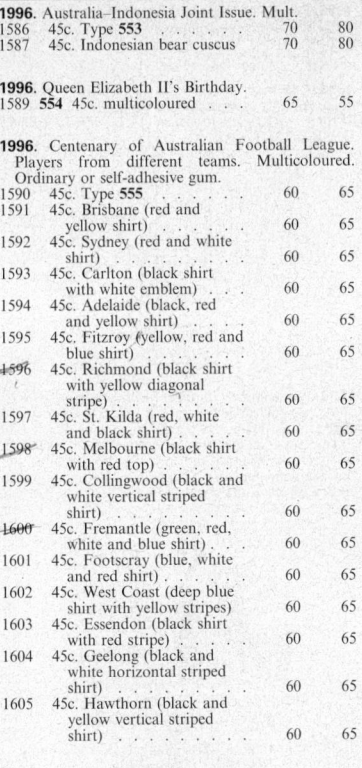

556 Leadbeater's Possum

1996. Fauna and Flora (1st series). Central Highlands
Forest, Victoria. Multicoloured.
1622 5c. Type **556** 10 10
1623 10c. Powerful owl 10 10
1624 $2 Blackwood wattle . . . 1·40 1·50
1625 $5 Soft tree fern and
mountain ash
(30 × 50 mm) . . . . . 3·50 3·75
See also Nos. 1679/90, 1854/66 and 2126/9.

557 Edwin Flack (800 and 1500
metres gold medal winner, 1896)

1996. Centennial Olympic Games and 10th
Paralympic Games, Atlanta. Multicoloured.
1627 45c. Type **557** 70 70
1628 45c. Fanny Durack (100
metres freestyle swimming
gold medal winner, 1912) 70 70
1629 $1.05 Wheelchair athletes . . 1·60 1·60

558 "Animalia" (Graeme Base)

1996. 50th Anniv of Children's Book Council
Awards. Designs taken from book covers. Ordinary
or self-adhesive gum. Multicoloured.
1630 45c. Type **558** 60 60
1631 45c. "Greetings from Sandy
Beach" (Bob Graham) . . 60 60
1632 45c. "Who Sank the Boat?"
(Pamela Allen) 60 60
1633 45c. "John Brown, Rose
and the Midnight Cat"
(Jenny Wagner, illustrated
by Ron Brooks) 60 60

559 American Bald Eagle, **560** Margaret
Kangaroo and Olympic Windeyer
Flame

1996. Passing of Olympic Flag to Sydney.
1638 **559** 45c. multicoloured . . . 55 50

1996. Centenary of the National Council of Women.
1639 **560** 45c. purple and yellow . . 50 50
1640 – $1 blue and yellow . . . 1·25 1·75
DESIGN: $1 Rose Scott.

561 Pearl

1996. Pearls and Diamonds. Multicoloured.
1641 45c. Type **561** 60 50
1642 $1.20 Diamond . . . . . . 1·40 1·50
The pearl on the 45c. is shown as an exelgram (holographic printing on ultra thin plastic film) and the diamond on the $1.20 as a hologram, each embossed on to the stamp.

562 Silhouettes of Female Dancer and Musician on Rural Landscape

1996. 50th Anniv of Arts Councils. Multicoloured.
1643 20c. Type **562** . . . . . 1·25 1·75
1644 45c. Silhouettes of musician and male dancer on landscape 35 40

563 Ginger Cats

1996. Australian Pets. Multicoloured.
1645 45c. Type **563** 60 60
1646 45c. Blue heeler dogs . . . 60 60
1647 45c. Cockatoo (30 × 25 mm) . 60 60
1648 45c. Duck with ducklings (25 × 30 mm) 60 60
1649 45c. Dog and cat (25 × 30 mm) 60 60
1650 45c. Ponies (30 × 50 mm) . . 60 60
Nos. 1645/6 also come self-adhesive.

564 Ferdinand von Mueller

1996. Australia–Germany Joint Issue. Death Centenary of Ferdinand von Mueller (botanist).
1654 **564** $1.20 multicoloured . . . 1·25 1·40

565 Willem de Vlamingh   **566** Madonna and Child

1996. 300th Anniv of the Visit of Willem de Vlamingh to Western Australia.
1655 **565** 45c. multicoloured . . . 75 75

1996. Christmas. Multicoloured.
1656 40c. Type **566** 55 30
1657 45c. Wise man with gift . . 55 30
1658 $1 Shepherd boy with lamb . 1·25 1·75
No. 1656 also comes self-adhesive.

567 "Landscape '74" (Fred Williams)

1997. Australia Day. Contemporary Paintings. Multicoloured.
1660 85c. Type **567** . . . . . 1·10 1·10
1661 90c. "The Balcony 2" (Brett Whiteley) . . . . 1·10 1·10
1662 $1.20 "Fire Haze at Gerringong" (Lloyd Rees) 1·40 1·40

568 Sir Donald Bradman   **569** Red Roses

1997. Australian Legends (1st series). Sir Donald Bradman (cricketer). Multicoloured.
1663 45c. Type **568** 55 55
1664 45c. Bradman playing stroke . 55 55
See also Nos. 1731/42 and 1838/9.

1997. St. Valentine's Day. Ordinary or self-adhesive gum.
1665 **569** 45c. multicoloured . . . 50 50

570 Ford Coupe Utility, 1934   **571** May Wirth and Horse

1997. Classic Cars. Multicoloured. Ordinary or self-adhesive gum.
1667 45c. Type **570** 60 60
1668 45c. GMH Holden 48-215 (FX), 1948 . . . . . 60 60
1669 45c. Austin Lancer, 1958 . . 60 60
1670 45c. Chrysler Valiant "R" Series, 1962 . . . . . 60 60

1997. 150th Anniv of the Circus in Australia. Multicoloured.
1675 45c. Type **571** 55 55
1676 45c. Con Colleano on tightrope 55 55
1677 45c. Clowns 55 55
1678 45c. Acrobats 55 55

1997. Fauna and Flora (2nd series). Kakadu Wetlands, Northern Territory. As T **556**. Mult.
1679 20c. Saltwater crocodile . . 15 20
1680 25c. Northern dwarf tree frog 20 25
1681 45c. Comb-crested jacana . . 75 60
1682 45c. Little kingfisher . . . 75 60
1683 45c. Brolga 75 60
1684 45c. Black-necked stork ("Jabiru") 75 60
1685 $1 "Cressida cressida" (butterfly) 70 75
1686 $10 Kakadu Wetlands (50 × 30 mm) . . . . 7·00 7·25
Nos. 1681/84 also come self-adhesive.

572 Royal Wedding 1d. Stamp of 1947   **573** Hand holding Globe and Lion's Emblem

1997. Queen Elizabeth II's Birthday.
1691 **572** 45c. purple 50 50

1997. 50th Anniv of First Australian Lions Club.
1692 **573** 45c. blue, brown and purple 50 50

574 Doll holding Teddy Bear (Kaye Wiggs)   **575** Police Rescue Helicopter

1997. Dolls and Teddy Bears. Multicoloured.
1693 45c. Type **574** 45 50
1694 45c. Teddy bear standing (Jennifer Laing) 45 50
1695 45c. Doll wearing white dress with teddy bear (Susie McMahon) 45 50
1696 45c. Doll in brown dress and bonnet (Lynda Jacobson) 45 50
1697 45c. Teddy bear sitting (Helen Williams) 45 50

1997. Emergency Services. Multicoloured.
1698 45c. Type **575** 80 65
1699 45c. Emergency Service volunteers carrying victim 80 65
1700 $1.05 Fire service at fire . . 1·60 1·75
1701 $1.20 Loading casualty into ambulance . . . . . 1·75 1·75

576 George Peppin Jnr (breeder) and Merino Sheep

1997. Bicentenary of Arrival of Merino Sheep in Australia. Multicoloured.
1702 45c. Type **576** 70 80
1703 45c. Pepe chair, cloth and wool logo . . . . . .

577 Dumbi the Owl

1997. "The Dreaming". Cartoons from Aboriginal Stories. Multicoloured.
1704 45c. Type **577** 65 30
1705 $1 The Two Willy-Willies . 1·40 95
1706 $1.20 How Brolga became a Bird . . . . 1·60 1·75
1707 $1.80 Tuggan-Tuggan . . . 2·25 2·50

578 "Rhoetosaurus brownei"   **579** Spotted-tailed Quoll

1997. Prehistoric Animals. Multicoloured.
1708 45c. Type **578** 45 50
1709 45c. "Mcnamaraspis kaprios" 45 50
1710 45c. "Ninjemys oweni" . . 45 50
1711 45c. "Paracylotosaurus davidi" 45 50
1712 45c. "Woolungasaurus glendowerensis" 45 50

1997. Nocturnal Animals. Multicoloured.
1713 45c. Type **579** 65 65
1714 45c. Barking owl 65 65
1715 45c. Platypus (30 × 25 mm) . 65 65
1716 45c. Brown antechinus (30 × 25 mm) 65 65
1717 45c. Dingo (30 × 25 mm) . . 65 65
1718 45c. Yellow-bellied glider (50 × 30 mm) 65 65
Nos. 1713/14 also come self-adhesive.

580 Woman

1997. Breast Cancer Awareness Campaign.
1722 **580** 45c. multicoloured . . . 70 45

581 Two Angels

1997. Christmas. Children's Nativity Play. Mult.
1723 40c. Type **581** 50 30
1724 45c. Mary 55 30
1725 $1 Three Kings . . . . . 1·25 1·75
No. 1723 also comes self-adhesive.

582 "Flying Cloud" (clipper) (J. Scott)

1998. Ship Paintings. Multicoloured.
1727 45c. Type **582** 60 30
1728 85c. "Marco Polo" (full-rigged ship) (T. Robertson) . . . . 1·00 1·00
1729 $1 "Chusan I" (steamship) (C. Gregory) . . . . 1·25 1·10
1730 $1.20 "Heather Belle" (clipper) . . . . . . 1·50 1·75

583 Betty Cuthbert (1956)   **584** "Champagne" Rose

1998. Australian Legends (2nd series). Olympic Gold Medal Winners. Multicoloured. Ordinary or self-adhesive gum.
1731 45c. Type **583** 45 50
1732 45c. Betty Cuthbert running . 45 50
1733 45c. Herb Elliott (1960) . . 45 50
1734 45c. Herb Elliott running . . 45 50
1735 45c. Dawn Fraser (1956, 1960 and 1964) . . . 45 50
1736 45c. Dawn Fraser swimming 45 50
1737 45c. Marjorie Jackson (1952) 45 50
1738 45c. Marjorie Jackson running 45 50
1739 45c. Murray Rose (1956) . . 45 50
1740 45c. Murray Rose swimming 45 50
1741 45c. Shirley Strickland (1952 and 1956) 45 50
1742 45c. Shirley Strickland hurdling 45 50

1998. Greeting Stamp. Ordinary or self-adhesive gum.
1755 **584** 45c. multicoloured . . . 55 45

585 Queen Elizabeth II

1998. Queen Elizabeth II's Birthday.
1757 **585** 45c. multicoloured . . . 50 40

586 Sea Hawk (helicopter) landing on Frigate

1998. 50th Anniv of Royal Australian Navy Fleet Air Arm.
1758 **586** 45c. multicoloured . . . 50 40

587 Sheep Shearer and Sheep

1998. Farming. Multicoloured. Ordinary or self-adhesive gum.

1759	45c. Type **587**		45	45
1760	45c. Barley and silo		45	45
1761	45c. Farmers herding beef cattle		45	45
1762	45c. Sugar cane harvesting		45	45
1763	45c. Two dairy cows		45	45

588 Cardiograph Trace and Heart

1998. Heart Disease Awareness.

1769	**588**	45c. multicoloured	40	45

589 Johnny OKeefe ("The Wild One", 1958)

1998. Australian Rock and Roll. Multicoloured. Ordinary or self-adhesive gum.

1770	45c. Type **589**		50	45
1771	45c. Col Joye ("Oh Yeah Uh Huh", 1959)		50	45
1772	45c. Little Pattie ("He's My Blonde Headed Stompie Wompie Real Gone Surfer Boy", 1963)		50	45
1773	45c. Normie Rowe ("Shakin all Over", 1965)		50	45
1774	45c. Easybeats ("She's so Fine", 1965)		50	45
1775	45c. Russell Morris ("The Real Thing", 1969)		50	45
1776	45c. Masters Apprentices ("Turn Up Your Radio", 1970)		50	45
1777	45c. Daddy Cool ("Eagle Rock", 1971)		50	45
1778	45c. Billy Thorpe and the Aztecs ("Most People I know think I'm Crazy", 1972)		50	45
1779	45c. Skyhooks ("Horror Movie", 1974)		50	45
1780	45c. AC/DC ("It's a Long Way to the Top", 1975)		50	45
1781	45c. Sherbet ("Howzat", 1976)		50	45

590 Helmeted Honeyeater (Yellow-tufted Honeyeater subspecies)

1998. Endangered Species. Multicoloured.

1794	5c. Type **590**		30	30
1795	5c. Orange-bellied parrot		30	30
1796	45c. Red-tailed black cockatoo		65	65
1797	45c. Gouldian finch		65	65

591 French Horn and Cello Players

1998. Youth Arts, Australia. Multicoloured.

1798	45c. Type **591**		50	50
1799	45c. Dancers		50	50

592 "Phalaenopsis rosenstromii"

1998. Australia–Singapore Joint Issue. Orchids. Multicoloured.

1800	45c. Type **592**		55	40
1801	85c. "Arundina graminifolia"		1·00	1·00
1802	$1 "Grammatophyllum speciosum"		1·25	1·25
1803	$1.20 "Dendrobium phalaenopsis"		1·50	1·60

593 Flying Angel with Teapot (cartoon by Michael Leunig)

1998. "The Teapot of Truth" (cartoons by Michael Leunig). Multicoloured.

1805	45c. Type **593**		50	55
1806	45c. Two birds in heart-shaped tree		50	55
1807	45c. Pouring tea		50	55
1808	$1 Mother and child (29 × 24 mm)		1·25	1·25
1809	$1.20 Cat with smiling face (29 × 24 mm)		1·50	1·60

594 Red Lacewing   **595** Flinders' Telescope and Map of Tasmania

1998. Butterflies. Multicoloured. Ordinary or self-adhesive gum.

1810	45c. Type **594**		65	65
1811	45c. Dull oakblue		65	65
1812	45c. Meadow argus		65	65
1813	45c. Ulysses butterfly		65	65
1814	45c. Common red-eye		65	65

1998. Bicentenary of the Circumnavigation of Tasmania by George Bass and Matthew Flinders. Multicoloured.

1820	45c. Type **595**		65	50
1821	45c. Sextant and letter from Bass		65	50

596 Weedy Seadragon   **597** Rose of Freedom

1998. International Year of the Ocean. Multicoloured.

1822	45c. Type **596**		65	65
1823	45c. Bottlenose dolphin		65	65
1824	45c. Fiery squid (24 × 29 mm)		65	65
1825	45c. Manta ray (29 × 24 mm)		65	65
1826	45c. White pointer shark (29 × 49 mm)		65	65
1827	45c. Southern right whale (49 × 29 mm)		65	65

Nos. 1822/3 also come self-adhesive.

1998. 50th Anniv of Universal Declaration of Human Rights.

1831	**597**	45c. multicoloured	50	50

598 Three Kings

1998. Christmas. Multicoloured.

1832	40c. Type **598**		40	25
1833	45c. Nativity scene		40	25
1834	$1 Mary and Joseph		1·10	1·50

No. 1832 also comes self-adhesive.

599 Australian Coat of Arms

1999. 50th Anniv of Australian Citizenship. Ordinary or self-adhesive gum.

1836	**599**	45c. multicoloured	50	50

600 Arthur Boyd

1999. Australian Legends (3rd series). Arthur Boyd (painter). Multicoloured. Ordinary or self-adhesive gum.

1838	45c. Type **600**		45	45
1839	45c. "Nebuchadnezzer on fire falling over Waterfall" (Arthur Boyd)		45	45

601 Red Roses

1999. Greetings Stamp. Romance. Ordinary or self-adhesive gum.

1842	**601**	45c. multicoloured	50	50

602 Elderly Man and Grandmother with Boy

1999. International Year of Older Persons. Mult.

1844	45c. Type **602**		45	45
1845	45c. Elderly woman and grandfather with boy		45	45

603 "Polly Woodside" (barque)   **604** Olympic Torch and 1956 7½d. Stamp

1999. Sailing Ships. Multicoloured.

1846	45c. Type **603**		60	35
1847	85c. "Alma Doepel" (topsail schooner)		1·00	90
1848	$1 "Enterprize" replica (topsail schooner)		1·25	1·10
1849	$1.05 "Lady Nelson" replica (topsail schooner)		1·40	1·60

1999. Olympic Torch Commemoration.

1853	**604**	$1.20 multicoloured	1·10	1·10

605 "Correa reflexa" (native fuchsia)   **607** "Here's Humphrey"

606 Queen Elizabeth II with The Queen Mother

1999. Fauna and Flora (3rd series). Coastal Environment. Multicoloured. Ordinary or self-adhesive gum.

1854	45c. Type **605**		30	35
1855	45c. "Hibbertia scandens" (guinea flower)		30	35
1856	45c. "Ipomoea pre-caprae" (beach morning glory)		30	35
1857	45c. "Wahlenbergia stricta" (Australian bluebells)		30	35
1858	70c. Humpback whales and zebra volute shell (29 × 24 mm)		50	55
1859	90c. Brahminy kite and checkerboard helmet shell (29 × 24 mm)		65	70
1860	90c. Fraser Island and chambered nautilus (29 × 24 mm)		65	70
1861	$1.05 Loggerhead turtle and melon shell (29 × 24 mm)		75	80
1862	$1.20 White-bellied sea eagle and Campbell's stromb shell (29 × 24 mm)		85	90

Nos. 1859/60 were printed together, se-tenant, forming a composite design.

1999. Queen Elizabeth II's Birthday.

1870	**606**	45c. multicoloured	50	40

1999. Children's Television Programmes. Multicoloured. Ordinary or self-adhesive gum.

1871	45c. Type **607**		45	45
1872	45c. "Bananas in Pyjamas"		45	45
1873	45c. "Mr. Squiggle"		45	45
1874	45c. "Play School" (teddy bears)		45	45
1875	45c. "Play School" (clock, toy dog and doll)		45	45

608 Obverse and Reverse of 1899 Sovereign

1999. Centenary of the Perth Mint.

1881	**608**	$2 gold, blue and green	2·00	1·75

609 Lineout against New Zealand   **610** Drilling at Burn's Creek and Rock Bolting in Tumut 2 Power Station Hall

1999. Centenary of Australian Test Rugby. Mult.

1882	45c. Type **609**		40	40
1883	45c. Kicking the ball against England		40	40
1884	$1 Try against South Africa (horiz)		85	85
1885	$1.20 Passing the ball against Wales (horiz)		1·10	1·25

Nos. 1882/3 also come self-adhesive.

1999. 50th Anniv of Snowy Mountain Scheme (hydro-electric project). Multicoloured. Ordinary or self-adhesive gum.

1888	45c. Type **610**		45	45
1889	45c. English class for migrant workers, Cooma		45	45
1890	45c. Tumut 2 Tailwater Tunnel and Eucumbene Dam		45	45
1891	45c. German carpenters and Island Bend Dam		45	45

611 Cálligraphy Pen and Letter   **612** Sydney Olympic Emblem

1999. Greetings Stamps. Multicoloured.

1896	45c. Type **611**		45	45
1897	45c. Wedding rings		45	45
1898	45c. Birthday cake		45	45
1899	45c. Christmas decoration		45	45
1900	45c. Teddy bear		45	45
1901	$1 Koala		80	85

See also No. 1921.

1999. Olympic Games, Sydney (2000) (1st issue).

1902	**612**	45c. multicoloured	50	40

613 Australia Post Symbol, 1975

1999. "Sydney Design '99" International Congress and Exhibition. Multicoloured.

1903	45c. Type **613**		45	30
1904	90c. Embryo chair, 1988		80	85
1905	$1.35 Possum skin textile, c.1985		1·25	1·25
1906	$1.50 Storey Hall, R.M.I.T. University, 1995		1·25	1·50

614 Magnificent Tree Frog **615** Madonna and Child

1999. National Stamp Collecting Month, Small Pond Life. Multicoloured. Ordinary or self-adhesive gum.

1907	45c. Type **614**	45	40
1908	45c. Sacred kingfisher	45	40
1909	45c. Roth's tree frog (29 × 24 mm)	45	40
1910	45c. Dragonfly (29 × 24 mm)	45	40
1911	50c. Javelin frog (24 × 29 mm)	50	40
1912	50c. Northern dwarf tree frog (24 × 29 mm)	50	40

1999. Christmas. Multicoloured.

1918	40c. Type **615**	45	30
1919	$1 Tree of Life (horiz)	1·00	1·00

No. 1918 also comes self-adhesive.

616 Fireworks and Hologram **617** Rachel Thomson (college administrator)

1999. Millennium Greetings stamp.

1921	**616** 45c. multicoloured	50	50

2000. New Millennium. "Face of Australia". Mult.

1922	45c. Nicholle and Meghan Triandis (twin babies)	45	50
1923	45c. David Willis (cattleman)	45	50
1924	45c. Natasha Bramley (scuba diver)	45	50
1925	45c. Cyril Watson (Aborigine boy)	45	50
1926	45c. Mollie Dowdall (wearing red hat) (vineyard worker)	45	50
1927	45c. Robin Dicks (flying instructor)	45	50
1928	45c. Mary Simons (retired nurse)	45	50
1929	45c. Peta and Samantha Nieuwerth (mother and baby)	45	50
1930	45c. John Matthews (doctor)	45	50
1931	45c. Edith Dizon-Fitzimmons (wearing drop earrings) (music teacher)	45	50
1932	45c. Philippa Weir (wearing brown hat) (teacher)	45	50
1933	45c. John Thurgar (in bush hat and jacket) (farmer)	45	50
1934	45c. Miguel Alzona (with face painted) (schoolboy)	45	50
1935	45c. Type **617**	45	50
1936	45c. Necip Akarsu (wearing blue shirt) (postmaster)	45	50
1937	45c. Justin Allan (R.A.N. sailor)	45	50
1938	45c. Wadad Dennaoui (wearing checked shirt) (student)	45	50
1939	45c. Jack Laity (market gardener)	45	50
1940	45c. Kelsey Stubbin (wearing cricket cap) (schoolboy)	45	50
1941	45c. Gianna Rossi (resting chin on hand) (church worker)	45	50
1942	45c. Paris Hansch (toddler)	45	50
1943	45c. Donald George Whatham (in blue shirt and tie) (retired teacher)	45	50
1944	45c. Stacey Coull (wearing pendant)	45	50
1945	45c. Alex Payne (wearing cycle helmet) (schoolgirl)	45	50
1946	45c. John Lodge (Salvation Army member)	45	50

618 Walter Parker

2000. Australian Legends (4th series). "The Last Anzacs". Multicoloured.

1947	45c. Type **618**	45	50
1948	45c. Roy Longmore	45	50
1949	45c. Alec Campbell	45	50
1950	45c. 1914–15 Star (medal)	45	50

Nos. 1947/50 also come self-adhesive.

619 Scenes from "Cloudstreet" (play) (Perth Festival) **620** Coast Banksia, False Sarsaparilla and Swamp Bloodwood (plants)

2000. Arts Festivals. Multicoloured.

1955	45c. Type **619**	45	50
1956	45c. Belgian dancers from Rosas Company (Adelaide Festival)	45	50
1957	45c. "Guardian Angel" (sculpture) and dancer (Sydney Festival)	45	50
1958	45c. Musician and Balinese dancer (Melbourne Festival)	45	50
1959	45c. Members of Vusa Dance Company of South Africa (Brisbane Festival)	45	50

2000. Gardens. Multicoloured. Ordinary or self-adhesive gum.

1960	45c. Type **620**	45	50
1961	45c. Eastern spinebill on swamp bottlebrush in foreground	45	50
1962	45c. Border of cannas	45	50
1963	45c. Roses, lake and ornamental bridge	45	50
1964	45c. Hibiscus with bandstand in background	45	50

621 Queen Elizabeth II in 1996

2000. Queen Elizabeth II's Birthday.

1970	**621** 45c. multicoloured	50	40

622 Medals and Korean Landscape

2000. 50th Anniv of Korean War.

1971	**622** 45c. multicoloured	50	40

623 Daisy **624** Taking the Vote, New South Wales

2000. Nature and Nation. Greeting stamps. Mult.

1972	45c. Type **623**	45	50
1973	45c. Australia on globe	45	50
1974	45c. Red kangaroo and flag	45	50
1975	45c. Sand, sea and sky	45	50
1976	45c. Rainforest	45	50

2000. Centenary of Commonwealth of Australia Constitution Act. Multicoloured.

1977	45c. Type **624**	45	40
1978	45c. Voters waiting for results, Geraldton, Western Australia	45	40
1979	$1.50 Queen Victoria (29 × 49 mm)	1·40	1·40
1980	$1.50 Women dancing ("The Fair New Nation") (29 × 49 mm)	1·40	1·40

625 Sydney Opera House, New South Wales

2000. International Stamps. Views of Australia (1st series). Multicoloured.

1982	50c. Type **625**	55	40
1983	$1 Nandroya Falls, Queensland	1·10	80
1984	$1.50 Sydney Harbour Bridge, New South Wales	1·50	1·25
1985	$2 Cradle Mountain, Tasmania	1·40	1·50
1986	$3 The Pinnacles, Western Australia	2·10	2·25
1987	$4.50 Flinders Ranges, South Australia (51 × 24 mm)	3·00	3·25
1988	$5 Twelve Apostles, Victoria (51 × 24 mm)	3·50	3·75
1989	$10 Devils Marbles, Northern Territory (51 × 24 mm)	7·00	7·25

Nos. 1982/9 were intended for international postage which, under changes in Australian tax laws from 1 July 2000, remained exempt from General Sales Tax.

See also Nos. 2121/5.

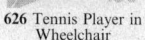

626 Tennis Player in Wheelchair **627** Sir Neville Howse (first Australian recipient of Victoria Cross, 1900)

2000. Paralympic Games, Sydney. Multicoloured. Ordinary or self-adhesive gum.

1990	45c. Type **626**	50	50
1991	45c. Amputee sprinting	50	50
1992	49c. Basketball player in wheelchair	50	50
1993	49c. Blind cyclist	50	50
1994	49c. Amputee putting the shot	50	50

2000. Cent of Australia's First Victoria Cross Award.

2000	**627** 45c. multicoloured	50	50
2001	– 45c. brown, gold and black	50	50
2002	– 45c. multicoloured	50	50
2003	– 45c. multicoloured	50	50
2004	– 45c. brown, gold and black	50	50

DESIGNS: No. 2001, Sir Roden Cutler, 1941; 2002, Victoria Cross; 2003, Private Edward Kenna, 1945; 2004, Warrant Officer Keith Payne, 1969.

628 Water Polo **629** Olympic Flag, Flame and Parthenon

2000. Olympic Games, Sydney. Multicoloured. Ordinary or self-adhesive gum. Competitors highlighted in varnish.

2005	45c. Type **628**	50	50
2006	45c. Hockey	50	50
2007	45c. Swimming	50	50
2008	45c. Basketball	50	50
2009	45c. Cycling (triathlon)	50	50
2010	45c. Horse riding	50	50
2011	45c. Tennis	50	50
2012	45c. Gymnastics	50	50
2013	45c. Running	50	50
2014	45c. Rowing	50	50

Nos. 2005/14 were printed together, se-tenant, with the backgrounds forming a composite design.

2000. Transfer of Olympic Flag from Sydney to Athens. Joint issue with Greece. Multicoloured.

2025	45c. Type **629**	50	40
2026	$1.50 Olympic Flag, Flame and Sydney Opera House	1·50	1·50

Stamps in similar designs were issued by Greece.

630 Ian Thorpe (Men's 400m Freestyle Swimming) **631** Martian Terrain

2000. Australian Gold Medal Winners at Sydney Olympic Games. Multicoloured.

2027A	45c. Type **630**	45	45
2028A	45c. Australian team (Men's 4 × 100 m Freestyle Swimming Relay)	45	45
2029A	45c. Michael Diamond (Men's Trap Shooting)	45	45
2030A	45c. Australian team (Three Day Equestrian Event)	45	45
2031A	45c. Susie O'Neill (Women's 200 m Freestyle Swimming)	45	45
2032A	45c. Australian team (Men's 4 × 200 m Freestyle Swimming Relay)	45	45
2033A	45c. Simon Fairweather (Men's Individual Archery)	45	45
2034A	45c. Australian team (Men's Madison Cycling)	45	45
2035A	45c. Grant Hackett (Men's 1500 m Freestyle Swimming)	45	45
2036A	45c. Australian team (Women's Water Polo)	45	45
2037A	45c. Australian team (Women's Beach Volleyball)	45	45
2038A	45c. Cathy Freeman (Women's 400 m Athletics)	45	45
2039A	45c. Lauren Burns (Women's under 49 kg Taekwondo)	45	45
2040A	45c. Australian team (Women's Hockey)	45	45
2041A	45c. Australian crew (Women's 470 Dinghy Sailing)	45	45
2042A	45c. Australian crew (Men's 470 Dinghy Sailing)	45	45

2000. Stamp Collecting Month. Exploration of Mars. Multicoloured. (a) Ordinary gum.

2043	45c. Type **631**	45	45
2044	45c. Astronaut using thruster	45	45
2045	45c. Spacecraft (50 × 30 mm)	45	45
2046	45c. Flight crew (30 × 25 mm)	45	45
2047	45c. Launch site (30 × 50 mm)	45	45
2048	45c. Robots on kelp rod (25 × 30 mm)	45	45

(b) Self-adhesive. Designs 21 × 32 mm.

2050	45c. Type **631**	45	45
2051	45c. Astronaut using thruster	45	45

632 Cathy Freeman with Olympic Torch and Ring of Flames

2000. Opening Ceremony, Olympic Games, Sydney.

2052	**632** 45c. multicoloured	50	50

633 Blind Athlete carrying Olympic Torch

2000. Paralympic Games, Sydney (2nd issue). Multicoloured.

2053	45c. Type **633**	55	50
2054	45c. Paralympic Games logo	55	50

634 Siobhan Paton (swimmer) **635** "Sleep in Heavenly Peace"

2000. Siobhan Paton, Paralympian of the Year.

2055	**634** 45c. multicoloured	50	45

2000. Christmas. "Silent Night" (carol). Multicoloured. (a) Ordinary gum.

2056	40c. Type **635**	45	25
2057	45c. "All is Calm, All is Bright"	50	25

(b) Self-adhesive.

2059	40c. Type **635**	45	35

(c) International Mail. As T **625** inscr "Season's Greetings".

2060	80c. Byron Bay, New South Wales	70	85

2001. International Mail. No. 1901 optd **International POST**.

2061	$1 Koala	1·00	80

637 Parade passing Federation Arch, Sydney

2001. Centenary of Federation. Multicoloured. (a) Ordinary gum.

2062 49c. Type **637** 45 40
2063 49c. Edmund Barton (first Federal Prime Minister) 45 40
2064 $2 "Australia For Ever" (song sheet) and celebration picnic (50 × 30 mm) . . . . . . 1·75 2·00
2065 $2 State Banquet, Sydney (30 × 50 mm) . . . . . . 1·75 2·00

(b) Self-adhesive.

2067 49c. Type **637** 45 40
2068 49c. Edmund Barton (first Federal Prime Minister) 45 40

638 Slim Dusty with Guitar in 1940s

2001. Australian Legends (5th series). Slim Dusty (country music singer). Multicoloured. Ordinary or self-adhesive gum.

2069 45c. Type **638** 45 45
2070 45c. Slim Dusty wearing "Sundowner" hat 45 45

639 Light Horse Parade, 1940, and Command Post, New Guinea, 1943

2001. Centenary of Australian Army. Multicoloured.

2073 45c. Type **639** 45 45
2074 45c. Soldier carrying Rwandan child and officers on the Commando Selection Course 45 45

640 Entry Canopy, Skylights and Site Plan

2001. Opening of the National Museum, Canberra. Multicoloured.

2075 49c. Type **640** 45 45
2076 49c. Skylights and "Pangk" (wallaby sculpture) . . . 45 45

2001. Sir Donald Bradman (cricketer) Commemoration. Nos. 1663/4 additionally inscribed "1908–2001" in red. Multicoloured.

2077 45c. Type **568** 45 45
2078 45c. Bradman playing stroke 45 45

641 "Khe Sanh" (Cold Chisel), 1978

2001. Australian Rock and Pop Music. Multicoloured. Ordinary or self-adhesive gum.

2079 45c. Type **641** 45 45
2080 45c. "Down Under" (Men at Work), 1981 . . . . . 45 45
2081 45c. "Power and the Passion" (Midnight Oil), 1983 . . . . 45 45
2082 45c. "Original Sin" (INXS), 1984 . . . . 45 45
2083 45c. "You're the Voice" (John Farnham), 1986 . . 45 45
2084 45c. "Don't Dream it's Over" (Crowded House), 1986 . . . . 45 45
2085 45c. "Treaty" (Yothu Yindi), 1991 . . . . . . 45 45
2086 45c. "Tomorrow" (Silverchair), 1994 . . . . 45 45
2087 45c. "Confide in Me" (Kylie Minogue), 1994 . . . . . 45 45
2088 45c. "Truly, Madly, Deeply" (Savage Garden), 1997 . . 45 45

642 Queen Elizabeth II holding Bouquet

643 Party Balloons

2001. Queen Elizabeth II's Birthday.

2099 **642** 45c. multicoloured . . . 50 40

2001. "Colour My Day". Greetings Stamps. (a) Domestic Mail.

2100 45c. Type **643** 45 50
2101 45c. Smiling Flower 45 50
2102 45c. Hologram and party streamers 45 50

(b) International Mail.

2103 $1 Kangaroo and joey . . . 85 80
2104 $1.50 The Bayulu Banner 1·25 1·50

644 "Opening of the First Federal Parliament" (Charles Nuttall)

2001. Centenary of Federal Parliament. Paintings. Multicoloured.

2105 45c. Type **644** 45 40
2106 $2.45 "Prince George opening the First Parliament of the Commonwealth of Australia" (Tom Roberts) 2·25 2·25

645 Telecommunications Tower

2001. Outback Services. Multicoloured. Ordinary or self-adhesive gum.

2108 45c. Type **645** 30 35
2109 45c. Road train 30 35
2110 45c. School of the Air pupil 30 35
2111 45c. Outback family and mail box 30 35
2112 45c. Royal Flying Doctor Service aircraft and ambulance 30 35

646 Dragon Boat and Hong Kong Convention and Exhibition Centre

2001. Joint Issue with Hong Kong. Dragon Boat Racing. Multicoloured. (a) Domestic Mail.

2118 45c. Type **646** 30 35

(b) International Mail.

2119 $1 Dragon boat and Sydney Opera House 70 75

2001. International Stamps. Views of Australia (2nd series). As T **625**. Multicoloured.

2121 50c. The Three Sisters, Blue Mountains, New South Wales 35 40
2122 $1 The Murrumbidgee River, Australian Capital Territory 70 75
2123 $1.50 Four Mile Beach, Port Douglas, Queensland . . 1·10 1·25
2124 $20 Uluru Rock at dusk, Northern Territory (52 × 24 mm) . . . . . . 14·00 14·50

No. 2121 also comes self-adhesive.

647 Variegated Wren

649 Christmas Tree

648 Daniel Solander (Swedish botanist) and Mango Tree

2001. Fauna and Flora (4th series). Desert Birds. Multicoloured. Ordinary or self-adhesive gum.

2126 45c. Type **647** 30 35
2127 45c. Painted finch ("Firetail") 30 35
2128 45c. Crimson chat 30 35
2129 45c. Budgerigar 30 35

2001. Australia–Sweden Joint Issue. Daniel Solander's Voyage with Captain Cook. Multicoloured. (a) Domestic Mail.

2134 45c. Type **648** 30 35

(b) International Mail.

2135 $1.50 H.M.S. *Endeavour* on reef and Kapok tree . . . 1·10 1·25

2001. Christmas (1st issue). Multicoloured. (a) Domestic Mail.

2136 40c. Type **649** 30 35

(b) International Mail.

2137 80c. Star 55 60

See also Nos. 2157/8.

650 Australia on Globe

2001. Commonwealth Heads of Government Meeting (No. 2138) and Commonwealth Parliamentary Conference (No. 2139). Mult.

2138 45c. Type **650** 30 35
2139 45c. Southern Cross 30 35

651 Wedge-tailed Eagle

2001. Centenary of Birds of Australia. Birds of Prey. Multicoloured.

2140 49c. Type **651** 35 40
2141 49c. Australian kestrel ("Nankeen Kestrel") . . . 35 40
2142 98c. Red goshawk (vert) . . 70 75
2143 98c. Spotted harrier (vert) 70 75

652 Cockatoos dancing to Animal Band

653 "Adoration of the Magi"

2001. National Stamp Collecting Month. "Wild Babies" (cartoons). Multicoloured. Ordinary or self-adhesive gum.

2144 45c. Type **652** 30 35
2145 45c. Kevin Koala with birthday cake 30 35
2146 45c. Ring-tailed possums eating 30 35
2147 45c. Bilbies at foot of tree 30 35
2148 45c. James Wombat on rope ladder 30 35
2149 45c. Wallaby, echidna and platypus on rope ladder 30 35

2001. Christmas (2nd issue). Miniatures from "Wharncliffe Hours Manuscript". Multicoloured.

2157 40c. Type **653** 20 25
2158 45c. "Flight into Egypt" . . 30 35

No. 2157 also comes self-adhesive.

654 Sir Gustav Nossal (immunologist)

2002. Australian Legends. (6th series). Medical Scientists. Ordinary or self-adhesive gum. Multicoloured.

2160 45c. Type **654** 30 35
2161 45c. Nancy Millis (microbiologist) 30 35
2162 45c. Peter Doherty (immunologist) 30 35
2163 45c. Fiona Stanley (epidemiologist) 30 35
2164 45c. Donald Metcalf (haematologist) 30 35

655 Queen Elizabeth in 1953

2002. Golden Jubilee. Multicoloured.

2170 45c. Type **655** 30 35
2171 $2.45 Queen Elizabeth in Italy, 2000 . . . . 1·75 1·90

656 Steven Bradbury (Men's 1000m Short Track Speed Skating)

2002. Australian Gold Medal Winners at Salt Lake City Winter Olympic Games. Multicoloured.

2173 45c. Type **656** 30 35
2174 45c. Alisa Camplin (Women's Aerials Freestyle Skiing) 30 35

657 Austin 7 and Bugatti Type 40, Australian Grand Prix, Phillip Island, 1928

658 Macquarie Lighthouse

2002. Centenary of Motor Racing in Australia and New Zealand. Multicoloured. (a) Ordinary or self-adhesive gum.

2175 45c. Type **657** 30 35
2176 45c. Jaguar Mark II, Australian Touring Car Championship, Mallala, 1963 . . . . 30 35
2177 45c. Repco-Brabham, Tasman Series, Sandown, 1966 . . . . 30 35
2178 45c. Holden Torana and Ford Falcon, Hardie-Ferodo 500, Bathurst, 1972 . . . . 30 35
2179 45c. William's Ford, Australian Grand Prix, Calder, 1980 . . . . . . 30 35
2180 45c. Benetton-Renault, Australian Grand Prix, Albert Park, 2001 . . . . 30 35

2002. Lighthouses. Multicoloured.

2187 45c. Type **658** 30 35
2188 49c. Cape Naturaliste . . . 35 40
2189 49c. Troubridge Island . . . 35 40
2190 $1.50 Cape Bruny . . . . . 1·10 1·25

Nos. 2188/9 also came self adhesive.

659 Nicolas Baudin, Kangaroo, *Geographe* (ship) and Map

2002. Australia—France Joint Issue. Bicentenary of Flinders—Baudin Meeting at Encounter Bay. Multicoloured. (a) Domestic Mail.
2193	45c. Type **659**	. . . . . .	30	35

(b) International Mail.
2194	$1.50 Matthew Flinders, Port Lincoln Parrot, *Investigator* (ship) and Map	. . . . . .	1·10	1·25

2002. International Stamps. Views of Australia (3rd series). As T **625.** Multicoloured.
2195	50c. Walker Flat, River Murray, South Australia		35	40
2196	$1 Mt. Roland, Tasmania		70	75
2197	$1.50 Cape Leveque, Western Australia		1·10	1·250

Nos. 2195/6 also came self adhesive.

OFFICIAL STAMPS

1931. Optd **O.S.** (a) Kangaroo issue.
O133	**1**	6d. brown	20·00	20·00

(b) King George V issue.
O128	**3**	½d. orange	4·75	1·50
O129		1d. green	3·25	45
O130		2d. red	7·00	55
O131		3d. blue	7·50	4·00
O126		4d. olive	16·00	3·75
O132		3d. brown	35·00	27·00

(c) Various issues.
O123	**13**	2d. red	55·00	16·00
O134	**18**	2d. red	5·00	2·00
O124	**13**	3d. blue	£200	32·00
O135	**18**	3d. blue	14·00	5·00
O136	**17**	1s. green	40·00	27·00

POSTAGE DUE STAMPS

D 1   **D 3**

1902. White space below value at foot.
D1	**D 1**	½d. green	3·25	4·25
D2		1d. green	12·00	6·00
D3		2d. green	30·00	7·00
D4		3d. green	30·00	20·00
D5		4d. green	42·00	12·00
D6		6d. green	55·00	9·50
D7		8d. green	95·00	75·00
D8		5s. green	£180	70·00

1902. White space filled in.
D22	**D 3**	½d. green	7·50	7·00
D23		1d. green	6·50	2·75
D24		2d. green	20·00	2·75
D25		3d. green	60·00	12·00
D26		4d. green	50·00	9·00
D17		5d. green	42·00	9·50
D28		6d. green	50·00	10·00
D29		8d. green	£120	50·00
D18		10d. green	70·00	17·00
D19		1s. green	55·00	10·00
D20		2s. green	£100	18·00
D33		5s. green	£180	21·00
D43		10s. green	£1600	£1300
D44		20s. green	£3500	£2250

1908. As Type **D 3**, but stroke after figure of value, thus "5/-".
D58	**D 3**	1s. green	75·00	8·50
D60		2s. green	£850	£1400
D59		5s. green	£200	48·00
D61		10s. green	£2000	£2500
D62		20s. green	£5500	£7000

D 7   **D 10**

1909.
D132	**D 7**	½d. red and green	2·00	2·00
D133		1d. red and green	3·00	3·50
D 93		1½d. red and green	1·50	9·00
D121		2d. red and green	5·00	1·25
D134		3d. red and green	1·75	3·00
D109		4d. red and green	6·50	2·25
D124		5d. red and green	12·00	3·50
D137		6d. red and green	2·75	3·50
D126		7d. red and green	4·25	8·50
D127		8d. red and green	11·00	26·00
D139		10d. red and green	4·50	3·25
D128		1s. red and green	18·00	1·75
D 70		2s. red and green	70·00	13·00
D 71		5s. red and green	90·00	15·00
D 72		10s. red and green	£250	£150
D 73		£1 red and green	£475	£275

1953.
D140	**D 10**	1s. red and green	5·00	2·75
D130		2s. red and green	18·00	12·00
D131a		5s. red and green	12·00	70

AUSTRALIAN ANTARCTIC TERRITORY   Pt. 1

By an Order in Council of 7 February 1933, the territory S. of latitude 60°S. between 160th and 145th meridians of East longitude (excepting Adelie Land) was placed under Australian administration. Until 1957 stamps of Australia were used from the base.

1957. 12 pence = 1 shilling;
20 shillings = 1 pound.
1966. 100 cents = 1 dollar.

1 1954 Expedition at Vestfold Hills and Map

1957.
1	**1**	2s. blue	. . . . . .	80	50

2 Members of Shackleton Expedition at S. Magnetic Pole, 1909   **3** Weazel and Team

1959.
2	**2**	5d. on 4d. black and sepia	60	15
3	**3**	8d. on 7d. black and blue	3·00	2·25
4	—	1s. myrtle	3·00	2·00
5	—	2s.3d. green	7·00	4·00

DESIGNS—VERT (as Type **3**): 1s. Dog-team and iceberg; 2s.3d. Map of Antarctica and emperor penguins.

6   **7** Sir Douglas Mawson (Expedition leader)

1961.
6	**6**	5d. blue	1·25	20

1961. 50th Anniv of 1911–14 Australian Antarctic Expedition.
7	**7**	5d. myrtle	35	20

8 Aurora and Camera Dome   **11** Sastrugi (Snow Ridges)

1966. Multicoloured.
8	1c. Type **8**		70	30
9	2c. Emperor penguins		3·00	80
10	4c. Ship and iceberg		90	90
11	5c. Banding southern elephant-seals		2·75	1·75
12	7c. Measuring snow strata		80	80
13	10c. Wind gauges		1·00	1·10
14	15c. Weather balloon		5·00	2·00
15	20c. Bell Trooper helicopter (horiz)		6·00	3·00
16	25c. Radio operator (horiz)		3·00	3·00
17	50c. Ice-compression tests (horiz)		4·50	5·50
18	$1 Parahelion ("mock sun") (horiz)		22·00	14·00

1971. 10th Anniv of Antarctic Treaty.
19	**11**	6c. blue and black	75	1·00
20	—	30c. multicoloured	2·75	6·00

DESIGN: 30c. Pancake ice.

12 Capt. Cook, Sextant and Compass   **13** Plankton

1972. Bicentenary of Cook's Circumnavigation of Antarctica. Multicoloured.
21	7c. Type **12**	. . . . .	1·00	75
22	35c. Chart and H.M.S. "Resolution"		3·50	3·50

1973. Multicoloured.
23	1c. Type **13**		30	15
24	5c. Mawson's De Havilland Gipsy Moth, 1931		70	70
25	7c. Adelie penguin		1·75	70
26	8c. De Havilland Fox Moth, 1934–37		75	90
27	9c. Leopard seal (horiz)		40	90
28	10c. Killer whale (horiz)		3·75	2·00
29	20c. Wandering albatross ("Albatross") (horiz)		1·00	1·00
30	25c. Wilkins's Lockheed Vega "San Francisco", 1928 (horiz)		75	1·00
31	30c. Ellsworth's Northrop Gamma "Polar Star", 1935		75	1·00
32	35c. Christensen's Avro Type 581 Avian, 1934 (horiz)		75	1·00
33	50c. Byrd's Ford Trimotor "Floyd Bennett", 1929		75	1·00
34	$1 Sperm whale		1·00	1·40

14 Admiral Byrd (expedition leader), Ford Trimotor "Floyd Bennett" and Map of South Pole   **15** "Thala Dan" (supply ship)

1979. 50th Anniv of First Flight over South Pole. Multicoloured.
35	20c. Type **14**		25	60
36	55c. Admiral Byrd, aircraft and Antarctic terrain		50	1·25

1979. Ships. Multicoloured.
37	1c. "Aurora" (horiz)		15	10
38	2c. "Penola" (Rymill's ship)		40	10
39	5c. Type **15**		30	40
40	10c. H.M.S. "Challenger" (survey ship) (horiz)		50	55
41	15c. "Morning" (bow view) (whaling ship) (horiz)		2·00	3·00
42	15c. "Nimrod" (stern view) (Shackleton's ship) (horiz)		1·40	60
43	20c. "Discovery II" (supply ship) (horiz)		1·25	1·50
44	22c. "Terra Nova" (Scott's ship) (horiz)		90	1·25
45	25c. "Endurance" (Shackleton's ship)		60	1·00
46	30c. "Fram" (Amundsen's ship) (horiz)		60	1·75
47	35c. "Nella Dan" (supply ship) (horiz)		80	1·75
48	40c. "Kista Dan" (supply ship)		1·25	1·00
49	45c. "L'Astrolabe" (D'Urville's ship) (horiz)		70	70
50	50c. "Norvegia" (supply ship) (horiz)		70	70
51	55c. "Discovery" (Scott's ship)		1·00	2·00
52	$1 H.M.S. "Resolution" (Cook's ship)		1·75	2·50

No. 41 is incorrectly inscr "S.Y. Nimrod".

16 Sir Douglas Mawson in Antarctic Terrain   **17** Light-mantled Sooty Albatross

1982. Birth Centenary of Sir Douglas Mawson (Antarctic explorer). Multicoloured.
53	27c. Type **16**		25	25
54	75c. Sir Douglas Mawson and map of Australian Antarctic Territory		75	1·50

1983. Regional Wildlife. Multicoloured.
55	27c. Type **17**		60	90
56	27c. King cormorant ("Macquarie Island shag")		60	90
57	27c. Southern elephant seal		60	90

18 Antarctic Scientist   **19** Prismatic Compass and Lloyd-Creak Dip Circle

58	27c. Royal penguin		60	90
59	27c. Dove prion ("Antarctic prion")		60	90

1983. 12th Antarctic Treaty Consultative Meeting. Canberra.
60	**18**	27c. multicoloured	55	55

1984. 75th Anniv of Magnetic Pole Expedition. Multicoloured.
61	**19**	30c. Type **19**	30	30
62		85c. Aneroid barometer and theodolite	70	1·25

20 Dog Team pulling Sledge   **21** Prince Charles Mountains near Mawson Station

1984. Antarctic Scenes. Multicoloured.
63	2c. Summer afternoon, Mawson Station		10	40
64	5c. Type **20**		15	15
65	10c. Late summer evening, MacRobertson Land		15	15
66	15c. Prince Charles Mountains		15	20
67	20c. Summer morning, Wilkesland		15	20
68	25c. Sea-ice and iceberg		60	1·00
69	30c. Mount Coates		25	30
70	33c. "Iceberg Alley", Mawson		25	60
71	36c. Early winter evening, Casey Station		30	35
72	45c. Brash ice (vert)		70	1·50
73	60c. Midwinter shadows, Casey Station		50	55
74	75c. Coastline		2·25	2·75
75	85c. Landing strip		2·50	3·00
76	90c. Pancake ice (vert)		75	80
77	$1 Emperor penguins		2·75	1·25

1986. 25th Anniv of Antarctic Treaty.
78	**21**	36c. multicoloured	1·25	1·10

22 Hourglass Dolphins and "Nella Dan"   **23** "Antarctica"

1988. Environment, Conservation and Technology. Multicoloured.
79	37c. Type **22**		1·10	1·25
80	37c. Emperor penguins and Davis Station		1·10	1·25
81	37c. Crabeater seal and Hughes 500D helicopters		1·10	1·25
82	37c. Adelie penguins and tracked vehicle		1·10	1·25
83	37c. Grey-headed albatross and photographer		1·10	1·25

1989. Antarctic Landscape Paintings by Sir Sidney Nolan. Multicoloured.
84	39c. Type **23**		1·00	1·00
85	39c. "Iceberg Alley"		1·00	1·00
86	60c. "Glacial Flow"		1·75	1·50
87	80c. "Frozen Sea"		2·25	1·75

24 "Aurora Australis"

1991. 30th Anniv of Antarctic Treaty (43c.) and Maiden Voyage of "Aurora Australis" (research ship) ($1.20). Multicoloured.
88	43c. Type **24**		75	60
89	$1.20 "Aurora Australis" off Heard Island		2·75	3·50

25 Adelie Penguin and Chick 26 Head of Husky

1992. Antarctic Wildlife. Multicoloured.

90	45c. Type 25	30	35
91	75c. Elephant seal with pup	55	60
92	85c. Hall's giant petrel ("Northern giant petrel") on nest with fledgeling	60	65
93	95c. Weddell seal and pup	65	70
94	$1 Royal penguin	70	75
95	$1.20 Emperor penguins with chicks (vert)	85	90
96	$1.40 Fur seal	1·00	1·10
97	$1.50 King penguin (vert)	1·10	1·25

1994. Departure of Huskies from Antarctica. Multicoloured.

104	45c. Type 26	1·25	65
105	75c. Dogs pulling sledge (horiz)	1·50	1·75
106	85c. Husky in harness	1·75	2·00
107	$1.05 Dogs on leads (horiz)	2·00	2·25

27 Humpback Whale with Calf

1995. Whales and Dolphins. Multicoloured.

108	45c. Type 27	1·25	80
109	45c. Pair of hourglass dolphins (vert)	1·25	1·25
110	45c. Pair of minke whales (vert)	1·25	1·25
111	$1 Killer whale	2·00	2·00

Nos. 109/10 were printed together, se-tenant, forming a composite design.

28 "Rafting Sea Ice" (Christian Clare Robertson) 29 Apple Huts

1996. Paintings by Christian Clare Robertson. Multicoloured.

113	45c. Type 28	80	70
114	45c. "Shadow on the Plateau"	80	70
115	$1 "Ice Cave"	1·75	1·40
116	$1.20 "Twelve Lake"	1·90	1·60

1997. 50th Anniv of Australian National Antarctic Research Expeditions (A.N.A.R.E.). Multicoloured.

117	45c. Type 29	55	55
118	45c. Tuning a radio receiver	55	55
119	95c. Summer surveying	90	1·10
120	$1.05 Scientists in cage above sea ice	1·00	1·25
121	$1.20 Scientists and tents	1·25	1·40

30 "Aurora Australis" (research ship)

1998. Antarctic Transport. Multicoloured.

122	45c. Type 30	1·25	1·25
123	45c. "Skidoo"	1·25	1·25
124	$1 Helicopter lifting quad-bike (vert)	2·25	2·25
125	$2 Hagglunds tractor and trailer (vert)	2·50	2·50

31 Sir Douglas Mawson (expedition leader, 1911–14) and "Aurora" (research ship)

1999. Restoration of Mawson's Huts, Cape Denison. Each including a background drawing of a hut. Multicoloured.

126	45c. Type 31	70	70
127	45c. Huts in blizzard	70	70
128	90c. Husky team	1·10	1·10
129	$1.35 Conservation in progress	1·40	1·40

32 Emperor Penguins

2000. Penguins. Multicoloured.

130	45c. Type 32	50	55
131	45c. Adelie penguins	50	55

33 Adelie Penguins with Egg

2001. Centenary of Australian Antarctic Exploration. Multicoloured.

132	5c. Type 33	10	15
133	5c. Louis Bernacchi (physicist)	10	15
134	5c. *Nimrod* (Shackleton)	10	15
135	5c. Mackay, Edgeworth David and Mawson at South Magnetic Pole, 1909	10	15
136	5c. Taylor and Debenham (geologists)	10	15
137	10c. Early radio set	10	15
138	10c. Lockheed-Vega aircraft and husky team	10	15
139	10c. Sir Douglas Mawson	10	15
140	10c. Members of BANZARE Expedition, 1929–31	10	15
141	10c. Hoisting Union Jack	10	15
142	25c. Hoisting Australian flag, 1948	20	25
143	25c. Hagglund vehicle and helicopter	20	25
144	25c. *Aurora australis* over Casey	20	25
145	25c. Scientist with weather balloon	20	25
146	25c. Modern Antarctic clothing and "apple" hut	20	25
147	45c. *Nella Dan* (supply ship) and emperor penguins	30	35
148	45c. Male and female scientists taking ice sample	30	35
149	45c. Scientist using satellite phone	30	35
150	45c. Weddell seal and tourists	30	35
151	45c. Satellite photograph of Antarctica	30	35

Nos. 132/51 were printed together, se-tenant, with the backgrounds forming a composite design.

Each stamp carries an inscription on the reverse, printed over the gum.

34 Female Leopard Seal and Pup

2001. Endangered Species. Leopard Seal. Mult.

152	45c. Type 34	30	35
153	45c. Male seal on ice floe chasing penguins	30	35
154	45c. Female seal and pup swimming underwater	30	35
155	45c. Adult seal chasing Adelie penguins underwater	30	35

AUSTRIA Pt. 2

A state of Central Europe, part of the Austro-Hungarian Monarchy and Empire until 1918. At the end of the First World War the Empire was dismembered and German-speaking Austria became a Republic.

Austria was absorbed into the German Reich in 1938 and remained part of Germany until 1945. Following occupation by the four Allied Powers the Austrian Republic was re-established on 14 May 1945.

1850. 60 kreuzer = 1 gulden.
1858. 100 kreuzer = 1 gulden.
1899. 100 heller = 1 krone.
1925. 100 groschen = 1 schilling.
1938. 100 pfennig = 1 German reichsmark.
1945. 100 groschen = 1 schilling.
2002. 100 cents = 1 euro.

1 Arms of Austria 4 5

1850. Imperf.

6a	1	1k. yellow	£1300	80·00
7		2k. black	£800	50·00
8a		3k. red	£275	2·00
9		6k. brown	£500	3·25
10		9k. blue	£500	1·40

For stamps in Type **1** with values in "CENTES", see Lombardy and Venetia.

1858.

22	5	2k. yellow	£600	38·00
23	4	3k. black	£1100	£150
24		3k. green	£1100	95·00
25	5	5k. red	£190	1·25
26		10k. brown	£500	3·25
27		15k. blue	£500	1·40

For stamps in Types **4** and **5** with values in "SOLDI", see Lombardy and Venetia.

The portraits on Austrian stamps to 1906 are of the Emperor Francis Joseph I.

10 12 Arms of Austria

1860.

33	10	2k. yellow	£300	24·00
34		3k. green	£325	19·00
35		5k. red	£300	40
36		10k. brown	£700	1·10
37		15k. blue	£800	75

1863.

45	12	2k. yellow	£100	8·00
46		3k. green	£100	7·50
47		5k. red	35·00	20
48		10k. blue	£100	1·75
49		15k. brown	£110	1·00

A H 14 A H 16 20

1867.

59	A H 14	2k. yellow	6·50	55
60		3k. green	24·00	40
62		5k. red	1·75	10
63		10k. blue	60·00	20
64		15k. brown	4·00	3·00
56a		25k. grey	17·00	10·50
66	A H 16	50k. brown	10·00	65·00

1883.

70	20	2k. brown	4·75	35
71		3k. green	4·25	20
72		5k. red	9·25	15
73		10k. blue	3·75	15
74		20k. grey	38·00	3·25
75a		50k. mauve	£250	50·00

23 24 25

1890.

79	23	1k. grey	1·50	15
80		2k. brown	30	15
81		3k. green	40	15
82		5k. red	40	15
83		10k. blue	85	10
84		12k. purple	2·50	25
85		15k. purple	2·00	25
86		20k. green	30·00	1·90
87		24k. blue	2·50	1·10
88		30k. brown	2·50	60
89		50k. mauve	6·50	6·50
90	24	1g. blue	2·00	1·90
105		1g. lilac	42·00	4·00
91		2g. red	3·75	5·00
106		2g. green	10·00	32·00

1891. Figures in black.

92	25	20k. green	1·40	15
93		24k. blue	2·75	65
94		30k. brown	1·40	20
95		50k. mauve	1·75	35

27 28

29 30

1899. Corner numerals in black on heller values.

107	27	1h. mauve	55	10
108		2h. grey	2·40	40
140		3h. brown	50	10
141		5h. green	25	10
142		6h. orange	25	10
143	28	10h. red	40	10
144		20h. brown	80	10
145		25h. blue	80	20
146		30h. mauve	2·10	1·00
147	29	35h. green	1·45	25
148		40h. green	2·10	3·25
149		50h. blue	4·50	6·50
150		60h. brown	2·25	90
119a	30	1k. red	3·25	15
120		2k. lilac	40·00	40
121		4k. green	4·25	9·00

33 35

1904. Types as before, but with corners containing figures altered as T **33** and **35**. Figures in black on white on 10h. to 30h. only.

169	33	1h. purple	10	35
170		2h. black	15	30
171		3h. brown	40	10
183		5h. green	30	10
173		6h. orange	40	10
160	28	10h. red	2·25	10
161		20h. brown	32·00	80
162		25h. blue	32·00	80
163		30h. mauve	40·00	1·60
178	35	35h. green	3·00	30
179		40h. purple	3·00	70
180		50h. blue	3·00	2·75
181		60h. brown	3·00	55
168		72h. red	1·40	1·50

1906. Figures on plain white ground and stamps printed in one colour.

184	28	10h. red	35	10
185		12h. violet	85	65
186		20h. brown	3·00	15
187		25h. blue	3·00	35
188		30h. red	5·75	15

37 Francis Joseph I 38 Francis Joseph I

41 Schonbrunn 42 Francis Joseph I

1908. 60th Anniv of Emperor's Accession.

189	–	1h. black	20	10
190	–	2h. violet	20	10
191	–	3h. purple	30	10
192	37	5h. green	20	10
193	–	6h. brown	55	55
194	37	10h. red	15	10
195	–	12h. red	1·25	75
196	–	20h. brown	3·00	20
197	37	25h. blue	2·40	15
198	–	30h. green	5·00	15
199	–	35h. grey	2·50	20
200	38	50h. green	40	10
201	–	60h. red	25	10
202	38	72h. brown	1·40	15
203	–	1k. violet	8·00	10
204	41	2k. green and red	13·00	20
205	–	5k. purple and brown	25·00	2·75
206	42	10k. brown, blue & ochre	£120	42·00

DESIGNS—As Type **37**: 1h. Charles VI; 2h. Maria Theresa; 3h. Joseph II; 6h. Leopold II; 12h. Francis I; 20h. Ferdinand; 30h. Francis Joseph I in 1848; 35h. Same in 1878. As Type **38**: 60h. Francis Joseph I on horseback; 1k. Same in ceremonial robes. As Type **41**: 5k. Hofburg.

45    **47**

1910. 80th Birthday of Francis Joseph I. As issue of
1908 but with dates added as T **45**.

223	1h. black	4·00	6·50
224	2h. violet	5·25	8·50
225	3h. purple	4·75	7·00
226	5h. green	15	25
227	6h. brown	2·75	5·00
228	10h. red	15	25
229	12h. red	3·25	6·50
230	20h. brown	5·75	6·50
231	25h. blue	1·40	1·25
232	30h. green	3·25	5·00
233	35h. grey	3·25	5·00
234	50h. green	5·25	8·50
235	60h. red	5·25	8·50
236	1k. violet	5·75	9·50
237	2k. green and red	£130	£190
238	5k. purple and brown	90·00	£150
239	10k. brown, blue and ochre	£160	£300

1914. War Charity Funds.

240	**47**	5h.+(2h.) green	10	40
241		10h.+(2h.) red	20	25

48 Cavalry

1915. War Charity Funds.

242	–	3h.+1h. brown	10	40
243	**48**	5h.+2h. green	10	10
244	–	10h.+2h. red	10	10
245	–	20h.+3h. green	40	1·90
246	–	35h.+3h. blue	2·40	4·75

DESIGNS: 3h. Infantry; 10h. Artillery; 20h.
Battleship "Viribus Unitas" (Navy); 35h. Lohner
Pfeilflieger B-1 biplane (Air Force).

49 Imperial Austrian   **50** Francis Joseph I
Crown

51 Arms of Austria    **52**

1916.

247	**49**	3h. violet	10	10
248		5h. green	10	10
249		6h. orange	25	65
250		10h. red	10	10
251		12h. blue	25	1·25
252	**50**	15h. red	35	10
253		20h. brown	2·75	20
254		25h. blue	4·50	35
255		30h. slate	4·00	60
256	**51**	40h. olive	15	10
257		50h. green	15	10
258		60h. blue	15	10
259		80h. brown	15	10
260		90h. purple	15	10
261		1k. red on yellow	25	10
262aa	**52**	2k. blue	10	15
263aa		3k. red	20	55
264a		4k. green	1·10	1·10
265au		10k. violet	8·50	21·00

On Nos. 254/5 the portrait is full face. The 1k. has
floral sprays each side of the coat-of-arms.

60 Charles I

1917.

290	**60**	15h. red	10	10
291a		20h. green	10	10

292		25h. blue	55	10
293		30h. violet	40	10

1918. Air. Optd **FLUGPOST** or surch also.

296	**52**	1k.50 on 2k. mauve	1·90	4·25
297		2k.50 on 3k. brown	8·00	16·00
298		4k. grey	5·25	12·00

1918. Optd **Deutschosterreich**.

299	**49**	3h. violet	10	10
300		5h. green	10	10
301		6h. orange	20	1·10
302		10h. red	10	10
303		12h. blue	20	1·50
304	**60**	15h. red	20	90
305		20h. green	10	10
306		25h. blue	10	40
307		30h. violet	10	10
308	**51**	40h. olive	10	10
309		50h. green	50	1·00
310		60h. blue	40	85
311		80h. brown	10	15
312		90h. red	15	40
313		1k. red on yellow	15	15
314	**52**	2k. blue	10	10
315		3k. red	35	80
316		4k. green	95	1·10
317		10k. violet	7·25	19·00

64 Posthorn   **65** Republican   **66** "New
   Arms   Republic"

1919. Imperf or perf.

336	**64**	3h. grey	10	10
337	**65**	5h. green	10	10
338	–	5h. grey	10	10
339	**64**	6h. orange	10	40
340	**65**	10h. red	10	10
342	**64**	12h. blue	10	65
343a	–	15h. brown	10	10
344	**66**	20h. green	10	10
346	**65**	25h. blue	10	10
347	**64**	25h. violet	10	10
348	**66**	30h. brown	10	10
349		40h. violet	10	10
350		40h. red	10	10
351	**65**	45h. green	10	65
352	**66**	50h. black	10	10
353	**64**	60h. green	10	10
354	**65**	1k. red on yellow	10	10
355		1k. blue	25	30

67 Parliament Building    **71** Republican
   Arms

1919.

356	**67**	2k. black and red	15	45
357		2½k. bistre	10	30
358		3k. brown and blue	10	10
359		4k. black and red	10	10
360		5k. black	10	15
361		7½k. purple	25	35
362		10k. brown and green	20	30
363		20k. brown and violet	10	40
364		50k. violet on yellow	35	1·00

1920.

402	**71**	80h. red	10	10
403		1k. brown	10	10
404		1½k. blue	25	10
405		2k. blue	10	10
406		3k. black and green	10	20
407		4k. claret and red	10	10
408		5k. red and lilac	10	80
409		7½k. brown and orange	10	10
410		10k. blue and violet	10	20

The frames of the 3 to 10k. differ.

1920. Issues for Carinthian Plebiscite. Optd **Karnten
Abstimmung** (T **65/7** in new colours). (a) Perf.

411	**65**	5h. (+10h.) grey on yell	10	1·25
412		10h. (+20h.) red on pink	40	95
413	**64**	15h. (+30h.) brn on yell	25	80
414	**66**	20h. (+40h.) green on bl	25	75
415	**64**	25h. (+50h.) pur on pink	30	65
416	**66**	30h. (+60h.) brn on buff	1·10	2·75
417		40h. (+80h.) red on yell	25	80
418		50h. (+100h.) indigo on blue	20	60
419		80h. (+120h.) green on bl	1·10	3·00
420	**71**	80h. (+160h.) red	35	80
421		1k. (+2k.) brown	35	80
422		2k. (+4k.) blue	35	85

(b) Imperf

423	**67**	2½k. (+5k.) brown	35	1·00
424		3k. (+6k.) green & blue	40	1·25
425		4k. (+8k.) violet & red	55	1·50
426		5k. (+10k.) black	55	1·25
427		7½k. (+15k.) green	55	1·25
428		10k. (+20k.) red & green	55	1·25
429		20k. (+40k.) brn & lilac	55	1·90

The plebiscite was to decide whether Carinthia
should be part of Austria or Yugoslavia, and the
premium was for a fund to promote a vote in favour

of remaining in Austria. The result was a vote for
Austria.

1921. Flood Relief Fund. Optd **Hochwasser 1920**
(colours changed).

430	**65**	5h. (+10h.) grey on yell	20	55
431		10h. (+20h.) brown	20	55
432	**64**	15h. (+30h.) grey	20	55
433	**66**	20h. (+40h.) green on yell	20	55
434	**64**	25h. (+50h.) blue on yell	20	55
435	**66**	30h. (+60h.) purple on bl	55	1·10
436		40h. (+80h.) brn on red	60	1·40
437		50h. (+100h.) green on bl	1·40	2·10
438	**64**	60h. (+120h.) pur on yell	10	1·10
439	**71**	80h. (+160h.) blue	40	1·10
440		1k. (+2k.) orange on blue	35	90
441		1½k. (+3k.) green on yell	20	55
442		2k. (+4k.) brown	20	55
443	**67**	2½k. (+5k.) red & green	25	55
444		3k. (+6k.) red & green	25	55
445		4k. (+8k.) brown & lilac	75	1·90
446		5k. (+10k.) green	25	70
447		7½k. (+15k.) red	25	80
448		10k. (+20k.) green & blue	25	85
449		20k. (+40k.) pur & red	50	1·25

80 Pincers and   **81** Ear of Corn
Hammer

1922.

461	**81**	½k. brown	10	55
462	**80**	1k. brown	10	10
463		2k. blue	10	10
464	**81**	2½k. brown	10	10
465	**80**	4k. purple	10	85
466		5k. green	10	10
467	**81**	7½k. violet	10	10
468	**80**	10k. red	10	10
469	**81**	12½k. green	10	10
470		15k. turquoise	10	10
471		20k. blue	10	10
472		25k. red	10	10
473	**80**	30k. grey	10	10
474		45k. red	10	10
475		50k. brown	10	10
476		60k. green	10	10
477		75k. blue	10	10
478		80k. yellow	10	10
479	**81**	100k. grey	10	10
480		120k. brown	10	10
481		150k. orange	10	10
482		160k. green	10	10
483		180k. red	10	10
484		200k. pink	10	10
485		240k. violet	10	10
486		300k. blue	10	10
487		400k. green	80	10
488		500k. yellow	10	10
489		600k. slate	10	10
490		700k. brown	1·40	10
491		800k. violet	65	1·75
492	**80**	1000k. mauve	1·25	40
493		1200k. red	70	40
494		1500k. orange	70	10
495		1600k. slate	2·75	2·40
496		2000k. blue	4·00	95
497		3000k. blue	7·25	1·40
498		4000k. blue on blue	4·75	2·75

82   **85** Mozart

1922.

499	**82**	20k. sepia	10	15
500		25k. blue	10	10
501		50k. red	10	10
502		100k. green	10	10
503		200k. purple	10	10
504		500k. orange	35	85
505		1000k. violet on yellow	10	10
506		2000k. green on yellow	10	10
507		3000k. red	8·00	65
508		5000k. black	1·90	1·50
509		10,000k. brown	4·75	5·00

1922. Musicians' Fund.

519	–	2½k. brown	6·25	10·00
520	**85**	5k. blue	1·00	1·90
521	–	7½k. black	2·00	3·00
522	–	10k. purple	2·10	3·25
523	–	25k. green	4·25	7·00
524	–	50k. red	2·40	3·75
525	–	100k. green	7·00	10·00

COMPOSERS: 2½k. Haydn; 7½k. Beethoven; 10k.
Schubert; 25k. Bruckner; 50k. J. Strauss; 100k. Wolf.

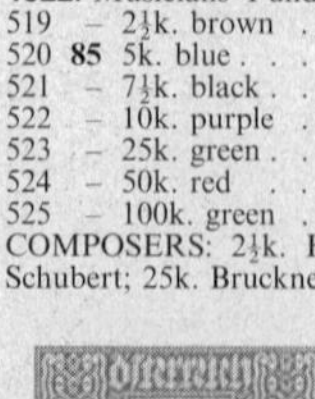

87 Hawk   **88** W. Kress

1922. Air.

546	**87**	300k. red	20	1·50

547		400k. green	3·75	17·00
548		600k. olive	15	1·10
549		900k. red	15	1·10
550	**88**	1200k. purple	15	1·10
551		2400k. slate	15	1·10
552		3000k. brown	2·50	8·00
553		4800k. blue	2·50	8·00

89 Bregenz   **90** "Art the
Comforter"

1923. Artists' Charity Fund.

554	**89**	100k. green	2·50	6·50
555	–	120k. blue	2·50	6·50
556	–	160k. purple	2·50	6·50
557	–	180k. purple	2·50	6·50
558	–	200k. red	2·50	6·50
559	–	240k. brown	3·25	6·50
560	–	400k. brown	2·50	6·50
561	–	600k. green	2·50	6·50
562	–	1000k. black	2·50	7·00

DESIGNS: 120k. Salzburg; 160k. Eisenstadt; 180k.
Klagenfurt; 200k. Innsbruck; 240k. Linz; 400k. Graz;
600k. Melk; 1000k. Vienna.

1924. Artists' Charity Fund.

563	**90**	100k.+300k. green	3·25	7·50
564	–	300k.+900k. green	3·25	7·50
565	–	500k.+1500k. purple	3·25	9·00
566	–	600k.+1800k. turquoise	3·25	15·00
567	–	1000k.+3000k. brown	7·50	17·00

DESIGNS: 300k. "Agriculture and Handicraft";
500k. "Mother Love"; 600k. "Charity"; 1000k.
"Fruitfulness".

91    **92** Plains   **93** Minorite
Church, Vienna

1925.

568	**91**	1g. grey	15	10
569		2g. red	30	10
570		3g. red	30	10
571		4g. blue	85	10
572		5g. brown	95	10
573		6g. blue	60	10
574		7g. brown	85	10
575		8g. green	2·75	10
576	**92**	10g. brown	30	10
577		15g. red	30	10
578		16g. blue	30	10
579		18g. green	65	65
580		20g. violet	50	10
581		24g. red	80	40
582		30g. brown	50	10
583		40g. blue	75	10
584		45g. brown	1·00	10
585		50g. grey	1·10	10
586		80g. blue	3·75	5·00
587	**93**	1s. green	15·00	1·25
588	–	2s. red	5·75	10·50

DESIGN—As T **92**—20g. to 80g. Golden eagle on
mountains.

96 Airman and Hansa   **97** De Havilland
Brandenburg C-1   D.H.34 and
Common Crane

1925. Air.

616	**96**	2g. brown	35	75
617		5g. red	15	25
618		6g. blue	80	1·75
619		8g. green	80	1·75
620	**97**	10g. red	95	2·50
621	**96**	10g. orange	95	1·75
622	**97**	15g. red	65	1·50
623	**96**	15g. mauve	40	85
624		20g. brown	10·00	6·50
625		25g. violet	3·75	7·50
626	**97**	30g. purple	1·00	2·40
627	**96**	30g. bistre	7·50	8·50
628	**97**	30g. grey	1·00	2·50
629	**96**	50g. blue	14·00	12·50
630		80g. green	1·10	4·75
631	**97**	1s. blue	4·75	7·25
632		2s. green	1·90	4·00
633		3s. brown	42·00	60·00
634		5s. blue	13·00	24·00
635		10s. brown on grey (25 × 32 mm)	8·00	17·00

98 Siegfried and Dragon

99 Dr. Michael Hainisch

1926. Child Welfare. Scenes from the Nibelung Legend.

636	**98**	3g.+2g. brown	65	65
637	–	8g.+2g. blue	10	35
638	–	15g.+5g. red	25	40
639	–	20g.+5g. green	25	55
640	–	24g.+6g. violet	25	60
641	–	40g.+10g. brown	3·75	4·25

DESIGNS: 8g. Gunther's voyage; 15g. Kriemhild and Brunhild; 20g. Hagen and the Rhine maidens; 24g. Rudiger and the Nibelungs; 40g. Dietrich's fight with Hagen.

1928. 10th Anniv of Republic and War Orphans and Invalid Children's Fund.

642	**99**	10g. (+10g.) brown	3·00	7·00
643		15g. (+15g.) red	3·00	7·00
644		30g. (+30g.) black	3·00	7·00
645		40g. (+40g.) blue	3·00	7·00

100 Gussing

101 National Library, Vienna

1929. Views. Size 25½ × 21½ mm.

646	**100**	10g. orange	50	10
647		10g. brown	50	10
648	–	15g. purple	50	95
649	–	16g. black	10	10
650	–	18g. green	25	40
651	–	20g. black	30	10
653	–	24g. purple	4·00	25
654	–	30g. violet	3·50	10
655	–	40g. blue	5·50	15
656	–	50g. violet	24·00	15
657	–	60g. green	14·00	20
658	**101**	1s. brown	3·75	20
659	–	2s. green	6·75	7·50

VIEWS—As T **100**: 15g. Hochosterwitz; 16, 20g. Durnstein; 18g. Traunsee; 24g. Salzburg; 30g. Seewiesen; 40g. Innsbruck; 50g. Worthersee; 60g. Hohenems. As T **101**: 2s. St. Stephen's Cathedral, Vienna.

See also Nos. 678/91.

102 Pres. Wilhelm Miklas

104 Johann Nestroy

1930. Anti-tuberculosis Fund.

660	**102**	10g. (+10g.) brown	5·00	11·50
661		20g. (+20g.) red	5·00	11·50
662		30g. (+30g.) purple	5·00	11·50
663		40g. (+40g.) blue	5·00	11·50
664		50g. (+50g.) green	5·00	11·50
665		1s. (+1s.) brown	5·00	11·50

1930. Rotarian Congress. Optd with Rotary Int emblem and **CONVENTION WIEN 1931**.

666	**100**	10g. (+10g.) brown	26·00	50·00
667	–	20g. (+20g.) grey (No. 651)	26·00	50·00
668	–	30g. (+30g.) vio (No. 654)	26·00	50·00
669	–	40g. (+40g.) bl (No. 655)	26·00	50·00
670	–	50g. (+50g.) vio (No. 656)	26·00	50·00
671	**101**	1s. (+1s.) brown	26·00	50·00

1931. Austrian Writers and Youth Unemployment Fund.

672	–	10g. (+10g.) purple	10·00	24·00
673	–	20g. (+20g.) grey	10·00	24·00
674	**104**	30g. (+30g.) red	10·00	24·00
675	–	40g. (+40g.) blue	10·00	24·00
676	–	50g. (+50g.) green	10·00	24·00
677	–	1s. (+1s.) brown	10·00	24·00

DESIGNS: 10g. F. Raimund; 20g. E. Grillparzer; 40g. A Stifter; 50g. L. Anzengruber; 1s. P. Rosegger.

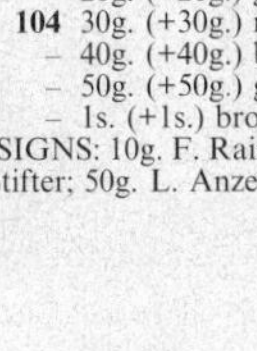

105

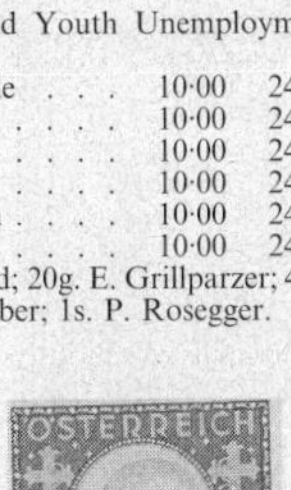

106 Dr. Ignaz Seipel

1932. Designs as No. 646 etc, but size reduced to 20½ × 16 mm as T **105**.

678	**105**	10g. brown	65	10
679	–	12g. green	1·40	10
680	–	18g. green	1·40	2·00
681	–	20g. black	65	10
682	–	24g. red	5·00	10
683	–	24g. violet	3·25	10
684	–	30g. violet	15·00	10
685	–	30g. red	4·00	10
686	–	40g. blue	18·00	95
687	–	40g. violet	6·00	30
688	–	50g. violet	23·00	30
689	–	50g. blue	5·75	30
690	–	60g. green	50·00	2·75
691	–	64g. green	11·50	35

DESIGNS (new values): 12g. Traunsee; 64g. Hohenems.

1932. Death of Dr. Seipel (Chancellor), and Ex-servicemen's Fund.

692	**106**	50g. (+50g.) blue	15·00	19·00

107 Hans Makart

108 The Climb

1932. Austrian Painters.

693	–	12g. (+12g.) green	14·50	35·00
694	–	24g. (+24g.) purple	14·50	35·00
695	–	30g. (+30g.) red	14·50	35·00
696	**107**	40g. (+40g.) grey	14·50	35·00
697	–	64g. (+64g.) brown	14·50	35·00
698	–	1s. (+1s.) red	14·50	35·00

DESIGNS: 12g. F. G. Waldmuller; 24g. Von Schwind; 30g. Alt; 64g. Klimt; 1s. A. Egger-Lienz.

1933. International Ski Championship Fund.

699	**108**	12g. (+12g.) green	7·00	10·00
700	–	24g. (+24g.) violet	75·00	£110
701	–	30g. (+30g.) red	11·00	19·00
702	–	50g. (+50g.) blue	75·00	£110

DESIGNS: 24g. Start; 30g. Race; 50g. Ski jump.

109 "The Honeymoon" (M. von Schwind)

111 John Sobieski

1933. International Philatelic Exn, Vienna (WIPA).

703	**109**	50g. (+50g.) blue	£110	£200

1933. 250th Anniv of Relief of Vienna and Pan-German Catholic Congress.

706	–	12g. (+12g.) green	21·00	38·00
707	–	24g. (+24g.) violet	17·00	29·00
708	–	30g. (+30g.) red	17·00	29·00
709	**111**	40g. (+40g.) grey	30·00	55·00
710	–	50g. (+50g.) blue	17·00	29·00
711	–	64g. (+64g.) brown	24·00	50·00

DESIGNS—VERT: 12g. Vienna in 1683; 24g. Marco d'Aviano; 30g. Count von Starhemberg; 50g. Charles of Lorraine; 64g. Burgomaster Liebenberg.

1933. Winter Relief Fund. Surch with premium and **Winterhilfe** (5g.) or **WINTERHILFE** (others).

712	**91**	5g.+2g. green	15	60
713	–	12g.+3g. blue (as 679)	15	65
714	–	24g.+6g. brn (as 682)	15	50
715	**101**	1s.+50g. red	24·00	48·00

114

115

1934.

716	**114**	1g. violet	10	10
717		3g. red	10	10
718	–	4g. green	10	10
719	–	5g. purple	10	10
720	–	6g. blue	15	10
722	–	8g. green	10	10
723	–	12g. brown	10	10
724	–	20g. brown	15	10
725	–	24g. turquoise	15	10
726	–	25g. violet	15	20
727	–	30g. red	10	10
728	–	35g. red	25	40
729	**115**	40g. grey	45	25
730	–	45g. brown	40	15
731	–	60g. blue	60	25
732	–	64g. brown	75	10
733	–	1s. purple	95	50
735	–	2s. green	3·25	5·75
736	–	3s. orange	11·00	18·00
737	–	5s. black	22·00	42·00

DESIGNS (Austrian costumes of the districts named)—As Type **114**: 1, 3g. Burgenland; 4, 5g. Carinthia; 6, 8g. Lower Austria; 12, 20g. Upper Austria; 24, 25g. Salzburg; 30, 35g. Styria (Steiermark). As Type **115**: 40, 45g. Tyrol; 60, 64g. Vorarlberg; 1s. Vienna; 2s. Army officer and soldiers. 30 × 31 mm: 3s. Harvesters; 5s. Builders.

117 Chancellor Dollfuss

118 Anton Pilgram

1934. Dollfuss Mourning Stamp.

738	**117**	24g. black	35	25

See also No. 762.

1934. Welfare Funds. Austrian Architects.

739	**118**	12g. (+12g.) black	7·50	17·00
740	–	24g. (+24g.) violet	7·50	17·00
741	–	30g. (+30g.) red	7·50	17·00
742	–	40g. (+40g.) brown	7·50	17·00
743	–	60g. (+60g.) blue	7·50	17·00
744	–	64g. (+64g.) green	7·50	17·00

DESIGNS: 24g. Fischer von Erlach; 30g. J. Prandtauer; 40g. A. von Siccardsburg and E. van der Null; 60g. H. von Ferstel; 64g. Otto Wagner.

119 "Mother and Child" (J. Danhauser)

1935. Mothers Day.

745	**119**	24g. blue	40	20

1935. 1st Anniv of Assassination of Dr. Dollfuss.

762	**117**	24g. blue	85	65

121 Maria Worth Castle, Carinthia

122 Zugspitze Aerial Railway

1935. Air. Designs showing Junkers airplane (except 10s.) and landscape.

763	–	5g. purple	15	40
764	**121**	10g. orange	10	15
765	–	15g. green	60	1·50
766	–	20g. blue	10	25
767	–	25g. purple	10	25
768	–	30g. red	10	25
769	–	40g. green	10	30
770	–	50g. blue	15	55
771	–	60g. sepia	20	80
772	–	80g. brown	35	1·10
773	–	1s. red	25	80
774	–	2s. green	3·25	7·25
775	–	3s. brown	8·25	20·00
776	**122**	5s. green	3·25	10·50
777	–	10s. blue	42·00	95·00

DESIGNS—As T **121**: 5g. Gussing Castle; 15g. Durnstein; 20g. Hallstatt; 25g. Salzburg; 30g. Dachstein Mts.; 40g. Wettersee; 50g. Stuben am Arlberg; 60g. St. Stephen's Cathedral, Vienna; 80g. Minorite Church, Vienna. As T **122**: 1s. River Danube; 2s. Tauern railway viaduct; 3s. Grossglockner mountain roadway; 10s. Glider and yachts on the Attersee.

1935. Winter Relief Fund. As Nos. 719, 723, 725 and 733, but colours changed, surch **Winterhilfe** (778/80) or **WINTERHILFE** (781) and premium.

778		5g.+2g. green	35	85
779		12g.+3g. blue	35	1·10
780		24g.+6g. brown	35	95
781		1s.+50g. red	24·00	48·00

123 Prince Eugene of Savoy (born 1663, not 1667 as given)

124 Slalom Course Skier

1935. Welfare Funds. Austrian Heroes.

782	**123**	12g. (+12g.) brown	8·00	18·00
783	–	24g. (+24g.) green	8·00	18·00
784	–	30g. (+30g.) purple	8·00	18·00
785	–	40g. (+40g.) blue	8·00	18·00
786	–	60g. (+60g.) blue	8·00	18·00
787	–	64g. (+64g.) violet	8·00	18·00

PORTRAITS: 24g. Baron von Laudon; 30g. Archduke Charles; 40g. Field-Marshal Radetzky; 60g. Vice-Admiral von Tegetthoff; 64g. Field-Marshal Conrad von Hotzendorff.

1936. International Ski Championship Fund. Inscr "WETTKAMPFE 1936".

788	**124**	12g. (+12g.) green	2·75	4·00
789	–	24g. (+24g.) violet	4·75	5·25
790	–	35g. (+35g.) red	24·00	48·00
791	–	60g. (+60g.) blue	24·00	48·00

DESIGNS: 24g. Skier on mountain slope; 35g. Woman slalom course skier; 60g. View of Maria Theresienstrasse, Innsbruck.

125 Madonna and Child

1936. Mothers' Day.

792	**125**	24g. blue	20	20

126 Chancellor Dollfuss

127 "St. Martin sharing Cloak"

1936. 2nd Anniv of Assassination of Dr. Dollfuss.

793	**126**	10s. blue	£500	£800

1936. Winter Relief Fund. Inscr "WINTERHILFE 1936/37".

794	**127**	5g.+2g. green	25	60
795	–	12g.+3g. violet	25	60
796	–	24g.+6g. blue	25	60
797	–	1s.+1s. red	6·50	12·00

DESIGNS: 12g. "Healing the sick"; 24g. "St. Elizabeth feeding the hungry"; 1s. "Warming the poor".

128 J. Ressel

129 Mother and Child

1936. Welfare Funds. Austrian Inventors.

798	**128**	12g. (+12g.) brown	2·50	5·00
799	–	24g. (+24g.) violet	2·50	5·00
800	–	30g. (+30g.) red	2·50	5·00
801	–	40g. (+40g.) black	2·50	5·00
802	–	60g. (+60g.) blue	2·50	5·00
803	–	64g. (+64g.) green	2·50	5·00

PORTRAITS: 24g. Karl Ritter von Ghega; 30g. J. Werndl; 40g. Carl Freih. Auer von Welsbach; 60g. R. von Lieben; 64g. V. Kaplan.

1937. Mothers' Day.

804	**129**	24g. red	15	20

130 "Maria Anna"

131 "Child Welfare"

1937. Centenary of Regular Danube Services of Danube Steam Navigation Co. Paddle-steamers.

805	**130**	12g. red	50	25
806	–	24g. blue	50	25
807	–	64g. green	50	1·00

DESIGNS: 24g. "Helios"; 64g. "Oesterreich".

1937. Winter Relief Fund. Inscr "WINTERHILFE 1937 1938"

808	**131**	5g.+2g. green	15	50
809	–	12g.+3g. brown	15	50
810	–	24g.+6g. blue	15	50
811	–	1s.+1s. red	2·75	8·25

DESIGNS: 12g. "Feeding the Children"; 24g. "Protecting the Aged"; 1s. "Nursing the Sick."

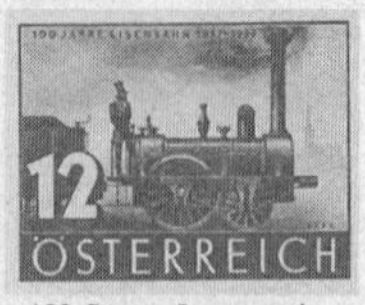

132 Steam Locomotive "Austria", 1837

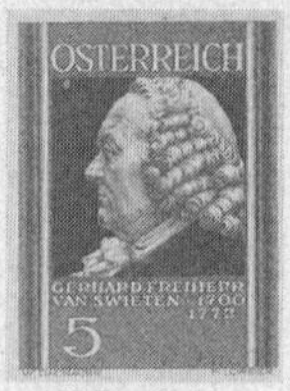

133 Dr. G. Van Swieten

1937. Railway Centenary.

812	132	12g. brown	15	10
813	–	25g. violet	80	1·10
814	–	35g. red	1·90	2·50

DESIGNS: 25g. Steam locomotive, 1936; 35g. Electric locomotive.

1937. Welfare Funds. Austrian Doctors.

815	133	5g. (+5g.) brown	1·75	4·25
816	–	8g. (+8g.) red	1·75	4·25
817	–	12g. (+12g.) brown	1·75	4·25
818	–	20g. (+20g.) green	1·75	4·25
819	–	24g. (+24g.) violet	1·75	4·25
820	–	30g. (+30g.) red	1·75	4·25
821	–	40g. (+40g.) olive	1·75	4·25
822	–	60g. (+60g.) blue	1·75	4·25
823	–	64g. (+64g.) purple	1·75	4·25

DESIGNS: 8g. L. A. von Auenbrugg; 12g. K. von Rokitansky; 20g. J. Skoda; 25g. F. von Hebra; 30g. F. von Arlt; 40g. J. Hyrtl; 60g. T. Billroth; 64g. T. Meynert.

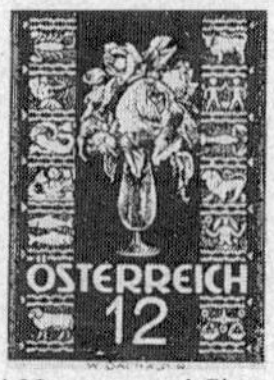

134 Nosegay and Signs of the Zodiac

1937. Christmas Greetings.

824	134	12g. green	10	10
825		24g. red	10	10

ALLIED OCCUPATION. Nos. 826/905 were issued in the Russian Zone of occupation and Nos. 906/22 were a joint issue for use in the British, French and American zones.

1945. Hitler portrait stamps of Germany optd.

(a) Optd **Osterreich** only.

826	173	5pf. green	10	70
827		8pf. red	20	55

(b) Optd **Osterreich** and bar.

828	173	6pf. violet	20	80
829		12pf. red	20	80

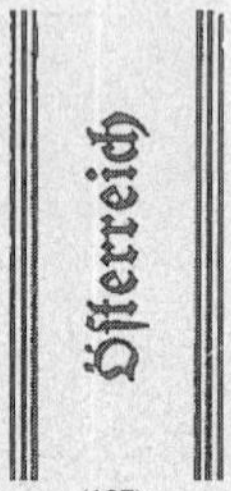

(137)

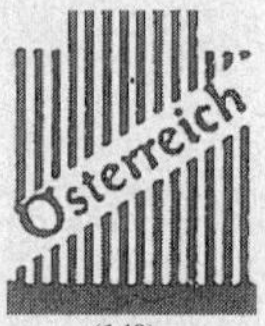

(140)

1945. 1941 and 1944 Hitler stamps of Germany optd as T **137**.

830	137	1pf. grey	2·50	5·50
831		3pf. brown	1·90	5·00
832		4pf. grey	10·00	26·00
833		5pf. green	2·40	6·00
834		6pf. violet	35	65
835		8pf. red	1·10	1·75
836		10pf. brown	3·25	6·00
837		12pf. red	40	55
838		15pf. red	1·25	3·25
839		16pf. green	24·00	60·00
840		20pf. blue	3·25	7·50
841		24pf. brown	24·00	65·00
842	173	25pf. blue	2·75	6·00
843		30pf. green	2·75	6·00
844		40pf. mauve	2·75	6·00
845	225	42pf. green	5·00	10·50
846	173	50pf. green	3·75	8·00
847		60pf. brown	4·00	10·00
848		80pf. blue	4·25	8·50
853	182	1rm. green	20·00	30·00
850		2rm. violet	20·00	32·00
855		3rm. red	30·00	70·00
856		5rm. blue	£250	£450

1945. Stamps of Germany surch **OSTERREICH** and new value.

857	186	5pf. on 12+88pf. green	60	2·00
858	–	6pf. on 6+14pf. brown and blue (No. 811)	6·00	14·50
859	220	8pf. on 42+108pf. brn	95	3·00
860	–	12pf. on 3+7pf. blue (No. 810)	60	1·75

1948. 1941 and 1944 Hitler stamps of Germany optd as T **140**.

862	173	5pf. green	55	3·25
863		6pf. violet	35	2·00
864		8pf. red	25	2·10
865		12pf. red	40	2·75
866		30pf. green	5·75	17·00
867a	225	42pf. green	10·50	38·00

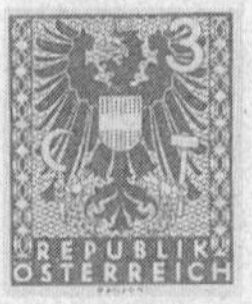

141 New National Arms

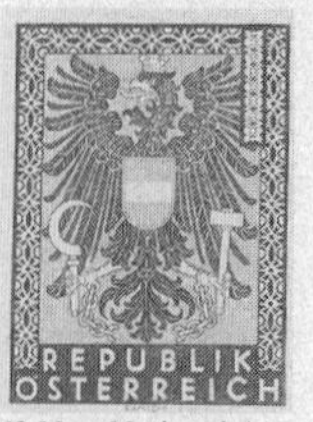

142 New National Arms

1945.

868	141	3pf. brown	15	15
869		4pf. blue	15	35
870		5pf. green	15	15
871		6pf. purple	15	15
872		8pf. orange	15	15
873		10pf. brown	15	15
874		12pf. red	15	15
875		15pf. orange	15	15
876		16pf. green	15	40
877		20pf. blue	15	20
878		24pf. orange	15	25
879		25pf. blue	15	20
880		30pf. green	15	15
881		38pf. blue	15	20
882		40pf. purple	15	20
883		42pf. grey	20	20
884		50pf. green	15	35
885		60pf. red	15	35
886		80pf. violet	15	35
887	142	1rm. green	15	60
888		2rm. violet	20	75
889		3rm. purple	30	1·10
890		5rm. brown	35	1·10

Nos. 877/86 are 24 × 28 mm.

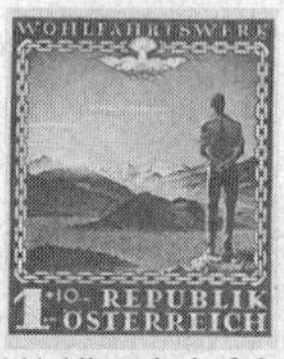

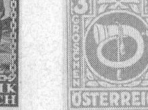

144 Allegorical of the Home Land

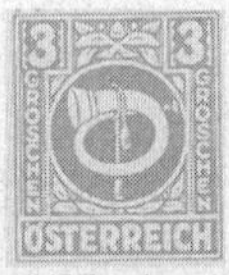

145 Posthorn

1945. Austrian Welfare Charities.

905	144	1s.+10s. green	65	2·10

1945.

906	145	1g. blue	10	50
907		3g. orange	10	20
908		4g. brown	10	20
909		5g. green	10	15
910		6g. purple	10	15
911		8g. red	10	15
912		10g. grey	10	15
913		12g. brown	10	15
914		15g. red	10	20
915		20g. brown	10	20
916		25g. blue	10	20
917		30g. mauve	10	20
918		40g. blue	10	20
919		60g. olive	10	20
920		1s. violet	20	55
921		2s. yellow	35	1·50
922		5s. blue	40	1·50

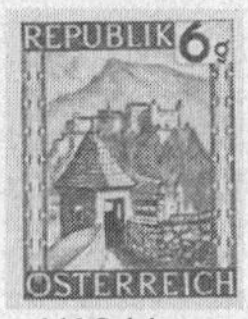

146 Salzburg

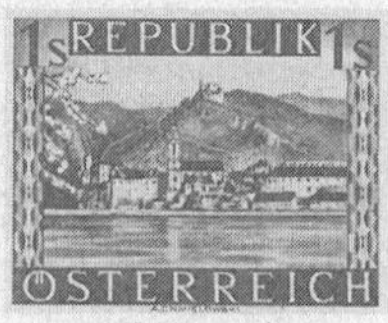

148 Durnstein

1945. Views as T **146/8**.

923	–	3g. blue	15	10
924	–	4g. red	15	10
925	–	5g. red	15	10
926	146	6g. green	15	10
927	–	8g. brown	15	10
928	–	8g. purple	15	10
929	–	8g. green	15	10
930	–	10g. green	15	10
931	–	10g. purple	15	10
932	–	12g. brown	15	10
933	–	15g. blue	15	10
934	–	16g. brown	15	10
935	–	20g. blue	15	10
936	–	24g. green	15	10
937	–	25g. grey	15	15
938	–	30g. red	15	15
939	–	30g. blue	45	40
940	–	35g. red	15	10
941	–	38g. green	15	10
942	–	40g. grey	15	10
943	–	42g. red	15	10
944	–	45g. blue	40	55
945	–	50g. blue	15	10
946	–	50g. purple	50	40
947	–	60g. blue	15	15
948	–	60g. violet	2·40	2·40
949	–	70g. blue	25	35
950	–	80g. brown	25	55
951	–	90g. green	1·25	1·50
952	148	1s. brown	65	65
953	–	2s. grey	2·50	3·25
954	–	3s. green	95	1·00
955	–	5s. red	1·50	1·90

DESIGNS—As Type **146**: 3g. Lermoos; 4g. Iron-ore mine, Erzberg; 5g. Leopoldsberg, Vienna; 8g. (927), Prater Woods, Vienna; 8g. (928/9), Town Hall Park, Vienna; 10g. (930/1), Hochosterwitz; 12g. Schafberg; 15g. Forchtenstein; 16g. Gesauseeingang. 23½ × 29 mm: 20g. Gebhartsberg; 24g. Holdrichsmuhle, near Modling; 25g. Vent im Otztal; 30g. (938/9), Neusiedler Lake; 35g. Belvedere Palace, Vienna; 38g. Langbath Lake; 40g. Mariazell; 42g. Traunstein; 45g. Burg Hartenstein; 50g. (945/6), Silvretta Peaks, Vorarlberg; 60g. (947/8), Semmering; 70g. Badgastein; 80g. Kaisergebirge; 90g. Wayside shrine near Tragoss. As T **148**: 2s. St. Christof; 3s. Heiligenblut; 5s. Schonbrunn Palace, Vienna.

See also Nos. 1072/86a.

1946. 1st Anniv of U.N.O. No. 938 surch **26. JUNI 1945+20 g 26. JUNI 1946** and globe.

971		30g.+20g. red	2·10	3·75

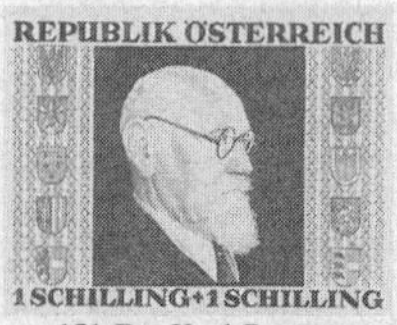

151 Dr. Karl Renner

1946. 1st Anniv of Establishment of Renner Government.

972	151	1s.+1s. green	2·50	6·50
973		2s.+2s. violet	2·50	6·50
974		3s.+3s. purple	2·50	6·50
975		5s.+5s. brown	2·50	6·50

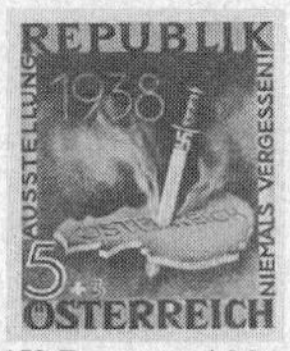

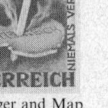

152 Dagger and Map

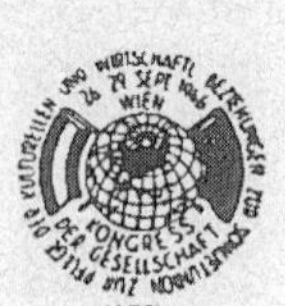

(153)

1946. "Anti-Fascist" Exhibition.

977	152	5g.+3g. sepia	40	80
978	–	6g.+4g. green	30	55
979	–	8g.+6g. orange	30	55
980	–	12g.+12g. blue	30	55
981	–	30g.+30g. violet	30	55
982	–	42g.+42g. brown	30	55
983	–	1s.+1s. red	40	1·00
984	–	2s.+2s. red	60	1·90

DESIGNS: 6g. Broom sweeping Nazi and Fascist emblems; 8g. St. Stephen's Cathedral in flames; 12g. Hand and barbed wire; 30g. Hand strangling snake; 42g. Hammer and broken column; 1s. Hand and Austrian flag; 2s. Eagle and smoking Nazi emblem.

1946. Congress of Society for Promotion of Cultural and Economic Relations with the Soviet Union. No. 932 optd with T **153**.

985		12g. brown	15	40

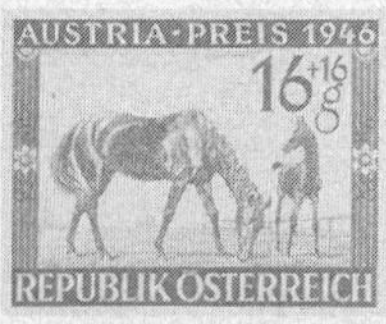

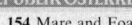

154 Mare and Foal

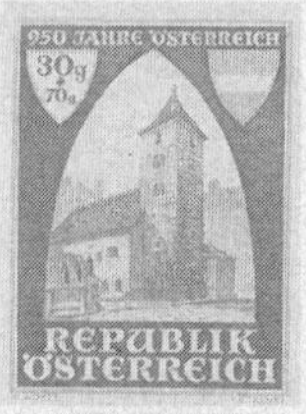

155 Ruprecht's Church, Vienna

1946. Austria Prize Race Fund.

986	154	16g.+16g. red	2·00	3·00
987	–	24g.+24g. violet	2·00	3·25
988	–	60g.+60g. green	2·00	3·25
989	–	1s.+1s. blue	2·00	3·25
990	–	2s.+2s. brown	2·00	5·25

DESIGNS: 24g. Two horses' heads; 60g. Racehorse clearing hurdle; 1s. Three racehorses; 2s. Three horses' heads.

1946. 950th Anniv of First recorded use of name "Osterreich".

991	155	30g.+70g. red	35	80

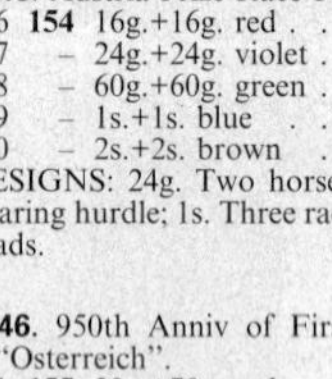

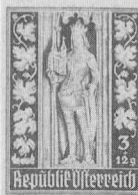

156 Statue of Duke Rudolf

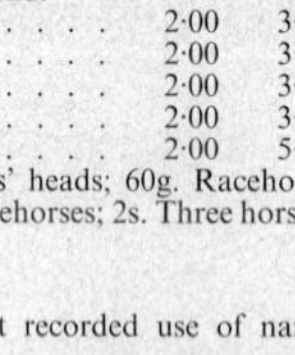

157 Franz Grillparzer (dramatic poet)

1946. St. Stephen's Cathedral Reconstruction Fund. Architectural and Sculptural designs.

992	156	3g.+12g. brown	15	45
993	–	5g.+20g. purple	15	55
994	–	6g.+24g. blue	15	55
995	–	8g.+32g. green	15	55
996	–	10g.+40g. blue	20	65
997	–	12g.+48g. violet	35	1·00
998	–	30g.+1s.20 red	65	1·75
999	–	50g.+1s.80 blue	85	3·00
1000	–	1s.+5s. purple	95	4·00
1001	–	2s.+10s. brown	1·90	8·00

DESIGNS: 5g. Tomb of Frederick III; 6g. Pulpit; 8g. Statue of St. Stephen; 10g. Statue of Madonna and Child; 12g. Altar; 30g. Organ; 50g. Anton Pilgram; 1s. N.E. Tower; 2s. S.W. Spire.

1947. Famous Austrians.

1002	–	12g. green	20	10
1003	157	18g. purple	15	10
1004	–	20g. green	40	20
1005	–	40g. brown	8·00	3·00
1006	–	40g. green	6·00	6·00
1007	–	60g. lake	40	25

PORTRAITS: 12g. Franz Schubert (composer); 20g. Carl Michael Ziehrer (composer); 40g. (No. 1005), Adalbert Stifter (poet); 40g. (No. 1006), Anton Bruckner (composer); 60g. Friedrich Amerling (painter).

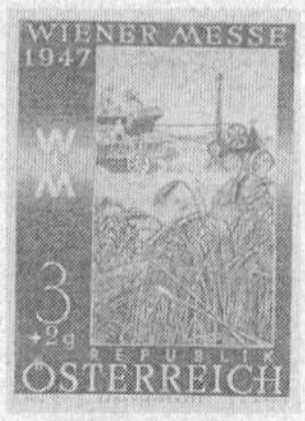

158 Harvesting

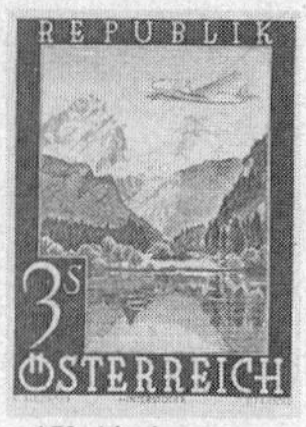

159 Airplane over Hinterstoder

1947. Vienna Fair Fund.

1009	158	3g.+2g. brown	35	60
1010	–	8g.+2g. green	35	60
1011	–	10g.+5g. slate	35	60
1012	–	12g.+8g. violet	35	60
1013	–	18g.+12g. olive	35	60
1014	–	30g.+10g. purple	35	60
1015	–	35g.+15g. red	35	60
1016	–	60g.+20g. blue	35	60

DESIGNS: 8g. Logging; 10g. Factory; 12g. Pithead; 18g. Oil wells; 30g. Textile machinery; 35g. Foundry; 60g. Electric cables.

1947. Air.

1017	–	50g. brown	15	55
1018	–	1s. purple	25	60
1019	–	2s. green	35	85
1020	159	3s. brown	2·00	4·00
1021	–	4s. green	1·50	4·00
1022	–	5s. blue	1·50	4·00
1023	–	10s. blue	65	5·00

DESIGNS—Airplane over: 50g. Windmill at St. Andra; 1s. Heidentor; 2s. Gmund; 4s. Pragraten; 5s. Torsaule; 10s. St. Charles's Church, Vienna.

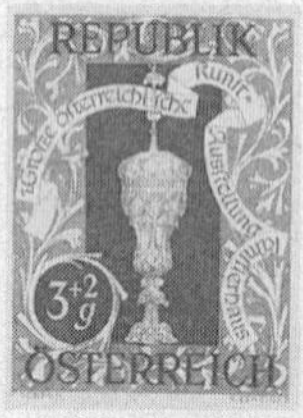

160 Beaker (15th century)

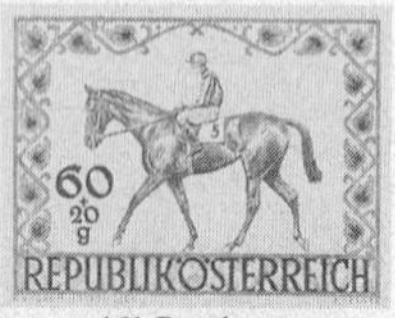

161 Racehorse

1947. National Art Exhibition Fund.

1024	160	3g.+2g. brown	20	55
1025	–	8g.+2g. green	20	55
1026	–	10g.+5g. red	20	55
1027	–	12g.+8g. violet	20	55
1028	–	18g.+12g. brown	20	55
1029	–	20g.+10g. violet	20	55
1030	–	30g.+10g. green	20	55
1031	–	35g.+15g. red	20	55
1032	–	48g.+12g. purple	20	55
1033	–	60g.+20g. blue	20	55

DESIGNS: 8g. Statue of "Providence" (Donner); 10g. Benedictine Monastery, Melk; 12g. "Wife of Dr. Brante of Vienna"; 18g. "Children in a Window" (Waldmuller); 20g. Belvedere Palace Gateway; 30g. Figure of "Egeria" on fountain at Schonbrunn; 35g. National Library, Vienna; 48g. "Copper Printer's (Ernst Rohm) Workshop" (Ferdinand Schmutzer); 60g. "Girl in Straw Hat" (Amerling).

1947. Vienna Prize Race Fund.

1034	161	60+20g. blue on pink	15	60

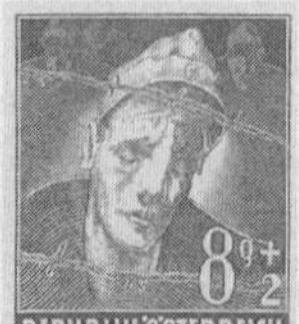

163 Prisoner-of-war

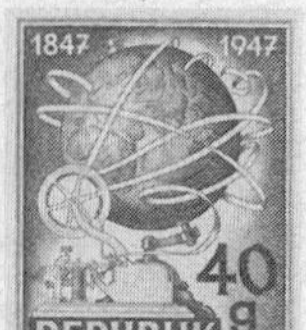

165 Globe and Tape Machine

1947. Prisoners-of-war Relief Fund.

1063	163	8g.+2g. green	10	35
1064	–	12g.+8g. brown	10	40
1065	–	18g.+12g. black	10	40
1066	–	35g.+15g. purple	10	40
1067	–	60g.+20g. blue	10	40
1068	–	1s.+40g. brown	15	60

DESIGNS: 12g. Letter from home; 18g. Gruesome

camp visitor; 35g. Soldier and family reunited; 60g. Industry beckons returned soldier; 1s. Soldier sowing.

1947. Nos. 934 and 941 surch.
1069 75g. on 38g. green 30 75
1070 1s.40 on 16g. brown 10 20

1947. Telegraph Centenary.
1071 **165** 40g. violet 15 30

1947. Currency Revaluation. (a) As T **146**.
1072 3g. red (Lermoos) 20 15
1073 5g. red (Leopoldsberg) . . . 20 10
1074 10g. red (Hochosterwitz) . . 20 10
1075 15g. red (Forchtenstein) . . 1·60 1·60

(b) As T **146** but larger (23½ × 29 mm).
1076 20g. red (Gebhartsberg) . . 35 10
1077 30g. red (Neusiedler Lake) 60 20
1078 40g. red (Mariazell) 60 10
1079 50g. red (Silvretta Peaks) . . 75 10
1080 60g. red (Semmering) . . . 8·50 1·40
1081 70g. red (Badgastein) . . . 3·00 15
1082 80g. red (Kaisergebirge) . . 3·00 15
1083 90g. red (Wayside shrine, Tragoss) . . . . 3·25 65

(c) As T **148**.
1084 1s. violet (Durnstein) . . . 60 10
1085 2s. violet (St. Christof) . . 65 20
1086 3s. violet (Heiligenblut) . . 11·00 1·00
1086a 5s. violet (Schonbrunn) . . 11·00 1·50
Nos. 1072/86a in new currency replaced previous issue at rate of 3s. (old) = 1s. (new).

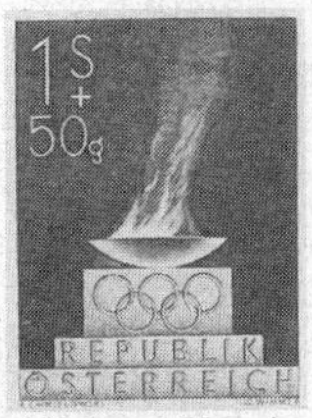
166 Sacred Olympic Flame

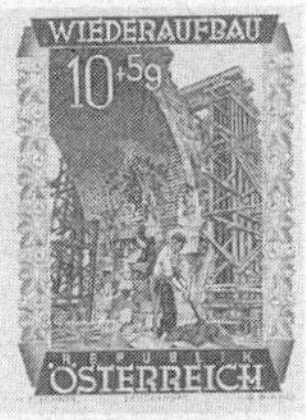
167 Laabenbach Viaduct, Neulenbach

1948. Fund for Entries to 5th Winter Olympic Games, St. Moritz.
1087 **166** 1s.+50g. blue 25 35

1948. Reconstruction Fund.
1088 **167** 10g.+5g. grey 40 40
1089 – 20g.+10g. violet 40 40
1090 – 30g.+10g. green 40 40
1091 – 40g.+20g. green 15 20
1092 – 45g.+20g. blue 10 20
1093 – 60g.+30g. red 10 20
1094 – 75g.+35g. purple 15 20
1095 – 80g.+40g. purple 15 20
1096 – 1s.+50g. blue 15 20
1097 – 1s.40+70g. lake 40 60
DESIGNS (showing reconstruction): 20g. Vermunt Lake Dam; 30g. Danube Port, Vienna; 40g. Erzberg open-cast mine; 45g. Southern Railway Station, Vienna; 60g. Flats; 75g. Vienna Gas Works; 80g. Oil refinery; 1s. Mountain roadway; 1s.40, Parliament Building.

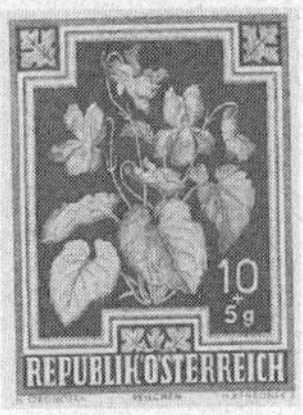
169 Violets

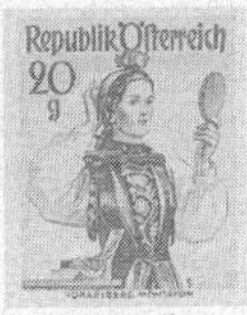
170 Vorarlberg Montafon

1948. Anti-tuberculosis Fund.
1098 **169** 10g.+5g. violet, mauve and green 25 15
1099 – 20g.+10g. green, light green and yellow . . . 15 15
1100 – 30g.+10g. brown, yellow and green . . . . . . 2·75 2·75
1101 – 40g.+20g. green, yellow and orange 55 45
1102 – 45g.+20g. purple, mauve and yellow 15 15
1103 – 60g.+30g. red, mauve and green 15 15
1104 – 75g.+35g. green, pink and yellow 15 15
1105 – 80g.+40g. blue, pink and green 30 30
1106 – 1s.+50g. blue, ultramarine and green 30 25
1107 – 1s.40+70g. green, blue and yellow . . . . . 1·25 1·25
FLOWERS: 20g. Anemone; 30g. Crocus; 40g. Primrose; 45g. Pasque flower; 60g. Rhododendron; 75g. Wild rose; 80g. Cyclamen; 1s. Gentian; 1s.40, Edelweiss.

1948. Provincial Costumes.
1108 – 3g. grey 65 80
1109 – 5g. green 20 10
1110 – 10g. blue 20 10
1111 – 15g. brown 40 10
1112 **170** 20g. green 20 10
1113 – 25g. brown 20 10
1114 – 30g. red . . . . 2·00 10
1115 – 30g. violet 40 10
1116 – 40g. violet . . . . . . 2·10 10
1117 – 40g. green 40 10
1118 – 45g. blue . . . . . . 1·90 20
1119 – 50g. brown 55 10
1120 – 60g. red 40 10
1121 – 70g. green 60 10
1122 – 75g. blue . . . . 4·00 40
1123 – 80g. rose 60 10
1124 – 90g. purple . . . . . . 25·00 30
1125 – 1s. blue . . . . 5·75 10
1126 – 1s. red . . . . 50·00 10
1127 – 1s. green 25 10
1128 – 1s.20 violet 55 10
1129 – 1s.40 brown . . . . . . 2·50 25
1130 – 1s.45 red 90 10
1131 – 1s.50 blue 90 10
1132 – 1s.60 red 35 10
1133 – 1s.70 blue . . . . 1·90 55
1134 – 2s. green 55 10
1135 – 2s.20 slate . . . . 1·75 20
1136 – 2s.40 blue . . . . 1·10 10
1137 – 2s.50 brown . . . . . . 1·90 1·25
1138 – 2s.70 brown 45 55
1139 – 3s. lake . . . . 1·90 10
1140 – 3s.50 green . . . . . . 16·00 10
1141 – 4s.50 purple 65 65
1142 – 5s. purple . . . . 1·00 10
1143 – 7s. olive . . . . 2·00 35
1144 – 10s. grey . . . . 26·00 3·25
DESIGNS—As T **170**: 3g. "Tirol Inntal"; 5 g "Salzburg Pinzgau"; 10, 75g. "Steiermark Salzkammergut" (different designs); 15 g "Burgenland Lutzmannsburg"; 25g., 1s.60, "Wien 1850" (two different designs); 30g. (2) "Salzburg Pongau"; 40g. (2) "Wien 1840"; 45 g "Karnten Lesachtal"; 50g. "Vorarlberg Bregenzerwald"; 60g. "Karnten Lavanttal"; 70g. "Niederosterreich Wachau"; 80 g "Steiermark Ennstal"; 90g. "Steiermark Mittelsteier"; 1s. (3) "Tirol Pustertal"; 1s.20, "Niederosterreich Wienerwald"; 1s.40, "Oberosterreich Innviertel"; 1s.45, "Wilter bei Innsbruck"; 1s.50, "Wien 1853"; 1s.70, "Ost Tirol Kals"; 2s. "Oberosterreich"; 2s.20, "Ischl 1820"; 2s.40, "Kitzbuhel"; 2s.50, "Obersteiermark 1850"; 2s.70, "Kleines Walsertal"; 3s. "Burgenland"; 3s.50, "Niederosterreich 1850"; 4s.50, "Gailtal"; 5s. "Zillertal"; 7s. "Steiermark Sulmtal". 25 × 35 mm: 10s. "Wien 1850".

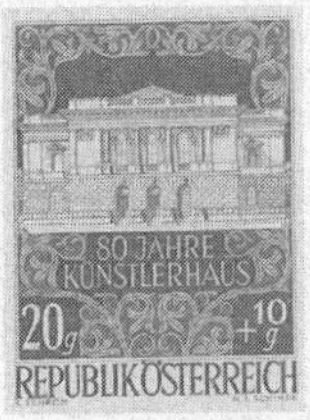
172 Kunstlerhaus

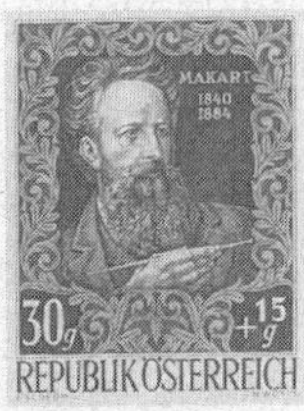
173 Hans Makart

1948. 80th Anniv of Creative Artists' Association.
1145 **172** 20g.+10g. green . . . . 6·00 5·25
1146 **173** 30g.+15g. brown . . . . 2·00 2·75
1147 – 40g.+20g. blue . . . . . 2·00 2·75
1148 – 50g.+25g. violet . . . . 3·25 4·00
1149 – 60g.+30g. red . . . . . 4·00 3·75
1150 – 1s.+50g. blue . . . . . 4·00 5·00
1151 – 1s.40+70g. brown . . . . 12·00 11·00
PORTRAITS: 40g. K. Kundmann; 50g. A. von Siccardsburg; 60g. H. Canon; 1s. W. Unger; 1s.40, Friedr. Schmidt.

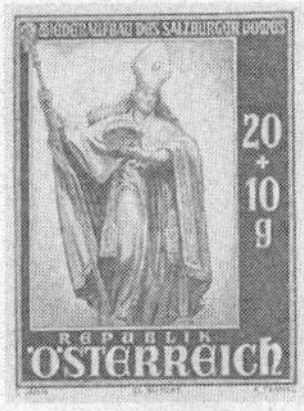
174 St. Rupert

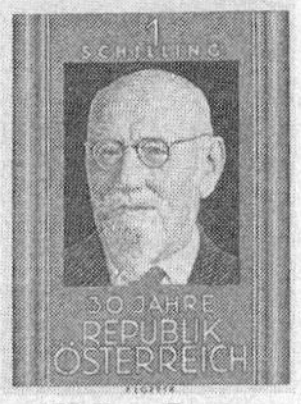
175 Pres. Renner

1948. Salzburg Cathedral Reconstruction Fund.
1152 **174** 20g.+10g. green . . . . 5·00 5·75
1153 – 30g.+15g. brown . . . . 2·00 2·50
1154 – 40g.+20g. green . . . . 1·90 1·90
1155 – 50g.+25g. brown 35 50
1156 – 60g.+30g. red 35 50
1157 – 80g.+40g. purple 35 50
1158 – 1s.+50g. blue 50 70
1159 – 1s.40+70g. green . . . . 1·10 1·50
DESIGNS: 30, 40, 50, 80g. Views of Salzburg Cathedral; 60g. St. Peter's; 1s. Cathedral and Fortress; 1s.40, Madonna.

1948. 30th Anniv of Republic.
1160 **175** 1s. blue . . . . 1·25 1·25
See also Nos. 1224 and 1333.

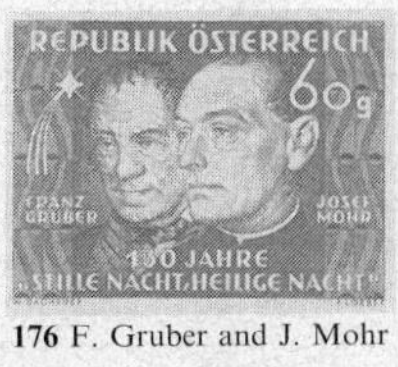
176 F. Gruber and J. Mohr

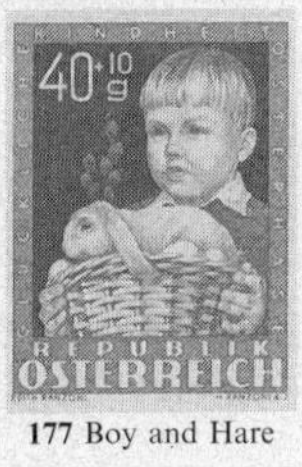
177 Boy and Hare

1948. 130th Anniv of Composition of Carol "Silent Night, Holy Night".
1161 **176** 60g. brown . . . . . . 4·25 4·25

1949. Child Welfare Fund.
1162 **177** 40g.+10g. purple . . . . 10·00 12·00
1163 – 60g.+20g. red . . . . . 10·00 12·00
1164 – 1s.+25g. blue . . . . . 10·00 12·00
1165 – 1s.40+35g. green . . . . 10·00 12·00
DESIGNS: 60g. Two girls and apples in boot; 1s. Boy and birthday cake; 1s.40, Girl praying before candle.

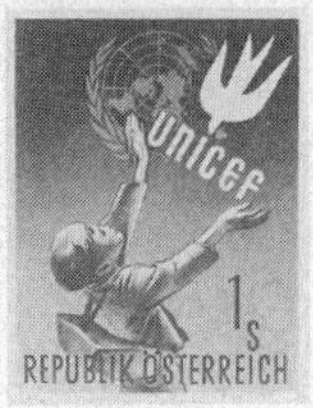
178 Boy and Dove

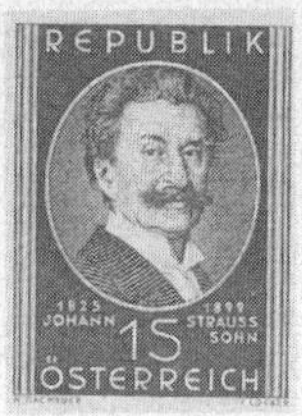
179 Johann Strauss

1949. U.N. Int. Children's Emergency Fund.
1166 **178** 1s. blue . . . . 6·50 1·75

1949. 50th Death Anniv of Johann Strauss the Younger (composer).
1167 **179** 1s. blue . . . . 2·10 1·90
See also Nos. 1174, 1207 and 1229.

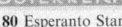

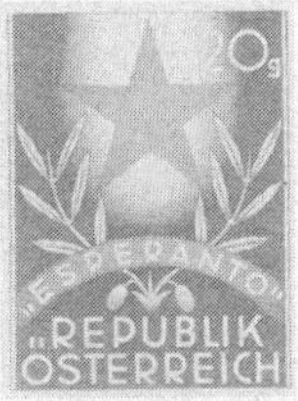
180 Esperanto Star

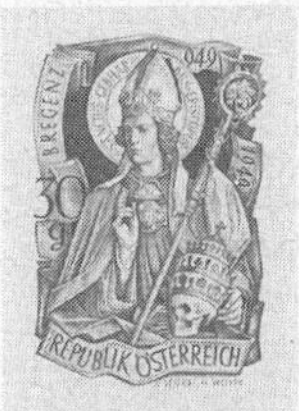
181 St. Gebhard

1949. Esperanto Congress, Vienna.
1168 **180** 20g. green 55 55

1949. Birth Millenary of St. Gebhard (Bishop of Vorarlberg).
1169 **181** 30g. violet . . . . 1·10 1·10

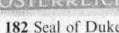

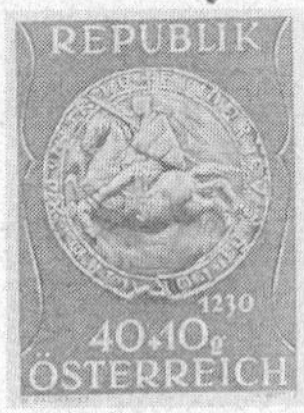
182 Seal of Duke Friedrich II, 1230

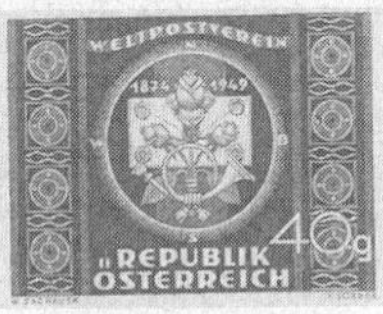
183 Allegory of U.P.U.

1949. Prisoners-of-war Relief Fund. Arms.
1170 **182** 40g.+10g. yell & brn . . 3·75 5·25
1171 – 60g.+15g. pink & pur . . 3·75 5·25
1172 – 1s.+25g. red & blue . . 3·75 5·25
1173 – 1s.60+40g. pink and green . . . . 3·75 5·25
ARMS: 60g. Princes of Austria, 1450; 1s. Austria, 1600; 1s.60, Austria, 1945.

1949. Death Centenary of Johann Strauss the Elder (composer). Portrait as T **179**.
1174 30g. purple . . . . 1·90 1·75

1949. 75th Anniv of U.P.U.
1175 **183** 40g. green . . . . 2·50 2·10
1176 – 60g. red . . . . 2·50 2·10
1177 – 1s. blue . . . . 5·75 4·00
DESIGNS: 60g. Children holding "75"; 1s. Woman's head.

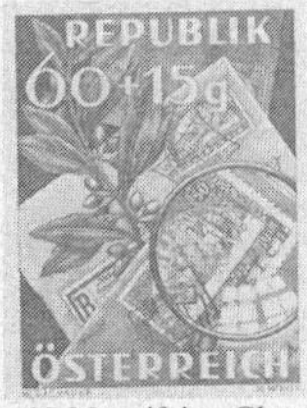
185 Magnifying Glass and Covers

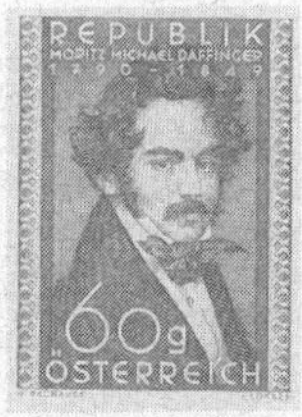
186 M. M. Daffinger

1949. Stamp Day.
1206 **185** 60g.+15g. brown . . . . 3·75 4·00

1949. 50th Death Anniv of Karl Millocker (composer). Portrait as T **179**.
1207 1s. blue . . . . 9·50 8·00

1950. 160th Birth Anniv of Moritz Michael Daffinger (painter).
1208 **186** 60g. brown . . . . . . 4·25 4·25

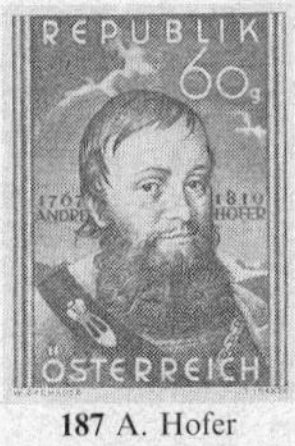
187 A. Hofer

1950. 140th Death Anniv of Andreas Hofer (patriot).
1209 **187** 60g. violet . . . . 8·25 7·00
See also Nos. 1211, 1223, 1232, 1234, 1243, 1253, 1288 and 1386.

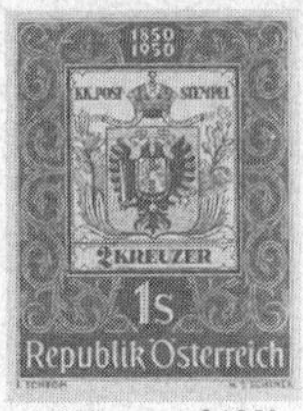
188 Stamp of 1850

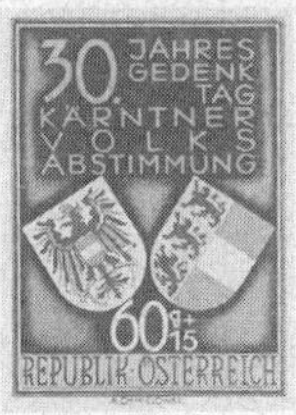
189 Arms of Austria and Carinthia

1950. Austrian Stamp Centenary.
1210 **188** 1s. black on yellow . . . 1·25 95

1950. Death Centenary of Josef Madersperger (sewing machine inventor). Portrait as T **187**.
1211 60g. violet . . . . 3·75 2·75

1950. 30th Anniv of Carinthian Plebiscite.
1212 **189** 60g.+15g. grn & brn . . 21·00 23·00
1213 – 1s.+25g. red & orange 25·00 26·00
1214 – 1s.70+40g. blue and turquoise . . . . . . 25·00 30·00
DESIGNS: 1s. Carinthian waving Austrian flag; 1s.70, Hand and ballot box.

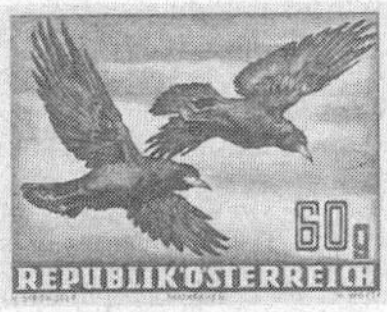
190 Rooks

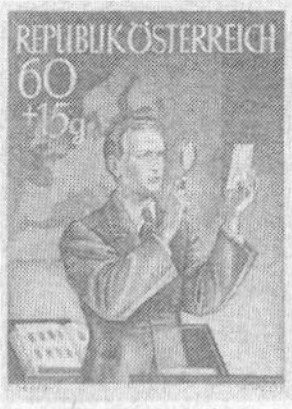
191 Philatelist

1950. Air.
1215 **190** 60g. violet . . . . 4·00 2·50
1216 – 1s. violet (Barn swallows) . . . . . . 24·00 17·00
1217 – 2s. blue (Black-headed gulls) . . . . 17·00 7·25
1218 – 3s. turquoise (Common cormorants) . . . . . £110 75·00
1219 – 5s. brown (Common buzzard) . . . . £110 75·00
1220 – 10s. purple (Grey heron) 50·00 38·00
1221 – 20s. sepia (Golden eagle) 8·50 3·75

1950. Stamp Day.
1222 **191** 60g.+15g. green . . . . 5·25 5·25

1950. Birth Centenary of Alexander Girardi (actor). Portrait as T **187**.
1223 30g. blue . . . . 1·10 85

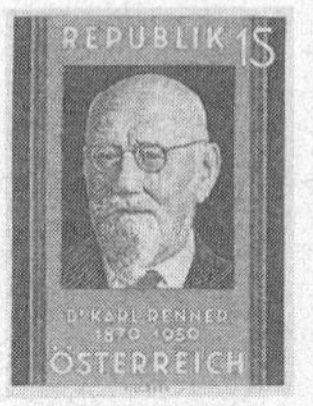
192 Dr. Renner

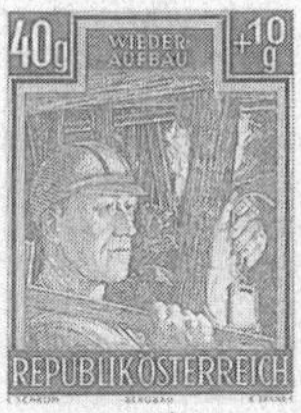
193 Miner

1951. Death of Pres. Karl Renner.
1224 **192** 1s. black on lemon . . . 1·00 35

1951. Reconstruction Fund.
1225 **193** 40g.+10g. purple . . . . 9·50 10·00
1226 – 60g.+15g. green . . . . 9·50 10·00
1227 – 1s.+25g. brown . . . . 9·50 10·00
1228 – 1s.70+40g. blue . . . . 9·50 10·00
DESIGNS: 60g. Bricklayer; 1s. Bridge-builder; 1s.70, Telegraph engineer.

1951. 150th Birth Anniv of Joseph Lanner (composer). Portrait as T **179**.
1229 60g. green . . . . 2·75 1·75

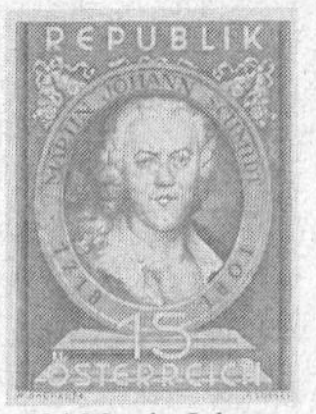
194 Martin Johann Schmidt

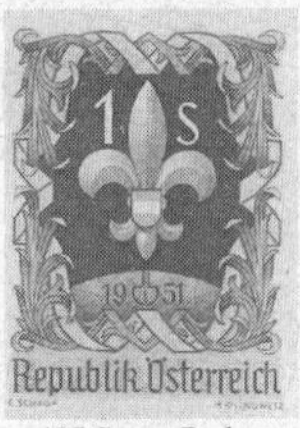
195 Scout Badge

1951. 150th Death Anniv of Schmidt (painter).
1230 **194** 1s. red . . . . 4·00 2·40

1951. Boy Scout Jamboree.
1231 **195** 1s. red, yellow & green 2·75 2·75

1951. 10th Death Anniv of Wilhelm Kienzl (composer). Portrait as T **187**.
1232 1s.50 blue . . . . 1·90 1·00

196 Laurel Branch and Olympic Emblem   **197** Schrammel

1952. 6th Winter Olympic Games, Oslo.
1233 **196** 2s.40+60g. green . . . . 11·00 14·00

1952. 150th Birth Anniv of Karl Ritter von Ghega (railway engineer). Portrait as T **187**.
1234 1s. green . . . . 4·75 1·25

1952. Birth Cent of Josef Schrammel (composer).
1235 **197** 1s.50 blue . . . . 4·25 1·40
See also No. 1239.

198 Cupid and Letter   **199** Breakfast Pavilion

1952. Stamp Day.
1236 **198** 1s.50+35g. purple . . . . 12·00 14·50

1952. Bicentenary of Schonbrunn Menagerie.
1237 **199** 1s.50 green . . . . 3·75 1·50

200   **202**

1952. Int Union of Socialist Youth Camp, Vienna.
1238 **200** 1s.50 blue . . . . 3·75 80

1952. 150th Birth Anniv of Nikolaus Lenau (writer). Portrait as T **197**.
1239 1s. green . . . . 4·00 1·25

1952. International Children's Correspondence.
1240 **202** 2s.40 blue . . . . 6·25 1·90

203 "Christus Pantocrator" (sculpture)   **204** Hugo Wolf

1952. Austrian Catholics' Day.
1241 **203** 1s.+25g. olive . . . . . 7·00 9·25

1953. 50th Death Anniv of Wolf (composer).
1242 **204** 1s.50 blue . . . . 5·25 1·10

1953. President Korner's 80th Birthday. As T **187** but portrait of Korner.
1243 1s.50 blue . . . . 4·00 95
For 1s.50 black, see No. 1288.

1953. 60th Anniv of Austrian Trade Union Movement. As No. 955 (colour changed) surch **GEWERKSCHAFTS BEWEGUNG 60 JAHRE 1s+25g.**
1244 1s.+25g. on 5s. blue . . . . 1·90 2·00

---

206 Linz National Theatre   **207** Meeting-house, Steyr

1953. 150th Anniv of Linz National Theatre.
1245 **206** 1s.50 turquoise . . . . . 11·00 2·40

1953. Vienna Evangelical School Rebuilding Fund.
1246 **207** 70g.+15g. purple 25 20
1247   – 1s.+25g. blue 35 25
1248   – 1s.50+40g. brown 55 55
1249   – 2s.40+60g. green . . . . 2·75 2·50
1250   – 3s.+75g. lilac . . . . 7·00 6·25
DESIGNS: 1s. J. Kepler (astronomer); 1s.50, Lutheran Bible, 1534; 2s.40, T. von Hansen (architect); 3s. School after reconstruction.

208 Child and Christmas Tree   **209**

1953. Christmas
1251 **208** 1s. green 75 20
See also No. 1266.

1953. Stamp Day.
1252 **209** 1s.+25g. brown . . . . 4·00 4·00

1954. 150th Birth Anniv of M. Von Schwind (painter). As T **187** but portrait of Von Schwind.
1253 1s.50 lilac . . . . 7·50 2·00

210 Baron K. von Rokitansky   **212** Surgeon with Microscope

1954. 150th Birth Anniv of Von Rokitansky (anatomist).
1254 **210** 1s.50 violet . . . . . 10·00 2·00
See also No. 1264.

1954. Avalanche Fund. As No. 953 (colour changed) surch **LAWINENOPFER 1954 1s+20g.**
1255 1s.+20g. blue 15 20

1954. Health Service Fund.
1256   – 30g.+10g. violet . . . . 95 1·25
1257 **212** 70g.+15g. brown 25 20
1258   – 1s.+25g. blue 25 25
1259   – 1s.45+35g. green 35 40
1260   – 1s.50+35g. red . . . . 4·25 4·50
1261   – 2s.40+60g. purple . . . . 4·50 6·00
DESIGNS: 30g. Boy patient and sun-ray lamp; 1s. Mother and children; 1s.45, Operating theatre; 1s.50, Baby on scales; 2s.40, Red Cross nurse and ambulance.

213 Esperanto Star   **214** J. M. Rottmayr von Rosenbrunn

1954. 50th Anniv of Esperanto in Austria.
1262 **213** 1s. green and brown . . 2·50 25

1954. Birth Tercentenary of Rottmayr von Rosenbrunn (painter).
1263 **214** 1s. green . . . . . . 6·25 2·75

1954. 25th Death Anniv of Dr. Auer von Welsbach (inventor). Portrait as T **210**.
1264 1s.50 blue . . . . . . 21·00 2·40

---

216 Great Organ, Church of St. Florian   **217** 18th-century River Boat

1954. 2nd International Congress of Catholic Church Music, Vienna.
1265 **216** 1s. brown . . . . . . 1·10 25

1954. Christmas. As No. 1251, but colour changed.
1266 **208** 1s. blue . . . . . . 2·10 40

1954. Stamp Day.
1267 **217** 1s.+25g. green . . . . . 4·00 4·75

218 Arms of Austria and Newspapers

1954. 150th Anniv of State Printing Works and 250th Anniv of "Wiener-Zeitung" (newspaper).
1268 **218** 1s. black and red . . . . 1·50 20

219 "Freedom"

1955. 10th Anniv of Re-establishment of Austrian Republic.
1269   – 70g. purple . . . . . 1·50 20
1270   – 1s. blue . . . . . 6·25 20
1271 **219** 1s.45 red . . . . . 7·00 3·25
1272   – 1s.50 brown . . . . . 20·00 30
1273   – 2s.40 green . . . . . 7·00 3·25
DESIGNS: 70g. Parliament Buildings; 1s. Western Railway terminus, Vienna; 1s.50, Modern houses; 2s.40, Limberg Dam.

1955. Austrian State Treaty. As No. 888, but colour changed, optd **STAATSVERTRAG 1955**.
1274 **142** 2s. grey . . . . 1·40 20

221 "Strength through Unity"

1955. 4th World Trade Unions Congress, Vienna.
1275 **221** 1s. blue . . . . 1·10 1·50

222 "Return to Work"

1955. Returned Prisoners-of-war Relief Fund.
1276 **222** 1s.+25g. brown . . . . 1·40 1·25

223 Burgtheater, Vienna

1955. Re-opening of Burgtheater and State Opera House, Vienna.
1277 **223** 1s.50 brown . . . . . 2·75 20
1278   – 2s.40 blue (Opera House) 3·25 2·00

---

224 Globe and Flags   **225** Stamp Collector

1955. 10th Anniv of U.N.O.
1279 **224** 2s.40 green . . . . . 6·50 1·75

1955. Stamp Day.
1280 **225** 1s.+25g. brown . . . . 2·00 2·40

226 Mozart   **227**

1956. Birth Bicentenary of Mozart (composer).
1281 **226** 2s.40 blue . . . . . . 2·50 85

1956. Admission of Austria into U.N.
1282 **227** 2s.40 brown . . . . . 6·00 1·10

228   **229** Vienna and Five New Towns

1956. 5th World Power Conference, Vienna.
1283 **228** 2s.40 blue . . . . . . 5·75 1·40

1956. 23rd International Town Planning Congress.
1284 **229** 1s.45 red, black & green 1·75 55

230 J. B. Fischer von Erlach   **231** "Stamp Day"

1956. Birth Tercentenary of Fischer von Erlach (architect).
1285 **230** 1s.50 brown . . . . . 65 1·00

1956. Stamp Day.
1286 **231** 1s.+25g. red . . . . . 1·75 2·00

1956. Hungarian Relief Fund. As No. 1173, but colours changed, surch **1956 1.50 +50 UNGARNHILFE**.
1287 1s.50+50g. on 1s.60+40g. red and grey 25 35

1957. Death of Pres. Korner. As No. 1243, but colour changed.
1288 1s.50 black . . . . 95 1·10

233 J. Wagner von Jauregg   **234** Anton Wildgans

1957. Birth Centenary of Wagner von Jauregg (psychiatrist).
1289 **233** 2s.40 brown . . . . . 2·40 1·25

1957. 25th Death Anniv of Anton Wildgans (poet).
1290 **234** 1s. blue 25 25

235 Early and Modern Postal Coaches

1957. 50th Anniv of Postal Coach Service.
1291 **235** 1s. black on yellow . . . 35 20

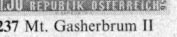

237 Mt. Gasherbrum II **236** Mariazell Basilica

1957. Austrian Himalaya–Karakorum Expedition, 1956.
1293 **237** 1s.50 blue 40 25

1957. Buildings. (a) Size 20½ × 24½ mm.

1295	–	20g. purple	10	10
1296	–	30g. green	20	10
1297	–	40g. red	10	10
1298	–	50g. grey	20	10
1299	–	60g. brown	25	10
1300	–	70g. blue	20	10
1301	–	80g. brown	25	10
1302	236	1s. brown	50	10
1303	–	1s. brown	25	10
1304	–	1s.20 purple	35	15
1305	–	1s.30 green	25	10
1306	–	1s.40 blue	25	15
1307	–	1s.50 red	40	15
1308	–	1s.80 blue	40	15
1309	–	2s. blue	3·75	10
1310	–	2s. blue	35	10
1311	–	2s.20 green	75	20
1312	–	2s.50 violet	60	15
1313	–	3s. blue	60	10
1314	–	3s.40 green	50	65
1315	–	3s.50 mauve	55	10
1316	–	4s. violet	65	10
1317	–	4s.50 green	75	15
1318	–	5s.50 green	75	15
1319	–	6s. violet	1·00	10
1320	–	6s.40 blue	1·10	1·10
1321	–	8s. purple	1·50	15
		(b) Larger.		
1322	–	10s. green	2·50	30
1323	–	20s. purple	2·50	55
		(c) Smaller, size 17½ × 21 mm.		
1324	–	50g. grey	20	10
1325	236	1s. brown	20	10
1326	–	1s.50 purple	20	10

DESIGNS: 20g. Old Courtyard, Morbisch; 30g. Vienna Town Hall; 40g. Porcia Castle, Spittal; 50g. Heiligenstadt flats; 60g. Lederer Tower, Wells; 70g. Archbishop's Palace, Salzburg; 80g. Old farmhouse, Pinzgau; 1s. (1303) Millstatt; 1s.20, Corn Measurer's House, Bruck-on-the-Mur; 1s.30, Schattenburg Castle; 1s.40, Klagenfurt Town Hall; 1s.50, "Rabenhof" Flats, Erdberg, Vienna; 1s.80, Mint Tower, Hall-in-Tyrol; 2s. (1309) Christkindl Church; 2s. (1310) Dragon Fountain, Klagenfurt; 2s.20, Beethoven's House, Heiligenstadt, Vienna; 2s.50, Danube Bridge, Linz; 3s. "Swiss Portal", Imperial Palace, Vienna; 3s.40, Stein Gate, Krems-on-the-Danube; 3s.50, Esterhazy Palace, Eisenstadt; 4s. Vienna Gate, Hainburg; 4s.50, Schwechat Airport; 5s.50, Chur Gate, Feldkirch; 6s. Graz Town Hall; 6s.40, "Golden Roof", Innsbruck; 8s. Steyr Town Hall. 22 × 28½ mm: 10s. Heidenreichstein Castle. 28½ × 37½ mm: 20s. Melk Abbey.

238 Post Office, Linz **239** Badgastein

1957. Stamp Day.
1327 **238** 1s.+25g. green . . . . . 1·90 2·10

1958. International Alpine Ski Championships, Badgastein.
1328 **239** 1s.50 blue 20 20

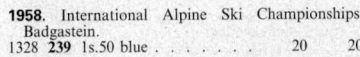

240 Vickers Viscount 800 **241** Mother and Child

1958. Austrian Airlines Inaugural Flight, Vienna–London.
1329 **240** 4s. red 55 20

1958. Mothers' Day.
1330 **241** 1s.50 blue 20 10

242 Walther von der Vogelweide (after 12th-century manuscript) **243** Dr. O. Redlich

1958. 3rd Austrian Choir Festival, Vienna.
1331 **242** 1s.50 multicoloured . . . 25 15

1958. Birth Cent of Dr. Oswald Redlich (historian).
1332 **243** 2s.40 blue 35 20

1958. 40th Anniv of Republic. As T **175** but inscr "40 JAHRE".
1333 **175** 1s.50 green 50 55

244 Post Office, Kitzbuhel

1958. Stamp Day.
1334 **244** 2s.40+60g. blue 55 70

245 "E" building on Map of Europe **246** Monopoly Emblem and Cigars

1959. Europa.
1335 **245** 2s.40 green 25 25

1959. 175th Anniv of Austrian Tobacco Monopoly.
1336 **246** 2s.40 brown 25 20

247 Archduke Johann **248** Western Capercailie

1959. Death Cent of Archduke Johann of Austria.
1337 **247** 1s.50 green 25 15

1959. International Hunting Congress, Vienna.

1338	248	1s. purple	40	15
1339	–	1s.50 blue (Roebuck)	40	15
1340	–	2s.40 grn (Wild boar)	55	70
1341	–	3s.50 brown (Red deer family)	40	40

249 Haydn **250** Tyrolean Eagle

1959. 150th Death Anniv of Haydn.
1342 **249** 1s.50 purple 55 20

1959. 150th Anniv of Tyrolese Rising.
1343 **250** 1s.50 red 20 15

251 Microwave Transmitting Aerial, Zugspitze **252** Handball Player

1959. Inaug of Austrian Microwave Network.
1344 **251** 2s.40 blue 25 15

1959. Sports.

1345	–	1s. violet	20	15
1346	252	1s.50 green	55	20
1347	–	1s.80 red	35	25
1348	–	2s. purple	25	25
1349	–	2s.20 blue	20	15

DESIGNS: 1s. Runner; 1s.80, Gymnast; 2s. Hurdling; 2s.20, Hammer thrower.

253 Orchestral Instruments **254** Roman Coach

1959. Vienna Philharmonic Orchestra's World Tour.
1350 **253** 2s.40 black and blue . . 35 20

1959. Stamp Day.
1351 **254** 2s.40+60g. blk & mve . . 55 55

255 Refugees **256** Pres. Adolf Scharf

1960. World Refugee Year.
1352 **255** 3s. turquoise 40 35

1960. President's 70th Birthday.
1353 **256** 1s.50 green 40 20

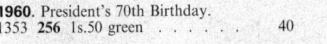

257 Youth Hostellers **258** Dr. Eiselsberg

1960. Youth Hostels Movement.
1354 **257** 1s. red 20 20

1960. Birth Cent of Dr. Anton Eiselsberg (surgeon).
1355 **258** 1s.50 sepia and cream . . 60 20

259 Gustav Mahler **260** Jakob Prandtauer

1960. Birth Centenary of Gustav Mahler (composer).
1356 **259** 1s.50 brown . . . . . . 1·00 20

1960. 300th Birth Anniv of Jakob Prandtauer (architect).
1357 **260** 1s.50 brown 40 20

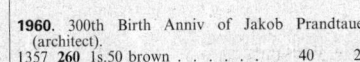

261 Grossglockner Highway **262** Ionic Capital

1960. 25th Anniv of Grossglockner Alpine Highway.
1358 **261** 1s.80 blue 40 35

1960. Europa.
1359 **262** 3s. black 95 60

263 Griffen, Carinthia

1960. 40th Anniv of Carinthian Plebiscite.
1360 **263** 1s.50 green 25 15

264 Examining Proof of Engraved Stamp **265** "Freedom"

1960. Stamp Day.
1361 **264** 3s.+70g. brown 55 70

1961. Austrian Freedom Martyrs' Commem.
1362 **265** 1s.50 red 20 15

266 Hansa Brandenburg C-1 **267** Transport and Multi-unit Electric Train

1961. "LUPOSTA" Exhibition, Vienna, and 1st Austrian Airmail Service Commemoration.
1363 **266** 5s. blue 60 35

1961. European Transport Ministers' Meeting.
1364 **267** 3s. olive and red 55 35

268 "Mower in the Alps" (Detail, A. Egger-Lienz) **269** Observatory on Sonnblick Mountain

1961. Centenary of Kunstlerhaus, Vienna. Inscr as in T **268**.

1365	268	1s. purple and brown	20	15
1366	–	1s.50 lilac and brown	20	25
1367	–	3s. green and brown	80	80
1368	–	5s. violet and brown	60	55

PAINTINGS: 1s.50, "The Kiss" (after A. von Pettenkofen). 3s. "Portrait of a Girl" (after A. Romako). 5s. "The Triumph of Ariadne" (detail of Ariadne, after Hans Makart).

1961. 75th Anniv of Sonnblick Meteorological Observatory.
1369 **269** 1s.80 blue 35 30

270 Lavanttaler Colliery   271 Mercury

1961. 15th Anniv of Nationalized Industries. Inscr "JAHRE VERSTAATLICHTE UNTERNEHMUNGEN".
1370	270	1s. black	15	10
1371	–	1s.50 green	20	25
1372	–	1s.80 red	55	55
1373	–	3s. mauve	75	55
1374	–	5s. blue	1·25	80

DESIGNS: 1s.50, Turbine; 1s.80, Industrial plant; 3s. Steelworks, Linz; 5s. Oil refinery, Schwechat.

1961. World Bank Congress, Vienna.
| 1375 | 271 | 3s. black | 40 | 35 |

272 Arms of Burgenland   273 Liszt

1961. 40th Anniv of Burgenland.
| 1376 | 272 | 1s.50 red, yellow & sepia | 35 | 20 |

1961. 150th Birth Anniv of Franz Liszt (composer).
| 1377 | 273 | 3s. brown | 60 | 35 |

274 Rust Post Office

1961. Stamp Day.
| 1378 | 274 | 3s.+70g. green | 60 | 65 |

275 Court of Accounts

1961. Bicentenary of Court of Accounts.
| 1379 | 275 | 1s. sepia | 15 | 15 |

276 Glockner-Kaprun Power Station

1962. 15th Anniv of Electric Power Nationalization. Inscr as in T 276.
1380	276	1s. blue	20	10
1381	–	1s.50 purple	30	20
1382	–	1s.80 green	75	65
1383	–	3s. brown	40	35
1384	–	4s. red	40	35
1385	–	6s.40 black	1·25	1·40

DESIGNS: 1s.50, Ybbs-Persenbeug (Danube); 1s.80, Luner See; 3s. Grossraming (Enns River); 4s. Bisamberg Transformer Station; 6s.40, St. Andra Power Stations.

1962. Death Cent of Johann Nestroy (playwright). Portrait as T 187.
| 1386 | | 1s. violet | 15 | 10 |

277 F. Gauermann   278 Scout Badge and Handclasp

1962. Death Cent of Friedrich Gauermann (painter).
| 1387 | 277 | 1s.50 blue | 15 | 15 |

1962. 50th Anniv of Austrian Scout Movement.
| 1388 | 278 | 1s.50 green | 40 | 25 |

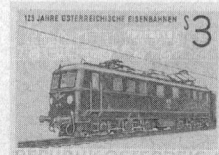

279 Forest and Lake

1962. "The Austrian Forest".
1389	279	1s. grey	10	15
1390	–	1s.50 brown	35	25
1391	–	3s. myrtle	95	65

DESIGNS: 1s.50, Deciduous forest; 3s. Fir and larch forest.

280 Electric Locomotive and Steam Locomotive "Austria" (1837)

1962. 125th Anniv of Austrian Railways.
| 1392 | 280 | 3s. black and buff | 95 | 45 |

281 Engraving Die   282 Postal Officials of 1863

1962. Stamp Day.
| 1393 | 281 | 3s.+70g. violet | 1·00 | 95 |

1963. Centenary of Paris Postal Conference.
| 1394 | 282 | 3s. sepia and yellow | 40 | 40 |

283 Hermann Bahr   284 St. Florian (statue)

1963. Birth Centenary of Hermann Bahr (writer).
| 1395 | 283 | 1s.50 sepia and blue | 20 | 15 |

1963. Cent of Austrian Voluntary Fire Brigade.
| 1396 | 284 | 1s.50 black and pink | 55 | 15 |

285 Flag and Emblem

1963. 5th Austrian Trade Unions Federation Congress.
| 1397 | 285 | 1s.50 red, sepia & grey | 25 | 10 |

286 Crests of Tyrol and Austria

1963. 600th Anniv of Tyrol as an Austrian Province.
| 1398 | 286 | 1s.50 multicoloured | 25 | 10 |

287 Prince Eugene of Savoy   288 Centenary Emblem

1963. Birth Tercent of Prince Eugene of Savoy.
| 1399 | 287 | 1s.50 violet | 25 | 15 |

1963. Centenary of Red Cross.
| 1400 | 288 | 3s. silver, red and black | 40 | 35 |

289 Skiing (slalom)

1963. Winter Olympic Games, Innsbruck, 1964. Centres black; inscr gold; background colours given.
1401	289	1s. grey	15	10
1402	–	1s.20 blue	15	15
1403	–	1s.50 grey	15	10
1404	–	1s.80 purple	25	25
1405	–	2s.20 green	65	60
1406	–	3s. slate	35	25
1407	–	4s. blue	80	75

DESIGNS: 1s.20, Skiing (biathlon); 1s.50, Ski jumping; 1s.80, Figure skating; 2s.20, Ice hockey; 3s. Tobogganing; 4s. Bobsleighing.

290 Vienna "101" P.O. and Railway Shed   291 "The Holy Family" (Josef Stammel)

1963. Stamp Day.
| 1408 | 290 | 3s.+70g. blk & drab | 60 | 65 |

1963. Christmas.
| 1409 | 291 | 2s. green | 20 | 15 |

292 Nasturtium

1964. Int Horticultural Exn, Vienna. Mult.
1410		1s. Type 292	15	10
1411		1s.50 Peony	15	10
1412		1s.80 Clematis	20	15
1413		2s.20 Dahlia	40	40
1414		3s. Convolvulus	55	25
1415		4s. Mallow	60	60

293 Gothic Statue and Stained-glass Window

1964. Romanesque Art Exhibition, Vienna.
| 1416 | 293 | 1s.50 blue and black | 25 | 20 |

294 Pallas Athene and Interior of Assembly Hall, Parliament Building

1964. 2nd Parliamentary and Scientific Conference, Vienna.
| 1417 | 294 | 1s.80 black and green | 25 | 20 |

295 "The Kiss" (Gustav Klimt)

1964. Re-opening of "Viennese Secession" Exn Hall.
| 1418 | 295 | 3s. multicoloured | 40 | 35 |

296 "Comforting the Sick"

1964. 350th Anniv of Order of Brothers of Mercy in Austria.
| 1419 | 296 | 1s.50 blue | 20 | 15 |

297 "Bringing News of the Victory at Kunersdorf" (Bellotto)

1964. 15th U.P.U. Congress, Vienna. Paintings.
1420	297	1s. purple	10	15
1421	–	1s.20 brown	25	15
1422	–	1s.50 blue	20	10
1423	–	1s.80 violet	25	25
1424	–	2s.20 black	25	30
1425	–	3s. purple	25	25
1426	–	4s. green	40	55
1427	–	6s.40 purple	1·25	1·40

PAINTINGS: 1s.20, "Changing Horses" (Hormann); 1s.50, "The Wedding Trip" (Schwind); 1s.80, "Postboys returning Home" (Raffalt); 2s.20, "The Vienna Mail Coach" (Klein); 3s. "Changing Horses" (Gauermann); 4s. "Postal Tracked-vehicle in Mountain Village" (Pilch); 6s.40, "Saalbach Post Office and Post-bus" (Pilch).

298 Vienna, from the Hochhaus (N.)   299 "Workers"

1964. "WIPA" Stamp Exhibition, Vienna (1965) (1st issue). Multicoloured.
1428		1s.50+30g. Type 298	20	20
1429		1s.50+30g. N.E.	20	20
1430		1s.50+30g. E.	20	20
1431		1s.50+30g. S.E.	20	20
1432		1s.50+30g. S.	20	20
1433		1s.50+30g. S.W.	20	20
1434		1s.50+30g. W.	20	20
1435		1s.50+30g. N.W.	20	20

The designs show a panoramic view of Vienna, looking to different points of compass (indicated on stamps). The inscription reads "Vienna welcomes you to WIPA 1965".

See also Nos. 1447/52.

1964. Centenary of Austrian Workers' Movement.
| 1436 | 299 | 1s. black | 15 | 15 |

300 Europa "Flower"

301 Radio Receiver Dial

1964. Europa.
1437 300 3s. blue 35 25

1964. 40th Anniv of Austrian Broadcasting Service.
1438 301 1s. sepia and red 15 15

302 Old Printing Press

1964. 6th International Graphical Federation Congress, Vienna.
1439 302 1s.50 black and drab . . . 20 15

303 Post-bus Station, St. Gilgen

1964. Stamp Day.
1440 303 3s.+70g. mult 40 40

304 Dr. Adolf Scharf   305 "Reconstruction"

1965. Pres. Scharf Commemoration.
1441 304 1s.50 blue and black . . . 20 20

1965. "20 Years of Reconstruction".
1442 305 1s.80 lake 20 15

306 University Seal, 1365   307 "St. George" (after engraving by Altdorfer)

1965. 600th Anniv of Vienna University.
1443 306 3s. red and gold 25 25

1965. Danubian Art.
1444 307 1s.80 blue 20 20

308 I.T.U. Emblem, Morse Key and T.V. Aerial   309 F. Raimund

1965. Centenary of I.T.U.
1445 308 3s. violet 25 20

1965. 175th Birth Anniv of Ferdinand Raimund (actor and playwright).
1446 309 3s. purple 25 15

310 Egyptian Hieroglyphs on Papyrus   311 Gymnasts with Wands

1965. "WIPA" Stamp Exhibition, Vienna (2nd issue). "Development of the Letter".
1447 310 1s.50+40g. black and pink 20 20
1448 — 1s.80+50g. black and yellow 25 25
1449 — 2s.20+60g. black and lilac 50 55
1450 — 3s.+80g. black & yell . . 50 50
1451 — 4s.+1s. black & blue . . 70 60
1452 — 5s.+1s.20 black & grn . . 80 80
DESIGNS: 1s.80, Cuneiform writing; 2s.20, Latin; 3c. Ancient letter and seal; 4s.19th-century letter; 5s. Typewriter.

1965. 4th Gymnaestrada, Vienna.
1453 311 1s.50 black and blue . . 15 15
1454 — 3s. black and brown . . 30 30
DESIGNS: 3s. Girls exercising with tambourines.

312 Dr. I. Semmelweis   313 F. G. Waldmuller (self-portrait)

1965. Death Cent of Ignaz Semmelweis (physician).
1455 312 1s.50 lilac 20 10

1965. Death Cent of F. G. Waldmuller (painter).
1456 313 3s. black 25 20

314 Red Cross and Gauze   315 Flag and Crowned Eagle

1965. Red Cross Conference, Vienna.
1457 314 3s. red and black 25 20

1965. 50th Anniv of Austrian Towns Union.
1458 315 1s.50 multicoloured . . . 15 15

316 Austrian Flag, U. N. Emblem and Headquarters

1965. 10th Anniv of Austria's Membership of U.N.O.
1459 316 3s. sepia, red and blue 35 20

317 University Building   318 Bertha von Suttner

1965. 150th Anniv of University of Technology, Vienna.
1460 317 1s.50 violet 15 10

1965. 60th Anniv of Nobel Peace Prize Award to Bertha von Suttner (writer).
1461 318 1s.50 black 15 15

319 Postman delivering Mail

1965. Stamp Day.
1462 319 3s.+70g. green 40 45

320 Postal Code Map

1966. Introduction of Postal Code System.
1463 320 1s.50 black, red & yell 15 10

321 P.T.T. Headquarters   322 M. Ebner-Eschenbach

1966. Centenary of Austrian Posts and Telegraphs Administration.
1464 321 1s.50 black on cream . . 15 15

1966. 50th Death Anniv of Maria Ebner-Eschenbach (writer).
1465 322 3s. purple 15 15

323 Big Wheel   324 Josef Hoffmann

1966. Bicentenary of Vienna Prater.
1466 323 1s.50 green 15 15

1966. 10th Death Anniv of Josef Hoffmann (architect).
1467 324 3s. brown 25 15

325 Bank Emblem

1966. 150th Anniv of Austrian National Bank.
1468 325 3s. brn, grn & drab . . 25 15

326 Arms of Wiener Neustadt

1966. "Wiener Neustadt 1440-93" Art Exhibition.
1469 326 1s.50 multicoloured . . . 15 10

327 Puppy   328 Columbine

1966. 120th Anniv of Vienna Animal Protection Society.
1470 327 1s.80 black and yellow 20 15

1966. Alpine Flora. Multicoloured.
1471 1s.50 Type 328 . . . . . . 20 15
1472 1s.80 Turk's cap 25 20
1473 2s.20 Wulfenia 40 35
1474 3s. Globe flower 40 35
1475 4s. Orange lily 55 50
1476 5s. Alpine anemone 65 55

329 Fair Building

1966. Wels International Fair.
1477 329 3s. blue 25 15

330 Peter Anich

1966. Death Bicent of Peter Anich (cartographer).
1478 330 1s.80 black 20 10

331 "Suffering"

1966. 15th International Occupational Health Congress, Vienna.
1479 331 3s. black and red 25 15

332 "Eunuchus" by Terence (engraving, Johann Gruninger)

1966. Austrian National Library, Vienna. Mult.
1480 1s.50 Type 332 (Theatre collection) 15 15
1481 1s.80 Detail of title page of Willem Blaeu's atlas (Cartography collection) 15 20
1482 2s.20 "Herrengasse, Vienna" (Anton Stutzinger (Pictures and portraits collection)) 35 35
1483 3s. Illustration from Rene of Anjou's "Livre du Cuer d'Amours Espris" (Manuscripts collection) 35 30

333 Young Girl

1966. Austrian "Save the Children" Fund.
1484 333 3s. black and blue . . . 30 15

334 Strawberries   335 16th-century Postman

1966. Fruits. Multicoloured.

1485	50g. Type **334**	10	15
1486	1s. Grapes	15	10
1487	1s.50 Apple	20	15
1488	1s.80 Blackberries	20	20
1489	2s.20 Apricots	25	25
1490	3s. Cherries	40	20

1966. Stamp Day.
1491 **335** 3s.+70g. multicoloured 35 40

336 Arms of Linz University 337 Skater of 1867

1966. Inauguration of Linz University.
1492 **336** 3s. multicoloured 30 15

1967. Centenary of Vienna Skating Assn.
1493 **337** 3s. indigo and blue 30 15

338 Dancer with Violin 339 Dr. Schonherr

1967. Centenary of "Blue Danube" Waltz.
1494 **338** 3s. purple 50 25

1967. Birth Cent of Dr. Karl Schonherr (poet).
1495 **339** 3s. brown 30 15

340 Ice Hockey Goalkeeper 341 Violin and Organ

1967. World Ice Hockey Championships, Vienna.
1496 **340** 3s. blue and green 30 15

1967. 125th Anniv of Vienna Philharmonic Orchestra.
1497 **341** 3s.50 blue 40 20

342 "Mother and Children" (aquarelle, Peter Fendi)

1967. Mother's Day.
1498 **342** 2s. multicoloured 20 15

343 "Madonna" (Gothic wood-carving)

1967. "Gothic Art in Austria" Exhibition, Krems.
1499 **343** 3s. green 25 15

344 Jewelled Cross 345 "The White Swan" (from Kokoschkas tapestry "Cupid and Psyche")

1967. "Salzburg Treasures" Exhibition, Salzburg Cathedral.
1500 **344** 3s.50 multicoloured ... 25 20

1967. "Art of the Nibelungen District" Exhibition, Pochlarn.
1501 **345** 2s. multicoloured 20 15

346 Vienna

1967. 10th European Talks, Vienna.
1502 **346** 3s. black and red 25 15

347 Champion Bull

1967. Centenary of Ried Fair.
1503 **347** 2s. purple 20 15

348 Colorado Potato Beetle

1967. 6th Int Plant Protection Congress, Vienna.
1504 **348** 3s. multicoloured 25 15

349 Locomotive No. 671 350 "Christ" (fresco detail)

1967. Centenary of Brenner Railway.
1505 **349** 3s.50 green and brown 50 25

1967. Lambach Frescoes.
1506 **350** 2s. multicoloured 20 15

351 Prater Hall, Vienna 352 Rector's Medallion and Chain

1967. International Trade Fairs Congress, Vienna.
1507 **351** 2s. purple and cream ... 20 15

1967. 275th Anniv of Fine Arts Academy, Vienna.
1508 **352** 2s. brown, yellow & blue ... 15 10

353 Bible on Rock (from commemorative coin of 1717) 355 Memorial, Vienna

354 Forest Trees

1967. 450th Anniv of the Reformation.
1509 **353** 3s.50 blue 25 15

1967. 100 Years of Austrian University Forestry Studies.
1510 **354** 3s.50 green 35 20

1967. 150th Anniv of Land Registry.
1511 **355** 2s. green 15 15

356 "St. Leopold" (stained-glass window, Heiligenkreuz Monastery) 357 "Music and Art"

1967. Margrave Leopold the Holy.
1512 **356** 1s.80 multicoloured ... 20 15

1967. 150th Anniv of Academy of Music and Dramatic Art, Vienna.
1513 **357** 3s.50 black and violet ... 40 20

358 St. Mary's Altar, Nonnberg Convent, Salzburg 359 "The Letter-carrier" (from playing-card)

1967. Christmas.
1514 **358** 2s. green 20 15

1967. Stamp Day.
1515 **359** 3s.50+80g. mult 35 40

360 Ski Jump, Stadium and Mountains

1968. Winter University Games, Innsbruck.
1516 **360** 2s. blue 20 20

361 C. Sitte 362 Mother and Child

1968. 125th Birth Anniv of Camillo Sitte (architect).
1517 **361** 2s. brown 20 20

1968. Mothers' Day.
1518 **362** 2s. olive 20 20

363 "Veterinary Medicine" 364 Bride with Lace Veil

1968. Bicentenary of Vienna Veterinary College.
1519 **363** 3s.50 gold, pur & drab 30 20

1968. Centenary of Vorarlberg Lace.
1520 **364** 3s.50 blue 40 25

365 Etrich Limousine

1968. "IFA Wien 1968" Airmail Stamp Exhibition, Vienna.

1521	**365**	2s. brown	35	35
1522	–	3s.50 green	55	50
1523	–	5s. blue	75	80

DESIGNS: 3s.50, Sud Aviation Caravelle; 5s. Douglas DC-8.

366 Horse-racing

1968. Centenary of Freudenau Gallop Races.
1524 **366** 3s.50 brown 40 25

367 Landsteiner 368 P. Rosegger

1968. Birth Centenary of Dr. Karl Landsteiner (physician and pathologist).
1525 **367** 3s.50 blue 40 25

1968. 50th Death Anniv of Peter Rosegger (writer).
1526 **368** 2s. green 25 15

369 A. Kauffmann (self-portrait) 370 Statue of Young Man (Helenenberg site)

1968. Exhibition of Angelica Kauffmann's Paintings, Bregenz.
1527 **369** 2s. violet 25 15

1968. Magdalensberg Excavations, Carinthia.
1528 **370** 2s. black and green 20 15

371 "The Bishop" (Romanesque carving)

372 K. Moser

1968. 750th Anniv of Graz-Seckau Diocese.
1529 **371** 2s. grey 20 15

1968. 50th Death Anniv of Koloman Moser (graphic artist).
1530 **372** 2s. brown and red . . . 20 15

373 Human Rights Emblem

374 Arms and Provincial Shields

1968. Human Rights Year.
1531 **373** 1s.50 red, green & grey 25 15

1968. 50th Anniv of Republic. Multicoloured.
1532 2s. Type **374** 25 25
1533 2s. Karl Renner (first President of Second Republic) 25 25
1534 2s. First Article of Constitution 25 25

375 Crib, Oberndorf, Salzburg

376 Mercury

1968. 150th Anniv of "Silent Night, Holy Night" (carol).
1535 **375** 2s. green 25 15

1968. Stamp Day.
1536 **376** 3s.50+80g. green 35 40

377 Fresco (Troger), Melk Monastery

378 "Madonna and Child"

1968. Baroque Frescoes. Designs showing frescoes in locations given. Multicoloured.
1537 2s. Type **377** 30 35
1538 2s. Altenburg Monastery . . 30 35
1539 2s. Rohrenbach-Greillenstein 30 35
1540 2s. Ebenfurth Castle 30 35
1541 2s. Halbthurn Castle 30 35
1542 2s. Maria Treu Church, Vienna 30 35
Nos. 1537/9 are the work of Anton Troger and Nos. 1540/2 that of Franz Maulbertsch.

1969. 500th Anniv of Vienna Diocese. Statues in St. Stephen's Cathedral, Vienna.
1543 **378** 2s. blue 30 35
1544 – 2s. grey 30 35
1545 – 2s. green 30 35
1546 – 2s. purple 30 35
1547 – 2s. black 30 35
1548 – 2s. brown 30 35
DESIGNS: No. 1544, "St. Christopher"; No. 1545, "St. George"; No. 1546, "St. Paul"; No. 1547, "St. Sebastian"; No. 1548, "St. Stephen".

379 Parliament Building, Vienna

1969. Interparliamentary Union Meeting, Vienna.
1549 **379** 2s. green 15 15

380 Colonnade

1969. Europa.
1550 **380** 2s. multicoloured 25 20

381 "Council Members"

382 Soldiers

1969. 20th Anniv of Council of Europe.
1551 **381** 3s.50 multicoloured . . . 35 35

1969. Austrian Armed Forces.
1552 **382** 2s. brown and red . . . 25 20

384 Maximilian's Armour

385 Viennese "Privilege" Seal

1969. "Maximilian I" Exhibition, Innsbruck.
1554 **384** 2s. black 20 15

1969. 19th International Union of Local Authorities Congress, Vienna.
1555 **385** 2s. red, brown & ochre 15 15

386 Young Girl

387 Hands clasping Spanner

1969. 20th Anniv of "SOS" Children's Villages Movement.
1556 **386** 2s. brown and green . . 15 15

1969. 50th Anniv of Int Labour Organization.
1557 **387** 2s. green 15 15

388 Austrian "Flag" encircling Globe

389 "El Cid killing a Bull" (Goya)

1969. "Austrians Living Abroad" Year.
1558 **388** 3s.50 red and green . . . 15 15

1969. Bicentenary of Albertina Art Collection, Vienna. Multicoloured.
1559 2s. Type **389** 30 30
1560 2s. "Young Hare" (Durer) 30 30
1561 2s. "Madonna with Pomegranate" (Raphael) 30 30
1562 2s. "The Painter and the Amateur" (Bruegel) . . . 30 30
1563 2s. "Rubens's Son, Nicholas" (Rubens) . . . 30 30
1564 2s. "Self-portrait" (Rembrandt) 30 30
1565 2s. "Madame de Pompadour" (detail, Guerin) 30 30
1566 2s. "The Artist's Wife" (Schiele) 30 30

390 Pres. Jonas

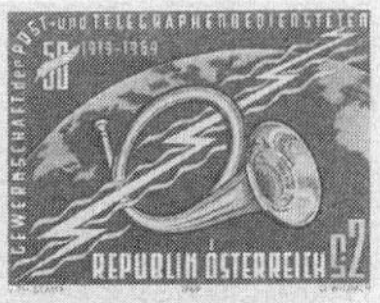
391 Posthorn and Lightning over Globe

1969. Pres. Franz Jonas's 70th Birthday.
1567 **390** 2s. blue and grey 20 10

1969. 50th Anniv of Post and Telegraph Employees Union.
1568 **391** 2s. multicoloured 20 15

392 Savings Bank (c. 1450)

393 "The Madonna" (Egger-Lienz)

1969. 150th Anniv of Austrian Savings Bank.
1569 **392** 2s. green and silver . . . 20 15

1969. Christmas.
1570 **393** 2s. purple and yellow . . 20 15

394 Unken, Salzburg, Post-house Sign (after F. Zeller)

395 J. Schoffel

1969. Stamp Day.
1571 **394** 3s.50+80g. black, red and stone 40 45

1970. 60th Death Anniv of Josef Schoffel ("Saviour of the Vienna Woods").
1572 **395** 2s. purple 20 15

396 St. Clement Hofbauer

398 Krimml Waterfalls

397 Chancellor Leopold Figl

1970. 150th Death Anniv of St. Clement Hofbauer (theologian).
1573 **396** 2s. brown and green . . 15 15

1970. 25th Anniv of Austrian Republic.
1574 **397** 2s. olive 20 20
1575 – 2s. brown 20 20
DESIGN: No. 1575, Belvedere Castle.

1970. Nature Conservation Year.
1576 **398** 2s. green 35 20

399 Oldest University Seal

401 Tower Clock, 1450–1550

400 "Musikverein" Organ

1970. 300th Anniv of Leopold Franz University, Innsbruck.
1577 **399** 2s. black and red 15 15

1970. Centenary of "Musikverein" Building.
1578 **400** 2s. purple and gold . . . 20 20

1970. Antique Clocks.
1579 **401** 1s.50 brown and cream 35 25
1580 – 1s.50 green & lt green . . 30 30
1581 – 2s. blue and pale blue . . 35 30
1582 – 2s. red and purple . . . 35 30
1583 – 3s.50 brown and buff . . 55 55
1584 – 3s.50 purple and lilac . . 55 55
DESIGNS: No. 1580, Empire "lyre" clock, 1790–1815; No. 1581, Pendant ball clock, 1600–50; No. 1582, Pocket-watch and signet, 1800–30; No. 1583, Bracket clock, 1720–60; No. 1584, "Biedermeier" pendulum clock and musical-box, 1820–50.

402 "The Beggar Student" (Millocker)

403 Scene from "The Gipsy Baron" (J. Strauss)

1970. Famous Operettas.
1585 **402** 1s.50 turquoise & green 35 25
1586 – 1s.50 blue and yellow . . 35 25
1587 – 2s. purple and pink . . . 50 40
1588 – 2s. brown and green . . 50 40
1589 – 3s.50 blue and light blue 50 55
1590 – 3s.50 blue and buff . . . 55 80
OPERETTAS: No. 1586, "Die Fledermaus" (Johann Strauss the younger); 1587, "A Waltz Dream" (O. Straus); 1588, "The Birdseller" (C. Zeller); 1589, "The Merry Widow" (F. Lehar); 1590, "Two Hearts in Waltz-time" (R. Stoiz).

1970. 25th Anniv of Bregenz Festival.
1591 **403** 3s.50 blue, buff & ult . . 40 25

404 Festival Emblem

405 T. Koschat

1970. 50th Anniv of Salzburg Festival.
1592 **404** 3s.50 multicoloured . . . 35 35

1970. 125th Birth Anniv of Thomas Koschat (composer and poet).
1593 **405** 2s. brown 25 20

406 "Head of St. John", from sculpture "Mount of Olives", Ried Church (attributed to T. Schwanthaler)

1970. 13th World Veterans Federation General Assembly.
1594 **406** 3s.50 sepia 35 20

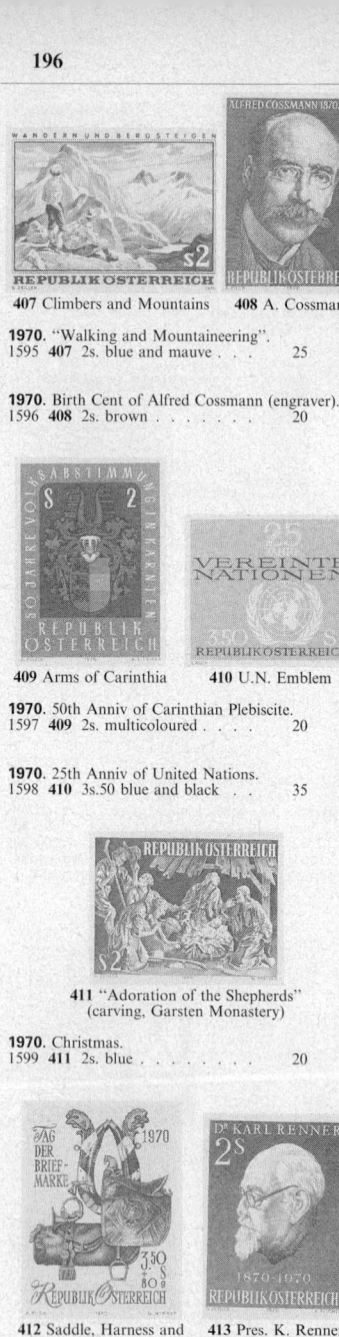

407 Climbers and Mountains **408** A. Cossmann

1970. "Walking and Mountaineering".
1595 **407** 2s. blue and mauve . . . 25 20

1970. Birth Cent of Alfred Cossmann (engraver).
1596 **408** 2s. brown 20 15

409 Arms of Carinthia **410** U.N. Emblem

1970. 50th Anniv of Carinthian Plebiscite.
1597 **409** 2s. multicoloured . . . 20 15

1970. 25th Anniv of United Nations.
1598 **410** 3s.50 blue and black . . 35 20

411 "Adoration of the Shepherds"
(carving, Garsten Monastery)

1970. Christmas.
1599 **411** 2s. blue 20 15

412 Saddle, Harness and **413** Pres. K. Renner
Posthorn

1970. Stamp Day.
1600 **412** 3s.50+80g. black, yellow
and grey 35 45

1970. Birth Centenary of Pres. Renner.
1601 **413** 2s. purple 15 15

414 Beethoven (after **415** E. Handel-
painting by Waldmuller) Mazzetti

1970. Birth Bicentenary of Beethoven.
1602 **414** 3s.50 black and stone . . 60 35

1971. Birth Centenary of Enrica Handel-Mazzetti
(novelist).
1603 **415** 2s. brown 20 15

416 "Safety for Children"

1971. Road Safety.
1604 **416** 2s. multicoloured 25 20

417 Florentine Bowl, c. 1580

1971. Austrian Art Treasures (1st series). Sculpture and Applied Art.
1605 **417** 1s.50 green and grey . . . 25 20
1606 — 2s. purple and grey . . . 25 20
1607 — 3s.50 yellow, brn & grey 55 55
DESIGNS: 2s. Ivory equestrian statuette of Joseph I, 1693 (Matthias Steinle); 3s.50, Salt-cellar, c. 1570 (Cellini).
See also Nos. 1609/11, 1632/4 and 1651/3.

418 Shield of Trade **419** "Jacopo de Strada"
Association (Titian)

1971. 23rd International Chamber of Commerce Congress, Vienna.
1608 **418** 3s.50 multicoloured . . . 25 20

1971. Austrian Art Treasures (2nd series).
1609 **419** 1s.50 purple 25 25
1610 — 2s. black 25 25
1611 — 3s.50 brown 35 55
PAINTINGS: 2s. "The Village Feast" (Brueghel); 3s.50, "Young Venetian Woman" (Durer).

420 Notary's Seal **421** "St. Matthew"
(altar sculpture)

1971. Austrian Notarial Statute Cent Congress.
1612 **420** 3s.50 purple and brown 35 35

1971. "Krems Millennium of Art" Exhibition.
1613 **421** 2s. brown and purple . . 15 15

422 Dr. A. Neilreich **423** Singer with Lyre

1971. Death Cent of Dr. August Neilreich (botanist).
1614 **422** 2s. brown 15 15

1971. International Choir Festival, Vienna.
1615 **423** 4s. blue, gold & pale
blue 60 35

424 Arms of Kitzbuhel

1971. 700th Anniv of Kitzbuhel.
1616 **424** 2s.50 multicoloured . . . 25 20

425 Stock Exchange Building

1971. Bicentenary of Vienna Stock Exchange.
1617 **425** 4s. brown 40 25

426 Old and New Fair Halls **427** O.G.B. Emblem

1971. "50 Years of Vienna International Fairs".
1618 **426** 2s.50 purple 25 15

1971. 25th Anniv of Austrian Trade Unions Federation.
1619 **427** 2s. multicoloured . . . 20 15

428 Arms and **429** "Marcus" Veteran Car
Insignia

1971. 50th Anniv of Burgenland Province.
1620 **428** 4s. multicoloured 20 20

1971. 75th Anniv of Austrian Automobile, Motor Cycle and Touring Club.
1621 **429** 4s. black and green . . . 35 25

430 Europa Bridge, **431** Iron-ore Workings,
Brenner Highway Erzberg

1971. Inauguration of Brenner Highway.
1622 **430** 4s. blue 35 25

1971. 25 Years of Nationalized Industries.
1623 **431** 1s.50 brown 20 20
1624 — 2s. blue 25 25
1625 — 4s. green 60 40
DESIGNS: 2s. Nitrogen Works, Linz; 4s. Iron and Steel works, Linz.

432 Electric Train on **433** E. Tschermak-
the Semmering Line Seysenegg

1971. Railway Anniversaries.
1626 **432** 2s. purple 45 25

1971. Birth Centenary of Dr. E. Tshermak-Seysenegg (biologist).
1627 **433** 2s. purple and grey . . 20 20

434 Angling **435** "The Infant Jesus
as Saviour" (from
miniature by Durer)

1971. Sports.
1628 **434** 2s. brown 25 20

1971. Christmas.
1629 **435** 2s. multicoloured . . . 25 20

436 "50 Years"

1971. 50th Anniv of Austrian Philatelic Clubs Association.
1630 **436** 4s.+1s.50 pur & gold . . 60 65

437 Franz Grillparzer **438** Roman Fountain,
(from miniature by Friesach
Daffinger)

1972. Death Centenary of Grillparzer (dramatist).
1631 **437** 2s. black, brown & stone 25 15

1972. Austrian Art Treasures (3rd series). Fountains.
1632 **438** 1s.50 purple 20 25
1633 — 2s. brown 35 25
1634 — 2s.50 green 40 45
DESIGNS: 2s. Lead Fountain, Heiligenkreuz Abbey; 2s.50. Leopold Fountain, Innsbruck.

 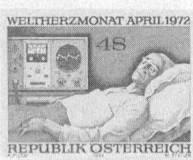

439 Hofburg Palace **440** Heart Patient

1972. 4th European Postal Ministers' Conf, Vienna.
1635 **439** 4s. violet 45 35

1972. World Heart Month.
1636 **440** 4s. brown 45 35

441 "Woman's Head" **442** Vienna Town Hall
(sculpture, Gurk and Congress Emblem
Cathedral)

1972. 900th Anniv of Gurk Diocese.
1637 **441** 2s. purple and gold . . . 25 15

1972. 9th International Public and Co-operative Economy Congress, Vienna.
1638 **442** 4s. black, red and yellow 45 25

443 Lienz–Pelos Pylon Line

1972. 25th Anniv of Electric Power Nationalization.
1639 **443** 70g. violet and grey . . 10 10
1640 — 2s.50 brown and grey . . 25 25
1641 — 4s. blue and grey 40 35
DESIGNS: 2s.50, Vienna-Semmering Power Station; 4s. Zemm Dam and lake.

444 Runner with Torch **445** "Hermes"
(C. Laib)

1972. Passage of the Olympic Torch through Austria.
1642 **444** 2s. brown and red . . . 25 20

1972. "Late Gothic Art" Exhibition, Salzburg.
1643 **445** 2s. purple 25 15

446 Pears   **448** University Arms

1972. Amateur Gardeners' Congress, Vienna.
1644 **446** 2s.50 multicoloured . . . 25 15

1972. Cent of University of Agriculture, Vienna.
1646 **448** 2s. multicoloured 25 20

449 Old University Buildings (after F. Danreiter)   **450** C. M. Ziehrer

1972. 350th Anniv of Paris Lodron University, Salzburg.
1647 **449** 4s. brown 40 20

1972. 50th Death Anniv of Carl M. Ziehrer (composer and conductor).
1648 **450** 2s. red 35 40

451 "Virgin and Child", Inzersdorf Church

1972. Christmas.
1649 **451** 2s. purple and green . . . 25 15

452 18th-century Viennese Postman

1972. Stamp Day.
1650 **452** 4s.+1s. green 50 65

453 State Sledge of Maria Theresa

1972. Austrian Art Treasures (4th series). Carriages from the Imperial Coach House.
1651 **453** 1s.50 brown and bistre . . 25 15
1652 — 2s. green and bistre . . . 30 25
1653 — 2s.50 purple and bistre . . 40 40
DESIGNS: 2s. Coronation landau; 2s.50, Hapsburg State Coach.

454 Telephone Network   **456** A. Petzold

---

455 "Drug Addict"

1972. Completion of Austrian Telephone System Automation.
1654 **454** 2s. black and yellow . . 30 15

1973. Campaign against Drug Abuse.
1655 **455** 2s. multicoloured . . . 55 40

1973. 50th Death Anniv of Alfons Petzold (writer).
1656 **456** 2s. purple 25 20

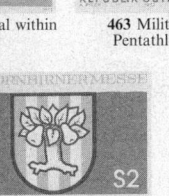

457 Korner   **458** Douglas DC-9-80 Super Eighty

1973. Birth Centenary of Pres. Theodor Korner (President, 1951–57).
1657 **457** 2s. purple and grey . . . 25 20

1973. Austrian Aviation Anniversaries.
1658 **458** 2s. blue and red 25 20

459 Otto Loewi   **460** "Succour"

1973. Birth Cent of Otto Loewi (pharmacologist).
1659 **459** 4s. violet 40 35

1973. 25th Anniv of National Federation of Austrian Social Insurance Institutes.
1660 **460** 2s. blue 25 20

461 Telephone Dial within Posthorn   **463** Military Pentathlon

462 Fair Emblem

1973. Europa.
1661 **461** 2s.50 black, yell & orge 35 20

1973. 25th Dornbirn Fair.
1662 **462** 2s. multicoloured . . . 25 20

1973. 25th Anniv of International Military Sports Council and 23rd Military Pentathlon Championships, Wiener Neustadt.
1663 **463** 4s. green 50 35

464 Leo Slezak   **465** Main Entrance, Hofburg Palace

1973. Birth Centenary of Leo Slezak (operatic tenor).
1664 **464** 4s. brown 55 40

1973. 39th International Statistical Institute's Congress, Vienna.
1665 **465** 2s. brown, red and grey 25 20

466 "Admiral Tegetthof Icebound" (J. Payer)   **467** I.U.L.C.S. Arms

1973. Centenary of Discovery of Franz Josef Land.
1666 **466** 2s.50 green 45 25

1973. 13th International Union of Leather Chemists' Societies Congress, Vienna.
1667 **467** 4s. multicoloured . . . 40 35

468 "Academy of Sciences, Vienna" (B. Bellotto)   **469** Max Reinhardt

1973. Cent of Int Meteorological Organization.
1668 **468** 2s.50 violet 30 20

1973. Birth Centenary of Max Reinhardt (theatrical director).
1669 **469** 2s. purple 30 20

470 F. Hanusch

1973. 50th Death Anniv of Ferdinand Hanusch (politician).
1670 **470** 2s. purple 30 15

471 Light Harness Racing

1973. Centenary of Vienna Trotting Assn.
1671 **471** 2s. green 35 25

472 Radio Operator

1973. 50th Anniv of International Criminal Police Organization (Interpol).
1672 **472** 4s. violet 55 35

473 Petzval Camera Lens

1973. "Europhot" (professional photographers) Congress, Vienna.
1673 **473** 2s.50 multicoloured . . . 35 20

474 Aqueduct, Hollen Valley

1973. Centenary of Vienna's 1st Mountain-spring Aqueduct.
1674 **474** 2s. brown, red & blue . . 30 20

475 Almsee   **476** "The Nativity" (stained-glass window, St. Erhard Church, Bretenau)

1973. Views. (a) Size 23 × 29 mm.
1674a — 20g. blue and light blue 25 25
1675 — 50g. green & lt green 15 10
1676 — 1s. sepia and brown . . 15 10
1677 — 1s.50 purple and pink 35 10
1678 — 2s. indigo and blue . . 35 10
1679 — 2s.50 deep lilac & lilac 35 10
1680 — 3s. ultramarine & blue 65 10
1680a — 3s.50 brown and orange 75 10
1681 **475** — 4s. violet and lilac . . 65 10
1681a — 4s.20 black and grey . . 65 40
1682 — 4s.50 dp green & green 80 10
1683 — 5s. violet and lilac . . 95 10
1683a — 5s.50 blue and violet . . 65 40
1683b — 5s.60 olive and green . . 75 85
1684 — 6s. lilac and pink . . . 1·40 10
1684a — 6s.50 blue & turquoise . 95 20
1685 — 7s. deep green & green . 1·10 15
1685a — 7s.50 purple & mauve . 1·50 35
1686 — 8s. brown and pink . . 1·10 15
1686a — 9s. red and pink . . . 1·50 70
1687 — 10s. myrtle and green . 1·10 10
1688 — 11s. red and orange . . 1·10 20
1688a — 12s. sepia and brown . 1·50 30
1688b — 14s. myrtle and green . 1·75 30
1688c — 16s. brown and orange . 1·50 40
1688d — 20s. green and bistre . 2·00 55

(b) Size 28 × 37 mm.
1689 — 50s. violet and grey . . 5·25 1·90

(c) Size 17 × 20 mm.
1690 — 3s. ultramarine and blue 45 15
DESIGNS: 20g. Friedstadt Keep, Muhlviertel; 50g. Zillertal; 1s. Kahlenbergerdorf, Vienna; 1s.50, Bludenz; 2s. Old bridge, Finstermunz; 2s.50, Murau, Styria; 3s. Bischofsmutze and Alpine farm; 3s.50, Osterkirche, Oberwart; 4s.20, Hirschegg, Kleinwalsertal; 4s.50, Windmill, Retz; 5s. Ruins of Aggstein Castle; 5s.50, Peace Chapel, Stoderzinken; 5s.60, Riezlern, Kleinwalsertal; 6s. Lindauer Hut, Ratikon Massif; 6s.50, Villach, Carinthia; 7s. Falkenstein Castle; 7s.50, Hohensalzburg Fortress; 8s. Votive column, Reiteregg, Styria; 9s. Asten valley; 10s. Neusiedlersee; 11s. Enns; 12s. Kufstein Fortress; 14s. Weiszsee, Salzburg; 16s. Bad Tatzmannsdorf open-air museum; 20s. Myra Falls, Muggendorf; 50s. Hofburg, Vienna.

1973. Christmas.
1691 **476** 2s. multicoloured 45 15

477 "Archangel Gabriel" (carving by Lorenz Luchsperger)   **478** Dr. Fritz Pregl

1973. Stamp Day.
1692 **477** 4s.+1s. purple 55 60

1973. 50th Anniv of Award of Nobel Prize for Chemistry to Fritz Pregl.
1693 **478** 4s. blue 35 25

479 Telex Machine and Globe   **480** Hugo Hofmannsthal

1974. 50th Anniv of Radio Austria.
1694 **479** 2s.50 blue & ultramarine   25   20

1974. Birth Cent of Hugo Hofmannsthal (writer).
1695 **480** 4s. blue   40   25

481 Anton Bruckner (composer)

1974. Inaug of Bruckner Memorial Centre, Linz.
1696 **481** 4s. brown   65   40

482 Vegetables

1974. 2nd Int Horticultural Show, Vienna. Mult.
1697   2s. Type **482**   30   25
1698 **483** 2s.50 Fruit   30   35
1699   4s. Flowers   55   55

483 Head from Ancient   484 Karl Kraus
      Seal

1974. 750th Anniv of Judenburg.
1700 **483** 2s. multicoloured   30   25

1974. Birth Centenary of Karl Kraus (poet).
1701 **484** 4s. red   40   35

485 "St. Michael"   486 "King Arthur"
(wood-carving, Thomas   (statue, Innsbruck)
Schwanthaler)

1974. "Sculptures by the Schwanthaler Family"
Exhibition, Reichersberg.
1702 **485** 2s.50 green   35   20

1974. Europa.
1703 **486** 2s.50 blue and brown . . .   35   20

487 Early Dion-Bouton   489 I.R.U. Emblem
Motor-tricycle

1974. 75th Anniv of Austrian Association of
Motoring, Motor Cycling and Cycling.
1704 **487** 2s. brown and grey   35   20

1974. "Renaissance in Austria" Exhibition,
Schallaburg Castle.
1705 **488** 2s. black, brown & gold . .   25   20

488 Mask of Satyr's Head

1974. 14th International Road Haulage Union
Congress, Innsbruck.
1706 **489** 4s. black and orange . . .   40   25

490 F. A.   491 Gendarmes of 1849 and
Maulbertsch   1974

1974. 205th Birth Anniv of Franz Maulbertsch
(painter).
1707 **490** 2s. brown   25   20

1974. 125th Anniv of Austrian Gendarmerie.
1708 **491** 2s. multicoloured   35   20

492 Fencing

1974. Sports.
1709 **492** 2s.50 black and orange   35   20

493 Transport Emblems

1974. European Transport Ministers' Conference,
Vienna.
1710 **493** 4s. multicoloured   35   30

494 "St. Virgilius"   495 Pres. F. Jonas
(wood-carving)

1974. 1200 Years of Christianity in Salzburg.
1711 **494** 2s. blue   25   20

1974. Pres. Franz Jonas Commemoration.
1712 **495** 2s. black   20   20

496 F. Stelzhamer   497 Diving

1974. Death Cent of Franz Stelzhamer (poet).
1713 **496** 2s. blue   25   20

1974. 13th European Swimming, Diving and Water-
polo Championships.
1714 **497** 4s. brown and blue . . .   55   35

498 F. R. von Hebra   499 A. Schonberg
(founder of German
scientific dermatology)

1974. 30th Meeting of German-speaking
Dermatologists Association, Graz.
1715 **498** 4s. brown   40   35

1974. Birth Cent of Arnold Schonberg (composer).
1716 **499** 2s.50 purple   40   20

500 Broadcasting Studios,   501 E. Eysler
Salzburg

1974. 50th Anniv of Austrian Broadcasting.
1717 **500** 2s. multicoloured   25   20

1974. 25th Death Anniv of Edmund Eysler
(composer).
1718 **501** 2s. green   35   20

502 19th-century Postman and Mail
Transport

1974. Centenary of U.P.U.
1719 **502** 2s. brown and mauve . .   35   20
1720 —   4s. blue and grey . .   35   40
DESIGN: 4s. Modern postman and mail transport.

503 Sports Emblem

1974. 25th Anniv of Football Pools in Austria.
1721 **503** 70g. red, black and green   15   10

504 Steel Gauntlet grasping Rose

1974. Nature Protection.
1722 **504** 2s. multicoloured   35   20

505 C. D. von   506 Mail Coach and
Dittersdorf   P.O., 1905

1974. 175th Death Anniv of Carl Ditters von
Dittersdorf (composer).
1723 **505** 2s. green   35   20

1974. Stamp Day.
1724 **506** 4s.+2s. blue   60   70

507 "Virgin Mary and   508 F. Schmidt
Child" (wood-carving)

1974. Christmas.
1725 **507** 2s. brown and gold . . .   30   15

1974. Birth Centenary of Franz Schmidt (composer).
1726 **508** 4s. black and stone . . .   40   35

509 "St. Christopher and   511 Seat-belt around
Child" (altarpiece)   Skeletal Limbs

1975. European Architectural Heritage Year and
125th Anniv of Austrian Commission for
Preservation of Monuments.
1727 **509** 2s.50 brown and grey . .   50   25

510 Slalom

1975. Winter Olympics, Innsbruck (1976) (1st issue).
Multicoloured.
1728 **510** 1s.+50g. Type **510**   15   15
1729   1s.50+70g. Ice hockey . . .   30   30
1730   2s.+90g. Ski-jumping . . .   40   45
1731   4s.+1s.90 Bobsleighing . . .   75   80
See also Nos. 1747/50.

1975. Car Safety-belts Campaign.
1732 **511** 70g. multicoloured . . .   15   10

512 Stained-glass   513 "The Buffer State"
Window, Vienna Town
Hall

1975. 11th European Communities' Day.
1733 **512** 2s.50 multicoloured . . .   35   20

1975. 30th Anniv of Foundation of Austrian Second
Republic.
1734 **513** 2s. black and brown . .   25   20

514 Forest Scene

1975. 50th Anniv of Foundation of Austrian Forests
Administration.
1735 **514** 2s. green   40   20

515 "The High Priest"   516 Gosaukamm
(M. Pacher)   Cable-way

1975. Europa.
1736 **515** 2s.50 multicoloured . . .   35   20

1975. 4th International Ropeways Congress, Vienna.
1737 **516** 2s. blue and red   30   20

517 J. Misson

1975. Death Centenary of Josef Misson (poet).
1738 **517** 2s. brown and red . . .   30   20

518 "Setting Sun"   520 L. Fall

519 F. Porsche

1975. Nat Pensioners' Assn Meeting, Vienna.
1739 **518** 1s.50 multicoloured . . . 25   20

1975. Birth Centenary of Prof. Ferdinand Porsche (motor engineer).
1740 **519** 1s.50 purple & green . . 25   15

1975. 50th Death Anniv of Leo Fall (composer).
1741 **520** 2s. violet 30   20

521 Judo "Shoulder Throw"   522 Heinrich Angeli

1975. World Judo Championships, Vienna.
1742 **521** 2s.50 multicoloured . . . 25   20

1975. 50th Death Anniv of Heinrich Angeli (court painter).
1743 **522** 2s. purple 25   20

523 J. Strauss

1975. 150th Birth Anniv of Johann Strauss the Younger (composer).
1744 **523** 4s. brown and ochre . . 60   35

524 "The Cellist"   525 "One's Own House"

1975. 75th Anniv of Vienna Symphony Orchestra.
1745 **524** 2s.50 blue and silver . . 40   25

1975. 50th Anniv of Austrian Building Societies.
1746 **525** 2s. multicoloured 25   20

1975. Winter Olympic Games, Innsbruck (1976) (2nd issue). As T **510.** Multicoloured.
1747   70g.+30g. Figure-skating
          (pairs) 20   25
1748   2s.+1s. Cross-country skiing   25   35
1749   2s.50+1s. Tobogganing . . .   35   35
1750   4s.+2s. Rifle-shooting
          (biathlon) 75   80

526 Scene on Folding Fan

1975. Bicentenary of Salzburg State Theatre.
1751 **526** 1s.50 multicoloured 40   30

527 Austrian Stamps of   528 "Virgin and
1850, 1922 and 1945   Child"
                          (Schottenaltar,
                           Vienna)

1975. Stamp Day. 125th Anniv of Austrian Postage Stamps.
1752 **527** 4s.+2s. multicoloured . . 60   70

1975. Christmas.
1753 **528** 2s. lilac and gold 30   15

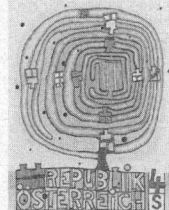

529 "Spiralbaum"   531 Dr. R. Barany
(F. Hundertwasser)

1975. Modern Austrian Art.
1754 **529** 4s. multicoloured 80   50

1976. Birth Centenary of Dr. Robert Barany (Nobel prizewinner for Medicine, 1915).
1756 **531** 3s. brown and blue . . . 50   30

532 Ammonite Fossil   533 9th-century
                        Coronation Throne

1976. Cent Exn, Vienna Natural History Museum.
1757 **532** 3s. multicoloured 55   25

1976. Millenary of Carinthia.
1758 **533** 3s. black and yellow . . 40   35

534 Stained-glass   535 "The Siege of
Window, Klosterneuburg   Linz" (contemporary
                          engraving)

1976. Babenberg Exhibition, Lilienfeld.
1759 **534** 3s. multicoloured 55   25

1976. 350th Anniv of the Peasants' War in Upper Austria.
1760 **535** 4s. black and green . . . 70   50

536 Bowler delivering Ball

1976. 11th World Skittles Championships, Vienna.
1761 **536** 4s. black and orange . . 70   40

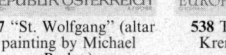

537 "St. Wolfgang" (altar   538 Tassilo Cup,
painting by Michael   Kremsmunster
Pacher)

1976. International Art Exhibition, St. Wolfgang.
1762 **537** 6s. purple 95   55

1976. Europa.
1763 **538** 4s. multicoloured 60   55

539 Fair Emblem   540 Constantin
                    Economo

1976. 25th Austrian Timber Fair, Klagenfurt.
1764 **539** 3s. multicoloured 40   25

1976. Birth Centenary of Constantin Economo (brain specialist).
1765 **540** 3s. brown 45   25

541 Bohemian Court Chancellery, Vienna

1976. Centenary of Administrative Court.
1766 **541** 6s. brown 80   60

543 Cancer the Crab   544 U.N. Emblem
                        and Bridge

1976. Fight against Cancer.
1768 **543** 2s.50 multicoloured . . . 40   25

1976. 10th Anniv of U.N. Industrial Development Organization.
1769 **544** 3s. blue and gold 40   25

545 Punched Tapes and Map of Europe

1976. 30th Anniv of Austrian Press Agency.
1770 **545** 1s.50 multicoloured . . . 20   10

546 V. Kaplan

1976. Birth Centenary of Viktor Kaplan (inventor of turbine).
1771 **546** 2s.50 multicoloured . . . 35   25

547 "The Birth of Christ" (Konrad von Friesach)

1976. Christmas.
1772 **547** 3s. multicoloured 50   25

548 Postilion's Hat and Posthorn

1976. Stamp Day.
1773 **548** 6s.+2s. black & lilac   1·10   1·10

549 R. M. Rilke   550 "Augustin the Piper"
                    (Arik Brauer)

1976. 50th Death Anniv of Rainer Maria Rilke (poet).
1774 **549** 3s. violet 40   25

1976. Austrian Modern Art.
1775 **550** 6s. multicoloured 95   60

551 City Synagogue   552 N. J. von Jacquin

1976. 150th Anniv of Vienna City Synagogue.
1776 **551** 1s.50 multicoloured . . . 35   15

1977. 250th Birth Anniv of Nikolaus Joseph Freiherrn von Jacquin (botanist).
1777 **552** 4s. brown 35   35

553 Oswald von   555 A. Kubin
Wolkenstein

554 Handball

1977. 600th Birth Anniv of Oswald von Wolkenstein (poet).
1778 **553** 3s. multicoloured 55   25

1977. World Indoor Handball Championships, Group B, Austria.
1779 **554** 1s.50 multicoloured . . . 20   15

1977. Birth Centenary of Alfred Kubin (writer and illustrator).
1780 **555** 6s. blue 80   50

556 Cathedral Spire

558 I.A.E.A. Emblem

557 F. Herzmanovsky-Orlando

1977. 25th Anniv of Re-opening of St. Stephen's Cathedral, Vienna.

1781	556	2s.50 brown	40	25
1782	–	3s. blue	55	45
1783	–	4s. purple	65	75

DESIGNS: 3s. West front; 4s. Interior.

1977. Birth Centenary of Fritz Herzmanovsky-Orlando (writer).
1784 **557** 6s. green and gold . . . 80 50

1977. 20th Anniv of Int Atomic Energy Agency.
1785 **558** 3s. lt blue, gold & blue . . 40 25

559 Arms of Schwanenstadt

561 Globe (Vincenzo Coronelli)

1977. 350th Anniv of Schwanenstadt.
1786 **559** 3s. multicoloured 55 35

1977. Europa.
1787 **560** 6s. green 80 55

1977. 5th International Symposium and 25th Anniv of Coronelli World Federation of Globe Friends.
1788 **561** 3s. black and stone . . . 45 25

560 Attersee

562 Canoeist

1977. World "White Water" Canoe Championships.
1789 **562** 4s. multicoloured 60 40

563 "The Samaritan" (Francesco Bassano)

1977. 50th Anniv of Austrian Workers' Samaritan Federation.
1790 **563** 1s.50 multicoloured . . . 25 25

564 Papermakers' Arms

565 "Freedom"

1977. 17th Conference of European Committee of Pulp and Paper Technology.
1791 **564** 3s. multicoloured 40 25

1977. Martyrs for Austrian Freedom.
1792 **565** 2s.50 blue and red . . . 35 25

566 Steam Locomotive, "Austria", 1837

1977. 140th Anniv of Austrian Railways. Mult.

1793	1s.50 Type **566**	35	25
1794	2s.50 Type 214 steam locomotive, 1928	60	40
1795	3s. Type 1044 electric locomotive, 1974	75	55

567 "Madonna & Child" (wood carving, Mariastein Pilgrimage Church)

1977. Christmas.
1796 **567** 3s. multicoloured 40 20

568 "Danube Maiden" (Wolfgang Hutter)

569 Emanuel Herrmann (inventor of postcard)

1977. Austrian Modern Art.
1797 **568** 6s. multicoloured 95 50

1977. Stamp Day.
1798 **569** 6s.+2s. brown and cinnamon . . . . . 1·10 1·10

570 Egon Friedell

1978. Birth Centenary of Egon Friedell (writer).
1799 **570** 3s. black and blue . . . 40 25

571 Underground Train

1978. Opening of Vienna Underground Railway.
1800 **571** 3s. multicoloured 95 35

572 Rifleman and Skier

1978. Biathlon World Championships, Hochfilzen.
1801 **572** 4s. multicoloured 60 35

573 Aztec Feather Shield

1978. 30th Anniv of Museum of Ethnology, Vienna.
1802 **573** 3s. multicoloured 40 25

574 Leopold Kunschak

575 "Mountain Peasants"

1978. 25th Death Anniv of Leopold Kunschak (politician).
1803 **574** 3s. blue 40 25

1978. Birth Centenary of Suitbert Lobisser (wood engraver).
1804 **575** 3s. brown and stone . . 40 35

576 Black Grouse, Hunting Satchel and Fowling Piece

577 Map of Europe and Austrian Parliament Building

1978. International Hunting Exn, Marchegg.
1805 **576** 6s. blue, brown & turq . . 75 50

1978. 3rd Interparliamentary European Security Conference, Vienna.
1806 **577** 4s. multicoloured 60 35

578 Riegersburg Castle, Styria

1978. Europa.
1807 **578** 6s. purple 80 60

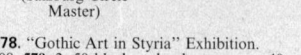

579 "Admont Pieta" (Salzburg Circle Master)

580 Ort Castle

1978. "Gothic Art in Styria" Exhibition.
1808 **579** 2s.50 black and ochre . . 40 25

1978. 700th Anniv of Gmunden Town Charter.
1809 **580** 3s. multicoloured 40 25

581 Face surrounded by Fruit and Flowers

582 Franz Lehar and Villa at Bad Ischl

1978. 25th Anniv of Austrian Association for Social Tourism.
1810 **581** 6s. multicoloured 80 45

1978. International Lehar Congress.
1811 **582** 6s. blue . . . . 1·10 45

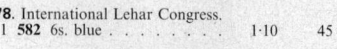

583 Tools and Globe

1978. 15th Congress of International Federation of Building and Wood Workers.
1812 **583** 1s.50 black, yellow & red . 20 15

584 Knights Jousting

1978. 700th Anniv of Battle of Durnkrut and Jedenspeigen.
1813 **584** 3s. multicoloured 40 25

585 Bridge over River Drau   586 City Seal, 1440

1978. 1100th Anniv of Villach.
1814 **585** 3s. multicoloured 40 25

1978. 850th Anniv of Graz.
1815 **586** 4s. brown, green & grey . . 50 40

587 Angler   588 Distorted Pattern

1978. 25th Sport Fishing Championships, Vienna.
1816 **587** 4s. multicoloured 60 40

1978. Handicapped People.
1817 **588** 6s. black and brown . . . 80 50

589 Concrete Chain   590 "Grace" (Albin Egger-Lienz)

1978. 9th International Concrete and Prefabrication Industry Congress, Vienna.
1818 **589** 2s.50 multicoloured . . . 35 25

1978. European Family Congress.
1819 **590** 6s. multicoloured 80 50

591 Lise Meitner   592 Victor Adler (bust, Anton Hamek)

1978. Birth Centenary of Lise Meitner (physicist).
1820 **591** 6s. violet 80   50

1978. 60th Death Anniv of Victor Adler (statesman).
1821 **592** 3s. black and red 40   25

593 Franz Schubert (after Josef Kriehuber)   594 "Madonna and Child" (Martino Altomonte, Wilhering Collegiate Church)

1978. 150th Death Anniv of Franz Schubert (composer).
1822 **593** 6s. brown . . . . 1·40   60

1978. Christmas.
1823 **594** 3s. multicoloured . . . 40   20

595 Post-bus, 1913

1978. Stamp Day.
1824 **595** 10s.+5s. multicoloured   2·00   1·75

596 "Archduke Johann Hut, Grossglockner" (E. T. Compton)

1978. Centenary of Austrian Alpine Club.
1825 **596** 1s.50 violet and gold . . 25   15

597 "Adam" (Rudolf Hausner)   598 Bound Hands

1978. Austrian Modern Art.
1826 **597** 6s. multicoloured 95   45

1978. 30th Anniv of Declaration of Human Rights.
1827 **598** 6s. purple 80   45

599 "CCIR"

1979. 50th Anniv of International Radio Consultative Committee.
1828 **599** 6s. multicoloured 80   40

600 Adult protecting Child

1979. International Year of the Child.
1829 **600** 2s.50 multicoloured . . . 35   30

601 Air Rifle, Pistol and Target

1979. Centenary of Austrian Shooting Club, and European Air Rifle and Air Pistol Shooting Championships.
1830 **601** 6s. multicoloured 80   40

602 "Franz I" (paddle-steamer)

1979. 150th Anniv of Danube Steam Navigation Company.
1831 **602** 1s.50 blue 25   20
1832   — 2s.50 brown 40   25
1833   — 3s. red 40   35
DESIGNS: 2s.50, Pusher tug "Linz"; 3s. "Theodor Korner" (passenger vessel).

603 Skater

1979. World Ice Skating and Dancing Championships. Vienna.
1834 **603** 4s. multicoloured 60   35

604 Fashion Drawing by Theo Zache, 1900   605 Wiener Neustadt Cathedral

1979. 50th Viennese Int Ladies' Fashion Week.
1835 **604** 2s.50 multicoloured . . . 30   25

1979. 700th Anniv of Wiener Neustadt Cathedral.
1836 **605** 4s. blue and grey 60   35

606 Relief from Emperor Joseph II Monument, Vienna   607 Population Graph

1979. Bicentenary of Education for the Deaf.
1837 **606** 2s.50 green, black & gold   35   25

1979. 150th Anniv of Austrian Central Statistical Office.
1838 **607** 2s.50 multicoloured . . . 35   25

608 Laurenz Koschier (postal reformer)   609 Section through Diesel Engine

1979. Europa.
1839 **608** 6s. brown and ochre . . . 80   45

1979. 13th Congress of International Combustion Engine Council.
1840 **609** 4s. multicoloured 55   35

610 Town Arms of Ried, Braunau and Scharding

1979. Bicentenary of Innviertel District.
1841 **610** 3s. multicoloured 40   25

611 Water Pollution

1979. Prevention of Water Pollution.
1842 **611** 2s.50 green and grey . . . 40   25

612 Arms of Rottenmann   613 Jodok Fink

1979. 700th Anniv of Rottenmann.
1843 **612** 3s. multicoloured 40   25

1979. 50th Death Anniv of Jodok Fink (politician).
1844 **613** 3s. brown 40   25

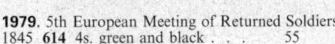

614 Arms of Wels and Returned Soldiers League Badge   615 Flower

1979. 5th European Meeting of Returned Soldiers.
1845 **614** 4s. green and black . . . 55   35

1979. U.N. Conference on Science and Technology for Development, Vienna.
1846 **615** 4s. blue 55   30

616 Vienna International Centre

1979. Opening of U.N.O. Vienna Int Centre.
1847 **616** 6s. slate 80   50

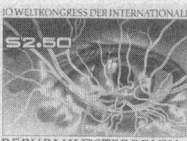

617 Eye and Blood Vessels of Diabetic

1979. 10th World Congress of International Diabetes Federation, Vienna.
1848 **617** 2s.50 multicoloured . . . 35   25

618 Stanzer Valley seen from Arlberg Road Tunnel

1979. 16th World Road Congress, Vienna.
1849 **618** 4s. multicoloured 60   35

619 Steam-driven Printing Press

1979. 175th Anniv of State Printing Works.
1850 **619** 3s. black and stone . . . 40   25

620 Richard Zsigmondy

1979. 50th Death Anniv of Dr. Richard Zsigmondy (Nobel Prize winner for Chemistry).
1851 **620** 6s. brown 80   55

621 Bregenz Festival and Congress Hall

1979. Bregenz Festival and Congress Hall.
1852 **621** 2s.50 lilac 35   25

622 Burning Match

1979. "Save Energy".
1853 **622** 2s.50 multicoloured . . . 35   20

623 Lions Emblem

1979. 25th European Lions Forum, Vienna.
1854 **623** 4s. yellow, gold and lilac   60   35

624 Wilhelm Exner (founder)   625 "The Suffering Christ" (Hans Fronius)

1979. Centenary of Industrial Museum and Technical School, Vienna.
1855 624 2s.50 dp purple & purple   35   25

1979. Austrian Modern Art.
1856 625 4s. black and stone . . .   55   40

626 Series 52 Goods Locomotive   627 August Musger

1979. Centenary of Raab (Gyor)–Odenburg (Sopron)-Ebenfurt Railway.
1857 626 2s.50 multicoloured . . .   60   35

1979. 50th Death Anniv of August Musger (pioneer of slow-motion photography).
1858 627 2s.50 black and grey . . .   35   25

628 "Nativity" (detail of icon by Moses Subotic, St. Barbara Church, Vienna)

1979. Christmas.
1859 628 4s. multicoloured   55   25

629 Neue Hofburg, Vienna

1979. "WIPA 1981" International Stamp Exhibition, Vienna (1st issue). Inscr "1. Phase".
1860 629 16s.+8s. multicoloured   3·25   2·75
See also No. 1890.

630 Arms of Baden   631 Loading Exports

1980. 500th Anniv of Baden.
1861 630 4s. multicoloured   55   35

1980. Austrian Exports.
1862 631 4s. blue, red and black   55   35

632 Rheumatic Hand holding Stick

1980. Fight against Rheumatism.
1863 632 2s.50 red and blue . . .   40   25

633 Emblems of 1880 and 1980

1980. Centenary of Austrian Red Cross.
1864 633 2s.50 multicoloured . . .   40   25

634 Kirchschlager   635 Robert Hamerling

1980. Pres. Rudolf Kirchschlager's 65th Birthday.
1865 634 4s. brown and red . . .   50   40

1980. 150th Birth Anniv of Robert Hamerling (writer).
1866 635 2s.50 green   35   25

636 Town Seal   637 "Maria Theresa as a Young Woman" (Andreas Moller)

1980. 750th Anniv of Hallein.
1867 636 4s. black and red   55   35

1980. Death Bicentenary of Empress Maria Theresa.
1868 637 2s.50 purple   40   25
1869 — 4s. blue   55   40
1870 — 6s. brown   80   65
DESIGNS: 4s. "Maria Theresa with St. Stephen's Crown" (Martin van Meytens); 6s. "Maria Theresa as Widow" (Joseph Ducreux).

638 Flags of Treaty Signatories   639 St. Benedict (statue, Meinrad Guggenbichler)

1980. 25th Anniv of Austrian State Treaty.
1871 638 4s. multicoloured   35   25

1980. Congress of Austrian Benedictine Orders, Mariazell.
1872 639 2s.50 green   35   25

640 "Hygieia" (Gustav Klimt)   641 Dish Aerial, Aflenz

1980. 175th Anniv of Hygiene Education.
1873 640 4s. multicoloured   55   35

1980. Inauguration of Aflenz Satellite Communications Earth Station.
1874 641 6s. multicoloured   80   40

642 Steyr (copperplate engraving, 1693)

1980. Millenary of Steyr.
1875 642 4s. brown, black & gold   60   35

643 Oil Driller   644 Town Seal of 1267

1980. 50th Anniv of Oil Production in Austria.
1876 643 2s.50 multicoloured . . .   35   25

1980. 800th Anniv of Innsbruck.
1877 644 2s.50 yellow, blk & red   35   25

645 Ducal Crown

1980. 800th Anniv of Elevation of Styria to Dukedom.
1878 645 4s. multicoloured   55   25

646 Leo Ascher   647 "Abraham" (illustration from "Viennese Genesis")

1980. Birth Cent of Leo Ascher (composer).
1879 646 3s. violet   70   40

1980. 10th Congress of International Organization for Study of the Old Testament.
1880 647 4s. multicoloured   55   35

648 Robert Stolz   649 Falkenstein Railway Bridge

1980. Europa and Birth Centenary of Robert Stolz (composer).
1881 648 6s. red . . . .   1·00   60

1980. 11th International Association of Bridge and Structural Engineering Congress, Vienna.
1882 649 4s. multicoloured   55   35

650 "Moon Figure" (Karl Brandstatter)   651 Customs Officer

1980. Austrian Modern Art.
1883 650 4s. multicoloured   55   35

1980. 150th Anniv of Customs Service.
1884 651 2s.50 brown and red . .   35   25

652 Masthead of 1810

1980. 350th Anniv of "Linzer Zeitung" (Linz newspaper).
1885 652 2s.50 black, red & gold   35   25

653 Frontispiece of Waidhofen Municipal Book   654 Heads

1980. 750th Anniv of Waidhofen.
1886 653 2s.50 multicoloured . . .   40   25

1980. 25th Anniv of Federal Army.
1887 654 2s.50 green and red . . .   35   25

655 Alfred Wegener   656 Robert Musil

1980. Birth Centenary of Alfred Wegener (explorer and geophysicist).
1888 655 4s. blue   55   35

1980. Birth Centenary of Robert Musil (writer).
1889 656 4s. brown   55   40

1980. "WIPA 1981" International Stamp Exhibition, Vienna (2nd issue). Inscr "2. Phase".
1890 629 16s.+8s. mult . . . . .   3·25   2·75

657 "Adoration of the Kings" (stained-glass window, Viktring Collegiate Church)   658 Ribbon in National Colours

1980. Christmas.
1891 657 4s. multicoloured   55   25

1981. 25th Anniv of General Social Insurance Act.
1892 658 2s.50 red, green & black   35   25

659 Unissued Design for 1926 Child Welfare Stamps   660 Disabled Person operating Machine Tool

1981. Birth Centenary of Wilhelm Dachauer (artist).
1894 659 3s. brown   40   20

1981. 3rd European Regional Conference of Rehabilitation International.
1895 660 6s. brown, blue and red   75   55

661 Sigmund Freud   662 Long-distance Heating System

1981. 125th Birth Anniv of Sigmund Freud (psychoanalyst).
1896 661 3s. purple   40   25

1981. 20th International Union of Long-distance Heat Distributors Congress, Vienna.
1897 662 4s. multicoloured   55   35

663 "Azzo and his Vassals" (cover of Monastery's "bearskin" Manuscript)

664 Maypole

1981. Kuenring Exhibition, Zwettl Monastery.
1898 **663** 3s. multicoloured 40 25

1981. Europa.
1899 **664** 6s. multicoloured 80 50

665 Early Telephone

1981. Centenary of Austrian Telephone System.
1900 **665** 4s. multicoloured 55 35

666 "The Frog King"

1981. Art Education in Schools.
1901 **666** 3s. multicoloured 55 25

667 Research Centre

1981. 25th Anniv of Seibersdorf Research Centre.
1902 **667** 4s. blue, dp blue & orge 60 35

668 Town Hall and Seal

669 Johann Florian Heller (chemist)

1981. 850th Anniv of St. Veit-on-Glan.
1903 **668** 4s. yellow, brown & red 55 35

1981. 11th Int Clinical Chemistry Congress, Vienna.
1904 **669** 6s. brown 80 50

670 Boltzmann

671 Otto Bauer

1981. 75th Death Anniv of Ludwig Boltzmann (physicist).
1905 **670** 3s. green 40 25

1981. Birth Centenary of Otto Bauer (writer and politician).
1906 **671** 4s. multicoloured 55 35

672 Chemical Balance

673 Impossible Construction (M. C. Escher)

1981. International Pharmaceutical Federation Congress, Vienna.
1907 **672** 6s. black, brown and red 80 40

1981. 10th International Austrian Mathematicians' Congress, Innsbruck.
1908 **673** 4s. lt blue, blue & dp blue 55 35

674 "Coronation of Virgin Mary" (detail)

675 Compass Rose

1981. 500th Anniv of Michael Pacher's Altarpiece at St. Wolfgang, Abersee.
1909 **674** 3s. blue 45 25

1981. 75th Anniv of Graz S.E. Exhibition.
1910 **675** 4s. multicoloured 55 35

676 "Holy Trinity" (illuminated MS, 12th century)

1981. 16th International Congress of Byzantine Scholars, Vienna.
1911 **676** 6s. multicoloured 80 40

677 Josef II

678 Hans Kelsen

1981. Bicentenary of Toleration Act (giving freedom of worship to Protestants).
1912 **677** 4s. black, blue & bistre 55 40

1981. Bicentenary of Hans Kelsen (law lecturer and contributor to shaping of Austrian Constitution).
1913 **678** 3s. red 40 25

679 Full and Empty Bowls and F.A.O. Emblem

1981. World Food Day.
1914 **679** 6s. multicoloured 80 50

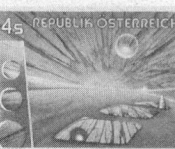

680 "Between the Times" (Oscar Asboth)

681 Workers and Emblem

1981. Austrian Modern Art.
1915 **680** 4s. multicoloured . . . 55 35

1981. 7th International Catholic Employees' Meeting, Vienna-Lainz.
1916 **681** 3s. multicoloured 40 25

682 Hammer-Purgstall

1981. 125th Death Anniv of Josef Hammer-Purgstall (orientalist).
1917 **682** 3s. multicoloured 40 25

683 Julius Raab

684 Stefan Zweig

1981. 90th Birth Anniv of Julius Raab (politician).
1918 **683** 6s. purple 80 40

1981. Birth Centenary of Stefan Zweig (writer).
1919 **684** 4s. lilac 55 35

685 Christmas Crib, Burgenland

1981. Christmas.
1920 **685** 4s. multicoloured 55 35

686 Arms of St. Nikola

1981. 800th Anniv of St. Nikola-on-Danube.
1921 **686** 4s. multicoloured . . . 55 40

687 Ambulance

1981. Cent of Vienna's Emergency Medical Service.
1922 **687** 3s. multicoloured 40 25

688 Skier

689 Dorotheum Building

1982. Alpine Skiing World Championship, Schladming-Haus.
1923 **688** 4s. multicoloured 55 35

1982. 275th Anniv of Dorotheum Auction, Pawn and Banking Society.
1924 **689** 4s. multicoloured 55 35

690 Lifesaving

691 St. Severin

1982. 25th Anniv of Austrian Water Lifesaving Service.
1925 **690** 5s. blue, red & light blue 70 50

1982. "St. Severin and the End of the Roman Period" Exhibition, Enns.
1926 **691** 3s. multicoloured 40 25

692 Sebastian Kneipp (pioneer of holistic medicine)

693 Printers' Coat-of-arms

1982. International Kneipp Congress, Vienna.
1927 **692** 4s. multicoloured 55 35

1982. 500th Anniv of Printing in Austria.
1928 **693** 4s. multicoloured 55 35

694 Urine Analysis from "Canon Medicinae" by Avicenna

695 St. Francis preaching to Animals (miniature)

1982. 5th European Union for Urology Congress, Vienna.
1929 **694** 6s. multicoloured 80 60

1982. "Franciscan Art and Culture in the Middle Ages" Exhibition, Krems-Stein.
1930 **695** 3s. multicoloured 40 25

696 Haydn and Birthplace, Rohrau

697 Globe within Milk Churn

1982. "Joseph Haydn and His Time" Exhibition, Eisenstadt.
1931 **696** 3s. green 50 25

1982. World Dairying Day.
1932 **697** 7s. multicoloured 80 60

698 Town Arms (1804 flag)

699 Tennis Player

1982. 800th Anniv of Gfohl.
1933 **698** 4s. multicoloured 55 35

1982. 80th Anniv of Austrian Lawn Tennis Assn.
1934 **699** 3s. multicoloured 40 25

700 Main Square, Langenlois **701** Town Arms

1982. 900th Anniv of Langenlois.
1935 **700** 4s. multicoloured 55 40

1982. 800th Anniv of Weiz.
1936 **701** 4s. multicoloured 50 35

702 Linz–Freistadt–Budweis Horse-drawn Railway

1982. Europa.
1937 **702** 6s. brown 85 60

703 Ignaz Seipel **704** Post-bus

1982. 50th Death Anniv of Ignaz Seipel (Federal Chancellor).
1938 **703** 3s. purple 35 25

1982. 75th Anniv of Post-bus Service.
1939 **704** 4s. multicoloured 65 40

705 Rocket Launch

1982. Second U.N. Conference on the Exploration and Peaceful Uses of Outer Space, Vienna.
1940 **705** 4s. multicoloured 55 35

706 Globe (Federal Office for Standardization and Surveying, Vienna)

1982. Geodesists' Day.
1941 **706** 3s. multicoloured 40 25

707 Great Bustard ("Grosstrappe")

1982. Endangered Animals. Multicoloured.
1942 3s. Type **707** 55 40
1943 4s. Eurasian beaver 70 60
1944 6s. Western capercaillie ("Auerhahn") 95 85

708 Institute Building, Laxenburg

1982. 10th Anniv of International Institute for Applied Systems Analysis.
1945 **708** 3s. black and brown . . 40 25

709 St. Apollonia (patron saint of dentists)

1982. 70th International Dentists Federation Congress, Vienna.
1946 **709** 4s. multicoloured 55 35

710 Emmerich Kalman **711** Max Mell

1982. Birth Cent of Emmerich Kalman (composer).
1947 **710** 3s. blue 70 35

1982. Birth Centenary of Max Mell (writer).
1948 **711** 3s. multicoloured 40 25

712 Christmas Crib, Damuls Church **713** Aerial View of Bosphorus

1982. Christmas.
1949 **712** 4s. multicoloured 55 35

1982. Centenary of St. George's Austrian College, Istanbul.
1950 **713** 4s. multicoloured 55 35

714 "Mainz-Weber" Mailbox, 1870

1982. Stamp Day.
1951 **714** 6s.+3s. multicoloured . . 1·25 1·25

715 "Muse of the Republic" (Ernst Fuchs) **716** Bank, Vienna

1982. Austrian Modern Art.
1952 **715** 4s. red and violet . . . 55 40

1983. Centenary of Postal Savings Bank.
1953 **716** 4s. yellow, black and blue 55 35

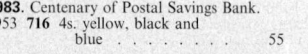

717 Hildegard Burjan

1983. Birth Centenary of Hildegard Burjan (founder of Caritas Socialis (religious sisterhood)).
1954 **717** 4s. red 55 35

718 Linked Arms

1983. World Communications Year.
1955 **718** 7s. multicoloured 80 60

719 Young Girl **720** Josef Matthias Hauer

1983. 75th Anniv of Children's Friends Organization.
1956 **719** 4s. black, blue and red 55 35

1983. Birth Centenary of Josef Matthias Hauer (composer).
1957 **720** 3s. purple 55 35

721 Douglas DC-9-80 Super Eighty

1983. 25th Anniv of Austrian Airlines.
1958 **721** 6s. multicoloured 80 55

722 Hands protecting Workers

1983. Cent of Government Work Inspection Law.
1959 **722** 4s. green, dp green & brn 55 35

723 Wels (engraving, Matthaeus Merian)

1983. "Millenary of Upper Austria" Exn, Wels.
1960 **723** 3s. multicoloured 40 25

724 Human Figure, Heart and Electrocardiogram **725** Monastery Arms

1983. 7th World Symposium on Pacemakers.
1961 **724** 4s. red, mauve and blue 60 50

1983. 900th Anniv of Gottweig Monastery.
1962 **725** 3s. multicoloured 40 25

726 Weitra

1983. 800th Anniv of Weitra.
1963 **726** 4s. black, red and gold 60 35

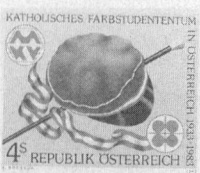

727 Cap, Stick, Ribbon and Emblems

1983. 50th Anniv of MKV and CCV Catholic Students' Organizations.
1964 **727** 4s. multicoloured 55 35

728 Glopper Castle and Town Arms **729** Hess

1983. 650th Anniv of Hohenems Town Charter.
1965 **728** 4s. multicoloured 55 35

1983. Europa. Birth Centenary of Viktor Franz Hess (physicist and Nobel Prize winner).
1966 **729** 6s. green 80 60

730 Vienna City Hall **731** Kiwanis Emblem and View of Vienna

1983. 25th Anniv of Vienna City Hall.
1967 **730** 4s. multicoloured 55 35

1983. Kiwanis International, World and European Conference, Vienna.
1968 **731** 5s. multicoloured 60 35

732 Congress Emblem **733** Hasenauer and Natural History Museum, Vienna

1983. 7th World Psychiatry Congress, Vienna.
1969 **732** 4s. multicoloured 55 35

1983. 150th Birth Anniv of Carl Freiherr von Hasenauer (architect).
1970 **733** 3s. brown 25 25

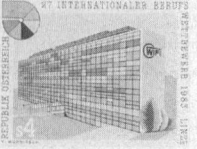

734 Institute for Promotion of Trade and Industry, Linz

1983. 27th International Professional Competition for Young Skilled Workers, Linz.
1971 **734** 4s. multicoloured 55 35

735 Symbols of Penicillin V
Efficacy and Cancer

736 Pope John Paul II

1983. 13th Int Chemotherapy Congress, Vienna.
1972 **735** 5s. red and green 70 50

1983. Papal Visit.
1973 **736** 6s. black, red and gold 1·00 60

738 Spectrum around Cross

739 Vienna Town Hall

1983. Austrian Catholics' Day.
1975 **738** 3s. multicoloured 40 25

1983. Centenary of Vienna Town Hall.
1976 **739** 4s. multicoloured 60 35

740 Karl von Terzaghi

1983. Birth Centenary of Karl von Terzaghi (soil mechanics and foundations engineer).
1977 **740** 3s. blue 40 25

741 Initials of Federation

1983. 10th Austrian Trade Unions Federation Congress.
1978 **741** 3s. red and black 40 25

742 "Evening Sun in Burgenland" (Gottfried Kumpf)

743 Tram No. 5, 1883

1983. Austrian Modern Art.
1979 **742** 4s. multicoloured 60 40

1983. Centenary of Modling–Hinterbruhl Electric Railway.
1980 **743** 3s. multicoloured 60 35

744 Boy looking at Stamped Envelope

1983. Stamp Day.
1981 **744** 6s.+3s. multicoloured . . 1·25 1·40

745 Francisco Carolinum Museum, Linz

1983. 150th Anniv of Upper Austrian Provincial Museum.
1982 **745** 4s. multicoloured 55 35

746 Crib by Johann Giner the Elder, Kitzbuhel Church

1983. Christmas.
1983 **746** 4s. multicoloured 70 35

747 Parliament Building

748 "St. Nicholas" (Maria Freund)

1983. Centenary of Parliament Building, Vienna.
1984 **747** 4s. blue 55 35

1983. Youth Stamp.
1985 **748** 3s. multicoloured 40 30

749 Wolfgang Pauli

1983. 25th Death Anniv of Wolfgang Pauli (Nobel Prize winner for Physics).
1986 **749** 6s. brown 80 55

750 Gregor Mendel

1984. Death Cent of Gregor Mendel (geneticist).
1987 **750** 4s. ochre and brown . . 55 35

751 Hanak at Work

1984. 50th Death Anniv of Anton Hanak (sculptor).
1988 **751** 3s. brown and black . . . 40 25

752 Disabled Skier

1984. 3rd World Winter Games for the Disabled, Innsbruck.
1989 **752** 4s.+2s. multicoloured . . 80 85

753 Memorial, Wollersdorf

1984. 50th Anniv of 1934 Insurrections.
1990 **753** 4s.50 red and black . . . 55 35

754 Founders' Stone

755 Geras Monastery

1984. 900th Anniv of Reichersberg Monastery.
1991 **754** 3s.50 stone, brown & bl 50 35

1984. Monasteries and Abbeys.
1992 — 50g. yellow, black & grey 10 10
1993 — 1s. yellow, black & mve 10 20
1994 — 1s.50 yellow, red & blue 10 20
1995 — 2s. yellow, green & black 25 10
1996 **755** 3s.50 yellow, sep & brn 50 10
1997 — 4s. yellow, purple & red 65 10
1998 — 4s.50 yellow, lilac & blue 60 10
1999 — 5s. yellow, purple & orge 65 10
2000 — 5s.50 yell, dp vio & vio 1·00 25
2001 — 6s. yellow, green & emer 1·10 10
2002 — 7s. yellow, green & blue 95 15
2003 — 7s.50 yell, dp brn & brn 1·00 25
2004 — 8s. yellow, blue and red 1·10 25
2005 — 10s. yellow, red & grey 1·40 20
2006 — 11s. yellow, black & brn 1·50 50
2007 — 12s. yellow, brn & orge 1·75 1·00
2008 — 17s. yellow, ultram & bl 2·50 70
2009 — 20s. yellow, brown & red 3·25 1·25
DESIGNS: 50g. Vorau Monastery; 1s. Wettingen Abbey, Mehrerau; 1s.50, Monastery of Teutonic Order, Vienna; 2s. Michaelbeuern Benedictine Monastery, Salzburg; 4s. Stams Monastery; 4s.50, Schlagl Monastery; 5s. St. Paul's Monastery, Lavanttal; 5s.50, St. Gerold's Priory, Vorarlberg; 6s. Rein Monastery; 7s. Loretto Monastery; 7s.50, Dominican Monastery, Vienna; 8s. Cistercian Monastery, Zwettl; 10s. Premonstratensian Monastery, Wilten; 11s. Trappist Monastery, Engelszell; 12s. Monastery of the Hospitallers, Eisenstadt; 17s. St. Peter's Abbey, Salzburg; 20s. Wernberg Convent, Carinthia.

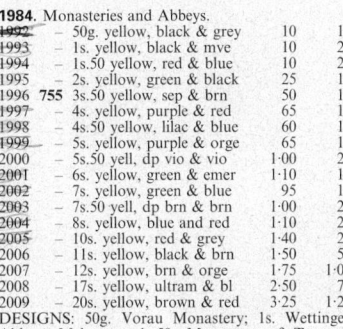

756 Cigar Band showing Tobacco Plant

757 Kostendorf

1984. Bicentenary of Tobacco Monopoly.
2012 **756** 4s.50 multicoloured . . . 60 40

1984. 1200th Anniv of Kostendorf.
2013 **757** 4s.50 multicoloured . . . 60 40

758 Wheel Bearing

1984. 20th International Federation of Automobile Engineers' Associations World Congress, Vienna.
2014 **758** 5s. multicoloured 70 50

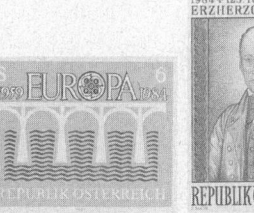

759 Bridge

760 Archduke Johann (after Schnorr von Carolsfeld)

1984. Europa. 25th Anniv of E.P.T. Conference.
2015 **759** 6s. blue and ultramarine 80 50

1984. 125th Death Anniv of Archduke Johann.
2016 **760** 4s.50 multicoloured . . . 60 40

761 Aragonite

762 Binding of "Das Buch vom Kaiser", by Max Herzig

1984. "Ore and Iron in the Green Mark" Exhibition, Eisenerz.
2017 **761** 3s.50 multicoloured . . . 45 35

1984. Lower Austrian "Era of Emperor Franz Joseph: From Revolution to Grunderzeit" Exhibition, Grafenegg Castle.
2018 **762** 3s.50 red and gold . . . 55 35

763 Upper City Tower and Arms

764 Dionysus (Virunum mosaic)

1984. 850th Anniv of Vocklabruch.
2019 **763** 4s.50 multicoloured . . . 60 40

1984. Centenary of Carinthia Provincial Museum, Klagenfurt.
2020 **764** 3s.50 stone, brn & grey 45 40

765 "Meeting of Austrian Army with South Tyrolean Reserves" (detail, Schnorr von Carolsfeld)

766 Ralph Benatzky

1984. "Jubilee of Tyrol Province" Exhibition.
2021 **765** 3s.50 multicoloured . . . 45 35

1984. Birth Cent of Ralph Benatzky (composer).
2022 **766** 4s. brown 80 50

767 Flood Control Barriers

768 Christian von Ehrenfels

1984. Centenary of Flood Control Systems.
2023 **767** 4s.50 green 60 50

1984. 125th Death Anniv of Christian von Ehrenfels (philosopher).
2024 **768** 3s.50 multicoloured . . . 50 35

769 Models of European Monuments

1984. 25th Anniv of Minimundus (model world), Worthersee.
2025 **769** 4s. yellow and black . . 55 35

770 Blockheide Eibenstein National Park

1984. Natural Beauty Spots.
2026 **770** 4s. pink and olive . . . 65 50

771 Electric Train on Schanatobel Bridge (Arlberg Railway Centenary)

1984. Railway Anniversaries.
2027 **771** 3s.50 brown, gold & red 60 50
2028 – 4s.50 blue, silver and red 75 60
DESIGN: 4s.50, Electric train on Falkenstein Bridge (75th anniv of Tauern Railway).

772 Johann Georg Stuwer's Ascent in Montgolfier Balloon

1984. Bicentenary of First Manned Balloon Flight in Austria.
2029 **772** 6s. multicoloured 80 55

773 Lake Neusiedl

1984. Natural Beauty Spots.
2030 **773** 4s. purple and blue . . . 75 55

774 Palace of Justice, Vienna

775 "Joseph Hyrtl" (window, Innsbruck Anatomy Institute)

1984. 20th Int Bar Assn Congress, Vienna.
2031 **774** 7s. multicoloured 80 60

1984. 7th European Anatomists' Congress, Innsbruck.
2032 **775** 6s. multicoloured 80 55

776 "Window" (Karl Korab)

777 Clock of Imms (astrolabe)

1984. Austrian Modern Art.
2033 **776** 4s. multicoloured . . . 60 35

1984. 600th Birth Anniv of Johannes von Gmunden (astronomer and mathematician).
2034 **777** 3s.50 multicoloured . . . 50 35

778 Quill

779 Fanny Elssler

1984. 125th Anniv of Concordia Press Club.
2035 **778** 4s.50 black, gold & red 55 35

1984. Death Centenary of Fanny Elssler (dancer).
2036 **779** 4s. multicoloured 55 35

780 "Holy Family" (detail, Aggsbach Old High Altar)

1984. Christmas.
2037 **780** 4s.50 multicoloured . . . 60 35

781 Detail from Burial Chamber Wall of Seschemnofer III

782 Coat of Arms

1984. Stamp Day.
2038 **781** 6s.+3s. multicoloured . . 1·25 1·40

1985. 400th Anniv of Graz University.
2039 **782** 3s.50 multicoloured . . . 50 35

783 Dr. Lorenz Bohler

1985. Birth Centenary of Prof. Dr. Lorenz Bohler (surgeon).
2040 **783** 4s.50 purple 55 35

784 Ski Jumping, Skiing and Emblem

1985. World Nordic Skiing Championship, Seefeld.
2041 **784** 4s. multicoloured . . . 60 40

785 Linz Cathedral

786 Alban Berg

1985. Bicentenary of Linz Diocese.
2042 **785** 4s.50 multicoloured . . . 70 40

1985. Birth Centenary of Alban Berg (composer).
2043 **786** 6s. blue . . . . 1·10 65

787 Institute Emblem   788 Stylized "B" and Clouds

1985. 25th Anniv of Institute for Vocational Advancement.
2044 **787** 4s.50 multicoloured . . . 55 35

1985. 2000th Anniv of Bregenz.
2045 **788** 4s. black, ultram & blue 45 40

789 1885 Registration Label

790 Josef Stefan

1985. Centenary of Registration Labels in Austria.
2046 **789** 4s.50 black, yell & grey 60 40

1985. 150th Birth Anniv of Josef Stefan (physicist).
2047 **790** 6s. brown, stone and red 80 55

791 St. Leopold (Margrave and patron saint)

792 "The Story-teller"

1985. Lower Austrian Provincial Exhibition, Klosterneuburg Monastery.
2048 **791** 3s.50 multicoloured . . . 55 35

1985. 150th Birth Anniv of Franz Defregger (artist).
2049 **792** 3s.50 multicoloured . . . 55 40

793 Barbed Wire, Broken Tree and New Shoot

794 Johann Joseph Fux (composer)

1985. 40th Anniv of Liberation.
2050 **793** 4s.50 multicoloured . . . 60 55

1985. Europa. Music Year.
2051 **794** 6s. brown and grey . . . 1·40 65

795 Flags and Caduceus   797 Bishop's Gate, St. Polten

796 Town and Arms

1985. 25th Anniv of European Free Trade Association.
2052 **795** 4s. multicoloured 60 50

1985. Millenary of Boheimkirchen.
2053 **796** 4s.50 multicoloured . . . 60 50

1985. Bicentenary of St. Polten Diocese.
2054 **797** 4s.50 multicoloured . . . 60 50

798 Johannes von Nepomuk Church, Innsbruck

799 Garsten (copperplate, George Matthaus Fischer)

1985. Gumpp Family (architects) Exn, Innsbruck.
2055 **798** 3s.50 multicoloured . . . 60 50

1985. Millenary of Garsten.
2056 **799** 4s.50 multicoloured . . . 70 55

800 U.N. Emblem and Austrian Arms

1985. 40th Anniv of U.N.O. and 30th Anniv of Austrian Membership.
2057 **800** 4s. multicoloured 60 55

801 Association Headquarters, Vienna

1985. 13th International Suicide Prevention Association Congress, Vienna.
2058 **801** 5s. brown, lt yell & yell 70 55

803 Operetta Emblem and Spa Building

804 Fireman and Emblem

1985. 25th Bad Ischl Operetta Week.
2060 **803** 3s.50 multicoloured . . . 65 45

1985. 8th International Fire Brigades Competition, Vocklabruck.
2061 **804** 4s.50 black, green & red 95 60

805 Grossglockner Mountain Road

1985. 50th Anniv of Grossglockner Mountain Road.
2062 **805** 4s. multicoloured 60 40

806 Chessboard as Globe

807 "Founding of Konigstetten" (August Stephan)

1985. World Chess Association Congress, Graz.
2063 **806** 4s. multicoloured 65 40

1985. Millenary of Konigstetten.
2064 **807** 4s.50 multicoloured . . . 65 40

808 Webern Church and Arms of Hofkirchen and Taufkircher

1985. 1200th Anniversaries of Hofkirchen, Weibern and Taufkirchen.
2065 **808** 4s.50 multicoloured . . . 65 50

809 Dr. Adam Politzer

1985. 150th Birth Anniv of Dr. Adam Politzer (otologist).
2066 **809** 3s.50 violet 50 35

810 Emblem and View of Vienna

1985. International Association of Forwarding Agents World Congress, Vienna.
2067 **810** 6s. multicoloured 75 55

811 "Clowns Riding High Bicycles" (Paul Flora)

1985. Austrian Modern Art.
2068 **811** 4s. multicoloured 80 55

812 St. Martin, Patron Saint of Burgenland

1985. 25th Anniv of Eisenstadt Diocese.
2069 **812** 4s.50 black, bistre & red 70 50

813 Roman Mounted Courier

1985. 50th Anniv of Stamp Day.
2070 **813** 6s.+3s. multicoloured . . 1·40 1·40

814 Hanns Horbiger   **815** "Adoration of the Christ Child" (marble relief)

1985. 125th Birth Anniv of Hanns Horbiger (design engineer).
2071 **814** 3s.50 purple and gold . . 45 35

1985. Christmas.
2072 **815** 4s.50 multicoloured . . . 70 30

816 Aqueduct

1985. 75th Anniv of Second Vienna Waterline.
2073 **816** 3s.50 black, red & blue . 50 35

818 Chateau de la Muette (headquarters)

1985. 25th Anniv of Organization of Economic Co-operation and Development.
2080 **818** 4s. black, gold & mauve . 55 40

819 Johann Bohm

1986. Birth Centenary of Johann Bohm (founder of Austrian Trade Unions Federation).
2081 **819** 4s.50 black and red . . . 60 40

820 Dove and Globe

1986. International Peace Year.
2082 **820** 6s. multicoloured 80 55

821 Push-button Dialling

1986. Introduction of Digital Preselection Telephone System.
2083 **821** 5s. multicoloured 65 40

822 Albrechtsberger and Organ

1986. 250th Birth Anniv of Johann Georg Albrechtsberger (composer).
2084 **822** 3s.50 multicoloured . . . 80 45

823 Main Square and Arms

1986. 850th Anniv of Korneuburg.
2085 **823** 5s. multicoloured 65 40

824 Kokoschka (self-portrait)   **825** Council Flag

1986. Birth Centenary of Oskar Kokoschka (artist).
2086 **824** 4s. black and pink . . . 55 40

1986. 30th Anniv of Membership of Council of Europe.
2087 **825** 6s. black, red and blue . 80 55

826 Holzmeister and Salzburg Festival Hall

1986. Birth Centenary of Professor Clemens Holzmeister (architect).
2088 **826** 4s. grey, brown & lt brn 55 40

827 Road, Roll of Material, and Congress Emblem

1986. 3rd International Geotextile Congress, Vienna.
2089 **827** 5s. multicoloured 65 45

828 Schlosshof Palace (after Bernardo Bellotto) and Prince Eugene

1986. "Prince Eugene and the Baroque Era" Exhibition, Schlosshof and Niederweiden.
2090 **828** 4s. multicoloured 60 40

829 St. Florian Monastery

1986. Upper Austrian "World of Baroque" Exhibition, St. Florian Monastery.
2091 **829** 4s. multicoloured 60 40

830 Herberstein Castle and Styrian Arms

1986. "Styria – Bridge and Bulwark" Exhibition, Herberstein Castle, near Stubenberg.
2092 **830** 4s. multicoloured 60 40

831 Large Pasque Flower

1986. Europa.
2093 **831** 6s. multicoloured . . . . 1·00 70

832 Wagner and Scene from Opera "Lohengrin"

1986. International Richard Wagner (composer) Congress, Vienna.
2094 **832** 4s. multicoloured . . . . 1·00 55

833 Antimonite Crystal

1986. Burgenland "Mineral and Fossils" Exhibition, Oberpullendorf.
2095 **833** 4s. multicoloured 60 45

834 Martinswall, Zirl

1986. Natural Beauty Spots.
2096 **834** 5s. brown and blue . . . 80 55

835 Waidhofen

1986. 800th Anniv of Waidhofen on Ybbs.
2097 **835** 4s. multicoloured 55 45

836 Tschauko Falls, Ferlach

1986. Natural Beauty Spots.
2098 **836** 5s. green and brown . . 80 55

837 19th-century Steam and Modern Articulated Trams

1986. Cent of Salzburg Local Transport System.
2099 **837** 4s. multicoloured 90 55

838 Enns and Seals of Signatories

1986. 800th Anniv of Georgenberg Treaty (between Duke Leopold V of Austria and Duke Otakar IV of Styria).
2100 **838** 5s. multicoloured 70 50

839 Tandler   **840** "Observatory, 1886" (A. Heilmann)

1986. 50th Death Anniv of Julius Tandler (social reformer).
2101 **839** 4s. multicoloured 55 40

1986. Centenary of Sonnblick Observatory.
2102 **840** 4s. black, blue and gold 55 40

841 Man collecting Mandragora (from "Codex Tacuinum Sanitatis")   **842** Fire Assistant

1986. 7th European Anaesthesia Congress, Vienna.
2103 **841** 5s. multicoloured 65 40

1986. 300th Anniv of Vienna Fire Brigade.
2104 **842** 4s. multicoloured 80 55

843 Stoessl   **844** Viennese Hunting Tapestry (detail)

1986. 50th Death Anniv of Otto Stoessl (writer).
2105 **843** 4s. multicoloured 55 40

1986. 5th International Oriental Carpets and Tapestry Conference, Vienna and Budapest.
2106 **844** 5s. multicoloured 65 45

845 Minister in Pulpit   **846** "Decomposition" (Walter Schmogner)

1986. 125th Anniv of Protestants Act and 25th Anniv of Protestants Law.
2107 **845** 5s. black and violet . . . 65 45

1986. Austrian Modern Art.
2108 **846** 4s. multicoloured 60 40

847 Liszt, Birthplace and Score

1986. 175th Birth Anniv of Franz Liszt (composer).
2109 **847** 5s. green and brown . . . 1·10 60

849 Strettweg Religious Carriage

1986. 175th Anniv of Styrian Joanneum Museum.
2111 **849** 4s. multicoloured 60 40

850 "Nuremberg Letter Messenger" (16th century woodcut)   **852** Headquarters

851 "Adoration of the Shepherds" (woodcut, Johann Georg Schwanthaler)

1986. Stamp Day.
2112 **850** 6s.+3s. multicoloured . . 1·40 1·50

1986. Christmas.
2113 **851** 5s. brown and gold . . . 75 40

1986. 40th Anniv of Federal Chamber of Trade and Industry.
2114 **852** 5s. multicoloured 75 45

853 Foundry Worker

1986. Austrian World of Work (1st series).
2115 **853** 4s. multicoloured 60 40
See also Nos. 2144, 2178, 2211, 2277, 2386, 2414, 2428, 2486, 2520, 2572 and 2605.

854 "The Educated Eye"

1987. Centenary of Adult Education in Vienna.
2116 **854** 5s. multicoloured 65 45

855 "Large Blue Madonna" (Anton Faistauer)

1987. Painters' Birth Centenaries. Multicoloured.
2117 4s. Type **855** 65 45
2118 6s. "Self-portrait" (Albert Paris Gutersloh) 80 60

856 Hundertwasser House, Vienna

1987. Europa and "Europalia 1987 Austria" Festival, Belgium.
2119 **856** 6s. multicoloured . . . . 1·10 1·75

857 Ice Hockey Players

1987. World Ice Hockey Championships, Vienna, and 75th Anniv of Austrian Ice Hockey Association.
2120 **857** 5s. multicoloured 75 55

858 Austria Centre

1987. Inaug of Austria Conference Centre, Vienna.
2121 **858** 5s. multicoloured 70 55

859 Salzburg   **860** Machine Shop, 1920

1987. 700th Anniv of Salzburg Town Charter.
2122 **859** 5s. multicoloured 75 45

1987. Upper Austrian "Work–Men–Machines, the Route to Industrialized Society" Exhibition, Steyr.
2123 **860** 4s. black and red 55 45

861 Man and Woman   **862** "Adele Bloch-Bauer I" (detail, Gustav Klimt)

1987. Equal Rights for Men and Women.
2124 **861** 5s. multicoloured 70 45

1987. Lower Austrian "Era of Emperor Franz Joseph: Splendour and Misery" Exhibition, Grafenegg Castle.
2125 **862** 4s. multicoloured 70 45

863 Archbishop and Salzburg

1987. 400th Anniv of Election of Prince Wolf Dietrich von Raitenau as Archbishop of Salzburg.
2126 **863** 4s. multicoloured 60 40

864 Schnitzler   **865** Lace and Arms

1987. 125th Birth Anniv of Arthur Schnitzler (dramatist).
2127 **864** 6s. multicoloured 80 55

1987. 1100th Anniv of Lustenau.
2128 **865** 5s. multicoloured 70 45

867 Dachstein Giant Ice Cave

1987. Natural Beauty Spots.
2130 **867** 5s. green and black . . . 95 55

868 Engraver at Work   **869** Dr. Karl Josef Bayer (chemist)

1987. 8th European Association of Engravers and Flexographers International Congress, Vienna.
2131 **868** 5s. brown, pink and grey 70 45

1987. 8th International Light Metal Meeting, Leoben and Vienna.
2132 **869** 5s. multicoloured 70 45

870 Passenger Ferry   **871** Office Building, Vienna

1987. Centenary of 1st Achensee Steam Service.
2133 **870** 4s. multicoloured 60 45

1987. 10th Anniv of Office of Ombudsmen.
2134 **871** 5s. black, yellow and red 70 45

872 Schrodinger   **873** Freistadt Town Square

1987. Birth Cent of Erwin Schrodinger (physicist).
2135 **872** 5s. brown, cream & bistre 70 45

1987. 125th Anniv of Freistadt Exhibitions.
2136 **873** 5s. multicoloured 75 45

874 Arbing Church

1987. 850th Anniv of Arbing.
2137 **874** 5s. multicoloured . . . 75 45

875 Gauertal and Montafon Valleys,
Voralberg

1987. Natural Beauty Spots.
2138 **875** 5s. brown and yellow . . . 95 45

876 Cyclist   **877** Emblem

1987. World Cycling Championship, Vienna and
Villach.
2139 **876** 5s. multicoloured 80 45

1987. World Congress of International Institute of
Savings Banks, Vienna.
2140 **877** 5s. multicoloured 70 40

878 Hofhaymer at Organ   **880** Lammergeier
("Bartgeier")

879 Haydn and Salzburg

1987. 450th Death Anniv of Paul Hofhaymer
(composer and organist).
2141 **878** 4s. blue, black and gold . 1·00 40

1987. 250th Birth Anniv of Michael Haydn
(composer).
2142 **879** 4s. lilac . . . . 1·00 45

1987. 25th Anniv of Alpine Zoo, Innsbruck.
2143 **880** 4s. multicoloured 70 45

881 Woman using Word Processor

1987. Austrian World of Work (2nd series).
2144 **881** 4s. multicoloured 55 40

882 "Tree Goddesses" (Arnulf
Neuwirth)

1987. Austrian Modern Art.
2145 **882** 5s. multicoloured 80 55

883 Lottery Wheel   **884** Helmer

1987. Bicentenary of Gambling Monopoly.
2146 **883** 5s. multicoloured 65 40

1987. Birth Centenary of Oskar Helmer (politician).
2147 **884** 4s. multicoloured 55 40

885 Gluck   **886** Stagecoach and
Passengers (lithograph,
Carl Schuster)

1987. Death Bicentenary of Christoph Willibald
Gluck (composer).
2148 **885** 5s. brown and ochre . . . 1·10 55

1987. Stamp Day.
2149 **886** 6s.+3s. multicoloured . . 1·40 1·50

887 Josef Mohr and Franz Xaver
Gruber (composers of "Silent
Night")

1987. Christmas.
2150 **887** 5s. multicoloured . . . . 1·10 45

888 Bosco and Boys   **889** Cross-country Sledging

1988. International Educational Congress of St. John
Bosco's Salesian Brothers, Vienna.
2151 **888** 5s. purple and orange . . 65 40

1988. 4th World Winter Games for the Disabled,
Innsbruck.
2152 **889** 5s.+2s.50 multicoloured 95 1·10

890 Mach   **891** "Village with
Bridge"

1988. 150th Birth Anniv of Ernst Mach (physicist and
philosopher).
2153 **890** 6s. multicoloured 80 55

1988. 25th Death Anniv of Franz von Zulow (artist).
2154 **891** 4s. multicoloured 60 45

892 "The Confiscation" (Ferdinand
Georg Waldmuller)

1988. "Patriotism and Protest: Viennese Biedermeier
and Revolution" Exhibition, Vienna.
2155 **892** 4s. multicoloured 60 45

893 Barbed Wire, Flag and Crosses

1988. 50th Anniv of Annexation of Austria by
Germany.
2156 **893** 5s. green, brown and red 65 40

894 Steam Locomotive   **895** European Bee
"Aigen", Muhlkreis Railway,   Eater
1887

1988. Railway Centenaries. Multicoloured.
2157 4s. Type **894** 85 55
2158 5s. Modern electric tram
and Josefsplatz stop
(Viennese Local Railways
Stock Corporation) . . . 1·00 60

1988. 25th Anniv of World Wildlife Fund, Austria.
2159 **895** 5s. multicoloured . . . . 1·10 60

896 Decanter and Beaker   **897** Late Gothic Silver
Censer

1988. Styrian "Glass and Coal" Exn, Barnbach.
2160 **896** 4s. multicoloured 55 40

1988. Lower Austrian "Art and Monastic Life at the
Birth of Austria" Exhibition, Seitenstetten
Benedictine Monastery.
2161 **897** 4s. multicoloured 55 35

898 Taking Casualty to   **900** Mattsee
Ambulance and Red Cross   Monastery

899 Dish Aerials, Aflenz

1988. 125th Anniv of Red Cross.
2162 **898** 12s. black, red and green 1·50 1·10

1988. Europa. Telecommunications.
2163 **899** 6s. multicoloured 80 55

1988. Salzburg "Bajuvars from Severin to Tassilo"
Exhibition, Mattsee Monastery.
2164 **900** 4s. multicoloured 60 45

901 Weinberg Castle   **902** Horvath

1988. Upper Austrian "Muhlviertel: Nature, Culture,
Life" Exhibition, Weinberg Castle, near
Kefermarkt.
2165 **901** 4s. multicoloured 55 35

1988. 50th Death Anniv of Odon von Horvath
(writer).
2166 **902** 6s. black and bistre . . . 75 50

903 Stockerau Town Hall

1988. 25th Anniv of Stockerau Festival.
2167 **903** 5s. multicoloured 70 50

904 Motorway   **905** Brixlegg

1988. Completion of Tauern Motorway.
2168 **904** 4s. multicoloured 55 40

1988. 1200th Anniv of Brixlegg.
2169 **905** 5s. multicoloured 75 50

906 Klagenfurt (after Matthaus
Merian)

1988. 400th Anniv of Regular Postal Services in
Carinthia.
2170 **906** 5s. multicoloured 70 40

907 Parish Church and Dean's
House

1988. 1200th Anniv of Brixen im Thale, Tyrol.
2171 **907** 5s. multicoloured 70 40

908 Krimml Waterfalls, Upper
Tauern National Park

1988. Natural Beauty Spots.
2172 **908** 5s. black and blue . . . 70 55

909 Town Arms

1988. 1100th Anniv of Feldkirchen, Carinthia.
2173 **909** 5s. multicoloured 65   40

910 Feldbach

1988. 800th Anniv of Feldbach.
2174 **910** 5s. multicoloured 65   45

911 Ansfelden   **912** Hologram of Export Emblem

1988. 1200th Anniv of Ansfelden.
2175 **911** 5s. multicoloured 65   45

1988. Federal Economic Chamber Export Congress.
2176 **912** 8s. multicoloured . . . . 2·00   1·90

913 Concert Hall

1988. 75th Anniv of Vienna Concert Hall.
2177 **913** 5s. multicoloured 65   45

914 Laboratory Assistant

1988. Austrian World of Work (3rd series).
2178 **914** 4s. multicoloured 55   35

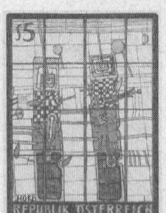

915 "Guards" (Giselbert Hoke)   **916** Schonbauer

1988. Austrian Modern Art.
2179 **915** 5s. multicoloured 65   45

1988. Birth Centenary of Dr. Leopold Schonbauer (neurosurgeon and politician).
2180 **916** 4s. multicoloured 55   45

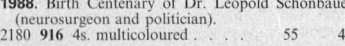

917 Carnation   **918** Loading Railway Mail Van at Pardubitz Station, 1914

1988. Cent of Austrian Social Democratic Party.
2181 **917** 4s. multicoloured 55   45

1988. Stamp Day.
2182 **918** 6s.+3s. multicoloured . . 1·40   1·40

919 "Nativity" (St. Barbara's Church, Vienna)   **920** "Madonna" (Lucas Cranach)

1988. Christmas.
2183 **919** 5s. multicoloured 65   35

1989. 25th Anniv of Diocese of Innsbruck.
2184 **920** 4s. multicoloured 55   45

921 Margrave Leopold II leading Abbot Sigibold and Monks to Melk (detail of fresco, Paul Troger)

1989. 900th Anniv of Melk Benedictine Monastery.
2185 **921** 5s. multicoloured 65   45

922 Marianne Hainisch   **923** Glider and Paraskier

1989. 150th Birth Anniv of Marianne Hainisch (women's rights activist).
2186 **922** 6s. multicoloured 75   55

1989. World Gliding Championships, Wiener Neustadt, and World Paraskiing Championships, Damuls.
2187 **923** 6s. multicoloured 75   55

924 "The Painting"   **926** Wittgenstein

925 "Bruck an der Leitha" (17th-century engraving, Georg Vischer)

1989. 50th Death Anniv of Rudolf Jettmar (painter).
2188 **924** 5s. multicoloured 65   40

1989. 750th Anniv of Bruck an der Leitha.
2189 **925** 5s. multicoloured 65   45

1989. Birth Centenary of Ludwig Wittgenstein (philosopher).
2190 **926** 5s. multicoloured 60   40

927 Holy Trinity Church, Stadl-Paura   **928** Suess (after Josef Kriehuber) and Map

1989. 250th Death Anniv of Johann Michael Prunner (architect).
2191 **927** 5s. multicoloured 65   40

1989. 75th Death Anniv of Eduard Suess (geologist and politician).
2192 **928** 6s. multicoloured 80   60

929 "Judenburg" (17th-century engraving, Georg Vischer)   **930** Steam Engine (Vinzenz Prick)

1989. Upper Styrian "People, Coins, Markets" Exhibition, Judenburg.
2193 **929** 4s. multicoloured 55   45

1989. Lower Austrian "Magic of Industry" Exhibition, Pottenstein.
2194 **930** 4s. blue and gold 55   45

931 Radstadt

1989. 700th Anniv of Radstadt.
2195 **931** 5s. multicoloured 65   40

932 Wooden Salt Barge from Viechtau

1989. Europa. Children's Toys.
2196 **932** 6s. multicoloured 80   65

933 "St. Adalbero and Family before Madonna and Child" (Monastery Itinerary Book)   **935** Hansa Brandenburg C-1 Mail Biplane at Vienna, 1918

934 "Gisela" (paddle-steamer)

1989. Upper Austrian "Graphic Art" Exhibition and 900th Anniv of Lambach Monastery Church.
2197 **933** 4s. multicoloured 60   45

1989. 150th Anniv of Passenger Shipping on Traunsee.
2198 **934** 5s. multicoloured 75   45

1989. Stamp Day.
2199 **935** 6s.+3s. multicoloured . . 1·25   1·40

936 St. Andra (after Matthaus Merian)

1989. 650th Anniv of St. Andra.
2200 **936** 5s. multicoloured 65   40

937 Strauss   **938** Locomotive

1989. 125th Birth Anniv of Richard Strauss (composer).
2201 **937** 6s. red, brown and gold   1·25   75

1989. Centenary of Achensee Steam Rack Railway.
2202 **938** 5s. multicoloured . . . . 1·00   60

939 Parliament Building, Vienna

1989. Centenary of Interparliamentary Union.
2203 **939** 6s. multicoloured 70   55

940 Anniversary Emblem

1989. Centenary of National Insurance in Austria.
2204 **940** 5s. multicoloured 60   50

941 U.N. Building, Vienna

1989. 10th Anniv of U.N. Vienna Centre.
2205 **941** 8s. multicoloured . . . . 1·00   65

942 Lusthaus Water, Prater Woods, Vienna

1989. Natural Beauty Spots.
2206 **942** 5s. black and buff 90   55

943 Wildalpen and Hammerworks

1989. 850th Anniv of Wildalpen.
2207 **943** 5s. multicoloured 65 50

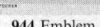

944 Emblem   946 "Tree of Life" (Ernst Steiner)

945 Palace of Justice, Vienna

1989. 33rd Congress of European Organization for Quality Control, Vienna.
2208 **944** 6s. multicoloured 70 60

1989. 14th Congress of Int Assn of Criminal Law.
2209 **945** 6s. multicoloured 80 55

1989. Austrian Modern Art.
2210 **946** 5s. multicoloured 65 50

947 Bricklayer   948 Ludwig Anzengruber (150th birth anniv)

1989. Austrian World of Work (4th series).
2211 **947** 5s. multicoloured 60 50

1989. Writers' Anniversaries. Multicoloured.
2212   4s. Type **948** 50 40
2213   4s. Georg Trakl (75th death
    anniv) 55 40

949 Fried   950 "Adoration of the Shepherds" (detail, Johann Carl von Reslfeld)

1989. 125th Birth Anniv of Alfred Fried (Peace Movement worker).
2214 **949** 6s. multicoloured 80 65

1989. Christmas.
2215 **950** 5s. multicoloured 65 35

951 "Courier"   952 Streif Downhill and
(Albrecht Durer)   Ganslern Slalom Runs

1990. 500th Anniv of Regular European Postal Services.
2216 **951** 5s. chocolate, cinnamon
    and brown 60 40

1990. 50th Hahnenkamm Ski Championships, Kitzbuhel.
2217 **952** 5s. multicoloured 65 40

953 Sulzer   954 Emich

1990. Death Centenary of Salomon Sulzer (creator of modern Synagogue songs).
2218 **953** 4s.50 multicoloured . . . 1·00 55

1990. 50th Death Anniv of Friedrich Emich (microchemist).
2219 **954** 6s. purple and green . . . 70 50

955 Emperor Friedrich III (miniature by Ulrich Schreier)

1990. 500th Anniv of Linz as Capital of Upper Austria.
2220 **955** 5s. multicoloured 70 50

956 University Seals

1990. 625th Anniv of Vienna University and 175th Anniv of Vienna University of Technology.
2221 **956** 5s. red, gold and lilac . . 60 50

957 South Styrian Vineyards

1990. Natural Beauty Spots.
2222 **957** 5s. black and yellow . . . 90 60

958 Parish Church   959 1897 May Day Emblem

1990. 1200th Anniv of Anthering.
2223 **958** 7s. multicoloured 85 70

1990. Centenary of Labour Day.
2224 **959** 4s.50 multicoloured . . . 60 50

960 "Our Dear   961 Ebene Reichenau Post
Housewife of   Office
Seckau" (relief)

962 Thematic Stamp   963 Makart (self-
Motifs   portrait)

1990. Stamp Day.
2227 **962** 7s.+3s. multicoloured . . 1·60 1·40

1990. 150th Birth Anniv of Hans Makart (painter).
2228 **963** 4s.50 multicoloured . . . 60 40

964 Schiele (self-portrait)   965 Raimund

1990. Birth Centenary of Egon Schiele (painter).
2229 **964** 5s. multicoloured 60 40

1990. Birth Bicentenary of Ferdinand Raimund (actor and playwright).
2230 **965** 4s.50 multicoloured . . . 60 40

966 "The Hundred Guilden Note" (Rembrandt)

1990. 2nd Int Christus Medicus Congress, Bad Ischl.
2231 **966** 7s. multicoloured 90 70

967 Hardegg

1990. 700th Anniv of Hardegg's Elevation to Status of Town.
2232 **967** 4s.50 multicoloured . . . 60 45

968 Oberdrauburg   970 Zdarsky skiing
(copperplate engraving,
Freiherr von Valvasor)

969 Church and Town Hall

1990. 750th Anniv of Oberdrauburg.
2233 **968** 5s. multicoloured 60 45

1990. 850th Anniv of Gumpoldskirchen.
2234 **969** 5s. multicoloured 60 45

1990. 50th Death Anniv of Mathias Zdarsky (developer of alpine skiing).
2235 **970** 5s. multicoloured 60 45

1990. 850th Anniv of Seckau Abbey.
2225 **960** 4s.50 blue 55 40

1990. Europa. Post Office Buildings.
2226 **961** 7s. multicoloured 90 70

971 "Telegraph", 1880, and "Anton Chekhov", 1978

1990. 150th Anniv of Modern (metal) Shipbuilding in Austria.
2236 **971** 9s. multicoloured . . . . 1·40 1·10

972 Perkonig   973 "Man of Rainbows" (Robert Zeppel-Sperl)

1990. Birth Centenary of Josef Friedrich Perkonig (writer).
2237 **972** 5s. sepia, brown & gold . . 65 45

1990. Austrian Modern Art.
2238 **973** 5s. multicoloured 70 45

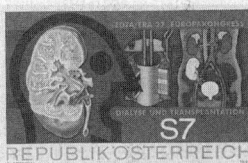

974 Kidney, Dialysis Machine and Anatomical Diagram

1990. 27th European Dialysis and Transplantation Federation Congress, Vienna.
2239 **974** 7s. multicoloured 85 65

975 Werfel

1990. Birth Centenary of Franz Werfel (writer).
2240 **975** 5s. multicoloured 65 55

976 U.N. and Austrian Flags

1990. 30th Anniv of Austrian Participation in U.N. Peace-keeping Forces.
2241 **976** 7s. multicoloured . . . . 1·00 80

977 Arms of Provinces

1990. 45th Anniv of First Provinces Conference (established Second Republic as Federal State).
2242 **977** 5s. multicoloured 65 45

978 University Seal   979 Vogelsang

1990. 150th Anniv of Mining University, Leoben.
2243 **978** 4s.50 black, red & green . . . 60 45

1990. Death Centenary of Karl von Vogelsang (Christian social reformer).
2244 **979** 4s.50 multicoloured . . . 60 45

980 Metal Workers

1990. Centenary of Metal, Mining and Energy Trade Union.
2245 **980** 5s. multicoloured 65 50

981 Player   **982** Greenhouse

1990. 3rd World Ice Curling Championships, Vienna.
2246 **981** 7s. multicoloured 85 65

1990. Re-opening of Schonbrunn Greenhouse.
2247 **982** 5s. multicoloured 65 50

983 "Birth of Christ"   **984** Grillparzer

1990. Christmas. Detail of Altarpiece by Master Nikolaus of Verdun, Klosterneuburg Monastery.
2248 **983** 5s. multicoloured 65 40

1991. Birth Bicent of Franz Grillparzer (dramatist).
2249 **984** 4s.50 multicoloured . . . 60 50

985 Skier   **986** Kreisky

1991. World Alpine Skiing Championships, Saalbach-Hinterglemm.
2250 **985** 5s. multicoloured 65 45

1991. 80th Birth Anniv of Bruno Kreisky (Chancellor, 1970–82).
2251 **986** 5s. multicoloured 60 45

987 Schmidt and Vienna Town Hall

1991. Death Centenary of Friedrich von Schmidt (architect).
2252 **987** 7s. multicoloured 90 70

988 Fountain, Vienna

1991. Anniversaries. Multicoloured.
2253 4s.50 Type **988** (250th death anniv of Georg Raphael Donner (sculptor)) . . . 60 45
2254 5s. "Kitzbuhel in Winter" (birth centenary of Alfons Walde (artist and architect)) . . . 65 45
2255 7s. Vienna Stock Exchange (death centenary of Theophil von Hansen (architect)) . . . 90 70
See also No. 2269.

989 M. von Ebner-Eschenbach

1991. 75th Death Anniv of Marie von Ebner-Eschenbach (writer).
2256 **989** 4s.50 purple 55 50

991 Obir Stalactite Caverns, Eisenkappel

1991. Natural Beauty Spots.
2258 **991** 5s. multicoloured 85 60

992 Spittal an der Drau (after Matthaus Merian)

1991. 800th Anniv of Spittal an der Drau.
2259 **992** 4s.50 multicoloured . . . 60 45

993 "ERS-1" European Remote Sensing Satellite

1991. Europa. Europe in Space.
2260 **993** 7s. multicoloured 90 85

994 "Garden Party" (Anthoni Bays)

1991. Vorarlberg "Clothing and People" Exhibition, Hohenems.
2261 **994** 5s. multicoloured 65 50

995 Grein

1991. 500th Anniv of Grein Town Charter.
2262 **995** 4s.50 multicoloured . . . 60 45

996 Bedding Plants forming Arms

1991. 1200th Anniv of Tulln.
2263 **996** 5s. multicoloured . . . 70 45

997 Military History Museum

1991. Vienna Museum Centenaries. Multicoloured.
2264 5s. Type **997** . . . 70 50
2265 7s. Museum of Art History . . . 90 80

998 "B" and "P"   **999** Tunnel Entrance

1991. Stamp Day.
2266 **998** 7s.+3s. brown, sepia and black . . . . 1·40 1·90
This is the first of a series of ten annual stamps, each of which will illustrate two letters. The complete series will spell out the words "Briefmarke" and "Philatelie".

1991. Opening of Karawanken Road Tunnel between Carinthia and Slovenia.
2267 **999** 7s. multicoloured 90 80

1000 Town Hall

1991. 5th Anniv of St. Polten as Capital of Lower Austria.
2268 **1000** 5s. multicoloured . . . 70 55

1991. 150th Birth Anniv of Otto Wagner (architect). As T **988**. Multicoloured.
2269 4s.50 Karlsplatz Station, Vienna City Railway . . 60 45

1001 Rowing

1991. Junior World Canoeing Championships and World Rowing Championships, Vienna.
2270 **1001** 5s. multicoloured 70 45

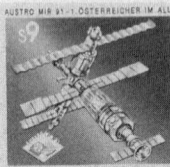

1002 X-ray Tube   **1003** Paracelsus

1991. European Radiology Congress, Vienna.
2271 **1002** 7s. multicoloured . . . 90 70

1991. 450th Death Anniv of Theophrastus Bombastus von Hohenheim (Paracelsus) (physician and scientist).
2272 **1003** 4s. black, red & brown . . 55 45

1004 "Mir" Space Station   **1005** Almabtrieb (driving cattle from mountain pastures) (Zell, Tyrol)

1991. "Austro Mir 91" Soviet–Austrian Space Flight.
2273 **1004** 9s. multicoloured . . . 1·25 1·25

1991. Folk Customs and Art (1st series). Mult.
2274 4s.50 Type **1005** 70 45
2275 5s. Vintage Crown (Neustift, Vienna) . . . 75 50
2276 7s. Harvest monstrance (Nestelbach, Styria) . 1·00 70
See also Nos. 2305/7, 2349/51, 2363/5, 2393/5, 2418, 2432/3, 2450, 2482, 2491, 2500/1, 2508, 2524, 2546, 2550, 2552, 2568, 2581, 2587 and 2595.

1006 Weaver

1991. Austrian World of Work (5th series).
2277 **1006** 4s.50 multicoloured . . 60 45

1007 "The General" (Rudolf Pointner)   **1008** Raab

1991. Austrian Modern Art.
2278 **1007** 5s. multicoloured . . . 70 55

1991. Birth Centenary of Julius Raab (Chancellor, 1953–61).
2279 **1008** 4s.50 brown & chestnut . 55 45

1009 "Birth of Christ" (detail of fresco, Baumgartenberg Church)

1991. Christmas.
2280 **1009** 5s. multicoloured . . . 70 45

1010 Clerks

1992. Centenary of Trade Union of Clerks in Private Enterprise.
2281 **1010** 5s.50 multicoloured . . . 60 45

1011 Emblems of Games and Olympic Rings

1992. Winter Olympic Games, Albertville, and Summer Games, Barcelona.
2282 **1011** 7s. multicoloured . . . 90 80

1012 Competitor

1992. 8th World Toboggan Championships on Natural Runs, Bad Goisern.
2283 **1012** 5s. multicoloured . . . 70 45

1013 Hollow Stone, Klostertal

1992. Natural Beauty Spots.
2284 **1013** 5s. multicoloured . . . 95 60

1014 Saiko   1015 "Athlete with Ball" (Christian Attersee)

1992. Birth Centenary of George Saiko (writer).
2285 **1014** 5s.50 brown 70 45

1992. Centenary of Workers' Sport Movement.
2286 **1015** 5s.50 multicoloured 75 55

1016 Franz Joseph Muller (chemist and mineralogist)

1992. Scientific Anniversaries. Multicoloured.
2287 5s. Type **1016** (250th birth anniv) 70 55
2288 5s.50 Paul Kitaibel (botanist, 175th death anniv) 75 60
2289 6s. Christian Doppler (physicist) (150th anniv of observation of Doppler Effect) 80 75
2290 7s. Richard Kuhn (chemist, 25th death anniv) . . 90 75

1018 First and Present Emblems

1992. Centenary of Railway Workers' Trade Union.
2292 **1018** 5s.50 red and black 80 55

1019 Hanrieder   1020 Scenes from "The Birdseller" (Zeller) and "The Beggar Student" (Millocker)

1992. 150th Birth Anniv of Norbert Hanrieder (writer).
2293 **1019** 5s.50 lilac & brown . . 70 45

1992. 150th Birth Anniversaries of Carl Zeller and Karl Millocker (composers).
2294 **1020** 6s. multicoloured . . . 1·00 85

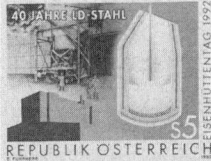

1021 Foundry and Process

1992. Ironworks Day. 40th Anniv of First LD-Process Steel Works, Linz.
2295 **1021** 5s. multicoloured . . . 60 45

1022 Woodcut of the Americas by Sebastian Munster (from "Geographia Universalis" by Claudius Ptolomaus)

1992. Europa. 500th Anniv of Discovery of America by Columbus.
2296 **1022** 7s. multicoloured . . . 90 80

1023 Dredger   1024 Rieger

1992. Centenary of Treaty for International Regulation of the Rhine.
2297 **1023** 7s. multicoloured . . . 1·00 80

1992. Centenary of Adoption of Pseudonym Reimmichl by Sebastian Rieger (writer).
2298 **1024** 5s. brown 60 45

1025 Flags and Alps   1026 Dr. Anna Dengel

1992. Alpine Protection Convention.
2299 **1025** 5s.50 multicoloured . . . 90 60

1992. Birth Centenary of Dr. Anna Dengel (founder of Medical Missionary Sisters).
2300 **1026** 5s.50 multicoloured . . 65 45

1027 "R" and "H"

1992. Stamp Day.
2301 **1027** 7s.+3s. multicoloured 1·40 1·75
See note below No. 2266.

1028 Town Hall

1992. 750th Anniv of First Documentation of Lienz as a Town.
2302 **1028** 5s. multicoloured . . . 65 45

1029 "Billroth in Lecture Room" (A. F. Seligmann)   1030 Waldheim

1992. Austrian Surgery Society International Congress, Eisenstadt.
2303 **1029** 6s. multicoloured . . . 70 70

1992. Presidency of Dr. Kurt Waldheim.
2304 **1030** 5s.50 black, red & grey 65 55

1992. Folk Customs and Art (2nd series). As T **1005**. Multicoloured.
2305 5s. Target with figure of Zieler, Lower Austria, 1732 . . . . 65 60
2306 5s.50 Chest, Carinthia . . . 65 65
2307 7s. Votive tablet from Venser Chapel, Vorarlberg 90 75

1031 Bridge over Canal

1992. Completion of Marchfeld Canal System.
2308 **1031** 5s. multicoloured . . . 65 45

1032 "The Purification of Sea Water" (Peter Pongratz)

1992. Austrian Modern Art.
2309 **1032** 5s.50 multicoloured . . 70 60

1033 Gateway, Hofburg Palace (venue)

1992. 5th Int Ombudsmen's Conference, Vienna.
2310 **1033** 5s.50 multicoloured . . 65 50

1034 Academy Seal   1035 "The Annunciation"

1992. 300th Anniv of Academy of Fine Arts, Vienna.
2311 **1034** 5s. blue and red 65 60

1992. Death Bicentenary of Veit Koniger (sculptor).
2312 **1035** 5s. multicoloured . . . 70 50

1036 "Birth of Christ" (Johann Georg Schmidt)

1992. Christmas.
2313 **1036** 5s.50 multicoloured . . 70 40

1037 Earth and Satellite

1992. Birth Centenary of Hermann Potocnik (alias Noordung) (space travel pioneer).
2314 **1037** 10s. multicoloured . . . 1·25 1·40

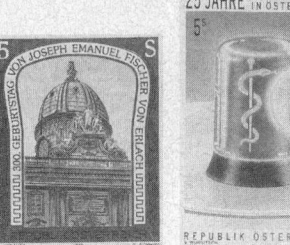

1038 Dome of Michael Wing, Hofburg Palace, Vienna   1039 Emergency Vehicle's Flashing Lantern

1993. Architects' Anniversaries. Multicoloured.
2315 5s. Type **1038** (Joseph Emanuel Fischer von Erlach, 300th birth) . . 65 50
2316 5s.50 Kinsky Palace, Vienna (Johann Lukas von Hildebrandt, 325th birth) 70 50
2317 7s. State Opera House, Vienna (Eduard van der Null and August Siccard von Siccardsburg, 125th death anniv) 90 80

1993. 25th Anniv of Radio-controlled Emergency Medical Service.
2318 **1039** 5s. multicoloured . . . 65 50

1040 Wilder Kaiser Massif, Tyrol

1993. Natural Beauty Spots.
2319 **1040** 6s. multicoloured . . . 90 80

1041 Mitterhofer Typewriter

1993. Death Centenary of Peter Mitterhofer (typewriter pioneer).
2320 **1041** 17s. multicoloured . . . 2·10 2·00

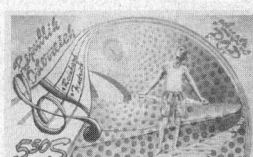

1042 "Strada del Sole" (record sleeve)

1993. "Austro Pop" (1st series). Rainhard Fendrich (singer).
2321 **1042** 5s.50 multicoloured . . . 70 50
See also Nos. 2356 and 2368.

1043 Games Emblem

1993. Winter Special Olympics, Salzburg and Schladming.
2322 **1043** 6s.+3s. multicoloured . 1·25 1·25

1044 Sealsfield   1045 Girl realizing her Rights

1993. Birth Bicent of Charles Sealsfield (novelist).
2323 **1044** 10s. red, blue and gold . . . . 1·25 90

1993. Ratification of U.N. Convention on Children's Rights.
2324 **1045** 7s. multicoloured . . . 90 80

1046 "Death" (detail of sculpture, Josef Stammel), Admont Monastery, Styria

1047 "Flying Harlequin" (Paul Flora)

1993. Monasteries and Abbeys.
2325 – 1s. brown, black & grn . . 10 10
2328 **1046** 5s.50 black, yell & grn . . 70 25
2329 – 6s. black, mauve & yell . . 80 20
2330 – 7s. brown, black & grey . . 90 35
2331 – 7s.50 brown, bl & blk . . 1·00 40
2332 – 8s. orange, black & bl . . 1·00 65
2334 – 10s. black, blue & orge . . 1·40 25
2339 – 20s. black, blue & yell . . 2·50 50
2340 – 26s. orange, black & bis . . 3·25 2·50
2341 – 30s. red, yellow & black . . 4·00 1·25
DESIGNS: 1s. The Annunciation (detail of crosier of Abbess), St. Gabriel Benedictine Abbey, Bertholdstein; 6s. St. Benedict of Nursia (glass painting), Mariastern Abbey, Gwiggen; 7s. Marble lion, Franciscan Monastery, Salzburg; 7s.50, Virgin Mary (detail of cupola painting by Paul Troger), Altenburg Monastery; 8s. Early Gothic doorway, Wilhering Monastery; 10s. "The Healing of St. Peregrinus" (altarpiece), Maria Luggau Monastery; 20s. Hartmann Crosier, St. Georgenberg Abbey, Fiecht; 26s. "Master Dolorosa" (sculpture), Franciscan Monastery, Schwaz; 30s. Madonna and Child, Monastery of the Scottish Order, Vienna.

1993. Europa. Contemporary Art.
2345 **1047** 7s. multicoloured . . . 90 80

1048 Silhouette, Script and Signature

1049 "Hohentwiel" (lake steamer) and Flags

1993. 150th Birth Anniv of Peter Rosegger (writer and newspaper publisher).
2346 **1048** 5s.50 black and green . . 70 45

1993. Lake Constance European Region.
2347 **1049** 6s. multicoloured . . . 90 60

1050 Knights in Battle and "I"s

1051 Human Rights Emblem melting Bars

1993. Stamp Day.
2348 **1050** 7s.+3s. gold, black and blue . . . . 1·40 1·40
See note below No. 2266.

1993. Folk Customs and Art (3rd series). As T **1005**. Multicoloured.
2349 5s. Corpus Christi Day procession, Hallstatt, Upper Austria 70 50
2350 5s.50 Drawing the block (log), Burgenland . . . 70 50
2351 7s. Aperschnalzen (whipping the snow away), Salzburg . 90 80

1993. U.N. World Conf on Human Rights, Vienna.
2352 **1051** 10s. multicoloured . . . 1·25 1·10

1052 Jagerstatter

1053 Train approaching Wolfgangsee

1993. 50th Death Anniv of Franz Jagerstatter (conscientious objector).
2353 **1052** 5s.50 multicoloured . . . 70 50

1993. Centenary of Schafberg Cog Railway.
2354 **1053** 6s. multicoloured . . . 1·00 70

1054 "Self-portrait with Doll"

1993. Birth Centenary of Rudolf Wacker (artist).
2355 **1054** 6s. multicoloured . . . 70 60

1993. "Austro Pop" (2nd series). Ludwig Hirsch (singer and actor). As T **1042**. Multicoloured.
2356 5s.50 "Die Omama" (record sleeve) 70 60

1055 "Concert in Dornbacher Park" (Balthasar Wigand)

1993. 150th Anniv of Vienna Male Choral Society.
2357 **1055** 5s. multicoloured . . . 70 55

1056 "Easter" (Max Weiler)

1057 "99 Heads" (detail, Friedensreich Hundertwasser)

1993. Austrian Modern Art.
2358 **1056** 5s.50 multicoloured . . 70 55

1993. Council of Europe Heads of State Conference, Vienna.
2359 **1057** 7s. multicoloured . . . 1·00 90

1058 Statue of Athene, Parliament Building

1060 "Birth of Christ" (Krainburg Altar, Styria)

1059 Workers

1993. 75th Anniv of Austrian Republic.
2360 **1058** 5s. multicoloured . . . 70 55

1993. Cent of 1st Austrian Trade Unions Congress.
2361 **1059** 5s.50 multicoloured . . . 70 55

1993. Christmas.
2362 **1060** 5s.50 multicoloured . . . 70 40

1994. Folk Customs and Art (4th series). As T **1005**. Multicoloured.
2363 5s.50 Rocking cradle, Vorarlberg 65 60
2364 6s. Carved sleigh, Styria . . 80 70
2365 7s. Godparent's bowl and lid, Upper Austria 90 90

1061 Winter Sports

1994. Winter Olympic Games, Lillehammer, Norway.
2366 **1061** 7s. multicoloured . . . 90 85

1062 Early Production of Coins

1994. 800th Anniv of Vienna Mint.
2367 **1062** 6s. multicoloured . . . 70 65

1994. "Austro Pop" (3rd series). Falco (Johann Holzel) (singer). As T **1042**. Multicoloured.
2368 6s. "Rock Me Amadeus" (record sleeve) 80 65

1063 "Reclining Lady" (detail, Herbert Boeckl)

1994. Birth Centenary of Herbert Boeckl (painter).
2369 **1063** 5s.50 multicoloured . . . 70 50

1064 N.W. Tower of City Wall

1994. 800th Anniv of Wiener Neustadt.
2370 **1064** 6s. multicoloured . . . 80 50

1065 Lurgrotte (caves), Styria

1994. Natural Beauty Spots.
2371 **1065** 6s. multicoloured . . . 90 65

1066 Lake Rudolf (Teleki–Hohnel expedition to Africa, 1887)

1994. Europa. Discoveries.
2372 **1066** 7s. multicoloured . . . 90 80

1067 "E" and "L" as Ruins in Landscape

1994. Stamp Day.
2373 **1067** 7s.+3s. multicoloured . . 1·40 1·40
See note below No. 2266.

1068 "Allegory of Theology, Justice, Philosophy and Medicine" (detail of fresco, National Library)

1994. 300th Birth Anniv of Daniel Gran (artist).
2374 **1068** 20s. multicoloured . . . 2·25 2·00

1069 Scene from "The Prodigal Son" (opera, Benjamin Britten)

1994. 25th Anniv of Carinthian Summer Festival, Ossiach and Villach.
2375 **1069** 5s.50 gold and red . . . 70 50

1070 Steam Locomotive and Diesel Railcar (Gailtal)

1994. Railway Centenaries. Multicoloured.
2376 5s.50 Type **1070** 65 50
2377 6s. Steam locomotive and diesel railcar (Murtal) . 1·00 65

1071 Gmeiner and Children

1072 Seitz (bust, G. Ambrosi)

1994. 75th Birth Anniv of Hermann Gmeiner (founder of S.O.S. children's villages).
2378 **1071** 7s. multicoloured . . . 80 80

1994. 125th Birth Anniv of Karl Seitz (acting President, 1920).
2379 **1072** 5s.50 multicoloured . . . 60 60

1073 Bohm

1075 Franz Theodor Csokor (dramatist and poet)

1074 Ethnic Minorities on Map

1994. Birth Centenary of Karl Bohm (conductor).
2380 **1073** 7s. blue and gold . . . 1·00 90

1994. Legal and Cultural Protection of Ethnic Minorities.
2381 **1074** 5s.50 multicoloured . . . 65 50

1994. Writers' Anniversaries. Multicoloured.
2382 6s. Type **1075** (25th death anniv) 60 70
2383 7s. Joseph Roth (novelist, birth cent) . . . . 1·00 1·10

1076 "Head" (Franz
Ringel)   1077 Money Box

1994. Austrian Modern Art.
2384 **1076** 6s. multicoloured . . .   80   60

1994. 175th Anniv of Savings Banks in Austria.
2385 **1077** 7s. multicoloured . . .   80   80

1078 Air Hostess and Child

1994. Austrian World of Work (6th series).
2386 **1078** 6s. multicoloured . . .   70   70

1079 Coudenhove-Kalergi and
Map of Europe

1994. Birth Cent of Richard Coudenhove-Kalergi
(founder of Paneuropa Union).
2387 **1079** 10s. multicoloured . . .   1·25   1·10

1080 "Birth of Christ"   1081 Map and Austrian
(Anton Wollenek)   and E.U. Flags

1994. Christmas.
2388 **1080** 6s. multicoloured . . .   70   45

1995. Austria's Entry into E.U.
2389 **1081** 7s. multicoloured . . .   90   85

1082 Loos House,
Michaelerplatz, Vienna

1995. 125th Birth Anniv of Adolf Loos (architect).
2390 **1082** 10s. multicoloured . . .   1·25   1·25

1083 Sporting Activities

1995. 50th Anniv of Austrian Gymnastics and Sports
Association.
2391 **1083** 6s. multicoloured . . .   80   60

1084 Workers

1995. 75th Anniv of Workers' and Employees'
Chambers (advisory body).
2392 **1084** 6s. multicoloured . . .   80   60

1995. Folk Costumes and Art (5th series). As T **1005.**
Multicoloured.
2393   5s.50 Belt, Carinthia   60   50
2394   6s. Costume of Hiata
     (vineyard guard), Vienna   90   60
2395   7s. Gold bonnet, Wachau   1·10   90

1085 State Seal   1086 Heft Ironworks

1995. 50th Anniv of Second Republic.
2396 **1085** 6s. multicoloured . . .   80   60

1995. Carinthian "History of Mining and Industry"
Exhibition, Heft, Huttenberg.
2397 **1086** 5s.50 multicoloured . . .   70   60

1087 Hiker in Mountains

1995. Centenary of Friends of Nature.
2398 **1087** 5s.50 multicoloured . .   70   60

1088 Heidenreichstein National Park

1995. Natural Beauty Spots.
2399 **1088** 6s. multicoloured . . .   80   80

1089 Woman and Barbed   1090 Map, Woman and
Wire around Skull   Child and Transport

1995. Europa. Peace and Freedom.
2400 **1089** 7s. multicoloured . . .   90   85

1995. Meeting of European Ministers of Transport
Conference, Vienna.
2401 **1090** 7s. multicoloured . . .   90   85

1091 "F" and "A" on   1093 St. Gebhard
Vase of Flowers   (stained-glass window,
       Martin Hausle)

1995. Stamp Day.
2402 **1091** 10s.+5s. mult . . . . .   2·00   2·00
See note below No. 2266.

1995. 50th Bregenz Festival.
2403 **1092** 6s. multicoloured . . .   80   60

1995. Death Millenary of St. Gebhard, Bishop of
Konstanz (patron saint of Vorarlberg chuches).
2404 **1093** 7s.50 multicoloured . .   1·00   85

1092 Set for "The Flying
Dutchman"

1094 Members' Flags   1095 Loschmidt

1995. 50th Anniv of U.N.O.
2405 **1094** 10s. multicoloured . . .   1·40   1·10

1995. Death Centenary of Josef Loschmidt (physical
chemist).
2406 **1095** 20s. black, stone & brn   2·50   2·10

1096 K. Leichter   1097 Scene from
              "Jedermann" (Hugo von
              Hofmannsthal)

1995. Birth Cent of Kathe Leichter (sociologist).
2407 **1096** 6s. cream, black & red   80   60

1995. 75th Anniv of Salzburg Festival.
2408 **1097** 6s. multicoloured . . .   80   60

1098 "European Scene" (Adolf
Frohner)

1995. Austrian Modern Art.
2409 **1098** 6s. multicoloured . . .   80   60

1099 Franz von Suppe and "The
Beautiful Galatea"

1995. Composers' Anniversaries. Scenes from
operettas. Multicoloured.
2410   6s. Type **1099** (death cent)   80   65
2411   7s. Nico Dostal and "The
     Hungarian Wedding"
     (birth centenary) . . . .   1·00   90

1100 University Building

1995. 25th Anniv of Klagenfurt University.
2412 **1100** 5s.50 multicoloured . . .   70   60

1101 Hollenburg Castle

1995. 75th Anniv of Carinthian Referendum.
2413 **1101** 6s. multicoloured . . .   80   60

1102 Postman

1995. Austrian World of Work (7th series).
2414 **1102** 6s. multicoloured . . .   80   60

1103 Anton von Webern   1104 Christ Child
(50th death)

1995. Composers' Anniversaries.
2415 **1103** 6s. blue and orange . .   80   60
2416   – 7s. red and orange . .   1·00   90
DESIGN: 7s. Ludwig van Beethoven (225th birth).

1995. Christmas. 300th Anniv of Christkindl Church.
2417 **1104** 6s. multicoloured . . .   80   60

1996. Folk Customs and Art (6th series). As T **1005.**
2418   6s. multicoloured . . .   70   60
DESIGN: 6s. Masked figures Roller and Scheller
(Imst masquerades, Tyrol).

1105 Empress Maria Theresia and
Academy Building

1996. 250th Anniv of Theresian Academy, Vienna.
2419 **1105** 6s. multicoloured . . .   80   60

1106 Ski Jumping

1996. World Ski Jumping Championships, Tauplitz
and Bad Mitterndorf.
2420 **1106** 7s. multicoloured . . .   90   85

1107 Terminal

1996. Completion of West Terminal, Vienna International Airport.
2421 **1107** 7s. multicoloured . . . 90 85

1108 Hohe Tauern National Park

1996. Natural Beauty Spots.
2422 **1108** 6s. multicoloured . . . 80 60

1109 "Mother and Child" (Peter Fendi)   1110 Organ and Music

1996. Artists' Birth Bicentenaries. Multicoloured.
2423 6s. Type **1109** 80 60
2424 7s. "Self-portrait" (Leopold Kupelwieser) 90 85

1996. Death Cent of Anton Bruckner (composer).
2425 **1110** 5s.50 multicoloured . . . 90 70

1111 Kollmitz Castle (from copper engraving)

1996. 300th Death Anniv of Georg Vischer (cartographer and engraver).
2426 **1111** 10s. black and stone . . 1·25 1·25

1112 Old Market Square

1996. 800th Anniv of Klagenfurt.
2427 **1112** 6s. multicoloured . . . 80 65

1113 Hotel Chef and Waitress

1996. Austrian World of Work (8th series).
2428 **1113** 6s. multicoloured . . . 80 70

1114 Paula von Preradovic (writer)   1115 "M" and "T" and Bluebirds (mosaic)

1996. Europa. Famous Women.
2429 **1114** 7s. stone, brown & grey 90 85

1996. Stamp Day.
2430 **1115** 10s.+5s. mult . . . . . 2·00 1·75
See note below No. 2266.

1116 Mascot with Olympic Flag

1996. Olympic Games, Atlanta.
2431 **1116** 10s. multicoloured . . . 1·40 1·25

1996. Folk Customs and Art (7th series). As T **1005**.
2432 5s.50 Flower-bedecked poles, Salzburg 85 65
2433 7s. Tyrol militia . . . . . . 1·10 90

1117 Landscape

1996. 75th Anniv of Burgenland.
2434 **1117** 6s. multicoloured . . . 80 65

1118 Mountaineers   1119 Deed of Otto III, 996

1996. Cent of Austrian Mountain Rescue Service.
2435 **1118** 6s. multicoloured . . . 80 65

1996. Millenary of Austria. Multicoloured.
2436 6s. Type **1119** 80 85
2437 6s. Archduke Joseph II (after Georg Weikert) and Archduchess Maria Theresia (after Martin van Meytens) 80 85
2438 7s. "Duke Heinrich II" (stained-glass window, Monastery of the Holy Cross) . . . . . 90 1·00
2439 7s. Arms in flames (1848 Revolution) . . . . . 90 1·00
2440 7s. Rudolf IV, the Founder 90 1·00
2441 7s. Karl Renner (first Federal Republic president) . . . . . 90 1·00
2442 10s. Archduke Maximilian I (Holy Roman Emperor) (miniature from Statute Book of Order of the Golden Fleece) . . . . . 1·25 1·40
2443 10s. Seal and signature of Leopold Figl (State Treaty of 1955) . . . . . 1·25 1·40
2444 20s. Imperial crown of Rudolf II . . . . . 2·50 3·25
2445 20s. State arms, stars of Europe and "The Horsebreaker" (bronze by Josef Lax) (Austria and Europe) . . . . . 2·50 3·25

1120 "Power Station" (Reinhard Artberg)

1996. Austrian Modern Art.
2446 **1120** 7s. multicoloured . . . 90 85

1121 Children of Different Nations

1996. 50th Anniv of U.N.I.C.E.F.
2447 **1121** 10s. multicoloured . . . 1·25 1·25

1122 Nativity and Vienna Town Hall

1996. Christmas.
2448 **1122** 6s. multicoloured . . . 80 65

1123 Kramer

1997. Birth Centenary of Theodor Kramer (poet).
2449 **1123** 5s.50 blue 65 50

1997. Folk Customs and Art (8th series). As T **1005**. Multicoloured.
2450 7s. Epiphany carol singers, Eisenstadt Burgenland . . . 80 80

1124 Vineyards on the Nussberg, Vienna

1997. Natural Beauty Spots.
2451 **1124** 6s. multicoloured . . . 65 60

1125 Academy and Light

1997. 150th Anniv of Austrian Academy of Sciences, Vienna.
2452 **1125** 10s. multicoloured . . . 1·25 90

1126 Emblem

1997. 50th Anniv of Verbund Electricity Company.
2453 **1126** 6s. multicoloured . . . 65 60

1127 The Cruel Rosalia of Forchtenstein   1128 Stage Set for "Die tote Stadt"

1997. Myths and Legends.
2459 – 6s.50 grn, pink & blk 70 65
2460 **1127** 7s. black, stone & brn 80 30
2461 – 8s. orange, blk & lilac 1·00 1·10
2462 – 9s. black, stone & pur 1·50 1·40
2462a – 10s. black, grey & red 1·10 1·10
2463 – 13s. black, brn & pur 1·75 1·75
2464 – 14s. black, lt blue & bl 1·75 1·90
2465 – 20s. green, blk & stone 2·25 1·90
2466 – 22s. black, bl & stone 2·75 2·75
2467 – 23s. black, ochre & grn . 2·75 2·75
2468 – 25s. stone, black & yell . 3·50 3·25
2469 – 32s. black, brn & pink 4·25 4·00
DESIGNS: 6s.50, Lindworm of Klagenfurt; 8s. The Black Lady of Hardegg; 9s. Charming Augustin; 10s. Basilisk of Vienna; 13s. The Pied Piper of Korneuburg; 14s. The Strudengau Water-nymph; 20s. St. Notburga; 22s. Witches Whirl; 23s. Loaf Agony; 25s. St. Konrad and Altems Castle; 32s. The Discovery of Erzberg (Mountain of Ore).

1997. Birth Cent of Erich Korngold (composer).
2470 **1128** 20s. black, blue & gold 2·25 1·90

1129 Stadium, Badge and Players

1997. Rapid Vienna, National Football Champions, 1995–96.
2471 **1129** 7s. multicoloured . . . 80 80

1130 Red Deer

1997. Hunting and the Environment. Deer Feeding in Winter.
2472 **1130** 7s. multicoloured . . . 80 80

1131 Canisius and Children (altar by Josef Bachlechner in Innsbruck Seminary)

1997. 400th Death Anniv of St. Petrus Canisius (patron saint of Innsbruck).
2473 **1131** 7s.50 multicoloured . . . 85 90

1132 Johannes Brahms (after L. Michalek)

1997. Composers' Anniversaries.
2474 **1132** 6s. violet and gold . . . 80 80
2475 – 10s. purple and gold . . . 1·25 1·25
DESIGNS: 6s. Type **1132** (death centenary); 10s. Franz Schubert (birth bicentenary).

1133 "A" and "E"   1134 The Four Friends

1997. Stamp Day.
2476 **1133** 7s. multicoloured . . .   80   85
See note below No. 2266.

1997. Europa. Tales and Legends. "The Town Band of Bremen" by the Brothers Grimm.
2477 **1134** 7s. multicoloured . . .   80   85

1135 1850 9k. Stamp and Postman

1997. "WIPA 2000" International Stamp Exhibition, Vienna (1st issue).
2478 **1135** 27s.+13s. mult . . . .   4·50   4·50
See also Nos. 2521 and 2543.

1136 Train on Hochschneeberg Line

1997. Railway Anniversaries. Multicoloured.
2479   6s. Type **1136** (centenary of
           Hochschneeberg rack-
           railway)   65   70
2480   7s.50 Steam locomotive
           "Licaon" and viaduct
           near Mattersburg (150th
           anniv of Odenburg–
           Wiener Neustadt line) . .   85   1·00

1137 Cogwheels   1138 Waggerl (self-
                              portrait)

1997. 125th Anniv of Austrian Technical Supervisory Association.
2481 **1137** 7s. multicoloured . . .   80   80

1997. Folk Customs and Art (9th series). As T **1005**. Multicoloured.
2482   6s.50 Tyrolean brass band   70   70

1997. Birth Centenary of Karl Waggerl (writer).
2483 **1138** 7s. green, yellow & blue   80   80

1139 Adolf Lorenz (founder of
German Society of Orthopaedia)

1997. Orthopaedics Congress, Vienna.
2484 **1139** 8s. multicoloured . . .   90   1·00

1140 Emblem   1142 Blind Man with
                          Guide Dog

1141 Patient, Nurse and Doctor

1997. 125th Anniv of College of Agricultural Sciences, Vienna.
2485 **1140** 9s. multicoloured . . .   1·00   1·10

1997. Austrian World of Work (9th series).
2486 **1141** 6s.50 multicoloured . .   70   65

1997. Cent of Austrian Association for the Blind.
2487 **1142** 7s. multicoloured . . .   80   80

1143 "House in Wind" (Helmut
Schickhofer)

1997. Austrian Modern Art.
2488 **1143** 7s. multicoloured . . .   80   80

1144 Klestil   1145 Werner

1997. 65th Birthday of Pres. Thomas Klestil.
2489 **1144** 7s. multicoloured . . .   80   85

1997. 75th Birth Anniv of Oskar Werner (actor).
2490 **1145** 7s. black, orge & grey   80   80

1997. Folk Customs and Art (10th series). As T **1005**. Multicoloured.
2491   6s.50 Tower wind-band,
           Upper Austria   70   85

1146 Glowing Light

1997. 25th Anniv of Light in Darkness (umbrella organization of children's charities).
2492 **1146** 7s. blue   80   85

1147 "Mariazell Madonna"

1997. Christmas.
2493 **1147** 7s. multicoloured . . .   80   80

1148 Kalkalpen National Park

1998. Natural Beauty Spots.
2494 **1148** 7s. multicoloured . . .   80   80

1149 Courting Pair

1998. Hunting and the Environment. Preservation of Breeding Habitat of the Black Grouse.
2495 **1149** 9s. multicoloured . . .   1·00   1·10

1150 Ice Skaters

1998. Winter Olympic Games, Nagano, Japan.
2496 **1150** 14s. multicoloured . . .   1·75   1·90

1151 Austrian Poster   1152 Alois Senefelder
Exposition Advertising   (inventor) on Lithographic
Poster, 1928   Stone

1998. Birth Cent of Joseph Binder (designer).
2497 **1151** 7s. multicoloured . . .   80   85

1998. Bicentenary of Invention of Lithography (printing process).
2498 **1152** 7s. blue, yellow & black   80   75

1153 Facade   1155 "St. Florian" (glass
                          painting)

1154 Player and Team Emblem

1998. Centenary of Vienna Secession (exn hall).
2499 **1153** 8s. brown, gold & blue   90   1·00

1998. Folk Customs and Art (11th series). As T **1005**. Multicoloured.
2500   6s.50 Fiacre, Vienna   80   80
2501   7s. Palm Sunday procession,
           Thaur, Tyrol   80   85

1998. Austria Memphis Football Club.
2502 **1154** 7s. multicoloured . . .   80   85

1998. St. Florian, Patron Saint of Firemen.
2503 **1155** 7s. multicoloured . . .   80   85

1156 Rupertus Cross

1998. 1200th Anniv of Salzburg Archdiocese.
2504 **1156** 7s. multicoloured . . .   80   80

1157 Series Yv Locomotive
No. 2, 1895

1998. Centenary of Completion of Ybbs Valley Railway.
2505 **1157** 6s.50 multicoloured . .   80   85

1158 "Tyrolia" (Ferdinand   1159 Vienna Town
Cosandier)   Hall (Viennese festive
                                     weeks)

1998. 175th Anniv of Tyrol Ferdinandeum (state museum), Innsbruck.
2506 **1158** 7s. multicoloured . . .   80   85

1998. Europa. National Festivals.
2507 **1159** 7s. multicoloured . . .   80   85

1998. Folk Customs and Art (12th series). As T **1005**. Multicoloured.
2508   6s.50 Samson and the
           dwarves, Salzburg . . .   80   85

1160 Christine Lavant

1998. 25th Death Anniv of Christine Lavant (poet).
2509 **1160** 7s. multicoloured . . .   80   85

1161 Electric Railcar No. 1   1162 "R" and "L"

1998. Centenary of Postlingberg Railway.
2510 **1161** 6s.50 multicoloured . .   80   90

1998. Stamp Day.
2511 **1162** 7s. multicoloured . . .   80   1·10
See note below No. 2266.

1163 Presidency   1164 Railcar No. 5090
Emblem

1998. Austrian Presidency of E.U.
2512 **1163** 7s. multicoloured . . . 80 85

1998. Centenary of Pinzgau Railway.
2513 **1164** 6s.50 multicoloured . . 80 85

1165 Volksoper, Vienna

1998. Centenary of Volksoper (theatre) and 50th Death Anniv of Franz Lehar (composer).
2514 **1165** 6s.50 multicoloured . . . 80 85

1166 Empress Elisabeth (after Franz Winterhalter)

1998. Death Centenary of Empress Elisabeth.
2515 **1166** 7s. multicoloured . . . 80 85

1167 School Building

1998. Centenary of Vienna Business School.
2516 **1167** 7s. multicoloured . . . 80 85

1168 Kudlich and Farmers   **1169** "My Garden" (Hans Staudacher)

1998. 175th Birth Anniv of Hans Kudlich (promoter of 1848 "Peasants' Liberation" Law).
2517 **1168** 6s.50 multicoloured . . 80 85

1998. Austrian Modern Art.
2518 **1169** 7s. multicoloured . . . 80 85

1170 Town Hall and Arms

1998. 350th Anniv of Declaration of Eisenstadt as a Free Town.
2519 **1170** 7s. multicoloured . . . 80 85

1171 Photographer and Reporter

1998. Austrian World of Work (10th series). Art, Media and Freelances.
2520 **1171** 6s.50 multicoloured . . . 75 85

1172 1929 2s. Stamp and Post Van

1998. "WIPA 2000" International Stamp Exhibition, Vienna (2nd issue).
2521 **1172** 32s.+13s. mult . . . . 5·25 5·50

1173 "Nativity" (fresco, Tainach Church)   **1174** Cross-country Skiing

1998. Christmas.
2522 **1173** 7s. multicoloured . . . 80 85

1999. World Nordic Skiing Championships, Ramsau.
2523 **1174** 7s. multicoloured . . . 80 85

1999. Folk Customs and Art (13th series). As T **1005**. Multicoloured.
2524   6s.50 Walking pilgrimage to Mariazell 80 85

1175 Stingl Rock, Bohemian Forest

1999. Natural Beauty Spots.
2525 **1175** 7s. multicoloured . . . 80 85

1176 Books and Compact Disc

1999. Centenary of Austrian Patent Office.
2526 **1176** 7s. multicoloured . . . 80 85

1177 Player and Club Emblem

1999. SK Puntigamer Sturm Graz Football Club.
2527 **1177** 7s. multicoloured . . . 80 85

1178 Palace Facade

1999. World Heritage Site. Schonbrunn Palace, Vienna.
2528 **1178** 13s. multicoloured . . . 1·50 1·75

1179 Partridges

1999. Hunting and the Environment. Living Space for Partridges.
2529 **1179** 6s.50 multicoloured . . 80 85

1180 Snowboarder

1999. 50th Anniv of Austrian General Sport Federation.
2530 **1180** 7s. multicoloured . . . 80 85

1181 Council Building, Strasbourg

1999. 50th Anniv of Council of Europe.
2531 **1181** 14s. multicoloured . . . 1·75 1·90
No. 2531 is denominated both in Austrian schillings and in euros.

1182 Steyr "Baby"

1999. Birth Centenary of Karl Jenschke (engineer and car manufacturer).
2532 **1182** 7s. multicoloured . . . 80 85

1183 "St. Martin" (marble relief, Peuerbach Church)

1999. Ancient Arts and Crafts.
2533 **1183** 8s. brown, blue & orange . . . . . . 90 1·00

1184 Symbols of Aid and Emblem

1999. 125th Anniv of Diakonie (professional charitable services).
2534 **1184** 7s. multicoloured . . . 80 85

1185 Johann Strauss, the Younger

1999. Composers' Death Anniversaries. Mult.
2535   7s. Type **1185** (centenary) 85 90
2536   8s. Johann Strauss, the Elder (150th anniv) . . . 90 1·00

1186 Rural Gendarmes   **1188** "K" and "I"

1999. 150th Anniv of National Gendarmerie.
2537 **1186** 7s. multicoloured . . . 80 85

1187 Donau-auen National Park

1999. Europa. Parks and Gardens.
2538 **1187** 7s. multicoloured . . . 80 85

1999. Stamp Day.
2539 **1188** 7s. multicoloured . . . 80 85
See note below No. 2266.

1189 Iron Stage Curtain

1999. Centenary of Graz Opera.
2540 **1189** 6s.50 multicoloured . . . 70 85

1190 Couple on Bench

1999. International Year of the Elderly.
2541 **1190** 7s. multicoloured . . . 80 85

1191 "St. Anne with Mary and Child Jesus" (wood-carving, St. George's Church, Purgg)

1999. Ancient Arts and Crafts.
2542 **1191** 9s. multicoloured . . . 1·00 1·10

1192 1949 25g. Stamp and Vienna Airport

1999. "WIPA 2000" International Stamp Exhibition, Vienna (3rd issue).
2543 **1192** 32s.+16s. mult . . . . 5·25 5·50

1193 "Security throughout Life" | 1194 "Cafe Girardi" (Wolfgang Herzig)

1999. 14th Congress of Federation of Austrian Trade Unions.
2544 1193 6s.50 multicoloured . . 70 80

1999. Austrian Modern Art.
2545 1194 7s. multicoloured . . . 80 85

1999. Folk Customs and Art (14th series). As T **1005**. Multicoloured.
2546 8s. Pumpkin Festival, Lower Austria . . . . 90 1·00

1999. Folk Customs and Art (15th series). As T **1005**. Multicoloured.
2547 7s. The Pummerin (great bell of St. Stephen's Cathedral) ringing in the New Year 80 85

1195 Institute and Fossils

1999. 150th Anniv of National Institute of Geology.
2548 1195 7s. multicoloured . . . 80 85

1196 "Nativity" (altar painting, Pinkafeld Church)

1999. Christmas.
2549 1196 7s. multicoloured . . . 80 85

2000. Folk Customs and Art (16th series). As T **1005**. Multicoloured.
2550 7s. Chapel procession, Carinthia 80 85

2000. Folk Customs and Art (17th series). As T **1005**. Multicoloured.
2552 6s.50 Three men wearing masks (Cavalcade of Beautiful Masks, Telfs) . . 70 80

1197 *Zantadeschica aethiopica*

2000. International Garden Show, Graz.
2553 1197 7s. multicoloured . . . 80 85

1198 Ibex

2000. Hunting and the Environment. Return of Ibex to Austrian Mountains.
2554 1198 7s. multicoloured . . . 80 85

1199 Players

2000. F.C. Tirol Innsbruck, National Football Champion 2000.
2555 1199 7s. multicoloured . . . 80 85

1200 Mt. Grossglockner and Viewing Point

2000. Bicentenary of First Ascent of Mt. Grossglockner.
2556 1200 7s. multicoloured . . . 80 85

1201 Weisssee Lake

2000. Natural Beauty Spots.
2557 1201 7s. multicoloured . . . 80 85

1202 "Building Europe" | 1203 Junkers Airplane and Air Traffic Control Tower

2000. Europa.
2558 1202 7s. multicoloured . . . 80 85

2000. 75th Anniv of Civil Aviation at Klagenfurt Airport.
2559 1203 7s. multicoloured . . . 80 85

1204 Madonna of Altenmarkt (statue) and Glass Roof, Palm House, Burggarten, Vienna

2000. 150th Anniv of Protection of Historic Monuments.
2560 1204 8s. multicoloured . . . 90 1·00

1205 Illuminated Letter and Text

2000. Life of St. Malachy (treatise) by St. Bernard of Clairvaux.
2561 1205 9s. multicoloured . . . 1·00 1·10

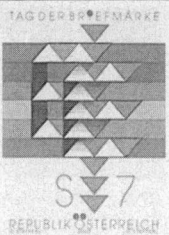

1206 "E" and "E"

2000. Stamp Day.
2562 1206 7s. multicoloured . . . 80 85
See note below No. 2266.

1207 1850 9 Kreuzer and 2000 Stamp Day Stamps

2000. 150th Anniv of Austrian Stamps.
2563 1207 7s. multicoloured . . . 80 85

1208 "Confetti"

2000. *Confetti* (children's television programme).
2565 1208 7s. multicoloured . . . 80 85

1210 Blood Droplets

2000. Centenary of Discovery of Blood Groups by Karl Landsteiner (pathologist).
2567 1210 8s. pink, silver & black 90 1·00

1211 Daimler Cannstatter Bus

2000. Centenary of First Regular Bus Route between Purkersdorf and Gablitz.
2568 1211 9s. black, blue & light blue . . . . . . 1·00 1·10

2000. Folk Customs and Art (18th series). As T **1005**. Multicoloured.
2569 7s. Men on raft (International Rafting Meeting, Carinthia) . . . 80 85

1212 Dachstein River and Hallstatt

2000. Natural Beauty Spots.
2570 1212 7s. multicoloured . . . 80 85

1213 String Instrument and Emblem

2000. Centenary of Vienna Symphony Orchestra.
2571 1213 7s. multicoloured . . . 80 85

1214 Dinghies

2000. Olympic Games, Sydney.
2572 1214 9s. multicoloured . . . 1·00 1·00

1215 Old and Modern Paper Production Methods

2000. Austrian World of Work (11th series). Printing and Paper.
2573 1215 6s.50 multicoloured . . 70 70

1216 "Turf Turkey" (Ida Szigethy)

2000. Austrian Modern Art.
2574 1216 7s. multicoloured . . . 80 85

1217 Codex 965 (National Library)

2000. Ancient Arts and Crafts (1st series).
2575 1217 8s. multicoloured . . . 80 1·00
See also Nos. 2600 and 2602.

1218 Child receiving Vaccination

2000. Bicentenary of Vaccination in Austria.
2576 1218 7s. black and cinnamon 80 85

1219 Urania Building, Vienna

2000. 50th Anniv of Adult Education Association.
2577 1219 7s. brown, grey & gold 80 85

1220 The Nativity (altar piece, Ludesch Church)

2000. Christmas.
2578 **1220** 7s. multicoloured . . . 80 85

1221 Downhill Skier

2000. World Skiing Championship (2001), St. Anton am Arlberg.
2579 **1221** 7s. multicoloured . . . 80 85

1222 Pair of Ducks

2001. Hunting and the Environment. Protection of Wetlands.
2580 **1222** 7s. multicoloured . . . 65 40

2001. Folk Customs and Art (19th series). As T **1005**. Multicoloured.
2581 8s. Boat mill, Mureck, Styria 70 45

1223 Steam Locomotive No. 3

2001. Centenary of Zillertal Railway.
2582 **1223** 7s. multicoloured . . . 65 40

1224 Players and Club Emblem

2001. SV Casino Salzburg, National Football Champion.
2583 **1224** 7s. multicoloured . . . 65 40

1225 Rolf Rudiger

2001. *Confetti* (children's television programme).
2584 **1225** 7s. multicoloured . . . 65 40

1226 Monoplane and Airport

2001. 75th Anniv of Salzburg Airport.
2585 **1226** 14s. multicoloured . . . 1·25 75

1227 Baerenschuetz Gorge

2001. Natural Beauty Spots.
2586 **1227** 7s. multicoloured . . . 65 40

2001. Folk Customs and Art (20th series). As T **1005**. Multicoloured.
2587 7s. Lent season cloth from Eastern Tyrol 65 40

1228 Water Droplet   1230 Air Balloon

1229 Post Office Railway Car

2001. Europa. Water Resources.
2588 **1228** 15s. multicoloured . . . 1·40 80

2001. Stamp Day.
2589 **1229** 20s.+10s. mult . . . 2·75 2·75

2001. Centenary of Austrian Flying Club.
2590 **1230** 7s. multicoloured . . . 65 40

1231 Refugee

2001. 50th Anniv of United Nations High Commissioner for Refugees.
2591 **1231** 21s. multicoloured . . . 1·90 1·10

1232 Kalte Rinne Viaduct

2001. U.N.E.S.C.O. World Heritage Site. The Semmering Railway.
2592 **1232** 35s. multicoloured . . . 3·25 1·90

1233 "Seppl" (mascot) (Michelle Schneeweiss)

2001. 7th International Hiking Olympics, Seefeld.
2593 **1233** 7s. multicoloured . . . 65 40

1234 Field Post Office at Famagusta

2001. Army Postal Services Abroad.
2594 **1234** 7s. multicoloured . . . 65 40

2001. Folk Customs and Art (21st series). As T **1005**. Multicoloured.
2595 7s. Rifle and Clubhouse, Preberschiessen, Salzburg (Rifleman's gathering) . . 65 40

1235 "Taurus" (Railway Engine)

2001. Conversion of East–West Railway to Four-tracked Railway.
2596 **1235** 7s. multicoloured . . . 65 40

1236 19th-century Theatrical Scene

2001. Birth Bicentenary of Johann Nestroy (playwright and actor).
2597 **1236** 7s. multicoloured . . . 65 40

1237 "The Continents" (detail Helmut Leherb)

2001. Austrian Modern Art.
2598 **1237** 7s. multicoloured . . . 65 40

1238 "False Friends" (Von Fuehrich)

2001. 125th Death Anniv of Joseph Ritter von Fuehrich (artist and engraver).
2599 **1238** 8s. deep green & green 70 45

2001. Ancient Arts and Crafts (2nd series). As T **1217**. Multicoloured.
2600 10s. Pluviale (embroidered religious robe) 90 95

1239 Dobler   1241 Cat

1240 Building and Scientific Equipment

2001. Birth Bicentenary of Leopold Ludwig Dobler (magician and inventor).
2601 **1239** 7s. multicoloured . . . 65 40

2001. Ancient Arts and Crafts (3rd series). As T **1217**. Multicoloured.
2602 7s. Dalmatik (religious vestment) (Carmelite Monastery, Silbergrasse, Vienna) 65 40

2001. 150th Anniv of the Central Institute for Meteorology and Geodynamics, Vienna.
2603 **1240** 12s. multicoloured . . . 1·10 65

2001.
2604 **1241** 19s. multicoloured . . . 1·75 1·00

1242 Civil Servants

2001. Austrian World of Work (12th series). Civil Service.
2605 **1242** 7s. multicoloured . . . 65 40

1243 Figure of Infant Jesus   1244 House of the Basilisk, Vienna

2001. Christmas. Glass Shrine, Fitzmoos Church.
2606 **1243** 7s. multicoloured . . . 65 40

New Currency

2002. Tourism. Multicoloured.
2607 51c. Type **1244** 60 40
2608 58c. Wine cellars, Hadres, Lower Austria 70 40
2609 73c. Alpine chalet, Salzburg 90 55
2610 87c. Alpach Valley, Tyrol 1·10 65
2611 €2.03 Heiligenkreuz, Lower Austria . . . . 1·25 75

1245 Stars, Map of Europe and €1 Coin

2002. Euro Currency.
2612 **1245** €3.27 multicoloured 4·00 2·40
No. 2612 is printed on the back under the gum with examples of Austrian schilling coins.

1246 Skiers and Olympic Rings

2002. Winter Olympic Games, Salt Lake City, U.S.A.
2613 **1246** 73c. multicoloured . . . 90 55

1247 Bouquet of Flowers

2002.
2614 **1247** 87c. multicoloured . . . 1·10 65

1248 Woman and Skyline

2002. Women's Day.
2615 **1248** 51c. multicoloured . . . 65 40

1249 Mel and Lucy

2002. "Philis" (children's stamp awareness programme) (1st issue)
2624 **1249** 58c. multicoloured . . . 75 45

1250 Red Roses

2002. Greetings Stamp.
2625 **1250** 58c. multicoloured . . . 75 45

1251 Kubin

2002. 125th Birth Anniv of Alfred Kubin (artist).
2626 **1251** 87c. black and buff . . . 1·10 65

1252 St. Elizabeth of Thuringia and Sick Man

2002. Caritas (Catholic charity organization).
2627 **1252** 51c. multicoloured . . . 60 35

IMPERIAL JOURNAL STAMPS

J 18    **J 21** Arms of   **J 22** Arms of
         Austria   Austria

1853. Imperf.
J67   1k. blue . . . . 12·00 1·25
J15   2k. green . . . . . . £1500 60·00
J68   2k. brown . . . . . . 9·00 1·25
J32   4k. brown £400 £1000
   The 2k. green has different corner ornaments.
   For similar values in black or red, see Lombardy and Venetia Imperial Journal stamps, Nos. J22/4.

1890. Imperf.
J76 J 21   1k. brown . . . . 6·50 1·00
J77   2k. green . . . . 6·50 1·00

1890. Perf.
J78 J 22 25k. red . . . . 80·00 £160

NEWSPAPER STAMPS

N 2 Mercury   **N 8** Francis   **N 11** Francis
                Joseph I   Joseph I

1851. Imperf.
N11b N 2 (0.6k.) blue . . . . . £140 95·00
N12   (6k.) yellow . . . £15000 £6000
N13   (6k.) red £31000 £40000
N14   (30k.) red £13000 £9000

1858. Imperf.
N28 N 8 (1k.05) blue £500 £550
N29   (1k.05) lilac . . . £700 £300

1861. Imperf.
N38 N 11 (1k.05) grey £150 £110

N 13 Arms of   **AHN 17**   **N 19** Mercury
Austria   Mercury

1863. Imperf.
N44 N 13 (1k.05) lilac . . . . . 26·00 13·00

1867. Imperf.
AHN58b AHN 17 (1k.) lilac . . . 35 15

1880. Imperf.
N69 N 19 ¼k. green . . . . . 4·50 80

N 31 Mercury    **N 43** Mercury

1899. Imperf.
N122 N 31 2h. blue 15 10
N123   6h. orange . . . . . 2·00 1·75
N124   10h. brown 65 65
N125   20h. pink . . . . 1·40 1·75

1908. Imperf.
N207 N 43 2h. blue 45 10
N208   6h. orange . . . . 3·25 35
N209   10h. red . . . . 3·25 35
N210   20h. brown . . . . 4·00

N 53 Mercury    **N 54** Mercury

1916. Imperf.
N266 N 53 2h. brown 10 10
N267   4h. green 30 60
N268   6h. blue 30 55
N269   10h. orange 35 60
N270   30h. red 25 55

1916. For Express. Perf.
N271 N 54 2h. red on yellow . . 65 1·75
N272   5h. green on yellow . . 65 1·75

N 61 Mercury    **N 68** Mercury

1917. For Express. Perf.
N294 N 61 2h. red on yellow . . 15 25
N295   5h. green on yellow . . 15 25

1919. Optd **Deutschosterreich**. Imperf.
N318 N 53 2h. brown 10 25
N319   4h. green 15 60
N320   6h. blue 15 60
N321   10h. orange 25 75
N322   30h. red . . . . 50 1·10

1919. For Express. Optd **Deutschosterreich**. Perf.
N334 N 61 2h. red on yellow . . 10 25
N335   5h. green on yellow . . 10 25

1920. Imperf.
N365 N 68 2h. violet 10 10
N366   4h. brown 10 15
N367   5h. slate 10 10
N368   6h. blue 10 10
N369   8h. green 10 10
N370   9h. bistre 10 10

N371   10h. red 10 10
N372   12h. blue 10 25
N373   15h. mauve 10 15
N374   18h. turquoise 10 20
N375   20h. orange 10 20
N376   30h. brown 10 10
N377   45h. green 10 35
N378   60h. red 10 15
N379   72h. brown 15 45
N380   90h. violet 25 60
N381   1k.20 red 25 55
N382   2k.40 green 25 65
N383   3k. grey 25 35

1921. For Express. No. N334 surch **50 50**.
N450 N 61 50 on 2h. red on yell . . 10 15

N 78 Mercury   **N 79** Posthorn and Arrow

1921. Imperf.
N452 N 78 45h. grey 15 15
N453   75h. red 10 35
N454   1k.50 green 10 50
N455   1k.80 blue 10 55
N456   2k.25 brown 10 75
N457   3k. green 10 50
N458   6k. purple 10 65
N459   7k.50 brown 15 85

1921. For Express. Perf.
N460 N 79 50h. lilac on yellow . . . 10 2·00

POSTAGE DUE STAMPS

D 26   **D 44**

1894. Perf.
D 96 D 26 1k. brown . . . . 2·00 95
D 97   2k. brown . . . . 3·25 1·90
D 98   3k. brown . . . . 3·25 80
D 99   5k. brown . . . . 3·25 40
D100   6k. brown . . . . 3·00 4·50
D101   7k. brown . . . . 1·00 4·25
D102   10k. brown . . . . 4·50 40
D103   20k. brown . . . . 1·00 4·25
D104   50k. brown . . . . 35·00 50·00

1899. As Type D **26**, but value in heller. Perf or imperf.
D126 D 26 1h. brown 30 35
D127   2h. brown 40 15
D128   3h. brown 40 10
D129   4h. brown 40 10
D130   5h. brown 40 10
D131   6h. brown 40 10
D132   10h. brown 55 10
D133   12h. brown 55 60
D134   15h. brown . . . . . 65 1·00
D135   20h. brown 65 35
D136   40h. brown . . . . . 1·00 65
D137   100h. brown . . . . . 3·75 2·10

1908. Perf.
D210 D 44 1h. red . . . . . 95 1·10
D211   2h. red 35 30
D212   4h. red 20 10
D213   6h. red 20 10
D214   10h. red 35 10
D215   14h. red . . . . . 4·00 1·90
D216   20h. red . . . . . 6·50 10
D217   25h. red . . . . . 5·25 4·25
D218   30h. red . . . . . 5·25 20
D219   50h. red . . . . . 8·50 4·25
D220   100h. red . . . . . 16·00 40
D221   5k. violet . . . . 48·00 10·50
D222   10k. violet . . . . £180 3·00

D 55    **D 56**

1916.
D273 D 55 5h. red 10 10
D274   10h. red 10 10
D275   15h. red 10 10
D276   20h. red 10 10
D277   25h. red 20 60
D278   30h. red 25 25
D279   40h. red 10 30
D280   50h. red . . . . . 1·10 1·50
D281 D 56 1k. blue 20 10
D282   5k. blue . . . . . 2·00 2·40
D283   10k. blue . . . . . 2·50 1·10

1916. Nos. 189/90 optd **PORTO** or surch **15 15** also.
D284   1h. black 10 10
D285   15 on 2h. violet 25 30

1917. Unissued stamps as T **50** surch **PORTO** and value.
D286 **50** 10 on 24h. blue . . . . 1·75 55
D287   15 on 36h. violet 40 15
D288   20 on 54h. orange 25 30
D289   50 on 42h. brown 25 20
   The above differ from Type **50** by showing a full-face portrait.

1919. Optd **Deutschosterreich**.
D323 D 55 5h. red 10 15
D324   10h. red 10 15
D325   15h. red 25 45
D326   20h. red 25 35
D327   25h. red . . . . . 8·50 15·00
D328   30h. red 25 35
D329   40h. red 25 60
D330   50h. red . . . . . 30 1·25
D331 D 56 1k. blue . . . . . 4·75 9·00
D332   5k. blue . . . . . 8·50 10·00
D333   10k. blue . . . . . 8·50 3·25

D 69   **D 70**

1920. Imperf or perf (D **69**), perf (D **70**).
D384 D 69 5h. pink 10 25
D385   10h. pink 10 15
D386   15h. pink . . . . . 10 1·25
D387   20h. pink 10 15
D388   25h. pink . . . . . 10 1·25
D389   30h. pink 10 20
D390   40h. pink 10 25
D391   50h. pink 10 15
D392   80h. pink 10 25
D393 D 70 1k. blue 10 15
D394   1½k. blue 10 15
D395   2k. blue 10 15
D396   3k. blue 10 45
D397   4k. blue 10 45
D398   5k. blue 10 15
D399   8k. blue 10 80
D400   10k. blue 10 25
D401   20k. blue . . . . . 35 1·25

1921. No. 343a surch **Nachmarke 7½ K**. Perf.
D451 **64** 7½k. on 15h. brown 10 10

D 83    **D 86**

1921.
D510 D 83 1k. brown 15 20
D511   2k. brown 15 25
D512   4k. brown 15 55
D513   5k. brown 15 20
D514   7½k. brown 15 80
D515   – 10k. blue 15 25
D516   – 15k. blue 15 50
D517   – 20k. blue 15 55
D518   – 50k. blue 15 50
   The 10k. to 50k. are larger (22 × 30 mm).

1922.
D526 D 83 10k. turquoise 10 30
D527   15k. turquoise 10 55
D528   20k. turquoise 10 40
D529   25k. turquoise 10 95
D530   40k. turquoise 10 30
D531   50k. turquoise 10 95
D532 D 86 100k. purple 10 10
D533   150k. purple 10 10
D534   200k. purple 10 10
D535   400k. purple 10 10
D536   600k. purple 20 50
D537   800k. purple 10 10
D538   1000k. purple 10 10
D539 D 86 1200k. purple . . . . 1·40 3·25
D540   1500k. purple 10 25

D541		1800k. purple	2·10	5·75
D542		2000k. purple	40	75
D543		3000k. purple	8·00	14·50
D544		4000k. purple	5·25	12·00
D545		6000k. purple	9·25	19·00

D 94

D 120

1925.

D589	D 94	1g. red	10	10
D590		2g. red	10	10
D591		3g. red	10	10
D592		4g. red	10	10
D593		5g. red	10	10
D594		6g. red	25	40
D595		8g. red	20	20
D596		10g. blue	20	10
D597		12g. blue	10	10
D598		14g. blue	10	10
D599		15g. blue	10	10
D600		16g. blue	25	20
D601		18g. blue	1·75	3·25
D602		20g. blue	15	10
D603		23g. blue	55	10
D604		24g. blue	1·75	10
D605		28g. blue	1·40	20
D606		30g. blue	25	10
D607		31g. blue	1·75	20
D608		35g. blue	1·75	15
D609		39g. blue	2·50	10
D610		40g. blue	1·40	1·90
D611		60g. blue	1·40	1·75
D612	–	1s. green	3·75	65
D613	–	2s. green	26·00	3·25
D614	–	5s. green	95·00	38·00
D615	–	10s. green	42·00	4·00

DESIGN: 1 to 10s. Horiz bands of colour.

1935.

D746	D 120	1g. red	10	15
D747		2g. red	15	15
D748		3g. red	10	15
D749		5g. red	10	10
D750	–	10g. blue	10	10
D751	–	12g. blue	10	10
D752	–	15g. blue	20	50
D753	–	20g. blue	20	10
D754	–	24g. blue	25	10
D755	–	30g. blue	25	15
D756	–	39g. blue	30	10
D757	–	60g. blue	65	1·10
D758	–	1s. green	85	25
D759	–	2s. green	1·75	80
D760	–	5s. green	3·75	3·25
D761	–	10s. green	5·25	65

DESIGNS: 10 to 60g. As Type D 120 but with background of horizontal lines; 1 to 10s. As last, but with positions of figures, arms and inscriptions reversed.

D 143

D 162

1945.

D891	D 143	1pf. red	10	15
D892		2pf. red	10	15
D893		3pf. red	10	15
D894		5pf. red	10	15
D895		10pf. red	10	15
D896		12pf. red	10	20
D897		20pf. red	10	20
D898		24pf. red	10	25
D899		30pf. red	10	35
D900		60pf. red	10	40
D901		1rm. violet	10	45
D902		2rm. violet	10	60
D903		5rm. violet	10	75
D904		10rm. violet	10	1·00

1946. Optd **PORTO**.

D956	145	3g. orange	10	10
D957		5g. green	10	10
D958		6g. purple	10	10
D959		8g. red	10	10
D960		10g. grey	10	15
D961		12g. brown	15	10
D962		15g. red	15	10
D963		20g. brown	15	10
D964		25g. blue	15	15
D965		30g. mauve	15	10
D966		40g. blue	10	10
D967		60g. green	10	10
D968		1s. violet	10	20
D969		2s. yellow	55	80
D970		5s. blue	40	55

1947.

D1035	D 162	1g. brown	10	10
D1036		2g. brown	10	10
D1037		3g. brown	10	20
D1038		5g. brown	10	10
D1039		8g. brown	10	10
D1040		10g. brown	10	10
D1041		12g. brown	10	10
D1042		15g. brown	10	10
D1043		16g. brown	35	80
D1044		17g. brown	20	80
D1045		18g. brown	20	80
D1046		20g. brown	45	10
D1047		24g. brown	20	85
D1048		30g. brown	10	20
D1049		36g. brown	55	75
D1050		40g. brown	10	10
D1051	D 162	42g. brown	60	1·25
D1052		48g. brown	60	1·25
D1053		50g. brown	60	25
D1054		60g. brown	15	25
D1055		70g. brown	10	20
D1056		80g. brown	3·25	1·90
D1057		1s. blue	10	10
D1058		1s.15 blue	2·50	25
D1059		1s.20 blue	3·00	1·40
D1060		2s. blue	25	20
D1061		5s. blue	25	25
D1062		10s. blue	35	25

D 184

D 817

1949.

D1178	D 184	1g. red	10	10
D1179		2g. red	15	10
D1180		4g. red	40	35
D1181		5g. red	1·50	35
D1182		8g. red	2·40	1·75
D1183		10g. red	15	10
D1184		20g. red	15	10
D1185		30g. red	15	10
D1186		40g. red	15	10
D1187		50g. red	15	10
D1188		60g. red	9·00	35
D1189		63g. red	3·75	5·25
D1190		70g. red	15	10
D1191		80g. red	20	10
D1192		90g. red	35	20
D1193		1s. violet	35	10
D1194		1s.20 violet	35	20
D1195		1s.35 violet	30	15
D1196		1s.40 violet	40	35
D1197		1s.50 violet	40	20
D1198		1s.65 violet	40	35
D1199		1s.70 violet	40	35
D1200		2s. violet	55	15
D1201		2s.50 violet	40	15
D1202		3s. violet	40	25
D1203		4s. violet	80	75
D1204		5s. violet	80	40
D1205		10s. violet	1·25	55

1985.

D2074	D 817	10g. yellow & black	10	10
D2075		20g. red and black	10	10
D2076		50g. orange & black	10	10
D2077		1s. blue and black	10	15
D2078		2s. brown & black	25	25
D2079		3s. violet and black	40	40
D2080		5s. yellow & black	75	75
D2081		10s. green & black	1·40	1·25

AUSTRIAN TERRITORIES ACQUIRED BY ITALY Pt. 2

Italian territory acquired from Austria at the close of the war of 1914–18, including Trentino and Trieste.

1918. 100 heller = 1 krone.
1918. 100 centesimi = 1 lira.
1919. 100 centesimi = 1 corona.

TRENTINO

1918. Stamps of Austria optd **Regno d'Italia Trentino 3 nov 1918.**

1	49	3h. purple	2·50	3·50
2		5h. green	2·10	2·00
3		6h. orange	27·00	35·00
4		10h. red	2·25	2·50
5		12h. green	75·00	£100
6	60	15h. brown	2·50	3·25
7		20h. green	1·50	2·50
8		25h. blue	19·00	25·00
9		30h. violet	7·00	10·00
10	51	40h. green	50·00	35·00
11		50h. green	14·00	20·00
12		60h. blue	22·00	32·00
13		80h. brown	30·00	42·00
14		90h. red	£600	£900
15		1k. red on yellow	30·00	42·00
16	52	2k. blue	£200	£250
17		4k. green	£950	£1400
18		10k. violet	£60000	

1918. Stamps of Italy optd **Venezia Tridentina**.

19	30	1c. brown	60	3·25
20	31	2c. brown	60	3·25
21	37	5c. green	60	3·25
22		10c. red	60	3·25
23	41	20c. orange	60	3·25
24	39	40c. brown	30·00	32·00
25	33	45c. olive	15·00	32·00
26	39	50c. mauve	15·00	32·00
27	34	1l. brown and green	15·00	32·00

1919. Stamps of Italy surch **Venezia Tridentina** and value.

28	37	5h. on 5c. green	60	1·60
29		10h. on 10c. red	60	1·60
30	41	20h. on 20c. orange	60	1·60

VENEZIA GIULIA

For use in Trieste and territory, Gorizia and province, and in Istria.

1918. Stamps of Austria optd **Regno d'Italia Venezia Giulia 3. XI. 18.**

31	49	3h. purple	45	80
32		5h. green	45	80
33		6h. orange	60	1·10
34		10h. red	1·90	1·90
35		12h. green	95	1·60
36	60	15h. brown	45	40
37		20h. green	45	40
38		25h. blue	3·00	5·25
39		30h. purple	95	1·60
40	51	40h. green	55·00	90·00
41		50h. green	3·00	5·75
42		60h. blue	8·50	15·00
43		80h. brown	5·00	8·75
44		1k. red on yellow	5·00	8·75
45	52	2k. blue	£110	£170
46		3k. red	£140	£225
47		4k. green	£200	£300
48		10k. violet	£20000	£23000

1918. Stamps of Italy optd **Venezia Giulia**.

49	30	1c. brown	80	2·25
50	31	2c. brown	80	2·25
51	37	5c. green	30	75
52		10c. red	30	75
53	41	20c. orange	40	95
54	39	25c. blue	45	1·25
55		40c. brown	4·25	9·50
56	33	45c. green	1·40	3·25
57	39	50c. mauve	2·25	4·25
58		60c. red	23·00	60·00
59	34	1l. brown and green	9·50	21·00

1919. Stamps of Italy surch **Venezia Giulia** and value.

60	37	5h. on 5c. green	55	1·25
61	41	20h. on 20c. orange	55	1·25

EXPRESS LETTER STAMPS

1919. Express Letter stamp of Italy optd **Venezia Giulia**.

E60	E 35	25c. red	17·00	35·00

POSTAGE DUE STAMPS

1918. Postage Due Stamps of Italy optd **Venezia Giulia**.

D60	D 12	5c. mauve and orange	15	35
D61		10c. mauve & orange	20	40
D62		20c. mauve & orange	40	85
D63		30c. mauve & orange	1·10	2·40
D64		40c. mauve & orange	12·50	23·00
D65		50c. mauve & orange	29·00	50·00
D66		1l. mauve and blue	75·00	£170

GENERAL ISSUE

For use throughout the liberated area of Trentino, Venezia Giulia and Dalmatia.

1919. Stamps of Italy surch in new currency.

62	30	1ce. di cor on 1c. brown	55	1·25
64	31	2ce. di cor on 2c. brown	55	1·25
65	37	5ce. di cor on 5c. green	55	50
67		10ce. di cor on 10c. red	50	50
68	41	20ce. di cor on 20c. orange	60	50
70	39	25ce. di cor on 25c. blue	60	1·10
71		40ce. di cor on 40c. brown	60	2·10
72	33	45ce. di cor on 45c. green	60	2·10
73	39	50ce. di cor on 50c. mauve	60	2·10
74		60ce. di cor on 60c. red	60	3·75
75	34	1cor. on 1l. brown & green	60	3·75
76		una corona on 1l. brn & grn	80	6·50
82		5cor. on 5l. blue and red	11·50	38·00
83		10cor. on 10l. green & red	11·50	38·00

EXPRESS LETTER STAMPS

1919. Express Letter stamps of Italy surch in new currency.

E76	E 35	25ce. di cor on 25c. red	60	1·60
E77	E 41	30ce. di cor on 30c. red and blue	95	1·90

POSTAGE DUE STAMPS

1919. Postage Due stamps of Italy surch in new currency.

D76	D 12	5ce. di cor on 5c. mauve and orange	25	70
D77		10ce. di cor. on 10c. mauve and orange	25	70
D78		20ce. di cor on 20c. mauve and orange	30	80
D79		30ce. di cor on 30c. mauve and orange	40	1·60
D80		40ce. di cor on 40c. mauve and orange	40	1·60
D81		50ce. di cor on 50c. mauve and orange	1·50	4·00
D82		una corona on 1l. mauve and blue	1·50	4·00
D86		1cor. on 1l. mve & blue	1·40	5·50
D83		due corona on 2l. mauve and blue	21·00	60·00
D87		2cor. on 2l. mve & blue	11·00	35·00
D84		cinque corona on 5l. mauve and blue	21·00	60·00
D88		5cor. on 5l. mve & blue	11·00	35·00

AUSTRO-HUNGARIAN MILITARY POST Pt. 2

A. GENERAL ISSUES

100 heller = 1 krone.

1915. Stamps of Bosnia and Herzegovina optd **K.U.K. FELDPOST**.

1	25	1h. olive	40	50
2		2h. blue	40	50
3		3h. lake	40	50
4		5h. green	40	50
5		6h. black	40	50
6		10h. red	25	30
7		12h. olive	45	60
8		20h. brown	55	65
9		25h. blue	50	60
10		30h. red	3·25	5·50
11	26	35h. green	2·75	4·00
12		40h. violet	2·75	4·00
13		45h. brown	2·75	4·00
14	26	50h. blue	2·75	4·00
15		60h. purple	60	2·00
16		72h. blue	2·75	3·50
17	25	1k. brown on cream	2·75	4·25
18		2k. indigo on blue	2·75	4·00
19	26	3k. red on green	22·00	32·00
20		5k. lilac on grey	22·00	28·00
21		10k. blue on grey	£150	£200

2 Francis Joseph

1915.

22	2	1h. green	10	10
23		2h. blue	10	10
24		3h. red	10	10
25		5h. green	10	10
26		6h. black	10	10
27		10h. red	10	10
28		10h. blue	10	10
29		12h. green	10	15
30		15h. red	10	10
31		20h. brown	20	25
32		20h. green	25	25
33		25h. blue	15	20
34		30h. red	10	25
35		35h. green	25	40
36		40h. violet	25	40
37		45h. brown	25	40
38		50h. deep green	25	40
39		60h. purple	25	40
40		72h. blue	25	40
41		80h. brown	25	25
42		90h. red	65	1·00
43	–	1k. purple on cream	1·25	1·75
44	–	2k. green on blue	1·00	85
45	–	3k. red on green	70	1·40
46	–	4k. violet on grey	70	1·60
47	–	5k. violet on grey	16·00	24·00
48	–	10k. blue on grey	3·00	5·25

The kronen values are larger, with profile portrait.

1917. As 1917 issue of Bosnia, but inscr "K.u.K. FELDPOST".

49		1h. blue	10	10
50		2h. orange	10	10
51		3h. grey	10	10
52		5h. green	10	10
53		6h. violet	10	10
54		10h. brown	10	10
55		12h. blue	10	15
56		15h. red	10	10
57		20h. brown	10	15
58		25h. blue	40	35
59		30h. grey	10	15
60		40h. bistre	10	15
61		50h. green	10	10
62		60h. red	10	15
63		80h. blue	10	10
64		90h. purple	40	60
65		2k. red on buff	10	10
66		3k. green on blue	1·00	1·40
67		4k. red on green	18·00	14·00
68		10k. violet on grey	2·25	4·00

The kronen values are larger and the border is different.

1918. Imperial and Royal Welfare Fund. As 1918 issue of Bosnia, but inscr "K. UND K. FELDPOST".

69	40	10h. (+10h.) green	25	45
70	–	20h. (+10h.) red	25	45
71	40	45h. (+10h.) blue	25	45

NEWSPAPER STAMPS

N 4 Mercury

1916.

N49	N 4	2h. blue	10	15
N50		6h. orange	45	65
N51		10h. red	45	65
N52		20h. brown	45	65

B. ISSUES FOR ITALY

100 centesimi = 1 lira.

1918. General Issue stamps of 1917 surch in figs and words.

1		2c. on 1h. blue	10	20
2		3c. on 2h. orange	10	20
3		4c. on 3h. grey	10	20
4		6c. on 5h. green	10	25
5		7c. on 6h. violet	10	25
6		11c. on 10h. brown	10	25
7		13c. on 12h. blue	10	25
8		16c. on 15h. red	10	25
9		22c. on 20h. brown	10	25
10		27c. on 25h. blue	25	60
11		32c. on 30h. grey	10	35
12		43c. on 40h. bistre	10	45
13		53c. on 50h. green	10	25
14		64c. on 60h. red	10	65
15		85c. on 80h. blue	10	35
16		95c. on 90h. purple	10	30
17		2l.11 on 2k. red on buff	20	45
18		3l.16 on 3k. green on blue	50	1·10
19		4l.22 on 4k. red on green	65	1·40

NEWSPAPER STAMPS

1918. Newspaper stamps of General Issue surch in figs and words.

N20	N 4	3c. on 2h. blue	20	35
N21		7c. on 6h. orange	40	70
N22		11c. on 10h. red	40	70
N23		22c. on 20h. brown	35	65

1918. For Express. Newspaper stamps of Bosnia surch in figs and words.

N24	N 35	3c. on 2h. red on yell	3·25	5·50
N25		6c. on 5h. green on yell	3·25	5·50

POSTAGE DUE STAMPS

1918. Postage Due stamps of Bosnia surch in figs and words.

D20	D 35	6c. on 5h. red	2·00	4·25
D21		11c. on 10h. red	1·75	3·50
D22		16c. on 15h. red	1·00	1·40
D23		27c. on 25h. red	1·00	1·40
D24		32c. on 30h. red	1·00	1·40
D25		43c. on 40h. red	1·00	1·40
D26		53c. on 50h. red	1·00	1·40

C. ISSUES FOR MONTENEGRO

100 heller = 1 krone.

1917. Nos. 28 and 30 of General Issues optd **K.U.K. MILIT. VERWALTUNG MONTENEGRO.**

1	2	10h. blue	6·75	7·25
2		15h. red	6·75	7·25

D. ISSUES FOR RUMANIA

100 bani = 1 leu.

1917. General Issue stamps of 1917 optd **BANI** or **LEI.**

1		3b. grey	1·00	1·25
2		5b. green	1·00	1·10
3		6b. violet	1·00	1·10
4		10b. brown	15	25
5		12b. blue	90	1·10
6		15b. red	80	1·10
7		20b. brown	15	25
8		25b. blue	25	25
9		30b. grey	35	45
10		40b. bistre	35	45
11		50b. green	35	45
12		60b. red	35	45
13		80b. blue	15	25
14		90b. purple	40	45
15		2l. red on buff	45	50
16		3l. green on blue	60	80
17		4l. red on green	60	80

3 Charles I

1918.

18	3	3b. grey	20	30
19		5b. green	20	30
20		6b. violet	25	40
21		10b. brown	30	45
22		12b. blue	25	30
23		15b. red	25	25
24		20b. brown	25	25
25		25b. blue	25	25
26		30b. grey	25	25
27		40b. bistre	25	35
28		50b. green	35	40
29		60b. red	35	40
30		80b. blue	20	40
31		90b. purple	35	50
32		2l. red on buff	25	50
33		3l. green on blue	40	65
34		4l. red on green	45	65

E. ISSUES FOR SERBIA

100 heller = 1 krone.

1916. Stamps of Bosnia optd **SERBIEN.**

22	25	1h. olive	1·60	3·00
23		2h. blue	2·10	3·00
24		3h. lake	2·10	3·00
25		5h. green	50	60
26		6h. black	1·10	1·60
27		10h. red	50	60
28		12h. olive	1·10	1·75
29		20h. brown	65	1·00
30		25h. blue	50	1·00
31		30h. red	50	1·00
32	26	35h. green	50	1·00
33		40h. violet	50	1·00
34		45h. brown	50	1·00
35		50h. blue	50	1·00
36		60h. brown	50	1·00
37		72h. blue	50	1·00
38	25	1k. brown on cream	85	1·00
39		2k. indigo on blue	85	1·00
40	26	3k. red on green	1·00	1·25
42		10k. blue on grey	9·50	19·00

AUSTRO-HUNGARIAN POST OFFICES IN THE TURKISH EMPIRE Pt. 2

Various Austro-Hungarian P.O.s in the Turkish Empire. Such offices had closed by 15 December 1914 except for several in Albania which remained open until 1915.

A. LOMBARDY AND VENETIA CURRENCY

100 soldi = 1 florin.

1

2

3

1867.

1	1	2s. yellow	1·75	19·00
9		3s. green	1·40	16·00
10		5s. red	35	12·00
11		10s. blue	32·00	65
5		15s. brown	20·00	7·50
6		25s. lilac	17·00	20·00
7a	2	50s. brown	1·40	23·00

1883.

14	3	2s. black and brown	20	45·00
15		3s. black and green	85	20·00
16		5s. black and red	25	6·50
17		10s. black and blue	65	35
18		20s. black and grey	1·40	4·50
19		50s. black and mauve	1·40	12·00

B. TURKISH CURRENCY

40 paras = 1 piastre.

1886. Surch **10 PARA 10.**

21a	3	10p. on 3s. green	65	11·00

1888. Nos. 71/75a of Austria surch.

22	20	10pa. on 3k. green	3·00	5·50
23		20pa. on 5k. red	45	5·25
24		1pi. on 10k. blue	50·00	70
25		2pi. on 20k. grey	1·75	3·00
26		5pi. on 50k. purple	1·75	10·00

1890. Stamps of Austria of 1890, the kreuzer values with lower figures of value removed, surch at foot.

27	23	8pa. on 2k. brown	15	55
28		10pa. on 3k. green	50	50
29		20pa. on 5k. red	35	50
30		1pi. on 10k. blue	35	10
31		2pi. on 20k. olive	6·25	23·00
32		5pi. on 50k. mauve	10·50	55·00
33	24	10pi. on 1g. blue	8·50	24·00
37		10pi. on 1g. lilac	9·50	19·00
34		20pi. on 2g. red	11·00	35·00
38		20pi. on 2g. green	35·00	60·00

1890. Stamps of Austria of 1891, with lower figures of value removed, surch at foot.

35	25	2pi. on 20k. green	3·50	1·25
36		5pi. on 50k. mauve	1·90	2·25

1900. Stamps of Austria of 1899, the heller values with lower figures of value removed, surch at foot.

46	27	10pa. on 5h. green	1·60	2·25
40	28	20pa. on 10h. red	5·00	75
48		1pi. on 25h. blue	1·00	50
49	29	2pi. on 50h. blue	2·50	4·50
43	30	5pi. on 1k. red	55	30
44		10pi. on 2k. lavender	1·75	2·75
45		20pi. on 4k. green	1·50	6·25

1903. Stamps of Austria of 1899, with all figures of value removed, surch at top and at foot.

55	27	10pa. green	55	1·50
56	28	20pa. red	1·40	1·50
57		30pa. mauve	55	3·00
58		1pi. blue	30	30
59	29	2pi. blue	60	75

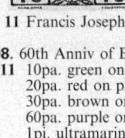

11 Francis Joseph I

12 Francis Joseph I

1908. 60th Anniv of Emperor's Accession.

60	11	10pa. green on yellow	10	20
61		20pa. red on pink	20	20
62		30pa. brown on buff	25	40
63		60pa. purple on blue	45	2·25
70		1pi. ultramarine on blue	45	55
65	12	2pi. red on yellow	35	30
66		5pi. brown on grey	45	65
67		10pi. green on yellow	85	1·10
68		20pi. blue on grey	1·90	1·10

POSTAGE DUE STAMPS

1902. Postage Due stamps as Type D 32 of Austria, but with value in heller, surch with new value.

D50	D 32	10pa. on 5h. green	1·00	2·50
D51		20pa. on 10h. green	1·10	3·25
D52		1pi. on 20h. green	1·50	3·75
D53		2pi. on 40h. green	1·50	3·75
D54		5pi. on 100h. green	1·50	3·50

D 13

1908.

D71	D 13	¼pi. green	3·25	6·25
D72		½pi. green	1·60	5·75
D73		1pi. green	2·00	5·75
D74		1½pi. green	90	14·00
D75		2pi. green	1·90	14·00
D76		5pi. green	1·90	8·50
D77		10pi. green	13·50	£100
D78		20pi. green	10·50	£120
D79		30pi. green	13·50	11·50

C. FRENCH CURRENCY

100 centimes = 1 franc.

1903. Stamps of Austria surch **CENTIMES** or **FRANC.**

F1	27	5c. on 5h. green and black	1·10	3·25
F2	28	10c. on 10h. red and black (No. 143)	80	3·50
F3		25c. on 25h. blue and black (No. 145)	24·00	21·00
F4	29	50c. on 50h. blue and black	6·75	£110
F5	30	1f. on 1k. red	95	£100
F6		2f. on 2k. lilac	7·00	£250
F7		4f. on 4k. green	9·00	£425

1904. Stamps of Austria surch **CENTIMES.**

F14	33	5c. on 5h. green	50	3·50
F13	28	10c. on 10h. red and black (No. 160)	55	11·00
F10		25c. on 25h. blue and black (No. 176)	65	95·00
F11	35	50c. on 50h. blue	1·40	£400

1906. Type of Austria surch **CENTIMES.**

F15	28	10c. on 10h. red (No. 184)	65	29·00
F16		15c. on 15h. violet and black (as No. 185)	65	26·00

No. F16 was not issued without the surch.

1908. 60th Anniv of Emperor's Accession. As T **11/12** but in centimes or franc.

F17	11	5c. green on yellow	15	65
F18		10c. red on pink	25	90
F19		15c. brown on buff	35	5·00
F20		25c. blue on blue	9·25	4·50
F21	12	50c. red on yellow	1·40	19·00
F22		1f. brown on grey	1·90	35·00

AZERBAIJAN Pt. 10

Formerly part of the Russian Empire. Became independent on 27 May 1918, following the Russian Revolution. Soviet troops invaded the country on 27 April 1920, and a Soviet Republic followed. From 1 October 1923 stamps of the Transcaucasian Federation were used but these were superseded by those of the Soviet Union in 1924.

With the dissolution of the Soviet Union in 1991, Azerbaijan once again became an independent state.

1919. 100 kopeks = 1 rouble.
1992. 100 qopik = 1 manat.

1 Standard-bearer

6 Famine Supplies

3 "Labour"

4 Petroleum Well

1919. Imperf. Various designs.

1	1	10k. multicoloured	40	50
2	–	20k. multicoloured	30	50
3	–	40k. olive, black and yellow	25	30
4	–	60k. orange, black & yellow	25	30
5	–	1r. blue, black and yellow	25	30
6	–	2r. red, black and yellow	25	30
7	–	5r. blue, black and yellow	25	40
8	–	10r. olive, black & yellow	50	75
9	–	25r. blue, black and red	50	1·00
10	–	50r. olive, black and red	75	1·50

DESIGNS—HORIZ: 40k. to 1r. Reaper; 2r. to 10r. Citadel, Baku; 25r., 50r. Temple of Eternal Fires.

1921. Imperf.

11	3	1r. green	30	40
12	4	2r. brown	30	40
13	–	5r. brown	30	40
14	–	10r. grey	50	50
15	–	25r. orange	30	40
16	–	50r. violet	30	70
17	–	100r. orange	30	70
18	–	150r. blue	30	40
19	–	250r. violet and buff	30	40
20	–	400r. blue	30	60
21	–	500r. black and lilac	30	60
22	–	1000r. red and blue	30	50
23	–	2000r. black and blue	30	60
24	–	3000r. brown and blue	30	60
25	–	5000r. green on olive	30	50

DESIGNS—HORIZ: 5r., 3000r. Bibi Eibatt Oilfield; 100r., 5000r. Goukasoff House (State Museum of Arts); 400r., 1000r. Hall of Judgment, Khan's Palace. VERT: 10r., 2000r. Minaret of Friday Mosque, Khan's Palace, Baku; 25r., 250r. Globe and Workers; 50r. Malden's Tower, Baku; 150r., 500r. Blacksmiths.

1921. Famine Relief. Imperf.

26	6	500r. blue	50	1·50
27	–	1000r. brown	85	2·50

DESIGN—VERT: 1000r. Starving family.

For stamps of the above issues surch with new values, see Stanley Gibbons Part 10 (Russia) Catalogue.

13 Azerbaijan Map and Flag

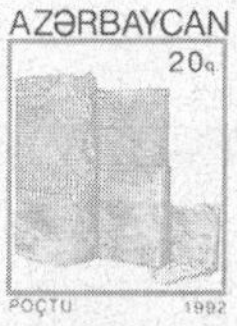

16 Maiden's Tower, Baku

1992. Independence.

83	13	35q. multicoloured	85	85

1992. Unissued stamp showing Caspian Sea surch **AZARBAYCAN** and new value.

84		25q. on 15k. multicoloured	20	20
85		35q. on 15k. multicoloured	30	30
86		50q. on 15k. multicoloured	50	50
87		1m.50 on 15k. multicoloured	1·40	1·40
88		2m.50 on 15k. multicoloured	2·25	2·25

1992. Dated "1992".

89	16	10q. green and black	10	10
90		20q. red and black	10	10
91		50q. yellow and black	10	10
92		1m.50 blue and black	50	50

See also Nos. 101/4.

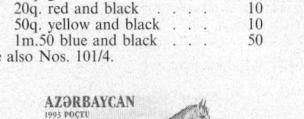

17 Akhalteka Horse

1993. Horses. Multicoloured.

93		20q. Type 17	10	10
94		30q. Kabarda horse	10	10
95		50q. Qarabair horse	10	10
96		1m. Don horse	10	10
97		2m.50 Yakut horse	30	30

98 5m. Orlov horse 55 55
99 10m. Diliboz horse 1·10 1·10

1993. Dated "1993"
101 **16** 50q. blue and black . . . 10 10
102 1m. mauve and black . . . 10 10
103 2m.50 yellow and black . . 10 10
104 5m. green and black . . . 50 50

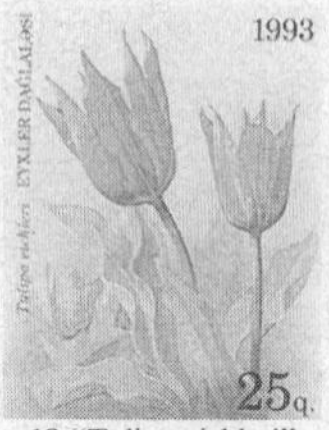

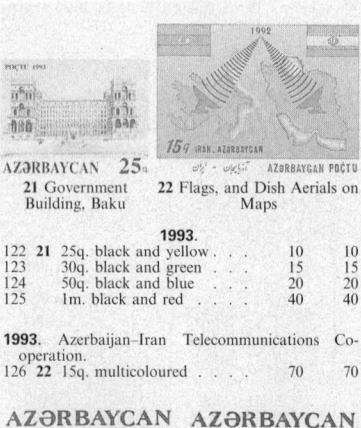

18 "Tulipa eichleri"

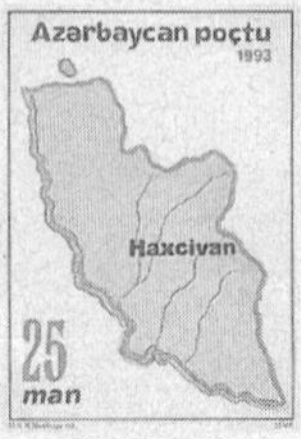

20 Map of Nakhichevan

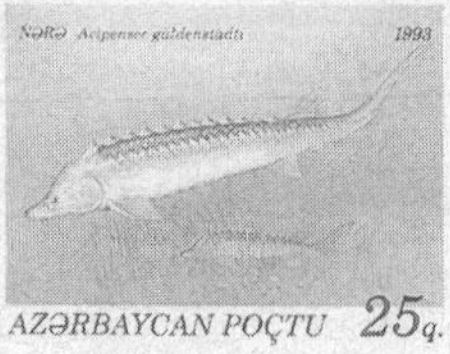

19 Russian Sturgeon

1993. Flowers. Multicoloured.
105 25q. Type **18** 10 10
106 50q. "Puschkinia scilloides" 10 10
107 1m. "Iris elegantissima" . . . 10 10
108 1m.50 "Iris acutiloba" . . . 25 25
109 5m. "Tulipa florenskyii" . . 70 70
110 10m. "Iris reticulata" . . . . 1·25 1·25

1993. Fishes. Multicoloured.
112 25q. Type **19** 10 10
113 50q. Stellate sturgeon 10 10
114 1m. Iranian roach 20 20
115 1m.50 Caspian roach 25 25
116 5m. Caspian trout 55 55
117 10m. Black-backed shad . . 1·25 1·25

1993. 70th Birthday of President Heydar Aliev.
119 – 25m. black and red . . . . 1·10 1·10
120 **20** 25m. multicoloured . . . . 1·10 1·10
DESIGN: No. 119, President Aliev.

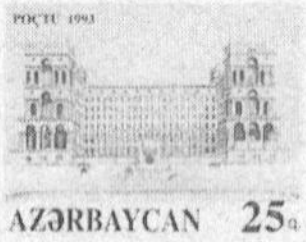

21 Government Building, Baku

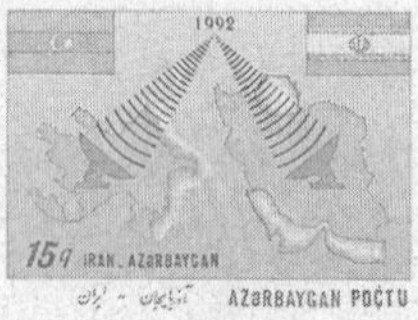

22 Flags, and Dish Aerials on Maps

1993.
122 **21** 25q. black and yellow . . . 10 10
123 30q. black and green . . . 15 15
124 50q. black and blue . . . 20 20
125 1m. black and red 40 40

1993. Azerbaijan–Iran Telecommunications Co-operation.
126 **22** 15q. multicoloured 70 70

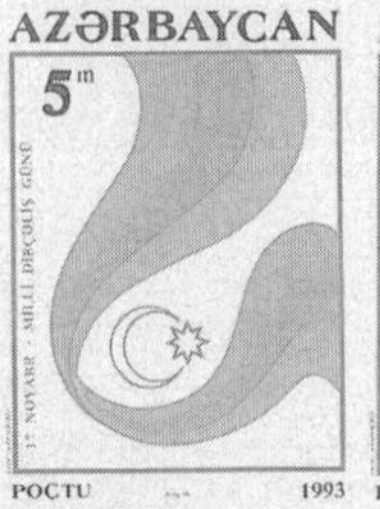

23 National Colours and Islamic Crescent

24 State Arms

1994. National Day.
127 **23** 5m. multicoloured 40 40

1994.
128 **24** 8m. multicoloured 40 40

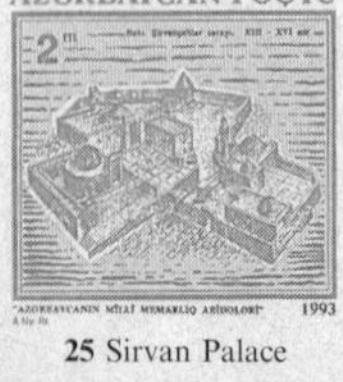

25 Sirvan Palace

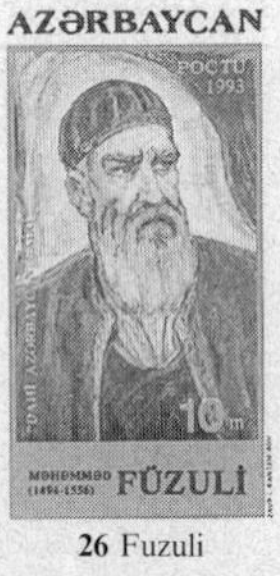

26 Fuzuli

1994. Baku Architecture.
129 **25** 2m. red, silver and black 10 10
130 – 4m. green, silver and black 20 20
131 – 8m. blue, silver and black 45 45
DESIGNS: 4m. 15th-century tomb; 8m. Divan-Khana.

1994. 500th Birth Anniv (1992) of Mohammed ibn Suleiman Fuzuli (poet).
132 **26** 10m. multicoloured 25 25

1994. No. 126 surch **IRAN–AZERBAYGAN** and value.
133 **22** 2m. on 15q. multicoloured 10 10
134 20m. on 15q. multicoloured 30 30
135 25m. on 15q. multicoloured 50 50
136 50m. on 15q. multicoloured 1·00 1·00

1994. Nos. 122/5 surch.
137 **21** 5m. on 1m. black and red 20 20
138 10m. on 30q. black & grn 20 20
139 15m. on 30q. black & grn 20 20
140 20m. on 50q. black & blue 20 20
141 25m. on 1m. black & red 25 25
142 40m. on 50q. black & blue 30 30
143 50m. on 25q. black & yell 45 45
144 100m. on 25q. black & yell 95 95

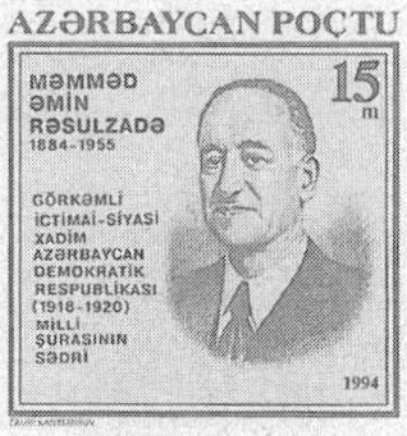

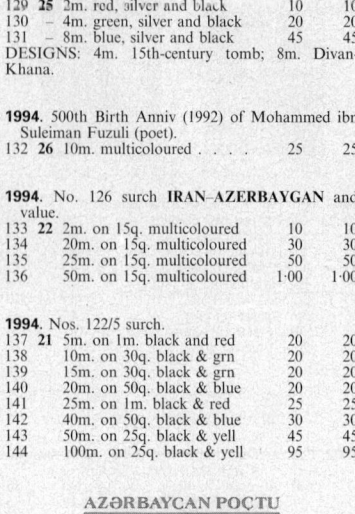

29 Rasulzade

1994. 110th Birth Anniv of Mammed Amin Rasulzade (politician).
145 **29** 15m. brown, ochre & black 55 55

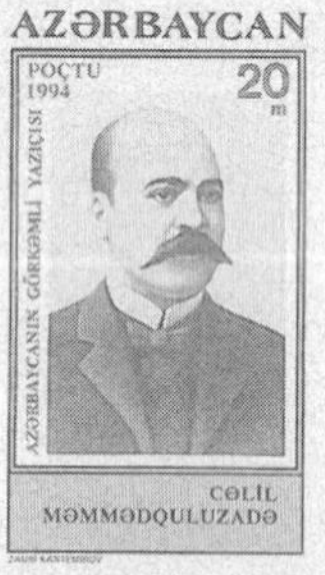

30 Mamedquluzade

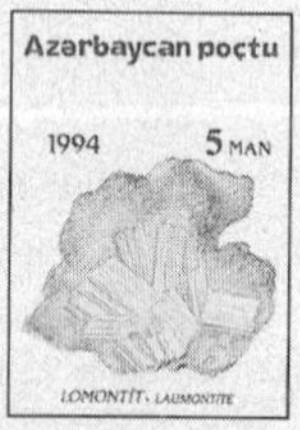

32 Laumontite

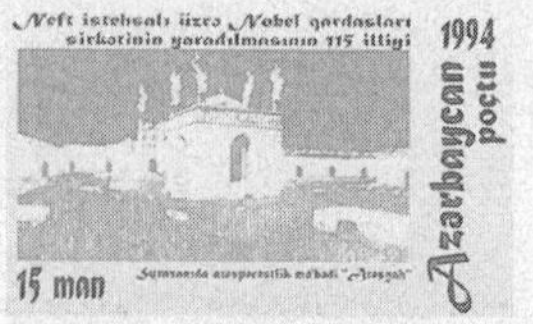

31 Temple of the Fire Worshippers of Atashgah

1994. 125th Birth Anniv of Jalil Mamedquluzade (writer).
146 **30** 20m. black, gold and blue 55 55

1994. 115th Anniv of Nobel Partnership to Exploit Black Sea Oil. Multicoloured.
147 15m. Type **31** 20 20
148 20m. Oil wells 25 25
149 25m. "Zoroastr" (first oil tanker in Caspian Sea) . . 40 40
150 50m. Nobel brothers and Petr Bilderling (partners) . . . 75 75

1994. Minerals. Multicoloured.
152 5m. Type **32** 20 20
153 10m. Epidot calcite 45 45
154 15m. Andradite 70 70
155 20m. Amethyst 95 95

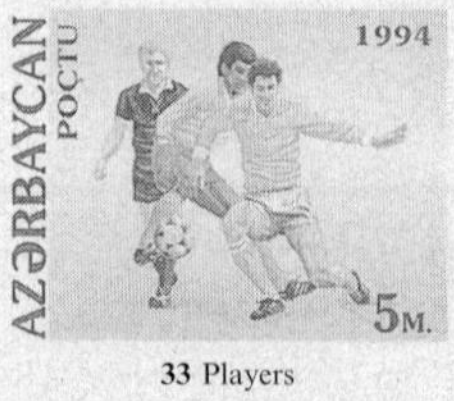

33 Players

1994. World Cup Football Championship, U.S.A.
157 **33** 5m. multicoloured 10 10
158 – 10m. multicoloured 10 10
159 – 20m. multicoloured 20 20
160 – 25m. multicoloured 25 25
161 – 30m. multicoloured 30 30
162 – 50m. multicoloured 55 55
163 – 80m. multicoloured 70 70
DESIGNS: 10m. to 80m. Match scenes.

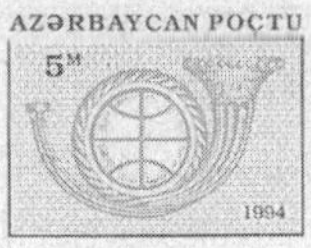

34 Posthorn

1994.
165 **34** 5m. red and black 10 10
166 10m. green and black . . . 10 10
167 20m. blue and black . . . 20 20
168 25m. yellow and black . . 20 20
169 40m. brown and black . . 25 25

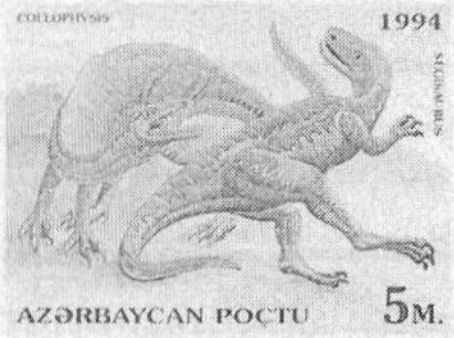

35 Coelophysis and Segisaurus

1994. Prehistoric Animals. Multicoloured.
170 5m. Type **35** 10 10
171 10m. Pentaceratops and tyrannosaurids 10 10
172 20m. Segnosaurus and oviraptor 20 20
173 25m. Albertosaurus and corythosaurus 25 25
174 30m. Igaunodons 25 25
175 50m. Stegosaurus and allosaurus 40 40
176 80m. Tyrannosaurus and saurolophus 65 65

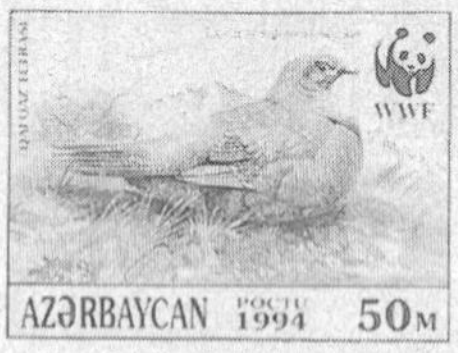

36 Nesting Grouse

1994. The Caucasian Black Grouse. Multicoloured.
178 50m. Type **36** 20 20
179 80m. Grouse on mountain . . 40 40
180 100m. Pair of grouse 55 55
181 120m. Grouse in spring meadow 90 90

1994. No. 84 further surch **400 M**.
182 400m. on 25q. on 15k. mult 35 35

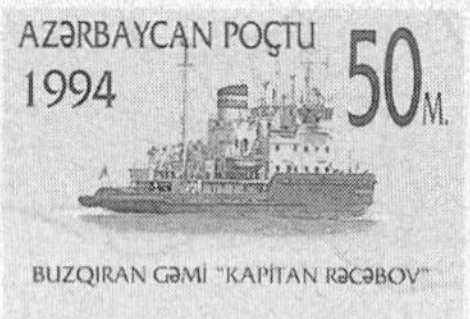

38 "Kapitan Razhabov" (tug)

1994. Ships. Multicoloured.
183 50m. Type **38** 25 25
184 50m. "Azerbaijan" (ferry) . . 25 25
185 50m. "Merkuri 1" (ferry) . . 25 25
186 50m. "Tovuz" (container ship) 25 25
187 50m. "Ganzha" (tanker) . . 25 25
Nos. 183/7 were issued together, se-tenant, the backgrounds of which form a composite design of a map.

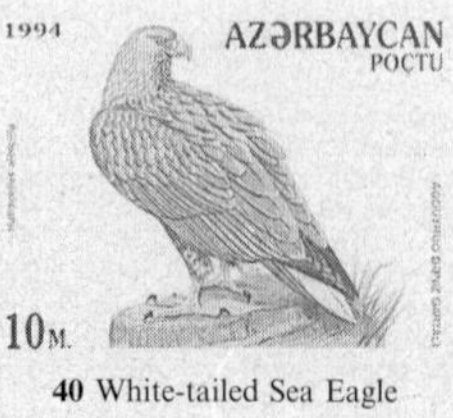

40 White-tailed Sea Eagle

1994. Birds of Prey. Multicoloured.
189 10m. Type **40** 25 25
190 15m. Imperial eagle 30 30
191 20m. Tawny eagle 45 45
192 25m. Lammergeier (vert) . . 50 50
193 50m. Saker falcon (vert) . . . 1·00 1·00
Nos. 190/1 are wrongly inscr "Aguila".

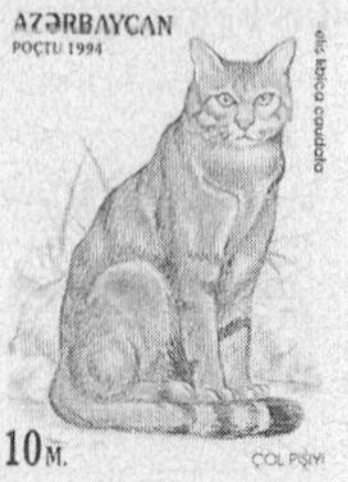

41 "Felis libica caudata"

1994. Wild Cats. Multicoloured.
195 10m. Type **41** 25 25
196 15m. Manul cat 30 30
197 20m. Lynx 45 45
198 25m. Leopard (horiz) 50 50
199 50m. Tiger (horiz) . . . . . 1·25 1·25

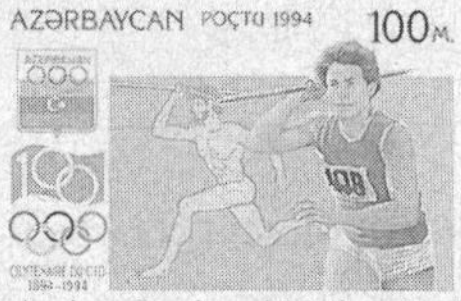

42 Ancient Greek and Modern Javelin Throwers

1994. Centenary of Int Olympic Committee. Mult.
201 100m. Type **42** 45 45
202 100m. Ancient Greek and modern discus throwers . . 45 45
203 100m. Baron Pierre de Coubertin (founder of modern games) and flame 45 45

1995. Nos. 89/92 and 101/4 surch.
204 **15** 250m. on 10q. green & blk 30 30
205 250m. on 20q. red & black 30 30
206 250m. on 50q. yell & blk 30 30
207 250m. on 1m.50 bl & blk 30 30
208 500m. on 50q. blue & blk 65 65
209 500m. on 1m. mve & blk 65 65
210 500m. on 2m.50 yellow and black 65 65
211 500m. on 5m. green & blk 65 65

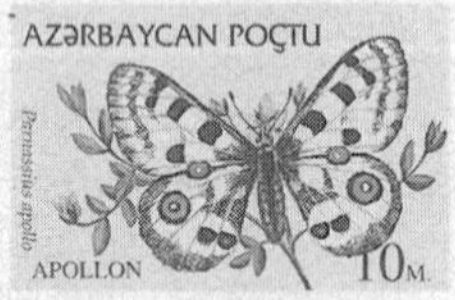

44 Apollo

1995. Butterflies. Multicoloured.
212 10m. Type **44** 20 20
213 25m. "Zegris menestho" . . . 30 30
214 50m. "Manduca atropos" . . 50 50
215 60m. "Pararge adrastoides" 70 70

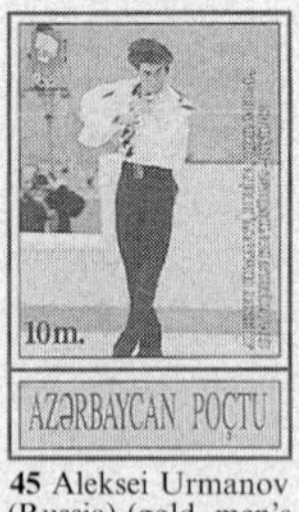

45 Aleksei Urmanov (Russia) (gold, men's figure skating)

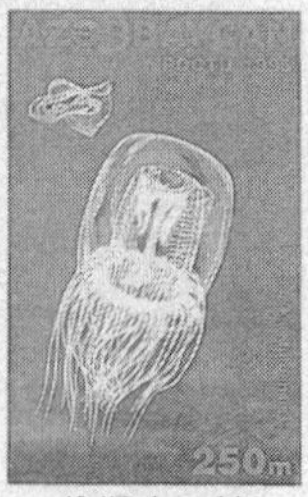

48 "Polyorchis karafutoensis"

1995. Winter Olympic Games, Lillehammer, Norway, Medal Winners. Multicoloured.
217 10m. Type **45** 10 10
218 25m. Nancy Kerrigan (U.S.A.) (silver, women's figure skating) 20 20
219 40m. Bonnie Blair (U.S.A.) (gold, women's 500m. speed skating) (horiz) . . . 25 25
220 50m. Takanori Kano (Japan) (gold, men's ski jumping) (horiz) 30 30
221 80m. Philip Laros (Canada) (silver, men's freestyle skiing) 50 50
222 100m. German team (gold, three-man bobsleigh) . . . 70 70

1995. Nos. 165/7 surch.
225 **34** 100m. on 5m. red & black 10 10
226 250m. on 10m. grn & blk 25 25
227 500m. on 20m. blue & blk 45 45

1995. Marine Animals. Multicoloured.
228 50m. "Loligo vulgaris" (horiz) 10 10
229 100m. "Orchistoma pileus" (horiz) 25 25
230 150m. "Pegea confoederata" (horiz) 40 40
231 250m. Type **48** 70 70
232 300m. "Agalma okeni" . . . 85 85

49 Matamata Turtle

1995. Tortoises and Turtles. Multicoloured.
234 50m. Type **49** 10 10
235 100m. Loggerhead turtle . . . 25 25
236 150m. Leopard tortoise . . . 40 40
237 250m. Indian star tortoise . . 70 70
238 300m. Hermann's tortoise . . 85 85

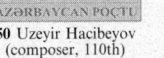

50 Uzeyir Hacibeyov (composer, 110th)

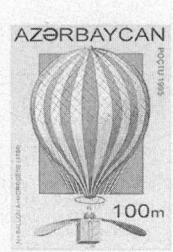

53 Charles's Hydrogen Balloon, 1783

1995. Birth Anniversaries.
240 **50** 250m. silver and black . . 40 40
241 – 400m. gold and black . . . 75 75
DESIGN: 400m. Vakhid (poet, centenary).

1995. Nos. 84/88 surch.
242 200m. on 2m.50 on 15k. mult 25 25
243 400m. on 25q. on 15k. mult 50 50
244 600m. on 35q. on 15k. mult 85 85
245 800m. on 50q. on 15k. mult 1·10 1·10
246 1000m. on 1m.50 on 15k.
mult . . . . 1·40 1·40

1995. Nos. 168/9 surch.
247 **34** 400m. on 25m. yell & blk 25 25
248 900m. on 40m. brn & blk 60 60

1995. History of Airships. Multicoloured.
249 100m. Type **53** 10 10
250 150m. Tissandier Brothers'
electrically-powered airship,
1883 . . . . 25 25
251 250m. J.-B. Meusnier's
elliptical balloon design,
1784 (horiz) 40 40
252 300m. Baldwin's dirigible
airship, 1904 (horiz) . . . 50 50
253 400m. U.S. Navy dirigible
airship, 1917 (horiz) . . . 60 60
254 500m. Pedal-powered airship,
1909 (horiz) 70 70
No. 249 is wrongly dated.

54 "Gymnopilus spectabilis"

1995. Fungi. Multicoloured.
256 100m. Type **54** 25 25
257 250m. Fly agaric 65 65
258 300m. Parasol mushroom . . 70 70
259 400m. "Hygrophorus
spectosus" . . . . . . 1·00 1·00
The 250m. is wrongly inscr "agaris".

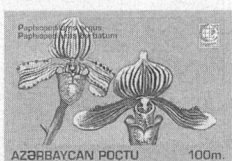

55 "Paphiopedilum argus" and "Paphiopedilum barbatum"

1995. "Singapore '95" International Stamp Exhibition. Orchids. Multicoloured.
261 100m. Type **55** 25 25
262 250m. "Maxillaria picta" . . 65 65
263 300m. "Laeliocattleya" . . 70 70
264 400m. "Dendrobium nobile" 1·00 1·00

56 Pres. Aliev and U.N. Secretary-General Boutros Boutros Ghali

1995. 50th Anniv of U.N.O.
266 **56** 250m. multicoloured . . 1·25 1·25

57 Players   **58** Eagle

1995. World Cup Football Championship, France (1998). Multicoloured.
267 100m. Type **57** 20 20
268 150m. Dribbling 40 40
269 250m. Tackling 60 60
270 300m. Preparing to kick ball 65 65
271 400m. Contesting for ball 90 90

1995. Air.
273 **58** 2200m. multicoloured . . 1·50 1·50

59 Persian   **60** Horse

1995. Cats. Multicoloured
274 100m. Type **59** 10 10
275 150m. Chartreux 25 25
276 250m. Somali 30 30
277 300m. Longhair Scottish fold 45 45
278 400m. Cymric 50 50
279 500m. Turkish angora . . . 70 70

1995. Flora and Fauna. Multicoloured.
281 100m. Type **60** 10 10
282 200m. Grape hyacinths (vert) 20 20
283 250m. Beluga 25 25
284 300m. Golden eagle 30 30
285 400m. Tiger 30 30
286 500m. Georgian black grouse
nesting 50 50
287 1000m. Georgian black
grouse in meadow . . 1·00 1·00

61 Lennon and Signature

1995. 15th Death Anniv of John Lennon (entertainer).
288 **61** 500m. multicoloured . . . 55 55

62 Early Steam Locomotive, U.S.A.

1996. Railway Locomotives. Multicoloured.
289 100m. Type **62** 40 40
290 100m. New York Central
Class J3 locomotive . . . 40 40
291 100m. Steam locomotive on
bridge 40 40
292 100m. Steam locomotive
No. 1959, Germany . . . 40 40
293 100m. Steam locomotive
No. 4113, Germany . . . 40 40
294 100m. Steam locomotive,
Italy 40 40
295 100m. Class 59 steam
locomotive, Japan . . . 40 40
296 100m. Class QJ steam
locomotive, China . . . 40 40
297 100m. Class Sn 23 steam
locomotive, China . . . 40 40

63 Operating Theatre and Topcubasov

1996. Birth Centenary of M. Topcubasov (surgeon).
299 **63** 300m. multicoloured . . . 65 65

64 Feast and Woman wearing Traditional Costume

1996. New Year.
300 **64** 250m. multicoloured . . . 65 65

65 Carl Lewis (athletics, Los Angeles, 1984)

1996. Olympic Games, Atlanta. Previous Gold Medallists. Multicoloured.
301 50m. Type **65** (wrongly inscr
"1994") 10 10
302 100m. Mohammed Ali
(Cassius Clay) (boxing,
Rome, 1960) 20 20
303 150m. Li Ning (gymnastics,
Los Angeles, 1984) 40 40
304 200m. Said Aouita (5000m,
Los Angeles, 1984) . . . 50 50
305 250m. Olga Korbut
(gymnastics, Munich, 1972) 65 65
306 300m. Nadia Comaneci
(gymnastics, Montreal,
1976) 85 85
307 400m. Greg Louganis (diving,
Los Angeles, 1984) . . . 1·00 1·00

66 "Maral-Gol"

1996. 5th Death Anniv of G. Aliev (painter). Mult.
309 100m. "Reka Cura" 50 50
310 200m. Type **66** . . . . . . 1·00 1·00

67 Behbudov and Globe

1996. 7th Death Anniv of Resid Behbudov (singer).
311 **67** 100m. multicoloured . . . 65 65

68 Mammadaliev and Flasks   **69** National Flag and Government Building

1996. 1st Death Anniv of Yusif Mammadaliev (scientist).
312 **68** 100m. multicoloured . . . 65 65

1996. 5th Anniv of Republic.
313 **69** 250m. multicoloured . . . 65 65

70 Dome of the Rock

1996. 3000th Anniv of Jerusalem. Multicoloured.
314 100m. Praying at the Wailing
Wall 40 40
315 250m. Interior of church . . . 1·00 1·00
316 300m. Type **70** . . . . . . 1·10 1·10

71 German Shepherd

1996. Dogs. Multicoloured.
318 50m. Type **71** 10 10
319 100m. Basset hounds 25 25
320 150m. Collies 35 35
321 200m. Bull terriers 50 50
322 300m. Boxers 70 70
323 400m. Cocker spaniels . . . 1·10 1·10

72 Shaft-tailed Whydah   **73** "Burgundy"

1996. Birds. Multicoloured.
325 50m. Type **72** 10 10
326 100m. Blue-naped mousebird 25 25
327 150m. Asian black-headed
oriole 35 35
328 200m. Golden oriole 50 50
329 300m. Common starling . . . 70 70
330 400m. Yellow-fronted canary 1·00 1·00

1996. Roses. Multicoloured.
332 50m. Type **73** 10 10
333 100m. "Virgo" 20 20
334 150m. "Rose Gaujard" . . . 30 30
335 200m. "Luna" 45 45
336 300m. "Lady Rose" 70 70
337 400m. "Landora" . . . . 1·00 1·00

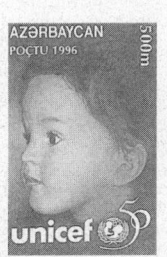

74 Child   **75** Spain v. Bulgaria

1996. 50th Anniv of U.N.I.C.E.F.
339 **74** 500m. multicoloured . . . 1·00 1·00

1996. European Football Championship, England. Multicoloured.
340 100m. Type **75** 20 20
341 150m. Rumania v. France . . 30 30
342 200m. Czech Republic v.
Germany 45 45
343 250m. England v. Switzerland 55 55
344 300m. Croatia v. Turkey . . 70 70
345 400m. Italy v. Russia . . . . 1·00 1·00

76 Chinese Junk

1996. Ships. Multicoloured.
347 100m. Type **76** 25 25
348 150m. "Danmark" (Danish
full-rigged cadet ship) . . . 40 40
349 200m. "Nippon-Maru II"
(Japanese cadet ship) . . . 45 45
350 250m. "Mircea" (Rumanian
barque) 55 55
351 300m. "Kruzenshtern"
(Russian cadet barque) . . 85 85
352 400m. "Ariadne" (German
cadet schooner) . . . . . 1·10 1·10

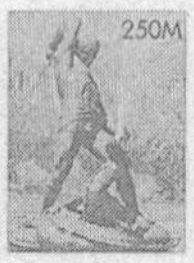

77 Baxram Gur killing Dragon (fountain by A. Shulgin at Baku)

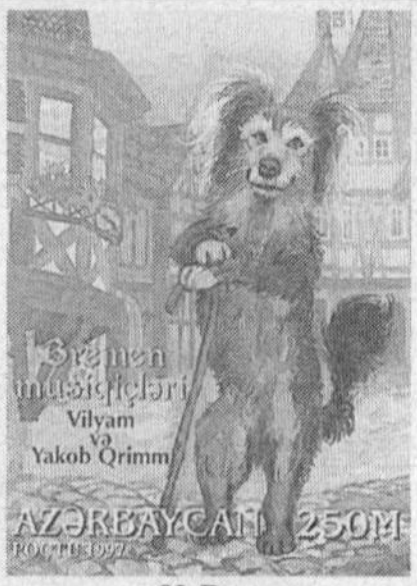

82 Dog

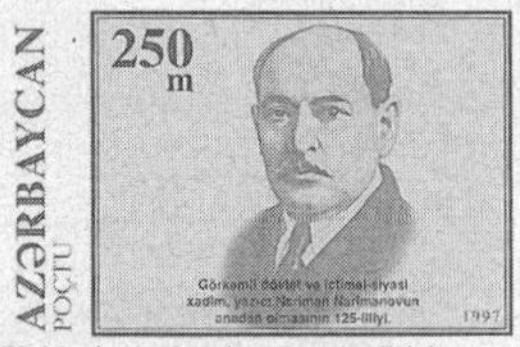

78 Nariman Narimanov (politician and writer)

1997.

354 **77** 100m. purple and black . . 55 55
356 250m. black and yellow . . 20 20
357 400m. black and red . . . 40 40
358 500m. black and green . . 45 45
359 1000m. black and blue . . 75 75

1997. Anniversaries. Multicoloured.
365 250m. Type **78** (125th birth anniv (1995)) 55 55
366 250m. Fatali Xoyskin (politician, 120th birth anniv (1995)) 55 55
367 250m. Aziz Mammed-Kerim ogli Aliyev (politician, birth centenary) 55 55
368 250m. Ilyas Afendiyev (writer, 1st death anniv) . . 55 55

1997. Red Cross. Various stamps optd **Red Cross** and cross. (a) Nos. 93/99.
370 20q. multicoloured 50 50
371 30q. multicoloured 50 50
372 50q. multicoloured 50 50
373 1m. multicoloured 75 75
374 2m.50 multicoloured 75 75
375 5m. multicoloured . . . . . 1·60 1·60
376 10m. multicoloured . . . . . 4·25 4·25

(b) Nos. 195/9.
378 10m. multicoloured 70 70
379 15m. multicoloured . . . . . 1·00 1·00
380 20m. multicoloured . . . . . 1·40 1·40
381 25m. multicoloured . . . . . 1·60 1·60
382 50m. multicoloured . . . . . 3·00 3·00

1997. 50th Anniv of Rotary Club International in Azerbaijan. Various stamps optd **50th Anniversary of the Rotary Club** and emblem. (a) Nos. 314/16.
384 100m. multicoloured 90 90
385 250m. multicoloured . . . . 3·00 3·00
386 300m. multicoloured . . . . 3·50 3·50

(b) Nos. 347/52.
388 100m. multicoloured 30 30
389 150m. multicoloured 55 55
390 200m. multicoloured 70 70
391 250m. multicoloured . . . . 1·00 1·00
392 300m. multicoloured . . . . 1·10 1·10
393 400m. multicoloured . . . . 1·40 1·40

1997. "The Town Band of Bremen" by the Brothers Grimm. Multicoloured.
395 250m. Type **82** . . . . 1·10 1·10
396 250m. Donkey and cat . . . 1·10 1·10
397 250m. Rooster . . . . 1·10 1·10
Nos. 395/7 were issued together, se-tenant, forming a composite design.

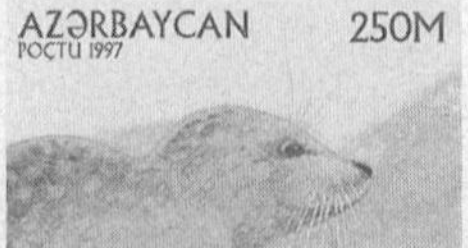

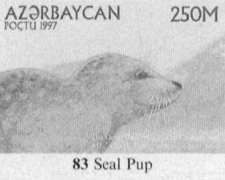

83 Seal Pup

1997. The Caspian Seal. Multicoloured.
399 250m. Type **83** 65 65
400 250m. Bull and mountain peak 65 65
401 250m. Bull and gull 65 65
402 250m. Cow (profile) 65 65
403 250m. Cow (full face) 65 65
404 250m. Young seal (three-quarter face) 65 65
Nos. 399/404 were issued together, se-tenant, forming a composite design.

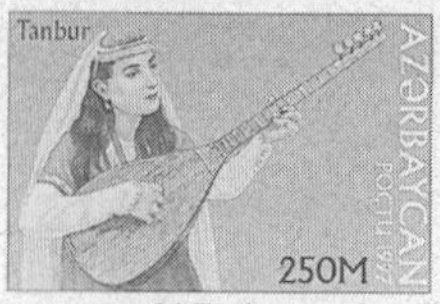

84 Tanbur

1997. Traditional Musical Instruments. Mult.
406 250m. Type **84** 50 50
407 250m. Gaval (tambourine) . . 50 50
408 500m. Jang (harp) . . . . . 1·00 1·00

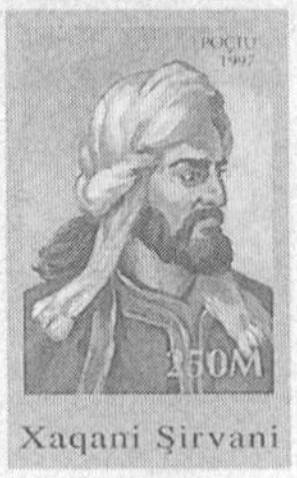

86 Sirvani

1997. 870th Birth Anniv (1996) of Xanqani Sirvani (poet).
410 **86** 250m. multicoloured . . . 90 90

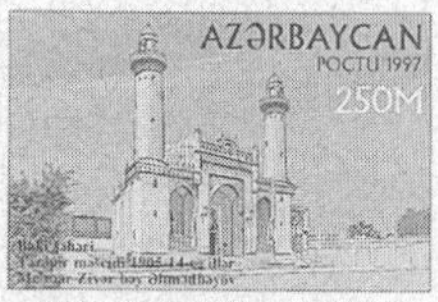

87 Taza-pir Mosque, Baku

1997. Mosques. Multicoloured.
411 250m. Type **87** 70 70
412 250m. Momuna-Xatun Mosque, Nakhichevan . . 70 70
413 250m. Govharaga Mosque, Shusha 70 70

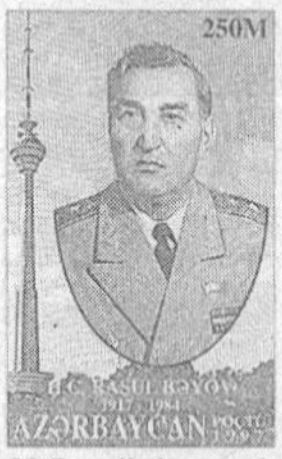

88 Rasulbekov and Baku T.V. Tower

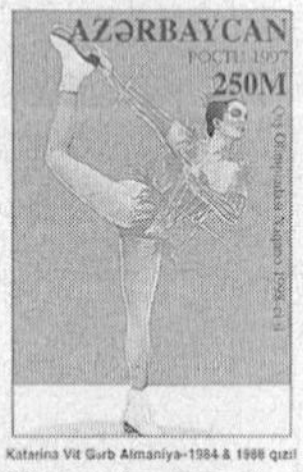

90 Katarina Wit, East Germany

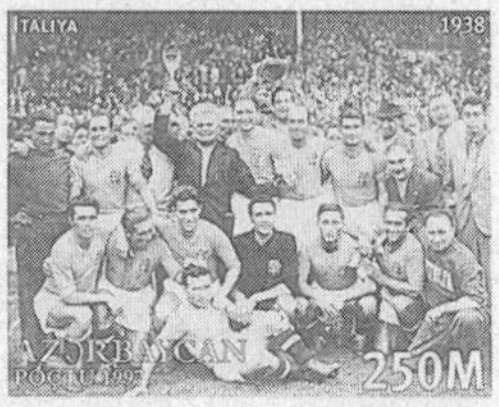

89 Italy, 1938

1997. 80th Birth Anniv of G. D. Rasulbekov (former Minister of Telecommunications).
414 **88** 250m. multicoloured . . . 65 65

1997. World Cup Football Championship, France (1998).
415 **89** 250m. black 55 55
416 – 250m. multicoloured . . . 55 55
417 – 250m. black 55 55
418 – 250m. multicoloured . . . 55 55
419 – 250m. multicoloured . . . 55 55
420 – 250m. multicoloured . . . 55 55
DESIGNS—World Champion Teams: No. 416, Argentina, 1986; 417, Uruguay, 1930 (wrongly inscr "1980"); 418, Brazil, 1994; 419, England, 1966; 420, West Germany, 1990.

1997. Winter Olympic Games, Nagano, Japan. Mult.
422 250m. Type **90** (figure skating gold medal, 1984 and 1988) 50 50
423 250m. Elvis Stoyko, Canada (figure skating silver medal, 1994) 50 50
424 250m. Midori Ito, Japan (figure skating silver medal, 1992) 50 50
425 250m. Azerbaijan flag and silhouettes of sports . . . 50 50
426 250m. Olympic torch and mountain 50 50
427 250m. Kristin Yamaguchi, U.S.A. (figure skating gold medal, 1992) 50 50
428 250m. John Curry, Great Britain (figure skating gold medal, 1976) 50 50
429 250m. Cen Lu, China (figure skating bronze medal, 1994) 50 50

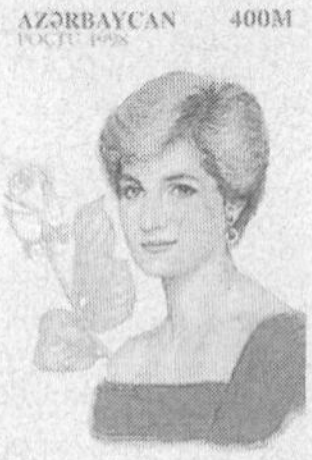

91 Diana, Princess of Wales

1998. Diana, Princess of Wales Commem. Mult.
431 400m. Type **91** 40 40
432 400m. Wearing black polo-neck jumper 40 40

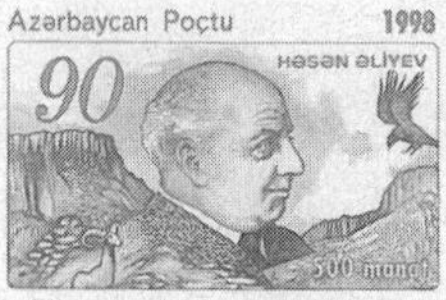

92 Aliyev and Mountain Landscape

1998. 90th Birth Anniv of Hasan Aliyev (ecologist).
433 **92** 500m. multicoloured . . . 65 65

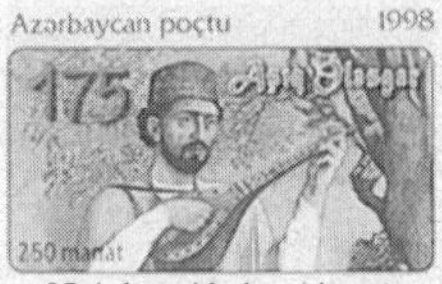

95 Ashug Alesker (singer)

1998. Birth Anniversaries. Multicoloured.
436 250m. Type **95** (175th anniv) 65 65
437 250m. Magomedhuseyn Shakhriyar (poet, 90th anniv) 65 65
438 250m. Qara Qarayev (composer, 80th anniv) . . 65 65

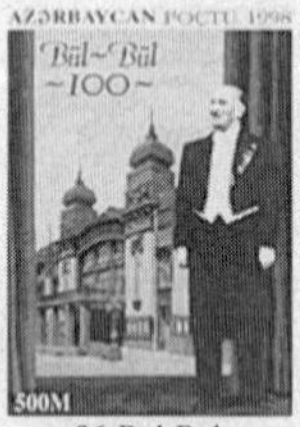

96 Bul-Bul

1998. Birth Centenary of Bul-Bul (Murtuz Meshadirza ogli Mamedov) (singer).
439 **96** 500m. multicoloured . . . 75 75

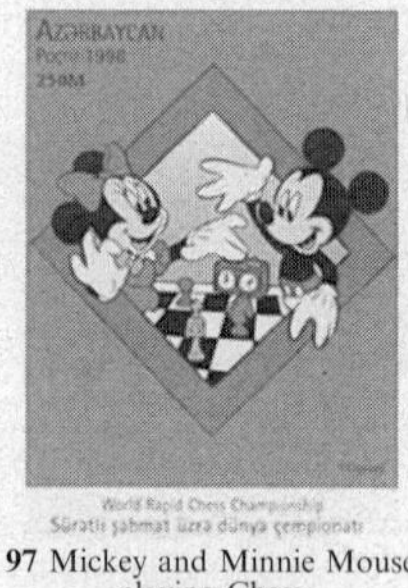

97 Mickey and Minnie Mouse playing Chess

1998. World Rapid Chess Championship, Georgia. Multicoloured.
440 250m. Type **97** 40 40
441 500m. Mickey, Minnie, pawn and rook 70 70
442 500m. Goofy, bishop and knight 70 70
443 500m. Donald Duck, king and bishop 70 70
444 500m. Pluto, rook, pawn and clockwork pawn 70 70
445 500m. Minnie and queen . . 70 70
446 500m. Daisy Duck, bishop and king 70 70
447 500m. Goofy, Donald and pawn 70 70
448 500m. Mickey, queen and rook 70 70

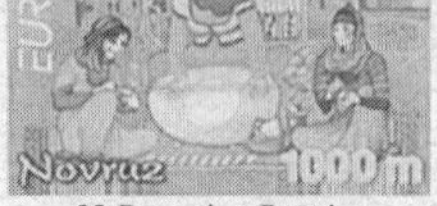

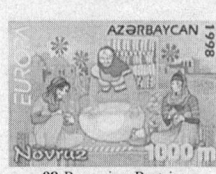

98 Preparing Pastries

1998. Europa. National Festivals: New Year. Mult.
450 1000m. Type **98** 85 85
451 3000m. Acrobat and wrestlers 2·40 2·40

1999. "iBRA" International Stamp Exhibition, Nuremberg, Germany. Nos. 450/1 optd with exhibition emblem.
452 1000m. multicoloured 90 90
453 3000m. multicoloured . . . . 2·75 2·75

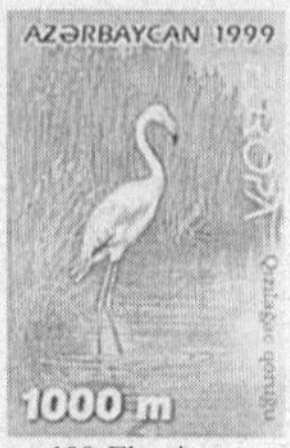

100 Flamingo, Gizilagach National Park

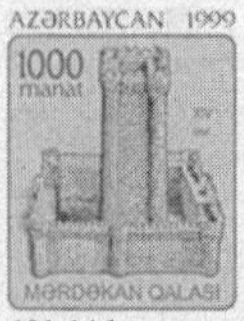

101 14th-century Square Tower

1999. Europa. Parks and Gardens. Multicoloured.
454 1000m. Type **100** 90 90
455 3000m. Stag, Girkan National Park . . . . . . 2·75 2·75

1999. Towers at Mardakyan.
456 **101** 1000m. black and blue . . 50 50
457 – 3000m. black and red . . 1·40 1·40
DESIGN: 3000m. 13th-century round tower.

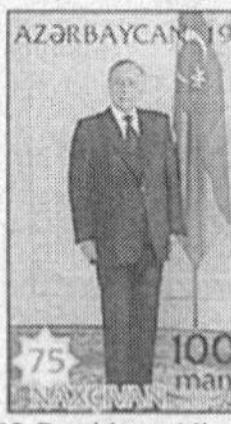

102 President Aliev and Flag

1999. 75th Anniv of Nakhichevan Autonomous Region. Multicoloured.
460 1000m. Type **102** 75 75
461 1000m. Map of Nakhichevan 75 75

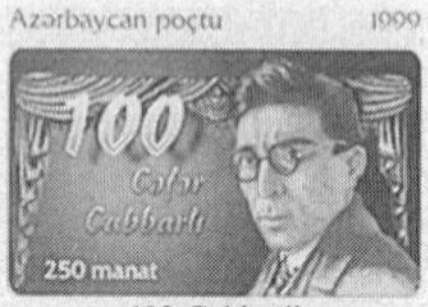

103 Cabbarli

1999. Birth Centenary of Cafar Cabbarli (dramatist).
463 **103** 250m. multicoloured . . . 1·10 1·10

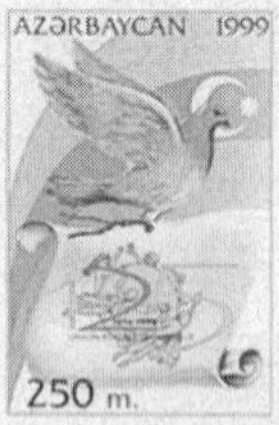

105 Flag, Pigeon and Emblem on Scroll

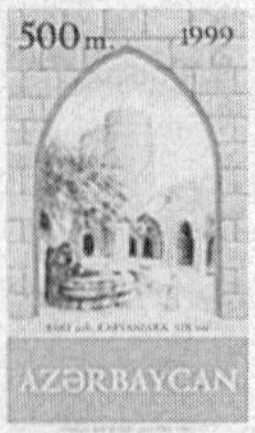

106 Caravanserai Inner Court and Maiden's Tower, Baku

1999. 125th Anniv of Universal Postal Union. Multicoloured.
465 250m. Type **105** 10 10
466 300m. Satellite, computer and emblem . . . . 2·00 2·00

1999. 19th-century Caravanserais. Multicoloured.
467 500m. Type **106** 95 95
468 500m. Camels outside caravanserai, Sheki 95 95

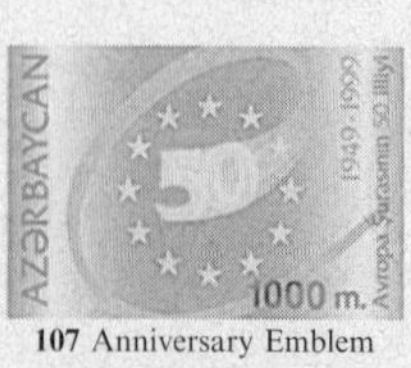

107 Anniversary Emblem

1999. 50th Anniv of Council of Europe.
469 **107** 1000m. multicoloured . . 1·00 1·00

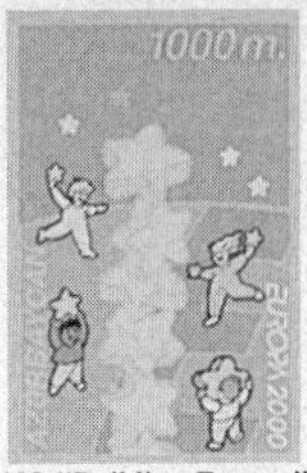
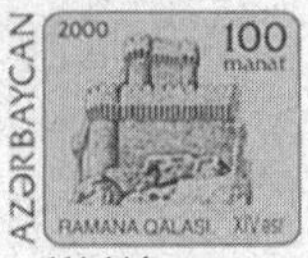
109 "Building Europe" 111 14th-century Square Tower, Ramana

2000. Europa.
471 **109** 1000m. multicoloured . . 90 90
472 3000m. multicoloured . . 2·75 2·75

2000. Towers of Mardakyan.
474 **111** 100m. black and orange 25 25
475 – 250m. black and green . . 55 55
DESIGN: 250m. 14th-century round tower, Nardaran.
See also Nos. 499/500.

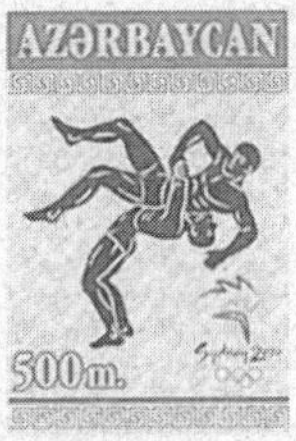
112 Wrestling

2000. Olympic Games, Sydney. Multicoloured.
476 500m. Type **112** 65 65
477 500m. Weightlifting 65 65
478 500m. Boxing 65 65
479 500m. Relay 65 65

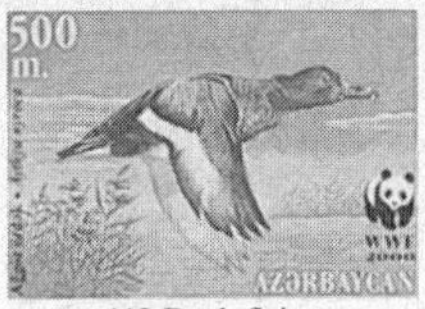
113 Duck flying

2000. The Ferruginous Duck. Multicoloured.
480 500m. Type **113** 45 45
481 500m. Ducks in water and standing on rocks 45 45
482 500m. Duck standing on rock and others swimming by grasses 45 45
483 500m. Ducks at sunset . . . 45 45

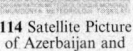

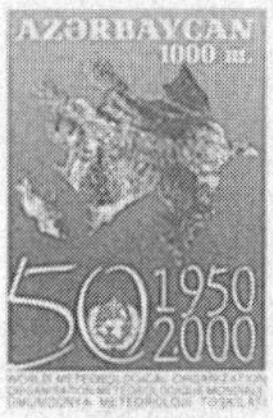
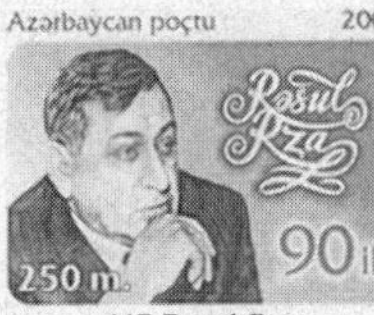
114 Satellite Picture of Azerbaijan and Emblem 117 Rasul-Rza

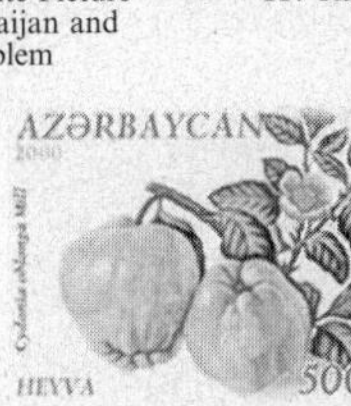
115 Quinces

2000. 50th Anniv of World Meteorological Organization.
484 **114** 1000m. multicoloured . . 65 65

2000. Fruits. Multicoloured.
485 500m. Type **115** 55 55
486 500m. Pomegranates (*Punica granatum*) 55 55
487 500m. Peaches (*Persica*) . . . 55 55
488 500m. Figs (*Ficus carica*) . . 55 55

2000. 90th Birth Anniv of Rasul-Rza (poet).
490 **117** 250m. multicoloured . . 50 50

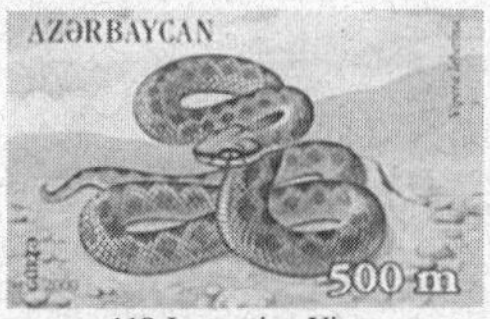
118 Levantine Viper

2000. Reptiles. Multicoloured.
491 500m. Type **118** 75 75
492 500m. Rock lizard (*Lacerta saxicola*) (wrongly inscr "Laserta saxcola") 75 75
493 500m. Ottoman viper (*Vipera xanthina*) 75 75
494 500m. Toad-headed agama (*Phrynocephalus mystaceus*) 75 75

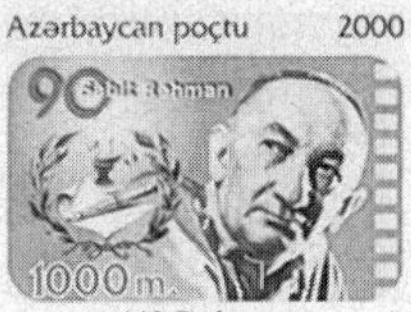
119 Rahman

2000. 90th Birth Anniv of Sabit Rahman (writer).
496 **119** 1000m. multicoloured . . 45 45

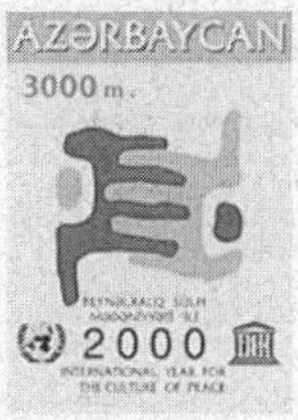
120 Emblem

2000. U.N.E.S.C.O. International Year of Culture and Peace.
497 **120** 3000m. multicoloured . . 1·40 1·40

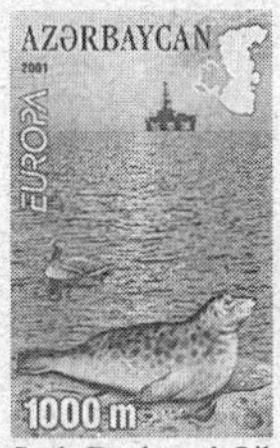
122 Seal, Duck and Oil Rig

2001. Europa. Water Resources. The Caspian Sea. Multicoloured.
499 1000m. Type **122** 55 55
500 3000m. Sturgeon, crab and oil rig . . . . 1·60 1·60

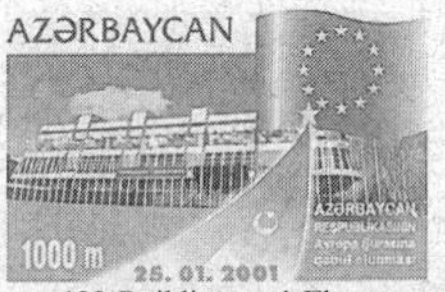
123 Building and Flags

2001. Admission of Azerbaijan to Council of Europe.
501 **123** 1000m. multicoloured . . 55 55

2001. Towers of Sheki. As T **111**
502 100m. black and lilac 10 10
503 250m. black and yellow . . . 25 25
DESIGNS: 100m. 18th-century round tower; 250m. Ruin of 12th-century tower.

AZORES — Pt. 9

A group of islands in the Atlantic Ocean.

1868. 1000 reis = 1 milreis.
1912. 100 centavos = 1 escudo.
2000. 100 cents = 1 euro.

NOTE. Except where otherwise stated, Nos. 1/393 are all stamps of Portugal optd **ACORES**.

1868. Curved value labels. Imperf.
1 **14** 5r. black £2250 £1500
2 10r. yellow £1000 £7500
3 20r. bistre £150 £130
4 50r. green £150 £130
5 80r. orange £170 £140
6 100r. purple £170 £140

1868. Curved value labels. Perf.
7 **14** 5r. black . . . . 55·00 55·00
9 10r. yellow . . . . . . 70·00 55·00
10 20r. bistre . . . . . . 55·00 50·00
11 25r. pink . . . . 55·00 8·50
12 50r. green £160 £150
13 80r. orange £160 £150
14 100r. lilac £160 £150
16 120r. blue . . . . . . £130 95·00
17 240r. lilac £475 £300

1871. Straight value labels.
38 **15** 5r. black . . . . 10·00 6·75
39 10r. yellow . . . . . . 22·00 13·00
73 10r. green . . . . . . 60·00 50·00
29 15r. brown . . . . . . 20·00 14·50
31 20r. bistre . . . . . . 22·00 20·00
109 20r. red . . . . £100 85·00
32 25r. pink . . . . 12·50 3·25
33 50r. green . . . . . . 65·00 32·00
54 50r. blue . . . . £110 65·00
101b 80r. orange . . . . . . 55·00 45·00
103 100r. mauve . . . . . . 45·00 40·00
25 120r. blue £120 £100
49 150r. blue £130 £120
104 150r. yellow . . . . . . 45·00 40·00
26 240r. lilac £650 £550
50 300r. lilac . . . . . . 65·00 45·00
94 1000r. black . . . . . . 90·00 85·00

1880.
58 **16** 5r. black . . . . 18·00 8·00
61 25r. grey . . . . 40·00 6·50
61b 25r. brown . . . . . . 40·00 6·50
60 **17** 25r. grey . . . . £100 32·00
67 **16** 50r. blue . . . . £120 29·00

1882.
136 **19** 5r. grey . . . . 10·50 4·00
125 10r. green . . . . . . 21·00 9·75
139 20r. red . . . . 22·00 13·00
126 25r. brown . . . . . . 14·50 3·00
141 25r. mauve . . . . . . 22·00 2·10
142 50r. blue . . . . 18·00 3·25
128 500r. black £120 £110
129 500r. mauve . . . . . . £100 70·00

1894. Prince Henry the Navigator.
143 **32** 5r. orange . . . . . . 2·25 2·25
144 10r. red . . . . 2·25 2·25
145 15r. brown . . . . . . 2·75 2·75
146 20r. lilac . . . . . . 3·00 3·00
147 25r. green . . . . . . 3·25 3·25
148 50r. blue . . . . . . 8·50 4·50
149 75r. red . . . . 15·00 6·50
150 80r. green . . . . . . 18·00 6·50
151 100r. brown on buff . . . 18·00 5·50
152 150r. red . . . . . . 26·00 12·50
153 300r. blue on buff . . . 28·00 20·00
154 500r. purple . . . . . . 50·00 30·00
155 1000r. black on buff . . . £100 48·00

1895. St. Anthony of Padua.
156 **35** 2½r. black . . . . . . 2·10 1·00
157 – 5r. orange . . . . . . 6·50 2·00
158 – 10r. mauve . . . . . . 6·50 3·00
159 – 15r. brown . . . . . . 10·00 4·50
160 – 20r. grey . . . . . . 10·00 6·50
161 – 25r. purple and green . . 7·00 2·10
162 **37** 50r. brown and blue . . . 22·00 10·00
163 – 75r. brown and red . . . 32·00 28·00
164 – 80r. brown and green . . 35·00 32·00
165 – 100r. black and brown . . 35·00 28·00
166 – 150r. red and brown . . . 65·00 70·00
167 – 200r. blue and brown . . 80·00 70·00
168 – 300r. black and brown . . £100 75·00
169 – 500r. brown & green . . . £140 £100
170 – 1000r. lilac and green . . £200 £150

1898. Vasco da Gama stamps as Nos. 378/385 of Portugal but inscr "ACORES".
171 2½r. green . . . . 2·25 95
172 5r. red . . . . 2·25 1·10
173 10r. purple . . . . . . 4·50 2·10
174 25r. green . . . . . . 4·50 2·10
175 50r. blue . . . . 6·75 6·50
176 75r. brown . . . . . . 14·00 10·00
177 100r. brown . . . . . . 18·00 10·00
178 150r. bistre . . . . . . 27·00 20·00

1906. "King Carlos" key-type inscr "ACORES" and optd with letters **A**, **H** and **PD** in three of the corners.
179 S 2½r. grey 30 30
180 5r. orange 30 30
181 10r. green 30 30
182 20r. lilac 45 40
183 25r. red 45 30
184 50r. blue . . . . . . 3·75 3·50
185 75r. brown on yellow . . . 1·25 90
186 100r. blue on blue . . . . 1·25 1·00
187 200r. purple on pink . . . 1·25 1·00
188 300r. blue on pink . . . . 4·25 3·50
189 500r. black on blue . . . 10·50 9·00

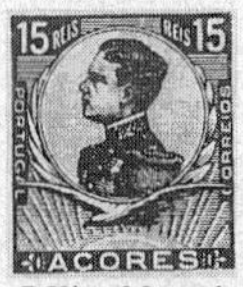
7 King Manoel

1910.
190 **7** 2½r. lilac 35 30
191 5r. black 40 35
192 10r. green 40 35
193 15r. brown 60 50
194 20r. red 85 70
195 25r. brown 40 35
196 50r. blue . . . . . . 2·00 1·00
197 75r. brown . . . . . . 2·00 1·00
198 80r. grey . . . . 2·00 2·00
199 100r. brown on green . . . 3·25 2·50
200 200r. green on pink . . . 3·25 2·50
201 300r. black on blue . . . 2·00 2·00
202 500r. brown and olive . . . 6·00 5·25
203 1000r. black and blue . . . 14·00 12·00

1910. Optd **REPUBLICA**.
204 **7** 2½r. lilac 30 25
205 5r. black 25 25
206 10r. green 30 25
207 15r. brown . . . . . . 1·25 1·00
208b 20r. red 75 75
209 25r. brown 25 25
210a 50r. blue . . . . . . 1·00 75
211 75r. brown . . . . . . 1·00 65
212 80r. grey . . . . 1·00 65
213 100r. brown on green . . . 80 60
214 200r. green on orange . . . 80 60
215 300r. black on blue . . . 2·40 1·60
216 500r. brown and green . . 2·75 2·25
217 1000r. black and blue . . . 5·75 3·75

1911. Vasco da Gama stamps of Azores optd **REPUBLICA**, some surch also.
218 2½r. green 50 40
219 15r. on 5r. red 50 40
220 25r. green 50 40
221 50r. blue . . . . 1·50 1·00
222 75r. brown . . . . . . 1·25 1·10
223 80r. on 150r. brown . . . 1·25 1·25
224 100r. brown . . . . . . 1·40 1·25
225 1000r. on 10r. purple . . . 13·00 9·50

1911. Postage Due stamps optd or surch **REPUBLICA ACORES**.
226 D **48** 5r. black 95 85
227 10r. mauve . . . . . . 2·00 85
228 20r. orange . . . . . . 3·25 2·50
229 200r. brown on buff . . . 14·50 12·50
230 300r. on 50r. grey . . . 14·50 12·50
231 500r. on 100r. red on pink . . . . 14·50 12·50

1912. "Ceres" type.
250 **56** ¼c. brown 35 30
273 ½c. black 40 20
252 1c. green 80 60
274 1c. brown 35 35
254 1½c. brown 80 60
255 1½c. green 40 40
256 2c. red 60 45
257 2c. orange 40 40
258 2½c. lilac 60 45
259 3c. red 40 40
278 3c. blue 30 30
260 3½c. green 40 40
261 4c. green 40 40
401 4c. orange 40 40
262 5c. blue 60 45
280 5c. brown 40 35
264 6c. purple 40 40
282 6c. brown 40 35
403 6c. red 25 25
265 7½c. brown . . . . . . 4·50 2·50
266 7½c. blue . . . . 1·25 1·10
267 8c. grey 60 45
283 8c. green 55 40
284 8c. orange 70 65
268 10c. brown . . . . . . 4·50 2·00
285 10c. red 80 40
286 12c. blue . . . . . . 1·75 1·25
287 12c. green 65 55
288 13½c. blue . . . . . . 1·75 1·25
249 14c. blue on yellow . . . 1·60 1·25
269 15c. purple 80 45
289 15c. black 40 35
290 16c. blue 65 60
243 20c. brown on green . . . 8·00 4·25
291 20c. brown 65 55
292 20c. green 80 65
293 20c. drab 55 40
294 24c. blue 60 35
295 25c. pink 45 40
244 30c. brown on pink . . . 45·00 35·00
245 30c. brown on yellow . . . 1·60 1·25
296 30c. brown . . . . . . 1·25 1·10
406 32c. green . . . . . . 1·75 1·25
298 36c. red 65 40
299 40c. blue 65 45
300 40c. brown . . . . . . 1·25 60
407 40c. green . . . . . . 1·00 50
408 48c. pink . . . . 2·50 2·00
246 50c. orange on orange . . 4·00 2·00
247 50c. orange on yellow . . 4·00 2·00
302 50c. yellow . . . . . . 1·25 1·00
410 50c. red . . . . 3·00 2·50
303 60c. blue . . . . 1·25 1·00
304 64c. blue . . . . 3·25 2·25
411 64c. red . . . . 3·00 2·50
305 75c. pink . . . . 3·25 2·50
412 75c. red . . . . 2·25 2·00
306 80c. purple . . . . . . 1·75 1·40
307 80c. lilac . . . . 1·75 1·25
413 80c. green . . . . . . 2·25 2·00
308 90c. blue . . . . 1·75 1·40
309 96c. red . . . . 4·75 2·25
248 1e. green on blue . . . . 4·50 3·75
310 1e. lilac . . . . 1·75 1·40
314 1e. purple . . . . . . 2·40 2·10
414 **56** 1e. red . . . . 28·00 20·00
311 1e.10 brown . . . . . . 1·90 1·40
312 1e.20 green . . . . . . 2·10 1·40
315 1e.20 buff . . . . . . 5·25 3·75
415 1e.25 blue . . . . . . 1·40 1·25
316 1e.50 purple . . . . . . 5·25 4·50
317 1e.50 lilac . . . . . . 5·25 4·50
400 1e.60 blue . . . . . . 2·50 1·10
313 2e. green . . . . 5·75 3·25
319 2e.40 green . . . . . . 48·00 32·00
320 3e. pink . . . . 55·00 32·00
321 3e.20 green . . . . . . 6·50 6·75
322 5e. green . . . . 12·00 6·75
323 10e. pink . . . . 32·00 19·00
324 20e. blue . . . . 75·00 50·00

1925. C. C. Branco Centenary.
325 **65** 2c. orange 20 20
326 3c. green 20 20
327 4c. blue 20 20
328 5c. red 20 20
329 – 10c. blue 20 20
330 – 16c. orange 25 25
331 **67** 25c. red 25 25
332 – 32c. green 40 40
333 **67** 40c. black and green . . . 40 40
334 48c. purple 85 85
335 – 50c. green 85 70
336 – 64c. brown 85 70
337 – 75c. grey 85 70
338 **67** 80c. brown 85 70
339 – 96c. red . . . . 1·00 85
340 – 1e.50 blue on blue . . . 1·00 85
341 **67** 1e.60 blue . . . . 1·10 1·00
342 – 2e. green on green . . . 1·60 1·50

343	– 2e.40 red on orange . . .	2·25	1·60
344	– 3e.20 black on green . . .	3·00	3·00

1926. 1st Independence Issue.

345	**76** 2c. black and orange . . .	30	30
346	– 3c. black and blue . . .	30	30
347	**76** 4c. black and green . . .	30	30
348	– 5c. black and brown . . .	30	30
349	**76** 6c. black and orange . . .	30	30
350	– 15c. black and green . . .	55	55
351	**77** 20c. black and violet . . .	55	55
352	– 25c. black and red . . .	55	55
353	**77** 32c. black and green . . .	55	55
354	– 40c. black and brown . . .	55	55
355	– 50c. black and olive . . .	1·10	1·10
356	– 75c. black and red . . .	1·10	1·10
357	– 1e. black and violet . . .	1·40	1·40
358	– 4e.50 black and green . . .	4·75	4·75

1927. 2nd Independence Issue.

359	**80** 2c. black and brown . . .	25	25
360	– 3c. black and blue . . .	25	25
361	**80** 4c. black and orange . . .	25	25
362	– 5c. black and brown . . .	25	25
363	– 6c. black and brown . . .	25	25
364	– 15c. black and brown . . .	25	25
365	**80** 25c. black and grey . . .	90	90
366	– 32c. black and green . . .	90	90
367	– 40c. black and green . . .	55	55
368	– 96c. black and red . . .	2·25	2·25
369	– 1e.60 black and blue . . .	2·25	2·25
370	– 4e.50 black and yellow . . .	5·00	5·00

1928. 3rd Independence Issue.

371	– 2c. black and blue . . .	25	25
372	**84** 3c. black and green . . .	25	25
373	– 4c. black and red . . .	25	25
374	– 5c. black and olive . . .	25	25
375	– 6c. black and brown . . .	25	25
376	**84** 15c. black and grey . . .	45	45
377	– 16c. black and purple . . .	55	55
378	– 25c. black and blue . . .	55	55
379	– 32c. black and green . . .	55	55
380	– 40c. black and brown . . .	55	55
381	– 50c. black and red . . .	1·10	1·10
382	**84** 80c. black and grey . . .	1·10	1·10
383	– 96c. black and red . . .	2·10	2·10
384	– 1e. black and mauve . . .	2·10	2·10
385	– 1e.60 black and blue . . .	2·10	2·10
386	– 4e.50 black and yellow . . .	5·00	5·00

1929. "Ceres" type surch **ACORES** and new value.

387	**56** 4c. on 25c. pink . . .	55	55
388	– 4c. on 60c. blue . . .	1·00	1·00
389	– 10c. on 25c. pink . . .	90	90
390	– 12c. on 25c. pink . . .	90	90
391	– 15c. on 25c. pink . . .	90	90
392	– 20c. on 25c. pink . . .	1·60	1·60
393	– 40c. on 1e.10 brown . . .	3·00	3·00

14 10r. Stamp of 1868

1980. 112th Anniv of First Azores Stamps.

416	**14** 6e.50 black, yellow & red	20	10
417	– 19e.50 blk, purple & blue	80	50

DESIGN: 19e.50, 100r. stamp of 1868.

15 Map of the Azores

1980. World Tourism Conference, Manila, Philippines. Multicoloured.

419	50c. Type **15**	10	10
420	1e. Church	10	10
421	5e. Windmill	40	10
422	6e.50 Traditional costume . .	45	10
423	8e. Coastal scene . . .	70	25
424	30e. Coastal village . . .	1·50	55

16 St. Peter's Cavalcade, Sao Miguel Island

1981. Europa. Folklore.

425	**16** 22e. multicoloured . . .	1·10	60

17 Bulls attacking Spanish Soldiers

1981. 400th Anniv of Battle of Salga. Mult.

427	8e.50 Type **17**	40	10
428	33e.50 Friar Don Pedro leading attack	1·60	70

18 "Myosotis azorica"

1981. Regional Flowers. Multicoloured.

429	4e. Type **18**	10	10
430	7e. "Tolpis azorica"	25	10
431	8e.50 "Ranunculus azoricus"	25	10
432	10e. "Lactuca watsoniana"	45	10
433	12e.50 "Hypericum foliosum"	20	10
434	20e. "Platanthera micranta"	60	35
435	27e. "Vicia dennesiana" . . .	1·10	60
436	30e. "Rubus hochstetterorum"	65	25
437	33e.50 "Azorina vidalii" . . .	1·10	65
438	37e.50 "Vaccinium cylindraceum" . . .	90	55
439	50e. "Laurus azorica" . . .	1·40	65
440	100e. "Juniperus brevifolia"	1·90	70

19 Embarkation of the Heroes of Mindelo

20 Chapel of the Holy Ghost

1982. Europa. Multicoloured.

445	**19** 33e.50 multicoloured . . .	1·60	65

1982. Regional Architecture. Multicoloured.

447	27e. Type **20**	1·10	55
448	33e.50 Chapel of the Holy Ghost (different) . . .	1·50	75

21 Geothermal Power Station, Pico Vermelho, Sao Miguel

1983. Europa.

449	**21** 37e.50 multicoloured . . .	1·25	50

22 Flag of Azores

1983. Flag.

451	**22** 12e.50 multicoloured . . .	65	10

23 Two "Holy Ghost" Jesters, Sao Miguel

1984. Traditional Costumes. Multicoloured.

452	16e. Type **23**	45	10
453	51e. Two women wearing Terceira cloak . . .	1·60	1·00

23a Bridge

1984. Europa.

454	**23a** 51e. multicoloured	1·75	95

24 "Megabombus ruderatus"

1984. Insects (1st series). Multicoloured.

456	16e. Type **24**	25	10
457	35e. Large white (butterfly)	85	50
458	40e. "Chrysomela banksi" (leaf beetle)	1·10	50
459	51e. "Phlogophora interrupta" (moth)	1·50	70

1985. Insects (2nd series). As T **24**. Multicoloured.

460	20e. "Polyspilla polyspilla" (leaf beetle) . . .	30	10
461	40e. "Sphaerophoria nigra" (hover fly) . . .	85	35
462	46e. Clouded yellow (butterfly) . . .	1·25	55
463	60e. Southern grayling (butterfly) . . .	1·40	65

25 Drummer

26 Jeque

1985. Europa. Music Year.

464	**25** 60e. multicoloured	1·75	75

1985. Traditional Boats. Multicoloured.

466	40e. Type **26**	1·10	70
467	60e. Bote	1·75	70

27 Northern Bullfinch

28 Alto das Covas Fountain, Terceira

1986. Europa.

468	**27** 68e.50 multicoloured . . .	1·90	80

1986. Regional Architecture. Drinking Fountains. Multicoloured.

470	22e.50 Type **28**	50	10
471	52e.50 Faja de Baixo, Sao Miguel . . .	1·40	65
472	68e.50 Portoes de S. Pedro, Terceira . . .	2·00	85
473	100e. Agua d'Alto, Sao Miguel . . .	2·75	95

29 Ox Cart, Santa Maria

1986. Traditional Carts. Multicoloured.

474	25e. Type **29**	45	10
475	75e. Ram cart, Sao Miguel	2·00	1·00

30 Regional Assembly Building (Correia Fernandes and Luis Miranda)

1987. Europa. Architecture.

476	**30** 74e.50 multicoloured . . .	1·75	85

31 Santa Cruz, Graciosa

1987. Windows and Balconies. Multicoloured.

478	51e. Type **31**	1·25	65
479	74e.50 Ribeira Grande, Sao Miguel	1·60	65

32 A. C. Read's Curtiss NC-4 Flying Boat, 1919

1987. Historic Airplane Landings in the Azores. Multicoloured.

480	25e. Type **32**	40	10
481	57e. E. F. Christiansen's Dornier Do-X flying boat, 1932 . . .	1·40	85
482	74e.50 Italo Balbo's Savoia Marchetti S-55X flying boat, 1933 . . .	2·00	75
483	125e. Charles Lindbergh's Lockheed 8 Sirius seaplane "Tingmissartoq", 1933 . . .	2·40	1·10

33 19th-century Mule-drawn Omnibus

1988. Europa. Transport and Communications.

484	**33** 80e. multicoloured	1·75	70

34 Wood Pigeon

1988. Nature Protection. Birds (1st series). Mult.

486	27e. Type **34**	45	10
487	60e. Eurasian woodcock . . .	1·25	65
488	80e. Roseate tern . . .	1·50	75
489	100e. Common buzzard . . .	2·00	70

See also Nos. 492/5 and 500/3.

35 Azores Arms

1988. Coats-of-arms. Multicoloured.

490	55e. Type **35**	1·25	60
491	80e. Bettencourt family arms	1·50	70

1989. Nature Protection (2nd series). Goldcrest. As T **34**. Multicoloured.

492	30e. Goldcrest perched on branch . . .	65	15
493	30e. Pair	65	15
494	30e. Goldcrest on nest . . .	65	15
495	30e. Goldcrest with outspread wings . . .	65	15

36 Boy in Boat

1989. Europa. Children's Games and Toys.

496	**36** 80e. multicoloured	1·60	75

37 Pioneers

1989. 550th Anniv of Portuguese Settlement in Azores. Multicoloured.

498	29e. Type **37**	40	10
499	87e. Settler breaking land	1·75	85

1990. Nature Protection (3rd series). Northern Bullfinch. As T **34**. Multicoloured.

500	32e. Two bullfinches	80	20
501	32e. Bullfinch on branch	80	20
502	32e. Bullfinch landing on twig	80	20
503	32e. Bullfinch on nest	80	20

38 Vasco da Gama P.O.

1990. Europa. P.O. Buildings.

504	**38** 80e. multicoloured	1·25	65

39 Cart Maker

1990. Traditional Occupations. Multicoloured.

506	5e. Type **39**	10	10
507	10e. Viol maker	10	10
508	32e. Potter	40	15
509	35e. Making roof tiles	35	10
510	38e. Carpenter	35	15
511	60e. Tinsmith	1·10	55
512	65e. Laying pavement mosaics	90	50
513	70e. Quarrying	1·00	55
514	85e. Basket maker	1·00	50
515	100e. Cooper	1·60	80
516	110e. Shaping stones	1·40	60
517	120e. Boat builders	1·25	65

40 "Hermes" Spaceplane

1991. Europa. Europe in Space.

520	**40** 80e. multicoloured	1·25	70

41 "Helena" (schooner)

1991. Inter-island Transport. Multicoloured.

522	35e. Type **41**	35	10
523	60e. Beech Model 18 airplane, 1947	75	35
524	80e. "Cruzeiro do Canal" (ferry), 1987	1·10	65
525	110e. British Aerospace ATP airliner, 1991	1·40	65

42 "Santa Maria" off Azores

1992. Europa. 500th Anniv of Discovery of America by Columbus.

526	**42** 85e. multicoloured	90	50

43 "Insulano" (steamer, 1868)

1992. The Empresa Insulana de Navegacao Shipping Fleet. Multicoloured.

527	38e. Type **43**	35	15
528	65e. "Carvalho Araujo" (ferry, 1930)	75	35
529	85e. "Funchal" (ferry, 1961)	95	50
530	120e. "Terceirense" (freighter, 1948)	1·25	65

44 Ox-mill

1993. Traditional Grinders. Multicoloured.

531	42e. Type **44**	40	15
532	130e. Hand-mill	1·50	75

45 "Two Sirens at the Entrance of a Grotto" (Antonio Dacosta)   **46** Main Entrance, Praia da Vitoria Church, Terceira

1993. Europa. Contemporary Art.

533	**45** 90e. multicoloured	1·25	55

1993. Doorways. Multicoloured.

535	42e. Type **46**	35	15
536	70e. South door, Praia da Vitoria Church	70	35
537	90e. Main door, Ponta Delgada Church, Sao Miguel	95	50
538	130e. South door, Ponta Delgada Church	1·25	55

47 Floral Decoration, Our Lady of Sorrows, Caloura, Sao Miguel

1994. Tiles. Multicoloured.

539	40e. Type **47**	35	15
540	70e. Decoration of crosses, Our Lady of Sorrows, Caloura, Sao Miguel	65	35
541	100e. "Adoration of the Wise Men", Our Lady of Hope Monastery, Ponta Delgada, Sao Miguel	95	50
542	150e. "St. Bras" (altar frontal), Our Lady of Anjos, Santa Maria	1·40	70

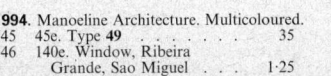

48 Monkey and Explorer with Model Caravel   **49** Doorway, St. Barbaras Church, Cedros, Faial

1994. Europa. Discoveries. Multicoloured.

543	**48** 100e. multicoloured	90	50

1994. Manoeline Architecture. Multicoloured.

545	45e. Type **49**	35	15
546	140e. Window, Ribeira Grande, Sao Miguel	1·25	65

50 Aristides Moreira da Motta

1995. Centenary of Decree decentralizing Government of the Azores and Madeira Islands. Pro-autonomy activists. Multicoloured.

547	42e. Type **50**	35	15
548	130e. Gil Mont' Alverne de Sequeira	1·10	60

51 Santana Palace, Ponta Delgada

1995. Architecture of Sao Miguel. Multicoloured.

549	45e. Type **51**	35	15
550	80e. Chapel of Our Lady of the Victories, Furnas	65	30
551	95e. Hospital, Ponta Delgada	80	35
552	135e. Ernesto do Canto's villa, Furnas	1·00	50

52 Contendas Lighthouse, Terceira (½-size illustration)

1996. Lighthouses. Multicoloured.

553	47e. Type **52**	35	15
554	78e. Molhe Lighthouse, Sao Miguel	65	40
555	98e. Arnel Lighthouse, Sao Miguel	80	40
556	140e. Santa Clara Lighthouse, Sao Miguel	1·25	55

53 Natalia Correia (poet)

1996. Europa. Famous Women.

558	**53** 98e. multicoloured	80	40

54 Bird eating Grapes (St. Peter's Church, Ponta Delgada)

1997. Gilded Wooden Altarpieces. Multicoloured.

560	49e. Type **54**	35	15
561	80e. Cherub (St. Peter of Alcantara Convent, Sao Roque)	65	30
562	100e. Cherub with wings (All Saints Church, Jesuit College, Ponta Delgada)	80	40
563	140e. Caryatid (St. Joseph's Church, Ponta Delgada)	1·10	60

55 Island of the Seven Cities

1997. Europa. Tales and Legends.

564	**55** 100e. multicoloured	85	40

56 Emperor and Empress and young Bulls (Festival of the Holy Spirit)

1998. Europa. National Festivals.

566	**56** 100e. multicoloured	75	40

57 Spotted Dolphin

1998. "Expo '98" World's Fair, Lisbon. Marine Life. Multicoloured.

568	50e. Type **57**	35	20
569	140e. Sperm whale (79 × 30 mm)	1·00	50

58 Mt. Pico Nature Reserve

1999. Europa. Parks and Gardens.

570	**58** 100e. multicoloured	75	35

59 "Emigrants" (Domingos Rebelo)

1999. Paintings. Multicoloured.

572	51e. Type **59**	35	15
573	95e. "Portrait of Vitorino Nemesio" (Antonio Dacosta) (vert)	70	35
574	100e. "Cattle loose on the Alto das Covas" (Ze van der Hagen Bretao)	70	35
575	140e. "Vila Franca Island" (Duarte Maia)	1·00	55

60 "Building Europe"

2000. Europa.

576	**60** 100e. multicoloured	70	35

61 Fishermen retrieving Mail Raft

2000. History of Mail Delivery in the Azores. Mult.

578	85e. Type **61**	50	25
579	140e. Zeppelin airship dropping mail sacks	80	40

62 Coast Line

2001. Europa. Water Resources.

580	**62** 105e. multicoloured	65	35

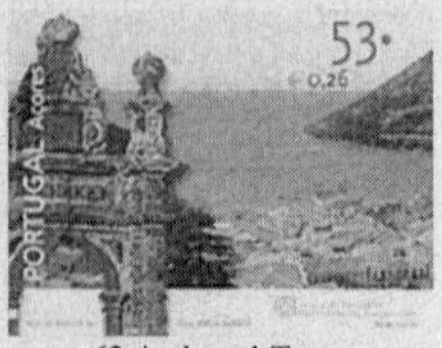

63 Arch and Town

2001. U.N.E.S.C.O. World Heritage Site, Angra do Heroismo. Multicoloured.

582		53e. Type **63**	35	15
583		85e. Monument and town	55	25
584		140e. Balcony and view over town	85	45

CHARITY TAX STAMPS

Used on certain days of the year as an additional postal tax on internal letters. The proceeds were devoted to public charities. If one was not affixed in addition to the ordinary postage, postage due stamps were used to collect the deficiency and the fine.

1911. No. 206 optd **ASSISTENCIA**.

C218a	**7**	10r. green	1·10	75

1913. No. 252 optd **ASSISTENCIA**.

C250	**56**	1c. green	3·50	2·50

1915. For the Poor. Charity stamp of Portugal optd **ACORES**.

C251	**C 58**	1c. red	45	30

1925. No. C251 surch **15 ctvs.**

C325	**C 58**	15c. on 1c. red	80	55

1925. Portuguese Army in Flanders issue of Portugal optd **ACORES**.

C345	**C 71**	10c. red	80	80
C346		10c. green	80	80
C347		10c. blue	80	80
C348		10c. brown	80	80

1925. As Marquis de Pombal issue of Portugal, inscr "ACORES".

C349	**C 73**	20c. green	80	80
C350	–	20c. green	80	80
C351	**C 75**	20c. green	80	80

NEWSPAPER STAMPS

1876. Stamps of Portugal optd **ACORES**.

N146	**N 16**	2r. black	4·00	2·10
N150b	**N 17**	2½r. green	4·00	1·25
N150a		2½r. brown	4·00	1·25

PARCEL POST STAMPS

1921. Stamps of Portugal optd **ACORES**.

P325	**P 59**	1c. brown	40	40
P326		2c. orange	40	40
P327		5c. brown	40	40
P328		10c. brown	55	40
P329		20c. blue	55	40
P330		40c. red	55	40
P331		50c. black	70	65
P332		60c. blue	70	65
P333		70c. brown	1·75	1·60
P334		80c. blue	1·75	1·60
P335		90c. violet	1·75	1·60
P336		1e. green	1·75	1·60
P337		2e. lilac	2·75	2·50
P338		3e. olive	5·00	2·50
P339		4e. blue	5·75	2·50
P340		5e. lilac	5·75	5·00
P341		10e. brown	25·00	14·50

POSTAGE DUE STAMPS

Nos. D179/351 are stamps of Portugal overprinted **ACORES**.

1904.

D179	**D 49**	5r. brown	90	80
D180		10r. orange	95	80
D181		20r. mauve	1·60	1·25
D182		30r. green	1·60	1·25
D183		40r. lilac	2·50	1·75
D184		50r. red	4·25	3·00
D185		100r. blue	5·50	4·50

1911. As last, optd **REPUBLICA**.

D218	**D 49**	5r. brown	45	45
D219		10r. orange	45	45
D220		20r. mauve	65	55
D221		30r. green	65	55
D222		40r. lilac	1·00	75
D223		50r. red	5·00	5·00
D224		100r. blue	2·00	2·00

1918. Value in centavos.

D325	**D 49**	½c. brown	50	50
D326		1c. orange	50	50
D327		2c. purple	50	50
D328		3c. green	50	50
D329		4c. lilac	50	50
D330		5c. red	50	50
D331		10c. blue	50	50

1922.

D332	**D 49**	½c. green	30	30
D333		1c. green	35	35
D334		2c. green	35	35
D335		3c. green	60	35
D336		8c. green	60	35
D337		10c. green	60	35
D338		12c. green	60	35
D339		16c. green	60	35
D340		20c. green	60	35
D341		24c. green	60	35
D342		32c. green	60	35
D343		36c. green	60	35
D344		40c. green	60	35
D345		48c. green	60	35
D346		50c. green	60	35
D347		60c. green	60	35
D348		72c. green	60	35
D349		80c. green	3·50	2·75
D350		1e.20 green	3·50	2·75

1925. Portuguese Army in Flanders.

D351	**D 72**	20c. brown	80	65

1925. As Nos. C349/51, optd **MULTA**.

D352	**D 73**	40c. green	80	80
D353	–	40c. green	80	80
D354	**D 75**	40c. green	80	80

BADEN Pt. 7

In S.W. Germany. Formerly a Grand Duchy, now part of the German Federal Republic.

60 kreuzer = 1 gulden.

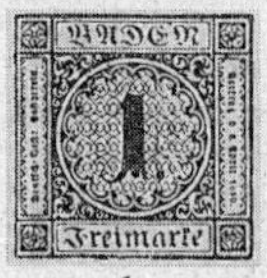

1

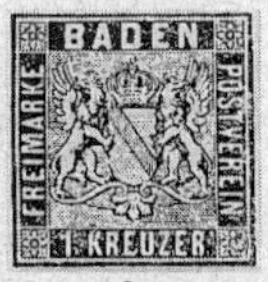

2

1851. Imperf.

1	**1**	1k. black on buff	£225	£200
8		1k. black on white	£140	20·00
3		3k. black on yellow	£110	11·50
9		3k. black on green	£130	5·50
10		3k. black on blue	£500	27·00
5		6k. black on green	£350	35·00
11		6k. black on orange	£225	17·00
6		9k. black on red	75·00	19·00

1860. Shaded background behind Arms. Perf.

13	**2**	1k. black	65·00	19·00
16		3k. blue	70·00	14·00
17		6k. orange	90·00	55·00
22		6k. blue	£100	60·00
19		9k. red	£200	£140
25		9k. brown	75·00	60·00

1862. Uncoloured background behind Arms.

27		1k. black	40·00	11·00
28		3k. red	40·00	1·25
30		6k. blue	6·50	20·00
33		9k. brown	11·50	25·00
36		18k. green	£325	£500
38		30k. orange	24·00	£1200

1868. "K R." instead of "KREUZER".

39		1k. green	3·25	4·00
41		3k. red	2·00	1·50
44		7k. blue	17·00	30·00

For issues of 1947 to 1964 see Germany: Allied Occupation (French Zone).

RURAL POSTAGE DUE STAMPS

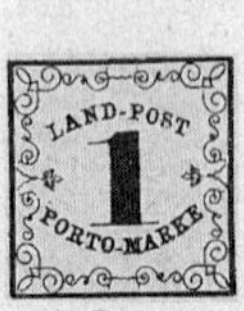

D 4

1862.

D39	**D 4**	1k. black on yellow	4·00	£250
D40		3k. black on yellow	2·00	95·00
D41		12k. black on yellow	26·00	£10000

BAGHDAD Pt. 1, Pt. 19

A city in Iraq. Special stamps issued during British occupation in the War of 1914–18.

16 annas = 1 rupee.

1917. Various issues of Turkey surch **BAGHDAD IN BRITISH OCCUPATION** and new value in annas.

A. Pictorial issues of 1913.

1	**32**	½a. on 2pa. red	£100	£120
2	**34**	½a. on 5pa. purple	75·00	80·00
3	–	½a. on 10pa. green (No. 516)	£550	£650
4	**31**	½a. on 10pa. green	£900	£1100
5	–	1a. on 20pa. red (No. 504)	£325	£350
6	–	2a. on 1pi. blue (No. 518)	£130	£160

B. As last, but optd with small star.

7	–	1a. on 20pa. red	£180	£200
8	–	2a. on 1pi. blue	£2750	£3500

C. Postal Jubilee issue.

9	**60**	½a. on 10pa. red	£350	£375
10b		1a. on 20pa. blue	£800	£950
11b		2a. on 1pi. black & violet	75·00	85·00

D. Optd with Turkish letter "B".

12	**30**	2a. on 1pi. blue	£300	£425

E. Optd with star and Arabic date within crescent.

13	**30**	½a. on 10pa. green	75·00	80·00
14		1a. on 20pa. red	£325	£350
15	**23**	1a. on 20pa. red	£375	£400
16	**21**	1a. on 20pa. red (No. N185)	£3000	£3750
17	**30**	2a. on 1pi. blue	85·00	£100
18	**21**	2a. on 1pi. blue	£140	£150

F. Optd as last, but with date between star and crescent.

19	**23**	½a. on 10pa. green	90·00	95·00
20	**60**	½a. on 10pa. red	£130	£140
21	**30**	1a. on 20pa. red	85·00	£110
22	**28**	1a. on 20pa. red	£325	£375
23	**15**	1a. on 10pa. on 20pa. red	£160	£160
24	**30**	2a. on 1pi. blue	£140	£150
25	**28**	2a. on 1pi. blue	£1200	£1400

BAHAMAS Pt. 1

A group of islands in the Br. W. Indies, S.E. of Florida. Self-Government introduced on 7 January 1964. The islands became an independent member of the British Commonwealth on 10 July 1973.

1859. 12 pence = 1 shilling;
20 shillings = 1 pound.
1966. 100 cents = 1 dollar.

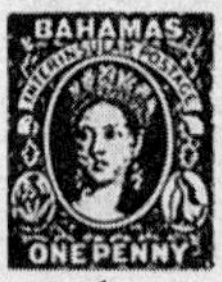

1

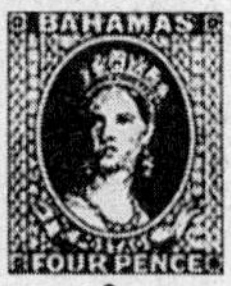

2

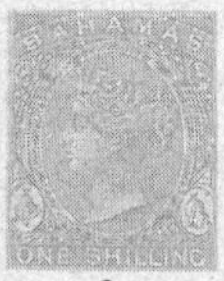

3

1859. Imperf.

2	**1**	1d. red	50·00	£1500

1860. Perf.

33	**1**	1d. red	50·00	15·00
26	**2**	4d. red	£275	60·00
31		6d. violet	£160	60·00
39b	**3**	1s. green	8·00	7·00

1883. Surch **FOURPENCE**.

45	**2**	4d. on 6d. violet	£550	£400

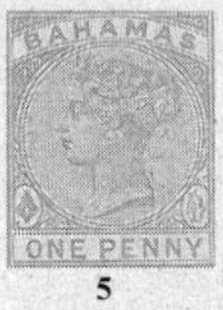

5

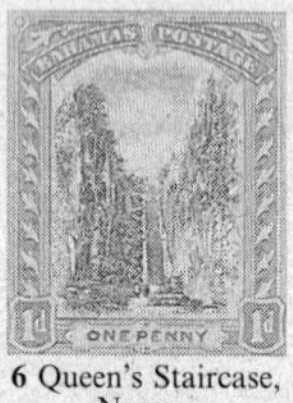

6 Queen's Staircase, Nassau

1884.

48	**5**	1d. red	7·00	2·50
52		2½d. blue	9·50	2·25
53		4d. yellow	9·50	4·00
54		6d. mauve	6·00	26·00
56		5s. green	65·00	75·00
57		£1 red	£275	£225

1901.

111	**6**	1d. black and red	80	1·25
76a		3d. purple on buff	5·50	4·50
77		3d. black and brown	2·00	2·25
59		5d. black and orange	8·50	48·00
78		5d. black and mauve	2·75	5·50
113		2s. black and blue	18·00	22·00
61		3s. black and green	35·00	60·00

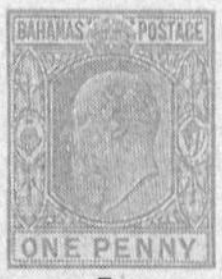

7

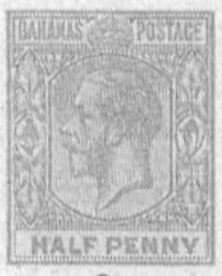

8

1902.

71	**7**	½d. green	5·00	2·75
62		1d. red	1·50	2·50
63		2½d. blue	6·50	1·25
64		4d. yellow	15·00	55·00
66		6d. brown	3·50	18·00
67		1s. black and red	20·00	48·00
69		5s. purple and blue	65·00	80·00
70		£1 green and black	£250	£325

1912.

115	**8**	½d. green	50	40
116		1d. red	1·00	15
117		1½d. red	3·25	1·00
118		2d. grey	1·25	2·75
119		2½d. blue	1·00	2·75
120		3d. purple on yellow	6·50	16·00
121		4d. yellow	1·50	5·00
122		6d. brown	70	1·25
123		1s. black and red	2·75	5·50
124		5s. purple and blue	35·00	65·00
125		£1 green and black	£160	£300

1917. Optd **1.1.17.** and Red Cross.

90	**6**	1d. black and red	40	2·00

1918. Optd **WAR TAX** in one line.

96	**8**	½d. green	1·75	1·75
97		1d. red	1·00	35
93	**6**	1d. black and red	3·50	4·00
98		3d. purple on yellow	1·00	1·50
100		3d. black and brown	45	4·00
99	**8**	1s. black and red	9·00	2·75

1919. Optd **WAR CHARITY 3.6.18.**

101	**6**	1d. black and red	30	2·50

1919. Optd **WAR TAX** in two lines.

102	**8**	½d. green	30	1·25
103		1d. red	1·50	1·50
105	**6**	3d. black and brown	75	8·00
104	**8**	1s. black and red	15·00	29·00

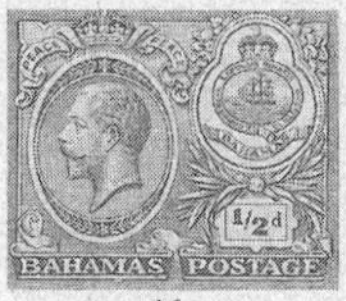

16

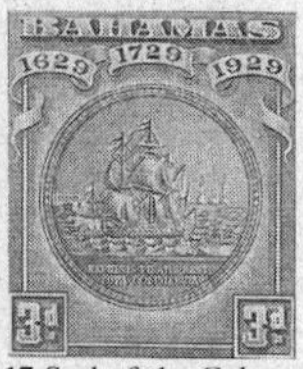

17 Seal of the Colony

1920. Peace Celebration.

106	**16**	½d. green	1·00	5·50
107		1d. red	2·75	1·00
108		2d. grey	2·75	7·50
109		3d. brown	2·75	9·00
110		1s. green	12·00	35·00

1930. Tercentenary of the Colony.

126	**17**	1d. black and red	2·00	2·75
127		3d. black and brown	4·00	15·00
128		5d. black and violet	4·00	15·00
129		2s. black and blue	18·00	45·00
130		3s. black and green	42·00	85·00

1931. As T **17**, but without dates at top.

131b		2s. black and blue	7·00	3·00
132a		3s. black and green	7·00	2·00

1935. Silver Jubilee. As T **13** of Antigua.

141		1½d. blue and red	1·00	2·75
142		2½d. brown and blue	5·00	9·00
143		6d. blue and olive	7·00	13·00
144		1s. grey and purple	7·00	9·00

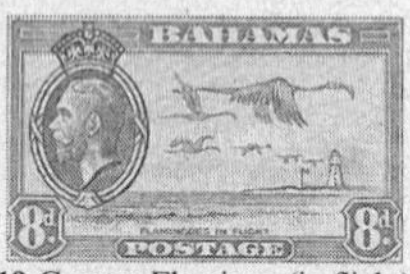

19 Greater Flamingo (in flight)

1935.

145	**19**	8d. blue and red	6·00	3·25

1937. Coronation. As T **2** of Aden.

146		½d. green	15	15
147		1½d. brown	30	75
148		2½d. blue	50	75

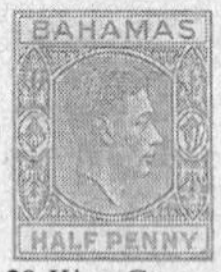

20 King George VI

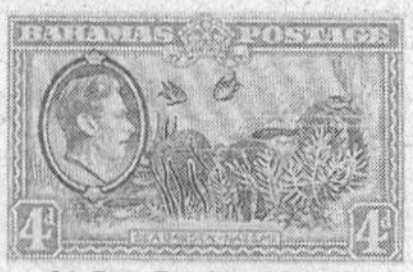

21 Sea Garden, Nassau

1938.

149	**20**	½d. green	50	1·25
149e		½d. purple	1·00	2·50
150		1d. red	8·50	4·75
150ab		1d. grey	60	70
151		1½d. brown	1·50	1·25
152		2d. grey	18·00	6·00
152b		2d. red	1·00	65
152c		2d. green	1·00	80
153		2½d. blue	3·25	2·00
153a		2½d. violet	1·25	1·25
154		3d. violet	16·00	4·25
154a		3d. blue	60	1·25
154b		3d. red	60	3·25
158	**21**	4d. blue and orange	1·00	1·00
159	–	6d. green and blue	60	1·00
160	–	8d. blue and red	6·75	2·25
154c	**20**	10d. orange	2·50	20
155c		1s. black and red	9·50	75
156b		5s. purple and blue	28·00	17·00
157a		£1 green and black	60·00	45·00

DESIGNS—As Type **21**: 6d. Fort Charlotte; 8d. Greater flamingos.

1940. Surch **3d.**

161	**20**	3d. on 2½d. blue	1·00	1·00

1942. 450th Anniv of Landing of Columbus. Optd **1492 LANDFALL OF COLUMBUS 1942**.

162	**20**	½d. green	30	60
163		1d. grey	30	60

164 1½d. brown 40 60
165 2d. red 30 65
166 2½d. blue 50 65
167 3d. blue 30 65
168 21 4d. blue and orange . . . 40 90
169 – 6d. green & blue (No. 159) . . . . . . 40 1·75
170 – 8d. blue and red (No. 160) . . . . . . 1·00 70
171 20 1s. black and red . . . . 5·50 3·50
172a 17 2s. black and blue . . . . 8·00 10·00
173 3s. black and green . . . . 5·50 6·50
174a 20 5s. purple and blue . . . 18·00 14·00
175a £1 green and black . . . 30·00 25·00

1946. Victory. As T **9** of Aden.
176 1½d. brown 10 40
177 3d. blue 10 40

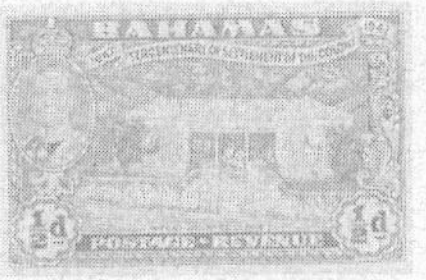

26 Infant Welfare Clinic

1948. Tercentenary of Settlement of Island of Eleuthera. Inscr as in T **26**.
178 26 ½d. orange 30 90
179 – 1d. olive 30 35
180 – 1½d. yellow 30 80
181 – 2d. red 30 40
182 – 2½d. brown 45 75
183 – 3d. blue . . . . 1·50 85
184 – 4d. black 60 70
185 – 6d. green . . . . 1·75 80
186 – 8d. violet 70 70
187 – 10d. red 60 35
188 – 1s. brown . . . . 1·00 50
189 – 2s. purple . . . . 4·00 8·50
190 – 3s. blue . . . . 8·00 8·50
191 – 5s. mauve . . . . 11·00 4·50
192 – 10s. grey . . . . 9·50 9·00
193 – £1 red . . . . 9·00 14·00
DESIGNS: 1d. Agriculture; 1½d. Sisal; 2d. Straw work; 2½d. Dairy; 3d. Fishing fleet; 4d. Island settlement; 6d. Tuna fishing; 8d. Paradise Beach; 10d. Modern hotels; 1s. Yacht racing; 2s. Water sports—skiing; 3s. Shipbuilding; 5s. Transportation; 10s. Salt production; £1 Parliament Buildings.

1948. Silver Wedding. As T **10/11** of Aden.
194 1½d. brown 20 25
195 £1 grey . . . . 32·00 32·00

1949. 75th Anniv of U.P.U. As T **20/23** of Antigua.
196 2½d. violet 35 40
197 3d. blue . . . . 2·25 2·25
198 6d. blue . . . . 55 2·25
199 1s. red 55 75

1953. Coronation. As T **13** of Aden.
200 6d. black and blue 60 50

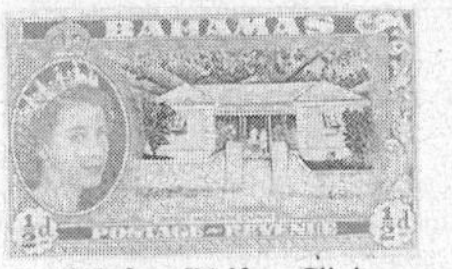

42 Infant Welfare Clinic

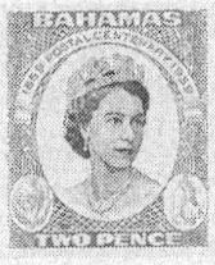

43 Queen Elizabeth II

1954. Designs as Nos. 178/93 but with portrait of Queen Elizabeth II and without commemorative inscr as in T **42**.
201 42 ½d. black and red . . . . 10 1·50
202 – 1d. olive and brown . . . 10 30
203 – 1½d. blue and black . . . 15 80
204 – 2d. brown and green . . . 15 30
205 – 3d. black and red . . . . 65 1·00
206 – 4d. turquoise and purple 30 30
207 – 5d. brown and blue . . . . 1·40 2·25
208 – 6d. blue and black . . . . 2·25 20
209 – 8d. black and lilac 70 40
210 – 10d. black and blue . . . 30 10
211 – 1s. blue and brown . . . . 1·00 10
212 – 2s. orange and black . . . 2·00 70
213 – 2s.6d. black and blue . . . 3·50 2·00
214 – 5s. green and orange . . . 18·00 75
215 – 10s. black and slate . . . . 20·00 2·50
216 – £1 black and violet . . . . 20·00 6·50
DESIGNS: 1½d. Hatchet Bay, Eleuthera; 4d. Water sports—skiing; 5d. Dairy; 6d. Transportation; 2s. Sisal; 2s.6d. Shipbuilding; 5s. Tuna fishing. Other values the same as for the corresponding values in Nos. 178/93.

1959. Centenary of 1st Bahamas Postage Stamp.
217 43 1d. black and red 35 20
218 2d. black and green . . . 35 1·00
219 6d. black and blue 45 40
220 10d. black and brown . . . 50 1·00

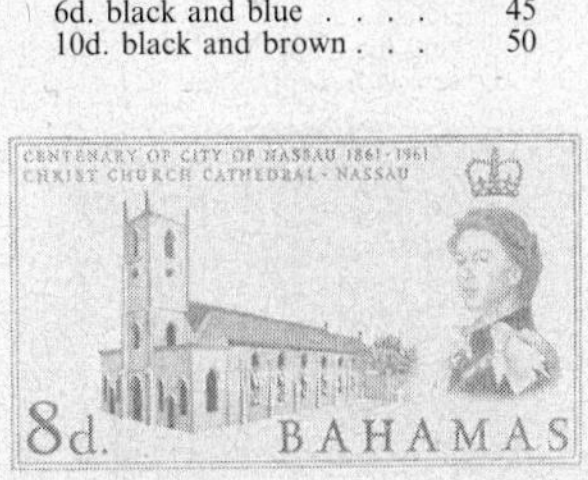

44 Christ Church Cathedral

1962. Centenary of Nassau.
221 44 8d. green 45 55
222 – 10d. violet 45 25
DESIGN: 10d. Nassau Public Library.

1963. Freedom from Hunger. As T **28** of Aden.
223 8d. sepia 40 40

1963. Bahamas Talks. Nos. 209/10 optd **BAHAMAS TALKS 1962**.
224 8d. black and lilac 40 75
225 10d. black and blue 50 75

1963. Centenary of Red Cross. As T **33** of Antigua.
226 1d. red and black 50 50
227 10d. red and blue . . . . . 1·75 2·50

1964. New Constitution. Nos. 201/16 optd **NEW CONSTITUTION 1964**.
228 42 ½d. black and red . . . . 15 1·25
229 – 1d. olive and brown . . . 15 15
230 – 1½d. blue and black . . . 70 1·25
231 – 2d. brown and green . . . 15 20
232 – 3d. black and red . . . . 1·50 1·50
233 – 4d. turquoise and purple 40 55
234 – 5d. brown and blue . . . . 40 1·50
235 – 6d. blue and black . . . . 2·25 30
236 – 8d. black and lilac 70 30
237 – 10d. black and blue . . . 30 15
238 – 1s. blue and brown . . . . 1·25 15
239 – 2s. brown and black . . . 1·50 1·75
240 – 2s.6d. black and blue . . . 3·00 2·75
241 – 5s. green and orange . . . 6·50 3·25
242 – 10s. black and slate . . . 7·00 5·50
243 – £1 black and violet . . . . 8·50 18·00

1964. 400th Birth Anniv of Shakespeare. As T **34** of Antigua.
244 6d. turquoise 20 10

1964. Olympic Games, Tokyo. No. 211 surch **8d.** and Olympic rings.
245 8d. on 1s. blue and brown . . 45 15

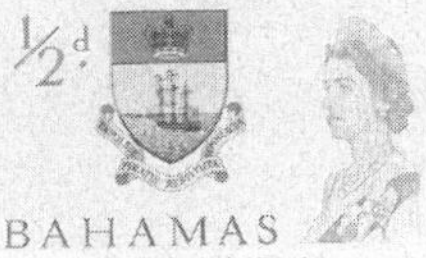

49 Colony's Badge

1965.
247 49 ½d. multicoloured . . . . 15 1·60
248 – 1d. slate, blue and orange 30 1·00
249 – 1½d. red, green and brown 15 2·00
250 – 2d. slate, green and blue 15 10
251 – 3d. red, blue and purple 2·75 20
252 – 4d. green, blue and brown 3·50 2·25
253 – 6d. green, blue and red 30 10
254 – 8d. purple, blue & bronze 50 30
255 – 10d. brown, green and violet 25 10
256a – 1s. multicoloured 30 10
257 – 2s. brown, blue and green 1·00 1·25
258 – 2s.6d. olive, blue and red 2·50 3·00
259 – 5s. brown, blue and green 2·75 1·00
260 – 10s. red, blue and brown 16·00 3·50
261 – £1 brown, blue and red 16·00 9·00
DESIGNS: 1d. Out Island regatta; 1½d. Hospital; 2d. High School; 3d. Greater flamingo; 4d. R.M.S. "Queen Elizabeth"; 6d. "Development"; 8d. Yachting; 10d. Public square; 1s. Sea garden; 2s. Old cannons at Fort Charlotte; 2s.6d. Sikorsky S-38 flying boat, 1929, and Boeing 707 airliner; 5s. Williamson film project, 1914, and undersea post office, 1939; 10s. Queen or pink conch; £1 Columbus's flagship.

1965. Centenary of I.T.U. As T **36** of Antigua.
262 1d. green and orange 15 10
263 2s. purple and olive 65 45

1965. No. 254 surch **9d.**
264 9d. on 8d. purple, blue & bronze 30 15

1965. I.C.Y. As T **37** of Antigua.
265 ½d. purple and turquoise . . 10 1·10
266 1s. green and lavender . . . 30 40

1966. Churchill Commemoration. As T **38** of Antigua.
267 ½d. blue 10 40
268 2d. green 40 30
269 10d. brown 75 85
270 1s. violet . . . . 75 1·40

1966. Royal Visit. As T **39** of Antigua but inscr "to the Caribbean" omitted.
271 6d. black and blue 90 50
272 1s. black and mauve . . . . 1·60 1·25

1966. Decimal currency. Nos. 247/61 surch.
273 49 1c. on ½d. multicoloured 10 30
274 – 2c. on 1d. slate, blue and orange 75 30
275 – 3c. on 2d. slate, green and blue 10 10
276 – 4c. on 3d. red, blue and purple . . . . 1·75 20
277 – 5c. on 4d. green, blue and brown . . . . 1·75 3·00
278 – 8c. on 6d. green, blue and red 20 20
279 – 10c. on 8d. purple, blue and bronze 30 75
280 – 11c. on 1½d. red, green and brown 15 30
281 – 12c. on 10d. brown, green and violet 15 10
282 – 15c. on 1s. multicoloured 25 10
283 – 22c. on 2s. brown, blue and green . . . . 60 1·00
284 – 50c. on 2s.6d. olive, blue and red . . . . 1·00 1·40
285 – $1 on 5s. brown, blue and green . . . . 1·75 1·50
286 – $2 on 10s. red, blue and brown . . . . 7·50 4·25
287 – $3 on £1 brown, blue and red . . . . 7·50 4·25

1966. World Cup Football Championships. As T **36** of Antigua.
288 8c. multicoloured 25 15
289 15c. multicoloured 30 25

1966. Inauguration of W.H.O. Headquarters, Geneva. As T **41** of Antigua.
290 11c. black, green and blue . . 50 90
291 15c. black, purple and ochre 50 50

1966. 20th Anniv of U.N.E.S.C.O. As T **54/6** of Antigua.
292 3c. multicoloured 10 10
293 15c. yellow, violet and olive 35 20
294 $1 black, purple and orange 1·10 2·00

1967. As Nos. 247/51, 253/9 and 261 but values in decimal currency, and new designs for 5c. and $2.
295 49 1c. multicoloured . . . . . 10 2·75
296 – 2c. slate, blue and green . . 50 60
297 – 3c. slate, green and violet 10 10
298 – 4c. red, light blue and blue 4·25 50
299 – 5c. black, blue and purple 1·00 3·00
300 – 8c. green, blue and brown 25 10
301 – 10c. purple, blue and red 30 70
302 – 11c. red, green and blue . . 25 80
303 – 12c. brown, green and olive 25 10
304 – 15c. multicoloured 55 10
305 – 22c. brown, blue and red 70 65
306 – 50c. olive, blue and green 2·00 75
307 – $1 maroon, blue and purple . . . . 2·00 60
308 – $2 multicoloured . . . . . 13·00 3·00
309 – $3 brown, blue and purple 3·75 2·00
NEW DESIGNS: 5c. "Oceanic"; $2 Conch shell (different).

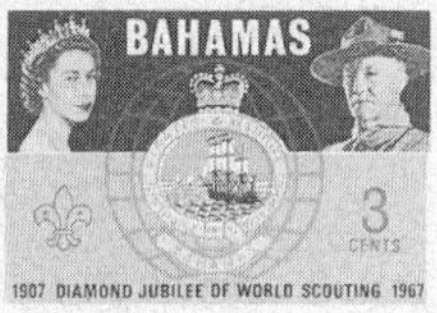

69 Bahamas Crest

1967. Diamond Jubilee of World Scouting. Mult.
310 3c. Type **69** 35 15
311 15c. Scout badge 40 15

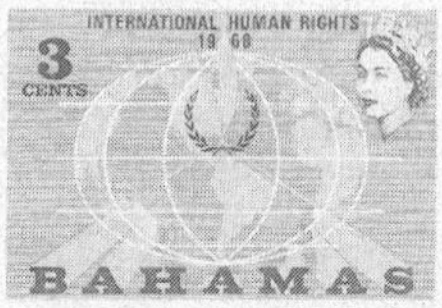

71 Globe and Emblem

1968. Human Rights Year. Multicoloured.
312 3c. Type **71** 10 10
313 12c. Scales of Justice and emblem 20 10
314 $1 Bahamas Crest and emblem 70 80

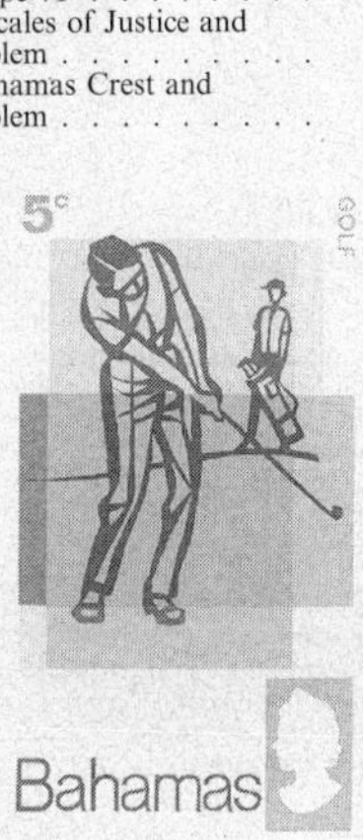

74 Golf

1968. Tourism. Multicoloured.
315 5c. Type **74** . . . . 1·75 1·75
316 11c. Yachting . . . . 1·25 40
317 15c. Horse-racing . . . . . . 1·75 45
318 50c. Water-skiing . . . . . 2·50 6·50

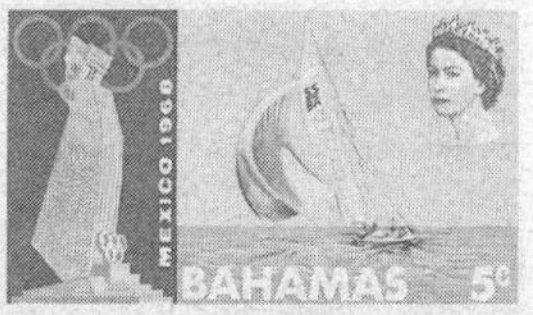

78 Racing Yacht and Olympic Monument

1968. Olympic Games, Mexico City.
319 78 5c. brown, yellow and green 40 75
320 – 11c. multicoloured 40 25
321 – 50c. multicoloured . . . . 60 1·75
322 78 $1 grey, blue and violet . . 2·00 3·75
DESIGNS: 11c. Long jumping and Olympic Monument; 50c. Running and Olympic Monument.

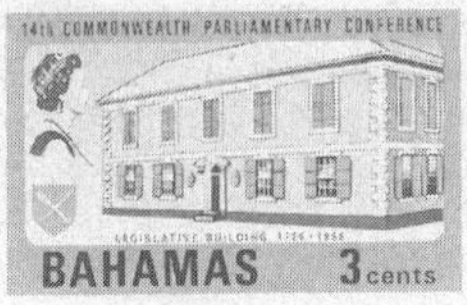

81 Legislative Building

1968. 14th Commonwealth Parliamentary Conference. Multicoloured.
323 3c. Type **81** 10 30
324 10c. Bahamas Mace and Westminster Clock Tower 15 30
325 12c. Local straw market . . . 15 25
326 15c. Horse-drawn surrey . . 20 35
Nos. 324/5 are vert.

85 Obverse and reverse of $100 Gold Coin

1968. Gold Coins commemorating the first General Election under the New Constitution.
327 85 3c. red on gold 40 40
328 – 12c. green on gold 60 50
329 – 15c. purple on gold 70 60
330 – $1 black on gold . . . . . 1·75 3·25
OBVERSE AND REVERSE OF: 12c. $50 gold coin; 15c. $20 gold coins; $1, $10 gold coin.

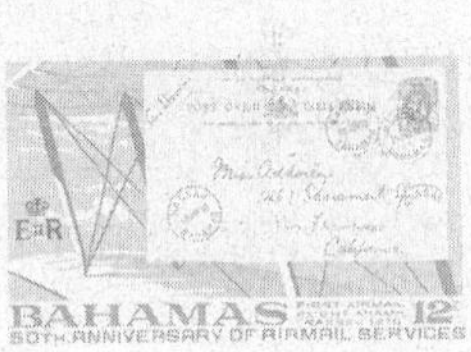

89 First Flight Postcard of 1919

1969. 50th Anniv of Bahamas Airmail Services.
331 89 12c. multicoloured 50 50
332 – 15c. multicoloured . . . . 60 1·75
DESIGN: 15c. Sikorsky S-38 flying boat of 1929.

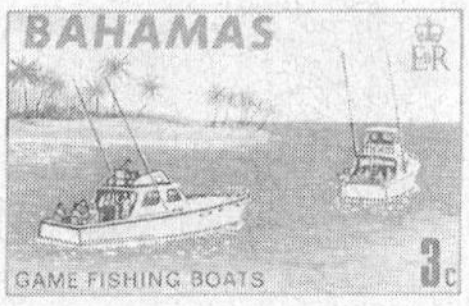

91 Game-fishing Boats

1969. Tourism. One Millionth Visitor to Bahamas. Multicoloured.
333 3c. Type **91** 25 10
334 11c. Paradise Beach 35 15
335 12c. "Sunfish" sailing boats 35 15
336 15c. Rawson Square and parade 45 25

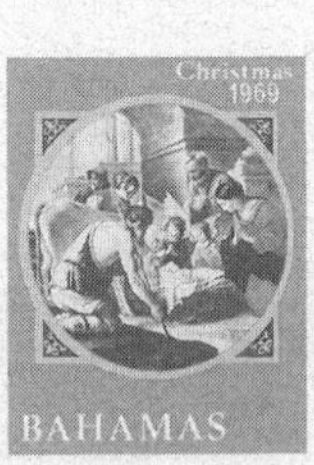

92 "The Adoration of the Shepherds" (Louis le Nain)

1969. Christmas. Multicoloured.
338 3c. Type **92** 10 20
339 11c. "The Adoration of the Shepherds" (Poussin) . . . 15 30
340 12c. "The Adoration of the Kings" (Gerard David) . . 15 20
341 15c. "The Adoration of the Kings" (Vincenzo Foppa) 20 65

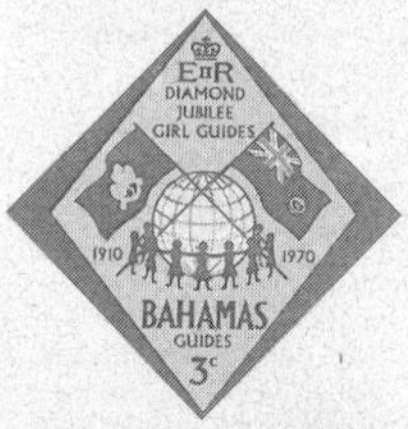

93 Badge of Girl Guides

1970. Diamond Jubilee of Girl Guides' Association. Multicoloured.
342	3c. Type **93**	30	10
343	12c. Badge of Brownies	45	20
344	15c. Badge of Rangers	50	35

94 New U.P.U. Headquarters and Emblem

1970. New U.P.U. Headquarters Building.
345	**94** 3c. multicoloured	10	15
346	15c. multicoloured	20	45

95 Coach and Globe

1970. "Goodwill Caravan". Multicoloured.
347	3c. Type **95**	75	20
348	11c. Diesel train and globe	1·50	60
349	12c. "Canberra" (liner), yacht and globe	1·50	60
350	15c. B.A.C. One Eleven airliner and globe	1·50	1·75

96 Nurse, Patients and Greater Flamingo

1970. Centenary of British Red Cross. Multicoloured.
352	3c. Type **96**	75	50
353	15c. Hospital and blue marlin	75	1·75

97 "The Nativity" (detail, Pittoni)

1970. Christmas. Multicoloured.
354	3c. Type **97**	15	15
355	11c. "The Holy Family" (detail, Anton Raphael Mengs)	20	25
356	12c. "The Adoration of the Shepherds" (detail, Giorgione)	20	20
357	15c. "The Adoration of the Shepherds" (detail, School of Seville)	30	75

98 International Airport

1971. Multicoloured.
359	1c. Type **98**	10	30
360	2c. Breadfruit	15	35
361	3c. Straw market	15	·30
362	4c. Hawksbill turtle	1·75	9·00
363	5c. Nassau grouper	60	60
364	6c. As 4c.	45	1·25
365	7c. Hibiscus	2·00	4·25
366	8c. Yellow elder	60	1·50
367	10c. Bahamian sponge boat	55	30
368	11c. Greater flamingos	2·50	3·00
369	12c. As 7c.	2·00	3·00
370	15c. Bonefish	55	55
466	17c. As 7c.	70	35
371	18c. Royal poinciana	65	65
467a	21c. As 2c.	80	1·25
372	22c. As 18c.	2·75	13·00
468	25c. As 4c.	90	40
469	40c. As 10c.	5·00	75
470	50c. Post Office, Nassau	1·75	1·75
471	$1 Pineapple (vert)	2·00	2·50
399	$2 Crawfish (vert)	1·50	6·00
473	$3 Junkanoo (vert)	2·00	9·00

99 Snowflake

101 Shepherd

100 High Jumping

1971. Christmas.
377	**99** 3c. purple, orange and gold	10	10
378	– 11c. blue and gold	20	15
379	– 15c. multicoloured	20	20
380	– 18c. blue, ultram & gold	25	25

DESIGNS: 11c. "Peace on Earth" (doves); 15c. Arms of Bahamas and holly; 18c. Starlit lagoon

1972. Olympic Games, Munich. Multicoloured.
382	10c. Type **100**	35	60
383	11c. Cycling	1·50	75
384	15c. Running	60	75
385	18c. Sailing	95	1·25

1972. Christmas. Multicoloured.
387	3c. Type **101**	10	10
388	6c. Bells	10	10
389	15c. Holly and Cross	15	20
390	20c. Poinsettia	25	45

1972. Royal Silver Wedding. As T **52** of Ascension, but with mace and galleon in background.
393	11c. pink	15	15
394	18c. violet	15	20

104 Weather Satellite

1973. Centenary of I.M.O./W.M.O. Multicoloured.
410	15c. Type **104**	50	25
411	18c. Weather radar	60	35

105 C. A. Bain (national hero)

106 "The Virgin in Prayer" (Sassoferrato)

1973. Independence. Multicoloured.
412	3c. Type **105**	10	10
413	11c. Coat of arms	15	10
414	15c. Bahamas flag	20	15
415	$1 Governor-General, M. B. Butler	65	1·00

1973. Christmas. Multicoloured.
417	3c. Type **106**	10	10
418	11c. "Virgin and Child with St. John" (Filippino Lippi)	15	15
419	15c. "A Choir of Angels" (Simon Marmion)	15	15
420	18c. "The Two Trinities" (Murillo)	25	25

107 "Agriculture and Sciences"

1974. 25th Anniv of University of West Indies. Multicoloured.
422	15c. Type **107**	20	25
423	18c. "Arts, Engineering and General Studies"	25	30

108 U.P.U. Monument, Berne

1974. Centenary of U.P.U.
424	**108** 3c. multicoloured	10	15
425	– 13c. multicoloured (vert)	20	25
426	– 14c. multicoloured	20	25
427	– 18c. multicoloured (vert)	25	40

DESIGNS—As Type **108** but showing different arrangements of the U.P.U. Monument.

109 Roseate Spoonbills

1974. 15th Anniv of Bahamas National Trust. Mult.
429	13c. Type **109**	1·40	85
430	14c. White-crowned pigeon	1·40	75
431	21c. White-tailed tropic birds	1·75	1·25
432	36c. Cuban amazon ("Bahamian parrot")	2·25	6·00

110 "The Holy Family" (Jacques de Stella)

1974. Christmas. Multicoloured.
434	8c. Type **110**	10	10
435	10c. "Madonna and Child" (16th-century Brescian School)	15	15
436	12c. "Virgin and Child with St. John the Baptist and St. Catherine" (Previtali)	15	15
437	21c. "Virgin and Child with Angels" (Previtali)	25	30

111 "Anteos maerula"

1975. Butterflies. Multicoloured.
439	3c. Type **111**	25	15
440	14c. "Eurema nicippe"	80	65
441	18c. "Papilio andraemon"	95	65
442	21c. "Euptoieta hegesia"	1·10	85

112 Sheep Husbandry

1975. Economic Diversification. Multicoloured.
444	3c. Type **112**	10	10
445	14c. Electric-reel fishing (vert)	20	15
446	18c. Farming	25	20
447	21c. Oil refinery (vert)	80	35

113 Rowena Rand (evangelist)

1975. International Women's Year.
449	**113** 14c. brown, lt blue & bl	20	50
450	– 18c. yellow, grn & brn	25	75

DESIGN: 18c. I.W.Y. symbol and harvest symbol.

114 "Adoration of the Shepherds" (Perugino)

1975. Christmas. Multicoloured.
451	3c. Type **114**	15	60
452	8c. "Adoration of the Magi" (Ghirlandaio)	20	10
453	18c. As 8c.	55	90
454	21c. Type **114**	60	95

115 Telephones, 1876 and 1976

1976. Centenary of Telephone. Multicoloured.
456	3c. Type **115**	20	50
457	16c. Radio-telephone link, Deleporte	40	50
458	21c. Alexander Graham Bell	50	65
459	25c. Satellite	60	1·00

116 Map of North America

1976. Bicentenary of American Revolution. Mult.
475	16c. Type **116**	30	30
476	$1 John Murray, Earl of Dunmore	1·50	1·75

117 Cycling

118 "Virgin and Child" (detail, Lippi)

1976. Olympic Games, Montreal.
478	**117** 8c. mauve, blue and light blue	1·25	20
479	– 16c. orange, brown and light blue	35	30
480	– 25c. blue, mauve and light blue	45	50
481	– 40c. brown, orange and blue	55	1·60

DESIGNS: 16c. Jumping; 25c. Sailing; 40c. Boxing.

1976. Christmas. Multicoloured.
483	3c. Type **118**	10	10
484	21c. "Adoration of the Shepherds" (School of Seville)	20	15
485	25c. "Adoration of the Kings" (detail, Foppa)	20	20
486	40c. "Virgin and Child" (detail, Vivarini)	35	40

119 Queen beneath Cloth of Gold Canopy

1977. Silver Jubilee. Multicoloured.
488	8c. Type **119**	10	10
489	16c. The Crowning	15	15
490	21c. Taking the Oath	15	15
491	40c. Queen with sceptre and orb	25	30

120 Featherduster

1977. Marine Life. Multicoloured.

493	3c. Type **120**	40	15
494	8c. Porkfish and cave	60	20
495	16c. Elkhorn coral	70	40
496	21c. Soft coral and sponge	80	55

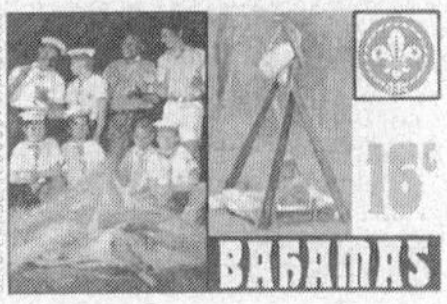

121 Scouts around Campfire and Home-made Shower

1977. 6th Caribbean Scout Jamboree. Multicoloured.

498	16c. Type **121**	75	30
499	21c. Boating scenes	85	35

1977. Royal Visit. Nos. 488/91 optd **Royal Visit October 1977.**

500	8c. Type **119**	15	10
501	16c. The Crowning	20	15
502	21c. Taking the Oath	25	25
503	40c. Queen with sceptre and orb	30	40

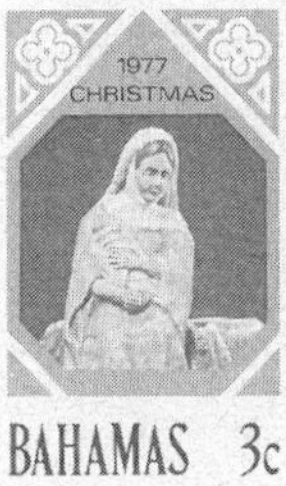

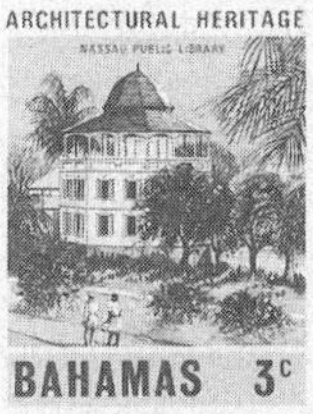

123 Virgin and Child **124** Public Library, Nassau (Colonial)

1977. Christmas. Multicoloured.

505	3c. Type **123**	10	10
506	16c. The Magi	20	25
507	21c. Nativity scene	25	40
508	25c. The Magi and star	30	45

1978. Architectural Heritage.

510	**124** 3c. black and green	10	10
511	– 8c. black and blue	15	10
512	– 16c. black and mauve	20	20
513	– 18c. black and pink	25	30

DESIGNS: 8c. St. Matthew's Church (Gothic); 16c. Government House (Colonial); 18c. Hermitage, Cat Island (Spanish).

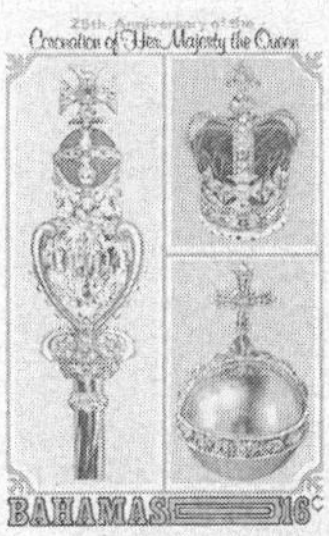

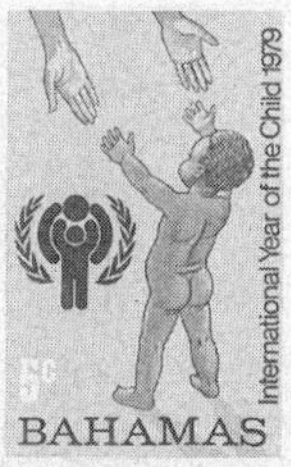

125 Sceptre, St. Edward's Crown and Orb **127** Child reaching for Adult

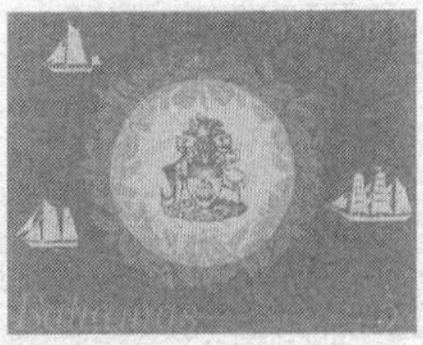
126 Coat of Arms within Wreath and Three Ships

1978. 25th Anniv of Coronation. Multicoloured.

515	16c. Type **125**	15	10
516	$1 Queen in Coronation regalia	50	65

1978. Christmas.

532	**126** 5c. gold, lake and red	15	10
533	– 21c. gold, deep blue and blue	30	25

DESIGN: 21c. Three angels with trumpets.

1979. International Year of the Child. Multicoloured.

535	5c. Type **127**	20	15
536	16c. Boys playing leapfrog	40	45
537	21c. Girls skipping	50	60
538	25c. Bricks with I.Y.C. emblem	50	75

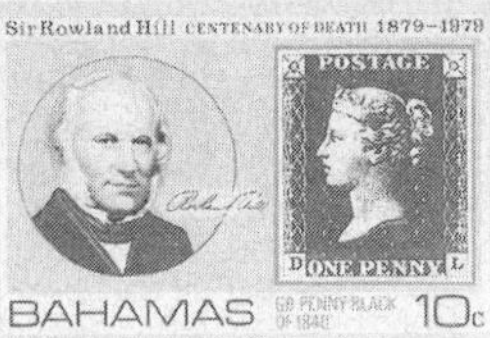

128 Sir Rowland Hill and Penny Black

1979. Death Centenary of Sir Rowland Hill. Multicoloured.

540	10c. Type **128**	30	10
541	21c. Printing press, 1840, and 6d. stamp of 1862	40	30
542	25c. Great Britain 1856 6d. with "A 05" (Nassau) cancellation, and 1840 2d. Blue	40	50
543	40c. Early mailboat and 1d. stamp of 1859	45	70

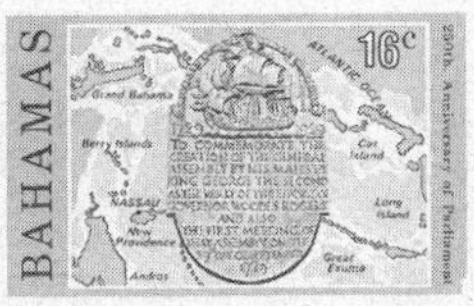

129 Commemorative Plaque and Map of Bahamas

1979. 250th Anniv of Parliament. Multicoloured.

545	16c. Type **129**	35	10
546	21c. Parliament buildings	40	15
547	25c. Legislative Chamber	40	15
548	$1 Senate Chamber	80	1·00

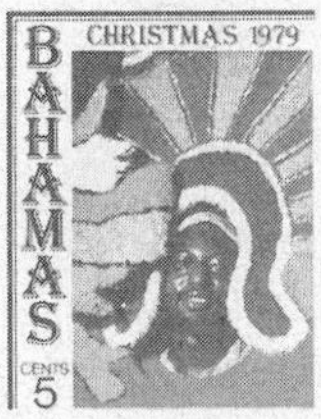

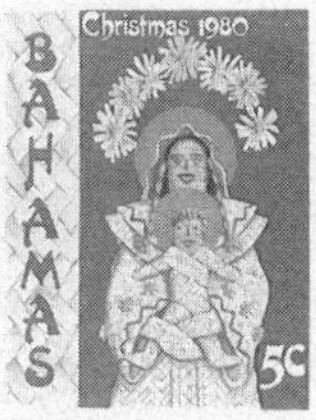

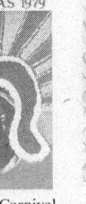

130 Goombay Carnival Headdress **132** Virgin and Child

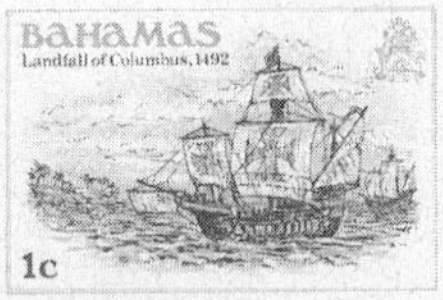

131 Landfall of Columbus, 1492

1979. Christmas.

550	**130** 5c. multicoloured	10	10
551	– 10c. multicoloured	15	10
552	– 16c. multicoloured	20	10
553	– 21c. multicoloured	20	20
554	– 25c. multicoloured	25	20
555	– 40c. multicoloured	30	45

DESIGNS: 10c. to 40c. Various Carnival costumes.

1980. Multicoloured.

557	1c. Type **131**	1·25	2·50
558	3c. Blackbeard the pirate	30	2·50
559	5c. Eleutheran Adventurers (Articles and Orders, 1647)	30	1·00
560	10c. Ceremonial mace	20	40
561	12c. The Loyalists, 1783–88	30	2·00
562	15c. Slave trading, Vendue House	5·50	1·00
563	16c. Wrecking in the 1800s	1·40	1·00
564	18c. Blockade running (American Civil War)	1·75	2·50
565	21c. Bootlegging, 1919–29	40	2·50
566	25c. Pineapple cultivation	40	2·50
567	40c. Sponge clipping	70	1·50
568	50c. Tourist development	75	1·50
569	$1 Modern agriculture	75	4·25
570	$2 Modern air and sea transport	4·00	5·50
571	$3 Banking (Central Bank)	1·25	4·00
572	$5 Independence, 10 July 1973	1·50	6·00

1980. Christmas. Straw-work. Multicoloured.

573	5c. Type **132**	10	10
574	21c. Three Kings	25	10
575	25c. Angel	25	15
576	$1 Christmas tree	75	85

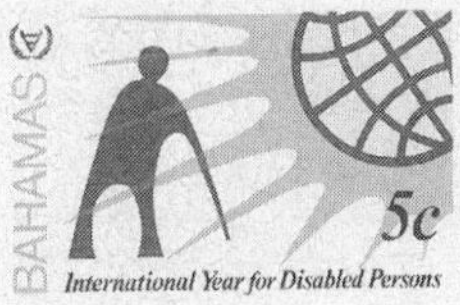

133 Disabled Persons with Walking Stick

1981. International Year of Disabled People. Mult.

578	5c. Type **133**	10	10
579	$1 Disabled person in wheelchair	1·25	1·25

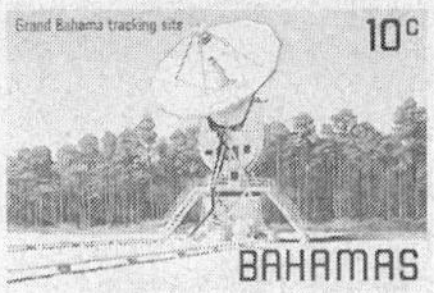

134 Grand Bahama Tracking Site

1981. Space Exploration. Multicoloured.

581	10c. Type **134**	30	15
582	20c. Satellite view of Bahamas (vert)	60	50
583	25c. Satelite view of Eleuthera	65	60
584	50c. Satellite view of Andros and New Province (vert)	1·00	1·25

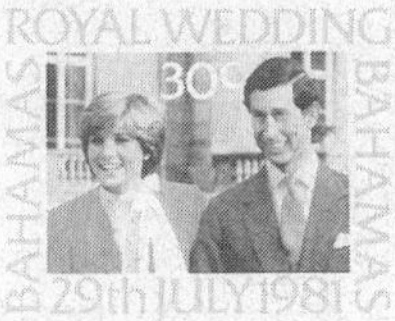

135 Prince Charles and Lady Diana Spencer

1981. Royal Wedding. Multicoloured.

586	30c. Type **135**	1·50	30
587	$2 Prince Charles and Prime Minister Pindling	1·50	1·25

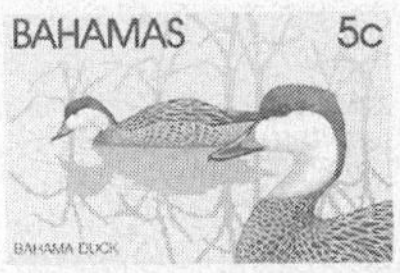

136 Bahamas Pintail ("Bahama Duck")

1981. Wildlife (1st series). Birds. Multicoloured.

589	5c. Type **136**	1·25	50
590	20c. Reddish egret	2·00	50
591	25c. Brown booby	2·00	55
592	$1 Black-billed whistling duck ("West Indian Tree Duck")	3·50	6·00

See also Nos. 626/9, 653/6 and 690/3.

1981. Commonwealth Finance Ministers' Meeting. Nos. 559/60, 566 and 568 optd **COMMONWEALTH FINANCE MINISTERS' MEETING 21–23 SEPTEMBER 1981.**

594	5c. Eleutheran Adventures (Articles and Orders, 1647)	15	15
595	10c. Ceremonial mace	20	20
596	25c. Pineapple cultivation	50	60
597	50c. Tourist development	85	1·50

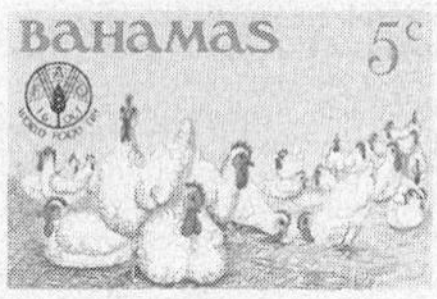

138 Poultry

1981. World Food Day. Multicoloured.

598	5c. Type **138**	20	10
599	20c. Sheep	35	35
600	30c. Lobsters	45	50
601	50c. Pigs	75	1·50

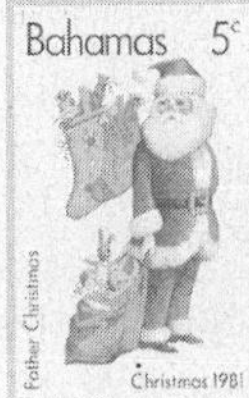

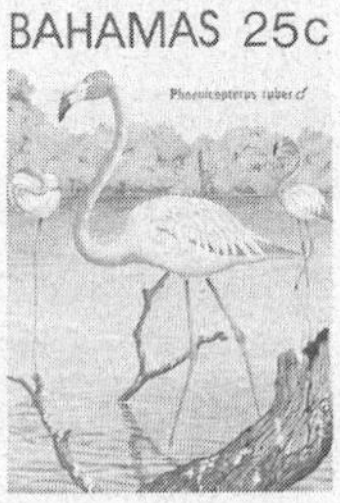

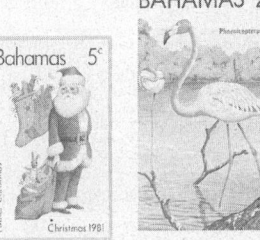

139 Father Christmas **141** Greater Flamingo (male)

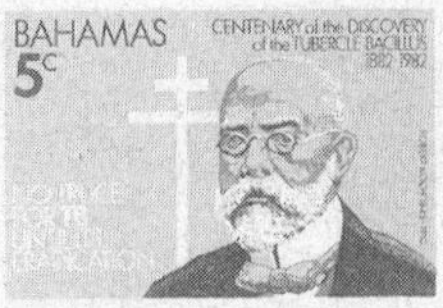

140 Robert Koch

1981. Christmas. Multicoloured.

603	5c. Type **139**	45	75
604	5c. Mother and child	45	75
605	5c. St. Nicholas, Holland	45	75
606	25c. Lussibruden, Sweden	60	85
607	25c. Mother and child (different)	60	85
608	25c. King Wenceslas, Czechoslovakia	60	85
609	30c. Mother with child on knee	60	85
610	30c. Mother carrying child	60	85
611	$1 Christkindl Angel, Germany	1·00	1·50

1982. Centenary of Discovery of Tubercle Bacillus by Robert Koch.

612	**140** 5c. black, brown and lilac	70	40
613	– 16c. black, brown & orge	1·25	50
614	– 21c. multicoloured	1·40	55
615	– $1 multicoloured	3·00	6·50

DESIGNS: 16c. Stylised infected person; 21c. Early and modern microscopes; $1 Mantoux test.

1982. Greater Flamingos. Multicoloured.

617	25c. Type **141**	1·60	1·00
618	25c. Female	1·60	1·00
619	25c. Female with nestling	1·60	1·00
620	25c. Juvenile	1·60	1·00
621	25c. Immature bird	1·60	1·00

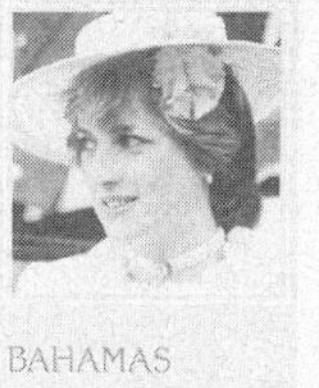

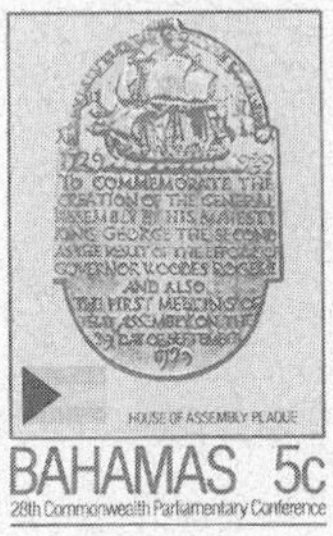

142 Lady Diana Spencer at Ascot, June 1981 **143** House of Assembly Plaque

1982. 21st Birthday of Princess of Wales. Mult.

622	16c. Bahamas coat of arms	20	10
623	25c. Type **142**	45	15
624	40c. Bride and Earl Spencer arriving at St. Paul's	60	20
625	$1 Formal portrait	1·00	1·25

1982. Wildlife (2nd series). Mammals. As T **136**. Multicoloured.

626	10c. Buffy flower bat	80	15
627	16c. Bahamian hutia	1·00	25
628	21c. Common racoon	1·25	55
629	$1 Common dolphin	3·00	1·75

1982. 28th Commonwealth Parliamentary Association Conference. Multicoloured.

631	5c. Type **143**	15	10
632	25c. Association coat of arms	50	35
633	40c. Coat of arms	80	60
634	50c. House of Assembly	1·10	75

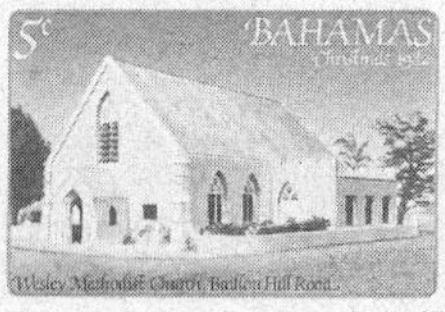

144 Wesley Methodist Church, Baillou Hill Road

1982. Christmas. Churches. Multicoloured.

635	5c. Type **144**	10	10
636	12c. Centreville Seventh Day Adventist Church	15	20
637	15c. The Church of God of Prophecy, East Street	15	30
638	21c. Bethel Baptist Church, Meeting Street	15	30
639	25c. St. Francis Xavier Catholic Church, Highbury Park	15	50
640	$1 Holy Cross Anglican Church, Highbury Park	60	2·75

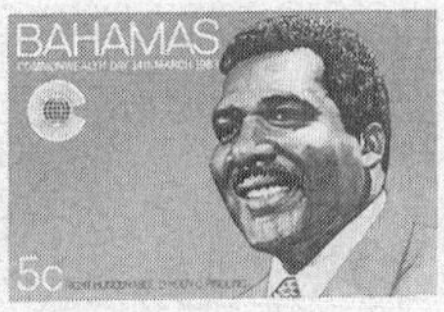

145 Prime Minister Lyndon O. Pindling

1983. Commonwealth Day. Multicoloured.

641	5c. Type **145**	10	10
642	25c. Bahamian and Commonwealth flags	40	40
643	35c. Map showing position of Bahamas	40	50
644	$1 Ocean liner	1·10	1·40

1983. Nos. 562/5 surch.

645	20c. on 15c. Slave trading, Vendue House	50	35
646	31c. on 21c. Bootlegging, 1919–29	60	55
647	35c. on 16c. Wrecking in the 1800s	1·25	60
648	80c. on 18c. Blockade running (American Civil War)	1·50	1·40

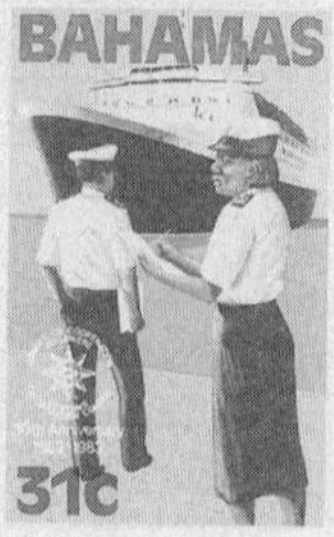

147 Customs Officers and "Queen Elizabeth 2" (liner)

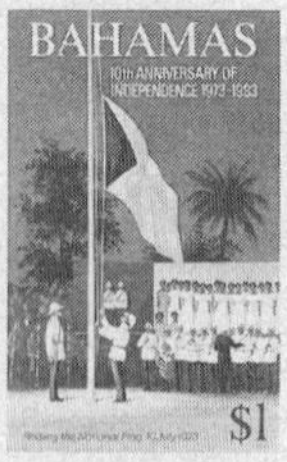

148 Raising the National Flag

1983. 30th Anniv of Customs Co-operation Council. Multicoloured.
649 31c. Type **147** . . . . 1·50 45
650 $1 Customs officers and Lockheed JetStar airliner 3·50 2·75

1983. 10th Anniv of Independence.
651 **148** $1 multicoloured . . . . 1·00 1·40

1983. Wildlife (3rd series). Butterflies. As T **136**.
653 5c. multicoloured . . . . . . 1·00 20
654 25c. multicoloured . . . . . 1·75 40
655 31c. black, yellow and red . . 1·75 55
656 50c. multicoloured . . . . . 2·00 85
DESIGNS: 5c. "Atalopedes carteri"; 25c. "Ascia monuste"; 31 c. "Phoebis agarithe"; 50c. "Dryas julia"

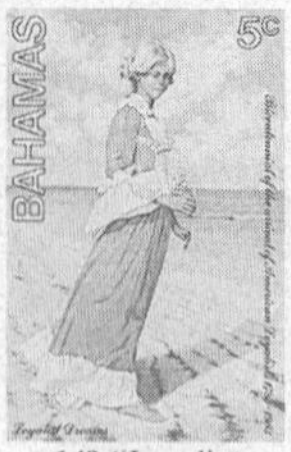

149 "Loyalist Dreams"

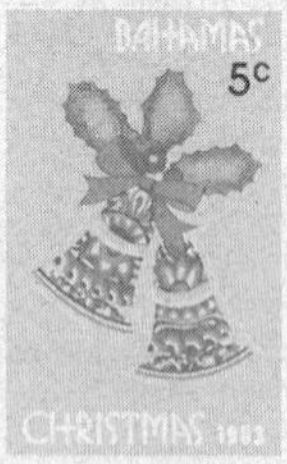

151 "Christmas Bells" (Monica Pinder)

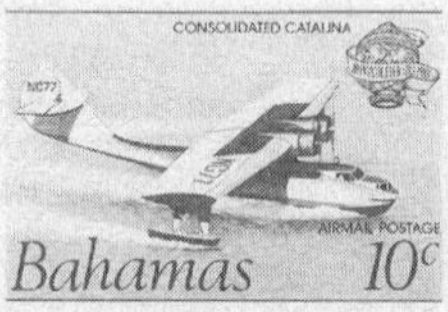

150 Consolidated Catalina

1983. Bicentenary of Arrival of American Loyalists in the Bahamas. Multicoloured.
658 5c. Type **149** 10 10
659 31c. New Plymouth, Abaco (horiz) 30 50
660 35c. New Plymouth Hotel (horiz) 40 70
661 50c. "Island Hope" 45 90

1983. Air. Bicentenary of Manned Flight. Mult.
663 10c. Type **150** 55 15
664 25c. Avro Tudor IV 75 30
665 31c. Avro Lancastrian . . . 85 45
666 35c. Consolidated Commodore . . . . 1·00 50
For these stamps without the Manned Flight logo, see Nos. 699/702.

1983. Christmas. Children's Paintings. Multicoloured.
667 5c. Type **151** 15 10
668 20c. "Flamingo" (Cory Bullard) 35 30
669 25c. "Yellow Hibiscus with Christmas Candle" (Monique Bailey) 45 40
670 31c. "Santa goes-a-sailing" (Sabrina Seiler) (horiz) . . 55 45
671 35c. "Silhouette scene with Palm Trees" (James Blake) 60 50
672 50c. "Silhouette scene with Pelicans" (Erik Russell) (horiz) 70 70

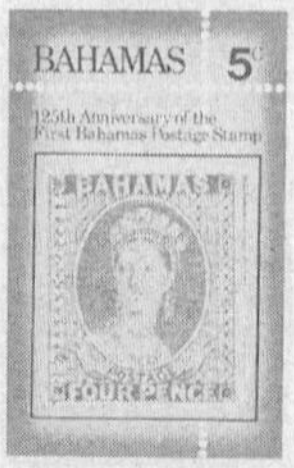

152 1861 4d. Stamp

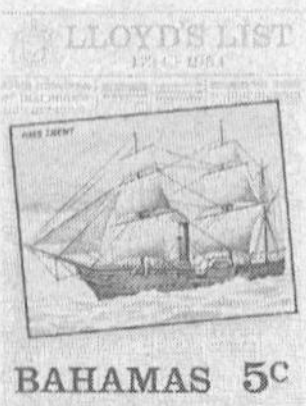

153 "Trent I" (paddle-steamer)

1984. 125th Anniv of First Bahamas Postage Stamp. Multicoloured.
673 5c. Type **152** 25 10
674 $1 1859 1d. stamp . . . . . 1·75 1·50

1984. 250th Anniv of "Lloyd's List" (newspaper). Multicoloured.
675 5c. Type **153** 50 10
676 31c. "Orinoco II" (mail ship), 1886 . . . . 1·00 60
677 35c. Cruise liners in Nassau harbour . . . . 1·10 75
678 50c. "Oropesa" (container ship) . . . . 1·40 1·60

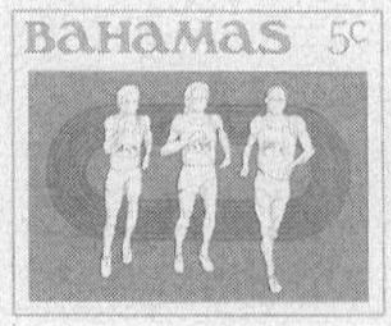

154 Running

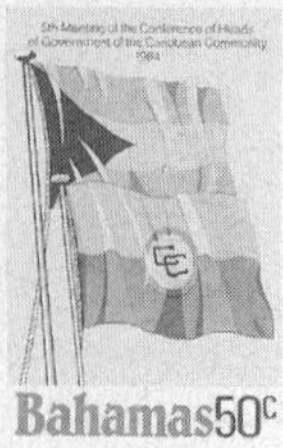

155 Bahamas and Caribbean Community Flags

1984. Olympic Games, Los Angeles.
679 **154** 5c. green, black and gold 15 15
680 – 25c. blue, black and gold 50 50
681 – 31c. red, black and gold 55 60
682 – $1 brown, black and gold 4·75 4·75
DESIGNS: 25c. Shot-putting; 31c. Boxing; $1 Basketball.

1984. 5th Conference of Caribbean Community Heads of Government.
684 **155** 50c. multicoloured . . . . 1·00 1·00

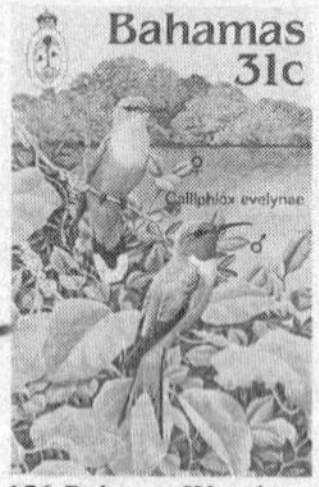

156 Bahama Woodstar

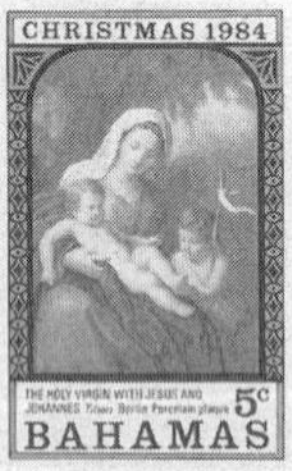

157 "The Holy Virgin with Jesus and Johannes" (19th-century porcelain plaque after Titian)

1984. 25th Anniv of National Trust. Multicoloured.
685 31c. Type **156** . . . . 3·25 3·25
686 31c. Belted kingfishers, greater flamingos and "Eleutherodactylus planirostris" (frog) . . . . 3·25 3·25
687 31c. Black-necked stilts, greater flamingos and "Phoebis sennae" (butterfly) . . . . . . 3·25 3·25
688 31c. "Urbanus proteus" (butterfly) and "Chelonia mydas" (turtle) . . . . . 3·25 3·25
689 31c. Osprey and greater flamingos . . . . 3·25 3·25
Nos. 685/9 were printed together in horiz strips of 5 forming a composite design.

1984. Wildlife (4th series). Reptiles and Amphibians. As T **136**.
690 5c. Allens' Cay iguana . . . 50 20
691 25c. Curly-tailed lizard . . . 1·25 60
692 35c. Greenhouse frog . . . . 1·50 85
693 50c. Atlantic green turtle . . 1·75 2·50

1984. Christmas. Religious Paintings. Multicoloured.
695 5c. Type **157** 30 10
696 31c. "Madonna with Child in Tropical Landscape" (aquarelle, Anais Colin) . . 80 60
697 35c. "The Holy Virgin with the Child" (miniature on ivory, Elena Caula) . . . . 1·00 65

1985. Air. As Nos. 663/6, but without Manned Flight logo.
699 10c. Type **150** 70 30
700 25c. Avro Tudor IV 85 40
701 31c. Avro Lancastrian . . . 85 55
702 35c. Consolidated Commodore . . . . 1·25 85

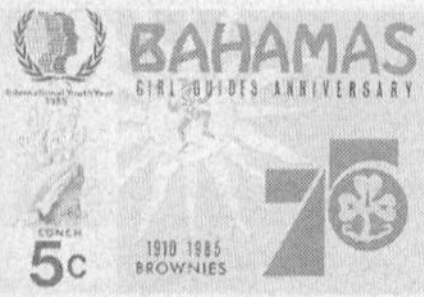

158 Brownie Emblem and Queen or Pink Conch

1985. International Youth Year. 75th Anniv of Girl Guide Movement. Multicoloured.
703 5c. Type **158** 60 50
704 25c. Tents and coconut palm 1·25 1·00
705 31c. Guide salute and greater flamingos . . . . 1·90 1·50
706 35c. Ranger emblem and marlin . . . . 1·90 1·50

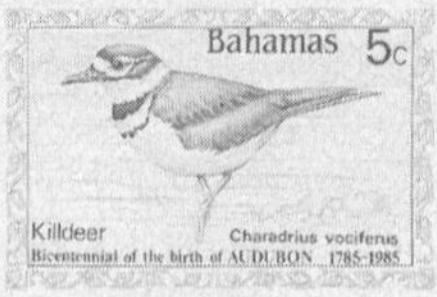

159 Killdeer Plover

1985. Birth Bicent of John J. Audubon (ornithologist). Multicoloured.
708 5c. Type **159** . . . . 1·00 60
709 31c. Mourning dove (vert) . . 2·25 60
710 35c. "Mourning dove" (John J. Audubon) (vert) . . . . 2·25 65
711 $1 "Killdeer Plover" (John J. Audubon) . . . . 4·00 4·50

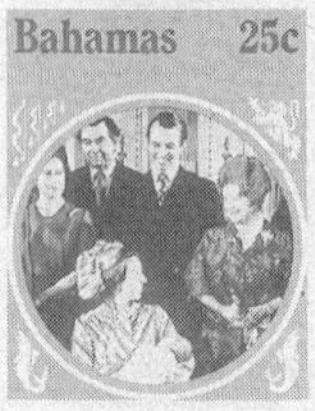

160 The Queen Mother at Christening of Peter Phillips, 1977

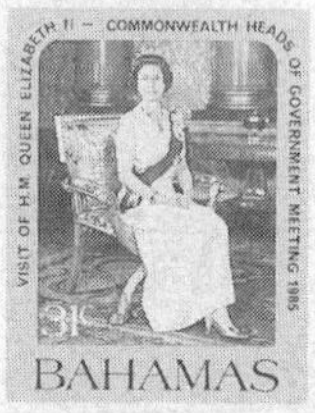

162 Queen Elizabeth II

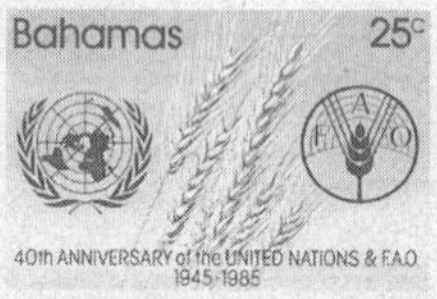

161 Ears of Wheat and Emblems

1985. Life and Times of Queen Elizabeth the Queen Mother. Multicoloured.
712 5c. Visiting Auckland, New Zealand, 1927 . . . . . . 35 20
713 25c. Type **160** 60 40
714 35c. The Queen Mother attending church 65 55
715 50c. With Prince Henry at his christening (from photo by Lord Snowdon) . . . . . 1·25 1·75

1985. 40th Anniv of U.N.O. and F.A.O.
717 **161** 25c. multicoloured 85 60

1985. Commonwealth Heads of Government Meeting, Nassau. Multicoloured.
718 31c. Type **162** . . . . 2·25 2·75
719 35c. Bahamas Prime Minister's flag and Commonwealth emblem . . 2·25 2·75

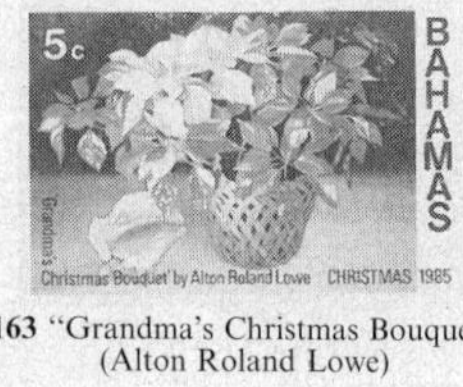

163 "Grandma's Christmas Bouquet" (Alton Roland Lowe)

1985. Christmas. Paintings by Alton Roland Lowe. Multicoloured.
736 5c. Type **163** 50 30
737 25c. "Junkanoo Romeo and Juliet" (vert) . . . . 1·25 1·00
738 31c. "Bunce Gal" (vert) . . . 1·50 1·50
739 35c. "Home for Christmas" 1·75 2·50

1986. 60th Birthday of Queen Elizabeth II. As T **110** of Ascension. Multicoloured.
741 10c. Princess Elizabeth aged one, 1927 . . . . 15 15
742 25c. The Coronation, 1953 30 30
743 35c. Queen making speech at Commonwealth Banquet, Bahamas, 1985 . . . . . 35 40
744 40c. In Djakova, Yugoslavia, 1972 . . . . 35 45
745 $1 At Crown Agents Head Office, London, 1983 . . . 80 1·40

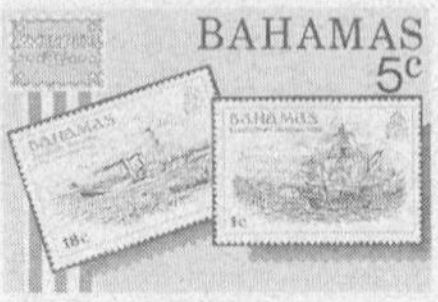

164 1980 1c. and 18c. Definitive Stamps

1986. "Ameripex '86" International Stamp Exn, Chicago.
746 **164** 5c. multicoloured 60 50
747 – 25c. multicoloured . . . . 1·40 50
748 – 31c. multicoloured . . . . 1·60 60
749 – 50c. multicoloured . . . . 2·25 3·50
750 – $1 black, green and blue 2·50 4·50
DESIGNS—HORIZ: (showing Bahamas stamps)—25c. 1969 50th Anniv of Bahamas Airmail Service pair; 31c. 1976 Bicentenary of American Revolution; 16c., 50c. 1981 Space Exploration miniature sheet. VERT: $1 Statue of Liberty.
No. 750 also commemorates the Centenary of the Statue of Liberty.

1986. Royal Wedding. As T **112** of Ascension. Mult.
756 10c. Prince Andrew and Miss Sarah Ferguson 20 20
757 $1 Prince Andrew . . . . . 1·25 2·10

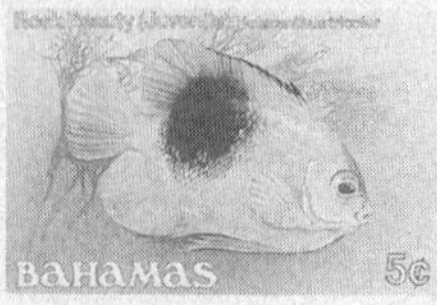

165 Rock Beauty (juvenile)

1986. Fishes. Multicoloured.
758A 5c. Type **165** 75 75
759A 10c. Stoplight parrotfish . . 80 1·00
760A 15c. Jackknife-fish . . . . 1·50 1·50
761A 20c. Flamefish . . . . . . 1·25 1·25
762A 25c. Peppermint basslet ("Swissguard basslet") . . 1·50 1·50
763A 30c. Spot-finned butterflyfish . . . . . . 1·10 1·50
764A 35c. Queen triggerfish . . . 1·10 2·25
765B 40c. Four-eyed butterflyfish 1·10 1·60
766A 45c. Royal gramma ("Fairy basslet") . . . . 1·50 1·25
767A 50c. Queen angelfish . . . 2·00 3·25
797 60c. Blue chromis . . . . . 2·25 5·00
769B $1 Spanish hogfish . . . . 2·75 3·00
799 $2 Harlequin bass . . . . 3·00 7·50
771A $3 Black-barred soldierfish 6·00 7·00
772A $5 Cherub angelfish ("Pygmy angelfish") . . . 6·50 8·00
773A $10 Red hind . . . . . . 16·00 21·00

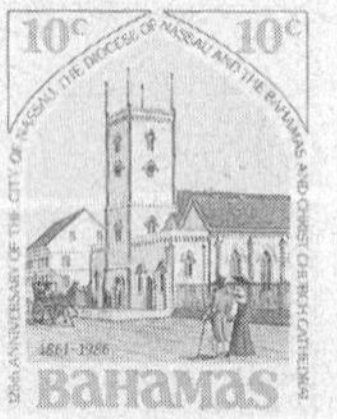

166 Christ Church Cathedral, Nassau, 1861

1986. 125th Anniv of City of Nassau. Diocese and Cathedral. Multicoloured.
774 10c. Type **166** 30 20
775 40c. Christ Church Cathedral, 1986 . . . . 70 80

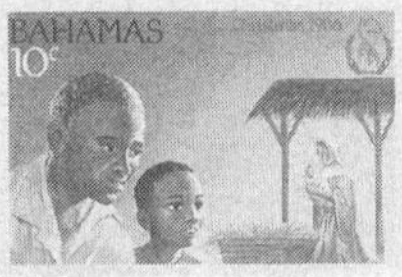

167 Man and Boy looking at Crib

1986. Christmas. International Peace Year. Mult.
777 10c. Type **167** 35 20
778 40c. Mary and Joseph journeying to Bethlehem 85 75
779 45c. Children praying and Star of Bethlehem . . . . 95 1·00
780 50c. Children exchanging gifts 1·00 2·00

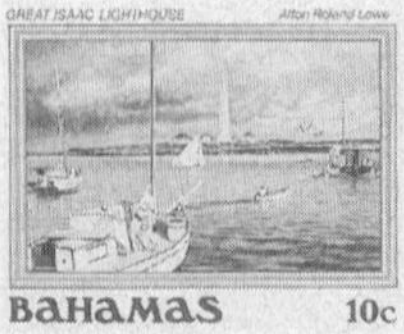

168 Great Isaac Lighthouse

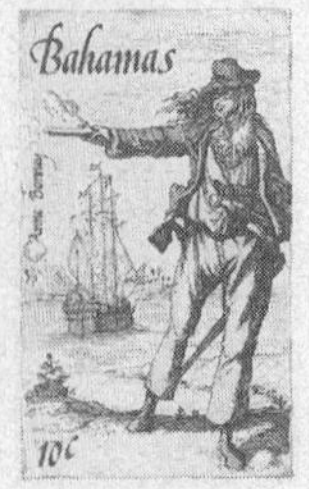

169 Anne Bonney

1987. Lighthouses. Multicoloured.
782 10c. Type **168** . . . . 2·25 85
783 40c. Bird Rock lighthouse . . 4·25 1·75
784 45c. Castle Island lighthouse 4·25 2·00
785 $1 "Hole in the Wall" lighthouse . . . . 7·00 11·00

1987. Pirates and Privateers of the Caribbean. Multicoloured.
786 10c. Type **169** . . . . 2·25 1·25
787 40c. Edward Teach ("Blackbeard") . . . . . 4·25 3·25
788 45c. Captain Edward England . . . . 4·25 3·25
789 50c. Captain Woodes Rogers 4·75 5·00

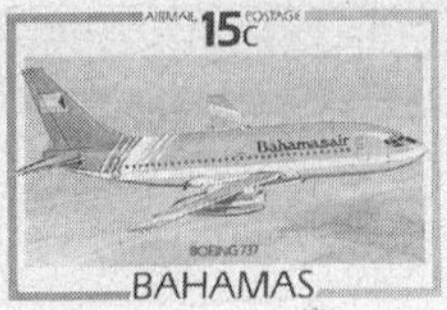

170 Boeing 737

1987. Air. Aircraft. Multicoloured.
800 15c. Type **170** . . . . 2·00 1·25
801 40c. Boeing 757-200 . . . . . 2·75 1·75
802 45c. Airbus Industrie A300 B4-200 . . . . 2·75 1·75
803 50c. Boeing 747-200 . . . . 2·75 3·00

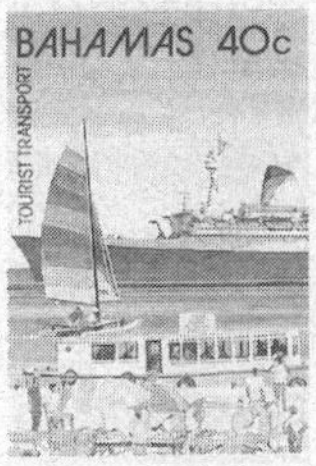

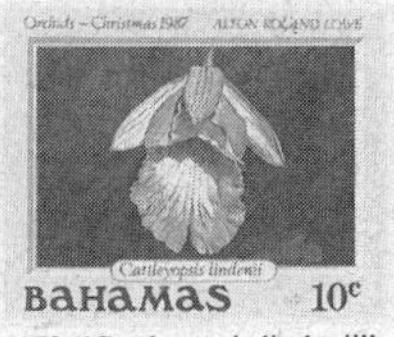

171 "Norway" (liner) and Catamaran **172** "Cattleyopsis lindenii"

1987. Tourist Transport. Multicoloured.
804 40c. Type **171** . . . . 2·00 2·00
805 40c. Liners and speedboat . . 2·00 2·00
806 40c. Game fishing boat and cruising yacht . . . . . . 2·00 2·00
807 40c. Game fishing boat and racing yachts . . . . . . 2·00 2·00
808 40c. Fishing boat and schooner . . . . 2·00 2·00
809 40c. Hawker Siddeley H.S.748 airliner . . . . . 2·00 2·00
810 40c. Boeing 737 and Boeing 727-200 airliners . . . . . 2·00 2·00
811 40c. Beech 200 Super King Air aircraft and radio beacon . . . . 2·00 2·00
812 40c. Aircraft and Nassau control tower . . . . . . 2·00 2·00
813 40c. Helicopter and parked aircraft . . . . 2·00 2·00
Nos. 804/8 and 809/13 were each printed together, se-tenant, forming composite design.

1987. Christmas. Orchids. Multicoloured.
814 10c. Type **172** . . . . 1·50 60
815 40c. "Encyclia lucayana" . . 2·75 1·50
816 45c. "Encyclia hodgeana" . . 2·75 1·50
817 50c. "Encyclia lleidae" . . . 2·75 2·50

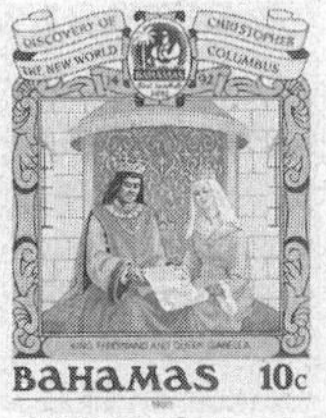

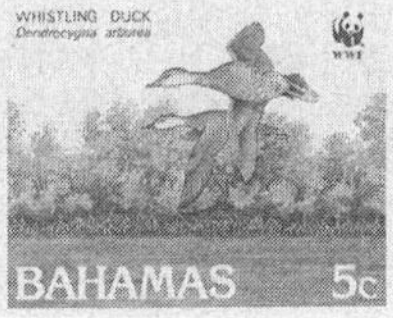

173 King Ferdinand and Queen Isabella of Spain **174** Whistling Ducks in Flight

1988. 500th Anniv (1992) of Discovery of America by Columbus (1st issue). Multicoloured.
819 10c. Type **173** 85 60
820 40c. Columbus before Talavera Committee . . . 1·75 1·75
821 45c. Lucayan village . . . . 1·90 1·90
822 50c. Lucayan potters . . . . 2·00 3·25
See also Nos. 844/7, 870/3, 908/11 and 933/6.

1988. Black-billed Whistling Duck. Multicoloured.
824 5c. Type **174** . . . . 2·25 1·50
825 10c. Whistling duck in reeds 2·25 1·50
826 20c. Pair with brood . . . . 4·00 2·50
827 45c. Pair wading . . . . . . 6·00 3·00

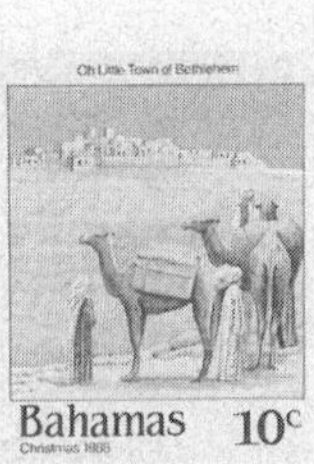

175 Grantstown Cabin, c. 1820 **177** "Oh Little Town of Bethlehem"

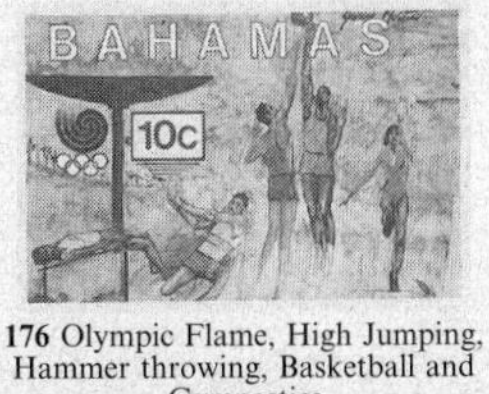

176 Olympic Flame, High Jumping, Hammer throwing, Basketball and Gymnastics

1988. 150th Anniv of Abolition of Slavery. Multicoloured.
828 10c. Type **175** 50 30
829 40c. Basket-making, Grantstown . . . . 1·25 95

1988. Olympic Games, Seoul. Designs taken from painting by James Martin. Multicoloured.
830 10c. Type **176** 75 50
831 40c. Athletics, archery, swimming, long jumping, weightlifting and boxing . . 90 60
832 45c. Javelin throwing, gymnastics, hurdling and shot put 90 60
833 $1 Athletics, hurdling, gymnastics and cycling . . 3·25 4·50

1988. 300th Anniv of Lloyd's of London. As T **123** of Ascension. Multicoloured.
835 10c. "Lloyd's List" of 1740 30 15
836 40c. Freeport Harbour (horiz) 1·50 60
837 45c. Space shuttle over Bahamas (horiz) . . . . . 1·50 60
838 $1 "Yarmouth Castle" (freighter) on fire . . . . . 2·50 1·90

1988. Christmas. Carols. Multicoloured.
839 10c. Type **177** 45 30
840 40c. "Little Donkey" . . . . 1·25 75
841 45c. "Silent Night" . . . . . 1·25 90
842 50c. "Hark the Herald Angels Sing" . . . . 1·40 2·00

1989. 500th Anniv (1992) of Discovery of America by Columbus (2nd issue). As T **173**. Multicoloured.
844 10c. Columbus drawing chart 2·00 75
845 40c. Types of caravel . . . . 3·00 1·50
846 45c. Early navigational instruments . . . . 3·00 1·50
847 50c. Arawak artefacts . . . . 3·00 4·00

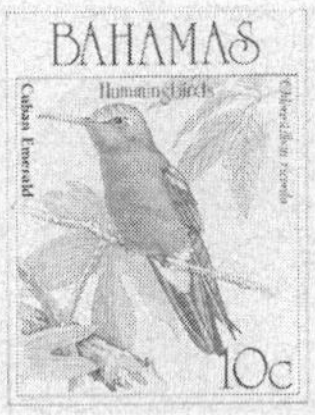

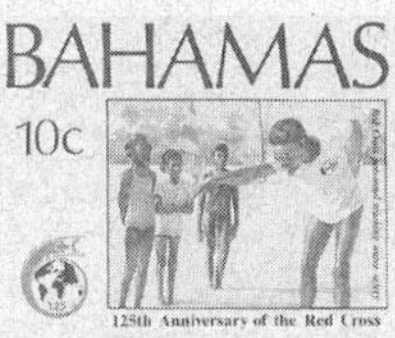

178 Cuban Emerald **179** Teaching Water Safety

1989. Hummingbirds. Multicoloured.
849 10c. Type **178** . . . . 1·75 1·25
850 40c. Ruby-throated hummingbird . . . . . . 3·00 2·00
851 45c. Bahama woodstar . . . 3·00 2·00
852 50c. Rufous hummingbird . . 3·25 4·50

1989. 125th Anniv of Int Red Cross. Mult.
853 10c. Type **179** . . . . 1·25 30
854 $1 Henri Dunant (founder) and Battle of Solferino . . 3·25 3·25

1989. 20th Anniv of First Manned Landing on Moon. As T **126** of Ascension. Multicoloured.
855 10c. "Apollo 8" Communications Station, Grand Bahama 75 50
856 40c. Crew of "Apollo 8" (30 × 30 mm) . . . . . . 1·25 90
857 45c. "Apollo 8" emblem (30 × 30 mm) . . . . . . 1·25 90
858 $1 The Earth seen from "Apollo 8" . . . . 2·25 3·50

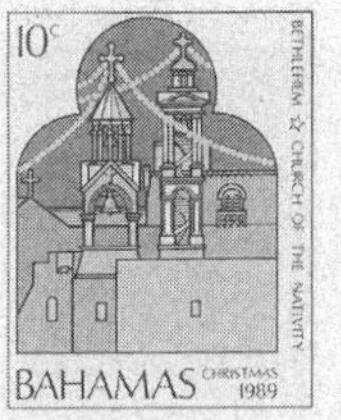

180 Church of the Nativity, Bethlehem

1989. Christmas. Churches of the Holy Land. Multicoloured.
860 10c. Type **180** 75 30
861 40c. Basilica of the Annunciation, Nazareth . . 1·50 70
862 45c. Tabgha Church, Galilee 1·50 70
863 $1 Church of the Holy Sepulchre, Jerusalem . . . 3·25 4·50

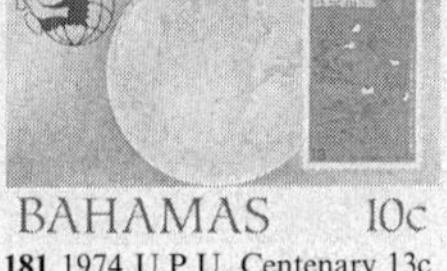

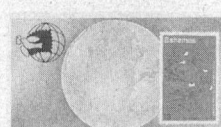

181 1974 U.P.U. Centenary 13c. Stamp and Globe

1989. "World Stamp Expo '89" International Stamp Exhibition, Washington. Multicoloured.
865 10c. Type **181** 70 40
866 40c. New U.P.U. Headquarters Building 3c. and building . . . . 1·40 85
867 45c. 1986 "Ameripex '86" $1 and Capitol, Washington 1·40 90
868 $1 1949 75th anniv of U.P.U. 2½d. and Boeing 737 airliner . . . . 5·50 7·00

1990. 500th Anniv (1992) of Discovery of America by Columbus (3rd issue). As T **173**. Multicoloured.
870 10c. Launching caravel . . . 1·75 80
871 40c. Provisional ship . . . . 2·75 2·00
872 45c. Shortening sail . . . . . 2·75 2·00
873 50c. Lucayan fisherman . . . 2·75 4·00

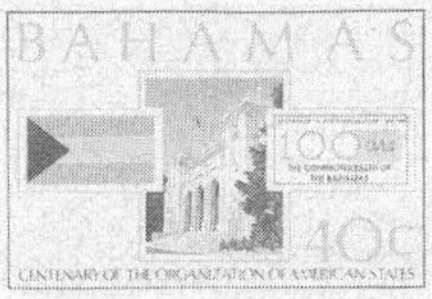

182 Bahamas Flag, O.A.S. Headquarters and Centenary Logo

1990. Centenary of Organization of American States.
875 **182** 40c. multicoloured . . . . 2·00 1·75

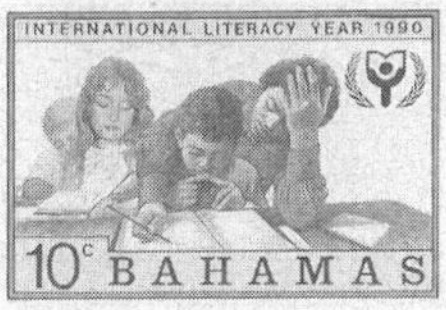

184 Teacher with Boy

1990. International Literacy Year. Multicoloured.
877 10c. Type **184** . . . . 1·00 50
878 40c. Three boys in class . . . 1·75 1·25
879 50c. Teacher and children with books . . . . 1·75 4·75

1990. 90th Birthday of Queen Elizabeth the Queen Mother. As T **134** of Ascension.
880 40c. multicoloured . . . . . 1·25 50
881 $1.50 black and ochre . . . 2·75 3·50
DESIGNS—21 × 36 mm: 40c. "Queen Elizabeth 1938" (Sir Gerald Kelly); 29 × 37 mm: $1.50, Queen Elizabeth at garden party, France, 1938.

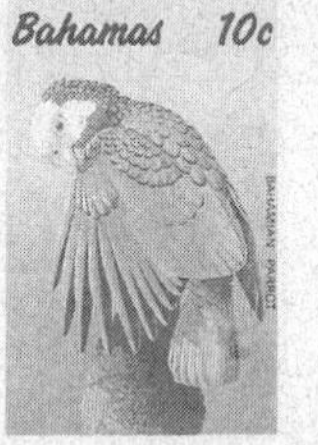

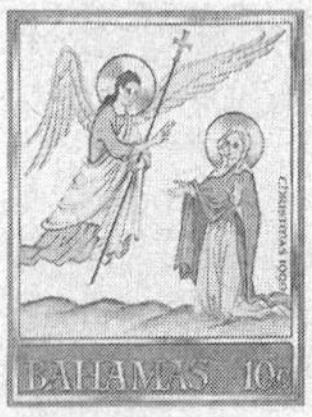

185 Cuban Amazon preening **186** The Annunciation

1990. Cuban Amazon ("Bahamian Parrot"). Mult.
882 10c. Type **185** . . . . 1·25 75
883 40c. Pair in flight . . . . . . 2·25 1·25
884 45c. Cuban amazon's head 2·25 1·25
885 50c. Perched on branch . . . 2·50 3·50

1990. Christmas. Multicoloured.
887 10c. Type **186** 65 50
888 40c. The Nativity . . . . . . 1·25 70
889 45c. Angel appearing to Shepherds . . . . 1·25 70
890 $1 The Three Kings . . . . 3·00 5·00

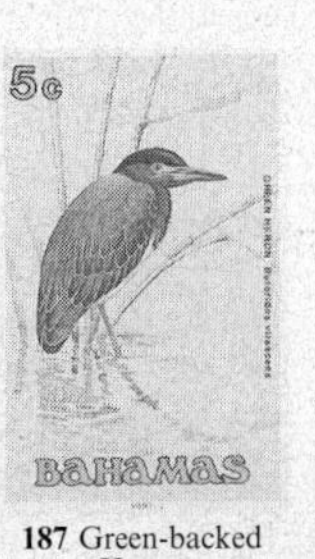

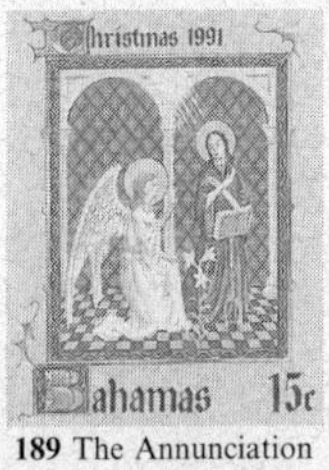

187 Green-backed Heron **189** The Annunciation

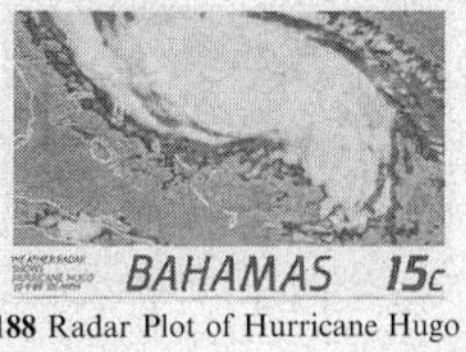

188 Radar Plot of Hurricane Hugo

1991. Birds. Multicoloured.
892 5c. Type **187** . . . . 85 1·00
893 10c. Turkey vulture . . . . . 1·00 1·25
976 15c. Osprey 80 70
895 20c. Clapper rail . . . . . . 1·00 80
978 25c. Royal tern 60 70
979 30c. Key West quail dove . . 1·75 90
898 40c. Smooth-billed ani . . . 1·75 55
899 45c. Burrowing owl . . . . . 2·75 80
900 50c. Hairy woodpecker . . . 2·25 80
983 55c. Mangrove cuckoo . . . 2·00 80
902 60c. Bahama mockingbird . . 2·00 1·75
903 70c. Red-winged blackbird 2·00 1·75
904 $1 Thick-billed vireo . . . . 2·50 1·50
905 $2 Bahama yellowthroat . . 5·50 6·00
988 $5 Stripe-headed tanager . . 6·50 8·50
907 $10 Greater Antillean bullfinch . . . . 13·00 15·00

1991. 500th Anniv (1992) of Discovery of America by Columbus (4th issue). As T **173**. Multicoloured.
908 15c. Columbus navigating by stars . . . . 1·75 85
909 40c. Fleet in mid-Atlantic . . 2·50 2·25
910 55c. Lucayan family worshipping at night . . . 2·50 2·50
911 60c. Map of First Voyage . . 3·25 4·50

1991. 65th Birthday of Queen Elizabeth II and 70th Birthday of Prince Philip. As T **139** of Ascension. Multicoloured.
913 15c. Prince Philip . . . . . 1·00 1·50
914 $1 Queen Elizabeth II . . . 1·75 2·00

1991. International Decade for Natural Disaster Reduction. Multicoloured.
915 15c. Type **188** . . . . 1·25 65
916 40c. Diagram of hurricane . . 1·75 1·50
917 55c. Flooding caused by Hurricane David, 1979 . . 2·00 2·25
918 60c. U.S. Dept of Commerce weather reconnaissance Lockhead WP-3D Orion 2·75 3·75

1991. Christmas. Multicoloured.
919 15c. Type **189** 65 30
920 55c. Mary and Joseph travelling to Bethlehem . . 1·50 1·00
921 60c. Angel appearing to the shepherds . . . . 1·60 1·50
922 $1 Adoration of the kings . . 2·50 3·75

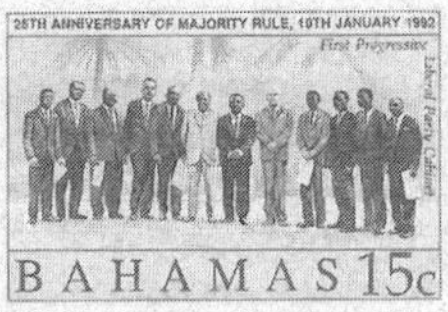

190 First Progressive Liberal Party Cabinet

1992. 25th Anniv of Majority Rule. Multicoloured.
924 15c. Type **190** 60 40
925 40c. Signing of Independence Constitution . . . . 1·40 1·10
926 55c. Prince of Wales handing over Constitutional Instrument (vert) . . . . . 1·50 1·50
927 60c. First Bahamian Governor-General, Sir Milo Butler (vert) . . . . 1·75 3·00

1992. 40th Anniv of Queen Elizabeth II's Accession. As T **143** of Ascension. Multicoloured.
928 15c. Queen Elizabeth with bouquet 60 30
929 40c. Queen Elizabeth with flags . . . . 1·10 70
930 55c. Queen Elizabeth at display . . . . 1·10 90
931 60c. Three portraits of Queen Elizabeth . . . . 1·25 1·50
932 $1 Queen Elizabeth II . . . 1·50 2·50

1992. 500th Anniv of Discovery of America by Columbus (5th issue). As T **173**. Multicoloured.
933 15c. Lucayans sighting fleet 1·75 1·00
934 40c. "Santa Maria" and dolphins . . . . 2·50 1·75
935 55c. Lucayan canoes approaching ships . . . . 2·50 2·25
936 60c. Columbus giving thanks for landfall . . . . 3·00 4·25

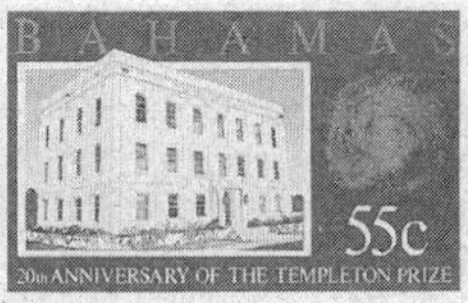

191 Templeton, Galbraith and Hansberger Ltd Building

1992. 20th Anniv of Templeton Prize for Religion.
938 **191** 55c. multicoloured . . . . 1·50 1·50

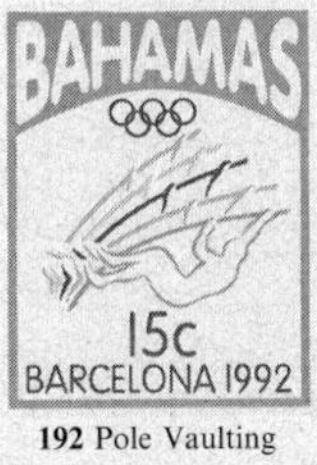

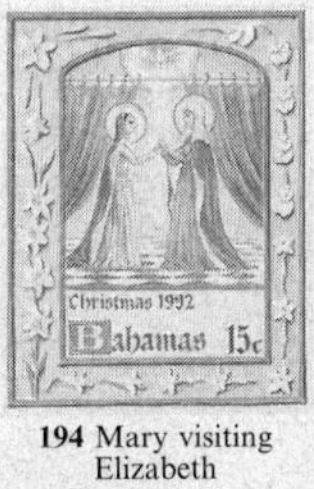

192 Pole Vaulting **194** Mary visiting Elizabeth

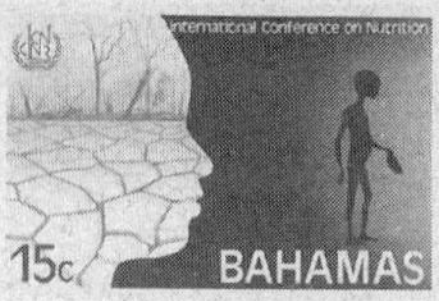

193 Arid Landscape and Starving Child

1992. Olympic Games, Barcelona. Multicoloured.

939	15c. Type **192**	60	50
940	40c. Javelin	1·00	90
941	55c. Hurdling	1·10	1·25
942	60c. Basketball	5·00	4·50

1992. International Conference on Nutrition, Rome. Multicoloured.

944	15c. Type **193**	1·00	75
945	55c. Seedling, cornfield and child	2·00	2·00

1992. Christmas. Multicoloured.

947	15c. Type **194**	40	20
948	55c. The Nativity	1·10	1·00
949	60c. Angel and shepherds	1·25	1·50
950	70c. Wise Men and star	1·40	2·50

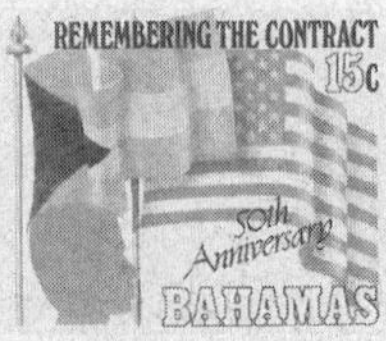

196 Flags of Bahamas and U.S.A. with Agricultural Worker

1993. 50th Anniv of The Contract (U.S.A.–Bahamas farm labour programme). Each including national flags. Multicoloured.

953	15c. Type **196**	1·75	70
954	55c. Onions	2·25	1·50
955	60c. Citrus fruit	2·25	2·50
956	70c. Apples	2·50	3·00

1993. 75th Anniv of Royal Air Force. As T **149** of Ascension. Multicoloured.

957	15c. Westland Wapiti IIA	1·25	85
958	40c. Gloster Gladiator I	2·00	1·00
959	55c. De Havilland Vampire F.3	2·25	1·75
960	70c. English Electric Lightning F.3	2·50	3·75

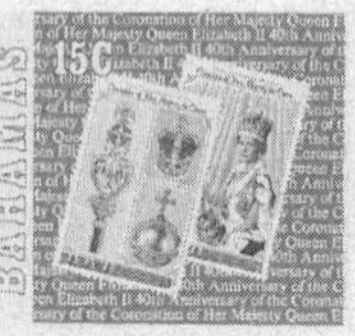

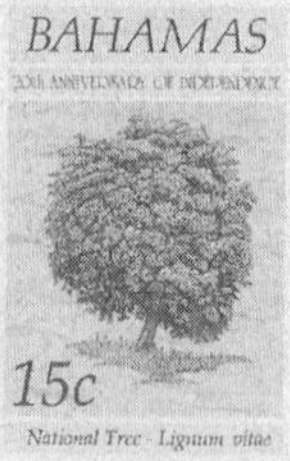

197 1978 Coronation Anniversary Stamps

198 "Lignum vitae" (national tree)

1993. 40th Anniv of Coronation. Multicoloured.

962	15c. Type **197**	70	50
963	55c. Two examples of 1953 Coronation stamp	1·75	1·75
964	60c. 1977 Silver Jubilee 8c. and 16c. stamps	1·75	2·00
965	70c. 1977 Silver Jubilee 21c. and 40c. stamps	2·00	2·75

1993. 20th Anniv of Independence. Mult.

966	15c. Type **198**	20	20
967	55c. Yellow elder (national flower)	90	90
968	60c. Blue marlin (national fish)	1·00	1·25
969	70c. Greater flamingo (national bird)	1·40	2·25

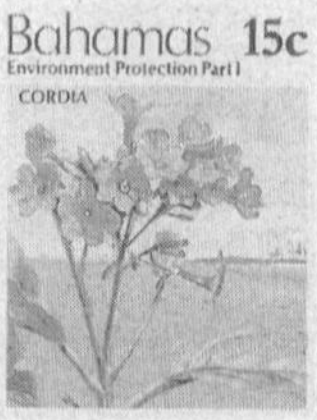

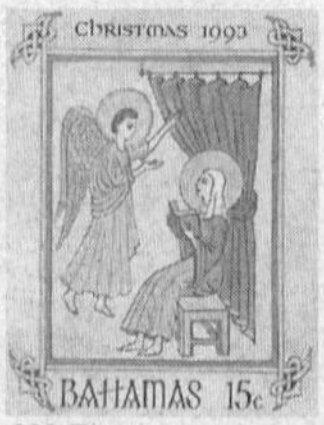

199 Cordia

200 The Annunciation

1993. Environment Protection (1st series). Wildflowers. Multicoloured.

970	15c. Type **199**	85	50
971	55c. Seaside morning glory	2·25	1·25
972	60c. Poinciana	2·50	2·25
973	70c. Spider lily	3·00	3·25

See also Nos. 1017/21, 1035/8, 1084/7, 1121/4, 1149/53 and 1193/6.

1993. Christmas. Multicoloured.

990	15c. Type **200**	85	50
991	55c. Angel and shepherds	2·50	1·75
992	60c. Holy Family	2·00	2·50
993	70c. Three Kings	3·00	3·25

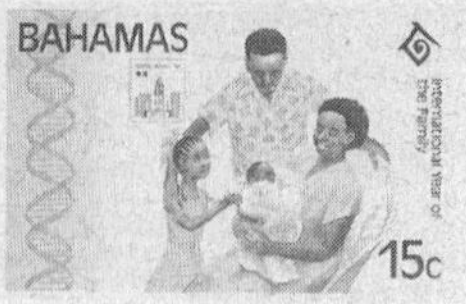

201 Family

1994. "Hong Kong '94" International Stamp Exhibition. International Year of the Family. Multicoloured.

995	15c. Type **201**	70	40
996	55c. Children doing homework	1·75	1·25
997	60c. Grandfather and grandson fishing	1·90	1·75
998	70c. Grandmother teaching grandchildren the Lord's Prayer	2·50	4·00

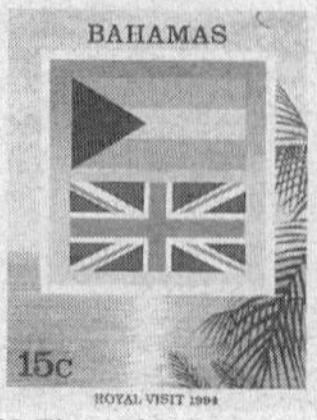

202 Flags of Bahamas and Great Britain

1994. Royal Visit. Multicoloured.

999	15c. Type **202**	1·00	50
1000	55c. Royal Yacht "Britannia"	2·25	1·75
1001	60c. Queen Elizabeth II	2·25	1·90
1002	70c. Queen Elizabeth and Prince Philip	2·25	3·50

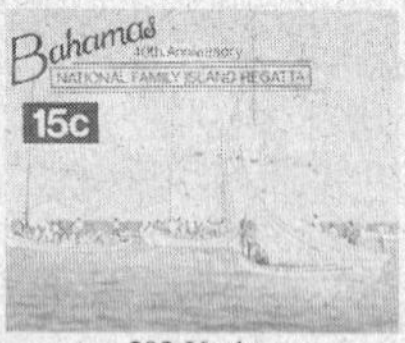

203 Yachts

1994. 40th Anniv of National Family Island Regatta. Multicoloured.

1003	15c. Type **203**	80	40
1004	55c. Dinghies racing	1·75	1·25
1005	60c. Working boats	1·75	1·75
1006	70c. Sailing sloop	2·25	4·00

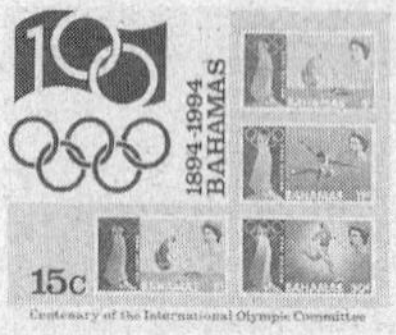

204 Logo and Bahamas 1968 Olympic Games Stamp

1994. Centenary of International Olympic Committee. Multicoloured.

1008	15c. Type **204**	1·25	50
1009	55c. 1976 Olympic Games stamps (vert)	2·25	1·25
1010	60c. 1984 Olympic Games stamps	2·25	2·25
1011	70c. 1992 Olympic Games stamps (vert)	2·50	3·50

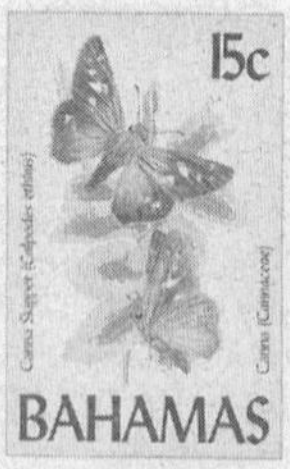

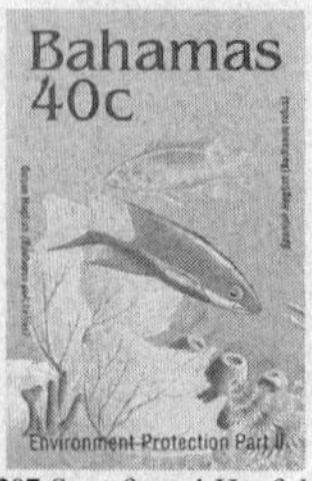

206 "Calpodes ethlius" and Canna

207 Spot-finned Hogfish and Spanish Hogfish

1994. Butterflies and Flowers. Multicoloured.

1013	15c. Type **206**	1·10	55
1014	55c. "Phoebis sennae" and cassia	2·00	1·50
1015	60c. "Anartia jatrophae" and passion flower	2·25	2·25
1016	70c. "Battus devilliersi" and calico flower	2·25	2·75

1994. Environment Protection (2nd series). Marine Life. Multicoloured.

1017	40c. Type **207**	1·00	1·25
1018	40c. Tomate and long-spined squirrelfish	1·00	1·25
1019	40c. French angelfish	1·00	1·25
1020	40c. Queen angelfish	1·00	1·25
1021	40c. Rock beauty	1·00	1·25

Nos. 1017/21 were printed together, se-tenant, with the backgrounds forming a composite design.

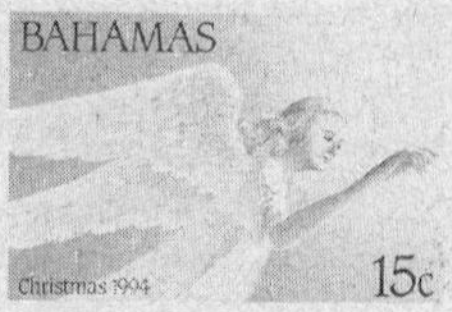

208 Angel

1994. Christmas. Multicoloured.

1023	15c. Type **208**	30	30
1024	55c. Holy Family	90	1·10
1025	60c. Shepherds	1·10	1·40
1026	70c. Wise Men	1·25	2·00

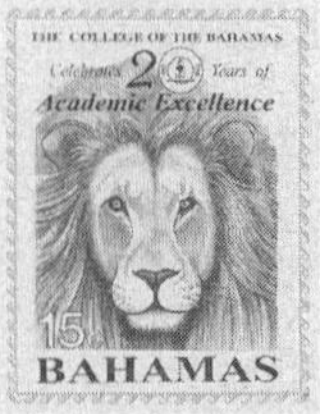

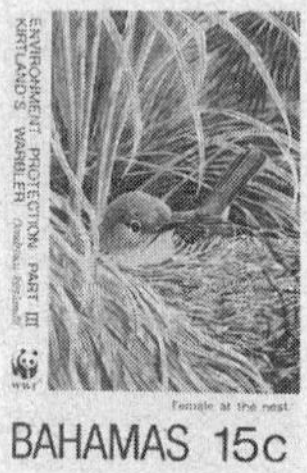

209 Lion and Emblem

210 Kirtlands Warbler on Nest

1995. 20th Anniv of the College of the Bahamas. Multicoloured.

1028	15c. Type **209**	30	30
1029	70c. Queen Elizabeth II and College building	1·25	1·75

1995. 50th Anniv of End of Second World War. As T **161** of Ascension. Multicoloured.

1030	15c. Bahamian infantry drilling	75	50
1031	55c. Consolidated PBY-5A Catalina flying boat	2·00	1·25
1032	60c. Bahamian women in naval operations room	2·00	2·25
1033	70c. Consolidated B-24 Liberator bomber	2·50	3·25

1995. Environment Protection (3rd series). Endangered Species. Kirtland's Warbler. Mult.

1035	15c. Type **210**	55	60
1036	15c. Singing on branch	55	60
1037	25c. Feeding chicks	55	60
1038	25c. Catching insects	55	60

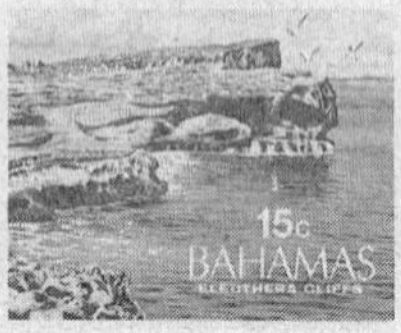

211 Eleuthera Cliffs

1995. Tourism. Multicoloured.

1040	15c. Type **211**	75	50
1041	55c. Clarence Town, Long Island	1·75	1·25
1042	60c. Albert Lowe Museum	2·00	2·25
1043	70c. Yachts	2·25	3·25

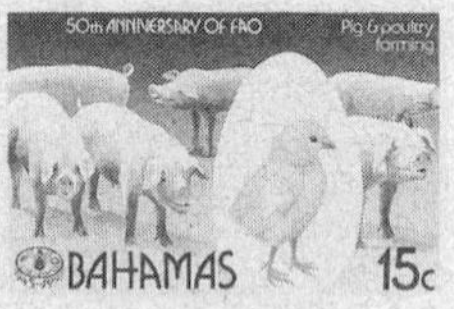

212 Pigs and Chick

1995. 50th Anniv of F.A.O. Multicoloured.

1044	15c. Type **212**	85	50
1045	55c. Seedling and hand holding seed	1·40	1·10
1046	60c. Family with fruit and vegetables	1·75	2·00
1047	70c. Fishes and crustaceans	2·50	3·25

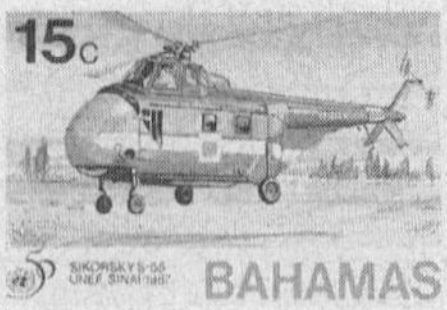

213 Sikorsky S-55 Helicopter, Sinai, 1957

1995. 50th Anniv of United Nations. Multicoloured.

1048	15c. Type **213**	70	50
1049	55c. Ferret armoured car, Sinai, 1957	1·25	1·25
1050	60c. Fokker F.27 Friendship (airliner), Cambodia, 1991–93	1·50	1·75
1051	70c. Lockheed C-130 Hercules (transport)	1·60	2·25

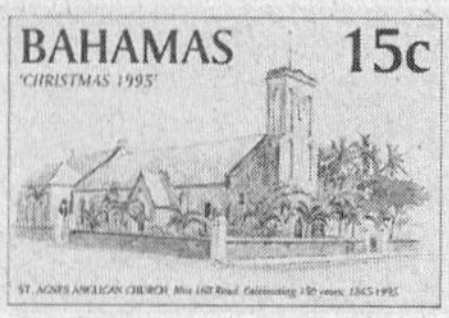

214 St. Agnes Anglican Church

1995. Christmas. Churches. Multicoloured.

1052	15c. Type **214**	30	25
1053	55c. Church of God, East Street	90	90
1054	60c. Sacred Heart Roman Catholic Church	95	1·25
1055	70c. Salem Union Baptist Church	1·10	1·75

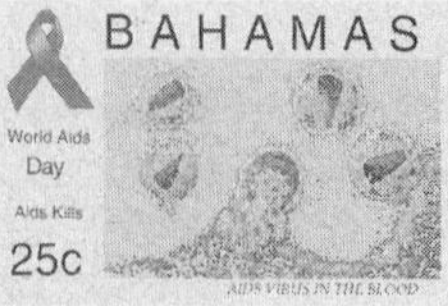

215 Microscopic View of AIDS Virus

1995. World AIDS Day. Multicoloured.

1056	25c. Type **215**	60	50
1057	70c. Research into AIDS	1·00	1·50

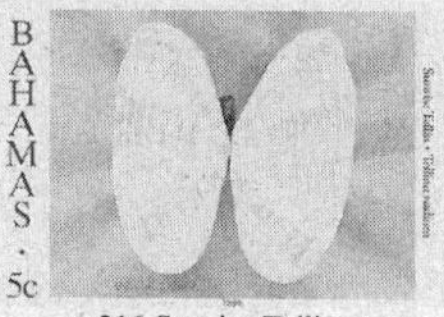

216 Sunrise Tellin

1996. Sea Shells. Multicoloured.

1098	5c. Type **216**	10	10
1099	10c. Queen conch	15	20
1100	15c. Angular triton	20	25
1101	20c. True tulip	30	35
1102	25c. Reticulated cowrie-helmet	35	40
1063	30c. Sand dollar	1·00	55
1103a	35c. As 30c.	50	55
1104	40c. Lace short-frond murex	55	60
1065	45c. Inflated sea biscuit	1·25	60
1106	50c. West Indian top shell	70	75
1067	55c. Spiny oyster	1·50	75
1108	60c. King helmet	85	90
1108a	65c. As 45c.	90	95
1109	70c. Lion's paw	1·00	1·10
1109a	80c. As 55c.	1·10	1·25
1110	$1 Crown cone	1·40	1·50
1111	$2 Atlantic partridge tun	2·75	3·00
1112	$5 Wide-mouthed purpura	7·00	7·25
1113	$10 Atlantic trumpet triton	14·00	14·50

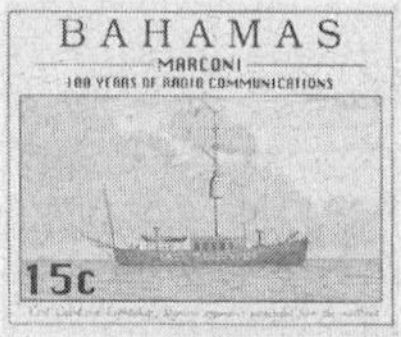

217 East Goodwin Lightship with Marconi Apparatus on Mast

1996. Centenary of Radio. Multicoloured.

1074	15c. Type **217**	1·50	65
1075	55c. Newspaper headline concerning Dr. Crippen	2·00	1·25
1076	60c. "Philadelphia" (liner) and first readable transatlantic message	2·00	2·00
1077	70c. Guglielmo Marconi and "Elettra" (yacht)	2·50	3·25

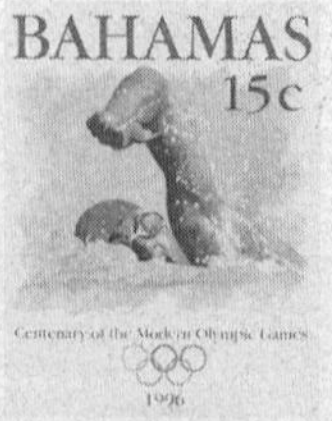

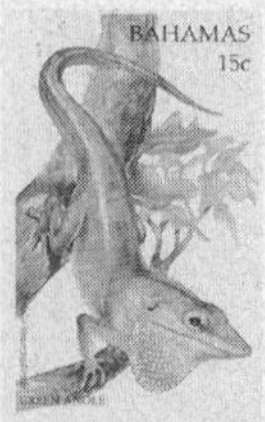

218 Swimming

219 Green Anole

1996. Centenary of Modern Olympic Games. Multicoloured.

1079	15c. Type **218**	40	35
1080	55c. Running	90	90
1081	60c. Basketball	1·75	1·75
1082	70c. Long jumping	1·40	2·25

1996. Environment Protection (4th series). Reptiles. Multicoloured.

1084	15c. Type **219**	55	50
1085	55c. Little Bahama bank boa	1·10	1·00
1086	60c. Inagua freshwater turtle	1·50	1·75
1087	70c. Acklins rock iguana	1·75	2·75

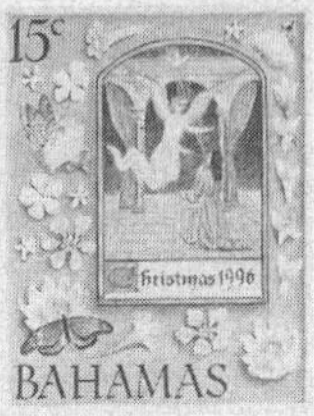
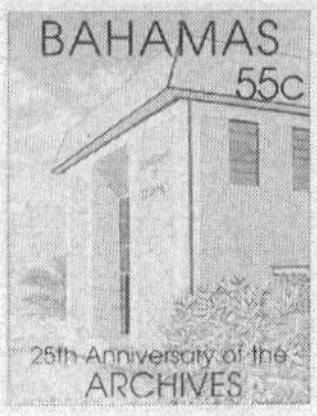

220 The Annunciation 221 Department of Archives Building

1996. Christmas. Multicoloured.
1089 15c. Type **220** 75 40
1090 55c. Joseph and Mary travelling to Bethlehem 1·75 85
1091 60c. Shepherds and angel . . 1·75 1·50
1092 70c. Adoration of the Magi 2·00 2·75

1996. 25th Anniv of Archives Department.
1094 **221** 55c. multicoloured . . . 1·25 1·00

1997. Golden Wedding of Queen Elizabeth and Prince Philip. As T **173** of Ascension. Multicoloured.
1114 50c. Queen Elizabeth II in Bonn, 1992 . . . . 1·40 1·60
1115 50c. Prince Philip and Prince Charles at Trooping the Colour . . . . 1·40 1·60
1116 60c. Prince Philip . . . . . 1·60 1·75
1117 60c. Queen at Trooping the Colour . . . . 1·60 1·75
1118 70c. Queen Elizabeth and Prince Philip at polo, 1970 . . . . 1·75 1·90
1119 70c. Prince Charles playing polo . . . . 1·75 1·90

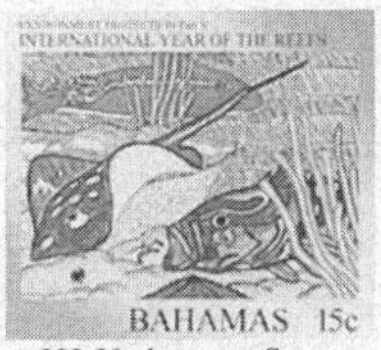

222 Underwater Scene

1997. Environment Protection (5th series). International Year of the Reefs.
1121 **222** 15c. multicoloured . . . 75 50
1122 – 55c. multicoloured . . . 1·60 1·00
1123 – 60c. multicoloured . . . 1·75 1·50
1124 – 70c. multicoloured . . . 2·00 2·50
DESIGNS: 55c. to 70c. Different children's paintings of underwater scenes.

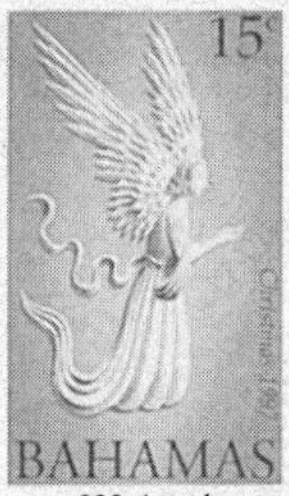
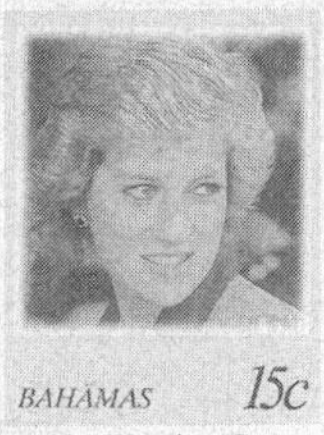

223 Angel 223a Wearing Grey Jacket, 1988

1997. Christmas. Multicoloured.
1125 15c. Type **223** 75 40
1126 55c. Mary and Baby Jesus 1·25 80
1127 60c. Shepherd . . . . . . 1·50 1·10
1128 70c. King . . . . 1·75 2·50

1998. Diana, Princess of Wales Commemoration.
1130 **223a** 15c. multicoloured . . . 40 40

1998. 80th Anniv of the Royal Air Force. As T **178** of Ascension. Multicoloured.
1132 15c. Handley Page Hyderabad 55 40
1133 55c. Hawker Demon . . . . 1·00 85
1134 60c. Gloster Meteor F.8 . . 1·10 1·25
1135 70c. Lockheed Neptune MR.1 . . . . 1·40 2·25

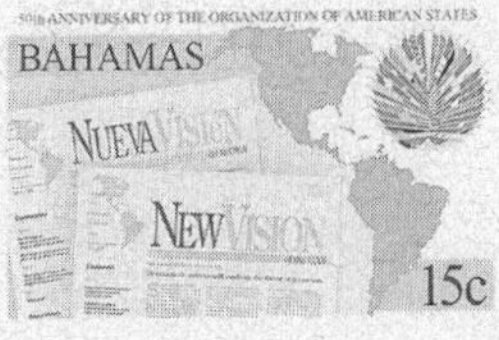

224 Newsletters

1998. 50th Anniv of Organization of American States. Multicoloured.
1137 15c. Type **224** 30 30
1138 55c. Headquarters building and flags, Washington . . 70 80

225 Start of Declaration and Birds

1998. 50th Anniv of Universal Declaration of Human Rights.
1139 **225** 55c. blue and black . . . 1·25 1·00

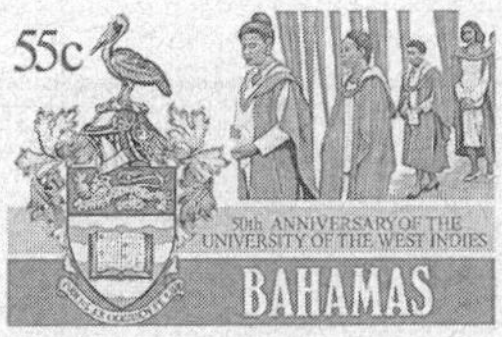

226 University Arms and Graduates

1998. 50th Anniv of University of the West Indies.
1140 **226** 55c. multicoloured . . . 1·25 1·00

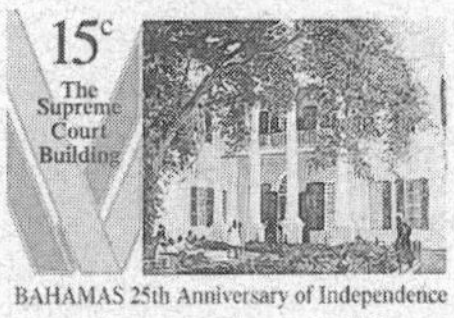

227 Supreme Court Building

1998. 25th Anniv of Independence. Multicoloured.
1141 15c. Type **227** 65 50
1142 55c. Nassau Library . . . . 1·25 1·00
1143 60c. Government House . . 1·40 1·40
1144 70c. Gregory Arch . . . . 1·60 2·00

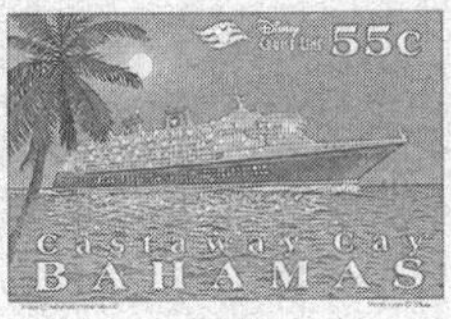

228 "Disney Magic" (cruise liner) at Night

1998. Disney Cruise Line's Castaway Cay Holiday Development. Multicoloured.
1146 55c. Type **228** . . . . . . 1·25 1·25
1147 55c. "Disney Magic" by day 1·25 1·25

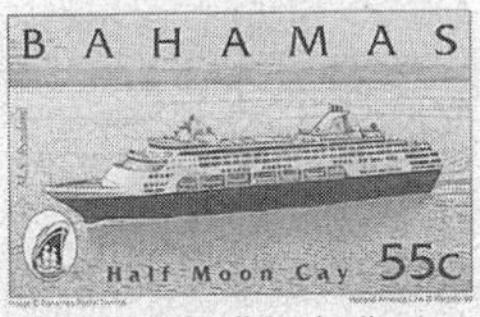

229 "Ryndam" (cruise liner)

1998. Holland America Line's Half Moon Cay Holiday Development.
1148 **229** 55c. multicoloured . . . 1·50 1·00

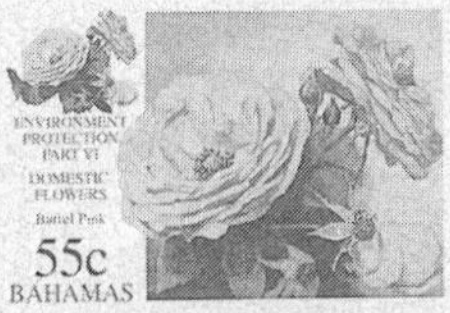

230 Barrel Pink Rose

1998. Environment Protection (6th series). Roses. Multicoloured.
1149 55c. Type **230** . . . . . . 1·00 1·25
1150 55c. Yellow cream . . . . . 1·00 1·25
1151 55c. Seven sisters . . . . . 1·00 1·25
1152 55c. Big red . . . . 1·00 1·25
1153 55c. Island beauty . . . . . 1·00 1·25

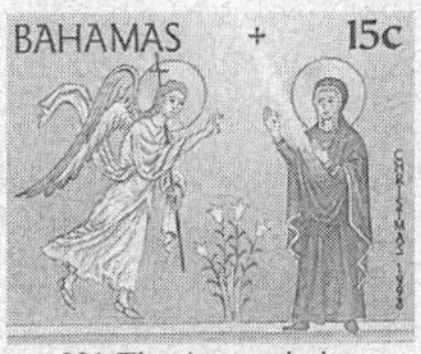

231 The Annunciation

1998. Christmas. Multicoloured.
1155 15c. Type **231** 50 30
1156 55c. Shepherds . . . . . . 1·00 70
1157 60c. Three Kings . . . . . 1·25 1·10
1158 70c. The Flight into Egypt 1·50 2·00

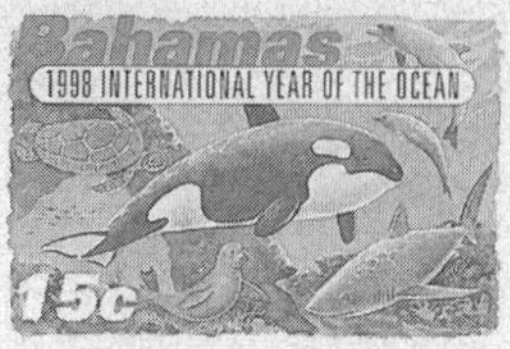

232 Killer Whale and other Marine Life

1998. International Year of the Ocean. Multicoloured.
1160 15c. Type **232** 65 50
1161 55c. Tropical fish 85 90

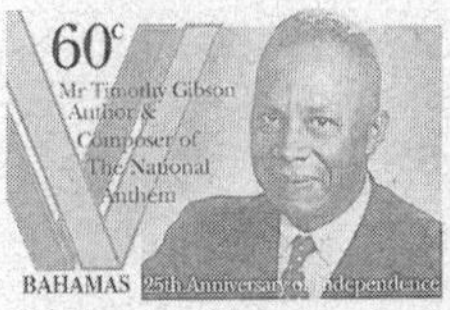

233 Timothy Gibson (composer)

1998. 25th Anniv of "March on Bahamaland" (national anthem).
1162 **233** 60c. multicoloured . . . 1·00 1·25

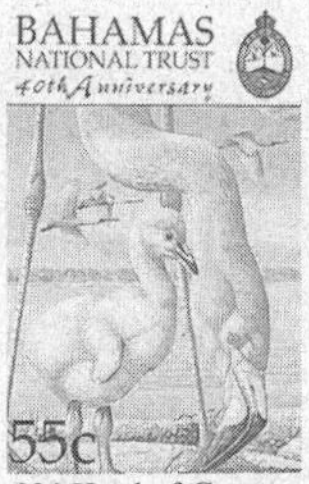

234 Head of Greater Flamingo and Chick

1999. 40th Anniv of National Trust (1st issue). Inagua National Park. Multicoloured.
1163 55c. Type **234** . . . . . . 1·00 1·25
1164 55c. Pair with two chicks . . 1·00 1·25
1165 55c. Greater flamingos asleep or stretching wings 1·00 1·25
1166 55c. Greater flamingos feeding . . . . 1·00 1·25
1167 55c. Greater flamingos in flight . . . . 1·00 1·25
Nos. 1163/7 were printed together, se-tenant, with the backgrounds forming a composite design.
See also Nos. 1173/7, 1198/1202 and 1207/11.

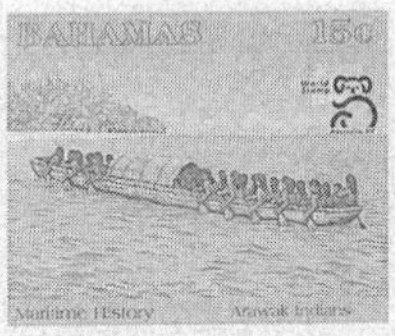

235 Arawak Indian Canoe

1999. "Australia '99" World Stamp Exhibition, Melbourne. Maritime History. Multicoloured.
1168 15c. Type **235** 30 30
1169 55c. "Santa Maria" (Columbus), 1492 . . . . 1·25 80
1170 60c. "Queen Anne's Revenge" (Blackbeard), 1716 . . . . 1·40 1·25
1171 70c. "The Banshee" (Confederate paddle-steamer) running blockade 1·50 2·00

1999. 40th Anniv of National Trust (2nd issue). Exuma Cays Land and Sea Park. As T **234**. Mult.
1173 55c. Dolphin . . . . 1·00 1·25
1174 55c. Angelfish and parrotfish 1·00 1·25
1175 55c. Queen triggerfish . . . 1·00 1·25
1176 55c. Turtle . . . . 1·00 1·25
1177 55c. Lobster . . . . 1·00 1·25
Nos. 1173/7 were printed together, se-tenant, with the backgrounds forming a composite design.

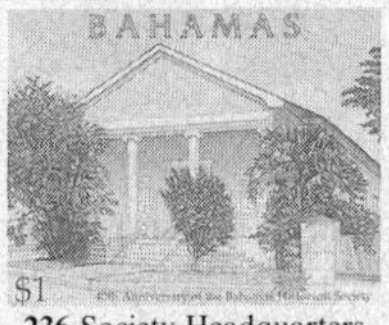

236 Society Headquarters Building

1999. 40th Anniv of Bahamas Historical Society.
1178 **236** $1 multicoloured . . . . 1·50 2·00

1999. 30th Anniv of First Manned Landing on Moon. As T **186** of Ascension. Multicoloured.
1179 15c. Constructing ascent module 45 35
1180 65c. Diagram of command and service module . . . 1·25 1·00
1181 70c. Lunar module descending . . . . 1·25 1·40
1182 80c. Lunar module preparing to dock with service module . . . . . 1·25 1·75

1999. "Queen Elizabeth the Queen Mother's Century". As T **187** of Ascension. Multicoloured.
1184 15c. Visiting Herts Hospital, 1940 . . . . 50 35
1185 65c. With Princess Elizabeth, Hyde Park, 1944 . . . . 1·40 1·00
1886 70c. With Prince Andrew, 1997 . . . . 1·40 1·40
1887 80c. With Irish Guards' mascot, 1997 . . . . . . 1·40 1·75

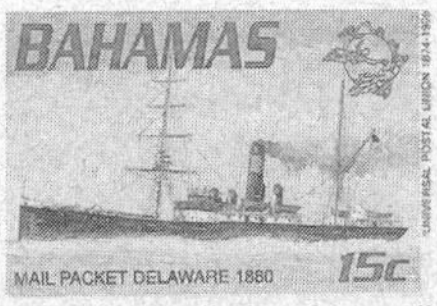

237 "Delaware" (American mail ship), 1880

1999. 125th Anniv of U.P.U. Ships. Multicoloured.
1189 15c. Type **237** 75 45
1190 65c. "Atlantis" (liner), 1923 1·50 1·00
1191 70c. "Queen of Bermuda 2" (liner), 1937 . . . . . . 1·50 1·50
1192 80c. U.S.S. "Saufley" (destroyer), 1943 . . . . 1·75 1·90

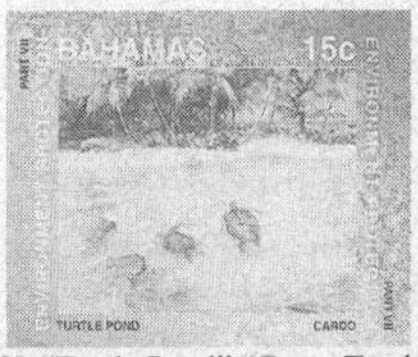

238 "Turtle Pond" (Green Turtle)

1999. Environment Protection (7th series). Marine Life Paintings by Ricardo Knowles. Multicoloured.
1193 15c. Type **238** 50 35
1194 65c. "Turtle Cliff" (Loggerhead turtle) . . . 1·25 1·00
1195 70c. "Barracuda" . . . . . 1·40 1·40
1196 80c. "Coral Reef" . . . . . 1·50 2·00
The 65c. is inscribed "GREEN TURTLES" in error.

1999. 40th Anniv of National Trust (3rd issue). Birds. As T **234**. Multicoloured.
1198 65c. Bridled tern and white-tailed tropic bird . . . . 1·00 1·25
1199 65c. Louisiana heron . . . 1·00 1·25
1200 65c. Bahama woodstar . . . 1·00 1·25
1201 65c. Black-billed whistling duck . . . . 1·00 1·25
1202 65c. Cuban amazon . . . . 1·00 1·25
Nos. 1198/1202 were printed together, se-tenant, with the backgrounds forming a composite design.

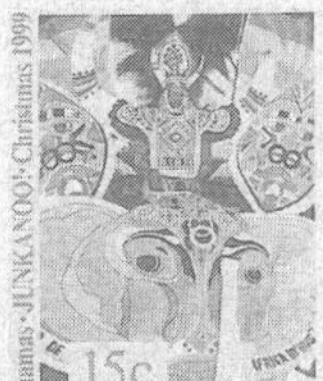

239 Man on Elephant Float

1999. Christmas. Junkanoo Festival. Multicoloured.
1203 15c. Type **239** 50 30
1204 65c. Man in winged costume 1·00 1·00
1205 70c. Man in feathered mask 1·25 1·25
1206 80c. Man blowing conch shell . . . . 1·50 1·75

1999. 40th Anniv of National Trust (4th issue). Flora and Fauna. As T **234**. Multicoloured.
1207 65c. Foxglove . . . . . . 1·25 1·40
1208 65c. Vole . . . . 1·25 1·40
1209 65c. Cuban emerald . . . . 1·25 1·40
1210 65c. Lizard . . . . 1·25 1·40
1211 65c. Red hibiscus . . . . . 1·25 1·40
Nos. 1207/11 were printed together, se-tenant, with the backgrounds forming a composite design.

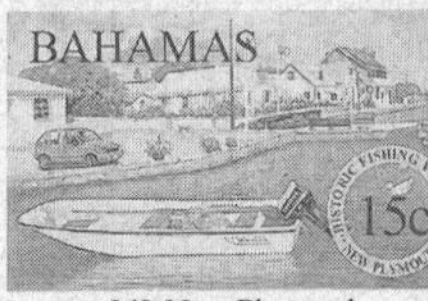

240 New Plymouth

2000. Historic Fishing Villages. Multicoloured.
1212 15c. Type **240** 50 30
1213 65c. Cherokee Sound . . . 1·25 1·00
1214 70c. Hope Town . . . . . 1·40 1·40
1215 80c. Spanish Wells . . . . 1·50 2·00

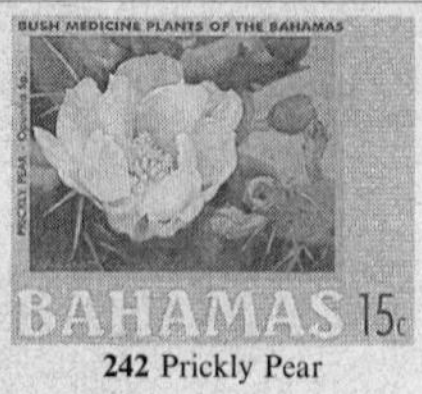

242 Prickly Pear

2000. Medicinal Plants. Multicoloured.

1217	15c. Type **242**	35	30
1218	65c. Buttercup	1·25	1·00
1219	70c. Shepherd's needle	1·25	1·25
1220	80c. Five fingers	1·40	1·60

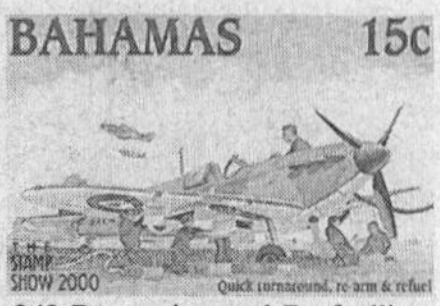

243 Re-arming and Re-fuelling Spitfire

2000. "The Stamp Show 2000" International Stamp Exhibition, London. 60th Anniv of Battle of Britain. Multicoloured.

1221	15c. Type **243**	50	35
1222	65c. Sqdn. Ldr. Stanford-Tuck's Hurricane Mk I	1·25	1·25
1223	70c. Dogfight between Spitfires and Heinkel IIIs	1·40	1·60

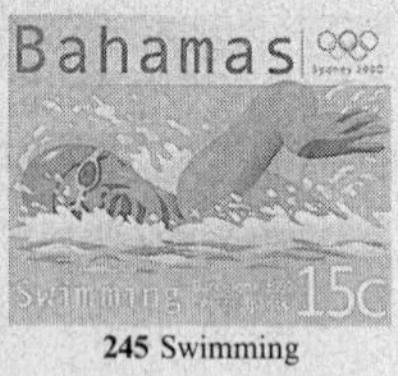

245 Swimming

2000. Olympic Games, Sydney. Each inscribed with details of previous Bahamian participation. Mult.

1227	15c. Type **245**	35	25
1228	65c. Triple jump	1·25	1·00
1229	70c. Women's 4 × 100 m relay	1·25	1·25
1230	80c. Sailing	1·40	1·60

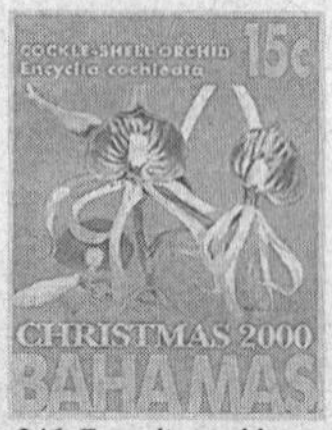

246 *Encyclia cochleata*

2000. Christmas. Orchids. Multicoloured.

1231	15c. Type **246**	45	30
1232	65c. *Encyclia plicata*	1·25	1·00
1233	70c. *Bletia purpurea*	1·40	1·40
1234	80c. *Encyclia gracilis*	1·50	1·60

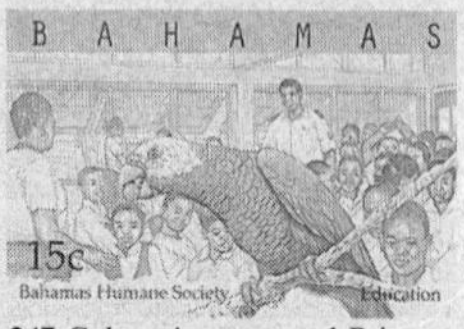

247 Cuban Amazon and Primary School Class

2000. Bahamas Humane Society. Multicoloured.

1235	15c. Type **247**	40	30
1236	65c. Cat and Society stall	1·25	1·00
1237	70c. Dogs and veterinary surgery	1·40	1·40
1238	80c. Goat and animal rescue van	1·50	1·60

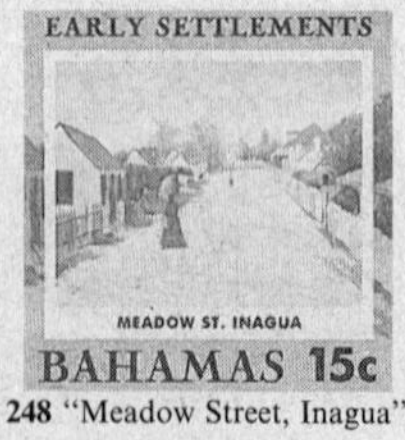

248 "Meadow Street, Inagua"

2001. Early Settlements. Paintings by Ricardo Knowles. Multicoloured.

1239	15c. Type **248**	40	30
1240	65c. "Bain Town"	1·25	1·00
1241	70c. "Hope Town, Abaco"	1·40	1·40
1242	80c. "Blue Hills"	1·50	1·60

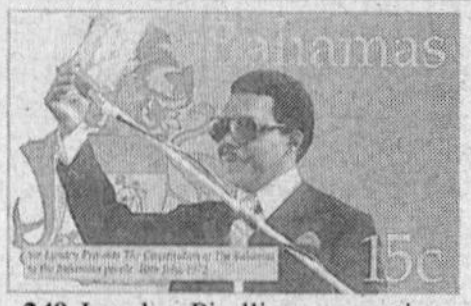

249 Lynden Pindling presenting Independence Constitution, 1972

2001. Sir Lynden Pindling (former Prime Minister) Commemoration. Multicoloured.

1243	15c. Type **249**	35	25
1244	65c. Sir Lynden Pindling with Bahamas flag	1·40	1·25

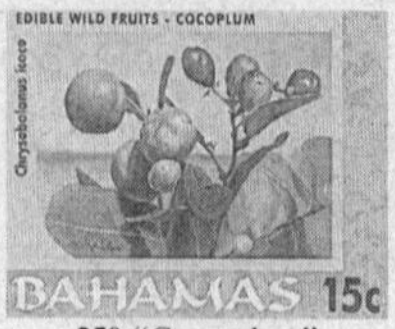

250 "Cocoaplum"

2001. Edible Wild Fruits. Paintings by Alton Roland Lowe. Multicoloured.

1245	15c. Type **250**	20	25
1246	65c. "Guana Berry"	90	95
1247	70c. "Mastic"	1·00	1·10
1248	80c. "Seagrape"	1·10	1·25

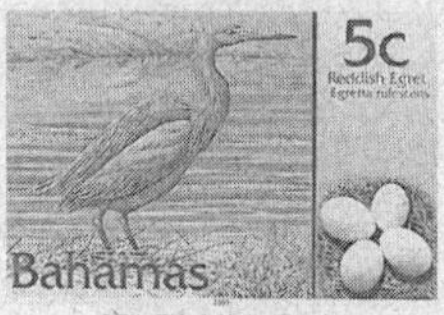

251 Reddish Egret

2001. Birds and their Eggs. Multicoloured.

1249	5c. Type **251**	10	15
1250	10c. American purple gallinule	10	15
1251	15c. Antillean nighthawk	20	25
1252	20c. Wilson's plover	30	35
1253	25c. Killdeer plover	35	40
1254	30c. Bahama woodstar	40	45
1255	40c. Bahama swallow	55	60
1256	50c. Bahama mockingbird	70	75
1257	60c. Black-cowled oriole	85	90
1258	65c. Great lizard cuckoo	90	95
1259	70c. Audubon's shearwater	1·00	1·10
1260	80c. Grey kingbird	1·10	1·25
1261	$1 Bananaquit	1·40	1·50
1262	$2 Yellow warbler	2·75	3·00
1263	$5 Greater Antillean bullfinch	7·00	7·25
1264	$10 Roseate spoonbill	14·00	14·50

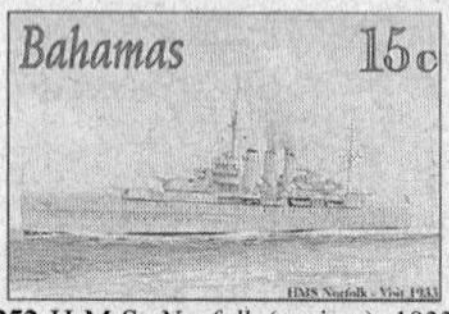

252 H.M.S. *Norfolk* (cruiser), 1933

2001. Royal Navy Ships connected to Bahamas. Multicoloured.

1265	15c. Type **252**	20	25
1266	25c. H.M.S. *Scarborough* (sloop), 1930s	30	35
1267	50c. H.M.S. *Bahamas* (frigate), 1944	70	75
1268	65c. H.M.S. *Battleaxe* (frigate), 1979	90	95
1269	70c. H.M.S. *Invincible* (aircraft carrier), 1997	1·00	1·10
1270	80c. H.M.S. *Norfolk* (frigate), 2000	1·10	1·25

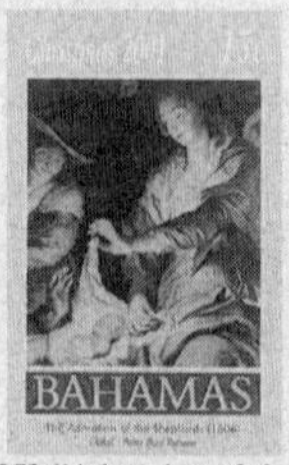

253 "Adoration of the Shepherds"

2001. Christmas. Paintings by Rubens. Multicoloured.

1271	15c. Type **253**	20	25
1272	65c. "Adoration of the Magi" (with Van Dyck)	90	95
1273	70c. "Holy Virgin in Wreath of Flowers" (with Breughel)	1·00	1·10
1274	80c. "Holy Virgin adored by Angels"	1·10	1·25

2002. Golden Jubilee. As T **200** of Ascension.

1275	15c. black, green and gold	20	25
1276	65c. multicoloured	90	95
1277	70c. multicoloured	1·00	1·25
1278	80c. multicoloured	1·10	1·25

DESIGNS: 15c. Princess Elizabeth; 65c. Queen Elizabeth in Bonn, 1992; 70c. Queen Elizabeth with Prince Edward, 1965; 80c. Queen Elizabeth at Sandringham, 1996.

SPECIAL DELIVERY STAMPS

1916. Optd **SPECIAL DELIVERY**.

S2 **6**	5d. black and orange	45	6·50
S3	5d. black and mauve	30	2·50

BAHAWALPUR Pt. 1

A former state of Pakistan.

12 pies = 1 anna, 16 annas = 1 rupee.

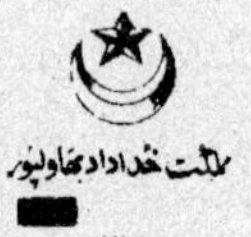

(1)

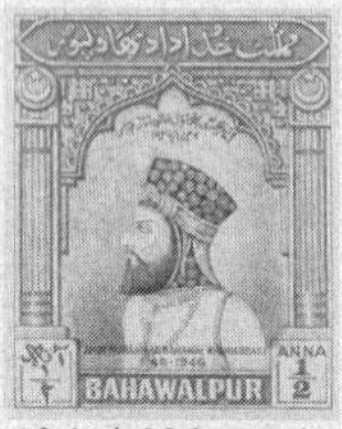

2 Amir Muhammad Bahawal Khan I Abbasi

1947. Nos. 265/8, 269a/77 and 259/62 of India optd with Type **1**.

1 **100a**	3p. slate	17·00
2	½a. purple	17·00
3	9p. green	17·00
4	1a. red	17·00
5 **101**	1½a. violet	17·00
6	2a. red	17·00
7	3a. violet	17·00
8	3½a. blue	17·00
9 **102**	4a. brown	17·00
10	6a. green	17·00
11	8a. violet	17·00
12	12a. lake	17·00
13	14a. purple	55·00
14 **93**	1r. grey and brown	22·00
15	2r. purple and brown	£1100
16	5r. green and blue	£1100
17	10r. purple and red	£1100

1948. Bicentenary Commemoration.

18 **2**	½a. black and red	1·75	2·00

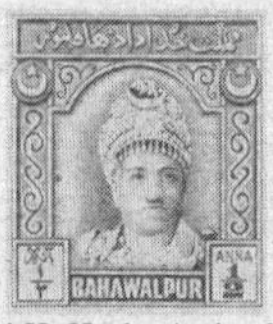

4 H. H. the Amir of Bahawalpur

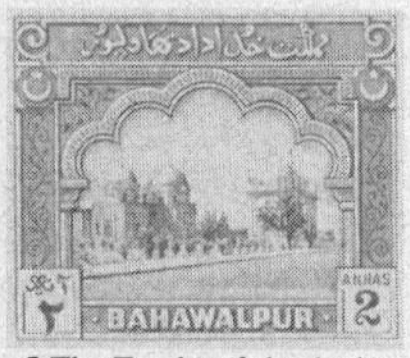

5 The Tombs of the Amirs

1948.

19 **4**	3p. black and blue	1·25	17·00
20	½a. black and red	1·25	17·00
21	9p. black and green	1·25	17·00
22	1a. black and red	1·25	17·00
23	1½a. black and violet	1·25	14·00
24 **5**	2a. green and red	1·50	18·00
25 –	4a. orange and brown	1·75	18·00
26 –	6a. violet and blue	1·75	18·00
27 –	8a. red and violet	1·75	18·00
28 –	12a. green and red	2·00	26·00
29 –	1r. violet and brown	19·00	38·00
35 –	1r. green and orange	1·25	16·00
30 –	2r. green and red	38·00	60·00
36 –	2r. black and red	1·50	19·00
31 –	5r. black and violet	38·00	75·00
37 –	5r. brown and blue	1·60	35·00
32 –	10r. red and black	32·00	90·00
38 –	10r. brown and green	1·75	40·00

DESIGNS—HORIZ: 6a. Fort Derawar from the lake; 8a. Nur-Mahal Palace; 12a. Sadiq-Garh Palace. 46 × 32 mm: 10r. Three generations of Rulers. VERT (As Type **5**): 4a. Mosque in Sadiq-Garh; 1, 2, 5r. H.H. the Amir of Bahawalpur.

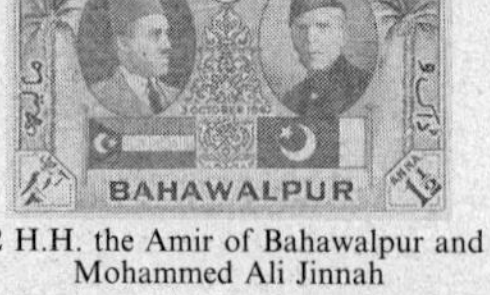

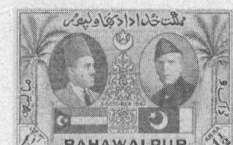

12 H.H. the Amir of Bahawalpur and Mohammed Ali Jinnah

1948. 1st Anniv of Union with Pakistan.

33 **12**	1½a. red and green	85	2·00

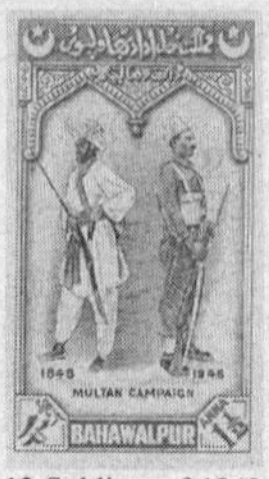

13 Soldiers of 1848 and 1948

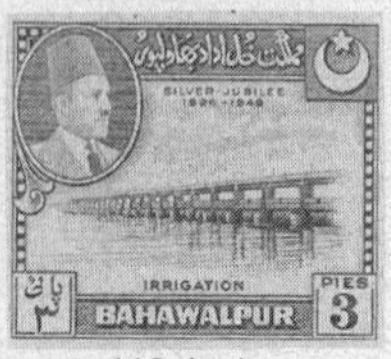

14 Irrigation

1948. Centenary of Multan Campaign.

34 **13**	1½a. black and red	70	8·00

1949. Silver Jubilee of Accession of H.H. the Amir of Bahawalpur.

39 **14**	3p. black and blue	10	8·00
40 –	½a. black and orange	10	8·00
41 –	9p. black and green	10	8·00
42 –	1a. black and red	10	8·00

DESIGNS: ½a. Wheat; 9p. Cotton; 1a. Sahiwal bull.

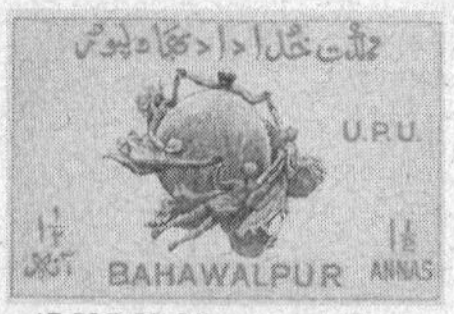

17 U.P.U. Monument, Berne

1949. 75th Anniv of U.P.U.

43 **17**	9p. black and green	20	1·25
44	1a. black and mauve	20	1·25
45	1½a. black and orange	20	1·25
46	2½a. black and blue	20	1·25

OFFICIAL STAMPS

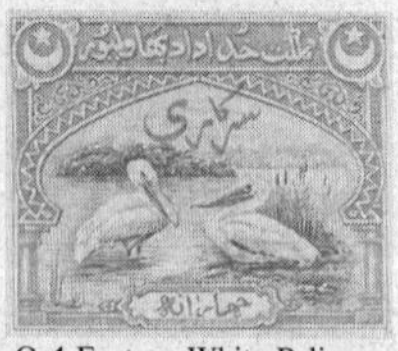

O 4 Eastern White Pelicans

1945. As Type O **4** with Arabic opt.

O1 –	½a. black and green	2·75	12·00
O2 –	1a. black and red	3·75	6·00
O7 –	1a. black and brown	32·00	48·00
O3 –	2a. black and violet	3·25	9·50
O4 O **4**	4a. black and olive	9·00	23·00
O5 –	8a. black and brown	21·00	13·00
O6 –	1r. black and orange	21·00	12·00

DESIGNS: ½a. Panjnad Weir; 1a. (No. O2), Camel and calf; 1a. (No. O7), Baggage camels; 2a. Blackbuck antelopes; 8a. Friday Mosque, Fort Derawar; 1r. Temple at Pattan Munara.

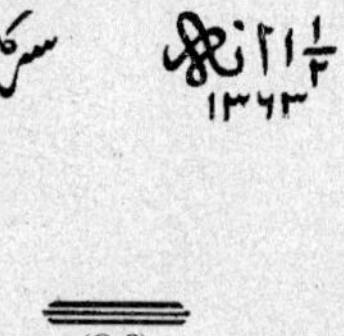

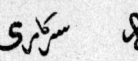

(O 8)

1945. Types as Nos. O1, etc., in new colours and without Arabic opt. (a) Surch as Type O **8**.

O11	½a. on 8a. black and purple (as No. O5)	4·25	3·50
O12	1½a. on 5r. black and orange (as No. O6)	35·00	9·00
O13	1½a. on 2r. black and blue (as No. O1)	£120	7·00

(b) Optd **SERVICE** and Arabic inscription.

O14	½a. black and red (as No. O1)	1·25	11·00
O15	1a. black and red (as No. O2)	2·00	13·00
O16	2a. black and orange (as No. O3)	3·25	42·00

1945. As Type **4** but inscr "SERVICE" at left.

O17	3p. black and blue	3·00	7·00
O18	1½a. black and violet	17·00	7·00

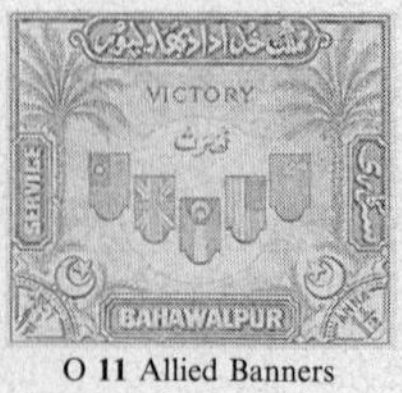

O 11 Allied Banners

1946. Victory.

O19 O **11**	1½a. green and grey	2·00	3·00

1948. Stamps of 1948 with Arabic opt as in Type O **4**.

O20 **4**	3p. black and blue	70	10·00

O21		1a. black and red	70	9·00
O22	5	2a. green and red	70	10·00
O23	–	4a. orange and brown	70	14·00
O24	–	1r. green and orange	70	16·00
O25	–	2r. black and red	70	22·00
O26	–	5r. chocolate and blue	70	35·00
O27	–	10r. brown and green	70	35·00

1949. 75th Anniv of U.P.U. optd as in Type O 4.

O28	17	9p. black and green	15	4·50
O29		1a. black and mauve	15	4·50
O30		1½a. black and orange	15	4·50
O31		2½a. black and blue	15	4·50

BAHRAIN Pt. 1, Pt. 19

An archipelago in the Persian Gulf on the Arabian coast. An independent shaikhdom with Indian and later British postal administration. The latter was closed on 1 January 1966, when the Bahrain Post Office took over.

1933. 12 pies = 1 anna; 16 annas = 1 rupee.
1957. 100 naya paise = 1 rupee.

Stamps of India optd **BAHRAIN**.

1933. King George V.

1	55	3p. grey	3·50	45
2	56	½a. green	7·50	3·25
15	79	½a. green	4·50	55
3	80	9p. green	3·75	1·50
4	57	1a. brown	7·00	2·50
16	81	1a. brown	10·00	40
5	82	1a.3p. mauve	5·00	1·00
6	70	2a. orange	10·00	12·00
17	59	2a. orange	40·00	7·50
7	62	3a. blue	19·00	45·00
18		3a. red	4·75	50
8	83	3a.6p. blue	3·75	30
9	71	4a. green	18·00	45·00
19	63	4a. olive	4·50	40
10	65	8a. mauve	6·00	30
11	66	12a. red	7·50	1·25
12	67	1r. brown and green	16·00	7·50
13		2r. red and orange	32·00	38·00
14		5r. blue and violet	£110	£140

1938. King George VI.

20	91	3p. slate	9·00	3·25
21		½a. brown	5·00	10
22		9p. green	5·00	5·50
23		1a. red	4·50	10
24	92	2a. red	6·50	1·50
26	–	3a. green (No. 253)	12·00	5·00
27	–	3a.6p. blue (No. 254)	4·75	3·25
28	–	4a. brown (No. 255)	£120	65·00
30	–	8a. violet (No. 257)	£140	35·00
31	–	12a. red (No. 258)	£100	45·00
32	93	1r. slate and brown	2·75	1·75
33		2r. purple and brown	13·00	4·75
34		5r. green and blue	15·00	13·00
35		10r. purple and red	65·00	35·00
36		15r. brown and green	60·00	35·00
37		25r. slate and purple	£100	85·00

1942. King George VI.

38	100a	3p. slate	2·25	1·00
39		½a. mauve	4·00	1·50
40		9p. green	13·00	14·00
41		1a. red	4·00	50
42	101	1a.3p. bistre	8·00	16·00
43		1½a. violet	4·75	4·25
44		2a. red	5·50	1·50
45		3a. violet	17·00	4·25
46		3½a. blue	4·00	15·00
47	102	4a. brown	2·25	1·50
48		6a. green	12·00	9·00
49		8a. violet	3·75	2·50
50		12a. purple	6·00	4·00

Stamps of Great Britain surch **BAHRAIN** and new value in Indian currency.

1948. King George VI.

51	128	½a. on ½d. green	50	1·25
71		½a. on ½d. orange	2·00	2·00
52		1a. on 1d. red	50	1·50
72		1a. on 1d. blue	2·50	20
53		1½a. on 1½d. brown	50	1·75
73		1½a. on 1½d. green	2·50	12·00
54		2a. on 2d. orange	50	20
74		2a. on 2d. brown	1·00	30
55		2½a. on 2½d. blue	50	2·75
75		2½a. on 2½d. red	2·50	12·00
56		3a. on 3d. violet	50	10
76	129	4a. on 4d. blue	2·50	1·50
57		6a. on 6d. purple	50	10
58	130	1r. on 1s. brown	1·25	10
59	131	2r. on 2s.6d. green	5·50	4·75
60		5r. on 5s. red	5·50	4·75
60a	–	10r. on 10s. blue (No. 478a)	65·00	48·00

1948. Silver Wedding.

61	137	2½a. on 2½d. blue	1·00	30
62	138	15r. on £1 blue	35·00	48·00

1948. Olympic Games.

63	139	2½a. on 2½d. blue	55	2·00
64	140	3a. on 3d. violet	55	2·50
65	–	6a. on 6d. purple	1·50	2·75
66	–	1r. on 1s. brown	1·50	2·75

1949. U.P.U.

67	143	2½a. on 2½d. blue	40	2·25
68	144	3a. on 3d. violet	60	2·75
69	–	6a. on 6d. purple	50	3·00
70	–	1r. on 1s. brown	1·25	2·00

1951. Pictorial stamps (Nos. 509/11).

77	147	2r. on 2s.6d. green	22·00	7·50
78	–	5r. on 5s. red	13·00	3·75
79	–	10r. on 10s. blue	26·00	7·50

1952. Queen Elizabeth II.

97	154	½a. on ½d. orange	10	15
81		1a. on 1d. blue	10	10
82		1½a. on 1½d. green	10	10
83		2a. on 2d. brown	30	10
84	155	2½a. on 2½d. red	20	1·75
85		3a. on 3d. lilac	3·00	10
86		4a. on 4d. blue	8·00	30
99	157	6a. on 6d. purple	50	50
88	160	12a. on 1s.3d. green	3·25	20
89		1r. on 1s.6d. blue	3·25	10

1953. Coronation.

90	161	2½a. on 2½d. red	1·25	75
91	–	4a. on 4d. blue	2·25	4·25
92	163	12a. on 1s.3d. green	3·25	4·25
93	–	1r. on 1s.6d. blue	7·50	50

1955. Pictorial stamps (Nos. 595a/598a).

94	166	2r. on 2s.6d. brown	5·50	2·00
95	–	5r. on 5s. red	12·00	2·75
96	–	10r. on 10s. blue	20·00	2·75

1957. Queen Elizabeth II.

102	157	1n.p. on 5d. brown	10	10
103	154	3n.p. on ½d. orange	30	2·25
104		6n.p. on 1d. blue	30	2·25
105		9n.p. on 1½d. green	30	2·25
106		12n.p. on 2d. pale brown	30	60
107	155	15n.p. on 2½d. red	30	15
108		20n.p. on 3d. lilac	30	10
109		25n.p. on 4d. blue	75	2·50
110	157	40n.p. on 6d. purple	40	10
111		50n.p. on 9d. olive	3·75	4·50
112		75n.p. on 1s.3d. green	2·25	50

1957. World Scout Jubilee Jamboree.

113	170	15n.p. on 2½d. red	25	35
114	171	25n.p. on 4d. blue	30	35
115	–	75n.p. on 1s.3d. green	40	45

16 Shaikh Sulman bin Hamed al-Khalifa

1960.

117	16	5n.p. blue	10	10
118		15n.p. orange	10	10
119		20n.p. violet	10	10
120		30n.p. bistre	10	10
121		40n.p. grey	15	10
122		50n.p. green	15	10
123		75n.p. brown	30	15
124	–	1r. black	1·75	30
125	–	2r. red	3·00	2·25
126	–	5r. blue	5·00	3·00
127	–	10r. green	12·00	4·75

The rupee values are larger, 27 × 32½ mm.

18 Shaikh Isa bin Sulman al-Khalifa

19 Air Terminal, Muharraq

1964.

128	18	5n.p. blue	10	10
129		15n.p. orange	10	10
130		20n.p. violet	10	10
131		30n.p. bistre	10	10
132		40n.p. slate	15	10
133		50n.p. green	15	20
134		75n.p. brown	25	10
135	19	1r. black	8·00	2·25
136		2r. red	8·50	2·25
137	–	5r. blue	13·00	12·00
138	–	10r. myrtle	13·00	12·00

DESIGN—As Type 19: 5r., 10r. Deep water harbour.

21 Sheikh Isa bin Sulman al-Khalifa

22 Ruler and Bahrain Airport

1966.

139	21	5f. green	10	10
140		10f. red	15	15
141		15f. blue	20	15
142		20f. purple	20	15
143	22	30f. black and green	25	15
144		40f. black and blue	30	15
145	–	50f. black and red	55	25
146	–	75f. black and violet	70	35
147	–	100f. blue and yellow	2·00	90
148	–	200f. green and orange	8·00	1·90
149	–	500f. brown and yellow	6·75	3·25
150	–	1d. multicoloured	14·00	7·00

DESIGNS—As Type 22: 50f., 75f. Ruler and Mina Sulman deep-water harbour. VERT (26½ × 42½ mm): 100f. Pearl-diving; 200f. Lanner falcon and horse-racing; 500f. Serving coffee, and ruler's palace. LARGER (37 × 52½ mm): 1d. Ruler, crest, date palm, horse, dhow, pearl necklace, mosque, coffee-pot and Bab-al-Bahrain (gateway).

23 Produce

24 W.H.O. Emblem and Map of Bahrain

1966. Trade Fair and Agricultural Show.

151	23	10f. turquoise and red	30	15
152		20f. lilac and green	65	35
153		40f. blue and brown	1·40	50
154		200f. red and blue	6·50	3·75

1968. 20th Anniv of W.H.O.

155	24	20f. black and grey	60	45
156		40f. black and turquoise	2·00	1·10
157		150f. black and red	8·00	4·25

25 View of Isa Town

1968. Inauguration of Isa New Town. Mult.

158		50f. Type 25	3·00	90
159		80f. Shopping centre	4·50	1·75
160		120f. Stadium	7·00	3·25
161		150f. Mosque	8·00	4·00

26 Symbol of Learning

1969. 50th Anniv of School Education in Bahrain.

162	26	40f. multicoloured	1·25	75
163		60f. multicoloured	2·40	1·25
164		150f. multicoloured	6·50	3·25

27 Dish Aerial and Map of Persian Gulf

1969. Opening of Satellite Earth Station, Ras Abu Jarjour. Multicoloured.

165		20f. Type 27	2·00	50
166		40f. Dish aerial and palms (vert)	4·00	80
167		100f. Type 27	9·00	3·25
168		150f. As 40f.	13·00	4·75

28 Arms, Map and Manama Municipality Building

1970. 2nd Arab Cities Organization Conf, Manama.

169	28	30f. multicoloured	1·25	1·25
170		150f. multicoloured	5·25	5·25

29 Copper Bull's Head, Barbar

1970. 3rd International Asian Archaeology Conference, Bahrain. Multicoloured.

171		60f. Type 29	2·50	1·60
172		80f. Palace of Dilmun excavations	3·25	2·00
173		120f. Desert gravemounds	4·75	2·75
174		150f. Dilmun seal	6·00	3·50

30 Vickers Super VC-10 Airliner, Big Ben, London, and Bahrain Minaret

1970. 1st Gulf Aviation Vickers Super VC-10 Flight, Doha–London.

175	30	30f. multicoloured	2·00	70
176		60f. multicoloured	4·50	1·50
177		120f. multicoloured	8·50	4·50

31 I.E.Y. Emblem and Open Book

1970. International Education Year. Multicoloured.

178		60f. Type 31	1·75	1·40
179		120f. Emblem and Bahraini children	4·25	3·75

32 Allegory of Independence

34 Human Heart

33 Arab Dhow with Arab League and U.N. Emblems

1971. Independence Day and 10th Anniv of Ruler's Accession. Multicoloured.

180		30f. Type 32	1·75	90
181		60f. Government House	3·25	1·75
182		120f. Arms of Bahrain	8·00	4·00
183		150f. Arms of Bahrain (gold background)	11·00	5·50

1972. Bahrain's Membership of Arab League and U.N. Multicoloured.

184		30f. Type 33	3·00	95
185		60f. Type 33	5·00	1·90
186		120f. Dhow sails (vert)	6·00	4·00
187		150f. As 120f.	11·00	5·50

1972. World Health Day.

188	34	30f. multicoloured	2·00	2·00
189		60f. multicoloured	5·00	5·00

35 F.A.O. and U.N. Emblems

1973. 10th Anniv of World Food Programme.

190	35	30f. brown, red and green	2·75	2·75
191		60f. brown, lt brown & grn	5·00	5·00

36 "Races of the World"

1973. 25th Anniv of Declaration of Human Rights.

192	36	30f. blue, brown and black	2·00	1·00
193		60f. red, brown and black	3·50	2·50

38 Flour Mill

1973. National Day. "Progress in Bahrain". Mult.
195	30f. Type **38**		1·00	75
196	60f. Muharraq Airport		2·50	1·00
197	120f. Sulmaniya Medical Centre		3·00	1·75
198	150f. Aluminium Smelter		3·50	3·00

39 U.P.U. Emblem within Letters

1974. Admission of Bahrain to U.P.U. Mult.
199	30f. Type **39**		1·50	55
200	60f. U.P.U. emblem on letters		2·50	90
201	120f. Ruler and emblem on dove with letter in beak (37 × 28 mm)		2·25	1·90
202	150f. As 120f. (37 × 28 mm)		3·25	2·75

40 Traffic Lights and Directing Hands

1974. International Traffic Day.
203	**40** 30f. multicoloured		1·75	1·60
204	60f. multicoloured		4·00	3·50

41 U.P.U. "Stamp" and Mail Transport

1974. Centenary of U.P.U.
205	**41** 30f. multicoloured		70	50
206	60f. multicoloured		1·25	90
207	120f. multicoloured		2·25	1·60
208	150f. multicoloured		2·75	1·90

42 Emblem and Sitra Power Station　　**43** Costume and Headdress

1974. National Day. Multicoloured.
209	**42** 30f. Type **42**		55	50
210	60f. Type **42**		95	85
211	120f. Emblem and Bahrain Dry Dock		2·50	2·00
212	150f. As 120f.		3·25	2·50

1975. Bahrain Women's Costumes.
213	**43** 30f. multicoloured		60	50
214	– 60f. multicoloured		1·25	1·10
215	– 120f. multicoloured		2·00	1·90
216	– 150f. multicoloured		2·50	2·40

DESIGNS: Nos. 214/16, Costumes as Type **43**.

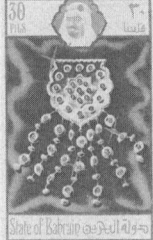　

44 Jewelled Pendant　　**45** Women planting "Flower"

1975. Costume Jewellery. Multicoloured.
217	30f. Type **44**		60	50
218	60f. Gold crown		1·25	1·10
219	120f. Jewelled necklace		2·00	1·90
220	150f. Gold necklace		2·50	2·40

1975. International Women's Year. Multicoloured.
221	30f. Type **45**		1·50	75
222	60f. Woman holding I.W.Y. emblem		3·00	1·75

46 Head of Horse

1975. Horses. Multicoloured.
223a	60f. Type **46**		4·00	4·00
223b	60f. Grey		4·00	4·00
223c	60f. Grey with foal (horiz)		4·00	4·00
223d	60f. Close-up of Arab with grey		4·00	4·00
223e	60f. Grey and herd of browns (horiz)		4·00	4·00
223f	60f. Grey and brown (horiz)		4·00	4·00
223g	60f. Arabs riding horses (horiz)		4·00	4·00
223h	60f. Arab leading grey beside sea (horiz)		4·00	4·00

47 National Flag　　**48** Map of Bahrain within Cog and Laurel

1976.
224	**47** 5f. red, pink and blue		15	10
225	10f. red, pink & green		15	10
226	15f. red, pink & black		15	15
227	20f. red, pink & brown		15	15
227a	**48** 25f. black and grey		20	15
228	40f. black and blue		20	15
228a	50f. green, black & olive		25	15
228b	60f. black and green		30	20
229	80f. black and mauve		45	30
229b	100f. black and red		55	45
230	150f. black and yellow		90	85
231	200f. black and yellow		1·10	1·00

49 Concorde Taking off

1976. 1st Commercial Flight of Concorde. Mult.
232	80f. Type **49**		2·25	2·00
233	80f. Concorde landing		2·25	2·00
234	80f. Concorde en route		2·25	2·00
235	80f. Concorde on runway		2·25	2·00

50 Soldier, Crest and Flag　　**52** Shaikh Isa bin Sulman al-Khalifa

51 King Khalid of Saudi Arabia and Shaikh of Bahrain with National Flags

1976. Defence Force Cadets' Day.
237	**50** 40f. multicoloured		1·40	1·25
238	80f. multicoloured		2·50	2·25

1976. Visit to Bahrain of King Khalid of Saudi Arabia.
239	**51** 40f. multicoloured		1·50	1·25
240	80f. multicoloured		3·00	2·50

1976.
241	**52** 300f. green and pale green		2·25	1·60
242	400f. purple and pink		3·00	2·25
243	500f. blue and pale blue		3·75	3·00
244	1d. black and grey		7·50	4·75
244a	2d. violet and lilac		15·00	11·00
244b	3d. brown and pink		23·00	17·00

53 Ministry of Housing Emblem, Designs for Houses and Mosque　　**54** A.P.U. Emblem

1976. National Day.
245	**53** 40f. multicoloured		1·25	1·00
246	80f. multicoloured		2·75	1·75

1977. 25th Anniv of Arab Postal Union.
247	**54** 40f. multicoloured		1·25	1·00
248	80f. multicoloured		2·75	1·75

55 Dogs on Beach

1977. Saluki Dogs. Multicoloured.
249a	80f. Type **55**		2·40	2·40
249b	80f. Dog and dromedaries		2·40	2·40
249c	80f. Dog and antelope		2·40	2·40
249d	80f. Dog on lawn of building		2·40	2·40
249e	80f. Head of dog		2·40	2·40
249f	80f. Heads of two dogs		2·40	2·40
249g	80f. Dog in scrubland		2·40	2·40
249h	80f. Dogs fighting		2·40	2·40

56 Arab Students and Candle

1977. International Literacy Day.
250	**56** 40f. multicoloured		1·25	1·00
251	80f. multicoloured		2·75	1·75

57 Shipyard Installations and Arab Flags

1977. Inauguration of Arab Shipbuilding and Repair Yard Co.
252	**57** 40f. multicoloured		1·25	1·00
253	80f. multicoloured		2·75	1·75

58 Microwave Antenna

1978. 10th World Telecommunications Day.
254	**58** 40f. multicoloured		1·25	1·00
255	80f. silver, dp blue & blue		2·75	1·75

59 Child being helped to Walk　　**60** Boom Dhow

1979. International Year of the Child. Mult.
256	**59** 50f. Type **59**		1·00	80
257	100f. Hands protecting child		2·50	1·60

1979. Dhows. Multicoloured.
258	100f. Type **60**		2·60	2·40
259	100f. Baghla		2·60	2·40
260	100f. Shu'ai (horiz)		2·60	2·40
261	100f. Ghanja (horiz)		2·60	2·40
262	100f. Kotia		2·60	2·40
263	100f. Sambuk		2·60	2·40
264	100f. Jaliboot (horiz)		2·60	2·40
265	100f. Zarook (horiz)		2·60	2·40

61 Dome of Mosque, Mecca

1980. 1400th Anniv of Hejira.
266	**61** 50f. multicoloured		65	40
267	100f. multicoloured		1·60	1·25
268	150f. multicoloured		1·90	1·50
269	200f. multicoloured		2·50	2·00

62 Arab with Gyr Falcon

1980. Falconry. Multicoloured.
271	100f. Type **62**		2·75	1·60
272	100f. Arab looking at Lanner falcon on wrist		2·75	1·60
273	100f. Peregrine falcon resting with outstretched wings		2·75	1·60
274	100f. Peregrine falcon in flight		2·75	1·60
275	100f. Gyr falcon on pillar (with camels in background) (vert)		2·75	1·60
276	100f. Gyr falcon on pillar (closer view) (vert)		2·75	1·60
277	100f. Close-up of gyr falcon facing right (vert)		2·75	1·60
278	100f. Close-up of Lanner falcon full-face (vert)		2·75	1·60

63 Map and I.Y.D.P. Emblem

1981. International Year for Disabled Persons.
279	**63** 50f. multicoloured		1·25	75
280	100f. multicoloured		2·25	1·75

64 Jubilee Emblem

1981. 50th Anniv of Electrical Power in Bahrain.
281 **64** 50f. multicoloured . . . . 1·25 75
282 100f. multicoloured . . . . 2·25 1·75

65 Carving   **66** Mosque

1981. Handicrafts. Multicoloured.
283 50f. Type **65** 55 45
284 100f. Pottery . . . . . . 1·00 90
285 150f. Weaving . . . . . . 1·90 1·60
286 200f. Basket-making . . . . 2·25 2·10

1981. Mosques.
287 **66** 50f. multicoloured 70 55
288 – 100f. multicoloured . . . . 1·40 1·10
289 – 150f. multicoloured . . . . 2·00 1·75
290 – 200f. multicoloured . . . . 2·75 2·50
DESIGNS: 100f. to 200f. As Type **66** but showing different mosques.

67 Shaikh Isa bin   **69** Flags and Clasped
Sulman al-Khalifa   Hands encircling
     Emblem

68 Dorcas Gazelle

1981. 20th Anniv of Coronation of Shaikh Isa bin Sulman al-Khalifa.
291 **67** 15f. gold, grey and mauve 25 20
292 50f. gold, grey and red 55 45
293 100f. gold, grey and brown 1·10 95
294 150f. gold, grey and blue 1·75 1·40
295 200f. gold, grey and blue 2·10 2·10

1982. Al-Areen Wildlife Park. Multicoloured.
296 100f. Goitred gazelle . . . . 1·75 1·75
297 100f. Type **68** . . . . . . 1·75 1·75
298 100f. Dhub lizard . . . . 1·75 1·75
299 100f. Brown hares . . . . 1·75 1·75
300 100f. Arabian oryx . . . . 1·75 1·75
301 100f. Addax . . . . . . 1·75 1·75

1982. 3rd Supreme Council Session of Gulf Co-operation Council.
302 **69** 50f. multicoloured 65 50
303 – 100f. multicoloured . . . . 1·40 1·10

70 Madinat Hamad

1983. Opening of Madinat Hamad New Town. Multicoloured.
304 **70** 50f. Type **70** 65 50
305 100f. View of Madinat Hamad (different) . . . . 1·40 1·10

71 Shaikh Isa bin Sulman al-Khalifa

1983. Bicentenary of Al-Khalifa Dynasty. Mult.
306 **71** 100f. Type **71** 70 70
307 100f. Cartouche of Ali bin Khalifa al-Khalifa 70 70
308 100f. Isa bin Ali al-Khalifa 70 70
309 100f. Hamad bin Isa al-Khalifa 70 70
310 100f. Salman bin Hamad al-Khalifa 70 70
311 100f. Cartouche of Ahmed bin Mohammed al-Khalifa 70 70
312 100f. Cartouche of Salman bin Ahmed al-Khalifa . . . 70 70
313 100f. Cartouche of Abdullah bin Ahmed al-Khalifa . . . 70 70
314 100f. Cartouche of Mohammed bin Khalifa al-Khalifa 70 70

72 G.C.C. and Traffic and Licensing Directorate Emblems

1984. Gulf Co-operation Council Traffic Week.
316 **72** 15f. multicoloured 25 20
317 50f. multicoloured 80 40
318 100f. multicoloured . . . . 1·25 75

73 Hurdling

1984. Olympic Games, Los Angeles. Multicoloured.
319 15f. Type **73** 20 20
320 50f. Show-jumping 70 55
321 100f. Swimming . . . . 1·25 1·10
322 150f. Fencing . . . . 1·75 1·50
323 200f. Shooting . . . . 2·40 2·25

74 Manama and Emblem

1984. Centenary of Postal Services.
324 **74** 15f. multicoloured 35 20
325 50f. multicoloured . . . . 1·00 50
326 100f. multicoloured . . . . 1·75 95

75 Narrow-barred Spanish Mackerel

1985. Fishes. Multicoloured.
327 100f. Type **75** . . . . . . 1·40 1·00
328 100f. Crocodile needlefish (three fishes) . . . . 1·40 1·00
329 100f. Sombre sweetlips (fish swimming to left, blue and lilac background) . . . . 1·40 1·00
330 100f. White-spotted rabbitfish (two fishes, blue and lilac background) . . . . 1·40 1·00
331 100f. Grey mullet (two fishes, green and pink background) . . . . 1·40 1·00
332 100f. Two-banded seabream (green and grey background) . . . . 1·40 1·00
333 100f. River seabream (blue background) . . . . 1·40 1·00
334 100f. Malabar grouper (green background) . . . . 1·40 1·00
335 100f. Small-toothed emperor (pink anemone background) . . . . 1·40 1·00
336 100f. Golden trevally (fish swimming to right, blue and lilac background) . . . . 1·40 1·00

76 Hands cupping Emblem

1985. Arabian Gulf States Social Work Week.
337 **76** 15f. multicoloured 20 15
338 50f. multicoloured 60 40
339 100f. multicoloured . . . . 1·00 70

77 I.Y.Y. Emblem

1986. International Youth Year.
340 **77** 15f. multicoloured 20 15
341 50f. multicoloured 60 40
342 100f. multicoloured . . . . 1·00 70

78 Aerial View of Causeway

1986. Opening of Saudi–Bahrain Causeway. Mult.
343 15f. Type **78** 25 20
344 50f. Aerial view of island . . 60 40
345 100f. Aerial view of road bridge . . . . 1·00 70

79 Shaikh Isa bin Sulman al-Khalifa

1986. 25th Anniv of Accession of Shaikh Isa bin Sulman al-Khalifa.
346 **79** 15f. multicoloured 25 20
347 50f. multicoloured 60 40
348 100f. multicoloured . . . . 1·00 70

80 Emblem

1988. 40th Anniv of W.H.O.
350 **80** 50f. multicoloured 40 25
351 150f. multicoloured . . . . 1·25 90

81 Centre

1988. Opening of Ahmed al-Fateh Islamic Centre.
352 **81** 50f. multicoloured 40 25
353 150f. multicoloured . . . . 1·25 90

82 Running

1988. Olympic Games, Seoul. Multicoloured.
354 **82** 50f. Type **82** 30 20
355 80f. Dressage 60 40
356 150f. Fencing . . . . 1·10 80
357 200f. Football . . . . 1·90 1·40

83 Emblem in "1988"

1988. 9th Supreme Council Meeting of Gulf Co-operation Council.
358 **83** 50f. multicoloured 35 25
359 150f. multicoloured . . . . 1·25 90

84 Arab leading Camel   **85** Shaikh Isa bin
     Sulman al-Khalifa

1989. Camels. Multicoloured.
360 150f. Type **84** . . . . . . 1·00 1·00
361 150f. Arab leading camel (different) . . . . 1·00 1·00
362 150f. Head of camel and pump-head . . . . 1·00 1·00
363 150f. Close-up of Arab on camel . . . . 1·00 1·00
364 150f. Arab riding camel . . . 1·00 1·00
365 150f. Two Arab camel-riders . . 1·00 1·00
366 150f. Head of camel and camel-rider . . . . 1·00 1·00
367 150f. Camels at rest in camp . . 1·00 1·00
368 150f. Camels with calf . . . 1·00 1·00
369 150f. Heads of three camels . . 1·00 1·00
370 150f. Camel in scrubland . . . 1·00 1·00
371 150f. Arab on camel . . . . 1·00 1·00
Nos. 366/71 are horiz.

1989. Multicoloured, colour of frame given.
372 **85** 25f. green 20 10
373 40f. grey 30 10
374 50f. pink 30 10
375 60f. brown 40 15
376 75f. mauve 50 15
377 80f. green 50 15
378 100f. orange 70 25
379 120f. violet 80 25
380 150f. grey . . . . . . 1·00 35
381 200f. blue . . . . . . 1·25 45

86 Houbara Bustards

1990. The Houbara Bustard. Multicoloured.
383 150f. Type **86** . . . . . . 1·00 1·00
384 150f. Two bustards (facing each other) . . . . 1·00 1·00
385 150f. Chicks and eggs . . . . 1·00 1·00
386 150f. Adult and chick . . . . 1·00 1·00
387 150f. Adult (vert) . . . . 1·00 1·00
388 150f. In flight . . . . 1·00 1·00
389 150f. Adult (facing right) . . . 1·00 1·00
390 150f. Young bird (vert) . . . 1·00 1·00
391 150f. Adult (facing left) . . . 1·00 1·00
392 150f. Bird in display plumage . . 1·00 1·00
393 150f. Two bustards in display plumage . . . . 1·00 1·00
394 150f. Two bustards with bridge in background . . . . 1·00 1·00

87 Anniversary Emblem

1990. 40th Anniv of Gulf Air.
395 **87** 50f. multicoloured 35 25
396 80f. multicoloured 55 35
397 150f. multicoloured . . . . 1·00 75
398 200f. multicoloured . . . . 1·40 95

88 Anniversary Emblem

1990. 50th Anniv of Bahrain Chamber of Commerce and Industry.
399 **88** 50f. multicoloured 30 20

400	80f. multicoloured	50	35
401	150f. multicoloured	95	65
402	200f. multicoloured	1·25	85

89 I.L.Y. Emblem

1990. International Literacy Year.

403	**89** 50f. multicoloured	30	20
404	80f. multicoloured	50	35
405	150f. multicoloured	95	65
406	200f. multicoloured	1·25	85

90 Crested Lark

1991. Birds. Multicoloured.

407	150f. Type **90**	90	90
408	150f. Hoopoe ("Upupa epops")	90	90
409	150f. White-cheeked bulbul ("Pycnonotus leucogenys")	90	90
410	150f. Turtle dove ("Streptopelia turtur")	90	90
411	150f. Collared dove ("Streptopelia decaocto")	90	90
412	150f. Common kestrel ("Falco tinnunculus")	90	90
413	150f. House sparrow ("Passer domesticus") (horiz)	90	90
414	150f. Great grey shrike ("Lanius excubitor") (horiz)	90	90
415	150f. Rose-ringed parakeet ("Psittacula krameri")	90	90

91 Shaikh Isa bin Sulman al-Khalifa

1991. 30th Anniv of Amir's Coronation.

416	**91** 50f. multicoloured	30	20
417	A 50f. multicoloured	30	20
418	**91** 80f. multicoloured	45	30
419	A 80f. multicoloured	45	30
420	**91** 150f. multicoloured	90	60
421	**91** 150f. multicoloured	90	60
422	**91** 200f. multicoloured	1·10	75
423	A 200f. multicoloured	1·10	75

DESIGN: A, The Amir and sunburst.

92 White Stork ("Ciconia ciconia")

1992. Migratory Birds. Multicoloured.

425	150f. Type **92**	80	80
426	150f. European bee eater ("Merops apiaster")	80	80
427	150f. Common starling ("Sturnus vulgaris")	80	80
428	150f. Grey hypocolius ("Hypocolius ampelinus")	80	80
429	150f. European cuckoo ("Cuculus canorus")	80	80
430	150f. Mistle thrush ("Turdus viscivorus")	80	80
431	150f. European roller ("Coracias garrulus")	80	80
432	150f. Eurasian goldfinch ("Carduelis carduelis")	80	80
433	150f. Red-backed shrike ("Lanius collurio")	80	80
434	150f. Redwing ("Turdus iliacus") (horiz)	80	80
435	150f. Pied wagtail ("Motacilla alba") (horiz)	80	80
436	150f. Golden oriole ("Oriolus oriolus") (horiz)	80	80
437	150f. European robin ("Erithacus rubecula")	80	80
438	150f. Nightingale ("Luscinia luscinia")	80	80

439	150f. Spotted flycatcher ("Muscicapa striata")	80	80
440	150f. Barn swallow ("Hirundo rustica")	80	80

93 Start of Race

1992. Horse-racing. Multicoloured.

441	150f. Type **93**	80	80
442	150f. Parading in paddock	80	80
443	150f. Galloping around bend	80	80
444	150f. Galloping past national flags	80	80
445	150f. Galloping past spectator stand	80	80
446	150f. Head-on view of horses	80	80
447	150f. Reaching winning post	80	80
448	150f. A black and a grey galloping	80	80

94 Show-jumping

1992. Olympic Games, Barcelona. Multicoloured.

449	50f. Type **94**	30	20
450	80f. Running	45	30
451	150f. Karate	85	55
452	200f. Cycling	1·10	75

95 Airport

1992. 60th Anniv of Bahrain International Airport.

453	**95** 50f. multicoloured	30	20
454	80f. multicoloured	45	30
455	150f. multicoloured	85	55
456	200f. multicoloured	1·10	75

96 Girl skipping   **98** Artillery Gun Crew

1992. Children's Paintings. Multicoloured.

457	50f. Type **96**	30	20
458	80f. Women	45	30
459	150f. Women preparing food (horiz)	85	55
460	200f. Pearl divers (horiz)	1·40	75

1992. Expansion of Aluminium Industry. Mult.

461	50f. Type **97**	30	20
462	80f. Worker in aluminium plant	45	30
463	150f. Aerial view of aluminium plant	85	55
464	200f. Processed aluminium	1·10	75

1993. 25th Anniv of Bahrain Defence Force. Mult.

465	50f. Type **98**	25	15
466	80f. General Dynamics Fighting Falcon jet fighters, tanks and patrol boat	40	25
467	150f. "Ahmed al Fatah" (missile corvette) (horiz)	75	50
468	200f. Fighting Falcon over Bahrain (horiz)	1·00	65

97 Cable-cars and Pylons

99 Satellite View of Bahrain   **100** Purple Heron

1993. World Meteorological Day. Multicoloured.

469	50f. Type **99**	30	20
470	150f. Satellite picture of world (horiz)	75	60
471	200f. Earth seen from space	1·25	85

1993. Water Birds. Multicoloured.

472	150f. Type **100**	90	90
473	150f. Moorhen ("Gallinula chloropus")	90	90
474	150f. Socotra cormorant ("Phalacrocorax nigrogularis")	90	90
475	150f. Crab plover ("Dromas ardeola")	90	90
476	150f. River kingfisher ("Alcedo atthis")	90	90
477	150f. Northern lapwing ("Vanellus vanellus")	90	90
478	150f. Oystercatcher ("Haematopus ostralegus") (horiz)	90	90
479	150f. Black-crowned night heron ("Nycticorax nycticorax")	90	90
480	150f. Caspian tern ("Sterna caspia") (horiz)	90	90
481	150f. Ruddy turnstone ("Arenaria interpres") (horiz)	90	90
482	150f. Water rail ("Rallus aquaticus") (horiz)	90	90
483	150f. Mallard ("Anas platyrhyncos) (horiz)	90	90
484	150f. Lesser black-backed gull ("Larus fuscus") (horiz)	90	90

101 Fawn

1993. The Goitered Gazelle. Multicoloured.

485	25f. Type **101**	15	10
486	50f. Doe walking	25	15
487	50f. Doe with ears pricked	25	15
488	150f. Male gazelle	75	60

102 "Lycium shawii"   **103** Children and Silhouettes of Parents' Heads

1993. Wild Flowers. Multicoloured.

489	150f. Type **102**	75	75
490	150f. "Alhagi maurorum"	75	75
491	150f. Caper-bush ("Caparis spinosa")	75	75
492	150f. "Cistanche phelypae"	75	75
493	150f. "Asphodelus tenuifolius"	75	75
494	150f. "Limonium axillare"	75	75
495	150f. "Cynomorium coccineum"	75	75
496	150f. "Calligonum polygonoides"	75	75

1994. International Year of the Family.

497	**103** 50f. multicoloured	20	15
498	80f. multicoloured	30	20
499	150f. multicoloured	65	45
500	200f. multicoloured	80	55

104 "Lepidochrysops arabicus"   **105** Anniversary Emblem

1994. Butterflies. Multicoloured.

501	50f. Type **104**	20	20
502	50f. "Ypthima bolanica"	20	20
503	50f. Desert grass yellow ("Eurema brigitta")	20	20
504	50f. "Precis limnoria"	20	20
505	50f. Small tortoiseshell ("Aglais urticae")	20	20
506	50f. Protomedia ("Colotis protomedia")	20	20
507	50f. Clouded mother-of-pearl ("Salamis anacardii")	20	20
508	50f. "Byblia ilithyia"	20	20
509	150f. Swallowtail ("Papilio machaon")	65	65
510	150f. Blue ("Agrodiaetus loewii")	65	65
511	150f. Painted lady ("Vanessa cardui")	65	65
512	150f. Chequered swallowtail ("Papilio demoleus")	65	65
513	150f. Guineafowl ("Hamanumida daedalus")	65	65
514	150f. "Funonia orithya"	65	65
515	150f. "Funonia chorimine"	65	65
516	150f. "Colias croceus"	65	65

Nos. 509/16 are horiz.

1994. 75th Anniv of International Red Cross and Red Crescent.

517	**105** 50f. multicoloured	20	15
518	80f. multicoloured	30	20
519	150f. multicoloured	65	45
520	200f. multicoloured	80	55

106 Goalkeeper

1994. World Cup Football Championship, U.S.A. Multicoloured.

521	50f. Type **106**	20	15
522	80f. Players	30	20
523	150f. Players' legs	65	45
524	200f. Player on ground	80	55

107 Earth Station

1994. 25th Anniv of Ras Abu Jarjour Satellite Earth Station.

525	**107** 50f. multicoloured	20	15
526	80f. multicoloured	30	20
527	150f. multicoloured	65	45
528	200f. multicoloured	80	55

108 Children on Open Book, Pen as Torch and School   **109** Dove with "Olive Branch" of Members' Flags

1994. 75th Anniv of Education in Bahrain.

529	**108** 50f. multicoloured	20	15
530	80f. multicoloured	30	20
531	150f. multicoloured	65	45
532	200f. multicoloured	80	55

1994. 15th Gulf Co-operation Council Supreme Council Session, Bahrain.

533	**109** 50f. multicoloured	20	15
534	80f. multicoloured	30	20
535	150f. multicoloured	65	45
536	200f. multicoloured	80	55

110 Date Palm in Bloom

1995. The Date Palm.
537 **110** 80f. Type **110** 25 15
538 100f. Date palm with
unripened dates 35 25
539 200f. Dates ripening 65 45
540 250f. Date palm trees with
ripened dates 80 55

111 Campaign Emblem

1995. World Health Day. Anti-poliomyelitis Campaign.
542 **111** 80f. multicoloured 25 15
543 200f. multicoloured . . . 65 45
544 250f. multicoloured . . . 80 55

112 Exhibition Emblem   114 Headquarters, Cairo

113 Crops

1995. 1st National Industries Exhibition.
545 **112** 80f. multicoloured 25 15
546 200f. multicoloured 65 45
547 250f. multicoloured 80 55

1995. 50th Anniv of F.A.O. Multicoloured.
548 **113** 80f. Type **113** 25 15
549 200f. Field of crops 65 45
550 250f. Field of cabbages . . 80 55

1995. 50th Anniv of Arab League.
551 **114** 80f. multicoloured 25 15
552 200f. multicoloured . . . 65 45
553 250f. multicoloured . . . 80 55

115 U.N. Headquarters and Map of Bahrain

1995. 50th Anniv of U.N.O.
554 **115** 80f. multicoloured 25 15
555 100f. multicoloured . . . 35 25
556 200f. multicoloured . . . 65 45
557 250f. multicoloured . . . 80 55

116 Tower

1995. Traditional Architecture. Multicoloured.
558 **116** 200f. Type **116** 65 65
559 200f. Balcony 65 65
560 200f. Doorway 65 65
561 200f. Multi-storied facade . 65 65

562 200f. Entrance flanked by
two windows 65 65
563 200f. Three arched windows 65 65

117 National Flag   118 Bookcase and Open
and Shaikh Isa Bin   Book
Sulman al-Khalifa

1995. National Day.
564 **117** 80f. multicoloured 25 15
565 100f. multicoloured . . . 35 25
566 200f. multicoloured . . . 65 45
567 250f. multicoloured . . . 85 55

1996. 50th Anniv of Public Library.
568 **118** 80f. multicoloured 25 15
569 200f. multicoloured . . . 65 45
570 250f. multicoloured . . . 85 55

119 Divers on Dhow

1996. Pearl Diving. Multicoloured.
571 80f. Type **119** 40 15
572 100f. Divers 70 25
573 200f. Diver on sea-bed and
dhow . . . . 1·00 45
574 250f. Diver with net 85 55

120 Globe, Ship and Olympic Rings

1996. Olympic Games, Atlanta.
576 **120** 80f. multicoloured 25 15
577 100f. multicoloured . . . 35 25
578 200f. multicoloured . . . 65 45
579 250f. multicoloured . . . 85 55

121 Interpol Emblem and Map, Arms
and Flag of Bahrain

1996. 24th Anniv of Membership of International Criminal Police (Interpol).
580 **121** 80f. multicoloured 25 15
581 100f. multicoloured . . . 35 25
582 200f. multicoloured . . . 65 45
583 250f. multicoloured . . . 85 55

122 Anniversary Emblems in English
and Arabic

1996. 25th Anniv of Aluminium Bahrain.
584 **122** 80f. multicoloured 25 15
585 100f. multicoloured . . . 30 20
586 200f. multicoloured . . . 65 45
587 250f. multicoloured . . . 80 55

123 National Flag, Map and Shaikh
Isa bin Sulman al-Khalifa

1996. 35th Anniv of Amir's Accession.
588 **123** 80f. multicoloured 25 15
589 100f. multicoloured . . . 30 20
590 200f. multicoloured . . . 65 45
591 250f. multicoloured . . . 80 55

124 Tanker, Refinery and Storage
Tanks

1997. 60th Anniv of Bahrain Refinery.
592 **124** 80f. multicoloured 25 20
593 200f. multicoloured . . . 65 50
594 250f. multicoloured . . . 85 70

125 Kuheilaan Weld umm Zorayr

1997. Arab Horses at Amiri Stud. Multicoloured.
595 200f. Musannaan (white
horse), Al-Jellabieh and
Rabdaan 65 65
596 200f. Type **125** 65 65
597 200f. Al-Jellaby 65 65
598 200f. Musannaan (brown
horse) 65 65
599 200f. Kuheilaan Aladiyat . 65 65
600 200f. Kuheilaan Aafas . . 65 65
601 200f. Al-Dhahma 65 65
602 200f. Mlolshaan 65 65
603 200f. Al-Kray 65 65
604 200f. Krush 65 65
605 200f. Al Hamdaany . . . 65 65
606 200f. Hadhfaan 65 65
607 200f. Rabda 65 65
608 200f. Al-Suwaitieh 65 65
609 200f. Al-Obeyah 65 65
610 200f. Al-Shuwaimeh . . . 65 65
611 200f. Al-Ma'anaghieh . . . 65 65
612 200f. Al-Tuwaisah 65 65
613 200f. Wadhna 65 65
614 200f. Al-Saqlawieh 65 65
615 200f. Al-Shawafah 65 65

126 Championship Emblem

1997. 9th World Men's Junior Volleyball Championship.
616 **126** 80f. multicoloured 25 15
617 100f. multicoloured . . . 30 20
618 200f. multicoloured . . . 65 45
619 250f. multicoloured . . . 80 55

127 Emblem

1997. 10th Anniv of Montreal Protocol (on reduction of use of chlorofluorocarbons).
620 **127** 80f. multicoloured 25 15
621 100f. multicoloured . . . 30 20
622 200f. multicoloured . . . 65 45
623 250f. multicoloured . . . 80 55

128 Close-up of Support

1997. Inauguration of Shaikh Isa bin Salman Bridge between Manama and Muharraq. Multicoloured.
624 80f. Type **128** 25 15
625 200f. Distant view of middle
section 65 45
626 250f. View of complete bridge
(75 × 26 mm) 80 55

129 Complex at Night

1998. Inauguration of Urea Plant at Gulf Petrochemical Industries Co Complex. Mult.
628 **129** 80f. Type **129** 25 15
629 200f. Refining towers 65 45
630 250f. Aerial view of complex 80 55

130 Map of Bahrain and Anniversary
Emblem

1998. 50th Anniv of W.H.O.
631 **130** 80f. multicoloured 25 15
632 200f. multicoloured . . . 65 45
633 250f. multicoloured . . . 80 55

131 Emblem

1998. World Cup Football Championship, France. Multicoloured.
634 80f. Type **131** 25 15
635 200f. Globes and football
forming "98" (vert) . . . 65 45
636 250f. Footballers and globe
(vert) 80 55

132 Football

1998. 14th Arabian Gulf Cup Football Championship, Bahrain. Multicoloured.
637 80f. Type **132** 25 15
638 200f. Close-up of football . . 65 45
639 250f. As No. 638 . . . . . 85 55

133 Emblem and Koran

1999. Holy Koran Reading Competition.
640 **133** 100f. multicoloured . . . 30 20
641 200f. multicoloured . . . 65 45
642 250f. multicoloured . . . 85 55

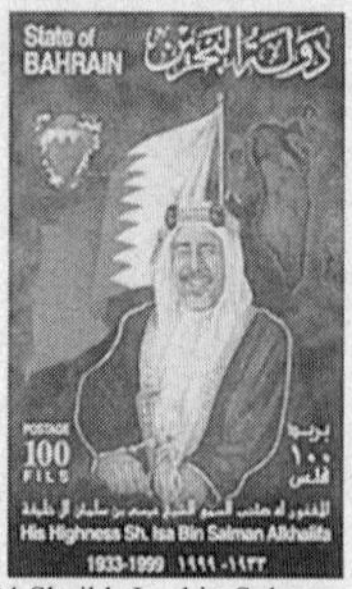

134 Shaikh Isa bin Sulman al-Khalifa and State Flag

1999. Shaikh Isa bin Sulman al-Khalifa Commemoration. Multicoloured.

643	100f. Type **134**	30	20
644	200f. Shaikh and map of Bahrain (41 × 31 mm)	65	45
645	250f. Shaikh, map of Bahrain and state flag	80	55

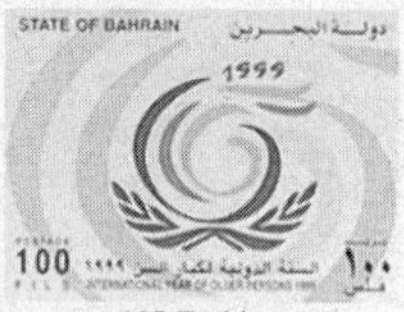

135 Emblem

1999. International Year of the Elderly. Mult.

647	100f. Type **135**	30	20
648	200f. Emblem and flame	65	45
649	250f. Emblem (different)	80	55

136 Emblem

1999. 10th Anniv of Bahrain Stock Exchange. Multicoloured.

650	100f. Type **136**	30	20
651	200f. Shaikh Isa bin Salman Bridge and emblem	65	40
652	250f. Globe and emblem	80	55

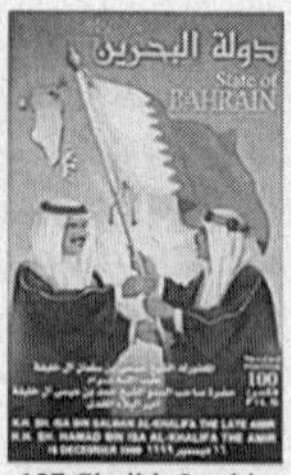

137 Shaikh Isa bin Salman and Shaikh Hamad bin Isa holding Flag

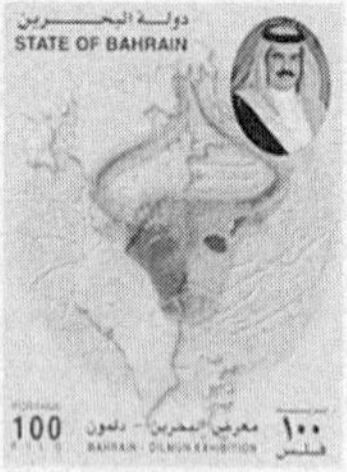

138 Map of Bahrain and Animal Skull

1999. National Day. Multicoloured.

653	100f. Type **137**	30	20
654	200f. Shaikh Hamad bin Isa and flag	65	40
655	250f. Shaikh Hamad bin Isa and globe	80	55

2000. Dilmun Exhibition. Multicoloured.

657	100f. Type **138**	35	25
658	200f. Map of Bahrain superimposed over animal skull	75	50
659	250f. Map of Bahrain and artefact	90	60

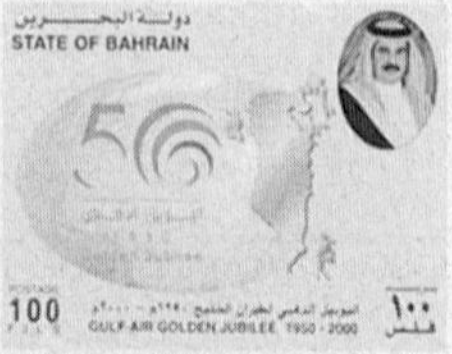

139 Map of Bahrain and Emblem

2000. 50th Anniv of Gulf Air. Multicoloured.

660	100f. Type **139**	35	25
661	200f. Map of Bahrain and emblem in circle	75	50
662	250f. Map of Bahrain, emblem and eagles	90	60

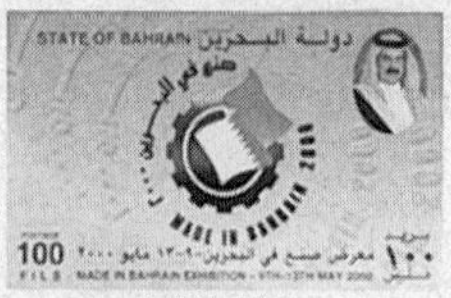

140 Emblem

2000. "Made in Bahrain 2000" Exhibition. Multicoloured.

663	100f. Type **140**	45	25
664	200f. Type **140**	75	50
665	250f. Oil refinery	90	60

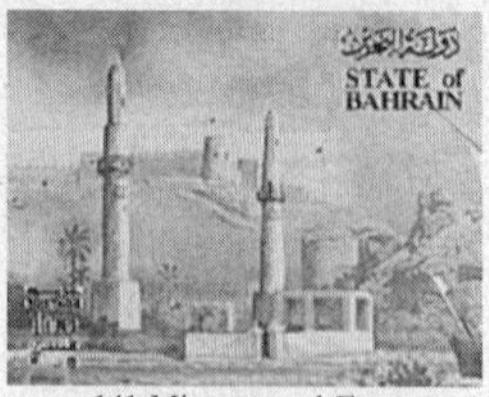

141 Minarets and Fort

2000. Millennium. Multicoloured.

666	100f. Type **141**	45	25
667	100f. Dhows and factories	45	25
668	100f. Man harvesting dates	45	25
669	100f. Fort, globe and dish aerial	45	25
670	200f. Lake and bridge	75	50
671	200f. Modern building and woman	75	50
672	200f. Dhows, jug and wicker basket	75	50
673	200f. Horseman and falconer	75	50
674	250f. Pearl divers	90	60
675	250f. Opening clams	90	60
676	250f. Fishermen	90	60
677	250f. Man mending fishing nets	90	60

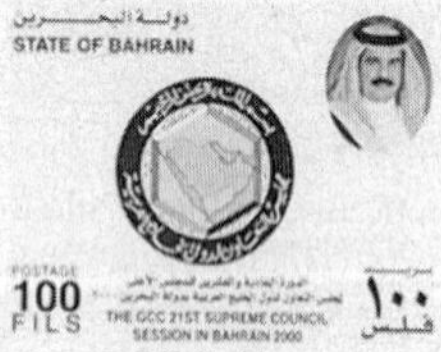

142 Emblem

2000. 21st Gulf Co-operation Council Supreme Council Session, Bahrain. Multicoloured.

678	100f. Type **142**	35	20
679	200f. Members' flags	70	40

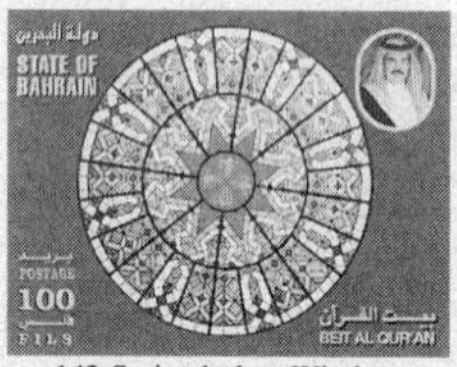

143 Stained-glass Window

2001. 10th Anniv of Beit Al Qur'an (Islamic institution). Multicoloured.

680	100f. Type **143**	35	20
681	200f. Beit Al Qur'an by night	70	40
682	250f. Facade	90	55

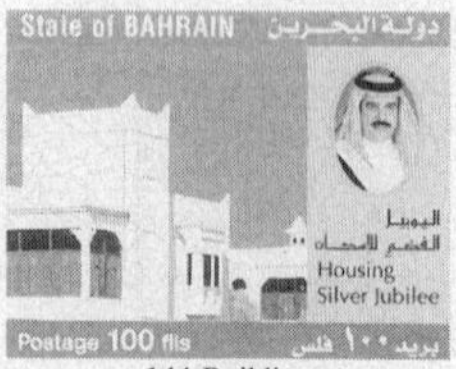

144 Building

2001. 25th Anniv of Ministry of Housing and Agriculture. Multicoloured.

684	100f. Type **144**	35	20
685	150f. Sculpture and building	55	35
686	200f. Building viewed through arch	70	40
687	250f. Tall, arched building	90	55

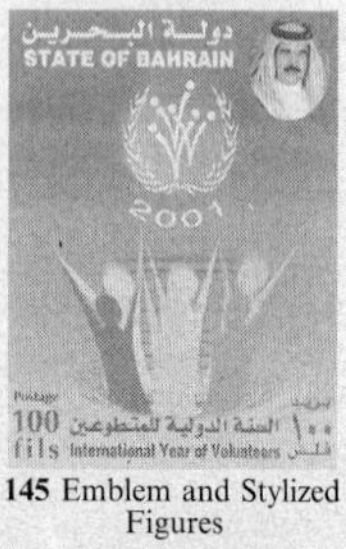

145 Emblem and Stylized Figures

2001. International Year of Volunteers. Multicoloured.

688	100f. Type **145**	35	20
689	150f. Hands encircling emblem	55	35
690	200f. Star pattern and emblem	70	40
691	250f. Paper cut figures	90	55

WAR TAX STAMPS

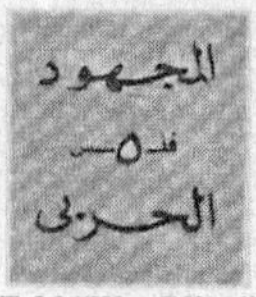
T 36 "War Effort"

T 37 "War Effort"

1973.

T192	T **36** 5f. blue and cobalt		

1973.

T194a	T **37** 5f. blue	1·00	10

BAMRA Pt. 1

A state in India. Now uses Indian stamps.

12 pies = 1 anna; 16 annas = 1 rupee.

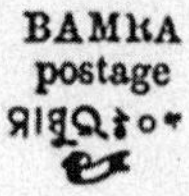

1

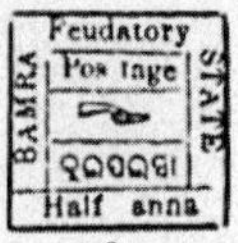

8

1888.

1 **1**	¼a. black on yellow	£325	
2	½a. black on red	70·00	
3	1a. black on blue	45·00	
4	2a. black on green	65·00	£225
5	4a. black on yellow	55·00	£225
6	8a. black on red	38·00	

1890. Imperf.

10 **8**	¼a. black on red	1·60	2·00
11	½a. black on green	2·00	2·50
30	1a. black on yellow	3·25	2·50
16	2a. black on red	3·50	4·00
19	4a. black on red	7·50	4·50
22	8a. black on red	11·00	14·00
25	1r. black on red	15·00	18·00

BANGLADESH Pt. 1

Formerly the Eastern wing of Pakistan. Following a landslide victory at the Pakistan General Election in December 1970 by the Awami League party the National Assembly was suspended. Unrest spread throughout the eastern province culminating in the intervention of India on the side of the East Bengalis. The new state became effective after the surrender of the Pakistan army in December 1971.

1971. 100 paisa = 1 rupee.
1972. 100 paisa = 1 taka.

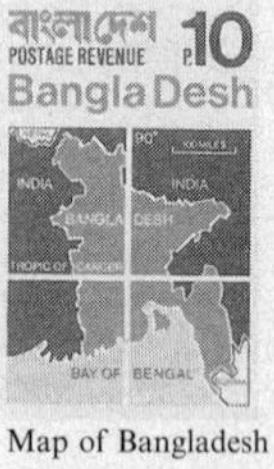

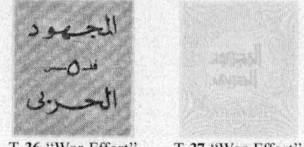

1 Map of Bangladesh

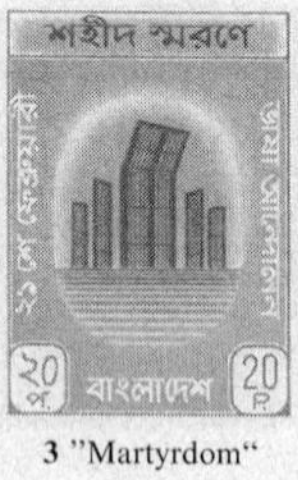

3 "Martyrdom"

1971.

1 **1**	10p. indigo, orange and blue	10	10
2 –	20p. multicoloured	10	10
3 –	50p. multicoloured	10	10
4 –	1r. multicoloured	10	10
5 –	2r. turquoise, blue and red	25	35
6 –	3r. light green, green and blue	30	55
7 –	5r. multicoloured	50	1·00
8 –	10r. gold, red and blue	1·00	2·00

DESIGNS: 20p. "Dacca University Massacre"; 50p. "75 Million People"; 1r. Flag of Independence; 2r. Ballot box; 3r. Broken chain; 5r. Shaikh Majibur Rahman; 10r. "Support Bangla Desh" and map.

1971. Liberation. Nos. 1 and 7/8 optd **BANGLADESH LIBERATED**.

9	10p. indigo, orange and blue	15	10
10	5r. multicoloured	1·75	2·25
11	10r. gold, red and blue	2·25	3·00

The remaining values of the original issue were also overprinted and placed on sale in Great Britian but were not issued in Bangladesh.

On 1 February 1972 the Agency placed on sale a further issue in the flag, map and Sheikh Mujib designs in new colours and new currency (100 paisa = 1 taka). This issue proved to be unacceptable to the Bangladesh authorities who declared them to be invalid for postal purposes, no supplies being sold within Bangladesh. The values comprise 1, 2, 3, 5, 7, 10, 15, 20, 25, 40, 50, 75p., 1, 2 and 5t.

1972. In Memory of the Martyrs.

12 **3**	20p. green and red	30	50

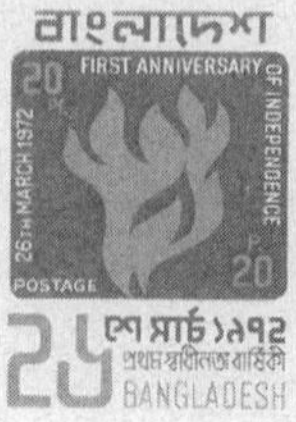

4 Flames of Independence

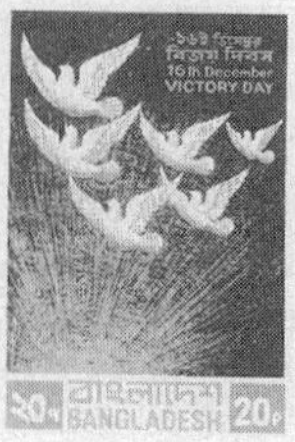

5 Doves of Peace

1972. 1st Anniv of Independence.

13 **4**	20p. lake and red	20	10
14	60p. blue and red	25	45
15	75p. violet and red	30	55

1972. Victory Day.

16 **5**	20p. multicoloured	15	10
17	60p. multicoloured	20	55
18	75p. multicoloured	20	55

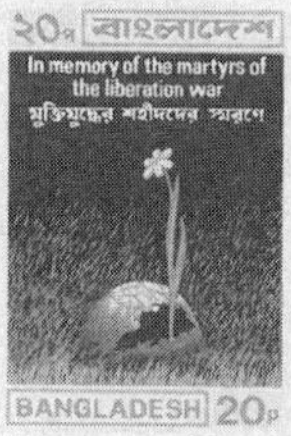

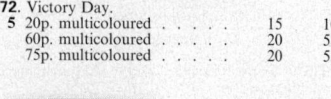

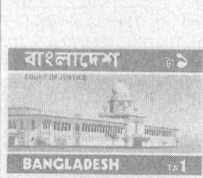

6 "Homage to Martyrs"

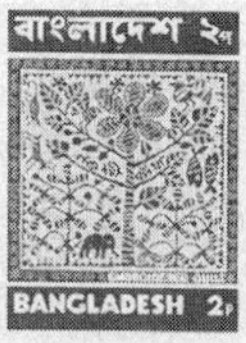

7 Embroidered Quilt

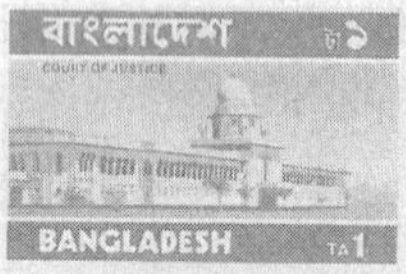

8 Court of Justice

9 Flame Emblem

1973. In Memory of the Martyrs.

19 **6**	20p. multicoloured	15	10
20	60p. multicoloured	30	40
21	1t.35 multicoloured	65	1·75

1973.

22 **7**	2p. black	10	80
23 –	3p. green	20	80
24 –	5p. brown	20	10
25 –	10p. black	20	10
26 –	20p. green	50	10
27 –	25p. mauve	2·75	10
28 –	50p. purple	1·50	30
29 –	60p. grey	75	75
30 –	75p. orange	80	75
31 –	90p. brown	90	1·00
32 **8**	1t. violet	4·00	30
33 –	2t. green	4·00	65
34 –	5t. blue	5·50	1·75
35 –	10t. pink	5·50	3·75

DESIGNS—As Type **7**: 3p. Jute field; 5p. Jack fruit; 10p. Bullocks ploughing; 20p. Rakta jaba (flower); 25p. Tiger; 60p. Bamboo grove; 75p. Plucking tea; 90p. Handicrafts. (28 × 22 mm): 50p. Hilsa (fish). As Type **8**. VERT: 2t. Date tree. HORIZ: 5t. Fishing boat; 10t. Sixty-dome mosque, Bagerhat.

See also Nos. 49/51a, 64/75 and 711.

1973. 25th Anniv of Declaration of Human Rights.

36 **9**	10p. multicoloured	10	10
37	1t.25 multicoloured	20	20

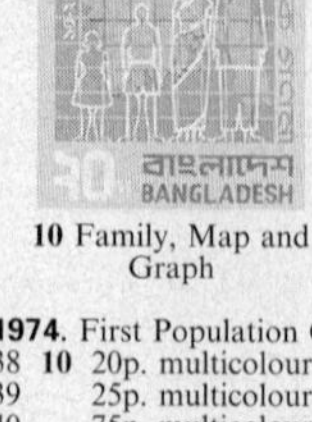

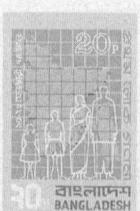

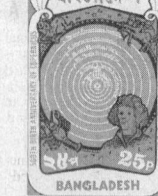

10 Family, Map and Graph

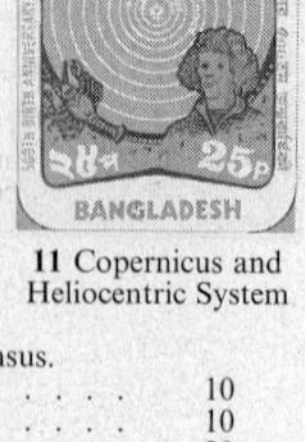

11 Copernicus and Heliocentric System

1974. First Population Census.

38 **10**	20p. multicoloured	10	10
39	25p. multicoloured	10	10
40	75p. multicoloured	20	20

1974. 500th Birth Anniv of Copernicus.

41 **11**	25p. orange, violet and black	10	10
42	75p. orange, green and black	25	50

12 U.N. H.Q. and Bangladesh Flag

13 U.P.U. Emblem

1974. Bangladesh's Admission to the U.N.

43	12	25p. multicoloured	10	10
44		1t. multicoloured	35	40

1974. Centenary of Universal Postal Union. Mult.

45		25p. Type **13**	10	10
46		1t.25 Mail runner	20	15
47		1t.75 Type **13**	20	25
48		5t. As 1t.25	80	1·60

14 Courts of Justice

1974. As Nos. 32/5 with revised inscriptions.

49	14	1t. violet	1·50	10
50	–	2t. olive	2·00	1·50
51	–	5t. blue	6·00	70
51a	–	10t. pink	14·00	11·00

For these designs redrawn to 32×20 mm or 20×32 mm, see Nos. 72/5 and, to 35×22 mm, see No. 711.

15 Tiger

16 Symbolic Family

1974. Wildlife Preservation. Multicoloured.

52		25p. Type **15**	70	10
53		50p. Tiger cub	1·00	70
54		2t. Tiger in stream	2·25	3·50

1974. World Population Year. "Family Planning for All". Multicoloured.

55		25p. Type **16**	15	10
56		70p. Village family	25	50
57		1t.25 Heads of family (horiz)	40	1·10

17 Radar Antenna

19 Telephones of 1876 and 1976

18 Woman's Head

1975. Inauguration of Betbunia Satellite Earth Station.

58	17	25p. black, silver and red	10	10
59		1t. black, silver and blue	20	70

1975. International Women's Year.

60	18	50p. multicoloured	10	10
61		2t. multicoloured	25	1·00

1976. As Nos. 24/31 and 49/51a but redrawn in smaller size.

64	–	5p. green	20	10
65	–	10p. black	20	10
66	–	20p. green	70	10
67	–	25p. mauve	3·00	10
68	–	50p. purple	3·00	10
69	–	60p. grey	40	20
70	–	75p. green	1·25	2·50
71	–	90p. brown	40	20
72	14	1t. violet	2·00	10
73	–	2t. green	6·50	10
74	–	5t. blue	3·25	2·50
75	–	10t. red	8·50	2·75

Nos. 64/71 are 23×18 mm (50p.) or 18×23 mm (others) and Nos. 72/75 are 20×32 mm (2t.) or 32×20 mm (others).

For the 10t. redrawn to 35×22 mm, see No. 711.

1976. Centenary of Telephone.

76	19	2t.25 multicoloured	25	20
77	–	5t. red, green and black	55	65

DESIGN: 5t. Alexander Graham Bell.

20 Eye and Nutriments

1976. Prevention of Blindness.

78	20	30p. multicoloured	50	10
79		2t.25 multicoloured	1·40	2·25

21 Liberty Bell

1976. Bicentenary of American Revolution. Mult.

80		30p. Type **21**	10	10
81		2t.25 Statue of Liberty	20	25
82		5t. "Mayflower"	55	50
83		10t. Mount Rushmore	55	80

22 Industry, Science, Agriculture and Education

23 Hurdling

1976. 25th Anniv of Colombo Plan.

85	22	30p. multicoloured	15	10
86		2t.25 multicoloured	35	75

1976. Olympic Games, Montreal. Multicoloured.

87		25p. Type **23**	10	10
88		30p. Running (horiz)	10	10
89		1t. Pole vaulting	15	10
90		2t.25 Swimming (horiz)	40	45
91		3t.50 Gymnastics	75	1·25
92		5t. Football	1·40	2·00

24 The Blessing

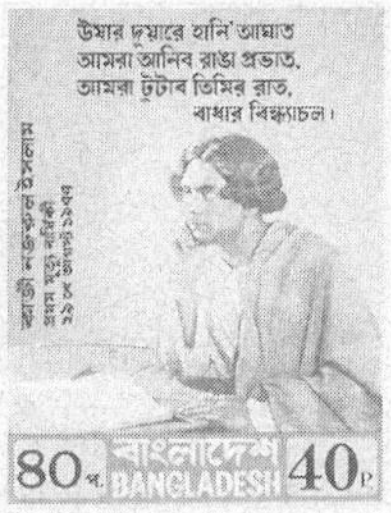

25 Qazi Nazrul Islam (poet)

1977. Silver Jubilee. Multicoloured.

93		30p. Type **24**	10	10
94		2t.25 Queen Elizabeth II	20	25
95		10t. Queen Elizabeth and Prince Philip	70	85

1977. Qazi Nazrul Islam Commemoration.

97	25	40p. green and black	10	10
98	–	2t.25 brown, red & lt brn	30	30

DESIGN—HORIZ: 2t.25, Head and shoulders portrait.

26 Bird with Letter

1977. 15th Anniv of Asian–Oceanic Postal Union.

99	26	30p. red, blue and grey	10	10
100		2t.25 red, blue and grey	20	25

27 Sloth Bear

28 Campfire and Tent

1977. Animals. Multicoloured.

101		40p. Type **27**	15	10
102		1t. Spotted deer	20	10
103		2t.25 Leopard (horiz)	40	20
104		3t.50 Gaur (horiz)	45	35
105		4t. Indian elephant (horiz)	1·00	50
106		5t. Tiger (horiz)	1·25	75

The Bengali numerals on the 40p. resemble "80", and that on the 4t. resembles "8".

1978. First National Scout Jamboree.

107	28	40p. red, blue and pale blue	30	10
108	–	3t.50 lilac, green and blue	1·25	30
109	–	5t. green, blue and red	1·40	45

DESIGNS—HORIZ: 3t.50, Scout stretcher-team. VERT: 5t. Scout salute.

29 "Michelia champaca"

1978. Flowers. Multicoloured.

110		40p. Type **29**	20	10
111		1t. "Cassia fistula"	40	15
112		2t.25 "Delonix regia"	55	30
113		3t.50 "Nymphaea nouchali"	60	60
114		4t. "Butea monosperma"	60	80
115		5t. "Anthocephalus indicus"	60	85

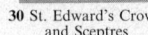

30 St. Edward's Crown and Sceptres

32 Fenchuganj Fertiliser Factory

31 Sir Alan Cobham's De Havilland D.H.50

1978. 25th Anniv of Coronation. Multicoloured.

116		40p. Type **30**	10	10
117		3t.50 Balcony scene	15	30
118		5t. Queen Elizabeth and Prince Philip	25	50
119		10t. Coronation portrait by Cecil Beaton	45	80

1978. 75th Anniv of Powered Flight.

121	31	40p. multicoloured	15	10
122	–	2t.25 brown and blue	50	45
123	–	3t.50 brown and yellow	65	65
124	–	5t. multicoloured	4·00	3·50

DESIGNS: 2t.25, Captain Hans Bertram's seaplane "Atlantis"; 3t.50, Wright brothers' Flyer III; 5t. Concorde.

1978.

125	–	5p. brown	10	10
126	32	10p. blue	10	10
127	–	15p. orange	10	10
128	–	20p. red	10	10
129	–	25p. blue	15	10
130	–	30p. green	2·00	10
131	–	40p. purple	30	10
132	–	50p. black	3·75	1·50
134	–	80p. brown	20	10
136	–	1t. violet	5·00	10
137	–	2t. blue	1·00	2·25

DESIGNS—HORIZ: 5p. Lalbag Fort; 25p. Jute on a boat; 40, 50p. Baitul Mukarram Mosque; 1t. Dotara (musical instrument); 2t. Karnaphuli Dam. VERT: 15p. Pineapple; 20p. Bangladesh gas; 30p. Banana tree; 80p. Mohastan Garh.

33 Tawaf-E-Ka'aba, Mecca

35 Moulana Abdul Hamid Khan Bhashani

34 Jasim Uddin

1978. Pilgrimage to Mecca. Multicoloured.

140		40p. Type **33**	20	10
141		3t. Pilgrims in Wuquf, Arafat (horiz)	60	45

1979. 3rd Death Anniv of Jasim Uddin (poet).

142	34	40p. multicoloured	20	50

1979. 3rd Death Anniv of Moulana Abdul Hamid Khan Bhashani (national leader).

143	35	40p. multicoloured	40	30

36 Sir Rowland Hill

37 Children with Hoops

1979. Death Centenary of Sir Rowland Hill.

144	36	40p. blue, red and light blue	10	10
145	–	3t.50 multicoloured	35	30
146	–	10t. multicoloured	80	1·00

DESIGNS: 3t.50, Sir Rowland Hill and first Bangladesh stamp; 10t. Sir Rowland Hill and Bangladesh U.P.U. stamp.

1979. International Year of the Child. Multicoloured.

148		40p. Type **37**	10	10
149		3t.50 Boy with kite	35	35
150		5t. Children jumping	50	50

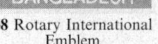

38 Rotary International Emblem

40 A. K. Fazlul Huq

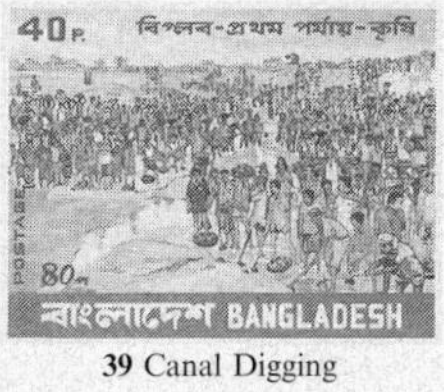

39 Canal Digging

1980. 75th Anniv of Rotary International.

152	38	40p. black, red and yellow	20	10
153	–	5t. gold and blue	65	45

DESIGN: 5t. Rotary emblem (different).

1980. Mass Participation in Canal Digging.

154	39	40p. multicoloured	40	30

1980. 18th Death Anniv of A. K. Fazlul Huq (national leader).

155	40	40p. multicoloured	30	30

41 Early Forms of Mail Transport

1980. "London 1980" International Stamp Exhibition. Multicoloured.
156 1t. Type **41** 15   10
157 10t. Modern forms of mail transport . . . . 1·25   90

42 Dome of the Rock   43 Outdoor Class

1980. Palestinian Welfare.
159 **42** 50p. lilac 70   30

1980. Education.
160 **43** 50p. multicoloured 40   30

44 Beach Scene

1980. World Tourism Conference, Manila. Mult.
161 50p. Type **44** 35   50
162 5t. Beach scene (different) . . 65   1·10

45 Mecca   46 Begum Roquaih

1980. Moslem Year 1400 A. H. Commemoration.
164 **45** 50p. multicoloured 20   20

1980. Birth Centenary of Begum Roquiah (campaigner for women's rights).
165 **46** 50p. multicoloured 10   10
166 2t. multicoloured 35   20

47 Spotted Deer and Scout Emblem   49 Queen Elizabeth the Queen Mother

1981. 5th Asia–Pacific and 2nd Bangladesh Scout Jamboree.
167 **47** 50p. multicoloured 40   15
168 5t. multicoloured . . . . . . 1·25   2·00

1981. 2nd Population Census. Nos. 38/40 optd **2nd. CENSUS 1981.**
169 **10** 20p. multicoloured 10   10
170 50p. multicoloured 10   10
171 75p. multicoloured 20   30

1981. 80th Birthday of the Queen Mother.
172 **49** 1t. multicoloured 15   15
173 15t. multicoloured . . . . . . 1·75   2·50

50 Revolutionary with Flag and Sub-machine-gun   52 Kemal Ataturk in Civilian Dress

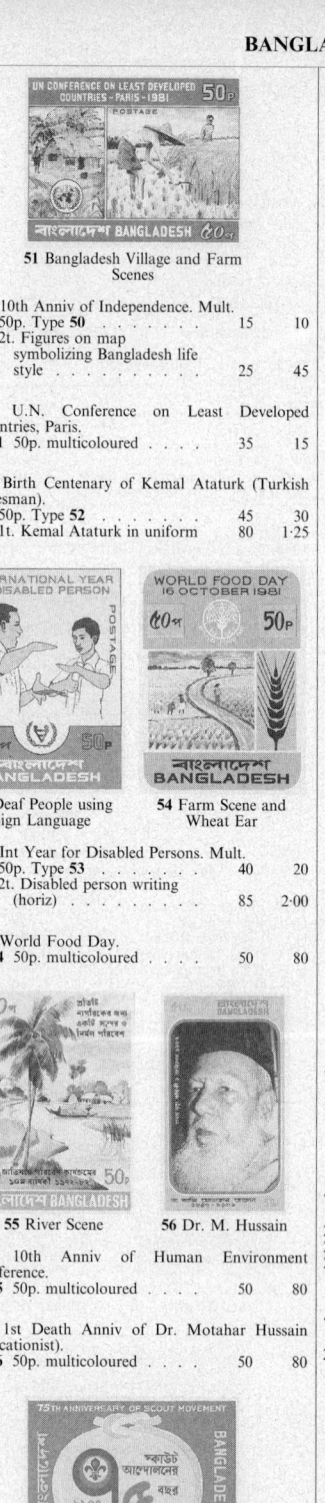

51 Bangladesh Village and Farm Scenes

1981. 10th Anniv of Independence. Mult.
175 50p. Type **50** 15   10
176 2t. Figures on map symbolizing Bangladesh life style 25   45

1981. U.N. Conference on Least Developed Countries, Paris.
177 **51** 50p. multicoloured 35   15

1981. Birth Centenary of Kemal Ataturk (Turkish statesman).
178 50p. Type **52** 45   30
179 1t. Kemal Ataturk in uniform 80   1·25

53 Deaf People using Sign Language   54 Farm Scene and Wheat Ear

1981. Int Year for Disabled Persons. Mult.
180 50p. Type **53** 40   20
181 2t. Disabled person writing (horiz) 85   2·00

1981. World Food Day.
182 **54** 50p. multicoloured 50   80

55 River Scene   56 Dr. M. Hussain

1982. 10th Anniv of Human Environment Conference.
183 **55** 50p. multicoloured 50   80

1982. 1st Death Anniv of Dr. Motahar Hussain (educationist).
184 **56** 50p. multicoloured 50   80

57 Knotted Rope surrounding Bengali "75"

1982. 75th Anniv of Boy Scout Movement and 125th Birth Anniv of Lord Baden-Powell. Multicoloured.
185 50p. Type **57** 30
186 2t. Lord Baden-Powell (vert) 2·25   4·00

(58)   60 Metric Scales

59 Captain Mohiuddin Jahangir

1982. Armed Forces' Day. No. 175 optd with T **58.**
187 50p. Type **50** . . . . 2·50   2·50

1983. Heroes and Martyrs of the Liberation. Multicoloured, background colour of commemorative plaque given.
188 50p. Type **59** (orange) 30   45
189 50p. Sepoy Hamidur Rahman (green) 30   45
190 50p. Sepoy Mohammed Mustafa Kamal (red) . . 30   45
191 50p. Muhammed Ruhul Amin (yellow) 30   45
192 50p. Flt. Lt. M. Matiur Rahman (brown) 30   45
193 50p. Lance-Naik Munshi Abdur Rob (brown) . . 30   45
194 50p. Lance-Naik Nur Mouhammad (green) . . 30   45

1983. Introduction of Metric Weights and Measures. Multicoloured.
195 50p. Type **60** 40   30
196 2t. Weights, jug and tape measure (horiz) . . . . 1·75   2·50

61 Dr. Robert Koch   63 Dr. Muhammed Shahidulla

62 Open Stage Theatre

1983. Centenary (1982) of Robert Koch's Discovery of Tubercle Bacillus. Multicoloured.
197 50p. Type **61** . . . . 1·00   40
198 1t. Microscope, slide and X-ray . . . . 2·25   3·25

1983. Commonwealth Day. Multicoloured.
199 1t. Type **62** 10   15
200 3t. Boat race 20   30
201 10t. Snake dance 50   90
202 15t. Picking tea 60   1·50

1983. Dr. Muhammed Shahidulla (Bengali scholar) Commemoration.
203 **63** 50p. multicoloured 75   1·00

64 Magpie Robin

1983. Birds of Bangladesh. Multicoloured.
204 50p. Type **64** . . . . 1·00   40
205 2t. White-throated kingfisher (vert) . . . . 1·75   2·25
206 3t.75 Lesser flame-backed woodpecker (vert) . . 1·75   3·00
207 5t. White-winged wood duck 2·00   3·50

65 "Macrobrachium rosenbergii"

1983. Marine Life. Multicoloured.
209 50p. Type **65** 80   30
210 2t. White pomfret . . . . 1·25   1·60
211 3t.75 Rohu . . . . . . 1·50   2·00
212 5t. Climbing perch . . . . 1·75   2·75

1983. Visit of Queen Elizabeth II. No. 95 optd **Nov. '83 Visit of Queen.**
214 10t. Queen Elizabeth and Prince Philip . . . . 3·75   4·75

67 Conference Hall, Dhaka

1983. 14th Islamic Foreign Ministers' Conference, Dhaka. Multicoloured.
215 50p. Type **67** 35   30
216 5t. Old Fort, Dhaka . . . . 1·25   2·75

68 Early Mail Runner   69 Carrying Mail by Boat

1983. World Communications Year. Multicoloured.
217 50p. Type **68** 30   15
218 5t. Sailing ship, steam train and Boeing 707 airliner . . 2·00   1·50
219 10t. Mail runner and dish aerial (horiz) . . . . 2·75   3·50

1983. Postal Communications.
220 **69** 5p. blue 10   10
221 – 10p. purple 10   10
222 – 15p. blue 10   10
223 – 20p. black 10   10
224 – 25p. grey 10   10
225 – 30p. brown 10   10
226 – 50p. brown 10   10
227 – 1t. blue 10   10
228 – 2t. green 10   10
228a – 3t. brown . . . . . . 1·75   70
229 – 5t. purple . . . . . . 1·75   80
DESIGNS—HORIZ (22 × 17 mm): 10p. Counter, Dhaka G.P.O.; 15p. I.W.T.A. Terminal, Dhaka; 20p. Inside railway travelling post office; 30p. Emptying pillar box; 50p. Mobile post office van. (30 × 19 mm): 1t. Kamalapur Railway Station, Dhaka; 2t. Zia International Airport; 3t. Sorting mail by machine; 5t. Khulna G.P.O. VERT (17 × 22 mm): 25p. Delivering a letter.

(70)

1984. 1st National Stamp Exhibition (1st issue). Nos. 161/2 optd with T **70** (5t.) or **First Bangladesh National Philatelic Exhibition—1984** (50p.)
230 **44** 50p. multicoloured . . . . 1·00   1·00
231 – 5t. multicoloured . . . . 1·25   1·75

71 Girl with Stamp Album (⅔-size illustration)

1984. 1st National Stamp Exhibition (2nd issue). Multicoloured.
232 50p. Type **71** 65   1·25
233 7t.50 Boy with stamp album 1·10   1·75

72 Sarus Crane and Gavial   73 Eagle attacking Hen with Chicks

1984. Dhaka Zoo. Multicoloured.
235 1t. Type **72** . . . . 1·75   85
236 2t. Common peafowl and tiger . . . . 2·50   4·00

1984. Centenary of Postal Life Insurance. Mult.
237 1t. Type **73** 50   25
238 5t. Bangladesh family and postman's hand with insurance cheque . . 1·50   2·00

74 Abbasuddin Ahmad (75)

1984. Abbasuddin Ahmad (singer) Commemoration.
239 74 3t. multicoloured 70 70

1984. "Khulnapex-84" Stamp Exhibition. No. 86 optd with T 75.
240 22 2t.25 multicoloured . . . . 1·00 1·50

76 Cycling

1984. Olympic Games, Los Angeles. Multicoloured.
241 1t. Type 76 . . . . 1·75 30
242 5t. Hockey . . . . 2·50 2·25
243 10t. Volleyball . . . . . . 2·75 4·00

77 Farmer with Rice and Sickle

1985. 9th Annual Meeting of Islamic Development Bank, Dhaka. Multicoloured.
244 1t. Type 77 . . . . 35 15
245 5t. Citizens of four races . . 1·25 1·75

78 Mother and Baby   80 Woman working at Tradional Crafts

উপজেলা নির্বাচন ১৯৮৫
(79)

1985. Child Survival Campaign. Multicoloured.
246 1t. Type 78 . . . . 30 10
247 10t. Young child and growth
graph . . . . 2·50 3·00

1985. Local Elections. Nos. 110/15 optd with T 79.
248 40p. Type 29 . . . . 25 25
249 1t. "Cassia fistula" 25 25
250 2t.25 "Delonix regia" . . . 40 55
251 3t.50 "Nymphaea nouchali" . 50 75
252 4t. "Butea monosperma" . . 50 75
253 5t. "Anthocephalus indicus" . 55 1·00

1985. U.N. Decade for Women. Multicoloured.
254 1t. Type 80 . . . . 25 10
255 10t. Women with microscope,
computer terminal and in
classroom . . . . 1·25 1·75

81 U.N. Building, New York, Peace Doves and Flags

1985. 40th Anniv of United Nations Organization and 11th Anniv of Bangladesh Membership. Multicoloured.
256 1t. Type 81 . . . . 10 10
257 10t. Map of world and
Bangladesh flag . . . . 80 1·10

82 Head of Youth, Flowers and Symbols of Commerce and Agriculture

83 Emblem and Seven Doves

1985. International Youth Year. Multicoloured.
258 1t. Type 82 . . . . 10 10
259 5t. Head of youth, flowers
and symbols of industry . . 40 60

1985. 1st Summit Meeting of South Asian Association for Regional Co-operation, Dhaka. Multicoloured.
260 1t. Type 83 . . . . 10 10
261 5t. Flags of member nations
and lotus blossom 40 60

84 Zainul Abedin (85)

1985. 10th Death Anniv of Zainul Abedin (artist).
262 84 3t. multicoloured 75 30

1985. 3rd National Scout Jamboree. No. 109 optd with T 85.
263 5t. green, blue and red . . 2·50 3·00

86 "Fishing Net" (Safiuddin Ahmed)

1986. Bangladesh Paintings. Multicoloured.
264 1t. Type 86 . . . . 15 10
265 5t. "Happy Return"
(Quamrul Hassan) 40 50
266 10t. "Levelling the Ploughed
Field" (Zainul Abedin) . . 70 80

87 Two Players competing for Ball

1986. World Cup Football Championship, Mexico. Multicoloured.
267 1t. Type 87 . . . . 50 10
268 10t. Goalkeeper and ball in
net . . . . 2·25 2·75

88 General M. A. G. Osmani

90 Butterflies and Nuclear Explosion

1986. General M. A. G. Osmani (army commander-in-chief) Commemoration.
270 88 3t. multicoloured . . . . . 1·25 75

1986. South Asian Association for Regional Co-operation Seminar. No. 183 optd **SAARC SEMINAR '86.**
271 55 50p. multicoloured . . . . 2·00 2·75

1986. International Peace Year. Multicoloured.
272 1t. Type 90 . . . . 50 25
273 10t. Flowers and ruined
buildings . . . . 2·75 3·50

1987. Conference for Development. Nos. 152/3 optd **CONFERENCE FOR DEVELOPMENT '87,** No. 275 also surch **TK. 1.00.**
275 38 1t. on 40p. black, red and
yellow 10 20
276 — 5t. gold and blue . . . . . 40 1·25

92 Demonstrators with Placards

1987. 35th Anniv of Bangla Language Movement. Multicoloured.
277 3t. Type 92 . . . . 1·00 1·75
278 3t. Martyrs' Memorial . . . 1·00 1·75
Nos. 277/8 were printed together, se-tenant, forming a composite design.

93 Nurse giving Injection

94 Pattern and Bengali Script

1987. World Health Day.
279 93 1t. black and blue . . . . 1·75 1·75
See also No 295.

1987. Bengali New Year Day. Multicoloured.
280 1t. Type 94 . . . . 10 10
281 10t. Bengali woman 40 60

95 Jute Shika   96 Ustad Ayet Ali Khan and Surbahar

1987. Export Products. Multicoloured.
282 1t. Type 95 . . . . 10 10
283 5t. Jute carpet (horiz) 30 35
284 10t. Cane table lamp 45 70

1987. 20th Death Anniv of Ustad Ayet Ali Khan (musician and composer).
285 96 5t. multicoloured . . . . . 1·25 60

97 Palanquin

1987. Transport. Multicoloured.
286 2t. Type 97 . . . . 20 15
287 3t. Bicycle rickshaw 40 20
288 5t. River steamer 80 35
289 7t. Express diesel train . . 2·00 50
290 10t. Bullock cart 50 75

98 H. S. Suhrawardy

1987. Hossain Shadid Suhrawardy (politician) Commemoration.
291 98 3t. multicoloured 20 30

99 Villagers fleeing from Typhoon

1987. International Year of Shelter for the Homeless. Multicoloured.
292 5t. Type 99 . . . . 20 30
293 5t. Villagers and modern
houses 20 30

100 President Ershad addressing Parliament

1987. 1st Anniv of Return to Democracy.
294 100 10t. multicoloured 40 60

1988. World Health Day. As T 93.
295 25p. brown 30 20
DESIGN: 25p. Oral rehydration.

101 Woman planting Palm Saplings

1988. I.F.A.D. Seminar on Agricultural Loans for Rural Women. Multicoloured.
296 3t. Type 101 . . . . 15 20
297 5t. Village woman milking
cow 20 40

102 Basketball

1988. Olympic Games, Seoul. Multicoloured.
298 5t. Type 102 . . . . 70 60
299 5t. Weightlifting 70 60
300 5t. Tennis 70 60
301 5t. Rifle-shooting 70 60
302 5t. Boxing 70 60

103 Interior of Shait Gumbaz Mosque, Bagerhat

1988. Historical Buildings. Multicoloured.
303 1t. Type 103 . . . . 20 10
304 4t. Paharpur Monastery . . . 35 15
305 5t. Kantanagar Temple,
Dinajpur 35 15
306 10t. Lalbag Fort, Dhaka . . . 50 30

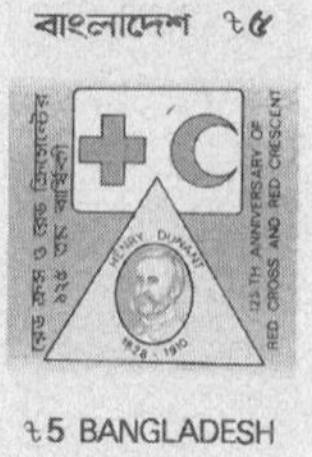

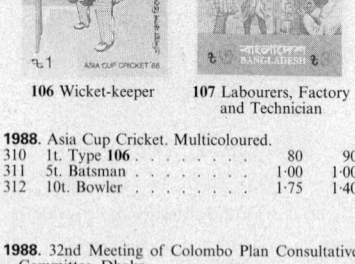

104 Henri Dunant (founder), Red Cross and Crescent

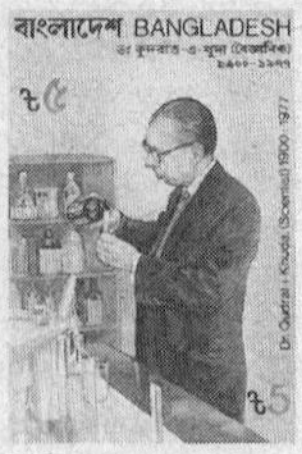

105 Dr. Qudrat-i-Khuda in Laboratory

1988. 125th Anniv of International Red Cross and Red Crescent. Multicoloured.

307	5t. Type **104**	80	30
308	10t. Red Cross workers with patient	1·10	95

1988. Dr. Qudrat-i-Khuda (scientist) Commem.

309 **105**	5t. multicoloured	30	30

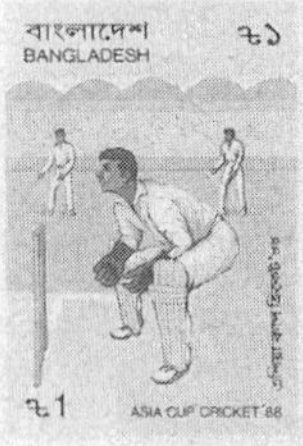

106 Wicket-keeper

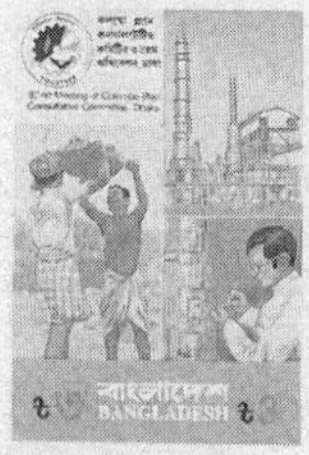

107 Labourers, Factory and Technician

1988. Asia Cup Cricket. Multicoloured.

310	1t. Type **106**	80	90
311	5t. Batsman	1·00	1·00
312	10t. Bowler	1·75	1·40

1988. 32nd Meeting of Colombo Plan Consultative Committee, Dhaka.

313 **107**	3t. multicoloured	10	10
314	10t. multicoloured	40	45

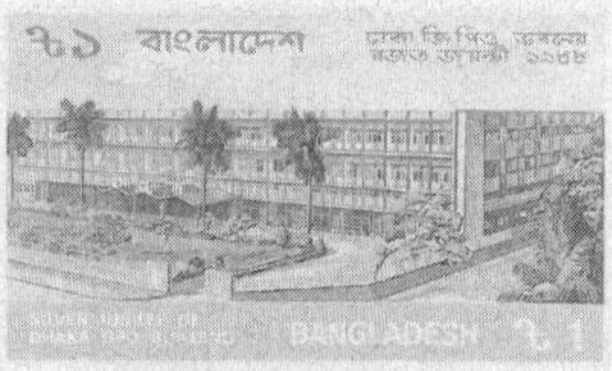

108 Dhaka G.P.O. Building

1988. 25th Anniv of Dhaka G.P.O. Building. Multicoloured.

315	1t. Type **108**	15	10
316	5t. Post Office counter	30	30

৫ম জাতীয় রোভার মুট
১৯৮৮-৮৯
(109)

1988. 5th National Rover Scout Moot. No. 168 optd with T **109**.

317 **47**	5t. multicoloured	1·75	1·75

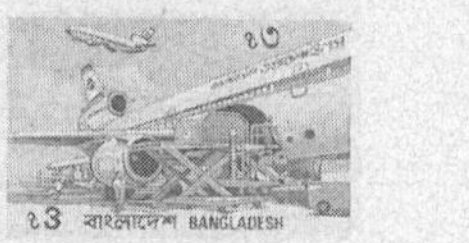

110 Bangladesh Airport

1989. Bangladesh Landmarks.

318 **110**	3t. black and blue	10	10
318a	– 4t. blue	10	15
710	– 5t. black and brown	10	15
320	– 10t. red	1·40	35
321	– 20t. multicoloured	50	55

DESIGNS—VERT (22 × 33 mm): 5t. Curzon Hall. (19½ × 31½ mm): 10t. Fertiliser factory, Chittagong. HORIZ (33 × 23 mm): 4t. Chittagong port; 20t. Postal Academy, Rajshahi.

চতুর্থ দ্বিবার্ষিক এশীয়
চারুকলা প্রদর্শনী
বাংলাদেশ ১৯৮৯
(111)

1989. 4th Biennial Asian Art Exhibition. No. 266 optd with T **111**.

322	10t. "Levelling the Ploughed Field" (Zainul Abedin)	40	45

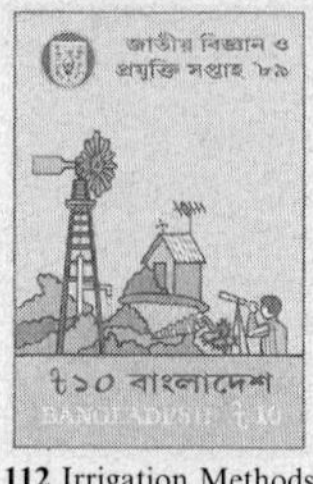

112 Irrigation Methods and Student with Telescope

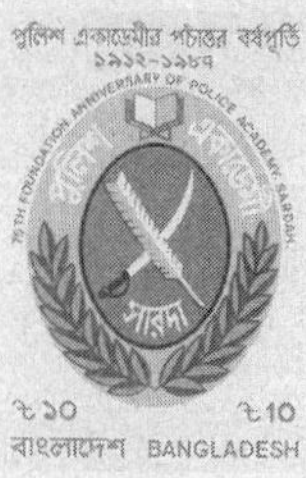

113 Academy Logo

1989. 12th National Science and Technology Week.

323 **112**	10t. multicoloured	40	45

1989. 75th Anniv of Police Academy, Sardah.

324 **113**	10t. multicoloured	50	45

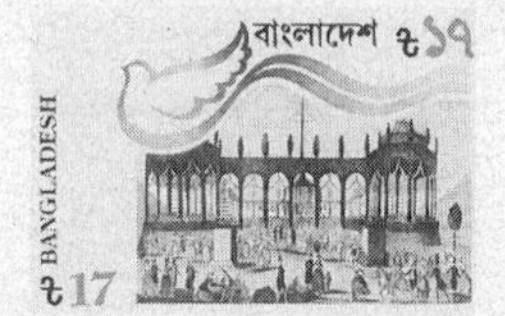

114 Rejoicing Crowds, Paris, 1789

1989. Bicentenary of French Revolution. Mult.

325	17t. Type **114**	70	75
326	17t. Storming the Bastille, 1789	70	75

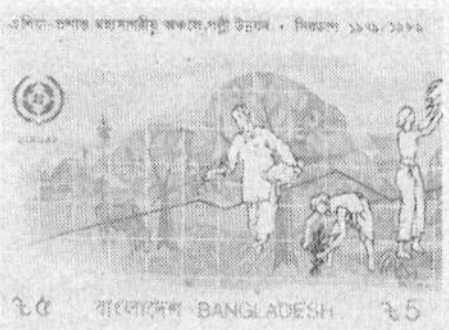

115 Sowing and Harvesting

1989. 10th Anniv of Asia–Pacific Integrated Rural Development Centre. Multicoloured.

329	5t. Type **115**	45	45
330	10t. Rural activities	55	55

Nos. 329/30 were printed together, se-tenant, forming a composite design.

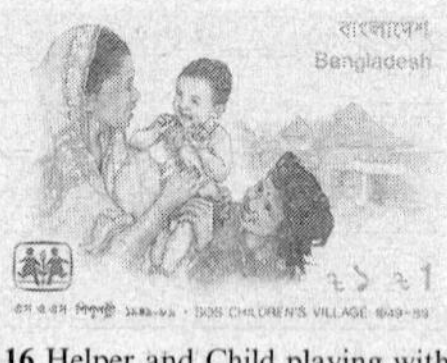

116 Helper and Child playing with Baby

1989. 40th Anniv of S.O.S. International Children's Village. Multicoloured.

331	1t. Type **116**	15	10
332	10t. Foster mother with children	55	55

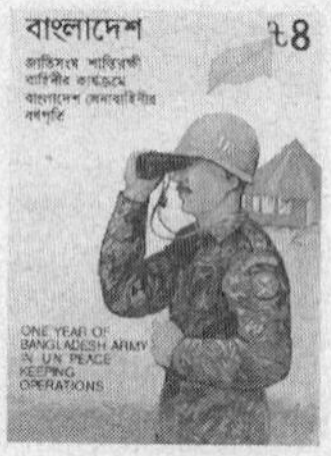

117 U.N. Soldier on Watch

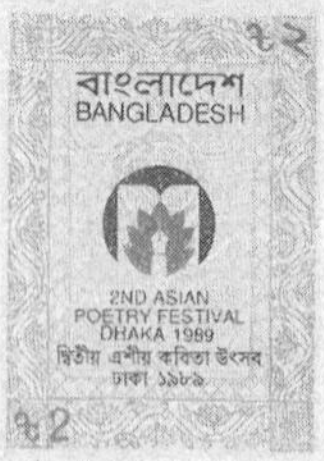

118 Festival Emblem

1989. 1st Anniv of Bangladesh Participation in U.N. Peace-keeping Force. Multicoloured.

333	4t. Type **117**	50	30
334	10t. Two soldiers checking positions	1·00	70

1989. 2nd Asian Poetry Festival, Dhaka.

335 **118**	2t. red, deep red and green	15	10
336	– 10t. multicoloured	60	65

DESIGN: 10t. Festival emblem and hall.

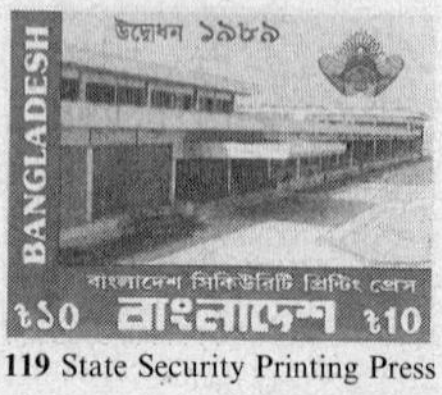

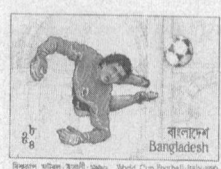

119 State Security Printing Press

1989. Inauguration of State Security Printing Press, Gazipur.

337 **119**	10t. multicoloured	65	65

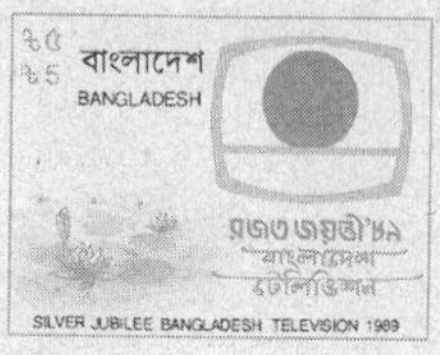

120 Water Lilies and T.V. Emblem

1989. 25th Anniv of Bangladesh Television. Multicoloured.

338	5t. Type **120**	35	30
339	10t. Central emblem and water lilies	65	80

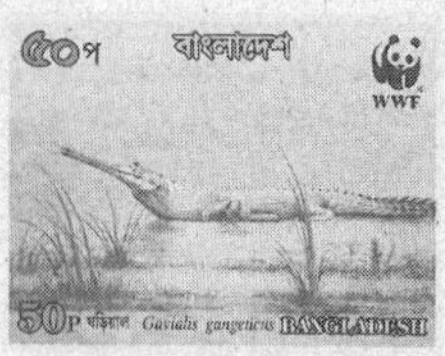

121 Gharial in Shallow Water

1990. Endangered Wildlife. Gharial. Multicoloured.

340	50p. Type **121**	80	45
341	2t. Gharial feeding	1·00	60
342	4t. Gharials basking on sand bank	1·40	70
343	10t. Two gharials resting	1·75	95

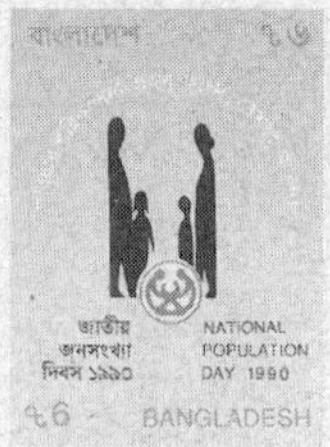

122 Symbolic Family

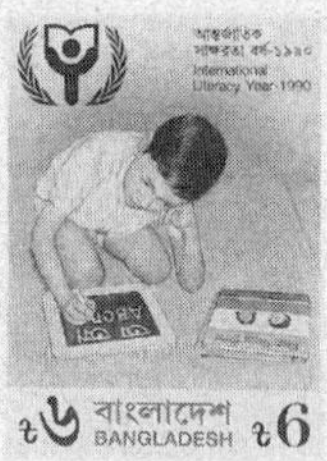

124 Boy learning Alphabet

1990. Population Day.

344 **122**	6t. multicoloured	55	35

1990. 10th Death Anniv of Justice Syed Mahbub Murshed.

345 **123**	5t. multicoloured	1·50	45

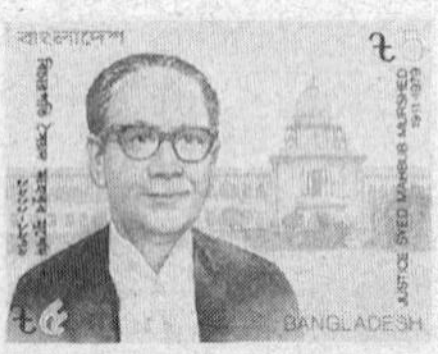

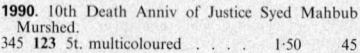

123 Justice S. M. Murshed

1990. International Literacy Year. Multicoloured.

346	6t. Type **124**	1·00	50
347	10t. Boy teaching girl to write	1·50	1·00

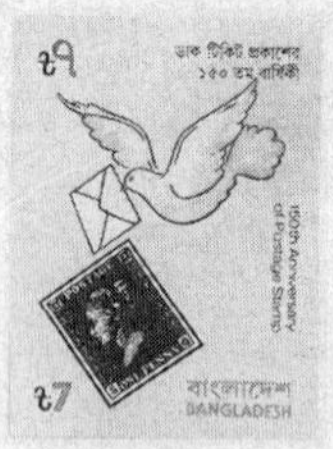

125 Penny Black with "Stamp World London 90" Exhibition Emblem

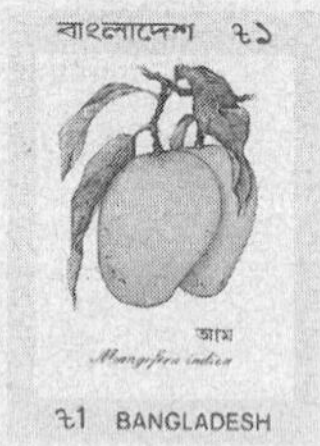

127 Mango

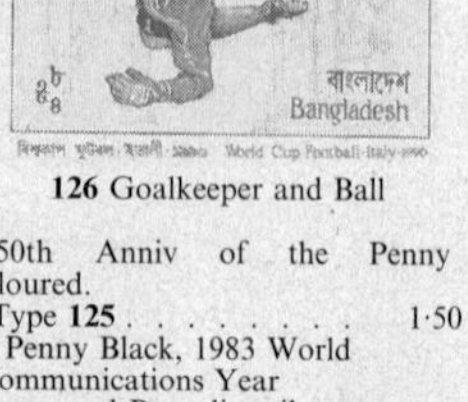

126 Goalkeeper and Ball

1990. 150th Anniv of the Penny Black. Multicoloured.

348	7t. Type **125**	1·50	1·50
349	10t. Penny Black, 1983 World Communications Year stamp and Bengali mail runner	1·75	1·75

1990. World Cup Football Championship, Italy. Multicoloured.

350	8t. Type **126**	1·75	1·50
351	10t. Footballer with ball	2·00	1·75

1990. Fruit. Multicoloured.

353	1t. Type **127**	30	10
354	2t. Guava	30	10
355	3t. Water melon	35	15
356	4t. Papaya	40	25
357	5t. Bread fruit	65	50
358	10t. Carambola	1·25	1·25

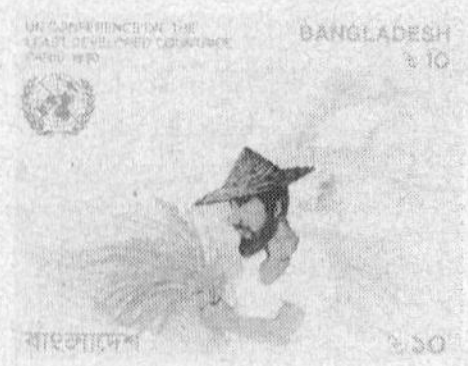

128 Man gathering Wheat

1990. U.N. Conference on Least Developed Countries, Paris.

359 **128**	10t. multicoloured	1·25	1·00

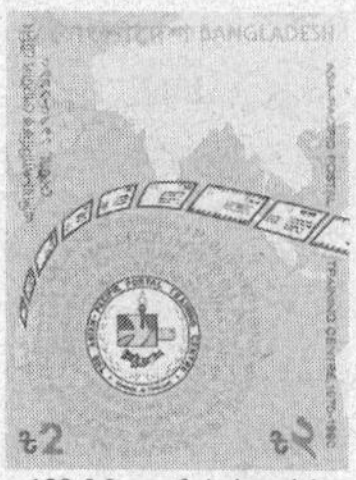

129 Map of Asia with Stream of Letters

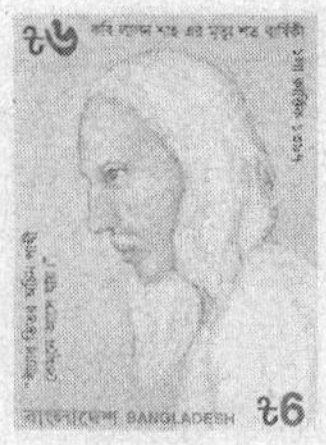

131 Lalan Shah

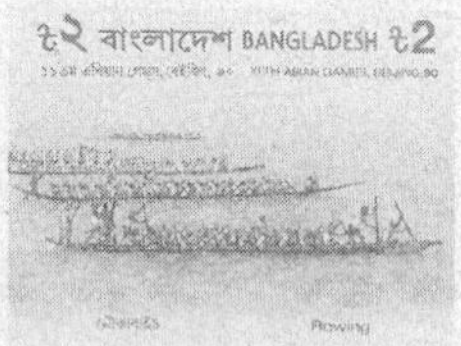

130 Canoe Racing

1990. 20th Anniv of Asia–Pacific Postal Training Centre. Multicoloured.

360	2t. Type **129**	1·25	1·25
361	6t. Map of Pacific with stream of letters	1·25	1·25

Nos. 360/1 were printed together, se-tenant, forming a composite map design.

1990. Asian Games, Beijing. Multicoloured.

362	2t. Type **130**	70	20
363	4t. Kabaddi	85	25
364	8t. Wrestling	1·40	1·00
365	10t. Badminton	2·25	1·50

1990. 1st Death Anniv of Lalan Shah (poet).

366 **131**	6t. multicoloured	1·00	35

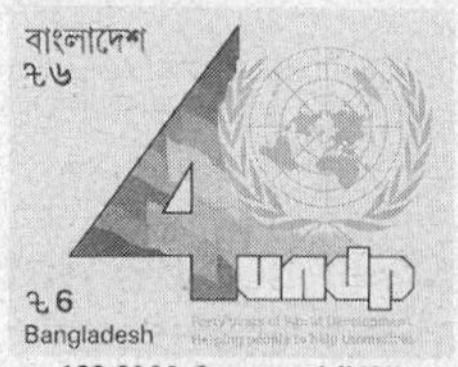

132 U.N. Logo and "40"

1990. 40th Anniv of United Nations Development Programme.

367 **132**	6t. multicoloured	80	35

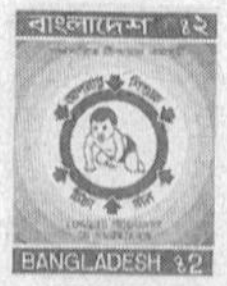

133 Baby

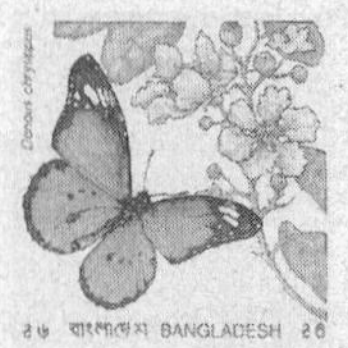

134 "Danaus chrysippus"

1990. Immunization.

368 **133**	1t. green	10	10
369	2t. brown	10	10

1990. Butterflies. Multicoloured.

370	6t. Type **134**	1·60	1·60
371	6t. "Precis almana"	1·60	1·60
372	10t. "Ixias pyrene"	1·75	1·75
373	10t. "Danaus plexippus"	1·75	1·75

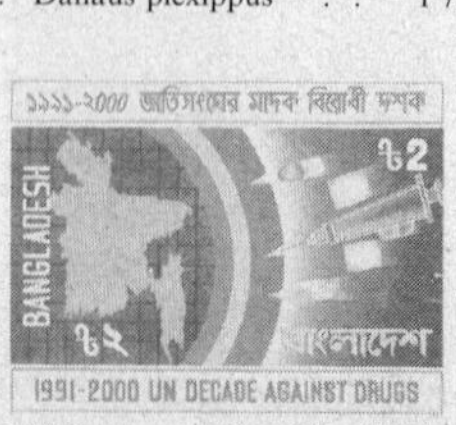

135 Drugs attacking Bangladesh

1991. U.N. Anti-drugs Decade. Multicoloured.
374 2t. Type **135** . . . . 1·00 50
375 4t. "Drug" snake around globe . . . . 1·25 1·25

136 Salimullah Hall

1991.
376 **136** 6t. blue and yellow . . . 20 25

137 Silhouetted People on Map

138 "Invincible Bangla" (statue)

1991. 3rd National Census.
382 **137** 4t. multicoloured 75 60

1991. 20th Anniv of Independence. Multicoloured.
383 4t. Type **138** 65 80
384 4t. "Freedom Fighter" (statue) 65 80
385 4t. Mujibnagar Memorial . . 65 80
386 4t. Eternal flame 65 80
387 4t. National Martyrs' Memorial 65 80
Nos. 383/7 were issued together, se-tenant, forming a composite design.

139 President Rahman Seated

141 Kaikobad

140 Red Giant Flying Squirrel

1991. 10th Death Anniv of President Ziaur Rahman. Multicoloured.
388 50p. Type **139** 20 15
389 2t. President Rahman's head in circular decoration . . . 65 85

1991. Endangered Species. Multicoloured.
391 2t. Type **140** . . . . 1·40 1·50
392 4t. Black-faced monkey (vert) 1·40 1·50
393 6t. Great Indian hornbill (vert) . . . . 1·40 1·50
394 10t. Armoured pangolin . . . 1·40 1·50

1991. 40th Death Anniv of Kaikobad (poet).
395 **141** 6t. multicoloured 80 60

142 Rabindranath Tagore and Temple

1991. 50th Death Anniv of Rabindranath Tagore (poet).
396 **142** 4t. multicoloured 70 55

143 Voluntary Blood Programme

144 Shahid Naziruddin and Crowd

1991. 14th Anniv of "Sandhani" (medical students' association).
397 **143** 3t. black and red 75 50
398 — 5t. multicoloured . . . . 1·25 1·50
DESIGN: 5t. Blind man and eye.

1991. 1st Death Anniv of Shahid Naziruddin Jahad (democrat).
399 **144** 2t. black, green and brown 70 50

145 Shaheed Noor Hossain with Slogan on Chest

1991. 4th Death Anniv of Shaheed Noor Hossain (democrat).
400 **145** 2t. multicoloured 60 40

146 Bronze Stupa

1991. Archaeological Relics from Mainamati. Multicoloured.
401 4t. Type **146** . . . . 1·25 1·40
402 4t. Earthenware and bronze pitchers . . . . 1·25 1·40
403 4t. Remains of Salban Vihara Monastery . . . . 1·25 1·40
404 4t. Gold coins . . . . . . 1·25 1·40
405 4t. Terracotta plaque . . . 1·25 1·40

147 Demostrators

1991. 1st Anniv of Mass Uprising.
406 **147** 4t. multicoloured . . . . 1·00 60

148 Munier Chowdhury

1991. 20th Anniv of Independence. Martyred Intellectuals (1st series). Each black and brown.
407 2t. Type **148** 35 35
408 2t. Ghyasuddin Ahmad . . . 35 35
409 2t. Rashidul Hasan 35 35
410 2t. Muhammad Anwar Pasha . 35 35
411 2t. Dr. Muhammad Mortaza . 35 35
412 2t. Shahid Saber 35 35
413 2t. Fazlur Rahman Khan . . 35 35
414 2t. Ranada Prasad Saha . . . 35 35
415 2t. Adhyaksha Joges Chandra Ghose 35 35
416 2t. Santosh Chandra Bhattacharyya 35 35
417 2t. Dr. Gobinda Chandra Deb 35 35
418 2t. A. Muniruzzaman 35 35
419 2t. Mufazzal Haider Chaudhury 35 35
420 2t. Dr. Abdul Alim Choudhury 35 35
421 2t. Sirajuddin Hossain . . . 35 35

422 2t. Shahidulla Kaiser 35 35
423 2t. Altaf Mahmud 35 35
424 2t. Dr. Jyotirmay Guha Thakurta 35 35
425 2t. Dr. Muhammad Abul Khair 35 35
426 2t. Dr. Serajul Haque Khan . 35 35
427 2t. Dr. Mohammad Fazle Rabbi 35 35
428 2t. Mir Abdul Quyyum . . . 35 35
429 2t. Golam Mostafa 35 35
430 2t. Dhirendranath Dutta . . . 35 35
431 2t. S. Mannan 35 35
432 2t. Nizamuddin Ahmad . . . 35 35
433 2t. Abul Bashar Chowdhury . 35 35
434 2t. Selina Parveen 35 35
435 2t. Dr. Abul Kalam Azad . . 35 35
436 2t. Saidul Hassan 35 35
See also Nos. 483/92, 525/40, 568/83, 620/35, 656/71, 691/706, 731/46 and 779/94.

149 "Penaeus monodon"

1991. Shrimps. Multicoloured.
437 6t. Type **149** . . . . 1·75 2·00
438 6t. "Metapenaeus monoceros" . . . . 1·75 2·00

150 Death of Raihan Jaglu

1992. 5th Death Anniv of Shaheed Mirze Abu Raihan Jaglu.
439 **150** 2t. multicoloured 80 50

151 Rural and Urban Scenes

152 Nawab Sirajuddaulah

1992. World Environment Day. Multicoloured.
440 4t. Type **151** 60 25
441 10t. World Environment Day logo (horiz) . . . . . . 1·40 2·00

1992. 235th Death Anniv of Nawab Sirajuddaulah of Bengal
442 **152** 10t. multicoloured . . . . 1·00 1·25

153 Syed Ismail Hossain Sirajee

1992. 61st Death Anniv of Syed Ismail Hossain Sirajee
443 **153** 4t. multicoloured 80 40

154 Couple planting Seedling

1992. Plant Week. Multicoloured.
444 2t. Type **154** 85 70
445 4t. Birds on tree (vert) . . . 1·25 70

155 Canoe Racing

1992. Olympic Games, Barcelona. Multicoloured.
446 4t. Type **155** . . . . 1·00 1·10
447 6t. Hands holding torch with Olympic rings . . . . . 1·00 1·10
448 10t. Olympic rings and doves 1·00 1·10
449 10t. Olympic rings and multiracial handshake . . . . 1·00 1·10

1992. "Banglapex '92", National Philatelic Exhibition (1st issue). No. 290 optd **Banglapex '92** in English and Bengali.
450 10t. Bullock cart . . . . . . 1·50 1·75
See also Nos. 452/3.

157 Masnad-e-Ala Isa Khan

1992. 393rd Death Anniv of Masnad-e-Ala Isa Khan.
451 **157** 4t. multicoloured 80 40

158 Ceremonial Elephant (19th-century ivory carving)

1992. "Banglapex '92" National Philatelic Exhibition (2nd issue). Multicoloured.
452 10t. Type **158** . . . . 1·25 1·75
453 10t. Victorian pillarbox between early and modern postmen . . . . 1·25 1·75

159 Star Mosque

1992. Star Mosque, Dhaka.
455 **159** 10t. multicoloured . . . . 1·50 1·50

160 Meer Nisar Ali Titumeer and Fort

1992. 161st Death Anniv of Meer Nisar Ali Titumeer.
456 **160** 10t. multicoloured . . . . 1·25 1·25

161 Terracotta Head and Seal

1992. Archaeological Relics from Mahasthangarh. Multicoloured.
457 10t. Type **161** . . . . 1·40 1·60
458 10t. Terracotta panel showing swan . . . . 1·40 1·60
459 10t. Terracotta statue of Surya . . . . 1·40 1·60
460 10t. Gupta stone column . . . 1·40 1·60

162 Young Child and Food

1992. Int Conference on Nutrition, Rome.
461 **162** 4t. multicoloured 75 40

163 National Flags

164 Syed Abdus Samad

1992. 7th South Asian Association for Regional Co-operation Summit Conference, Dhaka. Mult.
462 6t. Type **163** 75 75
463 10t. S.A.A.R.C. emblem . . . 1·00 1·25

1993. Syed Abdus Samad (footballer) Commem.
464 **164** 2t. multicoloured . . . . 1·00 50

165 Haji Shariat Ullah

1993. Haji Shariat Ullah Commemoration.
465 **165** 2t. multicoloured 80 40

166 People digging Canal

1993. Irrigation Canals Construction Project. Mult.
466 2t. Type **166** 55 65
467 2t. Completed canal and paddy-fields 55 65

167 Accident Prevention

1993. World Health Day. Multicoloured.
468 6t. Type **167** . . . . 1·50 75
469 10t. Satellite photograph and symbols of trauma (vert) 1·75 2·00

168 National Images

169 Schoolchildren and Bengali Script

1993. 1400th Year of Bengali Solar Calendar.
470 **168** 2t. multicoloured 80 40

1993. Compulsory Primary Education. Mult.
471 2t. Type **169** 60 70
472 2t. Books and slate (horiz) 60 70

170 Nawab Sir Salimullah and Palace

1993. 122nd Birth Anniv of Nawab Sir Salimullah.
473 **170** 4t. multicoloured 85 40

171 Fish Production

1993. Fish Fortnight.
474 **171** 2t. multicoloured 40 40

172 Sunderban

1993. Natural Beauty of Bangladesh. Mult.
475 10t. Type **172** 70 90
476 10t. Kuakata beach 70 90
477 10t. Madhabkunda waterfall (vert) 70 90
478 10t. River Piyain, Jaflang (vert) 70 90

173 Exhibition Emblem   **175** Burdwan House

174 Foy's Lake

1993. 6th Asian Art Biennale.
480 **173** 10t. multicoloured 60 80

1993. Tourism Month.
481 **174** 10t. multicoloured 70 90

1993. Foundation Day, Bangla Academy.
482 **175** 2t. brown and green . . . 60 40

1993. Martyred Intellectuals (2nd series). As T 148. Each black and brown.
483 2t. Lt. Cdr. Moazzam Hussain 20 30
484 2t. Muhammad Habibur Rahman 20 30
485 2t. Khandoker Abu Taleb . . 20 30
486 2t. Moshiur Rahman 20 30
487 2t. Md. Abdul Muktadir . . 20 30
488 2t. Nutan Chandra Sinha . . 20 30
489 2t. Syed Nazmul Haque . . . 20 30
490 2t. Dr. Mohammed Amin Uddin 20 30
491 2t. Dr. Faizul Mohee 20 30
492 2t. Sukha Ranjan Somaddar 20 30

176 Throwing the Discus

1993. 6th South Asian Federation Games, Dhaka. Multicoloured.
493 2t. Type **176** (vert) 15 15
494 4t. Running (vert) 25 25

177 Tomb of Sultan Ghiyasuddin Azam Shah

1993. Muslim Monuments.
495 **177** 10t. multicoloured 60 70

178 Scouting Activities and Jamboree Emblem

179 Emblem and Mother giving Solution to Child

1994. 14th Asian–Pacific and 5th Bangladesh National Scout Jamboree.
496 **178** 2t. multicoloured 30 30

1994. 25th Anniv of Oral Rehydration.
497 **179** 2t. multicoloured 30 30

180 Interior of Chhota Sona Mosque, Nawabgonj

1994. Ancient Mosques. Multicoloured.
498 4t. Type **180** 30 20
499 6t. Exterior of Chhota Sona Mosque 40 50
500 6t. Exterior of Baba Adam's Mosque, Munshigonj . . 40 50

181 Agricultural Workers and Emblem

1994. 75th Anniv of I.L.O. Multicoloured.
501 4t. Type **181** 25 20
502 10t. Worker turning cog (vert) . . . . 75 1·00

182 Priest releasing Peace Doves

184 Family, Globe and Logo

183 Scenes from Baishakhi Festival

1994. 1500th Year of Bengali Solar Calendar.
503 **182** 2t. multicoloured 25 25

1994. Folk Festivals. Multicoloured.
504 4t. Type **183** 25 25
505 4t. Scenes from Nabanna and Paush Parvana Festivals 25 25

1994. International Year of the Family.
506 **184** 10t. multicoloured . . . . 1·00 1·25

185 People planting Saplings

186 Player kicking Ball

1994. Tree Planting Campaign. Multicoloured.
507 4t. Type **185** 35 20
508 6t. Hands holding saplings 65 30

1994. World Cup Football Championship, U.S.A. Multicoloured.
509 20t. Type **186** . . . . . . 2·00 2·50
510 20t. Player heading ball . . . 2·00 2·50

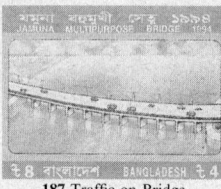
187 Traffic on Bridge

1994. Inauguration of Jamuna Multi-purpose Bridge Project.
511 **187** 4t. multicoloured 85 30

188 Asian Black-headed Oriole

190 Nawab Faizunnessa Chowdhurani

1994. Birds. Multicoloured.
512 4t. Type **188** 40 40
513 6t. Greater racquet-tailed drongo 60 80
514 6t. Indian tree pie 60 80
515 6t. Red junglefowl 60 80

189 Dr. Mohammad Ibrahim and Hospital

1994. 5th Death Anniv of Dr. Mohammad Ibrahim (diabetes treatment pioneer).
517 **189** 2t. multicoloured 30 20

1994. 160th Birth Anniv of Nawab Faizunnessa Chowdhurani (social reformer).
518 **190** 2t. muticoloured 50 20

191 Boxing

1994. Asian Games, Hiroshima, Japan.
519 **191** 4t. multicoloured 75 30

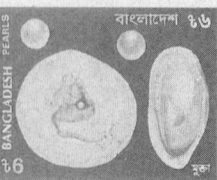
192 Pink and White Pearls with Windowpane Oysters

1994. Sea Shells. Multicoloured.
520 6t. Type **192** 85 90
521 6t. Tranquelous scallop and other shells 85 90

522 6t. Lister's conch, Asiatic
　　Arabian cowrie, bladder
　　moon and woodcock
　　murex 85 90
523 6t. Spotted tun, spiny frog
　　shell, spiral melongena and
　　gibbous olive (vert) 85 90

193 Dr. Milon and Demonstrators

1994. 4th Death Anniv of Dr. Shamsul Alam Khan Milon (medical reformer).
524 193 2t. multicoloured 20 20

1994. Martyred Intellectuals (3rd series). As T **148**. Each black and brown.
525 2t. Dr. Harinath Dey 20 25
526 2t. Dr. A. F. Ziaur Rahman . 20 25
527 2t. Mamun Mahmud . . . 20 25
528 2t. Mohsin Ali Dewan . . . 20 25
529 2t. Dr. N. A. M. Jahangir . . 20 25
530 2t. Shah Abdul Majid . . . 20 25
531 2t. Muhammad Akhter . . . 20 25
532 2t. Meherunnesa 20 25
533 2t. Dr. Kasiruddin Talukder . 20 25
534 2t. Fazlul Haque Choudhury . 20 25
535 2t. Md. Shamsuzzaman . . 20 25
536 2t. A. K. M. Shamsuddin . . 20 25
537 2t. Lt. Mohammad Anwarul
　　Azim 20 25
538 2t. Nurul Amin Khan . . . 20 25
539 2t. Mohammad Sadeque . . 20 25
540 2t. Md. Araz Ali 20 25

194 "Diplazium esculentum"

1994. Vegetables. Multicoloured.
541 4t. Type **194** 50 30
542 4t. "Momordica charantia" . 50 30
543 6t. "Lagenaria siceraria" . . 70 55
544 6t. "Trichosanthes dioica" . . 70 55
545 10t. "Solanum melongena" . 1·00 1·50
546 10t. "Cucurbita maxima"
　　(horiz) . . . . . 1·00 1·50

195 Sonargaon

1995. 20th Anniv of World Tourism Organization.
547 195 10t. multicoloured . . . 1·25 1·25

196 Exports

1995. Dhaka International Trade Fair '95. Mult.
548 4t. Type **196** 20 20
549 6t. Symbols of industry . . 45 65

197 Soldiers of Ramgarh Battalion (1795) and of Bangladesh Rifles (1995)

1995. Bicentenary of Bangladesh Rifles. Mult.
550 2t. Type **197** 45 35
551 4t. Riflemen on patrol . . . 80 65

198 Surgical Equipment and Lightning attacking Crab (cancer)

199 Fresh Food and Boy injecting Insulin

1995. Campaign against Cancer.
552 198 2t. multicoloured 30 20

1995. National Diabetes Awareness Day.
553 199 2t. multicoloured 30 20

200 Munshi Mohammad Meherullah

1995. Munshi Mohammad Meherullah (Islamic educator) Commemoration.
554 200 2t. multicoloured 20 20

রাজশ।হীপেক্স-৯৫
(201)

1995. "Rajshahipex '95" National Philatelic Exhibition. No. 499 optd with T **201**.
555 6t. Exterior of Chhota Sona
　　Mosque . . . . . 1·25 1·50

202 "Lagerstroemia speciosa"

203 Aspects of Farming

1995. Flowers. Multicoloured.
556 6t. Type **202** 65 65
557 6t. "Bombax ceiba" (horiz) . 65 65
558 10t. "Passiflora incarnata" . . 90 1·00
559 10t. "Bauhina purpurea" . . 90 1·00
560 10t. "Canna indica" . . . 90 1·00
561 10t. "Gloriosa superba" . . 90 1·00

1995. 50th Anniv of F.A.O.
562 203 10t. multicoloured 55 65

204 Anniversary Emblem, Peace Dove and U.N. Headquarters

1995. 50th Anniv of United Nations. Multicoloured.
563 2t. Type **204** 20 20
564 10t. Peace doves circling
　　dates and Globe . . . 75 1·10
565 10t. Clasped hands and U.N.
　　Headquarters . . . . 75 1·10

205 Diseased Lungs, Microscope, Family and Map

1995. 18th Eastern Regional Conference on Tuberculosis, Dhaka.
566 205 6t. multicoloured 60 50

206 Peace Doves, Emblem and National Flags

1995. 10th Anniv of South Asian Association for Regional Co-operation.
567 206 2t. multicoloured 60 20

1995. Martyred Intellectuals (4th series). As T **148**. Each black and brown.
568 2t. Abdul Ahad 15 20
569 2t. Lt. Col. Mohammad
　　Qadir 15 20
570 2t. Mozammel Hoque
　　Chowdhury 15 20
571 2t. Rafiqul Haider
　　Chowdhury 15 20
572 2t. Dr. Azharul Haque . . . 15 20
573 2t. A. K. Shamsuddin . . . 15 20
574 2t. Anudwaipayan
　　Bhattacharjee 15 20
575 2t. Lutfunnahar Helena . . . 15 20
576 2t. Shaikh Habibur Rahman . 15 20
577 2t. Major Naimul Islam . . . 15 20
578 2t. Md. Shahidullah 15 20
579 2t. Ataur Rahman Khan
　　Khadim 15 20
580 2t. A. B. M. Ashraful Islam
　　Bhuiyan 15 20
581 2t. Dr. Md. Sadat Ali . . . 15 20
582 2t. Sarafat Ali 15 20
583 2t. M. A. Sayeed 15 20

207 Aspects of COMDECA Projects

1995. 2nd Asia–Pacific Community Development Scout Camp.
584 207 2t. multicoloured 40 25

208 Volleyball Players

1995. Centenary of Volleyball.
585 208 6t. multicoloured 40 40

209 Man in Punjabi and Lungi

1995. Traditional Costumes. Multicoloured.
586 6t. Type **209** 65 65
587 6t. Woman in sari 65 65
588 10t. Christian bride and
　　groom . . . . . 1·00 1·00
589 10t. Muslim bride and groom 1·00 1·00
590 10t. Buddhist bride and
　　groom (horiz) . . . . 1·00 1·00
591 10t. Hindu bride and groom
　　(horiz) . . . . . 1·00 1·00

210 Shaheed Amanullah Mohammad Asaduzzaman

1996. 27th Death Anniv of Shaheed Amanullah Mohammad Asaduzzaman (student leader).
592 210 2t. multicoloured 20 20

211 Bowler and Map

1996. World Cup Cricket Championship. Multicoloured.
593 4t. Type **211** 80 35
594 6t. Batsman and wicket
　　keeper . . . . . 1·00 60
595 10t. Match in progress (horiz) 1·25 1·75

212 Liberation Struggle, 1971

1996. 25th Anniv of Independence. Multicoloured.
596 4t. Type **212** 30 40
597 4t. National Martyrs
　　Memorial 30 40
598 4t. Education 30 40
599 4t. Health 30 40
600 4t. Communications . . . 30 40
601 4t. Industry 30 40

213 Michael Madhusudan Dutt

214 Gymnastics

1996. Michael Madhusudan Dutt (poet) Commemoration.
602 213 4t. multicoloured 20 20

1996. Olympic Games, Atlanta. Multicoloured.
603 4t. Type **214** 25 20
604 6t. Judo 35 30
605 10t. Athletics (horiz) . . . 40 50
606 10t. High jumping (horiz) . . 40 50

215 Bangabandhu Sheikh Mujibur Rahman

1996. 21st Death Anniv of Bangabandhu Sheikh Mujibur Rahman.
609 215 4t. multicoloured 20 20

216 Maulana Mohammad Akrum Khan

1996. 28th Death Anniv of Maulana Mohammad Akrum Khan.
610 **216** 4t. multicoloured 20 20

217 Ustad Alauddin Khan

1996. 24th Death Anniv of Ustad Alauddin Khan (musician).
611 **217** 4t. multicoloured 50 20

218 "Kingfisher" (Mayeesha Robbani)

1996. Children's Paintings. Multicoloured.
612 2t. Type **218** 25 25
613 4t. "River Crossing" (Iffat Panchlais) (horiz) 30 25

219 Syed Nazrul Islam

1996. 21st Death Anniv of Jail Martyrs. Multicoloured.
614 4t. Type **219** 20 30
615 4t. Tajuddin Ahmad 20 30
616 4t. M. Monsoor Ali 20 30
617 4t. A. H. M. Quamaruzzaman 20 30

220 Children receiving Medicine

1996. 50th Anniv of U.N.I.C.E.F. Multicoloured.
618 4t. Type **220** 35 20
619 10t. Mother and child 50 75

1996. Martyred Intellectuals (5th series). As T **148**. Each black and brown.
620 2t. Dr. Jekrul Haque 25 25
621 2t. Munshi Kabiruddin Ahmed 25 25
622 2t. Md. Abdul Jabbar 25 25
623 2t. Mohammad Amir 25 25
624 2t. A. K. M. Shamsul Huq Khan 25 25
625 2t. Dr. Siddique Ahmed . . . 25 25
626 2t. Dr. Soleman Khan 25 25
627 2t. S. B. M. Mizanur Rahman 25 25
628 2t. Aminuddin 25 25
629 2t. Md. Nazrul Islam 25 25
630 2t. Zahirul Islam 25 25
631 2t. A. K. Lutfor Rahman . . . 25 25

632 2t. Afsar Hossain 25 25
633 2t. Abul Hashem Mian . . . 25 25
634 2t. A. T. M. Alamgir 25 25
635 2t. Baser Ali 25 25

221 Celebrating Crowds

1996. 25th Anniv of Victory Day. Multicoloured.
636 4t. Type **221** 25 25
637 6t. Soldiers and statue (vert) . . 40 50

222 Paul P. Harris

1997. 50th Death Anniv of Paul Harris (founder of Rotary International).
638 **222** 4t. multicoloured 20 20

223 Shaikh Mujibur Rahman making Speech

1997. 25th Anniv of Shaikh Mujibur's Speech of 7 March (1996).
639 **223** 4t. multicoloured 20 20

224 Sheikh Mujibur Rahman

226 Heinrich von Stephan

225 Sheikh Mujibur Rahman and Crowd with Banners

1997. 77th Birth Anniv of Sheikh Mujibur Rahman (first President).
640 **224** 4t. multicoloured 30 20

1997. 25th Anniv (1996) of Independence.
641 **225** 4t. multicoloured 20 20

1997. Death Centenary of Heinrich von Stephan (founder of U.P.U.).
642 **226** 4t. multicoloured 30 20

227 Sheep

1997. Livestock. Multicoloured.
643 4t. Type **227** 45 45
644 4t. Goat 45 45
645 6t. Buffalo bull 65 65
646 6t. Cow 65 65

228 "Tilling the Field - 2" (S. Sultan)

1997. Bangladesh Paintings. Multicoloured.
647 6t. Type **228** 40 30
648 10t. "Three Women" (Quamrul Hassan) 60 80

229 Trophy, Flag and Cricket Ball

1997. 6th International Cricket Council Trophy Championship, Malaysia.
649 **229** 10t. multicoloured . . . . 1·25 1·00

230 Kusumba Mosque, Naogaon

1997. Historic Mosques. Multicoloured.
650 4t. Type **230** 30 20
651 6t. Atiya Mosque, Tangail . . 40 30
652 10t. Bagha Mosque, Rajshahi . 70 1·00

231 Adul Karim Sahitya Vishard

232 River Moot Emblem and Scouts standing on top of World

1997. 126th Birth Anniv of Abdul Karim Sahitya Vishard (scholar).
653 **231** 4t. multicoloured 20 20

1997. 9th Asia-Pacific and 7th Bangladesh Rover Moot, Lakkatura.
654 **232** 2t. multicoloured 40 20

233 Officers and Flag

1997. 25th Anniv of Armed Forces.
655 **233** 2t. multicoloured 75 40

1997. Martyred Intellectuals (6th series). As T **148**. Each black and brown.
656 2t. Dr. Shamsuddin Ahmed . 45 45
657 2t. Mohammad Salimullah . . 45 45
658 2t. Mohiuddin Haider . . . 45 45
659 2t. Abdur Rahin 45 45
660 2t. Nitya Nanda Paul 45 45
661 2t. Abdel Jabber 45 45
662 2t. Dr. Humayun Kabir . . . 45 45
663 2t. Khaja Nizamuddin Bhuiyan 45 45
664 2t. Gulam Hossain 45 45
665 2t. Ali Karim 45 45
666 2t. Md. Moazzem Hossain . . 45 45
667 2t. Rafiqul Islam 45 45
668 2t. M. Nur Husain 45 45
669 2t. Captain Mahmood Hossain Akonda . . . 45 45
670 2t. Abdul Wahab Talukder . . 45 45
671 2t. Dr. Hasimoy Hazra . . . 45 45

234 Mohammad Mansooruddin

1998. Professor Mohammad Mansooruddin (folklorist) Commemoration.
672 **234** 4t. multicoloured 65 30

235 Standard-bearer and Soldiers

1998. 50th Anniv of East Bengal Regiment.
673 **235** 2t. multicoloured 50 25

236 Bulbul Chowdhury

1998. Bulbul Chowdhury (traditional dancer) Commemoration.
674 **236** 4t. multicoloured 30 20

237 World Cup Trophy

1998. World Cup Football Championship, France. Multicoloured.
675 6t. Type **237** 50 30
676 18t. Footballer and trophy . . 1·25 1·75

238 Eastern Approach Road, Bangabandhu Bridge

1998. Opening of Bangabandhu Bridge. Mult.
677 4t. Type **238** 45 20
678 6t. Western approach road . . 55 30
679 8t. Embankment 70 90
680 10t. Main span, Bangabandhu Bridge . . . 85 1·00

239 Diana, Princess of Wales

1998. Diana, Princess of Wales Commemoration. Multicoloured.
681 8t. Type **239** 75 60
682 18t. Wearing pearl choker . . 1·25 1·25
683 22t. Wearing pendant necklace . . . . . . 1·25 1·25

240 Means of collecting Solar Energy

1998. World Solar Energy Programme Summit.
684 **240** 10t. multicoloured 70 70

241 World Habitat Day Emblem and City Scene

1998. World Habitat Day.
685 **241** 4t. multicoloured 55 25

242 Farmworkers, Sunflower and "20"

1998. 20th Anniv of International Fund for Agricultural Development. Multicoloured.
686 6t. Type **242** 30 25
687 10t. Farmworker with baskets and harvested crops . . . 45 60

243 Batsman

1998. Wills International Cricket Cup, Dhaka.
688 **243** 6t. multicoloured . . . . 1·00 55

244 Begum Rokeya

1998. Begum Rokeya (campaigner for women's education) Commemoration.
689 **244** 4t. multicoloured 60 25

245 Anniversary Logo

1998. 50th Anniv of Universal Declaration of Human Rights.
690 **245** 10t. multicoloured 65 70

1998. Martyred Intellectuals (7th series). As T **148**. Each black and brown.
691 2t. Md. Khorshed Ali Sarker 30 30
692 2t. Abu Yakub Mahfuz Ali 30 30

693 2t. S. M. Nural Huda 30 30
694 2t. Nazmul Hoque Sarker . . 30 30
695 2t. Md. Taslim Uddin . . . 30 30
696 2t. Gulam Mostafa 30 30
697 2t. A. H. Nural Alam . . . 30 30
698 2t. Timir Kanti Dev 30 30
699 2t. Altaf Hossain 30 30
700 2t. Aminul Hoque 30 30
701 2t. S. M. Fazlul Hoque . . 30 30
702 2t. Mozammel Ali 30 30
703 2t. Syed Akbar Hossain . . 30 30
704 2t. Sk. Abdus Salam 30 30
705 2t. Abdur Rahman 30 30
706 2t. Dr. Shyamal Kanti Lala 30 30

246 Dove of Peace and U.N. Symbols

1998. 50th Anniv of U.N. Peace-keeping Operations.
707 **246** 10t. multicoloured 60 70

247 Kazi Nazrul Islam

1998. Birth Centenary (1999) of Kazi Nazrul Islam (poet).
708 **247** 6t. multicoloured 55 40

248 Jamboree Emblem and Scout Activities

1999. 6th Bangladesh National Scout Jamboree.
709 **248** 2t. multicoloured 50 25

1999. As No. 75 but redrawn. Size 35 × 22 mm.
711 10t. red 25 30
No. 711 has been redrawn so that "SIXTY-DOME MOSQUE" appears above the face value at bottom right instead of below the main inscription at top left.

249 Surjya Sen and Demonstrators

1999. Surjya Sen (revolutionary) Commemoration.
715 **249** 4t. multicoloured 55 20

251 National Team Badges

1999. Cricket World Cup, England. Multicoloured.
717 8t. Type **251** . . . . 1·25 2·00
718 10t. Bangladesh cricket team badge and flag . . . . . 1·50 1·25

252 Mother Teresa   **253** Sheikh Mujibur Rahman, New York Skyline and Dove

1999. Mother Teresa Commemoration.
720 **252** 4t. multicoloured 60 30

1999. 25th Anniv of Bangladesh's Admission to U.N.
721 **253** 6t. multicoloured 60 35

254 Shaheed Mohammad Maizuddin

1999. 15th Death Anniv of Shaheed Mohammad Maizuddin (politician).
722 **254** 2t. multicoloured 30 25

255 Faces in Tree

1999. International Year of the Elderly.
723 **255** 6t. multicoloured . . . . 1·50 20

256 Shanty Town and Modern Buildings between Hands

1999. World Habitat Day.
724 **256** 4t. multicoloured 40 15

257 Mobile Post Office

1999. 125th Anniv of U.P.U. Multicoloured.
725 4t. Type **257** 40 30
726 4t. Postman on motorcycle . . 40 30
727 6t. Postal motor launch . . . 55 45
728 6t. Two Bangladesh airliners 55 45

258 Sir Jagadis Chandra Bose

1999. Sir Jagadis Chandra Bose (physicist and botanist) Commemoration.
730 **258** 4t. multicoloured 50 20

1999. Martyred Intellectuals (8th series). As T **148**. Each black and brown.
731 2t. Dr. Mohammad Shafi . . 20 20
732 2t. Maulana Kasimuddin Ahmed 20 20
733 2t. Quazi Ali Imam 20 20
734 2t. Sultanuddin Ahmed . . . 20 20
735 2t. A. S. M. Ershadullah . . 20 20
736 2t. Mohammad Fazlur Rahman 20 20
737 2t. Captain A. K. M. Farooq 20 20
738 2t. Md. Latafot Hossain Joarder 20 20
739 2t. Ram Ranjan Bhattacharjya 20 20
740 2t. Abani Mohan Dutta . . . 20 20
741 2t. Sunawar Ali 20 20
742 2t. Abdul Kader Miah . . . 20 20
743 2t. Major Rezaur Rahman . . 20 20
744 2t. Md. Shafiqul Anowar . . 20 20
745 2t. A. A. M. Mozammel Hoque 20 20
746 2t. Khandkar Abul Kashem 20 20

259 Bangladesh Flag and Monument

2000. New Millennium. Multicoloured.
747 4t. Type **259** 30 20
748 6t. Satellite, computer and dish aerial (vert) 45 45

260 Cub Scouts, Globe and Flag

2000. 5th Bangladesh Cub Camporee.
749 **260** 2t. multicoloured 30 20

261 Jibananada Das

2000. Death Centenary (1999) of Jibananada Das (poet).
750 **261** 4t. multicoloured 35 20

262 Dr. Muhammad Shamsuzzoha

2000. 30th Death Anniv (1999) of Dr. Muhammad Shamsuzzoha.
751 **262** 4t. multicoloured 35 20

263 Shafiur Rahman

2000. International Mother Language Day. Mult.
752	4t. Type **263**	. . . .	40	40
753	4t. Abul Barkat	. . . . . .	40	40
754	4t. Abdul Jabbar	. . . . .	40	40
755	4t. Rafiq Uddin Ahmad	. . .	40	40

264 Meteorological Equipment

2000. 50th Anniv of World Meteorological Organization.
756	**264**	10t. multicoloured	60	60

265 Cricket Week Logo and Web Site Address

266 Wasp

2000. International Cricket Week.
757	**265**	6t. multicoloured	60	45

2000. Insects. Multicoloured.
758	2t. Type **266**	. . . .	20	15
759	4t. Grasshopper	. . . . . .	30	25
760	6t. Bumble bee	. . . . .	45	35
761	10t. Silkworms	. . . . .	70	75

267 Gecko

2000. Native Fauna. Multicoloured.
762	4t. Type **267**	. . . . .	35	30
763	4t. Indian crested porcupine		35	30
764	6t. Indian black-tailed python		50	45
765	6t. Bengal monitor	. . . .	50	45

268 Batsman

2000. Pepsi 7th Asia Cricket Cup.
766	**268**	6t. multicoloured	75	50

269 Water Cock

2000. Birds. Multicoloured.
767	4t. Type **269**	. . . . .	35	25
768	4t. White-breasted waterhen (*Amaurornis phoenicurus*)		35	25

769	6t. Javanese cormorant (*Phalacrocorax niger*) (vert)		50	45
770	6t. Indian pond heron (*Ardeola grayii*) (vert) . . .		50	45

270 Women's Shotput

2000. Olympic Games, Sydney. Multicoloured.
771	6t. Type **270**	. . . . .	35	25
772	10t. Men's Shotput	. . . . .	50	50

271 Clasped Hands, Landmarks and Flags

2000. 25th Anniv of Diplomatic Relations with People's Republic of China.
773	**271**	6t. multicoloured	40	25

272 Idrakpur Fort, Munshigonj

2000. Archaeology. Multicoloured.
774	4t. Type **272**	. . . . . .	30	20
775	6t. Statue of Buddha, Mainamati (vert)		45	35

273 Year Emblem

2000. International Volunteers' Year.
776	**273**	6t. multicoloured	30	25

274 Hason Raza

2000. 80th Death Anniv of Hason Raza (mystic poet).
777	**274**	6t. multicoloured	30	25

275 U.N.H.C.R. Logo

2000. 50th Anniv of United Nations High Commissioner for Refugees (U.N.H.C.R.).
778	**275**	10t. multicoloured	45	20

2000. Martyred Intellectuals (9th series). As T **148**. Each black and brown.
779	2t. M. A. Gofur	. . . . .	15	15
780	2t. Faizur Rahman Ahmed	.	15	15
781	2t. Muslimuddin Miah	. .	15	15
782	2t. Sgt. Shamsul Karim Khan		15	15

783	2t. Bhikku Zinananda	. . .	15	15
784	2t. Abdul Jabber	. . . .	15	15
785	2t. Sekander Hayat Chowdhury	. . . . .	15	15
786	2t. Chishty Shah Helalur Rahman	. . . . .	15	15
787	2t. Birendra Nath Sarker	.	15	15
788	2t. A. K. M. Nurul Haque	.	15	15
789	2t. Sibendra Nath Mukherjee		15	15
790	2t. Zahir Raihan	. . . .	15	15
791	2t. Ferdous Dowla Bablu	. .	15	15
792	2t. Capt A. K. M. Nurul Absur	. . . . . .	15	15
793	2t. Mizanur Rahman Miju	.	15	15
794	2t. Dr. Shamshad Ali	. .	15	15

276 Map of Faces

2001. Population and Housing Census.
795	**276**	4t. multicoloured	30	20

277 Producing Food

2001. "Hunger-free Bangladesh" Campaign.
796	**277**	6t. multicoloured	30	25

278 "Peasant Women" (Rashid Chowdbury)

2001. Bangladesh Paintings.
797	**278**	10t. multicoloured	25	30

279 Lalbagh Kella Mosque

2001. Historic Buildings. Multicoloured.
798	6t. Type **279**	. . . . .	15	20
799	6t. Uttara Ganabhavan, Natore		15	20
800	6t. Armenian Church, Armanitola		15	20
801	6t. Panam Nagar, Sonargaon		15	20

280 Smoking Accessories, Globe and Paper People

2001. World No Tobacco Day.
802	**280**	10t. multicoloured	25	30

281 Ustad Gul Mohammad Khan   282 Begum Sufia Kamal

2001. Artists. Multicoloured.
803	6t. Type **281**	. . . . .	15	20
804	6t. Ustad Khadem Hossain Khan		15	20
805	6t. Gouhar Jamil	. . . .	15	20
806	6t. Abdul Alim	. . . . .	15	20

2001. Begum Sufia Kamal (poet) Commemoration.
807	**282**	4t. multicoloured	10	10

283 Hilsa

2001. Fish. Multicoloured.
808	10t. Type **283**	. . . . .	25	30
809	10t. Tengra	. . . . .	25	30
810	10t. Punti	. . . . .	25	30
811	10t. Khalisa	. . . . .	25	30

284 Parliament House, Dhaka

2001. Completion of First Full National Parliamentary Term.
812	**284**	10t. multicoloured	25	30

285 Parliament House, Dhaka

2001. 8th Parliamentary Elections.
813	**285**	2t. multicoloured	10	10

286 "Children encircling Globe" (Urska Golob)

2001. U.N. Year of Dialogue among Civilizations.
814	**286**	10t. multicoloured	25	30

OFFICIAL STAMPS

1973. Nos. 22, etc. optd **SERVICE**.
O 1	**7**	2p. black	10	1·00
O 2		3p. green	10	1·00
O 3		5p. brown	20	10
O 4		10p. black	20	10
O 5		20p. green	1·50	10
O 6		25p. mauve	3·75	10
O 7		60p. grey	3·75	1·75
O 8		75p. orange	1·50	30
O 9	**8**	1t. violet	11·00	4·50
O10		5t. blue	5·00	8·00

1974. Nos. 49/51 optd **SERVICE**.
O11	**14**	1t. violet	4·50	30
O12		2t. olive	6·00	2·00
O13		5t. blue	11·00	10·00

1976. Nos. 64/70 and 72/4 optd **SERVICE**.
O14		5p. green	1·50	80
O15		10p. black	1·75	80
O16		20p. green	2·00	80
O17		25p. mauve	3·25	80
O18		50p. purple	3·25	50
O19		60p. grey	30	2·25
O20		75p. olive	30	3·00
O21	**14**	1t. blue	2·75	50
O22		2t. green	35	1·75
O23		5t. blue	30	1·75

1981. Nos. 125/37 optd **SERVICE**.
O24		5p. brown	1·50	2·00
O25	**32**	10p. blue	1·50	2·25
O26		15p. orange	1·50	2·00
O27		20p. red	1·50	2·00
O28		25p. blue	80	2·00
O29		30p. green	2·50	2·50
O30		40p. purple	2·50	1·50
O31		50p. black	30	10
O32		80p. brown	1·75	50

O33	–	1t. violet	30	10
O34	–	2t. blue	35	2·25

1983. Nos. 220/9, 318a and 710 (1989) optd **Service**.

O35	**69**	5p. blue	10	10
O36	–	10p. purple	10	10
O37	–	15p. blue	10	10
O38	–	20p. black	10	10
O39	–	25p. grey	10	10
O40	–	30p. brown	10	10
O41	–	50p. brown	10	10
O42	–	1 t. blue	50	10
O43	–	2t. green	10	10
O44	–	3t. black and blue	10	10
O45	–	4t. blue	10	15
O46	–	5t. purple	1·25	45

সার্ভিস (O **5**)

সার্ভিস (O **6**)

সার্ভিস (O 7)

1989. Nos. 227 and 710 (1989) optd with Type O **5**.

O47		1t. blue	10	10
O48		5t. black and brown	65	65

1990. Nos. 368/9 (Immunization) optd with Type O **6**.

O49	**133**	1t. green	10	10
O50		2t. brown	10	10

1992. No. 376 optd as Type O **6** but horiz.

O51	**136**	6t. blue and yellow	15	20

1995. No. 553 (National Diabetes Awareness Day) optd as Type O **6** but horiz.

O52	**199**	2t. multicoloured	55	55

1996. Nos. 221 and 223 optd with Type O **7**.

O53		10p. purple	20	20
O54		20p. black	30	30

1999. No. 710 optd as Type O **5** but vert.

O56		5t. black and brown	10	15

BARBADOS Pt. 1

An island in the Br. West Indies, E. of the Windward Islands, attained self-government on 16 October 1961 and achieved independence within the Commonwealth on 30 November 1966.

1852. 12 pence = 1 shilling;
20 shillings = 1 pound.
1950. 100 cents = 1 West Indian, later Barbados, dollar.

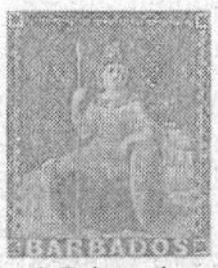
1 Britannia

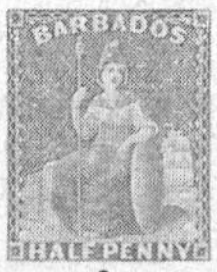
2

1852. Imperf.

8	**1**	(½d.) green	£110	£200
10		(1d.) blue	27·00	55·00
4a		(2d.) slate	£200	£1100
5		(4d.) red	80·00	£275
11	**2**	6d. red	£700	£120
12a		1s. black	£180	75·00

1860. Perf.

21	**1**	(½d.) green	14·00	10·00
24		(1d.) blue	28·00	3·50
25		(4d.) red	80·00	35·00
31	**2**	6d. red	75·00	19·00
33		6d. orange	95·00	26·00
35		1s. black	48·00	7·00

1873. Perf.

72	**2**	½d. green	9·50	50
74		1d. blue	50·00	65
63		3d. brown	£325	£110
75		3d. mauve	95·00	5·50
76		4d. red	95·00	8·00
79		6d. yellow	£100	1·00
81		1s. purple	£120	3·25

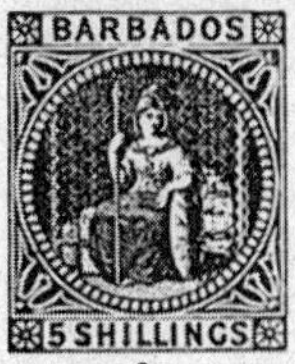
3

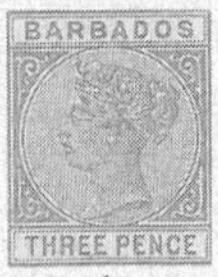
4

1873.

64	**3**	5s. red	£950	£300

1878. Half of No. 64 surch **1D**.

86	**3**	1d. on half 5s. red	£4000	£600

1882.

90	**4**	½d. green	14·00	1·50
92		1d. red	15·00	1·00
93		2½d. blue	80·00	1·50
96		3d. purple	4·25	15·00
97		4d. grey	£250	2·75
99		4d. brown	4·75	1·50
100		6d. brown	75·00	40·00
102		1s. brown	25·00	21·00
103		5s. bistre	£150	£190

1892. Surch **HALF-PENNY**.

104	**4**	½d. on 4d. brown	2·25	3·75

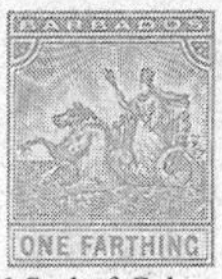
6 Seal of Colony

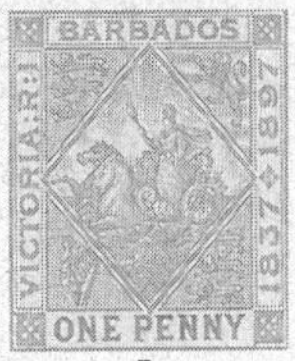
7

1892.

105	**6**	¼d. grey and red	2·25	10
163		¼d. brown	5·50	30
106		½d. green	2·50	10
107		1d. red	4·75	10
108		2d. black and orange	8·00	75
166		2d. grey	7·50	9·50
139		2½d. blue	13·00	15
110		5d. olive	7·00	4·50
111		6d. mauve and red	15·00	2·00
168		6d. deep purple and purple	9·50	15·00
112		8d. orange and blue	4·00	21·00
113		10d. green and red	8·00	6·50
169		1s. black on green	9·50	14·00
114		2s.6d. black and orange	48·00	48·00
144		2s.6d. violet and green	40·00	90·00

1897. Diamond Jubilee.

116	**7**	¼d. grey and red	3·50	60
117		½d. green	3·50	60
118		1d. red	3·50	60
119		2½d. blue	7·00	85
120		5d. brown	16·00	15·00
121		6d. mauve and red	21·00	21·00
122		8d. orange and blue	8·50	23·00
123		10d. green and red	48·00	55·00
124		2s.6d. black and orange	60·00	55·00

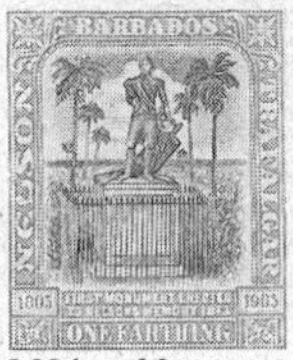
8 Nelson Monument

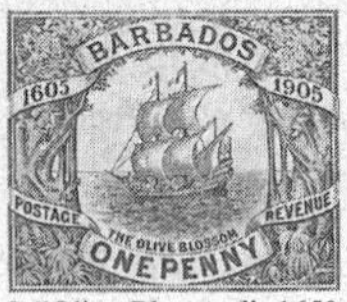
9 "Olive Blossom", 1650

1906. Death Centenary of Nelson.

145	**8**	¼d. black and grey	8·00	1·75
146		½d. black and green	9·50	15
147		1d. black and red	12·00	15
148		2d. black and yellow	1·75	4·50
149		2½d. black and blue	3·75	1·25
150		6d. black and mauve	18·00	25·00
151		1s. black and red	21·00	50·00

1906. Tercentenary of Annexation of Barbados.

152	**9**	1d. black, blue and green	10·00	25

1907. Surch **Kingston Relief Fund. 1d.**

153	**6**	1d. on 2d. black and orange	2·50	4·75

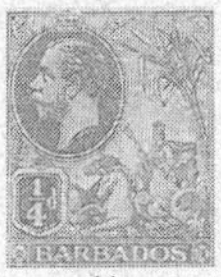
11

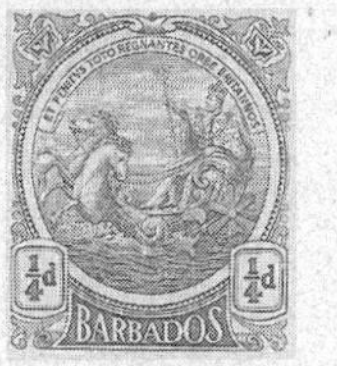
14

1912.

170	**11**	¼d. brown	1·50	1·50
171		½d. green	3·50	10
172		1d. red	7·50	10
173		2d. grey	2·75	14·00
174		2½d. blue	1·50	40
175		3d. purple on yellow	1·50	14·00
176		4d. red and black on yellow	1·50	16·00
177		6d. deep purple and purple	12·00	12·00

Larger type, with portrait at top centre.

178		1s. black on green	8·50	12·00
179		2s. blue and purple on blue	42·00	45·00
180		3s. violet and green	80·00	95·00

1916.

181	**14**	¼d. brown	75	40
182		½d. green	1·10	15
183a		1d. red	2·50	15
184		2d. grey	3·50	19·00
185		2½d. blue	3·50	2·00
186		3d. purple on yellow	2·25	5·50
187		4d. red on yellow	80	14·00
199		4d. black and red	80	3·75
188		6d. purple	3·00	3·75
189		1s. black on green	7·00	9·00
190		2s. purple on blue	16·00	7·50
191		3s. violet	48·00	£110
200		3s. green and violet	17·00	60·00

1917. Optd **WAR TAX**.

197	**11**	1d. red	50	15

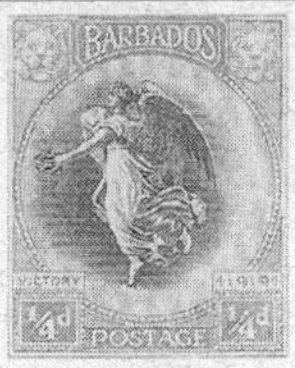
16

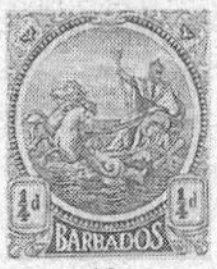
18

1920. Victory. Inscr "VICTORY 1919".

201	**16**	¼d. black and brown	30	70
202		½d. black and green	1·00	15
203		1d. black and red	4·00	10
204		2d. black and grey	2·00	7·00
205		2½d. indigo and blue	2·75	16·00
206		3d. black and purple	3·00	6·00
207		4d. black and green	3·25	7·00
208		6d. black and orange	3·75	14·00
209	–	1s. black and green	10·00	26·00
210	–	2s. black and brown	24·00	35·00
211	–	3s. black and orange	30·00	45·00

The 1s. to 3s. show Victory full-face.

1921.

217	**18**	¼d. brown	25	10
219		½d. green	1·50	10
220		1d. red	80	10
221		2d. grey	1·75	20
222		2½d. blue	1·50	6·50
213		3d. purple on yellow	2·00	6·00
214		4d. red on yellow	1·75	13·00
225		6d. purple	3·50	5·50
215		1s. black on green	5·50	11·00
227		2s. purple on blue	10·00	19·00
228		3s. violet	14·00	50·00

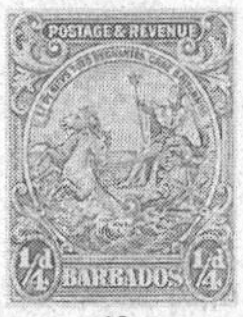
19

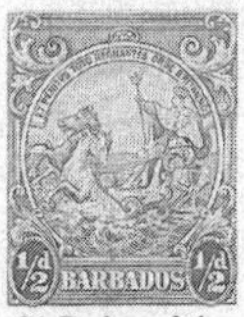
21 Badge of the Colony

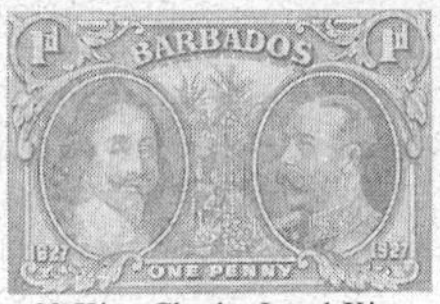
20 King Charles I and King George V

1925. Inscr "POSTAGE & REVENUE".

229	**19**	¼d. brown	25	10
230		½d. green	50	10
231		1d. red	50	10
231ba		1½d. orange	2·00	1·00
232		2d. grey	50	3·25
233		2½d. blue	50	80
234		3d. purple on yellow	1·00	45
235		4d. red on yellow	75	1·00
236		6d. purple	1·00	90
237		1s. black on green	2·00	6·50
238		2s. purple on blue	7·00	6·50
238a		2s.6d. red on blue	22·00	25·00
239		3s. violet	11·00	13·00

1927. Tercentenary of Settlement of Barbados.

240	**20**	1d. red	1·00	75

1935. Silver Jubilee. As T **13** of Antigua.

241		1d. blue and red	50	20
242		1½d. blue and grey	3·75	6·00
243		2½d. brown and blue	2·25	4·00
244		1s. grey and purple	17·00	18·00

1937. Coronation. As T **2** of Aden.

245		1d. red	30	15
246		1½d. brown	40	60
247		2½d. blue	70	45

1938. "POSTAGE & REVENUE" omitted.

248	**21**	½d. green	6·00	15
248c		½d. bistre	15	30
249a		1d. red	16·00	10
249c		1d. green	15	10
250		1½d. orange	15	40
250c		2d. purple	50	2·50
250d		2d. red	20	70
251		2½d. blue	50	60
252b		3d. brown	20	60
252c		3d. blue	20	1·75
253		4d. black	20	10
254		6d. violet	80	40
254a		8d. mauve	55	2·00
255a		1s. green	1·00	10
256		2s.6d. purple	7·00	1·50
256a		5s. blue	3·25	6·00

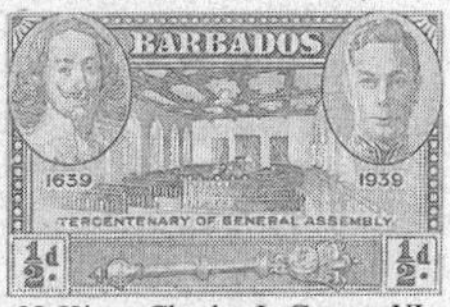
22 Kings Charles I, George VI, Assembly Chamber and Mace

1939. Tercentenary of General Assembly.

257	**22**	½d. green	2·25	70
258		1d. red	2·25	30
259		1½d. orange	2·25	60
260		2½d. blue	2·25	4·00
261		3d. brown	2·25	2·25

1946. Victory. As T **9** of Aden.

262		1½d. orange	15	15
263		3d. brown	15	15

1947. Surch **ONE PENNY**.

264	**17**	1d. on 2d. red	1·25	2·50

1948. Silver Wedding. As T **10/11** of Aden.

265		1½d. orange	30	10
266		5s. blue	10·00	6·50

1949. U.P.U. As T **20/23** of Antigua.

267		1½d. orange	30	40
268		3d. blue	1·50	1·75
269		4d. grey	35	2·25
270		1s. olive	35	60

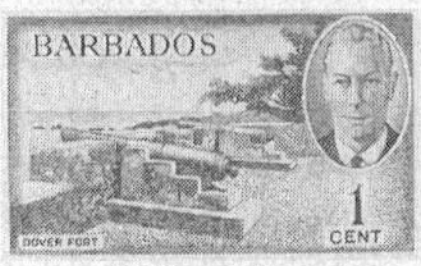
24 Dover Fort

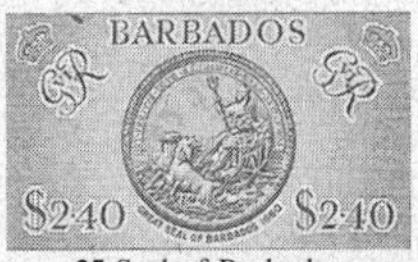
35 Seal of Barbados

1950.

271	**24**	1c. blue	30	2·25
272	–	2c. green	15	2·00
273	–	3c. brown and green	1·25	2·75
274	–	4c. red	15	40
275	–	6c. blue	15	2·00
276	–	8c. blue and purple	1·25	2·50
277	–	12c. blue and olive	1·00	1·00
278	–	24c. red and black	1·00	50
279	–	48c. violet	8·00	6·50
280	–	60c. green and lake	7·50	8·50
281	–	$1.20 red and olive	8·50	3·75
282	**35**	$2.40 black	15·00	15·00

DESIGNS—As Type **24**: HORIZ: 2c. Sugar cane breeding; 3c. Public buildings; 6c. Casting net; 8c. "Frances W. Smith" (schooner); 12c. Four-winged flyingfish; 24c. Old Main Guard Garrison; 60c. Careenage. VERT: 4c. Statue of Nelson; 48c. St. Michael's Cathedral; $1.20, Map and wireless mast.

1951. Inauguration of B.W.I. University College. As T **24/25** of Antigua.

283		3c. brown and blue	30	30
284		12c. blue and olive	55	1·75

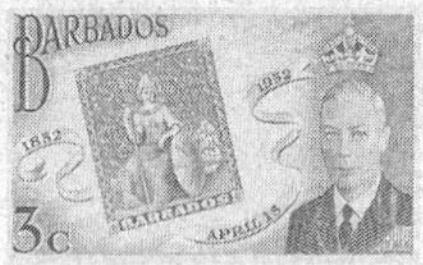
36 King George VI and Stamp of 1852

1952. Centenary of Barbados Stamps.

285	**36**	3c. green and slate	15	40
286		4c. blue and red	15	1·00
287		12c. slate and green	15	1·00
288		24c. brown and sepia	15	55

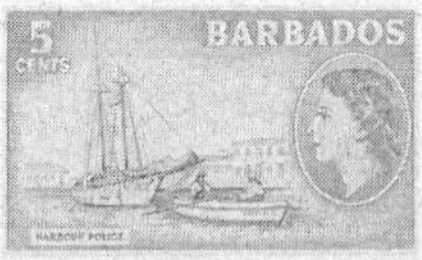
37 Harbour Police

1953. As 1950 issue but with portrait or cypher (No. 301) of Queen Elizabeth II as in T **37**.

289	**24**	1c. blue	10	80
290	–	2c. orange and turquoise	15	50
291	–	3c. black and green	1·00	75
292	–	4c. black and orange	20	20
293	**37**	5c. blue and red	1·00	60
294	–	6c. brown	50	60
314	–	8c. black and blue	60	35
296	–	12c. blue and olive	1·00	10
297	–	24c. red and black	50	10
298	–	48c. violet	6·00	1·00
318	–	60c. green and purple	10·00	4·00
300	–	$1.20 red and olive	19·00	3·25
319	**35**	$2.40 black	1·25	1·75

1953. Coronation. As T **13** of Aden.

302		4c. black and orange	40	10

1958. British Caribbean Federation. As T **28** of Antigua.

303		3c. green	35	20
304		6c. blue	50	2·25
305		12c. red	50	30

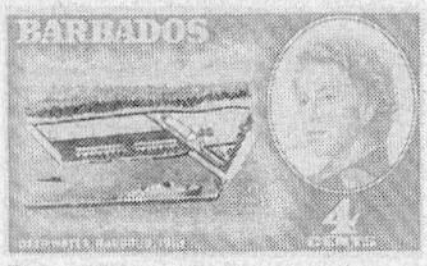

38 Deep Water Harbour, Bridgetown

1961. Opening of Deep Water Harbour.

306 **38**	4c. black and orange	25	50
307	8c. black and blue	25	60
308	24c. red and black	25	60

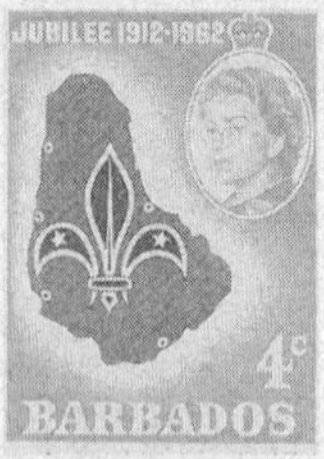

39 Scout Badge and Map of Barbados

1962. Golden Jubilee of Barbados Boy Scout Association.

309 **39**	4c. black and orange	50	10
310	12c. blue and brown	80	15
311	$1.20 red and green	1·50	3·50

1965. Centenary of I.T.U. As T **36** of Antigua.

320	2c. lilac and red	20	40
321	48c. yellow and drab	45	1·00

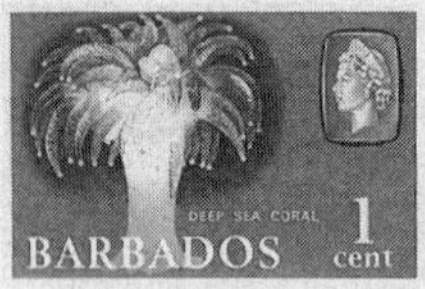

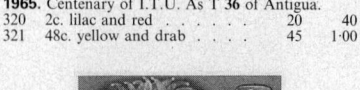

40 Deep Sea Coral

1965.

342 **40**	1c. black, pink and blue	10	20
323 –	2c. brown, yell & mve	20	15
324 –	3c. brown and orange	45	60
344 –	3c. brown and orange	30	2·75
325 –	4c. blue and green	15	10
326 –	5c. sepia, red and lilac	30	20
327 –	6c. multicoloured	45	20
328 –	8c. multicoloured	25	10
329 –	12c. multicoloured	35	10
330 –	15c. black, yellow and red	80	30
331 –	25c. blue and ochre	95	30
332 –	35c. red and green	1·50	15
333 –	50c. blue and green	2·00	40
334 –	$1 multicoloured	2·75	1·25
335 –	$2.50 multicoloured	2·75	3·00
355a –	$5 multicoloured	12·00	8·00

DESIGNS—HORIZ: 2c. Lobster; 3c. (No. 324) Lined seahorse (wrongly inscribed "Hippocanpus"); 3c. (No. 344) (correctly inscribed "Hippocampus"); 4c. Sea urchin; 5c. Staghorn coral; 6c. Spot-finned butterflyfish; 8c. Rough file shell; 12c. Porcupinefish ("Balloon fish"); 15c Grey angel-fish; 25c. Brain coral; 35c. Brittle star; 50c. Four-winged flyingfish: $1 Queen or pink conch shell; $2.50, Fiddler crab. VERT: $5 Dolphin.

1966. Churchill Commemoration. As T **38** of Antigua.

336	1c. blue	10	2·25
337	4c. green	30	10
338	25c. brown	70	50
339	35c. violet	80	60

1966. Royal Visit. As T **39** of Antigua.

340	3c. black and blue	35	40
341	35c. black and mauve	1·40	1·00

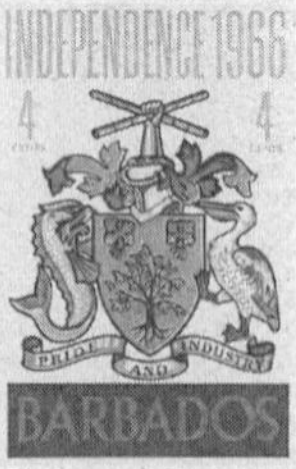

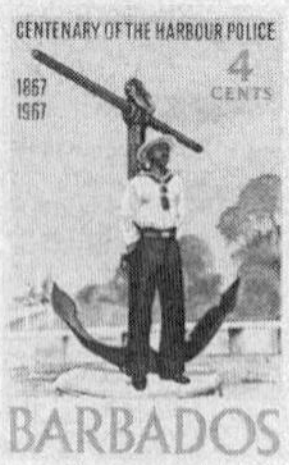

54 Arms of Barbados **58** Policeman and Anchor

1966. Independence. Multicoloured.

356	4c. Type **54**	10	10
357	25c. Hilton Hotel (horiz)	15	10
358	35c. G. Sobers (Test cricketer)	1·50	65
359	50c. Pine Hill Dairy (horiz)	70	1·10

1967. 20th Anniv of U.N.E.S.C.O. As T **54/56** of Antigua.

360	4c. multicoloured	20	10
361	12c. yellow, violet and olive	45	50
362	25c. black, purple and orange	75	1·25

1967. Centenary of Harbour Police. Multicoloured.

363	4c. Type **58**	25	10
364	25c. Policeman and telescope	40	15
365	35c. "BPI" (police launch) (horiz)	45	15
366	50c. Policeman outside H.Q.	60	1·60

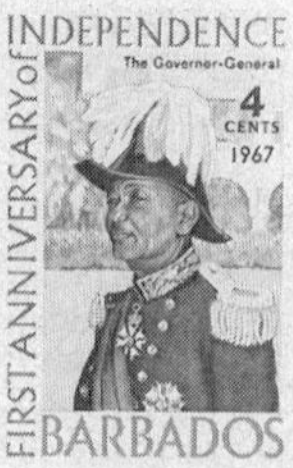

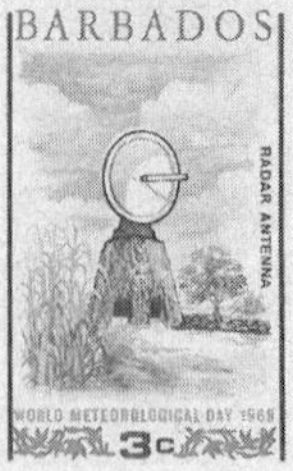

62 Governor-General Sir Winston Scott G.C.M.G **67** Radar Antenna

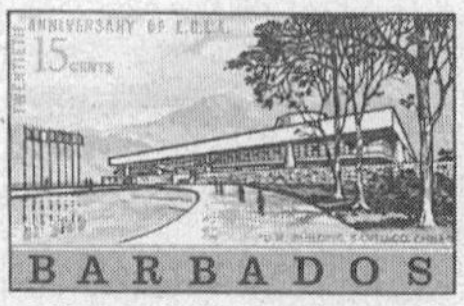

66 U.N. Building, Santiago, Chile

1967. 1st Anniv of Independence. Multicoloured.

367	4c. Type **62**	10	10
368	25c. Independence Arch	20	10
369	35c. Treasury Building	25	10
370	50c. Parliament Building	35	90

Nos. 368/70 are horizontal.

1968. 20th Anniv of Economic Commission for Latin America.

371 **66**	15c. multicoloured	10	10

1968. World Meteorological Day. Multicoloured.

372	3c. Type **67**	10	10
373	25c. Meteorological Institute (horiz)	25	10
374	50c. Harp Gun and Coat of Arms	30	90

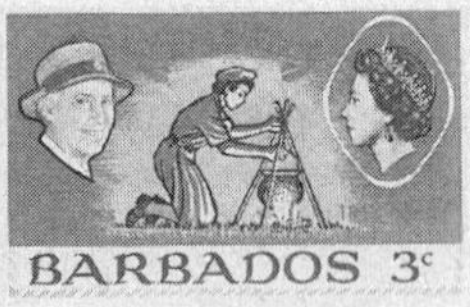

70 Lady Baden-Powell and Guide at Campfire

1968. Golden Jubilee of Girl Guiding in Barbados.

375 **70**	3c. blue, black and gold	20	60
376 –	25c. blue, black and gold	30	60
377 –	35c. yellow, black and gold	35	60

DESIGNS: 25c. Lady Baden-Powell and Pax Hill; 35c. Lady Baden-Powell and Guides' Badge.

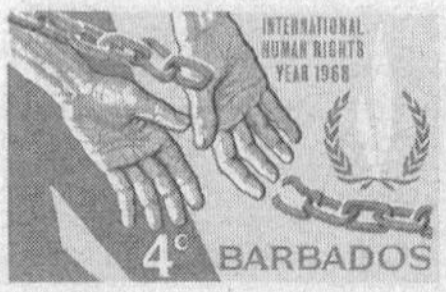

73 Hands breaking Chain, and Human Rights Emblem

1968. Human Rights Year.

378 **73**	4c. violet, brown and green	10	20
379 –	25c. black, blue and yellow	10	25
380 –	35c. multicoloured	15	25

DESIGNS: 25c. Human Rights emblem and family enchained; 35c. Shadows of refugees beyond opening fence.

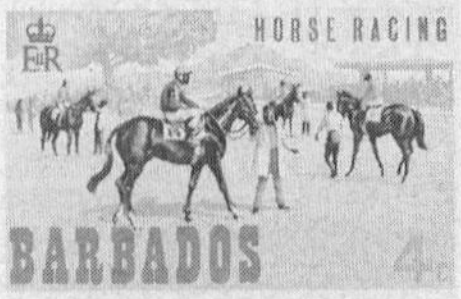

76 Racehorses in the Paddock

1969. Horse Racing. Multicoloured.

381	4c. Type **76**	25	15
382	25c. Starting-gate	25	15
383	35c. On the flat	30	15
384	50c. The winning-post	35	2·00

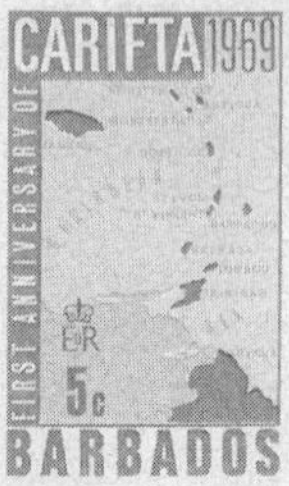

80 Map showing "CARIFTA" Countries

1969. 1st Anniv of "CARIFTA". Multicoloured.

386	5c. Type **80**	10	10
387	12c. "Strength in Unity" (horiz)	10	10
388	25c. Type **80**	10	10
389	50c. As 12c.	15	20

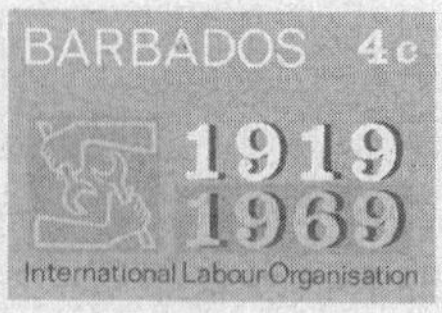

82 I.L.O. Emblem and "1919–1969"

1969. 50th Anniv of I.L.O.

390 **82**	4c. black, green and blue	10	10
391	25c. black, mauve and red	20	10

1969. No. 363 surch **ONE CENT**.

392 **58**	1c. on 4c. multicoloured	10	10

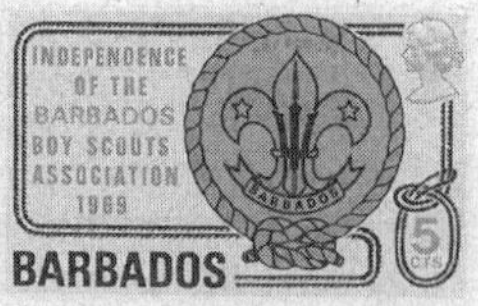

84 National Scout Badge

1969. Independence of Barbados Boy Scouts Association and 50th Anniv of Barbados Sea Scouts. Multicoloured.

393	5c. Type **84**	15	10
394	25c. Sea Scouts rowing	45	10
395	35c. Scouts around campfire	55	10
396	50c. Scouts and National Scout H.Q.	80	1·25

1970. No. 346 surch **4**.

398	4c. on 5c. sepia, red and lilac	10	10

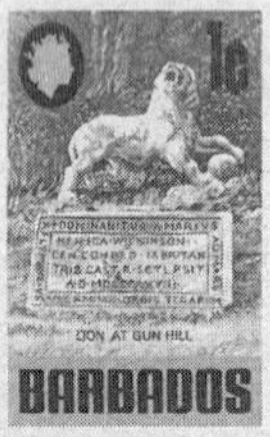

89 Lion at Gun Hill

1970. Multicoloured.

399	1c. Type **89**	10	1·25
400	2c. Trafalgar Fountain	30	1·25
401	3c. Montefiore Drinking Fountain	10	1·00
402a	4c. St. James' Monument	10	10
403	5c. St. Ann's Fort	10	10
404	6c. Old Sugar Mill, Morgan Lewis	35	2·75
405	8c. The Cenotaph	10	10
406a	10c. South Point Lighthouse	1·00	15
407	12c. Barbados Museum	1·25	10
408	15c. Sharon Moravian Church	30	15
409	25c. George Washington House	25	15
410	35c. Nicholas Abbey	30	85
411	50c. Bowmanston Pumping Station	40	1·00
412	$1 Queen Elizabeth Hospital	70	2·50
413	$2.50 Suger Factory	1·50	4·00
467	$5 Seawell International Airport	4·00	5·50

The 12c. to $5 are horiz.

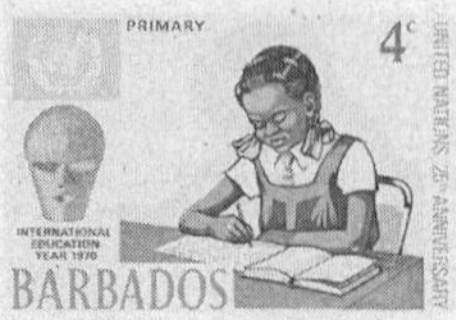

105 Primary Schoolgirl

1970. 25th Anniv of U.N. Multicoloured.

415	4c. Type **105**	10	10
416	5c. Secondary schoolboy	10	10
417	25c. Technical student	35	10
418	50c. University building	55	1·50

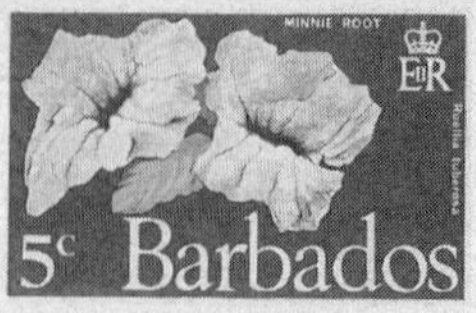

106 Minnie Root

1970. Flowers of Barbados. Multicoloured.

419	1c. Barbados Easter lily	10	2·00
420	5c. Type **106**	40	10
421	10c. Eyelash orchid	1·75	30
422	25c. Pride of Barbados	1·25	75
423	35c. Christmas hope	1·25	85

The 1c. and 25c. are vertical.

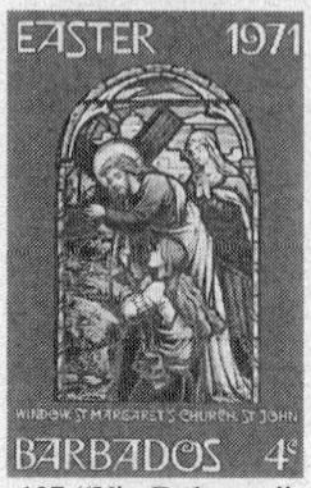

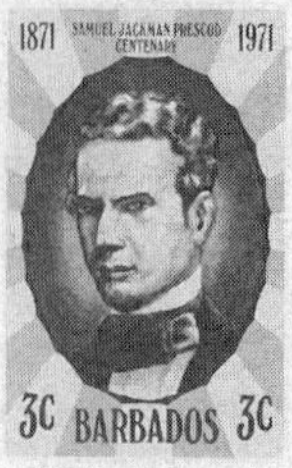

107 "Via Dolorosa" Window, St. Margaret's Church, St. John **109** S. J. Prescod (politician)

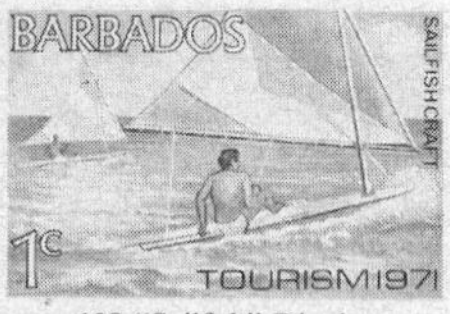

108 "Sailfish" Dinghy

1971. Easter. Multicoloured.

425	4c. Type **107**	10	10
426	10c. "The Resurrection" (Benjamin West)	10	10
427	35c. Type **107**	15	10
428	50c. As 10c.	30	1·50

1971. Tourism. Multicoloured.

429	1c. Type **108**	10	20
430	5c. Tennis	40	10
431	12c. Horse-riding	60	10
432	25c. Water-skiing	40	20
433	50c. Scuba-diving	50	80

1971. Death Centenary of Samuel Jackman Prescod.

434 **109**	3c. multicoloured	10	15
435	35c. multicoloured	15	15

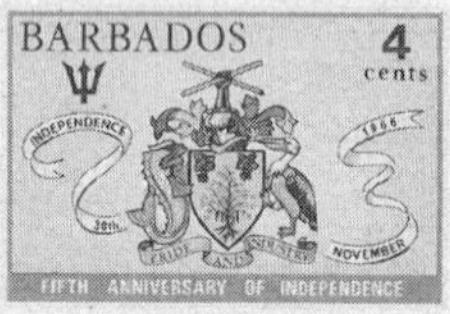

110 Arms of Barbados

1971. 5th Anniv of Independence. Multicoloured.

436	4c. Type **110**	20	10
437	15c. National flag and map	45	10
438	25c. Type **110**	45	10
439	50c. As 15c.	90	1·60

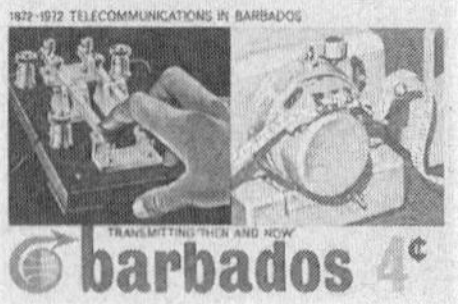

111 Transmitting "Then and Now"

1972. Centenary of Cable Link. Multicoloured.

440	4c. Type **111**	10	10
441	10c. Cable Ship "Stanley Angwin"	20	10
442	35c. Barbados Earth Station and "Intelsat 4"	35	20
443	50c. Mt. Misery and Tropospheric Scatter Station	50	1·40

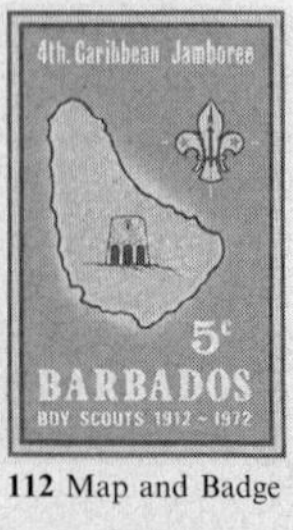

112 Map and Badge

1972. Diamond Jubilee of Scouts. Multicoloured.

444	5c. Type **112**	15	10
445	15c. Pioneers of scouting	15	10
446	25c. Scouts	30	15
447	50c. Flags	60	1·00

Nos. 445/7 are horiz.

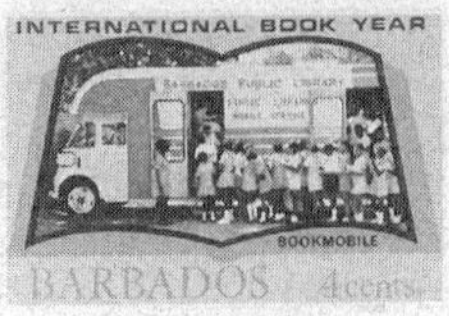

113 Mobile Library

1972. Int Book Year. Multicoloured.

448	4c. Type **113**	20	10
449	15c. Visual-aids van	25	10
450	25c. Public library	25	10
451	$1 Codrington College	1·00	1·50

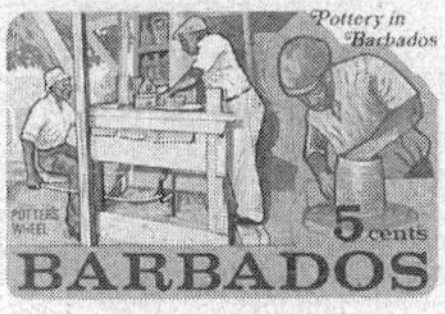

114 Potter's Wheel

1973. Pottery in Barbados. Multicoloured.

468	5c. Type **114**	10	10
469	15c. Kilns	20	10
470	25c. Finished products	25	10
471	$1 Market scene	90	1·10

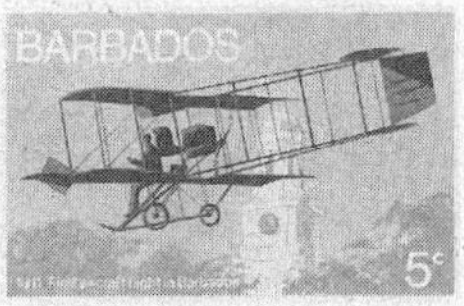

115 First Flight, 1911

1973. Aviation.

472 **115**	5c. multicoloured	30	10
473 –	15c. multicoloured	90	10
474 –	25c. blue, blk & cobalt	1·25	20
475 –	50c. multicoloured	2·00	1·90

DESIGNS: 15c. De Havilland Cirrus Moth on first flight to Barbados, 1928; 25c. Lockheed Super Electra, 1939; 50c. Vickers Super VC-10 airliner, 1973.

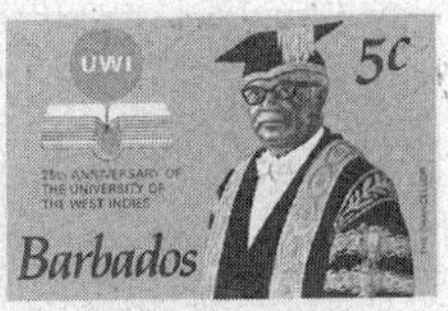

116 University Chancellor

1973. 25th Anniv of University of West Indies. Multicoloured.

476	5c. Type **116**	10	10
477	25c. Sherlock Hall	25	15
478	35c. Cave Hill Campus	30	25

1974. No. 462 surch **4c.**

479	4c. on 25c. multicoloured	15	15

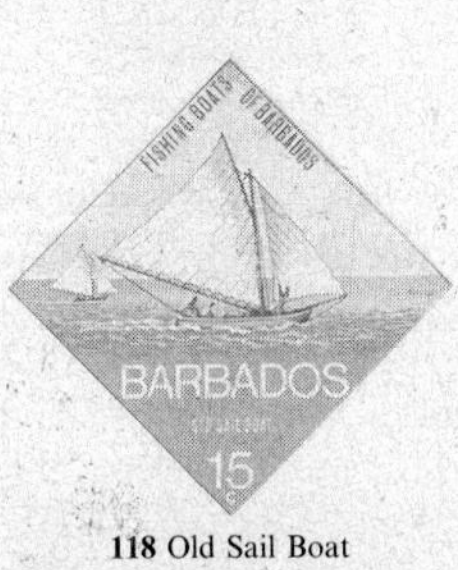

118 Old Sail Boat

1974. Fishing Boats of Barbados. Multicoloured.

480	15c. Type **118**	30	15
481	35c. Rowing-boat	55	25
482	50c. Motor fishing-boat	70	70
483	$1 "Calamar" (fishing boat)	1·10	1·40

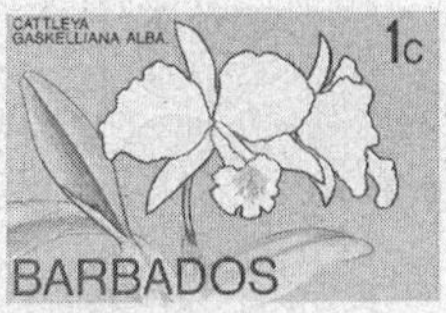

119 "Cattleya gaskelliana alba"

1974. Orchids. Multicoloured.

510	1c. Type **119**	15	1·25
511	2c. "Renanthera storiei"	15	1·25
512	3c. "Dendrobium" "Rose Marie"	15	1·00
488	4c. "Epidendrum ibaguense"	1·75	90
514	5c. "Schomburgkia humboldtii"	35	15
490	8c. "Oncidium ampliatum"	1·00	90
515	10c. "Arachnis maggie oei"	35	10
492	12c. "Dendrobium aggregatum"	45	2·50
517	15c. "Paphiopedilum puddle"	70	15
493b	20c. "Spathoglottis" "The Gold"	4·75	4·75
518	25c. "Epidendrum ciliare" (Eyelash)	70	10
550	35c. "Bletia patula"	2·00	1·75
519	45c. "Phalaenopsis schilleriana" "Sunset Glow"	60	15
496	50c. As 45c.	4·75	4·25
497	$1 "Ascocenda" "Red Gem"	8·00	3·25
498	$2.50 "Brassolaeliocattleya" "Nugget"	3·50	7·00
499	$5 "Caularthron bicornutum"	3·50	6·00
500	$10 "Vanda" "Josephine Black"	4·00	13·00

The 1, 20, 25c., $2.50 and $5 are horiz, the rest are vert.

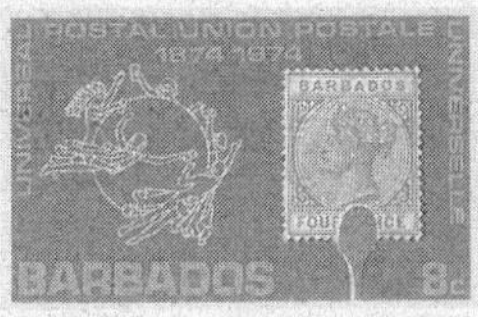

120 4d. Stamp of 1882, and U.P.U. Emblem

1974. Centenary of Universal Postal Union.

501 **120**	8c. mauve, orange & grn	10	10
502 –	35c. red, orge & brown	20	10
503 –	50c. ultram, bl & silver	25	35
504 –	$1 blue, brown & black	55	1·00

DESIGNS: 35c. Letters encircling the globe; 50c. U.P.U. emblem and arms of Barbados; $1 Map of Barbados, sailing ship and Boeing 747 airliner.

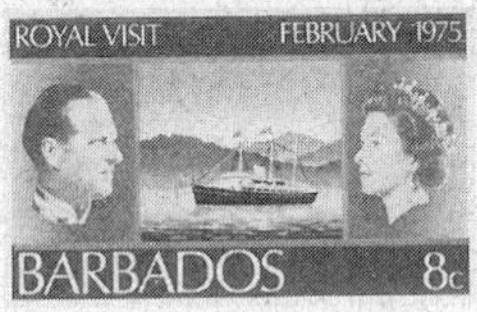

121 Royal Yacht "Britannia"

1975. Royal Visit. Multicoloured.

506	8c. Type **121**	75	20
507	25c. Type **121**	1·10	30
508	35c. Sunset and palms	60	35
509	$1 As 35c.	1·75	3·00

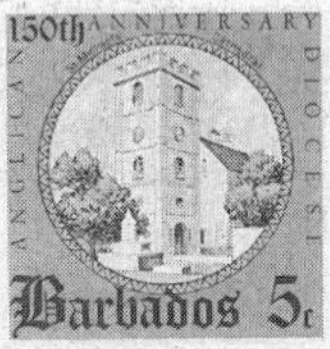

122 St. Michael's Cathedral

1975. 150th Anniv of Anglican Diocese. Mult.

526	5c. Type **122**	10	10
527	15c. Bishop Coleridge	15	10
528	50c. All Saints' Church	45	50
529	$1 "Archangel Michael and Satan" (stained glass window, St. Michael's Cathedral, Bridgetown)	70	80

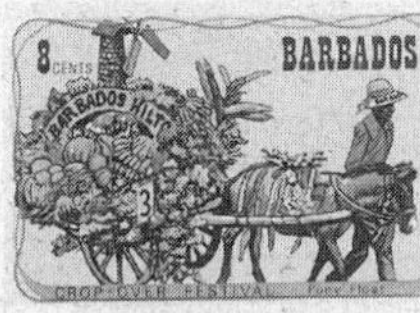

123 Pony Float

1975. Crop-over Festival. Multicoloured.

531	8c. Type **123**	10	10
532	25c. Man on stilts	10	10
533	35c. Maypole dancing	15	10
534	50c. Cuban dancers	30	80

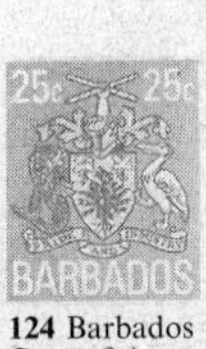

124 Barbados Coat of Arms

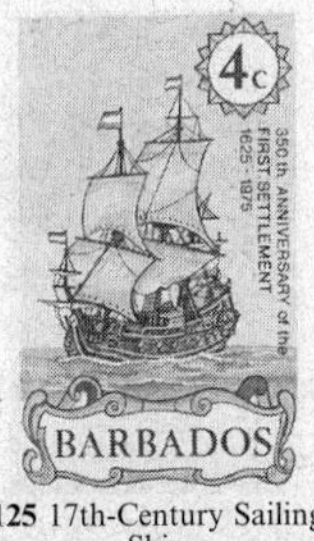

125 17th-Century Sailing Ship

1975. Coil Definitives.

536 **124**	5c. blue	15	80
537	25c. violet	25	1·10

1975. 350th Anniv of First Settlement. Multicoloured.

538	4c. Type **125**	50	20
539	10c. Bearded fig tree and fruit	30	15
540	25c. Ogilvy's 17th-century map	1·00	30
541	$1 Captain John Powell	1·50	5·00

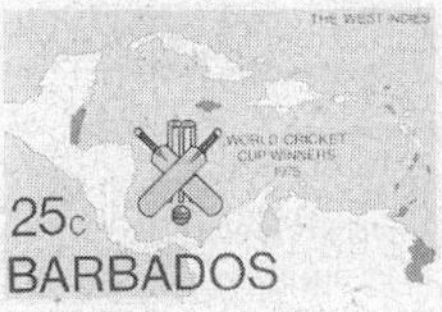

126 Map of Caribbean

1976. West Indian Victory in World Cricket Cup.

559 **126**	25c. multicoloured	1·00	1·00
560 –	45c. black and purple	1·00	2·00

DESIGN—VERT: 45c. The Prudential Cup.

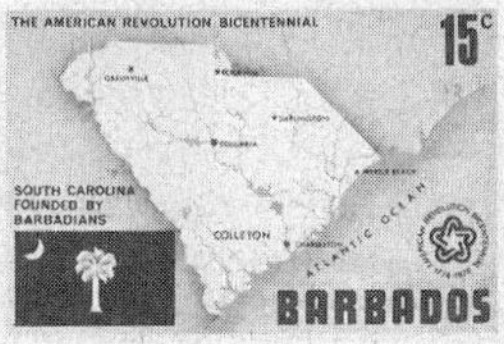

127 Flag and Map of South Carolina

1976. Bicentenary of American Revolution. Mult.

561	15c. Type **127**	45	15
562	25c. George Washington and map of Bridgetown	45	15
563	50c. Independence Declaration	60	1·00
564	$1 Prince Hall	75	3·00

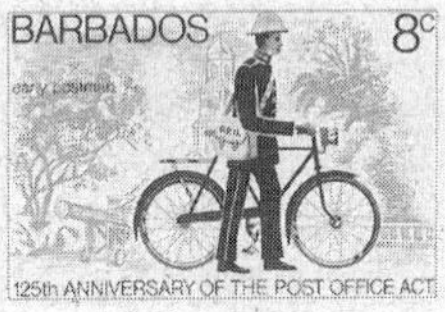

128 Early Postman

1976. 125th Anniv of Post Office Act. Multicoloured.

565	8c. Type **128**	10	10
566	35c. Modern postman	25	10
567	50c. Early letter	30	60
568	$1 Delivery van	50	1·60

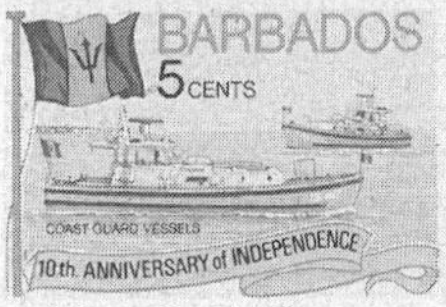

129 Coast Guard "Commander Marshall" and "T. T. Lewis" launches

1976. 10th Anniv of Independence. Multicoloured.

569	5c. Type **129**	30	10
570	15c. Reverse of currency note	30	10
571	25c. Barbados national anthem	30	20
572	$1 Independence Day parade	1·10	2·75

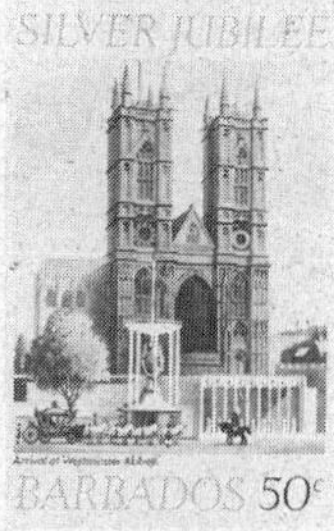

130 Arrival of Coronation Coach at Westminster Abbey

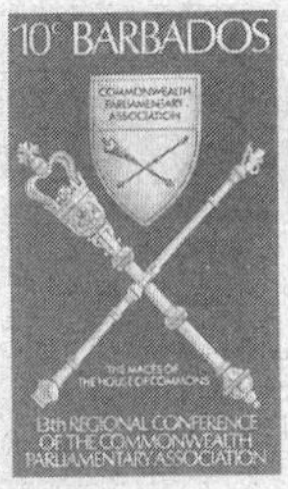

132 Maces of the House of Commons

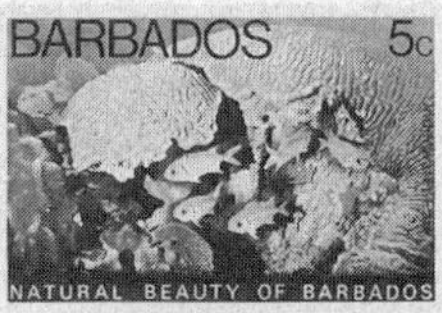

131 Underwater Park

1977. Silver Jubilee. Multicoloured.

574	15c. Queen knighting Garfield Sobers, 1975	30	25
575	50c. Type **130**	30	40
576	$1 Queen entering Abbey	30	70

1977. Natural Beauty of Barbados. Multicoloured.

577	5c. Type **131**	15	10
578	35c. Royal palms (vert)	30	10
579	50c. Underwater caves	40	50
580	$1 Stalagmite in Harrison's Cave (vert)	70	1·10

1977. 13th Regional Conference of Commonwealth Parliamentary Association.

582 **132**	10c. orange, yellow & brn	10	10
583 –	25c. green, orge & dp grn	10	10
584 –	50c. multicoloured	20	20
585 –	$1 blue, orange and dp bl	55	75

DESIGNS—VERT: 25c. Speaker's Chair; 50c. Senate Chamber. HORIZ: $1 Sam Lord's Castle.

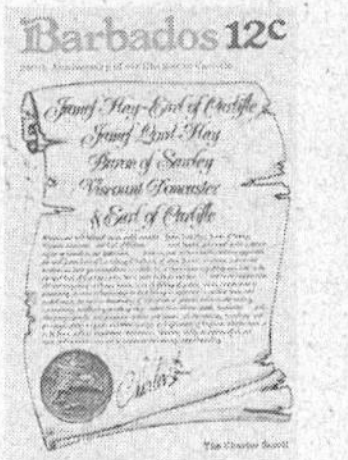

133 The Charter Scroll

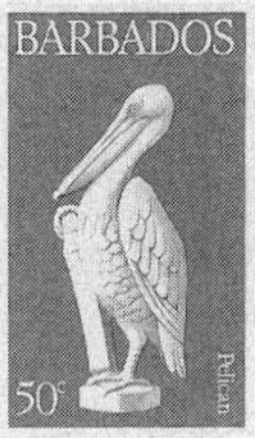

135 Brown Pelican

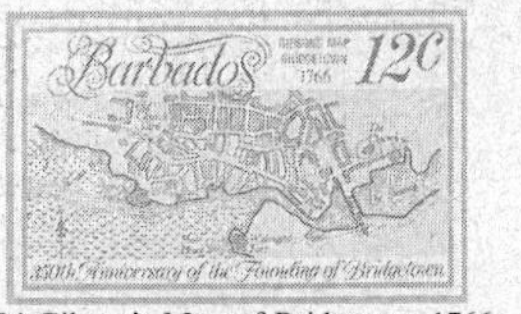

134 Gibson's Map of Bridgtown, 1766

1977. 350th Anniv of Granting of Charter to Earl of Carlisle. Multicoloured.

586	12c. Type **133**	15	10
587	25c. The earl receiving charter	15	10
588	45c. The earl and Charles I (horiz)	30	35
589	$1 Ligon's map, 1657 (horiz)	50	1·00

1977. Royal Visit. As Nos. 574/6 but inscr "SILVER JUBILEE ROYAL VISIT".

590	15c. Garfield Sobers being knighted, 1975	60	50
591	50c. Type **130**	20	75
592	$1 Queen entering Abbey	30	1·25

1978. 350th Anniv of Founding of Bridgetown.

593 **134**	12c. multicoloured	15	10
594 –	25c. black, green & gold	15	10
595 –	45c. multicoloured	20	15
596 –	$1 multicoloured	30	60

DESIGNS: 25c. "A Prospect of Bridgetown in Barbados" (engraving by S. Copens, 1695); 45c. "Trafalgar Square, Bridgetown" (drawing by J. M. Carter, 1835); $1 The Bridges, 1978.

1978. 25th Anniv of Coronation.

597 –	50c. olive, black & blue	25	50
598 –	50c. multicoloured	25	50
599 **135**	50c. olive, black & blue	25	50

DESIGNS: No. 597, Griffin of Edward III. No. 598, Queen Elizabeth II.

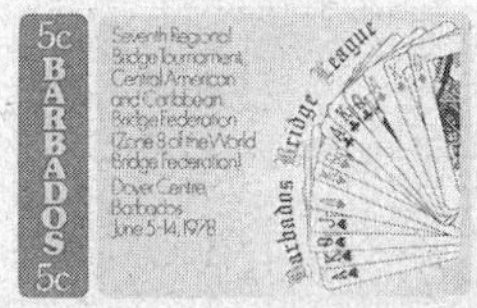

136 Barbados Bridge League Logo

1978. 7th Regional Bridge Tournament, Barbados. Multicoloured.

600	5c. Type **136**	10	10
601	10c. Emblem of World Bridge Federation	15	10
602	45c. Central American and Caribbean Bridge Federation emblem	25	10
603	$1 Playing cards on map of Caribbean	40	60

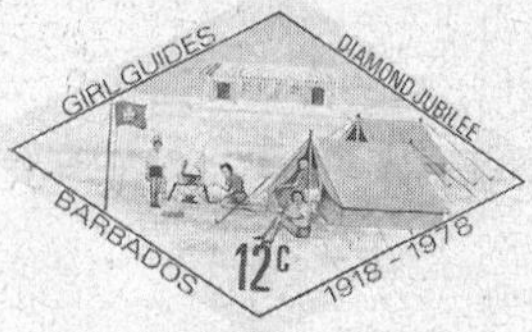

137 Camp Scene

1978. Diamond Jubilee of Guiding. Multicoloured.

605	12c. Type **137**	25	15
606	28c. Community work	40	15
607	50c. Badge and "60" (vert)	55	30
608	$1 Guide badge (vert)	75	1·00

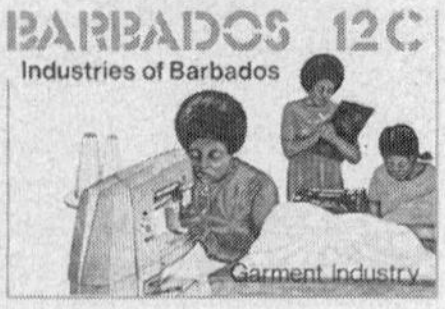

138 Garment Industry

1978. Industries of Barbados. Multicoloured.

609	12c. Type **138**	15	10
610	28c. Cooper (vert)	25	25
611	45c. Blacksmith (vert)	35	95
612	50c. Wrought iron working	40	95

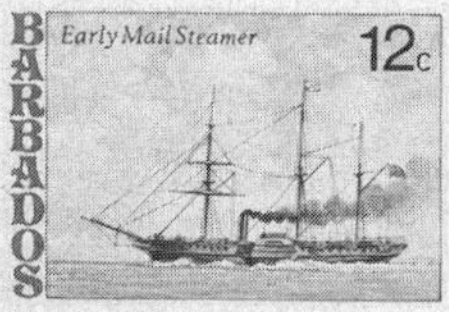

139 "Forth" (early mail steamer)

1979. Ships. Multicoloured.

613	12c. Type **139**	35	10
614	25c. "Queen Elizabeth 2" in Deep Water Harbour	55	15
615	50c. "Ra II" nearing Barbados	75	1·00
616	$1 Early mail paddle-steamer	1·00	2·50

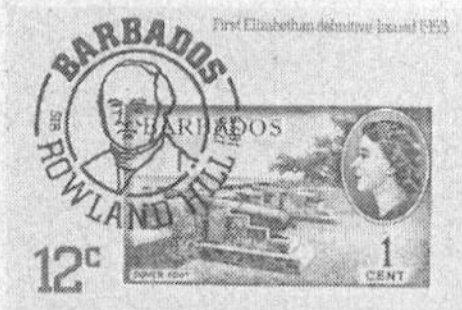

140 1953 1c. Definitive Stamp

1979. Death Cent of Sir Rowland Hill. Mult.

617	12c. Type **140**	15	15
618	28c. 1975 350th anniv of first settlement 25c. commemorative (vert)	20	30
619	45c. Penny Black with Maltese Cross postmark (vert)	30	45

1979. St. Vincent Relief Fund. No. 495 surch **28c+4c ST. VINCENT RELIEF FUND**.

621	28c.+4c. on 35c. "Bletia patula"	50	60

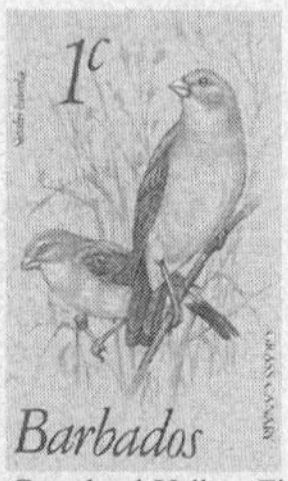

142 Grassland Yellow Finch ("Grass Canary")

1979. Birds. Multicoloured.

622	1c. Type **142**	10	1·00
623	2c. Grey kingbird ("Rainbird")	10	1·00
624	5c. Lesser Antillean bullfinch ("Sparrow")	10	70
625	8c. Magnificent frigate bird ("Frigate Bird")	50	2·00
626	10c. Cattle egret	10	40
627	12c. Green-backed heron ("Green Gaulin")	50	1·25
627a	15c. Carib grackle ("Blackbird")	4·50	5·00
628	20c. Antillean crested hummingbird ("Humming Bird")	20	55
629	25c. Scaly-breasted ground dove ("Ground Dove")	20	60
630	28c. As 15c.	1·75	1·75
631	35c. Green-throated carib	30	70
631b	40c. Red-necked pigeon ("Ramier")	4·50	5·50
632	45c. Zenaida dove ("Wood Dove")	1·50	1·25
633	50c. As 40c.	1·50	1·75
633a	55c. American golden plover ("Black breasted Plover")	4·00	3·50
633b	60c. Bananaquit ("Yellow Breasted")	4·50	6·00
634	70c. As 60c.	1·50	3·25
635	$1 Caribbean elaenia ("Peer whistler")	1·50	1·50
636	$2.50 American redstart ("Christmas Bird")	2·00	6·00
637	$5 Belted kingfisher ("Kingfisher")	3·25	9·00
638	$10 Moorhen ("Red-seal Coot")	5·50	14·00

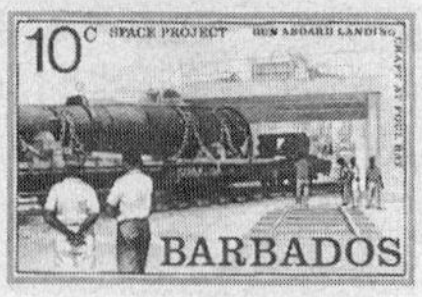

143 Unloading H.A.R.P. Gun on Railway Wagon at Foul Bay

1979. Space Projects Commemorations. Mult.

639	10c. Type **143**	15	10
640	12c. H.A.R.P. gun on railway wagon under tow (vert)	15	15
641	20c. Firing launcher (vert)	15	20
642	28c. Bath Earth Station and "Intelsat"	15	30
643	45c. "Intelsat" over Caribbean	25	50
644	50c. "Intelsat" over Atlantic (vert)	25	60

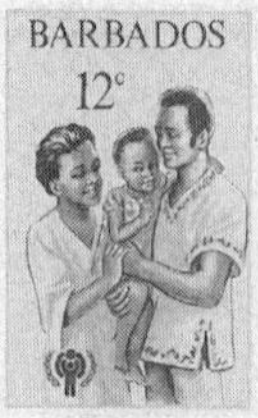

144 Family

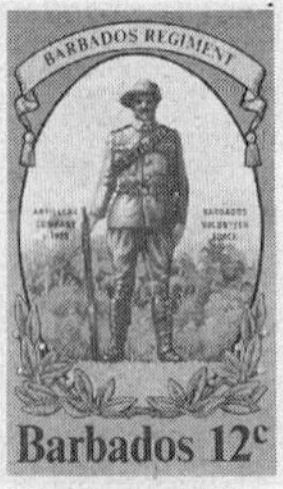

146 Private, Artillery Company, Barbados Volunteer Force, c. 1909

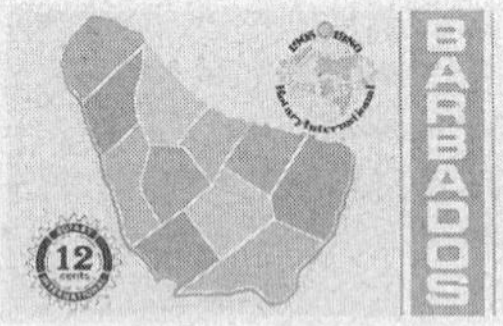

145 Map of Barbados

1979. International Year of the Child. Multicoloured.

646	12c. Type **144**	10	10
647	28c. Ring of children and map of Barbados	15	15
648	45c. Child with teacher	20	20
649	50c. Children playing	20	20
650	$1 Children and kite	35	45

1980. 75th Anniv of Rotary International. Multicoloured.

651	12c. Type **145**	15	10
652	28c. Map of Caribbean	15	15
653	50c. Rotary anniversary emblem	20	35
654	$1 Paul P. Harris (founder)	30	95

1980. Barbados Regiment. Multicoloured.

655	12c. Type **146**	25	10
656	35c. Drum Major, Zouave uniform	35	15
657	50c. Sovereign's and Regimental Colours	40	30
658	$1 Barbados Regiment Women's Corps	55	70

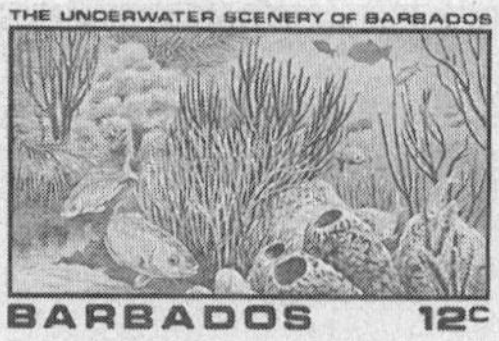

148 Yellow-tailed Snapper

1980. Underwater Scenery. Multicoloured

660	12c. Type **148**	20	10
661	28c. Banded butterflyfish	35	15
662	50c. Male and female blue-headed wrasse and princess parrotfish	45	25
663	$1 French grunt and French angelfish	70	70

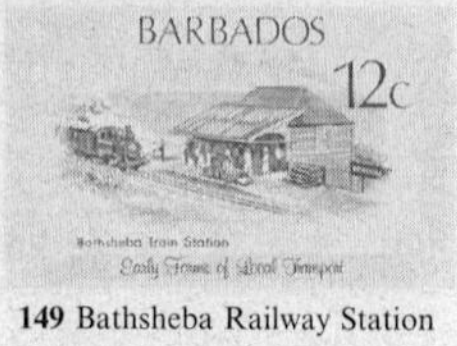

149 Bathsheba Railway Station

1981. Early Transport. Multicoloured.

665	12c. Type **149**	30	10
666	28c. Cab stand at The Green	20	15
667	45c. Animal-drawn tram	30	30
668	70c. Horse-drawn bus	45	60
669	$1 Railway Station, Fairchild Street	70	95

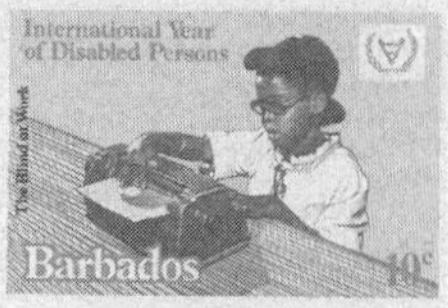

150 The Blind at Work

1981. Int Year for Disabled Persons. Mult.

670	10c. Type **150**	20	10
671	25c. Sign Language (vert)	25	15
672	45c. "Be alert to the white cane" (vert)	40	25
673	$2.50 Children at play	80	3·00

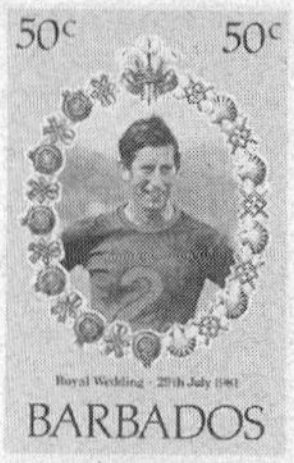

151 Prince Charles dressed for Polo

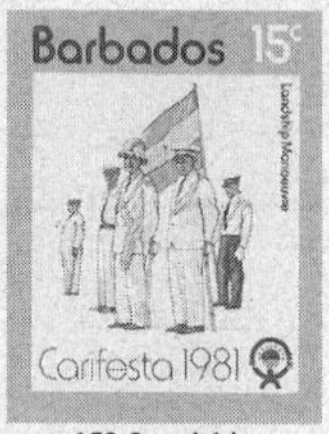

152 Landship Manoeuvre

1981. Royal Wedding. Multicoloured.

674	28c. Wedding bouquet from Barbados	15	10
675	50c. Type **151**	20	15
676	$2.50 Prince Charles and Lady Diana Spencer	55	1·25

1981. Carifesta (Caribbean Festival of Arts), Barbados. Multicoloured.

677	15c. Type **152**	15	15
678	20c. Yoruba dancers	15	15
679	40c. Tuk band	20	25
680	55c. Sculpture by Frank Collymore	25	35
681	$1 Harbour scene	50	75

1981. Nos. 630, 632 and 634 surch.

682	15c. on 28c. Carib grackle	30	15
683	40c. on 45c. Zenaida dove	30	35
684	60c. on 70c. Bananaquit	30	45

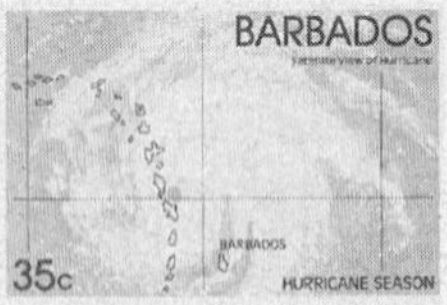

154 Satellite View of Hurricane

1981. Hurricane Season.

685 **154**	35c. black and blue	35	20
686	– 50c. multicoloured	45	35
687	– 60c. multicoloured	70	50
688	– $1 multicoloured	85	90

DESIGNS: 50c. Hurricane "Gladys" from "Apollo 7"; 60c. Police Department on hurricane watch; $1 McDonnell Banshee "hurricane chaser" aircraft.

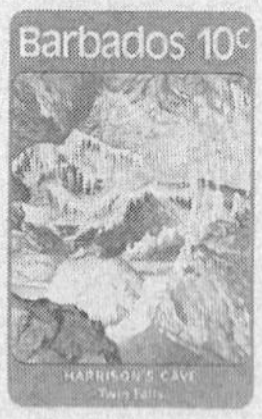

155 Twin Falls

1981. Harrison's Cave. Multicoloured.

689	10c. Type **155**	10	10
690	20c. Stream in Rotunda Room	20	15
691	55c. Formations in Rotunda Room	25	30
692	$2.50 Cascade Pool	60	2·25

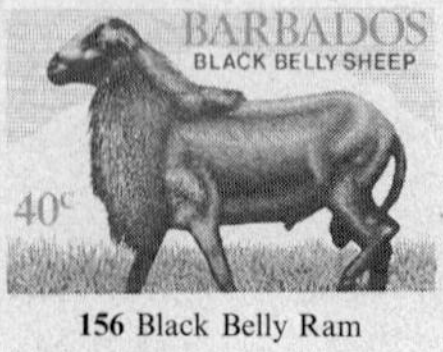

156 Black Belly Ram

1982. Black Belly Sheep. Multicoloured.

693	40c. Type **156**	15	20
694	50c. Black belly ewe	15	20
695	60c. Ewe with lambs	20	45
696	$1 Ram and ewe, with map of Barbados	35	1·50

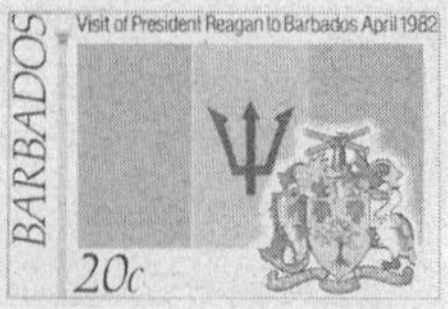

157 Barbados Coat of Arms and Flag

1982. President Reagan's Visit. Multicoloured.

697	20c. Type **157**	40	1·25
698	20c. U.S.A. coat of arms and flag	40	1·25
699	55c. Type **157**	50	1·50
700	55c. As No. 698	50	1·50

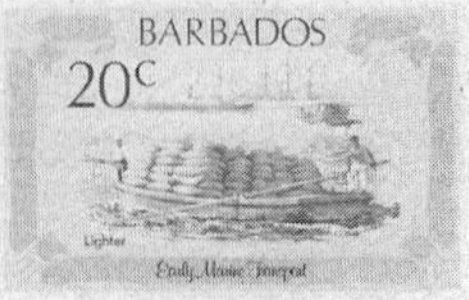

158 Lighter

1982. Early Marine Transport. Multicoloured.

701	20c. Type **158**	20	15
702	35c. Rowing boat	35	25
703	55c. Speightstown schooner	50	40
704	$2.50 Inter-colonial schooner	1·75	2·50

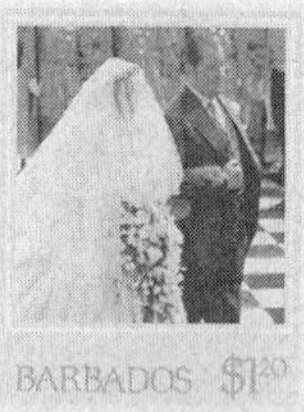

159 Bride and Earl Spencer Proceeding up the Aisle

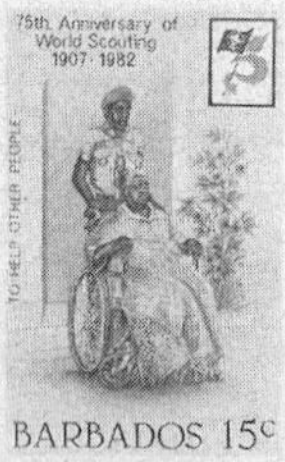

160 "To Help other People"

1982. 21st Birthday of Princess of Wales. Mult.

705	20c. Barbados coat of arms	20	15
706	60c. Princess at Llanelwedd, October, 1981	45	50
707	$1.20 Type **159**	75	1·10
708	$2.50 Formal portrait	1·25	1·90

1982. 75th Anniv of Boy Scout Movement. Mult.

709	15c. Type **160**	50	10
710	40c. "I Promise to do my Best" (horiz)	80	30
711	55c. "To do my Duty to God, the Queen and my Country" (horiz)	90	65
712	$1 National and Troop flags	1·40	1·75

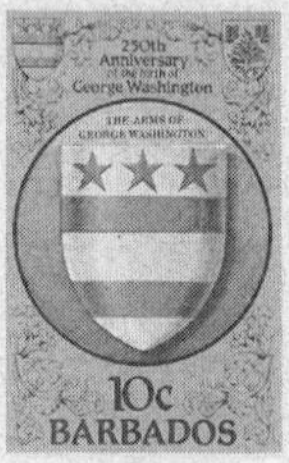

161 Arms of George Washington

1982. 250th Birth Anniv of George Washington. Multicoloured.

714	10c. Type **161**	10	10
715	55c. Washington House, Barbados	25	30
716	60c. Washington with troops	25	35
717	$2.50 Washington taking Oath	75	1·60

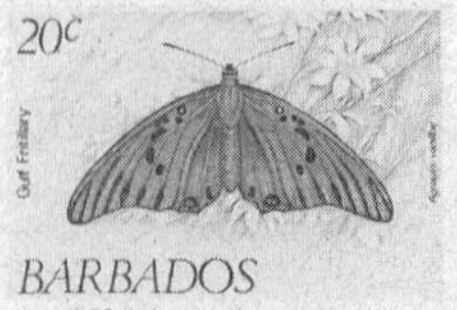

162 "Agraulis vanillae"

1983. Butterflies. Multicoloured.

718	20c. Type **162**	1·00	40
719	40c. "Danaus plexippus"	1·50	40
720	55c. "Hypolimnas misippus"	1·50	45
721	$2.50 "Hemiargus hanno"	3·25	3·75

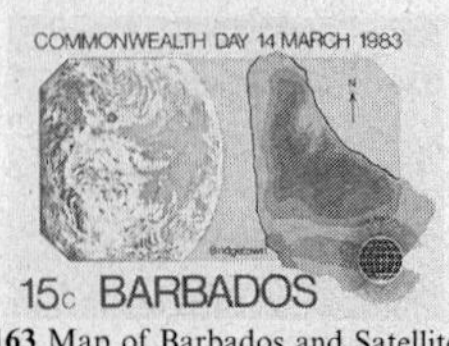

163 Map of Barbados and Satellite View

1983. Commonwealth Day. Multicoloured.
722 15c. Type **163** 20 10
723 40c. Tourist beach 25 20
724 60c. Sugar cane harvesting 35 40
725 $1 Cricket match 1·25 1·10

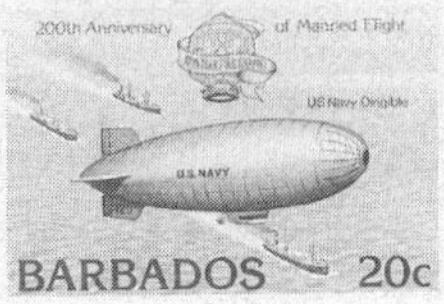

164 U.S. Navy "M" Class Airship M-20

1983. Bicentenary of Manned Flight.
726 20c. Type **164** 35 15
727 40c. Douglas DC-3 40 40
728 55c. Vickers Viscount 837 40 50
729 $1 Lockheed TriStar 500 65 2·50

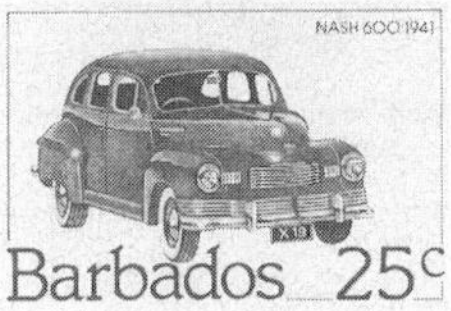

165 Nash "600", 1941

1983. Classic Cars. Multicoloured.
730 25c. Type **165** 45 20
731 45c. Dodge, 1938 60 30
732 75c. Ford "Model AA", 1930 80 1·50
733 $2.50 Dodge "Four", 1918 1·50 4·50

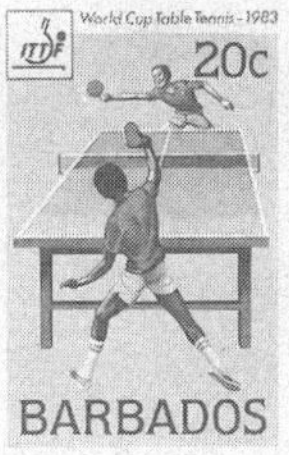

166 Game in Progress

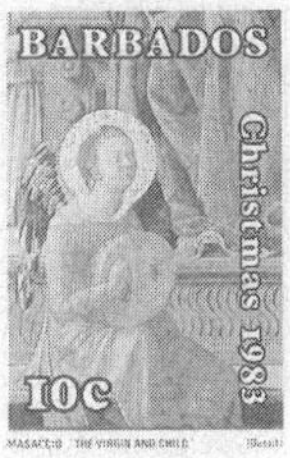

167 Angel playing Lute (detail "The Virgin and Child") (Masaccio)

1983. Table Tennis World Cup Competition. Multicoloured.
734 20c. Type **166** 25 20
735 65c. Map of Barbados 50 55
736 $1 World Table Tennis Cup 75 1·00

1983. Christmas. 50th Anniv of Barbados Museum.
737 **167** 10c. multicoloured 30 10
738 – 25c. multicoloured 60 20
739 – 45c. multicoloured 90 40
740 – 75c. black and gold 1·40 1·60
741 – $2.50 multicoloured 4·50 6·00
DESIGNS—HORIZ: 45c. "The Barbados Museum" (Richard Day); 75c. "St. Ann's Garrison" (W. S. Hedges); $2.50, Needham's Point, Carlisle Bay. VERT: 25c., $2 Different details from "The Virgin and Child" (Masaccio).

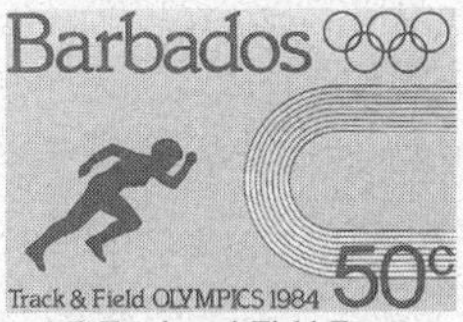

168 Track and Field Events

1984. Olympic Games, Los Angeles.
745 **168** 50c. green, black and brown 60 45
746 – 65c. orange, blk & brn 80 60
747 – 75c. blue, black & dp bl 1·00 85
748 – $1 brown, black and yellow 2·50 1·75
DESIGNS: 65c. Shooting; 75c. Sailing; $1 Cycling.

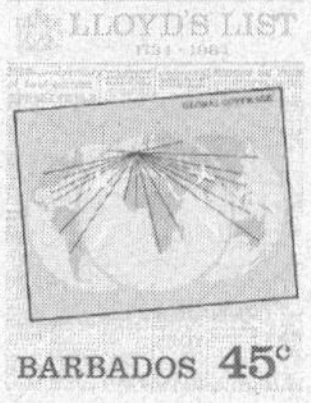

169 Global Coverage

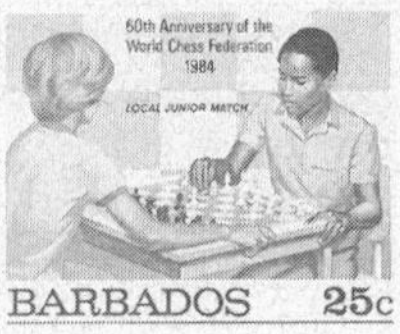

171 Local Junior Match

1984. 250th Anniv of "Lloyd's List" (newspaper). Multicoloured.
750 45c. Type **169** 80 40
751 50c. Bridgetown harbour 90 50
752 75c. "Philosopher" (full-rigged ship), 1857 1·40 1·25
753 $1 "Sea Princess" (liner), 1984 1·40 1·60

1984. 60th Anniv of International Chess Federation. Multicoloured.
755 25c. Type **171** 1·25 30
756 45c. Staunton and 19th-century knights 1·60 50
757 65c. Staunton queen and 18th-century queen from Macao 1·75 1·60
758 $2 Staunton and 17th-century rooks 3·50 6·00

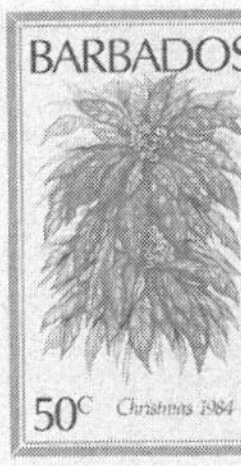

172 Poinsettia

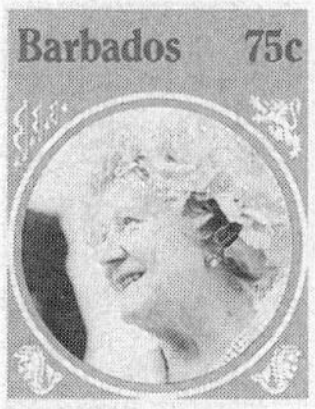

174 The Queen Mother at Docks

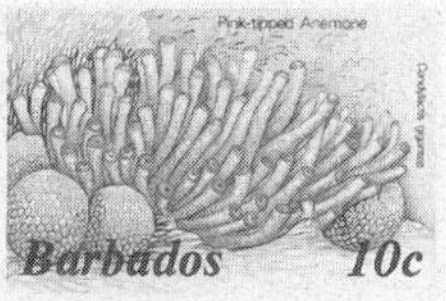

173 Pink-tipped Anemone

1984. Christmas. Flowers. Multicoloured.
759 50c. Type **172** 1·50 80
760 65c. Snow-on-the-Mountain 1·75 1·50
761 75c. Christmas Candle 2·00 3·00
762 $1 Christmas Hope 2·25 3·50

1985. Marine Life. Multicoloured.
794B 1c. Bristle worm 30 2·25
795B 2c. Spotted trunkfish 30 2·25
796A 5c. Coney 65 1·50
797B 10c. Type **173** 30 30
798B 20c. Christmas tree worm 30 40
799B 25c. Hermit crab 40 40
800A 35c. Animal flower 1·00 1·50
801B 40c. Vase sponge 50 50
802B 45c. Spotted moray 60 50
803B 50c. Ghost crab 60 60
804B 65c. Flamingo tongue snail 65 70
805B 75c. Sergeant major 70 75
806B $1 Caribbean warty anemone 85 85
807B $2.50 Green turtle 2·00 6·00
808B $5 Rock beauty (fish) 2·50 8·00
809B $10 Elkhorn coral 3·75 8·00

1985. Life and Times of Queen Elizabeth the Queen Mother. Multicoloured.
779 25c. In the White Drawing Room, Buckingham Palace, 1930s 30 20
780 65c. With Lady Diana Spencer at Trooping the Colour, 1981 1·75 80
781 75c. Type **174** 70 90
782 $1 With Prince Henry at his christening (from photo by Lord Snowdon) 85 1·00

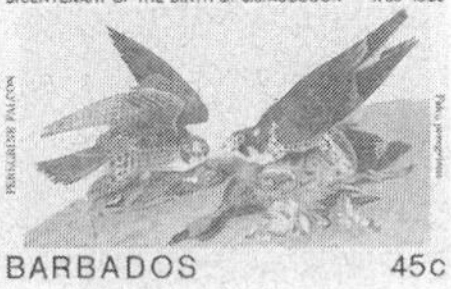

175 Peregrine Falcon

1985. Birth Bicentenary of John J. Audubon (ornithologist). Designs showing original paintings. Multicoloured.
784 45c. Type **175** 2·25 80
785 65c. Prairie warbler (vert) 2·50 2·25
786 75c. Great blue heron (vert) 2·75 3·00
787 $1 Yellow warbler (vert) 3·00 4·00

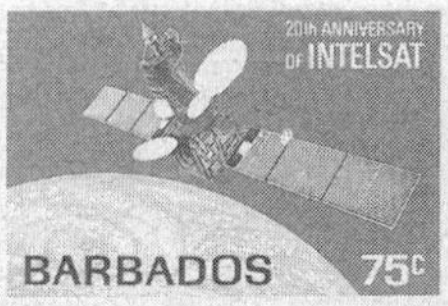

176 Intelsat Satellite orbiting Earth

1985. 20th Anniv of Intelsat Satellite System.
788 **176** 75c. multicoloured 1·00 70

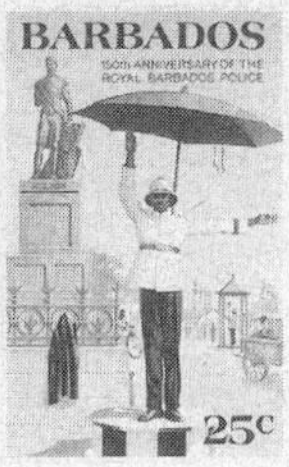

177 Traffic Policeman

1985. 150th Anniv of Royal Barbados Police. Multicoloured.
789 25c. Type **177** 80 20
790 50c. Police band on bandstand 1·40 80
791 65c. Dog handler 1·60 1·40
792 $1 Mounted policeman in ceremonial uniform 1·75 2·00

1986. 60th Birthday of Queen Elizabeth II. As T **110** of Ascension. Multicoloured.
810 25c. Princess Elizabeth aged two, 1928 20 20
811 50c. At University College of West Indies, Jamaica, 1953 35 40
812 65c. With Duke of Edinburgh, Barbados, 1985 55 50
813 75c. At banquet in Sao Paulo, Brazil, 1968 55 60
814 $2 At Crown Agents Head Office, London, 1983 1·00 1·50

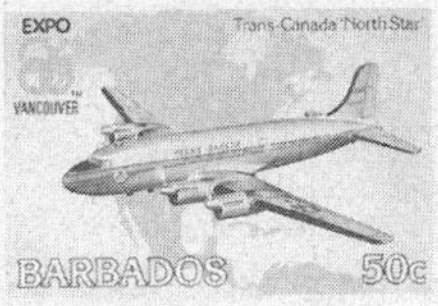

178 Canadair DC-4M2 North Star of Trans-Canada Airlines

1986. "Expo '86" World Fair, Vancouver. Mult.
815 50c. Type **178** 75 50
816 $2.50 "Lady Nelson" (cargo liner) 2·00 2·50

1986. "Ameripex '86" International Stamp Exhibition, Chicago. As T **164** of Bahamas, showing Barbados stamps. Multicoloured.
817 45c. 1976 Bicentenary of American Revolution 25c. 70 35
818 50c. 1976 Bicentenary of American Revolution 50c. 80 55
819 65c. 1981 Hurricane Season $1 90 1·00
820 $1 1982 Visit of President Reagan 55c. 1·00 1·75

1986. Royal Wedding. As T **112** of Ascension. Multicoloured.
822 45c. Prince Andrew and Miss Sarah Ferguson 75 35
823 $1 Prince Andrew in midshipman's uniform 1·25 75

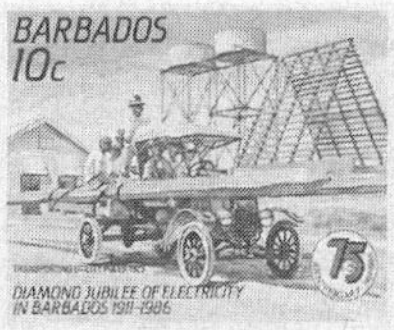

179 Transporting Electricity Poles, 1923

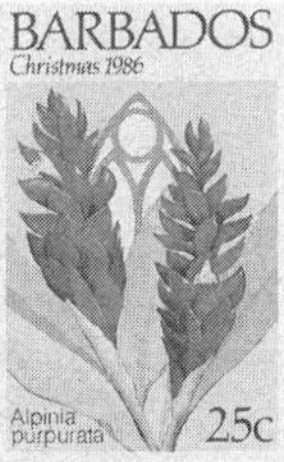

180 "Alpinia purpurata" and Church Window

1986. 75th Anniv of Electricity in Barbados. Multicoloured.
824 10c. Type **179** 15 10
825 25c. Heathman Ladder, 1935 (vert) 25 20
826 65c. Transport fleet, 1941 60 60
827 $2 Bucket truck, 1986 (vert) 1·60 2·00

1986. Christmas. Multicoloured.
828 25c. Type **180** 20 20
829 50c. "Anthurium andraeanum" 45 45
830 75c. "Heliconia rostrata" 75 80
831 $2 "Heliconia × psittacorum" 1·50 3·25

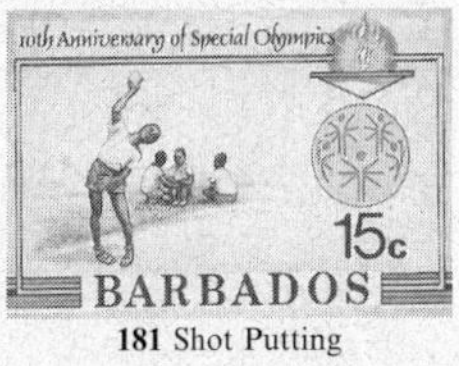

181 Shot Putting

1987. 10th Anniv of Special Olympics. Multicoloured.
832 15c. Type **181** 25 15
833 45c. Wheelchair racing 45 30
834 65c. Long jumping 60 65
835 $2 Logo and slogan 1·25 2·50

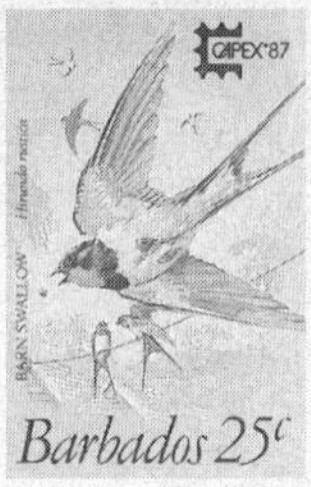

182 Barn Swallow

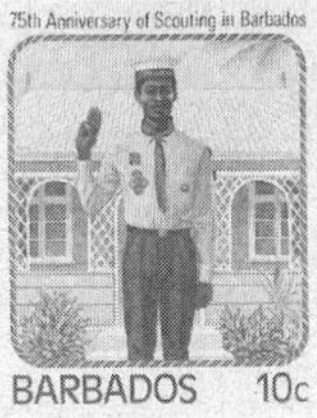

183 Sea Scout saluting

1987. "Capex '87" International Stamp Exhibition, Toronto. Birds. Multicoloured.
836 25c. Type **182** 2·00 50
837 50c. Yellow warbler 2·25 1·75
838 65c. Audubon's shearwater 2·25 1·75
839 75c. Black-whiskered vireo 2·50 3·25
840 $1 Scarlet tanager 2·75 4·00

1987. 75th Anniv of Scouting in Barbados. Multicoloured.
841 10c. Type **183** 20 10
842 25c. Scout jamboree 30 20
843 65c. Scout badges 65 45
844 $2 Scout band 1·60 1·75

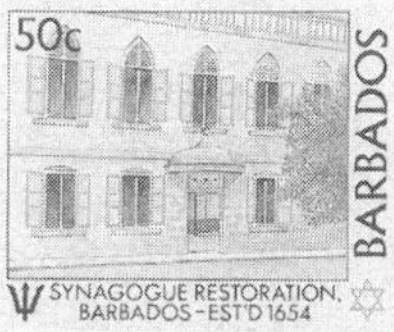

184 Bridgetown Synagogue

1987. Restoration of Bridgetown Synagogue. Multicoloured.
845 50c. Type **184** 1·75 1·75
846 65c. Interior of Synagogue 1·90 1·90
847 75c. Ten Commandments (vert) 2·25 2·25
848 $1 Marble laver (vert) 2·50 3·00

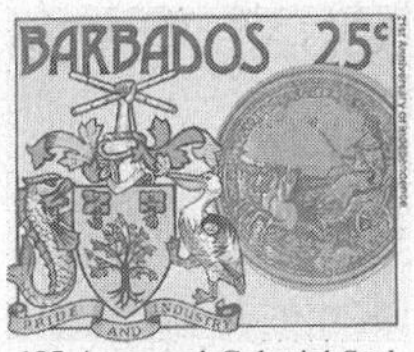

185 Arms and Colonial Seal

1987. 21st Anniv of Independence. Mult.
849 29c. Type **185** 35 20
850 45c. Flags of Barbados and Great Britain 75 35
851 65c. Silver dollar and one penny coins 1·00 55
852 $2 Colours of Barbados Regiment 2·25 2·50

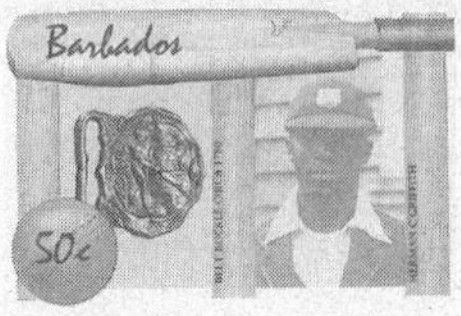

186 Herman C. Griffith

1988. West Indian Cricket. Each showing portrait, cricket equipment and early belt buckle. Multicoloured.
854 15c. E. A. (Manny) Martindale 2·25 75
855 45c. George Challenor 3·00 75
856 50c. Type **186** 3·25 2·25
857 75c. Harold Austin 3·75 3·50
858 $2 Frank Worrell 4·25 9·50

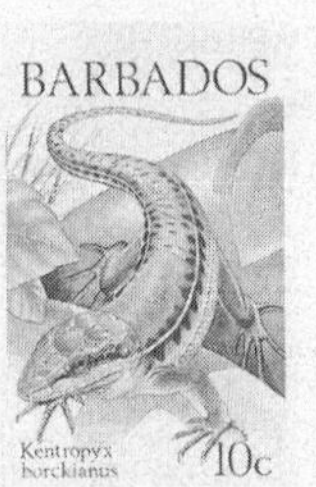

187 "Kentropyx borckianus"

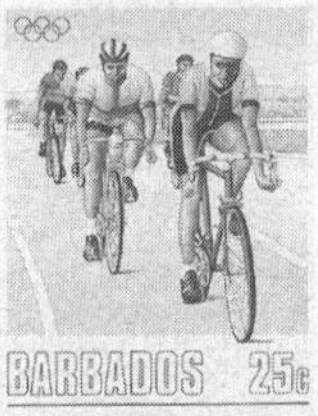

188 Cycling

1988. Lizards of Barbados. Multicoloured.
859 10c. Type **187** 1·50 45
860 50c. "Hemidactylus mabouia" 2·75 60
861 65c. "Anolis extremus" 2·75 1·00
862 $2 "Gymnophthalmus underwoodii" 5·50 8·50

1988. Olympic Games, Seoul. Multicoloured.
863 25c. Type **188** 1·25 30
864 45c. Athletics 60 30

865 75c. Relay swimming 75 65
866 $2 Yachting . . . . 1·75 2·25

1988. 300th Anniv of Lloyd's of London. As T **123** of Ascension.
868 40c. multicoloured 55 30
869 50c. multicoloured 65 35
870 65c. multicoloured . . . . . 1·50 45
871 $2 blue and red . . . . . . 3·75 2·00
DESIGNS—VERT: 40c. Royal Exchange, 1774; $2 Sinking of "Titanic", 1912. HORIZ: 50c. Early sugar mill; 65c. "Author" (container ship).

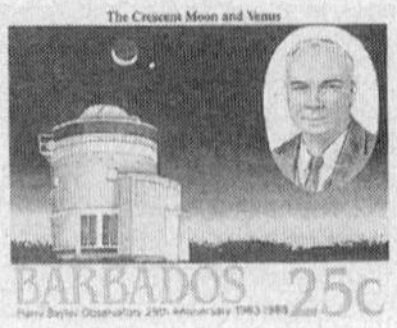

189 Harry Bayley and Observatory

1988. 25th Anniv of Harry Bayley Observatory. Multicoloured.
872 25c. Type **189** 60 20
873 65c. Observatory with North Star and Southern Cross constellations . . . . . . 1·25 65
874 75c. Andromeda galaxy . . . 1·50 80
875 $2 Orion constellation . . . 2·75 4·50

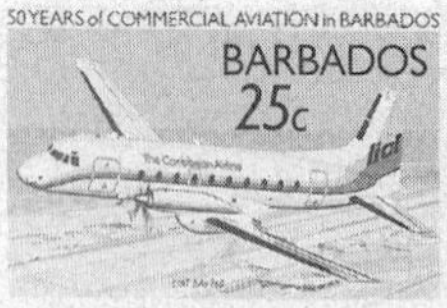

190 L.I.A.T. Hawker Siddeley H.S.748

1989. 50th Anniv of Commercial Aviation in Barbados. Multicoloured.
876 25c. Type **190** . . . . 2·00 40
877 65c. Pan Am Douglas DC-8-62 . . . . 2·75 1·00
878 75c. British Airways Concorde at Grantley Adams Airport . . . . . 2·75 1·00
879 $2 Caribbean Air Cargo Boeing 707-351C . . . . . 4·50 6·50

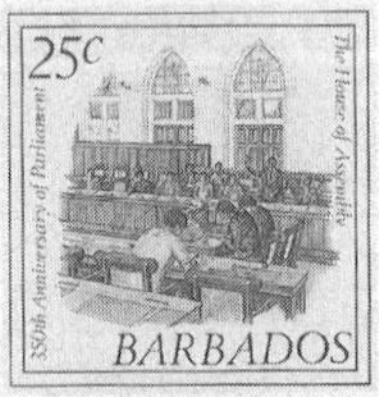

191 Assembly Chamber

1989. 350th Anniv of Parliament.
880 **191** 25c. multicoloured 40 20
881 – 50c. multicoloured 60 35
882 – 75c. blue and black . . . 1·00 50
883 – $2.50 multicoloured . . . 2·50 2·00
DESIGNS: 50c. The Speaker; 75c. Parliament Buildings, c. 1882; $2.50, Queen Elizabeth II and Prince Philip in Parliament.

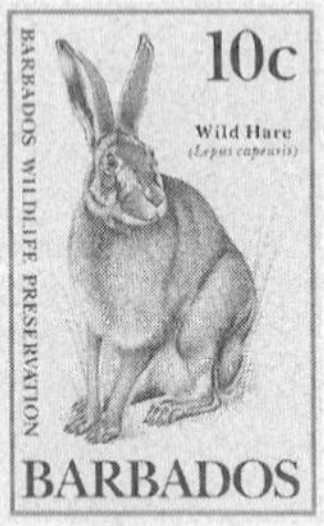

192 Brown Hare

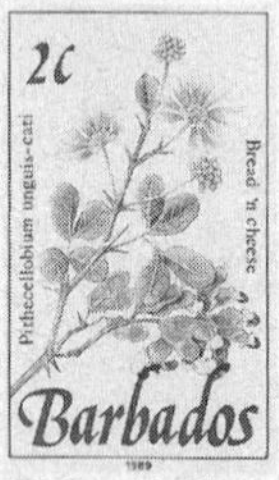

193 Bread 'n Cheese

1989. Wildlife Preservation. Multicoloured.
884 10c. Type **192** 70 30
885 50c. Red-footed tortoise (horiz) . . . . 1·50 70
886 65c. Savanna ("Green") monkey . . . . 1·75 1·25
887 $2 "Bufo marinus" (toad) (horiz) . . . . 3·25 6·00

1989. Wild Plants. Multicoloured.
921 2c. Type **193** . . . . 40 1·25
891 5c. Scarlet cordia 30 70
892 10c. Columnar cactus . . . 30 30
893 20c. Spiderlily 40 30
925 25c. Rock balsam 55 20
895 30c. Hollyhock 50 25
895a 35c. Red sage . . . . 1·00 1·00
927 45c. Yellow shak-shak . . . 65 35
928 50c. Whitewood 70 40
898 55c. Bluebell 80 55
930 65c. Prickly sage 80 55
900 70c. Seaside samphire . . . 80 80
901 80c. Flat-hand dildo . . . . 1·50 1·00
901a 90c. Herringbone . . . . . 1·50 2·00
902 $1.10 Lent tree . . . . . . 1·25 2·00
934 $2.50 Rodwood . . . . . . 1·90 4·00
935 $5 Cowitch . . . . 3·25 6·00
936 $10 Maypole . . . . 6·50 9·00

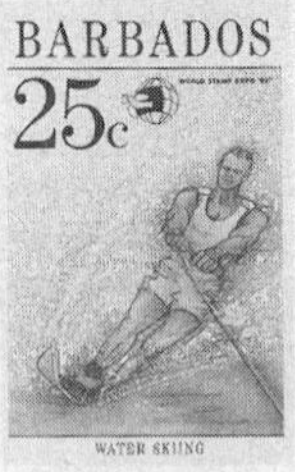

194 Water Skiing

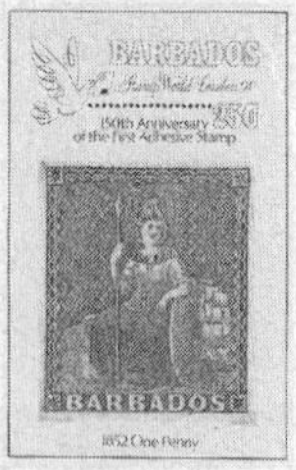

195 Barbados 1852 1d. Stamp

1989. "World Stamp Expo '89" International Stamp Exn., Washington. Watersports. Mult.
906 25c. Type **194** . . . . 1·25 40
907 50c. Yachting . . . . 2·25 1·00
908 65c. Scuba diving . . . . . 2·25 1·60
909 $2.50 Surfing . . . . 6·00 9·00

1990. 150th Anniv of the Penny Black and "Stamp World London '90" International Stamp Exn.
910 **195** 25c. green, black and yellow . . . . 1·25 40
911 – 50c. multicoloured . . . . 1·75 1·00
912 – 65c. multicoloured . . . . 1·75 1·25
913 – $2.50 multicoloured . . . 4·00 7·00
DESIGNS: 50c., 1d. 1882 Queen Victoria stamp; 65c. 1899 2d. stamp; $2.50, 1912 3d. stamp.

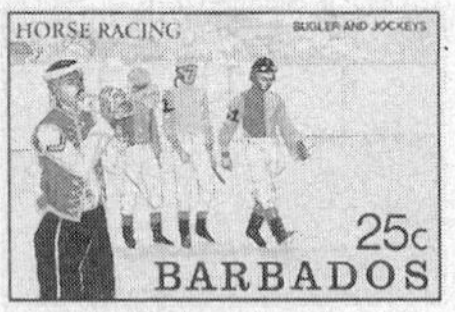

196 Bugler and Jockeys

1990. Horse Racing. Multicoloured.
915 25c. Type **196** 45 30
916 45c. Horse and jockey in parade ring 70 50
917 75c. At the finish 90 85
918 $2 Leading in the winner (vert) . . . . 2·50 4·50

1990. 90th Birthday of Queen Elizabeth the Queen Mother. As T **134** of Ascension.
919 75c. multicoloured 75 60
920 $2.50 black and green . . . . 2·25 2·75
DESIGNS—21 × 36 mm: 75c. Lady Elizabeth Bowes-Lyon, April 1923 (from painting by John Lander). 29 × 37 mm: $2.50, Lady Elizabeth Bowes-Lyon on her engagement, January 1923.

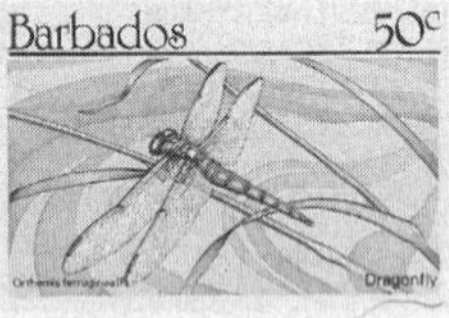

197 "Orthemis ferruginea" (dragonfly)

1990. Insects. Multicoloured.
937 50c. Type **197** . . . . 1·50 80
938 65c. "Ligyrus tumulosus" (beetle) . . . . 1·75 1·00
939 75c. "Neoconocephalus sp." (grasshopper) . . . . . . 2·00 1·25
940 $2 "Bostra maxwelli" (stick-insect) . . . . 3·50 5·50

1990. Visit of the Princess Royal. Nos. 925, 901 and 903 optd **VISIT OF HRH THE PRINCESS ROYAL OCTOBER 1990.**
941 25c. Rock balsam . . . . . 1·25 40
942 80c. Flat-hand dildo . . . . 2·50 1·75
943 $2.50 Rodwood . . . . . . 5·00 7·00

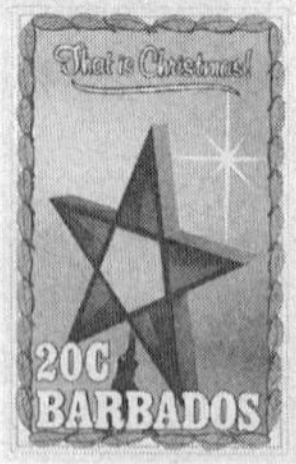

199 Star

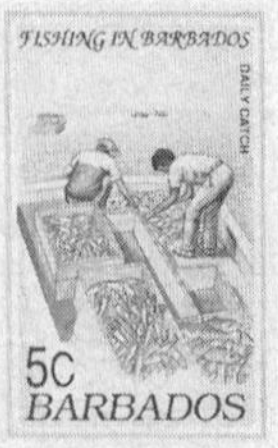

201 Sorting Daily Catch

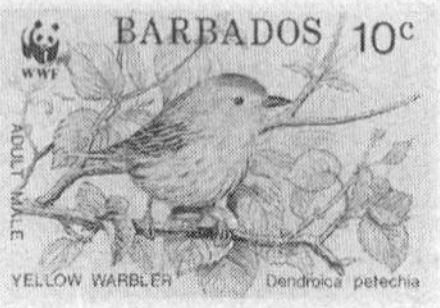

200 Adult Male Yellow Warbler

1990. Christmas. Multicoloured.
944 20c. Type **199** 65 20
945 50c. Figures from crib . . . 1·00 50

946 $1 Stained glass window . . 2·00 1·50
947 $2 Angel (statue) . . . . . . 3·00 5·50

1991. Endangered Species. Yellow Warbler. Multicoloured.
948 10c. Type **200** . . . . 1·40 80
949 20c. Pair feeding chicks in nest . . . . 2·00 80
950 45c. Female feeding chicks in nest . . . . 2·50 80
951 $1 Male with fledgeling . . . 4·00 5·25

1991. Fishing in Barbados. Multicoloured.
952 5c. Type **201** 50 50
953 50c. Line fishing (horiz) . . . 1·75 90
954 75c. Fish cleaning (horiz) . . 2·25 1·25
955 $2.50 Game fishing . . . . . 4·50 6·50

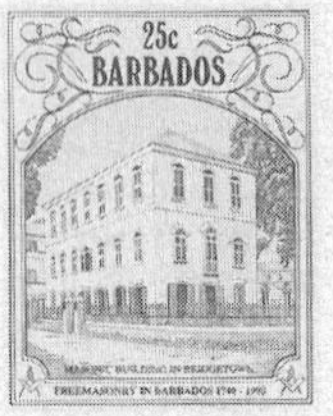

202 Masonic Building, Bridgetown

1991. 250th Anniv of Freemasonry in Barbados (1990).
956 **202** 25c. multicoloured . . . . 1·25 50
957 – 65c. multicoloured . . . . 2·00 1·25
958 – 75c. black, yellow & brn . 2·00 1·25
959 – $2.50 multicoloured . . . 4·75 7·00
DESIGNS: 65c. Compass and square (masonic symbols); 75c. Royal Arch jewel; $2.50, Ceremonial apron, columns and badge.

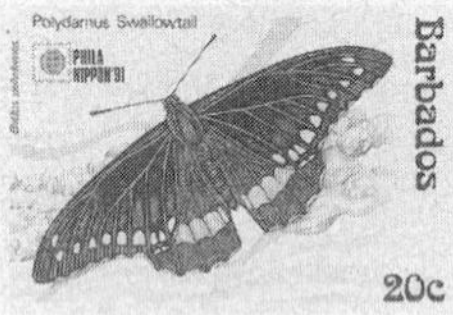

203 "Battus polydamus"

1991. "Phila Nippon '91" International Stamp Exhibition, Tokyo. Butterflies. Multicoloured.
960 20c. Type **203** . . . . 1·00 40
961 50c. "Urbanus proteus" (vert) 1·50 65
962 65c. "Phoebis sennae" . . . 1·60 95
963 $2.50 "Junonia evarete" (vert) . . . . 4·00 6·00

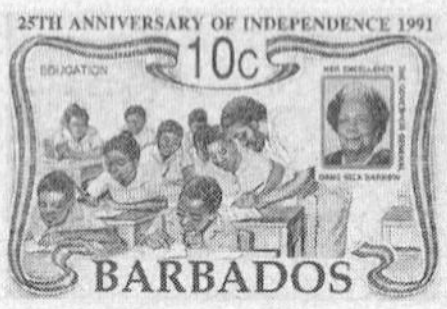

204 School Class

1991. 25th Anniv of Independence. Multicoloured.
965 10c. Type **204** 20 20
966 25c. Barbados Workers' Union Labour College . . 30 30
967 65c. Building a house 70 90
968 75c. Sugar cane harvesting 80 1·00
969 $1 Health clinic . . . . . . 1·00 2·00

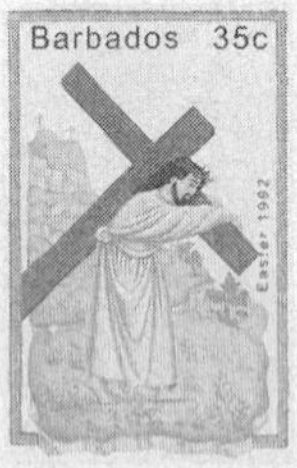

205 Jesus carrying Cross

1992. Easter. Multicoloured.
971 35c. Type **205** 80 30
972 70c. Crucifixion . . . . . . 1·40 90
973 90c. Descent from the Cross 1·50 1·25
974 $3 Risen Christ . . . . . . 4·00 6·50

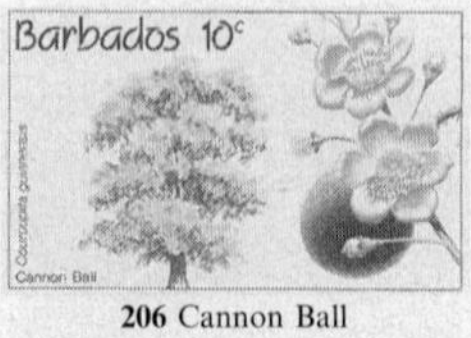

206 Cannon Ball

1992. Conservation. Flowering Trees. Multicoloured.
975 10c. Type **206** 60 40
976 30c. Golden shower tree . . . 1·00 50
977 80c. Frangipani . . . . . . 2·25 2·50
978 $1.10 Flamboyant . . . . . 2·75 3·00

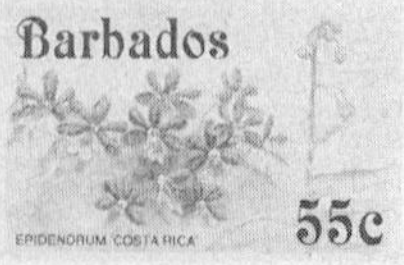

207 "Epidendrum" "Costa Rica"

1992. Orchids. Multicoloured.
979 55c. Type **207** 85 65
980 65c. "Cattleya guttaca" . . . 1·00 1·00
981 70c. "Laeliacattleya" "Splashing Around" . . . 1·00 1·00
982 $1.40 "Phalaenopsis" "Kathy Saegert" . . . . 1·60 3·00

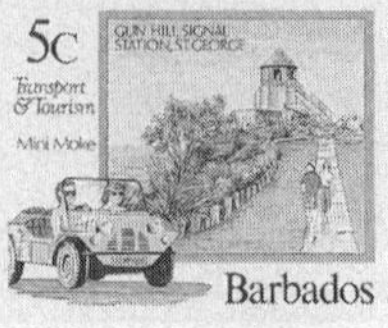

208 Mini Moke and Gun Hill Signal Station, St. George

1992. Transport and Tourism. Multicoloured.
983 5c. Type **208** 50 50
984 35c. Tour bus and Bathsheba Beach, St. Joseph . . . . 1·00 30
985 90c. B.W.I.A. McDonnell Douglas MD-83 over Grantley Adams Airport 2·50 2·25
986 $2 "Festivale" (liner) and Bridgetown harbour . . . 3·75 5·50

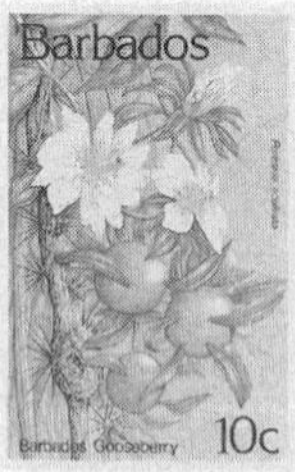

209 Barbados Gooseberry

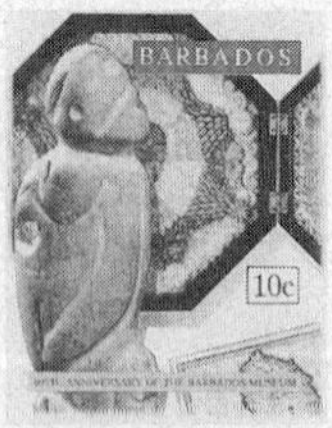

212 Sailor's Shell-work Valentine and Carved Amerindian

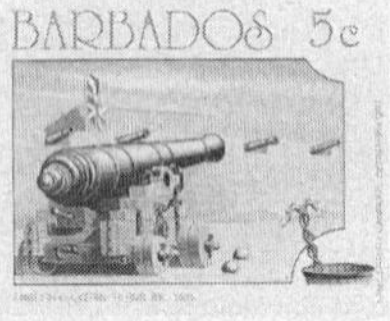

211 18 pdr Culverin of 1625, Denmark Fort

1993. Cacti and Succulents. Multicoloured.
987 10c. Type **209** 55 30
988 35c. Night-blooming cereus 1·25 35
989 $1.40 Aloe . . . . 3·00 3·50
990 $2 Scrunchineel . . . . . . 3·50 5·50

1993. 75th Anniv of Royal Air Force. As T **149** of Ascension. Multicoloured.
991 10c. Hawker Hunter F.6 . . 65 40
992 30c. Handley Page Victor K2 1·00 40
993 70c. Hawker Typhoon IB . . 1·50 1·50
994 $3 Hawker Hurricane Mk I 3·50 5·50

1993. 14th World Orchid Conference, Glasgow. Nos. 979/82 optd **WORLD ORCHID CONFERENCE 1993.**
996 55c. Type **207** . . . . 1·25 1·25
997 65c. "Cattleya guttaca" . . . 1·40 1·40
998 70c. "Laeliacattleya" "Splashing Around" . . . 1·40 1·40
999 $1.40 "Phalaenopsis" "Kathy Saegert" . . . . 2·25 3·50

1993. 17th-century English Cannon. Mult.
1000 5c. Type **211** 30 50
1001 45c. 6 pdr of 1649–60, St. Ann's Fort 85 50
1002 $1 9 pdr demi-culverin of 1691, The Main Guard 1·75 2·00
1003 $2.50 32 pdr demi-cannon of 1693–94, Charles Fort 2·75 4·50

1993. 60th Anniv of Barbados Museum. Mult.
1004 10c. Type **212** 50 50
1005 75c. "Barbados Mulatto Girl" (Agostino Brunias) 1·50 1·50
1006 90c. Morris Cup and soldier of West India Regiment, 1858 . . . . 1·75 1·90
1007 $1.10 Ogilby's map of Barbados, 1679, and Ashanti gold weights . . 2·00 2·50

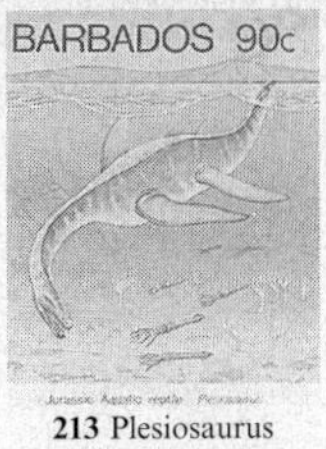

213 Plesiosaurus

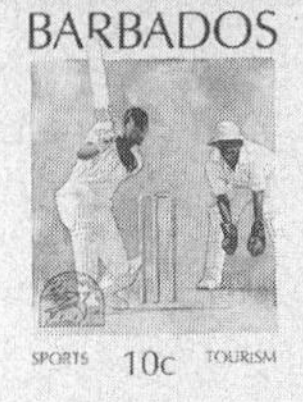

214 Cricket

1993. Prehistoric Aquatic Animals. Mult.

1008	90c. Type **213**	1·75	2·25
1009	90c. Ichthyosaurus	1·75	2·25
1010	90c. Elasmosaurus	1·75	2·25
1011	90c. Mosasaurus	1·75	2·25
1012	90c. Archelon	1·75	2·25

Nos. 1008/12 were printed together, se-tenant, with the background forming a composite design.

1994. Sports and Tourism. Multicoloured.

1013	10c. Type **214**	1·25	75
1014	35c. Rally driving	1·40	50
1015	50c. Golf	2·25	1·50
1016	70c. Long distance running	1·75	2·25
1017	$1.40 Swimming	2·00	3·25

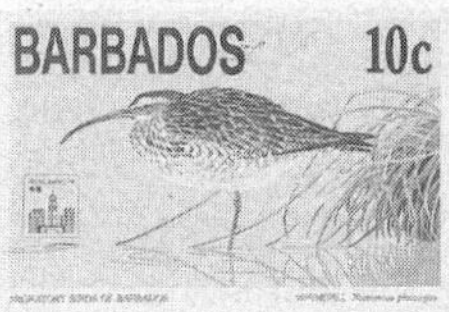

215 Whimbrel

1994. "Hong Kong '94" Int Stamp Exhibition. Migratory Birds. Multicoloured.

1018	10c. Type **215**	50	50
1019	35c. Pacific golden plover ("American Golden Plover")	1·00	50
1020	70c. Ruddy turnstone	1·50	1·50
1021	$3 Louisiana heron ("Tricoloured Heron")	3·50	5·50

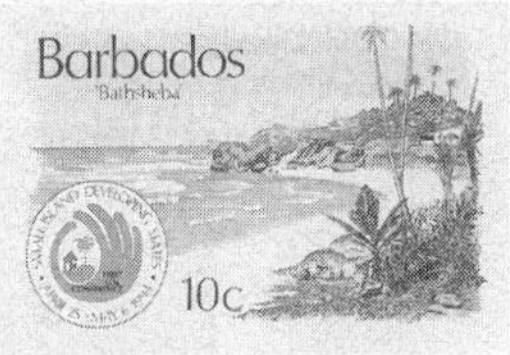

216 Bathsheba Beach and Logo

1994. 1st United Nations Conference of Small Island Developing States. Multicoloured.

1022	10c. Type **216**	20	15
1023	65c. Pico Tenneriffe	70	60
1024	90c. Ragged Point Lighthouse	1·75	1·50
1025	$2.50 Consett Bay	2·25	4·00

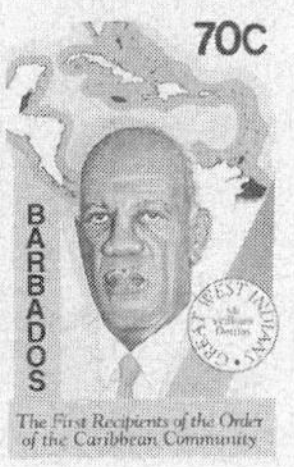

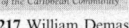

217 William Demas

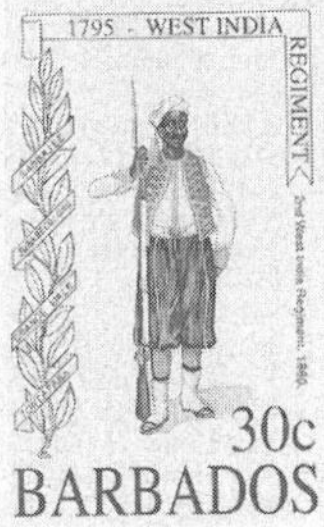

219 Private, 2nd West India Regt, 1860

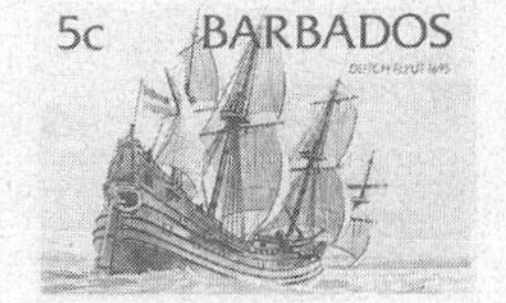

218 Dutch Flyut, 1695

1994. First Recipients of Order of the Caribbean Community. Multicoloured.

1026	70c. Type **217**	70	1·00
1027	70c. Sir Shridath Ramphal	70	1·00
1028	70c. Derek Walcott	70	1·00

1994. Ships. Multicoloured.

1075	5c. Type **218**	50	60
1076	10c. "Geestport" (freighter), 1994	30	40
1031B	25c. H.M.S. "Victory" (ship of the line), 1805	50	40
1078	30c. "Royal Viking Queen" (liner), 1994	50	30
1079	35c. H.M.S. "Barbados" (frigate), 1945	50	30
1080	45c. "Faraday" (cable ship), 1924	50	35
1081	50c. U.S.C.G. "Hamilton" (coastguard cutter), 1974	1·75	75
1082	65c. H.M.C.S. "Saguenay" (destroyer), 1939	75	70
1083	70c. "Inanda" (cargo liner), 1928	75	70
1084	80c. H.M.S. "Rodney" (battleship), 1944	75	70
1085	90c. U.S.S. "John F. Kennedy" (aircraft carrier), 1982	75	70
1086	$1.10 "William and John" (immigrant ship), 1627	1·00	1·00
1087	$5 U.S.C.G. "Champlain" (coastguard cutter), 1931	4·00	4·50
1042B	$10 "Artist" (full-rigged ship), 1877	7·00	8·00

1995. Bicentenary of Formation of West India Regiment. Multicoloured.

1043	30c. Type **219**	55	35
1044	50c. Light Company private, 4th West India Regt, 1795	70	55
1045	70c. Drum Major, 3rd West India Regt, 1860	85	1·10
1046	$1 Privates in undress and working dress, 5th West India Regt, 1815	1·00	1·40
1047	$1.10 Troops from 1st and 2nd West India Regts in Review Order, 1874	1·25	1·75

1995. 50th Anniv of End of Second World War. As T **161** of Ascension. Multicoloured.

1048	10c. Barbadian Bren gun crew	60	50
1049	35c. Avro Type 683 Lancaster bomber	90	50
1050	55c. Supermarine Spitfire	1·25	75
1051	$2.50 "Davisian" (cargo liner)	3·00	4·50

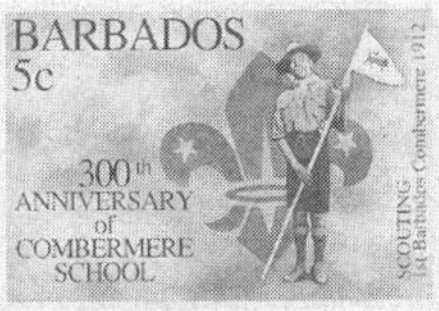

220 Member of 1st Barbados Combermere Scout Troop, 1912

1995. 300th Anniv of Combermere School. Mult.

1053	5c. Type **220**	25	40
1054	20c. Violin and sheet of music	45	30
1055	35c. Sir Frank Worrell (cricketer) (vert)	1·50	55
1056	$3 Painting by pupil	2·25	4·00

1995. 50th Anniv of United Nations. As T **213** of Bahamas. Multicoloured.

1058	30c. Douglas C-124 Globemaster (transport), Korea, 1950–53	70	40
1059	45c. Royal Navy Sea King helicopter	1·00	50
1060	$1.40 Westland Wessex helicopter, Cyprus, 1964	1·50	2·00
1061	$2 Sud Aviation SA 341 Gazelle helicopter, Cyprus, 1964	1·50	2·50

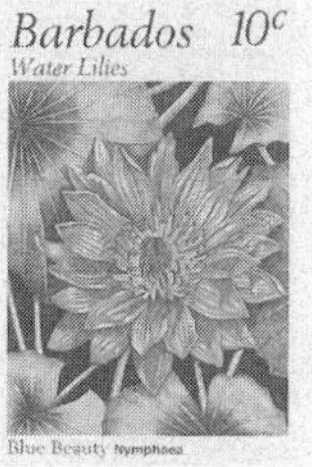

221 Blue Beauty

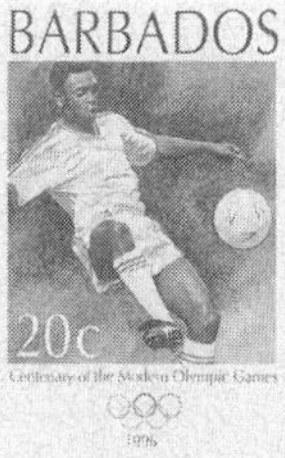

223 Football

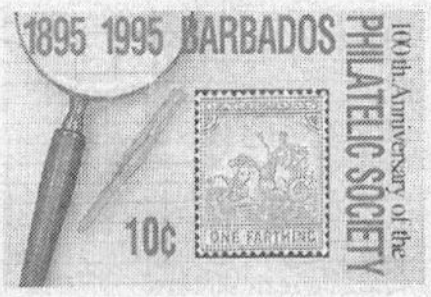

222 Magnifying Glass, Tweezers and 1896 Colony Seal ¼d. Stamp

1995. Water Lilies. Multicoloured.

1062	10c. Type **221**	35	30
1063	65c. White water lily	1·00	60
1064	70c. Sacred lotus	1·00	60
1065	$3 Water hyacinth	2·75	4·00

1996. Centenary of Barbados Philatelic Society. Each showing magnifying glass, tweezers and stamp. Multicoloured.

1066	10c. Type **222**	30	30
1067	55c. 1906 Tercentenary of Annexation 1d.	65	45
1068	$1.10 1920 Victory 1s.	1·25	1·40
1069	$1.40 1937 Coronation 2½d.	1·60	2·50

1996. Cent of Modern Olympic Games. Mult.

1070	20c. Type **223**	40	30
1071	30c. Relay running	45	30
1072	55c. Basketball	1·60	60
1073	$3 Rhythmic gymnastics	2·25	3·75

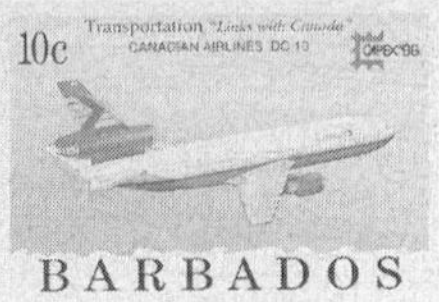

224 Douglas DC-10 of Canadian Airlines

1996. "CAPEX '96" International Stamp Exhibition, Toronto. Aircraft. Multicoloured.

1089	10c. Type **224**	40	30
1090	90c. Boeing 767 of Air Canada	1·00	80
1091	$1 Airbus Industrie A320 of Air Canada	1·00	1·10
1092	$1.40 Boeing 767 of Canadian Airlines	1·40	2·50

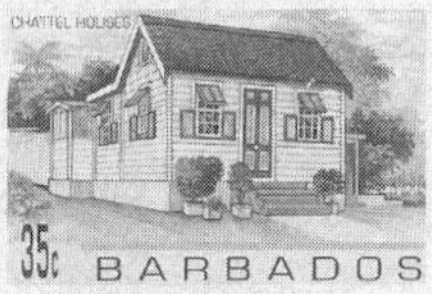

225 Chattel House

1996. Chattel Houses.

1093	**225**	35c. multicoloured	40	25
1094	–	70c. multicoloured	70	60
1095	–	$1.10 multicoloured	90	1·10
1096	–	$2 multicoloured	1·60	2·75

DESIGNS: 70c. to $2, Different houses.

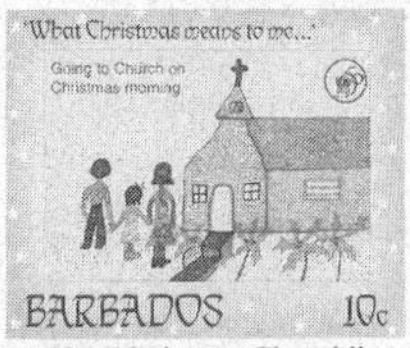

226 "Going to Church"

1996. Christmas. 50th Anniv of U.N.I.C.E.F. Children's Paintings. Multicoloured.

1097	10c. Type **226**	35	15
1098	30c. "The Tuk Band"	55	25
1099	55c. "Singing carols"	70	40
1100	$2.50 "Decorated house"	1·75	3·25

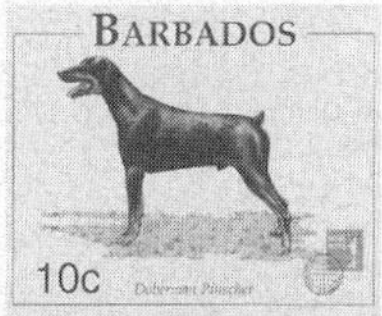

227 Doberman Pinscher

1997. "HONG KONG '97" International Stamp Exhibition. Dogs. Multicoloured.

1101	10c. Type **227**	55	40
1102	30c. German shepherd	1·00	40
1103	90c. Japanese akita	1·50	1·25
1104	$3 Irish red setter	3·50	5·00

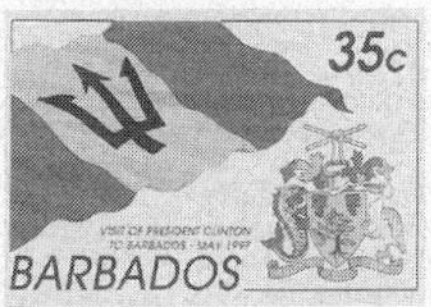

228 Barbados Flag and State Arms

1997. Visit of President Clinton of U.S.A. Multicoloured.

1105	35c. Type **228**	50	65
1106	90c. American flag and arms	70	85

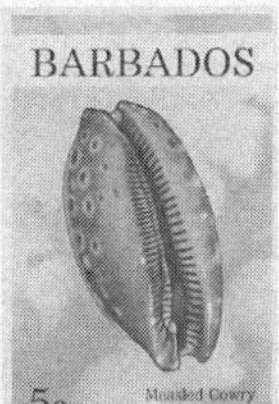

229 Measled Cowrie

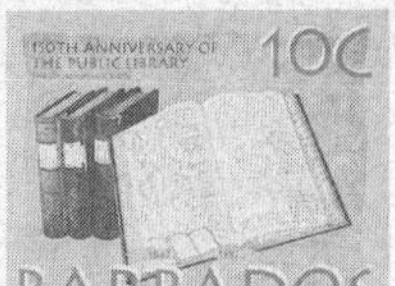

230 Lucas Manuscripts

1997. Shells. Multicoloured.

1107	5c. Type **229**	25	30
1108	35c. Trumpet triton	60	25
1109	90c. Scotch bonnet	1·25	90
1110	$2 West Indian murex	1·75	2·75

1997. 150th Anniv of the Public Library Service. Multicoloured.

1112	10c. Type **230**	20	15
1113	30c. Librarian reading to children	40	25
1114	70c. Mobile library van	80	60
1115	$3 Man using computer	2·25	3·50

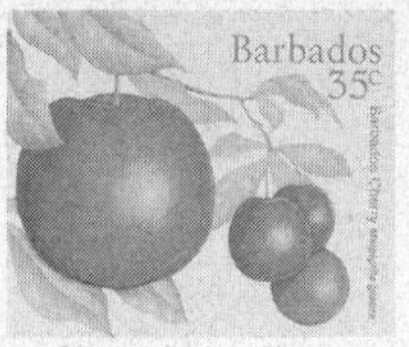

231 Barbados Cherry

1997. Local Fruits. Multicoloured.

1116	35c. Type **231**	35	30
1117	40c. Sugar apple	40	30
1118	$1.15 Soursop	95	1·00
1119	$1.70 Pawpaw	1·50	2·25

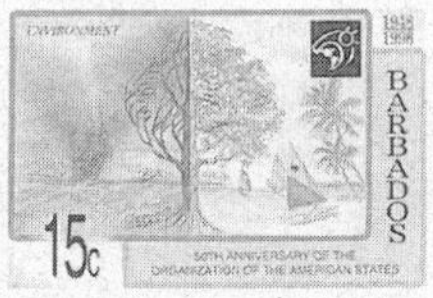

233 Environment Regeneration

1998. 50th Anniv of Organization of American States. Multicoloured.

1122	15c. Type **233**	20	15
1123	$1 Stilt dancing	70	70
1124	$2.50 Judge and figure of Justice	1·75	2·50

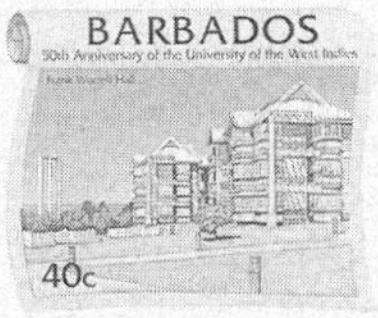

234 Frank Worrell Hall

1998. 50th Anniv of University of West Indies. Multicoloured.

1125	40c. Type **234**	30	30
1126	$1.15 Student graduating	1·00	1·10
1127	$1.40 50th anniversary plaque	1·25	1·75
1128	$1.75 Quadrangle	2·50	3·00

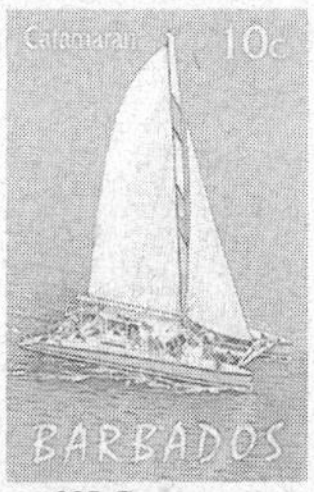

235 Catamaran

1998. Tourism. Multicoloured.

1129	10c. Type **235**	30	20
1130	45c. "Jolly Roger" (tourist schooner) (horiz)	75	35
1131	70c. "Atlantis" (tourist submarine) (horiz)	1·10	80
1132	$2 "Harbour Master" (ferry)	2·50	3·25

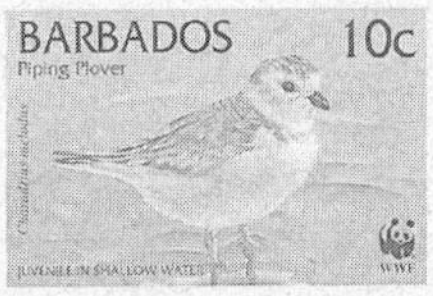

237 Juvenile Piping Plover in Shallow Water

1999. Endangered Species. Piping Plover. Mult.

1134	10c. Type **237**	20	20
1135	45c. Female with eggs	55	55
1136	50c. Male and female with fledglings	55	65
1137	70c. Male in shallow water	65	85

1999. 30th Anniv of First Manned Landing on Moon. As T **186** of Ascension. Multicoloured.

1138	40c. Astronaut in training	45	30
1139	45c. 1st stage separation	45	35
1140	$1.15 Lunar landing module	1·25	1·00
1141	$1.40 Docking with service module	1·40	1·75

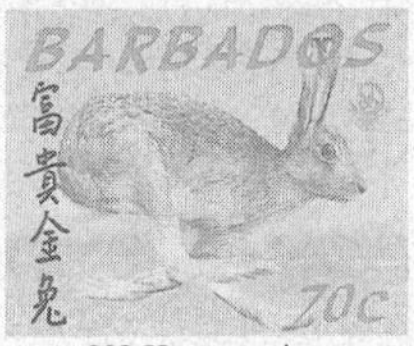

238 Hare running

1999. "China '99" International Stamp Exhibition, Beijing. Hares. Multicoloured.

1143	70c. Type **238**	1·10	1·10
1144	70c. Head of hare	1·10	1·10

1145	70c. Baby hares suckling	1·10	1·10
1146	70c. Hares boxing	1·10	1·10
1147	70c. Two leverets	1·10	1·10

Nos. 1143/7 were printed together, se-tenant, forming a composite background design.

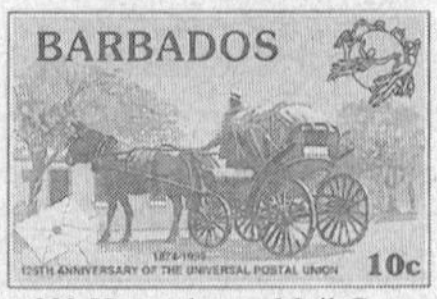

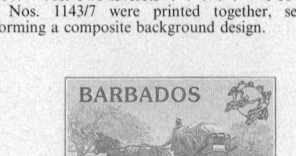

239 Horse-drawn Mail Cart

1999. 125th Anniv of U.P.U. Multicoloured.

1148	10c. Type **239**	30	15
1149	45c. Mail van	55	35
1150	$1.75 Sikorsky S42 flying boat	1·25	1·40
1151	$2 Computer and fax machine	1·25	1·75

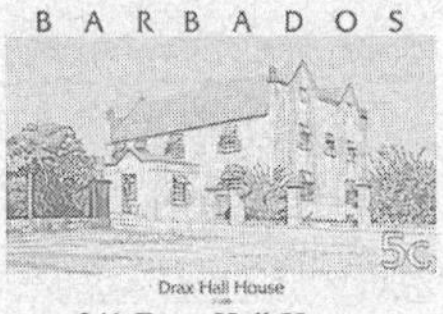

241 Drax Hall House

2000. Pride of Barbados. Multicoloured.

1153	5c. Type **241**	10	10
1154	10c. Reaping sugar cane (vert)	10	15
1155	40c. Needham's Point Lighthouse (vert)	30	35
1156	45c. Port St. Charles	30	35
1157	65c. Interior of Jewish synagogue	45	50
1158	70c. Bridgetown Port	50	55
1159	90c. Harrison's Cave	65	70
1160	$1.15 Villa Nova	80	85
1161	$1.40 Cricket at Kensington Oval	1·00	1·10
1162	$1.75 Sunbury House	1·25	1·40
1163	$2 Bethel Methodist Church	1·40	1·50
1164	$3 Peacock, Barbados Wildlife Reserve (vert)	2·10	2·25
1165	$5 Royal Westmoreland Golf Course (vert)	3·50	3·75
1166	$10 Grantley Adams International Airport	7·00	7·25

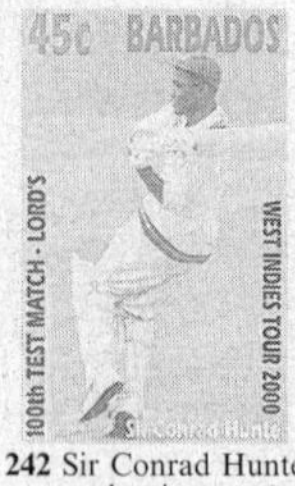

242 Sir Conrad Hunte batting

2000. West Indies Cricket Tour and 100th Test Match at Lord's. Multicoloured.

1167	45c. Type **242**	60	35
1168	90c. Malcolm Marshall bowling	1·25	75
1169	$2 Sir Garfield Sobers batting	2·00	2·50

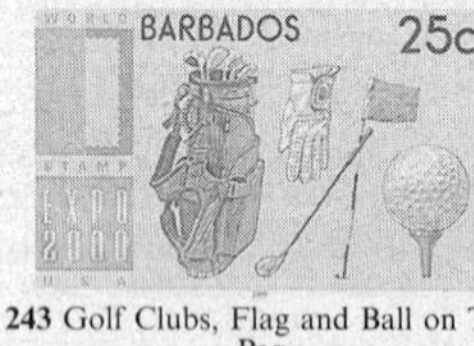

243 Golf Clubs, Flag and Ball on Tee Peg

2000. "EXPO 2000" World Stamp Exhibition, Anaheim, U.S.A. Golf. Multicoloured.

1171	25c. Type **243**	50	35
1172	40c. Golfer teeing off on top of giant ball	70	35
1173	$1.40 Golfer on green	1·50	1·60
1174	$2 Golfer putting	2·00	2·50

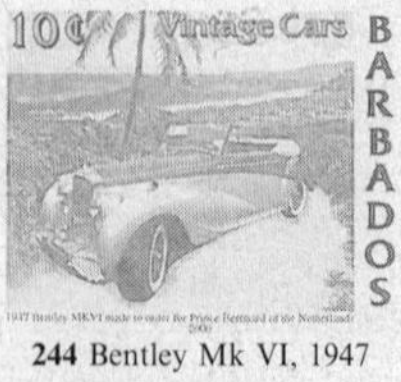

244 Bentley Mk VI, 1947

2000. Vintage Cars. Multicoloured.

1175	10c. Type **244**	25	15
1176	30c. Vanden Plas Princess, 1964	50	25
1177	90c. Austin Atlantic, 1952	1·00	70
1178	$3 Bentley Special, 1950	3·00	3·50

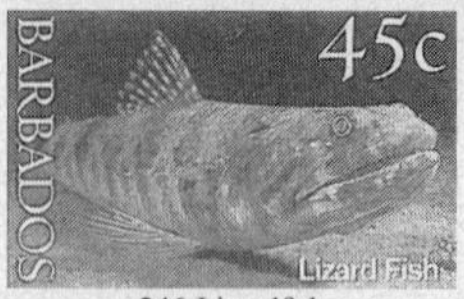

246 Lizardfish

2001. Deep Sea Creatures. Multicoloured.

1180	45c. Type **246**	30	35
1181	45c. Golden-tailed moray	30	35
1182	45c. Black-barred soldierfish	30	35
1183	45c. Golden zoanthid	30	35
1184	45c. Sponge brittle star	30	35
1185	45c. Magnificent feather duster	30	35
1186	45c. Bearded fireworm	30	35
1187	45c. Lima shell	30	35
1188	45c. Yellow tube sponge	30	35

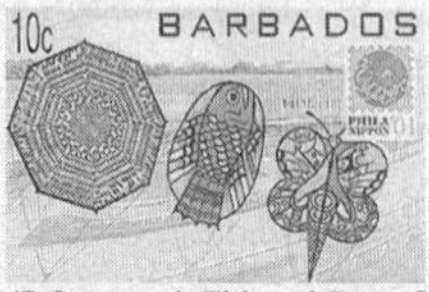

247 Octagonal, Fish and Butterfly Kites

2001. "Philanippon '01" International Stamp Exhibition, Tokyo. Kites. Multicoloured.

1189	10c. Type **247**	10	15
1190	65c. Hexagonal, bird and geometric kites	45	45
1191	$1.40 Policeman, Japanese and butterfly kites	1·00	1·10
1192	$1.75 Anti-drug, geisha and eagle kites	1·25	1·40

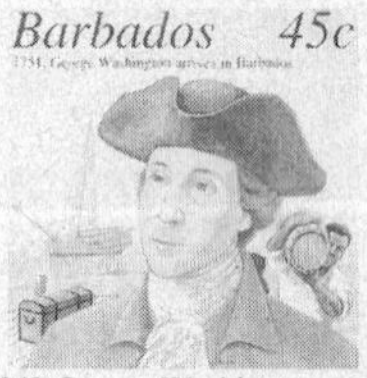

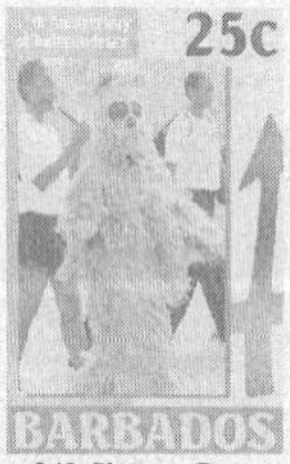

248 George Washington on the Quay, 1751 **249** Shaggy Bear (Traditional Carnival Character)

2001. 250th Anniv of George Washington's Visit to Barbados. Multicoloured.

1193	45c. Type **248**	25	30
1194	50c. George Washington in Barbados	25	30
1195	$1.15 George Washington superimposed on Declaration of Independence, 1776	60	65
1196	$2.50 Needham's Point Fort, 1750	1·25	1·40

2001. 35th Anniv of Independence. Multicoloured.

1198	25c. Type **249**	15	20
1199	45c. Tuk band	25	30
1200	$1 Landship Dancers	50	55
1201	$2 Guitar, saxophone and words of National Anthem	1·00	1·10

2002. Golden Jubilee. As T **200** of Ascension.

1202	10c. black, violet and gold	10	10
1203	70c. multicoloured	35	40
1204	$1 black, violet and gold	50	55
1205	$1.40 multicoloured	70	75

DESIGNS: 10c. Princess Elizabeth; 70c. Queen Elizabeth in cerise hat; $1 Queen Elizabeth wearing Imperial State Crown, Coronation 1953; $1.40, Queen Elizabeth in purple feathered hat.

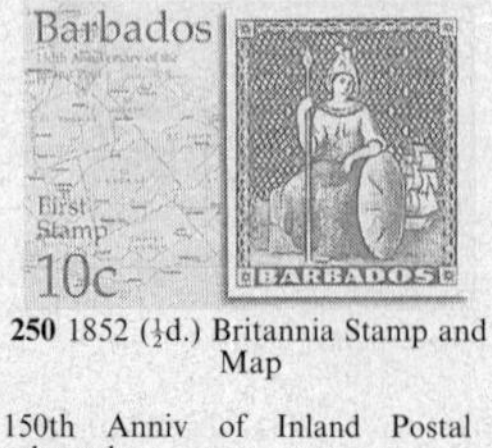

250 1852 (½d.) Britannia Stamp and Map

2002. 150th Anniv of Inland Postal Service. Multicoloured.

1207	10c. Type **250**	10	10
1208	45c. Early twentieth-century postman delivering letter	30	35
1209	$1.15 *Esk* (mail steamer)	80	85
1210	$2 B.W.I.A. Tri-Star airliner	1·00	1·50

POSTAGE DUE STAMPS

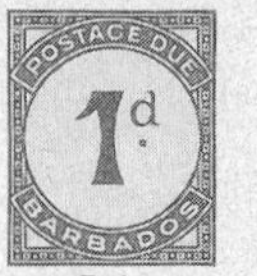

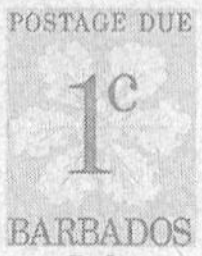

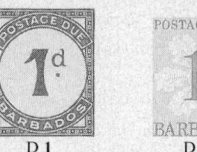

D 1 D 2

1934.

D1	D 1	½d. green	1·25	7·50
D2		1d. black	1·25	1·25
D3		3d. red	20·00	18·00

1950. Values in cents.

D4a	D 1	1c. green	30	3·00
D8		2c. black	30	5·00
D9		6c. red	50	7·00

1976.

D14a	D 2	1c. mauve and pink	10	10
D15a	–	2c. blue and light blue	10	10
D16a	–	5c. brown and yellow	10	15
D17a	–	10c. blue and lilac	15	20
D18a	–	25c. deep green and green	20	30
D19	–	$1 red and deep red	75	1·25

DESIGNS: Nos. D15/19 show different floral backgrounds.

BARBUDA Pt. 1

One of the Leeward Is., Br. W. Indies. Dependency of Antigua. Used stamps of Antigua and Leeward Is. concurrently. The issues from 1968 are also valid for use in Antigua. From 1971 to 1973 the stamps of Antigua were again used.

1922. 12 pence = 1 shilling;
20 shillings = 1 pound.
1951. 100 cents = 1 West Indian dollar.

1922. Stamps of Leeward Islands optd **BARBUDA**.

1	**11**	½d. green	1·50	8·50
2		1d. red	1·25	8·50
3		2d. grey	1·50	7·00
4		2½d. blue	1·25	7·50
9		3d. purple on yellow	1·75	12·00
5		6d. purple	2·00	18·00
10		1s. black on green	1·50	8·00
6		2s. purple and blue on blue	14·00	48·00
7		3s. green and violet	32·00	75·00
8		4s. black and red	38·00	75·00
11		5s. green and red on yellow	65·00	£130

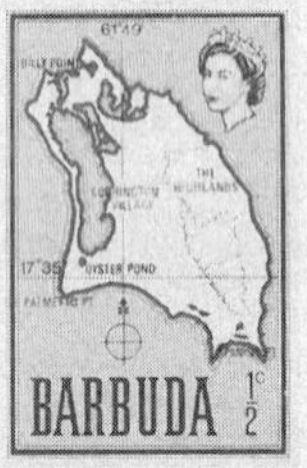

2 Map of Barbuda

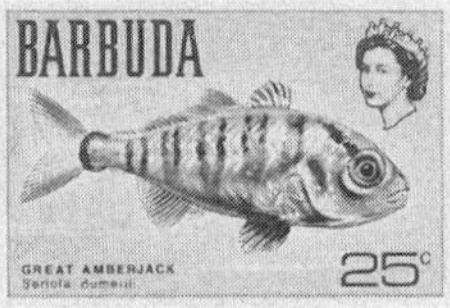

3 Greater Amberjack

1968.

12	**2**	½c. brown, black and pink	20	1·00
13		1c. orange, black and flesh	30	10
14		2c. brown, red and rose	50	10
15		3c. brown, yellow and lemon	30	10
16		4c. black, green & lt green	50	90
17		5c. turquoise and black	30	10
18		6c. black, purple and lilac	40	1·00
19		10c. black, blue and cobalt	30	30
20		15c. black, green & turq	30	1·25
20a	–	20c. multicoloured	1·50	2·00
21	**3**	25c. multicoloured	60	25
22	–	35c. multicoloured	80	25
23	–	50c. multicoloured	80	55
24	–	75c. multicoloured	80	80
25	–	$1 multicoloured	85	2·00
26	–	$2.50 multicoloured	1·50	5·00
27	–	$5 multicoloured	3·75	7·50

DESIGNS: As T **3**—20c. Great barracuda; 35c. French angelfish; 50c. Porkfish; 75c. Princess parrotfish; $1, Long-spined squirrelfish; $2.50, Bigeye; $5, Blue chromis.

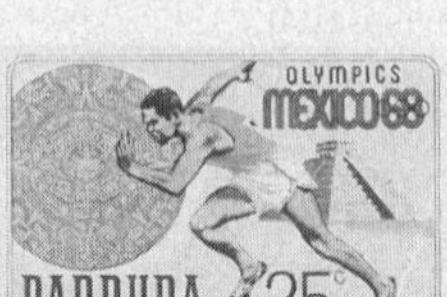

10 Sprinting and Aztec Sun-stone

1968. Olympic Games. Mexico. Multicoloured.

28	25c. Type **10**	45	25
29	35c. High-jumping and Aztec statue	50	25
30	75c. Dinghy-racing and Aztec lion mask	55	45

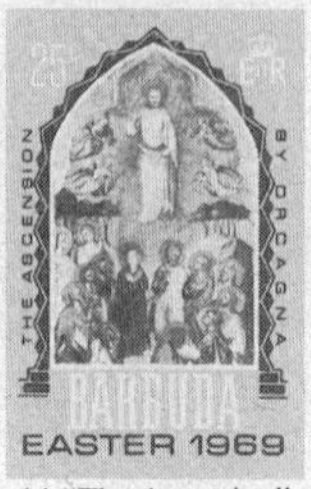

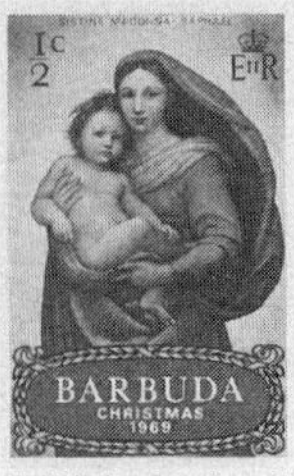

14 "The Ascension" (Orcagna) **18** "Sistine Madonna" (Raphael)

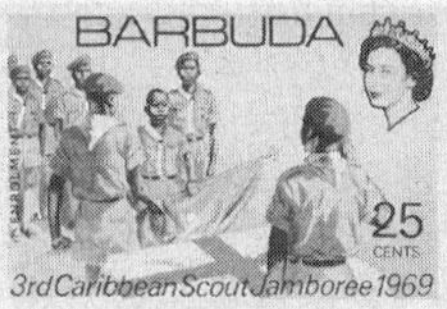

15 Scout Enrolment Ceremony

1969. Easter Commemoration.

32	**14**	25c. black and blue	15	45
33		35c. black and red	15	50
34		75c. black and lilac	15	55

1969. 3rd Caribbean Scout Jamboree. Multicoloured.

35	25c. Type **15**	45	55
36	35c. Scouts around camp fire	60	65
37	75c. Sea Scouts rowing boat	75	85

1969. Christmas.

38	**18**	½c. multicoloured	10	10
39		25c. multicoloured	10	15
40		35c. multicoloured	10	20
41		35c. multicoloured	20	35

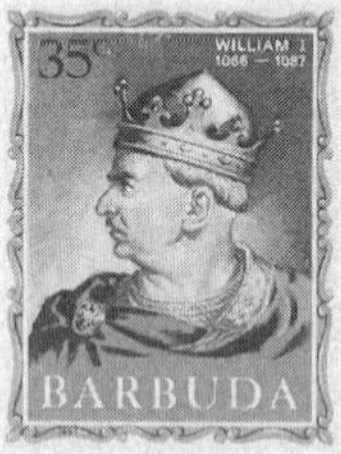

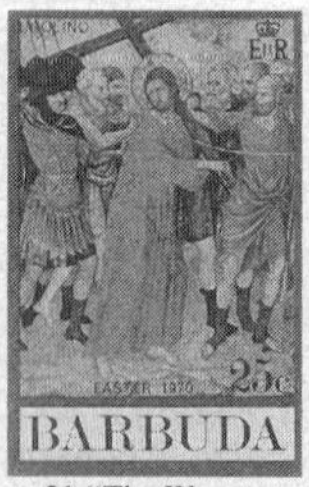

19 William I (1066–87) **21** "The Way to Calvary" (Ugolino)

1970. English Monarchs. Multicoloured.

42	35c. Type **19**	30	15
43	35c. William II (1087–1100)	10	15
44	35c. Henry I (1100–35)	10	15
45	35c. Stephen (1135–54)	10	15
46	35c. Henry II (1154–89)	10	15
47	35c. Richard I (1189–99)	10	15
48	35c. John (1199–1216)	10	15
49	35c. Henry III (1216–72)	10	15
50	35c. Edward I (1272–1307)	10	15
51	35c. Edward II (1307–27)	10	15
52	35c. Edward III (1327–77)	10	15
53	35c. Richard II (1377–99)	10	15
54	35c. Henry IV (1399–1413)	10	15
55	35c. Henry V (1413–22)	10	15
56	35c. Henry VI (1422–61)	10	15
57	35c. Edward IV (1462–83)	10	15
58	35c. Edward V (April–June 1483)	10	15
59	35c. Richard III (1483–85)	10	15
60	35c. Henry VII (1485–1509)	10	15
61	35c. Henry VIII (1509–47)	10	15
62	35c. Edward VI (1547–53)	10	15
63	35c. Lady Jane Grey (1553)	10	15
64	35c. Mary I (1553–8)	10	15
65	35c. Elizabeth I (1558–1603)	10	15
66	35c. James I (1603–25)	10	15
67	35c. Charles I (1625–49)	10	15
68	35c. Charles II (1649–1685)	10	15
69	35c. James II (1685–1688)	10	15
70	35c. William III (1689–1702)	10	15
71	35c. Mary II (1689–1694)	10	15
72	35c. Anne (1702–1714)	15	15
73	35c. George I (1714–1727)	15	15
74	35c. George II (1727–1760)	15	15
75	35c. George III (1760–1820)	15	15
76	35c. George IV (1820–1830)	15	15
77	35c. William IV (1830–1837)	15	60
78	35c. Victoria (1837–1901)	15	60

See also Nos. 710/5.

1970. No. 12 surch **20c**.

79	**2**	20c. on ½c. brn, blk & pink	10	20

1970. Easter. Paintings. Multicoloured.

80	25c. Type **21**	15	30
81	35c. "The Deposition from the Cross" (Ugolino)	15	30
82	75c. Crucifix (The Master of St. Francis)	15	35

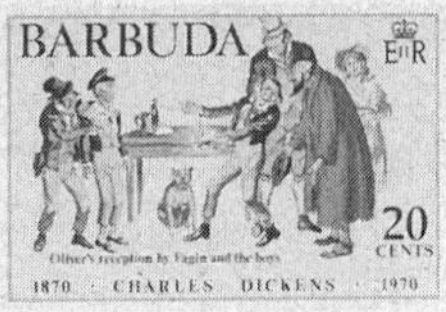

22 Oliver is introduced to Fagin ("Oliver Twist")

1970. Death Centenary of Charles Dickens. Mult.

83		20c. Type **22**	20	25
84		75c. Dickens and scene from "The Old Curiosity Shop"	45	65

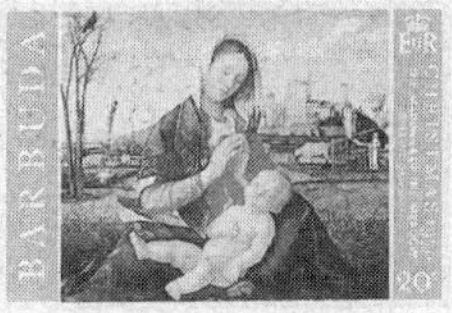

23 "Madonna of the Meadows" (G. Bellini)

1970. Christmas. Multicoloured.

85		20c. Type **23**	10	25
86		50c. "Madonna, Child and Angels" (from Wilton diptych)	15	30
87		75c. "The Nativity" (della Francesca)	15	35

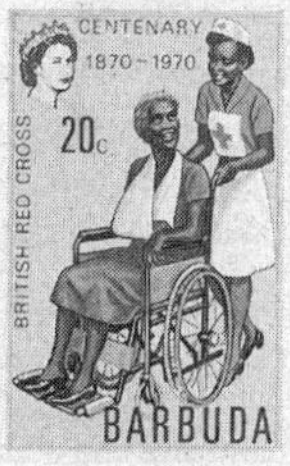

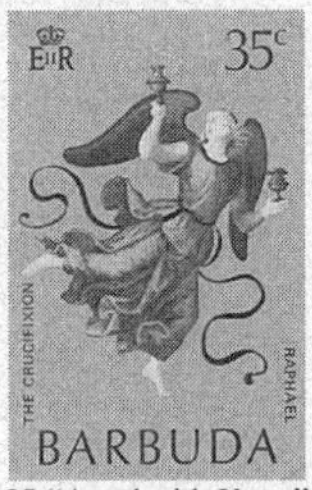

24 Nurse with Patient in Wheelchair **25** "Angel with Vases"

1970. Centenary of British Red Cross. Multicoloured.

88		20c. Type **24**	15	30
89		35c. Nurse giving patient magazines (horiz)	20	40
90		75c. Nurse and mother weighing baby (horiz)	25	70

1971. Easter. "Mond" Crucifixion by Raphael. Multicoloured.

91		35c. Type **25**	15	75
92		50c. "Christ crucified"	15	85
93		75c. "Angel with vase"	15	90

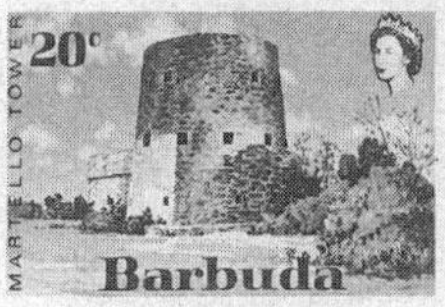

26 Martello Tower

1971. Tourism. Multicoloured.

94		20c. Type **26**	15	25
95		25c. "Sailfish" dinghy	25	30
96		50c. Hotel bungalows	25	35
97		75c. Government House and Mystery Stone	25	40

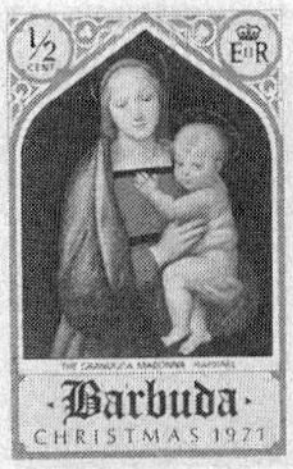

27 "The Granducal Madonna" (Raphael)

1971. Christmas. Multicoloured.

98		½c. Type **27**	10	10
99		35c. "The Ansidei Madonna" (Raphael)	10	20
100		50c. "The Madonna and Child" (Botticelli)	15	25
101		75c. "The Madonna of the Trees" (Bellini)	15	30

Four stamps to commemorate the 500th Birth Anniv of Durer were prepared in late 1971, but their issue was not authorised by the Antigua Government.

1973. Royal Wedding. Nos. 370/1 of Antigua optd **BARBUDA** twice.

102	**106**	25c. multicoloured	3·25	2·00
103		$2 multicoloured	1·25	1·25

1973. Ships. Nos. 269/85 of Antigua optd **BARBUDA**.

116	**92**	½c. multicoloured	15	20
104	–	1c. multicoloured	15	30
105	–	2c. multicoloured	25	30
117	–	3c. multicoloured	25	25
106	–	4c. multicoloured	30	30
107	–	5c. multicoloured	40	40
108	–	6c. multicoloured	40	40
109	–	10c. multicoloured	45	45
118	–	15c. multicoloured	45	50
110	–	20c. multicoloured	55	60
111	–	25c. multicoloured	55	60
112	–	35c. multicoloured	55	70
113	–	50c. multicoloured	55	70
114	–	75c. multicoloured	55	70
119	–	$1 multicoloured	55	70
115	–	$2.50 multicoloured	75	1·50
121	–	$5 multicoloured	1·10	2·50

1973. Military Uniforms. Nos. 353, 355 and 357 of Antigua optd **BARBUDA**.

122		½c. multicoloured	10	10
123		20c. multicoloured	15	10
124		75c. multicoloured	40	15

1973. Carnival. Nos. 360/2 of Antigua optd **BARBUDA**.

126		20c. multicoloured	10	10
127		35c. multicoloured	10	10
128		75c. multicoloured	20	25

1973. Christmas. Nos. 364/68 of Antigua optd **BARBUDA**.

130	**105**	3c. multicoloured	10	10
131	–	5c. multicoloured	10	10
132	–	20c. multicoloured	10	10
133	–	35c. multicoloured	15	15
134	–	$1 multicoloured	30	30

1973. Honeymoon Visit. Nos. 373/4 of Antigua additionally optd **BARBUDA**.

136		35c. multicoloured	30	20
137		$2 multicoloured	70	60

1974. University of West Indies. Nos. 376/9 of Antigua optd **BARBUDA**.

139		5c. multicoloured	10	10
140		20c. multicoloured	10	10
141		35c. multicoloured	15	15
142		75c. multicoloured	15	15

1974. Military Uniforms. Nos. 380/4 of Antigua optd **BARBUDA**.

143		½c. multicoloured	10	10
144		10c. multicoloured	15	10
145		20c. multicoloured	25	10
146		35c. multicoloured	25	10
147		75c. multicoloured	45	25

1974. Centenary of U.P.U. (1st issue). Nos. 386/92 of Antigua optd with either a or b. (a) **BARBUDA 13 JULY 1992**.

148		½c. multicoloured	10	10
150		1c. multicoloured	10	10
152		2c. multicoloured	20	15
154		5c. multicoloured	50	15
156		20c. multicoloured	40	70
158		35c. multicoloured	80	1·50
160		$1 multicoloured	2·25	4·00

(b) **BARBUDA 15 SEPT. 1874 G.P.U.** ("General Postal Union").

149		½c. multicoloured	10	10
151		1c. multicoloured	10	10
153		2c. multicoloured	20	15
155		5c. multicoloured	50	15
157		20c. multicoloured	40	70
159		35c. multicoloured	80	1·50
161		$1 multicoloured	2·25	4·00

1974. Antiguan Steel Bands. Nos. 394/97 of Antigua optd **BARBUDA**.

163		5c. deep red, red and black	10	10
164		20c. brown, lt brown & blk	10	10
165		35c. light green, green and black	10	10
166		75c. deep blue, blue and black	20	20

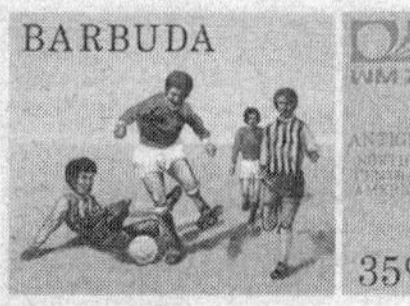

39 Footballers

1974. World Cup Football Championships (1st issue).

168	**39**	35c. multicoloured	10	10
169	–	$1.20 multicoloured	25	35
170	–	$2.50 multicoloured	35	50

DESIGNS: $1.20, $2.50, Footballers in action similar to Type **39**.

1974. World Cup Football Championships (2nd issue). Nos. 399/402 of Antigua optd **BARBUDA**.

172	**111**	5c. multicoloured	10	10
173	–	35c. multicoloured	20	10
174	–	75c. multicoloured	25	15
175	–	$1 multicoloured	25	25

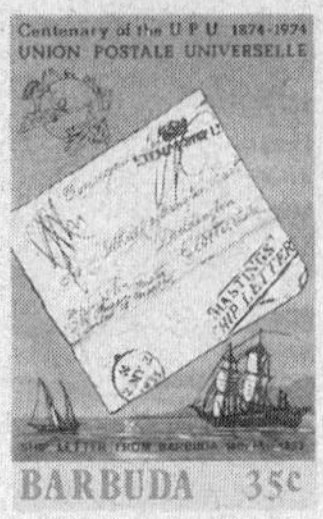

41 Ship Letter of 1833

1974. Cent of Universal Postal Union (2nd issue). Multicoloured.

177		35c. Type **41**	10	10
178		$1.20 Stamps and postmarks of 1922	25	50
179		$2.50 Britten Norman Islander mailplane over map of Barbuda	35	75

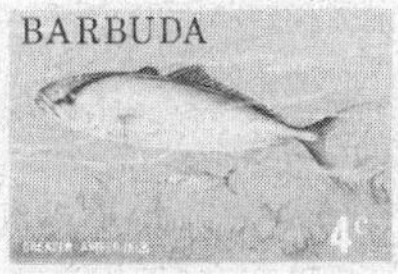

42 Greater Amberjack

1974. Multicoloured.

181		½c. Oleander, Rose Bay	10	40
182		1c. Blue petrea	15	40
183		2c. Poinsettia	15	40
184		3c. Cassia tree	15	40
185		4c. Type **42**	1·60	40
186		5c. Holy Trinity School	15	15
187		6c. Snorkeling	15	30
188		10c. Pilgrim Holiness Church	15	20
189		15c. New Cottage Hospital	15	20
190		20c. Post Office and Treasury	15	20
191		25c. Island jetty and boats	30	30
192		35c. Martello Tower	30	30
193		50c. Warden's House	30	30
194		75c. Britten Norman Islander aircraft	1·75	1·00
195		$1 Tortoise	70	80
196		$2.50 Spiny lobster	1·00	1·75
197		$5 Magnificent frigate bird	3·50	2·50
197b		$10 Hibiscus	1·50	4·50

The 50c. to $1 are 39×25 mm., $2.50 and $5 45×29 mm., $10 34×48 mm. The ½ to 3c., 25c. and $10 are vertical.

1974. Birth Centenary of Sir Winston Churchill (1st issue). Nos. 408/11 of Antigua optd **BARBUDA**.

198	**113**	5c. multicoloured	15	10
199	–	35c. multicoloured	25	15
200	–	75c. multicoloured	40	45
201	–	$1 multicoloured	75	70

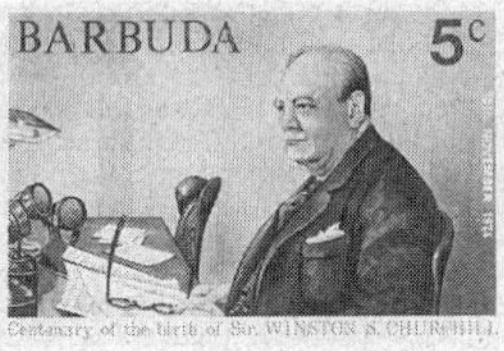

43 Churchill making Broadcast

1974. Birth Centenary of Sir Winston Churchill (2nd issue). Multicoloured.

203		5c. Type **43**	10	10
204		35c. Churchill and Chartwell	10	10
205		75c. Churchill painting	20	20
206		$1 Churchill making "V" sign	25	30

1974. Christmas. Nos. 413/20 of Antigua optd **BARBUDA**.

208	**114**	½c. multicoloured	10	10
209	–	1c. multicoloured	10	10
210	–	2c. multicoloured	10	10
211	–	3c. multicoloured	10	10
212	–	5c. multicoloured	10	10
213	–	20c. multicoloured	10	10
214	–	35c. multicoloured	15	15
215	–	75c. multicoloured	30	30

1975. Nelson's Dockyard. Nos. 427/31 of Antigua optd **BARBUDA**.

217	**116**	5c. multicoloured	15	15
218	–	15c. multicoloured	40	25
219	–	35c. multicoloured	55	35
220	–	50c. multicoloured	60	50
221	–	$1 multicoloured	65	80

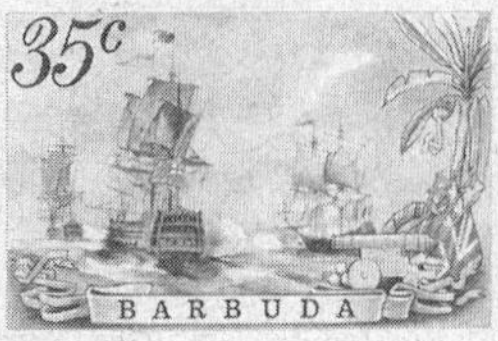

45 Ships of the Line

1975. Sea Battles. Battle of the Saints, 1782. Mult.

223		35c. Type **45**	50	65
224		50c. H.M.S. "Ramillies"	50	75
225		75c. "Bonhomme Richard" (American frigate) firing broadside	60	90
226		95c. "L'Orient" (French ship of the line) burning	60	1·25

1975. "Apollo–Soyuz" Space Project. No. 197 optd **U.S.A-U.S.S.R SPACE COOPERATION 1975** with **APOLLO** (No. 227) or **SOYUZ** (No. 228).

227		$5 multicoloured	3·25	6·00
228		$5 multicoloured	3·25	6·00

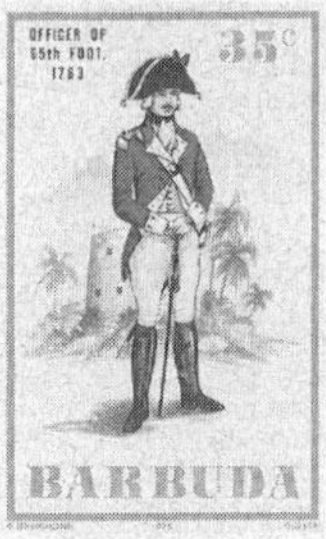

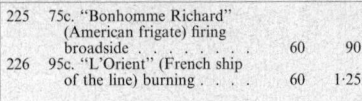

47 Officer, 65th Foot, 1763

1975. Military Uniforms. Multicoloured.

229		35c. Type **47**	75	75
230		50c. Grenadier, 27th Foot 1701–10	90	90
231		75c. Officer, 21st Foot, 1793–6	1·00	1·00
232		95c. Officer, Royal Regiment of Artillery, 1800	1·25	1·25

1975. 25th Anniv of United Nations. Nos. 203/6 optd **30TH ANNIVERSARY UNITED NATIONS 1945–1975**.

233	**43**	5c. multicoloured	10	10
234	–	35c. multicoloured	10	15
235	–	75c. multicoloured	15	20
236	–	$1 multicoloured	20	30

1975. Christmas. Nos. 457/64 of Antigua optd **BARBUDA**.

237	**121**	½c. multicoloured	10	10
238	–	1c. multicoloured	10	10
239	–	2c. multicoloured	10	10
240	–	3c. multicoloured	10	10
241	–	5c. multicoloured	10	10
242	–	10c. multicoloured	10	10
243	–	35c. multicoloured	15	20
244	–	$2 multicoloured	60	1·00

1975. World Cup Cricket Winners. Nos. 466/8 of Antigua optd **BARBUDA**.

246	**122**	5c. multicoloured	90	1·00
247	–	35c. multicoloured	1·75	2·00
248	–	$2 multicoloured	3·25	4·25

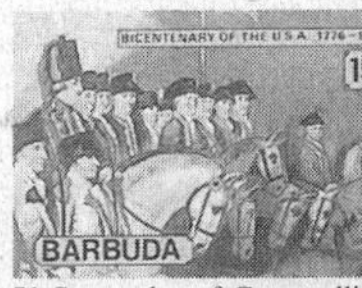

51 Surrender of Cornwallis at Yorktown (Trumbull)

1976. Bicentenary of American Revolution.

249	**51**	15c. multicoloured	10	15
250	–	15c. multicoloured	10	15
251	–	15c. multicoloured	10	15
252	–	35c. multicoloured	10	15
253	–	35c. multicoloured	10	15
254	–	35c. multicoloured	10	15
255	–	$1 multicoloured	15	25
256	–	$1 multicoloured	15	25
257	–	$1 multicoloured	15	25
258	–	$2 multicoloured	25	40
259	–	$2 multicoloured	25	40
260	–	$2 multicoloured	25	40

DESIGNS—As Type **51**: Nos. 249/51; 252/4, The Battle of Princeton; 255/7, Surrender of General Burgoyne at Saratoga; 258/60, Jefferson presenting Declaration of Independence.

Type **51** shows the left-hand stamp of the 15c. design.

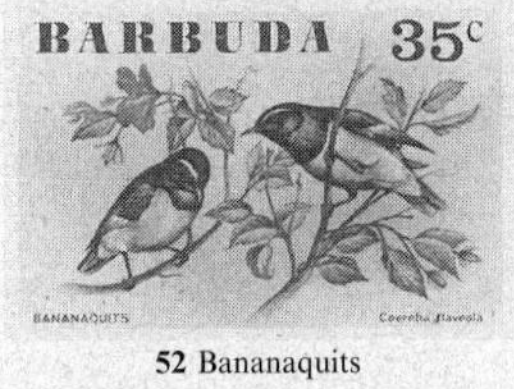

52 Bananaquits

1976. Birds. Multicoloured.

262		35c. Type **52**	70	50
263		50c. Blue-hooded euphonia	70	60
264		75c. Royal tern	70	80
265		95c. Killdeer plover ("Killdeer")	80	85
266		$1.25 Shiney-headed cowbird ("Glossy Cowbird")	85	1·00
267		$2 American purple gallinule ("Purple Gallinule")	90	1·25

1976. Royal Visit to the U.S.A. Nos. 249/60 additionally inscr "H.M. QUEEN ELIZABETH ROYAL VISIT 6TH JULY 1976 H.R.H. DUKE OF EDINBURGH".

268		15c. multicoloured	10	15

269 15c. multicoloured 10 15
270 15c. multicoloured 10 15
271 35c. multicoloured 10 20
272 35c. multicoloured 10 20
273 35c. multicoloured 10 20
274 $1 multicoloured 15 50
275 $1 multicoloured 15 50
276 $1 multicoloured 15 50
277 $2 multicoloured 25 70
278 $2 multicoloured 25 70
279 $2 multicoloured 25 70

1976. Christmas. Nos. 514/18 of Antigua optd **BARBUDA**.
281 **128** 8c. multicoloured 10 10
282 – 10c. multicoloured 10 10
283 – 15c. multicoloured 10 10
284 – 50c. multicoloured 15 15
285 – $1 multicoloured 25 30

1976. Olympic Games, Montreal. Nos. 495/501 of Antigua optd **BARBUDA**.
286 **125** ½c. brown, yellow and black 10 10
287 – 1c. violet and black . . . 10 10
288 – 2c. green and black . . . 10 10
289 – 15c. blue and black . . . 10 10
290 – 30c. brown, yellow & blk 10 10
291 – $1 orange, red and black 20 20
292 – $2 red and black 35 35

55 P.O. Tower, Telephones and Alexander Graham Bell

1977. Cent of First Telephone Transmission. Mult.
294 75c. Type **55** 15 35
295 $1.25 T.V. transmission by satellite 20 55
296 $2 Globe showing satellite transmission scheme . . . 30 75

56 St. Margaret's Church, Westminster

1977. Silver Jubilee (1st issue). Multicoloured.
298 75c. Type **56** 10 15
299 75c. Street decorations . . . 10 15
300 75c. Westminster Abbey . . . 10 15
301 $1.25 Household Cavalry . . 15 20
302 $1.25 Coronation Coach . . 15 20
303 $1.25 Postillions 15 20

1977. Nos. 469/86 of Antigua optd **BARBUDA**.
305 ½c. Antillean crested hummingbird 20 20
306 1c. Imperial amazon ("Imperial Parrot") 30 20
307 2c. Zenaida dove 30 20
308 3c. Loggerhead kingbird . . . 30 20
309 4c. Red-necked pigeon . . . 30 20
310 5c. Rufous throated solitaire 30 20
311 6c. Orchid tree 30 20
312 10c. Bougainvillea 30 20
313 15c. Geiger tree 30 25
314 20c. Flamboyant 30 25
315 25c. Hibiscus 30 25
316 35c. Flame of the Wood . . 35 30
317 50c. Cannon at Fort James 40 40
318 75c. Premier's Office 40 40
319 $1 Potworks Dam 50 60
320 $2.50 Irrigation scheme . . . 1·00 1·60
321 $5 Government House . . . 1·50 3·25
322 $10 Coolidge Airport . . . . 4·00 7·50

1977. Silver Jubilee (2nd issue). Nos. 526/30 of Antigua optd **BARBUDA**. (a) Ordinary gum.
323 10c. Royal Family 10 15
324 30c. Royal visit, 1966 . . . . 10 20
325 50c. The Queen enthroned . . 15 30
326 90c. The Queen after Coronation 15 40
327 $2.50 The Queen and Prince Charles . . . . 45 1·25

(b) Self-adhesive.
329 50c. Queen after Coronation 40 70
330 $5 The Queen and Prince Philip . . . . 3·00 9·00

1977. Caribbean Scout Jamboree, Jamaica. Nos. 534/40 of Antigua optd **BARBUDA**.
331 ½c. Type **131** 10 10
332 1c. Hiking 10 10
333 2c. Rock-climbing 10 10
334 10c. Cutting logs 10 10
335 30c. Map and sign reading 30 40
336 50c. First aid 35 65
337 $2 Rafting . . . . 75 2·25

1977. 21st Anniv of Carnival. Nos. 542/46 of Antigua optd **BARBUDA**.
339 10c. Type **312** 10 10
340 30c. Carnival Queen 10 10
341 50c. Butterfly costume . . . 15 20
342 90c. Queen of the Band . . . 20 35
343 $1 Calypso King and Queen 25 45

61 Royal Yacht "Britannia"

1977. Royal Visit (1st issue). Multicoloured.
345 50c. Type **61** 10 20
346 $1.50 Jubilee emblem 25 35
347 $2.50 Union Jack and flag of Antigua 35 55

1977. Royal Visit (2nd issue). Nos. 548/52 of Antigua optd **BARBUDA**.
349A 10c. Royal Family 10 10
350B 30c. Queen Elizabeth and Prince Philip in car . . . 10 15
351B 50c. Queen enthroned . . . 15 20
352B 90c. Queen after Coronation 20 30
353B $2.50 The Queen and Prince Charles 45 80

1977. Christmas. Nos. 554/60 of Antigua optd **BARBUDA**.
355 ½c. Type **134** 10 10
356 1c. Crivelli 10 10
357 2c. Lotto 10 10
358 8c. Pontormo 10 10
359 10c. Tura (different) 10 10
360 25c. Lotto (different) 15 10
361 $2 Crivelli (different) 45 45

64 Airship LZ-1

1977. Special Events, 1977. Multicoloured.
363 75c. Type **64** 30 30
364 75c. German battleship and German Navy airship L-31 30 30
365 75c. "Graf Zeppelin" in hangar 30 30
366 75c. Gondola of military airship 30 30
367 95c. Sputnik 1 . . . . 35 35
368 95c. Vostok rocket 35 35
369 95c. Voskhod rocket 35 35
370 95c. Space walk 35 35
371 $1.25 Fuelling for flight . . . 40 45
372 $1.25 Leaving New York . . 40 45
373 $1.25 "Spirit of St. Louis" . . 40 45
374 $1.25 Welcome to England 40 45
375 $2 Lion of England 50 70
376 $2 Unicorn of Scotland . . . 50 70
377 $2 Yale of Beaufort 50 70
378 $2 Falcon of Plantagenets . . 50 70
379 $5 "Daniel in the Lion's Den" (Rubens) . . . . . 50 1·25
380 $5 Different detail of painting 50 1·25
381 $5 Different detail of painting 50 1·25
382 $5 Different detail of painting 50 1·25
EVENTS: 75c. 75th anniv of navigable airships; 95c. 20th anniv of U.S.S.R. space programme; $1.25, 50th anniv of Lindbergh's transatlantic flight; $2 Silver Jubilee of Queen Elizabeth II; $5 400th birth anniv of Rubens.
Nos. 379/82 form a composite design.

1978. 10th Anniv of Statehood. Nos. 562/6 of Antigua optd **BARBUDA**.
384 10c. Type **135** 10 10
385 15c. State flag 15 10
386 50c. Police band . . . . . . 1·25 70
387 90c. Premier V. C. Bird . . . 20 40
388 $2 State Coat of Arms . . . 40 80

66 "Pieta" (sculpture) (detail)

1978. Easter. Paintings and Sculptures by Michelangelo. Multicoloured.
390 75c. Type **66** 15 15
391 95c. "The Holy Family" . . 15 20
392 $1.25 "Libyan sibyl" (from the Sistine Chapel) 15 35
393 $2 "The Flood" (from the Sistine Chapel) 20 45

1978. 75th Anniv of Powered Flight. Nos. 568/74 of Antigua optd **BARBUDA**.
395 ½c. Wright Glider No. III, 1902 . . . . 10 10
396 1c. Wright Flyer I, 1903 . . . 10 10
397 2c. Launch system and engine 10 10
398 10c. Orville Wright (vert) . . 10 10
399 50c. Wright Flyer III, 1905 25 20
400 90c. Wilbur Wright (vert) . . 35 25
401 $2 Wright Type B, 1910 . . . 60 45

1978. Sailing Week. Nos. 576/79 of Antigua optd **BARBUDA**.
403 10c. Sunfish regatta 20 10
404 50c. Fishing and work boat race 40 25
405 90c. Curtain Bluff race . . . 55 35
406 $2 Power boat rally 85 75

68 St. Edward's Crown

1978. 25th Anniv of Coronation (1st issue). Multicoloured.
408 75c. Type **68** 15 20
409 75c. Imperial State Crown . . 15 20
410 $1.50 Queen Mary's Crown 20 30
411 $1.50 Queen Mother's Crown 20 30
412 $2.50 Queen Consort's Crown 35 50
413 $2.50 Queen Victoria's Crown 35 50

1978. 25th Anniv of Coronation (2nd issue). Nos. 581/5 of Antigua optd **BARBUDA**.
415 10c. Queen Elizabeth and Prince Philip 10 10
416 30c. The Crowning 10 10
417 50c. Coronation procession 10 15
418 90c. Queen seated in St. Edward's Chair 15 20
419 $2.50 Queen wearing Imperial State Crown 30 60

1978. 25th Anniv of Coronation (3rd issue). As Nos. 587/9 of Antigua, additionally inscr "BARBUDA".
421 25c. Glass Coach 30 70
422 50c. Irish State Coach . . . 30 70
423 $5 Coronation Coach . . . . 1·00 2·25

1978. World Cup Football Championship, Argentina. Nos. 590/2 of Antigua optd **BARBUDA**.
424 10c. Player running with ball 10 10
425 15c. Players in front of goal 10 10
426 $3 Referee and player . . . . 1·00 1·25

1978. Flowers. As Nos. 594/7 of Antigua optd **BARBUDA**.
428 25c. Petrea 15 20
429 50c. Sunflower 25 40
430 90c. Frangipani 35 45
431 $2 Passion flower 60 90

1978. Christmas. As Nos. 599/601 of Antigua optd **BARBUDA**.
433 8c. "St. Ildefonso receiving the Chasuble from the Virgin" 10 10
434 25c. "The Flight of St. Barbara" 15 15
435 $2 "Madonna and Child, with St. Joseph, John the Baptist and Donor" . . . 60 1·25

70 Black-barred Soldierfish

1978. Flora and Fauna. Multicoloured.
437 25c. Type **70** . . . . 1·00 1·50
438 50c. "Cynthia cardui" (butterfly) . . . . 1·50 2·25
439 75c. Dwarf poinciana . . . . 1·00 2·25
440 95c. "Heliconius charithonia" (butterfly) . . . . 1·75 2·50
441 $1.25 Bougainvillea . . . . . 1·25 2·50

71 Footballers and World Cup

72 Sir Rowland Hill

1978. Anniversaries and Events.
442 75c. Type **71** 30 30
443 95c. Wright Brothers and Flyer I (horiz) 30 40
444 $1.25 Balloon "Double Eagle II" and map of Atlantic (horiz) 40 45
445 $2 Prince Philip paying homage to the Queen . . . 40 60
EVENTS: 75c. Argentina—Winners of World Cup Football Championship; 95c. 75th anniv of powered flight; $1.25, First Atlantic crossing by balloon; $2 25th anniv of Coronation.

1979. Death Centenary of Sir Rowland Hill (1st issue). Multicoloured.
447 75c. Type **72** 25 45
448 95c. Mail coach, 1840 (horiz) 25 50
449 $1.25 London's first pillar box, 1855 (horiz) 30 60
450 $2 Mail leaving St. Martin's Le Grand Post Office, London 45 85

1979. Death Centenary of Sir Rowland Hill (2nd issue). Nos. 603/6 of Antigua optd **BARBUDA**.
452 25c. 1d. Stamp of 1863 . . . 15 15
453 50c. Penny Black 20 20
454 $1 Stage-coach and woman posting letter, c. 1840 . . . 35 30
455 $2 Modern mail transport . . 80 60

1979. Easter. Works of Durer. Nos. 608/10 of Antigua optd **BARBUDA**.
457 10c. multicoloured 10 10
458 50c. multicoloured 20 20
459 $4 black, mauve and yellow 90 1·10

74 Passengers alighting from British Airways Boeing 747

1979. 30th Anniv of International Civil Aviation Organization. Multicoloured.
461 75c. Type **74** 25 50
462 95c. Air traffic control . . . 25 50
463 $1.25 Ground crew-man directing Douglas DC-8 on runway 25 50

1979. International Year of the Child (1st issue). Nos. 612/15 of Antigua optd **BARBUDA**.
464 25c. Yacht 20 15
465 50c. Rocket 30 25
466 90c. Car 40 35
467 $2 Toy train 80 60

1979. Fishes. Nos. 617/20 of Antigua optd **BARBUDA**.
469 30c. Yellow jack 20 15
470 50c. Blue-finned tuna 30 20
471 90c. Sailfish 40 30
472 $3 Wahoo . . . . 1·10 1·10

1979. Death Bicentenary of Captain Cook. Nos. 622/5 of Antigua optd **BARBUDA**.
474 25c. Cook's Birthplace, Marton 25 25
475 50c. H.M.S. "Endeavour" . . 70 35
476 90c. Marine chronometer . . 70 40
477 $3 Landing at Botany Bay 1·50 1·25

77 "Virgin with the Pear"

1979. International Year of the Child (2nd issue). Paintings by Durer. Multicoloured.
479 25c. Type **77** 15 15
480 50c. "Virgin with the Pink" (detail) 20 25
481 75c. "Virgin with the Pear" (different detail) 25 30
482 $1.25 "Nativity" (detail) . . 25 40

1979. Christmas. Nos. 627/630 of Antigua optd **BARBUDA**.
484 8c. The Holy Family 10 10
485 25c. Mary and Jesus on donkey 15 10
486 50c. Shepherd looking at star 25 15
487 $4 The Three Kings 85 80

1980. Olympic Games, Moscow. Nos. 632/5 of Antigua optd **BARBUDA**.
489 10c. Javelin 10 10
490 25c. Running 15 10
491 $1 Pole vault 35 20
492 $2 Hurdles 55 40

1980. "London 1980" International Stamp Exhibition. Nos. 452/5 optd **LONDON 1980**.
494 25c. 1d. stamp of 1863 . . . 35 20
495 50c. Penny Black 45 40
496 $1 Stage-coach and woman posting letter, c. 1840 . . . 85 65
497 $2 Modern mail transport . . 2·75 1·50

80 "Apollo 11" Crew Badge

1980. 10th Anniv of "Apollo 11" Moon Landing. Multicoloured.
498 75c. Type **80** 25 25
499 95c. Plaque left on Moon . . 25 30
500 $1.25 Rejoining the mother-ship 50 50
501 $2 Lunar module 50 75

81 American Wigeon ("American Widgeon")

1980. Birds. Multicoloured.
503 1c. Type **81** 70 70
504 2c. Snowy plover 70 70
505 4c. Rose-breasted grosbeak 75 70
506 6c. Mangrove cuckoo 75 70
507 10c. Adelaide's warbler . . . 75 70
508 15c. Scaly-breasted thrasher 80 70
509 20c. Yellow-crowned night heron 80 70
510 25c. Bridled quail dove . . . 80 70
511 35c. Carib grackle 85 70
512 50c. Northern pintail 90 55
513 75c. Black-whispered vireo 1·00 55
514 $1 Blue-winged teal . . . . . 1·25 80
515 $1.50 Green-throated carib (vert) . . . . 1·50 80
516 $2 Red-necked pigeon (vert) 2·25 1·25
517 $2.50 Wied's crested flycatcher ("Stolid Flycatcher") (vert) . . . . 2·75 1·50
518 $5 Yellow-bellied sapsucker (vert) . . . . 4·00 2·50
519 $7.50 Caribbean elaenia (vert) 5·00 5·00
520 $10 Great egret (vert) . . . . 5·00 5·00

1980. Famous Works of Art. Nos. 651/7 of Antigua optd **BARBUDA**.
521 10c. "David" (statue, Donatello) 10 10
522 30c. "The Birth of Venus" (painting, Sandro Botticelli) 15 15
523 50c. "Reclining Couple" (sarcophagus), Cerveteri . . 15 20
524 90c. "The Garden of Earthly Delights" (painting, Hieronymus Bosch) . . . 20 25
525 $1 "Portinari Altarpiece" (painting, Hugo van der Goes) 20 25
526 $4 "Eleanora of Toledo and her Son Giovanni de'Medici" (painting, Agnolo Bronzino) 60 80

1980. 75th Anniv of Rotary International. Nos. 651/4 of Antigua optd **BARBUDA**.
528 30c. Rotary Headquarters . . 15 15
529 50c. Antigua Rotary banner 20 20
530 90c. Map of Antigua 25 25
531 $3 Paul P. Harris (founder) 65 65

1980. 80th Birthday of the Queen Mother. Nos. 663/4 of Antigua optd **BARBUDA**.
533 10c. multicoloured 50 15
534 $2.50 multicoloured . . . . 1·25 1·50

1980. Birds. Nos. 666/9 of Antigua optd **BARBUDA**.
536 10c. Ringed kingfisher . . . 2·50 1·00
537 30c. Plain pigeon . . . . . . 3·00 1·10
538 $1 Green-throated carib . . . 4·00 2·75
539 $2 Black necked stilt . . . . 4·75 5·25

1981. Sugar Cane Railway Locomotives. Nos. 681/4 of Antigua optd **BARBUDA**.
541 25c. Diesel locomotive No. 15 1·00 25
542 50c. Narrow-gauge steam locomotive . . . . 1·25 35
543 90c. Diesel locomotive Nos. 1 and 10 . . . . 1·75 45
544 $3 Steam locomotive hauling sugar cane . . . . 3·25 1·40

84 Florence Nightingale

1981. Famous Women.
546 **84** 50c. multicoloured 15 30
547 – 90c. multicoloured 40 55
548 – $1 multicoloured 35 60
549 – $4 black, brown and lilac 50 1·75
DESIGNS: 90c. Marie Curie; $1 Amy Johnson; $4 Eleanor Roosevelt.

85 Goofy in Motor-boat

1981. Walt Disney Cartoon Characters. Multicoloured.
550 10c. Type **85** 70 15
551 20c. Donald Duck reversing car into sea 85 20
552 25c. Mickey Mouse asking tug-boat to take on more than it can handle 90 30
553 30c. Porpoise turning tables on Goofy 90 35
554 35c. Goofy in sailing boat . . 90 35
555 40c. Mickey Mouse and boat being lifted out of water by fish . . . . 1·00 40
556 75c. Donald Duck fishing for flying-fish with butterfly net 1·25 60
557 $1 Minnie Mouse in brightly decorated sailing boat . . . 1·25 80
558 $2 Chip and Dale on floating ship-in-bottle . . . . . . 1·75 1·40

1981. Birth Centenary of Picasso. Nos. 697/700 of Antigua optd with **BARBUDA**.
560 10c. "Pipes of Pan" 10 10
561 50c. "Seated Harlequin" . . 25 15
562 90c. "Paulo as Harlequin" . . 35 30
563 $4 "Mother and Child" . . . 90 1·00

87/8 Buckingham Palace (½-size illustration)

1981. Royal Wedding (1st issue). Buildings. Each printed in black on either pink, green or lilac backgrounds.
565 $1 Type **87** 25 40
566 $1 Type **88** 25 40
567 $1.50 Caernarvon Castle (right) 30 50
568 $1.50 Caernarvon Castle (left) 30 50
569 $4 Highgrove House (right) 55 90
570 $4 Highgrove House (left) . . 55 90
Same prices for any background colour. The two versions of each value form composite designs.

1981. Royal Wedding (2nd issue). Nos. 702/5 of Antigua optd **BARBUDA**.
572 25c. Prince Charles and Lady Diana Spencer 15 15
573 50c. Glamis Castle 25 25
574 $4 Prince Charles skiing . . . 75 1·00

89 "Integration and Travel"

1981. International Year of Disabled Persons (1st issue).
576 **89** 50c. multicoloured 25 20
577 – 90c. black, orange and green 25 25
578 – $1 black, blue and green 30 30
579 – $4 black, yellow and brown 45 85
DESIGNS: 90c. Braille and sign language; $1 "Helping hands"; $4 "Mobility aids for disabled".
See also Nos. 603/6.

1981. Royal Wedding (3rd issue). Nos. 706/12 of Antigua optd **BARBUDA**.
580 25c. Prince of Wales at Investiture, 1969 . . . . . 40 60
581 25c. Prince Charles as baby, 1948 . . . . 40 60
582 $1 Prince Charles at R.A.F. College, Cranwell, 1971 . . 50 70
583 $1 Prince Charles attending Hill House School, 1956 50 70
584 $2 Prince Charles and Lady Diana Spencer 75 90
585 $2 Prince Charles at Trinity College, 1967 . . . . . . 75 90
586 $5 Prince Charles and Lady Diana . . . . 2·75 3·75

1981. Independence. No. 686/96 of Antigua additionally optd **BARBUDA**.
587 6c. Orchid tree 50 15
588 10c. Bougainvillea 55 15
589 20c. Flamboyant 70 20
590 25c. Hibiscus 80 25
591 35c. Flame of the wood . . . 90 30
592 50c. Cannon at Fort James 1·10 45
593 75c. Premier's Office . . . . 1·25 75
594 $1 Potworks Dam . . . . . 1·50 80
595 $2.50 Irrigation scheme, Diamond Estate . . . . . 2·50 2·75
596 $5 Government House and Gardens . . . . 2·75 3·75
597 $10 Coolidge International Airport . . . . 4·50 6·00

1981. 50th Anniv of Antigua Girl Guide Movement. Nos. 713/16 of Antigua optd **BARBUDA**.
598 10c. Irene Joshua (founder) 55 10
599 50c. Campfire sing-song . . . 1·25 30
600 90c. Sailing . . . . 1·75 45
601 $2.50 Animal tending . . . . 3·00 1·40

1981. International Year of Disabled Persons (2nd issue). Sport for the Disabled. Nos. 728/31 of Antigua optd **BARBUDA**.
603 10c. Swimming 15 15
604 50c. Discus throwing 20 25
605 90c. Archery 45 45
606 $2 Baseball . . . . 60 1·50

1981. Christmas. Paintings. No. 726/6 of Antigua optd **BARBUDA**.
608 8c. "Holy Night" (Jacques Stella) 10 10
609 30c. "Mary with Child" (Julius Schnorr von Carolfeld) 20 20
610 $1 "Virgin and Child" (Alsono Cano) 40 40
611 $3 "Virgin and Child" (Lorenzo di Credi) . . . . 1·10 1·10

93 Princess of Wales

97 Vincenzo Lunardi's Balloon Flight, London, 1785

1982. Birth of Prince William of Wales (1st issue).
613 **93** $1 multicoloured 50 50
614 $2.50 multicoloured . . . 70 1·10
615 $5 multicoloured . . . . . 1·25 1·75

1982. South Atlantic Fund. Nos. 580/6 surch **S. Atlantic Fund + 50c.**
617 25c.+50c. Prince of Wales at Investiture, 1969 . . . . . 30 40
618 25c.+50c. Prince Charles as baby, 1948 . . . . 30 40
619 $1+50c. Prince Charles at R.A.F. College, Cranwell, 1971 . . . . 50 65
620 $1+50c. Prince Charles attending Hill House School, 1956 . . . . . . 50 65
621 $2+50c. Prince Charles and Lady Diana Spencer . . . 75 90
622 $2+50c. Prince Charles at Trinity College, 1967 . . . 75 90
623 $5+50c. Prince Charles and Lady Diana Spencer . . . 2·50 3·00

1982. 21st Birthday of Princess of Wales (1st issue). As Nos. 613/16 but inscr "Twenty First Birthday Greetings to H.R.H. The Princess of Wales."
624 $1 multicoloured . . . . . . 1·25 45
625 $2.50 multicoloured . . . . 2·00 1·25
626 $5 multicoloured . . . . . . 2·75 2·40

1982. 21st Birthday of Princess of Wales (2nd issue). Nos. 748/51 of Antigua optd **BARBUDA MAIL**.
628 90c. Queen's House, Greenwich 80 45
629 $1 Prince and Princess of Wales . . . . 1·10 50
630 $4 Princess of Wales . . . . 2·75 1·50

1982. Birth of Prince William of Wales (2nd issue). Nos. 757/9 of Antigua further optd **BARBUDA MAIL**.
632 90c. Queen's House, Greenwich 70 45
633 $1 Prince and Princess of Wales . . . . 1·00 50
634 $4 Princess of Wales . . . . 3·00 2·00

1982. Birth Centenary of Franklin D. Roosevelt and 250th Birth Anniv of George Washington. Nos. 761/6 of Antigua optd **BARBUDA MAIL**.
636 10c. Roosevelt in 1940 . . . 10 10
637 25c. Washington as blacksmith 15 15
638 45c. Churchill, Roosevelt and Stalin at Yalta Conference 75 25
639 60c. Washington crossing Delaware 20 25
640 $1 "Roosevelt Special" train 75 40
641 $3 Portrait of Roosevelt . . . 60 90

1982. Christmas. Religious Paintings by Raphael. Nos. 769/72 of Antigua optd **BARBUDA MAIL**.
644 10c. "Annunciation" 10 10
645 30c. "Adoration of the Magi" 15 15
646 $1 "Presentation at the Temple" 40 40
647 $4 "Coronation of the Virgin" . . . . 1·00 1·00

1983. 500th Birth Anniv of Raphael. Details from "Galatea" Fresco. Nos. 774/7 of Antigua optd **BARBUDA MAIL**.
649 45c. Tritons and dolphins . . 20 20
650 50c. Sea Nymph carried off by Triton 20 20
651 60c. Winged angel steering dolphins (horiz) 25 25
652 $4 Cupids shooting arrows . . 1·00 1·00

1983. Commonwealth Day. Nos. 779/82 of Antigua optd **BARBUDA MAIL**.
654 25c. Pineapple produce . . . 45 55
655 45c. Carnival 55 70
656 60c. Tourism . . . . 80 1·25
657 $3 Airport . . . . 2·50 3·50

1983. World Communications Year. Nos. 783/6 of Antigua optd **BARBUDA MAIL**.
658 15c. T.V. satellite coverage of Royal Wedding . . . . . 1·50 20
659 50c. Police communications 2·75 90
660 60c. House-to-diesel train telephone call . . . . . . 2·25 90
661 $3 Satellite earth station with planets Jupiter and Saturn 3·50 2·50

1983. Bicent of Manned Flight (1st issue). Mult.
663 $1 Type **97** 25 35
664 $1.50 Montgolfier brothers' balloon flight, Paris, 1783 40 55
665 $2.50 Blanchard and Jeffries' Cross-Channel balloon flight, 1785 . . . . 60 90
See also Nos. 672/5.

1983. Whales. Nos. 788/92 of Antigua optd **BARBUDA MAIL**.
667 15c. Bottlenose dolphin . . . 1·25 40
668 50c. Finback whale . . . . . 4·00 1·60
669 60c. Bowhead whale . . . . 4·50 1·75
670 $3 Spectacled porpoise . . . 5·50 4·25

1983. Bicentenary of Manned Flight (2nd issue). Nos. 811/15 of Antigua optd **BARBUDA MAIL**.
672 30c. Dornier Do-X flying boat 85 35
673 50c. Supermarine S6B seaplane . . . . 1·10 60
674 60c. Curtiss Sparrowhawk biplane and airship U.S.S. "Akron" . . . . 1·25 70
675 $4 Hot-air balloon "Pro-Juventute" . . . . 4·50 4·00

1983. Nos. 565/70 surch.
677 45c. on $1 Type **87** 25 45
678 45c. on $1 Type **88** 25 45
679 50c. on $1.45 Caernarvon Castle (right) 25 45
680 50c. on $1.45 Caernarvon Castle (left) 25 45
681 60c. on $4 Highgrove House (left) 25 45
682 60c. on $4 Highgrove House (right) 25 45

1983. Nos. 793/810 of Antigua optd **BARBUDA MAIL**.
683 1c. Cashew nut 10 10
684 2c. Passion fruit 15 10
685 3c. Mango 15 10
686 5c. Grapefruit 15 10
687 10c. Pawpaw 20 10
688 15c. Breadfruit 40 10
689 20c. Coconut 50 15
690 25c. Oleander 50 15
691 30c. Banana 55 20
692 40c. Pineapple 65 25
693 45c. Cordia 70 30
694 50c. Cassia 80 30
695 60c. Poui 80 30
696 $1 Frangipani . . . . 1·10 50
697 $2 Flamboyant . . . . 1·75 1·25
698 $2.50 Lemon . . . . 2·00 1·75
699 $5 Lignum vitae . . . . . . 3·00 2·75
700 $10 National flag and coat of arms . . . . 4·50 5·50

1983. Christmas. 500th Birth Anniv of Raphael. Nos. 816/20 of Antigua optd **BARBUDA MAIL**.
701 10c. multicoloured 10 10
702 30c. multicoloured 10 20
703 $1 multicoloured 30 50
704 $4 multicoloured . . . . . . 1·00 1·50

1983. Bicentenary (1984) of Methodist Church. Nos. 821/4 of Antigua optd **BARBUDA MAIL**.
706 15c. Type **181** 20 15
707 50c. Nathaniel Gilbert (founder in Antigua) . . . 30 25
708 60c. St. John Methodist Church steeple 30 30
709 $3 Ebenezer Methodist Church, St John's . . . . 80 1·00

100 Edward VII

1984. Members of British Royal Family. Mult.
710 $1 Type **100** 50 1·10
711 $1 George V 50 1·10
712 $1 George VI 50 1·10
713 $1 Elizabeth II 50 1·10
714 $1 Charles Prince of Wales 50 1·10
715 $1 Prince William of Wales 50 1·10

1984. Olympic Games, Los Angeles (1st issue). Nos. 825/8 of Antigua optd **BARBUDA MAIL**.
716 25c. Discus 25 20
717 50c. Gymnastics 40 40
718 90c. Hurdling 50 60
719 $3 Cycling 2·75 1·50

1984. Ships. Nos. 830/3 of Antigua optd **BARBUDA MAIL**.
721 45c. "Booker Vanguard" (freighter) 1·50 45
722 50c. "Canberra" (liner) 1·50 50
723 60c. Yachts 1·75 60
724 $4 "Fairwind" (cargo liner) 4·25 2·75

1984. Universal Postal Union Congress, Hamburg. Nos. 835/8 of Antigua optd **BARBUDA MAIL**.
726 15c. Chenille 25 15
727 50c. Shell flower 30 30
728 60c. Anthurium 40 40
729 $3 Angels trumpet 75 1·25

101 Olympic Stadium, Athens, 1896

1984. Olympic Games, Los Angeles (2nd issue). Multicoloured.
731 $1.50 Type **101** 60 90
732 $2.50 Olympic stadium, Los Angeles, 1984 80 1·50
733 $5 Athlete carrying Olympic torch 1·40 2·25

1984. Presidents of the United States of America. Nos. 856/63 of Antigua optd **BARBUDA MAIL**.
735 10c. Abraham Lincoln 10 10
736 20c. Harry Truman 15 15
737 30c. Dwight Eisenhower 20 25
738 40c. Ronald Reagan 25 30
739 90c. Gettysburg Address, 1863 50 55
740 $1.10 Formation of N.A.T.O., 1949 50 65
741 $1.50 Eisenhower during Second World War 60 70
742 $2 Reagan and Caribbean Basin Initiative 75 1·00

1984. Abolition of Slavery. Nos. 864/7 of Antigua optd **BARBUDA MAIL**.
743 40c. View of Moravian Mission 30 30
744 50c. Antigua Courthouse, 1823 40 40
745 60c. Planting sugar-cane, Monks Hill 45 45
746 $3 Boiling house, Delaps' Estate 1·40 1·40

1984. Songbirds. Nos. 869/73 of Antigua optd **BARBUDA MAIL**.
748 40c. Rufous-sided towhee 1·50 45
749 50c. Parula warbler 1·60 50
750 60c. House wren 1·75 55
751 $2 Ruby-crowned kinglet 3·00 1·50
752 $3 Common flicker ("Yellow-shafted Flicker") 3·50 2·25

1984. 450th Death Anniv of Correggio (painter). Nos. 878/81 of Antigua optd **BARBUDA MAIL**.
754 25c. "The Virgin and Infant with Angels and Cherubs" 15 20
755 60c. "The Four Saints" 40 45
756 90c. "St. Catherine" 50 55
757 $3 "The Campori Madonna" 1·25 1·75

1984. "Ausipex" International Stamp Exibition Melbourne. Australian Sports. Nos. 875/6 of Antigua optd **BARBUDA MAIL**.
759 $1 Grass-skiing 50 60
760 $5 Australian Football 2·00 3·00

1984. 150th Birth Anniv of Edgar Degas (painter). Nos. 883/6 of Antigua optd **BARBUDA MAIL**.
762 15c. "The Blue Dancers" 10 10
763 50c. "The Pink Dancers" 30 40
764 70c. "Two Dancers" 45 55
765 $4 "Dancers at the Bar" 1·75 3·50

1985. Famous People. Nos. 888/96 of Antigua optd **BARBUDA MAIL**.
767 60c. Winston Churchill 3·00 1·75
768 60c. Mahatma Gandhi 3·00 1·75
769 60c. John F. Kennedy 3·00 1·75
770 60c. Mao Tse-tung 3·00 1·75
771 $1 Churchill with General De Gaulle, Paris, 1944 (horiz) 3·00 1·75
772 $1 Gandhi leaving London by train, 1931 (horiz) 3·00 1·75
773 $1 Kennedy with Chancellor Adenauer and Mayor Brandt, Berlin, 1963 (horiz) 3·00 1·75
774 $1 Mao Tse-tung with Lin Piao, Peking, 1969 (horiz) 3·00 1·75

103 Lady Elizabeth Bowes-Lyon, 1907, and Camellias

104 Roseate Tern

1985. Life and Times of Queen Elizabeth the Queen Mother. Multicoloured.
776 15c. Type **103** 25 10
777 45c. Duchess of York, 1926, and "Elizabeth of Glamis" roses 30 25
778 50c. The Queen Mother after the Coronation, 1937 30 25
779 60c. In Garter robes, 1971, and dog roses 30 30
780 90c. Attending Royal Variety Show, 1967, and red Hibiscus 40 45
781 $1 The Queen Mother in 1982, and blue plumbago 65 1·10
782 $3 Receiving 82nd birthday gifts from children, and morning glory 90 1·60

1985. Birth Bicentenary of John J. Audubon (ornithologist) (1st issue). Designs showing original paintings. Multicoloured.
783 45c. Type **104** 25 30
784 50c. Mangrove cuckoo 25 30
785 60c. Yellow-crowned night heron 30 40
786 $5 Brown pelican 1·75 3·50
See also Nos. 794/7 and 914/17.

1985. Centenary (1986) of Statue of Liberty (1st issue). Nos. 907/13 of Antigua optd **BARBUDA MAIL**.
787 25c. Torch from statue in Madison Square Park, 1885 20 20
788 30c. Statue of Liberty and scaffolding ("Restoration and Renewal") (vert) 20 20
789 50c. Frederic Bartholdi (sculpture) supervising construction, 1876 30 30
790 90c. Close-up of Statue 55 55
791 $1 Statue and sailing ship ("Operation Sail", 1976) (vert) 60 60
792 $3 Dedication ceremony, 1886 (vert) 1·75 1·75
See also Nos. 987/96.

1985. Birth Bicentenary of John J. Audubon (ornithologist) (2nd issue). Nos. 924/8 of Antigua optd **BARBUDA MAIL**.
794 90c. Slavonian grebe ("Horned Grebe") 6·50 4·00
795 $1 British storm petrel ("Least Petrel") 6·50 4·25
796 $1.50 Great blue heron 7·50 5·50
797 $3 Double-crested cormorant (white phase) 11·00 10·00

1985. Butterflies. Nos. 929/33 of Antigua optd **BARBUDA MAIL**.
799 25c. "Anaea cyanea" 4·00 1·25
800 60c. "Leodonta dysoni" 6·00 2·00
801 90c. "Junea doraete" 7·00 2·50
802 $4 "Prepona pylene" 12·00 14·00

1985. Centenary of Motorcycle. Nos. 919/23 of Antigua optd **BARBUDA MAIL**.
804 10c. Triumph 2hp "Jap", 1903 40 10
805 30c. Indian "Arrow", 1949 70 20
806 60c. BMW "R100RS", 1976 1·10 40
807 $4 Harley Davidson "Model II", 1916 3·50 2·75

1985. 85th Birthday of Queen Elizabeth the Queen Mother. Nos. 776/82 optd **4TH AUG 1900–1985**.
809 15c. Type **103** 75 50
810 45c. Duchess of York, 1926 and "Elizabeth of Glamis" roses 1·10 60
811 50c. The Queen Mother after the Coronation, 1937 1·10 60
812 60c. In Garter robes, 1971, and dog roses 1·25 1·00
813 90c. Attending Royal Variey Show, 1967, and red hibiscus 1·25 1·25
814 $2 The Queen Mother in 1982, and blue plumbago 1·40 3·75
815 $3 Receiving 82nd birthday gifts from children, and morning glory 1·50 3·75

1985. Native American Artefacts. Nos. 914/18 of Antigua optd **BARBUDA MAIL**.
816 15c. Arawak pot sherd and Indians making clay utensils 15 10
817 50c. Arawak body design and Arawak Indians tattooing 25 25
818 60c. Head of the god "Yocahu" and Indians harvesting manioc 35 35
819 $3 Carib war club and Carib Indians going into battle 1·25 1·50

1985. 40th Anniv of International Civil Aviation Organization. Nos. 934/8 of Antigua optd **BARBUDA MAIL**.
821 30c. Cessna Skyhawk 1·50 65
822 90c. Fokker D.VII 2·25 1·25
823 $1.50 SPAD VII 2·75 3·75
824 $3 Boeing 747 4·00 5·50

1985. Life and Times of Queen Elizabeth the Queen Mother (2nd series). Nos. 946/8 of Antigua optd **BARBUDA MAIL**.
826 $1 The Queen Mother attending church 3·50 2·50
827 $1.50 Watching children playing in London garden 3·75 3·00
828 $2.50 The Queen Mother in 1979 4·75 3·50

1985. 850th Birth Anniv of Maimonides (physician philosopher and scholar). No. 939 of Antigua optd **BARBUDA MAIL**.
830 $2 green 4·50 3·75

1985. Marine Life. Nos. 950/3 of Antigua optd **BARBUDA MAIL**.
832 15c. Magnificent frigate bird 4·50 85
833 45c. Brain coral 4·50 70
834 60c. Cushion star 4·50 90
835 $3 Spotted moray 8·50 4·75

1986. International Youth Year. Nos. 941/5 of Antigua optd **BARBUDA MAIL**.
837 25c. Young farmers with produce 15 15
838 50c. Hotel management trainees 25 30
839 60c. Girls with goat and boys with football ("Environment") 30 35
840 $3 Windsurfing ("Leisure") 1·50 1·60

1986. Royal Visit. Nos. 965/8 of Antigua optd **BARBUDA MAIL**.
842 60c. Flags of Great Britain and Antigua 1·50 35
843 $1 Queen Elizabeth II (vert) 1·50 55
844 $4 Royal Yacht "Britannia" 4·75 2·10

1986. 75th Anniv of Girl Guide Movement. Nos. 955/8 of Antigua optd **BARBUDA MAIL**.
846 15c. Girl Guides nursing 1·50 80
847 45c. Open-air Girl Guide meeting 2·75 1·75
848 60c. Lord and Lady Baden-Powell 2·75 2·50
849 $3 Girl Guides gathering flowers 7·50 9·50

1986. 300th Birth Anniv of Johann Sebastian Bach (composer). Nos. 960/3 of Antigua optd **BARBUDA MAIL**.
851 25c. multicoloured 2·50 70
852 50c. multicoloured 2·75 1·40
853 $1 multicoloured 3·75 2·00
854 $3 multicoloured 6·50 8·00

1986. Christmas. Religious Paintings. Nos. 985/8 of Antigua optd **BARBUDA MAIL**.
856 10c. "Madonna and Child" (De Landi) 40 30
857 25c. "Madonna and Child" (Berlinghiero) 80 50
858 60c. "The Nativity" (Fra Angelico) 1·50 1·00
859 $4 "Presentation in the Temple" (Giovanni di Paolo) 4·00 7·00

108 Queen Elizabeth II meeting Members of Legislature

1986. 60th Birthday of Queen Elizabeth II (1st issue). Multicoloured.
861 $1 Type **108** 50 1·00
862 $2 Queen with Headmistress of Liberta School 60 1·10
863 $2.50 Queen greeted by Governor-General of Antigua 60 1·25
See also Nos. 872/4.

109 Halley's Comet over Barbuda Beach

1986. Appearance of Halley's Comet (1st issue). Multicoloured.
865 $1 Type **109** 60 1·25
866 $2.50 Early telescope and dish aerial (vert) 1·00 2·25
867 $5 Comet and world map 1·75 3·75
See also Nos. 886/9.

1986. 40th Anniv of United Nations Organization. Nos. 981/3 of Antigua optd **BARBUDA MAIL**.
868 40c. Benjamin Franklin and U.N. (New York) 1953 U.P.U. 5c. stamp 1·50 1·00
869 $1 George Washington Carver (agricultural chemist) and 1982 Nature Conservation 28c. stamp 2·25 2·25
870 $3 Charles Lindbergh (aviator) and 1978 I.C.A.O. 25c. stamp 4·00 5·00

1986. 60th Birthday of Queen Elizabeth II (2nd issue). Nos. 1005/7 of Antigua optd **BARBUDA MAIL**.
872 60c. black and yellow 2·25 1·25
873 $1 multicoloured 2·50 1·75
874 $4 muticoloured 4·00 4·25

1986. World Cup Football Championship, Mexico. Nos. 995/8 of Antigua optd **BARBUDA MAIL**.
876 30c. Football, boots and trophy 3·00 1·00
877 60c. Goalkeeper (vert) 4·25 2·00
878 $1 Referee blowing whistle (vert) 4·50 2·25
879 $4 Ball in net 8·50 7·00

1986. "Ameripex '86" International Stamp Exhibition, Chicago. Famous American Trains. Nos. 1014/17 of Antigua optd **BARBUDA MAIL**.
881 25c. "Hiawatha" express 2·00 1·50
882 50c. "Grand Canyon" express 2·75 2·25
883 $1 "Powhattan Arrow" express 3·50 3·00
884 $3 "Empire State" express 6·00 7·00

1986. Appearance of Halley's Comet (2nd issue). Nos. 1000/3 of Antigua optd **BARBUDA MAIL**.
886 5c. Edmond Halley and Old Greenwich Observatory 1·00 75
887 10c. Messerschmitt Me 163B Komet (fighter aircraft), 1944 1·00 75
888 60c. Montezuma (Aztec Emperor) and Comet in 1517 (from "Historias de las Indias de Neuva Espana") 2·75 2·00
889 $4 Pocahontas saving Capt. John Smith and Comet in 1607 8·50 7·00

1986. Royal Wedding. Nos. 1019/21 of Antigua optd **BARBUDA MAIL**.
891 45c. Prince Andrew and Miss Sarah Ferguson 75 50
892 60c. Prince Andrew 90 65
893 $4 Prince Andrew with Prince Philip 3·50 4·00

1986. Sea Shells. Nos. 1023/6 of Antigua optd **BARBUDA MAIL**.
895 15c. Fly-specked cerith 2·50 2·00
896 45c. Smooth Scotch bonnet 2·75 2·25
897 60c. West Indian crown conch 3·50 2·75
898 $3 Criboney murex 8·00 12·00

1986. Flowers. Nos. 1028/35 of Antigua optd **BARBUDA MAIL**.
900 10c. "Nymphaea ampla" (water lily) 20 30
901 15c. Queen of the night 30 30
902 50c. Cup of gold 50 70
903 60c. Beach morning glory 55 70
904 70c. Golden trumpet 70 90
905 $1 Air plant 85 90
906 $3 Purple wreath 2·25 3·50
907 $4 Zephyr lily 2·75 3·75

1986. Mushrooms. Nos. 1042/5 of Antigua optd **BARBUDA MAIL**.
909 10c. "Hygrocybe occidentalis var scarletina" 90 50
910 50c. "Trogia buccinalis" 3·25 1·75
911 $1 "Collybia subpruinosa" 4·75 2·75
912 $4 "Leucocoprinus brebissonii" 9·50 8·00

1986. Birth Bicentenary of John J. Audubon (ornithologist) (3rd issue). Nos. 990/3 of Antigua optd **BARBUDA MAIL**.
914 60c. Mallard 4·75 2·25
915 90c. North American black duck ("Dusky Duck") 6·50 2·50
916 $1.50 American pintail ("Common Pintail") 8·50 6·50
917 $3 American wigeon ("Wigeon") 12·00 11·00

1987. Local Boats. Nos. 1009/12 of Antigua optd **BARBUDA MAIL**.
918 30c. Tugboat 1·00 60

919 60c. Game fishing boat 1·50 80
920 $1 Yacht 2·00 1·25
921 $4 Lugger with auxiliary sail 4·25 6·00

1987. Centenary of First Benz Motor Car. Nos. 1052/9 of Antigua optd **BARBUDA MAIL**.
923 10c. Auburn "Speedster" (1933) 90 45
924 15c. Mercury "Sable" (1986) 1·00 50
925 50c. Cadillac (1959) 1·60 70
926 60c. Studebaker (1950) 1·60 70
927 70c. Lagonda "V-12" (1939) 1·75 1·00
928 $1 Adler "Standard" (1930) 2·25 1·00
929 $3 DKW (1956) 3·00 3·75
930 $4 Mercedes "500K" (1936) 3·00 3·75

1987. World Cup Football Championship Winners, Mexico. Nos. 1037/40 of Antigua optd **BARBUDA MAIL**.
932 30c. Football, boots and trophy 2·00 80
933 60c. Goalkeeper (vert) 2·50 1·00
934 $1 Referee blowing whistle (vert) 3·00 1·75
935 $4 Ball in net 7·00 8·00

1987. America's Cup Yachting Championship. Nos. 1072/5 of Antigua optd **BARBUDA MAIL**.
936 30c. "Canada I" (1981) 90 40
937 60c. "Gretel II" (1970) 1·25 50
938 $1 "Sceptre" (1958) 1·60 80
939 $3 "Vigilant" (1893) 2·25 3·50

1987. Marine Life. Nos. 1077/84 of Antigua optd **BARBUDA MAIL**.
941 15c. Bridled burrfish 4·00 80
942 30c. Common noddy ("Brown Noddy") 5·00 85
943 40c. Nassau grouper 4·50 1·00
944 50c. Laughing gull 7·00 1·75
945 60c. French angelfish 7·00 1·50
946 $1 Porkfish 7·00 2·00
947 $2 Royal tern 13·00 8·00
948 $3 Sooty tern 13·00 9·00

1987. Milestones of Transportation. Nos. 1100/9 of Antigua optd **BARBUDA MAIL**.
950 10c. "Spirit of Australia" (fastest powerboat), 1978 1·75 75
951 15c. Werner von Siemens's electric locomotive, 1879 2·50 90
952 30c. U.S.S. "Triton" (first submerged circumnavigation), 1960 2·50 90
953 50c. Trevithick's steam carriage (first passenger-carrying vehicle), 1801 3·00 1·50
954 60c. U.S.S. "New Jersey" (battleship), 1942 3·25 1·25
955 70c. Draisine bicycle, 1818 3·25 1·75
956 90c. "United States" (liner) (holder of the Blue Riband), 1952 3·50 1·75
957 $1.50 Cierva C.4 (first autogyro), 1923 3·75 4·00
958 $2 Curtiss NC-4 flying boat (first transatlantic flight), 1919 4·75 5·00
959 $3 "Queen Elizabeth 2" (liner), 1969 6·00 6·50

110 Shore Crab

1987. Marine Life. Multicoloured.
960 5c. Type **110** 10 20
961 10c. Sea cucumber 10 20
962 15c. Stop-light parrotfish 10 20
963 25c. Banded coral shrimp 15 20
964 35c. Spotted drum 15 20
965 60c. Thorny starfish 25 40
966 75c. Atlantic trumpet triton 30 60
967 90c. Feather star and yellow beaker sponge 30 65
968 $1 Blue gorgonian (vert) 30 65
969 $1.25 Slender filefish (vert) 40 85
970 $5 Barred hamlet (vert) 70 4·00
971 $7.50 Royal gramma ("Fairy basslet") (vert) 1·00 5·50
972 $10 Fire coral and banded butterflyfish (vert) 1·25 6·50

1987. Olympic Games, Seoul (1988). Nos. 1086/9 of Antigua optd **BARBUDA MAIL**.
973 10c. Handball 85 50
974 60c. Fencing 1·75 80
975 $1 Gymnastics 2·00 1·40
976 $3 Football 3·75 5·00

1987. Birth Centenary of Marc Chagall (artist). Nos. 1091/8 of Antigua optd **BARBUDA MAIL**.
978 10c. "The Profile" 10 20
979 30c. "Portrait of the Artist's Sister" 15 15
980 40c. "Bride with Fan" 20 30
981 60c. "David in Profile" 25 30
982 90c. "Fiancee with Bouquet" 40 50
983 $1 "Self Portrait with Brushes" 45 55
984 $3 "The Walk" 1·40 2·00
985 $4 "Three Candles" 1·75 2·25

1987. Centenary (1986) of Statue of Liberty (2nd issue). Nos. 1110/19 of Antigua optd **BARBUDA MAIL**.
987 15c. Lee Iacocoa at unveiling of restored statue 10 10
988 30c. Statue at sunset (side view) 15 15
989 45c. Aerial view of head 20 25
990 50c. Lee Iacocoa and torch 25 30
991 60c. Workmen inside head of statue (horiz) 25 30
992 90c. Restoration work (horiz) 40 50
993 $1 Head of statue 45 55
994 $2 Statue at sunset (front view) 90 1·40
995 $3 Inspecting restoration work (horiz) 1·40 2·00
996 $5 Statue at night 2·25 3·00

1987. Entertainers. Nos. 1120/7 of Antigua optd **BARBUDA MAIL**.
997 15c. Grace Kelly 1·50 70
998 30c. Marilyn Monroe 3·50 1·25
999 45c. Orson Welles 1·50 75
1000 50c. Judy Garland 1·50 85
1001 60c. John Lennon 6·00 1·75
1002 $1 Rock Hudson 2·50 1·50
1003 $1 John Wayne 3·75 3·25
1004 $3 Elvis Presley 11·00 7·50

1987. "Capex '87" International Stamp Exhibition, Toronto. Reptiles and Amphibians. Nos. 1133/6 of Antigua optd **BARBUDA MAIL**.
1005 30c. Whistling frog 3·00 1·00
1006 60c. Croaking lizard 3·75 1·50
1007 $1 Antiguan anole 4·00 1·60
1008 $3 Red-footed tortoise 8·00 10·00

1988. Christmas. Religious Paintings. Nos. 1144/7 of Antigua optd **BARBUDA MAIL**.
1010 45c. "Madonna and Child" (Bernardo Daddi) 1·25 30
1011 60c. St. Joseph (detail, "The Nativity" (Sano di Pietro)) 1·40 55
1012 $1 Virgin Mary (detail, "The Nativity" (Sano di Pietro)) 1·60 1·00
1013 $4 "Music-making Angel" (Melozzo da Forli) 4·00 6·50

1988. Salvation Army's Community Service. Nos. 1163/70 of Antigua optd **BARBUDA MAIL**.
1015 25c. First aid at daycare centre, Antigua 1·00 1·00
1016 30c. Giving penicillin injection, Indonesia 1·00 1·00
1017 40c. Children at daycare centre, Bolivia 1·00 1·00
1018 45c. Rehabilitation of the handicapped, India 1·00 1·00
1019 50c. Training blind man, Kenya 1·50 1·50
1020 60c. Weighing baby, Ghana 1·50 1·50
1021 $1 Training typist, Zambia 2·00 2·25
1022 $2 Emergency food kitchen, Sri Lanka 2·50 3·50

1988. Bicentenary of U.S. Constitution. Nos. 1139/42 of Antigua optd **BARBUDA MAIL**.
1024 15c. House of Burgesses, Virginia ("Freedom of Speech") 10 15
1025 45c. State Seal, Connecticut 20 25
1026 60c. State Seal, Delaware 25 40
1027 $4 Gouverneur Morris (Pennsylvania delegate) (vert) 1·75 3·25

1988. Royal Ruby Wedding. Nos. 1149/52 of Antigua optd **BARBUDA MAIL**.
1029 25c. brown, black and blue 1·25 40
1030 60c. multicoloured 1·75 65
1031 $2 brown, black and green 3·25 2·50
1032 $3 multicoloured 3·50 3·00

1988. Birds of Antigua. Nos. 1154/61 of Antigua optd **BARBUDA MAIL**.
1034 10c. Great blue heron 2·25 1·50
1035 15c. Ringed kingfisher (horiz) 2·50 1·50
1036 50c. Bananaquit (horiz) 3·25 1·50
1037 60c. American purple gallinule ("Purple Gallinule") (horiz) 3·25 1·50
1038 70c. Blue-hooded euphonia (horiz) 3·50 2·50
1039 $1 Brown-throated concure ("Caribbean Parakeet") 3·75 2·50
1040 $3 Troupial (horiz) 6·50 8·00
1041 $4 Purple-throated carib (horiz) 6·50 8·00

1988. 500th Anniv (1992) of Discovery of America by Columbus (1st issue). Nos. 1172/9 of Antigua optd **BARBUDA MAIL**.
1043 10c. Columbus's second fleet, 1493 1·50 1·00
1044 30c. Painos Indian village and fleet 1·50 80
1045 45c. "Santa Mariagalante" (flagship) and Painos village 2·00 80
1046 60c. Painos Indians offering Columbus fruit and vegetables 1·50 85
1047 90c. Painos Indian and Columbus with scarlet macaw 3·25 1·75
1048 $1 Columbus landing on island 3·00 1·75
1049 $3 Spanish soldier and fleet 4·00 4·50
1050 $4 Fleet under sail 4·00 4·50
See also Nos. 1112/15, 1177/84, 1285/92, 1374/9 and 1381/2.

1988. 500th Birth Anniv of Titian. Nos. 1181/8 of Antigua optd **BARBUDA MAIL**.
1052 30c. "Bust of Christ" 25 20
1053 40c. "Scourging of Christ" 30 25
1054 45c. "Madonna in Glory with Saints" 35 25
1055 50c. "The Averoldi Polyptych" (detail) 35 30
1056 $1 "Christ Crowned with Thorns" 55 55
1057 $2 "Christ Mocked" 90 1·25
1058 $3 "Christ and Simon of Cyrene" 1·40 2·00
1059 $4 "Crucifixion with Virgin and Saints" 1·75 2·50

1988. 16th World Scout Jamboree, Australia. Nos. 1128/31 of Antigua optd **BARBUDA MAIL**.
1061 10c. Scouts around campfire and red kangaroo 1·50 1·00
1062 60c. Scouts canoeing and blue-winged kookaburra 4·00 1·50
1063 $1 Scouts on assault course and ring-tailed rock wallaby 2·50 1·75
1064 $3 Field kitchen and koala 5·00 6·50

1988. Sailing Week. Nos. 1190/3 of Antigua optd **BARBUDA MAIL**.
1066 30c. Two yachts rounding buoy 60 35
1067 60c. Three yachts 1·00 70
1068 $1 British yacht under way 1·25 1·10
1069 $3 Three yachts (different) 2·25 2·75

1988. Flowering Trees. Nos. 1213/20 of Antigua optd **BARBUDA MAIL**.
1071 10c. Jacaranda 10 10
1072 30c. Cordia 15 15
1073 50c. Orchid tree 20 25
1074 90c. Flamboyant 40 45
1075 $1 African tulip tree 45 50
1076 $2 Potato tree 80 1·25
1077 $3 Crepe myrtle 1·25 1·75
1078 $4 Pitch apple 1·60 2·25

1988. Olympic Games, Seoul. Nos. 1222/5 of Antigua optd **BARBUDA MAIL**.
1080 40c. Gymnastics 1·00 40
1081 60c. Weightlifting 1·25 55
1082 $1 Water polo (horiz) 1·50 1·00
1083 $3 Boxing (horiz) 2·25 3·00

1988. Caribbean Butterflies. Nos. 1227/44 of Antigua optd **BARBUDA MAIL**.
1085 1c. "Danaus plexippus" 30 60
1086 2c. "Greta diaphanus" 30 60
1087 3c. "Calisto archebates" 40 60
1088 5c. "Hamadryas feronia" 40 60
1089 10c. "Mestra dorcas" 50 50
1090 15c. "Hypolimnas misippus" 60 40
1091 20c. "Dione juno" 70 50
1092 25c. "Heliconius charithonia" 75 50
1093 30c. "Eurema pyro" 85 50
1094 40c. "Papilio androgeus" 90 50
1095 45c. "Anteos maerula" 90 50
1096 50c. "Aphrissa orbis" 1·10 75
1097 60c. "Astraptes xagua" 1·10 60
1098 $1 "Heliopetes arsalte" 1·40 1·00
1099 $2 "Polites baracoa" 3·00 3·50
1100 $2.50 "Phocides pigmalion" 3·25 4·00
1101 $5 "Prepona amphitoe" 4·50 5·50
1102 $10 "Oarisma nanus" 7·50 8·50
1102a $20 "Parides lycimenes" 12·00 13·00

1989. 25th Death Anniv of John F. Kennedy (American statesman). Nos. 1245/52 of Antigua optd **BARBUDA MAIL**.
1103 1c. President Kennedy and family 10 30
1104 2c. Kennedy commanding "PT109" 10 30
1105 3c. Funeral cortege 10 30
1106 4c. In motorcade, Mexico 10 30
1107 30c. As 1c. 75 40
1108 60c. As 4c. 1·50 55
1109 $1 As 3c. 1·60 1·25
1110 $4 As 2c. 4·75 6·50

1989. 500th Anniv (1992) of Discovery of America by Columbus (2nd issue). Pre-Columbian Arawak Society. Nos. 1267/70 of Antigua optd **BARBUDA MAIL**.
1112 $1.50 Arawak warriors 2·50 3·00
1113 $1.50 Whip dancers 2·50 3·00
1114 $1.50 Whip dancers and chief with pineapple 2·50 3·00
1115 $1.50 Family and camp fire 2·50 3·00

1989. 50th Anniv of First Jet Flight. Nos. 1272/9 of Antigua optd **BARBUDA MAIL**.
1117 10c. Hawker Siddeley Comet 4 airliner 2·25 1·25
1118 30c. Messerschmitt Me 262 fighter 2·75 1·25
1119 40c. Boeing 707 airliner 3·00 1·00
1120 60c. Canadair CL-13 Sabre fighter 3·50 1·00
1121 $1 Lockheed Starfighters 4·00 1·50
1122 $2 Douglas DC-10 airliner 5·00 4·50
1123 $3 Boeing 747-300/400 airliner 6·00 6·50
1124 $4 McDonnell Douglas Phantom II fighter 6·00 6·50

1989. Caribbean Cruise Ships. Nos. 1281/8 of Antigua optd **BARBUDA MAIL**.
1126 25c. "Festivale" 2·25 1·00
1127 45c. "Southward" 2·50 1·00
1128 50c. "Sagafjord" 2·50 1·25
1129 60c. "Daphne" 2·75 1·25
1130 75c. "Cunard Countess" 2·75 2·50
1131 90c. "Song of America" 3·00 2·50
1132 $3 "Island Princess" 6·00 6·50
1133 $4 "Galileo" 6·00 6·50

1989. Japanese Art. Paintings by Hiroshige. Nos. 1290/7 of Antigua optd **BARBUDA MAIL**.
1135 25c. "Fish swimming by Duck half-submerged in Stream" 2·00 70
1136 45c. "Crane and Wave" 2·50 70
1137 50c. "Sparrows and Morning Glories" 2·75 1·00
1138 60c. "Crested Blackbird and Flowering Cherry" 2·75 1·00
1139 $1 "Great Knot sitting among Water Grass" 2·75 1·25
1140 $2 "Goose on a Bank of Water" 4·00 3·50
1141 $3 "Black Paradise Fly-catcher and Blossoms" 4·25 4·00
1142 $4 "Sleepy Owl perched on a Pine Branch" 5·00 4·50

1989. World Cup Football Championship, Italy (1990). Nos. 1308/11 of Antigua optd **BARBUDA MAIL**.
1144 15c. Goalkeeper 1·40 50
1145 25c. Goalkeeper moving towards ball 1·40 50
1146 $1 Goalkeeper reaching for ball 2·50 1·50
1147 $4 Goalkeeper saving goal 4·75 6·50

1989. Christmas. Paintings by Raphael and Giotto. Nos. 1351/8 of Antigua optd **BARBUDA MAIL**.
1149 10c. "The Small Cowper Madonna" (Raphael) 15 20
1150 25c. "Madonna of the Goldfinch" (Raphael) 20 20
1151 30c. "The Alba Madonna" (Raphael) 20 20
1152 50c. Saint (detail, "Bologna Altarpiece") (Giotto) 35 30
1153 60c. Angel (detail, "Bologna Altarpiece") (Giotto) 45 45
1154 70c. Angel slaying serpent (detail, "Bologna Altarpiece") (Giotto) 50 50
1155 $4 Evangelist (detail, "Bologna Altarpiece") (Giotto) 2·25 3·50
1156 $5 "Madonna of Foligno" (Raphael) 2·50 3·50

1990. Fungi. Nos. 1313/20 of Antigua optd **BARBUDA MAIL**.
1158 10c. "Mycena pura" 1·75 75
1159 25c. Psathyrella turberculata" (vert) 2·00 65
1160 50c. "Psilocybe cubensis" 2·50 1·00
1161 60c. "Leptonia caeruleocapitata" (vert) 2·50 1·00
1162 75c. "Xeromphalina tenuipes" (vert) 2·50 1·40
1163 $1 "Chlorophyllum molybdites" (vert) 2·50 1·40
1164 $3 "Marasmius haematocephalus" 5·00 5·50
1165 $4 "Cantharellus cinnabarinus" 5·00 5·50

1990. Local Fauna. Nos. 1322/5 optd **BARBUDA MAIL**.
1167 25c. Desmarest's hutia 75 60
1168 45c. Caribbean monk seal 2·00 1·00
1169 60c. Mustache bat (vert) 1·50 1·00
1170 $4 American manatee (vert) 4·00 5·50

1990. 20th Anniv of First Manned Landing on Moon. Nos. 1346/9 optd **BARBUDA MAIL**.
1172 10c. Launch of "Apollo 11" 1·50 1·00
1173 45c. Aldrin on Moon 2·50 70
1174 $1 Module "Eagle" over Moon (horiz) 3·50 2·00
1175 $4 Recovery of "Apollo 11" crew after splashdown (horiz) 7·00 9·00

1990. 500th Anniv (1992) of Discovery of America by Columbus (3rd issue). New World Natural History – Marine Life. Nos. 1360/7 of Antigua optd **BARBUDA MAIL**.
1177 10c. Star-eyed hermit crab 1·00 1·00
1178 20c. Spiny lobster 1·25 1·00
1179 25c. Magnificent banded fanworm 1·25 1·00
1180 45c. Cannonball jellyfish 1·75 75
1181 60c. Red-spiny sea star 2·00 75
1182 $2 Peppermint shrimp 3·00 3·25
1183 $3 Coral crab 3·50 4·25
1184 $4 Branching fire coral 3·50 4·25

1990. "EXPO 90" International Gardens and Greenery Exhibition, Osaka. Orchids. Nos. 1369/76 of Antigua optd **BARBUDA MAIL**.
1186 15c. "Vanilla mexicana" 1·50 80
1187 45c. "Epidendrum ibaguense" 2·00 80
1188 50c. "Epidendrum secundum" 2·00 90
1189 60c. "Maxillaria conferta" 2·25 1·10
1190 $1 "Onicidium altissimum" 2·50 1·75
1191 $2 "Spiranthes lanceolata" 4·50 4·50
1192 $3 "Tonopsis utricularioides" 5·00 5·50
1193 $5 "Epidendrum nocturnum" 6·50 7·50

1990. Reef Fishes. Nos. 1386/93 of Antigua optd **BARBUDA MAIL**.
1195 10c. Flamefish 1·50 1·00
1196 15c. Coney 1·60 1·00
1197 50c. Long-spined squirrelfish 2·25 1·10
1198 60c. Sergeant major 2·25 1·10
1199 $1 Yellow-tailed snapper 2·75 1·75
1200 $2 Rock beauty 4·50 4·50

1201 $3 Spanish hogfish 5·00 5·50
1202 $4 Striped parrotfish 5·00 5·50

1990. 1st Anniv of Hurricane Hugo. Nos. 971/2 surch **1st Anniversary Hurricane Hugo 16th September, 1989-1990** and new value.
1204 $5 on $7.50 Fairy basslet (vert) 7·50 8·00
1205 $7.50 on $10 Fire coral and butterfly fish (vert) 8·50 10·00

1990. 90th Birthday of Queen Elizabeth the Queen Mother. Nos. 1415/18 of Antigua optd **BARBUDA MAIL**.
1206 15c. multicoloured 2·75 1·25
1207 35c. multicoloured 4·25 1·25
1208 75c. multicoloured 7·00 2·25
1209 $3 multicoloured 12·00 11·00

1990. Achievements in Space. Nos. 1395/1414 of Antigua optd **BARBUDA MAIL**.
1211 45c. "Voyager 2" passing Saturn 2·00 2·00
1212 45c. "Pioneer 11" photographing Saturn 2·00 2·00
1213 45c. Astronaut in transporter 2·00 2·00
1214 45c. Space shuttle "Columbia" 2·00 2·00
1215 45c. "Apollo 10" command module on parachutes 2·00 2·00
1216 45c. "Skylab" space station 2·00 2·00
1217 45c. Astronaut Edward White in space 2·00 2·00
1218 45c. "Apollo" spacecraft on joint mission 2·00 2·00
1219 45c. "Soyuz" spacecraft on joint mission 2·00 2·00
1220 45c. "Mariner 1" passing Venus 2·00 2·00
1221 45c. "Gemini 4" capsule 2·00 2·00
1222 45c. "Sputnik 1" 2·00 2·00
1223 45c. Hubble space telescope 2·00 2·00
1224 45c. North American X-15 rocket plane 2·00 2·00
1225 45c. Bell XS-1 airplane 2·00 2·00
1226 45c. "Apollo 17" astronaut and lunar rock formation 2·00 2·00
1227 45c. Lunar rover 2·00 2·00
1228 45c. "Apollo 14" lunar module 2·00 2·00
1229 45c. Astronaut Buzz Aldrin on Moon 2·00 2·00
1230 45c. Soviet "Lunokhod" lunar vehicle 2·00 2·00

1990. Christmas. Paintings by Renaissance Masters. Nos. 1457/64 of Antigua optd **BARBUDA MAIL**.
1231 25c. "Madonna and Child with Saints" (detail, Sebastiano del Piombo) 1·10 60
1232 30c. "Virgin and Child with Angels" (detail, Grunewald) (vert) 1·25 60
1233 40c. "The Holy Family and a Shepherd" (detail, Titian) 1·25 60
1234 60c. "Virgin and Child" (detail, Lippi) (vert) 1·60 1·10
1235 $1 "Jesus, St. John and Two Angels" (Rubens) 2·25 1·50
1236 $2 "Adoration of the Shepherds" (detail, Vincenzo Catena) 3·25 3·75
1237 $4 "Adoration of the Magi" (detail, Giorgione) 4·50 6·00
1238 $5 "Virgin and Child adored by Warriors" (detail, Vincenzo Catena) 4·50 6·00

1991. 150th Anniv of the Penny Black. Nos. 1378/80 of Antigua optd **BARBUDA MAIL**.
1240 45c. green 2·75 80
1241 60c. mauve 2·75 85
1242 $5 blue 9·00 10·00

1991. "Stamp World London 90" International Stamp Exhibition. Nos. 1382/4 of Antigua optd **BARBUDA MAIL**.
1244 50c. green and red 2·75 85
1245 75c. brown and red 2·75 1·25
1246 $4 blue and red 9·00 10·00

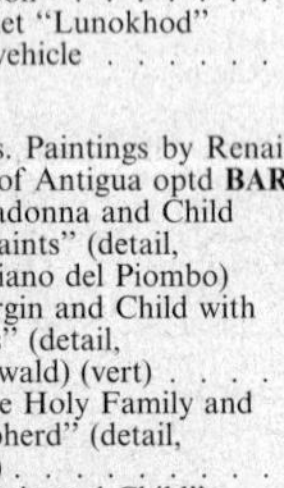

119 Troupial

1991. Wild Birds. Multicoloured.
1248 60c. Type **119** 1·50 65
1249 $2 Adelaide's warbler ("Christmas Bird") 2·75 2·50
1250 $4 Rose-breasted grosbeak 4·00 4·50
1251 $7 Wied's crested flycatcher ("Stolid Flycatcher") 6·00 8·50

1991. Olympic Games, Barcelona (1992). Nos. 1429/32 of Antigua optd **BARBUDA MAIL**.
1252 50c. Men's 20 kilometres walk 1·50 90
1253 75c. Triple jump 1·75 1·00
1254 $1 Men's 10,000 metres 2·00 1·75
1255 $5 Javelin 6·50 8·50

1991. Birds. Nos. 1448/55 of Antigua optd **BARBUDA MAIL**.
1257 10c. Pearly-eyed thrasher 1·75 1·50
1258 25c. Purple-throated carib 2·50 80
1259 50c. Common yellowthroat 2·75 1·00
1260 60c. American kestrel 2·75 1·10
1261 $1 Yellow-bellied sapsucker 3·00 1·75
1262 $2 American purple gallinule ("Purple Gallinule") 4·25 4·50
1263 $3 Yellow-crowned night heron 4·75 6·00
1264 $4 Blue-hooded euphonia 4·75 6·00

1991. 350th Death Anniv of Rubens. Nos. 1466/73 of Antigua optd **BARBUDA MAIL**.
1266 25c. "Rape of the Daughters of Leucippus" (detail) 1·25 70
1267 45c. "Bacchanal" (detail) 1·50 70
1268 50c. "Rape of the Sabine Women" (detail) 1·50 75
1269 60c. "Battle of the Amazons" (detail) 1·60 85
1270 $1 "Rape of the Sabine Women" (different detail) 2·25 1·50
1271 $2 "Bacchanal" (different detail) 3·50 3·75
1272 $3 "Rape of the Sabine Women" (different detail) 4·50 5·50
1273 $4 "Bacchanal" (different detail) 4·50 5·50

1991. 50th Anniv of Second World War. Nos. 1475/83 of Antigua optd **BARBUDA MAIL**.
1275 10c. U.S. troops cross into Germany, 1944 1·75 1·50
1276 15c. Axis surrender in North Africa, 1943 2·25 1·50
1277 25c. U.S. tanks invade Kwalajalein, 1944 2·50 1·10
1278 45c. Roosevelt and Churchill meet at Casablanca, 1943 4·50 1·50
1279 50c. Marshall Badoglio, Prime Minister of Italian anti-facist government, 1943 2·75 1·50
1280 $1 Lord Mountbatten, Supreme Allied Commander South-east Asia, 1943 6·50 3·00
1281 $2 Greek victory at Koritza, 1940 7·00 7·00
1282 $4 Anglo-Soviet mutual assistance pact, 1941 8·00 8·00
1283 $5 Operation Torch landings, 1942 8·00 8·00

1991. 500th Anniv (1992) of Discovery of America by Columbus (4th issue). History of Exploration. Nos. 1503/10 of Antigua optd **BARBUDA MAIL**.
1285 10c. multicoloured 1·10 1·00
1286 15c. multicoloured 1·25 1·00
1287 45c. multicoloured 1·75 80
1288 60c. multicoloured 2·00 1·00
1289 $1 multicoloured 2·75 1·75
1290 $2 multicoloured 3·75 3·75
1291 $4 multicoloured 6·00 6·00
1292 $5 multicoloured 6·00 6·00

1991. Butterflies. Nos. 1494/1501 of Antigua optd **BARBUDA MAIL**.
1294 10c. "Heliconius charithonia" 1·75 1·50
1295 35c. "Marpesia petreus" 2·50 1·25
1296 50c. "Anartia amathea" 3·00 1·40
1297 75c. "Siproeta stelenes" 3·50 1·60
1298 $1 "Battus polydamas" 3·50 1·75
1299 $2 "Historis odius" 4·75 4·75
1300 $4 "Hypolimnas misippus" 7·00 7·50
1301 $5 "Hamadryas feronia" 7·00 7·50

1991. 65th Birthday of Queen Elizabeth II. Nos. 1534/7 of Antigua optd **BARBUDA MAIL**.
1303 15c. Queen Elizabeth and Prince Philip in 1976 1·75 75
1304 20c. The Queen and Prince Philip in Portugal, 1985 1·75 75
1305 $2 Queen Elizabeth II 5·00 3·50
1306 $4 The Queen and Prince Philip at Ascot, 1986 7·50 7·50

1991. 10th Wedding Anniv of Prince and Princess of Wales. Nos. 1539/42 of Antigua optd **BARBUDA MAIL**.
1308 10c. Prince and Princess of Wales at party, 1986 2·00 1·00
1309 40c. Separate portraits of Prince, Princess and sons 3·25 80
1310 $1 Prince Henry and Prince William 3·50 2·00
1311 $5 Princess Diana in Australia and Prince Charles in Hungary 8·50 8·50

1991. Christmas. Religious Paintings by Fra Angelico. Nos. 1595/1602 of Antigua optd **BARBUDA MAIL**.
1313 10c. "The Annunciation" 1·25 1·00
1314 30c. "Nativity" 1·75 70
1315 40c. "Adoration of the Magi" 1·75 70
1316 60c. "Presentation in the Temple" 2·00 70
1317 $1 "Circumcision" 2·50 1·25
1318 $3 "Flight into Egypt" 4·50 5·00
1319 $4 "Massacre of the Innocents" 4·50 6·00
1320 $5 "Christ teaching in the Temple" 4·50 6·00

1992. Death Centenary (1990) of Vincent van Gogh (artist). Nos. 1512/23 of Antigua optd **BARBUDA MAIL**.
1321 5c. "Camille Roulin" 90 90
1322 10c. "Armand Roulin" 1·10 1·10
1323 15c. "Young Peasant Woman with Straw Hat sitting in the Wheat" 1·25 1·00
1324 25c. "Adeline Ravoux" 1·25 1·00
1325 30c. "The Schoolboy" 1·25 80
1326 40c. "Doctor Gachet" 1·50 80
1327 50c. "Portrait of a Man" 1·50 1·00
1328 75c. "Two Children" 2·00 1·50
1329 $2 "The Postman Joseph Roulin" 4·00 4·00
1330 $3 "The Seated Zouave" 4·50 5·00
1331 $4 "L'Arlesienne" 4·50 5·50
1332 $5 "Self-Portrait, November/December 1888" 4·50 5·50

1992. Birth Centenary of Charles de Gaulle (French statesman). Nos. 1562/9 of Antigua optd **BARBUDA MAIL**.
1334 10c. Pres. De Gaulle and Kennedy, 1961 1·40 1·25
1335 15c. General De Gaulle with Pres. Roosevelt, 1945 (vert) 1·40 1·25
1336 45c. President De Gaulle with Chancellor Adenauer, 1962 (vert) 2·00 80
1337 60c. De Gaulle at Arc de Triomphe, Liberation of Paris, 1944 (vert) 2·25 1·00
1338 $1 General De Gaulle crossing the Rhine, 1945 2·75 1·50
1339 $2 General De Gaulle in Algiers, 1944 4·50 4·50
1340 $4 Presidents De Gaulle and Eisenhower, 1960 6·00 7·50
1341 $5 De Gaulle returning from Germany, 1968 (vert) 6·00 7·50

1992. Easter. Religious Paintings. Nos. 1627/34 of Antigua optd **BARBUDA MAIL**.
1343 10c. "Supper at Emmaus" (Caravaggio) 1·00 90
1344 15c. "The Vision of St. Peter" (Zurbaran) 1·25 90
1345 30c. "Christ driving the Money-changers from the Temple" (Tiepolo) 1·50 70
1346 40c. "Martyrdom of St. Bartholomew" (detail) (Ribera) 1·50 70
1347 $1 "Christ driving the Money-changers from the Temple" (detail) (Tiepolo) 2·75 1·75
1348 $2 "Crucifixion" (detail) (Altdorfer) 4·00 4·25
1349 $4 "The Deposition" (detail) (Fra Angelico) 5·50 6·50
1350 $5 "The Deposition" (different detail) (Fra Angelico) 5·50 6·50

1992. Anniversaries and Events. Nos. 1573/82 of Antigua optd **BARBUDA MAIL**.
1352 25c. Germans celebrating Reunification 80 60
1353 75c. Cubs erecting tent 1·75 1·25
1354 $1.50 "Don Giovanni" and Mozart 5·50 2·75
1355 $2 Chariot driver and Gate at night 2·50 2·50
1356 $2 Lord Baden-Powell and members of the 3rd Antigua Methodist cub pack (vert) 2·50 2·50
1357 $2 Lilienthal's signature and glider "Flugzeug Nr. 5" 2·50 2·50
1358 $2.50 Driver in Class P36 steam locomotive (vert) 4·50 3·75
1359 $3 Statues from podium 2·75 3·75
1360 $3.50 Cubs and campfire 3·50 4·00
1361 $4 St. Peter's Cathedral, Salzburg 6·50 6·50

1992. 50th Anniv of Japanese Attack on Pearl Harbor. Nos. 1585/94 of Antigua optd **BARBUDA MAIL**.
1364 $1 "Nimitz" class carrier and "Ticonderoga" class cruiser 3·25 2·50
1365 $1 Tourist launch 3·25 2·50
1366 $1 U.S.S. "Arizona" memorial 3·25 2·50
1367 $1 Wreaths on water and aircraft 3·25 2·50
1368 $1 White tern 3·25 2·50
1369 $1 Japanese torpedo bombers over Pearl City 3·25 2·50
1370 $1 Zeros attacking 3·25 2·50
1371 $1 Battleship Row in flames 3·25 2·50
1372 $1 U.S.S. "Nevada" (battleship) underway 3·25 2·50
1373 $1 Zeros returning to carriers 3·25 2·50

1992. 500th Anniv of Discovery of America by Columbus (5th issue). World Columbian Stamp "Expo '92", Chicago. Nos. 1654/9 of Antigua optd **BARBUDA MAIL**.
1374 15c. Memorial cross and huts, San Salvador 75 80
1375 30c. Martin Pinzon with telescope 90 90
1376 40c. Christopher Columbus 1·00 90
1377 $1 "Pinta" 3·50 2·50
1378 $2 "Nina" 4·50 4·50
1379 $4 "Santa Maria" 6·50 7·50

1992. 500th Anniv of Discovery of America by Columbus (6th issue). Organization of East Caribbean States. Nos. 1670/1 of Antigua optd **BARBUDA MAIL**.
1381 $1 Columbus meeting Amerindians 2·00 1·50
1382 $2 Ships approaching island 5·50 4·25

1992. 40th Anniv of Queen Elizabeth II's Accession. Nos. 1604/7 of Antigua optd **BARBUDA MAIL**.
1384 10c. Queen Elizabeth II and bird sanctuary 2·50 1·25
1385 30c. Nelson's Dockyard 3·00 1·00
1386 $1 Ruins on Shirley Heights 4·25 2·25
1387 $5 Beach and palm trees 8·50 9·00

1992. Prehistoric Animals. Nos. 1618/25 of Antigua optd **BARBUDA MAIL**.
1389 10c. Pteranodon 1·75 1·50
1390 15c. Brachiosaurus 2·25 1·50
1391 30c. Tyrannosaurus Rex 2·75 1·25
1392 50c. Parasaurolophus 2·75 1·50
1393 $1 Deinonychus (horiz) 3·25 2·25
1394 $2 Triceratops (horiz) 5·00 4·50
1395 $4 Protoceratops hatching (horiz) 6·00 6·50
1396 $5 Stegosaurus (horiz) 6·00 6·50

1992. Christmas. Nos. 1691/8 of Antigua optd **BARBUDA MAIL**.
1398 10c. "Virgin and Child with Angels" (School of Piero della Francesca) 1·75 75
1399 25c. "Madonna degli Alberelli" (Giovanni Bellini) 1·75 75
1400 30c. "Madonna and Child with St. Anthony Abbot and St. Sigismund" (Neroccio) 1·75 75
1401 40c. "Madonna and the Grand Duke" (Raphael) 2·00 75
1402 60c. "The Nativity" (Georges de la Tour) 2·25 75
1403 $1 "Holy Family" (Jacob Jordaens) 2·75 1·50
1404 $4 "Madonna and Child Enthroned" (Magaritone) 6·50 8·00
1405 $5 "Madonna and Child on a Curved Throne" (Byzantine school) 6·50 8·00

1993. Fungi. Nos. 1645/52 of Antigua optd **BARBUDA MAIL**.
1407 10c. "Amanita caesarea" 1·75 1·25
1408 15c. "Collybia fusipes" 2·00 1·25
1409 30c. "Boletus aereus" 2·25 1·50
1410 40c. "Laccaria amethystina" 2·25 1·50
1411 $1 "Russula virescens" 3·25 2·00
1412 $2 "Tricholoma equestre" ("Tricholoma auratum") 4·50 4·00
1413 $4 "Calocybe gambosa" 5·50 6·00
1414 $5 "Lentinus tigrinus" ("Panus tigrinus") 5·50 6·00

1993. "Granada '92" International Stamp Exhibition, Spain. Spanish Paintings. Nos. 1636/43 of Antigua optd **BARBUDA MAIL**.
1416 10c. "The Miracle at the Well" (Alonzo Cano) 1·00 75
1417 15c. "The Poet Luis de Goingora y Argote" (Velazquez) 1·25 75
1418 30c. "The Painter Francisco Goya" (Vincente Lopez Portana) 1·50 1·00
1419 40c. "Maria de las Nieves Michaela Fourdinier" (Luis Paret y Alcazar) 1·50 1·00
1420 $1 "Carlos III eating before his Court" (Alcazar) (horiz) 2·50 2·00
1421 $2 "Rain Shower in Granada" (Antonio Munoz Degrain) (horiz) 4·00 4·00
1422 $4 "Sarah Bernhardt" (Santiago Ruisnol i Prats) 5·50 6·50
1423 $5 "The Hermitage Garden" (Joaquim Mir Trinxet) 5·50 6·50

1993. "Genova '92" International Thematic Stamp Exhibition. Hummingbirds and Plants. Nos. 1661/8 of Antigua optd **BARBUDA MAIL**.
1425 10c. Antillean crested hummingbird and wild plantain 1·75 1·50
1426 25c. Green mango and parrot's plantain 2·00 1·00
1427 45c. Purple-throated carib and lobster claws 2·25 1·25
1428 60c. Antillean mango and coral plant 2·50 1·50
1429 $1 Vervain hummingbird and cardinal's guard 3·00 2·00
1430 $2 Rufous-breasted hermit and heliconia 4·25 4·25
1431 $4 Blue-headed hummingbird and reed ginger 5·50 6·00
1432 $5 Green-throated carib and ornamental banana 5·50 6·00

1993. Inventors and Inventions. Nos. 1672/9 of Antigua optd **BARBUDA MAIL**.
1434 10c. Ts'ai Lun and paper 65 85
1435 25c. Igor Sikorsky and "Bolshoi Baltiskii" (first four-engined airplane) 2·00 80
1436 30c. Alexander Graham Bell and early telephone 1·25 80
1437 40c. Johannes Gutenberg and early printing press 1·25 80

1438 60c. James Watt and stationary steam engine 4·00 1·60
1439 $1 Anton van Leeuwenhoek and early microscope 3·25 2·00
1440 $4 Louis Braille and hands reading braille 5·00 6·00
1441 $5 Galileo and telescope 5·00 6·00

1993. Anniversaries and Events. Nos. 900/13 of Antigua optd **BARBUDA MAIL**.
1443 10c. Russian cosmonauts 1·50 1·40
1444 40c. "Graf Zeppelin" (airship), 1929 2·50 1·00
1445 45c. Bishop Daniel Davis 70 70
1446 75c. Konrad Adenauer making speech 90 90
1447 $1 Bus Mosbacher and "Weatherly" (yacht) 2·00 1·50
1448 $1.50 Rain forest 2·25 2·25
1449 $2 Tiger 7·50 5·00
1450 $2 National flag, plant and emblem (horiz) 4·00 2·50
1451 $2 Members of Community Players company (horiz) 2·50 2·50
1452 $2.25 Women carrying pots 2·50 3·00
1453 $3 Lions Club emblem 3·25 3·50
1454 $4 Chinese rocket on launch tower 4·50 4·50
1455 $4 West German and N.A.T.O. flags 4·50 4·50
1456 $6 Hugo Eckener (airship pioneer) 5·50 6·00

1993. Flowers. Nos. 1733/40 of Antigua optd **BARBUDA MAIL**.
1458 15c. Cardinal's guard 1·40 1·25
1459 25c. Giant granadilla 1·60 1·10
1460 30c. Spider flower 1·75 1·25
1461 40c. Gold vine 2·00 1·40
1462 $1 Frangipani 3·00 2·25
1463 $2 Bougainvillea 4·00 4·00
1464 $4 Yellow oleander 5·00 6·00
1465 $5 Spicy jatropha 5·00 6·00

1993. World Bird Watch. Nos. 1248/51 optd **WORLD BIRDWATCH 9-10 OCTOBER 1993**.
1467 60c. Type **119** 3·50 1·75
1468 $2 Adelaide's warbler 6·50 4·50
1469 $4 Rose-breasted grosbeak 8·50 9·00
1470 $7 Wied's crested flycatcher 11·00 12·00

1993. Endangered Species. Nos. 1759/70 of Antigua optd **BARBUDA MAIL**.
1471 $1 St. Lucia amazon ("St. Lucia Parrot") 3·50 3·00
1472 $1 Cahow 3·50 3·00
1473 $1 Swallow-tailed kite 3·50 3·00
1474 $1 Everglade kite ("Everglades Kite") 3·50 3·00
1475 $1 Imperial amazon ("Imperial Parrot") 3·50 3·00
1476 $1 Humpback whale 3·50 3·00
1477 $1 Plain pigeon ("Puerto Rican Plain Pigeon") 3·50 3·00
1478 $1 St. Vincent amazon ("St. Vincent Parrot") 3·50 3·00
1479 $1 Puerto Rican amazon ("Puerto Rican Parrot") 3·50 3·00
1480 $1 Leatherback turtle 3·50 3·00
1481 $1 American crocodile 3·50 3·00
1482 $1 Hawksbill turtle 3·50 3·00

1994. Bicentenary of the Louvre, Paris. Paintings by Peter Paul Rubens. Nos. 1742/9 of Antigua optd **BARBUDA MAIL**.
1484 $1 "The Destiny of Marie de' Medici" (upper detail) 2·75 2·75
1485 $1 "The Birth of Marie de' Medici" 2·75 2·75
1486 $1 "The Education of Marie de' Medici" 2·75 2·75
1487 $1 "The Destiny of Marie de' Medici" (lower detail) 2·75 2·75
1488 $1 "Henry VI receiving the Portrait of Marie" 2·75 2·75
1489 $1 "The Meeting of the King and Marie at Lyons" 2·75 2·75
1490 $1 "The Marriage by Proxy" 2·75 2·75
1491 $1 "The Birth of Louis XIII" 2·75 2·75

1994. World Cup Football Championship, 1994, U.S.A. (1st Issue). Nos. 1816/27 of Antigua optd **BARBUDA MAIL**.
1493 $2 Paul Gascoigne 3·00 2·25
1494 $2 David Platt 3·00 2·25
1495 $2 Martin Peters 3·00 2·25
1496 $2 John Barnes 3·00 2·25
1497 $2 Gary Lineker 3·00 2·25
1498 $2 Geoff Hurst 3·00 2·25
1499 $2 Bobby Charlton 3·00 2·25
1500 $2 Bryan Robson 3·00 2·25
1501 $2 Bobby Moore 3·00 2·25
1502 $2 Nobby Stiles 3·00 2·25
1503 $2 Gordon Banks 3·00 2·25
1504 $2 Peter Shilton 3·00 2·25
See also Nos. 1573/8.

1994. Anniversaries and Events. Nos. 1829/38, 1840 and 1842/6 of Antigua optd **BARBUDA MAIL**.
1506 10c. Grand Inspector W. Heath 2·00 1·50
1507 15c. Rodnina and Oulanov (U.S.S.R.) (pairs figure skating) (horiz) 1·50 1·25
1508 30c. Present Masonic Hall, St. John's (horiz) 2·75 1·50
1509 30c. Willy Brandt with Helmut Schmidt and George Leber (horiz) 1·25 1·00
1510 30c. "Cat and Bird" (Picasso) (horiz) 1·25 1·00
1511 40c. Previous Masonic Hall, St. John's (horiz) 2·75 1·50
1512 40c. "Fish on a Newspaper" (Picasso) (horiz) 1·25 1·00
1513 40c. Early astronomical equipment 1·25 1·00
1514 40c. Prince Naruhito and engagement photographs (horiz) 1·25 1·00
1515 60c. Grand Inspector J. Jeffery 3·50 1·75
1516 $3 Masako Owada and engagement photographs (horiz) 2·75 3·50
1517 $4 Willy Brandt and protest march (horiz) 3·50 4·00
1518 $4 Galaxy 3·50 4·00
1519 $5 Alberto Tomba (Italy) (giant slalom) (horiz) 3·50 4·00
1520 $5 "Dying Bull" (Picasso) (horiz) 3·50 4·00
1521 $5 Pres. Clinton and family (horiz) 3·50 4·00

1994. Aviation Anniversaries. Nos. 1848/54 of Antigua optd **BARBUDA MAIL**.
1523 30c. Hugo Eckener and Dr. W. Beckers with airship "Graf Zeppelin" over Lake George, New York 2·25 1·50
1524 40c. Chicago World's Fair from "Graf Zeppelin" 2·25 1·50
1525 40c. Gloster Whittle E28/39, 1941 2·25 1·50
1526 40c. George Washington writing balloon mail letter (vert) 2·25 1·50
1527 $4 Pres. Wilson and Curtiss "Jenny" 6·00 6·50
1528 $5 Airship LZ-129 "Hindenburg" over Ebbets Field baseball stadium, 1937 6·00 6·50
1529 $5 Gloster Meteor in dogfight 6·00 6·50

1994. Centenaries of Henry Ford's First Petrol Engine (Nos. 1531, 1533) and Karl Benz's First Four-wheeled Car (others). Nos. 1856/9 of Antigua optd **BARBUDA MAIL**.
1531 30c. Lincoln Continental 2·00 1·25
1532 40c. Mercedes racing car, 1914 2·00 1·25
1533 $4 Ford "GT40", 1966 7·00 7·50
1534 $5 Mercedes Benz "gull-wing" coupe, 1954 7·00 7·50

1994. Famous Paintings by Rembrandt and Matisse. Nos. 1881/8 of Antigua optd **BARBUDA MAIL**.
1536 15c. "Hannah and Samuel" (Rembrandt) 1·40 1·25
1537 15c. "Guitarist" (Matisse) 1·40 1·25
1538 30c. "The Jewish Bride" (Rembrandt) 1·75 1·10
1539 40c. "Jacob wrestling with the Angel" (Rembrandt) 1·75 1·10
1540 60c. "Interior with a Goldfish Bowl" (Matisse) 2·00 1·25
1541 $1 "Mlle. Yvonne Landsberg" (Matisse) 2·50 1·60
1542 $4 "The Toboggan" (Matisse) 5·50 6·50
1543 $5 "Moses with the Tablets of the Law" (Rembrandt) 5·50 6·50

1994. "Polska '93" International Stamp Exhibition, Poznan. Nos. 1839 and 1841 of Antigua optd **BARBUDA MAIL**.
1545 $1 "Woman Combing her Hair" (W. Slewinski) (horiz) 3·25 2·50
1546 $3 "Artist's Wife with Cat" (Konrad Kryzanowski) (horiz) 6·00 6·50

1994. Orchids. Nos. 1949/56 of Antigua optd **BARBUDA MAIL**.
1548 10c. "Spiranthes lanceolata" 1·75 1·50
1549 20c. "Ionopsis utricularioides" 2·50 1·50
1550 30c. "Tetramicra canaliculata" 2·75 1·25
1551 50c. "Oncidium picturatum" 3·00 1·50
1552 $1 "Epidendrum difforme" 3·75 2·25
1553 $2 "Epidendrum ciliare" 5·00 4·50
1554 $4 "Epidendrum ibaguense" 6·50 7·50
1555 $5 "Epidendrum nocturnum" 6·50 7·50

1994. Centenary of Sierra Club (environmental protection society) (1992). Endangered Species. Nos. 1907/21 of Antigua optd **BARBUDA MAIL**.
1557 $1.50 Sumatran rhinoceros lying down 2·50 2·50
1558 $1.50 Sumatran rhinoceros feeding 2·50 2·50
1559 $1.50 Ring-tailed lemur on ground 2·50 2·50
1560 $1.50 Ring-tailed lemur on branch 2·50 2·50
1561 $1.50 Red-fronted brown lemur on branch 2·50 2·50
1562 $1.50 Head of red-fronted brown lemur 2·50 2·50
1563 $1.50 Head of red-fronted brown lemur in front of trunk 2·50 2·50
1564 $1.50 Sierra Club Centennial emblem 1·60 1·60
1565 $1.50 Head of bactrian camel 2·50 2·50
1566 $1.50 Bactrian camel 2·50 2·50
1567 $1.50 African elephant drinking 2·50 2·50
1568 $1.50 Head of African elephant 2·50 2·50
1569 $1.50 Leopard sitting upright 2·50 2·50
1570 $1.50 Leopard in grass (emblem at right) 2·50 2·50
1571 $1.50 Leopard in grass (emblem at left) 2·50 2·50

1995. World Cup Football Championship, U.S.A. (2nd issue). Nos. 2039/44 of Antigua optd **BARBUDA MAIL**.
1573 15c. Hugo Sanchez (Mexico) 1·25 1·25
1574 35c. Jurgen Klinsmann (Germany) 1·75 1·25
1575 65c. Antiguan player 1·75 1·25
1576 $1.20 Cobi Jones (U.S.A.) 2·50 2·25
1577 $4 Roberto Baggio (Italy) 4·50 5·50
1578 $5 Bwalya Kalusha (Zambia) 4·50 5·50

1995. Christmas. Religious Paintings. Nos. 2058/65 of Antigua optd **BARBUDA MAIL**.
1580 15c. "Virgin and Child by the Fireside" (Robert Campin) 1·00 75
1581 35c. "The Reading Madonna" (Giorgione) 1·50 70
1582 40c. "Madonna and Child" (Giovanni Bellini) 1·50 70
1583 45c. "The Little Madonna" (Da Vinci) 1·50 70
1584 65c. "The Virgin and Child under the Apple Tree" (Lucas Cranach the Elder) 2·00 1·00
1585 75c. "Madonna and Child" (Master of the Female Half-lengths) 2·00 1·25
1586 $1.20 "An Allegory of the Church" (Alessandro Allori) 2·75 3·00
1587 $5 "Madonna and Child wreathed with Flowers" (Jacob Jordaens) 5·50 8·00

1995. "Hong Kong '94" International Stamp Exhibition (1st issue). Nos. 1890/1 of Antigua optd **BARBUDA MAIL**.
1589 40c. Hong Kong 1981 $1 Fish stamp and sampans, Shau Kei Wan 1·50 1·50
1590 40c. Antigua 1990 $2 Reef fish stamp and sampans, Shau Kei Wan 1·50 1·50
See also Nos. 1591/6.

1995. "Hong Kong '94" International Stamp Exhibition (2nd issue). Nos. 1892/7 of Antigua optd **BARBUDA MAIL**.
1591 40c. Terracotta warriors 30 40
1592 40c. Cavalryman and horse 30 40
1593 40c. Warriors in armour 30 40
1594 40c. Painted bronze chariot and team 30 40
1595 40c. Pekingese dog 30 40
1596 40c. Warriors with horses 30 40

1995. Centenary of International Olympic Committee. Nos. 1990/1 of Antigua optd **BARBUDA MAIL**.
1597 50c. Edwin Moses (U.S.A.) (400 metres hurdles), 1984 75 75
1598 $1.50 Steffi Graf (Germany) (tennis), 1988 4·50 3·50

1995. Dogs of the World. Chinese New Year ("Year of the Dog"). Nos. 1923/46 of Antigua optd **BARBUDA MAIL**.
1600 50c. West Highland white terrier 85 85
1601 50c. Beagle 85 85
1602 50c. Scottish terrier 85 85
1603 50c. Pekingese 85 85
1604 50c. Dachshund 85 85
1605 50c. Yorkshire terrier 85 85
1606 50c. Pomeranian 85 85
1607 50c. Poodle 85 85
1608 50c. Shetland sheepdog 85 85
1609 50c. Pug 85 85
1610 50c. Shih tzu 85 85
1611 50c. Chihuahua 85 85
1612 50c. Mastiff 85 85
1613 50c. Border collie 85 85
1614 50c. Samoyed 85 85
1615 50c. Airedale terrier 85 85
1616 50c. English setter 85 85
1617 50c. Rough collie 85 85
1618 50c. Newfoundland 85 85
1619 50c. Weimarana 85 85
1620 50c. English springer spaniel 85 85
1621 50c. Dalmatian 85 85
1622 50c. Boxer 85 85
1623 50c. Old English sheepdog 85 85

1995. Centenary of First English Cricket Tour to the West Indies (1995). Nos. 1994/6 of Antigua optd **BARBUDA MAIL**.
1625 35c. Mike Atherton (England) and Wisden Trophy 1·75 1·00
1626 75c. Viv Richards (West Indies) (vert) 2·50 2·25
1627 $1.20 Richie Richardson (West Indies) and Wisden Trophy 3·00 3·25

1995. "Philakorea '94" International Stamp Exhibition (1st issue). Nos. 1998/2008 of Antigua optd **BARBUDA MAIL**.
1629 40c. Entrance bridge, Songgwangsa Temple 85 70
1630 75c. Long-necked bottle 1·10 1·10
1631 75c. Punch'ong ware jar with floral decoration 1·10 1·10
1632 75c. Punch'ong ware jar with blue dragon pattern 1·10 1·10
1633 75c. Ewer in shape of bamboo shoot 1·10 1·10
1634 75c. Punch'ong ware green jar 1·10 1·10
1635 75c. Pear-shaped bottle 1·10 1·10
1636 75c. Porcelain jar with brown dragon pattern 1·10 1·10
1637 75c. Porcelain jar with floral pattern 1·10 1·10
1638 90c. Song-op Folk Village, Cheju 1·10 1·10
1639 $3 Port Sogwipo 2·75 3·00

1995. 1st Recipients of Order of the Caribbean Community. Nos. 2046/8 of Antigua optd **BARBUDA MAIL**.
1641 65c. Sir Shridath Ramphal 50 55
1642 90c. William Demas 70 75
1643 $1.20 Derek Walcott 1·75 1·75

1995. 25th Anniv of First Moon Landing. Nos. 1977/88 of Antigua optd **BARBUDA MAIL**.
1644 $1.50 Edwin Aldrin (astronaut) 2·00 2·00
1645 $1.50 First lunar footprint 2·00 2·00
1646 $1.50 Neil Armstrong (astronaut) 2·00 2·00
1647 $1.50 Aldrin stepping onto Moon 2·00 2·00
1648 $1.50 Aldrin and equipment 2·00 2·00
1649 $1.50 Aldrin and U.S.A. flag 2·00 2·00
1650 $1.50 Aldrin at Tranquility Base 2·00 2·00
1651 $1.50 Moon plaque 2·00 2·00
1652 $1.50 "Eagle" leaving Moon 2·00 2·00
1653 $1.50 Command module in lunar orbit 2·00 2·00
1654 $1.50 First day cover of U.S.A. 1969 10c. First Man on Moon stamp 2·00 2·00
1655 $1.50 Pres. Nixon and astronauts 2·00 2·00

1995. International Year of the Family. No. 1993 of Antigua optd **BARBUDA MAIL**.
1656 90c. Antiguan family 1·50 1·50

1995. 50th Anniv of D-Day. Nos. 2010/12 of Antigua optd **BARBUDA MAIL**.
1658 40c. Short S.25 Sunderland flying boat 1·75 1·00
1659 $2 Lockheed P-38 Lightning fighters attacking train 3·75 3·75
1660 $3 Martin B-26 Marauder bombers 4·50 4·50

122 Queen Elizabeth the Queen Mother (95th birthday)

1995. Anniversaries. Multicoloured.
1662 $7.50 Type **122** 8·50 8·50
1663 $8 German bombers over St. Paul's Cathedral, London (horiz) (50th anniv of end of Second World War) 11·00 11·00
1664 $8 New York skyline with U.N. and national flags (horiz) (50th anniv of United Nations) 7·50 8·50

1995. Hurricane Relief. Nos. 1662/4 surch **HURRICANE RELIEF** and premium.
1665 $7.50+$1 Type **122** (90th birthday) 6·50 7·50
1666 $8+$1 German bombers over St. Paul's Cathedral, London (horiz) (50th anniv of end of Second World War) 6·50 7·50
1667 $8+$1 New York skyline with U.N. and national flags (horiz) (50th anniv of United Nations) 6·50 7·50

1996. Marine Life. Nos. 1967/75 of Antigua optd **BARBUDA MAIL**.
1668 50c. Bottlenose dolphin 85 85
1669 50c. Killer whale 85 85
1670 50c. Spinner dolphin 85 85
1671 50c. Oceanic sunfish 85 85
1672 50c. Caribbean reef shark and short fin pilot whale 85 85
1673 50c. Copper-banded butterflyfish 85 85
1674 50c. Mosaic moray 85 85
1675 50c. Clown triggerfish 85 85
1676 50c. Red lobster 85 85

1996. Christmas. Religious Paintings. Nos. 2267/72 of Antigua optd **BARBUDA MAIL**.
1678 15c. "Rest on the Flight into Egypt" (Paolo Veronese) 50 40
1679 35c. "Madonna and Child" (Van Dyck) 65 40
1680 65c. "Sacred Conversation Piece" (Veronese) 80 55
1681 75c. "Vision of St. Anthony" (Van Dyck) 90 60

1682 90c. "Virgin and Child" (Van Eyck) . . . . 1·10 75
1683 $6 "The Immaculate Conception" (Giovanni Tiepolo) . . . . 4·25 5·50

1996. Stars of Country and Western Music. Nos. 2014/37 of Antigua optd **BARBUDA MAIL.**

1685 75c. Travis Tritt 75 75
1686 75c. Dwight Yoakam . . . 75 75
1687 75c. Billy Ray Cyrus . . . 75 75
1688 75c. Alan Jackson 75 75
1689 75c. Garth Brooks 75 75
1690 75c. Vince Gill 75 75
1691 75c. Clint Black 75 75
1692 75c. Eddie Rabbit 75 75
1693 75c. Patsy Cline 75 75
1694 75c. Tanya Tucker 75 75
1695 75c. Dolly Parton 75 75
1696 75c. Anne Murray 75 75
1697 75c. Tammy Wynette . . . 75 75
1698 75c. Loretta Lynn 75 75
1699 75c. Reba McEntire 75 75
1700 75c. Skeeter Davis 75 75
1701 75c. Hank Snow 75 75
1702 75c. Gene Autry 75 75
1703 75c. Jimmie Rodgers 75 75
1704 75c. Ernest Tubb 75 75
1705 75c. Eddy Arnold 75 75
1706 75c. Willie Nelson 75 75
1707 75c. Johnny Cash 75 75
1708 75c. George Jones 75 75

1996. Birds. Nos. 2067/81 of Antigua optd **BARBUDA MAIL.**

1710 15c. Magnificent frigate bird 10 15
1711 25c. Antillean euphonia ("Blue-hooded Euphonia") 15 20
1712 35c. Eastern meadowlark ("Meadowlark") 20 25
1713 40c. Red-billed tropic bird 20 25
1714 45c. Greater flamingo . . . 25 30
1715 60c. Yellow-faced grassquit 30 35
1716 65c. Yellow-billed cuckoo 35 40
1717 70c. Purple-throated carib 35 40
1718 75c. Bananaquit 40 45
1719 90c. Painted bunting 45 50
1720 $1.20 Red-legged honeycreeper 60 65
1721 $2 Northern jacana ("Jacana") . . . . 1·00 1·10
1722 $5 Greater Antillean bullfinch . . . . 2·50 2·75
1723 $10 Caribbean elaenia . . . 5·00 5·25
1724 $20 Brown trembler ("Trembler") . . . . . . 10·00 10·50

1996. Birds. Nos. 2050, 2052 and 2054/6 of Antigua optd **BARBUDA MAIL.**

1725 15c. Bridled quail dove . . 75 60
1726 40c. Purple-throated carib (vert) . . . . 1·25 50
1727 $1 Broad-winged hawk ("Antigua Broad-winged Hawk") (vert) . . . . . 2·00 1·25
1728 $4 Yellow warbler . . . . . 3·50 4·50

1996. Prehistoric Animals. Nos. 2082/99 of Antigua optd **BARBUDA MAIL.**

1730 15c. Head of pachycephalosaurus 90 90
1731 20c. Head of afrovenator . . 90 90
1732 65c. Centrosaurus 90 90
1733 75c. Kronosaurus (horiz) . . 90 90
1734 75c. Ichthyosaurus (horiz) 90 90
1735 75c. Plesiosaurus (horiz) . . 90 90
1736 75c. Archelon (horiz) . . . 90 90
1737 75c. Pair of tyrannosaurus (horiz) 90 90
1738 75c. Tyrannosaurus (horiz) 90 90
1739 75c. Parasaurolophus (horiz) 90 90
1740 75c. Pair of parasaurolophus (horiz) 90 90
1741 75c. Oviraptor (horiz) . . . 90 90
1742 75c. Protoceratops with eggs (horiz) 90 90
1743 75c. Pteranodon and protoceratops (horiz) . . 90 90
1744 75c. Pair of protoceratops (horiz) 90 90
1745 90c. Pentaceratops drinking 1·25 1·25
1746 $1.20 Head of tarbosaurus 1·60 1·60
1747 $5 Head of styracosaurus 4·00 4·50

1996. Olympic Games, Atlanta (1st issue). Previous Gold Medal Winners. Nos. 2101/6 of Antigua optd **BARBUDA MAIL.**

1749 15c. Al Oerter (U.S.A.) (discus – 1956, 1960, 1964, 1968) 75 70
1750 20c. Greg Louganis (U.S.A.) (diving – 1984, 1988) . . 75 70
1751 65c. Naim Suleymanoglu (Turkey) (weightlifting – 1988) . . . . 1·25 70
1752 90c. Louise Ritter (U.S.A.) (high jump – 1988) . . . 1·75 1·10
1753 $1.20 Nadia Comaneci (Rumania) (gymnastics – 1976) . . . . 2·00 1·90
1754 $5 Olga Bondarenko (Russia) (10,000 m – 1988) . . . . 4·00 6·00

See also Nos. 1922/43.

1996. 18th World Scout Jamboree, Netherlands. Tents. Nos. 2203/8 of Antigua optd **BARBUDA MAIL.**

1756 $1.20 The Explorer Tent . . 1·00 1·00
1757 $1.20 Camper tent . . . . 1·00 1·00
1758 $1.20 Wall tent . . . . . 1·00 1·00
1759 $1.20 Trail tent . . . . . . 1·00 1·00
1760 $1.20 Miner's tent . . . . . 1·00 1·00
1761 $1.20 Voyager tent . . . . 1·00 1·00

1996. Centenary of Nobel Prize Trust Fund. Nos. 2226/43 of Antigua optd **BARBUDA MAIL.**

1763 $1 Dag Hammarskjold (1961 Peace) 60 60
1764 $1 Georg Wittig (1979 Chemistry) 60 60
1765 $1 Wilhelm Ostwold (1909 Chemistry) 60 60
1766 $1 Robert Koch (1905 Medicine) 60 60
1767 $1 Karl Ziegler (1963 Chemistry) 60 60
1768 $1 Alexander Fleming (1945 Medicine) 60 60
1769 $1 Hermann Staudinger (1953 Chemistry) 60 60
1770 $1 Manfred Eigen (1967 Chemistry) 60 60
1771 $1 Arno Penzias (1978 Physics) 60 60
1772 $1 Shumal Agnon (1966 Literature) 60 60
1773 $1 Rudyard Kipling (1907 Literature) 60 60
1774 $1 Aleksandr Solzhenitsyn (1970 Literature) 60 60
1775 $1 Jack Steinburger (1988 Physics) 60 60
1776 $1 Andrei Sakharov (1975 Peace) 60 60
1777 $1 Otto Stern (1943 Physics) 60 60
1778 $1 John Steinbeck (1962 Literature) 60 60
1779 $1 Nadine Gordimer (1991 Literature) 60 60
1780 $1 William Faulkner (1949 Literature) 60 60

1996. 70th Birthday of Queen Elizabeth II. Nos. 2355/7 of Antigua optd **BARBUDA MAIL.**

1782 $2 Queen Elizabeth II in blue dress . . . . 1·10 1·10
1783 $2 With bouquet . . . . . 1·10 1·10
1784 $2 In Garter robes . . . . 1·10 1·10

1997. Christmas. Religious Paintings by Filippo Lippi. Nos. 2377/82 of Antigua optd **BARBUDA MAIL.**

1786 60c. "Madonna Enthroned" 35 35
1787 90c. "Adoration of the Child and Saints" 55 55
1788 $1 "The Annunciation" . . 60 60
1789 $1.20 "Birth of the Virgin" 75 75
1790 $1.60 "Adoration of the Child" 90 90
1791 $1.75 "Madonna and Child" 1·00 1·00

1997. 50th Anniv of F.A.O. Nos. 2121/3 of Antigua optd **BARBUDA MAIL.**

1793 75c. Woman buying produce from market 80 80
1794 90c. Women shopping . . . 90 90
1795 $1.20 Women talking . . . 1·10 1·10

1997. 90th Anniv of Rotary International (1995). No. 2125 of Antigua optd **BARBUDA MAIL.**

1797 $5 Beach and rotary emblem 2·75 3·00

1997. 50th Anniv of End of Second World War in Europe and the Pacific. Nos. 2108/15 and 2132/7 of Antigua optd **BARBUDA MAIL.**

1799 $1.20 Map of Berlin showing Russian advance 55 60
1800 $1.20 Russian tank and infantry 55 60
1801 $1.20 Street fighting in Berlin 55 60
1802 $1.20 German tank exploding 55 60
1803 $1.20 Russian air raid . . . 55 60
1804 $1.20 German troops surrendering 55 60
1805 $1.20 Hoisting the Soviet flag on the Reichstag . . 55 60
1806 $1.20 Captured German standards 55 60
1807 $1.20 Gen. Chiang Kai-shek and Chinese guerrillas . . 55 60
1808 $1.20 Gen. Douglas MacArthur and beach landing 55 60
1809 $1.20 Gen. Claire Chennault and U.S. fighter aircraft 55 60
1810 $1.20 Brig. Orde Wingate and supply drop 55 60
1811 $1.20 Gen. Joseph Stilwell and U.S. supply plane . . 55 60
1812 $1.20 Field-Marshal Bill Slim and loading cow onto plane 55 60

1997. Bees. Nos. 2172/5 of Antigua optd **BARBUDA MAIL.**

1814 90c. Mining bees 65 50
1815 $1.20 Solitary bee 80 80
1816 $1.65 Leaf-cutter bee . . . 1·10 1·25
1817 $1.75 Honey bees . . . . . 1·25 1·40

1997. Flowers. Nos. 177/88 of Antigua optd **BARBUDA MAIL.**

1819 75c. Narcissus 55 60
1820 75c. Camellia 55 60
1821 75c. Iris 55 60
1822 75c. Tulip 55 60
1823 75c. Poppy 55 60
1824 75c. Peony 55 60
1825 75c. Magnolia 55 60
1826 75c. Oriental lily 55 60
1827 75c. Rose 55 60
1828 75c. Pansy 55 60
1829 75c. Hydrangea 55 60
1830 75c. Azaleas 55 60

1997. Cats. Nos. 2190/201 of Antigua optd **BARBUDA MAIL.**

1832 45c. Somali 35 40
1833 45c. Persian and butterflies 35 40
1834 45c. Devon rex 35 40
1835 45c. Turkish angora 35 40
1836 45c. Himalayan 35 40
1837 45c. Maine coon 35 40
1838 45c. Ginger non-pedigree . . 35 40
1839 45c. American wirehair . . . 35 40
1840 45c. British shorthair . . . 35 40
1841 45c. American curl 35 40
1842 45c. Black non-pedigree and butterfly 35 40
1843 45c. Birman 35 40

1997. 95th Birthday of Queen Elizabeth the Queen Mother. Nos. 2127/30 of Antigua optd **BARBUDA MAIL.**

1845 $1.50 brown, lt brown & black . . . . 1·50 1·50
1846 $1.50 multicoloured . . . . 1·50 1·50
1847 $1.50 multicoloured . . . . 1·50 1·50
1848 $1.50 multicoloured . . . . 1·50 1·50

1997. 50th Anniv of United Nations. Nos. 2117/19 of Antigua optd **BARBUDA MAIL.**

1850 75c. Signatures and Earl of Halifax 35 40
1851 90c. Virginia Gildersleeve 40 45
1852 $1.20 Harold Stassen . . . 55 60

1997. Trains of the World. Nos. 2210/24 of Antigua optd **BARBUDA MAIL.**

1854 35c. Trans-Gabon diesel-electric train 40 30
1855 65c. Canadian Pacific diesel-electric locomotive 50 40
1856 75c. Santa Fe Railway diesel-electric locomotive, U.S.A. 50 50
1857 90c. High Speed Train, Great Britain 50 60
1858 $1.20 TGV express train, France 55 60
1859 $1.20 Diesel-electric locomotive, Australia . . 55 60
1860 $1.20 Pendolino "ETR 450" electric train, Italy 55 60
1861 $1.20 Diesel-electric locomotive, Thailand . . 55 60
1862 $1.20 Pennsylvania Railroad Type 4 steam locomotive, U.S.A. 55 60
1863 $1.20 Beyer-Garratt steam locomotive, East African Railways 55 60
1864 $1.20 Natal Govt steam locomotive 55 60
1865 $1.20 Rail gun, American Civil War 55 60
1866 $1.20 Locomotive "Lion" (red livery), Great Britain 55 60
1867 $1.20 William Hedley's "Puffing Billy" (green livery), Great Britain . . 55 60
1868 $6 Amtrak high speed diesel locomotive, U.S.A. . . . 2·75 3·50

1997. Golden Wedding of Queen Elizabeth II and Prince Philip (1st issue). Nos. 1662/3 optd **Golden Wedding of H.M. Queen Elizabeth II and Prince Philip 1947-1997.**

1870 $7.50 Type **122** . . . . . 3·50 4·00
1871 $8 German bombers over St. Paul's Cathedral, London (horiz) . . . . . 3·75 4·25

See also Nos. 1925/30.

1997. Fungi. Nos. 2274/81 of Antigua optd **BARBUDA MAIL.**

1872 75c. "Hygrophoropsis aurantiaca" 55 55
1873 75c. "Hygrophorus bakerensis" 55 55
1874 75c. "Hygrophorus conicus" 55 55
1875 75c. "Hygrophorus miniatus" ("Hygrocybe miniata") 55 55
1876 75c. "Suillus brevipes" . . . 55 55
1877 75c. "Suillus luteus" . . . 55 55
1878 75c. "Suillus granulatus" . . 55 55
1879 75c. "Suillus caerulescens" 55 55

1997. Birds. Nos. 2140/63 of Antigua optd **BARBUDA MAIL.**

1881 75c. Purple-throated carib 45 50
1882 75c. Antilean crested hummingbird 45 50
1883 75c. Bananaquit 45 50
1884 75c. Mangrove cuckoo . . . 45 50
1885 75c. Troupial 45 50
1886 75c. Green-throated carib 45 50
1887 75c. Yellow warbler 45 50
1888 75c. Antillean euphonia ("Blue-hooded Euphonia") 45 50
1889 75c. Scaly-breasted thrasher 45 50
1890 75c. Burrowing owl 45 50
1891 75c. Carib grackle 45 50
1892 75c. Adelaide's warbler . . 45 50
1893 75c. Ring-necked duck . . . 45 50
1894 75c. Ruddy duck 45 50
1895 75c. Green-winged teal . . . 45 50
1896 75c. Wood duck 45 50
1897 75c. Hooded merganser . . 45 50
1898 75c. Lesser scaup 45 50
1899 75c. Black-billed whistling duck ("West Indian Tree Duck") 45 50
1900 75c. Fulvous whistling duck 45 50
1901 75c. Bahama pintail 45 50
1902 75c. Northern shoveler ("Shoveler") 45 50
1903 75c. Masked duck 45 50
1904 75c. American wigeon . . . 45 50

1997. Sailing Ships. Nos. 2283/2300 of Antigua optd **BARBUDA MAIL.**

1906 15c. H.M.S. "Resolution" (Cook) 40 40
1907 25c. "Mayflower" (Pilgrim Fathers) 40 30
1908 45c. "Santa Maria" (Columbus) 40 30
1909 75c. "Aemilia" (Dutch galleon) 40 45
1910 75c. "Sovereign of the Seas" (English galleon) 40 45
1911 90c. H.M.S. "Victory" (Nelson) 50 55
1912 $1.20 As No. 1909 . . . . 55 60
1913 $1.20 As No. 1910 . . . . 55 60
1914 $1.20 "Royal Louis" (French galleon) 55 60
1915 $1.20 H.M.S. "Royal George" (ship of the line) 55 60
1916 $1.20 "Le Protecteur" (French frigate) 55 60
1917 $1.20 As No. 1911 . . . . 55 60
1918 $1.50 As No. 1908 . . . . 70 75
1919 $1.50 "Victoria" (Magellan) 70 75
1920 $1.50 "Golden Hind" (Drake) 70 75
1921 $1.50 As No. 1907 . . . . 70 75
1922 $1.50 "Griffin" (La Salle) 70 75
1923 $1.50 As No. 1906 . . . . 70 75

1997. Golden Wedding of Queen Elizabeth and Prince Philip (2nd issue). Nos. 2474/9 of Antigua optd **BARBUDA MAIL.**

1925 $1 Queen Elizabeth II . . . 90 90
1926 $1 Royal coat of arms . . . 90 90
1927 $1 Queen Elizabeth and Prince Philip at reception 90 90
1928 $1 Queen Elizabeth and Prince Philip in landau . . 90 90
1929 $1 Balmoral 90 90
1930 $1 Prince Philip 90 90

1997. Christmas. Religious Paintings. Nos. 2566/71 of Antigua optd **BARBUDA MAIL.**

1932 15c. "The Angel leaving Tobias and his Family" (Rembrandt) 30 30
1933 25c. "The Resurrection" (Martin Knoller) 35 30
1934 60c. "Astronomy" (Raphael) 50 40
1935 75c. "Music-making Angel" (Melozzo da Forli) . . . 55 45
1936 90c. "Amor" (Parmigianino) 70 60
1937 $1.20 "Madonna and Child with Saints" (Rosso Fiorentino) . . . . 90 1·10

1998. Sea Birds. Nos. 2325/32 of Antigua optd **BARBUDA MAIL.**

1939 75c. Black skimmer 70 70
1940 75c. Black-capped petrel . . 70 70
1941 75c. Sooty tern 70 70
1942 75c. Royal tern 70 70
1943 75c. Pomarine skua ("Pomarine Jaegger") . . 70 70
1944 75c. White-tailed tropic bird 70 70
1945 75c. Northern gannet . . . 70 70
1946 75c. Laughing gull 70 70

1998. Centenary of Radio. Entertainers. Nos. 2372/5 of Antigua optd **BARBUDA MAIL.**

1948 65c. Kate Smith 45 45
1949 75c. Dinah Shore 50 50
1950 90c. Rudy Vallee 60 60
1951 $1.20 Bing Crosby 75 75

1998. Olympic Games, Atlanta (2nd issue). Previous Medal Winners. Nos. 2302/23 of Antigua optd **BARBUDA MAIL.**

1953 65c. Florence Griffith Joyner (U.S.A.) (Gold – track, 1988) 60 60
1954 75c. Olympic Stadium, Seoul (1988) (horiz) 60 60
1955 90c. Allison Jolly and Lynne Jewell (U.S.A.) (Gold – yachting, 1988) (horiz) . . 60 60
1956 90c. Wolfgang Nordwig (Germany) (Gold – pole vaulting, 1972) 60 60
1957 90c. Shirley Strong (Great Britain) (Silver – 100 m hurdles, 1984) 60 60
1958 90c. Sergei Bubka (Russia) (Gold – pole vault, 1988) 60 60
1959 90c. Filbert Bayi (Tanzania) (Silver – 3000 m steeplechase, 1980) . . . 60 60
1960 90c. Victor Saneyev (Russia) (Gold – triple jump, 1968, 1972, 1976) 60 60
1961 90c. Silke Renk (Germany) (Gold – javelin, 1992) . . 60 60
1962 90c. Daley Thompson (Great Britain) (Gold – decathlon, 1980, 1984) . . 60 60
1963 90c. Robert Richards (U.S.A.) (Gold – pole vault, 1952, 1956) 60 60
1964 90c. Parry O'Brien (U.S.A.) (Gold – shot put, 1952, 1956) 60 60
1965 90c. Ingrid Kramer (Germany) (Gold – Women's platform diving, 1960) 60 60
1966 90c. Kelly McCormick (U.S.A.) (Silver – Women's springboard diving, 1984) 60 60
1967 90c. Gary Tobian (U.S.A.) (Gold – Men's springboard diving, 1960) 60 60

1968	90c. Greg Louganis (U.S.A.) (Gold – Men's diving, 1984 and 1988)	60	60
1969	90c. Michelle Mitchell (U.S.A.) (Silver – Women's platform diving, 1984 and 1988)	60	60
1970	90c. Zhou Jihong (China) (Gold – Women's platform diving, 1984)	60	60
1971	90c. Wendy Wyland (U.S.A.) (Bronze – Women's platform diving, 1984)	60	60
1972	90c. Xu Yanmei (China) (Gold – Women's platform diving, 1988)	60	60
1973	90c. Fu Mingxia (China) (Gold – Women's platform diving, 1992)	60	60
1974	$1.20 2000 m tandem cycle race (horiz)	1·00	1·00

1998. World Cup Football Championship, France. Nos. 2525/38 of Antigua optd **BARBUDA MAIL.**

1976	60c. multicoloured	60	60
1977	75c. brown	60	60
1978	90c. multicoloured	65	65
1979	$1 brown	65	65
1980	$1 brown	65	65
1981	$1 brown	65	65
1982	$1 black	65	65
1983	$1 brown	65	65
1984	$1 brown	65	65
1985	$1 brown	65	65
1986	$1 brown	65	65
1987	$1.20 multicoloured	70	70
1988	$1.65 multicoloured	85	85
1989	$1.75 multicoloured	95	95

1998. Cavalry through the Ages. Nos. 2359/62 of Antigua optd **BARBUDA MAIL.**

1991	60c. Ancient Egyptian cavalryman	60	60
1992	60c. 13th-century English knight	60	60
1993	60c. 16th-century Spanish lancer	60	60
1994	60c. 18th-century Chinese cavalryman	60	60

1998. 50th Anniv of U.N.I.C.E.F. Nos. 2364/6 of Antigua optd **BARBUDA MAIL.**

1996	75c. Girl in red sari	60	60
1997	90c. South American mother and child	70	70
1998	$1.20 Nurse with child	80	80

1998. 3000th Anniv of Jerusalem. Nos. 2368/70 of Antigua optd **BARBUDA MAIL.**

2000	75c. Tomb of Zachariah and "Verbascum sinuatum"	65	65
2001	90c. Pool of Siloam and "Hyacinthus orientalis"	75	75
2002	$1.20 Hurva Synagogue and "Ranunculus asiaticus"	1·10	1·10

1998. Diana, Princess of Wales Commemoration. Nos. 2573/84 of Antigua optd **BARBUDA MAIL.**

2004	$1.65 Diana, Princess of Wales	1·00	1·00
2005	$1.65 Wearing hoop earrings (red and black)	1·00	1·00
2006	$1.65 Carrying bouquet	1·00	1·00
2007	$1.65 Wearing floral hat	1·00	1·00
2008	$1.65 With Prince Harry	1·00	1·00
2009	$1.65 Wearing white jacket	1·00	1·00
2010	$1.65 In kitchen	1·00	1·00
2011	$1.65 Wearing black and white dress	1·00	1·00
2012	$1.65 Wearing hat (brown and black)	1·00	1·00
2013	$1.65 Wearing floral print dress (brown and black)	1·00	1·00
2014	$1.65 Dancing with John Travolta	1·00	1·00
2015	$1.65 Wearing white hat and jacket	1·00	1·00

1998. Broadway Musical Stars. Nos. 2384/92 of Antigua optd **BARBUDA MAIL.**

2017	$1 Robert Preston ("The Music Man")	65	65
2018	$1 Michael Crawford ("Phantom of the Opera")	65	65
2019	$1 Zero Mostel ("Fiddler on the Roof")	65	65
2020	$1 Patti Lupone ("Evita")	65	65
2021	$1 Raul Julia ("Threepenny Opera")	65	65
2022	$1 Mary Martin ("South Pacific")	65	65
2023	$1 Carol Channing ("Hello Dolly")	65	65
2024	$1 Yul Brynner ("The King and I")	65	65
2025	$1 Julie Andrews ("My Fair Lady")	65	65

1998. 20th Death Anniv of Charlie Chaplin (film star). Nos. 2404/12 of Antigua optd **BARBUDA MAIL.**

2027	$1 Charlie Chaplin as young man	65	65
2028	$1 Pulling face	65	65
2029	$1 Looking over shoulder	65	65
2030	$1 In cap	65	65
2031	$1 In front of star	65	65
2032	$1 In "The Great Dictator"	65	65
2033	$1 With movie camera and megaphone	65	65
2034	$1 Standing in front of camera lens	65	65
2035	$1 Putting on make-up	65	65

1998. Butterflies. Nos. 2414/35 of Antigua optd **BARBUDA MAIL.**

2037	90c. "Charaxes porthos"	70	70
2038	$1.10 "Charaxes protoclea protoclea"	75	75
2039	$1.10 "Byblia ilithyia"	75	75
2040	$1.10 Black-headed tchagra (bird)	75	75
2041	$1.10 "Charaxes nobilis"	75	75
2042	$1.10 "Pseudacraea boisduvali trimeni"	75	75
2043	$1.10 "Charaxes smaragdalis"	75	75
2044	$1.10 "Charaxes lasti"	75	75
2045	$1.10 "Pseudacraea poggei"	75	75
2046	$1.10 "Graphium colonna"	75	75
2047	$1.10 Carmine bee eater (bird)	75	75
2048	$1.10 "Pseudacraea eurytus"	75	75
2049	$1.10 "Hypolimnas monteironis"	75	75
2050	$1.10 "Charaxes anticlea"	75	75
2051	$1.10 "Graphium leonidas"	75	75
2052	$1.10 "Graphium illyris"	75	75
2053	$1.10 "Nephronia argia"	75	75
2054	$1.10 "Graphium policenes"	75	75
2055	$1.10 "Papilio dardanus"	75	75
2056	$1.20 "Aethiopana honorius"	75	75
2057	$1.60 "Charaxes hadrianus"	1·00	1·00
2058	$1.75 "Precis westermanni"	1·10	1·10

1998. Christmas. Dogs. Nos. 2771/7 of Antigua optd **BARBUDA MAIL.**

2060	15c. Border collie	30	30
2061	25c. Dalmatian	40	30
2062	65c. Weimaraner	70	50
2063	75c. Scottish terrier	75	55
2064	90c. Long-haired dachshund	85	60
2065	$1.20 Golden retriever	95	95
2066	$2 Pekingese	1·50	2·00

1999. Lighthouses of the World. Nos. 2612/19 of Antigua optd **BARBUDA MAIL.**

2068	45c. Europa Point Lighthouse, Gibraltar	65	50
2069	65c. Tierra del Fuego, Argentina (horiz)	70	70
2070	75c. Point Loma, California, U.S.A. (horiz)	70	70
2071	90c. Groenpoint, Cape Town, South Africa	80	80
2072	$1 Youghal, Cork, Ireland	90	90
2073	$1.20 Launceston, Tasmania, Australia	1·00	1·00
2074	$1.65 Point Abino, Ontario, Canada (horiz)	1·25	1·25
2075	$1.75 Great Inagua, Bahamas (horiz)	1·25	1·25

1999. Endangered Species. Nos. 2457/68 of Antigua optd **BARBUDA MAIL.**

2077	$1.20 Red bishop	80	85
2078	$1.20 Yellow baboon	80	85
2079	$1.20 Superb starling	80	85
2080	$1.20 Ratel	80	85
2081	$1.20 Hunting dog	80	85
2082	$1.20 Serval	80	85
2083	$1.65 Okapi	90	1·00
2084	$1.65 Giant forest squirrel	90	1·00
2085	$1.65 Lesser masked weaver	90	1·00
2086	$1.65 Small-spotted genet	90	1·00
2087	$1.65 Yellow-billed stork	90	1·00
2088	$1.65 Red-headed agama	90	1·00

1999. "Pacific 97" International Stamp Exhibition, San Francisco. Death Centenary of Heinrich von Stephan (founder of the U.P.U.). Nos. 2481/3 of Antigua optd **BARBUDA MAIL.**

2090	$1.75 blue	1·25	1·40
2091	$1.75 brown	1·25	1·40
2092	$1.75 mauve	1·25	1·40

DESIGNS: No. 2090, Kaiser Wilhelm I and Heinrich von Stephan; 2091, Von Stephan and Mercury; 2092, Carrier pigeon and loft.

1999. 175th Anniv of Brothers Grimm's Third Collection of Fairy Tales. *Cinderella*. Nos. 2485/7 of Antigua optd **BARBUDA MAIL.**

2094	$1.75 The Ugly Sisters and their Mother	1·25	1·40
2095	$1.75 Cinderella and her Fairy Godmother	1·25	1·40
2096	$1.75 Cinderella and the Prince	1·25	1·40

1999. Orchids of the World. Nos. 2502/23 of Antigua optd **BARBUDA MAIL.**

2098	45c. *Odontoglossum cervantesii*	50	35
2099	65c. *Phalaenopsis* Medford Star	60	65
2100	75c. *Vanda* Motes Resplendent	65	65
2101	90c. *Odontonia* Debutante	70	70
2102	$1 *Iwanagaara* Apple Blossom	80	80
2103	$1.65 *Cattleya* Sophia Martin	1·10	1·25
2104	$1.65 Dogface Butterfly	1·10	1·25
2105	$1.65 *Laeliocattleya* Mini Purple	1·10	1·25
2106	$1.65 *Cymbidium* Showgirl	1·10	1·25
2107	$1.65 *Brassolaeliocattleya* Dorothy Bertsch	1·10	1·25
2108	$1.65 *Disa blackii*	1·10	1·25
2109	$1.65 *Paphiopedilum leeanum*	1·10	1·25
2110	$1.65 *Paphiopedilum macranthum*	1·10	1·25
2111	$1.65 *Brassocattleya* Angel Lace	1·10	1·25
2112	$1.65 *Saphrolae liocattleya* Precious Stones	1·10	1·25
2113	$1.65 Orange Theope Butterfly	1·10	1·25
2114	$1.65 *Promenaea xanthina*	1·10	1·25
2115	$1.65 *Lycasle macrobulbon*	1·10	1·25
2116	$1.65 *Amestella philippinensis*	1·10	1·25
2117	$1.65 *Masdevallia* Machu Picchu	1·10	1·25
2118	$1.65 *Phalaenopsis* Zuma Urchin	1·10	1·25
2119	$2 *Dendrobium victoria-reginae*	1·25	1·40

1999. 50th Death Anniv of Paul Harris (founder of Rotary International). No. 2472 of Antigua optd **BARBUDA MAIL.**

2121	$1.65 Paul Harris and James Grant	1·40	1·60

1999. Royal Wedding. Nos. 2912/15 of Antigua optd **BARBOUDA MAIL.**

2123	$3 Sophie Rhys-Jones	1·50	1·75
2124	$3 Sophie and Prince Edward	1·50	1·75
2125	$3 Prince Edward	1·50	1·75

All examples of Nos. 2123/5 show the incorrect country overprint as above.

1999. Fungi. Nos. 2489/2500 of Antigua optd **BARBUDA MAIL.**

2127	45c. *Marasmius rotula*	50	35
2128	65c. *Cantharellus cibarius*	55	55
2129	70c. *Lepiota cristata*	60	60
2130	90c. *Auricularia mesenterica*	70	70
2131	$1 *Pholiota alnicola*	75	75
2132	$1.65 *Leccinum aurantiacum*	1·10	1·10
2133	$1.75 *Entoloma serrulatum*	1·10	1·10
2134	$1.75 *Panaeolus sphinctrinus*	1·10	1·10
2135	$1.75 *Volvariella bombycina*	1·10	1·10
2136	$1.75 *Conocybe percincta*	1·10	1·10
2137	$1.75 *Pluteus cervinus*	1·10	1·10
2138	$1.75 *Russula foetens*	1·10	1·10

1999. 1st Death Anniv of Diana, Princess of Wales. No. 2753 of Antigua optd **BARBUDA MAIL.**

2140	$1.20 Diana, Princess of Wales	75	75

1999. Railway Locomotives of the World. Nos. 2553/64 of Antigua optd **BARBUDA MAIL.**

2141	$1.65 Original drawing by Richard Trevithick, 1803	1·00	1·00
2142	$1.65 William Hedley's *Puffing Billy*, (1813–14)	1·00	1·00
2143	$1.65 Crampton locomotive of French Nord Railway, 1858	1·00	1·00
2144	$1.65 Lawrence Machine Shop locomotive, U.S.A., 1860	1·00	1·00
2145	$1.65 Natchez and Hamburg Railway steam locomotive *Mississippi*, U.S.A., 1834	1·00	1·00
2146	$1.65 Bury "Coppernob" locomotive, Furness Railway, 1846	1·00	1·00
2147	$1.65 David Joy's *Jenny Lind*, 1847	1·00	1·00
2148	$1.65 Schenectady Atlantic locomotive, U.S.A., 1899	1·00	1·00
2149	$1.65 Kitson Class 1800 tank locomotive, Japan, 1881	1·00	1·00
2150	$1.65 Pennsylvania Railroad express freight	1·00	1·00
2151	$1.65 Karl Golsdorf's 4 cylinder locomotive, Austria	1·00	1·00
2152	$1.65 Series "E" locomotive, Russia, 1930	1·00	1·00

1999. 175th Anniv of Cedar Hall Moravian Church. Nos. 2605/10 of Antigua optd **BARBUDA MAIL.**

2154	20c. First Church and Manse, 1822–40	25	25
2155	45c. Cedar Hall School, 1840	35	30
2156	75c. Hugh A. King, minister, 1945–53	50	45
2157	90c. Present Church building	55	50
2158	$1.20 Water tank, 1822	70	75
2159	$2 Former Manse, demolished 1978	1·00	1·25

1999. Christmas. Religious Paintings. Nos. 2945/50 of Antigua optd **BARBUDA MAIL.**

2161	15c. multicoloured	20	20
2162	25c. black, stone and yellow	25	20
2163	45c. multicoloured	35	30
2164	60c. multicoloured	60	35
2165	$2 multicoloured	1·25	1·50
2166	$4 black, stone and yellow	2·00	2·50

1999. Centenary of Thomas Oliver Robinson Memorial School. Nos. 2634/39 of Antigua optd **BARBUDA MAIL.**

2168	20c. green and black	20	20
2169	45c. multicoloured	35	30
2170	65c. green and black	50	40
2171	75c. multicoloured	55	50
2172	90c. multicoloured	60	60
2173	$1.20 brown, green and black	70	80

2000. Cats and Dogs. Nos. 2540/51 of Antigua optd **BARBUDA MAIL.**

2175	$1.65 Scottish fold kitten	1·00	1·00
2176	$1.65 Japanese bobtail	1·00	1·00
2177	$1.65 Tabby manx	1·00	1·00
2178	$1.65 Bicolor American shorthair	1·00	1·00
2179	$1.65 Sorel Abyssinian	1·00	1·00
2180	$1.65 Himalayan blue point	1·00	1·00
2181	$1.65 Dachshund	1·00	1·00
2182	$1.65 Staffordshire terrier	1·00	1·00
2183	$1.65 Shar-pei	1·00	1·00
2184	$1.65 Beagle	1·00	1·00
2185	$1.65 Norfolk terrier	1·00	1·00
2186	$1.65 Golden retriever	1·00	1·00

2000. Fishes. Nos. 2586/603 of Antigua optd **BARBUDA MAIL.**

2188	75c. Yellow damselfish	60	50
2189	90c. Barred hamlet	65	55
2190	$1 Yellow-tailed damselfish ("Jewelfish")	70	70
2191	$1.20 Blue-headed wrasse	80	80
2192	$1.50 Queen angelfish	1·00	1·00
2193	$1.65 Jackknife-fish	1·00	1·00
2194	$1.65 Spot-finned hogfish	1·00	1·00
2195	$1.65 Sergeant major	1·00	1·00
2196	$1.65 Neon goby	1·00	1·00
2197	$1.65 Jawfish	1·00	1·00
2198	$1.65 Flamefish	1·00	1·00
2199	$1.65 Rock beauty	1·00	1·00
2200	$1.65 Yellow-tailed snapper	1·00	1·00
2201	$1.65 Creole wrasse	1·00	1·00
2202	$1.65 Slender filefish	1·00	1·00
2203	$1.65 Long-spined squirrelfish	1·00	1·00
2204	$1.65 Royal gramma ("Fairy Basslet")	1·00	1·00
2205	$1.75 Queen triggerfish	1·10	1·10

2000. Ships of the World. Nos. 2679/84 of Antigua optd **BARBUDA MAIL.**

2207	$1.75 *Savannah* (paddle-steamer)	1·10	1·10
2208	$1.75 Viking longship	1·10	1·10
2209	$1.75 Greek galley	1·10	1·10
2210	$1.75 Sailing clipper	1·10	1·10
2211	$1.75 Dhow	1·10	1·10
2212	$1.75 Fishing catboat	1·10	1·10

2000. Modern Aircraft. Nos. 2700/11 of Antigua optd **BARBUDA MAIL.**

2214	$1.65 Lockheed-Boeing General Dynamics Yf-22	1·00	1·00
2215	$1.65 Dassault-Breguet Rafale BO 1	1·00	1·00
2216	$1.65 MiG 29	1·00	1·00
2217	$1.65 Dassault-Breguet Mirage 2000D	1·00	1·00
2218	$1.65 Rockwell B-1B "Lancer"	1·00	1·00
2219	$1.65 McDonnell-Douglas C-17A	1·00	1·00
2220	$1.65 Space Shuttle	1·00	1·00
2221	$1.65 SAAB "Grippen"	1·00	1·00
2222	$1.65 Eurofighter EF-2000	1·00	1·00
2223	$1.65 Sukhoi SU 27	1·00	1·00
2224	$1.65 Northrop B-2	1·00	1·00
2225	$1.65 Lockheed F-117 "Nighthawk"	1·00	1·00

BARWANI Pt. 1

A State of Central India. Now uses Indian stamps.

12 pies = 1 anna; 16 annas = 1 rupee.

1 Rana Ranjit Singh

2

1921.

5	1	¼a. green	18·00	65·00
19		¼a. blue	1·00	11·00
37 B		¼a. black	3·00	27·00
18		½a. pink	1·25	11·00
4		½a. blue	17·00	£130
29		½a. green	2·75	12·00
10	2	1a. red	2·25	19·00
39 B		1a. brown	11·00	22·00
11		2a. purple	2·25	22·00
41 B		2a. red	22·00	85·00
31		4a. orange	55·00	£150
42Ba	–	4a. green	11·00	35·00

DESIGN: 4 a. Another portrait of Rana Ranjit Singh.

4 Rana Devi Singh

5

1932.

32A	4	¼a. slate	1·50	17·00
33A		½a. green	2·00	17·00
34A		1a. brown	2·25	16·00
35A		2a. purple	3·50	27·00
36A		4a. olive	6·00	30·00

1938.

43	5	1a. brown	27·00	50·00

BASUTOLAND Pt. 1

An African territory under British protection, N.E. of Cape Province. Self-Government introduced on 1 April 1965. Attained independence on 4 October 1966, when the country was renamed Lesotho.

1933. 12 pence = 1 shilling;
20 shillings = 1 pound.
1961. 100 cents = 1 rand.

1 King George V, Nile Crocodile and Mountains

1933.

1 1	½d. green	1·00	1·75
2	1d. red	75	1·25
3	2d. purple	1·00	80
4	3d. blue	75	1·25
5	4d. grey	2·00	7·00
6	6d. yellow	2·25	1·75
7	1s. orange	2·25	4·50
8	2s.6d. brown	21·00	45·00
9	5s. violet	48·00	65·00
10	10s. olive	£110	£120

1935. Silver Jubilee. As T 13 of Antigua.

11	1d. blue and red	55	50
12	2d. blue and grey	65	1·25
13	3d. brown and blue	3·75	3·75
14	6d. grey and purple	3·75	3·75

1937. Coronation. As T 2 of Aden.

15	1d. red	35	50
16	2d. purple	50	85
17	3d. blue	60	85

1938. As T 1, but portrait of King George VI.

18	½d. green	30	1·25
19	1d. red	50	70
20	1½d. blue	40	50
21	2d. purple	30	60
22	3d. blue	30	1·25
23	4d. grey	1·50	3·50
24	6d. yellow	50	1·50
25	1s. orange	50	1·00
26	2s.6d. brown	8·50	8·50
27	5s. violet	22·00	9·50
28	10s. olive	22·00	17·00

1945. Victory. Stamps of South Africa optd **Basutoland**. Alternate stamps inscr in English or Afrikaans.

29 55	1d. brown and red	40	40
30	2d. blue and violet	40	40
31	3d. blue	40	70

Prices are for bi-lingual pairs.

5 King George VI and Queen Elizabeth

1947. Royal Visit.

32	1d. red	10	10
33 5	2d. green	10	10
34	3d. blue	10	10
35	1s. mauve	15	10

DESIGNS—VERT: 1d. King George VI. HORIZ: 3d. Queen Elizabeth II as Princess and Princess Margaret; 1s. The Royal Family.

1948. Silver Wedding. As T 10/11 of Aden.

36	1½d. blue	20	10
37	10s. green	30·00	27·00

1949. U.P.U. As T 20/23 of Antigua.

38	1½d. blue	20	1·00
39	3d. blue	1·75	2·00
40	6d. orange	1·00	2·00
41	1s. brown	50	1·00

1953. Coronation. As T 13 of Aden.

42	2d. black and purple	40	50

8 Qiloane  **9 Mohair (Shearing Goats)**

1954.

43 8	½d. black and sepia	10	10
44	1d. black and green	10	10
45	2d. blue and orange	60	10
46	3d. sage and red	80	30
47	4½d. indigo and blue	70	15
48	6d. brown and green	1·25	15
49	1s. bronze and purple	1·25	30
50	1s.3d. brown and turquoise	16·00	4·50

51	2s.6d. blue and red	14·00	7·50
52	5s. black and red	5·00	8·50
53 9	10s. black and purple	18·00	23·00

DESIGNS—HORIZ: 1d. Orange River; 2d. Mosuto horseman; 3d. Basuto household; 4½d. Maletsunyane Falls; 6d. Herd-boy playing lesiba; 1s. Pastoral scene; 1s.3d. De Havilland Comet 1 airplane over Lancers' Gap; 2s.6d. Old Fort, Leribe; 5s. Mission cave house.

1959. No. 45 Surch ½d. and bar.

54	½d. on 2d. blue and orange	10	15

20 "Chief Moshoeshoe I" (engraving by Delangle) **26 Basuto Household**

1959. Inauguration of National Council.

55 20	3d. black and olive	30	10
56	1s. red and green	30	10
57	1s.3d. blue and orange	50	45

DESIGNS: 1s. Council house; 1s.3d. Mosuto horseman.

1961. Nos. 43/53 surch.

58 8	1c. on 1d. black and sepia	10	10
59	1c. on 1d. black and green	10	10
60	2c. on 2d. blue and orange	10	10
61	2½c. on 3d. green and red	10	10
62	3½c. on 4½d. indigo and blue	10	10
63	5c. on 6d. brown and green	10	10
64	10c. on 1s. green and purple	10	10
65	12½c. on 1s.3d. brown and turquoise	1·25	30
66	25c. on 2s.6d. blue and red	30	30
67a	50c. on 5s. black and red	1·00	1·60
68b 9	1r. on 10s. black and purple	8·50	9·00

1961. As 1954 but value in new currency as in T **26**.

69 8	½c. black and brown	10	20
70	1c. black and green (as 1d.)	10	40
71	2c. blue and orange (as 2d.)	50	1·40
86 26	2½c. green and red	15	15
73	3½c. indigo and blue (as 4½d.)	30	1·50
88	5c. brown and green (as 6d.)	30	40
75	10c. green and purple (as 1s.)	30	40
90	12½c. brown & grn (as 1s.3d.)	2·75	1·50
77	25c. blue and red (as 2s.6d.)	6·50	6·50
92	50c. black and red (as 5s.)	7·25	10·00
79 9	1r. black and purple	25·00	12·00

1963. Freedom from Hunger. As T **28** of Aden.

80	12½c. violet	40	15

1963. Centenary of Red Cross. As T **33** of Antigua.

81	2½c. red and black	20	10
82	12½c. red and blue	80	60

28 Mosotho Woman and Child

1965. New Constitution. Inscr "SELF GOVERNMENT 1965". Multicoloured.

94	2½c. Type 28	20	10
95	3½c. Maseru border post	25	20
96	5c. Mountain scene	25	20
97	12½c. Legislative Buildings	45	70

1965. Centenary of I.T.U. As T **36** of Antigua.

98	1c. red and purple	15	10
99	20c. blue and brown	35	30

1965. I.C.Y. As T **37** of Antigua.

100	½c. purple and turquoise	10	10
101	12½c. green and lavender	45	35

1966. Churchill Commemoration. As T **38** of Antigua.

102	1c. blue	15	30
103	2½c. green	35	10
104	10c. brown	45	30
105	22½c. violet	70	60

OFFICIAL STAMPS

1934. Nos. 1/3 and 6 optd **OFFICIAL**.

O1 1	½d. green	£3500	£3500
O2	1d. red	£1500	£1000
O3	2d. purple	£900	£550
O4	6d. yellow	£10000	£4750

POSTAGE DUE STAMPS

1933. As Type D 1 of Barbados.

D1b	1d. red	1·00	2·25
D2a 1	2d. violet	30	9·50

D 2

1956.

D3 D 2	1d. red	30	2·75
D4	2d. violet	30	5·00

1961. Surch.

D5 D 2	1c. on 1d. red	10	35
D6	1c. on 2d. violet	10	35
D7	5c. on 2d. violet	15	45
D8 —	5c. on 2d. violet (No. D2a)	1·00	6·50

1964. As Type D **2**, but value in decimal currency.

D 9	1c. red	2·50	13·00
D10	5c. violet	2·50	13·00

For later issues see **LESOTHO**.

BATUM Pt. 1

Batum, a Russian port on the Black Sea, had been taken by Turkish troops during the First World War. Following the Armistice, British Forces occupied the town on 1 December 1918. Batum was handed over to the National Republic of Georgia on 7 July 1920.

100 kopeks = 1 rouble.

 БАТУМ. ОБ.

РУб 10 РУб

1 Aloe Tree (2)

1919. Imperf.

1 1	5k. green	6·50	11·00
2	10k. blue	6·50	11·00
3	50k. yellow	2·50	3·25
4	1r. brown	3·25	3·75
5	3r. violet	9·50	14·00
6	5r. brown	10·00	16·00

1919. Arms types of Russia surch as T **2**. Imperf (Nos. 7/8), perf (Nos. 9/10).

7	10r. on 1k. orange	42·00	50·00
8	10r. on 3k. red	18·00	23·00
9	10r. on 5k. purple	£325	£325
10	10r. on 10 on 7k. blue	£275	£275

1919. T **1** optd **BRITISH OCCUPATION**.

11 1	5k. green	11·00	12·00
12	10k. blue	11·00	12·00
13	25k. yellow	11·00	12·00
14	1r. blue	3·50	9·00
15	2r. pink	1·00	3·00
16	3r. violet	1·00	3·00
17	5r. brown	1·25	2·50
18	7r. red	4·00	6·50

1919. Arms types of Russia surch with Russian inscr, **BRITISH OCCUPATION** and new value.

19	10r. on 3k. red	14·00	18·00
20a	15r. on 1k. orange	38·00	42·00
29	25r. on 5k. purple	35·00	38·00
30a	25r. on 10 on 7k. blue	55·00	60·00
31a	25r. on 20 on 14k. red and blue	55·00	60·00
32a	25r. on 25k. purple and green	80·00	85·00
33	50r. on 50k. green and purple	55·00	60·00
21	50r. on 1k. orange	£325	£350
34	50r. on 2k. green	85·00	90·00
35	50r. on 3k. red	85·00	90·00
36	50r. on 4k. red	75·00	80·00
37	50r. on 5k. purple	55·00	60·00
27	50r. on 10k. blue	£1100	£1200
28	50r. on 15k. blue and brown	£425	£475

1920. Romanov type of Russia surch with Russian inscr, **BRITISH OCCUPATION** and new value.

41	50r. on 4k. red	45·00	55·00

1920. Nos. 11, 13 and 3 surch with new value (50r. with **BRITISH OCCUPATION** also).

42 1	25r. on 5k. green	26·00	28·00
43	25r. on 25k. yellow	21·00	22·00
44a	50r. on 50k. yellow	12·00	13·00

1920. T **1** optd **BRITISH OCCUPATION**.

45 1	1r. brown	70	6·00
46	2r. blue	80	6·00
47	3r. pink	1·00	6·00
48	5r. black	80	6·00
49	7r. yellow	80	6·00
50	10r. green	70	6·00
51	15r. violet	1·00	7·50
52	25r. red	90	7·00
53	50r. blue	90	10·00

BAVARIA Pt. 7

In S. Germany. A kingdom till 1918, then a republic. Incorporated into Germany in 1920.

1849. 60 kreuzer = 1 gulden.
1874. 100 pfennig = 1 mark.

1 **2 (Circle cut)**

1849. Imperf.

1 1	1k. black	£600	£1500

1849. Imperf. Circle cut by labels.

3 2	3k. blue	40·00	1·75
23	3k. red	35·00	4·25
7	6k. brown	£5000	£160

1850. Imperf. As T **2**, but circle not cut.

8a 2	1k. red	75·00	17·00
21	1k. yellow	50·00	17·00
11	6k. brown	35·00	2·75
25	6k. blue	50·00	8·00
16	9k. green	50·00	9·50
28	9k. brown	80·00	11·00
18	12k. red	£100	£120
31	12k. green	70·00	50·00
19	18k. yellow	£110	£180
32	18k. red	£110	£375

3 **6** **8**

1867. Imperf.

34 3	1k. green	50·00	7·50
37	3k. red	50·00	1·25
39	6k. blue	32·00	14·50
41	6k. brown	55·00	35·00
43	7k. blue	£325	9·50
46	9k. brown	38·00	27·00
48	12k. mauve	£300	75·00
18	18k. red	90·00	£140
65 6	1m. mauve	£500	60·00

1870. Perf.

51A 3	1k. green	4·00	1·25
69	3k. red	60	3·50
55A	6k. brown	25·00	24·00
56A	7k. blue	1·75	2·40
59A	9k. brown	4·00	3·25
60A	10k. yellow	4·00	11·00
61A	12k. mauve	£275	£850
63A	18k. red	8·00	11·50

1876. Perf.

120 8	2pf. grey	1·50	45
103	3pf. green	7·50	1·60
121	3pf. brown	10	35
122	5pf. green	10	35
107	5pf. mauve	14·00	1·40
123	10pf. red	10	10
124	20pf. blue	15	35
114	25pf. brown	23·00	3·75
125	25pf. orange	15	45
126	30pf. olive	40	55
127	40pf. yellow	40	55
86	50pf. red	40·00	4·50
117	50pf. brown	40·00	3·00
128	50pf. purple	40	1·25
129	80pf. green	2·25	1·10
100 6	1m. mauve	2·25	1·10
101a	2m. orange	3·00	4·25
136	3m. brown	7·50	18·00
137	5m. green	7·50	18·00

11 **13 Prince Luitpold**

1911. Prince Regent Luitpold's 90th Birthday.

138c 11	3pf. brown on drab	25	10
139c	5pf. green on green	20	10
140d	10pf. red on buff	20	10
141b	20pf. blue on blue	1·75	55
142a	25pf. deep brown on buff	2·25	1·25
143a	30pf. orange on buff	1·40	75
144a	40pf. olive on buff	2·00	75
145a	50pf. red on drab	2·00	75
146	60pf. green on buff	2·50	1·50
147a	80pf. violet red on buff	7·50	4·00
148a 13	1m. brown on drab	2·00	1·25
149a	2m. green on green	2·00	5·75
150a	3m. red on buff	12·00	23·00
151	5m. blue on buff	19·00	23·00
152	10m. orange on yellow	28·00	40·00
153	20m. brown on yellow	17·00	20·00

The 30 pf. to 80 pf. values are similar to Type **11**, but larger.

14

1911. 25th Anniv of Regency of Prince Luitpold.

169	14	5pf. yellow, green & black	50	75
170		10pf. yellow, red & black	60	1·50

15 King Ludwig III

16

1914. Imperf or perf.

171A	15	2pf. slate	20	1·00
172A		2½ on 2pf. slate	20	1·00
173A		3pf. brown	20	1·00
175A		5pf. green	20	1·00
176A		7½pf. green	20	1·00
178A		10pf. red	20	1·00
179A		15pf. red	20	1·00
181A		20pf. blue	20	1·00
183A		25pf. grey	20	1·00
184A		30pf. orange	30	1·00
185A		40pf. olive	30	1·00
186A		50pf. brown	20	1·00
187A		60pf. green	30	1·00
188A		80pf. violet	20	1·25
189A	16	1m. brown	20	1·25
190A		2m. violet	25	2·00
191A		3m. red	30	5·00
192A	–	5m. blue	50	8·25
193A	–	10m. green	1·25	50·00
194A	–	20m. brown	2·50	65·00

The 5, 10 and 20m. are larger.

1919. Peoples' State Issue. Overprinted **Volksstaat Bayern**. Imperf or perf.

195A	15	3pf. brown	10	1·00
196A		5pf. green	10	1·00
197A		7½pf. green	10	1·00
198A		10pf. lake	10	1·00
199A		15pf. red	10	1·00
200A		20pf. blue	10	1·00
201A		25pf. grey	10	1·00
202A		30pf. orange	10	1·00
203A		35pf. orange	10	2·00
204A		40pf. olive	10	1·10
205A		50pf. brown	10	1·10
206A		60pf. turquoise	10	1·10
207A		75pf. brown	10	1·10
208A		80pf. violet	10	1·40
209A	16	1m. brown	15	1·00
210A		2m. violet	30	1·40
211A		3m. red	45	4·00
212A	–	5m. blue (No. 192)	70	12·50
213A	–	10m. green (No. 193)	1·10	38·00
214A	–	20m. brown (No. 194)	1·90	42·00

1919. 1st Free State Issue. Stamps of Germany (inscr "DEUTSCHES REICH") optd **Freistaat Bayern**.

215	24	2½pf. grey	15	70
216	10	3pf. brown	15	70
217		5pf. green	15	70
218	24	7½pf. orange	15	1·00
219	10	10pf. red	15	1·25
220	24	15pf. violet	15	1·00
221	10	20pf. blue	15	65
222		25pf. black & red on yell	15	1·50
223	24	35pf. brown	15	1·75
224	10	40pf. black and red	30	1·60
225		75pf. black and green	40	2·00
226		80pf. black & red on rose	40	2·75
227	12	1m. red	85	4·75
228	13	2m. blue	1·10	8·50
229	14	3m. black	1·40	12·00
230	15	5m. red and black	1·60	12·00

1919. 2nd Free State Issue. Stamps of Bavaria overprinted **Freistaat Bayern**. Imperf or perf.

231A	15	3pf. brown	10	1·00
232A		5pf. green	10	30
233A		7½pf. green	10	11·50
234A		10pf. lake	10	30
235A		15pf. red	10	30
236A		20pf. blue	10	45
237A		25pf. grey	10	1·25
238A		30pf. orange	10	1·25
239A		40pf. olive	10	3·50
240A		50pf. brown	10	1·90
241A		60pf. turquoise	20	8·00
242A		75pf. brown	55	9·50
243A		80pf. violet	20	4·00
244A	16	1m. brown	30	3·00
245A		2m. violet	30	5·00
246A		3m. red	40	8·00
247A	–	5m. blue (No. 192)	70	16·00
248A	–	10m. green (No. 193)	1·60	29·00
249A	–	20m. brown (No. 194)	2·00	55·00

1919. War Wounded. Surch **5 Pf. fur Kriegs-beschadigte Freistaat Bayern**. Perf.

250	15	10pf.+5pf. lake	30	1·50
251		15pf.+5pf. red	30	1·50
252		20pf.+5pf. blue	30	2·00

1920. Surch **Freistaat Bayern** and value. Imperf or perf.

253A	16	1m.25pf. on 1m. green	20	1·40
254A		1m.50pf. on 1m. orange	20	3·00
255A		2m.50pf. on 1m. slate	25	5·00

1920. No. 121 surch **20** in four corners.

256	8	20 on 3pf. brown	15	1·10

26

27

28

29

30

1920.

257	26	5pf. green	20	1·00
258		10pf. orange	20	1·00
259		15pf. red	20	1·00
260	27	20pf. violet	20	1·00
261		30pf. blue	15	1·25
262		40pf. brown	15	1·25
263	28	50pf. red	15	1·40
264		60pf. turquoise	15	1·60
265		75pf. red	15	2·50
266	29	1m. red and grey	20	2·50
267		1¼m. blue and brown	20	2·50
268		1½m. green and grey	25	2·75
269		2½m. black and grey	30	13·00
270	30	3m. blue	20	11·50
271		5m. orange	40	11·50
272		10m. green	80	21·00
273		20m. black	1·00	29·00

OFFICIAL STAMPS

O 18

1916.

O195	O 18	3pf. brown	15	40
O196		5pf. green	15	40
O197		7½pf. green on green	25	55
O198		7½pf. green	15	15
O199		10pf. red	15	15
O200		15pf. red on buff	15	15
O201		15pf. red	40	85
O202		20pf. blue on blue	1·40	2·00
O203		20pf. blue	15	15
O204		25pf. grey	15	15
O205		30pf. orange	20	15
O206		60pf. turquoise	15	55
O207		1m. purple on buff	60	2·40
O208		1m. purple	2·10	£425

1919. Optd **Volksstaat Bayern**.

O215	O 18	3pf. brown	20	6·50
O216		5pf. green	20	1·00
O217		7½pf. green	20	8·00
O218		10pf. red	20	1·00
O219		15pf. red	20	85
O220		20pf. blue	20	1·00
O221		25pf. grey	20	1·00
O222		30pf. orange	20	1·00
O223		35pf. orange	20	1·00
O224		50pf. olive	20	1·00
O225		60pf. turquoise	25	3·25
O226		75pf. brown	25	2·00
O227		1m. purple on buff	90	3·00
O228		1m. purple	3·50	£350

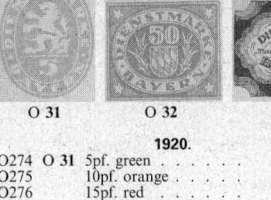

O 31

O 32

O 33

1920.

O274	O 31	5pf. green	10	5·75
O275		10pf. orange	10	5·75
O276		15pf. red	10	5·75
O277		20pf. violet	10	5·75
O278		30pf. blue	10	8·00
O279		40pf. brown	10	8·00
O280	O 32	50pf. red	10	20·00
O281		60pf. green	10	8·00
O282		70pf. lilac	10	22·00
O283		75pf. red	10	26·00
O284		80pf. blue	10	27·00
O285		90pf. olive	10	40·00
O286	O 33	1m. brown	10	35·00
O287		1¼m. green	10	45·00
O288		1½m. red	10	48·00
O289		2½m. blue	10	55·00
O290		3m. lake	30	75·00
O291		5m. green	1·50	85·00

POSTAGE DUE STAMPS

D 6

1862. Inscr "Bayer. Posttaxe" at top. Imperf.

D34	D 6	3k. black	£120	£300

1870. As Type D **6**, but inscr "Bayr. Posttaxe" at top. Perf.

D65B	D 6	1k. black	9·00	£625
D66B		3k. black	9·00	£375

1876. Optd **Vom Empfanger zahlbar.**

D130a	8	2pf. grey	55	1·25
D131a		3pf. grey	35	2·25
D132a		5pf. grey	70	1·50
D133a		10pf. grey	50	80

1895. No. D131a surch **2** in each corner.

D134	8	2 on 3pf. grey	†	£40000

RAILWAY OFFICIALS' STAMPS

1908. Stamps of 1876 optd **E**.

R133	8	3pf. brown	1·00	3·75
R134		5pf. green	25	25
R135		10pf. red	25	25
R136		20pf. blue	55	70
R137		50pf. purple	4·00	6·25

BECHUANALAND Pt. 1

A colony and protectorate in Central S. Africa. British Bechuanaland (colony) was annexed to Cape of Good Hope in 1895. Internal Self-Government in the protectorate was introduced on 1 March 1965. Attained independence on 30 September 1966, when the country was renamed Botswana.

1885. 12 pence = 1 shilling;
20 shillings = 1 pound.
1961. 100 cents = 1 rand.

A. BRITISH BECHUANALAND

1885. Stamps of Cape of Good Hope ("Hope" seated) optd **British Bechuanaland**.

4	6	½d. black	7·00	11·00
38		1d. red	2·25	2·25
32		2d. bistre	3·25	2·25
2		3d. red	35·00	40·00
3		4d. blue	55·00	65·00
7		6d. purple	90·00	38·00
8		1s. green	£250	£150

1887. Stamp of Great Britain (Queen Victoria) optd **BRITISH BECHUANALAND**.

9	71	½d. red	1·25	1·25

3

4

1887.

10	3	1d. lilac and black	15·00	1·75
11a		2d. lilac and black	42·00	23·00
12		3d. lilac and black	3·50	5·50
13		4d. lilac and black	42·00	2·25
14		6d. lilac and black	50·00	2·50
15	4	1s. green and black	29·00	5·50
16		2s. green and black	50·00	35·00
17		2s.6d. green and black	60·00	55·00
18		5s. green and black	80·00	£150
19		10s. green and black	£170	£350
20	–	£1 lilac and black	£800	£700
21	–	£5 lilac and black	£2750	£1500

Nos. 20/1 are as Type **4** but larger, 23 × 39½ mm.

1888. Surch.

22	3	"1d." on 1d. lilac and black	7·50	6·50
23		"2d." on 2d. lilac and black	20·00	3·00
25		"4d." on 4d. lilac and black	£225	£300
26		"6d." on 6d. lilac and black	90·00	10·00
28	4	"1s." on 1s. green and black	£130	75·00

1888. Surch **ONE HALF PENNY** and bars.

29	3	½d. on 3d. lilac and black	£130	£140

1891. Stamps of Great Britain (Queen Victoria) optd **BRITISH BECHUANALAND**.

33	57	1d. lilac	6·00	1·50
34	73	2d. green and red	8·00	4·00
35	76	4d. green and brown	2·50	50
36	79	6d. purple on red	3·00	2·00
37	82	1s. green	13·00	16·00

B. BECHUANALAND PROTECTORATE

1888. No. 9 to 19 optd **Protectorate** or surch also.

40	71	½d. red	3·50	25·00
41	3	1d. on 1d. lilac and black	8·00	14·00
42		2d. on 2d. lilac and black	23·00	17·00
43		3d. on 3d. lilac and black	£120	£170
51		4d. on 4d. lilac and black	70·00	32·00
45		6d. on 6d. lilac and black	70·00	40·00
46	4	1s. green and black	75·00	50·00
47		2s. green and black	£600	£850
48		2s.6s. green and black	£500	£750
49		5s. green and black	£1100	£1900
50		10s. green and black	£3250	£5000

1889. Stamp of Cape of Good Hope ("Hope" seated) optd **Bechuanaland Protectorate**.

52	6	½d. black	2·75	35·00

1889. No. 9 surch **Protectorate Fourpence**.

53	71	4d. on ½d. red	18·00	3·50

1897. Stamp of Cape of Good Hope ("Hope" seated) optd **BRITISH BECHUANALAND**.

56	6	½d. green	2·50	9·00

1897. Queen Victoria stamps of Great Britain optd **BECHUANALAND PROTECTORATE**.

59	71	½d. red	1·00	2·25
60		½d. green	1·40	3·50
61	57	1d. lilac	4·00	75
62	73	2d. green and red	3·25	4·25
63	75	3d. purple on yellow	5·50	8·50
64	76	4d. green and brown	15·00	11·00
65	79	6d. purple on red	23·00	11·00

1904. King Edward VII stamps of Great Britain optd **BECHUANALAND PROTECTORATE**.

66	83	½d. turquoise	2·00	2·00
68		1d. red	7·50	30
69		2½d. blue	7·00	5·00
70	–	1s. green and red (No. 314)	35·00	£120

1912. King George V stamps of Great Britain optd **BECHUANALAND PROTECTORATE**.

91	105	½d. green	1·50	1·75
72	102	1d. red	1·50	60
92	104	1d. red	2·00	70
75	105	1½d. brown	2·50	3·00
93	106	2d. orange	1·75	1·00
78	104	2½d. blue	3·50	20·00
79	106	3d. violet	6·00	12·00
80		4d. grey	6·50	14·00
81	107	6d. purple	7·00	16·00
82	108	1s. brown	9·50	20·00
88	109	2s.6d. brown	80·00	£160
89		5s. red	£110	£275

22 King George V, Baobab Tree and Cattle drinking

1932.

99	22	½d. green	1·00	30
100		1d. red	1·00	25
101		2d. brown	1·00	30
102		3d. blue	1·00	1·75
103		4d. orange	1·25	5·50
104		6d. purple	2·50	3·00
105		1s. black and olive	3·00	7·00
106		2s. black and orange	24·00	40·00
107		2s.6d. black and red	19·00	30·00
108		3s. black and purple	35·00	42·00
109		5s. black and blue	55·00	65·00
110		10s. black and brown	£110	£120

1935. Silver Jubilee. As T **13** of Antigua.

111		1d. blue and red	30	2·75
112		2d. blue and black	1·00	2·75

| 113 | 3d. brown and blue | 2·50 | 2·75 |
| 114 | 6d. grey and purple | 4·00 | 2·75 |

1937. Coronation. As T **2** of Aden.

115	1d. red	45	40
116	2d. brown	60	1·00
117	3d. blue	60	1·25

1938. As T **22**, but portrait of King George VI.

118	½d. green	2·00	2·25
119	1d. red	75	50
120a	1½d. blue	1·00	1·00
121	2d. brown	75	50
122	3d. blue	1·00	2·50
123	4d. orange	2·00	3·50
124a	6d. purple	4·00	2·50
125	1s. black and olive	4·00	4·25
126	2s.6d. black and red	14·00	14·00
127	5s. black and blue	30·00	16·00
128	10s. black and brown	14·00	19·00

1945. Victory. Stamps of South Africa optd **Bechuanaland**. Alternate stamps inscr in English or Afrikaans.

129	**55**	1d. brown and red	50	55
130		2d. blue and violet (No. 109)	50	1·00
131		3d. blue (No. 110)	50	1·00

Prices for bi-lingual pairs.

1947. Royal Visit. As Nos. 32/5 of Basutoland.

132	1d. red	10	10
133	2d. green	10	10
134	3d. blue	10	10
135	1s. mauve	10	10

1948. Silver Wedding. As T **10/11** of Aden.

| 136 | 1½d. blue | 30 | 10 |
| 137 | 10s. grey | 27·00 | 35·00 |

1949. U.P.U. As T **20/23** of Antigua.

138	1½d. blue	30	75
139	3d. blue	1·00	2·00
140	6d. mauve	45	1·00
141	1s. olive	45	1·00

1953. Coronation. As T **13** of Aden.

| 142 | 2d. black and brown | 30 | 30 |

1955. As T **22** but portrait of Queen Elizabeth II, facing right.

143	½d. green	50	30
144	1d. red	80	10
145	2d. brown	1·25	30
146	3d. blue	3·00	70
146b	4d. orange	6·50	7·00
147	4½d. blue	1·50	35
148	6d. purple	1·25	60
149	1s. black and olive	1·25	80
150	1s.3d. black and lilac	14·00	9·50
151	2s.6d. black and red	10·00	9·50
152	5s. black and blue	15·00	6·50
153	10s. black and brown	26·00	15·00

26 Queen Victoria. Queen Elizabeth II and Landscape

28 African Golden Oriole ("Golden Oriole")

1960. 75th Anniv of Protectorate.

154	**26**	1d. sepia and black	40	50
155		3d. mauve and black	40	30
156		6d. blue and black	40	50

1961. Stamps of 1955 surch.

157	1c. on 1d. red	30	10
158	2c. on 2d. brown	20	10
159	2½c. on 2d. brown	30	10
160	2½c. on 3d. blue	2·00	3·75
161d	3½c. on 4d. orange	20	60
162a	5c. on 6d. purple	20	10
163	10c. on 1s. black and olive	20	10
164	12½c. on 1s.3d. black and lilac	65	20
165	25c. on 2s.6d. black and red	2·00	50
166	50c. on 5s. black and blue	3·00	2·00
167b	1r. on 10s. black and brown	7·00	4·25

1961.

168	**28**	1c. multicoloured	1·50	40
169	–	2c. orange, black and olive	1·75	2·75
170	–	2½c. multicoloured	1·50	20
171	–	3½c. multicoloured	2·00	1·75
172	–	5c. multicoloured	3·25	1·00
173	–	7½c. multicoloured	2·00	2·25
174	–	10c. multicoloured	2·00	60
175	–	12½c. multicoloured	18·00	5·50
176	–	20c. brown and drab	1·00	1·25
177	–	25c. sepia and lemon	1·25	1·00
178	–	35c. blue and orange	1·00	2·25
179	–	50c. sepia and olive	1·00	2·25
180	–	1r. black and brown	3·00	2·50
181	–	2r. brown and turquoise	18·00	9·00

DESIGNS—VERT: 2c. Hoopoe ("African Hoopoe"); 2½c. Scarlet-chested sunbird; 3½c. Yellow-rumped bishop ("Cape Widow-bird"); 5c. Swallow-tailed bee eater; 7½c. African grey hornbill ("Grey Hornbill"); 10c. Red-headed weaver; 12½c. Brown-hooded kingfisher; 20c. Woman musician; 35c. Woman

grinding maize; 1r. Lion; 2r. Police camel patrol. HORIZ: 25c. Baobab tree; 50c. Bechuana ox.

1963. Freedom from Hunger. As T **28** of Aden.

| 182 | 12½c. green | 30 | 15 |

1963. Centenary of Red Cross. As T **33** of Antigua.

| 183 | 2½c. red and black | 20 | 10 |
| 184 | 12½c. red and blue | 40 | 50 |

1964. 400th Birth Anniv of Shakespeare. As T **34** of Antigua.

| 185 | 12½c. brown | 15 | 15 |

C. BECHUANALAND

42 Map and Gaberones Dam

1965. New Constitution.

186	**42**	2½c. red and gold	10	10
187		5c. blue and gold	15	40
188		12½c. brown and gold	20	40
189		25c. green and gold	20	55

1965. Centenary of I.T.U. As T **36** of Antigua.

| 190 | 2½c. red and yellow | 20 | 10 |
| 191 | 12½c. mauve and brown | 45 | 30 |

1965. I.C.Y. As T **37** of Antigua.

| 192 | 1c. purple and turquoise | 10 | 10 |
| 193 | 12½c. green and lavender | 60 | 55 |

1966. Churchill Commemoration. As T **38** of Antigua.

194	1c. blue	15	30
195	2½c. green	35	10
196	12½c. brown	70	30
197	20c. violet	75	50

43 Haslar Smoke Generator

1966. Bechuanaland Royal Pioneer Corps.

198	**43**	2½c. blue, red and green	25	10
199	–	5c. brown and blue	25	20
200	–	15c. blue, red and green	30	25
201	–	35c. multicoloured	30	80

DESIGNS: 5c. Bugler; 15c. Gun-site; 35c. Regimental cap badge.

POSTAGE DUE STAMPS

1926. Postage Due stamps of Great Britain optd **BECHUANALAND PROTECTORATE**.

D1	D **1**	½d. green	4·00	65·00
D2		1d. red	4·00	48·00
D3		2d. black	6·00	85·00

D 3

1932.

D4	D **3**	½d. green	6·00	38·00
D5a		1d. red	1·00	15·00
D6b		2d. violet	1·50	19·00

1961. Surch.

D7	D **3**	1c. on 1d. red	25	50
D8		2c. on 2d. violet	25	1·50
D9		5c. on ½d. green	20	60

1961. As Type D **3** but value in decimal currency.

D10	1c. red	15	1·75
D11	2c. violet	15	1·75
D12	5c. green	30	2·00

For later issues see **BOTSWANA**.

BELARUS   Pt. 10

Formerly a constituent republic of the Soviet Union, Belarus became independent in 1991.

100 kopeks = 1 rouble.

1 12th-century Cross

1992.

| 1 | **1** | 1r. multicoloured | 15 | 15 |

2 Shyrma    **3** Arms of Polotsk

1992. Birth Cent of R. R. Shyrma (composer).

| 2 | **2** | 20k. lt blue, blue and black | 15 | 15 |

1992.

| 3 | **3** | 2r. multicoloured | 15 | 15 |

See also Nos. 63 and 89/90.

4 Flag and Map   (5)

1992.

| 4 | **4** | 5r. multicoloured | 15 | 15 |
| 5 | – | 5r. black, yellow and red | 15 | 15 |

DESIGN: No. 5, State arms.

1992. Millenary of Orthodox Church in Belarus. No. 1 optd with T **5**.

| 6 | **1** | 1r. multicoloured | 15 | 15 |

6 Kamen Tower   **7** State Arms

1992. Ancient Buildings and Monuments. Mult.

8	**6**	2r. Type **6**	10	10
9	–	2r. Calvinist church, Zaslavl	10	10
10	–	2r. St. Euphrosyne's church, Polotsk	10	10
11	–	2r. St. Boris Gleb church, Grodno (horiz)	10	10
12	–	2r. Mir castle (horiz)	10	10
13	–	2r. Nesvizh castle (horiz)	10	10

1992.

14	**7**	30k. blue	10	10
15	–	45k. green	10	10
16	–	50k. green	10	10
17	–	1r. brown	10	10
18	–	2r. brown	10	10
19	–	3r. yellow	10	10
20	–	5r. blue	15	15
21	–	10r. red	15	15
22	–	15r. violet	20	20
23	–	25r. green	20	20
24	–	50r. mauve	25	25
25	–	100r. red	25	25
26	–	150r. purple	25	25
27	–	200r. green	10	10
28	–	300r. red	15	15
29	–	600r. mauve	20	25
30	–	1000r. red	25	25
31	–	3000r. blue	50	50

8 Jug and Bowl

1992. Pottery. Multicoloured.

40	**8**	1r. Type **8**	10	10
41		1r. Vases and jug on jug tree	10	10
42		1r. Flagon	10	10
43		1r. Jugs	10	10

9 Chickens

1993. Corn Dollies. Multicoloured.

44	**9**	5r. Type **9**	10	10
45		10r. Woman and gunman	15	15
46		15r. Woman (vert)	25	25
47		25r. Man and woman (vert)	50	50

 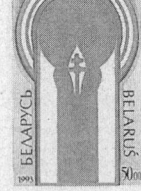

10 Harezki   **11** Emblem

1993. Birth Centenary of M. I. Harezki (author).

| 48 | **10** | 50r. purple | 15 | 15 |

1993. World Belarussian Congress, Minsk.

| 49 | **11** | 50r. red, gold and black | 60 | 60 |

12 "Man Over Vitebsk"

1993. Europa. Contemporary Art. Paintings by Marc Chagall. Multicoloured.

| 50 | | 1500r. Type **12** | 2·25 | 2·25 |
| 51 | | 1500r. "Promenade" (vert) | 2·25 | 2·25 |

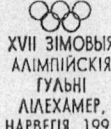

1993. Europa. Contemporary Art ... XVII ЗІМОВЫЯ АЛІМПІЙСКІЯ ГУЛЬНІ ЛІЛЕХАМЕР, НАРВЕГІЯ, 1994

1500 (13)

ЧЭМПІЯНАТ СВЕТУ ПА ФУТБОЛУ, ЗША, 1994

1500 (14)

1993. Sports Events. Nos. 4/5 variously surch. (a) Winter Olympic Games, Lillehammer, Norway (1994). Surch **Winter Pre-Olympic Games Lillehammer, Norway 1500** (in capitals on No. 44) or in Cyrillic as T **13**.

53	**4**	1500r. on 5r. mult (in Cyrillic)	2·50	2·50
54		1500r. on 5r. mult (in English)	2·50	2·50
55	–	1500r. on 5r. black, yellow and red (in Cyrillic)	2·50	2·50

56 – 1500r. on 5r. black, yellow
  and red (in English) . . . 2·50 2·50

(b) World Cup Football Championship, U.S.A.
(1994). **Surch WORLD CUP USA 94 1500** or in
  Cyrillic as T **14**.

58 **4** 1500r. on 5r. mult (in
  Cyrillic) . . . . 2·50 2·50
59 1500r. on 5r. mult (in
  English) . . . . 2·50 2·50
60 – 1500r. on 5r. black, yellow
  and red (in Cyrillic) . . 2·50 2·50
61 – 1500r. on 5r. black, yellow
  and red (in English) . . 2·50 2·50

1993. Town Arms. As T **3**. Multicoloured.
63 25r. Minsk 15 15

15 St. Stanislav's Church, Mogilev

1993.
64 **15** 150r. multicoloured 40 40

16 Kastus Kalinowski (leader)

1993. 130th Anniv of Peasants' Uprising.
65 **16** 50r. multicoloured 20 20

17 Princess Ragneda   **18** Statue of Budny

1993. 10th-century Rulers of Polotsk. Mult.
66 75r. Type **17** 30 30
67 75r. Prince Ragvalod and map . . 30 30

1993. 400th Death Anniv of Simon Budny (poet).
68 **18** 100r. multicoloured 50 50

19 Golden Eagle

1994. Birds in the Red Book. Multicoloured.
69 20r. Type **19** 10 10
70 40r. Mute swan ("Cygnus
  olor") 20 20
71 40r. River kingfisher ("Alcedo
  atthis") 20 20

1994. Nos. 14/16 surch.
72 **7** 15r. on 30k. blue 10 10
73 25r. on 45k. green 10 10
74 50r. on 50k. green 15 15
  See also Nos. 86/8.

21 Map and Rocket Launchers
  (Liberation of Russia)

1994. 50th Anniv of Liberation. Multicoloured.
75 500r. Type **21** 10 10
76 500r. Map and airplanes
  (Ukraine) 10 10
77 500r. Map, tank and soldiers
  (Byelorussia) 10 10

---

22 Yasev Drazdovich and "Persecution"

1994. Artists and Paintings. Multicoloured.
78 300r. Type **22** 10 10
79 300r. Pyotr Sergievich and
  "The Path through Life" . . 10 10
80 300r. Ferdinand Rushchyts
  and "The Land" 10 10

23 Figure Skating   **26** "Belarus"

25 Church, Synkavichai (16th-
  century)

1994. Winter Olympic Games, Lillehammer, Norway.
  Multicoloured.
81 1000r. Type **23** 15 15
82 1000r. Biathlon 15 15
83 1000r. Cross-country skiing . . 15 15
84 1000r. Speed skating 15 15
85 1000r. Ice hockey 15 15

1994. Birds in the Red Book. As Nos. 69/71 but
  values changed. Multicoloured.
86 300r. As Type **19** 10 10
87 400r. As No. 70 . . . . . . 10 10
88 400r. As No. 71 . . . . . . 10 10

1994. Town Arms. As T **3**. Multicoloured.
89 700r. Grodno 15 15
90 700r. Vitebsk 15 15

1994. Religious Buildings. Multicoloured.
91 700r. Type **25** 15 15
92 700r. Sts. Peter and Paul's
  Cathedral, Gomel (19th-
  century) 15 15

1994. 150th Birth Anniv of Ilya Repin (painter).
  Multicoloured.
93 1000r. Type **26** 15 15
94 1000r. Repin Museum 15 15
  Nos. 93/4 were issued together, se-tenant, forming
a composite design.

27 Tomasz Wojshezki and Battle
  Scene

1995. Bicentenary (1994) of Polish Insurrection.
  Multicoloured.
95 600r. Type **27** 10 10
96 600r. Jakub Jasinski 10 10
97 1000r. Mikhail Aginski 15 15
98 1000r. Tadeusz Kosciuszko . . 15 15

28 Memorial   **29** Aleksandr
      Stepanovich Popov
      (radio pioneer)

1995. 50th Anniv of End of Second World War.
  Multicoloured.
99 180r. Type **28** 10 10
100 600r. Clouds and memorial . . 10 10

1995. Centenary of First Radio Transmission (by
  Guglielmo Marconi).
101 **29** 600r. multicoloured 10 10

30 Obelisk to
  the Fallen of
  the Red
  Army, Minsk   **31** Cherski

1995.
102 **30** 180r. bistre and red . . . 10 10
103 200r. green and bistre . . 10 10
104 280r. green and blue . . . 15 15
107 600r. purple and bistre . . 15 15

1995. 150th Birth Anniv of Ivan Cherski (explorer).
115 **31** 600r. multicoloured 15 15

32 Motal   **33** Head of Beaver

1995. Traditional Costumes (1st series). Mult.
116 180r. Type **32** 10 10
117 600r. Vaukavysk-Kamyanets . . 10 10
118 1200r. Pukhavits 20 20
  See also Nos. 188/190 and 256/8.

1995. The Eurasian Beaver. Multicoloured.
119 300r. Type **33** 10 10
120 450r. Beaver gnawing branch . . 10 10
121 450r. Beaver (horiz) 10 10
122 800r. Beaver swimming . . . 15 15

34 Writer and Script   **35** Arms

1995. Writers' Day.
123 **34** 600r. multicoloured 15 15

1995. National Symbols. Multicoloured.
124 600r. Type **35** 15 15
125 600r. Flag over map and
  arms 15 15

36 Anniversary Emblem

1995. 50th Anniv of U.N.O.
126 **36** 600r. blue, black and gold . 15 15

37 Mstislavl Church

1995. Churches. Multicoloured.
127 600r. Type **37** 15 15
128 600r. Kamai Church 15 15
  See also Nos. 227/8.

1995
125 год
з дня нараджэння
(38)

1995. 125th Birth Anniv of Ferdinand Rushchyts
  (artist). No. 80 optd with T **38**.
129 360r. multicoloured 55 55

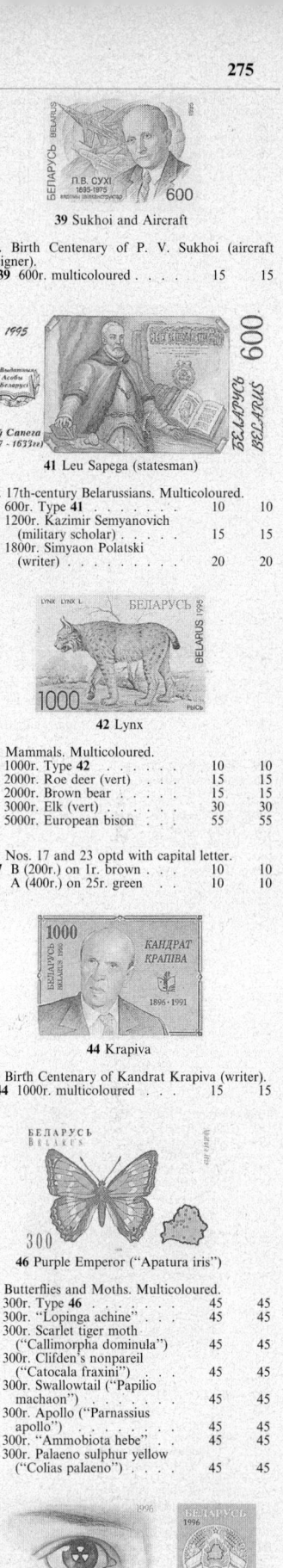

39 Sukhoi and Aircraft

1995. Birth Centenary of P. V. Sukhoi (aircraft
  designer).
130 **39** 600r. multicoloured 15 15

41 Leu Sapega (statesman)

1995. 17th-century Belarussians. Multicoloured.
132 600r. Type **41** 10 10
133 1200r. Kazimir Semyanovich
  (military scholar) 15 15
134 1800r. Simyaon Polatski
  (writer) 20 20

42 Lynx

1996. Mammals. Multicoloured.
135 1000r. Type **42** 10 10
136 2000r. Roe deer (vert) 15 15
137 2000r. Brown bear 15 15
138 3000r. Elk (vert) 30 30
139 5000r. European bison 55 55

1996. Nos. 17 and 23 optd with capital letter.
140 **7** B (200r.) on 1r. brown . . . 10 10
141 A (400r.) on 25r. green . . . 10 10

44 Krapiva

1996. Birth Centenary of Kandrat Krapiva (writer).
142 **44** 1000r. multicoloured 15 15

46 Purple Emperor ("Apatura iris")

1996. Butterflies and Moths. Multicoloured.
144 300r. Type **46** 45 45
145 300r. "Lopinga achine" . . . 45 45
146 300r. Scarlet tiger moth
  ("Callimorpha dominula") . 45 45
147 300r. Clifden's nonpareil
  ("Catocala fraxini") . . . 45 45
148 300r. Swallowtail ("Papilio
  machaon") 45 45
149 300r. Apollo ("Parnassius
  apollo") 45 45
150 300r. "Ammobiota hebe" . . . 45 45
151 300r. Palaeno sulphur yellow
  ("Colias palaeno") . . . 45 45

47 Radioactivity Symbol within   **48** State Arms
  Eye

1996. 10th Anniv of Chernobyl Nuclear Disaster.
  Multicoloured.
153 1000r. Type **47** 15 15
154 1000r. Radioactivity symbol
  on diseased leaf 15 15
155 1000r. Radioactivity symbol
  on boarded-up window . . 15 15

1996. Arms and value in black, background colours
  given.
159 **48** 100r. blue 10 10
160 200r. brown 10 10
161 400r. brown 10 10
162 500r. green 10 10
163 600r. red 10 10

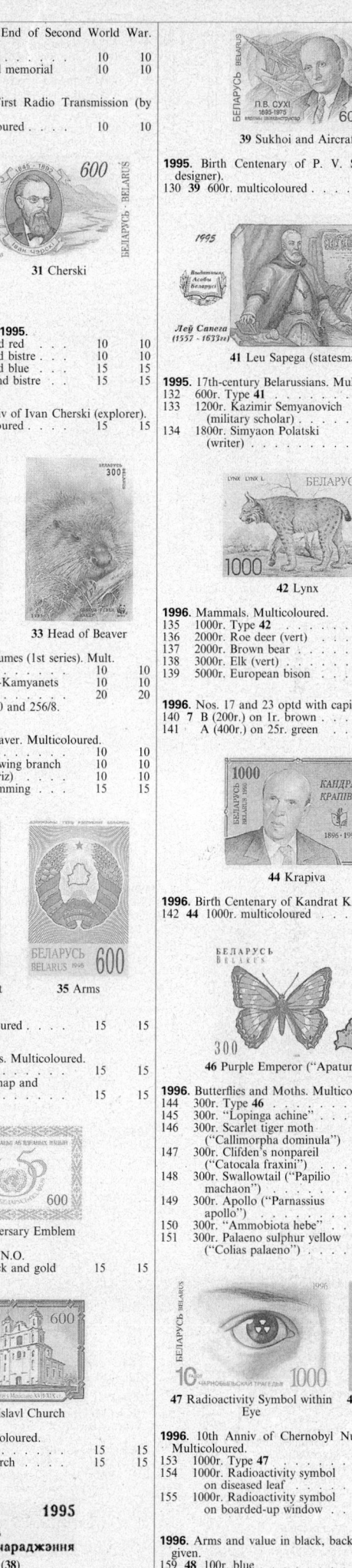

164	800r. blue	10	10
165	1000r. orange	10	10
166	1500r. mauve	10	10
167	1500r. blue	10	10
168	1800r. violet	10	10
169	2000r. green	10	10
170	2200r. mauve	10	10
171	2500r. blue	10	10
172	3000r. brown	15	15
173	3300r. yellow	15	15
174	5000r. blue	20	20
175	10000r. green	45	45
176	30000r. brown	1·25	1·25
177	50000r. purple	2·10	2·10

49 Russian and Belarussian Flags

1996. Russian–Belarussian Treaty.

182	49	1500r. multicoloured	15	15

50 Gymnastics   **51** Kapyl-Kletski

1996. Olympic Games, Atlanta. Multicoloured.

183	3000r. Type **50**	15	15
184	3000r. Throwing the discus	15	15
185	3000r. Weightlifting	15	15
186	3000r. Wrestling	15	15

1996. Traditional Costumes (2nd series). Mult.

188	1800r. Type **51**	10	10
189	2200r. David-Garadots Turau	10	10
190	3300r. Kobryn	15	15

See also Nos. 256/8.

52 "Acorus calamus"

1996. Medicinal Plants. Multicoloured.

192	1500r. Type **52**	10	10
193	1500r. "Sanguisorba officinalis"	10	10
194	2200r. "Potentilla erecta"	10	10
195	3300r. "Frangula alnus"	15	15

53 Grey Heron ("Ardea cinerea")

1996. Birds. Multicoloured.

197	400r. Type **53**	25	25
198	400r. Black storks ("Ciconia nigra")	25	25
199	400r. Great cormorant ("Phalacrocorax carbo")	25	25
200	400r. White stork ("Ciconia ciconia")	25	25
201	400r. Black-headed gulls ("Larus ridibundus")	25	25
202	400r. Common snipe ("Gallinago gallinago")	25	25
203	400r. White-winged black tern ("Chlidonias leucopterus")	25	25
204	400r. Penduline tit ("Remiz pendulinus")	25	25
205	400r. Eurasian bittern ("Botaurus stellaris")	25	25
206	400r. Black coot ("Fulica atra")	25	25
207	400r. Little bittern ("Ixobrychus minutus")	25	25
208	400r. River kingfisher ("Alcedo atthis")	25	25
209	400r. Green-winged teals ("Anas crecca")	25	25
210	400r. Gadwalls ("Anas strepera")	25	25
211	400r. Northern pintails ("Anas acuta")	25	25
212	400r. Mallards ("Anas platyrhynchos")	25	25
213	400r. Greater scaups ("Aythya marila")	25	25
214	400r. Long-tailed duck ("Clangula hyemalis")	25	25
215	400r. Northern shovelers ("Anas clypeata")	25	25
216	400r. Garganeys ("Anas querquedula")	25	25
217	400r. European wigeon ("Anas penelope")	25	25
218	400r. Ferruginous ducks ("Aythya nyroca")	25	25
219	400r. Common goldeneyes ("Bucephala clangula")	25	25
220	400r. Goosander ("Mergus merganser")	25	25
221	400r. Smew ("Mergus albellus")	25	25
222	400r. Tufted duck ("Aythya fuligula")	25	25
223	400r. Red-breasted merganser ("Mergus serrator")	25	25
224	400r. Common pochard ("Aythya ferina")	25	25

54 Title Page   **55** Shchakatsikhin

1996. 400th Anniv of Publication of First Belarussian Grammar.

226	54	1500r. multicoloured	10	10

1996. Churches. As T **37**. Multicoloured.

227	3300r. St. Nicholas's Church, Mogilev	10	10
228	3300r. Franciscan church, Pinsk	10	10

1996. Birth Centenary of Mikola Shchakatsikhin (artist).

229	55	2000r. multicoloured	10	10

56 Old and New Telephones

1996. Cent of Telephone Service in Minsk.

230	56	2000r. multicoloured	10	10

57 Lukashenka

1996. President Alyaksandr Rygoravich Lukashenka.

231	57	2500r. multicoloured	10	10

58 Kiryla Turovski (12th-century Bishop of Turov)   **59** Decorated Tree, Minsk

1996. Multicoloured.

232	3000r. Type **58**	15	15
233	3000r. Mikolaj Radziwill (16th-century Chancellor of Lithuania)	15	15
234	3000r. Mikola Gusovski (15th-16th century writer)	15	15

1996. New Year. Multicoloured.

235	1500r. Type **59**	10	10
236	2000r. Winter landscape (horiz)	10	10

60 "Paraskeva"

1996. Icons in National Museum, Minsk. Multicoloured.

237	3500r. Type **60**	15	15
238	3500r. "Illya" (17th-century)	15	15
239	3500r. "Three Holy Men" (Master of Sharashov)	15	15
240	3500r. "Madonna of Smolensk"	15	15

61 Zhukov

1997. Birth Cent of Marshal G. K. Zhukov.

242	61	2000r. black, gold and red	10	10

62 Theatre

1997. Kupala National Theatre, Minsk.

243	62	3500r. black and gold	20	20

63 Byalnitsky-Birulya

1997. 125th Birth Anniv of W. K. Byalnitsky-Birulya (painter).

244	63	2000r. black and brown	10	10

(64)

1997. 105th Birth Anniv of R. R. Shyrma (composer). No. 2 surch with T **64**.

245	2	3500r. on 20k. light blue, blue and black	20	20

65 Salmon

1997. Fishes. Multicoloured.

246	2000r. Type **65**	10	10
247	3000r. Vimba	15	15
248	4500r. Barbel ("Barbus barbus")	20	20
249	4500r. European grayling ("Thymallus thymallus")	20	20

66 "SOS" on Globe

1997. International Conference on Developing Countries, Minsk. Multicoloured.

251	3000r. Type **66**	10	10
252	4500r. Protective hand over ecosystem	15	15

Nos. 251/2 were issued together, se-tenant, with intervening label showing the Conference emblem, the whole strip forming a composite design.

67 Emblem   **69** Map, National Flag and Monument to the Fallen of Second World War, Minsk

1997. 50th Anniv of Belarussian Membership of Universal Postal Union.

253	67	3000r. multicoloured	10	10

1997. No. 18 surch **100 1997**.

254	7	100r. on 2r. brown	10	10

1997. Independence Day.

255	69	3000r. multicoloured	20	20

1997. Traditional Costumes (3rd series). As T **51**. Multicoloured.

256	2000r. Dzisensk	10	10
257	3000r. Navagrydsk	20	20
258	4500r. Bykhaisk	30	30

70 Page from Skorina Bible and Vilnius

1997. 480th Anniv of Printing in Belarus. Each red, black and grey.

259	3000r. Type **70**	20	20
260	3000r. Page from Skorina Bible and Prague	20	20
261	4000r. Franzisk Skorina and Polotsk	25	25
262	7500r. Skorina and Cracow	40	40

71 Jesuit College

1997. 900th Anniv of Pinsk.

263	71	3000r. multicoloured	20	20

72 Books and Entrance

1997. 75th Anniv of National Library.

264	72	3000r. multicoloured	20	20

73 Dark Glasses reflecting Hands reading Braille

1997. Cent of Schools for the Blind in Belarus.

265	73	3000r. multicoloured	20	20

74 Child in Hand "Flower"

1997. World Children's Day.
266 **74** 3000r. multicoloured . . . 20 20

75 Red Ribbon and Crowd

1997. Red Ribbon AIDS Solidarity Campaign.
267 **75** 4000r. multicoloured . . . 20 20

76 Model 1221

1997. Belarussian Tractors. Multicoloured.
268 3300r. Type **76** 20 20
269 4400r. First Belarussian
    tractor, 1953 . . . . . 25 25
270 7500r. Model 680 . . . . 40 40
271 7500r. Model 952 . . . . 40 40

(77)

1997. Restoration of Cross of St. Ephrosina of Polotsk. No. 1 surch with T **77**.
272 **1** 3000r. on 1r. multicoloured 20 20

78 St. Nicholas hang-gliding over Houses (New Year)

1997. Greetings Stamps. Multicoloured.
273 1400r. Type **78** 10 10
274 4400r. Procession of
    musicians (Christmas) . . . 25 25

79 Cross-country Skiing

1998. Winter Olympic Games, Nagano, Japan. Multicoloured.
275 2000r. Type **79** 15 15
276 3300r. Ice hockey 20 20
277 4400r. Biathlon 30 30
278 7500r. Freestyle skiing . . . 55 55

80 Mashcherov

1998. 80th Birth Anniv of P. M. Mashcherov (writer).
279 **80** 2500r. multicoloured . . . 15 15

81 MAZ-205 Lorry, 1947

1998. Lorries. Multicoloured.
280 1400r. Type **81** 10 10
281 2000r. MAZ-503B, 1968 . . 15 15
282 3000r. MAZ-5549, 1977 . . 20 20
283 4400r. MAZ-5551, 1985 . . 30 30
284 7500r. MAZ-5516, 1994 . . 50 50

82 Entrance to Nyasvizh Castle   **83** Mickiewicz

1998. Europa. National Festivals.
285 **82** 15000r. multicoloured . . . 55 55

1998. Birth Bicentenary of Adam Mickiewicz (political writer).
286 **83** 8600r. multicoloured . . . 35 35

(84)   **85** Bluethroat

1998. 225th Anniv of Postal Service between Mogilov and St. Petersburg. No. 64 surch with T **84**.
287 **15** 8600r. on 150r. mult . . . 35 35

1998. Birds. Multicoloured.
288 1500r. Type **85** 10 10
289 3200r. Penduline tit . . . 15 15
290 3800r. Aquatic warbler . . 15 15
291 5300r. Savi's warbler . . . 20 20
292 8600r. Azure tit 35 35

86 Watermill   **87** Bulldozer Model 7821

1998.
293 **86** 100r. black and green . . . 10 10
294 – 200r. black and brown . . 10 10
295 – 500r. black and blue . . 10 10
296 – 800r. black and violet . . 10 10
297 – 1000r. black and green . . 10 10
298 – 1000r. black and brown . . 10 10
299 – 2000r. black and blue . . 10 10
300 – 3000r. black and yellow . . 15 15
301 – 3200r. black and green . . 15 15
302 – 5000r. black and blue . . 25 25
303 – 5300r. black and yellow . . 25 25
304 – 10000r. black and orange . 45 45
305 **86** 30000r. black and blue . . 40 40
306 – 50000r. black, orange and
    deep orange 60 60
308 – 100000r. black and mauve . 1·40 1·40
309 – 500000r. black and brown . 3·00 3·00
DESIGNS—VERT: 200, 50000r. Windmill; 500r. Stork; 800r. Cathedral of the Holy Trinity, Ishkold; 1000r. Bison; 1500, 3200r. Dulcimer; 2000r. Star; 3000, 5300r. Lute; 5000r. Church; 10000r. Flaming wheel; 500000r. Lyavoniha (folk dance). HORIZ: 100000r. Exhibition centre, Minsk.

1998. 50th Anniv of Belaz Truck Works. Mult.
310 1500r. Type **87** 10 10
311 3200r. Tipper Model 75131 . 15 15
312 3800r. Tipper Model 75303 . 15 15
313 5300r. Tipper Model 75483 . 20 20
314 8600r. Tipper Model 7555 . . 35 35

88 Common Morel   **89** Lion's Head

1998. Fungi. Multicoloured.
315 2500r. Type **88** 10 10
316 3800r. "Morchella conica" . . 15 15
317 4600r. Shaggy parasol . . . 20 20
318 5800r. Parasol mushroom . . 25 25
319 9400r. Shaggy ink cap . . . 45 45

1998. Wood Sculptures. Multicoloured.
320 3400r. Type **89** 20 20
321 3800r. Archangel Michael . . 20 20
322 5800r. Prophet Zacharias . . 30 30
323 9400r. Madonna and Child . . 50 50

90 Emblem and Belarussian Stamps

1998. World Post Day.
324 **90** 5500r. multicoloured . . . 30 30

91 "Kalozha" (V. K. Tsvirka)

1998. Paintings. Multicoloured.
325 3000r. Type **91** 20 20
326 3500r. "Hotel Lounge"
    (S. Yu. Zhukoiski) . . 20 20
327 5000r. "Winter Sleep" (V. K.
    Byalynitski-Birulya) . . 30 30
328 5500r. "Portrait of a Girl"
    (I. I. Alyashkevich) (vert) 30 30
329 10000r. "Portrait of an
    Unknown Woman" (I. F.
    Khrutski) (vert) 60 60

92 Anniversary Emblem   **93** Girl, Rabbit and Fir Trees

1998. 50th Anniv of Universal Declaration of Human Rights.
330 **92** 7100r. multicoloured . . . 35 35

1998. Christmas and New Year. Multicoloured.
331 5500r. Type **93** 30 30
332 5500r. Girl, rabbit and house . 30 30

94 Pushkin and Adam Mickiewicz Monument, St. Petersburg (A. Anikeichyk)

1999. Birth Bicentenary of Aleksandr Pushkin (writer).
333 **94** 15300r. multicoloured . . . 1·00 1·00

95 Model 8007 and Excavator

1999. Minsk Truck and Military Works. Mult.
334 10000r. Type **95** 15 15
335 15000r. Model 543M and
    Smerch rocket system . . 20 20
336 30000r. Model 7907 crane . . 35 35
337 30000r. Model 543M Rubezh
    missile launcher 35 35

96 Dish, Jar and Vase

1999. Glasswork. Multicoloured.
339 30000r. Type **96** 40 40
340 30000r. Chalice 40 40
341 100000r. Oil lamp . . . . 1·40 1·40

(97)

1999. "iBRA '99" International Stamp Exhibition, Nuremberg. Nos. 69/71 surch with T **97**.
342 20r. multicoloured (Type **19**) . 10 10
343 40r. multicoloured (No. 70) . 35 35
344 40r. multicoloured (No. 71) . 35 35

98 Belavezhskaya Pushcha Reserve

1999. Europa. Parks and Gardens. Multicoloured.
345 150000r. Type **98** 55 55
346 150000r. Beaver in
    Byarezinski Reserve . . . 55 55

99 Well

1999. Wooden Buildings. Multicoloured.
347 50000r. Type **99** 20 20
348 50000r. Public house . . . 20 20
349 100000r. Windmill 40 40

100 "Portrait of Yu. M. Pen" (A. M. Brazer)

1999. Vitebsk Art School. Paintings. Multicoloured.

350	30000r. Type **100**	15	15
351	60000r. "St. Anthony's Church, Vitebsk" (S. B.Yudovin)	25	25
352	100000r. "Street in Vitebsk" (Yu. M. Pen)	30	30
353	100000r. "Kryvaya Street, Vitebsk" (M. P. Mikhalap) (horiz)	30	30

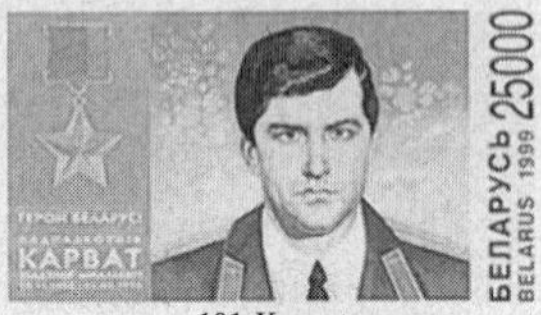

101 Karvat

1999. 3rd Death Anniv of Wing Commander Karvat.

355 **101**	25000r. multicoloured	10	10

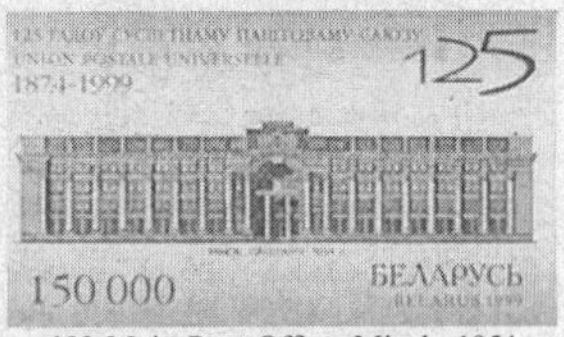

102 Main Post Office, Minsk, 1954

1999. 125th Anniv of Universal Postal Union. Mult.

356	150000r. Type **102**	50	50
357	150000r. First post office in Minsk, 1800	50	50

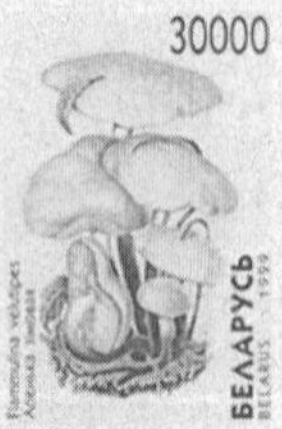

103 Golden Mushroom

1999. Fungi. Multicoloured.

358	30000r. Type **103**	10	10
359	50000r. Changeable agaric	15	15
360	75000r. *Lyophyllum connatum*	20	20
361	100000r. *Lyophyllum decastes*	30	30

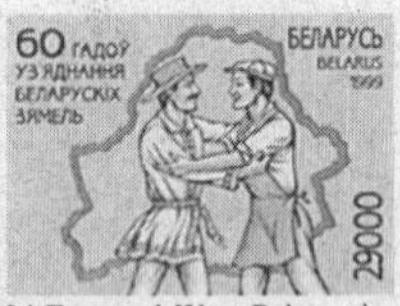

104 East and West Belarussians Embracing

1999. 60th Anniv of Re-unification of Republic of Byelorussia.

363 **104**	29000r. multicoloured	10	10

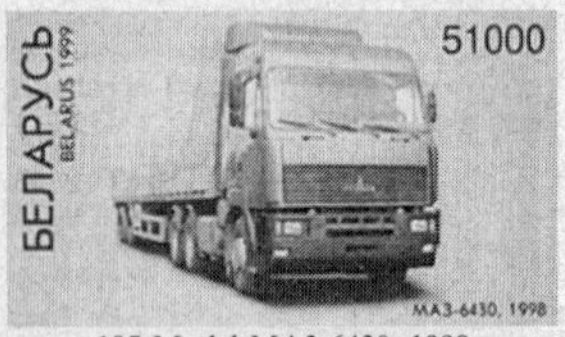

105 Model MA3-6430, 1998

1999. Minsk Truck and Military Works. Lorries. Multicoloured.

364	51000r. Type **105**	15	15
365	86000r. Lorry Model MA3-4370	30	30

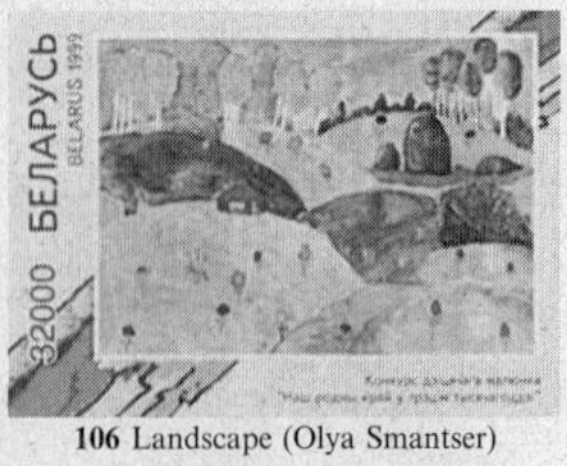

106 Landscape (Olya Smantser)

1999. Children's Painting Competition Winners. Mult.

366	32000r. Type **106**	10	10
367	59000r. Girl (Masha Dudarenko) (vert)	15	15

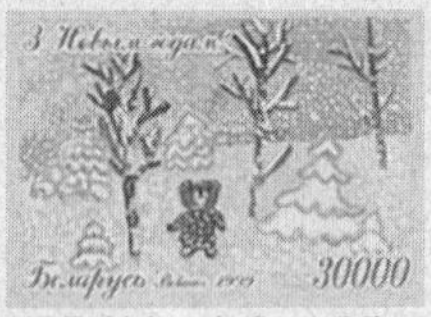

107 Teddybear in Snow (Mitya Kutas)

1999. Christmas and New Year. Children's Paintings. Multicoloured.

368	30000r. Type **107**	10	10
369	30000r. Children building snowman and ice-skating (Yulya Yakubovich)	10	10

Currency Revaluation

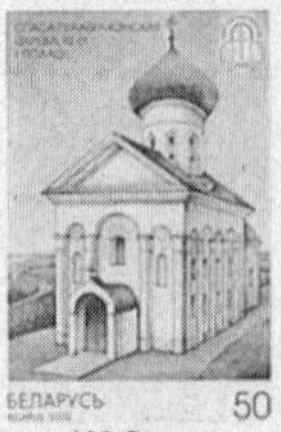

108 Spasa-Praabrazhenskaya Church, Polatsk

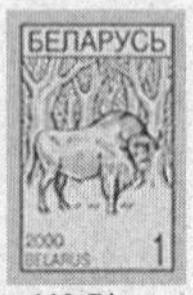

110 Bison

2000. Birth Bimillenary of Jesus Christ. Mult.

370	50r. Type **108**	25	25
371	75r. St. Atsistratsiga Cathedral, Slutsk	40	40
372	100r. The Reverend Serafim Sarovskaga Church, Belaazersk	55	55

2000.

374 **110**	1r. black and green	10	10
375 –	2r. black and blue	10	10
376 –	3r. black and yellow	10	10
377 –	5r. black and blue	10	10
378 –	10r. black and orange	10	10
380 –	20r. black and mauve	10	10
382 –	30r. black and green	15	15
383 –	50r. black and yellow	55	55
387 –	100r. black and mauve	1·00	1·10

DESIGNS—VERT: 2r. Star; 3r. Lyre; 5r. Synkovichy Church; 10r. Flaming wheel; 20r. Type **111**; 30r. Watermill; 50r. Windmill. HORIZ: 100r. Exhibition Centre.

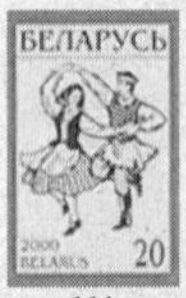

111 Kryzhachok (folk dance)

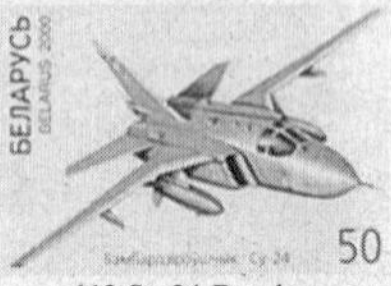

112 Su-24 Bomber

2000. Self-adhesive.

391 **111**	20r. black and red	10	10

2000. 25th Death Anniv of Pavel Sukhoi (aircraft designer). Multicoloured.

392	50r. Type **112**	50	50
393	50r. Su-27 fighter	50	50
394	50r. Su-25 battle fighter	50	50

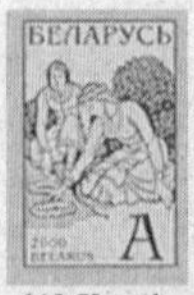

113 Kupala Holiday

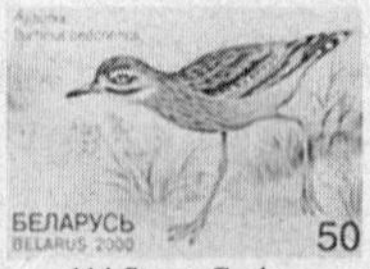

114 Stone-Curlew

2000.

396 **113**	A black and blue	15	15

No. 396 was for Inland Letter Post rate.

2000. Birds in the Red Book. Multicoloured.

397	50r. Type **114**	25	25
398	50r. Smew (*Mergellus albellus*)	25	25
399	75r. Willow grouse	40	40
400	100r. Lesser spotted eagle (vert)	55	55

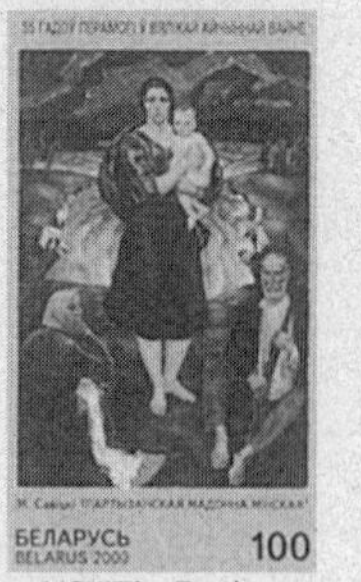

115 "The Partisan Madonna of Minsk" (M. Savitsky)

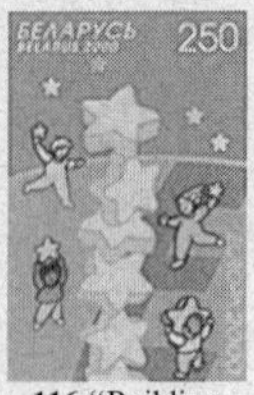

116 "Building Europe"

2000. 55th Anniv of End of Second World War.

401 **115**	100r. multicoloured	55	55

2000. Europa.

402 **116**	250r. multicoloured	1·10	1·10

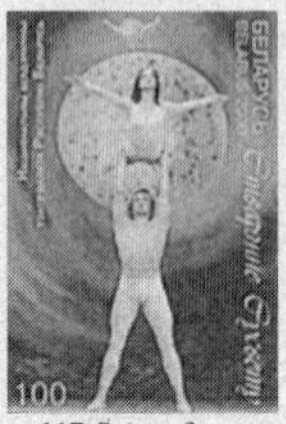

117 Scene from "Creation of the World"

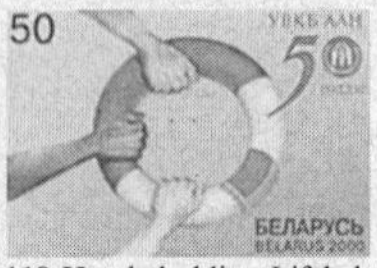

118 Hands holding Lifebelt

2000. National Ballet Company.

403 **117**	100r. multicoloured	55	55

2000. 50th Anniv of United Nations High Commission for Refugees.

405 **118**	50r. multicoloured	25	25

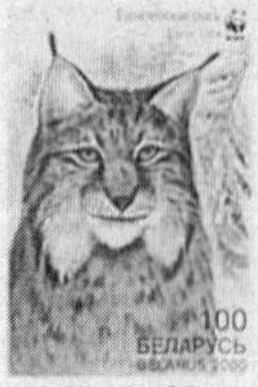

119 Head of Lynx

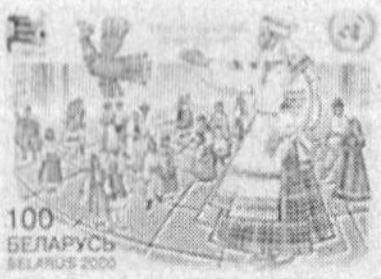

120 People wearing National Costumes

2000. Endangered Species. The Lynx. Multicoloured.

406	100r. Type **119**	55	55
407	100r. On branch	55	55
408	150r. Walking through woodland	80	80
409	150r. Adult and cub	80	80

2000. International Year of Culture.

410 **120**	100r. multicoloured	55	55

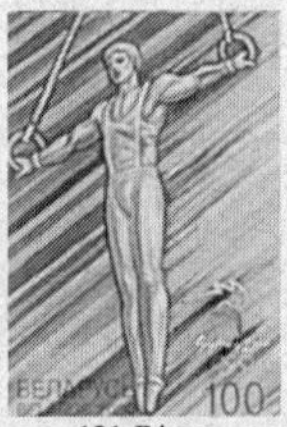

121 Rings

2000. Olympic Games, Sydney. Multicoloured.

411	100r. Type **121**	55	55
412	100r. Kayaking	55	55
413	100r. Rhythmic gymnastics	55	55

BELGIAN CONGO Pt. 4

A Belgian colony in Central Africa. Became independent in July 1960. For later issues see Congo, Zaire, Democratic Republic of Congo, Katanga and South Kasai.

100 centimes = 1 franc.

INDEPENDENT STATE OF THE CONGO

The Independent State of the Congo was established in 1885, with King Leopold II of the Belgians as ruler.

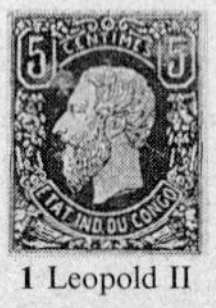

1 Leopold II

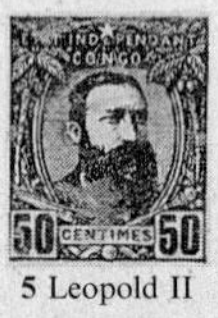

5 Leopold II

1886. Various frames.

1 **1**	5c. green	4·25	14·50
2	10c. red	2·40	3·25
3	25c. blue	30·00	26·00
4	50c. green	4·75	4·75
5	5f. lilac	£225	£180

1887. Surch **COLIS-POSTAUX Fr. 3.50**.

6 **1**	3f.50 on 5f. lilac	£700	£500

1887.

7 **5**	5c. green	60	60
8	10c. red	90	80
9	25c. blue	85	70
10	50c. brown	35·00	18·00
11	50c. grey	2·00	13·00
12	5f. lilac	£700	£300
13	5f. grey	90·00	70·00
14	10f. orange	£325	£225

1887. Surch **COLIS-POSTAUX Fr. 3.50**.

15 **5**	3f.50 on 5f. violet	£600	£350

1889. Surch **COLIS-POSTAUX Fr. 3.50** in frame.

16 **5**	3f.50 on 5f. violet	£450	£275
17	3f.50 on 5f. grey	90·00	80·00

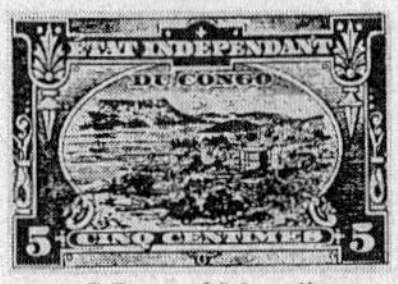

7 Port of Matadi

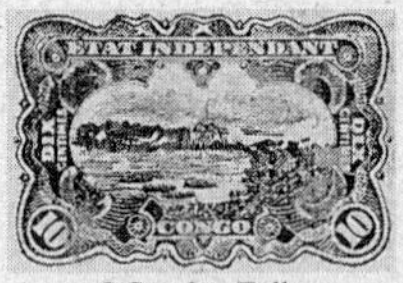

8 Stanley Falls

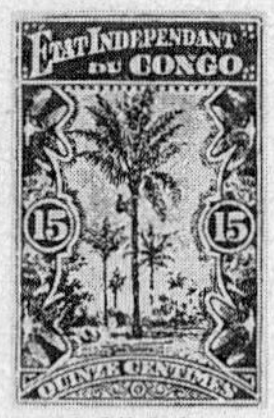

13 Oil Palms

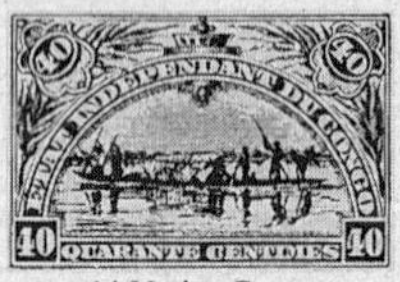

14 Native Canoe

1894. Inscr "ETAT INDEPENDANT DU "CONGO".

18 **7**	5c. black and blue	9·50	9·50
24	5c. black and brown	1·90	95
30	5c. black and green	1·10	35
19 **8**	10c. black and brown	10·50	10·50
25	10c. black and blue	1·10	90
31	10c. black and red	2·75	65
26 **13**	15c. black and brown	3·00	65
20 –	25c. black and orange	3·00	2·00
32 –	25c. black and blue	3·00	1·25
27 **14**	40c. black and green	3·00	2·40
21 –	50c. black and green	1·10	90
33 –	50c. black and brown	3·00	65
22 –	1f. black and violet	16·00	10·00
35 –	1f. black and red	£160	5·00
28 –	3f.50 black and red	£110	80·00
23 –	5f. black and red	32·00	22·00
29 –	10f. black and green	80·00	24·00

DESIGNS—HORIZ: 25c. Inkissi Falls; 50c. Railway Bridge over the M'pozo; 1f. African elephant hunt; 3f.50 Congo village; 10f. "Deliverance" (stern wheel paddle-steamer). VERT: 5f. Bangala Chief Morangi and wife.

BELGIAN CONGO

The Congo was annexed to Belgium in 1908 and was renamed the Belgian Congo.

1909. Nos. 23, 26/29 and 30/33 optd **CONGO BELGE**.

36 **7**	5c. black and green	1·60	1·25
37 **8**	10c. black and red	1·60	1·25
38 **13**	15c. black and brown	3·50	2·40
49 –	25c. black and blue	2·40	1·60
50 **14**	40c. black and green	2·00	2·00
51 –	50c. black and brown	3·25	1·60
52 –	1f. black and red	15·00	4·00
53 –	3f.50 black and red	21·00	16·00
54 –	5f. black and red	38·00	20·00
55b –	10f. black and green	75·00	20·00

1909. As 1894 issue but inscr "CONGO BELGE".

56 **7**	5c. black and green	60	50
57 **8**	10c. black and red	55	35
58 **13**	15c. black and brown	20·00	10·50
59 –	50c. black and bistre	2·25	1·60

1910. As 1894 issue but inscr "CONGO BELGE BELGISCH-CONGO" with values in French and Flemish.

60 **7**	5c. black and green	50	20
61 **8**	10c. black and red	60	15
62 **13**	15c. black and brown	40	15
63 –	25c. black and blue	1·25	25
64 **14**	40c. black and green	2·00	1·75
65 –	50c. black and bistre	2·50	1·50
66 –	1f. black and red	2·50	1·90
68 –	3f. black and red	13·00	8·00
67 –	5f. black and red	20·00	19·00
69 –	10f. black and green	18·00	17·00

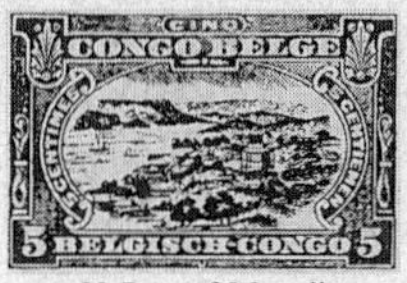
32 Port of Matadi

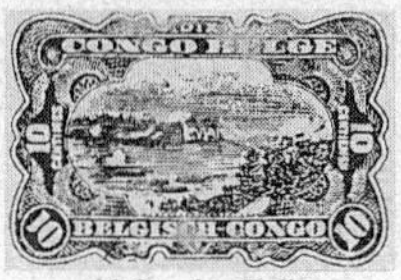
33 Stanley Falls

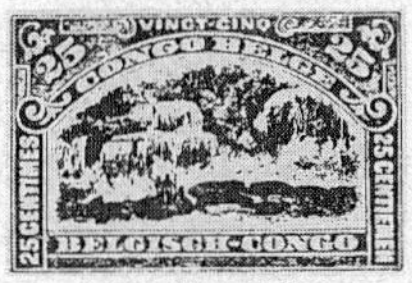
34 Inkissi Falls

1915. New types as **32** to **34** (with value in words at top) and other types as 1910 all inscr "CONGO BELGE" and "BELGISCH-CONGO".

70	32	5c. black and green	20	15
71	33	10c. black and red	20	15
72b	13	15c. black and green	25	20
73	34	25c. black and blue	95	25
74	14	40c. black and red	4·00	2·00
75	–	50c. black and red	5·25	1·60
76	–	1f. black and olive	1·75	60
77	–	5f. black and orange	1·40	60

1918. Types as before, surch with red cross and premium.

78	32	5c.+10c. blue and green	20	25
79	33	10c.+15c. blue and red	20	25
80	13	15c.+20c. blue and green	20	25
81	34	25c.+25c. blue	25	25
82	14	40c.+40c. blue and red	35	45
83	–	50c.+50c. blue and red	40	40
84	–	1f.+1f. blue and olive	1·40	1·40
85	–	5f.+5f. blue and orange	8·00	8·00
86	–	10f.+10f. blue and green	95·00	95·00

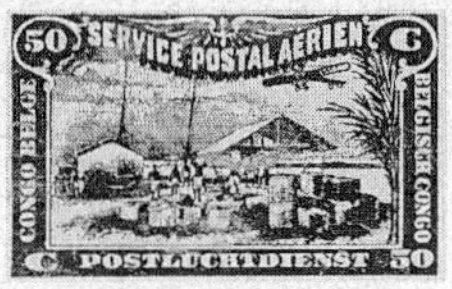
38 Congo Wharf

1920. Air.

87	38	50c. black and orange	20	10
88	–	1f. black and violet	20	10
89	–	2f. black and blue	55	20
90	–	5f. black and green	1·10	55

DESIGNS—HORIZ: 1f. District stores; 2f. Native canoes on beach. VERT: 5f. Provinicial prison.

1921. Stamps of 1910 surch.

91	14	5c. on 40c. black and green	20	20
92	–	10c. on 5c. black and green	20	20
93	–	15c. on 50c. black and olive	25	25
94	13	25c. on 15c. black & yellow	1·60	90
95	8	30c. on 10c. black and red	25	25
96	–	50c. on 25c. black and blue	1·40	90

1921. Stamps of 1910 optd **1921**.

97		1f. black and red	70	70
98		3f. black and red	2·10	2·10
99		5f. black and lake	6·50	6·50
100		10f. black and green	5·50	4·00

1922. Stamps of previous issues variously surch without bars.

101	–	5c. on 50c. black and lake (No. 75)	30	30
102	32	10c. on 5c. black and green (No. 70)	35	25
114	8	0.25 on 30c. on 10c. black and red (No. 95)	9·50	9·50
115	33	0.25 on 30c. on 10c. black and red (No. 104)	9·50	9·50
103	14	25c. on 40c. black and lake (No. 74)	2·00	30
104	33	30c. on 10c. black and red (No. 71)	20	20
105	34	50c. on 25c. black and blue (No. 73)	70	25

1922. Stamps of 1915 surch with new value and two bars through old values.

108	32	10c. on 5c. black & green	40	35
110	–	10c. on 1f. black & olive	50	50
112	14	25c. on 40c. black & lake	70	30
113	–	25c. on 5f. blk & orange	1·40	1·40

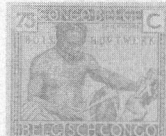

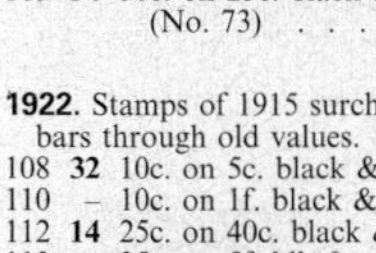
46 Wood Carver

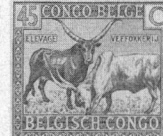

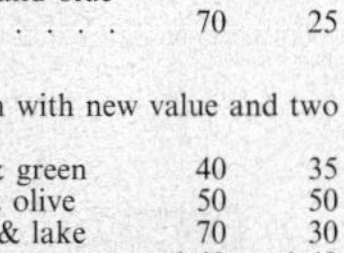
56 Native Cattle

1923.

117	A	5c. yellow	15	10
118	B	10c. green	15	10
119	C	15c. brown	15	10
120	D	20c. olive	15	10
121	E	20c. green	15	10
122	F	25c. brown	20	10
123	46	30c. red	30	40
124		30c. olive	15	10
125		35c. green	40	40
126	D	40c. purple	15	10
142	56	45c. purple	30	25
127	G	50c. blue	20	10
128		50c. orange	30	10
143	56	60c. red	30	15
129	E	75c. orange	30	20
130		75c. blue	30	20
131	46	75c. red	20	10
132	H	1f. brown	45	15
133		1f. blue	35	10
134		1f. red	60	10
135	D	1f.25 blue	30	20
136		1f.50 blue	30	15
137		1f.75 blue	3·50	3·00
138	I	3f. brown	3·00	1·60
139	J	5f. grey	9·25	3·75
140	K	10f. black	16·00	8·00

DESIGNS: A, Ubangi woman; B, Baluba woman; C, Babuende woman; D, Ubangi man; E, Weaver; F, Basketmaker; G, Archer; H, Potter; I, Rubber worker; J, Palm oil; K, African elephant.

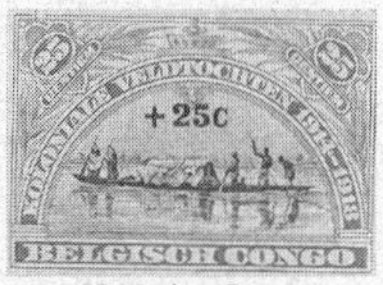
55 Native Canoe

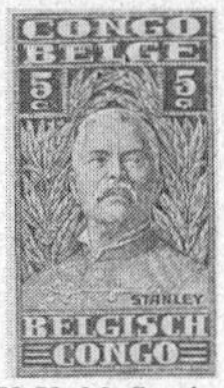
58 H. M. Stanley

1925. Great War Colonial Memorial Fund. Inscr in French or in Flemish.

141	55	25c.+25c. black and red	20	20

1927. No. 136 surch **1.75**.

144		1.75 on 1f. 50 blue	60	50

1928. 50th Anniv of Stanley's Exploration of the Congo.

145	58	5c. olive	10	10
146		10c. violet	10	10
147		20c. red	20	15
148		35c. green	65	60
149		40c. brown	25	15
150		60c. sepia	25	15
151		1f. red	25	10
152		1f.60 grey	4·50	3·75
153		1f.75 blue	1·10	60
154		2f. brown	75	50
155		2f.75 purple	4·50	30
156		3f.50 red	1·00	50
157		5f. turquoise	80	20
158		10f. blue	1·10	60
159		20f. red	4·50	2·75

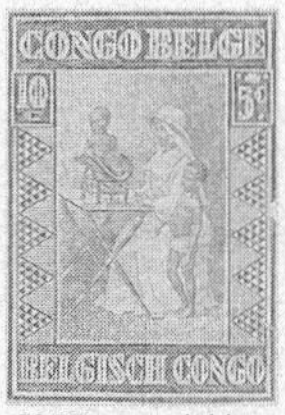
59 Nurse weighing Children

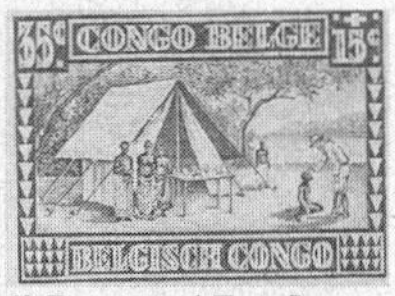
60 Doctor and Tent Surgery

1930. Congo Natives Protection Fund.

160	59	10c.+5c. red	45	45
161	–	20c.+10c. brown	60	60
162	60	35c.+15c. green	95	95
163	–	60c.+30c. purple	1·25	1·25
164	–	1f.+50c. red	1·60	1·60
165	–	1f.75+75c. blue	4·00	4·00
166	–	3f.50+1f.50 red	5·50	5·50
167	–	5f.+2f.50 brown	6·50	6·50
168	–	10f.+5f. black	8·00	8·00

DESIGNS—VERT: 20c. Missionary and child; 1f. Dispenser attending patients. HORIZ: 60c. Local hospital; 1f.75, Nurses and patients; 3f.50 Nurse bathing baby; 5f. Operating theatre; 10f. Children in school.

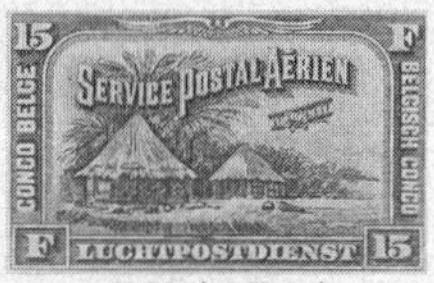
61 Native Kraal

1930. Air.

169	61	15f. black and sepia	1·60	85
170	–	30f. black and purple	1·90	90

DESIGN: 30f. Native porters.

1931. Surch.

171		40c. on 35c. grn (No. 148)	60	50
177		40c. on 35c. green (125)	2·75	2·75
178		50c. on 45c. purple (142)	1·75	1·00
172		1f.25 on 1f. red (151)	40	10
173		2f. on 1f.60 grey (152)	80	30
174		2f. on 1f.75 blue (153)	70	25
179		2f. on 1f.75 blue (137)	8·00	7·00
175		3f.25 on 2f.75 purple (155)	2·25	1·75
180		3f.25 on 3f. brown (138)	3·50	2·25
176		3f.25 on 3f.50 red (156)	4·00	3·25

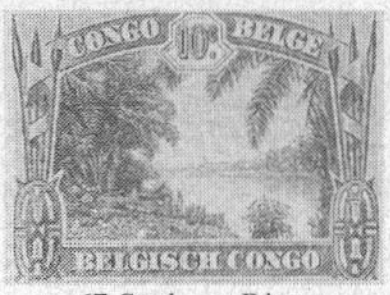
67 Sankuru River

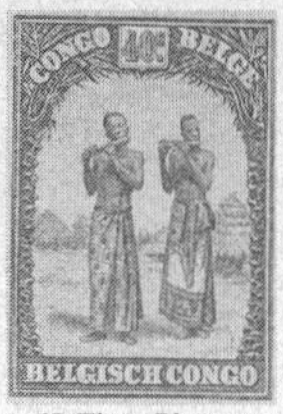
68 Flute Players

1931.

181	67	10c. brown	10	10
182	–	15c. grey	10	10
183	–	20c. mauve	10	10
184	–	25c. blue	10	10
185	68	40c. green	20	20
186	–	50c. violet	10	10
187	–	60c. purple	10	10
188	–	75c. red	10	10
189	–	1f. red	15	10
190	–	1f.25 brown	15	10
190b	–	1f.50 black	15	10
191	–	2f. blue	20	10
191a	–	2f.50 blue	50	15
192	–	3f.25 grey	75	30
193	–	4f. lilac	30	15
194	–	5f. purple	60	20
195	–	10f. orange	60	45
196	–	20f. sepia	1·40	1·25

DESIGNS—HORIZ: 15c. Native Kraal; 20c. Waterfall; 25c. Native Kraal; 50c. Native musicians; 1f.50, 2f., 4f. Riverside scenes (different views); 2f.50, 3f.25, Okapi. VERT: 60c. Native flute-players and drummers; 75c. Mangbethu woman; 1f. Elephant transport; 1f.25. Native chief; 5f. Pressing out tapioca; 10f. Witch doctor; 20f. Woman carrying latex.

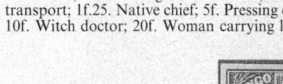

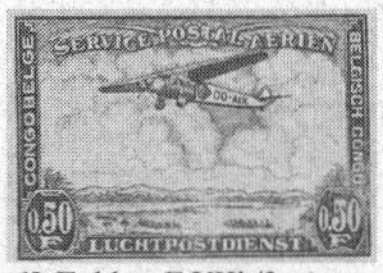
69 Fokker F.VIIb/3m over Congo

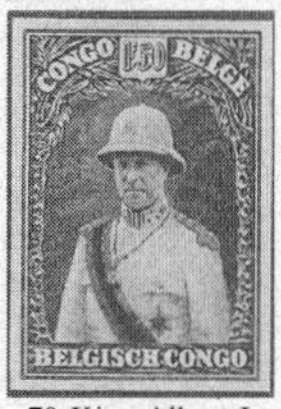
70 King Albert I

1934. Air

197	69	50c. black	15	15
198		1f. red	20	15
199		1f.50 green	20	15
200		3f. brown	25	10
201		4f.50 blue	30	15
202		5f. red	30	10
203		15f. purple	40	30
204		30f. red	90	85
205		50f. violet	2·50	1·60

1934. Death of King Albert.

206	70	1f.50 black	60	30

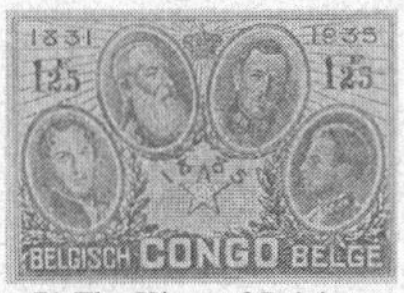
71 The Kings of Belgium

1935. 50th Anniv of Independent State of the Congo.

207	71	50c. green	1·00	50
208		1f.25 red	1·00	15
209		1f.50 purple	1·00	10
210		2f.40 orange	2·50	2·40
211		2f.50 blue	2·50	80
212		4f. violet	2·50	1·25
213		5f. brown	2·50	1·40

1936. Air. Surch **3.50F.**

214	69	3f.50 on 3f. brown	20	10

1936. King Albert Memorial Fund. Surch **+ 50 c.**

215	71	1f.50+50c. purple	3·25	2·75
216		2f.50+50c. blue	1·60	1·25

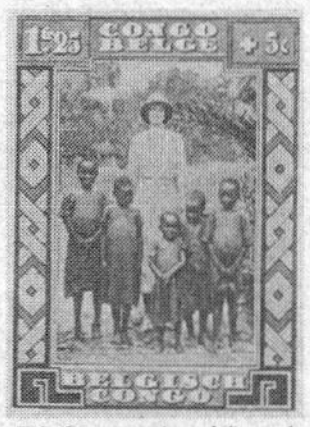
74 Queen Astrid and Congo Children

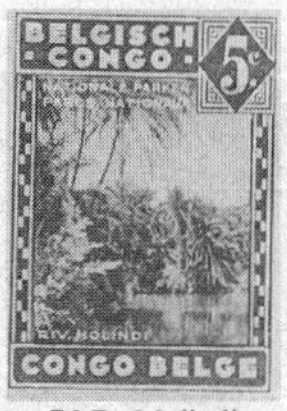
76 R. Molindi

1936. Queen Astrid Fund for Congo Children.

217	74	1f.25+5c. brown	50	45
218		1f.50+10c. red	50	45
219		2f.50+25c. blue	60	60

1938. Promotion of National Parks.

220	76	5c. black and violet	10	10
221	–	90c. brown and red	35	30
222	–	1f.50 black and purple	10	10
223	–	2f.40 brown and grey	10	10
224	–	2f.50 black and blue	25	15
225	–	4f.50 brown and green	25	15

DESIGNS—VERT: 90c. Bamboo-canes; 1f.50, R. Suza; 2f.40, R. Rutshuru. HORIZ: 2f.50, Mt. Karisimbi; 4f.50, Mitumba Forest.

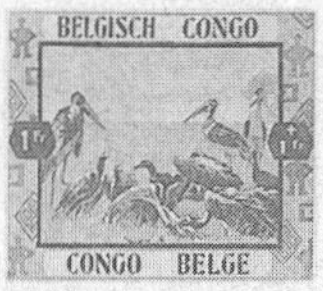
77 Marabou Stork and Ruppels Griffon

1939. Leopoldville Zoological Gardens.

226	77	1f.+1f. purple	5·75	5·50
227	–	1f.25+1f.25 red	4·50	4·50
228	–	1f.50+1f.50 violet	5·00	5·00
229	–	4f.50+4f.50 green	4·00	4·00
230	–	5f.+5f. brown	4·00	4·00

DESIGNS: 1f.25, Kob; 1f.50, Young chimpanzees; 4f.50, Crocodiles; 5f. Lioness.

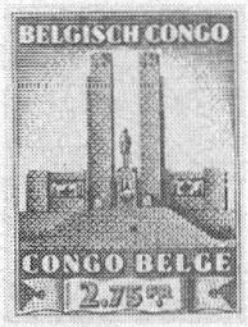
78 King Albert Memorial, Leopoldville

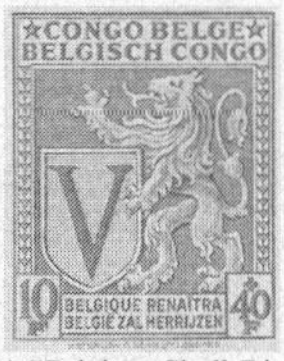
81 "Belgium Shall Rise Again"

1941.

231	78	10c. grey	20	20
232		15c. brown	20	20
233		25c. blue	30	25
234		50c. lilac	20	20
235		75c. pink	1·00	40
236		1f.25 brown	30	30
237		1f.75 orange	1·00	40
238		2f.50 red	60	15
239		2f.75 blue	90	75
240		5f. olive	3·25	3·25
241		10f. red	2·50	2·40

1941. Surch.

242	–	5c. on 1f.50 black & purple (No. 222) (postage)	10	10
243	78	75c. on 1f.75 orange	20	20
244	–	2f.50 on 2f.40 brown and grey (No. 223)	90	70
245	69	50c. on 1f.50 green (air)	20	20

1942. War Relief Fund.

246	81	10f.+40f. green	95	95
247		10f.+40f. blue	95	95

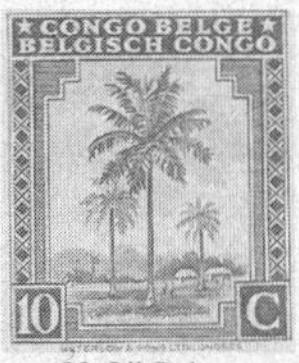
82 Oil Palms

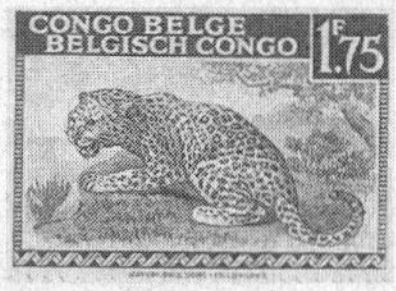
84 Leopard

1942. (a) Inscr "BELGISCH CONGO BELGE".

248	82	5c. red	10	10
249	–	50f. black and blue	3·25	1·00
250	–	100f. black and red	3·75	2·10

(b) Inscr "CONGO BELGE BELGISCH CONGO", or vice versa.

251	82	10c. olive	10	10
252		15c. brown	10	10
253		20c. blue	10	10
254		25c. purple	10	10
255		30c. blue	10	10
256		50c. green	10	10
257		60c. brown	10	10
258	–	75c. black and violet	10	10
259	–	1f. black and brown	15	10
260	–	1f.25 black and red	15	10
261	84	1f.75 brown	45	45
262		2f. yellow	45	15
263		2f.50 red	45	10
264	–	3f.50 olive	20	10
265	–	5f. orange	45	15
266	–	6f. blue	40	10
267	–	7f. black	40	10
268	–	10f. brown	50	10
269	–	20f. black and red	3·25	1·00

DESIGNS—As Type **82**: 75c. to 1f.25, Head of a native woman; 3f.50 to 10f. Askari sentry. As Type **84**: 20f. Okapi; 28 × 33 mm: 50 f. Head of woman; 100f. Askari sentry.

1944. Red Cross Fund. Surch **Au profit de la Croix Rouge Ten voordeele van het Roode Kruis** (or with French and Flemish reversed) and additional value.

269a	82	50c.+50f. green	1·90	1·90
269b	–	1f.25+100f. black and red (No. 260)	1·90	1·90
269c	84	1f.75+100f. brown	1·90	1·90
269d	–	3f.50+100f. green (No. 264)	1·90	1·90

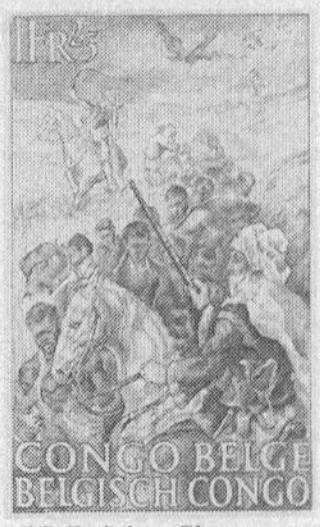
87 Driving Slaves to Market

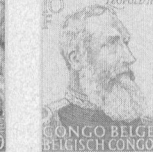

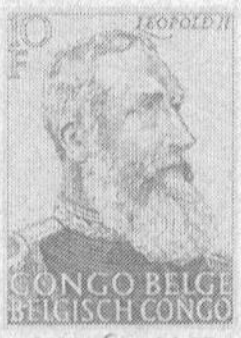
88 Leopold II

1947. 50th Anniv of Abolition of Slavery in Belgian Congo.

270	87	1f.25 brown	20	10
270a	–	1f.50 violet	1·50	25
270b	–	3f. brown	1·50	10
271	–	3f.50 blue	25	10
272	88	10f. orange	75	15

PORTRAITS–As Type **88**: 1f.50, Lavigerie. 3f. Dhanis. 3f.50, Lambermont.

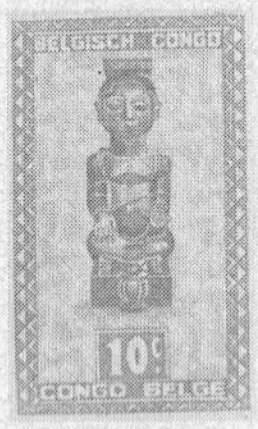
89 Seated Figure

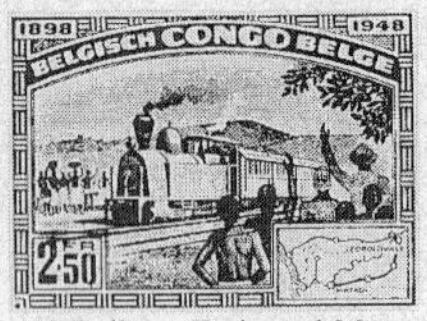
90 Railway Train and Map

1947. Native masks and carvings as T **89**.

273	89	10c. orange	10	10
274	A	15c. blue	10	10
275	B	20c. blue	10	10
276	C	25c. red	15	10
277	D	40c. purple	10	10
278	89	50c. brown	10	10
279	A	70c. green	10	10
280	B	75c. purple	10	10
281	C	1f. purple and orange	1·50	10
281a	A	1f.20 brown and grey	15	10
282	D	1f.25 purple and green	25	15
282a	E	1f.50 red and green	12·00	2·75
282b	B	1f.60 blue and grey	20	15
283	89	2f. red and orange	20	10
283a	C	2f.40 green and turquoise	30	15
284	A	2f.50 green and brown	20	10
284a	E	3f. indigo and blue	3·50	10
285	B	3f.50 green and blue	3·25	20
286	C	5f. purple and bistre	1·00	10
287	D	6f. green and orange	1·25	10
287a	F	6f.50 brown and red	1·40	10
287b	D	8f. green and blue	1·75	20
288	E	10f. brown and violet	6·50	10
289	F	20f. brown and red	3·00	10
290	E	50f. black and brown	4·75	25
291	F	100f. black and red	5·75	55

DESIGNS: A, Seated figure (different); B, Kneeling figure; C, Double mask; D, Mask; E, Mask with tassels; F, Mask with horns.

1948. 50th Anniv of Matadi–Leopoldville Railway.

292	90	2f.50 green and blue	1·25	20

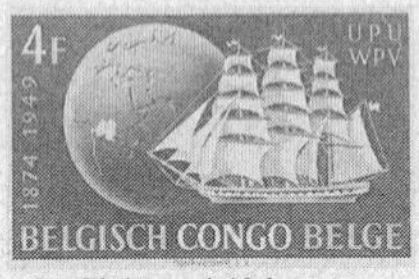
91 Globe and 19th-century Full-rigged Ship

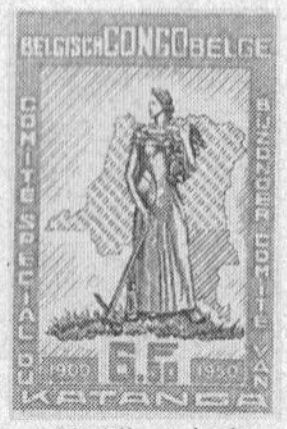
92 Allegorical Figure and Map

1949. 75th Anniv of U.P.U.

293	91	4f. blue	60	15

1950. 50th Anniv of "Comite Special du Katanga" (Chartered Company).

294	92	3f. slate and blue	1·60	15
295		6f.50 sepia and red	1·60	25

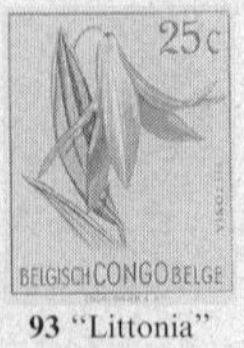
93 "Littonia"

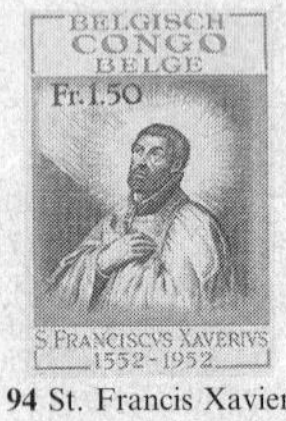
94 St. Francis Xavier

1952. Flowers. Multicoloured.

296	10c. "Dissotis"	10	10
297	15c. "Protea"	10	10
298	20c. "Vellozia"	10	10
299	25c. Type 93	10	10
300	40c. "Ipomoea"	10	10
301	50c. "Angraecum"	10	10
302	60c. "Euphorbia"	10	10
303	75c. "Ochna"	10	10
304	1f. "Hibiscus"	10	10
305	1f.25 "Protea"	1·00	35
306	1f.50 "Schizoglossum"	30	10
307	2f. "Ansellia"	30	10
308	3f. "Costus"	30	10
309	4f. "Nymphaea"	65	10
310	5f. "Thunbergia"	95	10
311	6f.50 "Thonningia"	1·00	10
312	7f. "Gerbera"	1·60	10
313	8f. "Gloriosa"	2·40	15
314	10f. "Silene"	2·75	10
315	20f. "Aristolochia"	3·25	10
316	50f. "Eulophia"	9·00	40
317	100f. "Cryptosepalum"	12·00	95

SIZES: Nos. 296/315, 21 × 25½ mm. Nos. 316/17, 22½ × 32½ mm.

1953. 400th Death Anniv of St. Francis Xavier.

318	94	1f.50c. black and blue	60	30

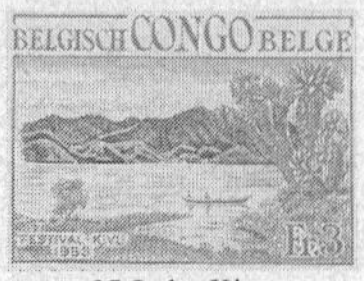
95 Lake Kivu

1953. Kivu Festival.

319	95	3f. black and red	1·25	20
320		7f. brown and blue	1·25	25

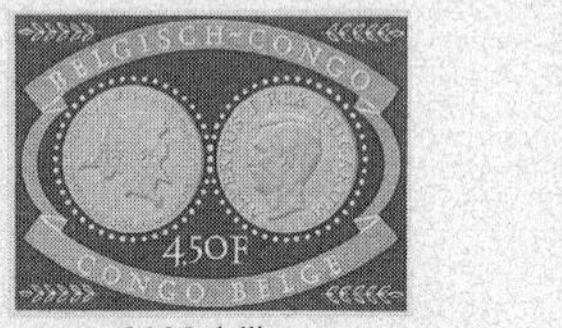
96 Medallion

1954. 25th Anniv of Belgian Royal Colonial Institute. No. 322 has different frame.

321	96	4f.50 grey and blue	1·25	30
322		6f.50 brown and green	75	10

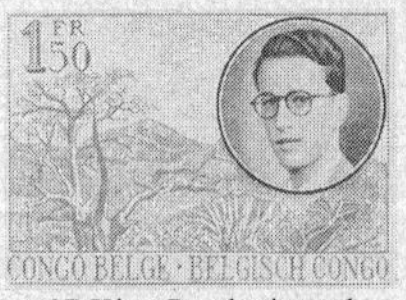
97 King Baudouin and Mountains

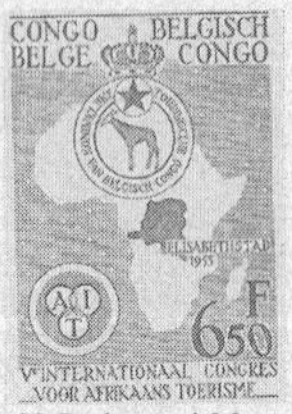
98 Badge and Map

1955. Inscr "CONGO BELGE . BELGISCH CONGO" or vice versa.

323	97	1f.50 black and red	8·75	1·10
324	–	3f. black and green	5·50	1·00
325	–	4f.50 black and blue	5·50	70
326	–	6f.50 black & purple	8·75	35

DESIGNS: 3f. Forest; 4f.50, River; 6f.50, Grassland.

1955. 5th Int Congress of African Tourism. Inscr in Flemish or French.

327	98	6f.50 blue	2·10	40

1956. Birth Bicentenary of Mozart. As T **316/17** of Belgium.

328	316	4f.50+1f.50 violet	3·00	1·40
329	317	6f.50+2f.50 blue	4·50	1·60

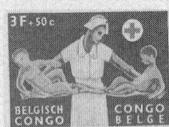

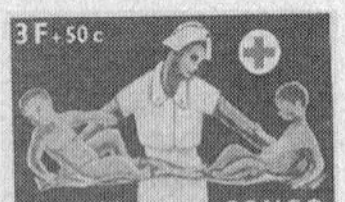
99 Nurse with Children

1957. Red Cross Fund. Cross in red.

330	99	3f.+50c. blue	85	40
331	–	4f.50+50c. green	85	40
332	–	6f.50+50c. brown	1·00	70

DESIGNS—HORIZ: 4f.50, Doctor inoculating patient; 6f.50, Nurse in tropical kit bandaging patient.

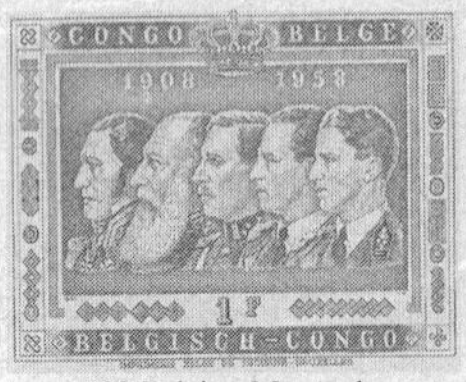
100 Belgian Monarchs

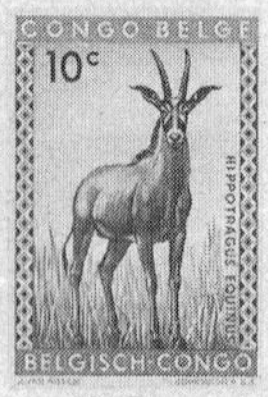
101 Roan Antelope

1958. 50th Anniv of Belgian Annexation of the Congo.

333	100	1f. red	50	10
334		1f.50 blue	50	10
335		3f. red	50	10
336		5f. green	1·00	30
337		6f.50 brown	80	10
338		10f. violet	1·00	10

1959. Wild Animals.

339	101	10c. brown, sepia & blue	10	10
340	–	20c. blue and red	25	25
341	–	40c. brown and blue	15	10
342	–	50c. multicoloured	15	10
343	–	1f. black, green & brown	25	10
344	–	1f.50 black and yellow	30	10
345	–	2f. black, brown and red	30	10
346	–	3f. black, purple & slate	50	10
347	–	5f. brown, green & sepia	65	15
348	–	6f.50 brn, yellow & blue	65	10
349	–	8f. bistre, violet & brown	75	15
350	–	10f. multicoloured	85	10

DESIGNS—HORIZ: 20c. White rhinoceros; 50c. Demidoff's galago; 1f.50, African buffaloes; 3f. African elephants; 6f.50, Impala; 10f. Eland and common zebras. VERT: 40c. Giraffe; 1f. Gorilla; 2f. Eastern Black and White Colobus monkey; 5f. Okapis; 8f. Giant ground pangolin.

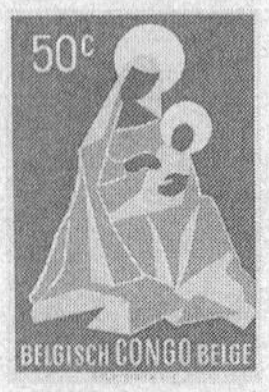
102 Madonna and Child

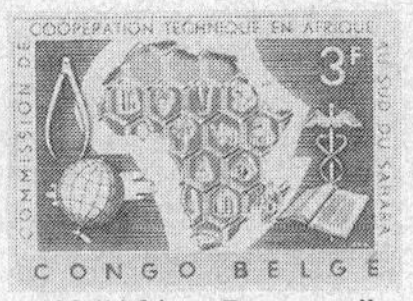
103 "African Resources"

1959. Christmas.

351	102	50c. brn, ochre & chestnut	10	10
352		1f. brown, violet & blue	10	10
353		2f. brown, blue and grey	15	10

1960. 10th Anniv of African Technical Co-operation Commission. Inscr in French or Flemish.

354	103	3f. orange and grey	20	10

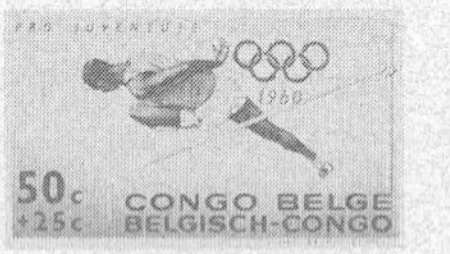
104 High Jumping

1960. Child Welfare Fund.

355	104	50c.+25c. blue and red	10	10
356	–	1f.50+50c. red & green	15	10
357	–	2f.+1f. green and red	20	10
358	–	3f.+1f.25 purple & bl	65	40
359	–	6f.50+3f.50 brn & red	80	40

DESIGNS: 1f.50, Hurdling; 2f. Football; 3f. Throwing the javelin; 6f.60, Throwing the discus.

POSTAGE DUE STAMPS

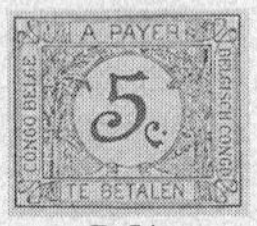
D 54

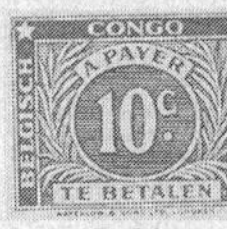
D 86

1923.

D141	D 54	5c. sepia	15	15
D142a		10c. red	15	15
D143		15c. violet	20	15
D144		30c. green	30	25
D145		50c. blue	40	35
D146		1f. grey	45	30

1943.

D270	D 86	10c. olive	10	10
D271		20c. blue	10	10
D272		50c. green	15	15
D273		1f. brown	15	15
D274		2f. orange	15	15

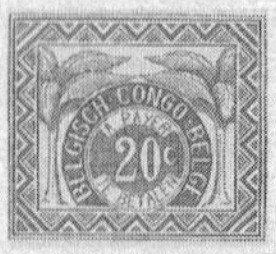
D 99

1957.

D330	D 99	10c. brown	10	10
D331		20c. purple	10	10
D332		50c. green	15	10
D333		1f. blue	25	20
D334		2f. red	35	30
D335		4f. violet	50	50
D336		6f. blue	60	50

For later issues see **CONGO (KINSHASA), ZAIRE REPUBLIC** and **DEMOCRATIC REPUBLIC OF CONGO**.

BELGIAN OCCUPATION OF GERMANY — Pt. 7

Stamps used in German territory occupied by Belgian Forces at the end of the War of 1914/18, and including the districts of Eupen and Malmedy, now incorporated in Belgium.

100 centimes = 1 Belgian franc.

1919. Stamps of Belgium optd **ALLEMAGNE DUITSCHLAND**.

1	51	1c. orange	25	15
2		2c. brown	25	35
3		3c. grey	50	1·40
4		5c. green	65	1·00
5		10c. red	1·60	1·90
6		15c. violet	75	90
7		20c. purple	1·25	1·10
8		25c. blue	1·25	1·50
9	63	25c. blue	3·75	5·75
10	52	35c. black and brown	1·25	1·10
11	–	40c. black and green	1·40	1·90
12	–	50c. black and red	6·50	9·00
13	–	65c. black and red	3·50	8·50
14	55	1f. violet	18·00	19·00
15	–	2f. grey	40·00	40·00
16	–	5f. blue (FRANK, No. 194)	8·00	8·50
17	–	10f. sepia	55·00	60·00

1920. Stamps of Belgium surch **EUPEN & MALMEDY** and value.

18	51	5pf. on 5c. green	40	50
19		10pf. on 10c. red	45	65
20		15pf. on 15c. violet	65	75
21		20pf. on 20c. purple	70	1·25
22		30pf. on 25c. blue	70	1·40
23	–	75pf. on 50c. black and red	15·00	19·00
24	55	1m.25 on 1f. violet	18·00	20·00

1920. Stamps of Belgium optd **Eupen**.

25	51	1c. orange	25	35
26		2c. brown	25	35
27		3c. grey	45	1·40
28		5c. green	60	80
29		10c. red	75	1·10
30		15c. violet	95	1·40
31		20c. purple	1·25	1·50
32		25c. blue	1·25	1·60
33	63	25c. blue	5·00	9·00
34	52	35c. black and brown	1·50	1·60
35	–	40c. black and green	1·75	1·90
36	–	50c. black and red	5·00	6·25
37	–	65c. black and red	3·25	9·50
38	55	1f. violet	18·00	17·00
39	–	2f. grey	38·00	38·00
40	–	5f. blue (FRANK, No. 194)	10·00	10·00
41	–	10f. sepia	45·00	48·00

1920. Stamps of Belgium optd **Malmedy**.

42	51	1c. orange	25	35
43		2c. brown	25	35
44		3c. grey	45	1·40
45		5c. green	60	80
46		10c. red	75	1·10
47		15c. violet	1·25	1·40
48		20c. purple	1·25	1·50
49		25c. blue	1·25	1·60
50	63	25c. blue	5·00	8·00
51	52	35c. black and brown	1·50	2·00
52	–	40c. black and green	1·75	2·00
53	–	50c. black and red	5·50	6·25
54	–	65c. black and red	3·25	9·50
55	55	1f. violet	17·00	16·00
56	–	2f. grey	38·00	45·00
57	–	5f. blue (FRANK, No. 194)	10·00	15·00
58	–	10f. sepia	45·00	50·00

POSTAGE DUE STAMPS

1920. Postage Due stamps of Belgium, 1919. (a) Optd **Eupen**.

D1	5c. green	75	1·40
D2	10c. red	1·50	2·00
D3	20c. green	4·25	4·50
D4	30c. blue	3·75	4·00
D5	50c. grey	13·00	13·00

(b) Optd **Malmedy**.

D 6	5c. green	1·25	1·10
D 7	10c. red	1·75	1·60
D 8	20c. green	9·25	10·50
D 9	30c. blue	4·50	8·50
D10	50c. grey	9·50	12·00

BELGIUM — Pt. 4

An independent Kingdom of N.W. Europe.

1849. 100 centimes = 1 franc.
2002. 100 cents = 1 euro.

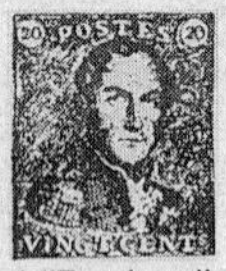
1 "Epaulettes"

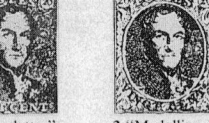

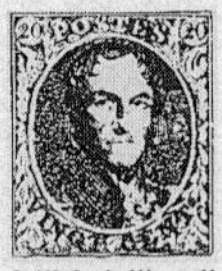
3 "Medallions"

1849. Imperf.

1	1	10c. brown	£1800	55·00
2a		20c. blue	£1900	38·00

1861. Imperf.

12	3	1c. green	£150	£100
13		10c. brown	£300	6·00

14		20c. blue	£325	5·75
15		40c. red	£2000	48·00

1863. Perf.

24	3	1c. green	35·00	22·00
25		10c. brown	48·00	2·75
26		20c. blue	48·00	2·75
27		40c. red	£325	20·00

5   8   10 "Small Lion"

1865. Various frames.

34	5	10c. grey	£100	1·60
35		20c. blue	£180	1·75
36		30c. brown	£450	9·00
37	8	40c. red	£475	14·00
38	5	1f. lilac	£1200	75·00

1866.

43	10	1c. grey	32·00	10·00
44		2c. blue	£110	70·00
45		5c. brown	£140	65·00

11   13   14

15   20

Types **13** to **20** and all later portraits to Type **38** are of Leopold II.

1869. Various frames.

46	11	1c. green	7·50	35
59a		2c. blue	22·00	1·25
60		5c. buff	45·00	55
49		8c. lilac	55·00	42·00
50	13	10c. green	20·00	25
51b	14	20c. blue	£100	90
62	15	25c. bistre	£120	1·60
53a	13	30c. buff	65·00	2·40
54b		40c. red	£100	5·75
55a	15	50c. grey	£200	9·00
56	13	1f. mauve	£275	12·00
57a	20	5f. brown	£1300	£1200

21   25

1883. Various frames.

63	21	10c. red	22·00	1·75
64		20c. grey	£140	5·50
65		25c. blue	£250	23·00
66		50c. violet	£225	24·00

1884. Various frames.

67	11	1c. olive	13·00	50
68		1c. grey	3·25	20
69		2c. brown	13·00	1·60
70		5c. green	32·00	10
71	25	10c. red	9·00	20
72		20c. olive	£130	1·00
73		25c. blue on red	10·00	40
74		35c. brown	13·00	2·25
75		50c. bistre	8·00	1·40
76		1f. brown on green	£550	12·00
77		2f. lilac	55·00	27·00

32   33   34 Arms of Antwerp

1893.

78a	32	1c. grey	50	20
79		2c. yellow	50	90
80		2c. brown	1·50	25
81		5c. green	5·75	20
82	33	10c. brown	2·00	20
83		10c. red	2·25	30
84		20c. olive	13·00	40
85		20c. blue	11·00	25
86a		35c. brown	17·00	1·60
87		50c. brown	45·00	11·50
88		50c. grey	50·00	1·75

89	1f. red on green	60·00	18·00
90	1f. orange	80·00	4·75
91	2f. mauve	70·00	48·00

The prices for the above and all following issues with the tablet are for stamps with the tablet attached. Without tablet, the prices will be about half those quoted.

See also Nos. 106/8.

1894. Antwerp Exhibition.

93	34	5c. green on red	4·75	2·75
94		10c. red on blue	2·25	1·75
95		25c. blue on red	95	90

35 St. Michael encountering Satan   36

1896. Brussels Exhibition of 1897.

96	35	5c. violet	35	40
97	36	10c. red	6·00	3·00
98		10c. brown	15	20

37   38   40 St. Martin and the Beggar (from altarpiece by Van Dyck)

1905. Various frames.

99	37	10c. red	1·00	40
100		20c. olive	24·00	75
101		25c. blue	10·50	60
102		35c. purple	24·00	1·60
103	38	50c. grey	80·00	1·75
104		1f. orange	£110	6·50
105		2f. mauve	65·00	13·50

1907. As T 32 but no scroll pattern between stamps and labels.

106	1c. grey	1·25	25
107	2c. red	15·00	5·50
108	5c. green	12·00	55

1910. Brussels Exhibition. A. Unshaded background. B. Shaded background. A.

109	40	1c. (+1c.) grey	1·25	1·10
110		2c. (+2c.) purple	8·25	8·00
111		5c. (+5c.) green	2·40	2·25
112		10c. (+5c.) red	2·40	2·25

B.

113	40	1c. (+1c.) green	2·40	2·25
114		2c. (+2c.) purple	6·50	6·00
115		5c. (+5c.) green	2·40	2·25
116		10c. (+5c.) red	2·40	2·25

1911. Nos. 109/16 optd 1911.A.

117	40	1c. (+1c.) grey	24·00	17·00
118		2c. (+2c.) purple	90·00	50·00
119		5c. (+5c.) green	8·25	7·00
120		10c. (+5c.) red	8·25	7·00

B.

121	40	1c. (+1c.) grey	35·00	25·00
122		2c. (+2c.) purple	48·00	23·00
123		5c. (+5c.) green	8·25	7·50
124		10c. (+5c.) red	8·25	7·50

1911. Charleroi Exhibition. Nos. 109/16 optd CHARLEROI—1911. A.

125	40	1c. (+1c.) grey	4·75	2·75
126		2c. (+2c.) purple	13·50	12·00
127		5c. (+5c.) green	8·50	8·25
128		10c. (+5c.) red	8·50	8·00

B.

129	40	1c. (+1c.) grey	4·75	2·75
130		2c. (+2c.) purple	14·00	10·00
131		5c. (+5c.) green	8·50	8·25
132		10c. (+5c.) red	8·50	8·25

42   43   44

45 Albert I   46 (Larger head)

1912.

133	42	1c. orange	10	10
134	43	2c. brown	20	20
135	44	5c. green	10	10
136	45	10c. red	65	40
137		20c. olive	14·50	4·25
138		35c. brown	75	55
139		40c. green	17·00	14·50
140		50c. grey	65	50
141		1f. orange	3·25	2·75
142		2f. violet	17·00	17·00
143	–	5f. purple	70·00	20·00

The 5f. is as Type 45 but larger (23×35 mm).

1912. Large head.

148	46	10c. red	10	10
145		20c. olive	35	35
150		25c. blue	15	20
147		40c. green	40	50

47 Merode Monument   48 Albert I

1914. Red Cross.

151	47	5c. (+5c.) red & green	2·75	2·75
152		10c. (+10c.) red & pink	4·50	4·75
153		20c. (+20c.) red & vio	48·00	42·00

1914. Red Cross.

154	48	5c. (+5c.) red and green	3·00	3·00
155		10c. (+10c.) red	20	25
156		20c. (+20c.) red & violet	9·50	10·00

49 Albert I

1915. Red Cross.

157	49	5c. (+5c.) red and green	6·50	2·00
158		10c. (+10c.) red and pink	20·00	11·50
159		20c. (+20c.) red & violet	32·00	15·00

51 Albert I   52 Cloth Hall, Ypres

55 Freeing of the Scheldt

1915.

170	51	1c. orange	20	15
171		2c. brown	15	15
179		3c. grey	30	15
172		5c. green	40	15
173		10c. red	95	15
174		15c. violet	1·10	15
187		20c. purple	2·75	25
176		25c. blue	55	35
188	52	35c. black and brown	55	20
189	–	40c. black and green	55	20
190	–	50c. black and red	4·25	20
191	55	1f. violet	30·00	70
192	–	2f. grey	20·00	1·70
193	–	5f. blue (FRANKEN)	£275	£120
194	–	5f. blue (FRANK)	1·25	1·10
195	–	10f. brown	19·00	20·00

DESIGNS: As T **52**: 40c. Dinant; 50c. Louvain. As T **55**: 2f. Annexation of the Congo; 5f. King Albert at Furnes; 10f. The Kings of Belgium.

1918. Red Cross. Surch with new value and cross. Some colours changed.

222	51	1c.+1c. orange	30	25
223		2c.+2c. brown	35	35
224		5c.+5c. green	1·10	1·10
225		10c.+10c. red	2·00	2·10
226		15c.+15c. purple	4·50	4·25

227		20c.+20c. brown	9·25	8·75
228		25c.+25c. blue	18·00	18·00
229	52	35c.+35c. black & violet	9·25	9·50
230	–	40c.+40c. black & brown	9·25	9·50
231	–	50c.+50c. black and blue	9·25	9·50
232	55	1f.+1f. grey	27·00	29·00
233	–	2f.+2f. green	65·00	65·00
234	–	5f.+5f. brn (FRANKEN)	£160	£150
235	–	10f.+10f. blue	£500	£450

63 "Perron" at Liege   64 Albert I

1919.

236a	63	25c. blue	2·40	30

1919.

237	64	1c. brown	10	10
238		2c. olive	10	10
239		5c. green	25	25
240		10c. red	20	20
241		15c. violet	20	20
242		20c. sepia	1·00	1·10
243		25c. blue	1·53	1·53
244		35c. brown	2·00	2·10
245		40c. red	5·25	6·00
246		50c. brown	12·00	10·00
247		1f. orange	35·00	40·00
248		2f. purple	£300	£300
249		5f. red	80·00	75·00
250		10f. red	£110	£110

SIZES: 1c., 2c., 18½×21½ mm. 5c. to 2f., 22½×26½ mm. 5f., 10f., 27½×33 mm.

67 Discus thrower   68 Charioteer

1920. Olympic Games, Antwerp.

256	67	5c. (+5c.) green	1·90	1·60
257	68	10c. (+5c.) red	1·40	1·40
258	–	15c. (+5c.) brown	2·00	1·40

DESIGN—VERT: 15c. Runner.

73 Hotel de Ville, Termonde   76 Albert I

1920.

308b	73	65c. black and purple	50	15

1921. Nos. 256/8 surch 20c. 20c.

309	67	20c. on 5c. green	50	25
310	68	20c. on 10c. red	25	20
311	–	20c. on 15c. brown	50	25

1921.

313	76	50c. blue	25	10
314		75c. red	20	25
315		75c. blue	35	10
316		1f. sepia	55	10
317		1f. blue	30	15
318		2f. green	80	20
319		5f. purple	11·50	12·00
320		5f. brown	6·75	7·25
321		10f. red	8·00	5·75

1921. Surch 55c 55c.

322	73	55c. on 65c. black & pur	2·25	35

80   81 Albert I

1922. War Invalids Fund.

348	80	20c.+20c. brown	1·50	1·10

1922.

349	81	1c. orange	10	10
350		2c. olive	15	20
351		3c. brown	10	10
352		5c. slate	10	10
353		10c. sepia	15	10
354		15c. plum	15	10
355		20c. brown	20	10
356		25c. purple	15	15
357		25c. violet	60	10
358		30c. red	35	10
359		30c. mauve	35	10
360		35c. brown	30	25
361		35c. green	90	30
362		40c. red	35	10
363		50c. bistre	45	10

364		60c. olive	2·75	10
365		75c. violet	90	55
366		1f. yellow	40	30
367		1f. red	90	10
368		1f.25 blue	1·10	1·10
369		1f.50 blue	1·60	40
370		1f.75 blue	1·50	10
371		2f. blue	2·25	30
372		5f. green	26·00	1·25
373		10f. brown	60·00	7·50

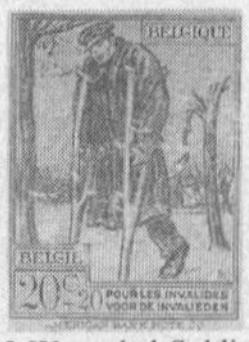
83 Wounded Soldier

1923. War Invalids Fund.

374	83	20c.+20c. slate	1·75	1·75

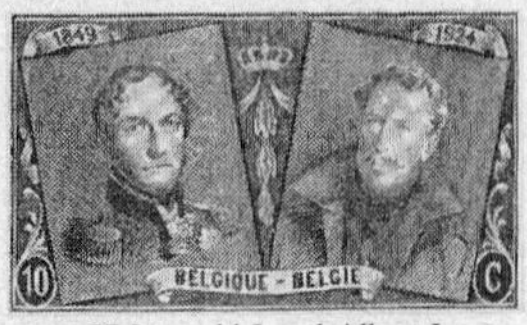
87 Leopold I and Albert I

1925. 75th Anniv of 1st Belgian Stamps.

410	87	10c. green	7·75	6·50
411		15c. violet	3·75	3·75
412		20c. brown	3·75	3·75
413		25c. slate	3·75	3·75
414		30c. red	3·75	3·75
415		35c. blue	3·75	3·75
416		40c. sepia	3·75	3·75
417		50c. brown	3·75	3·75
418		75c. blue	3·75	3·75
419		1f. purple	6·75	6·00
420		2f. blue	4·25	4·25
421		5f. black	4·25	4·00
422		10f. red	8·00	6·00

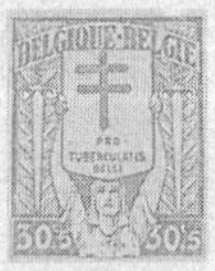
88

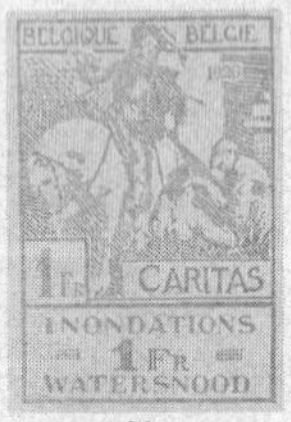
90

1925. Anti-T.B. Fund.

423	88	15c.+5c. red and mauve	20	20
424		30c.+5c. red and grey	20	10
425		1f.+10c. red and blue	1·10	1·10

1926. Flood Relief. Type of 1922 surch **Inondations 30 c Watersnood.**

426	81	30c.+30c. green	85	75

1926. Flood Relief Fund. A. Shaded background. B. Solid background. A.

427	90	1f.+1f. blue	6·00	5·75

B.

428	90	1f.+1f. blue	1·25	1·10

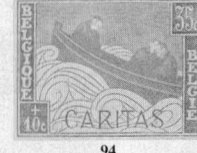

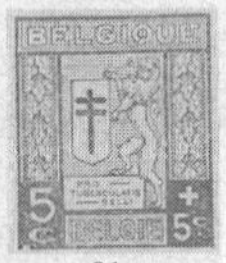
91

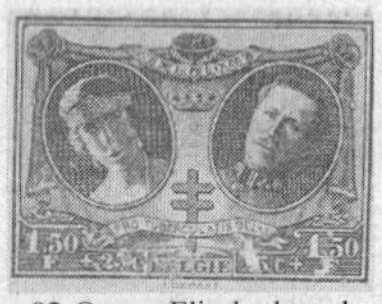
92 Queen Elisabeth and King Albert

1926. War Tuberculosis Fund.

429	91	5c.+5c. brown	15	15
430		20c.+5c. brown	35	35
431		50c.+5c. violet	25	15
432	92	1f.50+25c. blue	60	55
433		5f.+1f. red	6·00	6·00

1927. Stamps of 1922 surch.

434	81	3c. on 2c. olive	10	10
435		10c. on 15c. plum	10	10
436		35c. on 40c. red	25	15
437		1f.75 on 1f.50 blue	1·40	65

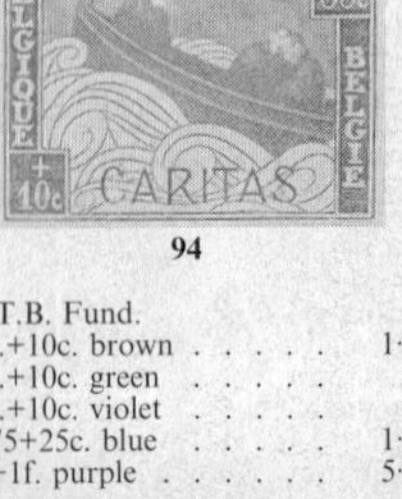
94

1927. Anti-T.B. Fund.

438	94	25c.+10c. brown	1·10	70
439		35c.+10c. green	55	60
440		60c.+10c. violet	25	25
441		1f.75+25c. blue	1·40	1·00
442		5f.+1f. purple	5·75	4·25

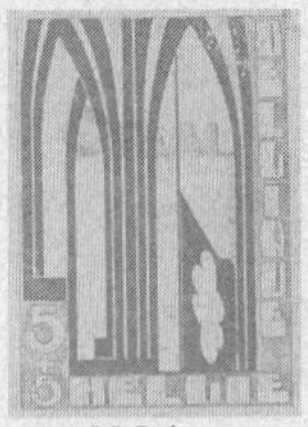
96 Ogives

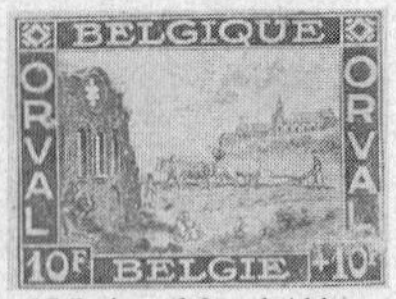
97 Ruins of Orval Abbey

1928. Orval Abbey Restoration Fund. Inscr "ORVAL 1928" or "ORVAL".

461	96	5c.+5c. red and gold	25	25
462	–	25c.+5c. violet and gold	35	35
463	–	35c.+10c. green	1·00	85
464	–	60c.+15c. brown	1·00	25
465	–	1f.75+25c. blue	3·50	1·75
466	–	2f.+40c. purple	17·00	15·00
467	–	3f.+1f. red	17·00	14·50
468	97	5f.+5f. lake	17·00	11·00
469	–	10f.+10f. sepia	17·00	11·00

DESIGNS—VERT: 35c., 2f. Cistercian monk stone-carving; 60c., 1f.75, 3f. Duchess Matilda retrieving her ring.

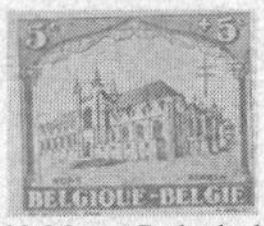
99 Mons Cathedral

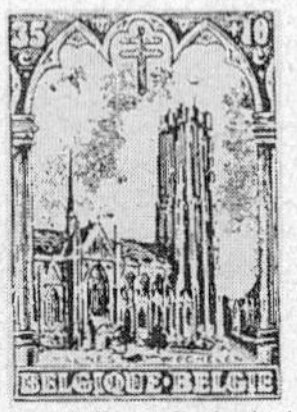
101 Malines Cathedral

1928. Anti-T.B. Fund.

472	99	5c.+5c. red	20	20
473	–	25c.+15c. sepia	30	30
474	101	35c.+10c. green	1·00	1·00
475	–	60c.+15c. brown	25	25
476	–	1f.75+25c. violet	9·00	7·00
477	–	5f.+5f. purple	16·00	18·00

DESIGNS—As Type **99**: 25c. Tournai Cathedral. As Type **101**: 60c. Ghent Cathedral; 1f.75, St. Gudule Cathedral, Brussels; 5f. Louvain Library.

1929. Surch **BRUXELLES 1929 BRUSSEL 5 c** in frame.

478	81	5c. on 30c. mauve	10	10
479		5c. on 75c. violet	20	15
480		5c. on 1f.25c. blue	10	10

The above cancellation, whilst altering the original face value of the stamps, also constitutes a precancel, although stamps also come with additional ordinary postmark. The unused prices are for stamps with full gum and the used prices are for stamps without gum, with or without postmarks. We do not list precancels where there is no change in face value.

104 The Belgian Lion

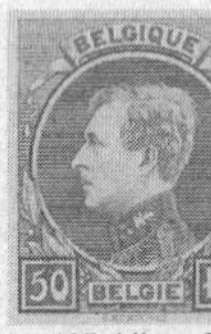
105 Albert I

1929.

487	104	1c. orange	10	10
488		2c. green	45	45
489		3c. brown	10	10
490		5c. green	10	10
491		10c. bistre	10	10
492		20c. mauve	1·10	20
493		25c. red	35	10
494		35c. green	45	10
495		40c. purple	35	10
496		50c. blue	35	10
497		60c. mauve	2·10	15
498		70c. brown	1·00	10
499		75c. blue	1·60	10
500		75c. brown	6·25	10
501	105	10f. brown	14·00	3·25
502		20f. green	70·00	19·00
503a		50f. purple	17·00	16·00
504a		100f. red	17·00	20·00

1929. Laying of first Stone towards Restoration of Orval Abbey. Nos. 461/9 optd with crown over ornamental letter "L" and **19-8-29.**

543	5c.+5c. red and gold	60·00	55·00
544	25c.+5c. violet and gold	60·00	55·00
545	35c.+10c. green	60·00	55·00
546	60c.+15c. brown	60·00	55·00
547	1f.75c.+25c. blue	60·00	55·00
548	2f.+40c. purple	60·00	55·00
549	3f.+1f. red	60·00	55·00
550	5f.+5f. lake	60·00	55·00
551	10f.+10f. sepia	60·00	55·00

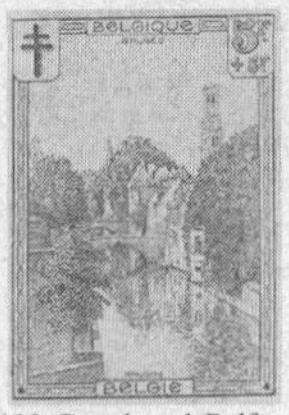
109 Canal and Belfry, Bruges

1929. Anti-T.B. Fund.

552	–	5c.+5c. brown	30	30
553	–	25c.+15c. grey	75	1·10
554	–	35c.+10c. green	75	80
555	–	60c.+15c. lake	35	40
556	–	1f.75+25c. blue	5·00	6·25
557	109	5f.+5f. purple	29·00	29·00

DESIGNS—HORIZ: 5c. Waterfall at Coo; 35c. Menin Gate, Ypres; 60c. Promenade d'Orleans, Spa; 1f.75, Antwerp Harbour. VERT: 25c. Bayard Rock, Dinant.

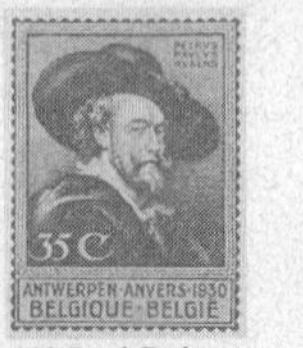
110 Paul Rubens

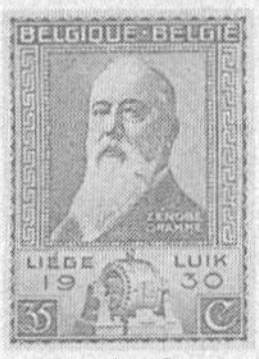
111 Zenobe Gramme

1930. Antwerp and Liege Exns.

558	110	35c. green	40	10
559	111	35c. green	40	10

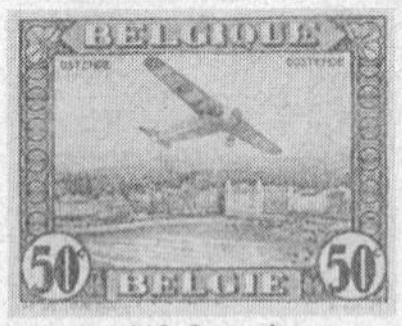
112 Ostend

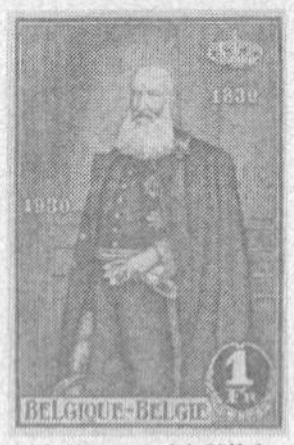
113 "Leopold II" by Jef Lempoels

1930. Air.

560	112	50c. blue	35	25
561	–	1f.50 brown (St. Hubert)	2·25	2·25
562	–	2f. green (Namur)	2·50	85
563	–	5f. red (Brussels)	1·75	95
564	–	5f. violet (Brussels)	29·00	29·00

1930. Centenary of Independence.

565	–	60c. purple	30	10
566	113	1f. red	1·00	50
567	–	1f.75 blue	2·00	1·40

PORTRAITS: 60c. "Leopold I" by Lievin de Winne. 1f.75, King Albert I.

1930. I.L.O. Congress. Nos. 565/7 optd **B.I.T. OCT. 1930.**

569	60c. purple	2·10	2·10
570	1f. red	8·50	10·00
571	1f.75 blue	16·00	16·00

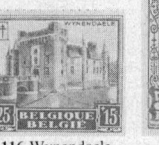

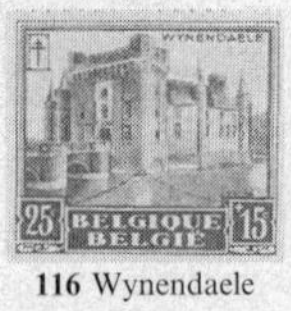
116 Wynendaele

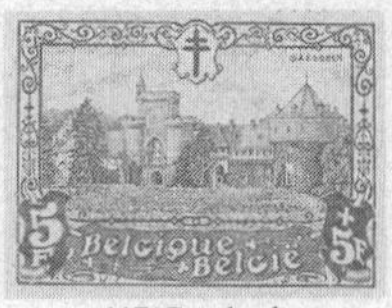
117 Gaesbeek

1930. Anti-T.B. Fund.

572	–	10c.+5c. mauve	20	25
573	116	25c.+15c. sepia	55	60
574	–	40c.+10c. purple	65	75
575	–	70c.+15c. slate	30	40
576	–	1f.+25c. red	3·00	4·00
577	–	1f.75+25c. blue	3·25	3·00
578	117	5f.+5f. green	32·00	32·00

DESIGNS: 10c. Bornhem; 40c. Beloeil; 70c. Oydonck, 1f. Ghent; 1f.75, Bouillon.

1931. Surch **2c.**

579	104	2c. on 3c. brown	10	25

1931. Surch **BELGIQUE 1931 BELGIE 10c.**

580	104	10c. on 60c. mauve	45	25

See note below No. 480.

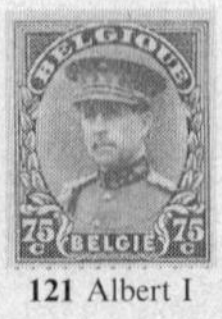
121 Albert I

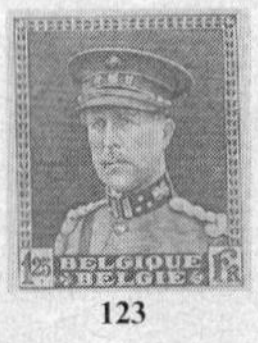
123

1931.

582	121	75c. brown (18 × 22 mm)	1·40	10
583		1f. lake (21 × 23½ mm)	25	20
584	123	1f.25 black	50	30
585		1f.50 purple	1·50	35
586		1f.75 blue	60	10
587		2f. brown	75	15
588		2f.45 violet	2·75	30
589		2f.50 sepia	10·00	70
590		5f. green	25·00	1·10
591		10f. red	40·00	12·00

See also No. 654.

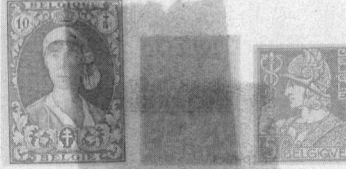

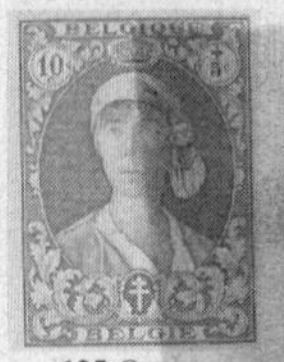
125 Queen Elisabeth

126 Reaper

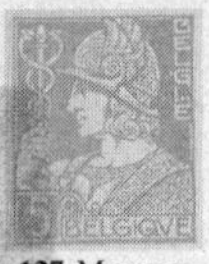
127 Mercury

1931. Anti-Tuberculosis Fund.

593	125	10c.+5c. brown	35	25
594		25c.+15c. violet	1·10	75
595		50c.+10c. green	70	45
596		75c.+15c. sepia	65	20
597		1f.+25c. lake	6·50	5·50
598		1f.75+25c. blue	5·75	3·25
599		5f.+5f. purple	50·00	50·00

1932. Surch **BELGIQUE 1932 BELGIE 10c.**

600	104	10c. on 40c. mauve	2·75	25
601		10c. on 70c. brown	2·75	15

See Note below No. 480.

1932.

602	126	2c. green	50	50
603	127	5c. red	20	10
604	126	10c. green	20	10
605	127	20c. lilac	40	20
606	126	25c. red	50	10
607	127	35c. green	2·50	10

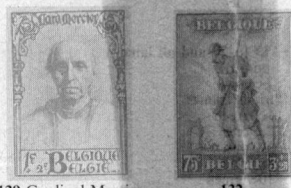

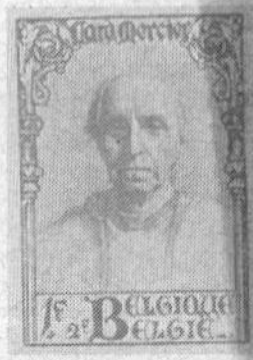
129 Cardinal Mercier

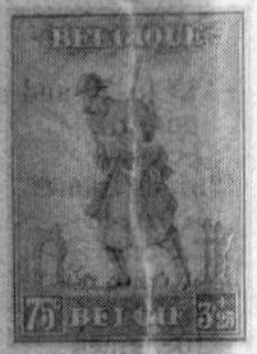
132

1932. Cardinal Mercier Memorial Fund.

609	129	10c.+10c. purple	25	25
610		50c.+30c. mauve	1·60	1·60
611		75c.+25c. brown	80	1·00
612		1f.+2f. red	4·50	4·50
613	–	1f.75+75c. blue	75·00	75·00
614	–	2f.50+2f.50 brown	75·00	75·00
615	–	3f.+4f.50 green	75·00	75·00
616	–	5f.+20f. purple	75·00	75·00
617	–	10f.+40f. red	£140	£140

DESIGNS: 1f.75, 3f. Mercier protecting refugees at Malines; 2f.50, 5f. Mercier with busts of Aristotle and Thomas Aquinas; 10f. Mercier when Professor at Louvain University.

1932. Infantry Memorial.

618	132	75c.+3f.25 red	60·00	60·00
619		1f.75+4f.25 blue	60·00	60·00

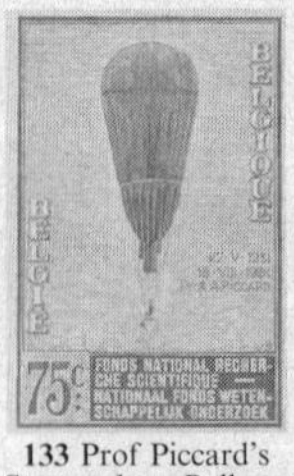
133 Prof Piccard's Stratosphere Balloon "F.N.R.S.", 1931

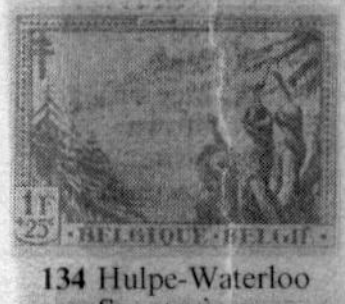
134 Hulpe-Waterloo Sanatorium

1932. Scientific Research Fund.

621	133	75c. brown	2·25	10
622		1f.75 blue	12·50	1·75
623		2f.50 violet	16·00	10·00

1932. Anti-T.B. Fund.

624	134	10c.+5c. violet	25	25
625		25c.+15c. mauve	1·40	90
626		50c.+10c. red	1·60	60
627		75c.+15c. brown	1·25	25
628		1f.+2c. red	10·50	10·00
629		1f.75+25c. blue	10·00	7·50
630		5f.+5f. green	80·00	80·00

1933. Lion type surch **BELGIQUE 1933 BELGIE 10c.**

631	104	10c. on 40c. mauve	12·50	2·40
632		10c. on 70c. brown	12·50	95

See note below No. 480.

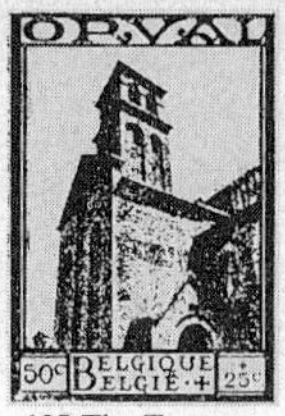

135 The Transept

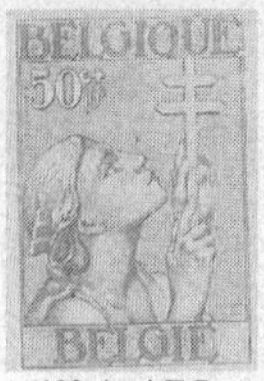

138 Anti-T.B. Symbol

1933. Orval Abbey Restoration Fund. Inscr "ORVAL".

633	–	5c.+5c. green	55·00	55·00
634	–	10c.+15c. green	42·00	42·00
635	–	25c.+15c. brown	42·00	42·00
636	135	50c.+25c. lake	42·00	42·00
637	–	75c.+50c. green	42·00	42·00
638	–	1f.+1f.25 lake	42·00	42·00
639	–	1f.25+1f.75 sepia	42·00	42·00
640	–	1f.75+2f.75 blue	55·00	55·00
641	–	2f.+3f. mauve	55·00	55·00
642	–	2f.50+5f. brown	55·00	55·00
643	–	5f.+20f. purple	55·00	55·00
644	–	10f.+40f. blue	£200	£200

DESIGNS—VERT: 10c. Abbey Ruins; 75c. Belfry, new abbey; 1f. Fountain, new abbey. HORIZ: 5c. The old abbey; 25c. Guests' Courtyard, new abbey; 1f.25, Cloister, new abbey; 1f.75, Foundation of Orval Abbey in 1131; 2f. Restoration of the abbey, XVI and XVII centuries; 2f.50, Orval Abbey, XVIII century; 5f. Prince Leopold laying foundation stone of new abbey; 10f. The Virgin Mary (30 × 45 mm).

1933. Anti-tuberculosis Fund.

646	138	10c.+5c. grey	65	45
647		25c.+15c. mauve	1·75	1·90
648		50c.+10c. brown	1·75	1·40
649		75c.+15c. sepia	12·50	35
650		1f.+25c. red	8·50	10·50
651		1f.75+25c. blue	11·00	12·00
652		5f.+5f. purple	£120	£120

1934. Lion type surch **BELGIQUE 1934 BELGIE 10c.**

653	104	10c. on 40c. mauve	13·00	2·50

See note below No. 480.

1934. King Albert's Mourning Stamp.

654	121	75c. black	20	10

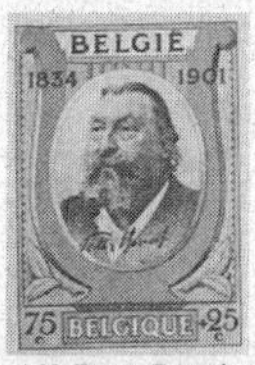

140 Peter Benoit

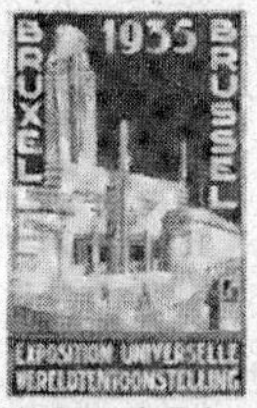

141 Brussels Palace

1934. Benoit Centenary Memorial Fund.

658	140	75c.+25c. brown	5·00	5·00

1934. International Exhibition, Brussels.

659	–	35c. green	1·10	20
660	141	1f. red	2·00	25
661	–	1f.50 brown	3·75	1·00
662	–	1f.75 blue	4·50	20

DESIGNS: 35c. Congo Palace; 1f.50, Old Brussels; 1f.75, Grand Palace of the Belgian section.

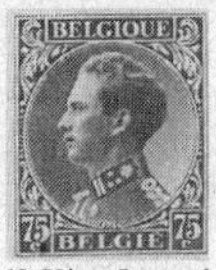

142 King Leopold III

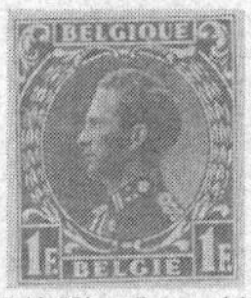

143 King Leopold III

1934. War Invalids' Fund. (a) Size 18 × 22 mm. (b) Size 21 × 24 mm. (i) Exhibition Issue.

663	142	75c.+25c. green (a)	15·00	15·00
664		1f.+25c. purple (b)	15·00	13·00

(ii) Ordinary postage stamps.

665	142	75c.+25c. purple (a)	3·50	3·25
666		1f.+25c. red (b)	55·75	4·50

1934.

667	142	70c. green	30	10
668		75c. brown	50	20
669	143	1f. red	3·25	25

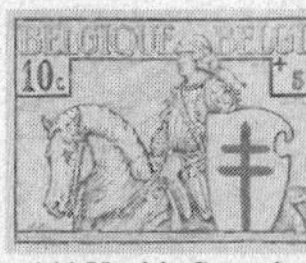

144 Health Crusader

1934. Anti-tuberculosis Fund. Cross in red.

670	144	10c.+5c. black	30	30
671		25c.+15c. brown	1·75	2·25
672		50c.+10c. green	1·10	1·25
673		75c.+15c. purple	70	45
674		1f.+25c. red	11·00	10·50
675		1f.75+25c. blue	9·00	7·00
676		5f.+5f. purple	£110	£110

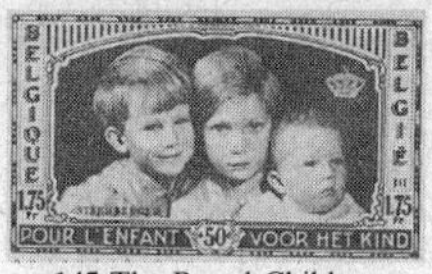

145 The Royal Children

1935. Queen Astrid's Appeal.

680	145	35c.+15c. green	90	90
681		70c.+30c. purple	90	90
682		1f.75+50c. blue	3·50	3·50

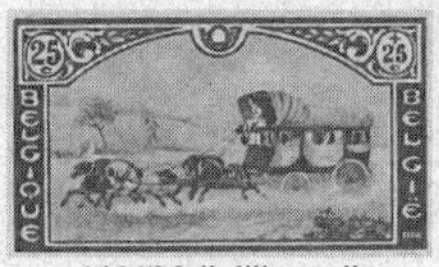

146 "Mail-diligence"

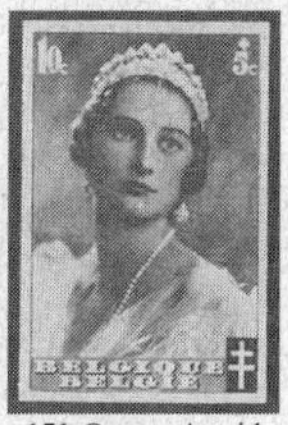

151 Queen Astrid

1935. Brussels Int Exn.

683	146	10c.+10c. olive	35	50
684		25c.+25c. brown	1·75	1·75
685		35c.+25c. green	2·75	2·75

1935. Air. Surch with new value twice.

686	112	1f. on 1f.50 brown	45	45
687		4f. on 5f. red	8·00	8·00

1935. Death of Queen Astrid. Mourning Stamp.

713	151	70c.+5c. black	15	15

1935. Anti-tuberculosis Fund. Black borders.

714	151	10c.+5c. olive	15	15
715		25c.+15c. brown	25	25
716		35c.+5c. green	25	25
717		50c.+10c. mauve	30	30
718		1f. +25c. red	1·00	1·00
719		1f.75+25c. blue	1·90	1·90
720		2f.45+55c. violet	3·25	3·25

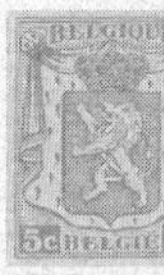

152 State arms

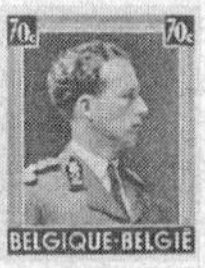

153

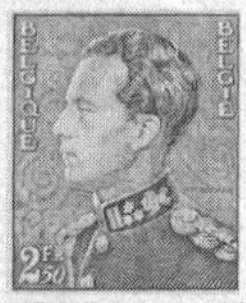

155 King Leopold III

1936.

727	152	2c. green	10	10
728		5c. orange	10	10
729		10c. olive	10	10
730		15c. blue	10	10
731		20c. violet	10	10
732		25c. red	10	10
733		25c. yellow	10	10
734		30c. brown	10	10
735		35c. green	10	10
736		40c. lilac	10	10
737		50c. blue	30	10
738		60c. grey	15	10
739		65c. mauve	80	10
740		70c. green	25	10
741		75c. mauve	25	10
742		80c. green	4·00	40
743		90c. violet	30	10
744		1f. brown	35	10

1936. Various frames. (a) Size 17½ × 22 mm.

745	153	70c. brown	25	10
746		75c. olive	25	10
747		1f. red	10	10

(b) Size 21 × 24 mm.

748	153	1f. red	25	10
749		1f.20 brown	90	10
750		1f.50 mauve	35	25
751		1f.75 blue	15	15
752		1f.75 red	10	10
753		2f. violet	1·10	95
754		2f.25 black	15	10
755		2f.50 red	2·00	20
756		3f.25 brown	25	20
757		5f. green	1·25	35

Nos. 746/7, 751/2, 754/5 and 757 are inscribed "BELGIE BELGIQUE".

1936.

760	155	1f.50 mauve	55	25
761		1f.75 blue	25	15
762		2f. violet	40	20
763		2f.25 violet	25	20
764		2f.45 black	35·00	40
765		2f.50 black	3·25	25
770		3f. brown	60	10
766		3f.25 brown	30	20
771		4f. blue	1·40	10
767		5f. green	2·75	40
772		6f. red	4·00	20
768		10f. purple	50	10
769		20f. red	1·25	25

See also No. 2775.

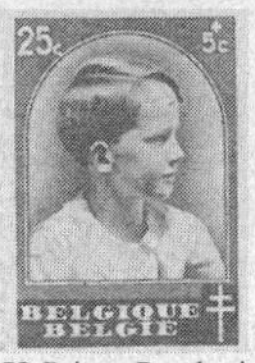

158 Prince Baudouin

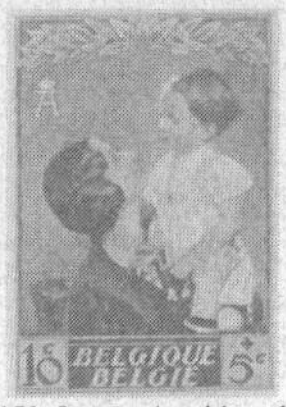

159 Queen Astrid and Prince Baudouin

1936. Anti-tuberculosis Fund.

777	158	10c.+5c. brown	10	10
778		25c.+5c. violet	10	10
779		35c.+5c. green	10	10
780		50c.+5c. brown	15	20
781		70c.+5c. olive	10	10
782		1f.+25c. red	1·00	1·25
783		1f.75+25c. blue	1·50	1·90
784		2f.45+2f.55 purple	3·25	4·75

1937. Stamp of 1929 surch **BELGIQUE 1937 BELGIE 10c.**

785	104	10c. on 40c. purple	20	20

See note below No. 480.

1937. International Stamp Day.

786	158	2f.45c.+2f.55c. slate	2·10	1·75

1937. Queen Astrid Public Utility Fund.

787	159	10c.+5c. purple	10	10
788		25c.+5c. olive	10	10
789		35c.+5c. green	10	10
790		50c.+5c. violet	15	15
791		70c.+5c. black	10	10
792		1f.+25c. red	1·10	95
793		1f.75c.+25c. blue	2·25	2·00
794		2f.45c.+1f.55c. brown	5·50	4·75

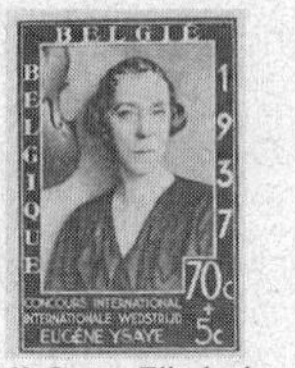

160 Queen Elisabeth

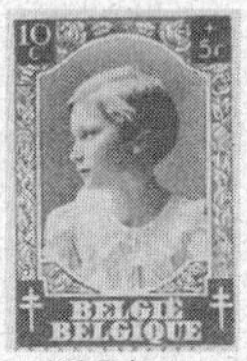

161 Princess Josephine Charlotte

1937. Eugene Ysaye Memorial Fund.

795	160	70c.+5c. black	25	10
796		1f.75+25c. blue	50	50

1937. Anti-tuberculosis Fund.

798	161	10c.+5c. green	10	10
799		25c.+5c. brown	10	10
800		35c.+5c. green	10	10
801		50c.+5c. olive	15	15
802		70c.+5c. purple	10	10
803		1f.+25c. red	80	80
804		1f.75+25c. blue	90	90
805		2f.45+2f.55 purple	2·40	2·40

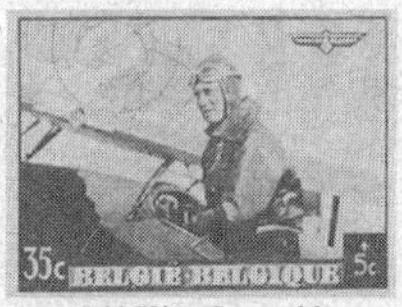

164 King Leopold

1938. Aeronautical Propaganda.

810	164	10c.+5c. purple	10	10
811		35c.+5c. green	15	10
812		70c.+5c. black	35	10
813		1f.75+25c. blue	2·10	2·25
814		2f.45+2f.55 violet	3·00	3·75

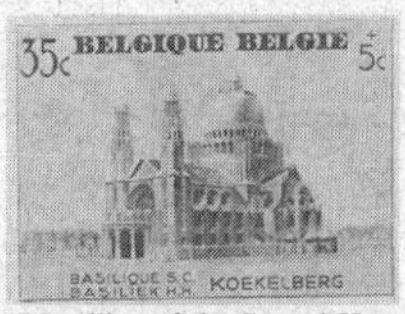

165 Basilica of the Sacred Heart, Koekelberg

1938. Building (Completion) Fund.

815	165	10c.+5c. brown	10	10
816	–	35c.+5c. green	10	10
817	165	70c.+5c. grey	10	10
818	–	1f.+25c. red	45	35
819	165	1f.75+25c. blue	45	35
820	–	2f.45+2f.55 red	3·00	2·75
821	–	5f.+5f. green	7·25	8·75

DESIGNS—HORIZ: 35c., 1f., 2f.45, Front view of Basilica. VERT: 5f. Interior view.

1938. Surch **2F50.**

823	155	2f.50 on 2f.45 black	11·00	25

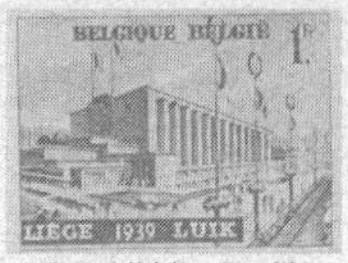

167 Exhibition Pavilion

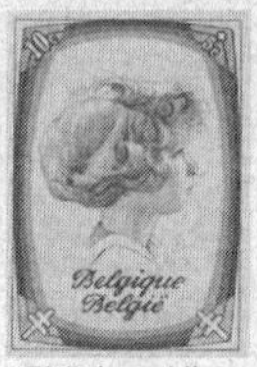

170 Prince Albert of Liege

1938. International Exhibition, Liege (1939). Inscr "LIEGE 1939 LUIK".

824	–	35c. green	10	10
825	167	1f. red	25	10
826	–	1f.50 brown	1·40	40
827	–	1f.75 blue	1·40	10

DESIGNS—VERT: 35c. View of Liege. HORIZ: 1f.50, R. Meuse at Liege; 1f.75, Albert Canal and King Albert.

1938. Koekelberg Basilica Completion Fund. Surch.

828	–	40c. on 35c.+5c. green (No. 816)	30	30
829	165	75c. on 70c.+5c. grey	30	30
830	–	2f.50+2f.50 on 2f.45+2f.55 red (No. 820)	6·00	6·00

1938. Anti-tuberculosis Fund.

831	170	10c.+5c. brown	10	10
832		30c.+5c. purple	10	10
833		40c.+5c. olive	10	10
834		75c.+5c. grey	10	10
835		1f.+25c. red	1·10	95
836		1f.75+25c. blue	1·40	1·10
837		2f.50+2f.50 green	5·50	5·25
838		5f.+5f. purple	10·50	10·50

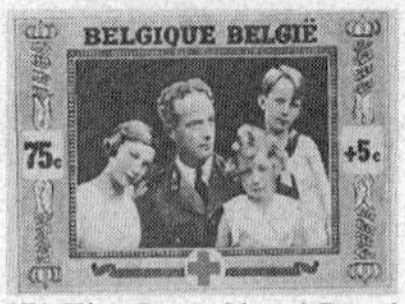

171 King Leopold and Royal Children

1939. 5th Anniv of Int Red Cross Society.

839	–	10c.+5c. brown	10	10
840	–	30c.+5c. red	10	10
841	–	40c.+5c. olive	10	10
842	171	75c.+5c. black	15	10
843	–	1f.+25c. red	1·40	1·25
844	171	1f.75+25c. blue	90	80
845	–	2f.50+2f.50 violet	1·75	1·90
846	–	5f.+5f. green	4·75	4·75

DESIGNS—VERT: 10c. H. Dunant; 30c. Florence Nightingale; 40c. and 1f. Queen Elisabeth and Royal children; 2f.50, Queen Astrid. HORIZ: 5f. Queen Elisabeth and wounded soldier (larger).

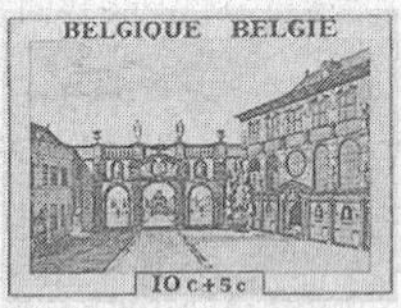

173 Rubens's House (after engraving by Harrewijn)

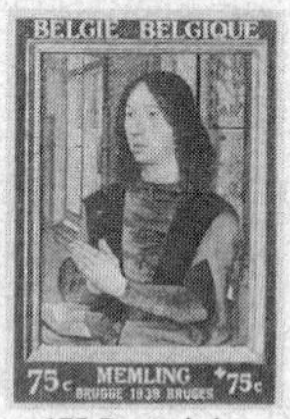

175 Portrait by Memling

1939. Rubens's House Restoration Fund.

847	173	10c.+5c. brown	10	10
848	–	40c.+5c. purple	10	10
849	–	75c.+5c. green	25	20
850	–	1f.+25c. red	1·60	1·40
851	–	1f.50+25c. brown	2·00	1·75
852	–	1f.75+25c. blue	3·00	2·75
853	–	2f.50+2f.50 purple	11·50	11·00
854	–	5f.+5f. grey	15·00	16·00

DESIGNS—As Type **173**: VERT: 40c. "Rubens's Sons, Albert and Nicholas"; 1f. "Helene Fourment (2nd wife) and Children"; 1f.50, "Rubens and Isabella Brant" (1st wife); 1f.75, Rubens (after engraving by Pontius); 2f.50, "Straw Hat" (Suzanne Fourment). HORIZ: 5c. Arcade of Rubens's house. 35 × 45 mm: 5f. "The Descent from the Cross".

1939. Exn of Memling's Paintings, Bruges.

855	175	75c.+75c. olive	1·50	1·50

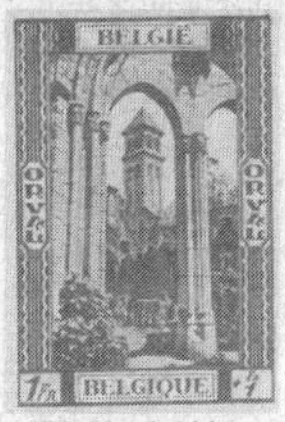

177 Orval Abbey Cloisters and Belfry

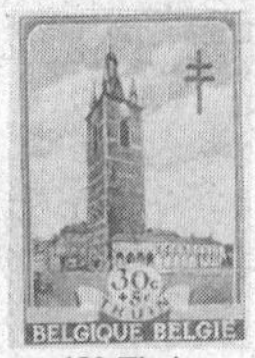

180 Thuin

1939. Orval Abbey Restoration Fund. Inscr "ORVAL".

861	–	75c.+75c. olive	3·25	3·25
862	177	1f.+1f. red	1·60	1·60
863	–	1f.50+1f.50 brown	1·60	1·60
864	–	1f.75+1f.75 blue	2·10	2·10
865	–	2f.50+2f.50 mauve	6·00	6·00
866	–	5f.+5f. purple	6·50	6·50

DESIGNS—As Type **177**: VERT: 75c. Monks in laboratory. HORIZ: 1f.50, Monks harvesting; 1f.75, Aerial view of Orval Abbey; 52½ × 35½ mm: 2f.50, Cardinal Van Roey, Statue of the Madonna and Abbot of Orval; 5f. Kings Albert and Leopold III and shrine.

1939. Anti-tuberculosis Fund. Belfries.

868	–	10c.+5c. olive	10	10
869	**180**	30c.+5c. brown	10	10
870	–	40c.+5c. purple	10	10
871	–	75c.+5c. grey	10	10
872	–	1f.+25c. red	85	85
873	–	1f.75+25c. blue	65	65
874	–	2f.50+2f.50 brown	6·50	6·50
875	–	5f.+5f. violet	8·00	8·00

DESIGNS—As Type **180**: 10c. Bruges; 40c. Lier; 75c. Mons. LARGER (21½ × 34 mm): 1f. Furnes; 1f.75, Namur; 2f.50, Alost; 5f. Tournai.

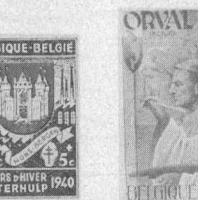

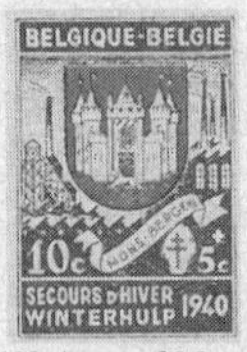
182 Arms of Mons

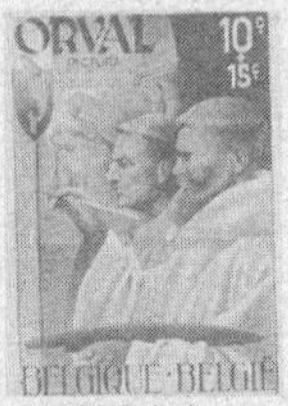
183 Painting

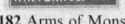

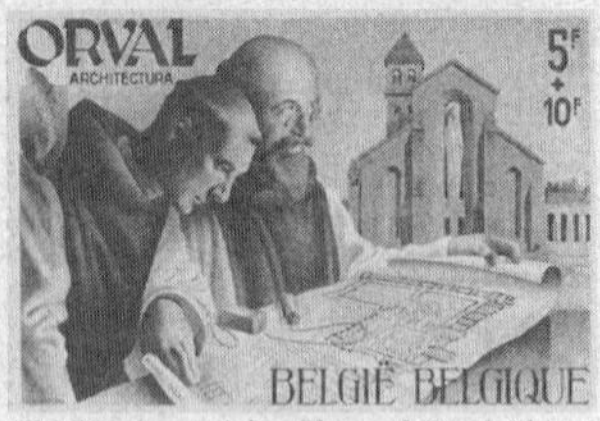
184 Monks studying Plans of Orval Abbey

1940. Winter Relief Fund.

901	**182**	10c.+5c. black, red and green	10	10
902	–	30c.+5c. multicoloured	10	10
903	–	40c.+10c. multicoloured	10	10
904	–	50c.+10c. multicoloured	10	10
905	–	75c.+15c. multicoloured	10	10
906	–	1f.+25c. multicoloured	25	20
907	–	1f.75c.+50c. mult	25	25
908	–	2f.50c.+2f.50c. olive, red and black	1·25	1·10
909	–	5f.+5f. multicoloured	1·60	1·40

DESIGNS: 30c. to 5f. Arms of Ghent, Arlon, Bruges, Namur, Hasselt, Brussels, Antwerp and Liege, respectively.

1941. Orval Abbey Restoration Fund.

935	**183**	10c.+15c. brown	40	30
936	–	30c.+30c. grey	40	30
937	–	40c.+60c. brown	40	30
938	–	50c.+65c. violet	40	30
939	–	75c.+1f. mauve	40	30
940	–	1f.+1f.50 red	40	30
941	**183**	1f.25+1f.75 green	40	30
942	–	1f.75+2f.50 blue	40	30
943	–	2f.+3f.50 mauve	40	30
944	–	2f.50+4f.50 brown	40	30
945	–	3f.+5f. green	40	30
946	**184**	5f.+10f. brown	1·40	1·10

DESIGNS—As Type **183**. 30c., 1f., 2f.50, Sculpture; 40c., 2f. Goldsmiths (Monks carrying candlesticks and cross); 50c., 1f.75, Stained glass (Monk at prayer); 75c., 3f. Sacred music.

1941. Surch.

955	**152**	10c. on 30c. brown	10	10
956		10c. on 40c. lilac	10	10
957	**153**	10c. on 70c. brown	10	10
958		50c. on 75c. olive	20	15
959	**155**	2f.25 on 2f.50 black	55	50

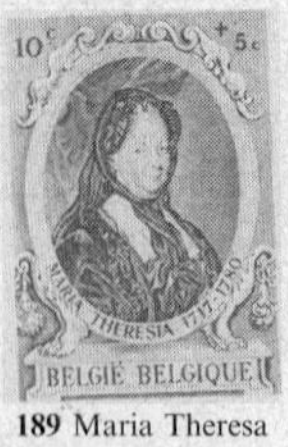
189 Maria Theresa

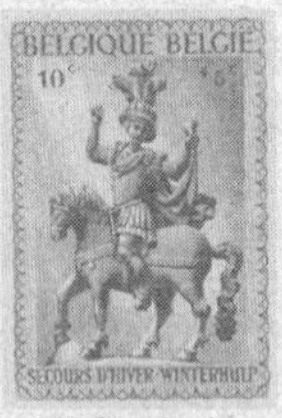
190 St. Martin, Dinant

1941. Soldiers' Families Relief Fund.

960	**189**	10c.+5c. black	10	10
961	–	35c.+5c. green	10	10
962	–	50c.+10c. brown	10	10
963	–	60c.+10c. violet	10	10
964	–	1f.+15c. red	10	10
965	–	1f.50+1f. mauve	25	20
966	–	1f.75+1f.75 blue	25	20
967	–	2f.25+2f.25 brown	25	25
968	–	3f.25+3f.25 brown	50	40
969	–	5f.+5f. green	75	70

PORTRAITS: 35c. to 5f. Charles of Lorraine, Margaret of Parma, Charles V, Johanna of Castile, Philip the Good, Margaret of Austria, Charles the Bold, Archduke Albert and Archduchess Isabella respectively.

1941. Winter Relief Fund. Statues.

970	**190**	10c.+5c. brown	10	10
971	–	35c.+5c. green	10	10
972	–	50c.+10c. violet	10	10
973	–	60c.+10c. brown	10	10
974	–	1f.+15c. red	10	10
975	**190**	1f.50+25c. green	20	20
976	–	1f.75+50c. blue	20	20
977	–	2f.25+2f.25 mauve	25	25
978	–	3f.25+3f.25 brown	25	25
979	–	5f.+5f. green	40	40

DESIGNS (Statues of St. Martin in churches)—As Type **190**: 35c., 1f. Lennick, St. Quentin; 50c., 3f. Beck, Limberg; 60c., 2f.25, Dave on the Meuse; 1f.75, Hal, Brabant. 35 × 50 mm: 5f. St. Trond.

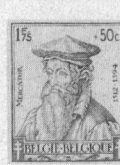

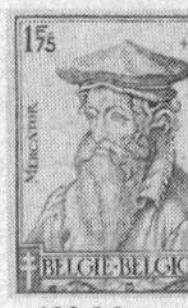
193 Mercator

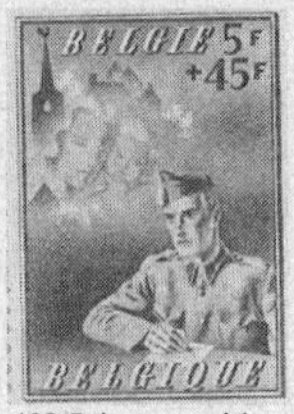
198 Prisoner writing Letter

1942. Anti-tuberculosis Fund. Portraits.

986	–	10c.+5c. brown	10	10
987	–	35c.+5c. green	10	10
988	–	50c.+10c. brown	10	10
989	–	60c.+10c. green	10	10
990	–	1f.+15c. red	10	10
991	**193**	1f.75+50c. blue	25	25
992	–	3f.25+3f.25 purple	20	20
993	–	5f.+5f. violet	25	25
994	–	10f.+30f. orange	1·10	1·10

SCIENTISTS—As T **193**: 10c. Bolland. 35c. Versale. 50c. S. Stevin. 60c. Van Helmont. 1f. Dodoens. 3f.25, Oertell. 5f. Juste Lipse. 25½ × 28½ mm: 10f. Plantin.

1942. Prisoners of War Fund.

1000	**198**	5f.+45f. grey	6·25	6·25

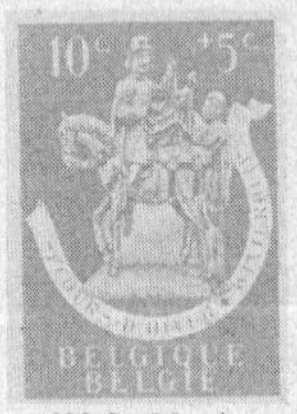
199 St. Martin

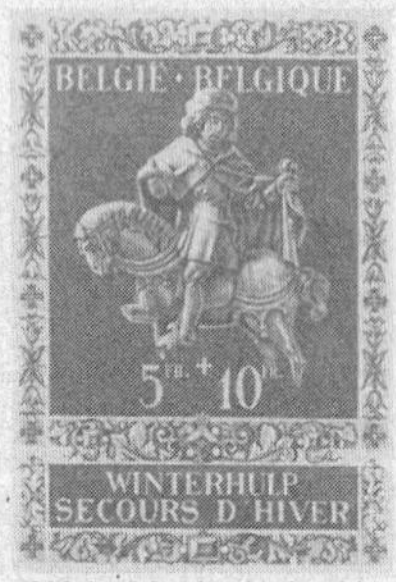
200 St. Martin sharing his cloak

1942. Winter Relief Fund.

1001	**199**	10c.+5c. orange	10	10
1002	–	35c.+5c. green	10	10
1003	–	50c.+10c. brown	10	10
1004	–	60c.+10c. black	10	10
1005	–	1f.+15c. red	10	10
1006	–	1f.50+25c. green	25	25
1007	–	1f.75+50c. blue	25	25
1008	–	2f.25+2f.25 brn	25	25
1009	–	3f.25+3f.25 purple	35	35
1010	**200**	5f.+10f. brown	1·25	1·25
1011		10f.+20f. brown & vio	1·25	1·25
1012		10f.+20f. red & violet	1·25	1·25

DESIGNS: 60c., 2f.25, 3f.25, horiz; others vert.

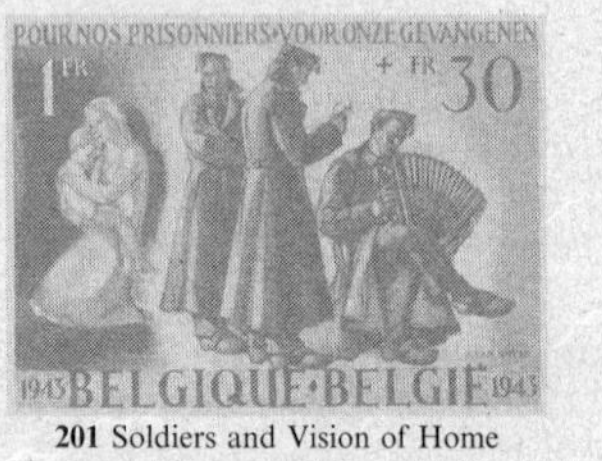
201 Soldiers and Vision of Home

1943. Prisoners of War Relief Fund.

1013	**201**	1f.+30f. red	1·90	2·00
1014	–	1f.+30f. brown	1·90	2·00

DESIGN: No. 1014, Soldiers emptying parcel of books and vision of home.

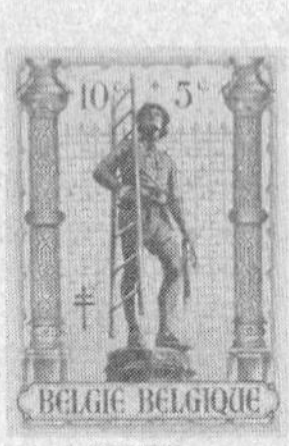
202 Tiler

1943. Anti-tuberculosis Fund. Trades.

1015	**202**	10c.+5c. brown	10	10
1016	–	35c.+5c. green	10	10
1017	–	50c.+10c. brown	10	10
1018	–	60c.+10c. green	10	10
1019	–	1f.+15c. red	25	25
1020	–	1f.75+75c. blue	25	25
1021	–	3f.25+3f.25 purple	45	45
1022	–	5f.+25f. violet	65	65

DESIGNS: 35c. Blacksmith; 50c. Coppersmith; 60c. Gunsmith; 1f. Armourer; 1f.75, Goldsmith; 3f.25, Fishmonger; 5f. Clockmaker.

203 Ornamental Letter

204 Ornamental Letters (⅔-size illustration)

1943. Orval Abbey Restoration Fund. Designs showing single letters forming "ORVAL".

1023	**203**	50c.+1f. black	30	35
1024	–	60c.+1f.90 violet	15	20
1025	–	1f.+3f. red	15	20
1026	–	1f.75+5f.25 blue	15	20
1027	–	3f.25+16f.75 green	60	55
1028	**204**	5f.+30f. brown	1·10	80

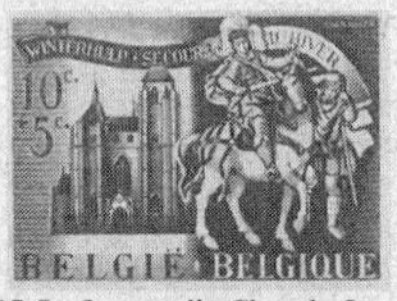
205 St. Leonard's Church, Leon, and St. Martin

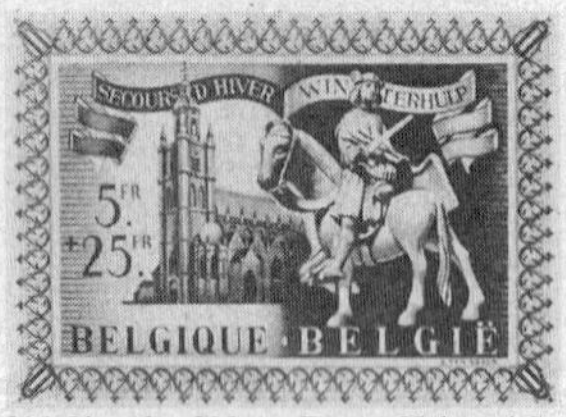
206 Church of Notre Dame, Hal, and St. Martin

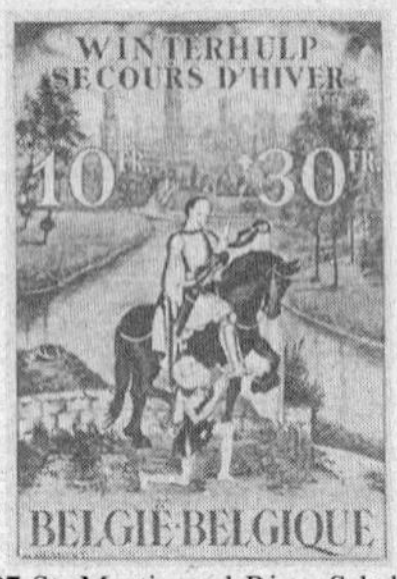
207 St. Martin and River Scheldt

1943. Winter Relief Fund.

1029	**205**	10c.+5c. brown	10	10
1030	–	35c.+5c. green	10	10
1031	–	50c.+15c. green	10	10
1032	–	60c.+20c. purple	10	10
1033	–	1f.+1f. red	25	20
1034	–	1f.75+4f.25 blue	70	60
1035	–	3f.25+11f.75 mauve	1·10	80
1036	**206**	5f.+25f. blue	1·60	1·40
1037	**207**	10f.+30f. green	1·60	1·10
1038	–	10f.+30f. brown	1·60	1·10

DESIGNS: (Various churches and statues of St. Martin sharing his cloak). As Type **205**: HORIZ: 35c. Dion-le-Val; 50c. Alost; 60c. Liege; 3f.25, Loppem. VERT: 1f. Courtrai; 1f.75, Angre. As Type **207**: 10f. brown Meuse landscape.

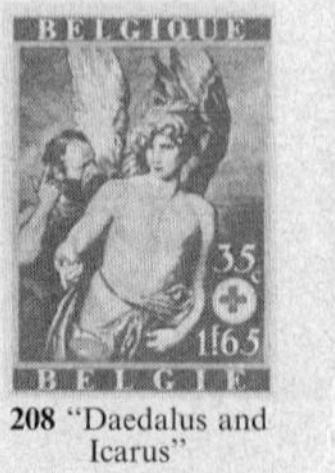
208 "Daedalus and Icarus"

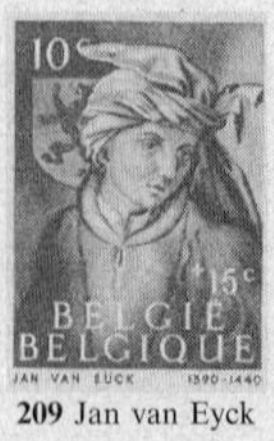
209 Jan van Eyck

1944. Red Cross.

1039	**208**	35c.+1f.65 green	30	30
1040	–	50c.+2f.50 grey	30	30
1041	–	60c.+3f.40 brown	30	30
1042	–	1f.+5f. red	60	60
1043	–	1f.75+8f.25 blue	35	35
1044	–	5f.+30f. brown	35	40

DESIGNS: 50c. "The Good Samaritan" (Jacob Jordsen); 60c. "Christ healing the Paralytic" (detail); 1f. "Madonna and Child"; 1f.75, "Self-portrait"; 5f. "St. Sebastian".

Nos. 1039 and 1041/4 depict paintings by Anthony van Dyck.

1944. Prisoners of War Relief Fund.

1045	**209**	10c.+15c. violet	25	25
1046	–	35c.+15c. green	25	25
1047	–	50c.+25c. brown	25	25
1048	–	60c.+40c. olive	25	30
1049	–	1f.+50c. red	25	25
1050	–	1f.75+4f.25 blue	25	30
1051	–	2f.25+8f.25 slate	70	60
1052	–	3f.25+11f.25 brown	25	30
1053	–	5f.+35f. grey	70	65

PORTRAITS: 35c. "Godefroid de Bouillon". 50c. "Jacob van Maerlant". 60c. "Jean Joses de Dinant". 1f. "Jacob van Artevelde". 1f.75, "Charles Joseph de Ligne". 2f.25, "Andre Gretry". 3f.25, "Jan Moretus-Plantin". 5f. "Ruusbroeck".

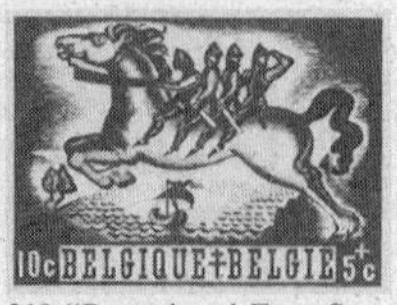
210 "Bayard and Four Sons of Aymon", Namur

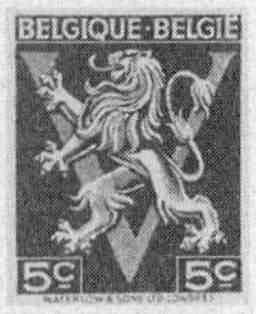
211 Lion Rampant

1944. Anti-tuberculosis Fund. Provincial legendary types.

1054	**210**	10c.+5c. brown	10	10
1055	–	35c.+5c. green	10	10
1056	–	50c.+10c. violet	10	10
1057	–	60c.+10c. brown	10	10
1058	–	1f.+15c. red	10	10
1059	–	1f.75+5f.25 blue	25	30
1060	–	3f.25+11f.75 green	25	30
1061	–	5f.+25f. blue	35	45

DESIGNS—VERT: 35c. "Brabo severing the giant's hand", Antwerp; 60c. "Thyl Ulenspiegel" and "Nele", Flanders; 1f. "St. George and the Dragon", Hainaut; 1f.75, "Genevieve of Brabant, with the Child and the Hind", Brabant. HORIZ: 50c. "St. Hubert encounters the Hind with the Cross", Luxemburg; 3f.25, "Tchantches wrestling with the Saracen", Liege; 5f. "St. Gertrude rescuing the Knight with the cards", Limburg.

1944. Inscr "BELGIQUE-BELGIE" or "BELGIE-BELGIQUE".

1062	**211**	5c. brown	10	10
1063		10c. green	10	10
1064		25c. blue	10	10
1065		35c. brown	10	10
1066		50c. green	10	10
1067		75c. violet	10	15
1068		1f. red	10	10
1069		1f.25 brown	10	20
1070		1f.50 orange	30	35
1071		1f.75 blue	10	10
1072		2f. blue	1·10	1·10
1073		2f.75 mauve	10	10
1074		3f. red	30	20
1075		3f.50 grey	30	25
1076		5f. olive	3·50	2·75
1077		10f. black	65	65

1944. Overprinted with large **V**.

1078	**152**	2c. green	10	10
1079		15c. blue	10	10
1080		20c. violet	10	10
1081		60c. grey	10	10

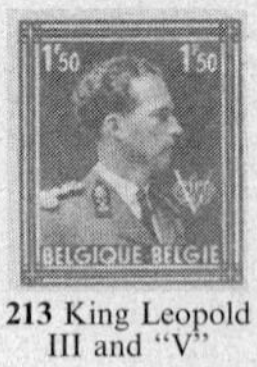
213 King Leopold III and "V"

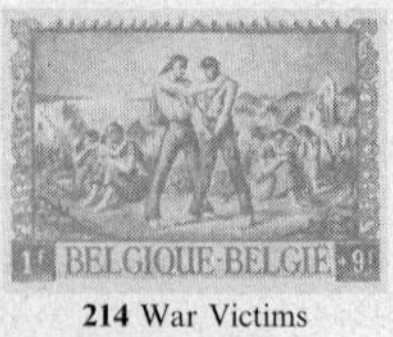
214 War Victims

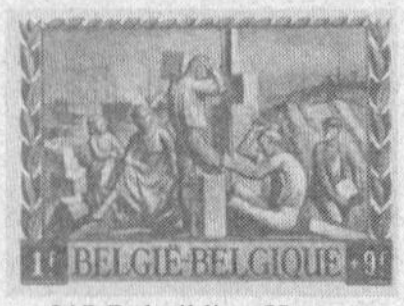
215 Rebuilding Homes

1944.

1082	**213**	1f. red	30	15
1083		1f.50 mauve	25	15
1084		1f.75 blue	30	50
1085		2f. violet	1·00	15
1086		2f.25 green	55	50
1087		3f.25 brown	30	15
1088		5f. green	1·00	15

1945. War Victims' Relief Fund.

1114	**214**	1f.+30f. red	1·25	70
1115	**215**	1¾f.+30f. blue	1·25	70

Nos. 1114/15 measure 50 × 35 mm.

1945. Post Office Employers' Relief Fund.

1119	**214**	1f.+9f. red	30	15
1120	**215**	1f.+9f. red	30	15

217 Resister

218 Group of Resisters

1945. Prisoners of War Relief Fund.

1121	217	10c.+15c. orange	10	10
1122	–	20c.+20c. violet	10	10
1123	–	60c.+25c. brown	10	10
1124	–	70c.+30c. green	10	10
1125	217	75c.+50c. brown	25	10
1126	–	1f.+75c. green	25	10
1127	–	1f.50+1f. red	25	10
1128	–	3f.50+3f.50 blue	1·25	95
1129	218	5f.+40f. brown	2·40	1·00

DESIGNS—VERT: 20c., 1f. Father and child; 60c., 1f.50, Victim tied to stake. HORIZ: 70c., 3f.50, Rifleman.

219 West Flanders

222 Douglas DC-4

1945. Anti-tuberculosis Fund.

1130	219	10c.+15c. green	10	10
1131	–	20c.+20c. red	10	10
1132	–	60c.+25c. brown	10	10
1133	–	70c.+30c. green	10	10
1134	–	75c.+50c. brown	10	10
1135	–	1f.+75c. violet	10	10
1136	–	1f.50+1f. red	10	10
1137	–	3f.50+1f.50 blue	20	10
1138	–	5f.+45f. mauve	2·25	3·00

ARMS DESIGNS—VERT: 20c. to 5f. Arms of Luxemburg, East Flanders, Namur, Limburg Hainaut, Antwerp, Liege and Brabant respectively.

1946. Air.

1165	222	6f. blue	40	25
1166		8f.50 red	50	70
1167		50f. green	4·50	80
1168		100f. grey	8·25	2·50

1946. Surch **-10%**, reducing the original value by 10%.

1171	213	"-10%" on 1f.50 mauve	50	10
1172		"-10%" on 2f. violet	1·90	60
1173		"-10%" on 5f. green	1·75	10

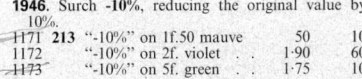

224 Paddle Steamer "Marie Henriette"

1946. Ostend–Dover Mail-boat Service Centenary.

1174a	–	1f.35 blue	20	10
1175	224	2f.25 green	45	20
1176	–	3f.15 grey	45	30

DESIGNS—21½ × 18½ or 21 × 17 mm: 1f.35, Mail steamer "Prince Baudouin". As T **224**: 3f.15, Paddle-steamer "Diamant", formerly "Le Chemin de Fer".

225 Paratrooper

1946. Air. Bastogne Monument Fund.

1177	225	17f.50+62f.50 green	1·50	85
1178		17f.50+62f.50 purple	1·50	85

226 Father Damien

227 E. Vandervelde

228 Francois Bovesse

1946. Belgian Patriots. (a) Father Damien.

1179	226	65c.+75c. blue	1·60	1·10
1180	–	1f.35+2f. brown	1·60	95
1181	–	1f.75+18f. lake	1·60	1·10

DESIGNS—HORIZ: 1f.35, Molokai Leper Colony. VERT: 1f.75, Damien's statue.

(b) Emile Vandervelde.

1182	227	65c.+75c. green	1·60	95
1183	–	1f.35+2f. blue	1·60	95
1184	–	1f.75+18f. red	1·60	1·00

DESIGNS—HORIZ: 1f.35, Vandervelde, miner, mother and child. VERT: 1f.75, Sower.

(c) Francois Bovesse.

1185	–	65c.+75c. violet	1·60	95
1186	228	1f.35+2f. brown	1·60	95
1187	–	1f.75+18f. red	1·60	95

DESIGNS—VERT: 65c. Symbols of Patriotism and Learning; 1f.75, Draped memorial figures holding wreath and torch.

229 Pepin d'Herstal

230 Allegory of "Flight"

1946. War Victims' Relief Fund.

1188	229	75c.+25c. green	55	20
1189	–	1f.+50c. violet	45	40
1190	–	1f.50+1f. purple	75	40
1191	–	3f.50+1f.50 blue	90	40
1192	–	5f.+45f. mauve	7·75	9·00
1194	–	5f.+45f. orange	7·75	9·00

DESIGNS: 1f. Charlemagne; 1f.50, Godfrey of Bouillon; 3f.50, Robert of Jerusalem; 5f. Baudouin of Constantinople.

See also Nos. 1207/11, 1258/9 and 1302/6.

1946. Air.

1193	230	2f.+8f. violet	50	45

231 Malines

232 Joseph Plateau

1946. Anti-tuberculosis Fund. No date.

1195	231	65c.+35c. red	85	30
1196	–	90c.+60c. olive	85	30
1197	–	1f.35+1f.15 green	85	45
1198	–	3f.15+1f.85 blue	95	45
1199	–	4f.50+45f.50 brown	12·50	11·00

DESIGNS—(Arms and Industries): 90c. Dinant; 1f.35, Ostend; 3f.15, Verviers; 4f.50, Louvain.

See also Nos. 1212/16.

1947. Air. "Cipex" International Stamp Exhibition, New York. Nos. 1179/87 surch **LUCHTPOST POSTE AERIENNE** or **POSTE AERIENNE LUCHTPOST** and new value. (a) Father Damien.

1199a		1f.+2f. on 65c.+75c. blue	65	50
1199b		1f.+50+2f.50 on 1f.35+2f. brown	65	50
1199c		2f.+45f. on 1f.75+18f. red	65	50

(b) Emile Vandervelde.

1199d		1f.+2f. on 65c.+75c. green	65	50
1199e		1f.50+2f.50 on 1f.35+2f. blue	65	50
1199f		2f.+45f. on 1f.75+18f. red	65	50

(c) Francois Bovesse.

1199g		1f.+2f. on 65c.+75c. vio	65	50
1199h		1f.50+2f.50 on 1f.35+2f. brown	65	50
1199i		2f.+45f. on 1f.75+18f. red	65	50

1947. Int Film and Belgian Fine Arts Festival.

1200	232	3f.15 blue	30	20

233 Adrien de Gerlache

234 Explorers landing from "Belgica"

1947. 50th Anniv of Belgian Antarctic Expedition.

1201	233	1f.35 red	25	10
1202	234	2f.25 grey	1·90	65

1947. War Victims' Relief Fund. Mediaeval Princes as T **229**.

1207	65c.+35c. blue	1·25	50
1208	90c.+60c. green	1·90	60
1209	1f.35+1f.15 red	3·00	1·00
1210	3f.15+1f.85 blue	3·25	1·10
1211	20f.+20f. purple	42·00	35·00

DESIGNS: 65c. John II, Duke of Brabant; 90c. Philippe of Alsace; 1f.35, William the Good; 3f.15, Notger, Bishop of Liege; 20f. Philip the Noble.

1947. Anti-Tuberculosis Fund. Arms designs as T **231**, but dated "1947".

1212	65c.+35c. orange	50	30
1213	90c.+60c. purple	50	30
1214	1f.35+1f.15 brown	50	30
1215	3f.15+1f.85 blue	2·25	80
1216	20f.+20f. green	20·00	13·50

DESIGNS (Arms and Industries): 65c. Nivelles; 90c. St. Truiden; 1f.35, Charleroi; 3f.15, St. Nicholas; 20f. Bouillon.

237 Chemical Industry

240 Textile Machinery

239 Antwerp Docks

1948. National Industries.

1217	237	60c. blue	25	10
1218		1f.20 brown	2·10	10
1219	–	1f.35 brown	25	10
1220	–	1f.75 green	40	10
1221	–	1f.75 red	30	20
1222	239	2f.25 grey	2·25	55
1223	–	2f.50 mauve	6·75	20
1224	239	3f. purple	15·00	25
1225	240	3f.15 blue	1·60	35
1226		4f. blue	8·75	25
1227	–	6f. blue	17·00	25
1228	–	6f.30 purple	3·00	2·40

DESIGNS—As Type **237**: 1f.35, 1f.75 green, Woman making lace; 1f.75 red, 2f.50, Agricultural produce. As Type **239**: 6f., 6f.30, Steel works.

242 St. Benedict and King Totila

243 St. Bega and Chevremont Castle

1948. Achel Abbey Fund. Inscr "ACHEL"

1232	242	65c.+65c. brown	1·00	45
1233	–	1f.35+1f.35 green	1·10	65
1234	–	3f.15+2f.85 blue	3·25	1·60
1235	–	10f.+10f. purple	12·50	8·75

DESIGNS—HORIZ: 1f.35, Achel Abbey. VERT: 3f.15, St. Benedict as Law-Giver; 10f. Death of St. Benedict.

1948. Chevremont Abbey Fund. Inscr "CHEVREMONT".

1236	243	65c.+65c. blue	80	45
1237	–	1f.35+1f.35 red	95	70
1238	–	3f.15+2f.85 blue	2·75	1·50
1239	–	10f.+10f. brown	12·50	7·75

DESIGNS—HORIZ: 1f.35, Chevremont Basilica and Convent. VERT: 3f.15, Madonna of Chevremont and Chapel; 10f. Monk and Madonna of Mt. Carmel.

244 Statue of Anseele

245 Ghent and E. Anseele

1948. Inauguration of Edward Anseele (Socialist Leader) Statue.

1245	244	65c.+35c. red	2·40	1·10
1246	245	90c.+60c. grey	3·00	2·10
1247	–	1f.35+1f.15 brn	1·60	1·10
1248	–	3f.15+1f.85 blue	5·75	3·75

DESIGNS: 1f.35, Statue and Ed. Anseele; 3f.15, Reverse side of statue.

247 "Liberty"

248 "Resistance"

1948. Antwerp and Liege Monuments Funds.

1253	247	10f.+10f. green	30·00	17·00
1254	248	10f.+10f. brown	14·00	9·50

249 Cross of Lorraine

1948. Anti-tuberculosis Fund.

1255	249	20c.+5c. green	25	10
1256		1f.20+30c. purple	95	50
1257		1f.75+25c. red	1·10	55
1258	–	4f.+3f.25 blue	7·75	4·00
1259	–	20f.+20f. green	42·00	26·00

DESIGNS—As Type **229**: 4f. Isabel of Austria; 20f. Albert, Archduke of Austria.

1949. Surch **1-1-49** at top, **31-XII-49** and value at bottom with posthorn in between. (a) Arms type.

1262	152	5c. on 15c. blue	10	10
1263		5c. on 30c. brown	10	10
1264		5c. on 40c. lilac	10	10
1265		20c. on 70c. green	10	10
1266		20c. on 75c. mauve	10	10

(b) Anseele Statue.

1267	244	10c. on 65c.+35c. red	3·25	2·50
1268	245	40c. on 90c.+60c. grey	1·60	1·40
1269	–	80c. on 1f.35+1f.15 brown	65	40
1270	–	1f.20 on 3f.15+1f.85 blue	2·10	2·10

251 King Leopold I

252 Forms of Postal Transport

1949. Belgian Stamp Cent.

1271	251	90c. green (postage)	45	30
1272		1f.75 brown	20	10
1273		3f. red	4·75	2·50
1274		4f. blue	3·50	60
1275	252	50f. brown (air)	35·00	15·00

253 St. Madeleine from "The Baptism of Christ"

255 Hemispheres and Allegorical Figure

1949. Exhibition of Paintings by Gerard David, Bruges.

1276	253	1f.75 brown	60	15

1949. 75th Anniv of U.P.U.

1296	255	4f. blue	3·00	2·00

256 Guido Gezelle

257 Arnica

1949. 50th Death Anniv of Gezelle (poet).

1297	**256**	1f.75+75c. green	1·40	1·10

1949. Anti-tuberculosis and other Funds. (a) Flowers.

1298	**257**	20c.+5c. black, yellow and green	20	10
1299	–	65c.+10c. black, green and buff	1·10	55
1300	–	90c.+10c. black, blue and red	1·75	80
1301	–	1f.20+30c. mult	1·75	95

FLOWERS: 65c. Thistle. 90c. Periwinkle. 1f.20, Poppy.

(b) Portraits as T **229**.

1302		1f.75+25c. orange	75	25
1303		3f.+1f.50 red	9·25	5·50
1304		4f.+2f. blue	8·00	6·50
1305		6f.+3f. brown	18·00	9·50
1306		8f.+4f. green	19·00	10·50

PORTRAITS: 1f.75, Philip the Good. 3f. Charles V. 4f. Maria Christina. 6f. Charles of Lorraine. 8f. Maria Theresa.

260 Anglo-Belgian Monument, Hertain

261 Allegory of Saving

1950. Anglo-Belgian Union and other Funds.

1307	–	80c.+20c. green	90	65
1308	–	2f.50+50c. red	4·00	2·50
1309	**260**	4f.+2f. blue	6·00	5·25

DESIGNS—HORIZ: 80c. Arms of Great Britain and Belgium; 2f.50, British tanks at Tournai.

1950. National Savings Bank Centenary.

1310	**261**	1f.75 sepia	50	25

262 Hurdling

263 Sikorski S-51 Helicopter and Douglas DC-4 leaving Melsbroeck

1950. European Athletic Championships. Inscr "HEYSEL 1950".

1311	**262**	20c.+5c. green	30	15
1312	–	90c.+10c. purple	3·25	1·60
1313	–	1f.75+25c. red	4·50	1·60
1314	–	4f.+2f. blue	35·00	18·00
1315	–	8f.+4f. green	38·00	21·00

DESIGNS—HORIZ: 1f.75, Relay racing. VERT: 90c. Javelin throwing; 4f. Pole vaulting; 8f. Sprinting.

1950. Air. Inauguration of Helicopter Airmail Services and Aeronautical Committee's Fund.

1317	**263**	7f.+3f. blue	7·25	4·25

265 Gentian

266 Sijsele Sanatorium

1950. Anti-tuberculosis and other Funds. Cross in red.

1326	**265**	20c.+5c. blue, green and purple	25	15
1327	–	65c.+10c. green and brown	95	60
1328	–	90c.+10c. light green and green	1·25	95
1329	–	1f.20+30c. blue, green and ultramarine	1·40	95
1330	**266**	1f.75+25c. red	1·75	95
1331	–	4f.+2f. blue	11·50	7·50
1332	–	8f.+4f. green	22·00	17·00

DESIGNS—Flowers as Type **265**: 65c. Rushes; 90c. Foxglove; 1f.20, Sea lavender. Sanatoria as Type **266**: HORIZ: 4f. Jauche. VERT: 8f. Tombeek.

267 The Belgian Lion

268 "Science"

1951. (a) 17½ × 20½ mm.

1334	**267**	2c. brown	15	10
1335		3c. violet	15	10
1336		5c. lilac	15	10
1336a		5c. pink	15	10
1337		10c. orange	15	10
1338		15c. mauve	15	10
1333		20c. blue	15	10
1339		20c. red	15	10
1340		25c. green	3·75	20
1341		25c. blue	15	10
1342		30c. green	15	10
1343		40c. brown	15	10
1344a		50c. blue	15	10
1345		60c. mauve	15	10
1346		65c. purple	10·50	25
1347		75c. lilac	15	10
1348		80c. green	60	10
1349		90c. blue	1·00	20
1350		1f. red	15	10
1351		1f.50 grey	15	10
1353		2f. green	15	10
1354		2f.50 brown	15	10
1355		3f. mauve	15	10
1355a		4f. purple	25	10
1355b		4f.50 blue	15	10
1355c		5f. purple	25	10

(b) 20½ × 24½ mm.

1356	**267**	50c. blue	35	15
1357		60c. purple	85	60
1358a		1f. red	15	10

(c) Size 17½ × 22 mm.

1359	**267**	50c. blue	15	10
1360		1f. pink	1·50	80
1361		2f. green	40	15

1951. U.N.E.S.C.O. Fund. Inscr "UNESCO".

1365	**268**	80c.+20c. green	1·60	60
1366	–	2f.50+50c. brown	8·75	5·75
1367	–	4f.+2f. blue	10·00	6·50

DESIGNS—HORIZ: 2f.50, "Education". VERT: 4f. "Peace".

269 Fairey Tipsy Belfair Trainer I

1951. Air. 50th Anniv of National Aero Club.

1368	–	6f. blue	22·00	14·00
1369	**269**	7f. red	22·00	14·00

DESIGN: 6f. Arsenal Air 100 glider.

1951. Air.

1370	–	6f. brown (glider)	3·50	15
1371	**269**	7f. green	4·75	70

270 Monument

272 Queen Elisabeth

1951. Political Prisoners' National Monument Fund.

1372	**270**	1f.75+25c. brown	2·00	65
1373	–	4f.+2f. blue	26·00	13·00
1374	–	8f.+4f. green	26·00	15·00

DESIGNS—HORIZ: 4f. Breendonk Fort. VERT: 8f. Side view of monument.

1951. Queen Elisabeth Medical Foundation Fund.

1376	**272**	90c.+10c. grey	4·25	85
1377		1f.75+25c. red	5·75	1·60
1378		3f.+1f. green	29·00	14·00
1379		4f.+2f. blue	28·00	14·00
1380		8f.+4f. sepia	38·00	22·00

273 Lorraine Cross and Dragon

274 Beersel Castle

1951. Anti-tuberculosis and other Funds.

1381	**273**	20c.+5c. red	25	10
1382		65c.+10c. blue	50	30
1383		90c.+10c. brown	50	40
1384		1f.20+30c. violet	1·10	75
1385	**274**	1f.75+75c. brown	3·00	1·10
1386	–	3f.+1f. green	13·00	7·00
1387	–	4f.+2f. blue	15·00	12·00
1388	–	8f.+4f. black	22·00	15·00

CASTLES—As Type **274**: VERT: 3f. Horst Castle. 8f. Veves Castle. HORIZ: 4f. Lavaux St. Anne Castle.

For stamps as Type **273** but dated "1952" see Nos. 1416/19 and for those dated "1953" see Nos. 1507/10.

276 Consecration of the Basilica

1952. 25th Anniv of Cardinalate of Primate of Belgium and Koekelberg Basilica Fund.

1389	–	1f.75+25c. brown	1·25	30
1390	–	4f.+2f. blue	13·00	6·00
1391	**276**	8f.+4f. purple	16·00	9·50

DESIGNS—24 × 35 mm: 1f.75, Interior of Koekelberg Basilica; 4f. Exterior of Koekelberg Basilica.

277 King Baudouin

278 King Baudouin

1952.

1393	**277**	1f.50 grey	1·10	10
1394		2f. red	30	10
1395		4f. blue	3·50	15
1396a	**278**	50f. purple	2·75	15
1397a		100f. red	4·75	25

279 Francis of Taxis

281 A. Vermeylen

1952. 13th U.P.U. Congress, Brussels. Portraits of Members of the House of Thurn and Taxis.

1398	**279**	80c. green	10	15
1399	–	1f.75 orange	10	10
1400	–	2f. brown	50	15
1401	–	2f.50 red	1·10	40
1402	–	3f. olive	1·10	15
1403	–	4f. blue	1·10	10
1404	–	5f. brown	3·00	40
1405	–	5f.75 violet	3·25	1·00
1406	–	8f. black	14·00	2·00
1407	–	10f. purple	20·00	6·50
1408	–	20f. grey	65·00	32·00
1409	–	40f.+10f. turquoise	£160	£100

DESIGNS—VERT: 1f.75, John Baptist; 2f. Leonard; 2f.50, Lamoral; 3f. Leonard Francis; 4f. Lamoral Claud; 5f. Eugene Alexander; 5f.75, Anselm Francis; 8f. Alexander Ferdinand; 10f. Charles Anselm; 20f. Charles Alexander; 40f. Beaulieu Chateau.

1952. Culture Fund. Writers.

1410	**281**	65c.+30c. lilac	5·00	1·75
1411	–	80c.+40c. green	5·00	1·75
1412	–	90c.+45c. olive	5·00	1·75
1413	–	1f.75+75c. lake	8·00	3·25
1414	–	4f.+2f. blue	32·00	15·00
1415	–	8f.+4f. sepia	32·00	16·00

PORTRAITS: 80c. K. van de Woestijne. 90c. C. de Coster. 1f.75, M. Maeterlinck. 4f. E. Verhaeren. 8f. H. Conscience.

A 4f. blue as No. 1414 and an 8f. lake as No. 1415 each se-tenant with a label showing a laurel wreath and bearing a premium "+ 9 fr." were put on sale by subscription only.

282 Arms, Malmedy

284 Dewe and Monument at Liege

1952. Anti-tuberculosis and other Funds. As T **273** but dated "1952" and designs as T **282**.

1416	**273**	20c.+5c. brown	10	10
1417		80c.+20c. green	65	35
1418		1f.20+30c. purple	1·25	70
1419		1f.50+50c. olive	1·25	70
1420	**282**	2f.+75c. red	1·70	70
1421	–	3f.+1f.50 brown	19·00	11·50
1422	–	4f.+2f. blue	19·00	9·25
1423	–	8f.+4f. purple	19·00	12·00

DESIGNS—HORIZ: 3f. Ruins, Burgreuland. VERT: 4f. Dam, Eupen; 8f. Saint and lion, St. Vith.

1953. Walthere Dewe Memorial Fund.

1435	**284**	2f.+1f. lake	2·10	1·25

285 Princess Josephine Charlotte

286 Fishing Boats "Marcel", "De Meeuw" and "Jacqueline Denise"

1953. Red Cross National Disaster Fund. Cross in red.

1436	**285**	80c.+20c. green	2·75	95
1437		1f.20+30c. brown	2·75	85
1438		2f.+50c. lake	2·75	85
1439		2f.50+50c. red	14·00	8·25
1440		4f.+1f. blue	14·00	7·25
1441		5f.+2f. black	14·00	7·25

1953. Tourist Propaganda and Cultural Funds.

1442	**286**	80c.+20c. green	2·25	65
1443	–	1f.20+30c. brown	7·50	2·40
1444	–	2f.+50c. sepia	7·50	2·40
1445	–	2f.50+50c. mauve	18·00	9·25
1446	–	4f.+2f. blue	18·00	10·00
1447	–	8f.+4f. green	18·00	12·50

DESIGNS—HORIZ: 1f.20, Bridge Bouillon; 2f. Antwerp. VERT: 2f.50, Namur; 4f. Ghent; 8f. Freyr Rocks and River Meuse.

289 King Baudouin

290

1953. (a) 21 × 24½ mm.

1453	**289**	1f.50 black	15	10
1454		2f. red	7·25	10
1455		2f. green	35	10
2188		2f.50 brown	25	10
1457		3f. purple	25	10
1458		3f.50 green	35	10
1459		4f. blue	45	10
1460		4f.50 brown	30	10
1462		5f. violet	95	10
1463		6f. mauve	35	10
1464		6f.50 grey	75·00	13·00
2189		7f. blue	60	15
1466		7f.50 brown	70·00	14·00
1467		8f. blue	70	10
1468		8f.50 purple	15·00	50
1469		9f. olive	70·00	1·25
1470		12f. turquoise	75	25
1471		30f. orange	2·10	30

(b) 17½ × 22 mm.

1472	**289**	1f.50 black	15	15
1473		2f.50 brown	6·75	5·75
1474		3f. mauve	25	10
1475		3f.50 green	35	10
1476		4f.50 brown	3·00	90

1953. European Child Welfare Fund.

1482	**290**	80c.+20c. green	4·75	2·10
1483		2f.50+1f. red	24·00	15·00
1484		4f.+1f.50 blue	29·00	18·00

293 Ernest Malvoz

296 King Albert Statue

1953. Anti-tuberculosis and other Funds. As T **273** but dated "1953" and portraits as T **293**.

1507	**273**	20c.+5c. blue	10	15
1508		80c.+20c. purple	1·25	50
1509		1f.20+30c. brown	1·25	90
1510		1f.50+50c. slate	1·60	95
1511	**293**	2f.+75c. green	1·90	1·25
1512	–	3f.+1f.50 red	18·00	9·00
1513	–	4f.+2f. blue	19·00	9·75
1514	–	8f.+4f. brown	19·00	11·50

PORTRAITS—VERT: 3f. Carlo Forlanini. 4f. Albert Calmette. HORIZ: 8f. Robert Koch.

1954. Surch **20c** and **I-I-54** at top, **31-XII-54** at bottom and bars in between.

1515	**267**	20c. on 65c. purple	1·50	25
1516		20c. on 90c. blue	1·50	25

See note below No. 480.

1954. King Albert Memorial Fund.

1520	**296**	2f.+50c. brown	6·00	2·50
1521	–	4f.+2f. blue	21·00	12·00
1522	–	9f.+4f.50 black	20·00	12·00

DESIGNS—HORIZ: 4f. King Albert Memorial. VERT: 9f. Marche-les-Dames Rocks and medallion portrait.

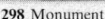

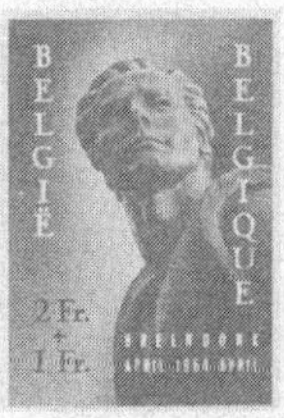
298 Monument

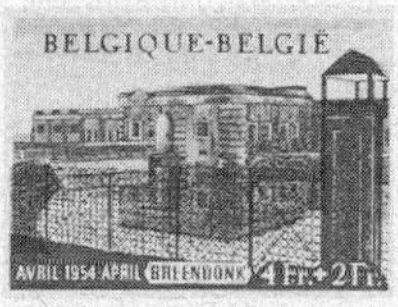
299 Breendonk Camp and Fort

1954. Political Prisoners' National Monument Fund.

1531	**298**	2f.+1f. red	16·00	8·00
1532	**299**	4f.+2f. brown	35·00	17·00
1533	–	9f.+4f.50 green	42·00	21·00

DESIGN—VERT: 9f. As Type **298** but viewed from different angle.

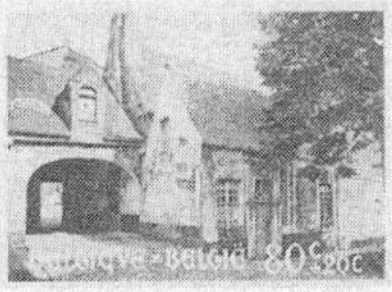
300 Entrance to Beguinal House

1954. Beguinage of Bruges Restoration Fund.

1534	**300**	80c.+20c. green	1·10	55
1535	–	2f.+1f. red	10·00	6·00
1536	–	4f.+2f. violet	14·00	8·00
1537	–	7f.+3f.50 purple	30·00	16·00
1538	–	8f.+4f. brown	30·00	16·00
1539	–	9f.+4f.50 blue	50·00	26·00

DESIGNS—HORIZ: 2f. River scene. VERT: 4f. Convent Buildings; 7f. Cloisters; 8f. Doorway; 9f. Statue of our Lady of the Vineyard (larger, 35 × 53 mm).

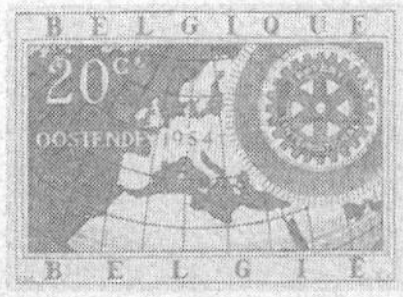
302 Map of Europe and Rotary Symbol

1954. 50th Anniv of Rotary International and 5th Regional Conference, Ostend.

1540	**302**	20c. red	10	10
1541	–	80c. green	25	25
1542	–	4f. blue	1·10	35

DESIGNS: 80c. Mermaid, "Mercury" and Rotary symbol; 4f. Rotary symbol and hemispheres.

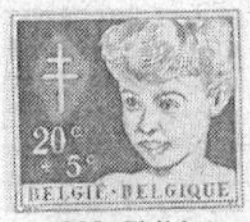
303 Child

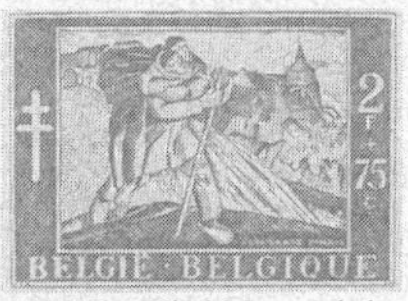
304 "The Blind Man and the Paralytic" (after Anto-Carte)

1954. Anti-T.B. and other Funds.

1543	**303**	20c.+5c. green	15	15
1544		80c.+20c. black	80	55
1545		1f.20+30c. brown	1·50	1·40
1546		1f.50+50c. violet	2·75	1·60
1547	**304**	2f.+75c. red	3·50	2·10
1548		4f.+1f. blue	16·00	11·00

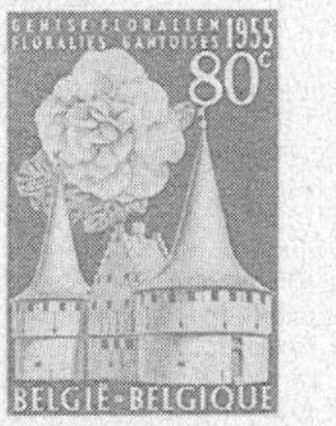
305 Begonia and the Rabot

1955. Ghent Flower Show.

1549	**305**	80c. red	35	25
1550	–	2f.50 sepia	6·25	2·50
1551	–	4f. lake	3·75	95

DESIGNS—VERT: 2f.50, Azaleas and Chateau des Comtes; 4f. Orchid and the "Three Towers".

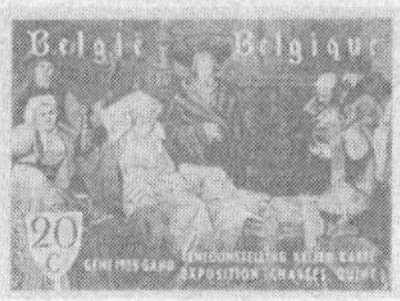
306 "Homage to Charles V" (A. De Vriendt)

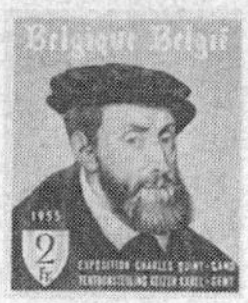
307 "Charles V" (Titian)

1955. Emperor Charles V Exhibition, Ghent.

1552	**306**	20c. red	15	10
1553	**307**	2f. green	70	10
1554	–	4f. blue	3·25	1·00

DESIGN—As Type **306**: 4f. "Abdication of Charles V" (L. Gallait).

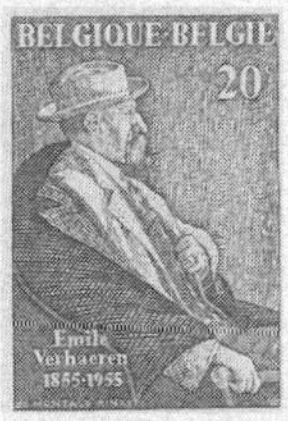
308 Emile Verhaeren (after C. Montald)

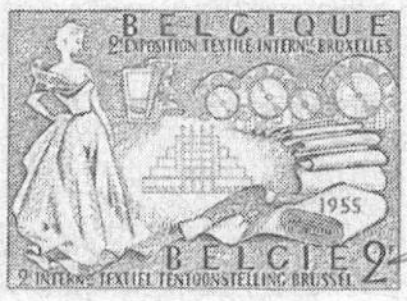
309 "Textile Industry"

1955. Birth Centenary of Verhaeren (poet).

1555	**308**	20c. black	15	10

1955. 2nd Int Textile Exhibition, Brussels.

1556	**309**	2f. purple	90	15

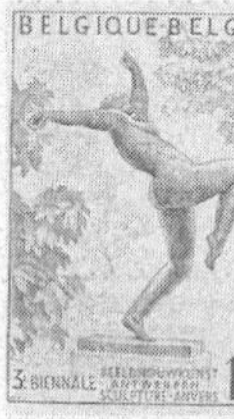
310 "The Foolish Virgin" (R. Wouters)

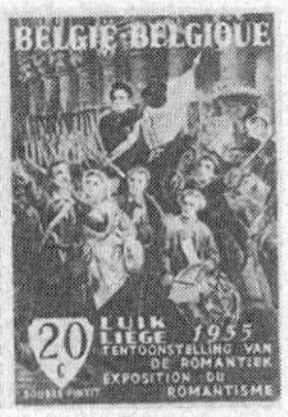
311 "The Departure of the Liege Volunteers in 1830" (Soubre)

1955. 3rd Biennial Sculpture Exn, Antwerp.

1557	**310**	1f.20 green	80	30
1558		2f. violet	1·25	15

1955. Liege Exn. 125th Anniv of 1830 Revolution.

1559	**311**	20c. green	10	10
1560		2f. brown	70	10

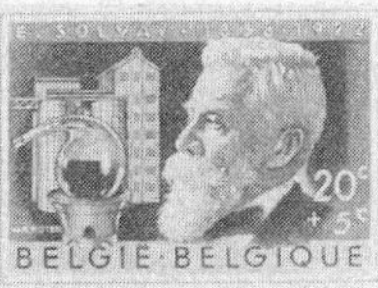
312 Ernest Solvay

1955. Cultural Fund. Scientists.

1561	**312**	20c.+5c. brown	10	10
1562	–	80c.+20c. violet	1·00	45
1563	–	1f.20+30c. blue	5·00	2·75
1564	–	2f.+50c. red	4·50	2·10
1565	–	3f.+1f. green	11·00	6·75
1566	–	4f.+2f. brown	11·00	6·75

PORTRAITS—VERT: 80c. Jean-Jacques Dony. 2f. Leo H. Baekeland. 3f. Jean-Etienne Lenoir. HORIZ: 1f.20, Egide Walschaerts. 4f. Emile Fourcault and Emile Gobbe.

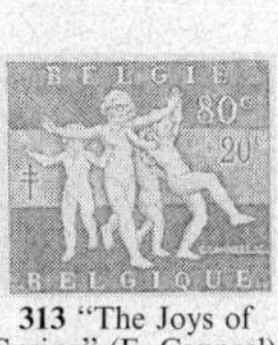
313 "The Joys of Spring" (E. Canneel)

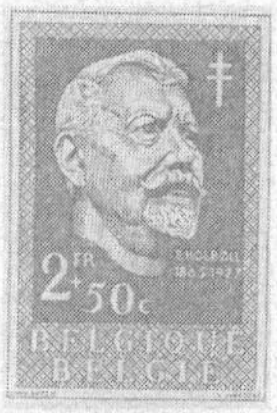
314 E. Holboll (Danish postal official)

1955. Anti-T.B. and other Funds.

1567	**313**	20c.+5c. mauve	10	15
1568		80c.+20c. green	60	35
1569		1f.20+30c. brown	2·25	50
1570		1f.50+50c. violet	1·90	75
1571	**314**	2f.+50c. red	8·00	4·00
1572	–	4f.+2f. blue	17·00	11·50
1573	–	8f.+4f. sepia	18·00	11·50

PORTRAITS—As Type **314**: 4f. J. D. Rockefeller (philanthropist). 8f. Sir R. W. Philip (physician).

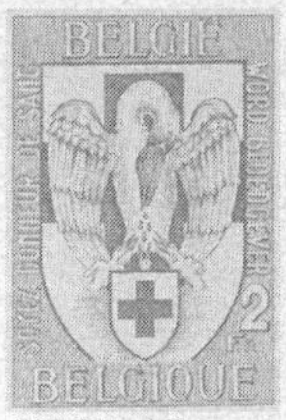
315 Blood Donors Emblem

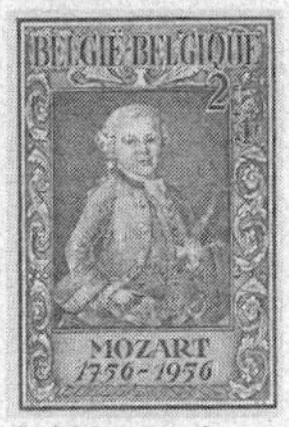
316 Mozart when a Child

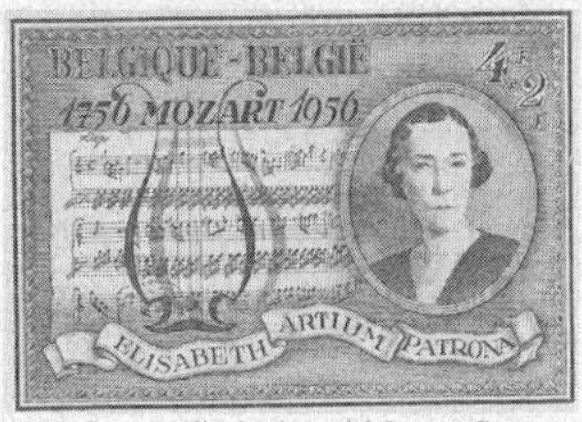
317 Queen Elisabeth and Mozart Sonata

1956. Blood Donors.

1574	**315**	2f. red	35	10

1956. Birth Bicentenary of Mozart. Inscr as in T **316**.

1575	–	80c.+20c. green	45	15
1576	**316**	2f.+1f. purple	3·25	1·75
1577	**317**	4f.+2f. lilac	7·00	4·50

DESIGN—As Type **316**: 80c. Palace of Charles de Lorraine, Brussels.

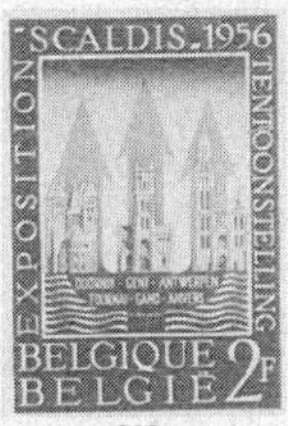
318

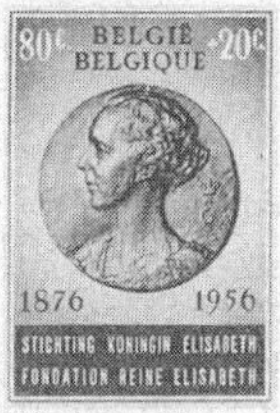
319 Queen Elisabeth Medallion (Courtens)

1956. "Scaldis" Exhibitions in Tournai, Ghent and Antwerp.

1578	**318**	2f. blue	15	15

1956. 80th Birthday of Queen Elisabeth and Foundation Fund.

1579	**319**	80c.+20c. green	50	20
1580		2f.+1f. lake	3·00	1·60
1581		4f.+2f. sepia	3·25	2·50

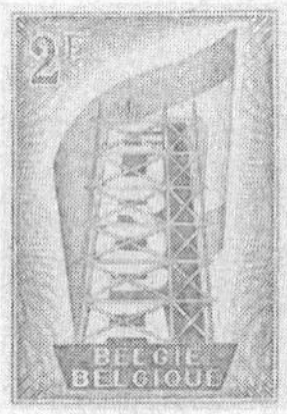
320

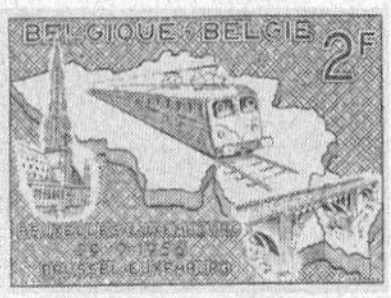
321 Electric Train and Railway Bridge

1956. Europa.

1582	**320**	2f. green	1·25	10
1583	–	4f. violet	6·50	35

1956. Electrification of Brussels–Luxembourg Railway Line.

1584	**321**	2f. blue	20	20

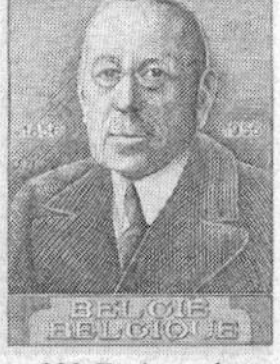
322 E. Anseele

1956. Birth Centenary of Anseele (statesman).

1588	**322**	20c. purple	10	10

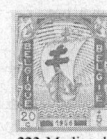

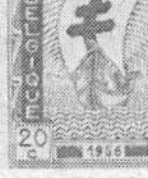
323 Medieval Ship

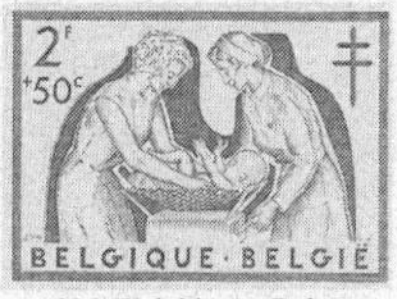
324 Weighing a Baby

1956. Anti-tuberculosis and other Funds.

1589	**323**	20c.+5c. brown	10	15
1590		80c.+20c. green	75	35
1591		1f.20+30c. purple	75	45
1592		1f.50+50c. slate	1·25	65
1593	**324**	2f.+50c. green	2·75	1·60
1594	–	4f.+2f. purple	10·50	6·75
1595	–	8f.+4f. red	11·50	8·00

DESIGNS—As Type **324**: HORIZ: 4f. X-ray examination. VERT: 8f. Convalescence and rehabilitation.

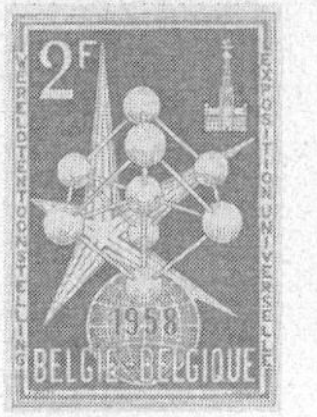
325 "Atomium" and Exhibition Emblem

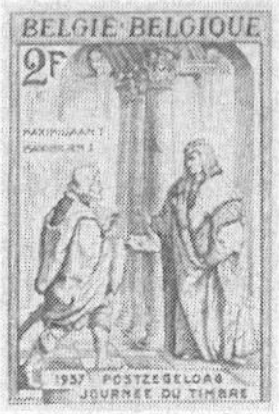
327 Emperor Maximilian I, with Messenger

1957. Brussels International Exhibition.

1596	**325**	2f. red	25	15
1597		2f.50 green	25	15
1598		4f. violet	60	30
1599		5f. purple	1·00	50

1957. Stamp Day.

1603	**327**	2f. red	15	15

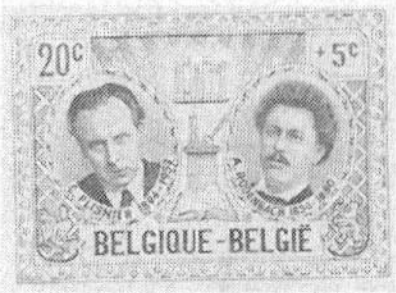
328 Charles Plisnier and Albrecht Rodenbach (writers)

1957. Cultural Fund. Belgian Celebrities.

1604	**328**	20c.+5c. violet	10	10
1605	–	80c.+20c. brown	40	25
1606	–	1f.20+30c. sepia	70	25
1607	–	2f.+50c. red	2·10	1·00
1608	–	3f.+1f. green	2·40	2·10
1609	–	4f.+2f. blue	2·75	2·50

DESIGNS: 80c. Professors Emiel Vliebergh and Maurice Wilmotte; 1f.20, Paul Pastur and Julius Hoste; 2f. Lodewijk de Raet and Jules Destree (politicians); 3f. Constantin Meunier and Constant Permeke (artists); 4f. Lieven Gevaert and Edouard Empain (industrialists).

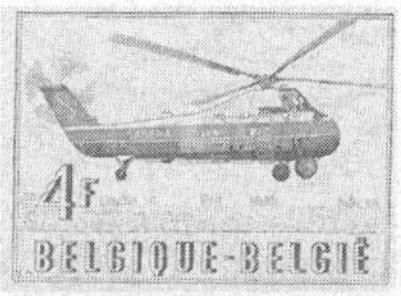
329 Sikorsky S-58 Helicopter

1957. Conveyance of 100,000th Passenger by Belgian Helicopter Service.

1610	**329**	4f. blue, green and grey	70	35

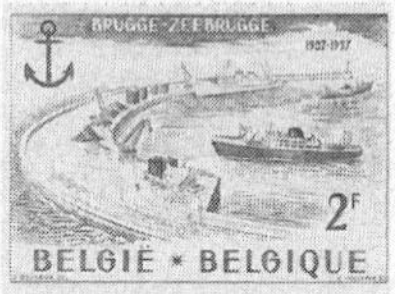
330 Zeebrugge Harbour

1957. 50th Anniv of Completion of Zeebrugge Harbour.

1611	**330**	2f. blue	30	10

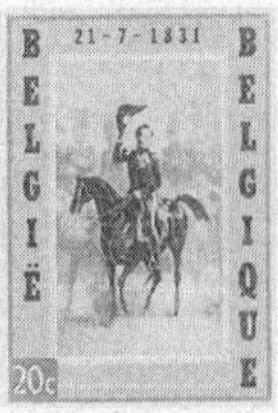
331 King Leopold I entering Brussels (after Simonau)

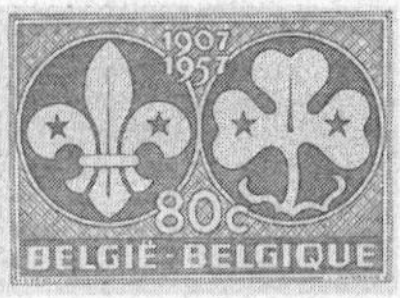
332 Scout and Guide Badges

1957. 126th Anniv of Arrival of King Leopold I in Belgium.

1612	**331**	20c. green	20	10
1613	–	2f. mauve	25	10

DESIGN—HORIZ: 2f. King Leopold I at frontier (after Wappers).

1957. 50th Anniv of Boy Scout Movement and Birth Centenary of Lord Baden-Powell.

1614	**332**	80c. brown	30	15
1615	–	4f. green	1·00	40

DESIGN—VERT: 4f. Lord Baden-Powell.

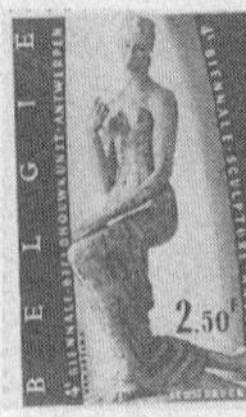
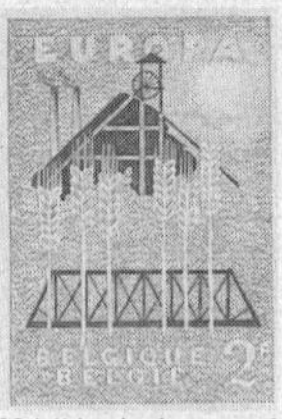

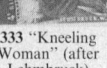

333 "Kneeling Woman" (after Lehmbruck)
334 "Agriculture and Industry"

1957. 4th Biennial Sculpture Exn, Antwerp.

1616	**333**	2f.50 green	1·00	60

1957. Europa.

1617	**334**	2f. purple	60	10
1618		4f. blue	1·10	35

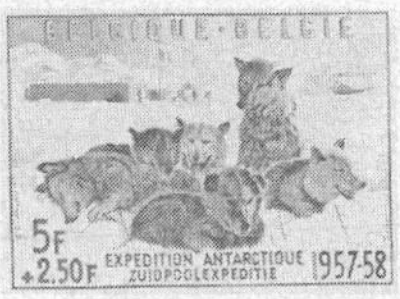

335 Sledge-dog Team

1957. Belgian Antarctic Expedition, 1957–58.

1619	**335**	5f.+2f.50 orange, brown and grey	2·50	2·10

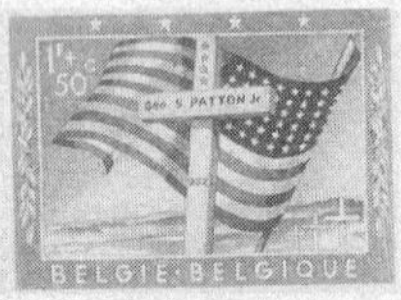
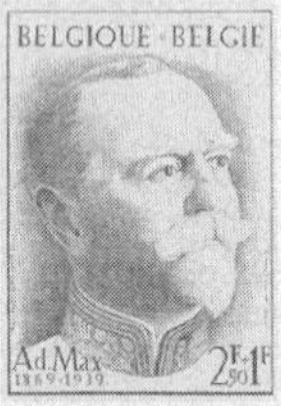

336 General Patton's Grave at Hamm
337 Adolphe Max

1957. General Patton Memorial Issue.

1621	**336**	1f.+50c. black	1·10	65
1622	–	2f.50+50c. green	1·75	60
1623	–	3f.+1f. brown	3·50	1·75
1624	–	5f.+2f.50 slate	6·25	3·75
1625	–	6f.+3f. red	8·75	6·00

DESIGNS—HORIZ: 2f.50, Patton Memorial project at Bastogne; 3f. Gen. Patton decorating Brig.-General A. MacAuliffe; 6f. (51 × 35½ mm) Tanks in action. VERT: 5f. General Patton.

1957. 18th Death Anniv of Burgomaster Adolphe Max (patriot).

1626	**337**	2f.50+1f. blue	1·10	65

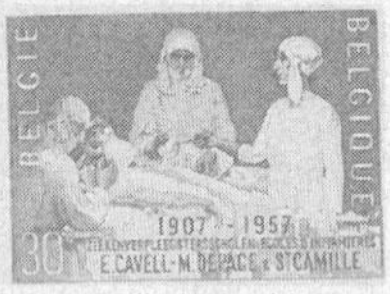

338 Queen Elisabeth with Doctors Depage and Debaisieux at a surgical operation

1957. 50th Anniv of "Edith Cavell-Marie Depage" and "St. Camille" Nursing Schools.

1627	**338**	30c. red	15	10

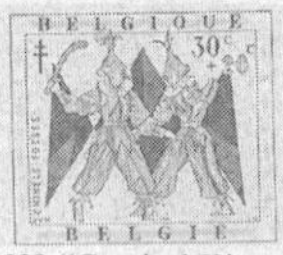
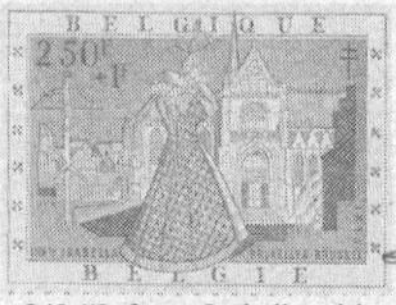

339 "Carnival Kings of Fosses" (Namur)
340 "Infanta Isabella with Crossbow" (Brussels)

1957. Anti-tuberculosis and other Funds. Provincial Legends.

1628	**339**	30c.+20c. pur & yell	10	15
1629	–	1f.+50c. sepia & blue	45	25
1630	–	1f.50+50c. grey & red	60	35
1631	–	2f.+1f. black & green	65	35
1632	**340**	2f.50+1f. grn & mve	1·90	80
1633	–	5f.+2f. black & blue	3·25	3·00
1634	–	6f.+2f.50 lake & red	4·50	3·75

DESIGNS: As Type **339**—HORIZ: 1f.50, "St. Remacle and the Wolf" (Liege). VERT: 1f. "Op Signoorken" (Antwerp); 2f. "The Long Man and the Pea Soup" (Limburg). As Type **340**—HORIZ: 6f. "Carnival Kings of Binche" (Hainaut). VERT: 5f. "The Virgin with the Inkwell" (West Flanders).

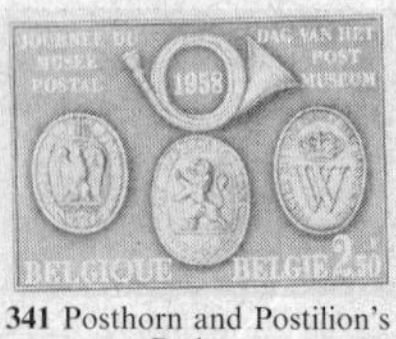

341 Posthorn and Postilion's Badges

1958. Postal Museum Day.

1635	**341**	2f.50 grey	25	10

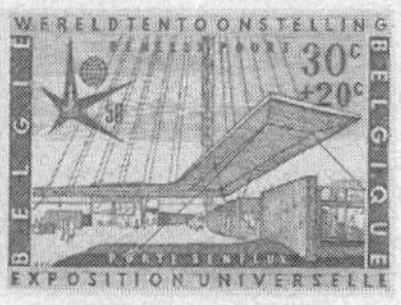

342 Benelux Gate

1958. Inauguration of Brussels International Exhibition. Inscr as in T **342**.

1636	**342**	30c.+20c. sepia, brown and violet	10	10
1637	–	1f.+50c. purple, slate and green	15	10
1638	–	1f.50+50c. violet, turquoise and green	15	15
1639	–	2f.50+1f. red, blue and vermilion	35	25
1640	–	3f.+1f.50 blue, black and red	80	60
1641	–	5f.+3f. mauve, black and blue	1·10	1·10

DESIGNS—HORIZ: 1f. Civil Engineering Pavilion; 1f.50, Belgian Congo and Ruanda-Urundi Pavilion; 2f.50, "Belgium, 1900"; 3f. Atomium; 5f. (49 × 33½ mm) Telexpo Pavilion.

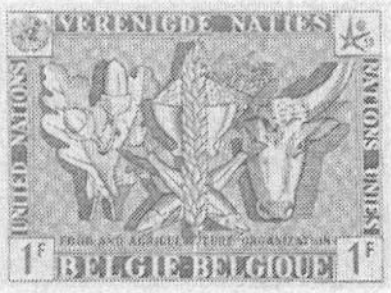

343 "Food and Agriculture Organization"

1958. United Nations Commemoration.

1642	–	50c. grey (postage)	2·10	1·75
1643	**343**	1f. red	10	15
1644	–	1f.50 blue	15	15
1645	–	2f. purple	45	40
1646	–	2f.50 green	10	15
1647	–	3f. turquoise	45	35
1648	–	5f. mauve	15	20
1649	–	8f. brown	70	60
1650	–	11f. lilac	1·25	90
1651	–	20f. red	2·10	1·60
1652	–	5f. blue (air)	15	15
1653	–	6f. green	30	30
1654	–	7f.50 violet	30	30
1655	–	8f. sepia	30	30
1656	–	9f. red	45	40
1657	–	10f. brown	45	40

DESIGNS (Emblems and symbols)—HORIZ: 50c. I.L.O. 2f.50, U.N.E.S.C.O. 3f. U.N. Pavilion, Brussels Int Exn; 6f. World Meteorological Organization; 8f. (No. 1649), Int Monetary Fund; 8f. (No. 1655), General Agreement on Tariffs and Trade; 10f. Atomic Energy Agency; 11f. W.H.O. 20f. U.P.U. VERT: 1f.50, U.N.O. 2f. World Bank; 5f. (No. 1648), I.T.U. 5f. (No. 1652), I.C.A.O. 7f.50, Protection of Refugees; 9f. UNICEF.

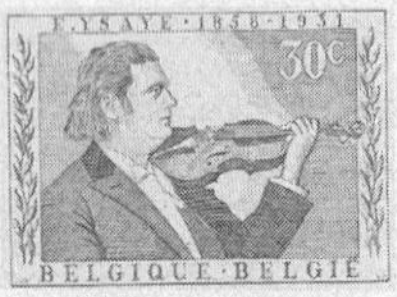
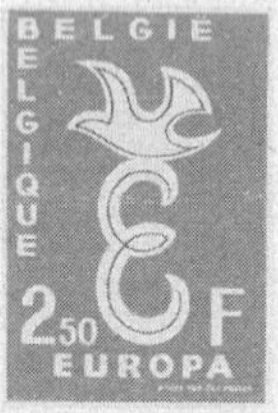

344 Eugene Ysaye
345 "Europa"

1958. Birth Centenary of Ysaye (violinist).

1658	**344**	30c. blue and red	25	10

1958. Europa.

1659	**345**	2f.50 blue and red	25	10
1660		5f. red and blue	40	20

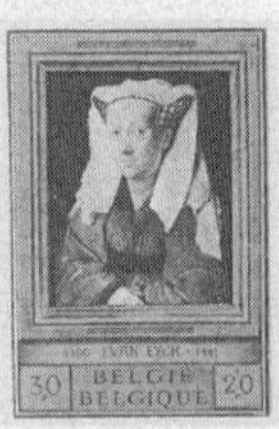

346 "Marguerite Van Eyck" (after Jan Van Eyck)

1958. Cultural Relief Funds. Paintings as T **346**. Frames in brown and yellow.

1661	**346**	30c.+20c. myrtle	10	15
1662	–	1f.+50c. lake	70	35
1663	–	1f.+50+50c. blue	1·10	65
1664	–	2f.50+1f. sepia	2·75	1·60
1665	–	3f.+1f.50 red	2·50	2·00
1666	–	5f.+3f. blue	5·00	3·75

PAINTINGS—HORIZ: 1f. "Carrying the Cross" (Hieronymus Bosch). 3f. "The Rower" (James Ensor). VERT: 1f.50, "St. Donatien" (Jan Gossaert). 2f.50, Self-portrait (Lambert Lombard). 5f. "Henriette with the Large Hat" (Henri Evenepoel).

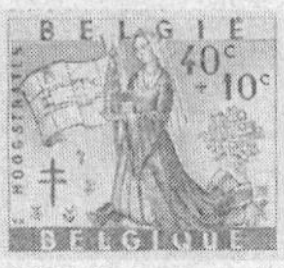
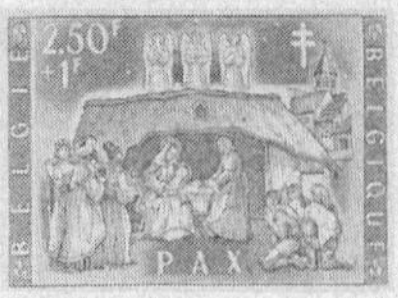

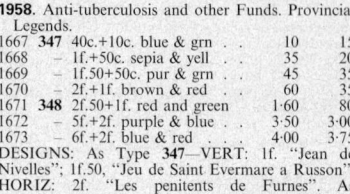

347 "Hoogstraten"
348 Pax—"Creche vivante"

1958. Anti-tuberculosis and other Funds. Provincial Legends.

1667	**347**	40c.+10c. blue & grn	10	15
1668	–	1f.+50c. sepia & yell	35	20
1669	–	1f.50+50c. pur & grn	45	35
1670	–	2f.+1f. brown & red	60	35
1671	**348**	2f.50+1f. red and green	1·60	80
1672	–	5f.+2f. purple & blue	3·50	3·00
1673	–	6f.+2f. blue & red	4·00	3·75

DESIGNS: As Type **347**—VERT: 1f. "Jean de Nivelles"; 1f.50, "Jeu de Saint Evermare a Russon". HORIZ: 2f. "Les penitents de Furnes". As Type **348**—HORIZ: "Marches de l'Entre Sambre et Meuse". VERT: 6f. "Pax—Vierge".

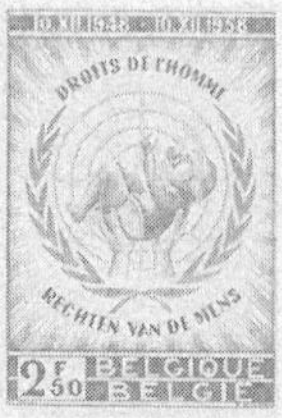
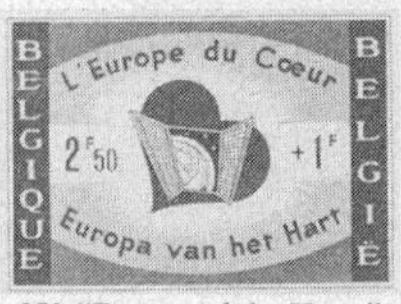

349 "Human Rights"
350 "Europe of the Heart"

1958. 10th Anniv of Human Rights Declaration.

1674	**349**	2f.50 slate	30	10

1959. "Heart of Europe". Fund for Displaced Persons.

1675	**350**	1f.+50c. purple	25	20
1676		2f.50+1f. green	75	50
1677		5f.+2f.50 brown	1·10	1·00

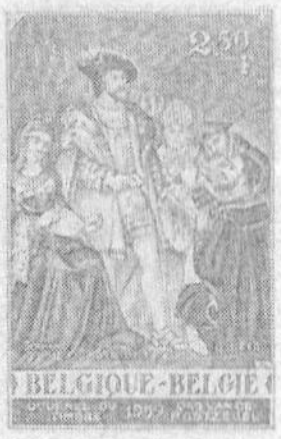
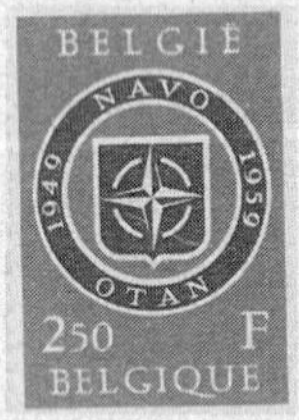

351 J. B. de Taxis taking the oath at the hands of Charles V (after J.-E. Van den Bussche)
352 N.A.T.O. Emblem

1959. Stamp Day.

1680	**351**	2f.50 green	35	10

1959. 10th Anniv of N.A.T.O.

1681	**352**	2f.50 blue and red	35	10
1682		5f. blue and green	95	60

On the 5f. value the French and Flemish inscriptions are transposed.

For similar design but inscr "1969", see No. 2112.

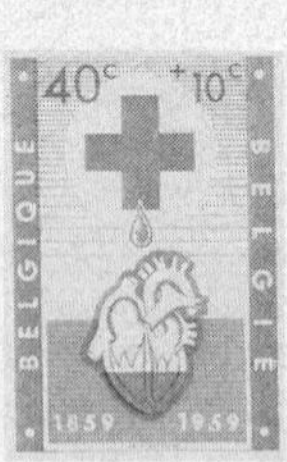

353 "Blood Transfusion"

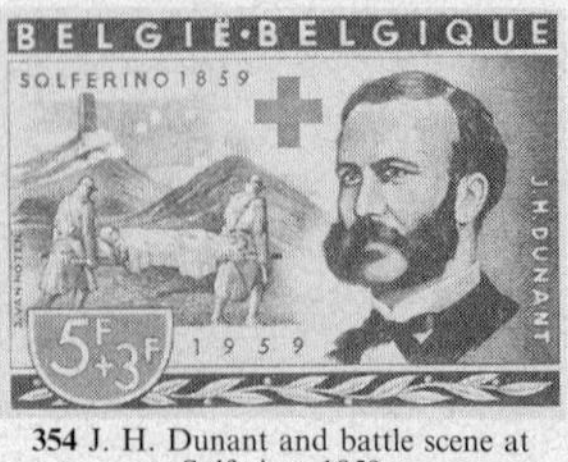

354 J. H. Dunant and battle scene at Solferino, 1859

1959. Red Cross Commem. Inscr "1859 1959".

1683	**353**	40c.+10c. red & grey	10	15
1684		1f.+50c. red & sepia	1·10	50
1685		1f.50+50c. red and lilac	2·10	1·00
1686	–	2f.50+1f. red & grn	2·50	1·40
1687	–	3f.+1f.50 red and blue	4·00	3·25
1688	**354**	5f.+3f. red and sepia	7·75	5·25

DESIGN—As Type **353**—HORIZ: 2f.50, 3f. Red Cross and broken sword ("Aid for the wounded").

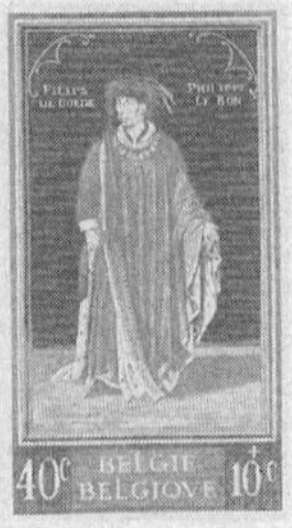
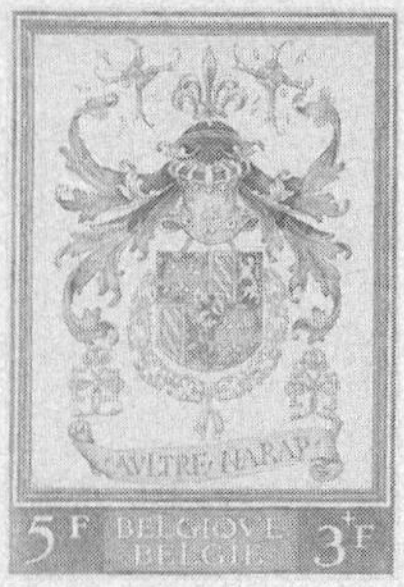

355 Philip the Good
356 Arms of Philip the Good

1959. Royal Library of Belgium Fund. Nos. 1689/94 have background in deep blue and bistre and bottom panel in deep olive.

1689	**355**	40c.+10c. red	10	15
1690	–	1f.+50c. red	45	30
1691	–	1f.50+50c. red	1·10	75
1692	–	2f.50+1f. red	2·10	1·60
1693	–	3f.+1f.50 red	2·50	2·25
1694	**356**	5f.+3f. multicoloured	4·00	3·25

DESIGNS—As Type **355** (Holders of Order of the Golden Fleece): 1f. Charles the Bold; 1f.50, Maximillian of Austria; 2f.50, Philip the Fair; 3f. Charles V.

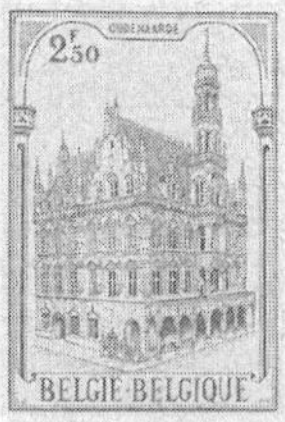
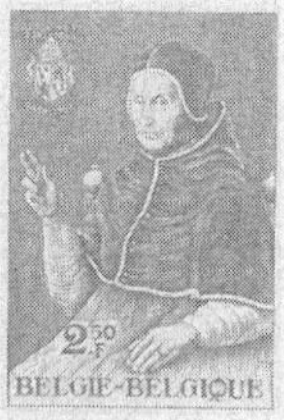

358 Town Hall, Oudenarde
359 Pope Adrian VI

1959. Oudenarde Town Hall Commem.

1699	**358**	2f.50 purple	30	10

1959. 500th Birth Anniv of Pope Adrian VI.

1700	**359**	2f.50 red	20	10
1701		5f. blue	35	35

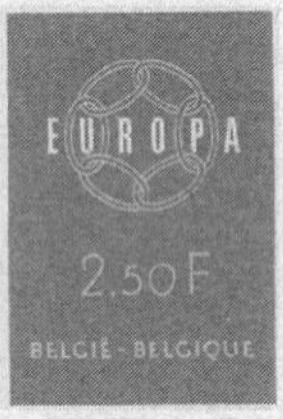
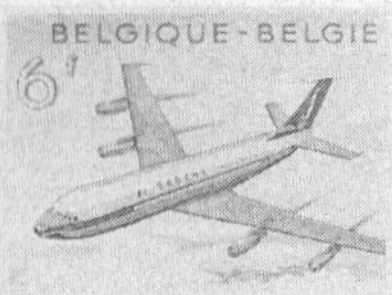

360 "Europa"
361 Boeing 707

1959. Europa.

1702	**360**	2f.50 red	20	10
1703		5f. turquoise	40	35

1959. Inauguration of Boeing 707 Airliners by SABENA.

1704	**361**	6f. blue, grey and red	1·50	50

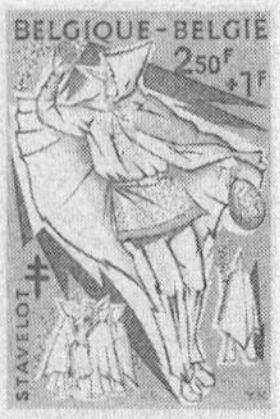

362 Antwerp fish (float)
363 Stavelot "Blancs Moussis" (carnival figures)

1959. Anti-tuberculosis and other Funds. Carnival scenes.

1705	**362**	40c.+10c. green, red and bistre	10	15
1706	–	1f.+50c. green, violet and olive	40	30
1707	–	2f.+50c. yellow, purple and brown	45	40
1708	**363**	2f.50+1f. blue, violet and grey	60	40
1709	–	3f.+1f. purple, yellow and grey	1·60	1·00
1710	–	6f.+2f. blue, red and olive	3·50	3·25
1711	–	7f.+3f. blk, yell, & bl	4·00	3·25

DESIGNS—As Type **362**—HORIZ: 1f. Mons dragon (float); 2f. Eupen and Malmedy clowns in chariot. As Type **363**—VERT: 3f. Ypres jester. HORIZ: 6f. Holy Family; 7f. Madonna and child.

364 Countess Alexandrine of Taxis (tapestry)
365 Indian Azalea

1960. Stamp Day.
1712 **364** 3f. blue 50 10

1960. Ghent Flower Show. Inscr as in T **365**.
1713 **365** 40c. red and violet . . . 10 10
1714 – 3f. yellow, red and green 45 10
1715 – 6f. red, green and blue 1·50 60
FLOWERS: 3f. Begonia. 6f. Anthurium and bromelia.

366 Refugee
367 "Labour" (after Meunier)

1960. World Refugee Year. Inscr as in T **366**.
1716 – 40c.+10c. purple 10 15
1717 **366** 3f.+1f.50 sepia 45 35
1718 – 6f.+3f. blue . . . . . . 1·10 80
DESIGNS: 40c. Child refugee; 6f. Woman refugee.

1960. 75th Anniv of Belgian Socialist Party. Inscr as in T **367**.
1720 **367** 40c. purple and red . . . 10 15
1721 – 3f. brown and red . . . 50 20
DESIGN—HORIZ: 3f. "Workers" (after Meunier).

369 Parachutist on ground

1960. Parachuting. Designs bearing emblem of National Parachuting Club.
1726 – 40c.+10c. black & blue 25 20
1727 – 1f.+50c. black & blue . . 1·50 60
1728 – 2f.+50c. black, blue and green . . . . 2·75 1·25
1729 – 2f.50+1f. black, turquoise and green 4·00 2·25
1730 **369** 3f.+1f. black, blue and green . . . . 4·00 2·25
1731 6f.+2f. black, blue and green . . . . 4·50 3·25
DESIGNS—HORIZ: 40c., 1f., Parachutists dropping from Douglas DC-4 aircraft. VERT: 2f., 2f.50, Parachutists descending.

370 Ship's Officer and Helmsman

1960. Congo Independence.
1732 **370** 10c. red 10 10
1733 – 40c. red 10 10
1734 – 1f. purple 60 20
1735 – 2f. green 45 20
1736 – 2f.50 blue 60 20
1737 – 3f. blue 60 10
1738 – 6f. violet . . . . 2·10 75
1739 – 8f. brown . . . . 6·25 5·25
DESIGNS—As Type **370**: 40c. Doctor and nurses with patient; 1f. Tree-planting; 2f. Sculptors; 2f.50, Sport (putting the shot); 3f. Broadcasting from studio. (52 × 35½ mm): 6f. Children with doll; 8f. Child with globe.

371 Refugee Airlift

1960. Congo Refugees Relief Fund.
1740 **371** 40c.+10c. turquoise . . . 10 15
1741 – 3f.+1f.50 red . . . . . 1·90 1·25
1742 – 6f.+3f. violet . . . . . 3·50 3·00
DESIGNS—As Type **371**: 3f. Mother and child. 35 × 51½ mm: 6f. Boeing 707 airplane spanning map of aircraft route.

1960. Surch.
1743 **267** 15c. on 30c. green . . . 10 10
1744 15c. on 50c. blue 15 10
1745 20c. on 30c. green . . . 10 10

373 Conference Emblem
374 Young Stamp Collectors

1960. 1st Anniv of E.P.T. Conference.
1746 **373** 3f. lake 45 10
1747 6f. green 80 35

1960. "Philately for the Young" Propaganda.
1748 **374** 40c. black and bistre . . 10 10

375 Pouring Milk for Child
376 Frere Orban (founder)

1960. United Nations Children's Fund.
1749 **375** 40c.+10c. yellow, green and brown 10 15
1750 – 1f.+50c. red, blue and drab 70 50
1751 – 2f.+50c. bistre, green and violet . . . . 1·25 1·25
1752 – 2f.50+1f. sepia, blue and red . . . . 2·10 1·40
1753 – 3f.+1f. violet, orange and turquoise . . . . . . 2·25 1·50
1754 – 6f.+2f. brown, green and blue . . . . 3·50 2·10
DESIGNS: 1f. Nurse embracing children; 2f. Child carrying clothes, and ambulance; 2f.50, Nurse weighing baby; 3f. Children with linked arms; 6f. Refugee worker and child.

1960. Centenary of Credit Communal (Co-operative Bank).
1755 **376** 10c. brown and yellow 10 10
1756 40c. brown and green . . 10 10
1757 1f.50 brown and violet 80 65
1758 3f. brown and red . . . 80 45

377 Tapestry

1960. Anti-T.B. and other Funds. Arts and Crafts.
1759 **377** 40c.+10c. ochre, brown and blue 10 15
1760 – 1f.+50c. blue, brown and indigo . . . . 1·00 55
1761 – 2f.+50c. green, black and brown . . . . 1·25 1·00
1762 – 2f.50+1f. yellow and brown . . . . 2·25 1·50
1763 – 3f.+1f. black, brown and blue . . . . 2·75 1·90
1764 – 6f.+2f. lemon and black 3·50 2·40
DESIGNS—VERT: 1f. Crystalware; 2f. Lace. HORIZ: 2f.50, Brassware; 3f. Diamond-cutting; 6f. Ceramics.

378 King Baudouin and Queen Fabiola
379 Nicolaus Rockox (after Van Dyck)

1960. Royal Wedding.
1765 **378** 40c. sepia and green . . 10 10
1766 3f. sepia and purple . . 45 10
1767 6f. sepia and blue . . . 1·25 40

1961. Surch in figs and **1961** at top, **1962** at bottom and bars in between.
1768 **267** 15c. on 30c. green . . . 80 10
1769 20c. on 30c. green . . . 1·90 1·50
See note below No. 480.

1961. 400th Birth Anniv of Nicolaus Rockox (Burgomaster of Antwerp).
1770 **379** 3f. black, bistre & brn 30 10

380 Seal of Jan Bode
381 K. Kats (playwright) and Father N. Pietkin (poet)

1961. Stamp Day.
1771 **380** 3f. sepia and brown . . 30 10

1961. Cultural Funds. Portrait in purple.
1772 40c.+10c. lake and pink . . 10 15
1773 1f.+50c. lake and brown . . 1·90 1·00
1774 2f.+50c. red and yellow . . 2·75 2·25
1775 2f.50+1f. myrtle and sage 2·75 2·25
1776 3f.+1f. blue and light blue 3·00 2·40
1777 6f.+2f. blue and lavender . . 4·25 3·25
PORTRAITS: 40c. Type **381**. 1f. A. Mockel and J. F. Willems (writers). 2f. J. van Rijswijck and X. Neujean (politicians). 2f.50, J. Demarteau (journalist) and A. van de Perre (politician). 3f. J. David (litterateur) and A. du Bois (writer). 6f. H. Vieuxtemps (violinist) and W. de Mol (composer).

382 White Rhinoceros
383 Cardinal A.P. de Granville (first Archbishop)

1961. Philanthropic Funds. Animals of Antwerp Zoo.
1778 40c.+10c. dp brown & brn 15 20
1779 1f.+50c. brown and green 75 65
1780 2f.+50c. sepia, red and black 1·50 1·10
1781 2f.50+1f. brown and red . . 1·50 1·50
1782 3f.+1f. brown and orange 1·50 1·40
1783 6f.+2f. ochre and blue . . . 1·90 1·60
ANIMALS—VERT: 40c. Type **382**; 1f. Przewalski horse and foal; 2f. Okapi. HORIZ: 2f.50, Giraffe; 3f. Lesser panda; 6f. Elk.

1961. 400th Anniv of Archbishopric of Malines.
1784 **383** 40c.+10c. brown, red and purple 10 15
1785 – 3f.+1f.50 mult 80 60
1786 – 6f.+3f. bistre, violet and purple . . . . 1·00 1·10
DESIGNS: 3f. Cardinal's Arms; 6f. Symbols of Archbishopric and Malines.

385 "Interparliamentary Union"

1961. 50th Interparliamentary Union Conference, Brussels.
1791 **385** 3f. brown and turquoise 50 10
1792 6f. purple and red . . . 70 60

386 Doves

1961. Europa.
1793 **386** 3f. black and olive . . . 20 10
1794 6f. black and brown . . . 35 30

387 Reactor BR 2, Mol
388 "The Mother and Child" (after Paulus)

1961. Euratom Commemoration.
1795 **387** 40c. green 10 10
1796 – 3f. mauve 15 10
1797 – 6f. blue 35 30
DESIGNS—VERT: 3f. Heart of reactor BR 3, Mol. HORIZ: 6f. View of reactor BR 3, Mol.

1961. Anti-T.B. and other Funds. Belgian paintings of mothers and children. Frames in gold.
1798 **388** 40c.+10c. sepia 10 15
1799 – 1f.+50c. blue 35 45
1800 – 2f.+50c. red . . . . . 1·00 95
1801 – 2f.50+1f. lake . . . . . 1·00 95
1802 – 3f.+1f. violet . . . . . 1·00 95
1803 – 6f.+2f. myrtle . . . . . 1·10 1·10
PAINTINGS: 1f. "Maternal Love" (Navez). 2f. "Maternity" (Permeke). 2f.50, "The Virgin and the Child" (Van der Weyden). 3f. "The Virgin with the Apple" (Memling), 6f. "The Myosotis Virgin" (Rubens).

389 Horta Museum
390 Male Castle

1962. Birth Cent of Victor Horta (architect).
1804 **389** 3f. brown 25 10

1962. Cultural and Patriotic Funds. Buildings.
1805 **390** 40c.+10c. green 10 15
1806 – 90c.+10c. mauve 20 30
1807 – 1f.+50c. lilac 45 45
1808 – 2f.+50c. violet 65 75
1809 – 2f.50+1f. brown . . . . 90 1·00
1810 – 3f.+1f. turquoise . . . . 95 1·10
1811 – 6f.+2f. red . . . . . 1·50 1·60
BUILDINGS—HORIZ: 90c. Royal Library, Brussels. 1f. Collegiate Church, Soignies. 6f. Ypres Halls. VERT: 1f. Notre-Dame Basilica, Tongres. 2f.50, Notre-Dame Church, Hanswijk, Malines. 3f. St. Denis-en-Broqueroie Abbey.

391 16th-Century Postilion
392 G. Mercator (after F. Hogenberg)

1962. Stamp Day.
1812 **391** 3f. brown and green . . 20 10
See also No. 1997.

1962. 450th Birth Anniv of Mercator (geographer).
1813 **392** 3f. sepia 20 10

393 Brother A. M. Gochet (scholar)
394 Guianan Cock of the Rock ("Coq de Roch, Rotshann")

1962. Gochet and Triest Commemoration.
1814 **393** 2f. blue 10 15
1815 – 3f. brown 20 15
PORTRAIT: 3f. Canon P.-J. Triest (benefactor of the aged).

1962. Philanthropic Funds. Birds of Antwerp Zoo. Birds, etc., in natural colours; colours of name panel and inscription given.
1816 **394** 40c.+10c. blue 10 15
1817 – 1f.+50c. blue and red . . 40 35
1818 – 2f.+50c. mauve & blk . . 70 65
1819 – 2f.50+1f. turq & red . . 90 85
1820 – 3f.+1f. brown & grn . . 1·10 1·10
1821 – 6f.+2f. blue and red . . 1·25 1·25
BIRDS: 1f. Red lory ("Rode Lori, Lori Rouge"); 2f.

Green turaco ("Touracou du Senegal, Senegal Toerakoe"); 2f.50, Keel-billed toucan ("Kortbek Toecan, Toucan a Bec Court"); 3f. Greater bird of paradise ("Grand Paradijsier, Grosse Paradisvogel"); 6f. Congo peacock ("Kongo Pauw, Paon du Congo").

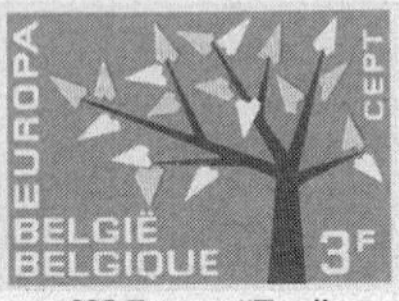

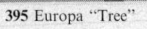

395 Europa "Tree"

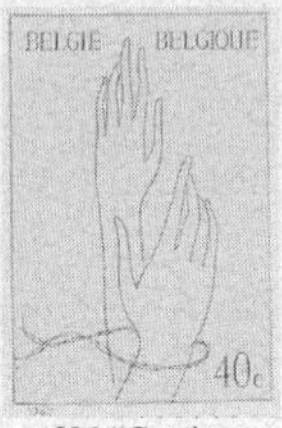

396 "Captive Hands" (after sculpture by Ianchelivici)

1962. Europa.

1822	395	3f. black, yellow & red	20	10
1823		6f. black, yellow & olive	40	30

1962. Concentration Camp Victims.

1824	396	40c. blue and black	10	10

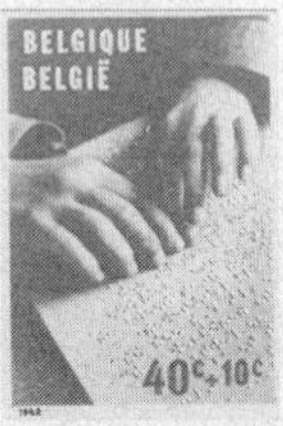

397 Reading Braille

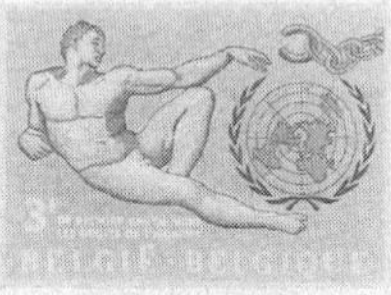
398 "Adam" (after Michelangelo)

1962. Handicapped Children Relief Funds.

1825	397	40c.+10c. brown	10	15
1826	–	1f.+50c. red	30	35
1827	–	2f.+50c. mauve	1·00	95
1828	–	2f.50+1f. green	90	1·00
1829	–	3f.+1f. blue	1·00	85
1830	–	6f.+2f. sepia	1·00	1·00

DESIGNS—VERT: 1f. Girl solving puzzle; 2f.50, Crippled child with ball; 3f. Girl walking with crutches. HORIZ: 2f. Child with earphones; 6f. Crippled boys with football.

1962. "The Rights of Man".

1831	398	3f. sepia and green	15	10
1832		6f. sepia and brown	40	30

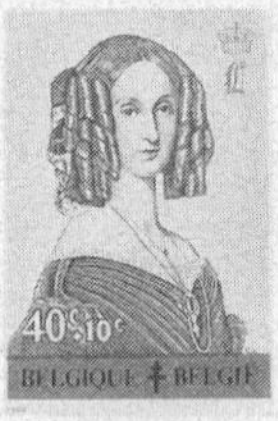

399 Queen Louise-Marie

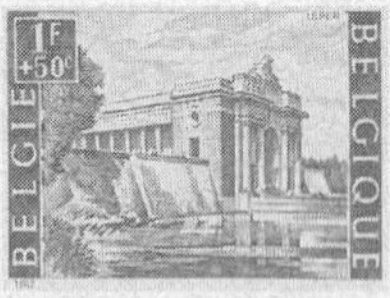

400 Menin Gate, Ypres

1962. Anti-tuberculosis and other Funds. Belgian Queens in green and gold.

1833		40c.+10c. Type 399	10	10
1834		40c.+10c. As T 399 but inscr "ML"	10	10
1835		1f.+50c. Marie-Henriette	65	45
1836		2f.+1f. Elisabeth	80	70
1837		3f.+1f.50 Astrid	1·00	1·10
1838		8f.+2f.50 Fabiola	1·10	1·25

1962. Ypres Millenary.

1839	400	1f.+50c. multicoloured	40	35

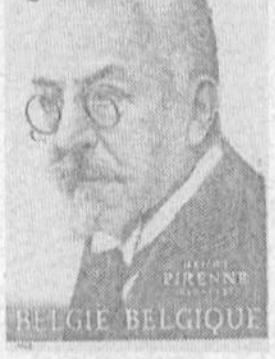

401 H. Pirenne

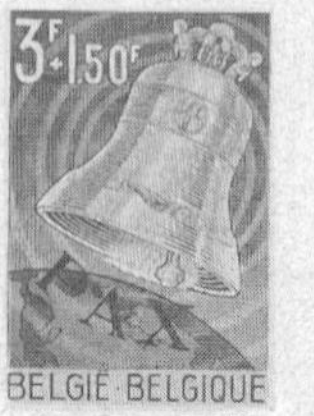

402 "Peace Bell"

1963. Birth Cent of Henri Pirenne (historian).

1841	401	3f. blue	30	10

1963. Cultural Funds and Installation of "Peace Bell" in Koekelberg Basilica. Bell in yellow; "PAX" in black.

1842	402	3f.+1f.50 green & bl	1·50	1·25
1843		6f.+3f. chestnut & brn	75	75

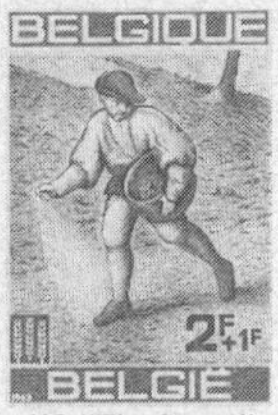

403 "The Sower" (after Brueghel)

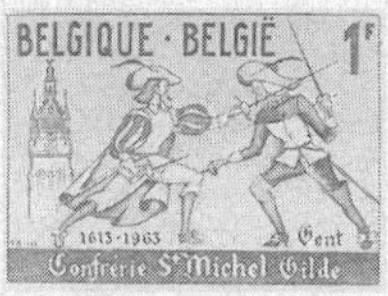

404 17th-century Duel

1963. Freedom from Hunger.

1845	403	2f.+1f. brown, black and green	20	25
1846	–	3f.+1f. brown, black and purple	25	25
1847	–	6f.+2f. yellow, black and brown	45	45

PAINTINGS—HORIZ: 3f. "The Harvest" (Brueghel). VERT: 6f. "The Loaf" (Anto Carte).

1963. 350th Anniv of Royal Guild and Knights of St. Michael.

1848	404	1f. red and blue	10	10
1849	–	3f. violet and green	30	10
1850	–	6f. multicoloured	40	30

DESIGNS—HORIZ: 3f. Modern fencing. VERT: 6f. Arms of the Guild.

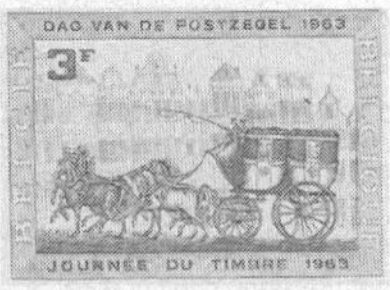

405 19th-century Mail-coach

1963. Stamp Day.

1851	405	3f. black and ochre	25	10

See also No. 1998.

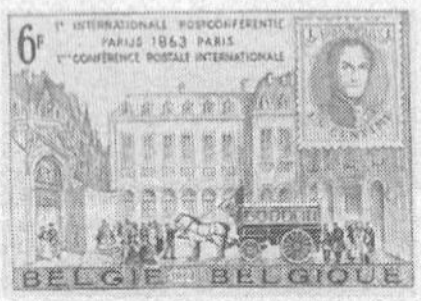

406 Hotel des Postes, Paris, and Belgian 1c. Stamp of 1863

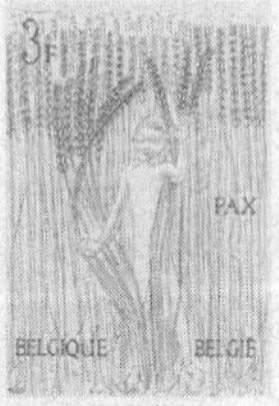

407 Child in Wheatfield

1963. Centenary of Paris Postal Conference.

1852	406	6f. sepia, mauve & grn	40	35

1963. "8th May" Peace Movement.

1853	407	3f. multicoloured	25	10
1854		6f. multicoloured	35	30

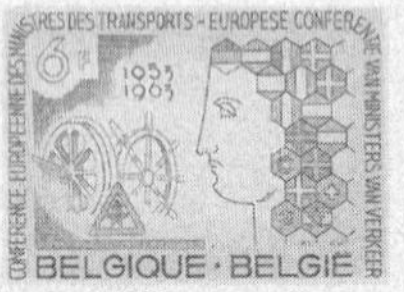

408 "Transport"

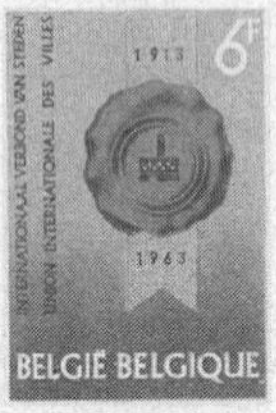

409 Town Seal

1963. European Transport Ministers' Conference, Brussels.

1855	408	6f. black and blue	40	35

1963. Int Union of Towns Congress, Brussels.

1856	409	6f. multicoloured	25	25

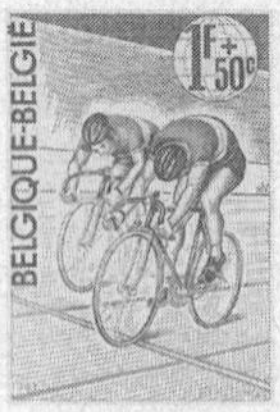

410 Racing Cyclists

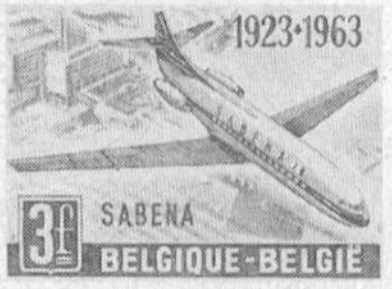

411 Sud Aviation SE 210 Caravelle

1963. Belgian Cycling Team's Participation in Olympic Games, Tokyo (1964).

1857	410	1f.+50c. multicoloured	10	15
1858	–	2f.+1f. multicoloured	20	20
1859	–	3f.+1f.50 mult	30	35
1860	–	6f.+3f. multicoloured	35	40

DESIGNS—HORIZ: 2f. Group of cyclists; 3f. Cyclists rounding bend. VERT: 6f. Cyclists being paced by motor-cyclists.

1963. 40th Anniv of SABENA Airline.

1861	411	3f. black and turquoise	25	10

412 "Co-operation"

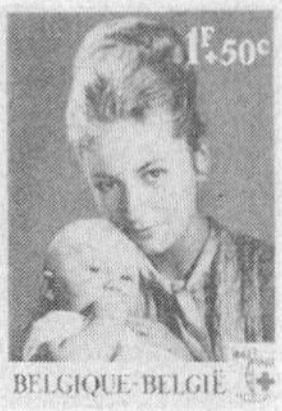

413 Princess Paola with Princess Astrid

1963. Europa.

1862	412	3f. black, brown & red	75	10
1863		6f. black, brown & blue	95	25

No. 1863 is inscr with "6 F" on the left, "BELGIE" at foot and "BELGIQUE" on right.

1963. Centenary of Red Cross and Belgian Red Cross Fund. Cross in red.

1864	–	40c.+10c. red & yell	10	10
1865	413	1f.+50c. grey & yellow	30	20
1866	–	2f.+50c. mauve & yell	35	30
1867	–	2f.50+1f. blue & yell	50	30
1868	–	3f.+1f. brown & yell	50	35
1869	–	3f.+1f. bronze & yell	1·60	1·90
1870	–	6f.+2f. green & yellow	75	1·10

DESIGNS—As T 413: 40c. Prince Philippe; 2f. Princess Astrid; 2f.50, Princess Paola; 6f. Prince Albert; 46 × 35 mm: 3f. (2), Prince Albert and family.

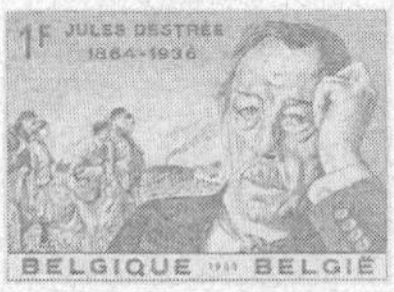

414 J. Destree (writer)

1963. Jules Destree and H. Van de Velde Commems.

1871	414	1f. purple	10	10
1872	–	1f. green	10	10

DESIGN: No. 1872, H. Van de Velde (architect).

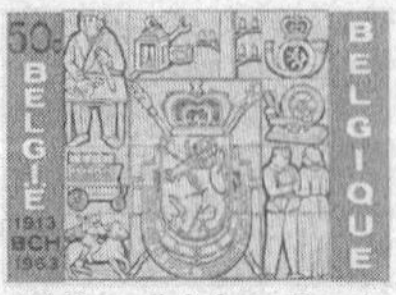

415 Bas-reliefs from Facade of Postal Cheques Office (after O. Jespars)

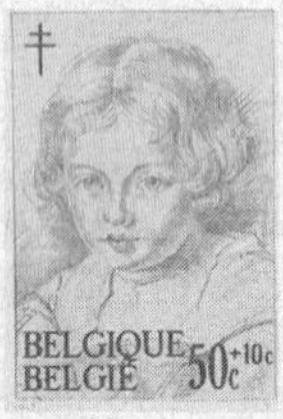

416 Balthasar Gerbier's Daughter

1963. 50th Anniv of Belgian Postal Cheques Office.

1873	415	50c. black, blue & red	10	10

1963. T.B. Relief and Other Funds. Rubens's Drawings. Background buff; inscr in black: designs colour given.

1874	416	50c.+10c. blue	10	10
1875	–	1f.+40c. red	10	15
1876	–	2f.+50c. violet	15	20
1877	–	2f.50+1f. green	35	40
1878	–	3f.+1f. brown	35	30
1879	–	6f.+2f. black	65	80

DRAWINGS—VERT: Rubens's children—1f. Nicolas (aged 2). 2f. Franz (aged 4). 2f.50, Nicolas (aged 6). 3f. Albert (aged 3). HORIZ: ($46\frac{1}{2} \times 35\frac{1}{2}$ mm): 6f. Infant Jesus, St. John and two angels.

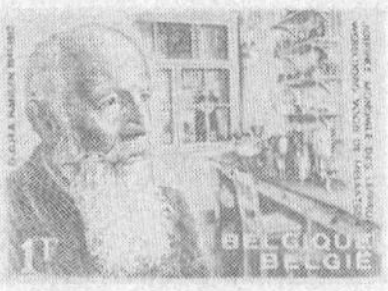

417 Dr. G. Hansen and Laboratory

1964. Leprosy Relief Campaign.

1880	417	1f. black and brown	10	25
1881	–	2f. brown and black	25	25
1882	–	5f. black and brown	40	30

DESIGNS: 2f. Leprosy hospital; 5f. Father Damien.

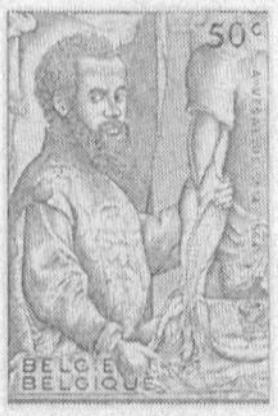

418 A. Vesale (anatomist) with Model of Human Arm

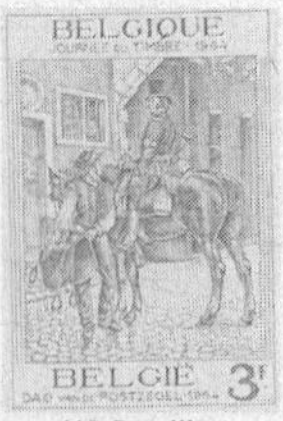

419 Postilion

1964. Belgian Celebrities.

1884	418	50c. black and green	10	20
1885	–	1f. black and green	10	20
1886	–	2f. black and green	20	15

DESIGNS—HORIZ: 1f. J. Boulvin (engineer) and internal combustion engine; 2f. H. Jaspar (statesman) and medallion.

1964. Stamp Day.

1887	419	3f. grey	25	10

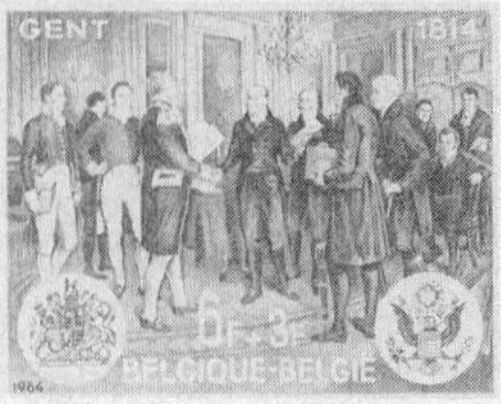

420 Admiral Lord Gambier and U.S. Ambassador J. Q. Adams after signing treaty (from painting by Sir A. Forestier)

1964. 150th Anniv of Signing of Treaty of Ghent.

1888	420	6f.+3f. blue	50	50

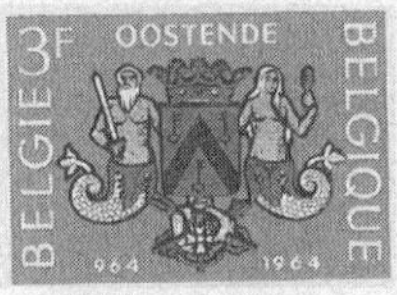

421 Arms of Ostend

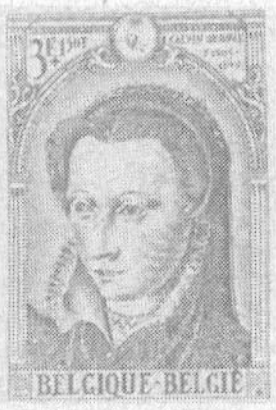

422 Ida of Bure (Calvin's wife)

1964. Millenary of Ostend.

1889	421	3f. multicoloured	25	10

1964. "Protestantism in Belgium".

1890	–	1f.+50c. blue	10	15
1891	422	3f.+1f.50 red	25	25
1892	–	6f.+3f. brown	45	45

PORTRAITS: 1f. P. Marnix of St. Aldegonde (Burgomaster of Antwerp). 6f. J. Jordaens (painter).

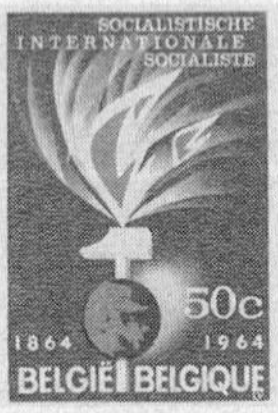

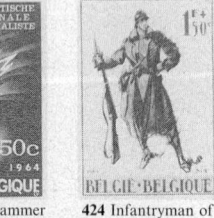

423 Globe, Hammer and Flame

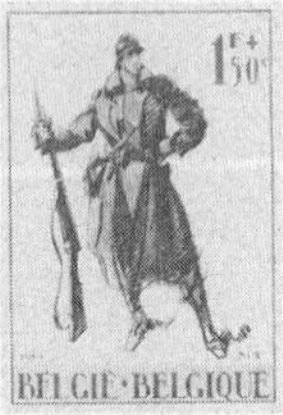

424 Infantryman of 1918

1964. Centenary of Socialist International.

1893	423	50c. red and blue	10	10
1894	–	1f. red and blue	10	10
1895	–	2f. red and blue	10	15

DESIGNS: 1f. "SI" on Globe; 2f. Flames.

1964. 50th Anniv of German Invasion of Belgium. Multicoloured.

1896	1f.+50c. Type 424	10	15
1897	2f.+1f. Colour sergeant of the Guides Regt, 1914	20	20
1898	3f.+1f.50 Trumpeter of the Grenadiers & Drummers of the Infantry and Carabiniers, 1914	25	25

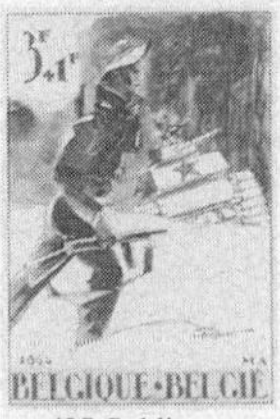

425 Soldier at Bastogne

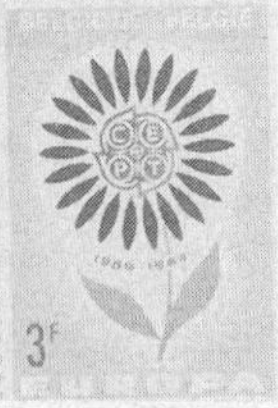

426 Europa "Flower"

1964. "Liberation–Resistance". Multicoloured.

1899	3f.+1f. Type 425	25	25
1900	6f.+3f. Soldier at estuary of the Scheldt	40	45

1964. Europa.

1901	426	3f. grey, red and green	20	10
1902		6f. blue, green and red	40	30

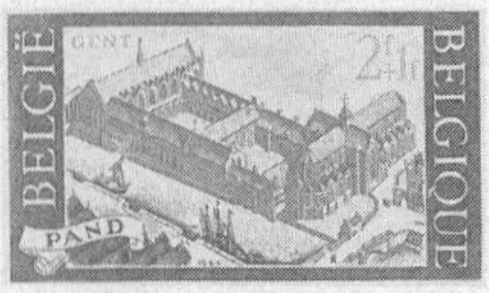

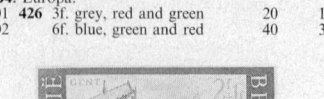

429 Pand Abbey, Ghent

1964. Pand Abbey Restoration Fund.

1905	429	2f.+1f. bl, turq & blk	20	20
1906	–	3f.+1f. brown, blue and purple	20	20

DESIGN: 3f. Waterside view of Abbey.

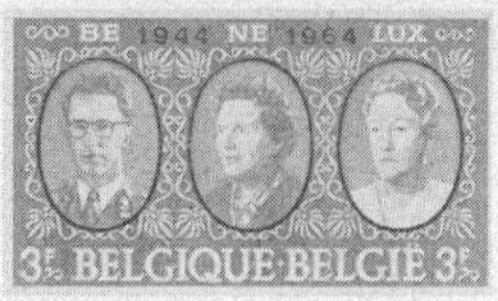

430 King Baudouin, Queen Juliana and Grand Duchess Charlotte

1964. 20th Anniv of "BENELUX".
1907 **430** 3f. purple, blue and olive 35 10

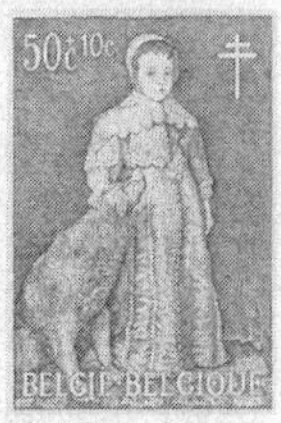

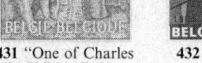

431 "One of Charles I's Children" (Van Dyck)

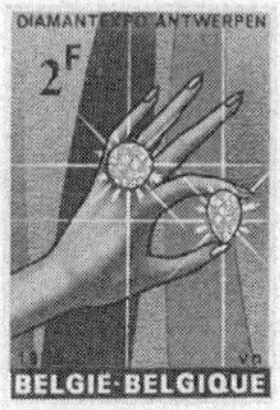

432 "Diamonds"

1964. T.B. Relief and Other Funds. Paintings of Royalty.
1908 **431** 50c.+10c. purple 10 10
1909 – 1f.+40c. red 10 15
1910 – 2f.+1f. purple 15 25
1911 – 3f.+1f. grey 30 25
1912 – 4f.+2f. violet 35 30
1913 – 6f.+3f. violet 40 35
DESIGNS—VERT: 1f. "William of Orange and his fiancee, Marie" (Van Dyck); 2f. "Portrait of a Little Boy" (E. Quellin and Jan Fyt); 3f. "Alexander Farnese at the age of 12 Years" (A. Moro); 4f. "William II, Prince of Orange" (Van Dyck). HORIZ—LARGER (46 × 35 mm): 6f. "Two Children of Cornelis De Vos" (C. de Vos).

1965. "Diamantexpo" (Diamonds Exn) Antwerp.
1914 **432** 2f. multicoloured 25 25

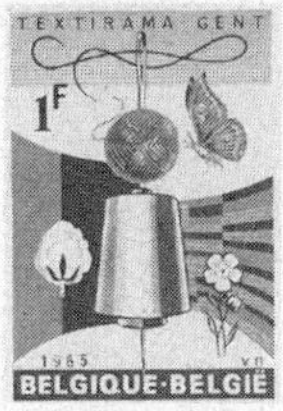

433 "Textiles"

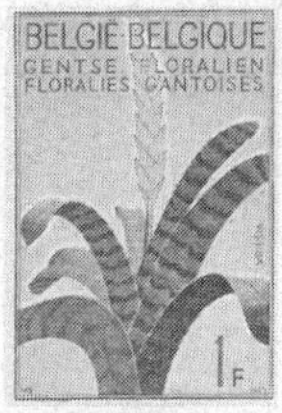

434 Vriesia

1965. "Textirama" (Textile Exn), Ghent.
1915 **433** 1f. black, red and blue 10 10

1965. Ghent Flower Show. Inscr "FLORALIES GANTOISES", etc. Multicoloured.
1916 1f. Type **434** 15 20
1917 2f. Echinocactus 25 20
1918 3f. Stapelia 15 15

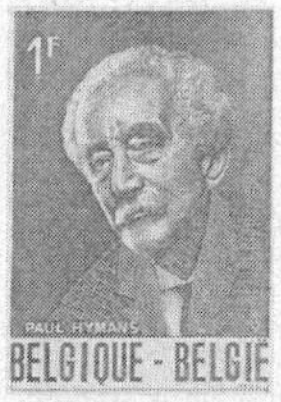

435 Paul Hymans

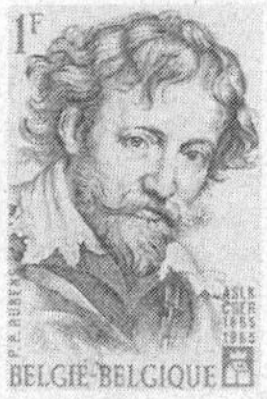

436 Rubens

1965. Birth Cent of Paul Hymans (statesman).
1919 **435** 1f. violet 10 10

1965. Centenary of General Savings and Pensions Funds. Painters.
1920 **436** 1f. sepia and mauve . . 10 10
1921 – 2f. sepia and turquoise 10 10
1922 – 3f. sepia and purple . . 10 10
1923 – 6f. sepia and red 30 20
1924 – 8f. sepia and blue . . . 45 40
PAINTERS: 2f. Franz Snyders. 3f. Adam van Noort. 6f. Anthony van Dyck. 8f. Jakob Jordaens.

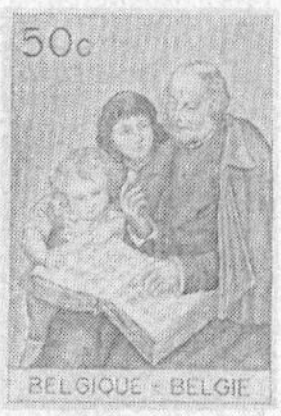

437 "Sir Rowland Hill with Young Collectors" (detail from mural by J. Van den Bussche)

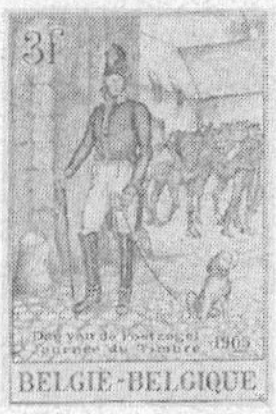

438 19th-century Postmaster

1965. "Philately for the Young".
1925 **437** 50c. green 10 10

1965. Stamp Day.
1926 **438** 3f. green 25 10

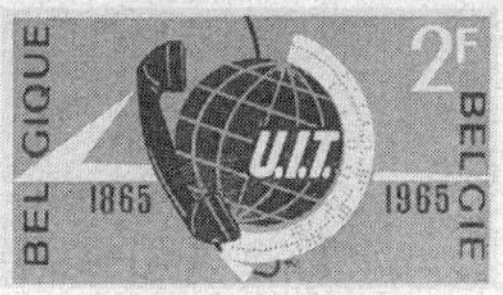

439 Globe and Telephone

1965. Centenary of I.T.U.
1928 **439** 2f. black and purple . . 15 15

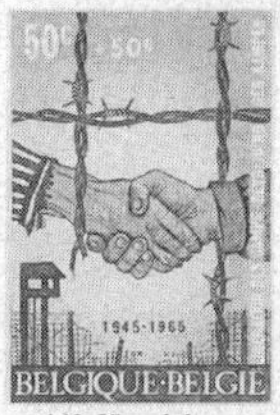

440 Handclasp

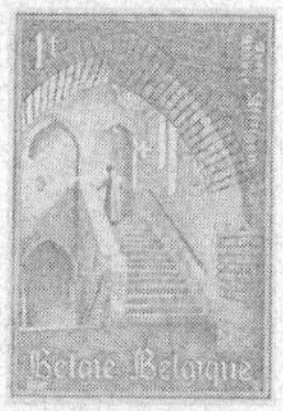

441 Abbey Staircase

1965. 20th Anniv of Liberation of Prison Camps.
1929 **440** 50c.+50c. purple, black and bistre 10 10
1930 – 1f.+50c. multicoloured 10 15
1931 – 3f.+1f.50 black, purple and green 25 25
1932 – 8f.+5f. multicoloured . . 75 75
DESIGNS—VERT: 1f. Hand reaching for barbed wire. HORIZ: 3f. Tank entering prison camp; 8f. Rose within broken wall.

1965. Affligem Abbey.
1933 **441** 1f. blue 10 10

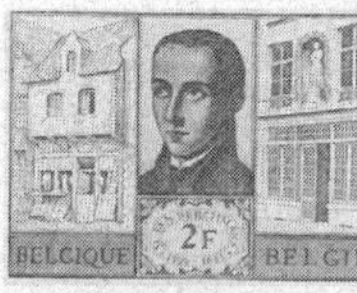

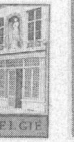

442 St. Jean Berchmans, Birthplace and Residence

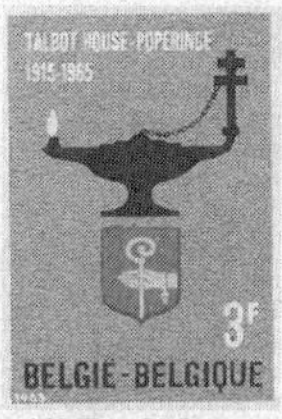

443 Toc H Lamp and Arms of Poperinge

1965. St. Jean Berchmans.
1934 **442** 2f. brown and purple . . 10 10

1965. 50th Anniv of Founding of Toc H Movement at Talbot House, Poperinge.
1935 **443** 3f. multicoloured 25 10

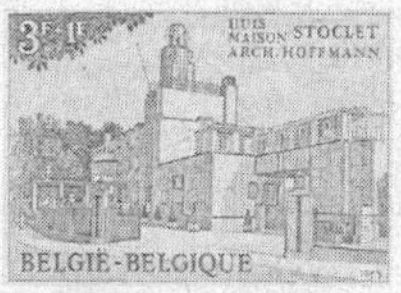

444 Maison Stoclet, Brussels

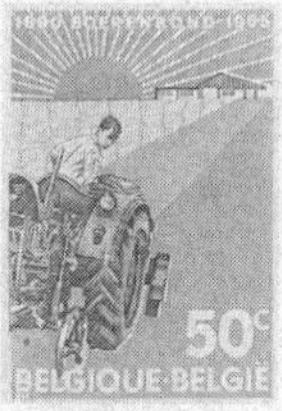

445 Tractor ploughing

1965. Josef Hoffman (architect) Commemoration.
1936 **444** 3f.+1f. grey and drab . . 25 25
1937 – 6f.+3f. brown 40 40
1938 – 8f.+4f. purple & drab . . 60 60
DESIGNS—Maison Stoclet: VERT: 6f. Entrance hall. HORIZ: 8f. Rear of building.

1965. 75th Anniv of Boerenbond (Belgian Farmers' Association). Multicoloured.
1939 50c. Type **445** 20 15
1940 3f. Horse-drawn plough . . 20 15

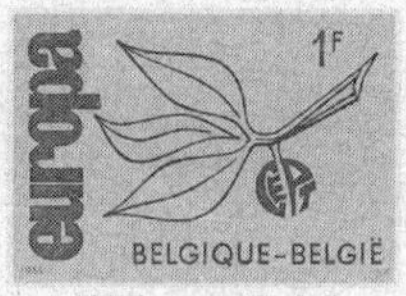

446 Europa "Sprig"

1965. Europa.
1941 **446** 1f. black and pink . . . 10 10
1942 3f. black and green . . . 10 10

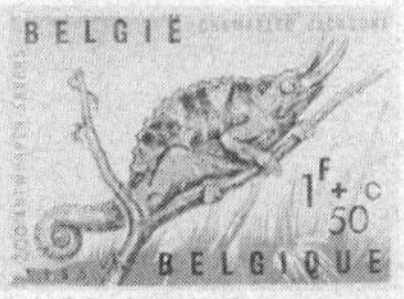

447 Jackson's Chameleon

1965. Philanthropic Funds. Reptiles of Antwerp Zoo. Multicoloured.
1943 1f.+50c. Type **447** 10 15
1944 2f.+1f. Iguana 25 20
1945 3f.+1f.50 Nile lizard 25 30
1946 6f.+3f. Komodo lizard . . . 50 45

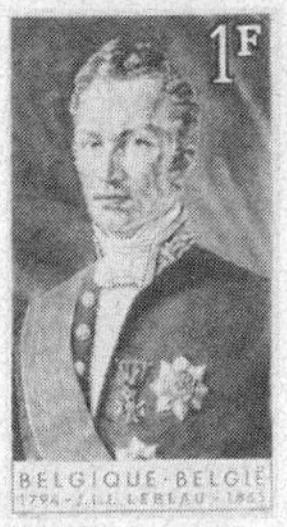

448 J. Lebeau (after A. Schollaert)

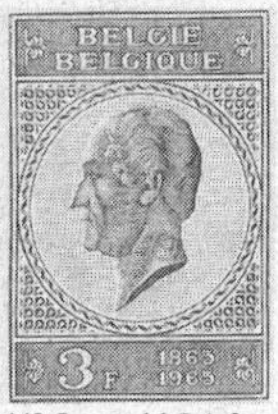

449 Leopold I (after 30c. and 1f. Stamps of 1865)

1965. Death Cent of Joseph Lebeau (statesman).
1948 **448** 1f. multicoloured 10 10

1965. Death Centenary of King Leopold I.
1949 **449** 3f. sepia 10 10
1950 – 6f. violet 35 30
DESIGN: 6f. As 3f. but with different portrait frame.

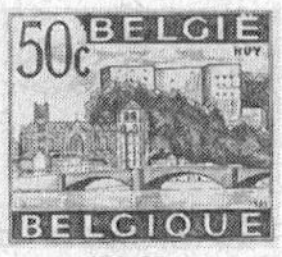

450 Huy

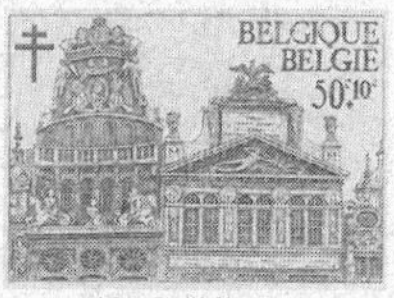

451 Guildhouse

1965. Tourist Publicity. Multicoloured.
1951 50c. Type **450** 10 10
1952 50c. Hoeilaart (vert) 10 10
See also Nos. 1995/6, 2025/6, 2083/4, 2102/3, 2123/4, 2159/60, 2240/1 and 2250/1.

1965. T.B. Relief and Other Funds. Public Buildings, Brussels.
1953 **451** 50c.+10c. blue 10 10
1954 – 1f.+40c. turquoise . . . 10 10
1955 – 2f.+1f. purple 15 20
1956 – 3f.+1f.50 violet 25 25
1957 – 10f.+4f.50 sepia and grey 60 65
BUILDINGS—HORIZ: 1f. Brewers' House; 2f. Builders' House; 3f. House of the Dukes of Brabant. VERT: (24½ × 44½ mm): 10f. Tower of Town Hall.

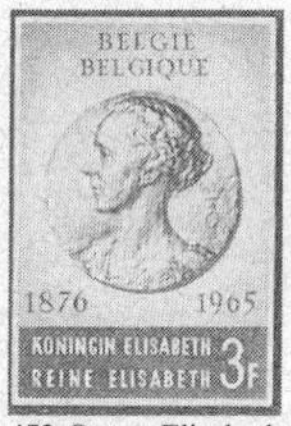

452 Queen Elisabeth (from medallion by A. Courtens)

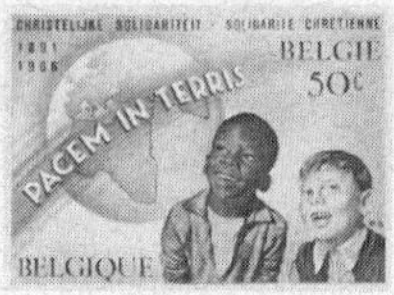

453 "Peace on Earth"

1965. Queen Elisabeth Commem.
1958 **452** 3f. black 25 10

1966. 75th Anniv of "Rerum Novarum" (papal encyclical). Multicoloured.
1959 50c. Type **453** 10 10
1960 1f. "Building for Tomorrow" (family and new building) 10 10
1961 3f. Arms of Pope Paul VI (vert 24½ × 45 mm) 10 10

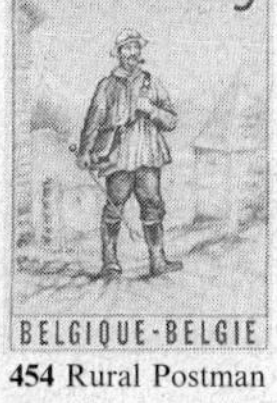

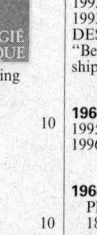

454 Rural Postman

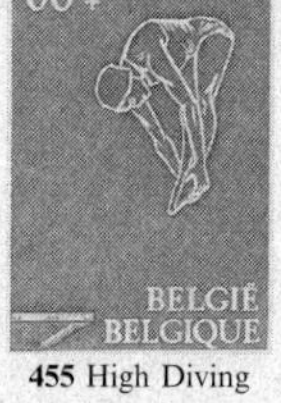

455 High Diving

1966. Stamp Day.
1964 **454** 3f. black, lilac & buff . . 25 10

1966. Swimming.
1965 **455** 60c.+40c. brown, green and blue 10 10
1966 – 10f.+4f. brown, purple and green 65 60
DESIGN: 10f. Diving from block.

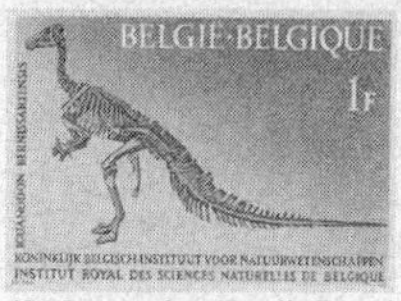

456 Iguanodon Fossil (Royal Institute of Natural Sciences)

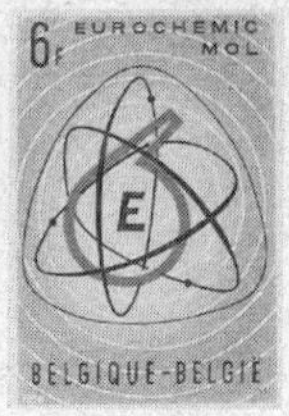

457 Eurochemic Symbol

1966. National Scientific Institutions.
1967 **456** 1f. black and green . . . 10 10
1968 – 2f. black, orge & cream 10 10
1969 – 2f. multicoloured 15 10
1970 – 3f. multicoloured 10 10
1971 – 3f. gold, black and red 10 10
1972 – 6f. multicoloured 40 20
1973 – 8f. multicoloured 45 45
DESIGNS—HORIZ: No. 1968, Kasai head (Royal Central African Museum); No. 1969, Snow crystals (Royal Meteorological Institute). VERT: No. 1970, "Scholar" (Royal Library); No. 1971, Seal (General Archives); No. 1972, Arend-Roland comet and telescope (Royal Observatory); No. 1973, Satellite and rocket (Space Aeronomy Inst.).

1966. European Chemical Plant, Mol.
1974 **457** 6f. black, red and drab 25 20

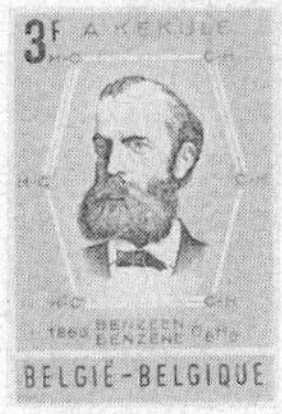

458 A. Kekule

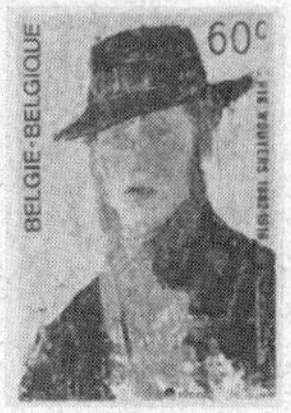

460 Rik Wouters (self-portrait)

1966. Centenary of Professor August Kekule's Benzene Formula.
1975 **458** 3f. brown, black & blue 25 10

1966. 19th World I.P.T.T. Congress, Brussels. Optd **XIXe CONGRES IPTT** and emblem.
1976 **454** 3f. black, lilac and buff 25 10

1966. 50th Death Anniv of Rik Wouters (painter).
1977 **460** 60c. multicoloured . . . 25 10

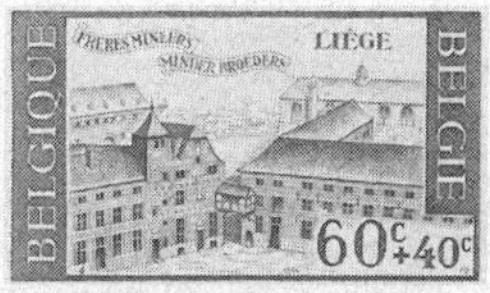

461 Minorites Convent, Liege

1966. Cultural Series.
1978 **461** 60c.+40c. purple, blue and brown 10 15
1979 – 1f.+50c. blue, purple and turquoise 10 15
1980 – 2f.+1f. red, purple and brown 10 15
1981 – 10f.+4f.50 purple, turquoise and green 70 65
DESIGNS: 1f. Val-Dieu Abbey, Aubel; 2f. Huy and town seal; 10f. Statue of Ambiorix and castle, Tongres.

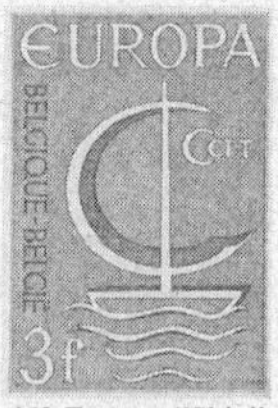

463 Europa "Ship"

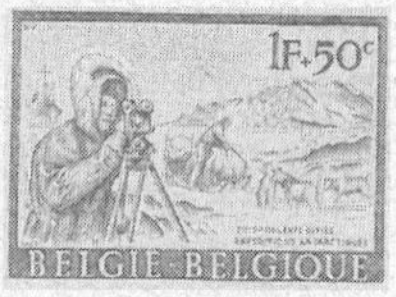

464 Surveying

1966. Europa.
1989 **463** 3f. green 10 10
1990 6f. purple 40 20

1966. Antarctic Expeditions.
1991 **464** 1f.+50c. green 10 10
1992 – 3f.+1f.50 violet 30 25
1993 – 6f.+3f. red 35 40
DESIGNS: 3f. Commander A. de Gerlache and "Belgica" (polar barque); 6f. "Magga Dan" (supply ship) and meteorological operations.

1966. Tourist Publicity. As T **450**. Multicoloured.
1995 2f. Bouillon 10 10
1996 2f. Lier (vert) 10 10

1966. 75th Anniv of Royal Federation of Belgian Philatelic Circles. Stamps similar to Nos. 1812 and 1851 but incorporating "1890 1996" and F.I.P. emblem.
1997 **391** 60c. purple and green . . 10 10
1998 **405** 3f. purple and ochre . . 10 10

466 Children with Hoops **467** Lions Emblem

1966. "Solidarity" (Child Welfare).
1999 – 1f.+1f. black & pink . . 10 10
2000 – 2f.+1f. black & green . . 25 20
2001 – 3f.+1f.50 black & lav . . 25 25
2002 **466** 6f.+3f. brown & flesh . . 35 35
2003 – 8f.+3f.50 brown & grn 45 45
DESIGNS—VERT: 1f. Boy with ball and dog; 2f. Girl with skipping-rope; 3f. Boy and girl blowing bubbles. HORIZ: 8f. Children and cat playing "Follow My Leader".

1967. Lions International.
2004 **467** 3f. sepia, blue and olive 15 10
2005 6f. sepia, violet and green 35 30

468 Part of Cleuter Pistol

1967. Arms Museum, Liege.
2006 **468** 2f. black, yellow & red 10 10

469 I.T.Y. Emblem

1967. International Tourist Year.
2007 **469** 6f. blue, red and black 35 25

471 Woodland and Trientalis (flowers), Hautes Fagnes

1967. Nature Conservation. Multicoloured.
2009 1f. Type **471** 10 10
2010 1f. Dunes and eryngium (flowers), Westhoek . . . 10 10

472 Paul-Emile Janson (statesman) **473** 19th-century Postman

1967. Janson Commemoration.
2011 **472** 10f. blue 50 35

1967. Stamp Day.
2012 **473** 3f. purple and red . . . 25 10

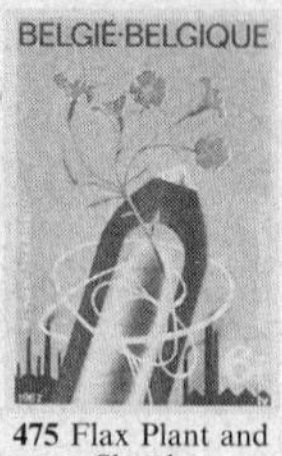

474 Cogwheels **475** Flax Plant and Shuttle

1967. Europa.
2013 **474** 3f. black, red and blue 15 15
2014 6f. black, yellow & green 40 35

1967. Belgian Linen Industry.
2015 **475** 6f. multicoloured 35 25

476 Kursaal in 19th Century

1967. 700th Anniv of Ostend's Rank as Town.
2016 **476** 2f. sepia, buff and blue 10 10

478 With F.I.T.C.E. Emblem **479** Robert Schuman (statesman)

1967. European Telecommunications Day. "Stamp Day" design of 1967 incorporating F.I.T.C.E. emblem as T **478** in green.
2021 **478** 10f. sepia and blue . . . 50 35
"F.I.T.C.E." "Federation des Ingenieurs des Telecommunications de la Communaute Europeenne."

1967. Charity.
2022 **479** 2f.+1f. green 15 15
2023 – 5f.+2f. brown, yellow and black 30 30
2024 – 10f.+5f. multicoloured 80 75
DESIGNS—HORIZ: 5f. Kongolo Memorial, Gentinnes (Congo Martyrs). VERT: 10f. "Colonial Brotherhood" emblem (Colonial Troops Memorial).

1967. Tourist Publicity. As T **450**. Mult.
2025 1f. Ypres 10 10
2026 1f. Spontin 10 10

480 "Caesar Crossing the Rubicon" (Tournai Tapestry) **481** "Jester in Pulpit" (from Erasmus's "Praise of Folly")

1967. Charles Plisnier and Lodewijk de Raet Foundations.
2028 **480** 1f. multicoloured 10 10
2029 – 1f. multicoloured 10 10
DESIGN No. 2029, "Maximilian hunting boar" (Brussels tapestry).

1967. Cultural Series. "Erasmus and His Time".
2030 1f.+50c. multicoloured . . . 10 10
2031 2f.+1f. multicoloured . . . 25 25
2032 3f.+1f.50 multicoloured . . 25 25
2033 5f.+2f. black, red & carmine 30 30
2034 6f.+3f. multicoloured . . . 35 40
DESIGNS—VERT: 1f. Type **481**. 2f. "Jester declaiming" (from Erasmus' "Praise of Folly"); 3f. Erasmus; 6f. Pierre Gilles ("Aegidius" from painting by Metzijs). HORIZ: 5f. "Sir Thomas More's Family" (Holbein).

482 "Princess Margaret of York" (from miniature) **483** Arms of Ghent University

1967. "British Week".
2035 **482** 6f. multicoloured 35 25

1967. Universities of Ghent and Liege. Mult.
2036 3f. Type **483** 15 10
2037 3f. Liege 15 10

485 Our Lady of Virga Jesse, Hasselt

1967. Christmas.
2039 **485** 1f. blue 10 10

486 "Children's Games" (section of Brueghel's painting)

1967. "Solidarity".
2040 **486** 1f.+50c. multicoloured 15 15
2041 – 2f.+50c. multicoloured 15 15
2042 – 3f.+1f. multicoloured . . 15 20
2043 – 6f.+3f. multicoloured . . 40 35
2044 – 10f.+4f. multicoloured 60 60
2045 – 13f.+6f. multicoloured 75 75
Nos. 2040/5 together form the complete painting.

487 Worker in Protective Hand **489** Army Postman (1916)

1968. Industrial Safety Campaign.
2046 **487** 3f. multicoloured 25 10

1968. Stamp Day.
2068 **489** 3f. purple, brown & blue 25 10

490 Belgian 1c. "Small Lion" Stamp of 1866 **491** Grammont and Seal of Baudouin VI

1968. Cent of State Printing Works, Malines.
2069 **490** 1f. olive 10 10

1968. "Historical Series". Multicoloured.
2070 2f. Type **491** 15 15
2071 3f. Theux-Franchimont Castle and battle emblems 15 10
2072 6f. Archaeological discoveries, Spiennes . . . 35 25
2073 10f. Roman oil lamp and town crest, Wervik . . . 50 35

492 Europa "Key" **493** Queen Elisabeth and Dr. Depage

1968. Europa.
2074 **492** 3f. gold, black & green 10 10
2075 6f. silver, black and red 40 30

1968. Belgian Red Cross Fund. Cross in red.
2076 **493** 6f.+3f. sepia, black and green 45 30
2077 – 10f.+5f. sepia, black and green 70 80
DESIGN: 10f. Queen Fabiola and baby.

494 Gymnastics **495** "Explosion"

1968. Olympic Games, Mexico. Multicoloured.
2078 1f.+50c. Type **494** 15 10
2079 2f.+1f. Weightlifting 15 10
2080 3f.+1f.50 Hurdling 25 15
2081 6f.+2f. Cycling 35 30
2082 13f.+5f. Yachting (vert 24½ × 45 mm) 75 95
Each design includes the Olympic "rings" and a Mexican cultural motif.

1968. Tourist Publicity. As Type **450**.
2083 2f. multicoloured 10 10
2084 2f. black, blue and green . . 10 10
DESIGNS: No. 2083, Farm-house and windmill, Bokrijk; No. 2084, Bath-house and fountain, Spa.

1968. Belgian Disasters. Victims Fund. Mult.
2085 10f.+5f. Type **495** 75 75
2086 12f.+5f. "Fire" 75 90
2087 13f.+5f. "Typhoon" 80 90

496 St. Laurent Abbey, Liege

1968. "National Interest".
2088 **496** 2f. black, bistre & blue 10 15
2089 – 3f. brown, grey & lt brn 25 10
2090 – 6f. black, blue & dp bl 35 25
2091 – 10f. multicoloured . . . 60 35
DESIGNS: 3f. Church, Lissewege; 6f. Canal-lock, Zandvliet; 10f. Canal-lift, Ronquieres.

497 Undulate Triggerfish

1968. "Solidarity" and 125th Anniv of Antwerp Zoo. Designs showing fish. Multicoloured.
2092 1f.+50c. Type **497** 15 25
2093 3f.+1f.50 Ear-spotted angelfish 25 25
2094 6f.+3f. Lionfish 40 40
2095 10f.+5f. Diagonal butterflyfish 60 65

498 King Albert in Bruges (October, 1918) **499** Lighted Candle

1968. Patriotic Funds.
2096 **498** 1f.+50c. multicoloured 10 15
2097 – 3f.+1f.50 mult 15 25
2098 – 6f.+3f. multicoloured . . 30 40
2099 – 10f.+5f. multicoloured 90 70
DESIGNS—HORIZ: 3f. King Albert entering Brussels (November, 1918); 6f. King Albert in Liege (November, 1918). LARGER (46 × 35 mm): 10f. Tomb of the Unknown Soldier, Brussels.

1968. Christmas.
2100 **499** 1f. multicoloured 10 10

500 "Mineral Searching" (ore carrier) in
Ghent Canal

1968. Ghent Maritime Canal.
2101 500 6f. black brown, & blue   35   25

1969. Tourist Publicity. As Type **450.**
2102   1f. black, blue & pur (vert)   10   10
2103   1f. black, olive and blue   10   10
DESIGNS: No. 2102, Town Hall, Louvain; No. 2103,
Valley of the Ourthe.

501 "Albert Magnis" (detail of wood
carving by Quellin, Confessional, St.
Paul's Church, Antwerp)

1969. St. Paul's Church, Antwerp, and Aulne Abbey
Commemoration.
2104 501 2f. sepia   10   10
2105   – 3f. black and mauve   10   10
DESIGN: 3f. Aulne Abbey.

502 "The Travellers"   503 Broodjes Chapel,
(sculpture,   Antwerp
Archaeological
Museum, Arlon)

1969. 2,000th Anniv of Arlon.
2106 502 2f. purple   15   20

1969. "150 Years of Public Education in Antwerp".
2107 503 3f. black and grey   25   10

504 Mail Train   505 Colonnade

1969. Stamp Day.
2108 504 3f. multicoloured   15   10

1969. Europa.
2109 505 3f. multicoloured   15   15
2110   6f. multicoloured   35   35

507 NATO Emblem   508 "The Builders"
                   (F. Leger)

1969. 20th Anniv of NATO.
2112 507 6f. blue and brown   35   35

1969. 50th Anniv of I.L.O.
2113 508 3f. multicoloured   25   15

509 "Houses"   510 Racing Cyclist
(I. Dimitrova)

1969. U.N.I.C.E.F. "Philanthropy" Funds. Mult.
2114   1f.+50c. Type **509**   10   15
2115   3f.+1f.50 "My Art"
     (C. Patric)   25   20
2116   6f.+3f. "In the Sun"
     (H. Rejchlova)   35   30
2117   10f.+5f. "Out for a Walk"
     (P. Sporn) (horiz)   65   80

1969. World Championship Cycle Races, Zolder.
2118 510 6f. multicoloured   35   25

511 Mgr. V.   512 National Colours
Scheppers

1969. Monseigneur Victor Scheppers (founder of
"Brothers of Mechlin") Commemoration.
2119 511 6f.+3f. purple   45   45

1969. 25th Anniv of BENELUX Customs Union.
2120 512 3f. multicoloured   25   10

513 Pascali Rose and Annevoie
Gardens

1969. Flowers and Gardens. Multicoloured.
2121   2f. Type **513**   10   10
2122   2f. Begonia and Lochristi
     Gardens   10   10

1969. Tourist Publicity. As Type **450.**
2123   2f. brown, red and blue   10   10
2124   2f. black, green and blue   10   10
DESIGNS: No. 2123, Veurne Furnes; No. 2124,
Vielsalm.

514 "Feats of Arms"   516 Wounded Soldier
from "History of
Alexander the Great"
(Tournai, 15th
century)

1969. "Cultural Works" Tapestries. Mult.
2125   1f.+50c. Type **514**   10   15
2126   3f.+1f.50 "The Violinist"
     from "Festival" (David
     Teniers II, Oudenarde,
     c. 1700)   15   20
2127   10f.+4f. "The Paralytic",
     from "The Acts of the
     Apostles" (Brussels,
     c. 1517)   75   70

515 Astronauts and Location of Moon
Landing

1969. 1st Man on the Moon.
2128 515 6f. sepia   35   35

1969. 50th Anniv of National War Invalids Works
(O.N.I.G.).
2130 516 1f. green   10   10

517 "The Postman"   519 Count H. Carton
de Wiart (from
painting by G. Geleyn)

518 John F. Kennedy Motorway
Tunnel, Antwerp

1969. "Philately for the Young".
2131 517 1f. multicoloured   10   10

1969. Completion of Belgian Road-works. Mult.
2132   3f. Type **518**   30   10
2133   6f. Loncin flyover, Wallonie
     motorway   25   30

1969. Birth Centenary of Count Henry Carton de
Wiart (statesman).
2134 519 6f. sepia   10   20

520 "Barbu d'Anvers" (Cockerel)

1969. "The Poultry-yard" (poultry-breeding).
2135 520 10f.+5f. multicoloured   90   85

521 "Le Denombrement de
Bethleem" (detail, Brueghel)

1969. Christmas.
2136 521 1f.50 multicoloured   10   10

522 Emblem, "Coin" and   523 Window, St.
Machinery   Waudru Church,
                  Mons

1969. 50th Anniv of National Credit Society
(S.N.C.I.).
2137 522 3f.50 brown and blue   25   10

1969. "Solidarity". Musicians in Stained-glass
Windows. Multicoloured.
2138   1f.50+50c. Type **523**   25   15
2139   3f.50+1f.50 's-Hereneldren
     Church   35   20
2140   7f.+3f. St. Jacques Church,
     Liege   50   50
2141   9f.+4f. Royal Museum of
     Art and History, Brussels   95   90
No. 2141 is larger, 36 × 52 mm.

524 Camellias   525 Beech Tree in
National Botanical
Gardens

1970. Ghent Flower Show. Multicoloured.
2142   1f.50 Type **524**   10   10
2143   2f.50 Water-lily   20   15
2144   3f.50 Azaleas   20   10

1970. Nature Conservation Year. Multicoloured.
2146   3f.50 Type **525**   25   10
2147   7f. Birch   30   30

526 Young "Postman"

1970. "Philately for the Young".
2148 526 1f.50 multicoloured   10   10

527 New U.P.U. Headquarters
Building

1970. New U.P.U. Headquarters Building.
2149 527 3f.50 green   25   10

528 "Flaming Sun"

1970. Europa.
2150 528 3f.50 cream, blk & lake   15   10
2151   7f. flesh, black and blue   35   30

529 Open-air Museum,   530 Clock-tower,
Bokrijk   Virton

1970. Cultural Works. Multicoloured.
2152   1f.50+50c. Type **529**   25   25
2153   3f.50+1f.50 Relay Post-
     house, Courcelles   30   30
2154   7f.+3f. "The Reaper of
     Trevires" (bas-relief,
     Virton)   40   45
2155   9f.+4f. Open-air Museum,
     Middelheim, (Antwerp)   45   45

1970. Historic Towns of Virton and Zelzate.
2156 530 2f.50 violet and ochre   10   15
2157   – 2f.50 black and blue   25   15
DESIGN—HORIZ: No. 2157, Canal bridge, Zelzate.

531 Co-operative Alliance Emblem

1970. 75th Anniv of Int Co-operative Alliance.
2158 531 7f. black and orange   35   25

1970. Tourist Publicity, As Type **450.**
2159   1f.50 green, blue and black   10   10
2160   1f.50 buff, blue & deep blue   10   10
DESIGNS—HORIZ: No. 2159, Kasterlee. VERT:
No. 2160, Nivelles.

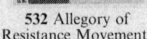

532 Allegory of Resistance Movements

533 King Baudouin

1970. 25th Anniv of Prisoner of War and Concentration Camps Liberation.
2161 **532** 3f.50+1f.50 black, red and green 35 35
2162 — 7f.+3f. black, red and mauve 50 50
DESIGN: 7f. Similar to Type **532**, but inscr "LIBERATION DES CAMPS", etc.

1970. King Baudouin's 40th Birthday.
2163 **533** 3f.50 brown 25 15
See also Nos. 2207/23c and 2335/9b.

534 Fair Emblem

535 U.N. Headquarters, New York

1970. 25th International Ghent Fair.
2164 **534** 1f.50 multicoloured . . . 10 10

1970. 25th Anniv of United Nations.
2165 **535** 7f. blue and black . . . 40 25

536 Queen Fabiola

537 Angler's Rod and Reel

1970. Queen Fabiola Foundation.
2166 **536** 3f.50 black and blue . . . 25 10

1970. Sports. Multicoloured.
2167 3f.50+1f.50 Type **537** . . . 25 30
2168 9f.+4f. Hockey stick and ball 65 60

539 "The Mason" (sculpture by G. Minne)

541 "Madonna and Child" (Jan Gossaert)

540 Man, Woman and Hillside Town

1970. 50th Anniv of National Housing Society.
2170 **539** 3f.50 brown & yell . . . 25 10

1970. 25th Anniv of Belgian Social Security.
2171 **540** 2f.50 multicoloured . . . 15 15

1970. Christmas.
2172 **541** 1f.50 brown 10 10

542 C. Huysmans (statesman)

543 Arms of Eupen, Malmedy and St. Vith

1970. Cultural Works. Famous Belgians.
2173 **542** 1f.50+50c. brown and red 15 15
2174 — 3f.50+1f.50 brown and purple 15 20
2175 — 7f.+3f. brown & green 40 40
2176 — 9f.+4f. brown & blue 60 60
PORTRAITS: 3f.50, Cardinal J. Cardijn. 7f. Maria Baers (Catholic social worker). 9f. P. Pastur (social reformer).

1970. 50th Anniv of Annexation of Eupen, Malmedy and St. Vith.
2177 **543** 7f. brown and sepia . . . 40 25

544 "The Uneasy Town" (detail, Paul Delvaux)

545 Telephone

1970. "Solidarity". Paintings. Multicoloured.
2178 3f.50+1f.50 Type **544** 35 35
2179 7f.+3f. "The Memory" (Rene Magritte) 50 65

1971. Inaug of Automatic Telephone Service.
2183 **545** 1f.50 multicoloured . . . 10 10

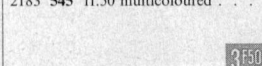

546 "Auto" Car

547 Touring Club Badge

1971. 50th Brussels Motor Show.
2184 **546** 2f.50 black and red . . . 15 10

1971. 75th Anniv of Royal Touring Club of Belgium.
2185 **547** 3f.50 gold, red & blue . . . 25 10

548 Tournai Cathedral

549 "The Letter-box" (T. Lobrichon)

1971. 800th Anniv of Tournai Cathedral.
2186 **548** 7f. blue 40 35

1971. "Philately for the Young".
2187 **549** 1f.50 brown 10 10

550 Notre-Dame Abbey, Marche-les-Dames

1971. Cultural Works.
2190 **550** 3f.50+1f.50 black, green and brown 35 30
2191 — 7f.+3f. black, red and yellow 60 45
DESIGN: 7f. Convent, Turnhout.

552 King Albert I, Jules Destree and Academy

1971. 50th Anniv of Royal Academy of French Language and Literature.
2201 **552** 7f. black and grey . . . 40 35

553 Postman of 1855 (from lithograph, J. Thiriar)

554 Europa Chain

1971. Stamp Day.
2202 **553** 3f.50 multicoloured . . . 10 10

1971. Europa.
2203 **554** 3f.50 brown and black . . . 15 10
2204 — 7f. green and black . . . 30 10

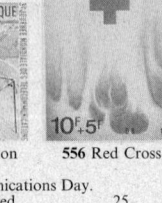

555 Satellite Earth Station

556 Red Cross

1971. World Telecommunications Day.
2205 **555** 7f. multicoloured 25 20

1971. Belgian Red Cross.
2206 **556** 10f.+5f. red & black . . 75 75

1971. As T **533**, but without dates.
2207 1f.75 green 15 20
2208 2f.25 green 15 20
2208a 2f.50 green 10 10
2209 3f. green 15 10
2209a 3f.25 plum 20 10
2210 3f.50 brown 30 10
2211 4f. blue 25 10
2212 4f.50 purple 25 10
2212a 4f.50 blue 25 10
2213 5f. violet 25 10
2214 6f. red 35 10
2214b 6f.50 violet 35 10
2215 7f. red 35 10
2215b 7f.50 mauve 40 10
2216a 8f. black 45 10
2217 9f. sepia 50 20
2217a 9f. brown 45 10
2218a 10f. mauve 50 10
2218b 11f. sepia 50 20
2219 12f. blue 70 10
2219b 13f. blue 70 10
2219c 14f. green 75 10
2220 15f. violet 75 10
2220b 16f. green 75 10
2220c 17f. purple 90 10
2221 18f. blue . . . . . 1·00 25
2221a 18f. turquoise 95 20
2222a 20f. blue . . . . . 1·00 10
2222b 22f. black . . . . . 1·10 1·00
2222c 22f. turquoise . . . . 1·10 25
2222d 25f. purple . . . . 1·25 10
2223a 30f. orange . . . . 1·25 10
2223b 35f. turquoise . . . . 1·90 25
2223c 40f. blue . . . . . 1·90 20
2223d 45f. brown . . . . 2·40 35
See also Nos. 2335/9.

557 Scientist, Adelie Penguins and "Erika Dan"

1971. 10th Anniv of Antarctic Treaty.
2230 **557** 10f. multicoloured . . . 60 45

558 "The Discus thrower" and Munich Cathedral

559 G. Hubin (statesman)

1971. Olympic Games, Munich (1972) Publicity.
2231 **558** 7f.+3f. black & blue . . . 60 50

1971. Georges Hubin Commemoration.
2232 **559** 1f.50 violet and black . . . 10 10

560 Notre-Dame Abbey, Orval

561 Processional Giants, Ath

1971. 900th Anniv of Notre-Dame Abbey, Orval.
2233 **560** 2f.50 brown 10 10

1971. Historic Towns.
2234 **561** 2f.50 multicoloured . . . 10 10
2235 — 2f.50 brown 10 10
DESIGN—HORIZ: (46×35 mm): No. 2235, View of Ghent.

562 Test-tubes and Diagram

1971. 50th Anniv of Discovery of Insulin.
2236 **562** 10f. multicoloured . . . 60 35

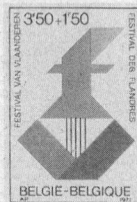

563 Flemish Festival Emblem

1971. Cultural Works. Festivals. Multicoloured.
2237 3f.50+1f.50 Type **563** . . . 10 25
2238 7f.+3f. Walloon Festival emblem 30 45

564 Belgian Family and "50"

565 Dr. Jules Bordet (medical scientist)

1971. 50th Anniv of "League of Large Families".
2239 **564** 1f.50 multicoloured . . . 10 10

1971. Tourist Publicity. Designs similar to T **450**.
2240 2f.50 black, brown and blue 15 10
2241 2f.50 black, brown and blue 15 10
DESIGNS: No. 2240, St. Martin's Church, Alost; No. 2241, Town Hall and belfry, Mons.

1971. Belgian Celebrities.
2242 **565** 3f.50 green 30 10
2243 — 3f.50 brown 30 10
DESIGN: No. 2242, Type **565** (10th death anniv); No. 2243, "Stijn Streuvels" (Frank Lateur, writer, birth cent.).

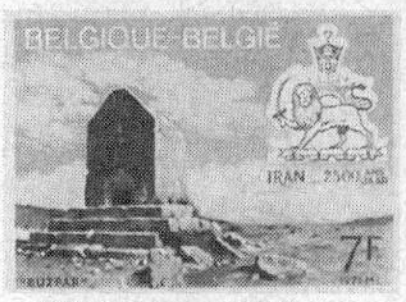
566 Achaemenid Tomb, Buzpar

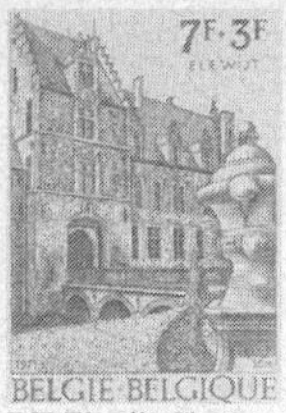
567 Elewijt Chateau

1971. 2500th Anniv of Persian Empire.
2244 **566** 7f. multicoloured 35 30

1971. "Belgica 72" Stamp Exhibition, Brussels (2nd issue).
2245 – 3f.50+1f.50 green 25 30
2246 **567** 7f.+3f. brown 35 40
2247 – 10f.+5f. blue 50 60
DESIGNS—HORIZ: (52×35½ mm): 3f. Attre Chateau; 10f. Royal Palace, Brussels.

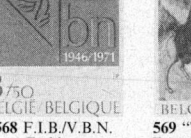

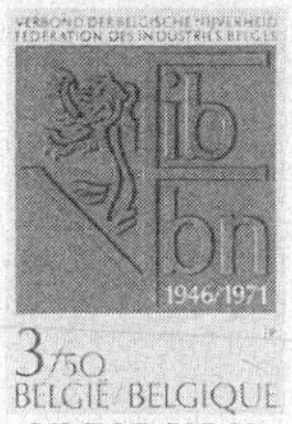
568 F.I.B./V.B.N. Emblem

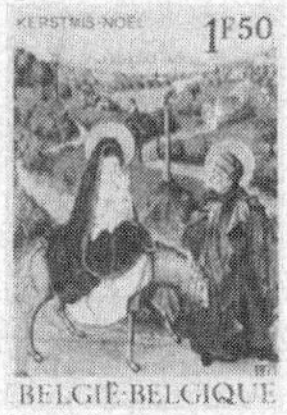
569 "The Flight into Egypt" (15th-century Dutch School)

1971. 25th Anniv of Federation of Belgian Industries.
2248 **568** 3f.50 gold, black & blue 10 10

1971. Christmas.
2249 **569** 1f.50 multicoloured . . . 10 10

1971. Tourist Publicity. Designs similar to T **450**.
2250 1f.50 blue and buff 10 10
2251 2f.50 blue and buff 10 10
DESIGNS—HORIZ: 1f.50, Town Hall, Malines. VERT: 2f.50, Basilica, St. Hubert.

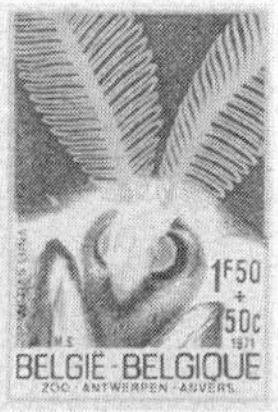
570 Luna Moth

1971. "Solidarity". Insects in Antwerp Zoo. Multicoloured.
2252 1f.50+50c. Type **570** 25 25
2253 3f.50+1f.50 "Tabanus bromius" (horse fly) (horiz) 30 30
2254 7f.+3f. "Polistes gallicus" (wasp) (horiz) 55 45
2255 9f.+4f. Green tiger beetle . . 65 65

572 Road Signs and Traffic Signals

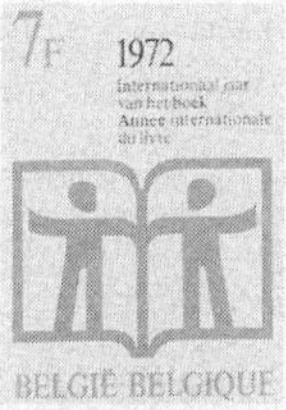
573 Book Year Emblem

1972. 20th Anniv of "Via Secura" Road Safety Organization.
2263 **572** 3f.50 multicoloured . . . 10 10

1972. International Book Year.
2264 **573** 7f. blue, brown & black 25 25

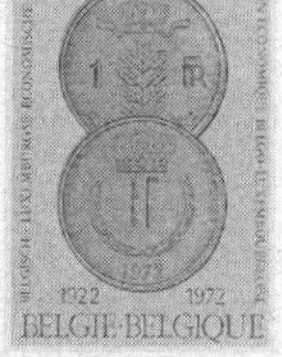
574 Coins of Belgium and Luxembourg

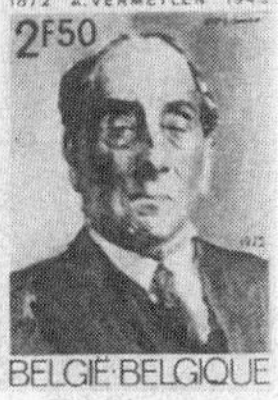
576 "Auguste Vermeylen" (I. Opsomer)

1972. 50th Anniv of Belgo–Luxembourgeoise Economic Union.
2265 **574** 1f.50 silver, black and orange 10 10

1972. Birth Centenary of Auguste Vemeylen (writer).
2267 **576** 2f.50 multicoloured . . . 10 20

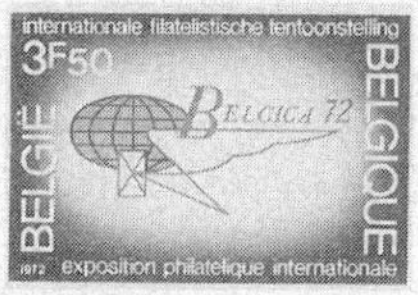
577 "Belgica 72" Emblem

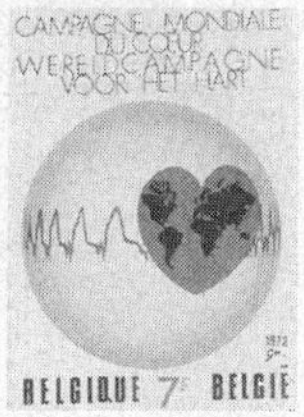
578 Heart Emblem

1972. "Belgica 72" Stamp Exn., Brussels (3rd Issue).
2268 **577** 3f.50 purple, blue & brn 10 10

1972. World Heart Month.
2269 **578** 7f. multicoloured 15 20

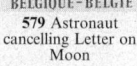

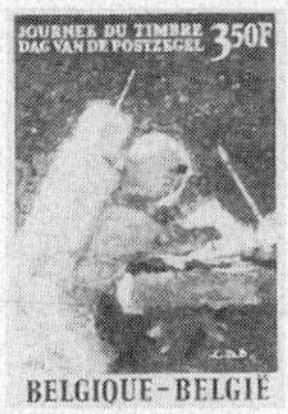
579 Astronaut cancelling Letter on Moon

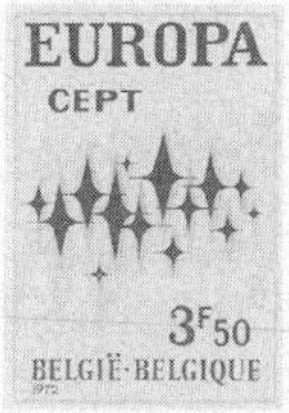
580 "Communications"

1972. Stamp Day.
2270 **579** 3f.50 multicoloured . . . 15 10

1972. Europa.
2271 **580** 3f.50 multicoloured . . . 10 10
2272 7f. multicoloured 30 35

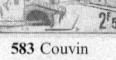

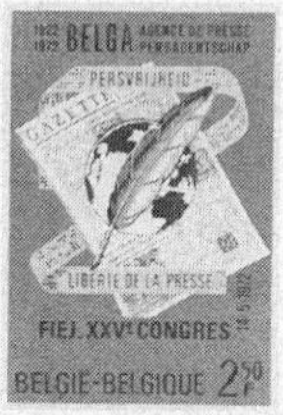
581 Quill Pen and Newspaper

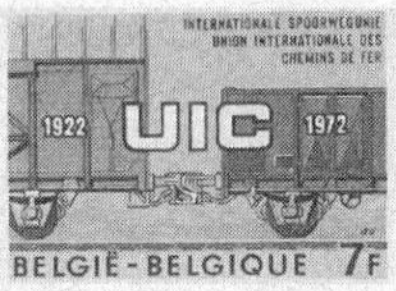
582 "UIC" on Coupled Wagons

1972. "Liberty of the Press". 50th Anniv of Belga News Agency and 25th Congress of International Federation of Newspaper Editors (F.I.E.J.).
2273 **581** 2f.50 multicoloured . . . 10 10

1972. 50th Anniv of Int Railways Union (U.I.C.).
2274 **582** 7f. multicoloured 25 20
See also No. P2266.

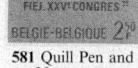

583 Couvin

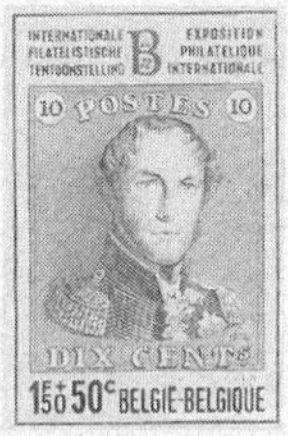
584 Leopold I 10c. "Epaulettes" Stamp of 1849

1972. Tourist Publicity.
2275 **583** 2f.50 purple, blue & grn 10 20
2276 – 2f.50 brown and blue . . 10 20
DESIGN—VERT: No. 2276, Aldeneik Church, Maaseik.

1972. "Belgica 72" Stamp Exn, Brussels (4th issue).
2277 **584** 1f.50+50c. brown, black and gold 25 20
2278 – 2f.+1f. red, brown and gold 25 25
2279 – 2f.50+1f. red, brown and gold 25 25
2280 – 3f.50+1f.50 lilac, black and gold 30 30
2281 – 6f.+3f. violet, black and gold 40 45
2282 – 7f.+3f. red, black and gold 50 55
2283 – 10f.+5f. blue, black and gold 75 70
2284 – 15f.+7f.50 green, turquoise and gold . . 65 90
2285 – 20f.+10f. chestnut, brown and gold . . . 1·60 1·50
DESIGNS: 2f. Leopold I 40c. "Medallion" of 1849; 2f.50, Leopold II 10c. of 1883. 3f.50, Leopold II 50c. of 1883; 6f. Albert I; 2f. "Tin Hat" of 1919; 7f. Albert I 50f. of 1929; 10f. Albert I 1f.75 of 1931; 15f. Leopold III 5f. of 1936; 20f. Baudouin 3f.50 of 1970.

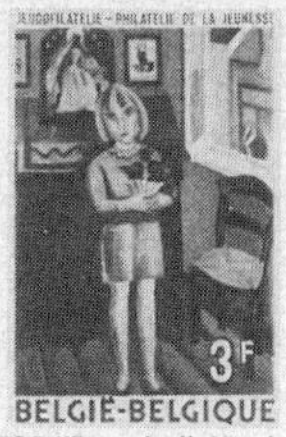
585 "Beatrice" (G. de Smet)

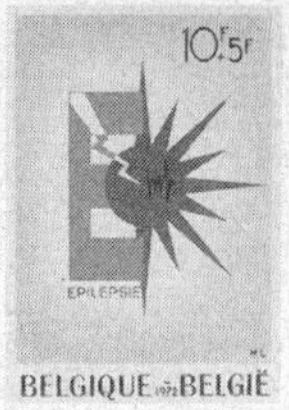
586 Emblem of Centre

1972. "Philately for the Young".
2287 **585** 3f. multicoloured 10 20

1972. Inauguration of William Lennox Epileptic Centre, Ottignies.
2288 **586** 10f.+5f. multicoloured 75 75

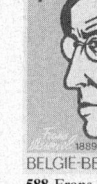

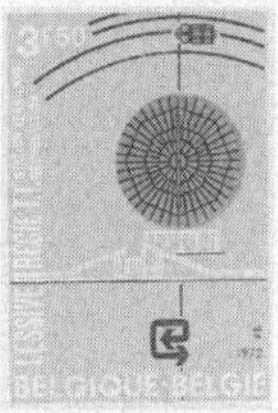
587 Dish Aerial and "Intelstat 4" Satellite

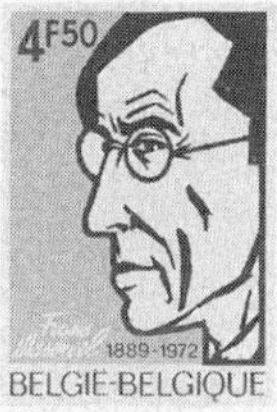
588 Frans Masereel (wood-carver and painter)

1972. Inaug of Satellite Earth Station, Lessive.
2289 **587** 3f.50 black, silver & bl 10 10

1972. Masereel Commem.
2290 **588** 4f.50 black and green . . 10 10

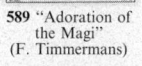

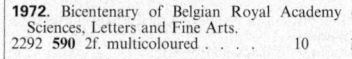

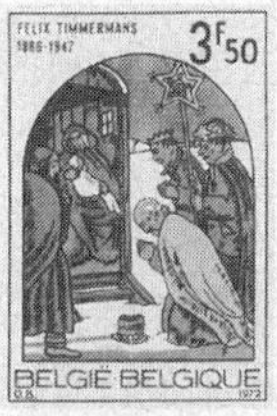
589 "Adoration of the Magi" (F. Timmermans)

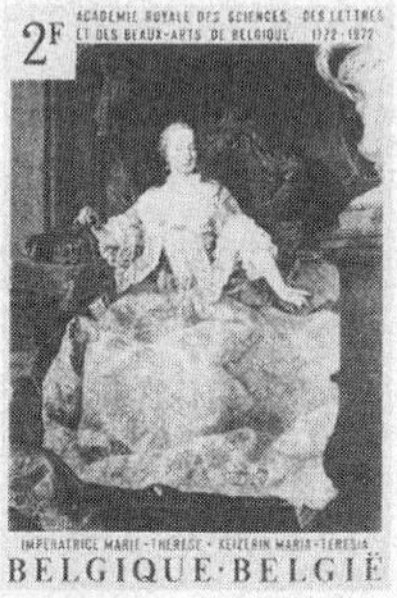
590 "Empress Maria Theresa" (unknown artist)

1972. Christmas.
2291 **589** 3f.50 multicoloured . . . 10 10

1972. Bicentenary of Belgian Royal Academy of Sciences, Letters and Fine Arts.
2292 **590** 2f. multicoloured 10 10

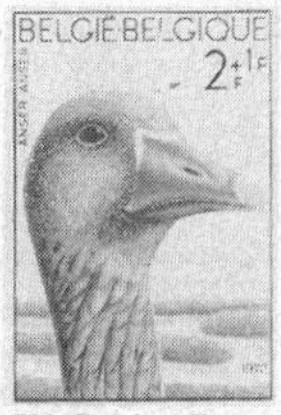
591 Greylag Goose

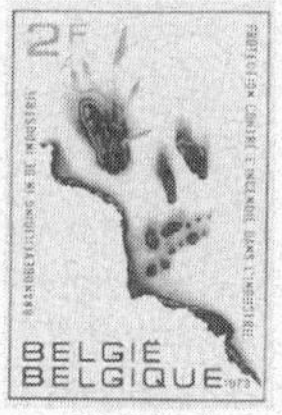
592 "Fire"

1972. "Solidarity". Birds from Zwin Nature Reserve. Multicoloured.
2293 2f.+1f. Type **591** 25 25
2294 4f.50+2f. Northern lapwing 40 35
2295 8f.+4f. White stork 55 60
2296 9f.+4f.50 Common kestrel (horiz) 90 75

1973. Industrial Buildings Fire Protection Campaign.
2297 **592** 2f. multicoloured 10 10

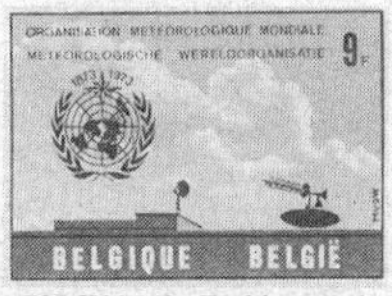
593 W.M.O. Emblem and Meteorological Equipment

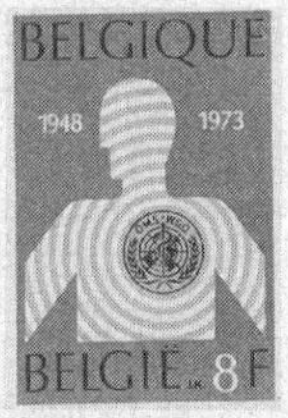
595 W.H.O. Emblem as Man's "Heart"

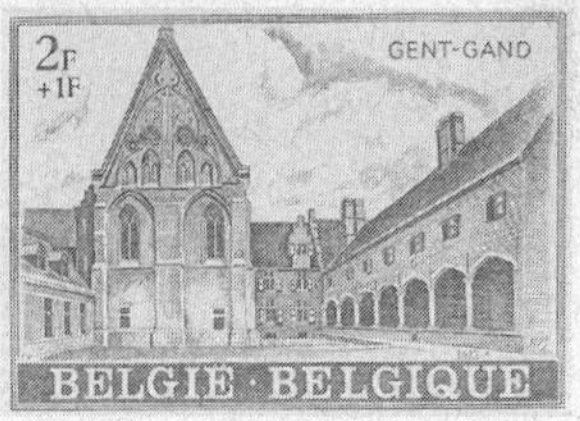
594 Bijloke Abbey and Museum, Ghent

1973. Centenary of World Meteorological Organization.
2298 **593** 9f. multicoloured 30 25

1973. Cultural Works. Religious Buildings.
2299 **594** 2f.+1f. green 25 25
2300 – 4f.50+2f. brown 35 30
2301 – 8f.+4f. red 50 55
2302 – 9f.+4f.50 blue 65 60
DESIGNS: 4f.50, Collegiate Church of St. Ursmer, Lobbes; 8f. Park Abbey, Heverlee; 9f. Floreffe Abbey.

1973. 25th Anniv of W.H.O.
2303 **595** 8f. black, yellow & red 25 20

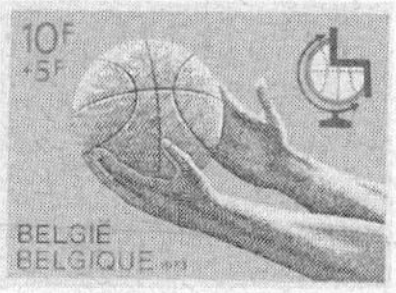
596 Ball in Hands

1973. 1st World Basketball Championships for the Handicapped, Bruges.
2304 **596** 10f.+5f. multicoloured 75 75

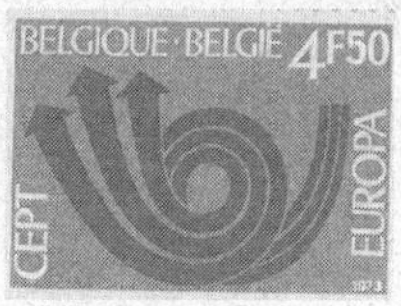
597 Europa "Posthorn"

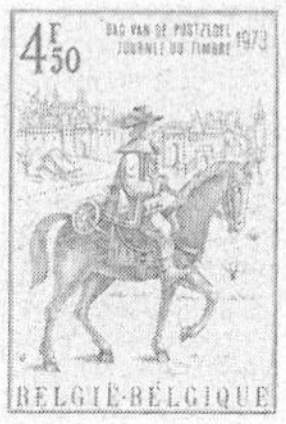
598 Thurn and Taxis Courier (17th-cent.)

1973. Europa.
2305 **597** 4f.50 blue, yellow & brn 15 10
2306 8f. blue, yellow & green 45 35

1973. Stamp Day.
2307 **598** 4f.50 brown and red . . 25 10

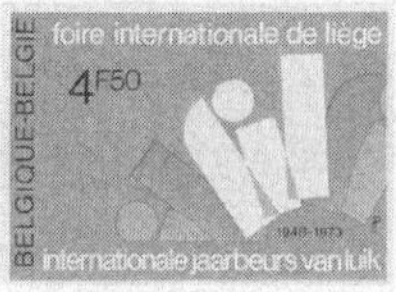
599 Fair Emblem

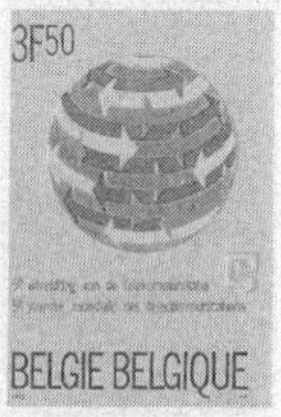
600 Arrows encircling Globe

1973. 25th International Fair, Liege.
2308 **599** 4f.50 multicoloured . . . 25 10

1973. 5th World Telecommunications Day.
2309 **600** 3f.50 multicoloured . . . 25 10

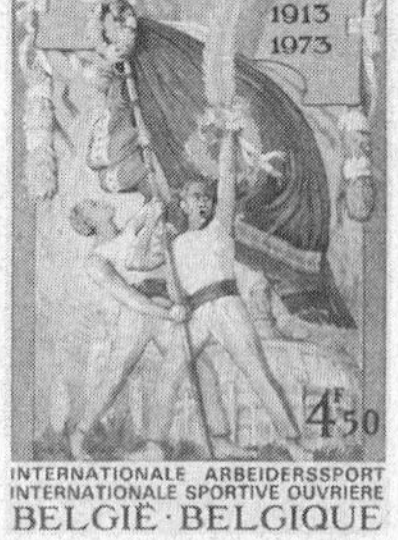
601 "Sport" (poster for Ghent Exhibition, 1913)

1973. 60th Anniv of Workers' International Sports Organization.
2310 **601** 4f.50 multicoloured . . . 25 10

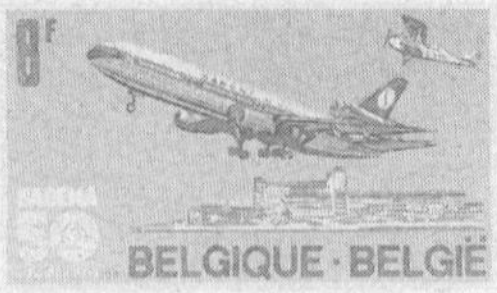

602 Douglas DC-10-30CF and De Havilland D.H.9

1973. 50th Anniv of SABENA.
2311 **602** 8f. black, blue and grey . . . 35 30

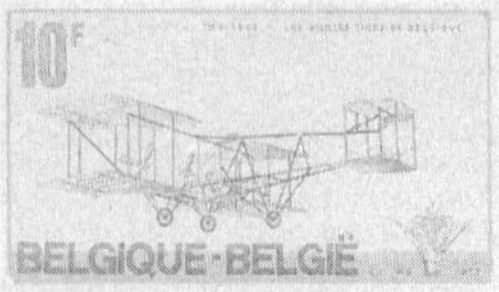

603 Ernest Tips's Biplane, 1908

1973. 35th Anniv (1972) of "Les Vieilles Tiges de Belgique" (pioneer aviators' association).
2312 **603** 10f. black, blue & green . . . 60 35

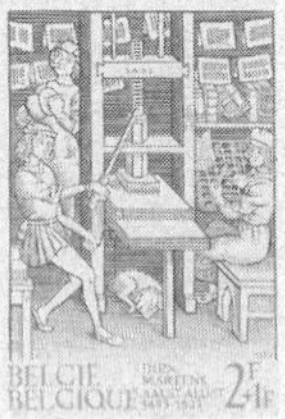

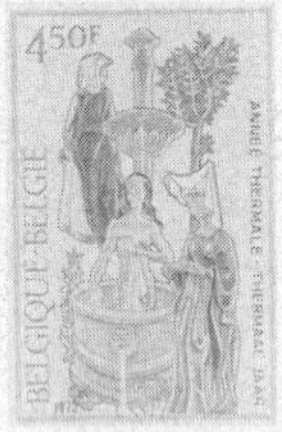

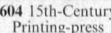

604 15th-Century Printing-press **605** "Woman Bathing" (fresco by Lemaire)

1973. Historical Events and Anniversaries.
2313 **604** 2f.+1f. blk, brn & red . . 10 20
2314 – 3f.50+1f.50 mult 10 25
2315 – 4f.50+2f. mult 15 30
2316 – 8f.+4f. multicoloured . . 65 60
2317 – 9f.+4f.50 mult 65 70
2318 – 10f.+5f. multicoloured . 1·00 1·10
DESIGNS—VERT (As Type **604**): 2f. (500th anniv of first Belgian printed book, produced by Dirk Martens); 3f.50, Head of Amon (Queen Elisabeth Egyptological Foundation. 50th anniv.); 4f.50, "Portrait of a Young Girl" (Petrus Christus, 500th death anniv). HORIZ (36 × 25 mm): 8f. Gold coins of Hadrian and Marcus Aurelius (Discovery of Roman treasure at Luttre-Liberchies); (52 × 35 mm); 9f. "Members of the Great Council" (Coessaert) (Great Council of Malines, 500th anniv.). 10f. "Jong Jacob" (East Indiaman) (Ostend Merchant Company, 250th anniv).

1973. Thermal Treatment Year.
2319 **605** 4f.50 multicoloured . . . 30 10

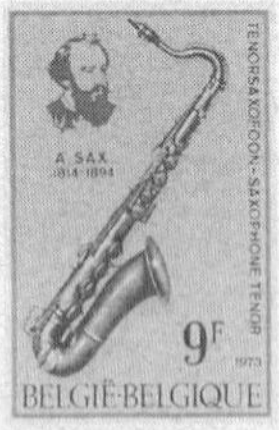

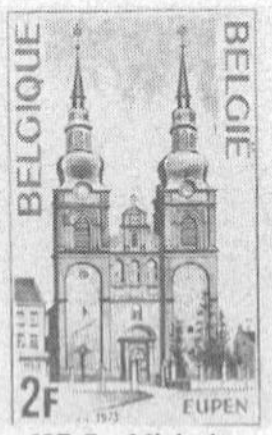

606 Adolphe Sax and Tenor Saxophone **607** St. Nicholas Church, Eupen

1973. Belgian Musical Instrument Industry.
2320 **606** 9f. multicoloured 30 30

1973. Tourist Publicity.
2321 **607** 2f. multicoloured 10 20
See also Nos. 2328/9, 2368/70, 2394/5, 2452/5, 2508/11, 2535/8, 2573/6, 2595/6 and 2614.

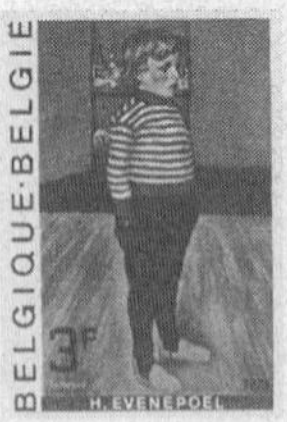

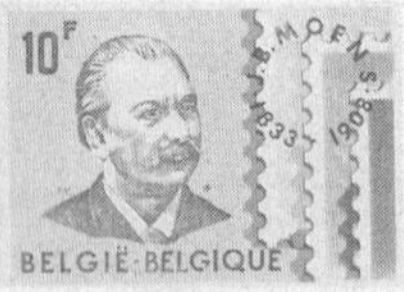

608 "Little Charles" (Evenepoel) **609** J. B. Moens (philatelist) and Perforations

1973. "Philately for the Young".
2322 **608** 3f. multicoloured 25 20

1973. 50th Anniv of Belgian Stamp Dealers Association.
2323 **609** 10f. multicoloured . . . 50 35

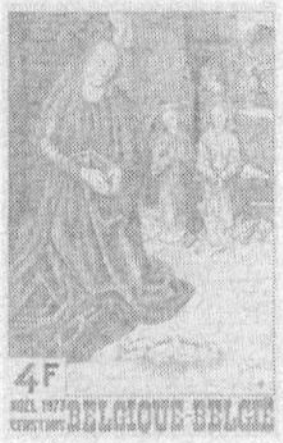

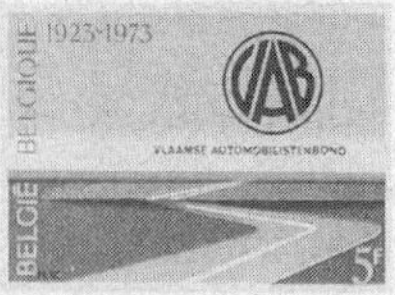

610 "Adoration of the Shepherds" (H. van der Goes) **611** Motorway and Emblem

1973. Christmas.
2324 **610** 4f. blue 30 20

1973. 50th Anniv of "Vlaamse Automobilisten-bond" (VAB) (motoring organization).
2325 **611** 5f. multicoloured 30 10

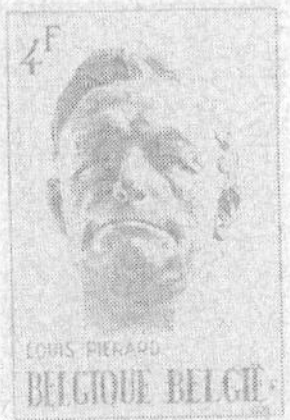

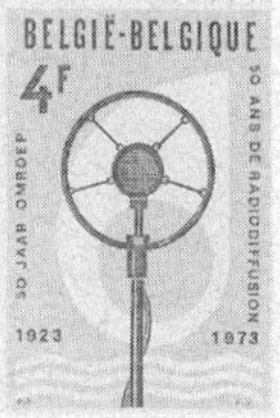

612 L. Pierard (after sculpture by Ianchelevici) **613** Early Microphone

1973. 21st Death Anniv of Louis Pierard (politician and writer).
2326 **612** 4f. red and cream . . . 25 15

1973. 50th Anniv of Belgium Radio.
2327 **613** 4f. black and blue . . . 25 20

1973. Tourist Publicity. As T **607**.
2328 3f. grey, brown and blue . . 25 10
2329 4f. grey and green 30 25
DESIGNS—HORIZ: 3f. Town Hall, Leau; 4f. Chimay Castle.

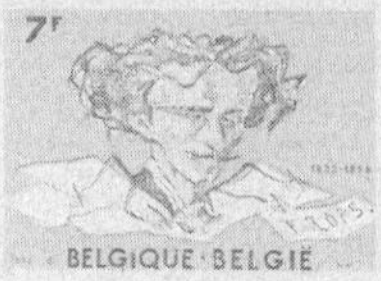

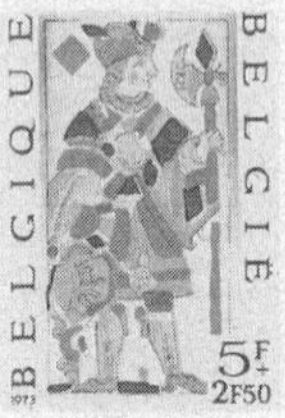

614 F. Rops (self-portrait) **615** Jack of Diamonds

1973. 75th Death Anniv of Felicien Rops (artist and engraver).
2330 **614** 7f. black and brown . . 35 30

1973. "Solidarity". Old Playing Cards. Mult.
2331 5f.+2f.50 Type **615** 40 35
2332 5f.+2f.50 Jack of Spades . . 40 35
2333 5f.+2f.50 Queen of Hearts 40 35
2334 5f.+2f.50 King of Clubs . . 40 35

1973. As Nos. 2207/23 but smaller, 22 × 17 mm.
2335 **583** 3f. green . . . . 1·10 85
2336 4f. blue 45 35
2337 4f.50 blue 35 20
2338 5f. mauve 25 20
2338c 6f. red 30 20
2339 6f.50 violet 45 25
2339b 8f. grey 35 20

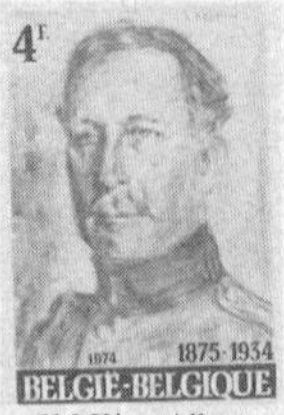

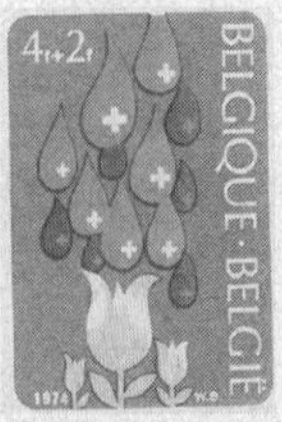

616 King Albert (Baron Opsomer) **617** "Blood Donation"

1974. 40th Death Anniv of King Albert I.
2340 **616** 4f. blue and black . . . 25 20

1974. Belgian Red Cross. Multicoloured.
2341 4f.+2f. Type **617** 35 35
2342 10f.+5f. "Traffic Lights" (Road Safety) 80 75

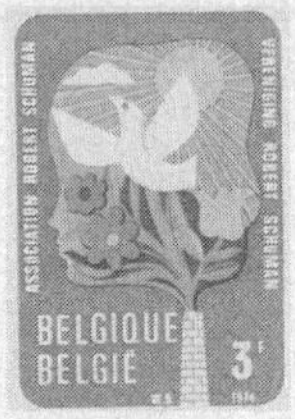

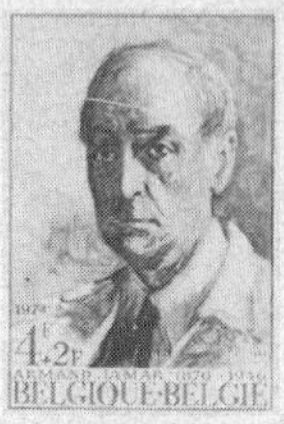

618 "Protection of the Environment" **619** "Armand Jamar" (Self-portrait)

1974. Robert Schuman Association for the Protection of the Environment.
2343 **618** 3f. multicoloured 15 10

1974. Belgian Cultural Celebrities. Multicoloured.
2344 4f.+2f. Type **619** 25 25
2345 5f.+2f.50 Tony Bergmann (author) and view of Lier 30 30
2346 7f.+3f.50 Henri Vieuxtemps (violinist) and view of Verviers 60 65
2347 10f.+5f. "James Ensor" (self-portrait with masks) (35 × 52 mm) 75 80

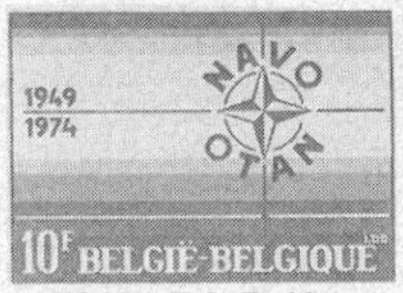

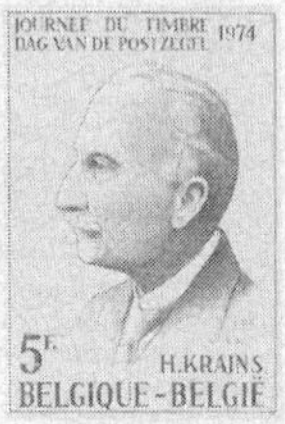

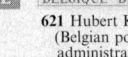

620 N.A.T.O. Emblem **621** Hubert Krains (Belgian postal administrator)

1974. 25th Anniv of North Atlantic Treaty Organization.
2348 **620** 10f. blue and light blue 50 30

1974. Stamp Day.
2349 **621** 5f. black and grey . . . 30 10

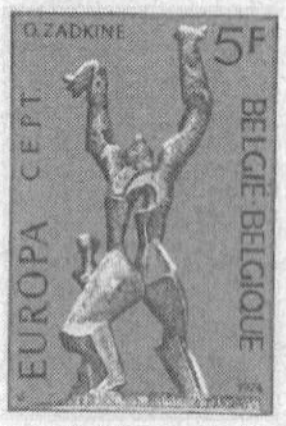

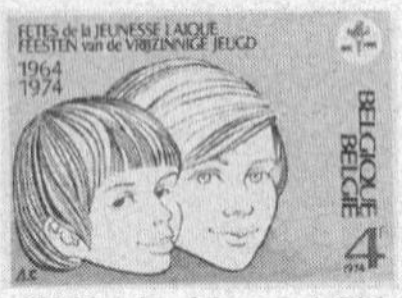

622 "Destroyed Town" (O. Zadkine) **623** Heads of Boy and Girl

1974. Europa. Sculptures.
2350 **622** 5f. black and red 25 10
2351 – 10f. black and blue . . . 50 40
DESIGN: 10f. "Solidarity" (G. Minne).

1974. 10th Lay Youth Festival.
2352 **623** 4f. multicoloured 25 20

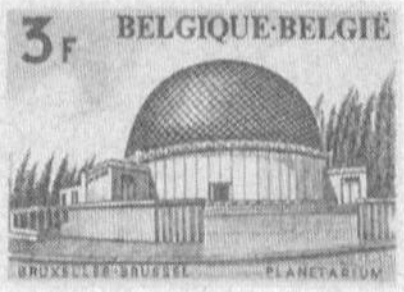

625 New Planetarium, Brussels

1974. Historical Buildings.
2354 **625** 3f. brown and blue . . . 25 10
2355 – 4f. brown and red . . . 30 25
2356 – 5f. brown and green . . 35 10
2357 – 7f. brown and yellow . . 40 25
2358 – 10f. brown, orange & bl 50 25
DESIGNS—As T **625**. HORIZ: 4f. Pillory, Braine-le-Chateau. VERT: 10f. Belfry, Bruges. 45 × 25 mm: 5f. Ruins of Soleilmont Abbey; 7f. "Procession" (fountain sculpture, Ghent).

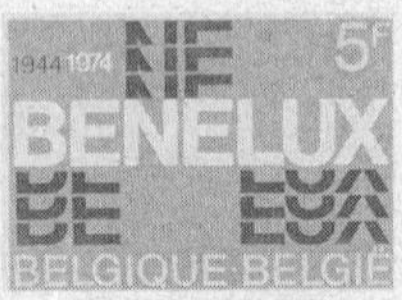

626 "BENELUX"

1974. 30th Anniv of Benelux Customs Union.
2359 **626** 5f. blue, green & lt blue 15 10

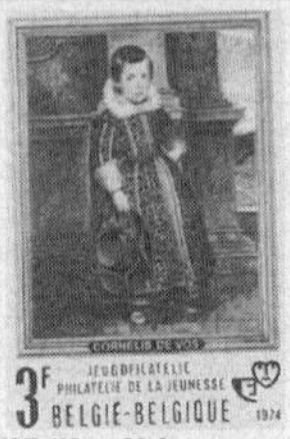

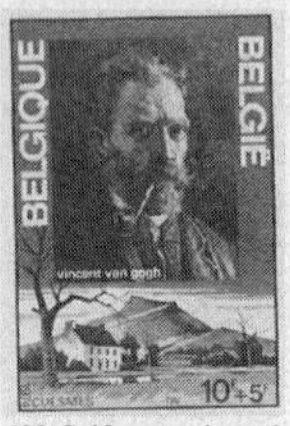

627 "Jan Vekemans at the Age of Five" (Cornelis de Vos) **628** Self-portrait and Van Gogh House, Cuesmes

1974. "Philately for the Young".
2360 **627** 3f. multicoloured 25 20

1974. Opening of Vincent Van Gogh House, Cuesmes.
2361 **628** 10f.+5f. multicoloured 75 75

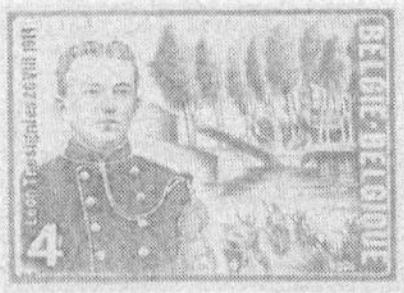

629 Corporal Tresignies and Brule Bridge

1974. 60th Death Anniv of Corporal Leon Tresignies (war hero).
2362 **629** 4f. green and brown . . 25 20

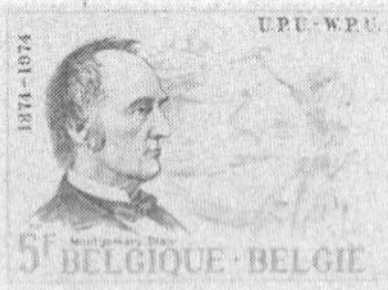

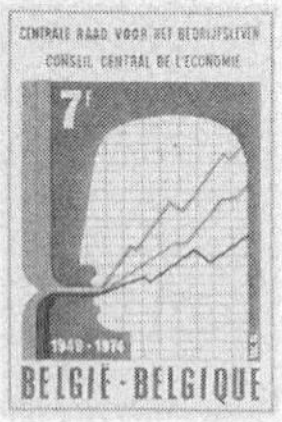

630 Montgomery Blair and U.P.U. Emblem **631** Graph within Head

1974. Centenary of U.P.U.
2363 **630** 5f. black and green . . . 30 10
2364 – 10f. black and red . . . 50 25
DESIGN: 10f. H. von Stephan and U.P.U. Monument.

1974. 25th Anniv of Central Economic Council.
2365 **631** 7f. multicoloured 40 25

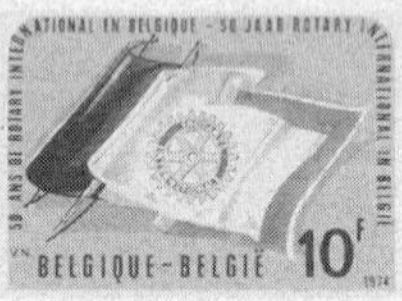

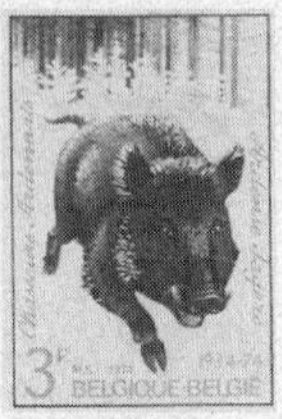

632 Rotary Emblem on Belgian Flag **633** Wild Boar

1974. 50th Anniv of Rotary Int in Belgium.
2366 **632** 10f. multicoloured . . . 50 30

1974. 40th Anniv of Granting of Colours to Ardennes Regiment of Chasseurs.
2367 **633** 3f. multicoloured 25 10

1974. Tourist Publicity. As T **607**.
2368 3f. brown and yellow . . . 25 20
2369 4f. green and blue 30 20
2370 4f. green and blue 30 25
DESIGNS—VERT: No. 2368, Aarschot. HORIZ: No. 2369, Meeting of three frontiers, Gemmenich; 2370, Nassogne.

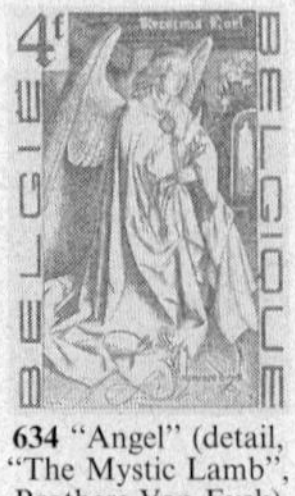

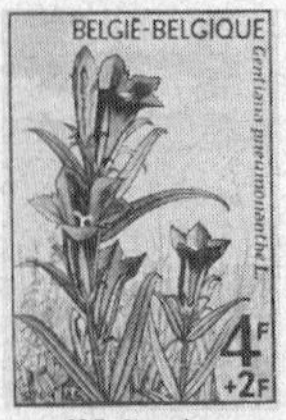

634 "Angel" (detail, "The Mystic Lamb", Brothers Van Eyck) **635** Gentian

1974. Christmas.
2371 **634** 4f. purple 25 20

1974. "Solidarity". Flora and Fauna. Multicoloured.
2372 4f.+2f. Type **635** 35 35
2373 5f.+2f.50 Eurasian badger (horiz) 40 35
2374 7f.+3f.50 Golden hunter (beetle) (horiz) 60 60
2375 10f.+5f. Spotted cat's-ear . . 80 80

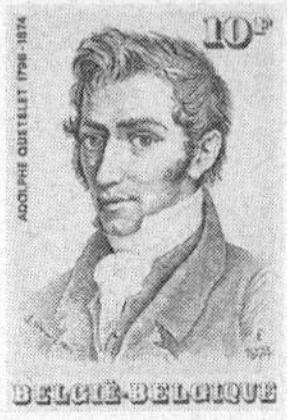
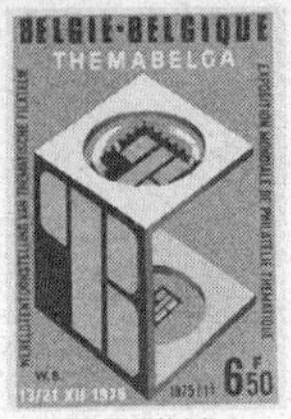

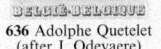

636 Adolphe Quetelet (after J. Odevaere)
637 Exhibition Emblem

1974. Death Centenary of Adolphe Quetelet. (scientist).
2376 **636** 10f. black and brown . . 45 25

1975. "Themabelga" Stamp Exhibition, Brussels (1st issue).
2377 **637** 6f.50 orange, blk & grn 30 10
See also Nos. 2411/16.

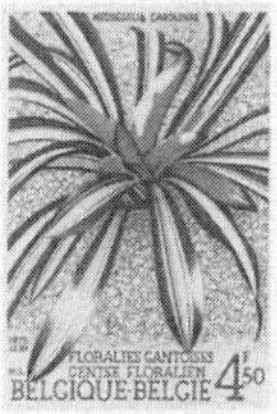
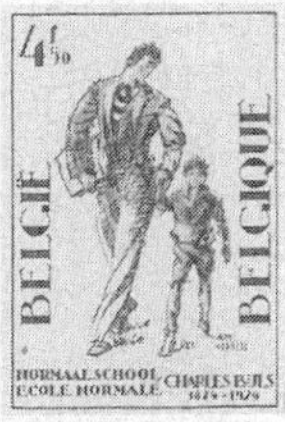

638 "Neoregelia carolinae"
639 Student and Young Boy

1975. Ghent Flower Show. Multicoloured.
2378 4f.50 Type **638** 25 15
2379 5f. "Tussilago petasites" . . 25 10
2380 6f.50 "Azalea japonica" . . 30 10

1975. Cent of Charles Buls Normal School.
2381 **639** 4f.50 multicoloured . . . 25 15

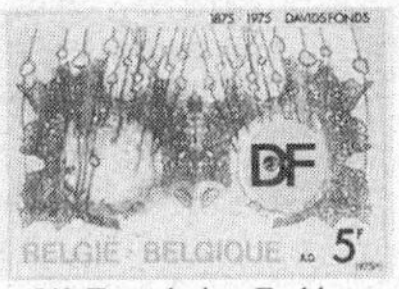
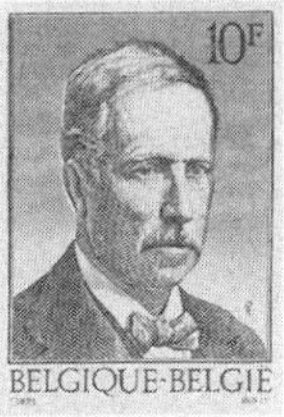

640 Foundation Emblem
641 King Albert I

1975. Centenary of Davids Foundation (Flemish cultural organisation).
2382 **640** 5f. multicoloured 30 10

1975. Birth Centenary of King Albert I.
2383 **641** 10f. black and purple . . 60 30

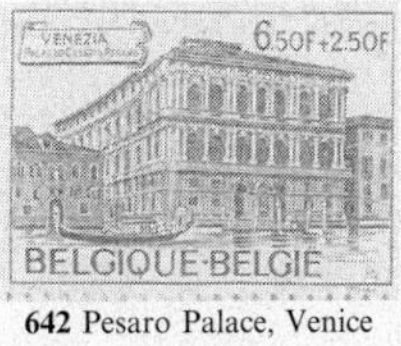
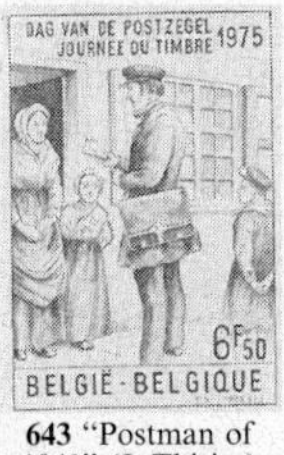

642 Pesaro Palace, Venice
643 "Postman of 1840" (J. Thiriar)

1975. Cultural Works.
2384 **642** 6f.50+2f.50 brown . . . 50 60
2385 – 10f.+4f.50 purple 65 75
2386 – 15f.+6f.50 blue . . . . . 1·10 1·10
DESIGNS—HORIZ: 10f. Sculpture Museum, St. Bavon Abbey, Ghent. VERT: 15f. "Virgin and Child" (Michelangelo, 500th Birth Anniv.)

1975. Stamp Day.
2387 **643** 6f.50 purple 30 10

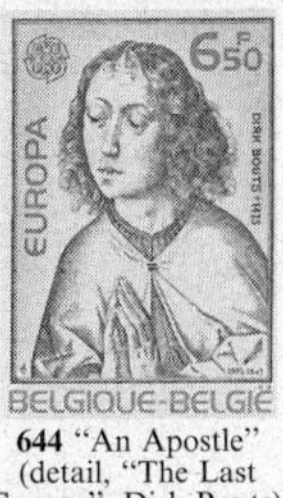
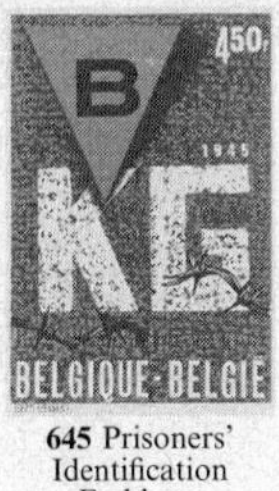

644 "An Apostle" (detail, "The Last Supper", Dirk Bouts)
645 Prisoners' Identification Emblems

1975. Europa. Paintings.
2388 **644** 6f.50 black, blue & grn 40 10
2389 – 10f. black, red & orange 50 35
DESIGN: 10f. "The Suppliant's Widow" (detail, "The Justice of Otho", Dirk Bouts).

1975. 30th Anniv of Concentration Camps' Liberation.
2390 **645** 4f.50 multicoloured . . . 25 10

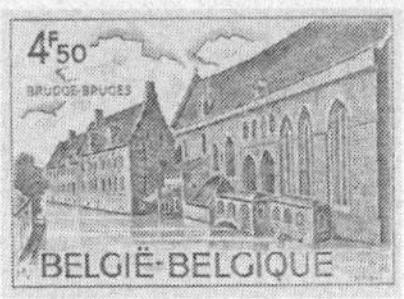

646 St John's Hospice, Bruges

1975. European Architectural Heritage Year.
2391 **646** 4f.50 purple 30 15
2392 – 5f. green 30 20
2393 – 10f. blue 45 30
DESIGNS—VERT: 5f. St. Loup's Church, Namur. HORIZ: 10f. Martyrs Square, Brussels.

1975. Tourist Publicity. As T **607**.
2394 4f.50 brown, buff and red 30 15
2395 5f. multicoloured 30 15
DESIGN—VERT: 4f.50, Church, Dottignies. HORIZ: 5f. Market Square, Saint Truiden.

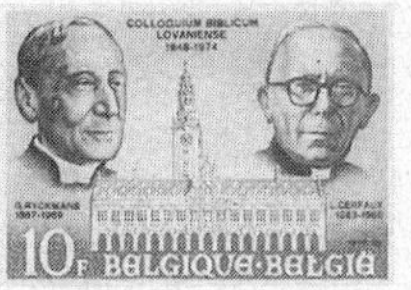
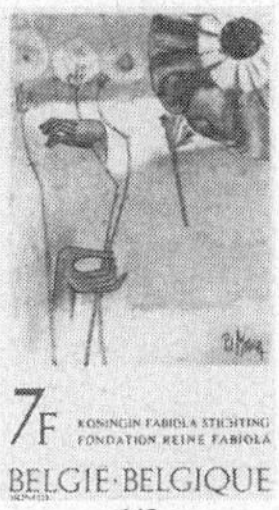

647 G. Ryckmans and L. Cerfaux (founders), and Louvain University Library
648 "Metamorphosis" (P. Mara)

1975. 25th Anniv of Louvain Colloquium Biblicum (Biblical Scholarship Association).
2396 **647** 10f. sepia and blue . . . 45 25

1975. Queen Fabiola Foundation for the Mentally Ill.
2397 **648** 7f. multicoloured 40 25

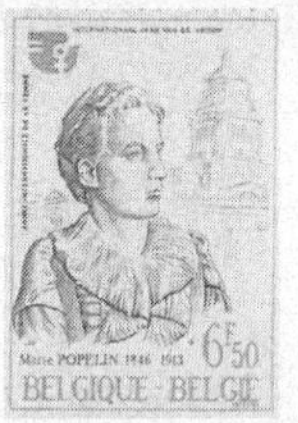
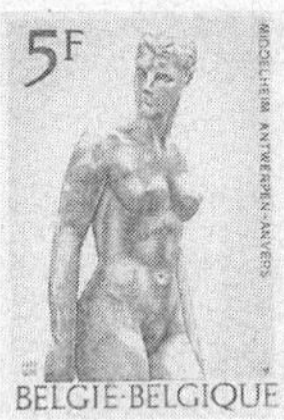

649 Marie Popelin (women's rights pioneer) and Palace of Justice
650 "Assia" (Charles Despiau)

1975. International Women's Year.
2398 **649** 6f.50 purple and green 40 10

1975. 25th Anniv of Middelheim Open-air Museum, Antwerp.
2399 **650** 5f. black and green . . . 30 15

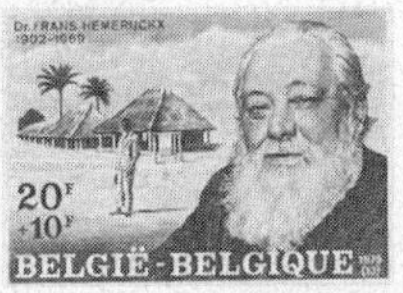

651 Dr. Hemerijckx and Leprosy Hospital, Zaire

1975. Dr. Frans Hemerijckx (treatment of leprosy pioneer) Commemoration.
2400 **651** 20f.+10f. mult . . . . . 1·50 1·50

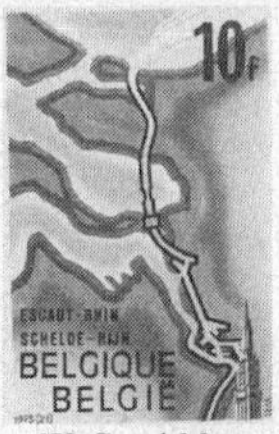
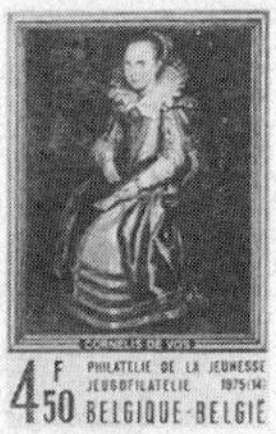

652 Canal Map
653 "Cornelia Vekemans at the Age of Seven" (Cornelis de Vos)

1975. Opening of Rhine–Scheldt Canal.
2401 **652** 10f. multicoloured . . . 45 30

1975. "Philately for the Young".
2402 **653** 4f.50 multicoloured . . . 30 20

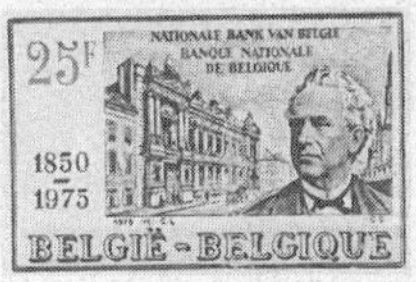

654 National Bank and F. Orban (founder)

1975. 125th Anniv of Belgian National Bank.
2403 **654** 25f. multicoloured . . . 1·10 35

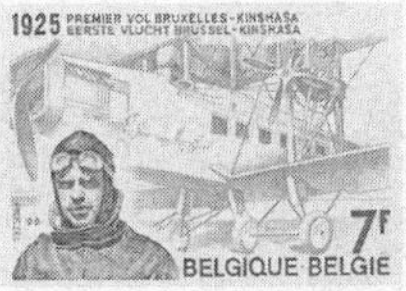
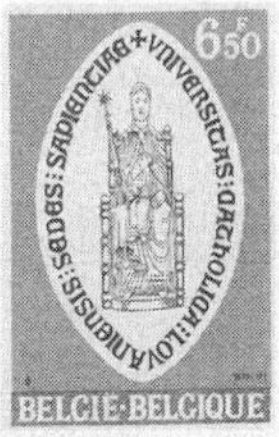

655 Edmond Thieffry (pilot) and "Princess Marie-Jose"
656 University Seal

1975. 50th Anniv of First Flight, Brussels–Kinshasa.
2404 **655** 7f. purple and black . . 35 25

1975. 550th Anniv of Louvain University.
2405 **656** 6f.50 black, green & bl 35 10

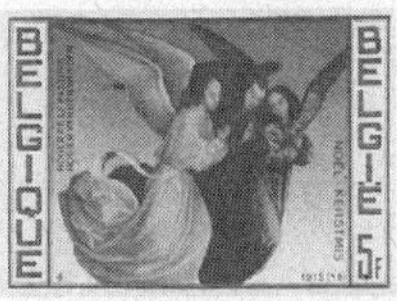
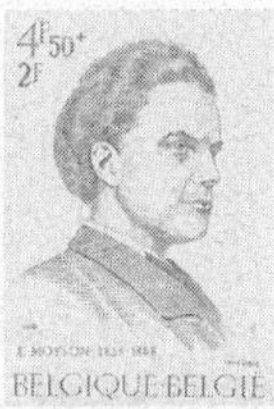

657 "Angels", (detail, "The Nativity", R. de le Pasture)
658 Emile Moyson (Flemish Leader)

1975. Christmas.
2406 **657** 5f. multicoloured 30 25

1975. "Solidarity".
2407 **658** 4f.50+2f. purple 35 35
2408 – 6f.50+3f. green 45 50
2409 – 10f.+5f. vio, blk & bl . . 70 70
2410 – 13f.+6f. multicoloured 1·00 1·00
DESIGNS—VERT: 6f.50, Dr. Augustin Snellaert (Flemish literature scholar); 13f. Detail of retable, St. Dymphne Church, Geel. HORIZ: 10f. Eye within hand, and Braille characters (150th anniv of introduction of Braille).

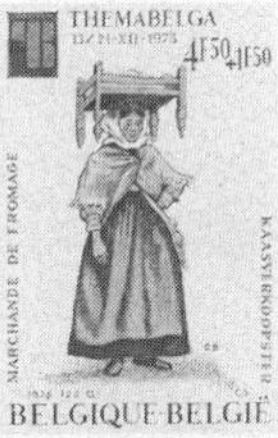
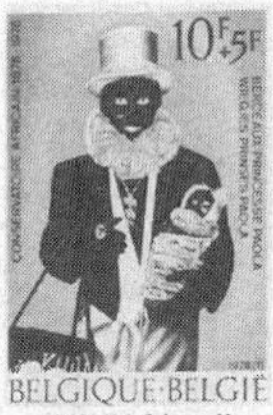

659 Cheese Seller
660 "African" Collector

1975. "Themabelga" International Thematic Stamp Exhibition, Brussels (2nd issue). Traditional Belgian Trades. Multicoloured.
2411 4f.50+1f.50 Type **659** . . . 30 30
2412 6f.50+3f. Potato seller . . . 45 45
2413 6f.50+3f. Basket-carrier . . . 45 45
2414 10f.+5f. Prawn fisherman and pony (horiz) 75 65
2415 10f.+5f. Knife-grinder and cart (horiz) 75 65
2416 30f.+15f. Milk-woman with dog-cart (horiz) . . . . . 1·90 2·10

1976. Centenary of "Conservatoire Africain" (Charity Organization).
2417 **660** 10f.+5f. multicoloured 75 75

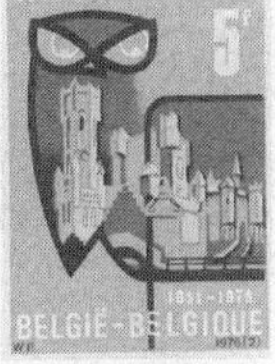
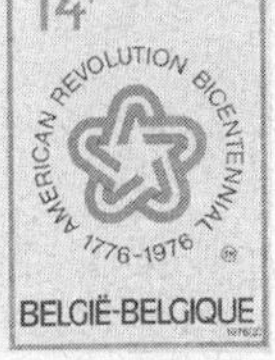

661 Owl Emblem and Flemish Buildings
662 Bicentennial Symbol

1976. 125th Anniv of Wilhems Foundation (Flemish cultural organization).
2418 **661** 5f. multicoloured 30 25

1976. Bicentenary of American Revolution.
2419 **662** 14f. multicoloured . . . 75 45

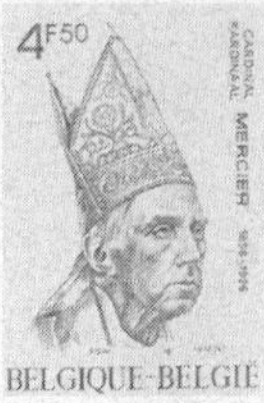
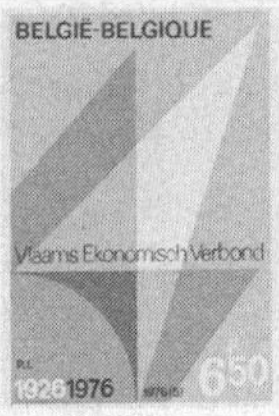

663 Cardinal Mercier
664 "Vlaams Ekonomisch Verbond"

1976. 50th Death Anniv of Cardinal Mercier.
2420 **663** 4f.50 purple 30 15

1976. 50th Anniv of Flemish Economic Federation.
2421 **664** 6f.50 multicoloured . . . 35 10

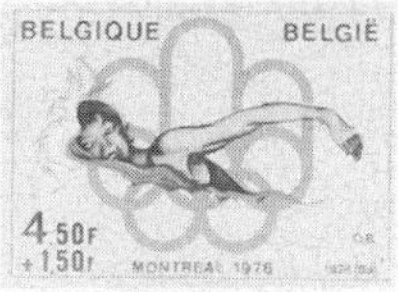

665 Swimming

1976. Olympic Games, Montreal. Multicoloured.
2422 4f.50+1f.50 Type **665** . . . 25 30
2423 5f.+2f. Running (vert) . . . 35 35
2424 6f.50+2f.50 Horse jumping 45 45

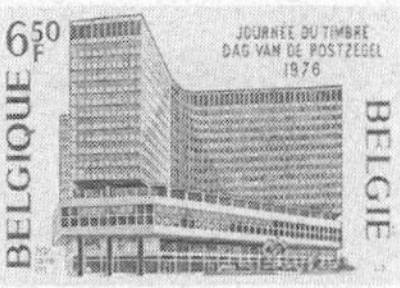

666 Money Centre Building, Brussels

1976. Stamp Day.
2425 **666** 6f.50 brown 35 10

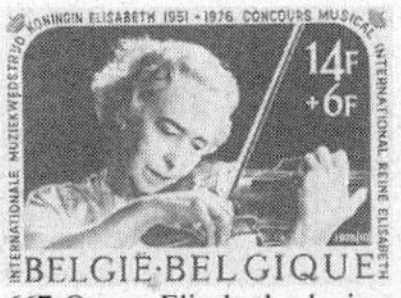
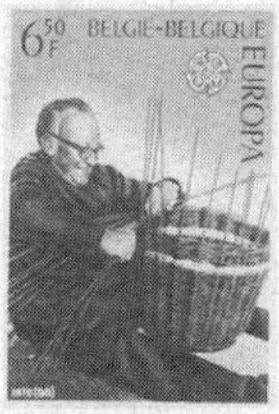

667 Queen Elisabeth playing Violin
668 Basket-making

1976. 25th Anniv of Queen Elisabeth International Music Competitions.
2426 **667** 14f.+6f. red & black . . 95 1·00

1976. Europa. Traditional Crafts. Multicoloured.
2427 6f.50 Type **668** 40 10
2428 14f. Pottery (horiz) 65 35

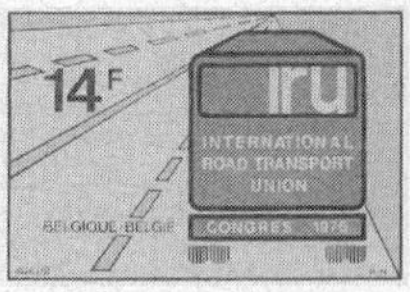
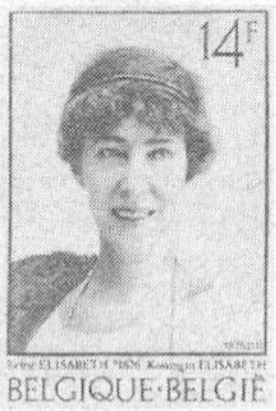

669 Lorry on Motorway
670 Queen Elisabeth

1976. 14th Congress of International Road Haulage Union, Brussels.
2429 **669** 14f. black, red & yellow 60 35

1976. Birth Centenary of Queen Elisabeth.
2430 **670** 14f. green 70 35

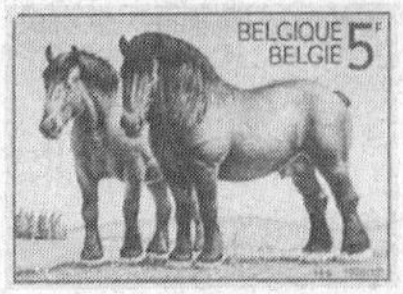

673 Ardennes Horses

1976. 50th Anniv of Ardennes Draught Horses Society.
2436 **673** 5f. multicoloured 30 25

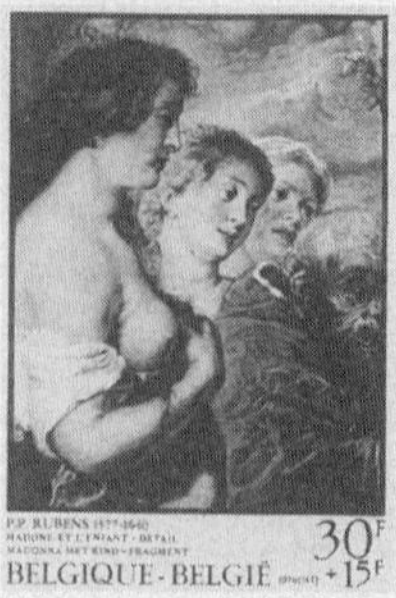

675 "Madonna and Child" (detail)

1976. 400th Birth Anniv of Peter Paul Rubens (artist) (1st issue). Multicoloured.
2438 4f.50+1f.50 "Descent from the Cross" (detail) 30 35
2439 6f.50+3f. "Adoration of the Shepherds" (detail) (24½ × 35 mm) 50 55
2440 6f.50+3f. "Virgin of the Parrot" (detail) (24½ × 35 mm) 50 55
2441 10f.+5f. "Adoration of the Kings" (detail) (24½ × 35 mm) 95 90
2442 10f.+5f. "Last Communion of St. Francis" (detail) (24½ × 35 mm) 95 75
2443 30f.+15f. Type **675** . . . . 2·25 2·00
See also Nos. 2459 and 2497.

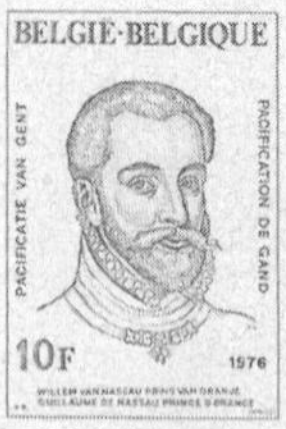

676 William the Silent, Prince of Orange

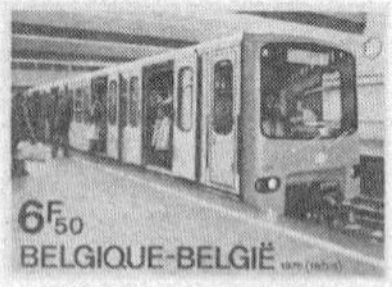

678 Underground Train

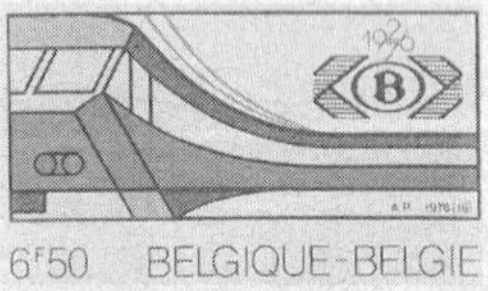

677 Modern Electric Train

1976. 400th Anniv of Pacification of Ghent.
2444 **676** 10f. green 50 25

1976. 50th Anniv of National Belgian Railway Company.
2445 **677** 6f.50 multicoloured . . . 40 10

1976. Opening of Brussels Metro (Underground) Service.
2446 **678** 6f.50 multicoloured . . . 40 10

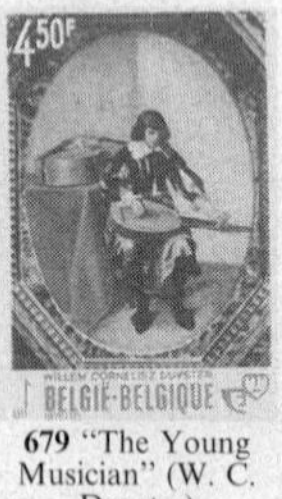

679 "The Young Musician" (W. C. Duyster)

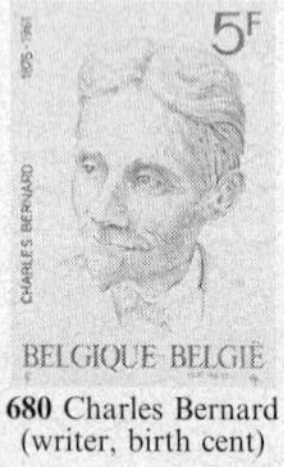

680 Charles Bernard (writer, birth cent)

1976. "Philately for the Young" and Young Musicians' Movement.
2447 **679** 4f.50 multicoloured . . . 30 10

1976. Cultural Anniversaries.
2448 **680** 5f. purple 25 20
2449 – 5f. red 25 20
2450 – 6f.50 brown 35 10
2451 – 6f.50 green 35 10
DESIGNS—VERT: No. 2449, Fernand Toussaint van Boelaere (writer, birth cent 1975); No. 2450, "St. Jerome in Mountain Landscape" (J. le Patinier) (25th anniv of Charles Plisnier Foundation). HORIZ: No. 2451, "Story of the Blind" (P. Brueghel) (25th anniv of "Vereniging voor Beschaafde Omgangstaal" (Dutch language organisation)).

1976. Tourist Publicity. As T **607**.
2452 4f.50 multicoloured 25 20
2453 4f.50 multicoloured 25 20
2454 5f. brown and blue 30 20
2455 5f. brown and olive 30 20
DESIGNS—HORIZ: No. 2452, Hunnegem Priory, Grammont; No. 2454, River Lys, Sint-Martens-Latem; No. 2455, Chateau, Ham-sur-Heure. VERT: No. 2453, Remouchamps Caves.

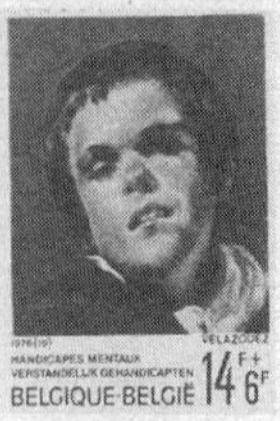

681 "Child with Impediment" (Velasquez)

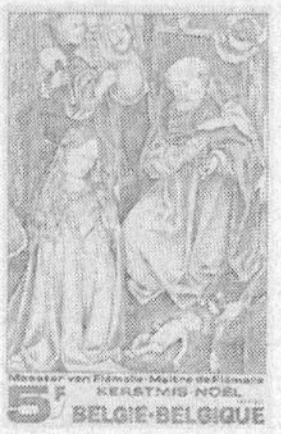

682 "The Nativity" (detail, Master of Flemalle)

1976. National Association for Aid to the Mentally Handicapped.
2456 **681** 14f.+6f. multicoloured 95 95

1976. Christmas.
2457 **682** 5f. violet 30 25

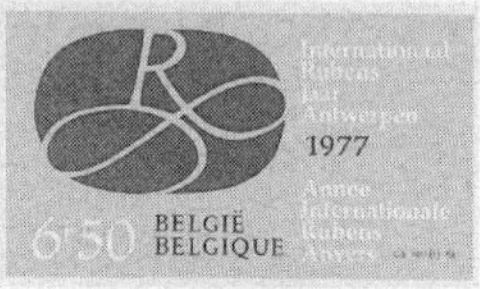

683 Monogram

1977. 400th Birth Anniv of Peter Paul Rubens (2nd issue).
2459 **683** 6f.50 black and lilac . . 35 15

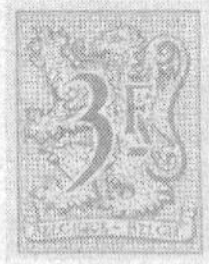
684 Belgian Lion

1977. (a) Size 17 × 20 mm.
2460 **684** 50c. brown 10 10
2461 65c. red 10 10
2462 1f. mauve 10 10
2463 1f.50 grey 10 10
2464a 2f. orange 15 10
2465 2f.50 green 30 15
2466 2f.75 blue 30 30
2467a 3f. violet 10 10
2468 4f. brown 25 10
2469 4f.50 blue 30 10
2470 5f. green 30 10
2471 6f. red 35 10
2472 7f. red 35 10
2473 8f. blue 40 10
2474 9f. orange 90 20

(b) 17 × 22 mm.
2475 **684** 1f. mauve 10 15
2476 2f. orange 25 25
2477 3f. violet 30 25

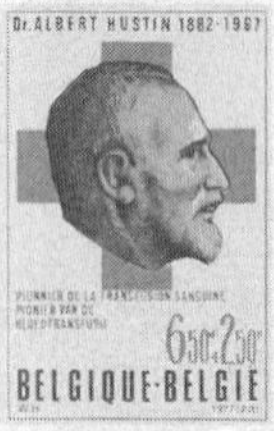

685 Dr. Albert Hustin (pioneer of blood transfusion)

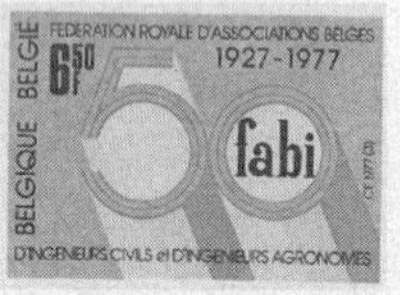

686 "50 Years of F.A.B.I."

1977. Belgian Red Cross.
2478 **685** 6f.50+2f.50 red and black 55 55
2479 – 14f.+7f. red, blue and black . . . . 1·10 1·00
DESIGN: 14f.+7f. Knee joint and red cross (World Rheumatism Year).

1977. 50th Anniv of Federation of Belgian Engineers.
2480 **686** 6f.50 multicoloured . . . 35 10

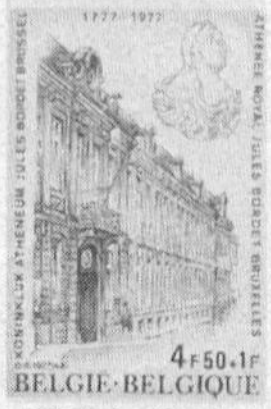

687 Jules Bordet School, Brussels (bicent)

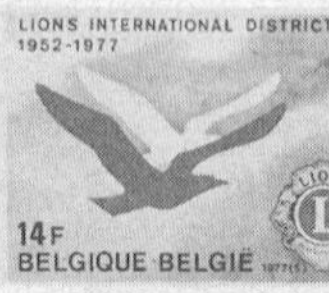

688 Gulls in Flight

1977. Cultural Anniversaries.
2481 **687** 4f.50+1f. mult 20 20
2482 – 4f.50+1f. mult 20 20
2483 – 5f.+2f. multicoloured . . 30 30
2484 – 6f.50+2f. mult 40 40
2485 – 6f.50+2f. red & black . . 40 40
2486 – 10f.+5 slate 50 50
DESIGNS—VERT: 24 × 37 mm: No. 2482, Marie-Therese College, Herve (bicentenary); 2483, Detail from "La Grande Pyramide Musicale" (E. Tytgat) (50th anniv of Brussels Philharmonic Society). 35 × 45 mm: No. 2486, Camille Lemonnier (75th anniv of Society of Belgian Authors writing in French). HORIZ: 35 × 24 mm: No. 2484, Lucien van Obbergh and stage scene (50th anniv of Union of Artists). 37 × 24 mm: No. 2485, Emblem of Humanist Society (25th anniv).

1977. 25th Anniv of District 112 of Lions International.
2487 **688** 14f. multicoloured . . . 75 25

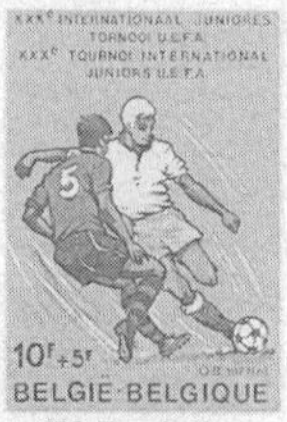

689 Footballers

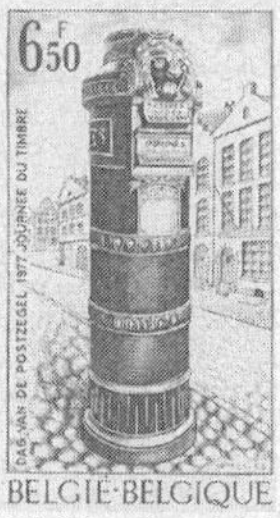

690 Pillar Box, 1852

1977. 30th International Youth Tournament of European Football Association.
2488 **689** 10f.+5f. multicoloured 75 60

1977. Stamp Day.
2489 **690** 6f.50 olive 25 10

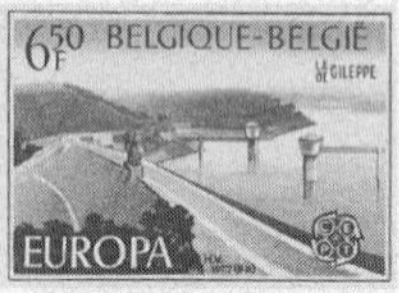

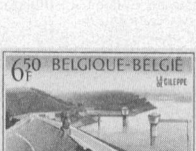

691 Gileppe Dam, Jalhay

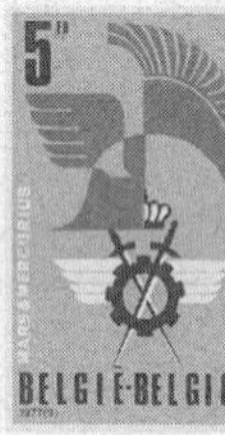

692 "Mars and Mercury Association Emblem"

1977. Europa. Multicoloured.
2490 6f.50 Type **691** 30 10
2491 14f. The Yser, Nieuport . . 55 25

1977. 50th Anniv of Mars and Mercury Association of Reserve and Retired Officers.
2492 **692** 5f. green, black & brown 15 10

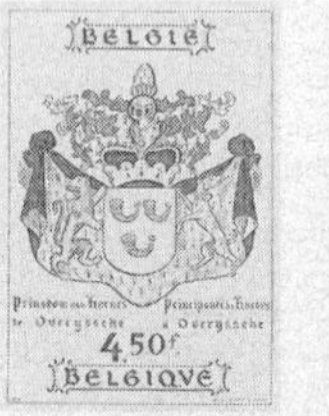

693 De Hornes Coat of Arms

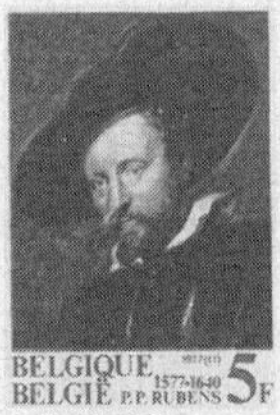

694 "Self-Portrait"

1977. Historical Anniversaries.
2493 **693** 4f.50 lilac 20 10
2494 – 5f. red 25 15
2495 – 6f.50 brown 30 10
2496 – 14f. green 50 25
DESIGNS AND EVENTS—VERT: 4f.50, Type **693** (300th anniv of creation of principality of Overijse under Eugene-Maximilien de Hornes); 6f.50, Miniature (600th anniv of Froissart's "Chronicles"); 14f. "The Conversion of St. Hubert" (1250th death anniv). HORIZ: (45 × 24 mm): 5f. Detail from "Oxford Chest" (675th anniv of Battle of Golden Spurs).

1977. 400th Birth Anniv of Peter Paul Rubens (3rd issue).
2497 **694** 5f. multicoloured 15 10

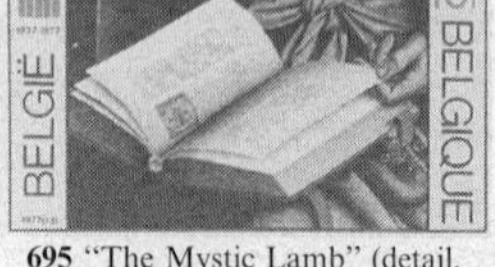

695 "The Mystic Lamb" (detail, Brothers Van Eyck)

1977. 50th Anniv of International Federation of Library Associations and Congress, Brussels.
2499 **695** 10f. multicoloured . . . 35 20

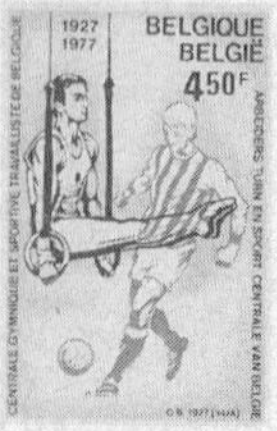

696 Gymnast and Footballer

1977. Sports Events and Anniversaries.
2500 **696** 4f.50 red, black & grn 20 20
2501 – 6f.50 black, violet and brown 25 10
2502 – 10f. turquoise, black and salmon 65 30
2503 – 14f. green, blk & ochre 70 35
DESIGNS—VERT: 4f.50, Type **696** (50th anniv of Workers' Central Sports Association); 10f. Basketball (20th European Championships); 14f. Hockey (International Hockey Cup competition). HORIZ: 6f.50, Disabled fencers (Rehabilitation through sport).

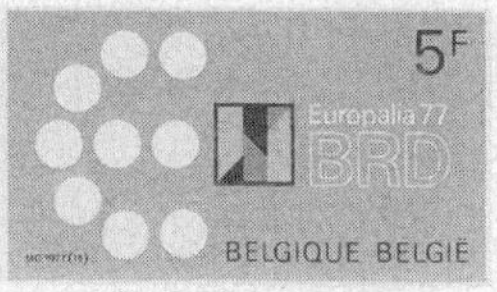

697 Festival Emblem

1977. "Europalia '77" Festival.
2504 **697** 5f. multicoloured 30 15

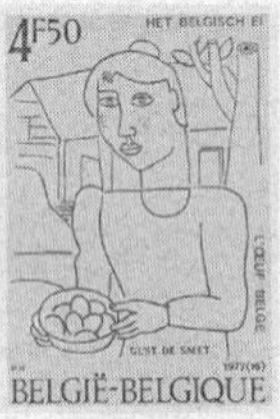

699 "The Egg-seller" (Gustave de Smet)

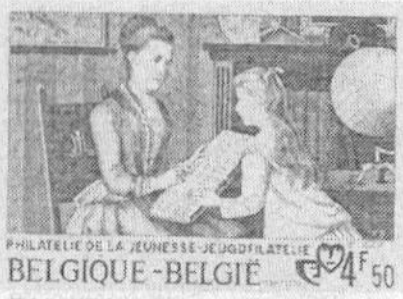

700 "The Stamp Collectors" (detail, Constant Cap)

1977. Promoting Belgian Eggs.
2506 **699** 4f.50 black and ochre . . 30 15

1977. "Philately for the Young".
2507 **700** 4f.50 sepia 30 15

1977. Tourist Publicity. As T**607**.
2508 4f.50 multicoloured 25 15
2509 4f.50 black, blue and green 25 15
2510 5f. multicoloured 25 25
2511 5f. multicoloured 25 25
DESIGNS—VERT: No. 2508, Bailiff's House, Gembloux; No. 2509, St. Aldegone's Church. HORIZ: No. 2510, View of Liege and statue of Mother and Child; No. 2511, View and statue of St. Nicholas.

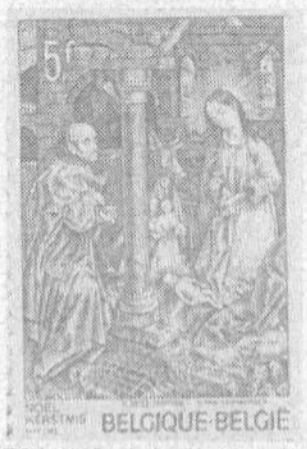

701 "Nativity" (detail, R. de la Pasture)

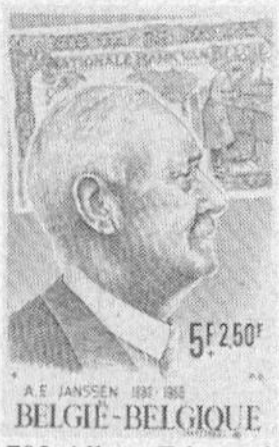

702 Albert-Edouard Janssen (financier)

1977. Christmas.
2512 **701** 5f. red 30 25

1977. "Solidarity".
2513 **702** 5f.+2f.50 black 35 35
2514 – 5f.+2f.50 red 35 35
2515 – 10f.+5f. purple 70 70
2516 – 10f.+5f. grey 70 70
DESIGNS: No. 2514, Joseph Wauters (politician); No. 2516, Jean Capart (egyptologist); No. 2515, August de Boeck (composer).

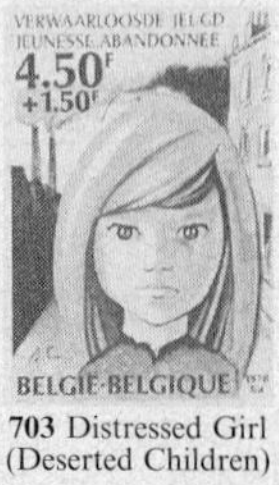

703 Distressed Girl (Deserted Children)

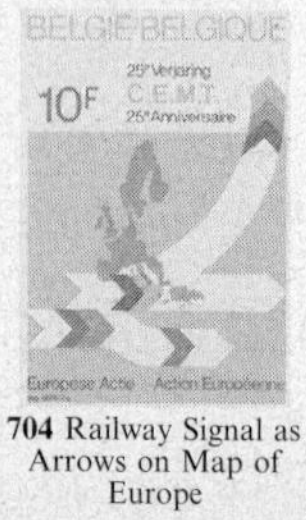

704 Railway Signal as Arrows on Map of Europe

1978. Philanthropic Works. Multicoloured.
2517 4f.50+1f.50 Type **703** . . . 25 30
2518 6f.+3f. Blood pressure
measurement (World
Hypertension Month) . . 35 40
2519 10f.+5f. De Mick
Sanatorium, Brasschaat
(Anti-tuberculosis) (horiz) 95 80

1978. "European Action". Multicoloured.
2520 10f. Type **704** (25th anniv of
European Conference of
Transport Ministers) . . . 95 25
2521 10f. European Parliament
Building, Strasbourg (first
direct elections) . . . 60 20
2522 14f. Campidoglio Palace,
Rome and map of EEC
countries (20th anniv of
Treaties of Rome) (horiz) 60 35
2523 14f. Paul Henri Spaak
(Belgian Prime Minister)
(horiz) 45 35

705 Grimbergen Abbey

1978. 850th Anniv of Premonstratensian Abbey,
Grimbergen.
2524 **705** 4f.50 brown 25 25

706 Emblem   **707** 5f. Stamp of 1878

1978. 175th Anniv of Ostend Chamber of Commerce
and Industry.
2525 **706** 8f. multicoloured 35 10

1978. Stamp Day.
2526 **707** 8f. brown, blk & drab 35 10

708 Antwerp Cathedral   **709** Theatre and
Characters from "The
Brussels Street Singer"

1978. Europa. Multicoloured.
2527 8f. Type **708** 40 20
2528 14f. Pont des Trous,
Tournai (horiz) 65 40

1978. Cultural Anniversaries.
2529 **709** 6f.+3f. multicoloured . . 40 40
2530 – 6f.+3f. multicoloured . . 40 40
2531 – 8f.+4f. brown 60 60
2532 – 10f.+5f. brown 70 70
DESIGNS AND EVENTS: No. 2529, (Type **709**)
(Royal Flemish Theatre Cent.); 2530, Arquebusier
with standard, arms and Company Gallery, Vise
(Royal Company of Crossbowmen of Vise 400th
anniv); 2531, Karel van der Woestijne (poet) (birth
cent); 2532, Don John of Austria (signing of Perpetual
Edict, 400th anniv).

710 "Education"   **711** "K.V.I."

1978. Teaching. Multicoloured.
2533 6f. Type **710** (Municipal
education in Ghent, 150th
anniv) 30 25
2534 8f. Paul Pastur Workers'
University, Charleroi
(75th anniv) 35 20

1978. Tourist Publicity. As T **607**.
2535 4f.50 sepia, buff and blue 25 25

2536 4f.50 multicoloured . . . 25 25
2537 6f. multicoloured 30 25
2538 6f. multicoloured 30 25
DESIGNS—VERT: No. 2535, Jonathas House,
Enghien. HORIZ: No. 2536, View of Wetteren and
couple in local costume; 2537, Brussels tourist hostess;
2538, Carnival Prince and church tower.

1978. 50th Anniv of Royal Flemish Association of
Engineers.
2539 **711** 8f. black and red 35 10

712 Young Stamp Collector   **713** Mountain
Scenery

1978. "Philately for the Young".
2540 **712** 4f.50 violet 30 25

1978. Olympic Games (1980) Preparation.
2541 **713** 6f.+2f.50 mult 40 40
2542 – 8f.+3f.50 green, brown
and black 60 50
DESIGN: 8f. Kremlin Towers.

714 "The Nativity" (detail,   **715** Tabernacle,
Bethlehem Door, Notre   Brussels Synagogue
Dame, Huy)   (centenary)

1978. Christmas.
2544 **714** 6f. black 30 25

1978. "Solidarity". Anniversaries.
2545 **715** 6f.+2f. brown, grey and
black 60 45
2546 – 8f.+3f. multicoloured . . 40 45
2547 – 14f.+7f. multicoloured 1·10 1·00
DESIGNS—HORIZ: (36×24 mm): 8f. Dancing
figures (Catholic Students Action, 50th anniv); 14f.
Father Dominique-Georges Pire and African Village
(Award of Nobel Peace Prize, 20th anniv).

716 Relief Workers   **717** "Till
giving First Aid   Eulenspiegel"
(legendary character)

1978. Belgian Red Cross. Multicoloured.
2548 8f.+3f. Type **716** 45 50
2549 16f.+8f. Skull smoking,
bottle and syringe
("Excess kills") . . . . . 1·10 1·10

1979. 10th Anniv of Lay Action Centres.
2550 **717** 4f.50 multicoloured . . . 30 25

718 "European Dove"   **719** Millenary Emblem

1979. 1st Direct Elections to European Assembly.
2551 **718** 8f. multicoloured 45 10

1979. Brussels Millenary (1st issue).
2552 **719** 4f.50 brown, blk & red 25 15
2553 – 8f. turquoise, blk & grn 35 10
See also Nos. 2559/62.

720 Sculpture at N.A.T.O.   **721** Drawing of
Headquarters and Emblem   Monument

1979. 30th Anniv of North Atlantic Treaty
Organization.
2554 **720** 30f. blue, gold and light
blue . . . . . . 1·25 45

1979. 25th Anniv of Breendonk Monument.
2555 **721** 6f. orange and black . . 30 25

722 Railway Parcels Stamp, 1879

1979. Stamp Day.
2556 **722** 8f. multicoloured 35 10

723 Mail Coach and Modern Post Van

1979. Europa. Multicoloured.
2557 8f. Type **723** 40 10
2558 14f. Semaphore posts,
satellite and dish aerial . . 65 40

724 "Legend of Our Lady of   **725** Caduceus and
Sablon" (detail of tapestry,   Factory
Town Museum of Brussels)

1979. Brussels Millenary (2nd issue). Multicoloured.
2559 6f.+2f. Type **724** 30 30
2560 8f.+3f. Different detail of
tapestry 40 50
2561 14f.+7f. "Legend of Our
Lady of Sablon"
(tapestry) . . . . . 1·10 1·00
2562 20f.+10f. Different detail of
tapestry . . . . . . 1·50 1·50
The tapestry shown on Nos. 2559/60 is from
Brussels Town Museum and that on Nos. 2561/2 from
the Royal Museum of Art and History.

1979. 175th Anniv of Verviers Chamber of
Commerce.
2564 **725** 8f. multicoloured 35 10

726 "50" and Bank Emblem

1979. 50th Anniv of Professional Credit Bank.
2565 **726** 4f.50 blue and gold . . . 30 25

727 Bas-relief

1979. 50th Anniv of Chambers of Trade and
Commerce.
2566 **727** 10f. crimson, orange and
red 45 25

728 Cambre Abbey

1979. Cultural Anniversaries.
2567 **728** 6f.+2f. multicoloured . . . 60 45
2568 – 8f.+3f. multicoloured . . 65 60
2569 – 14f.+7f. black, orange
and green . . . . 1·50 1·10
2570 – 20f.+10f. brown, red and
grey . . . . . . 2·10 1·75
DESIGNS: 6f. Type **728** (50th anniv of restoration);
8f. Beauvoorde Chateau; 14f. Barthelemy Dumortier
(founder) and newspaper "Courrier de L'Escaut"
(150th anniv); 20f. Crypt, shrine and Collegiate
Church of St. Hermes, Renaix (850th anniv of
consecration).

729 "Tintin" with Dog, Stamps
and Magnifier

1979. "Philately for the Young".
2571 **729** 8f. multicoloured . . . . 1·75 35

730 Le Grand-Hornu

1979. Le Grand-Hornu Industrial Archaeological
Site.
2572 **730** 10f.+5f. black & grey . . 75 75

1979. Tourist Publicity. As T **607**.
2573 5f. multicoloured 30 20
2574 5f. multicoloured 30 20
2575 6f. black, turquoise & green 30 20
2576 6f. multicoloured 30 20
DESIGNS—HORIZ: No. 2573, Royal African
Museum, Tervuren, and hunters with hounds; 2575,
St. John's Church, Poperinge, and statue of Virgin
Mary. VERT: No. 2574, Belfry, Thuin, and men
carrying religious image; 2576, St. Nicholas's Church
and cattle market, Ciney.

731 Francois Auguste   **732** Madonna and
Gevaert   Child, Foy-Notre-
Dame Church

1979. Music. Each brown and ochre.
2577 5f. Type **731** (150th birth
anniv) 30 20
2578 6f. Emmanuel Durlet . . . 30 20
2579 14f. Grand piano and string
instruments (40th anniv of
Queen Elisabeth Musical
Chapel) 70 35

1979. Christmas.
2580 **732** 6f. black and blue 35 25

 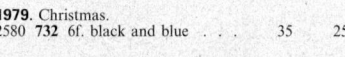

733 H. Heyman   **734** "1830–1980"
(politician, birth
centenary)

1979. "Solidarity".
2581 **733** 8f.+3f. brown, green and
black 45 45
2582 – 10f.+5f. multicoloured 60 60
2583 – 16f.+8f. black, green and
yellow . . . . . 1·25 1·10
DESIGNS—VERT: As Type **733**. 10f. War Invalids
Organization medal (50th anniv). HORIZ:

(44 × 24 mm): 16f. Child's head and International Year of the Child emblem.

1980. 150th Anniv of Independence (1st issue).
2584 **734** 9f. mauve & lt mauve . .   40   10
See also Nos. 2597/2601.

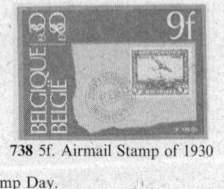

735 Frans Van   **736** Spring Flowers
Cauwelaert

1980. Birth Centenary of Frans Van Cauwelaert (politician).
2585 **735** 5f. black   30   10

1980. Ghent Flower Show. Multicoloured.
2586   5f. Type **736**   30   10
2587   6f.50 Summer flowers   35   30
2588   9f. Autumn flowers   40   10

737 Telephone and Diagram of Satellite Orbit

1980. 50th Anniv of Telegraph and Telephone Office.
2589 **737** 10f. multicoloured . . .   45   25

738 5f. Airmail Stamp of 1930

1980. Stamp Day.
2590 **738** 9f. multicoloured   45   10

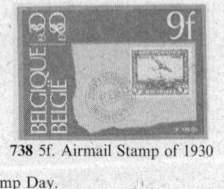

739 St. Benedict of Nursia

1980. Europa. Multicoloured.
2591   9f. Type **739**   40   10
2592   14f. Marguerite of Austria . .   70   45

740 Ivo van Damme   **741** Palais de la Nation

1980. Ivo van Damme (athlete) Commemoration.
2593 **740** 20f.+10f. mult . . . . .   1·50   1·50

1980. 4th Interparliamentary Conference on European Co-operation and Security, Brussels.
2594 **741** 5f. blue, lilac and black . .   30   25

742 Golden Carriage, Mons

1980. Tourist Publicity. Multicoloured.
2595   6f.50 Type **742**   30   25
2596   6f.50 Damme   30   25

743 King Leopold I and Queen Louise-Marie

1980. 150th Anniv of Belgian Independence (2nd issue).
2597 **743** 6f.50+1f.50 pur & blk . .   30   35
2598   – 9f.+3f. blue & black . .   50   50
2599   – 14f.+6f. green & blk . .   80   80
2600   – 17f.+8f. orange. & blk . .   1·25   1·25
2601   – 25f.+10f. green & blk . .   1·90   1·90
DESIGNS: 9f. King Leopold II and Queen Marie-Henriette; 14f. King Albert I and Queen Elisabeth; 17f. King Leopold III and Queen Astrid; 25f. King Baudouin and Queen Fabiola.

744 King   **745** "Brewer" (detail,
Baudouin   Reliquary of St. Lambert)

1980. King Baudouin's 50th Birthday.
2603 **744** 9f. red   45   10

1980. Millenary of Liège. Multicoloured.
2604   9f.+3f. Type **745**   45   60
2605   17f.+6f. "The Miner"
       (sculpture by Constantin
       Meunier) (horiz) . . . .   1·10   1·10
2606   25f.+10f. "Seat of Wisdom"
       (Madonna, Collegiate
       Church of St. John,
       Liege) . . . .   1·75   1·75

746 Chiny

1980. Tourist Publicity.
2608 **746** 5f. multicoloured   35   20

747 Emblem of Cardiological   **748** Rodenbach
League of Belgium   (statue at Roulers)

1980. Heart Week.
2609 **747** 14f. light blue, red and
       blue   60   35

1980. Death Cent of Albrecht Rodenbach (poet).
2610 **748** 9f. brown, blue and deep
       blue   40   10

749 "Royal Procession" (children of Thyl Uylenspiegel Primary School)

1980. "Philately for the Young".
2611 **749** 5f. multicoloured   30   25

750 Emblem   **751** "Garland of Flowers and Nativity" (attr. D. Seghers)

1980. 50th Anniv of Belgian Broadcasting Corporation.
2612 **750** 10f. black and grey . . .   45   25

1980. Christmas.
2613 **751** 6f.50 multicoloured . . .   35   25

   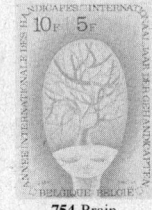

752 Gateway, Diest   **754** Brain

1980. Tourist Publicity.
2614 **752** 5f. multicoloured   30   25
See also Nos. 2648/51 and 2787/92.

1981. International Year of Disabled Persons. Multicoloured.
2637   10f.+5f. Type **754**   60   70
2638   25f.+10f. Eye . . . . . .   1·90   1·75

   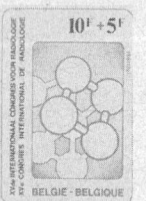

755 "Baron de   **756** Emblem of 15th
Gerlache" (after F. J.   International
Navez)   Radiology Convention

1981. Historical Anniversaries.
2639 **755** 6f. multicoloured   25   10
2640   – 9f. multicoloured   35   10
2641   – 50f. brown & yellow . .   2·50   65
DESIGNS—As T **755**: 6f. Type **755** (1st President of Chamber of Deputies) (150th anniv of Chamber); 9f. Baron de Stassart (1st President of Senate) (after F. J. Navez) (150th anniv of Senate). 35 × 51 mm: 50f. Statue of King Leopold I by Geefs (150th anniv of royal dynasty).

1981. Belgian Red Cross.
2642 **756** 10f.+5f. bl, blk & red . .   60   70
2643   – 25f.+10f. blue, red and
       black . . . .   1·75   1·75
DESIGN: 25f. Dove and globe symbolizing international emergency assistance.

757 Tchantches and Op-Signoorke (puppets)

1981. Europa. Multicoloured.
2644   9f. Type **757**   45   10
2645   14f. D'Artagnan and Woltje
       (puppets)   80   45

758 Stamp Transfer-   **759** Ovide Decroly
roller depicting A. de
Cock (founder of
Postal Museum)

1981. Stamp Day.
2646 **758** 9f. multicoloured   40   10

1981. 110th Birth Anniv of Dr. Ovide Decroly (educational psychologist).
2647 **759** 35f.+15f. brown & bl . .   2·40   2·25

1981. Tourist Publicity. As T **752**. Multicoloured.
2648   6f. Statue of our Lady of
       Tongre   30   25
2649   6f. Egmont Castle, Zottegem   30   25
2650   6f.50 Dams on Eau d'Heure
       (horiz)   35   25
2651   6f.50 Tongerlo Abbey,
       Antwerp (horiz)   30   25

760 Footballer   **761** Edouard Remouchamps (Walloon dramatist)

1981. Cent of Royal Antwerp Football Club.
2652 **760** 6f. red, brown & black . .   40   25

1981. 125th Anniv of Society of Walloon Language and Literature.
2653 **761** 6f.50 brown and stone . .   40   25

762 French Horn

1981. Centenary of De Vredekring Band, Antwerp.
2654 **762** 6f.50 blue, mve & blk . .   40   25

763 Audit Office

1981. 150th Anniv of Audit Office.
2655 **763** 10f. purple   45   25

765 Tombs of Marie of Burgundy and Charles the Bold

1981. Relocation of Tombs of Marie of Burgundy and Charles the Bold in Notre-Dame Church, Bruges.
2657 **765** 50f. multicoloured . . .   2·40   60

766 Boy holding   **767** King Baudouin
Globe in Tweezers

1981. "Philately for Youth".
2658 **766** 6f. multicoloured   30   25

1981.
2659 **767** 50f. light blue and blue .   2·75   10
2660   65f. mauve and black . .   4·50   70
2661   100f. brown and blue . .   5·25   10

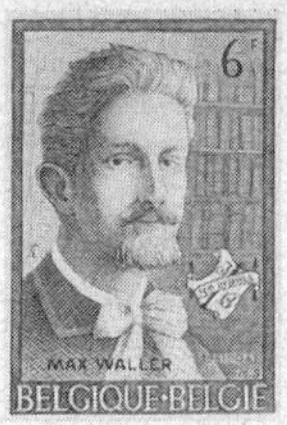

768 Max Waller (founder)

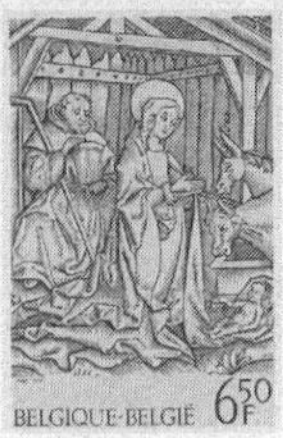

769 Nativity (miniature from "Missale ad usum d. Leodensis")

1981. Cultural Anniversaries.
2672 **768** 6f. multicoloured 25 15
2673 – 6f.50 multicoloured . . . 35 25
2674 – 9f. multicoloured 40 15
2675 – 10f. multicoloured . . . 70 30
2676 – 14f. lt brn & brn 70 45
DESIGNS: 6f. Type **768** (centenary of literary review "La Jeune Belgique"); 6f.50," Liqueur Drinkers" (detail, Gustave van de Woestyne) (birth centenary); 9f. Fernand Severin (poet, 50th death anniv); 10f. Jan van Ruusbroec (mystic, 600th death anniv); 14f. Owl (La Pensee et les Hommes organization, 25th anniv).

1981. Christmas.
2677 **769** 6f.50 brown and black 35 25

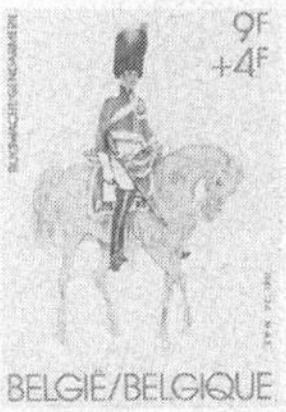

770 Mounted Gendarme, 1832

771 Cellist and Royal Conservatory of Music, Brussels

1981. "Solidarity". Multicoloured.
2678 9f.+4f. Type **770** 60 60
2679 20f.+7f. Carabinier . . . . 1·25 1·25
2680 40f.+20f. Mounted Guide, 1843 . . . . 2·50 2·50

1982. 150th Anniversaries. Multicoloured.
2681 6f.50 Type **771** 35 20
2682 9f. Front of former Law Court, Brussels (anniv of judiciary) 40 10

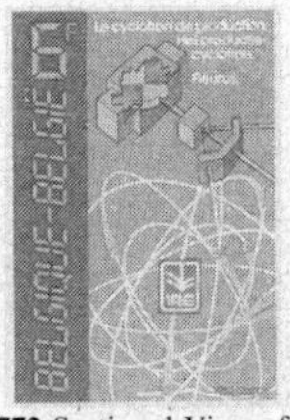

772 Sectional View of Cyclotron

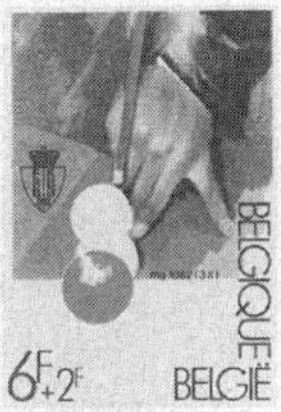

773 Billiards

1982. Science. Multicoloured.
2683 6f. Type **772** (Installation of cyclotron at National Radio-elements Institute, Fleurus) 30 15
2684 14f. Telescope and galaxy (Royal Observatory) . . . 75 30
2685 50f. Dr. Robert Koch and tubercle bacillus (centenary of discovery) 2·25 65

1982. Sports. Multicoloured.
2686 6f.+2f. Type **773** 50 50
2687 9f.+4f. Cycling 70 70
2688 10f.+5f. Football 95 95
2689 50f.+14f. Yacht "Treaty of Rome" . . . . 3·00 3·00

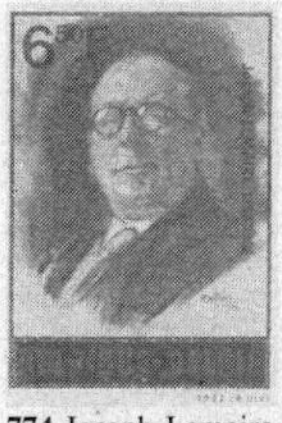
774 Joseph Lemaire (after Jean Maillard)

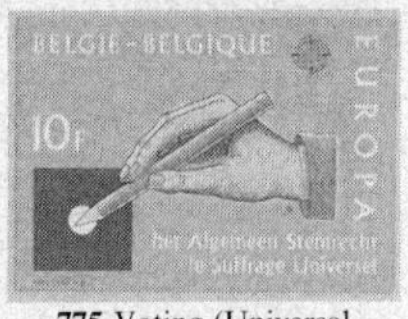

775 Voting (Universal Suffrage)

1982. Birth Centenary of Joseph Lemaire (Minister of State and social reformer).
2691 **774** 6f.50 multicoloured . . . 75 25

1982. Europa.
2692 **775** 10f. multicoloured . . . 45 15
2693 – 17f. green, black and grey 90 35
DESIGN: 17f. Portrait and signature of Emperor Joseph II (Edict of Toleration).

1982. Surch **1 F**.
2694 **684** 1f. on 5f. green 10 10

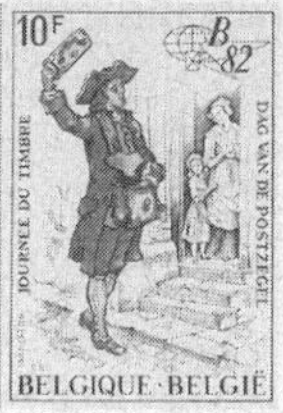

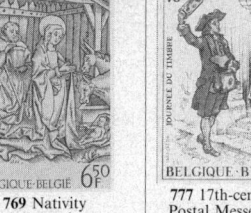

777 17th-century Postal Messenger

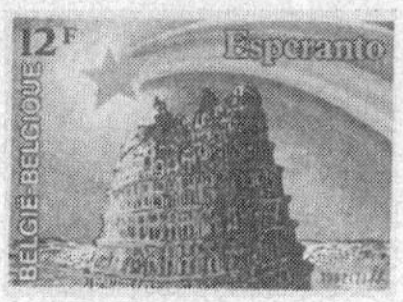

778 "Tower of Babel" (Brueghel the Elder)

1982. Stamp Day.
2695 **777** 10f. multicoloured . . . 45 10

1982. World Esperanto Congress, Antwerp.
2696 **778** 12f. multicoloured . . . 60 30

1982. Tourist Publicity. As T **752**.
2697 7f. blue and light blue . . . 40 20
2698 7f. black and green 40 20
2699 7f.50 brown and light brown 40 20
2700 7f.50 violet and lilac 40 20
2701 7f.50 black and grey 40 20
2702 7f.50 black and pink 40 20
DESIGNS—VERT: No. 2697, Gosselies Tower; 2698, Zwijveke Abbey, Termonde; 2701, Entrance gate, Grammont Abbey; 2702, Beveren pillory. HORIZ: No. 2699, Stavelot Abbey; 2700, Abbey ruins, Villers-la-Ville.

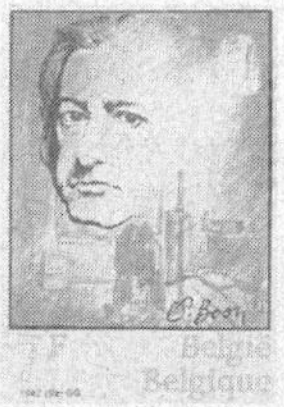

780 Louis Paul Boon (writer)

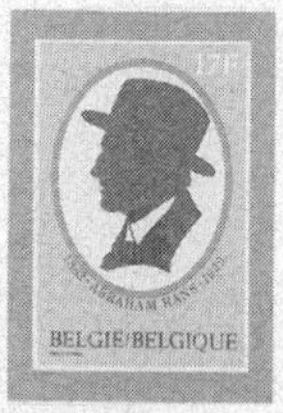

781 Abraham Hans

1982. Cultural Anniversaries.
2707 **780** 7f. black, red and grey 30 15
2708 – 10f. multicoloured . . . 40 10
2709 – 12f. multicoloured . . . 50 30
2710 – 17f. multicoloured . . . 80 35
DESIGNS: 7f. Type **780** (70th birth anniv); 10f. "Adoration of the Shepherds" (detail of Portinari retable) (Hugo van der Goes, 500th death anniv); 12f. Michel de Ghelderode (dramatist, 20th death anniv); 17f. "Motherhood" (Pierre Paulus, birth centenary (1981)).

1982. Birth Centenary of Abraham Hans (writer).
2711 **781** 17f. black, turquoise and blue 75 25

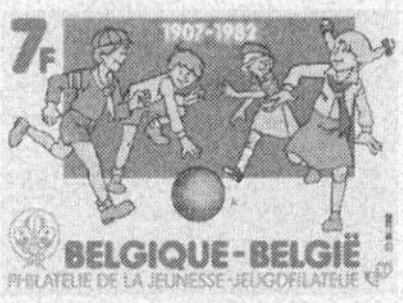

782 Children playing Football

1982. "Philately for the Young". Scout Year.
2712 **782** 7f. multicoloured 60 25

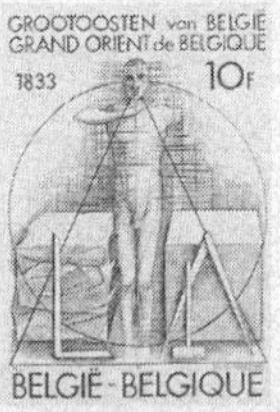

783 Masonic Emblems

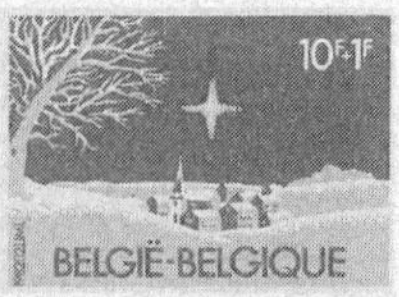

784 Star over Village

1982. 150th Anniv of Belgium Grand Orient (Freemasonry Lodge).
2713 **783** 10f. yellow and black . . 50 10

1982. Christmas.
2714 **784** 10f.+1f. multicoloured 70 70

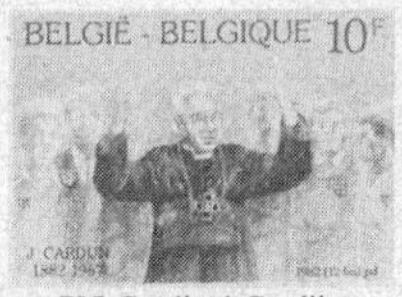

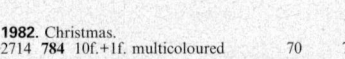

785 Cardinal Cardijn

1982. Birth Centenary of Cardinal Joseph Cardijn.
2715 **785** 10f. multicoloured . . . 50 10

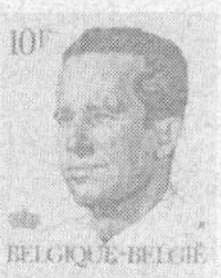

786 King Baudouin

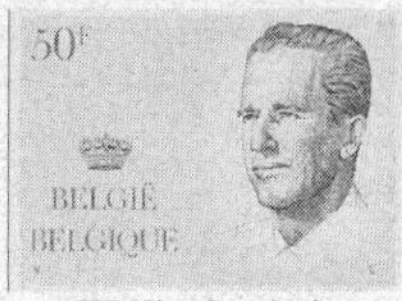

787 King Baudouin

1982.
2716 **786** 10f. blue 60 10
2717 11f. brown 60 10
2718 12f. green . . . . 1·50 10
2719 13f. red 75 10
2720 14f. black 75 10
2721 15f. red . . . . 1·60 30
2722 20f. blue . . . . 1·10 10
2723 22f. purple . . . . . . 2·10 90
2724 23f. green . . . . 1·90 45
2725 24f. grey . . . . 1·50 25
2726 25f. blue . . . . 1·50 25
2727 30f. brown . . . . . . 1·60 10
2728 40f. red . . . . 2·10 10
2729 **787** 50f. light brown, brown and black . . . . . . 2·75 15
2730 100f. blue, deep blue and black . . . . 5·00 25
2731 200f. light green, green and deep green . . . 10·50 70

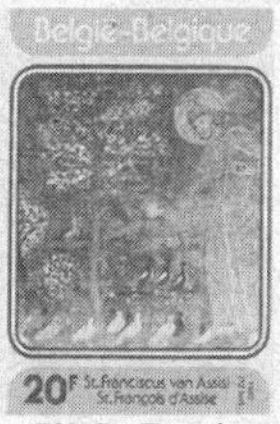

788 St. Francis preaching to the Birds

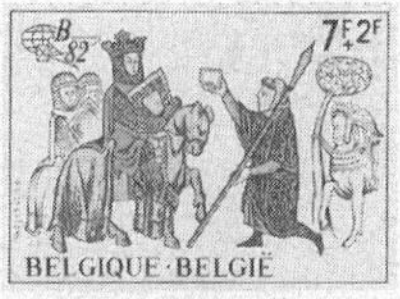

789 Messenger handing Letter to King in the Field

1982. 800th Birth Anniv of St. Francis of Assisi.
2736 **788** 20f. multicoloured . . . 95 35

1982. "Belgica 82" Postal History Exhibition. Multicoloured.
2737 7f.+2f. Type **789** 40 45
2738 7f.50+2f.50 Messenger, Basel (vert) 40 50
2739 10f.+3f. Messenger, Nuremburg (vert) 65 65
2740 17f.+7f. Imperial courier, 1750 (vert) . . . . 1·00 1·10
2741 20f.+9f. Imperial courier, 1800 . . . . 1·00 1·25
2742 25f.+10f. Belgian postman, 1886 . . . . 1·25 1·40

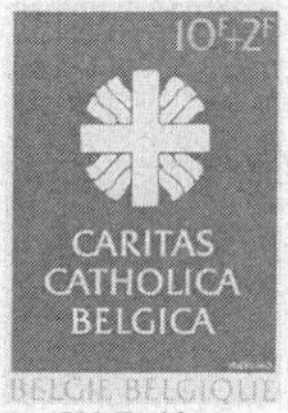

790 Emblem

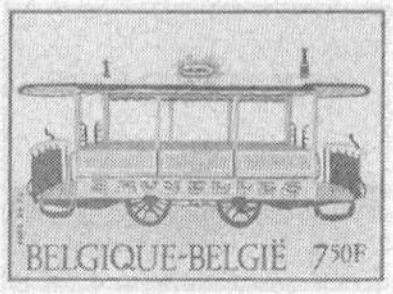

791 Horse Tram

1983. 50th Anniv of Caritas Catholica Belgica.
2744 **790** 10f.+2f. red and grey . . 60 65

1983. Trams. Multicoloured.
2745 7f.50 Type **791** 40 25
2746 10f. Electric tram 65 10
2747 50f. Tram with trolley (invented by K. van de Poele) . . . . 2·25 45

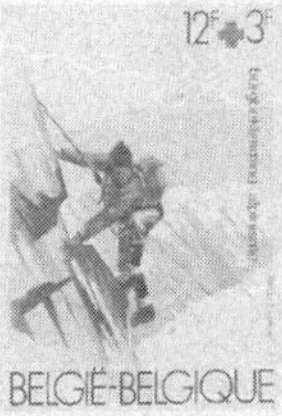

792 Mountaineer

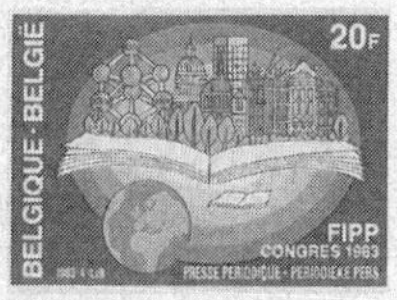

793 Brussels Buildings, Open Periodicals and Globe

1983. Belgian Red Cross. Multicoloured.
2748 12f.+3f. Type **792** 80 80
2749 20f.+5f. Walker . . . . . . 1·00 1·00

1983. 24th International Periodical Press Federation World Congress, Brussels.
2750 **793** 20f. multicoloured . . . 95 30

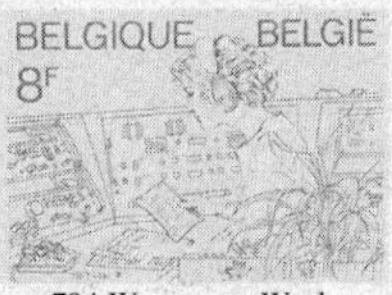

794 Woman at Work

1983. Women.
2751 **794** 8f. multicoloured 45 25
2752 – 11f. multicoloured . . . 60 10
2753 – 20f. yellow, brown & bl 1·00 35
DESIGNS: 11f. Woman at home; 20f. Woman manager.

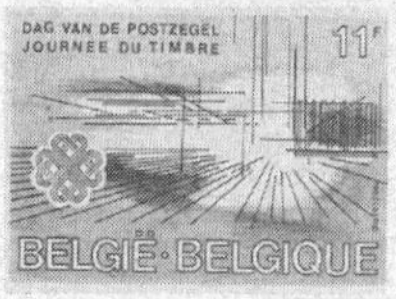

795 Graphic Representation of Midi Railway Station, Brussels

1983. Stamp Day. World Communications Year.
2754 **795** 11f. black, red and blue 50 20

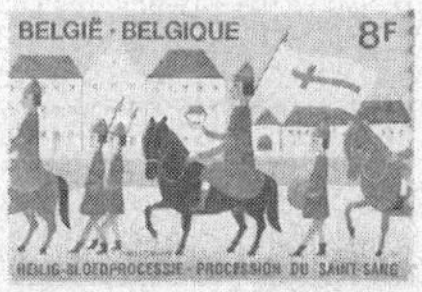

796 Procession of the Holy Blood

1983. Procession of the Holy Blood, Bruges.
2755 **796** 8f. multicoloured 50 25

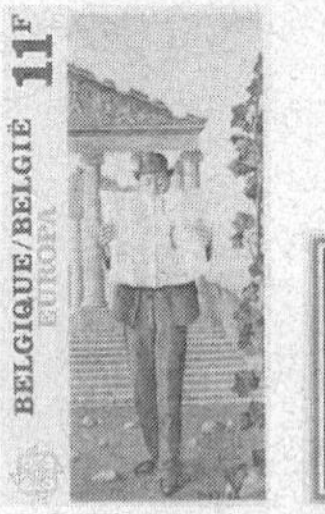

797 "The Man in the Street"

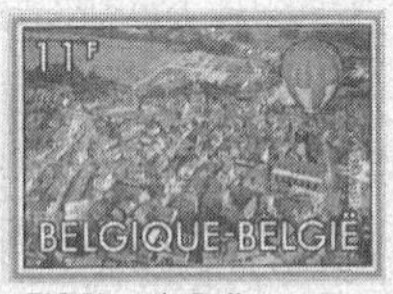

798 Hot-air Balloon over Town

1983. Europa. Paintings by P. Delvaux. Mult.
2756 11f. Type **797** 80 10
2757 20f. "Night Trains" (horiz) 95 45

1983. Bicentenary of Manned Flight. Mult.
2758 11f. Type **798** 45 10
2759 22f. Hot-air balloon over countryside . . . . 1·10 35

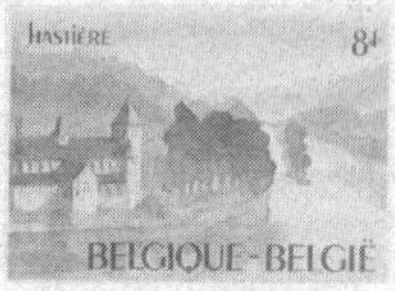

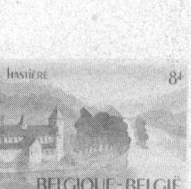

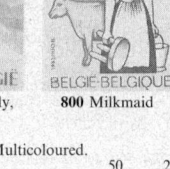

799 Church of Our Lady, Hastiere

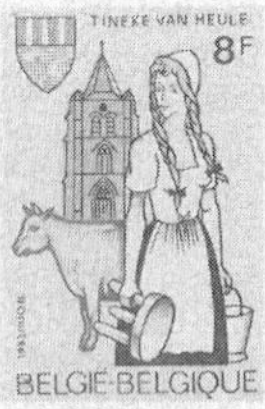

800 Milkmaid

1983. Tourist Publicity. Multicoloured.
2760 8f. Type **799** 50 20
2761 8f. Tumulus, Landen . . . 50 20
2762 8f. Park, Mouscron 50 20
2763 8f. Wijnendale Castle, Torhout 50 20

1983. Tineke Festival, Heule.
2764 **800** 8f. multicoloured 35 25

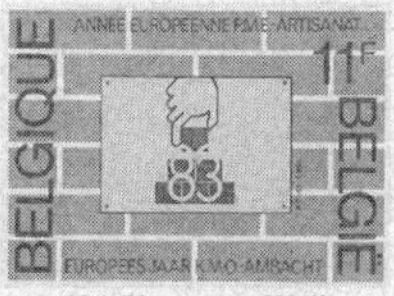

801 Plaque on Wall

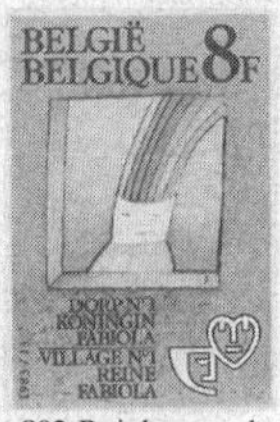

802 Rainbow and Child

1983. European Small and Medium-sized Industries and Crafts Year.
2765 **801** 11f. yellow, black & red 50 10

1983. "Philately for the Young". 20th Anniv of Queen Fabiola Village No. 1 (for handicapped people).
2766 **802** 8f. multicoloured 45 25

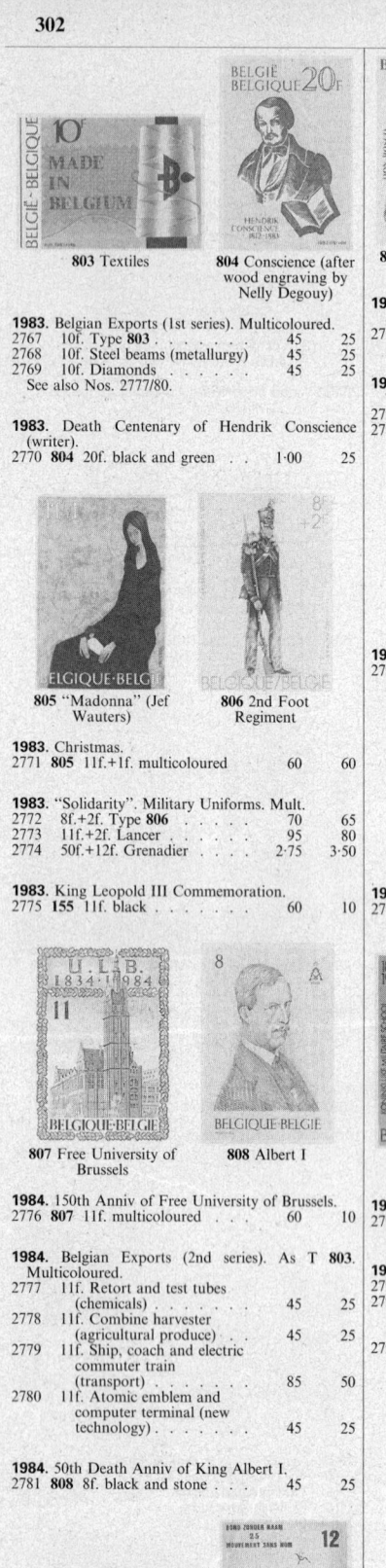

803 Textiles    804 Conscience (after wood engraving by Nelly Degouy)

1983. Belgian Exports (1st series). Multicoloured.
2767	10f. Type 803	45	25
2768	10f. Steel beams (metallurgy)	45	25
2769	10f. Diamonds	45	25

See also Nos. 2777/80.

1983. Death Centenary of Hendrik Conscience (writer).
| 2770 | 804 | 20f. black and green | 1·00 | 25 |

805 "Madonna" (Jef Wauters)   806 2nd Foot Regiment

1983. Christmas.
| 2771 | 805 | 11f.+1f. multicoloured | 60 | 60 |

1983. "Solidarity". Military Uniforms. Mult.
2772	8f.+2f. Type 806	70	65
2773	11f.+2f. Lancer	95	80
2774	50f.+12f. Grenadier	2·75	3·50

1983. King Leopold III Commemoration.
| 2775 | 155 | 11f. black | 60 | 10 |

807 Free University of Brussels   808 Albert I

1984. 150th Anniv of Free University of Brussels.
| 2776 | 807 | 11f. multicoloured | 60 | 10 |

1984. Belgian Exports (2nd series). As T 803. Multicoloured.
2777	11f. Retort and test tubes (chemicals)	45	25
2778	11f. Combine harvester (agricultural produce)	45	25
2779	11f. Ship, coach and electric commuter train (transport)	85	50
2780	11f. Atomic emblem and computer terminal (new technology)	45	25

1984. 50th Death Anniv of King Albert I.
| 2781 | 808 | 8f. black and stone | 45 | 25 |

809 Judo   810 Releasing Doves

1984. Olympic Games, Los Angeles. Multicoloured.
| 2782 | 8f.+2f. Type 809 | 65 | 65 |
| 2783 | 12f.+3f. Windsurfing (vert) | 85 | 85 |

1984. 25th Anniv of Movement without a Name.
| 2785 | 810 | 12f. multicoloured | 50 | 10 |

811 Clasped Hands

1984. 50th Anniv of National Lottery.
| 2786 | 811 | 12f.+3f. multicoloured | 75 | 75 |

812 St. John Bosco with Children   813 Bridge

1984. 50th Anniv of Canonization of St. John Bosco (founder of Salesians).
| 2787 | 812 | 8f. multicoloured | 35 | 10 |

1984. Europa. 25th Anniv of European Posts and Telecommunications Conference.
| 2788 | 813 | 12f. red and black | 70 | 10 |
| 2789 | | 22f. blue and black | 1·10 | 30 |

814 Leopold II 1884 10c. Stamp

1984. Stamp Day.
| 2790 | 814 | 12f. multicoloured | 60 | 10 |

815 Dove and Pencils

1984. 2nd European Parliament Elections.
| 2791 | 815 | 12f. multicoloured | 60 | 10 |

816 Shako   817 Church of Our Lady of the Chapel, Brussels

1984. 150th Anniv of Royal Military School.
| 2792 | 816 | 22f. multicoloured | 1·10 | 35 |

1984. Tourist Publicity. Multicoloured.
2793	10f. Type 817	50	25
2794	10f. St. Martin's Church and lime tree, Montigny-le-Tilleul	50	25
2795	10f. Belfry and Town Hall, Tielt (vert)	50	25

818 "Curious Masks" (detail, James Ensor)

1984. Inaug of Brussels Modern Art Museum.
2796	818	8f.+2f. multicoloured	75	60
2797		12f.+3f. multicoloured	95	85
2798		22f.+5f. multicoloured	1·25	1·25
2799		50f.+13f. grn, bl & blk	3·00	3·00

DESIGNS: 12f. "The Empire of Lights" (detail, Rene Magritte); 22f. "The End" (detail, Jan Cox); 50f. "Rhythm No. 6" (Jo Delahaut).

819 Symbolic Design   820 Averbode Abbey

1984. 50th Anniv of Chirojeugd (Christian youth movement).
| 2800 | 819 | 10f. yellow, violet & bl | 45 | 25 |

1984. Abbeys.
2801	820	8f. green and brown	35	25
2802		22f. brown & dp brown	1·10	35
2803		24f. green & light green	1·10	35
2804		50f. lilac and brown	2·25	70

DESIGNS—VERT: 22f. Chimay; 24f. Rochefort. HORIZ: 50f. Affligem.

821 Smurf as Postman   822 Child collecting Flowers

1984. "Philately for the Young".
| 2805 | 821 | 8f. multicoloured | 1·00 | 35 |

1984. Children.
2806	10f.+2f. Type 822	60	60
2807	12f.+3f. Children with globe	75	75
2808	15f.+3f. Child on merry-go-round	95	95

823 Meulemans   824 Three Kings

1984. Birth Cent of Arthur Meulemans (composer).
| 2809 | 823 | 12f. black and orange | 50 | 10 |

1984. Christmas.
| 2810 | 824 | 12f.+1f. multicoloured | 70 | 70 |

825 St. Norbert   826 "Virgin of Louvain" (attr. Jan Gossaert)

1985. 850th Death Anniv of St. Norbert.
| 2811 | 825 | 22f. brown & lt brown | 1·10 | 35 |

1985. "Europalia 85 Espana" Festival.
| 2812 | 826 | 12f. multicoloured | 50 | 15 |

827 Press Card in Hatband   828 Blood System as Tree

1985. Cent of Professional Journalists Association.
| 2814 | 827 | 9f. multicoloured | 40 | 25 |

1985. Belgian Red Cross. Blood Donations.
| 2815 | 828 | 9f.+2f. multicoloured | 65 | 65 |
| 2816 | | 23f.+5f. red, blue and black | 1·50 | 1·50 |

DESIGN: 23f. Two hearts.

829 "Sophrolaelio cattleya" "Burlingama"   830 Pope John Paul II

1985. Ghent Flower Festival. Orchids. Mult.
2817	12f. Type 829	50	15
2818	12f. Phalaenopsis "Malibu"	50	15
2819	12f. Tapeu orchid ("Vanda coerulea")	50	15

1985. Visit of Pope John Paul II.
| 2820 | 830 | 12f. multicoloured | 75 | 20 |

831 Rising Sun behind Chained Gates

1985. Centenary of Belgian Workers' Party.
| 2821 | 9f. Type 831 | 50 | 30 |
| 2822 | 12f. Broken wall, flag and rising sun | 50 | 20 |

832 Jean de Bast (engraver)

1985. Stamp Day.
| 2823 | 832 | 12f. blue | 50 | 10 |

834 Class 18 Steam Locomotive, 1896

1985. Public Transport Year. Multicoloured.
2826	9f. Type 834	60	20
2827	12f. Locomotive "Elephant", 1835	70	15
2828	23f. Class 23 tank engine, 1904	1·25	50
2829	24f. Class I Pacific locomotive, 1935	1·25	50

835 Cesar Franck and Score

1985. Europa. Music Year. Multicoloured.
| 2831 | 12f. Type 835 | 70 | 15 |
| 2832 | 23f. Queen and king with viola dressed in music score (Queen Elisabeth International Music Competition) | 1·25 | 45 |

836 Planned Canal Lock, Strepy-Thieu   837 Church of Our Lady's Assumption, Avernas-le-Bauduin

1985. Permanent International Navigation Congress Association Centenary Congress, Brussels. Multicoloured.
| 2833 | 23f. Type 836 | 1·25 | 50 |
| 2834 | 23f. Aerial view of Zeebrugge harbour | 1·25 | 50 |

1985. Tourist Publicity. Multicoloured.
2835	12f. Type 837	65	25
2836	12f. Saint Martin's Church, Marcinelle (horiz)	65	25
2837	12f. Roman tower and Church of old beguinage, Tongres	65	25
2838	12f. House, Wachtebeke (horiz)	65	25

838 Queen Astrid

839 Baking Matton Tart, Grammont

1985. 50th Death Anniv of Queen Astrid.
2839 **838** 12f. lt brown & brown ... 75 10

1985. Traditional Customs. Multicoloured.
2840 12f. Type **839** 65 25
2841 24f. Young people dancing on trumpet filled with flowers (cent of Red Youths, St. Lambert Cultural Circle, Hermalle-sous-Argenteau) ..... 1·10 45

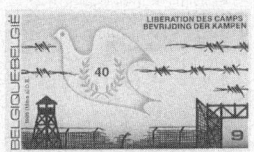
840 Dove and Concentration Camp

1985. 40th Anniv of Liberation. Multicoloured.
2842 9f. Type **840** 50 20
2843 23f. Battle of the Ardennes 1·00 50
2844 24f. Troops landing at Scheldt estuary ..... 1·60 45

841 Hawfinch ("Appelvink – Gros Bec")

842 Claes and Fictional Character

1985. Birds (1st series). Multicoloured.
2845 1f. Lesser spotted woodpecker ("Pic epeichette") 30 10
2846 2f. Eurasian tree sparrow ("Moineau friquet") ... 30 10
2847 3f. Type **841** 40 10
2847a 3f.50 European robin ("Rouge-gorge") ... 30 10
2848 4f. Bluethroat ("Gorge-bleue") 40 10
2848a 4f.50 Common stonechat ("Traquet patre") ... 30 20
2849 5f. Eurasian nuthatch ("Sittelle torchepot") .. 70 10
2850 6f. Northern bullfinch ("Bouvreuil") 75 10
2851 7f. Blue tit ("Mesange bleue") 50 10
2852 8f. River kingfisher ("Martin-pecheur") ... 50 20
2853 9f. Eurasian goldfinch ("Chardonneret") ... 50 10
2854 10f. Chaffinch ("Pinson") .. 70 20
See also Nos. 3073/86 and 3306/23.

1985. Birth Centenary of Ernest Claes (writer).
2855 **842** 9f. multicoloured ... 40 25

843 Youth

844 Trazegnies Castle

1985. "Philately for the Young". International Youth Year.
2856 **843** 9f. multicoloured ... 40 25

1985. "Solidarity". Castles. Multicoloured.
2857 9f.+2f. Type **844** 70 70
2858 12f.+3f. Laarne 80 80
2859 23f.+5f. Turnhout ..... 1·25 1·40
2860 50f.+12f. Colonster ..... 2·50 2·75

845 Miniature from "Book of Hours of Duc de Berry"

1985. Christmas.
2861 **845** 12f.+1f. multicoloured 70 70

846 King Baudouin and Queen Fabiola

1985. Royal Silver Wedding.
2862 **846** 12f. grey, blue and deep blue 90 20

847 Map and 1886 25c. Stamp

848 Giants and Belfry, Alost

1986. Centenary of First Independent State of Congo Stamp.
2863 **847** 10f. blue, grey & dp blue 50 25

1986. Carnivals. Multicoloured.
2864 9f. Type **848** 45 25
2865 12f. Clown, Binche 70 15

849 Dove as Hand holding Olive Twig

850 Emblem

1986. International Peace Year.
2866 **849** 23f. multicoloured ... 1·10 40

1986. 10th Anniv of King Baudouin Foundation.
2867 **850** 12f.+3f. blue, light blue and grey ..... 1·00 1·00

851 Virgin Mary

1986. "The Mystic Lamb" (altarpiece, Brothers Van Eyck). Multicoloured.
2868 9f.+2f. Type **851** 70 70
2869 13f.+3f. Christ in Majesty 95 95
2870 24f.+6f. St. John the Baptist 1·50 1·70

852 Exhibits

1986. Stamp Day. 50th Anniv of Postal Museum, Brussels.
2872 **852** 13f. multicoloured ... 60 10

853 Living and Dead Fish and Graph

854 Malinois Shepherd Dog

1986. Europa. Multicoloured.
2873 13f. Type **853** 70 15
2874 24f. Living and dead trees and graph .... 1·25 40

1986. Belgian Dogs. Multicoloured.
2875 9f. Type **854** 60 20
2876 13f. Tervuren shepherd dog 80 10
2877 24f. Groenendael cattle dog 1·10 50
2878 26f. Flanders cattle dog .. 1·25 50

855 St. Ludger Church, Zele

856 Boy, Broken Skateboard and Red Triangle

1986. Tourist Publicity.
2879 **855** 9f. brown and flesh ... 40 25
2880 – 9f. red and pink ... 45 25
2881 – 13f. green & light green 70 20
2882 – 13f. black and green . 70 20
2883 – 13f. blue and azure ... 70 20
2884 – 13f. brown & lt brown 70 20
DESIGNS—VERT: No. 2880, Town Hall, Wavre; 2882, Chapel of Our Lady of the Dunes, Bredene. HORIZ: 2881, Water-mills, Zwalm; 2883, Chateau Licot, Viroinval; 2884, Chateau d'Eynebourg, La Calamine.

1986. "Philately for the Young". 25th International Festival of Humour, Knokke.
2885 **856** 9f. black, green & red .. 40 25

857 Constant Permeke (artist)

1986. Celebrities. Multicoloured.
2886 9f. Type **857** (birth centenary) 50 20
2887 13f. Michael Edmond de Selys-Longchamps (naturalist) 70 15
2888 24f. Felix Timmermans (writer) (birth cent) .. 1·10 35
2889 26f. Maurice Careme (poet) 1·25 35

858 Academy Building, Ghent

1986. Centenary of Royal Academy for Dutch Language and Literature.
2890 **858** 9f. blue 40 25

859 Hops, Glass of Beer and Barley

1986. Belgian Beer.
2891 **859** 13f. multicoloured ... 70 20

860 Symbols of Provinces and National Colours

1986. 150th Anniv of Provincial Councils.
2892 **860** 13f. multicoloured ... 60 10

861 Lenoir, 1863

1986. "Solidarity". Cars. Multicoloured.
2893 9f.+2f. Type **861** 60 65
2894 13f.+3f. Pipe de Tourisme, 1911 .... 1·10 1·10
2895 24f.+6f. Minerva 22 h.p., 1930 .... 1·90 1·75
2896 26f.+6f. FN 8 cyl., 1931 ... 2·40 1·75

862 Snow Scene

1986. Christmas.
2897 **862** 13f.+1f. multicoloured 90 85

863 Tree and "100"

1986. Centenaries. Multicoloured.
2898 9f. Type **863** (Textile Workers Christian Union) 35 25
2899 13f. Tree and "100" (Christian Unions) ... 50 20

864 Corneel Heymans

865 Emblem

1987. Belgian Red Cross. Nobel Physiology and Medicine Prize Winners. Each black, red and stone.
2900 13f.+3f. Type **864** 90 90
2901 24f.+6f. Albert Claude ... 1·90 1·75

1987. "Flanders Technology International" Fair.
2902 **865** 13f. multicoloured ... 60 10

866 Bee Orchid

868 Jakob Wiener (engraver)

867 "Waiting" (detail of mural, Gustav Klimt)

1987. European Environment Year. Multicoloured.
2903 9f.+2f. Type 866 . . . . . 95 80
2904 24f.+6f. Small horse-shoe bat . . . . 1·60 1·75
2905 26f.+6f. Peregrine falcon ("Slechtvalk – Faucan Pelerin") . . . . 1·90 1·90

1987. "Europalia 87 Austria" Festival.
2906 **867** 13f. multicoloured . . . 60 10

1987. Stamp Day.
2907 **868** 13f. deep green and green 60 10

869 Penitents' Procession, Furnes
870 Louvain-la-Neuve Church (Jean Cosse)

1987. Folklore Festivals. Multicoloured.
2908 9f. Type 869 . . . . 40 30
2909 13f. "John and Alice" (play), Wavre 65 10

1987. Europa. Architecture. Multicoloured.
2910 13f. Type 870 . . . . 80 15
2911 24f. St.-Maartensdal (Regional Housing Association tower block), Louvain (Braem, de Mol and Moerkerke) . . . . . 1·25 45

871 Statue of Gretry and Stage Set
872 Virelles Lake

1987. 20th Anniv of Wallonia Royal Opera.
2912 **871** 24f. multicoloured . . . 1·25 45

1987. Tourist Publicity. Multicoloured.
2913 13f. St. Christopher's Church, Racour 70 20
2914 13f. Type 872 . . . . 70 20
2915 13f. Heimolen windmill, Keerbergen 70 20
2916 13f. Boondael Chapel 70 20
2917 13f. Statue of Jan Breydel and Pieter de Coninck, Bruges 70 20

873 Rowing

1987. Centenary of Royal Belgian Rowing Association (2918) and European Volleyball Championships (2919). Multicoloured.
2918 9f. Type 873 . . . . 35 25
2919 13f. Volleyball (27 × 37 mm) . . 70 20

874 Emblem

1987. Foreign Trade Year.
2920 **874** 13f. multicoloured . . . 60 10

875 "Leisure Time" (P. Paulus)

1987. Centenary of Belgian Social Law.
2921 **875** 26f. multicoloured . . . 1·10 35

876 Willy and Wanda (comic strip characters)

1987. "Philately for the Young".
2922 **876** 9f. multicoloured . . . . 1·25 30

878 Rixensart Castle

1987. "Solidarity". Castles. Multicoloured.
2928 9f.+2f. Type 878 . . . . . . 45 45
2929 13f.+3f. Westerlo . . . . . 1·00 70
2930 26f.+5f. Fallais . . . . . . 1·90 1·90
2931 50f.+12f. Gaasbeek . . . . 3·25 3·75

879 "Madonna and Child" (Remi Lens)
880 Cross and Road

1987. Christmas.
2932 **879** 13f.+1f. multicoloured . . 90 90

1987. 50th Anniv of Yellow and White Cross (home nursing organization).
2933 **880** 9f.+2f. multicoloured . . 90 90

881 Newsprint ("Le Soir")

1987. Newspaper Centenaries.
2934 **881** 9f. multicoloured 40 25
2935 – 9f. black and brown . . . 40 25
DESIGN—VERT: No. 2935, Type characters ("Het Laatste Nieuws" (1988)).

882 Lighthouse, "Snipe" (trawler) and Horse Rider in Sea
883 "Flanders Alive" (cultural activities campaign)

1988. The Sea. Multicoloured.
2936 10f. Type 882 . . . . 70 60
2937 10f. "Asannot" (trawler) and people playing on beach 70 60
2938 10f. Cross-channel ferry, yacht and bathing huts . . 70 60
2939 10f. Container ship, spotted redshank and oystercatcher 70 60
Nos. 2936/9 were issued together, se-tenant, forming a composite design.

1988. Regional Innovations.
2940 **883** 13f. multicoloured . . . 65 20
2941 – 13f. black, yellow & red . 65 20
DESIGN: No. 2941, "Operation Athena" emblem (technological advancement in Wallonia).

884 19th-century Postman (after James Thiriar)
885 "Bengale Triomphant"

1988. Stamp Day.
2942 **884** 13f. brown and cream . . 60 10

1988. Philatelic Promotion Fund. Illustrations from "60 Roses for a Queen" by Pierre-Joseph Redoute (1st series). Multicoloured.
2943 13f.+3f. Type 885 . . . . . 1·10 1·10
2944 24f.+6f. "Centfeuille cristata" . . . . 1·90 1·90
See also Nos. 2979/80 and 3009/10.

886 Non-polluting Motor

1988. Europa. Transport and Communications. Multicoloured.
2946 13f. Dish aerial 80 15
2947 24f. Type 886 . . . . 1·25 50

887 Table Tennis

1988. Olympic Games, Seoul. Multicoloured.
2948 9f.+2f. Type 887 . . . . . . 90 85
2949 13f.+3f. Cycling . . . . . . 1·10 1·10

888 Amay Tower
889 Monnet

1988. Tourist Publicity.
2951 **888** 9f. black and brown . . . 40 25
2952 – 9f. black and blue . . . 40 25
2953 – 9f. black, green and pink 40 25
2954 – 13f. black and pink . . 90 20
2955 – 13f. black and grey . . 90 20
DESIGNS—VERT: No. 2952, Lady of Hanswijk Basilica, Malines; 2954, Old Town Hall and village pump, Peer. HORIZ: No. 2953, St. Sernin's Church, Waimes; 2955, Basilica of Our Lady of Bon Secours, Peruwelz.

1988. Birth Centenary of Jean Monnet (statesman).
2956 **889** 13f. black and cream . . 60 20

890 Tapestry (detail) and Academy Building
891 Antwerp Ethnographical Museum Exhibits

1988. 50th Annivs of Royal Belgian Academy of Medicine (2957) and Royal Belgian Academy of Sciences, Literature and Fine Arts (2958). Multicoloured.
2957 9f. Type 890 . . . . 40 25
2958 9f. Symbols of Academy and building 40 25

1988. Cultural Heritage. Multicoloured.
2959 9f. Type 891 . . . . 40 25
2960 13f. Tomb of Lord Gilles Othon and Jacqueline de Lalaing, St. Martin's Church, Trazegnies 50 15

2961 24f. Organ, St. Bartholomew's Church, Geraardsbergen . . . . 1·50 45
2962 26f. St. Hadelin's reliquary, St. Martin's Church, Vise 1·25 45

892 Spirou (comic strip character) and Stamp

1988. "Philately for the Young". 50th Anniv of "Spirou" (comic).
2963 **892** 9f. multicoloured . . . . 1·10 30

893 Jacques Brel (songwriter)

1988. "Solidarity". Death Anniversaries. Mult.
2964 9f.+2f. Type 893 (10th) . . . 80 85
2965 13f.+3f. Jef Denyn (carilloner) (47th) . . . . 1·10 1·10
2966 26f.+6f. Fr. Ferdinand Verbiest (astronomer) (300th) . . . . 1·90 1·90

894 "75"

1988. 75th Anniv of Belgian Giro Bank.
2967 **894** 13f. multicoloured . . . 60 15

895 Winter Scene

1988. Christmas.
2968 **895** 9f. multicoloured 45 30

896 Standard Bearer and Guards of Royal Mounted Escort
897 Wooden Press, 1600

1988. 50th Anniv of Royal Mounted Escort.
2969 **896** 13f. multicoloured . . . 60 15

1988. Printing Presses.
2970 **897** 9f. black, pink and blue 40 15
2971 – 24f. brown, pink and deep brown . . . . . . 1·10 40
2972 – 26f. green, pink and light green . . . . 1·25 40
DESIGNS—VERT: 24f. 18th-cent Stanhope metal letterpress. HORIZ: 26f. 19th-cent Krause lithographic press.

898 "Crucifixion of Christ" (detail, Rogier van der Weyden)

1989. Belgian Red Cross. Paintings. Mult.
2973	9f.+2f. Type **898**	80	80
2974	13f.+3f. "Virgin and Child" (Gerard David)	1·10	1·10
2975	24f.+6f. "The Good Samaritan" (detail, Denis van Alsloot)	1·60	1·60

899 Marche en Famenne

1989. Lace-making Towns.
2976	**899**	9f. green, black & brown	50	30
2977	–	13f. blue, black & grey	70	20
2978	–	13f. red, black & grey . .	70	20

DESIGNS. No. 2977, Bruges; 2978, Brussels.

1989. Philatelic Promotion Fund. "60 Roses for a Queen" by Pierre-Joseph Redoute (2nd series). As T **885**. Multicoloured.
| 2979 | 13f.+5f. "Centfeuille unique melee de rouge" . . . | 1·00 | 1·10 |
| 2980 | 24f.+6f. "Bengale a grandes feuilles" . . . . . | 1·90 | 1·75 |

900 Post-chaise and Mail Coach

1989. Stamp Day.
| 2982 | **900** | 13f. yellow, black & brn | 60 | 15 |

901 Marbles

902 Palette on Column

1989. Europa. Children's Games and Toys. Multicoloured.
| 2983 | 13f. Type **901** . . . . . | 80 | 15 |
| 2984 | 24f. Jumping-jack . . . . . | 1·25 | 45 |

1989. 325th Anniv of Royal Academy of Fine Arts, Antwerp.
| 2985 | **902** | 13f. multicoloured . . . | 60 | 15 |

903 Brussels (½-size illustration)

1989. 3rd Direct Elections to European Parliament.
| 2986 | **903** | 13f. multicoloured . . . | 70 | 25 |

904 Hand (detail, "Creation of Adam", Michelangelo)

905 St. Tillo's Church, Izegem

1989. Bicentenary of French Declaration of Rights of Man.
| 2987 | **904** | 13f. black, red and blue | 65 | 25 |

1989. Tourist Publicity. Multicoloured.
2988	9f. Type **905**	50	30
2989	9f. Logne Castle, Ferrieres (vert)	50	30
2990	13f. Antoing Castle (vert)	75	20
2991	13f. St. Laurentius's Church, Lokeren (vert)	75	20

906 Mallard

1989. Ducks. Multicoloured.
2992	13f. Type **906**	1·10	45
2993	13f. Green-winged teal ("Sarcelle d'Hiver") . . .	1·10	45
2994	13f. Common shoveler ("Canard Souchet") . . .	1·10	45
2995	13f. Pintail ("Canard Pilet")	1·10	45

907 "Shogun Uesugi Shigefusa" (Kamakura period wood figure)

1989. "Europalia 89 Japan" Festival.
| 2996 | **907** | 24f. multicoloured . . . | 1·25 | 45 |

908 Profiles

909 Map

1989. 125th Anniv of League of Teaching and Permanent Education.
| 2997 | **908** | 13f. multicoloured . . . | 60 | 15 |

1989. 150th Anniv of Division of Limburg between Netherlands and Belgium.
| 2998 | **909** | 13f. multicoloured . . . | 60 | 15 |

910 Nibbs (comic strip character)

911 Flower Beds in Greenhouse

1989. "Philately for the Young".
| 2999 | **910** | 9f. multicoloured . . . . | 1·10 | 30 |

1989. "Solidarity". Royal Greenhouses, Laeken. Multicoloured.
3000	9f.+3f. Statue and greenhouses (horiz) . . .	75	75
3001	13f.+4f. Type **911** . . .	1·00	1·00
3002	24f.+5f. External view of greenhouse	1·60	1·60
3003	26f.+6f. Trees in greenhouse	1·75	1·75

912 Treble Clef

1989. 50th Anniv of Queen Elisabeth Musical Chapel, Waterloo.
| 3004 | **912** | 24f.+6f. multicoloured | 1·75 | 1·75 |

913 Army Musicians

1989. Christmas. Centenary of Salvation Army in Belgium.
| 3005 | **913** | 9f. multicoloured . . . . | 45 | 20 |

914 Fr. Damien and Church

915 Fr. Daens

1989. Death Cent of Fr. Damien (missionary).
| 3006 | **914** | 24f. multicoloured . . . | 1·50 | 45 |

1989. 150th Birth Anniv of Fr. Adolf Daens (social reformer).
| 3007 | **915** | 9f. turquoise and green | 45 | 15 |

916 "Courier" (Albrecht Durer)

917 "Iris florentina"

1990. 500th Anniv of Regular European Postal Services.
| 3008 | **916** | 14f. chocolate, buff and brown . . . . | 75 | 15 |

1990. Philatelic Promotion Fund. "60 Roses for a Queen" by Pierre-Joseph Redoute (3rd series). As T **885**. Multicoloured.
| 3009 | 14f.+7f. "Bengale Desprez" | 1·25 | 1·25 |
| 3010 | 25f.+12f. "Bengale Philippe" | 2·25 | 2·10 |

1990. Ghent Flower Show. Multicoloured.
3012	10f. Type **917**	50	25
3013	14f. "Cattleya harrisoniana"	75	15
3014	14f. "Lilium bulbiferum" . .	75	15

918 Emilienne Brunfaut (women's rights activist)

1990. International Women's Day.
| 3015 | **918** | 25f. red and black . . . | 1·25 | 45 |

919 Special Olympics

921 "Postman Roulin" (Vincent van Gogh)

920 Water, Tap and Heart

1990. Sporting Events. Multicoloured.
3016	10f. Type **919**	45	25
3017	14f. Football (World Cup football championship, Italy)	80	15
3018	25f. Disabled pictogram and ball (Gold Cup wheelchair basketball championship, Bruges)	1·10	45

1990. 75th Anniv of Foundation of National Water Supply Society (predecessor of present water-supply companies).
| 3019 | **920** | 14f. multicoloured . . . | 75 | 15 |

1990. Stamp Day.
| 3020 | **921** | 14f. multicoloured . . . | 75 | 15 |

922 Worker and Crowd

923 Liege I Post Office

1990. Centenary of Labour Day.
| 3021 | **922** | 25f. brown, pink & black | 1·25 | 45 |

1990. Europa. Post Office Buildings.
| 3022 | – | 14f. black and blue . . . | 95 | 15 |
| 3023 | **923** | 25f. black and red . . . | 1·10 | 45 |

DESIGN—HORIZ: 14f. Ostend I Post Office.

924 Monument of the Lys, Courtrai

1990. 50th Anniv of the 18 Days Campaign (resistance to German invasion).
| 3024 | **924** | 14f. black, yellow & red | 75 | 20 |

925 Battle Scene (⅔-size illustration)

1990. 175th Anniv of Battle of Waterloo.
| 3026 | **925** | 25f. multicoloured . . . | 1·25 | 95 |

926 Berendrecht Lock, Antwerp

927 King Baudouin

1990. Tourist Publicity. Multicoloured.
3027	10f. Type **926**	70	25
3028	10f. Procession of Bayard Steed, Termonde . . .	70	25
3029	14f. St. Rolende's March, Gerpinnes (vert)	70	15
3030	14f. Lommel (1000th anniv)	70	15
3031	14f. St. Clement's Church, Watermael	70	15

1990.
| 3032 | **927** | 14f. multicoloured . . . | 90 | 15 |

928 Eurasian Perch

1990. Fishes. Multicoloured.
3033	14f. Type **928**	1·50	55
3034	14f. Eurasian minnow ("Vairon")	1·50	55
3035	14f. European bitterling ("Bouviere")	1·50	55
3036	14f. Three-spined stickleback ("Epinoche") . . .	1·50	55

929 Orchestra and Children (½-size illustration)

1990. "Solidarity". Multicoloured.
3037 10f.+2f. Type **929** (50th anniv of Jeunesses Musicales) . . . . . . 1·50 1·50
3038 14f.+3f. Count of Egmont (16th-century campaigner for religious tolerance) and Beethoven (composer of "Egmont" overture) . . 1·90 1·90
3039 25f.+6f. Jozef Cantre (sculptor) and sculptures (birth centenary) . . . . 2·75 2·50

930 Lucky Luke (comic strip character)

1990. "Philately for the Young".
3040 **930** 10f. multicoloured . . . 1·00 30

931 St. Bernard

1990. 900th Birth Anniv of St. Bernard (Abbot of Clairvaux and Church mediator).
3041 **931** 25f. black and flesh . . . 1·25 45

932 "Pepingen, Winter 1977" (Jozef Lucas)

1990. Christmas.
3042 **932** 10f. multicoloured . . . 50 25

933 "Self-portrait"

1990. 300th Death Anniv of David Teniers, the Younger (painter). Multicoloured.
3043 10f. Type **933** 50 25
3044 14f. "Dancers" 70 15
3045 25f. "Peasants playing Bowls outside Village Inn" . . . 1·10 45

934 King Baudouin and Queen Fabiola (photograph by Valeer Vanbeckbergen)

1990. Royal 30th Wedding Anniversary.
3046 **934** 50f.+15f. mult . . . . 7·50 7·50

935 "Temptation of St. Anthony" (detail, Hieronymus Bosch) **936** "The Sower" (detail of "Monument to Labour", Brussels) (Constantin Meunier)

1991. Belgian Red Cross. Paintings. Mult.
3047 14f.+3f. Type **935** . . . . . 1·75 1·75
3048 25f.+6f. "The Annunciation" (detail, Dirck Bouts) . . . . . . 2·75 2·75

1991. 19th-Century Sculpture.
3049 14f. black & cinnamon 75 20
3050 – 25f. black and blue . . 1·25 45
DESIGN: 25f. Detail of Brabo Fountain, Antwerp (Jef Lambeaux).

937 Rhythmic Gymnastics (European Youth Olympic Days, Brussels)

1991. Sports Meetings.
3051 **937** 10f. grey, mauve & blk 50 20
3052 – 10f. grey, green & black 50 20
DESIGN: No. 3052, Korfball (Third World Championship, Belgium).

938 New Stamp Printing Office, Malines (Hugo van Hoecke)

1991. Stamp Day.
3053 **938** 14f. multicoloured . . . 75 20

939 Cogwheels

1991. Centenary of Liberal Trade Union.
3054 **939** 25f. blue, light blue and deep blue . . . . 1·25 45

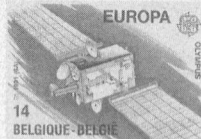

940 "Olympus 1" Communications Satellite

1991. Europa. Europe in Space. Multicoloured.
3055 14f. Type **940** 90 15
3056 25f. "Ariane 5" rocket carrying space shuttle "Hermes" . . . . . 1·60 45

941 Leo XIII's Arms and Standard, and Christian Labour Movement Banners

1991. Centenary of "Rerum Novarum" (encyclical letter from Pope Leo XIII on workers' rights).
3057 **941** 14f. multicoloured . . . 75 15

942 "Isabella of Portugal and Philip the Good" (anon)

1991. "Europalia 91 Portugal" Festival.
3058 **942** 14f. multicoloured . . . 75 20

943 Neptune Grottoes, Couvin

1991. Tourist Publicity. Multicoloured.
3059 14f. Type **943** 90 30
3060 14f. Dieleghem Abbey, Jette 70 30
3061 14f. Niel Town Hall (vert) 70 30
3062 14f. Hautes Fagnes nature reserve 70 30
3063 14f. Giant Rolarius, Roeselare (vert) 70 30

944 King Baudouin (photograph by Dimitri Ardelean)

1991. 60th Birthday (1990) and 40th Anniv of Accession to Throne of King Baudouin.
3064 **944** 14f. multicoloured . . . 1·25 15

945 Academy Building, Caduceus and Leopold I

1991. 150th Anniv of Royal Academy of Medicine.
3065 **945** 10f. multicoloured . . . 50 25

946 "The English Coast at Dover"   **948** Hands reaching through Bars

947 Death Cap

1991. 61st Death Anniv of Alfred Finch (painter and ceramic artist).
3066 **946** 25f. multicoloured . . . 1·25 45

1991. Fungi. Multicoloured.
3067 14f. Type **947** . . . . . 1·50 65
3068 14f. The Blusher (inscr "Golmotte") . . . . . 1·50 65
3069 14f. Flaky-stemmed witches' mushroom (inscr "Bolet a pied rouge") . . . . . 1·50 65
3070 14f. "Hygrocybe persistens" (inscr "Hygrophore jaune conique") . . . . . 1·50 65

1991. 30th Anniv of Amnesty International (3071) and 11th Anniv of Belgian Branch of Medecins sans Frontieres (3072). Multicoloured.
3071 25f. Type **948** . . . . . . 1·25 45
3072 25f. Doctor examining baby 1·25 45

1991. Birds (2nd series). As T **841**. Mult.
3073 50c. Goldcrest ("Roitelet Huppe") 10 10
3074 1f. Mealy redpoll ("Sizerin Flamme") 10 10
3075 2f. Blackbird ("Merle Noir") 15 10
3076 3f. Reed bunting ("Bruant des Roseaux") 30 10
3077 4f. Wagtail ("Bergeronette Grise") 30 10
3078 5f. Barn swallow ("Hirondelle de Cheminee") 30 10
3078b 5f.50 Jay ("Geai des Chenes") 35 15
3079 6f. White-throated dipper ("Cincle Plongeur") . . . 40 15
3079a 6f.50 Sedge-warbler ("Phragmite des Jones") 40 15
3080 7f. Oriole ("Loriot") . . . 50 15
3081 8f. Great tit ("Mesange Charbonniere") 50 15
3082 9f. Song thrush ("Grive Musicienne") 50 15
3083 10f. Greenfinch ("Verdier") 60 15
3084 11f. Winter wren ("Troglodyte Mignon") . . 60 15
3085 13f. House sparrow ("Moineau Domestique") 90 15
3085a 14f. Willow warbler ("Pouillot Fitis") 90 15
3086 16f. Waxwing ("Jaseur Boreal") . . . . . . 1·10 15

949 Exhibition Emblem

1991. "Telecom 91" International Telecommunications Exhibition, Geneva.
3089 **949** 14f. multicoloured . . . 75 20

950 Blake and Mortimer in "The Yellow Mark" (Edgar P. Jacobs)

1991. "Philately for the Young". Comic Strips. Multicoloured.
3090 14f. Type **950** . . . . . 1·25 70
3091 14f. Cori the ship boy in "The Ill-fated Voyage" (Bob de Moor) . . . . 1·50 70
3092 14f. "Cities of the Fantastic" (Francois Schuiten) . . . . . 1·25 70
3093 14f. "Boule and Bill" (Jean Roba) . . . . 1·25 70

951 Charles Dekeukeleire

1991. "Solidarity". Film Makers.
3094 **951** 10f.+2f. black, brown and green 95 70
3095 – 14f.+3f. black, orange and brown . . . . 1·50 1·25
3096 – 25f.+6f. black, ochre and brown . . . . 2·10 2·40
DESIGNS: 14f. Jacques Ledoux; 25f. Jacques Feyder.

952 Printing Press forming "100" ("Gazet van Antwerpen")

1991. Newspaper Centenaries. Multicoloured.
3097 **952** 10f. black, lt grn & grn 50 20
3098 – 10f. yellow, blue & blk 50 20
DESIGN: No. 3098, Cancellation on "stamp" ("Het Volk").

953 "Our Lady rejoicing in the Child" (icon, Chevetogne Abbey)

955 Speed Skating

954 Mozart and Score

1991. Christmas.
3099 **953** 10f. multicoloured 50 25

1991. Death Bicentenary of Wolfgang Amadeus Mozart (composer).
3100 **954** 25f. purple, bl & ultram 1·25 45

1992. Olympic Games, Albertville and Barcelona. Multicoloured.
3101 10f.+2f. Type **955** 1·00 1·00
3102 10f.+2f. Baseball 1·00 1·00
3103 14f.+3f. Tennis (horiz) 1·25 1·25
3104 25f.+6f. Clay-pigeon shooting 2·10 2·10

956 Fire Hose and Service Emblem

957 Flames and Silhouette of Man

1992. Fire Service.
3105 **956** 14f. multicoloured 75 15

1992. The Resistance.
3106 **957** 14f. yellow, black & red 75 15

958 Tapestry and Carpet

959 Belgian Pavilion and Exhibition Emblem

1992. Prestige Occupations. Multicoloured.
3107 10f. Type **958** 50 15
3108 14f. Chef's hat and cutlery (10th anniv (1991) of Association of Belgian Master Chefs) 80 15
3109 27f. Diamond and "100" (centenary (1993) of Antwerp Diamond Club) 1·75 40

1992. "Expo '92" World's Fair, Seville.
3110 **959** 14f. multicoloured 75 15

960 King Baudouin

961

1992.
3111 **960** 15f. red 75 10
3115 – 28f. green 1·60 45
3120 **961** 100f. green 5·25 65

962 Van Noten at Work

963 "White Magic No. VI"

1992. Stamp Day. 10th Death Anniv of Jean van Noten (stamp designer).
3124 **962** 15f. black and red 75 15

1992. Original Art Designs for Stamps. Mult.
3125 15f. Type **963** 75 20
3126 15f. "Colours" (horiz) 75 20

964 Compass Rose, Setting Sun and Harbour

1992. Europa. 500th Anniv of Discovery of America. Multicoloured.
3127 15f. Type **964** 75 15
3128 28f. Globe and astrolabe forming "500" 1·60 45

965 Faces of Different Colours

1992. Anti-racism.
3129 **965** 15f. grey, black & pink 75 15

966 "The Hamlet" (Jacob Smits)

1992. Belgian Paintings in Orsay Museum, Paris. Multicoloured.
3130 11f. Type **966** 50 15
3131 15f. "The Bath" (Alfred Stevens) 80 15
3132 30f. "Man at the Helm" (Theo van Rysselberghe) 1·50 50

967 Proud Margaret

968 Mannekin-Pis, Brussels

1992. Folk Tales. Multicoloured.
3133 11f.+2f. Type **967** 1·10 1·10
3134 15f.+3f. Witches ("Les Macrales") 1·60 1·60
3135 28f.+6f. Reynard the fox 2·50 2·50

1992. Tourist Publicity. Multicoloured.
3136 15f. Type **968** 70 20
3137 15f. Former Landcommandery of Teutonic Order, Alden Biesen (now Flemish cultural centre) (horiz) 70 20
3138 15f. Andenne (1300th anniv) 70 20
3139 15f. Carnival revellers on Fools' Monday, Renaix (horiz) 70 20
3140 15f. Great Procession (religious festival), Tournai (horiz) 70 20

969 European Polecat

1992. Mammals. Multicoloured.
3141 15f. Type **969** 1·25 60
3142 15f. Eurasian red squirrel 1·25 60
3143 15f. Eurasian hedgehog 1·25 60
3144 15f. Common dormouse 1·25 60

970 Henri van der Noot, Jean van der Meersch and Jean Vonck

1992. 203rd Anniv of Brabant Revolution.
3145 **970** 15f. multicoloured 75 15

971 Arms of Thurn and Taxis

972 Gaston Lagaffe (cartoon character)

1992. 500th Anniv of Mention of Thurn and Taxis Postal Services in Lille Account Books.
3146 **971** 15f. multicoloured 75 15

1992. "Philately for the Young".
3147 **972** 15f. multicoloured 95 25

973 Star, "B" and Map

1992. European Single Market.
3148 **973** 15f. multicoloured 75 15

974 Okapi

975 "Place Royale in Winter" (Luc de Decker)

1992. 150th Anniv of Antwerp Zoo. Mult.
3149 15f. Type **974** 75 15
3150 30f. Golden-headed tamarin 1·60 40

1992. Christmas.
3151 **975** 11f. multicoloured 50 25

976 "Man with Pointed Hat" (Adriaen Brouwer)

1993. Belgian Red Cross. Paintings. Mult.
3152 15f.+3f. Type **976** 1·50 1·50
3153 28f.+7f. "Nereid and Triton" (Peter Paul Rubens) (horiz) 3·00 3·00

977 Council of Leptines, 743

1993. Historical Events. Multicoloured.
3154 11f. Type **977** 60 15
3155 15f. Queen Beatrix and King Matthias I Corvinus of Hungary (detail of "Missale Romanum") (77 × 24 mm) 75 15
3156 30f. Battle scene (Battles of Neerwinden, 1673 and 1773) 1·60 45

978 Town Hall

1993. Antwerp, European City of Culture. Mult.
3158 15f. Panorama of Antwerp (76 × 24 mm) 75 15
3159 15f. Type **978** 75 15
3160 15f. "Study of Women's Heads and Male Torso" (Jacob Jordaens) 75 15
3161 15f. St. Job's altarpiece, Schoonbroek 75 15
3162 15f. "Angels" (stained glass window by Eugeen Yoors, Mother of God Chapel, Marie-Josee Institute, Elisabethville) (vert) 75 15

979 1893 2f. Stamp

980 "Florence 1960" (Gaston Bertrand)

1993. Stamp Day.
3163 **979** 15f. multicoloured 75 20

1993. Europa. Contemporary Art. Multicoloured.
3164 15f. Type **980** 80 15
3165 28f. "The Gig" (Constant Permeke) 1·50 45

981 Red Admiral ("Vanessa atalanta")

1993. Butterflies. Multicoloured.
3166 15f. Type **981** 70 25
3167 15f. Purple emperor ("Apatura iris") 70 25
3168 15f. Peacock ("Inachis io") 70 25
3169 15f. Small tortoiseshell ("Aglais urticae") 70 25

982 Knot　　　　**983** Mayan Warrior
　　　　　　　　　　　　　　(statuette)

1993. 150th Anniv of Alumni of Free University of Brussels Association.
3170 **982** 15f. blue and black . . . 　75　15

1993. "Europalia 93 Mexico" Festival.
3171 **983** 15f. multicoloured . . . . 　75　15

984 Ommegang, Brussels

1993. Folklore Festivals. Multicoloured.
3172　11f. Type **984** . . . . 　55　25
3173　15f. Royale Moncrabeau,
　　　　　Namur . . . . 　70　25
3174　28f. Stilt-walkers, Merchtem
　　　　　(vert) . . . . 　1·60　50

985 La Hulpe Castle

1993. Tourist Publicity.
3175 **985** 15f. black and blue . . . 　70　15
3176　 – 15f. black and lilac . . . 　70　15
3177　 – 15f. black and grey . . . 　70　15
3178　 – 15f. black and pink . . . 　70　15
3179　 – 15f. black and green . . . 　70　15
DESIGNS—HORIZ: No. 3176, Cortewalle Castle, Beveren; 3177, Jehay Castle; 3179, Raeren Castle. VERT: No. 3178, Arenberg Castle, Heverlee.

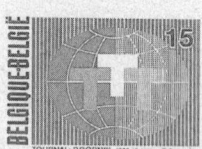

986 Emblem

1993. 2nd International Triennial Textile Exhibition, Tournai.
3180 **986** 15f. blue, red and black 　75　20

987 Presidency Emblem

1993. Belgian Presidency of European Community Council.
3181 **987** 15f. multicoloured . . . 　75　20

988 Magritte　　　**989** King
　　　　　　　　　　　　　　Baudouin

1993. 25th Death Anniv (1992) of Rene Magritte (artist).
3182 **988** 30f. multicoloured . . . 　1·50　45

1993. King Baudouin Commemoration.
3183 **989** 15f. black and blue . . . 　90　15

990 Red and White Cat

1993. Cats. Multicoloured.
3184　15f. Type **990** . . . . . . 　1·00　50
3185　15f. Tabby and white cat
　　　　　standing on rock . . . . 　1·00　50
3186　15f. Silver tabby lying on
　　　　　wall . . . . 　1·00　50
3187　15f. Tortoiseshell and white
　　　　　cat sitting by gardening
　　　　　tools . . . . 　1·00　50

991 Highlighted Cancer Cell　　**992** Frontispiece

1993. Anti-cancer Campaign.
3188 **991** 15f.+3f. multicoloured 　1·25　1·25

1993. 450th Anniv of "De Humani Corporis Fabrica" (treatise on human anatomy) by Andreas Vesalius.
3189 **992** 15f. black, brown & red 　75　15

993 Natacha (cartoon character)

1993. "Philately for the Young".
3190 **993** 15f. multicoloured . . . 　90　25

994 Sun's Rays　　　**995** "Madonna and Child"
　　　　　　　　　　　　　　(statue, Our Lady of the
　　　　　　　　　　　　　　Chapel, Brussels)

1993. 50th Anniv of Publication of "Le Faux Soir" (resistance newspaper).
3191 **994** 11f. multicoloured . . . 　50　30

1993. Christmas.
3192 **995** 11f. multicoloured . . . 　50　25

996 Child looking at Globe

1993. Children's Town Councils.
3193 **996** 15f. multicoloured . . . 　75　15

997 King Albert II　　**998** King Albert II

1993.
3194 **997** 16f. multicoloured . . . 　1·10　10
3196　 – 16f. turquoise and blue 　90　10
3198　 – 20f. brown and stone 　95　15
3203　 – 30f. purple and mauve 　1·25　15

3204　 – 32f. orange and yellow 　1·50　15
3205　 – 40f. red and mauve . . . 　1·90　15
3207　 – 50f. myrtle and green . . 　1·75　25
3208 **998** 100f. multicoloured . . . 　4·50　35
3209　 – 200f. multicoloured . . . 　9·50　85
See also No. 3621.

999 "Ma Toute Belle"　　**1000** Olympic Flames
(Serge Vandercam)　　　　　　and Rings

1994. Painters' Designs. Multicoloured.
3210　16f. Type **999** . . . . . . 　75　15
3211　16f. "The Malleable
　　　　　Darkness" (Octave
　　　　　Landuyt) (horiz) . . . . 　75　15

1994. Sports. Multicoloured.
3212　16f.+3f. Type **1000** (cent of
　　　　　International Olympic
　　　　　Committee) . . . . . . 　1·50　1·50
3213　16f.+3f. Footballers (World
　　　　　Cup Football
　　　　　Championship, U.S.A.) . 　1·50　1·50
3214　16f.+3f. Skater (Winter
　　　　　Olympic Games,
　　　　　Lillehammer, Norway) . 　1·50　1·50

1001 Hanriot HD-1　　**1002** Masthead of
　　　　　　　　　　　　　　"Le Jour-Le
　　　　　　　　　　　　　　Courrier"
　　　　　　　　　　　　　　(centenary)

1994. Biplanes. Multicoloured.
3215　13f. Type **1001** . . . . . . 　60　15
3216　15f. Spad XIII . . . . . . 　75　15
3217　30f. Schrenck FBA.H flying
　　　　　boat . . . . 　1·50　50
3218　32f. Stampe SV-4B . . . . 　1·50　50

1994. Newspaper Anniversaries. Multicoloured.
3219　16f. Type **1002** . . . . . . 　65　15
3220　16f. Masthead of "La
　　　　　Wallonie" (75th anniv)
　　　　　(horiz) . . . . 　65　15

1003 "Fall of the Golden Calf" (detail,
Fernand Allard l'Olivier)

1994. Centenary of Charter of Quaregnon (social charter).
3221 **1003** 16f. multicoloured . . . 　70　15

1004 1912 5f. Stamp

1994. Stamp Day. 60th Death Anniv of King Albert I.
3222 **1004** 16f. purple, mauve & bl 　70　15

1005 Reconciliation of Duke John I
and Arnold, Squire of Wezemaal

1994. 700th Death Anniv of John I, Duke of Brabant. Illustrations from 15th-century "Brabantse Yeesten". Multicoloured.
3223　13f. Type **1005** . . . . . . 　60　15
3224　16f. Tournament at wedding
　　　　　of his son John to
　　　　　Margaret of York, 1290 　75　15
3225　30f. Battle of Woeringen
　　　　　(77 × 25 mm) . . . . . . 　1·50　45

1006 Georges　　　**1008** St. Peter's Church,
Lemaitre　　　　　　　　　Bertem
(formulator of
expanding Universe
and of "big bang"
theory)

1007 Father Damien (missionary
and leprosy worker)

1994. Europa. Discoveries and Inventions. Mult.
3226　16f. Type **1006** . . . . . . 　75　15
3227　30f. Gerardus Mercator
　　　　　(inventor of Mercator
　　　　　projection in cartography) 　1·50　45

1994. Visit of Pope John Paul II. Mult.
3228　16f. Type **1007**
　　　　　(beatification) . . . . . . 　70　20
3229　16f. St. Mutien-Marie (5th
　　　　　anniv of canonization) . . 　70　20

1994. Tourist Publicity. Multicoloured.
3230　16f. Type **1008** . . . . . . 　70　15
3231　16f. St. Bavo's Church,
　　　　　Kanegem (vert) . . . . 　70　15
3232　16f. Royal St. Mary's
　　　　　Church, Schaarbeek . . . 　70　15
3233　16f. St. Gery's Church,
　　　　　Aubechies . . . . . . 　70　15
3234　16f. Sts. Peter and Paul's
　　　　　Church, St.-Severin en
　　　　　Condroz (vert) . . . . . . 　70　15

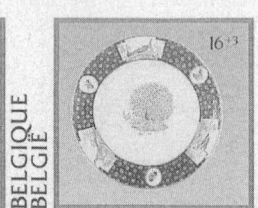

1009 Tournai Porcelain Plate from Duke
of Orleans Service (Mariemont Museum)

1994. Museum Exhibits. Multicoloured.
3235　16f.+3f. Type **1009** . . . . 　1·25　1·25
3236　16f.+3f. Etterbeek porcelain
　　　　　coffee cup and saucer
　　　　　(Louvain Municipal
　　　　　Museum) . . . . . . 　1·25　1·25

1010 Guillame Lekeu (composer)

1994. Anniversaries. Multicoloured.
3238　16f. Type **1010** (death cent) 　70　15
3239　16f. Detail of painting by
　　　　　Hans Memling (500th
　　　　　death anniv) . . . . . . 　70　15

1011 Generals Crerar, Montgomery and
Bradley and Allied Troops (½-size
illustration)

1994. 50th Anniv of Liberation.
3240 **1011** 16f. multicoloured . . . 　90　30

1012 Marsh Marigold ("Caltha palustris")

1994. Flowers. Multicoloured.
3241 16f. Type **1012** . . . . 1·10 50
3242 16f. White helleborine
("Cephalanthera
damasonium") . . . . . 1·10 50
3243 16f. Sea bindweed
("Calystegia soldanella") 1·10 50
3244 16f. Broad-leaved
helleborine ("Epipactis
helleborine") . . . . . 1·10 50

1013 Cubitus
(cartoon character)

1014 Simenon and Bridge of
Arches, Liege

1994. "Philately for the Young".
3245 **1013** 16f. multicoloured . . . 1·10 25

1994. 5th Death Anniv of Georges Simenon
(novelist).
3246 **1014** 16f. multicoloured . . . 1·10 25
The depiction of the bridge alludes to Simenon's
first novel "Au Pont des Arches".

1015 Deaf Man and Butterfly

1994. "Solidarity".
3247 **1015** 16f.+3f. mult 95 95

1016 Santa Claus on Rooftop

1994. Christmas.
3248 **1016** 13f. multicoloured . . . 60 25

1017 Field and Flax Knife (Flax
Museum, Courtrai)

1995. Museums. Multicoloured.
3249 16f.+3f. Type **1017** 95 95
3250 16f.+3f. River and pump
(Water and Fountain
Museum, Genval) 95 95
The premium was for the promotion of philately.

1018 Emblem

1995. Anniversaries. Anniversary emblems.
3252 **1018** 16f. red, blue & black 65 15
3253 – 16f. multicoloured . . . 65 15
3254 – 16f. red, grey & black . 65 15
3255 – 16f. black & brown . . 65 15
ANNIVERSARIES: No. 3252, 50th anniv of August
Vermeylen Fund; 3253, Centenary of Touring Club of
Belgium; 3254, Centenary of Federation of Belgian
Enterprises; 3255, 50th anniv of Social Security in
Belgium.

1019 "Hibiscus rosa-sinensis"

1995. Ghent Flower Show. Multicoloured.
3256 13f. Type **1019** 65 25
3257 16f. Azalea 75 20
3258 30f. Fuchsia . . . . 1·50 45

1020 Crossword
Puzzle

1021 Frans de Troyer
(promoter of thematic
philately)

1995. Games and Pastimes. Multicoloured.
3259 13f. Type **1020** 65 25
3260 16f. Chessman 75 25
3261 30f. Scrabble . . . . . . 1·50 45
3262 34f. Queen (playing cards) 1·50 45

1995. Post Day.
3263 **1021** 16f. black, stone & orge 75 15

1022 Watch Tower and Barbed Wire
Fence

1995. Europa. Peace and Freedom. Mult.
3264 16f. Type **1022** (50th anniv
of liberation of
concentration camps) . . 80 15
3265 30f. Nuclear cloud (25th
anniv of Non-
Proliferation Treaty) . . . 1·25 40

1023 Soldiers of the Irish
Brigade and Memorial Cross

1995. 250th Anniv of Battle of Fontenoy.
3266 **1023** 16f. multicoloured . . . 90 15

1024 U.N. Emblem

1995. 50th Anniv of U.N.O.
3267 **1024** 16f. multicoloured . . . 75 15

1025 "Sauvagemont, Maransart"
(Pierre Alechinsky)

1995. Artists' Philatelic Creations.
3268 **1025** 16f. red, black & yellow 75 15
3269 – 16f. multicoloured . . . 75 15
DESIGN: No. 3269, "Telegram-style" (Pol Mara).

1026 Paul Cauchie (Brussels)

1995. Tourist Publicity. Art nouveau house facades
by named architects. Multicoloured.
3270 16f. Type **1026** 75 10
3271 16f. Frans Smet-Verhas
(Antwerp) 75 10
3272 16f. Paul Jaspar (Liege) . . 75 10

1027 Anniversary Emblem

1995. Cent of Royal Belgian Football Assn.
3273 **1027** 16f.+4f. mult . . . . . 1·10 1·10

1028 "Mercator" (Belgian cadet barque)

1995. Sailing Ships. Multicoloured.
3274 16f. Type **1028** . . . . . . 1·00 50
3275 16f. "Kruzenshern" (Russian
cadet barque) (inscr
"Kruzenstern") . . . . . 1·00 50
3276 16f. "Sagres II" (Portuguese
cadet barque) . . . . . 1·00 50
3277 16f. "Amerigo Vespucci"
(Italian cadet ship) . . . 1·00 50

1029 Princess Astrid and Globe

1995. Red Cross. Multicoloured.
3278 16f.+3f. Type **1029**
(Chairwoman) . . . . . 1·00 1·00
3279 16f.+3f. Wilhelm Rontgen
(discoverer of X-rays) and
X-ray of hand . . . . . 1·00 1·00
3280 16f.+3f. Louis Pasteur
(chemist) and microscope . 1·00 1·00

1030 1908 Minerva

1995. Motor Cycles. Multicoloured.
3281 13f. Type **1030** 60 20
3282 16f. 1913 FN (vert) 70 20
3283 30f. 1929 La Mondiale . . . 1·50 45
3284 32f. 1937 Gillet (vert) . . . 1·50 45

1031 Sammy (cartoon character)

1995. "Philately for the Young".
3285 **1031** 16f. multicoloured . . . 95 30

1032 Couple and   1034 "Nativity" (from
Condom in Wrapper   15th-century breviary)

1033 King Albert II and Queen Paola
(photograph by Christian Louis)

1995. "Solidarity". AIDS Awareness.
3286 **1032** 16f.+4f. mult 95 95

1995. King's Day.
3287 **1033** 16f. multicoloured . . . 90 15

1995. Christmas.
3288 **1034** 13f. multicoloured . . . 65 15

1035 Puppets, Walloon Museum, Liege

1996. Museums. Multicoloured.
3289 16f.+4f. Type **1035** . . . . 95 1·00
3290 16f.+4f. National Gin
Museum, Hasselt . . . . 95 1·00
The premium was used for the promotion of
philately.

1036 "Emile Mayrisch"   1037
"LIBERALISME"

1996. 70th Death Anniv of Theo van Rysselberghe
(painter). No value expressed.
3292 **1036** A (16f.) mult 75 15

1996. 150th Anniv of Liberal Party.
3293 **1037** 16f. dp blue, violet & bl 75 15

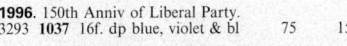

1038 Oscar Bonnevalle (stamp designer)
and "Gelatenheid"

1996. Stamp Day.
3294 **1038** 16f. multicoloured . . . 75 15

1039 Dragonfly ("Sympetrum
sanguineum")

1996. 150th Anniv of Royal Institute of Natural
Sciences of Belgium. Insects. Multicoloured.
3295 16f. Type **1039** 75 50
3296 16f. Buff-tailed bumble bee
("Bombus terrestris") . . . 75 50

3297 16f. Stag beetle ("Lucanus cervus") 75 50
3298 16f. May beetle ("Melolontha melolontha") . . . 75 50
3299 16f. European field cricket ("Gryllus campestris") . . 75 50
3300 16f. Seven-spotted ladybird ("Coccinella septempunctata") 75 50

1040 Yvonne Nevejean (rescuer of Jewish children)

1042 King Albert II

1996. Europa. Famous Women. Multicoloured.
3301 16f. Type 1040 . . . . 75 15
3302 30f. Marie Gevers (poet) . . 1·50 45

1996. Birds (3rd series). As T 841. Mult.
3306 1f. Crested tit ("Mesange Huppee") 10 10
3307 2f. Redwing ("Grive mauvis") 25 10
3308 3f. Eurasian skylark ("Alouette des champs") . 25 10
3309 4f. Pied flycatcher ("Gore-mouche noir") . . . 25 10
3310 5f. Common starling ("Etourneau sansonnet") 30 10
3312 6f. Spruce siskin ("Tarin des aulnes") 30 10
3313 7f. Yellow wagtail ("Bergeronnette printaniere") 35 10
3314 7f.50 Great grey shrike ("Pie-Grienche Grise") . 30 10
3315 9f. Green woodpecker ("Pic Vert") 35 10
3316 10f. Turtle dove ("Tourterelle des Bois") 40 10
3318 15f. Willow tit ("Mesange boreale") 70 15
3319 16f. Coal tit ("Mesange noire") 70 35
3320 16f. Red-backed shrike ("Pie grieche ecorcheur") . 1·10 15
3321 21f. Fieldfare ("Grive Litorne") (horiz) . . . 95 55
3323 150f. Black-billed magpie ("Pie bavarde") (35 × 25 mm) . . . . . 7·25 65

1996. 62nd Birthday of King Albert II.
3327 1042 16f. multicoloured . . . 70 15
See also Nos. 3341/8.

1043 Han sur Lesse Grottoes

1996. Tourist Publicity. Multicoloured.
3328 16f. Type 1043 . . . . . 65 15
3329 16f. Statue of beguine, Begijnendijk 65 15

1044 Royal Palace

1996. Brussels, Heart of Europe. Mult.
3330 16f. Type 1044 . . . . 70 20
3331 16f. St. Hubert Royal Galleries 70 20
3332 16f. Le Petit Sablon, Egmont Palace (horiz) . . 70 20
3333 16f. Jubilee Park (horiz) . . 70 20

1045 1900 Germain 6CV

1996. Cent of Motor Racing at Spa. Mult.
3334 16f. Type 1045 . . . . 70 20
3335 16f. 1925 Alfa Romeo P2 . 70 20
3336 16f. 1939 Mercedes Benz W154 . . . . . 70 20
3337 16f. 1967 Ferrari 330P . . 70 20

1046 Table Tennis

1996. Olympic Games, Atlanta. Mult.
3338 16f.+4f. Type 1046 . . . . 95 95
3339 16f.+4f. Swimming . . . 95 95

1996.
3341 1042 16f. blue 70 10
3342 17f. blue 75 10
3343 18f. green 90 10
3344 19f. lilac 90 15
3344a 20f. brown 90 15
3345 25f. brown . . . . 1·10 10
3346 28f. brown . . . . 1·10 25
3346a 32f. violet . . . . 1·25 10
3347 34f. blue . . . . 1·50 20
3348 36f. blue . . . . 1·25 25
3349 50f. green . . . . 2·40 55

1047 "The Straw Hat" (Peter Paul Rubens)

1048 Philip the Fair

1996. Paintings by Belgian Artists in the National Gallery, London. Multicoloured.
3351 14f. "St. Ivo" (Rogier van der Weyden) . . . 65 20
3352 16f. Type 1047 . . . 75 20
3353 30f. "Man in a Turban" (Jan van Eyck) . . . . . 1·50 45

1996. 500th Anniv of Marriage of Philip the Fair and Joanna of Castile and Procession into Brussels. Details of triptych by the Master of Affligem Abbey at Zierikzee Town Hall. Multicoloured.
3354 16f. Type 1048 . . . . 70 15
3355 16f. Joanna of Castile . . . 70 15

1049 Cloro (cartoon character)

1996. "Philately for the Young".
3356 1049 16f. multicoloured . . . 90 15

1050 Title of First Issue and Charles Letellier (founder)

1996. 150th Anniv of "Mons Almanac".
3357 1050 16f. black, yell & mve . . 90 15

1051 Arthur Grumiaux (violinist, 10th death anniv)

1996. Music and Literature Anniversaries.
3358 1051 16f. multicoloured . . . 70 15
3359 – 16f. multicoloured . . . 70 15
3360 – 16f. black and brown . . 70 15
3361 – 16f. multicoloured . . . 70 15
DESIGNS: No. 3359, Flor Peeters (organist, 10th death anniv); 3360, Christian Dotremont (poet, 5th death anniv); 3361, Paul van Ostaijen (writer, birth centenary) and cover drawing by Oscar Jespers for "Bezette Stad".

1052 Globe and Children of Different Races

1996. "Solidarity". 50th Anniv of U.N.I.C.E.F.
3362 1052 16f.+4f. mult 95 95

1054 Students

1997. Centenary of Catholic University, Mons.
3364 1054 17f. multicoloured . . . 70 15

1055 Barbed Wire and Buildings

1997. Museums. Multicoloured.
3365 17f.+4f. Type 1055 (Deportation and Resistance Museum, Dossin Barracks, Malines) . 1·10 1·00
3366 17f.+4f. Foundryman pouring molten metal (Fourneau Saint-Michel Iron Museum) . . . . 1·10 1·00
The premium was used for the promotion of philately.

1056 Deer and Landscape (½-size illustration)

1997. "Cantons of the East" (German-speaking Belgium).
3368 1056 17f. black and brown . . 75 20

1057 Marie Sasse

1997. Opera Singers. Multicoloured.
3369 17f. Type 1057 . . . . 75 15
3370 17f. Ernest van Dijck . . . 95 20
3371 17f. Hector Dufranne . . . 75 15
3372 17f. Clara Clairbert . . . 75 15

1058 Soldier on Duty

1997. Belgian Involvement in United Nations Peacekeeping Forces.
3373 1058 17f. multicoloured . . . 75 15

1059 The Goat Riders

1997. Europa. Tales and Legends. Mult.
3374 17f. Type 1059 . . . . 75 15
3375 30f. Jean de Berneau . . . 1·25 45

1060 Spinoy working on Recess Plate

1997. Stamp Day. 4th Death Anniv of Constant Spinoy (engraver).
3376 1060 17f. brown, yell & blk . . 75 15

1061 "The Man in the Street" (detail)

1062 Flower Arrangement

1997. Birth Centenary of Paul Delvaux (painter). Multicoloured.
3377 15f. Type 1061 . . . . 70 25
3378 17f. "The Public Voice" (horiz) 75 20
3379 32f. "The Messenger of the Night" . . . . . 1·50 45

1997. 2nd International Flower Show, Liege.
3380 1062 17f. multicoloured . . . 90 15

1063 Men's Judo

1997. Judo. Each black and red.
3381 17f.+4f. Type 1063 . . . 1·00 1·00
3382 17f.+4f. Women's judo (showing female symbol) 1·00 1·00

1064 Queen Paola and Belvedere Villa

1997. 60th Birthday of Queen Paola.
3383 1064 17f. multicoloured . . . 90 15

1065 Jommeke, Flip and Filiberke (comic strip characters)

1997. "Philately for the Young".
3384 1065 17f. multicoloured . . . 90 20

1066 "Rosa damascena" "Coccinea"

1067 St. Martin's Cathedral, Hal

1997. Roses. Illustrations by Pierre-Joseph Redoute. Multicoloured.
3385	17f. Type **1066**	75	15
3386	17f. "Rosa sulfurea"	75	15
3387	17f. "Rosa centifolia"	75	15

1997. Tourist Publicity. Multicoloured.
3388	17f. Type **1067**	75	15
3389	17f. Notre-Dame Church, Laeken (horiz)	75	15
3390	17f. St. Martin's Cathedral, Liege	75	15

1068 Stonecutter

1997. Trades. Multicoloured.
3391	17f. Type **1068**	80	15
3392	17f. Bricklayer	80	15
3393	17f. Carpenter	80	15
3394	17f. Blacksmith	80	15

1069 Queen amidst Workers

1997. Centenary and 35th Congress, Antwerp, of Apimondia (international apicultural association). Bees. Multicoloured.
3395	17f. Type **1069**	75	45
3396	17f. Development of egg	75	45
3397	17f. Bees emerging from cells	75	45
3398	17f. Bee collecting nectar from flower	75	45
3399	17f. Bee fanning at hive entrance and worker arriving with nectar	75	45
3400	17f. Worker feeding drone	75	45

1070 "Belgica" (polar barque) ice-bound

1997. Cent of Belgian Antarctic Expedition.
3401	**1070** 17f. multicoloured	90	15

1071 Mask   **1073** "Fairon" (Pierre Grahame)

1997. Centenary of Royal Central Africa Museum, Tervuren. Multicoloured.
3402	17f. Type **1071**	75	20
3403	17f. Museum (74 × 24 mm)	75	20
3404	34f. Statuette	1·50	50

1997. Christmas.
3408	**1073** 15f. multicoloured	70	25

1074 Disjointed Figure   **1075** Azalea "Mrs. Haerens"

1997. "Solidarity". Multiple Sclerosis.
3409	**1074** 17f.+4f. black & blue	1·00	90

1997. Willow Tit. As No. 3318 but horiz.
3410	15f. multicoloured	70	15

1997. Self-adhesive.
3411	**1075** (17f.) multicoloured	90	15

1076 Female Symbol   **1078** Gerard Walschap

1077 Thalys High Speed Train on Antoing Viaduct

1998. 50th Anniv of Women's Suffrage in Belgium.
3412	**1076** 17f. red, brown & sepia	90	10

1998. Paris–Brussels–Cologne-Amsterdam High Speed Rail Network.
3413	**1077** 17f. multicoloured	90	10

1998. Writers' Birth Centenaries. Mult.
3414	17f. Type **1078**	70	10
3415	17f. Norge (Georges Mogin)	70	10

1079 King Leopold III   **1080** "Black Magic"

1998. Kings of Belgium (1st series).
3416	**1079** 17f.+8f. green	1·25	1·10
3417	– 32f.+15f. brown	2·10	2·10

DESIGN: 32f. Baudouin I.
The premium was used for the promotion of philately.
See also Nos. 3466/7.

1998. Birth Centenary of Rene-Ghislain Magritte (painter) (1st issue). Multicoloured.
3419	17f. Type **1080**	75	10
3420	17f. "The Sensitive Chord" (horiz)	75	10
3421	17f. "The Castle of the Pyrenees"	75	10

See also No. 3432.

1081 "La Foire aux Amours" (Felicien Rops)

1998. Art Anniversaries. Multicoloured.
3422	17f. Type **1081** (death cent)	75	40
3423	17f. "Hospitality for the Strangers" (Gustave van de Woestijne) (bicentenary of Museum of Fine Arts, Ghent)	75	40
3424	17f. "Man with Beard" (self-portrait of Felix de Boeck, birth centenary)	75	40
3425	17f. "black writing mixed with colours..." (Karel Appel and Christian Dotremont) (50th anniv of Cobra art movement)	75	40

1082 Anniversary Emblem

1998. 75th Anniv of Belgian Postage Stamp Dealers' Association.
3426	**1082** 17f. multicoloured	90	10

1083 Avro RJ85 Airplane

1998. 75th Anniv of Sabena Airlines.
3427	**1083** 17f. multicoloured	90	10

1084 Fox

1998. Wildlife of the Ardennes. Mult.
3428	17f. Type **1084**	75	30
3429	17f. Red deer ("Cervus elaphus")	75	30
3430	17f. Wild boar ("Sus scrofa")	75	30
3431	17f. Roe deer ("Capreolus capreolus")	75	30

1085 "The Return" (Magritte)

1998. Birth Centenary of Rene-Ghislain Magritte (artist) (2nd issue).
3432	**1085** 17f. multicoloured	90	10

1086 Struyf   **1088** Pelote

1087 Guitarist (Torhout and Werchter Festival)

1998. Stamp Day. 2nd Death Anniv of Edmond Struyf (founder of Pro-Post (organization for promotion of philately)).
3433	**1086** 17f. black, red & yellow	90	10

1998. Europa. National Festivals.
3434	**1087** 17f. violet and yellow	75	10
3435	– 17f. violet and mauve	75	10

DESIGN: No. 3435, Music conductor (Wallonie Festival).

1998. Sports. Multicoloured.
3436	17f.+4f. Type **1088**	1·00	1·00
3437	17f.+4f. Handball	1·00	1·00

1089 Emblem   **1090** Marnix van Sint-Aldegonde

1998. European Heritage Days. Mult.
3439	17f. Type **1089**	60	15
3440	17f. Bourla Theatre, Antwerp	60	15
3441	17f. La Halle, Durbuy	60	15
3442	17f. Halletoren, Kortrijk	60	15
3443	17f. Louvain Town Hall	60	15
3444	17f. Perron, Liege	60	15
3445	17f. Royal Theatre, Namur	60	15
3446	17f. Aspremont-Lynden Castle, Rekem	60	15
3447	17f. Neo-Gothic kiosk, Sint Niklaas	60	15
3448	17f. Saint-Vincent's Chapel, Tournai	60	15
3449	17f. Villers-la-Ville Abbey	60	15
3450	17f. Saint-Gilles Town Hall	60	15

1998. 400th Death Anniv of Philips van Marnix van Sint-Aldegonde (writer).
3451	**1090** 17f. multicoloured	70	10

1091 Face

1998. Bicentenary of "Amis Philanthropes" (circle of free thinkers).
3452	**1091** 17f. black and blue	70	10

1092 Mniszech Palace

1998. Belgium Embassy, Warsaw, Poland.
3453	**1092** 17f. multicoloured	70	10

1093 King Albert II   **1096** Chick Bill and Ric Hochet

1094 "The Eighth Day" (dir. Jaco van Dormael)

1998.
3454	**1093** 19f. lilac	90	10

No. 3454 was for use on direct mail by large companies.

1998. 25th Anniv of Brussels and Ghent Film Festivals. Multicoloured.
3455	17f. Type **1094**	70	10
3456	17f. "Daens" (dir. Stijn Coninx)	70	10

1998. "Philately for the Young". Comic Strip Characters.
3460	**1096** 17f. multicoloured	70	10

1097 "Youth and Space"

1998. 14th World Congress of Association of Space Explorers.
3461	**1097** 17f. multicoloured	70	10

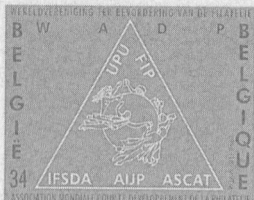

1098 Universal Postal Union Emblem

1998. World Post Day.
3462 **1098** 34f. blue & ultramarine . . . 1·40   30

1099 "The Three Kings" (Michel Provost)

1998. Christmas. No value indicated.
3463 **1099** (17f.) multicoloured . .   70   10

1100 Detail of Triptych by Constant Dratz   1101 Guide Dog and Man

1998. Cent of General Belgium Trade Union.
3464 **1100** 17f. multicoloured . . .   70   10

1998. "Solidarity". Guide Dogs for the Blind.
3465 **1101** 17f.+4f. multicoloured   1·00   1·00
The face value is embossed in Braille.

1999. Kings of Belgium (2nd series). As T **1079.**
3466   17f.+8f. deep green & green   1·10   1·10
3467   32f.+15f. black . . . . .   1·25   2·25
KINGS: 17f. Albert I; 32f. Leopold II.
The premium was used for the promotion of philately.

1102 Candle   1103 Barn Owl
("Happy Birthday")

1999. Greetings stamps. No value expressed. Mult.
3469   (17f.) Type **1102**   70   25
3470   (17f.) Stork carrying heart
     ("Welcome" (new baby))   70   25
3471   (17f.) Wristwatch ("Take
     your Time" (retirement))   70   25
3472   (17f.) Four-leafed clover
     ("For your pleasure") . .   70   25
3473   (17f.) White doves
     ("Congratulations"
     (marriage))   70   25
3474   (17f.) Arrow through heart
     ("I love you")   70   25
3475   (17f.) Woman with heart as
     head ("Happy Mother's
     Day")   70   25
3476   (17f.) Man with heart as
     head ("Happy Father's
     Day")   70   25

1999. Owls. Multicoloured.
3477   17f. Type **1103**   70   10
3478   17f. Little owl ("Athene
     noctua")   70   10
3479   17f. Tawny owl ("Strix
     aluco")   70   10
3480   17f. Long-eared owl ("Asio
     otus")   70   10

1104 Leopard Tank (Army)

1999. 50th Anniv of North Atlantic Treaty
Organization. Multicoloured.
3481   17f. Type **1104**   70   10
3482   17f. General Dynamics F-16
     jet fighters (Air Force) . .   70   10
3483   17f. "De Wandelaar"
     (frigate) (Navy)   70   10
3484   17f. Field hospital (Medical
     Service)   70   10
3485   17f. Display chart of
     military operations
     (General Staff)   70   10

1105 Letters and World Map

1999. 125th Anniv of U.P.U.
3486 **1105** 34f. multicoloured . . .   1·50   30

1106 De Bunt Nature Reserve, Hamme

1999. Europa. Parks and Gardens. Multicoloured.
3487   17f. Type **1106**   70   10
3488   17f. Harchies Marsh   70   10

1107 1849 10c. "Epaulettes" Stamp

1999. Stamp Day. 150th Anniv of First Belgian
Postage Stamp. Multicoloured.
3489   17f. Type **1107**   70   10
3490   17f. 1849 20c. "Epaulettes"
     stamp   70   10

BELGIQUE-BELGIË   17+4

1108 Racing

1999. Sport. Belgian Motor Cycling. Multicoloured.
3491   17f.+4f. Type **1108**   95   95
3492   17f.+4f. Trial (vert)   95   95

1109 "My Favourite Room"

1999. 50th Death Anniv of James Ensor (artist) (1st
issue).
3494 **1109** 17f. mullticoloured . .   65   10
See also Nos. 3501/3.

1110 Giant Family,   1111 Harvesting of Cocoa
Geraardsbergen   Beans

1999. Tourist Publicity. Multicoloured.
3495   17f. Type **1110**   65   10
3496   17f. Members of Confrerie
     de la Misericorde in Car
     d'Or procession, Mons
     (horiz)   65   10

1999. Belgian Chocolate. Multicoloured.
3497   17f. Type **1111**   60   10
3498   17f. Chocolate manufacture   60   10
3499   17f. Selling product   60   10

1112 Photographs of 1959 and 1999

1999. 40th Wedding Anniv of King Albert and Queen
Paola.
3500 **1112** 17f. multicoloured . . .   60   10

1113 "Woman eating Oysters"

1999. 50th Death Anniv of James Ensor (artist) (2nd
issue).
3501 **1113** 17f. multicoloured . . .   55   10
3502   – 30f. black, pale
     cinnamon and pale
     grey   95   30
3503   – 32f. multicoloured . . .   1·00   35
DESIGNS—30f. "Triumph of Death"; 32f. "Old
Lady with Masks".

1115 Henri la Fontaine
(President of International
Peace Bureau), 1913

1999. Belgian Winners of Nobel Peace Prize.
3509 **1115** 17f. red and gold . . .   55   10
3510   – 21f. blue and gold . . .   65   20
DESIGNS: 3510, Auguste Beernaert (Prime Minister
1884–94), 1909.

DENOMINATION. From No. 3511 Belgian stamps
are denominated both in Belgian francs and in euros.

1116 King   1116a King Albert II
Albert II

1999.
3511 **1116** 17f. multicoloured . .   55   10
3512   17f. blue   55   10
3513   19f. purple   60   15
3514   20f. brown   60   15
3516   25f. brown   75   20
3518   30f. purple   90   30
3519   32f. green . . . . .   1·00   30
3520   34f. blue . . . . . .   1·10   35
3521   36f. brown . . . . .   1·10   35
3522 **1116a** 50f. blue . . . . . .   1·50   50
3524   200f. lilac . . . . . .   6·25   1·90

1118 Geranium   1119 Reindeer holding
"Matador"   Glass of Champagne

1999. Flowers. No value expressed (geranium) or
inscr "ZONE A PRIOR" (tulip). Multicoloured.
Self-adhesive.
3526   (17f.) Type **1118**   55   10
3527   (21f.) Tulip (21 × 26 mm) . .   65   20
The geranium design was for use on inland letters

up to 20g. and the tulip design for letters within the
European Union up to 20g.

1999. Christmas.
3530 **1119** 17f. multicoloured . . .   55   10

1120 Child bandaging Teddy Bear

1999. "Solidarity". Red Cross. Multicoloured.
3531   17f.+4f. Type **1120**   65   65
3532   17f.+4f. Child and teddy
     bear cleaning teeth (vert)   65   65

1121 Prince Philippe and Mathilde
d'Udekem d'Acoz

1999. Engagement of Prince Philippe and Mathilde
d'Udekem d'Acoz.
3533 **1121** 17f. multicoloured   55   10

1123 Fireworks and Streamer forming
"2000"

2000. New Year.
3536 **1123** 17f. multicoloured . . .   55   10

1124 Red-backed   1125 Brussels Skyline
Shrike   and Group of People

2000. Birds. Multicoloured.
3537   50c. Goldcrest ("Roitelet
     Huppe")   10   10
3538   1f. Red crossbill ("Beccroisé
     des Sapins")   10   10
3539   2f. Short-toed treecreeper
     ("Grimpereau des
     Jardins")   10   10
3540   3f. Meadow pipit ("Pipit
     Farlouse")   10   10
3541   5f. Brambling ("Pinson du
     Nord")   15   10
3542   7f.50 Great grey shrike
     ("Pie-Grieche Grise") . .   25   10
3543   8f. Blue tit ("Mesange
     Charbonniere")   25   10
3544   10f. Wood warbler
     ("Pouillot Siffleur") . .   30   10
3546   16f. Type **1124**   50   15
3547   16f. Common tern ("Sterne
     Pierregarin")   50   15
3548   21f. Fieldfare ("Grive
     Litorne") (horiz) . . .   60   25
3552   150f. Black-billed magpie
     ("Pie Bavarde")
     (36 × 25 mm) . . . . .   4·50   1·25

2000. Brussels, European City of Culture. Mult.
3555   17f. Type **1125**   55   10
3556   17f. Toots Tielmans (jazz
     musician), Anne Teresa de
     Keersmaeker (gymnast)
     and skyline   55   10
3557   17f. Airplane, train and
     skyline   55   10
Nos. 3555/7 were issued together, se-tenant,
forming a composite design showing the Brussels
skyline.

1126 Queen Astrid

2000. Queens of Belgium.
3558 **1126** 17f.+8f. green and deep
    green 75 75
3559 – 32f.+15f. brown and
    black . . . . . . 1·50 1·50
DESIGN: 32f. Queen Fabiola.
  The premium was used for the promotion of philately.
  See also Nos. 3615/16.

1127 Mathematical   **1128** Globe and
   Formulae   Technology (Joachim
                Beckers)

2000. World Mathematics Year.
3561 **1127** 17f. multicoloured . . . 55 10

2000. "Stampin' the Future": Winning Entries in
  International Children's Painting Competition.
3562 **1128** 17f. multicoloured . . . 55 10

1129 "Charles V as Sovereign
Master of the Order of the Golden
Fleece" (anon)

2000. 500th Birth Anniv of Charles V, Holy Roman
  Emperor. Paintings of Charles V. Multicoloured.
3563   17f. Type **1129** 55 10
3564   21f. "Charles V" (Corneille
    de la Haye) 65 20

1130 Common Adder

2000. Amphibians and Reptiles. Multicoloured.
3566   17f. Type **1130** 55 10
3567   17f. Sand lizard (*Lacerta
    agilis*) (vert) 55 10
3568   17f. Common tree frog
    (*Hyla arborea*) (vert) . . . 55 10
3569   17f. Spotted salamander
    (*Salamander salamander*) . . 55 10

1131 Children flying Kites

2000. Red Cross and Red Crescent Movements.
3570 **1131** 17f.+4f. multicoloured 65 65

1132 Players Celebrating

2000. European Football Championship, Belgium
  and The Netherlands. Multicoloured. (a) With face
  value. Size 26 × 38 mm.
3571   17f. Type **1132** 55 10
3572   21f. Football 65 20
     (b) Size 20 × 26 mm. Self-adhesive.
3573   (17f.) As Type **1132** 55 10
  Nos. 3571/3 were printed together, se-tenant, with
the backgrounds forming the composite design of a
crowd of spectators and the Belgian flag.

1133 Cat and Rabbit reading Book

2000. Stamp Day. Winning Entry in Stamp Design
  Competition.
3574 **1133** 17f. black, blue and red 55 10

1134 Francois de Tassis   **1135** *Iris spuria*
  (detail of tapestry)

2000. "Belgica 2001" Int Stamp Exhibition, Brussels
  (1st issue).
3575 **1134** 17f. multicoloured . . . 55 10
  See also Nos. 3629/33.

2000. Ghent Flower Show. Multicoloured.
3576   16f. Type **1135** 55 10
3577   17f. Rhododendron (horiz) 55 10
3578   21f. Begonia (horiz) . . . 65 20

1136 Prince Philippe

2000. 2nd Anniv of Prince Philippe (cultural
  organization).
3579 **1136** 17f. brn, grey & sil . . 55 10

1137 Harpsichord   **1139** "Building
              Europe"

1138 Belgium Team and Emblem

2000. 250th Death Anniv of Johann Sebastian Bach.
  No value expressed. Multicoloured.
3580   (17f.) Type **1137** 55 10
3581   (17f.) Violin 55 10

3582   (17f.) Two tenor lutes . . . 55 10
3583   (17f.) Treble viol 55 10
3584   (17f.) Three trumpets . . . 55 10
3585   (17f.) Bach 55 10

2000. Olympic Games, Sydney. Multicoloured.
3586   17f. Type **1138** 65 65
3587   17f.+4f. Tae-kwon-do . . . 65 65
3588   17f.+4f. Paralympic athlete
    (horiz) 65 65

2000. Europa.
3590 **1139** 21f. multicoloured . . . 65 15

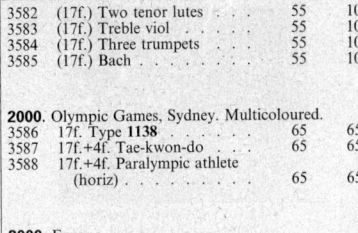

1140 Flemish Beguinages

2000. U.N.E.S.C.O. World Heritage Sites in Belgium.
  Multicoloured.
3591   17f. Type **1140** 50 10
3592   17f. Grand-Place, Brussels 50 10
3393   17f. Four lifts, Centre
    Canal, Wallonia 50 10

1141 Baroque Organ, Norbertine
Abbey Church, Grimbergen

2000. Tourism. Churches and Church Organs. Mult.
3594   17f. Type **1141** 50 10
3595   17f. St. Wandru Abbey,
    Mons 50 10
3596   17f. O.-L.-V.
    Hemelvaartkerk (former
    abbey church), Ninove . . 50 10
3597   17f. St. Peter's Church,
    Bastogne 50 10

1142 Red-backed   **1143** Marcel,
Shrike ("Pie grieche   Charlotte, Fanny and
ecorcheur")   Konstantinopel

2000.
3598 **1142** 16f. multicoloured . . . 50 10
3599 – 17f. mult (51 × 21 mm) 50 10
3600 – 23f. lilac 70 20
DESIGNS: 17f. Francois de Tassis (detail of tapestry)
and Belgica 2001 emblem; 23f. King Albert II.

2000. "Philately for the Young". Kiekeboe (cartoon
  series created by Robert Merhottein).
3601 **1143** 17f. multicoloured . . . 50 10

1144 "Springtime"

2000. Hainaut Flower Show.
3602 **1144** 17f. multicoloured . . . 50 10

1145 Violets   **1148** Postman

1147 "Bing of the Ferro Lusto X"
(Panamarenko)

2000. Flowers. No value expressed. Self-adhesive.
3603 **1145** (17f.) multicoloured . . 50 10

2000. Modern Art. Multicoloured.
3608   17f. Type **1147** 50 10
3609   17f. "Construction" (Anne-
    Mie van Kerckhoven)
    (vert) 50 10
3610   17f. "Belgique eternelle"
    (Jacques Charlier) 50 10
3611   17f. "Les Belles de Nuit"
    (Marie Jo Lafontaine) . . 50 10

2000. Christmas.
3612 **1148** 17f. multicoloured . . . 50 10

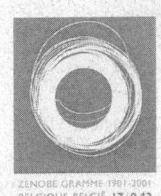 

1150 Stars

2000. New Year.
3614 **1150** 17f. gold, blue & blk 50 10

2001. Queens of Belgium. As T **1126**.
3615   17f.+8f. green & dp green 75 75
3616   32f.+15f. black and green 1·50 1·50
DESIGNS: 17f. Queen Elisabeth; 32f. Queen Marie-
Henriette; 50f. Queen Louise-Marie.
  The premium was used for the promotion of
philately.

1151 Movement of a   **1152** Virgin and Child
   Dynamo   (statue)

2001. Death Centenary of Zenode Gramme
  (physicist).
3619 **1151** 17f. black, red & black 50 10

2001. 575th Anniv of Louvain Catholic University.
3620 **1152** 17f. multicoloured . . . 50 10

2001. As T **998** but with face value expressed in
  Francs and Euros.
3621   100f. multicoloured . . . . 3·00 95

1153 Willem Elsschot (poet)

2001. Music and Literature.
3622 **1153** 17f. brown and black 50 10
3623 – 17f. grey and black . . 50 10
DESIGN: 17f. Albert Ayguesparse (poet).

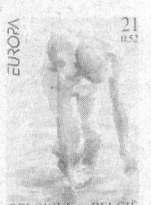

1154 Boy washing Hands

2001. Europa. Water Resources.
3625 **1154** 21f. multicoloured . . . 65 15

1155 Type 12 Steam Locomotive

2001. 75th Anniv of National Railway Company. Multicoloured.

3626	17f. Type **1155**	50	10
3627	17f. Series 06 dual locomotive No. 671	50	10
3628	17f. Series 03 locomotive No. 328	50	10

1156 16th-century Postman on horseback

2001. "Belgica 2001" International Stamp Exhibition, Brussels (2nd issue). 500th Anniv of European Post. Multicoloured.

3629	17f. Type **1156**	50	10
3630	17f. 17th-century postman with walking staff (vert)	50	10
3631	17f. 18th-century postman and hand using quill (vert)	50	10
3632	17f. Steam locomotive and 19th-century postman (vert)	50	10
3633	17f. 20th-century forms of communication (vert)	50	10

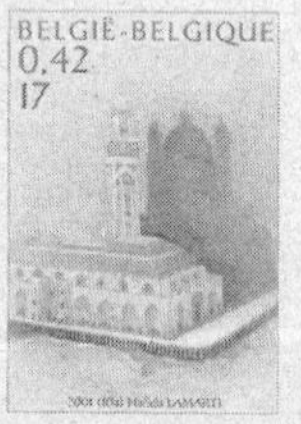

1157 Hassan II Mosque, Casablanca

2001. Religious Buildings. Multicoloured.

3635	17f. Type **1157**	50	10
3636	34f. Koekelberg Basilica	1·00	25

1158 "Winter Landscape with Skaters" (Pieter Bruegel the Elder)

2001. Art. Multicoloured.

3637	17f. Type **1158**	50	10
3638	17f. "Heads of Negros" (Peter Paul Rubens)	50	10
3639	17f. "Sunday" (Frits van den Berghe)	50	10
3640	17f. "Mussels" (Marcel Broodthaers)	50	10

1159 Pottery Vase

1160 Luc Orient

2001. Chinese Pottery. Multicoloured.

3641	17f. Type **1159**	50	10
3642	34f. Teapot	1·00	25

2001. "Philately for the Young". Cartoon Characters.

3643 **1160**	17f. multicoloured	50	10

1161 Cycling (World Cycling Championship, Antwerp)

2001. Sports. Multicoloured.

3644	17f.+4f. Type **1161**	65	65
3645	17f.+4f. Gymnast (World Gymnastics Championships, Ghent)	65	65

1162 Emblem

2001. Belgian Presidency of European Union.

3646 **1162**	17f. multicoloured	50	10

1163 Binche

2001. Town Hall Belfries.

3647 **1163**	17f. mauve and black	50	10
3648 –	17f. blue, mauve & blk	50	10

DESIGN: No. 3648, Diksmuide.

1164 Damme

2001. Large Farmhouses. Multicoloured.

3649	17f. Type **1164**	50	10
3650	17f. Beauvechain	50	10
3651	17f. Leuven	50	10
3652	17f. Honnelles	50	10
3653	17f. Hasselt	50	10

EXPRESS LETTER STAMPS

E 107 Ghent

1929.

E530 –	1f.75 blue	60	30
E531 E 107	2f.35 red	1·75	45
E581 –	2f.45 green	16·00	1·90
E532 –	3f.50 purple	10·50	10·50
E533 –	5f.25 olive	9·50	9·50

DESIGNS: 1f.75, Town Hall, Brussels; 2f.45, Eupen; 3f.50, Bishop's Palace, Liege; 5f.25, Antwerp Cathedral.

1932. No. E581 surch **2 Fr 50** and cross.

E608	2f.50 on 2f.45 green	17·00	1·90

MILITARY STAMPS

1967. As T **289** (Baudouin) but with letter "M" within oval at foot.

M2027	1f.50 green	10	10

1971. As No. 2207/8a and 2209a but with letter "M" within oval at foot.

M2224	1f.75 green	35	35
M2225	2f.25 green	35	30
M2226	2f.50 green	10	10
M2227	3f.25 plum	15	15

NEWSPAPER STAMPS

1928. Railway Parcels stamps of 1923 optd **JOURNAUX DAGBLADEN 1928.**

N443 P **84**	10c. red	45	25
N444	20c. green	45	25
N445	40c. olive	35	25
N446	60c. orange	80	25
N447	70c. brown	35	35
N448	80c. violet	80	25
N449	90c. slate	7·50	2·25
N450 –	1f. blue	1·50	35
N451 –	2f. olive	3·25	45
N452 –	3f. red	3·25	55
N453 –	4f. red	3·25	55
N454 –	5f. violet	3·25	55
N455 –	6f. brown	5·50	1·50
N456 –	7f. orange	15·00	2·40
N457 –	8f. brown	10·50	95
N458 –	9f. purple	28·00	7·25
N459 –	10f. green	10·50	1·60
N460 –	20f. pink	30·00	8·50

1929. Railway Parcels stamps of 1923 optd **JOURNAUX DAGBLADEN** only.

N505 P **84**	10c. red	30	25
N506	20c. green	30	30
N507	40c. olive	40	25
N508	60c. orange	70	30
N509	70c. brown	35	20
N510	80c. violet	80	40
N511	90c. slate	5·50	4·00
N512 –	1f. blue	1·10	25
N513 –	1f.10 brown	4·00	1·10
N514 –	1f.50 blue	4·00	1·10
N515 –	2f. olive	2·40	35
N516 –	2f.10 slate	12·00	7·75
N517 –	3f. red	2·25	45
N518 –	4f. red	2·25	50
N519 –	5f. violet	2·50	45
N520 –	6f. brown	5·50	1·00
N521 –	7f. orange	16·00	1·00
N522 –	8f. brown	11·00	1·00
N523 –	9f. purple	22·00	10·50
N524 –	10f. green	13·00	2·40
N525 –	20f. pink	30·00	9·25

PARCEL POST STAMPS

Stamps issued at Belgian Post Offices only.

1928. Optd **COLIS POSTAL POSTCOLLO.**

B470 **81**	4f. brown	3·00	90
B471	5f. bistre	3·00	90

B 106 G.P.O., Brussels

1929.

B526 B **106**	3f. sepia	1·50	10
B527	4f. slate	1·50	10
B528	5f. red	1·50	10
B529	6f. purple	21·00	21·00

1933. Surch **X4 4X.**

B645 B **106**	4f. on 6f. purple	21·00	10

POSTAGE DUE STAMPS

D 21

D 35

1870.

D63 D **21**	10c. green	3·00	1·90
D64	20c. blue	38·00	3·00

1895.

D 96a D **35**	5c. green	10	10
D 97	10c. brown	10·00	1·00
D101	10c. red	10	10
D 98a	20c. green	10	10
D102	30c. blue	15	10
D 99	50c. brown	20·00	4·00
D103	50c. grey	45	25
D100	1f. red	14·50	9·00
D104	1f. yellow	4·50	3·75

1919. As Type D **35**, but value in colour on white background.

D 251 D **35**	5c. green	35	25
D 323	5c. grey	10	10
D 252	10c. red	1·00	25
D 324	10c. green	10	10
D 253	20c. green	4·75	1·00
D 325	20c. brown	10	10
D 254	30c. blue	2·00	30
D 326	30c. red	60	40
D 327	35c. green	25	10
D 328	40c. brown	15	10
D 330	50c. grey	15	15
D 329	50c. blue	1·10	15
D 331	60c. red	25	15
D1146	65c. green	5·25	2·50
D 332	70c. brown	25	10
D 333	80c. grey	25	10
D 334	1f. violet	45	10
D 335	1f. purple	45	15
D 336	1f.20 olive	55	15
D 337	1f.40 green	50	35
D 338	1f.50 olive	55	35
D1147	1f.60 mauve	10·50	5·00
D1148	1f.80 red	12·00	5·00
D 339	2f. mauve	55	15
D1149	2f.40 lavender	7·25	2·75
D1150	3f. red	1·75	40
D 340	3f.50 blue	55	10
D1151	4f. blue	8·25	35
D1152	5f. brown	3·00	25
D1153	7f. violet	3·00	1·50
D1154	8f. purple	9·50	7·50
D1155	10f. violet	6·00	2·50

D 220

D 462

1945. Inscr "A PAYER" at top and "TE BETALEN" at bottom, or vice versa.

D1139 D **220**	10c. olive	10	10
D1140	20c. blue	10	10
D1141	30c. red	10	10
D1142	40c. blue	10	10
D1143	50c. green	10	10
D1144	1f. brown	10	10
D1145	2f. orange	10	10

1966.

D2812 D **462**	1f. mauve	10	10
D2813	2f. green	10	10
D2814	3f. blue	25	25
D2815	4f. green	25	25
D1985ab	5f. purple	35	20
D2816	5f. lilac	30	30
D1986	6f. brown	35	20
D1987	7f. red	40	15
D2818	7f. orange	45	45
D2819	8f. grey	45	45
D2820	9f. red	45	45
D2821	10f. brown	45	45
D1988	20f. green	1·10	45
D2822	20f. green	95	90

On No. D1988 the "F" is outside the shield; on No. D2822 it is inside.

RAILWAY PARCELS STAMPS

In Belgium the parcels service is largely operated by the Belgian Railways for which the following stamps were issued.

Certain stamps under this heading were also on sale at post offices in connection with a "small parcels" service. These show a posthorn in the design except for Nos. P1116/18.

P 21

1879.

P63 P **21**	10c. brown	55·00	5·75
P64	20c. blue	£170	14·00
P65	25c. green	£200	8·00
P66	50c. red	£1200	9·50
P67	80c. yellow	£1100	50·00
P68	1f. grey	£170	11·50

P 22

1882.

P69 P **22**	10c. brown	21·00	1·25
P73	15c. grey	7·25	7·25
P75	20c. blue	70·00	2·75
P77	25c. green	70·00	3·75
P78	50c. red	70·00	80
P81	80c. yellow	80·00	90
P84	80c. brown	70·00	90
P86	1f. grey	£400	1·75
P87	1f. purple	£375	3·00
P88	2f. buff	£170	55·00

P 35

1895. Numerals in black except 1f. and 2f.

P 96 P **35**	10c. brown	9·50	60
P 97	15c. slate	9·50	70
P 98	20c. blue	15·00	75
P 99	25c. green	15·00	1·00
P100	30c. orange	18·00	1·50
P101	40c. green	24·00	1·75
P102	50c. red	24·00	65
P103	60c. lilac	48·00	65
P104	70c. blue	48·00	1·00
P105	80c. yellow	48·00	1·00
P106	90c. red	70·00	1·90
P107	1f. purple	£190	2·10
P108	2f. buff	£225	15·00

P 37 Winged Railway Wheel

1902.

P109a	P 35	10c. slate and brown	10	10
P110		15c. purple and slate	30	25
P111		20c. brown and blue	30	25
P112		25c. red and green . .	40	25
P113		30c. green and orange	30	30
P114		35c. green and brown	30	30
P115		40c. mauve and green	35	30
P116		50c. mauve and pink	20	20
P117		55c. blue and purple	35	30
P118		60c. red and lilac . .	20	15
P119		70c. red and blue . .	10	15
P120		80c. purple and yellow	10	15
P121		90c. green and red . .	10	15
P122	P 37	1f. orange and purple	10	15
P123		1f.10 black and red . .	10	15
P124		2f. green and bistre	30	20
P125		3f. blue and black . .	30	25
P126		4f. red and green . . .	1·10	1·10
P127		5f. green and orange	70	65
P128		10f. purple and yellow	90	75

1915. Stamps of 1912–14 optd **CHEMINS DE FER SPOORWEGEN** and Winged Railway Wheel.

P160	44	5c. green	£140
P161	46	10c. red	£170
P162		20c. green	£190
P163		25c. blue	£190
P164	45	35c. brown	£250
P165	46	40c. green	£225
P166	45	50c. grey	£225
P167		1f. orange	£225
P168		2f. violet	£1300
P169	–	5f. purple (No. 143) . . .	£2750

P 59 Winged Railway Wheel    P 60 Steam Locomotive

1916.

P201	P 59	10c. blue	75	60
P202		15c. olive	1·50	1·60
P203		20c. red	1·25	1·00
P204		25c. brown	1·25	1·00
P205		30c. mauve	1·25	75
P206		35c. grey	1·25	75
P207		40c. orange	2·10	2·10
P208		50c. bistre	1·75	80
P209		55c. brown	2·40	2·10
P210		60c. lilac	1·90	85
P211		70c. green	1·10	75
P212		80c. brown	1·10	75
P213		90c. blue	1·75	1·10
P214	P 60	1f. grey	1·10	70
P215		1f.10 bl (FRANKEN)	26·00	26·00
P216		1f.10 blue (FRANK)	1·90	75
P217		2f. red	38·00	1·10
P218		3f. violet	38·00	1·10
P219		4f. green	42·00	2·40
P220		5f. brown	75·00	2·50
P221		10f. orange	75·00	2·50

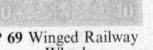

P 69 Winged Railway   P 70 Steam Train
Wheel

1920.

P259	P 69	10c. green	1·60	60
P280		10c. red	35	25
P281		15c. green	35	25
P261		20c. red	1·60	65
P282		20c. green	60	30
P262		25c. brown	1·60	85
P283		25c. blue	60	25
P263		30c. mauve	28·00	22·00
P284		30c. brown	60	20
P285		35c. brown	60	35
P286		40c. orange	60	20
P265		50c. bistre	8·00	1·10
P287		50c. red	60	20
P266		55c. brown	8·75	6·25
P288		55c. yellow	4·75	4·00
P267		60c. purple	10·50	95
P289		60c. red	60	25
P290		70c. green	2·75	45
P269		80c. brown	45·00	10
P291		80c. violet	1·90	35
P270		90c. blue	12·00	1·00
P292		90c. green	32·00	28·00
P293		90c. purple	6·00	35
P271	P 70	1f. grey	80·00	1·40
P272		1f.10 blue	1·75	65
P273		1f.20 green	16·00	1·60
P274		1f.40 brown	16·00	1·60
P275		2f. red	£120	1·00
P276		3f. mauve	£120	80
P277		4f. green	£120	1·25

P278		5f. brown	£120	85
P279		10f. orange	£120	90

On Nos. P271/9 the engine has one head lamp.

1920. Three head lamps on engine.

P294	P 70	1f. brown	6·00	25
P296		1f.10 blue	1·75	25
P297		1f.20 orange	2·40	25
P298		1f.40 yellow	14·00	2·50
P299		1f.60 green	35·00	65
P300		2f. red	28·00	25
P301		3f. red	28·00	25
P302		4f. green	28·00	25
P303		5f. violet	27·00	25
P304		10f. yellow	£120	17·00
P305		10f. brown	32·00	25
P306		15f. red	32·00	25
P307		20f. blue	£325	3·00

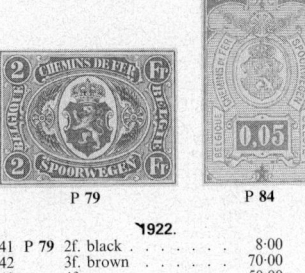

P 79    P 84

1922.

P341	P 79	2f. black	8·00	30
P342		3f. brown	70·00	30
P343		4f. green	50·00	30
P344		5f. red	50·00	30
P345		10f. brown	50·00	30
P346		15f. red	50·00	65
P347		20f. blue	£120	1·60

1923.

P375	P 84	5c. brown	25	10
P376		10c. red	10	10
P377		15c. blue	20	20
P378		20c. green	10	10
P379		30c. purple	10	10
P380		40c. olive	10	10
P381		50c. red	10	10
P382		60c. orange	10	10
P383		70c. brown	10	10
P384		80c. violet	15	10
P385		90c. slate	75	10

Similar type, but horiz.

P386		1f. blue	25	15
P388		1f.10 orange	1·75	40
P389		1f.50 green	1·75	40
P390		1f.70 brown	45	50
P391		1f.80 red	2·50	75
P392		2f. olive	25	20
P393		2f.10 green	4·75	85
P394		2f.40 violet	2·10	90
P395		2f.70 grey	32·00	75
P396		3f. red	25	15
P397		3f.30 brown	50·00	15
P398		4f. red	25	15
P399		5f. violet	50	15
P400		6f. brown	25	15
P401		7f. orange	25	15
P402		8f. brown	25	15
P403		9f. purple	1·50	15
P404		10f. green	60	15
P405		20f. pink	90	15
P406		30f. green	3·00	35
P407		40f. slate	38·00	85
P408		50f. bistre	5·00	40

See Nos. P876/7 and P911/34.

1924. No. P394 surch **2F30**.

P409		2f.30 on 2f.40 violet . .	2·50	35

P 139 Steam locomotive   P 149 Diesel
"Goliath"   Locomotive

1934.

P655	P 139	3f. green	10·00	2·10
P656		4f. mauve	3·75	15
P657		5f. red	60·00	15

1935. Centenary of Belgian Railway.

P 89	P 149	10c. red	35	20
P690		20c. violet	35	20
P691		30c. brown	45	25
P692		40c. blue	60	20
P693		50c. orange	60	15
P694		60c. green	45	15
P695		70c. blue	45	15
P696		80c. black	45	15
P697		90c. red	1·00	60

Horiz type. Early engine, "Le Belge".

P698		1f. purple	65	25
P699		2f. black	1·75	20
P700		3f. orange	2·25	20
P701		4f. purple	2·25	20
P702		5f. purple	3·50	20
P703		6f. green	4·50	20
P704		7f. violet	19·00	20
P705		8f. black	19·00	25
P706		9f. blue	21·00	25
P707		10f. red	21·00	25
P708		20f. green	35·00	25

P709		30f. violet	£100	3·75
P710		40f. brown	£100	3·75
P711		50f. red	£140	3·75
P712		100f. blue	£250	48·00

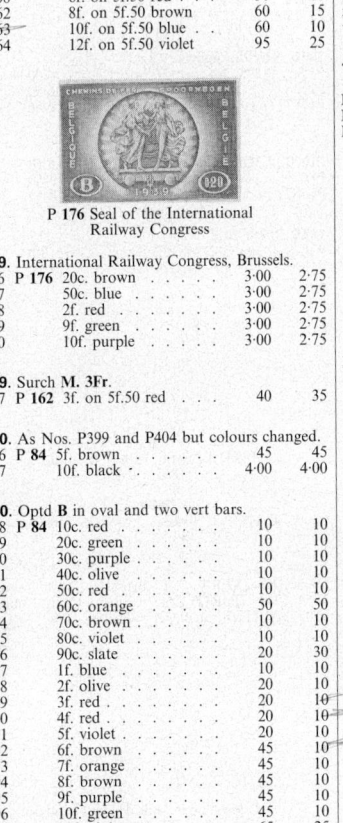

P 162 Winged Railway Wheel
and Posthorn

1938.

P 806	P 162	5f. on 3f.50 green . .	19·00	30
P 807		5f. on 6f.50 purple	10	10
P 808		6f. on 5f.50 red . . .	30	10
P1162		8f. on 5f.50 brown	60	15
P1163		10f. on 5f.50 blue .	60	10
P1164		12f. on 5f.50 violet	95	25

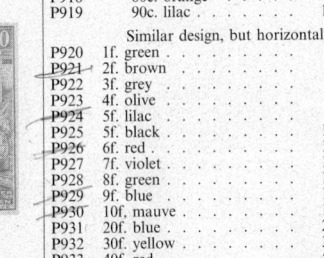

P 176 Seal of the International
Railway Congress

1939. International Railway Congress, Brussels.

P856	P 176	20c. brown	3·00	2·75
P857		50c. blue	3·00	2·75
P858		2f. red	3·00	2·75
P859		9f. green	3·00	2·75
P860		10f. purple	3·00	2·75

1939. Surch **M. 3Fr.**

P867	P 162	3f. on 5f.50 red . .	40	35

1940. As Nos. P399 and P404 but colours changed.

P876	P 84	5f. brown	45	45
P877		10f. black	4·00	4·00

1940. Optd **B** in oval and two vert bars.

P878	P 84	10c. red	10	10
P879		20c. green	10	10
P880		30c. purple	10	10
P881		40c. olive	10	10
P882		50c. red	10	10
P883		60c. orange	50	50
P884		70c. brown	10	10
P885		80c. violet	10	10
P886		90c. slate	20	30
P887		1f. blue	10	10
P888		2f. olive	20	10
P889		3f. red	20	10
P890		4f. green	20	10
P891		5f. violet	20	10
P892		6f. brown	45	10
P893		7f. orange	45	10
P894		8f. brown	45	10
P895		9f. purple	45	10
P896		10f. green	45	10
P897		20f. pink	65	25
P898		30f. green	80	1·00
P899		40f. slate	1·90	2·25
P900		50f. bistre	1·00	1·50

1940. As Type P 84 but colours changed.

P911	P 84	10c. olive	10	10
P912		20c. violet	10	10
P913		30c. red	10	10
P914		40c. blue	10	10
P915		50c. green	10	10
P916		60c. grey	10	10
P917		70c. brown	10	10
P918		80c. green	25	10
P919		90c. lilac	1·90	10

Similar design, but horizontal.

P920		1f. green	30	10
P921		2f. brown	40	10
P922		3f. grey	50	10
P923		4f. olive	65	10
P924		5f. lilac	80	10
P925		5f. black	1·10	35
P926		6f. red	1·00	10
P927		7f. violet	1·00	10
P928		8f. green	1·00	10
P929		9f. blue	1·00	10
P930		10f. mauve	1·10	10
P931		20f. blue	2·40	25
P932		30f. yellow	3·75	95
P933		40f. red	5·00	95
P934		50f. red	7·50	90

P 195 Engine Driver    P 216 Mercury

1942. Various designs.

P1090	P 195	10c. grey	10	10
P1091		20c. violet	10	10
P1092		30c. red	10	20
P1093		40c. blue	10	20
P1094		50c. blue	10	10
P1095		60c. black	10	10
P1096		70c. green	25	45
P1097		80c. orange	15	35
P1098		90c. brown	20	10

P1099	–	1f. green	10	10
P1100		2f. purple	10	10
P1101		3f. black	40	10
P1102		4f. blue	10	10
P1103		5f. brown	10	10
P1104		6f. green	40	50
P1105		7f. violet	15	15
P1106		8f. red	15	15
P1107		9f. blue	25	15
P996		9f.20 red	50	50
P1108		10f. red	1·00	10
P1109		10f. brown	70	35
P997	P 195	12f.30 green . . .	25	25
P998		14f.30 red	25	25
P1110		20f. green	30	15
P1111		30f. violet	40	15
P1112		40f. red	30	15
P1113		50f. blue	6·00	30
P 999		100f. blue	16·00	16·00

DESIGNS—As Type P 195: 1f. to 9f.20, Platelayer; 10f. and 14f.30 to 50f. Railway porter; 24½ × 34½ mm: 100f. Electric train.

1945. Inscribed "BELGIQUE-BELGIE" or vice-versa.

P1116	P 216	3f. green	30	10
P1117		5f. blue	10	10
P1118		6f. red	10	10

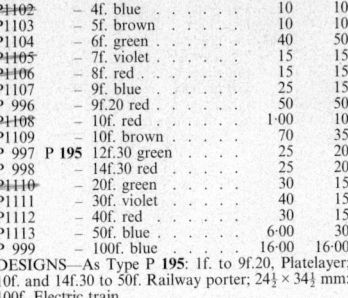

P 235 Level Crossing

1947.

P1203	P 235	100f. green	5·75	30

P 236 Archer

1947.

P1204	P 236	8f. brown	85	30
P1205		10f. blue and black	85	15
P1206		12f. violet	1·00	25

1948. Surch.

P1229	P 236	9f. on 8f. brown . .	85	15
P1230		11f. on 10f. blue and black	85	20
P1231		13f.50 on 12f. violet	95	15

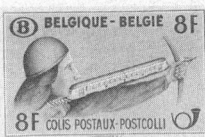

P 246 "Parcel Post"

1948.

P1250	P 246	9f. brown	5·75	15
P1251		11f. red	5·25	10
P1252		13f.50 black	9·00	15

P 254 Locomotive, 1862

1949. Locomotives from 1835 to 1951. Year given in brackets.

P1277		1f. brown (1835) . . .	35	25
P1278		1f. red (Type P 254)	45	25
P1279		2f. blue (1875) . . .	70	10
P1280		3f. red (1884) . . .	1·50	20
P1281		4f. green (1901) . . .	90	20
P1282		5f. red (1902) . . .	90	20
P1283		6f. purple (1904) . .	1·40	20
P1284		7f. green (1905) . .	2·10	20
P1285		8f. blue (1906) . . .	2·40	20
P1286		9f. brown (1909) . .	3·75	20
P1287		10f. olive (1910) . .	4·00	20
P1295		10f. black and red (1905)	7·00	85
P1288		20f. orange (1920)	7·50	20
P1289		30f. blue (1928) . .	12·00	20
P1290		40f. red (1930) . . .	15·00	20
P1291		50f. mauve (1935) .	27·00	20
P1292		60f. brown (1949) .	15·00	20
P1293		100f. red (1939) . .	60·00	35
P1294		300f. violet (1951) .	£110	45

The 300f. is larger (37½ × 25 mm).

P 264 Loading Parcels

1950.

P1318	–	11f. orange	4·25	20
P1319	–	12f. purple	15·00	1·50
P1320	–	13f. green	4·75	15
P1321	–	15f. blue	13·00	25
P1322	P **264**	16f. grey	4·25	15
P1323	–	17f. brown	4·75	20
P1324	P **264**	18f. red	11·00	95
P1325	–	20f. orange	5·00	20

DESIGNS—HORIZ: 11, 12, 17f. Dispatch counter; 13f., 15f. Sorting compartment.

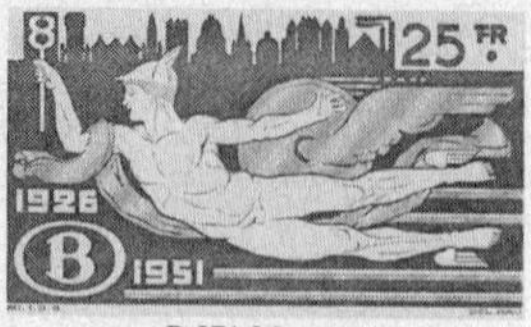

P **271** Mercury

1951. 25th Anniv of National Belgian Railway Society.

P1375	P **271**	25f. blue	10·00	8·75

1953. Nos. P1318, P1321 and P1324 surch.

P1448	–	13f. on 15f. blue	50·00	3·50
P1449	–	17f. on 11f. orange	24·00	85
P1450	P **264**	20f. on 18f. red	13·00	2·00

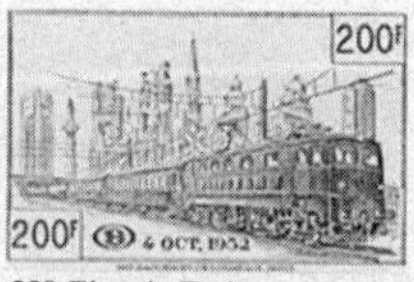

P **288** Electric Train and Brussels Skyline

1953. Inauguration of Nord-Midi Junction.

P1451	P **288**	200f. green	£190	70
P1452		200f. green & brown	£190	3·00

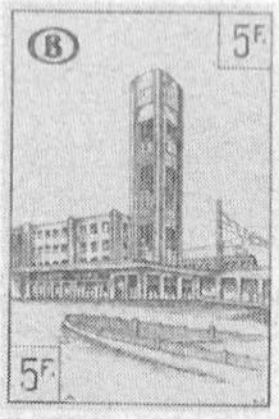

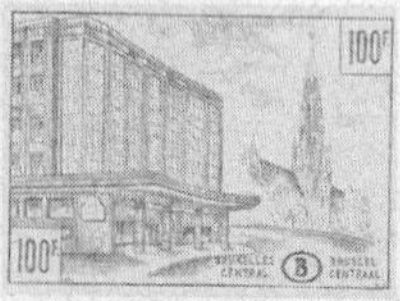

P **291** Nord Station P **292** Central Station

1953. Brussels Railway Stations.

P1485	P **291**	1f. ochre	25	10
P1486		2f. black	40	10
P1487		3f. green	45	10
P1488		4f. orange	60	10
P1489		5f. brown	2·10	15
P1490	–	5f. brown	8·00	15
P1491	P **291**	6f. purple	90	10
P1492		7f. green	90	10
P1493		8f. red	1·10	10
P1494		9f. blue	1·50	10
P1495	–	10f. green	1·90	10
P1496	–	10f. black	1·10	20
P1497	–	15f. red	11·00	40
P1498	–	20f. blue	3·00	10·00
P1498a	–	20f. green	1·75	35
P1499	–	30f. purple	4·75	10
P1500	–	40f. mauve	6·25	10
P1501	–	50f. mauve	8·00	10
P1501a	–	50f. blue	2·75	50
P1502	–	60f. violet	16·00	10
P1503	–	80f. purple	24·00	20
P1504	P **292**	100f. green	16·00	35
P1505		200f. blue	80·00	60
P1506		300f. mauve	£140	1·10

DESIGNS—VERT: 5f. (P1490), 10f. (P1496), 15, 20f. (P1498a), 50f. (P1501a), Congress Station; 10f. (P1495), 20f. (P1498) to 50f. (P1501), Midi Station. HORIZ: 60, 80f. Chapelle Station.

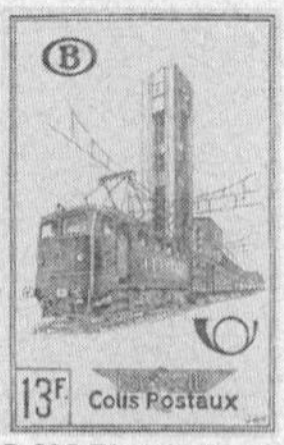

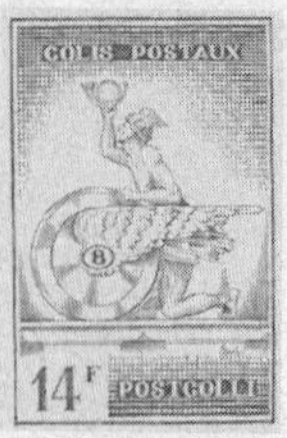

P **295** Electric Train and Nord Station, Brussels P **326** Mercury and Railway Winged Wheel

1953.

P1517	P **295**	13f. brown	17·00	25
P1518		18f. blue	17·00	15
P1519		21f. mauve	17·00	40

1956. Surch in figures.

P1585	P **295**	14f. on 13f. brown	6·50	15
P1586		19f. on 18f. blue	6·50	15
P1587		22f. on 21f. mauve	6·50	20

1957.

P1600	P **326**	14f. green	6·50	15
P1601		19f. sepia	6·50	15
P1602		22f. red	6·50	25

1959. Surch **20 F**.

P1678	P **326**	20f. on 19f. sepia	21·00	20
P1679		20f. on 22f. red	21·00	60

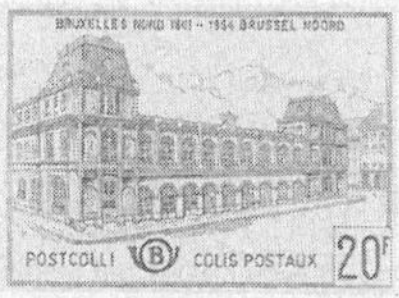

P **357** Brussels "Nord" Station, 1861–1954

1959.

P1695	P **357**	20f. olive	10·50	15
P1696	–	24f. red	4·75	25
P1697	–	26f. blue	4·75	1·75
P1698	–	28f. purple	4·75	1·25

DESIGNS—VERT: 24f. Brussels "Midi" station, 1869–1949. HORIZ: 26f. Antwerp Central station, 1905; 28f. Ghent St. Pieter's station.

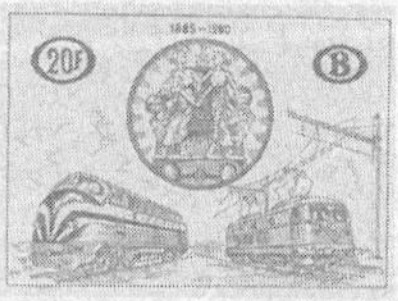

P **368** Congress Seal, Diesel and Electric Locomotives

1960. 75th Anniv of Int Railway Congress Assn.

P1722	P **368**	20f. red	38·00	26·00
P1723		50f. blue	38·00	26·00
P1724		60f. purple	38·00	26·00
P1725		70f. green	38·00	26·00

1961. Nos. P1695/8 surch.

P1787	P **357**	24f. on 20f. olive	48·00	25
P1788	–	26f. on 24f. red	4·75	25
P1789	–	28f. on 26f. blue	4·75	25
P1790	–	35f. on 28f. purple	4·75	25

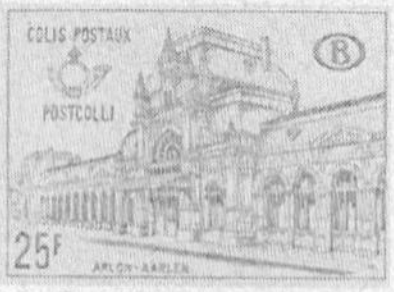

P **477** Arlon Station

1967.

P2017	P **477**	25f. ochre	7·00	25
P2018		30f. green	2·25	25
P2019		35f. blue	2·75	30
P2020		40f. red	20·00	30

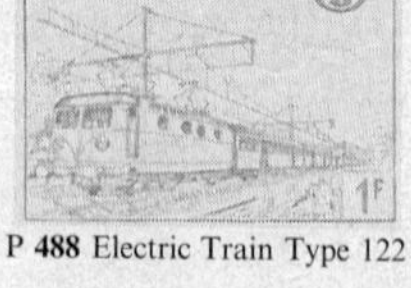

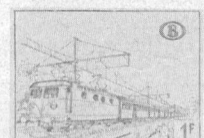

P **488** Electric Train Type 122

1968.

P2047	P **488**	1f. bistre	25	10
P2048		2f. green	25	15
P2049		3f. green	45	15
P2050		4f. orange	45	15
P2051		5f. brown	60	15
P2052		6f. plum	45	15
P2053		7f. green	60	15
P2054		8f. red	70	15
P2055		9f. blue	1·10	15
P2056	–	10f. green	2·40	15
P2057	–	20f. blue	1·25	15
P2058	–	30f. lilac	4·00	15
P2059	–	40f. violet	4·75	15
P2060	–	50f. purple	5·50	10
P2061	–	60f. violet	6·00	20
P2062	–	70f. brown	6·25	20
P2063	–	80f. purple	5·50	20
P2063a	–	90f. green	6·00	30
P2064	–	100f. green	9·50	15
P2065	–	200f. violet	11·00	30
P2066	–	300f. mauve	21·00	1·10
P2067	–	500f. yellow	32·00	1·50

DESIGNS: 10f. to 40f. Electric train Type 126; 50, 60, 70, 80, 90f. Electric train Type 160; 100, 200, 300f. Diesel-electric train Type 205; 500f. Diesel-electric train Type 210.

1970. Surch.

P2180	P **477**	37f. on 25f. ochre	45·00	6·00
P2181		48f. on 35f. blue	4·25	4·50
P2182		53f. on 40f. red	4·25	4·50

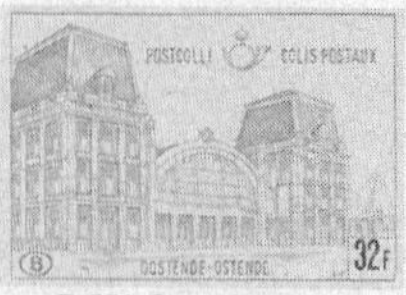

P **551** Ostend Station

1971. Figures of value in black.

P2192	P **551**	32f. ochre	1·25	1·10
P2193		37f. grey	11·00	11·00
P2194		42f. blue	1·75	1·90
P2195		44f. mauve	1·75	1·90
P2196		46f. violet	2·10	1·90
P2197		50f. red	1·75	1·60
P2198		52f. brown	11·00	11·00
P2199		54f. green	4·75	3·75
P2200		61f. blue	2·50	1·90

1972. Nos. P2192/5 and P2198/200 surch in figures.

P2256	P **551**	34f. on 32f. ochre	1·90	90
P2257		40f. on 37f. grey	1·90	90
P2258		47f. on 44f. mauve	2·10	90
P2259		53f. on 42f. blue	2·75	90
P2260		56f. on 52f. brown	2·50	90
P2261		59f. on 54f. green	2·75	1·00
P2262		66f. on 61f. blue	3·00	70

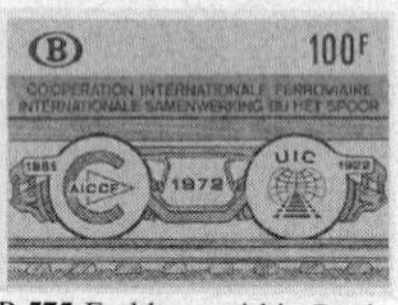

P **575** Emblems within Bogie Wheels

1972. 50th Anniv of Int Railways Union (U.I.C.).

P2266	P **575**	100f. black, red and green	6·25	1·50

See also No. 2274.

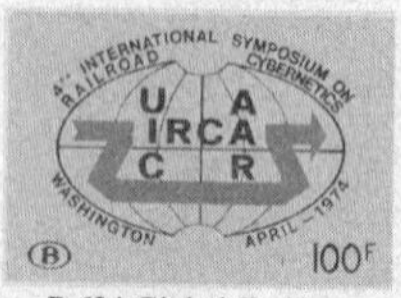

P **624** Global Emblem

1974. 4th International Symposium of Railway Cybernetics, Washington.

P2353	P **624**	100f. black, red and yellow	5·25	1·50

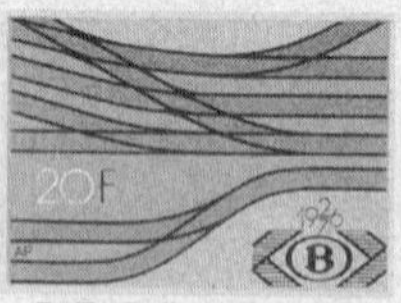

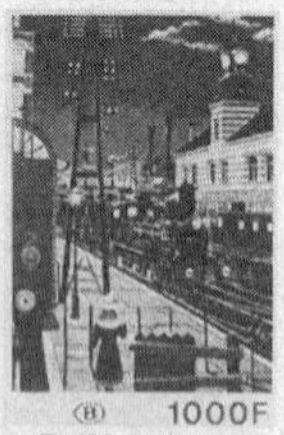

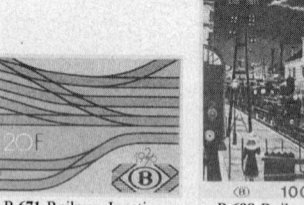

P **671** Railway Junction P **698** Railway Station at Night

1976.

P2431	P **671**	20f. black, bl & lilac	1·25	1·00
P2432		50f. black, green and turquoise	2·10	1·00
P2433		100f. black & orange	3·75	1·10
P2434		150f. black, mauve and deep mauve	6·00	1·10

1977.

P2505	P **698**	1000f. mult	48·00	16·00

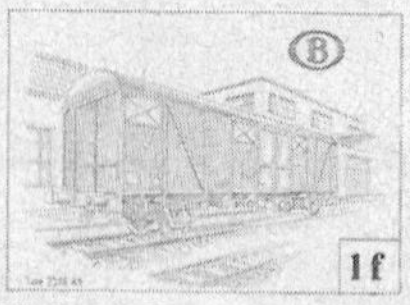

P **753** Goods Wagon, Type 2216 A8

1980. Values in black.

P2615	P **753**	1f. ochre	15	15
P2616		2f. red	15	15
P2617		3f. blue	15	15
P2618		4f. blue	15	15
P2619		5f. brown	25	15
P2620		6f. orange	30	25
P2621		7f. violet	30	25
P2622		8f. black	35	25
P2623		9f. green	50	45
P2624	–	10f. brown	50	35
P2625	–	20f. blue	1·25	35
P2626	–	30f. ochre	2·10	35
P2627	–	40f. mauve	2·75	35
P2628	–	50f. purple	3·25	35
P2629	–	60f. olive	3·75	35
P2630	–	70f. blue	4·50	2·50
P2631	–	80f. purple	4·50	70
P2632	–	90f. mauve	5·25	2·50
P2633	–	100f. red	6·00	1·25
P2634	–	200f. brown	11·00	1·50
P2635	–	300f. olive	17·00	1·90
P2636	–	500f. purple	30·00	3·75

DESIGNS: 10f. to 40f. Goods wagon, Type 3614 A5; 50f. to 90f. Self-discharging wagon, Type 1000 D; 100f. to 500f. Tanker wagon, Type 2000 G.

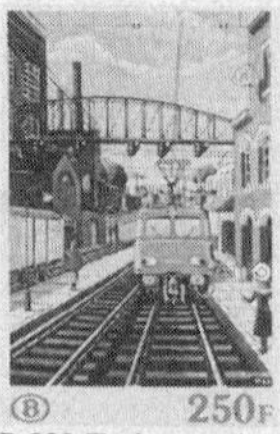

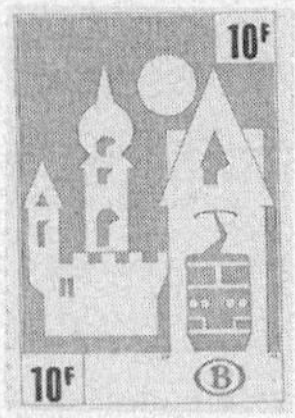

P **833** Train entering Station P **877** Buildings and Railway Locomotive

1985. 150th Anniv of Belgian Railways. Paintings by P. Delvaux. Multicoloured.

P2824		250f. Type P **833**	14·00	6·00
P2825		500f. Trains in station	26·00	12·00

1987.

P2923	P **877**	10f. red	60	65
P2924		20f. green	1·10	1·25
P2925		50f. brown	2·75	1·25
P2926		100f. purple	5·75	2·75
P2927		150f. brown	6·75	2·75

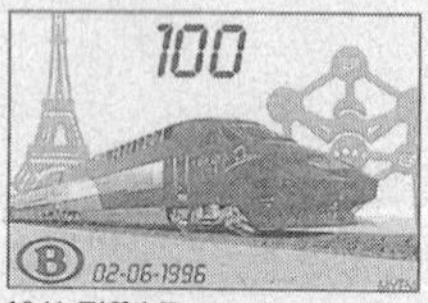

P **1041** Eiffel Tower (Paris), Thalys Train and Atomium (Brussels)

1996. Inauguration of Thalys Amsterdam–Paris via Belgium High-speed Train. Multicoloured.

P3325		100f. Type P **1041**	5·25	4·50
P3326		300f. Eiffel Tower, Thalys train (facing left) and Atomium	13·50	14·50

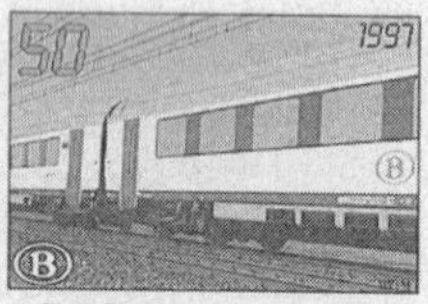

P **1072** Type III Coaches

1997. Inauguration of New Rolling Stock. Mult.

P3405		50f. Type P **1072**	2·50	1·50
P3406		100f. MS96 motor coach No. 449	5·00	2·75
P3407		200f. Type 13 electric locomotive No. 1302	9·00	5·75

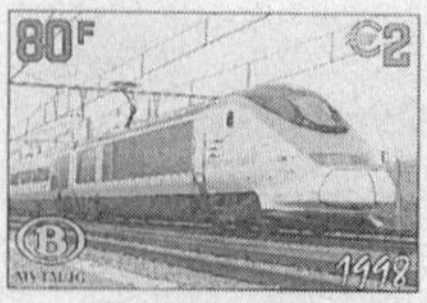

P **1095** Eurostar

1998. High-speed Trains. Multicoloured.

P3457		80f. Type P **1095**	3·00	1·90
P3458		80f. Thalys	3·00	1·90
P3459		160f. Eurostar and Thalys	6·00	3·75

Nos. P3457/9 are denominated both in Belgian francs and in euros.

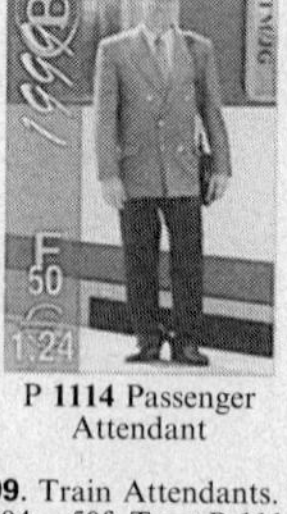

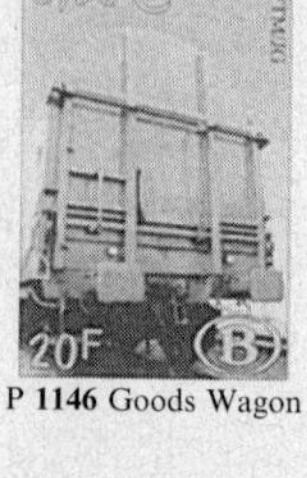

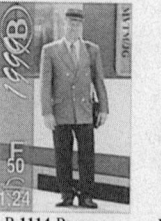

P **1114** Passenger Attendant P **1146** Goods Wagon

1999. Train Attendants. Multicoloured.

P3504		50f. Type P **1114**	1·50	75
P3505		75f. Passenger attendant	2·25	1·10

P3506 100f. Attendant and male passenger 3·00 1·50
P3507 125f. Attendant and female passenger 3·75 1·90
Nos. P3504/7 are denominated both in Belgian francs and in euros.

2000. Trains. Multicoloured.
P3604 20f. Type P **1146** 60 20
P3605 30f. Goods wagon 90 25
P3606 50f. Tanker 1·50 50

RAILWAY PARCEL POSTAGE DUE STAMPS

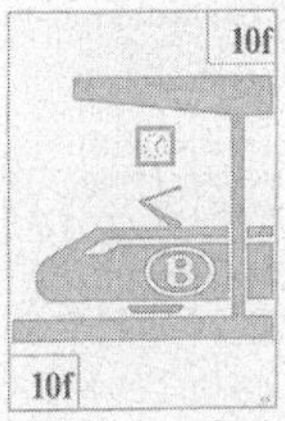

PD **779** Train at Station

1982.
PD2703 PD **779** 10f. red & black 1·60 30
PD2704 20f. green & blk 1·75 1·50
PD2705 50f. brown & blk 3·25 40
PD2706 100f. blue & blk 5·75 90

RAILWAY OFFICIAL STAMPS

For use on the official mail of the Railway Company.

1929. Stamps of 1922 optd with winged wheel.
O481 **81** 5c. slate 10 15
O482 10c. green 35 15
O483 35c. green 50 15
O484 60c. olive 35 15
O485 1f.50 blue 13·50 8·50
O486 1f.75 blue 3·00 25

1929. Stamps of 1929 optd with winged wheel.
O534 **104** 5c. green 10 10
O535 10c. bistre 15 15
O536 25c. red 2·25 60
O537 35c. green 90 25
O538 40c. purple 90 15
O539 50c. blue 35 15
O540 60c. mauve 10·00 8·25
O541 70c. brown 3·50 95
O542 75c. blue 6·25 70

1932. Stamps of 1931–34 optd with winged wheel.
O620 **126** 10c. green 80 80
O677 **127** 35c. green 12·00 45
O678 **142** 70c. green 4·25 25
O679 **121** 75c. brown 2·10 30

1936. Stamps of 1936 optd with winged wheel.
O721 **152** 10c. olive 20 10
O722 35c. green 15 10
O723 40c. lilac 35 15
O724 50c. blue 45 50
O725 **153** 70c. brown 2·50 3·00
O726 75c. olive 65 15

1941. Optd **B** in oval frame.
O948 **152** 10c. green 10 10
O949 40c. lilac 20 20
O950 50c. blue 10 10
O951 **153** 1f. red (No. 747) 10 10
O952a 1f. red (No. 748) 20 20
O953 2f.25 black 25 25
O954 **155** 2f.25 violet 45 40

1942. Nos. O722, O725 and O726 surch.
O983 **152** 10c. on 35c. green 10 15
O984 **153** 50c. on 70c. brown 10 20
O985 50c. on 75c. olive 10 20

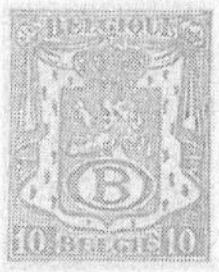

O **221**

O **283**

1946. Designs incorporating letter "B".
O1156 O **221** 10c. green 20 20
O1157 20c. violet 3·25 80
O1158 50c. blue 20 15
O1159 65c. purple 4·00 70
O1160 75c. mauve 20 20
O1161 90c. violet 5·00 35
O1240 – 1f.35 brn (as 1219) 2·10 45
O1241 – 1f.75 green (as 1220) 5·25 45
O1242 **239** 3f. purple 24·00 6·75
O1243 **240** 3f.15 blue 12·00 6·25
O1244 4f. blue 19·00 9·25

1952.
O1424 O **283** 10c. orange 35 10
O1425 20c. red 3·00 60
O1426 30c. green 1·25 40
O1427 40c. brown 30 10
O1428 50c. blue 25 10
O1429 60c. mauve 60 25
O1430 65c. purple 26·00 19·00
O1431 80c. green 4·25 1·00
O1432 90c. blue 6·25 1·10
O1433 1f. red 50 10
O1433a 1f.50 grey 15 10
O1434 2f.50 brown 25 10

1954. As T **289** (King Baudouin) but with letter "B" incorporated in design.
O1523 1f.50 black 35 20
O1524 2f. red 32·00 35
O1525 2f. green 35 20
O1526 2f.50 brown 26·00 55
O1527 3f. mauve 1·50 20
O1528 3f.50 green 70 20
O1529 4f. blue 95 25
O1530 6f. red 1·50 50

1971. As Nos. 2209/20 but with letter "B" incorporated in design.
O2224 3f. green 1·10 60
O2225 3f.50 brown 30 15
O2226 4f. blue 1·10 45
O2227 4f.50 purple 30 20
O2228 4f.50 blue 30 20
O2229 5f. violet 35 20
O2230 6f. red 35 20
O2231 6f.50 violet 45 25
O2232a 7f. red 30 25
O2233 8f. black 45 20
O2233a 9f. brown 45 20
O2234 10f. red 45 20
O2235 15f. violet 60 30
O2236 25f. purple 1·25 45
O2237 30f. brown 1·50 30

1977. As T **684** but with letter "B" incorporated in design.
O2455 50c. brown 15 10
O2456 1f. mauve 15 10
O2457 2f. orange 15 10
O2458 4f. brown 25 10
O2459 5f. green 20 25

BELIZE Pt. 1

British Honduras was renamed Belize on 1 June 1973 and the country became independent within the Commonwealth on 21 September 1981.

100 cents = 1 dollar

1973. Nos. 256/66 and 277/8 of British Honduras optd **BELIZE** and two stars.
347 – ½c. multicoloured 10 20
348 **63** 1c. black, brown and yellow 10 20
349 – 2c. black, green and yellow 10 20
350 – 3c. black, brown and lilac 10 10
351 – 4c. multicoloured 10 20
352 – 5c. black and red 10 20
353 – 10c. multicoloured 15 15
354 – 15c. multicoloured 20 20
355 – 25c. multicoloured 35 35
356 – 50c. multicoloured 65 75
357 – $1 multicoloured 75 1·50
358 – $2 multicoloured 1·25 2·75
359 – $5 multicoloured 1·40 4·75

1973. Royal Wedding. As T **47** of Anguilla. Background colours given. Multicoloured.
360 26c. blue 15 10
361 50c. brown 15 20

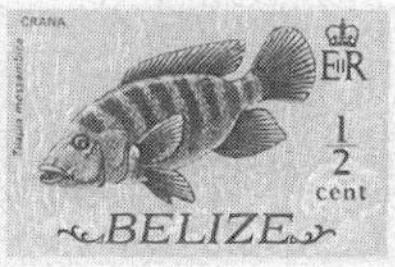

82 Mozambique Mouthbrooder

1974. As Nos. 256/66 and 276/78 of British Honduras. Multicoloured.
362 ½c. Type **82** 10 20
363 1c. Spotted jewfish 10 20
364 2c. White-lipped peccary ("Waree") 10 20
365 3c. Misty grouper 10 20
366 4c. Collared anteater 10 20
367 5c. Bonefish 10 20
368 10c. Paca ("Gibnut") 15 15
369 15c. Dolphin 20 20
370 25c. Kinkajou ("Night Walker") 35 35
371 50c. Mutton snapper 60 70
372 $1 Tayra ("Bush Dog") 75 1·50
373 $2 Great barracuda 1·25 2·25
374 $5 Puma 1·50 5·50

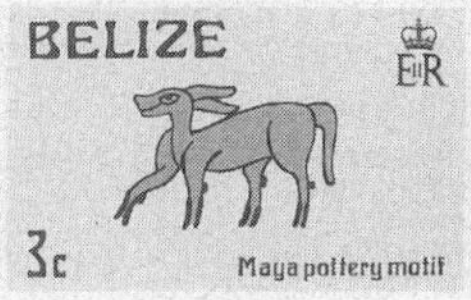

83 Deer

1974. Mayan Artefacts (1st series). Pottery Motifs. Multicoloured.
375 3c. Type **83** 10 10
376 6c. Jaguar deity 10 10
377 16c. Sea monster 15 10
378 26c. Cormorant 25 10
379 50c. Scarlet macaw 40 40
See also Nos. 398/402.

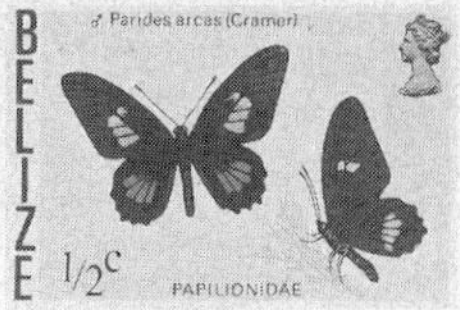

84 "Parides arcas"

1974. Butterflies of Belize. Multicoloured.
380 ½c. Type **84** 90 3·75
381 1c. "Evenus regalis" 90 1·75
405 2c. "Colobura dirce" 50 70
406 3c. "Catonephele numilia" 1·25 70
407 4c. "Battus belus" 3·00 30
408 5c. "Callicore patelina" 3·25 30
386 10c. "Diaethria astala" 1·50 70
410 15c. "Nessaea aglaura" 75 70
388 16c. "Prepona pseudojoiceyi" 4·50 6·50
412 25c. "Papilio thoas" 5·50 40
390 26c. "Hamadryas arethusa" 2·50 4·25
413 35c. Type **84** 11·00 4·50
391 50c. "Panthiades bathildis" 2·75 65
392 $1 "Caligo uranus" 6·50 5·50
393 $2 "Heliconius sapho" 4·00 1·25
394 $5 "Eurytides philolaus" 5·50 6·00
395 $10 "Philaethria dido" 10·00 4·00

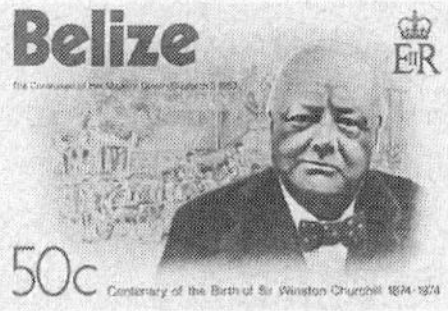

85 Churchill when Prime Minister, and Coronation Scene

1974. Birth Centenary of Sir Winston Churchill. Multicoloured.
396 50c. Type **85** 20 20
397 $1 Churchill in stetson, and Williamsburg Liberty Bell 30 30

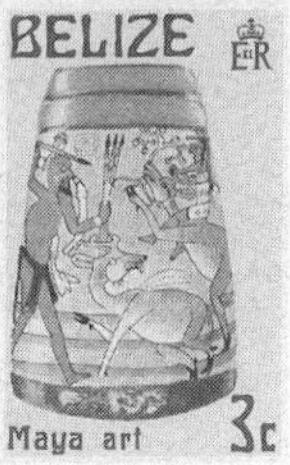

86 The Actun Balam Vase

1975. Mayan Artefacts (2nd series). Multicoloured.
398 3c. Type **86** 10 10
399 6c. Seated figure 10 10
400 16c. Costumed priest 25 15
401 26c. Head with headdress 35 20
402 50c. Layman and priest 45 1·75

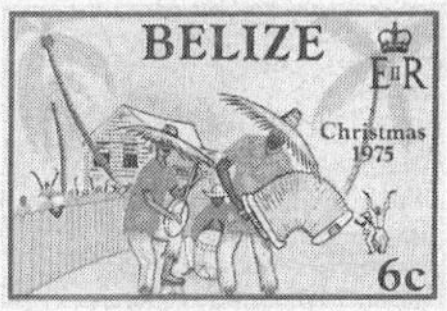

87 Musicians

1975. Christmas. Multicoloured.
435 6c. Type **87** 10 10
436 26c. Children and "crib" 20 10
437 50c. Dancer and drummers (vert) 30 55
438 $1 Family and map (vert) 55 1·60

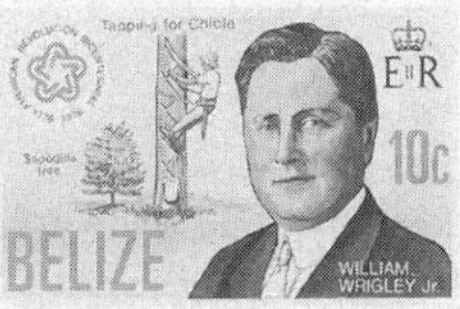

88 William Wrigley Jr. and Chicle Tapping

1976. Bicent of American Revolution. Mult.
439 10c. Type **88** 10 10
440 35c. Charles Lindbergh 20 40
441 $1 J. L. Stephens (archaeologist) 50 1·50

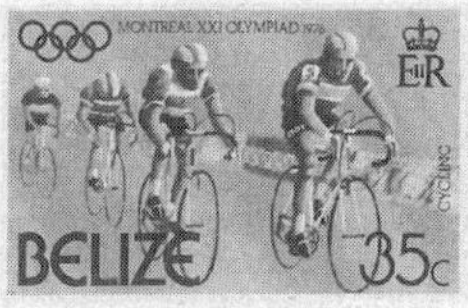

89 Cycling

1976. Olympic Games, Montreal. Multicoloured.
442 35c. Type **89** 15 10
443 45c. Running 20 15
444 $1 Shooting 35 1·40

1976. No. 390 surch **20c**.
445 20c. on 26c. multicoloured 1·50 1·00

1976. West Indian Victory in World Cricket Cup. As Nos. 559/60 of Barbados.
446 35c. multicoloured 40 50
447 $1 black and purple 60 2·00

1976. No. 426 surch **5c**.
448 5c. on 15c. multicoloured 1·10 2·50

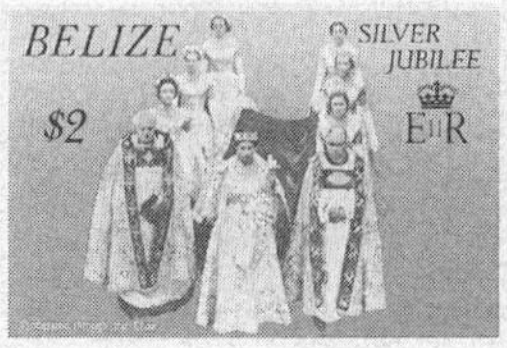

92 Queen and Bishops

1977. Silver Jubilee. Multicoloured.
449 10c. Royal Visit, 1975 10 10
450 35c. Queen and Rose Window 15 15
451 $2 Type **92** 45 90

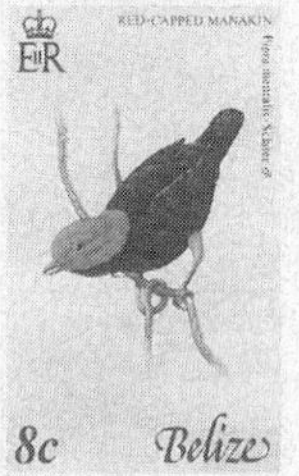

93 Red-capped Manakin

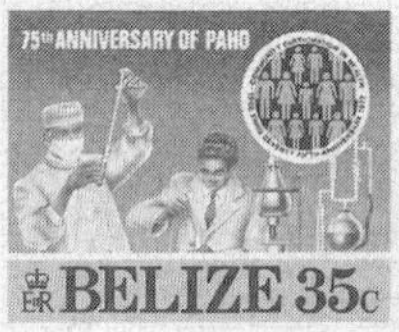

94 Laboratory Workers

1977. Birds (1st series). Multicoloured.
452 8c. Type **93** 75 55
453 10c. Hooded oriole 90 30
454 25c. Blue-crowned motmot 1·25 55
455 35c. Slaty-breasted tinamou 1·50 75
456 45c. Ocellated turkey 1·75 1·25
457 $1 White hawk 3·00 5·50
See also Nos. 467/72, 486/91 and 561/6.

1977. 75th Anniv of Pan-American Health Organization. Multicoloured.
459 35c. Type **94** 20 20
460 $1 Mobile medical unit 40 65

1978. Nos. 386 and 413 optd **BELIZE DEFENCE FORCE 1ST JANUARY 1978**.
462 10c. "Diaethria astala" 75 75
463 35c. Type **84** 1·50 2·25

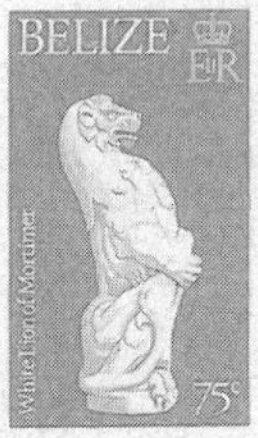

96 White Lion of Mortimer

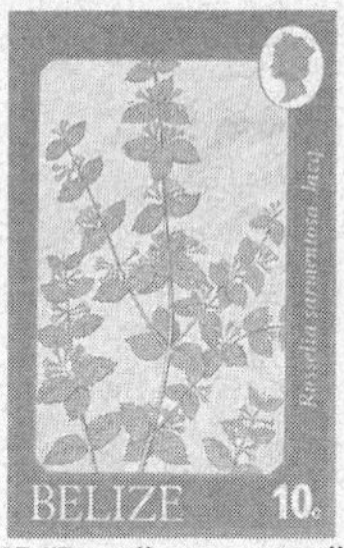

97 "Russelia sarmentosa"

1978. 25th Anniv. of Coronation.
464 **96** 75c. brown, red and silver 20 30
465 – 75c. multicoloured 20 30
466 – 75c. brown, red and silver 20 30
DESIGNS: No. 465, Queen Elizabeth II; 466, Jaguar (Maya god of Day and Night).

1978. Birds (2nd series). As T **93**. Multicoloured.
467 10c. White-capped parrot ("White-crowned Parrot") 55 30
468 25c. Crimson-collared tanager 80 45
469 35c. Black-headed trogon ("Citreoline Trogon") 1·10 55
470 45c. American finfoot ("Sungrebe") 1·25 1·75
471 50c. Muscovy duck 1·40 2·50
472 $1 King vulture 2·00 6·50

1978. Christmas. Wild Flowers and Ferns. Mult.
474 10c. Type **97** 15 10
475 15c. "Lygodium polymorphum" 20 15
476 35c. "Heliconia aurantiaca" 20 20
477 45c. "Adiantum tetraphyllum" 20 40
478 50c. "Angelonia ciliaris" 35 50
479 $1 "Thelypteris obliterata" 50 1·25

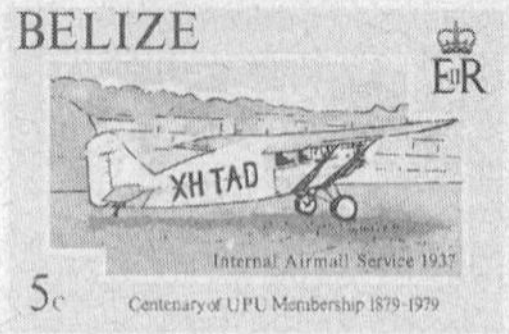

98 Fairchild Monoplane of Internal Airmail Service, 1937

1979. Centenary of U.P.U. Membership. Mult.

480 5c. Type **98** 25 30
481 10c. "Heron H" (mail boat), 1949 25 10
482 35c. Internal mail service, 1920 (canoe) 25 20
483 45c. Steam Creek Railway mail, 1910 45 55
484 50c. Mounted mail courier, 1882 45 60
485 $1 "Eagle" (mail boat), 1856 80 2·50

1979. No. 413 surch **15c.**

487 **84** 15c. on 35c. multicoloured 2·00 1·75

1979. Birds (3rd series). As T **93**. Multicoloured.

488 10c. Boat-billed heron 65 30
489 25c. Grey-necked wood rail 90 30
490 35c. Lineated woodpecker 1·10 55
491 45c. Blue-grey tanager 1·25 70
492 50c. Laughing falcon 1·25 1·25
493 $1 Long-tailed hermit 1·60 4·00

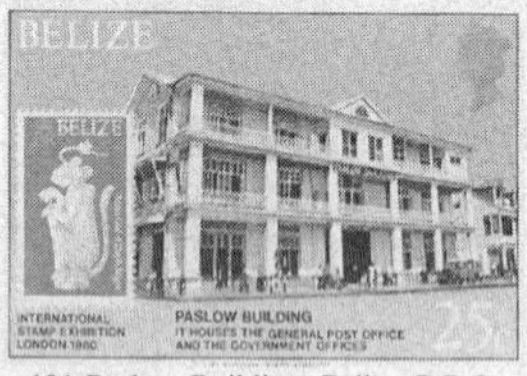

101 Paslow Building, Belize G.P.O.

1979. 25th Anniv of Coronation. Multicoloured.

495 25c. Type **101** 1·25 10
496 50c. Houses of Parliament 1·75 10
497 75c. Coronation State Coach 2·25 15
498 $1 Queen on horseback (vert) 3·00 15
499 $2 Prince of Wales (vert) 3·00 25
500 $3 Queen and Duke of Edinburgh (vert) 3·00 25
501 $4 Portrait of Queen (vert) 3·25 30
502 $5 St. Edward's Crown (vert) 3·50 30

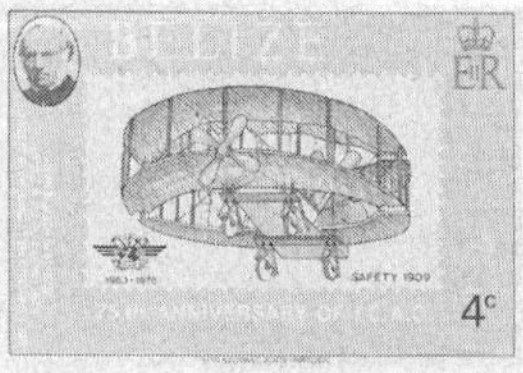

102 Mortimer and Vaughan "Safety" Airplane, 1910

1979. Death Centenary of Sir Rowland Hill. 60th Anniv of I.C.A.O. (International Civil Aviation Organization), previously Int Commission for Air Navigation. Multicoloured.

504 4c. Type **102** 50 10
505 25c. Boeing 720 1·50 20
506 50c. Concorde 3·75 30
507 75c. Handley Page H.P.18 W.8b (1922) 1·75 30
508 $1 Avro Type F (1912) 1·75 30
509 $1.50 Samuel Cody's biplane (1910) 2·50 30
510 $2 A.V. Roe Triplane I (1909) 2·50 40
511 $3 Santos Dumont's biplane "14 bis" (1906) 2·50 45
512 $4 Wright Type A 3·00 65

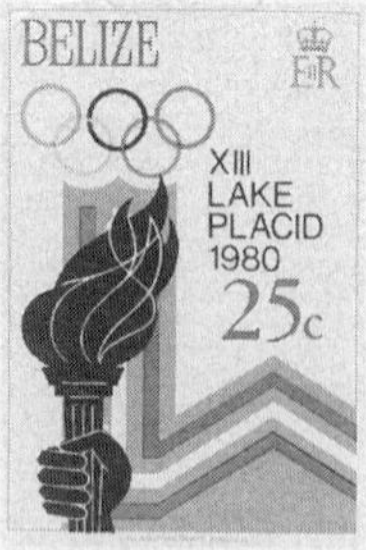

103 Handball **104** Olympic Torch

1979. Olympic Games, Moscow (1980). Mult.

514 25c. Type **103** 45 10
515 50c. Weightlifting 65 10
516 75c. Athletics 90 15
517 $1 Football 1·25 20
518 $2 Yachting 1·75 25
519 $3 Swimming 2·00 30
520 $4 Boxing 2·50 30
521 $5 Cycling 7·00 75

1979. Winter Olympic Games, Lake Placid (1980). Multicoloured.

523 25c. Type **104** 20 10
524 50c. Giant slalom 45 15
525 75c. Figure-skating 65 15
526 $1 Downhill skiing 80 15
527 $2 Speed-skating 1·60 20
528 $3 Cross-country skiing 2·50 30
529 $4 Shooting 3·00 40
530 $5 Gold, Silver and Bronze medals 3·50 45

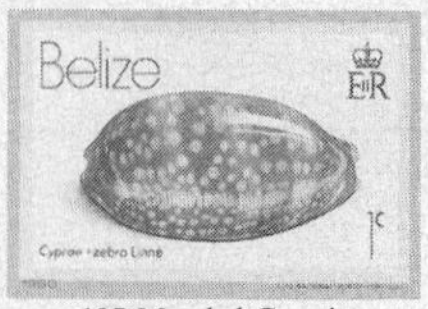

105 Measled Cowrie

1980. Shells. Multicoloured.

532 1c. Type **105** 55 10
533 2c. Callico clam 70 10
534 3c. Altantic turkey wing (vert) 80 10
535 4c. Leafy jewel box (vert) 80 10
536 5c. Trochlear latirus 80 10
537 10c. Alphabet cone (vert) 1·00 10
538 15c. Cabrits murex (vert) 1·40 10
539 20c. Stiff pen shell 1·50 10
540 25c. Little knobbed scallop (vert) 1·50 10
541 35c. Glory of the Atlantic cone (vert) 1·75 10
542 45c. Sunrise tellin (vert) 2·00 10
543 50c. "Leucozonia nassa leucozonalis" 2·00 10
544 85c. Triangular typhis 3·00 10
545 $1 Queen or pink conch (vert) 3·25 10
546 $2 Rooster-tail conch (vert) 5·00 30
547 $5 True tulip 7·50 50
548 $10 Star arene 9·50 90

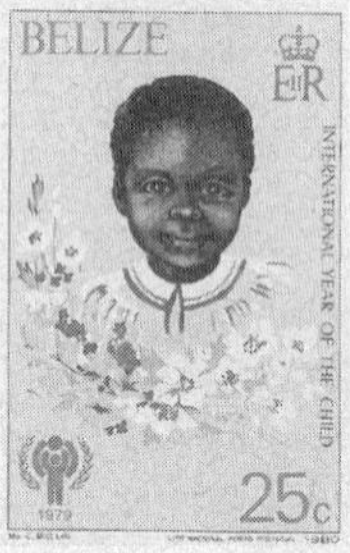

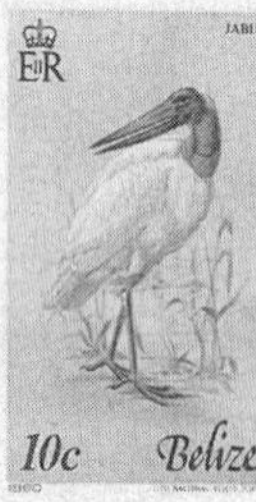

106 Girl and Flower Arrangement **108** Jabiru

1980. International Year of the Child (1st issue). Multicoloured.

550 25c. Type **106** 45 10
551 50c. Boy holding football 70 10
552 75c. Boy with butterfly 1·00 10
553 $1 Girl holding doll 1·00 10
554 $1.50 Boy carrying basket of fruit 1·50 15
555 $2 Boy holding reticulated cowrie-helmet shell 1·75 20
556 $3 Girl holding posy 2·25 25
557 $4 Boy and girl wrapped in blanket 2·50 30

See also Nos. 583/90.

1980. No. 412 surch **10c.**

560 10c. on 25c. "Papilio thoas" 75 1·00

1980. Birds (4th series). Multicoloured.

561 10c. Type **108** 6·00 2·75
562 25c. Barred antshrike 7·00 2·75
563 35c. Northern royal flycatcher ("Royal Flycatcher") 7·00 2·75
564 45c. White-necked puffbird 7·00 3·00
565 50c. Ornate hawk-eagle 7·00 3·00
566 $1 Golden-masked tanager 7·50 3·75

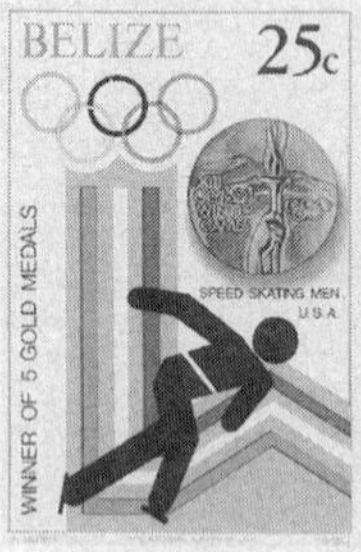

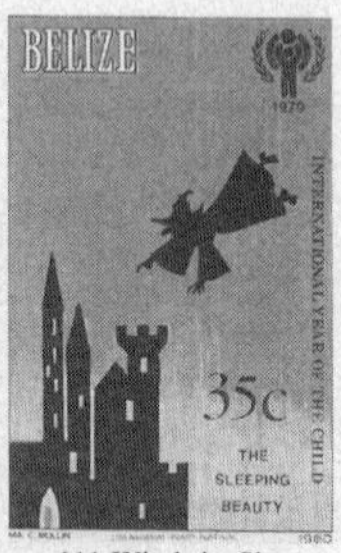

109 Speed Skating **111** Witch in Sky

1980. Winter Olympic Games, Lake Placid. Medal Winners. Multicoloured.

568 25c. Type **109** 30 15
569 50c. Ice-hockey 50 15
570 75c. Figure-skating 60 15
571 $1 Alpine-skiing 85 15
572 $1.50 Giant slalom (women) 1·25 25
573 $2 Speed-skating (women) 1·50 30
574 $3 Cross-country skiing 2·25 40
575 $5 Giant slalom 3·50 55

1980. "ESPAMER" International Stamp Exhibition, Madrid. Nos. 560/5 optd **BELIZE ESPAMER '80 MADRID 3-12 OCT 1980** and emblem (Nos. 577/9) or surch also.

577 10c. Type **107** 6·00 2·50
578 25c. Barred antshrike 6·50 2·75
579 35c. Northern royal flycatcher 6·50 2·75
580 40c. on 45c. White-necked puffbird 7·00 3·00
581 40c. on 50c. Ornate hawk eagle 7·00 3·00
582 40c. on $1 Golden-masked tanager 7·50 3·00

1980. International Year of the Child (2nd issue). "Sleeping Beauty".

583 **111** 25c. multicoloured 1·25 15
584 – 40c. multicoloured 1·50 15
585 – 50c. multicoloured 1·75 15
586 – 75c. multicoloured 1·90 15
587 – $1 multicoloured 2·00 20
588 – $1.50 multicoloured 2·50 30
589 – $3 multicoloured 3·50 35
590 – $4 multicoloured 3·50 45

DESIGNS: 40c. to $4, Illustrations from the story.

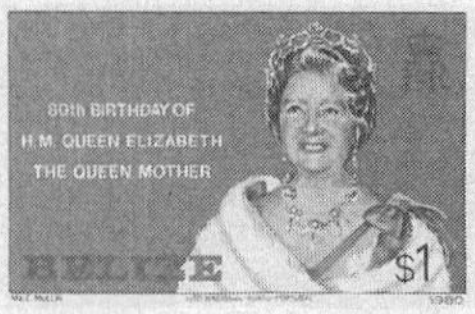

112 H.M. Queen Elizabeth the Queen Mother

1980. 80th Birthday of H.M. Queen Elizabeth the Queen Mother.

592 **112** $1 multicoloured 1·50 40

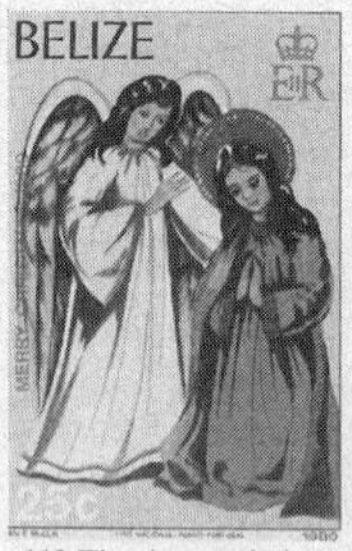

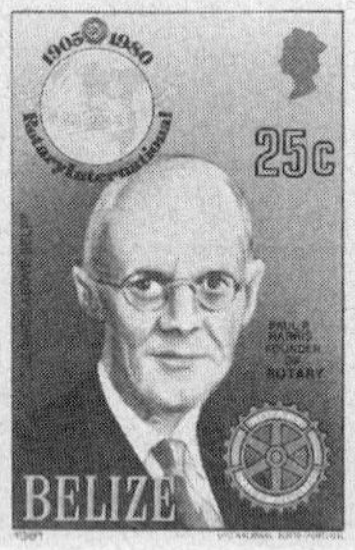

113 The Annunciation **115** Paul Harris (founder)

1980. Christmas. Multicoloured.

594 25c. Type **113** 55 10
595 50c. Bethlehem 1·00 10
596 75c. The Holy Family 1·25 10
597 $1 The Nativity 1·40 10
598 $1.50 The Flight into Egypt 1·60 15
599 $2 Shepherds following the Star 1·75 20
600 $3 Virgin, Child and Angel 2·25 25
601 $4 Adoration of the Kings 2·25 30

1981. "WIPA" International Stamp Exhibition, Vienna. Nos. 598 and 601 surch.

603 $1 on $1.50 The Flight into Egypt 5·00 1·25
604 $2 on $4 Adoration of the Kings 5·50 2·00

1981. 75th Anniv of Rotary International. Mult.

606 25c. Type **115** 1·50 25
607 50c. Emblems of Rotary activities 2·00 35
608 $1 75th Anniversary emblem 2·50 65
609 $1.50 Educational scholarship programme (horiz) 3·25 1·00
610 $2 "Project Hippocrates" 3·75 1·40
611 $3 Emblems 4·50 2·00
612 $5 Emblems and handshake (horiz) 5·50 3·25

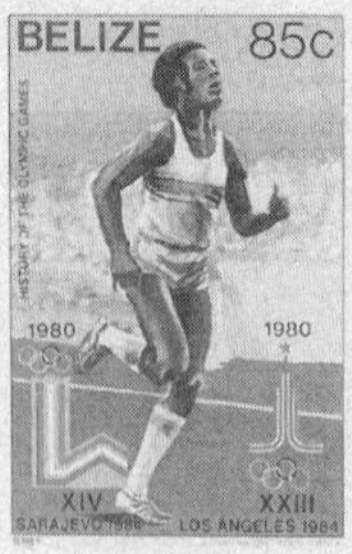

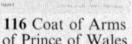

116 Coat of Arms of Prince of Wales **118** Athletics

1981. Royal Wedding. Mult. (a) Size 22 × 38 mm.

614 50c. Type **116** 35 40
615 $1 Prince Charles in military uniform 70 75
616 $1.50 Royal couple 1·10 1·25

(b) Size 25 × 42 mm, with gold borders.

617 50c. Type **116** 35 15
618 $1 As No. 615 70 35
619 $1.50 As No. 616 1·10 45

1981. No. 538 surch **10c.**

621 10c. on 15c. "Murex cabritii" 3·50 3·50

1981. History of the Olympics. Multicoloured.

622 85c. Type **118** 1·75 30
623 $1 Cycling 5·00 30
624 $1.50 Boxing 2·75 30
625 $2 1984 Games–Los Angeles and Sarajevo 3·50 30
626 $3 Baron de Coubertin 4·25 45
627 $5 Olympic Flame 5·00 60

1981. Independence Commemoration (1st issue). Optd **Independence 21 Sept., 1981.** (a) On Nos. 532/44 and 546/8.

629 1c. Type **105** 1·00 10
630 2c. Callico clam 1·00 10
631 3c. Atlantic turkey wing (vert) 1·00 10
632 4c. Leafy jewel box (vert) 1·00 10
633 5c. Trochlear latirus 1·25 10
634 10c. Alphabet cone (vert) 1·50 10
635 15c. Cabrits murex (vert) 2·25 10
636 20c. Stiff pen shell 2·25 15
637 25c. Little knobbed scallop (vert) 2·50 25
638 35c. Glory of the Atlantic cone 2·50 30
639 45c. Sunrise tellin (vert) 3·00 40
640 50c. "Leucozonia nassa leucozonalis" 3·00 40
641 85c. Triangular typhis 4·25 90
642 $2 Rooster-tail conch (vert) 8·00 2·50
643 $5 True tulip 9·50 5·50
644 $10 Star arene 13·00 9·50

(b) On Nos. 606/12.

646 25c. Type **115** 2·00 25
647 50c. Emblems of Rotary activities 2·25 35
648 $1 75th Anniversary emblem 2·75 65
649 $1.50 Educational scholarship programme 3·50 1·25
650 $2 "Project Hippocrates" 4·25 1·60
651 $3 Emblems 4·75 2·50
652 $5 Emblems and hand-shake 6·50 3·75

See also Nos. 657/62.

1981. "ESPAMER" International Stamp Exhibition, Buenos Aires. No. 609 surch **$1 ESPAMER 81 BUENOS AIRES 13-22 NOV** and emblem.

654 $1 on $1.50 Educational scholarship programme 7·00 2·75

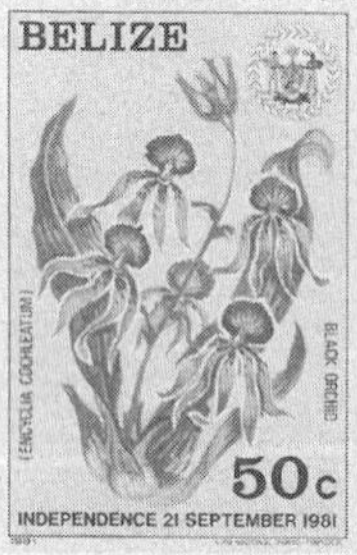

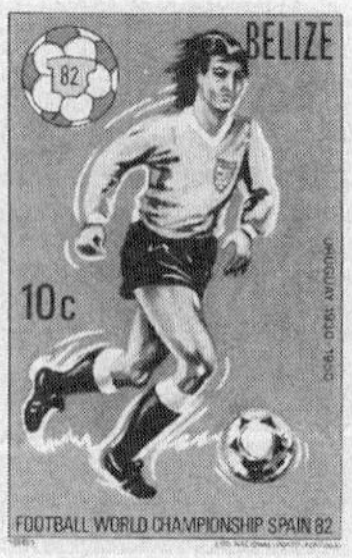

122 Black Orchid **123** Uruguayan Footballer

1981. Independence Commemoration (2nd issue). Multicoloured.

657 10c. Belize Coat of Arms (horiz) 1·75 20
658 35c. Map of Belize 3·25 40
659 50c. Type **122** 7·50 1·00
660 85c. Baird's tapir (horiz) 2·25 1·00
661 $1 Mahogany tree 2·25 1·10
662 $2 Keel-billed toucan (horiz) 11·00 3·75

1981. World Cup Football Championship, Spain (1st issue). Multicoloured.

664 10c. Type **123** 1·75 20
665 25c. Italian footballer 2·75 20
666 50c. German footballer 3·50 40
667 $1 Brazilian footballer 4·50 50
668 $1.50 Argentinian footballer 5·50 90
669 $2 English footballer 6·00 1·10

See also Nos. 721/6.

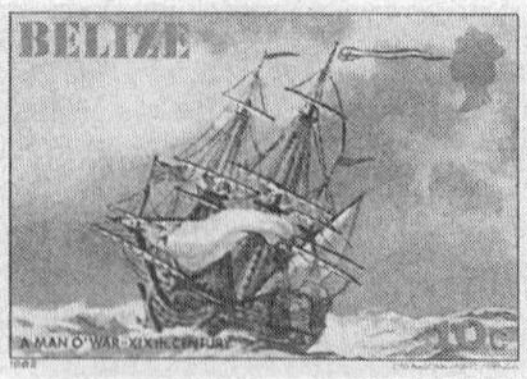

124 H.M.S. "Centurion" (frigate)

1981. Sailing Ships. Multicoloured.

671 10c. Type **124** 2·50 35
672 25c. "Madagascar" (1837) 3·75 45
673 35c. Brig "Whitby" (1838) 4·25 50
674 55c. "China" (1838) 4·75 85
675 85c. "Swiftsure" (1850) 6·00 1·25
676 $2 "Windsor Castle" (1857) 8·50 2·50

1982. "ESSEN '82" Int Stamp Exn, West Germany. Nos. 662 and 669 surch **$1 ESSEN 82.**

678 $1 on $2 Keel-billed toucan 7·00 2·25
679 $1 on $2 English footballer 7·00 2·25

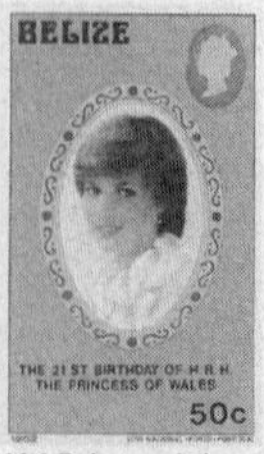

126 Princess Diana

1982. 21st Birthday of Princess of Wales. (a) Size 22 × 38 mm.

680	126	50c. multicoloured	1·40	45
681	–	$1 multicoloured	1·75	75
682	–	$1.50 multicoloured . . .	2·00	1·50
		(b) Size 25 × 43 mm.		
683	126	50c. multicoloured	1·40	30
684	–	$1 multicoloured	1·75	60
685	–	$1.50 multicoloured . . .	2·00	1·10

DESIGNS: Portraits of Princess of Wales with different backgrounds.

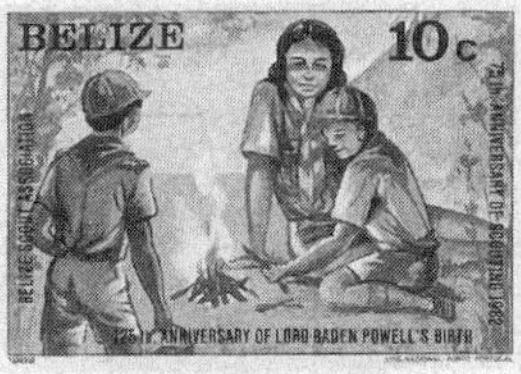

127 Lighting Campfire

1982. 125th Birth Anniv of Lord Baden-Powell. Multicoloured.

687	10c. Type **127**	1·50	20
668	25c. Bird watching	4·00	30
689	35c. Three scouts, one playing guitar	2·50	30
690	50c. Hiking	2·75	55
691	85c. Scouts with flag	3·75	1·00
692	$2 Saluting	4·25	2·50

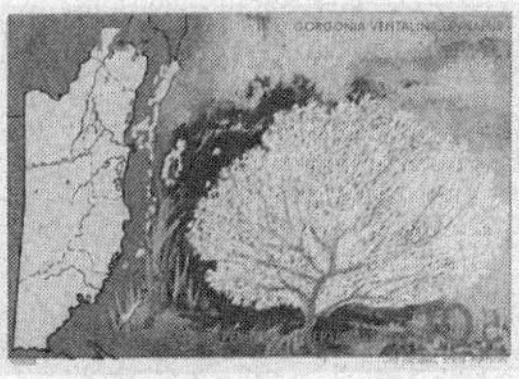
128 "Gorgonia ventalina"

1982. 1st Anniv of Independence. Marine Life. Multicoloured.

694	10c. Type **128**	2·00	20
695	35c. "Carpiuis corallinus" . .	3·25	20
696	50c. "Plexaura flexuasa" . .	3·75	45
697	85c. "Candylactis gigantea"	4·00	60
698	$1 "Stenopus hispidus" . . .	5·00	90
699	$2 Sergeant major	6·00	1·60

1982. "BELGICA 82" International Stamp Exhibition, Brussels. Nos. 687/92 optd **BELGICA 82 INT. YEAR OF THE CHILD SIR ROWLAND HILL 1795 1879 Picasso CENTENARY OF BIRTH** and emblems.

701	10c. Type **127**	2·00	30
702	25c. Bird watching	4·50	75
703	35c. Three scouts, one playing guitar	3·25	1·00
704	50c. Hiking	3·50	1·50
705	85c. Scouts with flag	7·50	2·50
706	$2 Saluting	9·00	6·50

1982. Birth of Prince William of Wales (1st issue). Nos. 680/5 optd **BIRTH OF H.R.H. PRINCE WILLIAM ARTHUR PHILIP LOUIS 21ST JUNE 1982.** (a) Size 22 × 38 mm.

707	50c. multicoloured	35	35
708	$1 multicoloured	45	50
709	$1.50 multicoloured	65	75
	(b) Size 25 × 43 mm.		
710	50c. multicoloured	35	35
711	$1 multicoloured	45	50
712	$1.50 multicoloured	65	75

1982. Birth of Prince William of Wales (2nd issue). Nos. 614/19 optd **BIRTH OF H.R.H. PRINCE WILLIAM ARTHUR PHILIP LOUIS 21ST JUNE 1982.** (a) Size 22 × 38 mm.

714	50c. Type **116**	2·50	1·00
715	$1 Prince Charles in military uniform	5·00	2·00
716	$1.50 Royal couple	7·50	3·00
	(b) Size 25 × 42 mm.		
717	50c. Type **116**	35	35
718	$1 As No. 715	70	70
719	$1.50 As No. 716	1·10	1·10

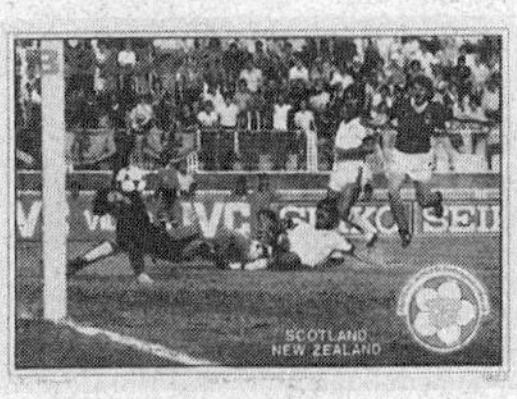

131 Scotland v New Zealand

1982. World Cup Football Championship, Spain (2nd issue). Multicoloured.

721	20c.+10c. Type **131**	2·00	1·00
722	30c.+15c. Scotland v New Zealand (different)	2·00	1·00
723	40c.+20c. Kuwait v France	2·25	1·00
724	60c.+50c. Italy v Brazil . . .	2·75	1·40
725	$1+50c. France v Northern Ireland	3·25	1·60
726	$1.50+75c. Austria v Chile	4·00	2·00

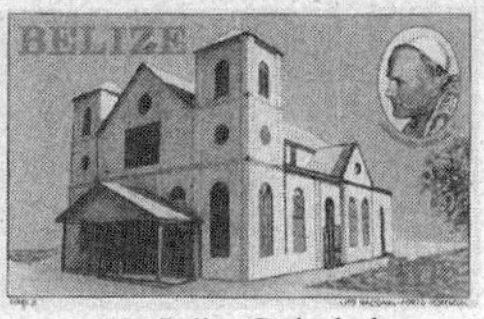

133 Belize Cathedral

1983. Visit of Pope John Paul II.

729	133	50c. multicoloured	2·25	1·25

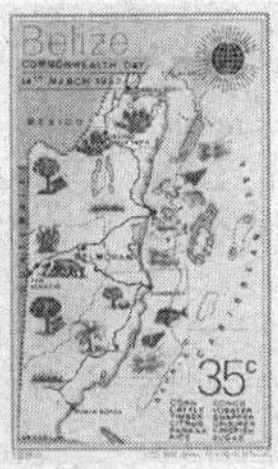

134 Map of Belize

1983. Commonwealth Day. Multicoloured.

731	35c. Type **134**	35	35
732	50c. "Maya Stella" from Lamanai Indian church (horiz)	50	50
733	85c. Supreme Court Building (horiz)	60	75
734	$2 University Centre, Belize (horiz)	1·25	2·25

1983. No. 658 surch **10c.**

735	10c. on 35c. Map of Belize		

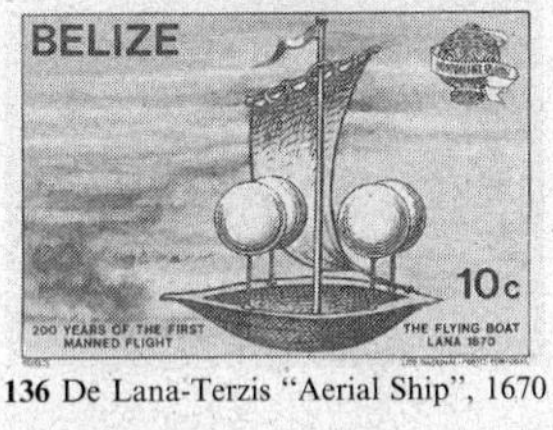

136 De Lana-Terzis "Aerial Ship", 1670

1983. Bicentenary of Manned Flight. Multicoloured.

736	10c. Type **136**	2·25	65
737	25c. De Gusmao's "La Passarole", 1709	3·00	70
738	50c. Guyton de Morveau's balloon with oars, 1784 . .	3·25	1·00
739	85c. Airship	4·00	1·25
740	$1 Airship "Clement Bayard"	4·25	1·60
741	$1.50 Beardmore airship R-34	4·75	3·25

1983. Nos. 662 and 699 surch **$1.25.**

743	$1.25 on $2 Keel-billed toucan	9·00	9·00
744	$1.25 on $2 Sergeant major	6·00	8·00

1983. No. 541 surch **10c.**

746	10c. on 35c. Glory of the Atlantic cone	32·00	

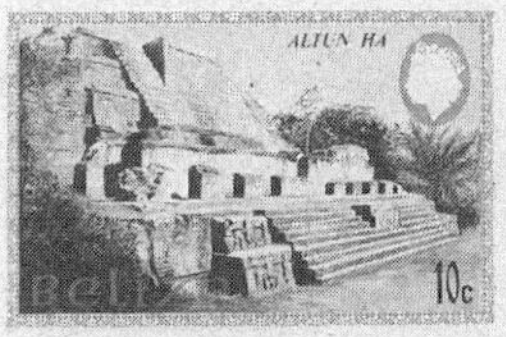

141 Altun Ha

1983. Maya Monuments. Multicoloured.

747	10c. Type **141**	10	10
748	15c. Xunantunich	10	10
749	75c. Cerros	30	40
750	$3 Lamanal	70	1·25

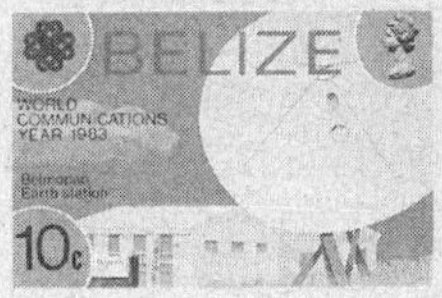

142 Belmopan Earth Station

1983. World Communications Year. Multicoloured.

752	10c. Type **142**	30	10
753	15c. "Telstar 2"	40	25
754	75c. U.P.U. logo	70	1·75
755	$2 M.V. "Heron H" mail service	1·25	4·50

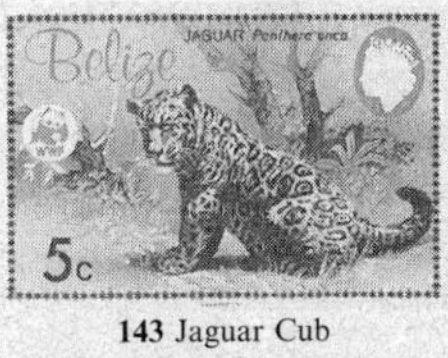

143 Jaguar Cub

1983. The Jaguar. Multicoloured.

756	5c. Type **143**	30	75
757	10c. Adult jaguar	35	45
758	85c. Jaguar in river	1·75	3·00
759	$1 Jaguar on rock	2·00	3·25

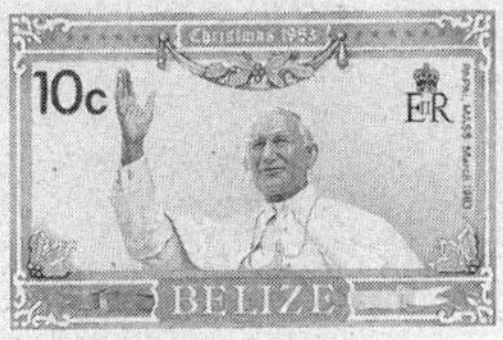

144 Pope John Paul II

1983. Christmas.

761	144	10c. multicoloured	25	10
762		15c. multicoloured	25	10
763		75c. multicoloured	50	60
764		$2 multicoloured	80	1·40

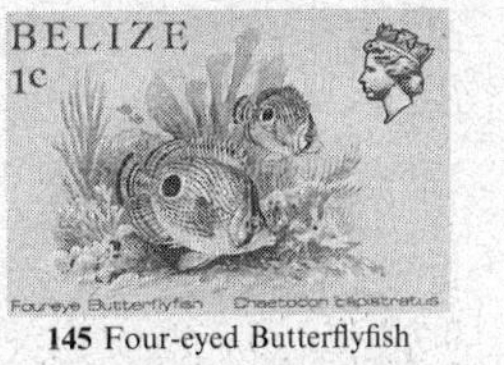

145 Four-eyed Butterflyfish

1984. Marine Life from the Belize Coral Reef. Multicoloured.

766	1c. Type **145**	15	80
767	2c. Cushion star	20	60
768	3c. Flower coral	25	60
769	4c. Royal gramma ("Fairy basslet")	25	60
770	5c. Spanish hogfish	30	60
771	6c. Star-eyed hermit crab . .	30	60
772a	10c. Sea fans and fire sponge	35	35
773a	15c. Blue-headed wrasse . .	50	60
774a	25c. Blue-striped grunt . . .	70	80
775a	50c. Coral crab	1·00	1·75
776a	60c. Tube sponge	1·00	1·75
777	75c. Brain coral	1·00	1·50
778	$1 Yellow-tailed snapper . .	1·00	1·25
779	$2 Common lettuce slug . .	1·25	65
780	$5 Three-spotted damselfish	1·50	80
781	$10 Rock beauty	2·00	1·40

1984. Visit of the Archbishop of Canterbury. Nos. 772 and 775 optd **VISIT OF THE LORD ARCHBISHOP OF CANTERBURY 8th-11th MARCH 1984.**

782	10c. Sea fans and fire sponge	75	50
783	50c. Coral crab	1·50	1·50

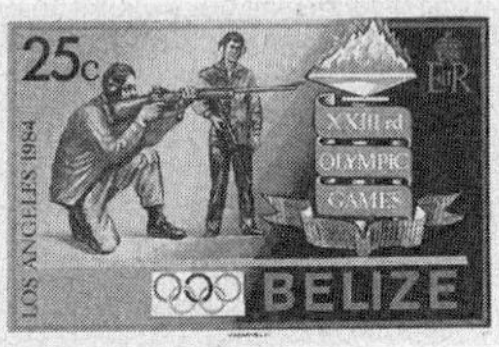

147 Shooting

1984. Olympic Games, Los Angeles. Multicoloured. (a) As T **147**.

784	25c. Type **147**	30	25
785	75c. Boxing	50	70
786	$1 Marathon	60	90
787	$2 Cycling	2·25	2·25
	(b) Similar designs to T **147** but Royal cypher replaced by Queen's Head.		
789	5c. Marathon	20	80
790	20c. Sprinting	25	80
791	25c. Shot-putting	25	80
792	$2 Olympic torch	35	1·10

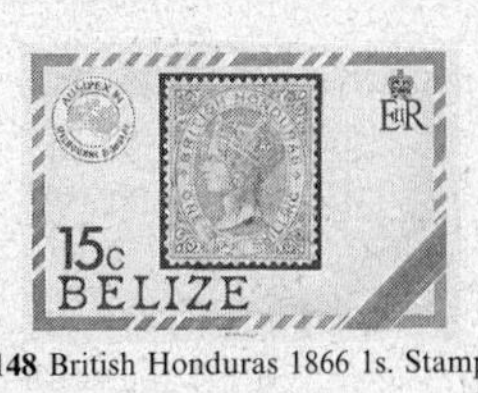

148 British Honduras 1866 1s. Stamp

1984. "Ausipex" International Stamp Exhibition, Melbourne. Multicoloured.

793	15c. Type **148**	25	15
794	30c. British mail coach, 1784	35	25
795	65c. Sir Rowland Hill and Penny Black	65	65
796	75c. British Honduras railway locomotive, 1910	70	75
797	$2 Royal Exhibition Buildings, Melbourne (46 × 28 mm)	1·00	2·00

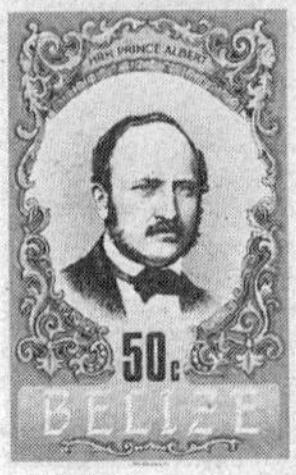

149 Prince Albert

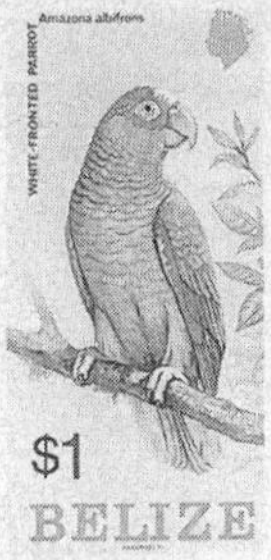

150 White-fronted Amazon ("White-fronted Parrot")

1984. 500th Anniv (1985) of British Royal House of Tudor. Multicoloured.

799	50c. Type **149**	25	35
800	50c. Queen Victoria	25	35
801	75c. King George VI	30	45
802	75c. Queen Elizabeth the Queen Mother	30	45
803	$1 Princess of Wales	40	70
804	$1 Prince of Wales	40	70

1984. Parrots. Multicoloured.

806	$1 Type **150**	1·75	2·00
807	$1 White-capped parrot (horiz)	1·75	2·00
808	$1 Mealy amazon ("Mealy Parrot") (horiz)	1·75	2·00
809	$1 Red-lored amazon ("Red-lored Parrot")	1·75	2·00

Nos. 806/9 were issued together, se-tenant, forming a composite design.

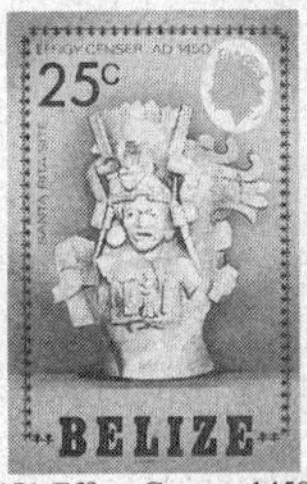

151 Effigy Censer, 1450 (Santa Rita Site)

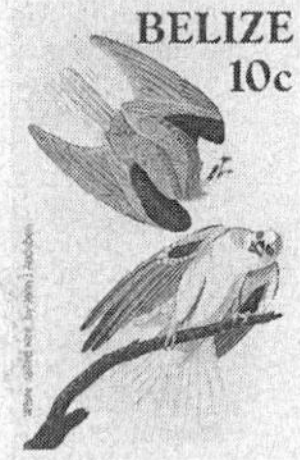

153 White-tailed Kite

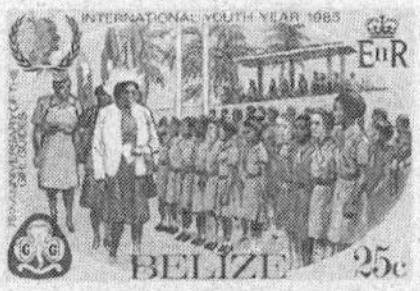

152 Governor-General inspecting Girl Guides

1984. Maya Artefacts. Multicoloured.

811	25c. Type **151**	30	25
812	75c. Vase, 675 (Actun Chapat)	60	80
813	$1 Tripod vase, 500 (Santa Rita site)	65	1·00
814	$2 Sun god Kinich Ahau, 600 (Altun Ha site)	90	2·50

1985. International Youth Year and 75th Anniv of Girl Guides Movement. Multicoloured.

815	25c. Type **152**	30	15
816	50c. Girl Guides camping . .	45	30
817	90c. Checking map on hike	60	45
818	$1.25 Students in laboratory	70	60
819	$2 Lady Baden-Powell (founder)	90	75

1985. Birth Bicentenary of John J. Audubon (ornithologist). Designs showing original paintings. Multicoloured.

820	10c. Type **153**	60	60
821	15c. Ruby-crowned kinglet ("Cuvier's Kinglet") (horiz)	70	60
822	25c. Painted bunting	80	60
822a	60c. As 25c.	16·00	7·00
823	75c. Belted kingfisher . . .	80	1·40
824	$1 Common cardinal ("Northern Cardinal") . .	80	2·25
825	$3 Long-billed curlew (horiz)	1·25	3·00

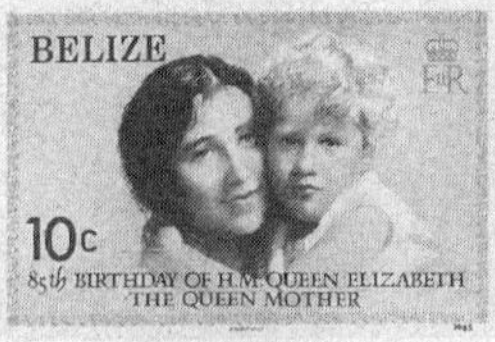

154 The Queen Mother with Princess Elizabeth, 1928

1985. Life and Times of Queen Elizabeth the Queen Mother. Multicoloured.

827	10c. Type **154**	10	10
828	15c. The Queen Mother, 1980	10	10

829	75c. Waving to the crowd, 1982	40	40
830	$5 Four generations of Royal Family at Prince William's Christening	1·50	2·75

1985. Inauguration of New Government. Nos. 772/3 and 775 optd **INAUGURATION OF NEW GOVERNMENT – 21st. DECEMBER 1984.**

832	10c. Sea fans and fire sponge	1·00	50
833	15c. Blue-headed wrasse	1·10	50
834	50c. Coral crab	1·60	3·00

156 British Honduras 1935 Silver Jubilee 25c. stamp and King George V with Queen Mary in Carriage (½-size illustration)

1985. 50th Anniv of First Commonwealth Omnibus Issue. Designs showing British Honduras/Belize stamps. Multicoloured.

835	50c. Type **156**	40	60
836	50c. 1937 Coronation 3c., and King George VI and Queen Elizabeth in Coronation robes	40	60
837	50c. 1946 Victory 3c. and Victory celebrations	40	60
838	50c. 1948 Royal Silver Wedding 4c. and King George VI and Queen Elizabeth at Westminster Abbey service	40	60
839	50c. 1953 Coronation 4c. and Queen Elizabeth II in Coronation robes	40	60
840	50c. 1966 Churchill 25c., Sir Winston Churchill and fighter aircraft	40	60
841	50c. 1972 Royal Silver Wedding 50c. and 1948 Wedding photograph	40	60
842	50c. 1973 Royal Wedding 50c. and Princess Anne and Capt. Mark Phillips at their Wedding	40	60
843	50c. 1977 Silver Jubilee $2 and Queen Elizabeth II during tour	40	60
844	50c. 1978 25th anniversary of Coronation 75c. and Imperial Crown	40	60

157 Mounted Postboy and Early Letter to Belize

1985. 350th Anniv of British Post Office. Mult.

846	10c. Type **157**	40	25
847	15c. "Hinchinbrook II" (sailing packet) engaging "Grand Turk" (American privateer)	55	25
848	25c. "Duke of Marlborough II" (sailing packet)	70	30
849	75c. "Diana" (packet)	1·25	1·50
850	$1 Falmouth packet ship	1·25	1·75
851	$3 "Conway" (mail paddle-steamer)	2·25	5·00

1985. Commonwealth Heads of Government Meeting, Nassau, Bahamas. Nos. 827/30 optd **COMMONWEALTH SUMMIT CONFERENCE, BAHAMAS 16th-22nd OCTOBER 1985.**

852	10c. Type **154**	30	30
853	15c. The Queen Mother, 1980	40	35
854	75c. Waving to the crowd, 1982	80	80
855	$4 Four generations of Royal Family at Prince William's christening	2·00	3·75

1985. 80th Anniv of Rotary International. Nos. 815/19 optd **80TH ANNIVERSARY OF ROTARY INTERNATIONAL.**

857	25c. Type **152**	60	40
858	50c. Girl Guides camping	1·00	75
859	90c. Checking map on hike	1·50	1·75
860	$1.25 Students in laboratory	2·00	2·50
861	$2 Lady Baden-Powell (founder)	2·50	3·25

160 Royal Standard and Belize Flag

1985. Royal Visit. Multicoloured.

862	25c. Type **160**	80	95
863	75c. Queen Elizabeth II	1·25	2·00
864	$4 Royal Yacht "Britannia" (81 × 39 mm)	3·75	3·75

161 Mountie in Canoe (Canada)

1985. Christmas. 30th Anniv of Disneyland, U.S.A. Designs showing dolls from "It's a Small World" exhibition. Multicoloured.

866	1c. Type **161**	10	15
867	2c. Indian chief and squaw (U.S.A.)	10	15
868	3c. Incas climbing Andes (South America)	10	15
869	4c. Africans beating drums (Africa)	10	15
870	5c. Snake-charmer and dancer (India and Far East)	10	15
871	6c. Boy and girl with donkey (Belize)	10	15
872	50c. Musician and dancer (Balkans)	1·50	1·50
873	$1.50 Boys with camel (Egypt and Saudi Arabia)	2·50	3·25
874	$3 Woman and girls playing with kite (Japan)	3·25	4·50

1985. World Cup Football Championship, Mexico (1986) (1st issue). Nos. 835/44 optd **PRE "WORLD CUP FOOTBALL" MEXICO 1986** and trophy.

876	50c. Type **156**	65	75
877	50c. 1937 Coronation 3c., and King George VI and Queen Elizabeth in Coronation robes	65	75
878	50c. Victory 3c., and Victory celebrations	65	75
879	50c. 1948 Royal Silver Wedding 4c., and King George VI and Queen Elizabeth at Westminster Abbey service	65	75
880	50c. 1953 Coronation 4c., and Queen Elizabeth II in Coronation robes	65	75
881	50c. 1966 Churchill 25c., Sir Winston Churchill and fighter aircraft	65	75
882	50c. 1972 Royal Silver Wedding 50c. and 1948 wedding photograph	65	75
883	50c. 1973 Royal Wedding 5c., and Princess Anne and Capt. Mark Phillips at their Wedding	65	75
884	50c. 1977 Silver Jubilee $2 and Queen Elizabeth II during tour	65	75
885	50c. 1978 25th anniv of Coronation 75c. and Imperial Crown	65	75

See also Nos. 936/9.

163 Indian Costume   **165** Princess Elizabeth aged Three

1986. Costumes of Belize. Multicoloured.

887	5c. Type **163**	75	30
888	10c. Maya	80	30
889	15c. Garifuna	1·00	35
890	25c. Creole	1·25	35
891	50c. Chinese	1·75	1·25
892	75c. Lebanese	2·00	2·00

164 Pope Pius X

893	$1 European c. 1900	2·00	2·50
894	$2 Latin	2·75	3·75

1986. Easter. 20th-century Popes. Multicoloured.

896	50c. Type **164**	1·10	1·40
897	50c. Benedict XV	1·10	1·40
898	50c. Pius XI	1·10	1·40
899	50c. Pius XII	1·10	1·40
900	50c. John XXIII	1·10	1·40
901	50c. Paul VI	1·10	1·40
902	50c. John Paul I	1·10	1·40
903	50c. John Paul II	1·10	1·40

1986. 60th Birthday of Queen Elizabeth II. Mult.

905	25c. Type **165**	30	55
906	50c. Queen wearing Imperial State Crown	50	75
907	75c. At Trooping the Colour	65	85
908	$3 Queen wearing diadem	1·25	2·25

166 Halley's Comet and Japanese "Planet A" Spacecraft

1986. Appearance of Halley's Comet. Multicoloured.

910	10c. Type **166**	35	60
911	15c. Halley's Comet, 1910	40	70
912	50c. Comet and European "Giotto" spacecraft	50	80
913	75c. Belize Weather Bureau	70	80
914	$1 Comet and U.S.A. space telescope	95	1·10
915	$2 Edmond Halley	1·50	1·60

167 George Washington

1986. United States Presidents. Multicoloured.

917	10c. Type **167**	35	60
918	20c. John Adams	35	65
916	30c. Thomas Jefferson	40	70
920	50c. James Madison	50	70
921	$1.50 James Monroe	80	1·25
922	$2 John Quincy Adams	1·00	1·50

168 Auguste Bartholdi (sculptor) and Statue's Head

1986. Centenary of Statue of Liberty. Multicoloured.

924	25c. Type **168**	40	65
925	50c. Statue's head at U.S. Centennial Celebration, Philadelphia, 1876	55	85
926	75c. Unveiling ceremony, 1886	55	90
927	$4 Statue of Liberty and flags of Belize and U.S.A.	1·00	2·00

169 British Honduras 1866 1s. Stamp

1986. "Ameripex" International Stamp Exhibition, Chicago. Multicoloured.

929	10c. Type **169**	40	55
930	15c. 1981 Royal Wedding $1.50 stamps	55	75
931	50c. U.S.A. 1918 24c. airmail inverted centre error	75	80
932	75c. U.S.S. "Constitution" (frigate)	75	1·10
933	$1 Liberty Bell	80	1·40
934	$2 White House	90	1·60

170 English and Brazilian Players

1986. World Cup Football Championship, Mexico (2nd issue). Multicoloured.

936	25c. Type **170**	1·50	1·75
937	50c. Mexican player and Maya statues	1·75	2·00
938	75c. Two Belizean players	2·00	2·25
939	$3 Aztec stone calendar	2·25	2·50

171 Miss Sarah Ferguson

1986. Royal Wedding. Multicoloured.

941	25c. Type **171**	55	40
942	75c. Prince Andrew	90	90
943	$3 Prince Andrew and Miss Sarah Ferguson (92 × 41 mm)	1·60	2·50

1986. World Cup Football Championship Winners, Mexico. Nos. 936/9 optd **ARGENTINA – WINNERS 1986.**

945	25c. Type **170**	1·50	1·75
946	50c. Mexican player and Maya statues	1·75	2·00
947	75c. Two Belizean players	2·00	2·25
948	$3 Aztec stone calendar	3·00	3·25

1986. "Stockholmia '86" International Stamp Exhibition, Sweden. Nos. 929/34 optd **STOCKHOLMIA 86** and emblem.

950	10c. Type **169**	50	70
951	15c. 1981 Royal Wedding $1.50 stamp	65	85
952	50c. U.S.A. 1918 24c. airmail inverted centre error	80	1·00
953	75c. U.S.S. "Constitution"	1·00	1·40
954	$1 Liberty Bell	1·25	1·50
955	$2 White House	1·60	1·75

174 Amerindian Girl

1986. International Peace Year. Multicoloured.

957	25c. Type **174**	55	75
958	50c. European boy and girl	70	1·00
959	75c. Japanese girl	90	1·50
960	$3 Indian boy and European girl	1·50	2·50

175 "Amanita lilloi"   **176** Jose Carioca

1986. Fungi and Toucans. Multicoloured.

962	5c. Type **175**	1·00	1·00
963	10c. Keel-billed toucan	1·40	1·40
964	20c. "Boletellus cubensis"	1·50	1·50
965	25c. Collared aracari	1·50	1·50
966	75c. "Psilocybe caerulescens"	1·75	1·75
967	$1 Emerald toucanet	1·75	1·75
968	$1.25 Crimson-rumped toucanet ("Crimson-rumped Toucan")	2·00	2·00
969	$2 "Russula puiggarii"	2·25	2·25

1986. Christmas. Designs showing Walt Disney cartoon characters in scenes from "Saludos Amigos". Multicoloured.

970	2c. Type **176**	20	20
971	3c. Jose Carioca, Panchito and Donald Duck	20	20

972	4c. Daisy Duck as Rio Carnival dancer	20	20
973	5c. Mickey and Minnie Mouse as musician and dancer	20	20
974	6c. Jose Carioca using umbrella as flute	20	20
975	50c. Donald Duck and Panchito	1·00	1·75
976	65c. Joe Carioca and Donald Duck playing hide and seek	1·25	2·00
977	$1.35 Donald Duck playing maracas	2·00	3·00
978	$2 Goofy as matador	2·75	3·50

177 Princess Elizabeth in Wedding Dress, 1947

179 "Mother and Child"

178 "America II", 1983

1987. Royal Ruby Wedding. Multicoloured.

980	25c. Type 177	20	20
981	75c. Queen and Duke of Edinburgh, 1972	35	50
982	$1 Queen on her 60th birthday	40	60
983	$4 In Garter robes	1·00	2·00

1987. America's Cup Yachting Championship. Multicoloured.

985	25c. Type 178	30	25
986	75c. "Stars and Stripes", 1987	40	50
987	$1 "Australia II", 1983	50	60
988	$4 "White Crusader"	1·00	2·00

1987. Wood Carvings by George Gabb. Mult.

990	25c. Type 179	15	25
991	75c. "Standing Form"	35	50
992	$1 "Love-doves"	40	60
993	$4 "Depiction of Music"	1·10	2·00

180 Black-handed Spider Monkey

1987. Primates. Multicoloured.

995	25c. Type 180	25	20
996	75c. Black howler monkey	40	55
997	$1 Spider monkeys with baby	45	65
998	$4 Two black howler monkeys	1·10	2·25

181 Guides on Parade

1987. 50th Anniv of Girl Guide Movement in Belize. Multicoloured.

1000	25c. Type 181	45	20
1001	75c. Brownie camp	80	1·00
1002	$1 Guide camp	1·00	1·25
1003	$4 Olave, Lady Baden-Powell	3·00	5·00

182 Indian Refugee Camp

1987. Int Year of Shelter for the Homeless. Mult.

1005	25c. Type 182	50	25

1006	75c. Filipino family and slum	90	90
1007	$1 Family in Middle East shanty town	1·00	1·25
1008	$4 Building modern house in Belize	2·00	4·50

183 "Laelia euspatha"

1987. Christmas. Orchids. Illustrations from Sander's "Reichenbachia". Multicoloured.

1009	1c. Type 183	75	75
1010	2c. "Cattleya citrina"	75	75
1011	3c. "Masdevallia backhousiana"	75	75
1012	4c. "Cypripedium tautzianum"	75	75
1013	5c. "Trichopilia suavis alba"	75	75
1014	6c. "Odontoglossum hebraicum"	75	75
1015	7c. "Cattleya trianaei schroederiana"	75	75
1016	10c. "Saccolabium giganteum"	75	75
1017	30c. "Cattleya warscewiczii"	90	90
1018	50c. "Chysis bractescens"	1·25	1·25
1019	70c. "Cattleya rochellensis"	1·40	1·40
1020	$1 "Laelia elegans schilleriana"	1·50	1·50
1021	$1.50 "Laelia anceps percivaliana"	1·60	1·60
1022	$3 "Laelia gouldiana"	2·25	2·25

184 Christ condemned to Death

1988. Easter. The Stations of the Cross. Mult.

1024	40c. Type 184	30	50
1025	40c. Christ carrying the Cross	30	50
1026	40c. Falling for the first time	30	50
1027	40c. Christ meets Mary	30	50
1028	40c. Simon of Cyrene helping to carry the Cross	30	50
1029	40c. Veronica wiping the face of Christ	30	50
1030	40c. Christ falling a second time	30	50
1031	40c. Consoling the women of Jerusalem	30	50
1032	40c. Falling for the third time	30	50
1033	40c. Christ being stripped	30	50
1034	40c. Christ nailed to the Cross	30	50
1035	40c. Dying on the Cross	30	50
1036	40c. Christ taken down from the Cross	30	50
1037	40c. Christ being laid in the sepulchre	30	50

185 Basketball

1988. Olympic Games, Seoul. Multicoloured.

1038	10c. Type 185	1·25	55
1039	25c. Volleyball	1·00	30
1040	60c. Table tennis	1·00	60
1041	75c. Diving	1·00	70
1042	$1 Judo	1·10	1·00
1043	$2 Hockey	4·25	4·00

186 Public Health Nurse, c. 1912

1988. 125th Anniv of Int Red Cross. Mult.

1045	60c. Type 186	2·25	1·25

187 Collared Anteater ("Ants Bear")

1046	75c. "Aleda E. Lutz" (hospital ship) and ambulance launch, 1937	2·50	1·50
1047	$1 Ambulance at hospital tent, 1956	3·00	1·75
1048	$2 Auster ambulance plane, 1940	3·75	4·75

1989. Small Animals of Belize. Multicoloured.

1049	10c. Paca ("Gibnut")	1·75	1·75
1050	25c. Four-eyed opossum (vert)	1·75	1·50
1051	50c. Type 187	2·25	2·00
1052	60c. As 10c.	2·25	2·25
1053	75c. Red brocket	2·25	2·25
1054	$1 Collared peccary	3·75	5·50

1989. 20th Anniv of First Manned Landing on Moon. As T 126 of Ascension. Multicoloured.

1055	25c. Docking of "Apollo 9" modules	1·00	30
1056	50c. "Apollo 9" command service module in Space (30 × 30 mm)	1·50	75
1057	75c. "Apollo 9" emblem (30 × 30 mm)	1·75	1·25
1058	$1 "Apollo 9" lunar module in space	2·00	1·75

1989. No. 771 surch 5c.

1060	5c. on 6c. Star-eyed hermit crab	6·00	2·00

190 Wesley Church

191 White-winged Tanager and "Catonephele numilia"

1989. Christmas. Belize Churches.

1062	190 10c. black, pink and brown	20	10
1063	– 25c. black, lilac and mauve	25	20
1064	– 60c. black, turq & bl	50	70
1065	– 75c. black, grn & lt grn	65	90
1066	– $1 black, lt yell & yell	80	1·25

DESIGNS: 25c. Baptist Church; 60c. St. John's Anglican Cathedral; 75c. St. Andrew's Presbyterian Church; $1 Holy Redeemer Roman Catholic Cathedral.

1990. Birds and Butterflies. Multicoloured.

1067A	5c. Type 191	60	60
1068B	10c. Keel-billed toucan and "Nessaea aglaura"	80	70
1069A	15c. Magnificent frigate bird and "Eurytides philolaus"	80	40
1070A	25c. Jabiru and "Heliconius sapho"	80	40
1071A	30c. Great blue heron and "Colobura dirce"	80	50
1072A	50c. Northern oriole and "Hamadyras arethusia"	1·00	60
1073A	60c. Scarlet macaw and "Evenus regalis"	1·25	70
1074A	75c. Red-legged honey-creeper and "Callicore patelina"	1·25	75
1075A	$1 Spectacled owl and "Caligo uranus"	2·25	1·60
1076A	$2 Green jay and "Philaethria dido"	2·75	3·50
1077A	$5 Turkey vulture and "Battus belus"	4·50	6·00
1078A	$10 Osprey and "Papilio thoas"	8·50	10·00

1990. First Belize Dollar Coin. No. 1075 optd **FIRST DOLLAR COIN 1990**.

1079	$1 Spectacled owl and "Caligo uranus"	4·25	2·75

193 Green Turtle

1990. Turtles. Multicoloured.

1080	10c. Type 193	65	40
1081	25c. Hawksbill turtle	1·00	40
1082	60c. Saltwater loggerhead turtle	1·50	1·50

1083	75c. Freshwater loggerhead turtle	1·60	1·60
1084	$1 Bocatora turtle	2·00	2·00
1085	$2 Hicatee turtle	2·75	5·00

194 Fairey Battle

1990. 50th Anniv of the Battle of Britain. Multicoloured.

1086	10c. Type 194	80	50
1087	25c. Bristol Type 152 Beaufort	1·40	50
1088	60c. Bristol Type 142 Blenheim Mk IV	2·00	2·00
1089	75c. Armstrong-Whitworth Whitley	2·00	2·00
1090	$1 Vickers-Armstrong Wellington Mk 1c	2·00	2·00
1091	$1 Handley Page Hampden	2·50	3·50

195 "Cattleya bowringiana"

1990. Christmas. Orchids. Multicoloured.

1092	25c. Type 195	85	20
1093	50c. "Rhyncholaelia digbyana"	1·25	50
1094	60c. "Sobralia macrantha"	1·50	1·00
1095	75c. "Chysis bractescens"	1·50	1·00
1096	$1 "Vanilla planifolia"	1·75	1·75
1097	$2 "Epidendrum polyanthum"	2·50	4·00

196 Common Iguana

1991. Reptiles and Mammals. Multicoloured.

1098	25c. Type 196	80	35
1099	50c. Morelet's crocodile	1·25	90
1100	60c. American manatee	1·50	1·50
1101	75c. Boa constrictor	1·75	1·75
1102	$1 Baird's tapir	2·00	2·00
1103	$2 Jaguar	2·75	3·75

1991. 65th Birthday of Queen Elizabeth II and 70th Birthday of Prince Philip. As T 139 of Ascension. Multicoloured.

1104	$1 Queen Elizabeth II wearing tiara	1·00	1·40
1105	$1 Prince Philip wearing panama	1·00	1·40

197 Weather Radar

1991. International Decade for Natural Disaster Reduction.

1106	197 60c. multicoloured	1·50	1·25
1107	– 75c. multicoloured	1·60	1·40
1108	– $1 blue and black	1·75	1·75
1109	– $2 multicoloured	2·50	3·25

DESIGNS: 75c. Weather station; $1 Floods in Belize after Hurricane Hattie, 1961; $2 Satellite image of Hurricane Gilbert.

198 Thomas Ramos and Demonstration

1991. 10th Anniv of Independence. Famous Belizeans (1st series). Multicoloured.

1110	25c. Type 198	60	30
1111	60c. Sir Isaiah Morter and palm trees	1·25	1·50

1112	75c. Antonio Soberanis and political meeting	1·25	1·75
1113	$1 Santiago Ricalde and cutting sugar-cane	1·50	2·00

See also Nos. 1126/9 and 1148/5.

199 "Anansi the Spider"

1991. Christmas. Folklore. Multicoloured.

1114	25c. Type **199**	80	20
1115	60c. "Jack-o-Lantern"	1·25	55
1116	60c. "Tata Duende" (vert)	1·50	1·25
1117	75c. "Xtabai"	1·50	1·25
1118	$1 "Warrie Massa" (vert)	1·75	1·75
1119	$2 "Old Heg"	2·75	5·00

200 "Gongora quinquenervis"

1992. Easter. Orchids. Multicoloured.

1120	25c. Type **200**	90	20
1121	50c. "Oncidium sphacelatum"	1·50	75
1122	60c. "Encyclia bratescens"	1·75	1·75
1123	75c. "Epidendrum ciliare"	1·75	1·75
1124	$1 "Psygmorchis pusilla"	2·00	2·25
1125	$2 "Galeandra batemanii"	2·75	4·50

1992. Famous Belizeans (2nd series). As T **198**, but inscr "EMINENT BELIZEANS" at top. Multicoloured.

1126	25c. Gwendolyn Lizarraga (politician) and High School	65	30
1127	60c. Rafael Fonseca (civil servant) and Government Offices, Belize	1·25	1·50
1128	75c. Vivian Seay (health worker) and nurses	1·50	1·75
1129	$1 Samuel Haynes (U.N.I.A. worker) and words of National Anthem	1·75	2·25

201 Xunantunich and National Assembly

1992. 500th Anniv of Discovery of America by Columbus. Mayan sites and modern buildings. Multicoloured.

1130	25c. Type **201**	1·00	25
1131	60c. Altun Ha and Supreme Court	1·50	1·00
1132	75c. Santa Rita and Tower Hill Sugar Factory	1·60	1·25
1133	$5 Lamanai and Citrus Company works	7·50	10·00

202 Hashishi Pampi

1992. Christmas. Folklore. Multicoloured.

1134	25c. Type **202**	30	20
1135	60c. Cadejo	60	60
1136	$1 La Sucia (vert)	90	1·00
1137	$5 Sisimito	4·00	6·50

1993. 75th Anniv of Royal Air Force. As T **149** of Ascension. Multicoloured.

1138	25c. Sud Aviation SA 330L Puma helicopter	1·00	60
1139	50c. Hawker Siddeley Harrier GR3	1·25	80
1140	60c. De Havilland DH98 Mosquito Mk XVIII	1·40	1·10
1141	75c. Avro Type 683 Lancaster	1·40	1·10
1142	$1 Consolidated Liberator I	1·60	1·40
1143	$3 Short Stirling Mk I	3·25	5·50

203 "Lycaste aromatica"

1993. 14th World Orchid Conference, Glasgow. Multicoloured.

1144	25c. Type **203**	40	25
1145	60c. "Sobralia decora"	75	80
1146	$1 "Maxillaria alba"	1·00	1·10
1147	$2 "Brassavola nodosa"	1·75	2·75

1993. Famous Belizeans (3rd series). As T **198**, but inscr "EMINENT BELIZEANS" at top. Multicoloured.

1148	25c. Herbert Watkin Beaumont, Post Office and postmark	40	25
1149	60c. Dr. Selvyn Walford Young and score of National Anthem	75	85
1150	75c. Cleopatra White and health centre	90	1·25
1151	$1 Dr. Karl Heusner and early car	1·10	1·40

204 Boom and Chime Band

1993. Christmas. Local Customs. Mult.

1152	25c. Type **204**	60	20
1153	60c. John Canoe dance	1·25	75
1154	75c. Cortez dance	1·25	80
1155	$2 Maya musical group	2·75	4·50

1994. "Hong Kong '94" International Stamp Exhibition. No. 1075 optd **HONG KONG '94** and emblem.

1156	$1 Spectacled owl and "Caligo uranus"	2·25	2·25

1994. Royal Visit. As T **202** of Bahamas. Mult.

1157	25c. Flags of Belize and Great Britain	80	25
1158	60c. Queen Elizabeth II in yellow coat and hat	1·25	85
1159	75c. Queen Elizabeth in evening dress	1·50	1·00
1160	$1 Queen Elizabeth, Prince Philip and Yeomen of the Guard	1·75	1·75

205 "Lonchorhina aurita" (bat)

1994. Bats. Multicoloured.

1161	25c. Type **205**	35	20
1162	60c. "Vampyrodes caraccioli"	65	65
1163	75c. "Noctilio leporinus"	80	80
1164	$2 "Desmodus rotundus"	2·00	3·00

1994. 75th Anniv of I.L.O. No. 1074 surch **10c** and anniversary emblem.

1165	10c. on 75c. multicoloured	1·00	1·00

207 "Cycnoches chlorochilon"

1994. Christmas. Orchids. Multicoloured.

1166	25c. Type **207**	45	20
1167	60c. "Brassavola cucullata"	75	70
1168	75c. "Sobralia mucronata"	90	90
1169	$1 "Nidema boothii"	1·10	1·25

208 Ground Beetle   (**209**)

1995. Insects. Multicoloured.

1170A	5c. Type **208**	30	50
1171A	10c. Harlequin beetle	30	50
1172A	15c. Giant water bug	40	60
1173A	25c. Peanut-head bug	50	20
1174A	30c. Coconut weevil	55	25
1175A	50c. Mantis	70	40
1176B	60c. Tarantula wasp	80	50
1177B	75c. Rhinoceros beetle	85	60
1178B	$1 Metallic wood borer	1·00	90
1179B	$2 Dobson fly	2·50	3·00
1180B	$5 Click beetle	4·25	5·00
1181B	$10 Long-horned beetle	7·00	8·50

1995. 50th Anniv of End of Second World War. As T **161** of Ascension. Multicoloured.

1182	25c. War memorial	30	25
1183	60c. Remembrance Day parade	75	80
1184	75c. British Honduras forestry unit	90	1·00
1185	$1 Vickers-Armstrong Wellington bomber	1·10	1·40

1995. "Singapore '95" International Stamp Exhibition. Nos. 1166/9 optd with T **209**.

1186	25c. Type **207**	40	25
1187	60c. "Brassavola cucullata"	75	80
1188	75c. "Sobralia mucronata"	90	95
1189	$1 "Nidema boothii"	1·10	1·40

1995. 50th Anniv of United Nations. As T **213** of Bahamas. Multicoloured.

1190	25c. M113-light reconnaisance vehicle	25	20
1191	60c. Sultan armoured command vehicle	60	65
1192	75c. Leyland-Daf 8 × 4 drops lorry	75	80
1193	$2 Warrior infantry combat vehicle	1·50	2·50

210 Male and Female Blue Ground Dove

1995. Christmas. Doves. Multicoloured.

1194	25c. Type **210**	35	20
1195	60c. White-fronted doves	70	70
1196	75c. Pair of ruddy ground doves	85	90
1197	$1 White-winged doves	1·25	1·25

1996. "CHINA '96" 9th Asian International Stamp Exhibition, Peking. Nos. 1172, 1174/5 and 1179 optd **'96 CHINA** and emblem.

1198	15c. Giant water bug	15	15
1199	30c. Coconut weevil	30	30
1200	50c. Mantis	45	50
1201	$2 Dobson fly	1·60	2·25

212 Unloading Banana Train, Commerce Bight Pier

1996. "CAPEX '96" International Stamp Exhibition, Toronto. Railways. Multicoloured.

1202	25c. Type **212**	75	30
1203	60c. Locomotive No. 1 Stann Creek station	1·25	80
1204	75c. Locomotive No. 4 pulling mahogany log train	1·25	90
1205	$3 L.M.S. No. 5602 "British Honduras" locomotive	3·00	4·50

213 "Epidendrum stamfordianum"   **214** Red Poll

1996. Christmas. Orchids. Multicoloured.

1206	25c. Type **213**	40	20
1207	60c. "Oncidium cartha-genense"	70	70
1208	75c. "Oerstedella verrucosa"	80	90
1209	$1 "Coryanthes speciosa"	1·10	1·25

1997. "HONG KONG '97" International Stamp Exhibition. Chinese New Year ("Year of the Ox"). Cattle Breeds. Multicoloured.

1210	25c. Type **214**	50	25
1211	60c. Brahman	85	85

1212	75c. Longhorn	1·00	1·00
1213	$1 Charbray	1·25	1·40

215 Coral Snake   **216** Adult Male Howler Monkey

1997. Snakes. Multicoloured.

1214	25c. Type **215**	35	20
1215	60c. Green vine snake	60	60
1216	75c. Yellow-jawed tommygoff	70	70
1217	$1 Speckled racer	85	1·00

1997. Endangered Species. Howler Monkey. Multicoloured.

1218	10c. Type **216**	20	15
1219	25c. Female feeding	30	20
1220	60c. Female with young	60	65
1221	75c. Juvenile monkey feeding	80	95

217 "Maxillaria elatior"

1997. Christmas. Orchids. Multicoloured.

1222	25c. Type **217**	25	20
1223	60c. "Dimmerandra emarginata"	50	50
1224	75c. "Macradenia brassavolae"	60	60
1225	$1 "Ornithocephalus gladiatus"	75	80

218 School Children using the Internet

1998. 50th Anniv of Organization of American States. Multicoloured.

1227	25c. Type **218**	25	20
1228	$1 Map of Central America	1·00	1·10

219 University Arms

1998. 50th Anniv of University of West Indies.

1229	**219** $1 multicoloured	1·00	1·00

220 Baymen Gun Flats

1998. Bicentenary of Battle of St. George's Cay. Multicoloured.

1230	10c. Boat moored at quayside (vert)	30	40
1231	10c. Three sentries and cannon (vert)	30	40
1232	10c. Cannon and rowing boats (vert)	30	40
1233	25c. Type **220**	45	20
1234	60c. Baymen sloops	70	70
1235	75c. British schooners	75	75
1236	$1 H.M.S. "Merlin" (sloop)	85	85
1237	$2 Spanish flagship	1·40	2·00

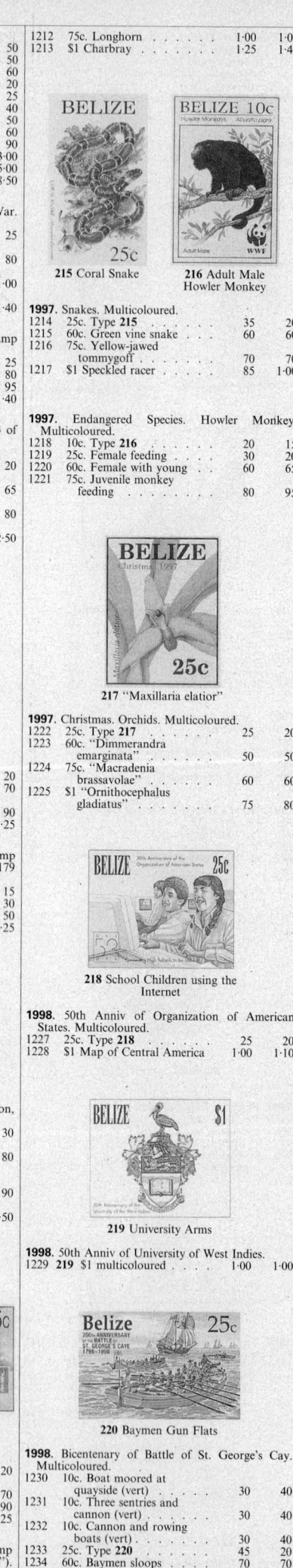

221 "Brassia maculata"

222 "Eucharis grandiflora"

1998. Christmas. Orchids. Multicoloured.

1238	25c. Type **221**	35	20
1239	60c. "Encyclia radiata"	50	40
1240	75c. "Stanhopea ecornuta"	50	55
1241	$1 "Isochilus carnosiflorus"	60	80

1999. Easter. Flowers. Multicoloured.

1242	10c. Type **222**	20	10
1243	25c. "Hippeastrum puniceum"	30	20
1244	60c. "Zephyranthes citrina"	50	50
1245	$1 "Hymenocallis littoralis"	60	80

223 Postman on Bicycle

1999. 125th Anniv of U.P.U. Multicoloured.

1246	25c. Type **223**	40	30
1247	60c. Postal truck	55	55
1248	75c. "Dee" (mail ship)	75	70
1249	$1 Modern airliner	90	1·00

224 "Holy Family with Jesus and St. John" (School of Rubens)

1999. Christmas. Religious Paintings. Multicoloured.

1250	25c. Type **224**	20	20
1251	60c. "Holy Family with St. John" (unknown artist)	50	45
1252	75c. "Madonna and Child with St. John and Angel" (unknown artist)	55	60
1253	$1 "Madonna with Child and St. John" (Andrea del Salerno)	75	75

225 Iguana

2000. Wildlife. Multicoloured.

1254	5c. Type **225**	10	10
1255	10c. Gibnut	10	10
1256	15c. Howler monkey	10	15
1257	25c. Collared anteater	20	25
1258	30c. Hawksbill turtle	20	25
1259	50c. Red brocket antelope	35	40
1260	60c. Jaguar	40	45
1261	75c. American manatee	55	60
1262	$1 Crocodile	70	75
1263	$2 Baird's tapir	1·40	1·50
1264	$5 Collared peccary	3·50	3·75
1265	$10 Boa constrictor	7·00	7·25

226 Mango

2000. Fruits. Multicoloured.

1266	25c. Type **226**	30	25
1267	60c. Cashew	55	50
1268	75c. Papaya	70	70
1269	$1 Banana	90	1·00

227 Meeting in Battlefield Park and Supreme Court, 1950

2000. 50th Anniv of People's United Party. Mult.

1270	10c. Type **227**	15	10
1271	25c. Voters queuing, 1954	30	25
1272	60c. Legislative Council and Mace, 1964	55	50
1273	75c. National Assembly Building (under construction and completed), Belmopan, 1967–70	70	70
1274	$1 Belizean flag in searchlights, Independence, 1981	90	1·00

228 *Bletia purpurea*

2000. Christmas. Orchids. Multicoloured

1275	25c. Type **228**	30	25
1276	60c. *Cyrtopodium punctatum*	55	50
1277	75c. *Cycnoches egertonianum*	70	70
1278	$1 *Catasetum integerrimum*	90	1·00

229 Children at Computers

2001. 20th Anniv of Independence. Multicoloured.

1279	25c. Type **229**	20	25
1280	60c. Shrimp farm	40	45
1281	75c. Privassion Cascade (vert)	55	60
1282	$2 Map of Belize (vert)	1·40	1·25

230 *Sobralia fragrans*

2001. Christmas. Orchids. Multicoloured.

1283	25c. Type **230**	20	25
1284	60c. *Encyclia cordigera*	40	45
1285	75c. *Maxillaria fulgens*	55	60
1286	$1 *Epidendrum nocturnum*	70	75

2002. Golden Jubilee. As T **200** of Ascension.

1287	25c. black, violet and gold	20	25
1288	60c. multicoloured	40	45
1289	75c. black, violet and gold	55	60
1290	$1 multicoloured	70	75

DESIGNS: 25c. Princess Elizabeth in pantomime, Windsor, 1943; 60c. Queen Elizabeth in floral hat; 75c. Queen Elizabeth in garden with Prince Charles and Princess Anne, 1952; $1 Queen Elizabeth in South Africa, 1995.

POSTAGE DUE STAMPS

D 2

1976.

D 6 D 2	1c. red and green	10	1·00
D 7 –	2c. purple and violet	15	1·00
D 8 –	5c. green and brown	20	1·25
D 9 –	15c. green and red	30	1·50
D10 –	25c. orange and green	40	1·75

DESIGNS: Nos. D7/10 as Type D **2** but with different frames.

BENIN Pt. 6; Pt. 12

A French possession on the W. coast of Africa incorporated, in 1899, into the colony of Dahomey.

100 centimes = 1 franc.

A. FRENCH COLONY

1892. Stamps of French Colonies. "Commerce" type, optd **BENIN**.

1 J	1c. black on blue	£120	£110
2	2c. brown on yellow	£110	£100
3	4c. brown on grey	48·00	45·00
4	5c. green on light green	17·00	15·00
5	10c. black on lilac	60·00	60·00
6	15c. blue on light blue	35·00	13·00
7	20c. red on green	£190	£170
8	25c. black on red	80·00	50·00
9	30c. brown on drab	£140	£120
10	35c. black on orange	£140	£120
11	40c. red on yellow	£120	£110
12	75c. red on pink	£250	£225
13	1f. green	£275	£225

1892. Nos. 4 and 6 surch.

14 J	01 on 5c. green on lt green	£220	£170
15	40 on 15c. blue on lt blue	£130	70·00
16	75 on 15c. blue on lt blue	£600	£400

1893. "Tablet" key-type inscr "GOLFE DE BENIN" in red (1, 5, 15, 25, 75c., 1f.) or blue (others).

17 D	1c. black on blue	1·90	4·00
18	2c. brown on buff	2·25	3·75
19	4c. brown on grey	2·00	4·00
20	5c. green on light green	5·50	7·00
21	10c. black on lilac	6·25	6·50
22	15c. blue	28·00	21·00
23	20c. red on green	8·00	9·25
24	25c. black on pink	27·00	14·50
25	30c. brown on drab	16·00	10·50
26	40c. red on yellow	2·50	4·25
27	50c. red on pink	2·25	3·75
28	75c. brown on orange	9·00	11·00
29	1f. green	55·00	55·00

1894. "Tablet" key-type inscr "BENIN" in red (1, 5, 15, 25, 75c., 1f.) or blue (others).

33 D	1c. black on blue	2·25	3·25
34	2c. brown on buff	2·50	4·00
35	4c. brown on grey	1·75	3·75
36	5c. green on light green	3·50	3·75
37	10c. black on lilac	4·50	4·25
38	15c. blue	9·00	2·25
39	20c. red on green	7·75	7·25
40	25c. black on pink	10·00	3·00
41	30c. brown on drab	4·00	6·00
42	40c. red on yellow	14·00	9·00
43	50c. red on pink	19·00	15·00
44	75c. brown on orange	14·00	12·00
45	1f. green	4·25	5·00

POSTAGE DUE STAMPS

1894. Postage Due stamps of French Colonies optd **BENIN**. Imperf.

D46 U	5c. black	£120	55·00
D47	10c. black	£120	55·00
D48	20c. black	£120	55·00
D49	30c. black	£120	55·00

B. PEOPLE'S REPUBLIC

The Republic of Dahomey was renamed the People's Republic of Benin on 30 November 1975.

185 Celebrations

1976. Republic of Benin Proclamation. Mult.

603	50f. Type **185**	50	30
604	60f. President Kerekou making Proclamation	70	30
605	100f. Benin arms and flag	1·25	65

186 Skiing

1976. Air. Winter Olympic Games, Innsbruck. Multicoloured.

606	60f. Type **186**	90	45
607	150f. Bobsleighing (vert)	1·60	95
608	300f. Figure-skating	3·50	2·00

1976. Various Dahomey stamps surch **POPULAIRE DU BENIN** and new value (609/11) or surch only (617/18).

617 **108**	50f. on 1f. multicoloured (postage)	50	25
618 –	60f. on 2f. multicoloured (No. 415)	60	35
609 –	135f. brown, purple and blue (No. 590) (air)	1·40	75
610 –	210f. on 300f. brown, red and blue (No. 591)	2·10	1·10
611 –	380f. on 500f. brown, red and green (No. 592)	3·75	1·90

188 Alexander Graham Bell, Early Telephone and Satellite

1976. Telephone Centenary.

612 **188**	200f. red, violet & brown	2·25	1·50

189 Basketball

1976. Air. Olympic Games, Montreal. Mult.

613	60f. Long jump (horiz)	75	40
614	150f. Type **189**	1·50	90
615	200f. Hurdling (horiz)	2·10	1·25

191 Scouts and Camp-fire

1976. African Scout Jamboree, Jos, Nigeria.

619 **191**	50f. purple, brown & blk	75	60
620 –	70f. brown, green & blk	1·25	70

DESIGN: 70f. "Comradeship".

192 Konrad Adenauer

193 Benin 1c. Stamp, 1893, and Lion Cub

1976. Air. Birth Centenary of Konrad Adenauer (German statesman).

621 **192**	90f. slate, blue and red	1·25	50
622 –	250f. blue, red & lt blue	3·25	1·40

DESIGN—HORIZ: 250f. Adenauer and Cologne Cathedral.

1976. Air. "Juvarouen 76" Youth Stamp Exhibition, Rouen.

623 –	60f. blue and turquoise	1·00	40
624 **193**	210f. red, brown & olive	2·25	1·25

DESIGN—HORIZ: 60f. Dahomey 60f. Stamp of 1965, and children's silhouettes.

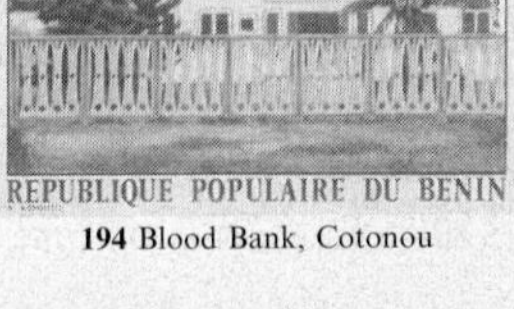

194 Blood Bank, Cotonou

1976. National Days of Blood Transfusion Service. Multicoloured.
625 5f. Type **194** 20 10
626 50f. Casualty and blood clinic 50 40
627 60f. Donor, patient and ambulance 90 50

195 Manioc   **196** "Apollo" Emblem and Rocket

1976. National Products Campaign Year. Mult.
628 20f. Type **195** 25 15
629 50f. Maize cultivation 60 25
630 60f. Cocoa trees 80 35
631 150f. Cotton plantation . . . 1·75 75

1976. Air. 5th Anniv of "Apollo 14" Space Mission.
632 **196** 130f. lake, brown & blue 1·25 65
633 – 270f. blue, turquoise & red . . . . 2·50 1·25
DESIGN: 270f. Landing on Moon.

197 Classroom   **198** Roan Antelope

1976. 3rd Anniv of Bariba Periodical "Kparo".
634 **197** 50f. multicoloured 75 40

1976. Mammals in Pendjari National Park. Multicoloured.
635 10f. Type **198** 40 30
636 30f. African buffalo 75 60
637 50f. Hippopotamus (horiz) 1·25 80
638 70f. Lion . . . . 1·50 1·00

199 "Freedom"   **200** "The Annunciation" (Master of Jativa)

1976. 1st Anniv of Proclamation of Republic. Multicoloured.
639 40f. Type **199** 45 25
640 150f. Maize cultivation . . . 1·40 75

1976. Air. Christmas. Multicoloured.
641 50f. Type **200** 65 30
642 60f. "The Nativity" (David) 75 40
643 270f. "Adoration of the Magi" (Dutch school) 3·00 1·60
644 300f. "The Flight into Egypt" (Fabriano) (horiz) . . . . 3·25 2·00

201 Table Tennis and Games Emblem

1976. West African University Games, Cotonou. Multicoloured.
645 10f. Type **201** 20 15
646 50f. Sports Hall, Cotonou 55 25

202 Loser with Ticket and Winner with Money

1977. Air. 10th Anniv of National Lottery.
647 **202** 50f. multicoloured 65 30

203 Douglas DC-10 crossing Globe   **205** Adder

204 Chateau Sassenage, Grenoble

1977. Europafrique.
648 **203** 200f. multicoloured . . . 2·25 2·00

1977. Air. 10th Anniv of International French Language Council.
649 **204** 200f. multicoloured . . . 1·90 95

1977. Reptiles and Domestic Animals. Mult.
650 2f. Type **205** 30 20
651 3f. Tortoise 30 20
652 5f. Zebus 50 30
653 10f. Cats 75 30

206 Concorde

1977. Air. Aviation.
654 **206** 80f. red and blue . . . 80 45
655 – 150f. red, violet & green 1·75 80
656 – 300f. violet, red & mauve 2·50 1·60
657 – 500f. red, blue & green . 5·00 2·75
DESIGNS: 150f. "Graf Zeppelin"; 300f. Charles Lindbergh and "Spirit of St. Louis"; 500f. Charles Nungesser and Francois Coli with "L'Oiseau".

207 Footballer heading Ball   **208** Rheumatic Patients

1977. Air. World Football Cup Eliminators. Multicoloured.
658 60f. Type **207** 65 25
659 200f. Goalkeeper and players 1·90 90

1977. World Rheumatism Year.
660 **208** 100f. multicoloured . . . 1·25 65

209 Karate   **210** Mao Tse-tung

1977. 2nd African Games, Lagos. Multicoloured.
661 90f. Type **209** 95 55
662 100f. Javelin (horiz) . . . 1·10 70
663 150f. Hurdling . . . . . 1·75 1·10

1977. 1st Death Anniv of Mao Tse-tung.
665 **210** 100f. multicoloured . . . 1·25 75

211 Sterilising Scalpels   **212** "Miss Haverfield" (Gainsborough)

1977. 150th Birth Anniv of Joseph Lister.
666 **211** 150f. grey, red & carmine 1·60 75
667 – 210f. olive, green & red 2·25 1·10
DESIGN: 210f. Lister and antiseptic spray.

1977. Air. Paintings.
668 **212** 100f. green and brown . . 1·25 40
669 – 150f. brown, bistre & red 1·90 90
670 – 200f. red and bistre . . 2·50 1·25
DESIGNS: 150f. "Self-Portrait" (Rubens); 200f. "Study of an Old Man" (da Vinci).

213 "Jarre Trouee" Emblem of King Ghezo (D'Abomey Museum)   **214** Atacora Waterfall

1977. Historic Museums of Benin. Mult.
671 50f. Type **213** 55 35
672 60f. Mask (Porto-Novo Museum) (horiz) . . . 80 45
673 210f. D'Abomey Museum . . 2·10 1·10

1977. Tourism. Multicoloured.
674 50f. Type **214** 50 30
675 60f. Stilt houses, Ganvie (horiz) 75 45
676 150f. Hut village, Savalou . . 1·90 95

1977. Air. 1st Commercial Concorde Flight. Paris–New York. No. 654 optd **1er VOL COMMERCIAL 22.11.77 PARIS NEW-YORK.**
678 **206** 80f. red and blue . . . 1·25 75

216 "Viking" on Mars ("Operation Viking", 1977)

1977. Air. Space Conquest Anniversaries.
679 **216** 100f. brown, olive & red 90 50
680 – 150f. blue, turq & mve . 1·40 75
681 – 200f. brown, blue & red 2·25 95
682 – 500f. blue, brn & olive . 5·50 2·75
DESIGNS AND EVENTS: 150f. Sir Isaac Newton, apple and stars (250th death anniv); 200f. Komarov and "Soyuz 2" over Moon (10th death anniv); 500f. Space dog "Laika" and rocket (20th anniv of ascent into Space).

217 Monument, Red Flag Square, Cotonou   **218** Mother and Child with Owl of Wisdom

1977. Air. 1st Anniv of Inauguration of Red Flag Square Monument.
683 **217** 500f. multicoloured . . . 5·00 2·25

1977. Fight against Witchcraft. Multicoloured.
684 60f. Type **218** 80 50
685 150f. Felling the tree of sorcery . . . . 2·00 1·00

219 "Suzanne Fourment"

1977. Air. 400th Birth Anniv of Rubens.
686 **219** 200f. brown, red & green 2·50 1·10
687 – 380f. orange and brown 4·50 2·00
DESIGN: 380f. "Albert Rubens".

220 Battle Scene

1978. "Victory over Imperialism".
688 **220** 50f. multicoloured . . . 80 40

221 Benin Houses and Map of Heads   **223** Abdoulaye Issa

222 Sir Alexander Fleming, Microscope and Drugs

1978. General Population Census.
689 **221** 50f. multicoloured 65 25

1978. 50th Anniv of Discovery of Antibiotics.
690 **222** 300f. multicoloured . . . 3·75 1·90

1978. 1st Death Anniv of Abdoulaye Issa.
691 **223** 100f. multicoloured . . . 90 45

224 El Hadj Omar

1978. Heroes of Anti-colonial Resistance.
692 – 90f. multicoloured 80 40
693 224 100f. green, grey & blue 95 55
DESIGN: 90f. Samory Toure.

225 "Communications"

1978. 10th World Telecommunications Day.
694 225 100f. multicoloured . . . 1·25 65

226 Footballer and Stadium

1978. World Cup Football Championship, Argentina. Multicoloured.
695 200f. Type 226 . . . . . 1·60 85
696 300f. Tackling (vert) . . . . 2·50 1·40
697 500f. Footballer and world
map . . . . 4·50 2·10

1978. Argentina's Victory in World Cup Football Championship. Nos. 695/7 optd.
699 226 200f. multicoloured . . . 1·75 1·10
700 – 300f. multicoloured . . . 2·50 1·75
701 – 500f. multicoloured . . . 4·50 3·00
OPTS: 200f. **FINALE ARGENTINE: 3
HOLLANDE: 1**; 300f. **CHAMPION 1978
ARGENTINE**; 500f. **3e BRESIL 4e ITALIE.**

228 Map, Olympic Flag and Basketball
Players

1978. 3rd African Games, Algiers. Multicoloured.
703 50f. Type 228 . . . . . 60 30
704 60f. African map and
Volleyball 85 50
705 80f. Cyclists and map of
Algeria . . . . 1·00 60

229 Martin Luther   230 Bicycle Taxi (Oueme)
King

1978. 10th Anniv of Martin Luther King's Assassination.
707 229 300f. multicoloured . . . . 2·75 1·50

1978. Benin Provinces. Multicoloured.
708 50f. Type 230 . . . . . . 60 30
709 60f. Leather work (Borgou) 70 35
710 70f. Drums (Oueme) . . . 90 45
711 100f. Calabash with burnt-
work ornamentation (Zou) 1·25 50

231 "Stamps" and Magnifying Glass

1978. Philatelic Exhibition, Riccione, Italy.
712 231 200f. multicoloured . . . . 1·90 95

232 Parthenon and Frieze showing
Horsemen

1978. Air. U.N.E.S.C.O. Campaign for the Preservation of the Acropolis. Multicoloured.
713 70f. Acropolis and Frieze
showing Procession . . . 70 30
714 250f. Type 232 . . . . . . 2·10 1·00
715 500f. The Parthenon (horiz) 4·25 1·90

235 Turkeys   236 Post Runner and
Boeing 747

1978. Domestic Poultry. Multicoloured.
722 10f. Type 235 . . . . . . 15 15
723 20f. Ducks 30 15
724 50f. Chickens 80 35
725 60f. Helmeted guineafowl . . 95 45

1978. Centenary of U.P.U. Paris Congress. Mult.
726 50f. Messenger of the
Dahomey Kings (horiz) . . 70 30
727 60f. Pirogue oarsman, boat
and car 80 35
728 90f. Type 236 . . . . . . 1·00 50

237 Red-breasted Merganser and Baden
1851 1k. Stamp

1978. Air. "Philexafrique" Exhibition, Libreville (Gabon) (1st issue) and International Stamp Fair, Essen, West Germany. Multicoloured.
729 100f. Type 237 . . . . 2·50 1·25
730 100f. African Buffalo and
Dahomey 1966 50f. African
Pygmy Goose stamp . . . 2·50 1·25
See also Nos. 747/8.

238 Raoul Follereau

1978. 1st Death Anniv of Raoul Follereau (leprosy pioneer).
731 238 200f. multicoloured . . . . 1·50 75

239 Wilbur and Orville Wright and Wright
Flyer 1

1978. Air. 75th Anniv of First Powered Flight.
732 239 500f. blue, yellow & brn 5·00 2·25

240 I.Y.C. Emblem   241 Hydrangea

1979. International Year of the Child. Mult.
733 10f. Type 240 . . . . 15 15
734 20f. Children in balloon . . 20 15
735 50f. Children dancing around
globe 40 20

1979. Flowers. Multicoloured.
736 20f. Type 241 . . . . . . 30 30
737 25f. Assangokan 35 30
738 30f. Geranium 50 40
739 40f. Water Lily (horiz) . . . 65 40

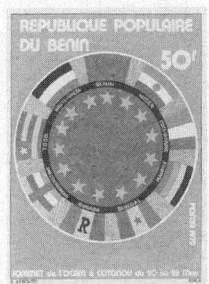

242 Flags around Map of Africa

1979. O.C.A.M. Summit Meeting, Cotonou (1st series). Multicoloured.
740 50f. Type 242 . . . . . . 50 30
741 60f. Flags and map of Benin 65 40
742 80f. O.C.A.M. flag and map
of member countries . . . 90 45
See also Nos. 754/6.

1979. Various stamps surch.
743 205 50f. on 2f. multicoloured
(postage) . . . . .
743a – 50f. on 3f. multicoloured
(651) . . . . . .
743b – 50f. on 70f. brown, green
and black (620) . . .
744 207 50f. on 60f. mult (air) . .
745 192 50f. on 90f. blue, deep
blue and red . . . .
746 – 50f. on 150f. mult (607)
747 189 50f. on 150f. mult . . . .

244 Antenna, Satellite and Wave
Pattern

1979. World Telecommunications Day.
748 244 50f. multicoloured 65 30

245 Headquarters Building

1979. West African Savings Bank Building Opening.
749 245 50f. multicoloured 55 30

246 "Resolution" and "Discovery" in
Karakakoa Bay, Hawaii

1979. Air. Death Bicentenary of Capt. James Cook.
750 246 20f. blue, green & brown 85 45
751 – 50f. brown, green & blue 1·00 60
DESIGN: 50f. Cook's death at Kowrowa.

247 Guelede Mask, Abomey Tapestry and
Fiery-breasted Bush Shrike

1979. "Philexafrique" Stamp Exhibition, Gabon (2nd issue).
752 247 15f. multicoloured 75 20
753 – 50f. orange, yellow & turq 95 55
DESIGN: 50f. Lockheed Tristar 500, satellite, U.P.U. emblem and canoe post.

1979. Common African and Mauritian Organization Summit Conference, Cotonou (2nd issue). Nos. 740/2 optd **26 Au 28 Juin 1979.**
754 50f. Type 242 . . . . . . 55 30
755 60f. Map of Benin and flags
of members 70 40
756 80f. OCAM flag and map
showing member countries 90 45

249 Olympic Flame, Benin Flags
and Pictograms

1979. Pre-Olympic Year. Multicoloured.
757 10f. Type 249 . . . . . . 20 15
758 50f. High jump 65 40

250 Roan Antelope

1979. Endangered Animals. Multicoloured.
759 5f. Type 250 . . . . . . 30 20
760 10f. Giraffes (vert) 40 30
761 20f. Chimpanzee 60 40
762 50f. African elephants (vert) 1·25 40

251 Emblem, Concorde and   252 Post Offices,
Map of Africa   Antenna, Telephone
and Savings Book

1979. 20th Anniv of ASECNA (African Air Safety Organization). Multicoloured.
763 50f. Type 251 . . . . . . 40 20
764 60f. As No. 763 but emblem
at bottom right and
without dates 50 25

1979. 20th Anniv of Posts and Telecommunications Office. Multicoloured.
765 50f. Type 252 . . . . . . 60 40
766 60f. Collecting, sorting and
delivering mail 85 50

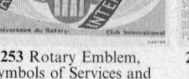

253 Rotary Emblem, Symbols of Services and Globe

324 Copernicus and Planetary System

1980. 75th Anniv of Rotary International. Mult.
767 90f. Cotonou Rotary Club
   banner (vert) 75 40
768 200f. Type 253 . . . . 1·50 75

1980. 50th Anniv of Discovery of Planet Pluto. Multicoloured.
769 70f. Kepler and astrolabe . . 65 40
770 100f. Type 254 . . . . 90 50

255 Pharaonic Capital

1980. 20th Anniv of Nubian Monuments Preservation Campaign. Multicoloured.
771 50f. Type 255 . . . . 45 25
772 60f. Rameses II, Abu Simbel 55 40
773 150f. Temple, Abu Simbel
   (horiz) . . . . 1·25 75

256 Lenin in Library

1980. 110th Birth Anniv of Lenin. Mult.
774 50f. Lenin and globe 50 25
775 150f. Type 256 . . . . 1·60 65

257 Monument

1980. Martyrs Square, Cotonou.
776 257 50f. multicoloured 40 15
777 – 60f. multicoloured 50 20
778 – 70f. multicoloured 55 25
779 – 100f. multicoloured . . . 80 30
DESIGNS—HORIZ: 60f. to 100f. Different views of the monument.

258 Farmer using Telephone

259 Assan

1980. World Telecommunications Day. Mult.
780 50f. Type 258 . . . . 40 25
781 60f. Telephone 50 25

1980. Traditional Musical Instruments. Mult.
782 5f. Type 259 . . . . 20 10

783 10f. Tinbo (horiz) 20 10
784 15f. Tam-tam sato 25 15
785 20f. Kora (horiz) 25 15
786 30f. Gangan (horiz) 60 35
787 50f. Sinhoun (horiz) 85 50

260 Monument

1980. King Gbehanzin Monument.
788 260 1000f. multicoloured . . . 9·50 6·25

261 Dieudonne Costes, Maurice Bellonte and "Point d'Interrogation"

1980. 50th Anniv of First Paris–New York Non-stop Flight.
789 – 90f. red, lt blue & blue . . 1·00 50
790 261 100f. red, blue and flesh 1·25 60
DESIGN: 90f. Airplane "Point d'Interrogation" and scenes of New York and Paris.

262 "Lunokhod I"

1980. 10th Anniv of "Lunokhod I".
791 – 90f. brown, blue and
   violet (postage) 75 50
792 262 210f. purple, blue and
   yellow (air) . . . . . . 2·25 1·10
DESIGN (48 × 36 mm): 90f. Rocket and "Lunokhod I".

263 Show-jumping

1980. Olympic Games, Moscow. Multicoloured.
793 50f. Olympic Flame, running
   track, emblem and mascot
   Mischa the bear (horiz) . . 45 20
794 60f. Type 263 . . . . 50 30
795 70f. Judo (horiz) 70 40
796 200f. Olympic flag and globe
   surrounded by sports
   pictogram . . . . 1·50 75
797 300f. Weightlifting . . . . . 2·50 1·25

264 O.C.A.M. Building

1980. Common African and Mauritian Organization Village, Cotonou. Multicoloured.
798 50f. Entrance to O.C.A.M.
   village 45 20
799 60f. View of village 50 20
800 70f. Type 264 . . . . 70 55

265 Dancers

1980. Agbadja Dance. Multicoloured.
801 30f. Type 265 . . . . 50 25
802 50f. Singer and musicians . . 75 40
803 60f. Dancers and musicians 85 50

266 Casting a Net

267 Philippines under Magnifying Glass

1980. Fishing. Multicoloured.
804 5f. Type 266 . . . . 10 10
805 10f. Fisherman with catch
   (vert) 25 15
806 15f. Line fishing 35 20
807 20f. Fisherman emptying eel-
   pot 40 20
808 50f. Hauling in a net 65 30
809 60f. Fish farm . . . . 1·25 40

1980. World Tourism Conference, Manila. Mult.
810 50f. Type 267 . . . . 55 25
811 60f. Conference flag on globe 70 25

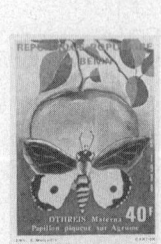

268 "Othreis materna"

269 Map of Africa and Posthorn

1980. Insects. Multicoloured.
812 40f. Type 268 . . . . 65 30
813 50f. "Othreis fullonia"
   (butterfly) 90 40
814 200f. "Oryctes" sp. (beetle) 2·75 1·25

1980. 5th Anniv of African Posts and Telecommunications.
815 269 75f. multicoloured 80 25

270 Hands freed from Chains

271 "Self-portrait"

1980. 30th Anniv of Signing of Human Rights Convention. Multicoloured.
816 30f. Type 270 . . . . 25 15
817 50f. African pushing through
   bars 45 20
818 60f. Figure holding Human
   Rights flame 55 20

1980. 90th Death Anniv of Van Gogh (artist). Multicoloured.
819 100f. Type 271 . . . . 1·75 80
820 300f. "The Postman Roulin" 4·25 2·10

272 Offenbach and Scene from "Orpheus in the Underworld"

1980. Death Centenary of Jacques Offenbach (composer).
821 272 50f. black, red and green 75 50
822 – 60f. blue, brown & dp brn 1·25 75
DESIGN: 60f. Offenbach and scene from "La Vie Parisienne".

273 Kepler and Astronomical Diagram

1980. 30th Death Anniv of Johannes Kepler (astronomer).
823 273 50f. red, blue and grey . . 55 25
824 – 60f. blue, black and green 70 25
DESIGN: 60f. Kepler, satellite and dish aerials.

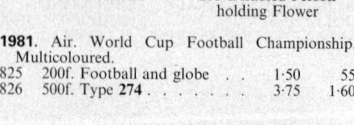

274 Footballers

275 Disabled Person holding Flower

1981. Air. World Cup Football Championship. Multicoloured.
825 200f. Football and globe . . 1·50 55
826 500f. Type 274 . . . . 3·75 1·60

1981. International Year of Disabled People.
827 275 115f. multicoloured . . . 1·00 40

276 Yuri Gagarin

1981. 20th Anniv of First Man in Space.
828 276 500f. multicoloured . . . . 4·50 2·50

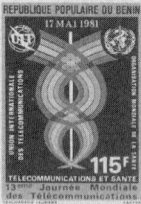

277 I.T.U. and W.H.O. Emblems and Ribbons forming Caduceus

278 Amaryllis

1981. World Telecommunications Day.
829 277 115f. multicoloured 90 40

1981. Flowers. Multicoloured.
830 10f. Type 278 . . . . 25 20
831 20f. "Eischornia crassipes" 40 30
832 80f. "Parkia biglobosa" . . . 1·25 60

279 Hotel and Map

1981. Opening of Benin Sheraton Hotel.
833 279 100f. multicoloured 90 40

1981. Surch 50F.
834 216 50f. on 100f. brown, green
   and red 45 20
835 193 50f. on 210f. red, brown
   and green 45 20

281 Prince Charles, Lady Diana Spencer and Tower Bridge

1981. Air. British Royal Wedding.
836 281 500f. multicoloured . . . 3·75 1·75

282 Guinea Pig

1981. Domestic Animals. Multicoloured.
837   5f. Type 282   25   20
838   60f. Cat   70   40
839   80f. Dogs . . . .   1·00   60

283 Heinrich von Stephan (founder of U.P.U.)

1981. World Universal Postal Union Day.
840 283 100f. slate and red   75   40

284 Heads, Quill, Paper Darts and U.P.U. Emblem

1981. International Letter Writing Week.
841 284 100f. blue and purple . . .   75   40

285 "The Dance"

1981. Air. Birth Centenary of Pablo Picasso. Multicoloured.
842 300f. Type 285 . . . .   2·75   95
843 500f. "The Three Musicians"   4·75   1·60

286 Globe, Map of Member Countries and Communication Symbols

287 St. Theodore Stratilates (tile painting)

1981. 5th Anniv of E.C.O.W.A.S. (Economic Community of West African States).
844 286 60f. multicoloured   65   25

1981. Air. 1300th Anniv of Bulgarian State.
845 287 100f. multicoloured . . .   75   35

288 Tractor and Map

1981. 10th Anniv of West African Rice Development Association.
846 288 60f. multicoloured   65   25

289 Pope John Paul II

1982. Air. Papal Visit.
847 289 80f. multicoloured . . . .   1·50   65

290 John Glenn

1982. Air. 20th Anniv of First United States Manned Space Flight.
848 290 500f. multicoloured . . .   4·25   1·90

291 Dr. Robert Koch

1982. Centenary of Discovery of Tubercle Bacillus.
849 291 115f. multicoloured . . .   1·25   45

292 Washington, U.S. Flag and Map

1982. 250th Birth Anniv of George Washington.
850 292 200f. multicoloured . . .   1·90   75

1982. Red Cross. Surch **Croix Rouge 8 Mai 1982 60f**.
851 266 60f. on 5f. multicoloured   50   25

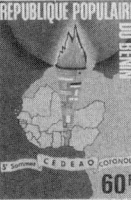

294 Map of Member Countries and Torch

295 Scouts round Campfire

1982. 5th Economic Community of West African States Summit, Cotonou.
852 294 60f. multicoloured   50   25

1982. Air. 75th Anniv of Boy Scout Movement.
853 295 105f. multicoloured . . .   1·25   75

296 Footballers

1982. World Cup Football Championship, Spain. Multicoloured.
854   90f. Type 296   75   40
855   300f. Leg with sock formed from flags of participating countries and globe/football . . . .   2·40   1·10

1982. African Posts and Telegraph Union. Surch **UAPT 1982 60f**.
856 282 60f. on 5f. multicoloured   65   30

298 Stamp of Map of France and Magnifying Glass

1982. "Philexfrance 82" International Stamp Exhibition, Paris.
857 298 90f. multicoloured . . . .   1·00   50

1982. World Cup Football Championship Results. Nos. 854/5 optd.
858   90f. Type 296 . . . .   1·00   50
859   300f. Leg with flags of participating countries and football "globe" . . . .   2·75   1·25
OVERPRINTS: 90f. **COUPE 82 ITALIE bat RFA 3-1**; 300f. **COUPE 82 1 ITALIE 2 RFA 3 POLOGNE**.

1982. Riccione Stamp Exhibition. Optd **RICCIONE 1982**.
860 231 200f. multicoloured . . .   1·50   65

301 Laughing Kookaburra ("Dacelo Gigas")

302 World Map and Satellite

1982. Birds. Multicoloured.
861   5f. Type 301   30   20
862   10f. Bluethroat ("La Gorge Bleue") (horiz)   45   20
863   15f. Barn swallow ("L'Hirondelle")   45   20
864   20f. Woodland kingfisher ("Martin-Pecheur") and Village weaver ("Tisserin")   70   25
865   30f. Reed warbler ("La Rousserolle") (horiz) . . .   1·10   35
866   60f. Warbler sp. ("Faurette Commoune") (horiz) . . .   1·40   50
867   80f. Eagle owl ("Hibou Grand Doc") . . . . . .   2·50   95
868   100f. Sulphur-crested cockatoo ("Cacatoes") . . .   3·00   1·25

1982. I.T.U. Delegates' Conference, Nairobi.
869 302 200f. turq, blue & blk . . .   1·50   65

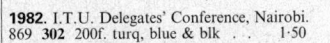

303 U.P.U. Emblem and Heads

1982. U.P.U. Day.
870 303 100f. green, blue & brown   90   40

305 "Claude Monet in his Studio"

1982. Air. 150th Birth Anniv of Edouard Manet (artist).
876 305 300f. multicoloured . . .   5·50   2·25

306 "Virgin and Child" (Grunewald)

1982. Air. Christmas. Multicoloured.
877   200f. Type 306 . . . . . .   2·25   1·10
878   300f. "Virgin and Child with Angels and Cherubins" (Correggio) . . . .   2·75   1·40

307 Pres. Mitterrand and Pres. Kerekou

1983. Visit of President Mitterrand.
879 307 90f. multicoloured . . . .   1·10   45

1983. Various stamps surch.
880   – 60f. on 50f. multicoloured (No. 798) (postage) . .   45   20
881   – 60f. on 70f. multicoloured (No. 778)   45   20
882 279 60f. on 100f. mult . . .   45   25
883   – 75f. on 80f. multicoloured (No. 832)   75   40
884   – 75f. on 80f. multicoloured (No. 839)   75   40
885 262 75f. on 210f. red, blue and yellow (air)   65   35

309 "Tender Benin" (tug) and "Amazone" (oil rig)

1983. Seme Oilfield.
886 309 125f. multicoloured . . .   1·40   60

1983. Various stamps surch.
887 267 5f. on 50f. multicoloured   10   10
888 284 10f. on 100f. blue & pur   10   10
889   – 10f. on 200f. mult (No. 659)   10   10
890   – 15f. on 200f. red and bistre (No. 670)   10   10
891   – 15f. on 200f. mult (No. 796)   10   10
892   – 15f. on 210f. green, deep green and red (No. 667)   10   10
893   – 15f. on 270f. mult (No. 643)   10   10
894 219 20f. on 200f. brown, red and olive   20   10
895   – 25f. on 70f. mult (No. 795)   25   10
896   – 25f. on 210f. mult (No. 673)   20   10
897   – 25f. on 270f. blue, turq & red (No. 633)   20   10
898   – 25f. on 380f. brown and red (No. 687)   25   10
899   – 30f. on 200f. brown, blue and red (No. 681) . . .   30   20
900 290 40f. on 500f. mult . . .   40   20
901 282 75f. on 5f. multicoloured   55   40

902 – 75f. on 100f. red, blue and pink (No. 790) 55 40
903 – 75f. on 150f. mult (No. 631) 55 40
904 – 75f. on 150f. violet, red and green (No. 655) 65 40
905 **211** 75f. on 150f. grey, orange and red 55 40
906 – 75f. on 150f. dp brown, brown & red (No. 669) 65 40

311 W.C.Y. Emblem

1983. World Communications Year.
907 **311** 185f. multicoloured . . . 1·50 65

312 Stamps of Benin and Thailand and World Map

1983. Air. "Bangkok 1983" International Stamp Exhibition.
908 **312** 300f. multicoloured . . . 2·50 1·25

313 Hand with Tweezers and Stamp

1983. "Riccione 83" Stamp Fair, San Marino.
909 **313** 500f. multicoloured . . . 3·75 1·60

314 First Aid   **315 Carved Table and Chairs**

1983. 20th Anniv of Benin Red Cross.
910 **314** 105f. multicoloured . . . 95 50

1983. Benin Woodwork. Multicoloured.
911 75f. Type **315** 65 25
912 90f. Rustic table and chairs 90 40
913 200f. Monkeys holding box 1·60 65

316 Boeing 747, World Map and U.P.U. Emblem

1983. U.P.U. Day.
914 **316** 125f. green, blue & brown 1·25 60

317 Egoun   **318 Rockcoco**

1983. Religious Cults. Multicoloured.
915 75f. Type **317** 65 30
916 75f. Zangbeto 65 30

1983. Hair-styles. Multicoloured.
917 30f. Type **318** 25 20
918 65f. Serpent 65 40
919 90f. Songas 90 45

319 Alfred Nobel

1983. 150th Birth Anniv of Alfred Nobel.
920 **319** 300f. multicoloured . . . 2·75 1·50

320 "Madonna of Lorette" (Raphael)

1983. Air. Christmas.
921 **320** 200f. multicoloured . . . 1·90 95

1984. Various stamps surch.
922 – 5f. on 150f. mult (No. 685) (postage) . . 15 15
923 **316** 5f. on 125f. green, blue and brown . . . 1·50 1·25
924 **292** 10f. on 200f. mult . . . 15 15
925 – 10f. on 300f. mult (No. 913) . . . 20 20
926 – 15f. on 300f. mult (No. 820) . . . 20 20
927 – 25f. on 300f. mult (No. 644) . . . 25 10
928 **276** 40f. on 500f. mult . . . 1·00 90
929 **314** 75f. on 105f. mult . . . 70 60
930 **275** 75f. on 115f. mult . . . 70 45
931 **277** 75f. on 115f. mult . . . 70 60
932 **291** 75f. on 115f. mult . . . 70 60
933 **311** 75f. on 185f. mult . . . 70 60
934 **302** 75f. on 200f. turquoise, blue and black . . . 70 60
935 **320** 15f. on 200f. mult (air) . . 10 10
936 **285** 15f. on 300f. mult . . . 10 10
937 **312** 25f. on 300f. mult . . . 25 10
938 **281** 40f. on 500f. mult . . . 30 25
939 **295** 75f. on 105f. mult . . . 1·00 90
940 **306** 90f. on 200f. mult . . . 70 45
941 **305** 90f. on 300f. mult . . . 70 45

322 Flags, Agriculture and Symbol of Unity and Growth   **323 U.P.U. Emblem and Magnifying Glass**

1984. 25th Anniv of Council of Unity.
942 **322** 75f. multicoloured 65 25
943 90f. multicoloured 75 30

1984. 19th Universal Postal Union Congress, Hamburg.
944 **323** 90f. multicoloured . . . . 1·00 40

324 Abomey-Calavi Ground Station   **325 Koumboro (Borgou)**

1984. Inauguration of Abomy-Calavi Ground Station.
945 **324** 75f. multicoloured . . . 65 40

1984. Traditional Costumes. Multicoloured.
946 5f. Type **325** 25 25
947 10f. Taka (Borgou) 35 30
948 20f. Toko (Atacora Province) 50 40

326 Olympic Mascot   **327 Plant and Starving Child**

1984. Air. Olympic Games, Los Angeles.
949 **326** 300f. multicoloured . . . 2·50 1·25

1984. World Food Day.
950 **327** 100f. multicoloured . . . 75 35

328 Anatosaurus

1984. Prehistoric Animals. Multicoloured.
951 75f. Type **328** 90 50
952 90f. Brontosaurus . . . . . 1·25 60

329 "Virgin and Child" (detail, Murillo)

1984. Air. Christmas.
953 **329** 500f. multicoloured . . . 4·25 1·90

1984. Various stamps surch.
954 **203** 75f. on 200f. mult (post) 1·50 1·25
955 **226** 75f. on 300f. mult . . . 1·25 1·00
956 – 75f. on 300f. mult (No. 696) . . . . . 1·25 1·00
957 **229** 75f. on 300f. mult . . . 70 45
958 – 90f. on 300f. mult (No. 855) . . . . . 1·25 1·00
959 – 90f. on 500f. mult (No. 697) . . . . . 1·25 1·00
960 – 90f. on 500f. mult (No. 701) . . . . . 1·25 1·00
961 **204** 75f. on 200f. mult (air) 55 40
962 – 75f. on 200f. mult (No. 825) . . . . . 1·25 1·00
963 – 75f. on 300f. violet, red and mauve (No. 656) 1·50 1·25
964 – 75f. on 300f. mult (No. 878) 55 40
965 **239** 90f. on 500f. blue, yellow and brown 1·50 1·25
966 – 90f. on 500f. mult (No. 715) 70 40
967 – 90f. on 500f. mult (No. 843) 70 40

331 Sidon Merchant Ship (2nd century)

1984. Air. Ships.
968 **331** 90f. black, green & blue 1·10 60
969 – 125f. multicoloured 1·75 90
DESIGN—VERT: 125f. Sail merchantman "Wavertree", 1895.

332 Emblem on Globe and Hands reaching for Cultural Symbols   **333 Benin Arms**

1985. 15th Anniv of Cultural and Technical Co-operation Agency.
970 **332** 300f. multicoloured . . . 2·25 95

1985. Air. Postal Convention between Benin and Sovereign Military Order of Malta. Multicoloured.
971 75f. Type **333** 60 25
972 75f. Arms of Sovereign Military Order 60 25

334 Soviet Flag, Soldier and Tank   **335 Teke Dance, Borgou**

1985. 40th Anniv of End of Second World War.
973 **334** 100f. multicoloured . . . .

1985. Traditional Dances. Multicoloured.
974 75f. Type **335** 75 50
975 100f. Tipen ti dance, Atacora 1·10 60

1985. Various Dahomey Stamps optd **POPULAIRE DU BENIN** (985/6) or **REPUBLIQUE POPULAIRE DU BENIN** (others), Nos. 976/7 and 979/85 surch also.
976 **174** 15f. on 40f. mult (post) 20 10
977 **182** 25f. on 40f. brown, blue and violet (air) 20 10
978 **115** 40f. black, purple & bl 25 10
978a – 75f. on 85f. brown, blue and green (No. 468) 50 25
979 – 75f. on 85f. brown, blue and green (No. 482) 50 25
980 **135** 75f. on 100f. purple, violet and green 50 25
981 – 75f. on 125f. green, blue and purple (No. 509) 50 25
982 **127** 90f. on 20f. brown, blue and green 65 40
983 – 90f. on 150f. purple, blue & brown (No. 456) 65 40
984 – 90f. on 200f. green, red and blue (No. 438) 65 40
985 – 90f. on 200f. mult (No. 563) 65 40
986 – 150f. mult (No. 562) . . . 1·00 65

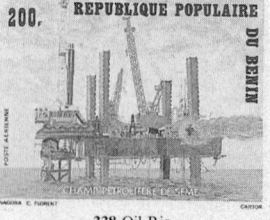
338 Oil Rig

1985. Air. "Philexafrique" International Stamp Exhibition, Lome, Togo (1st issue). Mult.
987 200f. Type **338** . . . . . . 2·50 1·75
988 200f. Footballers . . . . . . 2·40 1·50
See also Nos. 999/1000.

339 Emblem

1985. International Youth Year.
989 **339** 150f. multicoloured . . . 1·10 55

340 Football between Globes

1985. World Cup Football Championship, Mexico (1986) (1st issue).
990 **340** 200f. multicoloured . . . 1·50 80
See also No. 1015.

341 Boeing 727, Map and Emblem

1985. 25th Anniv of Aerial Navigation Security Agency for Africa and Malagasy.
991 **341** 150f. multicoloured . . . 1·25 90

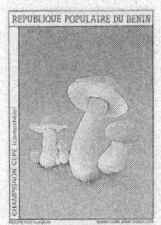 

342 "Boletus edulis"   343 Audubon and Arctic Skua ("Labbe Parasite")

1985. Fungi. Multicoloured.
992 35f. Type **342** . . . . . 1·60 60
993 40f. "Amanita phalloides" . . 2·10 1·10
994 100f. "Paxillus involutus" . . 4·75 2·10

1985. Birth Bicentenary of John J. Audubon (ornithologist). Multicoloured.
995 150f. Type **343** . . . . . 2·00 1·10
996 300f. Audubon and oystercatcher ("Huitrier Pie") . . . . 4·50 2·40

344 Emblem, Hands and Dove

1985. 40th Anniv of United Nations Organization and 25th Anniv of Benin's Membership.
997 **344** 250f. multicoloured . . . 1·90 90

345 Stamps and Globe

1985. "Italia '85" International Stamp Exhibition, Rome.
998 **345** 200f. multicoloured . . . 1·50 80

1985. "Philexafrique" International Stamp Exhibition, Lome, Togo (2nd issue). As Type **338**. Multicoloured.
999 250f. Forest and hand holding tools . . . . . 2·50 1·60
1000 250f. Magnifying glass over judo stamp . . . . . . 2·50 1·60

1985. Various Dahomey stamps optd **Republique Populaire du Benin**. Nos. 1001/9 and 1011 surch also.
1001 – 75f. on 35f. mult (No. 596) (postage) . . 50 25
1002 – 90f. on 70f. multicoloured (No. 419) 70 35
1003 – 90f. on 140f. multicoloured (No. 446) 70 35
1004 **113** 100f. on 40f. red, brown and green 75 40
1005 – 150f. on 45f. multicoloured (No. 597) . . . . . . 1·10 65
1006 – 75f. on 70f. multicoloured (No. 342) (air) . . . . 6·50 6·50
1007 – 75f. on 100f. multicoloured (No. 251) . . . . 2·00 60
1008 **59** 75f. on 200f. mult 2·00 60
1009 – 90f. on 250f. multicoloured (No. 272) . . . . 2·00 60
1010 **110** 100f. multicoloured . . . 45 40
1011 – 150f. on 500f. multicoloured (No. 252) . . . . 3·00 1·40
No. 1010 is surcharged on the unoverprinted unissued stamp subsequently issued as No. 422.

349 Church, Children playing and Nativity Scene

1985. Air. Christmas.
1012 **349** 500f. multicoloured . . . 4·00 1·60

350 Emblem

1986. 10th Anniv of African Parliamentary Union and Ninth Conference, Cotonou.
1013 **350** 100f. multicoloured . . . 75 40

351 Halley, Comet and "Giotto" Space Probe

1986. Appearance of Halley's Comet.
1014 **351** 205f. multicoloured . . . 2·25 1·25

352 Footballers

1986. World Cup Football Championship, Mexico (2nd issue). Multicoloured.
1015 **352** 500f. Footballers . . . . 3·75 1·75

 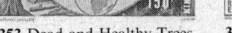

353 Dead and Healthy Trees   354 Amazone

1986. Anti-desertification Campaign.
1016 **353** 150f. multicoloured . . . 1·25 65

1986.
1017 **354** 100f. blue 65 20
1018 150f. purple 95 25

355 "Haemanthus"   356 "Inachis io", "Aglais urticae" and "Nymphalis antiopa"

1986. Flowers. Multicoloured.
1019 100f. Type **355** . . . . . . 1·10 75
1020 205f. "Hemerocallis" . . . 2·25 1·25

1986. Butterflies. Multicoloured.
1021 150f. Type **356** . . . . . . 1·75 1·10
1022 150f. "Anthocharis cardamines", "Papilio machaon" and "Cynthia cardui" . . . . 1·75 1·10

1986. Various stamps of Dahomey surch **Republique Populaire du Benin** and new value.
1024 – 150f. on 100f. mult (444) (postage) . . . . .
1025 – 15f. on 85f. mult (600) (air) . . . .
1026 – 25f. on 200f. mult (432)
1027 **150** 25f. on 200f. deep green, violet and green . . .
1030 **175** 100f. purple, indigo & bl
1031 **128** 150f. on 100f. blue, violet and red . . . .

358 Statue and Buildings   359 Bust of King Behanzin

1986. Centenary of Statue of Liberty.
1032 **358** 250f. multicoloured . . . 2·25 1·00

1986. King Behanzin.
1033 **359** 440f. multicoloured . . . 3·75 1·90
For design in smaller size, see Nos. 1101/4.

360 Family with Crib, Church and Nativity Scene

1986. Air. Christmas.
1034 **360** 300f. multicoloured . . . 2·50 1·10

361 Rainbow and Douglas DC-10

1986. Air. 25th Anniv of Air Afrique.
1035 **361** 100f. multicoloured . . . 1·00 60

362 Emblem around Map in Cog

1987. Brazil Culture Week, Cotonou.
1036 **362** 150f. multicoloured . . . 1·75 70

363 Cotonou Centre for the Blind and Partially Sighted

1987. Rotary International 910 District Conference, Cotonou.
1037 **363** 300f. multicoloured . . . 2·50 1·10

1987. Various stamps of Dahomey optd **Republique Populaire du Benin**. Nos. 1038/9 and 1042/53 surch also.
1038 **129** 10f. on 65f. black, violet and red (postage) . . .
1039 – 15f. on 100f. red, blue and green (434) . . .
1040 **98** 40f. green, blue and brown . . . . .
1042 – 150f. on 200f. mult (560) . . . .
1043 **144** 10f. on 65f. black, yellow & purple (air)
1046 – 25f. on 150f. mult (487)
1047 – 30f. on 100f. mult (602)
1048 **140** 40f. on 15f. purple, green and blue
1049 – 40f. on 100f. mult (453)
1051 – 50f. on 140f. mult (601)
1052 – 50f. on 100f. mult (252)
1053 – 70f. on 250f. mult (462)
1054 – 80f. mult (286) . . . .
1055 – 100f. mult (429) . . . .
1055a – 100f. mult (447) . . . .

365 De Dion-Bouton and Trepardoux Steam Tricycle and Modern Ford Motor Car

1987. Centenary of Motor Car. Multicoloured.
1058 150f. Type **365** . . . . . . 1·50 75
1059 300f. Daimler petrol motor car "Victoria" and modern Mercedes car . 2·75 1·50

366 Baptism in the Python Temple   368 G. Hansen and R. Follereau (leprosy pioneers) and Patients

1987. Ritual Ceremonies.
1060 **366** 100f. multicoloured . . . 95 50

1987. Shellfish. Multicoloured.
1061 100f. Type **367** . . . . . . 1·10 60
1062 150f. Crab . . . . 1·40 90

1987. Anti-leprosy Campaign.
1063 **368** 200f. multicoloured . . . 1·90 95

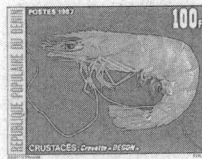

367 Shrimp

369 Crop-spraying and Locusts

1987. Anti-locust Campaign.
1064 **369** 100f. multicoloured . . . 1·10 60

370 Fisherman and Farmer

1987. Air. 10th Anniv of International Agricultural
Development Fund.
1065 **370** 500f. multicoloured . . .   3·75   1·90

371 Nativity Scene in Moon and
Father Christmas giving Sweets to
Crowd

1987. Christmas.
1066 **371** 150f. multicoloured . . .   1·25   75

372 Rally   **375** Hands holding Pot
Aloft

1988. 15th Anniv (1987) of Start of Benin Revolution.
1067 **372** 100f. multicoloured . . . .

1988. Various stamps surch. (a) Stamps of Dahomey
surch **Populaire du Benin** (1081c) or **Republique**
Populaire du Benin (others).
1068   – 5f. on 3f. black and
         blue (173) (postage)
1069   – 20f. on 100f. mult (506)
1071   – 25f. on 100f. mult (576)
1073   – 50f. on 45f. mult (320)
1074 **178** 55f. on 200f. olive,
         brown and green . .
1075a   125f. on 100f. mult
         (557) . . . . .
1076 **116** 10f. on 50f. black,
         orange and blue (air)
1077 **161** 15f. on 150f. red and
         black . . . . .
1078   – 25f. on 100f. mult (526)
1079 **156** 25f. on 100f. blue,
         brown and violet . .
1079a **153** 40f. on 35f. mult
1080   – 40f. on 100f. mult (495)
1081 **162** 40f. on 150f. red,
         brown and blue . .
1081b **148** 100f. brown and green
1081b **181** 125f. on 75f. lilac, red
         and green . . . .
1081c   – 125f. on 150f. blue and
         purple (541) . . . .
1082   – 125f. on 250f. mult
         (491) . . . .
1082a   – 125f. red and brown
         (540) . . . . . .
1083   – 190f. on 250f. brown,
         green and red (594)
1084   – 1000f. on 150f.
         multicoloured (545)

(b) No. 618 of Benin surch **Republique Populaire du**
Benin.
1085 – 10f. on 60f. on 2f. mult . .

         (c) Stamps of Benin surch only.
1086 **359** 125f. on 440f. mult
         (postage) . . . . .
1087 **338** 125f. on 200f. mult (air)
1088   – 190f. on 250f. mult (999)
1089   – 190f. on 250f. mult
         (1000) . . . .

1988. 25th Anniv of Organization of African Unity.
1094 **375** 125f. multicoloured . . .   95   40

376 Resuscitation of Man pulled from
River

1988. 125th Anniv of Red Cross Movement.
1095 **376** 200f. multicoloured . . .   1·50   1·00

377 King   **378** Scout and Camp

1988. 20th Death Anniv of Martin Luther King (Civil
Rights leader).
1096 **377** 200f. multicoloured . . .   1·50   75

1988. 1st Benin Scout Jamboree, Savalou.
1097 **378** 125f. multicoloured . . .   1·25   90

379 Healthy Family and Health Care

1988. 40th Anniv of W.H.O. and 10th Anniv of
"Health for All by 2000" Declaration.
1098 **379** 175f. multicoloured . . .   1·25   65

380 Dugout Canoes and Houses

1988. Ganvie (lake village). Multicoloured.
1099   125f. Type **380**   95   50
1100   190f. Boatman and houses   1·60   75

1988. As T **359** but smaller (17 × 24 mm).
1101 **359** 40f. black   25   15
1102   125f. red   75   25
1103   190f. blue . . . . . .   1·25   25
1104   220f. green . . . . . .   1·50   40

381 Adoration of the Magi

1988. Air. Christmas.
1105 **381** 500f. multicoloured . . .   3·75   1·90

382 Offering to Hebiesso, God
of Thunder

1988. Ritual Ceremony.
1106 **382** 125f. multicoloured . . .   95   50

383 Roseate Tern

1989. Endangered Animals. Roseate Tern. Mult.
1107 **383** 10f. Type **383**   25   15
1108   15f. Tern with fish   50   20
1109   50f. Tern on rocks . . . .   1·00   40
1110   125f. Tern flying . . . .   2·50   85

384 Eiffel Tower   **386** Tractor, Map and Pump

1989. Centenary of Eiffel Tower.
1111 **384** 190f. multicoloured . . .   1·60   1·00

1989. 30th Anniv of Agriculture Development
Council.
1113 **386** 75f. multicoloured . . . .

387 Symbols of Revolution and
France 1950 National Relief Fund
Stamps

1989. Bicentenary of French Revolution and
"Philexfrance 89" International Stamp Exhibition,
Paris.
1114 **387** 190f. multicoloured . . .   1·90   1·25

388 Burbot

1989. Fishes. Multicoloured.
1115   125f. Type **388** . . . . .   1·50   75
1116   190f. Northern pike and
         Atlantic salmon . . . .   2·25   1·25

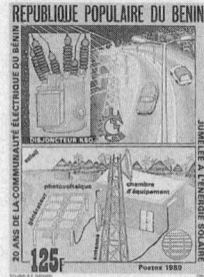

389 Circuit Breaker, Illuminated
Road and Solar Energy Complex

1989. 20th Anniv of Benin Electricity Community.
1117 **389** 125f. multicoloured . . .   95   50

390 Lion within Wreath

1989. Death Centenary of King Glele.
1118 **390** 190f. multicoloured . . .   1·40   75

391 Nativity

1989. Christmas.
1119 **391** 200f. multicoloured . . .   1·50   90

392 Anniversary Emblem and
Means of Communications

1990. Centenary of Postal and Telecommunications
Ministry (1st issue).
1120 **392** 125f. multicoloured . . .   95   50
See also No. 1127.

393 Oranges

1990. Fruit and Flowers. Multicoloured.
1121   60f. Type **393**   45   30
1122   190f. Kaufmannia tulips
         (vert) . . . . . .   1·75   90
1123   250f. Cashew nuts (vert) . .   1·90   1·10

394 Launch of "Apollo 11" and
Footprint on Moon

1990. 21st Anniv of First Manned Moon Landing.
1124 **394** 190f. multicoloured . . .   1·40   75

395 Footballers

1990. World Cup Football Championship, Italy.
Multicoloured.
1125   125f. Type **395** . . . . .   1·10   60
1126   190f. Mascot holding torch
         and pennant (vert) . . .   1·75   75

396 Balloons, Emblem   **398** De Gaulle
and Means of
Communication

1990. Centenary of Postal and Telecommunications Ministry (2nd issue).
1127 **396** 150f. multicoloured . . . 1·10 55

1990. World Cup Finalists. No. 1125 optd **FINALE R.F.A.-ARGENTINE 1-0.**
1128 **395** 125f. multicoloured . . . 80 50

1990. Birth Centenary of Charles de Gaulle (French statesman) (1st issue).
1129 **398** 190f. multicoloured . . . 1·50 1·00
See also No. 1160.

399 "Galileo" Space Probe orbiting Jupiter   **400** Nativity

1990. Space Exploration.
1130 **399** 100f. multicoloured . . . 75 50

1990. Christmas.
1131 **400** 200f. multicoloured . . . 1·50 1·00

401 Hands pointing to Scales of Justice

1990. National Conference of Active Forces.
1132 **401** 125f. multicoloured . . . . . .

406 Different Cultures and Emblem

1991. African Tourism Year.
1150 **406** 190f. multicoloured . . . 1·50 1·00

407 Tennis Player   **408** Flag and Arms

1991. Cent of French Open Tennis Championships.
1151 **407** 125f. multicoloured . . . 1·50 75

1991. 31st Anniv of Independence.
1152 **408** 125f. multicoloured . . . 1·50 75

1991. "Riccione 91" Stamp Fair. No. 1130 optd "Riccione 91".
1153 **399** 100f. multicoloured . . . 1·00 60

410 Adoration of the Magi

1991. Christmas.
1154 **410** 125f. multicoloured . . . 95 40

411 Guelede Dancer   **412** Mozart

1991.
1155 **411** 190f. multicoloured . . . 1·50 65

1991. Death Bicentenary of Wolfgang Amadeus Mozart (composer).
1156 **412** 1000f. multicoloured . . . 8·00 5·00

413 Slave in Chains and Route Map

1992. 500th Anniv of Discovery of America by Columbus.
1157 **413** 500f. black, brown & bl 3·75 2·50
1158 – 1000f. multicoloured . . 7·00 5·00
DESIGN—HORIZ: 1000f. Columbus landing at Guanahami, Bahamas.

1992. Birth Centenary (1990) of Charles de Gaulle (French statesman) (2nd issue). As No. 1129 but value changed.
1160 **398** 300f. multicoloured . . . 2·25 1·50

414 Child, Produce and Emblems   **415** Pope John Paul II

1992. International Nutrition Conference, Rome.
1161 **414** 190f. multicoloured . . . 1·40 1·00

1993. Papal Visit.
1162 **415** 190f. multicoloured . . . 1·25 90

416 Emblem and Voodoo Culture

1993. "Ouidah 92" Voodoo Culture Festival.
1163 **416** 125f. multicoloured . . . 75 50

417 Well and Blue-throated Roller

1993. Possotome Artesian Well.
1164 **417** 125f. multicoloured . . . 75 50

418 Map, Clasped Hands and Flags of Member Countries

1993. 30th Anniv of Organization of African Unity.
1165 **418** 125f. multicoloured . . . 70 40

419 John F. Kennedy (President of United States, 1961–63)

1993. Death Anniversaries. Multicoloured.
1166 190f. Type **419** (30th anniv) 85 45
1167 190f. Dr. Martin Luther King (American civil rights campaigner, 25th anniv) (vert) 85 45

1993. Stamps of Dahomey variously optd or surch.
(a) **REPUBLIQUE DU BENIN.**
1167a **139** 5f. multicoloured (postage) . . . . .
1170 **108** 50f. on 1f. multicoloured (617)
1171 **113** 80f. on 40f. red, brown and green
1173 135f. on 20f. black, green and red (190)
1175 135f. on 30f. black, brown and violet (472)
1177 **107** 135f. on 40f. mult . . .
1179 – 135f. on 60f. olive, red and purple (181)
1181 – 200f. on 100f. mult (322)
1186 – 15f. on 40f. mult (458) (air)
1190 **126** 100f. multicoloured . .
1190a **119** 125f. on 40f. mult . . .
1191 – 125f. on 65f. red and blue (552)
1201 – 200f. on 250f. mult (569)

(b) **DU BENIN.**
1207 **60** 5f. on 1f. multicoloured (postage) . . . . .
1208 – 10f. on 3f. black and blue (173) . .
1211 – 25f. multicoloured (441)
1220 – 135f. on 3f. mult (274)
1223 – 20f. on 200f. mult (451) (air)
1225 – 25f. on 85f. mult (600)
1227 **140** 30f. on 15f. purple, green and blue
1231 – 125f. on 70f. mult (383)
1235 – 150f. purple, blue and brown (456) . . .
1236 – 150f. multicoloured (527)
1239 **150** 200f. green, violet and emerald . . . .
1242 – 200f. on 150f. mult (562)
1243 **179** 300f. multicoloured . .

(c) **BENIN.**
1257 – 25f. on 500f. brown, red and green (592) (air)
1258 – 30f. on 200f. mult (528)
1260a – 100f. brown, green and blue (522) . .
1261 **116** 125f. on 50f. black, orange and blue . .
1263a – 190f. on 200f. mult (478) . . . .
1266 – 300f. brn, red & bl (591) . . . .

422 Conference Emblem

1994. U.N.E.S.C.O. Conference on the Slave Route, Ouidah.
1275 **422** 300f. multicoloured . . . 75 40

423 World Map

1994. International Year of the Family.
1276 **423** 200f. multicoloured . . . 50 25

425 Water Polo

1995. Olympic Games, Atlanta (1996) (1st issue). Multicoloured.
1278 45f. Type **425** 20 20
1279 50f. Throwing the javelin (vert) 25 20
1280 75f. Weightlifting (vert) . . 35 25
1281 100f. Tennis (vert) 50 40
1282 135f. Baseball (vert) 60 50
1283 200f. Synchronised swimming (vert) 90 70
See also Nos. 1347/52.

426 Paddle-steamer

1995. Ships. Multicoloured.
1285 40f. Type **426** 20 20
1286 50f. "Charlotte" (paddle steamer) 25 20
1287 75f. "Citta di Catania" (Italian liner) 35 25
1288 100f. "Mountbatten" SR-N4 (hovercraft) 50 40
1289 135f. "Queen Elizabeth 2" (liner) 60 50
1290 200f. "Matsu-Nef" (Japanese nuclear-powered freighter) 90 70

427 Chimpanzee

1995. Primates. Multicoloured.
1292 50f. Type **427** 25 20
1293 75f. Mandrill 35 30
1294 100f. Colobus 50 40
1295 135f. Barbary ape 70 50
1296 200f. Hamadryas baboon . . . 1·00 75

428 Tabby Shorthair

1995. Cats. Multicoloured.
1298 40f. Type **428** 20 20
1299 50f. Sorrel Abyssinian ("Ruddy red") 25 20
1300 75f. White Persian long-hair 35 30
1301 100f. Seal colourpoint 50 40
1302 135f. Tabby point 60 50
1303 200f. Black shorthair 90 70

429 German Shepherd

1995. Dogs. Multicoloured.
1305 40f. Type **429** 20 20
1306 50f. Beagle 25 20
1307 75f. Great dane 35 30
1308 100f. Boxer 50 40
1309 135f. Pointer 60 50
1310 200f. Long-haired fox terrier 90 70

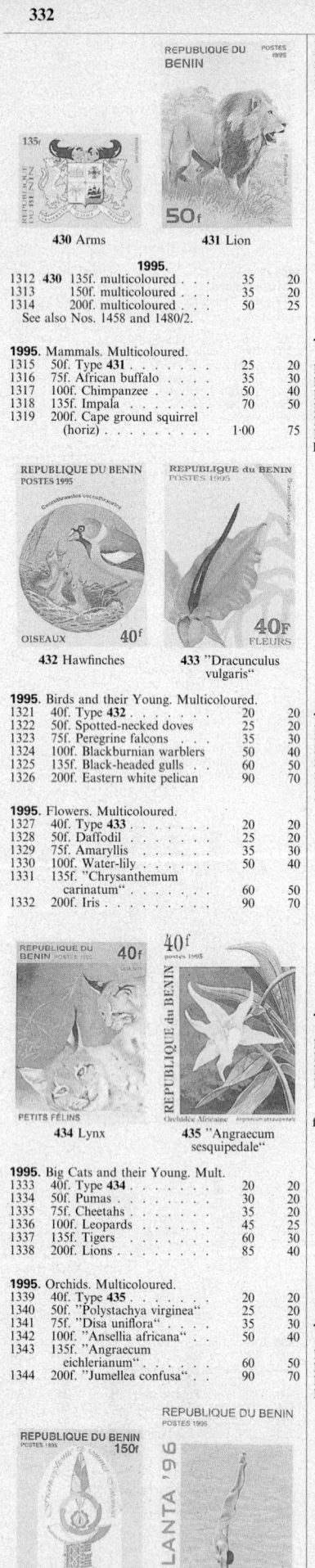

430 Arms   **431** Lion

1995.
1312	**430**	135f. multicoloured	35	20
1313		150f. multicoloured	35	20
1314		200f. multicoloured	50	25

See also Nos. 1458 and 1480/2.

1995. Mammals. Multicoloured.
1315	50f. Type **431**	25	20
1316	75f. African buffalo	35	30
1317	100f. Chimpanzee	50	20
1318	135f. Impala	70	50
1319	200f. Cape ground squirrel (horiz)	1·00	75

432 Hawfinches   **433** "Dracunculus vulgaris"

1995. Birds and their Young. Multicoloured.
1321	40f. Type **432**	20	20
1322	50f. Spotted-necked doves	25	20
1323	75f. Peregrine falcons	35	20
1324	100f. Blackburnian warblers	50	40
1325	135f. Black-headed gulls	60	50
1326	200f. Eastern white pelican	90	70

1995. Flowers. Multicoloured.
1327	40f. Type **433**	20	20
1328	50f. Daffodil	25	20
1329	75f. Amaryllis	35	30
1330	100f. Water-lily	50	40
1331	135f. "Chrysanthemum carinatum"	60	50
1332	200f. Iris	90	70

434 Lynx   **435** "Angraecum sesquipedale"

1995. Big Cats and their Young. Mult.
1333	40f. Type **434**	20	20
1334	50f. Pumas	30	20
1335	75f. Cheetahs	35	20
1336	100f. Leopards	45	25
1337	135f. Tigers	60	30
1338	200f. Lions	85	40

1995. Orchids. Multicoloured.
1339	40f. Type **435**	20	20
1340	50f. "Polystachya virginea"	25	20
1341	75f. "Disa uniflora"	35	30
1342	100f. "Ansellia africana"	50	40
1343	135f. "Angraecum eichlerianum"	60	50
1344	200f. "Jumellea confusa"	90	70

436 Emblem   **437** Diving

1995. 6th Francophone Summit, Cotonou.
1345	**436**	150f. multicoloured	35	20
1346		200f. multicoloured	50	25

1996. Olympic Games, Atlanta (2nd issue). Multicoloured.
1347	40f. Type **437**	20	20
1348	50f. Tennis	25	20

1349	75f. Running	35	30
1350	100f. Gymnastics	50	40
1351	135f. Weightlifting	60	50
1352	200f. Shooting	90	70

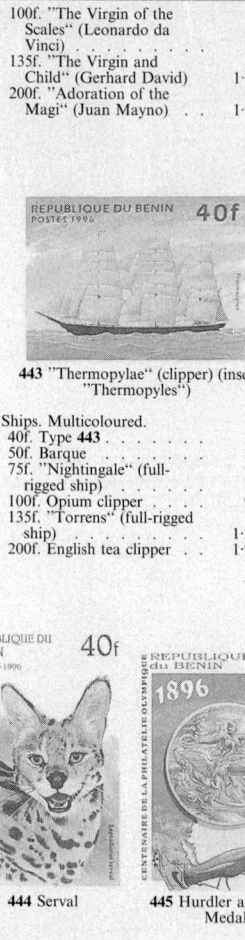

438 Player with Ball

1996. World Cup Football Championship, France (1998) (1st issue).
1354	**438**	40f. multicoloured	35	20
1355	–	50f. multicoloured	35	20
1356	–	75f. multicoloured	75	50
1357	–	100f. multicoloured	90	60
1358	–	135f. multicoloured	1·25	1·00
1359	–	200f. multicoloured	1·90	1·50

DESIGNS: 50f. to 200f. Different players. See also Nos. 1473/8.

439 Small Striped Swallowtail

1996. Butterflies. Multicoloured.
1361	40f. Type **439**	35	20
1362	50f. Red admiral	35	20
1363	75f. Common blue	75	50
1364	100f. African monarch	90	60
1365	135f. Painted lady	1·25	1·00
1366	200f. "Argus celbulina ortbitulus"	1·90	1·50

440 Dancer

1996. "China '96" International Stamp Exhibition, Peking. Multicoloured.
1368	40f. Type **440**	75	50
1369	50f. Exhibition emblem	1·00	75
1370	75f. Water-lily	1·50	1·00
1371	100f. Temple of Heaven, Peking	2·00	1·50

Nos. 1368/71 were issued together, se-tenant, forming a composite design.

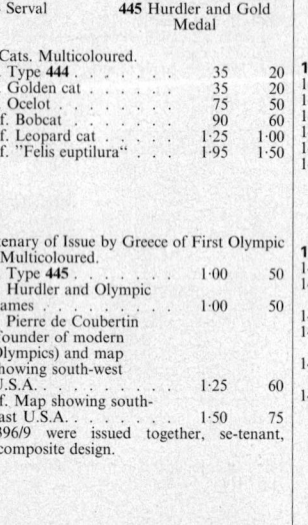

441 Emblem

1996. 15th Convention of Lions Club International, Cotonou.
1457	**441**	100f. multicoloured	75	50
1372		135f. multicoloured	1·10	75
1373		150f. multicoloured	1·10	75
1374		200f. multicoloured	1·50	1·00

442 "Holy Family of Rouvre" (Raphael)

1996. Christmas. Multicoloured.
1375	40f. Type **442**	35	20
1376	50f. "The Holy Family" (Raphael)	35	20
1377	75f. "St. John the Baptist" (Bartolome Murillo)	75	60

1378	100f. "The Virgin of the Scales" (Leonardo da Vinci)	95	60
1379	135f. "The Virgin and Child" (Gerhard David)	1·25	1·00
1380	200f. "Adoration of the Magi" (Juan Mayno)	1·90	1·50

443 "Thermopylae" (clipper) (inscr "Thermopyles")

1996. Ships. Multicoloured.
1382	40f. Type **443**	35	20
1383	50f. Barque	35	20
1384	75f. "Nightingale" (full-rigged ship)	75	50
1385	100f. Opium clipper	90	60
1386	135f. "Torrens" (full-rigged ship)	1·25	1·00
1387	200f. English tea clipper	1·90	1·50

444 Serval   **445** Hurdler and Gold Medal

1996. Big Cats. Multicoloured.
1389	40f. Type **444**	35	20
1390	50f. Golden cat	35	20
1391	75f. Ocelot	75	50
1392	100f. Bobcat	90	60
1393	135f. Leopard cat	1·25	1·00
1394	200f. "Felis euptilura"	1·95	1·50

1996. Centenary of Issue by Greece of First Olympic Stamps. Multicoloured.
1396	40f. Type **445**	1·00	50
1397	50f. Hurdler and Olympic flames	1·00	50
1398	75f. Pierre de Coubertin (founder of modern Olympics) and map showing south-west U.S.A.	1·25	60
1399	100f. Map showing south-east U.S.A.	1·50	75

Nos. 1396/9 were issued together, se-tenant, forming a composite design.

446 Running   **447** "Parodia subterranea"

1996. "Olymphilex '96" Olympics and Sports Stamp Exhibition, Atlanta. Multicoloured.
1400	40f. Type **446**	35	20
1401	50f. Canoeing	35	20
1402	75f. Gymnastics	75	50
1403	100f. Football	90	60
1404	135f. Tennis	1·25	1·00
1405	200f. Baseball	1·90	1·50

1996. Flowering Cacti. Multicoloured.
1407	40f. Type **447**	35	20
1408	50f. "Astrophytum senile"	35	20
1409	75f. "Echinocereus melanocentrus"	75	50
1410	100f. "Turbinicarpus klinkerianus"	90	60
1411	135f. "Astrophytum capricorne"	1·25	1·00
1412	200f. "Nelloydia grandiflora"	1·90	1·50

448 Chestnut Horse   **449** Longisquama

1996. Horses. Multicoloured.
1413	40f. Type **448**	35	20
1414	50f. Horse on hillside	35	20
1415	75f. Foal by fence	75	50
1416	100f. Mother and foal	95	60
1417	135f. Pair of horses	1·40	1·00
1418	200f. Grey horse (horiz)	2·00	1·50

1996. Prehistoric Animals. Multicoloured.
1419	40f. Type **449**	35	20
1420	50f. Dimorphodon	35	20
1421	75f. Dunkleosteus (horiz)	75	50
1422	100f. Eryops (horiz)	90	60
1423	135f. Peloneustes (horiz)	1·25	1·00
1424	200f. Deinonychus (horiz)	1·90	1·50

450 Ivory-billed Woodpecker   **451** Golden Tops

1996. Birds. Multicoloured.
1425	40f. Type **450**	35	20
1426	50f. Grey-necked bald crow	35	20
1427	75f. Kakapo	75	50
1428	100f. Puerto Rican amazon	90	60
1429	135f. Japanese crested ibis	1·25	1·00
1430	200f. California condor	1·90	1·50

1996. Fungi. Multicoloured.
1432	40f. Type **451**	35	20
1433	50f. "Psilocybe zapotecorum"	35	20
1434	75f. "Psilocybe mexicana"	75	50
1435	100f. "Conocybe siligineoides"	90	60
1436	135f. "Psilocybe caerulescens mazatecorum"	1·25	1·00
1437	200f. "Psilocybe caerulescens nigripes"	1·90	1·50

452 Impala

1996. Mammals. Multicoloured.
1439	40f. Type **452**	35	20
1440	50f. Waterbuck	35	20
1441	75f. African buffalo	75	50
1442	100f. Blue wildebeest	90	60
1443	135f. Okapi	1·25	1·00
1444	200f. Greater kudu	1·90	1·40

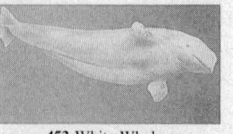

453 White Whale

1996. Marine Mammals. Multicoloured.
1445	40f. Type **453**	35	20
1446	50f. Bottle-nosed dolphin	35	20
1447	75f. Blue whale	75	50
1448	100f. "Eubalaena australis"	90	60
1449	135f. "Gramphidelphis griseus"	1·25	1·00
1450	200f. Killer whale	1·90	1·40

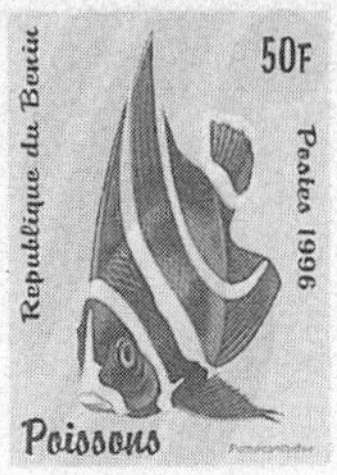

454 Grey Angelfish

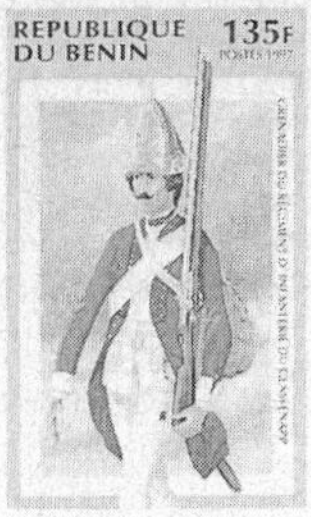

455 Grenadier, Glassenapps Regiment

1996. Fishes. Multicoloured.

1451	50f. Type **454**	10	10
1452	75f. Sail-finned tang (horiz)	15	10
1453	100f. Golden trevally (horiz)	20	10
1454	135f. Pyramid butterflyfish (horiz)	25	15
1455	200f. Racoon butterflyfish (horiz)	40	20

1996. Arms. Dated "1996".

1458	**430**	100f. multicoloured	95	40

1996. Stamps of Benin variously surch.

1469	**311**	15f. on 185f. mult (postage)		
1470	**379**	25f. on 175f. mult		
1473	**359**	50f. on 220f. green (1104)		
1479	**414**	150f. on 190f. mult		
1480	**415**	150f. on 190f. mult		
1484	**412**	250f. on 1000f. mult		
1494	**193**	40f. on 210f. red, brown and green (air)		
1495	–	40f. on 210f. purple, blue and yellow (792)		
1499	–	150f. on 500f. red, ultramarine and green (657)		

1996. Stamps of Dahomey variously optd or surch. (a) **Republique de Benin** (1510, 1516, 1519, 1522, 1526/9, 1535, 1544, 1556, 1558 and 1568) or **REPUBLIQUE DU BENIN** (others).

1510	–	35f. on 85f. brown, orange and green (493) (postage)		
1511	–	125f. on 100f. violet, red and black (510)		
1516	**85**	150f. on 30f. mult		
1519	**113**	150f. on 40f. red, brown and green		
1522	–	150f. on 45f. mult (597)		
1526	–	35f. on 100f. deep blue and blue (326) (air)		
1527	–	35f. on 100f. on 200f. multicoloured (409)		
1528	–	35f. on 125f. green, blue and light blue (553)		
1529	–	35f. on 300f. brown, red and blue (591)		
1535	–	150f. multicoloured (527)		
1544	**112**	150f. on 40f. multicoloured		
1556	–	150f. on 110f. mult (386)		
1558	–	150f. on 120f. mult (404)		
1568	–	200f. on 500f. mult (252)		

(b) **DU BENIN**.

1578		35f. on 125f. brown and green (540) (air)		
1579		125f. on 65f. mult (465)		
1580	**168**	135f. on 35f. mult		

(c) **BENIN**.

1587	**68**	150f. on 30f. mult (post)		
1591		25f. on 85f. mult (600) (air)		

1997. Military Uniforms. Multicoloured.

1600	135f. Type **455**	35	20
1601	150f. Officer, Von Groben's Regiment	35	20
1602	200f. Private, Dohna's Regiment	75	50
1603	270f. Artilleryman	90	60
1604	300f. Cavalry trooper	1·25	1·00
1605	400f. Trooper, Mollendorf's Dragoons	1·90	1·40

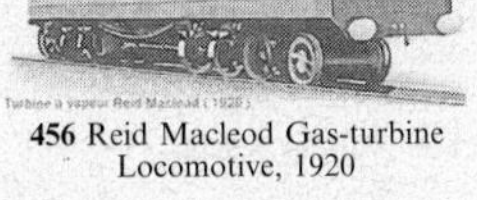

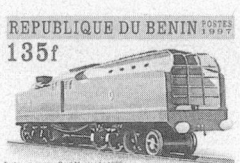

456 Reid Macleod Gas-turbine Locomotive, 1920

1997. Railway Locomotives. Multicoloured.

1607	135f. Type **456**	25	15
1608	150f. Class O5 steam locomotive, 1935, Germany	30	15
1609	200f. Locomotive "Silver Fox", Great Britain	40	20
1610	270f. Class "Merchant Navy" locomotive, 1941, Great Britain	55	30
1611	300f. Diesel locomotive, 1960, Denmark	60	30
1612	400f. GM Type diesel locomotive, 1960	80	40

No. 1607 is wrongly inscr "Reid Maclead 1920".

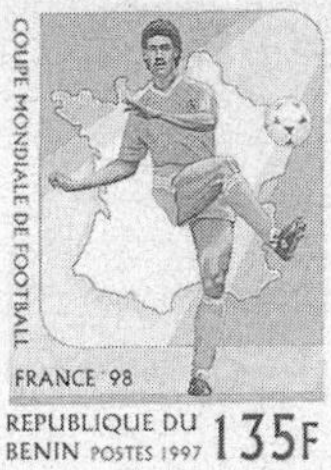

457 Footballer and Map

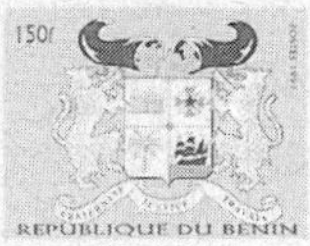

458 Arms

1997. World Cup Football Championship, France (1998) (2nd issue).

1614	**457**	135f. multicoloured	35	20
1615	–	150f. multicoloured	35	20
1616	–	200f. multicoloured	75	50
1617	–	270f. multicoloured	90	60
1618	–	300f. mult (horiz)	1·25	1·00
1619	–	400f. mult (horiz)	1·90	1·50

DESIGNS: 150f. to 400f. Each showing map of France and player.

1997. T **430** redrawn as T **458**. Dated "1997".

1621	**458**	135f. multicoloured	40	25
1622		150f. multicoloured	70	35
1623		200f. multicoloured	90	50

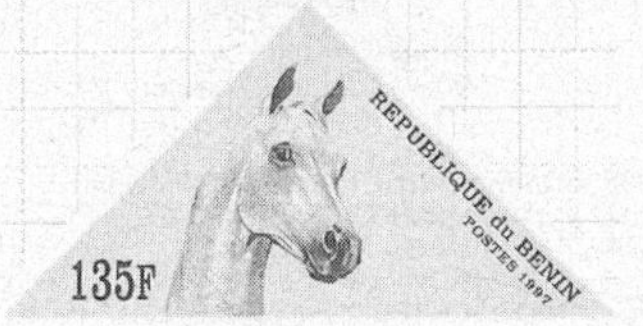

459 Horse's Head

1997. Horses. Multicoloured.

1624	135f. Type **459**	40	25
1625	150f. Bay horse	55	35
1626	200f. Chestnut horse looking forward	70	45
1627	270f. Chestnut horse looking backwards	80	60
1628	300f. Black horse	1·00	70
1629	400f. Profile of horse	1·25	85

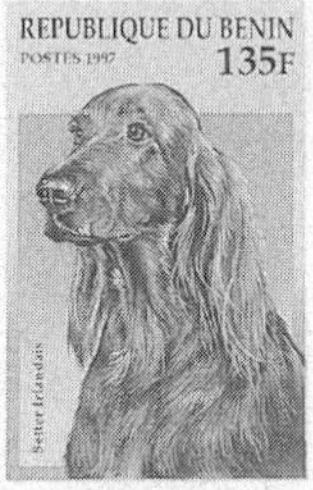

460 Irish Setter

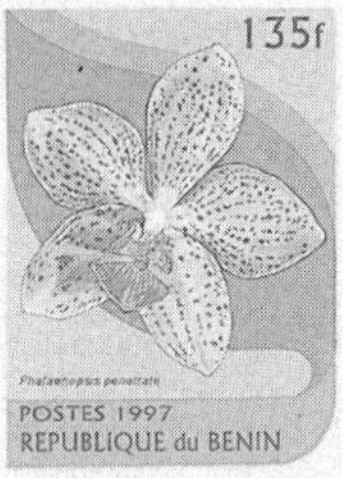

461 "Phalaenopsis penetrate"

1997. Dogs. Multicoloured.

1631	135f. Type **460**	40	25
1632	150f. Saluki	55	35
1633	200f. Dobermann pinscher	70	45
1634	270f. Siberian husky	80	60
1635	300f. Basenji	1·00	90
1636	400f. Boxer	1·25	85

1997. Orchids. Multicoloured.

1638	135f. Type **461**	40	25
1639	150f. "Phalaenopsis" "Golden Sands"	55	35
1640	200f. "Phalaenopsis" "Sun Spots"	70	45
1641	270f. "Phalaenopsis fuscata"	80	60
1642	300f. "Phalaenopsis christi floyd"	1·00	70
1643	400f. "Phalaenopsis cayanne"	1·25	85

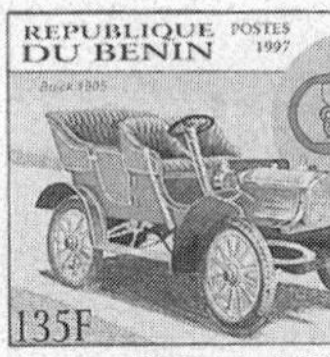

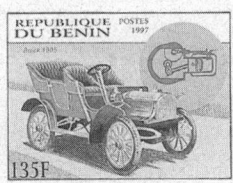

462 Buick, 1905

1997. Motor Cars. Multicoloured.

1645	135f. Type **462**	40	25
1646	150f. Ford, 1903	55	35
1647	200f. Stanley, 1913	70	45
1648	270f. Stoddar-Dayton, 1911	80	60
1649	300f. Cadillac, 1934	1·00	70
1650	400f. Cadillac, 1931	1·25	85

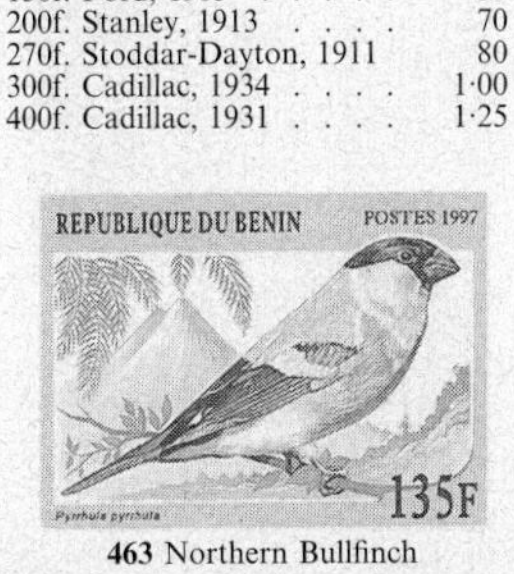

463 Northern Bullfinch

1997. Birds. Multicoloured.

1652	135f. Type **463**	40	25
1653	150f. Spruce siskin	50	35
1654	200f. Ring ousel	70	50
1655	270f. Crested tit	90	70
1656	300f. Spotted nutcracker	1·00	75
1657	400f. Nightingale	1·50	1·00

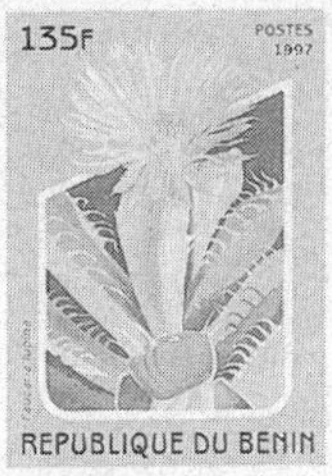

464 "Faucaria lupina"

1997. Cacti. Multicoloured.

1659	135f. Type **464**	40	25
1660	150f. "Conophytum bilobun"	50	35
1661	200f. "Lithops aucampiae"	70	50
1662	270f. "Lithops helmutii"	90	70
1663	300f. "Stapelia grandiflora"	1·00	75
1664	400f. "Lithops fulviceps"	1·50	1·00

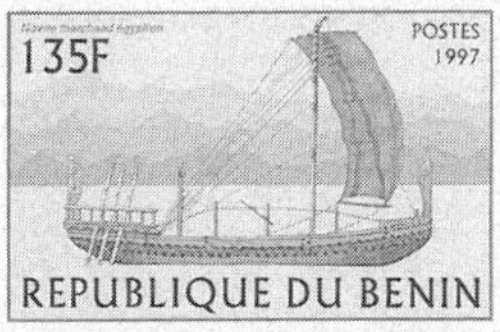

465 Egyptian Merchant Ship

1997. Ancient Sailing Ships. Multicoloured.

1666	135f. Type **465**	45	30
1667	150f. Greek merchant ship	45	30
1668	200f. Phoenician galley	75	50
1669	270f. Roman merchant ship	1·00	60
1670	300f. Norman knarr	1·10	70
1671	400f. Mediterranean sailing ship	1·50	90

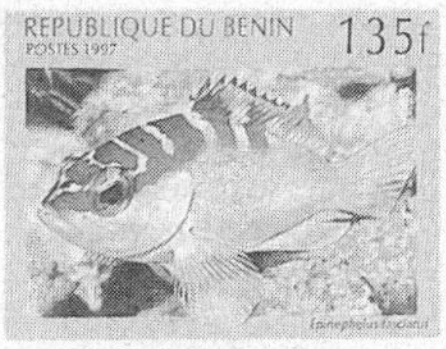

466 Black-tipped Grouper

1997. Fishes. Multicoloured.

1673	135f. Type **466**	30	15
1674	150f. Cardinal fish	30	15
1675	200f. Indo-Pacific humpheaded parrotfish	45	25
1676	270f. Regal angelfish	60	30
1677	300f. Wrasse	65	35
1678	400f. Hawkfish	85	45

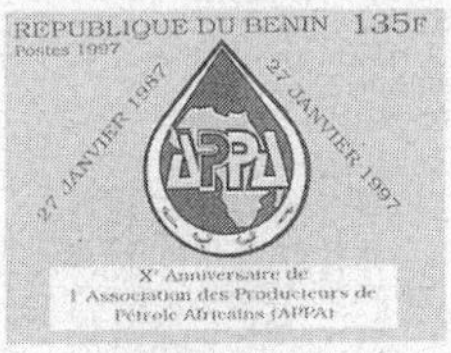

467 Emblem

1997. 10th Anniv of African Petroleum Producers' Association.

1680	**467**	135f. multicoloured	50	25
1681		200f. multicoloured	85	35
1682		300f. multicoloured	1·10	50
1683		500f. multicoloured	1·75	70

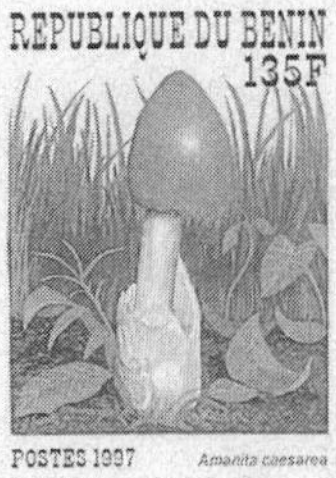

468 Caesar's Mushroom

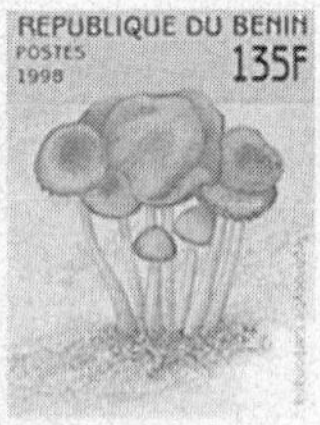

470 "Tephrocybe carbonaria"

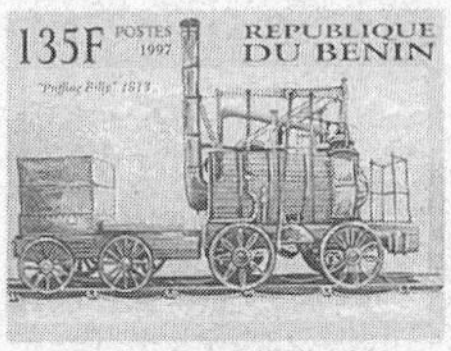

469 "Puffing Billy", 1813

1997. Fungi. Multicoloured.

1684	135f. Type **468**	40	25
1685	150f. Slimy-banded cort	50	35
1686	200f. "Amanita bisporigera"	70	50
1687	270f. The blusher	90	70
1688	300f. Cracked green russula	1·00	75
1689	400f. Strangulated amanita	1·50	1·00

1997. Steam Railway Locomotives. Mult.

1691	135f. Type **469**	30	15
1692	150f. "Rocket", 1829	30	15
1693	200f. "Royal George", 1827	45	25
1694	270f. "Novelty", 1829	60	30
1695	300f. "Locomotion", 1825 (vert)	65	35
1696	400f. "Sans Pareil", 1829 (vert)	85	45

1998. Fungi. Multicoloured.

1698	135f. Type **470**	25	15
1699	150f. Butter mushroom	30	15
1700	200f. Oyster fungus	40	20
1701	270f. "Hohenbuehelia geogenia"	50	25
1702	300f. Bitter bolete	60	30
1703	400f. "Lepiota leucothites"	80	40

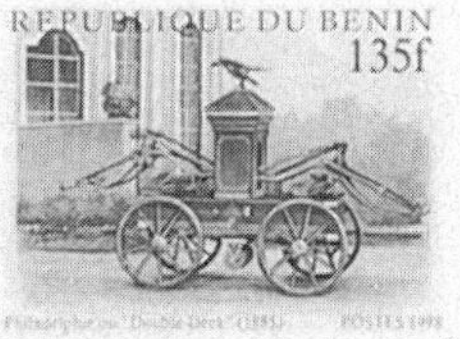

471 Philadelphia or "Double Deck", 1885

1998. Fire Engines. Multicoloured.

1705	135f. Type **471**	25	15
1706	150f. "Veteran", 1850	30	15
1707	200f. Merryweather, 1894	40	20
1708	270f. 19 th-century Hippomobile	50	25
1709	300f. Jeep "Willy", 1948	60	30
1710	400f. Chevrolet 6400	80	40

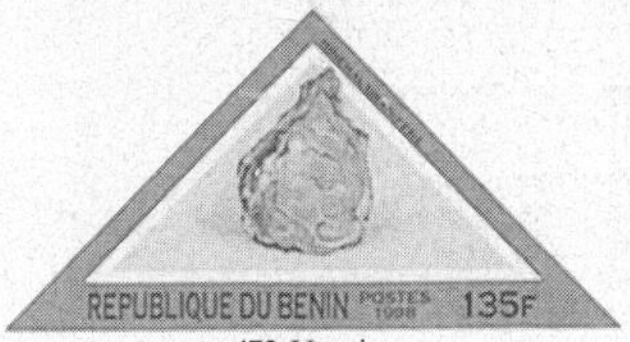

472 Uranite

1998. Minerals. Multicoloured.

1712	135f. Type **472**	25	15
1713	150f. Quartz	30	15
1714	200f. Aragonite	40	20
1715	270f. Malachite	50	25
1716	300f. Turquoise	60	30
1717	400f. Corundum	80	40

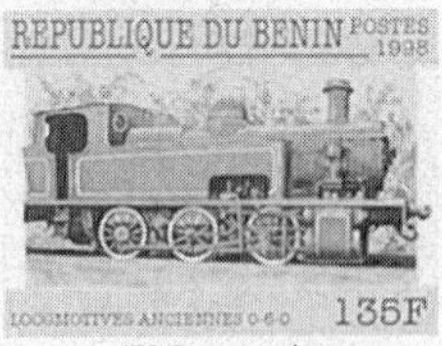

473 Locomotive

1998. Steam Railway Locomotives. Multicoloured.

1719	135f. Type **473**	25	15
1720	150f. Green locomotive	30	15
1721	200f. Brown locomotive	40	20
1722	270f. Lilac locomotive	50	25
1723	300f. Toledo Furnace Co No. 1	60	30
1724	400f. No. 1 "Helvetia"	80	40

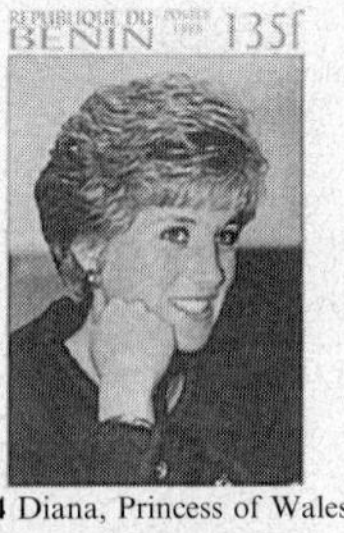

474 Diana, Princess of Wales

1998. 1st Death Anniv of Diana, Princess of Wales. Multicoloured.

1726	135f. Type **474**	25	15
1727	150f. Wearing pink dress	25	15
1728	200f. Wearing beige jacket	35	20
1729	270f. Wearing white jacket with revers	50	25
1730	300f. Making speech	55	30
1731	400f. Wearing collarless single-breasted white jacket	70	35
1732	500f. Wearing red jacket	90	45
1733	600f. Wearing black jacket	1·10	55
1734	700f. Wearing double-breasted white jacket	1·25	65

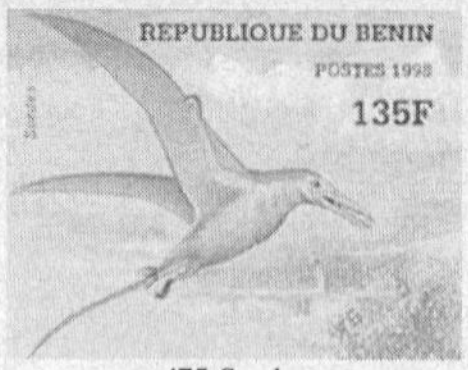

475 Sordes

1998. Prehistoric Animals. Multicoloured.

1735	135f. Type **475**	25	15
1736	150f. Scaphognatus	25	15
1737	200f. Dsungaripterus	35	20
1738	270f. Brontosaurus	50	25
1739	300f. Diplodocus	55	30
1740	400f. Coelurus and baryonyx	70	35
1741	500f. Kronosaurus and ichthyosaurus	90	45
1742	600f. Ceratosaurus	1·10	55
1743	700f. Yangchuansaurus	1·25	65

Nos. 1735/43 were issued together, se-tenant, forming a composite design.

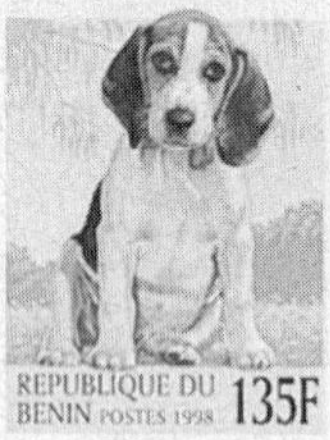

476 Beagle

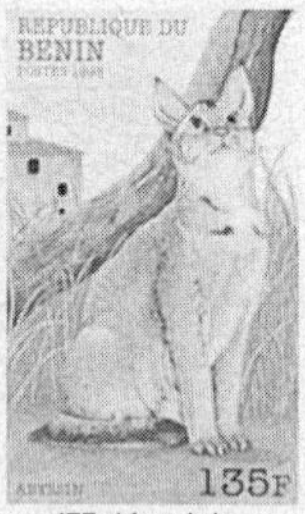

477 Abyssinian

1998. Dogs. Multicoloured.

1744	135f. Type **476**	25	15
1745	150f. Dalmatians	25	15
1746	200f. Dachshund	35	20
1747	270f. Cairn terrier	50	25
1748	300f. Shih-tzus	55	30
1749	400f. Pug	70	35

1998. Cats. Multicoloured.

1751	135f. Type **477**	25	15
1752	150f. Striped silver tabby	25	15
1753	200f. Siamese	35	20
1754	270f. Red tabby (horiz)	50	25
1755	300f. Wild cat (horiz)	55	30
1756	400f. Manx (horiz)	70	35

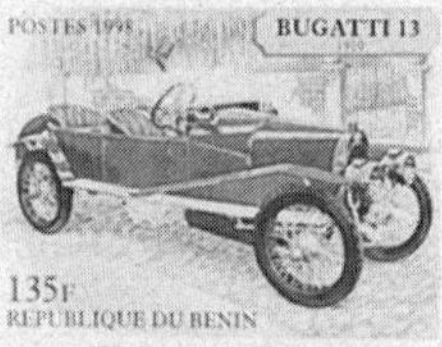

478 Bugatti 13, 1910

1998. Motor Cars. Multicoloured.

1758	135f. Type **478**	25	15
1759	150f. Clement, 1903	25	15
1760	200f. Stutz Bearcat, 1914	35	20
1761	270f. Darracq, 1907	50	25
1762	300f. Napier, 1913	55	30
1763	400f. Pierce-Arrow, 1911	70	35

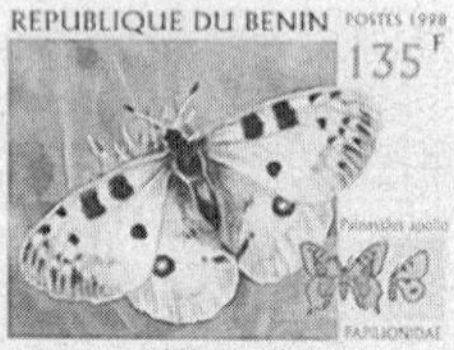

479 Apollo

1998. Butterflies. Multicoloured.

1765	135f. Type **479**	25	15
1766	150f. Orange-tip	25	15
1767	200f. Camberwell beauty	35	20
1768	250f. Speckled wood	40	20
1769	300f. Purple-edged copper	55	30
1770	400f. Chequered skipper	70	35

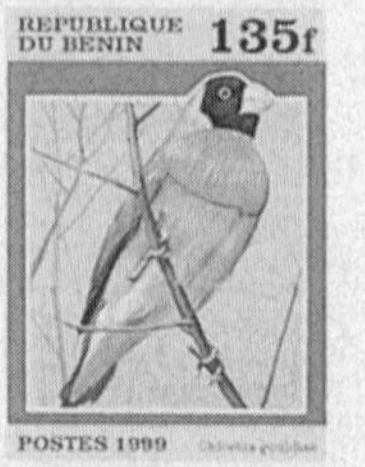

480 Gouldian Finch

1999. Birds. Multicoloured.

1772	135f. Type **480**	25	15
1773	150f. Saffron finch	25	15
1774	200f. Red-billed quelea	35	20
1775	270f. Golden bishop	50	25
1776	300f. Red-crested cardinal	55	30
1777	400f. Golden-breasted bunting	70	35

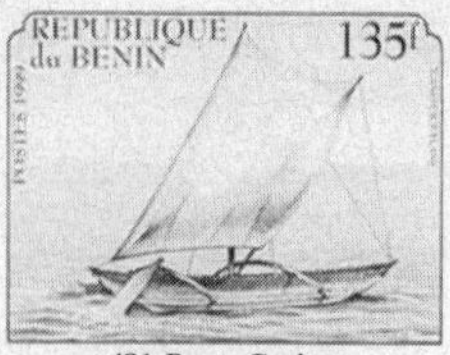

481 Boat, Ceylon

1999. Sailing Boats. Multicoloured.

1779	135f. Type **481**	25	15
1780	150f. Tanka-Tim, Canton, Macao	25	15
1781	200f. Sampan, Hong Kong	35	20
1782	270f. Outrigger sailing canoe, Polynesia	50	25
1783	300f. Junk, Japan	55	30
1784	400f. Dacca-Pulwar, Bengal	70	35

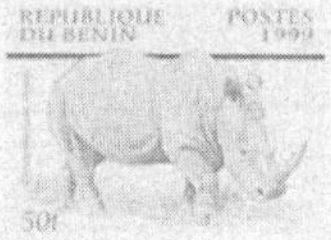

482 White Rhinoceros

1999. Mammals.

1786	**482** 50f. grey	10	10
1787	– 100f. violet	20	10
1788	– 135f. green	25	15
1789	– 135f. black	25	15
1790	– 150f. blue	25	15
1791	– 150f. green	25	15
1792	– 200f. blue	35	20
1793	– 200f. brown	35	20
1794	– 300f. brown	55	25
1795	– 300f. red	55	35
1796	– 400f. brown	70	35
1797	– 500f. brown	90	45

DESIGNS: No. 1787, Sable antelope; 1788, Warthog (*Phacochoerus aethiopicus*); 1789, Brown hyena (*Hyaena brunnea*); 1790, Eastern black-and-white colobus (*Colobus guereza*); 1791, Hippopotamus (*Hippopotamus amphibius*); 1792, Mountain zebra (*Equus zebra*); 1793, African buffalo (*Synceros caffer*) (wrongly inscr "Cyncerus"); 1794, Lion (*Panthera leo*); 1795, Cheetah (*Acinonyx jubatus*); 1796, Hunting dog; 1797, Potto.

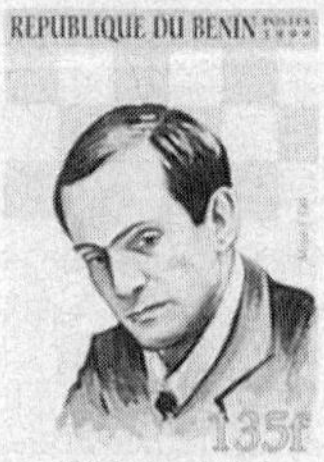

483 Mikhail Tal

1999. Chess Players. Multicoloured.

1798	135f. Type **483**	25	15
1799	150f. Emanuel Lasker	25	15
1800	200f. Jose Raul Capablanca	35	20
1801	270f. Aleksandr Alekhine	50	25
1802	300f. Max Euwe	55	25
1803	400f. Mikhail Botvinnik	70	35

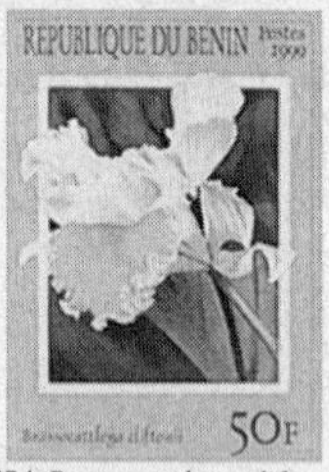

484 *Brassocattleya cliftonii*

1999. Orchids. Multicoloured.

1805	50f. Type **484**	10	10
1806	100f. Wilsonara	20	10
1807	150f. *Cypripedium paeony*	25	15
1808	300f. *Cymbidium babylon*	55	25
1809	400f. Cattleya	70	35
1810	500f. *Miltonia minx*	90	45

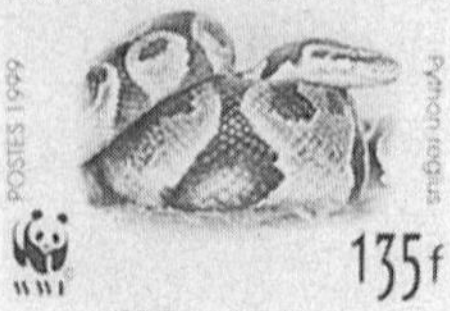

485 Royal Python

1999. Snakes. Multicoloured.

1812	135f. Type **485**	25	15
1813	150f. Royal python (different)	25	15
1814	200f. African rock python	35	20
1815	2000f. Head of African rock python	3·50	1·75

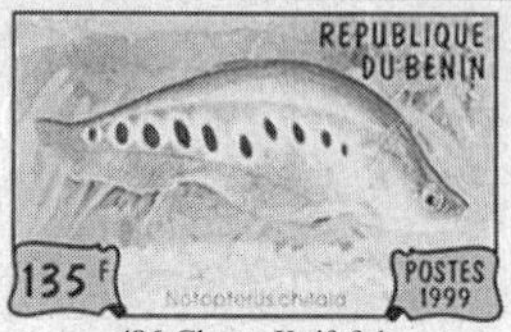

486 Clown Knifefish

1999. Fishes. Multicoloured.

1816	135f. Type **486**	25	15
1817	150f. Puntius filamentosus	25	15
1818	200f. *Epalzeorhynchos bicolor*	35	20
1819	270f. Spotted rasbora	50	25
1820	300f. Tigernander	55	25
1821	400f. Siamese fighting fish	70	35

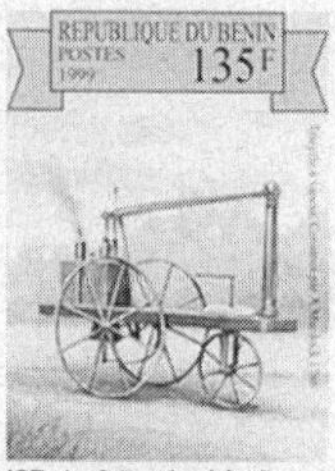

487 A. Murdock's Steam Tricycle, 1786

1999. Steam-powered Vehicles. Multicoloured.

1823	135f. Type **487**	25	15
1824	150f. Richard Trevithick's locomotive, 1800	25	15
1825	200f. Trevithick's locomotive, 1803	35	20
1826	270f. John Blenkinsop's locomotive, 1811	50	25
1827	300f. Foster and Rastik's *Stourbridge Lion*, 1829	55	30
1828	400f. Peter Cooper's *Tom Thumb*, 1829	70	35

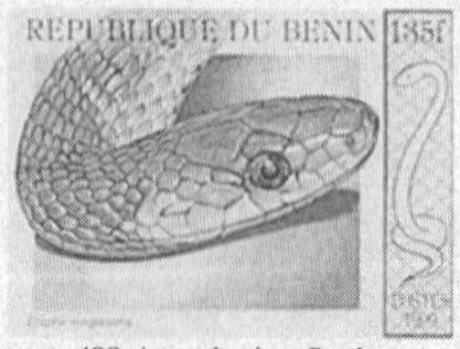

488 Aesculapian Snake

1999. Snakes. Multicoloured.

1830	135f. Type **488**	25	15
1831	150f. Common pine snake	25	15
1832	200f. Grass snake	35	20
1833	270f. Green whip snake	50	25
1834	300f. Jamaica boa	55	30
1835	400f. Diamond-back rattlesnake	70	35

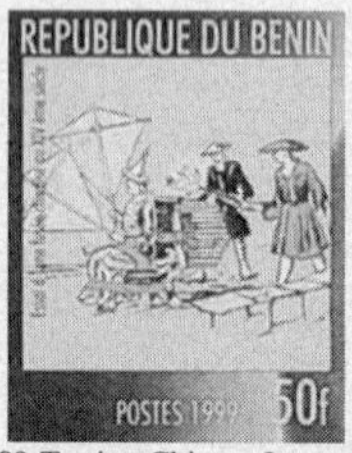

489 Testing Chinese Lantern (14th-century)

1999. "China 1999" International Stamp Exhibition, Peking. Multicoloured.

1837	50f. Type **486**	10	10
1838	100f. Satellite launching centre, Jiuquan	20	10
1839	135f. DFH-3 communications satellite	25	15
1840	150f. Satellite launch	25	15
1841	200f. Launch of *Long March* (rocket)	35	20
1842	300f. *Yuan Wang* (passenger ferry) at sea	55	30
1843	400f. Dish aerial	70	35
1844	500f. Items of space post	90	45

Nos. 1837/44 were issued together, se-tenant, with the backgrounds forming a composite design of the Earth.

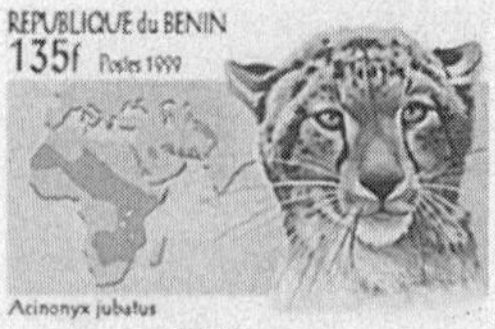

490 Cheetah

1999. Big Cats. Multicoloured.

1845	135f. Type **490**	25	15
1846	150f. Jaguar	25	15
1847	200f. Snow leopard	35	20
1848	270f. Leopard	50	25
1849	300f. Puma	55	25
1850	400f. Tiger	70	35

PARCEL POST STAMPS

1982. Optd or surch **Colis Postaux**.

P871	– 100f. multicoloured (No. 779) (postage)	75	40
P872	**256** 100f. on 150f. mult	75	40
P873	– 300f. mult (No. 797)	2·25	1·10
P874	**260** 1000f. multicoloured	6·75	3·25
P875	**274** 5000f. on 500f. mult (air)	35·00	17·00

1988. No. 543 of Dahomey surch **Republique Populaire du Benin colis postaux**.

P1089	**174** 5f. on 40f. multicoloured (postage)		
P1093	– 500f. on 200f. mult	3·00	1·90
P1092	– 300f. on 200f. blue, yellow & brown (air)		

POSTAGE DUE STAMPS

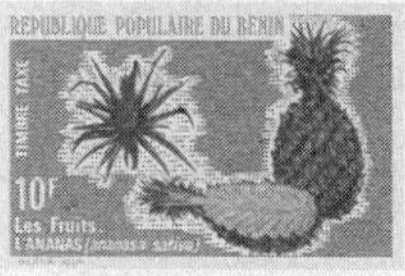

D **233** Pineapples

1978. Fruits. Multicoloured.

D716	10f. Type D **233**	30	30
D717	20f. Cashew nuts (vert)	50	40
D718	40f. Oranges	85	70
D719	50f. Breadfruit	1·10	80

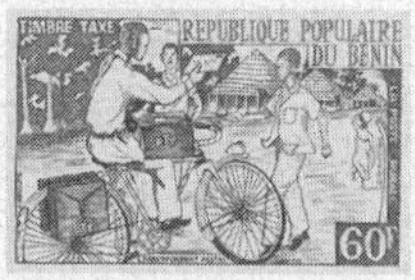

D **234** Village Postman on Bicycle

1978. Rural Post.

D720	D **234** 60f. brown, grn & red	95	60
D721	– 80f. blue, brn & red	1·10	75

DESIGN: 80f. River village and postman in canoe.

BERGEDORF Pt. 7

A German city on the Elbe, governed by Hamburg and Lubeck until 1867 when it was purchased by the former. In 1868 became part of North German Confederation.

16 schilling = 1 Hamburg mark.

1

1861. Various sizes. Imperf.

1	**1** ½s. black on lilac	£375	
2	½s. black on blue	32·00	£550
4	1s. black on white	32·00	£250
5	1½s. black on yellow	15·00	£950
6	3s. black on red	£550	
7	3s. blue on red	18·00	£1200
8	4s. black on brown	18·00	£1600

BERMUDA Pt. 1

A group of islands in the W. Atlantic, E. of N. Carolina. Usually regarded by collectors as part of the Br. W. Indies group, though this is not strictly correct.

1865. 12 pence = 1 shilling;
20 shillings = 1 pound.
1970. 100 cents = 1 dollar (U.S.).

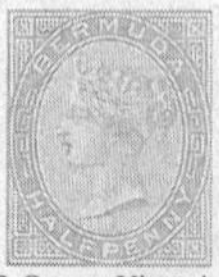

9 Queen Victoria

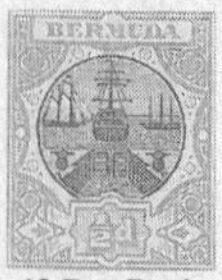

13 Dry Dock

1865. Portrait. Various frames.

19	**9** ½d. stone	2·75	4·25
21a	½d. green	2·50	80
24a	1d. red	9·00	20
25	2d. blue	55·00	3·50
26a	2d. purple	3·50	1·50
27b	2½d. blue	5·00	40
10	3d. yellow	£170	60·00
28	3d. grey	22·00	6·50
20	4d. red	17·00	1·75
28a	4d. brown	27·00	48·00
7	6d. mauve	23·00	12·00
11	1s. green	11·00	£120
29b	1s. brown	13·00	16·00

1874. Surch in words.

15	**9** 1d. on 2d. blue	£700	£375

16		1d. on 3d. yellow	£450	£350
17		1d. on 1s. green	£500	£250
12		3d. on 1d. red	£15000	
14		3d. on 1s. green	£1400	£650

1901. Surch **ONE FARTHING** and bar.

30	**9**	¼d. on 1s. grey	1·50	50

1902.

34	**13**	¼d. brown and violet	1·75	1·50
31		½d. black and green	12·00	1·50
36		½d. green	13·00	2·75
32		1d. brown and red	8·00	10
38		1d. red	18·00	10
39		2d. grey and orange	7·50	11·00
40		2½d. brown and blue	15·00	7·00
41		2½d. blue	12·00	6·50
33		3d. mauve and green	3·00	2·00
42		4d. blue and brown	3·00	16·00

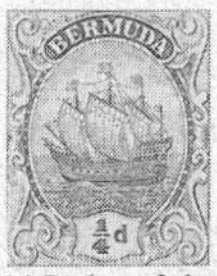

14 Badge of the Colony

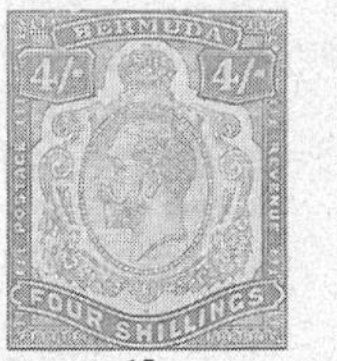

15

1910.

44a	**14**	¼d. brown	60	1·50
77		½d. green	1·50	15
78d		1d. red	10·00	80
79b		1½d. brown	9·00	35
80		2d. grey	1·50	1·50
82b		2½d. blue	1·75	75
81a		2½d. green	1·75	1·50
84		3d. purple on yellow	4·00	1·00
83		3d. blue	16·00	26·00
85		4d. red on yellow	2·00	1·00
86		6d. purple	1·00	80
51		1s. black on green	4·00	4·00
51b	**15**	2s. purple and blue on blue	18·00	50·00
52		2s.6d. black and red on blue	28·00	80·00
52b		4s. black and red	60·00	£160
53c		5s. green and red on yellow	45·00	90·00
92		10s. green and red on green	£120	£250
93		12s.6d. black and orange	£250	£350
55		£1 purple and black on red	£325	£550

1918. Optd **WAR TAX**.

56	**14**	1d. red	50	1·00

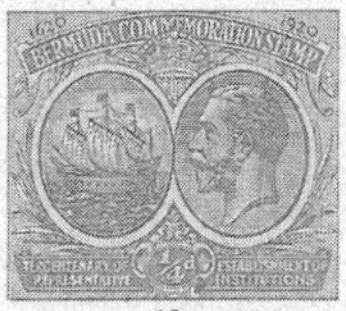

18

1920. Tercentenary of Representative Institutions.
(a) 1st Issue.

59	**18**	¼d. brown	3·25	17·00
60		½d. green	3·25	9·00
65		1d. red	3·75	30
61		2d. grey	13·00	38·00
66		2½d. blue	13·00	11·00
62		3d. purple on yellow	12·00	35·00
63		4d. black and red on yellow	12·00	35·00
67		6d. purple	26·00	65·00
64		1s. black on green	16·00	48·00

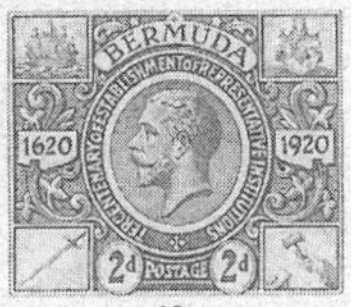

19

(b) 2nd Issue.

74	**19**	¼d. brown	1·25	3·75
75		½d. green	2·75	6·00
76		1d. red	2·50	35
68		2d. grey	5·50	28·00
69		2½d. blue	9·00	3·00
70		3d. purple on yellow	5·50	16·00
71		4d. red on yellow	16·00	21·00
72		6d. purple	12·00	48·00
73		1s. black on green	23·00	48·00

1935. Silver Jubilee. As T **13** of Antigua.

94		1d. blue and red	45	60
95		1½d. blue and grey	70	2·25
96		2½d. brown and blue	1·40	1·00
97		1s. grey and purple	15·00	24·00

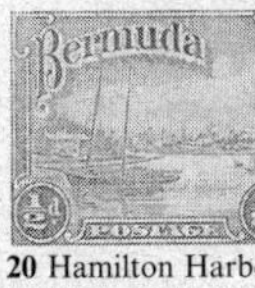

20 Hamilton Harbour

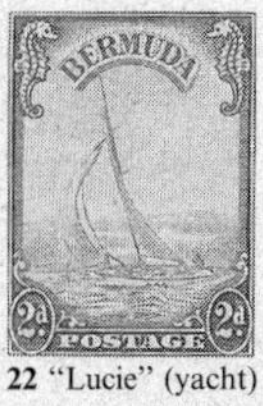

22 "Lucie" (yacht)

1936.

98	**20**	½d. green	10	10
99	–	1d. black and red	30	30
100	–	1½d. black and brown	1·00	50
101	**22**	2d. black and blue	5·00	2·00
102	–	2½d. blue	1·00	25
103	–	3d. black and red	2·75	1·40
104	–	6d. red and violet	80	10
105	–	1s. green	5·00	8·50
106	**20**	1s.6d. brown	50	10

DESIGNS—HORIZ: 1d., 1½d. South Shore, near Spanish Rock; 3d. Point House, Warwick Parish. VERT: 2½d., 1s. Grape Bay, Paget Parish; 6d. House at Par-la-Ville, Hamilton.

The 1d., 1½d., 2½d. and 1s. values include a portrait of King George V.

1937. Coronation. As T **2** of Aden.

107		1d. red	50	50
108		1½d. brown	60	1·50
109		2½d. blue	70	1·50

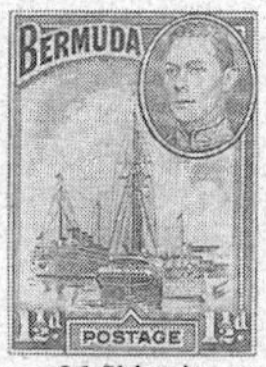

26 Ships in Hamilton Harbour

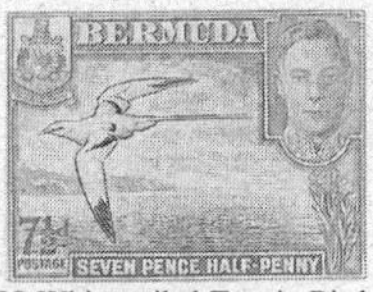

28 White-tailed Tropic Bird, Arms of Bermuda and Native Flower

1938.

110	**26**	1d. black and red	85	20
111b		1½d. blue and brown	2·25	35
112	**22**	2d. blue and brown	45·00	8·50
112a		2d. blue and red	1·50	1·00
113	–	2½d. blue and deep blue	11·00	1·25
113b	–	2½d. blue and black	2·75	1·50
114	–	3d. black and red	18·00	2·50
114a	–	3d. black and blue	1·75	40
114c	**28**	7½d. black, blue and green	4·50	2·75
115	–	1s. green	2·00	50

DESIGNS—VERT: 3d. St. David's Lighthouse. The 2½d. and 1s. are as 1935, but with King George VI portrait.

1938. As T **15**, but King George VI portrait.

116c		2s. purple and blue on blue	7·00	1·50
117d		2s.6d. black and red on blue	16·00	12·00
118f		5s. green and red on yellow	23·00	20·00
119e		10s. green and red on green	35·00	42·00
120b		12s.6d. grey and orange	95·00	50·00
121d		£1 purple and black on red	48·00	75·00

1940. Surch **HALF PENNY**.

122	**26**	½d. on 1d. black and red	40	45

1946. Victory. As T **9** of Aden.

123		1½d. brown	15	15
124		3d. blue	15	15

1948. Silver Wedding. As T **10/11** of Aden.

125		1½d. brown	30	50
126		£1 red	40·00	48·00

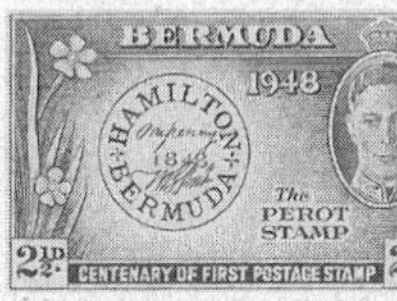

31 Postmaster Perot's Stamp

1949. Centenary of Postmaster Perot's Stamp.

127	**31**	2½d. blue and brown	15	15
128		3d. black and blue	15	15
129		6d. violet and green	15	15

1949. U.P.U. As T **20/23** of Antigua.

130		2½d. black	30	75
131		3d. blue	1·40	1·25
132		6d. purple	40	75
133		1s. green	40	75

1953. Coronation. As T **13** of Aden.

134		1½d. black and blue	60	15

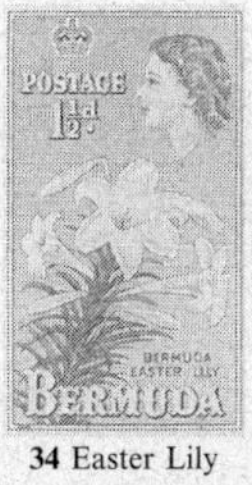

34 Easter Lily

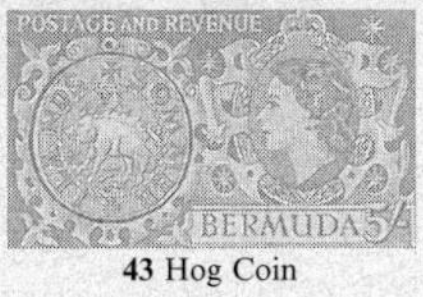

43 Hog Coin

1953.

135a	–	½d. olive	40	60
136	–	1d. black and red	1·50	50
137	**34**	1½d. green	30	10
138	–	2d. blue and red	50	40
139	–	2½d. red	2·00	50
140	–	3d. purple	30	10
141	–	4d. black and blue	30	40
142	–	4½d. green	1·25	1·00
143	–	6d. black and turquoise	5·50	60
156	–	6d. black and mauve	70	15
143a	–	8d. black and red	2·50	30
143b	–	9d. violet	7·50	2·50
144	–	1s. orange	50	15
145	–	1s.3d. blue	3·50	30
146	–	2s. brown	4·00	85
147	–	2s.6d. red	4·50	45
148	**43**	5s. red	19·00	85
149	–	10s. blue	13·00	5·00
150	–	£1 multicoloured	25·00	21·00

DESIGNS—HORIZ: ½d. Easter lilies; 1d., 4d. Postmaster Perot's stamp; 2d. "Victory II" (racing dinghy); 2½d. Sir George Somers and "Sea Venture"; 3d., 1s.3d. Map of Bermuda; 4½d. 9d. "Sea Venture" (galleon), coin and Perot stamp; 6d. (No. 143), 8d. White-tailed tropic bird; 6d. (No. 156), Perot's Post Office; 1s. Early Bermuda coins; 2s. Arms of St. George's 10s. Obverse and reverse of hog coin; £1 Arms of Bermuda. VERT: 2s.6d. Warwick Fort; No. 156 commemorates the restoration and reopening of Perot's Post Office.

1953. Royal Visit. As No. 143a but inscr "ROYAL VISIT 1953".

151		6d. black and turquoise	50	20

1953. Three Power Talks. Nos. 140 and 145 optd **Three Power Talks December, 1953.**

152		3d. purple	10	10
153		1s.3d. blue	10	10

1956. 50th Anniv of United States-Bermuda Yacht Race. Nos. 143a and 145 optd **50TH ANNIVERSARY US – BERMUDA OCEAN RACE 1956.**

154		8d. black and red	20	45
155		1s.3d. blue	20	55

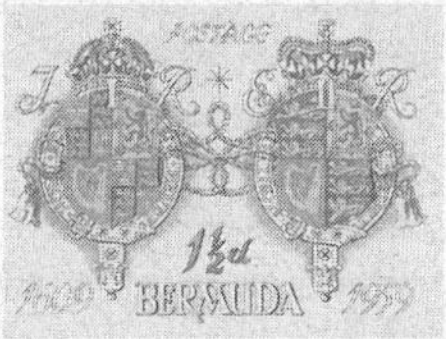

49 Arms of King James I and Queen Elizabeth II

1959. 350th Anniv of Settlement. Arms in red, yellow and blue. Frame colours given.

157	**49**	1½d. blue	25	10
158		3d. grey	30	50
159		4d. purple	35	55
160		8d. violet	35	15
161		9d. olive	35	1·25
162		1s.3d. brown	35	30

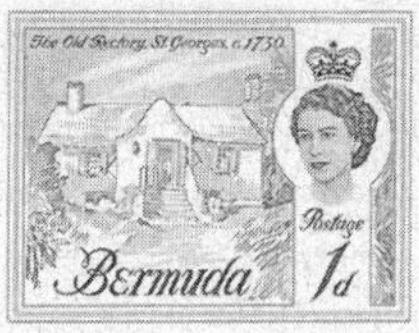

50 The Old Rectory, St George's, c. 1730

1962.

163	**50**	1d. purple, black and orange	10	60
164	–	2d. multicoloured	50	25
165	–	3d. brown and blue	10	10
166	–	4d. brown and mauve	20	40
167	–	5d. blue and red	1·00	2·50
168	–	6d. blue, green & lt blue	20	30
169	–	8d. blue, green and orange	30	35
170	–	9d. blue and brown	25	30
197	–	10d. violet and ochre	75	60
171	–	1s. multicoloured	20	10
172	–	1s.3d. lake, grey and bistre	75	15
173	–	1s.6d. violet and ochre	1·00	1·00
199	–	1s.6d. blue and red	2·25	50
200	–	2s. brown and orange	2·25	75
175	–	2s.3d. sepia and green	1·25	6·50
176	–	2s.6d. sepia, green & yell	55	50
177	–	5s. purple and green	1·25	1·50
178	–	10s. mauve, green and buff	4·25	6·50
179	–	£1 black, olive and orange	14·00	14·00

DESIGNS: 2d. Church of St. Peter, St. George's; 3d. Government House, 1892; 4d. The Cathedral. Hamilton, 1894; 5d., 1s.6d. (No. 199) H.M. Dockyard, 1811; 6d. Perot's Post Office, 1848; 8d. G.P.O., Hamilton, 1869; 9d. Library, Par-la-Ville; 10d., 1s.6d. (No. 173) Bermuda cottage, c. 1705; 1s. Christ Church, Warwick, 1719; 1s.3d. City Hall, Hamilton, 1960; 2s. Town of St. George; 2s.3d. Bermuda house, c. 1710; 2s.6d. Bermuda house, early 18th century; 5s. Colonial Secretariat, 1833; 10s. Old Post Office, Somerset, 1890; £1 The House of Assembly, 1815.

1963. Freedom from Hunger. As T **28** of Aden.

180		1s.3d. sepia	60	40

1963. Centenary of Red Cross. As T **33** of Antigua.

181		3d. red and black	50	25
182		1s.3d. red and blue	1·25	2·50

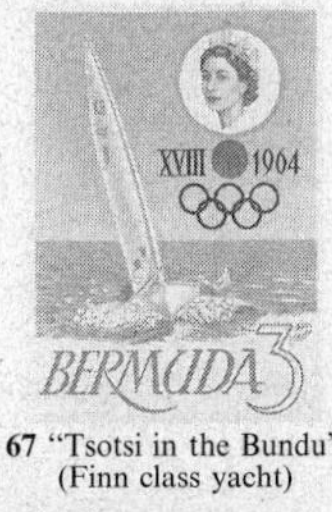

67 "Tsotsi in the Bundu" (Finn class yacht)

1964. Olympic Games, Tokyo.

183	**67**	3d. red, violet and blue	10	10

1965. Centenary of I.T.U. As T **36** of Antigua.

184		3d. blue and green	35	25
185		2s. yellow and blue	65	1·25

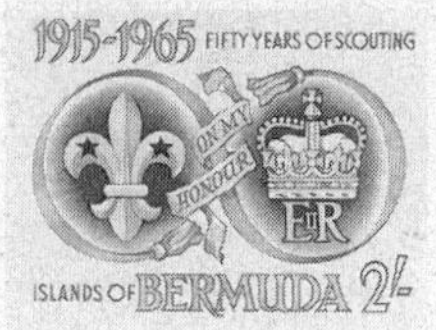

68 Scout Badge and St. Edward's Crown

1965. 50th Anniv of Bermuda Boy Scouts Association.

186	**68**	2s. multicoloured	50	50

1965. I.C.Y. As T **37** of Antigua.

187		4d. purple and turquoise	50	20
188		2s.6d. green and lavender	75	80

1966. Churchill Commemoration. As T **38** of Antigua.

189		3d. blue	25	20
190		6d. green	50	70
191		10d. brown	70	75
192		1s.3d. violet	80	2·50

1966. World Cup Football Championship. As T **40** of Antigua.

193		10d. multicoloured	60	15
194		2s.6d. multicoloured	90	1·25

1966. 20th Anniv of U.N.E.S.C.O. As T **54/56** of Antigua.

201		4d. multicoloured	45	15
202		1s.3d. yellow, violet and olive	1·00	50
203		2s. black, purple and orange	1·60	1·10

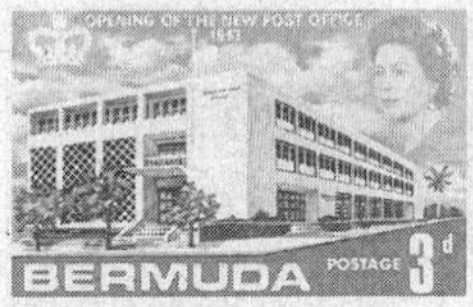

69 G.P.O. Building

1967. Opening of New General Post Office.

204	**69**	3d. multicoloured	10	10
205		1s. multicoloured	10	10
206		1s.6d. multicoloured	20	25
207		2s.6d. multicoloured	20	70

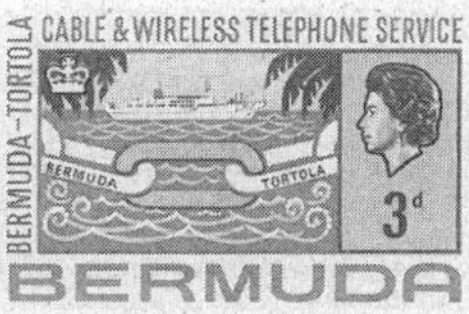

70 "Mercury" (cable ship) and Chain Links

1967. Inauguration of Bermuda–Tortola Telephone Service. Multicoloured.

208		3d. Type **70**	15	10
209		1s. Map, telephone and microphone	25	10
210		1s.6d. Telecommunications media	25	25
211		2s.6d. "Mercury" (cable ship) and marine fauna	40	70

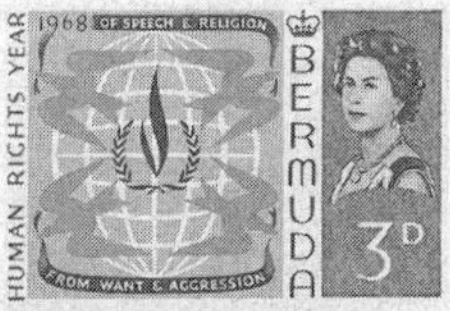

74 Human Rights Emblem and Doves

1968. Human Rights Year.

212	**74**	3d. indigo, blue and green	10	10
213		1s. brown, blue and light blue	10	10
214		1s.6d. black, blue and red	10	15
215		2s.6d. green, blue and yellow	15	25

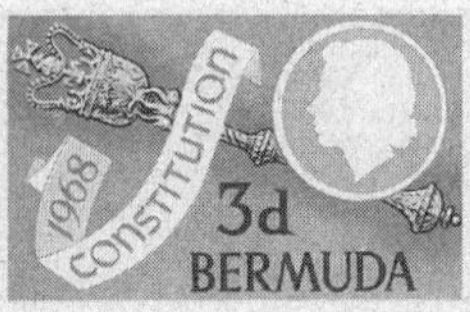

75 Mace and Queen's Profile

1968. New Constitution.

216	**75**	3d. multicoloured	10	10
217		1s. multicoloured	10	10

218 – 1s.6d. yellow, black and
blue 10 20
219 – 2s.6d. lilac, black and
yellow 15 75
DESIGNS: 1s.6d., 2s.6d., Houses of Parliament, and House of Assembly, Bermuda.

77 Football, Athletics and Yachting

1968. Olympic Games, Mexico.
220 77 3d. multicoloured 15 10
221 1s. multicoloured 25 10
222 1s.6d. multicoloured 50 30
223 2s.6d. multicoloured . . . . 50 1·40

78 Brownie and Guide

1969. 50th Anniv of Girl Guides. Multicoloured.
224 3d. Type 78 . . . . 10 10
225 1s. Type 78 . . . . 20 10
226 1s.6d. Guides and Badge . . 25 40
227 2s.6d. As 1s.6d. . . . . . . 35 1·40

80 Emerald-studded Gold Cross
and Seaweed

1969. Underwater Treasure. Multicoloured.
228 4d. Type 80 . . . . 20 10
229 1s.3d. Emerald-studded gold
cross and sea-bed 35 15
230 2s. As Type 80 . . . . . . 45 90
231 2s.6d. As 1s.3d. . . . . . . 45 1·75

1970. Decimal Currency. Nos. 163/79 surch.
232 1c. on 1d. purple, black &
orge . . . . 10 1·75
233 2c. on 2d. multicoloured . . 10 10
234 3c. on 3d. brown and blue . 10 10
235 4c. on 4d. brown and mauve . 10 10
236 5c. on 8d. blue, green & orge 15 2·00
237 6c. on 8d. blue, green & lt
blue . . . . 15 1·00
238 9c. on 9d. blue and brown . 30 2·25
239 10c. on 10d. violet and ochre 30 25
240 12c. on 1s. multicoloured . . 30 1·00
241 15c on 1s.3d. lake, grey & bis 1·50 1·00
242 18c on 1s.6d. blue and red . 80 65
243 24c. on 2s. brown and orange 85 1·00
244 30c. on 2s.6d. sepia, grn &
yell . . . . 1·00 2·75
245 36c. on 2s.3d. sepia and green 1·75 6·50
246 60c. on 5s. purple and green 2·25 3·25
247 $1.20 on 10s. mve, grn &
buff . . . . 4·00 15·00
248 $2.40 on £1 black, ol & orge 5·50 19·00

83 Spathiphyllum

1970. Flowers. Multicoloured.
249 1c. Type 83 . . . . 10 20
250 2c. Bottlebrush 20 25
251 3c. Oleander (vert) 15 10
252 4c. Bermudiana 15 10
253 5c. Poinsettia 30 20
254 6c. Hibiscus 30 30
255 9c. Cereus 20 45
256 10c. Bougainvillea (vert) . . 20 15
257 12c. Jacaranda 80 60
258 15c. Passion flower . . . . 90 1·40
258a 17c. As 15c. . . . . 2·75 3·75
259 18c. Coralita . . . . . . 2·25 2·25
259a 20c. As 18c. . . . . 2·75 3·75
260 24c. Morning glory . . . . 1·50 3·50
260a 25c. As 24c. . . . . 2·75 4·50
261 30c. Tecoma . . . . . . 1·00 1·25
262 36c. Angel's trumpet . . . 1·25 2·25
262a 40c. As 36c. . . . . 2·75 5·50
263 60c. Plumbago . . . . . . 1·75 1·75
263a $1 As 60c. . . . . 3·25 6·50

264 $1.20 Bird of paradise
flower . . . . 2·75 3·00
264a $2 As $1.20 . . . . 5·50 8·50
265 $2.40 Chalice cup . . . . 5·50 6·00
265a $3 As $2.40 . . . . 10·00 11·00

84 The State House, St. George's

1970. 350th Anniv of Bermuda Parliament. Multicoloured.
266 4c. Type 84 . . . . 10 10
267 15c. The Sessions House,
Hamilton 25 20
268 18c. St. Peter's Church, St.
George's 25 25
269 24c. Town Hall, Hamilton . . 35 60

85 Street Scene, St. George's

1971. "Keep Bermuda Beautiful". Multicoloured.
271 4c. Type 85 . . . . 20 10
272 15c. Horseshoe Bay 65 65
273 18c. Gibbs Hill Lighthouse . 1·50 2·25
274 24c. Hamilton Harbour . . . 1·25 2·50

86 Building of the "Deliverance"

1971. Voyage of the "Deliverance". Multicoloured.
275 4c. Type 86 . . . . 60 20
276 15c. "Deliverance" and
"Patience" at Jamestown
(vert) . . . . 1·50 1·75
277 18c. Wreck of the "Sea
Venture" (vert) . . . . 1·50 2·25
278 24c. "Deliverance" and
"Patience" on high seas . 1·75 2·50

87 Green overlooking Ocean View

1971. Golfing in Bermuda. Multicoloured.
279 4c. Type 87 . . . . 85 10
280 15c. Golfers at Port Royal . 1·75 80
281 18c. Castle Harbour . . . . 1·75 1·50
282 24c. Belmont . . . . . . 2·00 2·00

1971. Anglo-American Talks. Nos. 252, 258, 259 and 260 optd **HEATH-NIXON DECEMBER 1971.**
283 4c. Bermudiana 10 10
284 15c. Passion flower 10 20
285 18c. Coralita 15 65
286 24c. Morning glory 20 80

89 Bonefish

1972. World Fishing Records. Multicoloured.
287 4c. Type 89 . . . . 30 10
288 15c. Wahoo 30 50
289 18c. Yellow-finned tuna . . 35 75
290 24c. Greater amberjack . . 40 1·25

1972. Silver Wedding. As T 52 of Ascension, but with "Admiralty Oar" and Mace in background.
291 4c. violet 15 10
292 15c. red 15 50

91 Palmetto

1973. Tree Planting Year. Multicoloured.
293 4c. Type 91 . . . . 25 10
294 15c. Olivewood bark 65 75
295 18c. Bermuda cedar . . . . 70 1·25
296 24c. Mahogany . . . . . . 75 1·60

1973. Royal Wedding. As T 47 of Anguilla, background colour given. Multicoloured.
297 15c. mauve 15 15
298 18c. blue 15 15

92 Bernard Park, Pembroke, 1973

1973. Centenary of Lawn Tennis. Multicoloured.
299 4c. Type 92 . . . . 30 10
300 15c. Clermont Court, 1873 . 60 65
301 18c. Leamington Spa Court,
1872 . . . . 70 1·75
302 24c. Staten Island Courts,
1874 . . . . 85 2·25

93 Weather Vane, City Hall

1974. 50th Anniv of Rotary in Bermuda. Mult.
320 5c. Type 93 . . . . 15 10
321 17c. St. Peter's Church, St.
George's 45 35
322 20c. Somerset Bridge . . . 50 1·50
323 25c. Map of Bermuda, 1626 . 60 2·25

94 Jack of Clubs and "good
bridge hand"

1975. World Bridge Championships, Bermuda. Multicoloured.
324 5c. Type 94 . . . . 20 10
325 17c. Queen of Diamonds and
Bermuda Bowl 35 50
326 20c. King of Hearts and
Bermuda Bowl . . . . 40 1·75
327 25c. Ace of Spades and
Bermuda Bowl . . . . 40 2·25

95 Queen Elizabeth II and the Duke of
Edinburgh

1975. Royal Visit.
328 95 17c. multicoloured . . . 60 65
329 20c. multicoloured . . . . 65 2·10

96 Short S.23 Flying Boat "Cavalier",
1937

1975. 50th Anniv of Air-mail Service to Bermuda. Multicoloured.
330 5c. Type 96 . . . . 40 10
331 17c. U.S. Navy airship "Los
Angeles", 1925 . . . . 1·25 85
332 20c. Lockheed Constellation,
1946 . . . . 1·40 2·75
333 25c. Boeing 747-100, 1970 . . 1·50 3·50

97 Supporters of American Army
raiding Royal Magazine

1975. Bicentenary of Gunpowder Plot, St. George's. Multicoloured.
335 5c. Type 97 . . . . 20 10
336 17c. Setting off for raid . . . 40 40
337 20c. Loading gunpowder
aboard American ship . . 45 1·40
338 25c. Gunpowder on beach . . 50 1·50

98 Launching "Ready"
(bathysphere)

1976. 50th Anniv of Bermuda Biological Station. Multicoloured.
357 5c. Type 98 . . . . 30 10
358 17c. View from the sea
(horiz) 60 60
359 20c. H.M.S. "Challenger",
1873 (horiz) . . . . . . 65 2·25
360 25c. Beebe's Bathysphere
descent, 1934 . . . . . 70 2·75

99 "Christian Radich" (cadet ship)

1976. Tall Ships Race. Multicoloured.
361 5c. Type 99 . . . . 75 20
362 12c. "Juan Sebastian de
Elcano" (Spanish cadet
schooner) . . . . . . 80 2·00
363 17c. "Eagle" (U.S.
coastguard cadet ship) . 80 1·50
364 20c. "Sir Winston Churchill"
(cadet schooner) . . . . 80 2·00
365 40c. "Kruzenshtern" (Russian
cadet barque) . . . . . 1·00 2·75
366 $1 "Cutty Sark" trophy . . . 1·25 7·00

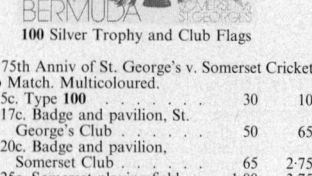

100 Silver Trophy and Club Flags

1976. 75th Anniv of St. George's v. Somerset Cricket Cup Match. Multicoloured.
367 5c. Type 100 . . . . 30 10
368 17c. Badge and pavilion, St.
George's Club 50 65
369 20c. Badge and pavilion,
Somerset Club . . . . 65 2·75
370 25c. Somerset playing field . 1·00 3·75

101 Royal Visit, 1975

1977. Silver Jubilee. Multicoloured.
371 5c. Type 101 . . . . 10 10
372 20c. St. Edward's Crown . . 15 20
373 $1 The Queen in Chair of
Estate . . . . 40 1·25

102 Stockdale House, St. George's, 1784–1812

1977. Centenary of U.P.U. Membership. Mult.
374	5c. Type **102**	15	10
375	15c. Perot Post Office and stamp	25	50
376	17c. St. George's P.O. c. 1860	25	50
377	20c. Old G.P.O., Hamilton, c. 1935	30	60
378	40c. New G.P.O., Hamilton, 1967	45	1·10

103 17th-Century Ship approaching Castle Island

1977. Piloting. Multicoloured.
379	5c. Type **103**	40	10
380	15c. Pilot leaving ship, 1795	70	60
381	17c. Pilots rowing out to paddle-steamer	80	60
382	20c. Pilot gig and brig "Harvest Queen"	85	2·25
383	40c. Modern pilot cutter and R.M.S. "Queen Elizabeth 2"	1·40	3·75

104 Great Seal of Queen Elizabeth I

1978. 25th Anniv of Coronation. Multicoloured.
384	8c. Type **104**	10	10
385	50c. Great Seal of Queen Elizabeth II	30	30
386	$1 Queen Elizabeth II	60	75

105 White-tailed Tropic Bird

1978. Wildlife. Multicoloured.
387	3c. Type **105**	2·50	2·00
388	4c. White-eyed vireo	2·25	2·00
389	5c. Eastern bluebird	1·25	1·75
390	7c. Whistling frog	50	1·50
391	8c. Common cardinal ("Cardinal Redbird")	1·25	55
392	10c. Spiny lobster	20	10
393	12c. Land crab	30	70
394	15c. Lizard (Skink)	30	15
395	20c. Four-eyed butterflyfish	30	30
396	25c. Red hind	30	20
397	30c. "Danaus plexippus" (butterfly)	2·25	2·50
398	40c. Rock beauty	45	1·50
399	50c. Banded butterflyfish	55	1·25
400	$1 Blue angelfish	2·25	1·75
401	$2 Humpback whale	2·00	2·75
402	$3 Green turtle	2·50	3·00
403	$5 Cahow	6·00	6·00

106 Map by Sir George Somers, 1609

1979. Antique Maps. Multicoloured.
404	8c. Type **106**	15	10
405	15c. Map by John Seller, 1685	20	15
406	20c. Map by H. Moll, 1729–40 (vert)	25	25

407	25c. Map by Desbruslins, 1740	30	30
408	50c. Map by Speed, 1626	45	80

107 Policeman and Policewoman

1979. Centenary of Police Force. Multicoloured.
409	8c. Type **107**	30	10
410	20c. Policeman directing traffic (horiz)	50	55
411	25c. "Blue Heron" (police launch) (horiz)	60	65
412	50c. Police car and motor cycle	80	1·50

108 1d. "Perot" Stamp of 1848 and 1840 Penny Black

1980. Death Cent of Sir Rowland Hill. Mult.
413	8c. Type **108**	20	10
414	20c. "Perot" and Sir Rowland Hill	30	25
415	25c. "Perot" and early letter	30	30
416	50c. "Perot" and "Paid 1" cancellation	35	70

109 Lockheed TriStar 500 approaching Bermuda

1980. "London 1980" International Stamp Exhibition. Multicoloured.
417	25c. Type **109**	30	15
418	50c. "Orduna I" (liner) at Grassy Bay, 1926	45	35
419	$1 "Delta" (screw steamer) at St. George's Harbour, 1856	85	1·00
420	$2 "Lord Sidmouth" (sailing packet) in Old Ship Channel, St. George's	1·40	2·00

110 Gina Swainson ("Miss World 1979–80")

1980. "Miss World 1979–80" Commem. Mult.
421	8c. Type **110**	15	10
422	20c. Miss Swainson after crowning ceremony	20	20
423	50c. Miss Swainson on Peacock Throne	35	35
424	$1 Miss Swainson in Bermuda carriage	70	90

111 Queen Elizabeth the Queen Mother

1980. 80th Birthday of The Queen Mother.
425	**111** 25c. multicoloured	30	1·00

112 Bermuda from Satellite

1980. Commonwealth Finance Ministers Meeting. Muticoloured.
426	8c. Type **112**	10	10
427	20c. "Camden"	20	40
428	25c. Princess Hotel, Hamilton	20	50
429	50c. Government House	35	1·25

113 Kitchen, 18th-century

1981. Heritage Week. Multicoloured.
430	8c. Type **113**	15	10
431	25c. Gathering Easter lilies, 20th-century	30	35
432	30c. Fishing, 20th-century	40	50
433	40c. Stone cutting, 19th-century	40	80
434	50c. Onion shipping, 19th-century	65	90
435	$1 Privateering, 17th-century	1·25	2·50

114 Wedding Bouquet from Bermuda   **115** "Service", Hamilton

1981. Royal Wedding. Multicoloured.
436	30c. Type **114**	20	20
437	50c. Prince Charles as Royal Navy Commander	35	40
438	$1 Prince Charles and Lady Diana Spencer	55	80

1981. 25th Anniv of Duke of Edinburgh Award Scheme. Multicoloured.
439	10c. Type **115**	15	10
440	25c. "Outward Bound", Paget Island	20	20
441	30c. "Expedition", St. David's Island	20	30
442	$1 Duke of Edinburgh	55	1·25

116 Lightbourne's Cone

1982. Sea Shells. Multicoloured.
443	10c. Type **116**	30	10
444	25c. Finlay's frog shell	55	55
445	30c. Royal bonnet	60	60
446	$1 Lightbourne's murex	1·75	3·25

117 Regimental Colours and Colour Party

1982. Bermuda Regiment. Multicoloured.
447	10c. Type **117**	55	10
448	25c. Queen's Birthday Parade	1·00	80
449	30c. Governor inspecting Guard of Honour	1·25	1·40
450	40c. Beating the Retreat	1·40	1·75
451	50c. Ceremonial gunners	1·40	2·00
452	$1 Guard of Honour, Royal visit, 1975	2·25	3·50

118 Charles Fort   **119** Arms of Sir Edwin Sandys

1982. Historic Bermuda Forts. Multicoloured.
453	10c. Type **118**	20	20
454	25c. Pembroks Fort	50	85
455	30c. Southampton Fort (horiz)	60	1·25
456	$1 Smiths Fort and Pagets Fort (horiz)	1·75	4·25

1983. Coat of Arms (1st series). Multicoloured.
457	10c. Type **119**	45	15
458	25c. Arms of the Bermuda Company	1·40	1·00
459	50c. Arms of William Herbert, Earl of Pembroke	2·25	3·25
460	$1 Arms of Sir George Somers	3·00	5·50

See also Nos. 482/5 and 499/502.

120 Early Fitted Dinghy   **122** Joseph Stockdale

121 Curtiss N-9 Seaplane

1983. Fitted Dinghies. Multicoloured.
461	12c. Type **120**	45	15
462	30c. Modern dinghy inshore	60	75
463	40c. Early dinghy (different)	70	90
464	$1 Modern dinghy with red and white spinnaker	1·40	3·25

1983. Bicentenary of Manned Flight. Multicoloured.
465	12c. Type **121** (First flight over Bermuda)	60	20
466	30c. Stinson Pilot Radio seaplane (First completed flight between U.S. and Bermuda)	1·25	1·25
467	40c. S.23 Flying boat "Cavalier" (First scheduled passenger flight)	1·50	1·75
468	$1 U.S.N. "Los Angeles" (airship) moored to U.S.S. "Patoka"	2·75	5·00

1984. Bicentenary of Bermuda's First Newspaper and Postal Service. Multicoloured
469	12c. Type **122**	30	15
470	30c. "The Bermuda Gazette"	60	80
471	40c. Stockdale's postal service (horiz)	80	1·10
472	$1 "Lady Hammond" (mail boat) (horiz)	2·50	3·25

123 Sir Thomas Gates and Sir George Somers

1984. 375th Anniv of First Settlement. Mult.
473	12c. Type **123**	20	15
474	30c. Jamestown, Virginia	50	1·25
475	40c. Wreck of "Sea Venture"	90	1·25
476	$1 Fleet leaving Plymouth, Devon	2·00	5·50

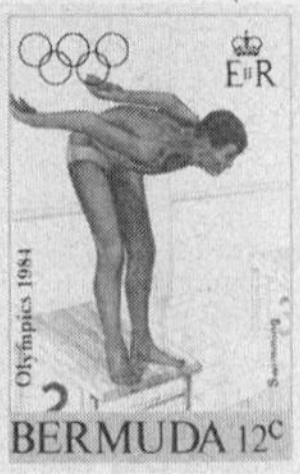

124 Swimming

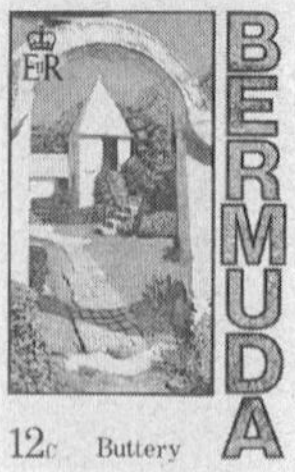

125 Buttery

1984. Olympic Games, Los Angeles. Multicoloured.

478	12c. Type **124**	40	15
479	30c. Track and field events (horiz)	70	75
480	40c. Equestrian	1·25	1·25
481	$1 Sailing (horiz)	2·50	5·00

1984. Coat of Arms (2nd series). As T **119**. Mult.

482	12c. Arms of Henry Wriothesley, Earl of Southampton	50	15
483	30c. Arms of Sir Thomas Smith	1·00	85
484	40c. Arms of William Cavendish, Earl of Devonshire	1·25	1·50
485	$1 Town arms of St. George	2·75	4·25

1985. Bermuda Architecture. Multicoloured.

486	12c. Type **125**	35	15
487	30c. Limestone rooftops (horiz)	80	70
488	40c. Chimneys (horiz)	95	1·00
489	$1.50 Entrance archway	3·00	3·75

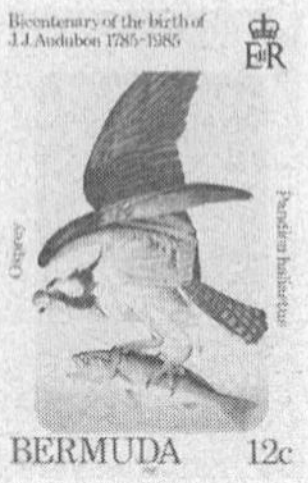

126 Osprey

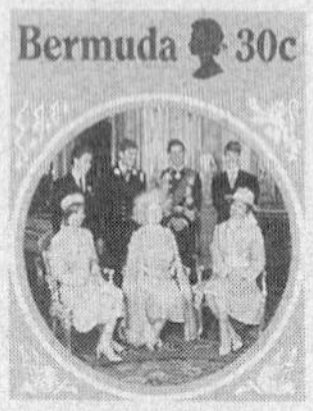

127 The Queen Mother with Grandchildren, 1980

1985. Birth Bicentenary of John J. Audubon (ornithologist). Designs showing original drawings. Multicoloured.

490	12c. Type **126**	2·00	65
491	30c. Yellow-crowned night heron	2·00	95
492	40c. Great egret (horiz)	2·25	1·25
493	$1.50 Eastern bluebird ("Bluebird")	3·75	6·50

1985. Life and Times of Queen Elizabeth the Queen Mother. Multicoloured.

494	12c. Queen Consort, 1937	25	15
495	30c. Type **127**	40	50
496	40c. At Clarence House on 83rd birthday	50	60
497	$1.50 With Prince Henry at his christening (from photo by Lord Snowdon)	2·00	2·75

1985. Coats of Arms (3rd series). As T **119**. Mult.

499	12c. Hamilton	75	15
500	30c. Paget	1·40	80
501	40c. Warwick	1·60	1·40
502	$1.50 City of Hamilton	3·75	4·25

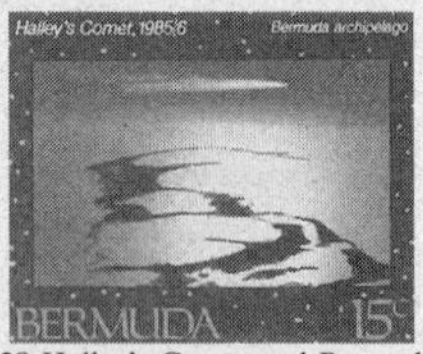

128 Halley's Comet and Bermuda Archipelago

1985. Appearance of Halley's Comet. Multicoloured.

503	15c. Type **128**	85	25
504	40c. Halley's Comet, A.D. 684 (from Nuremberg Chronicles, 1493)	1·60	1·75
505	50c. "Halley's Comet, 1531" (from Peter Apian woodcut, 1532)	1·90	2·50
506	$1.50 "Halley's Comet, 1759" (Samuel Scott)	3·50	5·00

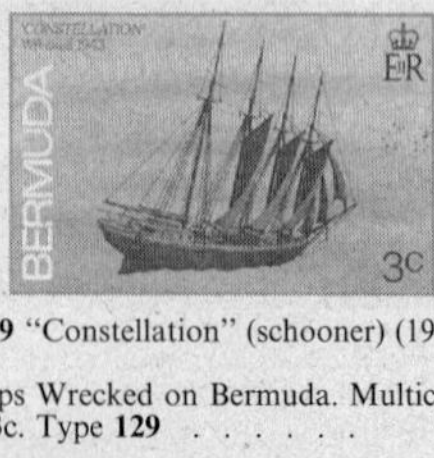

129 "Constellation" (schooner) (1943)

1986. Ships Wrecked on Bermuda. Multicoloured.

507A	3c. Type **129**	70	1·00
508A	5c. "Early Riser" (pilot boat), 1876	20	20
509A	7c. "Madiana" (screw steamer), 1903	65	1·75
510A	10c. "Curlew" (sail/steamer), 1856	30	30
511A	12c. "Warwick" (galleon), 1619	60	80
512A	15c. H.M.S. "Vixen" (gun-boat), 1890	40	60
512cA	18c. As 7c.	5·00	3·75
513A	20c. "San Pedro" (Spanish galleon), 1594	1·10	80
514A	25c. "Alert" (fishing sloop), 1877	60	2·25
515A	40c. "North Carolina" (barque), 1880	65	1·25
516A	50c. "Mark Antonie" (Spanish privateer), 1777	1·50	2·50
517A	60c. "Mary Celestia" (Confederate paddle-steamer), 1864	1·50	1·75
517cA	70c. "Caesar" (brig), 1818	5·50	6·00
518B	$1 "L'Herminie" (French frigate), 1839	1·50	1·60
519A	$1.50 As 70c.	4·50	4·50
520B	$2 "Lord Amherst" (transport), 1778	2·50	4·00
521B	$3 "Minerva" (sailing ship), 1849	4·25	6·00
522A	$5 "Caraquet" (cargo liner), 1923	4·75	11·00
523A	$8 H.M.S. "Pallas" (frigate), 1783	6·00	12·00

1986. 60th Birthday of Queen Elizabeth II. As T **110** of Ascension. Multicoloured.

524	15c. Princess Elizabeth aged three, 1929	35	30
525	40c. With Earl of Rosebery at Oaks May Meeting, Epsom, 1954	70	60
526	50c. With Duke of Edinburgh, Bermuda, 1975	70	75
527	60c. At British Embassy, Paris, 1972	80	90
528	$1.50 At Crown Agents Head Office, London, 1983	2·00	2·50

1986. "Ameripex '86" International Stamp Exhibition, Chicago. As T **164** of Bahamas, showing Bermuda stamps. Multicoloured.

529	15c. 1984 375th Anniv of Settlement miniature sheet	1·25	30
530	40c. 1973 Lawn Tennis Centenary, 24c.	2·00	70
531	50c. 1983 Bicentenary of Manned Flight 12c.	2·00	1·00
532	$1 1976 Tall Ships Race 17c.	3·50	3·00

1986. 25th Anniv of World Wildlife Fund. No. 402 surch **90c**.

534	90c. on $3 Green turtle	3·00	4·00

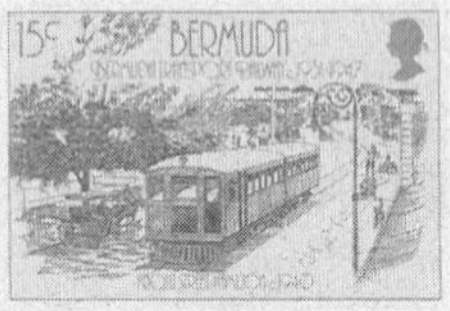

131 Train in Front Street, Hamilton, 1940

1987. Transport (1st series). Bermuda Railway. Multicoloured.

535	15c. Type **131**	1·75	25
536	40c. Train crossing Springfield Trestle	2·25	90
537	50c. "St. George Special" at Bailey's Bay Station	2·25	1·50
538	$1.50 Boat train at St. George	3·75	3·50

See also Nos. 557/60, 574/7 and 624/9.

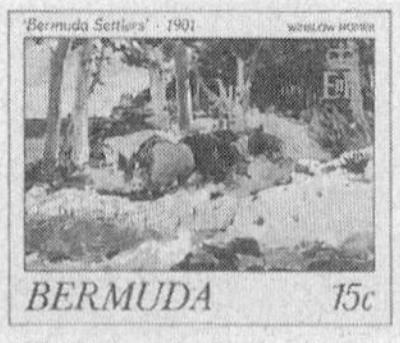

132 "Bermuda Settlers", 1901

1987. Bermuda Paintings (1st series). Works by Winslow Homer. Multicoloured.

539	15c. Type **132**	60	25
540	30c. "Bermuda", 1900	85	45
541	40c. "Bermuda Landscape", 1901 (buff frame)	95	55
544	40c. Type **132**	90	1·60
545	40c. As No. 540	90	1·60
546	40c. As No. 541 (grey frame)	90	1·60
547	40c. As No. 542	90	1·60
548	40c. As No. 543	90	1·60
542	50c. "Inland Water", 1901	1·10	70
543	$1.50 "Salt Kettle", 1899	2·50	2·50

See also Nos. 607/10 and 630/3.

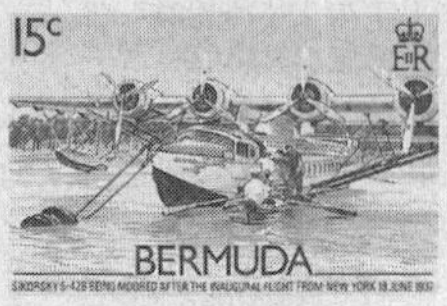

133 Sikorsky S-42B Flying Boat "Bermuda Clipper"

1987. 50th Anniv of Inauguration of Bermuda–U.S.A. Air Service. Multicoloured.

549	15c. Type **133**	1·75	15
550	40c. Short S.23 flying boat "Cavalier"	2·75	70
551	50c. "Bermuda Clipper" in flight over signpost	3·00	80
552	$1.50 "Cavalier" on apron and "Bermuda Clipper" in flight	5·50	3·50

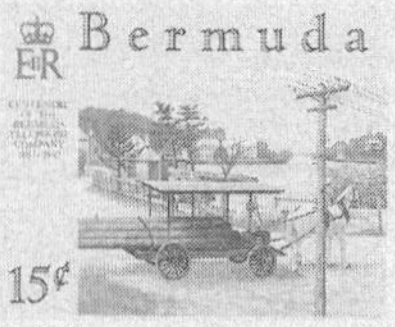

134 19th-century Wagon carrying Telephone Poles

1987. Centenary of Bermuda Telephone Company. Multicoloured.

553	15c. Type **134**	75	15
554	40c. Early telephone exchange	1·40	60
555	50c. Early and modern telephones	1·75	70
556	$1.50 Communications satellite orbiting Earth	2·75	3·50

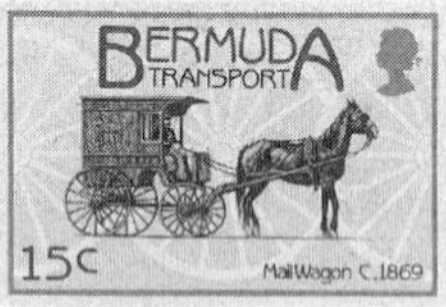

135 Mail Wagon, c. 1869

1988. Transport (2nd series). Horse-drawn Carts and Wagons. Multicoloured.

557	15c. Type **135**	25	15
558	40c. Open cart, c. 1823	55	55
559	50c. Closed cart, c. 1823	65	65
560	$1.50 Two-wheeled wagon, c. 1930	2·00	2·50

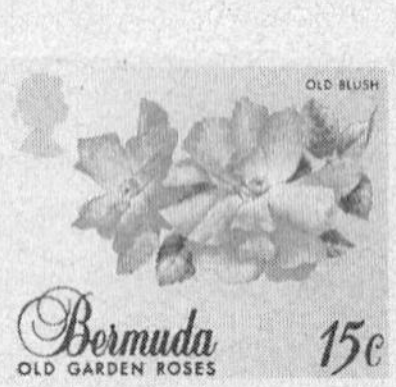

136 "Old Blush"

1988. Old Garden Roses (1st series). Multicoloured.

561	15c. Type **136**	75	25
562	30c. "Anna Olivier"	1·00	45
563	40c. "Rosa chinensis semperflorens" (vert)	1·10	85
564	50c. "Archduke Charles"	1·25	1·25
565	$1.50 "Rosa chinensis viridiflora" (vert)	2·75	4·50

See also Nos. 584/8 and, for designs with the royal cypher instead of the Queen's head, Nos. 589/98 and 683/6.

1988. 300th Anniv of Lloyd's of London. As T **123** of Ascension. Multicoloured.

566	18c. Loss of H.M.S. "Lutine" (frigate), 1799	75	25
567	50c. "Sentinel" (cable ship) (horiz)	1·40	65
568	60c. "Bermuda" (liner), Hamilton, 1931 (horiz)	1·60	75
569	$2 Loss of H.M.S. "Valerian" (sloop) in hurricane, 1926	3·00	3·25

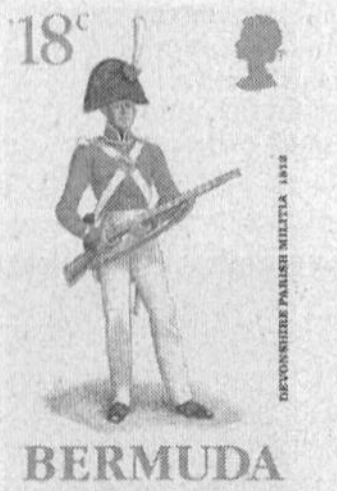

137 Devonshire Parish Militia, 1812

1988. Military Uniforms. Multicoloured.

570	18c. Type **137**	1·25	25
571	50c. 71 st (Highland) Regiment, 1831–34	1·75	1·10
572	60c. Cameron Highlanders, 1942	2·00	1·25
573	$2 Troop of horse, 1774	4·50	6·50

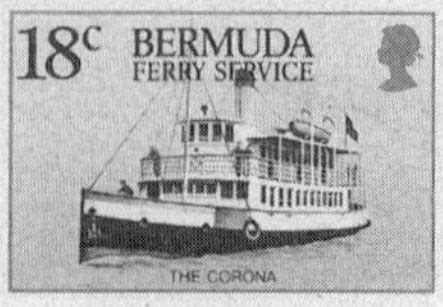

138 "Corona" (ferry)

1989. Transport (3rd series). Ferry Services. Mult.

574	18c. Type **138**	35	25
575	50c. Rowing boat ferry	75	65
576	60c. St. George's barge ferry	85	75
577	$2 "Laconia"	2·50	3·00

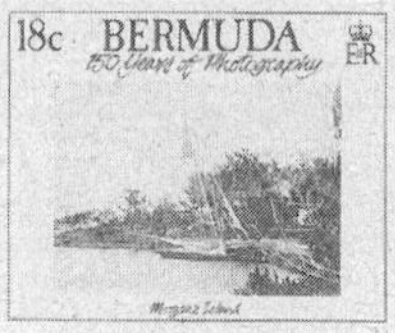

139 Morgan's Island

1989. 150 Years of Photography. Multicoloured.

578	18c. Type **139**	75	25
579	30c. Front Street, Hamilton	1·00	45
580	50c. Waterfront, Front Street, Hamilton	1·40	1·25
581	60c. Crow Lane from Hamilton Harbour	1·60	1·40
582	70c. Shipbuilding, Hamilton Harbour	1·75	2·50
583	$1 Dockyard	2·00	3·00

1989. Old Garden Roses (2nd series). As T **136**. Multicoloured.

584	18c. "Agrippina" (vert)	80	25
585	30c. "Smith's Parish" (vert)	1·00	60
586	50c. "Champney's Pink Cluster"	1·50	1·40
587	60c. "Rosette Delizy"	1·60	1·60
588	$1.50 "Rosa bracteata"	2·50	4·50

1989. Old Garden Roses (3rd series). Designs as Nos. 561/5 and 584/8, but with royal cypher at top left instead of Queen's head. Multicoloured.

589	50c. As No. 565 (vert)	1·40	1·75
590	50c. As No. 563 (vert)	1·40	1·75
591	50c. Type **136**	1·40	1·75
592	50c. As No. 562	1·40	1·75
593	50c. As No. 564	1·40	1·75
594	50c. As No. 585 (vert)	1·40	1·75
595	50c. As No. 584 (vert)	1·40	1·75
596	50c. As No. 586	1·40	1·75
597	50c. As No. 587	1·40	1·75
598	50c. As No. 588	1·40	1·75

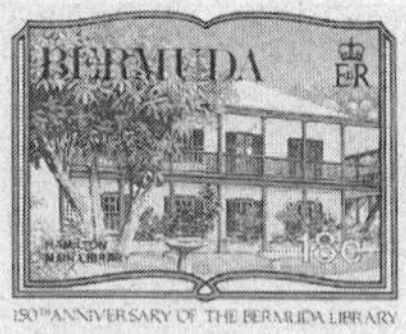

140 Main Library, Hamilton

1989. 150th Anniv of Bermuda Library. Mult.

599	18c. Type **140**	50	25
600	50c. The Old Rectory, St. George's	1·00	65
601	60c. Somerset Library, Springfield	1·10	75
602	$2 Cabinet Building, Hamilton	3·00	3·00

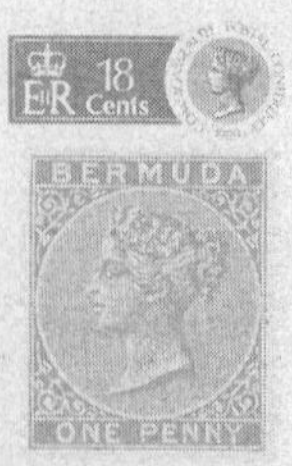

141 1865 1d. Rose

1989. Commonwealth Postal Conference. Mult.

603	**141**	18c. grey, pink and red	1·25	25
604	–	50c. grey, blue & lt blue	1·75	75
605	–	60c. grey, purple and mauve	2·00	1·25
606	–	$2 grey, green and emerald	3·50	5·50

DESIGNS: 50c. 1866 2d. blue; 60c. 1865 6d. purple; $2 1865 1s. green.

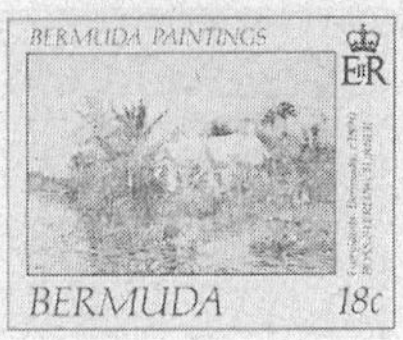

142 "Fairylands, c. 1890" (Ross Turner)

1990. Bermuda Paintings (2nd series). Multicoloured.

607	18c. Type **142**	75	25
608	50c. "Shinebone Alley, c. 1953" (Ogden Pleissner)	1·25	1·25
609	60c. "Salt Kettle, 1916" (Prosper Senat)	1·25	1·50
610	$2 "St. George's, 1934" (Jack Bush)	3·25	6·50

1990. "Stamp World London 90" International Stamp Exhibition. Nos. 603/6 optd **Stamp World London 90** and logo.

611	18c. grey, pink and red	1·25	25
612	50c. grey, blue and light blue	1·75	1·50
613	60c. grey, purple and mauve	2·00	1·75
614	$2 grey, green and emerald	3·50	6·50

1990. Nos. 511, 516 and 519 surch.

615	30c. on 12c. "Warwick" (galleon), (1619)	1·25	1·00
616	55c. on 50c. "Mark Antonie" (Spanish privateer), 1777	1·75	1·75
617	80c. on $1.50 "Caesar" (brig), 1818	2·25	3·75

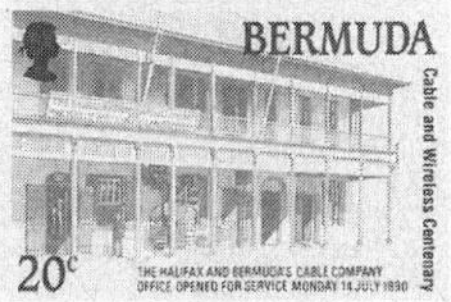

145 The Halifax and Bermudas Cable Company Office, Hamilton

1990. Centenary of Cable and Wireless in Bermuda.

618	**145** 20c. brown and black	70	25
619	– 55c. brown and black	2·00	1·25
620	– 70c. multicoloured	2·00	2·50
621	– $2 multicoloured	4·75	6·50

DESIGNS: 55c. "Westmeath" (cable ship), 1890; 70c. Wireless transmitter station, St. George's, 1928; $2 "Sir Eric Sharp" (cable ship).

1991. President Bush–Prime Minister Major Talks, Bermuda. Nos. 618/19 optd **BUSH-MAJOR 16 MARCH 1991.**

622	**145** 20c. brown and black	1·50	1·00
623	– 55c. brown and black	2·50	3·00

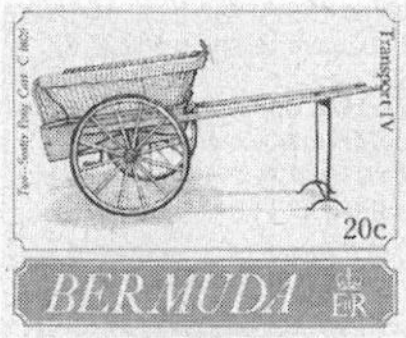

147 Two-seater Pony Cart, 1805

1991. Transport (4th series). Horse-drawn Carriages. Multicoloured.

624	20c. Type **147**	80	30
625	30c. Varnished rockaway, 1830	90	60
626	55c. Vis-a-Vis victoria, 1895	1·60	1·10
627	70c. Semi-formal phaeton, 1900	2·25	2·50
628	80c. Pony runabout, 1905	2·50	3·50
629	$1 Ladies phaeton, 1910	2·75	4·00

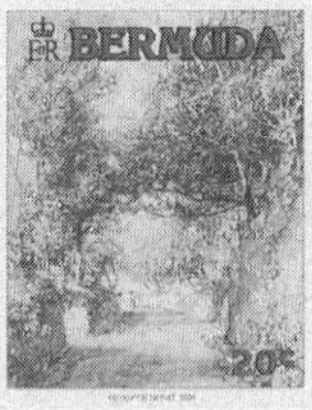

148 "Bermuda, 1916" (Prosper Senat)

1991. Bermuda Paintings (3rd series). Multicoloured.

630	20c. Type **148**	1·00	30
631	55c. "Bermuda Cottage" 1930 (Frank Allison) (horiz)	2·00	1·40
632	70c. "Old Maid's Lane", 1934 (Jack Bush)	2·50	3·00
633	$2 "St. George's", 1953 (Ogden Pleissner) (horiz)	5·00	7·50

1991. 65th Birthday of Queen Elizabeth II and 70th Birthday of Prince Philip. As T **139** of Ascension. Multicoloured.

634	55c. Prince Philip in tropical naval uniform	1·25	1·50
635	70c. Queen Elizabeth II in Bermuda	1·25	1·50

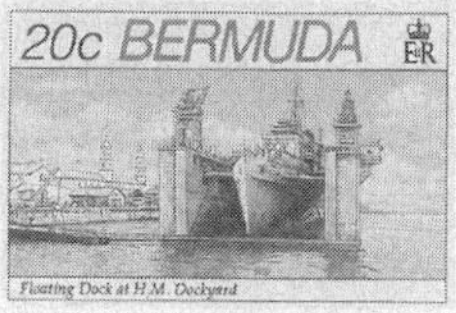

149 H.M.S. "Argonaut" (cruiser) in Floating Dock

1991. 50th Anniv of Second World War. Mult.

636	20c. Type **149**	1·50	40
637	55c. Kindley Airfield	2·25	1·40
638	70c. Boeing 314A flying boat and map of Atlantic route	2·75	3·25
639	$2 Censored trans-Atlantic mail	4·50	7·50

1992. 40th Anniv of Queen Elizabeth II's Accession. As T **143** of Ascension. Multicoloured.

640	20c. Old fort on beach	60	30
641	30c. Public gardens	75	55
642	55c. Cottage garden	1·25	90
643	70c. Beach and hotels	1·60	2·25
644	$1 Queen Elizabeth II	1·90	2·75

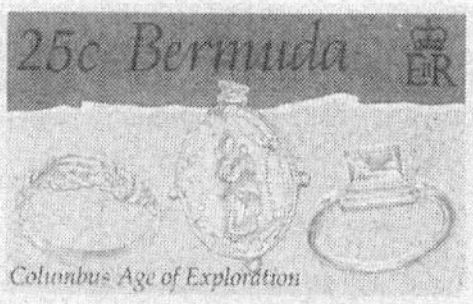

150 Rings and Medallion

1992. 500th Anniv of Discovery of America by Columbus. Spanish Artifacts. Multicoloured.

645	25c. Type **150**	1·00	35
646	35c. Ink wells	1·10	75
647	60c. Gold ornaments	2·00	2·00
648	75c. Bishop buttons and crucifix	2·25	3·00
649	85c. Earrings and pearl buttons	2·50	3·25
650	$1 Jug and bowls	2·75	4·00

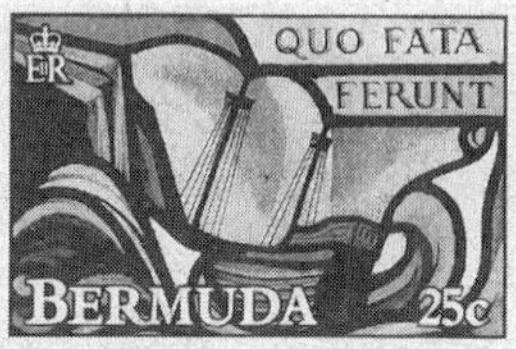

151 "Wreck of 'Sea Venture' "

1992. Stained Glass Windows. Multicoloured.

651	25c. Type **151**	1·25	40
652	60c. "Birds in tree"	2·50	2·00
653	75c. "St. Francis feeding bird"	3·00	3·00
654	$2 "Shells"	6·50	8·00

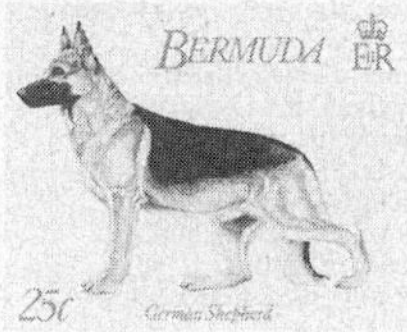

152 German Shepherd

1992. 7th World Congress of Kennel Clubs. Mult.

655	25c. Type **152**	1·25	40
656	35c. Irish setter	1·50	70
657	60c. Whippet (vert)	2·25	2·25
658	75c. Border terrier (vert)	2·25	3·00
659	85c. Pomeranian (vert)	2·50	3·50
660	$1 Schipperke (vert)	2·50	4·00

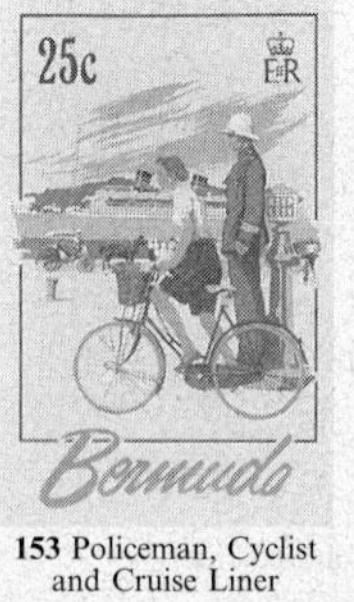

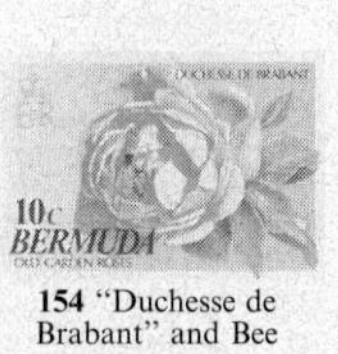

153 Policeman, Cyclist and Cruise Liner

154 "Duchesse de Brabant" and Bee

1993. Tourism Posters by Adolph Treidler. Mult.

679	25c. Type **153**	1·75	70
680	60c. Seaside golf course	2·50	2·50
681	75c. Deserted beach	2·50	2·75
682	$2 Dancers in evening dress and cruise liner	4·25	6·50

1993. Garden Roses (4th series).

683	**154** 10c. multicoloured	50	85
684	25c. multicoloured	50	50
685	50c. multicoloured	1·00	1·75
686	60c. multicoloured	80	1·10

1993. 75th Anniv of Royal Air Force. As T **149** of Ascension. Multicoloured.

687	25c. Consolidated PBY-5 Catalina	75	35
688	60c. Supermarine Spitfire Mk IX	1·75	2·00
689	75c. Bristol Type **156** Beaufighter Mk X	1·90	2·25
690	$2 Handley Page Halifax Mk III	3·50	4·50

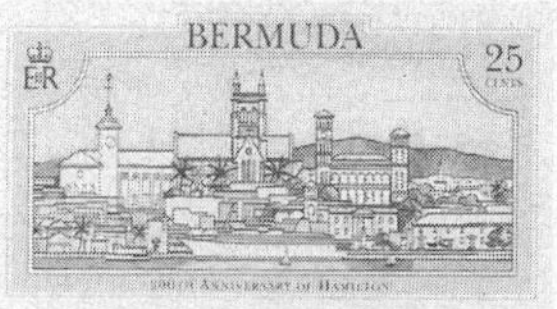

155 Hamilton from the Sea

1993. Bicentenary of Hamilton. Mult.

691	25c. Type **155**	1·00	35
692	60c. Waterfront	2·00	2·00
693	75c. Barrel warehouse	2·00	2·50
694	$2 Sailing ships off Hamilton	4·50	6·00

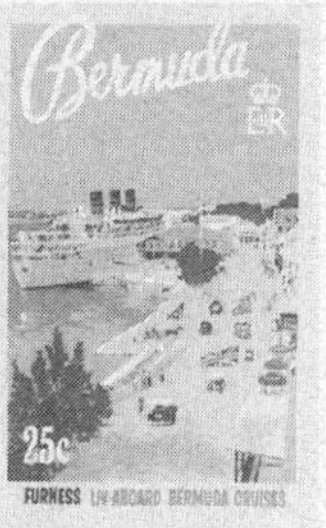

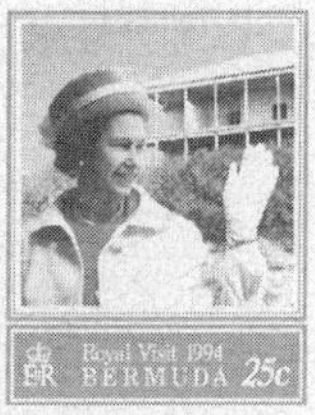

156 "Queen of Bermuda" (liner) at Hamilton

157 Queen Elizabeth II in Bermuda

1994. 75th Anniv of Furness Line's Bermuda Cruises. Adolphe Treidler Posters. Multicoloured.

695	25c. Type **156**	65	35
696	60c. "Monarch of Bermuda" entering port (horiz)	1·50	1·60
697	75c. "Queen of Bermuda" and "Ocean Monarch" (liners) (horiz)	1·60	1·75
698	$2 Passengers on promenade deck at night	3·50	5·00

1994. Royal Visit. Multicoloured.

699	25c. Type **157**	75	35
700	60c. Queen Elizabeth and Prince Philip in open carriage	1·75	1·75
701	75c. Royal Yacht "Britannia"	3·25	3·00

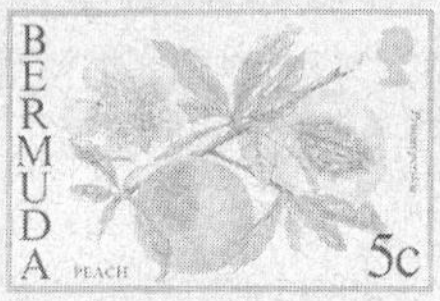

158 Peach

1994. Flowering Fruits. Multicoloured.

792	5c. Type **158**	10	10
703A	7c. Fig	10	10
704A	10c. Calabash (vert)	15	20
795	15c. Natal plum	20	25
796	18c. Locust and wild honey	25	30
797	20c. Pomegranate	30	35
798	25c. Mulberry (vert)	35	40
709A	35c. Grape (vert)	50	55
710A	55c. Orange (vert)	75	80
711A	60c. Surinam cherry	85	90
802	75c. Loquat	1·00	1·10
803	90c. Sugar apple	1·25	1·40
804	$1 Prickly pear (vert)	1·40	1·50
715A	$2 Paw paw	2·75	3·00
716A	$3 Bay grape	4·25	4·50
717A	$5 Banana (vert)	7·00	7·25
718A	$8 Lemon	11·00	11·50

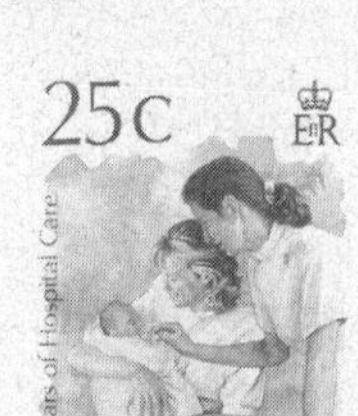

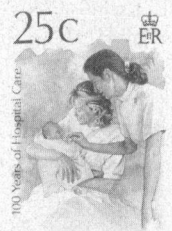

159 Nurse with Mother and Baby

1994. Centenary of Hospital Care. Multicoloured.

719	25c. Type **159**	1·00	35
720	60c. Patient on dialysis machine	2·00	1·90
721	75c. Casualty on emergency trolley	2·25	2·25
722	$2 Elderly patient in wheelchair with physiotherapists	4·75	6·50

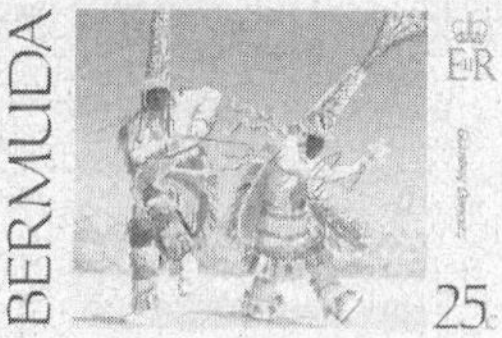

160 Gombey Dancers

1994. Cultural Heritage (1st series). Multicoloured.

723	25c. Type **160**	75	35
724	60c. Christmas carol singers	1·40	1·50
725	75c. Marching band	1·90	2·00
726	$2 National Dance Group performers	4·00	6·00

See also Nos. 731/4.

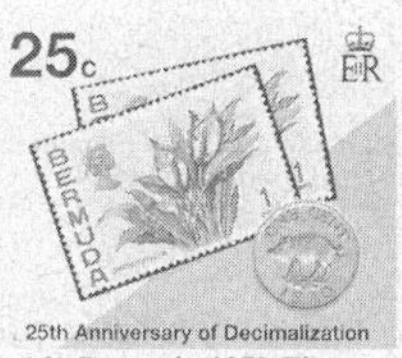

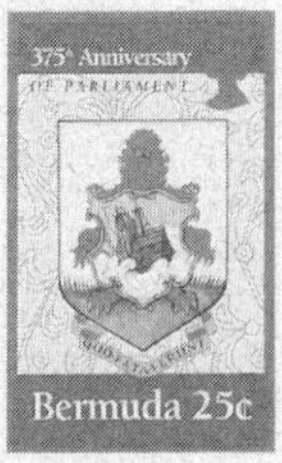

161 Bermuda 1970 Flower 1c. Stamps and 1c. Coin

162 Bermuda Coat of Arms

1995. 25th Anniv of Decimal Currency. Mult.

727	25c. Type **161**	45	35
728	60c. 1970 5c. stamps and coin	1·00	1·25
729	75c. 1970 10c. stamps and coin	1·25	1·75
730	$2 1970 25c. stamps and coin	3·50	4·50

1995. Cultural Heritage (2nd series). As T **160**. Multicoloured.

731	25c. Kite flying	55	35
732	60c. Majorettes	1·50	1·50
733	75c. Portuguese dancers	1·75	2·00
734	$2 Floral float	3·75	5·50

1995. 375th Anniv of Bermuda Parliament.

735	**162** 25c. multicoloured	75	35
736	$1 multicoloured	1·75	2·25

For design as No. 736 but inscr "Commonwealth Finance Ministers Meeting", see No. 765.

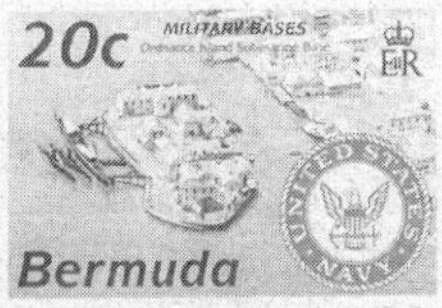

163 U.S. Navy Ordnance Island Submarine Base

1995. Military Bases. Multicoloured.

737	20c. Type **163**	50	30
738	25c. Royal Naval Dockyard	60	35
739	60c. U.S.A.F. Fort Bell and Kindley Field	1·25	1·25
740	75c. R.A.F. Darrell's Island flying boat base	1·50	1·75
741	90c. U.S. Navy operating base	1·50	2·25
742	$1 Canadian Forces Communications Station, Daniel's Head	1·60	2·25

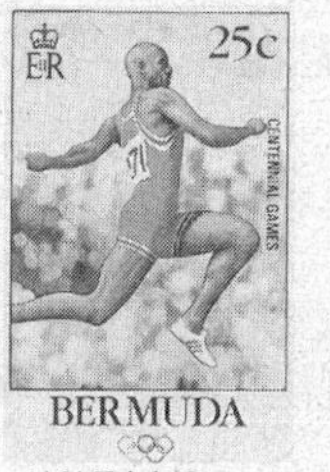

164 Triple Jump

1996. Olympic Games, Atlanta. Multicoloured.

743	25c. Type **164**	60	35
744	30c. Cycling	1·50	75
745	65c. Yachting	1·60	1·75
746	80c. Show jumping	1·75	2·25

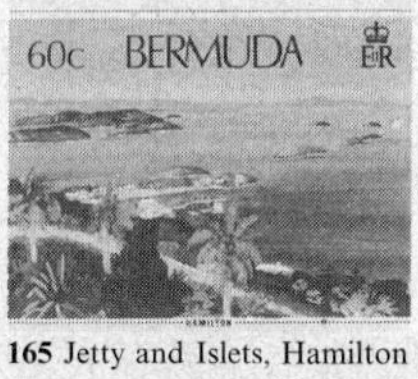

165 Jetty and Islets, Hamilton

1996. Panoramic Paintings of Hamilton (Nos. 747/51) and St. George's (Nos. 752/6) by E. J. Holland. Multicoloured.

747 60c. Type **165** . . . . 90 1·25
748 60c. End of island and buildings . . . . 90 1·25
749 60c. Yachts and hotel . . . . 90 1·25
750 60c. Islet, hotel and cathedral 90 1·25
751 60c. Cliff and houses by shore . . . . 90 1·25
752 60c. Islet and end of main island . . . . 90 1·25
753 60c. Yacht and houses on hillside . . . . 90 1·25
754 60c. Yacht and St. George's Hotel on hilltop . . . . . 90 1·25
755 60c. Shoreline and fishing boats . . . . 90 1·25
756 60c. Entrance to harbour channel . . . . 90 1·25

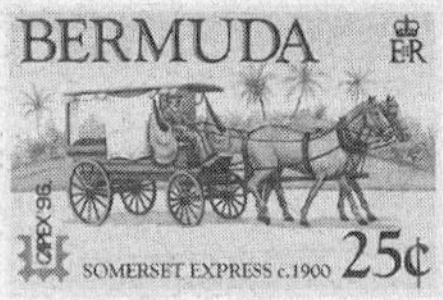

166 Somerset Express Mail Cart, c. 1900

1996. "CAPEX '96" International Stamp Exhibition, Toronto. Local Transport. Multicoloured.

757 25c. Type **166** 85 35
758 60c. Victoria carriage and railcar, 1930s . . . . . . 2·00 1·75
759 75c. First bus, 1946 . . . . 2·00 2·00
760 $2 Sightseeing bus, c. 1947 4·00 5·50

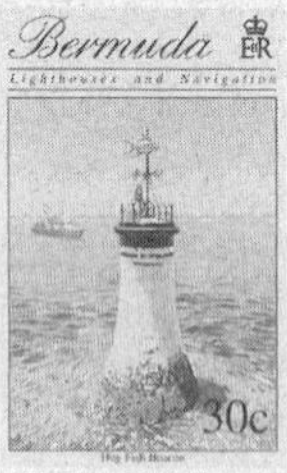

167 Hog Fish Beacon

1996. Lighthouses. Multicoloured.

761 30c. Type **167** . . . . 1·00 50
762 65c. Gibbs Hill Lighthouse 1·60 1·25
763 80c. St. David's Lighthouse 2·25 2·00
764 $2 North Rock Beacon . . . 3·50 5·00

See also Nos. 770/3.

1996. Commonwealth Finance Ministers' Meeting. As No. 736, but inscr "Commonwealth Finance Ministers Meeting" at top and with wider gold frame.

765 $1 multicoloured . . . . . . 1·50 2·00

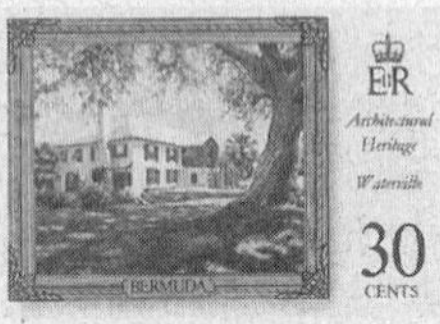

168 Waterville

1996. Architectural Heritage. Multicoloured.

766 30c. Type **168** 80 45
767 65c. Bridge House . . . . . 1·25 1·50
768 80c. Fannie Fox's Cottage . . 1·60 2·00
769 $2.50 Palmetto House . . . . 3·75 6·00

1997. "HONG KONG '97" International Stamp Exhibition. Designs as Nos. 761/4, but incorporating "HONG KONG '97" logo and with some values changed.

770 30c. As Type **167** . . . . . 1·25 50
771 65c. Gibbs Hill Lighthouse 2·00 1·50
772 80c. St David's Lighthouse 2·25 2·00
773 $2.50 North Rock Beacon . . 4·50 6·50

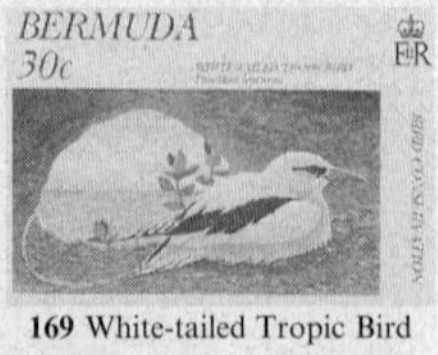

169 White-tailed Tropic Bird

1997. Bird Conservation. Multicoloured.

774 30c. Type **169** 60 50
775 60c. White-tailed tropic bird and chick (vert) . . . . . 1·25 1·25
776 80c. Cahow and chick (vert) 1·75 2·00
777 $2.50 Cahow . . . . 4·00 5·50

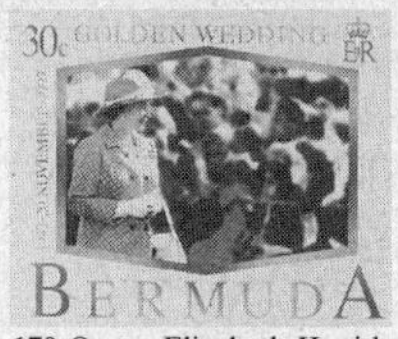

170 Queen Elizabeth II with Crowd

1997. Golden Wedding of Queen Elizabeth and Prince Philip. Multicoloured.

778 30c. Type **170** 50 40
779 $2 Queen Elizabeth and Prince Philip . . . . . . 2·75 3·75

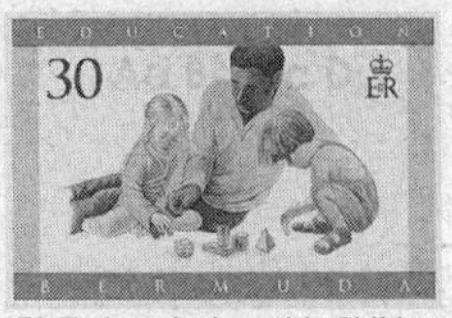

171 Father playing with Children

1997. Education. Multicoloured.

781 30c. Type **171** 50 40
782 40c. Teacher and children with map 60 55
783 60c. Boys holding sports trophy . . . . 85 1·25
784 65c. Pupils outside Berkeley Institute . . . . 90 1·25
785 80c. Scientific experiments . . 1·25 1·75
786 90c. New graduates . . . . . 1·40 2·25

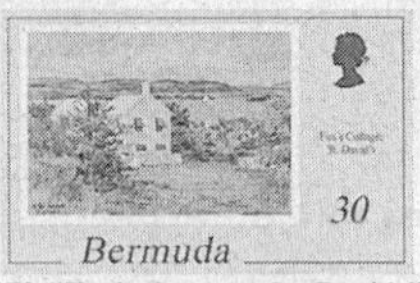

172 "Fox's Cottage, St. Davids" (Ethel Tucker)

1998. Paintings by Catherine and Ethel Tucker. Multicoloured.

788 30c. Type **172** 80 40
789 40c. "East Side, Somerset" 95 70
790 65c. "Long Bay Road, Somerset" . . . . 1·60 1·25
791 $2 "Flatts Village" . . . . . 3·75 5·00

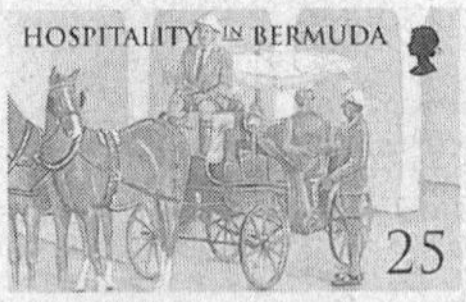

173 Horse and Carriage

1998. Hospitality in Bermuda. Multicoloured.

809 25c. Type **173** 55 35
810 30c. Golf club desk 80 60
811 65c. Chambermaid preparing room . . . . 1·00 1·25
812 75c. Kitchen staff under training . . . . 1·10 1·40
813 80c. Waiter at beach hotel . . 1·25 1·50
814 90c. Nightclub bar . . . . . 1·25 2·25

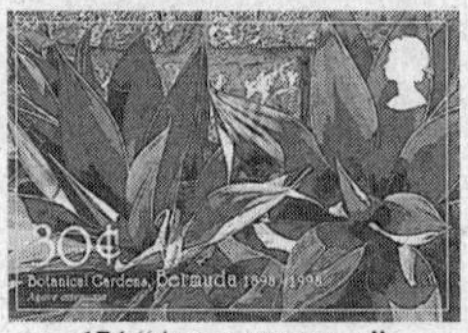

174 "Agave attenuata"

1998. Centenary of Botanical Gardens. Multicoloured.

815 30c. Type **174** 75 40
816 65c. Bermuda palmetto tree 1·50 90
817 $1 Banyan tree . . . . 2·00 2·00
818 $2 Cedar tree . . . . 3·25 4·50

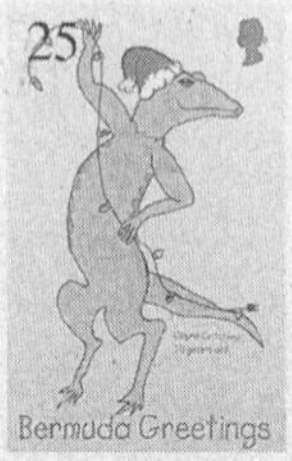

175 Lizard with Fairy Lights (Claire Critchley)

1998. Christmas. Children's Paintings. Multicoloured.

819 25c. Type **175** 50 35
820 40c. "Christmas stairway" (Cameron Rowling) (horiz) 75 90

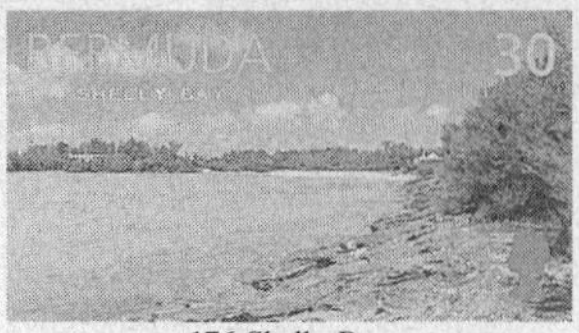

176 Shelly Bay

1999. Bermuda Beaches. Multicoloured.

821 30c. Type **176** 75 40
822 60c. Catherine's Bay . . . . 1·00 90
823 65c. Jobson's Cove . . . . . 1·10 1·00
824 $2 Warwick Long Bay . . . 3·25 4·25

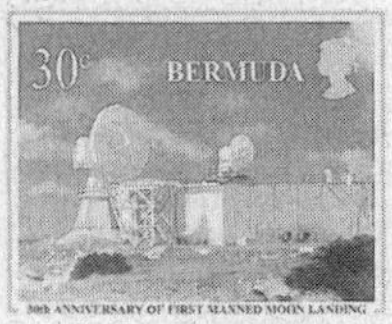

177 Tracking Station

1999. 30th Anniv of First Manned Landing on Moon. Multicoloured.

825 30c. Type **177** 65 40
826 60c. Mission launch (vert) . . 1·00 90
827 75c. Aerial view of tracking station, Bermuda . . . . . 1·25 1·25
828 $2 Astronaut on Moon (vert) 3·00 4·00

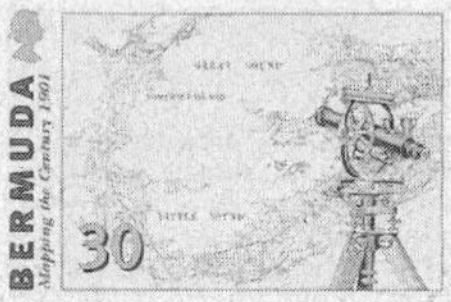

178 Theodolite and Map, 1901

1999. Centenary of First Digital Map of Bermuda.

830 **178** 30c. multicoloured 75 40
831 – 65c. black, stone & silver 1·40 1·25
832 – 80c. multicoloured . . . . 1·60 1·50
833 – $1 multicoloured . . . . 1·75 2·00

DESIGNS: 65c. Street map, 1901; 80c. Street plan and aerial photograph, 1999; $1 Satellite and Bermuda from Space, 1999.

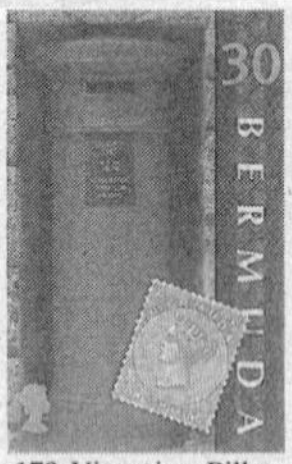

179 Victorian Pillar Box and Bermuda 1865 1s. Stamp

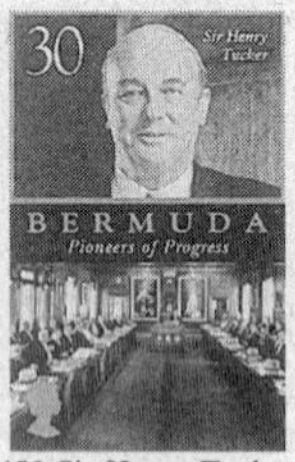

180 Sir Henry Tucker and Meeting of House of Assembly

1999. Bermuda Postal History. Multicoloured.

834 30c. Type **179** 65 40
835 75c. King George V pillar box and 1920 2s. stamp . . 1·40 1·25
836 95c. King George VI wall box and 1938 3d. stamp . . 1·60 1·75
837 $1 Queen Elizabeth II pillar box and 1953 Coronation 1½d. stamp . . . . 1·60 1·75

2000. Pioneers of Progress. Each brown, black and gold.

838 30c. Type **180** 60 70
839 30c. Gladys Morrell and suffragettes 60 70
840 30c. Dr. E. F. Gordon and workers 60 70

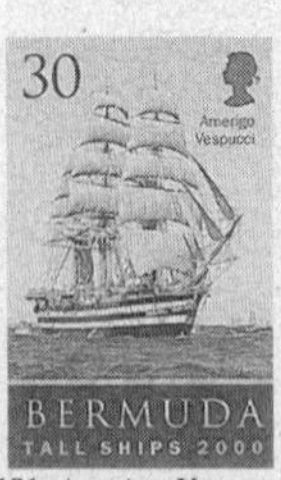

181 *Amerigo Vespucci* (full-rigged ship)

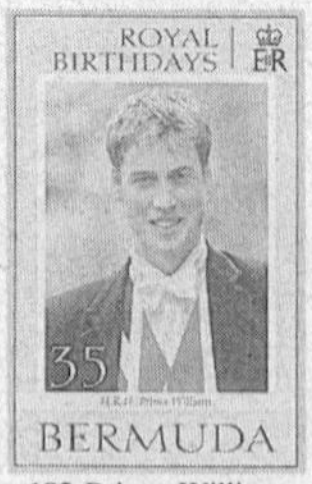

182 Prince William

2000. Tall Ships Race. Multicoloured.

841 30c. Type **181** 75 45
842 60c. *Europa* (barque) . . . . 1·10 1·25
843 80c. *Juan Sebastian de Elcano* (schooner) . . . . 1·25 1·50

2000. Royal Birthdays. Multicoloured.

844 35c. Type **182** 80 45
845 40c. Duke of York 85 50
846 50c. Princess Royal 90 70
847 70c. Princess Margaret . . . 1·10 1·40
848 $1 Queen Elizabeth the Queen Mother . . . . . . 1·60 2·00

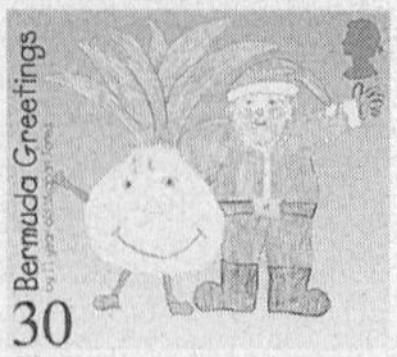

183 Santa Claus with Smiling Vegetable (Meghan Jones)

2000. Christmas. Children's Paintings. Multicoloured.

850 30c. Type **183** 60 45
851 45c. Christmas tree and presents (Carlita Lodge) . . 80 80

2001. Endangered Species. Bird Conservation. Designs as Nos. 774/7, but with different face values, inscriptions redrawn and WWF panda emblem added. Multicoloured.

852 15c. As Type **169** 45 50
853 15c. Cahow 45 50
854 20c. White-tailed tropic bird with chick (vert) 45 50
855 20c. Cahow with chick (vert) 45 50

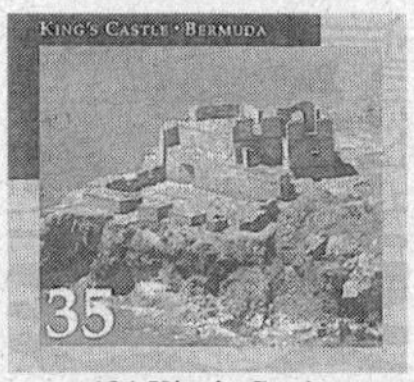

184 King's Castle

2001. Historic Buildings, St. George's. Multicoloured.

857 35c. Type **184** 70 55
858 50c. Bridge House 90 75
859 55c. Whitehall 95 80
860 70c. Fort Cunningham . . . 1·25 1·40
861 85c. St. Peter's Church . . . 1·50 1·75
862 95c. Water Street . . . . . . 1·60 1·90

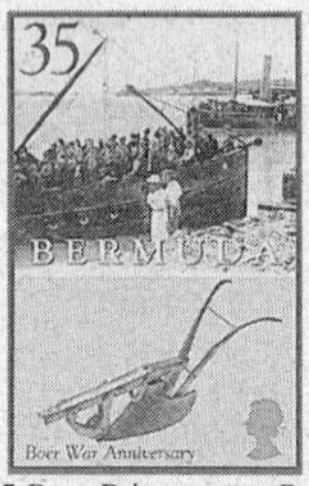

185 Boer Prisoners on Boat and Plough

2001. Centenary of Anglo-Boer War. Multicoloured.

863 35c. Type **185** 70 55
864 50c. Prisoners in shelter and boot 90 75
865 70c. Elderly Boer with children and jewellery . . . 1·25 1·40
866 95c. Bermuda residents and illustrated envelope of 1902 1·75 2·00

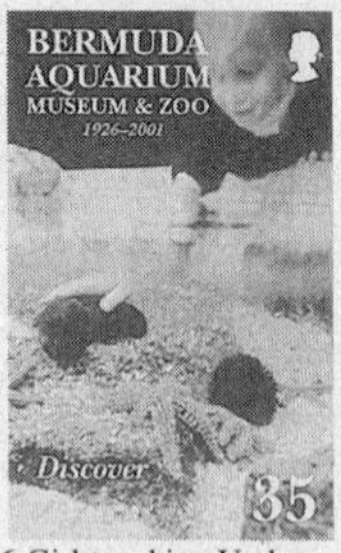

186 Girl touching Underwater Environment

2001. 75th Anniv of Bermuda Aquarium. Multicoloured.

867 35c. Type **186** 50 55
868 50c. Museum exhibits (horiz) 70 75
869 55c. Feeding giant tortoise (horiz) 75 80
870 70c. Aquarium building (horiz) . . . . 1·00 1·10
871 80c. Lesson from inside tank 1·10 1·25
872 95c. Turtle . . . . 1·40 1·50

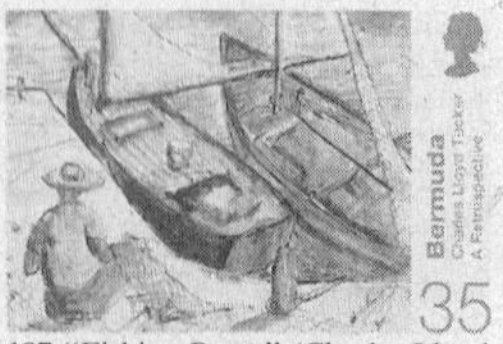

187 "Fishing Boats" (Charles Lloyd Tucker)

2001. Paintings of Charles Lloyd Tucker. Multicoloured.

873 35c. Type **187** 50 55
874 70c. "Bandstand and City Hall, Hamilton" . . . . . 1·00 1·10

875		85c. "Hamilton Harbour"	1·25	1·40
876		$1 "Train in Front Street, Hamilton"	1·40	1·50

2002. Golden Jubilee. As T **200** of Ascension.

877		10c. black, violet and gold	15	20
878		35c. multicoloured	1·00	1·10
879		70c. black, violet and gold	1·25	1·40
880		85c. multicoloured	1·40	1·50

DESIGNS: 10c. Princess Elizabeth with corgi; 35c. Queen Elizabeth in evening dress, 1965; 70c. Queen Elizabeth in car, 1952; 85c. Queen Elizabeth on Merseyside, 1991.

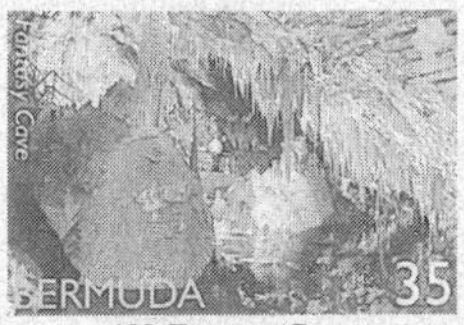

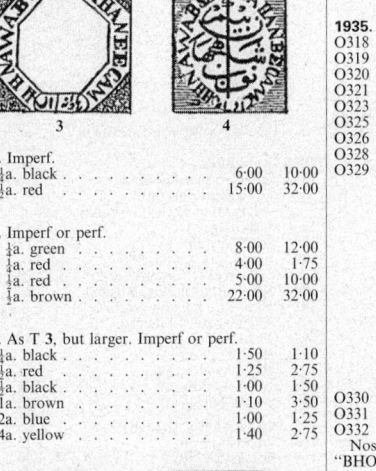

188 Fantasy Cave

2002. Caves. Multicoloured.

882		35c. Type **188**	50	55
883		70c. Crystal Cave	1·00	1·10
884		80c. Prospero's Cave	1·10	1·25
885		$1 Cathedral Cave	1·40	1·50

EXPRESS LETTER STAMP

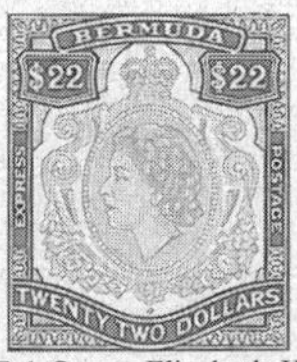

E **1** Queen Elizabeth II

1996.

E1	E **1**	$22 orange and blue	30·00	32·00

BHOPAL Pt. 1

A state of C. India. Now uses Indian stamps.

12 pies = 1 anna; 16 annas = 1 rupee.

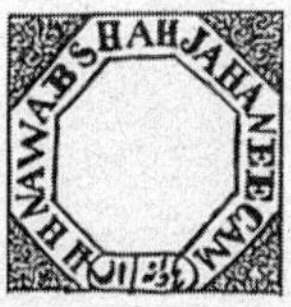

3

4

1876. Imperf.

5	**3**	¼a. black	6·00	10·00
2		½a. red	15·00	32·00

1878. Imperf or perf.

7	**4**	¼a. green	8·00	12·00
15		¼a. red	4·00	1·75
8		½a. red	5·00	10·00
9		½a. brown	22·00	32·00

1881. As T **3**, but larger. Imperf or perf.

29		¼a. black	1·50	1·10
37		½a. red	1·25	2·75
46		½a. black	1·00	1·50
30		1a. brown	1·10	3·50
31		2a. blue	1·00	1·25
32		4a. yellow	1·40	2·75

13

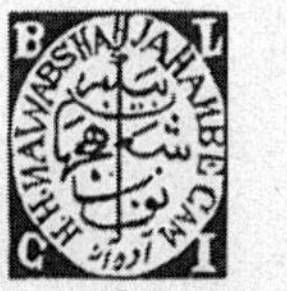

15

1884. Perf.

49	**13**	¼a. green	4·00	11·00
76		¼a. black	85	85

1884. Imperf or perf.

64	**15**	¼a. green	40	35
65		¼a. black	30	30
53		½a. black	50	2·25
56		½a. red	50	1·00

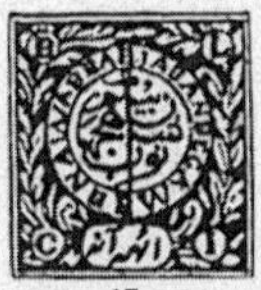

17

1890. Imperf or perf.

71	**17**	8a. greenish black	11·00	18·00

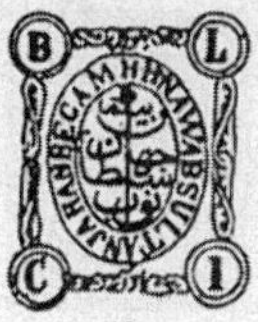

19

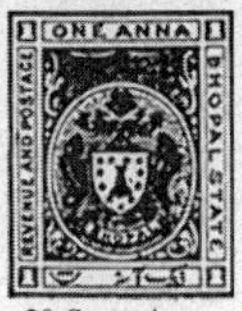

20 State Arms

1902. Imperf.

90	**19**	¼a. red	70	3·25
91		½a. black	65	4·00
92		1a. brown	1·10	4·75
94		2a. blue	4·00	18·00
96		4a. yellow	14·00	40·00
97		8a. lilac	38·00	95·00
98		1r. red	55·00	£130

1908. Perf.

100	**20**	1a. green	3·00	3·00

OFFICIAL STAMPS

1908. As T **20** but inscr "H.H. BEGUM'S SERVICE" optd **SERVICE**.

O301		½a. green	2·00	10
O302		1a. red	3·75	35
O307		2a. blue	3·00	40
O304		4a. brown	9·50	30

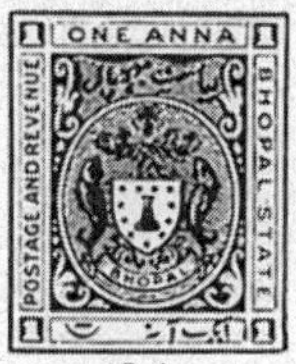

O 4

1930. Type O **4** optd **SERVICE**.

O309	O **4**	½a. green	8·00	1·25
O310		1a. red	9·00	15
O311		2a. blue	8·50	45
O312		4a. brown	8·00	80

1932. As T **20**, but inscr "POSTAGE" at left and "BHOPAL STATE" at right, optd **SERVICE**.

O313		¼a. orange	2·50	50

1932. As T **20**, but inscr "POSTAGE" at left and "BHOPAL GOVT" at right, optd **SERVICE**.

O314		½a. green	4·50	10
O315		1a. red	8·00	15
O316		2a. blue	8·00	45
O317		4a. brown	6·50	1·00

1935. Nos. O314, etc, surch.

O318		¼a. on ½a. green	21·00	12·00
O319		3p. on ½a. green	2·50	3·00
O320		¼a. on 2a. blue	22·00	15·00
O321		3p. on 2a. blue	3·75	3·25
O323		¼a. on 4a. brown	55·00	20·00
O325		3p. on 4a. brown	2·50	2·75
O326		1a. on ½a. green	3·25	1·50
O328		1a. on 2a. blue	70	1·10
O329		1a. on 4a. brown	4·25	4·50

O 8

1935.

O330	O **8**	1a.3p. blue and red	3·50	50
O331		1a.6p. blue and red	1·75	50
O332		1a.6p. red	4·75	1·00

Nos. O331/2 are similar to Type O **8**, but inscr "BHOPAL STATE POSTAGE".

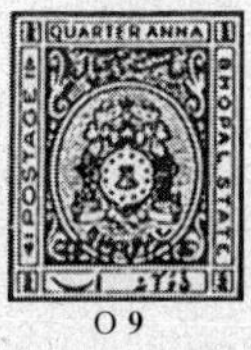

O 9

1936. Type O **9** optd **SERVICE**.

O333	O **9**	¼a. yellow	90	30
O335		1a. red	1·50	10

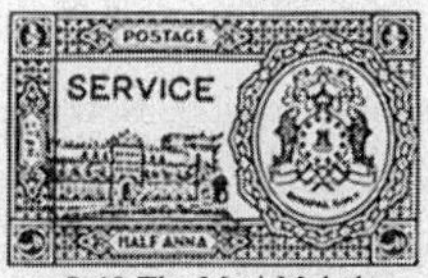

O **10** The Moti Mahal

1936. As Type O **4** optd **SERVICE**.

O336d	O **10**	½a. purple and green	70	30
O337	–	2a. brown and blue	1·60	40
O338	–	2a. green and violet	7·50	30
O339	–	4a. blue and brown	3·25	50
O340	–	8a. purple and blue	4·00	1·25
O341	–	1r. blue and purple	14·00	6·00

DESIGNS: 2a. The Moti Masjid; 4a. Taj Mahal and Be-Nazir Palaces; 8a. Ahmadabad Palace; 1r. Rait Ghat.

Nos. O336 is inscr "BHOPAL GOVT" below the arms, other values have "BHOPAL STATE".

1940. Animal designs, as Type O **10** but inscr "SERVICE" in bottom panel.

O344		¼a. blue (Tiger)	3·25	1·10
O345		1a. purple (Spotted deer)	17·00	1·40

1941. As Type O **8** but "SERVICE" inscr instead of optd.

O346	O **8**	1a.3p. green	1·00	1·00

1944. Palaces as Type O **10** but smaller.

O347		½a. green (Moti Mahal)	85	70
O348		2a. violet (Moti Masjid)	7·00	3·00
O348c		2a. purple (Moti Masjid)	1·90	2·75
O349		4a. brown (Be-Nazir)	4·25	1·40

The 2a. and 4a. are inscr "BHOPAL STATE", and the other "BHOPAL GOVT".

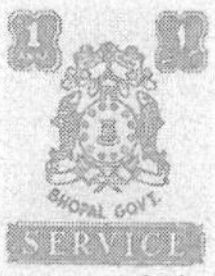

O **14** Arms of Bhopal

1944.

O350	O **14**	3p. blue	65	50
O351b		9p. brown	2·00	2·75
O352		1a. purple	4·25	1·10
O352b		1a. violet	7·00	2·25
O353		1½a. red	1·25	50
O354		3a. yellow	8·50	9·00
O354d		3a. brown	80·00	70·00
O355		6a. red	12·00	35·00

1949. Surch **2 As.** and bars.

O356	O **14**	2a. on 1½a. red	2·50	5·50

1949. Surch **2 As.** and ornaments.

O357	O **14**	2a. on 1½a. red	£650	£650

BHOR Pt. 1

A state of W. India, Bombay district. Now uses Indian stamps.

12 pies = 1 anna; 16 annas = 1 rupee.

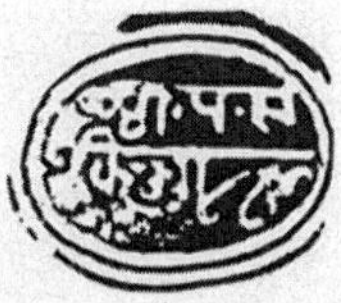

1

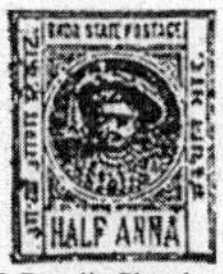

3 Pandit Shankar Rao

1879. Imperf.

1	**1**	½a. red	2·00	3·75

Similar to T **1**, but rectangular.

2		1a. red	4·00	5·50

1901. Imperf.

3	**3**	½a. red	11·00	32·00

BHUTAN Pt. 21

An independent territory in treaty relations with India and bounded by India, Sikkim and Tibet.

100 chetrum = 1 ngultrum.

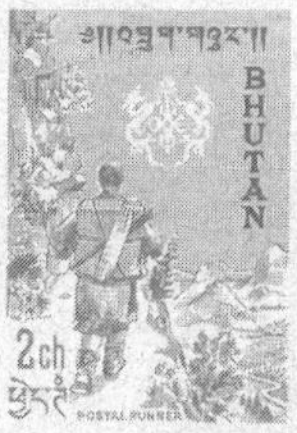

1 Postal Runner

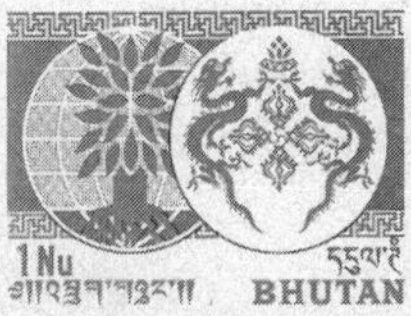

2 "Uprooted Tree" Emblem and Crest of Bhutan

1962.

1	**1**	2ch. red and grey	10	10
2	–	3ch. red and blue	20	20
3	–	5ch. brown and green	1·00	1·00
4	–	15ch. yellow, black and red	10	10
5	**1**	33ch. green and violet	20	20
6	–	70ch. ultramarine and blue	60	60
7	–	1n.30 black and blue	1·25	1·25

DESIGNS—HORIZ: 3, 70ch. Archer. 5ch., 1n.30, Yak. 15ch. Map of Bhutan, Maharaja Druk Gyalpo and Paro Dzong (fortress and monastery).

1962. World Refugee Year.

8	**2**	1n. red and blue	45	45
9		2n. violet and green	1·40	1·40

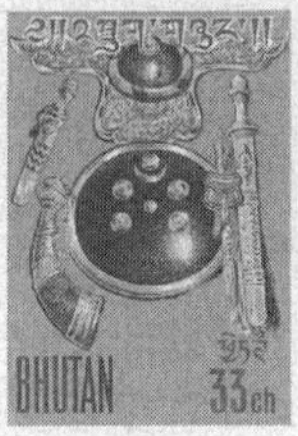

3 Accoutrements of Ancient Warrior

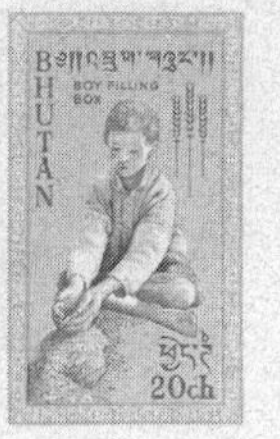

4 "Boy filling box" (with grain)

1962. Membership of Colombo Plan.

10	**3**	33ch. multicoloured	20	20
11		70ch. multicoloured	35	35
12		1n.30 red, brown & yellow	80	80

1963. Freedom from Hunger.

13	**4**	20ch. brown, blue & yellow	25	25
14		1n.50 purple, brown & blue	90	90

1964. Winter Olympic Games, Innsbruck, and Bhutanese Winter Sports Committee Fund. Nos. 10/12 surch **INNSBRUCK 1964 +50 ch**, Olympic rings and emblem.

15	**3**	33ch.+50ch. multicoloured	2·75	2·75
16		70ch.+50ch. multicoloured	2·75	2·75
17		1n.30+50ch. multicoloured	2·75	2·75

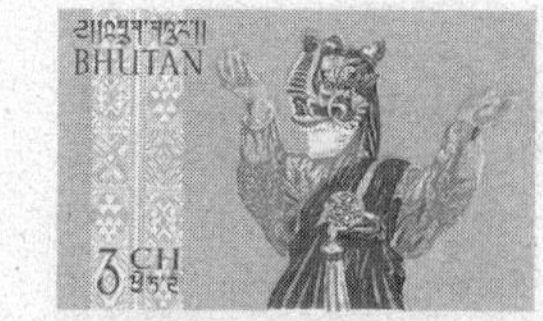

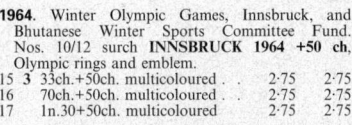

6 Dancer with upraised hands

1964. Bhutanese Dancers. Multicoloured.

18		2ch. Standing on one leg (vert)	10	10
19		3ch. Type **6**	10	10
20		5ch. With tambourine (vert)	10	10
21		20ch. As 2ch.	10	10
22		33ch. Type **6**	15	15
23		70ch. With sword	25	25
24		1n. With tasselled hat (vert)	55	55
25		1n.30 As 5ch.	70	70
26		2n. As 70ch.	1·25	1·25

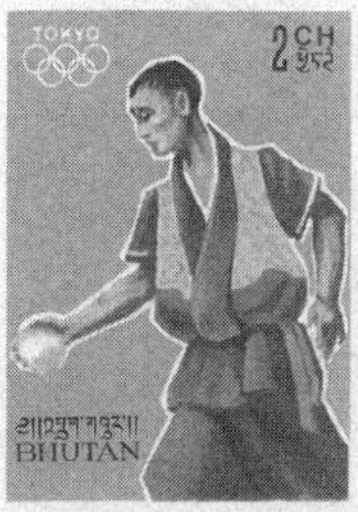

7 Bhutanese Athlete

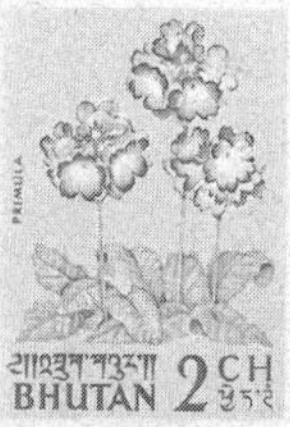

9 Primula

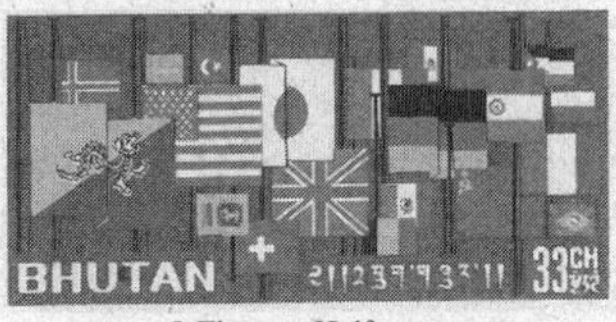

8 Flags at Half-mast

1964. Olympic Games, Tokyo. Multicoloured.

27		2ch. Type **7**	10	10
28		5ch. Boxing	10	10
29		15ch. Type **7**	10	10
30		33ch. As 5ch.	15	15
31		1n. Archery	55	55
32		2n. Football	90	90
33		3n. As 1n.	1·50	1·50

1964. Pres. Kennedy Commemoration.

34	**8**	33ch. multicoloured	20	20
35		1n. multicoloured	55	55
36		3n. multicoloured	1·25	1·25

1965. Flowers. Multicoloured.

37		2ch. Type **9**	10	10
38		5ch. Gentian	10	10
39		15ch. Type **9**	10	10
40		33ch. As 5ch.	15	15
41		50ch. Rhododendron	20	20
42		75ch. Peony	30	30
43		1n. As 50ch.	30	30
44		2n. As 75ch.	70	70

1965. Churchill Commemoration. Optd **WINSTON CHURCHILL 1874 1965**.

45	**1**	33ch. green and violet	15	15
46	**8**	1n. multicoloured	45	45
47	–	1n. multicoloured (No. 43)	45	45
48	–	2n. multicoloured (No. 44)	75	75
49	**8**	3n. multicoloured	1·25	1·25

11 Pavilion and Skyscrapers

1965. New York World's Fair. Mult.

50		1ch. Type **11**	10	10
51		10ch. Buddha and Michelangelo's "Pieta"	10	10
52		20ch. Bhutan houses and New York skyline	10	10
53		33ch. Bhutan and New York bridges	10	10
54		1n.50 Type **11**	55	55
55		2n. As 10ch.	90	90

1965. Surch.

56	**2**	5ch. on 1n. (No. 8)	24·00	24·00
57		5ch. on 2n. (No. 9)	27·00	27·00
58	–	10ch. on 70ch. (No. 23)	6·75	6·75
59	–	10ch. on 2n. (No. 26)	6·75	6·75
60	–	15ch. on 70ch. (No. 6)	5·00	5·00
61	–	15ch. on 1n.30 (No. 7)	5·00	5·00
62	–	20ch. on 1n. (No. 24)	6·75	6·75
63	–	20ch. on 1n.30 (No. 25)	6·75	6·75

13 "Telstar" and Portable Transmitter

1966. Centenary of I.T.U. Multicoloured.

64		35ch. Type **13**	20	20
65		2n. "Telstar" & morse key	65	65
66		3n. "Relay" and headphones	1·00	1·00

14 Asiatic Black Bear

1966. Animals. Multicoloured.

68		1ch. Type **14**	10	10
69		2ch. Snow leopard	10	10
70		4ch. Pygmy hog	10	10
71		8ch. Tiger	10	10
72		10ch. Dhole	10	10
73		75ch. As 8ch.	30	30
74		1n. Takin	30	30
75		1n.50 As 10ch.	45	45
76		2n. As 4ch.	80	80
77		3n. As 2ch.	1·00	1·00
78		4n. Type **14**	1·25	1·25
79		5n. As 1n.	1·60	1·60

15 Simtoke Dzong (fortress)

1966.

80	–	5c. brown	15	15
81	**15**	15ch. brown	15	15
82		20ch. green	20	20

DESIGN: 5ch. Rinpung Dzong (fortress).

16 King Jigme Dorji Wangchuck (obverse of 50n.p. coin)

1966. 40th Anniv of King Jigme Wangchuck's Accession (father of King Jigme Dorji Wangchuck). Circular designs, embossed on gold foil, backed with multicoloured patterned paper. Imperf.

Sizes: (a) Diameter 38 mm; (b) Diameter 50 mm; (c) Diameter 63 mm.

		(i) 50n.p. Coin		
83	**16**	10ch. green (a)	20	20
		(ii) 1r. Coin		
84	**16**	25ch. green (b)	25	25
		(iii) 3r. Coin		
85	**16**	50ch. green (c)	50	50
		(iv) 1 sertum Coin		
86	**16**	1n. red (a)	90	90
87	–	1n.30 red (a)	1·25	1·25
		(v) 2 sertum Coin		
88	**16**	2n. red (b)	1·75	1·75
89	–	3n. red (b)	2·75	2·75
		(vi) 5 sertum Coin		
90	**16**	4n. red (c)	3·75	3·75
91	–	5n. red (c)	4·50	4·50

Nos. 87, 89 and 91 show the reverse side of the coins (Symbol).

17 "Abominable Snowman"

1966. "Abominable Snowman". Various triangular designs.

92	**17**	1ch. multicoloured	10	10
93	–	2ch. multicoloured	10	10
94	–	3ch. multicoloured	10	10
95	–	4ch. multicoloured	10	10
96	–	5ch. multicoloured	10	10
97	–	15ch. multicoloured	10	10
98	–	30ch. multicoloured	10	10
99	–	40ch. multicoloured	20	20
100	–	50ch. multicoloured	20	20
101	–	1n.25 multicoloured	35	35
102	–	2n.50 multicoloured	70	70
103	–	3n. multicoloured	80	80
104	–	5n. multicoloured	1·40	1·40
105	–	6n. multicoloured	1·40	1·40
106	–	7n. multicoloured	1·75	1·75

1967. Air. Optd **AIR MAIL** and helicopter motif.

107	**6**	33ch. multicoloured	10	10
108	–	50ch. mult (No. 41)	15	15
109	–	70ch. mult (No. 23)	20	20
110	–	75ch. mult (No. 42)	25	25
111	–	1n. mult (No. 24)	30	30
112	–	1n.50 mult (No. 75)	35	35
113	–	2n. mult (No. 76)	35	35
114	–	3n. mult (No. 77)	65	65
115	**14**	4n. multicoloured	90	90
116	–	5n. mult (No. 79)	1·40	1·40

20 "Lilium sherriffiae"

1967. Flowers. Multicoloured.

117		3ch. Type **20**	10	10
118		5ch. "Meconopsis"	10	10
119		7ch. "Rhododendron dhwoju"	10	10
120		10ch. "Pleione hookeriana"	10	10
121		50ch. Type **20**	20	20
122		1n. As 5ch.	35	35
123		2n.50 As 7ch.	90	90
124		4n. As 10ch.	1·40	1·40
125		5n. "Rhododendron giganteum"	1·75	1·75

21 Scouts planting Sapling

1967. Bhutanese Boy Scouts. Multicoloured.

126		5ch. Type **21**	10	10
127		10ch. Scouts preparing meal	10	10
128		15ch. Scout mountaineering	20	20
129		50ch. Type **21**	30	30
130		1n.25. As 10ch.	45	45
131		4n. As 15ch.	1·25	1·25

1967. World Fair, Montreal. Nos. 53/5 optd **expo67** and emblem.

133	–	33ch. multicoloured	20	20
134	**11**	1n.50 multicoloured	40	40
135	–	2n. multicoloured	55	55

23 Avro Lancaster Bomber

1967. Churchill and Battle of Britain Commemoration. Multicoloured.

137		45ch. Type **23**	25	25
138		2n. Supermarine Spitfire fighter	50	50
139		4n. Hawker Hurricane Mk IIC fighter	1·00	1·00

1967. World Scout Jamboree, Idaho. Nos. 126/31 optd. **WORLD JAMBOREE IDAHO, U.S.A. AUG. 1-9/67.**

141	**21**	5ch. multicoloured	10	10
142	–	10ch. multicoloured	10	10
143	–	15ch. multicoloured	10	10
144	–	50ch. multicoloured	30	30
145	–	1n.25 multicoloured	55	55
146	–	4n. multicoloured	1·60	1·60

25 Painting

1967. Bhutan Girl Scouts. Multicoloured.

148		5ch. Type **25**	10	10
149		10ch. Playing musical instrument	10	10
150		15ch. Picking fruit	10	10
151		1n.50 Type **25**	30	30
152		2n.50 As 10ch.	45	45
153		5n. As 15ch.	1·10	1·10

26 Astronaut in Space

1967. Space Achievements. With laminated prismatic-ribbed plastic surface. Multicoloured.

155		3ch. Type **26** (postage)	15	15
156		5ch. Space vehicle and astronaut	15	15
157		7ch. Astronaut and landing vehicle	20	20
158		10ch. Three astronauts in space	30	30
159		15ch. Type **26**	35	35
160		30ch. As 5ch.	70	70
161		50ch. As 7ch.	90	90
162		1n.25 As 10ch.	2·75	2·75
163		2n.50 Type **26** (air)	90	90
164		4n. As 5ch.	1·40	1·40
165		5n. As 7ch.	2·25	2·25
166		9n. As 10ch.	3·25	3·25

The laminated plastic surface gives the stamps a three-dimensional effect.

27 Tashichho Dzong

1968.

168	**27**	10ch. purple and green	20	15

28 Elephant

1968. Mythological Creatures.

169	**28**	2ch. red, blue and brown (postage)	15	15
170	–	3ch. pink, blue & green	15	15
171	–	4ch. orange, green & blue	15	15
172	–	5ch. blue, yellow & pink	15	15
173	–	15ch. green, purple & blue	15	15
174	**28**	20ch. brown, blk & orge	15	15
175	–	30ch. yellow, black & blue	20	20
176	–	50ch. bistre, green & black	25	25
177	–	1n.25 black, green & red	25	25
178	–	2n. yellow, violet & black	35	35
179	**28**	1n.50 green, purple and yellow (air)	35	35
180	–	2n.50 red, black & blue	45	45
181	–	4n. orange, green & black	65	65
182	–	5n. brown, grey & orange	90	90
183	–	10n. violet, grey & black	1·75	1·75

DESIGNS: 3, 30ch., 2n.50, Garuda; 4, 50ch., 4n. Tiger; 5ch., 1n.25, 5n. Wind horse; 15ch., 2, 10n. Snow lion.

29 Tongsa Dzong

1968.

184	**29**	50ch. green	30	30
185	–	75ch. brown and blue	35	35
186	–	1n. blue and violet	40	40

DESIGNS: 75ch. Daga Dzong; 1n. Lhuntsi Dzong.

30 Ward's Trogon

1968. Rare Birds.

187		2ch. Red-faced liocichla ("Crimson-winged Laughing Thrush") (horiz) (postage)	10	10
188		3ch. Type **30**	15	15
189		4ch. Burmese ("Grey") Peacock-pheasant (horiz)	20	20
190		5ch. Rufous-necked hornbill	25	25
191		15ch. Fire-tailed myzornis ("Myzornis") (horiz)	35	35
192		20ch. As No. 187	45	45
193		30ch. Type **30**	50	50
194		50ch. As No. 189	55	55
195		1n.25 As No. 190	75	75
196		2n. As No. 191	1·25	1·25
197		1n.50 As No. 187 (air)	85	85
198		2n.50 Type **30**	1·25	1·25
199		4n. As No. 189	1·90	1·90
200		5n. As No. 190	2·75	2·75
201		10n. As No. 191	5·25	5·25

31 Mahatma Gandhi

1969. Birth Centenary of Mahatma Gandhi.

202	**31**	20ch. brown and blue	45	45
203		2n. brown and yellow	1·10	1·10

1970. Various stamps surch **5 CH** or **20 CH.**

		(a) Freedom from Hunger (No. 14).		
223		20ch. on 1n.50 purple, brown and blue	2·25	2·25
		(b) Animals (Nos. 75/9).		
224		20ch. on 1n.50 multicoloured	2·25	2·25
225		20ch. on 2n. multicoloured	2·25	2·25
204		20ch. on 3n. multicoloured	90	90
205		20ch. on 4n. multicoloured	90	90
206		20ch. on 5n. multicoloured	90	90
		(c) Abominable Snowmen (Nos. 101/6).		
226		20ch. on 1n.25 multicoloured	2·25	2·25
227		20ch. on 2n.50 multicoloured	2·25	2·25

207 20ch. on 3n. multicoloured 90 90
208 20ch. on 5n. multicoloured 90 90
209 20ch. on 6n. multicoloured 90 90
210 20ch. on 7n. multicoloured 90 90

(d) Flowers (Nos. 124/5).
211 20ch. on 4n. multicoloured 90 90
212 20ch. on 5n. multicoloured 90 90

(e) Boy Scouts (Nos. 130/1).
228 20ch. on 1n.25 multicoloured 2·25 2·25
213 20ch. on 4n. multicoloured 90 90

(f) Churchill (Nos. 138/9).
229 20ch. on 2n. multicoloured 2·25 2·25
230 20ch. on 4n. multicoloured 2·25 2·25

(g) 1968 Pheasants (Appendix).
231 20ch. on 2n. multicoloured 3·50 3·50
214 20ch. on 4n. multicoloured 2·00 2·00
232 20ch. on 7n. multicoloured 3·50 3·50

(h) Mythological Creatures (Nos. 175/80 and 182/3).
233 5ch. on 30ch. yellow, black and blue (postage) 70 70
234 5ch. on 50ch. bistre, green and black 70 70
235 5ch. on 1n.25 black, green and red 70 70
236 5ch. on 2n. yellow, vio & blk 70 70
215 20ch. on 2n. yellow, violet and black 90 90
237 5ch. on 1n.50 green, purple and brown (air) 70 70
238 5ch. on 2n.50 red, black and blue 70 70
216 20ch. on 5n. brown, grey and orange 90 90
217 20ch. on 10n. violet, grey and black 90 90

(i) Rare Birds (Nos. 193/201).
239 20ch. on 30ch. mult (postage) 3·50 3·50
240 20ch. on 50ch. multicoloured 3·50 3·50
241 20ch. on 1n. 25. multicoloured 3·50 3·50
218 20ch. on 2n. multicoloured 1·75 1·75
242 20ch. on 1n.50. mult (air) 3·50 3·50
219 20ch. on 2n.50. multicoloured 2·00 2·00
220 20ch. on 4n. multicoloured 2·00 2·00
221 20ch. on 5n. multicoloured 2·00 2·00
222 20ch. on 10n. multicoloured 2·00 2·00

(j) 1969 U.P.U. (Appendix).
243 20ch. on 1n.05. multicoloured 2·25 2·25
244 20ch. on 1n.40. multicoloured 2·25 2·25
245 20ch. on 4n. multicoloured 2·25 2·25

For stamps surcharged with 55 or 90ch. values, see Nos. 253/65 and for 25ch. surcharges see Nos. 385/410.

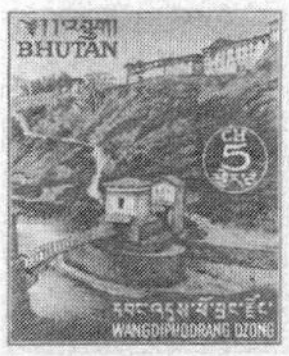

33 Wangdiphodrang Dzong and Bridge

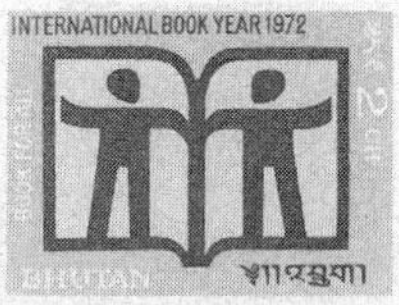

34 Book Year Emblem

1971.
246 33 2ch. grey 10 10
247 3ch. mauve 10 10
248 4ch. violet 10 10
249 5ch. green 10 10
250 10ch. brown 10 10
251 15ch. blue 15 15
252 20ch. purple 20 20

1971. Various stamps surch **55 CH** or **90 CH**. I. Dancers (Nos. 25/6).
253 55ch. on 1n.30 multicoloured 90 90
254 90ch. on 2n. multicoloured 90 90

II. Animals (Nos. 77/8).
255 55ch. on 3n. multicoloured 90 90
256 90ch. on 4n. multicoloured 90 90

III. Boy Scouts (No. 131).
257 90ch. on 4n. multicoloured 90 90

IV. 1968 Pheasants (Appendix).
258 55ch. on 5n. multicoloured 3·00 3·00
259 90ch. on 9n. multicoloured 3·00 3·00

V. Air. Mythological Creatures (No. 181).
260 55ch. on 4n. orange, green and black 55 55

VI. 1968 Mexico Olympics (Appendix).
261 90ch. on 1n.05 multicoloured 1·40 1·40

VII. Rare Birds (No. 196).
262 90ch. on 2n. multicoloured 3·00 3·00

VIII. 1969 U.P.U. (Appendix).
263 55ch. on 60ch. multicoloured 90 90

IX. 1970 New U.P.U. Headquarters (Appendix).
264 90ch. on 2n. 50 gold and red 7·50 7·50

X. 1971 Moon Vehicles (plastic-surfaced) (Appendix).
265 90ch. on 1n. 70 multicoloured 90 90

1972. International Book Year.
266 34 2ch. green and blue 15 15
267 3ch. brown and yellow 15 15
268 5ch. brown, orange & red 20 20
269 20ch. brown and blue 15 15

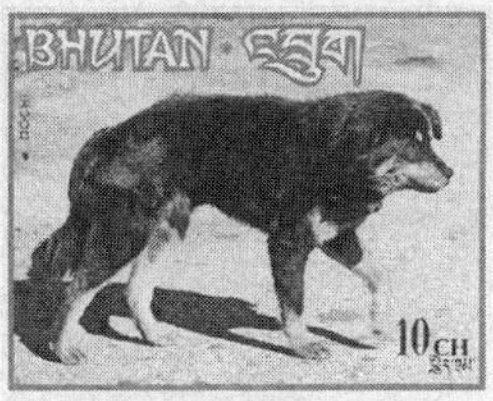

35 Dochi

1972. Dogs. Multicoloured.
270 5ch. Apsoo standing on hind legs (vert) 10 10
271 10ch. Type **35** 10 10
272 15ch. Brown and white damci 15 15
273 25ch. Black and white damci 15 15
274 55ch. Apsoo lying down 20 20
275 8n. Two damci 1·60 1·60

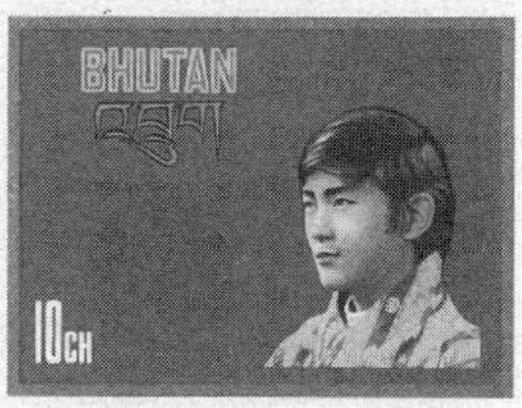

36 King and Royal Crest

1974. Coronation of King Jigme Singye Wangchuck. Multicoloured.
277 10ch. Type **36** 10 10
278 25ch. Bhutan Flag 10 10
279 1n.25 Good Luck signs 35 35
280 2n. Punakha Dzong 55 55
281 3n. Royal Crown 70 70

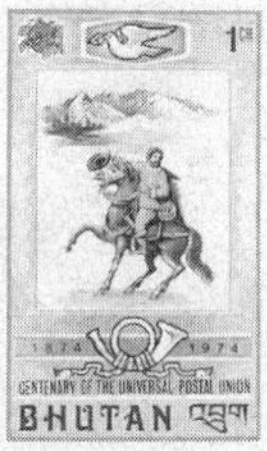

37 Mail Delivery by Horse

1974. Centenary of U.P.U. Multicoloured.
283 1ch. Type **37** (postage) 10 10
284 2ch. Early and modern locomotives 10 10
285 3ch. "Hindoostan" (paddle-steamer) and "Iberia" (liner) 20 20
286 4ch. Vickers Vimy and Concorde aircraft 30 30
287 25ch. Mail runner and jeep 15 15
288 1n. As 25ch. (air) 30 30
289 1n.40 As 2ch. 1·50 1·50
290 2n. As 4ch. 1·50 1·50

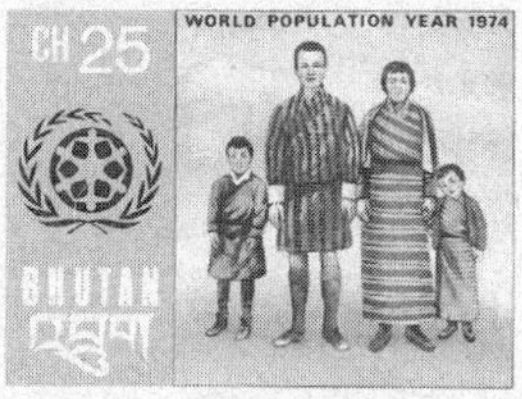

38 Family and W.P.Y. Emblem

1974. World Population Year.
292 38 25ch. multicoloured 10 10
293 50ch. multicoloured 20 20
294 90ch. multicoloured 35 35
295 2n.50 multicoloured 80 80

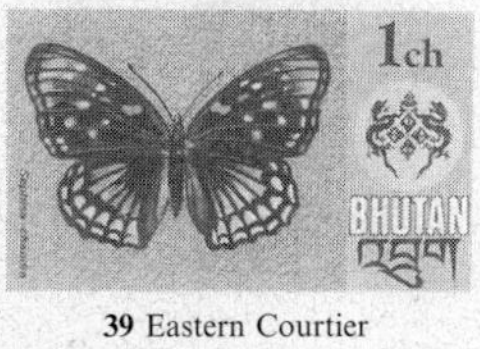

39 Eastern Courtier

1975. Butterflies. Multicoloured.
297 1ch. Type **39** 10 10
298 2ch. Bamboo forester 10 10
299 3ch. Tailed labyrinth 10 10
300 4ch. Blue duchess 10 10
301 5ch. Cruiser 15 15
302 10ch. Bhutan glory 15 15
303 3n. Bi-coloured commodore 65 65
304 5n. Red-breasted jezebel 1·40 1·40

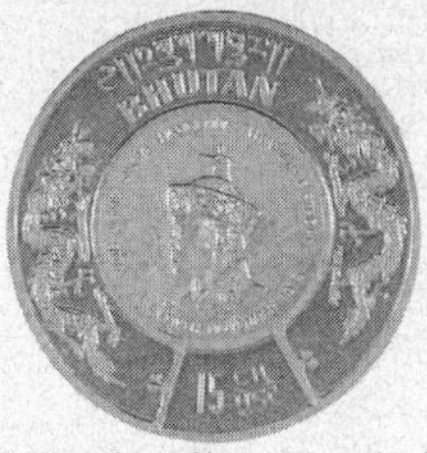

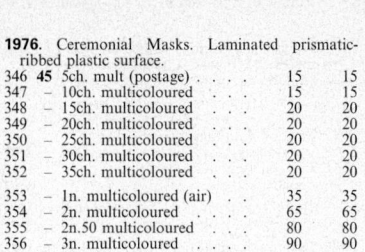

40 King Jigme Singye Wangchuck

1976. King Jigme's 20th Birthday. Imperf.
(a) Diameter 39 mm.
306 40 15ch. green on gold 10 10
307 1n. red on gold 30 30
308 – 1n.30 red on gold 35 35

(b) Diameter 50 mm.
309 40 25ch. green on gold 10 10
310 2n. red on gold 45 45
311 – 3n. red on gold 70 70

(c) Diameter 63 mm.
312 40 90ch. green on gold 25 25
313 4n. red on gold 1·10 1·10
314 – 5n. red on gold 1·25 1·25

DESIGN: 1n.30, 3, 5n. Decorative motif.

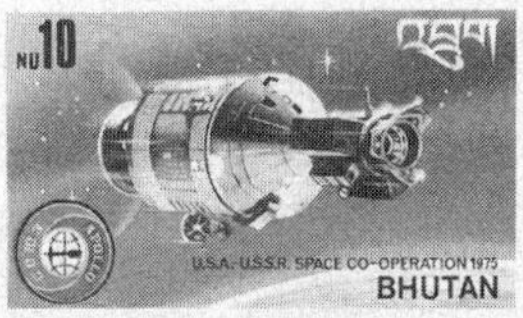

41 "Apollo"

1976. "Apollo"–"Soyuz" Space Link. Mult.
315 10n. Type **41** 2·40 2·40
316 10n. "Soyuz" 2·40 2·40

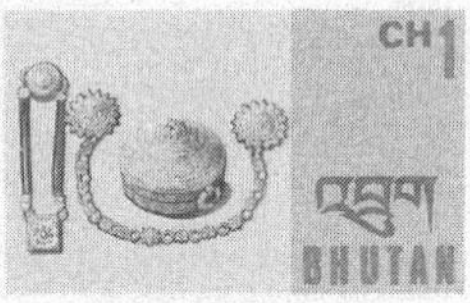

42 Jewellery

1976. Handicrafts and Craftsmen. Mult.
318 1ch. Type **42** 10 10
319 2ch. Coffee-pot, hand bell and sugar dish 10 10
320 3ch. Powder horns 10 10
321 4ch. Pendants and inlaid box 10 10
322 5ch. Painter 10 10
323 15ch. Silversmith 15 15
324 20ch. Wood carver with tools 15 15
325 1n.50 Textile printer 35 35
326 10n. Printer 2·75 2·75

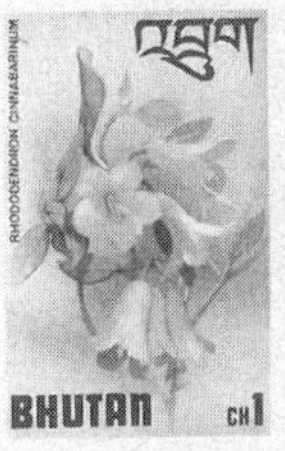

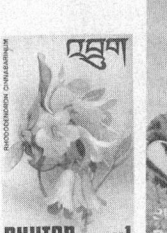

43 "Rhododendron cinnabarinum"

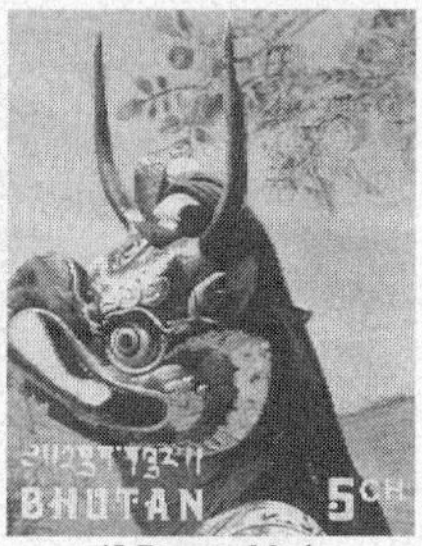

45 Dragon Mask

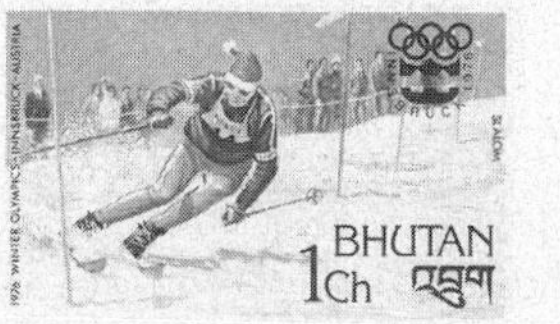

44 Skiing

1976. Rhododendrons. Multicoloured.
328 1ch. Type **43** 10 10
329 2ch. "R. campanulatum" 10 10
330 3ch. "R. fortunei" 10 10
331 4ch. "R. arboreum" 10 10
332 5ch. "R. arboreum" (different) 10 10
333 1n. "R. falconeri" 35 35
334 3n. "R. hodgsonii" 70 70
335 5n. "R. keysii" 1·40 1·40

1976. Winter Olympic Games, Innsbruck. Mult.
337 1ch. Type **44** 10 10
338 2ch. Bobsleighing 10 10
339 3ch. Ice hockey 10 10
340 4ch. Cross-country skiing 10 10
341 5ch. Women's figure skating 10 10
342 2n. Downhill skiing 45 45
343 4n. Speed skating 1·10 1·10
344 10n. Pairs figure skating 2·40 2·40

1976. Ceremonial Masks. Laminated prismatic-ribbed plastic surface.
346 45 5ch. mult (postage) 15 15
347 – 10ch. multicoloured 15 15
348 – 15ch. multicoloured 20 20
349 – 20ch. multicoloured 20 20
350 – 25ch. multicoloured 20 20
351 – 30ch. multicoloured 20 20
352 – 35ch. multicoloured 20 20
353 – 1n. multicoloured (air) 35 35
354 – 2n. multicoloured 65 65
355 – 2n.50 multicoloured 80 80
356 – 3n. multicoloured 90 90

DESIGNS: 10ch. to 3n. Similar Bhutanese masks.

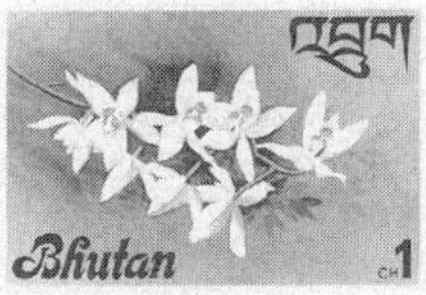

46 Orchid

1976. Flowers. Multicoloured.
358 1ch. Type **46** 10 10
359 2ch. Orchid (different) 10 10
360 3ch. Orchid (different) 10 10
361 4ch. "Primula denticulata" 10 10
362 5ch. Arum 10 10
363 2n. Orchid (different) 40 40
364 4n. "Leguminosa" 70 70
365 6n. Rhododendron 1·40 1·40

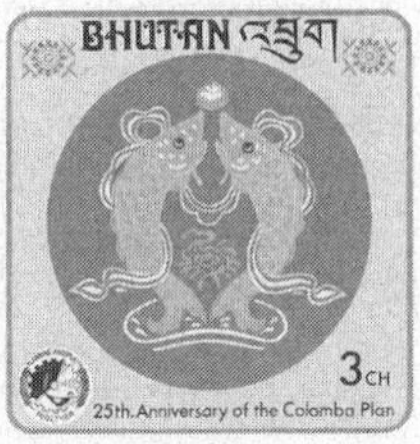

47 Double Carp Emblem

1976. 25th Anniv of Colombo Plan.
367 3ch. Type **47** 10 10
368 4ch. Vase emblem 10 10
369 5ch. Geometric design 10 10
370 25ch. Design incorporating animal's face 30 30
371 1n.25 Ornamental design 35 35
372 2n. Floral design 70 70
373 2n.50 Carousel design 90 90
374 3n. Wheel design 1·10 1·10

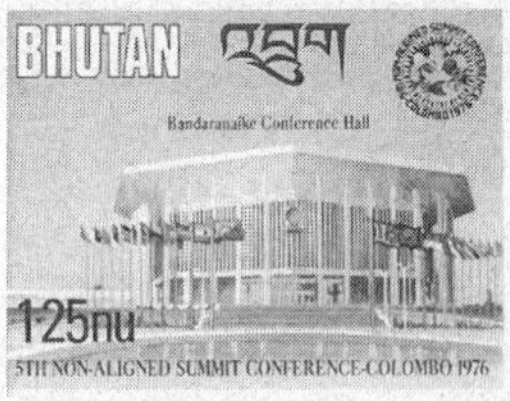

48 Bandaranaike Conference Hall

1976. 5th Non-aligned Countries Summit Conference, Colombo.
375 48 1n.25 multicoloured 35 35
376 2n.50 multicoloured 70 70

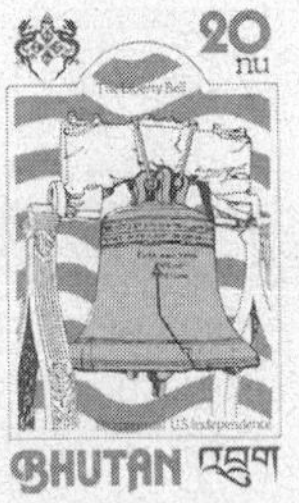

49 Liberty Bell

1978. Anniversaries and Events. Mult.
377 20n. Type **49** (bicentenary of U.S. independence) 4·50 4·50
378 20n. Alexander Graham Bell early telephone (telephone centenary) 4·50 4·50
379 20n. Archer (Olympic Games, Montreal) 4·50 4·50
380 20n. Alfred Nobel (75th anniv of Nobel Prizes) 4·50 4·50
381 20n. "Spirit of St. Louis" (50th anniv of Lindbergh's transatlantic flight) 4·50 4·50

382	20n. Airship LZ3 (75th anniv of Zeppelin)	4·50	4·50
383	20n. Queen Elizabeth II (25th anniv of Coronation) . . .	4·50	4·50

1978. Provisionals. Various stamps surch **25 Ch** (385, 394) or **25 CH** (others). I. Girl Scouts (No. 153).

385	25ch. on 5n. mult (postage)	1·40	1·40

II. Air, 1968 Mythological Creatures (Nos. 181 and 183).

386	25ch. on 4n. orange, green and black	1·40	1·40
387	25ch. on 10n. violet, grey and black	1·40	1·40

III. 1971 Admission to U.N. (Appendix).

388	25ch. on 3n. mult (postage)	1·40	1·40
389	25ch. on 5n. mult (air)	1·40	1·40
390	25ch. on 6n. multicoloured	1·40	1·40

IV. Boy Scouts Anniv (Appendix).

391	25ch. on 6n. multicoloured	1·40	1·40

V. 1972 Dogs (No. 275).

392	25ch. on 8n. multicoloured	1·40	1·40

VI. 1973 Dogs (Appendix).

393	25ch. on 6n. multicoloured	1·40	1·40

VII. 1973 "Indipex 73" (Appendix).

394	25ch. on 3n. mult (postage)	1·40	1·40
395	25ch. on 5n. mult (air)	1·40	1·40
396	25ch. on 6n. multicoloured	1·40	1·40

VIII. U.P.U. (Nos. 289/90).

397	25ch. on 1n. 40 multicoloured	6·50	6·50
398	25ch. on 2n. multicoloured	1·50	1·50

IX. World Population Year (No. 295).

399	25ch. on 2n.50 multicoloured	1·40	1·40

X. Butterflies (Nos. 303/4).

400	25ch. on 3n. multicoloured	1·40	1·40
401	25ch. on 5n. multicoloured	1·40	1·40

XI. "Apollo"–"Soyuz" (Nos. 315/16).

402	25ch. on 10n. mult (315)	1·40	1·40
403	25ch. on 10n. mult (316)	1·40	1·40

XII. Handicrafts (No. 326).

404	25ch. on 10n. multicoloured	1·40	1·40

XIII. Rhododendrons (No. 335).

405	25ch. on 5n. multicoloured	1·40	1·40

XIV. Winter Olympics (Nos. 343/4).

406	25ch. on 4n. multicoloured	1·40	1·40
407	25ch. on 5n. multicoloured	1·40	1·40

XV. Flowers (Nos. 364/5).

408	25ch. on 4n. multicoloured	1·40	1·40
409	25ch. on 6n. multicoloured	1·40	1·40

XVI. Colombo Plan (No. 373).

410	25ch. on 2n.50 multicoloured	1·75	1·75

50 Mother and Child

1979. International Year of the Child. Mult.

411	2n. Type **50**	55	55
412	5n. Mother carrying two children	1·25	1·25
413	10n. Children at school	2·25	2·25

51 Conference Emblem and Dove

1979. 6th Non-Aligned Countries Summit Conference, Havana. Multicoloured.

415	25ch. Type **51**	20	20
416	10n. Emblem and Bhutanese symbols	2·75	2·75

52 Dorji (rattle)

1979. Antiquities. Multicoloured.

417	5ch. Type **52**	10	10
418	10ch. Dilbu (hand bell) (vert)	10	10
419	15ch. Jadum (cylindrical pot) (vert)	10	10
420	25ch. Jamjee (teapot)	10	10
421	1n. Kem (cylindrical container) (vert)	20	20
422	1n.25 Jamjee (different)	30	30
423	1n.70 Sangphor (ornamental vessel) (vert)	35	35

424	2n. Jamjee (different) (vert)	45	45
425	3n. Yangtho (pot with lid) (vert)	65	65
426	4n. Battha (circular case)	90	90
427	5n. Chhap (ornamental flask) (vert)	1·10	1·10

53 Rinpiang Dzong, Bhutan Stamp and Rowland Hill Statue

1980. Death Cent of Sir Rowland Hill. Mult.

428	1n. Type **53**	15	15
429	2n. Dzong, Bhutan stamp and statue	35	35
430	5n. Ounsti Dzong, Bhutan stamp and statue	1·10	1·10
431	10n. Lingzi Dzong and British 1912 1d. stamp	2·25	2·25

54 Dungtse Lhakhang, Paro   **55** St. Paul's Cathedral

1981. Monasteries. Multicoloured.

433	1n. Type **54**	30	30
434	2n. Kich Lhakhang, Paro (horiz)	65	65
435	2n.25 Kurjey Lhakhang (horiz)	70	70
436	3n. Tangu, Thimphu (horiz)	90	90
437	4n. Cheri, Thimphu (horiz)	1·10	1·10
438	5n. Chorten, Kora (horiz)	1·40	1·40
439	7n. Tak-Tsang, Paro	1·75	1·75

1981. Wedding of Prince of Wales. Multicoloured.

440	1n. Type **55**	20	20
441	5n. Type **55**	90	90
442	20n. Prince Charles and Lady Diana Spencer	3·50	3·50
443	25n. As No. 442	4·75	4·75

56 Orange-bellied Leafbird ("Orange-billed Chiropsis")   **57** Footballers

1982. Birds. Multicoloured.

445	2n. Type **56**	85	85
446	3n. Himalayan monal pheasant ("Monal Pheasant")	1·40	1·40
447	5n. Ward's trogon	2·40	2·40
448	10n. Mrs. Gould's sunbird	4·25	4·25

1982. World Cup Football Championship, Spain.

450	**57** 1n. multicoloured	15	15
451	– 2n. multicoloured	35	35
452	– 3n. multicoloured	45	45
453	– 20n. multicoloured	3·50	3·50

DESIGNS: 2n. to 20n. Various football scenes.

58 St. James's Palace   **59** Lord Baden-Powell (founder)

1982. 21st Birthday of Princess of Wales. Mult.

455	1n. Type **58**	25	25
456	10n. Prince and Princess of Wales	1·75	1·75

457	15n. Windsor Castle	2·75	2·75
458	25n. Princess in wedding dress	4·50	4·50

1982. 75th Anniv of Boy Scout Movement. Multicoloured.

460	3n. Type **59**	45	45
461	5n. Scouts around campfire	90	90
462	15n. Map reading	2·75	2·75
463	20n. Pitching tents	3·50	3·50

60 Rama finds Mowgli

1982. "The Jungle Book" (cartoon film). Mult.

465	1ch. Type **60**	10	10
466	2ch. Bagheera leading Mowgli to Man-village	10	10
467	3ch. Kaa planning attack on Bagheera and Mowgli	10	10
468	4ch. Mowgli and elephants	10	10
469	5ch. Mowgli and Baloo	10	10
470	10ch. Mowgli and King Louie	10	10
471	30ch. Kaa and Shere Khan	15	15
472	2n. Mowgli, Baloo and Bagheera	45	45
473	20n. Mowgli carrying jug for girl	4·75	4·75

1982. Birth of Prince William of Wales. Nos. 455/8 optd **ROYAL BABY 21.6.82.**

475	1n. multicoloured	25	25
476	10n. multicoloured	1·75	1·75
477	15n. multicoloured	2·75	2·75
478	25n. multicoloured	4·50	4·50

62 Washington surveying

1982. 250th Birth Anniv of George Washington and Birth Centenary of Franklin D. Roosevelt. Mult.

480	50ch. Type **62**	10	10
481	1n. Roosevelt and Harvard University	15	15
482	2n. Washington at Valley Forge	35	35
483	3n. Roosevelt's mother and family	55	55
484	4n. Washington at Battle of Monmouth	70	70
485	5n. Roosevelt and the White House	90	90
486	15n. Washington and Mount Vernon	2·75	2·75
487	20n. Churchill, Roosevelt and Stalin at Yalta	3·50	3·50

1983. "Druk Air" Bhutan Air Service. Various stamps optd **DRUK AIR** (491) or **Druk Air** (others), No. 489 surch also.

489	**42** 30ch. on 1n. multicoloued (postage)	2·25	2·25
490	– 5n. multicoloured (Scouts, Appendix)	2·25	2·25
491	– 8n. mult (No. 275)	2·25	2·25
492	– 5n. mult ("Indipex 73", Appendix) (air)	2·75	2·75
493	– 7n. mult (Munich Olympics, Appendix)	2·75	2·75

64 "Angelo Doni"

1983. 500th Birth Anniv of Raphael (artist). Multicoloured.

494	1n. Type **64**	20	20
495	4n. "Maddalena Doni"	70	70
496	5n. "Baldassare Castiglione"	90	90
497	20n. "Woman with Veil"	3·50	3·50

65 Ta-Gyad-Boom-Zu (the eight luck-bringing symbols)

1983. Religious Offerings. Multicoloured.

499	25ch. Type **65**	10	10
500	50ch. Doeyun Nga (the five sensory symbols)	15	15
501	2n. Norbu Chadun (the seven treasures) (47 × 41 mm)	55	55
502	3n. Wangpo Nga (the five sensory organs)	80	80
503	8n. Sha Nga (the five kinds of flesh)	1·75	1·75
504	9n. Men-Ra-Tor Sum (the sacrificial cake) (47 × 41 mm)	2·00	2·00

66 Dornier Wal Flying Boat "Boreas"

1983. Bicentenary of Manned Flight. Mult.

506	50ch. Type **66**	15	15
507	3n. Savoia-Marchetti S.66 flying boat	65	65
508	10n. Hawker Osprey biplane	2·50	2·50
509	20n. Astra airship "Ville de Paris"	4·50	4·50

67 Mickey Mouse as Caveman   **68** Golden Langur

1984. World Communications Year. Mult.

511	4ch. Type **67**	10	10
512	5ch. Goofy as printer	10	10
513	10ch. Chip 'n' Dale with morse key	10	10
514	20ch. Pluto talks to girlfriend on telephone	10	10
515	25ch. Minnie Mouse pulling record from bulldog	10	10
516	50ch. Morty and Ferdie with microphone and loudhailers	15	15
517	1n. Huey, Dewey, and Louie listening to radio	25	25
518	5n. Donald Duck watching television on buffalo	1·00	1·00
519	20n. Daisy Duck with computers and abacus	4·00	4·00

1984. Endangered Species. Multicoloured.

521	50ch. Type **68**	15	15
522	1n. Golden langur family in tree (horiz)	25	25
523	2n. Male and female Golden langurs with young (horiz)	45	45
524	4n. Group of langurs	1·00	1·00

69 Downhill Skiing   **70** "Sans Pareil", 1829

1984. Winter Olympic Games, Sarajevo. Mult.

526	50ch. Type **69**	10	10
527	1n. Cross-country skiing	20	20
528	3n. Speed skating	65	65
529	20n. Four-man bobsleigh	3·75	3·75

1984. Railway Locomotives. Multicoloured.

531	50ch. Type **70**	15	15
532	1n. "Planet", 1830	40	40
533	3n. "Experiment" 1832	90	90
534	4n. "Black Hawk", 1835	1·25	1·25

535 5n.50 "Jenny Lind", 1847 (horiz) . . . . 1·50 1·50
536 8n. "Bavaria", 1851 (horiz) 2·40 2·40
537 10n. Great Northern locomotive No. 1, 1870 (horiz) . . . . 2·75 2·75
538 25n. Steam locomotive Type 110, Prussia, 1880 (horiz) . . . . 7·25 7·25

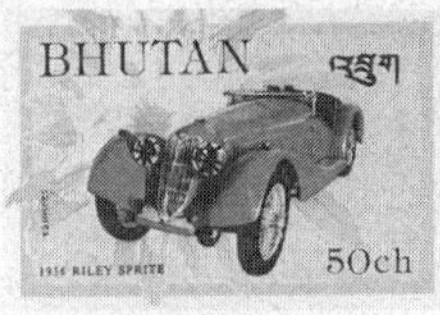

71 Riley "Sprite", 1936

1984. Cars. Multicoloured.
540 50ch. Type **71** 10 10
541 1n. Lanchester, 1919 . . . . 20 20
542 3n. Itala, 1907 . . . . 55 55
543 4n. Morris "Oxford (Bullnose)", 1913 . . . . . 70 70
544 5n.50 Lagonda "LG6", 1939 1·00 1·00
545 6n. Wolseley, 1903 . . . . . 1·10 1·10
546 8n. Buick "Super", 1952 . . 1·60 1·60
547 20n. Maybach "Zeppelin", 1933 . . . . 3·75 3·75

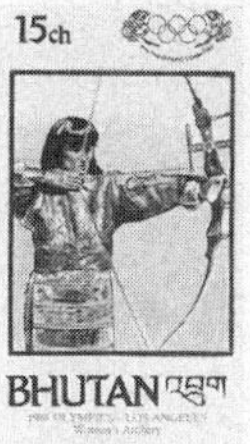

72 Women's Archery

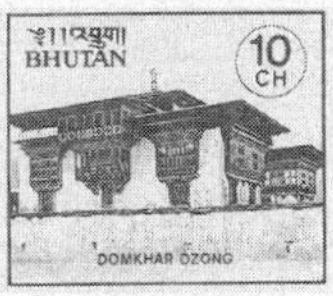

73 Domkhar Dzong

1984. Olympic Games, Los Angeles. Multicoloured.
549 15ch. Type **72** 10 10
550 25ch. Men's archery 10 10
551 2n. Table tennis 35 35
552 2n.25 Basketball 40 40
553 5n.50 Boxing . . . . 1·00 1·00
554 6n. Running . . . . 1·25 1·25
555 8n. Tennis . . . . 1·60 1·60

1984. Monasteries.
557 **73** 10ch. blue 10 10
558 – 25ch. red 10 10
559 – 50ch. violet 10 10
560 – 1n. brown 15 15
561 – 2n. red 35 35
562 – 5n. green 95 95
DESIGNS: 25ch. Shemgang Dzong; 50ch. Chapcha Dzong; 1n. Tashigang Dzong; 2n. Pungthang Dzong; 5n. Dechhenphoda Dzong.

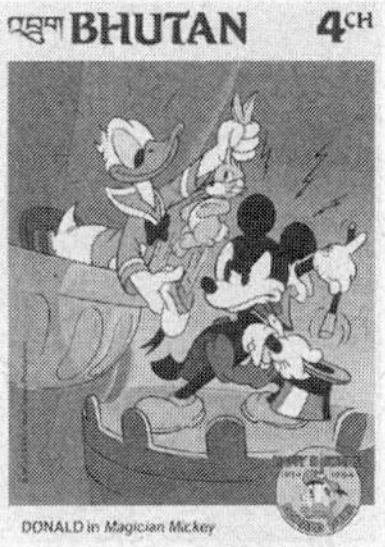

74 "Magician Mickey"

1984. 50th Anniv of Donald Duck. Scenes from films. Multicoloured.
563 4ch. Type **74** 10 10
564 5ch. "Slide, Donald, Slide" 10 10
565 10ch. "Donald's Golf Game" 10 10
566 20ch. "Mr. Duck Steps Out" 10 10
567 25ch. "Lion Around" 10 10
568 50ch. "Alpine Climbers" . . 15 15
569 1n. "Flying Jalopy" 25 25
570 5n. "Frank Duck brings 'Em Back Alive" . . . . 1·10 1·10
571 20n. "Good Scouts" . . . . 4·25 4·25

1984. Various stamps surch. (a) World Cup Football Championship, Spain (Nos. 450/3).
573 5n. on 1n. multicoloured . . 1·25 1·25
574 5n. on 2n. multicoloured . . 1·25 1·25
575 5n. on 3n. multicoloured . . 1·25 1·25
576 5n. on 20n. multicoloured . . 1·25 1·25

(b) 21st Birthday of Princess of Wales (Nos. 455/8).
578 5n. on 1n. multicoloured . . 85 85
579 5n. on 10n. multicoloured . . 85 85
580 5n. on 15n. multicoloured . . 85 85
581 40n. on 25n. multicoloured 8·75 8·75

(c) Birth of Prince William of Wales (Nos. 475/8).
583 5n. on 1n. multicoloured . . 85 85
584 5n. on 10n. multicoloured . . 85 85
585 5n. on 15n. multicoloured . . 85 85
586 40n. on 25n. multicoloured 7·75 7·75

(d) Wedding of Prince of Wales (Nos. 440/3).
588 10n. on 1n. multicoloured . . 2·10 2·10
589 10n. on 5n. multicoloured . . 2·10 2·10
590 10n. on 20n. multicoloured 2·10 2·10
591 10n. on 25n. multicoloured 2·10 2·10

(e) 75th Anniv of Boy Scout Movement (Nos. 460/3).
593 10n. on 3n. multicoloured . . 2·10 2·10
594 10n. on 5n. multicoloured . . 2·10 2·10
595 10n. on 15n. multicoloured 2·10 2·10
596 10n. on 20n. multicoloured 2·10 2·10

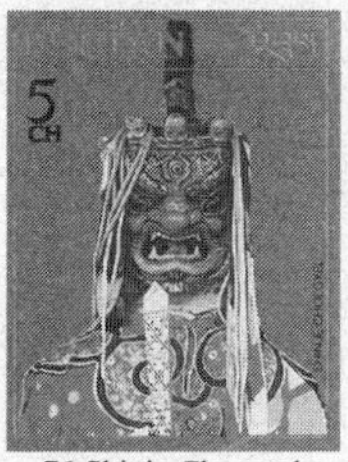

76 Shinje Choegyel

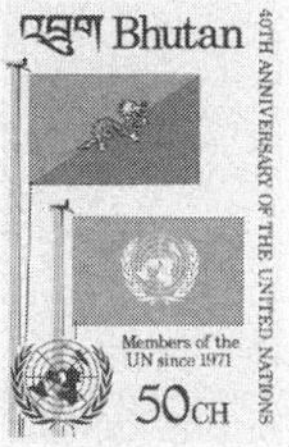

77 Bhutan and U.N. Flags

1985. The Judgement of Death Mask Dance. Multicoloured.
598 5ch. Type **76** 10 10
599 35ch. Raksh Lango 15 15
600 50ch. Druelgo 15 15
601 2n.50 Pago 55 55
602 3n. Telgo 60 60
603 4n. Due Nakcung 70 70
604 5n. Lha Karpo . . . . . . 1·00 1·00
605 5n.50 Nyalbum . . . . . . 1·10 1·10
606 6n. Khimda Pelkyi . . . . . 1·25 1·25

1985. 40th Anniv of U.N.O.
608 **77** 50ch. multicoloured . . . 10 10
609 – 15n. multicoloured . . . . 2·10 2·10
610 – 20n. black and blue . . . 3·00 3·00
DESIGNS—VERT: 15n. U.N. building, New York. HORIZ: 20n. Veterans' War Memorial Building, San Francisco (venue of signing of charter, 1945).

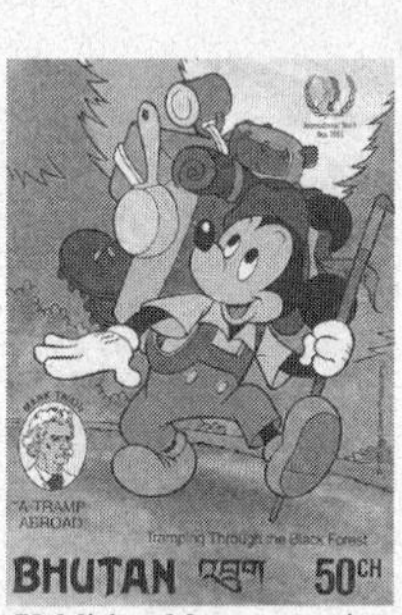

78 Mickey Mouse tramping through Black Forest

1985. 150th Birth Anniv of Mark Twain (writer) and International Youth Year. Multicoloured.
612 50ch. Type **78** 15 15
613 2n. Mickey Mouse, Donald Duck and Goofy on steamboat trip on Lake Lucerne 40 40
614 5n. Mickey Mouse, Donald Duck and Goofy climbing Rigi-Kulm 80 80
615 9n. Mickey Mouse and Goofy rafting to Heidelberg on River Neckar . . . . 1·25 1·25
616 20n. Mickey Mouse leading Donald Duck on horse back up the Riffelberg . . 3·50 3·50
Nos. 612/16 show scenes from "A Tramp Abroad" (cartoon film of Twain novel).

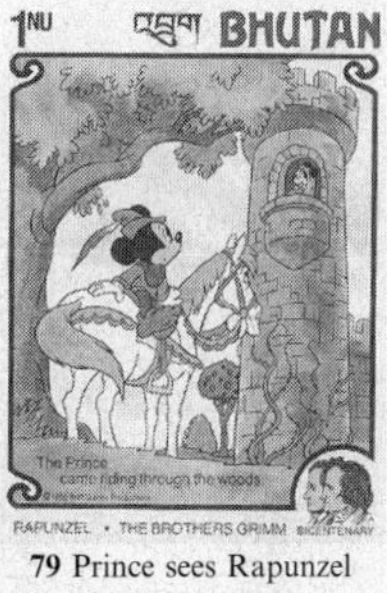

79 Prince sees Rapunzel

1985. Birth Bicentenaries (1985 and 1986) of Grimm Brothers (folklorists). Multicoloured.
618 1n. Type **79** 15 15
619 4n. Rapunzel (Minnie Mouse) in tower 55 55
620 7n. Mother Gothel calling to Rapunzel to let down her hair 85 85
621 8n. Prince climbing tower using Rapunzel's hair . . . 1·25 1·25
622 15n. Prince proposing to Rapunzel . . . . 1·90 1·90

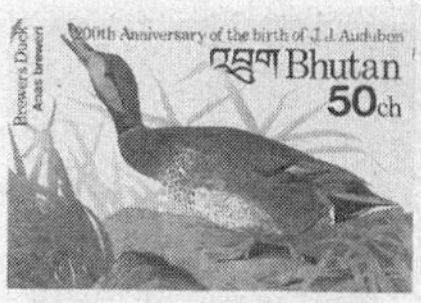

80 "Brewers Duck" (mallard)

1985. Birth Bicentenary of John J. Audubon (ornithologist). Audubon illustrations. Mult.
624 50ch. Type **80** 10 10
625 1n. "Willow Ptarmigan" (Willow/red Grouse) . . . 15 15
626 2n. "Mountain Plover" . . . 45 45
627 3n. "Red-throated Loon" (Red-throated Diver) . . . 70 70
628 4n. "Spruce Grouse" 85 85
629 5n. "Hooded Merganser" . . 1·10 1·10
630 15n. "Trumpeter Swan" (Whooper Swan) . . . . 3·00 3·00
631 20n. "Common Goldeneye" 4·00 4·00

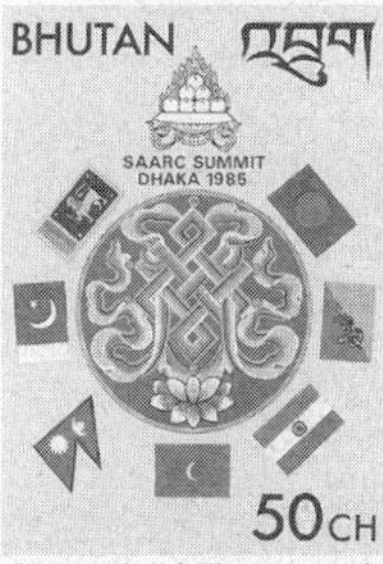

81 Members' Flags around Buddhist Design

1985. South Asian Regional Co-operation Summit, Dhaka, Bangladesh.
634 **81** 50ch. multicoloured . . . 10 10
635 5n. multicoloured 80 80

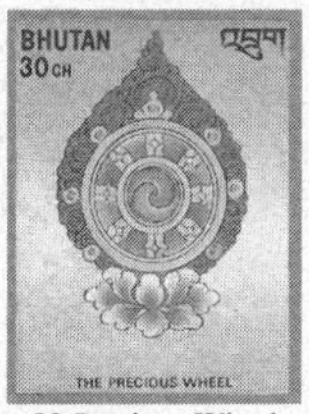

82 Precious Wheel

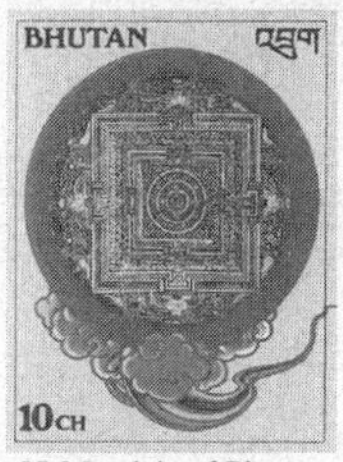

85 Mandala of Phurpa (Ritual Dagger)

1986. The Precious Symbols. Multicoloured.
636 30ch. Type **82** 10 10
637 50ch. Precious Gem 15 15
638 1n.25 Precious Queen 15 15
639 2n. Precious Minister 30 30
640 4n. Precious Elephant 55 55
641 6n. Precious Horse 85 85
642 8n. Precious General . . . . 1·25 1·25

1986. Olympic Games Gold Medal Winners. Nos. 549/50 and 552/5 optd.
643 **72** 15ch. **GOLD HYANG SOON SEO SOUTH KOREA** 15 15
644 – 25ch. **GOLD DARRELL PACE USA** 15 15
645 – 2n.25 **GOLD MEDAL USA** 25 25
646 – 5n.50 **GOLD MARK BRELAND USA** . . . 80 80
647 – 6n. **GOLD DALEY THOMPSON ENGLAND** 85 85
648 – 8n. **GOLD STEFAN EDBERG SWEDEN** . . 1·25 1·25

1986. "Ameripex 86" International Stamp Exhibition, Chicago. Various stamps optd **AMERIPEX 86**.
653 8n. mult (No. 621) . . . . . 1·10 1·10
650 9n. mult (No. 615) . . . . . 1·25 1·25
654 15n. mult (No. 622) . . . . . 2·00 2·00
651 20n. mult (No. 616) . . . . . 3·00 3·00

1986. Kilkhor Mandalas of Mahayana Buddhism. Multicoloured.
656 10ch. Type **85** 10 10
657 25ch. Mandala of Amitayus in Wrathful Form 10 10
658 50ch. Mandala of Overpowering Deities . . . 15 15
659 75ch. Mandala of the Great Wrathful One 20 20
660 1n. Type **85** 20 20
661 3n. As 25ch. 50 50
662 5n. As 50ch. 75 75
663 7n. As 75ch. . . . . 1·00 1·00

1986. 75th Anniv of Girl Guides. Nos. 460/3 optd **75th ANNIVERSARY GIRL GUIDES**.
664 3n. multicoloured 45 45
665 5n. multicoloured 65 65
666 15n. multicoloured . . . . . 2·00 2·00
667 20n. multicoloured . . . . . 3·00 3·00

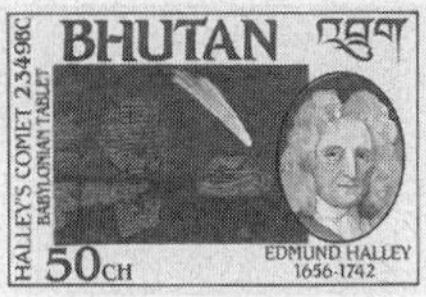

87 Babylonian Tablet and Comet over Noah's Ark

1986. Appearance of Halley's Comet. Mult.
669 50ch. Type **87** 15 15
670 1n. 17th-century print 15 15
671 2n. 1835 French silhouette . . 35 35
672 3n. Bayeux tapestry 50 50
673 4n. Woodblock from "Nuremburg Chronicle" 70 70
674 5n. Illustration of Revelation 6, 12–13 from 1650 Bible 85 85
675 15n. Comet in constellation of Cancer . . . . 2·25 2·25
676 20n. Decoration on Delft plate . . . . 3·25 3·25

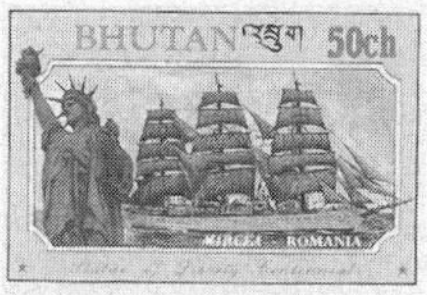

88 Statue and "Libertad" (Argentine full-rigged cadet ship)

1986. Centenary of Statue of Liberty. Multicoloured.
678 50ch. Type **88** 15 15
679 1n. "Shalom" (Israeli liner) 15 15
680 2n. "Leonardo da Vinci" (Italian liner) 35 35
681 3n. "Mircea" (Rumanian cadet barque) 50 50
682 4n. "France" (French liner) 70 70
683 5n. S.S. "United States" (American liner) 85 85
684 15n. "Queen Elizabeth 2" (British liner) . . . . . . 2·25 2·25
685 20n. "Europa" (West German liner) . . . . . . 2·75 2·75
The descriptions of the ships on Nos. 678 and 681 were transposed in error.

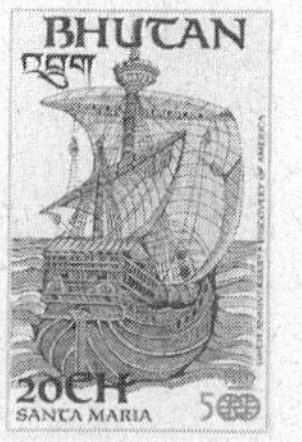

89 "Santa Maria"

1987. 500th Anniv (1992) of Discovery of America by Columbus. Multicoloured.
687 20ch. Type **89** 30 30
688 25ch. Queen Isabella of Spain 15 15
689 50ch. Flying fish 60 40
690 1n. Columbus's coat of arms 25 25
691 2n. Christopher Columbus . . 45 45
692 3n. Columbus landing with Spanish soldiers 80 80

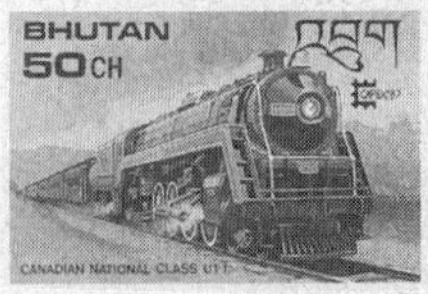

90 Canadian National Class "U1-f" Steam Locomotive No. 6060

1987. "Capex '87" International Stamp Exhibition, Toronto. Canadian Railways. Multicoloured.
695 50ch. Type **90** 20 20
696 1n. Via Rail "L.R.C." electric locomotive No. 6903 . . . 20 20
697 2n. Canadian National GM "GF30t" diesel locomotive No. 5341 . . . . 45 45
698 3n. Canadian National steam locomotive No. 6157 . . . 60 60
699 8n. Canadian Pacific steam locomotive No. 2727 . . . 1·60 1·60
700 10n. Via Express diesel locomotive No. 6524 . . . 2·00 2·00
701 15n. Canadian National "Turbotrain" . . . . . . 3·00 3·00
702 20n. Canadian Pacific diesel-electric locomotive No. 1414 . . . . 4·00 4·00

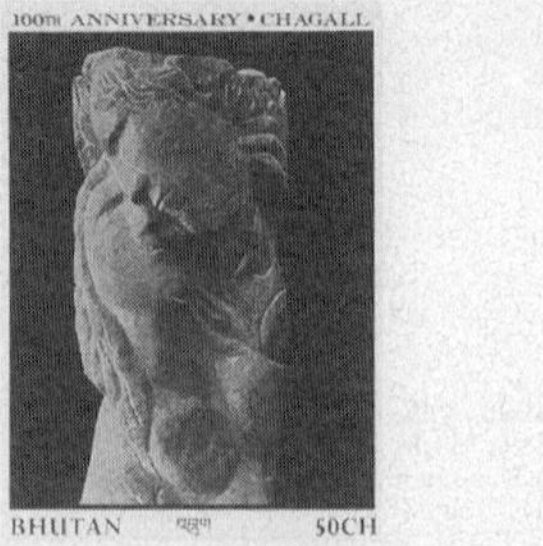

91 "Two Faces" (sculpture)

1987. Birth Centenary of Marc Chagall (artist). Multicoloured.
704 50ch. Type **91** 15 15
705 1n. "At the Barber's" 15 15
706 2n. "Old Jew with Torai" . . 35 35
707 3n. "Red Maternity" 50 50
708 4n. "Eve of Yom Kippur" . . 70 70
709 5n. "The Old Musician" . . 85 85
710 6n. "The Rabbi of Vitebsk" 85 85
711 7n. "Couple at Dusk" . . . 1·25 1·25
712 9n. "The Artistes" . . . . . 1·25 1·25
713 10n. "Moses breaking the Tablets" . . . . 1·50 1·50
714 12n. "Bouquet with Flying Lovers" . . . . 1·75 1·75
715 20n. "In the Sky of the Opera" . . . . 3·00 3·00

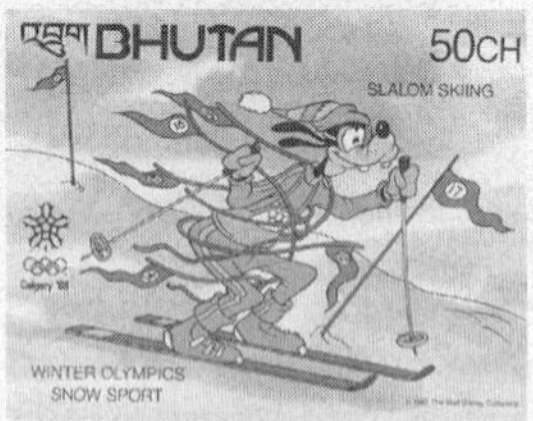

92 Goofy (slalom)

1988. Winter Olympic Games, Calgary. Mult.
717 50ch. Type **92** 15 15
718 1n. Donald Duck pushing Goofy at start (downhill skiing) 15 15
719 2n. Goofy in goal (ice hockey) 25 25
720 4n. Goofy (biathlon) 50 50
721 7n. Goofy and Donald Duck (speed skating) 85 85
722 8n. Minnie Mouse (figure skating) . . . . 1·00 1·00
723 9n. Minnie Mouse (free-style skating) . . . . 1·25 1·25
724 20n. Goofy and Mickey Mouse (two-man bobsleigh) . . . . 2·50 2·50

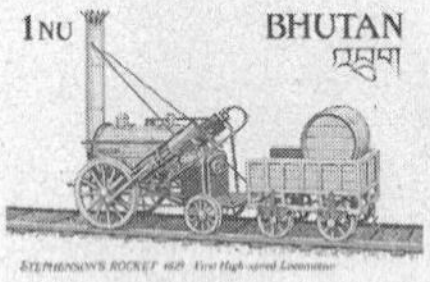

93 Stephenson's Railway Locomotive "Rocket", 1829

1988. Transport. Multicoloured.
726 50ch. Pullman "Pioneer" sleeper, 1985 . . . . 35 35
727 1n. Type **93** 35 35
728 2n. Pierre Lallement's "Velocipede", 1866 . . . . 25 25
729 3n. Benz "Patent Motor Wagon", 1866 . . . . . . 45 45
730 4n. Volkswagen "Beetle" . . 60 60
731 5n. Mississippi paddle-steamers "Natchez" and "Robert E. Lee", 1870 . . 70 70
732 6n. American "La France" motor fire engine, 1910 . . 85 85
733 7n. Frigate U.S.S. "Constitution", 1797 (vert) 85 85
734 9n. Bell rocket belt, 1961 (vert) . . . . 1·25 1·25
735 10n. Trevithick's railway locomotive, 1804 . . . . 2·25 2·25

No. 731 is wrongly inscribed "Natches" and No. 733 is wrongly dated "1787".

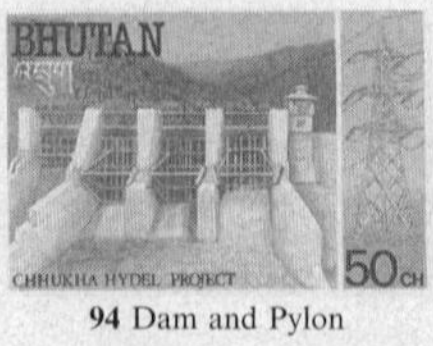

94 Dam and Pylon

1988. Chhukha Hydro-electric Project.
737 **94** 50ch. multicoloured . . . 15 15

1988. World Aids Day. Nos. 411/13 optd **WORLD AIDS DAY**.
738 **50** 2n. multicoloured 35 35
739 – 5n. multicoloured 95 95
740 – 10n. multicoloured . . . . 1·75 1·75

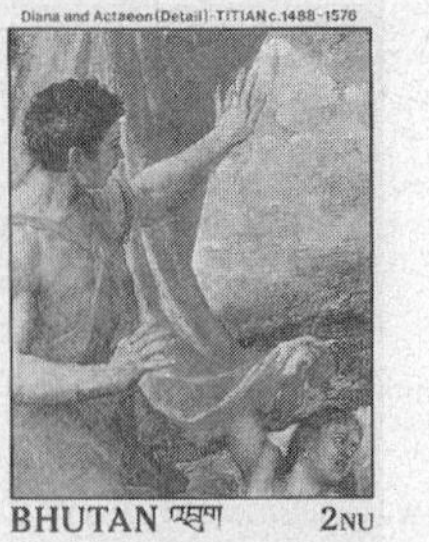

96 "Diana and Actaeon" (detail)

1989. 500th Birth Anniv of Titian (painter). Multicoloured.
741 50ch. "Gentleman with a Book" 15 15
742 1n. "Venus and Cupid, with a Lute Player" (detail) . . 15 15
743 2n. Type **96** 25 25
744 3n. "Cardinal Ippolito dei Medici" 45 45
745 4n. "Sleeping Venus" (detail) 50 50
746 5n. "Venus risen from the Waves" (detail) 80 80
747 6n. "Worship of Venus" (detail) 95 95
748 7n. "Fete Champetre" (detail) 85 85
749 10n. "Perseus and Andromeda" (detail) . . . 1·75 1·75
750 15n. "Danae" (detail) . . . . 2·10 2·10
751 20n. "Venus at the Mirror" 2·50 2·50
752 25n. "Venus and the Organ Player" (detail) . . . . . 3·25 3·25

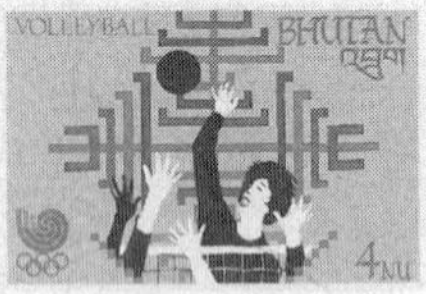

97 Volleyball

1989. Olympic Games, Seoul (1988). Mult.
754 50ch. Gymnastics 15 15
755 1n. Judo 15 15
756 2n. Putting the shot 25 25
757 4n. Type **97** 50 50
758 7n. Basketball (vert) . . . . 1·00 1·00
759 8n. Football (vert) . . . . . 1·25 1·25
760 9n. High jumping (vert) . . . 1·50 1·50
761 20n. Running (vert) . . . . 3·00 3·00

1989. "Fukuoka '89" Asia-Pacific Exhibition. Nos. 598/606 optd **ASIA-PACIFIC EXPOSITION FUKUOKA '89**.
763 5ch. multicoloured 10 10
764 35ch. multicoloured 10 15
765 50ch. multicoloured 15 15
766 2n.50 multicoloured 25 25
767 3n. multicoloured 35 35
768 4n. multicoloured 45 45
769 5n. multicoloured 60 60
770 5n.50 multicoloured 75 75
771 6n. multicoloured 95 95

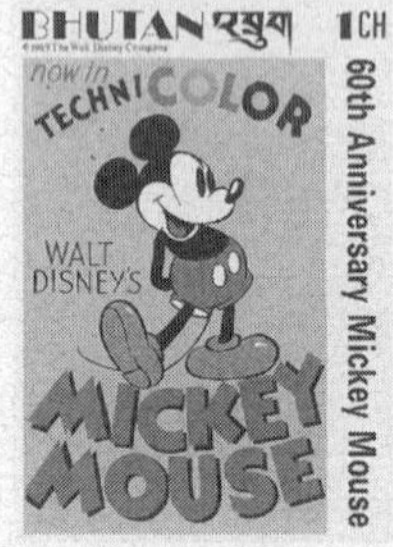

99 Mickey Mouse

1989. 60th Anniv of Mickey Mouse. Film Posters. Multicoloured.
772 1ch. Type **99** 10 10
773 2ch. "Barnyard Olympics" . . 15 15
774 3ch. "Society Dog Show" . . 15 15
775 4ch. "Fantasia" 15 15
776 5ch. "The Mad Dog" 15 15
777 10ch. "A Gentleman's Gentleman" 15 15
778 50ch. "Symphony hour" . . 15 15
779 10n. "The Moose Hunt" . . 1·25 1·25
780 15n. "Wild Waves" . . . . 2·00 2·00
781 20n. "Mickey in Arabia" . . 2·50 2·50
782 25n. "Tugboat Mickey" . . . 3·25 3·25
783 30n. "Building a Building" . 3·75 3·75

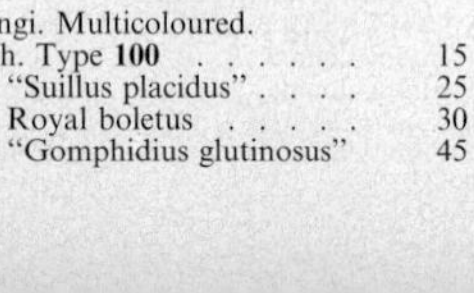

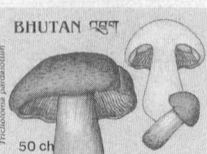

100 "Tricholoma pardalotum"

1989. Fungi. Multicoloured.
785 50ch. Type **100** 15 15
786 1n. "Suillus placidus" 25 15
787 2n. Royal boletus 30 25
788 3n. "Gomphidius glutinosus" 45 40
789 4n. Scarlet-stemmed boletus 60 50
790 5n. Elegant boletus 70 60
791 6n. "Boletus appendiculatus" 95 80
792 7n. Griping toadstool . . . . 1·00 85
793 10n. "Macrolepiota rhacodes" . . . . 1·60 1·40
794 15n. The blusher . . . . . . 2·40 2·10
795 20n. Death cap . . . . . . 3·25 2·75
796 25n. False death cap . . . . 4·00 3·50

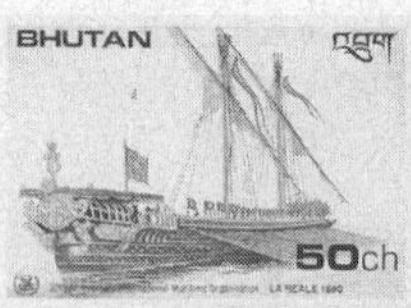

101 "La Reale" (Spanish galley), 1680

1989. 30th Anniv of International Maritime Organization. Multicoloured.
798 50ch. Type **101** 15 15
799 1n. "Turtle" (submarine), 1776 . . . . 15 15
800 2n. "Charlotte Dundas" (steamship), 1802 . . . . . 25 25
801 3n. "Great Eastern" (paddle-steamer), 1858 . . . . . 40 40
802 4n. H.M.S. "Warrior" (armoured ship), 1862 . . 50 50
803 5n. Mississippi river steamer, 1884 . . . . 80 80
804 6n. "Preussen" (full-rigged ship), 1902 . . . . . . 1·00 1·00
805 7n. U.S.S. "Arizona" (battleship), 1915 . . . . . 1·10 1·10
806 10n. "Bluenose" (fishing schooner), 1921 . . . . . 1·75 1·75
807 15n. Steam trawler, 1925 . . 1·75 1·75
808 20n. "Liberty" freighter, 1943 2·75 2·75
809 25n. "United States" (liner), 1952 . . . . 3·50 3·50

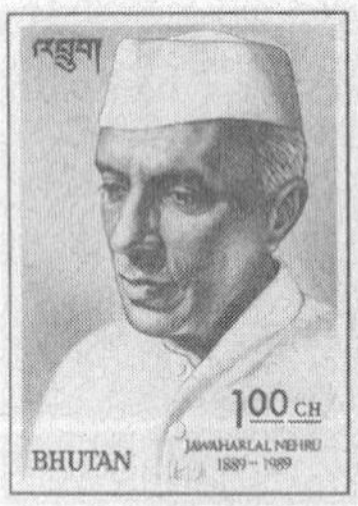

102 Nehru

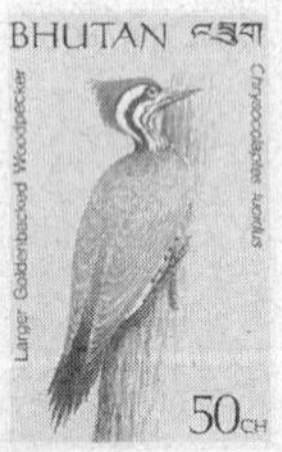

103 Greater Flamed-backed Woodpecker

1989. Birth Centenary of Jawaharlal Nehru (Indian statesman).
811 **102** 1n. brown 15 15
No. 811 is erroneously inscribed "ch".

1989. Birds. Multicoloured.
812 50ch. Type **103** 15 15
813 1n. Black-naped blue monarch ("Black naped Monarch") 15 15
814 2n. White-crested laughing thrush 25 20
815 3n. Blood pheasant 35 25
816 4n. Plum-headed ("Blossom-headed") parakeet . . . 45 35
817 5n. Rosy minivet 60 45
818 6n. Chestnut-headed fulvetta ("Tit-Babbler") (horiz) . . 65 50
819 7n. Blue pitta (horiz) 80 60
820 10n. Black-naped oriole (horiz) . . . . 1·25 90
821 15n. Green magpie (horiz) . . 1·75 1·25
822 20n. Three-toed kingfisher ("Indian Three-toed Kingfisher")(horiz) . . . . 2·25 1·75
823 25n. Ibis bill (horiz) . . . . 3·00 2·25

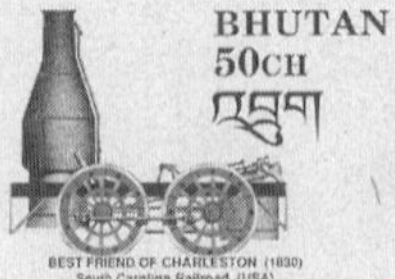

104 "Best Friend of Charleston", 1830, U.S.A.

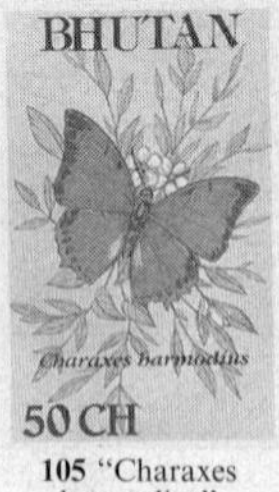

105 "Charaxes harmodius"

1990. Steam Railway Locomotives. Mult.
825 50ch. Type **104** 15 15
826 1n. Class U locomotive, 1948, France 20 20
827 2n. Consolidation locomotive, 1866, U.S.A. 40 40
828 3n. Luggage engine, 1843, Great Britain 55 55
829 4n. Class 60-3 Shay locomotive No. 18, 1913, U.S.A. 75 75
830 5n. "John Bull", 1831, U.S.A. 80 80
831 6n. "Hercules", 1837, U.S.A. 85 85
832 7n. Locomotive No. 947, 1874, Great Britain 90 90
833 10n. "Illinois", 1852, U.S.A. 1·50 1·50
834 15n. Class O5 locomotive, 1935, Germany . . . . . 3·00 3·00
835 20n. Standard locomotive, 1865, U.S.A. . . . . . . 4·00 4·00
836 25n. Class Ps-4 locomotive, 1936, U.S.A. . . . . . . 4·50 4·50

1990. Butterflies. Multicoloured.
838 50ch. Type **105** 10 10
839 1n. "Prioneris thestylis" . . . 15 15
840 2n. Eastern courtier 35 35
841 3n. "Penthema lisarda" (horiz) 50 50
842 4n. Golden birdwing 55 55
843 5n. Great nawab 65 65
844 6n. "Polyura dolon" (horiz) 1·00 1·00
845 7n. Tailed labyrinth (horiz) 1·10 1·10
846 10n. "Delias descombesi" . . 1·75 1·75
847 15n. "Childreni childrena" (horiz) . . . . 2·00 2·00
848 20n. Leaf butterfly (horiz) . . 3·50 3·50
849 25n. "Elymnias malelas" (horiz) . . . . 4·00 4·00

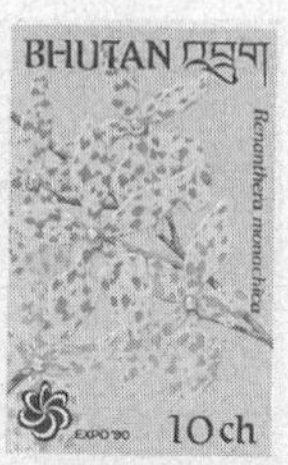

106 "Renanthera monachica"

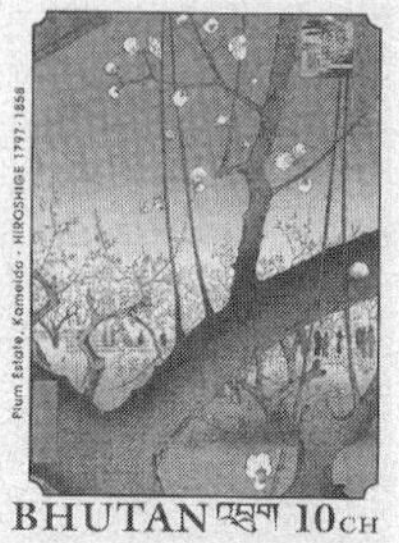

107 "Plum Estate, Kameido"

1990. "Expo '90" International Garden and Greenery Exposition, Osaka. Orchids. Mult.
851 10ch. Type **106** 15 15
852 50ch. "Vanda coerulea" . . . 15 15
853 1n. "Phalaenopsis violacea" 15 15
854 2n. "Dendrobium nobile" . . 35 35
855 5n. "Vandopsis lissochiloides" 85 85
856 6n. "Paphiopedilum rothschildianum" 95 95
857 7n. "Phalaenopsis schilleriana" . . . . 1·10 1·10
858 9n. "Paphiopedilum insigne" 1·40 1·40
859 10n. "Paphiopedilum bellatulum" . . . . 1·75 1·75
860 20n. "Doritis pulcherrima" 3·50 3·50
861 25n. "Cymbidium giganteum" 4·25 4·25
862 35n. "Phalaenopsis mariae" 5·75 5·75

1990. Death of Emperor Hirohito and Accession of Emperor Akihito of Japan. "100 Famous Views of Edo" by Ando Hiroshige. Multicoloured.
864 10ch. Type **107** 15 15
865 20ch. "Yatsumi Bridge" . . . 15 15
866 50ch. "Ayase River and Kanegafuchi" 15 15
867 75ch. "View of Shiba Coast" 15 15
868 1n. "Grandpa's Teahouse, Meguro" 15 15
869 2n. "Inside Kameido Tenjin Shrine" 30 30
870 6n. "Yoroi Ferry, Koami-cho" 75 75
871 7n. "Sakasai Ferry" 80 80
872 10n. "Fukagawa Lumberyards" . . . . . . 1·25 1·25
873 15n. "Suido Bridge and Surugadai" . . . . 2·00 2·00
874 20n. "Meguro Drum Bridge and Sunset Hill" . . . . . 3·50 3·50
875 25n. "Atagoshita and Yabu Lane" . . . . 4·25 4·25

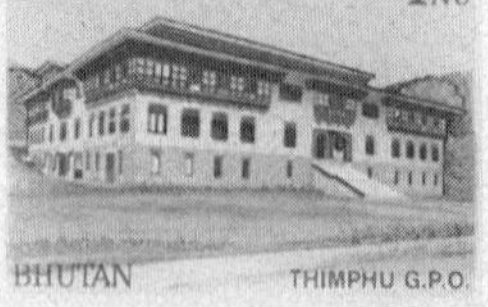

108 Thimphu Post Office

1990.
877 **108** 1n. multicoloured 15 15

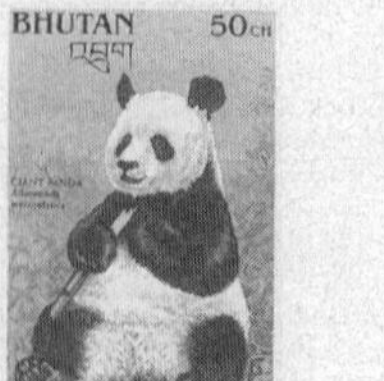

109 Giant Panda

1990. Mammals. Multicoloured.
878 50ch. Type **109** 10 10
879 1n. Giant panda in tree . . . 15 15
880 2n. Giant panda with cub . . 35 35
881 3n. Giant panda (horiz) . . . 50 50
882 4n. Giant panda eating (horiz) 50 50

883 5n. Tiger (horiz) 60 60
884 6n. Giant pandas pulling up bamboo (horiz) 80 80
885 7n. Giant panda and cub resting (horiz) 85 85
886 10n. Indian elephant (horiz) 1·40 1·40
887 15n. Giant panda beside fallen tree 1·90 1·90
888 20n. Indian muntjac (inscr "Barking deer") (horiz) 3·50 3·50
889 25n. Snow leopard (horiz) 4·25 4·25

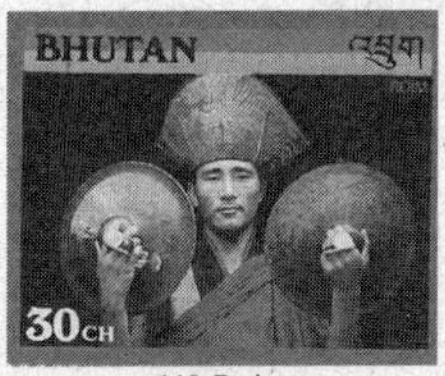

110 Roim

1990. Religious Musical Instruments. Mult.
891 10ch. Dungchen (large trumpets) 10 10
892 20ch. Dungkar (Indian chank shell) 10 10
893 30ch. Type **110** 10 10
894 50ch. Tinchag (cup cymbals) 10 10
895 1n. Dradu and drilbu (pellet drum and hand bell) 15 15
896 2n. Gya-ling (oboes) 25 25
897 2n.50 Nga (drum) 30 30
898 3n.50 Kang-dung (trumpets) 50 50

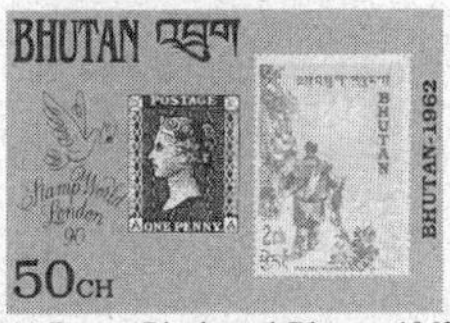

111 Penny Black and Bhutan 1962 2ch. Stamp

1990. "Stamp World London 90" International Stamp Exhibition. 150th Anniv of the Penny Black. Multicoloured.
900 50ch. Type **111** 10 10
901 1n. Oldenburg 1852 $^1/_{30}$th. stamp 15 15
902 2n. Bergedorf 1861 1½s. stamp 25 25
903 4n. German Democratic Republic 1949 50pf. stamp 45 45
904 5n. Brunswick 1852 1 sgr. stamp 60 60
905 6n. Basel 1845 2½r. stamp 65 65
906 8n. Geneva 1843 5c.+5c. stamp 85 85
907 10n. Zurich 1843 4r. stamp 1·10 1·10
908 15n. France 1849 20c. stamp 2·00 2·00
909 20n. Vatican City 1929 5c. stamp 2·40 2·40
910 25n. Israel 1948 3m. stamp 2·75 2·75
911 30n. Japan 1871 48m. stamp 3·50 3·50

Each value also depicts the Penny Black.
No. 901 is wrongly inscribed "Oldenberg".

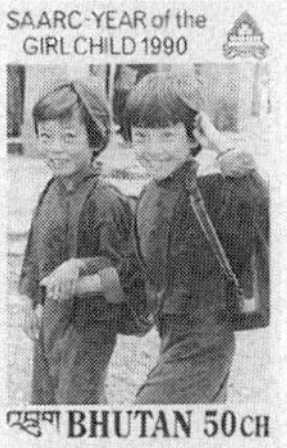

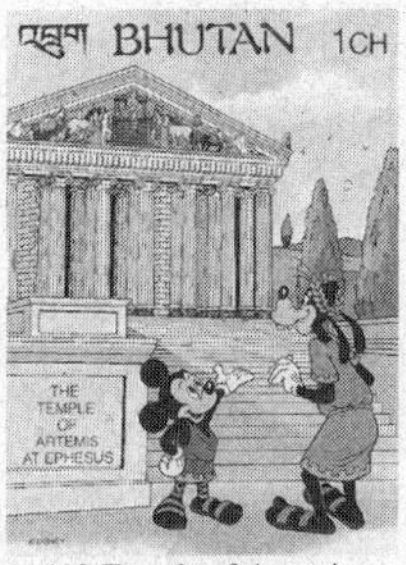

112 Girls

113 Temple of Artemis, Ephesus

1990. South Asian Association for Regional Co-operation Girl Child Year. Multicoloured.
913 50ch. Type **112** 10 10
914 20n. Girl 2·50 2·50

1991. Wonders of the World. Designs featuring Walt Disney cartoon characters. Multicoloured.
915 1ch. Type **113** 10 10
916 2ch. Statue of Zeus, Olympia 10 10
917 3ch. Pyramids of Egypt 10 10
918 4ch. Lighthouse of Alexandria, Egypt 10 10
919 5ch. Mausoleum, Halicarnassus 10 10
920 10ch. Colossus of Rhodes 10 10
921 50ch. Hanging Gardens of Babylon 10 10
922 5n. Mauna Loa Volcanoes, Hawaii (horiz) 65 65
923 6n. Carlsbad Caverns, New Mexico (horiz) 80 80
924 10n. Rainbow Bridge National Monument, Utah (horiz) 1·40 1·40
925 15n. Grand Canyon, Colorado (horiz) 1·90 1·90
926 20n. Old Faithful, Yellowstone National Park, Wyoming (horiz) 2·50 2·50
927 25n. Sequoia National Park, California (horiz) 3·00 3·00
928 30n. Crater Lake and Wizard Island, Oregon (horiz) 3·50 3·50

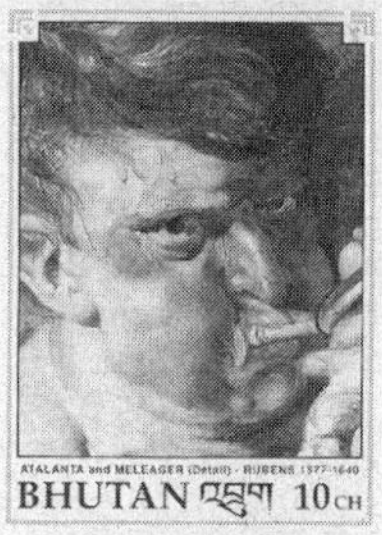

114 "Atalanta and Meleager" (detail)

1991. 350th Death Anniv (1990) of Peter Paul Rubens (painter). Multicoloured.
930 10ch. Type **114** 10 10
931 50ch. "The Fall of Phaeton" (detail) 10 10
932 1n. "Feast of Venus Verticordia" (detail) 15 15
933 2n. "Achilles slaying Hector" (detail) 25 25
934 3n. "Arachne punished by Minerva" (detail) 35 35
935 4n. "Jupiter receives Psyche on Olympus" (detail) 45 45
936 5n. "Atalanta and Meleager" (different detail) 55 55
937 6n. "Atalanta and Meleager" (different detail) 70 70
938 7n. "Venus in Vulcan's Furnace" (detail) 1·00 1·00
939 10n. "Atalanta and Meleager" (different detail) 1·25 1·25
940 20n. "Briseis returned to Achilles" (detail) 2·50 2·50
941 30n. "Mars and Rhea Sylvia" (detail) 3·50 3·50

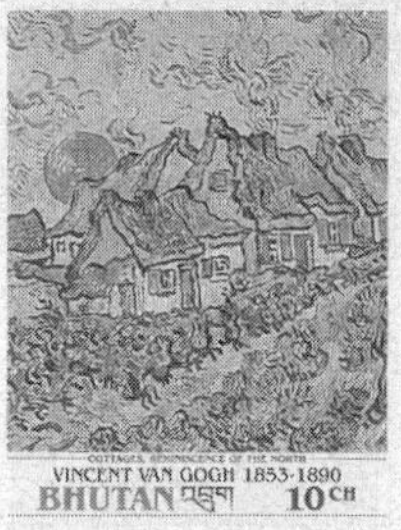

115 "Cottages, Reminiscence of the North"

1991. Death Centenary (1990) of Vincent van Gogh (painter). Multicoloured.
943 10ch. Type **115** 10 10
944 50ch. "Head of a Peasant Woman with Dark Cap" 10 10
945 1n. "Portrait of a Woman in Blue" 15 15
946 2n. "Head of an Old Woman with White Cap (the Midwife)" 35 35
947 8n. "Vase with Hollyhocks" 95 95
948 10n. "Portrait of a Man with a Skull Cap" 1·25 1·25
949 12n. "Agostina Segatori sitting in the Cafe du Tambourin" 1·40 1·40
950 15n. "Vase with Daisies and Anemones" 2·00 2·00
951 18n. "Fritillaries in a Copper Vase" 2·25 2·25
952 20n. "Woman sitting in the Grass" 2·50 2·50
953 25n. "On the Outskirts of Paris" (horiz) 3·25 3·25
954 30n. "Chrysanthemums and Wild Flowers in a Vase" 4·00 4·00

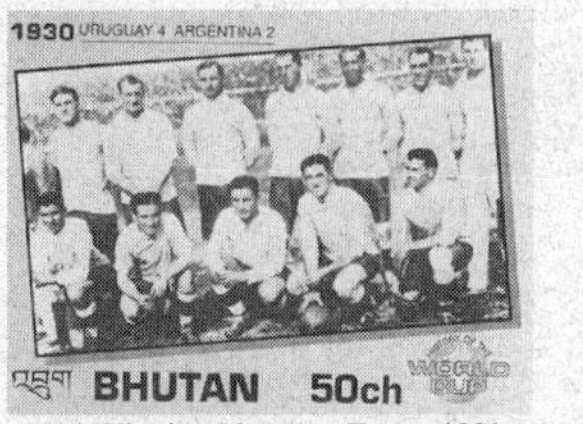

116 Winning Uruguay Team, 1930

1991. World Cup Football Championship. Mult.
956 50ch. Type **116** 10 10
957 1n. Italy, 1934 15 15
958 2n. Italy, 1938 25 25
959 3n. Uruguay, 1950 35 35
960 5n. West Germany, 1954 60 60
961 10n. Brazil, 1958 1·25 1·25
962 20n. Brazil, 1962 2·50 2·50
963 25n. England, 1966 3·00 3·00
964 29n. Brazil, 1970 4·00 4·00
965 30n. West Germany, 1974 4·00 4·00
966 31n. Argentina, 1978 4·00 4·00
967 32n. Italy, 1982 4·00 4·00
968 33n. Argentina, 1986 4·25 4·25
969 34n. West Germany, 1990 4·25 4·25
970 35n. Stadium, Los Angeles (venue for 1994 World Cup) 4·25 4·25

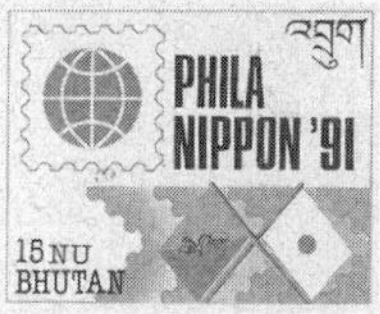

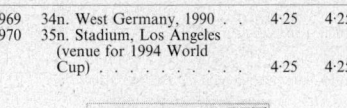

117 Bhutan and Japan State Flags

1991. "Phila Nippon '91" International Stamp Exhibition, Tokyo.
972 **117** 15n. multicoloured 2·10 2·10

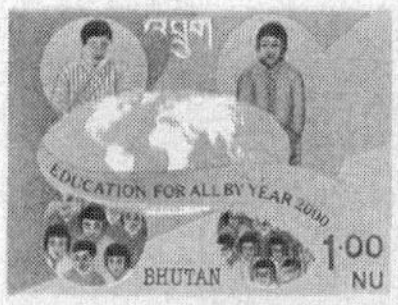

118 Teachers, Pupils and Hemisphere

1992. "Education for All by Year 2000".
973 **118** 1n. multicoloured 15 15

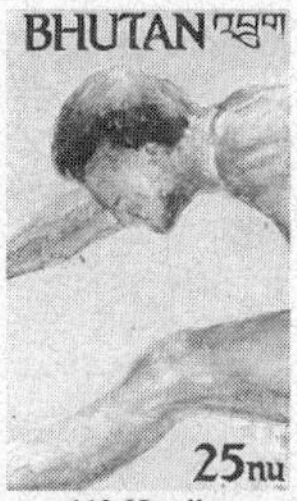

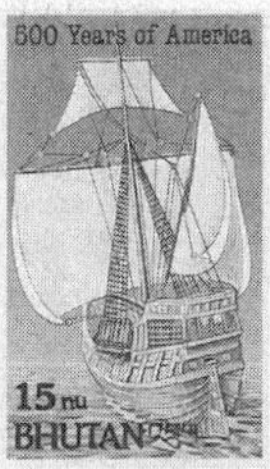

119 Hurdler

120 "Santa Maria"

1992. Olympic Games, Barcelona. Mult.
974 25n. Type **119** 3·00 3·00
975 25n. Body of hurdler 3·00 3·00

Nos. 974/5 were issued together, se-tenant, forming a composite design.

1992. 500th Anniv of Discovery of America by Columbus. Multicoloured.
977 15n. Type **120** 1·10 1·10
978 20n. Columbus 1·50 1·50

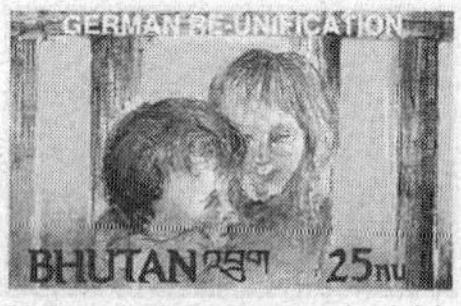

121 Brandenburg Gate and rejoicing Couple

1992. 2nd Anniv of Reunification of Germany.
980 **121** 25n. multicoloured 1·75 1·75

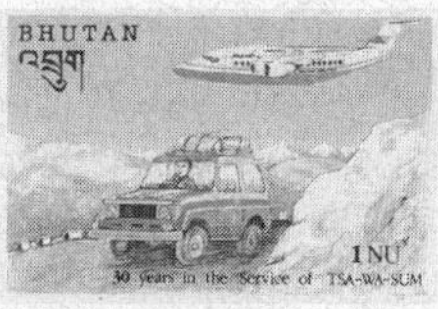

122 British Aerospace BAe 146 and Post Van

1992. 30th Anniv of Bhutan Postal Organization. Multicoloured.
982 1n. Type **122** 20 20
983 3n. Rural letter courier 25 25
984 5n. Emptying post box 45 45

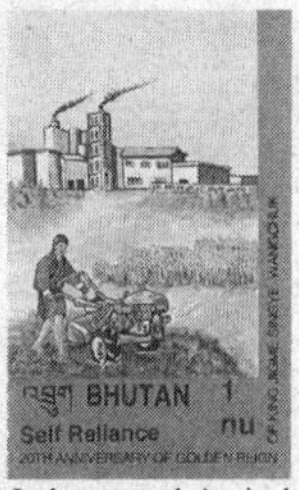

123 Industry and Agriculture

1992. 20th Anniv of Accession of King Jigme Singye Wangchuck. Multicoloured.
985 1n. Type **123** 10 10
986 5n. British Aerospace RJ70 of National Airline 35 35
987 10n. House with water-pump 70 70
988 15n. King Jigme Singye Wangchuk 1·00 1·00

Nos. 985/8 were issued together, se-tenant, each horizontal pair within the block forming a composite design.

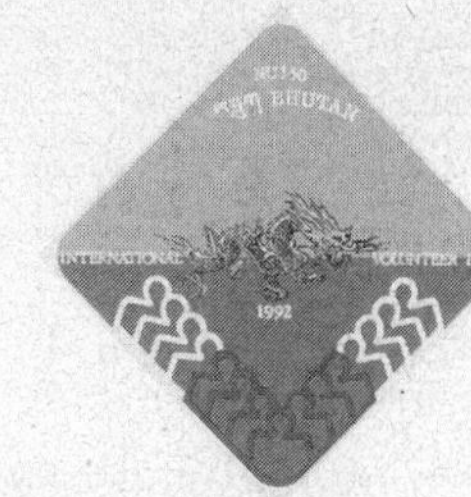

124 Dragon

1992. International Volunteer Day.
990 **124** 1n.50 multicoloured 15 15
991 9n. multicoloured 75 75
992 15n. multicoloured 1·10 1·10

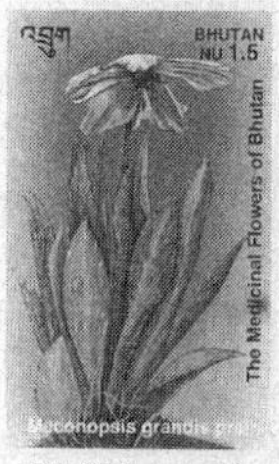

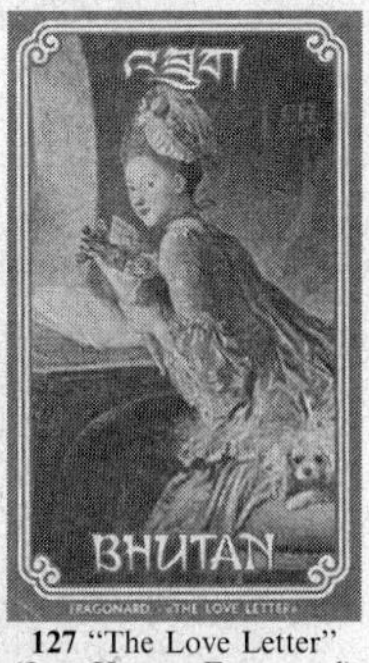

125 "Meconopsis grandis"

127 "The Love Letter" (Jean Honore Fragonard)

1993. Medicinal Flowers. Designs showing varieties of the Asiatic Poppy. Multicoloured.
993 1n.50 Type **125** 10 10
994 7n. "Meconopsis" sp. 50 50
995 10n. "Meconopsis wallichii" 70 70
996 12n. "Meconopsis horridula" 80 80
997 20n. "Meconopsis discigera" 1·40 1·40

1993. Paintings. Multicoloured.
1000 1ch. Type **127** (postage) 10 10
1001 2ch. "The Writer" (Vittore Carpaccio) 10 10
1002 3ch. "Mademoiselle Lavergne" (Jean Etienne Liotard) 10 10
1003 5ch. "Portrait of Erasmus" (Hans Holbein) 10 10
1004 10ch. "Woman writing a Letter" (Gerard Terborch) 10 10
1005 15ch. Type **127** 10 10
1006 25ch. As No. 1001 10 10
1007 50ch. As No. 1002 10 10
1008 60ch. As No. 1003 10 10
1009 80ch. As No. 1004 10 10
1010 1n. Type **127** 15 15
1011 1n.25 As No. 1001 20 20
1012 2n. As No. 1002 (air) 30 30
1013 3n. As No. 1003 40 40
1014 6n. As No. 1004 85 85

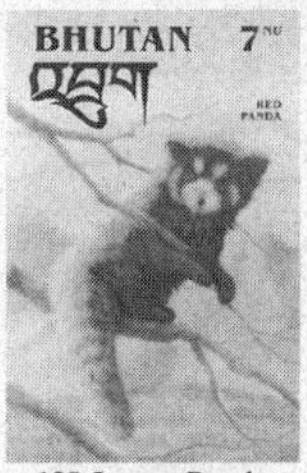

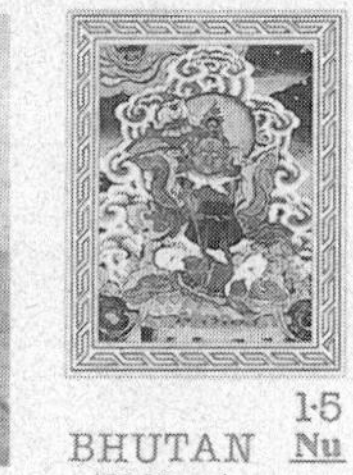

128 Lesser Panda

130 Namtheo-say

1993. Environmental Protection. Multicoloured.
1016 7n. Type **128** 45 45
1017 10n. One-horned rhinoceros 70 70
1018 15n. Black-necked crane and blue poppy 1·00 1·00
1019 20n. Takin 1·25 1·25

Nos. 1016/19 were issued together, se-tenant, forming a composite design.

1993. Door Gods. Multicoloured.
1021 1n.50 Type **130** 10 10
1022 5n. Pha-ke-po 40 40
1023 10n. Chen-mi Jang 80 80
1024 15n. Yul-khor-sung 1·25 1·25

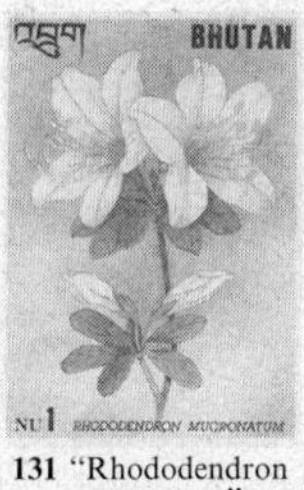

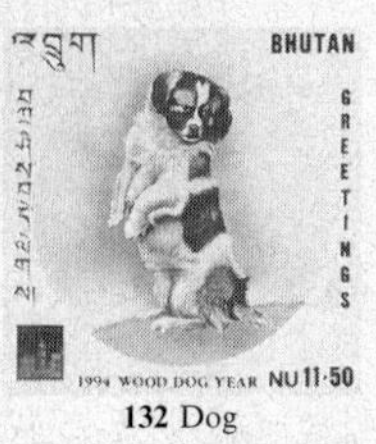

131 "Rhododendron mucronatum"

132 Dog

1994. Flowers. Multicoloured.
1025 1n. Type **131** 10 10
1026 1n.50 "Anemone rupicola" 10 10

1027 2n. "Polemonium coeruleum" 15 15
1028 2n.50 "Rosa marophylla" 20 20
1029 4n. "Paraquilegia microphylla" 30 30
1030 5n. "Aquilegia nivalis" . . . 40 40
1031 6n. "Geranium wallichianum" 45 45
1032 7n. "Rhododendron campanulatum" (wrongly inscr "Rhodendron") . . 55 55
1033 9n. "Viola suavis" 70 70
1034 10n. "Cyananthus lobatus" 80 80

1994. New Year. Year of the Dog. "Hong Kong '94" International Stamp Exhibition.
1036 **132** 11n.50 multicoloured . . 90 90

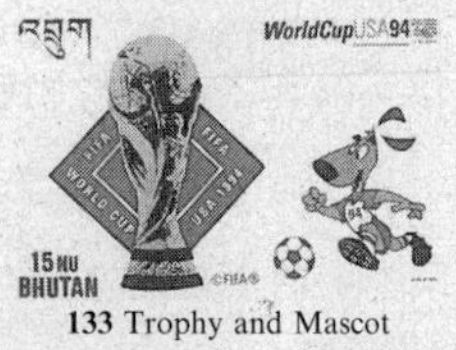

133 Trophy and Mascot

1994. World Cup Football Championship, U.S.A.
1038 **133** 15n. multicoloured . . . 55 55

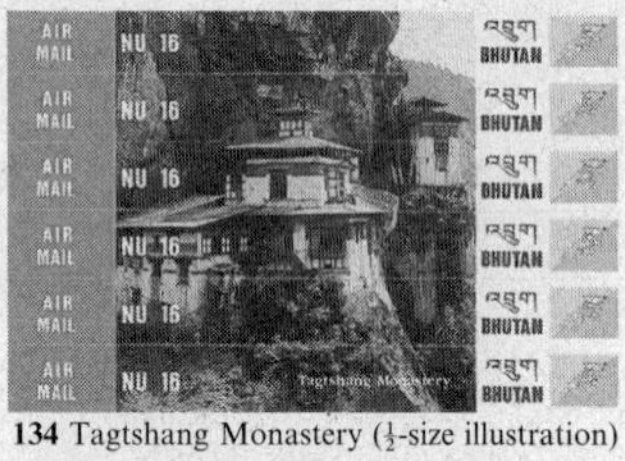

134 Tagtshang Monastery (½-size illustration)

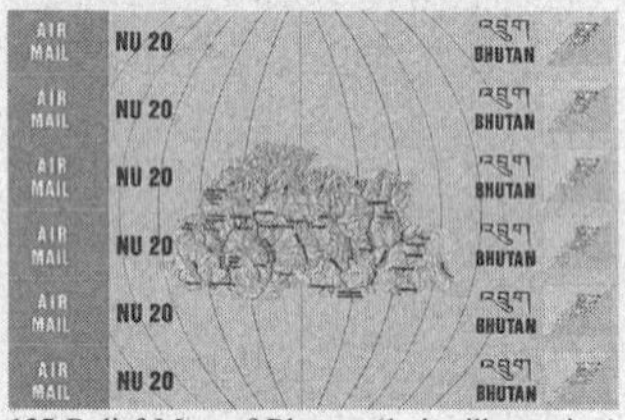

135 Relief Map of Bhutan (½-size illustration)

1994. Air. Self-adhesive.
1039 **134** 16n. multicoloured . . . 60 60
1040 **135** 20n. multicoloured . . . 75 75

The individual stamps are peeled directly from the card backing. Each card contains six different designs with the same face value forming the composite designs illustrated. Each stamp is a horizontal strip with a label indicating the main class of mail covered by the rate at the left, separated by a vertical line of rouletting. The outer edges of the cards are imperforate.

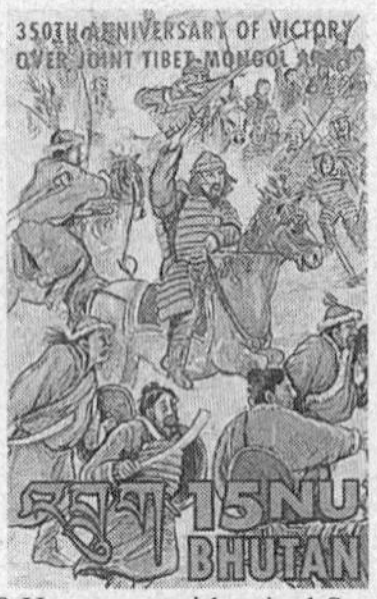

138 Horseman with raised Sword

1994. 350th Anniv of Victory over Tibet-Mongol Army. Multicoloured.
1043 15n. Type **138** 55 55
1044 15n. Archers and hand-to-hand sword fighting . . . 55 55
1045 15n. Horseman with insignia on helmet amongst infantry 55 55
1046 15n. Drummer, piper and troops 55 55

Nos. 1043/6 were issued together, se-tenant, forming a composite design of a battle scene and the Drugyel Dzong.

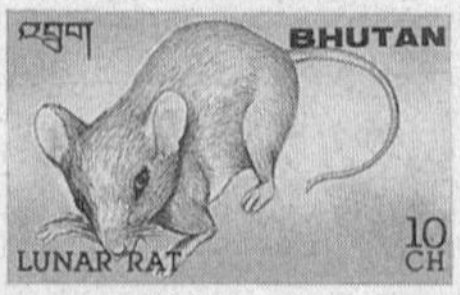

140 Lunar Rat

1995. New Year. Year of the Boar. Mult.
1048 10ch. Type **140** 10 10
1049 20ch. Lunar ox 10 10
1050 30ch. Lunar tiger 10 10
1051 40ch. Lunar rabbit 10 10
1052 1n. Lunar dragon 10 10
1053 2n. Lunar snake 10 10
1054 3n. Lunar horse 10 10
1055 4n. Lunar sheep 15 15
1056 5n. Lunar monkey 20 20
1057 7n. Lunar rooster 25 25
1058 8n. Lunar dog 30 30
1059 9n. Lunar boar 35 35

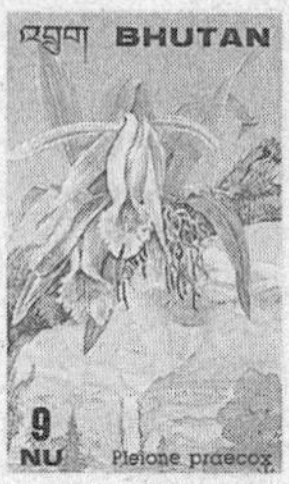

141 "Pleione praecox"

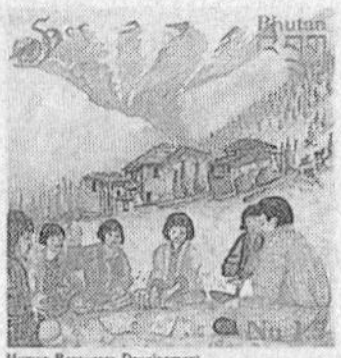

142 Human Resources Development

1995. Flowers. Multicoloured.
1061 9n. Type **141** 35 35
1062 10n. "Primula calderina" . . 35 35
1063 16n. "Primula whitei" . . . 60 60
1064 18n. "Notholirion macrophyllum" 65 65

1995. 50th Anniv of U.N.O. Multicoloured.
1065 1n.50 Type **142** 10 10
1066 5n. Transport and Communications 20 20
1067 9n. Health and Population 35 35
1068 10n. Water and Sanitation 35 35
1069 11n.50 U.N. in Bhutan . . . 45 45
1070 16n. Forestry and Environment 60 60
1071 18n. Peace and Security . . 65 65

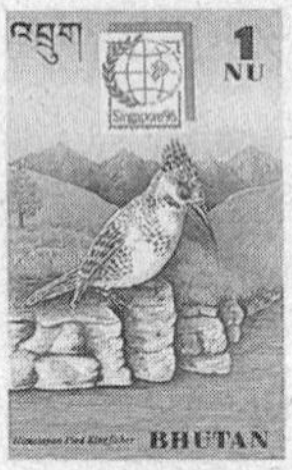

143 Greater Pied Kingfisher ("Himalayan Pied Kingfisher")

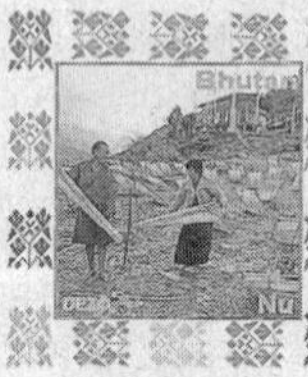

144 Making Paper

1995. "Singapore '95" International Stamp Exhibition. Birds. Multicoloured.
1072 1n. Type **143** 10 10
1073 2n. Blyth's tragopan 10 10
1074 3n. Long-tailed minivets . . 10 10
1075 10n. Red junglefowl 35 35
1076 15n. Black-capped sibia . . 55 55
1077 20n. Red-billed chough . . 70 70

1995. Traditional Crafts. Multicoloured.
1079 1n. Type **144** 10 10
1080 2n. Religious painting . . . 10 10
1081 3n. Clay sculpting 10 10
1082 10n. Weaving 35 35
1083 15n. Making boots 55 55
1084 20n. Carving wooden bowls 70 70

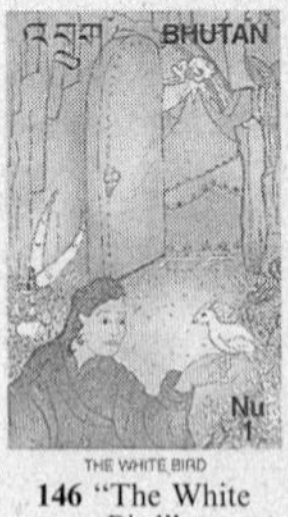

146 "The White Bird"

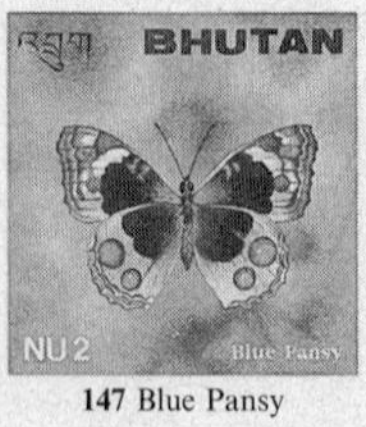

147 Blue Pansy

1996. Folk Tales. Multicoloured.
1087 1n. Type **146** 10 10
1088 2n. "Sing Sing Lhamo and the Moon" 10 10
1089 3n. "The Hoopoe" 10 10
1090 5n. "The Cloud Fairies" . . 20 20
1091 10n. "The Three Wishes" . . 35 35
1092 20n. "The Abominable Snowman" 70 70

1996. Butterflies. Multicoloured.
1094 2n. Type **147** 10 10
1095 3n. Blue peacock 10 10
1096 5n. Great mormon 20 20
1097 10n. Fritillary 35 35
1098 15n. Blue duke 55 55
1099 25n. Brown gorgon 90 90

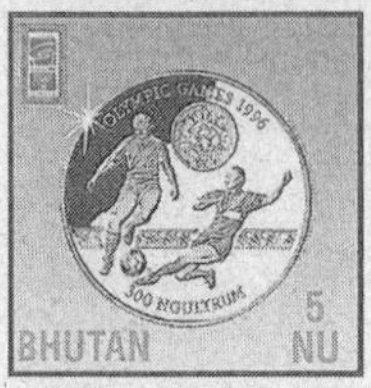

148 300n. Football Coin

1996. Olympic Games, Atlanta. Mult.
1101 5n. Type **148** 20 20
1102 7n. 300n. basketball coin . . 25 25
1103 10n. 5s. judo coin 35 35

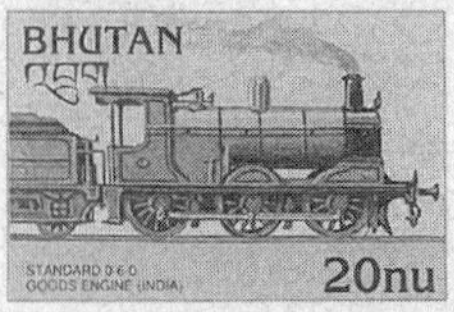

149 Standard Goods Locomotive, India

1996. Trains. Multicoloured.
1105 20n. Type **149** 70 70
1106 20n. Diesel-electric locomotive, Finland . . . 70 70
1107 20n. Shunting tank locomotive, Russia 70 70
1108 20n. Alco PA-1 diesel-electric locomotive, U.S.A. 70 70
1109 20n. Class C11 passenger tank locomotive, Japan 70 70
1110 20n. Settebello high speed electric train, Italy 70 70
1111 20n. Tank locomotive No. 191, Chile 70 70
1112 20n. Pacific locomotive, France 70 70
1113 20n. Steam locomotive No. 10, Norway 70 70
1114 20n. Atlantic express locomotive, Germany . . 70 70
1115 20n. Express steam locomotive, Belgium . . . 70 70
1116 20n. Type 4 diesel-electric locomotive, Great Britain 70 70

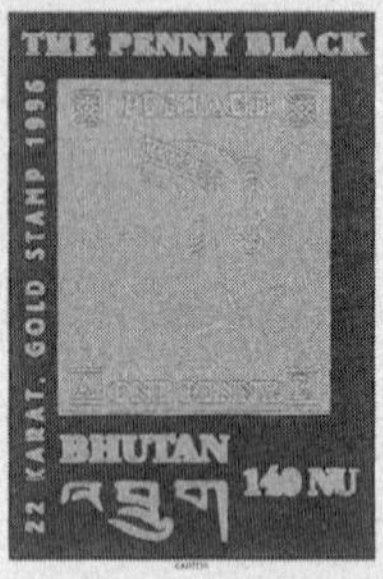

150 Penny Black

1996.
1118 **150** 140n. gold and black . . 4·25 4·25

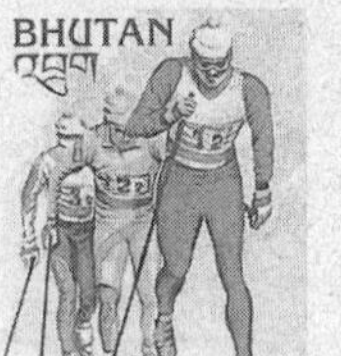

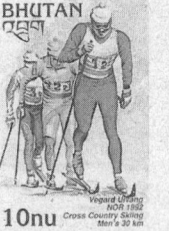

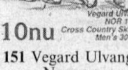

151 Vegard Ulvang, Norway

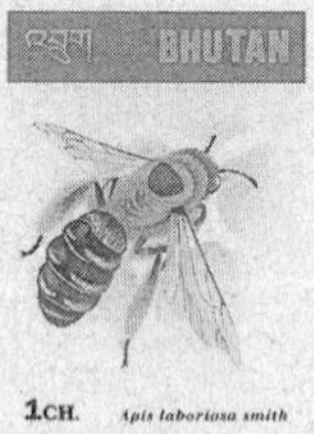

152 Bee

1997. Winter Olympic Gold Medallists. Multicoloured. (a) Without frame.
1119 10n. Type **151** (30km. cross-country skiing, 1992) . . 30 30
1120 15n. Kristi Yamaguchi, U.S.A. (women's figure skating, 1992) 45 45
1121 25n. Markus Wasmeier, Germany (men's super giant slalom, 1994) 75 75
1122 30n. Georg Hackl, Germany (luge, 1992) 95 95

(b) As T **151** but with black frame around design.
1123 15n. Andreas Ostler, West Germany (two-man bobsleighing, 1952) . . . 45 45
1124 15n. East German team (four-man bobsleighing, 1984) 45 45
1125 15n. Stein Eriksen, Norway (men's giant slalom, 1952) 45 45
1126 15n. Alberto Tomba, Italy (men's giant slalom, 1988) 45 45

1997. Insects and Arachnidae. Multicoloured.
1128 1ch. Type **152** 10 10
1129 2ch. "Neptunides polychromus" (beetle) . . 10 10
1130 3ch. "Conocephalus maculctus" (grasshopper) 10 10
1131 4ch. "Blattidae" sp. (beetle) 10 10
1132 5ch. Great diving beetle . . 10 10
1133 10ch. Hercules beetle . . . 10 10
1134 15ch. Ladybird 10 10
1135 20ch. "Sarcophaga haemorrhoidalis" (fly) . . 10 10
1136 25ch. Stag beetle 10 10
1137 30ch. Caterpillar 10 10
1138 35ch. "Lycia hirtaria" (moth) 10 10
1139 40ch. "Clytarius pennatus" (beetle) 10 10
1140 45ch. "Ephemera denica" (mayfly) 10 10
1141 50ch. European field cricket 10 10
1142 60ch. Elephant hawk moth 10 10
1143 65ch. "Gerris" sp. (beetle) 10 10
1144 70ch. Banded agrion 10 10
1145 80ch. "Tachyta nana" (beetle) 10 10
1146 90ch. "Eurydema pulchra" (shieldbug) 10 10
1147 1n. "Hadrurus hirsutus" (scorpion) 10 10
1148 1n.50 "Vespa germanica" (wasp) 10 10
1149 2n. "Pyrops" sp. (beetle) . . 10 10
1150 2n.50 Praying mantis . . . 10 10
1151 3n. "Araneus diadematus" (spider) 10 10
1152 3n.50 "Atrophaneura" sp. (butterfly) 10 10

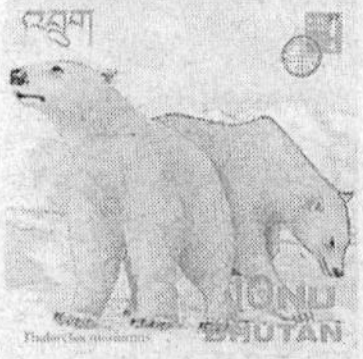

153 Polar Bears

1997. "Hong Kong '97" International Stamp Exhibition. Multicoloured.
1154 10n. Type **153** 30 30
1155 10n. Koalas ("Phascolarctos cinereus") 30 30
1156 10n. Asiatic black bear ("Selenarctos thibetanus") 30 30
1157 10n. Lesser panda ("Ailurus fulgens") 30 30

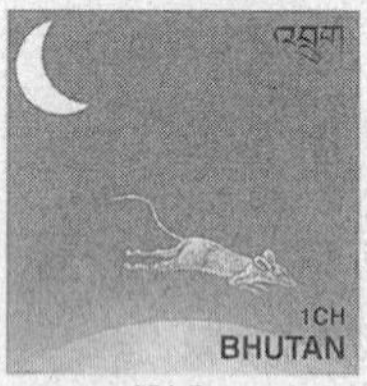

154 Rat

1997. New Year. Year of the Ox. Multicoloured.
1159 1ch. Type **154** 10 10
1160 2ch. Ox 10 10
1161 3ch. Tiger 10 10
1162 4ch. Rabbit 10 10
1163 90ch. Monkey 10 10
1164 5n. Dragon 15 15
1165 6n. Snake 20 20
1166 7n. Horse 20 20
1167 8n. Ram 25 25
1168 10n. Cock 30 30
1169 11n. Dog 30 30
1170 12n. Boar 35 35

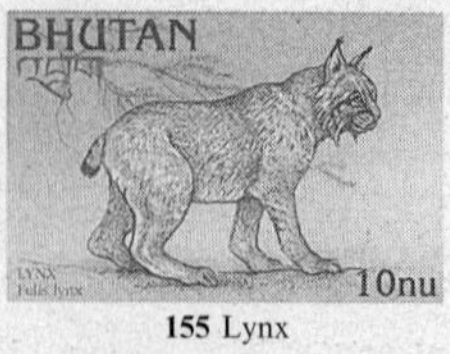

155 Lynx

1997. Endangered Species. Multicoloured.
1172 10n. Type **155** 30 30
1173 10n. Lesser ("Red") panda ("Ailurus fulgens") . . . 30 30
1174 10n. Takin ("Budorcas taxicolor") 30 30
1175 10n. Forest musk deer ("Moschus chrysogaster") 30 30
1176 10n. Snow leopard ("Panthera uncia") . . . 30 30
1177 10n. Golden langur ("Presbytis geei") 30 30
1178 10n. Tiger ("Panthera tigris") 30 30
1179 10n. Indian muntjac ("Muntiacus muntjak") 30 30
1180 10n. Bobak marmot ("Marmota bobak") . . . 30 30
1181 10n. Dhole ("Cuon alpinis") running 30 30
1182 10n. Dhole walking 30 30
1183 10n. Mother dhole nursing cubs 30 30
1184 10n. Two dhole 30 30

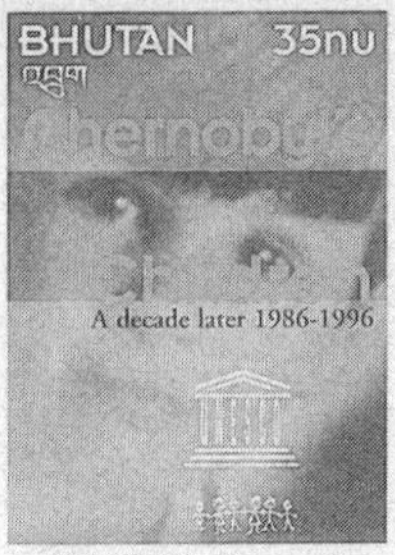

156 Child's Face and U.N.E.S.C.O. Emblem

1997. 10th Anniv of Chernobyl Nuclear Disaster.
1186 **156** 35n. multicoloured . . . 1·00 1·00

157 Mount Huangshah, China

1997. 50th Anniv of U.N.E.S.C.O. World Heritage Sites. Multicoloured.
1187 10n. Type **157** 30 30
1188 10n. Statue of Emperor Qin, China 30 30
1189 10n. Imperial bronze dragon, China 30 30
1190 10n. Pyramids, Tikal National Park, Guatemala 30 30
1191 10n. Fountain, Evora, Portugal 30 30
1192 10n. Forest path, Shirakami-Sanchi, Japan 30 30
1193 10n. View from Eiffel Tower, Paris, France 30 30
1194 10n. Wooden walkway, Valley Below the Falls, Croatia 30 30
1195 15n. Bamberg Cathedral, Germany 45 45
1196 15n. Aerial view of Bamberg 45 45
1197 15n. St. Michael's Church, Hildesheim, Germany 45 45
1198 15n. Potsdam Palace, Germany 45 45
1199 15n. Church, Potsdam 45 45
1200 15n. Waterfront, Lubeck, Germany 45 45
1201 15n. Quedlinberg, Germany 45 45
1202 15n. Benedictine church, Lorsch, Germany 45 45

158 Turkish Angora

159 Stuart Pearce (England)

1997. Domestic Animals. Mult. (a) Cats.
1204 10n. Type **158** 30 30
1205 15n. Oriental shorthair 45 45
1206 15n. Japanese bobtail 45 45
1207 15n. Ceylon 45 45
1208 15n. Exotic 45 45
1209 15n. Rex 45 45
1210 15n. Ragdoll 45 45
1211 15n. Russian blue 45 45
1212 20n. British shorthair 55 55
1213 25n. Burmese 70 70

(b) Dogs.
1214 10n. Dalmatian 30 30
1215 15n. Siberian husky 45 45
1216 20n. Saluki 55 55
1217 20n. Dandie Dinmont terrier 55 55
1218 20n. Chinese crested 55 55
1219 20n. Norwich terrier 55 55
1220 20n. Basset hound 55 55
1221 20n. Cardigan Welsh corgi 55 55
1222 20n. French bulldog 55 55
1223 25n. Shar-Pei 70 70

Nos. 1206/11 and 1217/22 respectively were issued together, se-tenant, forming composite designs.

1997. World Cup Football Championship, France (1998). Black (Nos. 1225, 1231, 1235, 1237, 1241, 1243) or multicoloured (others).
1225 5n. Type **159** 15 15
1226 10n. Paul Gascoigne (England) 30 30
1227 10n. Diego Maradona (Argentina 1986) (horiz) 30 30
1228 10n. Carlos Alberto (Brazil 1970) (horiz) 30 30
1229 10n. Dunga (Brazil 1994) (horiz) 30 30
1230 10n. Bobby Moore (England 1966) (horiz) 30 30
1231 10n. Fritz Walter (West Germany 1954) (horiz) 30 30
1232 10n. Walter Matthaus (Germany 1990) (horiz) 30 30
1233 10n. Franz Beckenbauer (West Germany 1974) (horiz) 30 30
1234 10n. Daniel Passarella (Argentina 1978) (horiz) 30 30
1235 10n. Italy team, 1938 (horiz) 30 30
1236 10n. West Germany team, 1954 (horiz) 30 30
1237 10n. Uruguay team, 1958 (horiz) 30 30
1238 10n. England team, 1966 (horiz) 30 30
1239 10n. Argentina team, 1978 (horiz) 30 30
1240 10n. Brazil team, 1962 (horiz) 30 30
1241 10n. Italy team, 1934 (horiz) 30 30
1242 10n. Brazil team, 1970 (horiz) 30 30
1243 10n. Uruguay team, 1930 (horiz) 30 30
1244 10n. David Beckham (England) 45 45
1245 20n. Steve McManaman (England) 55 55
1246 25n. Tony Adams (England) 70 70
1247 30n. Paul Ince (England) 85 85

160 Buddha in Lotus Position

161 Jawaharlal Nehru and King Jigme Dorji Wangchuck

1997. "Indepex '97" International Stamp Exhibition, New Delhi. 50th Anniv of Independence of India. Multicoloured.
1249 3n. Type **160** 10 10
1250 7n. Mahatma Gandhi with hands together 20 20
1251 10n. Gandhi (three-quarter face portrait) 30 30
1252 15n. Buddha with feet on footstool 45 45

1997. Int Friendship between India and Bhutan.
1254 **161** 3n. black and pink 10 10
1255 – 10n. multicoloured 30 30
DESIGN: 10n. Prime Minister Rajiv Gandhi of India and King Jigme Singye Wangchuck.

162 Tiger

1998. New Year. Year of the Tiger.
1257 **162** 3n. multicoloured 10 10

163 Safe Motherhood and Anniversary Emblems

1998. 50th Anniv of W.H.O.
1259 **163** 3n. multicoloured 10 10
1260 10n. multicoloured 30 30

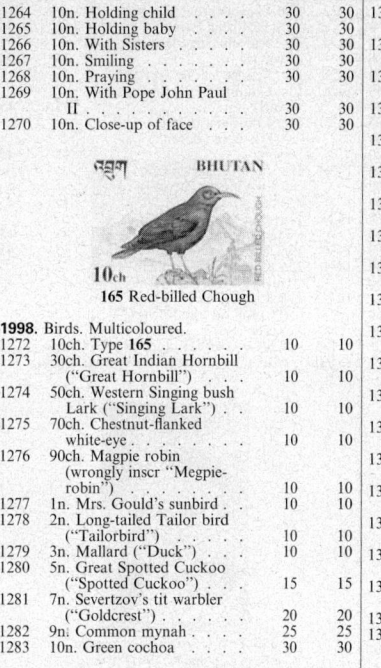

164 Mother Teresa

1998. Mother Teresa (founder of Missionaries of Charity) Commemoration. Multicoloured.
1262 10n. Type **164** 30 30
1263 10n. With Diana, Princess of Wales 30 30
1264 10n. Holding child 30 30
1265 10n. Holding baby 30 30
1266 10n. With Sisters 30 30
1267 10n. Smiling 30 30
1268 10n. Praying 30 30
1269 10n. With Pope John Paul II 30 30
1270 10n. Close-up of face 30 30

165 Red-billed Chough

1998. Birds. Multicoloured.
1272 10ch. Type **165** 10 10
1273 30ch. Great Indian Hornbill ("Great Hornbill") 10 10
1274 50ch. Western Singing bush Lark ("Singing Lark") 10 10
1275 70ch. Chestnut-flanked white-eye 10 10
1276 90ch. Magpie robin (wrongly inscr "Megpie-robin") 10 10
1277 1n. Mrs. Gould's sunbird 10 10
1278 2n. Long-tailed Tailor bird ("Tailorbird") 10 10
1279 3n. Mallard ("Duck") 10 10
1280 5n. Great Spotted Cuckoo ("Spotted Cuckoo") 15 15
1281 7n. Severtzov's tit warbler ("Goldcrest") 20 20
1282 9n. Common mynah 25 25
1283 10n. Green cochoa 30 30

166 Rabbit

1999. New Year. Year of the Rabbit. Multicoloured.
1285 4n. Type **166** 10 10
1286 16n. Rabbit on hillock 45 45

168 King Wangchuck

1999. 25th Anniv of Coronation of King Jigme Singye Wangchuck. Multicoloured.
1289 25n. Type **168** 75 75
1290 25n. Facing left (yellow background) 75 75
1291 25n. Facing forwards (orange background) 75 75
1292 25n. With arm raised (green background) 75 75

169 Early German Steam Locomotive

1999. Trains. Multicoloured.
1294 5n. Type **169** 15 15
1295 10n. Electric locomotive 30 30
1296 10n. "Hikari" express train, Japan 30 30
1297 10n. Steam locomotive, South Africa, 1953 30 30
1298 10n. Super Chief locomotive, U.S.A., 1946 30 30
1299 10n. Magleus Magnet train, Japan, 1991 30 30
1300 10n. *Flying Scotsman*, Great Britain, 1992 30 30
1301 10n. Kodama locomotive, Japan, 1958 30 30
1302 10n. "Blue Train", South Africa, 1969 30 30
1303 10n. Intercity train, Germany, 1960 30 30
1304 10n. ET 403 high speed electric locomotive, Germany, 1973 30 30
1305 10n. 4-4-0 steam locomotive, U.S.A., 1855 30 30
1306 10n. Beyer-Garratt steam locomotive, South Africa, 1954 (wrongly inscr "BAYER GARRATT") 30 30
1307 10n. Settebello locomotive, Italy, 1953 30 30
1308 15n. Pacific Class 01 steam locomotive, Germany 45 45
1309 15n. Neptune Express, Germany 45 45
1310 15n. 4-6-0 steam locomotive, Great Britain 45 45
1311 15n. Shovelnose Streamliner diesel locomotive, U.S.A. 45 45
1312 15n. Electric locomotive, Germany 45 45
1313 15n. Early steam locomotive, Germany 45 45
1314 15n. Union Pacific diesel locomotive, U.S.A. 45 45
1315 15n. 1881 Borsig steam locomotive, Germany 45 45
1316 15n. Borsig 4-6-4 diesel locomotive, Germany 45 45
1317 15n. Diesel-electric locomotive, France 45 45
1318 15n. Pennsylvania Railroad locomotive, U.S.A. 45 45
1319 15n. Steam locomotive, Germany 45 45
1320 15n. Amtrak locomotive, U.S.A. 45 45
1321 15n. 2-2-2 steam locomotive, Great Britain 45 45
1322 15n. P class steam locomotive, Denmark 45 45
1323 15n. Electric locomotive, France 45 45
1324 15n. First Japanese locomotive 45 45
1325 15n. 2-8-2 steam locomotive, Germany 45 45
1326 20n. Steam locomotive 45 45
1327 30n. Electric locomotive 45 45

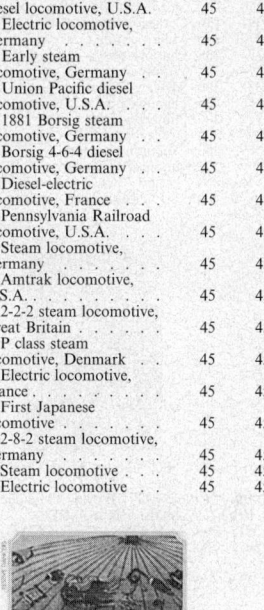

170 "Festive Dancers"

1999. 150th Death Anniv of Katsushika Hokusai (artist). Multicoloured.
1329 15n. Type **170** 45 45
1330 15n. "Drawings of Women" (woman reading) 45 45
1331 15n. "Festive Dancers" (man wearing pointed hat) 45 45
1332 15n. "Festive Dancers" (man looking up) 45 45
1333 15n. "Drawings of Women" (woman sitting on ground) 45 45
1334 15n. "Festive Dancers" (woman) 45 45
1335 15n. "Suspension Bridge between Hida and Etchu" 45 45
1336 15n. "Drawings of Women" (woman dressing hair) 45 45
1337 15n. "Exotic Beauty" 45 45
1338 15n. "The Poet Nakamaro in China" 45 45
1339 15n. "Drawings of Women" (woman rolling up sleeve) 45 45
1340 15n. "Chinese Poet in Snow" 45 45
1341 15n. "Mount Fuji seen above Mist on the Tama River" (horiz) 45 45
1342 15n. "Mount Fuji seen from Shichirigahama" (horiz) 45 45
1343 15n. "Sea Life" (turtle) (horiz) 45 45
1344 15n. "Sea Life" (fish) (horiz) 45 45
1345 15n. "Mount Fuji reflected in a Lake" (horiz) 45 45
1346 15n. "Mount Fuji seen through the Piers of Mannenbashi" (horiz) 45 45

171 Tyrannosaurus Rex

1999. Prehistoric Animals. Multicoloured.
1348 10n. Type **171** 30 30
1349 10n. Dimorphodon 30 30
1350 10n. Diplodocus 30 30
1351 10n. Pterodaustro 30 30
1352 10n. Tyrannosaurus Rex (different) 30 30
1353 10n. Edmontosaurus 30 30
1354 10n. Apatosaurus 30 30
1355 10n. Deinonychus 30 30
1356 10n. Hypsilophodon 30 30
1357 10n. Oviraptor 30 30
1358 10n. Stegosaurus beside lake 30 30
1359 10n. Head of Triceratops 30 30
1360 10n. Pterodactylus and Brachiosaurus 30 30
1361 10n. Pteranodon 30 30

1362 10n. Anurognathus and Tyrannosaurus Rex . . . 30 30
1363 10n. Brachiosaurus 30 30
1364 10n. Corythosaurus 30 30
1365 10n. Iguanodon 30 30
1366 10n. Lesothosaurus 30 30
1367 10n. Allosaurus 30 30
1368 10n. Velociraptor 30 30
1369 10n. Triceratops in water . . 30 30
1370 10n. Stegosaurus in water 30 30
1371 10n. Compsognathus . . . 30 30
1372 20n. Moeritherium 60 60
1373 20n. Platybelodon 60 60
1374 20n. Woolly mammoth . . . 60 60
1375 20n. African elephant . . . 60 60
1376 20n. Deinonychus 60 60
1377 20n. Dimorphodon 60 60
1378 20n. Archaeopteryx 60 60
1379 20n. Common pheasant ("Ring-necked Pheasant") 60 60

Nos. 1348/59 and 1360/71 were issued together, se-tenant, with the backgrounds forming a composite design

172 Siberian Musk Deer

1999. "China '99" World Philatelic Exhibition, Peking. Animals. Multicoloured.

1381 20n. Type **172** 60 60
1382 20n. Takin (*Budorcas taxicolor*) 60 60
1383 20n. Bharal ("Blue sheep") (*Pseudois nayur*) (wrongly inscr "nayour") 60 60
1384 20n. Yak (*Bos gunniens*) . . 60 60
1385 20n. Common goral (*Nemorhaedus goral*) . . . 60 60

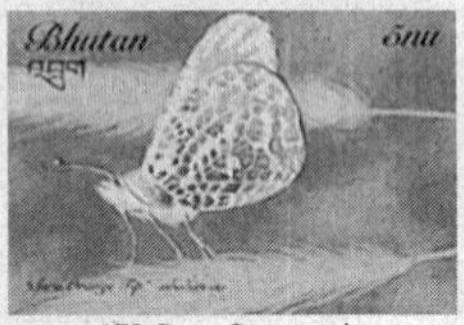

173 Sara Orange-tip

1999. Butterflies. Multicoloured.

1386 5n. Type **173** 15 15
1387 10n. Pipe-vine swallowtail 30 30
1388 15n. Longwings 45 45
1389 20n. Viceroy 60 60
1390 20n. Frosted skipper 60 60
1391 20n. Fiery skipper 60 60
1392 20n. Banded hairstreak . . 60 60
1393 20n. Cloudless ("Clouded") sulphur 60 60
1394 20n. Milbert's tortoiseshell 60 60
1395 20n. Eastern tailed blue . . 60 60
1396 20n. Jamaican kite ("Zebra") swallowtail . . 60 60
1397 20n. Colorado hairstreak . . 60 60
1398 20n. Pink-edged sulphur . . 60 60
1399 20n. Barred sulphur (wrongly inscr "Fairy Yellow") 60 60
1400 20n. Red-spotted purple . . 60 60
1401 20n. Aphrodite 60 60
1402 25n. Silver-spotted skipper (vert) 75 75
1403 30n. Great spangled fritillary (vert) 90 90
1404 35n. Little copper (vert) . . 1·00 1·00

Nos. 1390/95 and 1396/1401 were issued together, se-tenant, forming a composite design.

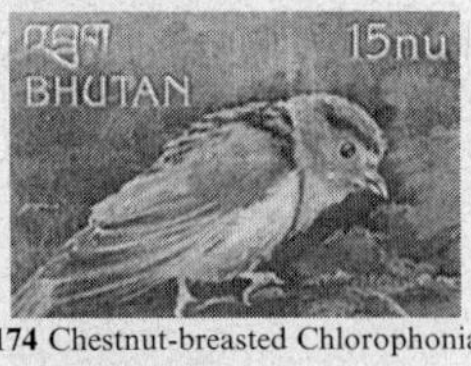

174 Chestnut-breasted Chlorophonia

1999. Birds. Multicoloured.

1406 15n. Type **174** 45 45
1407 15n. Yellow-faced amazon 45 45
1408 15n. White ibis 45 45
1409 15n. Parrotlet sp. ("Caique") 45 45
1410 15n. Green jay 45 45
1411 15n. Tufted coquette 45 45
1412 15n. Troupial 45 45
1413 15n. American purple gallinule ("Purple Gallinule") 45 45
1414 15n. Copper-rumped hummingbird 45 45
1415 15n. Great egret ("Common egret") 45 45
1416 15n. Rufous-browed pepper shrike 45 45
1417 15n. Glittering-throated emerald 45 45
1418 15n. Great kiskadee 45 45
1419 15n. Cuban green woodpecker 45 45
1420 15n. Scarlet ibis 45 45
1421 15n. Belted kingfisher . . . 45 45
1422 15n. Barred antshrike . . . 45 45
1423 15n. Brown-throated conure ("Caribbean Parakeet") 45 45
1424 15n. Rufous-tailed jacamar (vert) 45 45
1425 15n. Scarlet macaw (vert) . . 45 45
1426 15n. Channel-billed toucan (vert) 45 45
1427 15n. Louisiana heron ("Tricolored heron") (vert) 45 45
1428 15n. St. Vincent amazon ("St. Vincent Parrot") (vert) 45 45
1429 15n. Blue-crowned motmot (vert) 45 45
1430 15n. Horned screamer (vert) 45 45
1431 15n. Grey plover ("Black-billed Plover") (vert) . . . 45 45
1432 15n. Eastern meadowlark ("Common meadowlark") (vert) 45 45

Nos. 1406/14, 1415/23 and 1424/32 were issued together, se-tenant, forming a composite design.

175 Yuri Gagarin (first person in space, 1961)

1999. 30th Anniv of First Manned Moon Landing. Multicoloured.

1434 20n. Type **175** 60 60
1435 20n. Alan Shepard (first American in space, 1961) 60 60
1436 20n. John Glenn (first American to orbit Earth, 1962) 60 60
1437 20n. Valentina Tereshkova (first woman in space, 1963) 60 60
1438 20n. Edward White (first American to walk in space, 1965) 60 60
1439 20n. Neil Armstrong (first person to set foot on Moon, 1969) 60 60
1440 20n. Neil Armstrong (wearing N.A.S.A. suit) 60 60
1441 20n. Michael Collins 60 60
1442 20n. Edwin (Buzz) Aldrin 60 60
1443 20n. *Columbia* (pointing upwards) 60 60
1444 20n. *Eagle* on lunar surface 60 60
1445 20n. Edwin Aldrin on lunar surface 60 60
1446 20n. N.A.S.A. X-15 rocket (1960) 60 60
1447 20n. Gemini 8 (1966) . . . 60 60
1448 20n. Saturn V rocket (1969) 60 60
1449 20n. *Columbia* (pointing downwards) 60 60
1450 20n. *Eagle* above Moon . . 60 60
1451 20n. Edwin Aldrin descending ladder 60 60

Nos. 1434/9, 1440/5 and 1446/51 were issued together, se-tenant, forming a composite design.

176 Tortoiseshell Cat

1999. Animals. Multicoloured.

1453 5n. Type **176** 15 15
1454 5n. Man watching blue and white cat 15 15
1455 5n. Girl and pet cat 15 15
1456 10n. Chinchilla golden longhair adult and kittens 30 30
1457 12n. Russian blue adult and kitten 35 35
1458 12n. Birman 35 35
1459 12n. Devon rex 35 35
1460 12n. Pewter longhair 35 35
1461 12n. Bombay 35 35
1462 12n. Sorrel somali 35 35
1463 12n. Red tabby manx . . . 35 35
1464 12n. Blue smoke longhair 35 35
1465 12n. Oriental tabby shorthair adult and kitten 35 35
1466 12n. Australian silky terrier 35 35
1467 12n. Samoyed 35 35
1468 12n. Basset bleu de Gascogne 35 35
1469 12n. Bernese mountain dog 35 35
1470 12n. Pug 35 35
1471 12n. Bergamasco 35 35
1472 12n. Basenji 35 35
1473 12n. Wetterhoun 35 35
1474 12n. Drever 35 35
1475 12n. Przewalski horse . . . 35 35
1476 12n. Shetland pony 35 35
1477 12n. Dutch gelderlander horse 35 35
1478 12n. Shire horse 35 35
1479 12n. Arab 35 35
1480 12n. Boulonnais 35 35
1481 12n. Falabella 35 35
1482 12n. Orlov trotter 35 35
1483 12n. Suffolk punch 35 35
1484 15n. Lipizzaner 45 45
1485 20n. Andalusian 60 60
1486 25n. Weimaraner (dog) . . . 60 60

177 Bharal

1999. Animals and Birds of the Himalayas. Multicoloured. (a) Animals.

1489 20n. Type **177** 60 60
1490 20n. Lynx 60 60
1491 20n. Rat snake 60 60
1492 20n. Indian elephant 60 60
1493 20n. Langur 60 60
1494 20n. Musk deer 60 60
1495 20n. Otter 60 60
1496 20n. Tibetan wolf 60 60
1497 20n. Himalayan black bear 60 60
1498 20n. Snow leopard 60 60
1499 20n. Flying squirrel 60 60
1500 20n. Red fox 60 60
1501 20n. Ibex 60 60
1502 20n. Takin 60 60
1503 20n. Agama lizard 60 60
1504 20n. Marmot 60 60
1505 20n. Red panda 60 60
1506 20n. Leopard cat 60 60

(b) Birds.

1508 20n. Red-crested pochard 60 60
1509 20n. Satyr tragopan 60 60
1510 20n. Lammergeier ("Lammergeier Vulture") 60 60
1511 20n. Kalij pheasant 60 60
1512 20n. Great Indian hornbill 60 60
1513 20n. White stork ("Stork") 60 60
1514 20n. Rufous-necked hornbill (wrongly inscr "Rofous") 60 60
1515 20n. Black drongo ("Drongo") 60 60
1516 20n. Himalayan monal pheasant 60 60
1517 20n. Black-necked crane . . 60 60
1518 20n. Little green bee-eater 60 60
1519 20n. Oriental ibis ("Ibis") 60 60
1520 20n. Crested lark 60 60
1521 20n. Ferruginous duck . . . 60 60
1522 20n. Blood pheasant 60 60
1523 20n. White-crested laughing thrush ("Laughing Thrush") 60 60
1524 20n. Golden eagle 60 60
1525 20n. Siberian rubythroat . . 60 60

178 Elephant, Monkey, Rabbit and Bird (Four Friends)

1999. Year 2000.

1527 **178** 10n. multicoloured . . . 30 30
1528 20n. multicoloured . . . 60 60

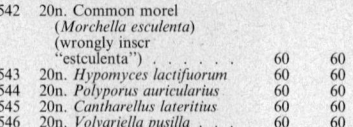

179 Elegant Stink Horn

1999. Fungi. Multicoloured.

1529 20n. Type **179** 60 60
1530 20n. *Pholiota squarrosoides* 60 60
1531 20n. Scaly inky cap (*Coprinus quadrifidus*) . . 60 60
1532 20n. Golden spindles (*Clavulinopsis fusiformis*) 60 60
1533 20n. *Spathularia velutipes* . . 60 60
1534 20n. *Ganoderma lucidum* . . 60 60
1535 20n. *Microglossum rufum* . . 60 60
1536 20n. *Lactarius hygrophoroides* 60 60
1537 20n. *Lactarius speciosus complex* 60 60
1538 20n. *Calostoma cinnabarina* 60 60
1539 20n. *Clitocybe clavipes* . . . 60 60
1540 20n. *Microstoma floccosa* . . 60 60
1541 20n. Frost's bolete (*Boletus frostii*) 60 60
1542 20n. Common morel (*Morchella esculenta*) (wrongly inscr "estculenta") 60 60
1543 20n. *Hypomyces lactifuorum* 60 60
1544 20n. *Polyporus auricularius* 60 60
1545 20n. *Cantharellus lateritius* 60 60
1546 20n. *Volvariella pusilla* . . . 60 60

180 Green Dragon with Red Flames

2000. New Year. Year of the Dragon. Multicoloured.

1548 3n. Type **180** 10 10
1549 5n. Green dragon encircling moon 15 15
1550 8n. Dragon and symbols of Chinese zodiac 20 20
1552 12n. Brown dragon encircling moon 35 35

181 LZ-1 (first flight), 1900

2000. Centenary of First Zeppelin Flight. Multicoloured.

1554 25n. Type **181** 70 70
1555 25n. LZ-2, 1906 . . . . . . 70 70
1556 25n. LZ-3 over hills (first flight, 1906) 70 70
1557 25n. LZ-127 *Graf Zeppelin* (first flight, 1928) 70 70
1558 25n. LZ-129 *Hindenberg* (first flight, 1936) 70 70
1559 25n. LZ-130 *Graf Zeppelin II* (first flight, 1938) . . . 70 70
1560 25n. LZ-1 over hill with tree 70 70
1561 25n. LZ-2 over mountains 70 70
1562 25n. LZ-3 against sky . . . 70 70
1563 25n. LZ-4 (first flight, 1908) 70 70
1564 25n. LZ-5 (first flight, 1909) 70 70
1565 25n. LZ-6 (formation of Deutsche Liftschiffahrts Aktien Gesellschaft (DELAG) (world's first airline), 1909) 70 70
1566 25n. LZ-1 over grassy hills, 1900 . . . . 70 70
1567 25n. Z11 *Ersatz*, 1913 . . . 70 70
1568 25n. LZ-6 exiting hanger, 1909 . . . . 70 70
1569 25n. LZ-10 *Schwabein* first flight, 1911) 70 70
1570 25n. LZ-7 *Deutschland* (inscr "Ersatz Deutschland") . . 70 70
1571 25n. LZ-11 *Viktoria Luise* 70 70

182 Lunix III

2000. "WORLD STAMP EXPO 2000" International Stamp Exhibition, Anaheim, California. Space. Multicoloured.

1573 25n. Type **182** 70 70
1574 25n. Ranger 9 . . . . 70 70
1575 25n. Lunar Orbiter 70 70
1576 25n. Lunar Prospector spacecraft 70 70
1577 25n. *Apollo 11* spacecraft . . 70 70
1578 25n. Selen satellite 70 70
1579 25n. Space shuttle *Challenger* 70 70
1580 25n. North American X-15 experimental rocket aircraft 70 70
1581 25n. Space shuttle *Buran* . . 70 70
1582 25n. Hermes (experimental space plane) 70 70
1583 25n. X-33 Venturi Star (re-usable launch vehicle) . . 70 70
1584 25n. Hope (unmanned experimental spacecraft) 70 70
1585 25n. Victor Patsayev (cosmonaut) 70 70
1586 25n. Yladisloav Volkov (cosmonaut) 70 70
1587 25n. Georgi Dobrvolski (cosmonaut) 70 70
1588 25n. Virgil Grissom (astronaut) 70 70
1589 25n. Roger Chaffee (astronaut) 70 70
1590 25n. Edward White (astronaut) 70 70

183 Trashigang Dzong

2000. "EXPO 2000" World's Fair, Hanover, Germany (1st issue). Monasteries. Multicoloured.

1592	3n. Type **183**	10	10
1593	4n. Lhuentse Dzong	10	10
1594	6n. Gasa Dzong	15	15
1595	7n. Punakha Dzong	20	20
1596	10n. Trashichhoe Dzong	30	30
1597	20n. Paro Dzong	55	55

184 Snow Leopard

2000. "EXPO 2000" World's Fair, Hanover, Germany (2nd issue). Wildlife. Multicoloured.

1599	10n. Type **184**	30	30
1600	10n. Raven	30	30
1601	10n. Golden langur	30	30
1602	10n. Rhododendron	30	30
1603	10n. Black-necked crane	30	30
1604	10n. Blue poppy	30	30

185 Jesse Owens (U.S.A.) (Berlin, 1936)

2000. Olympic Games, Sydney. Multicoloured.

1605	20n. Type **185**	55	55
1606	20n. Kayaking (modern games)	55	55
1607	20n. Fulton County Stadium, Atlanta, Georgia (1996 games)	55	55
1608	20n. Ancient Greek athlete	55	55

186 G. and R. Stephenson's (first steam locomotive) *Rocket*

2000. 175th Anniv of Opening of Stockton and Darlington Railway. Multicoloured.

1609	20n. Type **186**	55	55
1610	20n. Steam locomotive (opening of London and Birmingham railway, 1828)	55	55
1611	20n. Northumbrian locomotive, 1825	55	55

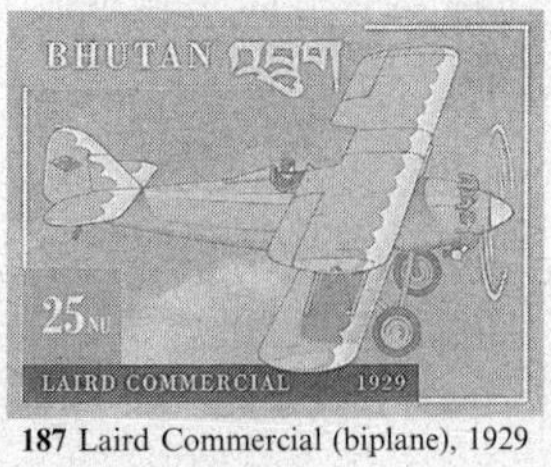

187 Laird Commercial (biplane), 1929

2000. Airplanes. Multicoloured.

1613	25n. Type **187**	70	70
1614	25n. Ryan B-5 Brougham, 1927 (wrongly inscr "Broughm")	70	70
1615	25n. Cessna AW, 1928	70	70
1616	25n. Travel Air 4000 biplane, 1927	70	70
1617	25n. Fairchild F-71, 1927	70	70
1618	25n. Command Aire biplane, 1928	70	70
1619	25n. Waco YMF biplane, 1935	70	70
1620	25n. Piper J-4 Cub Coupe, 1938	70	70
1621	25n. Ryan ST-A, 1937	70	70
1622	25n. Spartan Executive, 1939	70	70
1623	25n. Luscombe 8, 1939	70	70
1624	25n. Stinson SR5 Reliant seaplane, 1935	70	70
1625	25n. Cessna 195 seaplane, 1949	70	70
1626	25n. Waco SRE biplane, 1940	70	70
1627	25n. Erco Ercope, 1948	70	70
1628	25n. Boeing Stearman biplane, 1941	70	70
1629	25n. Beech Staggerwing biplane, 1944	70	70
1630	25n. Republic Seabee, 1947	70	70

APPENDIX

The following stamps have either been issued in excess of postal needs or have not been available to the public in reasonable quantities at face value. Such stamps may later be given full listing if there is evidence of regular postal use.

1968.

Bhutan Pheasants, 1, 2, 4, 8, 15ch., 2, 4, 5, 7, 9n.

Winter Olympic Games, Grenoble. Optd on 1966 Abominable Snowmen issue. 40ch., 1n.25, 3, 6n.

Butterflies (plastic-surfaced). Postage 15. 50ch., 1n.25, 2n., Air 3, 4, 5, 6n.

Paintings (relief-printed). Postage 2, 4, 5, 10 45, 80ch., 1n.05, 1n.40, 2, 3, 4, 5n.; Air 1n.50, 2n.50, 6, 8n.

Olympic Games, Mexico. 5, 45, 60, 80ch., 1n.05, 2, 3, 5n.

Human Rights Year. Die-stamped surch on unissued "Coins". 15ch. on 50n.p., 33ch. on 1r., 9n. on 3r.75.

1969.

Flood Relief. Surch on 1968 Mexico Olympics issue. 5ch.+5ch., 80ch.+25ch., 2n.+50ch.

Fish (plastic-surfaced). Postage 15, 20, 30ch.; Air 5, 6, 7n.

Insects (plastic-surfaced). Postage 10, 75ch., 1n.25, 2n.; Air 3, 4, 5, 6n.

Admission of Bhutan to Universal Postal Union. 5, 10, 15, 45, 60ch., 1n.05, 1n.40, 4n.

5000 Years of Steel Industry. On steel foil. Postage 2, 5, 15, 45, 75ch., 1 n 50, 1n.75, 2n.; Air 3, 4, 5, 6n.

Birds (plastic-surfaced). Postage 15, 50ch., 1n.25, 2n.; Air 3, 4, 5, 6n.

Buddhist Prayer Banners. On silk rayon. 15, 75ch., 2, 5, 6n.

Moon Landing of "Apollo 11" (plastic-surfaced). Postage 3, 5, 15, 20, 25, 45, 50ch., 1n.75; Air 3, 4, 5, 6n.

1970.

Famous Paintings (plastic-surfaced). Postage 5, 10, 15ch., 2n.75; Air 3, 4, 5, 6n.

New U.P.U. Headquarters Building, Berne. 3, 10, 20ch., 2n.50.

Flower Paintings (relief-printed). Postage 2, 3, 5, 10, 15, 75ch., 1n., 1n.40; Air 80, 90ch., 1n.10, 1n.40, 1n.60, 1n.70, 3n., 3n.50.

Animals (plastic-surfaced). Postage 5, 10, 20, 25, 30, 40, 65, 75, 85ch.; Air 2, 3, 4, 5n.

Conquest of Space (plastic-surfaced). Postage 2, 5, 15, 25, 30, 50, 75ch., 1n.50; Air 2, 3, 6, 7n.

1971.

History of Sculpture (plastic-moulded). Postage 10, 75ch., 1n.25, 2n.; Air 3, 4, 5, 6n.

Moon Vehicles (plastic-surfaced). Postage 10ch., 1n.70; Air 2n.50, 4n.

History of the Motor Car (plastic-surfaced). Postage 2, 5, 10, 15, 20, 30, 60, 75, 85ch., 1n., 1n.20, 1n.55, 1n.80, 2n., 2n.50; Air 4, 6, 7, 9, 10n.

Bhutan's Admission to United Nations. Postage 5, 10, 20ch., 3 n; Air 2n.50, 5, 6n.

60th Anniv of Boy Scout Movement. 10, 20, 50, 75ch., 2, 6n.

World Refugee Year. Optd on 1971 United Nations issue. Postage 5, 10, 20ch., 3n.; Air 2n.50, 5, 6n.

1972.

Famous Paintings (relief-printed). Postage 15, 20, 90ch., 2n.50; Air 1n.70, 4n.60, 5n.40, 6n.

Famous Men (plastic-moulded). Postage 10, 15, 55ch.; Air 2, 6, 8n.

Olympic Games, Munich. Postage 10, 15, 20, 30, 45ch.; Air 35ch., 1n.35, 7n.

Space Flight of "Apollo 16" (plastic-surfaced). Postage 15, 20, 90ch., 2n.50; Air 1n.70, 4n.60, 5n.40, 6n.

1973.

Dogs. 2, 3, 15, 20, 30, 99ch., 2n.50, 4n.

Roses (on scent-impregnated paper). Postage 15, 25, 30ch., 3n.; Air 6, 7n.

Moon Landing of "Apollo 17" (plastic-surfaced). Postage 10, 15, 55ch. 2n.; Air 7n., 9n.

"Talking Stamps" (miniature records). Postage 10, 25ch., 1n.25, 7, 8n.; Air 3, 9n.

Death of King Jigme Dorji Wangchuck. Embossed on gold foil. Postage 10, 25ch., 3n.; Air 6, 8n.

Mushrooms. 15, 25, 30ch., 3, 6, 7n.

"Indipex 73" Stamp Exhibition, New Delhi. Postage 5, 10, 15, 25ch., 1n.25, 3n.; Air 5, 6n.

BIAFRA Pt. 1

The Eastern Region of Nigeria declared its Independence on 30 May 1967 as the Republic of Biafra. Nigerian military operations against the breakaway Republic commenced in July 1967.

The Biafran postal service continued to use Nigerian stamps when supplies of these became low. In July 1967 "Postage Paid" cachets were used pending the issue of Nos. 1/3.

12 pence = 1 shilling;
20 shillings = 1 pound

1 Map of Republic

5 Flag and Scientist

1968. Independence. Multicoloured.

1	2d. Type **1**	10	65
2	4d. Arms, flag and date of Independence	10	65
3	1s. Mother and child (17×22 mm)	15	1·75

1968. Nos. 172/5 and 177/85 of Nigeria optd **SOVEREIGN BIAFRA** and arms.

4	½d. multicoloured (No. 172)	1·50	3·50
5	1d. multicoloured (No. 173)	1·50	5·50
6	1½d. multicoloured (No. 174)	6·00	11·00
7	2d. multicoloured (No. 175)	23·00	48·00
8	4d. multicoloured (No. 177)	17·00	48·00
9	6d. multicoloured (No. 178)	6·00	11·00
10	9d. blue and red (No. 179)	3·00	2·50
11	1s. multicoloured (No. 180)	60·00	£110
12	1s.3d. multicoloured (No. 181)	35·00	50·00
13	2s.6d. multicoloured (No. 182)	1·75	11·00
14	5s. multicoloured (No. 183)	2·25	10·00
15	10s. multicoloured (No. 184)	10·00	35·00
16	£1 multicoloured (No. 185)	10·00	35·00

The overprint on No. 15 does not include **SOVEREIGN**.

1968. 1st Anniv of Independence. Multicoloured.

17	4d. Type **5**	15	10
18	1s. Victim of atrocity	20	20
19	2s.6d. Nurse and refugees	45	2·75
20	5s. Biafran arms and banknote	60	3·25
21	10s. Orphaned child	1·00	3·75

16 Child in Chains, and Globe

17 Pope Paul VI, Africa, and Papal Arms

1969. 2nd Anniv of Independence. Multicoloured; frame colours given.

35	**16**	2d. orange	1·25	4·00
36		4d. red	1·25	4·00
37		1s. blue	1·75	6·50
38		2s.6d. green	2·00	13·00

1969. Visit of Pope Paul to Africa. Multicoloured; background colours given.

39	**17**	4d. orange	40	2·75
40	–	6d. blue	55	6·00
41	–	9d. green	75	8·00
42	–	3s. mauve	2·25	13·00

DESIGNS: Pope Paul VI, map of Africa and 6d. Arms of Vatican; 9d. St. Peter's Basilica; 3s. Statue of St. Peter.

BIJAWAR Pt. 1

A state of Central India. Now uses Indian stamps.

12 pies = 1 anna; 16 annas = 1 rupee.

1 Maharaja Sarwant Singh

2 Maharaja Sarwant Singh

1935.

6	**1**	3p. brown	3·50	3·50
2		6p. red	4·50	3·75
3		9p. violet	5·50	4·25
4		1a. blue	6·00	4·50
5		2a. green	6·00	4·75

1937.

11	**2**	4a. orange	9·00	65·00
12		6a. lemon	10·00	65·00
13		8a. green	11·00	80·00
14		12a. blue	11·00	80·00
15		1r. violet	32·00	£120

BOHEMIA AND MORAVIA Pt. 5

Following the proclamation of Slovak Independence on 14 March, 1939, the Czech provinces of Bohemia and Moravia became a German Protectorate. The area was liberated in 1945 and returned to Czechoslovakia.

100 haleru = 1 koruna.

1939. Stamps of Czechoslovakia optd **BOHMEN u. MAHREN CECHY a MORAVA.**

1	**34**	5h. blue	10	1·00
2		10h. brown	10	1·00
3		20h. red	20	1·00
4		25h. green	10	1·00
5		30h. purple	10	1·00
6	**59**	40h. blue	2·75	4·75
7	**77**	50h. green	25	1·00
8	**60a**	60h. violet	2·75	4·50
9	**61**	1k. purple (No. 348)	1·00	1·50
10		1k. purple (No. 395)	35	1·00
11	–	1k.20 purple (No. 354)	4·00	4·50
12	**64**	1k.50 red	4·00	4·50
13	–	1k.60 green (No. 355a)	2·75	4·50
14	–	2k. green (No. 356)	1·40	1·90
15	–	2k.50 blue (No. 357)	3·50	4·50
16	–	3k. brown (No. 358)	3·50	4·50
17	**65**	4k. violet	3·75	6·00
18	–	5k. green (No. 361)	3·75	9·00
19	–	10k. blue (No. 362)	4·50	13·50

2 Linden Leaves and Buds

3 Karluv Tyn Castle

5 Zlin

1939.

20	**2**	5h. blue	10	10
21		10h. brown	10	10
22		20h. red	10	10
23		25h. green	10	10
24		30h. purple	10	10
25	–	40h. blue	10	10
26	**3**	50h. green	10	10
27	–	60h. violet	10	10
28	–	1k. red	10	10
29	–	1k.20 purple	10	35
30	–	1k.50 red	10	10
31	–	2k. green	10	10
32	–	2k.50 blue	10	10
33	**5**	3k. mauve	10	10
34	–	4k. grey	10	10
35	–	5k. green	15	45
36	–	10k. blue	10	75
37	–	20k. brown	45	1·25

DESIGNS—As Type **3**: 40h. Svikov Castle; 60h. St. Barbara's Church, Kutna Hora; 1k. St. Vitus's Cathedral, Prague. As Type **5**—VERT: 1k.20, 1k.50, Brno Cathedral; 2k., 2k.50, Olomouc. HORIZ: 4k. Ironworks, Moravska-Ostrava; 5k., 10k., 20k. Karlsburg, Prague.

1940. As 1939 issue, but colours changed and new values.

38	**2**	30h. brown	10	10
39		40h. orange	10	10
40		50h. green	10	10
44	–	50h. green	10	10
41	**2**	60h. violet	10	10
42		80h. orange	10	10
45	–	80h. blue	10	25
43	**2**	1k. brown	10	10
46	–	1k.20 brown	10	25
47	–	1k.20 red	10	10
48	–	1k.50 pink	10	10
49	–	2k. green	10	10
50	–	2k. blue	10	15
51	–	2k.50 blue	10	10
52	–	3k. green	10	15
53	–	5k. green	10	10
54	–	6k. brown	10	20
55	–	8k. green	10	20
56	–	10k. blue	10	30
57	–	20k. brown	35	1·25

DESIGNS—As Type **3**: 50h. (No. 44), Neuhaus Castle; 80h. (No. 45), 3k. Pernstyn Castle; 1k.20 (No. 46), 2k.50, Brno Cathedral; 1k.20 (No. 47), St. Vitus's Cathedral, Prague; 1k.50 St. Barbara's Church, Kutna Hora; 2k. Pardubitz Castle. As **5**—HORIZ: 5k. Bridge at Beching; 6k. Samson Fountain, Budweis; 8k. Kremsier; 10k. Wallenstein Palace, Prague; 20k. Karlsburg, Prague.

6 Red Cross Nurse and Wounded Soldier

7 Patient in Hospital

1940. Red Cross Relief Fund.

58	6	60h.+40h. blue	25	45
59		1k.20+80h. plum	30	50

1941. Red Cross Relief Fund.

60	7	60h.+40h. blue	10	35
61		1k.20+80h. plum	10	45

8 Anton Dvorak

9 Harvesting

10 Blast-furnace, Pilsen

1941. Birth Centenary of Dvorak (composer).

62	8	60h. violet	10	30
63		1k.20 brown	20	35

1941. Prague Fair.

64	9	30h. brown	10	10
65		60h. green	10	10
66	10	1k.20 plum	10	20
67		2k.50 blue	10	35

11 "Stande- theater", Prague

12 Mozart

1941. 150th Death Anniv of Mozart.

68	11	30h.+30h. brown	10	20
69		60h.+60h. green	10	20
70	12	1k.20+1k.20 red	10	30
71		2k.50+2k.50 blue	15	50

(13)

1942. 3rd Anniv of German Occupation. Optd with T 13.

72		1k.20 red (No. 47)	20	55
73		2k.50 blue (No. 51)	30	70

14 Adolf Hitler

15 Adolf Hitler

1942. Hitler's 53rd Birthday.

74	14	30h.+20h. brown	10	10
75		60h.+40h. green	10	10
76		1k.20+80h. purple	10	10
77		2k.50+1k.50 blue	10	75

1942. Various sizes.

78	15	10h. black	10	10
79		30h. brown	10	10
80		40h. blue	10	10
81		50h. green	10	10
82		60h. violet	10	10
83		80h. orange	10	10
84		1k. brown	10	10
85		1k.20 red	10	10
86		1k.50 red	10	10
87		1k.60 green	10	20
88		2k. blue	10	10
89		2k.40 brown	10	10
90		2k.50 blue	10	10
91		3k. olive	10	10
92		4k. purple	10	10
93		5k. green	10	10
94		6k. brown	10	10
95		8k. blue	10	10
96		10k. green	10	80
97		20k. violet	20	1·00
98		30k. red	25	1·40
99		50k. blue	1·00	3·00

SIZES—17½ × 21½ mm: 10h. to 80h.; 18½ × 21 mm: 1k. to 2k.40; 19 × 24 mm: 2k.50 to 8k.; 24 × 30 mm: 10k. to 50k.

16 Nurse and Patient

17 Mounted Postman

1942. Red Cross Relief Fund.

100	16	60h.+40h. blue	10	15
101		1k.20+80h. red	10	15

1943. Stamp Day.

102	17	60h. purple	10	10

18 Peter Parler

19 Adolf Hitler

1943. Winter Relief Fund.

103	–	60h.+40h. violet	10	10
104	18	1k.20+80h. red	10	10
105	–	2k.50+1k.50 blue	10	10

DESIGNS: 60h. Charles IV; 2k.50, King John of Luxembourg.

1943. Hitler's 54th Birthday.

106	19	60h.+1k.40 violet	10	15
107		1k.20+3k.80 red	10	25

20 Scene from "The Mastersingers of Nuremberg"

21 Richard Wagner

1943. 130th Birth Anniv of Wagner.

108	20	60h. violet	10	10
109	21	1k.20 red	10	10
110	–	2k.50 blue	10	15

DESIGN: 2k.50, Blacksmith scene from "Siegfried".

22 Reinhard Heydrich

23 Arms of Bohemia and Moravia and Red Cross

1943. 1st Death Anniv of Reinhard Heydrich (German Governor).

111	22	60h.+4k.40 black	10	30

1943. Red Cross Relief Fund.

112	23	1k.20+8k.80 blk & red	10	10

24 National Costumes

25 Arms of Bohemia and Moravia

1944. 5th Anniv of German Occupation.

113	24	1k.20+3k.80 red	10	10
114	25	4k.20+18k.80 brown	10	10
115	24	10k.+20k. blue	10	20

26 Adolf Hitler

27 Smetana

1944. Hitler's 55th Birthday.

116	26	60h.+1k.40 brown	10	10
117		1k.20+3k.80 green	10	15

1944. 600th Death Anniv of Bedrich Smetana (composer).

118	27	60h.+1k.40 green	10	10
119		1k.20+3k.80 red	10	15

28 St. Vitus's Cathedral, Prague

29 Adolf Hitler

1944.

120	28	1k.50 purple	10	10
121		2k.50 violet	10	20

1944.

122	29	4k.20 green	10	30

NEWSPAPER STAMPS

N 6 Dove

N 19 Dove

1939. Imperf.

N38	N 6	2h. brown	10	25
N39		5h. blue	10	25
N40		7h. red	10	25
N41		9h. green	10	25
N42		10h. red	10	25
N43		12h. blue	10	25
N44		20h. green	10	25
N45		50h. brown	10	25
N46		1k. green	10	25

1940. For bulk postings. No. N42 optd **GD-OT**.

N60	N 6	10h. red	25	40

1943. Imperf.

N106	N 19	2h. brown	10	10
N107		5h. blue	10	10
N108		7h. red	10	10
N109		9h. green	10	10
N110		10h. red	10	10
N111		12h. blue	10	10
N112		20h. green	10	10
N113		50h. brown	10	10
N114		1k. green	10	15

OFFICIAL STAMPS

O 7 Numeral and Laurel Wreath

O 19 Eagle and Numeral

1941.

O60	O 7	30h. brown	10	10
O61		40h. blue	10	10
O62		50h. green	10	10
O63		60h. green	10	10
O64		80h. red	50	20
O65		1k. brown	20	10
O66		1k.20 red	20	10
O67		1k.50 purple	35	25
O68		2k. blue	35	10
O69		3k. green	35	10
O70		4k. purple	50	70
O71		5k. yellow	1·25	1·10

1943.

O106	O 19	30h. brown	10	50
O107		40h. blue	10	50
O108		50h. green	10	50
O109		60h. violet	10	50
O110		80h. red	10	50
O111		1k. brown	10	50
O112		1k.20 red	10	15
O113		1k.50 brown	10	25
O114		2k. blue	10	30
O115		3k. green	10	30
O116		4k. purple	10	30
O117		5k. green	10	80

PERSONAL DELIVERY STAMPS

P 6

1939.

P38	P 6	50h. blue	35	1·10
P39		50h. red	60	1·40

POSTAGE DUE STAMPS

D 6

1939.

D38	D 6	5h. red	10	10
D39		10h. red	10	10
D40		20h. red	10	10
D41		30h. red	10	10
D42		40h. red	10	10
D43		50h. red	10	10
D44		60h. red	10	10
D45		80h. red	10	10
D46		1k. blue	10	25
D47		1k.20 blue	15	25
D48		2k. blue	35	80
D49		5k. blue	50	90
D50		10k. blue	65	1·40
D51		20k. blue	1·90	3·75

BOLIVAR Pt. 20

One of the states of the Granadine Confederation. A department of Colombia from 1886, now uses Colombian stamps.

1863. 100 centavos = 1 peso.

1

2

3

1863. Imperf.

1	1	10c. green	£350	£275
2		10c. red	20·00	20·00
3		1p. red	10·00	10·00

1872. Various frames. Imperf.

4	2	5c. blue	5·00	5·50
5	3	10c. mauve	7·00	7·50
6	–	20c. green	15·00	16·00
7	–	80c. red	38·00	30·00

6

7

8

1874. Imperf.

8	6	5c. blue	12·00	7·50
9	7	5c. blue	6·00	5·00
10	8	10c. mauve	2·00	2·00

9 Simon Bolivar

10 Simon Bolivar

1879. Various frames. Dated "1879". White or blue paper. Perf.

14	9	5c. blue	20	20
12		10c. mauve	20	20
13		20c. red	25	20

1880. Various frames. Dated "1880". White or blue paper.

19	9	5c. blue	15	15
20		10c. mauve	25	25
21		20c. red	25	25
22		80c. green	2·00	2·00
23		1p. orange	2·75	2·75

1882.

30	10	5p. red and blue	1·00	1·00
31		10p. blue and purple	1·00	1·00

11 Simon Bolivar

12 Simon Bolivar

1882. Various frames. Dated "1882".

32	11	5c. blue	20	20
33		10c. mauve	20	20
34		20c. red	25	35

35		80c. green	55	55
36		1p. orange	65	60

1883. Various frames. Dated "1883".

37	**11**	5c. blue	15	15
38		10c. mauve	20	20
39		20c. red	20	20
40		80c. green	45	55
41		1p. orange	55	80

1884. Various frames. Dated "1884".

42	**11**	5c. blue	40	40
43		10c. mauve	15	15
44		20c. red	15	15
45		80c. green	20	25
46		1p. orange	45	55

1885. Various frames. Dated "1885".

47	**11**	5c. blue	10	10
48		10c. mauve	10	10
49		20c. red	10	10
50		80c. green	20	25
51		1p. orange	55	35

1891.

56	**12**	1c. black	15	20
57		5c. orange	35	25
58		10c. red	55	55
59		20c. blue	65	65
60		50c. green	95	95
61		1p. violet	95	95

13 Simon Bolivar

1903. Various sizes and portraits. Imperf or perf. On paper of various colours.

63	**13**	50c. green	45	45
64		50c. blue	30	30
65		50c. violet	90	1·00
67		– 1p. red	50	50
68		– 1p. green	70	70
69		– 5p. red	35	35
70b		– 10p. blue		
71		– 10p. violet	2·50	2·50

PORTRAITS: 1p. Fernandez Madrid. 5p. Rodriguez Torices. 10p. Garcia de Toledo.

20 J. M. del Castillo **23**

1904. Various portraits. Imperf or perf.

77	**20**	5c. black	15	15
78		– 10c. brown (M. Anguiano)	15	15
80		– 20c. red (P.G. Ribon)	40	40

1904. Figures in various frames. Imperf.

81	**23**	½c. green	30	25
82		1c. blue (horiz)	50	50
83		2c. violet	75	70

ACKNOWLEDGMENT OF RECEIPT STAMPS

AR 19 **AR 27**

1903. Imperf. On paper of various colours.

AR75	AR 19	20c. orange	60	60
AR76		20c. blue	50	50

1904. Imperf.

AR85	AR 27	2c. red	1·00	1·00

LATE FEE STAMPS

L 18

1903. Imperf. On paper of various colours.

L73	L 18	20c. brown	30	30
L74		20c. violet	30	30

REGISTRATION STAMPS

1879. As T **9** but additionally inscr "CERTIFICADA".

R17	**9**	40c. brown	60	60

1880. As previous issue dated "1880".

R28	**9**	40c. brown	30	35

1882. As T **11**, but additionally inscr "CERTIFICADA". Dated as shown.

R52	**11**	40c. brown ("1882")	25	40
R53		40c. brown ("1883")	40	40
R54		40c. brown ("1884")	15	15
R55		40c. brown ("1885")	35	40

R 17

1903. Imperf. On paper of various colours.

R72	R **17**	20c. orange	50	50

R 26

1904. Imperf.

R84	R **26**	5c. black	2·00	2·00

BOLIVIA Pt. 20

A republic of Central South America.

1867. 100 centavos = 1 boliviano.
1963. 100 centavos = 1 peso boliviano ($b).
1987. 100 centavos = 1 boliviano.

1 Condor **4 (9 Stars)**

1867. Imperf.

3a	**1**	5c. green	2·40	3·00
10		5c. mauve	£120	90·00
7		10c. brown	£140	90·00
8		50c. yellow	12·50	19·00
11		50c. blue	£200	£160
9		100c. blue	38·00	48·00
12		100c. green	90·00	85·00

1868. Nine stars below Arms. Perf.

32	**4**	5c. green	11·00	5·50
33		10c. red	16·00	5·50
34		50c. blue	28·00	16·00
35		100c. orange	28·00	17·00
36		500c. black	£300	£225

1871. Eleven stars below Arms. Perf.

37	**4**	5c. green	6·25	4·00
38		10c. red	8·75	6·25
39		50c. blue	23·00	11·00
40		100c. orange	22·00	11·00
41		500c. black	£1100	£1100

7 **11**

1878. Perf.

42	**7**	5c. blue	5·75	2·50
43		10c. orange	4·75	1·90
44		20c. green	14·00	2·40
45		50c. red	70·00	7·50

1887. Eleven stars below Arms. Roul.

46	**4**	1c. red	1·50	1·40
47		2c. violet	1·50	1·40
48		5c. blue	4·50	2·00
49		10c. orange	4·50	2·00

1890. Nine stars below Arms. Perf.

50	**4**	1c. red	90	50
58		2c. violet	2·75	1·40
52		5c. blue	2·50	50
53		10c. orange	4·00	60
54		20c. green	8·00	1·00
55		50c. red	4·00	1·00
56		100c. yellow	8·00	2·00

1893. Eleven stars below Arms. Perf.

59	**4**	5c. blue	3·75	1·40

1894.

63	**11**	1c. bistre	60	60
64		2c. red	60	60

65		5c. green	60	60
66		10c. brown	60	40
67		20c. blue	2·00	85
68		50c. red	4·75	1·25
69		100c. red	11·00	4·00

12 Frias **13**

1897.

77	**12**	1c. green	70	50
78		– 2c. red (Linares)	1·00	90
79		– 5c. green (Murillo)	1·40	40
80		– 10c. purple (Monteagudo)	1·60	40
81		– 20c. black and red (J. Ballivian)	3·00	70
82		– 50c. orange (Sucre)	3·00	1·40
83		– 1b. blue (Bolivar)	3·00	3·50
84	**13**	2b. multicoloured	23·00	30·00

18 Sucre **19 A. Ballivian** **24**

1899.

92	**18**	1c. blue	1·40	40
93		2c. red	1·00	25
94		5c. green	3·75	85
95		5c. red	1·00	50
96		10c. orange	1·40	70
97		20c. red	1·75	30
98		50c. brown	3·75	1·40
99		1b. lilac	1·00	1·00

1901.

100	**19**	1c. red	35	15
101		– 2c. green (Camacho)	40	25
102		– 5c. red (Campero)	40	25
103		– 10c. blue (J. Ballivian)	1·00	15
104		– 20c. black and purple (Santa Cruz)	45	15
105	**24**	2b. brown	2·40	1·75

25 **26 Murillo**

1909. Issued in La Paz. Centenary of Revolution of July, 1809. Centres in black.

110	**25**	5c. blue	5·50	3·00
111	**26**	10c. green	5·50	3·00
112		– 20c. orange (Lanza)	5·50	3·00
113		– 2b. red (Montes)	5·50	3·00

37 P. D. Murillo **F 8 Figure of Justice**

1909. Centenary of Beginning of War of Independence, 1809–25.

115		– 1c. black and brown	25	15
116		– 2c. black and green	35	25
117	**37**	5c. black and red	35	10
118		– 10c. black and blue	35	10
119		– 20c. black and violet	40	25
120		– 50c. black and bistre	60	35
121		– 1b. black and brown	60	50
122		– 2b. black and brown	1·00	70

PORTRAITS: 1c. M. Betanzos. 2c. I. Warnes. 10c. B. Monteagudo. 20c. E. Arze. 50c. A. J. Sucre. 1b. S. Bolivar. 2b. M. Belgrano.

1910. Centenary of Liberation of Santa Cruz, Potosi and Cochabamba. Portraits as T **37**.

123		5c. black and green	25	10
124		10c. black and red	25	10
125		20c. black and blue	55	35

PORTRAITS: 5c. I. Warnes. 10c. M. Betanzos. 20c. E. Arze.

1911. Nos. 101 and 104 surch **5 Centavos 1911.**

127		5c. on 2c. green	40	20
128		5c. on 20c. black & purple	10·00	10·00

1912. Stamps similar to Type F **8** optd **CORREOS 1912.** or surch also.

130	F **8**	2c. green	40	25
131		5c. orange	35	35

132		10c. red	85	50
129		10c. on 1c. blue	35	15

1913. Portraits as 1901 and new types.

133	**19**	1c. pink	35	25
134		– 2c. orange	35	20
135		– 5c. green	40	10
136		– 8c. yellow (Frias)	70	30
137		– 10c. grey	70	25
139		– 50c. purple (Sucre)	95	35
140		– 1b. blue (Bolivar)	1·40	85
141	**24**	2b. black	2·75	1·75

46 Monolith **47 Mt. Potosi**

1916. Various sizes.

142	**46**	½c. brown	20	20
143	**47**	1c. green	25	15
144		– 2c. black and red	30	15
145		– 5c. blue	50	10
147		– 10c. blue and orange	85	10

DESIGNS—HORIZ: 2c. Lake Titicaca; 5c. Mt. Illimani; 10c. Parliament Building, La Paz.

51 **54 Morane Saulnier Type P Airplane**

1919.

158a	**51**	1c. lake	15	10
158b		2c. violet	25	15
151		5c. green	35	10
152		10c. red	35	10
179		15c. blue	50	15
180		20c. blue	35	15
154		22c. blue	50	45
155		24c. violet	35	25
162		50c. orange	1·75	35
163		1b. brown	40	15
164		2b. brown	25	15

See also Nos. 194/206.

1923. Surch **Habilitada** and value.

165	**51**	5c. on 1c. lake	35	25
169		15c. on 10c. red	40	35
168		15c. on 22c. blue	40	35

1924. Air. Establishment of National Aviation School.

170	**54**	10c. black and red	30	25
171		15c. black and lake	1·10	70
172		25c. black and blue	55	35
173		50c. black and orange	1·10	70
174		– 1b. black and brown	1·10	1·00
175		– 2b. black and brown	2·25	2·00
176		– 5b. black and violet	3·50	3·25

Nos. 174/6 have a different view.

57 Andean Condor

1925. Centenary of Independence.

184		– 5c. red on green	50	25
185		– 10c. red on yellow	85	45
186		– 15c. red	35	10
187	**57**	25c. blue	2·00	50
188		– 50c. purple	35	10
189		– 1b. red	85	85
190		– 2b. yellow	1·25	1·25
191		– 5b. brown	1·40	1·40

DESIGNS—VERT: 5c. Torch of Freedom; 10c. Kantuta (national flower); 15c. Pres. B. Saavedra; 50c. Head of Liberty; 1b. Mounted archer; 5b. Marshal Sucre. HORIZ: 2b. Hermes.

1927. Surch **1927** and value.

192	**51**	5c. on 1c. lake	1·40	50
193		10c. on 24c. violet	1·40	85

1928.

194	**51**	2c. yellow	35	25
195		2c. pink	40	35
196		4c. red	40	35
197		20c. olive	60	25
198		25c. blue	60	35
199		30c. violet	60	50
200		40c. orange	1·00	85
201		50c. brown	1·00	50
202		1b. red	1·25	85
203		2b. purple	1·75	1·75
204		3b. green	1·75	1·60

| 205 | 4b. lake | 2·75 | 2·40 |
| 206 | 5b. brown | 3·25 | 2·75 |

1928. Optd **Octubre 1927** and star.

207	**51**	5c. green	25	15
208		10c. grey	35	15
209		15c. red	50	35

1928. Surch **15 cts. 1928**.

211	**51**	15c. on 20c. blue	5·50	5·50
213		15c. on 24c. violet	95	50
216		15c. on 50c. orange	70	40

66 "L.A.B." (Lloyd Aereo Boliviano)　　68 Andean Condor

1928. Air.

217	**66**	15c. green	55	55
218		20c. blue	20	10
219		35c. red	35	35

1928.

221	**68**	5c. green	2·25	30
222		10c. blue	35	10
223		15c. red	35	10

DESIGNS: 10c. Pres. Siles; 15c. Map of Bolivia.

1930. Stamps of 1913 and 1916 surch **R. S. 21-4 1930** and value.

224		0.01c. on 2c. (No. 134)	70	70
225		0.03c. on 2c. (No. 144)	85	70
226	**46**	25c. on ⅓c. brown	70	50
227		25c. on 2c. (No. 144)	70	50

1930. Air. Optd **CORREO AEREO R. S. 6-V-1930** or surch **5 Cts.** also.

228	**54**	5c. on 10c. black & red	8·00	10·00
229		10c. black and red	8·00	10·00
231		15c. black and lake	8·00	10·00
232		25c. black and blue	8·00	10·00
233		50c. black and orange	8·00	10·00
235		1b. black and brown	£100	£100

1930. "Graf Zeppelin" Air stamps. Stamps of 1928 surch **Z 1930** and value.

241	**66**	1b.50 on 15c. green	20·00	27·00
242		3b. on 20c. blue	20·00	27·00
243		6b. on 35c. red	35·00	45·00

75 Junkers F-13 over Bullock Cart　　77 Pres. Siles

78 Map of Bolivia　　79 Marshal Sucre

1930. Air.

244	**75**	5c. violet	1·60	65
245		15c. red	1·60	65
246		20c. yellow	65	40
247	**75**	35c. green	65	15
248		50c. blue	65	15
249	**75**	1b. brown	65	20
250		2b. red	65	30
251	**75**	3b. grey	3·75	1·60

DESIGN: 15, 20, 50c., 2b. Junkers F-13 seaplane over river boat.

1930.

252	**77**	1c. brown	25	25
253		2c. green (Potosi)	85	35
254		5c. blue (Illimani)	85	15
255		10c. red (E. Abaroa)	85	15
256	**78**	15c. violet	70	15
257		35c. red	1·40	40
258		40c. orange	1·40	40
259	**79**	50c. slate	70	50
260		1b. brown (Bolivar)	35	35

80 Symbols of Revolution

1931. 1st Anniv of Revolution.

| 263 | **80** | 15c. red | 1·40 | 35 |
| 264 | | 50c. lilac | 45 | 50 |

81

1932. Air.

265	**81**	5c. blue	45	50
266		10c. grey	50	25
267		15c. red	45	35
268		25c. orange	45	35
269		30c. green	40	35
270		50c. purple	40	35
271		1b. brown	40	35

1933. Surch **Habilitada D. S. 13-7-1933** and value.

273	**51**	5c. on 1b. red	40	20
274	**78**	15c. on 35c. red	20	20
275		15c. on 45c. orange	20	20
276	**51**	15c. on 50c. brown	85	15
277		25c. on 40c. orange	40	15

83　　84 M. Baptista

1933.

278	**83**	2c. green	25	15
279		5c. blue	15	10
280		10c. red	40	25
281		15c. violet	25	15
282		25c. blue	60	40

1935. Ex-President Baptista Commemoration.

| 283 | **84** | 15c. violet | 50 | 20 |

85 Map of Bolivia　　86 Fokker Super Universal

1935.

284	**85**	2c. blue	25	15
285		3c. yellow	25	15
286		5c. green	25	15
287		5c. red	25	15
288		10c. brown	25	15
289		15c. blue	25	15
290		15c. red	25	15
291		20c. green	25	15
292		25c. blue	35	15
293		30c. red	35	25
294		40c. orange	60	20
295		50c. violet	60	15
296		1b. yellow	60	40
297		2b. brown	60	40

1935. Air.

298	**86**	5c. brown	15	15
299		10c. green	15	15
300		20c. violet	15	15
301		30c. blue	15	15
302		50c. orange	35	15
303		1b. brown	35	30
304		1½b. yellow	1·00	15
305		2b. red	1·00	45
306		5b. green	1·25	45
307		10b. brown	2·10	85

1937. Surch **Comunicaciones D.S. 25-2-37** and value in figures.

308	**83**	5c. on 2c. green	20	20
310		15c. on 25c. blue	25	25
311		30c. on 25c. blue	40	40
312	**51**	45c. on 1b. brown	50	50
313		1b. on 2b. purple	60	60
314	**83**	2b. on 25c. blue	60	60
315	**80**	3b. on 50c. lilac	85	85
316		5b. on 50c. lilac	70	70

1937. Air. Surch **Correo Aereo D. S. 25-2-37** and value in figures.

321	**75**	5c. on 35c. green	35	35
322	**66**	20c. on 35c. red	40	25
323		50c. on 35c. red	75	40
324		1b. on 35c. red	90	50
325	**54**	2b. on 50c. black & orge	1·75	70
317		3b. on 50c. pur (No. 188)	90	35
318		4b. on 1b. red (No. 189)	75	70
319	**57**	4b. on 2b. orange	95	85
320		10b. on 5b. sepia (No. 191)	2·40	1·75
326	**54**	12b. on 10c. black & red	6·00	3·50
327		15b. on 10c. black & red	6·00	2·25

89 Native School　　92 Junkers Ju52/3m over Cornfield

1938.

| 328 | **89** | 2c. red (postage) | 10 | 10 |
| 329 | | 10c. orange | 15 | 10 |

330		15c. green	25	25
331		30c. yellow	40	35
332		45c. red	5·25	2·75
333		60c. violet	50	35
334		75c. blue	70	35
335		1b. brown	1·00	35
336		2b. buff	95	35

DESIGNS—VERT: 10c. Oil Wells; 15c. Industrial buildings; 30c. Pincers and torch; 75c. Indian and condor. HORIZ: 45c. Sucre-Camiri railway map; 60c. Natives and book; 1b. Machinery; 2b. Agriculture.

337		20c. red (air)	25	20
338		30c. grey	25	20
339		40c. yellow	25	20
340	**92**	50c. green	35	20
341		60c. blue	35	20
342		1b. red	50	50
343		2b. buff	1·25	20
344		3b. brown	90	20
345		5b. violet	60	1·25

DESIGNS—VERT: 20c. Mint, Potosi; 30c. Miner; 40c. Symbolical of women's suffrage; 1b. Pincers, torch and slogan; 3b. New Government emblem; 5b. Junkers aircraft over map of Bolivia. HORIZ: 60c. Airplane and monument; 2b. Airplane over river.

102 Llamas　　103 Arms

1939.

346	**102**	2c. green	70	50
347		4c. brown	70	50
348		5c. mauve	70	35
349		10c. black	70	50
350		15c. green	70	55
351		20c. green	70	35
352	**103**	25c. yellow	60	25
353		30c. blue	60	35
354		40c. red	2·75	60
355		45c. black	2·50	60
356		60c. red	1·40	70
357		75c. slate	1·40	70
358		90c. orange	4·25	75
359		1b. blue	4·25	75
360		2b. red	5·50	75
361		3b. violet	6·50	1·00
362		4b. brown	4·00	1·40
363		5b. purple	5·00	1·60

DESIGNS—HORIZ: 10, 15, 20c. Vicuna; 60, 75c. Mountain viscacha; 90c., 1b. Toco toucan; 2, 3b. Andean condor; 4, 5b. Jaguar. VERT: 40, 45c. Cocoi herons.

107 Virgin of Copacabana　　111 Workman

1939. Air. 2nd National Eucharistic Congress. Inscr "II CONGRESO EUCARISTICO NACIONAL".

364		5c. violet	25	35
365	**107**	30c. green	20	20
366		45c. blue	60	20
367		60c. red	60	40
368		75c. red	45	40
369		90c. blue	30	25
370		2b. brown	50	25
371		4b. mauve	70	40
372	**107**	5b. blue	1·75	25
373		10b. yellow	3·50	25

DESIGNS—TRIANGULAR: 5c., 10b. Allegory of the Light of Religion. VERT: 45c., 4b. The "Sacred Heart of Jesus"; 75c., 90c. S. Anthony of Padua. HORIZ: 60c., 2b. Facade of St. Francis's Church, La Paz.

1939. Obligatory Tax. Workers' Home Building Fund.

| 374 | **111** | 5c. violet | 35 | 10 |

112 Flags of 21 American Republics

1940. 50th Anniv of Pan-American Union.

| 375 | **112** | 9b. red, blue & yellow | 70 | 70 |

114 Urns of Murillo and Sagarnaga　　117 Shadow of Aeroplane on Lake Titicaca

1941. 130th Death Anniv of P. D. Murillo (patriot).

376		10c. purple	10	10
377	**114**	15c. green	15	10
378		45c. red	15	15
379		1b.05 blue	35	15

DESIGNS—VERT: 10c. Murillo statue; 1b.05 Murillo portrait. HORIZ: 45c. "Murillo dreaming in Prison".

1941. Air.

380	**117**	10b. green	4·00	50
381		20b. blue	4·50	85
382		50b. mauve	9·25	1·75
383		100b. brown	18·00	6·00

DESIGN: 50, 100b. Andean condor over Mt. Illimani.

119 1867 and 1941 Issues　　120 "Union is Strength"

1942. 1st Students' Philatelic Exn, La Paz.

384	**119**	5c. mauve	65	55
385		10c. orange	65	55
386		20c. green	1·10	60
387		40c. red	1·25	65
388		90c. blue	2·50	80
389		1b. violet	3·75	2·00
390		10b. brown	12·00	7·50

1942. Air. Chancellors' Meeting, Rio de Janeiro.

391	**120**	40c. red	35	25
392		50c. blue	35	25
393		1b. brown	40	35
394		5b. mauve	1·40	25
395		10b. purple	1·75	1·60

121 Mt. Potosi　　122 Chaquiri Dam

1943. Mining Industry.

396	**121**	15c. brown	25	15
397		45c. blue	25	15
398		1b.25 purple	1·40	85
399		1b.50 green	35	25
400		2b. brown	1·40	85
401	**122**	2b.10 blue	50	40
402		3b. orange	2·50	90

DESIGNS—VERT: 45c. Quechisla (at foot of Mt. Choroloque); 1b.25, Miner Drilling. HORIZ: 1b.50, Dam; 2b. Truck Convoy; 3b. Entrance to Pulacayo Mine.

125 Gen. Ballivian leading Cavalry Charge

1943. Centenary of Battle of Ingavi.

403	**125**	2c. green	10	10
404		3c. orange	10	10
405		25c. purple	15	10
406		45c. blue	25	15
407		3b. red	25	15
408		4b. purple	40	25
409		5b. sepia	55	35

126 Gen. Ballivian and Trinidad Cathedral

1943. Centenary of Founding of El Beni. Centres in brown.

| 410 | **126** | 5c. green (postage) | 10 | 10 |
| 411 | | 10c. purple | 15 | 15 |

412		30c. red	15	15
413		45c. blue	25	25
414		2b.10 orange	35	35
415	–	10. violet (air)	10	10
416	–	20c. green	15	10
417	–	30c. red	20	15
418	–	3b. blue	25	20
419	–	5b. black	60	35

DESIGN: Nos. 415/19, Gen. Ballivian and mule convoy crossing bridge below airplane.

127 Trans. "Honour-Work-Law/All for the Country"

129 Allegory of "Flight"

1944. Revolution of 20th December, 1943.

420	127	20c. orange (postage)	10	10
421		20c. green	10	10
422		90c. blue	10	10
423		90c. red	10	10
424	–	1b. purple	15	10
425	–	2b.40 brown	20	15

DESIGN—VERT: 1b., 2b.40, Clasped hands and flag.

426	129	40c. mauve (air)	10	10
427	–	1b. violet	15	10
428	–	1b.50 green	15	10
429	–	2b.50 blue	35	15

DESIGN—HORIZ: 1b.50, 2b.50, Lockheed 10 Electra airplane and sun.

131 Posthorn and Envelope

132 Douglas DC-2 and National Airways Route Map

1944. Obligatory Tax.

430	131	10c. red	1·00	25
432		10c. blue	1·00	25

Smaller Posthorn and Envelope.

469	10c. red	1·60	60
470	10c. yellow	1·40	60
471	10c. green	1·40	60
472	10c. brown	1·40	60

1945. Air. Panagra Airways, 10th Anniv of First La Paz–Tacna Flight.

433	132	10c. red	15	10
434		50c. orange	20	10
435		90c. green	30	10
436		5b. blue	45	15
437		20b. brown	1·40	45

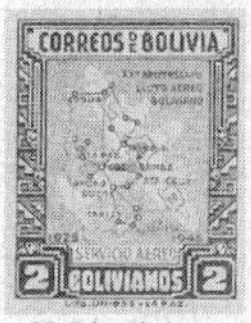
133 Lloyd-Aereo Boliviano Air Routes

134 L. B. Vincenti and J. I. de Sanjines, Composers of National Anthem

1945. Air. 20th Anniv of First National Air Service.

438	133	20c. blue, orange & vio	10	10
439		30c. blue, orange & brn	10	10
440		50c. blue, orange & grn	10	10
441		90c. blue, orange & pur	10	10
442		2b. blue and orange	15	10
443		3b. blue, orange & red	20	15
444		4b. blue, orange & bistre	40	15

1946. Centenary of National Anthem.

445	134	5c. black and mauve	10	10
446		10c. black and blue	10	10
447		15c. black and green	10	10
448		30c. brown and red	15	10
449		90c. brown and blue	15	15
450		2b. brown and black	40	15

1947. Surch **1947 Habilitada Bs. 1.40**.

451	1b.40 on 75c. blue (No. 334) (postage)	15	10
452	1b.40 on 75c. slate (No. 357)	15	10
455	1b.40 on 75c. red (No. 368) (air)	15	10

136 Seizure of Government Palace

137 Mt. Iillimani

1947. Popular Revolution of 21 July 1946.

456	136	20c. green (postage)	10	10
457		50c. purple	10	10
458		1b.40 blue	10	10
459		3b.70 orange	15	10
460		4b. violet	25	15
461		10b. olive	30	30
462	137	1b. red (air)	10	10
463		1b.40 green	10	10
464		2b.50 blue	15	15
465		3b. orange	25	20
466		4b. mauve	35	20

138 Arms of Bolivia and Argentina

140 Cross and Child

1947. Meeting of Presidents of Bolivia and Argentina.

467	138	1b.40 orange (postage)	10	10
468		2b.90 blue (air)	25	25

1948. 3rd Inter-American Catholic Education Congress.

473	–	1b.40 bl & yell (postage)	35	10
474	140	2b. green and orange	50	15
475	–	3b. green and blue	55	20
476	–	5b. violet and orange	60	25
477	–	5b. brown and green	75	25
478	–	2b.50 orange & yell (air)	30	35
479	140	3b.70 red and buff	40	35
480	–	4b. mauve and blue	40	25
481	–	4b. blue and orange	40	15
482	–	13b.60 blue and green	50	25

DESIGNS: 1b.40, 2b.50, Christ the Redeemer, Monument; 3b., 4b. (No. 480), Don Bosco; 5b. (No. 476), 4b. (No. 481), Virgin of Copacabana; 5b. (No. 477), 13b.60, Pope Pius XII.

141 Map of S. America and Bolivian Auto Club Badge

142 Posthorn, Globe and Pres. G. Pacheco

1948. Pan-American Motor Race.

483	141	5b. blue & pink (postage)	1·00	20
484		10b. green & cream (air)	1·10	25

1950. 75th Anniv of U.P.U.

485	142	1b.40 blue (postage)	10	10
486		4b.20 red	10	10
487		1b.40 brown (air)	10	10
488		2b.50 orange	10	10
489		3b.30 purple	10	10

1950. Air. Surch **XV ANIVERSARIO PANAGRA 1935–1950** and value.

490	132	4b. on 10c. red	10	10
491		10b. on 20b. brown	25	20

1950. No. 379 surch **Bs. 2.- Habilitada D.S.6.VII.50**.

492	2b. on 1b.05 blue	15	10

145 Apparition at Potosi

146 Douglas DC-2

1950. 400th Anniv of Apparition at El Potosi.

493	145	20c. violet	10	10
494		30c. orange	10	10
495		50c. purple	10	10
496		1b. red	10	10
497		2b. blue	15	10
498		6b. brown	25	10

1950. Air. 25th Anniv of Lloyd Aereo Boliviano.

499	146	20c. orange	15	10
500		30c. violet	15	10
501		50c. green	15	10
502		1b. yellow	15	10
503		3b. blue	15	10
504		15b. red	50	15
505		50b. brown	1·40	40

1950. Air. Surch **Triunfo de la Democracia 24 de Sept. 49 Bs. 1.40**.

506	137	1b.40 on 3b. orange	15	15

148 U.N. Emblem and Globe

150 St. Francis Gate

149 Gate of the Sun, Tiahuanacu

1950. 5th Anniv of U.N.O.

507	148	60c. blue (postage)	70	10
508		2b. green	95	25
509		3b.60 red (air)	35	15
510		4b.70 brown	45	15

1951. 4th Centenary of Founding of La Paz. Centres in black.

511	149	20c. green (postage)	10	10
512	150	30c. orange	10	10
513	A	40c. brown	10	10
514	B	50c. red	10	10
515	C	1b. purple	10	10
516	D	1b.40 violet	15	15
517	E	2b. purple	15	15
518	F	3b. mauve	20	15
519	G	5b. red	25	15
520	H	10b. sepia	50	25
521	149	20c. red (air)	15	15
522	150	30c. violet	15	15
523	A	40c. slate	15	15
524	B	50c. green	15	15
525	C	1b. red	20	20
526	D	2b. orange	35	35
527	E	3b. blue	35	35
528	F	4b. red	40	40
529	G	5b. green	40	40
530	H	10b. brown	45	45

DESIGNS—HORIZ: As Type **149**: A, Camacho Avenue; B, Consistorial Palace; C, Legislative Palace; D, G.P.O. E, Arms; F, Pedro de la Casca authorizes plans of City; G, Founding the City; H, City Arms and Captain A. de Mendoza.

151 Tennis

1951. Sports. Centres in black.

531	–	20c. blue (postage)	15	10
532	151	50c. red	15	10
533	–	1b. purple	20	10
534	–	1b.40 yellow	20	15
535	–	2b. red	25	15
536	–	3b. brown	55	50
537	–	4b. blue	70	50
538	–	20c. violet (air)	25	10
539	–	30c. purple	35	10
540	–	50c. orange	50	10
541	–	1b. brown	50	10
542	–	2b.50 orange	70	40
543	–	3b. sepia	70	50
544	–	5b. red	1·40	1·00

DESIGNS—Postage: 20c. Boxing; 1b. Diving; 1b.40, Football; 2b. Skiing; 3b. Pelota; 4b. Cycling. Air: 20c. Horse-jumping; 30c. Basketball; 50c. Fencing; 1b. Hurdling; 2b.50, Javelin; 3b. Relay race; 5b. La Paz Stadium.

152 Condor and Flag

1951. 100th National Flag Anniv. Flag in red, yellow and green.

545	152	2b. green	10	10
546		3b.50c. blue	10	10
547		5b. violet	15	15
548		7b.50c. grey	35	15
549		15b. red	40	25
550		30b. brown	85	50

153 Posthorn and Envelope

154 E. Abaroa

1951. Obligatory Tax.

551	–	20c. orange	30	15
551b	–	20c. green	30	15
552	–	20c. blue	30	15
553	153	50c. green	40	15
553d		50c. red	40	15
553e		3b. green	40	15
553f		3b. bistre	60	45
553g		5b. violet	65	15

DESIGN: 20c. Condor over posthorn and envelope.

1952. 73rd Death Anniv of Abaroa (patriot).

554	154	80c. red (postage)	10	10
555		1b. orange	10	10
556		2b. green	15	10
557		5b. blue	20	15
558		10b. mauve	35	15
559		20b. brown	70	40
560		70c. red (air)	10	10
561		2b. yellow	15	15
562		3b. green	15	15
563		5b. blue	15	15
564		50b. purple	70	50
565		100b. black	75	70

155 Isabella the Catholic

156 Columbus Lighthouse

1952. 500th Birth Anniv of Isabella the Catholic.

566	155	2b. blue (postage)	10	10
567		6b.30 red	25	15
568		50b. green (air)	40	25
569		100b. brown	45	35

1952. Columbus Memorial Lighthouse. On tinted papers.

570	156	2b. blue (postage)	20	15
571		5b. red	40	20
572		9b. green	65	35
573		2b. purple (air)	15	10
574		3b.70 turquoise	15	10
575		4b.40 orange	20	10
576		20b. brown	45	10

157 Miner

159 Revolutionaries

158 Villarroel, Paz Estenssoro and Siles Zuazo

1953. Nationalization of Mining Industry.

577	157	2b.50c. red	10	10
578		8b. violet	15	10

1953. 1st Anniv of Revolution of April 9th, 1952.

579	158	50c. mauve (postage)	10	10
580		1b. red	10	10
581		2b. blue	10	10
582		3b. green	10	10
583		4b. yellow	10	10
584		5b. violet	15	10
585		3b.70 brown (air)	15	15
590	159	6b. mauve	15	15
586	158	9b. red	15	15
587		10b. turquoise	15	15
588		16b. orange	15	15
591	159	22b.50 brown	25	20
589	158	40b. grey	40	15

1953. Obligatory Tax. No. 551b and similar stamp surch **50 cts**.

592	50c. on 20c. mauve	30	30
593	50c. on 20c. green	15	15

161

162 Ear of Wheat and Map

1954. Obligatory Tax.

594	161	1b. lake	25	10
595		1b. brown	25	10

1954. 1st National Agronomical Congress.

596	162	25b. blue	15	10
597		85b. brown	35	15

163 Pres. Paz Estenssoro embracing Indian

167 Derricks

166 Refinery

1954. Air. 3rd Inter-American Indigenous Congress.

598	163	20b. brown	10	10
599		100b. turquoise	25	10

1954. 1st Anniv of Agrarian Reform. As T **162**, but designs inscr "REFORMA AGRARIA".

600		5b. red (postage)	10	10
601		17b. turquoise	10	10
602		27b. mauve (air)	10	15
603		30b. orange	15	10
604		45b. purple	25	10
605		300b. green	70	25

DESIGNS—5b., 17b. Cow's head and map; 27b. to 300b. Indian peasant woman.

1955. Obligatory Tax. Nos. 553e and 553f surch **Bs. 5.—D. S. 21-IV-55**.

606	153	5b. on 3b. green	25	10
607		5b. on 3b. bistre	25	10

1955. Development of Petroleum Industry.

608	166	10b. blue (postage)	10	10
609		35b. red	10	10
610		40b. green	10	10
611		50b. purple	15	10
612		80b. brown	25	10
613	167	55b. blue (air)	10	10
614		70b. black	20	10
615		90b. green	30	10
616		500b. mauve	45	40
617		1000b. brown	85	75

168 Control Tower

169 Douglas DC-6B Aircraft

1957. Obligatory Tax. Airport Building Fund.

618	168	5b. blue	50	10
620		5b. red	50	10
619	169	10b. green	40	10
620b		20b. brown	55	25

DESIGNS: 5b. (No. 620), Douglas DC-6B over runway; 20b. Lockheed Constellation in flight.

1957. Currency revaluation. Founding of La Paz stamps of 1951 surch. Centres in black.

621	F	50b. on 3b. mauve (post)	10	10
622	E	100b. on 2b. purple	10	10
623	C	200b. on 1b. purple	15	10
624	D	300b. on 1b.40 violet	20	10
625	149	350b. on 20c. green	30	10
626	A	400b. on 40c. brown	30	10
627	150	600b. on 30c. orange	40	10
628	B	800b. on 50c. red	45	10
629	H	1000b. on 10b. sepia	45	15
630	G	2000b. on 5b. red	50	25
631	E	100b. on 3b. blue (air)	10	10
632	D	200b. on 2b. orange	10	10
633	F	500b. on 4b. red	15	10
634	C	600b. on 1b. red	15	10
635	149	700b. on 20c. red	30	15
636	A	800b. on 40c. slate	40	20
637	150	900b. on 30c. violet	45	10
638	B	1800b. on 50c. green	45	35
639	G	3000b. on 5b. green	70	30
640	H	5000b. on 10b. brown	1·10	50

172 Congress Buildings (Santiago de Chile and La Paz)

173 "Latin America" on Globe

1957. 7th Latin-America Economic Congress, La Paz.

641	172	150b. bl & grey (postage)	10	10
642		350b. grey and brown	20	10
643		550b. sepia and blue	25	10
644		750b. green and red	35	10
645		900b. brown and green	50	15
646	173	700b. violet & lilac (air)	15	10
647		1200b. brown	25	15
648		1350b. red and mauve	40	25
649		2700b. olive and turq	75	45
650		4000b. violet and blue	95	50

174 Steam Train and Presidents of Bolivia and Argentina

1957. Yacuiba-Santa Cruz Railway Inauguration.

651	174	50b. orange (postage)	55	45
652		350b. blue and light blue	1·75	60
653		1000b. brown & cinna	4·25	1·25
654		600b. purple & pink (air)	1·60	60
655		700b. violet and blue	3·00	1·25
656		900b. green	4·25	75

175 Presidents and Flags of Bolivia and Mexico

1960. Visit of Mexican President to Bolivia.

657	175	350b. olive (postage)	15	10
658		600b. brown	25	10
659		1,500b. sepia	50	15
660		400b. red (air)	25	10
661		800b. blue	45	20
662		2,000b. green	70	40

The President's visit to Bolivia did not take place.

176 Indians and Mt. Illimani

177 "Gate of the Sun", Tiahuanacu

1960. Tourist Publicity.

663	176	500b. bistre (postage)	30	10
664		1000b. blue	50	15
665		2000b. sepia	1·40	35
666		4000b. green	2·50	1·75
667	177	3000b. grey (air)	1·25	75
668		5000b. orange	1·90	75
669		10,000b. purple	3·00	1·75
670		15,000b. violet	4·25	3·00

178 Refugees

179 "Uprooted Tree"

1960. World Refugee Year.

671	178	50b. brown (postage)	10	10
672		350b. purple	15	10
673		400b. blue	15	10
674		1000b. sepia	50	15
675		3000b. green	70	70
676	179	600b. blue (air)	35	35
677		700b. brown	35	35
678		900b. turquoise	40	35
679		1800b. violet	40	35
680		2000b. black	45	40

180 Jaime Laredo (violinist)

181 Jaime Laredo (violinist)

1960. Jaime Laredo Commem.

681	180	100b. green (postage)	10	10
682		350b. lake	20	10
683		500b. blue	25	10
684		1000b. brown	35	15
685		1500b. violet	60	60
686		5000b. black	2·00	2·00
687	181	600b. plum (air)	50	25
688		700b. olive	50	35
689		800b. brown	50	35
690		900b. blue	70	35
691		1800b. turquoise	1·00	1·00
692		4000b. grey	2·00	70

182 Rotary Emblem and Nurse with Children

183

1960. Founding of Children's Hospital by La Paz Rotary Club. Wheel in blue and yellow, foreground in yellow; background given.

693	182	350b. green (postage)	15	10
694		500b. sepia	25	10
695		600b. violet	35	10
696		1000b. grey	45	15
697		600b. brown (air)	45	25
698		1000b. olive	40	25
699		1800b. purple	70	70
700		5000b. black	2·00	80

1960. Air. Unissued stamp, surch as in T **183**.

701	183	1200b. on 10b. orange	2·75	1·75

184 Design from Gate of the Sun

185 Flags of Argentina and Bolivia

1960. Unissued Tiahuanacu Excavation stamps surch as in T **184**. Gold backgrounds.

702	50b. on ½c. red	30	20
703	100b. on 1c. red	35	15
704	200b. on 2c. black	50	15
705	300b. on 5c. green	25	15
706	350b. on 10c. green	25	50
707	400b. on 15c. blue	35	15
708	500b. on 20c. red	35	15
709	500b. on 50c. red	40	15
710	600b. on 22½c. green	30	25
711	600b. on 60c. violet	40	35
712	700b. on 25c. violet	50	20
713	700b. on 1b. green	85	80
714	800b. on 30c. red	40	20
715	900b. on 40c. green	30	25
716	1000b. on 2b. blue	40	35
717	1800b. on 3b. grey	3·25	2·40
718	4000b. on 4b. grey	19·00	16·00
719	5000b. on 5b. grey	5·00	4·75

DESIGNS: Various gods, motifs and ornaments. SIZES: Nos. 702/6, As Type **184**. Nos. 707/17, As Type **184** but horiz. No. 718, 49 × 23 mm. No. 719, 50 × 52½ mm.

1961. Air. Visit of Pres. Frondizi of Argentina.

720	185	4000b. multicoloured	70	60
721	–	6000b. sepia and green	1·00	85

DESIGN: 6000b. Presidents of Argentina and Bolivia.

186 Miguel de Cervantes (First Mayor of La Paz)

187 "United in Christ"

1961. M. de Cervantes Commem and 4th Centenary of Santa Cruz de la Sierra (1500b.).

722	186	600b. violet and ochre (postage)	40	10
723	–	1500b. blue and orange	60	20
724	–	1400b. brown & green (air)	60	25

DESIGNS: 1400b. Portrait as Type **186** (diamond shape, 30½ × 30½ mm); 1500b. Nuflo de Chaves (vert: as Type **186**).

See also Nos. 755/6.

1962. 4th National Eucharistic Congress, Santa Cruz.

725	187	1000b. yellow, red and green (postage)	45	35
726	–	1400b. yellow, pink and brown (air)	45	35

DESIGN: 1400b. Virgin of Cotoca.

1962. Nos. 671/80 surch.

727	178	600b. on 50b. brown (postage)	25	15
728		900b. on 350b. purple	30	15
729		1000b. on 400b. blue	25	15
730		2000b. on 1000b. brown	25	30
731		3500b. on 3000b. green	45	45
732	179	1200b. on 600b. blue (air)	40	35
733		1300b. on 700b. brown	35	35
734		1400b. on 900b. green	40	35
735		2800b. on 1800b. violet	60	50
736		3000b. on 2000b. black	60	50

189 Hibiscus

190 Infantry

1962. Flowers in actual colours; background colours given.

737	189	200b. green (postage)	25	10
738	–	400b. brown	25	10
739	–	600b. deep blue	50	10
740	–	1000b. violet	85	20
741	–	100b. blue (air)	10	10
742	–	800b. green	40	15
743	–	1800b. violet	90	35
744	–	10,000b. deep blue	4·50	2·25

FLOWERS: Nos. 738, 740 Orchids; 739, St. James' lily; 741/4, Types of Kantuta (national flowers).

1962. Armed Forces Commemoration.

745	190	400b. mult (postage)	10	10
746	–	500b. multicoloured	15	10
747	–	600b. multicoloured	20	15
748	–	2000b. multicoloured	60	40
749	–	600b. mult (air)	35	15
750	–	1200b. multicoloured	45	20
751	–	2000b. multicoloured	65	35
752	–	5000b. multicoloured	1·75	85

DESIGNS: No. 746, Cavalry; 747, Artillery; 748, Engineers; 749, Parachutists and aircraft; 750, 752, "Overseas Flights" (Lockheed Super Electra airplane over oxen-cart); 751, "Aerial Survey" (Douglas DC-3 airplane photographing ground).

191 Campaign Emblem

192 Goal-Keeper diving to save Goal

1962. Malaria Eradication.

753	191	600b. yellow, violet and lilac (postage)	25	15
754	–	2000b. yellow, green and blue (air)	55	50

DESIGN: 2000b. As No. 753 but with laurel wreath and inscription encircling emblem.

1962. Spanish Discoverers. As T **186** but inscribed "1548–1962".

755	600b. mauve on blue (postage)	35	15
756	1200b. brown on yellow (air)	45	20

PORTRAITS: 600b. A. de Mendoza. 1200b. P. de la Gasca.

(Currency reform. 1000 (old) pesos = 1 (new) peso)

1963. 21st South American Football Championships, La Paz. Multicoloured.

757	192	60c. Type **192** (postage)	40	10
758		1p. Goalkeeper saving ball	60	15
759		1p.40 Andean condor on football (air)	2·40	1·50
760		1p.80 Ball in corner of net	70	70

Nos. 758/60 are vertical.

193 Globe and Emblem

194 Alliance Emblem

1963. Freedom from Hunger.

761	193	60c. yellow, blue and indigo (postage)	25	10
762	–	1p.20 yellow, blue and myrtle (air)	50	50

DESIGN: 1p.20, Ear of wheat across Globe.

1963. Air. "Alliance for Progress".

763	194	1p.20 green, blue & bis	55	35

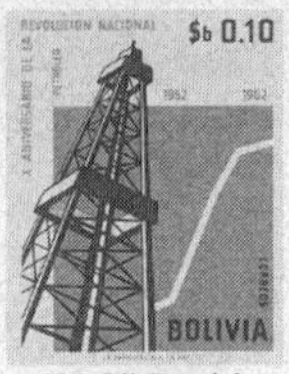

195 Oil Derrick

1963. 10th Anniv of Revolution (1962).
764 **195** 10c. grn & brn (postage) 10 10
765 – 60c. sepia and orange . . 30 10
766 – 1p. yellow, violet & green 35 15
767 – 1p.20 pink, brown and grey (air) 45 20
768 – 1p.40 green and ochre . . 55 25
769 – 2p.80 buff and slate . . . 70 50
DESIGNS: 60c. Map of Bolivia; 1p. Students; 1p.20, Ballot box and voters; 1p.40, Peasant breaking chain; 2p.80, Miners.

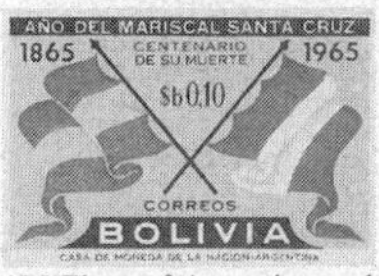

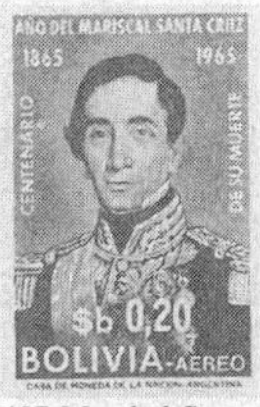

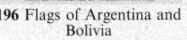

196 Flags of Argentina and Bolivia **197** Marshal Santa Cruz

1966. Death Centenary of Marshal Santa Cruz.
770 **196** 10c. mult (postage) . . . 10 10
771 60c. multicoloured 20 10
772 1p. multicoloured 35 15
773 2p. multicoloured 50 20
774 **197** 20c. blue (air) 10 10
775 60c. green 20 10
776 1p.20 brown 50 35
777 2p.80 black 65 40

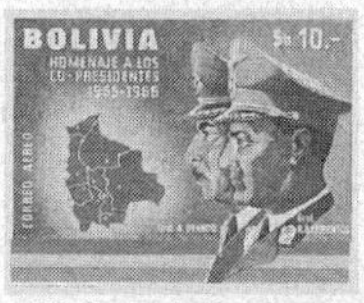

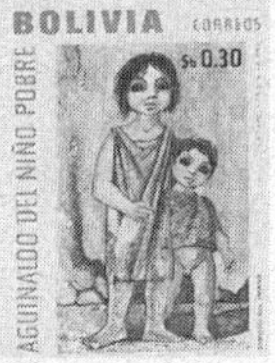

198 Generals Barrientos and Ovando, Bolivian Map and Flag **199** Needy Children

1966. Co-Presidents Commemoration.
778 **198** 60c. mult (postage) . . . 20 10
779 1p. multicoloured 30 10
780 2p.80 mult (air) 95 70
781 10p. multicoloured . . . 1·10 35

1966. Aid for Poor Children.
783 **199** 30c. brown, sepia and ochre (postage) 15 10
784 – 1p.40 black & blue (air) 70 45
DESIGN: 1p.40, Mother and needy children.

1966. Commemorative Issues. Various stamps surch with inscr (as given below) and value. (i) Red Cross Centenary. Surch **Centenario de la Cruz Roja Internacional**.
785 20c. on 150b. (No. 641) (post) 10 10
786 4p. on 4000b. (No. 650) (air) 95 70

(ii) General Azurduy de Padilla. Surch **Homenaje a la Generala J. Azurduy de Padilla**.
787 30c. on 550b. (No. 643) . . . 10 10
788 2p.80 on 750b. (No. 644) . . 70 35

(iii) Air. Tupiza Cent. Surch **Centenario de Tupiza**.
789 60c. on 1350b. (No. 648) . . 20 20

(iv) Air. 25th Anniv of Bolivian Motor Club. Surch **XXV Aniversario Automovil Club Boliviano**.
790 2p.80 on 2700b. (No. 649) . . 1·40 1·10

(v) Air. Cochabamba Philatelic Society Anniv. Surch **Aniversario Centro Filatelico Cochabamba**.
791 1p.20 on 800b. (No. 742) . . 35 25
792 1p.20 on 1800b. (No. 743) . . 35 25

(vi) Rotary Help for Children's Hospital. Surch with value only. (a) Postage.
793 1p.60 on 350b. (No. 693) . . 45 15
794 2p.40 on 500b. (No. 694) . . 70 25

(b) Air.
795 1p.40 on 1000b. (No. 698) . . 45 45
796 1p.40 on 1800b. (No. 699) . . 45 45

(vii) 150th Anniv of Coronilla Heroines. Surch **CL Aniversario Heroinas Coronilla**. (a) Postage.
797 60c. on 350b. (No. 682) . . . 15 10

(b) Air.
798 1p.20 on 800b. (No. 689) . . 40 35

(viii) Air. Centenary of Hymn La Paz. Surch **Centenario Himno Paceno**.
799 1p.40 on 4000b. (No. 692) . . 40 35

(ix) Air. 12th Anniv of Agrarian Reform. Surch **XII Aniversario Reforma Agraria**.
800 10c. on 27b. (No. 602) . . . 15 15

(x) Air. 25th Anniv of Chaco Peace Settlement. Surch **XXV Aniversario Paz del Chaco**.
801 10c. on 55b. (No. 613) . . . 15 15

All the following are surch on Revenue stamps. The design shows a beach scene with palms, size 27 × 21½mm.

(xi) Centenary of Rurrenabaque. Surch **Centenario de Rurrenabaque**.
802 1p. on 10b. brown 30 10

(xii) 25th Anniv of Busch Government. Surch **XXV Aniversario Gobierno Busch**.
803 20c. on 5b. red 10 10

(xiii) 20th Anniv of Villarroel Government. Surch **XX Aniversario Gob. Villarroel**.
804 60c. on 2b. green 15 10

(xiv) 25th Anniv of Pando Department. Surch **XXV Aniversario Dpto. Pando**. (a) Postage.
805 1p.60 on 50c. violet 45 15

(b) Air. Surch **Aereo** also.
806 1p.20 on 1b. blue 50 40

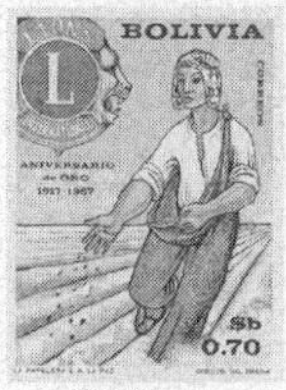

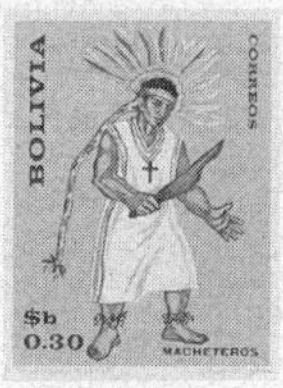

201 Sower **202** "Macheteros"

1967. 50th Anniv of Lions International. Mult.
807 **201** 70c. Type **201** (postage) 35 10
808 2p. Lions emblem and Inca obelisks (horiz) (air) 55 45

1968. 9th Congress of the U.P.A.E. (Postal Union of the Americas and Spain). Bolivian Folklore. Designs showing costumed figures. Multicoloured.
810 **202** 30c. Type **202** (postage) 10 10
811 60c. "Chunchos" 15 10
812 1p. "Wiphala" 25 15
813 2p. "Diablada" 50 20
814 1p.20 "Pujllay" (air) . . . 25 15
815 1p.40 "Ujusiris" 35 20
816 2p. "Morenada" 50 25
817 3p. "Auki-aukis" 85 50

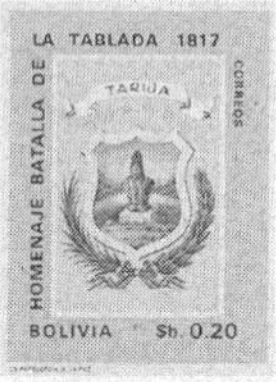

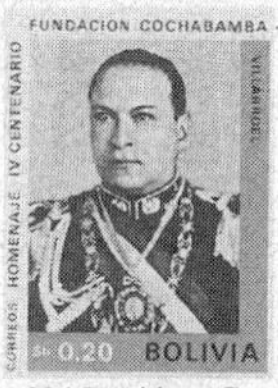

203 Arms of Tarija **204** President G. Villarroel

1968. 150th Anniv of Battle of the Tablada (1817).
819 **203** 20c. mult (postage) . . . 10 10
820 30c. multicoloured 10 10
821 40c. multicoloured 15 10
822 60c. multicoloured 20 10
823 – 1p. multicoloured (air) . . 35 15
824 – 1p.20 multicoloured . . . 40 15
825 – 2p. multicoloured 70 35
826 – 4p. multicoloured 70 50
DESIGNS: Nos. 823/6, Moto Mendez.

1968. 400th Anniv of Cochabamba.
827 **204** 20c. brn & orge (postage) 15 10
828 30c. brown & turquoise 15 10
829 40c. brown and purple . . 15 10
830 50c. brown and green . . 15 10
831 1p. brown and bistre . . 35 10
832 – 1p.40 black & red (air) . . 35 25
833 – 3p. black and blue . . . 35 40
834 – 4p. black and red 50 50
835 – 5p. black and green . . . 60 40
836 – 10p. black and violet . . 1·10 75
DESIGN—HORIZ: 1p.40 to 10p. Similar portrait of President.

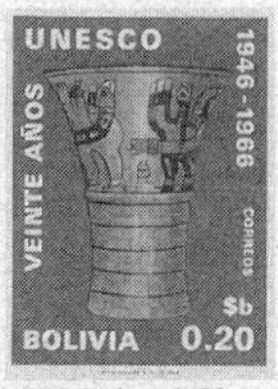

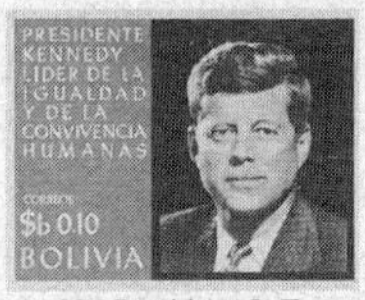

205 Painted Clay Cup **206** President J. F. Kennedy

1968. 20th Anniv of U.N.E.S.C.O. (1966).
837 **205** 20c. mult (postage) . . . 15 10
838 60c. multicoloured 40 25
839 1p.20 black & blue (air) 40 20
840 2p.80 black and green . . 45 45
DESIGNS: Nos. 839/40, U.N.E.S.C.O. emblem.

1968. 5th Death Anniv of John F. Kennedy (U.S. President).
841 **206** 10c. black & grn (postage) 15 10
842 4p. black and violet . . . 95 95
843 1p. black and green (air) 35 20
844 10p. black and red . . . 1·90 1·90

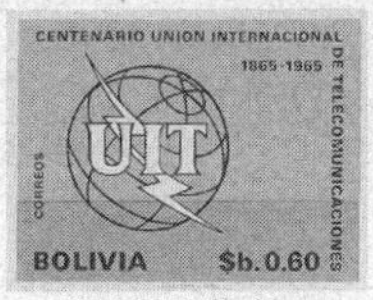

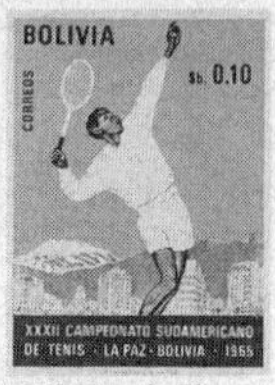

207 I.T.U. Emblem **208** Tennis Player

1968. Centenary (1965) of I.T.U.
846 **207** 10c. black grey and yellow (postage) 15 10
847 60c. black, orange & bistre 35 10
848 1p.20 black, grey and yellow (air) 30 10
849 1p.40 black, blue & brn 40 20

1968. South American Tennis Championships, La Paz.
850 **208** 10c. black, brown and grey (postage) 20 10
851 20c. black, brown & yell 20 10
852 30c. black, brown & blue 20 10
853 1p.40 black, brown and orange (air) 45 25
854 2p.80 black, brown & bl 50 50

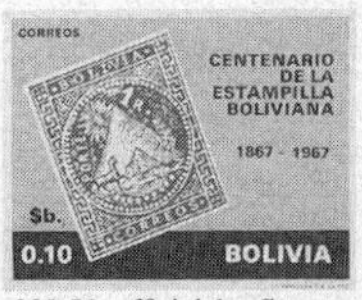

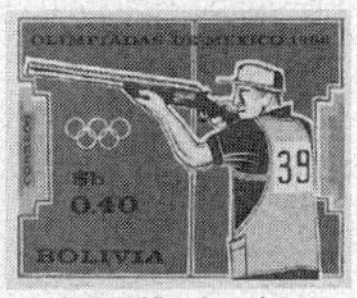

209 Unofficial 1r. Stamp of 1863 **210** Rifle-shooting

1963. Stamp Centenary.
856 **209** 10c. brown, black and green (postage) 15 10
857 30c. brown, black & blue 15 10
858 2p. brown, black & drab 25 10
859 – 1p.40 green, black and yellow (air) 50 25
860 – 2p.80 green, blk & pink 70 50
861 – 3p. green, black & lilac 70 50
DESIGNS: Nos. 859/61 First Bolivian stamp.

1969. Olympic Games, Mexico (1968).
863 **210** 40c. black, red and orange (postage) 15 10
864 – 50c. black, red and green 15 10
865 – 60c. black, blue & green 25 10
866 – 1p.20 black, green and ochre (air) 40 15
867 – 2p.80 black, red & yell . . 85 35
868 – 5p. multicoloured . . . . 1·00 1·00
DESIGNS—HORIZ: 50c. Horse-jumping; 60c. Canoeing; 5p. Hurdling. VERT: 1p.20, Running; 2p.80, Throwing the discus.

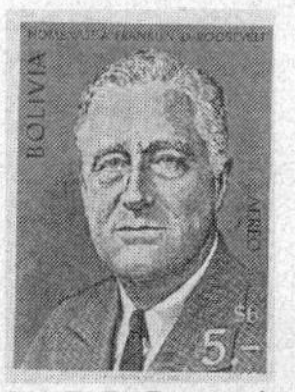

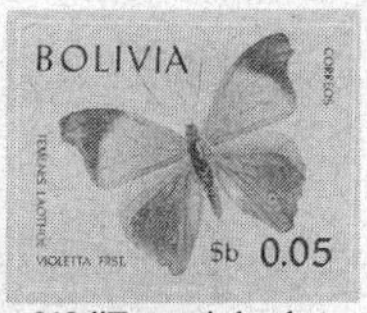

211 F. D. Roosevelt **212** "Temensis laothoe violetta"

1969. Air. Franklin D. Roosevelt Commem.
870 **211** 5p. black, orange & brown . . . . 1·40 75

1970. Butterflies. Multicoloured.
871 5c. Type **212** (postage) . . . 35 35
872 10c. "Papilio crassus" 70 70
873 20c. "Catagramma cynosura" 70 70
874 30c. "Eunica eurota flora" . . 70 70
875 80c. "Ituna phenarete" . . . 70 70
876 1p. "Metamorpha dido wernichei" (air) 90 50
877 1p.80 "Heliconius felix" . . . 1·25 65
878 2p.80 "Morpho casica" . . . 1·75 1·75
879 3p. "Papilio yuracares" . . . 1·90 1·75
880 4p. "Heliconsus melitus" . . 2·50 2·00

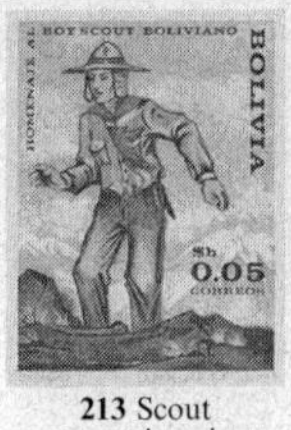

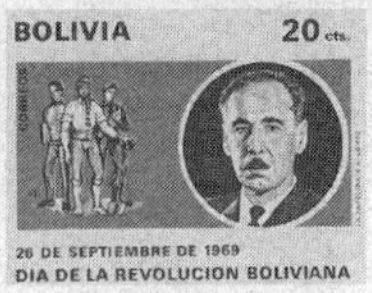

213 Scout mountaineering **214** President A. Ovando and Revolutionaries

1970. Bolivian Scout Movement. Multicoloured.
882 **213** 5c. Type **213** (postage) . . 15 10
883 10c. Girl-scout planting shrub 15 10
884 50c. Scout laying bricks (air) 15 10
885 1p.20 Bolivian scout badge 35 15

1970. Obligatory Tax. Revolution and National Day.
886 **214** 20c. blk & red (postage) 25 15
887 30c. black & green (air) 25 15
DESIGN: 30c. Pres. Ovando, oil derricks and laurel sprig.

1970. "Exfilca 70" Stamp Exhibition, Caracas, Venezuela. No. 706 further surch **EXFILCA 70** and new value.
888 30c. on 350b. on 10c. . . . 15 10

1970. Provisionals. Various stamps surch.
889 **178** 60c. on 900b. on 350b. (postage) 30 10
890 – 1p.20 on 1500b. (No. 723) 50 15
891 **185** 1p.20 on 4000b. (air) . . 35 15

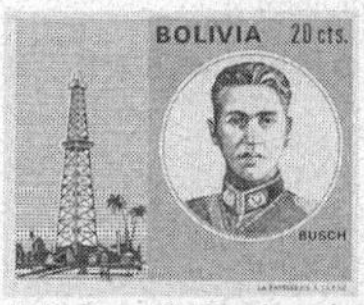

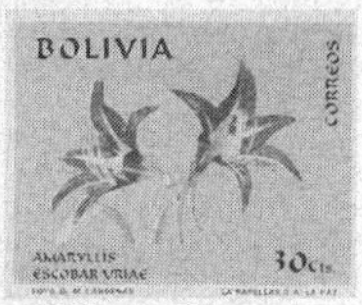

217 Pres. G. Busch and Oil Derrick **218** "Amaryllis escobar uriae"

1971. 32nd Death Anniv of President G. Busch and 25th Death Anniv of Pres. Villarroel.
892 **217** 20c. blk & lilac (postage) 35 10
893 – 30c. black and blue (air) 30 10
DESIGN: 30c. Pres. Villarroel and oil refinery.

1971. Bolivian Flora. Multicoloured.
894 30c. Type **218** (postage) . . . 15 10
895 40c. "Amaryllis evansae" . . 15 10
896 50c. "Amaryllis yungacensis" (vert) 20 15
897 2p. "Gymnocalycium chiquitanum" (vert) . . . 55 35
898 1p.20 "Amaryllis pseudopardina" (air) . . . 45 15
899 1p.40 "Rebutia kruegeri" (vert) 60 15
900 2p.80 "Lobivia pentlandii" 95 25
901 4p. "Rebutia tunariensis" (vert) . . . . 1·60 50

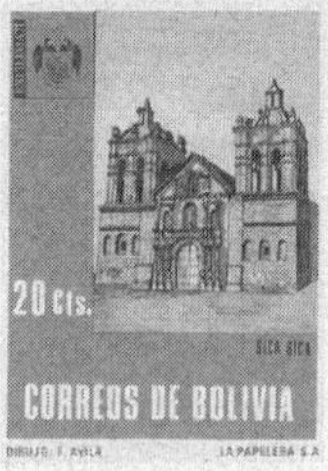

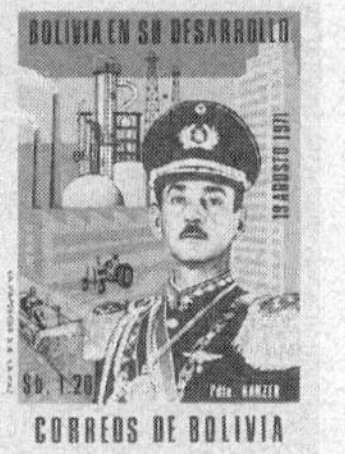

219 Sica Sica Cathedral **220** Pres. H. Banzer

1971. "Exfilima" Stamp Exhibition, Lima, Peru.
903 **219** 20c. multicoloured 15 10

1972. "Bolivia's Development".
904 **220** 1p.20 multicoloured . . . 35 15

221 Chiriwano de Achocalla Dance   **222 "Virgin and Child" (B. Bitti)**

1972. Folk Dances. Multicoloured.

905	20c. Type 221 (postage)	10	10
906	40c. Rueda Chapaca	20	15
907	60c. Kena-Kena	30	15
908	1p. Waca Thokori	40	25
909	1p.20 Kusillo (air)	40	15
910	1p.40 Taquirari	45	15

1972. Bolivian Paintings. Multicoloured.

911	10c. "The Washerwoman" (M. P. Holguin) (postage)	10	10
912	50c. "Coronation of the Virgin" (G. M. Berrio)	20	10
913	70c. "Arquebusier" (anon.)	25	10
914	80c. "St. Peter of Alcantara" (M. P. Holguin)	25	15
915	1p. Type 222	35	15
916	1p.40 "Chola Pacena" (G. de Rojas) (air)	40	10
917	1p.50 "Adoration of the Kings" (G. Gamarra)	40	10
918	1p.60 "Pachamama Vision" (A. Borda)	40	10
919	2p. "Idol's Kiss" (G. de Rojas)	40	25

223 Tarija Cathedral

1972. "EXFILIBRA 72" Stamp Exhibition, Rio de Janeiro.

920	223 30c. multicoloured	15	10

224 National Arms

1972. Air.

921	224 4p. multicoloured	95	35

225 Santos Dumont and "14 bis"

1973. Air. Birth Centenary of Alberto Santos Dumont (aviation pioneer).

922	225 1p.40 black and yellow	1·25	45

226 "Echinocactus   227 Power Station, Santa Isabel notocactus"

1973. Cacti. Multicoloured.

923	20c. Type 226 (postage)	10	10
924	40c. "Echinocactus lenninghaussii"	15	10
925	50c. "Mammillaria bocasana"	20	10
926	70c. "Echinocactus lenninghaussii" (different)	30	10
927	1p.20 "Mammillaria bocasana" (different) (air)	40	15
928	1p.90 "Opuntia cristata"	60	20
929	2p. "Echinocactus rebutia"	85	25

1973. Bolivian Development Multicoloured.

930	10c. Type 227 (postage)	10	10

931	20c. Tin foundry	15	10
932	90c. Bismuth plant	40	10
933	1p. Gas plant	40	10
934	1p.40 Bridge, Highways 1 and 4 (air)	50	15
935	2p. Inspection car crossing bridge, Al Beni	8·00	2·50

228 "Cattleya nobilior"   229 Morane Saulnier Type P and Emblem

1974. Orchids. Multicoloured.

936	20c. Type 228 (postage)	10	10
937	50c. "Zygopetalum bolivianum"	20	10
938	1p. "Huntleya melagris"	35	10
939	2p.50 "Cattleya luteola" (horiz).(air)	90	25
940	3p.80 "Stanhopaea"	1·00	35
941	4p. "Catasetum" (horiz)	1·00	45
942	5p. "Maxillaria"	1·75	50

1974. Air. 50th Anniv of Bolivian Air Force. Multicoloured.

944	3p. Type 229	75	50
945	3p.80 Douglas DC-3 crossing Andes	1·25	70
946	4p.50 Triplane trainer and Morane Saulnier Paris I aircraft	1·25	70
947	8p. Col. Rafael Pabon and biplane fighter	1·75	1·40
948	15p. Jet airliner on "50"	3·75	2·00

230 General Sucre (after J. Wallpher)

1974. 150th Anniv of Battle of Avacucho.

949	230 5p. multicoloured	75	55

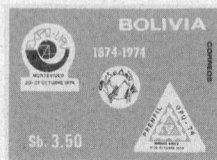

231 U.P.U. and Exhibition Emblems

1974. Centenary of U.P.U. and Expo U.P.U. (Montevideo) and Prenfil U.P.U. (Buenos Aires) Stamp Exhibitions.

950	231 3p.50 green, black & bl	70	45

232 Lions Emblem and Steles

1975. 50th Anniv of Lions International in Bolivia.

951	232 30c. multicoloured	35	10

233 Exhibition Emblem

1975. "Espana 75" International Stamp Exhibition, Madrid.

952	233 4p.50 multicoloured	55	35

234 Emblem of Meeting   235 Arms of Pando

1975. Cartagena Agreement. First Meeting of Postal Ministers, Quito, Ecuador.

953	234 2p.50 silver, violet & blk	45	30

1975. 150th Anniv of Republic (1st issue). Provincial Arms. Multicoloured.

955	20c. Type 235 (postage)	10	10
956	2p. Chuzuisaca	50	35
957	3p. Cochabamba	70	50
958	20c. Beni (air)	10	10
959	30c. Tarija	10	10
960	50c. Potosi	10	10
961	1p. Oruro	4·50	1·50
962	2p.50 Santa Cruz	50	50
963	3p. La Paz	70	50

See also Nos. 965/78.

236 Presidents Perez and Banzer   237 Pres. Victor Paz Estenssoro

1975. Air. Visit of Pres. Perez of Venezuela.

964	236 3p. multicoloured	75	55

1975. 150th Anniv of Republic (2nd issue).

965	30c. Type 237 (postage)	10	10
966	60c. Pres. Thomas Frias	15	10
966a	1p. Ismael Montes	20	10
967	2p.50 Aniceto Arce	50	25
968	7p. Bautista Saavedra	95	35
969	10p. Jose Manuel Pando	1·40	50
970	15p. Jose Maria Linares	1·75	1·75
971	50p. Simon Bolivar	6·25	6·25
972	50c. Rene Barrientos Ortuno (air)	15	10
973	2p. Francisco B. O'Connor	50	25
973a	3p.80 Gualberto Villaroel	70	50
974	4p.20 German Busch	70	70
975	4p.50 Pres. Hugo Banzer Suarez	70	70
976	20p. Jose Ballivian	2·50	1·40
977	30p. Pres. Andres de Santa Cruz	3·25	3·25
978	40p. Pres. Antonio Jose de Sucre	4·25	4·25

Nos. 965/70, 972/4 and 976/78 are smaller, 24 × 33 mm.

238 Laurel Wreath and L.A.B. Emblem   239 "EXFIVIA"

1975. Air. 50th Anniv of Lloyd-Aereo Boliviano (national airline). Multicoloured.

979	1p. Type 238	15	10
980	1p.50 Douglas DC-9 and L.A.B. route map (horiz)	35	15
981	2p. Guillermo Kyllmann (founder) and Junkers F-13 aircraft (horiz)	45	25

1975. Obligatory Tax. As No. 893 but inscr "XXV ANIVERSARIO DE SU GOBIERNO".

982	30c. black and blue	30	10

1975. "Exfivia 75". Stamp Exhibition.

983	239 3p. multicoloured	70	35

240 U.P.U. Emblem

1975. Air. Centenary (1974) of U.P.U.

984	240 25p. multicoloured	2·00	2·00

241 Chiang Kai-shek

1976. 1st Death Anniv of President Chiang Kai-shek.

985	241 2p.50 multicoloured	60	25

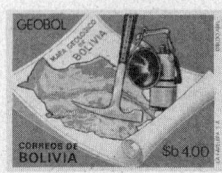

242 Geological Hammer, Lamp and Map

1976. Bolivian Geological Institute.

986	242 4p. multicoloured	55	55

243 Naval Insignia

1976. Navy Day.

987	243 50c. multicoloured	25	10

244 Douglas DC-10 and Divided Roundel

1976. 50th Anniv of Lufthansa Airline.

988	244 3p. multicoloured	90	35

245 Bolivian Boy Scout and Badge

1976. 60th Anniv of Bolivian Boy Scouts.

989	245 1p. multicoloured	50	20

246 Battle Scene   247 Brother Vicente Bernedo (missionary)

1976. Bicentenary of American Revolution.

990	246 4p.50 multicoloured	95	45

1976. Brother Vincente Bernedo Commemoration.

992	247 1p.50 multicoloured	35	15

248 Rainbow over La Paz, Police Handler with Dog   **249** Bolivian Family

1976. 150th Anniv of Police Service.
993   248   2p.50 multicoloured . . .   40   25

1976. National Census.
994   249   2p.50 multicoloured . . .   55   35

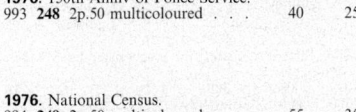

250 Pedro Poveda (educator)

1976. Poveda Commemoration.
995   250   1p.50 multicoloured . . .   35   15

251 Arms, Bolivar and Sucre   **252** "Numeral"

1976. International Bolivarian Societies Congress.
996   251   1p.50 multicoloured . . .   55   25

1976.
997   252   20c. brown   10   10
998   1p. blue   25   10
999   1p.50 green   40   10

253 Boy and Girl   **254** Caduceus

1977. Christmas 1976 and 50th Anniv of Inter-American Children's Institute.
1000   253   50c. multicoloured . . .   15   10

1977. National Seminar on "Chagas Disease".
1001   254   3p. multicoloured . . .   70   10

255 Court Buildings, La Paz   **256** Tower and Map

1977. 150th Anniv of Bolivian Supreme Court. Multicoloured.
1002   2p.50 Type **255** . . .   30   10
1003   4p. Dr. Manuel M. Urcullu, first President .   45   10
1004   4p.50 Dr. Pantaleon Dalence, President, 1883–89 . . .   50   10

1977. 90th Anniv of Oruro Club.
1005   256   3p. multicoloured . . .   50   15

257 Newspaper Mastheads   **258** Games Poster

1977. Bolivian Newspapers. Multicoloured.
1006   1p.50 Type **257**   25   10
1007   2p.50 "Ultima Hora" and Alfredo Alexander (horiz)   35   10
1008   3p. "El Diario" and Jose Carrasco (horiz)   45   15
1009   4p. "Los Tiempos" and Demetrio Canelas . . .   50   15
1010   5p.50 "Presencia"   70   20

1977. 8th Bolivarian Games, La Paz.
1011   258   5p. multicoloured . . .   70   20

259 Tin Miner and Mining Corporation Emblem   **260** Miners, Globe and Chemical Symbol for Tin

1977. 25th Anniv of Bolivian Mining Corporation.
1012   259   3p. multicoloured . . .   4·25   2·00

1977. International Tin Symposium, La Paz.
1013   260   6p. multicoloured . . .   55   30

261 Map of Bolivia and Radio Masts   **263** "Eye", Compass, Key and Law Book

1977. 50th Anniv of Bolivian Radio.
1014   261   2p.50 multicoloured . . .   35   10

1977. "Exfivia 77" Philatelic Exhibition, Cochabamba. No. 719 surch **EXFIVIA — 77 $b. 5.—**.
1015   5p. on 5,000b. on $b. 5 grey and gold   85   15

1978. 50th Anniv of Audit Department.
1016   263   5p. multicoloured . . .   45   15

264 Aesculapius Staff and Map of Andean Countries   **265** Map of the Americas   **266** Mt. Illimani

1978. 5th Meeting of Andean Countries' Health Ministers.
1017   264   2p. orange and black . .   40   10

1978. World Rheumatism Year (1977).
1018   265   2p.50 blue and red . . .   35   15

1978.
1019   266   50c. green and blue . .   10   10
1020   1p. yellow and brown . .   15   10
1021   1p.50 grey and red . . .   25   10
DESIGNS—HORIZ: 1p.50, Mt. Cerro de Potosi. VERT: 1p. Pre-Columbian monolith.

267 Central Bank   **268** Jesus with Children

1978. 50th Anniv of Bank of Bolivia.
1022   267   7p. multicoloured . . .   70   25

1979. International Year of the Child.
1023   268   8p. multicoloured . . .   60   15

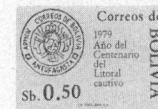

269 Antofagasta Cancellation

270 Antofagasta

1979. Centenary of Loss of Litoral Department to Chile.
1024   269   50c. brown and black . .   10   10
1025   1p. mauve and black . .   15   10
1026   1p.50 green and black . .   25   10
1027   270   5p.50 multicoloured . . .   40   15
1028   6p.50 multicoloured . . .   55   20
1029   7p. multicoloured . . .   55   20
1030   8p. multicoloured . . .   60   25
1031   10p. multicoloured . . .   75   35
DESIGNS—HORIZ: 1p. La Chimba cancel; 1p. Mejillonos cancel. VERT: (As Type **270**). 6p.50, Woman in chains; 7p. Eduardo Arbaroa; 8p. Map of Department, 1876; 10p. Arms of Litoral.

271 Map and Radio Club Emblem   **272** Runner and Games Emblem

1979. Radio Club of Bolivia.
1032   271   3p. multicoloured . . .   40   10

1979. 1st "Southern Cross" Games. Mult.
1033   6p.50 Type **272**   55   20
1034   10p. Gymnast   75   35

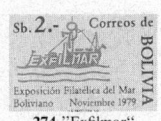

273 Bulgarian Stamp of 1879   **274** "Exfilmar" Emblem

1979. "Philaserdica 79" Philatelic Exhibition, Sofia, Bulgaria.
1035   273   2p.50 black, yellow and light yellow   30   10

1979. "Exfilmar 79" Maritime Philatelic, Exhibition, La Paz.
1036   274   2p. blue, black and light blue   20   20

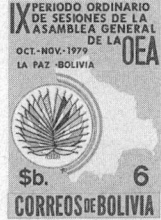

275 O.A.S. Emblem and Map   **276** Franz Tamayo (lawyer)

1979. 9th Congress of Organization of American States, La Paz.
1037   275   6p. multicoloured . . .   50   20

1979. Anniversaries and Events.
1038   276   2p.80 light grey, black and grey . . .   35   10
1039   5p. multicoloured . . .   35   20
1040   5p. multicoloured . . .   35   20
1041   6p. multicoloured . . .   45   20
1042   9p.50 multicoloured . . .   2·00   80
DESIGNS—VERT: 2p.80, Type **276** (birth centenary); 5p. (No. 1039) U.N. emblem and delegates (18th CEPAL Sessions, La Paz); 5p. (No. 1042), Gastroenterological laboratory (Japanese health co-operation); 6p. Radio mast (50th anniv of national radio). HORIZ: 9p.50, Puerto Suarez iron ore deposits.

277 500c. Stamp of 1871, Exhibition Emblem and Flag

1980. "Exfilmar" Bolivian Maritime Stamp Exhibition, La Paz.
1043   277   4p. multicoloured . . .   50   15

278 Juana Azurduy de Padilla

1980. Birth Bicentenary of Juana Azurduy de Padilla (Independence heroine).
1044   278   4p. multicoloured . . .   55   15

279 Jean Baptiste de la Salle (founder)

1980. 300th Anniv of Brothers of Christian Schools.
1045   279   9p. multicoloured . . .   75   30

280 "Victory in a Chariot", Emblem and Flags

1980. "Espamer 80" International Stamp Exhibition, Madrid.
1046   280   14p. multicoloured . . .   1·10   45

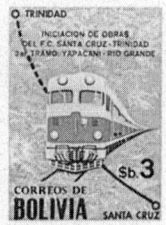

281 Flags over Map of South America   **282** Diesel Locomotive

1980. Meeting of Public Works and Transport Ministers of Argentina, Bolivia and Peru.
1047   281   2p. multicoloured . . .   25   10

1980. Inauguration of Santa Cruz-Trinidad Railway, Third Section.
1048   282   3p. multicoloured . . .   90   50

283 Soldier and Citizen with Flag destroying Communism

284 Scarlet Macaw

1981. 1st Anniv of 17 July Revolution. Mult.
1049 **283** 1p. Type 283 . . . . 15 10
1050 3p. Flag shattering hammer and sickle on map . . . 35 10
1051 40p. Flag on map of Bolivia showing provinces . . . 3·25 85
1052 50p. Rejoicing crowd (horiz) 3·75 85

1981. Macaws. Multicoloured.
1053 **284** 4p. Type 284 . . . . 65 35
1054 7p. Green-winged macaw . . 1·00 50
1055 8p. Blue and yellow macaw . 1·25 60
1056 9p. Red-fronted macaw . . 1·40 65
1057 10p. Yellow-collared macaw . 1·40 65
1058 12p. Hyacinth macaw . . . 1·90 90
1059 15p. Military macaw . . . . 1·50 1·10
1060 20p. Chestnut-fronted macaw . . . . 3·00 1·25

285 Virgin and Child receiving Flower

286 Emblem

1981. Christmas.
1061 **285** 1p. pink and red 15 10
1062 – 2p. light blue and blue . 30 10
DESIGN: 2p. Child and star (horiz).
See also No. 1080.

1982. 22nd American Air Force Commanders' Conference, Buenos Aires.
1063 **286** 14p. multicoloured . . . 1·10 35

287 Cobija

288 Simon Bolivar

1982. 75th Anniv of Cobija City.
1064 **287** 28p. multicoloured . . . 30 20

1982. Birth Bicentenary of Simon Bolivar.
1065 **288** 18p. multicoloured . . . 35 25

289 Dish Antenna

290 Footballers

1982. World Communication Year.
1066 **289** 26p. multicoloured . . . 30 20

1982. World Cup Football Championship, Spain. Multicoloured.
1067 **290** 4p. Type 290 . . . . . . 20 10
1068 100p. "The Final Number" (Picasso) . . . . 1·25 65

291 Boy playing Football

1982. Bolivian Youth. Multicoloured.
1069 **291** 16p. Type 291 . . . . . . 20 20
1070 20p. Girl playing piano (horiz) 25 30

292 Harvesting

1982. China-Bolivian Agricultural Co-operation.
1071 **292** 30p. multicoloured . . . 50 20

293 Flowers

1982. 1st Bolivian-Japanese Gastroenterological Days.
1072 **293** 22p. multicoloured . . . 25 20

294 Bolivian Stamps

295 Hernando Siles

1982. 10th Anniv of Bolivian Philatelic Federation.
1073 **294** 19p. multicoloured . . . 35 15

1982. Birth Centenary of Hernando Siles (former President).
1074 **295** 20p. buff and brown . . 40 20

296 Baden-Powell

297 "Liberty", Cochabamba

1982. 125th Birth Anniv of Lord Baden-Powell and 75th Anniv of Boy Scout Movement.
1075 **296** 5p. multicoloured . . . 15 10

1982. 25th Anniv of Cochabamba Philatelic Centre.
1076 **297** 3p. buff, black & blue . 10 10

298 High Court, Cochabamba

299 Virgin of Copacabana

1982. 150th Anniv of High Court, Cochabamba.
1077 **298** 10p. black, red and bronze 25 10

1982. 400th Anniv of Enthronement of Virgin of Copacabana.
1078 **299** 13p. multicoloured . . . 30 15

300 Puerto Busch Naval Base

1982. Navy Day.
1079 **300** 14p. multicoloured . . . 60 20

1982. Christmas. Design as Type **285**, inscribed "NAVIDAD 1982".
1080 **285** 10p. grey and green . . . 20 10

301 Footballer and Emblem

1983. 10th American Youth Football Championships.
1081 **301** 50p. multicoloured . . . 55 45

302 Sun Gate

1983. "Exfivia 83" Stamp Exhibition.
1082 **302** 150p. red 90 35

303 Presidents Figueiredo and Zuazo

1984. Visit of President of Brazil.
1083 **303** 150p. multicoloured . . 40 15

1984. Various stamps surch.
1084 **276** 40p. on 2p.80 light grey, black and grey 15 10
1085 – 60p. on 1p.50 green and black (1026) 15 10
1086 **265** 60p. on 2p.50 blue and red 15 10
1087 **274** 100p. on 2p. blue, black and light blue 30 15
1088 **174** 200p. on 350b. blue and light blue . . . . . . 2·25 90

1984. "Mladost 84". Youth Stamp Exn, Pleven, Bulgaria. No. 1035 surch.
1089 **273** 40p. on 2p.50 black, yellow and light yellow 15 10

306 "Simon Bolivar" (Mulato Gil de Quesada)

308 Pedestrian walking in Road

1984. Birth Bicentenary of Simon Bolivar. Mult.
1090 **306** 50p. Type 306 . . . . . 15 10
1091 200p. "Simon Bolivar entering La Paz" (Carmen Baptista) 35 20

1984. Various stamps surch.
1092 **297** 500p. on 3p. buff, black and blue (postage) . . 45 30
1093 **290** 1000p. on 4p. mult . . . 90 65
1094 **285** 2000p. on 10p. grey and green . . . . 2·00 85
1095 **296** 5000p. on 5p. mult . . . 4·75 2·00
1096 – 10000p. on 3p.80 mult (No. 940) (air) . . . . 6·25 3·75

1984. Road Safety Campaign. Multicoloured.
1097 80p. Type 308 . . . . . 10 10
1098 120p. Police motor-cyclist and patrol car 10 10

309 "Mendezs Birthplace" (Jorge Campos)

310 Legs and Feet on Map and Bata Emblem

1984. Birth Bicentenary of Jose Eustaquio Mendez. Multicoloured.
1099 **309** 300p. Type 309 . . . . . . 15 10
1100 500p. "Battle of La Tablada" (M. Villegas) . . 20 10

1984. World Footwear Festival. Mult.
1101 **310** 100p. Type 310 . . . . . . 10 10
1102 200p. Legs and feet on map and Power emblem . . 10 10
1103 600p. Football and globes (World Cup, Mexico, 1986) (horiz) 15 10

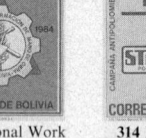

311 Inca Postal Runner

312 Vicuna

1985.
1104 **311** 11000p. blue 30 15

1985. Endangered Animals.
1105 **312** 23000p. brown and deep brown 35 15
1106 – 25000p. brown, blue and orange . . . . . 1·00 20
1107 – 30000p. red and green 45 20
DESIGNS—VERT: 25000p. Andean condor; 30000p. Marsh deer.

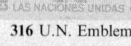

313 National Work Education Service Emblem

314 Hand with Syringe, Victim in Droplet and Campaign Emblem

1985. International Professional Education Year.
1108 **313** 2000p. blue and red . . . 10 10

1985. Anti-polio Campaign.
1109 **314** 20000p. blue and violet . . 30 15

315 Vicenta Juaristi Eguino

316 U.N. Emblem

1985. Birth Bicentenary of Vicenta Juaristi Eguino (Independence heroine).
1110 **315** 300000p. multicoloured . . 30 15

1985. 40th Anniv of U.N.O.
1111 **316** 1000000p. blue and gold . . 45 30

317 Emblem

318 Emblem, Envelope and Posthorn

1985. 75th Anniv of "The Strongest" Football Club.
1112 **317** 200000p. multicoloured . . 20 10

1986. Cent of Bolivian U.P.U. Membership.
1113 **318** 800000p. multicoloured . . 65 30

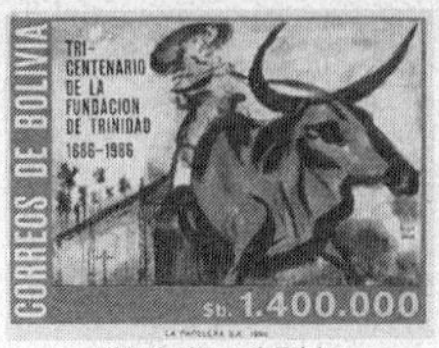

319 Bull and Rider

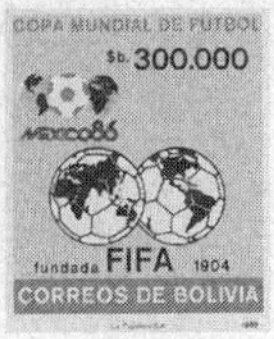

321 Football as Globes

1986. 300th Anniv of Trinidad City.
1114 **319** 1400000p. multicoloured 1·00 45

1986. No. 1108 surch.
1115 **313** 200000p. on 2000p. blue and red 15 10
1116 5000000p. on 2000p. blue and red 3·50 1·60

1986. World Cup Football Championship, Mexico.
1117 **321** 300000p. red and black 25 10
1118 – 550000p. multicoloured 45 20
1119 – 1000000p. black and green (horiz) 80 40
1120 – 2500000p. green & yell 1·90 85
DESIGNS—VERT: 550000p. Pique (mascot); 2500000p. Trophy. HORIZ: 1000000p. Azteca Stadium, Mexico City.

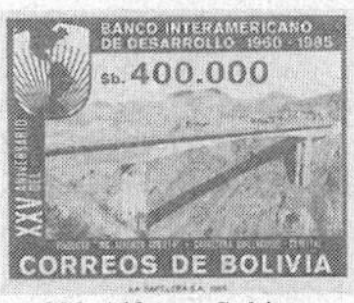

322 Alfonso Subieta Viaduct

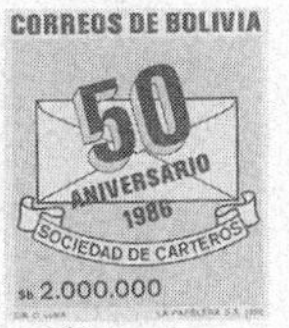

323 Envelope

1986. 25th Anniv of American Development Bank.
1121 **322** 400000p. blue 35 15

1986. 50th Anniv of Society of Postmen.
1122 **323** 2000000p. brown 1·60 70

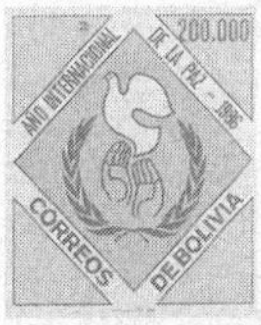

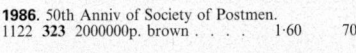

324 Emblem and Dove

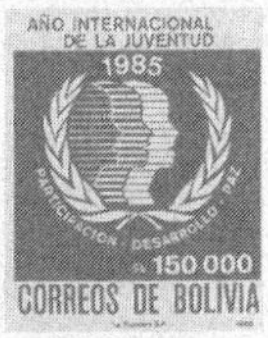

325 Emblem

1986. International Peace Year.
1123 **324** 200000p. green 15 10

1986. International Youth Year (1985).
1124 **325** 150000p. red 15 10
1125 500000p. green 45 30
1126 – 3000000p. multicoloured 2·10 1·00
DESIGNS: 3000000p. Child clutching trophy and flag (25th anniv of Enrique Happ Sports Club, Cochabamba).

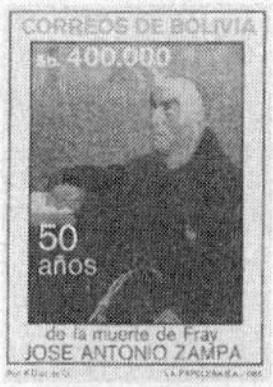

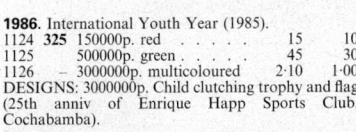

326 Zampa (after F. Diaz de Ortega)

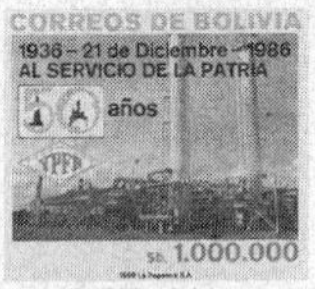

328 Refinery

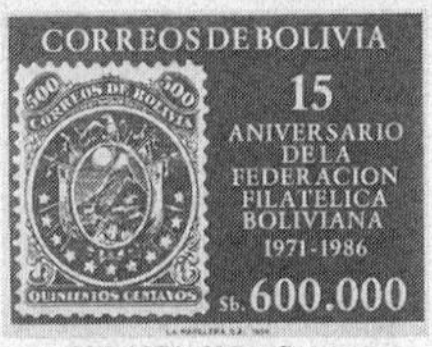

327 1870 500c. Stamp

1986. 50th Death Anniv of Friar Jose Antonio Zampa.
1127 **326** 400000p. multicoloured 35 15

1986. 15th Anniv of Bolivian Philatelic Federation.
1128 **327** 600000p. brown 50 20

1986. 50th Anniv of National Petroleum Refining Corporation.
1129 **328** 1000000p. multicoloured 1·00 30

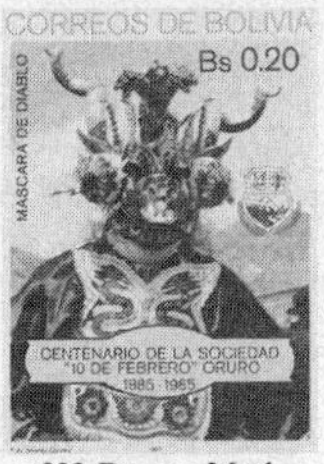

329 Demon Mask

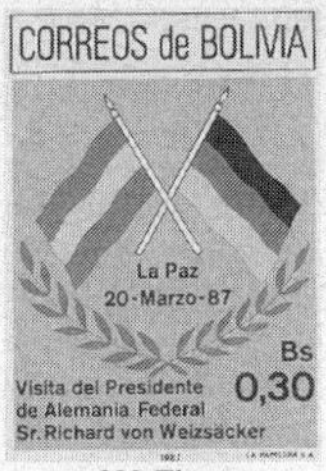

330 Flags

1987. Centenary of 10th February Society, Oruro.
1130 **329** 20c. multicoloured 10 10

1987. State Visit of President Richard von Weizsacker of German Federal Republic.
1131 **330** 30c. multicoloured 15 15

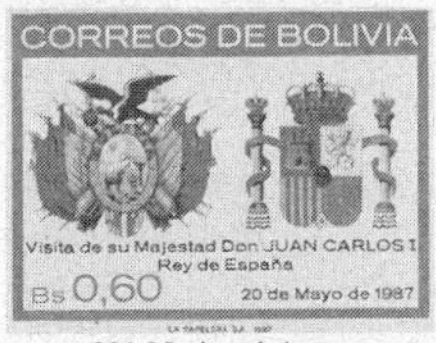

331 National Arms

1987. Visit of King Juan Carlos of Spain.
1132 **331** 60c. multicoloured 60 20

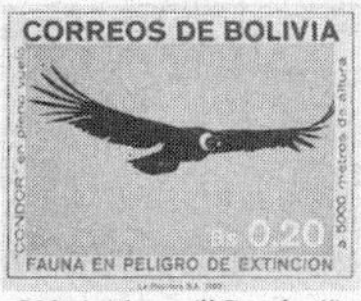

332 Andean ("Condor")

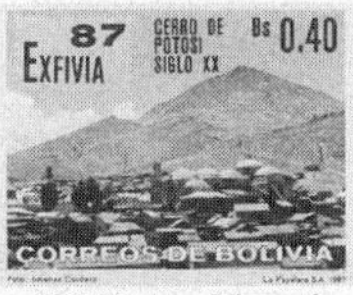

333 Modern View of Potosi

1987. Endangered Animals. Multicoloured.
1133 20c. Type **332** 35 25
1134 20c. Tapir 10 10
1135 30c. Vicuna (new-born) 15 15
1136 30c. Armadillo 15 15
1137 40c. Spectacled bear 25 20
1138 60c. Keel-billed toucans ("Tucan") 1·10 50

1987. "Exfivia 87" Stamp Exhibition, Potosi. Multicoloured.
1139 40c. Type **333** 25 20
1140 50c. 18th-century engraving of Potosi 30 25

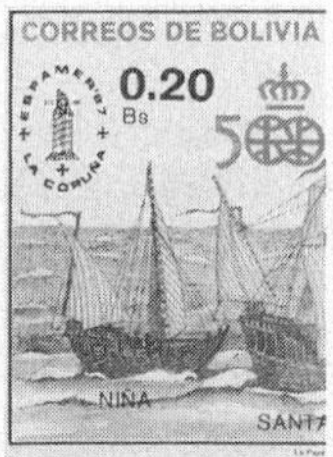

334 "Nina" and Stern of "Santa Maria"

1987. "Espamer '87" Stamp Exhibition, La Coruna. Multicoloured.
1141 20c. Type **334** 30 15
1142 20c. "Pinta" and bow of "Santa Maria" 30 15
Nos. 1141/2 were printed together, se-tenant, forming a composite design.

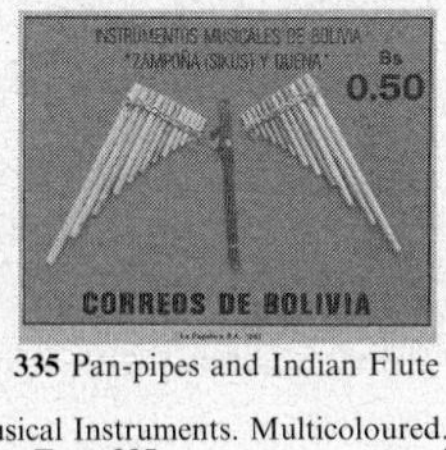

335 Pan-pipes and Indian Flute

1987. Musical Instruments. Multicoloured.
1143 50c. Type **335** 30 20
1144 1b. Indian guitars 1·00 35

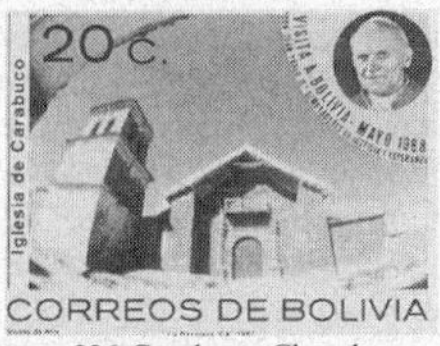

336 Carabuco Church

1988. Visit of Pope John Paul II. Mult.
1145 20c. Type **336** 10 10
1146 20c. Tihuanacu church 10 10
1147 20c. Cathedral of the Kings, Beni 10 10
1148 30c. St. Joseph church, Chiquitos 15 15
1149 30c. St. Francis's church, Sucre 15 15
1150 40c. Cobija chapel (vert) 20 15
1151 50c. Cochabamba cathedral (vert) 25 20
1152 50c. Jayu Kcota church 25 20
1153 60c. St. Francis's Basilica, La Paz (vert) 30 25
1154 70c. Church of Jesus, Machaca 60 30
1155 70c. St. Lawrence's church, Potosi (vert) 60 30
1156 80c. Vallegrande church 70 35
1157 80c. Copacabana Virgin (vert) 70 35
1158 80c. "The Holy Family" (Peter Paul Rubens) (vert) 70 35
1159 1b.30 Concepcion church 1·10 55
1160 1b.30 Tarija cathedral (vert) 1·10 55
1161 1b.50 Pope and Arms of John Paul II and Bolivia 1·40 65

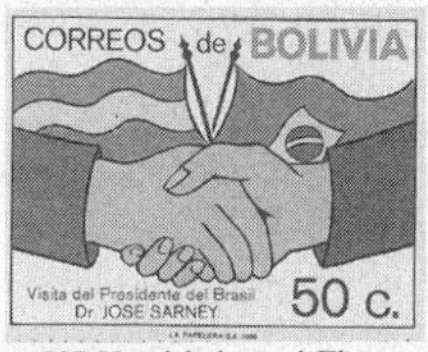

337 Handshake and Flags

1988. Visit of President Jose Sarney of Brazil.
1162 **337** 50c. multicoloured 25 20

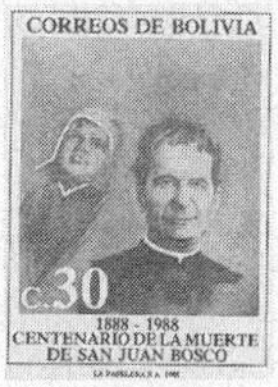

338 St. John Bosco

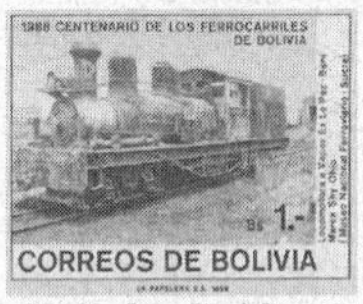

339 La Paz–Beni Steam Locomotive

1988. Death Centenary of St. John Bosco (founder of Salesian Brothers).
1163 **338** 30c. multicoloured 15 15

1988. Centenary of Bolivian Railways.
1164 **339** 1b. multicoloured 2·25 1·10

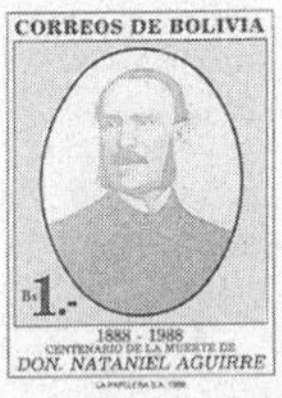

340 Aguirre

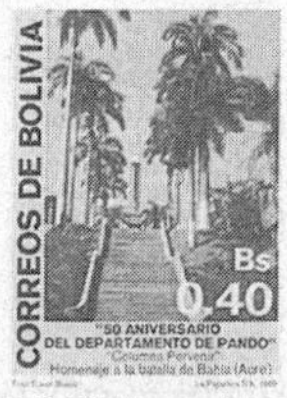

341 "Column of the Future" (Battle of Bahia Monument)

1988. Death Cent of Nataniel Aguirre (writer).
1165 **340** 1b. black and brown 80 35

1988. 50th Anniv of Pando Department. Mult.
1166 40c. Type **341** 15 10
1167 60c. Rubber production 50 20

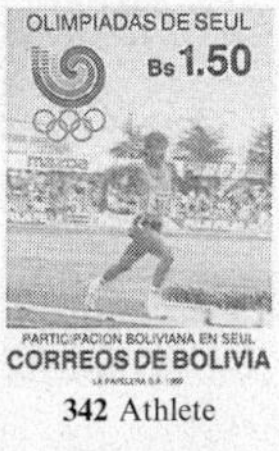

342 Athlete

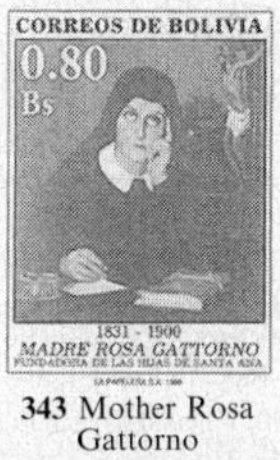

343 Mother Rosa Gattorno

1988. Olympic Games, Seoul.
1168 **342** 1b.50 multicoloured 1·25 55

1988. 88th Death Anniv of Mother Rosa Gattorno (Founder of the Daughters of St. Anne).
1169 **343** 80c. multicoloured 70 30

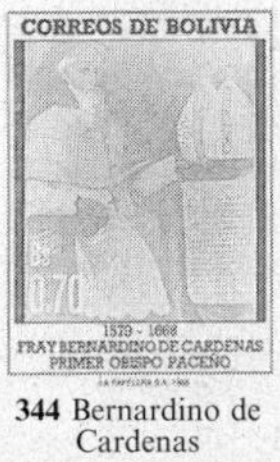

344 Bernardino de Cardenas

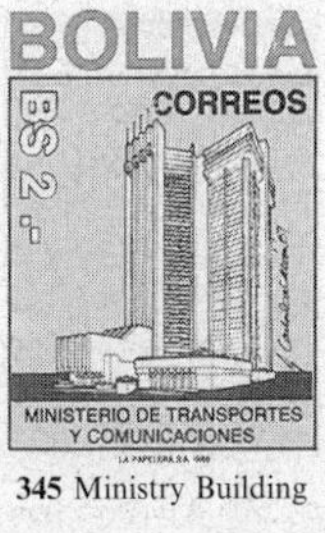

345 Ministry Building

1988. 220th Death Anniv of Br. Bernardino de Cardenas (first Bishop of La Paz).
1170 **344** 70c. black and brown 60 25

1988. Ministry of Transport and Communications.
1171 **345** 2b. black, green & red 1·60 70

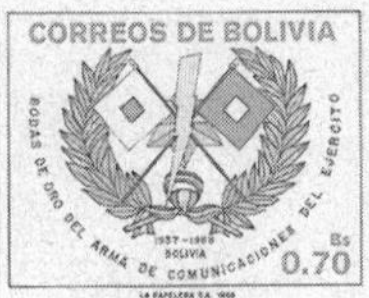

346 Arms

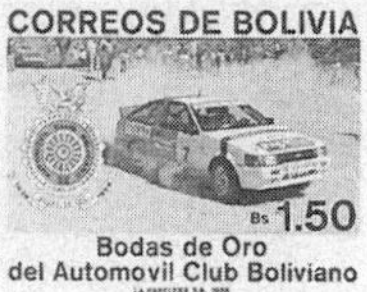

347 Rally Car

1988. 50th Anniv of Army Communications Corps.
1172 **346** 70c. multicoloured 65 25

1988. 50th Anniv of Bolivian Automobile Club.
1173 **347** 1b.50 multicoloured 1·00 55

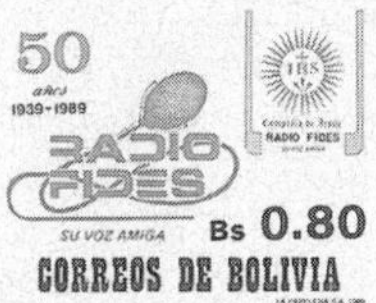

348 Microphone and Emblem

1989. 50th Anniv of Radio Fides.
1174 **348** 80c. multicoloured 65 30

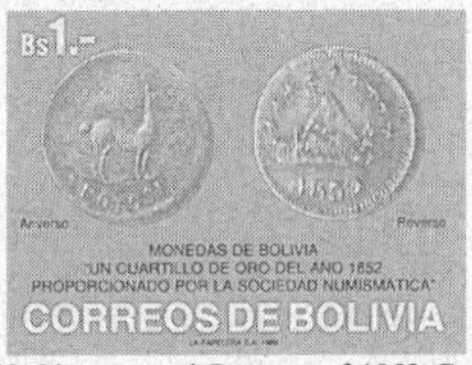

349 Obverse and Reverse of 1852 Gold Cuartillo

1989. Coins.
1175 **349** 1b. multicoloured 80 35

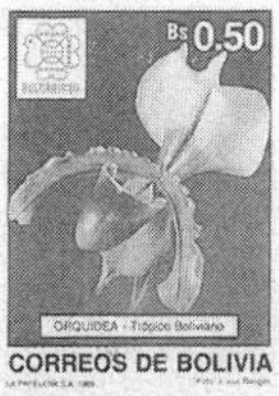

350 "Bulgaria 89" Stamp Exhibition Emblem and Orchid

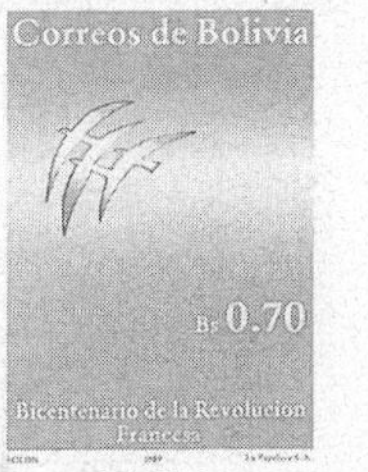

351 Birds

1989. Events and Plants. Multicoloured.
1176 50c. Type **350** 20 15
1177 60c. "Italia '90" World Cup football championship emblem and kantuta (national flower) (horiz) 50 20
1178 70c. "Albertville 1986" emblem and "Heliconia humilis" 55 25
1179 1b. Olympic Games, Barcelona emblem and "Hoffmanseggia" 80 35
1180 2b. Olympic Games, Seoul emblem and bromeliad 1·60 70

1989. Bicentenary of French Revolution.
1181 **351** 70c. multicoloured 60 25

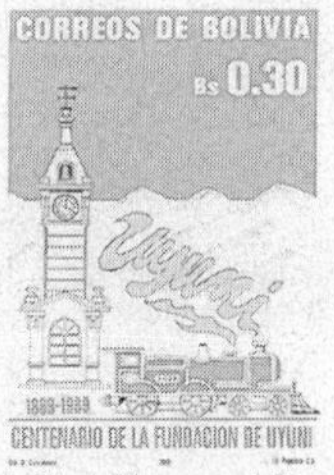

352 Clock Tower and Steam Locomotive

1989. Centenary of Uyuni.
1182 **352** 30c. grey, black & blue 75 40

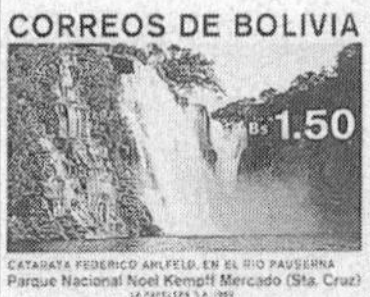

353 Federico Ahlfeld Waterfall, River Pauserna

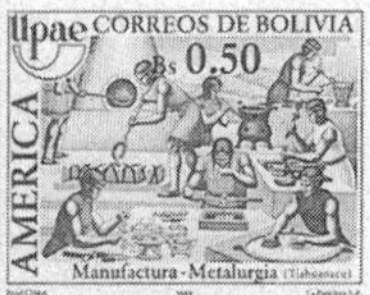

354 Making Metal Articles

1989. Noel Kempff Mercado National Park. Multicoloured.
1183　1b.50 Type **353** . . . . .　1·25　60
1184　3b. Pampas deer . . . . . .　2·40　1·00

1989. America. Tiahuanacu Culture. Mult.
1185　50c. Type **354** . . . .　20　15
1186　1b. Kalasasaya Temple . . .　70　35

355 Dr. Carlos Perez and Jaime Zamora　**356** Cobija Arch

1989. Meeting of Presidents of Bolivia and Venezuela.
1187　**355**　2b. multicoloured . . .　1·40　70

1989. World Heritage Site, Potosi. Mult.
1188　60c. Type **356** . . . .　50　15
1189　80c. Mint . . . .　60　20

357 ''Andean Lake'' (Arturo Borda)

1989. Christmas. Paintings. Multicoloured.
1190　40c. Type **357** . . . .　15　10
1191　60c. ''Virgin of the Roses'' (anon) . . . .　45　15
1192　80c. ''Conquistador'' (Jorge de la Reza) . . . .　55　20
1193　1b. ''Native Harmony'' (Juan Rimsa) . . . . . .　70　25
1194　1b.50 ''Woman with Pitcher'' (Cecilio Guzman de Rojas) . . . .　1·10　40
1195　2b. ''Flower of Tenderness'' (Gil Imana) . . . . . .　1·40　55

358 Foot crushing Syringe　**359** Map of Americas

1990. Anti-drugs Campaign.
1196　**358**　80c. multicoloured . . .　60　20

1990. Centenary of Organization of American States.
1197　**359**　80c. blue and deep blue　55　20

360 Colonnade　**361** Penny Black, Sir Rowland Hill and Bolivian 5c. Condor Stamp

1990. 450th Anniv of White City.
1198　**360**　1b.20 multicoloured . . .　85　35

1990. 150th Anniv of the Penny Black.
1199　**361**　4b. multicoloured . . .　2·75　1·25

362 Giuseppe Meaza Stadium, Milan　**363** Emblem

1990. World Cup Football Championship, Italy. Multicoloured.
1200　2b. Type **362** . . . . . .　1·40　55
1201　6b. Match scene . . . . .　4·00　1·50

1990. Cent of Bolivian Chamber of Commerce.
1202　**363**　50c. black, blue & gold　40　10

364 Satellite, Map and Globe　**366** Chipaya Village, Oruro

365 Hall

1990. Telecommunications Development Year.
1203　**364**　70c. multicoloured . . .　50　15

1990. Centenary of Cochabamba Social Club.
1204　**365**　40c. multicoloured . . .　15　10

1990. America. Multicoloured.
1205　80c. Type **366** . . . . . .　50　15
1206　1b. Nevado Huayna, Cordillera Real (mountain) (vert) . . . .　65　20

367 Emblem　**368** Trees and Mountains

1990. ''Meeting of Two Worlds. United towards Progress''. 500th Anniv (1992) of Discovery of America by Columbus.
1207　**367**　2b. multicoloured . . .　1·25　40

1990. 400th Anniv of Larecaja District.
1208　**368**　1b.20 multicoloured . .　70　25

369 Dove and German National Colours　**370** Boys playing Football (Omar Espana)

1990. Unification of Germany.
1209　**369**　2b. multicoloured . . .　1·25　55

1990. Christmas. Rights of the Child.
1210　**370**　50c. multicoloured . . .　15　10

371 Arms of Bolivia and Ecuador　**373** Andes

372 Flags and Andes

1990. Visit of Pres. Rodrigo Borja Cevallos of Ecuador.
1211　**371**　80c. multicoloured . . .　60　15

1990. 4th Andean Presidents' Council, La Paz.
1212　**372**　1b.50 multicoloured . . .　90　30

1990. ''Exfivia 90'' National Stamp Exhibition.
1213　**373**　40c. blue . . . . . .　15　10

374 Arms of Bolivia and Mexico　**376** Emblem

375 Emblem, Globe and Flags

1990. Visit of Pres. Carlos Salinas de Gortari of Mexico.
1214　**374**　60c. multicoloured . . .　50　15

1990. Express Mail Service.
1215　**375**　1b. multicoloured . . .　60　20

1991. 50th Anniv of Bolivian Radio Club.
1216　**376**　2b.40 multicoloured . .　1·40　50

377 Head of Bear　**378** National Museum of Archaeology

1991. The Spectacled Bear. Multicoloured.
1217　30c. Type **377** . . . . . .　10　10
1218　30c. Bear on branch . . . .　10　10
1219　30c. Bear and cub at water's edge . . . .　10　10
1220　30c. Bear and cubs on branches . . . .　10　10

1991. ''Espamer '91'' Spain–Latin America Stamp Exhibition, Buenos Aires. Multicoloured.
1221　50c. Type **378** . . . . . .　15　10
1222　50c. National Art Museum .　15　10
1223　1b. National Museum of Ethnography and Folklore . . . .　60　20

379 Map　**380** Statue of Our Lady of La Paz and Cathedral

1991. 56th Anniv of Ending of Chaco War and Beginning of Construction of ''Heroes of Chaco'' Road.
1224　**379**　60c. multicoloured . . .　20　15

1991. La Paz Cathedral.
1225　**380**　1b.20 multicoloured . . .　80　25

381 Presidents Lacalle and Paz Zamora

1991. Meeting of Uruguayan and Bolivian Presidents.
1226　**381**　1b. multicoloured . . .　60　20

---

382 Presidents Paz Zamora and Menem

1991. Meeting of Bolivian and Argentine Presidents.
1227　**382**　1b. multicoloured . . .　60　20

383 ''Exfivia 83'', ''87'' and ''90'' Stamps　**385** Route Map, Motor Cycle and Rally Car

384 Presidents Fujimori and Paz Zamora

1991. 20th Anniv of Bolivian Philatelic Federation.
1228　**383**　70c. multicoloured . . .　45　10

1991. Presidential Summit of Bolivia and Peru.
1229　**384**　50c. multicoloured . . .　15　10

1991. Pres. Jaime Paz Zamora National Grand Prix Motor Rally, Tarija-Cobija.
1230　**385**　50c. multicoloured . . .　15　10

386 Data Retrieval Systems

1991. ''Ecobol'' Postal Security.
1231　**386**　1b.40 multicoloured . . .　90　30

387 ''First Discovery of Chuquiago'' (Arturo Reque)　**388** Stylized Figures and City Skyline

1991. America. Voyages of Discovery. Mult.
1232　60c. Type **387** . . . . . .　20　10
1233　1b.20 ''Foundation of City of Our Lady of La Paz'' (J. Rimsa) (vert) . . . .　80　30

1991. National Population and Housing Census.
1234　**388**　50c. multicoloured . . .　15　10

389 ''Landscape'' (Daniel Pena y Sarmiento)

1991. Christmas. Multicoloured.
1235　2b. Type **389** . . . . . .　1·00　40
1236　5b. ''Fruit Seller'' (Cecilio Guzman de Rojas) . . . .　2·50　1·00
1237　15b. ''Native Mother'' (Crespo Gastelu) . . . .　7·50　3·00

390 Camp-site and Emblem

1992. 75th Anniv (1990) of Bolivian Scout Movement and Los Andes Jamboree, Cochabamba.
1238 **390** 1b.20 multicoloured . . . 80 30

 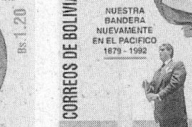

391 Simon Bolivar   392 Raising Flag

1992. "Exfilbo 92" National Stamp Exhibition, La Paz.
1239 **391** 1b.20 deep brown, brown and stone . . . 80 30

1992. Creation of Bolivian Free Zone in Ilo, Peru. Multicoloured.
1240   1b.20 Type **392** 65 30
1241   1b.50 Presidents Fujimori (Peru) and Paz Zamora (horiz) 80 30
1242   1b.80 Beach at Ilo (horiz) 95 35

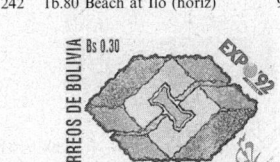

393 Logotype of Pavilion

1992. "Expo '92" World's Fair, Seville, and "Granada '92" Int Stamp Exhibition. Mult.
1243   30c. Type **393** 10 10
1244   50c. Columbus's fleet . . 30 10

394 Rotary International Emblem and Prize

1992. Rotary Club Miraflores District 4690 "Illimani de Oro" Prize.
1245 **394** 90c. gold, blue & black 30 20

395 School and Perez

1992. Birth Centenary of Elizardo Perez (founder of Ayllu School, Warisata).
1246 **395** 60c. blue, black & yellow 50 10

396 Government Palace

1992. U.N.E.S.C.O. World Heritage Site, Sucre.
1247 **396** 50c. multicoloured . . . 15 10

397 Mario Martinez   398 Front Page
Guzman

1992. Olympic Games, Barcelona.
1248 **397** 1b.50 multicoloured . . . 80 30

1992. 25th Anniv of "Los Tiempos" (newspaper).
1249 **398** 50c. multicoloured . . . 15 10

399 Canoeing   400 Columbus leaving Palos (after Bejarano)

1992. 1st International River Bermejo Canoeing Championship.
1250 **399** 1b.20 multicoloured . . . 75 30

1992. America. 500th Anniv of Discovery of America by Columbus.
1251 **400** 60c. brown and black . . 20 10
1252   – 2b. multicoloured . . . 95 40
DESIGN—HORIZ: 2b. "Columbus meeting the Caribisis Tribe" (Luis Vergara).

401 Football Match   402 "Chenopodium quinoa"

1992. World Cup Football Championship, U.S.A. (1994).
1253 **401** 1b.20 multicoloured . . 1·25 30

1992. 50th Anniv of Interamerican Institute for Agricultural Co-operation.
1254 **402** 1b.20 multicoloured . . 80 30

403 University Arms and Minerals

1992. Cent of Oruro Technical University.
1255 **403** 50c. multicoloured . . . 15 10

404 Mascots

1992. 12th Bolivarian Games, Cochabamba and Santa Cruz (1st issue).
1256 **404** 2b. multicoloured . . . 1·00 40
See also No. 1271.

405 Cayman

1992. Ecology and Conservation. Multicoloured.
1257   20c. Type **405** 10 10
1258   50c. Spotted cavy 15 10
1259   1b. Chinchilla 30 20
1260   2b. Anteater . . . . 1·00 40
1261   3b. Jaguar . . . . 1·50 65
1262   4b. Long-tailed sylph ("Picaflor") (vert) . . . 3·50 1·60
1263   5b. Piranhas . . . . 2·50 1·10
Each stamp also bears the emblem of an anniversary or event.

406 Battle Scene

1992. 150th Anniv of Battle of Ingavi.
1264 **406** 1b.20 brown and black 65 30

407 Man following Star in Boat

1992. Christmas. Multicoloured.
1265   1b.20 Type **407** 60 20
1266   2b.50 Star over church . . . 1·40 50
1267   6b. Infant in manger and church . . . . 3·00 1·25

408 Nicolas   409 Mother Nazaria
Copernicus (450th   (after Victor Eusebio
death anniv)   Choque)

1993. Astronomy.
1268   – 50c. multicoloured . . . 15 10
1269 **408** 2b. black . . . . 1·00 35
DESIGN—HORIZ: 50c. Santa Ana International Astronomical Observatory, Tarija (10th anniv (1992)).

1993. Beatification (1992) of Mother Nazaria Ignacia March Meza.
1270 **409** 60c. multicoloured . . . 40 10

410 Pictograms and Flags of Ecuador, Venezuela, Peru, Bolivia, Colombia and Panama

1993. 12th Bolivarian Games, Cochabamba and Santa Cruz (2nd issue).
1271 **410** 2b.30 multicoloured . . 1·10 35

411 Bolivia 1962 10000b. Kantuta and Brazil 90r. "Bull's Eye" Stamps

1993. 150th Anniv of First Brazilian Stamps.
1272 **411** 2b.30 multicoloured . . 1·10 35

412 "Morpho sp."

1993. Butterflies. Multicoloured.
1273   60c. Type **412** 40 10
1274   60c. "Archaeoprepona demophon" 40 10
1275   80c. "Papilio sp." 45 10
1276   80c. Orion ("Historis odius") 45 10
1277   80c. Mexican fritillary ("Euptoieta hegesia") . . 45 10
1278   1b.80 "Morpho deidamia" 1·10 30
1279   1b.80 Orange swallowtail ("Papilio thoas") . . . 1·10 30
1280   1b.80 Monarch ("Danaus plexippus") . . . . 1·10 30
1281   2b.30 Scarlet emperor ("Anaea marthesia") . . 1·25 35
1282   2b.30 "Caligo sp." . . . 1·25 35
1283   2b.30 "Rothschildia sp." . . 1·25 35
1284   2b.70 "Heliconius sp." . . 1·50 45
1285   2b.70 "Marpesia corinna" . 1·50 45
1286   2b.70 "Prepona chromus" . 1·50 45
1287   3b.50 Rusty-tipped page ("Siproeta epaphus") . 1·90 60
1288   3b.50 "Heliconius sp." . . . 1·90 60

 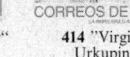

413 "Eternal Father"   414 "Virgin of
(wood statuette,   Urkupina"
Gaspar de la Cueva)

1993.
1289 **413** 1b.80 multicoloured . . . 90 30

1993. 400th Anniv of Quillacollo.
1290 **414** 50c. multicoloured . . . 15 10

415 Student, Machinery and Emblem

1993. 50th Anniv (1992) of Pedro Domingo Murillo Technical College.
1291 **415** 60c. multicoloured . . . 15 10

416 Owl (painting,   417 Common
Chuquisaca)   Squirrel-monkeys

1993. Cave Art. Multicoloured.
1292   80c. Type **416** 20 10
1293   80c. Animals (painting, Cochabamba) 20 10
1294   80c. Geometric patterns (engraving, Chuquisaca) (vert) 20 10
1295   80c. Sun (engraving, Beni) (vert) 20 10
1296   80c. Llama (painting, Oruro) 20 10
1297   80c. Human figure (engraving, Potosi) . . 20 10
1298   80c. Church and tower (painting, La Paz) (vert) 20 10
1299   80c. Warrior (engraving, Tarija) (vert) 20 10
1300   80c. Religious mask (engraving, Santa Cruz) (vert) 20 10

1993. America. Endangered Animals. Mult.
1301   80c. Type **417** 20 10
1302   2b.30 Ocelot . . . . 1·00 35

418 Emblems and Map   419 Yolanda Bedregal
(poet)

1993. 90th Anniv (1992) of Pan-American Health Organization. Anti-AIDS Campaign.
1303 **418** 80c. multicoloured . . . 20 10

1993. Personalities. Each brown.
1304   50c. Type **419** 15 10
1305   70c. Simon Martinic (President of Cochabamba Philatelic Centre) . . . 20 10
1306   90c. Eugenio von Boeck (politician and President of Bolivian Philatelic Federation) 25 15
1307   1b. Marina Nunez del Prado (sculptor) 25 15

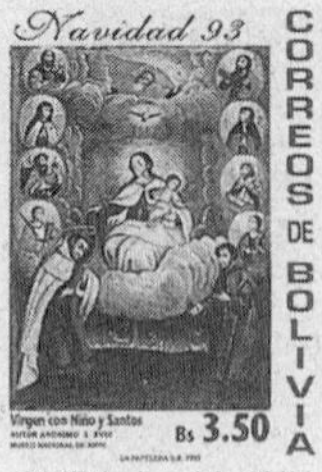

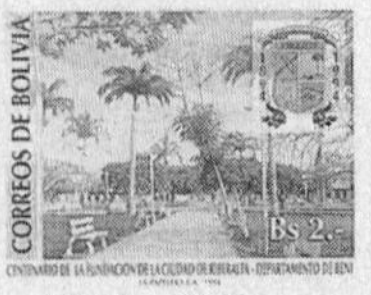

420 "Virgin with Child and Saints" (anonymous)

421 Riberalta Square

1993. Christmas. Multicoloured.

1308	2b.30 "Adoration of the Shepherds" (Leonardo Flores)	95	35
1309	3b.50 Type **420**	1·50	60
1310	6b. "Virgin of the Milk" (Melchor Perez de Holguin)	2·50	1·00

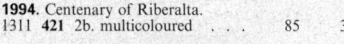

1994. Centenary of Riberalta.

1311 **421**	2b. multicoloured	85	35

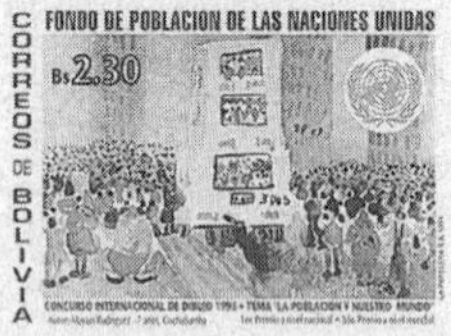

422 "Population and Our World" (Mayari Rodriguez)

1994. 2nd Prize-winning Design (6–8 year group) in United Nations Fund for Population Activities International Design Contest.

1312 **422**	2b.30 multicoloured	1·00	35

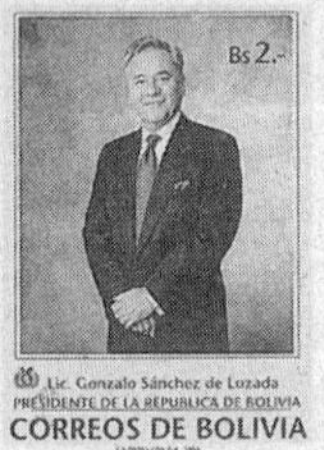

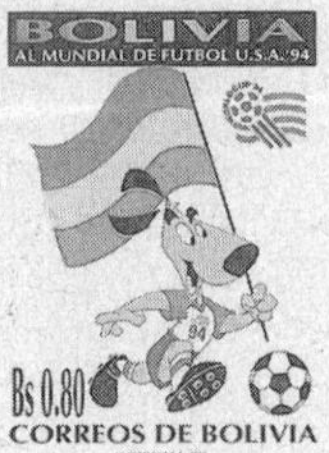

423 Sanchez de Lozada

424 Mascot

1994. Presidency of Gonzalo Sanchez de Lozada.

1313 **423**	2b. multicoloured	85	35
1314	2b.30 multicoloured	1·00	35

1994. World Cup Football Championship, U.S.A. Multicoloured.

1315	80c. Type **424**	20	10
1316	1b.80 Bolivia v Uruguay	75	30
1317	2b.30 Bolivia v Venezuela	95	35
1318	2b.50 Bolivian team (left half)	1·00	35
1319	2b.50 Bolivian team (right half)	1·00	35
1320	2b.70 Bolivia v Ecuador	1·10	45
1321	3b.50 Bolivia v Brazil	1·50	60

Nos. 1318/19 were issued together, se-tenant, forming a composite design.

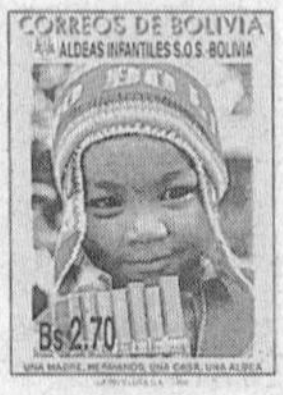

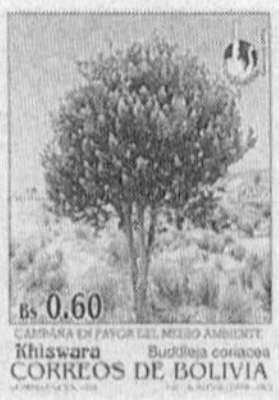

425 Child

427 "Buddleja coriacea"

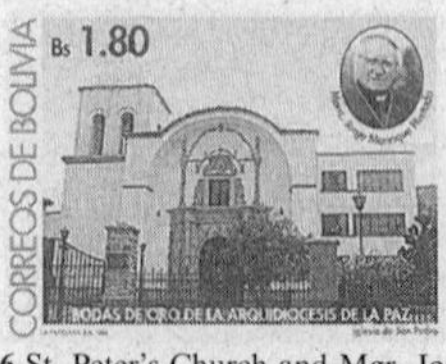

426 St. Peter's Church and Mgr. Jorge Manrique Hurtado (Archbishop, 1967–87)

1994. S.O.S. Children's Villages.

1322 **425**	2b.70 multicoloured	1·10	45

1994. 50th Anniv (1993) of Archdiocese of La Paz. Multicoloured.

1323	1b.80 Type **426**	75	30
1324	2b. Church of the Sacred Heart of Mary and Mgr. Abel Antezana y Rojas (first Archbishop, 1943–67) (vert)	85	35
1325	3b.50 Santo Domingo Church and Mgr. Luis Sainz Hinojosa (Archbishop since 1987) (vert)	1·50	60

1994. Environmental Protection. Trees. Mult.

1326	60c. Type **427**	15	10
1327	1b.80 "Bertholletia exelsa"	50	30
1328	2b. "Schinus molle" (horiz)	80	35
1329	2b.70 "Polylepis racemosa"	1·00	45
1330	3b. "Tabebuia chrysantha"	1·25	50
1331	3b.50 "Erythrina falcata" (horiz)	1·40	60

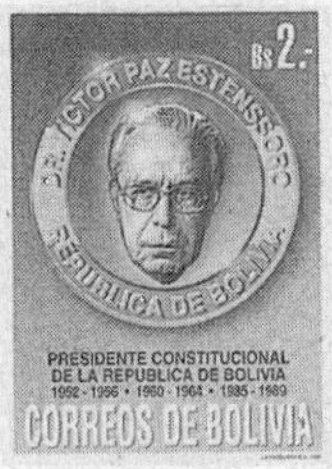

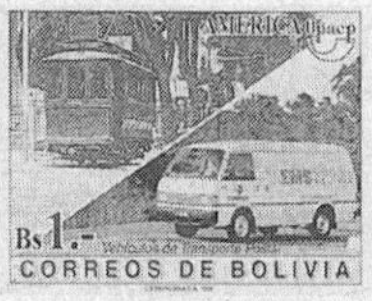

428 Paz

429 Tramcar and Mail Van

1994. Dr. Victor Paz Estenssoro (former President).

1332 **428**	2b. multicoloured	55	35

1994. America. Postal Transport. Mult.

1333	1b. Type **429**	2·25	1·50
1334	5b. Airplane and ox cart	1·25	80

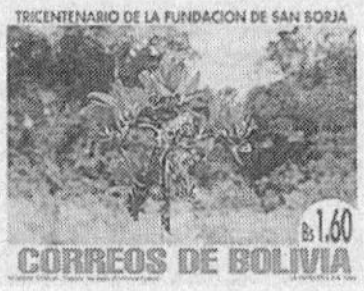

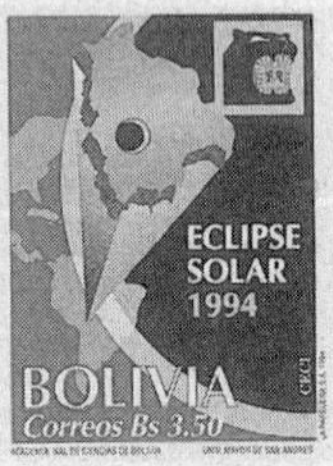

430 Coral Tree

431 Diagram of Eclipse

1994. 300th Anniv of San Borja.

1335 **430**	1b.60 multicoloured	40	25

1994. Solar Eclipse.

1336 **431**	3b.50 multicoloured	1·40	60

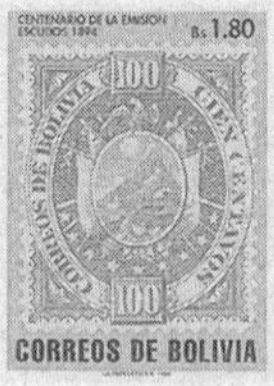

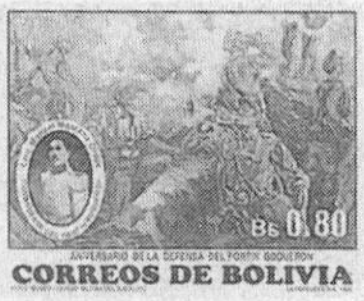

432 1894 100c. Stamp

433 Col. Marzana and Soldiers

1994. Centenary of Arms Issue of 1894.

1337 **432**	1b.80 multicoloured	50	30

1994. 62nd Anniv of Defence of Fort Boqueron.

1338 **433**	80c. multicoloured	20	10

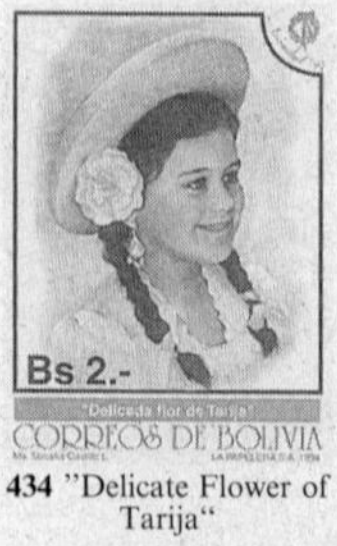

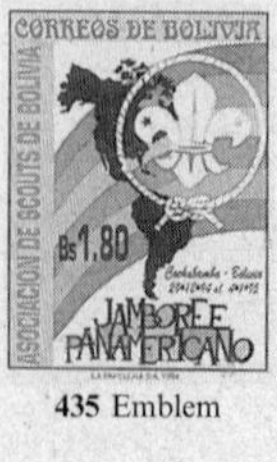

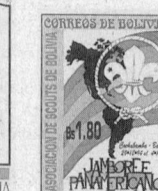

434 "Delicate Flower of Tarija"

435 Emblem

1994. Christmas. Pastels of children by Maria Susana Castillo. Multicoloured.

1339	2b. Type **434**	55	35
1340	5b. "Child of the High Plateau"	1·75	40
1341	20b. "Shoot of the Bolivian East"	6·75	2·40

1994. Pan-American Scout Jamboree, Cochabamba.

1342 **435**	1b.80 multicoloured	50	30

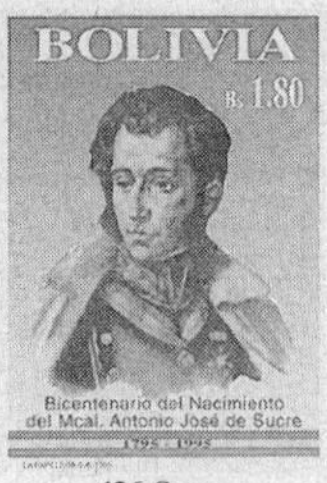

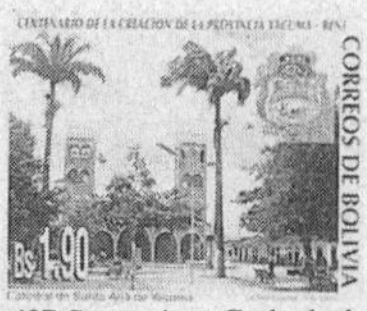

436 Sucre

437 Santa Ana Cathedral

1995. Birth Bicentenary of General Antonio Jose de Sucre. Multicoloured.

1343	1b.80 Type **436**	50	30
1344	3b.50 Sucre and national colours	90	60

1995. Centenary (1994) of Yacuma Province, Beni Department.

1345 **437**	1b.90 multicoloured	80	35
1346	2b.90 multicoloured	1·10	50

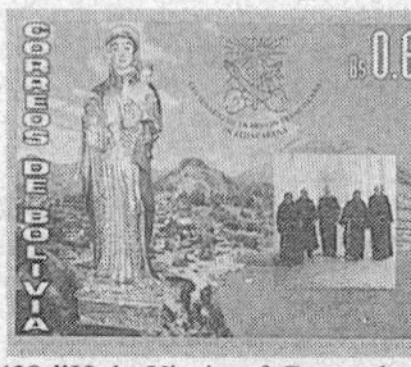

438 "Holy Virgin of Copacabana", Sanctuary and Franciscans

1995. Centenary of Franciscan Presence at Copacabana Sanctuary.

1347 **438**	60c. multicoloured	15	10
1348	80c. multicoloured	20	10

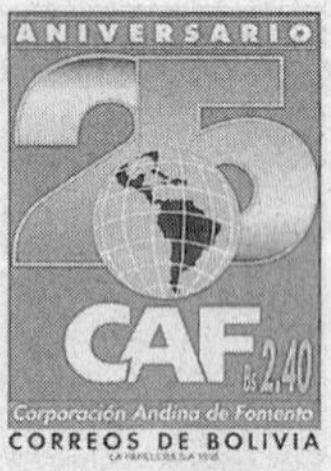

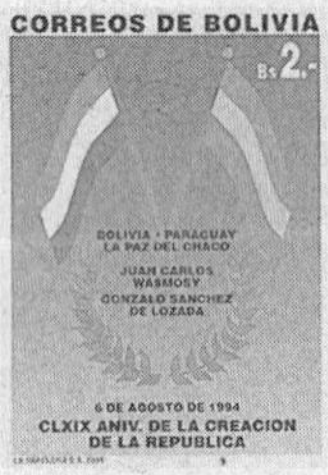

439 Anniversary Emblem

440 Paraguay and Bolivia Flags (Chaco Peace Treaty, 1938)

1995. 25th Anniv of Andean Development Corporation.

1349 **439**	2b.40 multicoloured	80	35

1995. Visit of President Juan Carlos Wasmosy of Paraguay and 169th Anniv (1994) of Republic of Bolivia.

1350 **440**	2b. multicoloured	45	30

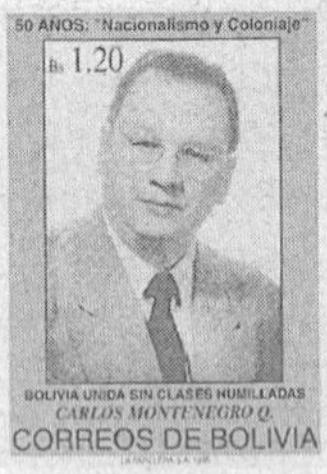

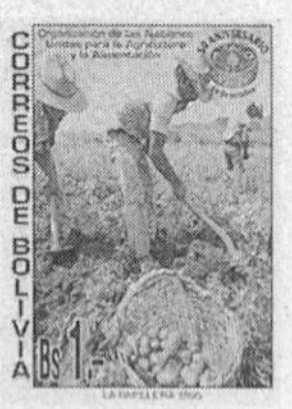

441 Montenegro

442 Digging Potatoes

1995. 50th Anniv of Publication of "Nationalism and Colonialism" by Carlos Montenegro.

1351 **441**	1b.20 black and pink	25	15

1995. 50th Anniv of F.A.O.

1352 **442**	1b. multicoloured	20	10

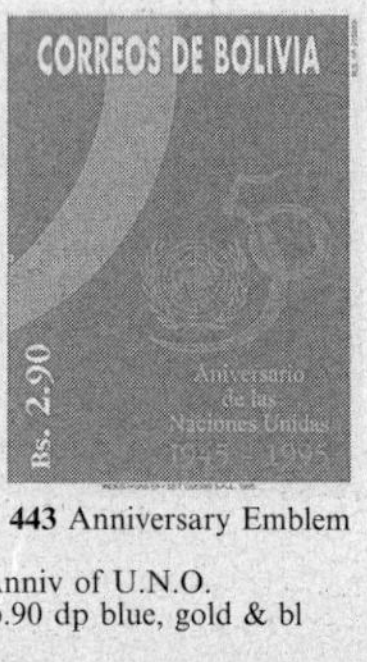

443 Anniversary Emblem

1995. 50th Anniv of U.N.O.

1353 **443**	2b.90 dp blue, gold & bl	90	40

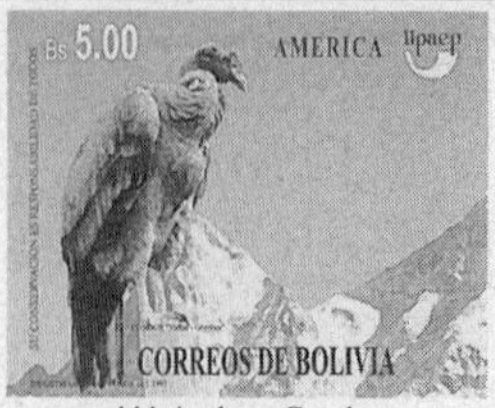

444 Andean Condor

1995. America. Endangered Species. Mult.

1354	5b. Type **444**	1·60	70
1355	5b. Llamas	1·60	70

Nos. 1354/5 were issued together, se-tenant, forming a composite design.

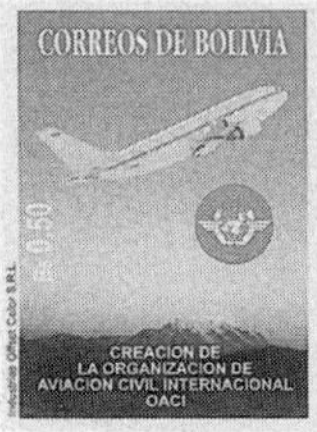

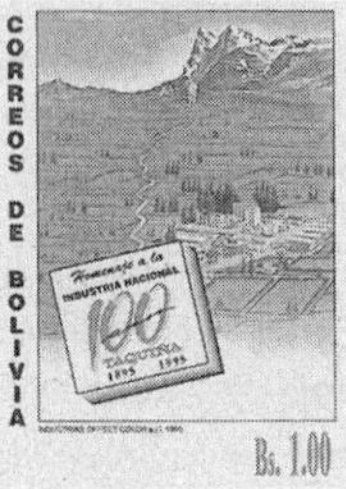

445 Airbus Industrie A320

447 Brewery Complex

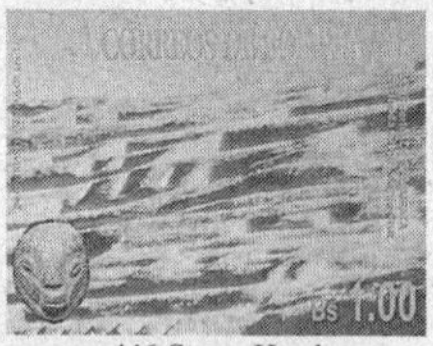

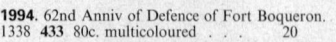

446 Stone Head

1995. 50th Anniv (1994) of I.C.A.O.

1356 **445**	50c. multicoloured	10	10

1995. Archaeology. Samaipata Temple, Florida. Multicoloured.

1357	1b. Type **446**	20	10
1358	1b.90 Stone head (different)	40	25
1359	2b. Excavation and stone head	45	30
1360	2b.40 Entrance and animal-shaped vessel	55	35

Nos. 1357/60 were issued together, se-tenant, forming a composite design.

1995. Centenary of Taquina Brewery.

1361 **447**	1b. multicoloured	20	10

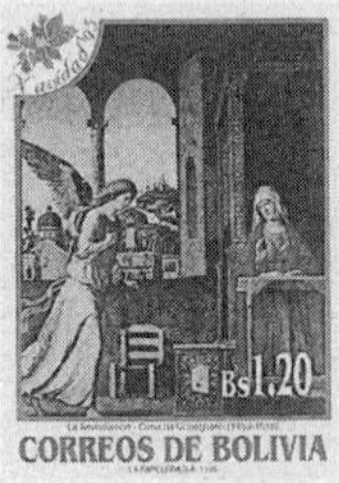

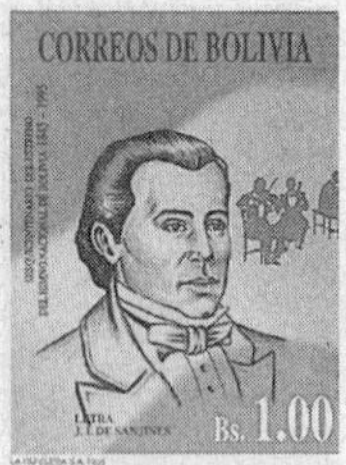

448 "The Annunciation" (Cima da Conegliano)

449 Jose de Sanjines (lyricist)

1995. Christmas. Multicoloured.

1362	1b.20 Type **448**	25	15
1363	3b. "The Nativity" (Hans Baldung)	90	40
1364	3b.50 "Adoration of the Wise Men" (altarpiece, Rogier van der Weyden)	1·10	50

1995. 150th Anniv of National Anthem. Mult.

1365	1b. Type **449**	20	10
1366	2b. Benedetto Vincenti (composer)	45	30

Nos. 1365/6 were issued together, se-tenant, forming a composite design.

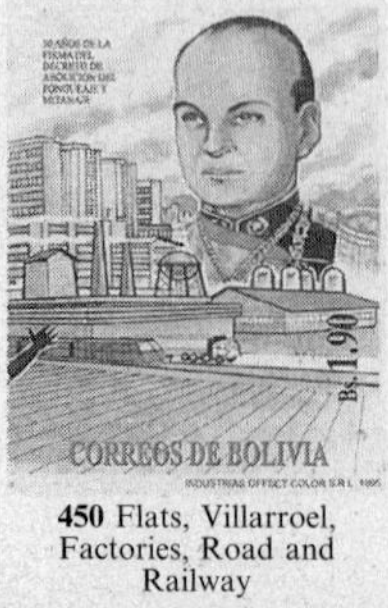

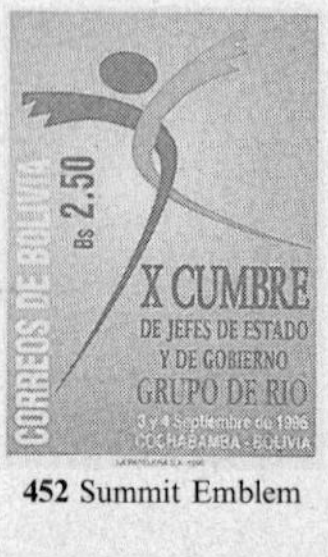

450 Flats, Villarroel, Factories, Road and Railway

452 Summit Emblem

1996. 50th Anniv of Decree for Abolition of Enforced Amerindian Labour. Mult.

1367		1b.90 Type **450**	1·25	1·10
1368		2b.90 Pres. Gualberto Villarroel addressing Congress and freed workers	2·25	1·90

Nos. 1367/8 were issued together, se-tenant, forming a composite design.

1996. Various stamps surch.

1369		50c. on 3000000p. multicoloured (No. 1126) (postage)	10	10
1370	**265**	60c. on 2p.50 blue and red	10	10
1371	**313**	60c. on 5000000p. on 2000p. blue and red (No. 1116)	10	10
1372	**319**	60c. on 1400000p. mult	10	10
1373		1b. on 2500000p. green and yellow (No. 1120)	20	10
1374	**311**	1b.50 on 11000p. blue	30	20
1375	**312**	2b.50 on 23000p. brown and sepia	55	35
1376	**316**	3b. on 1000000p. blue and gold	65	40
1377	**272**	3b.50 on 6p.50 mult	80	50
1378	**279**	3b.50 on 9p. mult	80	50
1379	**323**	3b.50 on 2000000p. brown	80	50
1380	**298**	20b. on 10p. black, purple and bronze	5·00	2·00
1381	**299**	20b. on 13p. mult	5·00	2·00
1382		3b.80 on 3p.80 mult (No. 945) (air)	85	55
1383		20b. on 3p.80 mult (No. 973a)	5·00	2·00

1996. 10th Rio Group Summit Meeting, Cochabamba. Multicoloured.

1384		2b.50 Type **452**	55	35
1385		3b.50 Rio Group emblem	80	50

453 Summit Emblem **454** Facade

1996. Summit of the Americas on Sustainable Development, Santa Cruz de la Sierra.

1386	**453**	2b.50 multicoloured	55	35
1387		5b. multicoloured	1·10	70

1996. National Bank.

1388	**454**	50c. black and blue	10	10

455 De Lemoine **456** Family

1996. 220th Birth Anniv of Jose Joaquin de Lemoine (first postal administrator).

1389	**455**	1b. brown and stone	20	10

1997. CARE (Co-operative for American Relief Everywhere). Multicoloured.

1390		60c. Type **456** (20th anniv in Bolivia)	10	10
1391		70c. Hands cradling globe (50th anniv) (vert)	15	10

457 Musicians playing Piccolo and Saxophone **458** Casa Dorada (cultural centre)

1997. 50th Anniv of National Symphony Orchestra. "Overture" by G. Rodo Boulanger. Multicoloured.

1392		1b.50 Type **457**	30	20
1393		2b. Musicians playing violin and cello	45	30

Nos. 1392/3 were issued together, se-tenant, forming a composite design of the complete painting.

1997. Tarija. Multicoloured.

1394		50c. Type **458**	10	10
1395		60c. Entre Rios Church and musician	10	10
1396		80c. Narrows of San Luis (horiz)	15	10

1397		1b. Memorial to the Fallen of the Chaco War (territorial dispute with Paraguay) (horiz)	20	10
1398		3b. Virgin and shrine of Chaguaya (horiz)	60	40
1399		20b. Birthplace and statue of Jose Eustaquio Mendez (Independence hero), San Lorenzo (horiz)	4·75	1·90

459 La Glorieta, Sucre

1997. Chuquisaca. Multicoloured.

1400		60c. Type **459**	10	10
1401		1b. Government Palace, Sucre (vert)	20	10
1402		1b.50 Footprints and drawing of dinosaur	30	20
1403		1b.50 Interior of House of Freedom	30	20
1404		2b. Man playing traditional wind instrument (vert)	40	25
1405		3b. Statue of Juana Azurduy de Padilla (Independence heroine) (vert)	60	40

460 Miners' Monument

1997. Oruro. Multicoloured.

1406		50c. Type **460**	35	25
1407		60c. Demon carnival mask	10	10
1408		1b. Vigin of the Cave (statue)	20	10
1409		1b.50 Sajama (volcano) (horiz)	30	20
1410		2b.50 Chipaya child and belfry	50	30
1411		3b. Moreno (Raul Shaw) (singer and musician) (horiz)	60	40

461 Pres. Gonzalo Sanchez de Lozada of Bolivia and Pres. Chirac

1997. Visit to Bolivia of President Jacques Chirac of France.

1412	**461**	4b. multicoloured	80	50

462 Children playing (Pamela G. Villarroel) **463** St. John Bosco (founder)

1997. 50th Anniv of U.N.I.C.E.F. Children's Drawings. Multicoloured.

1413		50c. Type **462**	10	10
1414		90c. Boy leaping across clifftop (Lidia Acapa)	20	10
1415		1b. Children of different races on top of world (Gabriela Philco)	20	10
1416		2b.50 Children and swing (Jessica Grundy)	50	30

1997. Centenary of Salesian Brothers in Bolivia. Multicoloured.

1417		1b.50 Type **463**	30	20
1418		2b. Church and statue of Bosco with child	40	25

464 Chulumani **465** Emblem

1997. La Paz. Multicoloured.

1419		50c. Type **464**	10	10
1420		80c. Inca stone monolith	15	10
1421		1b.50 La Paz and Mt. Illimani	30	20
1422		2b. Gate of the Sun, Tiahuanaco (horiz)	40	25
1423		2b.50 Dancers	50	30
1424		10b. "Virgin of Copacabana" and balsa raft on Lake Titicaca (horiz)	2·50	1·75

1997. Football Events. Multicoloured.

1425		3b. Type **465** (America Cup Latin-American Football Championship, Bolivia)	60	40
1426		5b. Eiffel Tower and trophy (World Cup Football Championship, France (1998) Eliminating Rounds)	1·00	65

466 Parliamentary Session and Building **467** Valley

1997. National Congress.

1427	**466**	1b. multicoloured	20	10

1997. America. Traditional Costumes. Mult.

1428		5b. Type **467**	1·00	65
1429		15b. Eastern region	3·50	1·40

468 Members Flags and Southern Cross **469** "Virgin of the Hill" (anon)

1997. 6th Anniv of Mercosur (South American Common Market).

1430	**468**	3b. multicoloured	60	40

1997. Christmas. Multicoloured.

1431		2b. Type **469**	40	25
1432		5b. "Virgin of the Milk" (anon)	1·00	65
1433		10b. "Holy Family" (Melchor Perez Holguin)	2·00	1·25

470 Diana, Princess of Wales

1997. Diana, Princess of Wales Commemoration. Multicoloured.

1434		2b. Type **470**	40	25
1435		3b. Diana, Princess of Wales beside minefield warning sign (horiz)	60	40

471 Presidents of Boliva and Spain

1998. State Visit of Prime Minister Jose Maria Aznar of Spain.

1436	**471**	6b. multicoloured	2·00	80

472 Juan Munoz Reyes (President) and Medallion **473** Linked Arms and Globe

1998. 75th Anniv of Bolivian Engineers' Association.

1437	**472**	3b.50 multicoloured	60	40

1998. 70th Anniv of Rotary International in Bolivia.

1438	**473**	5b. multicoloured	1·00	60

474 Delivering Letter, 1998 **475** Werner Guttentag Tichauer (35th anniv of his bibliography)

1998. America. The Postman. Multicoloured.

1439		3b. Type **474**	60	40
1440		4b. Postmen on parade, 1942 (horiz)	80	50

1998. Anniversaries.

1441	**475**	1b.50 brown	20	10
1442		2b. green	40	25
1443		3b.50 black	60	40

DESIGNS—VERT: 2b. Martin Cardenas Hermosa (botanist, birth centenary (1999)); 3b. Adrian Patino Carpio (composer, 47th death anniv).

476 Amazon Water-lily

1998. Beni. Multicoloured.

1444		50c. Type **476**	10	10
1445		1b. "Callandria" sp.	20	10
1446		1b.50 White tajibo tree (vert)	20	10
1447		3b.50 Ceremonial mask	60	40
1448		5b. European otter	1·00	60
1449		7b. King vulture ("Tropical Condor")	1·40	90

477 River Acre

1998. Pando. Multicoloured.

1450		50c. Type **477**	10	10
1451		1b. Pale-throated sloth (vert)	20	10
1452		1b.50 Arroyo Bahia (vert)	20	10
1453		4b. Boa constrictor	80	50
1454		5b. Capybara with young	1·00	60
1455		7b. Palm trees, Cobija (vert)	1·40	90

478 Rural Activities and First Lady

1998. America. Women. Multicoloured.
| 1456 | 1b.50 Type **478** . . . . . . | 20 | 10 |
| 1457 | 2b. First Lady, girl at blackboard and woman using computer . . . . . . | 40 | 25 |

Nos. 1456/7 were issued together, se-tenant, forming a composite design.

479 Town Arms and Church

1998. 450th Anniv of La Paz.
| 1458 | **479** | 2b. multicoloured . . . | 40 | 25 |

480 Emblem   **481** Magnifying Glass and 1998 7b. Stamp

1998. 50th Anniv of Organization of American States.
| 1459 | **480** | 3b.50 blue and yellow . . | 60 | 40 |

1998. "Espamer 98" Stamp Exhibition, Buenos Aires and 25th Anniv of Bolivian Philatelic Federation.
| 1460 | **481** | 2b. multicoloured . . . | 40 | 25 |

482 "People going to Church" (Kathia Lucuy Saenz)

1998. Christmas. Multicoloured.
1461	2b. Type **482**	40	25
1462	6b. Pope John Paul II (vert)	1·25	80
1463	7b. Pope John Paul II with Mother Teresa (vert) . . .	1·40	90

483 U.P.U. Monument, Berne

1999. 125th Anniv of Universal Postal Union.
| 1464 | **483** | 3b.50 multicoloured . . | 70 | 45 |

484 Statue of Football Player

1999. 75th Anniv of Cochabamba Football Association.
| 1465 | **484** | 5b. multicoloured . . . | 1·40 | 65 |

485 Red Cross Lorries at Earthquake Site

1999. 50th Anniv of Geneva Conventions.
| 1466 | **485** | 5b. multicoloured . . . | 1·00 | 65 |

486 Bernardo Guarachi and Mt. Everest

1999. 1st Ascent (1998) of Mt. Everest by a Bolivian.
| 1467 | **486** | 6b. multicoloured . . . | 1·25 | 85 |

487 Winners on Podium

1999. 30th Anniv of First Special Olympics. Multicoloured.
| 1468 | 2b. Type **487** . . . . . . | 40 | 25 |
| 1469 | 2b.50 Athletes on race track and winners on podium | 50 | 30 |

488 Golden Palace

1999. Centenary of Japanese Immigration to Bolivia. Multicoloured.
| 1470 | 3b. Type **488** . . . . . | 60 | 40 |
| 1471 | 6b. View over lake and flags (vert) . . . . | 1·25 | 85 |

489 Children dancing

1999. Anti-drugs Campaign.
| 1472 | **489** | 3b.50 multicoloured . . | 70 | 45 |

490 Route Map and Presidents Hugo Banzer Suarez of Bolivia and Fernando Cardoso of Brazil

1999. Inauguration of Gas Pipeline from Santa Cruz, Bolivia, to Campinas, Brazil. Multicoloured.
| 1473 | 3b. Type **490** . . . . . | 60 | 40 |
| 1474 | 6b. Presidents Hugo Banzer Suarez and Fernando Cardoso embracing . . . | 1·25 | 85 |

491 Village Scene   **493** International Lions Emblem

492 "Hacia la Gloria" (directed Rau Duran, Mario Camacho and Jose Jimenez)

1999. 50th Anniv of S.O.S. Children's Villages.
| 1475 | **491** | 3b.50 multicoloured . . | 70 | 45 |

1999. Centenary of Motion Pictures in Bolivia. Multicoloured.
1476	50c. Type **492**	10	10
1477	50c. "Jonah and the Pink Whale" (dir. J. Carlos Valdivia)	10	10
1478	1b. "Wara Wara" (dir. Jose Velasco)	20	15
1479	1b. "Vuelve Sebastiana" (dir. Jorge Ruiz)	20	15
1480	3b. "The Chaco Campaign" (dir. Juan Penaranda, Jose Velasco and Mario Camacho)	60	40
1481	3b. "The Watershed" (dir. Jorge Ruiz)	60	40
1482	6b. "Yawar Mallku" (dir. Jorge Sanjines)	1·25	85
1483	6b. "Mi Socio" (dir. Paolo Agazzi)	1·25	85

1999. 50th Anniv (1998) of La Paz Lions Club.
| 1485 | **493** | 3b.50 multicoloured . . | 70 | 45 |

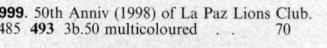

494 Mt. Tunari

1999. Cochabamba. Multicoloured.
1486	50c. Type **494**	10	10
1487	1b. Forest, Cochabamba Valley	20	15
1488	2b. Omereque vase and fertility goddess (vert) . .	40	25
1489	3b. Totora	60	40
1490	5b. Teofilo Vargas Candia (composer) and music score (vert)	1·00	65
1491	6b. "Christ of Harmony" (mountain-top statue) (vert)	1·25	85

495 Tarapaya Lagoon (Inca spa)   **496** Globe with Children, Fish, Flower, Pencil, Heart and Stars

1999. Potosi. Multicoloured.
1492	50c. Type **495**	10	10
1493	1b. First republican coins, minted in 1827 (horiz) . .	20	10
1494	2b. Mt. Chorolque (horiz)	45	30
1495	3b. Green Lagoon (horiz)	65	40
1496	4b. "The Mestizo sitting on a Trunk" (Teofilo Loaiza)	90	60
1497	6b. Alfredo Dominguez Romeo (Tupiceno singer)	1·25	80

1999. America. A New Millennium without Arms. Multicoloured.
| 1498 | 3b.50 Type **496** . . . . | 75 | 50 |
| 1499 | 3b.50 Globe emerging from flower . . . . . . | 75 | 50 |

497 Children from S.O.S. Childrens Village   **498** Ugarte

1999. Christmas. Multicoloured.
1500	2b. Type **497**	45	30
1501	6b. "The Birth of Jesus" (Gaspar Miguel de Berrios) (vert)	1·25	80
1502	7b. "Our Family in the World" (Omar Medina) (vert)	1·50	1·00

2000. 5th Death Anniv of Victor Agustin Ugarte (football player).
| 1503 | **498** | 3b. grey, green and yellow | 65 | 40 |

499 El Arenal Park

2000. Santa Cruz. Multicoloured.
1504	50c. Type **499**	10	10
1505	1b. Ox cart	20	10
1506	2b. Raul Otero Reiche, Gabriel Rene Moreno and Hernando Sanabria Fernandez (writers) . .	45	30
1507	3b. Cotoca Virgin (statue) (vert)	65	40
1508	5b. Anthropomorphic vase (vert)	1·10	70
1509	6b. Bush dog	1·25	80

500 "The Village of Serinhaem in Brazil" (Frans Post)

2000. 500th Anniv of Discovery of Brazil.
| 1510 | **500** | 5b. multicoloured . . . | 1·10 | 70 |

501 Granado

2000. Javier del Granado (poet) Commemoration.
| 1511 | **501** | 3b. grey, blue and red | 65 | 40 |

502 Cyclists   **503** Oriental Clay Figure

2000. "Double Copacabana" Cycle Race.
1512	**502**	1b. multicoloured . . .	20	10
1513	–	3b. multicoloured . . .	65	40
1514	–	5b. multicoloured . . .	1·10	70
1515	–	7b. multicoloured . . .	1·50	1·00

DESIGNS: 3b. to 7b. Various race scenes.

2000. National Archaeology Museum Exhibits. Each brown and gold.
1516	50c. Type **503**	10	10
1517	50c. Clay figure, Potosi . .	10	10
1518	70c. Oriental clay head, Beni	15	10
1519	90c. Clay vase, Tarija . . .	20	10
1520	1b. Clay head, Oruro . . .	20	10
1521	1b. Yampara clay urn . . .	20	10
1522	3b. Inca wood carving . . .	65	40
1523	5b. Oriental anthropomorphic vase . .	1·10	70
1524	20b. Tiwanaku clay mask . .	4·50	3·00

504 Male and Female Symbols in Red Vortex

2000. America. Anti-A.I.D.S. Campaign. Multicoloured.
| 1525 | 3b.50 Type **504** . . . . | 75 | 45 |
| 1526 | 3b.50 Couple walking through wall . . . . . . | 75 | 45 |

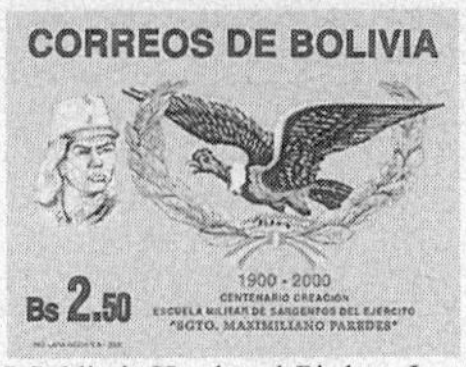

505 Soldier's Head and Bird on Laurel Wreath

2000. Centenary of Maximiliano Parades Military School.
1527 **505** 2b.50 multicoloured . . 55 35

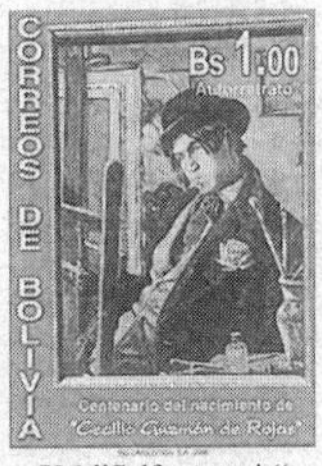

506 "Self-portrait"

2000. Birth Centenary of Cecilio Guzman de Rojas (artist). Showing paintings. Multicoloured.
1528 1b. Type **506** 25 15
1529 2b.50 "Triumph of Nature" (horiz) 55 35
1530 5b. "Andina" . . . . 1·10 65
1531 6b. "Students' Quarrel" (horiz) . . . . 1·25 75

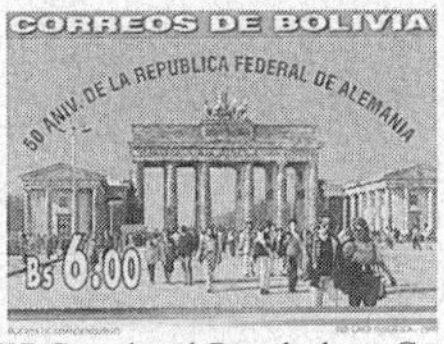

507 Crowd and Brandenburg Gate

2000. 50th Anniv of German Federal Republic.
1532 **507** 6b. multicoloured . . . 1·25 75

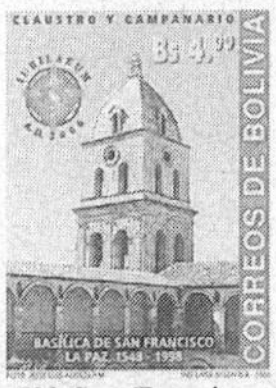
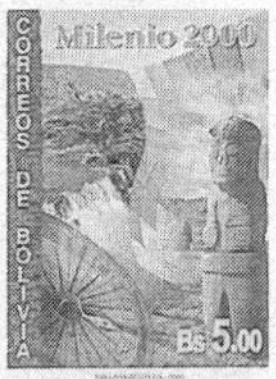

508 San Francisco Basilica, La Paz
509 Waterfall and Statue

2000. Holy Year 2000. Bolivian Episcopal Conference. Multicoloured.
1533 4b. Type **508** 90 55
1534 6b. Stalks of grain breaking through barbed-wire . . . 1·25 75

2000. New Millennium.
1535 **509** 5b. multicoloured . . . 1·10 65

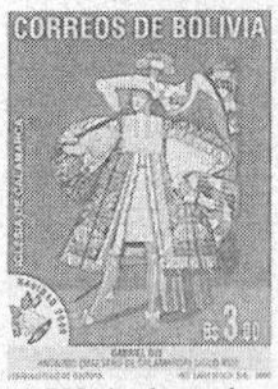

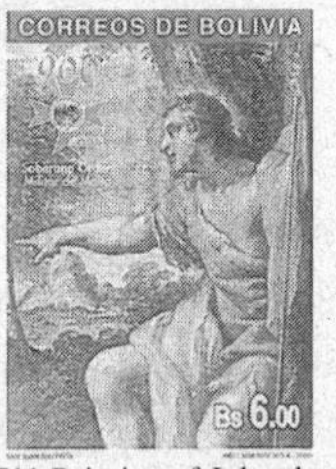

510 Archangel Gabriel
511 Painting of John the Baptist and Emblem

2000. Christmas. Showing 17th-century paintings of Angels from Calamarca Church. Multicoloured.
1536 3b. Type **510** 65 40
1537 5b. Angel of Virtue . . . . 1·10 65
1538 10b. Angel with ear of corn 2·25 1·40

2000. 900th Anniv of Sovereign Military Order of St. John.
1539 **511** 6b. multicoloured . . . 1·25 75

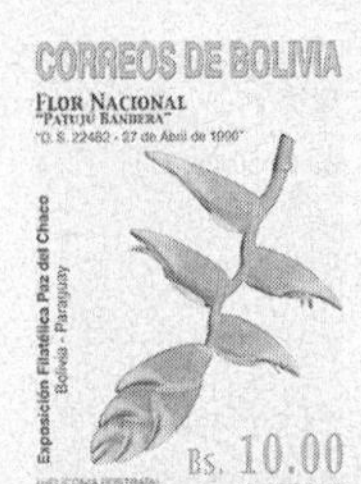

512 Lobster Claw (*Heliconia rostrata*)

2001. Patriotic Symbols. Multicoloured.
1540 10b. Type **512** (designated national flower, 1990) . . 2·25 1·40
1541 20b. *Periphrangus dependens* (designated national flower 1924) . . . . . . 4·50 2·75
1542 30b. First Bolivian coat of arms (instated 1825) . . . 6·50 4·00
1543 50b. Second Bolivian coat of arms (instated 1826) . . . 11·00 6·50
1544 100b. Present day Bolivian coat of arms (instated 1851) . . . . 20·00 12·00

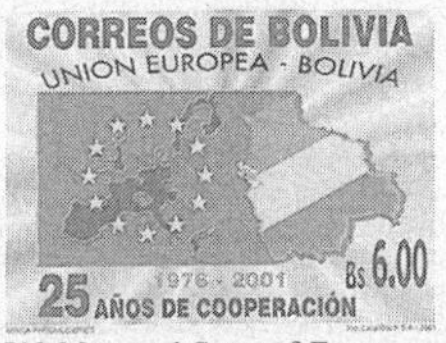

513 Map and Stars of European Union and Map of Bolivia

2001. 25th Anniv of Co-operation between Bolivia and European Union.
1550 **513** 6b. multicoloured . . . 1·25 75

POSTAGE DUE STAMPS

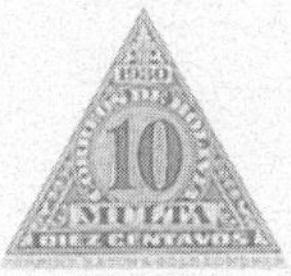
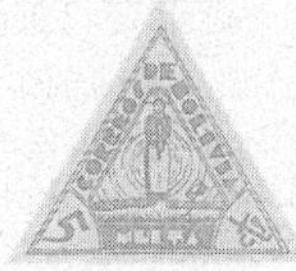

D **81** D **93** "Youth"

1931.
D265 D **81** 5c. blue 70 85
D266 10c. red 70 85
D267 15c. yellow . . . . . 1·00 85
D268 30c. green . . . . . . 1·00 85
D269 40c. violet . . . . . . 1·75 1·75
D270 50c. sepia . . . . . . 2·40 2·40

1938. Triangular designs.
D346 D **93** 5c. red 50 50
D347 – 10c. green 50 50
D348 – 30c. blue 50 50
DESIGNS: 10c. Torch of Knowledge; 30c. Date and Symbol of 17 May 1936 Revolution.

BOPHUTHATSWANA Pt. 1

The republic of Bophuthatswana was established on 6 December 1977 as one of the "black homelands" constructed from the territory of the Republic of South Africa.

Although this independence did not receive international political recognition we are satisfied that the stamps had "de facto" acceptance as valid for the carriage of mail outside Bophuthatswana.

Bophuthatswana was formally re-incorporated into South Africa on 27 April 1994.

100 cents = 1 rand

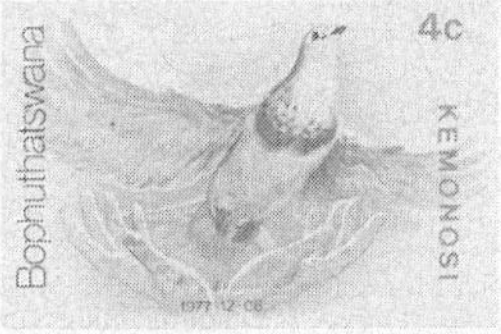

1 Hand releasing Dove

1977. Independence. Multicoloured.
1 4c. Type **1** 35 35
2 10c. Leopard (national emblem) 75 60
3 15c. Coat of arms . . . . . . 1·25 1·00
4 20c. National flag . . . . . . 1·50 1·40

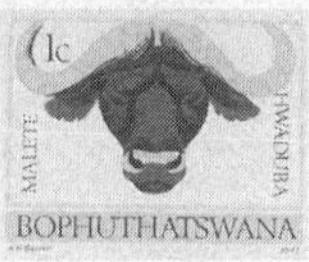

2 African Buffalo

1977. Tribal Totems. Multicoloured.
5a 1c. Type **2** 20 15
6a 2c. Bush pig 20 15
7a 3c. Chacma baboon 20 15
8a 4c. Leopard 20 10
9a 5c. Crocodile 20 10
10 6c. Savanna monkey 20 10
11a 7c. Lion 30 15
12a 8c. Spotted hyena 20 15
13 9c. Cape porcupine 25 15
14 10c. Aardvark 25 10
15 15c. Tilapia (fish) 65 15
16 20c. Hunting dog 25 20
17 25c. Common duiker 40 30
18 30c. African elephant . . . 60 35
19 50c. Python 70 40
20 1r. Hippopotamus . . . . . 1·40 1·00
21 2r. Greater kudu . . . . . 1·50 2·25

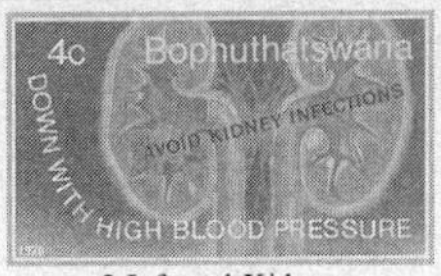

3 Infected Kidney

1978. World Hypertension Month. Multicoloured.
22 4c. Type **3** 50 25
23 10c. Heart and spoon of salt 70 70
24 15c. Spoon reflecting skull, knife and fork . . . . . . 1·25 1·25

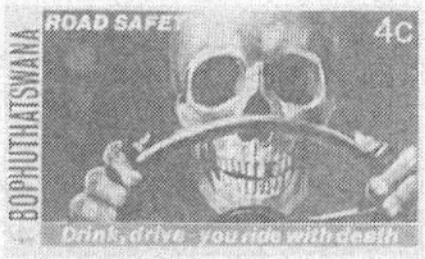

4 Skull behind Wheel of Car

1978. Road Safety. Multicoloured.
25 4c. Type **4** 70 40
26 10c. Child knocked off tricycle 90 80
27 15c. Pedestrian stepping in front of car . . . . 1·00 1·10
28 20c. Cyclist ignoring stop sign 1·40 1·75

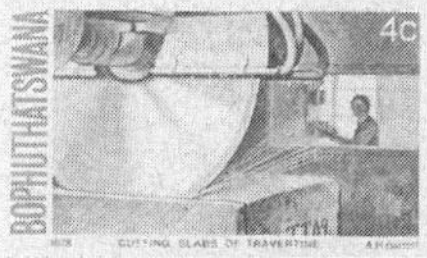

5 Cutting slabs of Travertine

1978. Semi-precious Stones. Multicoloured.
29 4c. Type **5** 65 25
30 10c. Polishing travertine . . . 1·25 85
31 15c. Sorting semi-precious stones . . . . 1·50 1·25
32 20c. Factory at Taung . . . . 2·25 1·60

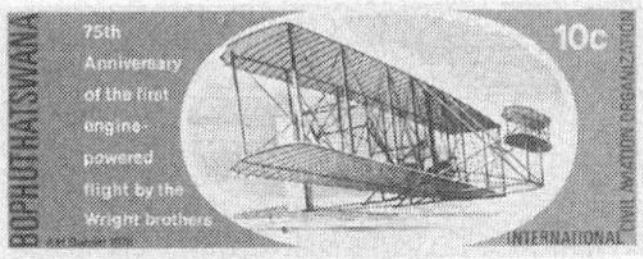

6 Wright Flyer I

1978. 75th Anniv of First Powered Flight by Wright Brothers.
33 **6** 10c. black, blue and red . . . 1·00 1·00
34 – 15c. black, blue and red . . . 1·40 1·50
DESIGN: 15c. Orville and Wilbur Wright.

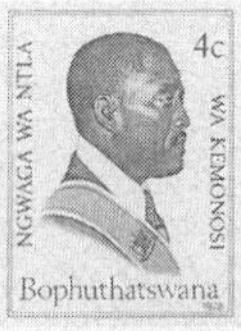

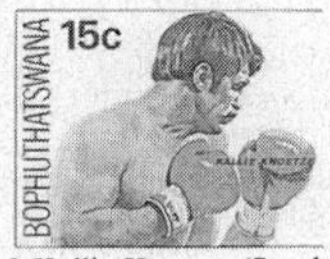

7 Pres. Lucas M. Mangope
9 Kallie Knoetze (South Africa)

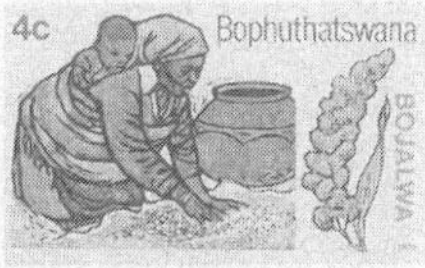

8 Drying Germinated Wheat Sorghum

1978. 1st Anniv of Independence. Multicoloured.
35 4c. Type **7** 25 20
36 15c. Full face portrait of President 75 60

1978. Sorghum Beer-making. Multicoloured.
37 4c. Type **8** 25 20
38 15c. Cooking the ground grain 65 70
39 20c. Sieving the liquid 70 75
40 25c. Drinking the beer . . . . 80 1·00

1979. Knoetze–Tate Boxing Match. Multicoloured.
41 15c. Type **9** 75 75
42 15c. John Tate (U.S.A.) . . . 75 75

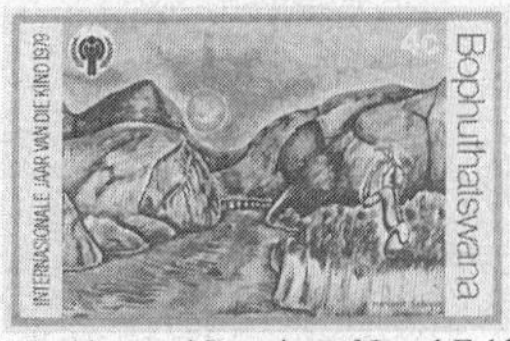

10 Emblem and Drawing of Local Fable (Hendrick Sebapo)

1979. International Year of the Child. Children's Drawings of Local Fables. Multicoloured.
43 4c. Type **10** 20 20
44 15c. Family with animals (Daisy Morapedi) 25 25
45 20c. Man's head and landscape (Peter Tladi) . . . 35 35
46 25c. Old man, boy and donkey (Hendrick Sebapo) 45 60

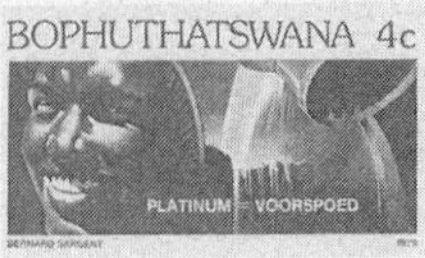

11 Miner and Molten Platinum

1979. Platinum Industry.
47 **11** 4c. multicoloured 25 10
48 – 15c. multicoloured 35 30
49 – 20c. multicoloured 45 45
50 – 25c. black and grey 60 65
DESIGNS: 15c. Platinum granules and industrial use; 20c. Telecommunications satellite; 25c. Jewellery.

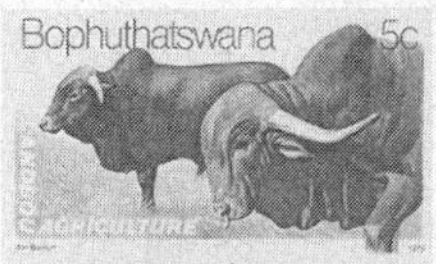

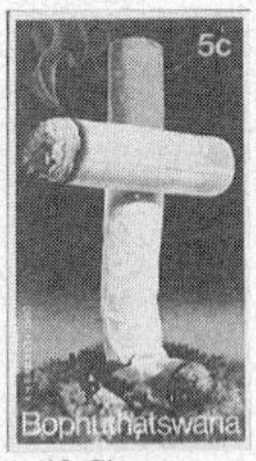

12 Cattle
13 Cigarettes forming Cross

1979. Agriculture. Multicoloured.
51 5c. Type **12** 20 20
52 15c. Picking cotton 25 25
53 20c. Scientist examining maize 30 30
54 25c. Catch of fish 35 35

1979. Anti-smoking Campaign.
55 **13** 5c. multicoloured 40 20

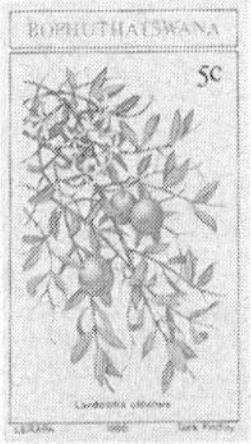

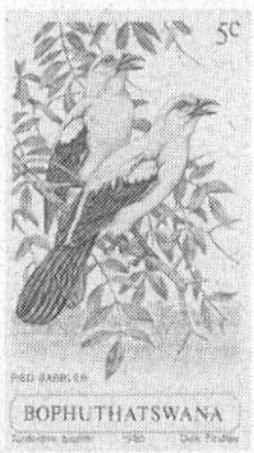

14 "Landolphia capensis"
15 Pied Babbler

1980. Edible Wild Fruits. Multicoloured.
56 5c. Type **14** 15 15
57 10c. "Vangueria infausta" . . 30 30
58 15c. "Bequaertiodendron magalismontanum" 40 40
59 20c. "Sclerocarya caffra" . . . 55 55

1980. Birds. Multicoloured.
60 5c. Type **15** 30 20
61 10c. Carmine bee eater 40 35
62 15c. Shaft-tailed whydah . . . 60 60
63 20c. Brown parrot ("Meyer's Parrot") 70 65

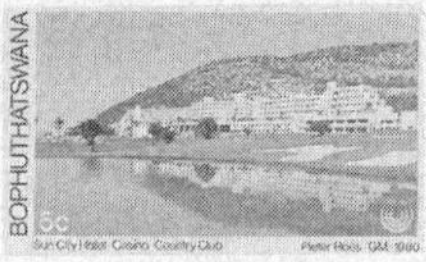

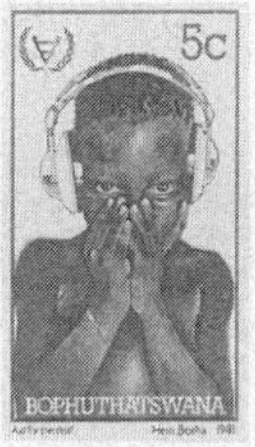

16 Sun City Hotel
17 Deaf Child

1980. Tourism. Sun City. Multicoloured.
64 5c. Type **16** 10 15
65 10c. Gary Player Country Club 40 30
66 15c. Casino 45 50
67 20c. Extravaganza 50 70

1981. Int Year of Disabled Persons. Mult.
68 5c. Type **17** 15 10
69 15c. Blind child 30 20
70 20c. Archer in wheelchair . . 45 35
71 25c. Tuberculosis X-ray . . . 60 60

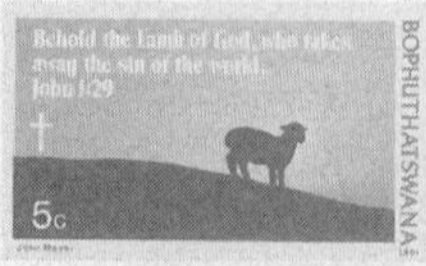

18 "Behold the Lamb of God ..."

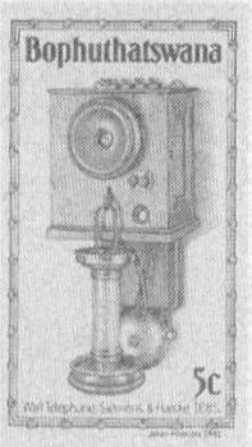

19 Siemens and Halske Wall Telephone, 1885

1981. Easter. Multicoloured.

72	5c. Type **18**	10	10
73	15c. Bread ("I am the bread of life")	25	25
74	20c. Shepherd ("I am the good shepherd")	35	35
75	25c. Wheatfield ("Unless a grain of wheat falls into the earth and dies ...")	45	45

1981. History of the Telephone (1st series). Multicoloured.

76	5c. Type **19**	10	10
77	15c. Ericsson telephone, 1895	25	25
78	20c. Hasler telephone, 1900	35	35
79	25c. Mix and Genest wall telephone, 1904	45	45

See also Nos. 92/5, 108/11 and 146/9.

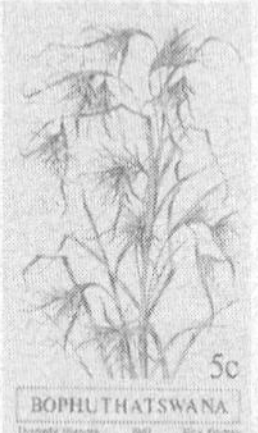

20 "Themeda triandra"

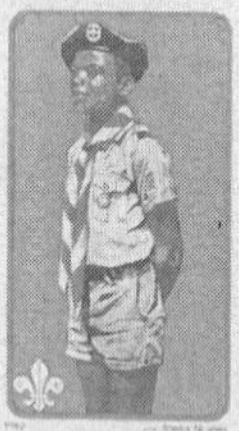

21 Boy Scout

1981. Indigenous Grasses (1st series). Multicoloured.

80	5c. Type **20**	10	10
81	15c. "Rhynchelytrum repens"	20	25
82	20c. "Eragrostis capensis"	20	30
83	25c. "Monocymbium ceresiiforme"	30	45

See also Nos. 116/19.

1982. 75th Anniv of Boy Scout Movement. Multicoloured.

84	5c. Type **21**	15	10
85	15c. Mafeking siege stamps	35	35
86	20c. Original cadet	40	40
87	25c. Lord Baden-Powell	45	45

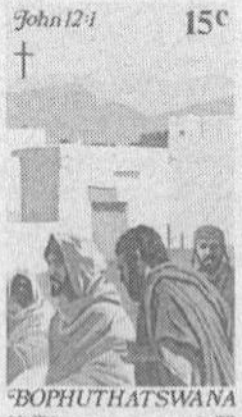

22 Jesus arriving at Bethany (John 12:1)

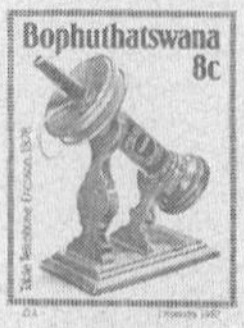

23 Ericsson Telephone, 1878

1982. Easter. Multicoloured.

88	15c. Type **22**	25	25
89	20c. Jesus sending disciples for donkey (Matthew 21:1,2)	30	30
90	25c. Disciples taking donkey (Mark 11:5,6)	40	40
91	30c. Disciples with donkey and foal (Matthew 21:7)	45	45

1982. History of the Telephone (2nd series). Multicoloured.

92	8c. Type **23**	15	10
93	15c. Ericsson telephone, 1885	20	20
94	20c. Ericsson telephone, 1893	20	20
95	25c. Siemens and Halske telephone, 1898	30	30

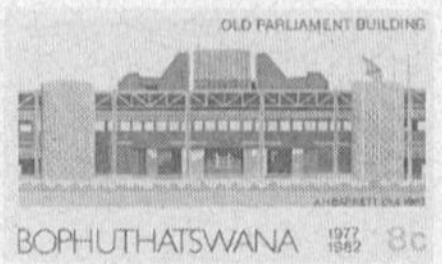

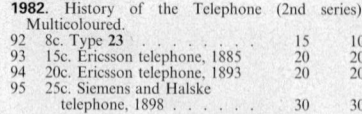

24 Old Parliament Building

1982. 5th Anniv of Independence. Multicoloured.

96	8c. Type **24**	10	10
97	15c. New government offices	20	20
98	20c. University, Mmabatho	25	25
99	25c. Civic Centre, Mmabatho	30	30

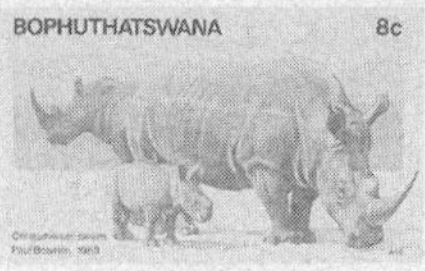

25 White Rhinoceros

1983. Pilanesberg Nature Reserve. Multicoloured.

100	8c. Type **25**	30	10
101	20c. Common zebras	40	30
102	25c. Sable antelope	40	35
103	40c. Hartebeest	60	60

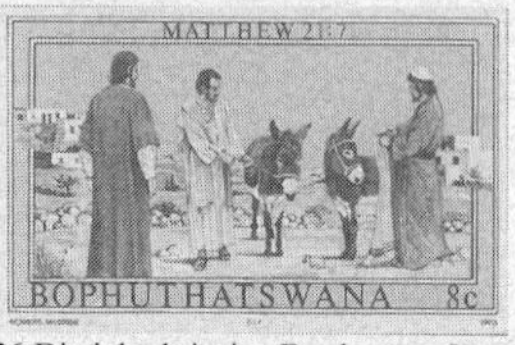

26 Disciples bringing Donkeys to Jesus (Matthew 21:7)

1983. Easter. Palm Sunday. Multicoloured.

104	8c. Type **26**	10	10
105	20c. Jesus stroking colt (Mark 11:7)	30	30
106	25c. Jesus enters Jerusalem on donkey (Matthew 21:8)	35	35
107	40c. Crowd welcoming Jesus (Mark 11:9)	60	60

1983. History of the Telephone (3rd series). As T **19**. Multicoloured.

108	10c. A.T.M. table telephone c. 1920	15	10
109	20c. A/S Elektrisk wall telephone, c. 1900	30	30
110	25c. Ericsson wall telephone c. 1900	35	35
111	40c. Ericsson wall telephone c. 1900 (different)	60	60

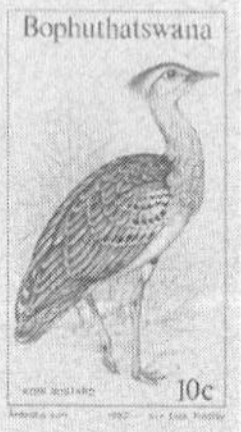

27 Kori Bustard

1983. Birds of the Veld. Multicoloured.

112	10c. Type **27**	30	20
113	20c. Black bustard ("Black Korhaan")	45	45
114	25c. Crested bustard ("Red-crested Korhaan")	55	55
115	40c. Denhan's ("Stanley Bustard")	70	80

1984. Indigenous Grasses (2nd series). As T **20**. Multicoloured.

116	10c. "Panicum maximum"	15	10
117	20c. "Hyparrhenia dregeana"	20	20
118	25c. "Cenchrus ciliaris"	25	35
119	40c. "Urochloa brachyura"	50	70

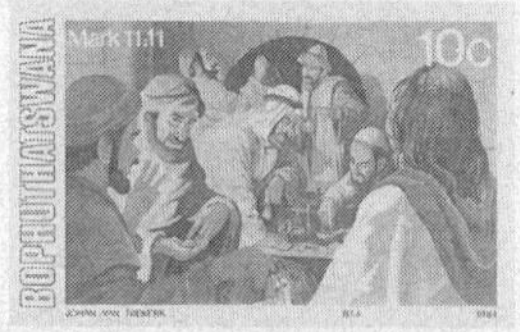

28 Money-lenders in the Temple (Mark 11:11)

1984. Easter. Multicoloured.

120	10c. Type **28**	15	10
121	20c. Jesus driving the money-lenders from the Temple (Mark 11:15)	25	20
122	25c. Jesus and fig tree (Matthew 21:9)	35	35
123	40c. The withering of the fig tree (Matthew 21:9)	60	70

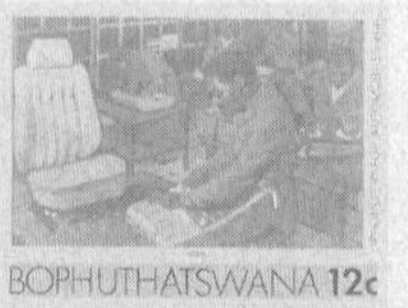

29 Car Upholstery, Ga-Rankuwa

1984. Industries. Multicoloured.

124	1c. Textile mill	10	10
125	2c. Sewing sacks, Selosesha	10	10
126	3c. Ceramic tiles, Babelegi	10	10
127	4c. Sheepskin car seat covers	10	10
128	5c. Crossbow manufacture	15	10
129	6c. Automobile parts, Babelegi	15	10
130	7c. Hosiery, Babelegi	15	10
131	8c. Specialised bicycle factory, Babelegi	30	10
132	9c. Lawn mower assembly line	30	15
133	10c. Dress factory, Thaba 'Nchu	20	10
134	11c. Molten platinum	60	20
135	12c. Type **29**	40	15
136	14c. Maize mill, Mafeking	50	15
137	15c. Plastic bags, Babelegi	25	15
137b	16c. Brick factory, Mmabatho	60	15
137c	18c. Cutlery manufacturing, Mogwase	60	15
138	20c. Men's clothing, Babelegi	25	15
138b	21c. Welding bus chassis	50	50
138c	21c. Fitting engine to bus chassis	50	50
138d	21c. Bus body construction	50	50
138e	21c. Spraying and finishing bus	50	50
138f	21c. Finished bus	50	50
139	25c. Chromium plating pram parts	30	20
140	30c. Spray painting metal beds	40	25
141	50c. Milk processing plant	65	40
142	1r. Modern printing works	90	75
143	2r. Industrial complex, Babelegi	2·00	2·75

1984. History of the Telephone (4th series). As T **19**. Multicoloured.

146	11c. Schuchhardt table telephone, 1905	15	10
147	20c. Siemens wall telephone, 1925	25	20
148	25c. Ericsson table telephone, 1900	30	30
149	30c. Oki table telephone, 1930	40	50

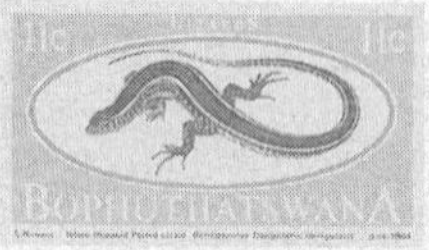

30 Yellow-throated Plated Lizard

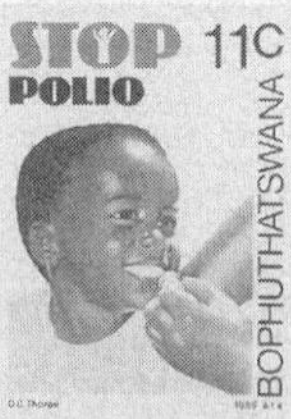

31 Giving Oral Vaccine against Polio

1984. Lizards. Multicoloured.

150	11c. Type **30**	20	10
151	25c. Transvaal girdled lizard	30	30
152	30c. Ocellated sand lizard	35	40
153	45c. Bibron's thick-toed gecko	50	60

1985. Health. Multicoloured.

154	11c. Type **31**	35	10
155	25c. Vaccinating against measles	45	30
156	30c. Examining child for diphtheria	50	40
157	50c. Examining child for whooping cough	70	80

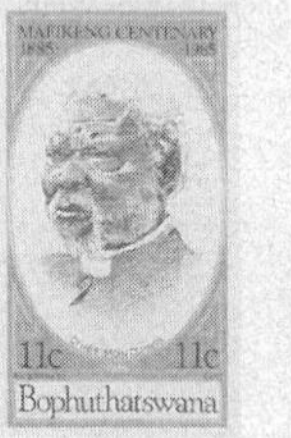

32 Chief Montshiwa of Barolong booRatshidi

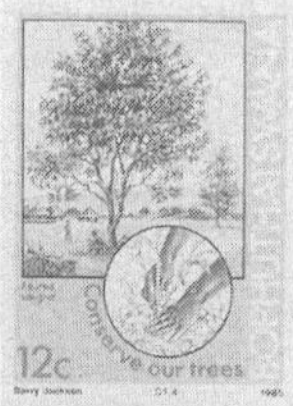

34 "Faurea saligna" and planting Sapling

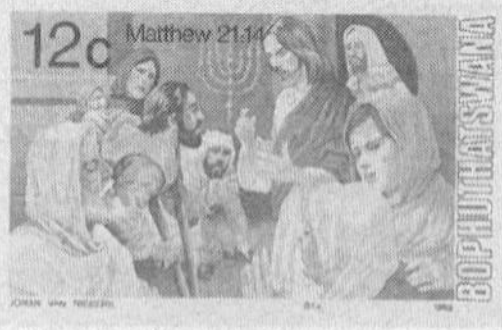

33 The Sick flock to Jesus in the Temple (Matthew, 21:41)

1985. Centenary of Mafeking.

158	**32**	11c. black, grey and orange	20	10
159	–	25c. black, grey and blue	40	30

DESIGN: 25c. Sir Charles Warren.

1985. Easter. Multicoloured.

160	12c. Type **33**	20	10
161	25c. Jesus cures the sick (Matthew 21:14)	30	20
162	30c. Children praising Jesus (Matthew 21:15)	35	30
163	50c. Community leaders discussing Jesus's acceptance of praise (Matthew 21:15, 16)	50	60

1985. Tree Conservation. Multicoloured.

164	12c. Type **34**	20	10
165	25c. "Boscia albitrunca" and kudu	25	20
166	30c. "Erythrina lysistemon" and mariqua sunbird	35	30
167	50c. "Bequaertiondendron magalismontanum" and bee	55	50

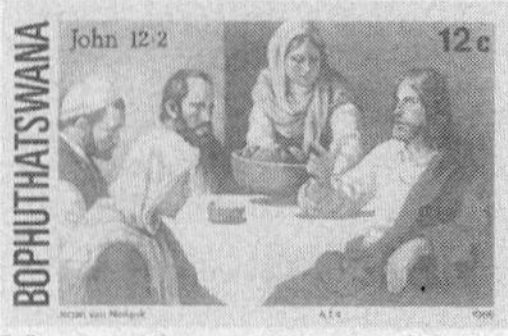

35 Jesus at Mary and Martha's, Bethany (John 12:2)

1986. Easter. Multicoloured.

168	12c. Type **35**	25	10
169	20c. Mary anointing Jesus's feet (John 12:3)	30	20
170	25c. Mary drying Jesus's feet with her hair (John 12:3)	35	25
171	30c. Disciple condemns Mary for anointing Jesus's head with oil (Matthew 26:7)	45	50

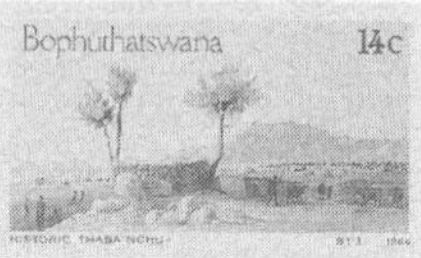

36 "Wesleyan Mission Station and Residence of Moroka, Chief of the Barolong, 1834" (C. D. Bell)

1986. Paintings of Thaba 'Nchu. Multicoloured.

172	14c. Type **36**	30	15
173	20c. "James Archbell's Congregation, 1834" (Charles Davidson Bell)	50	50
174	25c. "Mission Station at Thaba 'Nchu, 1850" (Thomas Baines)	55	70

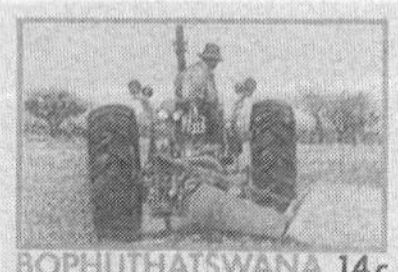

37 Farmer using Tractor (agricultural development)

1986. Temisano Development Project. Mult.

175	14c. Type **37**	20	10
176	20c. Children at school (community development)	30	20
177	25c. Repairing engine (training)	35	30
178	30c. Grain elevator (secondary industries)	50	50

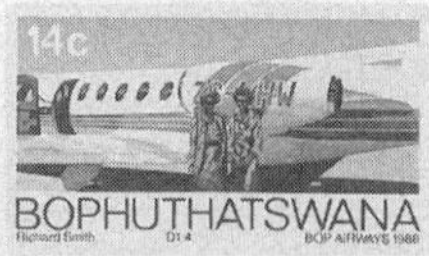

38 Stewardesses and Cessna Citation II

1986. "B.O.P." Airways. Multicoloured.

179	14c. Type **38**	25	10
180	20c. Passengers disembarking from Boeing 707	40	20
181	25c. Mmabatho International Airport	50	35
182	30c. Cessna Citation II	60	50

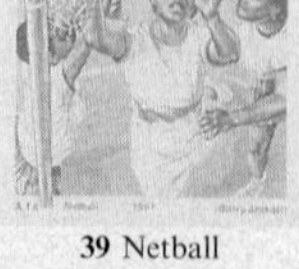

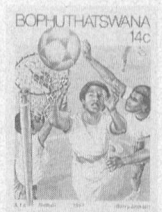

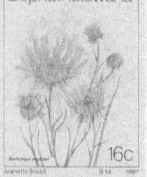

39 Netball

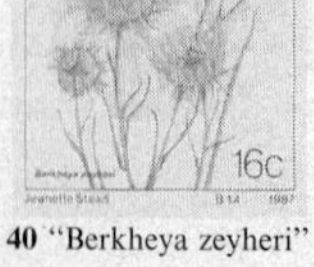

40 "Berkheya zeyheri"

1987. Sports. Multicoloured.

183	14c. Type **39**	20	15
184	20c. Tennis	30	30
185	25c. Football	30	30
186	30c. Athletics	45	50

1987. Wild Flowers. Multicoloured.

187	16c. Type **40**	25	15
188	20c. "Plumbago auriculata"	35	35
189	25c. "Pterodiscus speciosus"	35	35
190	30c. "Gazania krebsiana"	40	50

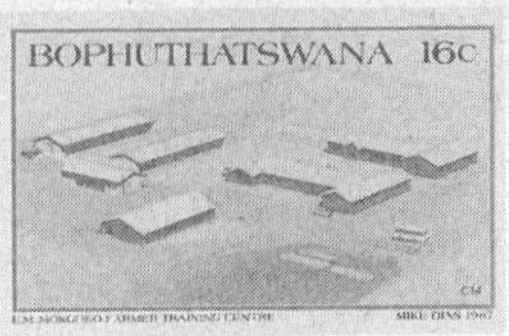

41 E. M. Mokgoko Farmer Training Centre

1987. Tertiary Education. Multicoloured.

191	16c. Type **41**	20	15
192	20c. Main lecture block, University of Bophuthatswana	30	35
193	25c. Manpower Centre	30	35
194	30c. Hotel Training School	30	50

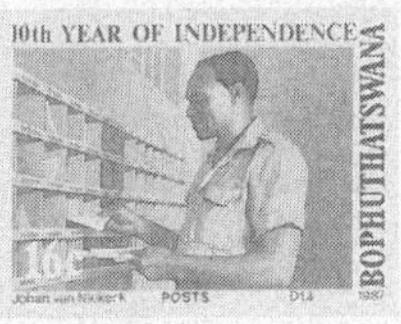

42 Posts

1987. 10th Anniv of Independence. Communications. Multicoloured.

195	16c. Type **42**	25	15
196	30c. Telephone	35	35
197	40c. Radio	35	35
198	50c. Television	40	50

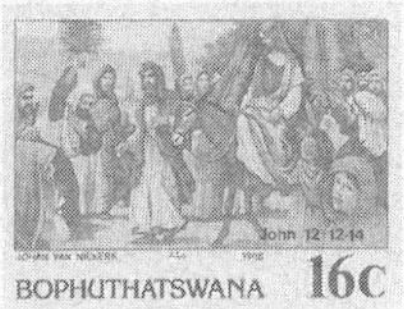

43 Jesus entering Jerusalem on Donkey (John 12:12–14)

1988. Easter. Multicoloured.

199	16c. Type **43**	25	15
200	30c. Judas negotiating with chief priests (Mark 14:10–11)	35	35
201	40c. Jesus washing the disciples' feet (John 13:5)	35	35
202	50c. Jesus handing bread to Judas (John 13:26)	40	50

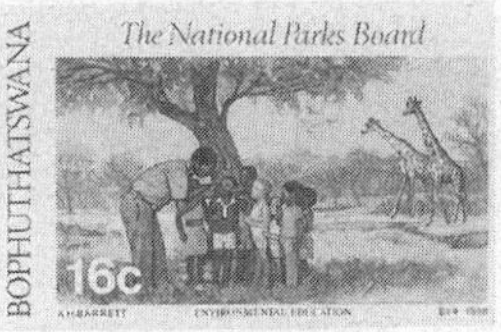

44 Environment Education

1988. National Parks Board. Multicoloured.

203	16c. Type **44**	25	15
204	30c. Rhinoceros (Conservation)	40	40
205	40c. Catering workers	40	40
206	50c. Cheetahs (Tourism)	55	65

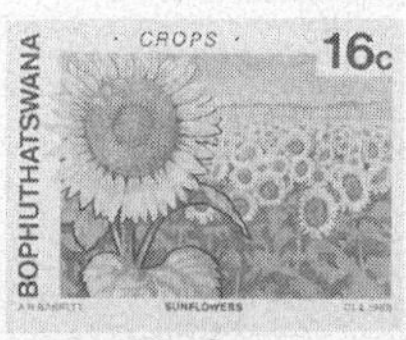

45 Sunflowers

1988. Crops. Multicoloured.

207	16c. Type **45**	25	15
208	30c. Peanuts	35	35
209	40c. Cotton	45	45
210	50c. Cabbages	60	60

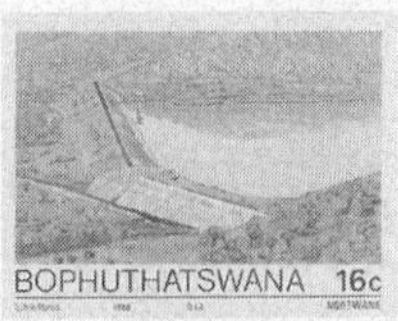

46 Ngotwane Dam

1988. Dams. Multicoloured.

211	16c. Type **46**	30	20
212	30c. Groothoek Dam	50	50
213	40c. Sehujwane Dam	50	50
214	50c. Molatedi Dam	70	70

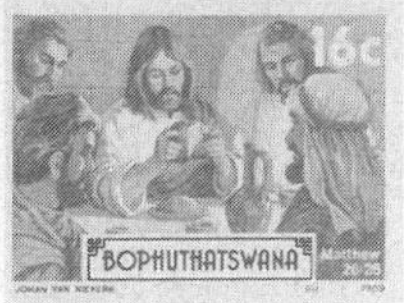

47 The Last Supper (Matthew 26:26)

1989. Easter. Multicoloured.

215	16c. Type **47**	35	20
216	30c. Jesus praying in Garden of Gethsemane (Matthew 26:39)	50	50
217	40c. Judas kissing Jesus (Mark 14:45)	60	60
218	50c. Peter severing ear of High Priest's slave (John 18:10)	75	90

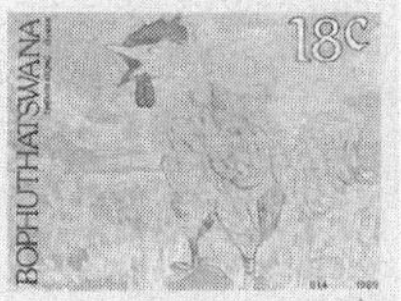

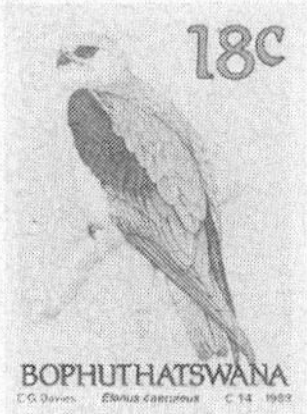

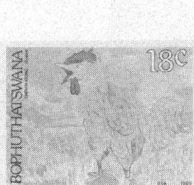

48 Cock (Thembi Atong) **49** Black-shouldered Kite

1989. Children's Art. Designs depicting winning entries in National Children's Day Art Competition.

219	18c. Type **48**	30	20
220	30c. Traditional thatched hut (Muhammad Mahri)	40	40
221	40c. Airplane, telephone wires and houses (Tshepo Mashokwi)	45	45
222	50c. City scene (Miles Brown)	50	60

1989. Birds of Prey. Paintings by Claude Finch-Davies. Multicoloured.

223	18c. Type **49**	1·10	30
224	30c. Pale chanting goshawk	1·25	75
225	40c. Lesser kestrel	1·50	1·10
226	50c. Short-toed eagle	1·60	1·50

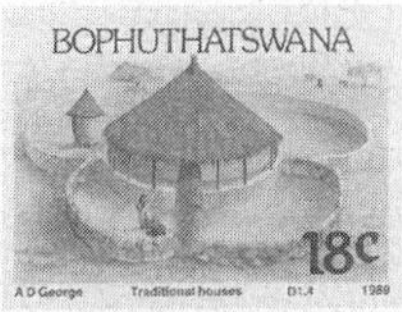

50 Bilobial House

1989. Traditional Houses. Multicoloured.

227	18c. Type **50**	25	20
228	30c. House with courtyards at front and side	35	35
229	40c. House with conical roof	35	35
230	50c. House with rounded roof	40	50

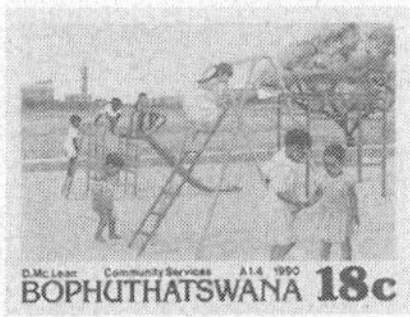

51 Early Learning Schemes

1990. Community Services. Multicoloured.

231	18c. Type **51**	25	20
232	30c. Clinics	35	35
233	40c. Libraries	35	35
234	50c. Hospitals	40	45

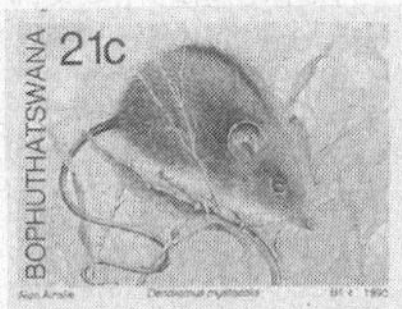

52 Lesser Climbing Mouse

1990. Small Mammals. Multicoloured.

235	21c. Type **52**	30	20
236	30c. Zorilla	40	40
237	40c. Transvaal elephant shrew	60	60
238	50c. Large-toothed rock hyrax	80	85

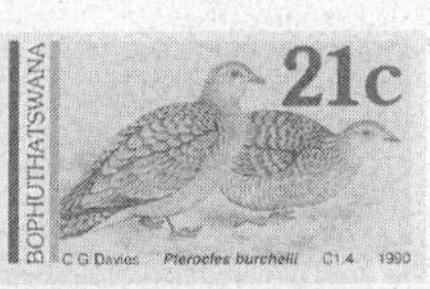

53 Variegated Sandgrouse

1990. Sandgrouse. Paintings by Claude Finch-Davies. Multicoloured.

239	21c. Type **53**	90	30
240	35c. Double-banded sandgrouse	1·10	75
241	40c. Namaqua sandgrouse	1·10	90
242	50c. Yellow-throated sandgrouse	1·40	1·40

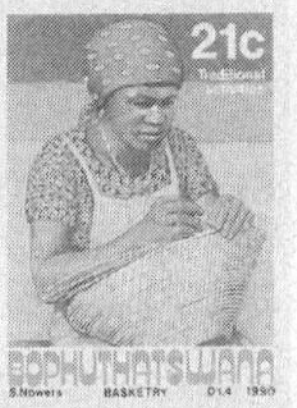

54 Basketry

1990. Traditional Crafts. Multicoloured.

243	21c. Type **54**	40	20
244	35c. Training	60	60
245	40c. Beer making	60	65
246	50c. Pottery	65	75

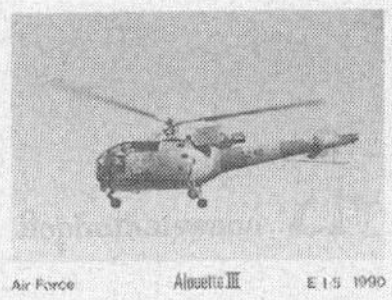

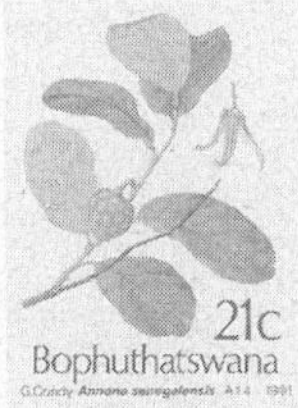

55 Sud Aviation Alouette II Helicopter **56** Wild Custard Apple

1990. Bophuthatswana Air Force. Multicoloured.

247	21c. Type **55**	1·10	1·10
248	21c. MBB-Kawasaki BK-117 helicopter	1·10	1·10
249	21c. Pilatus PC-7 turbo trainer	1·10	1·10
250	21c. Pilatus PC-6	1·10	1·10
251	21c. CASA C-212 Aviocar	1·10	1·10

1991. Edible Wild Fruit. Multicoloured.

252	21c. Type **56**	35	25
253	35c. Spine-leaved monkey orange	50	60
254	40c. Sycamore fig	55	65
255	50c. Kei apple	60	75

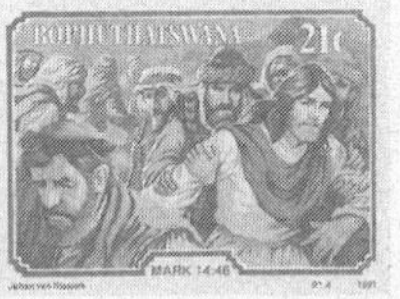

57 Arrest of Jesus (Mark 14:46)

1991. Easter. Multicoloured.

256	21c. Type **57**	40	25
257	35c. First trial by the Sanhedrin (Mark 14:53)	55	55
258	40c. Assault and derision of Jesus after sentence (Mark 14:65)	60	60
259	50c. Servant girl recognizing Peter (Mark 14:67)	65	80

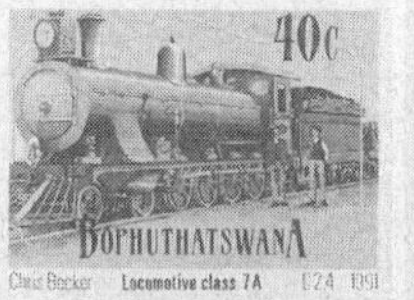

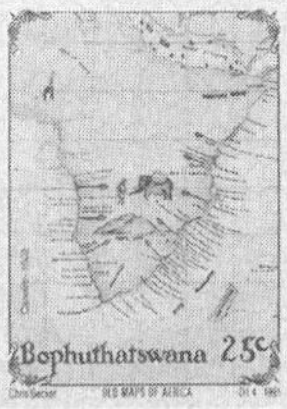

58 Class 7A Locomotive No. 350, 1897 **59** Caneiro Chart, 1502

1991. Steam Locomotives. Multicoloured.

260	25c. Class 6A locomotive No. 194, 1897, trucks and caboose (71 × 25 mm)	75	55
261	40c. Type **58**	95	75
262	50c. Double-boiler Class 6Z locomotives pulling Cecil Rhodes's funeral train (71 × 25 mm)	1·10	1·10
263	60c. Class 8 locomotive at Mafeking station, 1904	1·25	1·50

1991. Old Maps (1st series). Multicoloured.

264	25c. Type **59**	85	40
265	40c. Cantino Chart, 1502	1·25	85
266	50c. Giovanni Contarini's map, 1506	1·40	1·25
267	60c. Martin Waldseemuller's map, 1507	1·40	1·75

See also Nos. 268/71 and 297/300.

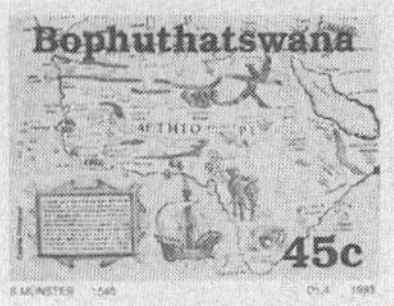

60 Fracanzano Map, 1508

1992. Old Maps (2nd series). Multicoloured.

268	27c. Type **60**	85	40
269	45c. Martin Waldseemuller's map (from edition of Ptolemy), 1513	1·25	85
270	65c. Section of Waldseemuller's woodcut "Carta Marina Navigatora Portugallan Navigationes", 1516	1·40	1·25
271	85c. Map from Laurent Fries's "Geographia", 1522	1·40	1·75

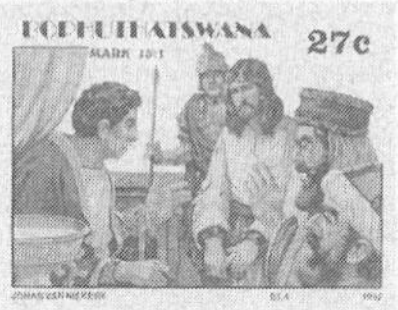

61 Delivery of Jesus to Pilate (Mark 15:1)

1992. Easter. Multicoloured.

272	27c. Type **61**	25	20
273	45c. Scourging of Jesus (Mark 15:15)	40	40
274	65c. Placing crown of thorns on Jesus's head (Mark 15: 17–18)	50	70
275	85c. Soldiers mocking Jesus (Mark 15:19)	60	90

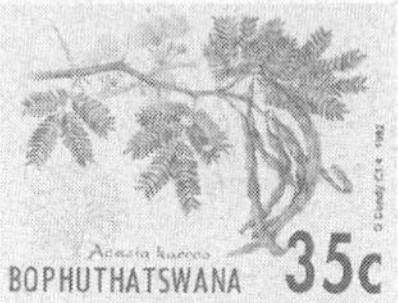

62 Sweet Thorn

1992. Acacia Trees. Multicoloured.

276	35c. Type **62**	30	25
277	70c. Camel thorn	50	60
278	90c. Umbrella thorn	60	80
279	1r.05 Black thorn	70	1·00

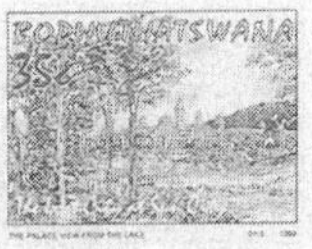

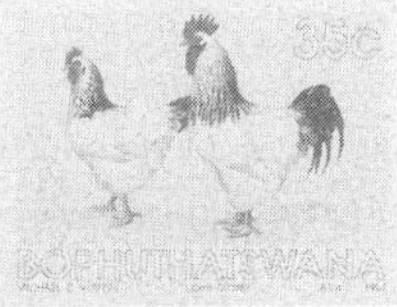

63 View of Palace across Lake **64** Light Sussex

1992. The Lost City Complex, Sun City. Mult.

280	35c. Type **63**	35	45
281	35c. Palace facade	35	45
282	35c. Palace porte cochere	35	45
283	35c. Palace lobby	35	45
284	35c. Tusk Bar, Palace	35	45

1993. Chickens. Multicoloured.

285	35c. Type **64**	30	25
286	70c. Rhode Island red	50	50
287	90c. Brown leghorn	60	80
288	1r.05 White leghorn	70	1·10

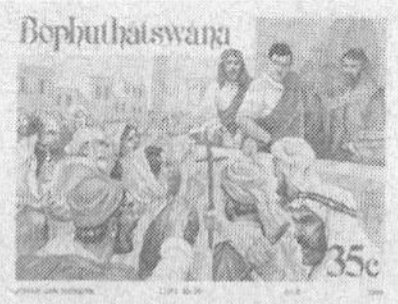

65 Pilate offering Release of Barabbas (Luke 23:25)

1993. Easter. Multicoloured.

289	35c. Type **65**	55	30
290	70c. Jesus falling under cross (John 19:17)	85	75
291	90c. Simon of Cyrene carrying cross (Mark 15:21)	1·00	1·00
292	1r.05 Jesus being nailed to cross (Mark 15:23)	1·25	1·60

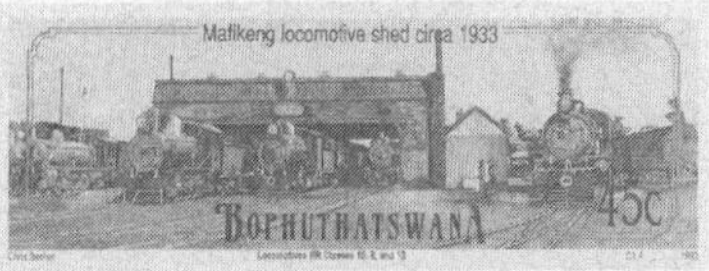

66 Mafeking Locomotive Shed, 1933 ($\frac{2}{3}$-size illustration)

1993. Steam Locomotives (2nd series). Multicoloured.

293		45c. Type **66**	55	55
294		65c. Rhodesian Railways steam locomotive No. 5, 1901 (34 × 25 mm)	65	65
295		85c. Class 16B locomotive pulling "White Train" during visit of Prince George, 1934	85	85
296		1r.05 Class 19D locomotive, 1923 (34 × 25 mm)	1·10	1·25

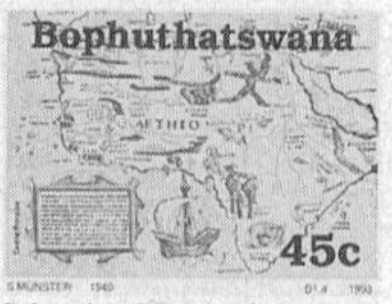

67 Sebastian Munster's Map (from edition of Ptolemy), 1540

1993. Old Maps (3rd series). Multicoloured.

298		45c. Type **67**	50	40
299		65c. Jacopo Gastaldi's map, 1564	65	65
300		85c. Map from Mercator's "Atlas", 1595	75	90
301		1r.05 Map from Ortelius's "Theatrum Orbis Terrarum", 1570	90	1·25

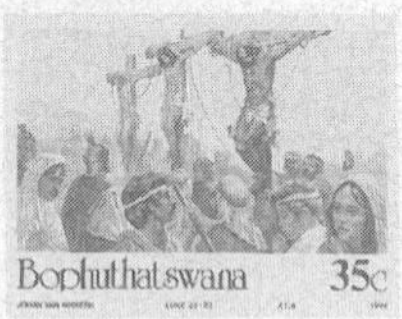

68 Crucifixion (Luke 23:33)

1994. Easter. Multicoloured.

302		35c. Type **68**	55	45
303		65c. Soldiers and Jews mocking Jesus (Luke 23: 35–36)	85	75
304		85c. Soldier offering Jesus vinegar (Luke 23:36)	95	95
305		1r.05 Jesus on cross and charge notice (Luke 23:38)	1·40	1·60

BOSNIA AND HERZEGOVINA

Pts. 2, 3

Turkish provinces administered by Austria from 1878 and annexed by her in 1908. In 1918 it became part of Yugoslavia.

In 1992 Bosnia and Herzegovina declared itself independent. Hostilities subsequently broke out between the Croat, Moslem and Serbian inhabitants, which ultimately led to the establishment of three de facto administrations: the mainly Moslem Bosnian government, based in Sarajevo; the Croats in Mostar; and the Serbian Republic in Pale. Under the Dayton Agreement in November 1995 the Republic was split between a Moslem-Croat Federation and the Serbian Republic.

A. AUSTRO-HUNGARIAN MILITARY POST

1879. 100 kreuzer = 1 gulden.
1900. 100 heller = 1 krone.
1993. 100 paras = 1 dinar.
2002. 100 cents = 1 euro.

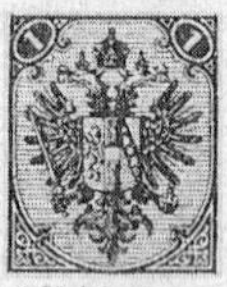

1 Value at top

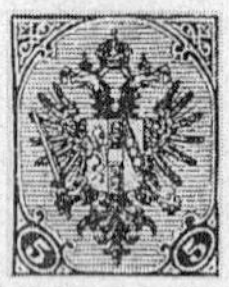

2 Value at bottom

1879.

106	**1**	½k. black	11·00	23·00
135		1k. grey	3·00	1·10
136		2k. yellow	1·90	50
137		3k. green	3·00	1·25
146		5k. red	4·00	55
139		10k. blue	4·00	75
140		15k. brown	3·25	3·75
141		20k. green	4·00	4·25
142		25k. purple	5·00	6·00

1900.

148	**2**	1h. black	20	15
149		2h. grey	20	15
151		3h. yellow	20	15
152		5h. green	15	10
154		6h. brown	30	15
155		10h. red	15	10
156		20h. pink	£100	8·00
158		25h. blue	90	35
173		30h. brown	£110	8·25
160		40h. orange	£120	13·00
161		50h. purple	60	45

Larger stamps with value in each corner.

162		1k. red	80	50
163		2k. blue	1·40	1·50
164		5k. green	3·00	4·50

1901. Black figures of value.

177	**2**	20h. pink and black	60	45
178		30h. brown and black	55	45
180		35h. blue and black	1·00	65
181		40h. orange and black	70	65
182		45h. turquoise and black	80	70

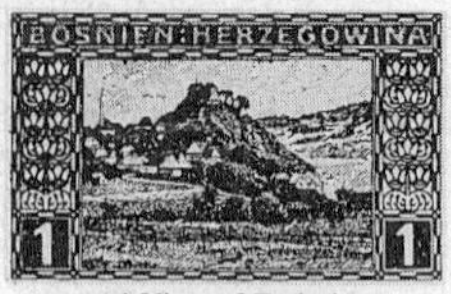

4 View of Doboj

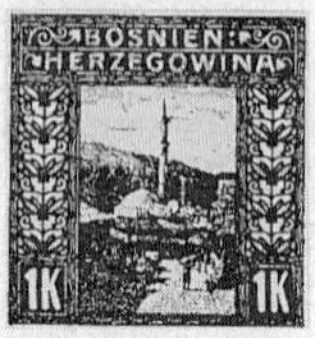

5 In the Carshija (business quarter) Sarajevo

1906.

186	**4**	1h. black	10	15
187	–	2h. violet	10	15
188	–	3h. yellow	10	15
189	–	5h. green	35	10
190	–	6h. brown	20	20
191	–	10h. red	40	10
192	–	20h. brown	65	20
193	–	25h. blue	1·40	90
194	–	30h. green	1·40	45
195	–	35h. green	1·40	45
196	–	40h. orange	1·40	45
197	–	45h. red	1·40	75
198	–	50h. brown	1·60	90
199	**5**	1k. red	4·75	3·00
200	–	2k. green	6·25	11·50
201	–	5k. blue	4·75	7·75

DESIGNS—As Type **4**: 2h. Mostar; 3h. The old castle, Jajce; 5h. Naretva pass and Prenz Planina; 6h. Valley of the Rama; 10h. Valley of the Vrbas; 20h. Old Bridge, Mostar; 25h. The Begova Djamia (Bey's Mosque), Sarajevo; 30h. Post by beast of burden; 35h. Village and lake, Jezero; 40h. Mail wagon; 45h. Bazaar at Sarajevo, 50h. Postal motor-car. As Type **5**: 2k. St. Luke's Campanile at Jajce; 5k. Emperor Francis Joseph I.

See also Nos. 359/61.

1910. 80th Birthday of Francis Joseph I. As stamps of 1906 but with date-label at foot.

343		1h. black	50	25
344		2h. violet	60	25
345		3h. yellow	60	25
346		5h. green	65	25
347		6h. brown	70	45
348		10h. red	65	15
349		20h. brown	1·60	1·40
350		25h. blue	3·00	2·50
351		30h. green	2·00	2·25
352		35h. green	2·75	2·25
353		40h. orange	3·00	2·25
354		45h. red	5·25	5·50
355		50h. brown	5·25	6·00
356		1k. red	5·25	6·25
357		2k. green	19·00	21·00
358		5k. blue	3·50	6·00

1912. As T **4** (new values and views).

359		12h. blue	4·50	5·00
360		60h. grey	3·25	4·25
361		72h. red	12·50	16·00

DESIGNS: 12h. Jajce; 60h. Konjica; 72h. Vishegrad.

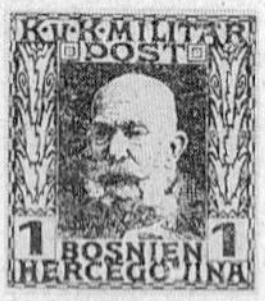

25 Francis Joseph I

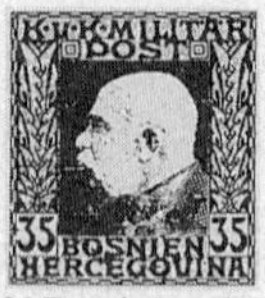

26 Francis Joseph I

1912. Various frames. Nos. 378/82 are larger (27 × 22 mm).

362	**25**	1h. olive	30	10
363		2h. blue	30	10
364		3h. lake	30	10
365		5h. green	30	10
366		6h. black	30	10
367		10h. red	30	10
368		12h. green	50	20
369		20h. brown	3·50	10
370		25h. blue	1·75	10
371		30h. red	1·75	10
372	**26**	35h. green	1·75	10
373		40h. violet	6·00	10
374		45h. brown	3·00	20
375		50h. blue	2·50	10
376		60h. brown	2·25	10
377		72h. blue	3·00	3·25
378	**25**	1k. brown on cream	12·00	35
379		2k. blue on blue	7·25	50
380	**26**	3k. red on green	11·00	10·00
381		5k. lilac and grey	21·00	25·00
382		10k. blue on grey	65·00	95·00

1914. Nos. 189 and 191 surch **1914.** and new value.

383		7h. on 5h. green	40	40
384		12h. on 10h. red	40	40

1915. Nos. 189 and 191 surch **1915.** and new value.

385		7h. on 5h. green	9·00	9·00
386		12h. on 10h. red	30	40

1915. Surch **1915.** and new value.

387	**25**	7h. on 5h. green	70	1·75
388		12h. on 10h. red	1·50	1·75

1916. Surch **1916.** and new value.

389	**25**	7h. on 5h. green	60	60
390		12h. on 10h. red	60	65

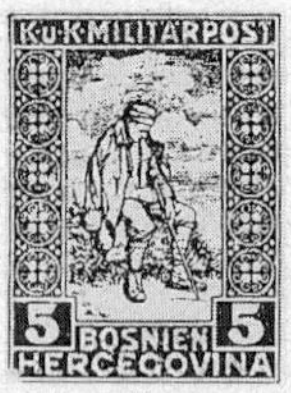

31

1916. War Invalids' Fund.

391	**31**	5h. (+2h.) green	85	80
392	–	10h. (+2h.) purple	1·40	1·40

DESIGN: 10h. Blind soldier and girl.

See also Nos. 434/5.

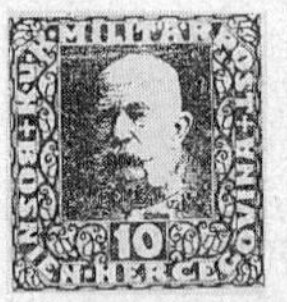

33 Francis Joseph I

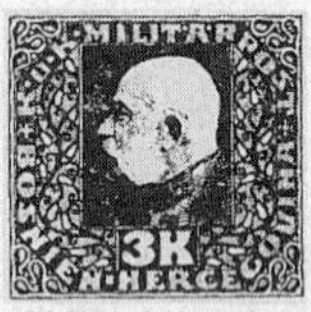

34 Francis Joseph I

1916.

393	**33**	3h. black	25	25
394		5h. olive	45	50
395		6h. violet	45	50
396		10h. bistre	2·00	2·25
397		12h. grey	45	60
398		15h. red	45	25
399		20h. brown	45	60
400		25h. blue	45	60
401		30h. green	45	60
402		40h. red	45	60
403		50h. green	45	60
404		60h. lake	45	60
405		80h. brown	1·40	40
406		90h. purple	1·60	80
407	**34**	2k. red on yellow	65	1·00
408		3k. green on blue	80	2·10
409		4k. red on green	5·50	10·00
410		10k. violet on grey	28·00	20·00

1917. War Widows' Fund. Optd **WITWEN-UND WAISENWOCHE 1917**.

411	**33**	10h. (+2h.) bistre	10	20
412		15h. (+2h.) pink	10	20

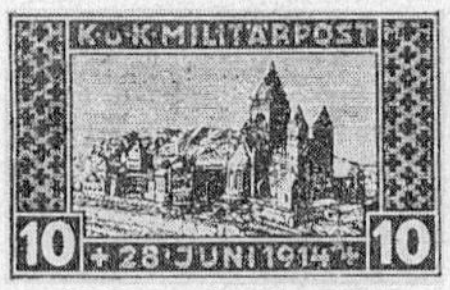

36 Design for Memorial Church, Sarajevo

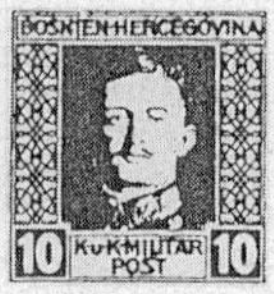

39 Emperor Charles

1917. Assassination of Archduke Ferdinand. Fund for Memorial Church at Sarajevo.

413	**36**	10h. (+2h.) black	10	30
414	–	15h. (+2h.) red	10	30
415	–	40h. (+2h.) blue	10	30

PORTRAITS—HORIZ: 40h. Francis Ferdinand and Sophie. VERT: 15h. Archduke Francis Ferdinand.

1917.

416	**39**	3h. grey	10	20
417		5h. olive	10	10
418		6h. violet	60	70
419		10h. brown	20	10
420		12h. blue	60	70
421		15h. red	10	10
422		20h. brown	10	10
423		25h. blue	90	65
424		30h. green	25	20
425		40h. bistre	25	20
426		50h. green	90	50
427		60h. red	90	45
428		80h. blue	20	25
429		90h. lilac	1·00	1·40
430	–	2k. red on yellow	60	35
431	–	3k. green on blue	15·00	16·00
432	–	4k. red on green	6·00	8·00
433	–	10k. violet on grey	4·00	6·25

The kronen values are larger (25 × 25 mm) and with different border.

1918. War Invalids' Fund.

434	–	10h. (+2h.) green (as No. 392)	60	70
435	**31**	15h. (+2h.) brown	60	70

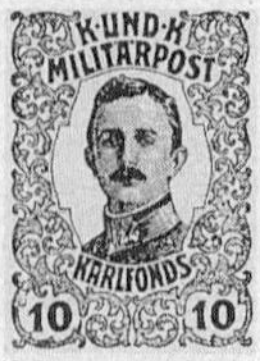

40 Emperor Charles

1918. Emperor's Welfare Fund.

436	**40**	10h. (+10h.) green	40	85
437	–	15h. (+10h.) brown	40	85
438	**40**	40h. (+10h.) purple	40	85

DESIGN—15h. Empress Zita.

1918. Optd **1918**.

439	–	2h. violet (No. 344)	50	1·00
440	**25**	2h. blue	50	1·10

NEWSPAPER STAMPS

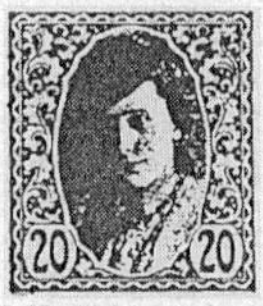

N 27 Girl in Bosnian Costume

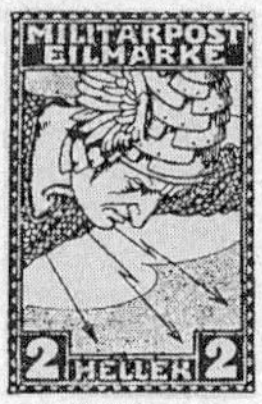

N 35 Mercury

1913. Imperf.

N383	**N 27**	2h. blue	40	40
N384		6h. mauve	1·40	1·40
N385		10h. red	1·60	1·40
N386		20h. green	2·10	1·60

For these stamps perforated see Yugoslavia, Nos. 25 to 28.

1916. For Express.

N411	**N 35**	2h. red	25	25
N412		5h. green	45	45

POSTAGE DUE STAMPS

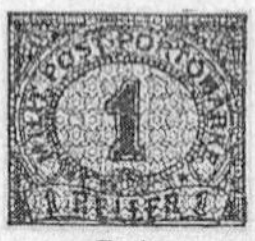

D 4

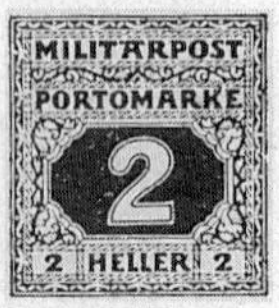

D 35

1904. Imperf. or perf.

D183	**D 4**	1h. black, red & yellow	30	10
D184		2h. black, red & yellow	30	15
D185		3h. black, red & yellow	30	10
D186		4h. black, red & yellow	30	10
D187		5h. black, red & yellow	1·40	10
D188		6h. black, red & yellow	25	10
D189		7h. black, red & yellow	2·25	3·25
D190		8h. black, red & yellow	2·25	1·50
D191		10h. black, red & yellow	50	10
D192		15h. black, red & yellow	40	10
D193		20h. black, red & yellow	3·00	25
D194		50h. black, red & yellow	1·10	30
D195		200h. black, red & grn	4·00	2·25

1916.

D411	**D 35**	2h. red	40	1·00
D412		4h. red	35	60
D413		5h. red	40	60
D414		6h. red	35	85
D415		10h. red	35	50
D416		15h. red	2·75	5·25
D417		20h. red	35	50
D418		25h. red	90	2·00
D419		30h. red	90	2·00
D420		40h. red	7·25	12·50
D421		50h. red	23·00	40·00
D422		1k. blue	2·50	5·25
D423		3k. blue	12·00	23·00

B. INDEPENDENT REPUBLIC

I. SARAJEVO GOVERNMENT

The following issues were used for postal purposes in those areas controlled by the Sarajevo government.

1993. 100 paras = 1 dinar.
1997. 100 fennig = 1 mark.

50 State Arms   **51** Games Emblem

1993. Imperf.

450	**50**	100d. blue, lemon & yellow	10	10
451		500d. blue, yellow & pink	15	15
452		1000d. ultramarine, yellow and blue	25	25
453		5000d. blue, yellow & grn	75	75
454		10000d. blue, lemon & yell	1·50	1·50
455		20000d. blue, yellow & bis	3·00	3·00
456		50000d. blue, yellow & grey	7·50	7·50

1994. 10th Anniv of Winter Olympic Games, Sarajevo. Imperf.

457	**51**	50000d. black and orange	5·00	5·00

Currency Reform
10000 (old) dinars = 1 (new) dinar.

53 Facade   **55** Postman and Globe

54 Historical Map, 10th–15th Centuries

1995. Sarajevo Head Post Office. Multicoloured.

460		10d. Type **53**	10	10
461		20d. Interior	15	15
462		30d. As No. 461	30	30
463		35d. Before conflict	35	35
464		50d. As No. 463	45	45
465		100d. Present day	90	90
466		200d. As No. 465	1·75	1·75

1995. Bosnian History. Multicoloured.

467		35d. Type **54**	30	30
468		100d. 15th-century Bogomil tomb, Oplicici (vert)	80	80
469		200d. Arms of Kotromanic Dynasty (14th-15th centuries) (vert)	1·60	1·60
470		300d. Charter by Ban Kulin of Bosnia, 1189	2·50	2·00

1995. World Post Day.

471	**55**	100d. multicoloured	95	95

56 Dove with Olive Branch

1995. Europa. Peace and Freedom.

472	**56**	200d. multicoloured	1·75	1·75

57 Children and Buildings (A. Softic)

1995. Children's Week.

473	**57**	100d. multicoloured	95	95

58 Tramcar, 1895   **59** "Simphyandra hofmannii"

1995. Centenary of Sarajevo Electric Tram System.

474	**58**	200d. multicoloured	1·75	1·75

1995. Flowers. Multicoloured.

475		100d. Type **59**	95	95
476		200d. Turk's-head lily	1·90	1·90

60 Dalmatian Barbel Gudgeon

1995. Fishes. Multicoloured.

477		100d. Type **60**	95	95
478		200d. Adriatic minnow	1·90	1·90

61 Kozija Bridge, Sarajevo

1995. Bridges. Multicoloured.

479		20d. Type **61**	15	15
480		30d. Arslanagica Bridge, Trebinje	25	25
481		35d. Latinska Bridge, Sarajevo	35	35
482		50d. Old bridge, Mostar	45	45
483		100d. Visegrad	90	90

62 Visiting Friends

1995. Christmas. Multicoloured.

484		100d. Type **62**	1·00	1·00
485		200d. Madonna and Child (vert)	2·00	2·00

63 Queen Jelena of Bosnia and Tomb (600th death anniv)

1995. Multicoloured.

486		30d. Type **63**	20	20
487		35d. Husein Kapetan Gradascevic "Dragon of Bosnia" (leader of 1831 uprising against Turkey)	30	30
488		100d. Mirza Safvet Basagic (125th death anniv) (horiz)	95	95

64 Places of Worship and Graveyards

1995. Religious Pluralism.

489	**64**	35d. multicoloured	35	35

65 Stadium and Sports

1995. Destruction of Olympic Stadium, Sarajevo. Multicoloured.

490		35d. Type **65**	30	30
491		100d. Stadium ablaze (vert)	95	95

66 Bahrija Hadzic (opera singer)   **67** Child's Handprint

1996. Europa. Famous Women. Multicoloured.

492		80d. Type **66**	75	75
493		120d. Nasiha Hadzic (children's writer and radio presenter)	1·10	1·10

1996. 50th Anniv of U.N.I.C.E.F. Multicoloured.

494		50d. Child stepping on landmine (P. Mirna and K. Princes)	65	65
495		150d. Type **67**	1·25	1·25

68 Bobovac Castle   **69** Roofed Fountain and Extract from Holy Koran

1996.

496	**68**	35d. black, blue and violet	35	35

1996. Bairam Festival.

497	**69**	80d. multicoloured	75	75

70 Town Hall

1996. Centenary of Sarajevo Town Hall.

498	**70**	80d. multicoloured	75	75

71 Hands on Computer Keyboard and Title Page of "Bosanki Prijatelj"

1996. 150th Anniv of Journalists' Association.

499	**71**	100d. multicoloured	95	95

72 Essen

1996. "Essen 96" International Stamp Fair, Essen.

500	**72**	200d. multicoloured	1·75	1·75

73 Running   **74** "Campanula hercegovina"

1996. Centenary of Modern Olympic Games and Olympic Games, Atlanta. Multicoloured.

501		30d. Type **73**	25	25
502		35d. Games emblem	30	30
503		80d. Torch bearer and Olympic flag	75	75
504		120d. Pierre de Coubertin (founder)	1·10	1·10

Nos. 501/4 were issued together, se-tenant, with the backgrounds forming a composite design of athletes.

1996. Flowers. Multicoloured.

505		30d. Type **74**	30	30
506		35d. "Iris bosniaca"	35	35

75 Barak

1996. Dogs. Multicoloured.

507		35d. Type **75**	35	35
508		80d. Tornjak	85	85

76 Globe, Telephone and Alexander Bell

1996. Anniversaries. Multicoloured.

509		80d. Type **76** (120th anniv of Bell's invention of telephone)	80	80
510		120d. 1910 50h. stamp (cent of post vans in Bosnia and Herzegovina)	1·10	1·10

77 Charter with Seal   **78** Hot-air Balloons

1996. Granting of Privileges to Dubrovnik by Ban Stepan II Kotromanic, 1333.

511	**77**	100d. multicoloured	95	95

1996. SOS Children's Village, Sarajevo.

512	**78**	100d. multicoloured	95	95

79 Muslim Costume of Bjelasnice   **80** Bogomil Soldier

1996. Traditional Costumes. Multicoloured.

513		50d. Type **79**	40	40
514		80d. Croatian	75	75
515		100d. Muslim costume of Sarajevo	1·10	1·10

1996. Military Uniforms. Multicoloured.

516		35d. Type **80**	30	30
517		80d. Austro-Hungarian rifleman	75	75
518		100d. Turkish light cavalryman	1·10	1·10
519		120d. Medieval Bosnian king	1·25	1·25

81 Mosque

1996. Winter Festival, Sarajevo.
520 **81** 100d. multicoloured 90   90

82 Map and State Arms

1996. Bosnia Day.
521 **82** 120d. multicoloured . . . 1·00   1·00

83 Crowd around Baby Jesus

1996. Christmas.
522 **83** 100d. multicoloured 90   90

84 Pope John Paul II   **85** Palaeolithic Rock
                                    Carving, Badanj

1996. Papal Visit.
523 **84** 500d. multicoloured . . . 4·00   4·00

1997. Archaeological Finds. Multicoloured.
524   35d. Type **85**   30   30
525   50d. Neolithic ceramic head,
           Butmir   40   40
526   80d. Bronze Age "birds"
           wagon, Glasinac   65   65

86 Ferhad Pasha   **87** "Clown" (Martina
Mosque, Banja Luka   Nokto)

1997. Bairam Festival.
528 **86** 200d. multicoloured . . . 1·50   1·50

1997. Children's Week.
529 **87** 100d. multicoloured 75   75

88 Komadina   **89** Trojan Warriors
                              and Map

1997. 72nd Death Anniv of Mujaga Komadina
(developer and Mayor of Mostar).
530 **88** 100d. multicoloured 75   75

1997. Europa. Tales and Legends. Mult.
531   100d. Type **89** (theory of
           Roberto Prays) 75   75
532   120d. Man on prayer-mat
           and castle ("The
           Miraculous Spring of
           Ajvatovica") 90   90

90 "Rainbow Warrior"

1997. 26th Anniv of Greenpeace (environmental
organization). Designs showing the "Rainbow
Warrior". Multicoloured.
533   35d. Type **90**   35   35
534   80d. inscr "Dorreboom" . .   80   65
535   100d. inscr "Beltra" . . . . 1·10   1·10
536   120d. inscr "Morgan" . . .   1·40   1·40

91 Open Air Cinema, Sarajevo

1997. 3rd International Film Festival, Sarajevo.
537 **91** 110d. multicoloured 90   90

92 Games Emblem   **93** Diagram of Electrons

1997. Mediterranean Games, Bari. Mult.
538   40d. Type **92**   35   35
539   130d. Boxing, basketball and
           kick boxing . . . . 1·10   1·10

1997. Anniversaries and Event. Mult.
540   40d. Type **93** (centenary of
           discovery of electrons) . 35   35
541   110d. Vasco da Gama
           (navigator) and map (500th
           anniv of science of
           navigation) (vert) . . . . 1·75   1·25
542   130d. Airmail envelope and
           airplane (Stamp Day) . . . 1·40   1·40
543   150d. Steam locomotive
           "Bosna" (125th anniv of
           railway in Bosnia and
           Herzegovina) . . . . . . 1·25   1·25

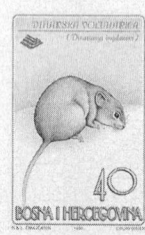   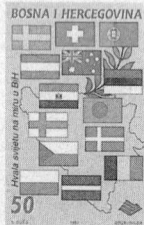

94 Vole   **95** Map and Flags

1997. Flora and Fauna. Multicoloured.
544   40d. Type **94**   35   35
545   50d. "Oxytropis prenja" . . . 35   35
546   80d. Alpine newt   65   65
547   110d. "Dianthus freynii" . . . 1·10   1·10

1997. International Peace Day. Mult.
548   50d. Type **95**   50   50
549   60d. Flags and right half of
           globe showing Europe and
           Africa 55   55
550   70d. Flags and left half of
           globe showing the
           Americas 60   60
551   110d. Map and flags
           (including U.S.A. and
           U.K.) . . . . 1·10   1·10
Nos. 548/51 were issued together, se-tenant,
Nos. 549/50 forming a composite design.

96 House with Attic

1997. Architecture. Multicoloured.
552   40d. Type **96**   35   35
553   50d. Tiled stove and door . . 50   50
554   130d. Three-storey house . .   1·40   1·40

97 Sarajevo in 1697 and 1997

1997. 300th Anniv of Great Fire of Sarajevo.
555 **97** 110d. multicoloured . . . 1·10   1·10

98 Augustin Tin Ujevic

1997. Personalities. Multicoloured.
556   1m.30 Type **98** (lyricist and
           essayist)   90   90
557   2m. Zaim Imanovic (singer)
           (vert) . . . . 1·40   1·40

99 Sarajevo and Corps Emblem

1997. Contribution of Italian Pioneer Corps in
Reconstruction of Sarajevo.
558 **99** 1m.40 multicoloured . . . 95   95

100 Diana, Princess of Wales, and Roses

1997. Diana, Princess of Wales, Commem.
559 **100** 2m.50 multicoloured . . . 1·90   1·90

101 "Gnijezdo" (Fikret Libovac)

1997. Art. Multicoloured.
560   35f. Type **101** 20   20
561   80f. "Sarajevo Library"
           (sculpture, Nusret Pasic) . 55   55

102 Youth Builders Emblem
attached to Route Map

1997. 50th Anniv of Samac-Sarajevo Railway.
562 **102** 35f. multicoloured . . . 30   30

103 Nativity (icon)   **105** Mosque Fountain

1997. Religious Events. Multicoloured.
563   50f. Type **103** (Orthodox
           Christmas) 35   35
564   1m.10 Wreath on door
           (Christmas)   80   80
565   1m.10 Pupils before teacher
           (14th-century miniature)
           (Haggadah) 80   80

1998. Bairam Festival.
567 **105** 1m. multicoloured 70   70

106 Zvornik

1998. Old Fortified Towns. Multicoloured.
568   35f. Type **106** 25   25
569   70f. Bihac   50   50
570   1m. Pocitelj   70   70
571   1m.20 Gradacac   85   85

107 Muradbegovic

1998. Birth Centenary of Ahmed Muradbegovic
(dramatist and actor-director).
572 **107** 1m.50 multicoloured . . . 1·10   1·10

108 Branislav Djurdjev   **109** White Storks

1998. Former Presidents of the University of Arts and
Science. Multicoloured.
573   40f. Type **108** 30   30
574   70f. Alojz Benac   50   50
575   1m.30 Edhem Camo   95   95

1998. Endangered Species. The White Stork.
Multicoloured.
576   70f. Type **109** 50   50
577   90f. Two storks flying . . .   65   65
578   1m.10 Two adult storks on
           nest 80   80
579   1m.30 Adult stork with
           young   95   95

110 International Theatre
Festival, Sarajevo

1998. Europa. National Festivals.
580 **110** 1m.10 multicoloured . . . 80   80

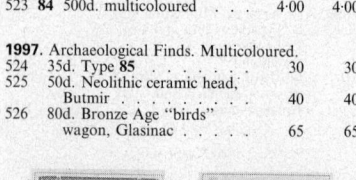

111 Footballs

1998. World Cup Football Championship, France. Multicoloured.
581 50f. Type **111** 35 35
582 1m. Map of Bosnia and ball . 70 70
583 1m.50 Asim Ferhatovic Hase (footballer) . . . . . . 1·10 1·10

113 Common Morel   **114** Tunnel

1998. Fungi. Multicoloured.
585 50f. Type **113** 35 35
586 80f. Chanterelle 55 55
587 1m.10 Edible mushroom . . 80 80
588 1m.35 Caesar's mushroom . . 95 95

1998. 5th Anniv of Sarajevo's Supply Tunnels.
589 **114** 1m.10 multicoloured . . . 80 80

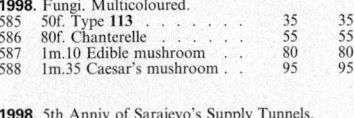

115 Eiffel Tower and Underground Train

1998. Paris Metro.
590 **115** 2m. multicoloured . . . . 1·40 1·40

116 Henri Dunant   **118** Travnik
(founder of Red Cross)

1998. Anti-tuberculosis Week.
591 **116** 50f. multicoloured . . . 35 35

1998. Old Towns.
593 **118** 5f. black and green . . 10 10
597 – 38f. black and brown . . 25 25
DESIGN: 38f. Sarajevo.

119 Postal Workers in   **120** Lutes
New Uniforms

1998. World Post Day.
605 **119** 1m. multicoloured 70 70

1998. Musical Instruments.
606 **120** 80f. multicoloured . . . 55 55

121 "The Creation of Adam" (detail of fresco on ceiling of Sistine Chapel, Michelangelo)

1998. World Disabled Day.
607 **121** 1m. multicoloured 70 70

122 Bjelasnica Mountain Range

1998.
608 **122** 1m. multicoloured 70 70

123 People

1998. 50th Anniv of Universal Declaration of Human Rights.
609 **123** 1m.35 multicoloured . . . 90 90

124 Christmas Tree (Lamija Pehilj)

1998. Christmas and New Year. Multicoloured.
610 1m. Type **124** 70 70
611 1m.50 Father Andeo Zvizdovic . . . . . . 1·00 1·00

125 Sarajevo   **127** Astronaut, Earth
University and   and Moon
"Proportion of Man"
(Leonardo da Vinci)

126 Feral Rock Pigeons

1999. Anniversaries. Multicoloured.
612 40f. Type **125** (50th anniv) 25 25
613 40f. Sarajevo High School (120th anniv) (horiz) . . . 25 25

1999. Flora and Fauna. Multicoloured.
614 80f. Type **126** 55 55
615 1m.10 "Knautia sarajevensis" 75 75

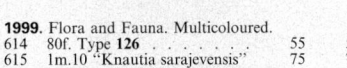

128 Slapovi Une

1999. 30th Anniv of First Manned Moon Landing.
616 **127** 2m. multicoloured . . . .

1999. Europa. Parks and Gardens.
617 **128** 2m. multicoloured . . . . 1·40 1·40

129 Gorazde

1999.
618 **129** 40f. multicoloured 25 25

130 Children playing Football in Sun (Pranjkovic Nenad)

1999. Children's Week.
619 **130** 50f. multicoloured 35 35

131 House

1999. World Environment Day.
620 **131** 80f. multicoloured 55 55

132 Church, Mosque and Emblem

1999. "Philexfrance 99" International Stamp Exhibition, Paris, France.
621 **132** 2m. multicoloured . . . . 1·40 1·40

133 Sarajevo on Stamp

1999. 120th Anniv of First Bosnia and Herzegovina Stamps.
622 **133** 1m. multicoloured 70 70

134 Letters encircling Globe and Telephones

1999. 125th Anniv of Universal Postal Union.
623 **134** 1m.50 multicoloured . . . 1·00 1·00

135 Tuzlait from Tuoanj

1999. Minerals. Multicoloured.
624 40f. Type **135** 20 20
625 60f. Siderit from Vitez . . . 40 40
626 1m.20 Hijelofan from Busovaca 80 80
627 1m.80 Quartz from Srebrenica (vert) . . . 1·25 1·25

136 Dove and Cathedral   **137** Kursum
Medresa, Sarajevo,
1537 (site of library)

1999. Southern Europe Stability Pact, Sarajevo.
628 **136** 2m. multicoloured . . . 1·40 1·40

1999. Gazi-Husref Library. Multicoloured.
629 1m. Type **137** 70 70
630 1m.10 Miniature from Hval Codex, 1404 . . . . 75 75

138 Koran, 1550

1999.
631 **138** 1m.50 multicoloured . . . 1·00 1·00

139 X-Ray and Thermal Image of Hands

1999. Centenary of Radiology in Bosnia and Herzegovina.
632 **139** 90f. multicoloured 60 60

140 Kresevljakovic

1999. 40th Death Anniv of Hamdija Kresvljakovic (historian).
633 **140** 1m.30 multicoloured . . . 90 90

141 Chess Emblems and Stars

1999. 15th European Chess Clubs Championship Final, Bugojno.
634 **141** 1m.10 multicoloured . . . 75 75

142 Twipsy (exhibition mascot)

1999. "Expo 2000" World's Fair, Hanover, Germany.
635 **142** 1m. multicoloured 60 60

143 Painting (Afan Ramic)

1999.
636 **143** 1m.20 multicoloured . . . 75 75

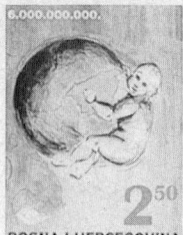

144 Globe and Baby

1999. Birth of World's Six Billionth Inhabitant in Sarajevo.
637 **144** 2m.50 multicoloured . . . 1·50 1·50

146 Philharmonic Orchestra Building, Sarajevo   **147** Woman

1999. International Music Festival, Sarajevo.
639 **146** 40f. black and red 25 25
640 – 1m.10 multicoloured . . . 65 65
DESIGN: 1m.10, Festival poster

2000. Bairam Festival.
641 **147** 1m.10 multicoloured 65 65

149 Spaho   **150** Morse Apparatus

2000. 60th (1999) Death Anniv of Mehmed Spaho (politician).
643 **149** 1m. multicoloured 60 60

2000. 50th Anniv of Amateur Radio in Bosnia and Herzegovina.
644 **150** 1m.50 multicoloured 95 95

151 Illuminated Manuscript

2000. 50th Anniv of Institute of Oriental Studies, Sarajevo University.
645 **151** 2m. multicoloured . . . . 1·25 1·25

152 Boracko River

2000. 15th Anniv of Emerald River Nature Protection Organization. Multicoloured.
646 40f. Type **152** 25 25
647 1m. Figure of woman and
   river (vert) 60 60

154 Griffon Vulture

2000. Birds. Multicoloured.
649 1m. Type **154** 60 60
650 1m.50 White spoonbill . . . 95 95

155 "Building Europe"

2000. Europa.
651 **155** 2m. multicoloured . . . . 1·25 1·25

156 Count Ferdinand von Zeppelin and LZ-1

2000. Centenary of 1st Zeppelin Flight.
652 **156** 1m.50 multicoloured . . . 95 95

II. CROATIAN POSTS

Issues made by the Croat administration in Mostar.

1993. 100 paras = 1 Croatian dinar.
1994. 100 lipa = 1 kuna.

C 1 Statue and Church   **C 2** Silvije Kranjcevic (poet)

1993. Sanctuary of Our Lady Queen of Peace Shrine, Medugorje.
C1 **C 1** 2000d. multicoloured . . . 50 50

1993. Multicoloured.
C2 200d. Type **C 2** 10 10
C3 500d. Jajce 15 15
C4 1000d. Mostar (horiz) . . . 20 20

C 3 Medieval Gravestone   **C 4** "Madonna of the Grand Duke" (Raphael)

1993. 250th Anniv of Census in Bosnia and Herzegovina.
C5 **C 3** 100d. multicoloured . . . 10 10

1993. Christmas.
C6 **C 4** 6000d. multicoloured . . . 1·25 1·25

C 5 "Uplands in Bloom"

1993. Europa. Contemporary Art. Paintings by Gabrijel Jurkic. Multicoloured.
C7 3500d. Type **C 5** . . . . . . 1·75 1·75
C8 5000d. "Wild Poppy" . . . . 2·25 2·25

C 6 Kravica Waterfall

1993.
C9 **C 6** 3000d. multicoloured . . . 60 60

C 7 Hrvoje (from "Hrvoje's Missal" by Butko)

1993. 577th Death Anniv of Hrvoje Vukcic Hrvatinic, Duke of Split, Viceroy of Dalmatia and Croatia and Grand Duke of Bosnia.
C10 **C 7** 1500d. multicoloured . . 30 30

C 8 Plehan Monastery

1993.
C11 **C 8** 2200d. multicoloured . . 45 45

C 9 Arms   **C 11** "Campanula hercegovina"

C 10 Bronze Cross, Rama-Scit (Mile Blazevic)

1994. Proclamation (August 1993) of Croatian Community of Herceg Bosna.
C12 **C 9** 10000d. multicoloured . . 2·00 2·00

1994.
C13 **C 10** 2k.80 multicoloured . . . 55 55

1994. Flora and Fauna. Multicoloured.
C14 3k.80 Type **C 11** 75 75
C15 4k. Mountain dog 80 80

C 12 Hutova Swamp

1994.
C16 **C 12** 80l. multicoloured . . . 20 20

C 13 Penny Farthing Bicycles

1994. Europa. Discoveries and Inventions. Mult.
C17 8k. Type **C 13** . . . . 1·50 1·50
C18 10k. Mercedes motor cars,
   1901 . . . . 2·00 2·00

C 14 Views of Town and Fortress

1994. 550th Anniv of First Written Record of Ljubuski.
C19 **C 14** 1k. multicoloured . . . 20 20

C 15 Hospital and Christ   **C 16** Anniversary Emblem

1994. 2nd Anniv of Dr. Nikolic Franciscan Hospital, Nova Bila.
C20 **C 15** 5k. multicoloured . . . 1·00 1·00

1995. 50th Anniv of U.N.O. Self-adhesive. Rouletted.
C21 **C 16** 1k.50 blue, red & black 30 30

C 17 Crib

1995. Christmas.
C22 **C 17** 5k.40 multicoloured . . 1·10 1·10

C 18 Franciscan Monastery, Kraljeva Sutjeska   **C 19** Srebrenica

1995.
C23 **C 18** 3k. multicoloured . . . 60 60

1995. Towns. Multicoloured.
C24 2k. Type **C 19** 40 40
C25 4k. Franciscan Monastery,
   Mostar 80 80

C 20 Christ on the Cross   **C 21** Statue and Church

1995. Europa. Peace and Freedom.
C26 **C 20** 6k.50 multicoloured . . 1·25 1·25

1996. 15th Anniv of Sanctuary of Our Lady Queen of Peace Shrine, Medugorje.
C27 **C 21** 10k. multicoloured . . . 2·00 2·00

C 22 Queen Katarina Kosaca Kotromanic   **C 23** Monastery

1996. Europa. Famous Women.
C28 **C 22** 2k.40 multicoloured . . 50 50

1996. 150th Anniv of Franciscan Monastery and Church, Siroki Brijeg.
C29 **C 23** 1k.40 multicoloured . . 30 30

C 24 Virgin Mary   **C 26** "Madonna and Child" (anon)

1996. Self-adhesive. Rouletted.
C30 C **24** 2k. mult (postage) . . . 40 40
C31   9k. multicoloured (air)   1·75 1·75

1996. "Taipeh '96" International Stamp Exn. Nos.
C30/1 surch **1.10** and emblem.
C32 C **24** 1k.10 on 2k. mult
         (postage) . . .   20 20
C33   1k.10 on 9k. mult (air)   20 20

1996. Christmas.
C34 C **26** 2k.20 multicoloured . . .   45 45

C **27** St. George and the Dragon
C **28** Pope John Paul II

1997. Europa. Tales and Legends. Mult.
C35   2k. Type C **27** . . .   40 40
C36   5k. Zeus as bull and Europa
       (39 × 34 mm)   1·00 1·00

1997. Papal Visit.
C37 C **28** 3k.60 multicoloured . .   70 70

C **29** Chapel, Samatorje, Gorica
C **30** Purple Heron

1997.
C39 C **29** 1k.40 multicoloured . . .   25 25

1997. Flora and Fauna. Multicoloured.
C40   1k. Type C **30** . . .   20 20
C41   2k.40 "Symphyandra
       hofmannii" (orchid)   45 45

C **31** "Birth of Christ" (fresco, Giotto)

1997. Christmas.
C42 C **31** 1k.40 multicoloured . . .   25 25

C **32** Cats

1998. Europa. Animated Film Festival.
C43 C **32** 6k.50 multicoloured . .   1·10 1·10

C **33** Seal
C **35** "Sibiraea croatica"

C **34** Livno

1998. 550th Anniv of Herzegovina.
C44 C **33** 2k.30 red, black and
           gold   40 40

1998. 1100th Anniv of Livno.
C45 C **34** 1k.20 multicoloured . .   20 20

1998.
C46 C **35** 1k.40 multicoloured . .   25 25

C **36** Griffon Vulture
C **37** Adoration of the Wise Men

1998.
C47 C **36** 2k.40 multicoloured . .   40 40

1998. Christmas.
C48 C **37** 5k.40 multicoloured . .   90 90

C **38** Woman, Posavina Region
C **39** Ruins of Bobovac

1999. Regional Costumes.
C49 C **38** 40l. multicoloured . . .   10 10

1999. Old Towns.
C50 C **39** 10l. multicoloured . . .   10 10

C **40** Simic
C **41** Blidinje Nature Park

1999. Birth Centenary (1998) of Antun Simic (writer).
C51 C **40** 30l. multicoloured . . .   10 10

1999. Europa. Parks and Gardens.
C52 C **41** 1k.50 multicoloured . .   25 25

C **42** Dianthus freynii

1999.
C53 C **42** 80l. multicoloured . . .   50 50

C **43** Pine Marten

1999.
C54 C **43** 40l. multicoloured . . .   25 25

C **44** Gradina Osanici, Stolac
C **45** The Nativity (mosaic)

1999. Archaeology.
C55 C **44** 10l. multicoloured . . .   10 10

1999. Christmas.
C56 C **45** 30l. multicoloured . . .   20 20

C **46** Sop
C **47** Emblem

2000. 96th Birth Anniv of Nikola Sop (poet).
C57 C **46** 40l. multicoloured . . .   25 25

2000. World Health Day.
C58 C **47** 40l. multicoloured . . .   25 25

III. REPUBLIKA SRPSKA

Issued by the Serb administration based in Pale.

100 paras = 1 dinar.
1998. 100 fennig = 1 mark.

(S **1**)
S **2** Stringed Instrument

1992. Nos. 2587/98 of Yugoslavia surch as Type S **1**.
S 1   5d. on 10p. violet and green   10 10
S 2   30d. on 3d. blue and red . .   60·00 60·00
S 3a   50d. on 40p. green & purple   50 50
S 4   60d. on 20p. red and yellow   60 60
S 5   60d. on 30p. green & orange   60 60
S 6   100d. on 1d. blue and
       purple   1·00 1·00
S 7a   100d. on 2d. blue and red   1·00 1·00
S 8   100d. on 3d. blue and red   1·00 1·00
S 9a   300d. on 5d. ultram & blue   3·00 3·00
S10   500d. on 50p. green & violet   5·00 5·00
S11   500d. on 60p. mauve & red   5·00 5·00

1993. Dated "1992".
S12 S **2** 10d. black and yellow . .   10 10
S13   20d. black and blue . . .   25 25
S14   30d. black and pink . . .   35 35
S15   – 50d. black and red . . .   60 60
S16   – 100d. black and red . . .   1·25 1·25
S17   – 500d. black and blue . .   6·25 6·25
DESIGNS—VERT: 50, 100d. Coat of arms. HORIZ: 500d. Monastery.

1993. Dated "1993".
S18 S **2** 5000d. black and lilac . .   10 10
S19   6000d. black and yellow   15 15
S20   10000d. black and blue . .   25 25
S21   – 20000d. black and red . .   55 55
S22   – 30000d. black and red . .   85 85
S23   – 50000d. black and lilac . .   1·40 1·40
DESIGNS—VERT: 20000, 30000d. Coat of arms. HORIZ: 50000d. Monastery.

(S **3**)
S **4** Symbol of St. John the Evangelist

1993. Referendum. Nos. S15/16 surch as Type S **3**.
S24   7500d. on 50d. black and red   60 60
S25   7500d. on 100d. black and
       red . . .   60 60
S26   9000d. on 50d. black and red   80 80

1993. No value expressed.
S27 S **4** A red . . .   40 40
No. S27 was sold at the rate for internal letters.

Currency Reform

S **5** Icon of St. Stefan

1994. Republic Day.
S28 S **5** 1d. multicoloured . . .   4·00 4·00

S **6** King Petar I

1994. 150th Birth Anniv of King Petar I of Serbia.
S29 S **6** 80p. sepia and brown . .   2·50 2·50

S **7** Banja Luka

1994. 500th Anniv of Banja Luka.
S30 S **7** 1d.20 multicoloured . . .   2·00 2·50

1994. Issued at Doboj. Surch with letter. (a) On Nos. S13/16.
S31 S **2** A on 20d. black and blue
S32   R on 20d. black and blue
S33   R on 30d. black and pink
S34   – R on 50d. black and red
S35   – R on 100d. black and red
       (b) On Nos. S18/19 and S21/2.
S36 S **2** R on 5000d. black and
           lilac .
S37   R on 6000d. black and
       yellow .
S38   – A on 20000d. black and
       red . .
S39   – R on 20000d. black and
       red .
S40   – R on 30000d. black and
       red .
       Set of 10 . . .   65·00
Stamps surcharged "A" were sold at the current rate for internal letters and those surcharged "R" at the rate for internal registered letters. The "R" on No. S32 is reversed.

S **9** "Madonna and Child" (icon)

1994. Cajnicka Church.
S41 S **9** 1d. multicoloured . . . .   2·00 2·00

1994. Nos. S18/20 and S23 surch (Nos. 542/3 with letter).
S42 S **2** A on 5000d. black & lilac   1·10 1·10
S43   R on 6000d. black & yell   1·10 1·10
S44   40p. on 10000d. blk & bl   1·10 1·10
S45   – 2d. on 50000d. black and
       lilac . . .   1·10 1·10
No. S42 was sold at the current rate for internal letters and No. S43, which shows the surcharge as the cyrillic letter resembling "P", at the rate for internal registered letters.

S **11** Tavna Monastery

1994. Monasteries. Multicoloured.
S46   60p. Type S **11** . . .   2·00 2·00
S47   1d. Mostanica (horiz) . .   2·00 2·00
S48   1d.20 Zitomislic . . . .   2·25 2·25

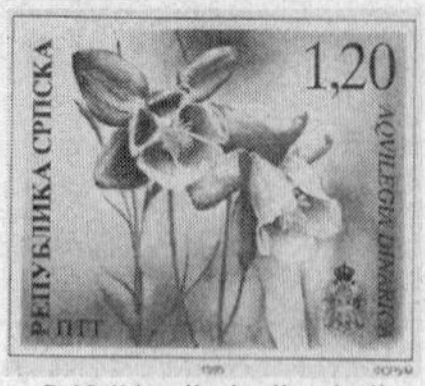

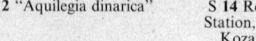

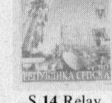

S 12 "Aquilegia dinarica"

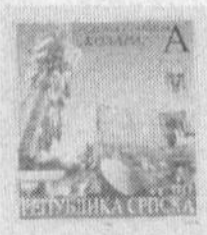

S 14 Relay Station, Mt. Kozara

1996. Nature Protection. Multicoloured.

S49	1d.20 Type S **12**	1·25	1·25
S50	1d.20 "Edraianthus niveus" (plant)	1·25	1·25
S51	1d.20 Shore lark	1·25	1·25
S52	1d.20 "Dinaromys bogdanovi" (dormouse)	1·25	1·25

1996. Nos. S14/16, S19 and S22 surch.

S53	S **2** 70p. on 30d. black and pink	30	30
S54	– 1d. on 100d. black & red	40	40
S55	– 2d. on 30000d. blk & red	80	80
S56	– 3d. on 50d. black and red	1·25	1·25
S57	S **2** 5d. on 6000d. black and yellow	2·25	2·25

1996.

S58	S **14** A green and bistre		
S59	– R purple and brown		
S60	– 1d.20 violet and blue		
S61	– 2d. lilac and mauve		
S62	– 5d. purple and blue		
S63	– 10d. brown and sepia		
	Set of 6	6·50	6·50

DESIGNS—VERT: R, Kraljica relay station, Mt. Ozren; 2d. Relay station, Mt. Romanija; 5d. Stolice relay station, Mt. Maljevica. HORIZ: 1d.20, Bridge over river Drina at Srbinje; 10d. Bridge at Visegrad.

No. S58 was sold at the current rate for an internal letter and No. S59 at the rate for an internal registered letter.

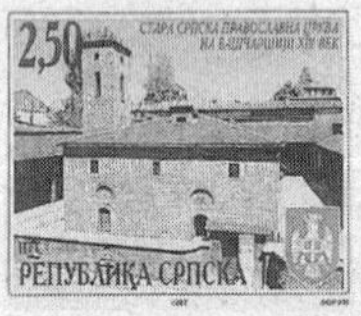

S 15 Orthodox Church, Bascarsiji

1997.

S64	S **15** 2d.50 multicoloured	1·00	1·00

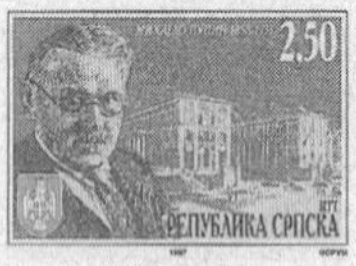

S 16 Pupin

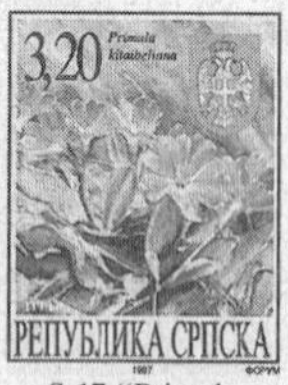

S 17 "Primula kitaibeliana"

1997. 62nd Death Anniv of Michael Pupin (physicist and inventor).

S65	S **16** 2d.50 multicoloured	1·00	1·00

1997. Flowers. Multicoloured.

S66	3d.20 Type S **17**	85	85
S67	3d.20 "Pedicularis hoermanniana"	85	85
S68	3d.20 "Knautia sarajevensis"	85	85
S69	3d.20 "Oxytropis campestris"	85	85

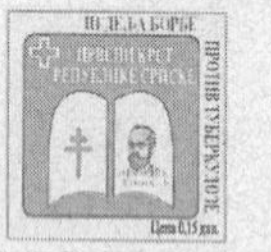

S 18 Robert Koch

S 19 Branko Copic

1997. Obligatory Tax. Anti-tuberculosis Week. Self-adhesive

S70	S **18** 15f. red and blue	10	10

1997. Writers. Each mauve and yellow.

S71	A (60p.) Type S **19**	25	25
S72	R (90p.) Jovan Ducic	35	35
S73	1d.50 Mesa Selimovic	35	35
S74	3d. Aleksa Santic	85	85
S75	5d. Petar Kocic	1·25	1·25
S76	10d. Ivo Andric	2·50	2·50

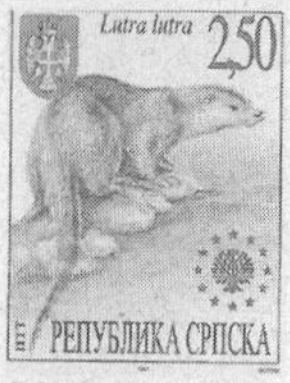

S 20 European Otter

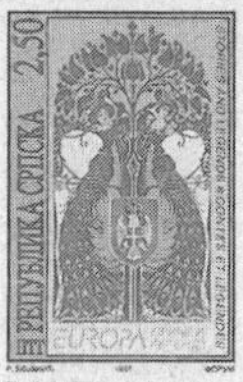

S 21 Two Queens

1997. Nature Protection. Multicoloured.

S77	2d.50 Type S **20**	50	50
S78	4d.50 Roe deer	1·10	1·10
S79	6d.50 Brown bear	1·75	1·75

1997. Europa. Tales and Legends. Multicoloured.

S80	2d.50 Type S **21**	1·00	1·00
S81	6d.50 Prince on horseback	2·50	2·50

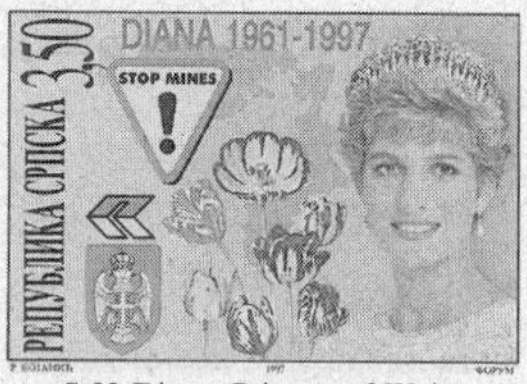

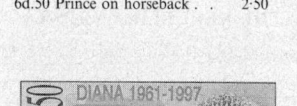

S 22 Diana, Princess of Wales

1998. Diana, Princess of Wales Commemoration.

S82	S **22** 3d.50 multicoloured ("DIANA" in Roman alphabet)	1·25	1·25
S83	3d.50 multicoloured ("DIANA" in Cyrillic alphabet)	1·25	1·25

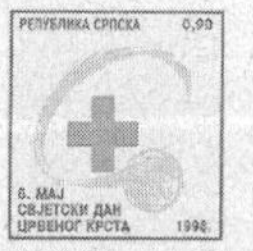

S 23 Cross and Globe

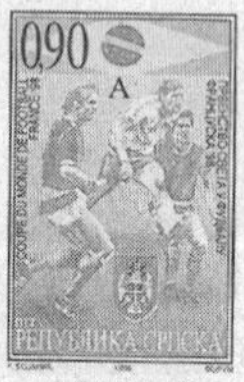

S 24 Brazil

1998. Obligatory Tax. Red Cross. Self-adhesive.

S84	S **23** 90f. red, blue and ultram	60	60

1998. World Cup Football Championship, France. Showing flags and players of countries in final rounds. Multicoloured.

S 85	90f. Type S **24**	60	60
S 86	90f. Morocco	60	60
S 87	90f. Norway	60	60
S 88	90f. Scotland	60	60
S 89	90f. Italy	60	60
S 90	90f. Chile	60	60
S 91	90f. Austria	60	60
S 92	90f. Cameroun	60	60
S 93	90f. France	60	60
S 94	90f. Saudi Arabia	60	60
S 95	90f. Denmark	60	60
S 96	90f. South Africa	60	60
S 97	90f. Spain	60	60
S 98	90f. Nigeria	60	60
S 99	90f. Paraguay	60	60
S100	90f. Bulgaria	60	60
S101	90f. Netherlands	60	60
S102	90f. Belgium	60	60
S103	90f. Mexico	60	60
S104	90f. South Korea	60	60
S105	90f. Germany	60	60
S106	90f. United States of America	60	60
S107	90f. Yugoslavia	60	60
S108	90f. Iran	60	60
S109	90f. Rumania	60	60
S110	90f. England (U.K. flag)	60	60
S111	90f. Tunisia	60	60
S112	90f. Colombia	60	60
S113	90f. Argentina	60	60
S114	90f. Jamaica	60	60
S115	90f. Croatia	60	60
S116	90f. Japan	60	60

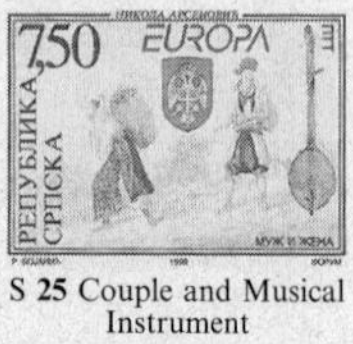

S 25 Couple and Musical Instrument

1998. Europa. National Festivals. Multicoloured.

S117	7m.50 Type S **25**	5·00	5·00
S118	7m.50 Couple from Neretva and musical instrument	5·00	5·00

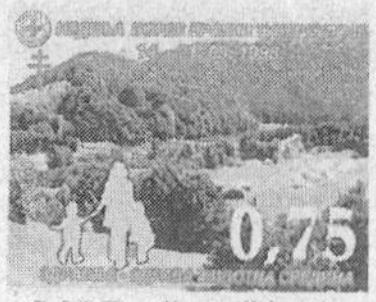

S 26 Family walking in Countryside

1998. Obligatory Tax. Anti-tuberculosis Week.

S119	S **26** 75f. multicoloured	50	50

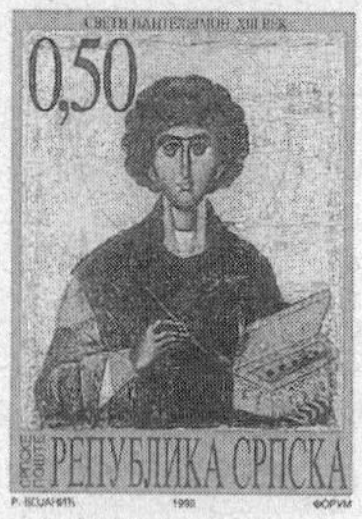

S 27 St. Pantelejmon

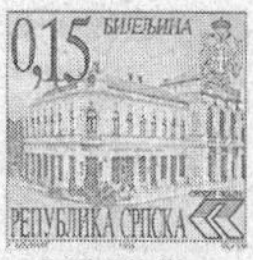

S 28 Bijelijna

1998. 800th Anniv of Hilandar Monastery. Icons. Multicoloured.

S120	50f. Type S **27**	35	35
S121	70f. Jesus Christ	45	45
S122	1m.70 St. Nikola	1·10	1·10
S123	2m. St. John of Rila	1·40	1·40

1999. Towns. Multicoloured. (a) With face value.

S124	15f. Type S **28**	10	10
S125	20f. Sokolac	15	15
S126	75f. Prijedor	50	50
S127	2m. Brcko	1·40	1·40
S128	4m.50 Zvornik	3·00	3·00
S129	10m. Doboj	6·75	6·75

(b) Face value expressed by letter.

S130	A (50f.) Banja Luka	35	35
S131	R (1m.) Trebinje	70	70

No. S130 was sold at the current rate for an internal letter and No. S131 at the rate for an internal registered letter.

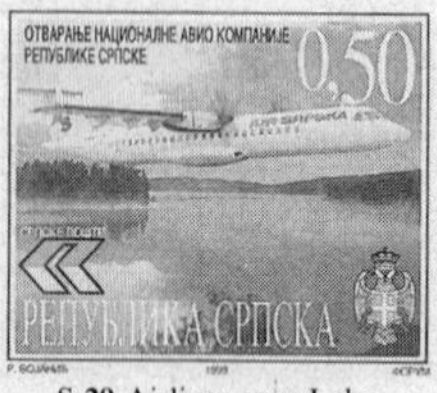

S 29 Airliner over Lake

1999. Founding of Air Srpska (state airline). Multicoloured.

S132	50f. Type S **29**	35	35
S133	50f. Airliner above clouds	35	35
S134	75f. Airliner over beach	50	50
S135	1m.50 Airliner over lake (different)	1·00	1·00

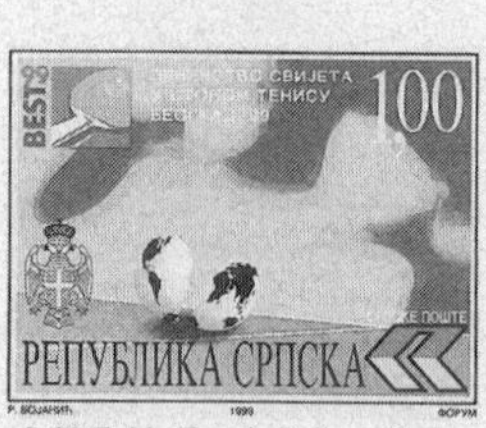

S 30 Table Tennis Ball as Globe

1999. International Table Tennis Championships, Belgrade. Multicoloured.

S136	1m. Type S **30**	70	70
S137	2m. Table tennis table, bat and ball	1·40	1·40

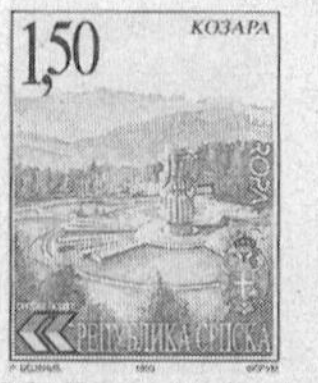

S 31 Kozara National Park

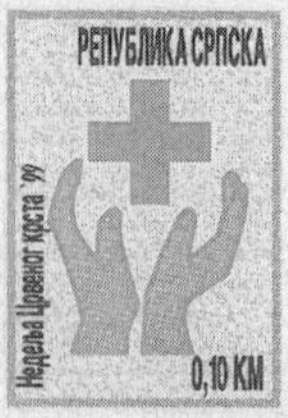

S 32 Open Hands

1999. Europa. National Parks. Multicoloured.

S138	1m.50 Type S **31**	1·00	1·00
S139	2m. Perucica National Park	1·40	1·40

1999. Obligatory Tax. Red Cross.

S140	S **32** 10f. multicoloured	10	10

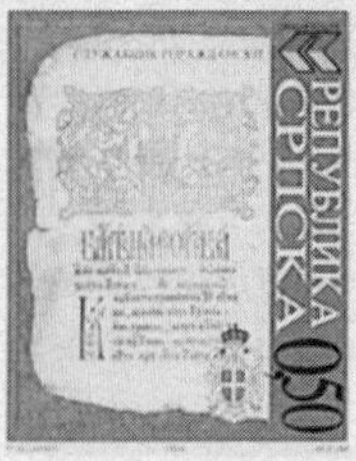

S 33 Manuscript

1999. 780th Anniv of Bosnia and Herzegovina Archbishopric (S142, S144/8) and 480th Anniv of Garazole Printing Works (S141, S143). Mult.

S141	50f. Type S **33**	30	30
S142	50f. Dobrun Monastery	30	30
S143	50f. "G"	30	30
S144	50f. Zhitomislib Monastery	30	30
S145	50f. Gomionitsa Monastery	30	30
S146	50f. Madonna and Child with angels and prophets (icon, 1578)	30	30
S147	50f. St. Nicolas (icon)	30	30
S148	50f. Wise Men (icon)	30	30

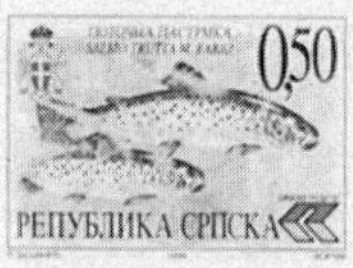

S 34 Brown Trout

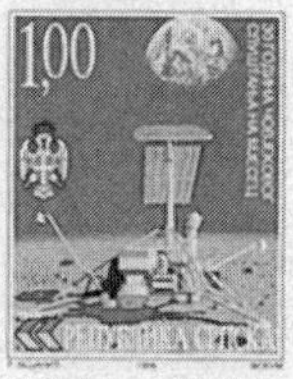

S 35 Lunar Module on Moon's Surface

1999. Fishes. Multicoloured.

S149	50f. Type S **34**	30	30
S150	50f. Lake trout (*Salmo trutta morpha lacustris*)	30	30
S151	75f. Huchen	45	45
S152	1m. European grayling	65	65

1999. 30th Anniv of First Manned Landing on Moon. Multicoloured.

S153	1m. Type S **35**	65	65
S154	2m. Astronaut on Moon	1·25	1·25

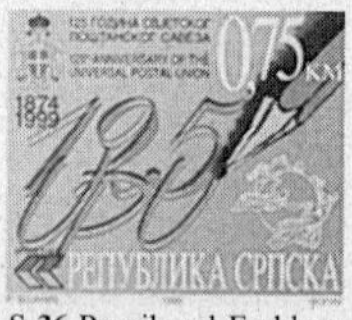

S 36 Pencil and Emblem

1999. 125th Anniv of Universal Postal Union. Mult.

S155	75f. Type S **36**	45	45
S156	1m.25 Earth and emblem	75	75

BOTSWANA Pt. 1

Formerly Bechuanaland Protectorate, attained independence on 30 September 1966, and changed its name to Botswana.

1966. 100 cents = 1 rand.
1976. 100 thebe = 1 pula.

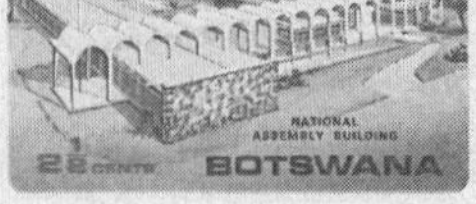

47 National Assembly Building

1966. Independence. Multicoloured.

202	2½c. Type **47**	15	10
203	5c. Abattoir, Lobatsi	20	10
204	15c. National Airways Douglas DC-3	65	20
205	35c. State House, Gaberones	40	30

1966. Nos. 168/81 of Bechuanaland optd **REPUBLIC OF BOTSWANA**.

206	**28** 1c. multicoloured	25	10
207	– 2c. orange, black and olive	30	1·25
208	– 2½c. multicoloured	30	10
209	– 3½c. multicoloured	40	20
210	– 5c. multicoloured	40	1·50
211	– 7½c. multicoloured	40	1·75
212	– 10c. multicoloured	60	20
213	– 12½c. multicoloured	2·00	2·75
214	– 20c. brown and drab	30	1·00
215	– 25c. sepia and lemon	30	2·00
216	– 35c. blue and orange	40	2·25
217	– 50c. sepia and olive	30	70
218	– 1r. black and brown	40	1·25
219	– 2r. brown and turquoise	1·00	2·50

52 Golden Oriole

1967. Multicoloured.
220	1c. Type **52**	30	15
221	2c. Hoopoe ("African Hoopese")	40	70
222	3c. Groundscraper thrush	55	10
223	4c. Cordon-bleu ("Blue Waxbill")	55	10
224	5c. Secretary bird	55	10
225	7c. Southern Yellow-billed hornbill ("Yellow-billed Hornbill")	60	90
226	10c. Burchell's gonolek ("Crimson-breasted Strike")	60	15
227	15c. Malachite kingfisher	7·00	3·00
228	20c. African fish eagle ("Fish Eagle")	7·00	2·00
229	25c. Go-away bird ("Grey Loerie")	4·00	1·50
230	35c. Scimitar-bill	6·00	2·25
231	50c. Comb duck ("Knob-Billed Duck")	2·75	2·75
232	1r. Levaillant's barbet ("Crested Barbet")	7·00	3·50
233	2r. Didric cuckoo ("Diederick Cuckoo")	8·00	16·00

66 Students and University

1967. 1st Conferment of University Degrees.
234	**66** 3c. sepia, blue and orange	10	10
235	7c. sepia, blue and turquoise	10	10
236	15c. sepia, blue and red	10	10
237	35c. sepia, blue and violet	20	20

67 Bushbuck

1967. Chobe Game Reserve. Multicoloured.
238	3c. Type **67**	10	20
239	7c. Sable Antelope	15	30
240	35c. Fishing on the Chobe River	80	1·10

70 Arms of Botswana and Human Rights Emblem

1968. Human Rights Year.
241	**70** 3c. multicoloured	10	1070
242	– 15c. multicoloured	25	45
243	– 25c. multicoloured	25	60

The designs of Nos. 242/3 are similar, but are arranged differently.

73 Eland and Giraffe Rock Paintings, Tsodilo Hills

1968. Opening of National Museum and Art Gallery. Multicoloured.
244	3c. Type **73**	20	20
245	7c. Girl wearing ceremonial beads (31 × 48 mm)	25	40
246	10c. "Baobab Trees" (Thomas Baines)	25	30
247	15c. National Museum and art gallery (72 × 19 mm)	40	1·50

77 African Family, and Star over Village

1968. Christmas.
249	**77** 1c. multicoloured	10	10
250	2c. multicoloured	10	10
251	5c. multicoloured	10	10
252	25c. multicoloured	15	50

78 Scout, Lion and Badge in frame

1969. 22nd World Scout Conference, Helsinki. Mult.
253	3c. Type **78**	30	30
254	15c. Scouts cooking over open fire (vert)	35	1·00
255	25c. Scouts around camp fire	35	1·00

81 Woman, Child and Christmas Star 82 Diamond Treatment Plant, Orapa

1969. Christmas.
256	**81** 1c. blue and brown	10	10
257	2c. olive and brown	10	10
258	4c. yellow and brown	10	10
259	35c. brown and violet	20	20

1970. Developing Botswana. Multicoloured.
261	3c. Type **82**	70	20
262	7c. Copper-nickel mining	95	20
263	10c. Copper-nickel mine, Selebi-Pikwe (horiz)	1·25	15
264	35c. Orapa Diamond mine and diamonds (horiz)	2·75	1·25

83 Mr. Micawber ("David Copperfield")

1970. Death Centenary of Charles Dickens. Mult.
265	3c. Type **83**	20	10
266	7c. Scrooge ("A Christmas Carol")	25	10
267	15c. Fagin ("Oliver Twist")	45	40
268	25c. Bill Sykes ("Oliver Twist")	70	60

84 U.N. Building and Emblem

1970. 25th Anniv of United Nations.
270	**84** 15c. blue, brown and silver	70	30

85 Crocodile

1970. Christmas. Multicoloured.
271	1c. Type **85**	10	10
272	2c. Giraffe	10	10
273	7c. Elephant	15	15
274	25c. Rhinoceros	60	80

86 Sorghum

1971. Important Crops. Multicoloured.
276	3c. Type **86**	15	10
277	7c. Millet	20	10
278	10c. Maize	20	10
279	35c. Groundnuts	70	55

87 Map and Head of Cow 88 King bringing Gift of Gold

1971. 5th Anniv of Independence.
280	**87** 3c. black, brown and green	10	10
281	– 4c. black, light blue and blue	10	10
282	– 7c. black and orange	20	15
283	– 10c. multicololured	20	15
284	– 20c. multicoloured	55	2·00

DESIGNS: 4c. Map and cogs; 7c. Map and common zebra; 10c. Map and sorghum stalk crossed by tusk; 20c. Arms and map of Botswana.

1971. Christmas. Multicoloured.
285	2c. Type **88**	10	10
286	3c. King bringing frankincense	10	10
287	7c. King bringing myrrh	10	10
288	20c. Three Kings behold the star	35	65

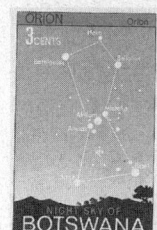

89 Orion 90 Postmark and Map

1972. "Night Sky".
290	**89** 3c. blue, black and red	75	30
291	– 7c. blue, black and yellow	1·10	80
292	– 10c. green, black and orange	1·25	85
293	– 20c. blue, black and green	1·75	3·00

CONSTELLATIONS: 7c. The Scorpion; 10c. The Centaur; 20c. The Cross.

1972. Mafeking-Gubulawayo Runner Post. Mult.
294	3c. Type **90**	30	10
295	4c. Bechuanaland stamp and map	30	35
296	7c. Runners and map	45	50
297	20c. Mafeking postmark and map	1·10	1·25

For these designs with changed inscription see Nos. 652/5.

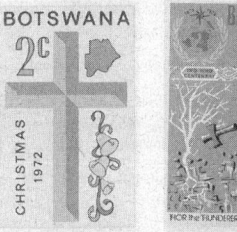

91 Cross, Map and Bells 92 Thor

1972. Christmas. Each with Cross and Map. Mult.
299	2c. Type **91**	10	75
300	3c. Cross, map and candle	10	10
301	7c. Cross, map and Christmas tree	15	25
302	20c. Cross, map, star and holly	40	85

1973. Centenary of I.M.O./W.M.O. Norse Myths. Multicoloured.
304	3c. Type **92**	20	10
305	4c. Sun God's chariot (horiz)	25	15
306	7c. Ymir, the frost giant	30	15
307	20c. Odin and Sleipnir (horiz)	75	70

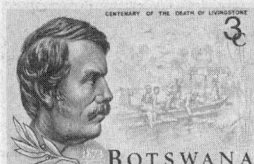

93 Livingstone and River Scene

1973. Death Centenary of Dr. Livingstone. Mult.
308	3c. Type **93**	20	10
309	20c. Livingstone meeting Stanley	90	90

94 Donkey and Foal at Village Trough

1973. Christmas. Multicoloured.
310	3c. Type **94**	10	10
311	4c. Shepherd and flock (horiz)	10	10
312	7c. Mother and Child	10	10
313	20c. Kgotla meeting (horiz)	40	85

95 Gaborone Campus

1974. 10th Anniv of University of Botswana, Lesotho and Swaziland. Multicoloured.
314	3c. Type **95**	10	10
315	7c. Kwaluseni Campus	10	10
316	20c. Roma Campus	15	20
317	35c. Map and flags of the three countries	20	35

96 Methods of Mail Transport

1974. Centenary of U.P.U. Multicoloured.
318	2c. Type **96**	55	35
319	3c. Post Office, Palapye, circa 1889	55	35
320	7c. Bechuanaland Police Camel Post, circa 1900	95	70
321	20c. Hawker Siddeley H.S.748 and De Havilland D.H.9 mail planes of 1920 and 1974	2·75	2·50

97 Amethyst

1974. Botswana Minerals. Multicoloured.
322	1c. Type **97**	60	1·50
323	2c. Agate-"Botswana Pink"	60	1·50
324	3c. Quartz	65	80
325	4c. Copper nickel	70	60
326	5c. Moss agate	70	1·00
327	7c. Agate	80	60
328	10c. Stilbite	1·60	65
329	15c. Moshaneng banded marble	2·00	3·50
330	20c. Gem diamonds	4·00	4·25
331	25c. Chrysotile	5·00	2·50
332	35c. Jasper	5·00	5·00
333	50c. Moss quartz	4·50	7·00
334	1r. Citrine	7·50	10·00
335	2r. Chalcopyrite	20·00	20·00

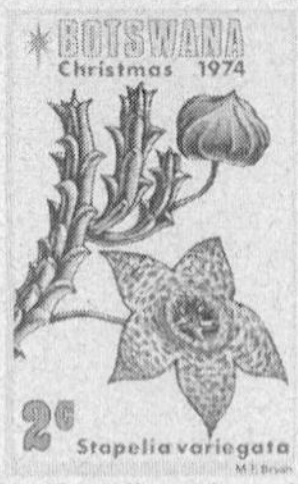
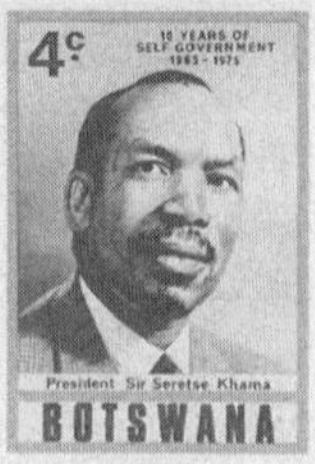

98 "Stapelia variegata" **99** President Sir Seretse Khama

1974. Christmas. Multicoloured.

336	2c. Type **98**	20	40
337	7c. "Hibiscus lunarifolius"	40	20
338	15c. "Ceratotheca triloba"	60	1·00
339	20c. "Nerine laticoma"	70	1·25

1975. 10th Anniv of Self-Government.

341	**99** 4c. multicoloured	10	10
342	10c. multicoloured	15	10
343	20c. multicoloured	25	25
344	35c. multicoloured	45	50

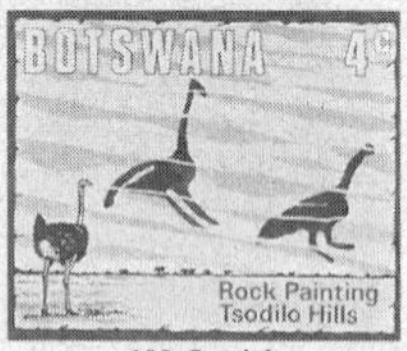

100 Ostrich

1975. Rock Paintings, Tsodilo Hills. Multicoloured.

346	4c. Type **100**	60	10
347	10c. White rhinoceros	1·00	10
348	25c. Spotted hyena	2·00	55
349	35c. Scorpion	2·00	1·10

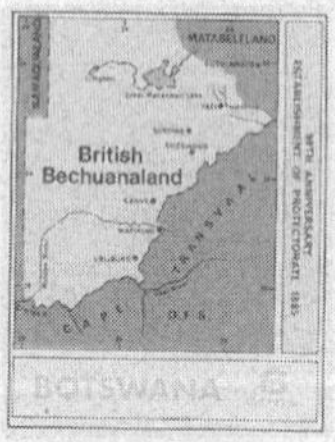
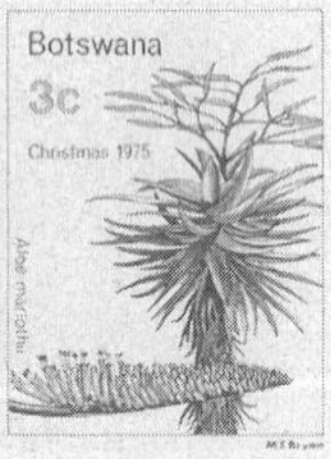

101 Map of British Bechuanaland, 1885 **102** "Aloe marlothii"

1975. Anniversaries. Multicoloured.

351	6c. Type **101**	30	20
352	10c. Chief Khama, 1875	40	15
353	25c. Chiefs Sebele, Bathoen and Khama, 1895 (horiz)	80	75

EVENTS: 6c.90th anniv of Protectorate; 10c. Centenary of Khama's accession; 25c.80th anniv of Chiefs' visit to London.

1975. Christmas. Aloes. Multicoloured.

354	3c. Type **102**	25	10
355	10c. "Aloe lutescens"	50	20
356	15c. "Aloe zebrina"	75	1·50
357	25c. "Aloe littoralis"	90	2·50

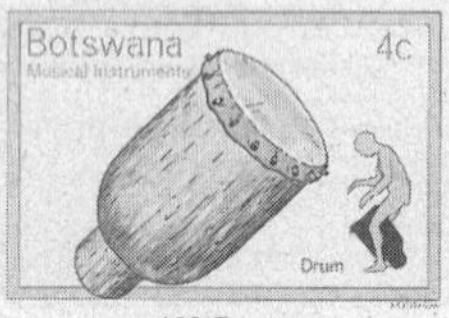

103 Drum

1976. Traditional Musical Instruments. Mult.

358	4c. Type **103**	15	10
359	10c. Hand piano	20	10
360	15c. Segankuru (violin)	25	50
361	25c. Kudu signal horn	30	1·25

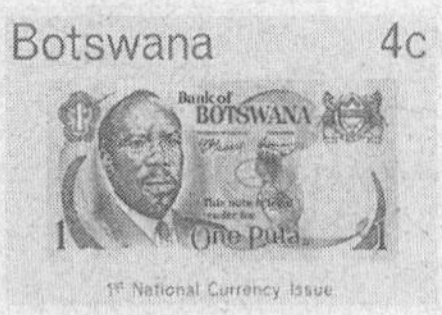

104 One Pula Note

1976. 1st National Currency. Multicoloured.

362	4c. Type **104**	15	10
363	10c. Two pula note	20	10
364	15c. Five pula note	35	20
365	25c. Ten pula note	45	45

1976. Nos. 322/35 surch in new currency.

367	1t. on 1c. multicoloured	2·00	70
368	2t. on 2c. multicoloured	2·00	1·25
369	3t. on 3c. multicoloured	1·50	60
370	4t. on 4c. multicoloured	2·50	40
371	5t. on 5c. multicoloured	2·50	40
372	7t. on 7c. multicoloured	1·25	2·50
373	10t. on 10c. multicoloured	1·25	80
374	15t. on 15c. multicoloured	4·25	3·00
375	20t. on 20c. multicoloured	7·50	80
376	25t. on 25c. multicoloured	5·00	1·25
377	35t. on 35c. multicoloured	4·50	5·00
378	50t. on 50c. multicoloured	7·00	9·00
379	1p. on 1r. multicoloured	8·00	9·50
380	2p. on 2r. multicoloured	11·00	11·00

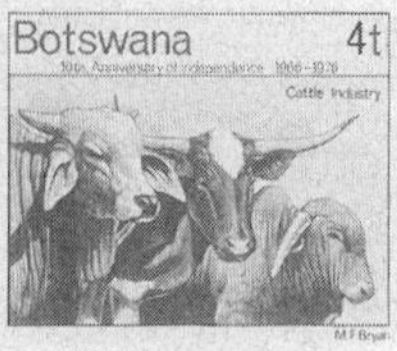

106 Botswana Cattle

1976. 10th Anniv of Independence. Multicoloured.

381	4t. Type **106**	15	10
382	10t. Deer, Okavango Delta (vert)	20	10
383	15t. School and pupils	20	40
384	25t. Rural weaving (vert)	20	50
385	35t. Miner (vert)	75	85

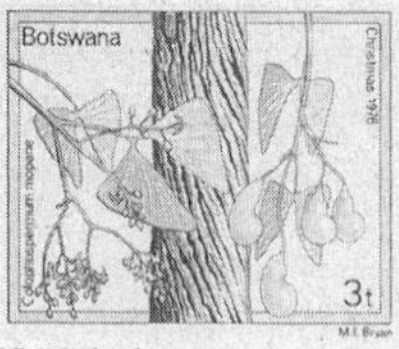

107 "Colophospermum mopane"

1976. Christmas. Trees. Multicoloured.

386	3t. Type **107**	15	10
387	4t. "Baikiaea plurijuga"	15	10
388	10t. "Sterculia rogersii"	20	10
389	25t. "Acacia nilotica"	45	50
390	40t. "Kigelia africana"	75	1·25

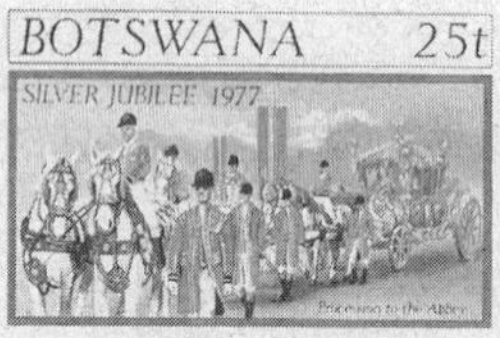

108 Coronation Coach

1977. Silver Jubilee. Multicoloured.

391	4t. The Queen and Sir Seretse Khama	10	10
392	25t. Type **108**	20	15
393	40t. The Recognition	35	90

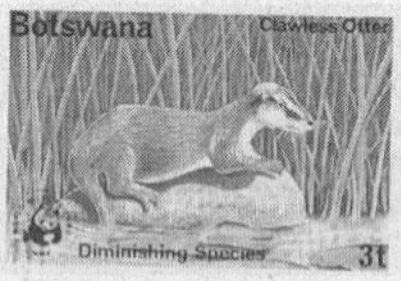

109 African Clawless Otter

1977. Diminishing Species. Multicoloured.

394	3t. Type **109**	3·50	40
395	4t. Serval	3·50	40
396	10t. Bat-eared fox	4·25	40
397	25t. Temminck's ground pangolin	10·00	2·00
398	40t. Brown hyena	12·00	7·50

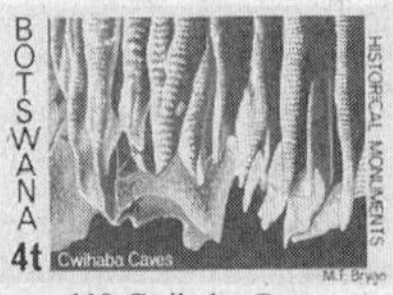

110 Cwihaba Caves

1977. Historical Monuments. Multicoloured.

399	4t. Type **110**	20	10
400	5t. Khama Memorial	20	10
401	15t. Green's Tree	30	40
402	20t. Mmajojo Ruins	30	45
403	25t. Ancient morabaraba board	30	50
404	35t. Matsieng's footprint	40	60

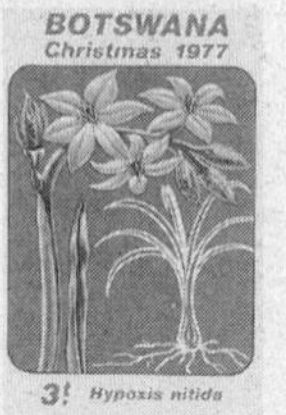
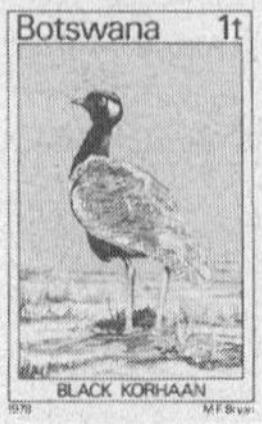

111 "Hypoxis nitida" **112** Black Bustard

1977. Christmas. Lilies. Multicoloured.

406	3t. Type **111**	15	10
407	5t. "Haemanthus magnificus"	15	10
408	10t. "Boophane disticha"	20	10
409	25t. "Vellozia retinervis"	40	55
410	40t. "Ammocharis coranica"	55	1·25

1978. Birds. Multicoloured.

411	1t. Type **112**	70	1·25
412	2t. Marabou stork	70	1·25
413	3t. Green wood hoopoe ("Red Billed Hoopoe")	70	85
414	4t. Carmine bee eater	70	75
415	5t. African jacana	70	40
416	7t. African paradise flycatcher ("Paradise Flycatcher")	70	2·75
417	10t. Bennett's woodpecker	1·75	60
418	15t. Red bishop	1·00	2·75
419	20t. Crowned plover	1·50	2·00
420	25t. Giant kingfisher	70	2·75
421	30t. White-faced whistling duck ("White-faced Duck")	70	70
422	35t. Green-backed heron	70	3·25
423	45t. Black-headed heron	1·00	3·00
424	50t. Spotted eagle owl	5·00	4·50
425	1p. Gabar goshawk	2·50	4·50
426	2p. Martial eagle	3·00	8·00
427	5p. Saddle-bill stork	8·00	16·00

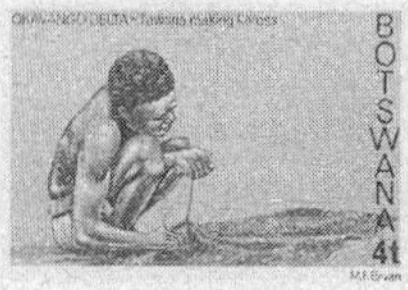

113 Tawana making Kaross

1978. Okavango Delta. Multicoloured.

428	4t. Type **113**	10	10
429	5t. Tribe localities	10	10
430	15t. Bushman collecting roots	25	40
431	20t. Herero woman milking	35	55
432	25t. Yei poling "mokoro" (canoe)	40	60
433	35t. Mbukushu fishing	45	1·50

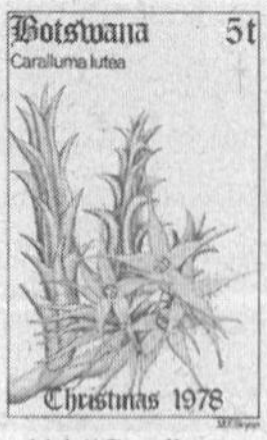
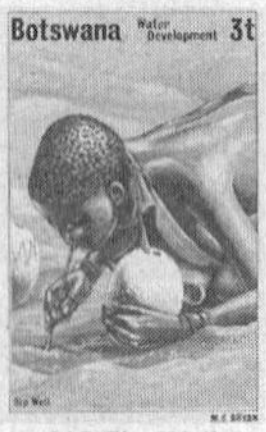

114 "Caralluma lutea" **115** Sip Well

1978. Christmas. Flowers. Multicoloured.

435	5t. Type **114**	35	10
436	10t. "Hoodia lugardii"	50	15
437	15t. "Ipomoea transvaalensis"	90	55
438	25t. "Ansellia gigantea"	1·10	70

1979. Water Development. Multicoloured.

439	3t. Type **115**	10	10
440	5t. Watering pit	10	10
441	10t. Hand dug well	15	10
442	22t. Windmill	20	30
443	50t. Modern drilling rig	40	55

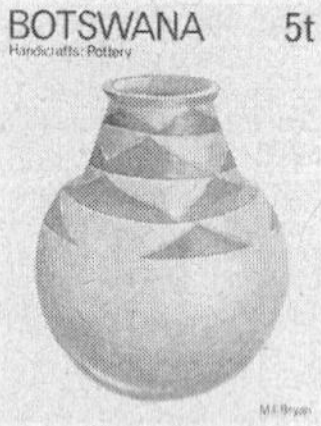

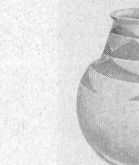

116 Pottery

1979. Handicrafts. Multicoloured.

444	5t. Type **116**	10	10
445	10t. Clay modelling	10	10
446	25t. Basketry	20	25
447	40t. Beadwork	40	50

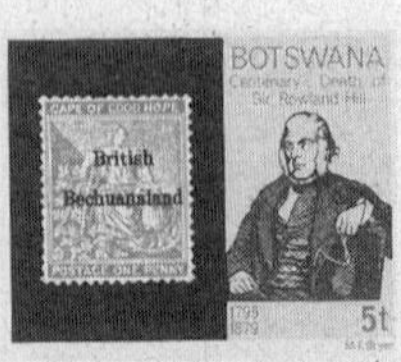

117 British Bechuanaland 1885 1d. Stamp and Sir Rowland Hill

1979. Death Centenary of Sir Rowland Hill. Mult.

449	5t. Type **117**	20	10
450	25t. Bechuanaland Protectorate 1932 2d. stamp	45	50
451	45t. 1967 Hoopoe 2c. definitive stamp	55	1·25

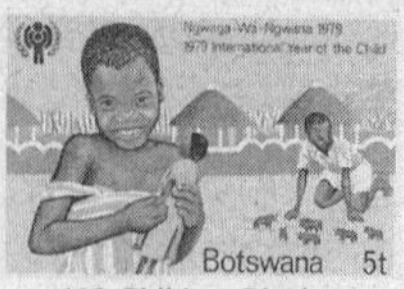

118 Children Playing

1979. International Year of the Child. Multicoloured.

452	5t. Type **118**	20	10
453	10t. Child playing with doll (vert)	30	20

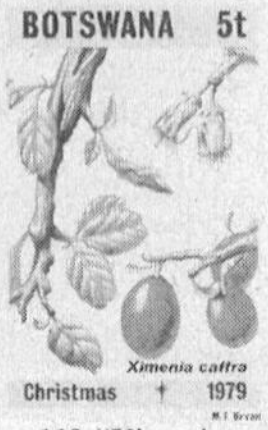
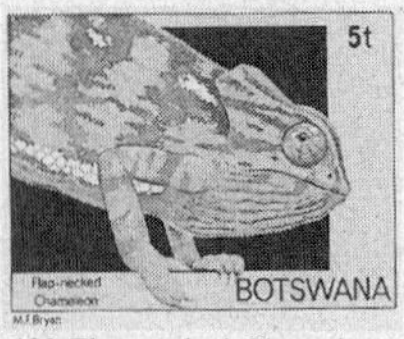

119 "Ximenia caffra" **120** Flap-necked Chameleon

1979. Christmas. Flowers. Multicoloured.

454	5t. Type **119**	10	10
455	10t. "Sclerocarya caffra"	20	20
456	15t. "Hexalobus monopetalus"	35	35
457	25t. "Ficus soldanella"	45	45

1980. Reptiles. Multicoloured.

458	5t. Type **120**	30	10
459	10t. Leopard tortoise	30	15
460	25t. Puff adder	50	65
461	40t. White-throated monitor	60	2·50

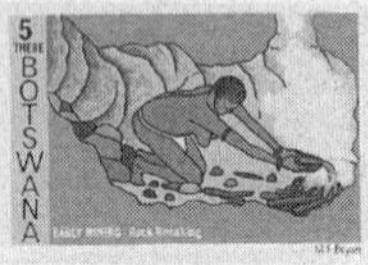

121 Rock Breaking

1980. Early Mining. Multicoloured.

462	5t. Type **121**	25	15
463	10t. Ore hoisting	30	15
464	15t. Ore transport	70	60
465	20t. Ore crushing	75	70
466	25t. Smelting	80	90
467	35t. Tool and products	1·00	1·40

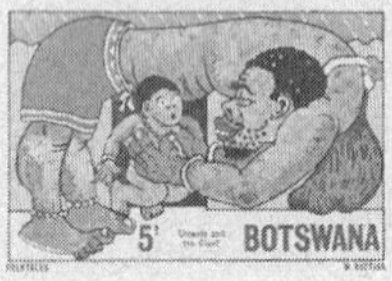

122 "Chiwele and the Giant"

1980. Folktales. Multicoloured.

468	5t. Type **122**	10	10
469	10t. "Kgori is not deceived" (vert)	15	10
470	30t. "Nyambi's wife and Crocodile" (vert)	45	45
471	45t. "Clever Hare" (horiz)	60	60

The 10t. and 30t. are 28 × 37 mm and the 45t. 44 × 27 mm.

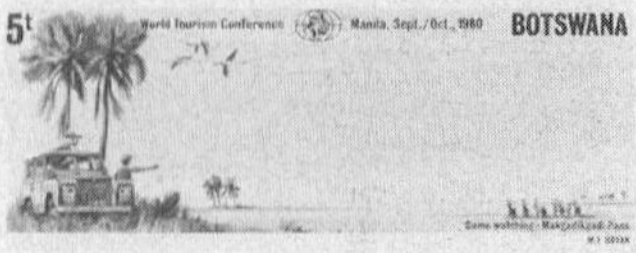

123 Game watching, Makgadikgadi Pans

1980. World Tourism Conference, Manila.

472	**123** 5t. multicoloured	45	20

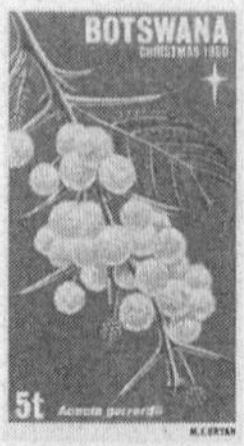
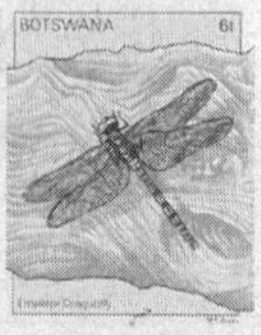

124 "Acacia gerrardii" **126** "Anax imperator" (dragonfly)

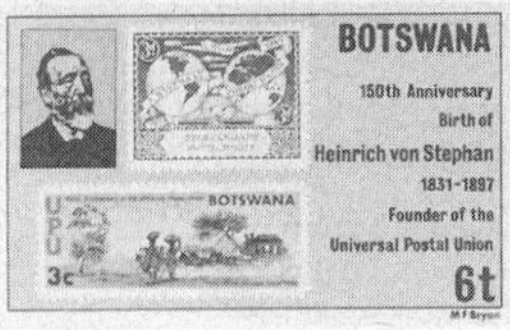

125 Heinrich von Stephan and Botswana 3d. and 3c. U.P.U. Stamps

1980. Christmas. Multicoloured.

473	6t. Type **124**	10	10
474	1t. "Acacia nilotica"	20	10
475	25t. "Acacia erubescens"	45	30
476	40t. "Dichrostachys cinerea"	70	70

1981. 150th Birth Anniv of Heinrich von Stephan (founder of Universal Postal Union). Multicoloured.

477	6t. Type **125**	75	30
478	20t.6d. and 7c. U.P.U. stamps	1·75	2·25

1981. Insects. Multicoloured.

479	6t. Type **126**	15	10
480	7t. "Sphodromantis gastrica" (mantid)	15	20
481	10t. "Zonocerus elegans" (grasshopper)	15	20
482	20t. "Kheper nigroaeneus" (beetle)	25	50
483	30t. "Papilio demodocus" (butterfly)	35	70
484	45t. "Acanthocampa belina" (moth larva)	40	1·10

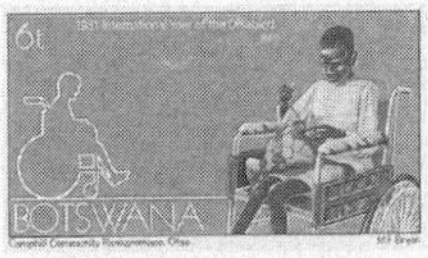

127 Camphill Community Rankoromane, Otse

1981. International Year for Disabled Persons. Multicoloured.

486	6t. Type **127**	20	10
487	20t. Resource Centre for the Blind, Mochudi	55	35
488	30t. Tlamelong Rehabilitation Centre, Tlokweng	75	45

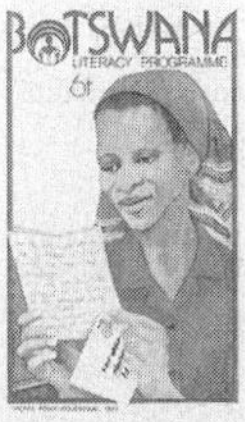

128 Woman reading Letter

1981. Literacy Programme. Multicoloured.

489	6t. Type **128**	20	10
490	7t. Man filling in form	20	15
491	20t. Boy reading newspaper	60	35
492	30t. Child being taught to read	80	45

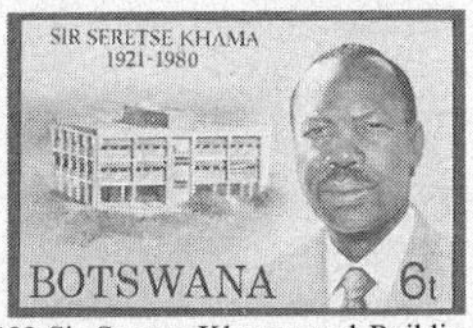

129 Sir Seretse Khama and Building

1981. 1st Death Anniv of Sir Seretse Khama (former President). Multicoloured.

493	6t. Type **129**	15	10
494	10t. Seretse Khama and building (different)	25	15
495	30t. Seretse Khama and Botswana flag	40	45
496	45t. Seretse Khama and building (different)	55	70

1981. Nos. 417 and 422 surch.

497	25t. on 35t. Green-backed heron	3·50	2·00
498	30t. on 10t. Bennett's woodpecker	3·50	2·00

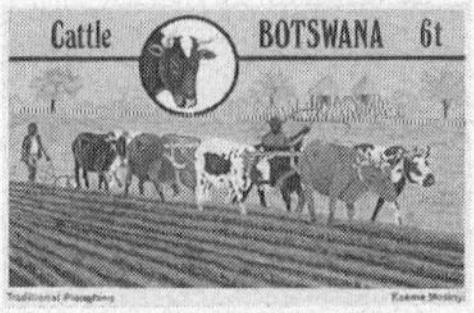

131 Traditional Ploughing

1981. Cattle Industry. Multicoloured.

499	6t. Type **131**	10	10
500	20t. Agricultural show	30	50
501	30t. Botswana Meat Commission	35	60
502	45t. Vaccine Institute, Botswana	50	1·00

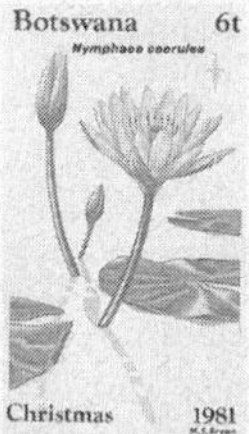

132 "Nymphaea caerulea"

1981. Christmas. Flowers. Multicoloured.

503	6t. Type **132**	20	10
504	10t. "Nymphoides indica"	25	10
505	25t. "Nymphaea lotus"	60	90
506	40t. "Ottelia kunenensis"	80	2·25

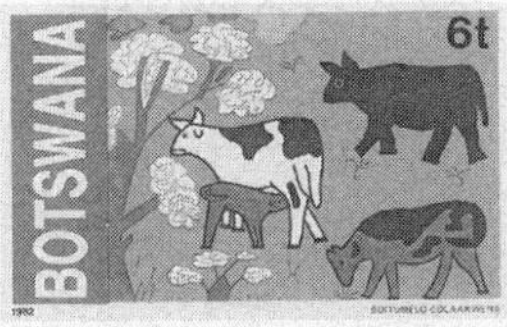

133 "Cattle Post Scene" (Boitumelo Golaakwena)

1982. Children's Art. Multicoloured.

507	6t. Type **133**	40	10
508	10t. "Kgotla Meeting" (Reginald Klinck)	50	15
509	30t. "Village Water Supply" (Keronmemang Matswiri)	1·75	1·25
510	45t. "With the Crops" (Kennedy Balemoge)	1·75	2·75

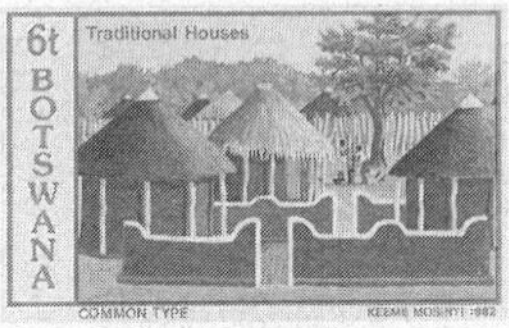

134 Common Type

1982. Traditional House. Multicoloured.

511	6t. Type **134**	40	15
512	10t. Kgatleng type	50	15
513	30t. North Eastern type	2·00	1·10
514	45t. Sarwa type	2·00	3·00

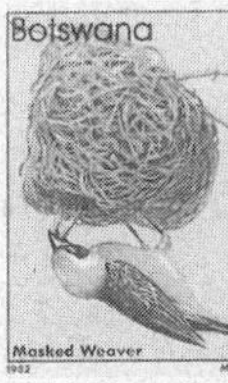

135 African Masked Weaver

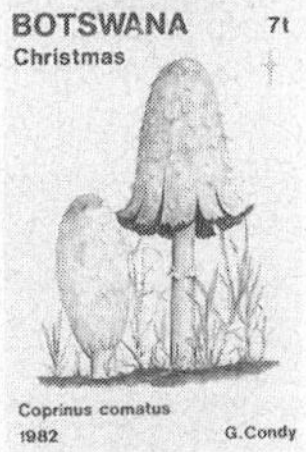

136 "Coprinus comatus"

1982. Birds. Multicoloured.

515	1t. Type **135**	80	1·50
516	2t. Miombo double-collared sunbird ("Lesser double-collared Sunbird")	90	1·60
517	3t. Red-throated bee eater	1·00	1·60
518	4t. Ostrich	1·00	1·60
519	5t. Grey-headed gull	1·00	1·60
520	6t. African pygmy ("Pygmy Goose")	1·00	40
521	7t. Cattle egret	1·00	15
522	8t. Lanner falcon	2·50	1·50
523	10t. Yellow-billed stork	1·00	20
524	15t. Red-billed pintail ("Red-billed Teal") (horiz)	2·75	25
525	20t. Barn owl (horiz)	5·50	3·50
526	25t. Hammerkop ("Hammerkop") (horiz)	3·25	70
527	30t. South African stilt ("Stilt") (horiz)	3·75	90
528	35t. Blacksmith plover (horiz)	3·75	80
529	45t. Senegal wattled plover ("Watted Plover") (horiz)	3·75	1·75
530	50t. Helmeted guineafowl ("Crowned Guineafowl") (horiz)	4·75	2·50
531	1p. Cape vulture (horiz)	9·00	12·00
532	2p. Augur buzzard (horiz)	11·00	16·00

1982. Christmas. Fungi. Multicoloured.

533	7t. Type **136**	2·00	20
534	15t. "Lactarius deliciosus"	3·25	65
535	35t. "Amanita pantherina"	5·00	2·00
536	50t. "Boletus edulis"	6·50	7·00

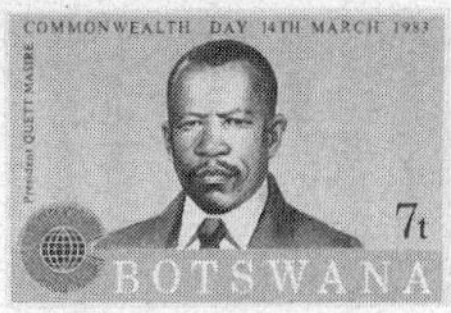

137 President Quett Masire

1983. Commonwealth Day. Multicoloured.

537	7t. Type **137**	10	10
538	15t. Native dancers	15	20
539	35t. Melbourne conference centre	45	55
540	45t. Meeting of Heads of State, Melbourne	55	80

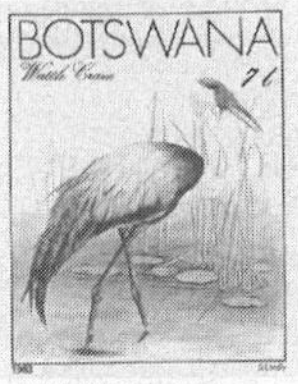

138 Wattled Crane

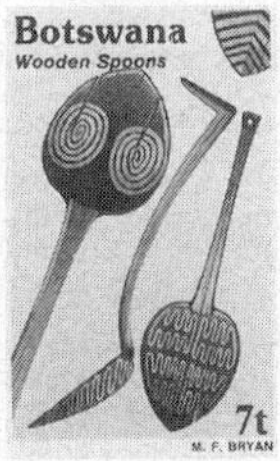

139 Wooden Spoons

1983. Endangered Species. Multicoloured.

541	7t. Type **138**	3·00	55
542	15t. "Aloe lutescens"	2·50	80
543	35t. Roan antelope	3·00	3·25
544	50t. Ivory palm	3·50	6·00

1983. Traditional Artifacts. Multicoloured.

545	7t. Type **139**	25	10
546	15t. Personal ornaments	45	30
547	35t. Ox-hide milk bag	75	65
548	50t. Decorated knives	1·00	1·10

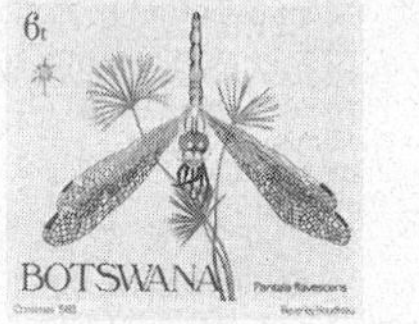

140 "Pantala flavescens"

1983. Christmas. Dragonflies. Multicoloured.

550	6t. Type **140**	85	10
551	15t. "Anax imperator"	1·75	50
552	25t. "Trithemis arteriosa"	2·00	85
553	45t. "Chlorolestes elegans"	2·75	4·50

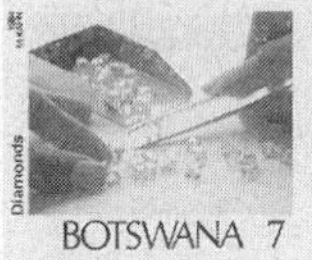

141 Sorting Diamonds

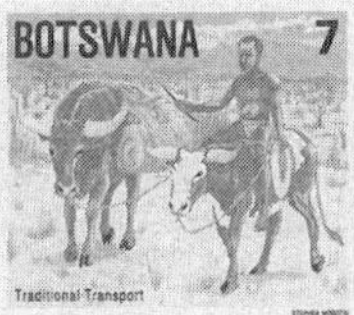

142 Riding Cattle

1984. Mining Industry. Multicoloured.

554	7c. Type **141**	2·00	50
555	15c. Lime kiln	2·00	75
556	35c. Copper-nickel smelter plant (vert)	3·25	3·00
557	60c. Stockpiled coal (vert)	3·75	8·00

1984. Traditional Transport. Multicoloured.

558	7t. Type **142**	20	10
559	25t. Sledge	65	50
560	35t. Wagon	85	1·25
561	50t. Two-wheeled donkey cart	1·25	3·75

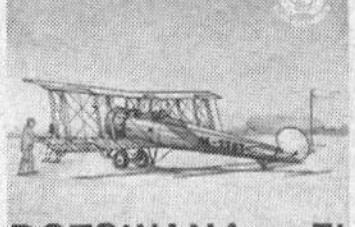

143 Avro 504 Aircraft

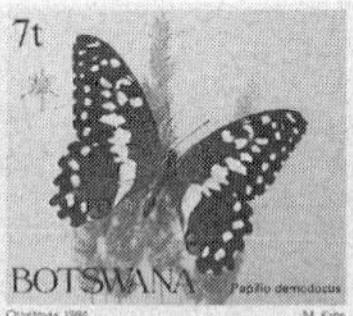

144 "Papilio demodocus"

1984. 40th Anniv of International Civil Aviation Organization. Multicoloured.

562	7t. Type **143**	75	20
563	10t. Westland Wessex trimotor	1·00	30
564	15t. Junkers Ju 52/3m	1·40	85
565	25t. De Havilland Dominie	2·00	1·50
566	35t. Douglas DC-3 "Wenala"	2·25	3·25
567	50t. Fokker Friendship	2·50	6·00

1984. Christmas. Butterflies. Multicoloured.

568	7t. Type **144**	2·00	30
569	25t. "Byblia anvatara"	2·25	1·50
570	35t. "Danaus chrysippus"	3·50	3·00
571	50t. "Graphium taboranus"	4·75	9·00

No. 570 is incorrectly inscr "Hypolimnas misippus".

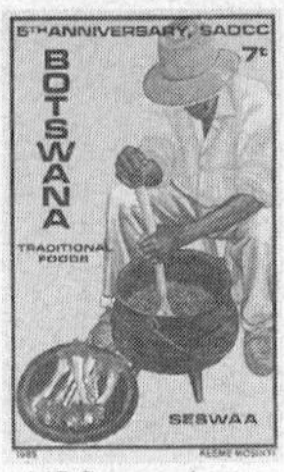

145 Seswaa (meat dish)

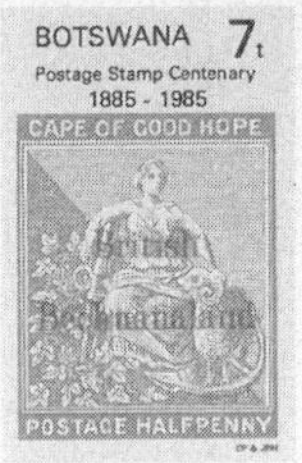

146 1885 British Bechuanaland Overprint on Cape of Good Hope ½d.

1985. 5th Anniv of Southern African Development Co-ordination Conference. Traditional Foods. Multicoloured.

572	7t. Type **145**	30	10
573	15t. Bogobe (cereal porridge)	55	35
574	25t. Madila (soured coagulated cow's milk)	80	55
575	50t. Phane (caterpillars)	1·25	1·75

1985. Centenary of First Bechuanaland Stamps.

577	**146** 7t. black, grey and red	1·00	20
578	– 15t. black, brown yell	1·75	50
579	– 25t. black and red	2·25	80
580	– 35t. black, blue and gold	2·50	2·00
581	– 50t. multicoloured	2·75	3·25

DESIGNS—VERT: 15t. 1897 Bechuanaland Protectorate overprint on G.B. 3d.; 25t. Bechuanaland Protectorate 1932 1d. definitive. HORIZ: 35t. Bechuanaland 1965 Internal Self-Government 5c.; 50t. Botswana 1966 Independence 2½c.

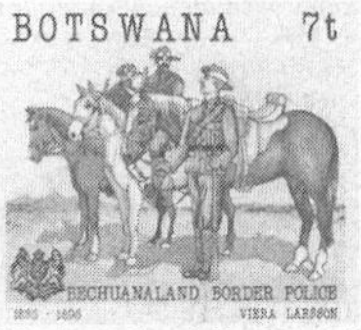

147 Bechuanaland Border Police, 1885–95

1985. Centenary of Botswana Police. Multicoloured.

582	7t. Type **147**	2·00	50
583	10t. Bechuanaland Mounted Police, 1895–1902	2·25	50
584	25t. Bechuanaland Protectorate Police, 1903–66	3·25	2·00
585	50t. Botswana Police, from 1966	4·50	6·00

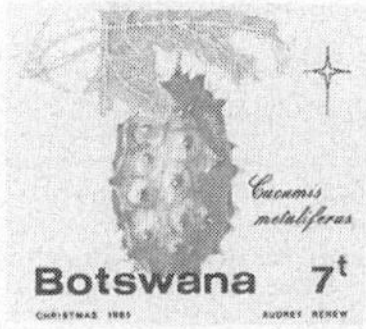

148 "Cucumis metuliferus"

1985. Christmas. Edible Wild Cucumbers. Mult.

586	7t. Type **148**	90	10
587	15t. "Acanthosicyos naudinianus"	1·75	70
588	25t. "Coccinia sessifolia"	2·50	1·10
589	50t. "Momordica balsamina"	4·00	7·50

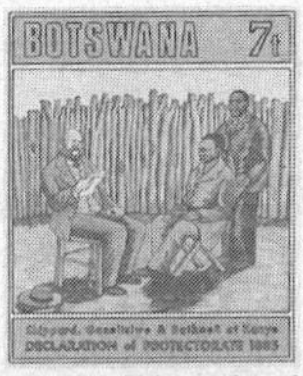

149 Mr. Shippard and Chief Gaseitsiwe of the Bangwaketse

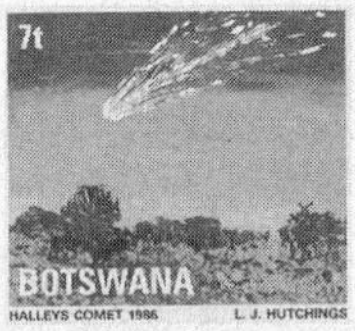

150 Halley's Comet over Serowe

1985. Centenary of Declaration of Bechuanaland Protectorate. Multicoloured.

590	7t. Type **149**	35	10
591	15t. Sir Charles Warren and Chief Sechele of the Bakwena	70	45
592	25t. Revd. Mackenzie and Chief Khama of the Bamangwato	1·25	85
593	50t. Map showing Protectorate	2·75	2·75

1986. Appearance of Halley's Comet. Multicoloured.

595	7t. Type **150**	80	15
596	15t. Comet over Bobonong at sunset	1·50	70
597	35t. Comet over Gomare at dawn	2·00	1·50
598	50t. Comet over Thamaga and Letlhakeng	2·25	3·50

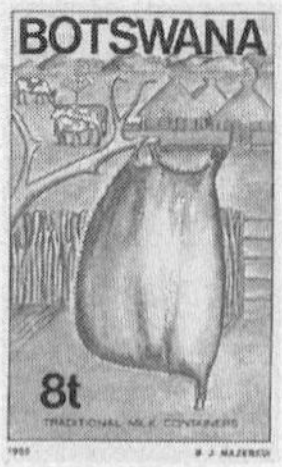

151 Milk Bag

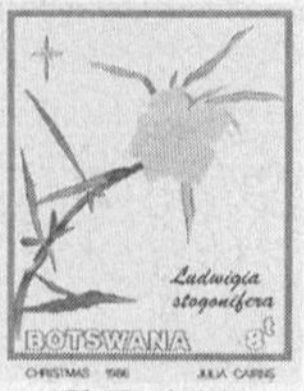

153 "Ludwigia stogonifera"

1986. Traditional Milk Containers. Multicoloured.

599	8t. Type **151**	15	10
600	15t. Clay pot and calabashes	25	30
601	35t. Wooden milk bucket	50	65
602	50t. Milk churn	70	1·10

1986. Christmas. Flowers of Okavango. Mult.

604	8t. Type **153**	1·25	10
605	15t. "Sopubia mannii"	2·25	1·10
606	35t. "Commelina diffusa"	3·50	3·00
607	50t. "Hibiscus diversifolius"	4·00	10·00

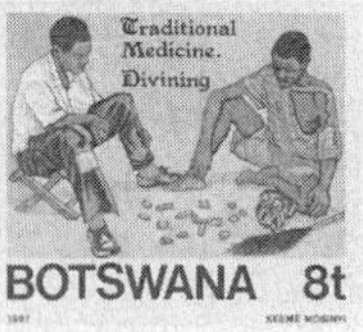

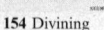

154 Divining

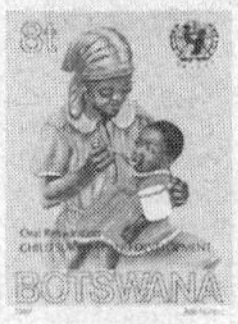

156 Oral Rehydration Therapy

1987. Traditional Medicine. Multicoloured.

608	8t. Type **154**	80	10
609	15t. Lightning prevention	1·50	80
610	35t. Rain making	2·25	2·50
611	50t. Blood letting	2·75	6·50

1987. Nos. 520, 523 and 530 surch.

612	3t. on 6t. African pygmy goose	1·75	60
613	5t. on 10t. Yellow-billed stork	1·75	60
614	20t. on 50t. Helmeted guineafowl (horiz)	3·75	1·40

1987. U.N.I.C.E.F. Child Survival Campaign. Multicoloured.

615	8t. Type **156**	35	10
616	15t. Growth monitoring	60	55
617	35t. Immunization	1·25	1·75
618	50t. Breast feeding	1·50	4·25

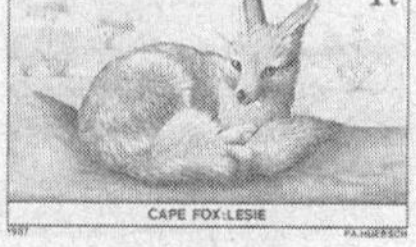

157 Cape Fox

1987. Animals of Botswana. Multicoloured.

619	1t. Type **157**	10	70
620	2t. Lechwe	20	80
621	3t. Zebra	15	70
622	4t. Duiker	15	1·25
623	5t. Banded mongoose	20	1·25
624	6t. Rusty-spotted genet	20	1·25
625	8t. Hedgehog	30	10
626	10t. Scrub hare	30	10
627	12t. Hippopotamus	1·75	2·75
628	15t. Suricate	1·50	1·00
629	20t. Caracal	70	65
630	25t. Steenbok	70	1·25
631	30t. Gemsbok	1·25	1·00
632	35t. Square-lipped rhinoceros	1·50	1·25
633	40t. Mountain reedbuck	1·40	1·25
634	50t. Rock dassie	90	1·75
635	1p. Giraffe	2·50	3·75
636	2p. Tsessebe	2·50	4·75
637	3p. Side-striped jackal	3·75	7·00
638	5p. Hartebeest	6·00	11·00

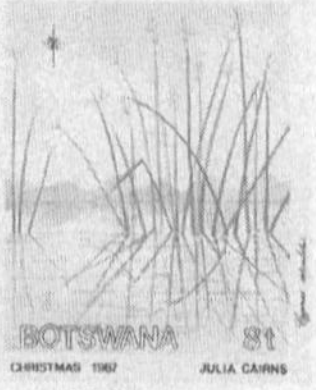

158 "Cyperus articulatus"

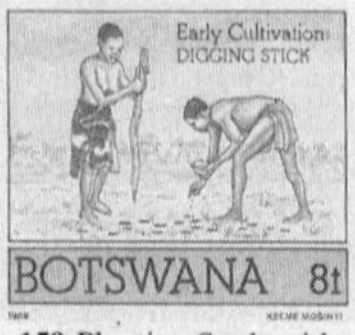

159 Planting Seeds with Digging Stick

1987. Christmas. Grasses and Sedges of Okavango. Multicoloured.

639	8t. Type **158**	40	10
640	15t. Broomgrass	60	40
641	30t. "Cyperus alopurcides"	1·25	75
642	1p. Bulrush sedge	2·50	4·50

1988. Early Cultivation. Multicoloured.

644	8t. Type **159**	40	10
645	15t. Using iron hoe	60	35
646	35t. Wooden ox-drawn plough	1·00	1·00
647	50t. Villagers using lesotlas	1·40	2·00

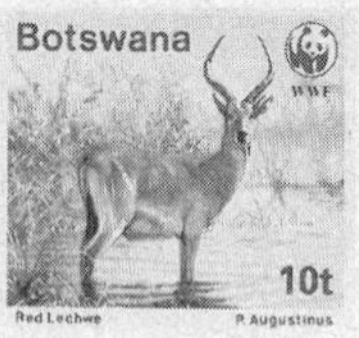

160 Red Lechwe at Water-hole

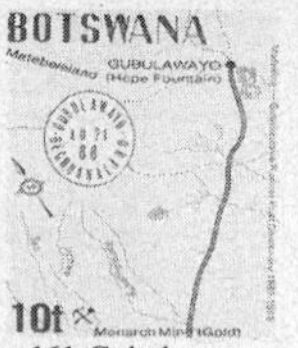

161 Gubulawayo Postmark and Route Southwards to Tati

1988. Red Lechwe. Multicoloured.

648	10t. Type **160**	90	15
649	15t. Red lechwe and early morning sun	1·75	65
650	35t. Female and calf	2·50	1·75
651	75t. Herd on the move	3·75	7·50

1988. Cent of Mafeking–Gubalawayo Runner Post. Designs as Nos. 294/7, but redrawn smaller with changed inscriptions as in T **161**. Multicoloured.

652	10t. Type **161**	35	10
653	15t. Bechuanaland 1888 6d. on 6d. stamp and route from Tati southwards	55	30
654	30t. Runners and twin routes south from Shoshong	95	75
655	60t. Mafeking postmark and routes to Bechuanaland and Transvaal	1·60	2·75

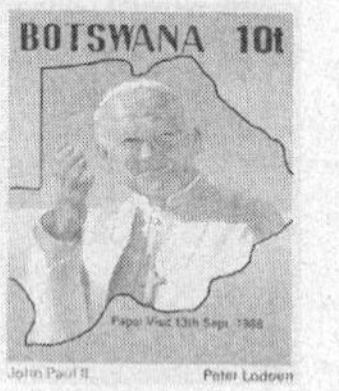

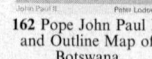

162 Pope John Paul II and Outline Map of Botswana

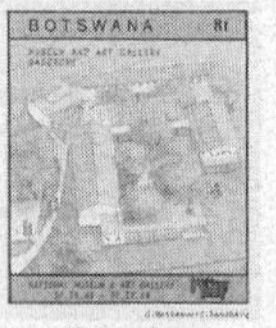

163 National Museum and Art Gallery, Gaborone

1988. Visit of Pope John Paul II. Multicoloured.

657	10t. Type **162**	1·25	20
658	15t. Pope John Paul II	1·50	30
659	30t. Pope giving blessing and outline map	2·00	70
660	80t. Pope John Paul II (different)	2·75	2·75

1988. 20th Anniv of National Museum and Art Gallery, Gaborone. Multicoloured.

661	8t. Type **163**	15	10
662	15t. Pottery	20	25
663	30t. Blacksmith's buffalo bellows	35	40
664	60c. Children and mobile museum van	70	1·00

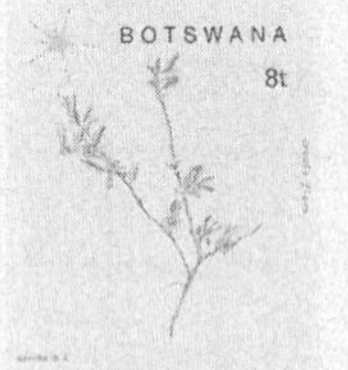

164 "Grewia flava"

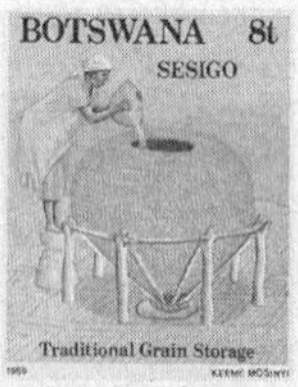

165 Basket Granary

1988. Flowering Plants of South-eastern Botswana. Multicoloured.

665	8t. Type **164**	20	10
666	15t. "Cienfuegosia digitata"	30	25
667	40t. "Solanum seaforthianum"	60	55
668	75t. "Carissa bispinosa"	1·00	1·40

1989. Traditional Grain Storage. Multicoloured.

669	8t. Type **165**	55	10
670	15t. Large letlole granary	85	40
671	30t. Pot granary	1·40	60
672	60t. Two types of serala	2·00	2·25

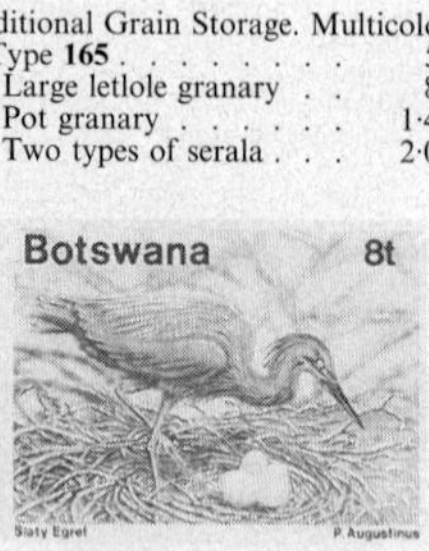

166 Female with Eggs

1989. Slaty Egret. Multicoloured.

673	8t. Type **166**	55	15
674	15t. Chicks in nest	75	40
675	30t. In flight	1·00	75
676	60t. Pair building nest	1·40	1·60

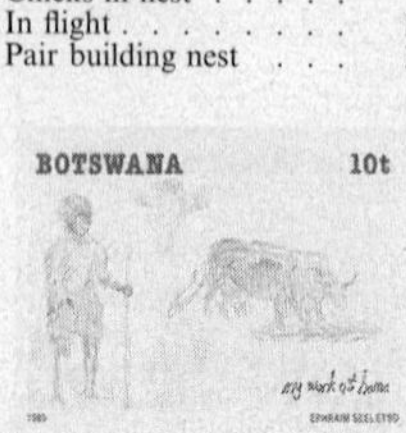

167 "My Work at Home" (Ephraim Seeletso)

1989. Children's Paintings. Multicoloured.

678	10t. Type **167**	35	10
679	15t. "My Favourite Game" (hopscotch) (Neelma Bhatia) (vert)	50	35
680	30t. "My Favourite Toy" (clay animals) (Thabo Habana)	75	70
681	1p. "My School Day" (Thabo Olesitse)	2·00	3·25

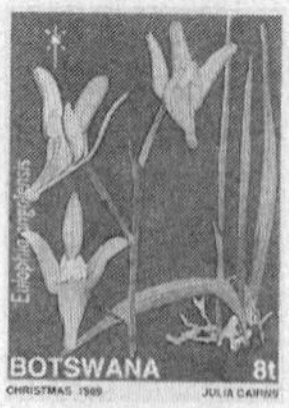

168 "Eulophia angolensis"

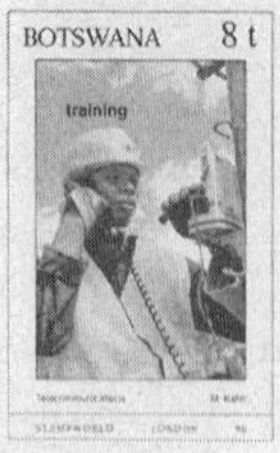

171 Telephone Engineer

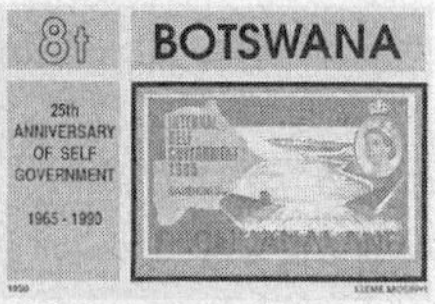

169 Bechuanaland 1965 New Constitution 25c. Stamp (25th anniv of Self-Government)

1989. Christmas. Orchids. Multicoloured.

682	8t. Type **168**	70	10
683	15t. "Eulophia hereroensis"	1·25	60
684	30t. "Eulophia speciosa"	1·75	1·00
685	60t. "Eulophia petersii"	2·50	6·50

1990. Anniversaries.

686 **169**	8t. multicoloured	70	15
687 –	15t. multicoloured	75	50
688 –	30t. multicoloured	2·25	1·40
689 –	60t. black, blue and yellow	2·75	5·50

DESIGNS: 15t. Casting vote in ballot box (25th anniv of First Elections); 30t. Outline map and flags of Southern Africa Development Co-ordination Conference countries (10th anniv); 60t. Penny Black (150th anniv of first postage stamp).

1990. Nos. 619, 624 and 627 surch.

690	10t. on 1t. Type **157**	45	20
691	20t. on 6t. Rusty-spotted genet	60	70
692	50t. on 12t. Hippopotamus	2·00	3·00

1990. "Stamp World London 90" International Stamp Exhibition. Multicoloured.

693	8t. Type **171**	35	10
694	15t. Transmission pylon	65	40
695	30t. Public telephone	1·00	75
696	2p. Testing circuit board	3·00	6·00

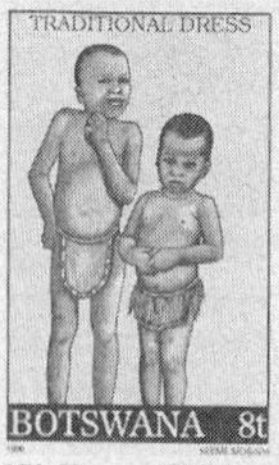

172 Young Children

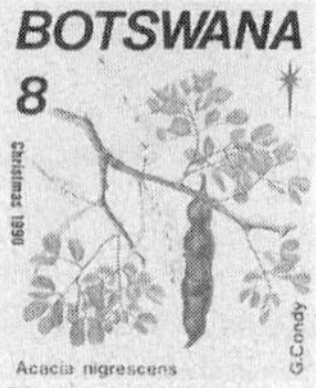

173 "Acacia nigrescens"

1990. Traditional Dress. Multicoloured.

697	8t. Type **172**	35	10
698	15t. Young woman	65	40
699	30t. Adult man	1·00	70
700	2p. Adult woman	3·00	6·00

1990. Christmas. Flowering Trees. Multicoloured.

702	8t. Type **173**	50	10
703	15t. "Peltophorum africanum"	85	35
704	30t. "Burkea africana"	1·50	75
705	2p. "Pterocarpus angolensis"	3·50	6·00

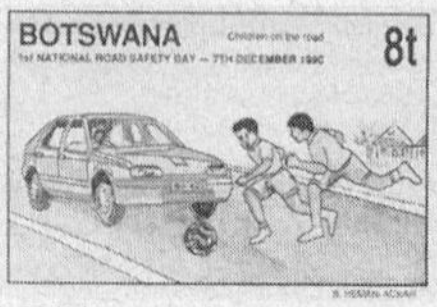

174 Children running in Front of Car

1990. 1st National Road Safety Day. Multicoloured.

706	8t. Type **174**	1·75	30
707	15t. Careless overtaking	2·25	1·00
708	30t. Cattle on road	2·75	2·75

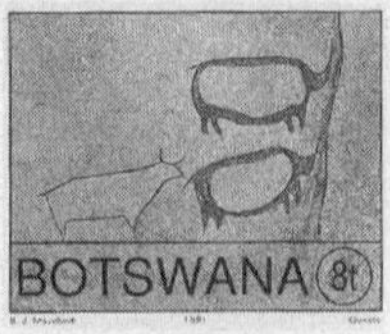

175 Cattle

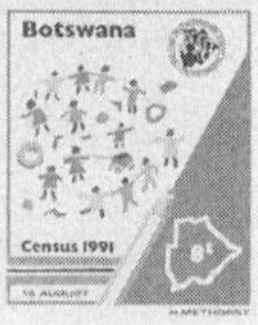

176 Children

1991. Rock Paintings. Multicoloured.

709	8t. Type **175**	1·50	40
710	15t. Cattle, drying frames and tree	2·00	85
711	30t. Animal hides	2·50	1·25
712	2p. Family herding cattle	4·50	7·50

1991. National Census. Multicoloured.

713	8t. Type **176**	70	10
714a	15t. Village	1·25	55
715	30t. School	1·50	75
716	2p. Hospital	5·50	7·50

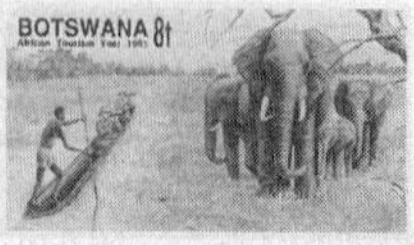

177 Tourists viewing Elephants

1991. African Tourism Year. Okavango Delta. Mult.

717	8t. Type **177**	1·50	70
718	15t. Crocodiles basking on river bank	1·75	90
719	35t. Fish eagles and De Havilland D.H.C.7 Dash Seven aircraft	3·50	3·25
720	2p. Okavango wildlife (26 × 44 mm)	5·50	8·00

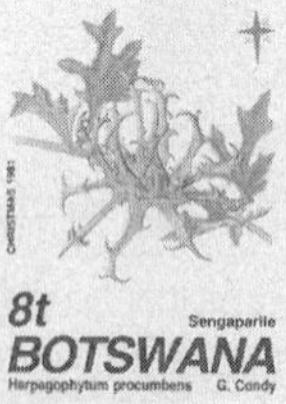

178 "Harpagophytum procumbens"

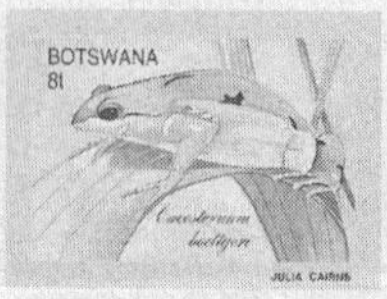

179 "Cacosternum boettgeri"

1991. Christmas. Seed Pods. Multicoloured.

721	8t. Type **178**	60	10
722	15t. "Tylosema esculentum"	1·00	40
723	30t. "Abrus precatorius"	1·75	80
724	2p. "Kigelia africana"	4·00	7·00

1992. Nos. 621, 624 and 627 surch.

725	8t. on 12t. Hippopotamus	1·00	60
726	10t. on 12t. Hippopotamus	1·00	60
727	25t. on 6t. Rusty-spotted genet	1·25	1·40
728	40t. on 3t. Zebra	2·25	3·25

1992. Climbing Frogs. Multicoloured.

729	8t. Type **179**	45	20
730	10t. "Hyperolius marmoratus angolensis" (vert)	45	20
731	40t. "Bufo fenoulheti"	1·40	1·25
732	1p. "Hyperolius sp." (vert)	2·00	4·50

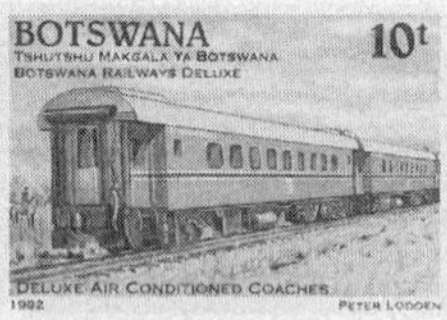

180 Air-conditioned Carriages

1992. Deluxe Railway Service. Multicoloured.

733	10t. Type **180**	1·25	40
734	25t. Diesel locomotive No. BD001 (vert)	2·00	80
735	40t. Carriage interior (vert)	2·25	1·00
736	2p. Diesel locomotive No. BD028	3·50	6·50

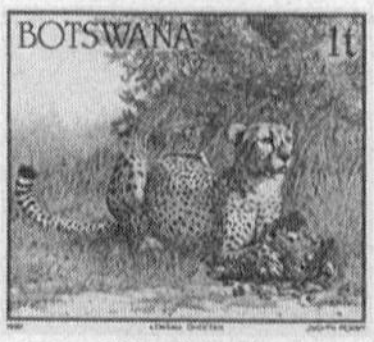

181 Cheetah

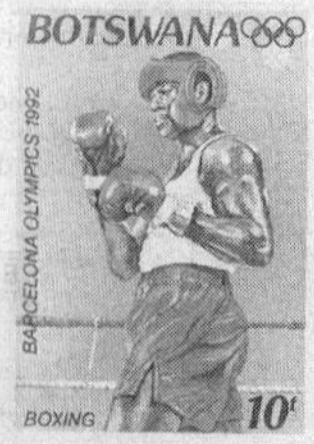

182 Boxing

1992. Animals. Multicoloured.

738	1t. Type **181**	30	1·25
739	2t. Spring hare	30	1·25
740	4t. Blackfooted cat	40	1·25
741	5t. Striped mouse	40	90
742	10t. Oribi	45	10
743	12t. Pangolin	75	1·75
744	15t. Aardwolf	75	40
745	20t. Warthog	75	40

746	25t. Ground squirrel	75	20
747	35t. Honey badger	1·00	30
748	40t. Common mole rat	1·00	30
749	45t. Wild dog	1·00	30
750	50t. Water mongoose	1·00	35
751	80t. Klipspringer	1·75	1·75
752	1p. Lesser bushbaby	1·75	1·75
753	2p. Bushveld elephant shrew	2·50	3·50
754	5p. Zorilla	4·25	6·50
755	10p. Vervet monkey	6·50	9·50

1992. Olympic Games, Barcelona. Multicoloured.

756	10t. Type **182**	50	10
757	50t. Running	1·25	50
758	1p. Boxing (different)	1·75	2·25
759	2p. Running (different)	2·25	4·00

183 "Adiantum incisum"

184 Helping Blind Person (Lions Club International)

1992. Christmas. Ferns. Multicoloured.

761	10t. Type **183**	40	10
762	25t. "Actiniopteris radiata"	70	35
763	40t. "Ceratopteris cornuta"	1·00	55
764	1p.50 "Pellaea calomelanos"	3·00	5·50

1993. Charitable Organizations in Botswana. Mult.

765	10t. Type **184**	70	20
766	15t. Nurse carrying child (Red Cross Society) (horiz)	80	35
767	25t. Woman watering seedling (Ecumenical Decade)	80	40
768	35t. Deaf children (Round Table) (horiz)	1·00	1·25
769	40t. Crowd of people (Rotary International)	1·00	1·60
770	50t. Hands at prayer (Botswana Christian Council) (horiz)	1·25	2·25

185 Bechuanaland Railways Class "6" Locomotive No. 1

186 Long-crested Eagle

1993. Railway Centenary. Multicoloured.

771	10t. Type **185**	75	30
772	40t. Class "19" locomotive No. 317	1·40	75
773	50t. Class "12" locomotive No. 256	1·40	80
774	1p.50 Class "7" locomotive No. 71	2·00	4·00

1993. Endangered Eagles. Multicoloured.

776	10t. Type **186**	55	35
777	25t. Short-toed eagle ("Snake eagle")	1·00	65
778	50t. Bateleur ("Bateleur Eagle")	1·40	1·75
779	1p.50 Secretary bird	2·50	4·50

187 "Aloe zebrina"

1993. Christmas. Flora. Multicoloured.

780	12t. Type **187**	40	10
781	25t. "Croton megalobotrys"	60	25
782	50t. "Boophane disticha"	85	70
783	1p. "Euphoria davyi"	1·25	2·75

188 Boy with String Puppet

1994. Traditional Toys. Multicoloured.

784	10t. Type **188**	20	10
785	40t. Boys with clay cattle	45	30
786	50t. Boy with spinner	50	50
787	1p. Girls playing in make-believe houses	1·10	2·25

189 Interior of Control Tower, Gaborone Airport

1994. 50th Anniv of I.C.A.O. Multicoloured.

788	10t. Type **189**	40	10
789	25t. Crash tender	55	30
790	40t. Loading supplies onto airliner (vert)	75	75
791	50t. Control tower, Gaborone (vert)	80	1·50

1994. No. 743 surch **10t.**

792	10t. on 12t. Pangolin	3·50	75

191 Lesser Flamingos at Sua Pan

192 "Ziziphus mucronata"

1994. Environment Protection. Makgadikgadi Pans. Multicoloured.

793	10t. Type **191**	75	40
794	35t. Baobab trees (horiz)	50	40
795	50t. Zebra and palm trees	65	80
796	2p. Map of area (horiz)	2·50	4·50

1994. Christmas. Edible Fruits. Multicoloured.

797	10t. Type **192**	25	10
798	25t. "Strychnos cocculoides"	40	30
799	40t. "Bauhinia petersiana"	60	70
800	50t. "Schinziphyton rautoneii"	70	1·10

193 Fisherman with Bow and Arrow

194 Boys watering Horses (F.A.O.)

1995. Traditional Fishing. Multicoloured.

801	15t. Type **193**	35	20
802	40t. Men in canoe and boy with fishing rod	60	40
803	65t. Fisherman with net	80	75
804	80t. Fisherman with basket fish trap	1·00	1·60

1995. 50th Anniv of United Nations. Multicoloured.

805	20t. Type **194**	20	10
806	50t. Schoolchildren queueing for soup (W.F.P.)	35	30
807	80t. Letters and postman delivering to village (U.N.D.P.)	60	80
808	1p. Weighing baby (U.N.I.C.E.F.)	70	1·50

195 Brown Hyena

1995. Endangered Species. Brown Hyena. Mult.

809	20t. Type **195**	45	50
810	50t. Pair of hyenas	65	65
811	80t. Hyena stealing ostrich eggs	1·10	1·25
812	1p. Adult hyena and cubs	1·25	1·75

196 "Adenia glauca"

198 Spears

1995. Christmas. Plants. Multicoloured.

813	20t. Type **196**	25	10
814	50t. "Pterodiscus ngamicus"	45	30

815	80t. "Sesamothamnus lugardii"	75	80
816	1p. "Fockea multiflora"	80	1·50

1996. Nos. 738/40 surch.

817	20t. on 2t. Spring hare	40	30
818	30t. on 1t. Type **181**	40	30
819	70t. on 4t. Blackfooted cat	1·00	1·60

1996. Traditional Weapons. Multicoloured.

820	20t. Type **198**	20	10
821	50t. Axes	35	30
822	80t. Shield and knobkerries	55	65
823	1p. Knives and sheaths	60	1·10

199 Child with Basic Radio

200 Olympic Flame, Rings and Wreath

1996. Centenary of Radio. Multicoloured.

824	20t. Type **199**	25	10
825	50t. Radio Botswana's mobile transmitter	40	30
826	80t. Police radio control	60	70
827	1p. Listening to radio	70	1·25

1996. Centenary of Modern Olympic Games. Mult.

828	20t. Type **200**	25	10
829	50t. Pierre de Coubertin (founder of modern Olympics)	40	30
830	80t. Map of Botswana with flags and athletes	75	75
831	1p. Ruins of ancient stadium at Olympia	75	1·25

201 Family Planning Class (Botswana Family Welfare Association)

202 "Adansonia digitata" Leaf and Blossom

1996. Local Charities. Multicoloured.

832	20t. Type **201**	20	10
833	30t. Blind workers (Pudulogong Rehabilitation Centre)	20	15
834	50t. Collecting seeds (Forestry Association of Botswana)	30	30
835	70t. Secretarial class (Y.W.C.A.)	40	70
836	80t. Children's day centre (Botswana Council of Women)	50	75
837	1p. Children's village, Tlokweng (S.O.S. Children's village)	60	1·10

1996. Christmas. Parts of Life Cycle for "Adansonia digitata". Multicoloured.

838	20t. Type **202**	25	10
839	50t. Fruit	40	25
840	80t. Tree in leaf	60	70
841	1p. Tree with bare branches	70	1·25

203 Tati Hotel

204 Steam Locomotive, Bechuanaland Railway, 1897

1997. Francistown Centenary. Multicoloured.

842	20t. Type **203**	15	10
843	50t. Railway Station	55	35
844	80t. Company Manager's House	60	70
845	1p. Monarch Mine	80	1·25

1997. Railway Centenary. Multicoloured.

846	35t. Type **204**	30	20
847	50t. Elephants crossing railway line	50	35
848	80t. First locomotive in Bechuanaland, 1897	60	45
849	1p. Beyer-Garratt type steam locomotive No. 352	65	65

850	2p. Diesel locomotive No. BD339	90	1·50
851	2p.50 Fantuzzi container stacker	1·00	1·75

205 Pel's Fishing Owl

206 "Combretum zeyheri"

1997. Birds. Multicoloured.

852	5t. Type **205**	10	10
853	10t. African Harrier Hawk ("Gymnogene") (horiz)	10	10
854	15t. Brown parrot ("Meyer's Parrot")	10	10
855	20t. Harlequin quail (horiz)	10	10
856	25t. Mariqua sunbird ("Marico Sunbird") (horiz)	10	10
857	30t. Kurrichane thrush (horiz)	10	10
858	40t. Paradise Sparrow ("Redheaded Finch")	10	10
859	50t. Red-billed buffalo weaver ("Buffalo Weaver")	10	15
860	60t. Sacred ibis (horiz)	15	20
861	70t. Cape shoveler (horiz)	15	20
862	80t. Black-throated honeyguide ("Greater Honeyguide") (horiz)	20	25
863	1p. Woodland kingfisher (horiz)	20	25
864	1p.25 Purple heron	30	35
865	1p.50 Yellow-billed oxpecker (horiz)	35	40
866	2p. Shaft-tailed whydah	45	50
867	2p.50 White stork	50	55
868	5p. Ovampo sparrow hawk ("Sparrowhawk")	1·10	1·25
869	10p. Spotted crake	2·25	2·40

No. 861 is inscribed "Shoveller" in error.

1997. Golden Wedding of Queen Elizabeth and Prince Philip. As T **173** of Ascension. Multicoloured.

870	35t. Prince Philip with carriage	20	40
871	35t. Queen Elizabeth with binoculars	20	40
872	2p. Queen Elizabeth with horse team	90	1·40
873	2p. Prince Philip and horse	90	1·40
874	2p.50 Queen Elizabeth and Prince Philip	1·10	1·40
875	2p.50 Princess Anne and Prince Edward	1·10	1·40

1997. Christmas. Plants. Multicoloured.

877	35t. Type **206**	30	10
878	1p. "Combretum apiculatum"	75	35
879	2p. "Combretum molle"	1·40	1·40
880	2p.50 "Combretum imberbe"	1·60	1·75

207 Baobab Trees

1998. Tourism (1st series). Multicoloured.

881	35t. Type **207**	25	15
882	1p. Crocodile	50	40
883	2p. Stalactites (vert)	85	1·10
884	2p.50 Tourists and rock paintings (vert)	1·10	1·60

See also Nos. 899/902.

1998. Diana, Princess of Wales Commemoration. As T **223a** of Bahamas. Multicoloured.

885	35t. Princess Diana, 1990	25	15
886	1p. In green hat, 1992	40	35
887	2p. In white blouse, 1993	75	1·10
888	2p.50 With crowd, Cambridge, 1993	90	1·50

208 "Village Life" (tapestry)

209 "Ficus ingens"

1998. Botswana Weavers. Multicoloured.

890	35t. Type **208**	25	15
891	55t. Weaver dyeing threads	30	20
892	1p. "African wildlife" (tapestry)	75	65
893	2p. Weaver at loom	95	1·60

1998. Christmas. Plants. Multicoloured.

895	35t. Type **209**	30	10
896	55t. "Ficus pygmaea"	40	20

897 1p. "Ficus abutilifolia" ... 70 45
898 2p.50 "Ficus sycomorus" .. 1·40 2·25

1999. Tourism (2nd series). As T **207**. Multicoloured.
899 35t. Rock painting of men and cattle ... 25 10
900 55t. Expedition at Salt Pan 30 20
901 1p. Rock painting of elephant and antelope (vert) ... 50 45
902 2p. Tourists under Baobab tree (vert) ... 70 1·25

211 Modern Post Office

1999. 125th Anniv of Universal Postal Union.
904 **211** 2p. multicoloured .... 1·00 1·10

212 Mpule Kwelagobe winning contest

1999. Mpule Kwelagobe ("Miss Universe 1999"). Multicoloured.
905 35t. Type **212** ... 20 10
906 1p. In traditional dress (horiz) ... 50 30
907 2p. In traditional dancing costume with lion ... 85 60
908 2p.50 Wearing "Botswana" sash (horiz) ... 95 75
909 15p. With leopard in background (horiz) ... 5·50 7·00

213 Saddle-bill Stork and Limpopo River

2000. Scenic Rivers. Multicoloured.
911 35t. Type **213** ... 25 10
912 1p. Hippopotamuses in water lilies (vert) ... 50 30
913 2p. African skimmer and makoro (dugout canoe) ... 85 85
914 2p.50 African elephant at sunset, Chobe River (vert) ... 1·00 1·25

214 Mopane Moth

2000. Moths. Multicoloured.
915 35t. Type **214** ... 15 10
916 70t. Wild silk moth ... 25 20
917 1p. Crimson speckled footman ("Tiger Moth") ... 35 30
918 2p. African lunar moth ... 65 60
919 15p. Speckled emperor moth 4·75 6·50

215 Mother reading Medicine Label with Child ("Protect Your Children")

2000. United Nations Literacy Decade. Mult.
921 35t. Type **215** ... 15 10
922 70t. Adult literacy class ("Never Too Old To Learn") ... 25 20
923 2p. Man smoking next to petrol pump ("Be Aware Of Danger") ... 65 65
924 2p.50 Man at Automatic Teller Machine ("Be Independent") ... 85 1·10

216 Pres. Sir Seretse Khama

217 Doctor giving Eye Test

2000. Chiefs and Presidents.
925 **216** 35t. black, red and gold ... 10 10
926 – 1p. multicoloured ... 20 25
927 – 2p. multicoloured ... 55 60
928 – 2p.50 multicoloured ... 70 90
DESIGNS—HORIZ (60 × 40 mm): 35t. Chiefs Sebele I of Bakwena, Bathoen I of Bangwaketse and Khama III of Bangato, 1895. VERT (as T **216**): 2p. Pres. Sir Ketumile Masire; 2p.50, Pres. Festus Mogae.

2000. Airborne Medical Service. Multicoloured.
929 35t. Type **217** ... 15 10
930 1p. Medical team and family ... 40 30
931 2p. Aircraft over canoes ... 75 75
932 2p.50 Donkeys and mule cart on airstrip ... 85 1·00

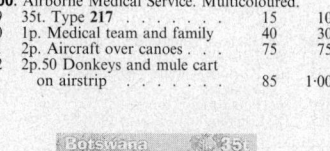

218 Hippopotamus

2000. Wetlands (1st series). Okavango Delta. Mult.
933 35t. Type **218** ... 15 10
934 1p. Tiger fish and tilapia ... 35 30
935 1p.75 Painted reed frog and wattled crane (vert) ... 70 75
936 2p. Pels fishing owl and vervet monkey (vert) ... 70 75
937 2p.50 Nile crocodile, Sitatunga and red lechwe ... 70 85
See also Nos. 958/62.

219 Diamonds

2001. Diamonds. Multicoloured. Self-adhesive.
940 35t. Type **219** ... 15 10
941 1p.75 J.C.B. in open-cast mine ... 70 65
942 2p. Quality inspector ... 75 75
943 2p.50 Diamonds in jewellery ... 80 90

220 African Pygmy Falcon

2001. Kgalagadi Transfrontier Wildlife Park. Joint Issue with South Africa. Multicoloured.
944 35t. Type **220** ... 10 15
945 1p. Leopard ... 20 25
946 2p. Gemsbok ... 45 50
947 2p.50 Bat-eared fox ... 50 55

221 Shallow Basket

2001. Traditional Baskets. Multicoloured.
949 35t. Type **221** ... 10 15
950 1p. Tall basket ... 20 25
951 2p. Woman weaving basket ... 45 50
952 2p.50 Spherical basket ... 50 55

222 Boys by River at Sunset

2001. Scenic Skies. Multicoloured.
954 50t. Type **222** ... 10 15
955 1p. Woman with baby at sunset ... 20 25
956 2p. Girls carrying firewood at sunset ... 45 50
957 10p. Traditional village at sunset near huts ... 2·25 2·40

2001. Wetlands (2nd series). Chobe River. As T **218**. Multicoloured.
958 50t. Water monitor and carmine bee-eater ... 10 15
959 1p.75 Buffalo ... 40 45
960 2p. Savanna baboons (vert) ... 45 50
961 2p.50 Lion (vert) ... 50 55
962 3p. African elephants in river ... 65 70

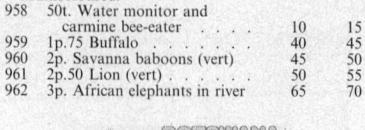

223 Black Mamba

2002. Snakes. Multicoloured.
964 50t. Type **223** ... 10 15
965 1p.75 Spitting cobra (vert) ... 40 45
966 2p.50 Puff adder ... 50 55
967 3p. Boomslang (vert) ... 65 70

POSTAGE DUE STAMPS

1967. Nos. D10/12 of Bechuanaland optd **REPUBLIC OF BOTSWANA.**
D13 D **1** 1c. red ... 15 1·75
D14 2c. violet ... 15 1·75
D15 5c. green ... 20 1·75

D **5** African Elephant

D **6** Common Zebra

1971.
D16 D **5** 1c. red ... 1·10 3·25
D17 2c. violet ... 1·40 3·50
D18 6c. brown ... 1·75 5·50
D19 14c. green ... 2·00 7·50

1977.
D25a D **6** 1t. black and red ... 30 75
D26a 2t. black and green ... 30 75
D27a 4t. black and red ... 30 75
D28a 10t. black and blue ... 30 75
D29a 16t. black and brown ... 35 1·00

BOYACA   Pt. 20

One of the states of the Granadine Confederation. A Department of Colombia from 1886, now uses Colombian stamps.

100 centavos = 1 peso.

1 Mendoza Perez

1899. Imperf or perf.
1 **1** 5c. green ... 60 1·50

2

6 Battle of Boyaca Monument

1903. Imperf or perf.
3 **2** 10c. grey ... 15 15
4 10c. blue ... 60 60

12 – 10c. orange ... 20 15
5 **2** 20c. brown ... 20 20
5a 20c. lake ... 25 25
6 – 50c. turquoise ... 15 15
8 – 1p. red ... 20 15
9 – 1p. red ... 1·40 1·40
10 **6** 5p. black on red ... 50 35
11 – 10p. black on buff ... 50 40
DESIGNS—As Type **2**: 10c. orange, Building; 50c. Gen. Pinzon; 1p. Figure of value. As Type **6**: 10p. Pres. Marroquin.

BRAZIL   Pt. 20

A country in the N.E. of S. America. Portuguese settlement, 1500. Kingdom, 1815. Empire, 1822. Republic from 1889.

1843. 1000 reis = 1 milreis.
1942. 100 centavos = 1 cruzeiro.
1986. 100 centavos = 1 cruzado.
1990. 100 centavos = 1 cruzeiro.
1994. 100 centavos = 1 real.

1 "Bull's Eye"

1843. Imperf.
4 **1** 30r. black ... £2250 £375
5 60r. black ... £600 £200
6 90r. black ... £2250 £950

2   3   4

1844. Imperf.
10 **2** 10r. black ... £120 24·00
11 30r. black ... £150 35·00
12 60r. black ... £120 24·00
13 90r. black ... £900 £140
14 180r. black ... £3750 £1100
15 300r. black ... £4750 £1400
16 600r. black ... £4500 £1600

1850. Imperf.
17 **3** 10r. black ... 30·00 26·00
18 20r. black ... 90·00 £110
19 30r. black ... 12·00 3·50
20 60r. black ... 12·00 2·50
21 90r. black ... 95·00 12·00
22 180r. black ... £120 55·00
23 300r. black ... £350 70·00
24 600r. black ... £450 80·00

1854. Imperf.
25 **3** 10r. blue ... 12·00 9·00
26 30r. blue ... 35·00 55·00
27 **4** 280r. red ... £120 85·00
28 430r. yellow ... £190 £120

5   6

17 Emperor Dom Pedro II

1866. Various frames, but in T **5** the Emperor has a dark beard. Perf or roul.
43 **5** 10r. red ... 9·00 5·25
44a **6** 20r. purple ... 12·00 3·00
45 **5** 50r. blue ... 20·00 1·75
46a 80r. purple ... 55·00 4·75
47a 100r. green ... 20·00 1·25
55 **6** 200r. black ... 48·00 4·75
67 **17** 300r. green and orange ... 90·00 24·00
56 **5** 500r. orange ... £160 24·00

12   13

1878. Various frames, but in T **13** the Emperor's beard is white. Roulette.

57	**12**	10r. red	9·00	3·00
58	**13**	20r. mauve	12·00	2·40
59	**12**	50r. blue	18·00	1·75
60		80r. red	20·00	9·50
61		100r. green	20·00	1·25
62		200r. black	£110	15·00
63		260r. brown	60·00	20·00
64		300r. brown	60·00	6·00
65		700r. red	£130	80·00
66		1000r. grey	£140	35·00

21

27 Pedro II

1881. Various frames. Perf.

71	**21**	10r. black	12·00	26·00
72		10r. orange	3·00	1·75
73		50r. blue	30·00	3·00
74		100r. olive	50·00	3·00
77		100r. lilac	£175	1·75
75a		200r. red	42·00	3·50

No. 77 is inscr "CORREIO".

1884.

81	**27**	100r. lilac	£175	3·50

25

26

29

30 Southern Cross

31

32

33 Entrance to Bay of Rio de Janeiro

35 Southern Cross

1884.

78	**25**	20r. green	24·00	3·50
80	**26**	50r. blue	20·00	5·25
83	**29**	100r. lilac	48·00	1·75
84	**30**	300r. blue	£200	26·00
85a	**31**	500r. olive	£110	12·00
86	**32**	700r. lilac	75·00	£125
87	**33**	1000r. blue	£225	£125

1890.

97a	**35**	20r. green	2·40	2·40
89		50r. green	4·75	2·40
110a		100r. purple	30·00	1·75
91		200r. violet	10·50	2·40
100		300r. slate	70·00	6·00
92		300r. blue	70·00	6·00
93		500r. buff	18·00	10·50
94		500r. grey	18·00	10·50
95		700r. brown	26·00	35·00
96		1000r. yellow	18·00	3·50

37 Head of Liberty

38 Head of Liberty

1891.

111d	**37**	100r. red and blue	35·00	1·75

1893.

114	**38**	100r. red	70·00	1·75

39 Sugar-loaf Mountain

41 Head of Liberty

43 Head of Mercury

1894.

124	**39**	10r. blue and red	1·90	60
125		20r. blue and orange	90	45
126		50r. blue	5·25	3·50
232		50r. green	9·00	3·75
127	**41**	100r. black and red	3·50	40
239		100r. red	18·00	35
128		200r. black and orange	90	35
234		200r. blue	10·50	35
129		300r. black and green	14·00	60
153		500r. black and blue	26·00	1·75
131a		700r. black and mauve	14·50	1·75
132	**43**	1000r. mauve and green	55·00	1·75
133		2000r. purple and grey	55·00	12·00

1897. As T **39** but inscr "REIS REIS" instead of "DEZ REIS".

165a		10r. blue and red	1·60	60

1898. Newspaper stamps of 1889 surch **1898** between value twice in figures.

168	N **34**	100r. on 50r. orange	1·90	55·00
169		200r. on 100r. mauve	3·50	95
170		300r. on 200r. black	3·50	95
171		500r. on 300r. red	5·25	4·00
173		700r. on 500r. green	7·00	1·75
172		700r. on 500r. orange	7·00	18·00
174		1000r. on 700r. orange	35·00	35·00
175		1000r. on 700r. blue	25·00	18·00
176		2000r. on 1000r. orange	25·00	18·00
177		2000r. on 1000r. brown	19·00	7·00

1898. Newspaper stamp of 1890 surch **200** over **1898**.

180	N **37**	200r. on 100r. mauve	14·00	9·00

1898. Newspaper stamps of 1890 surch **1898** over new value.

182	N **38**	20r. on 10r. blue	1·75	3·50
183		50r. on 20r. green	9·00	10·50
184		100r. on 50r. green	18·00	21·00

1899. Postage stamps of 1890 surch **1899** over new value.

194	**35**	50r. on 20r. green	1·75	3·50
195		100r. on 50r. green	1·75	3·50
196		300r. on 200r. violet	9·00	18·00
190b		500r. on 300r. slate	55·00	12·50
190		500r. on 300r. blue	55·00	12·50
191		700r. on 500r. buff	35·00	10·50
192a		1,000r. on 700r. brown	25·00	10·50
193		2,000r. on 1,000r. yellow	35·00	5·25

50 Discovery of Brazil

52 Emancipation of Slaves

1900. 400th Anniv of Discovery of Brazil.

226	**50**	100r. red	7·00	3·50
227	–	200r. green and yellow	7·00	3·50
228	**52**	500r. blue	7·00	3·50
229	–	700r. green	7·00	3·50

DESIGNS—HORIZ: 200r. Declaration of Independence. VERT: 700r. Allegory of Republic.

56 Pan-American Congress

1906.

259a	**56**	100r. red	42·00	26·00
259b		200r. blue	90·00	8·75

57 Aristides Lobo

61 Liberty

1906.

260	**57**	10r. grey	90	20
261	–	20r. violet	90	20
262	–	50r. green	90	20
264	–	100r. red	1·75	20
265	–	200r. blue	1·75	20
267	–	300r. brown	3·50	60
268	–	400r. olive	26·00	1·75
269	–	500r. violet	5·25	60
272	–	600r. olive	2·75	90
273	–	700r. brown	5·25	2·75
274	**61**	1000r. red	28·00	90
275	–	1000r. green	3·50	35
276	–	1000r. grey	19·00	60
277	**61**	2000r. green	18·00	60
278		2000r. blue	9·00	90
279		5000r. pink	7·00	1·75
280	–	5000r. brown	55·00	10·50
281	–	10000r. brown	7·00	1·75

PORTRAITS: 20r. B. Constant. 50r. A. Cabral. 100r. Wandendkolk. 200r. D. da Fonseca. 300r. F. Peixoto. 400r., 600r. P. de Moraes. 500r. C. Salles. 700r., 5000r. (No. 280) R. Alves. 1000r. (Nos. 275/6) B. do Rio Branco. 10000r. N. Pecanha.

64 King Carlos and Pres. Affonso Penna and Emblems of Portuguese-Brazilian Amity

65 Emblems of Peace, Commerce and Industry

1908. Centenary of Opening of Brazilian Ports to Foreign Commerce.

282	**64**	100r. red	14·50	1·75

1908. National Exhibition, Rio de Janeiro.

283	**65**	100r. red	45·00	2·40

66 Bonifacio, San Martin, Hidalgo, Washington, O'Higgins, Bolivar

67 Cape Frio

1909. Pan-American Congress, Rio de Janeiro.

284	**66**	200r. blue	14·50	1·25

1915. 300th Anniv of Discovery of Cape Frio.

285	**67**	100r. turquoise on yellow	7·00	5·25

69 Bay of Guajara

1916. 300th Anniv of City of Belem.

286	**69**	100r. red	12·50	5·00

70 Revolutionary Flag

1917. Centenary of Pernambuco Revolution.

287	**70**	100r. blue	18·00	9·00

71 Liberty

72 Liberty

74 Inscr "BRAZIL"

1918. Various frames.

288	**71**	10r. brown	60	35
289		20r. violet	60	35
290		25r. grey	60	35
291		50r. green	1·75	60
292	**72**	100r. red	1·75	35
293		200r. blue	7·00	45
294		300r. orange	19·00	3·50
295		500r. purple	19·00	3·50
296		600r. orange	2·75	8·75
297	**74**	1000r. blue	7·00	35
298		2000r. brown	26·00	7·00
299		5000r. lilac	7·00	7·00
300		10,000r. red	9·00	1·00

77 Steam Locomotive

78 "Industry"

79 "Agriculture"

80 "Aviation"

81 Mercury

82 "Shipping"

1920. T **74** inscr "BRASIL".

317	**77**	10r. purple	60	60
387	**80**	10r. brown	35	35
318	**77**	20r. grey	60	60
388	**80**	20r. violet	35	35
389	**78**	25r. purple	35	1·10
354	**79**	40r. brown	60	60
306	**78**	50r. green	1·25	60
355		50r. brown	60	60
390	**80**	50r. purple	35	35
391		50r. green	35	35
308	**79**	80r. green	20	3·50
309	**80**	100r. red	3·50	60
392		100r. orange	60	35
367		100r. green	1·25	60
420		100r. yellow	1·75	35
311		150r. violet	1·75	60
312		200r. blue	5·25	60
330		200r. red	1·25	60
383		200r. green	4·75	60
405	**81**	300r. grey	60	35
394		300r. green	1·50	35
333		300r. red	1·25	35
406		400r. blue	1·50	35
335		400r. orange	1·25	3·50
407		500r. brown	1·75	35
385		500r. blue	2·40	60
397		600r. brown	9·00	30
422		600r. orange	5·25	35
341	**82**	600r. orange	1·75	60
409	**81**	700r. violet	3·50	35
342	**82**	1000r. purple	3·50	35
410	**81**	1000r. blue	9·00	35
362c	**74**	2000r. blue	10·50	1·25
411		2000r. violet	10·50	1·25
363a		5000r. brown	21·00	1·25
364		10000r. purple	21·00	1·75

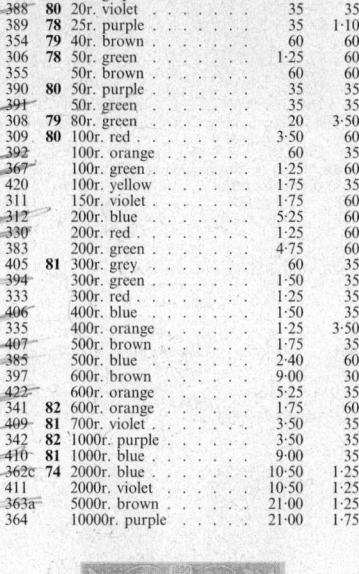

93 King Albert and Pres. Pessoa

1920. Visit of King of the Belgians.

431	**93**	100r. red	70	50

94 Declaration of Ypiranga

97 Brazilian Army entering Bahia

1922. Centenary of Independence.

432	**94**	100r. blue	5·25	90
433	–	200r. red	10·50	60
434	–	300r. green	10·50	60

DESIGNS: 200r. Dom Pedro I and J. Bonifacio; 300r. National Exn. and Pres. Pessoa.

1923. Centenary of Capture of Bahia from the Portuguese.

435	**97**	200r. red	12·00	7·00

98 Arms of the Confederation

99 Ruy Barbosa

1924. Centenary of Confederation of the Equator.

436	**98**	200r. multicoloured	3·50	1·90

1927.

438b	**99**	1000r. red	2·40	1·25

100 "Justice"

1927. Centenary of Law Courses.

439	**100**	100r. blue	1·75	60
440	–	200r. red	1·25	35

DESIGN: 200r. Map and Balances.

1928. Air. Official stamps of 1913, Type O **67**, surch **SERVICO AEREO** and new value. Centres in black.

441	50r. on 10r. grey	35	35
442	200r. on 1000r. brown	2·40	4·50
443	200r. on 2000r. brown	1·25	9·50
444	200r. on 5000r. bistre	1·50	1·25
445	300r. on 500r. yellow	1·50	1·90
446	300r. on 600r. purple	90	65
447	500r. on 50r. grey	1·50	65
448	1000r. on 20r. olive	1·25	35
449	2000r. on 100r. red	2·25	1·50
450	2000r. on 200r. blue	3·00	1·60
451	2000r. on 10,000r. black	2·25	65
452	5000r. on 20,000r. blue	8·75	3·75
453	5000r. on 50,000r. green	8·75	3·75
454	5000r. on 100,000r. red	24·00	30·00
455	10,000r. on 500,000r. brown	24·00	24·00
456	10,000r. on 1,000,000r. sepia	24·00	24·00

104 Liberty holding Coffee Leaves **106** Ruy Barbosa

1928. Bicent of Introduction of the Coffee Plant.
457 **104** 100r. green . . . . 3·50 2·40
458 200r. red . . . . 1·75 1·25
459 300r. black . . . . 10·50 60

1928. Official stamps of 1919 surch.
460 **O 77** 700r. on 500r. orange . . 9·00 9·00
461 1000r. on 100r. red . . . 5·25 60
462 2000r. on 200r. blue . . 7·00 1·25
463 5000r. on 50r. green . . 7·00 1·75
464 10,000r. on 10r. brown 25·00 1·75

1929.
465 **106** 5000r. blue . . . . 21·00 1·25

108 Santos Dumonts Airship "Ballon No. 6" **109** Santos Dumont

1929. Air.
469 – 50r. green 15 10
470 **108** 200r. red . . . . 1·50 15
471 – 300r. blue . . . . 2·00 15
472 – 500r. purple . . . . . . 2·40 15
473 – 1000r. brown . . . . . 7·00 25
479 – 2000r. green . . . . . . 12·00 1·25
480 – 5000r. red . . . . . . 14·50 1·40
481 **109** 10,000r. grey . . . . . . 14·50 3·00
DESIGNS: 50r. De Gusmao's monument; 300r. A. Severo's airship "Pax"; 500r. Santos Dumont's biplane "14 bis"; 1000r. R. de Barros's flying boat "Jahu"; 2000r. De Gusmao; 5000r. A. Severo.

110 **112**

1930. Air.
486 **110** 3000r. violet . . . . . . 1·75 1·75

1930. 4th Pan-American Architectural Congress.
487 – 100r. turquoise . . . . . 3·50 3·50
488 **112** 200r. grey . . . . 6·00 2·40
489 – 300r. red . . . . 8·25 3·50
DESIGNS: 100r. Sun rays inscr "ARCHITECTOS"; 300r. Architrave and Southern Cross.

113 G. Vargas and J. Pessoa – "Redemption of Brazil" **114** O. Aranha – "What is the matter?"

1931. Charity. Revolution of 3 October 1930.
490 **113** 10r.+10r. blue . . . . . 15 12·00
491 20r.+20r. brown . . . . . 15 9·00
492 **114** 50r.+50r. green, red and yellow 15 15
493 **113** 100r.+50r. orange . . . . 1·25 60
494 200r.+100r. green 60 60
495 – 300r.+150r. mult 60 60
496 **113** 400r.+200r. red . . . . . 1·75 1·75
497 500r.+250r. blue . . . . 1·25 90
498 600r.+300r. purple . . . 90 18·00
499 700r.+350r. mult . . . . 1·25 90
500 1$+500r. green, red and yellow . . . . 3·50 60
501 – 2$+1$ grey and red . . . 12·00 1·25
502 – 5$+2$ 500r. blk & red . . 24·00 12·00
503 – 10$+5$ green & yellow . . 60·00 18·00
DESIGNS: 300r., 700r. as Type **113**, but portraits in circles and frames altered. Milreis values as Type **114** with different portraits and frames.

1931. No. 333 surch **1931 200 Reis**.
507 **81** 200r. on 300r. red 60 35

1931. Zeppelin Air Stamps. Surch **ZEPPELIN** and value.
508 **108** 2$500 on 200r. red (No. 470) . . . . . . 35·00 35·00
511 **106** 3$500 on 5000r. blue (No. 468b) . . . . . . 25·00 25·00
509 – 5$000 on 300r. blue (No. 471) . . . . . . 45·00 45·00
512 **74** 7$000 on 10,000r. red (No. 364) . . . . . . 28·00 28·00

1931. Air. No. 486 surch **2.500 REIS**.
510 **110** 2500r. on 3000r. violet . . 26·00 26·00

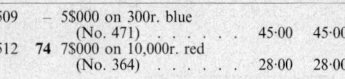

121 Brazil

1932. 400th Anniv of Colonization of Sao Vicente.
513 **121** 20r. purple 35 35
514 – 100r. black 90 90
515 – 200r. violet . . . . 1·75 35
516 – 600r. brown . . . . . . 3·00 2·75
517 – 700r. blue . . . . 3·50 3·00
DESIGNS: 100r. Natives; 200r. M. Afonso de Souza; 600r. King John III of Portugal; 700r. Founding of Sao Vicente.

125 Soldier and Flag **130** "Justice"

1932. Sao Paulo Revolutionary Government issue.
518 – 100r. brown . . . . 1·25 3·50
519 **125** 200r. red . . . . 60 1·25
520 – 300r. green . . . . 2·40 7·00
521 – 400r. blue . . . . 5·25 9·00
522 – 500r. sepia . . . . 7·00 9·00
523 – 600r. red . . . . 7·00 9·00
524 **125** 700r. violet . . . . 3·50 9·00
525 – 1000r. orange . . . . . . 2·40 9·00
526 – 2000r. brown . . . . . . 21·00 35·00
527 – 5000r. green . . . . . . 26·00 60·00
528 **130** 10,000r. purple . . . . . 30·00 70·00
DESIGNS—As Type **125**: 100r., 500r. Map of Brazil; 300r., 600r. Symbolical of freedom, etc., 400r., 1000r. Soldier in tin helmet. As Type **130**: 2000r. "LEX" and sword; 5000r. "Justice" and soldiers with bayonets.

131 Campo Bello Square and memorial. Vassouras

1933. Centenary of Vassouras.
529 **131** 200r. red . . . . 1·25 1·25

132 Flag and Dornier Wal Flying Boat

1933. Air.
532 **132** 3500r. blue, green & yell 1·75 1·75

1933. Surch **200 REIS**.
536 **81** 200r. on 300r. red 60 60

134 Flag of the Race

1933. 441st Anniv of Departure of Columbus from Polos.
537 **134** 200r. red . . . . 1·75 1·25

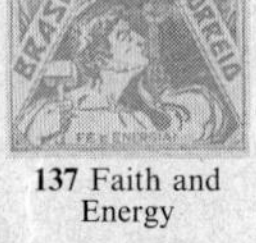

135 Christian Symbols **137** Faith and Energy

136 From Santos Dumont Statue, St. Cloud

1933. 1st Eucharistic Congress, Sao Salvador.
538 **135** 200r. red 70 40

1933. Obligatory Tax for Airport Fund.
539 **136** 100r. purple 60 10

1933.
540 **137** 200r. red 60 35
543 200r. violet . . . . 1·25 35

138 "Republic" and Flags **139** Santos Dumont Statue, St. Cloud

1933. Visit of Pres. Justo of Argentina.
545 **138** 200r. blue 65 60
546 400r. green . . . . 1·75 1·75
547 600r. red . . . . 5·25 7·00
548 1000r. violet . . . . . . 7·00 5·25

1934. 1st National Aviation Congress, Sao Paulo.
549 **139** 200r. blue . . . . 1·25 70

140 Exhibition Building

1934. 7th International Sample Fair, Rio de Janeiro.
550 **140** 200r. brown 65 65
551 400r. red . . . . 3·50 3·50
552 700r. blue . . . . 3·50 3·00
553 1000r. orange . . . . . . 7·00 1·75

141 Brazilian Stamp of 1844

1934. National Philatelic Exhibition, Rio. Imperf.
555 **141** 200r.+100r. purple . . . 1·25 3·00
556 300r.+100r. red . . . . 1·25 3·00
557 700r.+100r. blue . . . . 6·00 24·00
558 1000r.+100r. black . . . 6·00 24·00

142 Christ of Mt. Corcovado **143** Jose de Anchieta

1934. Visit of Cardinal Pacelli.
559 **142** 300r. red . . . . 3·00 3·00
560 700r. blue . . . . 12·00 12·00

1934. 400th Anniv of Founding of Sao Paulo by Anchieta.
561 **143** 200r. brown . . . . 1·25 1·25
562 300r. violet . . . . 1·25 60
563 700c. blue . . . . 3·00 3·50
564 1000r. green . . . . . . 5·25 2·40

145 "Brazil" and "Uruguay" **146** Town of Igarassu

1935. Visit of President Terra of Uruguay.
565 – 200r. orange 65 60
566 **145** 300r. yellow . . . . . . 1·25 1·75
567 700r. blue . . . . 8·75 15·00
568 – 1000r. violet . . . . . . 18·00 10·50
DESIGN—HORIZ: 200r., 1000r. Female figures as in Type **145** and bridge.

1935. 400th Anniv of Founding of Pernambuco.
569 **146** 200r. brown and red . . . 1·75 1·25
570 300r. olive and violet . . 1·75 90

147 Nurse and Patient

1935. 3rd Pan-American Red Cross Conference.
571 **147** 200r.+100r. violet . . . . 3·00 3·00
572 300r.+100r. brown . . . 3·00 3·00
573 700r.+100r. blue . . . . 15·00 13·00

149 Gen. da Silva

1935. Cent of Farroupilha "Ragged Revolution".
574 – 200r. black . . . . 1·75 1·25
575 – 300r. red . . . . 1·25 65
576 **149** 700r. blue . . . . 4·00 10·50
577 – 1000r. violet . . . . . . 5·25 5·25
DESIGNS: 200r., 300r. Mounted Gaucho; 1000r. Marshal Caxias.

151 Gavea

1935. Children's Day.
578 **151** 300r. violet and brown . . 2·40 1·60
579 300r. turquoise and black 2·40 1·60
580 300r. blue and green . . . 2·40 1·60
581 300r. black and red . . . 2·40 1·60

152 Federal District Coat of Arms

1935. 8th International Fair.
582 **152** 200r. blue . . . . 3·50 3·50

153 Coutinho's ship "Gloria", 1535

1935. 400th Anniv of Colonization of State of Espirito Santo.
583 **153** 300r. red . . . . 6·00 3·00
584 – 700r. blue . . . . 9·00 6·00
DESIGN—VERT: 700r. Arms of Coutinho.

154a Viscount Cairu **155** Cameta

1936. Death Centenary of Cairu.
585 **154a** 1200r. violet . . . . . . 14·00 9·00

1936. Tercentenary of Founding of Cameta.
586 **155** 200r. buff . . . . 2·40 2·40
587 500r. green . . . . 2·40 1·25

156 Coin Press **157** Scales of "Justice"

1936. Numismatic Congress, Sao Paulo.
588 156 300r. brown . . . . 1·75 1·75

1936. 1st National Juridical Congress, Rio.
589 157 300r. red . . . . 1·25 1·25

158 A. Carlos Gomes

159 "Il Guarany"

1936. Birth Centenary of C. Gomes (composer).
590 158 300r. red . . . . 1·25 1·25
591 " 300r. brown . . . . 1·25 1·25
592 159 700r. blue . . . . 3·50 1·75
593 " 700r. buff . . . . 4·75 3·00

1936. 9th International Sample Fair, Rio. As T 152
with inscription and date altered.
594 152 200r. red . . . . 1·75 1·25

160 Congress Seal   161 Botafogo Bay

1936. 2nd National Eucharistic Congress, Belo Horizonte.
595 160 300r. multicoloured . . . 1·75 1·25

1937. Birth Centenary of Dr. Francisco Pereira Passos.
596 161 700r. blue . . . . 1·25 1·25
597 " 700r. black . . . . 1·25 1·25

162 Esperanto Star and National Flags

1937. 9th Brazilian Esperanto Congress, Rio de Janeiro.
598 162 300r. green . . . . 1·75 1·25

163 Bay of Rio de Janeiro

1937. 2nd S. American Radio Conference.
599 163 300r. black and orange . 1·25 1·25
600 " 700r. brown and blue . . 3·00 1·75

164 Globe

1937. Golden Jubilee of Esperanto.
601 164 300r. green . . . . 1·75 1·25

---

166 Iguazu Falls

1937. Tourist Propaganda.
602 – 200r. blue and brown . . 1·25 1·25
603 – 300r. green and orange . . 1·25 1·25
604 166 1000r. brown and sepia . 3·50 2·40
605 – 2000r. red and green . . 15·00 16·00
606 166 5000r. green and black . . 30·00 30·00
607 – 10,000r. blue and red . . 60·00 60·00
DESIGNS—HORIZ: 200r., 2000r. Monroe Palace, Rio. VERT: 300r., 10,000r. Botanical Gardens, Rio.

168 J. Da Silva Paes   169 Eagle and Shield

1937. Bicent of Founding of Rio Grande do Sul.
608 168 300r. blue . . . . 1·25 60

1937. 150th Anniv of U.S. Constitution.
609 169 400r. blue . . . . 1·25 60

170 Coffee   171 "Grito" Memorial

1938. Coffee Propaganda.
610 170 1200r. multicoloured . . . 7·00 60

1938. Commemoration of Abortive Proclamation of Republic.
611 171 400r. brown . . . . . . 1·25 60

172 Arms of Olinda

1938. 4th Centenary of Olinda.
612 172 400r. violet . . . . . . 1·25 60

173 Couto de Magalhaes   174 National Archives

1938. Birth Centenary of De Magalhaes.
613 173 400r. green 90 60

1938. Centenary of Founding of National Archives.
614 174 400r. brown 90 60

175 Rio de Janeiro   176 Santos

1939.
615 175 1200r. purple . . . . . . 2·40 15

1939. Centenary of Santos City.
616 176 400r. blue 65 60

177 Chalice-vine and Cup-of-gold Blossoms   178 Seal of Congress

---

1939. 1st S. American Botanical Congress, Rio.
617 177 400r. green . . . . 1·25 60

1939. 3rd National Eucharistic Congress, Recife.
618 178 400r. red 65 60

179 Duke of Caxias   180 Washington

1939. Soldiers' Day.
619 179 400r. blue 65 60

1939. New York World's Fair. Inscr "FEIRA MUNDIAL DE NOVA YORK".
620 180 400r. orange 50 25
621 – 800r. green 30 15
633 – 1m. violet . . . . . . 3·00 3·00
622 – 1200r. red 60 15
623 – 1600r. blue 60 25
634 – 5m. red . . . . . . 12·00 12·00
635 – 10m. slate . . . . . . 12·00 6·00
DESIGNS—HORIZ: 1200r. Grover Cleveland. VERT: 800r. Dom Pedro II; 1m. Water lily; 1600r. Statue of Liberty, Rio de Janeiro; 5m. Bust of Pres. Vargas; 10m. Relief map of Brazil.

184 Benjamin Constant   188 Child and Southern Cross

1939. 50th Anniv of Constitution.
624 184 400r. green 90 60
625 – 800r. black 60 60
626 – 1200r. brown . . . . . . 1·50 60
DESIGNS—VERT: 800r. Marshal da Fonseca. HORIZ: 1200r. Marshal da Fonseca and Pres. Vargas.

1940. Child Welfare.
627 – 100r.+100r. violet 60 60
628 – 200r.+100r. blue . . . . 1·00 95
629 188 400r.+200r. olive . . . 70 60
630 – 1200r.+400r. red . . . . 3·00 1·60
DESIGNS: 100r. Three Wise Men; 200r. Angel and Child; 1200r. Mother and Child.

189 Roosevelt, Vargas and American Continents   190 Map of Brazil

1940. 50th Anniv of Pan-American Union.
631 189 400r. blue 90 65

1940. 9th National Geographical Congress, Florianopolis.
632 190 400r. red 60 60

1940. Birth Centenary of Machado de Assis (poet and novelist). As T 173 but portrait of de Assis, dated "1839–1939".
636 400r. black 50 50

193 Two Workers   195 Brazilian Flags and Head of Liberty

194 Acclaiming King John IV of Portugal

1940. Bicentenary of Colonization of Porto Alegre.
637 193 400r. green 65 60

1940. Centenaries of Portugal (1140–1640-1940) (1st issue).
638 194 1200r. grey . . . . . . 3·50 60
See also Nos. 642/5.

1940. 10th Anniv of Govt. of President Vargas.
639 195 400r. purple 50 50

196 Date of Fifth Census   197 Globe showing Spotlight on Brazil

1941. 5th General Census.
640 196 400r. blue & red (postage) 30 10
641 197 1200r. brown (air) . . . . 5·25 90

199 Father Antonio Vieira   202 Father Jose Anchieta

1941. Centenaries of Portugal (2nd issue).
642 – 200r. pink 15 10
643 199 400r. blue 15 10
644 – 800r. violet 20 10
645 – 5400r. green . . . . . . 2·40 90
DESIGNS—VERT: 200r. Alfonso Henriques; 800r. Governor-Gen. Benevides. HORIZ: 5,400r. Carmona and Vargas.

1941. 400th Anniv of Order of Jesuits.
646 202 1m. violet . . . . . . 1·25 70

205 Oil Wells   210 Count of Porto Alegre

1941. Value in reis.
647 205 10r. orange 10 10
648 – 20r. olive 10 10
649 – 50r. brown 10 10
650 – 100r. turquoise 15 10
651 – 200r. brown 60 35
652 – 300r. red 15 10
653 – 400r. blue 20 10
654 – 500r. red 15 10
655 – 600r. violet . . . . . . 1·75 35
656 – 700r. red 60 35
657 – 1000r. grey . . . . . . 3·50 35
658 – 1200r. blue . . . . . . 5·25 35
659 – 2000r. purple . . . . . . 7·00 35
660 – 5000r. blue . . . . . . 9·00 60
661 210 10,000r. red . . . . . . 18·00 60
662 – 20,000r. brown . . . . . . 16·00 60
663 – 50m. red . . . . . . 26·00 26·00
664 – 100m. blue . . . . . . 1·25 7·00
DESIGNS: 200r. to 500r. Wheat harvesting machinery; 600r. to 1200r. Smelting works; 2000r. "Commerce"; 5000r. Marshal F. Peixoto; 20,000r. Admiral Maurity; 50m. "Armed Forces"; 100m. Pres. Vargas.
For stamps with values in centavos and cruzeiros see Nos. 751, etc.

213 Amador Bueno   214 Brazilian Air Force Emblem

1941. 300th Anniv of Amador Bueno as King of Sao Paulo.
665 213 400r. black 55 35

1941. Aviation Week.
666 214 5400r. green . . . . . . 5·25 2·40

1941. Air. 4th Anniv of President Vargas's New Constitution. Optd **AEREO "10 Nov."** 937-941.
667 5400r. green (No. 645) . . . . 5·25 1·75

215 Indo-Brazilian Cow

216 Bernardino de Campos

1942. 2nd Agriculture and Cattle Show, Uberaba.
668a **215** 200r. blue 90 60
669a 400r. brown 90 60

1942. Birth Centenaries of B. de Campos and P. de Morais (lawyers and statesmen).
670 **216** 1000r. red . . . . 3·50 95
671 – 1200r. blue . . . . 9·00 65
PORTRAIT: 1200r. Prudente de Morais.

217 Torch of Learning

218 Map of Brazil showing Goiania

1942. 8th National Education Congress, Goiania.
672 **217** 400r. brown 45 25

1942. Founding of Goiania City.
673 **218** 400r. violet 45 25

219 Congressional Seal

221 Tributaries of R. Amazon

1942. 4th National Eucharistic Congress, Sao Paulo.
674 **219** 400r. brown 60 40

1942. Air. 5th Anniv of President Vargas's New Constitution. No. 645 surch **AEREO "10 Nov." 937-942** and value.
675 5cr.40 on 5400r. green . . . 4·75 2·40

1943. 400th Anniv of Discovery of River Amazon.
676 **221** 40c. brown 90 60

222 Early Brazilian Stamp

223 Memorial Tablet

1943. Centenary of Petropolis.
677 **222** 40c. violet . . . . 1·25 60

1943. Air. Visit of Pres. Morinigo of Paraguay.
678 **223** 1cr.20 blue . . . . 4·75 1·25

224 Map of S. America showing Brazil and Bolivia

1943. Air. Visit of President Penaranda of Bolivia.
679 **224** 1cr.20 multicoloured . . . 3·50 90

225 "Bulls-eye"

226

1943. Centenary of 1st Brazilian Postage Stamps.
(a) Postage. Imperf.
680 **225** 30c. black . . . . 1·75 90
681 60c. black . . . . 2·40 60
682 90c. black . . . . 1·25 90

(b) Air. Perf.
683 **226** 1cr. black and yellow . . 3·50 1·25
684 2cr. black and green . . . 4·75 1·25
685 5cr. black and red . . . . 6·00 1·75

227 Book of the Law

228 Ubaldino do Amaral

1943. Air. Inter-American Advocates Conference.
686 **227** 1cr.20 red and brown . . 2·40 60

1943. Birth Centenary of Ubaldino do Amaral.
687 **228** 40c. grey 60 20

229 Indo-Brazilian Cow

1943. 9th Cattle Show, Bahia.
688 **229** 40c. brown . . . . 1·50 50

230 Justice and Seal

231 Santa Casa de Misericordia Hospital

1943. Centenary of Institute of Brazilian Lawyers.
689 **230** 2cr. red . . . . 3·50 1·75

1943. 400th Anniv of Santa Casa de Misericordia de Santos.
690 **231** 1cr. blue . . . . 1·25 60

232 Barbosa Rodrigues

233 Pedro Americo

1943. Birth Centenary of B. Rodrigues (botanist).
691 **232** 40c. green 40 15

1943. Birth Cent of Americo (artist and author).
692 **233** 40c. brown 90 20

1944. Air. No. 629 surch. **AEREO** and value.
693 **188** 20c. on 400r.+200r. . . . 1·75 90
694 40c. on 400r.+200r. . . . 3·50 90
695 60c. on 400r.+200r. . . . 5·25 60
696 1cr. on 400r.+200r. . . . 5·25 90
697 1cr.20 on 400r.+200r. . . 10·50 60

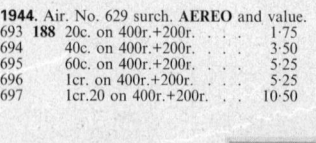

235 Gen. Carneiro and Defenders of Lapa

236 Baron do Rio Branco

1944. 50th Anniv of Siege of Lapa.
698 **235** 1cr.20c. red . . . . 1·75 60

1944. Inauguration of Monument to Baron do Rio Branco.
699 **236** 1cr. blue . . . . 1·50 60

237 Duke of Caxias

238 Emblems of Y.M.C.A.

1944. Centenary of Pacification of Revolutionary Uprising of 1842.
700 **237** 1cr.20 green and yellow 1·75 60

1944. Centenary of Y.M.C.A.
701 **238** 40c. blue, red and yellow 90 20

239 Rio Grande Chamber of Commerce

240 "Bartolomeo de Gusmao and the Aerostat" (Bernardino de Souza Pereira)

1944. Centenary of Founding of Rio Grande Chamber of Commerce.
702 **239** 40c. brown 90 25

1944. Air. Air Week.
703 **240** 1cr.20 red . . . . 1·25 15

241 Ribeiro de Andrada

1945. Death Cent of M. de Andrada (statesman).
704 **241** 40c. blue 90 15

242 Meeting between Caxias and Canabarro

1945. Cent of Pacification of Rio Grande do Sul.
705 **242** 40c. blue 90 15

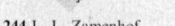

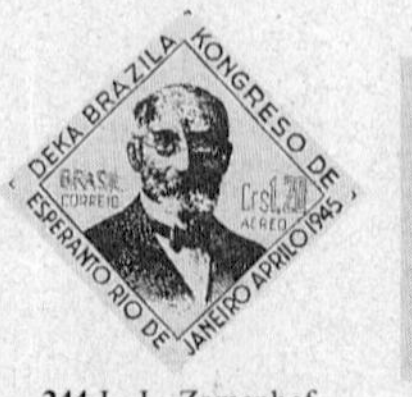
244 L. L. Zamenhof

247 Baron do Rio Branco (statesman)

1945. 10th Brazilian Esperanto Congress, Rio de Janeiro.
706 – 40c. green (postage) . . . 90 60
707 **244** 1cr.20 brown (air) . . . . 1·25 60
DESIGN: 40c. Woman and map.

1945. Birth Centenary of Baron do Rio Branco.
708 – 40c. blue (postage) . . . 60 15
709 – 1cr.20 purple (air) . . . . 1·25 50
710 **247** 5cr. purple . . . . 4·75 60
DESIGNS—HORIZ: 40c. Bookplate VERT: 1cr.20, S. America.

248 "Glory"

250 "Co-operation"

1945. Victory of Allied Nations in Europe. Roul.
711 – 20c. violet 50 10
712 **248** 40c. red 50 10
713 – 1cr. orange . . . . 1·75 60
714 – 2cr. blue . . . . 1·75 90
715 **250** 5cr. green . . . . 3·50 1·25
SYMBOLICAL DESIGNS—VERT: 20c. Tranquility (inscr "SAUDADE"). HORIZ: 1cr. "Victory" (inscr "VITORIA"); 2cr. "Peace" (inscr "PAZ").

251 F. M. da Silva

252 Bahia Institute

1945. 150th Birth Anniv of Francisco Manoel da Silva (composer of Brazilian National Anthem).
716 **251** 40c. red . . . . 1·25 60

1945. 50th Anniv of Founding of Bahia Institute of Geography and History.
717 **252** 40c. blue . . . . 1·75 15

253 Shoulder Flash

255 "V" Sign and Flashes

1945. Return of Brazilian Expeditionary Force.
718 **253** 20c. blue, red and green 50 15
719 – 40c. multicoloured 50 15
720 – 1cr. multicoloured . . . . 2·40 50
721 – 2cr. multicoloured . . . . 3·50 1·25
722 **255** 5cr. multicoloured . . . . 6·00 1·25
DESIGNS (embodying shoulder flashes) As Type **253**: 40c. B.E.F. flash. As Type **255**. HORIZ: 1cr. U.S.A. flag; 2cr. Brazilian flag.

256 Wireless Mast and Map

257 Admiral Saldanha da Gama

1945. 3rd Inter-American Radio Communication Conference.
723 **256** 1cr.20 black . . . . 1·25 15

1946. Birth Centenary of Admiral S. da Gama.
724 **257** 40c. grey . . . . 90 1·25

258 Princess Isabel d'Orleans-Braganza

261 P.O., Rio de Janeiro

260 Lockheed Super Electra over Bay of Rio de Janeiro

1946. Birth Centenary of Princess Isabel d'Orleans-Braganza.
725 **258** 40c. black . . . . 90 1·75

1946. 5th P.U. Congress of the Americas and Spain.
726 – 40c. orange and black . . . 50 15
727 **260** 1cr.30 orange and green . . 90 60
728 1cr.70 orange and red . . 1·25 90
729 **261** 2cr. blue and slate . . . 1·75 90
730 **260** 2cr.20 orange and blue . . 1·25 90
731 **261** 5cr. blue and brown . . . 4·75 1·25
732 10cr. blue and violet . . . 6·00 90
DESIGN (25 × 37 mm): 40c. Post-horn, V and envelope.

262 Proposed Columbus Lighthouse   263 "Liberty"

1946. Construction of Columbus Lighthouse, Dominican Republic.
733 **262** 5cr. blue . . . . 9·00 2·50

1946. New Constitution.
734 **263** 40c. grey 10 10

264 Orchid

1946. 4th National Exn of Orchids, Rio de Janeiro.
735 **264** 40c. blue, red and yellow . 65 10

265 Gen. A. E.   266 Academy of Arts
Gomes Carneiro

1946. Birth Cent of Gen. A. E. Gomes Carneiro.
736 **265** 40c. green 35 10

1946. 50th Anniv of Brazilian Academy of Arts.
737 **266** 40c. blue 35 10

267 Antonio de   268 Pres. Gonzalez
Castro Alves

1947. Birth Centenary of Castro Alves (poet).
738 **267** 40c. turquoise 35 10

1947. Visit of Chilean President.
739 **268** 40c. brown 35 10

269 "Peace and   270 "Dove of Peace"
Security"

1947. Inter-American Defence Conference, Rio de Janeiro.
740 **269** 1cr.20 blue (postage) . . . 90 10
741 **270** 2cr.20 green (air) . . . . 1·25 50

271 Pres. Truman, Map of S. America and Statue of Liberty

1947. Visit of President Truman.
742 **271** 40c. blue 50 10

272 Pres. Enrico   273 Woman and Child
Gaspar Dutra

1947. Commemorating Pres. Dutra.
743 **272** 20c. green 10 10
744 40c. red 15 10
745 1cr.20 blue 50 10

1947. Children's Week. 1st Brazilian Infant Welfare Convention and Paediatrics.
747 **273** 40c. blue 50 10

274 Icarus

1947. Obligatory Tax. "Week of the Wing" Aviation Fund.
748 **274** 40c.+10c. orange 50 10

275 Santos Dumont   276 Arms of Belo
Monument, St. Cloud,   Horizonte
France

1947. Air. Homage to Santos Dumont (aviation pioneer).
749 **275** 1cr.20c. brown & green . . 1·25 50

1947. 50th Anniv of Founding of City of Belo Horizonte.
750 **276** 1cr.20c. red 65 10

1947. As postage stamps of 1941, but values in centavos or cruzeiros.
751 **205** 2c. olive 20 10
752 5c. brown 20 10
753 10c. turquoise 20 10
754 – 20c. brown (No. 651) . . 50 10
755 – 30c. red (No. 652) . . . 1·25 10
756 – 40c. blue (No. 653) . . . 50 10
757 – 50c. red (No. 654) . . . 1·25 10
758 – 60c. violet (No. 655) . . 1·75 10
759 – 70c. red (No. 656) . . . 60 10
760 – 1cr. grey (No. 657) . . . 3·50 10
761 – 1cr.20 blue (No. 658) . . 5·25 10
762 – 2cr. purple (No. 659) . . 9·00 10
763 – 5cr. blue (No. 660) . . . 18·00 10
764 **210** 10cr. red . . . . 14·00 10
765 – 20cr. brown (No. 662) . . 25·00 10
766 – 50cr. red (No. 663) . . . 55·00 10

277 Rio de Janeiro   278 Globe
and Rotary Emblem

279 Quitandinha Hotel

1948. Air. 39th Rotary Congress Rio de Janeiro.
769 **277** 1cr.20 red . . . . . . 1·25 50
770 3cr.80 violet . . . . . 3·50 60

1948. International Industrial and Commercial Exhibition, Quitandinha.
771 **278** 40c. grn & mve (postage) . 15 10
772 **279** 1cr.20 brown (air) 50 15
773 3cr.80 violet . . . . . 1·75 15

280 Arms of   281 Girl Reading
Paranagua

1948. Tercentenary of Founding of Paranagua.
774 **280** 5cr. brown . . . . . . 4·75 1·25

1948. National Children's Campaign.
775 **281** 40c. green 15 35

282 Three Muses (after Henrique Bernardelli)

1948. Air. Centenary of National School of Music.
776 **282** 1cr.20 blue . . . . . . 1·25 10

283 President Berres

1948. Air. Visit of Uruguayan President.
777 **283** 1cr.70 blue 50 10

284 Merino Ram

1948. Air. International Livestock Show, Bage.
778 **284** 1cr.20 orange . . . . . 1·75 50

285 Congress Seal   286 "Tiradentes" (trans. "Tooth-puller")

1948. Air. 5th National Eucharistic Congress, Porto Alegre.
779 **285** 1cr.20 purple 50 10

1948. Birth Bicentenary of A. J. J. da Silva Xavier (patriot).
780 **286** 40c. orange 10 10

287 Crab and Globe   288 Adult Student

1948. Anti-cancer Campaign.
781 **287** 40c. purple 50 60

1949. Campaign for Adult Education.
782 **288** 60c. purple 50 10

289 Battle of Guararapes

1949. 300th Anniv of 2nd Battle of Guararapes.
783 **289** 60c. blue (postage) . . . 2·40 50
784 – 1cr.20 pink (air) . . . . . 4·75 1·75
DESIGN: 1cr.20, View of Guararapes.

290 St. Francis of   291 Father Nobrega
Paula Church

292 De Souza   293 Franklin D. Roosevelt
meeting Indians

1949. Bicentenary of Ouro Fino.
785 **290** 60c. brown 50 10

1949. 4th Centenary of Founding of Bahia. (a) Postage. Imperf.
786 **291** 60c. violet 50 10
          (b) Air. Perf.
787 **292** 1cr.20 blue . . . . . . 1·25 15

1949. Air. Homage to Franklin D. Roosevelt. Imperf.
788 **293** 3cr.80 blue . . . . . . 2·40 1·75

294 Douglas DC-3 and Air Force Badge

1949. Homage to Brazilian Air Force. Imperf.
789 **294** 60c. violet 50 10

295 Joaquim Nabuco   296 "Revelation"

1949. Air. Birth Centenary of J. Nabuco (lawyer and author).
790 **295** 3cr.80 purple . . . . . 2·40 10

1949. 1st Sacerdotal Vocational Congress, Bahia.
791 **296** 60c. purple 50 10

297 Globe

1949. 75th Anniv of U.P.U.
792 **297** 1cr.50 blue 90 10

298 Ruy Barbosa   **299** Cardinal Arcoverde

1949. Birth Cent of Ruy Barbosa (statesman).
793 **298** 1cr.20 red . . . . 1·25   15

1950. Birth Cent of Cardinal Joaquim Arcoverde.
794 **299** 60c. pink 50   10

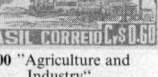

300 "Agriculture and Industry"   **301** Virgin of the Globe

1950. 75th Anniv of Arrival of Italian Immigrants.
795 **300** 60c. red 60   10

1950. Centenary of Establishment of Daughters of Charity of St. Vincent de Paul.
796 **301** 60c. blue and black . . . 50   10

302 Globe and Footballers   **303** Stadium

1950. 4th World Football Championship, Rio de Janeiro.
797 **302** 60c. grey & bl (postage) . 1·25   15
798 **303** 1cr.20 orange and blue (air) . . . . 1·60   50
799   – 5cr.80 yellow, green and blue . . . . 7·00   60
DESIGN—VERT: 5cr.80 Linesman and flag.

304 Three Heads, Map and Graph   **305** Line of People and Map

1950. 6th Brazilian Census, 1950.
800 **304** 60c. red (postage) 50   10
801 **305** 1cr.20 brown (air) . . . . 1·25   10

306 Oswaldo Cruz   **307** Blumenau and Itajai River

1950. 5th International Microbiological Congress. Rio de Janeiro.
802 **306** 60c. brown 50   10

1950. Centenary of Founding of Blumenau.
803 **307** 60c. pink 50   10

308 Government Offices   **309** Arms

1950. Centenary of Amazon Province.
804 **308** 60c. red 60   10

1950. Centenary of Juiz de Fora City.
805 **309** 60c. red 60   10

310 P.O. Building, Recife

1951. Inauguration of Head Post Office, Pernambuco Province.
806 **310** 60c. red 50   10
807   1cr.20 red 60   10

311 Arms of Joinville   **312** S. Romero

1951. Centenary of Founding of Joinville.
808 **311** 60c. brown 60   10

1951. Birth Centenary of Sylvio Romero (poet).
809 **312** 60c. brown 60   10

313 De La Salle   **314** Heart and Flowers

1951. Birth Tricentenary of Jean-Baptiste de la Salle (educational reformer).
810 **313** 60c. blue 65   10

1951. Mothers' Day.
811 **314** 60c. purple 90   50

315 J. Caetano and Stage   **316** O. A. Derby

1951. 1st Brazilian Theatrical Congress.
812 **315** 60c. blue 50   10

1951. Birth Centenary of Derby (geologist).
813 **316** 2cr. slate 65   35

317 Crucifix and Congregation   **318** E. P. Martins and Map

1951. 4th Inter-American Catholic Education Congress, Rio de Janeiro.
814 **317** 60c. brown and buff . . . 65   10

1951. 29th Anniv of First Rio–New York Flight.
815 **318** 3cr.80 brown & lemon . . 3·25   50

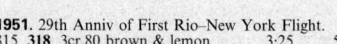

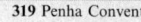
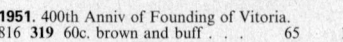

319 Penha Convent   **320** Santos Dumont and Boys with Model Aircraft

1951. 400th Anniv of Founding of Vitoria.
816 **319** 60c. brown and buff . . . 65   10

1951. "Week of the Wing" and 50th Anniv of Santos Dumont's Flight over Paris.
817 **320** 60c. brn & orge (postage) 65   15
818   – 3cr.80 violet (air) . . . 1·90   20
DESIGN: 3cr.80, "Ballon No. 6" airship over Eiffel Tower.

321 Wheat Harvesters   **322** Bible and Map

1951. Wheat Festival, Bage.
819 **321** 60c. green and grey . . . 50   50

1951. Bible Day.
820 **322** 1cr.20 brown . . . . . . 1·25   35

323 Isabella the Catholic   **324** Henrique Oswald

1952. 500th Birth Anniv of Isabella the Catholic.
821 **323** 3cr.80 blue . . . . 1·90   50

1952. Birth Centenary of Oswald (composer).
822 **324** 60c. brown 65   10

325 Map and Symbol of Labour   **326** Dr. L. Cardoso

1952. 5th Conf of American Members of I.L.O.
823 **325** 1cr.50 red 65   10

1952. Birth Centenary of Cardoso (scientist) and 4th Brazilian Homoeopathic Congress, Porto Alegre.
824 **326** 60c. blue 50   15

327 Gen. da Fonseca   **328** L. de Albuquerque

1952. Centenary of Telegraphs in Brazil.
825 **327** 2cr.40 red 65   15
826   – 5cr. blue . . . . 3·50   15
827   – 10cr. turquoise . . . . 3·50   15
PORTRAITS—VERT: 5cr. Baron de Capanema. 10cr. E. de Queiros.

1952. Bicentenary of Mato Grosso City.
828 **328** 1cr.20 violet 65   10

329 Olympic Flame and Athletes   **330** Councillor J. A. Saraiva

1952. 50th Anniv of Fluminense Football Club.
829 **329** 1cr.20 blue . . . . 1·25   60

1952. 100th Anniv of Terezina City.
830 **330** 60c. mauve 65   10

331 Emperor Dom Pedro II   **332** Globe, Staff and Rio de Janeiro Bay

1952. Stamp Day and 2nd Philatelic Exhibition, Sao Paulo.
831 **331** 60c. black and blue . . . 65   10

1952. 2nd American Congress of Industrial Medicine.
832 **332** 3cr.80 green and brown . 1·60   60

333 Dove, Globe and Flags

1952. United Nations Day.
833 **333** 3cr.80 blue . . . . 2·40   50

334 Compasses and Modern Buildings, Sao Paulo   **335** D. A. Feijo (Statesman)

1952. City Planning Day.
834 **334** 60c. yellow, green & blue 50   10

1952. Homage to D. A. Feijo.
835 **335** 60c. brown 60   10

336 Father Damien

1952. Obligatory Tax. Leprosy Research Fund.
836 **336** 10c. brown 50   15
837   10c. green 15   10

337 R. Bernardelli

1952. Birth Centenary of Bernardelli (sculptor).
838 **337** 60c. blue 65   10

338 Arms of Sao Paulo and Settler   **339** "Expansion"

1953. 400th Anniv of Sao Paulo (1st issue).

839	**338**	1cr.20 black and brown	1·75	50
840	–	2cr. green and yellow	3·50	50
841	–	2cr.80 brown and orange	1·90	15
842	**339**	3cr.80 brown and green	1·90	15
843		5cr.80 blue and green	1·50	15

DESIGNS—VERT: (Inscr as Type **339**): 2cr. Coffee blossom and berries; 2cr.80, Monk planting tree.

See also Nos. 875/9.

340   **341** J. Ramalho

1953. 6th Brazilian Accountancy Congress, Port Alegre.

844 **340** 1cr.20 brown 95 10

1953. 4th Centenary of Santo Andre.

845 **341** 60c. blue 10 10

342 A. Reis and Plan of Belo Horizonte   **343** "Almirante Saldanha" (cadet ship)

1953. Birth Centenary of A. Reis (engineer).

846 **342** 1cr.20 brown 15 10

1953. 4th Voyage of Circumnavigation by Training Ship "Almirante Saldanha".

847 **343** 1cr.50 blue 90 20

344 Viscount de Itaborahy   **345** Lamp and Rio-Petropolis Highway

1953. Centenary of Bank of Brazil.

848 **344** 1cr.20 violet 15 10

1953. 10th Int Nursing Congress, Petropolis.

849 **345** 1cr.20 grey 15 10

346 Bay of Rio de Janeiro

1953. 4th World Conference of Young Baptists.

850 **346** 3cr.80c. turquoise 95 10

347 Ministry of Health and Education   **348** Arms and Map

1953. Stamp Day and 1st National Philatelic Exhibition of Education, Rio de Janeiro.

851 **347** 1cr.20 turquoise 15 10

1953. Centenary of Jau City.

852 **348** 1cr.20 violet 15 10

349 Maria Quiteria de Jesus   **350** Pres. Odria

1953. Death Centenary of Maria Quiteria de Jesus.

853 **349** 60c. blue 10 10

1953. Visit of President of Peru.

854 **350** 1cr.40 purple 15 10

351 Caxias leading Troops   **352** Quill-pen and Map

1953. 150th Birth Anniv of Duke of Caxias.

855	**351**	60c. turquoise	35	15
856	–	1cr.20 purple	50	15
857	–	1cr.70 blue	50	15
858	–	3cr.80 brown	1·60	15
859	–	5cr.80 violet	85	15

DESIGNS: 1cr.20, Tomb; 1cr.70, 5cr.80, Portrait of Caxias; 3cr.80, Coat of arms.

1953. 5th National Congress of Journalists, Curitiba.

860 **352** 60c. blue 10 10

353 H. Hora   **354** President Somoza

1953. Birth Centenary of H. Hora (painter).

861 **353** 60c. purple and orange . . 35 10

1953. Visit of President Somoza of Nicaragua.

862 **354** 1cr.40 purple 20 15

355 A. de Saint-Hilaire   **356** J. do Patrocinio and "Spirit of Emancipation" (after R. Amoedo)

1953. Death Centenary of A. de Saint-Hilaire (explorer and botanist).

863 **355** 1cr.20 lake 20 10

1953. Death Centenary of J. do Patrocinio (slavery abolitionist).

864 **356** 60c. slate 10 10

357 Clock Tower, Crato   **358** C. de Abreu

1953. Centenary of Crato City.

865 **357** 60c. green 15 10

1953. Birth Centenary of Abreu (historian).

866	**358**	60c. blue	20	10
867		5cr. violet	1·90	20

359 "Justice"   **360** Harvesting

1953. 50th Anniv of Treaty of Petropolis.

868	**359**	60c. blue	15	10
869		1cr.20 purple	15	10

1953. 3rd National Wheat Festival, Erechim.

870 **360** 60c. turquoise 15 10

361 Teacher and Pupils   **362** Porters with Trays of Coffee Beans

1953. 1st National Congress of Elementary Schoolteachers, Salvador.

871 **361** 60c. red 15 10

1953. Centenary of State of Parana.

872a	–	2cr. brown and black	1·75	60
873	**362**	5cr. orange and black	2·40	60

DESIGN: 2cr. Portrait of Z. de Gois e Vasconellos.

363 A. de Gusmao   **364** Growth of Sao Paulo

365 Sao Paulo and Arms

1954. Death Bicent of Gusmao (statesman).

874 **363** 1cr.20 purple 50 10

1954. 400th Anniv of Sao Paulo (2nd issue).

875	**364**	1cr.20 brown	1·25	90
876	–	2cr. mauve	1·90	65
877	–	2cr.80 violet	3·00	55
878	**365**	3cr.80 green	3·00	55
879		5cr.80 red	3·00	55

DESIGNS—VERT: 2cr. Priest, pioneer and Indian; 2cr.80, J. de Anchieta.

366 J. F. Vieira, A. V. de Negreiros, A. F. Camarao and H. Dias

1954. 300th Anniv of Recovery from the Dutch of Pernambuco.

880 **366** 1cr.20 blue 50 10

367 Sao Paulo and Allegorical Figure

1954. 10th International Congress of Scientific Organization, Sao Paulo.

881 **367** 1cr.50 purple 15 10

368 Grapes and Winejar   **369** Immigrants' Monument

1954. Grape Festival, Rio Grande do Sul.

882 **368** 40c. lake 15 10

1954. Immigrants' Monument, Caxias do Sul.

883 **369** 60c. violet 15 10

370 "Baronesa", 1852 (first locomotive used in Brazil)   **371** Pres. Chamoun

1954. Centenary of Brazilian Railways.

884 **370** 40c. red . . . . 1·25 40

1954. Visit of President of Lebanon.

885 **371** 1cr.50 lake 20 10

372 Sao Jose College, Rio de Janeiro   **373** Vel Marcelino Champagnat

1954. 50th Anniv of Marists in Brazil.

886	**372**	60c. violet	20	15
887	**373**	1cr.20 blue	20	15

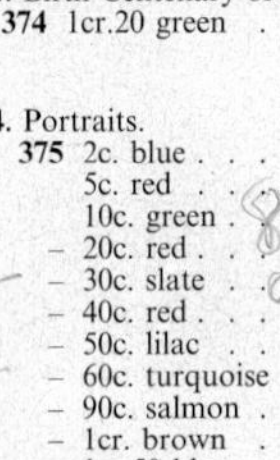
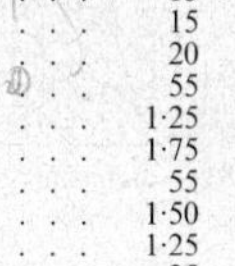

374 Apolonia Pinto   **375** Admiral Tamandare

1954. Birth Centenary of Apolonia Pinto (actress).

888 **374** 1cr.20 green 10 10

1954. Portraits.

889	**375**	2c. blue	15	15
890		5c. red	15	10
891		10c. green	15	10
892	–	20c. red	20	10
893	–	30c. slate	55	10
894	–	40c. red	1·25	10
895	–	50c. lilac	1·75	10
896	–	60c. turquoise	55	10
897	–	90c. salmon	1·50	15
904a	–	1cr. brown	1·25	50
899	–	1cr.50 blue	25	10
904b	–	2cr. green	1·75	50
904c	–	5cr. purple	5·25	10
902	–	10cr. green	2·75	10
903	–	20cr. red	3·50	30
904	–	50cr. blue	10·50	10

PORTRAITS—20c., 30c., 40c. O. Cruz. 50c. to 90c. J. Murtinho. 1cr., 1cr.50, 2cr. Duke of Caxias. 5cr., 10cr., R. Barbosa. 20cr., 50cr. J. Bonifacio.

376 Boy Scout

377 B. Fernandes

1954. International Scout Encampment, Sao Paulo.
905 376 1cr.20 blue 95 15

1954. Tercentenary of Sorocaba City.
906 377 60c. red 10 10

378 Cardinal Piazza

379 Virgin and Map

1954. Visit of Cardinal Piazza (Papal Legate).
907 378 4cr.20 red 95 10

1954. Marian Year. Inscr "ANO MARIANO".
908 379 60c. lake 55 10
909 – 1cr.20 blue 65 10
DESIGN: 1cr.20, Virgin and globe.
No. 909 also commemorates the Centenary of the Proclamation of the Dogma of the Immaculate Conception.

380 Benjamin Constant and Braille Book

1954. Cent of Education for the Blind in Brazil.
910 380 60c. green 15 10

381 River Battle of Riachuelo   382 Admiral Barroso

1954. 150th Birth Anniv of Admiral Barroso.
911 381 40c. brown 90 15
912 382 60c. violet 25 10

383 S. Hahnemann (physician)

384 Nisia Floresta (suffragist)

1954. 1st World Congress of Homoeopathy.
913 383 2cr.70 green 95 10

1954. Removal of Ashes of Nisia Floresta (suffragist) from France to Brazil.
914 384 60c. mauve 10 10

385 Ears of Wheat   386 Globe and Basketball Player

1954. 4th Wheat Festival, Carazinho.
915 385 60c. olive 15 10

1954. 2nd World Basketball Championship.
916 386 1cr.40 red 95 15

387 Girl, Torch and Spring Flowers

388 Father Bento

1954. 6th Spring Games.
917 387 60c. brown 50 10

1954. Obligatory Tax. Leprosy Research Fund.
918 388 10c. blue 15 10
919 10c. mauve 15 10
919a 10c. salmon 15 10
919b 10c. green 15 10
919c 10c. lilac 15 10
919d 10c. brown 15 10
919e 10c. slate 15 10
919f 2cr. lake 15 10
919g 2cr. lilac 15 10
919h 2cr. orange 15 10
See also Nos. 1239/40.

389 Sao Francisco Power Station

1955. Inauguration of Sao Francisco Hydro-electric Station.
920 389 60c. orange 15 10

390 Itutinga Power Plant

1955. Inaug of Itutinga Hydro-electric Station.
921 390 40c. blue 15 10

391 Rotary Symbol and Rio Bay

392 Aviation Symbols

1955. 50th Anniv of Rotary International.
922 391 2cr.70 green and black . . 2·40 10

1955. 3rd Aeronautical Congress, Sao Paulo.
923 392 60c. grey and black . . . 15 10

393 Fausto Cardoso Palace

1955. Centenary of Aracaiu.
924 393 40c. brown 10 10

394 Arms of Botucatu

1955. Centenary of Botucatu.
925 394 60c. brown 10 10
926 1cr.20 green 15 10

395 Young Athletes

396 Marshal da Fonseca

1955. 5th Children's Games, Rio de Janeiro.
927 395 60c. brown 50 10

1955. Birth Centenary of Marshal da Fonseca.
928 396 60c. violet 10 10

397 Congress Altar, Sail and Sugar-loaf Mountain

398 Cardinal Masella

1955. 36th International Eucharistic Congress.
929 397 1cr.40 green 10 10
930 – 2cr.70 lake (St. Pascoal) 90 90

1955. Visit of Cardinal Masella (Papal Legate) to Eucharistic Congress.
931 398 4cr.20 blue . . . . 1·75 15

399 Gymnasts

1955. 7th Spring Games.
932 399 60c. mauve 20 10

400 Monteiro Lobato

401 A. Lutz

1955. Honouring M. Lobato (author).
933 400 40c. green 10 10

1955. Birth Cent of Lutz (public health pioneer).
934 401 60c. green 15 10

402 Lt.-Col. T. C. Vilagran Cabrita

403 Salto Grande Dam

1955. Centenary of 1st Battalion of Engineers.
935 402 60c. blue 15 10

1956. Salto Grande Dam.
936 403 60c. red 15 10

404

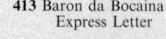
405 Arms of Mococa

1955. Centenary of Botucatu.
925 394 60c. brown 10 10
926 1cr.20 green 15 10

1956. 18th International Geographical Congress, Rio de Janeiro.
937 404 1cr.20 blue 50 10

1956. Centenary of Mococa, Sao Paulo.
938 405 60c. red 35 10

406 Girls Running

407 Douglas DC-3 and Map

1956. 6th Children's Games.
939 406 2cr.50 blue 65 10

1956. 25th Anniv of National Air Mail.
940 407 3cr.30 blue 95 10

408 Rescue Work

1956. Centenary of Firemen's Corps, Rio de Janeiro.
941 408 2cr.50 red 90 35

409 Franca Cathedral

410 Open book with Inscription and Map

1956. Centenary of City of Franca.
942 409 2cr.50 blue 60 10

1956. 50th Anniv of Arrival of Marist Brothers in N. Brazil.
943 410 2cr.50 blue (postage) . . . 50 10
944 – 3cr.30 purple (air) 15 10
DESIGN—VERT: 3cr.30, Father J. B. Marcelino Champagnat.

411 Hurdler

412 Forest and Map of Brazil

1956. 8th Spring Games.
945 411 2cr.50 red . . . . 1·25 35

1956. Afforestation Campaign.
946 412 2cr.50 green 50 10

413 Baron da Bocaina and Express Letter   414 Commemorative Stamp from Panama

1956. Birth Centenary of Baron da Bocaina.
947 413 2cr.50 brown 50 10

1956. Pan-American Congress. Panama.
948 414 3cr.30 black and green . . 95 15

415 Santos Dumont's Biplane "14 bis"

1956. Air. Alberto Santos Dumont (aviation pioneer) Commemoration.
949 415 3cr. green . . . . 1·60 40
950 3cr.30 blue 20 10
951 4cr. purple . . . . 1·25 10
952 6cr.50 brown 20 10
953 11cr.50 orange . . . . . . 2·50 30

416 Volta Redonda Steel Mill, and Molten Steel
417 J. E. Gomes da Silva (civil engineer)

1957. Nat Steel Company's Expansion Campaign.
955 416 2cr.50 brown 40 10

1957. Birth Cententary of Gomes da Silva.
956 417 2cr.50 green 50 10

418 Allan Kardec, Code and Globe

1957. Centenary of Spiritualism Code.
957 418 2cr.50 brown 15 10

419 Young Gymnast
420 Gen. Craveiro Lopes

1957. 7th Children's Games.
958 419 2cr.50 lake . . . . . . 1·25 10

1957. Visit of President of Portugal.
959 420 6cr.50 blue 95 10

421 Stamp of 1932
422 Lord Baden-Powell

1957. 25th Anniv of Sao Paulo Revolutionary Government.
960 421 2cr.50 red 60 10

1957. Air. Birth Centenary of Lord Baden-Powell.
961 422 3cr.30 lake 95 10

423 Convent of Santo Antonio

1957. 300th Anniv of Emancipation of Santo Antonio Province.
962 423 2cr.50 purple 15 10

424 Volleyball
425 Basketball

1957. 9th Spring Games.
963 424 2cr.50 brown . . . . . . 1·25 10

1957. 2nd Women's World Basketball Championships.
964 425 3cr.30 green and brown . . 1·25 10

426 U.N. Emblem, Map of Suez Canal and Soldier

1957. Air. United Nations Day.
965 426 5cr.30 blue 15 30

427 Count of Pinhal (founder), Arms and Locomotive
428 Auguste Comte (philosopher)

1957. Centenary of City of San Carlos.
966 427 2cr.50 red 90 30

1957. Death Centenary of Comte.
967 428 2cr.50 brown 50 10

429 Sarapui Radio Station

1957. Inauguration of Sarapui Radio Station.
968 429 2cr.50 myrtle 50 10

430 Admiral Tamandare (founder) and "Almirante Tamandare" (cruiser)
431 Coffee Beans and Emblem

1957. 150th Anniv of Brazilian Navy.
969 430 2cr.50 blue 55 15
970 – 3cr.30 green 70 15
DESIGN: 3cr.30, Aircraft-carrier "Minas Gerais".

1957. Centenary of City of Ribeirao Preto.
971 431 2cr.50 red 60 10

432 King John VI of Portugal and Sail Merchantman

1958. 150th Anniv of Opening of Ports to Foreign Trade.
972 432 2cr.50 purple 60 10

433 Bugler
434 Locomotive "Baronesa", 1852, and Dom Pedro II Station, Rio de Janeiro

1958. 150th Anniv of Corps of Brazilian Marines.
973 433 2cr.50 red 50 10

1958. Centenary of Central Brazil Railway.
974 434 2cr.50 brown 85 20

435 High Court Building
436 Brazilian Pavilion

1958. 150th Anniv of Military High Courts.
975 435 2cr.50 green 15 10

1958. Brussels International Exhibition.
976 436 2cr.50 blue 10 10

437 Marshal C. M. da Silva Ronden
438 Jumping

1958. Rondon Commem and "Day of the Indian".
977 437 2cr.50 purple 15 10

1958. 8th Children's Games, Rio de Janeiro.
978 438 2cr.50 red 50 10

439 Hydro-electric Station

1958. Inaug of Salto Grande Hydro-electric Station.
979 439 2cr.50 purple 15 10

440 National Printing Works
441 Marshal Osorio

1958. 150th Anniv of National Printing Works.
980 440 2cr.50 brown 10 10

1958. 150th Birth Anniv of Marshal Osorio.
981 441 2cr.50 violet 10 10

442 Pres. Morales of Honduras
443 Botanical Gardens, Rio de Janeiro

1958. Visit of President of Honduras.
982 442 6cr.50 green . . . . . . 3·50 90

1958. 150th Anniv of Botanical Gardens, Rio de Janeiro.
983 443 2cr.50 green 10 10

444 Hoe, Rice and Cotton
445 Prophet Joel

1958. 50th Anniv of Japanese Immigration.
984 444 2cr.50 red 10 10

1958. Bicentenary of Basilica of the Good Jesus, Matosinhos.
985 445 2cr.50 blue 35 10

446 Brazil on Globe

1958. Int Investments Conf, Belo Horizonte.
986 446 2cr.50 brown 10 10

447 Tiradentes Palace, Rio de Janeiro
448 J. B. Brandao (statesman)

1958. 47th Inter-Parliamentary Union Conf.
987 447 2cr.50 brown 10 10

1958. Centenary of Brandao.
988 448 2cr.50 brown 10 10

449 Dawn Palace, Brasilia

1958. Construction of Presidential Palace.
989 449 2cr.50 blue 10 10

450 Freighters

1958. Govt Aid for Brazilian Merchant Navy.
990 450 2cr.50 blue 55 10

451 J. C. da Silva
452 Pres. Gronchi

1958. Birth Centenary of Da Silva (author).
991 451 2cr.50 brown 10 10

1958. Visit of President of Italy.
992 452 7cr. blue . . . . . . 1·75 10

453 Archers

454 Old People within Hour-glass

1958. 10th Spring Games, Rio de Janeiro.
993 453 2cr.50 orange 90 10

1958. Old People's Day.
994 454 2cr.50 lake 15 10

455 Machado de Assis (writer)

456 Pres. Vargas with oily Hand

1958. 50th Death Anniv of Machado de Assis.
995 455 2cr.50 brown 10 10

1958. 5th Anniv of State Petroleum Law.
996 456 2cr.50 blue 10 10

457 Globe showing Brazil and the Americas

458 Gen. L. Sodre

1958. 7th Inter-American Municipalities Congress, Rio de Janeiro.
997 457 2cr.50 blue 50 10

1958. Birth Centenary of Sodre.
998 458 3cr.30 green 10 10

459 U.N. Emblem

460 Footballer

1958. 10th Anniv of Human Rights Declaration.
999 459 2cr.50 blue 10 10

1959. World Football Cup Victory, 1958.
1000 460 3cr.30 brown & green . . 95 10

461 Map and Railway Line

462 Pres. Sukarno

1959. Centenary of Opening of Patos-Campina Grande Railway.
1001 461 2cr.50 brown 30 15

1959. Visit of President of Indonesia.
1002 462 2cr.50 blue 10 10

463 Basketball Player

464 King John VI of Portugal

1959. Air. World Basketball Championships 1959.
1003 463 3cr.30 brown & blue 90 10

1959.
1004 464 2cr.50 red 15 10

465 Polo Players

1959. Children's Games.
1005 465 2cr.50 brown 20 10

466 Dockside Scene

467 Church Organ, Diamantina

1959. Rehabilitation of National Ports Law.
1006 466 2cr.50 green 15 10

1959. Bicent of Carmelite Order in Brazil.
1007 467 3cr.30 lake 10 10

468 Dom J. S. de Souza (First Archbishop)

469 Sugar-loaf Mountain and Road

1959. Birth Cent of Archbishop of Diamantina.
1008 468 2cr.50 brown 10 10

1959. 11th International Roads Congress.
1009 469 3cr.30 blue and green . . 15 10

470 Londrina and Parana

471 Putting the Shot

1959. 25th Anniv of Londrina.
1010 470 2cr.50 green 10 10

1959. Spring Games.
1011 471 2cr.50 mauve 65 10

472 Daedalus

473 Globe and "Snipe" Class Yachts

1959. Air. Aviation Week.
1012 472 3cr.30 blue 10 10

1959. World Sailing Championships, Porto Alegre.
1013 473 6cr.50 green 10 10

474 Lusignan Cross and Arms of Salvador, Bahia

475 Gunpowder Factory

1959. 4th International Brazilian–Portuguese Study Conference, Bahia University.
1014 474 6cr.50 blue 10 10

1959. 50th Anniv of President Vargas Gunpowder Factory.
1015 475 3cr.30 brown 10 10

476

477 Sud Aviation Caravelle

1959. Thanksgiving Day.
1016 476 2cr.50 blue 50 10

1959. Air. Inauguration of "Caravelle" Airliners by Brazilian National Airlines.
1017 477 6cr.50 blue 15 10

478 Burning Bush

1959. Centenary of Presbyterian Work in Brazil.
1018 478 3cr.30 green 10 10

479 P. da Silva and "Schistosoma mansoni"

1959. 50th Anniv of Discovery and Identification of "Schistosoma mansoni" (fluke).
1019 479 2cr.50 purple 50 10

480 L. de Matos and Church

481 Pres. Lopez Mateos of Mexico

1960. Birth Centenary of Luiz de Matos (Christian evangelist).
1020 480 3cr.30 brown 10 10

1960. Air. Visit of Mexican President.
1021 481 6cr.50 brown 10 10

482 Pres. Eisenhower

483 Dr. L. Zamenhof

1960. Air. Visit of United States President.
1022 482 6cr.50 brown 15 10

1960. Birth Centenary of Zamenhof (inventor of Esperanto).
1023 483 6cr.50 green 35 10

484 Adel Pinto (engineer)

485 "Care of Refugees"

1960. Birth Centenary of Adel Pinto.
1024 484 11cr.50 red 25 10

1960. Air. World Refugee Year.
1025 485 6cr.50 blue 20 10

486 Plan of Brasilia

1960. Inauguration of Brasilia as Capital.
1026 – 2cr.50 green (postage) . . 15 10
1027 – 3cr.30 violet (air) 10 10
1028 – 4cr. blue . . . . . 1·25 10
1029 – 6cr.50 mauve 10 10
1030 486 11cr.50 brown 15 10
DESIGNS—Outlines representing: HORIZ: 2cr.50, President's Palace of the Plateau; 3cr.30, Parliament Buildings; 4cr. Cathedral. VERT: 6cr.50, Tower.

487 Congress Emblem

1960. Air. 7th Nat Eucharistic Congress, Curitiba.
1032 487 3cr.30 mauve 10 10

488 Congress Emblem, Sugar-loaf Mountain and Cross

489 Boy Scout

1960. Air. 10th Baptist World Alliance Congress, Rio de Janeiro.
1033 488 6cr.50 blue 10 10

1960. Air. 50th Anniv of Scouting in Brazil.
1034 489 3cr.30 orange 10 10

490 "Agriculture"

491 Caravel

1960. Cent of Brazilian Ministry of Agriculture.
1035 490 2cr.50 brown 15 10

1960. Air. 5th Death Centenary of Prince Henry the Navigator.
1036 491 6cr.50 black 30 10

492 P. de Frontin   **493** Locomotive Piston Gear

1960. Birth Cent of Paulo de Frontin (engineer).
1037 **492** 2cr.50 orange 10   10

1960. 10th Pan-American Railways Congress.
1038 **493** 2cr.50 blue 35   10

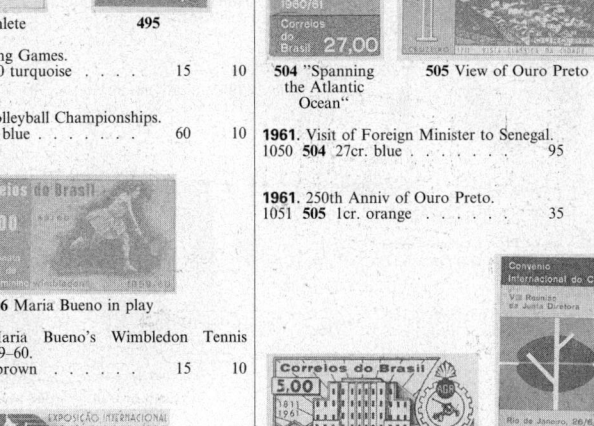

494 Athlete   **495**

1960. 12th Spring Games.
1039 **494** 2cr.50 turquoise 15   10

1960. World Volleyball Championships.
1040 **495** 11cr. blue 60   10

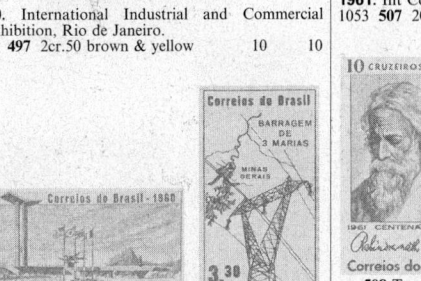

496 Maria Bueno in play

1960. Air. Maria Bueno's Wimbledon Tennis Victories, 1959–60.
1041 **496** 6cr. brown 15   10

497 Exhibition Emblem

1960. International Industrial and Commercial Exhibition, Rio de Janeiro.
1042 **497** 2cr.50 brown & yellow 10   10

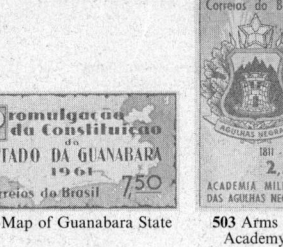

502 Map of Guanabara State   **503** Arms of Academy

1961. Promulgation of Guanabara Constitution.
1047 **502** 7cr.50 brown 60   10

1961. 150th Anniv of Agulhas Negras Military Academy.
1048 **503** 2cr.50 green 20   10
1049 – 3cr.30 red 10   10
DESIGN: 3cr.30, Military cap and sabre.

504 "Spanning the Atlantic Ocean"   **505** View of Ouro Preto

1961. Visit of Foreign Minister to Senegal.
1050 **504** 27cr. blue 95   10

1961. 250th Anniv of Ouro Preto.
1051 **505** 1cr. orange 35   10

506 Arsenal, Rio de Janeiro   **507** Coffee Plant

1961. 150th Anniv of Rio de Janeiro Arsenal.
1052 **506** 5cr. brown 45   10

1961. Int Coffee Convention, Rio de Janeiro.
1053 **507** 20cr. brown . . . . . . 2·40   10

508 Tagore   **509** 280r. Stamp of 1861 and Map of France

1960. Birth Cent of Rabindranath Tagore (poet).
1054 **508** 10cr. mauve 90   10

1961. "Goat's Eyes" Stamp Centenary.
1055 **509** 10cr. red . . . . . . 1·25   10
1056 – 20cr. orange . . . . . . 3·75   10
DESIGN: 20cr. 430r. stamp and map of the Netherlands.

510 Cloudburst   **511** Pinnacle, Rope and Haversack

1962. World Meteorological Day.
1057 **510** 10cr. brown . . . . . . 1·25   10

1962. 50th Anniv of 1st Ascent of "Finger of God" Mountain.
1058 **511** 8cr. green 10   10

512 Dr. G. Vianna and parasites

1962. 50th Anniv of Vianna's Cure for Leishman's Disease.
1059 **512** 8cr. blue 20   10

513 Campaign Emblem   **514** Henrique Dias (patriot)

1962. Air. Malaria Eradication.
1060 **513** 21cr. blue 10   10

1962. 300th Death Anniv of Dias.
1061 **514** 10cr. purple 15   10

515 Metric Measure   **516** "Snipe" Sailing-boats

1962. Cent of Brazil's Adoption of Metric System.
1062 **515** 100cr. red . . . . . . 1·25   10

1962. 13th "Snipe" Class Sailing Championships, Rio de Janeiro.
1063 **516** 8cr. turquoise 20   10

517 J. Mesquita and Newspaper "O Estado de Sao Paulo"

1962. Birth Centenary of Mesquita (journalist and founder of "O Estado de Sao Paulo").
1064 **517** 8cr. bistre . . . . . . 1·25   10

518 Empress Leopoldina   **519** Brasilia

1962. 140th Anniv of Independence.
1065 **518** 8cr. mauve 15   10

1962. 51st Interparliamentary Conference, Brasilia.
1066 **519** 10cr. orange 40   10

520 Foundry Ladle   **521** U.P.A.E. Emblem

1962. Inauguration of "Usiminas" (national iron and steel foundry).
1067 **520** 8cr. orange 10   10

1962. 50th Anniv of Postal Union of the Americas and Spain.
1068 **521** 8cr. mauve 10   10

522 Emblems of Industry   **523** Q. Bocaiuva

1962. 10th Anniv of National Bank.
1069 **522** 10cr. turquoise 15   10

1962. 50th Death Anniv of Bocaiuva (journalist and patriot).
1070 **523** 8cr. brown 10   10

524 Footballer

1962. Brazil's Victory in World Football Championships, 1962.
1071 **524** 10cr. turquoise . . . . . . 1·25   10

 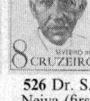

525 Carrier Pigeon   **526** Dr. S. Neiva (first Brazilian P.M.G.)

1962. Tercentenary of Brazilian Posts.
1072 **525** 8cr. multicoloured 10   10

1963.
1073 **526** 8cr. violet 50   10
1073a – 30cr. turquoise (Euclides da Cunha) . . 4·75   10
1073b – 50cr. brown (Prof. A. Moreira da Costa Lima) . . 3·50   10
1073c – 100cr. blue (G. Dias) . . 1·75   10
1073d – 200cr. red (Tiradentes) . . 7·00   10
1073e – 500cr. brown (Emperor Pedro I) . . 35·00   20
1073f – 1000cr. blue (Emperor Pedro II) . . 90·00   60

527 Rockets and "Dish" Aerial   **528** Cross

1963. Int Aeronautics and Space Exn, Sao Paulo.
1074 **527** 21cr. blue 60   10

1963. Ecumenical Council, Vatican City.
1075 **528** 8cr. purple 10   10

529 "abc" Symbol   **530** Basketball

1963. National Education Week.
1076 **529** 8cr. blue 10   10

1963. 4th World Basketball Championships.
1077 **530** 8cr. mauve 50   10

— note: (left-bottom block) **500** Emperor Haile Selassie   **501** Sacred Book and Map of Brazil

1961. Visit of Emperor of Ethiopia.
1045 **500** 2cr.50 brown 10   10

1961. 50th Anniv of Sacre-Coeur de Marie College.
1046 **501** 2cr.50 blue 15   10

498 War Memorial, Rio de Janeiro   **499** Pylon and Map

1960. Air. Return of Ashes of World War II Heroes from Italy.
1043 **498** 3cr.30 lake 15   10

1961. Air. Inauguration of Tres Marias Hydro-electric Station.
1044 **499** 3cr.30 mauve 15   10

531 Torch Emblem

1963. 4th Pan-American Games, Sao Paulo.
1078 **531** 10cr. red 65 10

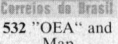

532 "OEA" and Map   533 J. B. de Andrada e Silva

1963. 15th Anniv of Organization of American States.
1079 **532** 10cr. orange 50 10

1963. Birth Bicentenary of Jose B. de Andrada e Silva ("Father of Independence")
1080 **533** 8cr. bistre 10 10

534 Campaign Emblem

1963. Freedom from Hunger.
1081 **534** 10cr. blue 50 10

535 Centenary Emblem   536 J. Caetano

1963. Red Cross Centenary.
1082 **535** 8cr. red and yellow . . . 20 10

1963. Death Centenary of Joao Caetano (actor).
1083 **536** 8cr. black 10 10

537 "Atomic" Development   538 Throwing the Hammer

1963. 1st Anniv of National Nuclear Energy Commission.
1084 **537** 10cr. mauve 50 10

1963. International Students' Games, Porto Alegre.
1085 **538** 10cr. black and grey . . 65 10

539 Pres. Tito   540 Cross and Map

1963. Visit of President Tito of Yugoslavia.
1086 **539** 80cr. drab . . . . . . 2·40 10

1963. 8th Int Leprology Congress, Rio de Janeiro.
1087 **540** 8cr. turquoise 10 10

541 Petroleum Installations   543 A. Borges de Medeiros

542 "Jogos da Primavera"

1963. 10th Anniv of National Petroleum Industry.
1088 **541** 8cr. green 10 10

1963. Spring Games.
1089 **542** 8cr. yellow 10 10

1963. Birth Centenary of A. Borges de Medeiros (politician).
1090 **543** 8cr. brown 10 10

544 Bridge of Sao Joao del Rey   546 Viscount de Maua

545 Dr. A. Alvim

1963. 250th Anniv of Sao Joao del Rey.
1091 **544** 8cr. blue 10 10

1963. Birth Cent of Dr. Alvaro Alvim (scientist).
1092 **545** 8cr. slate 10 10

1963. 150th Birth Anniv of Viscount de Maua (builder of Santos–Jundiai Railway).
1093 **546** 8cr. mauve 45 20

547 Cactus   548 C. Netto

1964. 10th Anniv of North-East Bank.
1094 **547** 8cr. green 10 10

1964. Birth Centenary of Coelho Netto (author).
1095 **548** 8cr. violet 10 10

549 L. Muller   550 Child with Spoon

1964. Birth Cent of Lauro Muller (patriot).
1096 **549** 8cr. red 10 10

1964. Schoolchildren's Nourishment Week.
1097 **550** 8cr. yellow and brown 10 10

551 "Chalice" (carved rock), Vila Velha, Parana   552 A. Kardec (author)

1964. Tourism.
1098 **551** 80cr. red 65 10

1964. Cent of Spiritual Code, "O Evangelho".
1099 **552** 30cr. green 95 10

553 Pres. Lubke   554 Pope John XXIII

1964. Visit of Pres. Lubke of West Germany.
1100 **553** 100cr. brown . . . . . 1·25 10

1964. Pope John Commemoration.
1101 **554** 20cr. lake 60 35

555 Pres. Senghor

1964. Visit of Pres. Senghor of Senegal.
1102 **555** 20cr. sepia 15 10

556 "Visit Rio de Janeiro"

1964. 400th Anniv (1965) of Rio de Janeiro.
1103 **556** 15cr. blue and orange . . 25 10
1104 — 30cr. red and blue 65 10
1105 — 30cr. black and blue . 1·60 40
1106 — 35cr. black and orange 15 10
1107 — 100cr. brn & grn on yell 65 10
1108 — 200cr. red and green . 6·00 10
DESIGNS: As Type 556—HORIZ: 30cr. (No. 1105), Tramway viaduct; 200cr. Copacabana Beach. VERT: 35cr. Estacio de Sa's statue; 100cr. Church of Our Lady of the Rock. SMALLER (24½ × 37 mm): 30cr. (No. 1104), Statue of St. Sebastian.

558 Pres. De Gaulle   559 Pres. Kennedy

1964. Visit of Pres. De Gaulle.
1110 **558** 100cr. brown 95 10

1964. Pres. Kennedy Commemoration.
1111 **559** 100cr. black 15 15

560 Nahum (statue)

1964. 150th Death Anniv of A. F. Lisboa (sculptor).
1112 **560** 10cr. black 30 10

561 Cross and Sword   562 V. Brazil (scientist)

1965. 1st Anniv of Democratic Revolution.
1113 **561** 120cr. grey 15 10

1965. Birth Cent of Vital Brazil.
1114 **562** 120cr. orange . . . . . 1·25 10

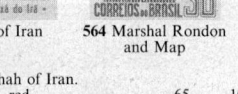

563 Shah of Iran   564 Marshal Rondon and Map

1965. Visit of Shah of Iran.
1115 **563** 120cr. red 65 10

1965. Birth Cent of Marshal C. M. da S. Rondon.
1116 **564** 30cr. purple 50 10

565 Lions Emblem   566 I.T.U. Emblem and Symbols

1965. Brazilian Lions Clubs National Convention, Rio de Janeiro.
1117 **565** 35cr. black and lilac . . 15 10

1965. I.T.U. Centenary.
1118 **566** 120cr. green and yellow 65 10

567 E. Pessoa   568 Barrosos Statue

1965. Birth Centenary of Epitacio Pessoa.
1119 **567** 35cr. slate 10 10

1965. Centenary of Naval Battle of Riachuelo.
1120 **568** 30cr. blue 15 10

569 Author and Heroine   **570** Sir Winston Churchill

1965. Centenary of Publication of Jose de Alencar's "Iracema".
1121 **569** 30cr. purple 15 10

1965. Churchill Commemoration.
1122 **570** 200cr. slate . . . . . . 1·25 10

571 Scout Badge and Emblem of Rio's 400th Anniv   **572** I.C.Y. Emblem

1965. 1st Pan-American Scout Jamboree, Rio de Janeiro.
1123 **571** 30r. multicoloured . . . 1·10 10

1965. International Co-operation Year.
1124 **572** 120cr. black and blue . . 1·25 10

573 L. Correia   **574** Exhibition Emblem

1965. Birth Centenary of Leoncia Correia (poet).
1125 **573** 35cr. green 10 10

1965. Sao Paulo Biennale (Art Exn).
1126 **574** 30cr. red 10 10

575 President Saragat   **576** Grand Duke and Duchess of Luxembourg

1965. Visit of President of Italy.
1127 **575** 100cr. green on pink . . 15 10

1965. Visit of Grand Duke and Duchess of Luxembourg.
1128 **576** 100cr. brown 15 10

577 Curtiss Fledgling on Map   **578** O.E.A. Emblem

1965. Aviation Week and 3rd Philatelic Exn.
1129 **577** 35cr. blue 15 10

1965. Inter-American Conference, Rio de Janeiro.
1130 **578** 100cr. black and blue . . 45 10

579 King Baudouin and Queen Fabiola   **580** Coffee Beans

1965. Visit of King and Queen of the Belgians.
1131 **579** 100cr. slate 50 10

1965. Brazilian Coffee.
1132 **580** 30cr. brown on cream 65 10

581 F. A. Varnhagen   **583** Sister and Globe

582 Emblem and Map

1965. Air. 150th Birth Anniv of Francisco Varnhagen (historian).
1133 **581** 45cr. brown 15 10

1966. Air. 5th Anniv of "Alliance for Progress".
1134 **582** 120cr. blue & turquoise 95 10

1966. Air. Centenary of Dorothean Sisters Educational Work in Brazil.
1135 **583** 35cr. violet 10 10

584 Loading Ore at Quayside   **585** "Steel"

1966. Inauguration of Rio Doce Iron-ore Terminal Tubarao, Espirito Santo.
1136 **584** 110cr. black and bistre 50 10

1966. Silver Jubilee of National Steel Company.
1137 **585** 30cr. black on orange . . 35 10

586 Prof. Rocha Lima   **587** Battle Scene

1966. 50th Anniv of Professor Lima's Discovery of the Characteristics of "Rickettsia prowazeki" (cause of typhus fever).
1138 **586** 30cr. turquoise 65 10

1966. Centenary of Battle of Tuiuti.
1139 **587** 30cr. green 65 10

 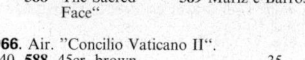

588 "The Sacred Face"   **589** Mariz e Barros

1966. Air. "Concilio Vaticano II".
1140 **588** 45cr. brown 35 35

1966. Air. Death Centenary of Commander Mariz e Barros.
1141 **589** 35cr. brown 15 10

590 Decade Symbol   **591** Pres. Shazar

1966. International Hydrological Decade.
1142 **590** 100cr. blue and brown 65 10

1966. Visit of President Shazar of Israel.
1143 **591** 100cr. blue 95 10

592 "Youth"   **593** Imperial Academy of Fine Arts

1966. Air. Birth Centenary of Eliseu Visconti (painter).
1144 **592** 120cr. brown . . . . . 1·90 10

1966. 150th Anniv of French Art Mission's Arrival in Brazil.
1145 **593** 100cr. brown . . . . . 1·75 10

594 Military Service Emblem   **595** R. Dario

1966. New Military Service Law.
1146 **594** 30cr. blue and yellow . . 15 10

1966. 50th Death Anniv of Ruben Dario (Nicaraguan poet).
1148 **595** 100cr. purple 65 10

596 Santarem Candlestick   **597** Arms of Santa Cruz do Sul

1966. Centenary of Goeldi Museum.
1149 **596** 30cr. brown on salmon 15 10

1966. 1st National Tobacco Exn, Santa Cruz.
1150 **597** 30cr. green 15 10

598 U.N.E.S.C.O. Emblem   **599** Capt. A. C. Pinto and Map

1966. 20th Anniv of U.N.E.S.C.O.
1151 **598** 120cr. black . . . . . . 1·25 35

1966. Bicentenary of Arrival of Captain A. C. Pinto.
1153 **599** 30cr. red 15 10

600 Lusignan Cross and Southern Cross   **601** Madonna and Child

1966. "Lubrapex 1966" Stamp Exn, Rio de Janeiro.
1154 **600** 100cr. green 95 10

1966. Christmas.
1155 **601** 30cr. green 20 10
1156 – 35cr. blue and orange . . 20 15
1157 – 150cr. pink and blue . . 3·50 3·50
DESIGN—DIAMOND(34 × 34 mm). 35cr. Madonna and child (different). VERT (46 × 103 mm). 150cr. As 35cr. inscr "Pax Hominibus" but not "Brazil Correio".

602 Arms of Laguna

1967. Centenary of Laguna Postal and Telegraphic Agency.
1158 **602** 60cr. sepia 10 10

603 Grota Funda Viaduct and 1866 Viaduct

1967. Centenary of Santos–Jundiai Railway.
1159 **603** 50cr. orange . . . . . 1·40 30

604 Polish Cross and "Black Madonna"

1967. Polish Millennium.
1160 **604** 50cr. red, blue & yellow 50 10

605 Research Rocket   **606** Anita Garibaldi

1967. World Meteorological Day.
1161 **605** 50cr. black and blue . . 95 10

1967.
1162 – 1c. blue 10 10
1163 – 2c. red 10 10
1164 – 3c. green 15 10
1165 **606** 5c. black 15 10
1166 – 6c. brown 15 10
1167 – 10c. green . . . . . . 1·40 10
PORTRAITS: 1c. Mother Angelica. 2c. Marilia de

Dirceu. 3c. Dr. R. Lobato. 6c. Ana Neri. 10c. Darci Vargas.

607 "VARIG 40   608 Lions Emblem and Globes
Years"

1967. 40th Anniv of Varig Airlines.
1171 607 6c. black and blue . . .   15   10

1967. 50th Anniv of Lions International.
1172 608 6c. green   25   10

609 "Madonna   610 Prince Akihito and Princess
and Child"   Michiko

1967. Mothers' Day.
1174 609 5c. violet   10   10

1967. Visit of Crown Prince and Princess of Japan.
1176 610 10c. black and red . . .   15   10

611 Radar Aerial   612 Brother Vicente
and Pigeon   do Salvador

1967. Inaug of Communications Ministry, Brasilia.
1177 611 10c. black and mauve . .   15   10

1967. 400th Birth Anniv of Brother Vicente do Salvador (founder of Franciscan Brotherhood, Rio de Janeiro).
1178 612 5c. brown   15   10

613 Emblem and Members   614 Mobius
Symbol

1967. National 4-S ("4-H") Clubs Day.
1179 613 5c. green and black . . .   15   10

1967. 6th Brazilian Mathematical Congress. Rio de Janeiro.
1180 614 5c. black and blue . . .   15   10

615 Dorado (fish) and "Waves"

1967. Bicentenary of Piracicaba.
1181 615 5c. black and blue . . .   20   10

616 Papal Arms and "Golden Rose"

1967. Pope Paul's "Golden Rose" Offering to Our Lady of Fatima.
1182 616 20c. mauve and yellow   1·25   35

617 General A. de Sampaio

1967. Gen. Sampaio Commem.
1183 617 5c. blue   15   10

618 King Olav of   619 Sun and Rio de
Norway   Janeiro

1967. Visit of King Olav.
1184 618 10c. brown   15   10

1967. Meeting of International Monetary Fund, Rio de Janeiro.
1185 619 10c. black and red . . .   15   10

620 N. Pecanha   621 Our Lady of the
(statesman)   Apparition and Basilica

1967. Birth Centenary of Nilo Pecanha.
1186 620 5c. purple   10   10

1967. 250th Anniv of Discovery of Statue of Our Lady of the Apparition.
1187 621 5c. blue and ochre . . .   15   10

622 "Song Bird"   623 Balloon, Rocket and
Airplane

1967. International Song Festival.
1189 622 20c. multicoloured . . .   55   35

1967. Aviation Week.
1190 623 10c. blue   60   10

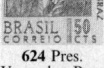

624 Pres.   625 Rio Carnival
Venceslau Braz

1967.
1192 – 10c. blue   35   10
1193 – 20c. brown . . . . . .   1·75   10
1195 624 50c. black . . . .   12·00   10
1198 – 1cr. purple . . . . . .   18·00   10
1199 – 2cr. green . . . .   3·75   10
Portraits of Brazilian Presidents: 10c. Arthur Bernardes. 20c. Campos Salles. 1cr. Washington Luiz. 2cr. Castello Branco.

1967. International Tourist Year.
1200 625 10c. multicoloured . . .   15   10

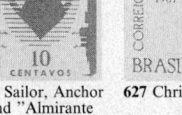

626 Sailor, Anchor   627 Christmas Decorations
and "Almirante
Tamandare"
(cruiser)

1967. Navy Week.
1202 626 10c. blue   30   15

1967. Christmas.
1203 627 5c. multicoloured . . .   15   10

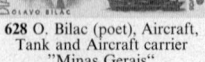

628 O. Bilac (poet), Aircraft,   629 J. Rodrigues
Tank and Aircraft carrier   de Carvalho
"Minas Gerais"

1967. Reservists Day.
1204 628 5c. blue and yellow . . .   60   15

1967. Birth Centenary of Jose Rodriques de Carvalho (jurist and writer).
1205 629 10c. green   10   10

630 O. Rangel

1968. Birth Cent of Orlando Rangel (chemist).
1206 630 5c. black and blue . . .   15   10

631 Madonna and   632 Map of Free
Diver   Zone

1968. 250th Anniv of Paranagua Underwater Exploration.
1207 631 10c. green and slate . . .   20   10

1968. Manaus Free Zone.
1208 632 10c. red, green and
yellow   15   10

633 Human Rights   634 Paul Harris
Emblem

1968. 20th Anniv of Declaration of Human Rights.
1209 633 10c. red and blue   10   10

> GUM. All the following issues to No. 1425 are without gum, except where otherwise stated.

1968. Birth Centenary of Paul Harris (founder of Rotary International).
1210 634 20c. brown and green . .   1·25   60

635 College Arms

1968. Centenary of St. Luiz College. With gum.
1211 635 10c. gold, blue and red . .   25   10

636 Cabral and his Fleet, 1500

1968. 500th Birth Anniv of Pedro Cabral (discoverer of Brazil).
1212 636 10c. multicoloured . . .   30   15
1213 – 20c. multicoloured . . .   90   60
DESIGN: 20c. "The First Mass" (C. Portinari).

637 "Maternity" (after
H. Bernardeli)

1968. Mother's Day.
1214 637 5c. multicoloured   20   15

638 Harpy Eagle

1968. 150th Anniv of National Museum. With gum.
1215 638 20c. black and blue . .   2·50   60

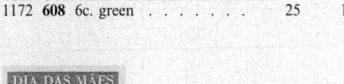

639 Women of Brazil and Japan

1968. Inaug of "VARIG" Brazil–Japan Air Service.
1216 **639** 10c. multicoloured . . . 25 15

640 Horse-racing

1968. Centenary of Brazilian Jockey Club.
1217 **640** 10c. multicoloured . . . 20 10

641 Musician Wren

1968. Birds.
1218 – 10c. multicoloured . . . 50 25
1219 **641** 20c. brown, green & bl 1·50 25
1220 – 50c. multicoloured . . . 1·90 40
DESIGNS—VERT: 10c. Red-crested cardinal; 50c.
Royal flycatcher.

642 Ancient Post-box   643 Marshal E.
Luiz Mallet

1968. Stamp Day. With gum.
1221 **642** 5c. black, green & yellow 10 10

1968. Mallet Commemoration. With gum.
1222 **643** 10c. lilac 10 10

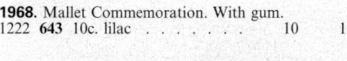

644 Map of South   645 Lyceum Badge
America

1968. Visit of Chilean President. With gum.
1223 **644** 10c. orange 10 10

1968. Centenary of Portuguese Literacy Lyceum
(High School). With gum.
1224 **645** 5c. green and pink . . . 10 10

646 Map and Telex Tape

1968. "Telex Service for 25th City (Curitiba)". With
gum.
1225 **646** 20c. green and yellow . . 55 35

647 Soldiers on   648 "Cock" shaped as Treble
Medallion   Clef

1968. 8th American Armed Forces Conference
1226 **647** 5c. black and blue . . . 15 10

1968. 3rd Int Song Festival, Rio de Janeiro.
1227 **648** 6c. multicoloured . . . 25 15

649 "Petrobras" Refinery   650 Boy walking
towards Rising
Sun

1968. 15th Anniv of National Petroleum Industry.
1228 **649** 6c. multicoloured . . . 50 15

1968. U.N.I.C.E.F.
1229 **650** 5c. black and blue . . . 20 15
1230 – 10c. black, red & blue . . 20 15
1231 – 20c. multicoloured . . . 50 15
DESIGNS—HORIZ: 10c. Hand protecting child.
VERT: 20c. Young girl in plaits.

651 Children with Books

1968. Book Week.
1232 **651** 5c. multicoloured . . . 15 10

652 W.H.O. Emblem and Flags

1968. 20th Anniv of W.H.O.
1233 **652** 20c. multicoloured . . . 30 15

653 J. B. Debret (painter)

1968. Birth Bicentenary of Jean Baptiste Debret (1st
issue).
1234 **653** 10c. black and yellow . . 20 10
See Nos. 1273/4.

654 Queen Elizabeth II

1968. State Visit of Queen Elizabeth II.
1235 **654** 70c. multicoloured . . . 1·50 90

655 Brazilian Flag   656 F. Braga and
part of "Hymn of
National Flag"

1968. Brazilian Flag Day.
1236 **655** 10c. multicoloured . . . 20 15

1968. Birth Cent of Francisco Braga (composer).
1237 **656** 5c. purple 25 10

657 Clasped Hands

1968. Blood Donors' Day.
1238 **657** 5c. red, black and blue 15 10

1968. Obligatory Tax. Leprosy Research Fund.
Revalued currency. With gum.
1239 **388** 5c. green . . . . 5·25 1·25
1240 – 5c. red . . . . 2·40 60

658 Steam Locomotive No. 1 "Maria
Fumaca", 1868

1968. Centenary of Sao Paulo Railway.
1241 **658** 5c. multicoloured . . . 2·50 2·50

659 Angelus Bell   660 F.A.V. Caldas
Jr

1968. Christmas. Multicoloured.
1242 5c. Type **659** 15 10
1243 6c. Father Christmas giving
present 15 10

1968. Birth Centenary of Francisco Caldas Junior
(founder of "Correio do Povo" newspaper).
1244 **660** 10c. black, pink & red 15 10

661 Reservists Emblem and Memorial

1968. Reservists' Day. With gum.
1245 **661** 5c. green and brown . . 15 10

662 Dish Aerial   663 Viscount do Rio
Branco

1969. Inaug of Satellite Communications System.
1246 **662** 30c. black and blue . . 90 60

1969. 150th Birth Anniv of Viscount do Rio Branco.
1247 **663** 5c. sepia and drab . . 15 10

664 St. Gabriel   666 Kardec and Monument

665 Shoemaker's Last and Globe

1969. St. Gabriel's Day (Patron Saint of
Telecommunications).
1248 **664** 5c. multicoloured . . . 15 10

1969. 4th Int Shoe Fair, Novo, Hamburgo.
1249 **665** 5c. multicoloured . . . 15 10

1969. Death Centenary of "Allan Kardec" (Professor
H. Rivail) (French educationalist and spiritualist).
1250 **666** 5c. brown and green . . 15 10

667 Men of Three Races and Arms of
Cuiaba

1969. 250th Anniv of Cuiaba (capital of Mato Grosso
state).
1251 **667** 5c. multicoloured 10 10

668 Mint and Banknote Pattern

1969. Opening of New State Mint Printing Works.
1252 **668** 5c. bistre and orange . . 20 15

669 Society Emblem and Stamps

1969. 50th Anniv of Sao Paulo Philatelic Society.
1253 **669** 5c. multicoloured 10 10

670 "Our Lady of Santana"
(statue)

1969. Mothers' Day.
1254 **670** 5c. multicoloured 20 15

671 ILO Emblem

1969. 50th Anniv of I.L.O. With gum.
1255 **671** 5c. gold and red 10 10

672 Diving Platform and Swimming Pool

673 "Mother and Child at Window" (after Di Cavalcanti)

1969. 40th Anniv of Cearense Water Sports Club, Fortaleza.
1256 **672** 20c. black, green & brn   40   15

1969. 10th Art Exhibition Biennale, Sao Paulo. Multicoloured.
1257   10c. Type **673**   60   15
1258   20c. Modern sculpture
     (F. Leirner)   90   30
1259   50c. "Sunset in Brasilia" (D.
     di Prete) . . . .   1·75   1·25
1260   1cr. "Angelfish"
     (A. Martins) . . . . . .   1·75   80
No. 1258 is square, size 33 × 33 mm and Nos. 1259/60 vertical, size 33 × 53mm.

674 Freshwater Angelfish

675 I. O. Teles de Manezes (founder)

1969. A.C.A.P.I. Fish Preservation and Development Campaign.
1261 **674** 20c. multicoloured . . .   45   15

1969. Centenary of Spiritualist Press. With gum.
1263 **675** 50c. green and orange   1·50   90

676 Postman delivering Letter

677 General Fragoso

1969. Stamp Day. With gum.
1264 **676** 30c. blue . . . . . .   1·25   60

1969. Birth Centenary of General Tasso Fragoso. With gum.
1265 **677** 20c. green   90   60

678 Map of Army Bases

1969. Army Week. Multicoloured.
1266   10c. Type **678**   25   15
1267   20c. Monument and railway
     bridge (39 × 22 mm) . . .   1·75   60

679 Jupia Dam

1969. Inauguration of Jupia Dam.
1268 **679** 20c. multicoloured . . .   55   55

680 Mahatma Gandhi and Spinning-wheel

1969. Birth Centenary of Mahatma Gandhi.
1269 **680** 20c. black and yellow . .   1·25   60

681 Alberto Santos Dumont, "Ballon No. 6", Eiffel Tower and Moon Landing

1969. 1st Man on the Moon and Santos Dumont's Flight (1906). Commemoration.
1270 **681** 50c. multicoloured . . .   1·75   1·25

682 Smelting Plant

1969. Expansion of USIMINAS Steel Consortium.
1271 **682** 20c. multicoloured . . .   55   15

683 Steel Furnace   **685** Exhibition Emblem

1969. 25th Anniv of ACESITA Steel Works.
1272 **683** 10c. multicoloured . . .   55   15

684 "The Water Cart" (after Debret)

1969. Birth Centenary of J. B. Debret (painter) (2nd issue). Multicoloured. No. 1274 dated "1970".
1273   20c. Type **684** . . . . .   1·25   60
1274   30c. "Street Scene" . . . .   1·00   95

1969. "Abuexpo 69" Stamp Exn.
1275 **685** 10c. multicoloured . . .   20   15

686 Embraer Bandeirante Airplane

1969. Brazilian Aeronautical Industry Expansion Year.
1276 **686** 50c. multicoloured . . .   1·75   1·25

687 Pele scoring Goal

1969. Footballer Pele's 1,000th Goal.
1277 **687** 10c. multicoloured . . .   1·25   1·75

688 "Madonna and Child" (painted panel)

1969. Christmas.
1279 **688** 10c. multicoloured . . .   55   35

689 "Pernambuco" (destroyer) and "Bahia" (submarine)

1969. Navy Day. With gum.
1281 **689** 5c. blue . . . .   1·00   15

690 Dr. H. Blumenau

1969. 150th Birth Anniv of Dr. Hermann Blumenau (German immigrant leader). With gum.
1282 **690** 20c. green   60   60

691 Carnival Dancers

1969. Carioca Carnival, Rio de Janeiro (1970). Multicoloured.
1283   5c. Type **691**   25   20
1284   10c. Samba dancers (horiz)   25   20
1285   20c. Clowns (horiz) . . .   25   30
1286   30c. Confetti and mask . .   2·75   1·50
1287   50c. Tambourine-player . .   2·75   1·40

692 Carlos Gomes conducting

1970. Centenary of Opera "O. Guarani" by A. Carlos Gomes.
1288 **692** 20c. multicoloured . . .   60   20

693 Monastery

1970. 400th Anniv of Penha Monastery, Vilha Velha.
1289 **693** 20c. multicoloured . . .   25   15

694 National Assembly Building

1970. 10th Anniv of Brasilia. Multicoloured.
1290   20c. Type **694**   25   15
1291   50c. Reflecting Pool . . . .   1·75   1·50
1292   1cr. Presidential Palace . . .   1·75   1·50

695 Emblem on Map

1970. Rondon Project (students' practical training scheme).
1293 **695** 50c. multicoloured . . .   1·50   1·50

696 Marshal Osorio and Arms

1970. Opening of Marshal Osorio Historical Park.
1294 **696** 20c. multicoloured . . .   1·25   45

697 "Madonna and Child" (San Antonio Monastery)

698 Brasilia Cathedral (stylized)

1970. Mothers' Day
1295 **697** 20c. multicoloured . . .   55   20

1970. 8th National Eucharistic Congress, Brasilia. With gum.
1296 **698** 20c. green   15   15

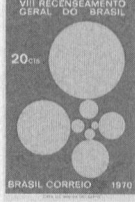

699 Census Symbol   **700** Jules Rimet Cup, and Map

1970. 8th National Census.
1297 **699** 20c. yellow and green . .   55   50

1970. World Cup Football Championships Mexico.
1298 **700** 50c. black, gold & blue   50   40

701 Statue of Christ

1970. Marist Students. 6th World Congress.
1299 **701** 50c. multicoloured . . . 1·50 1·50

702 Bellini and Swedish Flag (1958)

1970. Brazil's Third Victory in World Cup Football Championships. Multicoloured.
1300 1cr. Type **702** . . . . . 1·75 90
1301 2cr. Garrincha and Chilean flag (1962) . . . . . 5·25 1·75
1302 3cr. Pele and Mexican flag (1970) . . . . 2·75 90

703 Pandia Calogeras
704 Brazilian Forces Badges and Map

1970. Birth Centenary of Calogeras (author and politician).
1303 **703** 20c. green . . . . . 1·75 60

1970. 25th Anniv of World War II. Victory.
1304 **704** 20c. multicoloured . . . 50 15

705 "The Annunciation" (Cassio M'Boy)

1970. St. Gabriel's Day (Patron Saint of Telecommunications).
1305 **705** 20c. multicoloured . . . 90 40

706 Boy in Library
707 U.N. Emblem

1970. Book Week.
1306 **706** 20c. multicoloured . . . 90 60

1970. 25th Anniv of United Nations.
1307 **707** 50c. blue, silver & ultram 90 75

708 "Rio de Janeiro, circa 1820"

1970. 3rd Brazilian–Portuguese Stamp Exhibition "Lubrapex 70", Rio de Janeiro.
1308 **708** 20c. multicoloured . . . 60 60
1309 – 50c. brown and black . . 2·75 1·75
1310 – 1cr. multicoloured . . . 2·75 2·75
DESIGNS: 50c. Post Office Symbol; 1cr. Rio de Janeiro (modern view).

709 "The Holy Family" (C. Portinari)
710 "Graca Aranha" (destroyer)

1970. Christmas.
1312 **709** 50c. multicoloured . . . 90 90

1970. Navy Day.
1314 **710** 20c. multicoloured . . . 1·75 80

711 Congress Emblem
712 Links and Globe

1971. 3rd Inter-American Housing Congress, Rio de Janeiro.
1315 **711** 50c. red and black . . . 80 80

1971. Racial Equality Year.
1316 **712** 20c. multicoloured . . . 60 30

713 "Morpho melacheilus"

1971. Butterflies. Multicoloured.
1317 20c. Type **713** . . . . . 1·25 35
1318 1cr. "Papilio thoas brasiliensis" . . . . . 6·00 2·40

714 Madonna and Child
715 Hands reaching for Ball

1971. Mothers' Day.
1319 **714** 20c. multicoloured . . . 60 15

1971. 6th Women's Basketball World Championships.
1320 **715** 70c. multicoloured . . . 1·25 95

716 Eastern Part of Highway Map

1971. Trans-Amazon Highway Project. Mult.
1321 40c. Type **716** . . . . . 6·25 3·75
1322 1cr. Western part of Highway Map . . . . 6·25 5·25
Nos. 1321/2 were issued together se-tenant, forming a composite design.

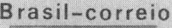

717 "Head of Man" (V. M. Lima)

1971. Stamp Day. Multicoloured.
1323 40c. Type **717** . . . . . 1·25 45
1324 1cr. "Arab Violinist" (Pedro Americo) . . . . 3·00 1·25

718 General Caxias and Map
719 Anita Garibaldi

1971. Army Week.
1325 **718** 20c. red and green . . . 50 15

1971. 150th Birth Anniv of Anita Garibaldi.
1326 **719** 20c. multicoloured . . . 20 15

720 Xavante and Santos Dumont's Biplane "14 bis"

1971. 1st Flight of Embraer Xavante Jet Fighter.
1327 **720** 40c. multicoloured . . . 1·25 45

721 Flags of Central American Republics
722 Exhibition Emblem

1971. 150th Anniv of Central American Republics' Independence.
1328 **721** 40c. multicoloured . . . 80 40

1971. "Franca 71" Industrial, Technical and Scientific Exhibition, Sao Paulo.
1329 **722** 1cr.30 multicoloured . . 1·25 90

723 "The Black Mother" (L. de Albuquerque)
724 Archangel Gabriel

1971. Centenary of Slaves Emancipation Law.
1330 **723** 40c. multicoloured . . . 40 20

1971. St. Gabriel's Day (Patron Saint of Communications).
1331 **724** 40c. multicoloured . . . 45 50

725 "Couple on Bridge" (Marisa da Silva Chaves)

1971. Children's Day. Multicoloured.
1332 35c. Type **725** 35 30
1333 45c. "Couple on Riverbank" (Mary Rosa e Silva) . . . 90 30
1334 60c. "Girl in Hat" (Teresa A. P. Ferreira) 35 30

726 "Laelia purpurata Werkhauserii superba"
727 Eunice Weaver

1971. Brazilian Orchids.
1335 **726** 40c. multicoloured . . . 1·50 50

1971. Obligatory Tax. Leprosy Research Fund.
1336 **727** 10c. green . . . . . 1·25 65
1337 10c. purple 55 15

728 "25 Senac"

1971. 25th Anniv of SENAC (apprenticeship scheme) and SESC (workers' social service).
1338 **728** 20c. blue and black . . 90 60
1339 – 40c. orange and black 90 60
DESIGN: 40c. As Type **728**, but inscribed "25 SESC".

729 "Parati" (gunboat)

1971. Navy Day.
1340 **729** 20c. multicoloured . . . 2·00 50

730 Cruciform Symbol
731 Washing Bomfim Church

1971. Christmas.
1341 **730** 20c. lilac, red and blue 30 15
1342 75c. black on silver . . . 55 1·75
1343 1cr.30 multicoloured . . 2·40 1·50

1972. Tourism. Multicoloured.
1344 20c. Type **731** . . . . . 1·75 90
1345 40c. Cogwheel and grapes (Grape Festival, Rio Grande do Sul) . . . . . 1·75 20
1346 75c. Nazareth Festival procession, Belem . . . 1·75 1·75
1347 1cr.30 Street scene (Winter Festival of Ouro Preto) 3·50 1·75

732 Pres. Lanusse

1972. Visit of President Lanusse of Argentina.
1348 **732** 40c. multicoloured . . . 90 75

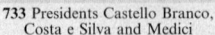

733 Presidents Castello Branco, Costa e Silva and Medici

734 Post Office Symbol

1972. 8th Anniv of 1964 Revolution.
1349 **733** 20c. multicoloured . . . 40 30

1972.
1350 **734** 20c. brown . . . . . . 1·50 10

735 Pres. Tomas

1972. Visit of Pres. Tomas of Portugal.
1351 **735** 75c. multicoloured . . . 1·25 95

736 Exploratory Borehole (C.P.R.M.)

1972. Mineral Resources. Multicoloured.
1352 20c. Type **736** 60 15
1353 40c. Oil rig (PETROBRAS) (vert) . . . . 2·75 50
1354 75c. Power station and dam (ELECTROBRAS) . . . 95 1·25
1355 1cr.30 Iron ore production (Vale do Rio Doce Co.) . . 3·25 1·25

738 Postman and Map (Post Office)

1972. Communications. Multicoloured.
1357 35c. Type **738** 90 20
1358 45c. Microwave Transmitter (Telecommunications) (vert) 90 90
1359 60c. Symbol and diagram of Amazon microwave system 90 70
1360 70c. Worker and route map (Amazon Basin development) . . . . . . 1·25 70

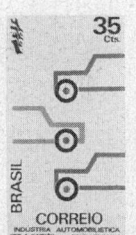

739 Motor Cars

740 Footballer (Independence Cup Championships)

1972. Major Industries.
1361 **739** 35c. orange, red & black 45 25
1362 – 45c. multicoloured . . . 45 40
1363 – 70c. multicoloured . . . 45 25
DESIGNS—HORIZ: 45c. Three hulls (Shipbuilding); 70c. Metal Blocks (Iron and Steel Industry).

1972. "Sports and Pastimes".
1364 **740** 20c. black and brown . . 40 15
1365 – 75c. black and red . . . 1·25 1·50
1366 – 1cr.30 black and blue . . 2·00 1·50
DESIGNS: 75c. Treble clef in open mouth ("Popular Music"); 1cr.30, Hand grasping plastic ("Plastic Arts").

741 Diego Homem's Map of Brazil, 1568

1972. "EXFILBRA 72" 4th International Stamp Exhibition, Rio de Janeiro. Multicoloured.
1367 70c. Type **741** 60 35
1368 1cr. Nicolau Visscher's Map of Americas, c. 1652 . . 5·25 60
1369 2cr. Lopo Homem's World Map, 1519 . . . . . . 2·40 90

742 Figurehead, Sao Francisco River

743 "Institution of Brazilian Flag"

1972. Brazilian Folklore. Multicoloured.
1371 45c. Type **742** 45 15
1372 60c. Fandango, Rio Grande do Sul 75 75
1373 75c. Capoeira (game), Bahia 30 15
1374 1cr.15 Karaja statuette . . . 30 25
1375 1cr.30 "Bumba-Meu-Boi" (folk play) . . . . . . 2·50 1·10

1972. 150th Anniv of Independence.
1376 **743** 30c. green and yellow . . 1·75 1·00
1377 – 70c. mauve and pink . . 75 30
1378 – 1cr. red and brown . . . 4·00 85
1379 – 2cr. black and brown . . 2·40 85
1380 – 3cr.50 black and grey . . 4·00 2·40
DESIGNS—HORIZ: 70c. "Proclamation of Emperor Pedro I" (lithograph after Debret); 2cr. Commemorative gold coin of Pedro I; 3cr.50, Declaration of Ypiranga monument. VERT: 1cr. "Emperor Pedro I" (H. J. da Silva).

744 Numeral and P.T.T. Symbol

747 Writing Hand and People ("Mobral" Literacy Campaign)

745 Scroll

1972.
1383 **744** 5c. orange 30 10
1384 10c. brown 40 10
1394 15c. blue 15 10
1385 20c. blue . . . . . 2·40 10
1396 25c. brown 15 10
1386 30c. red . . . . . . 1·50 10
1387 40c. green 15 10
1388 50c. green . . . . . 1·50 10
1398 70c. purple 60 10
1389 **745** 1cr. purple 60 10
1390 2cr. blue . . . . . 1·75 10
1391 4cr. orange and lilac . . 3·50 35
1392 5cr. brown, cinnamon and red . . . . . 3·50 10
1393 10cr. green, brown & blk 7·00 35
Nos. 1392/3 have a background of multiple P.T.T. symbols.

1972. Social Development. Multicoloured.
1412 10c. Type **747** 20 20
1413 20c. Graph and people (National Census Cent) 50 40
1414 1cr. House in hand (Pension Fund system) . . . . 9·00 20
1415 2cr. Workers and factory (Gross National Product) 1·25 45

748 Legislative Building, Brasilia

1972. National Congress Building, Brasilia.
1416 **748** 1cr. black, orange & bl 9·00 4·50

749 Pottery Crib

750 Farm-worker and Pension Book (Rural Social Security Scheme)

1972. Christmas.
1417 **749** 20c. black and brown . . 40 20

1972. Government Services.
1418 **750** 10c. black, orange & bl 25 20
1419 – 10c. multicoloured . . . 90 90
1420 – 70c. black, brown & red 4·50 2·00
1421 – 2cr. multicoloured . . . 5·50 2·50
DESIGNS—VERT: 70c. Dr. Oswald Cruz, public health pioneer (birth cent.). HORIZ: 10c. (No. 1419), Children and traffic lights (Transport system development); 2cr. Bull, fish and produce (Agricultural exports).

751 Brazilian Expeditionary Force Monument

1972. Armed Forces' Day.
1422 **751** 10c. black, purple & brn 1·40 85
1423 – 30c. multicoloured . . . 2·00 85
1424 – 30c. multicoloured . . . 1·40 85
1425 – 30c. black, brn & lilac 1·40 85
DESIGNS: No. 1423, Sail-training ship (Navy); No. 1424, Trooper (Army); No. 1425, Dassault Mirage IIIC jet fighter (Air Force).

GUM. All the following issues are with gum, except where otherwise stated.

752 Emblem and Cogwheels

1973. 50th Anniv of Rotary in Brazil.
1426 **752** 1cr. blue, lt blue & yell 1·75 1·00

753 Swimming

1973. Sporting Events.
1427 **753** 40c. brown and blue . . 25 20
1428 – 40c. red and green . . . 2·75 55
1429 – 40c. brown and purple 90 45
DESIGNS AND EVENTSHORIZ: No. 1427, ("Latin Cup" Swimming Championships); No. 1428, Gymnast (Olympic Festival of Gymnastics, Rio de Janeiro). VERT: No. 1429, Volleyball player (Internation Volleyball Championships, Rio de Janeiro).

754 Paraguayan Flag

1973. Visit of Pres. Stroessner of Paraguay.
1430 **754** 70c. multicoloured . . . 1·40 80

755 "Communications"

1973. Inauguration of Ministry of Communications Building, Brasilia.
1431 **755** 70c. multicoloured . . . 90 50

756 Neptune and Map

1973. Inauguration of "Bracan I" Underwater Cable, Recife to Canary Islands.
1432 **756** 1cr. multicoloured . . . 4·25 2·40

757 Congress Emblem

758 Swallow-tailed Manakin and "Acacia decurrens"

1973. 24th Int Chamber of Commerce Congress.
1433 **757** 1cr. purple and orange 4·25 2·40

1973. Tropical Birds and Plants. Mult.
1434 20c. Type **758** 65 30
1435 20c. Troupial and "Cereus peruvianus" 65 30
1436 20c. Brazilian ruby and "Tecoma umbellata" . . 65 30

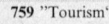

759 "Tourism"

760 "Caboclo" Festival Cart

1973. National Tourism Year.
1437 **759** 70c. multicoloured . . . 60 30

1973. Anniversaries. Multicoloured.
1438 20c. Type **760** 90 30
1439 20c. Arariboia (Indian chief) 90 30
1440 20c. Convention delegates 90 30
1441 20c. "The Graciosa Road" 90 30
EVENTS: No. 1438, 150th anniv of Liberation Day. No. 1439, 400th anniv of Niteroi. No. 1440, Cent of Itu Convention. No. 1441, Cent of Nhundiaquara highway.

761 "Institute of Space Research"

1973. Scientific Research Institute. Mult.
1442 20c. Type **761** 50 25
1443 70c. "Federal Engineering School", Itajuba . . . 1·50 50
1444 1cr. "Institute for Pure and Applied Mechanics" . . 2·00 45

762 Santos Dumont and Biplane "14 bis"

1973. Birth Centenary of Alberto Santos Dumont (aviation pioneer).
1445 **762** 20c. brown, grn & lt grn   50   20
1446 – 70c. brown, red & yellow   1·25   1·25
1447 – 2cr. brown, ultram & bl   1·60   1·25
DESIGNS: 70c. Airship "Ballon No. 6"; 2cr. Monoplane No. 20 "Demoiselle".

763 Map of the World

1973. Stamp Day.
1448 **763** 40c. black and red   1·90   1·25
1449 – 40c. black and red   1·90   1·25
The design of No. 1449 differs from Type **763** in that the red portion is to the top and right, instead of to the top and left.

764 G. Dias   **766** Festival Banner

1973. 150th Birth Anniv of Goncalves Dias (poet).
1450 **764** 40c. black and violet   60   30
See also Nos. 1459 and 1477.

1973. National Folklore Festival.
1452 **766** 40c. multicoloured   60   20

767 Masonic Emblems

1973. 150th Anniv of Masonic Grand Orient Lodge of Brazil.
1453 **767** 1cr. blue   2·00   95

768 Fire Protection

1973. National Protection Campaign. Mult.
1454 40c. Type **768**   60   20
1455 40c. Cross and cornice (cultural protection)   60   20
1456 40c. Winged emblem (protection in flight)   60   20
1457 40c. Leaf (protection of nature)   60   20

1973. Birth Centenary of St. Theresa of Lisieux. As T **764**.
1459   2cr. brown and orange   2·75   1·40
DESIGN: Portrait of St. Theresa.

770 M. Lobato and "Emilia"

1973. Monteiro Lobato's Children's Stories. Multicoloured.
1460 **770** 40c. Type **770**   50   50
1461 40c. "Aunt Nastasia"   50   50
1462 40c. "Nazarinho", "Pedrinho" and "Quindim"   50   50
1463 40c. "Visconde de Sabugosa"   50   50
1464 40c. "Dona Benta"   50   50

771 Father J. M. Nunes Garcia

1973. "The Baroque Age". Multicoloured.
1465 40c. Wood carving, Church of St. Francia, Bahia   60   50
1466 40c. "Prophet Isaiah" (detail, sculpture by Aleijadinho)   60   50
1467 70c. Type **771**   1·75   1·75
1468 1cr. Portal, Church of Conceicao da Praia   5·25   2·75
1469 2cr. "Glorification of Holy Virgin", ceiling, St. Francis Assisi Church, Ouro Preto   4·25   2·75

772 Early Telephone and Modern Instruments

1973. 50th Anniv of Brazilian Telephone Company.
1470 **772** 40c. multicoloured   35   15

773 "Angel" (J. Kopke)

1973. Christmas.
1471 **773** 40c. multicoloured   25   10

774 "Gailora" (river steamboat)

1973. Brazilian Boats. Multicoloured.
1472 40c. Type **774**   70   50
1473 70c. "Regatao" (river trading boat)   1·40   1·75
1474 1cr. "Jangada" (coastal raft)   4·75   2·40
1475 2cr. "Saveiro" (passenger boat)   4·75   2·40

775 Scales of Justice

1973. Judiciary Power.
1476 **775** 40c. violet and mauve   30   15

1973. Birth Centenary of Placido de Castro. As T **764**.
1477   40c. black and red   55   20
DESIGN: Portrait of Castro.

776 Scarlet Ibis and "Victoria Regia" Lilies   **777** Saci Perere (goblin)

1973. Brazilian Flora and Fauna. Mult.
1478 40c. Type **776**   1·00   50
1479 70c. Jaguar and Indian tulip   4·75   45

1480 1cr. Scarlet macaw and palm   8·50   3·75
1481 2cr. Greater rhea and mulunga plant   9·50   2·75

1974. Brazilian Folk Tales. Multicoloured.
1482 40c. Type **777**   35   15
1483 80c. Zumbi (warrior)   90   40
1484 1cr. Chico Rei (African king)   1·25   20
1485 1cr.30 Little black boy of the pasture (32 × 33 mm)   2·40   80
1486 2cr.50 Iara, queen of the waters (32 × 33 mm)   9·00   4·25

778 View of Bridge

1974. Inauguration of President Costa e Silva (Rio de Janeiro–Niteroi) Bridge.
1487 **778** 40c. multicoloured   35   20

779 "Press"

1974. Brazilian Communications Pioneers.
1488 **779** 40c. red, blue & bistre   30   15
1489 – 40c. brown, blue & bistre   25   15
1490 – 40c. blue, pink & brown   30   15
DESIGNS AND EVENTS: No. 1488, Birth bicentenary of Hipolito da Costa (founder of newspaper "Correio Brasiliense", 1808); No. 1489, "Radio waves" (Edgar R. Pinto, founder of Radio Sociedade do Rio de Janeiro, 1923); No. 1490, "Television screen" (F. de Assis Chateaubriand, founder of first T.V. station, Sao Paulo, 1950).

780 "Construction"

1974. 10th Anniv of March Revolution.
1491 **780** 40c. multicoloured   25   20

781 Christ of the Andes

1974. Birth Cent of G. Marconi (radio pioneer).
1492 **781** 2cr.50 multicoloured   7·00   3·50

782 Heads of Three Races

1974. Ethnical Origins and Immigration. Mult.
1493 40c. Type **782**   25   20
1494 40c. Heads of many races   10   20
1495 2cr.50 German immigration   3·75   1·25
1496 2cr.50 Italian immigration   9·00   1·25
1497 2cr.50 Japanese immigration   2·75   1·25

783 Artwork and Stamp-printing Press

1974. State Mint.
1498 **783** 80c. multicoloured   95   20

784 Sete Cidades National Park

1974. Tourism. Multicoloured.
1499 40c. Type **784**   60   25
1500 80c. Ruins of church of St. Michael of the Missions   60   25

786 Caraca College

1974. Bicentenary of Caraca College.
1502 **786** 40c. multicoloured   20   15

787 Wave Pattern

1974. 3rd Brazilian Telecommunications Congress, Brasilia.
1503 **787** 40c. black and blue   15   15

788 Fernao Dias Paes

1974. 300th Anniv of Paes Expedition.
1504 **788** 20c. multicoloured   15   15

1974. Visit of President Alvarez of Mexico. As T **754**. Multicoloured.
1505 80c. Mexican Flag   1·75   1·25

789 Flags and Crowd in Stadium   **791** Pederneiras (after J. Carlos)

1974. World Cup Football Championships, West Germany (2nd issue).
1506 **789** 40c. multicoloured   50   50

1974. Birth Centenary of Raul Pederneiras (lawyer, author and artist).
1508 **791** 40c. black & yell on brn   20   20

792 Emblem and Seascape

1974. 13th Int Union of Building Societies and Savings Associations Congress, Rio de Janeiro.
1509   **792**   1cr.30 multicoloured   75   60

794 "UPU" on World Map

1974. Centenary of U.P.U.
1511   **794**   2cr.50 black and blue   . .   7·00   3·50

795 Aruak Hammock

1974. "Popular Culture".
1512   **795**   50c. purple   75   30
1513   –   50c. light blue and blue   1·25   30
1514   –   50c. brown, red & yellow   40   30
1515   –   50c. brown and yellow   50   30
DESIGNS—SQUARE: No. 1513, Bilro Lace. VERT: (24 × 37 mm), No. 1514, Guitar player (folk literature); No. 1515, Horseman (statuette by Vitalino).

796 Coffee Beans

1974. Bicentenary of City of Campinas.
1516   **796**   50c. multicoloured   90   50

797 Hornless Tabapua

1974. Domestic Animals. Multicoloured.
1517   80c. Type **797**   95   60
1518   1cr.30 Creole horse   . . .   90   70
1519   2cr.50 Brazilian mastiff   . .   9·00   1·75

798 Ilha Solteira Dam   **799** Herald Angel

1974. Ilha Solteira Hydro-electric Power Project.
1520   **798**   50c. brown, grey & yell   65   20

1974. Christmas.
1521   **799**   50c. multicoloured   . . .   30   15

800 "The Girls"   **802** Athlete
(Carlos Reis)

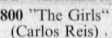

801 "Justice for Juveniles"

1974. "Lubrapex 74" Stamp Exhibition, Sao Paulo (2nd issue).
1522   **800**   1cr.30 multicoloured   40   25

1974. 50th Anniv of Brazilian Juvenile Court.
1523   **801**   90c. multicoloured   . . .   20   20

1974. 50th Anniv of Sao Silvestre Long-distance Race.
1524   **802**   3cr.30 multicoloured   90   55

803 Mounted Newsvendor and Newspaper Masthead

1975. Cent of Newspaper "O Estado de S. Paulo".
1525   **803**   50c. multicoloured   . . .   60   30

804 Industrial Complex, Sao Paulo

1975. Economic Resources.
1526   **804**   50c. yellow and blue   . .   95   25
1527   –   1cr.40 yellow & brown   60   60
1528   –   4cr.50 yellow & black   .   3·00   25
DESIGNS: 1cr.40 Rubber industry, Acre; 4cr.50, Manganese industry, Amapa.

805 Santa Cruz Fortress, Rio de Janeiro

1975. Colonial Forts. Each brown on yellow.
1529   50c. Type **805**   10   15
1530   50c. Reis Magos Fort, Rio Grande do Norte   30   15
1531   50c. Monte Serrat Fort, Bahia   50   15
1532   90c. Nossa Senhora dos Remedios Fort, Fernando de Noronha   10   25

806 "Palafita" House, Amazonas

1975. Brazilian Architecture. Multicoloured.
1533   50c. Modern Architecture, Brasilia   . . . . . .   1·50   1·50
1534   50c. Modern Architecture, Brasilia (yellow line at left)   . . . .   16·00   8·00
1535   1cr. Type **806**   30   15
1536   1cr.40 Indian hut, Rondonia (yellow line at left)   . .   3·00   3·00
1537   1cr.40 As No. 1536 but yellow line at right   . .   55   60
1538   3cr.30 "Enxaimel" house, Santa Catarina (yellow line at right)   . . .   95   95
1539   3cr.30 As No. 1538 but yellow line at left   . . . .   4·25   4·25

807 Oscar ("Astronotus ocellatus")

1975. Freshwater Fishes. Multicoloured.
1540   50c. Type **807**   . . . . .   1·40   25
1541   50c. South American pufferfish ("Colomesus psitacus")   55   35
1542   50c. Tail-spot livebearer ("Phallocerus caudimaculatus")   . . .   55   40
1543   50c. Red discus ("Symphysodon discus")   85   35

808 Flags forming Serviceman's Head   **809** Brazilian Pines

1975. Honouring Ex-Servicemen of Second World War.
1544   **808**   50c. multicoloured   25   15

1975. Fauna and Flora Preservation. Mult.
1545   70c. Type **809**   . . . . .   1·60   20
1546   1cr. Giant otter (vert)   . . .   1·00   40
1547   3cr.30 Marsh cayman   . . .   95   40

810 Inga Carved Stone, from Paraiba   **811** Statue of the Virgin Mary

1975. Archaeology. Multicoloured.
1548   70c. Type **810**   95   20
1549   1cr. Marajoara pot from Para   25   20
1550   1cr. Fossilized garfish from Ceara (horiz)   30   20

1975. Holy Year. 300th Anniv of Franciscan Province of Our Lady of the Immaculate Conception.
1551   **811**   3cr.30 multicoloured   . .   95   60

812 Ministry of Communications Building, Rio de Janeiro   **813** "Congada" Sword Dance, Minas Gerais

1975. Stamp Day.
1552   **812**   70c. red   45   15

1975. Folk Dances. Multicoloured.
1553   70c. Type **813**   25   30
1554   70c. "Frevo" umbrella dance, Pernambuco   . .   25   30
1555   70c. "Warrior" dance, Alagoas   25   30

814 Stylized Trees

1975. Tree Festival.
1556   **814**   70c. multicoloured   . . .   25   10

815 Dish Aerial and Globe   **816** Woman holding Globe

1975. Inauguration of Tangua Satellite Telecommunications Station.
1557   **815**   3cr.30 multicoloured   90   60

1975. International Women's Year.
1558   **816**   3cr.30 multicoloured   . .   1·25   45

817 Tile, Balcony Rail and Memorial Column, Alcantara

1975. Historic Towns. Multicoloured.
1559   70c. Type **817**   40   25
1560   70c. Belfry, weather vane and jug, Goias (26 × 38 mm)   40   25
1561   70c. Sao Francisco Convent, Sao Cristovao (40 × 22 mm)   40   25

818 Crowd welcoming Walking Book

1975. Day of the Book.
1562   **818**   70c. multicoloured   . . .   20   15

819 ASTA Emblem and Arrows

1975. 45th American Society of Travel Agents Congress.
1563   **819**   70c. multicoloured   . . .   20   15

820 Two Angels   **821** Aerial, and Map of America

1975. Christmas.
1564   **820**   70c. brown and red   . .   15   10

1975. 2nd International Telecommunications Conference, Rio de Janeiro.
1565   **821**   5cr.20 multicoloured   . .   3·50   1·75

822 Friar Nicodemus   **823** People in front of Cross

1975. Obligatory Tax. Leprosy Research Fund.
1566   **822**   10c. brown   20   10

1975. Thanksgiving Day.
1567   **823**   70c. turquoise and blue   30   25

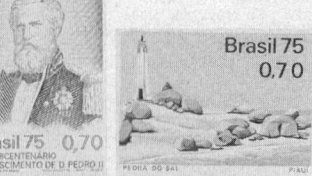

824 Emperor Pedro II in Naval Uniform (after P. P. da Silva Manuel)   **825** Sal Stone Beach, Piaui

1975. 150th Birth Anniv of Emperor Pedro II.
1568   **824**   70c. brown   40   20

1975. Tourism. Multicoloured.
1569   70c. Type **825**   30   20
1570   70c. Guarapari Beach, Espirito Santo   30   20
1571   70c. Torres Cliffs Rio Grande do Sul   30   20

826 Triple Jump

1975. 7th Pan-American Games, Santo Domingo, Dominican Republic.
1572 826 1cr.60 turquoise & black ... 20 20

827 U.N. Emblem and H.Q. Building, New York

1975. 30th Anniv of United Nations.
1573 827 1cr.30 violet on blue ... 15 15

828 Light Bulbs and House

1976. "Preservation of Fuel Resources". Mult.
1574 70c. Type 828 ... 25 10
1575 70c. Drops of petrol and car ... 25 10

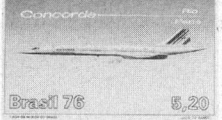

829 Concorde

1976. Concorde's First Commercial Flight, Paris–Rio de Janeiro.
1576 829 5cr.20 black and grey ... 1·10 40

831 Early and Modern Telephone Equipment

832 "Eye"-part of Exclamation Mark

1976. Telephone Centenary.
1578 831 5cr.20 black & orange ... 1·25 1·25

1976. World Health Day.
1579 832 1cr. red, brown & violet ... 30 50

833 Kaiapo Body-painting

834 Itamaraty Palace, Brasilia

1976. Brazil's Indigenous Culture. Mult.
1580 1cr. Type 833 ... 20 10
1581 1cr. Bakairi ceremonial mask ... 20 10
1582 1cr. Karaja feather head-dress ... 20 10

1976. Diplomats' Day.
1583 834 1cr. multicoloured ... 35 60

835 "The Sprinkler" (3D composition by J. Tarcisio)

836 Basketball

1976. Modern Brazilian Art. Multicoloured.
1584 1cr. Type 835 ... 15 10
1585 1cr. "Beribboned Fingers" (P. Checcacci) (horiz) ... 15 10

1976. Olympic Games, Montreal.
1586 836 1cr. black and green ... 10 10
1587 – 1cr.40 black and blue ... 25 10
1588 – 5cr.20 black and orange ... 1·25 1·25
DESIGNS: 1cr.40, Olympic yachts; 5cr.20, Judo.

837 Golden Lion-Tamarin

838 Cine Camera on Screen

1976. Nature Protection. Multicoloured.
1589 1cr. Type 837 ... 25 20
1590 1cr. Orchid ("Acacallis cyanea") ... 25 30

1976. Brazilian Cinematograph Industry.
1591 838 1cr. multicoloured ... 20 10

839 Ox-cart Driver

1976.
1592 839 10c. red ... 10 10
1593 – 15c. brown ... 25 10
1594 – 20c. blue ... 20 10
1595 – 30c. red ... 20 10
1596 – 40c. orange ... 20 10
1597a – 50c. brown ... 25 10
1598 – 70c. black ... 15 10
1599 – 80c. green ... 1·75 10
1600a – 1cr. black ... 20 10
1601 – 1cr.10 purple ... 20 10
1602 – 1cr.30 red ... 20 10
1603a – 1cr.80 violet ... 20 10
1604a – 2cr. brown ... 1·50 10
1605 – 2cr.50 brown ... 25 10
1605a – 3cr.20 blue ... 25 10
1606a – 5cr. lilac ... 95 10
1607 – 7cr. violet ... 6·00 10
1608a – 10cr. green ... 95 10
1609 – 15cr. green ... 1·75 10
1610 – 20cr. blue ... 1·75 10
1611 – 21cr. purple ... 1·25 10
1612 – 27cr. brown ... 1·40 10
DESIGNS—HORIZ: 20c. Pirogue fisherman; 40c. Cowboy; 3cr.20, Sao Francisco boatman; 27cr. Muleteer. VERT: 15c. Bahia woman; 30c. Rubber gatherer; 50c. Gaucho; 70c. Women breaking Babacu chestnuts; 80c. Gold-washer; 1cr. Banana gatherer; 1cr.10, Grape harvester; 1cr.30, Coffee harvester; 1cr.80, Carnauba cutter; 2cr. Potter; 2cr.50, Basket maker; 5cr. Sugar-cane cutter; 7cr. Salt worker; 10cr. Fisherman; 15cr. Coconut vendor; 20cr. Lace maker; 21cr. Ramie cutter.

840 Neon Tetra ("Paracheirodon innesi")

1976. Brazilian Freshwater Fishes. Mult.
1613 1cr. Type 840 ... 50 45
1614 1cr. Splash tetra ("Copeina arnold") ... 50 45
1615 1cr. Prochilodus ("Prochilodus insignis") ... 50 45
1616 1cr. Spotted pike cichlid ("Crenicichla lepidota") ... 50 45
1617 1cr. Bottle-nosed catfish ("Ageneiosus sp.") ... 50 45
1618 1cr. Reticulated corydoras ("Corydoras reticulatus") ... 50 45

841 Santa Marta Lighthouse

842 Postage Stamps as Magic Carpet

1976. 300th Anniv of Laguna.
1619 841 1cr. blue ... 40 15

1976. Stamp Day.
1620 842 1cr. multicoloured ... 15 10

843 Oil Lamp and Profile

1976. 50th Anniv of Brazilian Nursing Assn.
1621 843 1cr. multicoloured ... 20 10

844 Puppet Soldier

845 Winner's Medal

1976. Mamulengo Puppet Theatre. Mult.
1622 1cr. Type 844 ... 20 15
1623 1cr.30 Puppet girl ... 20 15
1624 1cr.60 Finger puppets (horiz) ... 20 15

1976. 27th International Military Athletics Championships, Rio de Janeiro.
1625 845 5cr.20 multicoloured ... 45 20

846 Family within "House"

847 Rotten Tree

1976. SESC and SENAC National Organizations for Apprenticeship and Welfare.
1626 846 1cr. blue ... 15 10

1976. Conservation of the Environment.
1627 847 1cr. multicoloured ... 15 10

848 Electron Orbits and Atomic Agency Emblem

1976. 20th International Atomic Energy Conference, Rio de Janeiro.
1628 848 5cr.20 multicoloured ... 45 25

849 Underground Train

851 School Building

850 St. Francis

1976. Inauguration of Sao Paulo Underground Railway.
1629 849 1cr.60 multicoloured ... 45 25

1976. 750th Death Anniv of St. Francis of Assisi.
1630 850 5cr.20 multicoloured ... 45 20

1976. Centenary of Ouro Preto Mining School.
1631 851 1cr. violet ... 25 30

852 "Three Kings" (J. A. da Silva)

1976. Christmas. Multicoloured.
1632 80c. Type 852 ... 30 20
1633 80c. "Father Christmas" (T. Onivaldo Cogo) ... 30 20
1634 80c. "Nativity Scene" (R. Yabe) ... 30 20
1635 80c. "Angels" (E. Folchini) ... 30 20
1636 80c. "Nativity" (A.L. Cintra) ... 30 20

854 "Our Lady of Monte Serrat" (Friar A. da Piedade)

1976. Brazilian Sculpture. Multicoloured.
1638 80c. Type 854 ... 15 10
1639 5cr. "St. Joseph" (unknown artist) (25 × 37 mm) ... 40 20
1640 5cr.60 "The Dance" (J. Bernardelli) (square) ... 45 20
1641 6cr.50 "The Caravel" (B. Giorgi) (As 5cr.) ... 35 20

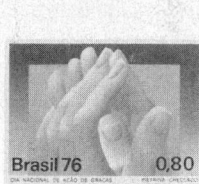 

855 Hands in Prayer

856 Sailor of 1840

1976. Thanksgiving Day.
1642 855 80c. multicoloured ... 15 10

1976. Brazilian Navy Commemoration. Mult.
1643 80c. Type 856 ... 20 10
1644 2cr. Marine of 1808 ... 25 15

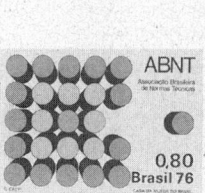 

857 "Natural Resources"

858 "Wheel of Life" (wood-carving, G. T. de Oliveira)

1976. Brazilian Bureau of Standards.
1645 857 80c. multicoloured ... 15 10

1977. 2nd World Black and African Festival of Arts and Culture, Lagos (Nigeria). Multicoloured.
1646 5cr. Type 858 ... 50 20
1647 5cr.60 "The Beggar" (wood-carving, A. dos Santos) ... 50 20
1648 6cr.50 Benin pectoral mask ... 90 20

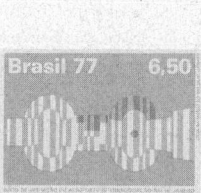 

859 Airport Layout

860 Seminar Emblem

1977. Inauguration of Operation of International Airport, Rio de Janeiro.
1649 859 6c.50 multicoloured ... 85 25

1977. 6th InterAmerican Budget Seminar.
1650 860 1cr.10 turq, bl & stone ... 20 10

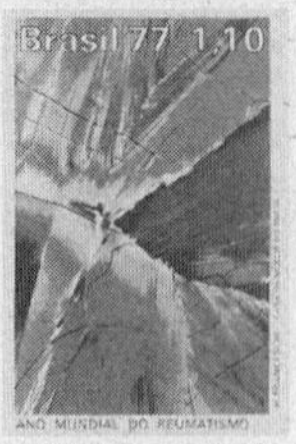

861 Salicylic Acid Crystals

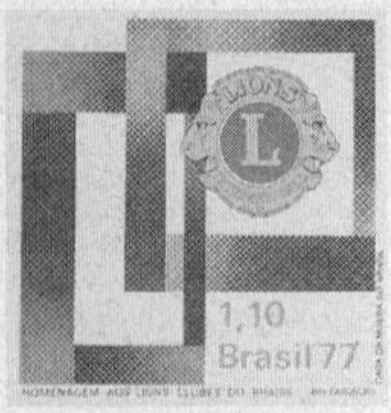

862 Emblem of Lions Clubs

1977. World Rheumatism Year.
1651 **861** 1cr.10 multicoloured . . 20 10

1977. 25th Anniv of Brazilian Lions Clubs.
1652 **862** 1cr.10 multicoloured . . 20 10

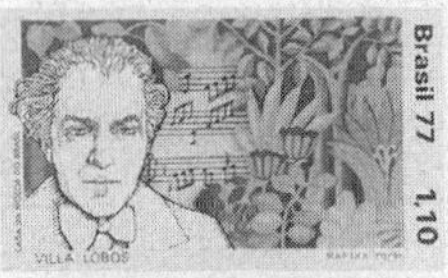

863 H. Villa-Lobos and Music

1977. Brazilian Composers. Multicoloured.
1653 1cr.10 Type **863** 25 10
1654 1cr.10 Chiquinha Gonzaga and guitar 25 10
1655 1cr.10 Noel Rosa and guitar 25 10

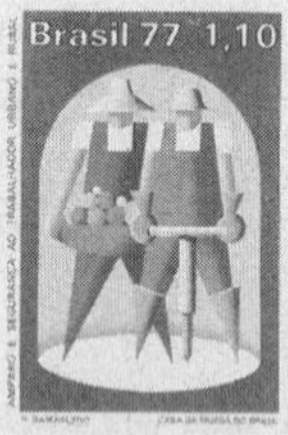

864 Rural and Urban Workers

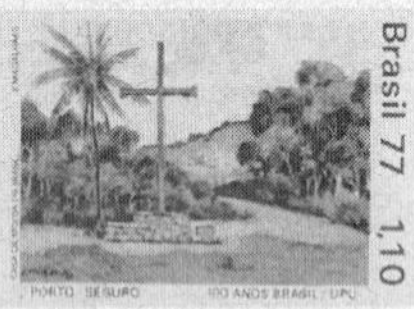

865 Memorial, Porto Seguro

1977. Industrial Protection and Safety. Mult.
1656 1cr.10 Type **864** 15 10
1657 1cr.10 Laboratory vessels . . 15 10

1977. Centenary of U.P.U. Membership. Views of Porto Seguro. Multicoloured.
1658 1cr.10 Type **865** 15 10
1659 5cr. Beach . . . . 1·25 20
1660 5cr.60 Old houses 55 20
1661 6cr.50 Post Office 50 25

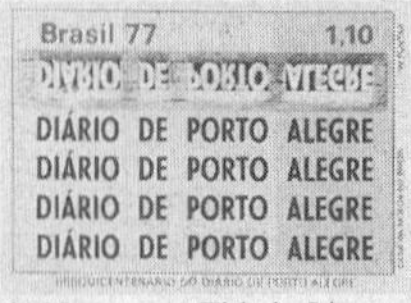

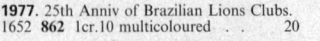

866 Newspaper Title in Linotype and Print

1977. 150th Anniv of Brazilian Newspaper "Diario de Porto Allegre".
1662 **866** 1cr.10 black & purple . . 15 10

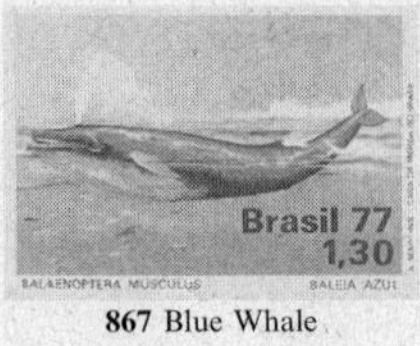

867 Blue Whale

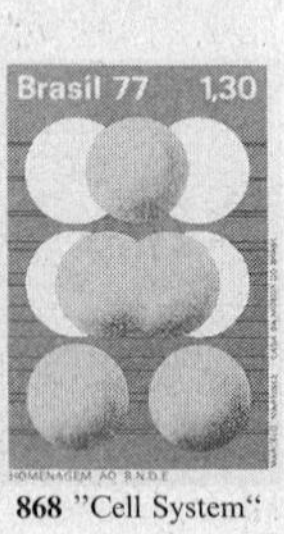

868 "Cell System"

1977. Fauna Preservation.
1663 **867** 1cr.30 multicoloured . . 55 15

1977. 25th Anniv of National Economic Development Bank.
1664 **868** 1cr.30 multicoloured . . 15 10

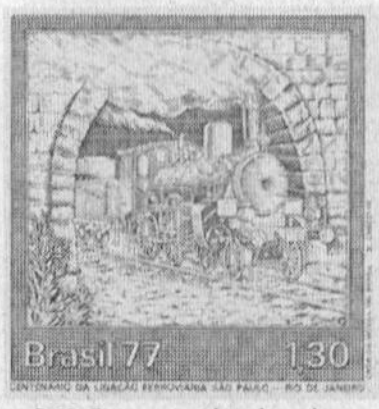

869 Locomotive leaving Tunnel

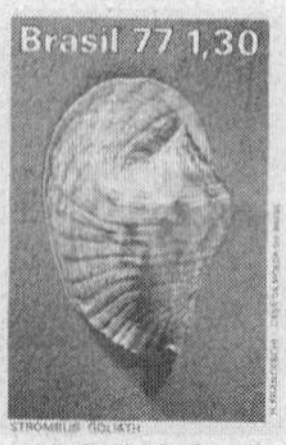

870 Goliath Conch

1977. Centenary of Rio de Janeiro–Sao Paulo Railway.
1665 **869** 1c.30 black 60 25

1977. Brazilian Molluscs. Multicoloured.
1666 1cr.30 Type **870** 30 15
1667 1cr.30 Thin-bladed murex ("Murex tenuivaricosus") 30 15
1668 1cr.30 Helmet vase ("Vasum cassiforme") 30 15

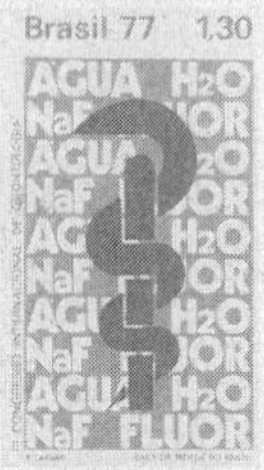

871 Caduceus

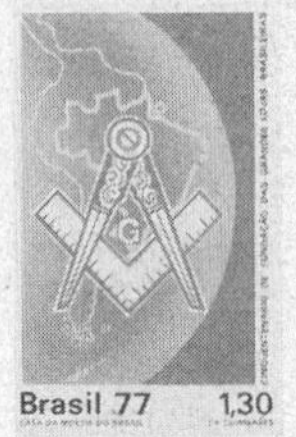

872 Masonic Symbols

1977. 3rd International Congress of Odontology.
1669 **871** 1cr.30 brown, bis & orge 20 10

1977. 50th Anniv of Brazilian Grand Masonic Lodge.
1670 **872** 1cr.30 blue, dp bl & blk 25 10

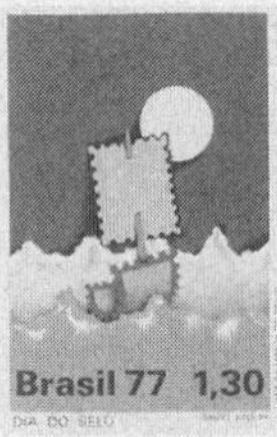

873 "Sailboat"

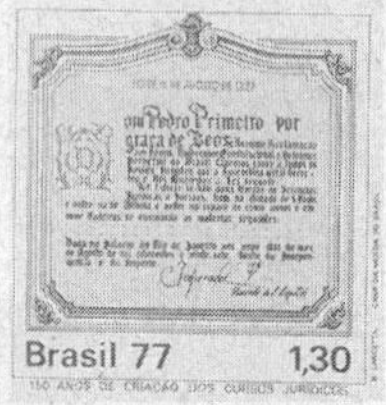

874 Law Proclamation

1977. Stamp Day.
1671 **873** 1cr.30 multicoloured . . 15 10

1977. 150th Anniv of Juridical Courses.
1672 **874** 1cr.30 multicoloured . . 15 10

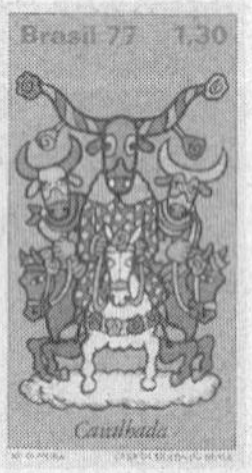

875 "Cavalhada" (horsemen)

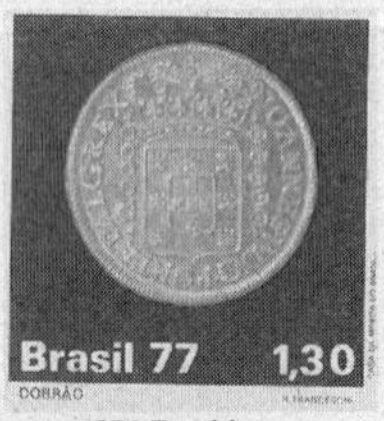

876 Doubloon

1977. Folklore. Multicoloured.
1673 1cr.30 Type **875** 20 10
1674 1cr.30 Horseman with flag 20 10
1675 1cr.30 Jousting (horiz) . . 20 10

1977. Brazilian Colonial Coins. Multicoloured.
1676 1cr.30 Type **876** 20 10
1677 1cr.30 Pataca 20 10
1678 1cr.30 Vintem 20 10

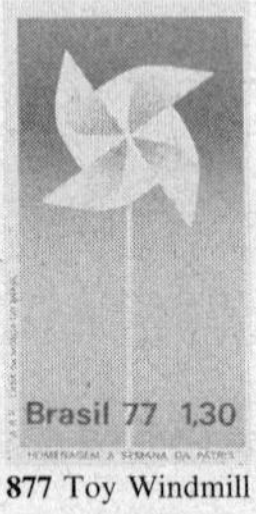

877 Toy Windmill

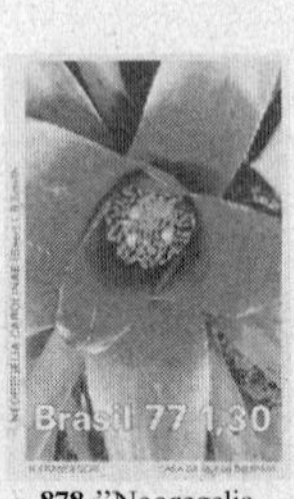

878 "Neoregelia carolinae"

1977. National Day.
1679 **877** 1cr.30 multicoloured . . 15 10

1977. Nature Conservation.
1680 **878** 1cr.30 multicoloured . . 20 10

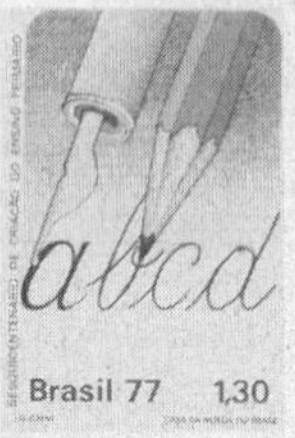

879 Pen, Pencil and Writing

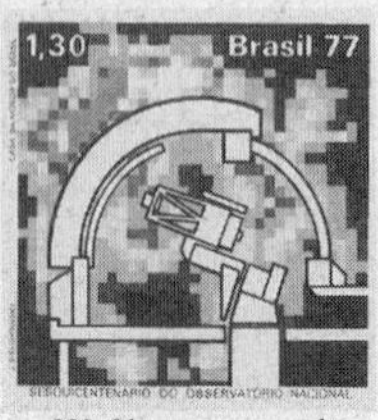

880 Observatory and Electrochromograph of Supernova

1977. 150th Anniv of Official Elementary Schooling.
1681 **879** 1cr.30 multicoloured . . 15 10

1977. 150th Anniv of National Observatory.
1682 **880** 1cr.30 multicoloured . . 20 10

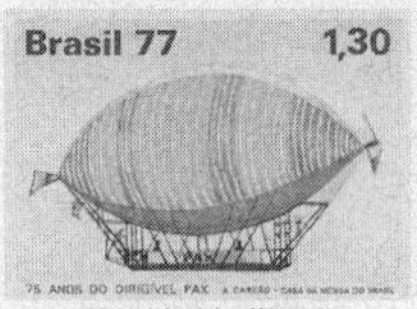

881 Airship "Pax"

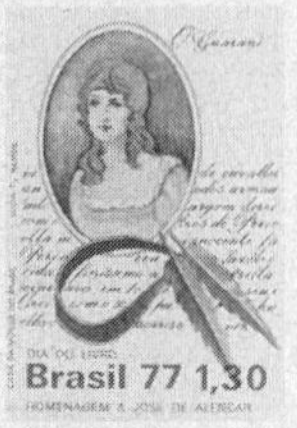

882 Text from "O Guarani" and Ceci

1977. Aviation Anniversaries. Multicoloured.
1683 1cr.30 Type **881** 20 10
1684 1cr.30 Savoia Marchetti flying boat "Jahu" . . . 20 10

ANNIVERSARIES: No. 1683, 75th anniv of "Pax" flight. No. 1684, 50th anniv of "Jahu" South Atlantic crossing.

1977. Day of the Book and Jose de Alencar Commemoration.
1685 **882** 1cr.30 multicoloured . . 15 10

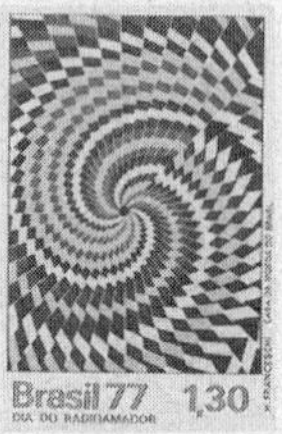

883 Radio Waves

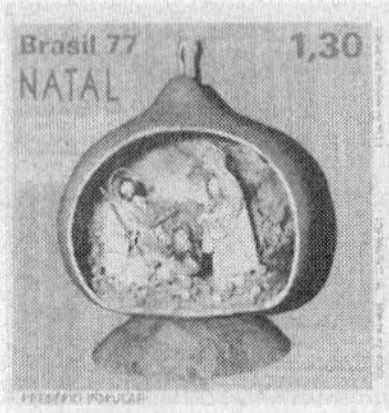

884 Nativity (in carved gourd)

1977. Amateur Radio Operators' Day.
1686 **883** 1cr.30 multicoloured . . 15 10

1977. Christmas. Multicoloured.
1687 1cr.30 Type **884** 15 10
1688 2cr. The Annunciation . . . 25 10
1689 5cr. Nativity 55 15

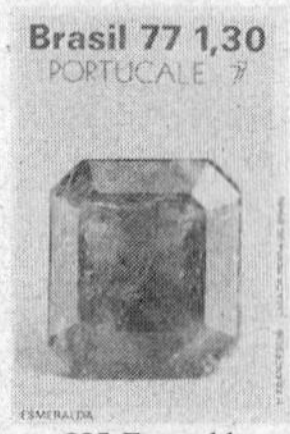

885 Emerald

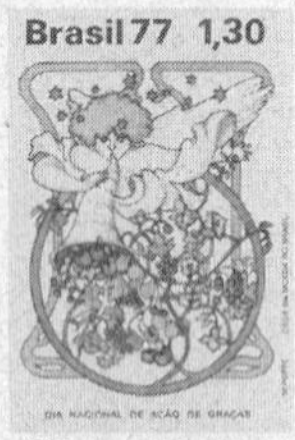

886 Angel holding Cornucopia

1977. "Portucale 77" Thematic Stamp Exhibition. Multicoloured.
1690 1cr.30 Type **885** 20 10
1691 1cr.30 Topaz 20 10
1692 1cr.30 Aquamarine 20 10

1977. Thanksgiving Day.
1693 **886** 1cr.30 multicoloured . . 15 10

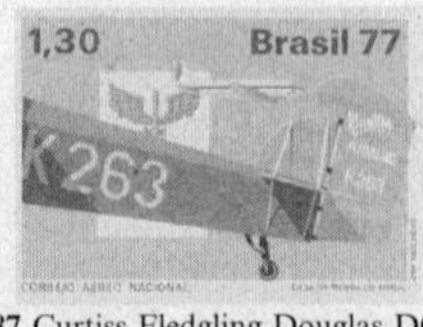

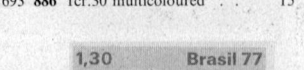

887 Curtiss Fledgling Douglas DC-3 and Badge (National Airmail Service)

1977. National Integration. Multicoloured.
1694 1cr.30 Type **887** 30 10
1695 1cr.30 Amazon River naval patrol boat and badge (Amazon Fleet) 50 10
1696 1cr.30 Train crossing bridge and badges (Engineering Corps and Railway Battalion) 75 25

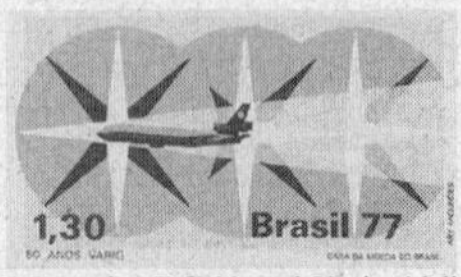

888 Douglas DC-10 and Varig Airline Emblems

1977. 50th Anniv of Varig State Airline.
1697 **888** 1cr.30 black, lt bl & bl 15 10

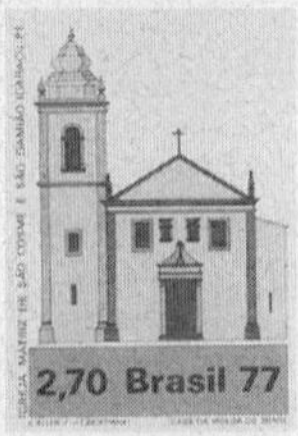

889 Sts. Cosmus and Damian Church, Igaracu

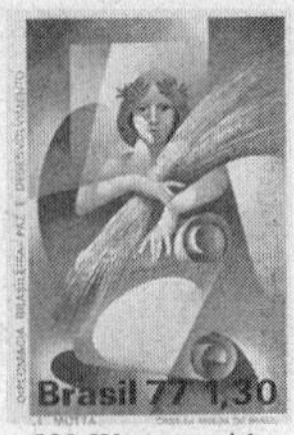

890 Woman with Wheat Sheaf

1977. Regional Architecture, Churches. Mult.
1698 2cr.70 Type **889** 20 10
1699 7cr.50 St. Bento Monastery Church, Rio de Janeiro 60 25
1700 8cr.50 St. Francis Assisi Church, Ouro Preto . . . 65 25
1701 9cr.50 St. Anthony Convent Church, Joao Pessoa . . 80 30

1977. Diplomats' Day.
1702 **890** 1cr.30 multicoloured . . 15 10

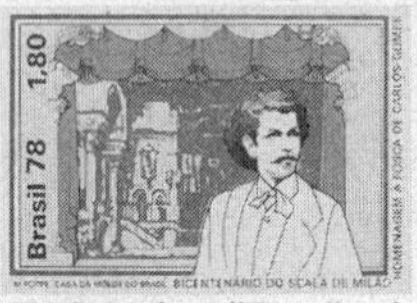

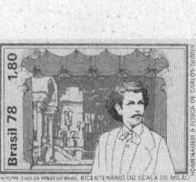

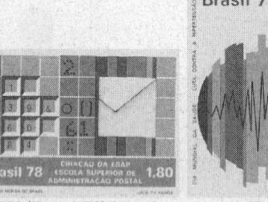

891 Scene from "Fosca" and Carlos Gomes (composer)

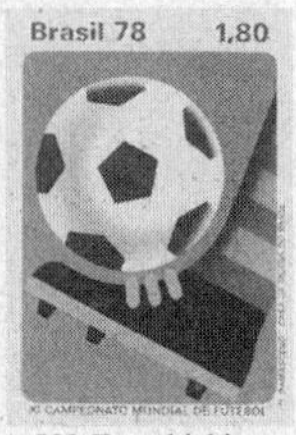

892 Foot kicking Ball

1978. Bicentenary of La Scala Opera House, Milan, and Carlos Gomes Commemoration.
1703 **891** 1cr.80 multicoloured . . 30 10

1978. World Cup Football Championship, Argentina. Multicoloured.
1704 1cr.80 Type **892** 20 10
1705 1cr.80 Ball in net 20 10
1706 1cr.80 Stylized player with cup 20 10

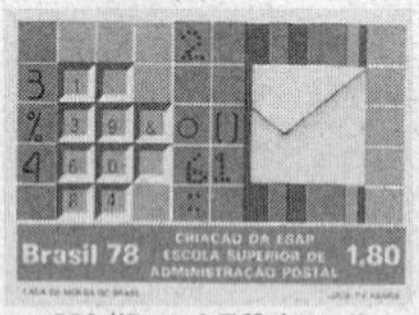

893 "Postal Efficiency"

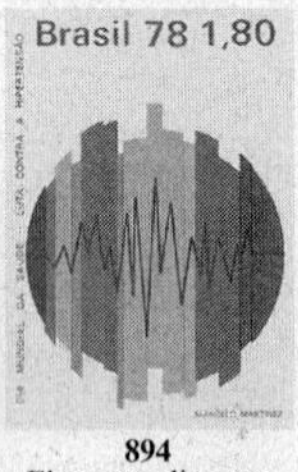

894 Electrocardiogram

1978. Postal Staff College.
1707 **893** 1cr.80 multicoloured . . 15 10

1978. World Hypertension Month.
1708 **894** 1cr.80 multicoloured . . 20 10

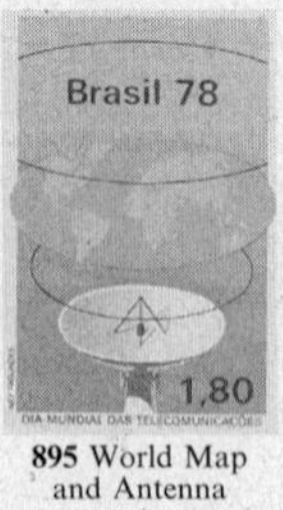

895 World Map and Antenna

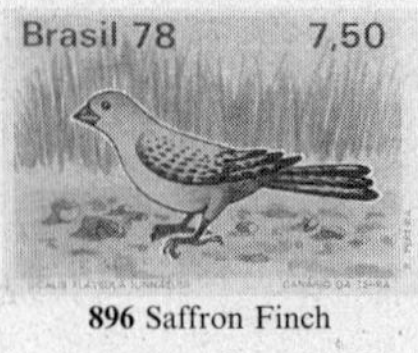

896 Saffron Finch

1978. World Telecommunications Day.
1709 **895** 1cr.80 multicoloured . . 15 10

1978. Birds. Multicoloured.
1710 7cr.50 Type **896** . . . . . 1·25 50
1711 8cr.50 Banded cotinga . . . 1·60 60
1712 9cr.50 Seven-coloured tanager . . . . 1·90 85

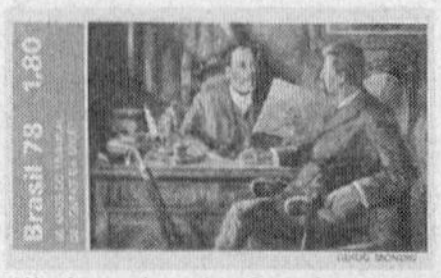

897 "Discussing the Opening Speech" (G. Mondin)

1978. 85th Anniv of Union Court of Audit.
1713 **897** 1cr.80 multicoloured . . 15 10

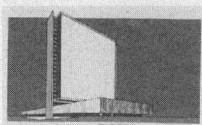

898 Post and Telegraph Headquarters, Brasilia

1978. Opening of Post and Telegraph Headquarters.
1714 **898** 1cr.80 multicoloured . . 15 10

899 President Geisel **900** Savoia Marchetti S-64 and Map

1978. President Geisel Commemoration.
1716 **899** 1cr.80 olive 20 10

1978. 50th Anniv of South Atlantic Flight by del Prete and Ferrarin.
1717 **900** 1cr.80 multicoloured . . 25 10

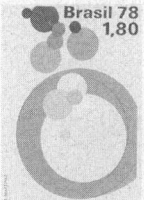 

901 "Smallpox" **902** 10r. Pedro II "White Beard" Stamp of 1878

1978. Global Eradication of Smallpox.
1718 **901** 1cr.80 multicoloured . . 20 10

1978. Stamp Day.
1719 **902** 1cr.80 multicoloured . . 15 10

903 "Jangadeiros"

1978. Birth Centenary of Helios Seelinger (painter).
1720 **903** 1cr.80 multicoloured . . 15 10

904 Musicians with Violas

1978. Folk Musicians. Multicoloured.
1721 1cr.80 Type **904** 20 10
1722 1cr.80 Two fife players . . 20 10
1723 1cr.80 Berimbau players . . 20 10

905 Children playing Football

1978. National Week.
1724 **905** 1cr.80 multicoloured . . 20 10

906 Patio de Colegio Church

1978. Restoration of Patio de Colegio Church, Sao Paulo.
1725 **906** 1cr.80 brown 15 10

907 "Justice" (A. Ceschiatti)

1978. 150th Anniv of Federal Supreme Court.
1726 **907** 1cr.80 black and bistre 15 10

908 Ipe (flowering tree)

1978. Environment Protection. Iguacu Falls National Park. Multicoloured.
1727 1cr.80 Type **908** 25 10
1728 1cr.80 Iguacu Falls 25 10

909 Stages of "Intelsat" Assembly

1978. 3rd Assembly. Users of "Intelsat" Telecommunications Satellite.
1729 **909** 1cr.80 multicoloured . . 15 10

910 Flag of the Order of Christ

1978. "Lubrapex 78" Stamp Exhibition. Flags. Multicoloured.
1730 1cr.80 Type **910** 60 30
1731 1cr.80 Principality of Brazil 60 30
1732 1cr.80 United Kingdom of Brazil 60 30
1733 8cr.50 Empire of Brazil . . 60 30
1734 8cr.50 National Flag of Brazil 60 30

911 Postal Tramcar

1978. 18th U.P.U. Congress, Rio de Janeiro.
1735 **911** 1cr.80 brown, blk & bl 1·10 1·00
1736 – 1cr.80 brown, blk & bl 60 60
1737 – 1cr.80 grey, blk & rose 60 60
1738 – 7cr.50 grey, blk & rose 2·00 1·10
1739 – 8cr.50 brown, blk & grn 1·00 60
1740 – 9cr.50 brown, blk & grn 1·00 60
DESIGNS: No. 1736, Mail container truck; No. 1737, Mail van, 1914; No. 1738, Travelling post office; No. 1739, Mail coach; No. 1740, Mule caravan.

912 Gaucho **913** "Morro de Santo Antonio" (Nicolas Antoine Taunay)

1978. Day of the Book and J. Guimaraes Rosa Commemoration.
1741 **912** 1cr.80 multicoloured . . 20 10

1978. Landscape Paintings. Multicoloured.
1742 1cr.80 Type **913** 20 10
1743 1cr.80 "View of Pernambuco" (Frans Post) 20 10
1744 1cr.80 "Morro de Castelo" (Victor Meirelles) 20 10
1745 1cr.80 "Landscape at Sabara" (Alberto da Veiga Guignard) 20 10

914 Angel with Lute **915** "Thanksgiving"

1978. Christmas. Multicoloured.
1746 1cr.80 Type **914** 15 10
1747 1cr.80 Angel with lyre . . . 15 10
1748 1cr.80 Angel with trumpet 15 10

1978. Thanksgiving Day.
1749 **915** 1cr.80 ochre, blk & red 15 10

916 Red Cross Services

1978. 70th Anniv of Brazilian Red Cross.
1750 **916** 1cr.80 red and black . . 15 10

917 Peace Theatre, Belem **918** Underground Trains

1978. Brazilian Theatres. Multicoloured.
1751 10cr.50 Type **917** 50 15
1752 12cr. Jose de Alencar Theatre, Fortaleza . . . 55 20
1753 12cr.50 Rio de Janeiro Municipal Theatre 60 20

1979. Inauguration of Rio de Janeiro Underground Railway.
1754 **918** 2cr.50 multicoloured . . 50 10

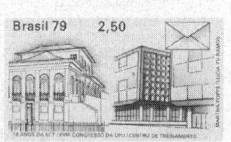

919 Old and New Post Offices

1979. 10th Anniv of Post & Telegraph Department and 18th U.P.U. Congress (2nd issue). Multicoloured.
1755 2cr.50 Type **919** 25 15
1756 2cr.50 Mail boxes 25 15
1757 2cr.50 Mail sorting 25 15
1758 2cr.50 Mail planes 25 15
1759 2cr.50 Telegraph and telex machines 25 15
1760 2cr.50 Postmen 25 15

920 "O'Day 23" Class Yacht

1979. "Brasiliana 79" 3rd World Thematic Stamp Exhibition (1st issue). Multicoloured.
1761 2cr.50 Type **920** 25 10
1762 10cr.50 "Penguin" class dinghy 55 20
1763 12cr. "Hobie Cat" class catamaran 55 20
1764 12cr.50 "Snipe" class dinghy 55 25
See Nos. 1773/6 and 1785/90.

921 Joao Bolinha (characters from children's story)

1979. Children's Book Day.
1765 **921** 2cr.50 multicoloured . . 20 10

922 "Victoria amazonica"

1979. 18th U.P.U. Congress (3rd issue). Amazon National Park. Multicoloured.
1766 10cr.50 Type **922** 60 20
1767 12cr. Amazon manatee . . 65 25
1768 12cr.50 Tortoise 70 25

923 Bank Emblem

1979. 25th Anniv of Northeast Bank of Brazil.
1769 **923** 2cr.50 multicoloured . . 15 10

924 Physicians and Patient (15th cent woodcut)

1979. 150th Anniv of National Academy of Medicine.
1770 **924** 2cr.50 yellow and black 15 10

925 Clover with Hearts as Leaves

1979. 35th Brazilian Cardiology Congress.
1771 **925** 2cr.50 multicoloured . . 15 10

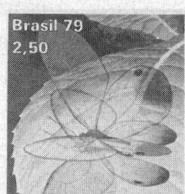

927 "Cithaerias aurora"

1979. "Brasiliana 79" (2nd issue). Butterflies. Multicoloured.
1773 2cr.50 Type **927** 30 15
1774 10cr.50 "Evenus regalis" . . 90 25
1775 12cr. "Caligo eurilochus" . 1·00 35
1776 12cr.50 "Diaethria clymena janeira" . . . . 1·10 40

928 Embraer Xingu **929** Globe illuminating Land

1979. 10th Anniv of Brazilian Aeronautical Industry.
1777 **928** 2cr.50 dp blue and blue 15 10

1979. National Week.
1778 **929** 3cr.20 blue, green & yell 15 10

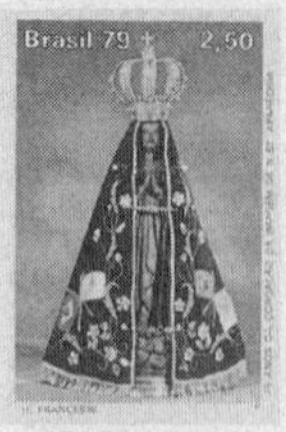

930 Our Lady Aparecida

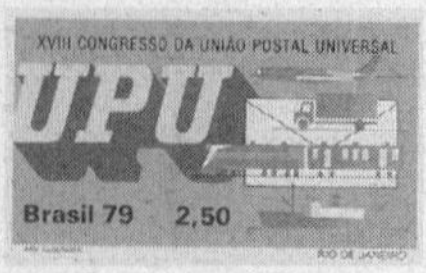

931 Envelope and Transport

1979. 75th Anniv of Coronation of Our Lady Aparecida.
1779 **930** 2cr.50 multicoloured . . 15 10

1979. 18th U.P.U. Congress, Rio de Janeiro (4th issue). Multicoloured.
1780 2cr.50 Type **931** 75 30
1781 2cr.50 Post Office emblems 20 10
1782 10cr.50 Globe 35 20
1783 12cr. Flags of Brazil and U.P.U 40 20
1784 12cr.50 U.P.U. emblem . . 40 20

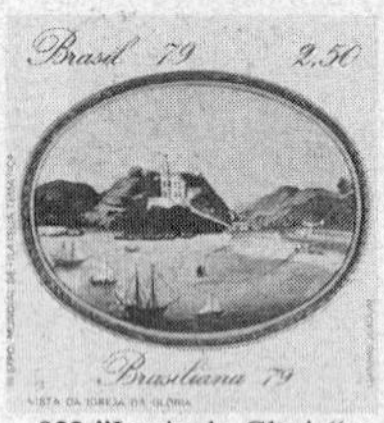

932 "Igreja da Gloria"

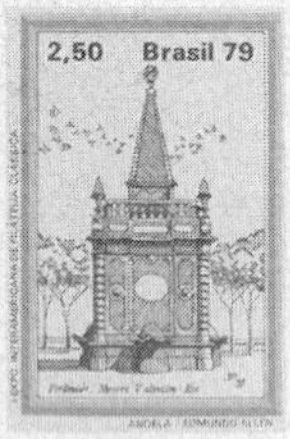

933 Pyramid Fountain, Rio de Janeiro

1979. "Brasiliana 79" Third World Thematic Stamp Exhibition (3rd issue). Paintings by Leandro Joaquim. Multicoloured.
1785 2cr.50 Type **932** 15 10
1786 12cr. "Fishing on Guanabara Bay" 35 20
1787 12cr.50 "Boqueirao Lake and Carioca Arches" . . 45 25

1979. "Brasiliana 79" (4th issue). 1st International Exhibition of Classical Philately. Fountains.
1788 **933** 2cr.50 black, grn & emer 10 10
1789 – 10cr.50 black, turq & bl 35 20
1790 – 12cr. black, red and pink 40 25
DESIGNS—VERT: 12cr. Boa Vista, Recife. HORIZ: 10cr.50, Marilia Fountain, Ouro Preto.

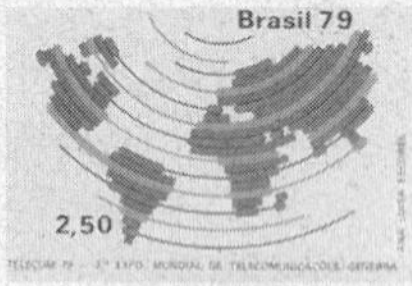

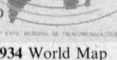

934 World Map

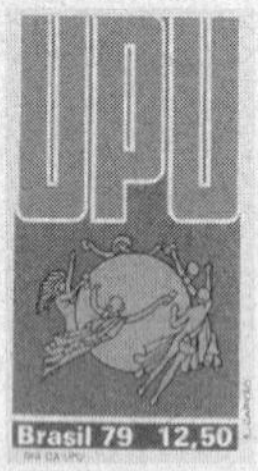

935 "UPU" and Emblem

1979. 3rd World Telecommunications Exhibition, Geneva.
1791 **934** 2cr.50 multicoloured . . 15 10

1979. U.P.U. Day.
1792 **935** 2cr.50 multicoloured . . 15 10
1793 10cr.50 multicoloured . . 35 15
1794 12cr. multicoloured . . . 35 15
1795 12cr.50 multicoloured . . 35 20

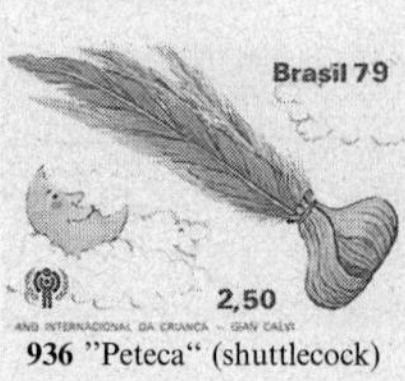

936 "Peteca" (shuttlecock)

1979. International Year of the Child. Mult.
1796 2cr.50 Type **936** 20 10
1797 3cr.20 Spinning top 20 10
1798 3cr.20 Jumping Jack 20 10
1799 3cr.20 Rag doll 20 10

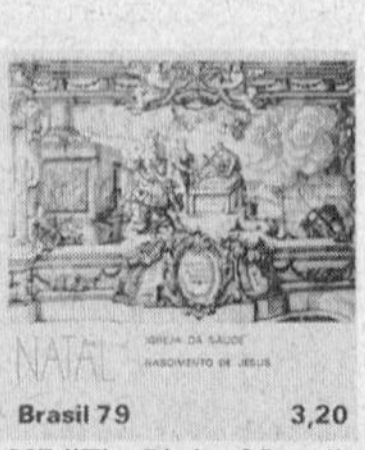

937 "The Birth of Jesus"

1979. Christmas. Tiles from the Church of Our Lady of Health and Glory, Salvador. Multicoloured.
1800 3cr.20 Type **937** 15 10
1801 3cr.20 "Adoration of the Kings" 15 10
1802 3cr.20 "The Boy Jesus among the Doctors" . . . 15 10

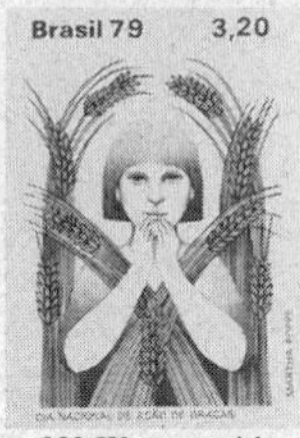

939 Woman with Wheat

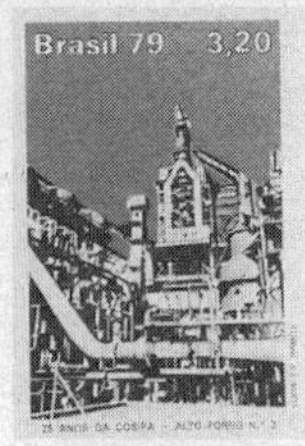

940 Steel Mill

1979. Thanksgiving Day.
1804 **939** 3cr.20 multicoloured . . 15 10

1979. 25th Anniv of Cosipa Steel Works, Sao Paulo.
1805 **940** 3cr.20 multicoloured . . 15 10

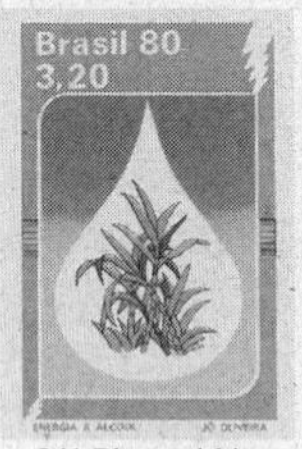

941 Plant within Raindrop

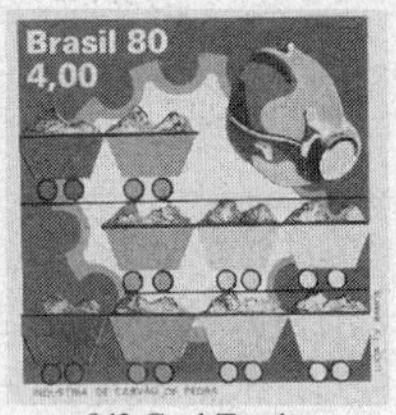

942 Coal Trucks

1980. Energy Conservation. Multicoloured.
1806 3cr.20 Type **941** 25 10
1807 17cr.+7cr. Sun and lightbulb 35 10
1808 20cr.+8cr. Windmill and lightbulb 90 55
1809 21cr.+9cr. Dam and lightbulb . . . . 1·50 30

1980. Coal Industry.
1810 **942** 4cr. black, orge & red 65 30

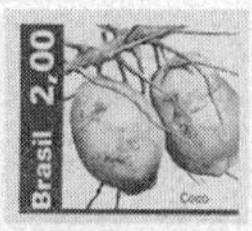

943 Coconuts

1980.
1811 **943** 2cr. brown 15 10
1812 – 3cr. red 15 10
1813 – 4cr. orange 15 10
1814 – 5cr. violet 15 10
1815 – 7cr. orange 35 10
1816 – 10cr. green 15 10
1817 – 12cr. green 10 10
1818 – 15cr. brown 15 10
1819 – 17cr. red 35 10
1820 – 20cr. brown 15 10
1821 – 24cr. orange 90 10
1822 – 30cr. black 90 10
1823 – 34cr. brown . . . . . 5·25 1·25
1824 – 38cr. red . . . . 3·50 50
1825 – 42cr. green . . . . . . 7·00 1·25
1825a – 45cr. brown 10 10
1826 – 50cr. orange 20 10
1826a – 57cr. brown . . . . . 2·40 60
1826b – 65cr. purple 15 10
1827 – 66cr. violet . . . . . . 5·25 1·25
1827a – 80cr. red 90 45
1828 – 100cr. brown 55 10
1828a – 120cr. blue 20 10
1829 – 140cr. red . . . . . . 7·00 60
1829a – 150cr. green 20 10
1830 – 200cr. green . . . . . 1·75 10
1830a – 300cr. purple . . . . 2·40 10
1831 – 500cr. brown . . . . . 2·40 10
1832 – 800cr. green . . . . . 1·75 10
1833 – 1000cr. olive . . . . . 1·75 10
1834 – 2000cr. orange . . . . 2·40 10
DESIGNS: 3cr. Mangoes; 4cr. Corn; 5cr. Onions; 7cr. Oranges; 10cr. Passion fruit; 12cr. Pineapple; 15cr. Bananas; 17cr. Guarana; 20cr. Sugar cane; 24cr. Bee and honeycomb; 30cr. Silkworm and mulberry; 34cr. Cocoa beans; 38cr. Coffee; 42cr. Soya bean; 45cr. Manioc; 50cr. Wheat; 57cr. Peanuts; 65cr. Rubber; 66cr. Grapes; 80cr. Brazil nuts; 100cr. Cashews; 120cr. Rice; 140cr. Tomatoes; 150cr. Eucalyptus; 200cr. Castor-oil bean; 300cr. Parana pine; 500cr. Cotton; 800cr. Carnauba palm; 1000cr. Babassu palm; 2000cr. Sunflower.

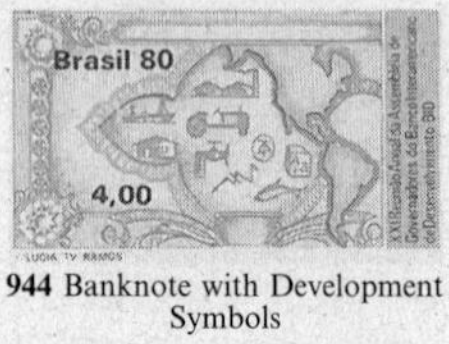

944 Banknote with Development Symbols

1980. 21st Inter-American Bank of Development Directors' Annual Assembly Meeting, Rio de Janeiro.
1836 **944** 4cr. blue, brown & blk 15 10

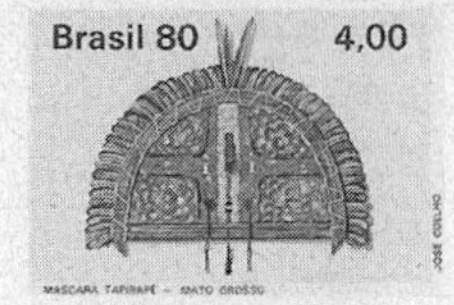

945 Tapirape Mask

1980. Indian Art. Ritual Masks. Mult.
1837 4cr. Type **945** 20 10
1838 4cr. Tukuna mask (vert) . . 20 10
1839 4cr. Kanela mask (vert) . . 20 10

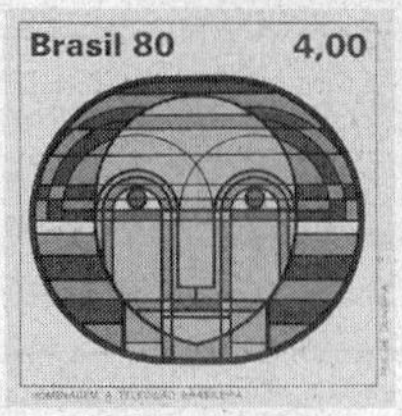

946 Geometric Head

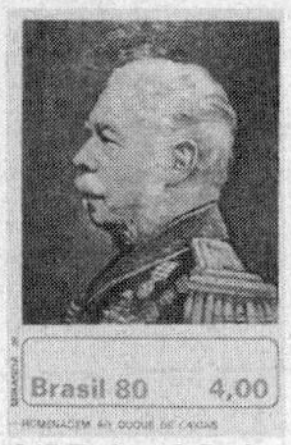

947 Duke of Caxias (after Miranda Junior)

1980. 30th Anniv of Brazilian Television.
1840 **946** 4cr. multicoloured . . . 15 10

1980. Death Centenary of Duke de Caxias (General and statesman).
1841 **947** 4cr. multicoloured . . . 15 10

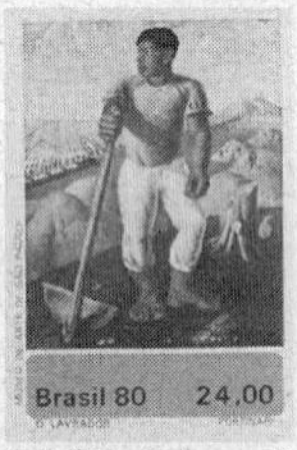

948 "The Labourer" (Candido Portinari)

1980. Art in Brazilian Museums. Mult.
1842 24cr. Type **948** 75 25
1843 28cr. "Mademoiselle Pogany" (statuette, Constantin Brancusi) . . 75 25
1844 30cr. "The Glass of Water" (A. de Figueiredo) 95 30
MUSEUMS. 24cr. Sao Paulo Museum of Art. 28cr. Rio de Janeiro Museum of Modern Art. 30cr. Rio de Janeiro Museum of Fine Art.

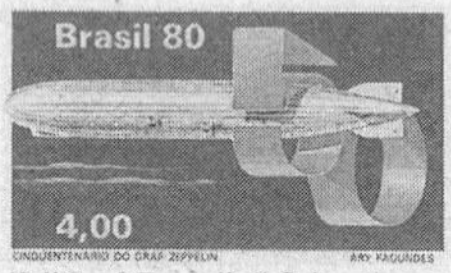

949 "Graf Zeppelin" flying through "50"

1980. 50th Annivs of "Graf Zeppelin" and First South Atlantic Air Mail Flight.
1845 **949** 4cr. black, blue & violet 20 15
1846 – 4cr. multicoloured . . . 20 15
DESIGN: No. 1846, Latecoere seaplane "Comte de la Vaulx".

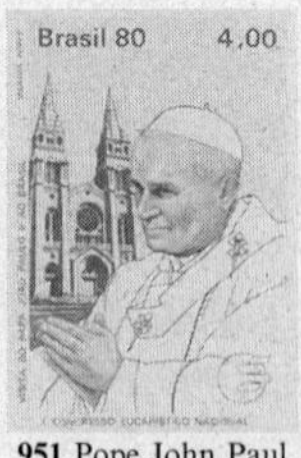

951 Pope John Paul II and Fortaleza Cathedral

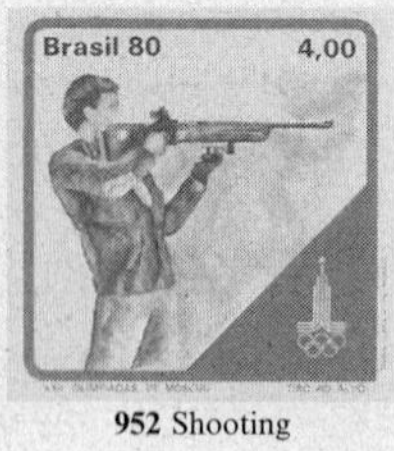

952 Shooting

1980. Papal Visit and 10th National Eucharistic Congress. Pope John Paul II and cathedrals. Multicoloured.
1848 4cr. Type **951** 25 15
1849 4cr. St. Peter's, Rome (horiz) 25 15
1850 24cr. Apericida (horiz) . . . 65 40
1851 28cr. Rio de Janeiro (horiz) 65 20
1852 30cr. Brasilia (horiz) . . . . 1·50 25

1980. Olympic Games, Moscow. Mult.
1853 4cr. Type **952** 20 10
1854 4cr. Cycling 20 10
1855 4cr. Rowing 20 10

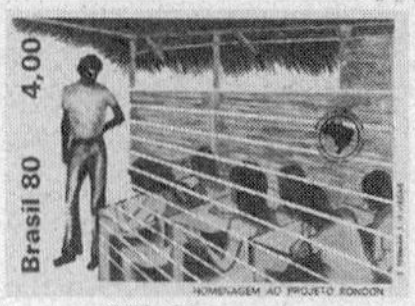

953 Classroom

1980. Rondon Project (voluntary student work in rural areas).
1856 **953** 4cr. multicoloured . . . 20 10

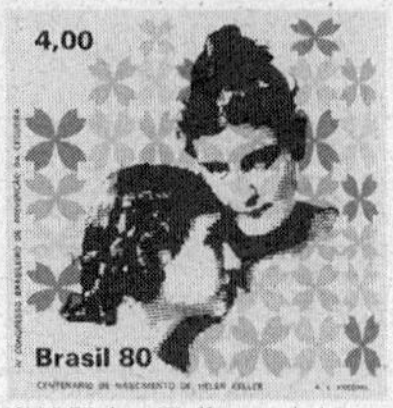

954 Helen Keller and Anne Sullivan

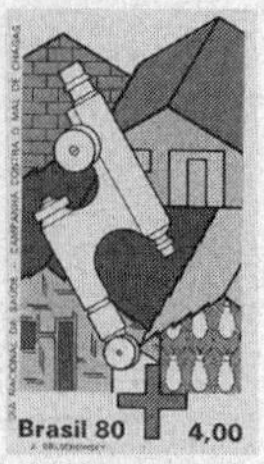

956 Houses and Microscope

1980. Birth Centenary of Helen Keller, and 4th Brazilian Congress on Prevention of Blindness, Belo Horizonte.
1857 **954** 4cr. multicoloured . . . 20 10

1980. National Health Day. Campaign against Chagas Disease (barber bug fever).
1859 **956** 4cr. multicoloured . . . 20 10

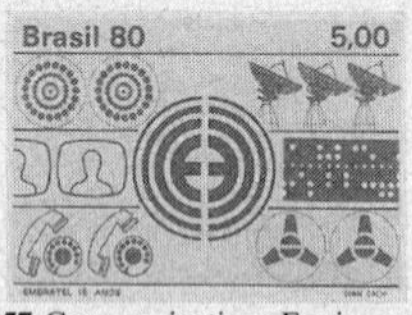

957 Communications Equipment

1980. 15th Anniv of National Telecommunications System.
1860 **957** 5cr. stone, blue & green 20 10

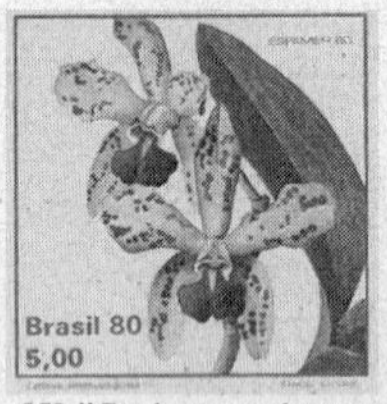

959 "Cattleya amethystoglossa"

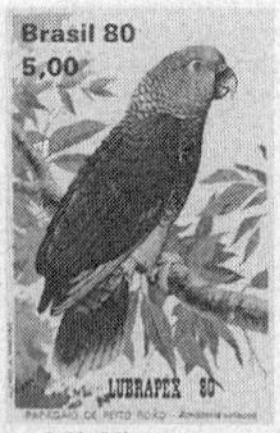

960 Vinaceous Amazon

1980. "Espamer 80" International Stamp Exhibition, Madrid. Orchids. Multicoloured.
1862 5cr. Type **959** 30 10
1863 5cr. "Laelia cinnabarina" 30 10
1864 24cr. "Zygopetalum crinitum" . . . . 1·75 35
1865 28cr. "Laelia tenebrosa" . . 1·75 40

1980. "Lubrapex 80" Portuguese–Brazilian Stamp Exhibition, Lisbon. Parrots. Multicoloured.
1866 5cr. Type **960** 60 40
1867 5cr. Red-tailed amazon . . 60 40
1868 28cr. Red-spectacled amazon 2·75 1·00
1869 28cr. Brown backed parrotlet . . . . 2·75 1·00

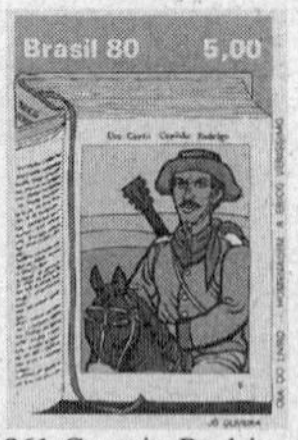

961 Captain Rodrigo (fictional character)

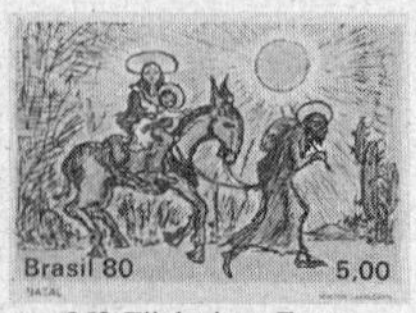

962 Flight into Egypt

1980. Book Day and Erico Verissimo (writer). Commemoration.
1870 **961** 5cr. multicoloured . . . 20 10

1980. Christmas.
1871 **962** 5cr. multicoloured . . . 20 10

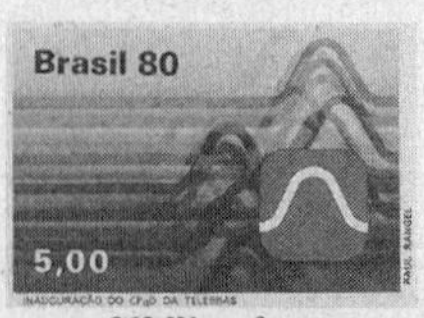

963 Wave-form

1980. Inauguration of Telecommunications Centre for Research and Development, Campanas City.
1872 **963** 5cr. multicoloured . . . 20 10

964 Carvalho Viaduct, Paranagua–Curitiba Railway Line

1980. Centenary of Engineering Club.
1873 **964** 5cr. multicoloured . . . 45 25

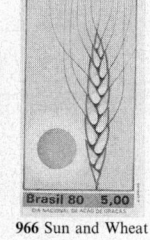

965 Postal Chessboard   **966** Sun and Wheat

1980. Postal Chess.
1874 **965** 5cr. multicoloured . . . 55 20

1980. Thanksgiving Day.
1875 **966** 5cr. multicoloured . . . 20 15

967 Father Anchieta writing Poem in Sand

1980. Beatification of Father Jose de Anchieta.
1876 **967** 5cr. multicoloured . . . 20 10

968 Christ on the Mount of Olives

1980. 250th Birth Anniv of Antonio Lisboa (Aleijadinho) (sculptor). Wood sculptures of Christ's head. Multicoloured.
1877 5cr. Type **968** 30 30
1878 5cr. The Arrest in the
     Garden 30 30
1879 5cr. Flagellation 30 30
1880 5cr. Wearing Crown of
     Thorns 30 30
1881 5cr. Carrying the cross . . . 30 30
1882 5cr. Crucifixion 30 30

969 Agricultural Produce

1981. Agricultural Development. Mult.
1883 30cr. Type **969** . . . . . . 1·25 25
1884 35cr. Shopping 80 30
1885 40cr. Exporting 80 30

970 Scout sitting by Camp Fire

1981. 4th Pan-American Jamboree. Multicoloured.
1886 5cr. Type **970** 25 10
1887 5cr. Troop cooking 25 10
1888 5cr. Scout with totem pole 25 10

973 Lima Barreto and Rio de Janeiro Street Scene

1981. Birth Centenary of Lima Barreto (author).
1891 **973** 7cr. multicoloured . . . 60 25

974 Tupi-Guarani Ceramic Funeral Urn

1981. Artefacts from Brazilian Museums. Mult.
1892 7cr. Type **974** (Archaeology
     and Popular Arts
     Museum, Paranagua) . . 20 15
1893 7cr. Marajoara "tanga"
     ceramic loincloth (Emilio
     Goeldi Museum, Para) . 20 15
1894 7cr. Maraca tribe funeral
     urn (National Museum,
     Rio de Janeiro) 20 15

975 Ruby-topaz Hummingbird

1981. Hummingbirds. Multicoloured.
1895 7cr. Type **975** 85 25
1896 7cr. Horned sungem 85 25
1897 7cr. Frilled coquette 85 25
1898 7cr. Planalto hermit 85 25

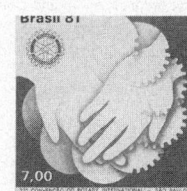

976 Hands and Cogwheels

1981. 72nd Int Rotary Convention, Sao Paulo.
1899 **976** 7cr. red and black . . . 15 10
1900 – 35cr. multicoloured . . . 1·50 60
DESIGN: 35cr. Head and cogwheels.

977 "Protection of the Water"

1981. Environment Protection. Multicoloured.
1901 7cr. Type **977** 25 15
1902 7cr. "Protection of the
     forests" 25 15
1903 7cr. "Protection of the air" 25 15
1904 7cr. "Protection of the soil" 25 15

978 Curtiss Fledgling

1981. 50th Anniv of National Air Mail Service.
1905 **978** 7cr. multicoloured . . . 20 10

979 Locomotive "Colonel Church" and Map of Railway

1981. 50th Anniv of Madeira–Mamore Railway Nationalization.
1906 **979** 7cr. multicoloured . . . 55 30

980 Esperanto Star and Arches of Alvorada Governmental Palace, Brasilia

1981. 66th World Esperanto Congress, Brasilia.
1907 **980** 7cr. green, grey & black 15 10

981 Pedro II and 50r. "Small Head" Stamp

1981. Cent of Pedro II "Small Head" Stamps.
1908 **981** 50cr. brown, blk & bl . . 1·10 25
1909 – 55cr. mauve and green 1·10 25
1910 – 60cr. blue, black & orge 95 30
DESIGNS: 55cr. Pedro II and 100r. "Small Head" stamp; 60r. Pedro II and 200r. "Small Head" stamp.

982 Military Institute of Engineering

1981. 50th Anniv of Military Institute of Engineering.
1911 **982** 12cr. multicoloured . . . 15 10

983 Caboclinhos Folkdance

1981. Festivities. Multicoloured.
1912 50cr. Type **983** 90 15
1913 55cr. Marujada folk festival 90 15
1914 60cr. Resado parade 90 20

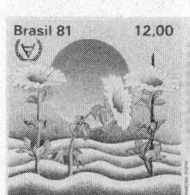

984 Sun and Erect, Drooping, and Supported Flowers

1981. International Year of Disabled Persons.
1915 **984** 12cr. multicoloured . . . 20 10

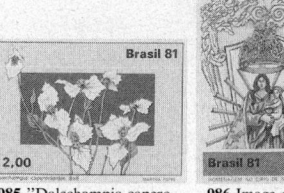

985 "Dalechampia capero-niodes"   **986** Image of Our Lady of Nazareth

1981. Flowers of the Central Plateau. Multicoloured.
1916 12cr. Type **985** 20 15
1917 12cr. "Palicourea rigida" . . 20 15
1918 12cr. "Eremanthus
     sphaerocephalus"(vert) . . 20 15
1919 12cr. "Cassia clausseni"
     (vert) 20 15

1981. Festival of Our Lady of Nazareth, Belem.
1920 **986** 12cr. multicoloured . . . 15 10

987 Christ the Redeemer Monument   **988** Farmhands seeding the Land

1981. 50th Anniv of Christ the Redeemer Monument, Rio de Janeiro.
1921 **987** 12cr. multicoloured . . . 15 10

1981. World Food Day.
1922 **988** 12cr. multicoloured . . . 15 10

989 Santos Dumont and Biplane "14 bis" landing at Paris

1981. 75th Anniv of Santos Dumont's First Powered Flight.
1923 **989** 60cr. multicoloured . . . 75 20

990 Friar Santos Rita Durao, Title Page and Scene from "Caramuru"

1981. Book Day and Bicentenary of Publication of Epic Poem "Caramuru".
1924 **990** 12cr. multicoloured . . . 15 10

991 Crib, Juazeiro de Norte (Cica)

1981. Christmas. Various designs showing Cribs. Multicoloured.
1925 12cr. Type **991** 15 10
1926 50cr. Caruaru (Vitalino
     Filho) 75 15
1927 55cr. Sao Jose dos Campos
     (Eugenia) (vert) 75 15
1928 60cr. Taubate (Candida)
     (vert) . . . . 1·10 20

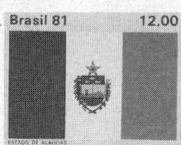

992 Alagoas

1981. State Flags (1st series). Multicoloured.
1929 12cr. Type **992** 50 50
1930 12cr. Bahia 50 50
1931 12cr. Federal District . . . 50 50
1932 12cr. Pernambuco 50 50
1933 12cr. Sergipe 50 50
See also Nos. 1988/92, 2051/5, 2113/17, 2204/7 and 3043/4.

993 Girls with Wheat   **994** Heads and Symbols of Occupations

1981. Thanksgiving Day.
1934 **993** 12cr. multicoloured . . . 15 10

1981. 50th Anniv of Ministry of Labour.
1935 **994** 12cr. multicoloured . . . 15 10

995 Federal Engineering School, Itajuba

1981. Birth Centenary of Theodomiro Carneiro Santiago (founder of Federal Engineering School).
1936 **995** 15cr. green and mauve 15 10

996 Musician of Police Military Band and Headquarters

997 Army Library "Ex Libris"

1981. 150th Anniv of Sao Paulo Military Police. Multicoloured.
1937 12cr. Type **996** 25 10
1938 12cr. Lancers of Ninth of July Regiment, Mounted Police 25 10

1981. Centenary of Army Library.
1939 **997** 12cr. multicoloured . . . 15 10

999 Brigadier Eduardo Gomes

1982. Brigadier Eduardo Gomes Commem.
1941 **999** 12cr. blue and black . . 15 10

1000 Lage, Coal Trucks, "Ita" freighter and HL-1 Airplane

1981. Birth Cent of Henrique Lage (industrialist)
1942 **1000** 17cr. multicoloured . . 1·60 45

1001 Tackle

1002 Microscope, Bacillus and Lung

1982. World Cup Football Championship, Spain. Multicoloured.
1943 75cr. Type **1001** . . . . 1·75 50
1944 80cr. Kicking ball . . . . . 1·75 50
1945 85cr. Goalkeeper . . . . . 1·75 50

1982. Centenary of Robert Koch's Discovery of Tubercle Bacillus. Multicoloured.
1947 90cr. Type **1002** . . . . . 4·25 1·75
1948 100cr. Flasks, tablets, syringe, bacillus and lung . . 4·25 1·75

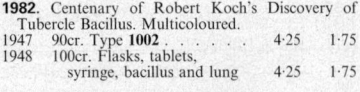
1004 Oil Rig Workers

1982. Birth Centenary of Monteiro Lobato (writer).
1950 **1004** 17cr. multicoloured . . 20 10

1005 St. Vincent de Paul

1982. 400th Birth Anniv of St. Vincent de Paul.
1951 **1005** 17cr. multicoloured . . 15 10

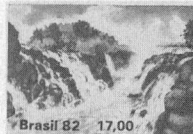
1006 Fifth Fall

1982. Guaira's Seven Falls. Multicoloured.
1952 17cr. Type **1006** 20 10
1953 21cr. Seventh fall 25 10

1007 Envelope, Telephone, Antenna and Postcode

1982. 15th Anniv of Ministry of Communications.
1954 **1007** 21cr. multicoloured . . 15 10

1008 The Old Arsenal (National Historical Museum)

1982. 50th Anniv of Museology Course.
1955 **1008** 17cr. black and pink . . 15 10

1009 Cogwheels and Ore Mountains

1982. 40th Anniv of Vale do Rio Doce Company.
1956 **1009** 17cr. multicoloured . . 15 10

1010 Martim Afonso de Souza proclaiming Sao Vicente a Town

1982. 450th Anniv of Sao Vicente.
1957 **1010** 17cr. multicoloured . . 15 10

1011 Giant Anteater

1982. Animals. Multicoloured.
1958 17cr. Type **1011** 40 10
1959 21cr. Maned wolf 90 15
1960 30cr. Pampas deer . . . . . 1·75 25

1012 Film and "Golden Palm" 1014 Church of Our Lady of O, Sabara

1982. 20th Anniv of "Golden Palm" Film Award to "The Given World".
1961 **1012** 17cr. multicoloured . . 20 10

1982. Baroque-style Architecture in Minas Gerais. Multicoloured.
1963 17cr. Type **1014** 55 10
1964 17cr. Church of Our Lady of Carmo, Mariana (horiz) 55 10
1965 17cr. Church of Our Lady of Rosary, Diamantina (horiz) 55 10

1015 St. Francis of Assisi

1016 "Large Head" Stamp of 1882

1982. 800th Birth Anniv of St. Francis of Assisi.
1966 **1015** 21cr. multicoloured . . 15 10

1982. Centenary of Pedro II "Large Head" Stamps.
1967 **1016** 21cr. yellow, brn & blk . . 15 10

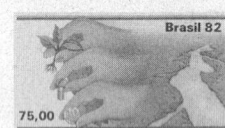
1017 Amazon River and Hands holding Seedling, Screw and Coin

1982. Manaus Free Trade Zone.
1968 **1017** 75cr. multicoloured . . 95 20

1019 Xango

1982. Orixas Religious Costumes. Mult.
1970 20cr. Type **1019** 20 10
1971 20cr. Iemanja 20 10
1972 20cr. Oxumare 20 10

1020 XII Florin

1982. 10th Anniv of Brazilian Central Bank Values Museum. Multicoloured.
1973 25cr. Type **1020** 20 10
1974 25cr. Pedro I Coronation piece 20 10

1021 "Ipiranga Cry" (Dom Pedro proclaiming independence)

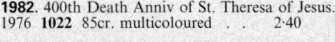
1022 St. Theresa of Jesus

1982. Independence Week.
1975 **1021** 25cr. multicoloured . . 20 10

1982. 400th Death Anniv of St. Theresa of Jesus.
1976 **1022** 85cr. multicoloured . . 2·40 50

1023 Musical Instrument Maker

1024 Embraer Tucano Trainers

1982. "Lubrapex 82" Brazilian–Portuguese Stamp Exhibition, Curitiba. The Paranaense Fandango. Multicoloured.
1977 75cr. Type **1023** . . . . . 1·75 50
1978 80cr. Dancers . . . . 1·75 50
1979 85cr. Musicians . . . . 1·75 50

1982. Aeronautical Industry Day.
1981 **1024** 24cr. multicoloured . . 20 25

1025 Bastos Tigre and Verse from "Saudade"

1982. Day of the Book and Birth Centenary of Bastos Tigre (poet).
1982 **1025** 24cr. multicoloured . . 15 10

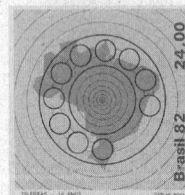
1026 Telephone Dial on Map of Brazil

1982. 10th Anniv of Telebras (Brazilian Telecommunications Corporation).
1983 **1026** 24cr. multicoloured . . 15 10

1027 "Nativity" (C.S. Miyaba)

1982. Christmas. Children's Paintings. Mult.
1984 24cr. Type **1027** . . . . . 1·25 10
1985 24cr. "Choir of Angels" (N. N. Aleluia) . . . . . 1·25 10
1986 30cr. "Holy Family" (F. T. Filho) . . . . 1·25 15
1987 30cr. "Nativity with Angel" (N. Arand) . . . . 1·25 15

1982. State Flags (2nd series). As T **992**. Mult.
1988 24cr. Ceara . . . . . . 1·75 60
1989 24cr. Espirito Santo . . . . . 1·75 60
1990 24cr. Paraiba . . . . . 1·75 60
1991 24cr. Rio Grande do Norte . . 1·75 60
1992 24cr. Rondonia . . . . . . 1·75 60

1028 "Germination"

1029 "Efeta" (S. Tempel)

1982. Thanksgiving Day.
1993 **1028** 24cr. multicoloured . . 50 10

1982. The Hard of Hearing.
1994 **1029** 24cr. multicoloured . . 15 10

1030 "Benjamin Constant" (cadet ship)

1982. Bicentenary of Naval Academy. Mult.
1995	24cr. Type **1030**	85	25
1996	24cr. "Almirante Saldanha" (cadet ship)	85	25
1997	24cr. "Brasil" (training frigate)	85	25

1032 Samba Parade Drummers

1983. "Brasiliana 83" International Stamp Exhibition, Rio de Janeiro. Carnival. Multicoloured.
1999	24cr. Type **1032**	90	35
2000	130cr. Masked clowns . . .	3·00	90
2001	140cr. Dancer	3·00	90
2002	150cr. Indian	3·00	90

1033 Support Ship "Barao de Teffe" in Antarctic

1983. 1st Brazilian Antarctic Expedition.
2003	**1033** 150cr. multicoloured . .	1·75	45

1034 Woman with Ballot Paper   1035 Itaipu Dam

1983. 50th Anniv of Women's Suffrage in Brazil.
2004	**1034** 130cr. multicoloured . .	1·75	50

1983. Itaipu Brazilian–Paraguayan Hydro-electric Project.
2005	**1035** 140cr. multicoloured . .	1·75	50

1036 Luther   1037 Microscope and Crab

1983. 500th Birth Anniv of Martin Luther (Protestant reformer).
2006	**1036** 150cr. dp grn, grn & blk	2·40	50

1983. Cancer Prevention. 30th Anniv of Antonio Prudente Foundation and A.C. Camargo Hospital. Multicoloured.
2007	30cr. Type **1037**	25	20
2008	38cr. Antonio Prudente, hospital and crab	25	20

1038 Tissue Culture

1983. Agricultural Research. Multicoloured.
2009	30cr. Type **1038**	20	10
2010	30cr. Brazilian wild chestnut tree	20	10
2011	38cr. Tropical soya beans	20	10

1039 Friar Rogerio Neuhaus before Altar   1040 Council Emblem and World Map

1983. Cent of Ordination of Friar Rogerio Neuhaus.
2012	**1039** 30cr. multicoloured . .	20	10

1983. 30th Anniv of Customs Co-operation Council.
2013	**1040** 30cr. multicoloured . .	20	10

1041 Satellite

1983. World Communications Year.
2014	**1041** 250cr. multicoloured . .	3·50	1·25

1042 Toco Toucan

1983. Toucans. Multicoloured.
2015	30cr. Type **1042**	90	20
2016	185cr. Red-billed toucan . .	3·00	85
2017	205cr. Red-breasted toucan	3·00	90
2018	215cr. Channel-billed toucan	3·00	1·10

1044 Baldwin Locomotive No. 1, 1881   1045 Basketball Players

1983. Locomotives. Multicoloured.
2020	30cr. Type **1044**	55	30
2021	30cr. Hohenzollern locomotive No. 980, 1875	55	30
2022	38cr. Locomotive No. 1 "Maria Fumaca", 1868	55	30

1983. 9th Women's World Basketball Championship, Sao Paulo.
2023	30cr. Type **1045**	25	10
2024	30cr. Basketball players (different)	25	10

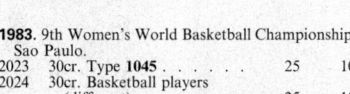

1046 Bolivar (after Tito Salas)

1983. Birth Bicentenary of Simon Bolivar.
2025	**1046** 30cr. multicoloured . .	20	10

1047 Boy with Kite and Boy waiting for Polio Vaccination   1048 Minerva and Computer Punched Tape

1983. Polio and Measles Vaccination Campaign. Multicoloured.
2026	30cr. Type **1047**	30	10
2027	30cr. Girl on bicycle and girl receiving measles vaccination	30	10

1983. 20th Anniv of Post-graduate Master's Programmes in Engineering.
2028	**1048** 30cr. light brown, blue and brown	20	10

1049 30r. "Bulls Eye" Stamp and Rio de Janeiro Bay

1983. "Brasiliana 83" International Stamp Exhibition, Rio de Janeiro. 140th Anniv of "Bull's Eye" Stamps.
2029	**1049** 185cr. black and blue	1·50	90
2030	– 205cr. black and blue	1·50	90
2031	– 215cr. black and violet	1·50	90

DESIGNS: Nos. 2030/1, As Type **1049** but showing 60r. and 90r. "Bull's Eye" stamp respectively.

1052 Embraer EMB-120

1983. Brazilian Aeronautics Industry.
2035	**1052** 30cr. multicoloured . .	25	10

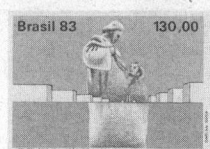

1053 Bosco and State Departments Esplanade, Brasilia

1983. Dom Bosco's Dream of Brazil.
2036	**1053** 130cr. multicoloured . .	75	10

1054 "Council of State decides on Independence" (detail, Georgina de Albuquerque)

1983. National Week.
2037	**1054** 50cr. multicoloured . .	15	10

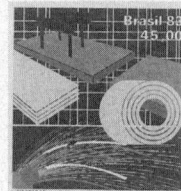

1055 Iron and Steel Production

1983. 10th Anniv of Siderbras (Brazilian Steel Corporation).
2038	**1055** 45cr. multicoloured . .	15	10

1056 "Pilosocereus gounellei"

1983. Cacti. Multicoloured.
2039	45cr. Type **1056**	95	10
2040	45cr. "Melocactus bahiensis"	95	10
2041	57cr. "Cereus jamacari" . .	95	10

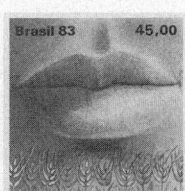

1057 Monstrance   1058 Mouth and Wheat

1983. 50th Anniv of National Eucharistic Congress.
2042	**1057** 45cr. multicoloured . .	15	10

1983. 20th Anniv of World Food Programme. Fishery Resources. Multicoloured.
2043	45cr. Type **1058**	20	15
2044	57cr. Fish and fishing pirogue	80	15

1060 "Our Lady of Angels" (wood, Franisco Xavier de Brito)

1983. Christmas. Statues of the Madonna. Multicoloured.
2046	45cr. Type **1060**	90	10
2047	315cr. "Our Lady of Birth"	2·75	90
2048	335cr. "Our Lady of Joy" (fired clay, Agostinho de Jesus)	2·75	90
2049	345cr. "Our Lady of Presentation"	2·75	90

1061 Moraes and Map of Italian Campaign

1983. Birth Centenary of Marshal Mascarenhas de Moraes.
2050	**1061** 45cr. pink, green & pur	20	15

1983. State Flags (3rd series). As Type **992**. Multicoloured.
2051	45cr. Amazonas	90	55
2052	45cr. Goias	90	55
2053	45cr. Rio de Janeiro . .	90	55
2054	45cr. Mato Grosso do Sul	90	55
2055	45cr. Parana	90	55

1062 Praying Figure and Wheat

1983. Thanksgiving Day.
2056	**1062** 45cr. multicoloured . .	15	10

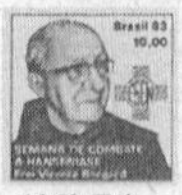

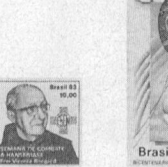

1063 Friar Vincente Borgard

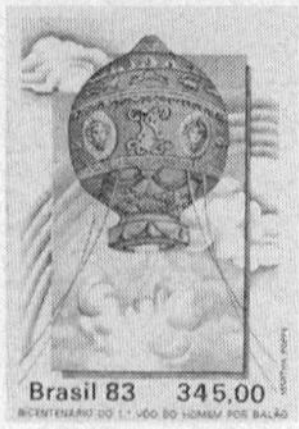

1064 Montgolfier Balloon

1983. Obligatory Tax. Anti-leprosy Week.
2057 **1063** 10cr. brown . . . . . 2·75 90

1983. Bicentenary of Manned Flight.
2058 **1064** 345cr. multicoloured . . 4·25 2·40

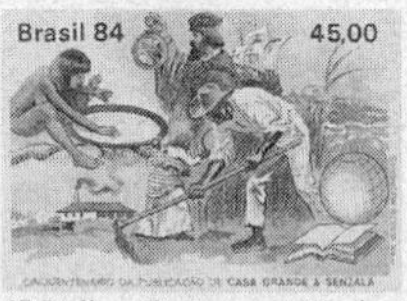

1065 Indian, Portuguese Navigator and Negro

1984. 50th Anniv of Publication of "Masters and Slaves" by Gilberto Freyre.
2059 **1065** 45cr. multicoloured . . 60 10

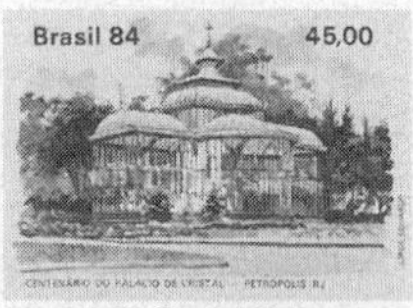

1066 Crystal Palace

1984. Centenary of Crystal Palace, Petropolis.
2060 **1066** 45cr. multicoloured . . 25 10

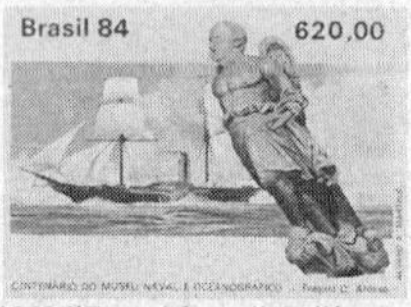

1068 "Don Afonso" (sail/steam warship) and Figurehead

1984. Cent of Naval Oceanographic Museum.
2062 **1068** 620cr. multicoloured . . 1·25 35

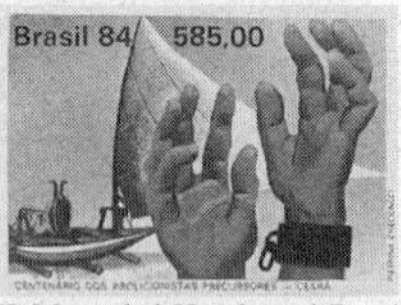

1069 Manacled Hands and Beached Fishing Pirogue

1984. Centenary of Abolition of Slavery in Ceara and Amazonas. Multicoloured.
2063 585cr. Type **1069** . . . . . 1·75 90
2064 610cr. Emancipated slave . . 1·75 90

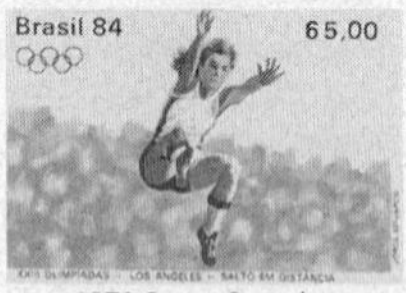

1071 Long Jumping

1984. Olympic Games, Los Angeles. Mult.
2066 65cr. Type **1071** 90 50
2067 65cr. 100 metres 90 50
2068 65cr. Relay 90 50
2069 585cr. Pole vaulting 90 75
2070 610cr. High jumping 90 75
2071 620cr. Hurdling 90 75

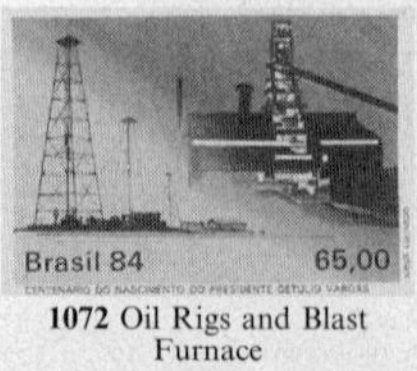

1072 Oil Rigs and Blast Furnace

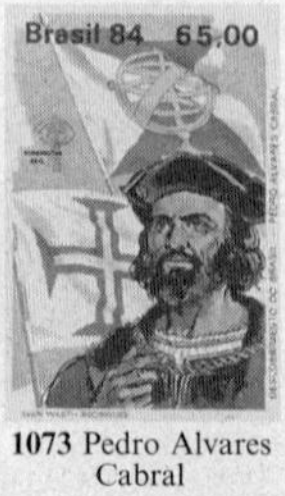

1073 Pedro Alvares Cabral

1984. Birth Cent (1983) of Getulio Vargas (President 1930–45 and 1951–54). Multicoloured.
2072 65cr. Type **1072** 15 10
2073 65cr. Ballot boxes and symbols of professions and trades 15 10
2074 65cr. Sugar refinery and electricity pylons 15 10

1984. "Espana 84" International Stamp Exhibition, Madrid. Explorers. Multicoloured.
2075 65cr. Type **1073** 15 10
2076 610cr. Christopher Columbus . . . . 1·75 20

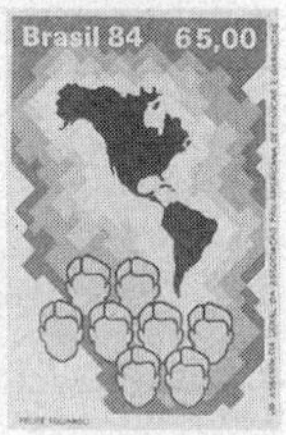

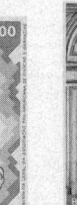

1074 Heads and Map of Americas

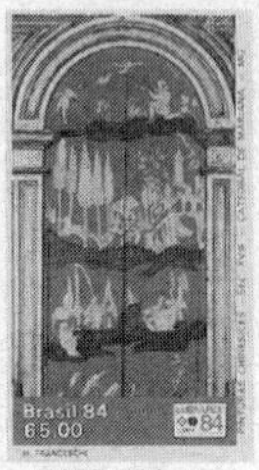

1075 Chinese Painting

1984. 8th Pan-American Surety Association General Assembly.
2077 **1074** 65cr. multicoloured . . 15 10

1984. "Lubrapex 84" Brazilian-Portuguese Stamp Exhibition, Lisbon.
2078 **1075** 65cr. multicoloured . . 15 10
2079 – 585cr. multicoloured . . 90 50
2080 – 610cr. multicoloured . . 90 50
2081 – 620cr. multicoloured . . 90 50
DESIGNS: 585 to 620cr. Chinese paintings from Mariana Cathedral.

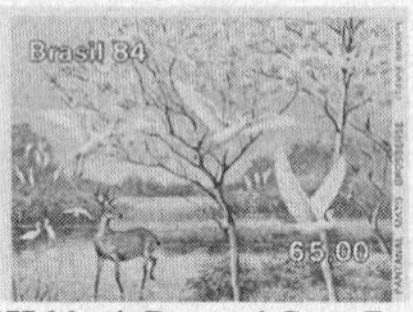

1077 Marsh Deer and Great Egret

1984. Mato Grosso Flood Plain. Multicoloured.
2083 65cr. Type **1077** 80 50
2084 65cr. Jaguar, capybara and roseate spoonbill 80 50
2085 80cr. Alligator, jabiru and red-cowled cardinals . . . 85 55

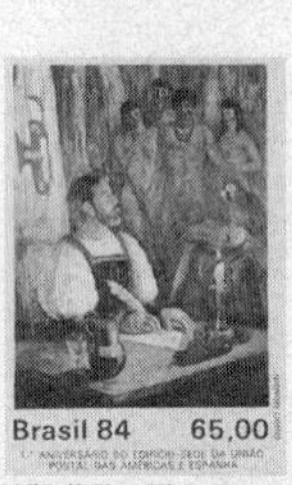

1078 "The First Letter Sent from Brazil" (Guido Mondin)

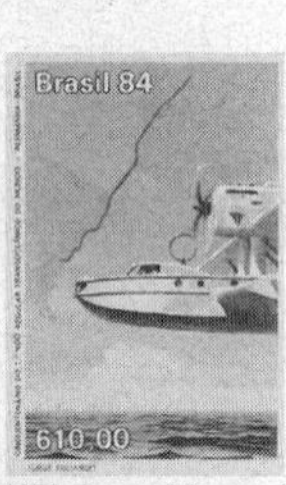

1079 Route Map and Dornier Wal Flying Boat

1984. 1st Anniv of Postal Union of the Americas and Spain H.Q., Montevideo, Uruguay.
2086 **1078** 65cr. multicoloured . . 40 15

1984. 50th Anniv of First Trans-Oceanic Air Route. Multicoloured.
2087 610cr. Type **1079** . . . . . 1·60 50
2088 620cr. Support ship "Westfalen" and Dornier Wal . . . . 2·00 45

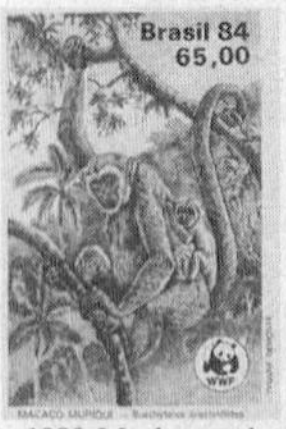

1080 Mother and Baby

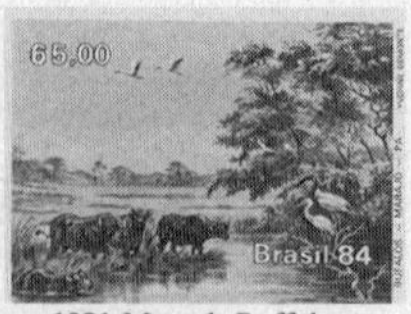

1081 Murrah Buffaloes

1984. Wildlife Preservation. Woolley Spider Monkey. Multicoloured.
2089 65cr. Type **1080** 50 10
2090 80cr. Monkey in tree . . . 25 10

1984. Marajo Island Water Buffaloes. Designs showing different races. Multicoloured.
2091 65cr. Type **1081** 40 30
2092 65cr. Carabao buffaloes . . 40 30
2093 65cr. Mediterranean buffaloes 30 25
Nos. 2091/3 were issued together; se-tenant, forming a composite design.

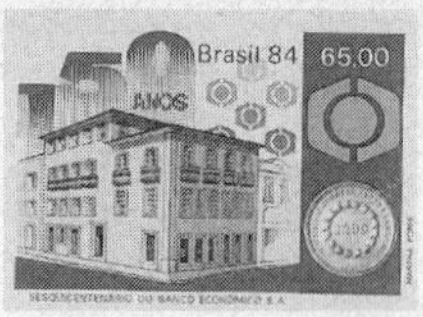

1082 Headquarters, Salvador

1984. 150th Anniv of Economic Bank.
2094 **1082** 65cr. multicoloured . . 15 10

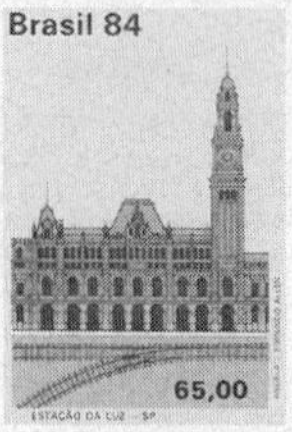

1083 Da Luz Station, Sao Paulo

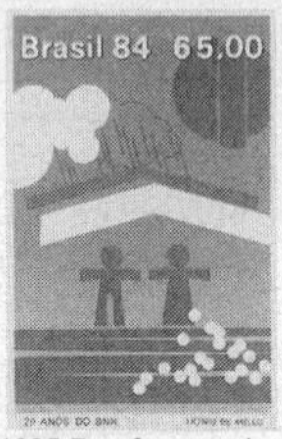

1085 Roof protecting Couple

1984. Preservation of Historic Railway Stations. Multicoloured.
2095 65cr. Type **1083** . . . . . . 1·00 35
2096 65cr. Japeri station Rio de Janeiro . . . . 1·00 35
2097 80cr. Sao Joao del Rei station, Minas Gerais . . 1·00 35

1984. 20th Anniv of National Housing Bank.
2099 **1085** 65cr. multicoloured . . 10 10

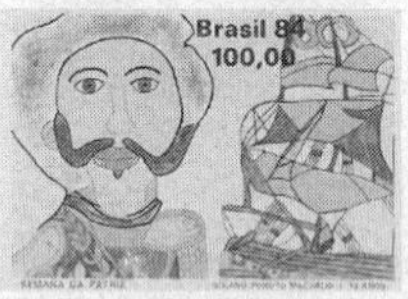

1086 "Pedro I" (Solano Peixoto Machado)

1984. National Week. Designs showing children's paintings. Multicoloured.
2100 100cr. Type **1086** 15 10
2101 100cr. Girl painting word "BRASIL" (Juruce Maria Klein) 15 10
2102 100cr. Children of different races under rainbow (Priscela Barreto da Fonseca Bara) 15 10
2103 100cr. Caravels (Carlos Peixoto Mangueira) . . . 15 10

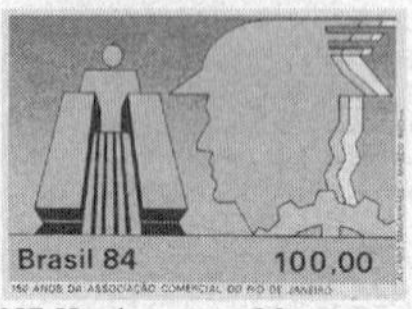

1087 Headquarters, Mercury and Cogwheel

1984. 150th Anniv of Rio de Janeiro Commercial Association.
2104 **1087** 100cr. multicoloured . . 15 10

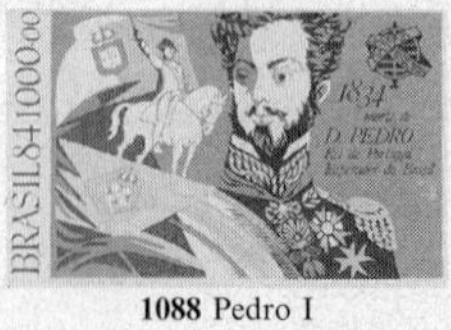

1088 Pedro I

1984. 150th Death Anniv of Emperor Pedro I.
2105 **1088** 1000cr. multicoloured 3·50 1·75

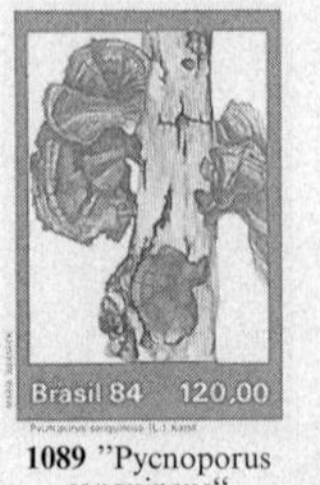

1089 "Pycnoporus sanguineus"

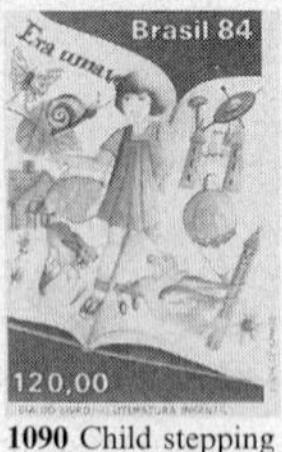

1090 Child stepping from Open Book

1984. Fungi. Multicoloured.
2106 120cr. Type **1089** 40 15
2107 1050cr. "Calvatia" sp. . . . 2·75 60
2108 1080cr. "Pleurotus" sp. (horiz) . . . . 2·75 60

1984. Book Day. Children's Literature.
2109 **1090** 120cr. multicoloured . . 20 10

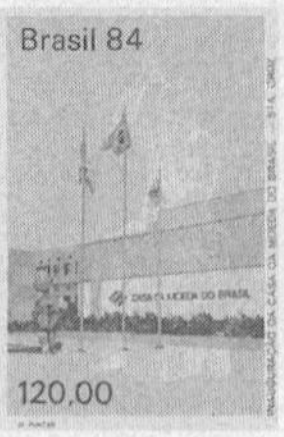

1091 New State Mint and 17th-century Minter

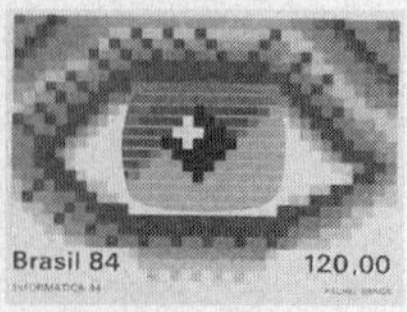

1092 Computer Image of Eye

1984. Inauguration of New State Mint, Santa Cruz, Rio de Janeiro.
2110 **1091** 120cr. blue & deep blue 15 10

1984. "Informatica 84" 17th National Information Congress and 4th International Informatics Fair, Rio de Janeiro.
2111 **1092** 120cr. multicoloured . . 15 10

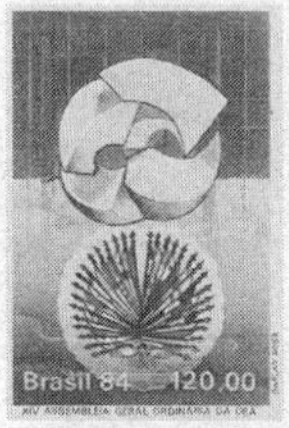

1093 Sculpture by Bruno Giorgi and Flags

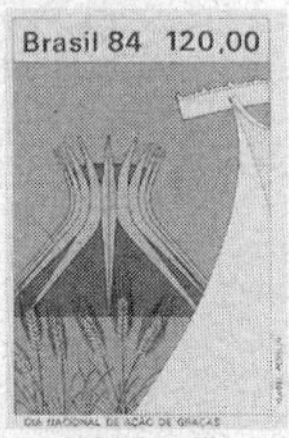

1094 Brasilia Cathedral and Wheat

1984. 14th General Assembly of Organization of American States, Brasilia.
2112 **1093** 120cr. multicoloured . . 15 10

1984. State Flags (4th series). As T **992**.
2113 120cr. red, black & buff . . 90 50
2114 120cr. multicoloured 90 50
2115 120cr. multicoloured 90 50
2116 120cr. multicoloured 90 50
2117 120cr. multicoloured 90 50
DESIGNS: No. 2113, Minas Gerais; 2114, Mato Grosso; 2115, Piaui; 2116, Maranhao; 2117, Santa Catarina.

1984. Thanksgiving Day.
2118 **1094** 120cr. multicoloured . . 15 10

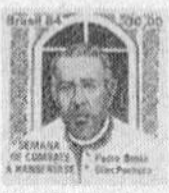
1095 Father Bento Dias Pacheco

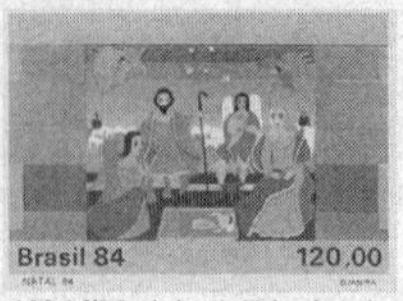

1096 "Nativity" (Djanira da Mota e Silva)

1984. Obligatory Tax. Anti-leprosy Week.
2119 **1095** 30cr. blue 50 10
See also Nos. 2208, 2263 and 2291.

1984. Christmas. Paintings from Federal Savings Bank collection. Multicoloured.
2120 120cr. Type **1096** 15 10
2121 120cr. "Virgin and Child" (Glauco Rodrigues) . . . 75 25
2122 1050cr. "Flight into Egypt" (Paul Garfunkel) . . . . 2·75 50
2123 1080cr. "Nativity" (Emiliano Augusto di Cavalcanti) . . 2·75 50

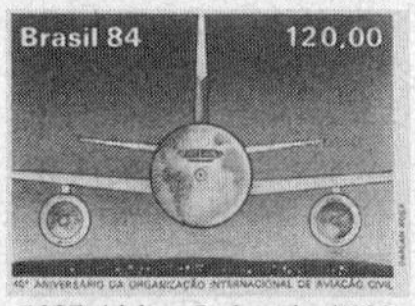

1097 Airbus Industrie A300

1984. 40th Anniv of I.C.A.O.
2124 **1097** 120cr. multicoloured . . 15 10

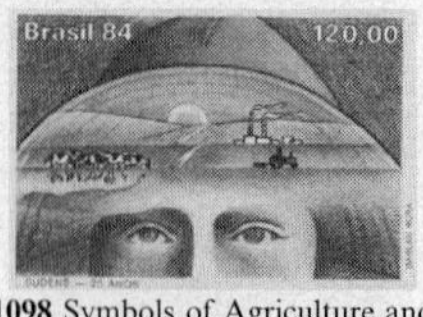

1098 Symbols of Agriculture and Industry on Hat

1984. 25th Anniv of North-east Development Office.
2125 **1098** 120cr. multicoloured . . 15 10

1099 "Virgin of Safe Journeys Church" (detail)

1985. 77th Death Anniv of Emilio Rouede (artist).
2126 **1099** 120cr. multicoloured . . 20 10

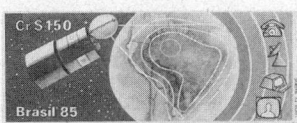

1100 "Brasilsat" over Brazil

1985. Launch of "Brasilsat" (first Brazilian telecommunications satellite).
2127 **1100** 150cr. multicoloured . . 25 10

1101 Electric Trains and Plan of Port Alegre Station

1985. Inauguration of Metropolitan Surface Railway, Recife and Porto Alegre.
2128 **1101** 200cr. multicoloured . . 60 20

1102 Butternut Tree   **1103** Parachutist

1985. Opening of Botanical Gardens, Brasilia.
2129 **1102** 200cr. multicoloured . . 20 10

1985. 40th Anniv of Military Parachuting.
2130 **1103** 200cr. multicoloured . . 20 10

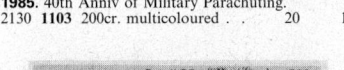

1104 Map, Temperature Graph and Weather Scenes

1985. National Climate Programme.
2131 **1104** 500cr. multicoloured . . 20 10

1105 Campolina   **1107** "Polyvolume" (Mary Vieira)

1106 Ouro Preto

1985. Brazilian Horses. Multicoloured.
2132 1000cr. Type **1105** . . . . 1·25 15
2133 1500cr. Marajoara . . . . . 1·25 15
2134 1500cr. Mangalarga pacer . 1·25 15

1985. U.N.E.S.C.O. World Heritage Sites. Multicoloured.
2135 220cr. Type **1106** 15 10
2136 220cr. Sao Miguel das Missoes 15 10
2137 220cr. Olinda 15 10

1985. 40th Anniv of Rio-Branco Institute (diplomatic training academy).
2138 **1107** 220cr. multicoloured . . 10 10

1108 National Theatre

1985. 25th Anniv of Brasilia. Multicoloured.
2139 220cr. Type **1108** 10 10
2140 220cr. Catetinho (home of former President Juscelino Keubitschek) and memorial 10 15

1109 Rondon and Morse Telegraph   **1110** Fontoura and Pharmaceutical Equipment

1985. 120th Birth Anniv of Marshal Candido Mariano da Silva Rondon (military engineer and explorer).
2141 **1109** 220cr. multicoloured . . 10 10

1985. Birth Centenary of Candido Fontoura (pharmacist).
2142 **1110** 220cr. multicoloured . . 15 10

1111 Lizards    **1112** Numeral

1113 Numeral

1985. Rock Paintings. Multicoloured.
2143 300cr. Type **1111** 10 10
2144 300cr. Deer 10 10
2145 2000cr. Various animals . . 75 15

1985.
2147 **1112** 50cr. red 10 10
2148 100cr. purple 10 10
2149 150cr. lilac 10 10
2150 200cr. blue 10 10
2151 220cr. green 50 10
2152 300cr. blue 10 10
2153 500cr. black 10 10
2154 **1113** 1000cr. brown 10 10
2155 2000cr. green 15 10
2156 3000cr. lilac 15 10
2157 5000cr. brown . . . . 1·75 10

1114 Common Noddies

1985. National Marine Park, Abrolhos. Mult.
2168 220cr. Type **1114** 55 35
2169 220cr. Magnificent frigate birds and blue-faced booby 55 35
2170 220cr. Blue-faced boobies and red-billed tropic bird 55 35
2171 2000cr. Grey plovers . . . 2·75 65

1115 Breast-feeding    **1116** Bell 47J Ranger Helicopter rescuing Man, "Brasil" (corvette) and Diver

1985. United Nations Children's Fund Child Survival Campaign. Multicoloured.
2172 220cr. Type **1115** 15 10
2173 220cr. Growth chart and oral rehydration . . 15 10

1985. International Sea Search and Rescue Convention, Rio de Janeiro.
2174 **1116** 220cr. multicoloured . . 1·00 30

1118 Children holding Hands    **1119** Hands holding Host

1985. International Youth Year.
2176 **1118** 220cr. multicoloured . . 15 10

1985. 11th Nat Eucharistic Congress, Aparecida.
2177 **1119** 2000cr. multicoloured 75 50

1120 Scene from "Mineiro Blood", Camera and Mauro

1985. 60th Anniv of Humberto Mauro's Cataguases Cycle of Films.
2178 **1120** 300cr. multicoloured . . 15 10

1121 Escola e Sacro Museum    **1122** Inconfidencia Museum, Ouro Preto

1985. 400th Anniv of Paraiba State.
2179 **1121** 330cr. multicoloured . . 15 10

1985. Museums. Multicoloured.
2180 300cr. Type **1122** 15 10
2181 300cr. Historical and Diplomatic Museum Itamaraty 15 10

1123 "Cabano" (Guido Mondin)    **1124** Aeritalia/Aermacchi AM-X Fighter

1985. 150th Anniv of Cabanagem Insurrection, Belem City.
2182 **1123** 330cr. multicoloured . . 15 10

1985. AM-X (military airplane) Project.
2183 **1124** 330cr. multicoloured . . 15 10

1125 Captain and Crossbowman (early 16th century)

1985. Military Dress. Multicoloured.
2184 300cr. Type **1125** 15 10
2185 300cr. Arquebusier and sergeant (late 16th cent) 15 10
2186 300cr. Musketeer and pikeman (early 17th century) 15 10
2187 300cr. Mulatto fusilier and pikeman with scimitar (early 17th century) . . 15 10

1126 "Farroupilha Rebels" (Guido Mondin)

1985. 150th Anniv of Farroupilha Revolution.
2188 **1126** 330cr. multicoloured . . 15 10

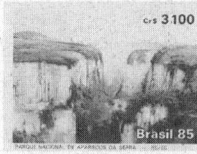

1127 Itaimbezinho Canyon

1985. Aparados da Serra National Park. Mult.
2189 3100cr. Type **1127** 95 15
2190 3320cr. Mountain range . . 95 15
2191 3480cr. Pine forest 95 15

1128 Neves and Brasilia Buildings

1985. Tancredo Neves (President-elect) Commem.
2192 **1128** 330cr. black & orange . . 15 10

1129 "FEB" on Envelope

1985. 40th Anniv (1984) of Brazilian Expeditionary Force Postal Service.
2193 **1129** 500cr. multicoloured . . 15 10

1130 "Especuladora", 1835

1985. 150th Anniv of Rio de Janeiro–Niteroi Ferry Service. Multicoloured.
2194 500cr. Type **1130** 70 20
2195 500cr. "Segunda", 1862 . . 70 20
2196 500cr. "Terceira", 1911 . . 70 20
2197 500cr. "Urca", 1981 . . . . 70 20

1131 Muniz M-7

1985. 50th Anniv of Muniz M-7 Biplane's Maiden Flight.
2198 **1131** 500cr. multicoloured . . 30 15

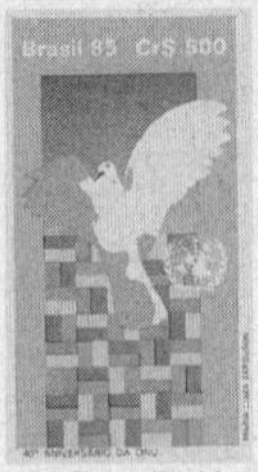

1132 Dove Emblem and Stylized Flags

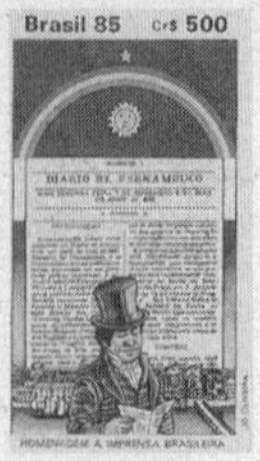

1133 Front Page of First Edition

1985. 40th Anniv of U.N.O.
2199 **1132** 500cr. multicoloured . . 15 10

1985. 160th Anniv of "Pernambuco Daily News".
2200 **1133** 500cr. multicoloured . . 15 10

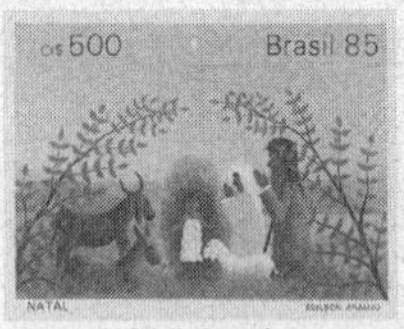

1134 Adoration

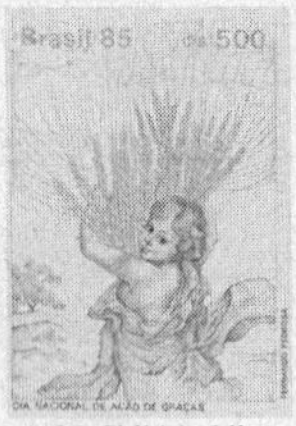

1135 Child holding Wheat

1985. Christmas. Multicoloured.
2201 500cr. Type **1134** 15 10
2202 500cr. Adoration of the Magi 15 10
2203 500cr. Flight into Egypt . . 15 10

1985. State Flags (5th series). As T **992**. Mult.
2204 500cr. Para 15 10
2205 500cr. Rio Grande do Sul 15 10
2206 500cr. Acre 15 10
2207 500cr. Sao Paulo 15 10

1985. Obligatory Tax. Anti-leprosy Week.
2208 **1095** 100cr. red 25 25

1985. Thanksgiving Day.
2209 **1135** 500cr. multicoloured . . 10 10

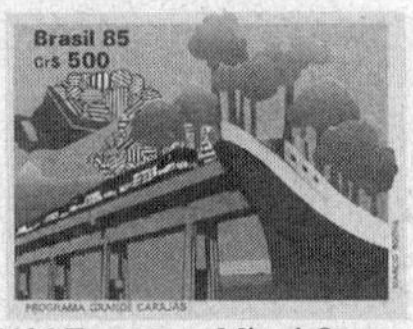

1136 Transport, Mined Ore and Trees

1985. Carajas Development Programme.
2210 **1136** 500cr. multicoloured . . 20 10

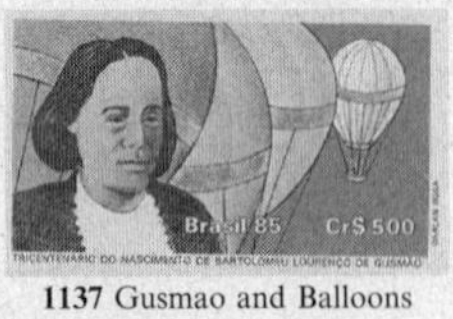

1137 Gusmao and Balloons

1985. 300th Birth Anniv of Bartolomeu Lourenco de Gusmao (inventor).
2211 **1137** 500cr. multicoloured . . 10 10

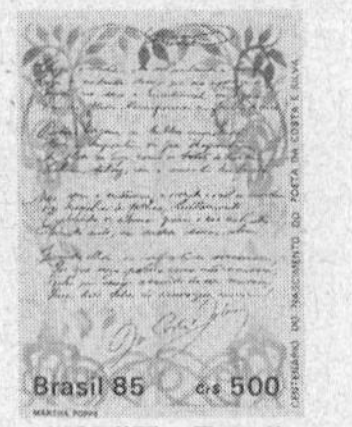

1138 "The Trees"

1985. Birth Centenary of Antonio Francisco da Costa e Silva (poet).
2212 **1138** 500cr. multicoloured . . 10 10

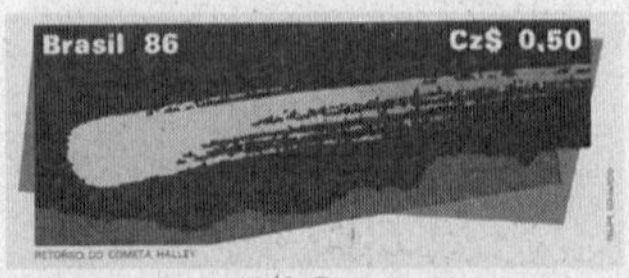

1140 Comet

1986. Appearance of Halley's Comet.
2214 **1140** 50c. multicoloured . . . 35 15

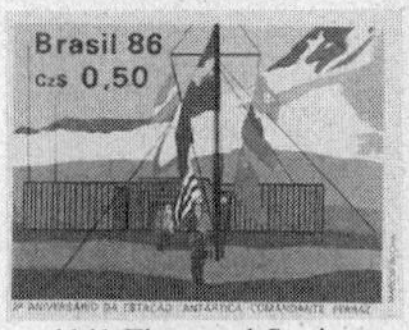

1141 Flags and Station

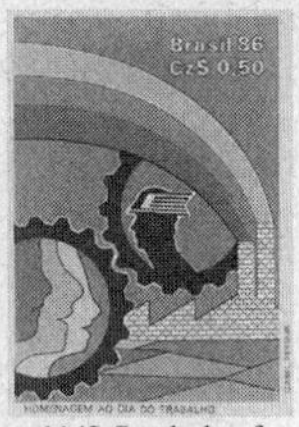

1142 Symbols of Industry, Agriculture and Commerce

1986. 2nd Anniv of Commander Ferraz Antarctic Station.
2215 **1141** 50c. multicoloured . . . 10 15

1986. Labour Day.
2216 **1142** 50c. multicoloured . . . 10 10

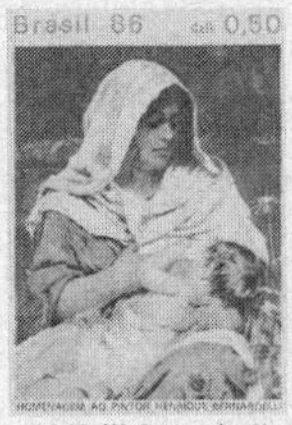

1143 "Maternity"

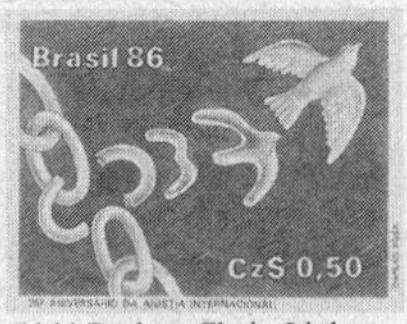

1144 Broken Chain Links as Birds

1986. 50th Death Anniv of Henrique Bernardelli (artist).
2217 **1143** 50c. multicoloured . . . 10 10

1986. 25th Anniv of Amnesty International.
2218 **1144** 50c. multicoloured . . . 10 10

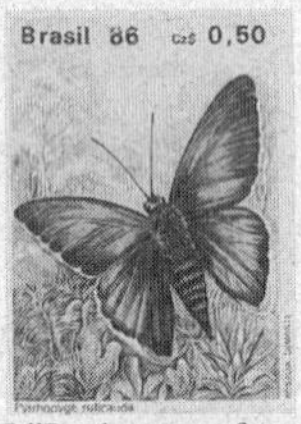

1145 "Pyrrhopyge ruficauda"

1986. Butterflies. Multicoloured.
2219 50c. Type **1145** 85 30
2220 50c. "Pierriballia mandela molione" 85 30
2221 50c. "Prepona eugenes diluta" 85 30

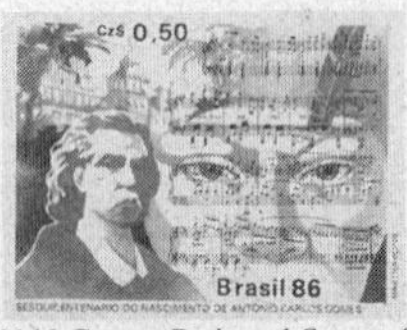

1146 Gomes Peri, and Score of "O Guarani"

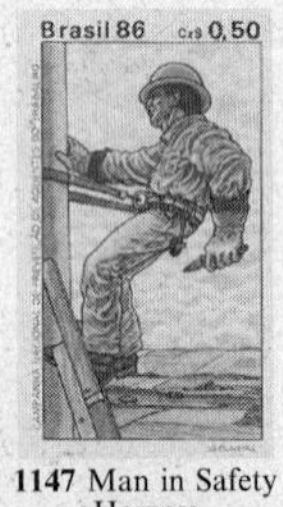

1147 Man in Safety Harness

1986. 150th Birth Anniv of Antonio Carlos Gomes (composer).
2222 **1146** 50c. multicoloured . . . 15 10

1986. Prevention of Industrial Accidents.
2223 **1147** 50c. multicoloured . . . 15 10

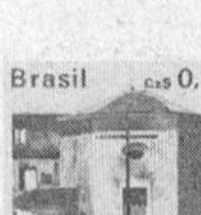

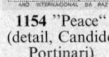

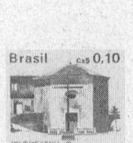

1149 Garcia D'Avilas House Chapel, Nazare de Mata

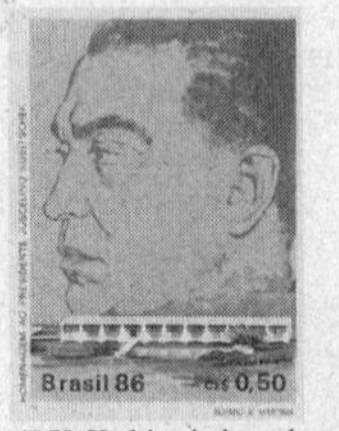

1150 Kubitschek and Alvorada Palace

1986.

2225	**1149**	10c. green	10	10
2226	–	20c. blue	10	10
2228	–	50c. orange	55	10
2230	–	1cz. brown	10	10
2231	–	2cz. red	10	10
2233	–	5cz. green	10	10
2235	–	10cz. blue	10	10
2236	–	20cz. red	10	10
2238	–	50cz. orange	15	15
2240	–	100cz. green	30	25
2241	–	200cz. blue	50	30
2242	–	500cz. brown	50	10

DESIGNS—HORIZ: 20c. Church of Our Lady of the Assumptiom, Anchieta; 50c. Reis Magos Fortress, Natal; 1cz. Pelourinho, Alcantara; 2cz. St. Francis's Monastery, Olinda; 5cz. St. Anthony's Chapel, Sao Roque; 10cz. St Lawrence of the Indians Church, Niteroi; 20cz. Principe da Beira Fortress, Costa Marques, Rondobua; 100cz. Church of Our Lady of Sorrows, Campanha; 200cz. Counting House, Ouro Preto; 500cz. Customs building, Belem. VERT: 50cz. Church of the Good Jesus, Matasinhos.

1986. 10th Death Anniv of Juscelino Kubitschek (President 1956–61).
2244 **1150** 50c. multicoloured . . . 25 10

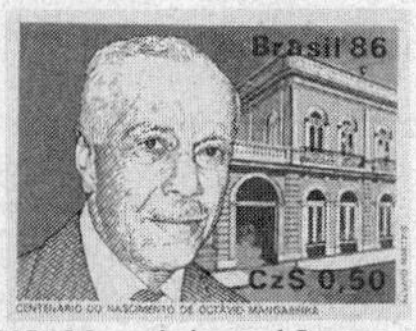

1151 Mangabeira and Itamaraty Palace, Rio de Janeiro

1986. Birth Cent of Octavio Mangabeira (politician).
2245 **1151** 50c. multicoloured . . . 10 10

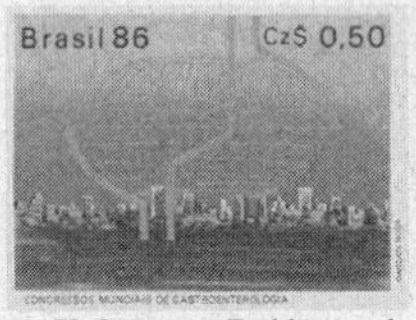

1152 Congress Emblem and Sao Paulo

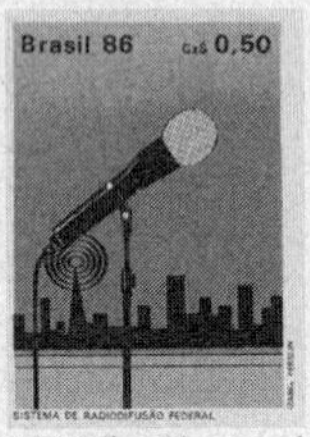

1153 Microphone and Radio Waves

1986. 8th World Gastroenterology Congress, Sao Paulo.
2246 **1152** 50c. multicoloured . . . 10 10

1986. 50th Annivs. of National Radio and Education and Culture Ministry Radio.
2247 **1153** 50c. multicoloured . . . 10 10

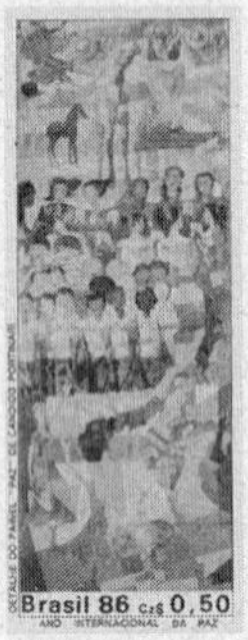

1154 "Peace" (detail, Candido Portinari)

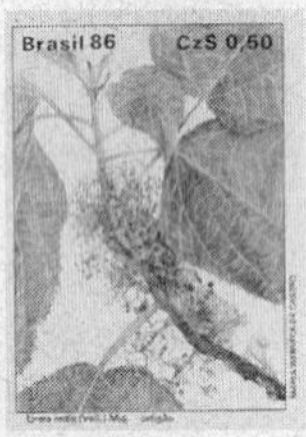

1155 "Urera mitis"

1986. International Peace Year.
2248 **1154** 50c. multicoloured . . . 10 10

1986. Flowers. Multicoloured.
2249 50c. Type **1155** 15 10
2250 6cz.50 "Couroupita guyanensis" 85 20
2251 6cz.90 Mountain ebony (horiz) 90 20

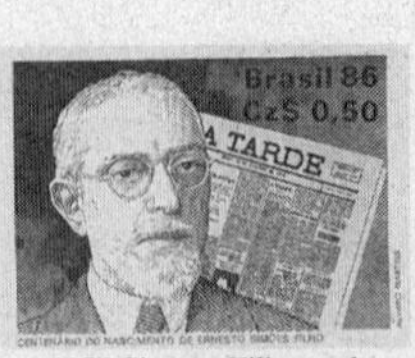

1156 Simoes Filho and Newspaper

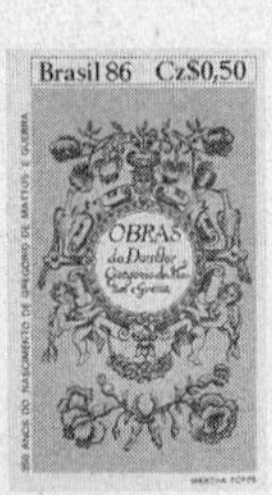

1157 Title Page of Gregorio de Matto's MS

1986. Birth Centenary of Ernesto Simoes Filho (politician and founder of "A Tarde").
2252 **1156** 50c. multicoloured . . . 10 10

1986. Book Day. Poets' Birth Anniversaries.
2253 **1157** 50c. brown & lt brown 10 10
2254 – 50c. green and red . . . 10 10

DESIGNS: No. 2253, Type **1157** (350th anniv); 2254, Manuel Bandeira and last verse of "I'll Return to Pasargada" (centenary).

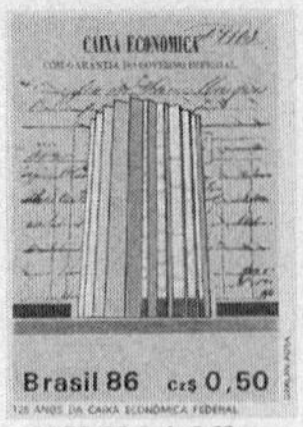

1158 Head Office, Brasilia

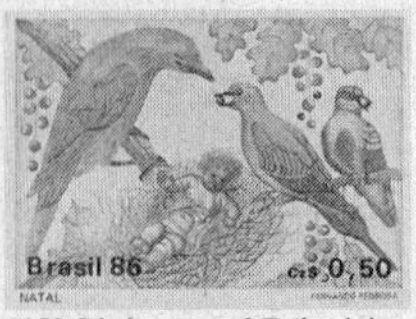

1159 Birds around Baby lying in Nest

1986. 125th Anniv of Federal Savings Bank.
2255 **1158** 50c. multicoloured . . . 10 10

1986. Christmas. Multicoloured.
2256 50c. Type **1159** 75 15
2257 6cz.50 Birds around tree with Christmas decorations . . . . 1·50 25
2258 7cz.30 Birds wearing Santa Claus caps . . . . 1·25 30

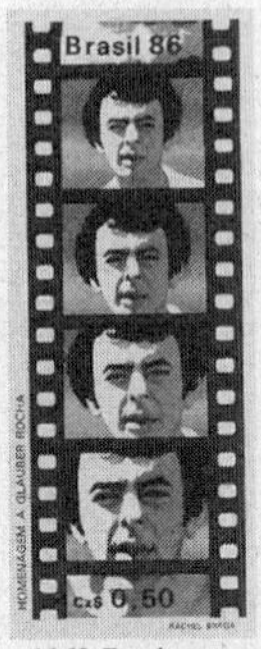

1160 Rocha on Strip of Film

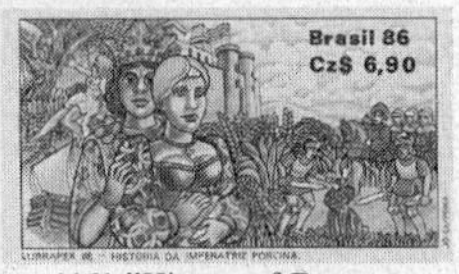

1161 "History of Empress Porcina"

1986. 5th Death Anniv of Glauber Rocha (film producer).
2259 **1160** 50c. multicoloured . . . 10 10

1986. "Lubrapex 86" Brazilian–Portuguese Stamp Exhibition, Rio de Janeiro. Design showing scenes from Cordel Literature. Multicoloured.
2260 6cz.90 Type **1161** 55 40
2261 6cz.90 "Romance of the Mysterious Peacock" . . 55 40

1986. Obligatory Tax. Anti-leprosy Week.
2263 **1095** 10c. brown 10 10

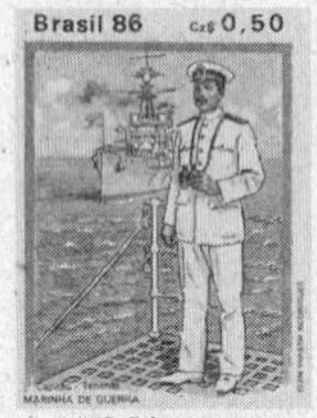

1162 Lieutenant Commander, 1930

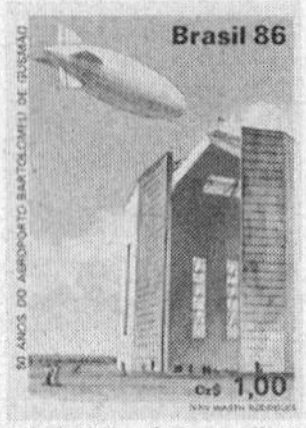

1163 "Graf Zeppelin" over Hangar

1986. Military Uniforms. Multicoloured.
2264 50c. Type **1162** 60 10
2265 50c. Military Aviation flight lieutenant, 1930 . . . . . 10 10

1986. 50th Anniv of Bartolomeu de Gusmao Airport, Santa Cruz.
2266 **1163** 1cz. multicoloured . . . 10 10

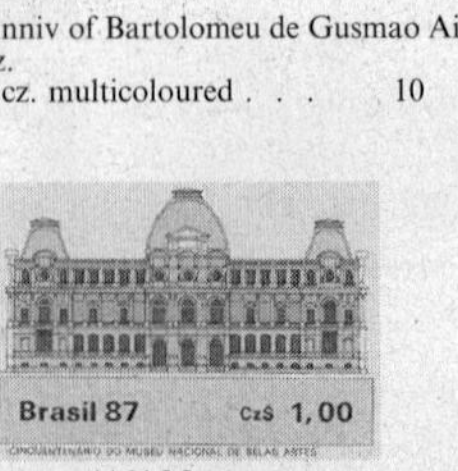

1164 Museum

1987. 50th Anniv of National Fine Arts Museum, Rio de Janeiro.
2267 **1164** 1cz. multicoloured . . . 10 10

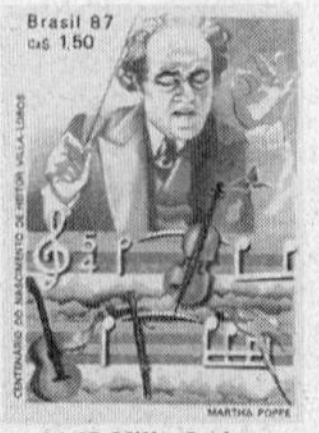

1165 Villa-Lobos conducting and Musical Motifs

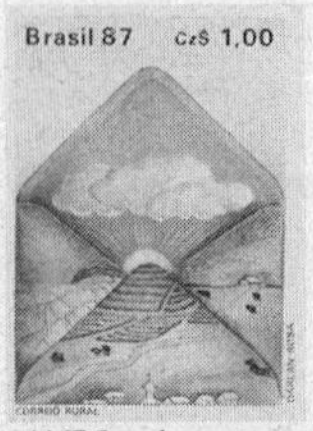

1167 Landscape on Open Envelope (Rural Post Office Network)

1166 Flag, Lockheed Hercules Aircraft and Antarctic Landscape

1987. Birth Cent of Heitor Villa-Lobos (composer).
2268 **1165** 1cz.50 multicoloured . . . 30 10

1987. Air Force Participation in Brazilian Antarctic Programme.
2269 **1166** 1cz. multicoloured . . . 90 20

1987. Special Mail Services. Multicoloured.
2270 1cz. Type **1167** 10 10
2271 1cz. Satchel and globe (International Express Mail Service) 10 10

1168 "Brasilsat" Satellite, Radio Wave and Globe   **1169** Modern Pentathlon

1987. "Telecom 87" World Telecommunications Exhibition, Geneva.
2272 **1168** 2cz. multicoloured . . . 10 10

1987. 10th Pan-American Games, Indianapolis, U.S.A.
2273 **1169** 18cz. multicoloured . . . 1·75 50

1170 Hawksbill Turtle

1987. Endangered Animals. Multicoloured.
2274 2cz. Type **1170** 60 35
2275 2cz. Right whale 60 35

1171 Old and New Court Buildings and Symbol of Justice   **1172** Arms

1987. 40th Anniv of Federal Appeal Court.
2276 **1171** 2cz. multicoloured . . . 10 10

1987. Centenary of Military Club.
2277 **1172** 3cz. multicoloured . . . 10 10

1173 Institute and Foodstuffs

1987. Centenary of Agronomic Institute, Campinas.
2278 **1173** 2cz. multicoloured . . . 10 10

1174 "Fulgora servillei"

1987. 50th Anniv of Brazilian Entomology Society. Multicoloured.
2279 3cz. Type **1174** 60 35
2280 3cz. "Zoolea lopiceps" . . . 60 35

1175 Features of Northern and North-east Regions   **1176** Main Tower

1987. National Tourism Year. Multicoloured.
2281 3cz. Type **1175** 50 15
2282 3cz. Features of mid-west, south-east and south regions 10 10

1987. 150th Anniv of Royal Portuguese Reading Cabinet, Rio de Janeiro.
2283 **1176** 30cz. green and red . . . 25 20

1177 International Sport Club (1975, 1976, 1979)

1987. Brazilian Football Championship Gold Cup Winners (1st series). Designs showing footballers and Club emblems.
2284 **1177** 3cz. red, black & yellow   35 10
2285 – 3cz. red, yellow & black   35 10
2286 – 3cz. multicoloured . . .   35 10
2287 – 3cz. red, black & yellow   35 10
DESIGNS: No. 2285, Sao Paulo Football Club (1977, 1986); 2286, Guarani Football Club (1978); 2287, Regatas do Flamengo Club (1980, 1982, 1983). See also Nos. 2322/5, 2398 and 2408.

1178 St. Francis's Church and Tiled Column

1987. 400th Anniv of St. Francis's Monastery, Salvador.
2288 **1178** 4cz. multicoloured . . . 10 10

1179 Almeida and Scenes from "A Bagaceira"

1987. Birth Centenary of Jose Americo de Almeida (writer).
2289 **1179** 4cz. multicoloured . . . 10 10

1180 Barra do Picao

1987. 450th Anniv of Recife.
2290 **1180** 5cz. multicoloured . . . 30 10

1987. Obligatory Tax. Anti-leprosy Week.
2291 **1095** 30cz. green 15 15

1181 Rainbow, Dove and Open Hands   **1182** Angels

1987. Thanksgiving Day.
2292 **1181** 5cz. multicoloured . . . 10 10

1987. Christmas. Multicoloured.
2293 6cz. Type **1182** 10 10
2294 6cz. Dancers on stage . . . 10 10
2295 6cz. Shepherd playing flute . . 10 10

1183 Bernardo Pereira de Vasconcelos (founder) and Pedro II

1987. 150th Anniv of Pedro II School, Rio de Janeiro.
2296 **1183** 6cz. yellow, blk & red . . 10 10

1184 "Cattleya guttata"

1987. 50th Anniv of Brazilian Orchid Growers Society. Multicoloured.
2297 6cz. Type **1184** 50 10
2298 6cz. "Laelia lobata" 50 10

1185 Statue and Fatima Basilica, Portugal

1987. Marian Year. Visit to Brazil of Statue of Our Lady of Fatima.
2299 **1185** 50cz. multicoloured . . 90 60

1186 Sousa, Indians and Fauna

1987. 400th Anniv of "Descriptive Treaties of Brazil" by Gabriel Soares de Sousa.
2300 **1186** 7cz. multicoloured . . . 40 15

1187 Page from Book of Gregorian Chants and Computer Terminal

1988. 150th Anniv of National Archives.
2301 **1187** 7cz. multicoloured . . . 10 10

1188 National Colours, Caravel and Modern Ship

1988. 180th Anniv of Opening of Brazilian Ports to Free Trade.
2302 **1188** 7cz. multicoloured . . . 10 10

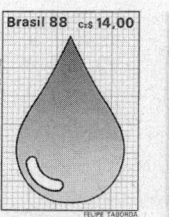 

1190 Petrol Droplet   **1192** Bonifacio and Emblems of his Life

1988. Energy Conservation. Multicoloured.
2304 14cz. Type **1190** 10 10
2305 14cz. Flash of electricity . . . 10 10

1988. 150th Death Anniv of Jose Bonifacio de Andrada e Silva (scientist, writer and "Patriarch of the Independence").
2307 **1192** 20cz. multicoloured . . 10 10

1193 Quill Pen on Page of Aurea Law

1988. Centenary of Abolition of Slavery. Mult.
2308 20cz. Type **1193** 10 10
2309 50cz. Norris map of Africa, 1773, slave ship and plan of trading routes 20 10

1194 Church of the Good Jesus of Matosinhos   **1195** Concentric Circles on Map of Americas

1988. U.N.E.S.C.O. World Heritage Sites. Mult.
2310 20cz. Type **1194** 10 10
2311 50cz. Brasilia 15 15
2312 100cz. Pelourinho, Salvador . . 15 15

1988. "Americas Telecom 88" Telecommunications Exhibition, Rio de Janeiro.
2313 **1195** 50cz. multicoloured . . 15 15

1196 "Kasato Maru" (first immigrant ship) and Japanese Family   **1197** Postal Authority Emblem

1988. 80th Anniv of Japanese Immigration into Brazil.
2314 **1196** 100cz. multicoloured . . 55 25

1988. No value expressed.
2315 **1197** (–) blue 80 10
No. 2315 was valid for use at the current first class inland letter rate. It could not be used to pay postage to foreign countries.

1198 Judo   **1199** Giant Anteater

1988. Olympic Games, Seoul.
2316 **1198** 25cz. multicoloured . . 80 10

1988. Endangered Mammals. Multicoloured.
2317 20cz. Type **1199** 50 10
2318 50cz. Thin-spined porcupine . . 60 15
2319 100cz. Bush dog . . . . . 1·25 25

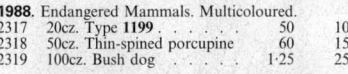 

1201 Industrial Symbols

1988. 50th Anniv of National Confederation of Industry.
2321 **1201** 50cz. multicoloured . . 15 15

1988. Brazilian Football Championship Gold Cup Winners (2nd series). As T **1177.** Multicoloured.
2322 50cz. Sport Club do Recife (1987) . . . 40 15
2323 50cz. Coritiba Football Club (1985) . . . 40 15
2324 100cz. Gremio Football Porto Alegrense (1981) . . 55 25
2325 200cz. Fluminense Football Club (1984) . . 75 40

1203 Raul Pompeia and Lines from "O Ateneu"

1988. Book Day. Centenaries of Publication of "O Ateneu" and "Verses". Multicoloured.
2327 50cz. Type **1203** . . . 15 15
2328 100cz. Olavo Bilac and lines from "Verses" 30 25

1204 Church

1205 Father Santiago Uchoa

1988. Christmas. Origami by Marcia Bloch. Multicoloured.
2329 50cz. Type **1204** 15 15
2330 100cz. Nativity 30 25
2331 200cz. Santa Claus and parcels 55 45

1988. Obligatory Tax. Anti-leprosy Week.
2332 1cz.30 brown 50 10
See also Nos. 2614 and 2686.

1206 Mate and Rodeo Rider

1988. "Abrafex" Argentine–Brazilian Stamp Exhibition, Buenos Aires.
2333 **1206** 400cz. multicoloured . . 2·25 1·10

1207 Hatchetfish ("Gasteropelecus sp.")

1988. Freshwater Fishes. Multicoloured.
2334 55cz. Type **1207** 30 30
2335 55cz. Black arawana ("Osteoglossum ferreira") 30 30
2336 55cz. Green moenkhausia ("Moenkhausia sp.") 30 30
2337 55cz. Pearlfish ("Xavantei") 30 30
2338 55cz. Armoured bristlemouth catfish ("Ancistrus hoplogenys") 30 30
2339 55cz. Emerald catfish ("Brochis splendens") . . 30 30

1209 Dish Aerials

1210 "Four Arts"

1988. 10th Anniv of Ansat 10 (first Brazilian dish aerial), Macapa.
2341 **1209** 70cz. multicoloured . . 20 15

1988. Establishment of National Foundation of Scenic Arts.
2342 **1210** 70cz. multicoloured . . 20 15

1211 Court Building

1989. 380th Anniv of Bahia Court of Justice.
2343 **1211** 25c. multicoloured . . . 10 10

1212 Library Building and Detail of Main Door

1989. Public Library Year. 178th Anniv of First Public Library, Bahia.
2344 **1212** 25c. multicoloured . . . 10 10

1213 Facsimile Machine

1215 Emblem

1989. 20th Anniv of Post and Telegraph Department. Postal Services. Multicoloured.
2345 25c. Type **1213** 10 10
2346 25c. Hand holding parcel (Express Mail Service) . 10 10
2347 25c. Airbus Industrie 300 airplane on runway (SEDEX express parcel service) 10 10
2348 25c. Putting coin in savings box (CEF postal savings) 10 10

1989. "Our Nature" Programme.
2350 **1215** 25c. multicoloured . . . 10 10

1216 Hand reaching for Symbol of Freedom

1989. Bicentenary of Inconfidencia Mineira (independence movement). Multicoloured.
2351 30c. Type **1216** 10 10
2352 30c. Man's profile and colonial buildings . . . 10 10
2353 40c. Baroque buildings in disarray 10 10

1217 School

1989. Cent of Rio de Janeiro Military School.
2354 **1217** 50c. multicoloured . . . 10 10

1218 "Pavonia alnifolia"

1989. Endangered Plants. Multicoloured.
2355 50c. Type **1218** 90 10
2356 1cz. "Worsleya rayneri" (vert) 90 10
2357 1cz.50 "Heliconia farinosa" (vert) . . . . . 1·10 10

1219 Barreto and Pedro II Square, Recife Law School

1220 "Quiabentia zehntneri"

1989. 150th Birth Anniv of Tobias Barreto (writer).
2358 **1219** 50c. multicoloured . . . 10 10

1989. Flowers. Currency expressed as "NCz $". Multicoloured.
2359 10c. "Dichorisandra" sp. . . 10 10
2360 20c. Type **1220** 10 10
2361 50c. "Bougainvillea glabra" 10 10
2363 1cz. "Impatiens" sp. . . . 50 10
2364 3cz. "Chorisia crispiflora" (vert) 10 15
2366 5cz. "Hibiscus trilineatus" 10 10
See also Nos. 2413/24.

1221 Shooting of "Revistinha"

1989. 20th Anniv of TV Cultura.
2371 **1221** 50c. multicoloured . . . 10 10

1222 Postal Authority Emblem

1223 Brasilia T.V. Tower and Microlight

1989. No value expressed.
2372 **1222** (–) blue and orange . . 80 10
No. 2372 was sold at the current rate for first class internal postage.

1989. Aerosports and 80th Anniv of Santos Dumont's Flight in "Demoiselle". Mult.
2373 50c. Type **1223** 50 10
2374 1cz.50 Eiffel Tower and "Demoiselle" 60 10

1225 Tourmaline

1989. Precious Stones. Multicoloured.
2376 50c. Type **1225** 10 10
2377 1cz.50 Amethyst 15 10

1226 Rainbow and Association H.Q. Mercury

1989. 150th Anniv of Pernambuco Trade Assn.
2379 **1226** 50c. multicoloured . . . 10 10

1228 Pioneers' Names and 19th-century to Modern Photographs

1989. International Photography Year.
2380 **1228** 1cz.50 multicoloured . . 15 10

1229 Power Station

1989. Centenary of Marmelos-o Power Station (first South American hydro-electric power station).
2381 **1229** 50c. multicoloured . . . 10 10

1230 Hebrew Volute

1231 Muiraquita

1989. Molluscs. Multicoloured.
2382 50c. Type **1230** 50 10
2383 1cz. Matthew's morum . . . 55 15
2384 1cz.50 Travasso's ancilla . . 60 20

1989. America. Pre-Columbian Artefacts. Mult.
2385 1cz. Type **1231** 80 10
2386 4cz. Caryatid vase (horiz) . . 80 10

1233 Casimiro de Abreu

1234 Postal Authority Emblem

1989. Book Day. Writers' Birth Annivs. Mult.
2388 1cz. Type **1233** (150th anniv) 10 10
2389 1cz. Machado de Assis (150th anniv) . . . 10 10
2390 1cz. Cora Coralina (cent) . . 10 10

1989. No value expressed. Burelage in second colour.
2391 **1234** (–) red and orange . . 3·25 35
No. 2391 was sold at the current rate for first class international postage.

1235 Police Emblem

1989. 25th Anniv of Federal Police Department.
2392 **1235** 1cz. multicoloured . . . 10 10

1237 Angel

1238 Candle Flame as Dove

1989. Christmas. Multicoloured.
2394 70c. Type **1237** 10 10
2395 1cz. Nativity 10 10

1989. Thanksgiving Day.
2396 **1238** 1cz. multicoloured . . . 10 10

1239 Fr. Damien de Veuster

1240 "The Yellow Man"

1989. Obligatory Tax. Anti-leprosy Week.
2397 **1239** 2c. red 10 10
See also Nos. 2458, 2509 and 2565.

1989. Football Clubs. As T **1177.** Multicoloured.
2398 50c. Bahia Sports Club . . . 10 10

1989. Birth Cent of Anita Malfatti (painter).
2399 **1240** 1cz. multicoloured . . . 10 10

1241 Archive and Proclamation by Bento Goncalves

1990. Cent of Bahia State Public Archive.
2400 **1241** 2cz. multicoloured . . . 20 15

1242 "Mimosa caesalpiniifolia"

1990. 40th Anniv of Brazilian Botanical Society. Multicoloured.
2401 2cz. Type **1242** 10 10
2402 13cz. "Caesalpinia echinata" . . 10 10

1243 Cathedral of St. John the Baptist, Santa Cruz do Sul   **1244** Sailing Barque and Modern Container Ship

1990. Churches. Multicoloured.
2403 2cz. Type **1243** 10 10
2404 3cz. Our Lady of Victory Church, Oeiras (horiz) . . 10 10
2405 5cz. Our Lady of the Rosary Church, Ouro Preto . . 10 10

1990. Cent of Lloyd Brasileiro Navigation Company.
2406 **1244** 3cz. multicoloured . . . 30 10

1990. Brazilian Football Clubs As T **1177**. Multicoloured.
2408 10cz. Vasco da Gama Regatas Club 15 10

1246 Collor and Newspaper Mastheads   **1247** Sarney

1990. Birth Cent of Lindolfo Collor (journalist).
2409 **1246** 20cz. multicoloured . . 25 20

1990. Tribute to Jose Sarney (retiring President).
2410 **1247** 20cz. blue 25 20

 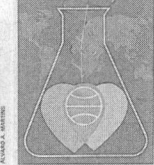

1248 Gold Coin, Anniversary Emblem and Bank Headquarters, Brasilia   **1249** Hearts sprouting in Flask

1990. 25th Anniv of Brazil Central Bank.
2411 **1248** 20cr. multicoloured . . 25 20

1990. World Health Day. Anti-AIDS Campaign.
2412 **1249** 20cr. multicoloured . . 25 20

1990. Flowers. As T **1220** but with currency expressed as "Cr$".
2413 1cr. "Impatiens sp" 10 10
2414 2cr. "Chorisia crispiflora" (vert) 10 10
2415 5cr. "Hibiscus trilineatus" . . 10 10
2417 10cr. "Tibouchina granulosa" (vert) 15 10
2418 20cr. "Cassia micranthera" (vert) 25 20
2420 50cr. "Clitoria fairchildiana" (vert) 30 10
2421 50cr. "Tibouchina mutabilis" (vert) 75 65
2422 100cr. "Erythrina crista-galli" (vert) 65 10

2423 200cr. "Jacaranda mimosifolia" (vert) . . . 65 10
2424 500cr. "Caesalpinia peltophoroides" (vert) . . 65 15
2424a 1000cr. "Pachira aquatica" (vert) 15 10
2424b 2000cr. "Hibiscus pernambucensis" (vert) . . 25 20
2424c 5000cr. "Tripolaris surinamensis" (vert) . . 90 30
2424d 10000cr. "Tabebuia heptaphylia" (vert) . . 65 10
2424e 20000cr. "Erythrina speciosa" (vert) 65 10

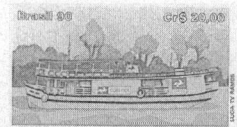

1250 Amazon Post Launch

1990. River Post Network.
2425 **1250** 20cr. multicoloured . . 55 25

1253 Lorry and Coach

1990. 22nd World Congress of Int Road Transport Union, Rio de Janeiro. Multicoloured.
2428 20cr. Type **1253** . . . . . 1·00 55
2429 80cr. Van and motor car . . 1·25 55
Nos. 2428/29 were printed together, se-tenant, forming a composite design.

1254 Imperial Crown (Imperial Museum, Petropolis)

1990. Museum 50th Anniversaries. Multicoloured.
2430 20cr. Type **1254** 25 20
2431 20cr. "Our Lady of the Immaculate Conception" (woodcarving) (Missionary Museum, Sao Miguel das Missoes) . . . 25 20

1990. Creation of State of Tocantins. As T **992**, showing state flag.
2432 20cr. yellow, blue and black 25 20

1255 Service Building. Hildebrand Theodolite and Map of Rio de Janeiro

1990. Centenary of Army Geographic Service.
2433 **1255** 20cr. multicoloured . . 25 20

1256 Adhemar Gonzaga (producer)

1990. Brazilian Film Industry. Each maroon and purple.
2434 25cr. Type **1256** 80 25
2435 25cr. Carmen Miranda (actress) 80 25
2436 25cr. Carmen Santos (actress) 80 25
2437 25cr. Oscarito (actor) . . . 80 25

1257 Aerial View of House   **1258** Ball and Net

1990. 5th Anniv of France–Brazil House, Rio de Janeiro.
2438 **1257** 50cr. multicoloured . . 60 10

1990. 12th World Men's Volleyball Championship, Brazil.
2439 **1258** 10cr. multicoloured . . 55 10

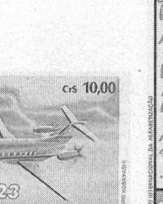

1259 Embraer/FMA Vector   **1260** Globe, Pencil and Alphabet

1990. Aeronautics Industry.
2440 **1259** 10cr. multicoloured . . 15 10

1990. International Literacy Year.
2441 **1260** 10cr. multicoloured . . 15 10

1261 Institute

1990. Cent of Granbery Institute, Juiz de Fora.
2442 **1261** 13cr. multicoloured . . 15 10

1262 Map, Track and Diesel Locomotive

1990. 18th Pan-American Railways Congress, Rio de Janeiro.
2443 **1262** 95cr. multicoloured . . 1·50 1·50

1263 Satellite and Computer Communication

1990. 25th Anniv of Embratel (Telecommunications Enterprise).
2444 **1263** 13cr. multicoloured . . 15 10

1264 "Bathers" (Alfredo Ceschiatti)

1990. "Lubrapex 90" Brazilian–Portuguese Stamp Exhibition, Brasilia. Brasilia Sculptures. Mult.
2445 25cr. Type **1264** 30 25
2446 25cr. "Warriors" (Bruno Giorgi) 30 25
2447 100cr. "St. John" (Ceschiatti) . . . . . . 1·40 50
2448 100cr. "Justice" (Ceschiatti) 1·40 50

1265 "Bromelia antiacantha"

1990. America. 500th Anniv of Discovery of America by Columbus. Praia do Sul Nature Reserve. Multicoloured.
2450 15cr. Type **1265** 90 10
2451 105cr. Wooded shoreline of Lagoa do Sul . . . . . 1·25 50
Nos. 2450/1 were printed together, se-tenant, forming a composite design.

1266 Oswald de Andrade (birth centenary) and Illustration from "Anthropophagic Manifesto"

1990. Book Day. Anniversaries. Mult.
2452 15cr. Type **1266** 15 10
2453 15cr. Guilherme de Almeida (birth cent) and illustration of "Greek Songs" 15 10
2454 15cr. National Library (180th anniv) and illuminated book 15 10

1267 Emblem and Tribunal Offices, Brasilia

1990. Centenary of National Accounts Tribunal.
2455 **1267** 15cr. multicoloured . . 15 10

1268 National Congress Building   **1269** Fingers touching across Map of Americas

1990. Christmas. Brasilia Lights. Mult.
2456 15cr. Type **1268** 15 10
2457 15cr. Television Tower . . . 15 10

1990. Obligatory Tax. Anti-Leprosy Week. As No. 2397 but value and colour changed.
2458 **1239** 50c. blue 10 10

1990. Centenary of Organization of American States.
2459 **1269** 15cr. multicoloured . . 15 10

1270 "Nike Apache" Rocket on Launch Pad   **1271** Sao Cristovao City

1990. 25th Anniv of Launch of "Nike Apache" Rocket.
2460 **1270** 15cr. multicoloured . . 15 10

1990. 400th Anniv of Colonization of Sergipe State.
2461 **1271** 15cr. multicoloured . . 15 10

1272 Gymnasts

1991. World Congress on Physical Education, Sports and Recreation, Foz do Iguacu.
2462 **1272** 17cr. multicoloured . . 20 15

1273 Cazuza

1991. "Rock in Rio" Concert. Multicoloured.
2463 25cr. Type **1273** 60 60
2464 185cr. Raul Seixas 80 80
Nos. 2463/4 were printed together, se-tenant, forming a composite design.

1274 Aeritalia/Aermacchi AM-X and Republic Thunderbolt

1991. 50th Anniv of Aeronautics Ministry.
2465 **1274** 17cr. multicoloured . . 20 15

1275 Effigies of Day Woman and Midnight Man, Olinda

1276 Antarctic Wildlife

1991. Carnival. Multicoloured.
2466 25cr. Type **1275** 10 10
2467 30cr. Electric trio on truck, Salvador 10 10
2468 280cr. Samba dancers, Rio de Janeiro 80 45

1991. Visit of President Collor to Antarctica.
2469 **1276** 300cr. multicoloured . . 3·25 2·00

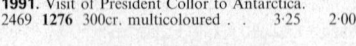

1277 Hang-gliders

1991. 8th World Free Flight Championships, Governador Valadares.
2470 **1277** 36cr. multicoloured . . 15 10

1278 Yachting

1991. 11th Pan-American Games, Cuba, and Olympic Games, Barcelona (1992). Mult.
2471 36cr. Type **1278** 30 10
2472 36cr. Rowing 10 10
2473 300cr. Swimming 85 75

1279 Cross over Bottle (alcoholism)

1991. Anti-addiction Campaign. Mult.
2474 40cr. Type **1279** 10 10
2475 40cr. Cross over cigarette (smoking) 10 10
2476 40cr. Cross over syringe (drug abuse) 10 10

1280 Old and Present Offices and Mastheads

1281 Yanomami Youth in Ceremonial Paint

1991. Cent of "Jornal do Brasil" (newspaper).
2477 **1280** 40cr. multicoloured . . 10 10

1991. Indian Culture. The Yanomami. Mult.
2478 40cr. Type **1281** 10 10
2479 400cr. Hunter (horiz) . . . 80 70

1282 Orinoco Goose

1991. United Nations Conference on Environment and Development.
2480 **1282** 45cr. multicoloured . . 55 30

1283 Jararaca

1284 National Flag

1991. 90th Anniv of Butantan Institute (2481/2) and 173rd Anniv of National Museum (others). Multicoloured.
2481 45cr. Type **1283** 35 10
2482 45cr. Green tree boa 35 10
2483 45cr. Theropoda (dinosaurs) 35 10
2484 350cr. Sauropoda (dinosaurs) . . . . 1·25 60

1991. No value expressed.
2485 **1284** (–) multicoloured . . . 80 10

1285 Early Steam Pump and Santos City 6th Fire Group's Headquarters

1991. Fire Fighting.
2486 **1285** 45cr. multicoloured . . 10 10

1286 Pedra Pintada, Boa Vista, Roraima

1991. Tourism. Centenaries of Boa Vista (1990) and Teresopolis. Multicoloured.
2487 45cr. Type **1286** 10 10
2488 350cr. God's Finger, Teresopolis, Rio de Janeiro 70 60

1287 Welder, "Justice" and Farmer

1991. 50th Anniv of Labour Justice Legal System.
2489 **1287** 45cr. multicoloured . . 10 10

1288 Folklore Characters, Singers and Mota

1991. 5th International Festival of Folklore and Birth Centenary of Leonardo Mota (folklorist).
2490 **1288** 45cr. red, ochre & black 10 10

1289 Jose Basilio da Gama (poet)

1290 Pope John Paul II

1991. Writers' Birth Anniversaries. Mult.
2491 45cr. Type **1289** (250th anniv) 10 10
2492 50cr. Luis Nicolau Fagundes Varela (poet, 150th anniv) 10 10
2493 50cr. Jackson de Figueiredo (essayist and philosopher, centenary) 10 10

1991. Papal Visit and 12th National Eucharistic Congress, Natal. Multicoloured.
2494 50cr. Type **1290** 60 50
2495 400cr. Congress emblem . . 90 70
Nos. 2494/5 were issued together, se-tenant, forming a composite design.

1291 "The Constitutional Commitment" (Aurelio de Figueiredo)

1292 Exhibition Emblem and dish Aerial

1991. Centenary of 1891 Constitution.
2496 **1291** 50cr. multicoloured . . 10 10

1991. "Telecom 91" International Telecommunications Exhibition, Geneva.
2497 **1292** 50cr. multicoloured . . 10 10

1293 Ferdinand Magellan

1294 White-vented Violetear and "Cattleya warneri"

1991. America. Voyages of Discovery. Mult.
2498 50cr. Type **1293** 15 10
2499 400cr. Francisco de Orellana on River Amazon . . . . 1·25 75

1991. "Brapex 91" National Stamp Exhibition, Vitoria. Humming Birds and Orchids in Mata Atlantica Forest. Multicoloured.
2500 50cr. Type **1294** 60 15
2501 65cr. Glittering-bellied emerald and "Rodriguezia venusta" 80 35
2502 65cr. Brazilian ruby and "Zygopetalum intermedium" 80 35

1295 "Self-portrait III"

1296 Agricultural Projects

1991. Birth Cent of Lasar Segall (artist).
2504 **1295** 400cr. multicoloured . . 80 30

1991. Centenary of Bureau of Agriculture and Provision, Sao Paulo.
2505 **1296** 70cr. multicoloured . . 20 10

1297 Dr. Manuel Ferraz de Campos Salles (President, 1898–1902)

1298 Madonna and Child

1991. 150th Birth Anniversaries. Mult.
2506 70cr. Type **1297** 10 10
2507 90cr. Dr. Prudente de Moraes (President, 1894–98) and Catete Palace, Rio de Janeiro (former Executive Headquarters) 10 10
Nos. 2506/7 were issued together, se-tenant, forming a composite design.

1991. Christmas.
2508 **1298** 70cr. multicoloured . . 10 10

1991. Obligatory Tax. Anti-leprosy Week.
2509 **1239** 3cr. green 35 10

1299 Hand holding Prayer Book

1991. Thanksgiving Day.
2510 **1299** 70cr. multicoloured . . 10 10

1301 Policeman in Historic Uniform and Tobias de Aguiar Battalion Building, Sao Paulo

1302 First Baptist Church, Niteroi (centenary)

1991. Military Police.
2512 **1301** 80cr. multicoloured . . 10 10

1992. Church Anniversaries. Multicoloured.
2513 250cr. Type **1302** 20 15
2514 250cr. Presbyterian Cathedral, Rio de Janeiro (130th anniv) 20 15

1303 Afranio Costa (silver, free pistol)

1992. Olympic Games, Barcelona (1st issue). 1920 Olympics Shooting Medal Winners. Multicoloured.
2515 300cr. Type **1303** 55 20
2516 2500cr. Guilherme Paraense (gold, 30 m revolver) . . 1·75 60
See also No. 2526.

1304 Old and Modern Views of Port

1992. Centenary of Port of Santos.
2517 **1304** 300cr. multicoloured . . 50 20

1305 White-tailed Tropic Birds

1992. 2nd United Nations Conference on Environment and Development, Rio de Janeiro (1st issue). Multicoloured.
2518 400cr. Type **1305** 75 60
2519 2500cr. Spinner dolphins . . . 2·00 1·90
See also Nos. 2532/5, 2536/8, 2539/42 and 2543/6.

1306 Ipe

1307 Hunting using Boleadeira

1992. No value expressed.
2520 **1306** (–) multicoloured . . . 1·25 10
No. 2520 was valid for use at the second class inland letter rate.

1992. "Abrafex '92" Argentinian–Brazilian Stamp Exhibition, Porto Alegre. Mult.
2521 250cr. Type **1307** 35 35
2522 250cr. Traditional folk
        dancing 20 15
2523 250cr. Horse and cart . . . 20 15
2524 1000cr. Rounding-up cattle 85 75

1308 Sportsmen on Globe

1992. Olympic Games, Barcelona (2nd issue).
2526 **1308** 300cr. multicoloured . . 20 15

1310 Columbus's Fleet

1992. America. 500th Anniv of Discovery of America by Columbus. Multicoloured.
2528 500cr. Type **1310** 75 25
2529 3500cr. Columbus, route
        map and quadrant . . . 75 60
Nos. 2528/9 were issued together, se-tenant, forming a composite design.

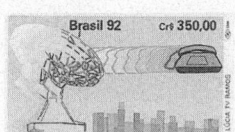

1311 Dish Aerial, Telephone and City

1992. Installation of 10,000,000th Telephone Line in Brazil.
2530 **1311** 350cr. multicoloured . . 15 10

1313 Hercule Florence (botanist)

1992. 2nd U.N. Conference on Environment and Development (2nd issue). 170th Anniv of Langsdorff Expedition. Multicoloured.
2532 500cr. Type **1313** 20 15
2533 500cr. Aime-Adrien Taunay
        (ethnographer) and
        Amerindians 20 15
2534 500cr. Johann Moritz
        Rugendas (zoologist) . . 20 15
2535 3000cr. Gregory Ivanovich
        Langsdorff and route map 60 60

1314 Urban and Rural Symbols

1992. 2nd U.N. Conference on Environment and Development (3rd issue). Multicoloured.
2536 450cr. Type **1314** 20 15
2537 450cr. Flags of Sweden (host
        of first conference) and
        Brazil around globe . . . 20 15
2538 3000cr. Globe, map, flora
        and fauna 60 30

1315 Monica sitting by Waterfall

1992. 2nd U.N. Conference on Environment and Development (4th issue). Ecology. Designs showing cartoon characters. Multicoloured.
2539 500cr. Type **1315** 20 15
2540 500cr. Cebolinha in canoe 20 15
2541 500cr. Cascao
        photographing wildlife . . 20 15
2542 500cr. Magali picking wild
        fruit 20 15
Nos. 2539/42 were issued together, se-tenant, forming a composite design.

1316 "Nidularium innocentii"

1317 Humming-bird's Wings forming Flower

1992. 2nd U.N. Conference on Environment and Development (5th issue). 3rd Anniv of Margaret Mee Brazilian Botanical Foundation. Flower paintings by Margaret Mee. Multicoloured.
2543 600cr. Type **1316** 25 20
2544 600cr. "Canistrum exiguum" 25 20
2545 700cr. "Nidularium rubens" 25 20
2546 700cr. "Canistrum
        cyathiforme" 25 20

1992. National Diabetes Day.
2547 **1317** 600cr. multicoloured . . 20 15

1318 Training Tower and First Manual Pump

1319 Animals, Cave Paintings and Map of Piaui State

1992. Centenary of Joinville Volunteer Fire Service.
2548 **1318** 550cr. multicoloured . . 20 15

1992. 13th Anniv of Capivara Mountain National Park. Multicoloured.
2549 550cr. Type **1319** 20 15
2550 550cr. Canyons and map of
        Brazil 20 15
Nos. 2549/50 were issued together, se-tenant, forming a composite design.

1320 Projects within Flask

1322 Santa Cruz Fortress, Anhatomirim Island

1321 Students at Work

1992. 24th Anniv of Financing Agency for Studies and Projects.
2551 **1320** 550cr. multicoloured . . 1·25 40

1992. 50th Anniv of National Industrial Training Service.
2552 **1321** 650cr. multicoloured . . 15 10

1992. Santa Catarina Fortresses. Multicoloured.
2553 650cr. multicoloured . . 15 10
2554 3000cr. Santo Antonio Fort,
        Ratones Grande island . . 65 60

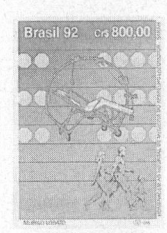

1323 Masonic Emblem and Palace, Brasilia

1324 Profiles of Child and Man forming Hourglass

1992. 170th Anniv of Grande Oriente (Federation of Brazil's Freemasonry Lodges).
2555 **1323** 650cr. multicoloured . . 10 10

1992. 50th Anniv of Brazilian Legion of Assistance.
2556 **1324** 650cr. multicoloured . . . 10 10

1325 Medical Equipment and Patients

1326 Menotti del Picchia

1992. Sarah Locomotor Hospital, Brasilia.
2557 **1325** 800cr. multicoloured . . 10 10

1992. Book Day. Writers' Birth Centenaries. Multicoloured.
2558 900cr. Type **1326** 10 10
2559 900cr. Graciliano Ramos . . 10 10
2560 1000cr. Assis Chateaubriand
        (journalist) (horiz) 15 10

1327 Meridian Circle, Map, Cruls and Tent

1992. Centenary of Luiz Cruls's Exploration of Central Plateau.
2561 **1327** 900cr. multicoloured . . 10 10

1328 Productivity Graph on Flag

1992. 2nd Anniv of Brazilian Quality and Productivity Programme.
2562 **1328** 1200cr. multicoloured 15 10

1330 Father Christmas

1992. Christmas. No value expressed.
2564 **1330** (–) multicoloured . . . 90 10

1992. Obligatory Tax. Anti-leprosy Week.
2565 **1239** 30cr. brown 35 10

1331 Sister Dulce, Patients and Lacerda Lift, Salvador

1993. Sister Dulce (founder of Santo Antonio Hospital and Simoes Filho Educational Centre) Commemoration.
2566 **1331** 3500cr. multicoloured 20 20

1333 Tube Station, Pine Trees and Church of the Third Order of St. Francis of Assisi and Stigmata

1993. 300th Anniv of Curitiba.
2568 **1333** 4500cr. multicoloured 25 20

1334 Heart dripping Blood onto Flowers

1335 "Night with the Geniuses of Study and Love"

1993. Health and Preservation of Life. Mult.
2569 4500cr. Type **1334** (blood
        donation) 20 20
2570 4500cr. Crab attacking
        healthy cell (anti-cancer
        campaign) 20 20
2571 4500cr. Rainbow, head and
        encephalogram (mental
        health) 20 20

1993. 150th Birth Anniv of Pedro Americo (painter). Multicoloured.
2572 5500cr. Type **1335** 20 20
2573 36000cr. "David and
        Abizag" (horiz) 30 20
2574 36000cr. "A Carioca" . . . 30 20

1336 Flag

1337 "Dynastes hercules"

1993. No value expressed. Self-adhesive. Die-cut.
2575 **1336** (–) blue, yellow & grn 1·75 20
No. 2575 was valid for use at the current first class inland letter rate. It could not be used to pay postage to foreign countries.

1993. World Environment Day. Beetles. Mult.
2576 8000cr. Type **1337** 30 25
2577 55000cr. "Batus
        barbicornis" 90 25

1338 Map, Flags and Discussion Themes

1993. 3rd Iberian–American Summit Conference, Salvador.
2578 **1338** 12000cr. multicoloured 25 20

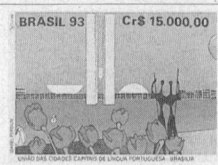

1339 Lake, Congress Building and "Os Candangos" (statue), Brasilia

1993. Union of Portuguese-speaking Capital Cities. Multicoloured.
2579 15000cr. Type **1339** 30 25
2580 71000cr. Copacabana beach and "Christ the Redeemer" (statue), Rio de Janeiro 30 25
Nos. 2579/80 were issued together, se-tenant, forming a composite design.

1340 30r. "Bulls Eye" Stamp

1993. 150th Anniv of First Brazilian Stamps (1st issue) and "Brasiliana 93" International Stamp Exhibition, Rio de Janeiro. Each black, red and yellow.
2581 30000cr. Type **1340** 90 50
2582 60000cr.60r. "Bull's Eye" stamp 90 50
2583 90000cr.90r. "Bull's Eye" stamp 90 50
See also Nos. 2585/8.

1341 Cebolinha designing Stamp

1993. 150th Anniv of First Brazilian Stamps (2nd issue). No value expressed. Cartoon characters. Multicoloured.
2585 (–) Type **1341** 90 15
2586 (–) Cascao as King and 30r. "Bull's Eye" stamp . . . 90 15
2587 (–) Monica writing letter and 60r. "Bull's Eye" stamp 90 15
2588 (–) Magali receiving letter and 90r. "Bull's Eye" stamp 90 15
Nos. 2585/8 were issued together, se-tenant, forming a composite design.
Nos. 2585/8 were valid for use at the current first class inland letter rate. They could not be used to pay postage to other countries.

1342 Imperial Palace (former postal H.Q.), Rio de Janeiro
1344 Forest Mound and Tools

1993. 330th Anniv of Postal Service. Mult.
2589 20000cr. Type **1342** . . . 40 35
2590 20000cr. Petropolis post office 40 35
2591 20000cr. Main post office, Rio de Janeiro . . . 40 35
2592 20000cr. Niteroi post office 40 35

1343 Polytechnic School, Sao Paulo University

1993. 330th Anniv of Postal Service. Mult.

Currency Reform
1 (new) cruzeiro real = 1000 (old) cruzeiros.

1993. Engineering Schools. Multicoloured.
2593 17cr. Type **1343** (centenary, 1994) 30 25
2594 17cr. Old and new engineering schools, Rio de Janeiro Federal University (bicent, 1992) 30 25

1993. Preservation of Archaeological Sites. Mult.
2595 17cr. Type **1344** 20 15
2596 17cr. Coastal mound, shells and tools 20 15

1345 Guimaraes and National Congress

1993. Ulysses Guimaraes (politician).
2597 **1346** 22cr. Multicoloured. . . 25 20

1346 Hands holding Candles and Rope around Statue
1347 Hyacinth Macaw, Glaucous Macaw and Indige Macaw

1993. Bicentenary of Procession of "Virgin of Nazareth", Belem.
2598 **1346** 22cr. multicoloured . . 25 20

1993. America. Endangered Macaws. Mult.
2599 22cr. Type **1346** 25 20
2600 130cr. Spix's macaw . . . . 1·10 90

1348 Vinicius de Moraes
1349 Liberty

1993. Composers' Anniversaries. Mult.
2601 22cr. Type **1348** (80th birth anniv) 25 20
2602 22cr. Alfredo da Rocha Vianna (pseud. Pixinguinha) and score of "Carinhoso" (20th death anniv) 25 20

1993. No value expressed.
2603 **1349** (–) blue, turq & yell . . 1·75 45
No. 2603 was sold at the current rate for first class international postage.

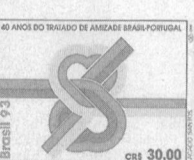

1350 Mario de Andrade
1351 Knot

1993. Book Day. Writers' Birth Centenaries. Multicoloured.
2604 30cr. Type **1350** 30 25
2605 30cr. Alceu Amoroso Lima (pseud. Tristao de Athayde) 30 25
2606 30cr. Gilka Machado (poet) 30 25

1993. 40th Anniv of Brazil–Portugal Consultation and Friendship Treaty.
2607 **1351** 30cr. multicoloured . . 30 25

1352 Nho-Quim

1993. 2nd International Comic Strip Biennial. No value expressed. Multicoloured.
2608 (–) Type **1352** 90 30
2609 (–) Benjamin (Louneiro) . . 60 25
2610 (–) Lamparina 60 25
2611 (–) Reco-Reco, Bolao and Azeitona (Luiz Sa) . . . 60 25
See note below Nos. 2585/8.

1353 Diagram and "Tamoio" (submarine)

1993. Launch of First Brazilian-built Submarine.
2612 **1353** 240cr. multicoloured . . 1·10 70

1354 Nativity

1993. Christmas. No value expressed.
2613 **1354** (–) multicoloured . . . 80 25
See note below Nos. 2585/8.

1993. Obligatory Tax. Anti-leprosy Week.
2614 **1205** 50c. blue 20 15

1355 Republic P-47 Thunderbolt Fighters over Tarquinia Camp, Italy
1356 Flag

1993. 50th Anniv of Formation of 1st Fighter Group, Brazilian Expeditionary Force.
2615 **1355** 42cr. multicoloured . . 60 25

1994. No value expressed. Self-adhesive. Imperf.
2616 **1356** (–) blue, yellow & green 60 30
See note below Nos. 2585/8.

1357 Foundation of Republican Memory, Convent and Cloisters

1994. 340th Anniv of Convent of Merces (now Cultural Centre), Sao Luis.
2617 **1357** 58cr. multicoloured . . 40 35

1358 "Mae Menininha"

1994. Birth Centenary of Mae Menininha do Gantois (Escolastica Maria da Conceiao Nazare).
2618 **1358** 80cr. multicoloured . . 20 20

1359 Olympic Rings and Rower
1360 Blue and White Swallow

1994. Centenaries of International Olympic Committee and Rowing Federation, Rio Grande do Sul. No value expressed.
2619 **1359** (–) multicoloured . . . 1·75 90
See note below No. 2603.

1994. Birds. Multicoloured.
2620 10cr. Type **1360** 10 10
2621 20cr. Roadside hawk . . . 10 10
2622 50cr. Rufous-bellied thrush 10 10
2623 100cr. Ruddy ground dove 15 10
2624 200cr. Southern lapwing . . 30 25
2625 500cr. Rufous-collared sparrow 80 70
See after Nos. 2649/61.

1361 Map and Prince Henry

1994. 600th Birth Anniv of Prince Henry the Navigator.
2626 **1361** 635cr. multicoloured . . 1·75 90

1362 Bicycle

1994. America. Postal Vehicles. Mult.
2627 110cr. Type **1362** 15 10
2628 635cr. Motor cycle . . . . 1·75 20

1363 Statue, Grain Store and Chapel of Help, Juazeiro do Norte

1994. 150th Anniv of Birth of Father Cicero Romao Batista. With service indicator.
2629 **1363** (–) multicoloured . . . 60 15
See note below Nos. 2585/8.

1364 Sabin and Children

1994. 1st Death Anniv of Albert Sabin (developer of oral polio vaccine).
2630 **1364** 160cr. multicoloured . . 25 20

1365 Castello Branco and Brasilia

1994. Carlos Castello Branco (journalist).
2631 **1365** 160cr. multicoloured . . 25 20

1366 "Euterpe oleracea"   1367 "Brazil"

1994. Birth Bicentenary of Karl Friedrich Phillip von Martius (botanist). With service indicator. Multicoloured.
(a) Inscr "1. PORTE NACIONAL".
2632 (–) Type 1366 . . . . . . 85 15
2633 (–) "Jacaranda
    paucifoliolata" 85 15
(b) Inscr "1. PORTE INTERNACIONAL TAXE PERCUE".
2634 (–) "Barbacenia tomentosa" 1·50 30
Nos. 2632/3 were for use at the current first class inland letter rate and Nos. 2634 for first class international postage.

1994. With service indicator. (a) Size 21 × 28mm. Self-adhesive. Rouletted. (i) PRINTED MATTER. Inscr "1. PORTE IMPRESSO CATEGORIA II".
2635 1367 (–) blue 10 10
(ii) INLAND POSTAGE. Inscr "3. PORTE NACIONAL".
2636 1367 (3rd) red 30 20
(b) INLAND POSTAGE. Inscr "PORTE NACIONAL". Size 26 × 35mm.
2637 1367 (4th) green 40 30
2638   (5th) red 75 30
Nos. 2635/8 were valid for internal use in the category described.

1368 Brazilian Player wearing "100"

1994. Centenary of Football in Brazil and World Cup Football Championship, U.S.A. With service indicator.
2639 1368 (–) multicoloured . . . 2·40 90
See note below No. 2603.

1369 Emperor Tamarin   1371 Pencils Crossing
("Saguinus imperator")   over Fingerprint

1994. Endangered Mammals. With service indicator. Multicoloured.
2640 (–) Type 1369 . . . . . . 60 15
2641 (–) Bare-faced tamarin
    ("Saguinus bicolor") . . . 60 15
2642 (–) Golden lion tamarin
    ("Leontopithecus rosalia") 60 15
See note below Nos. 2585/8.

1994. 10 Year Education Plan. With service indicator. Multicoloured.
2644 (–) Type 1371 (literacy
    campaign) 60 15
2645 (–) PRONAICA pencil and
    school (National
    Programme of Integral
    Care to Children and
    Teenagers) 60 15
2646 (–) Lecture scene and graph
    (increase in qualified
    teachers) 60 15
2647 (–) Pencil and "lecturers" on
    television (distance
    learning by video) . . . 60 15
See note below Nos. 2585/8.

1994. Birds. As T 1360 but with value expressed as "R$". Multicoloured.
2649 1c. Type 1360 . . . . . . 10 10
2650 2c. As No. 2621 . . . . . 10 10
2652 5c. As No. 2622 . . . . . 10 10
2654 10c. As No. 2623 . . . . 15 10
2655 15c. Saffron finch 20 15
2656 20c. As No. 2624 . . . . 30 25
2657 22c. Fork-tailed fly-catcher 30 25
2658 50c. As No. 2625 . . . . 75 65
2661 1r. Rufous hornero . . . . 1·50 1·25

1373 Edgard Santos (founder   1374 "Petrobras X"
of Bahia University)   (drilling platform),
    Campos Basin. Rio
    de Janeiro

1994. Anniversaries. With service indicator. Multicoloured.
2662 (–) Type 1373 (birth
    centenary) 20 15
2663 (–) Oswaldo Aranha
    (politician, birth
    centenary) 20 15
2664 (–) Otto Lara Resende
    (author and journalist,
    2nd death anniv) . . . 20 15
See note below Nos. 2585/8.

1994. 40th Anniv of Petrobras (state oil company).
2665 1374 12c. multicoloured . . . 40 15

1375 17th century   1376 Loaf of Bread
Coin Production

1994. 300th Anniv of Brazilian Mint.
2666 1375 12c. multicoloured . . . 20 15

1994. Campaign against Famine and Misery. With service indicator.
2667 1376 (–) multicoloured . . . 20 15
2668   (–) black and blue . . . 20 15
DESIGN: No. 2668, Fish.
See note below Nos. 2585/8.

1377 Writing with Quill and Scales of Justice

1994. 150th Anniv of Brazilian Lawyers Institute.
2669 1377 12c. multicoloured . . . 20 15

1378 Family within Heart

1994. International Year of the Family.
2670 1378 84c. multicoloured . . . 1·25 60

1379 Hospital, White Stork and Babies forming "1000000"

1994. Centenary of Sao Paulo Maternity Hospital. Its Millionth Birth.
2671 1379 12c. multicoloured . . . 20 15

1380 Celestino performing and "Maternal Heart" (record sleeve)

1994. Birth Centenary of Vicente Celestino (singer).
2672 1380 12c. multicoloured . . . 20 15

1381 Fernando de Azevedo (educationist)

1994. Writers' Birth Anniversaries. Mult.
2673 12c. Type 1381 (cent) . . . 20 15
2674 12c. Tomas Antonio
    Gonzaga (poet, 250th) . . 20 15

1382 "Joao and Maria" (Hansel and Gretel)

1994. Centenary of Publication of "Fairy Tales" by Alberto Figueiredo Pimentel (first Brazilian children's book). Multicoloured.
2675 12c. Type 1382 . . . . . . 20 15
2676 12c. "Dona Baratinha"
    (Little Mrs Cockroach) 20 15
2677 84c. "Puss in Boots" . . . 1·25 1·10
2678 84c. "Tom Thumb" . . . 1·25 1·10

1383 St. Clare, St. Damian's Convent and Statue of St. Francis

1994. 800th Birth Anniv of St. Clare of Assisi (founder of order of Poor Clares).
2679 1383 12c. multicoloured . . . 20 15

1384 Racing Car and Brazilian Flag

1994. Ayrton Senna (racing driver) Commemoration. Multicoloured.
2680 12c. Type 1384 . . . . . . 90 60
2681 12c. Senna and crowd
    waving farewell 90 60
2682 84c. Brazilian and chequered
    flags, racing cars and
    Senna giving victory
    salute . . . . 1·75 60
Nos. 2680/2 were issued together, se-tenant, forming a composite design.

1385 Books and Globe

1994. Centenary of Historical and Geographical Institute, Sao Paulo.
2683 1385 12c. multicoloured . . . 20 15

1386 Adoniran Barbosa and "11 o'Clock Train"

1994. Composers. Multicoloured.
2684 12c. Type 1386 . . . . . . 20 15
2685 12c. Score of "The Sea"
    (Dorival Caymmi) . . . 20 15

1994. Obligatory Tax. Anti-Leprosy Week.
2686 1205 1c. purple 10 10

1387 Maggot wearing Santa Claus Hat in Apple

1994. Christmas. Multicoloured.
2687 12c. Type 1387 . . . . . . 20 15
2688 12c. Carol singers 20 15
2689 12c. Boy smoking pipe and
    letter in boot 20 15
2690 84c. Boy wearing saucepan
    on head and Santa Claus
    cloak 90 60

1389 Pasteur

1995. Death Centenary of Louis Pasteur (chemist).
2692 1389 84c. multicoloured . . . 1·10 30

1390 Duke of Caxias and   1391 Pres. Franco
Soldiers

1995. 150th Anniv of Peace of Ponche Verde (pacification of Farroupilha Revolution) (2693) and 50th Anniv of Battle of Monte Castello (2694). Multicoloured.
2693 12c. Type 1390 . . . . . . 15 10
2694 12c. Soldier, Brazilian flag
    and battle scene 15 10

1995. Itamar Franco (President 1992–94).
2695 1391 12c. multicoloured . . . 15 10

1392 Meal before   1393 Alexandre de Gusmao
Child   (diplomat)

1995. 50th Anniv of F.A.O.
2696 1392 84c. multicoloured . . . 1·10 30

1995. Birth Anniversaries. Multicoloured.
2697 12c. Type 1393 (300th
    anniv) 15 10
2698 12c. Visconde (Viscount) de
    Jequitinhonha (lawyer,
    bicent (1994) 15 10
2699 15c. Barao (Baron) do Rio
    Branco (diplomat, 150th
    anniv) 20 15

1394 Guglielmo Marconi and his Transmitter

1995. Centenary of First Radio Transmission.
2700 1394 84c. multicoloured . . . 1·10 30

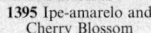

1395 Ipe-amarelo and Cherry Blossom **1396** Solitary Tinamou ("Tinamus solitarius")

1995. Centenary of Brazil–Japan Friendship Treaty.
2701 **1395** 84c. multicoloured . . . 1·10 30

1995. Birds. Multicoloured.
2702 12c. Type **1396** 15 10
2703 12c. Razor-billed curassow ("Mitu mitu") 15 10

1397 St. John's Party, Campina Grande

1995. June Festivals. Multicoloured.
2704 12c. Type **1397** 15 10
2705 12c. Country wedding, Caruaru 15 10

1398 St. Antony holding Child Jesus (painting, Vieira Lusitano)

1995. 800th Birth Anniv of St. Antony of Padua.
2706 **1398** 84c. multicoloured . . . 1·10 30

1400 Laurel and "Republic" **1401** Player, Net and Anniversary Emblem

1995. 1st Anniv of Real Currency.
2708 **1400** 12c. brown, green & blk 15 10

1995. Centenary of Volleyball.
2709 **1401** 15c. multicoloured . . . 20 15

1402 "Angaturama limai"

1995. 14th Brazilian Palaeontology Society Congress, Uberaba. Dinosaurs. Multicoloured.
2710 15c. Type **1402** 20 10
2711 1r.50 Titanosaurus . . . . 2·00 1·75

1403 Crash Test Dummies in Car

1995. Road Safety Campaign. Multicoloured.
2712 12c. Type **1403** 15 10
2713 71c. Car crashing into glass of whisky 95 85

1404 "Calathea burle-marxii" **1405** Paratroopers

1995. "Singapore '95" International Stamp Exhibition. 10th Anniv of Donation to Nation by Roberto Burle Marx of his Botanical Collection. Multicoloured.
2714 15c. Type **1404** 20 15
2715 15c. "Vellozia burle-marxii" 20 15
2716 1r.50 "Heliconia aemygdiana" . . . . . . 2·00 1·75

1995. 50th Anniv of Parachutist Infantry Brigade.
2717 **1405** 15c. multicoloured . . . 20 15

1406 Paulista Museum and "Fernao Dias Paes Leme" (statue, Luigi Brizzolara)

1995. Centenary of Paulista Museum of the University of Sao Paulo.
2718 **1406** 15c. multicoloured . . . 20 15

1407 Olinda **1408** Scarlet Ibis and Stoat catching Fish

1995. Lighthouses. Multicoloured.
2719 15c. Type **1407** 35 25
2720 15c. Sao Joao 35 25
2721 15c. Santo Antonio da Barra 35 25

1995. "Lubrapex 95" Brazilian–Portuguese Stamp Exhibition, Sao Paulo. Fauna of the Tiete River Valley. Multicoloured.
2722 15c. Type **1408** 30 15
2723 84c. Great egret flying over canoe . . . . 1·10 95

1409 X-Ray of Hand

1995. 150th Birth Anniv of Wilhelm Rontgen and Centenary of his Discovery of X-Rays.
2725 **1409** 84c. multicoloured . . . 1·10 30

1410 Arms and Crowd

1995. Centenary of Flamengo Regatta Club.
2726 **1410** 15c. multicoloured . . . 20 15

1411 Fungi and Alligator

1995. America. Environmental Protection. Mult.
2727 15c. Type **1411** 20 15
2728 84c. Black-necked swans on lake . . . . 1·10 95

Nos. 2727/8 were issued together, se-tenant, forming a composite design.

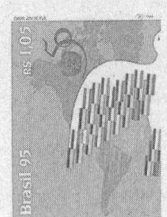

1412 Dove over World Map (left detail) **1413** Jose Maria Eca de Queiroz

1995. 50th Anniv of U.N.O. Multicoloured.
2729 1r.05 Type **1412** . . . . . 1·40 1·25
2730 1r.05 Dove over world map (right detail) . . . . . 1·40 1·25
Nos. 2729/30 were issued together, se-tenant, forming a composite design.

1995. Book Day. Writers' Anniversaries. Mult.
2731 15c. Type **1413** (150th birth) 20 15
2732 15c. Rubem Braga (5th death) 20 15
2733 23c. Carlos Drummond de Andrade (8th death) . . . 30 25

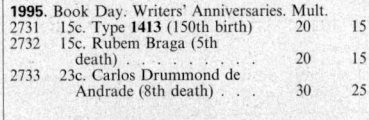

1415 Front Crawl (Freestyle)

1995. 11th World Short-course Swimming Championships, Rio de Janeiro. Multicoloured.
2735 23c. Type **1415** 30 25
2736 23c. Backstroke 30 25
2737 23c. Butterfly 30 25
2738 23c. Breaststroke 30 25
Nos. 2735/8 were issued together, se-tenant, forming a composite design of a swimming pool.

1416 Cherub

1995. Christmas. Multicoloured.
2739 15c. Type **1416** 20 15
2740 23c. Cherub (different) . . . 30 25
Nos. 2739/40 were issued together, se-tenant, forming a composite design.

1417 Flag, Former Headquarters and "Manequinho" (statue)

1995. Centenary (1994) of Botafogo Football and Regatta Club.
2741 **1417** 15c. multicoloured . . . 20 15

1418 Computer, Mouse and Masthead

1995. 170th Anniv of "Diario de Pernambuco" (newspaper)
2742 **1418** 23c. multicoloured . . . 30 25

1420 Prestes Maia and Sao Paulo

1996. Birth Centenary of Francisco Prestes Maia (Mayor of Sao Paulo).
2744 **1420** 18c. multicoloured . . . 20 15

1421 Bornhausen and Santa Catarina

1996. Birth Centenary of Irineu Bornhausen (Governor of State of Santa Catarina).
2745 **1421** 27c. multicoloured . . . 35 30

1422 "Ouro Preto Landscape" (Alberto da Veiga Guignard) **1423** Doll

1996. Artists' Birth Centenaries. Mult.
2746 15c. Type **1422** 20 15
2747 15c. "Boat with Little Flags and Birds" (Alfredo Volpi) 20 15

1996. 50th Anniv of United Nations Children's Fund. Campaign against Sexual Abuse.
2748 **1423** 23c. multicoloured . . . 30 25

1424 Anniversary Emblem **1426** Pantanal

1425 Pinheiro da Silva and National Congress

1996. 500th Anniv (2000) of Discovery of Brazil by the Portuguese.
2749 **1424** 1r.05 multicoloured . . . 1·25 1·10

1996. Birth Centenary of Israel Pinheiro da Silva (politician).
2750 **1425** 18c. multicoloured . . . 20 15

1996. Tourism. Multicoloured. Self-adhesive. Imperf (backing paper rouletted).
2751 23c. Amazon River 30 25
2752 23c. Type **1426** 30 25
2753 23c. Jangada raft 30 25
2754 23c. "The Sugarloaf", Guanabara Bay 30 25
2755 23c. Iguazu Falls 30 25

1427 Crimson Topaz

1996. "Espamer 96" Spanish and Latin-American Stamp Exhibition, Seville, Spain. Hummingbirds. Multicoloured.
2756 15c. Type **1427** 20 15
2757 1r.05 Black-breasted plover-crest . . . . 1·25 1·10
2758 1r.15 Swallow-tailed hummingbird . . . . . . 1·40 1·25

1428 Marathon Runners

1996. Cent of Modern Olympic Games. Mult.
2759	18c. Type **1428**	. . . . .	20	15
2760	23c. Gymnastics	. . . .	30	25
2761	1r.05 Swimming	. . . . .	1·25	1·10
2762	1r.05 Beach volleyball	. . .	1·25	1·10

1430 Dish Aerial, Satellite over Earth and Sports

1996. "Americas Telecom 96" International Telecommunications Exn, Rio de Janeiro.
2764 **1430** 1r.05 multicoloured . . 1·25   25

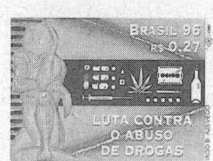

1432 Addict and Drugs

1996. Anti-drug Abuse Campaign.
2766 **1432** 27c. multicoloured . . . 35   30

1433 Coloured Pencils   **1435** Gomes and Peace Theatre

1434 Princess Isabel and Aurea Law

1996. Education Year.
2767 **1433** 23c. multicoloured . . . 30   25

1996. 150th Birth Anniv of Princess Isabel the Redeemer.
2768 **1434** 18c. multicoloured . . . 20   15
The Aurea Law abolished slavery in Brazil.

1996. Death Centenary of Carlos Gomes (opera composer).
2769 **1435** 50c. multicoloured . . . 60   50

1436 "Cattleya eldorado"

1996. 15th International Orchid Conference, Rio de Janeiro. Multicoloured.
2770	15c. Type **1436**	. . . . .	20	15
2771	15c. "Cattleya loddigesii"	. .	20	15
2772	15c. "Promenaea stapellioides"	. . . . . .	20	15

1437 Melania and Maximino and Virgin Mary

1996. 150th Anniv of Apparition of Our Lady at La Salette, France.
2773 **1437** 1r. multicoloured . . . 1·25   1·10

1439 "Marilyn Monroe" (Andy Warhol)

1996. 23rd International Biennale, Sao Paulo. Paintings. Multicoloured.
2775	55c. Type **1439**	. . . . .	60	50
2776	55c. "The Scream" (Edvard Munch)	. . . .	60	50
2777	55c. "Mirror for the red Room" (Louise Bourgeois)	. . . . .	60	50
2778	55c. "Lent" (Pablo Picasso)		60	50

1440 Emblem

1996. Defenders of Nature (environmental organization).
2779 **1440** 10r. multicoloured . . . 11·00   9·50

1441 Vaqueiro   **1442** Poinsettia and Lighted Candle

1996. America. Traditional Costumes. Mult.
2780	50c. Type **1441**	. . . . .	60	50
2781	1r. Baiana (seller of beancakes)	. . . .	1·25	1·10

1996. Christmas.
2782 **1442** (–) multicoloured . . . 20   15
See second note below No. 2588.

1443 "Melindrosa" (cover of 1931 "O Cruzeiro" magazine)   **1444** Ipiranga Monument

1996. 46th Death Anniv of Jose Carlos (caricaturist).
2783 **1443** (–) multicoloured . . . 20   15
See second note below No. 2588.

1996. Tourism. Multicoloured. Self-adhesive. Imperf (backing paper rouletted).
2784	(–) Type **1444**	. . . . .	15	10
2785	(–) Hercilio Luz Bridge	. .	15	10
2786	(–) National Congress building	. . . . . .	15	10
2787	(–) Pelourinho	. . . . .	15	10
2788	(–) Ver-o-Peso market	. .	15	10

Nos. 2784/8 were valid for use at the current first stage inland letter rate.

1445 Campaign Emblem and Guanabara Bay

1997. Bid by Rio de Janeiro for 2004 Olympic Games.
2789 **1445** (–) multicoloured . . . 60   50
No. 2789 was valid for use at the current first stage international letter rate.

1446 Postman and Letter Recipients

1997. America. The Postman.
2790 **1446** (–) multicoloured . . . 15   10
No. 2790 was valid for use at the current first stage inland letter rate.

1447 Alves, Flogging and Salvador Harbour

1997. 150th Birth Anniv of Antonio de Castro Alves (poet).
2791 **1447** 15c. multicoloured . . . 30   10

1448 Tamandare (after Miranda Junior) and "Rescue of 'Ocean Monarch by 'Don Afonso '" (Samuel Walters)

1997. Death Centenary of Marquis of Tamandare (naval reformer).
2792 **1448** 23c. multicoloured . . . 40   20

1449 "Joy. Joy"

1997. Winning Entry in "Art on Stamps" Competition.
2793 **1449** 15c. multicoloured . . . 15   10

1450 Globe in Glass of Water   **1451** Embraer EMB-145

1997. World Water Day.
2794 **1450** 1r.05 multicoloured . . . 1·10   95

1997. Brazilian Aircraft. Multicoloured. Self-adhesive. Imperf (backing paper rouletted).
2795	15c. Type **1451**	. . . . .	15	10
2796	15c. Aeritalia/Aermacchi AM-X jet fighter	. . .	15	10
2797	15c. Embraer EMB-312 H Super Tucano	. . . .	15	10
2798	15c. Embraer EMB-120 Brasilia	. . . . .	15	10
2799	15c. Embraer EMB-312 Tucano trainer	. . .	15	10

1452 Red Ribbon inside Condom   **1454** Emblem

1997. Family Health Association (A.S.F.) Anti-AIDS Campaign.
2810 **1452** 23c. multicoloured . . . 25   20

1997. 500th Anniv (2000) of Discovery of Brazil by the Portuguese.
2812 **1454** 1r.05 multicoloured . . 1·10   95

1455 Pixinguinha   **1457** Inscription

1997. Birth Centenary of Pixinguinha (musician).
2813 **1455** 15c. multicoloured . . . 15   10

1997. "Human Rights, Rights of All".
2815 **1457** 18c. black and red . . . 20   15

1459 Melon   **1460** Mahogany ("Swietenia macropylla")

1997. Fruits. Self-adhesive. (a) Imperf (backing paper rouletted). (i) With service indicator.
2817 **1459** (–) red and green . . . 20   15

(ii) With face values.
2818	– 1c. yellow, orange & grn		10	10
2819	– 2c. yellow, brown & blk .		10	10
2820	– 5c. orange, yellow & blk		10	10
2821	– 10c. yellow, brown & grn		10	10
2822	– 20c. yellow, red & green		20	15

(b) Die-cut wavy edge.
2823	– 1c. yellow, orange & grn		10	10
2826	– 10c. yellow, brown & grn		10	10
2828	– 20c. lt green, grn & blk .		20	15
2829	– 22c. red, purple & green		20	15
2830	– 50c. multicoloured . . .		30	25
2831	– 51c. green, lt grn & brn .		50	45
2832	– 80c. red, green & yellow		80	70
2833	– 82c. lt grn, grn & dp grn		80	70
2834	– 1r. red, green & yellow .		1·00	90

DESIGNS—HORIZ: Nos. 2818, 2823, Oranges; 2819, Bananas; 2820, Mango. VERT: Nos. 2821, 2826, Pineapple; 2822, Cashew nuts; 2828, Sugarapple; 2829, Grapes; 2830, Suriname cherry ("Pitanga"); 2831, Coconut; 2832, Apples; 2833, Limes; 2834, Strawberries.
No. 2817 was valid for use at the current first stage inland letter rate.

1997. World Environment Day. Amazon Flora and Fauna. Multicoloured.
2836	27c. Type **1460**	. . . . . .	30	25
2837	27c. Arapaima (55 × 22 mm)		30	25

1461 Antonio Vieira in Pulpit

1997. Death Anniversaries of Missionaries to Brazil. Multicoloured.
2838	1r.05 Type **1461** (300th)	. . .	1·10	95
2839	1r.05 Indian children and Jose de Auchieta (400th)		1·10	95

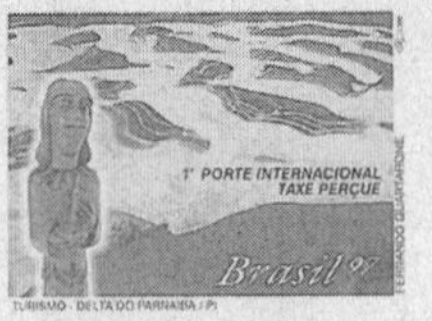

1462 Parnaiba Delta and Sculpture (Mestre Dezinho)

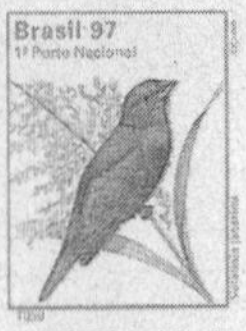

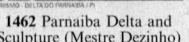

1463 Blue-black Grassquit

1997. Tourism. With service indicator. Mult.
2840 (–) Type **1462** . . . . . . 1·25 1·10
2841 (–) Lencois Maranhenses National Park and costume . . . . 1·25 1·10
Nos. 2840/1 were valid for use at the current rate for first class international postage.

1997. Birds. Multicoloured. Self-adhesive. Imperf (backing paper rouletted). (a) With service indicator.
2842 (–) Type **1463** 20 15
(b) With face value.
2843 22c. Social flycatcher ("Vermilion-crowned Flycatcher") 20 15
No. 2842 was valid for use at the current first stage inland letter rate.

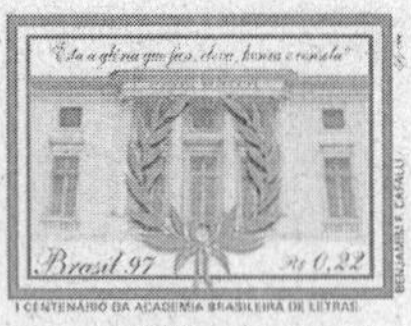

1464 Academy

1998. Cent of Brazilian Literature Academy.
2850 **1464** 22c. multicoloured . . . 20 15

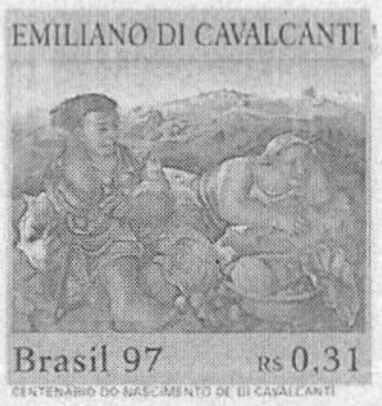

1465 "Gipsies" (Di Cavalcanti)

1997. Birth Centenary of Emiliano di Cavalcanti (artist).
2851 **1465** 31c. multicoloured . . . 30 25

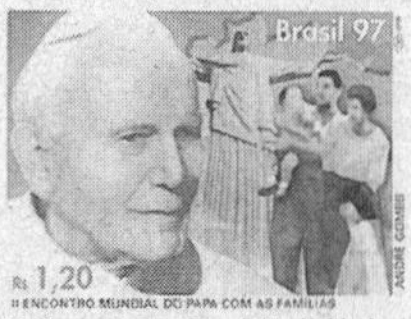

1466 Pope John Paul II, "Christ the Redeemer" and Family

1997. 2nd World Meeting of Pope with Families, Rio de Janeiro.
2852 **1466** 1r.20 multicoloured . . 1·25 1·10

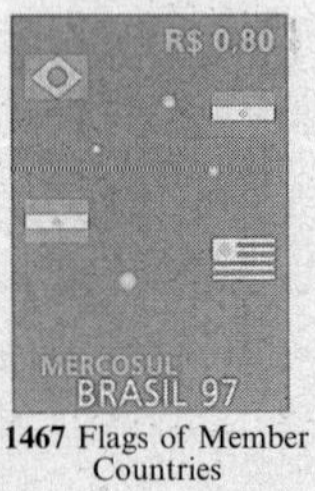

1467 Flags of Member Countries

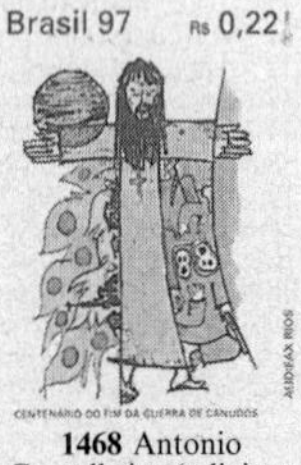

1468 Antonio Conselheiro (religious leader)

1997. Mercosur (South American Common Market).
2853 **1467** 80c. multicoloured . . . 80 70

1997. Centenary of End of Canudos War.
2854 **1468** 22c. multicoloured . . . 20 15

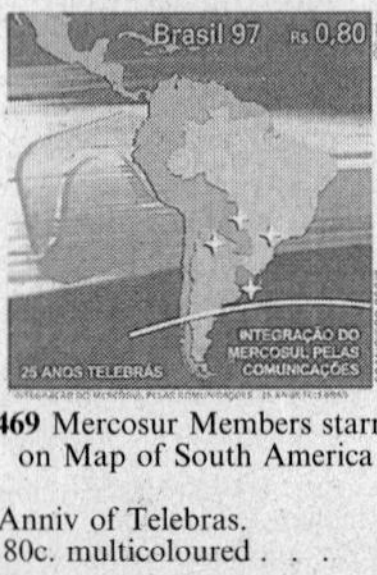

1469 Mercosur Members starred on Map of South America

1997. 25th Anniv of Telebras.
2855 **1469** 80c. multicoloured . . . 80 70

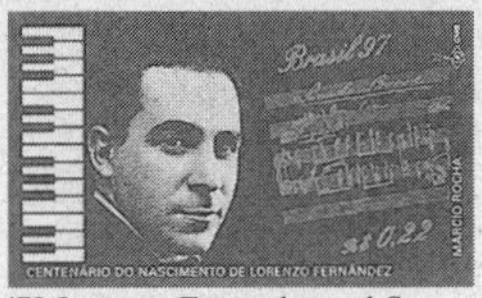

1470 Lorenzo Fernandez and Score of "Sonata Breve"

1997. Composers' Birth Centenaries. Each black and gold.
2856 22c. Type **1470** 20 15
2857 22c. Francisco Mignone and score of "Second Brazilian Fantasia" 20 15

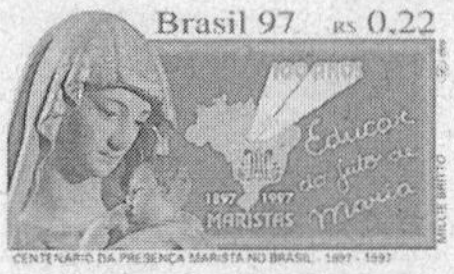

1471 "Our Good Mother" and Blackboard with Marist Motto

1997. Centenary of Marist Brothers in Brazil.
2858 **1471** 22c. multicoloured . . . 20 15

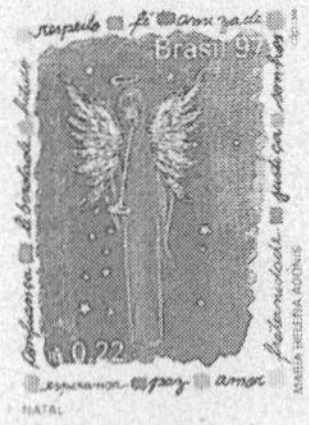

1472 Angel playing Trumpet

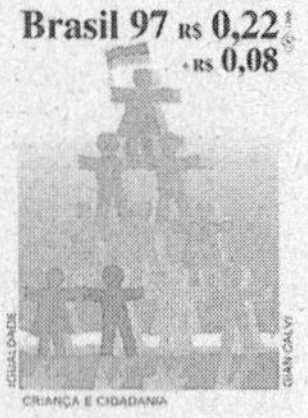

1473 "Equality" (Gian Calvi)

1997. Christmas.
2859 **1472** 22c. multicoloured . . . 20 15

1997. Children and Citizenship. Multicoloured.
2860 22c.+8c. Type **1473** 30 25
2861 22c.+8c. "Love and Tenderness" (Alcy Linares) 30 25
2862 22c.+8c. "Admission to School" (Ziraldo) 30 25
2863 22c.+8c. "Healthy Pregnancy" (Claudio Martins) 30 25
2864 22c.+8c. "Being Happy" (Cica Fittipaldi) 30 25
2865 22c.+8c. "Work for Parents, School for Children" (Roger Mello) 30 25
2866 22c.+8c. "Breast-feeding" (Angela Lago) 30 25
2867 22c.+8c. "Civil Registration" (Mauricio de Sousa) 30 25
2868 22c.+8c. "Integration of the Handicapped" (Nelson Cruz) 30 25
2869 22c.+8c. "Presence of Parents during Illness" (Eliardo Franca) 30 25
2870 22c.+8c. "Quality of Teaching" (Graca Lima) 30 25
2871 22c.+8c. "Safe Delivery" (Eva Furnari) 30 25
2872 22c.+8c. "Family and Community Life" (Gerson Conforti) 30 25
2873 22c.+8c. "Music playing" (Ana Raquel) 30 25
2874 22c.+8c. "Respect and Dignity" (Helena Alexandrino) 30 25
2875 22c.+8c. "Summary of Children's Statute" (Darlan Rosa) 30 25

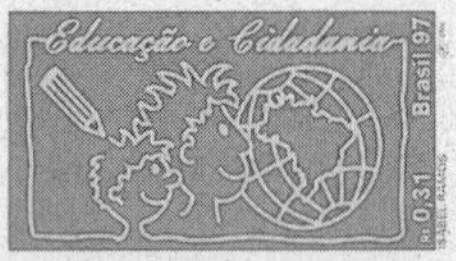

1474 Children and Globe

1997. Education and Citizenship.
2876 **1474** 31c. blue and yellow . . 30 25

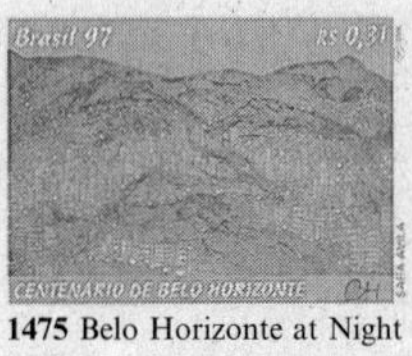

1475 Belo Horizonte at Night

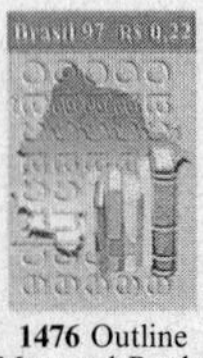

1476 Outline Map and Books (Education)

1997. Centenary of Belo Horizonte.
2877 **1475** 31c. multicoloured . . . 30 25

1997. Citizens' Rights. Mult. Self-adhesive.
2878 22c. Type **1476** 20 15
2879 22c. Map and hand holding labour card (work) . . . 20 15
2880 22c. Map and fruit (agriculture) 20 15
2881 22c. Map and stethoscope (health) 20 15
2882 22c. Clapper-board and paint brush (culture) . . . 20 15

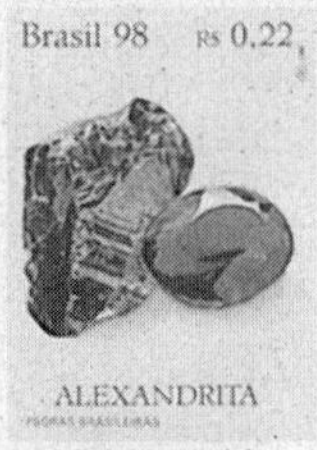

1477 Alexandrite

1998. Minerals. Multicoloured.
2883 22c. Type **1477** 15 10
2884 22c. Chrysoberyl cat's-eye 15 10
2885 22c. Indicolite 15 10

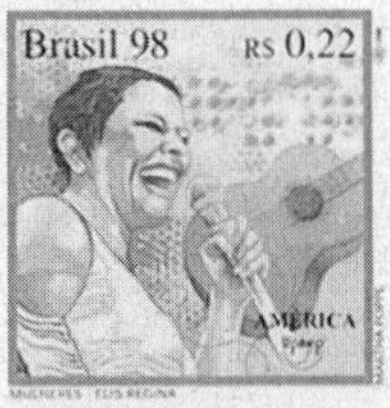

1478 Elis Regina (singer)

1998. America. Famous Women. Multicoloured.
2886 22c. Type **1478** 15 10
2887 22c. Clementina de Jesus (singer) 15 10
2888 22c. Dulcina de Moraes (actress) 15 10
2889 22c. Clarice Lispector (writer) 15 10

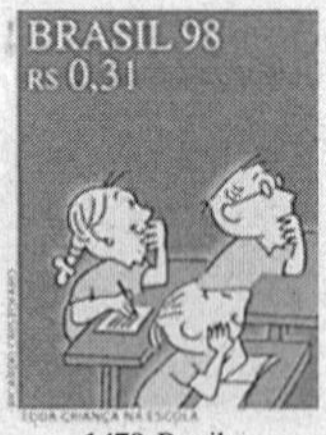

1479 Pupils

1998. Education. Multicoloured.
2890 31c. Type **1479** (universal schooling) 20 15
2891 31c. Teacher (teacher appraisal) 20 15
Nos. 2390/1 were issued together, se-tenant, forming a composite design of a classroom.

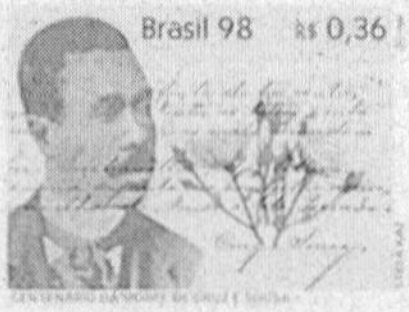

1480 Cruze Sousa

1998. Death Centenary of Joao da Cruze Sousa (poet).
2892 **1480** 36c. multicoloured . . . 20 15

1481 Map, 1519

1998. 500th Anniv (2000) of Discovery of Brazil by the Portuguese. Multicoloured.
2893 1r.05 Type **1481** 65 55
2894 1r.05 Galleon . . . . 1·10 90
Nos. 2893/4 were issued together, se-tenant, forming a composite design.

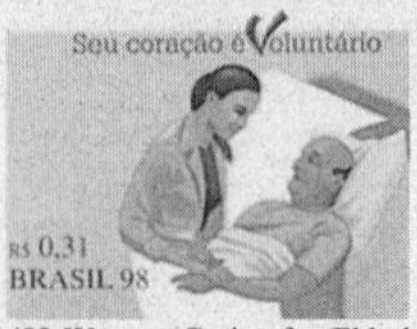

1482 Woman Caring for Elderly Man

1998. Voluntary Work. Multicoloured.
2895 31c. Type **1482** 20 15
2896 31c. Woman caring for child 20 15
2897 31c. Fighting forest fire . . 20 15
2898 31c. Adult's and child's hands 20 15
Nos. 2895/8 were issued together, se-tenant, forming a composite design.

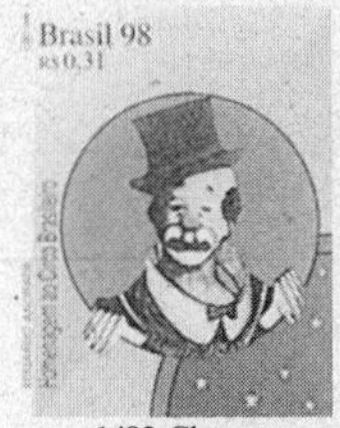

1483 Clown

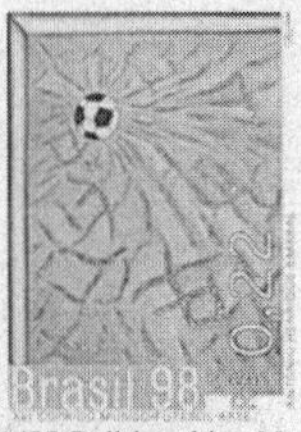

1485 Ball breaking Net (Antonio Henrique Amaral)

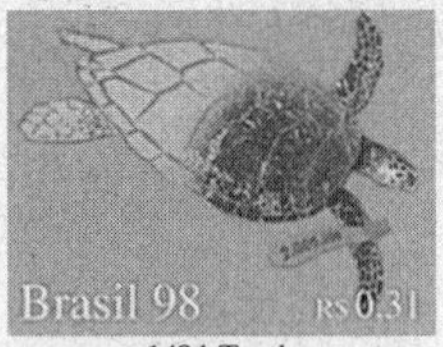

1484 Turtle

1998. Circus. Multicoloured.
2899 31c. Type **1483** 20 15
2900 31c. Clown resting on stick 20 15
2901 31c. Clown (left half) and outside of Big Top . . . 20 15
2902 31c. Clown (right half) and inside of Big Top 20 15
Nos. 2899/2902 were issued together, se-tenant, forming a composite design.

1998. Expo '98 World's Fair, Lisbon. International Year of the Ocean. Multicoloured.
2903 31c. Type **1484** 20 15
2904 31c. Tail of whale 20 15
2905 31c. Barracuda 20 15
2906 31c. Jellyfish and fishes . . 20 15
2907 31c. Diver and school of fishes 20 15
2908 31c. Two dolphins 20 15
2909 31c. Angelfish (brown spotted fish) 20 15
2910 31c. Two whales 20 15
2911 31c. Two long-nosed butterflyfishes (with black stripe across eye) 20 15
2912 31c. Sea perch (red and yellow fish) 20 15
2913 31c. Manatee 20 15
2914 31c. Seabream (blue, yellow and white fish) 20 15
2915 31c. Emperor angelfish and coral 20 15
2916 31c. School of snappers (blue and yellow striped fishes) 20 15
2917 31c. Flying gurnard 20 15
2918 31c. Manta ray 20 15
2919 31c. Two butterflyfishes (black and green fishes) 20 15
2920 31c. Pipefish 20 15
2921 31c. Moray eel 20 15
2922 31c. Angelfish (blue, yellow and black) and coral . . . 20 15
2923 31c. Red and yellow fish, starfish and coral 20 15
2924 31c. Crab and coral 20 15
2925 31c. Snapper and coral . . . 20 15
2926 31c. Seahorse and coral . . . 20 15
Nos. 2903/26 were issued together, se-tenant, forming a composite design.

1998. World Cup Football Championship, France. Designs depicting football art by named artists. Multicoloured.
2927 22c. Type **1485** 15 10
2928 22c. Aldemir Martins 15 10
2929 22c. Glauco Rodrigues . . . 15 10
2930 22c. Marcia Grostein . . . 15 10
2931 22c. Claudio Tozzi 15 10
2932 22c. Zelio Alves Pinto . . . 15 10
2933 22c. Guto Lacaz 15 10
2934 22c. Antonio Peticov . . . 15 10
2935 22c. Cildo Meireles 15 10
2936 22c. Mauricio Nogueira Lima 15 10
2937 22c. Roberto Magalhaes . . 15 10
2938 22c. Luiz Zerbine 15 10
2939 22c. Maciej Babinski (horiz) 15 10
2940 22c. Wesley Duke Lee (horiz) 15 10
2941 22c. Joao Camara (horiz) 15 10
2942 22c. Jose Zaragoza (horiz) 15 10
2943 22c. Mario Gruber (horiz) 15 10
2944 22c. Nelson Leirner (horiz) 15 10
2945 22c. Carlos Vergara (horiz) 15 10
2946 22c. Tomoshige Kusuno (horiz) 15 10

2947	22c. Gregorio Gruber (horiz)	15	10
2948	22c. Jose Roberto Aguilar (horiz)	15	10
2949	22c. Ivald Granato (horiz)	15	10
2950	22c. Leda Catunda (horiz)	15	10

1486 Bean Casserole and Vegetables

1998. Cultural Dishes.

2951	**1486**	31c. multicoloured	20	15

1487 "Araucaria angustifolia"

1998. Environmental Protection. Multicoloured.

2952	22c. Type **1487**	15	10
2953	22c. Azure jay ("Cyanocorax caeruleus")	15	10

Nos. 2952/3 were issued together, se-tenant, forming a composite design.

1488 "Tapajo"

1998. Launching of Submarine "Tapajo".

2954	**1488**	51c. multicoloured	60	35

1489 Bust of Queiroz and College Building

1998. Death Centenary of Luiz de Queiroz (founder of Agricultural College, Piracicaba).

2955	**1489**	36c. multicoloured	20	15

1490 Statue of St. Benedict and Monastery

1998. 400th Anniv of St. Benedict's Monastery, Sao Paulo.

2956	**1490**	22c. multicoloured	15	10

1491 Santos-Dumont and his First Balloon "Brasil"

1998. Aviation. Aircraft Designs by Alberto Santos-Dumont (aviator). Multicoloured.

2957	31c. Type **1491**	20	15
2958	31c. Santos-Dumont and Dirigible "No.1"	20	15

1492 Early Film of Guanabara Bay

1998. Centenary (1997) of Brazilian Cinema. Multicoloured.

2959	31c. Type **1492**	20	15
2960	31c. Taciana Reis (actress) in "Limite" (dir. Mario Peixoto, 1912)	20	15
2961	31c. Grande Otela and Oscarito in "A Dupla do Barulho" (dir. Carlos Manga, 1953) (inscr "Chanchada")	20	15
2962	31c. Mazzaropi (actor) and film titles (Vera Cruz film company)	20	15
2963	31c. Glauber Rocha (director) ("New Cinema")	20	15
2964	31c. Titles of prize-winning films, 1962–98	20	15

1493 Andrade, Entrance to St. Antony's Church (Tiradentes) and Church of Our Lady of the Rosary (Ouro Preto)

1998. Birth Centenary of Rodrigo Melo Franco de Andrade (founder of Federal Institution for Preservation of the National Historic and Artistic Patrimony).

2965	**1493**	51c. multicoloured	30	25

1494 Cascudo and Folk Characters

1998. Birth Centenary of Luis da Camara Cascudo (writer).

2966	**1494**	22c. multicoloured	15	10

1495 Fencing

1998. 42nd World Aeronautical Pentathlon Championships, Natal. Multicoloured.

2967	22c. Type **1495**	15	10
2968	22c. Running	15	10
2969	22c. Swimming	15	10
2970	22c. Shooting	15	10
2971	22c. Basketball	15	10

1496 Missionary Cross and St. Michael of the Missions Church

1998. Mercosur. Missions.

2972	**1496**	80c. multicoloured	50	45

1497 Untitled Work (Jose Leonilson) (Biennale emblem)

1998. 24th Art Biennale, Sao Paulo. Paintings. Mult.

2973	31c. Type **1497**	20	15
2974	31c. "Tapuia Dance" (Albert von Eckhout)	20	15
2975	31c. "The Schoolboy" (Vincent van Gogh) (vert)	20	15
2976	31c. "Portrait of Michel Leiris" (Francis Bacon) (vert)	20	15
2977	31c. "The King's Museum" (Rene Magritte) (vert)	20	15
2978	31c. "Urutu" (Tarsila do Amaral)	20	15
2979	31c. "Facade with Arcs, Circle and Fascia" (Alfredo Volpi) (vert)	20	15
2980	31c. "The Raft of the Medusa" (Asger Jorn)	20	15

1498 "Citizenship" (Erika Albuquerque)

1998. Child and Citizenship.

2981	**1498**	22c. multicoloured	15	10

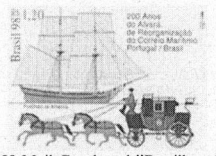

1499 Mail Coach and "Postilhao da America" (brigantine)

1998. Bicentenary of Reorganization of Maritime Mail Service between Portugal and Brazil.

2982	**1499**	1r.20 multicoloured	1·10	90

1500 "D. Pedro I" (Simplicio Rodrigues da Sa), Crown and Sceptre

1501 Mangoes and Glasses of Juice

1998. Birth Bicentenary of Emperor Pedro I.

2983	**1500**	22c. multicoloured	15	10

1998. Frisco (fruit juice) Publicity Campaign. Self-adhesive.

2984	**1501**	36c. multicoloured	20	15

1502 "Solanum lycocarpum"

1998. Cerrado Flowers. Multicoloured.

2985	31c. Type **1502**	20	15
2986	31c. "Cattleya walkeriana"	20	15
2987	31c. "Kielmeyera coriacea"	20	15

1503 Mother Teresa (founder of Missionaries of Charity)

1998. Peace and Fraternity. Multicoloured.

2988	31c. Type **1503**	20	15
2989	31c. Friar Galvao (first Brazilian to be beatified, 1998)	20	15
2990	31c. Betinho (Herbert Jose de Souza)	20	15
2991	31c. Friar Damiao	20	15

Nos. 2988/91 were issued together, se-tenant, forming a central composite design of the Earth.

1504 Sergio Motta and Headquarters, Brasilia

1998. 1st Anniv of National Telecommunications Agency.

2992	**1504**	31c. multicoloured	20	15

Motta was Minister of Communications when the agency was established.

1505 Tiles and Church of Our Lady of Fatima, Brasilia

1998. Christmas.

2993	**1505**	22c. multicoloured	15	10

1506 Moxoto Goat **1507** Man casting Winged Shadow

1998. Domestic Animals. Mult. Self-adhesive.

2994	22c. Type **1506**	15	10
2995	22c. North-eastern donkey	15	10
2996	22c. Junqueira ox	15	10
2997	22c. Brazilian terrier (vert)	15	10
2998	22c. Brazilian shorthair (vert)	15	10

1998. 50th Anniv of Universal Declaration of Human Rights.

2999	**1507**	1r.20 multicoloured	75	65

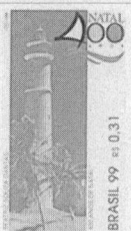

1508 Mother Luiza Lighthouse, Natal

1510 Stamp Vending Machines of 1940s and 1998

1509 Extent of Economic Zone, Satellite and Belmonte Lighthouse

1999. 400th Annivs of Natal (1999) and of Wise Men's Fortress (1998). Multicoloured.
3000 31c. Type **1508** 20 15
3001 31c. Wise Men's Fortress, Natal (horiz) 20 15

1999. Evaluation Programme of Sustainable Potential of Living Resources in the Exclusive Economic Zone (REVIZEE). Multicoloured.
3002 31c. Type **1509** (Sao Pedro and Sao Paulo Archipelago Research Programme) 20 15
3003 31c. Blue-faced booby on buoy 20 15
3004 31c. "Riobaldo" (research ship) 20 15
3005 31c. Turtle 20 15
3006 31c. Dolphin 20 15
3007 31c. Diver 20 15
Nos. 3002/7 were issued together, se-tenant, forming a composite design.
No. 3004 includes the emblem of "Australia 99" International Stamp Exhibition, Melbourne.

1999. 125th Anniv of Universal Postal Union. Multicoloured.
3008 31c. Type **1510** 20 15
3009 31c. Postal products vending machines of 1906 and 1998 . . . . . . 20 15
3010 31c. Postboxes of 1870 and 1973 . . . . . . 20 15
3011 31c. Brazilian Quality and Productivity Programme silver award to Rio Grande postal region, 1998 . . . . 20 15
Nos. 3008/11 were issued together, se-tenant, forming a composite design of the U.P.U. emblem.

1511 Lacerda Lift, Barra Lighthouse and Church of Our Lady of the Rosary

1999. 450th Anniv of Salvador.
3012 **1511** 1r.05 multicoloured . . 65 55

1512 Footprint, Iguanodon, Stegosaurus and Allosaurus

1999. "iBRA 99" International Stamp Exhibition, Nuremberg, Germany. Valley of the Dinosaurs, Sousa.
3013 **1512** 1r.05 multicoloured . . 65 55

1513 Fortress

1999. 415th Anniv of St. Amaro of Barra Grande Fortress, Guaruja.
3014 **1513** 22c. multicoloured . . . 15 10

1515 Camouflaged Airplane, Emblem, Dove and Globe

1999. 30th Anniv of 6th Air Transportation Squadron.
3016 **1515** 51c. multicoloured . . . 30 25

1516 Banner and Revellers

1519 Santos-Dumont and Ballon No.3

1999. Feast of the Holy Spirit, Planaltina.
3017 **1516** 22c. multicoloured . . . 15 10

1518 Symbols of Computer Science, Chemistry, Engineering, Metallurgy and Geology

1999. Centenary of Institute for Technological Research, Sao Paulo.
3019 **1518** 36c. multicoloured . . . 20 15

1999. Centenary of Flight of Alberto Santos-Dumont's Airship Ballon No.3.
3020 **1519** 1r.20 multicoloured . . 75 70

1520 Anteater and Emblem   **1522** Stitched Heart

1999. National Campaign for Prevention and Combat of Forest Fires (PREVFOGO). Mult. Self-adhesive.
3021 51c. Type **1520** 35 30
3022 51c. Flower and IBAMA emblem 35 30
3023 51c. Leaf and IBAMA emblem 35 30
3024 51c. Burnt tree trunk and PREVFOGO emblem . . 35 30
Nos. 3021/4 were issued together, se-tenant, forming a composite design of a map and flames.
Nos. 3021/4 are also impregnated with the scent of burnt wood.

1999. 20th Anniv of Political Amnesty in Brazil.
3026 **1522** 22c. multicoloured . . . 15 10

1523 Joaquim Nabuco (politician)

1999. 150th Birth Anniversaries. Multicoloured.
3027 22c. Type **1523** 15 10
3028 31c. Rui Barbosa (politician) . 20 15

1524 Dorado

1999. "China '99" International Stamp Exhibition, Peking. Fishes. Multicoloured.
3029 22c. Type **1524** 15 10
3030 31c. *Brycon microlepis* . . . 20 15
3031 36c. *Acestrorhynchus pantaneiro* 25 20
3032 51c. Tetra "*Hyphessobrycon eques*" 35 30
3033 80c. *Rineloricaria* sp. . . . 55 45
3034 90c. *Leporinus macrocephalus* 65 55
3035 1r.05 *Abramites* sp. 75 65
3036 1r.20 Bristle-mouthed catfish 85 75
Nos. 3029/36 were issued together, se-tenant, with the backgrounds forming a composite design.
No. 3036 also includes a hologram of the exhibition emblem.

1525 Open Book and Flags of Member Countries

1999. Mercosur. The Book.
3037 **1525** 80c. multicoloured . . . 55 45

1526 Aguas Emendadas Ecological Station

1999. Water Resources. Multicoloured.
3038 31c. Type **1526** 20 15
3039 31c. House and jetty 20 15
3040 31c. Cedro Dam 20 15
3041 31c. Oros Dam 20 15
Nos. 3038/41 were issued together, se-tenant, forming a composite design of a whirlpool.

1527 "Ex Libris" (Eliseu Visconti)

1999. National Library, Rio de Janeiro.
3042 **1527** 22c. multicoloured . . . 15 10

1999. State Flags (6th series). As T **992**.
3043 31c. Amapa 20 15
3044 36c. Roraima 25 20

1528 Piano and Woman

1999. 5th Death Anniv of Antonio Carlos Jobim (composer).
3045 **1528** 31c. multicoloured . . . 20 15

1529 The Annunciation

1999. Christmas. Birth Bimillenary of Jesus Christ. Multicoloured.
3046 22c. Type **1529** 15 10
3047 22c. Adoration of the Magi . 15 10
3048 22c. Presentation of Jesus in the Temple 15 10
3049 22c. Baptism of Jesus by John the Baptist 15 10
3050 22c. Jesus and the Twelve Apostles 15 10
3051 22c. Death and resurrection of Jesus 15 10

1530 Open Book and Globe

1999. New Middle School Education Programme.
3052 **1530** 31c. multicoloured . . . 20 15

1531 Itamaraty Palace, Rio de Janeiro

1999. Centenary of Installation of Ministry of Foreign Relations Headquarters in Itamaraty Palace, Rio de Janeiro.
3053 **1531** 1r.05 brown and stone 75 65

1532 Buildings and Trees (Milena Karoline Ribeiro Reis)

2000. "Stampin the Future". Winning Entries in Children's International Painting Competition. Mult.
3054 22c.+8c. Type **1532** 20 15
3055 22c.+8c. Globe, sun, trees, children and whale (Caio Ferreira Guimaraes de Oliveira) 20 15
3056 22c.+8c. Woman with globe on dress (Clarissa Cazane) 20 15
3057 22c.+8c. Children hugging globe (Jonas Sampaio de Freitas) 20 15

1533 "2000"

2000. New Millennium.
3058 **1533** 90c. multicoloured . . . 65 55

1534 Map of South America and Children holding Books

2000. National School Book Programme.
3059 **1534** 31c. multicoloured . . . 20 15

1535 Ada Rogato

2000. Women Aviators. Multicoloured.
3060   22c. Type **1535**   15   10
3061   22c. Thereza de Marzo . . .   15   10
3062   22c. Anesia Pinheiro   15   10

1536 Moqueca Capixaba

2000. Cultural Dishes. Multicoloured.
3063   1r.05 Type **1536**   75   65
3064   1r.05 Moqueca baiana . . .   75   65

1537 Freyre and Institute Facade

2000. Birth Centenary of Gilberto Freyre (writer).
3065   **1537** 36c. multicoloured . . .   25   15

1538 Painting and Emblem

2000. 500th Anniv of the Discovery of Brazil.
3066   **1538** 51c. multicoloured . . .   30   25

1539 Natives

2000. 500th Anniv of the Discovery of Brazil.
Multicoloured.
3067   31c. Type **1539**   15   10
3068   31c. Natives watching ships   15   10
3069   31c. Sailors in rigging . . .   15   10
3070   31c. Ships sails and natives   15   10

1540 Sailing Ship and Brazilian
Flag

2000. 500th Anniv of the Discovery of Brazil.
Multicoloured.
3071   45c. Type **1540**   25   10
3072   45c. Man dressed in red
          suit, pineapple and
          telephone dial   25   10
3073   45c. Red-spectacled amazon
          and silhouettes of sailing
          ships   25   10
3074   45c. Four babies   25   10
3075   45c. Go-kart, Formula 1
          racing car and Ayrton
          Senna   25   10
3076   45c. Sloth, Toco toucan,
          crocodile, penguin and
          tiger   25   10
3077   45c. Outline of Brazil and
          compass roses   25   10
3078   45c. Peace dove   25   10
3079   45c. Child with decorated
          face   25   10
3080   45c. "500" emblem   25   10
3081   45c. Man wearing feather
          headdress   25   10
3082   45c. Man in boat, sails and
          town (Nataly M. N.
          Moriya)   25   10
3083   45c. Wristwatch, balloon,
          Alberto Santos-Dumont
          and his biplane *14 bis* . .   25   10
3084   45c. Sailing ship and
          document (first report of
          discovery)   25   10
3085   45c. Jules Rimet Cup and
          World Cup trophies,
          player, football and year
          dates (Brazilian victories
          in World Cup Football
          Championship)   25   10
3086   45c. Hand writing, street
          lights and fireworks . . .   25   10
3087   45c. Banners and Brazilian
          flag forming cow   25   10
3088   45c. Golden conure perched
          on branch   25   10
3089   45c. Bakairi masks   25   10
3090   45c. Globe, ship and
          emblem   25   10

1541 Globe and Map of Brazil

2000. 2nd Anniv of BrazilTradeNet (business
information web site).
3091   **1541** 27c. multicoloured . . .   10   10

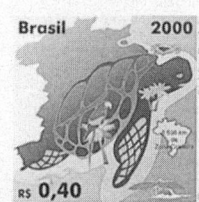

1542 Turtle, Scarlet Macaw and
Map

2000. National Coastal Management Programme
(G.E.R.C.O.).
3092   **1542** 40c. multicoloured . . .   20   10

1544 Cruz, Students and Building Facade

2000. Centenary of the Oswaldo Cruz Foundation
(medical research institution).
3094   **1544** 40c. multicoloured . . .   20   10

1545 Mask, Musical Instruments
and Jewellery

2000. Africa Day.
3095   **1545** 1r.10 multicoloured . .   60   20

1546 Klink in Rowing Boat and
Portion of Globe showing Route

2000. Voyages by Amyr Klink (navigator).
Multicoloured.
3096   1r. Type **1546** (first South
          Atlantic crossing by
          rowing boat (1984)) . . .   55   30
3097   1r. *Paratii* (polar sailing
          boat) in Antarctica and
          portion of globe showing
          route (first single-handed
          circumnavigation of
          Antarctica (1999))   55   30
Nos. 3096/7 were issued together, se-tenant,
forming a composite design.

1547 Flag, Buildings, Map and City Arms

2000. 150th Anniv of Juiz de Fora.
3098   **1547** 60c. multicoloured . . .   35   20

1548 Hang Gliding

2000. Outdoor Pursuits. Multicoloured. Self-
adhesive.
3099   27c. Type **1548**   10   10
3100   27c. Surfing   10   10
3101   40c. Rock climbing   20   10
3102   40c. Skateboarding   20   10

1549 Forest

2000. Environmental Protection. Multicoloured.
3103   40c. Type **1549**   20   10
3104   40c. Oncilla standing on
          branch in forest   20   10
3105   40c. Vegetation, adult
          oncilla and head of kitten   20   10
3106   40c. Vegetation, adult
          oncilla and body of kitten   20   10
Nos. 3103/6 were issued together, se-tenant,
forming a composite design.

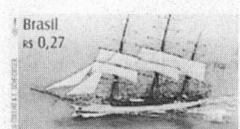

1550 *Cisne Branco* (full-rigged cadet
ship)

2000. Brazilian Navy. Cadet Ships. Multicoloured.
3107   27c. Type **1550**   10   10
3108   27c. *Brasil* (cadet frigate) . .   10   10

1553 Teixeira, Carneiro Ribeiro Education
Center, Salvador and Pupils

2000. Birth Centenary of Anisio Teixeira (education
reformer).
3111   **1553** 45c. multicoloured . . .   25   10

1554 Child walking to School

2000. 10th Anniv of the Children and Teenagers
Statute (3112) and 15th Anniv of National
Movement of Street Boys and Girls (3113).
Multicoloured.
3112   27c. Type **1554**   10   10
3113   40c. Rainbow with girl and
          boy holding star   20   10

EXPRESS STAMP

1930. Surch **1000 REIS EXPRESSO** and bars.
E490   **66** 1000r. on 200r. blue . . .   5·25   2·40

NEWSPAPER STAMPS

N 34   N 37

1889. Roul.
N88   N **34** 10r. orange . . . . . .   3·50   3·50
N89   20r. orange . . . . . .   9·00   9·00
N90   50r. orange . . . . . .   15·00   7·00
N91   100r. orange . . . . . .   6·00   3·50
N92   200r. orange . . . . . .   3·50   1·75
N93   300r. orange . . . . . .   4·00   1·75
N94   500r. orange . . . . . .   30·00   9·00
N95   700r. orange . . . . . .   4·75   15·00
N96   1000r. orange . . . . . .   4·75   15·00

1889. Roul.
N 97   N **34** 10r. green . . . . .   1·75   60
N 98   20r. green . . . . .   1·75   60
N 99   50r. buff . . . . . .   2·40   1·25
N100a   100r. mauve . . . . .   4·75   1·75
N101   200r. black . . . . .   4·00   1·75
N102   300r. red . . . . . .   18·00   15·00
N103   500r. green . . . . .   70·00   90·00
N104   700r. blue . . . . .   38·00   60·00
N105   1000r. brown . . . . .   18·00   45·00

1890. Perf.
N111   N **37** 10r. blue . . . . .   18·00   15·00
N112   20r. green . . . . .   55·00   21·00
N113   100r. mauve . . . . .   18·00   18·00

N **38** Southern Cross and
Sugar-loaf Mountain

1890. Perf.
N119   N **38** 10r. blue . . . . .   2·40   1·75
N123a   20r. green . . . . .   7·00   4·00
N127   50r. green . . . . .   18·00   15·00

OFFICIAL STAMPS

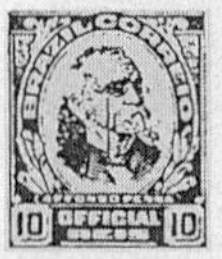
O 64 Pres. Affonso Penna

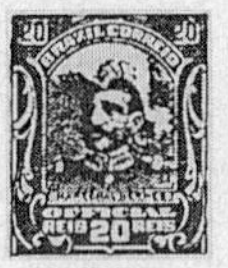
O 67 Pres. Hermes de Fonseca

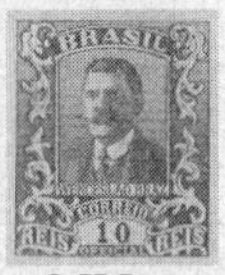
O 77 Pres. Wenceslao Braz

1906. Various frames.

O282	O 64	10r. green & orange	90	10
O283		20r. green & orange	1·25	10
O284		50r. green & orange	1·75	10
O285		100r. green & orange	90	10
O286		200r. green & orange	1·25	35
O287		300r. green & orange	3·50	60
O288		400r. green & orange	7·00	3·00
O289		500r. green & orange	3·50	1·75
O290		700r. green & orange	4·75	4·00
O291		1000r. green & orange	4·75	1·25
O292		2000r. green & orange	5·25	2·40
O293		5000r. green & orange	10·50	1·75
O294		10000r. green & orange	10·50	1·40

1913. Various frames.

O295	O 67	10r. black and grey	20	60
O296		20r. black and olive	20	60
O297		50r. black and grey	25	60
O298		100r. black and red	90	35
O299		200r. black and blue	1·25	35
O300		500r. black & yellow	3·00	60
O301		600r. black & purple	3·50	3·00
O302		1000r. black & brown	4·00	1·75
O303		2000r. black & brown	7·00	2·40
O304		5000r. black & bistre	9·00	3·50
O305		10000r. black	15·00	7·00
O306		20000r. black & blue	27·00	27·00
O307		50000r. black & green	48·00	48·00
O308		100000r. black & red	£140	£140
O309		500000r. black & brn	£200	£200
O310		1000000r. black & brn	£225	£225

1919.

O311	O 77	10r. brown	25	3·50
O312		50r. green	90	1·25
O313		100r. red	1·75	60
O314		200r. blue	2·40	60
O315		500r. orange	9·00	18·00

POSTAGE DUE STAMPS

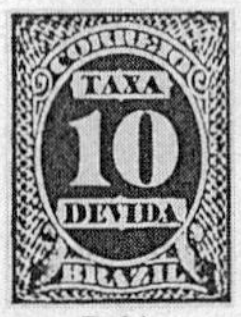
D 34

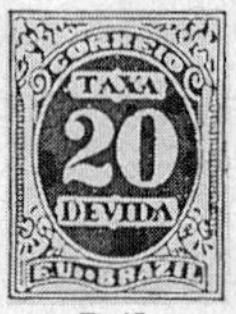
D 45

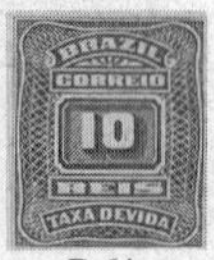
D 64

1889. Roul.

D88	D 34	10r. red	3·50	1·25
D89		20r. red	5·25	2·40
D90		50r. red	7·00	4·75
D91		100r. red	3·50	1·75
D92		200r. red	70·00	21·00
D93		300r. red	10·50	10·50
D94		500r. red	9·00	9·00
D95		700r. red	16·00	18·00
D96		1000r. red	16·00	14·00

1890. Roul.

D 97	D 34	10r. orange	60	35
D 98		20r. blue	60	35
D 99		50r. olive	1·25	35
D100		200r. red	7·00	1·25
D101		300r. green	3·50	1·75
D102		500r. grey	4·75	3·50
D103		700r. violet	5·25	10·50
D104		1000r. purple	7·00	7·00

1895. Perf.

D172	D 45	10r. blue	1·75	1·25
D173		20r. green	9·00	7·00
D174		50r. green	14·00	9·00
D175		100r. red	7·00	2·40
D176b		200r. lilac	7·00	1·75
D177a		300r. blue	3·00	2·40
D178		2000r. brown	18·00	18·00

1906.

D282	D 64	10r. slate	35	35
D283		20r. violet	35	35
D284		50r. green	40	35
D285		100r. red	1·25	60
D286		200r. blue	90	40
D287		300r. grey	60	1·25
D288		400r. deep olive	1·25	50
D289		500r. lilac	30·00	30·00
D290		600r. purple	1·25	2·40
D291		700r. brown	26·00	26·00
D292		1000r. red	3·00	3·50
D293		2000r. green	4·75	5·25
D294		5000r. brown	1·25	38·00

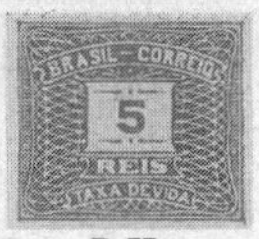
D 77

1919.

D345	D 77	5r. brown	40	40
D403		10r. mauve	35	35
D365		20r. olive	40	40
D404		20r. black	40	35
D405		50r. green	45	45
D375		100r. red	60	60
D407		200r. blue	1·75	60
D408		400r. brown	1·25	1·25
D401		600r. violet	60	60
D350		600r. orange	1·25	1·25
D409		1000r. turquoise	60	60
D439		2000r. brown	1·25	1·25
D411		5000r. blue	85	85

BREMEN Pt. 7

A free city of the Hanseatic League, situated on the R. Weser in northern Germany. Joined the North German Confederation in 1868.

72 grote = 1 thaler.
22 grote = 10 silbergroschen.

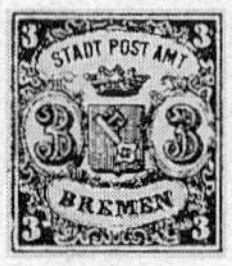
1

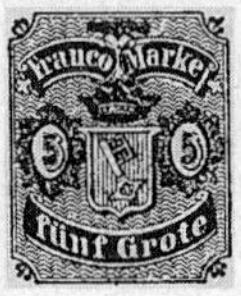
2

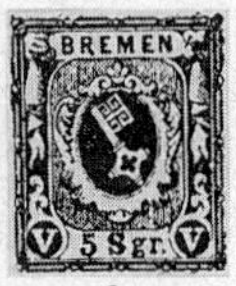
3

1855. Imperf.

1	1	3g. black on blue	£160	£250

1856. Imperf.

3	2	5g. black on red	£150	£250
4		7g. black on yellow	£190	£550
5	3	5sg. green	£110	£200

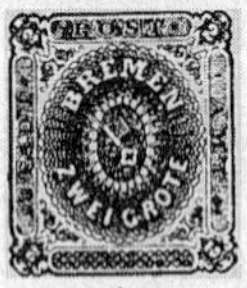
4

5

1861. Zigzag roulette or perf.

17	4	2g. orange	55·00	£250
19	1	3g. black on blue	60·00	£275
20	2	5g. black on red	£110	£225
21		7g. black on yellow	£120	£3000
22	5	10g. black	£170	£550
24	3	5sg. green	£140	£140

BRITISH ANTARCTIC TERRITORY Pt. 1

Constituted in 1962 comprising territories south of latitude 60°S., from the former Falkland Island Dependencies.

1963. 12 pence = 1 shilling;
20 shillings = 1 pound.
1971. 100 (new) pence = 1 pound.

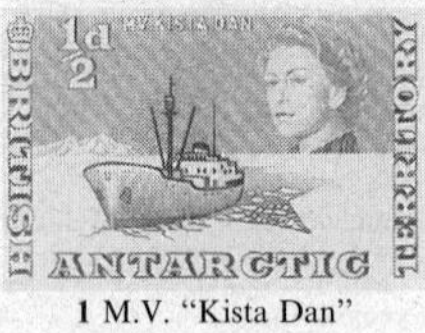
1 M.V. "Kista Dan"

1963.

1	1	½d. blue	1·25	1·75
2	–	1d. brown	1·25	80
3	–	1½d. red and purple	1·25	1·50
4	–	2d. purple	1·25	80
5	–	2½d. myrtle	3·00	1·25
6	–	3d. turquoise	3·75	1·25
7	–	4d. sepia	2·75	1·50
8	–	6d. olive and blue	4·50	2·25
9	–	9d. green	3·50	2·00
10	–	1s. turquoise	3·75	70
11	–	2s. violet and brown	20·00	9·00
12	–	2s.6d. blue	20·00	9·50
13	–	5s. orange and red	21·00	14·00
14	–	10s. blue and green	45·00	26·00
15	–	£1 black and blue	48·00	48·00
15a	–	£1 red and black	£120	£120

DESIGNS: 1d. Manhauling; 1½d. Muskeg (tractor); 2d. Skiing; 2½d. De Havilland D.H.C.2 Beaver (aircraft); 3d. R.R.S. "John Biscoe II"; 4d. Camp scene; 6d. H.M.S. "Protector"; 9d. Sledging; 1s. De Havilland D.H.C.3 Otter (aircraft); 2s. Huskies; 2s.6d. Westland Whirlwind helicopter; 5s. Snocat (tractor); 10s. R.R.S. "Shackleton"; £1 (No. 15), Antarctic map; £1 (No. 15a), H.M.S. "Endurance I".

1966. Churchill Commemoration. As T **38** of Antigua.

16	½d. blue	80	3·25
17	1d. green	3·00	3·25
18	1s. brown	21·00	6·50
19	2s. violet	24·00	7·00

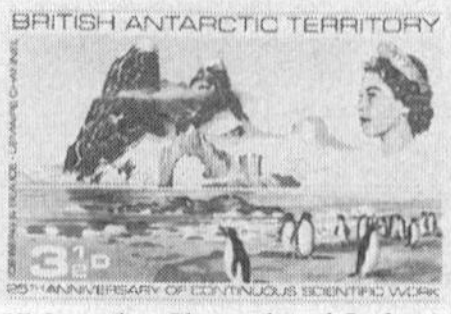

17 Lemaire Channel and Icebergs

1969. 25th Anniv of Continuous Scientific Work.

20	17	3½d. black, blue and ultram	3·50	3·00
21	–	6d. multicoloured	1·25	2·50
22	–	1s. black, blue and red	1·25	2·00
23	–	2s. black, orange and turquoise	1·25	3·00

DESIGNS: 6d. Radio Sonde balloon; 1s. Muskeg pulling tent equipment; 2s. Surveyors with theodolite.

1971. Decimal Currency. Nos. 1/14 surch.

24	½p. on ½d. blue	60	3·00
25	1p. on 1d. brown	1·00	90
26	1½p. on 1½d. red and purple	1·25	75
27	2p. on 2d. purple	1·25	40
28	2½p. on 2½d. green	3·00	2·25
29	3p. on 3d. blue	2·50	75
30	4p. on 4d. brown	2·25	75
31	5p. on 6d. green and blue	4·75	3·50
32	6p. on 9d. green	16·00	8·00
33	7½p. on 1s. blue	17·00	8·50
34	10p. on 2s. violet and brown	20·00	14·00
35	15p. on 2s.6d. blue	20·00	15·00
36	25p. on 5s. orange and red	24·00	17·00
37	50p. on 10s. blue and green	42·00	30·00

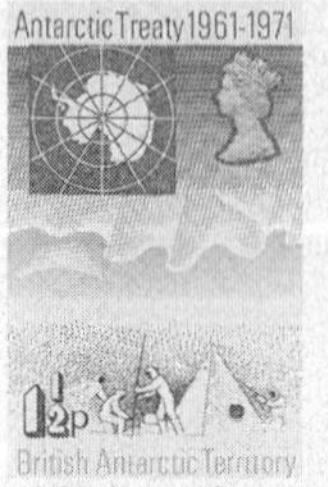

19 Setting up Camp, Graham Land

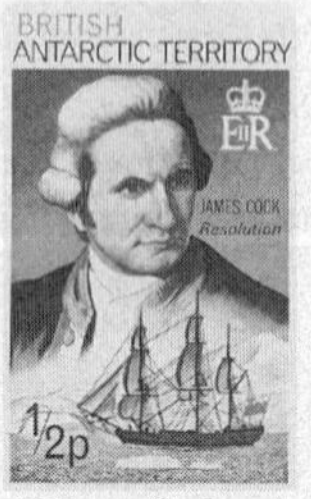

21 James Cook and H.M.S. "Resolution"

1971. 10th Anniv of Antarctic Treaty. Muticoloured.

38	1½p. Type **19**	6·00	5·50
39	4p. Snow petrels	16·00	8·00
40	5p. Weddell seals	9·50	8·00
41	10p. Adelie penguins	22·00	9·00

Nos. 38/41 each include Antarctic map and Queen Elizabeth in their design.

1972. Royal Silver Wedding. As T **52** of Ascension, but with Kerguelen fur seals and Emperor penguins in background.

42	5p. brown	3·00	3·00
43	10p. green	3·00	3·00

1973. Multicoloured.

64a	½p. Type **21**	75	2·50
65	1p. Thaddeus von Bellingshausen and "Vostok"	60	2·25
66	1½p. James Weddell and "Jane"	60	2·25
47	2p. John Biscoe and "Tula"	2·25	1·75
48	2½p. J. S. C. Dumont d'Urville and "L'Astrolabe"	1·50	1·75
49	3p. James Clark Ross and H.M.S. "Erebus"	95	1·75
50	4p. C. A. Larsen and "Jason"	95	1·75
51	5p. Adrien de Gerlache and "Belgica"	1·00	1·75
52	6p. Otto Nordenskjold and "Antarctic"	1·25	1·75
53	7½p. W. S. Bruce and "Scotia"	1·50	2·25
74a	10p. Jean-Baptiste Charcot and "Pourquoi Pas?"	50	3·00
75	15p. Ernest Shackleton and "Endurance"	1·25	2·25
76	25p. Hubert Wilkins and Lockheed Vega "San Francisco"	1·25	1·50
77b	50p. Lincoln Ellsworth and Northrop Gamma "Polar Star"	85	2·75
78	£1 John Rymill and "Penola"	2·75	2·00

The 25p. and 50p. show aircraft; the rest show ships.

1973. Royal Wedding. As T **47** of Anguilla. Background colour given. Multicoloured.

59	5p. brown	40	20
60	15p. blue	70	30

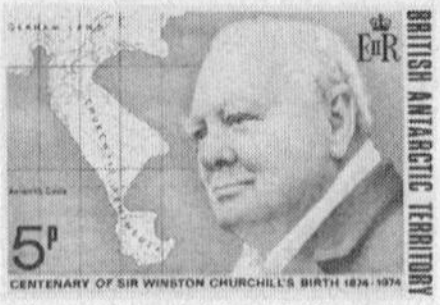

22 Churchill and Churchill Peninsula, B.A.T.

1974. Birth Centenary of Sir Winston Churchill. Multicoloured.

61	5p. Type **22**	1·50	1·75
62	15p. Churchill and "Trepassey"	1·75	2·25

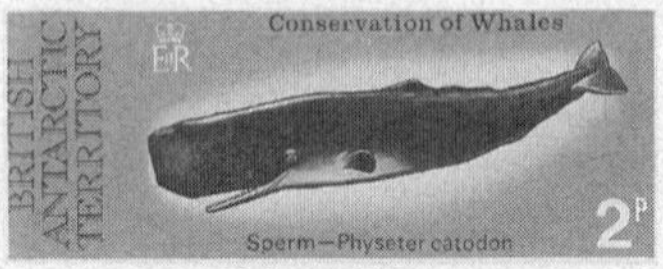

23 Sperm Whale

1977. Whale Conservation. Multicoloured.

79	2p. Type **23**	6·50	4·00
80	8p. Fin whale	7·50	4·50
81	11p. Humpback whale	8·00	4·50
82	25p. Blue whale	8·50	6·00

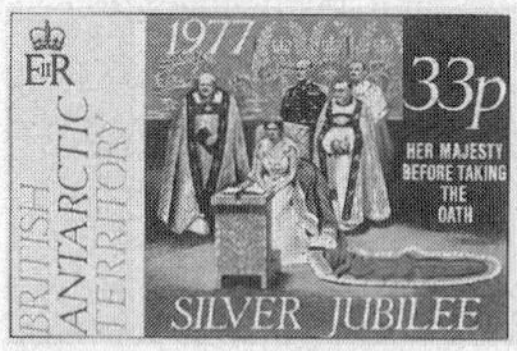

24 The Queen before Taking the Oath

1977. Silver Jubilee. Multicoloured.

83	6p. Prince Philip's visit, 1956/7	70	40
84	11p. The Coronation Oath	80	50
85	33p. Type **24**	1·25	65

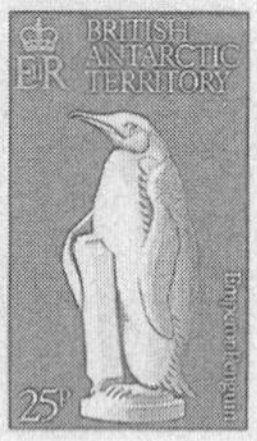

25 Emperor Penguin

1978. 25th Anniv of Coronation.

86	–	25p. green, deep green and silver	80	1·00
87	–	25p. multicoloured	80	1·00
88	25	25p. green, deep green and silver	80	1·00

DESIGNS: No. 86, Black Bull of Clarence; No. 87, Queen Elizabeth II.

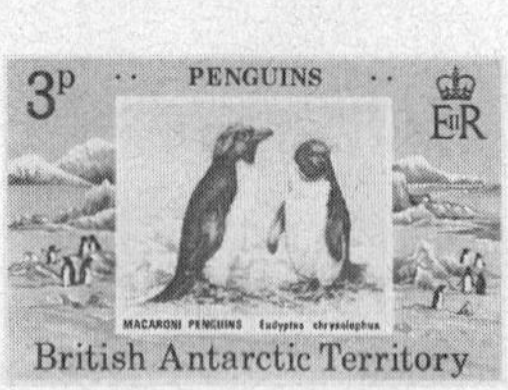

26 Macaroni Penguins

1979. Penguins. Multicoloured.

89	3p. Type **26**	11·00	11·00
90	8p. Gentoo penguins	3·00	3·00
91	11p. Adelie penguins	3·50	3·50
92	25p. Emperor penguins	4·50	4·50

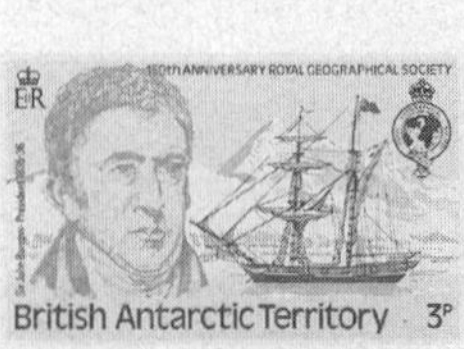

27 Sir John Barrow and "Tula"

1980. 150th Anniv of Royal Geographical Society. Former Presidents. Multicoloured.

93	3p. Type **27**	20	15
94	7p. Sir Clement Markham and "Discovery"	20	25
95	11p. Lord Curzon and whaleboat "James Caird"	25	30
96	15p. Sir William Goodenough	30	35
97	22p. Sir James Wordie	35	55
98	30p. Sir Raymond Priestley	40	65

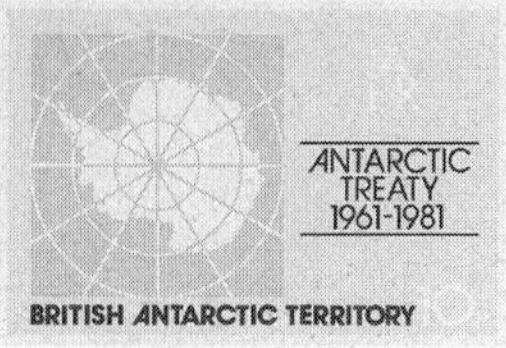

28 Map of Antarctic

1981. 20th Anniv of Antarctic Treaty.

99 **28**	10p. black, blue and light blue	40	80
100 –	13p. black, blue and green	45	90
101 –	25p. black, blue and mauve	55	1·00
102 –	26p. black, brown and red	55	1·00

DESIGNS: 13p. Conservation research ("scientific co-operation"); 25p. Satellite image mapping ("technical co-operation"); 26p. Global geophysics ("scientific co-operation").

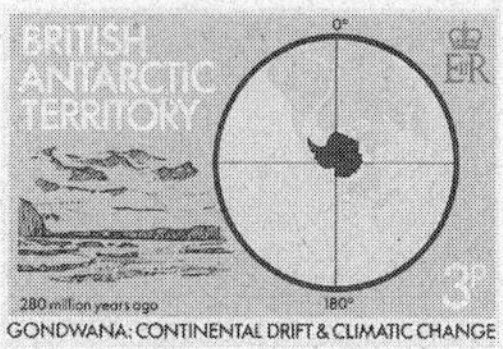

29 Map of Gondwana 280 million years ago and Contemporary Landscape Scene

1982. Gondwana – Continental Drift and Climatic Change. Maps of Gondwana showing position of continents, and contemporary landscapes. Mult.

103	3p. Type **29**	25	40
104	6p. 260 million years ago	30	50
105	10p. 230 million years ago	35	60
106	13p. 175 million years ago	45	70
107	25p. 50 million years ago	55	75
108	26p. Present day	55	75

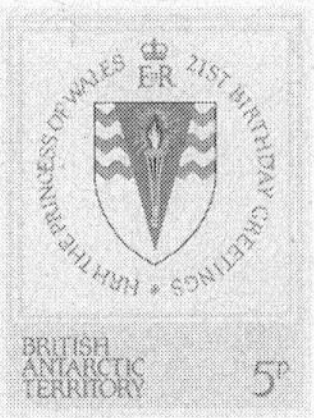

30 British Antarctic Territory Coat of Arms

1982. 21st Birthday of Princess of Wales. Multicoloured.

109	5p. Type **30**	20	20
110	17p. Princess of Wales (detail of painting by Bryan Organ)	45	50
111	37p. Wedding ceremony	70	80
112	50p. Formal portrait	1·10	1·10

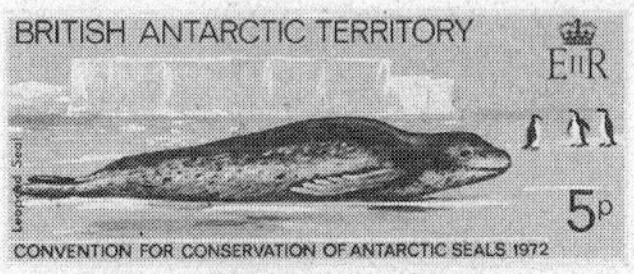

31 Leopard Seal

1983. 10th Anniv of Antarctic Seal Conservation Convention. Multicoloured.

113	5p. Type **31**	30	35
114	10p. Weddell seals	35	40
115	13p. Southern elephant seals	40	45
116	17p. Kerguelen fur seals	40	55
117	25p. Ross seals	40	65
118	34p. Crabeater seals	50	85

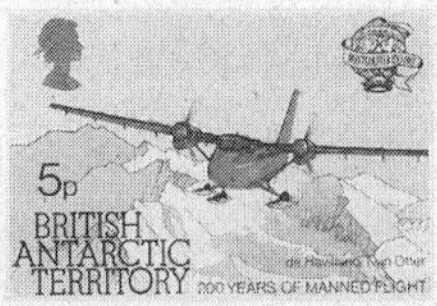

32 De Havilland Twin Otter 200/300

1983. Bicentenary of Manned Flight. Multicoloured.

119	5p. Type **32**	25	30
120	13p. De Havilland D.H.C.3 Otter	40	45
121	17p. Consolidated PBY-5A Canso amphibian	55	60
122	50p. Lockheed Vega "San Francisco"	1·10	1·25

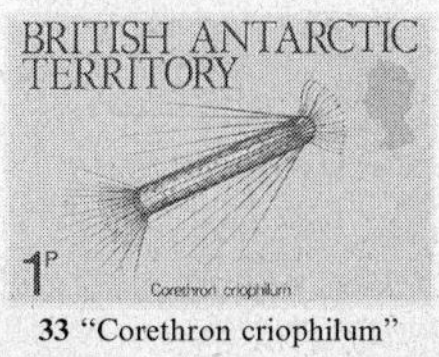

33 "Corethron criophilum"

1984. Marine Life. Multicoloured.

123	1p. Type **33**	60	1·40
124	2p. "Desmonema gaudichaudi"	65	1·40
125	3p. "Tomopteris carpenteri"	65	1·40
126	4p. "Pareuchaeta antarctica"	70	1·50
127	5p. "Antarctomysis maxima"	70	1·50
128	6p. "Antarcturus signiensis"	70	1·50
129	7p. "Serolis cornuta"	70	1·50
130	8p. "Parathemisto gaudichaudii"	70	1·50
131	9p. "Bovallia gigantea"	70	1·50
132	10p. "Euphausia superba"	70	1·50
133	15p. "Colossendeis australis"	70	1·75
134	20p. "Todarodes sagittatus"	75	1·75
135	25p. Antarctic rockcod	80	1·75
136	50p. Black-finned icefish	1·25	2·00
137	£1 Crabeater seal	1·75	2·50
138	£3 Antarctic marine food chain	5·00	6·50

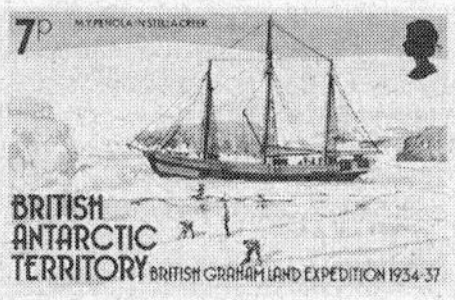

34 M.Y. "Penola" in Stella Creek

1985. 50th Anniv of British Graham Land Expedition. Multicoloured.

139	7p. Type **34**	40	75
140	22p. Northern Base, Winter Island	70	1·40
141	27p. De Havilland Fox Moth at Southern Base, Barry Island	80	1·60
142	54p. Dog Team, near Ablation Point, George VI Sound	1·50	2·25

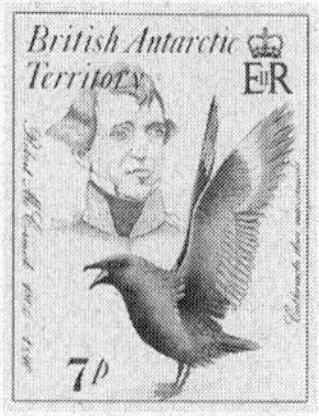

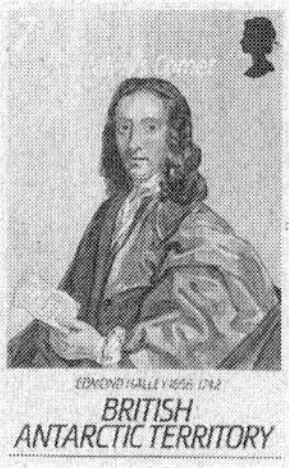

35 Robert McCormick and South Polar Skua

36 Dr. Edmond Halley

1985. Early Naturalists. Multicoloured.

143	7p. Type **35**	1·25	1·50
144	22p. Sir Joseph Dalton Hooker and "Deschampsia antarctica"	1·75	2·75
145	27p. Jean Rene C. Quoy and hourglass dolphin	1·90	2·75
146	54p. James Weddell and Weddell seal	2·75	4·00

1986. Appearance of Halley's Comet. Multicoloured.

147	7p. Type **36**	1·00	1·25
148	22p. Halley Station, Antarctica	1·75	2·25
149	27p. "Halley's Comet, 1531" (from Peter Apian woodcut, 1532)	2·00	2·50
150	44p. "Giotto" spacecraft	3·50	4·50

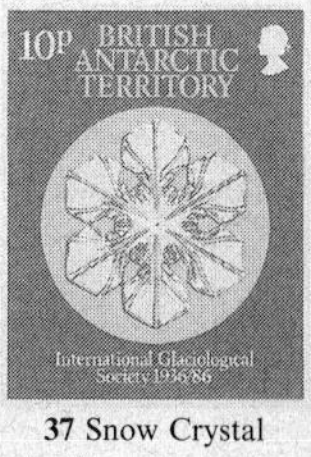

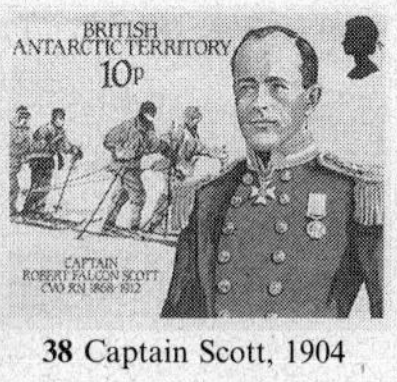

37 Snow Crystal

38 Captain Scott, 1904

1986. 50th Anniv of International Glaciological Society. Snow Crystals.

151 **37**	10p. light blue and blue	60	75
152 –	24p. green and deep green	90	1·40
153 –	29p. mauve and deep mauve	1·00	1·50
154 –	58p. blue and violet	1·40	2·50

1987. 75th Anniv of Captain Scott's Arrival at South Pole. Multicoloured.

155	10p. Type **38**	85	95
156	24p. Hut Point and "Discovery" Ross Island, 1902–4	1·40	2·00
157	29p. Cape Evans Hut, 1911–13	1·75	2·25
158	58p. Scott's expedition at South Pole, 1912	2·25	3·00

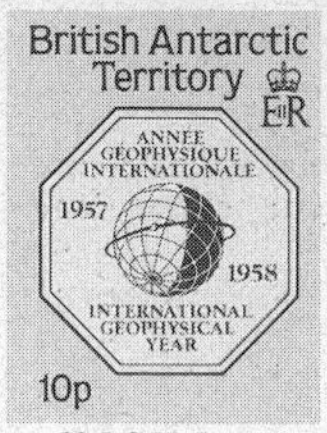

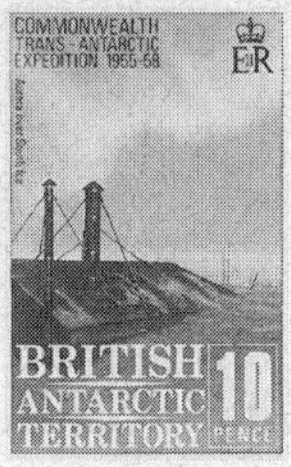

39 I.G.Y. Logo

40 Aurora over South Ice Plateau Station

1987. 30th Anniv of International Geophysical Year.

159 **39**	10p. black and green	30	75
160 –	24p. multicoloured	60	1·40
161 –	29p. multicoloured	75	1·75
162 –	58p. multicoloured	1·40	2·50

DESIGNS: 24p. Port Lockroy; 29p. Argentine Islands; 58p. Halley Bay.

1988. 30th Anniv of Commonwealth Trans-Antarctic Expedition. Multicoloured.

163	10p. Type **40**	30	55
164	24p. "Otter" aircraft at Theron Mountains	60	90
165	29p. Seismic ice-depth sounding	70	1·10
166	58p. "Sno-cat" over crevasse	1·25	1·75

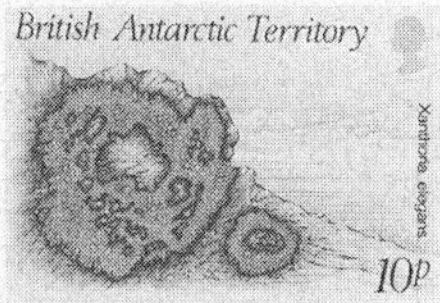

41 "Xanthoria elegans"

1989. Lichens. Multicoloured.

167	10p. Type **41**	90	90
168	24p. "Usnea aurantiaco-atra"	1·60	1·75
169	29p. "Cladonia chlorophaea"	1·75	1·90
170	58p. "Umbilicaria antarctica"	2·50	3·25

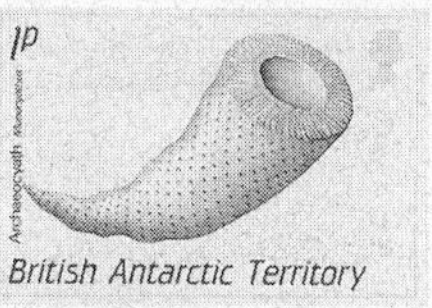

42 "Monocyathus" (archaeocyath)

1990. Fossils. Multicoloured.

171	1p. Type **42**	85	1·00
172	2p. "Lingulella" (brachiopod)	85	1·00
173	3p. "Triplagnoslus" (trilobite)	85	1·00
174	4p. "Lyriaspis" (trilobite)	1·00	1·00
175	5p. "Glossopteris" leaf (gymnosperm)	1·00	1·00
176	6p. "Gonatosorus" (fern)	1·00	1·10
177	7p. "Belemnopsis aucklandica" (belemnite)	1·00	1·10
178	8p. "Sanmartinoceras africanum insignicostatum" (ammonite)	1·00	1·10
179	9p. "Pinna antarctica" (mussel)	1·00	1·10
180	10p. "Aucellina andina" (mussel)	1·00	1·10
181	20p. "Pterotrigonia malagninoi" (mussel)	1·50	1·60
182	25p. "Perissoptera" (conch shell)	1·50	1·60
183	50p. "Ainoceras sp." (ammonite)	2·00	2·75
184	£1 "Gunnarites zinsmeisteri" (ammonite)	3·50	4·25
185	£4 "Hoploparia" (crayfish)	7·00	8·00

1990. 90th Birthday of Queen Elizabeth the Queen Mother. As T **134** of Ascension.

186	26p. multicoloured	1·75	2·50
187	£1 black and brown	3·75	4·50

DESIGNS: 29 × 36 mm: 26p. Wedding of Prince Albert and Lady Elizabeth Bowes-Lyon, 1923. 29 × 37 mm: £1 The Royal Family, 1940.

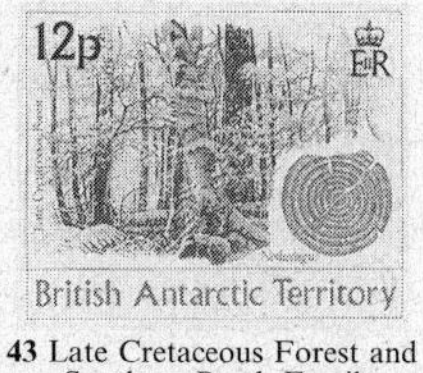

43 Late Cretaceous Forest and Southern Beech Fossil

1991. Age of the Dinosaurs. Multicoloured.

188	12p. Type **43**	1·25	1·25
189	26p. Hypsilophodont dinosaurs and skull	2·00	2·25
190	31p. Frilled sharks and tooth	2·25	2·50
191	62p. Mosasaur, plesiosaur, and mosasaur vertebra	3·50	4·00

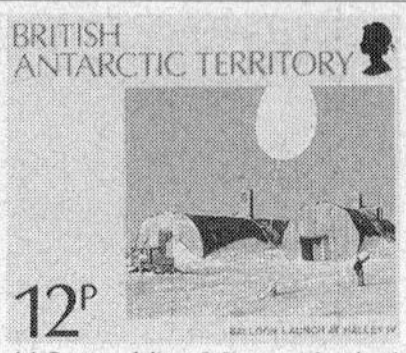

44 Launching Meteorological Balloon, Halley IV Station

1991. Discovery of Antarctic Ozone Hole. Mult.

192	12p. Type **44**	90	1·25
193	26p. Measuring ozone with Dobson spectrophotometer	1·60	2·25
194	31p. Satellite map showing ozone hole	1·75	2·50
195	62p. Lockheed ER-2 aircraft and graph of chlorine monoxide and ozone levels	3·00	3·50

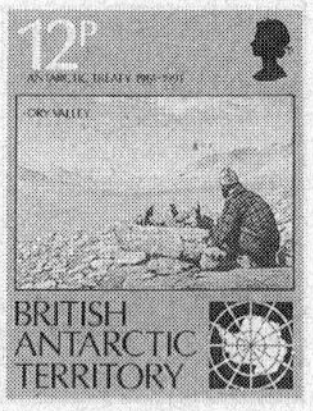

45 Researching Dry Valley

1991. 30th Anniv of Antarctic Treaty.

196 **45**	12p. multicoloured	90	90
197 –	26p. multicoloured	1·60	1·75
198 –	31p. black and green	1·75	1·90
199 –	62p. multicoloured	3·00	3·25

DESIGNS: 26p. Relief map of ice sheet; 31p. BIOMASS logo; 62p. Ross seal.

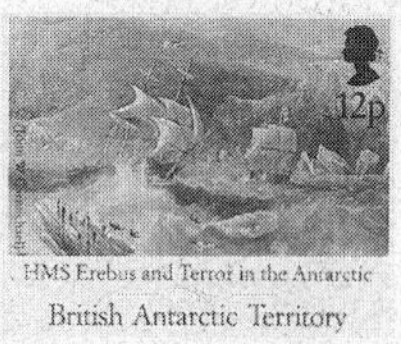

46 "H.M.S. 'Erebus' and H.M.S. 'Terror' in the Antarctic" (J. Carmichael)

1991. Maiden Voyage of "James Clark Ross" (research ship). Multicoloured.

200	12p. Type **46**	90	1·25
201	26p. Launch of "James Clark Ross"	1·60	2·25
202	31p. "James Clark Ross" in Antarctica	1·75	2·50
203	62p. Scientific research	3·00	3·50

1991. Birth Bicentenary of Michael Faraday (scientist). Nos. 200/3 additionally inscr "200th Anniversary M. Faraday 1791–1867".

204	12p. Type **46**	90	1·25
205	26p. Launch of "James Clark Ross"	1·60	2·25
206	31p. "James Clark Ross" in Antarctica	1·75	2·50
207	62p. Scientific research	3·00	3·50

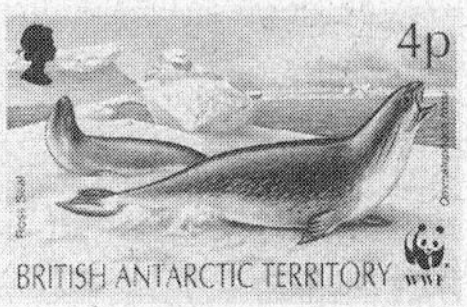

47 Ross Seals

1992. Endangered Species. Seals and Penguins. Multicoloured.

208	4p. Type **47**	80	1·00
209	5p. Adelie penguins	80	1·00
210	7p. Weddell seal with pup	80	1·10
211	29p. Emperor penguins with chicks	2·00	2·00
212	34p. Crabeater seals with pup	1·75	2·00
213	68p. Bearded penguins ("Chinstrap Penguin") with young	2·25	2·50

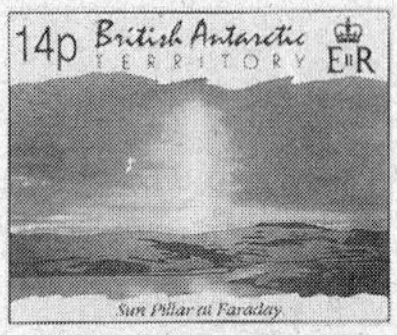

48 Sun Pillar at Faraday

1992. Lower Atmospheric Phenomena. Mult.

214	14p. Type **48**	80	1·00
215	29p. Halo over iceberg	1·40	1·25
216	34p. Lee Wave cloud	1·75	1·50
217	68p. Nacreous clouds	2·75	2·75

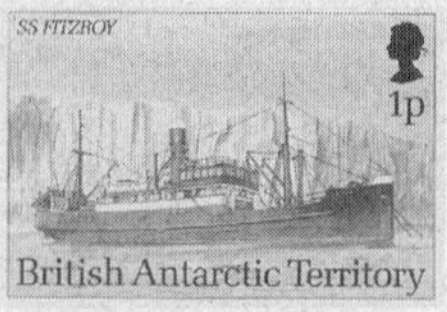

49 "Fitzroy" (mail and supply ship)

1993. Antarctic Ships. Multicoloured.

218	1p. Type **49**	50	80
219	2p. "William Scoresby" (research ship)	60	80
220	3p. "Eagle" (sealer)	70	80
221	4p. "Trepassey" (supply ship)	70	80
222	5p. "John Biscoe I" (research ship)	70	80
223	10p. "Norsel" (supply ship)	1·00	1·25
224	20p. H.M.S. "Protector" (ice patrol ship)	1·25	1·50
225	30p. "Oluf Sven" (supply ship)	1·40	1·75
226	50p. "John Biscoe II" and "Shackleton" (research ships)	1·75	2·00
227	£1 "Tottan" (supply ship)	2·75	3·25
228	£3 "Perla Dan" (supply ship)	6·50	7·50
229	£5 H.M.S. "Endurance I" (ice patrol ship)	10·00	11·00

1994. "Hong Kong '94", International Stamp Exhibition. Nos. 240/5 optd **HONG KONG '94** and emblem.

230	15p. Type **51**	85	1·00
231	24p. De Havilland Turbo Beaver III aircraft	1·25	1·75
232	31p. De Havilland Otter aircraft and dog team	1·50	1·90
233	36p. De Havilland Twin Otter 200/300 aircraft and dog team	1·60	2·00
234	62p. De Havilland Dash Seven aircraft over landing strip, Rothera Point	2·25	2·75
235	72p. De Havilland Dash Seven aircraft on runway	2·25	2·75

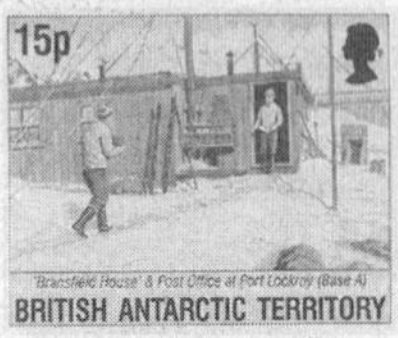

50 Bransfield House Post Office, Port Lockroy

1994. 50th Anniv of Operation Tabarin. Multicoloured.

236	15p. Type **50**	80	80
237	31p. Survey team, Hope Bay	1·25	1·25
238	36p. Dog team, Hope Bay	2·00	1·60
239	72p. "Fitzroy" (supply ship) and H.M.S. "William Scoresby" (minesweeper)	2·75	2·75

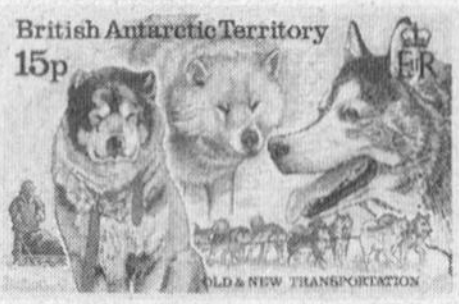

51 Huskies and Sledge

1994. Forms of Transportation. Multicoloured.

240	15p. Type **51**	60	70
241	24p. De Havilland Turbo Beaver III aircraft	80	90
242	31p. De Havilland Otter aircraft and dog team	90	1·00
243	36p. De Havilland Twin Otter 200/300 aircaft and dog team	1·00	1·25
244	62p. De Havilland Dash Seven aircraft over landing strip, Rothera Point	1·90	2·50
245	72p. De Havilland Dash Seven aircraft on runway	2·00	2·75

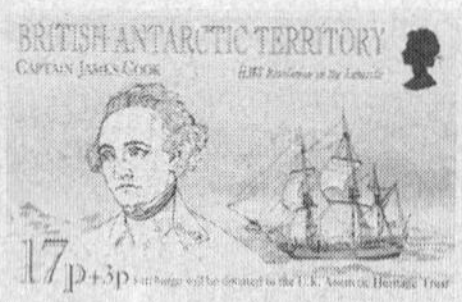

52 Capt. James Cook and H.M.S. "Resolution"

1994. Antarctic Heritage Fund. Multicoloured.

246	17p.+3p. Type **52**	1·50	1·60
247	35p.+15p. Sir James Clark Ross with H.M.S. "Erebus" and H.M.S. "Terror"	1·75	1·90
248	40p.+10p. Capt. Robert Falcon Scott and interior of hut	1·75	1·90
249	76p.+4p. Sir Ernest Shackleton and "Endurance"	2·50	2·75

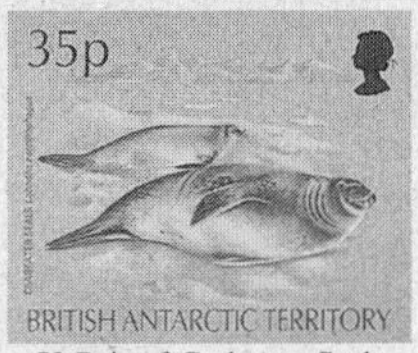

53 Pair of Crabeater Seals

1994. Antarctic Food Chain. Multicoloured.

250	35p. Type **53**	1·25	1·50
251	35p. Blue whale	1·25	1·50
252	35p. Wandering albatross	1·25	1·50
253	35p. Mackerel icefish	1·25	1·50
254	35p. Krill	1·25	1·50
255	35p. Seven star flying squid	1·25	1·50

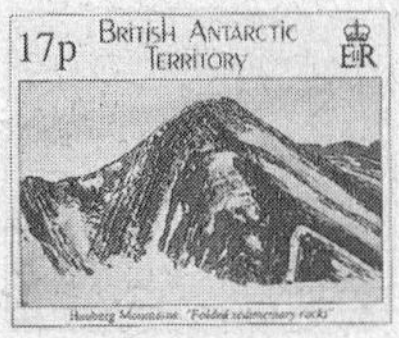

54 Hauberg Mountains

1995. Geological Structures. Multicoloured.

256	17p. Type **54**	75	75
257	35p. Arrowsmith Peninsula	1·50	1·50
258	40p. Colbert Mountains	1·75	1·75
259	76p. Succession Cliffs	2·50	2·50

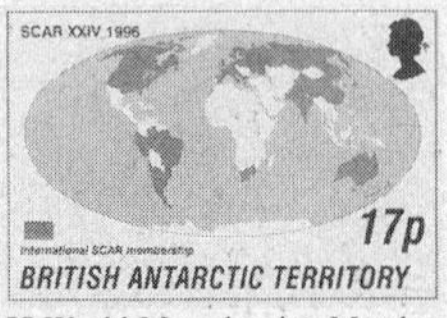

55 World Map showing Member Countries

1996. 24th Meeting of Scientific Committee on Antarctic Research. Multicoloured.

260	17p. Type **55**	75	75
261	35p. Scientist analysing ice samples	1·50	1·50
262	40p. Releasing balloon	1·75	1·75
263	76p. Antarctic research ship catching marine life	2·50	2·50

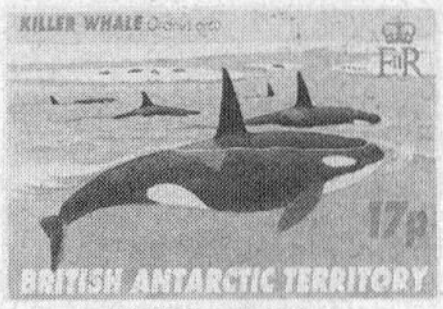

56 Killer Whales

1996. Whales. Multicoloured.

265	17p. Type **56**	70	60
266	35p. Sperm whales	1·25	1·10
267	40p. Minke whales	1·50	1·40
268	76p. Blue whale and calf	2·25	2·00

1996. 70th Birthday of Queen Elizabeth II. As T **165** of Ascension, each incorporating a different photograph of the Queen. Mult.

270	17p. At premiere of "Chaplin", Leicester Square, 1992	70	60
271	35p. At Buckingham Palace dinner, 1991	1·25	1·25
272	40p. In Aberdeen, 1993	1·50	1·50
273	76p. At Royal Military School of Music, 1990	2·00	2·25

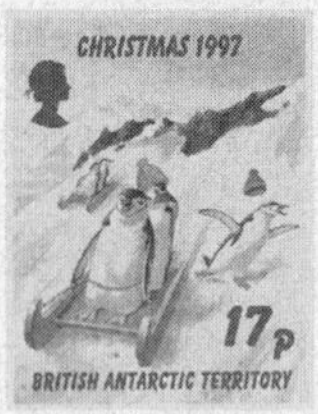

57 Chinstrap Penguins sledging

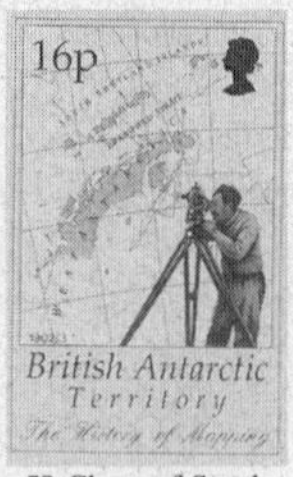

58 Chart of South Shetland Islands (Swedish South Polar Expedition, 1902–3)

1997. Christmas. Multicoloured.

276	17p. Type **57**	1·00	75
277	35p. Emperor penguins carol singing	1·60	1·40
278	40p. Adelie penguins throwing snowballs	1·75	1·60
279	76p. Gentoo penguins ice-skating	2·25	2·75

1998. History of Mapping in Antarctica. Multicoloured.

281	16p. Type **58**	85	75
282	30p. Map of Antarctic Peninsula (1949)	1·40	1·25
283	35p. Map of AntarcticPeninsula (1964)	1·60	1·40
284	40p. Map of Antarctic Peninsula from Landsat (1981)	1·60	1·50
285	65p. Map of Antarctic Peninsula from satellite (1995)	2·00	2·25

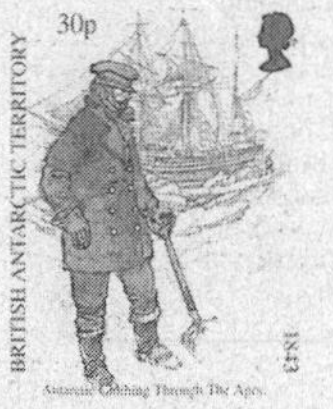

59 Antarctic Explorer and H.M.S. "Erebus", 1843

1998. Antarctic Clothing. Multicoloured.

286	30p. Type **59**	80	80
287	35p. Explorer with dog, and "Discovery I", 1900	90	90
288	40p. Surveyor, and "Fitzroy", 1943	1·10	1·10
289	65p. Scientist with Adelie penguins, and "James Clark Ross", 1998	1·60	1·60

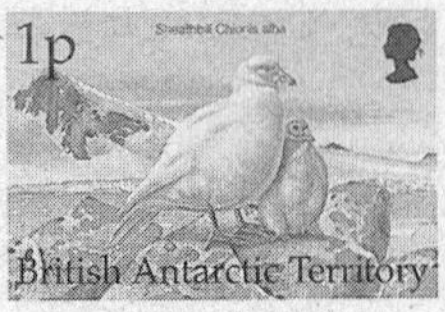

60 Snowy Sheathbill

1998. Antarctic Birds. Multicoloured.

290	1p. Type **60**	10	10
291	2p. Dove prion ("Antarctic Prion")	10	10
292	5p. Adelie penguin	10	10
293	10p. Emperor penguin	20	25
294	20p. Antarctic tern	40	45
295	30p. Black-bellied storm petrel	60	65
296	35p. Southern fulmar ("Antarctic Fulmar")	70	75
297	40p. Blue-eyed cormorant ("Blue-eyed Shag")	80	85
298	50p. South polar skua ("McCormick's Skua")	1·00	1·10
299	£1 Southern black-backed gull ("Kelp Gull")	2·00	2·10
300	£3 Wilson's storm petrel	6·00	6·25
301	£5 Antactic skua ("Brown Skua")	10·00	10·50

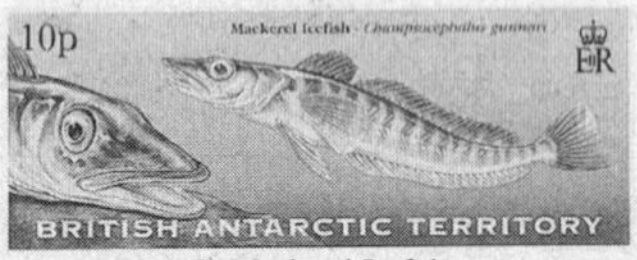

61 Mackerel Icefish

1999. Fish of the Southern Ocean. Multicoloured.

302	10p. Type **61**	30	25
303	20p. Blenny rockcod ("Toothfish")	55	45
304	25p. Borch	65	55
305	50p. Marbled rockcod ("Marbled notothen")	1·25	1·10
306	80p. Bernacchi's rockcod ("Bernach")	1·75	1·75

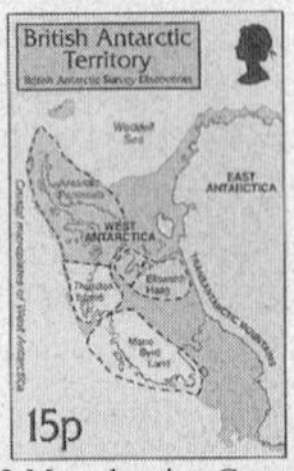

62 Map showing Crustal Microplates of West Antarctica

1999. British Antarctic Survey Discoveries. Mult.

307	15p. Type **62**	75	60
308	30p. Testing lead levels in ice	1·00	85
309	35p. Decolopodid sea spider (Gigantism in marine invertebrates) (horiz)	1·10	90
310	40p. Scientist operating Dobson Spectrophotometer for testing ozone layer (horiz)	1·25	95
311	70p. Radar antenna (aurora electric field research) (horiz)	1·40	1·10

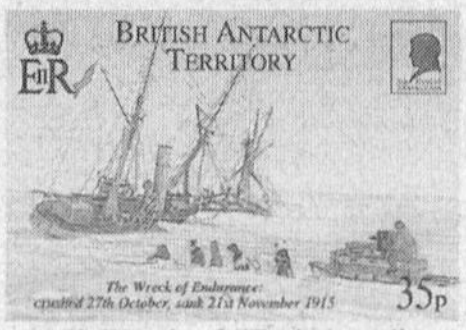

63 Wreck of "Endurance"

2000. Shackleton's Trans-Antarctic Expedition, 1914–17, Commemoration. Multicoloured.

312	35p. Type **63**	1·25	1·00
313	40p. Ocean Camp on ice	1·25	1·00
314	65p. Launching "James Caird" from Elephant Island	1·75	2·00

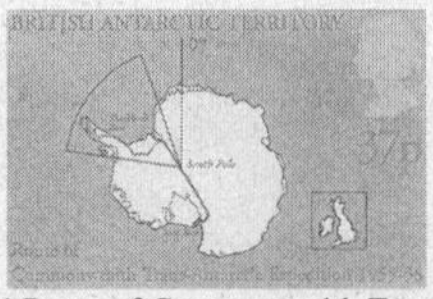

64 Route of Commonwealth Trans-Antarctic Expedition, 1955–58

2000. "Heroic Age of Antarctica" (1st series). Commonwealth Trans-Antarctic Expedition, 1955–8. Multicoloured.

315	37p. Type **64**	95	1·00
316	37p. Expedition at South Pole, 1958	95	1·00
317	37p. *Magga Dan* (Antarctic supply ship)	95	1·00
318	37p. "Sno-cat" repair camp	95	1·00
319	37p. "Sno-cat" over crevasse	95	1·00
320	37p. Seismic explosion	95	1·00

See also Nos. 333/8.

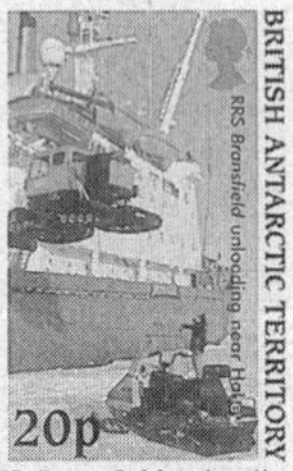

65 *Bransfield* unloading "Sno-cat", Halley

2000. Survey Ships. Multicoloured.

321	20p. Type **65**	60	60
322	33p. *Ernest Shackelton* unloading supplies into *Tula*	85	85
323	37p. *Bransfield* in the ice (horiz)	95	95
324	43p. *Ernest Shackelton* with helicopter (horiz)	1·10	1·10

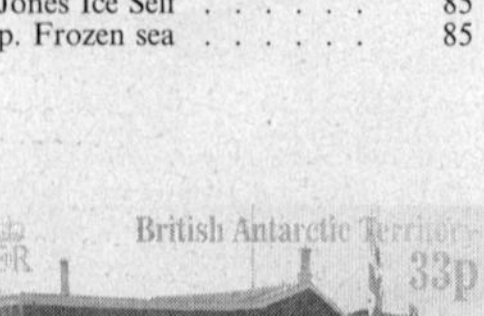

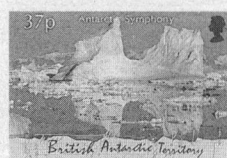

66 Iceberg and Opening Bars

2000. Composition of *Antarctic Symphony* by Sir Peter Maxwell Davies. Multicoloured.

325	37p. Type **66**	75	80
326	37p. Stern of *James Clark Ross* and pack ice	75	80
327	43p. Aircraft and camp on Jones Ice Self	85	90
328	43p. Frozen sea	85	90

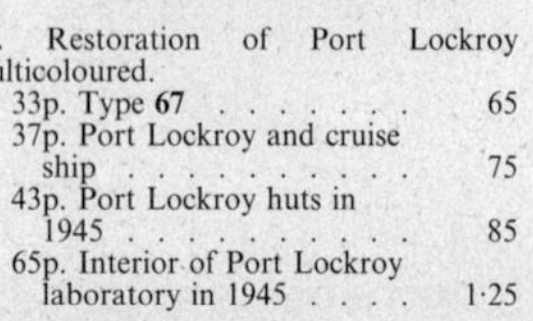

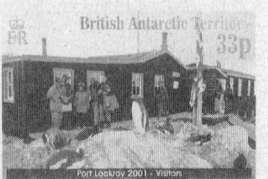

67 Tourists at Port Lockroy

2001. Restoration of Port Lockroy Base. Multicoloured.

329	33p. Type **67**	65	70
330	37p. Port Lockroy and cruise ship	75	80
331	43p. Port Lockroy huts in 1945	85	90
332	65p. Interior of Port Lockroy laboratory in 1945	1·25	1·40

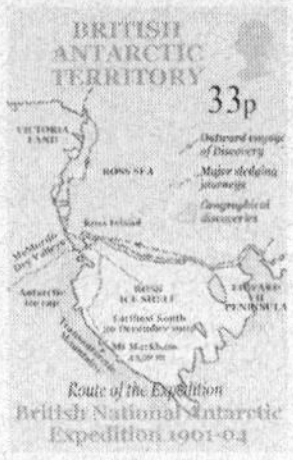

68 Map of Ross Sea Area

2001. "Heroic Age of Antarctica" (2nd series). Captain Scott's 1901–04 Expedition. Multicoloured.

333	33p. Type **68**	65	70
334	37p. Captain Robert F. Scott	75	80
335	43p. First Antarctic balloon ascent, 1902 (horiz)	85	90
336	65p. "Emperor Penguin chick" (drawing by Edward Wilson)	1·25	1·40
337	70p. Shackleton, Scott and Wilson and most southerly camp, 1902 (horiz)	1·40	1·50
338	80p. *Discovery I* trapped in ice off Hut Point (horiz)	1·60	1·75

2002. Golden Jubilee. As T **200** of Ascension.

339	20p. black, mauve and gold	40	45
340	37p. multicoloured	75	80
341	43p. black, mauve and gold	85	90
342	50p multicoloured	1·00	1·10

DESIGNS: 20p. Princess Elizabeth and Princess Margaret making radio broadcast, 1940; 37p. Queen Elizabeth in Garter robes, 1998; 43p. Queen Elizabeth at Balmoral, 1952; 50p. Queen Elizabeth in London, 1996.

BRITISH COLUMBIA AND VANCOUVER ISLAND Pt. 1

Former British colonies, now a Western province of the Dominion of Canada, whose stamps are now used.

1860. 12 pence = 1 shilling;
20 shillings = 1 pound.
1865. 100 cents = 1 dollar.

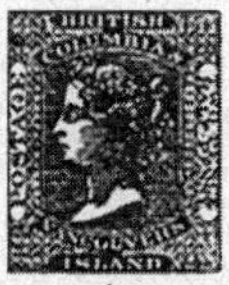

1

1860. Imperf or perf.

2	**1**	2½d. pink	£325	£180

VANCOUVER ISLAND

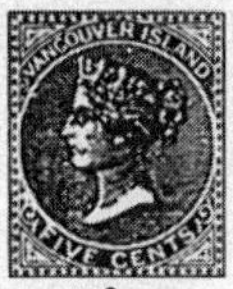

2

1865. Imperf or perf. Various frames.

13	**2**	5c. red	£250	£150
14	–	10c. blue	£225	£140

BRITISH COLUMBIA

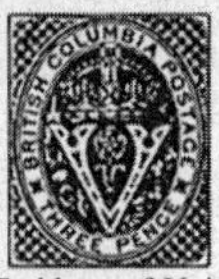

4 Emblems of United Kingdom

1865.

21	**4**	3d. blue	80·00	65·00

1868. Surch in words or figures and words.

28	**4**	2c. brown	£110	£110
29		5c. red	£140	£130
24		10c. red	£550	£475
31		25c. yellow	£140	£130
26		50c. mauve	£475	£425
27		$1 green	£750	£800

BRITISH COMMONWEALTH OCCUPATION OF JAPAN Pt. 1

Stamps used by British Commonwealth Occupation Forces, 1946–49.

12 pence = 1 shilling;
20 shillings = 1 pound.

1946. Stamps of Australia optd **B.C.O.F. JAPAN 1946.**

J1	**27**	½d. orange	3·25	4·75
J2	**46**	1d. purple	2·50	2·25
J3	**31**	3d. brown	2·00	2·00
J4	–	6d. brown (No. 189a)	15·00	9·00
J5	–	1s. green (No. 191)	15·00	11·00
J6	**1**	2s. red	42·00	45·00
J7	**38**	5s. red	95·00	£120

BRITISH EAST AFRICA Pt. 1

Now incorporated in Kenya and Uganda.

16 annas = 100 cents = 1 rupee.

1890. Stamps of Great Britain (1881) surch **BRITISH EAST AFRICA COMPANY** and value in annas.

1	**57**	½a. on 1d. lilac	£275	£200
2	**73**	1a. on 2d. green and red	£450	£275
3	**78**	4a. on 5d. purple and blue	£475	£300

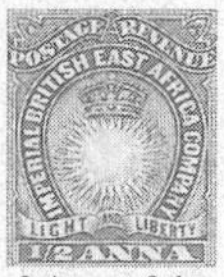

3 Arms of the Company

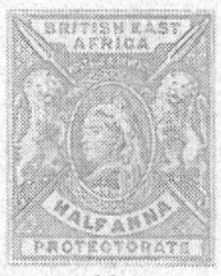

11

1890. Nos. 16/19 are larger (24 × 25 mm).

4b	**3**	½a. brown	70	4·00
5		1a. green	4·00	5·00
6		2a. red	2·75	4·00
7c		2½a. black on yellow	4·50	5·00
8a		3a. black on red	2·00	5·50
9		4a. brown	2·50	5·50
11a		4½a. purple	2·50	16·00
29		5a. black on blue	1·25	10·00
30		7½a. black	1·25	15·00
12		8a. blue	5·50	9·50
13		8a. grey	£275	£225
14		1r. red	6·00	9·00
15		1r. grey	£225	£225
16	–	2r. red	14·00	27·00
17	–	3r. purple	8·50	38·00
18	–	4r. blue	12·00	38·00
19	–	5r. green	30·00	70·00

1891. With handstamped or pen surcharges. Initialled in black.

20	**3**	½a. on 2a. red	£4250	£850
31		½a. on 3a. black on red	£425	50·00
32		1a. on 3a. black on red	£5000	£2500
26		1a. on 4a. brown	£4000	£1400

1894. Surch in words and figures.

27	**3**	5a. on 8a. blue	65·00	85·00
28		7½a. on 1r. red	65·00	85·00

1895. Optd **BRITISH EAST AFRICA.**

33	**3**	½a. brown	70·00	42·00
34		1a. green	£140	95·00
35		2a. red	£180	95·00
36		2½a. black on yellow	£180	55·00
37		3a. black on red	80·00	45·00
38		4a. brown	45·00	35·00
39		4½a. purple	£200	£100
40		5a. black on blue	£190	£130
41		7½a. black	£110	80·00
42		8a. blue	95·00	75·00
43		1r. red	55·00	50·00
44	–	2r. red	£400	£200
45	–	3r. purple	£225	£120
46	–	4r. blue	£170	£160
47	–	5r. green	£400	£250

1895. Surch with large **2½.**

48	**3**	2½a. on 4½a. purple	£150	70·00

1895. Stamps of India (Queen Victoria) optd **British East Africa.**

49	**23**	½a. turquoise	6·50	5·50
50	–	1a. purple	5·50	6·00
51	–	1½a. brown	4·00	4·00
52	–	2a. blue	5·00	3·00
53	–	2a.6p. green	6·00	2·50
54	–	3a. orange	9·50	11·00
55a	–	4a. green (No. 96)	28·00	24·00
56	–	6a. brown (No. 80)	30·00	48·00
57c	–	8a. mauve	28·00	50·00
58	–	12a. purple on red	22·00	30·00
59	–	1r. grey (No. 101)	85·00	65·00
60	**37**	1r. green and red	42·00	£110
61	**38**	2r. red and orange	85·00	£130
62		3r. brown and green	85·00	£130
63		5r. blue and violet	£110	£140

1895. No. 51 surch with small **2½.**

64		2½ on 1½a. brown	85·00	42·00

1896.

65	**11**	½a. green	2·50	80
66		1a. red	5·00	40
67		2a. brown	3·50	4·25
68		2½a. blue	7·00	1·75
69		3a. grey	2·75	6·00
70		4a. green	6·00	3·50
71		4½a. yellow	7·00	16·00
72		5a. brown	7·50	4·25
73		7½a. mauve	5·00	22·00
74		8a. grey	3·50	5·50
75		1r. blue	45·00	23·00
76		2r. orange	65·00	25·00
77		3r. violet	65·00	30·00
78		4r. red	55·00	65·00
79		5r. brown	55·00	40·00

1897. Stamps of Zanzibar, 1896, optd **British East Africa.**

80	**13**	½a. green and red	55·00	45·00
81		1a. blue and red	95·00	90·00
82		2a. brown and red	38·00	21·00
83		4½a. orange and red	50·00	30·00
84		5a. brown and red	55·00	35·00
85		7½a. mauve and red	50·00	35·00

1897. As last, surch **2½.**

86	**13**	2½ on 1a. blue and red	£100	60·00
89		2½ on 3a. grey and red	95·00	50·00

1897. As Type **11**, but larger.

92a		1r. blue	55·00	29·00
93		2r. orange	75·00	75·00
94		3r. violet	90·00	£110
95		4r. red	£275	£325
96		5r. brown	£200	£275
97		10r. brown	£275	£300
98		20r. green	£600	£1400
99		50r. mauve	£1600	£6000

BRITISH FORCES IN EGYPT Pt. 1

SPECIAL SEALS AND STAMPS FOR THE USE OF BRITISH FORCES IN EGYPT

A. SEALS

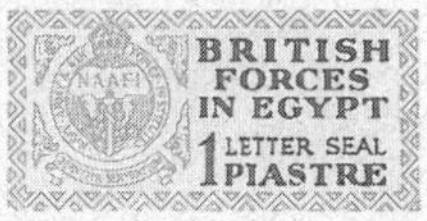

A 1

1932. (a) Inscr "POSTAL SEAL".

A1	A **1**	1p. blue and red	80·00	3·50

(b) Inscr "LETTER SEAL".

A2	A **1**	1p. blue and red	25·00	85

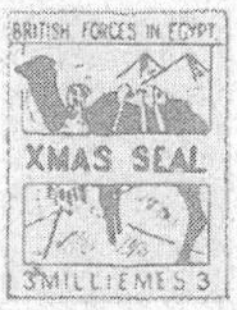

A 2

1932. Christmas Seals.

A3	A **2**	3m. black on blue	48·00	70·00
A4		3m. lake	7·50	48·00
A5		3m. blue	7·00	25·00
A6a		3m. red	7·50	18·00

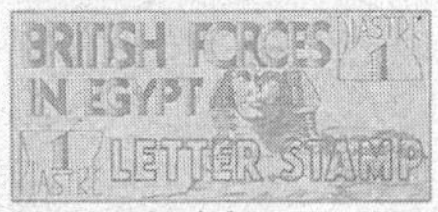

A 3

1934.

A9	A **3**	1p. red	2·25	3·00
A8		1p. green	4·00	4·00

1935. Silver Jubilee. Optd **JUBILEE COMMEMORATION 1935.**

A10	A **3**	1p. blue	£200	£180

1935. Provisional Christmas Seal. Surch **Xmas 1935 3 Milliemes.**

A11	A **3**	3m. on 1p. red	16·00	70·00

B. POSTAGE STAMPS

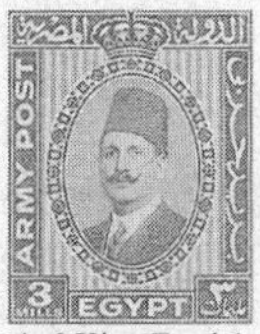

A **6** King Fuad I

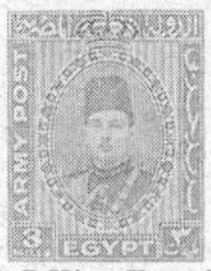

A **7** King Farouk

1936.

A12	A **6**	3m. green	1·00	1·00
A13		10m. red	3·00	10

1939.

A14	A **7**	3m. green	3·00	4·50
A15		10m. red	3·75	10

BRITISH GUIANA Pt. 1

Situated on the N.E. coast of S. America. A British colony granted full internal self-government in August 1951. Attained independence on 26 May 1966, when the country was renamed Guyana.

100 cents = 1 dollar.

1

1850. Imperf.

1	**1**	2c. black on red	—	£70000
2		4c. black on orange	£26000	£4250
4		8c. black on green	£15000	£3250
5		12c. black on blue	£5500	£2000

Prices are for used stamps cut round. Stamps cut square are worth much more.

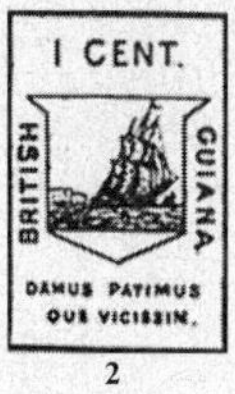

2

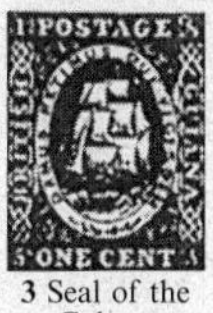

3 Seal of the Colony

1852. Imperf.

9	**2**	1c. black on magenta	£8500	£4250
10		4c. black on blue	£11000	£6000

1853. Imperf.

12	**3**	1c. red	£2750	£1000
20		4c. blue	£900	£350

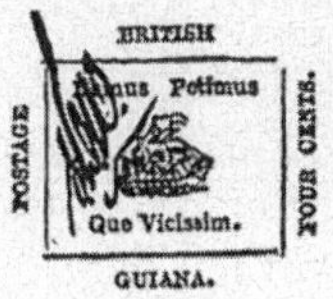

6

1856. Imperf.

23	**6**	1c. black on magenta	†	—
24		4c. black on magenta	†	£6000
25		4c. black on blue	£20000	£8500

7

9

1860. Perf.

29	**7**	1c. red	£1300	£200
40		1c. brown	£325	95·00
85		1c. black	9·50	4·00
87		2c. orange	24·00	3·00
89		4c. blue	80·00	13·00
92	**9**	6c. blue	£110	29·00
95	**7**	8c. red	£110	23·00
98		12c. lilac	£160	13·00
99		12c. grey	£150	16·00
64		24c. green	£170	50·00
79	**9**	24c. green	£140	8·50
82		48c. red	£225	48·00

The prices quoted for Nos. 29/82 are for fine copies with four margins. Medium specimens can be supplied at much lower rates.

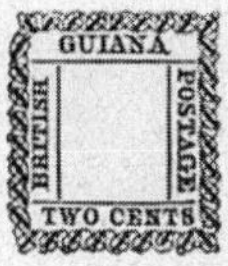

10

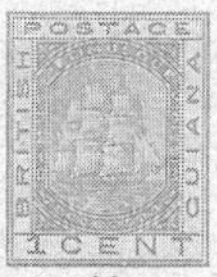

16

1862. Various borders. Roul.

116	**10**	1c. black on red	£2500	£475
119		2c. black on yellow	£2500	£325
122		4c. black on blue	£2750	£550

The above prices are for stamps signed in the centre by the Postmaster. Unsigned stamps are worth considerably less.

1876.

126	**16**	1c. grey	2·75	1·40
171		2c. orange	22·00	15
172		4c. blue	90·00	5·00
173		6c. brown	5·00	6·50
174		8c. red	85·00	40
131		12c. violet	50·00	1·25
132		24c. green	60·00	3·00

133 48c. brown . . . . £110 27·00
134 96c. olive £475 £250

1878. Optd with thick horiz or horiz and vert bars.
(a) On postage stamps.
137 **16** 1c. on 6c. brown . . . . . 38·00 £110
141 **9** 1c. on 6c. blue . . . . . . £150 75·00

(b) On official stamps of 1875 and 1877.
138 **7** 1c. black . . . . £200 70·00
139 **16** 1c. grey . . . . £150 55·00
140 2c. orange . . . . £300 65·00
144 4c. blue . . . . £250 95·00
145 6c. brown . . . . £375 90·00
146 **7** 8c. red £1500 £250
148 **16** 8c. red . . . . £325 95·00

1881. Surch with figure. Old value barred out in ink.
(a) On postage stamps.
152 **9** "1" on 48c. red . . . . . 42·00 5·00
149 **16** "1" on 96c. olive . . . . . 3·50 6·00
150 "2" on 96c. olive . . . . . 4·25 11·00

(b) On stamps optd **OFFICIAL**.
153 **7** "1" on 12c. lilac . . . . . £120 70·00
154 **16** "1" on 48c. brown . . . . £130 90·00
155 "2" on 12c. violet . . . . 65·00 26·00
157 "2" on 24c. green . . . . 75·00 42·00

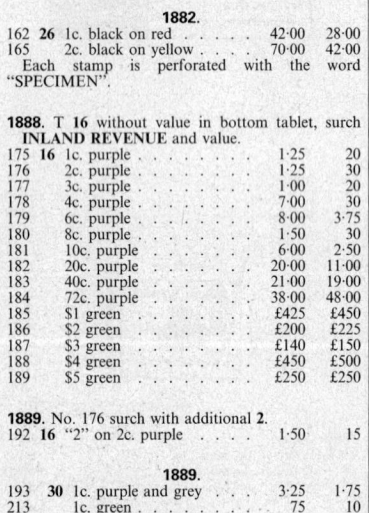

26

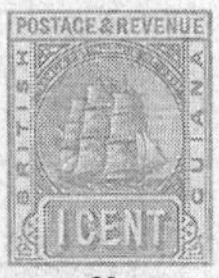
30

1882.
162 **26** 1c. black on red . . . . . 42·00 28·00
165 2c. black on yellow . . . . 70·00 42·00
Each stamp is perforated with the word "SPECIMEN".

1888. T **16** without value in bottom tablet, surch **INLAND REVENUE** and value.
175 **16** 1c. purple . . . . 1·25 20
176 2c. purple . . . . 1·25 30
177 3c. purple . . . . 1·00 20
178 4c. purple . . . . 7·00 30
179 6c. purple . . . . 8·00 3·75
180 8c. purple . . . . 1·50 30
181 10c. purple . . . . 6·00 2·50
182 20c. purple . . . . 20·00 11·00
183 40c. purple . . . . 21·00 19·00
184 72c. purple . . . . 38·00 48·00
185 $1 green £425 £450
186 $2 green £200 £225
187 $3 green £140 £150
188 $4 green £450 £500
189 $5 green £250 £250

1889. No. 176 surch with additional **2**.
192 **16** "2" on 2c. purple . . . . 1·50 15

1889.
193 **30** 1c. purple and grey . . . 3·25 1·75
213 1c. green 75 10
194 2c. purple and orange . . 1·75 10
234 2c. purple and red . . . . 3·25 30
241a 2c. purple & black on red 3·50 10
253a 2c. red . . . . 8·50 10
195 4c. purple and blue . . . 4·50 1·75
254 4c. brown and purple . . 2·25 60
214 5c. blue . . . . 2·75 10
243a 5c. purple & blue on blue 3·50 6·50
198 6c. purple and brown . . 7·00 11·00
236 6c. black and blue . . . 6·50 11·00
256 6c. grey and black . . . 13·00 7·00
199 8c. purple and red . . . 12·00 1·00
215 8c. purple and black . . . 2·75 1·10
200a 12c. purple and mauve . . 8·50 2·25
257 12c. orange and purple . . 4·00 4·00
246a 24c. purple and green . . 3·75 4·50
202 48c. purple and red . . . 16·00 9·00
247a 48c. grey and brown . . . 14·00 20·00
248a 60c. green and red . . . 14·00 85·00
203 72c. purple and brown . . 28·00 38·00
205 96c. purple and red . . . 65·00 70·00
250 96c. black & red on yellow . . . . 35·00 45·00

1890. Nos. 185/8 surch **ONE CENT**.
207 **16** 1 cent on $1 green . . . . 1·25 35
208 1 cent on $2 green . . . . 2·00 60
209 1 cent on $3 green . . . . 2·00 1·25
210 1 cent on $4 green . . . . 2·00 6·50

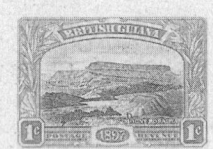

32 Mount Roraima

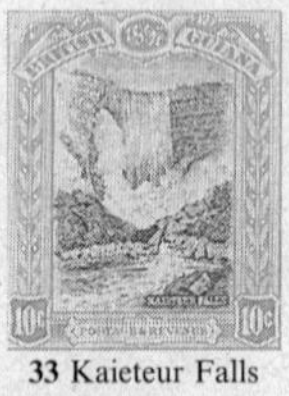
33 Kaieteur Falls

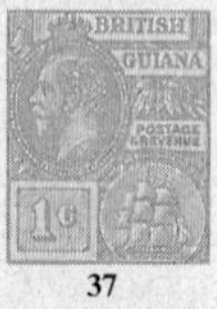
37

1898. Jubilee.
216 **32** 1c. black and red . . . . 4·00 75
217 **33** 2c. brown and blue . . . . 20·00 2·25
219 **32** 5c. green and brown . . . 42·00 3·50
220 **33** 10c. black and red . . . . 22·00 20·00
221 **32** 15c. brown and blue . . . 30·00 16·00

1899. Nos. 219/21 surch **TWO CENTS**.
222 **32** 2c. on 5c. green and brown 3·25 2·00
223 **33** 2c. on 10c. black and red 2·25 2·00
224 **32** 2c. on 15c. brown and blue 1·50 1·25

1905. T **30** but inscr "REVENUE", optd **POSTAGE AND REVENUE**.
251 **30** $2.40 green and violet . . £160 £275

1913.
259a **37** 1c. green . . . . 1·50 25
260 2c. red . . . . 1·25 10
274 2c. violet . . . . 2·50 10
261b 4c. brown and purple . . 3·75 25
262 5c. blue . . . . 1·75 1·00
263 6c. grey and black . . . 2·75 1·00
276 6c. blue . . . . 3·00 30
264 12c. orange and violet . . 1·25 1·00
278 24c. purple and green . . 2·00 4·50
279 48c. grey and purple . . 9·50 3·50
280 60c. green and red . . . 10·00 48·00
281 72c. purple and brown . . 22·00 55·00
269a 96c. black and red on yellow . . . . 18·00 45·00

1918. Optd **WAR TAX**.
271 **37** 2c. red . . . . 1·00 15

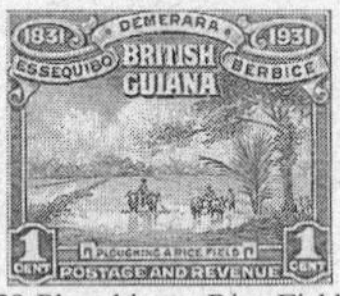
39 Ploughing a Rice Field

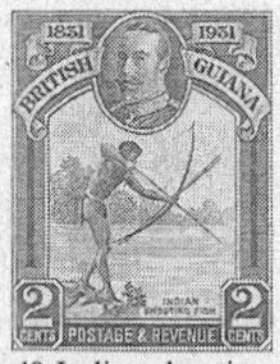
40 Indian shooting Fish

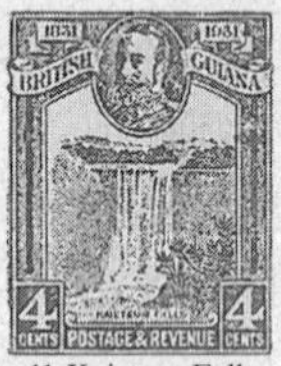
41 Kaieteur Falls

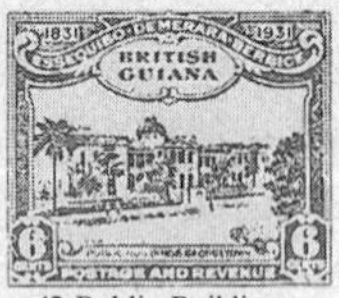
42 Public Buildings, Georgetown

1931. Centenary of County Union.
283 **39** 1c. green . . . . 2·50 1·25
284 **40** 2c. brown . . . . 2·00 10
285 **41** 4c. red . . . . 1·75 45
286 **42** 6c. blue . . . . 2·25 2·75
287 **41** $1 violet . . . . 21·00 48·00

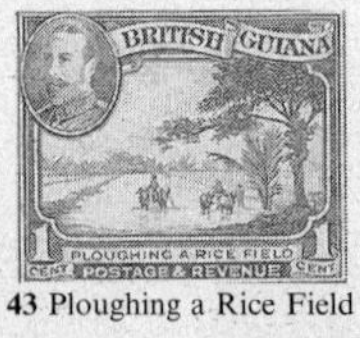
43 Ploughing a Rice Field

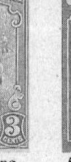

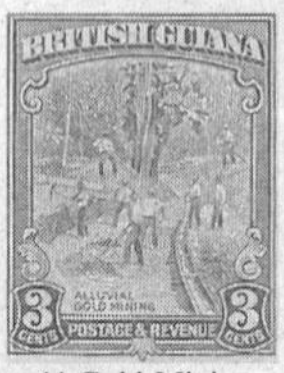
44 Gold Mining

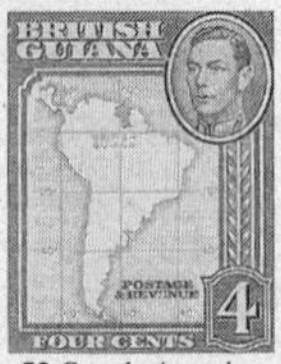
53 South America

1934.
288 **43** 1c. green 60 80
289 **40** 2c. brown . . . . 1·50 70
290 **44** 3c. red 30 10
291 **41** 4c. violet . . . . 2·00 1·75
292 – 6c. blue . . . . 2·75 3·50
293 – 12c. orange 20 20
294 – 24c. purple . . . . 3·50 5·50
295 – 48c. black . . . . 7·00 8·50
296 **41** 50c. green . . . . 10·00 17·00
297 – 60c. brown . . . . 26·00 27·00
298 – 72c. purple . . . . 1·25 2·25
299 – 96c. black . . . . 20·00 30·00
300 – $1 violet . . . . 32·00 30·00
DESIGNS—HORIZ: 6c. Shooting logs over falls; 12c. Stabroek Market; 24c. Sugar canes in punts; 48c. Forest road; 60c. Victoria Regia lilies; 72c. Mount Roraima; $1 Botanical Gardens. VERT: 96c. Sir Walter Raleigh and his son.
The 2c., 4c. and 50c. are without the dates shown in Types **40/44** and the 12, 48, 72 and 96c. have no portrait.

1935. Silver Jubilee. As T **13** of Antigua.
301 2c. blue and grey 20 10
302 6c. brown and blue . . . . . 1·00 1·75
303 12c. green and blue . . . . . 4·00 8·00
304 24c. grey and purple . . . . 5·50 8·00

1937. Coronation. As T **2** of Aden.
305 2c. brown 15 10
306 4c. grey 50 30
307 6c. blue . . . . 60 1·00

1938. Designs as for same values of 1934 issue (except where indicated) but with portrait of King George VI (as in T **53**) where portrait of King George V previously appeared.
308aa **43** 1c. green 30 10
309a – 2c. violet (As 4c.) . . . 30 10
310b **53** 4c. red and black 50 15
311 – 6c. blue (As 2c.) 40 10
312a – 24c. green . . . . 1·25 10
313 – 36c. violet (As 4c.) . . . 2·00 20
314 – 48c. orange 60 40
315 – 60c. brown (As 6c.) . . . 11·00 3·75
316 – 96c. purple . . . . 2·50 2·75
317 – $1 violet . . . . 11·00 35
318 – $2 purple (As 72c.) . . . 4·50 14·00
319 – $3 brown . . . . 27·00 25·00
DESIGN—HORIZ: $3 Victoria Regia lilies.

1946. Victory. As T **9** of Aden.
320 3c. red 10 20
321 6c. blue 30 50

1948. Silver Wedding. As T **10/11** of Aden.
322 3c. red 10 40
323 $3 brown . . . . 12·00 23·00

1949. U.P.U. As T **20/23** of Antigua.
324 4c. red 10 20
325 6c. blue . . . . 1·00 65
326 12c. orange 15 45
327 24c. green 15 60

1951. Inauguration of B.W.I. University College. As T **24/25** of Antigua.
328 3c. black and red 30 30
329 6c. black and blue 30 60

1953. Coronation. As T **13** of Aden.
330 4c. black and red 20 10

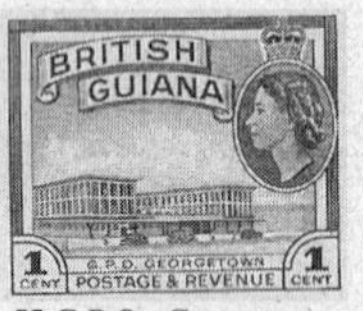
55 G.P.O., Georgetown

1954.
331 **55** 1c. black 10 10
332 – 2c. myrtle 10 10
333 – 3c. olive and brown . . . 3·50 20
334 – 4c. violet 20 10
335 – 5c. red and black 30 10
336 – 6c. green 40 10
337 – 8c. blue 15 20
338a – 12c. black and brown . . 15 10
360 – 24c. black and orange . . 4·00 10
361 – 36c. red and black 60 60
341a – 48c. blue and brown . . . 50 60
342 – 72c. red and green . . . . 12·00 2·75
364 – $1 multicoloured . . . . 7·00 90
344 – $2 mauve . . . . 18·00 6·00
345 – $5 blue and black . . . . 14·00 22·00
DESIGNS—HORIZ: 2c. Botanical Gardens; 3c. Victoria Regia lilies; 5c. Map of Caribbean; 6c. Rice combine-harvester; 8c. Sugar cane entering factory; 24c. Bauxite mining; 36c. Mount Roraima; $1 Channel-billed toucan; $2 Dredging gold. VERT: 4c. Amerindian shooting fish; 12c. Felling greenheart; 48c. Kaieteur Falls; 72c. Arapaima (fish); $5 Arms of British Guiana.

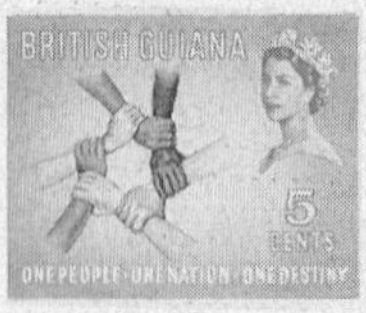
70

1961. History and Culture Week.
346 **70** 5c. sepia and red 20 10
347 6c. sepia and green 20 15
348 30c. sepia and orange . . . 45 45

1963. Freedom from Hunger. As T **28** of Aden.
349 20c. violet 30 10

1963. Centenary of Red Cross. As T **33** of Antigua.
350 5c. red and black 20 20
351 20c. red and blue 55 35

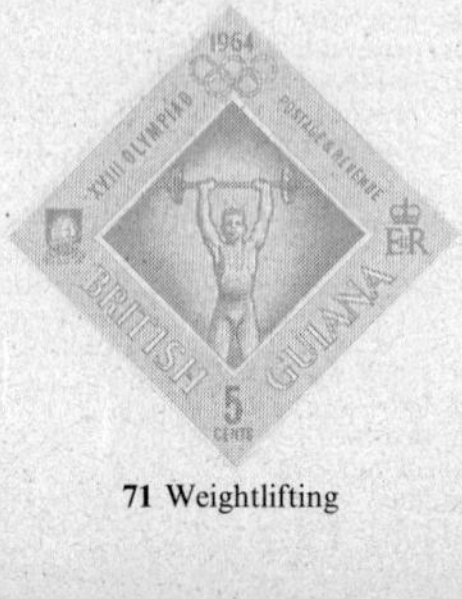
71 Weightlifting

1964. Olympic Games, Tokyo.
367 **71** 5c. orange 10 10
368 8c. blue 15 35
369 25c. mauve 25 40

1965. Centenary of I.T.U. As T **36** of Antigua.
370 5c. green and olive 10 15
371 25c. blue and mauve 20 15

1965. I.C.Y. As T **37** of Antigua.
372 5c. purple and turquoise . . 15 10
373 25c. green and lavender . . . 30 20

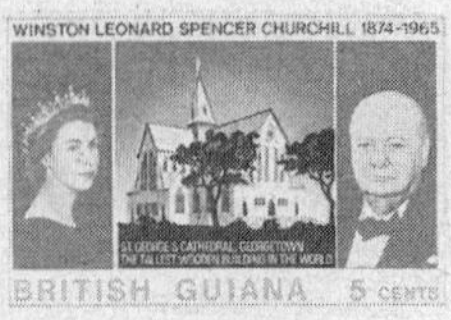
72 St George's Cathedral, Georgetown

1966. Churchill Commemoration.
374 **72** 5c. black, red and gold . . 50 10
375 25c. black, blue and gold 1·75 50

1966. Royal Visit. As T **39** of Antigua.
376 3c. black and blue 50 15
377 25c. black and mauve . . . . 1·50 60

OFFICIAL STAMPS

1875. Optd **OFFICIAL**.
O1 **7** 1c. black . . . . 48·00 17·00
O2 2c. orange . . . . £170 14·00
O3 8c. red £325 £120
O4 12c. lilac £1800 £500
O5 **9** 24c. green £1000 £225

1877. Optd **OFFICIAL**.
O 6 **16** 1c. grey . . . . £225 65·00
O 7 2c. orange . . . . £100 15·00
O 8 4c. blue . . . . 80·00 20·00
O 9 6c. brown £4750 £600
O10 8c. red £1900 £450

POSTAGE DUE STAMPS

1940. As Type D **1** of Barbados, but inscr "BRITISH GUIANA".
D1a 1c. green . . . . 1·50 10·00
D2a 2c. black . . . . 1·50 3·50
D3 4c. blue . . . . 30 9·00
D4 12c. red . . . . 27·00 4·00

For later issues see **GUYANA**.

BRITISH HONDURAS Pt. 1

A British colony on the East coast of Central America. Self-government was granted on 1 January 1964. The country was renamed Belize from 1 June 1973.

1866. 12 pence = 1 shilling;
20 shillings = 1 pound.
1888. 100 cents = 1 dollar.

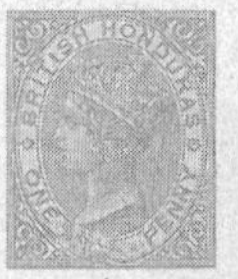
1

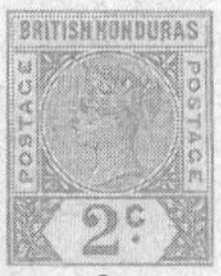
8

1866.
17 **1** 1d. blue . . . . 40·00 13·00
18 1d. red . . . . 23·00 13·00
13 3d. brown . . . . £120 17·00
20 4d. mauve . . . . 70·00 4·75
9 6d. red . . . . £225 35·00
21 6d. yellow £275 £190
16 1s. green . . . . £190 11·00
22 1s. grey £250 £160

1888. Surch as **2 CENTS**.
36 **1** 1c. on 1d. green . . . . . 80 1·50
37 2c. on 1d. red . . . . . . 60 2·25
25 2c. on 6d. red . . . . . . £100 90·00
38 3c. on 3d. brown . . . . . 3·00 1·40
39 6c. on 3d. blue . . . . . . 2·75 13·00
40 10c. on 4d. mauve . . . . 8·50 50
41 20c. on 6d. yellow . . . . 12·00 14·00
42 50c. on 1s. grey . . . . . 29·00 75·00

1888. No. 42 surch **TWO**.
35 **1** "TWO" on 50c. on 1s. grey 45·00 90·00

1891. No. 40 surch **6** and bar.
44 **1** 6c. on 10c. on 4d. mauve . . 1·25 1·50

1891. Nos. 38 and 39 surch.
49 **1** "FIVE" on 3c. on 3d. brown 1·25 1·40
50 "15" on 6c. on 3d. blue . . . 13·00 24·00

1891.
51 **8** 1c. green . . . . 2·50 1·25
52 2c. red . . . . 2·00 20
53 3c. brown . . . . 6·00 4·00

54 5c. blue . . . . 12·00 75
55 5c. black and blue on blue 16·00 2·50
56 6c. blue . . . . 6·00 2·00
57 10c. mauve and green (A) 10·00 8·50
58 10c. purple and green (B) 11·00 7·50
59a 12c. mauve and green . . . 2·50 2·00
60 24c. yellow and blue . . . . 5·50 14·00
61 25c. brown and green . . . 65·00 £110
62 50c. green and red . . . . 24·00 55·00
63 $1 green and red . . . . . 70·00 £110
64 $2 green and blue . . . . . 85·00 £140
65 $5 green and black £275 £325
NOTE: 10c. (A) inscr "POSTAGE POSTAGE"; (B) inscr "POSTAGE & REVENUE".

1899. Optd **REVENUE**.
66 **8** 5c. blue . . . . 11·00 2·50
67 10c. mauve and green . . . . 3·50 16·00
68 25c. brown and green . . . . 2·75 35·00
69 **1** 50c. on 1s. grey £140 £300

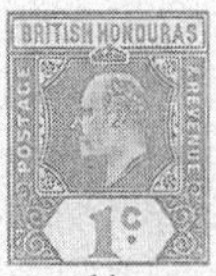

14

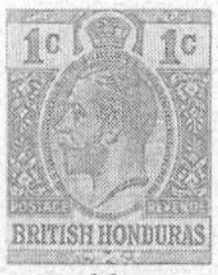

16

1902.
84a **14** 1c. green . . . . 75 1·75
85a 2c. purple and black on red 75 20
96 2c. red . . . . 12·00 10
86 5c. black and blue on blue 1·75 20
97 5c. blue . . . . 1·75 10
87 10c. purple and green . . 5·00 11·00
83 20c. purple . . . . 6·00 17·00
89 25c. purple and orange . . 7·00 48·00
100 25c. black on green . . . 3·00 45·00
90 50c. green and red . . . . 15·00 70·00
91 $1 green and red . . . . 50·00 75·00
92 $2 green and blue . . . . 90·00 £150
93 $5 green and black . . . £200 £250

1913.
101 **16** 1c. green . . . . 3·75 1·50
102 2c. red . . . . 3·50 1·00
103 3c. orange 80 20
104 5c. blue . . . . 2·00 85
105 10c. purple and green . . . 3·00 6·50
106 25c. black on green . . . . 1·25 12·00
107 50c. purple and blue on blue . . . . 10·00 15·00
108 $1 black and red . . . . . 19·00 45·00
109 $2 purple and green . . . 65·00 80·00
110 $5 purple and black on red £200 £225

1915. Optd with pattern of wavy lines.
111a **16** 1c. green . . . . 50 13·00
112 2c. red . . . . 3·50 50
113 5c. blue . . . . 30 6·00

1916. Optd **WAR**.
114 **16** 1c. green (No. 111a) . . . 10 1·25
119 1c. green (No. 101) 10 30
120 3c. orange (No. 103) . . . 70 1·75

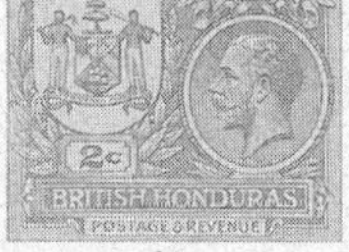

21

1921. Peace.
121 **21** 2c. red . . . . 3·25 50

As last, but without word "PEACE"
123 4c. grey . . . . 6·50 50

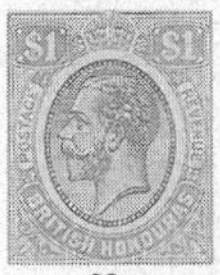
22

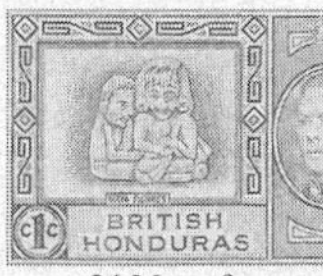

24 Maya figures

1922.
126 **22** 1c. green . . . . 4·00 6·50
127 2c. brown . . . . 1·50 1·50
128 2c. red . . . . 2·25 1·50
129 3c. orange . . . . 15·00 4·00
130 4c. grey . . . . 6·00 85
131 5c. blue . . . . 1·50 55
132 10c. purple and olive . . . 1·25 30
133 25c. black on green . . . . 1·25 8·50
134 50c. purple and blue on blue . . . . 4·75 16·00
136 $1 black and red . . . . . 8·00 23·00
137 $2 green and purple . . . 32·00 80·00
125 $5 purple and black on red £190 £200

1932. Optd **BELIZE RELIEF FUND PLUS** and value.
138 **22** 1c.+1c. green . . . . . . 70 7·00
139 2c.+2c. red . . . . 75 6·50
140 3c.+3c. orange . . . . . . 85 16·00
141 4c.+4c. grey . . . . . . 10·00 21·00
142 5c.+5c. blue . . . . 6·50 14·00

1935. Silver Jubilee. As T **13** of Antigua.
143 3c. blue and black . . . . . 1·75 50
144 4c. green and blue . . . . . 1·75 3·50
145 5c. brown and blue . . . . . 1·75 1·00
146 25c. grey and purple . . . . 3·75 4·00

1937. Coronation. As T **2** of Aden.
147 3c. orange 30 30
148 4c. grey 70 30
149 5c. blue . . . . 80 1·60

1938.
150 **24** 1c. purple and green . . . 10 1·50
151 – 2c. black and red . . . . 20 1·00
152 – 3c. purple and brown . . . 30 80
153 – 4c. black and green 30 70
154 – 5c. purple and blue . . . 1·00 70
155 – 10c. green and brown . . . 1·00 60
156 – 15c. brown and blue . . . 2·25 70
157 – 25c. blue and green . . . . 2·25 1·25
158 – 50c. black and purple . . 11·00 3·50
159 – $1 red and olive . . . . 20·00 10·00
160 – $2 blue and purple . . . 27·00 16·00
161 – $5 red and brown . . . . 27·00 23·00
DESIGNS—VERT: 2c. Chicle tapping; 3c. Cohune palm; $1 Court House, Belize; $2 Mahogany felling; $5 Arms of Colony. HORIZ: 4c. Local products; 5c. Grapefruit; 10c. Mahogany logs in river; 15c. Sergeant's Cay; 25c. Dorey; 50c. Chicle industry.

1946. Victory. As T **9** of Aden.
162 3c. brown 10 10
163 5c. blue 10 10

1948. Silver Wedding. As T **10** and **11** of Aden.
164 4c. green 15 20
165 $5 brown . . . . 16·00 40·00

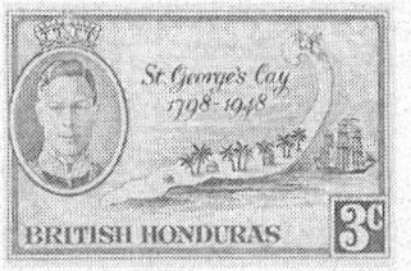

36 Island of Saint George's Cay

1949. 150th Anniv of Battle of Saint George's Cay.
166 **36** 1c. blue and green 10 75
167 3c. blue and brown . . . . 10 1·25
168 4c. olive and violet 10 50
169 – 5c. brown and blue 80 20
170 – 10c. green and brown . . . 70 30
171 – 15c. green and blue 70 30
DESIGNS: 5, 10 and 15c. H.M.S. "Merlin".

1949. U.P.U. As T **20/23** of Antigua.
172 4c. green 30 30
173 5c. blue . . . . 1·25 50
174 10c. brown . . . . 30 2·50
175 25c. blue 35 50

1951. Inauguration of B.W.I. University College. As T **24/25** of Antigua.
176 3c. violet and brown . . . . 45 1·50
177 10c. green and brown 45 30

1953. Coronation. As T **13** of Aden.
178 4c. black and green 40 30

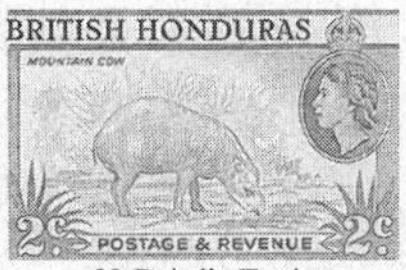

39 Baird's Tapir

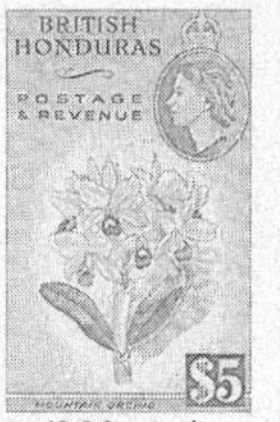

49 Mountain Orchid

1953.
179 – 1c. green and black . . . 10 40
180a **39** 2c. brown and black . . . 50 10
181a – 3c. lilac and mauve . . . 10 10
182 – 4c. brown and green . . . 40 30
183 – 5c. olive and red 10 10
184 – 10c. slate and blue . . . 10 10
185 – 15c. green and violet . . . 15 10
186 – 25c. blue and brown . . . 6·00 2·25
187 – 50c. brown and purple . . 7·50 1·75
188 – $1 slate and brown . . . 5·50 5·00
189 – $2 red and grey . . . . . 6·50 4·50
190 **49** $5 purple and slate . . . 48·00 17·00
DESIGNS—HORIZ: 1c. Arms of British Honduras; 3c. Mace and Legislative Council Chamber; 4c. Pine industry; 5c. Spiny lobster; 10c. Stanley Field Airport; 15c. Maya frieze, Xunantunich; 25c. "Morpho peleides" (butterfly); $1 Nine-banded armadillo; $2 Hawkesworth Bridge. VERT: 50c. Maya indian.

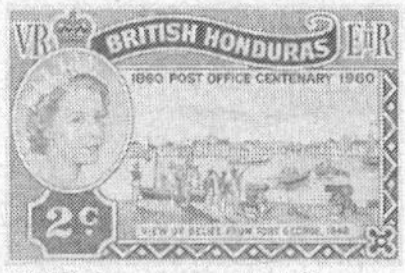

50 "Belize from Fort George, 1842" (C. J. Hullmandel)

1960. Post Office Centenary.
191 **50** 2c. green . . . . 30 1·25
192 – 10c. red 30 10
193 – 15c. blue 35 35
DESIGNS: 10c. Public seals, 1860 and 1960; 15c. Tamarind tree, Newtown Barracks.

1961. New Constitution. Stamps of 1953 optd **NEW CONSTITUTION 1960.**
194 **39** 2c. brown and black . . . 25 20
195 – 3c. lilac and mauve 30 20
196 – 10c. slate and blue 30 10
197 – 15c. green and violet . . . 30 20

1962. Hurricane Hattie Relief Fund. Stamps of 1953 optd **HURRICANE HATTIE**.
198 1c. green and black 10 65
199 10c. slate and blue 30 10
200 25c. blue and brown . . . . 1·40 80
201 50c. brown and purple . . . 50 1·00

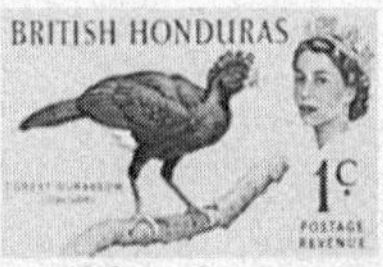

55 Great Curassow

1962. Birds in natural colours; portrait and inscr in black; background colours given.
239 **55** 1c. yellow 10 50
240 – 2c. grey 30 75
204 – 3c. green . . . . 2·50 3·00
241 – 4c. grey . . . . 1·75 1·50
242 – 5c. buff 40 10
243 – 10c. stone 40 10
244 – 15c. stone 40 10
209 – 25c. slate . . . . 4·50 30
210 – 50c. grey . . . . 6·00 35
211 – $1 blue . . . . 9·00 1·00
212 – $2 stone . . . . 14·00 3·00
213 – $5 grey . . . . 25·00 15·00
BIRDS: 2c. Red-legged honeycreeper; 3c. Northern jacana ("American Jacana"); 4c. Great kiskadee; 5c. Scarlet-rumped tanager; 10c. Scarlet macaw; 15c.Slaty-tailed trogon ("Massena Trogon"); 25c. Red-footed booby; 50c. Keel-billed toucan; $1 Magnificent frigate bird; $2 Rufous-tailed jacamar; $5 Montezuma oropendola.

1963. Freedom from Hunger. As T **28** of Aden.
214 22c. green 30 15

1963. Centenary of Red Cross. As T **33** of Antigua.
215 4c. red and black 20 55
216 22c. red and blue 40 85

1964. New Constitution. Nos. 202, 204, 205, 207 and 209 optd **SELF GOVERNMENT 1964**.
217 **55** 1c. yellow 10 30
218 – 3c. green 45 30
219 – 4c. pale grey 45 30
220 – 10c. stone 45 10
221 – 25c. slate 55 30

1965. Centenary of I.T.U. As T **36** of Antigua.
222 2c. red and green 10 10
223 50c. yellow and purple . . . 35 25

1965. I.C.Y. As T **37** of Antigua.
224 1c. purple and turquoise . . 10 15
225 22c. green and lavender . . . 20 15

1966. Churchill Commemoration. As T **38** of Antigua.
226 1c. blue 10 40
227 4c. green 20 10
228 22c. brown 40 10
229 25c. violet 50 45

1966. Dedication of new Capital Site. Nos. 202, 204/5 207 and 209 optd **DEDICATION OF SITE NEW CAPITAL 9th OCTOBER 1965**.
230 **55** 1c. yellow 10 40
231 – 3c. green 45 40
232 – 4c. grey 45 40
233 – 10c. stone 45 10
234 – 25c. slate 55 35

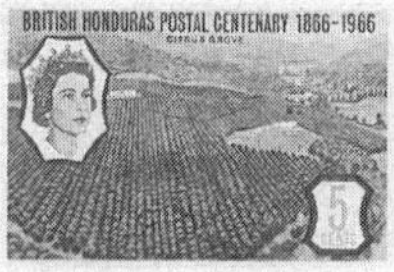

58 Citrus Grove

1966. Stamp Centenary. Multicoloured.
235 5c. Type **58** 10 10
236 10c. Half Moon Cay 10 10
237 22c. Hidden Valley Falls . . 10 10
238 25c. Maya ruins, Xunantunich 15 45

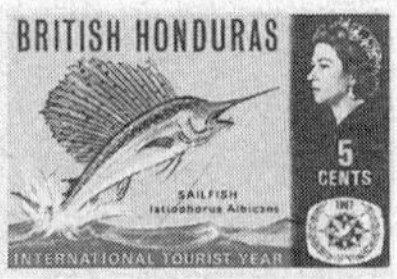

59 Sailfish

1967. International Tourist Year.
246 **59** 5c. blue, black and yellow 15 30
247 – 10c. brown, black and red 15 10
248 – 22c. orange, black and green 30 10
249 – 25c. blue, black and yellow 30 60
DESIGNS: 10c. Red brocket; 22c. Jaguar; 25c. Atlantic tarpon.

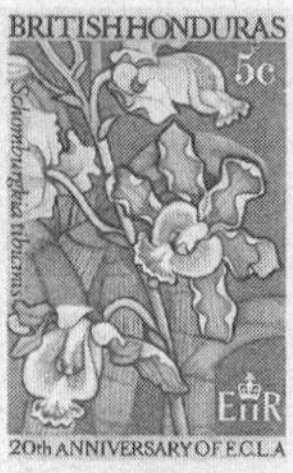

60 "Schomburgkia tibicinis"

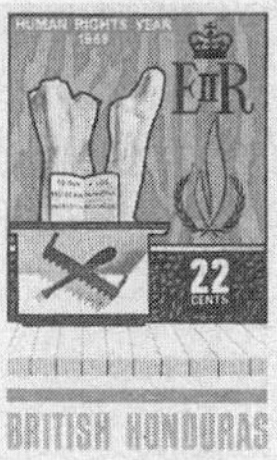

61 Monument Belizean Patriots

1968. 20th Anniv of Economic Commission for Latin America. Orchids. Multicoloured.
250 5c. Type **60** 20 15
251 10c. "Maxillaria tenuifolia" 25 10
252 22c. "Bletia purpurea" . . . 30 10
253 25c. "Sobralia macrantha" 40 20

1968. Human Rights Year. Multicoloured.
254 22c. Type **61** 15 10
255 50c. Monument at site of new capital 15 20

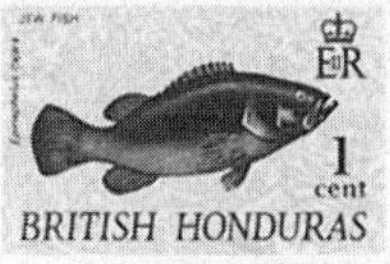

63 Spotted Jewfish

1968. Wildlife.
276 – ½c. multicoloured and blue 10 10
277 – ½c. multicoloured and yellow . . . . 2·25 1·00
256 **63** 1c. black, brown and yellow 20 10
257 – 2c. black, green and yellow 10 10
258 – 3c. black, brown and lilac 20 10
259 – 4c. multicoloured 15 95
260 – 5c. black and red 15 95
261 – 10c. multicoloured 15 10
262 – 15c. multicoloured . . . . 1·00 20
263 – 25c. multicoloured 30 20
264 – 50c. multicoloured . . . . 70 1·25
265 – $1 multicoloured . . . . . 2·50 1·25
266 – $2 multicoloured . . . . . 2·50 2·00
278 – $5 multicoloured . . . . . 6·50 12·00
DESIGNS: ½c. (Nos. 276 and 277) Mozambique mouthbrooder ("Crana"); 2c. White-lipped peccary; 3c. Misty grouper; 4c. Collared anteater; 5c. Bonefish; 10c. Paca; 15c. Dolphin; 25c. Kinkajou; 50c. Mutton snapper; $1 Tayra; $2 Great barracuda; $5 Puma.

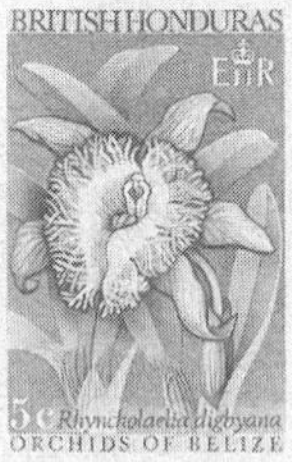

64 "Rhyncholaelia digbyana"

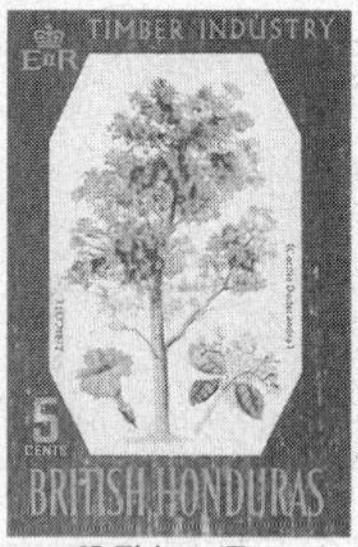

65 Ziricote Tree

1969. Orchids of Belize (1st series). Multicoloured.
268 5c. Type **64** 50 20
269 10c. "Cattleya bowringiana" 55 15
270 22c. "Lycaste cochleatum" 85 15
271 25c. "Coryanthes speciosum" 1·10 1·10
See also Nos. 287/90.

1969. Indigenous Hardwoods (1st series). Mult.
272 5c. Type **65** 10 20
273 10c. Rosewood 10 10
274 22c. Mayflower 20 10
275 25c. Mahogany 20 45
See also Nos. 291/4, 315/18 and 333/7.

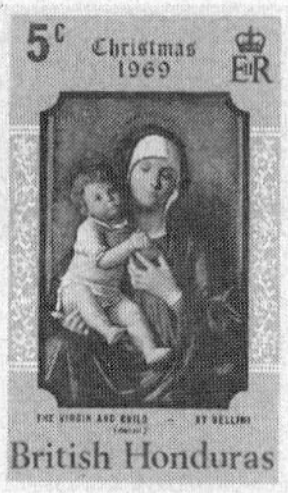

66 "The Virgin and Child" (Bellini)

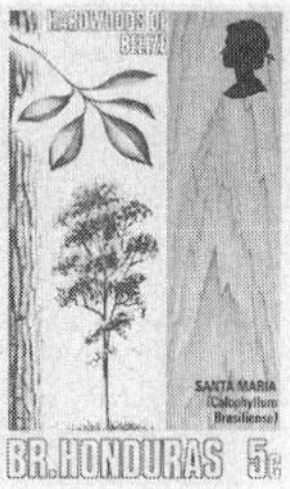

69 Santa Maria

1969. Christmas. Paintings. Multicoloured.
279 5c. Type **66** 10 10
280 15c. Type **66** 10 10
281 22c. "The Adoration of the Magi" (Veronese) 10 10
282 25c. As No. 281 . . . . . . 10 20

1970. Population Census. Nos. 260/3 optd **POPULATION CENSUS 1970**.
283 5c. multicoloured 10 10
284 10c. multicoloured 15 10

285	15c. multicoloured	20	10
286	25c. multicoloured	20	15

1970. Orchids of Belize (2nd series). As T **64**. Mult.

287	5c. Black orchid	35	15
288	15c. White butterfly orchid	50	10
289	22c. Swan orchid	70	10
290	25c. Butterfly orchid	70	40

1970. Indigenous Hardwoods (2nd series). Mult.

291	5c. Type **69**	25	10
292	15c. Nargusta	40	10
293	22c. Cedar	45	10
294	25c. Sapodilla	45	35

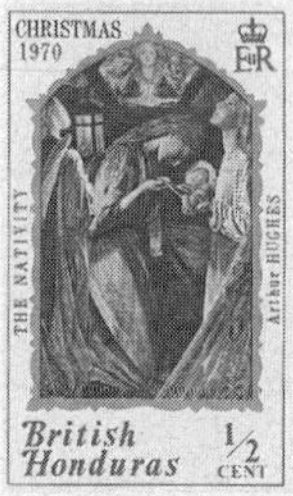

70 "The Nativity" (A. Hughes)

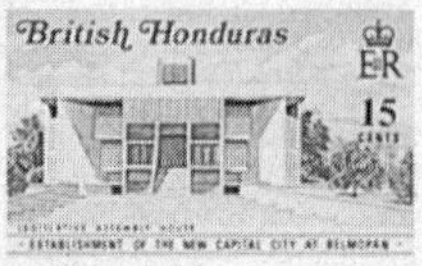

71 Legislative Assembly House

1970. Christmas. Multicoloured.

295	½c. Type **70**	10	10
296	5c. "The Mystic Nativity" (Botticelli)	10	10
297	10c. Type **70**	10	10
298	15c. As 5c.	20	10
299	22c. Type **70**	25	10
300	50c. As 5c.	40	85

1971. Establishment of New Capital, Belmopan. Multicoloured.

301	5c. Old capital, Belize	10	10
302	10c. Government Plaza	10	10
303	15c. Type **71**	10	10
304	22c. Magistrates' Court	15	10
305	25c. Police H.Q	15	15
306	50c. New G.P.O	25	40

The 5c. and 10c. are larger, 60 × 22 mm.

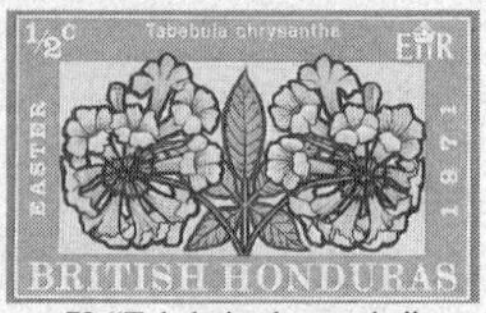

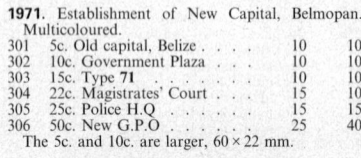

72 "Tabebuia chrysantha"

1971. Easter. Flowers. Multicoloured.

307	½c. Type **72**	10	10
308	5c. "Hymenocallis littoralis"	10	10
309	10c. "Hippeastrum equestre"	10	10
310	15c. Type **72**	20	10
311	22c. As 5c.	20	10
312	25c. As 10c.	20	30

1971. Racial Equality Year. Nos. 261 and 264 optd **RACIAL EQUALITY YEAR–1971**.

313	10c. multicoloured	25	10
314	50c. multicoloured	55	20

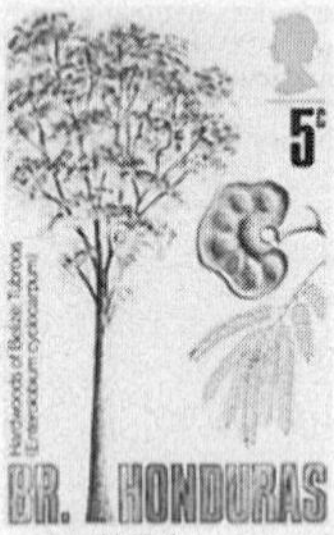

74 Tubroos

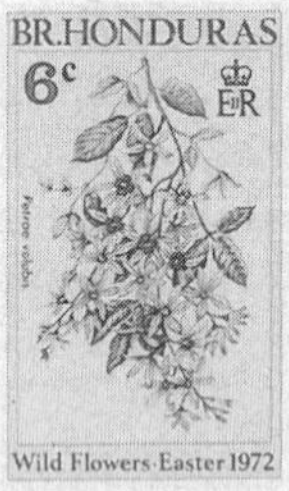

76 "Petrae volubis"

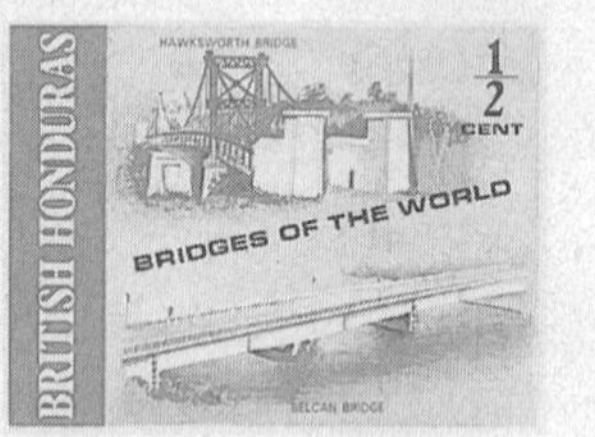

75 Hawksworth and Belcan Bridges

1971. Indigenous Hardwoods (3rd series). Mult.

315	5c. Type **74**	50	10
316	15c. Yemeri	70	30
317	26c. Billywebb	95	35
318	50c. Logwood	1·75	4·00

1971. Bridges of the World. Multicoloured.

320	½c. Type **75**	10	20
321	5c. Narrows Bridge, N.Y. and Quebec Bridge	30	15
322	26c. London Bridge (1871) and reconstructed, Arizona (1971)	70	15
323	50c. Belize Mexican Bridge and Swing Bridge	90	1·25

1972. Easter. Wild Flowers. Multicoloured.

324	6c. Type **76**	15	10
325	15c. Yemeri	25	30
326	26c. Mayflower	50	45
327	50c. Tiger's Claw	80	1·40

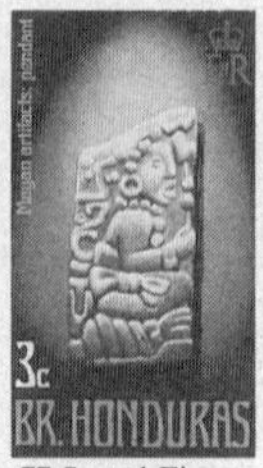

77 Seated Figure

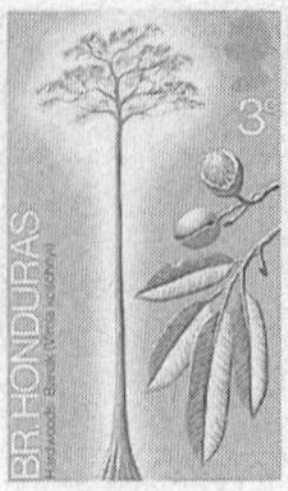

78 Banak

1972. Mayan Artefacts. Multicoloured.

328	3c. Type **77**	20	10
329	6c. Priest in "dancing" pose	20	10
330	16c. Sun God's head (horiz)	40	15
331	26c. Priest and Sun God	60	20
332	50c. Full-front figure	1·25	3·25

1972. Indigenous Hardwoods (4th series). Mult.

333	3c. Type **78**	20	10
334	5c. Quamwood	20	10
335	16c. Waika Chewstick	45	15
336	26c. Mamee-Apple	60	25
337	50c. My Lady	1·40	3·25

1972. Royal Silver Wedding. As T **52** of Ascension, but with Orchids of Belize in background.

341	26c. green	25	10
342	50c. violet	40	65

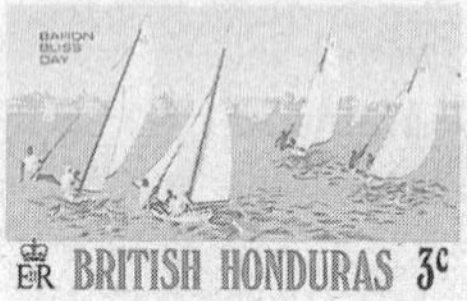

80 Baron Bliss Day

1973. Festivals of Belize. Multicoloured.

343	3c. Type **80**	15	10
344	10c. Labour Day	15	10
345	26c. Carib Settlement Day	30	10
346	50c. Pan American Day	50	85

POSTAGE DUE STAMPS

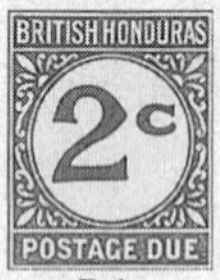

D 1

1923.

D1	D **1** 1c. black	2·25	13·00
D4	2c. black	2·75	5·50
D5	4c. black	90	6·00

For later issues see **BELIZE**.

BRITISH INDIAN OCEAN TERRITORY Pt. 1

A Crown Colony, established 8 November 1965, comprising the Chagos Archipelago (previously administered by Mauritius) and Aldabra, Farquhar and Desroches, previously administered by Seychelles to which country they were returned on 29 June 1976.

The Chagos Archipelago has no indigenous population, but stamps were provided from 1990 for use by civilian workers at the U.S. Navy base on Diego Garcia.

1968. 100 cents = 1 rupee.
1990. 100 pence = 1 pound.

1968. Nos 196/200, 202/4 and 206/12 of Seychelles optd **B.I.O.T.**

1	**24** 5c. multicoloured	1·00	1·25
2	– 10c. multicoloured	10	15
3	– 15c. multicoloured	10	15
4	– 20c. multicoloured	15	15
5	– 25c. multicoloured	15	15
6	– 40c. multicoloured	20	20
7	– 45c. multicoloured	20	30
8	– 50c. multicoloured	20	30
9	– 75c. multicoloured	20	35
10	– 1r. multicoloured	60	35
11	– 1r.50 multicoloured	1·75	1·50
12	– 2r.25 multicoloured	3·00	3·75
13	– 3r.50 multicoloured	3·00	4·50
14	– 5r. multicoloured	10·00	7·50
15	– 10r. multicoloured	20·00	20·00

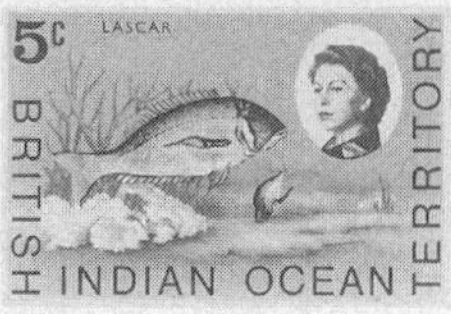

2 Lascar

1968. Marine Life. Multicoloured.

16	5c. Type **2**	70	2·00
17	10c. Smooth hammerhead (vert)	30	1·25
18	15c. Tiger shark	30	1·50
19	20c. Spotted eagle ray ("Bat ray")	30	1·00
20	25c. Yellow-finned butterflyfish and ear-spot angelfish (vert)	80	1·00
20a	30c. Robber crab	3·50	2·75
21	40c. Blue-finned trevalley ("Caranx")	40	40
22	45c. Crocodile needlefish ("Garfish") (vert)	2·25	2·50
23	50c. Pickhandle barracuda	45	30
23a	60c. Spotted pebble crab	3·50	3·25
24	75c. Indian Ocean steep-headed parrotfish	2·50	2·75
24a	85c. Rainbow runner ("Dorade")	6·00	3·50
25	1r. Giant hermit crab	1·50	35
26	1r.50 Parrotfish ("Humphead")	2·50	3·00
27	2r.25 Yellow-edged lyre-tail andAredate grouper ("Rock cod")	11·00	10·00
28	3r.50 Black marlin	4·00	3·75
29	5r. black, green and blue (Whale shark) (vert)	10·00	9·00
30	10r. Lionfish	9·00	8·00

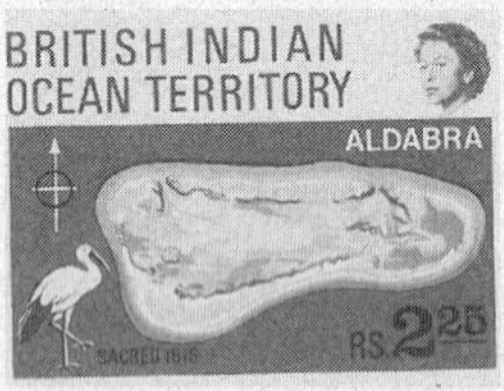

3 Sacred Ibis and Aldabra Coral Atoll

1969. Coral Atolls

31	**3** 2r.25 multicoloured	1·75	1·00

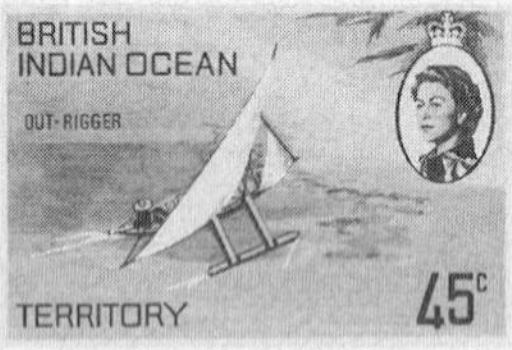

4 Outrigger Canoe

1969. Ships of the Islands. Multicoloured.

32	45c. Type **4**	65	75
33	75c. Pirogue	65	80
34	1r. M.V. "Nordvaer"	70	90
35	1r.50 "Isle of Farquhar"	80	1·00

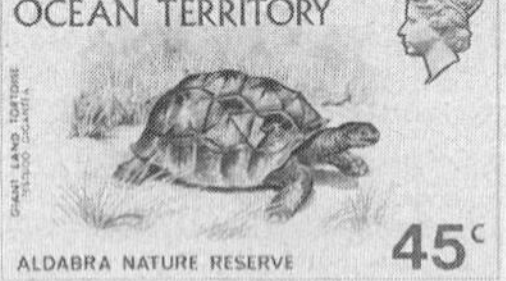

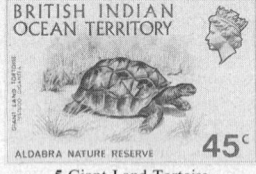

5 Giant Land Tortoise

1971. Aldabra Nature Reserve. Multicoloured.

36	45c. Type **5**	2·50	2·50
37	75c. Aldabra lily	3·00	2·50
38	1r. Aldabra tree snail	3·50	2·75
39	1r.50 Western reef heron ("Dimorphic Egrets")	12·00	10·00

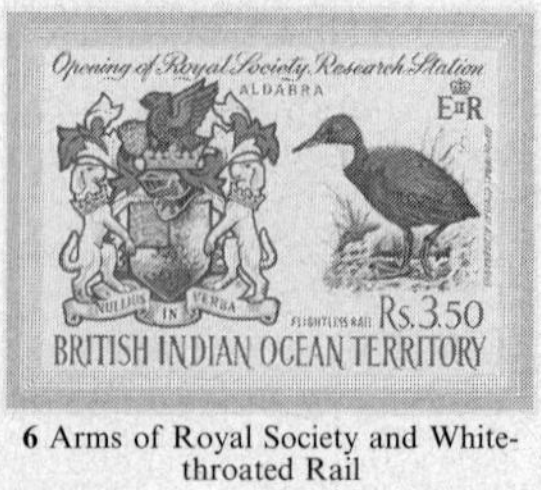

6 Arms of Royal Society and White-throated Rail

1971. Opening of Royal Society Research Station, Aldabra.

40	**6** 3r.50 multicoloured	15·00	8·50

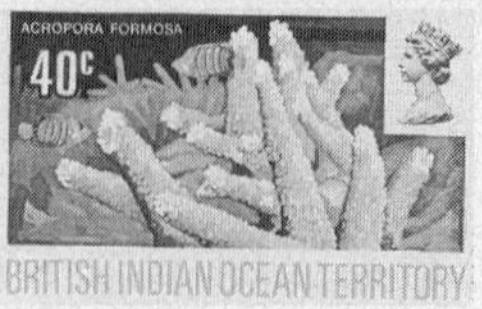

7 Staghorn Coral

1972. Coral. Multicoloured.

41	40c. Type **7**	3·50	4·00
42	60c. Brain coral	4·00	4·25
43	1r. Mushroom coral	4·00	4·25
44	1r.75 Organ pipe coral	5·00	6·50

1972. Royal Silver Wedding. As T **52** of Ascension, but with White-throated rail and Sacred ibis in background.

45	95c. green	50	40
46	1r.50 violet	50	40

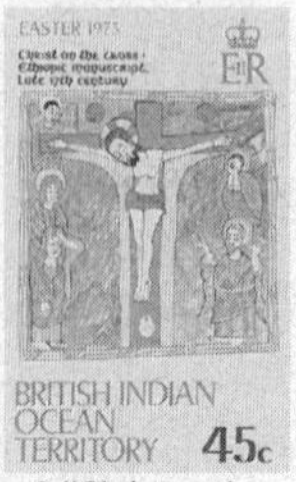

9 "Christ on the Cross"

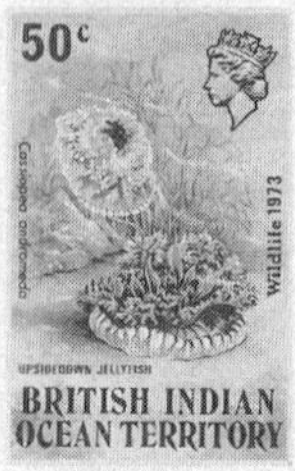

10 Upsidedown Jellyfish

1973. Easter. Multicoloured.

47	45c. Type **9**	20	40
48	75c. "Joseph and Nicodemus burying Jesus"	30	55
49	1r. Type **9**	30	60
50	1r.50 As 75c.	30	70

1973. Wildlife (1st series). Multicoloured.

53	50c. Type **10**	3·50	3·00
54	1r. "Hypolimnas misippus" and "Belenois aldabrensis" (butterflies)	4·00	3·00
55	1r.50 "Nephila madagascariensis" (spider)	4·25	3·00

See also Nos. 58/61, 77/80 and 86/9.

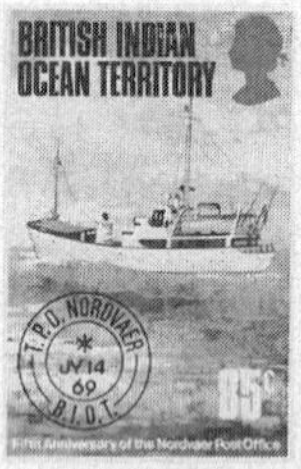

11 M.V. "Nordvaer"

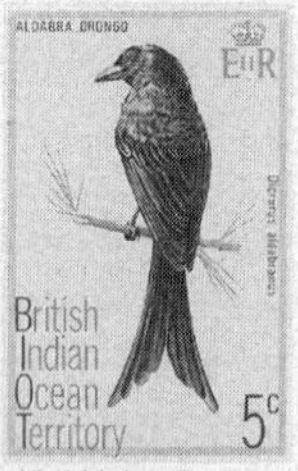

13 Aldabra Drongo

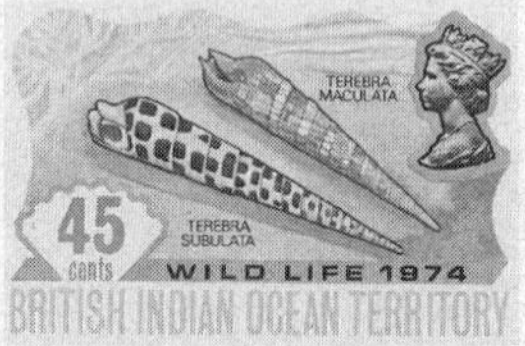

12 Red-cloud Auger and Subulat Auger

1974. 5th Anniv of "Nordvaer" Travelling Post Office. Multicoloured.

56	85c. Type **11**	85	75
57	2r.50 "Nordvaer" off shore	1·40	1·25

1974. Wildlife (2nd series). Shells. Multicoloured.

58	45c. Type **12**	2·25	1·25
59	75c. Great green turban	2·50	1·50
60	1r. Strawberry drupe	2·75	1·75
61	1r.50 Bull-mouth helmet	3·00	2·00

1975. Birds. Multicoloured.

62	5c. Type **13**	1·25	2·75
63	10c. Black coucal ("Malagasy Coucal")	1·25	2·75
64	20c. Mascarene fody ("Red-Headed Forest Foddy")	1·25	2·75
65	25c. White tern	1·25	2·75
66	30c. Crested tern	1·25	2·75
67	40c. Brown booby	1·25	2·75
68	50c. Common noddy (horiz)	1·25	3·00
69	60c. Grey heron	1·25	3·00
70	65c. Blue-faced booby (horiz)	1·25	3·00
71	95c. Madagascar white eye ("Malagasy White-eye") (horiz)	1·25	3·00
72	1r. Green-backed heron (horiz)	1·25	3·00
73	1r.75 Lesser frigate bird (horiz)	2·00	5·00
74	3r.50 White-tailed tropic bird (horiz)	2·75	5·00
75	5r. Souimanga sunbird (horiz)	4·00	5·00
76	10r. Madagascar turtle dove ("Malagasy Turtle Dove") (horiz)	8·00	9·00

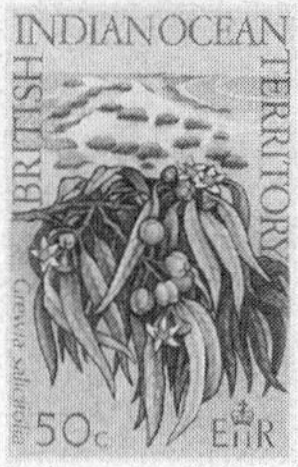

14 "Grewia salicifolia"

1975. Wildlife (3rd series). Seashore Plants. Multicoloured.

77	50c. Type **14**	50	1·25
78	65c. "Cassia aldabrensis"	55	1·40
79	1r. "Hypoestes aldabrensis"	65	1·50
80	1r.60 "Euphorbia pyrifolia"	80	1·60

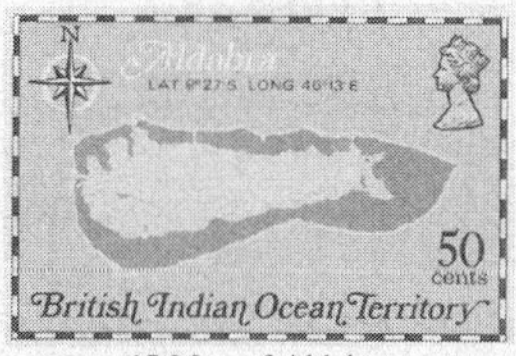

15 Map of Aldabra

1975. 10th Anniv of Territory. Maps. Multicoloured.

81	50c. Type **15**	70	65
82	1r. Desroches	85	85
83	1r.50 Farquhar	95	1·00
84	2r. Diego Garcia	1·00	1·25

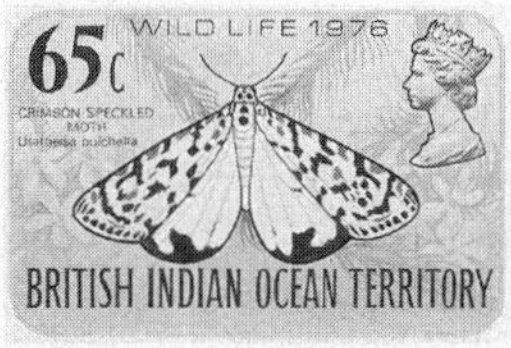

16 "Utetheisa pulchella" (moth)

1976. Wildlife (4th series). Multicoloured.

86	65c. Type **16**	60	1·10
87	1r.20 "Dysdercus fasciatus" (bug)	75	1·25
88	1r.50 "Sphex torridus" (wasp)	80	1·40
89	2r. "Oryctes rhinoceros" (beetle)	85	1·40

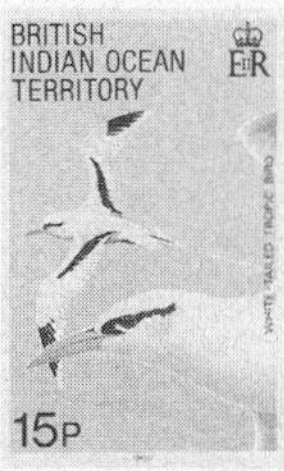

17 White-tailed Tropic Bird

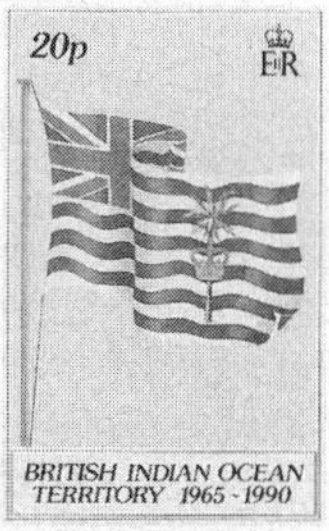

19 Territory Flag

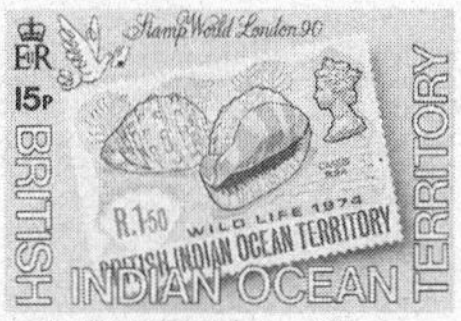

18 1974 Wildlife 1r.50 Stamp

1990. Birds. Multicoloured.

90	15p. Type **17**	1·10	2·00
91	20p. Madagascar turtle dove ("Turtle Dove")	1·25	2·00
92	24p. Great frigate bird ("Greater Frigate")	1·40	2·00
93	30p. Green-backed heron ("Little Green Heron")	1·50	2·25
94	34p. Great sand plover ("Greater Sand Plover")	1·60	2·25
95	41p. Crab plover	1·75	2·50
96	45p. Crested tern	2·00	2·50
97	54p. Lesser crested tern	2·25	2·75
98	62p. White tern ("Fairy Tern")	2·25	2·75
99	71p. Red-footed booby	2·25	3·00
100	80p. Common mynah ("Indian Mynah")	2·50	3·25
101	£1 Madagascar red fody ("Madagascar Fody")	2·50	3·50

1990. "Stamp World London 90" International Stamp Exhibition. Multicoloured.

102	15p. Type **18**	2·75	2·75
103	20p. 1976 Wildlife 2r. stamp	3·00	3·00
104	34p. 1975 Diego Garcia map 2r. stamp	4·50	4·50
105	54p. 1969 "Nordvaer" 1r. stamp	6·50	6·50

1990. 90th Birthday of Queen Elizabeth the Queen Mother. As T **34** of Ascension.

106	24p. multicoloured	3·50	3·50
107	£1 black and ochre	6·50	6·50

DESIGNS—21 × 36 mm: Lady Elizabeth Bowes-Lyon, 1923. 29 × 37 mm: £1 Queen Elizabeth and her daughters, 1940.

1990. 25th Anniv of British Indian Ocean Territory. Multicoloured.

108	20p. Type **19**	4·00	4·50
109	24p. Coat of arms	4·00	4·50

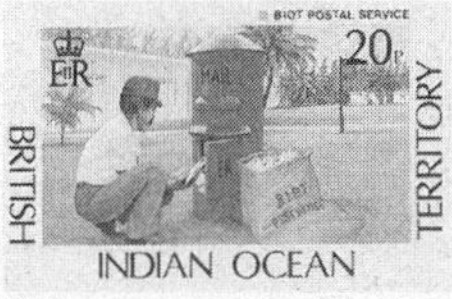

20 Postman emptying Pillar Box

1991. British Indian Ocean Territory Administration. Multicoloured.

111	20p. Type **20**	2·00	2·50
112	24p. Commissioner inspecting guard of Royal Marines	2·25	2·50
113	34p. Policeman outside station	4·00	4·50
114	54p. Customs officers boarding yacht	5·50	6·00

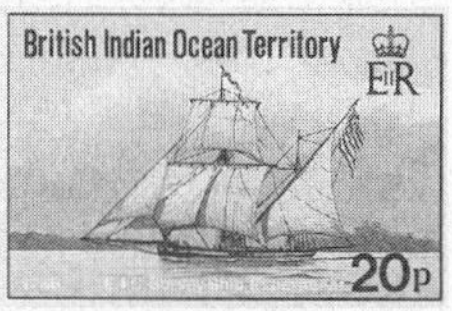

21 "Experiment" (E.I.C. survey brig), 1786

1991. Visiting Ships. Multicoloured.

115	20p. Type **21**	2·75	3·00
116	24p. "Pickering" (American brig), 1819	3·00	3·25
117	34p. "Emden" (German cruiser), 1914	4·00	4·25
118	54p. H.M.S. "Edinburgh" (destroyer), 1988	5·00	5·50

1992. 40th Anniv of Queen Elizabeth II's Accession. As T **143** of Ascension. Multicoloured.

119	15p. Catholic chapel, Diego Garcia	1·25	1·25
120	20p. Planter's house, Diego Garcia	1·40	1·40
121	24p. Railway tracks on wharf, Diego Garcia	3·00	2·00
122	34p. Three portraits of Queen Elizabeth	2·50	2·25
123	54p. Queen Elizabeth II	2·50	2·50

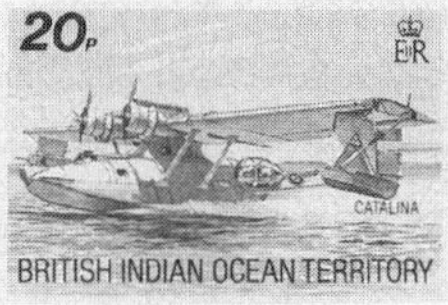

22 R.A.F. Consolidated PBY-5 Catalina (flying boat)

1992. Visiting Aircraft. Multicoloured.

124	20p. Type **22**	2·00	2·50
125	24p. R.A.F. Hawker Siddeley Nimrod M.R.2 (maritime reconnaissance aircraft)	2·25	2·50
126	34p. Lockheed P-3 Orion (transport aircraft)	2·75	3·25
127	54p. U.S.A.A.F. Boeing B-52 Stratofortress (heavy bomber)	3·50	4·50

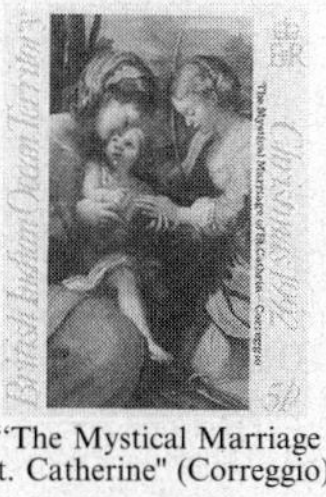

23 "The Mystical Marriage of St. Catherine" (Correggio)

1992. Christmas. Religious Paintings. Multicoloured.

128	5p. Type **23**	70	80
129	24p. "Madonna" (anon)	1·50	1·60
130	34p. "Madonna" (anon) (different)	1·75	2·25
131	54p. "The Birth of Jesus" (Kaspar Jele)	2·50	3·50

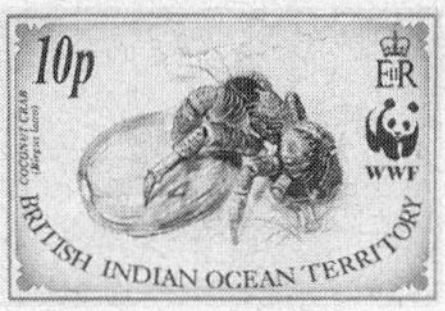

24 Coconut Crab and Rock

1993. Endangered Species. Coconut Crab. Multicoloured.

132	10p. Type **24**	1·25	1·25
133	10p. Crab on beach	1·25	1·25
134	10p. Two crabs	1·25	1·25
135	15p. Crab climbing coconut tree	1·50	1·50

1993. 75th Anniv of Royal Air Force. As T **149** of Ascension. Multicoloured.

136	20p. Vickers Virginia Mk X	1·25	1·50
137	24p. Bristol Bulldog IIA	1·40	1·50
138	34p. Short S.25 Sunderland Mk III	1·75	2·00
139	54p. Bristol Blenheim Mk IV	2·75	3·25

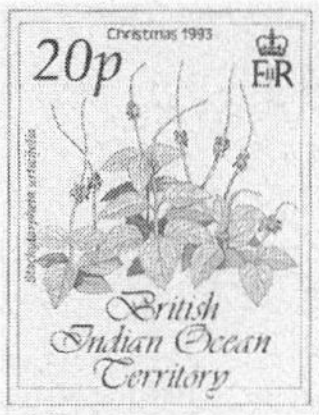

25 "Stachytarpheta urticifolia"

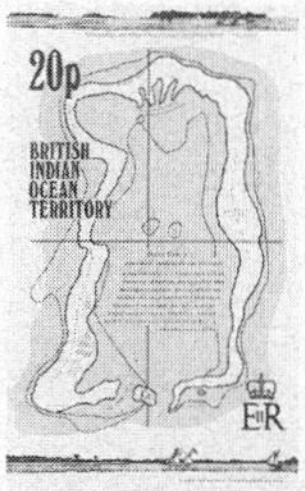

26 Forrest's Map of Diego Garcia, 1778

1993. Christmas. Flowers. Multicoloured.

141	20p. Type **25**	1·25	1·50
142	24p. "Ipomea pes-caprae"	1·25	1·50
143	34p. "Sida pusilla"	1·50	2·25
144	54p. "Catharanthus roseus"	2·50	3·00

1994. "Hong Kong '94" International Stamp Exhibition. Nos. 92 and 101 optd **HONG KONG '94** and emblem.

145	24p. Great frigate bird	2·00	1·50
146	£1 Madagascar red fody	3·50	5·00

1994. 18th-century Maps. Each black and blue.

147	20p. Type **26**	90	1·40
148	24p. Blair's plan of Diego Garcia harbour, 1786–87	1·00	1·50
149	34p. Blair's chart of Chagos Archipelago, 1786–87	1·10	1·60
150	44p. Plan of part of Diego Garcia, 1774	1·40	1·75
151	54p. Fontaine's plan of Diego Garcia, 1770	1·60	1·90

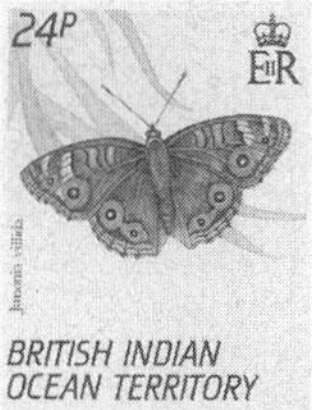

27 "Junonia villida"

1994. Butterflies. Multicoloured.

152	24p. Type **27**	1·75	1·75
153	30p. "Petrelaea dana"	2·25	2·50
154	56p. "Hypolimnas misippus"	3·75	4·00

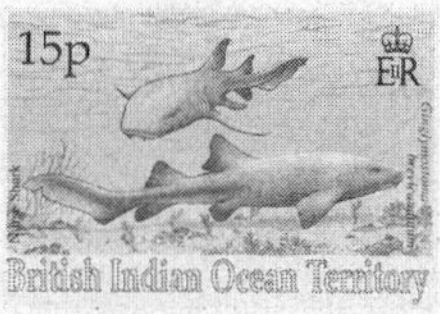

28 Short-tailed Nurse Sharks

1994. Sharks. Multicoloured.

155	15p. Type **28**	1·25	1·25
156	20p. Silver-tipped sharks	1·25	1·25
157	24p. Black-finned reef shark	1·25	1·25
158	30p. Oceanic white-tipped sharks	1·50	1·50
159	35p. Black-tipped shark	1·75	1·75
160	41p. Smooth hammerhead	1·75	1·75
161	46p. Sickle-finned lemon shark	1·75	1·75
162	55p. White-tipped reef shark	2·00	2·00
163	65p. Tiger sharks	2·00	2·00
164	74p. Indian sand tiger	2·25	2·50
165	80p. Great hammerhead	2·25	2·50
166	£1 Great white shark	2·25	2·75

1995. 50th Anniv of End of Second World War. As T **161** of Ascension. Multicoloured.

167	20p. Military cemetery	1·50	1·75
168	24p. Rusty 6-inch naval gun at Cannon Point	1·75	1·75
169	30p. Short S.25 Sunderland flying boat	2·00	2·25
170	56p. H.M.I.S. "Clive"(sloop)	3·00	3·75

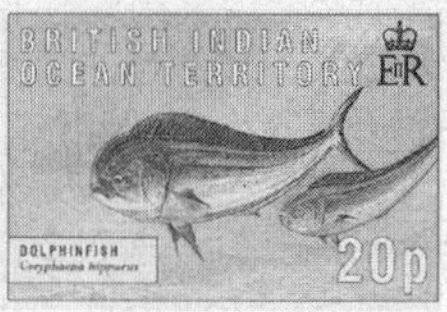

29 Dolphin (fish)

1995. Gamefish. Multicoloured.

172	20p. Type **29**	1·50	1·60
173	24p. Sailfish	1·60	1·60
174	30p. Wahoo	2·25	2·50
175	56p. Striped marlin	3·25	3·75

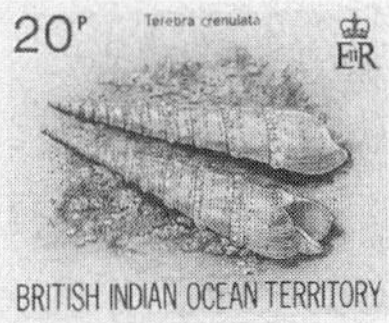

30 "Terebra crenulata"

1996. Sea Shells. Multicoloured.

176	20p. Type **30**	1·25	1·50
177	24p. "Bursa bufonia"	1·25	1·50
178	30p. "Nassarius papillosus"	1·75	2·00
179	56p. "Lopha cristagalli"	3·00	3·25

1996. 70th Birthday of Queen Elizabeth II. As T **165** of Ascension, each incorporating a different photograph of the Queen. Multicoloured.

180	20p. View of lagoon from south	75	1·00
181	24p. Manager's House, Peros Banhos	80	1·00
182	30p. Wireless hut, Peros Banhos	1·00	1·40
183	56p. Sunset	1·50	2·00

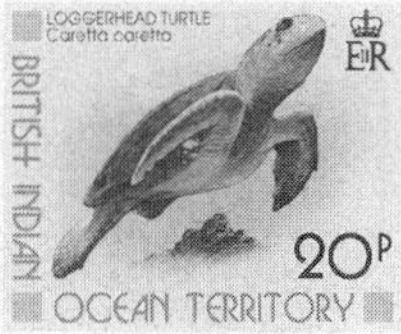

31 Loggerhead Turtle

1996. Turtles. Multicoloured.

185	20p. Type **31**	1·00	1·10
186	24p. Leatherback turtle	1·10	1·10
187	30p. Hawksbill turtle	1·40	1·60
188	56p. Green turtle	2·00	2·25

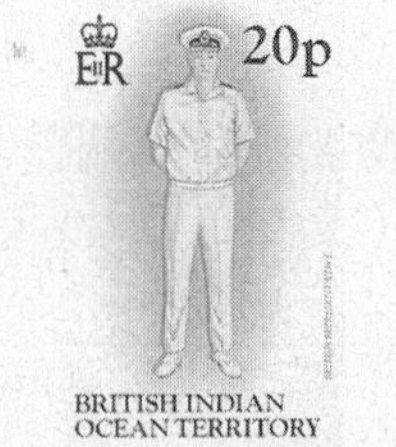

32 Commissioner's Representative (naval officer)

1996. Uniforms. Multicoloured.

189	20p. Type **32**	1·00	1·10
190	24p. Royal Marine officer	1·10	1·10
191	30p. Royal Marine in battle-dress	1·50	1·75
192	56p. Police officers	2·25	2·75

1997. Golden Wedding of Queen Elizabeth and Prince Philip. As T **173** of Ascension. Mult.

195	20p. Queen Elizabeth at Bristol, 1994	1·10	1·40
196	20p. Prince Philip competing in Royal Windsor Horse Show, 1996	1·10	1·40
197	24p. Queen Elizabeth in phaeton, Trooping the Colour, 1987	1·10	1·40
198	24p. Prince Philip	1·10	1·40
199	30p. Queen Elizabeth and Prince Philip with Land Rover	1·10	1·40
200	30p. Queen Elizabeth at Balmoral	1·10	1·40

Nos. 195/6, 197/8 and 199/20 respectively were printed together, se-tenant, with the backgrounds forming a compsite design.

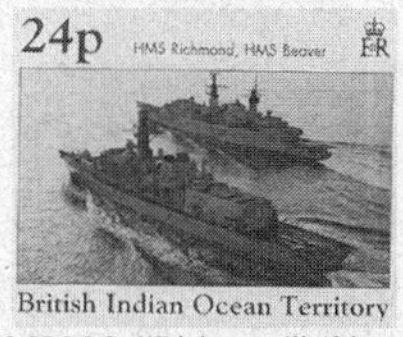

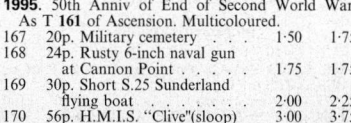

33 H.M.S. "Richmond" (frigate) and H.M.S. "Beaver" (frigate)

1997. Exercise Ocean Wave. Multicoloured.

202	24p. Type **33**	90	1·00
203	24p. H.M.S. "Illustrious" (aircraft carrier) launching aircraft	90	1·00
204	24p. H.M.S. "Beaver"	90	1·00
205	24p. Royal Yacht "Britannia", R.F.A. "Sir Percival" and H.M.S. "Beaver"	90	1·00
206	24p. Royal Yacht "Britannia"	90	1·00
207	24p. H.M.S. "Richmond", H.M.S. "Beaver" and H.M.S. "Gloucester" (destroyer)	90	1·00
208	24p. H.M.S. "Richmond"	90	1·00
209	24p. Aerial view of H.M.S. "Illustrious"	90	1·00
210	24p. H.M.S. "Gloucester" (wrongly inscr "Sheffield")	90	1·00
211	24p. H.M.S. "Trenchant" (submarine) and R.F.A. "Diligence"	90	1·00
212	24p. R.F.A. "Fort George" replenishing H.M.S. "Illustrious" and H.M.S. "Gloucester"	90	1·00
213	24p. Aerial view of H.M.S. "Richmond", H.M.S. "Beaver" and H.M.S. "Gloucester"	90	1·00

1998. 80th Anniv of the Royal Air Force. As T **178** of Ascension. Multicoloured.

215	26p. Blackburn Iris	1·00	1·10
216	34p. Gloster Gamecock	1·25	1·40
217	60p. North American Sabre F.4	2·25	2·50
218	80p. Avro Lincoln	2·75	3·00

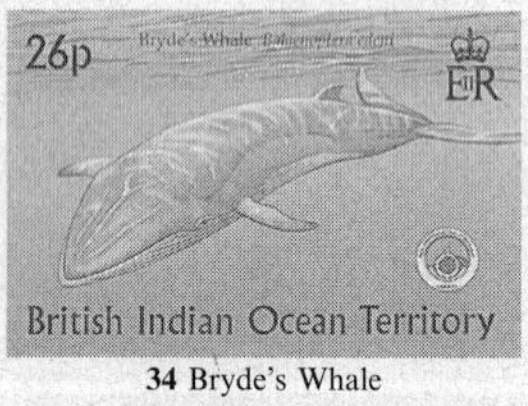

34 Bryde's Whale

1998. International Year of the Ocean. Multicoloured.

220	26p. Type **34**	1·00	1·10
221	26p. Striped dolphin	1·00	1·10
222	34p. Pilot whale	1·00	1·10
223	34p. Spinner dolphin	1·00	1·10

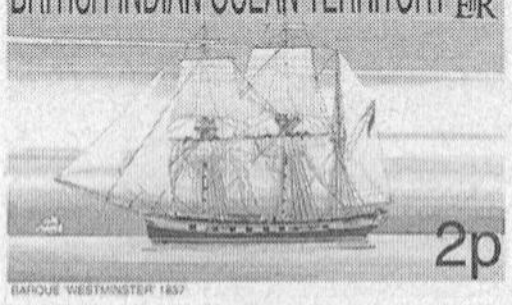

35 "Westminster" (East Indiaman), 1837

1999. Ships. Multicoloured.

224	2p. Type **35**	10	10
225	15p. "Sao Cristovao" (Spanish galleon), 1589	30	35
226	20p. "Sea Witch" (U.S. clipper), 1849	40	45
227	26p. H.M.S. "Royal George" (ship of the line), 1778	55	60
228	34p. "Cutty Sark" (clipper), 1883	70	75
229	60p. "Mentor" (East Indiaman), 1789	1·25	1·40
230	80p. H.M.S. "Trinculo" (brig), 1809	1·60	1·70
231	£1 "Enterprise" (paddle-steamer), 1825	2·00	2·10
232	£1.15 "Confiance" (French privateer), 1800	2·25	2·40
233	£2 "Kent" (East Indiaman), 1820	4·00	4·25

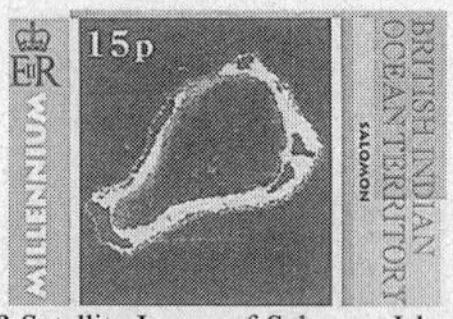

38 Satellite Image of Salomon Island

2000. New Millennium. Satellite Images of Islands. Multicoloured.

236	15p. Type **38**	65	75
237	20p. Egmont	75	85
238	60p. Blenheim Reef	1·50	1·75
239	80p. Diego Garcia	1·75	2·00

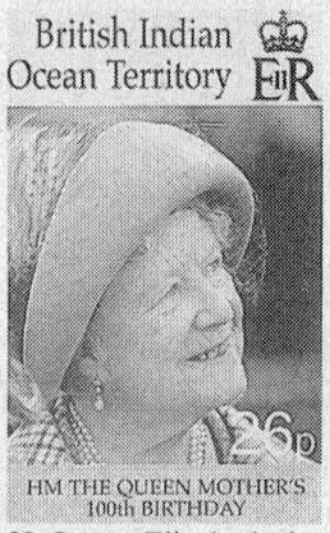

39 Queen Elizabeth the Queen Mother

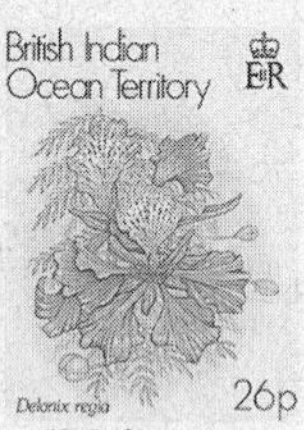

40 *Delonix regia*

2000. Queen Elizabeth the Queen Mother's 100th Birthday. Multicoloured.

240	26p. Type **39**	90	95
241	34p. Wearing green hat and outfit	1·00	1·10

2000. Christmas Flowers. Multicoloured.

243	26p. Type **40**	60	65
244	34p. *Barringtonia asiatica*	80	85
245	60p. *Zephyranthes rosea*	1·50	1·60

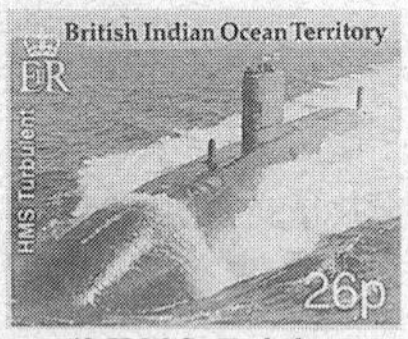

42 H.M.S. *Turbulent*

2001. Centenary of Royal Navy Submarine Service. Multicoloured (except Nos. 248 and 250).

247	26p. Type **42**	60	65
248	26p. H.M.S. *Churchill* (grey and black)	60	065
249	34p. H.M.S. *Resolution*	80	75
250	34p. H.M.S. *Vanguard*	80	85
251	60p. H.M.S. *Otter* (73 × 27 mm)	1·50	1·60
252	60p. H.M.S. *Oberon* (73 × 27 mm) (grey and black)	1·50	1·60

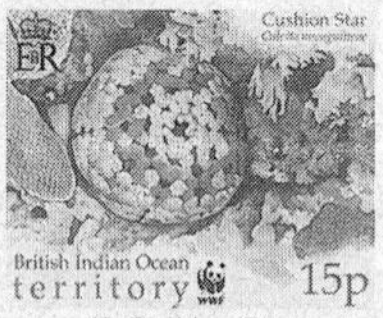

43 Cushion Star

2001. Endangered Species. Seastars. Multicoloured.

253	15p. Type **43**	30	35
254	26p. Azure sea star	50	55
255	34p. Crown-of-Thorns	70	75
256	56p. Banded bubble star	1·10	1·25

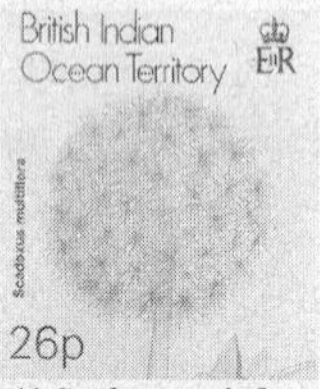

44 *Scadoxus multiflora*

2001. Plants (1st series). Flowers. Multicoloured.

257	26p. Type **44**	50	55
258	34p. *Striga asiatica*	70	75

2002. Golden Jubilee. As T **200** of Ascension.

261	10p. brown, blue and gold	20	25
262	25p. multicoloured	50	55
263	35p. black, blue and gold	70	75
264	55p. multicoloured	1·10	1·25

DESIGNS: 10p. Princess Elizabeth in pantomime, Windsor, 1943; 25p. Queen Elizabeth in floral hat, 1967; 35p. Princess Elizabeth and Prince Philip on their engagement, 1947; 55p. Queen Elizabeth in evening dress.

BRITISH LEVANT Pt. 1

Stamps used at British post offices in the Turkish Empire. These offices closed in 1914. The stamps were again in use after 1918, during the British Occupation of Turkey.

Stamps of Great Britain surcharged or overprinted

A. BRITISH POST OFFICES IN TURKISH EMPIRE

I. TURKISH CURRENCY.

40 paras = 1 piastre.

1885. Queen Victoria stamps surch in **PARAS** or **PIASTRES**.

7	**71**	40pa. on ½d. red	£425	£100
1	**64**	40pa. on 2½d. lilac	90·00	1·25
4	**74**	40pa. on 2½d. purple on blue	2·75	10
2	**62**	80pa. on 5d. green	£180	9·50
5	**78**	80pa. on 5d. purple & blue	15·00	30
6	**81**	4pi. on 10d. purple and red	42·00	8·00
3a	**58**	12pi. on 2s.6d. lilac	45·00	22·00

1902. King Edward VII stamps surch in **PARAS** or **PIASTRES**.

29	–	30pa. on 1½d. purple & grn	6·50	55
8	**83**	40pa. on 2½d. blue	12·00	10
9	–	80pa. on 5d. purple and blue	4·75	2·50
13	**83**	1pi. on 2½d. blue	11·00	10
30	–	2pi. on 5d. purple and blue	9·50	1·50
10	–	4pi. on 10d. purple and red	9·50	4·00
21	–	5pi. on 1s. green and red	4·25	8·50
11	–	12pi. on 2s.6d. purple	35·00	35·00
12	–	24pi. on 5s. red	32·00	40·00

1906. Surch **1 Piastre**.

15	–	1pi. on 2d. green and red	£1300	£600

1909. King Edward VII stamps surch in **PIASTRE PARAS**.

17	–	1pi. 10pa. on 3d. pur on yell	12·00	30·00
18	–	1pi. 30pa. on 4d. grn & brn	5·00	17·00
19	–	1pi. 30pa. on 4d. orange	17·00	50·00
20	**83**	2pi. 20pa. on 6d. purple	18·00	50·00

1910. King Edward VII stamps surch in **PIASTRES**.

22	–	1¼pi. on 3d. purple on yellow	40	1·00
23	–	1¾pi. on 4d. orange	40	60
24	**83**	2½pi. on 6d. purple	1·40	65

1913. King George V stamps surch.

41	**105**	30pa. on ½d. green	75	11·00
35		30pa. on 1½d. brown	3·50	14·00
36a	**104**	1pi. on 2½d. blue	3·75	15
37	**106**	1¼pi. on 3d. violet	4·50	4·25
42	**104**	1½pi. on 1d. red	1·50	1·00
38	**106**	1¾pi. on 4d. grey-green	3·00	6·00
43	**104**	3¾pi. on 2½d. blue	1·25	25
39	**108**	4pi. on 10d. blue	7·50	17·00
44	**106**	4½pi. on 3d. violet	2·00	3·75
40	**108**	5pi. on 1s. brown	40·00	60·00
45	**107**	7½pi. on 5d. brown	30	10
46	**108**	15pi. on 10d. blue	70	15
47		18¾pi. on 1s. brown	4·25	3·75
48	**109**	45pi. on 2s.6d. brown	20·00	45·00
49		90pi. on 5s. red	25·00	30·00
50		180pi. on 10s. blue	45·00	40·00

II. BRITISH CURRENCY

1905. King Edward VII stamps optd **LEVANT**.

L 1	**83**	½d. green	8·50	15
L 2		1d. red	6·00	15
L 3	–	1½d. purple and green	4·50	1·75
L 4a	–	2d. green and red	3·00	7·00
L 5	**83**	2½d. blue	8·50	20·00
L 6	–	3d. purple and yellow	6·00	12·00
L 7	–	4d. green and brown	8·00	35·00
L 8	–	5d. purple and blue	16·00	27·00
L 9	**83**	6d. purple	12·00	25·00
L10		1s. green and red	35·00	48·00

1911. King George V stamps optd **LEVANT**.

L12	**98**	½d. green	1·00	1·00
L14	**101**	½d. green	50	20
L16	**105**	½d. green	30	1·00
L13	**99**	1d. red	50	4·50
L15	**102**	1d. red	50	1·60
L17	**104**	1d. red	30	4·25
L18	**106**	2d. orange	1·25	27·00
L19		3d. violet	7·50	10·00
L20		4d. green	5·00	13·00
L21	**107**	5d. brown	12·00	28·00
L22a		6d. purple	26·00	8·50
L23	**108**	1s. brown	13·00	8·50
L24	**109**	2s.6d. brown	38·00	85·00

B. BRITISH FIELD OFFICE IN SALONICA

1916. King George V stamps of Great Britain optd **Levant**.

S1	**105**	½d. green	38·00	£180
S2	**104**	1d. red	38·00	£180
S3	**106**	2d. orange	£120	£300
S4		3d. violet	90·00	£300
S5		4d. green	£120	£300
S6	**107**	6d. purple	70·00	£250
S7	**108**	9d. black	£275	£500
S8		1s. brown	£225	£450

The above stamps were optd at Salonica during the war of 1914–18.

BRITISH OCCUPATION OF ITALIAN COLONIES Pt. 1

Issues for use in Italian colonies occupied by British Forces. Middle East Forces overprints were used in Cyrenaica, Dodecanese Islands, Eritrea, Italian Somaliland and Tripolitania.

MIDDLE EAST FORCES

12 pence = 1 shilling;
20 shillings = 1 pound.

1942. Stamps of Great Britain optd **M.E.F.**

M11	**128**	1d. red	1·50	10
M12		2d. orange	1·50	1·25
M13		2½d. blue	45	10
M 4		3d. violet	30	10
M 5	**129**	5d. brown	30	15
M16		6d. purple	40	10
M17	**130**	9d. olive	85	10
M18		1s. brown	50	10
M19	**131**	2s.6d. green	7·00	1·00
M20		5s. red	11·00	17·00
M21		10s. blue (No. 478a)	14·00	10·00

PRICES. Our prices for Nos. M1/21 in used condition are for stamps with identifiable postmarks of the territories in which they were issued. These stamps were also used in the United Kingdom with official sanction, from the summer of 1950 onwards, and with U.K. postmarks are worth about 25 per cent less.

POSTAGE DUE STAMPS

1942. Postage Due stamps of Great Britain optd **M.E.F.**

MD1	**D 1**	½d. green	30	10·00
MD2		1d. red	30	1·75
MD3		2d. black	1·25	1·25
MD4		3d. violet	50	4·25
MD5		1s. blue	3·25	11·00

CYRENAICA

10 milliemes = 1 piastre;
100 piastres = 1 Egyptian pound.

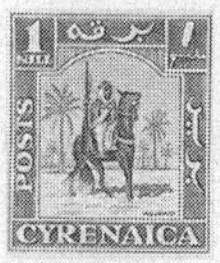

24 Mounted Warrior

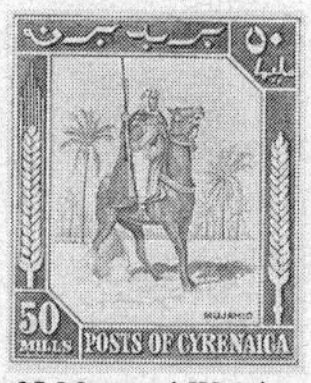

25 Mounted Warrior

1950.

136	**24**	1m. brown	1·25	2·75
137		2m. red	1·50	2·75
138		3m. yellow	1·50	2·75
139		4m. green	1·50	3·25
140		5m. grey	1·25	1·25
141		8m. orange	1·50	1·50
142		10m. violet	1·50	1·25
143		12m. red	1·50	1·00
144		20m. blue	1·50	1·00
145	**25**	50m. blue and brown	2·50	3·00
146		100m. red and black	6·50	9·00
147		200m. violet and blue	11·00	25·00
148		500m. yellow and green	42·00	65·00

POSTAGE DUE STAMPS

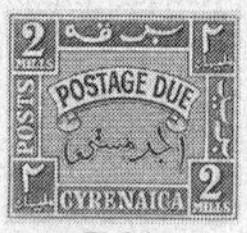

D 26

1950.

D149	**D 26**	2m. brown	45·00	95·00
D150		4m. green	45·00	95·00
D151		8m. red	45·00	£100
D152		10m. orange	45·00	£100
D153		20m. yellow	45·00	£110
D154		40m. blue	45·00	£130
D155		100m. brown	45·00	£140

ERITREA

100 cents = 1 shilling.

BRITISH MILITARY ADMINISTRATION

1948. Stamps of Great Britain surch **B.M.A. ERITREA** and value in cents or shillings.

E 1	**128**	5c. on ½d. green	60	65
E 2		10c. on 1d. red	75	2·50
E 3		20c. on 2d. orange	50	2·25
E 4		25c. on 2½d. blue	50	60
E 5		30c. on 3d. violet	1·25	4·50
E 6	**129**	40c. on 5d. brown	30	4·25
E 7		50c. on 6d. purple	30	1·00
E 7a	**130**	65c. on 8d. red	7·00	2·00
E 8		75c. on 9d. olive	50	75
E 9		1s. on 1s. brown	50	50
E10	**131**	2s.50 on 2s.6d. green	7·00	10·00
E11		5s. on 5s. red	7·00	16·00
E12	–	10s. on 10s. blue (No. 478a)	20·00	22·00

BRITISH ADMINISTRATION

1950. Stamps of Great Britain surch **B.A. ERITREA** and value in cents or shillings.

E13	**128**	5c. on ½d. green	65	7·00
E26		5c. on ½d. orange	30	60
E14		10c. on 1d. red	30	2·75
E27		10c. on 1d. blue	30	60
E15		20c. on 2d. orange	30	70
E28		20c. on 2d. brown	30	30
E16		25c. on 2½d. blue	30	60
E29		25c. on 2½d. red	30	30
E17	**128**	30c. on 3d. violet	30	1·75
E18	**129**	40c. on 5d. brown	40	1·50
E19		50c. on 6d. purple	30	20
E20	**130**	65c. on 8d. red	1·25	1·50
E21		75c. on 9d. olive	30	25
E22		1s. on 1s. brown	30	15
E23	**131**	2s.50 on 2s.6d. green	4·50	4·75

E24		5s. on 5s. red	6·00	10·00
E25	–	10s. on 10s. blue (No. 478a)	55·00	55·00

1951. Nos. 509/11 of Great Britain surch **B.A. ERITREA** and value in cents and shillings.

E30	147	2s.50 on 2s.6d. green	7·50	21·00
E31	–	5s. on 5s. red	21·00	21·00
E32	–	10s. on 10s. blue	21·00	21·00

POSTAGE DUE STAMPS

1948. Postage Due stamps of Great Britain surch **B.M.A ERITREA** and new value in cents and shillings.

ED1	D 1	5c. on ½d. green	9·50	20·00
ED2		10c. on 1d. red	9·50	22·00
ED3		20c. on 2d. black	7·00	15·00
ED4		30c. on 3d. violet	9·50	14·00
ED5		1s. on 1s. blue	17·00	28·00

1950. Postage Due stamps of Great Britain surch **B.A. ERITREA** and new value in cents or shillings.

ED 6	D 1	5c. on ½d. green	11·00	45·00
ED 7		10c. on 1d. red	9·00	15·00
ED 8		20c. on 2d. black	9·50	13·00
ED 9		30c. on 3d. violet	11·00	17·00
ED10		1s. on 1s. blue	15·00	22·00

SOMALIA

BRITISH OCCUPATION

1943. Stamps of Great Britain optd **E.A.F.** (East African Forces).

S1	128	1d. red	60	40
S2		2d. orange	1·50	1·25
S3		2½d. blue	30	3·50
S4		3d. violet	50	15
S5	129	5d. brown	50	40
S6		6d. purple	30	90
S7	130	9d. olive	80	2·25
S8		1s. brown	1·50	15
S9	131	2s.6d. green	7·50	6·50

PRICES. Our prices for Nos. S1/9 in used condition are for stamps with identifiable postmarks of the territories in which they were issued. These stamps were also used in the United Kingdom with official sanction, from the summer of 1950, and with U.K. postmarks are worth about 25 per cent less.

BRITISH MILITARY ADMINISTRATION

1948. Stamps of Great Britain surch **B.M.A. SOMALIA** and new value in cents and shillings.

S10	128	5c. on ½d. green	1·00	1·75
S11		15c. on 1½d. brown	1·50	14·00
S12		20c. on 2d. orange	2·50	4·00
S13		25c. on 2½d. blue	2·25	4·50
S14		30c. on 3d. violet	2·25	9·00
S15	129	40c. on 5d. brown	85	20
S16		50c. on 6d. purple	50	2·00
S17	130	75c. on 9d. olive	2·00	17·00
S18		1s. on 1s. brown	1·25	20
S19	131	2s.50 on 2s.6d. green	3·75	25·00
S20		5s. on 5s. red	8·50	35·00

BRITISH ADMINISTRATION

1950. Stamps of Great Britain surch **B.A. SOMALIA** and value in cents and shillings.

S21	128	5c. on ½d. green	20	3·00
S22		15c. on 1½d. brown	60	16·00
S23		20c. on 2d. orange	60	6·50
S24		25c. on 2½d. blue	50	7·00
S25		30c. on 3d. violet	1·00	4·25
S26	129	40c. on 5d. brown	55	85
S27		50c. on 6d. purple	50	1·00
S28	130	75c. on 9d. olive	1·25	6·50
S29		1s. on 1s. brown	60	1·50
S30	131	2s.50 on 2s.6d. green	4·00	24·00
S31		5s. on 5s. red	9·50	29·00

TRIPOLITANIA

BRITISH MILITARY ADMINISTRATION

1948. Stamps of Great Britain surch **B.M.A. TRIPOLITANIA** and value in **M.A.L.** (Military Administration lire).

T 1	128	1l. on ½d. green	50	1·00
T 2		2l. on 1d. red	30	15
T 3		3l. on 1½d. brown	30	50
T 4		4l. on 2d. orange	30	50
T 5		5l. on 2½d. blue	30	20
T 6		6l. on 3d. violet	30	40
T 7	129	10l. on 5d. brown	30	15
T 8		12l. on 6d. purple	30	20
T 9	130	18l. on 9d. olive	50	65
T10		24l. on 1s. brown	50	1·00
T11	131	60l. on 2s.6d. green	2·50	7·50
T12		120l. on 5s. red	13·00	16·00
T13		240l. on 10s. blue (No. 478a)	20·00	90·00

BRITISH ADMINISTRATION

1950. As Nos. T1/13 but surch **B.A. TRIPOLITANIA** and value in **M.A.L.**

T14	128	1l. on ½d. green	1·50	11·00
T27		1l. on ½d. orange	20	5·00
T15		2l. on 1d. red	1·75	40
T28		2l. on 1d. blue	20	90
T16		3l. on 1½d. brown	50	11·00
T29		3l. on 1½d. green	30	7·50
T17		4l. on 2d. orange	40	4·50
T30		4l. on 2d. brown	20	1·25
T18		5l. on 2½d. blue	30	70
T31		5l. on 2½d. red	30	7·50
T19		6l. on 3d. violet	1·25	3·25
T20	129	10l. on 5d. brown	30	4·00
T21		12l. on 6d. purple	1·25	50
T22	130	18l. on 9d. olive	1·50	2·50
T23		24l. on 1s. brown	1·50	3·50
T24	131	60l. on 2s.6d. green	4·50	12·00
T25		120l. on 5s. red	17·00	22·00
T26	–	240l. on 10s. blue (No. 478a)	28·00	60·00

1951. Nos. 509/11 of Great Britain surch **B.A. TRIPOLITANIA** and value in **M.A.L.**

T32	147	60l. on 2s.6d. green	4·50	20·00
T33	–	120l. on 5s. red	8·00	26·00
T34	–	240l. on 10s. blue	35·00	42·00

POSTAGE DUE STAMPS

1948. Postage Due stamps of Great Britain surch **B.M.A. TRIPOLITANIA** and value in **M.A.L.**

TD1	D 1	1l. on ½d. green	5·50	48·00
TD2		2l. on 1d. red	2·50	30·00
TD3		4l. on 2d. black	7·50	28·00
TD4		6l. on 3d. violet	7·50	20·00
TD5		24l. on 1s. blue	28·00	£100

1950. As Nos. TD1/5 but surch **B.A. TRIPOLITANIA** and value in **M.A.L.**

TD 6	D 1	1l. on ½d. green	12·00	80·00
TD 7		2l. on 1d. red	2·50	27·00
TD 8		4l. on 2d. black	2·75	30·00
TD 9		6l. on 3d. violet	18·00	60·00
TD10		24l. on 1s. blue	48·00	£140

BRITISH POSTAL AGENCIES IN EASTERN ARABIA Pt. 1

British stamps surcharged for use in parts of the Persian Gulf.

The stamps were used in Muscat from 1 April 1948 to 29 April 1966; in Dubai from 1 April 1948 to 6 January 1961; In Qatar: Doha from August 1950, Umm Said from February 1956 to 31 March 1957; and in Abu Dhabi from 30 March 1963 (Das Island from December 1960) to 29 March 1964.

Nos. 21/2 were placed on sale in Kuwait Post Offices in 1951 and from February to November 1953 due to shortages of stamps with "KUWAIT" overprint. Isolated examples of other values can be found commercially used from Bahrain and Kuwait.

1948. 12 pies = 1 anna; 16 annas = 1 rupee.
1957. 100 naya paise = 1 rupee.

Stamps of Great Britain surch in Indian currency.

1948. King George VI.

16	128	½a. on ½d. green	2·75	6·50
35		½a. on ½d. orange	30	9·00
17		1a. on 1d. red	2·75	20
36		1a. on 1d. blue	30	7·50
18		1½a. on 1½d. brown	7·00	2·00
37		1½a. on 1½d. green	7·00	22·00
19		2a. on 2d. orange	1·75	2·25
38		2a. on 2d. brown	30	8·50
20		2½a. on 2½d. blue	3·00	5·50
39		2½a. on 2½d. red	30	16·00
21		3a. on 3d. violet	3·00	10
40	129	4a. on 4d. blue	30	3·50
22		6a. on 6d. purple	3·00	10
23	130	1r. on 1s. brown	3·50	50
24	131	2r. on 2s.6d. green	8·50	32·00

1948. Royal Silver Wedding.

25	137	2½a. on 2½d. blue	2·00	2·00
26	138	15r. on £1 blue	23·00	35·00

1948. Olympic Games.

27	139	2½a. on 2½d. blue	35	2·00
28	140	3a. on 3d. violet	45	2·00
29	–	6a. on 6d. purple	45	2·00
30	–	1r. on 1s. brown	1·25	2·25

1949. 75th Anniv of U.P.U.

31	143	2½a. on 2½d. blue	50	2·50
32	144	3a. on 3d. violet	50	2·50
33	–	6a. on 6d. purple	50	1·75
34	–	1r. on 1s. brown	2·00	2·75

1951. Pictorial.

41	147	2r. on 2s.6d. green	24·00	7·00

1952. Queen Elizabeth.

42	154	½a. on ½d. orange	10	2·00
43		1a. on 1d. blue	10	2·00
44		1½a. on 1½d. green	10	2·00
45		2a. on 2d. brown	10	10
46	155	2½a. on 2½d. red	10	10
47		3a. on 3d. lilac	20	1·00
48		4a. on 4d. blue	55	3·75
49	157	6a. on 6d. purple	35	10
50	160	12a. on 1s.3d. green	2·00	30
51		1r. on 1s.6d. blue	2·00	10

1953. Coronation.

52	161	2½a. on 2½d. red	1·75	1·40
53	–	4a. on 4d. blue	1·75	1·00
54	163	12a. on 1s.3d. green	2·25	1·00
55	–	1r. on 1s.6d. blue	2·50	45

1955. Pictorials.

56	166	2r. on 2s.6d. brown	5·50	70
57	–	5r. on 5s. red	10·00	2·00

1957. Value in naye paise. Queen Elizabeth II stamps surch **NP** twice (once only on 75n.p.) and value.

79	157	1n.p. on 5d. brown	10	20
80	154	3n.p. on ½d. orange	55	80
81		5n.p. on 1d. blue	1·00	1·50
67		6n.p. on 1d. blue	20	2·25
68		9n.p. on 1½d. green	20	1·75
83		10n.p. on 1½d. green	50	2·00
69		12n.p. on 2d. brown	30	1·75
85	155	15n.p. on 2½d. red	25	10
71		20n.p. on 3d. lilac	20	10
72		25n.p. on 4d. blue	70	3·00
87		30n.p. on 4½d. brown	40	50
73	157	40n.p. on 6d. purple	30	10
89	158	50n.p. on 9d. olive	1·00	1·75
75	160	75n.p. on 1s.3d. green	2·00	35

1957. World Scout Jubilee Jamboree.

76	170	15n.p. on 2½d. red	25	85
77	171	25n.p. on 4d. blue	30	85
78	–	75n.p. on 3d. green	35	85

BRITISH POST OFFICES IN CHINA Pt. 1

Stamps for use in Wei Hai Wei, and the neighbouring islands, leased to Great Britain from 1898 to 1 October 1930, when they were returned to China. The stamps were also used in the Treaty Ports from 1917 until 1922.

100 cents = 1 dollar.

1917. Stamps of Hong Kong (King George V) optd **CHINA**.

1	24	1c. brown	3·00	1·50
2		2c. green	4·00	30
3		4c. red	3·75	30
4		6c. orange	4·00	60
5		8c. grey	10·00	1·25
6		10c. blue	9·50	30
7		12c. purple on yellow	7·50	2·50
8		20c. purple and olive	11·00	60
9		25c. purple	7·50	15·00
11		30c. purple and orange	26·00	5·00
12b		50c. black on green	26·00	5·50
13		$1 purple and blue on blue	65·00	2·50
14		$2 red and black	£190	50·00
15		$3 green and purple	£400	£170
16		$5 green and red on green	£350	£225
17		$10 purple and black on red	£850	£425

BRITISH POST OFFICES IN CRETE Pt. 1

40 paras = 1 piastre.

B 1

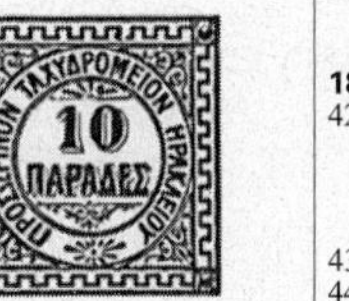

B 2

1898.

B1	B 1	20pa. violet	£425	£225

1898.

B2	B 2	10pa. blue	8·00	17·00
B4		10pa. brown	8·00	24·00
B3		20pa. green	12·00	15·00
B5		20pa. red	17·00	15·00

BRITISH POST OFFICES IN SIAM Pt. 1

Used at Bangkok.

100 cents = 1 dollar.

1882. Stamps of Straits Settlements optd **B** on issue of 1867.

1	19	32c. on 2a. yellow	£35000	

On issues of 1867 to 1883.

14	5	2c. brown	£475	£350
13	9	2c. on 32c. red (No. 60)	£2500	£2750
15	5	2c. red	55·00	45·00
16		4c. red	£500	£300
17		4c. brown	75·00	70·00
4	18	5c. brown	£275	£300
18		5c. blue	£225	£160
5	5	6c. lilac	£200	£110
20		8c. orange	£140	65·00
21	19	10c. grey	£150	85·00
8	5	12c. blue	£900	£475
22		12c. purple	£275	£150
9		24c. green	£700	£150
10	8	30c. red	£30000	£20000
11	9	96c. grey	£5000	£2750

BRITISH VIRGIN ISLANDS Pt. 1

A group of the Leeward Islands, Br. W. Indies. Used general issues for Leeward Islands concurrently with Virgin Islands stamps until 1 July 1956. A Crown Colony.

1951. 100 cents = 1 West Indian dollar.
1962. 100 cents = 1 U.S. dollar.

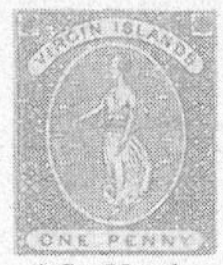

1 St. Ursula

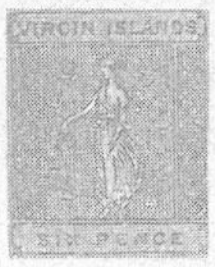

2

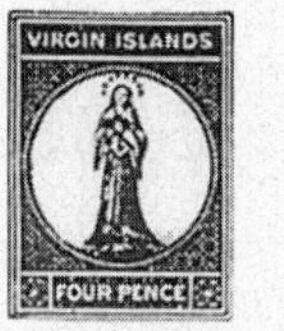

3

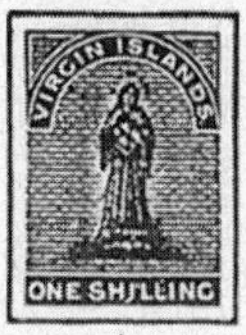

4

1866.

1	1	1d. green	45·00	60·00
16	3	4d. red	40·00	60·00
7	2	6d. red	60·00	90·00
11	4	1s. black and red	£225	£300

No. 11 has a double-lined frame.

1867. With heavy coloured border.

18	4	1s. black and red	48·00	60·00

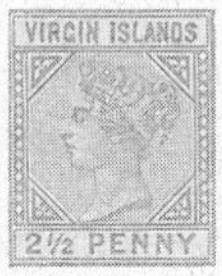

6

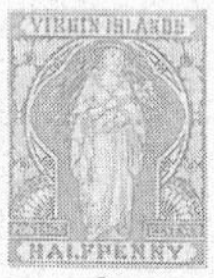

8

1880.

26	6	½d. yellow	85·00	80·00
27		½d. green	4·25	8·00
24		1d. green	65·00	85·00
29		1d. red	24·00	27·00
25		2½d. brown	90·00	£120
31		2½d. blue	2·50	14·00

1887.

32	1	1d. red	2·00	7·00
35	3	4d. brown	35·00	65·00
39	2	6d. violet	12·00	42·00
41	4	1s. brown	45·00	70·00

1888. No. 18 surch **4D.**

42	4	4d. on 1s. black and red	£110	£150

1899.

43	8	½d. green	1·00	55
44		1d. red	2·75	3·00
45		2½d. blue	12·00	4·00
46		4d. brown	4·00	18·00
47		6d. violet	4·50	4·50
48		7d. green	7·00	8·00
49		1s. yellow	22·00	35·00
50		5s. blue	70·00	85·00

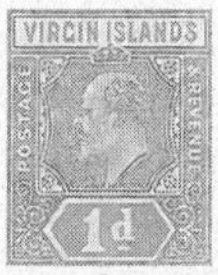

9

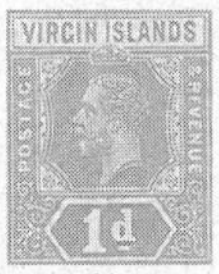

11

1904.

54	9	½d. purple and green	75	40
55		1d. purple and red	2·50	35
56		2d. purple and brown	6·00	4·50
57		2½d. purple and blue	2·00	2·00
58		3d. purple and black	3·50	3·00
59		6d. purple and brown	2·75	3·00
60		1s. green and red	4·00	5·00
61		2s.6d. green and black	23·00	55·00
62		5s. green and blue	48·00	65·00

1913.

69	11	½d. green	50	3·50
70		1d. red	2·25	14·00
71		2d. grey	4·00	23·00
72		2½d. blue	5·50	9·00
73		3d. purple on yellow	2·75	6·50
74		6d. purple	5·00	10·00
75		1s. black on green	3·25	9·00
76		2s.6d. black and red on blue	48·00	50·00
77		5s. green and red on yellow	35·00	£110

1917. Optd **WAR STAMP**.

78c	11	1d. red	30	3·75
79a		3d. purple on yellow	3·00	10·00

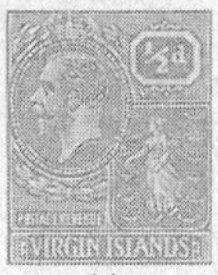

14

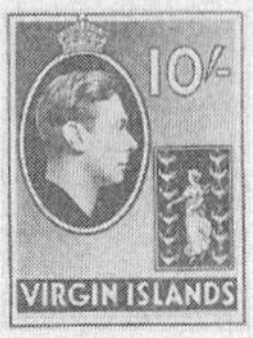

15 King George VI and Badge of Colony

1922.

86 **14** ½d. green . . . . 85 2·75
87 1d. red 60 60
88 1d. violet . . . . 1·00 3·50
91 1½d. red . . . . 1·75 2·00
92 2d. grey . . . . 1·00 6·00
95 2½d. blue . . . . 2·50 3·50
94 2½d. orange . . . . 1·25 1·50
96 3d. purple on yellow . . . 2·25 11·00
97 5d. purple and olive . . . 5·50 45·00
98 6d. purple . . . . 1·50 6·50
83 1s. black on green . . . . 75 14·00
84 2s.6d. black and red on blue . . . . 5·50 11·00
101 5s. green and red on yellow 19·00 70·00

1935. Silver Jubilee. As T **13** of Antigua.
103 1d. blue and red . . . . . . 1·25 3·50
104 1½d. blue and grey . . . . . 1·25 3·50
105 2½d. brown and blue . . . . 1·25 3·50
106 1s. grey and purple . . . . . 6·50 16·00

1937. Coronation. As T **2** of Aden.
107 1d. red . . . . 20 1·00
108 1½d. brown . . . . 50 2·50
109 2½d. blue . . . . 50 1·00

1938.

110a **15** ½d. green . . . . 30 1·00
111a 1d. red 30 60
112a 1½d. brown . . . . 1·00 1·00
113a 2d. grey . . . . 1·00 90
114a 2½d. blue . . . . 70 2·50
115a 3d. orange 70 80
116a 6d. mauve . . . . 2·00 80
117a 1s. brown . . . . 1·50 70
118a 2s.6d. brown . . . . . . 15·00 3·00
119a 5s. red . . . . 13·00 4·00
120 10s. blue . . . . 6·00 8·00
121 £1 black . . . . 8·00 20·00

1946. Victory. As T **9** of Aden.
122 1½d. brown 10 10
123 3d. orange 10 10

1949. Silver Wedding. As T **10/11** of Aden.
124 2½d. blue 10 10
125 £1 grey . . . . 13·00 16·00

1949. 75th Anniv of U.P.U. As T **20/23** of Antigua.
126 2½d. blue 30 45
127 3d. orange . . . . 80 2·00
128 6d. mauve 30 40
129 1s. olive 30 40

1951. Inauguration of B.W.I. University College. As T **24/25** of Antigua.
130 3c. black and red . . . . . 40 1·25
131 12c. black and violet . . . . 60 1·25

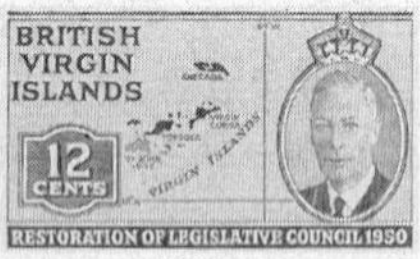

16 Map

1951. Restoration of Legislative Council.
132 **16** 6c. orange . . . . 30 1·00
133 12c. purple 30 50
134 24c. olive 30 50
135 $1.20 red . . . . 80 1·00

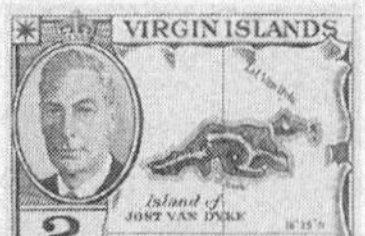

18 Map of Jost Van Dyke

1952.

136 – 1c. black . . . . 80 1·25
137 **18** 2c. green 70 30
138 – 3c. black and brown . . . 80 1·00
139 – 4c. red . . . . 70 1·00
140 – 5c. red and black . . . . 1·50 50
141 – 8c. blue . . . . 70 1·25
142 – 12c. violet . . . . 80 1·40
143 – 24c. brown 70 50
144 – 60c. green and blue . . . 3·50 11·00
145 – $1.20 black and blue . . . 4·25 12·00
146 – $2.40 green and brown . . 10·00 16·00
147 – $4.80 blue and red . . . 11·00 16·00

DESIGNS—VERT: 1c. Sombrero lighthouse; 24c. Badge of Presidency. HORIZ—VIEWS: 3c. Sheep industry; 5c. Cattle industry; 60c. Dead Man's Chest (Is); $1.20, Sir Francis Drake Channel; $2.40, Road Town. HORIZ—MAPS: 4c. Anegada Island; 8c. Virgin Gorda Island; 12c. Tortola Island; $4.80, Virgin Islands.

1953. Coronation. As T **13** of Aden.
148 2c. black and green . . . . . 30 1·00

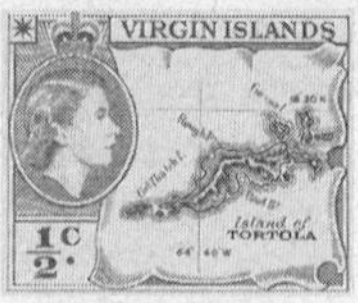

29 Map of Tortola

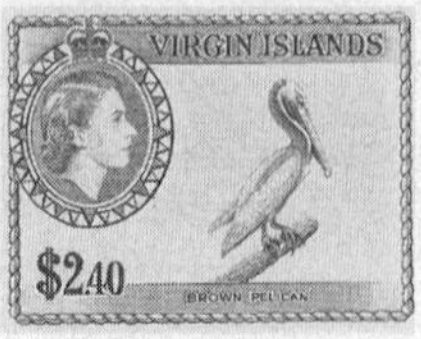

30 Brown Pelican

1956.

149 **29** ½c. black and purple . . . 40 20
150 – 1c. turquoise and slate . . 1·50 75
151 – 2c. red and black 30 10
152 – 3c. blue and olive 30 30
153 – 4c. brown and turquoise . . 45 30
154 – 5c. black 45 10
155 – 8c. orange and blue . . . 1·50 40
156 – 12c. blue and red . . . . 3·00 75
157 – 24c. green and brown . . . 1·00 65
158 – 60c. blue and orange . . . 8·00 8·00
159 – $1.20 green and red . . . 2·00 8·00
160 **30** $2.40 yellow and purple . . 38·00 13·00
161 – $4.80 sepia and turquoise 38·00 13·00

DESIGNS—HORIZ: As Type **13**: 1c. Virgin Islands sloop; 2c. Nelthrop Red Poll bull; 3c. Road Harbour; 4c. Mountain travel; 5c. Badge of the Presidency; 8c. Beach scene; 12c. Boat launching; 24c. White cedar tree; 60c. Skipjack tuna ("Bonito"); $1.20, Treasury Square Coronation celebrations. As Type **30**: $4.80, Magnificent frigate bird ("Man-o'-War Bird").

1962. New Currency. Nos. 149/53, 155/61 surch in U.S. Currency.
162 **29** 1c. on ½c. black and purple 30 10
163 – 2c. on 1c. turq & vio . . . 1·50 10
164 – 3c. on 2c. red and black . . 50 10
165 – 4c. on 3c. blue and olive . . 30 10
166 – 5c. on 4c. brown & turq . . 30 10
167 – 8c. on 8c. orange and blue . 30 10
168 – 10c. on 12c. blue and red . 1·50 10
169 – 12c. on 24c. green & brn . . 30 10
170 – 25c. on 60c. blue and orange . . . . 2·50 45
171 – 70c. on $1.20 green and red 35 45
172 **30** $1.40 on $2.40 yellow and purple . . . . 9·00 3·75
173 – $2.80 on $4.80 sepia & turq . . . . 9·00 3·75

1963. Freedom from Hunger. As T **28** of Aden.
174 25c. violet 20 10

1963. Centenary of Red Cross. As T **33** of Antigua.
175 2c. red and black 15 20
176 25c. red and blue 50 20

1964. 400th Birth Anniv of Shakespeare. As T **34** of Antigua.
177 10c. blue 20 10

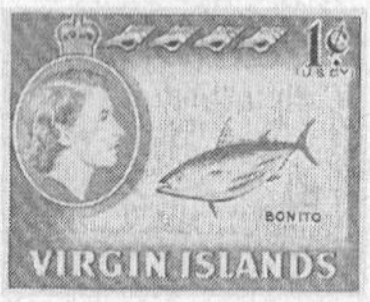

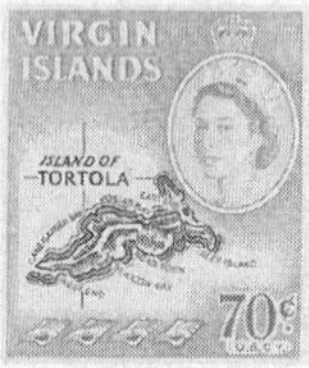

43 Skipjack Tuna 44 Map of Tortola

1964.

178 **43** 1c. blue and olive . . . . 30 1·25
179 – 2c. olive and red 15 30
180 3c. sepia and turquoise . . 3·00 1·25
181 – 4c. black and red . . . . 80 1·75
182 – 5c. black and green . . . 65 1·75
183 – 6c. black and orange . . . 30 85
184 – 8c. black and mauve . . . 30 45
185 – 10c. lake and lilac . . . . 1·50 30
186 – 12c. green and blue . . . 2·00 2·00
187 – 15c. green and black . . . 35 2·25
188 – 25c. green and purple . . . 11·00 1·75
189 **44** 70c. black and brown . . . 3·75 5·00
190 – $1 green and brown . . . 3·00 2·00
191 – $1.40 blue and red . . . 24·00 9·00
192 – $2.80 black and purple . . 24·00 9·00

DESIGNS—HORIZ (As Type **43**): 2c. Soper's Hole; 3c. Brown pelican; 4c. Dead Man's Chest; 5c. Road Harbour; 6c. Fallen Jerusalem; 8c. The Baths, Virgin Gorda; 10c. Map of Virgin Islands; 12c. "Youth of Tortola" (Tortola–St Thomas ferry); 15c. The Towers, Tortola; 25c. Beef Island Airfield. VERT (As Type **44**): $1 Virgin Gorda: $1.40, Yachts at anchor. (27½ × 37½ mm): $2.80, Badge of the Colony.

1965. Centenary of I.T.U. As T **36** of Antigua.
193 4c. yellow and turquoise . . 20 10
194 25c. blue and buff 45 20

1965. I.C.Y. As T **37** of Antigua.
195 1c. purple and turquoise . . 10 15
196 25c. green and lavender . . . 30 15

1966. Churchill Commemoration. As T **38** of Antigua.
197 1c. blue 10 30
198 2c. green 15 30
199 10c. brown 30 10
200 25c. violet 60 25

1966. Royal Visit. As T **39** of Antigua.
201 4c. black and blue 40 10
202 70c. black and mauve . . . . 1·40 45

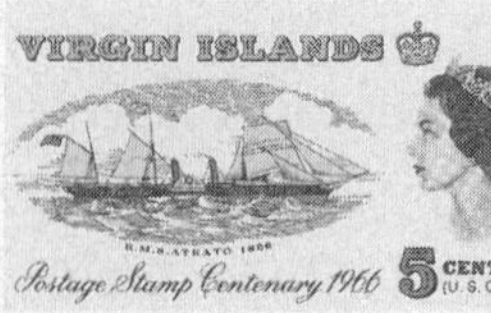

58 "Atrato I" (paddle-steamer), 1866

1966. Stamp Centenary. Multicoloured.
203 5c. Type **58** 35 10
204 10c. 1d. and 6d. stamps of 1866 . . . . 35 10
205 25c. Mail transport, Beef Island, and 6d. stamp of 1866 . . . . 55 10
206 60c. Landing mail at Roadtown, 1866 and 1d. stamp of 1866 . . . . . . 1·00 2·50

1966. Nos. 189 and 191/2 surch.
207 **44** 50c. on 70c. blk & brn . . 1·25 90
208 – $1.50 on $1.40 blue and red . . . . 2·25 2·00
209 – $3 on $2.80 black and purple . . . . 2·25 2·75

1966. 20th Anniv of U.N.E.S.C.O. As T **54/6** of Antigua.
210 2c. multicoloured 10 10
211 12c. yellow, violet and olive 20 10
212 60c. black, purple and orange 50 45

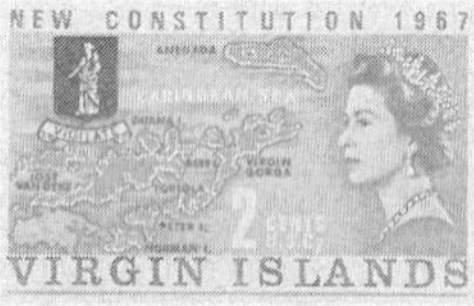

63 Map of Virgin Islands

1967. New Constitution.
213 **63** 2c. multicoloured 10 10
214 10c. multicoloured 15 10
215 25c. multicoloured 15 10
216 $1 multicoloured 55 40

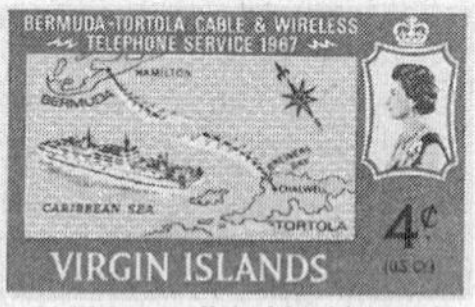

64 "Mercury" (cable ship) and Bermuda–Tortola Link

1967. Inauguration of Bermuda–Tortola Telephone Service. Multicoloured.
217 4c. Type **64** 20 10
218 10c. Chalwell Telecommunications Station 20 10
219 50c. "Mercury" (cable ship) 50 30

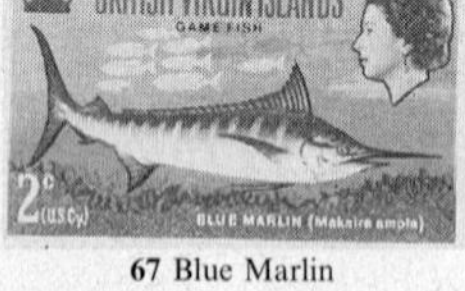

67 Blue Marlin

1968. Game Fishing. Multicoloured.
220 2c. Type **67** 10 65
221 10c. Cobia 25 10
222 25c. Wahoo 55 10
223 40c. Fishing launch and map 85 75

1968. Human Rights Year. Nos. 185 and 188 optd **1968 INTERNATIONAL YEAR FOR HUMAN RIGHTS**.
224 10c. lake and lilac 20 10
225 25c. green and purple 30 40

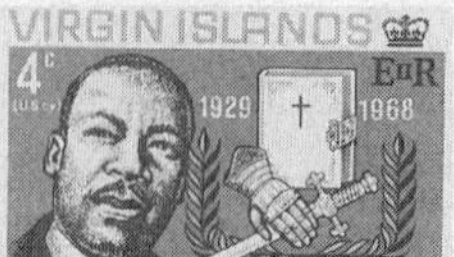

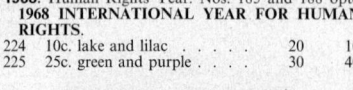

72 Dr. Martin Luther King, Bible, Sword and Armour Gauntlet

1968. Martin Luther King Commemoration.
226 **72** 4c. multicoloured 25 20
227 25c. multicoloured 40 40

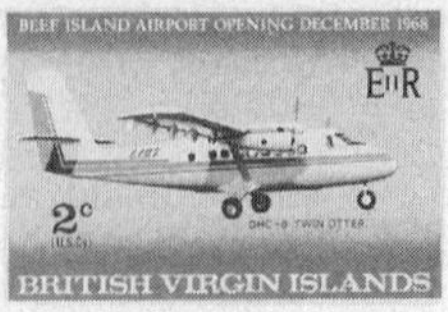

73 De Havilland Twin Otter 100

1968. Opening of Beef Island Airport Extension. Multicoloured.
228 2c. Type **73** 15 70
229 10c. Hawker Siddeley H.S.748 airliner 20 10
230 25c. De Havilland Heron 2 airplane 40 10
231 $1 Royal Engineers' cap badge . . . . 50 2·00

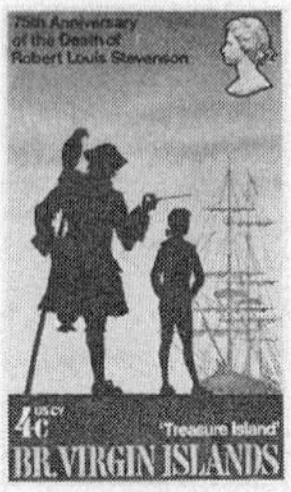

77 Long John Silver and Jim Hawkins

1969. 75th Death Anniv of Robert Louis Stevenson. Scenes from "Treasure Island".
232 **77** 4c. blue, yellow and red . . 20 15
233 – 10c. multicoloured 20 10
234 – 40c. brown, black and blue 25 30
235 – $1 multicoloured . . . . . 45 1·00

DESIGNS—HORIZ: 10c. Jim Hawkins escaping from the pirates; $1 Treasure trove. VERT: 40c. The fight with Israel Hands.

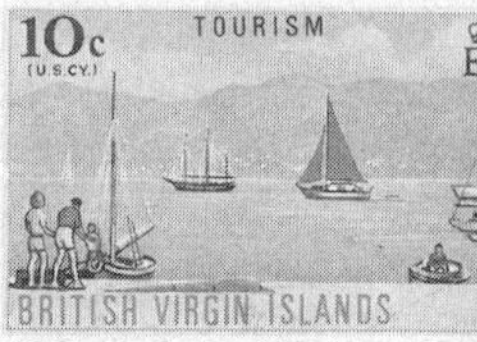

82 Yachts in Road Harbour, Tortola

1969. Tourism. Multicoloured.
236 2c. Tourist and yellow-finned grouper (fish) 15 50
237 10c. Type **82** 30 10
238 20c. Sun-bathing at Virgin Gorda National Park . . . 40 20
239 $1 Tourist and Pipe Organ cactus at Virgin Gorda . . 90 1·50

Nos. 236 and 239 are vert.

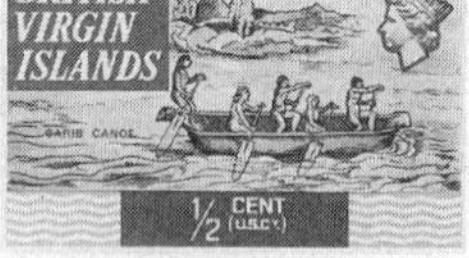

85 Carib Canoe

1970.

240 **85** ½c. buff, brown and sepia . 10 1·00
241 – 1c. blue and green 15 30
242 – 2c. orange, brown and slate 40 1·00
243 – 3c. red, blue and sepia . . 30 1·25
244 – 4c. turquoise, blue & brn . 30 50
245 – 5c. green, pink and black . 30 10
246 – 6c. violet, mauve and green 40 1·75
247 – 8c. green, yellow and sepia 50 3·00
248 – 10c. blue and brown . . . 50 15
249 – 12c. yellow, red and brown 65 1·00
250 – 15c. green, orange and brown . . . . 6·00 85
251 – 25c. green, blue and purple 4·00 1·75
252 – 50c. mauve, green and brown . . . . 2·75 1·50
253 – $1 salmon, green and brown . . . . 3·00 3·75
254 – $2 buff, slate and grey . . 6·50 7·00
255 – $3 ochre, blue and sepia . 2·75 4·50
256 – $5 violet and grey . . . . 2·75 5·00

DESIGNS: 1c. "Santa Maria" (Columbus's flagship); 2c. "Elizabeth Bonaventure" (Drake's flagship); 3c. Dutch buccaneer, c. 1660; 4c. "Thetis", 1827 (after etching by E. W. Cooke); 5c. Henry Morgan's ship (17th-century); 6c. H.M.S. "Boreas" (Captain Nelson, 1784); 8c. H.M.S. "Eclair", 1804; 10c. H.M.S. "Formidable", 1782; 12c. H.M.S. "Nymph", 1778; 15c. "Windsor Castle" (sailing packet) engaging "Jeune Richard" (French brig), 1807; 25c. H.M.S. "Astrea", 1808; 50c. Wreck of R.M.S. "Rhone", 1867; $1 Tortola sloop; $2 H.M.S. "Frobisher"; $3 "Booker Viking" (cargo liner), 1967; $5 Hydrofoil "Sun Arrow".

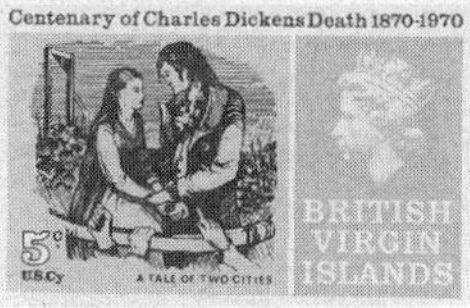

102 "A Tale of Two Cities"

1970. Death Centenary of Charles Dickens.

257	**102**	5c. black, red and grey	10	40
258	–	10c. black, blue and green	20	10
259	–	25c. black, green and yellow	30	25

DESIGNS: 10c. "Oliver Twist"; 25c. "Great Expectations".

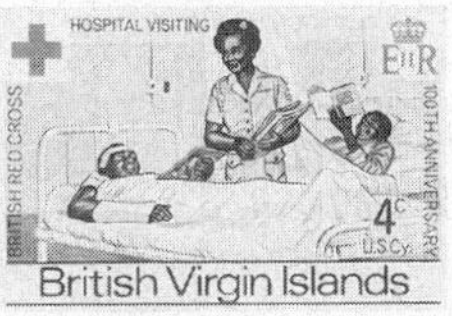

103 Hospital Visit

1970. Centenary of British Red Cross. Multicoloured.

260		4c. Type **103**	20	10
261		10c. First Aid class	20	10
262		25c. Red Cross and coat of arms	50	55

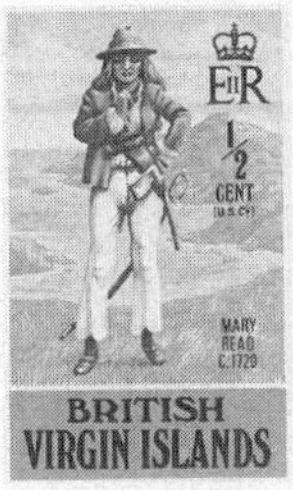

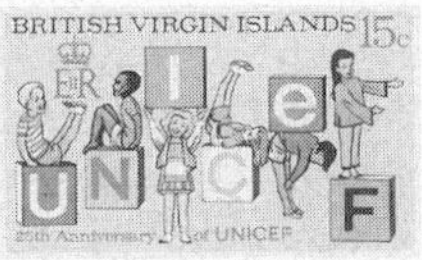

104 Mary Read **105** Children and "UNICEF"

1970. Pirates. Multicoloured.

263		½c. Type **104**	10	15
264		10c. George Lowther	30	10
265		30c. Edward Teach (Blackbeard)	60	25
266		60c. Henry Morgan	80	1·00

1971. 25th Anniv of U.N.I.C.E.F.

267	**105**	15c. multicoloured	10	10
268		30c. multicoloured	20	25

1972. Royal Visit of Princess Margaret. Nos 244 and 251 optd **VISIT OF H.R.H. THE PRINCESS MARGARET 1972 1972.**

269		4c. blue, light blue and brown	20	15
270		25c. green, blue and plum	30	45

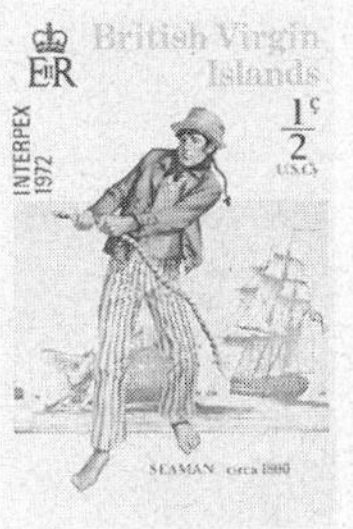

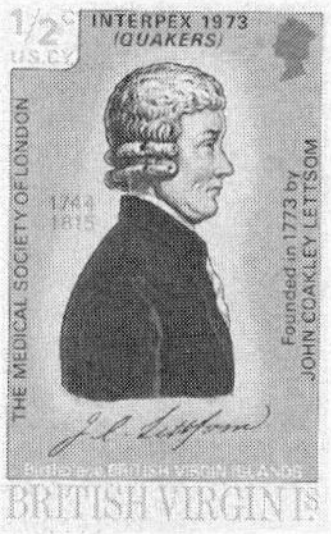

107 Seaman of 1800 **110** J. C. Lettsom

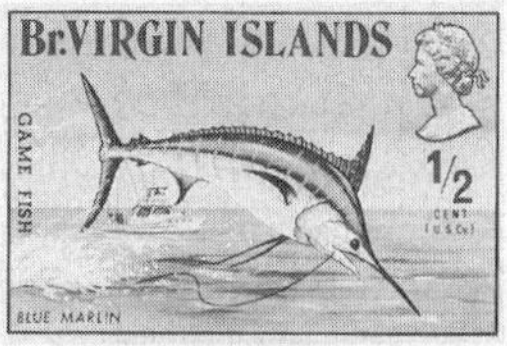

109 Blue Marlin

1972. "Interpex" Stamp Exhibition, New York. Naval Uniforms. Multicoloured.

271		½c. Type **107**	10	40
272		10c. Boatswain, 1787–1807	35	10
273		30c. Captain, 1795–1812	85	55
274		60c. Admiral, 1787–95	1·50	2·50

1972. Royal Silver Wedding. As T **52** of Ascension, but with sailfish and "Sir Winston Churchill" (cadet schooner) in background.

275		15c. blue	25	15
276		25c. blue	25	15

1972. Game Fish. Multicoloured.

277		½c. Type **109**	10	90
278		½c. Wahoo	15	90
279		15c. Yellow-finned tuna ("Allison tuna")	65	25
280		25c. White marlin	75	30
281		50c. Sailfish	1·25	1·50
282		$1 Dolphin	2·00	2·75

1973. "Interpex 1973" (Quakers). Multicoloured.

284		½c. Type **110**	10	15
285		10c. Lettsom House (horiz)	15	10
286		15c. Dr. W. Thornton	20	10
287		30c. Dr. Thornton and Capitol, Washington (horiz)	25	20
288		$1 William Penn (horiz)	60	1·10

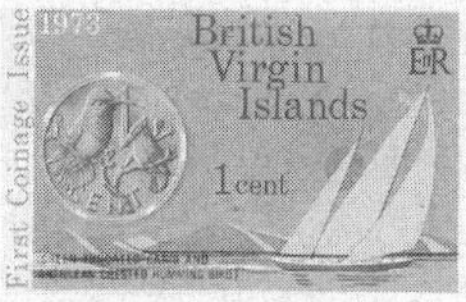

111 Green-throated Carib and Antillean Crested Hummingbird

1973. First Issue of Coinage. Coins and local scenery. Multicoloured.

289		1c. Type **111**	10	30
290		5c. "Zenaida Dove" (5c. coin)	60	10
291		10c. "Ringed Kingfisher" (10c. coin)	75	10
292		25c. "Mangrove Cuckoo" (25c. coin)	95	15
293		50c. "Brown Pelican" (50c. coin)	1·10	1·00
294		$1 "Magnificent Frigate-bird ($1 coin)	1·40	2·00

1973. Royal Wedding. As T **47** of Anguilla. Multicoloured. Background colours given.

301		5c. brown	10	10
302		50c. blue	20	20

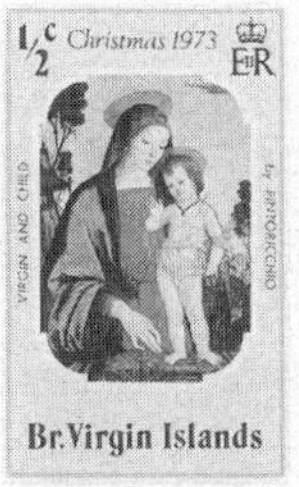

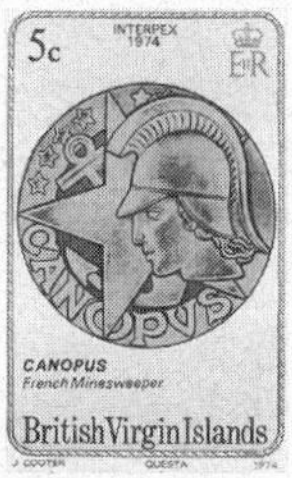

112 "Virgin and Child" (Pintoricchio) **113** Crest of the "Canopus" (French)

1973. Christmas. Multicoloured.

303		½c. Type **112**	10	10
304		3c. "Virgin and Child" (Lorenzo di Credi)	10	10
305		25c. "Virgin and Child" (Crivelli)	15	10
306		50c. "Virgin and Child with St. John" (Luini)	30	40

1974. "Interpex 1974". Naval Crests. Multicoloured.

307		5c. Type **113**	15	10
308		18c. U.S.S. "Saginaw"	25	25
309		25c. H.M.S. "Rothesay"	25	30
310		50c. H.M.C.S. "Ottawa"	45	60

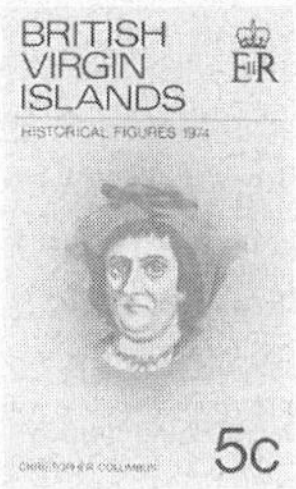

114 Christopher Columbus

1974. Historical Figures.

312	**114**	5c. orange and black	20	10
313	–	10c. blue and black	30	10
314	–	25c. violet and black	35	25
315	–	40c. brown and deep brown	60	75

PORTRAITS: 10c. Sir Walter Raleigh; 25c. Sir Martin Frobisher; 40c. Sir Francis Drake.

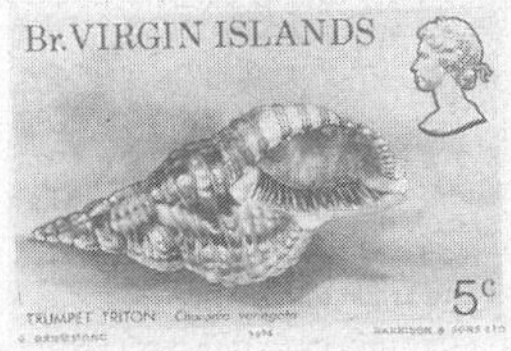

115 Atlantic Trumpet Triton

1974. Seashells. Multicoloured.

317		5c. Type **115**	30	15
318		18c. West Indian murex	60	30
319		25c. Bleeding tooth	75	35
320		75c. Virgin Islands latirus	1·75	2·00

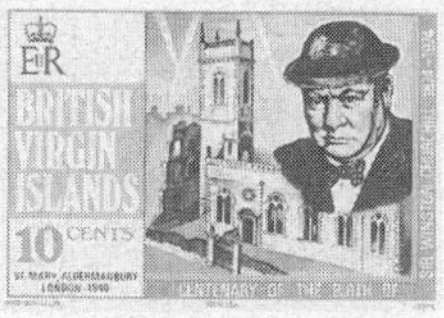

116 Churchill and St. Mary, Aldermanbury, London

1974. Birth Centenary of Sir Winston Churchill. Multicoloured.

322		10c. Type **116**	15	10
323		50c. St. Mary, Fulton, Missouri	35	50

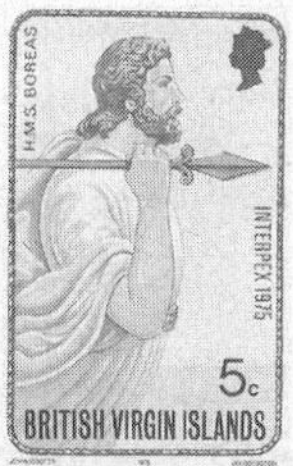

117 H.M.S. "Boreas"

1975. "Interpex 1975" Stamp Exhibition, New York. Ships' Figure-heads. Multicoloured.

325		5c. Type **117**	20	10
326		18c. "Golden Hind"	50	15
327		40c. H.M.S. "Superb"	70	25
328		85c. H.M.S. "Formidable"	1·50	1·50

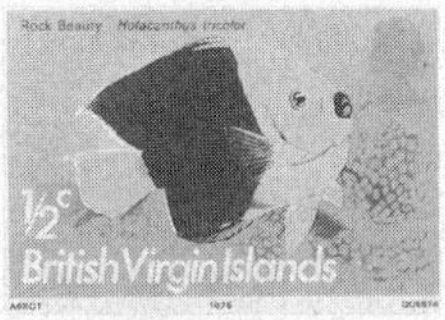

118 Rock Beauty

1975. Fishes. Multicoloured.

330		½c. Type **118**	15	50
331		1c. Long-spined squirrelfish	40	2·00
332		3c. Queen triggerfish	1·00	2·00
333		5c. Blue angelfish	30	20
334		8c. Stoplight parrotfish	30	25
335		10c. Queen angelfish	30	25
336		12c. Nassau grouper	40	30
337		13c. Blue tang	40	30
338		15c. Sergeant major	40	35
339		18c. Spotted jewfish	80	80
340		20c. Bluehead wrasse	60	80
341		25c. Grey angelfish	1·00	60
342		60c. Glass-eyed snapper	1·25	2·25
343		$1 Blue chromis	1·75	1·75
344		$2.50 French angelfish	2·50	4·50
345		$3 Queen parrotfish	3·00	4·50
346		$5 Four-eyed butterflyfish	3·50	6·00

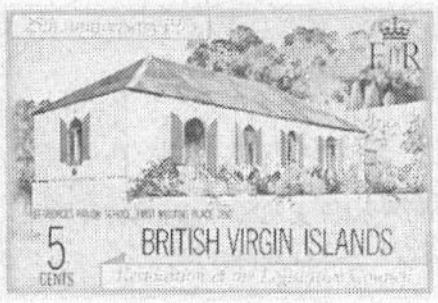

119 St. George's Parish School (first meeting-place, 1950)

1975. 25th Anniv of Restoration of Legislative Council. Multicoloured.

347		5c. Type **119**	10	10
348		25c. Legislative Council Building	20	10
349		40c. Mace and gavel	25	15
350		75c. Commemorative scroll	35	65

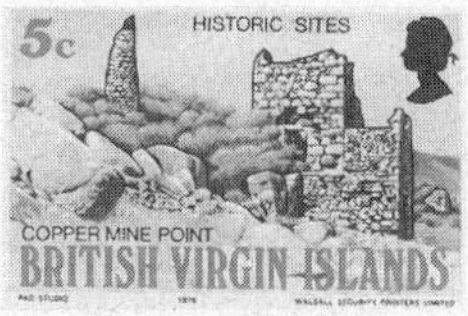

120 Copper Mine Point

1976. Historic Sites. Multicoloured.

351		5c. Type **120**	10	10
352		18c. Pleasant Valley	20	10
353		50c. Callwood Distillery	40	30
354		75c. The Dungeon	60	65

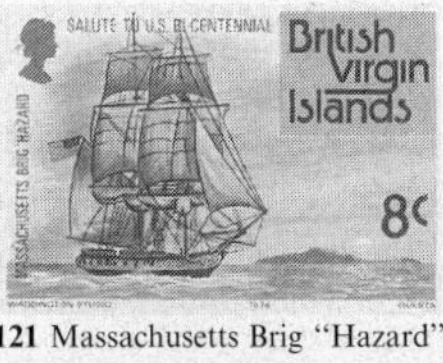

121 Massachusetts Brig "Hazard"

1976. Bicentenary of American Revolution. Mult.

355		8c. Type **121**	30	15
356		22c. American privateer "Spy"	45	20
357		40c. "Raleigh" (American frigate)	55	60
358		75c. Frigate "Alliance" and H.M.S. "Trepassy"	80	1·25

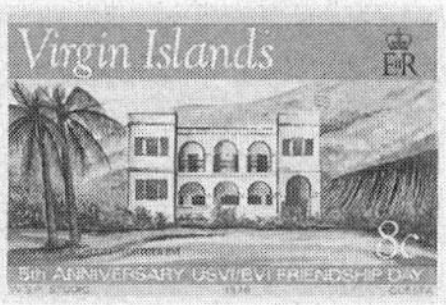

122 Government House, Tortola

1976. 5th Anniv of Friendship Day with U.S. Virgin Islands. Multicoloured.

360		8c. Type **122**	10	10
361		15c. Government House, St. Croix (vert)	10	10
362		30c. Flags (vert)	15	10
363		75c. Government seals	30	40

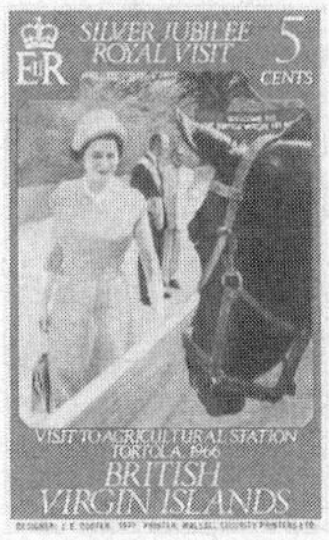

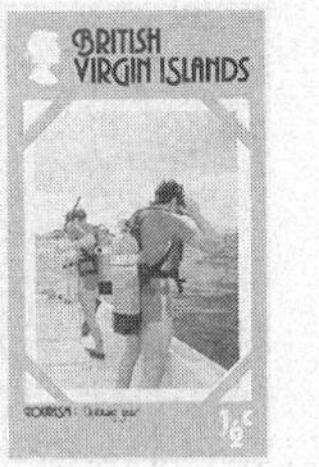

123 Royal Visit, 1966 **125** Divers checking Equipment

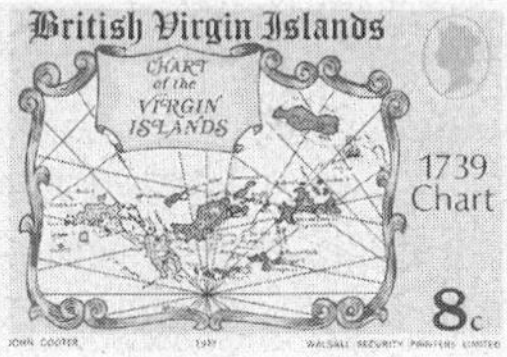

124 Chart of 1739

1977. Silver Jubilee. Multicoloured.

364		8c. Type **123**	10	10
365		30c. The Holy Bible	15	15
366		60c. Presentation of Holy Bible	25	40

1977. 18th-century Maps. Multicoloured.

367		8c. Type **124**	40	10
368		22c. French map, 1758	55	30
369		30c. Map from English and Danish surveys, 1775	65	65
370		75c. Map of 1779	85	1·50

1977. Royal Visit. As Nos. 364/6 inscr "SILVER JUBILEE ROYAL VISIT".

371		5c. Type **123**	10	10
372		25c. The Holy Bible	20	10
373		50c. Presentation of Holy Bible	35	25

1978. Tourism. Multicoloured.

374		½c. Type **125**	10	10
375		5c. Cup coral on wreck of "Rhone"	20	10
376		8c. Sponge formation on wreck of "Rhone"	25	10
377		22c. Cup coral and sponges	45	15
378		30c. Sponges inside cave	60	20
379		75c. Marine life	90	85

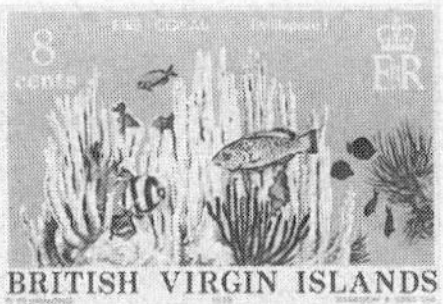

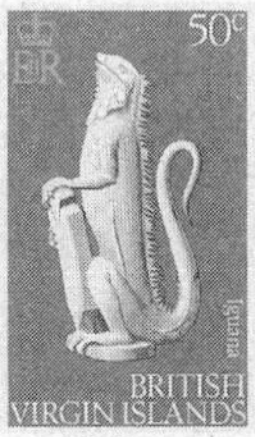

126 Fire Coral **127** Iguana

1978. Corals. Multicoloured.

380		8c. Type **126**	25	15
381		15c. Staghorn coral	40	30
382		40c. Brain coral	75	85
383		75c. Elkhorn coral	1·50	1·60

1978. 25th Anniv of Coronation.

384	–	50c. brown, green and silver	20	40
385	–	50c. multicoloured	20	40
386	**127**	50c. brown, green and silver	20	40

DESIGNS: No. 384, Plantagenet Falcon; No. 385, Queen Elizabeth II.

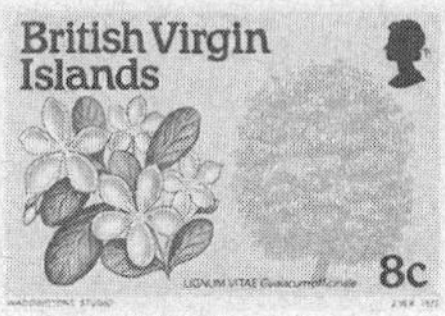

128 Lignum Vitae

1978. Flowering Trees. Multicoloured.

387	8c. Type **128**	15	10
388	22c. Ginger Thomas	20	15
389	40c. Dog almond	30	20
390	75c. White cedar	45	70

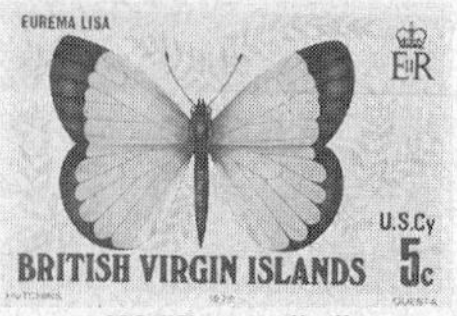

129 "Eurema lisa"

1978. Butterflies. Multicoloured.

392	5c. Type **129**	25	10
393	22c. "Agraulis vanillae"	40	20
394	30c. "Heliconius charithonia"	1·10	30
395	75c. "Hemiargus hanno"	1·40	1·25

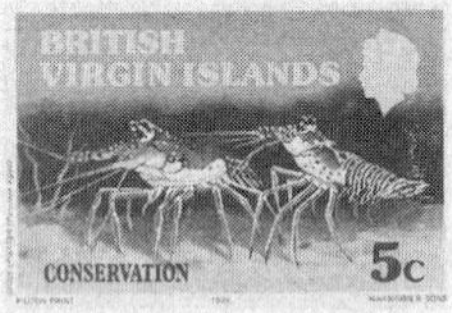

130 Spiny Lobster

1978. Wildlife Conservation. Multicoloured.

397	5c. Type **130**	15	10
398	15c. Large iguana (vert)	25	10
399	22c. Hawksbill turtle	40	15
400	75c. Black coral (vert)	75	90

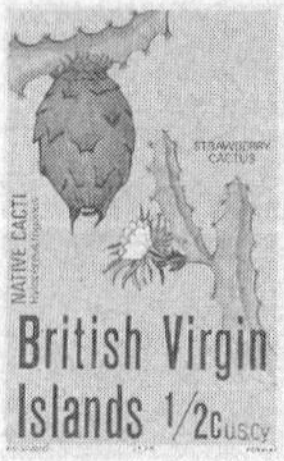

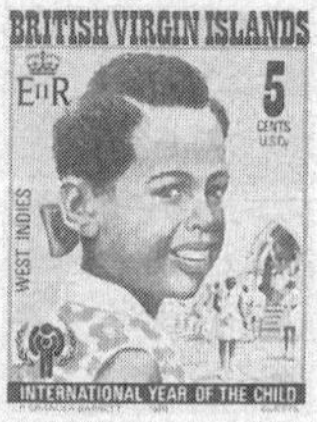

131 Strawberry Cactus **132** West Indian Girl

1979. Native Cacti. Multicoloured.

402	½c. Type **131**	10	10
403	5c. Snowy cactus	15	10
404	13c. Barrel cactus	20	20
405	22c. Tree cactus	25	35
406	30c. Prickly pear	30	40
407	75c. Dildo cactus	40	1·00

1979. International Year of the Child. Multicoloured.

408	5c. Type **132**	10	10
409	10c. African boy	10	10
410	13c. Asian girl	10	10
411	$1 European boy	50	85

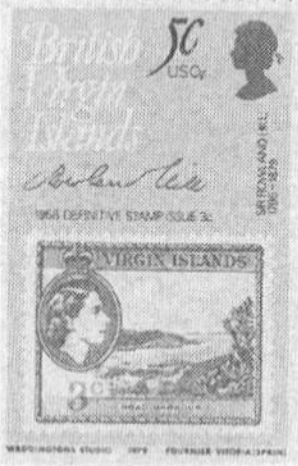

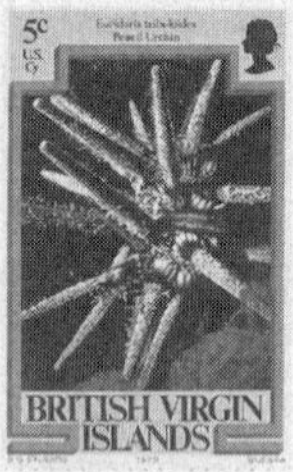

133 1956 Road Harbour 3c. Definitive Stamp **134** Pencil Urchin

1979. Death Centenary of Sir Rowland Hill.

413	**133** 5c. dp blue, blue & green	10	10
414	– 13c. blue and mauve	10	10
415	– 75c. blue and purple	45	50

DESIGNS—HORIZ: 13c. 1880 2½d. red-brown; 75c. Great Britain 1910 unissued 2d. Tyrian plum.

1979. Marine Life. Multicoloured.

417	½c. Calcified algae	40	2·00
418	1c. Purple-tipped sea anemone	55	2·00
419	3c. Common starfish	1·00	2·00
420	5c. Type **134**	1·00	1·75
421	8c. Atlantic trumpet triton	1·25	1·75
422	10c. Christmas tree worms	30	1·00
423a	13c. Flamingo tongue snail	1·50	75
424	15c. Spider crab	40	1·00
425	18c. Sea squirts	2·00	3·50
426	20c. True tulip	55	1·25
427	25c. Rooster-tail conch	1·25	3·50
428	30c. West Indian fighting conch	2·00	1·50
429	60c. Mangrove crab	1·50	2·50
430	$1 Coral polyps	1·50	3·50
431	$2.50 Peppermint shrimp	1·75	4·00
432	$3 West Indian murex	1·75	4·50
433	$5 Carpet anemone	2·25	5·50

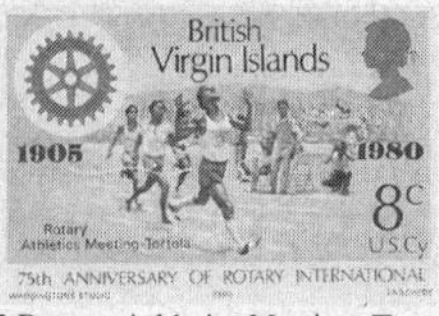

135 Rotary Athletics Meeting, Tortola

1980. 75th Anniv of Rotary International. Mult.

434	8c. Type **135**	10	10
435	22c. Paul P. Harris (founder)	15	10
436	60c. Mount Saga, Tortola ("Creation of National Park")	30	40
437	$1 Rotary anniversary emblem	55	75

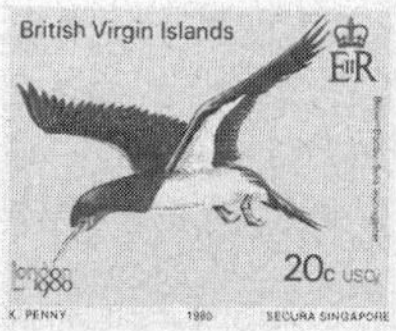

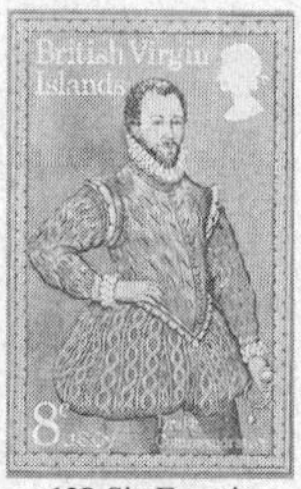

136 Brown Booby **138** Sir Francis Drake

1980. "London 1980" International Stamp Exhibition. Birds. Multicoloured.

439	20c. Type **136**	20	20
440	25c. Magnificent frigate bird	25	25
441	50c. White-tailed tropic bird	40	40
442	75c. Brown pelican	55	55

1980. Caribbean Commonwealth Parliamentary Association Meeting, Tortola. Nos. 414/15 optd **CARIBBEAN COMMONWEALTH PARLIAMENTARY ASSOCIATION MEETING TORTOLA 11–19 JULY 1980.**

444	13c. blue and red	15	10
445	75c. deep blue and blue	40	40

1980. Sir Francis Drake Commemoration. Mult.

446	8c. Type **138**	50	10
447	15c. Queen Elizabeth I	70	15
448	30c. Drake receiving knighthood	90	30
449	75c. "Golden Hind" and coat of arms	1·75	1·25

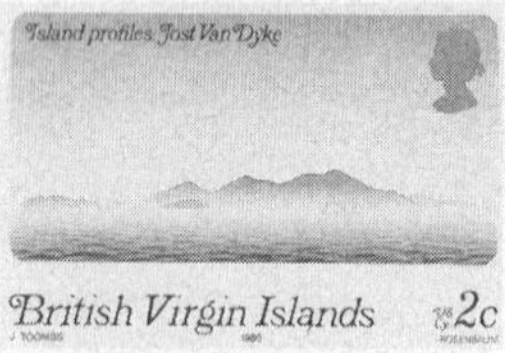

139 Jost Van Dyke

1980. Island Profiles. Multicoloured

451	2c. Type **139**	10	10
452	5c. Peter Island	10	10
453	13c. Virgin Gorda	15	10
454	22c. Anegada	20	10
455	30c. Norman Island	25	15
456	$1 Tortola	70	1·00

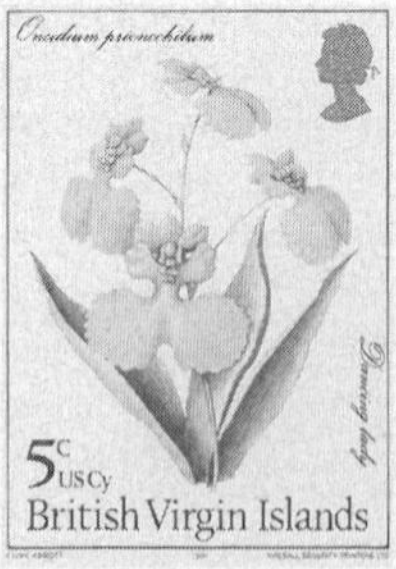

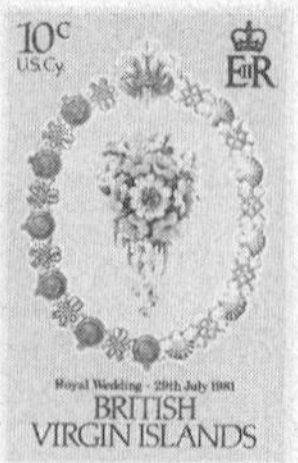

140 Dancing Lady **141** Wedding Bouquet from British Virgin Islands

1981. Flowers. Multicoloured.

458	5c. Type **140**	10	10
459	20c. Love in the mist	15	15
460	22c. "Pitcairnia angustifolia"	15	15
461	75c. Dutchman's pipe	35	65
462	$1 Maiden apple	35	80

1981. Royal Wedding. Multicoloured.

463	10c. Type **141**	10	10
464	35c. Prince Charles and Queen Elizabeth the Queen Mother in Garter robes	20	15
465	$1.25 Prince Charles and Lady Diana Spencer	60	80

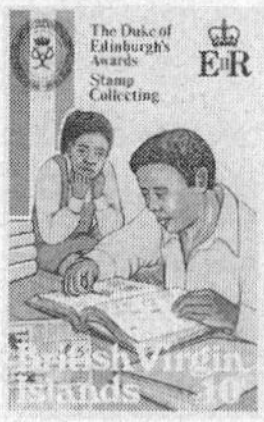

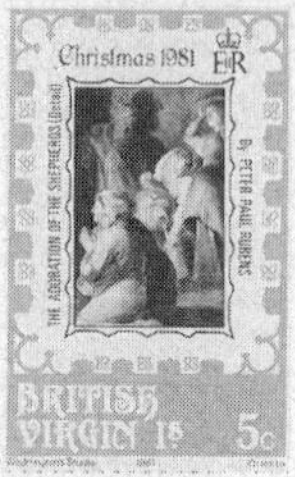

142 Stamp Collecting **144** Detail from "The Adoration of the Shepherds" (Rubens)

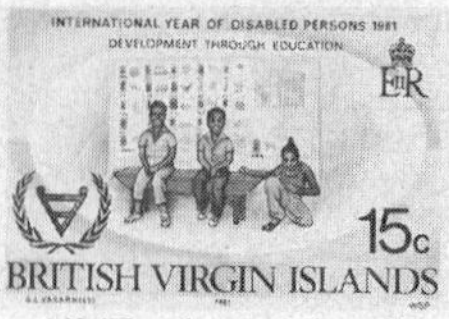

143 "Development through Education"

1981. 25th Anniv of Duke of Edinburgh Award Scheme. Multicoloured.

466	10c. Type **142**	10	10
467	15c. Athletics	10	10
468	50c. Camping	25	25
469	$1 Duke of Edinburgh	40	45

1981. International Year for Disabled Persons. Multicoloured.

470	15c. Type **143**	15	15
471	20c. Fort Charlotte Children's Centre	15	20
472	30c. "Developing cultural awareness"	20	30
473	$1 Fort Charlotte Children's Centre (different)	60	1·25

1981. Christmas.

474	**144** 5c. multicoloured	15	10
475	– 15c. multicoloured	25	10
476	– 30c. multicoloured	45	15
477	– $1 multicoloured	1·10	1·10

DESIGNS: 15c. to $1 Further details from "The Adoration of the Shepherds" by Rubens.

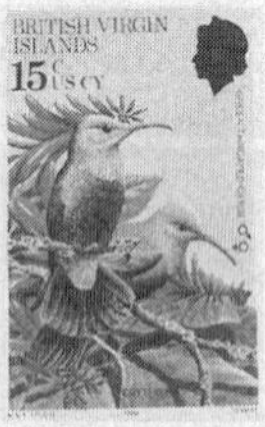

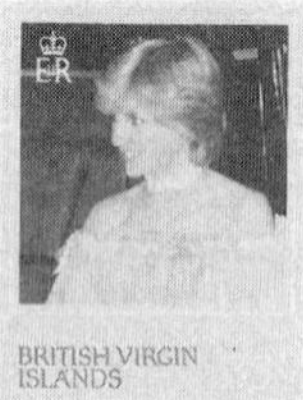

145 Green-throated Caribs and Erythrina **147** Princess at Victoria and Albert Museum, November, 1981

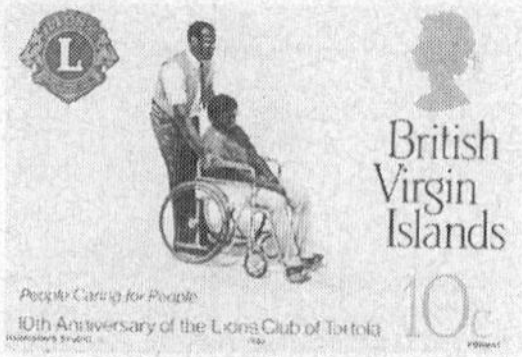

146 "People caring for People"

1982. Hummingbirds. Multicoloured.

479	15c. Type **145**	50	15
480	30c. Green-throated carib and bougainvillea	60	45
481	35c. Antillean crested hummingbirds and "granadilla passiflora"	70	55
482	$1.25 Antillean crested hummingbirds and hibiscus	1·75	3·00

1982. 10th Anniv of Lions Club of Tortola. Mult.

483	10c. Type **146**	20	15
484	20c. Tortola Headquarters	30	15
485	30c. "We Serve"	35	20
486	$1.50 "Lions" symbol	80	1·40

1982. 21st Birthday of Princess of Wales. Mult.

488	10c. British Virgin Islands coat of arms	15	10
489	35c. Type **147**	30	15
490	50c. Bride and groom proceeding into Vestry	45	35
491	$1.50 Formal portrait	1·10	1·10

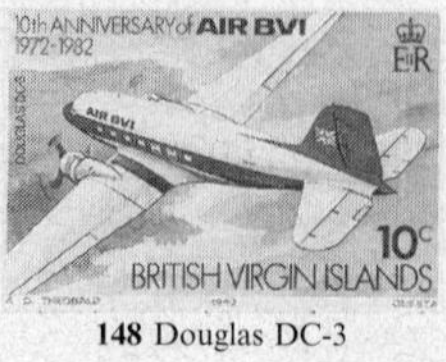

148 Douglas DC-3

1982. 10th Anniv of Air BVI. Multicoloured.

492	10c. Type **148**	45	15
493	15c. Britten Norman Islander	60	20
494	60c. Hawker Siddeley H.S.748	1·10	75
495	75c. Runway scene	1·25	90

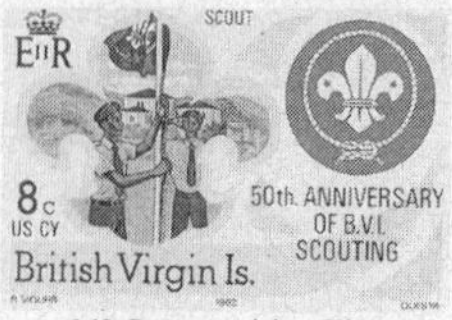

149 Scouts raising Flag

1982. 75th Anniv of Boy Scout Movement and 50th Anniv of Scouting in B.V.I. Multicoloured.

496	8c. Type **149**	20	10
497	20c. Cub Scout	45	25
498	50c. Sea Scout	60	55
499	$1 First camp, Brownsea Island, and portrait of Lord Baden-Powell	1·00	1·50

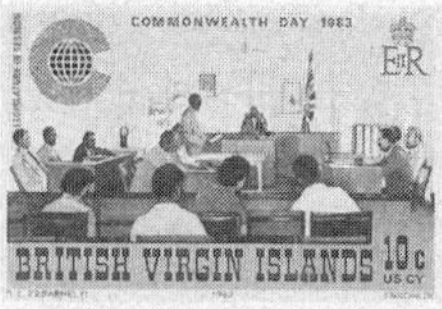

150 Legislature in Session

1983. Commonwealth Day. Multicoloured.

500	10c. Type **150**	10	10
501	30c. Tourism	25	20
502	35c. Satellite view of Earth showing Virgin Islands	25	25
503	75c. B.V.I. and Commonwealth flags	70	90

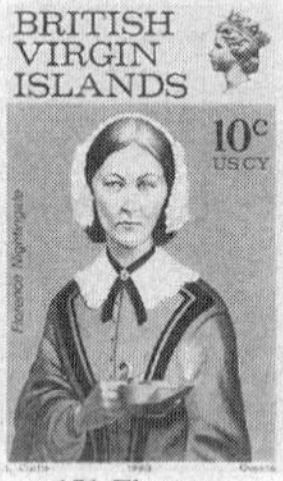

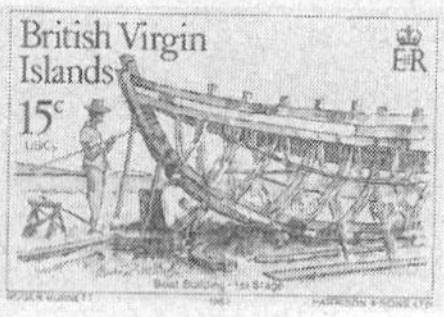

151 Florence Nightingale **152** Frame Construction

1983. Nursing Week. Multicoloured.

504	10c. Type **151**	50	15
505	30c. Staff nurse and assistant nurse	90	45
506	60c. Public Health nurses testing blood pressure (horiz)	1·75	1·25
507	75c. Peebles Hospital (horiz)	1·90	1·75

1983. Traditional Boat-building. Multicoloured.

508	15c. Type **152**	35	25
509	25c. Planking	40	45
510	50c. Launching	60	80
511	$1 Maiden voyage	85	1·75

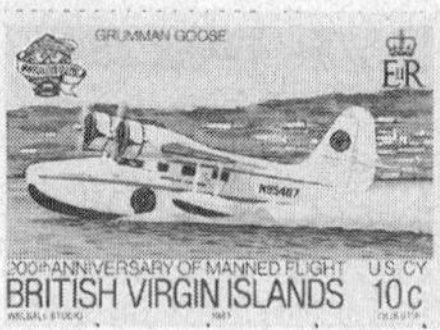

153 Grumman Goose Amphibian

1983. Bicentenary of Manned Flight. Multicoloured.

513	10c. Type **153**	20	15
514	30c. Riley Turbo Skyliner	45	45
515	60c. Embraer Bandeirante	65	85
516	$1.25 Hawker Siddeley H.S.748	90	1·60

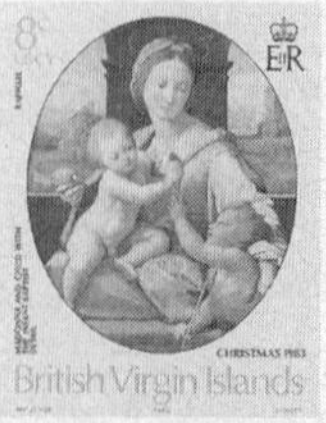

154 "Madonna and Child with the Infant Baptist"

1983. Christmas. 500th Birth Anniv of Raphael. Multicoloured.

517	8c. Type **154**	10	10
518	15c. "La Belle Jardiniere"	20	15
519	50c. "Madonna del Granduca"	50	60
520	$1 "The Terranuova Madonna"	90	1·10

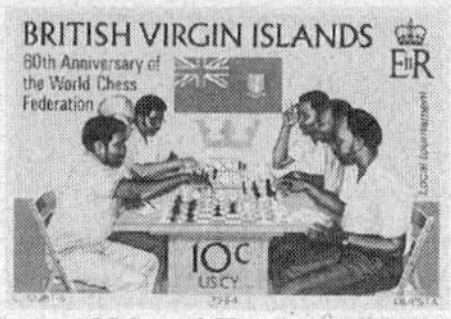

155 Local Tournament

1984. 60th Anniv of International Chess Federation. Multicoloured.
522 10c. Type **155** . . . . 1·00 40
523 35c. Staunton king, rook and pawn (vert) . . . . 2·00 1·50
524 75c. Karpov's winning position against Jakobsen in 1980 Olympiad (vert) . . 3·75 4·25
525 $1 B.V.I. Gold Medal won by Bill Hook at 1980 Chess Olympiad . . . . 4·25 5·50

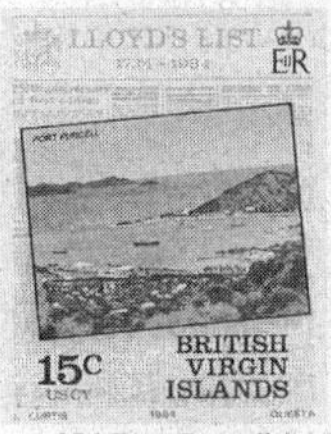

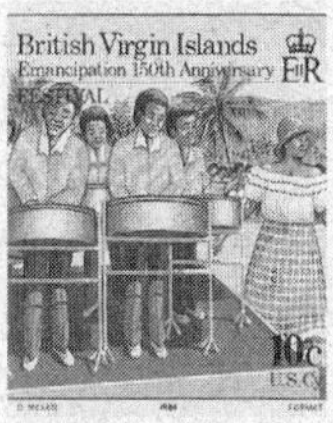

156 Port Purcell 159 Steel Band

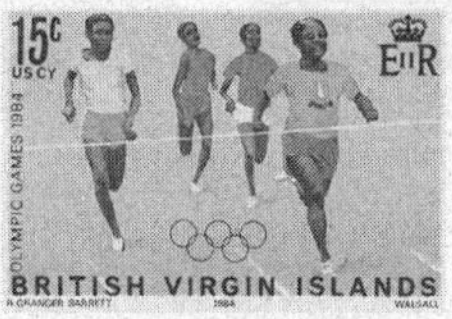

158 Running

1984. 250th Anniv of "Lloyd's List" (newspaper). Multicoloured.
526 15c. Type **156** 25 30
527 25c. Boeing 747-100 . . . . . 45 50
528 50c. Wreck of "Rhone" (mail steamer), 1867 . . . . . . 90 95
529 $1 "Booker Viking" (cargo liner) . . . . 1·50 1·60

1984. Olympic Games, Los Angeles. Multicoloured.
531 15c. Type **158** 40 40
532 15c. Runner 40 40
533 20c. Wind-surfing 45 45
534 20c. Surfer 45 45
535 30c. Sailing 65 65
536 30c. Yacht 65 65

1984. 150th Anniv of Abolition of Slavery. Mult.
538 10c. Type **159** 30 35
539 10c. Dancing girls 30 35
540 10c. Men in traditional costumes 30 35
541 10c. Girl in traditional costumes 30 35
542 10c. Festival Queen 30 35
543 30c. Green and yellow dinghies 45 50
544 30c. Blue and red dinghies . . 45 50
545 30c. White and blue dinghies 45 50
546 30c. Red and yellow dinghies 45 50
547 30c. Blue and white dinghies 45 50
DESIGNS: Various aspects of Emancipation Festival. Nos. 543/7 form a composite design, the sail colours of the dinghies being described.

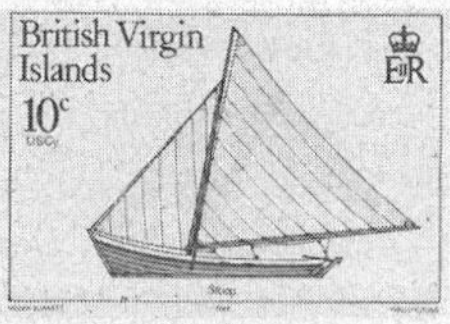

160 Sloop

1984. Boats. Multicoloured.
548 10c. Type **160** 40 20
549 35c. Fishing boat 80 65
550 60c. Schooner . . . . 1·10 1·25
551 75c. Cargo boat . . . . . . 1·10 1·60

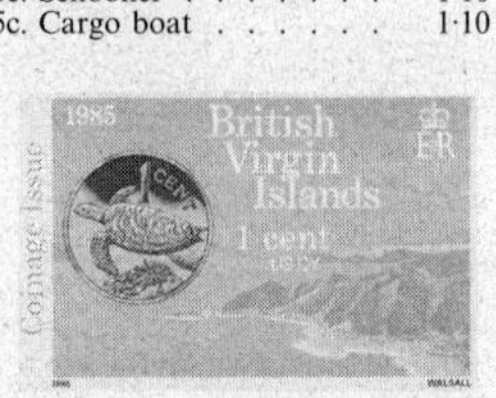

161 One Cent Coin and Aerial View

1985. New Coinage. Coins and Local Scenery. Multicoloured.
553 1c. Type **161** 10 10
554 5c. Five cent coin and boulders on beach 10 10
555 10c. Ten cent coin and scuba diving 20 20
556 25c. Twenty-five cent coin and yachts 45 50
557 50c. Fifty cent coin and jetty 90 1·25
558 $1 One dollar coin and beach at night . . . . 1·75 2·25

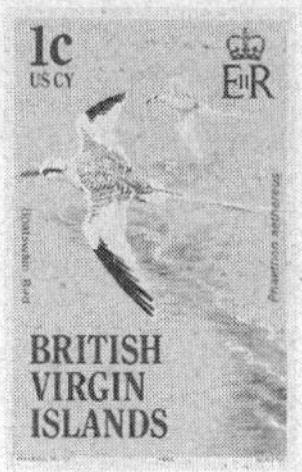

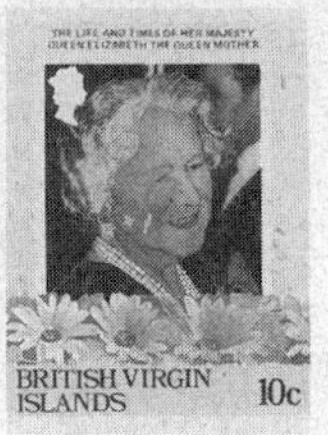

162 Red-billed Tropic Bird 163 The Queen Mother at Festival of Remembrance

1985. Birds of the British Virgin Islands. Multicoloured.
560 1c. Type **162** . . . . 70 1·75
561 2c. Yellow-crowned night heron ("Night Gaulin") . . 70 1·75
562 5c. Mangrove cuckoo ("Rain Bird") . . . . 1·00 1·75
563 8c. Northern mockingbird ("Mockingbird") . . . . . 1·00 2·25
564 10c. Grey kingbird ("Chinchary") . . . . . . 1·00 40
565 12c. Red-necked pigeon ("Wild Pigeon") . . . . . 1·50 80
649 15c. Least bittern ("Bittlin") 1·50 1·00
567 18c. Smooth-billed ani ("Black Witch") . . . . . 2·00 2·50
651 20c. Clapper rail ("Pond Shakey") . . . . 1·50 1·00
652 25c. American kestrel ("Killy-killy") . . . . 2·00 1·00
570 30c. Pearly-eyed thrasher ("Thrushie") . . . . 2·00 1·10
654 35c. Bridled quail dove ("Marmi Dove") . . . . . 2·00 1·00
572 40c. Green-backed heron ("Little Gaulin") . . . . . 2·25 1·75
573 50c. Scaly-breasted ground dove ("Ground Dove") . . 2·50 2·75
574 60c. Little blue heron ("Blue Gaulin") . . . . 2·75 4·00
658 $1 Audubon's shearwater ("Pimleco") . . . . 3·25 4·00
576 $2 Blue-faced booby ("White Booby") . . . . 4·50 7·00
577 $3 Cattle egret ("Cow Bird") 5·50 8·50
578 $5 Zenaida dove ("Turtle Dove") . . . . 7·50 11·00

1985. Life and Times of Queen Elizabeth the Queen Mother. Multicoloured.
579A 10c. Type **163** 10 20
580A 10c. At Victoria Palace Theatre, 1984 . . . . . 10 20
581A 25c. At the engagement of the Prince of Wales, 1981 15 40
582A 25c. Opening Celia Johnson Theatre, 1985 . . . . . 15 40
583A 50c. The Queen Mother on her 82nd birthday . . . 20 70
584A 50c. At the Tate Gallery, 1983 . . . . 20 70
585A 75c. At the Royal Smithfield Show, 1983 . . 25 1·00
586A 75c. Unveiling Mountbatten Statue, 1983 . . . . . . 25 1·00

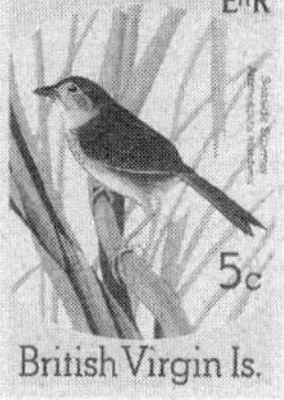

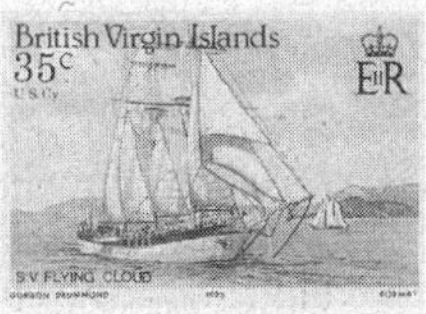

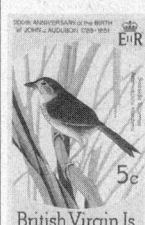

164 Seaside Sparrow 165 S.V. "Flying Cloud"

1985. Birth Bicentenary of John J. Audubon (ornithologist). Designs showing original paintings. Multicoloured.
588 5c. Type **164** 30 20
589 30c. Passenger pigeon 40 70
590 50c. Yellow-breasted chat . . 45 1·75
591 $1 American kestrel . . . . . 50 2·75

1986. Visiting Cruise Ships. Multicoloured.
592 35c. Type **165** 80 85
593 50c. M.V. "Newport Clipper" 1·10 1·50
594 75c. M.V. "Cunard Countess" . . . . 1·10 2·50
595 $1 M.V. "Sea Goddess" . . . 1·25 3·00

1986. Inaugural Flight of Miami–Beef Island Air Service. Nos 581/2 and 585/6 optd **MIAMI B.V.I. INAUGURAL FLIGHT**.
596A 25c. At the engagement of the Prince of Wales, 1981 40 50
597A 25c. Opening Celia Johnson Theatre, 1985 . . . . . 40 50
598A 75c. At the Royal Smithfield Show, 1983 . . 1·25 1·50
599A 75c. Unveiling Mountbatten statue, 1983 . . . . . . 1·25 1·50

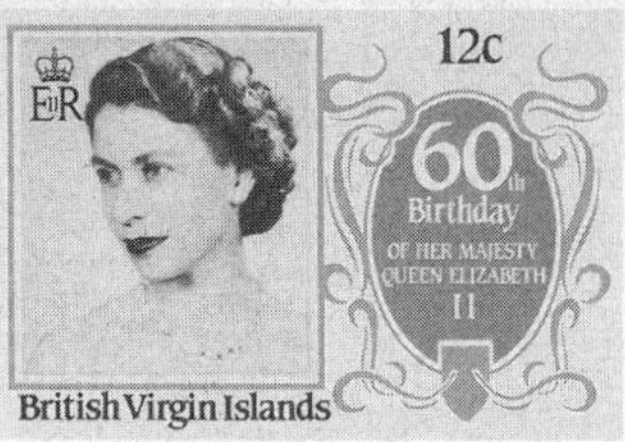

167 Queen Elizabeth II in 1958

1986. 60th Birthday of Queen Elizabeth II. Multicoloured.
600 12c. Type **167** 15 20
601 35c. At a Maundy Service . . 20 45
602 $1.50 Queen Elizabeth . . . 45 1·75
603 $2 During a visit to Canberra, 1982 (vert) . . . 60 2·25

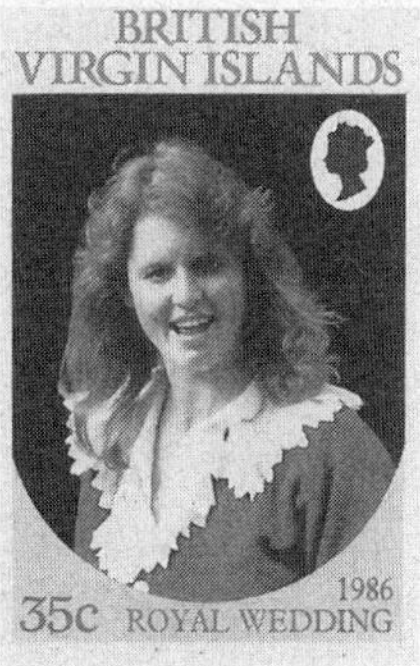

168 Miss Sarah Ferguson

1986. Royal Wedding. Multicoloured.
605 35c. Type **168** 30 70
606 35c. Prince Andrew and Miss Sarah Ferguson 30 70
607 $1 Prince Andrew in morning dress (horiz) . . . . 50 1·25
608 $1 Miss Sarah Ferguson (different) (horiz) . . . . . 50 1·25

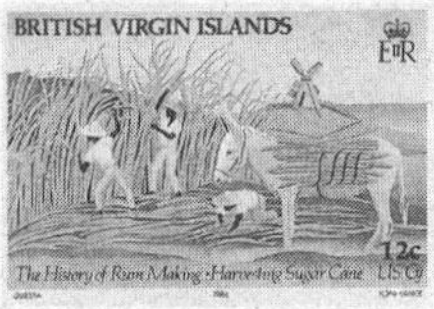

169 Harvesting Sugar Cane

1986. History of Rum Making. Multicoloured.
610 12c. Type **169** 80 20
611 40c. Bringing sugar cane to mill . . . . 1·50 1·25
612 60c. Rum distillery . . . . . 2·00 3·25
613 $1 Delivering barrels of rum to ship . . . . 4·25 4·75

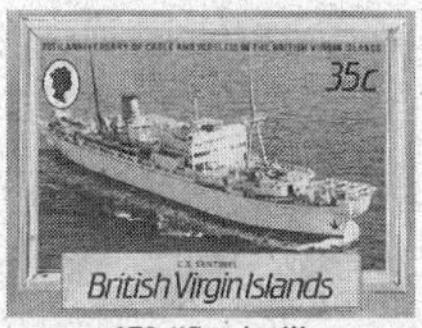

170 "Sentinel"

1986. 20th Anniv of Cable and Wireless Caribbean Headquarters, Tortola. Cable Ships. Multicoloured.
615 35c. Type **170** 60 80
616 35c. "Retriever" (1961) . . . 60 80
617 60c. "Cable Enterprise" (1964) . . . . 75 1·50
618 60c. "Mercury" (1962) . . . 75 1·50
619 75c. "Recorder" (1955) . . . 75 1·75
620 75c. "Pacific Guardian" (1984) . . . . 75 1·75
621 $1 "Great Eastern" (1860's) 80 2·00
622 $1 "Cable Venture" (1977) 80 2·00

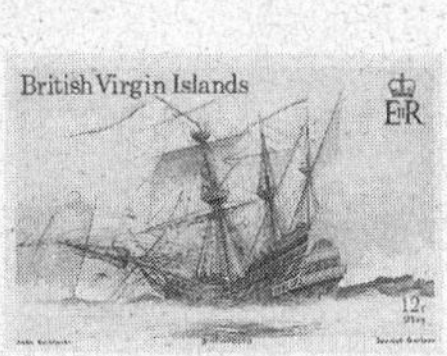

172 18th-century Spanish Galleon

1987. Shipwrecks. Multicoloured
625 12c. Type **172** . . . . 1·75 55
626 35c. H.M.S. "Astrea" (frigate), 1808 . . . . . . 3·00 1·40
627 75c. "Rhone" (mail steamer), 1867 . . . . 4·50 4·50
628 $1.50 "Captain Rokos" (freighter), 1929 . . . . . 6·50 9·00

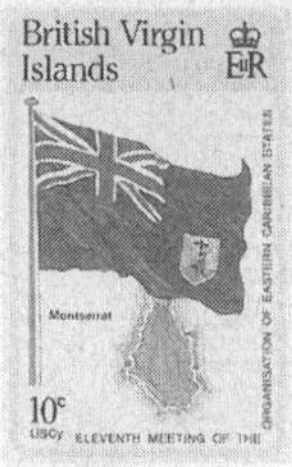

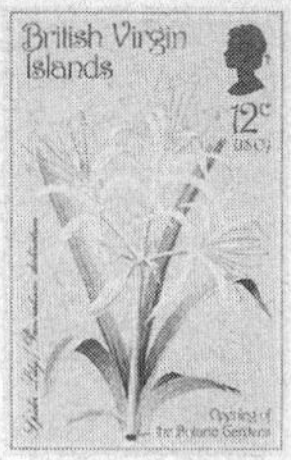

173 Outline Map and Flag of Montserrat 174 Spider Lily

1987. 11th Meeting of Organization of Eastern Caribbean States. Each showing map and flag. Multicoloured.
630 10c. Type **173** 70 70
631 15c. Grenada 80 75
632 20c. Dominica 85 80
633 25c. St. Kitts-Nevis . . . . . 90 1·00
634 35c. St. Vincent and Grenadines . . . . 1·40 1·00
635 50c. British Virgin Islands . . 2·00 2·50
636 75c. Antigua and Barbuda . . 2·25 3·25
637 $1 St. Lucia . . . . 2·75 3·50

1987. Opening of Botanical Gardens. Multicoloured.
638 12c. Type **174** 80 35
639 35c. Barrel cactus . . . . . 1·75 1·00
640 $1 Wild plantain . . . . . . 2·75 3·25
641 $1.50 Little butterfly orchid 8·00 8·50

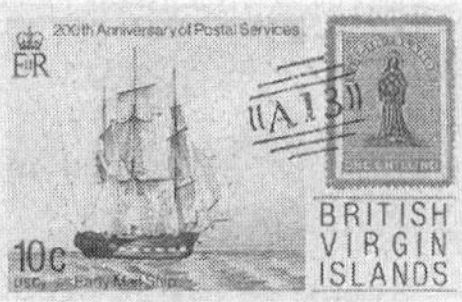

175 Early Mail Packet and 1867 1s. Stamp

1987. Bicentenary of Postal Services. Multicoloured.
662 10c. Type **175** . . . . 1·75 80
663 20c. Map and 1899 1d. stamp 2·25 1·25
664 35c. Road Town Post Office and Customs House, c. 1913, and 1847 4d. stamp 2·50 1·75
665 $1.50 Piper Apache mail plane and 1964 25c. definitive . . . . 7·50 11·00

1988. 500th Birth Anniv of Titian (artist). As T **238** of Antigua. Multicoloured.
667 10c. "Salome" 55 55
668 12c. "Man with the Glove" 60 60
669 20c. "Fabrizio Salvaresio" . . 80 80
670 25c. "Daughter of Roberto Strozzi" 90 90
671 40c. "Pope Julius II" . . . . 1·40 2·00
672 50c. "Bishop Ludovico Beccadelli" . . . . 1·60 2·00
673 60c. "King Philip II" . . . . 1·75 2·50
674 $1 "Empress Isabella of Portugal" . . . . 2·25 2·75

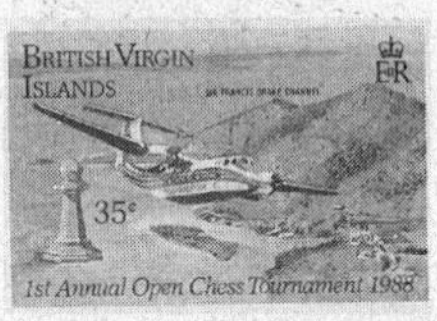

176 De Havilland D.H.C.5 over Sir Francis Drake Channel and Staunton Pawn

1988. First British Virgin Islands Open Chess Tournament. Multicoloured.
676 35c. Type **176** . . . . 5·00 1·50
677 $1 Jose Capablanca (former World Champion) and Staunton king . . . . . . 9·00 8·50

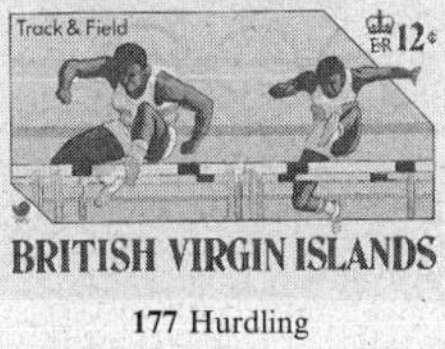

177 Hurdling

1988. Olympic Games, Seoul. Multicoloured.
679 12c. Type **177** 35 25
680 20c. Windsurfing 60 45
681 75c. Basketball . . . . 3·75 3·25
682 $1 Tennis . . . . 3·75 3·75

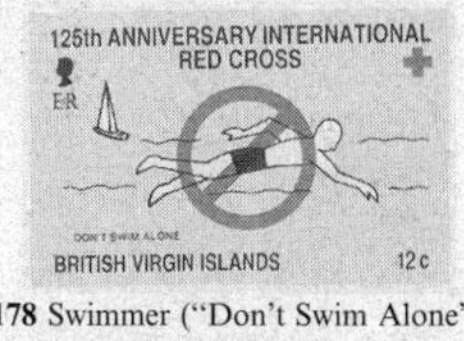

178 Swimmer ("Don't Swim Alone")

1988. 125th Anniv of International Red Cross
684 **178** 12c. black, red and blue 85 40
685 – 30c. black, red and blue 1·50 80

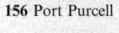

686 – 60c. black, red and blue 2·75 3·00
687 – $1 black, red and blue . . 3·25 4·00
DESIGNS: 30c. Swimmers ("No swimming during electrical storms"); 60c. Beach picnic ("Don't eat before swimming"); $1 Boat and equipment ("Proper equipment for boating").

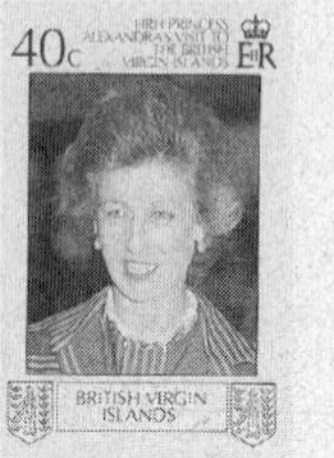
179 Princess Alexandra

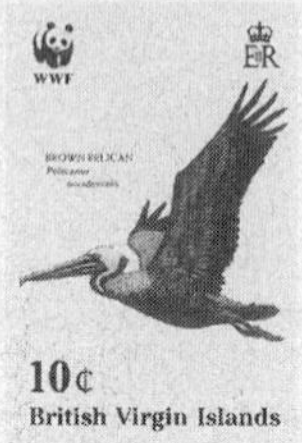
180 Brown Pelican in Flight

1988. Visit of Princess Alexandra. Designs showing different portraits.
689 179 40c. multicoloured . . . . 1·75 75
690 – $1.50 multicoloured . . . 3·75 4·75

1988. Wildlife (1st series). Aquatic Birds. Multicoloured.
692 10c. Type **180** . . . . 1·60 50
693 12c. Brown pelican perched on post . . . . 1·60 55
694 15c. Brown pelican . . . . . 1·75 1·10
695 35c. Brown pelican swallowing fish . . . . . 2·75 3·00

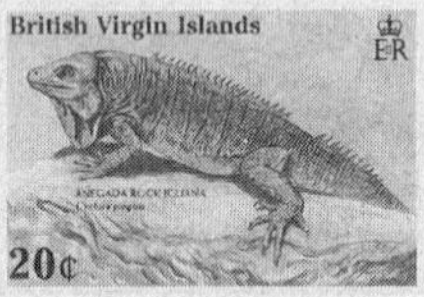
181 Anegada Rock Iguana

1988. Wildlife (2nd series). Endangered Species. Multicoloured.
697 20c. Type **181** . . . . 1·25 75
698 40c. Virgin Gorda dwarf gecko . . . . 1·50 1·40
699 60c. Hawksbill turtle . . . . 2·50 3·50
700 $1 Humpback whale . . . . 7·00 8·00

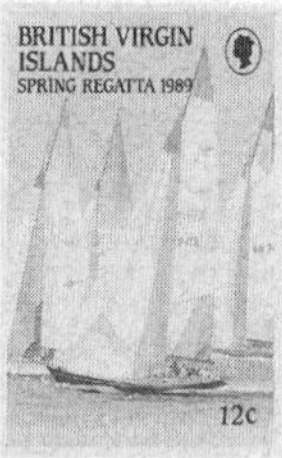
182 Yachts at Start

1989. Spring Regatta. Multicoloured.
702 12c. Type **182** 45 40
703 40c. Yacht tacking (horiz) . . 1·00 1·00
704 75c. Yachts at sunset . . . . 1·60 2·50
705 $1 Yachts rounding buoy (horiz) . . . . 2·00 2·75

1989. 500th Anniv (1992) of Discovery of America by Columbus (1st issue). Pre-Columbian Arawak Society. As T **247** of Antigua. Multicoloured.
707 10c. Arawak in hammock . . 70 45
708 20c. Making fire . . . . . . 1·00 50
709 25c. Making implements . . 1·00 60
710 $1.50 Arawak family . . . . 4·50 7·00
See also Nos. 741/4, 793/6 and 818/26.

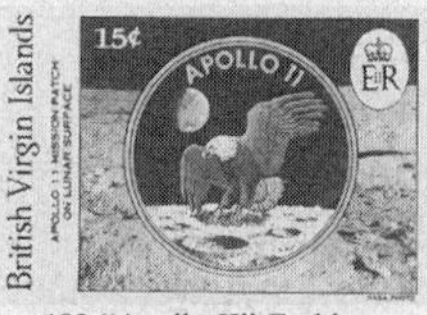
183 "Apollo II" Emblem

1989. 20th Anniv of First Manned Landing on the Moon. Multicoloured.
712 15c. Type **183** . . . . 1·00 60
713 30c. Edwin Aldrin deploying scientific experiments . . . 2·00 1·00
714 65c. Aldrin and U.S. flag on Moon . . . . 2·75 3·75
715 $1 "Apollo II" capsule after splashdown . . . . 3·75 4·00

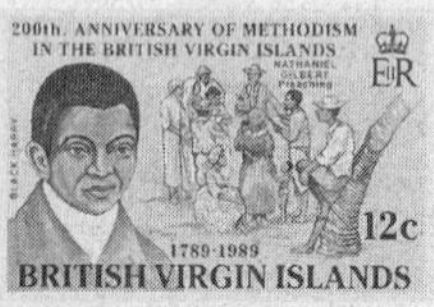
184 Black Harry and Nathaniel Gilbert preaching to Slaves

1989. Bicentenary of Methodist Church in British Virgin Islands. Multicoloured
717 12c. Type **184** . . . . 1·00 50
718 25c. Methodist school exercise book . . . . . . 1·40 75
719 35c. East End Methodist Church, 1810 . . . . . . 1·60 85
720 $1.25 Reverend John Wesley (founder of Methodism) and church youth choir . . 3·25 6·50

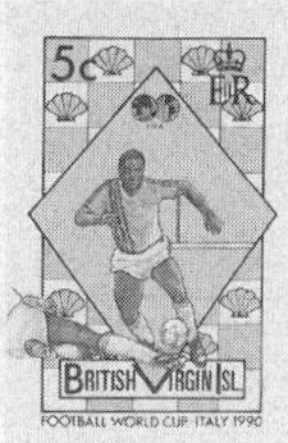
185 Player tackling

1989. World Cup Football Championships, Italy, 1990. Multicoloured.
722 5c. Type **185** 80 80
723 10c. Player dribbling ball . . 80 80
724 20c. Two players chasing ball 1·50 80
725 $1.75 Goalkeeper diving for ball . . . . 7·00 7·50

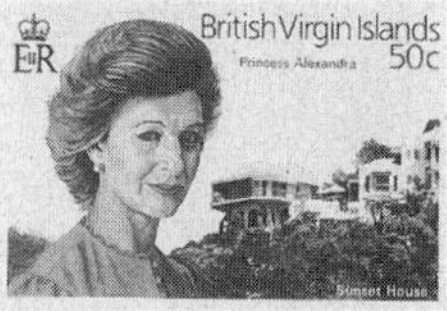
186 Princess Alexandra and Sunset House

1990. "Stamp World London 90" International Stamp Exhibition. Royal Visitors. Multicoloured.
727 50c. Type **186** . . . . 2·25 2·50
728 50c. Princess Margaret and Government House . . . . 2·25 2·50
729 50c. Hon. Angus Ogilvy and Little Dix Bay Hotel . . . 2·25 2·50
730 50c. Princess Diana with Princes William and Henry and Necker Island Resort 2·25 2·50

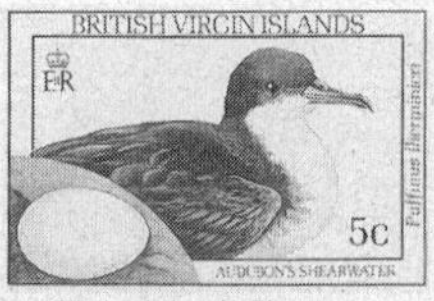
187 Audubon's Shearwater

1990. Birds. Multicoloured.
732 5c. Type **187** 70 80
733 12c. Red-necked pigeon . . . 1·00 40
734 20c. Moorhen ("Common Gallinule") . . . . 1·25 50
735 25c. Green-backed heron ("Green Heron") . . . . . 1·25 50
736 40c. Yellow warbler . . . . 1·50 1·25
737 60c. Smooth-billed ani . . . 1·75 2·50
738 $1 Antillean crested hummingbird . . . . 1·75 2·75
739 $1.25 Black-faced grassquit 2·00 3·50

1990. 500th Anniv (1992) of Discovery of America by Columbus (2nd issue). New World Natural History–Fishes. As T **260** of Antigua. Mult.
741 10c. Blue tang (horiz) . . . . 1·00 60
742 35c. Glass-eyed snapper (horiz) . . . . 2·00 70
743 50c. Slippery dick (horiz) . . 2·50 3·00
744 $1 Porkfish (horiz) . . . . . 3·75 4·00

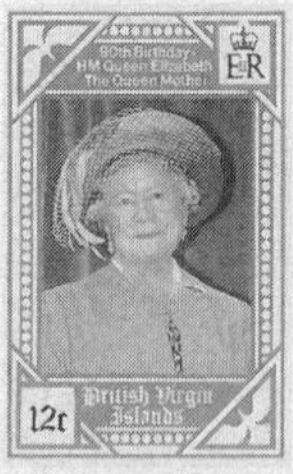
188 Queen Elizabeth the Queen Mother

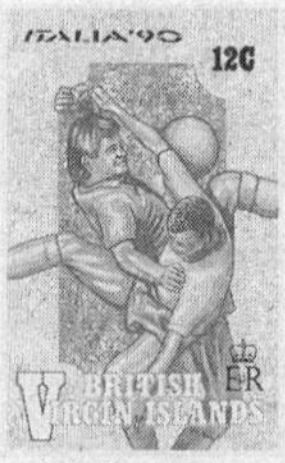
189 Footballers

1990. 90th Birthday of Queen Elizabeth the Queen Mother.
746 188 12c. multicoloured 50 25
747 – 25c. multicoloured 90 55
748 – 60c. multicoloured . . . . 1·75 2·25
749 – $1 multicoloured . . . . . 2·00 2·50
DESIGNS: 25, 60c., $1 Recent photographs.

1990. World Cup Football Championships, Italy.
751 189 12c. multicoloured 60 40
752 – 20c. multicoloured 90 50
753 – 50c. multicoloured . . . . 1·75 2·00
754 – $1.25 multicoloured . . . 2·50 3·75
DESIGNS: 20, 50c., $1.25, Footballers.

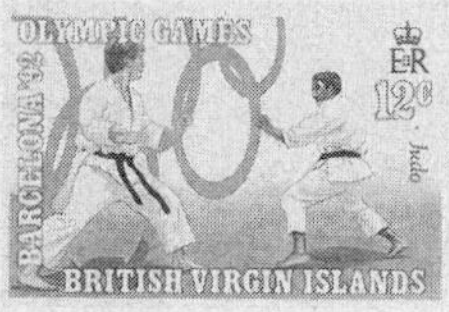
190 Judo

1990. Olympic Games, Barcelona (1992). Mult.
756 12c. Type **190** . . . . 1·00 45
757 40c. Yachting . . . . 1·75 1·40
758 60c. Hurdling . . . . 2·25 3·00
759 $1 Show jumping . . . . . 3·50 3·75

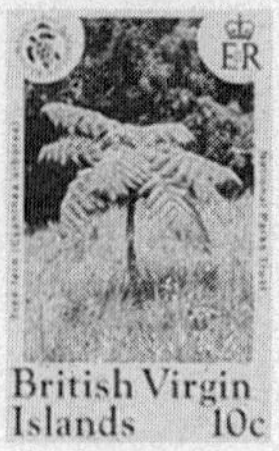
191 Tree-fern, Sage Mountain National Park

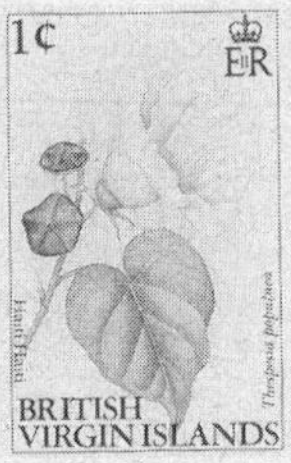
192 Haiti Haiti

1991. 30th Anniv of National Parks Trust. Multicoloured.
761 10c. Type **191** 70 80
762 25c. Coppermine ruins, Virgin Gorda (horiz) . . . 1·00 80
763 35c. Ruined windmill, Mt. Healthy . . . . 1·25 80
764 $2 The Baths (rock formation), Virgin Gorda (horiz) . . . . 7·00 9·00

1991. Flowers. Multicoloured.
765 1c. Type **192** 20 75
766 2c. Lobster claw 20 75
767 5c. Frangipani 20 75
887 10c. Autograph tree 50 80
769 12c. Yellow allamanda . . . 40 30
889 15c. Lantana 65 40
771 20c. Jerusalem thorn 50 30
772 25c. Turk's cap 55 40
892 30c. Swamp immortelle . . . 70 50
893 35c. White cedar 85 55
775 40c. Mahoe tree 75 65
895 45c. Pinguin 95 80
896 50c. Christmas orchid . . . . 2·25 1·75
778 70c. Lignum vitae . . . . . 1·10 2·00
779 $1 African tulip tree . . . . 1·25 2·00
899 $2 Beach morning glory . . . 3·00 4·50
781 $3 Organ pipe cactus . . . . 4·00 6·00
901 $5 Tall ground orchid . . . 8·50 11·00
783 $10 Ground orchid . . . . . 14·00 16·00

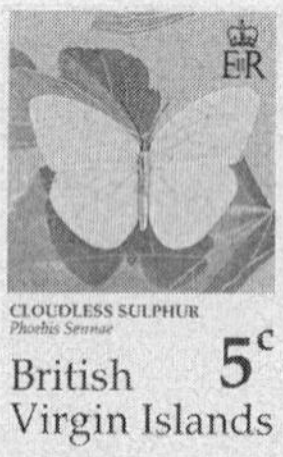
193 "Phoebis sennae"

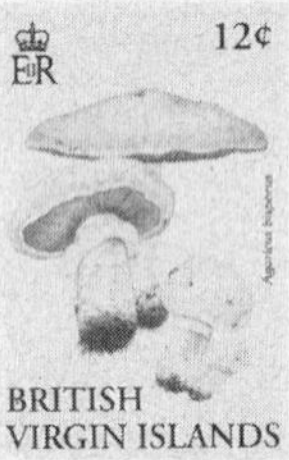
194 "Agaricus bisporus"

1991. Butterflies. Multicoloured.
784 5c. Type **193** 70 90
785 10c. "Dryas iulia" 80 90
786 15c. "Junonia evarete" . . . 1·00 75
787 20c. "Dione vanillae" . . . . 1·10 80
788 25c. "Battus polydamus" . . 1·25 1·00
789 30c. "Eurema lisa" . . . . . 1·40 1·00
790 35c. "Heliconius charitonius" 1·50 1·10
791 $1.50 "Siproeta stelenes" . . 3·50 5·50

1991. 500th Anniv (1992) of Discovery of America by Columbus (3rd issue). History of Exploration. As T **277** of Antigua. Multicoloured.
793 12c. "Vitoria" in Pacific (Magellan, 1519–21) . . . 1·25 50
794 50c. La Salle on the Mississippi, 1682 . . . . . 2·25 2·00
795 75c. John Cabot landing in Nova Scotia, 1497–98 . . . 3·00 2·75
796 $1 Cartier discovering the St. Lawrence, 1534 . . . . . 3·50 3·50

1991. Death Centenary (1990) of Vincent Van Gogh (artist). As T **278** of Antigua. Multicoloured.
798 15c. "Cottage with Decrepit Barn and Stooping Woman" (horiz) . . . . . 1·25 50
799 30c. "Paul Gauguin's Armchair" . . . . 1·75 80
800 75c. "Breton Women" (horiz) 3·00 3·00
801 $1 "Vase with Red Gladioli" 3·50 3·50

1991. Christmas. Religious Paintings by Quinten Massys. As T **291** of Antigua. Multicoloured.
803 15c. "The Virgin and Child Enthroned" (detail) . . . . 1·25 25
804 30c. "The Virgin and Child Enthroned" (different detail) . . . . 2·00 50
805 60c. "Adoration of the Magi" (detail) . . . . 3·50 3·75
806 $1 "Virgin in Adoration" . . 3·75 4·00

1992. Fungi. Multicoloured.
808 12c. Type **194** . . . . 1·50 55
809 30c. "Lentinula edodes" (horiz) . . . . 2·25 85
810 45c. "Hygocybe acutoconica" 2·25 1·00
811 $1 "Gymnopilus chrysopellus" (horiz) . . . 4·00 6·00

1992. 40th Anniv of Queen Elizabeth II's Accession. As T **288** of Antigua. Multicoloured.
813 12c. Little Dix Bay, Virgin Gorda 75 30
814 25c. Deadchest Bay, Peter Island . . . . 1·50 90
815 60c. Pond Bay, Virgin Gorda 1·90 2·25
816 $1 Cane Garden Bay, Tortola 2·00 2·75

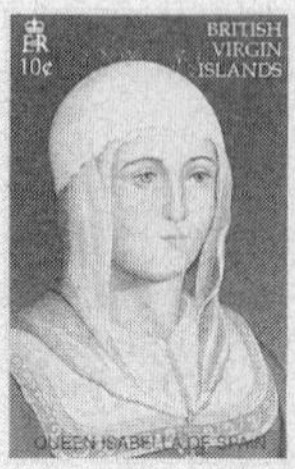
195 Queen Isabella of Spain

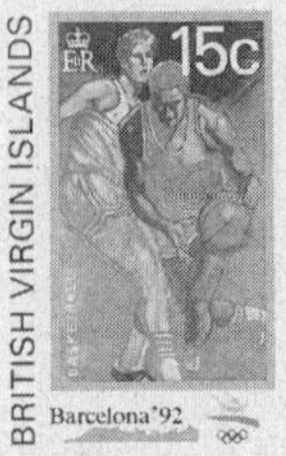
196 Basketball

1992. 500th Anniv of Discovery of America by Columbus (4th issue). Multicoloured.
818 10c. Type **195** 80 75
819 15c. Fleet of Columbus (horiz) . . . . 1·40 90
820 20c. Arms awarded to Columbus . . . . 1·40 90
821 30c. Landing Monument, Watling Island and Columbus's signature (horiz) . . . . 1·40 1·00
822 45c. Christopher Columbus 1·90 1·40
823 50c. Landing in New World and Spanish royal standard (horiz) . . . . 1·90 1·90
824 70c. Convent at La Rabida 2·25 3·25
825 $1.50 Replica of "Santa Maria" and Caribbean Pavilion, New York World's Fair (horiz) . . . 3·50 4·75

1992. Olympic Games, Barcelona. Multicoloured.
827 15c. Type **196** . . . . 2·50 75
828 30c. Tennis . . . . 2·50 90
829 60c. Volleyball . . . . 2·75 3·00
830 $1 Football . . . . 3·00 3·75

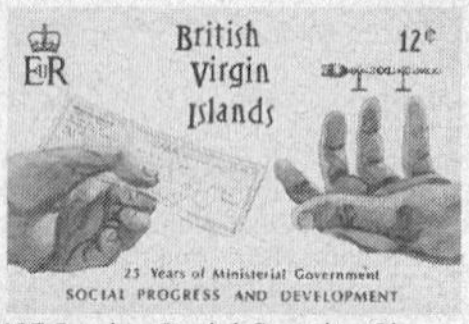
197 Issuing Social Security Cheque

1993. 25th Anniv of Ministerial Government. Multicoloured.
832 12c. Type **197** 40 40
833 15c. Map of British Virgin Islands . . . . 1·25 70
834 45c. Administration building 80 70
835 $1.30 International currency abbreviations . . . . . . 2·25 4·25

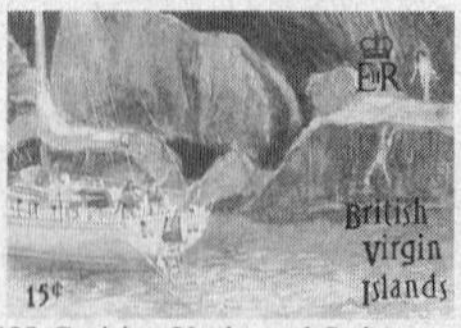
198 Cruising Yacht and Swimmers, The Baths, Virgin Gorda

1993. Tourism. Multicoloured.
836 15c. Type **198** . . . . 1·25 50
837 30c. Cruising yacht under sail (vert) . . . . 1·50 60
838 60c. Scuba diving . . . . . 2·25 2·50
839 $1 Cruising yacht at anchor and snorklers (vert) . . . . 2·50 3·00

1993. 40th Anniv of Coronation. As T **307** of Antigua.
841 12c. multicoloured . . . . . 90 1·25
842 45c. multicoloured . . . . . 1·25 1·50
843 60c. grey and black . . . . 1·40 1·75
844 $1 multicoloured . . . . . . 1·60 1·90
DESIGNS: 12c. Queen Elizabeth II at Coronation (photograph by Cecil Beaton); 45c. Orb; 60c. Queen with Prince Philip, Queen Mother and Princess Margaret, 1953; $1 Queen Elizabeth II on official visit.

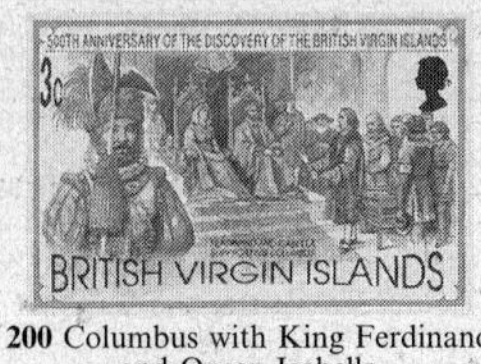

200 Columbus with King Ferdinand and Queen Isabella

1993. 500th Anniv of Discovery of Virgin Islands by Columbus. Multicoloured.

846	3c. Type **200**	15	40
847	12c. Columbus's ship leaving port	40	40
848	15c. Blessing the fleet	45	45
849	25c. Arms and flag of B.V.I.	60	60
850	30c. Columbus and "Santa Maria"	70	70
851	45c. Ships of second voyage	95	95
852	60c. Columbus in ship's boat	1·50	2·25
853	$1 Landing of Columbus	2·00	2·50

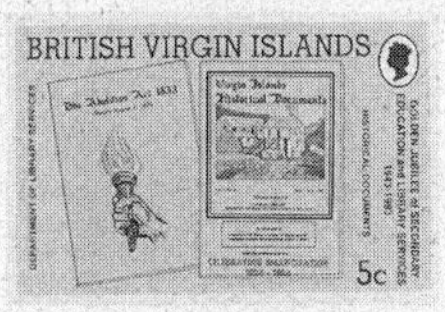

201 Library Services Publications

1993. 50th Anniv of Secondary Education and Library Services. Multicoloured.

855	5c. Type **201**	50	80
856	10c. Secondary school sports	1·00	90
857	15c. Stanley Nibbs (school teacher) (vert)	70	60
858	20c. Mobile library	1·00	70
859	30c. Dr. Norwell Harrigan (adminstrator and lecturer) (vert)	1·00	70
860	35c. Children in library	1·10	70
861	70c. Commemorative inscription on book	2·00	3·25
862	$1 B.V.I. High School	2·25	3·25

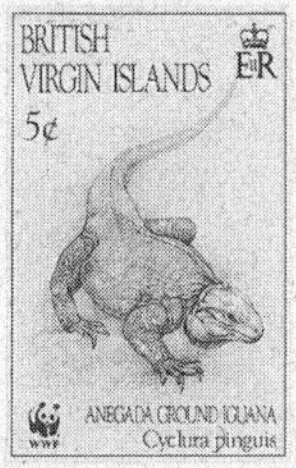

202 Anegada Ground Iguana

1994. Endangered Species. Anegada Ground Iguana.

863	**202**	5c. multicoloured	70	70
864	–	10c. multicoloured	70	70
865	–	15c. multicoloured	80	60
866	–	45c. multicoloured	1·25	1·25

DESIGNS: 10c. to 45c. Different iguanas.

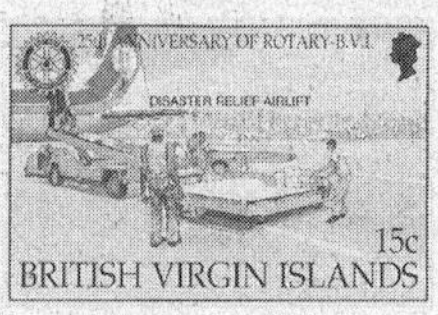

203 Loading Disaster Relief Aircraft

1994. Centenary of Rotary International in B.V.I. Multicoloured.

868	15c. Type **203**	35	35
869	45c. Training children in marine safety	85	85
870	50c. Donated operating table	90	1·00
871	90c. Paul Harris (founder) and emblem	1·60	2·50

1994. 25th Anniv of First Manned Moon Landing. As T **326** of Antigua. Multicoloured.

872	50c. Anniversary logo	2·00	2·25
873	50c. Lunar landing training vehicle	2·00	2·25
874	50c. Launch of "Apollo 11"	2·00	2·25
875	50c. Lunar module "Eagle" in flight	2·00	2·25
876	50c. Moon's surface	2·00	2·25
877	50c. Neil Armstrong (astronaut) taking first step	2·00	2·25

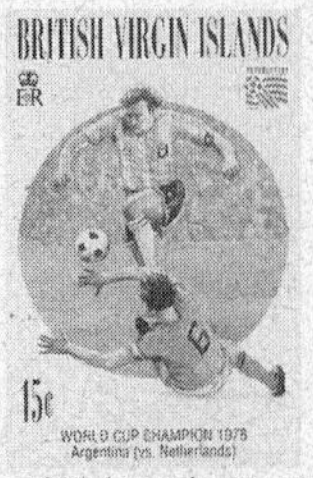

204 Argentina v. Netherlands, 1978

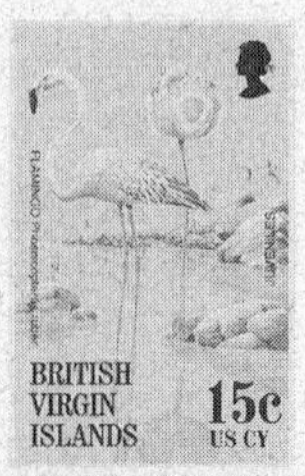

205 Pair of Juvenile Greater Flamingos

1994. World Cup Football Championship, U.S.A. Previous Winners. Multicoloured.

879	15c. Type **204**	1·25	50
880	35c. Italy v. West Germany, 1982	2·00	70
881	50c. Argentina v. West Germany, 1986	2·75	2·25
882	$1.30 West Germany v. Argentina, 1990	4·50	6·50

1995. 50th Anniv of United Nations. As T **213** of Bahamas. Multicoloured.

903	15c. Peugeot P4 all-purpose field cars	45	40
904	30c. Foden medium road tanker	75	60
905	45c. SISU all-terrain vehicle	1·00	90
906	$2 Westland Lynx AH7 helicopter	3·75	5·50

1995. Anegada Flamingos Restoration Project. Multicoloured.

907	15c. Type **205**	75	50
908	20c. Pair of adults	75	55
909	60c. Adult feeding	1·25	1·75
910	$1.45 Adult feeding chick	2·25	3·50

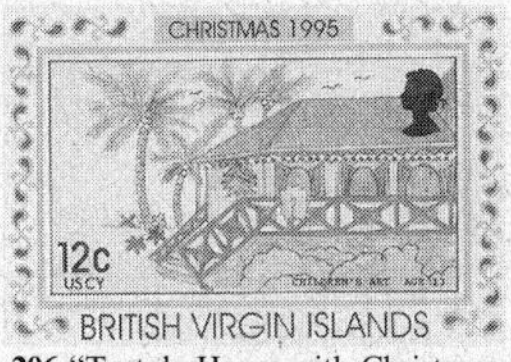

206 "Tortola House with Christmas Tree" (Maureen Walters)

1995. Christmas. Children's Paintings. Multicoloured.

912	12c. Type **206**	1·00	30
913	50c. "Father Christmas in Rowing Boat" (Collin Collins)	2·25	1·40
914	70c. "Christmas Tree and Gifts" (Clare Wassell)	2·50	2·50
915	$1.30 "Peace Dove" (Nicholas Scott)	3·25	4·50

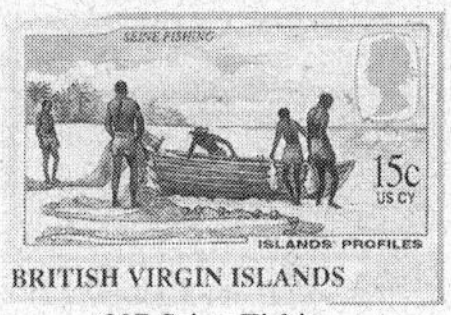

207 Seine Fishing

1996. Island Profiles (1st series). Jost Van Dyke. Multicoloured.

916	15c. Type **207**	1·00	40
917	35c. Sandy Spit	1·25	55
918	90c. Map	3·25	3·25
919	$1.50 Foxy's Regatta	3·50	4·50

See also Nos. 1003/6.

1996. 70th Birthday of Queen Elizabeth II. As T **165** of Ascension, each incorporating a different photograph of the Queen. Multicoloured.

920	10c. Government House, Tortola	20	20
921	30c. Legislative Council Building	55	55
922	45c. Liner in Road Harbour	1·00	70
923	$1.50 Map of British Virgin Islands	2·75	4·50

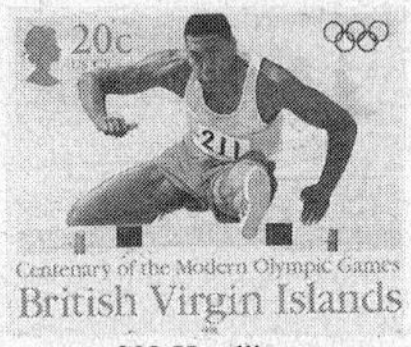

208 Hurdling

1996. Centenary of Modern Olympic Games. Multicoloured.

925	20c. Type **208**	35	30
926	35c. Volley ball	60	60
927	50c. Swimming	90	1·50
928	$1 Yachting	1·75	2·50

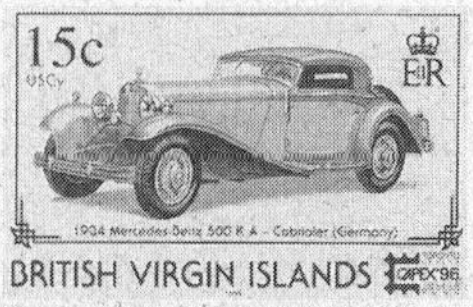

209 Mercedes-Benz "500 K A", 1934

1996. "CAPEX '96" International Stamp Exhibition, Toronto. Early Motor Cars. Multicoloured.

929	15c. Type **209**	30	30
930	40c. Citroen "12", 1934	70	70
931	60c. Cadillac "V-8 Sport Phaeton", 1932	1·00	1·50
932	$1.35 Rolls Royce "Phantom II", 1934	2·25	3·00

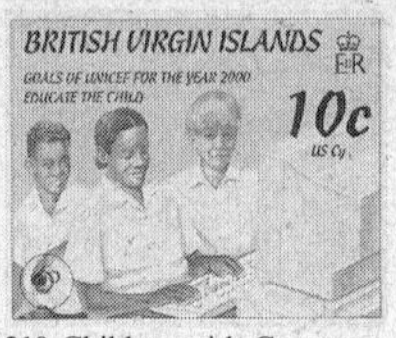

210 Children with Computer

1996. 50th Anniv of U.N.I.C.E.F. Multicoloured.

934	10c. Type **210**	40	40
935	15c. Carnival costume	50	50
936	30c. Children on Scales of Justice	80	80
937	45c. Children on beach	1·25	1·25

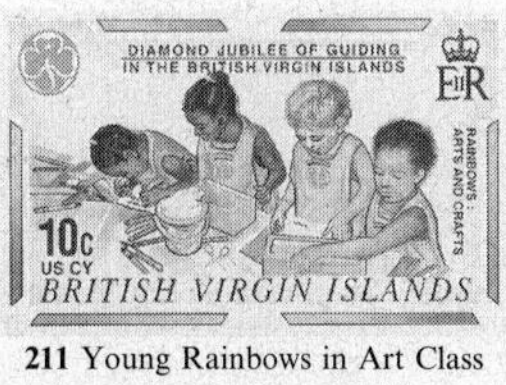

211 Young Rainbows in Art Class

1996. 75th Anniv of Guiding in the British Virgin Islands. Multicoloured.

938	10c. Type **211**	20	20
939	15c. Brownies serving meals	30	25
940	30c. Guides around campfire	50	45
941	45c. Rangers on parade	65	60
942	$2 Lady Baden-Powell	2·75	4·00

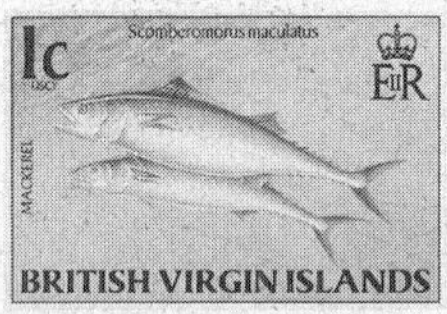

212 Spanish Mackerel

1997. Game Fishes. Multicoloured.

943	1c. Type **212**	10	10
944	10c. Wahoo	15	20
945	15c. Great barracuda	20	25
946	20c. Tarpon	30	35
947	25c. Tiger shark	35	40
948	35c. Sailfish	50	55
949	40c. Dolphin	55	60
950	50c. Black-finned tuna	70	75
951	60c. Yellow-finned tuna	85	90
952	75c. King mackerel ("Kingfish")	1·00	1·10
953	$1.50 White marlin	2·10	2·25
954	$1.85 Amberjack	2·50	2·75
955	$2 Atlantic bonito	2·75	3·00
956	$5 Bonefish	7·00	7·25
957	$10 Blue marlin	14·00	14·50

1997. Golden Wedding of Queen Elizabeth and Prince Philip. As T **173** of Ascension. Multicoloured.

959	30c. Prince Philip with horse	60	80
960	30c. Queen Elizabeth at Windsor, 1989	60	80
961	45c. Queen in phaeton, Trooping the Colour	80	1·00
962	45c. Prince Philip in Scots Guards uniform	80	1·00
963	70c. Queen Elizabeth and Prince Philip at the Derby, 1993	1·10	1·40
964	70c. Prince Charles playing polo, Mexico, 1993	1·10	1·40

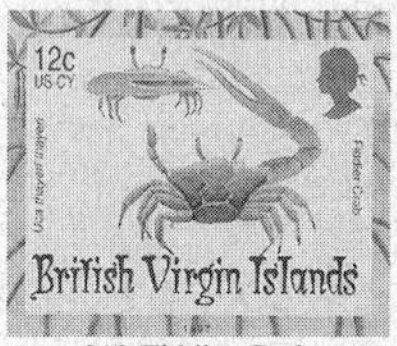

213 Fiddler Crab

1997. Crabs. Multicoloured.

966	12c. Type **213**	55	50
967	15c. Coral crab	60	50
968	35c. Blue crab	85	60
969	$1 Giant hermit crab	1·75	2·75

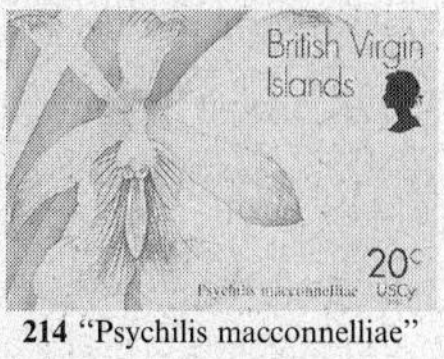

214 "Psychilis macconnelliae"

1997. Orchids of the World. Multicoloured.

971	20c. Type **214**	60	85
972	50c. "Tolumnia prionochila"	90	1·10
973	60c. "Tetramicra canaliculata"	95	1·25
974	75c. "Liparis elata"	1·00	1·25

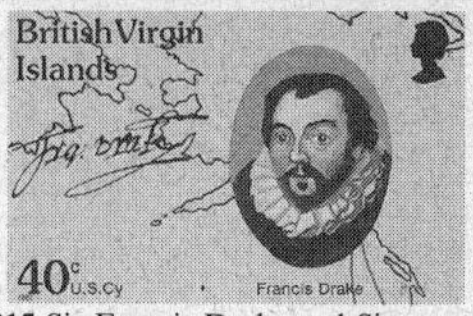

215 Sir Francis Drake and Signature

1997. 420th Anniv of Drake's Circumnavigation of the World. Multicoloured.

976	40c. Type **215**	85	90
977	40c. Drake's coat of arms	85	90
978	40c. Queen Elizabeth I and signature	85	90
979	40c. "Christopher" and "Marigold"	85	90
980	40c. "Golden Hind"	85	90
981	40c. "Swan"	85	90
982	40c. "Cacafuego" (Spanish galleon)	85	90
983	40c. "Elizabeth"	85	90
984	40c. "Maria" (Spanish merchant ship)	85	90
985	40c. Drake's astrolabe	85	90
986	40c. "Golden Hind's" figurehead	85	90
987	40c. Compass rose	85	90

1998. 80th Anniv of Royal Air Force. As T **178** of Ascension. Multicoloured.

990	20c. Fairey IIIF (seaplane)	60	40
991	35c. Supermarine Scapa (flying boat)	85	50
992	50c. Westland Sea King H.A.R.3 (helicopter)	1·40	1·10
993	$1.50 BAe Harrier GR7	2·50	3·25

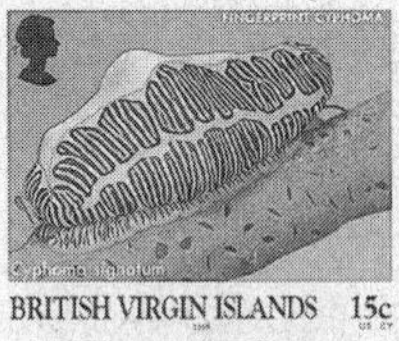

216 Fingerprint Cyphoma

1998. Marine Life. Multicoloured.

995	15c. Type **216**	70	40
996	30c. Long-spined sea urchin	90	55
997	45c. Split crown feather duster worm	1·25	70
998	$1 Upside down jelly	2·00	2·75

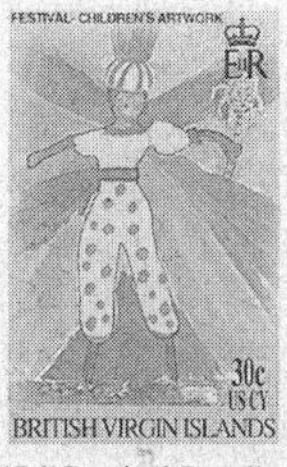

217 "Carnival Reveller" (Rebecca Peck)

1998. Festival. Children's Paintings. Multicoloured.

1000	30c. Type **217**	75	50
1001	45c. "Leader of a Troupe" (Jehiah Maduro)	90	65
1002	$1.30 "Steel Pans" (Rebecca McKenzie) (horiz)	2·50	3·25

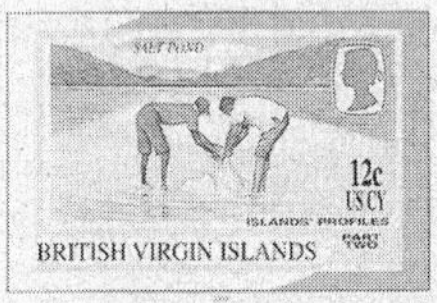

218 Salt Pond

1998. Island Profiles (2nd series). Salt Island. Multicoloured.

1003	12c. Type **218**	65	50
1004	30c. Wreck of "Rhone" (mail steamer)	1·00	55
1005	70c. Traditional house	1·25	1·60
1006	$1.45 Salt Island from the air	2·25	3·00

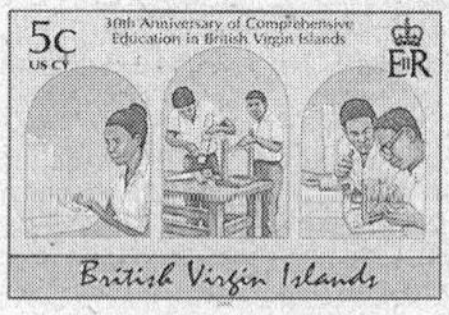

219 Business Studies, Woodwork and Technology Students

1998. Anniversaries. Multicoloured.

1008	5c. Type **219**	25	50
1009	15c. Comprehensive school band	45	30
1010	30c. Chapel, Mona Campus, Jamaica	60	40
1011	45c. Anniversary plaque and University arms	75	60

1012 50c. Dr. John Coakley Lettsom and map of Little Jost Van Dyke . . . . . 1·00 1·10
1013 $1 The Medical Society of London building and arms . . . . 1·60 2·25

EVENTS: 5, 15c. 30th anniv of Comprehensive Education in B.V.I.; 30, 45c. 50th anniv of University of West Indies; 50c., $1 250th anniv of Medical Society of London.

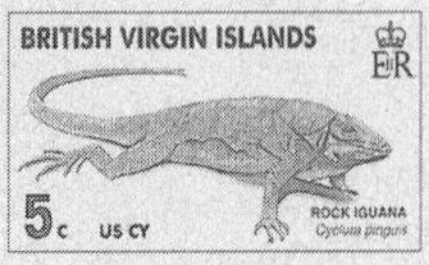

220 Rock Iguana

1999. Lizards. Multicoloured.
1014 5c. Type **220** 30 40
1015 35c. Pygmy gecko 85 45
1016 60c. Slippery back skink . . 1·50 1·00
1017 $1.50 Wood slave gecko . . 2·25 3·00

1999. Royal Wedding. As T **185** of Ascension. Multicoloured.
1019 20c. Photographs of Prince Edward and Miss Sophie Rhys-Jones 75 40
1020 $3 Engagement photograph 4·50 5·50

1999. 30th Anniv of First Manned Landing on Moon. As T **186** of Ascension. Multicoloured.
1021 10c. "Apollo 11" on launch pad 45 35
1022 40c. Firing of second stage rockets . . . . 1·00 65
1023 50c. Lunar module on Moon . . . . 1·10 85
1024 $2 Astronauts transfer to command module . . . . 3·00 4·00

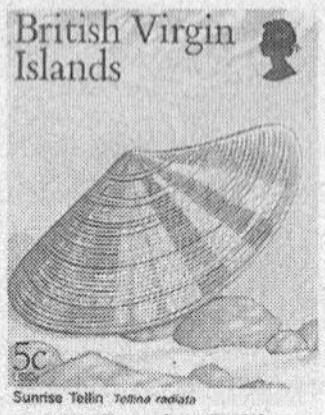

221 Sunrise Tellin

1999. Sea Shells. Multicoloured.
1026A 5c. Type **221** 45 55
1027A 10c. King helmet 45 55
1028A 25c. Measle cowrie 65 75
1029A 35c. West Indian top shell 75 85
1030A 75c. Zigzag scallop . . . . 1·00 1·25
1031A $1 West Indian fighting conch . . . . 1·25 1·50

Nos. 1026A/31A were printed together, se-tenant, with the backgrounds forming a composite design.

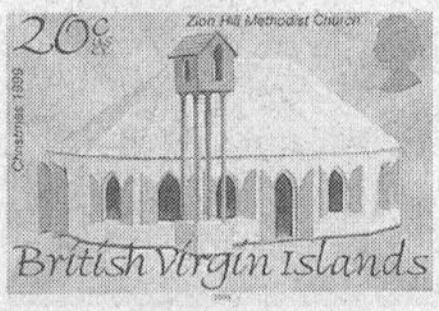

222 Zion Hill Methodist Church

1999. Christmas. Church Buildings. Multicoloured.
1032 20c. Type **222** 45 35
1033 35c. Seventh Day Adventist Church, Fat Hogs Bay, 1982 . . . . 60 45
1034 50c. Ruins of St. Phillip's Anglican Church, Kingstown 85 85
1035 $1 St. William's Catholic Church, Road Town . . . 1·60 2·00

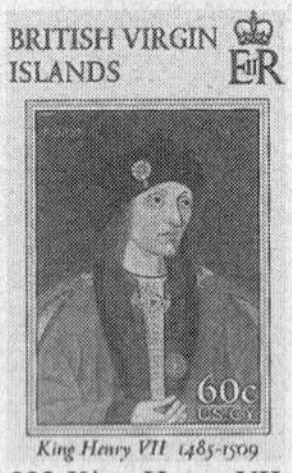

223 King Henry VII

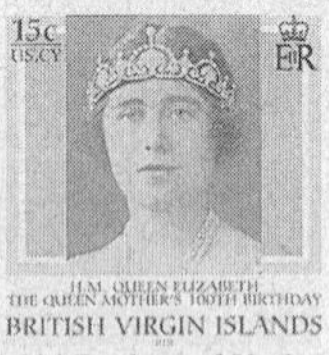

224 Duchess of York, 1920s

2000. "Stamp Show 2000" International Stamp Exhibition, London. Kings and Queens of England. Multicoloured.
1036 60c. Type **223** . . . . . . 1·00 1·10
1037 60c. Lady Jane Grey . . . . 1·00 1·10
1038 60c. King Charles I . . . . 1·00 1·10
1039 60c. King William III . . . 1·00 1·10
1040 60c. King George III . . . 1·00 1·10
1041 60c. King Edward VII . . . 1·00 1·10

2000. 18th Birthday of Prince William. As T **191** of Ascension. Multicoloured.
1042 20c. Prince William as baby (horiz) 60 35
1043 40c. Prince William playing with ball, 1984 . . . . . 90 60
1044 50c. Skiing in British Columbia, 1998 . . . . . 1·25 1·00
1045 $1 In evening dress, 1997 (horiz) . . . . 2·00 2·50

2000. 100th Birthday of Queen Elizabeth the Queen Mother. Multicoloured.
1047 15c. Type **224** 50 25
1048 35c. As Queen Mother in 1957 . . . . 1·00 55
1049 70c. In evening dress, 1970 1·50 1·50
1050 $1.50 With family on 99th birthday . . . . 2·50 3·25

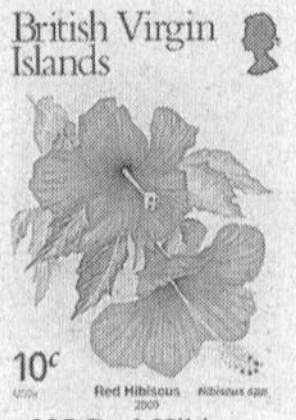

225 Red Hibiscus

2000. Flowers. Multicoloured.
1051 10c. Type **225** 25 30
1052 15c. Pink oleander 30 30
1053 35c. Yellow bell 65 55
1054 50c. Yellow and white frangipani 90 75
1055 75c. Flamboyant . . . . . 1·40 1·50
1056 $2 Bougainvillea . . . . . 3·00 3·50

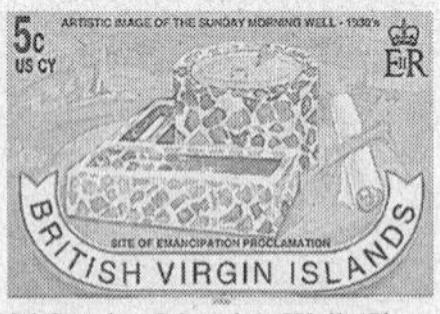

226 Sunday Morning Well (Site of Emancipation Proclamation)

2000. New Millennium. Multicoloured.
1057 5c. Type **226** 15 25
1058 20c. Nurse Mary Louise Davies M.B.E. 45 35
1059 30c. Cheyney University, U.S.A. 60 45
1060 45c. Enid Leona Scatliffe (former chief education officer) 80 70
1061 50c. H. Lavity Stoutt Community College . . . 90 1·00
1062 $1 Sir J. Olva Georges . . . 1·60 2·00

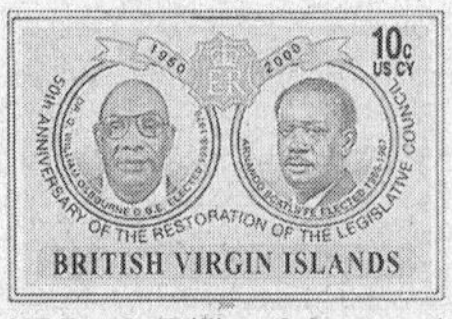

227 Dr. Q. William Osborne and Arnando Scatliffe

2000. 50th Anniv of Restoration of Legislative Council. Multicoloured.
1064 10c. Type **227** 25 30
1065 15c. H. Robinson O'Neal and A. Austin Henley . . 35 30
1066 20c. Wilfred W. Smith and John C. Brudenell-Bruce 45 35
1067 35c. Howard R. Penn and I. G. Fonseca 65 55
1068 50c. Carlton L. de Castro and Theodolph H. Faulkner 90 90
1069 60c. Willard W. Wheatley (Chief Minister, 1971–79) 1·25 1·40
1070 $1 H. Lavity Stoutt (Chief Minister, 1967–71, 1979–83 and 1986–95) . . . . 1·60 2·00

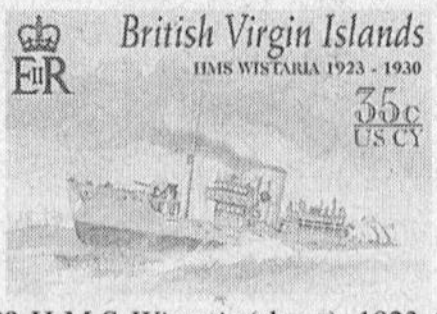

229 H.M.S. *Wistaria* (sloop), 1923–30

2001. Royal Navy Ships connected to British Virgin Islands. Multicoloured.
1072 35c. Type **229** 50 55
1073 50c. H.M.S. *Dundee* (sloop), 1934–35 . . . . 70 75
1074 60c. H.M.S. *Eurydice* (frigate), 1787 . . . . . 85 90
1075 75c. H.M.S. *Pegasus* (frigate), 1787 . . . . . 1·00 1·10
1076 $1 H.M.S. *Astrea* (frigate), 1807 . . . . 1·40 1·50
1077 $1.50 Royal Yacht *Britannia*, 1966 . . . . . 2·10 2·25

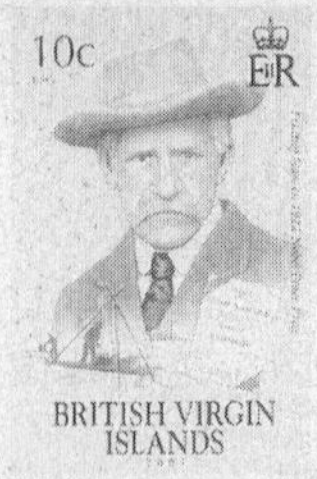

230 Fridtjof Nansen (Peace Prize, 1922)

2001. Centenary of Nobel Prize. Multicoloured.
1078 10c. Type **230** 15 20
1079 20c. Albert Einstein (Physics Prize,1921) 30 35
1080 25c. Sir Arthur Lewis (Economic Sciences Prize, 1979) 35 40
1081 40c. Saint-John Perse (Literature Prize, 1960) . . 55 60
1082 70c. Mother Teresa (Peace Prize, 1979) . . . . . . 1·00 1·10
1083 $2 Christian Lous Lange (Peace Prize, 1921) . . . 2·75 3·00

2002. Golden Jubilee. As T **200** of Ascension.
1084 15c. brown, mauve and gold 15 20
1085 50c. multicoloured 70 75
1086 60c. multicoloured 85 90
1087 75c. multicoloured . . . . . 1·00 1·10

DESIGNS: 15c. Princess Elizabeth in A.T.S. uniform, changing wheel; 50c. Queen Elizabeth in fur hat, 1977; 60c. Queen Elizabeth carrying bouquet; 75c. Queen Elizabeth at banquet, Prague, 1996.

OFFICIAL STAMPS

1985. Nos. 418/21 and 423/33 optd **OFFICIAL**.
O 1 1c. Purple-tipped sea anemone . . . . 30 1·00
O 2 3c. Common starfish . . . . 45 1·00
O 3 5c. Type **134** 45 45
O 4 8c. Triton's trumpet (shell) 55 60
O 5 13c. Flamingo tongue snail 80 75
O 6 15c. Spider crab 85 70
O 7 18c. Sea squirts . . . . . . 90 1·50
O 8 20c. True tulip (shell) . . . 90 80
O 9 25c. Rooster tail conch (shell) . . . . 1·25 1·50
O10 30c. Fighting conch (shell) 1·40 1·00
O11 60c. Mangrove crab . . . . 2·00 2·50
O12 $1 Coral polyps . . . . . . 3·00 3·75
O13 $2.50 Peppermint shrimp . . 4·50 9·00
O14 $3 West Indian murex (shell) 5·50 10·00
O15 $5 Carpet anemone . . . . 7·50 10·00

1986. Nos. 560/78 optd **OFFICIAL**.
O16 1c. Type **162** . . . . 40 1·00
O17 2c. Yellow-crowned night heron . . . . 40 1·00
O18 5c. Mangrove cuckoo . . . 55 1·00
O19 8c. Northern mockingbird 55 1·25
O20 10c. Grey kingbird . . . . 70 1·00
O21 12c. Red-necked pigeon . . 70 40
O22 15c. Least bittern 70 40
O23 18c. Smooth-billed ani . . 70 75
O24 20c. Clipper rail . . . . . . 1·00 1·00
O25 25c. American kestrel . . . 1·00 1·00
O26 30c. Pearly-eyed thrasher . . 1·25 1·00
O27 35c. Bridled quail dove . . 1·25 1·00
O28 40c. Green-backed heron . . 1·25 1·00
O29 50c. Scaly-breasted ground dove . . . . 1·40 1·75
O30 60c. Little blue heron . . . 1·50 2·50
O31 $1 Audubon's shearwater . . 2·25 3·50
O32 $2 Blue-faced booby . . . . 2·50 4·00
O33 $3 Cattle egret . . . . . . 6·00 7·00
O34 $5 Zenaida dove . . . . . . 6·50 7·50

1991. Nos. 767/8, 771, 773/9 and 781 optd **OFFICIAL**.
O35 5c. Frangipani 45 60
O36 10c. Autograph tree 45 60
O37 20c. Jerusalem thorn 55 55
O38 30c. Swamp immortelle . . . 70 55
O39 35c. White cedar 70 55
O40 40c. Mahoe tree 80 70
O41 45c. Pinguin 80 75
O42 50c. Christmas orchid . . . 1·50 90
O43 70c. Lignum vitae . . . . . 1·50 2·25
O44 $1 African tulip tree . . . . 1·50 2·50
O45 $3 Organ pipe cactus . . . . 4·00 5·50

BRUNEI Pt. 1

A Sultanate on the North Coast of Borneo.

100 cents = 1 dollar.

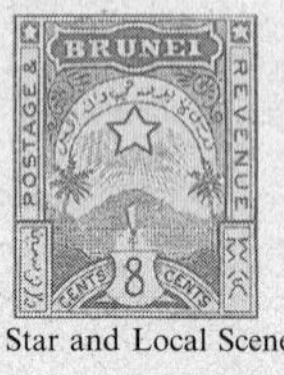

1 Star and Local Scene

1895.
1 **1** ½c. brown . . . . 2·75 20·00
2 1c. brown . . . . 3·00 15·00
3 2c. black . . . . 4·00 15·00
4 3c. blue . . . . 3·50 14·00
5 5c. green . . . . 6·50 16·00
6 8c. purple . . . . 6·50 26·00
7 10c. red . . . . 8·00 26·00
8 25c. green . . . . 60·00 75·00
9 50c. green . . . . 18·00 90·00
10 $1 green . . . . 20·00 £110

1906. Stamps of Labuan optd **BRUNEI.** or surch also.
11 **18** 1c. black and purple . . . . 28·00 55·00
12 2c. on 3c. black and brown 2·75 9·00
13 2c. on 8c. black and orange 27·00 80·00
14 3c. black and brown . . . . 28·00 85·00
15 4c. on 12c. black and yellow 3·75 5·00
16 5c. on 16c. green and brown 45·00 75·00
17 8c. black and orange . . . 9·00 32·00
18 10c. on 16c. green and brown . . . . 6·50 22·00
19 25c. on 16c. green and brown £100 £120
20 30c. on 16c. green and brown . . . . 95·00 £120
21 50c. on 16c. green and brown . . . . 95·00 £120
22 $1 on 8c. black and orange 95·00 £120

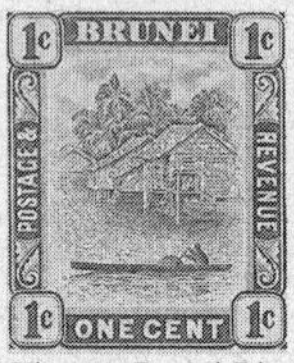

5 View on Brunei River

1907.
23 **5** 1c. black and green . . . . . 2·25 11·00
24 2c. black and red . . . . . 2·50 4·50
25 3c. black and brown . . . . 10·00 22·00
26 4c. black and mauve . . . . 7·50 10·00
27 5c. black and blue . . . . . 50·00 90·00
28 8c. black and orange . . . . 7·50 23·00
29 10c. black and green . . . . 4·50 7·00
30 25c. blue and brown . . . . 32·00 48·00
31 30c. violet and black . . . . 23·00 22·00
32 50c. green and brown . . . . 15·00 22·00
33 $1 red and grey . . . . . . 60·00 90·00

1908.
35 **5** 1c. green . . . . 60 2·00
60 1c. black . . . . 1·00 75
79 1c. brown . . . . 50 1·75
36 2c. black and brown . . . . 3·00 1·25
61 2c. brown . . . . 90 6·00
62 2c. green . . . . 1·50 1·00
80 2c. grey . . . . 60 3·50
37 3c. red . . . . 3·00 1·25
63 3c. green . . . . 80 6·50
64 4c. purple . . . . 1·50 1·25
65 4c. orange . . . . 2·00 1·00
40 5c. black and orange . . . . 7·00 7·00
82 5c. orange . . . . 80 1·25
67 5c. grey . . . . 11·00 12·00
68 5c. brown . . . . 11·00 70
41 8c. blue and indigo . . . . . 7·00 11·00
71 8c. blue . . . . 6·00 5·00
72 8c. black . . . . 11·00 75
84 8c. red . . . . 40 1·00
42 10c. purple on yellow . . . . 2·00 1·75
85 10c. violet 70 30
86 15c. blue . . . . 1·50 60
87 25c. purple . . . . 2·25 1·00
44 30c. purple and yellow . . . 9·00 12·00
88 30c. black and orange . . . 1·50 1·00
77 50c. black on green . . . . . 7·50 15·00
89 50c. black . . . . 3·00 70
46 $1 black and red on blue . . 20·00 48·00
90 $1 black and red . . . . . . 6·50 75
47 $5 red on green £110 £180
91 $5 green and orange . . . . 16·00 17·00
92 $10 black and purple . . . . 55·00 30·00
48 $25 black on red £475 £850

1922. Optd **MALAYA- BORNEO EXHIBITION. 1922.**
51 **5** 1c. green . . . . 3·50 24·00
52 2c. black and brown . . . . 4·50 29·00
53 3c. red . . . . 6·00 38·00
54 4c. red . . . . 8·00 45·00
55 5c. orange . . . . 11·00 55·00
56 10c. purple on yellow . . . . 6·50 55·00
57 25c. lilac . . . . 14·00 80·00
58 50c. black on green . . . . . 45·00 £150
59 $1 black and red on blue . . 70·00 £190

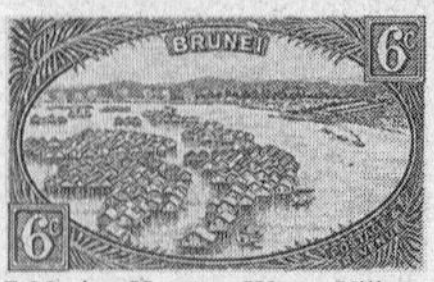

7 Native Houses, Water Village

1924.
81 **7** 3c. green . . . . 1·00 5·00
83 6c. black . . . . 1·00 4·00
70 6c. red . . . . 3·75 11·00
74 12c. blue . . . . 4·50 9·00

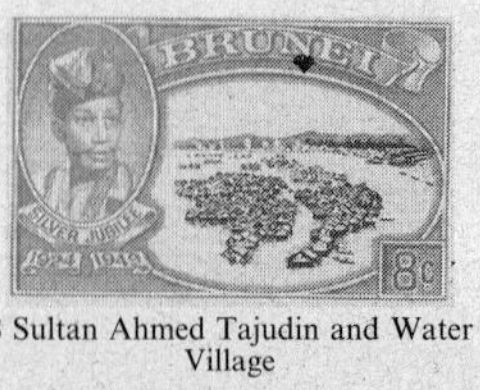

8 Sultan Ahmed Tajudin and Water Village

1949. Silver Jubilee of H.H. the Sultan.

93	8	8c. black and red	70	1·00
94		25c. purple and orange	70	1·40
95		50c. black and blue	70	1·40

1949. 75th Anniv of U.P.U. As T **20/23** of Antigua.

96	8c. red	1·00	1·25
97	15c. blue	3·50	1·50
98	25c. mauve	1·00	1·50
99	50c. black	1·00	1·25

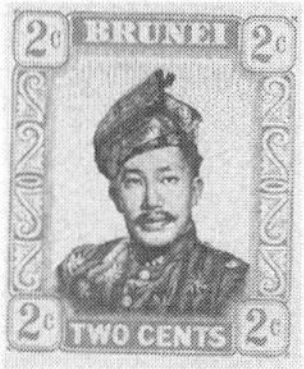

9 Sultan Omar Ali Saifuddin

1952. Dollar values as T **8**, but with arms instead of portrait inset.

100	9	1c. black	10	50
101		2c. black and orange	10	50
102		3c. black and brown	10	30
103		4c. black and green	10	20
104		6c. black and grey	30	10
123		8c. black and red	60	10
106		10c. black and sepia	15	10
125		12c. black and violet	1·50	10
126		15c. black and blue	55	10
109		25c. black and purple	2·50	10
110		50c. black and blue	1·75	10
111		$1 black and green (horiz)	1·50	1·40
112		$2 black and red (horiz)	4·50	2·50
113		$5 black and purple (horiz)	14·00	7·00

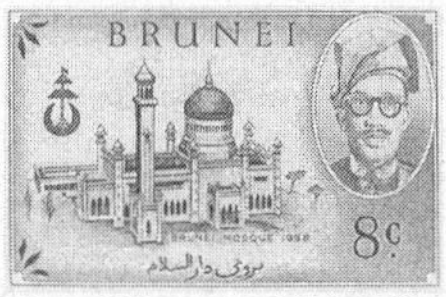

11 Brunei Mosque and Sultan Omar

1958. Opening of the Brunei Mosque.

114	11	8c. black and green	20	65
115		15c. black and red	25	15
116		35c. black and lilac	30	90

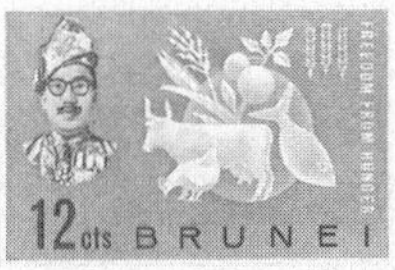

12 "Protein Foods"

1963. Freedom from Hunger.

117	12	12c. sepia	2·75	1·00

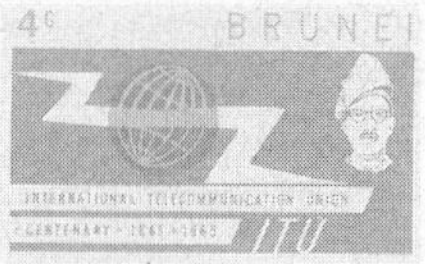

13 I.T.U. Emblem

1965. Centenary of I.T.U.

132	13	4c. mauve and brown	35	10
133		75c. yellow and green	1·00	75

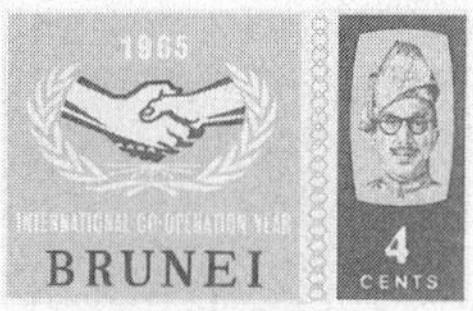

14 I.C.Y. Emblem

1965. International Co-operation Year.

134	14	4c. purple and turquoise	20	10
135		15c. green and lavender	55	35

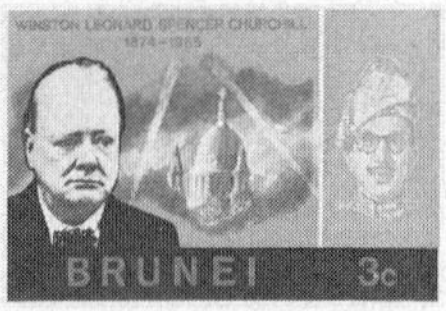

15 Sir Winston Churchill and St. Paul's Cathedral in Wartime

1966. Churchill Commemoration. Designs in black, red and gold and with backgrounds in colours given.

136	15	3c. blue	30	20
137		10c. green	1·50	20
138		15c. brown	1·75	35
139		75c. violet	4·25	2·25

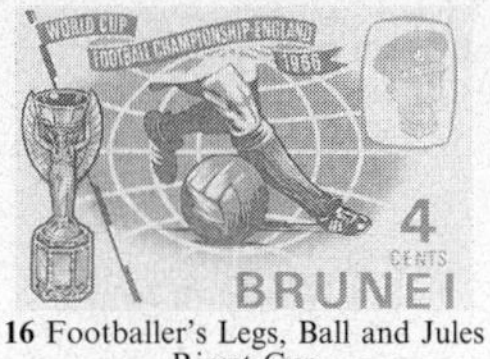

16 Footballer's Legs, Ball and Jules Rimet Cup

1966. World Cup Football Championships.

140	16	4c. multicoloured	20	15
141		75c. multicoloured	80	60

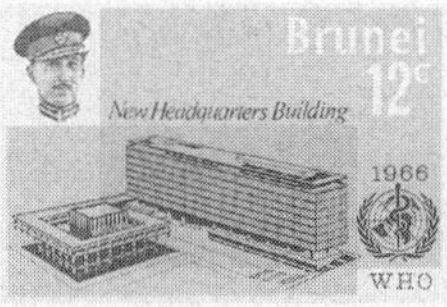

17 W.H.O. Building

1966. Inauguration of W.H.O. Headquarters, Geneva.

142	17	12c. black, green and blue	40	65
143		25c. black, purple and ochre	60	1·25

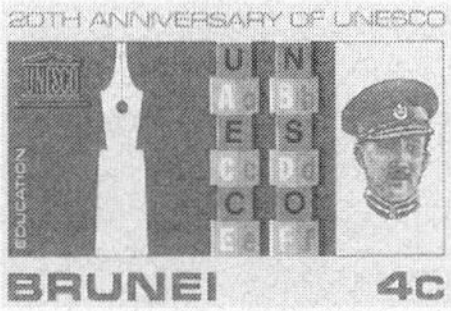

18 "Education"

1966. 20th Anniv of U.N.E.S.C.O.

144	18	4c. multicoloured	35	10
145	–	15c. yellow, violet and olive	75	50
146	–	75c. black, purple and orange	2·50	6·00

DESIGNS: 15c. "Science"; 75c. "Culture".

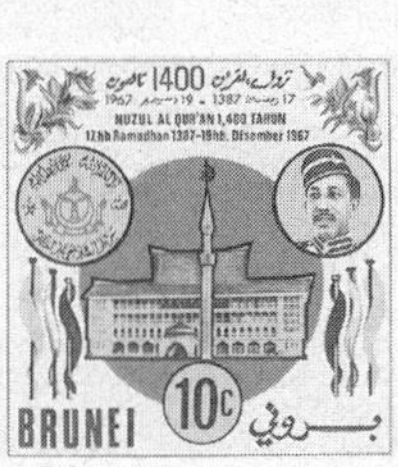

21 Religious Headquarters Building

1967. 1400th Anniv of Revelation of the Koran.

147	21	4c. multicoloured	10	10
148		10c. multicoloured	15	10
149	–	25c. multicoloured	20	30
150	–	50c. multicoloured	35	1·50

Nos. 149/50 have sprigs of laurel flanking the main design (which has a smaller circle) in place of flagpoles.

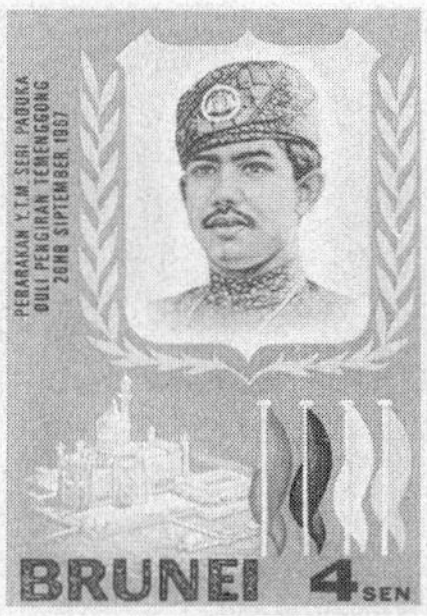

22 Sultan of Brunei, Mosque and Flags

1968. Installation of Y.T.M. Seri Paduka Duli Pengiran Temenggong. Multicoloured.

151	4c. Type **22**	15	50
152	12c. Sultan of Brunei, Mosque and Flags (different) (horiz)	40	1·00
153	25c. Type **22**	55	1·60

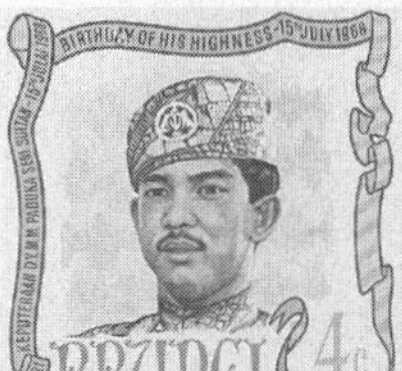

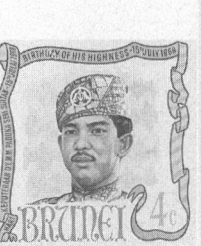

23 Sultan of Brunei

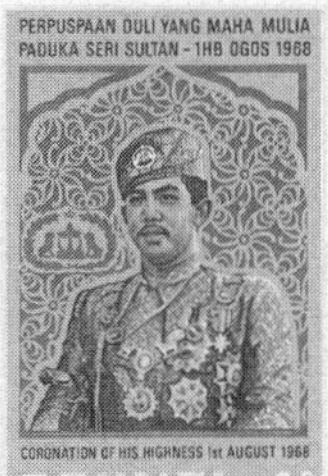

24 Sultan of Brunei

1968. Birthday of Sultan.

154	23	4c. multicoloured	10	35
155		12c. multicoloured	20	60
156		25c. multicoloured	30	1·00

1968. Coronation of Sultan of Brunei.

157	4c. multicoloured	15	25
158	12c. multicoloured	25	50
159	25c. multicoloured	40	75

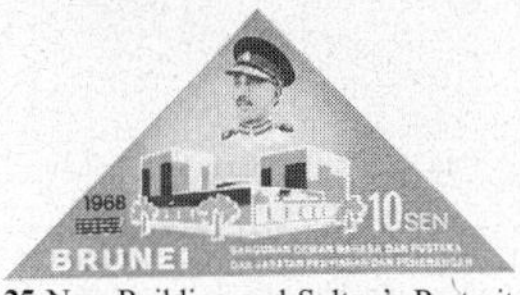

25 New Building and Sultan's Portrait

1968. Opening of Hall of Language and Literature Bureau. Multicoloured.

160	10c. Type **25**	20	1·75
161	15c. New Building and Sultan's portrait ($48\frac{1}{2}\times22$ mm)	20	35
162	30c. As 15c.	45	90

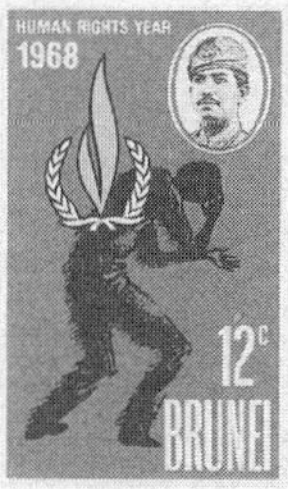

27 Human Rights Emblem and struggling Man

1968. Human Rights Year.

163	27	12c. black, yellow and green	10	20
164		25c. black, yellow and blue	15	25
165		75c. black, yellow and purple	45	1·75

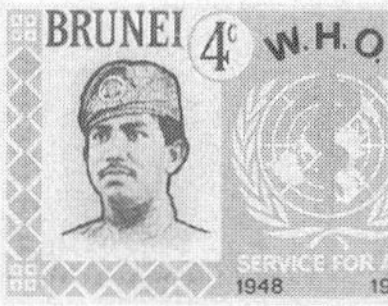

28 Sultan of Brunei and W.H.O. Emblem

1968. 20th Anniv of World Health Organization.

166	28	4c. yellow, black and blue	30	30
167		15c. yellow, black and violet	55	65
168		25c. yellow, black and olive	65	1·25

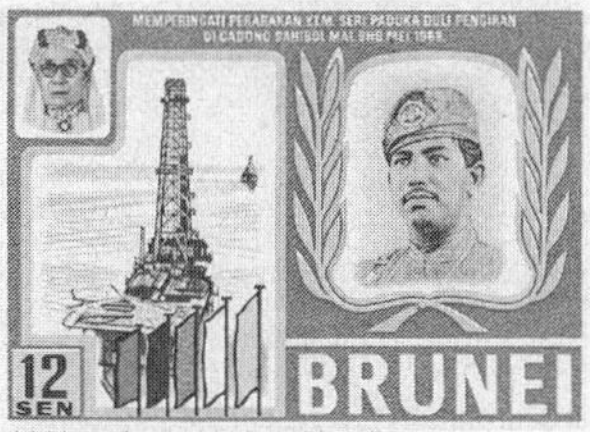

29 Deep Sea Oil-Rig, Sultan of Brunei and inset portrait of Pengiran Di-Gadong

1969. Installation (9th May, 1968) of Pengiran Shar-bandar as Y.T.M. Seri Paduka Duli Pengiran Di-Gadong Sahibol Mal.

169	29	12c. multicoloured	85	50
170		40c. multicoloured	1·25	2·00
171		50c. multicoloured	1·25	2·00

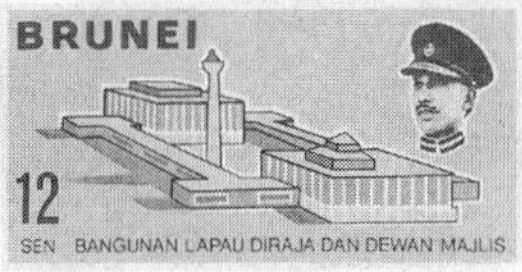

30 Aerial View of Parliament Buildings

1969. Opening of Royal Audience Hall and Legislative Council Chamber.

172	30	12c. multicoloured	20	25
173		25c. multicoloured	30	45
174	–	50c. red and violet	60	1·75

DESIGN: 50c. Elevation of new buildings.

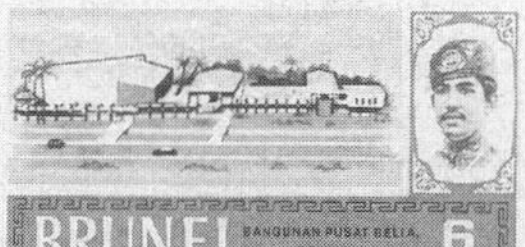

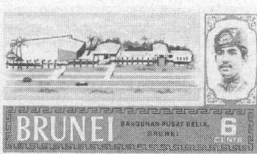

32 Youth Centre and Sultan's Portrait

1969. Opening of New Youth Centre.

175	32	6c. multicoloured	20	1·00
176		10c. multicoloured	25	10
177		30c. multicoloured	70	1·00

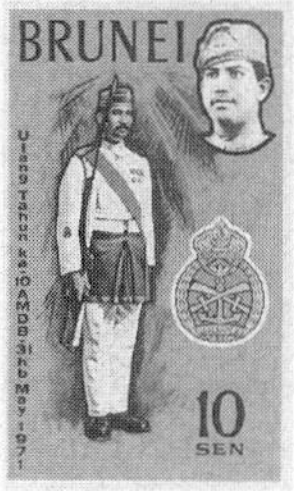

33 Soldier, Sultan and Badge

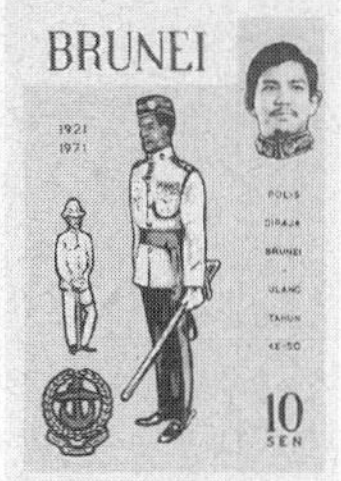

34 Badge, and Officer in Full-dress Uniform

1971. 10th Anniv of Royal Brunei Malay Regiment. Multicoloured.

178	10c. Type **33**	80	30
179	15c. Bell 205 Iroquois helicopter, Sultan and badge (horiz)	1·75	70
180	75c. "Pahlawan" (patrol boat), Sultan and badge (horiz)	3·25	6·50

1971. 50th Anniv of Royal Brunei Police Force. Multicoloured.

181	10c. Type **34**	50	30
182	15c. Badge and Patrol Constable	60	90
183	50c. Badge and Traffic Constable	1·10	6·00

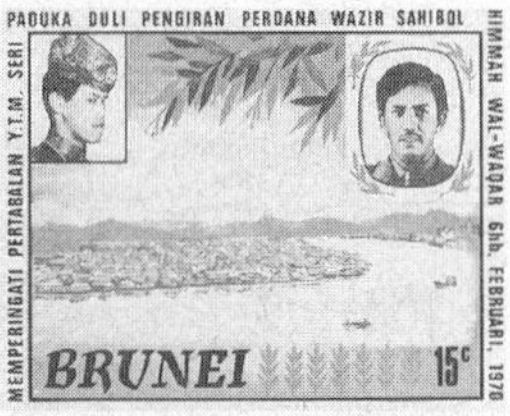

35 Perdana Wazir, Sultan of Brunei and View of Water Village

1971. Installation of the Yang Teramat Mulia as the Perdana Wazir.

184	35	15c. multicoloured	40	50
185	–	25c. multicoloured	70	1·00
186	–	50c. multicoloured	1·40	5·00

Nos. 185/6 show various views of Brunei Town.

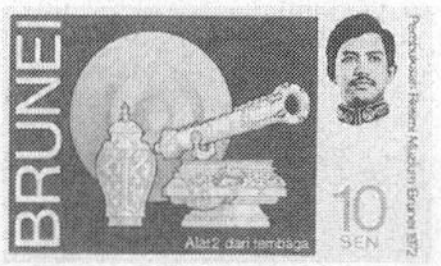

36 Pottery

1972. Opening of Brunei Museum. Mult.

187	10c. Type **36**	30	10
188	12c. Straw-work	40	20
189	15c. Leather-work	45	20
190	25c. Gold-work	1·25	1·25
191	50c. Museum Building (58×21 mm)	2·25	4·75

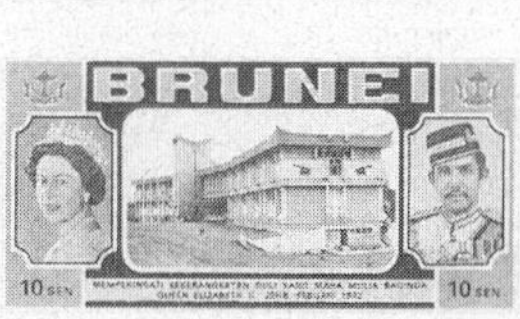

37 Modern Building, Queen Elizabeth and Sultan of Brunei

1972. Royal Visit. Each design with portrait of Queen and Sultan. Multicoloured.

192	10c. Type **37**	70	20
193	15c. Native houses	95	55
194	25c. Mosque	2·00	1·60
195	50c. Royal Assembly Hall	3·75	7·00

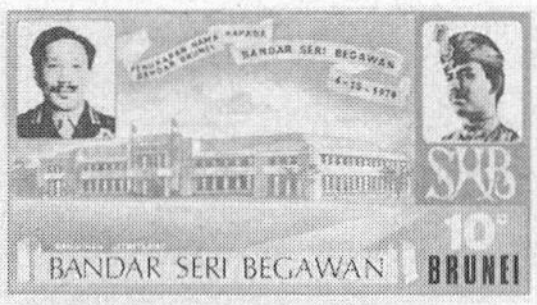

38 Secretariat Building

1972. Renaming of Brunei Town as Bandar Seri Begawan.

196	38	10c. multicoloured	30	15
197	–	15c. green, yellow and black	35	15
198	–	25c. blue, yellow and black	60	50
199	–	50c. red, blue and black	95	2·25

VIEWS: 15c. Darul Hana Palace; 25c. Old Brunei Town; 50c. Town and Water Village.

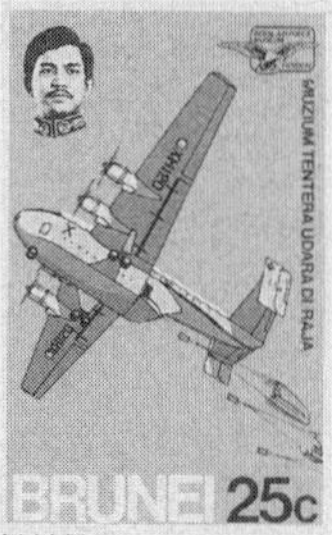

39 Blackburn Beverley C1 parachuting Supplies

1972. Opening of R.A.F. Museum, Hendon. Multicoloured.

200	25c. Type **39**	1·75	1·25
201	75c. Blackburn Beverley C1 landing	3·25	4·75

1972. Royal Silver Wedding. As T **52** of Ascension, but with girl with traditional flower-pot, and boy with bowl and pipe in background.

210	12c. red	10	10
211	75c. green	20	50

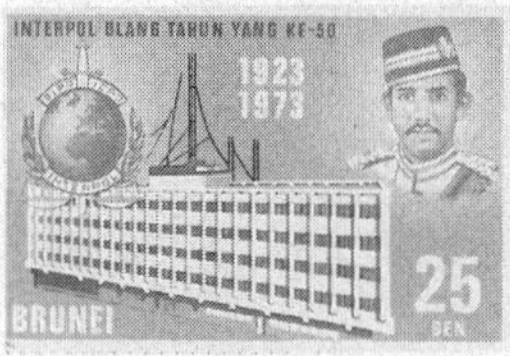

41 Interpol H.Q., Paris

1973. 50th Anniv of Interpol.

212 **41**	25c. green, purple and black	1·50	1·25
213 –	50c. blue, ultram & red	1·50	1·25

DESIGN: 50c. Different view of the H.Q.

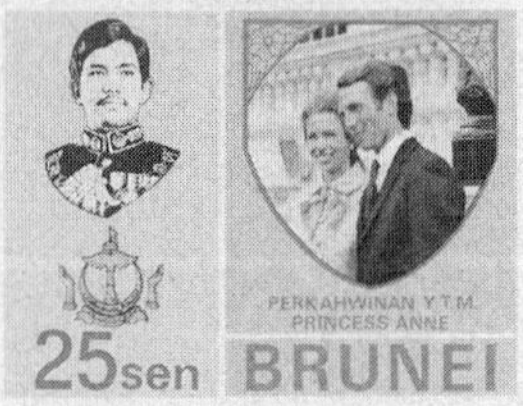

42 Sultan, Princess Anne and Captain Phillips

1973. Royal Wedding.

214 **42**	25c. multicoloured	15	10
215	50c. multicoloured	15	25

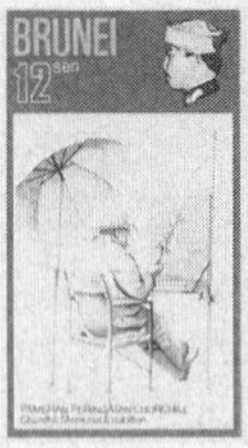

43 Churchill Painting

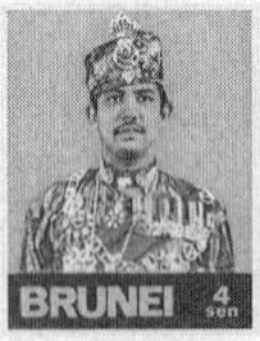

44 Sultan Sir Hassanal Bolkiah Mu'izzaddin Waddaulah

1973. Opening of Churchill Memorial Building. Multicoloured.

216	12c. Type **43**	10	20
217	50c. Churchill statue	30	1·40

1975. Multicoloured. Background colours given.

218 **44**	4c. green	20	20
219	5c. blue	20	30
220	6c. green	2·75	4·00
221	10c. lilac	30	10
222	15c. brown	1·50	10
223	20c. stone	30	20
224	25c. green	40	15
225	30c. blue	40	15
226	35c. grey	40	20
227	40c. purple	40	20
228	50c. brown	40	20
229	75c. green	60	3·25
256	$1 orange	1·50	3·25
231	$2 yellow	2·25	10·00
232	$5 silver	3·00	17·00
233	$10 gold	5·00	30·00

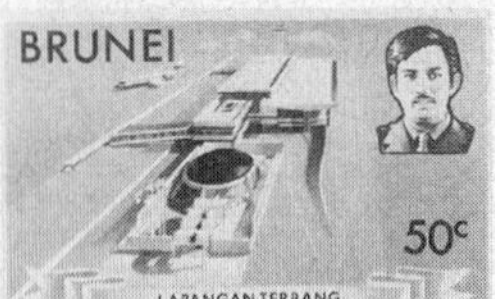

45 Aerial View of Airport

1974. Inauguration of Brunei International Airport. Multicoloured.

234	50c. Type **45**	1·25	1·00
235	75c. Sultan in Army uniform, and airport (48 × 36 mm)	1·50	1·50

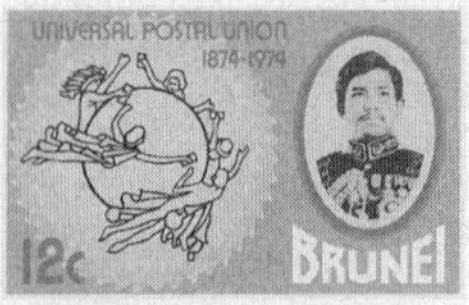

46 U.P.U. Emblem and Sultan

1974. Centenary of Universal Postal Union.

236 **46**	12c. multicoloured	20	20
237	50c. multicoloured	40	1·40
238	75c. multicoloured	50	1·75

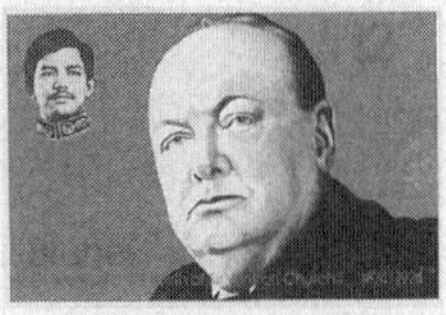

47 Sir Winston Churchill

1974. Birth Centenary of Sir Winston Churchill.

239 **47**	12c. black, blue and gold	25	20
240 –	75c. black, green and gold	45	1·40

DESIGN: 75c. Churchill smoking cigar (profile).

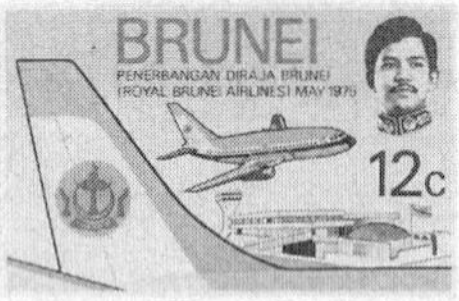

48 Boeing 737 and R.B.A. Crest

1975. Inauguration of Royal Brunei Airlines. Mult.

241	12c. Type **48**	1·00	25
242	35c. Boeing 737 over Bandar Seri Begawan Mosque	1·75	1·25
243	75c. Boeing 737 in flight	2·50	2·50

1976. Surch **10 sen**.

263 **44**	10c. on 6c. brown	1·75	1·50

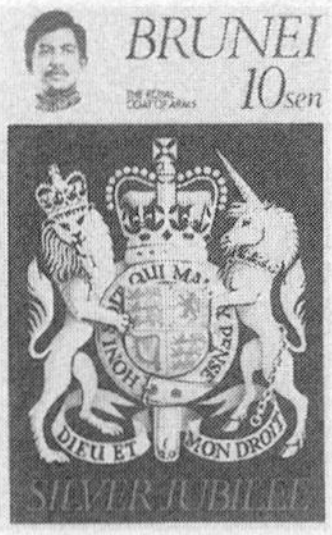

50 Royal Coat of Arms

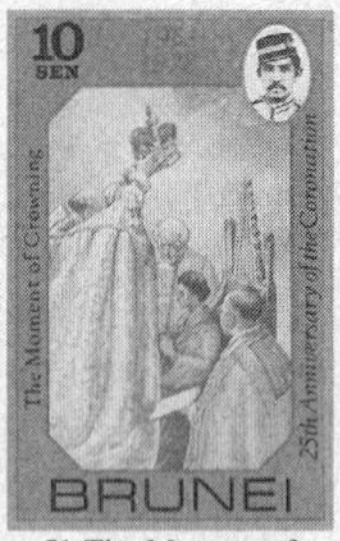

51 The Moment of Crowning

1977. Silver Jubilee. Multicoloured.

264	10c. Type **50**	15	15
265	20c. Imperial State Crown	20	20
266	75c. Queen Elizabeth (portrait by Annigoni)	45	60

1978. 25th Anniv of Coronation. Multicoloured.

267	10c. Type **51**	15	10
268	20c. Queen in Coronation regalia	20	20
269	75c. Queen's departure from Abbey	55	80

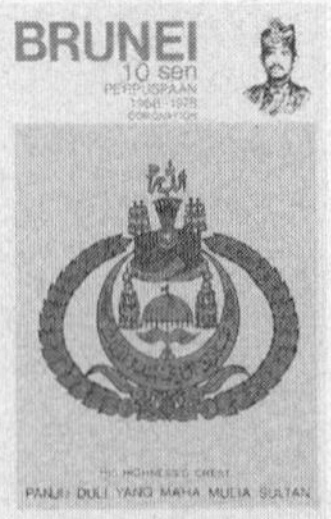

52 Royal Crest

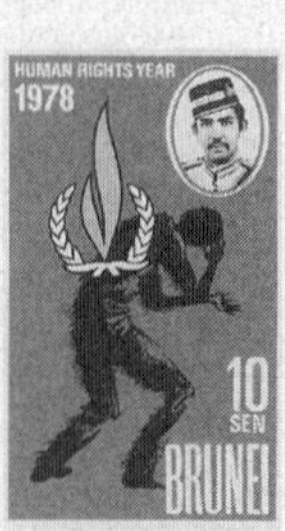

53 Human Rights Emblem and Struggling Man

1978. 10th Anniv of Coronation of Sultan.

270 **52**	10c. black, red and yellow	20	10
271 –	20c. multicoloured	40	25
272 –	75c. multicoloured	1·10	2·75

DESIGNS: 20c. Coronation; 75c. Sultan's Crown.

1978. Human Rights Year.

274 **53**	10c. black, yellow and red	15	10
275	20c. black, yellow and violet	20	35
276	75c. black, yellow and bistre	40	2·25

Type **53** is similar to the design used for the previous Human Rights issue in 1968.

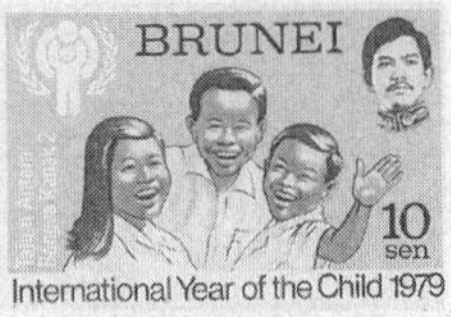

54 Smiling Children

1979. International Year of the Child.

277 **54**	10c. multicoloured	20	10
278 –	$1 black and green	1·25	2·50

DESIGN: $1 I.Y.C. emblem.

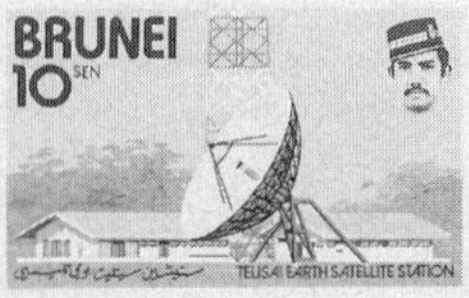

55 Earth Satellite Station

1979. Telisai Earth Satellite Station. Multicoloured.

279	10c. Type **55**	25	15
280	20c. Satellite and antenna	45	40
281	75c. Television camera, telex machine and telephone	85	2·75

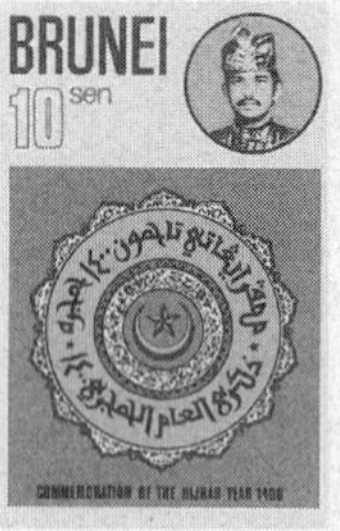

56 Hegira Symbol

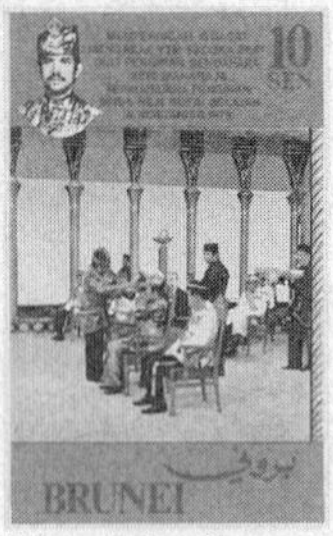

57 Installation Ceremony

1979. Moslem Year 1400 A.H. Commemoration.

282 **56**	10c. black, yellow and green	10	15
283	20c. black, yellow and blue	15	30
284	75c. black, yellow and lilac	45	2·00

1980. 1st Anniv of Prince Sufri Bolkiah's Installation as First Wazir. Multicoloured. Blue borders.

286	10c. Type **57**	15	10
287	75c. Prince Sufri	85	2·00

1980. 1st Anniv of Prince Jefri Bolkiah's Installation as Second Wazir. Designs similar to T **57**. Multicoloured. Green borders.

288	10c. Installation ceremony	15	10
289	75c. Prince Jefri	85	2·00

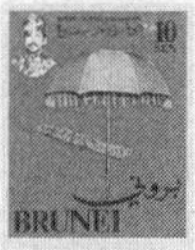

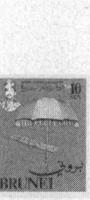

58 Royal Umbrella and Sash

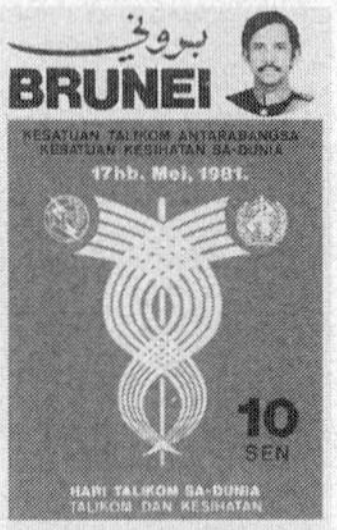

59 I.T.U. and W.H.O. Emblems

1981. Royal Regalia (1st series). Multicoloured.

290	10c. Type **58**	20	15
291	15c. Sword and Shield	35	25
292	20c. Lance and Sheath	40	40
293	30c. Betel Leaf Container	60	1·25
294	50c. Coronation Crown (39 × 22 mm)	1·25	4·00

See Nos. 298/303, 314/19 and 320/5.

1981. World Telecommunications and Health Day.

296 **59**	10c. black and red	50	25
297	75c. black, blue and violet	2·25	4·25

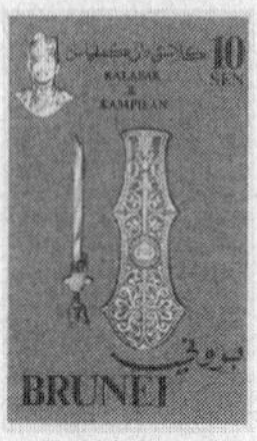

60 Shield and Broadsword

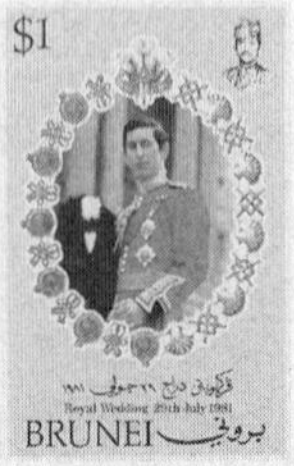

61 Prince Charles as Colonel of the Welsh Guards

1981. Royal Regalia (2nd series). Multicoloured.

298	10c. Type **60**	10	10
299	15c. Blunderbuss and Pouch	20	20
300	20c. Crossed Lances and Sash	30	30
301	30c. Sword, Shield and Sash	40	65
302	50c. Forked Lance	60	2·25
303	75c. Royal Drum (29 × 45 mm)	80	3·75

1981. Royal Wedding. Multicoloured.

304	10c. Wedding bouquet from Brunei	15	15
305	$1 Type **61**	50	1·50
306	$2 Prince Charles and Lady Diana Spencer	70	2·50

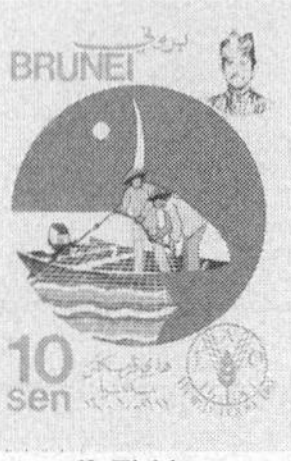

62 Fishing

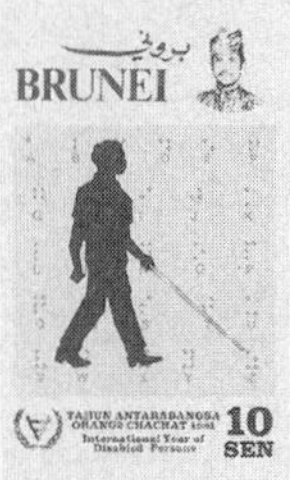

63 Blind Man and Braille Alphabet

1981. World Food Day. Multicoloured.

307	10c. Type **62**	50	15
308	$1 Farm produce and machinery	4·50	6·50

1981. International Year for Disabled Persons. Multicoloured.

309	10c. Type **63**	65	20
310	20c. Deaf people and sign language	1·50	80
311	75c. Disabled person and wheelchairs	3·00	6·25

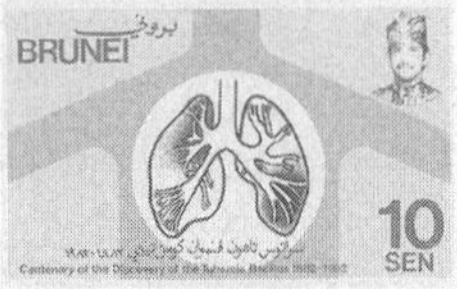

64 Drawing of Infected Lungs

1982. Centenary of Robert Koch's Discovery of Tubercle Bacillus. Multicoloured.

312	10c. Type **64**	50	25
313	75c. Magnified tubercle bacillus and microscope	3·00	4·50

1982. Royal Regalia (3rd series). As T **60**. Mult.

314	10c. Ceremonial Ornament	10	10
315	15c. Silver Betel Caddy	20	20
316	20c. Traditional Flowerpot	25	30
317	30c. Solitary Candle	50	80
318	50c. Golden Pipe	70	2·25
319	75c. Royal Chin Support (28 × 45 mm)	90	3·50

1982. Royal Regalia (4th series). As T **60**. Mult.

320	10c. Royal Mace	25	10
321	15c. Ceremonial Shield and Spears	35	20
322	20c. Embroidered Ornament	45	40
323	30c. Golden-tasseled Cushion	75	1·40
324	50c. Ceremonial Dagger and Sheath	1·25	3·25
325	75c. Religious Mace (28 × 45 mm)	1·60	4·25

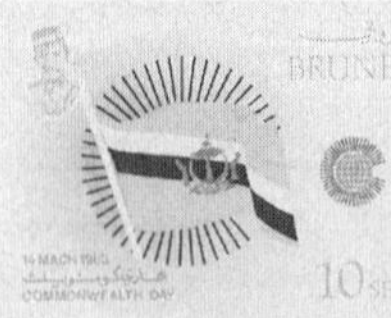

65 Brunei Flag

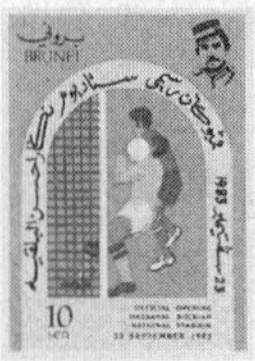

67 Football

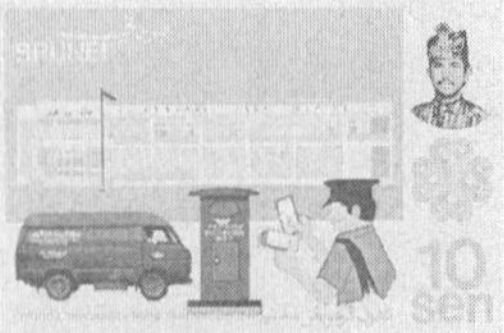

66 "Postal Service"

1983. Commonwealth Day.

326 **65**	10c. multicoloured	15	60
327 –	20c. blue, black and buff	20	70
328 –	75c. blue, black and green	45	1·10
329 –	$2 blue, black and yellow	1·10	1·75

DESIGNS: 20c. Brunei Mosque; 75c. Machinery; $2 Sultan of Brunei.

1983. World Communications Year.

330 **66**	10c. multicoloured	15	10
331 –	75c. yellow, brown and black	60	75
332 –	$2 multicoloured	1·75	2·25

DESIGNS: 75c. "Telephone Service"; $2 "Communications".

1983. Official Opening of the National Hassanal Bolkiah Stadium. Multicoloured.

333	10c. Type **67**	55	15
334	75c. Athletics	2·25	1·50
335	$1 View of stadium (44 × 27 mm)	2·75	4·00

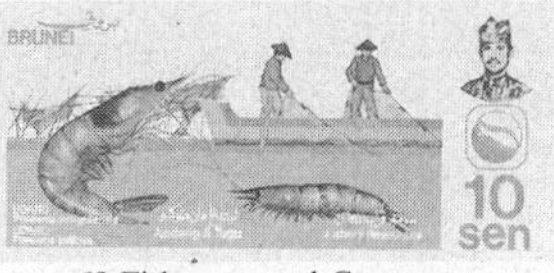

68 Fishermen and Crustacea

1983. Fishery Resources. Multicoloured.

336	10c. Type **68**	90	15
337	50c. Fishermen with net	2·75	1·50
338	75c. Fishing trawler	3·00	3·00
339	$1 Fishing with hook and tackle	3·25	3·75

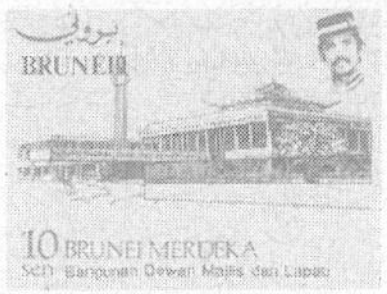

69 Royal Assembly Hall

1984. Independence.

340 **69**	10c. brown and orange	20	10
341 –	20c. pink and red	30	20
342 –	35c. pink and purple	60	60
343 –	50c. light blue and blue	1·75	1·25
344 –	75c. light green and green	1·75	2·00
345 –	$1 grey and brown	2·00	2·50
346 –	$3 multicoloured	6·00	9·00

DESIGNS—34 × 25 mm: 20c. Government Secretariat Building; 35c. New Supreme Court; 50c. Natural gas well; 75c. Omar Ali Saifuddin Mosque; $1 Sultan's Palace. 68 × 24 mm: $3 Brunei flag and map of South-East Asia.

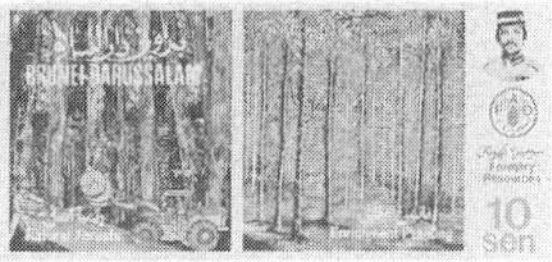

70 Natural Forests and Enrichment Planting

1984. Forestry Resources. Multicoloured.

349	10c. Type **70**	90	25
350	50c. Forests and water resources	2·25	2·25
351	75c. Recreation forests	3·00	4·25
352	$1 Forests and wildlife	4·50	5·50

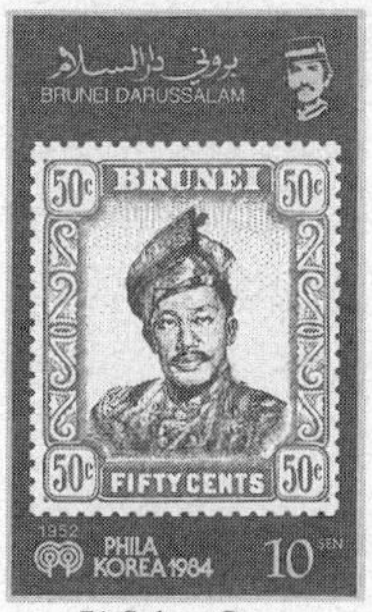

71 Sultan Omar Saiffuddin 50c. Stamp of 1952

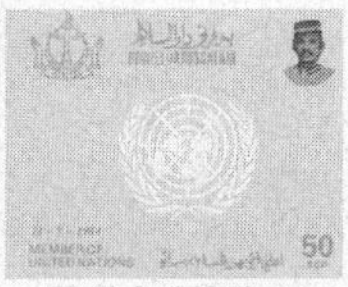

72 United Nations Emblem

1984. "Philakorea" International Stamp Exhibition, Seoul. Multicoloured.

353	10c. Type **71**	50	15
354	75c. Brunei River view 10c.stamp of 1907	1·50	2·25
355	$2 Star and view $\frac{1}{2}$c. stamp of 1895	2·50	6·00

1985. Admission of Brunei to World Organizations (1st issue).

357 **72**	50c. black, gold and blue	50	70
358 –	50c. multicoloured	50	70
359 –	50c. multicoloured	50	70
360 –	50c. multicoloured	50	70

DESIGNS: No. 358, Islamic Conference Organization logo; 359, Commonwealth logo; 360, A.S.E.A.N. emblem.

See also Nos. 383/6.

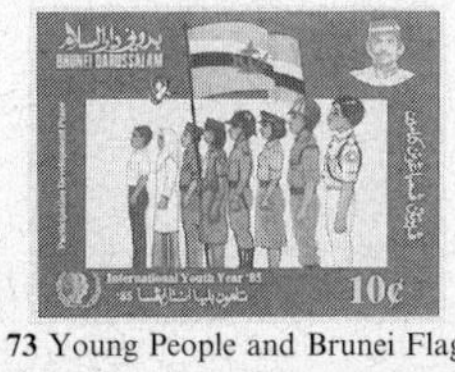

73 Young People and Brunei Flag

1985. International Youth Year. Multicoloured.

362	10c. Type **73**	1·25	20
363	75c. Young people at work	5·00	6·00
364	$1 Young people serving the community	6·00	7·00

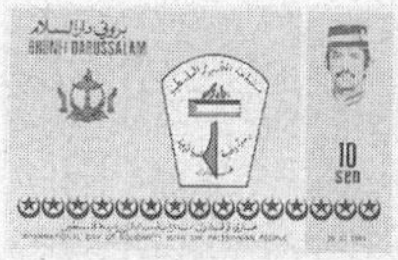

74 Palestinian Emblem

1985. International Palestinian Solidarity Day.

365 **74**	10c. multicoloured	1·50	20
366	50c. multicoloured	3·75	1·50
367	$1 multicoloured	4·50	3·00

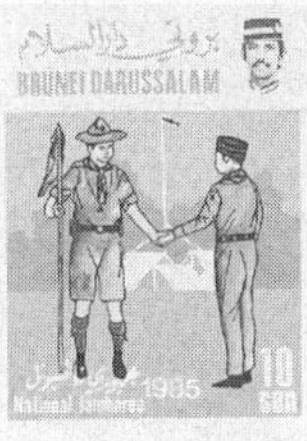

75 Early and Modern Scout Uniforms

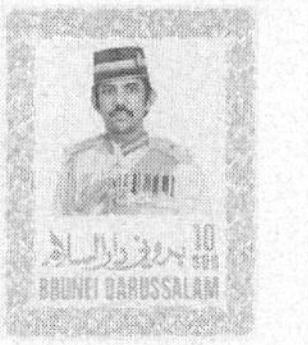

76 Sultan Sir Hassanal Bolkiah Mu'izzaddin Waddaulah

1985. National Scout Jamboree. Multicoloured.

368	10c. Type **75**	60	10
369	20c. Scout on tower signalling with flag	90	40
370	$2 Jamboree emblem	2·75	3·25

1985.

371 **76**	10c. multicoloured	30	10
372	15c. multicoloured	30	10
373	20c. multicoloured	40	10
374	25c. multicoloured	40	15
375	35c. multicoloured	55	20
376	40c. multicoloured	60	25
377	50c. multicoloured	70	35
378	75c. multicoloured	90	50
379	$1 multicoloured	1·25	70
380	$2 multicoloured	2·25	1·75
381	$5 multicoloured	4·25	5·00
382	$10 multicoloured	8·00	11·00

Nos. 379/82 are larger, size 32 × 39 mm.

1986. Admission of Brunei to World Organizations (2nd issue). As T **72**.

383	50c. black, gold and green	50	60
384	50c. black, gold and mauve	50	60
385	50c. black, gold and red	50	60
386	50c. black, gold and blue	50	60

DESIGNS: No. 383, World Meteorological Organization emblem; 384, International Telecommunication Union emblem; 385, Universal Postal Union emblem; 386, International Civil Aviation Organization emblem.

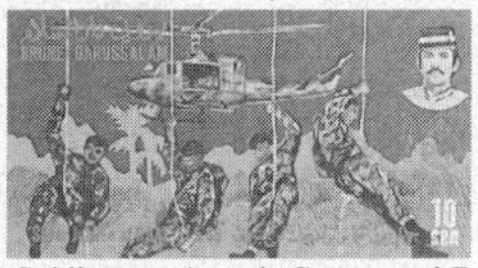

78 Soldiers on Assault Course and Bell 205 Iroquois Helicopter

1986. 25th Anniv of Brunei Armed Forces. Multicoloured.

388	10c. Type **78**	3·25	3·25
389	20c. Operating computer	3·50	3·50
390	50c. Anti-aircraft missile, MBB-Bolkow Bo 150L helicopter and missile boat	4·50	4·50
391	75c. Army, commanders and parade	4·75	4·75

Nos. 388/91 were printed together, se-tenant, forming a composite design.

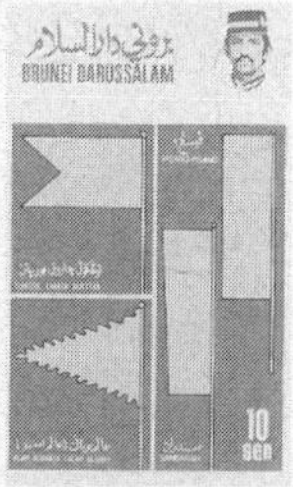

79 Tunggul Charok Buritan, Alam Bernaga (Alam Besar), Pisang-Pisang and Sandaran

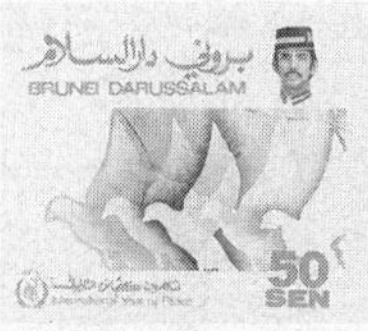

80 Stylized Peace Doves

1986. Royal Ensigns (1st series).

392 **79**	10c. black, yellow and red	30	10
393 –	75c. multicoloured	1·10	1·10
394 –	$2 black, yellow and green	2·25	2·75

DESIGNS: 75c. Ula-Ula Besar, Sumbu Layang and Payong Haram; $2 Panji-Panji, Chogan Istiadat (Chogan Di-Raja) and Chogan Ugama.

1986. Royal Ensigns (2nd series). As T **79**.

395	10c. multicoloured	30	10
396	75c. black, red and yellow	1·10	1·10
397	$2 multicoloured	2·25	2·75

DESIGNS: 10c. Dadap, Tunggul Kawan, Ambal, Payong Ubor-Ubor, Sapu-Sapu Ayeng and Rawai Lidah; 75c. Payong Tinggi and Payong Ubor-Ubor Tiga Ringkat; $2 Lambang Duli Yang Maha Mulia and Mahligai.

1986. International Peace Year. Multicoloured.

398	50c. Type **80**	75	75
399	75c. Stylized hands and "1986"	1·00	1·10
400	$1 International Peace Year emblem and arms of Brunei	1·25	1·50

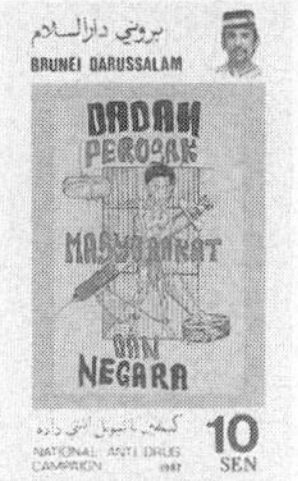

81 Drug Addict in Cage and Syringe (poster by Othman bin Ramboh)

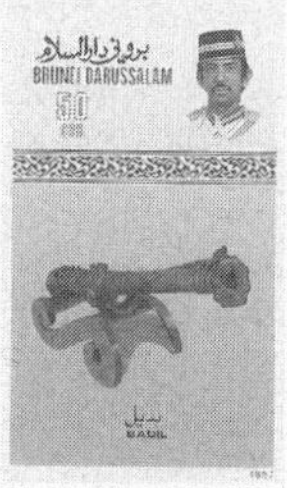

82 Cannon ("badil")

1987. National Anti-drug Campaign. Children's Posters. Multicoloured.

401	10c. Type **81**	1·00	25
402	75c. Drug addict and noose (Arman bin Mohd. Zaman)	2·50	3·75
403	$1 Blindfolded drug addict and noose (Abidin bin Hj. Rashid)	3·00	4·75

1987. Brassware (1st series). Multicoloured.

404	50c. Type **82**	50	50
405	50c. Lamp ("pelita")	50	50
406	50c. Betel container ("langguai")	50	50
407	50c. Water jug ("kiri")	50	50

See also Nos. 434/7.

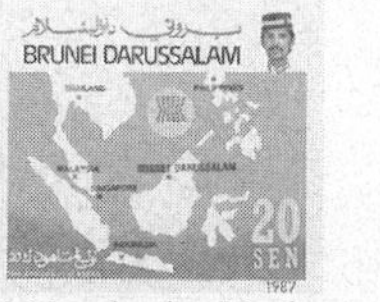

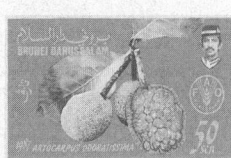

83 Map showing Member Countries

1987. 20th Anniv of Association of South East Asian Nations. Multicoloured.

408	20c. Type **83**	35	20
409	50c. Dates and figures "20"	60	50
410	$1 Flags of member states	1·25	1·25

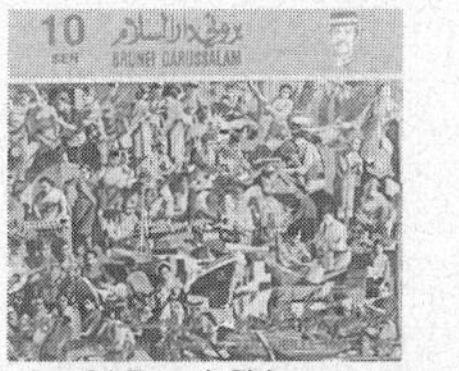

84 Brunei Citizens

1987. 25th Anniv (1986) of Language and Literature Bureau. Multicoloured.

411	10c. Type **84**	30	30
412	50c. Flame emblem and hands holding open book	60	060
413	$2 Scenes of village life	1·50	1·50

Nos. 411/13 were printed together, se-tenant, forming a composite design taken from a mural.

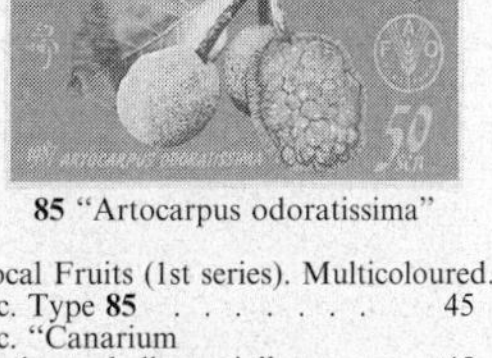

85 "Artocarpus odoratissima"

1987. Local Fruits (1st series). Multicoloured.

414	50c. Type **85**	45	55
415	50c. "Canarium odontophyllum mig"	45	55
416	50c. "Litsea garciae"	45	55
417	50c. "Mangifera foetida lour"	45	55

See also Nos. 421/4, 459/62, 480/2 and 525/8.

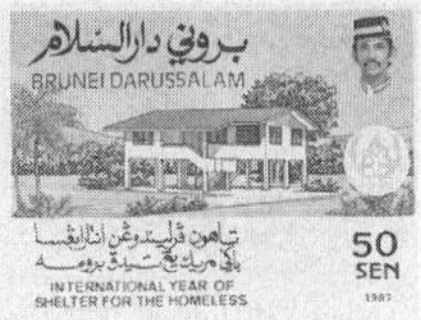

86 Modern House

1987. International Year of Shelter for the Homeless.

418 **86**	50c. multicoloured	40	50
419 –	75c. multicoloured	55	65
420 –	$1 multicoloured	80	90

DESIGNS: 75c., $1 Modern Brunei housing projects.

1988. Local Fruits (2nd series). As T **85**. Mult.

421	50c. "Durio spp"	65	90
422	50c. "Durio oxleyanus"	65	90
423	50c. "Durio graveolens" (blue background)	65	90
424	50c. "Durio graveolens" (white background)	65	90

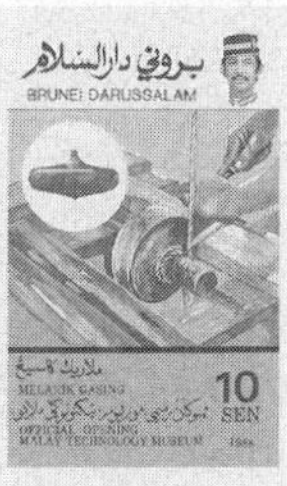

87 Wooden Lathe

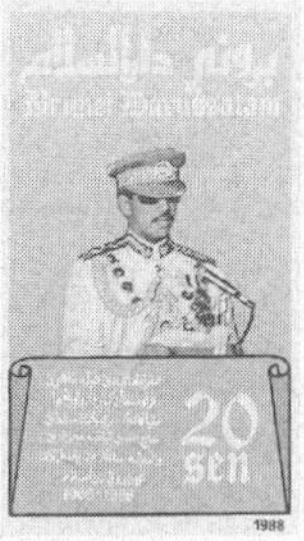

89 Sultan reading Proclamation

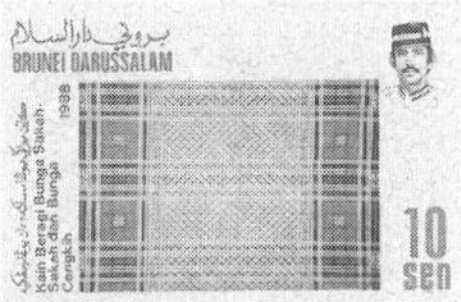

88 Patterned Cloth

1988. Opening of Malay Technology Museum. Multicoloured.

425	10c. Type **87**	15	10
426	75c. Crushing sugar cane	55	70
427	$1 Bird scarer	70	85

1988. Handwoven Material (1st series). Mult.

428	10c. Type **88**	10	10
429	20c. Jong Sarat cloth	15	15
430	25c. Si Pugut cloth	20	25
431	40c. Si Pugut Bunga Berlapis cloth	30	35
432	75c. Si Lobang Bangsi Bunga Belitang Kipas cloth	55	80

See also Nos. 442/6.

1988. Brassware (2nd series). As T **82**. Multicoloured.

434	50c. Lidded two-handled pot ("periok")	40	50
435	50c. Candlestick ("lampong")	40	50
436	50c. Shallow circular dish with stand ("gangsa")	40	50
437	50c. Repousse box with lid ("celapa")	40	50

1988. 20th Anniv of Sultan's Coronation. Mult.

438	20c. Type **89**	15	15
439	75c. Sultan reading from Koran	55	60
440	$2 In Coronation robes (26 × 63 mm)	1·50	1·60

1988. Handwoven Material (2nd series). As T **88**. Multicoloured.

442	10c. Beragi cloth	15	10
443	20c. Bertabur cloth	20	20
444	25c. Sukma Indra cloth	25	25
445	40c. Si Pugut Bunga cloth	40	65
446	75c. Beragi Si Lobang Bangsi Bunga Cendera Kesuma cloth	75	1·25

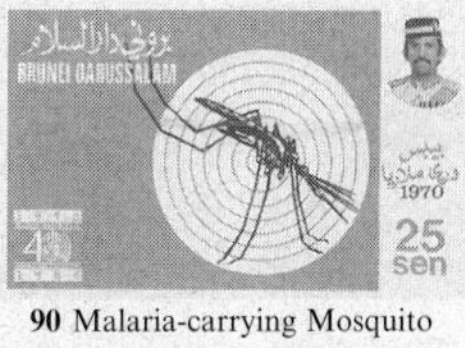

90 Malaria-carrying Mosquito

1988. 40th Anniv of W.H.O. Multicoloured.

448	25c. Type **90**	90	30
449	35c. Man with insecticide spray and sample on slide	1·00	45
450	$2 Microscope and magnified malaria cells	2·75	2·00

91 Sultan and Council of Ministers

1989. 5th Anniv of National Day. Mult.
451　20c. Type **91** . . . . 15　10
452　30c. Guard of honour . . . . 20　15
453　45c. Firework display
　　　　(27 × 55 mm) . . . . . 45　40
454　$2 Congregation in mosque . 1·50　1·75

92 Dove escaping from Cage

1989. "Freedom of Palestine". Multicoloured.
456　20c. Type **92** . . . . 30　20
457　75c. Map and Palestinian flag 90　85
458　$1 Dome of the Rock,
　　　　Jerusalem . . . . 1·10　1·25

1989. Local Fruits (3rd series). As T **85**. Mult.
459　60c. "Daemonorops fissa" . . 2·00　2·25
460　60c. "Eleiodoxa conferta" . . 2·00　2·25
461　60c. "Salacca zalacca" . . . 2·00　2·25
462　60c. "Calamus ornatus". . . 2·00　2·25

93 Oil Pump

1989. 60th Anniv of Brunei Oil and Gas Industry. Multicoloured.
463　20c. Type **93** . . . . 1·75　30
464　60c. Loading tanker . . . . 2·75　2·25
465　90c. Oil well at sunset . . . 3·00　3·00
466　$1 Pipe laying . . . . . . 3·25　3·00
467　$2 Oil terminal . . . . . . 5·75　6·50

94 Museum Building and Exhibits

1990. 25th Anniv of Brunei Museum. Multicoloured.
468　30c. Type **94** . . . . 1·50　70
469　60c. Official opening, 1965 . 2·25　2·25
470　$1 Brunei Museum . . . . 3·00　3·50

95 Letters from Malay Alphabet

1990. International Literacy Year. Multicoloured.
471　15c. Type **95** . . . . 80　40
472　90c. English alphabet . . . 3·25　3·75
473　$1 Literacy Year emblem and
　　　　letters . . . . 3·25　3·75

96 Tarsier in Tree　**97** Symbolic Family

1990. Endangered Species. Western Tarsier. Multicoloured.
474　20c. Western Tarsier on
　　　　branch . . . . 1·25　45
475　60c. Western Tarsier feeding . 2·50　2·75
476　90c. Type **96** . . . . 3·50　4·00

1990. Worldwide Campaign against AIDS. Multicoloured.
477　20c. Type **97** . . . . 1·75　60
478　30c. Sources of infection . . 2·50　1·75
479　90c. "AIDS" headstone
　　　　surrounded by skulls . . 6·25　7·00

1990. Local Fruits (4th series). As T **85**. Mult.
480　60c. "Willoughbea sp."
　　　　(brown fruit) . . . . . 2·75　3·25
481　60c. Ripe "Willoughbea sp."
　　　　(yellow fruit) . . . . . 2·75　3·25
482　60c. "Willoughbea
　　　　angustifolia" . . . . . . 2·75　3·25

98 Proboscis Monkey on Ground

1991. Endangered Species. Proboscis Monkey. Multicoloured.
483　15c. Type **98** . . . . 1·50　60
484　20c. Head of monkey . . . . 1·60　70
485　50c. Monkey sitting on
　　　　branch . . . . 3·00　3·25
486　60c. Female monkey with
　　　　baby climbing tree . . . 3·25　3·75

99 Junior School Classes

1991. Teachers' Day. Multicoloured.
487　60c. Type **99** . . . . 2·25　2·50
488　90c. Secondary school class . 2·75　3·50

100 Young Brunei Beauty

1991. Fishes. Brunei Beauty. Multicoloured.
489　30c. Type **100** . . . . . . 1·50　85
490　60c. Female fish . . . . . . 2·50　3·50
491　$1 Male fish . . . . 3·00　4·00

　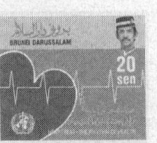

101 Graduate with Family　**102** Symbolic Heart and Trace

1991. Happy Family Campaign. Multicoloured.
492　20c. Type **101** . . . . . . 70　50
493　60c. Mothers with children . 1·75　2·00
494　90c. Family . . . . 2·00　3·25

1992. World Health Day.
495　**102** 20c. multicoloured . . 1·25　50
496　　–　50c. multicoloured . . 2·50　2·25
497　　–　75c. multicoloured . . 3·50　4·50
DESIGNS: 50c., 70c. (48 × 27 mm) Heart and heartbeat trace.

103 Map of Cable System

1992. Launching of Singapore–Borneo–Philippines Fibre Optic Submarine Cable System. Mult.
498　20c. Type **103** . . . . . . 1·75　50
499　30c. Diagram of Brunei
　　　　connection . . . . 1·75　1·25
500　90c. Submarine cable . . . . 3·75　4·50

104 Modern Sculptures

1992. Visit A.S.E.A.N. Year. Multicoloured.
501　20c. Type **104** . . . . . . 1·75　2·00
502　60c. Traditional martial arts . 2·00　2·50
503　$1 Modern sculptures
　　　　(different) . . . . 2·25　2·75
Nos. 501/3 were printed together, se-tenant, the backgrounds forming a composite design.

105 "A.S.E.A.N. 25" and Logo　**106** Sultan in Procession

1992. 25th Anniv of A.S.E.A.N (Association of South East Asian Nations). Multicoloured.
504　20c. Type **105** . . . . . . 1·25　65
505　60c. Headquarters building . 2·75　2·75
506　90c. National landmarks . . 3·50　4·25

1992. 25th Anniv of Sultan's Accession. Mult.
507　25c. Type **106** . . . . . . 1·25　1·40
508　25c. Brunei International
　　　　Airport . . . . 1·25　1·40
509　25c. Sultan's Palace . . . . 1·25　1·40
510　25c. Docks and Brunei
　　　　University . . . . 1·25　1·40
511　25c. Mosque . . . . 1·25　1·40
Nos. 507/11 were printed together, se-tenant, forming a composite design.

107 Crested Wood Partridge　**108** National Flag and "10"

1992. Birds (1st series). Multicoloured.
512　30c. Type **107** . . . . . . 75　50
513　60c. Asiatic paradise
　　　　flycatcher ("Asian Paradise
　　　　Flycatcher") . . . . . . 1·60　2·25
514　$1 Great argus pheasant . . 1·90　3·00
See also Nos. 515/17, 518/20, 575/7 and 602/5.

1993. Birds (2nd series). As T **107**. Multicoloured.
515　30c. Long-tailed parakeet . . 1·00　50
516　60c. Magpie robin . . . . . 2·00　2·25
517　$1 Blue-crowned hanging
　　　　parrot ("Malay Lorikeet") . 2·50　3·00

1993. Birds (3rd series). As T **107**. Multicoloured.
518　30c. Chesnut-breasted
　　　　malkoha . . . . 1·25　50
519　60c. White-rumped shama . . 2·25　2·50
520　$1 Black and red broadbill
　　　　(vert) . . . . 3·00　3·50

1994. 10th Anniv of National Day. Multicoloured.
521　10c. Type **108** . . . . . . 50　70
522　20c. Symbolic hands . . . . 60　75
523　30c. Previous National Day
　　　　symbols . . . . 75　85
524　60c. Coat of arms . . . . . 1·00　1·25

1994. Local Fruits (5th issue). As T **85**, but each 36 × 26 mm. Multicoloured.
525　60c. "Nephelium mutabile" . 85　1·40
526　60c. "Nephelium
　　　　xerospermoides" . . . . 85　1·40
527　60c. "Nephelium spp" . . . 85　1·40
528　60c. "Nephelium
　　　　macrophyllum" . . . . . 85　1·40

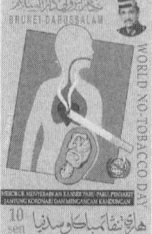

109 Cigarette burning Heart and Deformed Baby in Womb　**110** Raja Isteri (wife of Sultan in Guide uniform)

1994. World No Tobacco Day. Multicoloured.
529　10c. Type **109** . . . . . . 25　20
530　15c. Symbols of smoking
　　　　over crowd of people . . . 25　20
531　$2 Globe crushing cigarettes . 2·75　4·00

1994. 40th Anniv of Brunei Girl Guides' Association. Multicoloured.
532　40c. Type **110** . . . . . . 90　1·25
533　40c. Guide receiving award . 90　1·25
534　40c. Guide reading . . . . . 90　1·25
535　40c. Group of guides . . . . 90　1·25
536　40c. Guides erecting tent . . 90　1·25

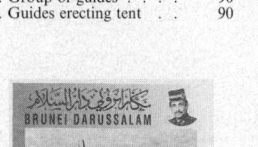

111 Turbo-prop Airliner on Runway

1994. 20th Anniv of Royal Brunei Airlines. Multicoloured.
537　10c. Type **111** . . . . . . 55　20
538　20c. Jet airliner on runway . 85　35
539　$1 Jet airliner in the air . . . 2·00　3·00

112 Malay Family　**113** Aerial View of City, 1970

1994. International Day against Drug Abuse and Trafficking. Multicoloured.
540　20c. Type **112** . . . . . . 70　1·00
541　60c. Chinese family . . . . . 1·10　1·40
542　$1 Doctor, police officers and
　　　　members of youth
　　　　organizations . . . . . . 1·50　1·75
Nos. 540/2 were printed together, se-tenant, forming a composite design.

1995. 25th Anniv of Bandar Seri Begawan. Mult.
543　30c. Type **113** . . . . . . 65　45
544　50c. City in 1980 . . . . . . 1·00　1·00
545　$1 City in 1990 . . . . . . 1·75　2·50

114 United Nations General Assembly　**115** Students in Laboratory

1995. 50th Anniv of United Nations. Multicoloured.
546　20c. Type **114** . . . . . . 40　25
547　60c. Security Council in
　　　　session . . . . 75　80
548　90c. United Nations Building,
　　　　New York (27 × 44 mm) . 1·25　2·00

1995. 10th Anniv of University of Brunei. Mult.
549　30c. Type **115** . . . . . . 45　35
550　50c. University building . . . 70　70
551　90c. Sultan visiting University 1·25　2·00

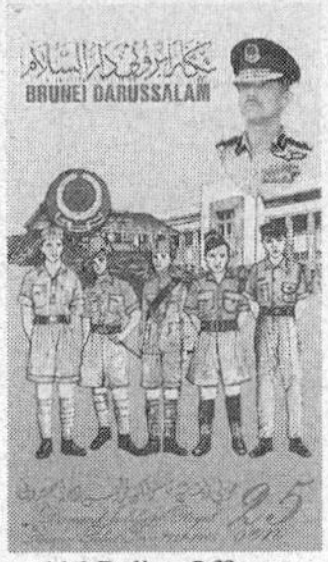

116 Police Officers

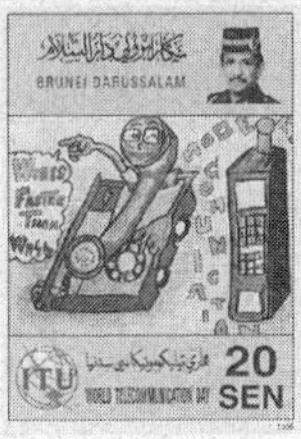

117 Telephones

1996. 75th Anniv of Royal Brunei Police Force. Multicoloured.

552	25c. Type **116**	75	40
553	50c. Aspects of police work	1·10	1·10
554	75c. Sultan inspecting parade	1·75	2·50

1996. World Telecommunications Day. Children's Paintings. Multicoloured.

555	20c. Type **117**	50	30
556	35c. Telephone dial and aspects of telecommunications	65	45
557	$1 Globe and aspects of telecommunications	2·00	2·50

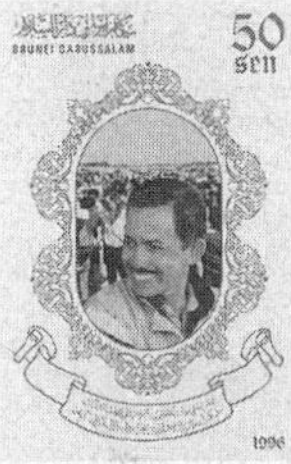

118 Sultan and Crowd

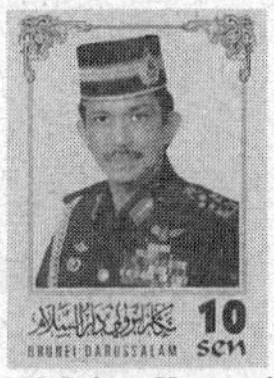

119 Sultan Hassanal Bolkiah Mu'izzaddin Waddaulah

1996. 50th Birthday of Sultan Hassanal Bolkiah Mu'izzaddin Waddaulah. Multicoloured.

558	50c. Type **118**	75	1·00
559	50c. Sultan in ceremonial dress	75	1·00
560	50c. Sultan receiving dignitaries at mosque	75	1·00
561	50c. Sultan with subjects	75	1·00

1996.

563 **119**	10c. multicoloured	10	15
564	15c. multicoloured	10	15
565	20c. multicoloured	15	20
566	30c. multicoloured	25	30
567	50c. multicoloured	40	45
568	60c. multicoloured	45	50
569	75c. multicoloured	60	65
570	90c. multicoloured	70	75
571 –	$1 multicoloured	80	85
572 –	$2 multicoloured	1·50	1·60
573 –	$5 multicoloured	3·75	4·00
574 –	$10 multicoloured	7·50	7·75

DESIGN—27 × 39 mm: $1 to $10 Sultan in ceremonial robes.

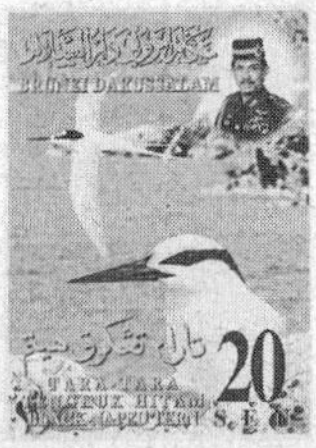

121 Black-naped Tern

1996. Birds (4th series). Sea Birds. Multicoloured.

575	20c. Type **121**	65	40
576	30c. Roseate tern	65	50
577	$1 Bridled tern	1·50	2·25

No. 576 is inscr "ROSLATE TERN" in error.

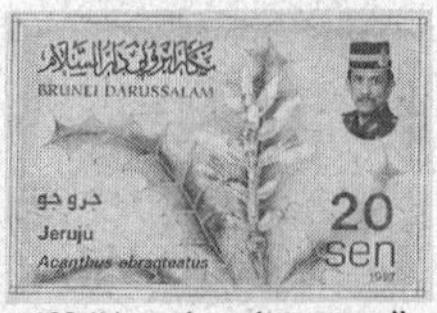

122 "Acanthus ebracteatus"

1997. Mangrove Flowers. Multicoloured.

578	20c. Type **122**	35	25
579	30c. "Lumnitzera littorea"	45	35
580	$1 "Nypa fruticans"	1·25	1·75

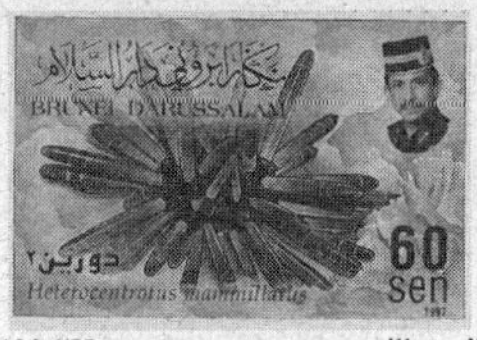

123 "Heterocentrotus mammillatus"

1997. Marine Life. Multicoloured.

581	60c. Type **123**	60	75
582	60c. "Linckia laevigata" (starfish)	60	75
583	60c. "Oxycomanthus bennetti" (plant)	60	75
584	60c. "Bohadschia argus" (sea slug)	60	75

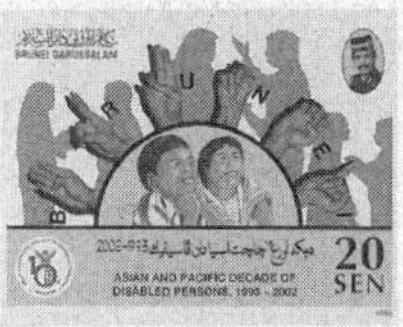

124 Children and Sign Language

1998. Asian and Pacific Decade of Disabled Persons, 1993–2002. Multicoloured.

585	20c. Type **124**	30	25
586	50c. Woman typing and firework display	60	60
587	$1 Disabled athletes	1·00	1·40

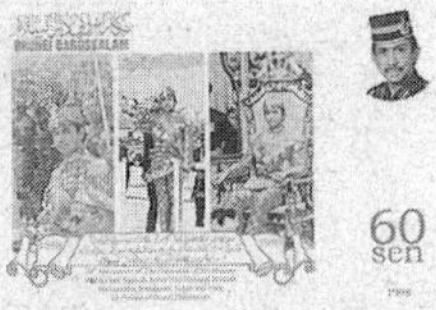

125 Sultan performing Ceremonial Duties

1998. 30th Anniv of Coronation of Sultan Hassanal Bolkiah Mu'izzaddin Waddaulah. Multicoloured.

588	60c. Type **125**	60	50
589	90c. Sultan on Coronation throne	90	1·25
590	$1 Coronation parade	1·00	1·25

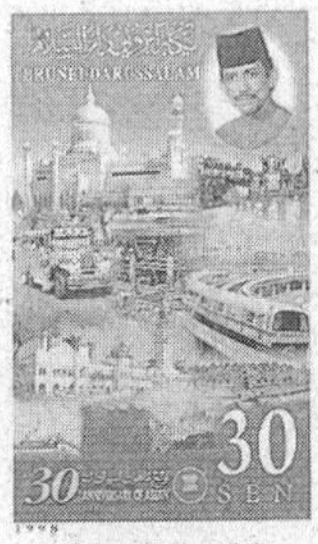

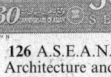

126 A.S.E.A.N. Architecture and Transport

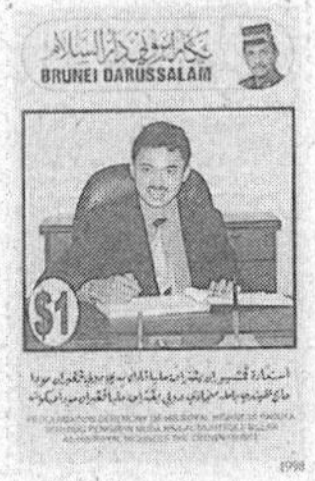

127 Crown Prince at Desk

1998. 30th Anniv of Association of South-east Asian Nations. Multicoloured.

592	30c. Type **126**	60	60
593	30c. Map of Brunei and city scenes	60	60
594	30c. Flags of member nations	60	60

1998. Proclamation of Prince Al-Muhtadee Billah as Crown Prince. Multicoloured.

595	$1 Type **127**	1·00	1·00
596	$2 Crown Prince in military uniform	1·75	2·50
597	$3 Crown Prince's emblem	2·25	3·50

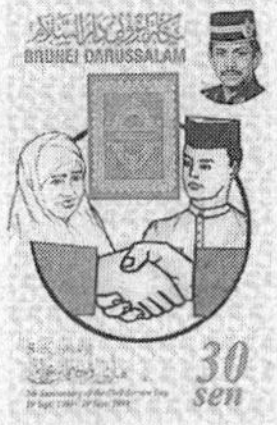

128 Koran, Civil Servants and Handshake

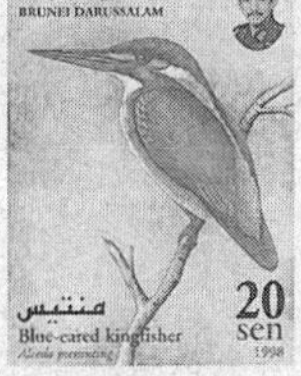

129 Blue-eared Kingfisher

1998. 5th Anniv of Civil Service Day. Multicoloured.

599	30c. Type **128**	40	30
600	60c. Symbols of progress	65	65
601	90c. Civil servants at work	95	1·25

1998. Birds (5th series). Kingfishers. Multicoloured.

602	20c. Type **129**	60	40
603	30c. River kingfisher ("Common Kingfisher")	70	40
604	60c. White-collared kingfisher	1·00	85
605	$1 Stork-billed kingfisher	1·25	1·50

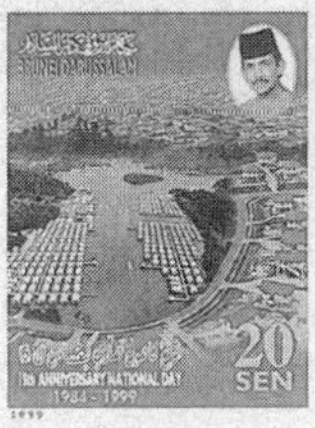

130 Water Village, Bandar Seri Begawan

1999. 15th Anniv of National Day. Multicoloured.

606	20c. Type **130**	30	20
607	60c. Modern telecommunications and air travel	80	80
608	90c. Aspects of modern Brunei	1·25	1·50

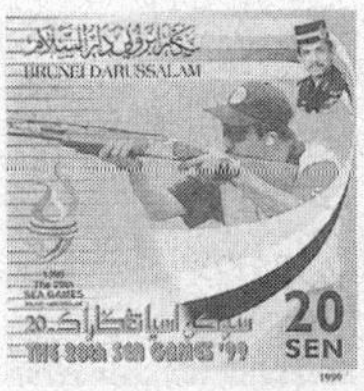

131 Rifle-shooting

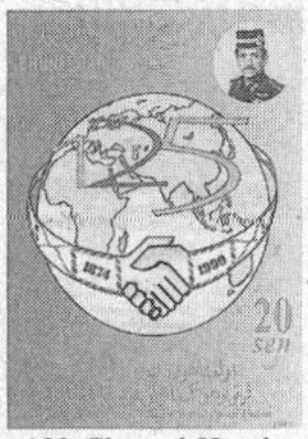

132 Clasped Hands and Globe

1999. 20th South-east Asia Games, Brunei. Mult.

610	20c. Type **131**	30	35
611	20c. Golf and tennis	30	35
612	20c. Boxing and judo	30	35
613	20c. Squash and table tennis	30	35
614	20c. Swimming and canoe racing	30	35
615	20c. Hockey and cycling	30	35
616	20c. Basketball and football	30	35
617	20c. High jumping, shot putting and running	30	35
618	20c. Snooker	30	35
619	20c. Bowling	30	35

1999. 125th Anniv of Universal Postal Union. Multicoloured.

621	20c. Type **132**	30	20
622	30c. "125" and logos	40	25
623	75c. Aspects of postal service	85	1·00

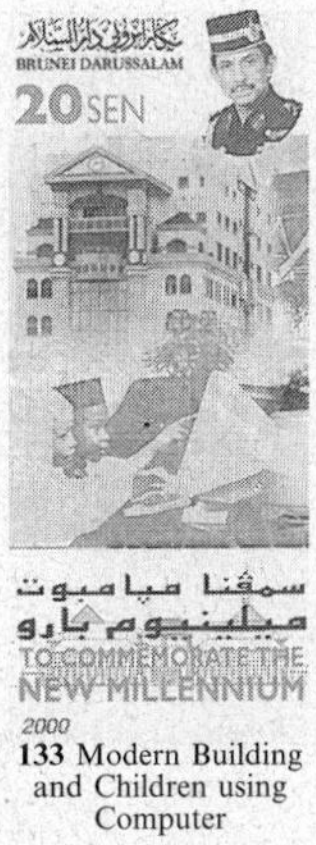

133 Modern Building and Children using Computer

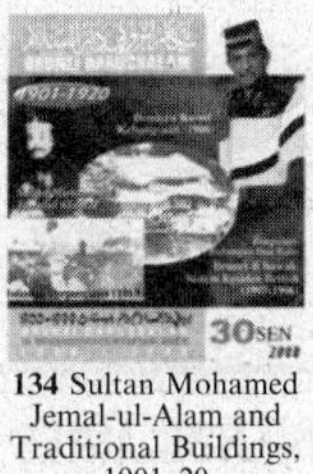

134 Sultan Mohamed Jemal-ul-Alam and Traditional Buildings, 1901–20

2000. New Millennium. Multicoloured.

624	20c. Type **133**	25	30
625	20c. Royal Palace, tree and people using computer	25	30
626	20c. Aerial view of mosque and factory	25	30
627	20c. Plan of Parterre Gardens	25	30
628	20c. Container ships and airliner	25	30
629	20c. Satellite dish aerials	25	30

Nos. 624/9 were printed together, se-tenant, with the backgrounds forming a composite design.

2000. Brunei in the 20th Century. Multicoloured.

631	30c. Type **134**	35	40
632	30c. Sultan Ahmed Tajudin, oil well and Brunei police, 1921–40	35	40
633	30c. Signing of the Constitution and Brunei Mosque, 1941–60	35	40
634	30c. Oil installation, satellite dish, Royal Brunei Airlines and bank note, 1961–80	35	40
635	30c. Sultan on throne, international organisation emblems and crowd with trophy, 1981–99	35	40

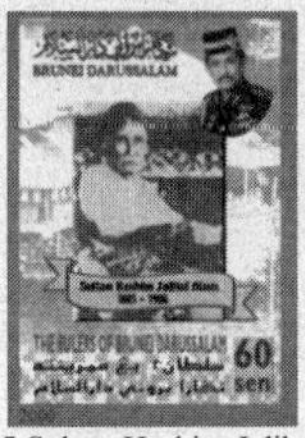

135 Sultan Hashim Jalil-ul-Alam, 1885–1906

2000. The Sultans of Brunei. Multicoloured.

636	60c. Type **135**	65	70
637	60c. Sultan Mohamed Jemal-ul-Alam, 1906–24	65	70
638	60c. Sultan Ahmed Tajudin, 1924–50	65	70
639	60c. Sultan Omar Ali Saifuddin, 1950–67	65	70
640	60c. Sultan Hassanal Bolkiah, 1967	65	70

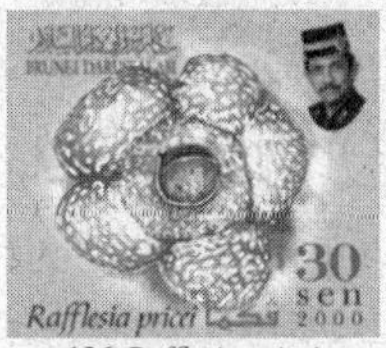

136 *Rafflesia pricei*

2000. Local Flowers. Multicoloured.

642	30c. Type **136**	35	30
643	50c. *Rhizanthes lowi*	55	55
644	60c. *Nepenthes rafflesiana*	65	70

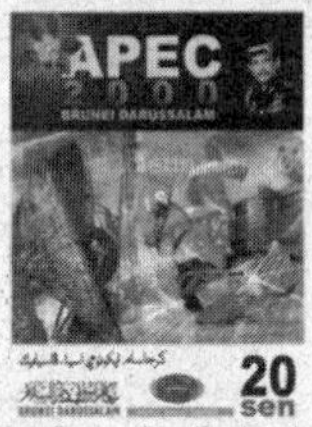

137 Information Technology

2000. Asia–Pacific Economic Cooperation. Heads of Government Meeting. Multicoloured.

645	20c. Type **137**	30	25
646	30c. Small and medium businesses	35	30
647	60c. Tourism	65	75

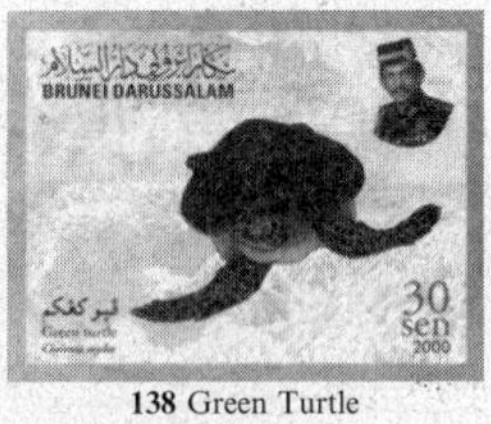

138 Green Turtle

2000. Turtles. Multicoloured.

649	30c. Type **138**	35	40
650	30c. Hawksbill turtle	35	40
651	30c. Olive Ridley turtle	35	40

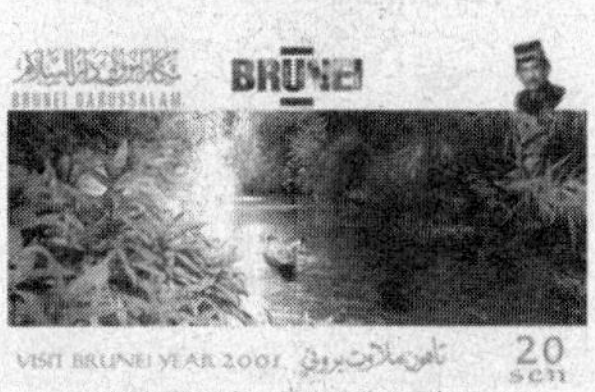

139 Tourist Canoe on River

2001. "Visit Brunei Year" (1st series). Multicoloured.

652	20c. Type **139**	30	25
653	30c. Traditional water village	35	30
654	60c. Carved building facade	65	75

See also Nos. 669/72

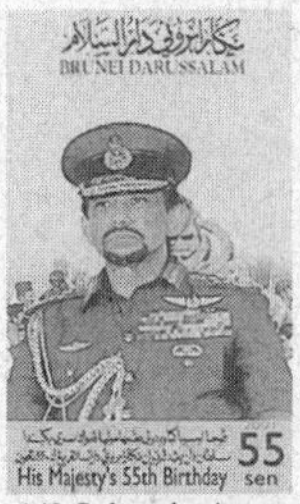

140 Sultan in Army Uniform

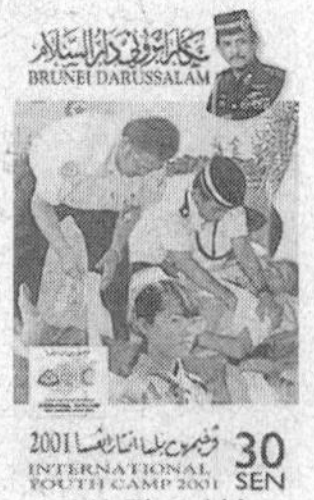

141 First Aid Demonstration

2001. 55th Birthday of Sultan Hassanal Bolkiah Muizzaddin Waddaulah. Multicoloured.

655	55c. Type **140**	40	45

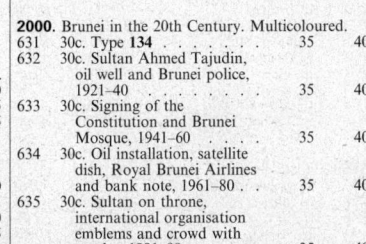

656		55c. Sultan in Air Force uniform	40	45
657		55c. Sultan in traditional dress	40	45
658		55c. Sultan in Army camouflage jacket	40	45
659		55c. Sultan in Navy uniform	40	45

2001. International Youth Camp. Multicoloured.

661		30c. Type **141**	25	30
662		30c. Brunei guides and tent demonstration	25	30
663		30c. Scouts with cooking pot	25	30

Nos. 661/3 were printed together, se-tenant, forming a composite design.

142 Islamic Regalia

2001. 1st Islamic International Exhibition, Brunei. Multicoloured.

665		20c. Type **142**	15	20
666		20c. Exhibition centre	15	20
667		20c. Computer communications	15	20
668		20c. Opening ceremony	15	20

143 Forest Walkway

2001. Visit Brunei (2nd series). Multicoloured.

669		20c. Type **143**	15	20
670		20c. Waterfall	15	20
671		20c. Jerudong Theme Park	15	20
672		20c. Footbridges across lake	15	20

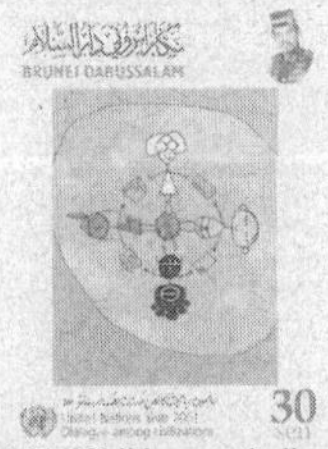

144 "Children encircling Globe" (Urska Golob)

2001. U.N. Year of Dialogue among Civilisations. Multicoloured.

673		30c. Type **144**	25	30
674		30c. Quotation marks illustrated with faces	25	30
675		30c. Cubist portrait and Japanese girl	25	30
676		30c. Coloured leaves	25	30

145 Male and Female Bulwer's Pheasants

2001. Endangered Species. Bulwer's Pheasant. Multicoloured.

677		30c. Type **145**	25	30
678		30c. Male pheasant	25	30
679		30c. Female pheasant with chicks	25	30
680		30c. Female pheasant	25	30

JAPANESE OCCUPATION OF BRUNEI

These stamps were valid throughout British Borneo (i.e. in Brunei, Labuan, North Borneo and Sarawak).

100 cents = 1 dollar.

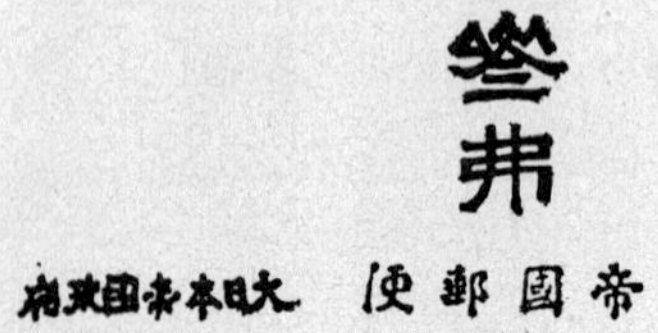

(1) ("Imperial Japanese Government") (2) ("Imperial Japanese Postal Service $3")

1942. Stamps of Brunei optd with T **1**.

J 1	**5**	1c. black	6·00	23·00
J 2		2c. green	50·00	£110
J 3		2c. orange	3·50	9·00
J 4		3c. green	28·00	75·00
J 5		4c. orange	3·00	13·00
J 6		5c. brown	3·00	13·00
J 7	**7**	6c. grey	40·00	£200
J 8		6c. red	£550	£550
J 9	**5**	8c. black	£650	£850
J10	**7**	8c. red	4·00	12·00
J11	**5**	10c. purple on yellow	8·50	26·00
J12	**7**	12c. blue	24·00	26·00
J13		15c. blue	13·00	26·00
J14	**5**	25c. lilac	23·00	50·00
J15		30c. purple and orange	95·00	£180
J16		50c. black on green	38·00	60·00
J17		$1 black and red on blue	55·00	70·00
J18		$5 red on green	£850	£1800
J19		$25 black on red	£900	£1800

1944. No. J1 surch with T **2**.

J20	**5**	$3 on 1c. black	£6000	£5500

BRUNSWICK — Pt. 7

Formerly a duchy of N. Germany. Joined North German Confederation in 1868.

30 silbergroschen = 1 thaler.

1

1852. Imperf.

1	**1**	1sg. red	£4500	£250
2		2sg. blue	£2750	£200
3		3sg. red	£2750	£200

1853. Imperf.

4	**1**	¼gg. black on brown	£500	£250
5		⅓gg. black	£110	£300
15		½sg. black on green	22·00	£200
7		1sg. black on buff	£250	55·00
8		2sg. black on blue	£225	£140
11		3sg. black on red	£325	65·00

3

4

1857. Imperf

12	**3**	4/4gg. black on brown	30·00	85·00

1864. Rouletted

22	**1**	⅓gg. black	£400	£1700
23		½sg. black on green	£180	£2250
24		1sg. black on yellow	£2250	£1300
25		1sg. yellow	£300	£120
26		2sg. black on blue	£300	£275
27		3sg. pink	£650	£450

1865. Roul.

28	**4**	⅓g. black	25·00	£325
29		1g. red	2·00	40·00
32		2g. blue	7·00	£100
34		3g. brown	5·75	£130

BUENOS AIRES — Pt. 20

A province of the Argentine Republic. Issued its own stamps from 1858 to 1862.

8 reales = 1 peso.

1 Paddle Steamer

2 Head of Liberty

1858. Imperf.

P13	**1**	4r. brown	£100	80·00
P17		1 (IN) p. brown	£125	80·00
P20		1 (IN) p. blue	65·00	50·00
P25		1 (TO) p. blue	£150	£100
P 1		2p. blue	90·00	50·00
P 4		3p. green	£450	£250
P 7		4p. red	£1500	£900
P10		5p. yellow	£1500	£900

1859. Imperf.

P37	**2**	4r. green on blue	90·00	50·00
P38		1p. blue	12·00	7·50
P45		1p. red	60·00	30·00
P43		2p. red	£120	80·00
P48		2p. blue	£120	45·00

BULGARIA — Pt. 3

Formerly a Turkish province; a principality under Turkish suzerainty from 1878 to 1908, when an independent kingdom was proclaimed. A People's Republic since 1946.

1879. 100 centimes = 1 franc.
1881. 100 stotinki = 1 lev.

1 Large Lion

2 Large Lion

1879. Value in centimes and franc.

1	**1**	5c. black and yellow	85·00	25·00
3		10c. black and green	£375	75·00
5		25c. black and purple	£200	20·00
7		50c. black and blue	£350	80·00
8		1f. black and red	50·00	22·00

1881. Value in stotinki.

10	**2**	3s. red and grey	17·00	3·50
11		5s. black and yellow	17·00	3·50
14		10s. black and green	85·00	10·00
15		15s. red and green	85·00	10·00
18		25s. black and purple	£400	50·00
19		30s. blue and brown	17·00	10·00

See also No. 275/9.

A

B

C

D

1882.

46	**2**	1s. violet (Type A)	12·50	5·00
48		1s. violet (Type C)	85	20
47		2s. green (Type B)	11·50	3·75
49		2s. green (Type D)	85	20
21		3s. orange and yellow	85	35
23		5s. green	6·75	75
26		10s. red	8·50	75
28		15s. purple and mauve	6·75	50
31		25s. blue	6·75	90
33		30s. lilac and green	7·00	85
34		50s. blue and red	7·00	1·00
50		1l. black and red	30·00	4·00

1884. Surch with large figure of value.

38	**2**	3 on 10s. red	45·00	35·00
43		5 on 30s. blue and brown	45·00	40·00
45		15 on 25s. blue	65·00	50·00
40		50 on 1f. black and red	£300	£190

7

11 Arms of Bulgaria

13 Cherry wood Cannon used against the Turks

1889.

85	**7**	1s. mauve	10	10
88		2s. grey	45	20
89		3s. brown	15	10
90		5s. green	15	10
94		10s. red	50	10
96		15s. orange	35	10
100		25s. blue	50	10
58		30s. brown	4·00	10
59		50s. green	50	10
60		1l. red	45	40
83		2l. red and pink	1·60	1·40
84		3l. black and buff	3·25	2·75

1892. Surch **15**.

61	**7**	15 on 30s. brown	8·50	70

1895. Surch **01**.

74	**2a**	01 on 2s. green (No. 49)	65	15

1896. Baptism of Prince Boris.

78	**11**	1s. green	35	15
79		5s. blue	35	15
81		15s. violet	45	15
82		25s. red	4·00	30

1901. Surch in figures.

101	**7**	5 on 3s. brown	1·60	70
103		10 on 50s. green	1·60	90

1901. 25th Anniv of Uprising against Turkey.

104	**13**	5s. red	1·00	85
105		15s. green	1·00	85

14 Prince Ferdinand

16 Fighting at Shipka Pass

1901.

106	**14**	1s. black and purple	10	10
107		2s. blue and green	20	10
108		3s. black and orange	20	10
109		5s. brown and green	1·00	10
110		10s. brown and red	1·25	10
113		15s. black and lake	65	10
114		25s. black and blue	65	10
116		30s. black and brown	18·00	50
117		50s. brown and blue	1·00	15
118		1l. green and red	2·00	15
120		2l. black and red	3·75	50
123		3l. red and grey	4·50	85

1902. 25th Anniv of Battle of Shipka Pass.

124	**16**	5s. red	1·25	50
125		10s. green	1·25	50
126		15s. blue	4·50	1·75

1903. Surch.

140	**15**	5 on 15s. black and red	1·25	75
141		10 on 15s. black and red	2·50	40
143		25 on 30s. black & brown	7·50	90

18 Ferdinand I in 1887 and 1907

1907. 20th Anniv of Prince Ferdinand's Accession.

132	**18**	5s. green	7·00	90
134		10s. brown	12·50	90
137		25s. blue	24·00	1·90

1909. Optd **1909**.

146	**7**	1s. mauve	1·00	45
149		5s. green	1·00	45

1909. Surch **1909** and new value.

151	**7**	5 on 30s. brown	1·50	35
153		10 on 15s. orange	11·50	50
156		10 on 50s. green	1·50	55

1910. Surch **1910** and new value.

157	**14**	1 on 3s. black and orange	3·50	75
158		5 on 15s. black and lake	1·00	60

23 King Asen Tower

24 Tsar in General's Uniform

25 Veliko Turnovo

1911.

159	**23**	1s. green	10	10
182a		1s. slate	10	10
160	**24**	2s. black and red	10	10
161	**25**	3s. black and lake	1·50	25
162	–	5s. black and green	60	10
181	–	5s. purple and green	1·25	10
163	–	10s. black and red	55	10
181a	–	10s. sepia and brown	10	10
164	–	15s. bistre	7·50	30
183	–	15s. olive	1·00	30
165	–	25s. black and blue	30	10
166	–	30s. black and blue	2·75	15
182	–	30s. brown and olive	1·00	30
167	–	50s. black and yellow	16·00	15
168	–	1l. brown	4·25	15
169	–	2l. black and purple	1·00	60
170	–	3l. black and violet	9·00	2·75

DESIGNS—VERT: 5, 10, 25s., 1l. Portraits of Tsar Ferdinand. HORIZ: 15s. R. Isker; 30s. Rila Monastery; 50s. Tsars and Princes (after Ya. Veshin); 2l. Monastery of the Holy Trinity, Veliko Turnovo; 3l. Varna.

See also Nos. 229/30 and 236/7.

35 Tsar Ferdinand

1912. Tsar's Silver Jubilee

171	**35**	5s. grey	2·25	65
172		10s. red	3·50	1·25
173		25s. blue	4·50	1·90

ОСВОБ. ВОЙНА

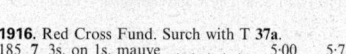

1912-1913

(**36**) "War of Liberation" 1912–13

3 СТОТИНКИ

(**37a**)

1913. Victory over Turks. Stamps of 1911 optd as T **36**.

174	**23**	1s. green	25	10
175	**24**	2s. black and red	25	10
176	**25**	3s. black and lake	90	40
177	–	5s. black and green	25	10
178	–	10s. black and red	30	10
179	–	15s. bistre	2·75	75
180	–	25s. black and blue	1·75	40

1915. No. 165 surch **10 CT.** and bar.

180a	–	10s. on 25s. blk & blue	45	10

1916. Red Cross Fund. Surch with T **37a**.

185	**7**	3s. on 1s. mauve	5·00	5·75

45 Veles

46 Bulgarian Ploughman

38

39 Bulgarian Peasant

1917. Liberation of Macedonia.

193	**45**	1s. grey	10	10
194	**46**	1s. green	10	10
195	–	5s. green	10	10
186	**38**	5s. green	45	20
187	**39**	15s. grey	15	15
188	–	25s. blue	15	15
189	–	30s. orange	15	20
190	–	50s. violet	45	30
191	–	2l. brown	50	30
192	–	3l. red	75	45

DESIGNS—As Type **45**: 5s. Monastery of St. John, Ohrid. As Type **38**: 25s. Soldier and Mt. Sonichka; 50s. Ohrid and Lake. As Type **39**: 30s. Nish. 2l. Demir Kapija; 3l. Gevgeli.

48 Tsar Ferdinand

1918. 30th Anniv of Tsar's Accession.

196	**48**	1s. slate	10	10
197		2s. brown	10	10
198		3s. blue	25	20
199		10s. red	25	20

49 Parliament Building

50 King Boris III

1919.

201	**49**	1s. black	10	10
202		2s. olive	10	10

1919. 1st Anniv of Enthronement of King Boris III.

203	**50**	3s. red	10	10
204		5s. green	10	10
205		10s. red	10	10
206		15s. violet	10	10
207		25s. blue	10	10
208		30s. brown	10	10
209		50s. brown	10	10

ЗА НАШИТЬ ПЛѢННИЦИ 2½

(**52**)

ЗА НАШИТЬ ПЛѢННИЦИ 50

(**53**)

1920. Prisoners of War Fund. Surch as T **52/53**.

210	**49**	1 on 2s. olive	10	10
211	**50**	2½ on 5s. green	10	10
212		5 on 10s. red	10	10
213		7½ on 15s. violet	10	10
214		12½ on 25s. blue	10	10
215		15 on 30s. brown	10	10
216		25 on 50s. brown	10	10
217	–	50 on 1l. brown (No. 168)	10	10
218	–	1 on 2l. brown (No. 191)	15	15
219	–	1½ on 3l. red (No. 192)	30	35

54 Vazov's Birthplace at Sopot and Cherry-wood Cannon

55 "The Bear-fighter", character from "Under the Yoke"

1920. 70th Birth Anniv of Ivan Vazov (writer).

220	**54**	30s. red	10	10
221	**55**	50s. green	10	10
222	–	1l. sepia	20	15
223	–	2l. brown	60	40
224	–	3l. violet	75	60
225	–	5l. blue	95	75

DESIGNS—HORIZ: 1l. Ivan Vazov in 1870 and 1920; 3l. Vazov's Houses in Plovdiv and Sofia. VERT: 2l. Vazov; 5l. Father Paisii Khilendarski (historian).

59 Aleksandr Nevski Cathedral, Sofia

62 King Boris III

1921.

226	**59**	10s. violet	10	10
227	–	20s. green	10	10
228	**62**	25s. blue	10	10
229	**25**	50s. orange	75	20
230		50s. blue	8·50	2·50
231	–	75s. violet	10	10
232	–	75s. blue	20	10
233	**62**	1l. red	15	10
234		1l. blue	10	10
235	–	2l. brown	25	10
236	–	3l. purple	45	10
237	–	5l. blue	2·00	30
238	**62**	10l. red	6·75	2·25

DESIGNS—HORIZ: 20s. Alexander II "The Liberator" Monument, Sofia; 75s. Shipka Pass Monastery; 5l. Rila Monastery. VERT: 2l. Harvester; 3l. King Asen Tower.

66 Tsar Ferdinand and Map

68 Mt. Shar

1921.

239	**66**	10s. red	10	10
240	–	10s. red	10	10
241	**68**	10s. red	10	10
242	–	10s. mauve	15	10
243	–	20s. blue	45	10

DESIGNS—VERT: No. 240, Tsar Ferdinand. HORIZ: No. 242, Bridge over Vardar, at Skopje; 243, St. Clement's Monastery, Ohrid.

71 Bourchier in Bulgarian Costume

72 J. D. Bourchier

73 Rila Monastery, Bourchier's Resting-place

1921. James Bourchier ("Times" Correspondent) Commemoration.

244	**71**	10s. red	10	10
245		20s. orange	10	10
246	**72**	30s. grey	10	10
247		50s. lilac	10	10
248		1l. purple	20	10
249	**73**	1½l. green	20	20
250		2l. green	20	10
251		3l. blue	45	20
252		5l. red	75	30

1924. Surch.

253	**49**	10s. on 1s. black	10	10
254	D **37**	10s. on 20s. orange	10	10
255		20s. on 5s. green	5·00	5·00
256		20s. on 10s. violet	1·40	1·40
257		20s. on 30s. orange	10	10
258	**50**	1l. on 5s. green	15	10
259	**25**	3l. on 50s. blue	1·10	40
260	**62**	6l. on 1l. red	50	30

77

78

79 King Boris III

81 Aleksandr Nevski Cathedral, Sofia

82 Harvesters

83 Proposed Rest-home, Verona

1925.

261	**77**	10s. blue & red on rose	10	10
262		15s. orange & red on blue	10	10
263		30s. buff and black	10	10
264	**78**	50s. brown on green	15	10
265	**79**	1l. olive	35	10
266		1l. green	50	10
267	**81**	2l. green and buff	85	10
267a	**79**	2l. brown	40	10
268	**82**	4l. red and yellow	75	10

1925. Sunday Delivery Stamps.

268b	**83**	1l. black on green	2·75	15
268c		1l. brown	2·50	15
268d		1l. orange	3·50	15
268e		1l. pink	3·50	15
268f		1l. violet on red	3·50	15
268g	–	2l. green	40	15
268h	–	2l. violet	40	20
268i	–	5l. blue	3·75	45
268j	–	5l. red	40	45

DESIGN: 2, 5l., Proposed Sanatorium, Bankya.

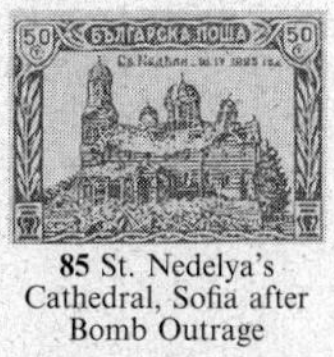

85 St. Nedelya's Cathedral, Sofia after Bomb Outrage

86 C. Botev (poet)

1926.

269	**85**	50s. black	10	10

1926. Botev Commemoration.

270	**86**	1l. green	30	15
271		2l. blue	65	15
272		4l. red	65	50

87

89 King Boris III

90 Saint Clement of Ohrid

1926.

273	**87**	6l. olive and blue	75	20
274		10l. brown and sepia	3·00	75

1927. As T **2** in new colours.

275		10s. red and green	10	10
276		15s. black and yellow	15	10
277		30s. slate and buff	10	10
278		30s. blue and buff	15	10
279		50s. black and red	15	10

1927. Air. Various stamps optd with Albatros biplane and No. 281 surch **1l** also.

281	**87**	1l. on 6l. green and blue	1·60	1·60
282	**79**	2l. brown	1·60	1·60
283	**82**	4l. red and yellow	2·75	2·00
284	**87**	10l. orange and brown	50·00	30·00

1928.

285	**89**	1l. green	75	10
286		2l. brown	1·25	10

1929. 50th Anniv of Liberation of Bulgaria and Millenary of Tsar Simeon.

287	**90**	10s. violet	15	10
288	–	15a. purple	15	10
289	–	30s. red	15	10
290	–	50s. green	25	10
291	–	1l. red	70	10
292	–	2l. blue	95	15
293	–	3l. green	2·10	50
294	–	4l. brown	3·00	25
295	–	5l. brown	95	55
296	–	6l. blue	2·75	1·25

PORTRAITS—23½ × 33½ mm: 15s. Konstantin Miladinov (poet and folklorist); 1l. Father Paisii Khilendarski (historian); 2l. Tsar Simeon; 4l. Vasil Levski (revolutionary); 5l. Georgi Benkovski (revolutionary); 6l. Tsar Alexander II of Russia, "The Liberator". 19 × 28½ mm: 30s. Georgi Rakovski (writer). 19 × 26 mm: 3l. Lyuben Karavelov (journalist).

98 Convalescent Home, Varna

1930. Sunday Delivery stamps.

297	**98**	1l. green and purple	5·00	15
298		1l. yellow and green	50	15
299		1l. brown and red	50	15

99

101 King Boris III

1930. Wedding of King Boris and Princess Giovanna of Italy.

300	**99**	1l. green	20	20
301	–	2l. purple	35	20
302	**99**	4l. red	35	30
303	–	6l. blue	45	35

DESIGN: 2, 6l. Portraits in separate ovals.

1931.

304a	**101**	1l. green (A)	15	10
305		2l. red (A)	50	10
306		4l. orange (A)	30	10
308a		4l. orange (B)	70	10
307		6l. blue (A)	35	10
308b		6l. blue (B)	70	10
308c		7l. blue (B)	25	20
308d		10l. slate (B)	10·00	55
308		12l. brown (A)	45	10
308e		14l. brown (B)	35	20
308f	–	20l. brown & pur (B)	85	60

(A) Without coloured frame-lines at top and bottom; (B) with frame-lines.

The 20l. is 24½ × 33½ mm.

103 Gymnastics

1831. Balkan Olympic Games.

309	**103**	1l. green	60	60
326		1l. turquoise	2·25	1·75
310	–	2l. red	1·10	60
327	–	2l. blue	3·00	1·75
311	–	4l. red	1·75	75

328	–	4l. purple	4·00	1·75
312	–	6l. green	4·75	1·50
329	–	6l. red	8·00	3·50
313	–	10l. red	10·00	5·00
330	–	10l. brown	45·00	20·00
314	–	12l. blue	45·00	10·50
331	–	12l. red	75·00	40·00
315	–	50l. brown	35·00	30·00
332	–	50l. red	£225	£200

DESIGNS—VERT (23 × 28 mm): 2l. Footballer; 4l. Horse-riding. As Type **103**—HORIZ: 6l. Fencing; 10l. Cycling. VERT: 12l. Diving; 50l. Spirit of Victory.

108

109 Rila Monastery

1931. Air.

316	**108**	1l. green	25	10
316a		1l. purple	10	10
317		2l. purple	25	10
317a		2l. green	15	10
318		6l. blue	35	20
318a		6l. red	40	20
319		12l. red	60	25
319a		12l. blue	50	30
320		20l. violet	60	40
321		30l. orange	1·25	75
322		50l. brown	1·50	95

1932. Air.

323	**109**	18l. green	55·00	40·00
324		24l. red	50·00	35·00
325		28l. blue	35·00	24·00

1934. Surch **2**.

333	**101**	2 on 3l. olive	3·75	35

111 Defending the Pass

113 Convalescent Home, Troyan

1934. Unveiling of Shipka Pass Memorial.

334	**111**	1l. green	45	50
340		1l. green	45	50
335	–	2l. red	45	20
341	–	2l. orange	45	20
336	–	3l. brown	1·50	1·50
342	–	3l. yellow	1·50	1·50
337	–	4l. red	1·25	40
343	–	4l. red	1·25	40
338	–	7l. blue	2·25	1·75
344	–	7l. light blue	2·25	1·75
339	–	14l. purple	7·50	7·50
345	–	14l. bistre	7·50	7·50

DESIGNS—VERT: 2l. Shipka Memorial; 3, 7l. Veteran standard-bearer; 14l. Widow showing memorial to orphans. HORIZ: 4l. Bulgarian veteran.

1935. Sunday Delivery stamps.

346	**113**	1l. red and brown	45	10
347		1l. blue and green	45	10
348	–	5l. blue and red	1·75	60

DESIGN: 5l. Convalescent Home, Bakya.

114 Capt. Georgi Mamarchef

115 Aleksandr Nevski Cathedral, Sofia

1935. Centenary of Turnovo Insurrection.

349	–	1l. blue	85	35
350	**114**	2l. purple	85	60

DESIGN: 1l. Velcho Atanasov Dzhamdzhiyata.

1935. 5th Balkan Football Tournament.

351	–	1l. green	1·60	1·50
352	**115**	2l. grey	3·00	2·50
353	–	4l. red	5·50	4·00
354	–	7l. blue	12·50	9·00
355	–	14l. orange	10·00	8·00
356	–	50l. brown	£140	£150

DESIGNS—HORIZ: 1l. Match in progress at Yunak Stadium, Sofia; 4l. Footballers. VERT: 7l. Herald and Balkan map; 14l. Footballer and trophy; 50l. Trophy.

116 Girl Gymnast

117 Janos Hunyadi

1935. 8th Bulgarian Gymnastic Tournament. Dated "12–14. VII. 1935".

357	–	1l. green	1·75	2·00
358	–	2l. blue	2·50	2·00
359	**116**	4l. red	6·00	5·00
360	–	7l. blue	6·50	6·50
361	–	14l. brown	6·50	7·00
362	–	50l. orange	90·00	£100

DESIGNS—VERT: 1l. Parallel bars; 2l. Male gymnast in uniform; 7l. Pole vault; 50l. Athlete and lion. HORIZ: 14l. Yunak Stadium, Sofia.

1935. Unveiling of Monument to Ladislas III of Poland at Varna. Inscr "WARNEN CZYK(A)", etc.

363	**117**	1l. orange	75	45
364	–	2l. red	2·25	60
365	–	4l. red	9·00	4·50
366	–	7l. blue	1·75	1·40
367	–	14l. green	1·75	1·10

DESIGNS—VERT: 2l. King Ladislas of Hungary enthroned (22 × 32 mm); 7l. King Ladislas in armour (20 × 31 mm). HORIZ: 4l. Varna Memorial (33 × 24 mm); 14l. Battle scene (30 × 25 mm).

118 Dimitur

119

120

1935. 67th Death Anniv of Khadzhi Dimitur (revolutionary).

368	–	1l. green	1·75	55
369	**118**	2l. brown	2·25	1·10
370	–	4l. red	5·00	3·25
371	–	7l. blue	6·50	5·00
372	–	14l. orange	6·50	6·00

DESIGNS—VERT: 1l. Dimitur's monument at Sliven; 7l. Revolutionary group (dated 1868). HORIZ: 4l. Dimitur and Stefan Karadzha (revolutionary); 14l. Dimitur's birthplace at Sliven.

1936.

373	**119**	10s. red	10	10
373a		15s. green	10	10
374	**120**	30s. red	10	10
374a		30s. brown	10	10
374b		30s. blue	10	10
375		50s. blue	10	10
375a		50s. red	10	10
375b		50s. green	10	10

121 Nesebur

122 St. Cyril and St. Methodius

1936. Slav Geographical and Ethnographical Congress, Sofia.

376	–	1l. violet	1·00	1·50
377	–	2l. blue	1·00	1·25
378	**121**	7l. blue	3·25	2·50

DESIGNS—25 × 34 mm: 1l. Meteorological Bureau, Mt. Musala; 23 × 34 mm: 2l. Peasant girl.

1937. Millenary of Introduction of Cyrillic Alphabet and Slavonic Liturgy.

379	**122**	1l. green	35	15
380		2l. purple	35	15
381	–	4l. red	45	15
382	**122**	7l. blue	1·50	1·10
383	–	14l. red	1·50	1·25

DESIGN: 4l., 14l. The Saints Preaching.

124 Princess Marie Louise

125 King Boris III

1937.

384	**124**	1l. green	35	10
385		2l. red	40	15
386		4l. red	40	20

1937. 19th Anniv of Accession.

387	**125**	2l. red	30	30

126 Harvesting

129 Prince Simeon

1938. Agricultural Products.

388	**126**	10s. orange	10	10
389		10s. red	10	10
390	–	15s. red	30	10
391	–	15s. purple	30	10
392	–	30s. brown	15	10
393	–	30s. brown	15	10
394	–	50s. blue	55	10
395	–	50s. black	55	10
396	–	1l. green	60	10
397	–	1l. green	60	10
398	–	2l. red	55	10
399	–	2l. brown	55	10
400	–	3l. purple	1·10	35
401	–	3l. purple	1·10	35
402	–	4l. brown	70	20
403	–	4l. purple	70	20
404	–	7l. violet	1·40	55
405	–	7l. blue	1·40	55
406	–	14l. brown	2·25	1·40
407	–	14l. brown	2·25	1·40

DESIGNS—VERT: 15s. Sunflower; 30s. Wheat; 50s. Chickens and eggs; 1l. Grapes; 3l. Strawberries; 4l. Girl carrying grapes; 7l. Roses; 14l. Tobacco leaves. HORIZ: 2l. "Attar of Roses".

1938. 1st Birthday of Heir Apparent.

408	**129**	1l. green	10	10
409		2l. red	15	10
410	–	4l. red	20	10
411	**129**	7l. blue	80	35
412	–	14l. brown	80	35

DESIGN: 4, 14l. Another portrait.

131 King Boris III

132 First Locomotive in Bulgaria, 1866

1938. 20th Anniv of King's Accession. Portraits of King in various uniforms.

413	**131**	1l. green	10	10
414	–	2l. red	75	10
415	–	4l. brown	10	10
416	–	7l. blue	30	30
417	–	14l. mauve	30	30

1939. 50th Anniv of Bulgarian State Railways. Locomotive types dated "1888–1938".

418	**132**	1l. green	55	50
419	–	2l. brown	70	50
420	–	4l. orange	2·00	80
421	–	7l. blue	7·25	6·50

DESIGNS: 2l. Class 01 steam locomotive; 4l. Train crossing viaduct; 7l. King Boris as engine-driver.

133 P.O. Emblem

135 Gymnast

1939. 60th Anniv of Bulgarian P.O. Inscr "1879 1939".

422	**133**	1l. green	15	10
423	–	2l. red (G.P.O., Sofia)	20	10

1939. Yunak Gymnastic Society's Rally, Sofia.

424	**135**	1l. green	25	15
425	–	2l. red	25	15
426	–	4l. brown	40	15
427	–	7l. blue	1·40	60
428	–	14l. mauve	6·00	4·50

DESIGNS: 2l. Yunak badge; 4l. "The Discus-thrower" (statue by Miron); 7l. Rhythmic dancer; 14l. Athlete holding weight aloft.

Наводнението
1939
1+1
лева

(**136**) ("Inundation 1939")

1939. Sevlievo and Turnovo Floods Relief Fund. Surch as T **136** and value.

429	**39**	1l.+1l. on 15s. grey	15	15
430	**73**	2l.+1l. on 1½l. olive	15	15
431		4l.+2l. on 2l. green	20	20
432		7l.+4l. on 3l. blue	55	55
433		14l.+7l. on 5l. red	1·10	1·10

137 Mail Plane

138 King Boris III

1940. Air.

434	**137**	1l. green	15	10
435	–	2l. red	2·10	10
436	–	4l. orange	20	10
437	–	6l. blue	25	15
438	–	10l. brown	3·75	1·25
439	–	12l. brown	1·00	35
440		16l. violet	1·10	55
441	–	19l. blue	1·25	75
442	–	30l. mauve	1·90	1·10
443	–	45l. violet	4·75	2·25
444	–	70l. red	5·00	2·75
445	–	100l. blue	12·00	8·00

DESIGNS—VERT: Aircraft over: King Asen's Tower (2l.), Bachovo Monastery (4l.), Aleksandr Nevski Cathedral, Sofia (45l.), Shipka Pass Memorial (70l.); 10l. Airplane, mail train and express motor cycle; 30l. Airplane and swallow; 100l. Airplane and Royal cypher. HORIZ: 6l. Loading mails at aerodrome. Aircraft over: Sofia Palace (12l.), Mt. El Tepe (16l.), Rila Lakes and mountains (19l.).

1940.

445a	**138**	1l. green	15	10
446		2l. red	30	10

139 First Bulgarian Postage Stamp

1940. Cent of 1st Adhesive Postage Stamp.

447	**139**	10l. olive	1·50	1·25
448	–	20l. blue	1·50	1·25

DESIGN: 20l. has scroll dated "1840–1940".

140 Grapes

142 King Boris III

141 Ploughing

1940.

449	**140**	10s. orange	10	10
450	–	15s. blue	10	10
451	**141**	30s. brown	10	10
452	–	50s. violet	10	10
452a	–	50s. green	10	10
453	**142**	1l. green	10	10
454		2l. red	10	10
455		4l. orange	10	10
456		6l. violet	20	10
457		7l. blue	25	10
458		10l. green	25	10

DESIGNS—VERT: 15s. Beehive. HORIZ: 50s. Shepherd and flock.

143 Peasant Couple and King Boris

144 King Boris and Map of Dobrudja

1940. Recovery of Dobrudja from Rumania. Designs incorporating miniature portrait of King Boris.

464	**143**	1l. green	15	10
465	–	2l. red	15	10
466	**144**	4l. brown	15	10
467		7l. blue	55	30

DESIGN—VERT: 2l. Bulgarian flags and wheat-field.

145 Bee-keeping

1940. Agricultural Scenes.

468	–	10s. purple	10	10
469	–	10s. blue	10	10
470	–	15s. green	10	10
471	–	15s. olive	10	10
472	**145**	30s. orange	10	10
473		30s. green	10	10
474	–	50s. violet	10	10
475	–	50s. purple	10	10
476	–	3l. brown	55	10
477	–	3l. black	60	40
478	–	5l. brown	1·25	50
479	–	5l. blue	75	40

DESIGNS: 10s. Threshing; 15s. Ploughing with oxen; 50s. Picking apples; 3l. Shepherd; 5l. Cattle.

146 Pencko Slaveikov (poet) **147** St. Ivan Rilski

1940. National Relief.

480	**146**	1l. green	10	10
481	–	2l. red	15	10
482	**147**	3l. brown	15	10
483	–	4l. orange	15	10
484	–	7l. blue	1·00	75
485	–	10l. brown	2·00	75

DESIGNS: 2l. Bishop Sofronii of Vratsa; 4l. Marin Drinov (historian); 7l. Chernorisets Khratur (monk); 10l. Kolo Ficheto (writer).

148 Johannes Gutenberg **149** Nikola Karastoyanov

1940. 500th Anniv of Invention of Printing and Centenary of Bulgarian Printing.

486	**148**	1l. green	15	10
487	**149**	2l. brown	15	10

150 Botev **151** Arrival in Koslodui

1941. 65th Death Anniv of Khristo Botev (poet and revolutionary).

488	**150**	1l. green	10	10
489	**151**	2l. red	15	10
490	–	3l. brown	55	35

DESIGN—VERT: 3l. Botev Memorial Cross.

152 National History Museum

1941. Buildings in Sofia.

491	**152**	14l. brown	95	60
492	–	20l. green	35	15
493	–	50l. blue	1·75	1·25

DESIGNS: 20l. Tsarita Icanna Workers' Hospital; 50l. National Bank.

153 Thasos Island **154** Ohrid

1941. Reacquisition of Macedonia.

494	–	1l. green	10	10
495	**153**	2l. orange	10	10
496	–	2l. red	10	10
497	–	4l. brown	15	10
498	**154**	7l. blue	45	30

DESIGNS—VERT: 1l. Macedonian girl. HORIZ: 2l. (No. 496) King Boris and map dated "1941"; 4l. Poganovski Monastery.

155 Children on Beach

1942. Sunday Delivery. Inscr as in T **155**.

499	–	1l. green	10	10
500	**155**	2l. orange	10	10
501	–	5l. blue	30	25

DESIGNS: 1l. St. Konstantin Sanatorium, Varna; 5l. Sun-bathing terrace, Bankya.

156 Bugler at Camp **157** Folk Dancers

1942. "Work and Joy". Inscr as at foot of T **157**.

502	–	1l. green	10	10
503	–	2l. red	15	10
504	–	4l. black	15	10
505	**156**	7l. blue	20	10
506	**157**	14l. brown	35	20

DESIGNS—VERT: 1l. Guitarist and accordion player; 2l. Camp orchestra; 4l. Hoisting the flag.

158 Wounded Soldier **159** Queen visiting Wounded

1942. War Invalids. Inscr as T **158/9**.

507	**158**	1l. green	10	10
508	–	2l. red	10	10
509	–	4l. orange	10	10
510	–	7l. blue	10	10
511	–	14l. brown	10	10
512	**159**	20l. black	30	10

DESIGNS—HORIZ: 2l. Soldier and family; 4l. First aid on battlefield; 7l. Widow and orphans at grave; 14l. Unknown Soldiers Memorial.

160 Khan Kubrat (ruled 595–642) **161** King Boris III

1942. Historical series.

513	**160**	10s. black	10	10
514	–	15s. blue	10	10
515	–	30s. mauve	10	10
516	–	50s. blue	10	10
517	–	1l. green	10	10
518	–	2l. red	10	10
519	–	3l. brown	10	10
520	–	4l. orange	10	10
521	–	5l. green	15	10
522	–	7l. blue	15	10
523	–	10l. black	15	10
524	–	14l. olive	15	10
525	–	20l. brown	50	20
526	–	30l. black	90	30

DESIGNS: 15s. Cavalry charge (Khan as parukh, 680–701); 30s. Equestrian statue of Khan Krum (803–814); 50s. Baptism of King Boris I; 1l. St. Naum's School; 2l. King Boris crowns his son, Tsar Simeon; 3l. Golden Era of Bulgarian literature; 4l. Trial of Bogomil Vasilii; 5l. Proclamation of Second Bulgarian Empire; 7l. Ivan Asen II (1214–81) at Tebizond; 10l. Expulsion of Eutimil Patriarch of Turnovo; 14l. Wandering minstrels; 20l. Father Paisii Khilendarski (historian); 30l. Shipka Pass Memorial.

1944. King Boris Mourning Issue. Portraits dated "1894–1943". Perf or imperf.

527	**161**	1l. olive	10	10
528	–	2l. brown	15	15
529	–	4l. brown	15	15
530	–	5l. violet	35	35
531	–	7l. blue	35	35

ВСИЧКО
ЗА
ФРОНТА

163 King Simeon II **(164)**

1944.

532	**163**	3l. orange	10	10

1945. "All for the Front". Parcel Post stamps optd as T **164** or surch also.

533	P **163**	1l. red	10	10
534		4l. on 1l. red	10	10
535		7l. purple	10	10
536		20l. brown	15	10
537		30l. purple	15	10
538		50l. orange	40	20
539		100l. blue	70	45

1945. Air. Optd with airplane or surch also.

540	**142**	1l. green	10	10
541		4l. orange	15	10
542	P **163**	10l. on 100l. yellow	30	15
543		45l. on 100l. yellow	35	15
544		75l. on 100l. yellow	55	30
545		100l. yellow	85	40

Nos. 540/1 are perf; the rest imperf.

167

1945. Slav Congress. Perf or imperf.

546	**167**	4l. red	10	10
547		10l. blue	10	10
548		50l. red	30	30

СЪБИРАЙТЕ
ВСЪКАКВИ
ПАРЦАЛИ
(168) "Collect All Rags"

СЪБИРАЙТЕ
СТАРО
ЖЕЛЪЗО
(169) "Collect Old Iron"

СЪБИРАЙТЕ
ХАРТИЕНИ
ОТПАДЪЦИ
(170) "Collect Wastepaper"

1945. Salvage Campaign. Nos. 457/9 optd with T **168/70**.

549	**142**	1l. green	15	10
550		2l. red	50	10
551		4l. orange	30	10

Prices are the same for these stamps with any one of the overprints illustrated.

171 Lion Rampant **172**

1945. Lion Rampant, in various frames.

552	–	30s. green	10	10
553	–	50s. blue	10	10
554	**171**	1l. green	10	10
555	–	2l. brown	10	10
556	–	4l. blue	10	10
557	–	5l. violet	10	10
558	**172**	9l. grey	10	10
559	–	10l. blue	10	10
560	–	15l. brown	20	10
561	–	20l. black	20	10
562	–	20l. red	20	10

173 Chain-breaker **174** "VE Day"

1945. Liberty Loan. Imperf.

563	**173**	50l. orange	15	10
564		50l. lake	15	10
565	–	100l. blue	20	10
566	–	100l. brown	20	10
567	–	150l. red	45	20
568	–	150l. green	45	20
569	–	200l. olive	75	60
570	–	200l. blue	75	60

DESIGNS: 100l. Hand holding coin; 150l. Water-mill; 200l. Coin and symbols of industry and agriculture.

1945. "Victory in Europe".

571	**174**	10l. green and brown	10	10
572		50l. green and red	30	10

175 **176**

1945. 1st Anniv of Fatherland Front Coalition.

573	**175**	1l. olive	10	10
574		4l. blue	10	10
575		5l. mauve	10	10
576	**176**	10l. blue	10	10
577		20l. red	15	10
578	**175**	50l. green	30	20
579		100l. brown	50	30

177 Refugee Children **178** Red Cross Train

1946. Red Cross. Cross in red.

580	**177**	2l. olive	10	10
645d		2l. brown	10	10
581	–	4l. violet	10	10
645e	–	4l. black	10	10
582	**177**	10l. purple	10	10
645f		10l. green	15	10
583	–	20l. dark blue	15	10
645g	–	20l. light blue	25	15
584	–	30l. brown	15	15
645h	–	30l. green	35	25
585	**178**	35l. black	2·25	1·50
645i		35l. green	1·75	1·10
586	–	50l. purple	35	25
645j	–	50l. lake	70	45
587	**178**	100l. brown	4·25	2·75
645k		100l. blue	3·50	2·00

DESIGNS—HORIZ: 4l., 20l. Soldier on stretcher. VERT: 30l., 50l. Nurse and wounded soldier.

179 Postal Savings Emblem **180** Savings Bank-Note

1946. 50th Anniv of Savings Bank.

588	**179**	4l. red	40	25
589	**180**	10l. olive	15	10
590	–	20l. blue	15	10
591	–	50l. black	60	55

DESIGNS—VERT: 20l. Child filling money-box; 50l. Postal Savings Bank.

181 Arms of Russia and Bulgaria and Spray of Oak **182** Lion Rampant

1946. Bulgo-Russian Congress.

592	**181**	4l. red	7·00	7·00
593		4l. orange	10	10
594		20l. blue	7·00	7·00
595		20l. green	20	20

1946. Stamp Day. Imperf.

596	**182**	20l. blue	40	30

183 **190**

1946. Air. Inscr "PAR AVION".

597	**183**	1l. purple	15	10
598		2l. grey	15	10
599	–	4l. black	30	15
600	–	6l. blue	40	30
601	–	10l. green	10	10
602	–	12l. brown	10	10
603	–	16l. purple	10	10
604	–	19l. red	10	10
605	–	30l. orange	15	10
606	–	45l. green	45	15
607	–	75l. brown	55	15
608	**190**	100l. red	1·10	25
609	–	100l. grey	1·10	25

DESIGNS—23 × 18 mm: 4l. Bird carrying envelope; 100l. (No. 609), Airplane. 18 × 23 mm: 6l. Airplane and envelope; 10, 12, 19l. Wings and posthorn; 16l. Wings and envelope; 30l. Airplane; 45, 75l. Dove and posthorn.

192 Stamboliiski

193 Flags of Albania, Bulgaria, Yugoslavia and Rumania

1946. 25th Death Anniv of Aleksandur Stamboliiski (Prime Minister 1919–23).

610	**192**	100l. orange	7·00	7·00

1946. Balkan Games.

611	**193**	100l. brown	1·40	1·40

196 Artillery

195 Junkers Ju87B "Stuka" Dive Bombers

1946. Military and Air Services.

612	–	2l. red	10	10
613	–	4l. grey	10	10
614	**196**	5l. red	10	10
615	**195**	6l. brown	10	10
616	–	9l. mauve	10	10
617	–	10l. violet	10	10
618	–	20l. blue	35	15
619	–	30l. orange	35	15
620	–	40l. olive	40	20
621	–	50l. green	50	50
622	–	60l. brown	75	50

DESIGNS—HORIZ: 2, 20l. Grenade thrower and machine-gunner; 9l. Building pontoon-bridge; 10, 30l. Cavalry charge; 40l. Supply column; 50l. Motor convoy; 60l. Tanks. VERT: 4l. Grenade thrower.

203 St. Ivan Rilski

208 "New Republic"

1946. Death Millenary of St. Ivan Rilski.

623	**203**	1l. brown	10	10
624	–	4l. sepia	10	10
625	–	10l. green	25	10
626	–	20l. blue	30	10
627	–	50l. red	1·25	55

DESIGNS—HORIZ: 4l. Rila Monastery; 10l. Monastery entrance; 50l. Cloistered courtyard. VERT: 20l. Aerial view of Monastery.

1946. Referendum.

628	**208**	4l. red	10	10
629		20l. blue	10	10
630		50l. brown	25	15

209 Assault

210 Ambuscade

211 Nurse and Children

1946. Partisan Activities.

631	**209**	1l. purple	10	10
632	**210**	4l. green	10	10
633	–	5l. brown	10	10
634	**210**	10l. red	10	10
635	**209**	20l. blue	30	10
636	–	30l. brown	30	15
637	–	50l. black	40	25

DESIGNS—VERT: 5l., 50l. Partisan riflemen; 30l. Partisan leader.

1947. Winter Relief.

638	**211**	1l. violet	10	10
639	–	4l. red	10	10
640	–	9l. olive	10	10
641	**211**	10l. grey	10	10
642	–	20l. blue	15	10
643	–	30l. brown	15	10
644	–	40l. red	30	25
645	**211**	50l. green	50	35

DESIGNS: 4l., 9l. Child carrying gifts; 20l., 40l. Hungry child; 30l. Destitute mother and child.

212a Partisans

1947. Anti-fascists of 1923, 1941 and 1944 Commem.

645a	–	10l. brown and orange	40	40
645b	**212a**	20l. dp blue & lt blue	40	40
645c	–	70l. brown and red	35·00	35·00

DESIGNS—HORIZ: 10l. Group of fighters; 70l. Soldier addressing crowd.

213 Olive Branch

214 Dove of Peace

1947. Peace.

646	**213**	4l. olive	10	10
647	**214**	10l. brown	10	10
648		20l. blue	20	15

"BULGARIA" is in Roman characters on the 20l.

215 "U.S.A." and "Bulgaria"

216 Esperanto Emblem and Map of Bulgaria

1947. Air. Stamp Day and New York International Philatelic Exhibition.

649	**215**	70l.+30l. brown	1·75	2·00

1947. 30th Esperanto Jubilee Congress, Sofia.

650	**216**	20l.+10l. purple & green	75	50

217 G.P.O., Sofia

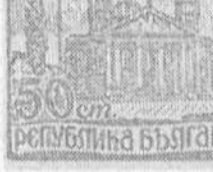

218 National Theatre, Sofia

219 Parliament Building

220 President's Palace

221 G.P.O., Sofia

1947. Government Buildings. (a) T **217**.

651		1l. green	10	10
		(b) T **218**.		
652		50s. green	10	10
653		2l. red	10	10
654		4l. blue	10	10
655		9l. red	25	10
		(c) T **219**.		
656		50s. green	10	10
657		2l. blue	10	10
658		4l. blue	10	10
659		20l. blue	85	30
		(d) T **220**.		
660		1l. green	10	10
		(e) T **221**.		
661		1l. green	10	10
662		2l. red	10	10
663		4l. blue	10	10

222 Hydro-electric Power Station and Dam

223 Emblem of Industry

1947. Reconstruction.

664	**222**	4l. green	15	15
665	–	9l. brown (Miner)	15	15
666	**223**	20l. blue	25	25
667	–	40l. green (Motor plough)	85	85

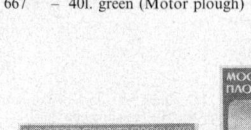

224 Exhibition Building

225 Former Residence of the French Poet Lamartine

226 Rose and Grapes

227 Airplane over City

1947. Plovdiv Fair. (a) Postage.

668	**224**	4l. red	10	10
669	**225**	9l. red	10	10
670	**226**	20l. blue	25	15
		(b) Air. Imperf.		
671	**227**	40l. green	1·10	1·00

228 Cycle Racing

229 Basketball

231 V. E. Aprilov

1947. Balkan Games.

672	**228**	2l. lilac	40	20
673	**229**	4l. green	40	20
674	–	9l. brown	1·10	40
675	–	20l. blue	1·25	50
676	–	60l. red	3·00	2·00

DESIGNS—VERT: 9l. Chess; 20l. Football; 60l. Balkan flags.

1947. Death Cent of Vasil Aprilov (educationist).

678	–	4l. red	15	10
677	**231**	40l. blue	35	25

DESIGN: 4l. Another portrait of Aprilov.

233 Postman

235 Geno Kirov

1947. Postal Employees' Relief Fund.

679	**233**	4l.+2l. olive	10	10
680	–	10l.+5l. red	20	20
681	–	20l.+10l. blue	25	25
682	–	40l.+20l. brown	1·00	1·00

DESIGNS: 10l. Linesman; 20l. Telephonists; 40l. Wireless masts.

1947. Theatrical Artists' Benevolent Fund.

683	**235**	50s. brown	10	10
684	–	1l. green	10	10
685	–	2l. green	10	10
686	–	3l. blue	10	10
687	–	4l. red	10	10
688	–	5l. purple	10	10
689	–	9l.+5l. blue	15	15
690	–	10l.+6l. red	20	20
691	–	15l.+7l. violet	25	25
692	–	20l.+15l. blue	50	25
693	–	30l.+20l. purple	1·00	85

PORTRAITS: 1l. Zlotina Nedeva; 2l. Ivan Popov; 3l. Atanas Kirchev; 4l. Elena Snezhina; 5l. Stoyan Buchvarov; 9l. Khristo Ganchev; 10l. Adriana Budevska; 15l. Vasil Kirkov; 20l. Save Orgnyanov; 30l. Krustyn Sarafov.

236 "Rodina" (freighter)

1947. National Shipping Revival.

694	**236**	50l. blue	1·25	35

237 Worker and Flag

238 Worker and Globe

1948. 2nd General Workers' Union Congress.

695	**237**	4l. blue (postage)	15	10
696	**238**	60l. brown (air)	65	50

239

240

1948. Leisure and Culture.

697	**239**	4l. red	15	10
698	**240**	20l. blue	25	15
699	–	40l. green	40	20
700	–	60l. brown	65	40

DESIGNS—VERT: 40l. Workers' musical interlude; 60l. Sports girl.

241 Kikola Vaptsarov

242 Petlyakov Pe-2 Bomber over Baldwin's Tower

1948. Poets.

701	**241**	4l. red on cream	10	10
702	–	9l. brown on cream	15	10
703	–	15l. purple on cream	15	15
704	–	20l. blue on cream	20	15
705	–	45l. green on cream	65	75

PORTRAITS: 9l. Peya Yavorov; 15l. Khristo Smirnenski; 20l. Ivan Vazov; 45l. Petko Slaveikov.

1948. Air. Stamp Day.

706	**242**	50l. brown on cream	1·40	1·10

243 Soldier

244 Peasants and Soldiers

1948. Soviet Army Monument.
707 **243** 4l. red on cream 10 10
708 **244** 10l. green on cream . . . 15 10
709 – 20l. blue on cream . . . 25 15
710 – 60l. olive on cream . . . 75 45
DESIGNS—HORIZ: 20l. Soldiers of 1878 and 1944. VERT: 60l. Stalin and Spassky Tower, Kremlin.

245 Bath, Gorna Banya

246 Lion Emblem

1948. Bulgarian Health Resorts.
711 **245** 2l. red 10 10
712 – 3l. orange 10 10
713 – 4l. blue 15 10
717 – 5l. brown 15 10
714 – 10l. purple 25 10
718 – 15l. olive 35 10
715 **245** 20l. blue . . . . 1·00 15
716 – 20l. blue . . . . 1·50 15
DESIGNS: 3l., 10l. Bath, Bankya; 4l., 20l. (No. 716), Mineral bath, Sofia; 5l., 15l. Malyovitsa Peak.

1948.
719 **246** 50s. orange 10 10
719a 50s. brown 10 10
720 1l. green 10 10
721 9l. black 15 10

247 Dimitur Blagoev

248 Youths marching

1948. 25th Anniv of September Uprising.
722 **247** 4l. brown 10 10
723 – 9l. orange 10 10
724 – 20l. blue 40 25
725 **248** 60l. brown . . . . 1·00 75
DESIGNS—VERT: 9l. Gabrit Genov. HORIZ: 20l. Bishop Andrei Monument.

249 Khristo Smirnenski

250 Miner

1948. 500th Birth Anniv of Smirnenski (poet and revolutionary).
726 **249** 4l. blue 10 10
727 16l. brown 15 10

1948.
728 **250** 4l. blue 75 25

251 Battle of Grivitsa

1948. Treaty of Friendship with Rumania.
729 **251** 20l. blue (postage) 20 10
730 – 40l. black (air) 25 15
731 – 100l. mauve 95 85
DESIGNS: 40l. Parliament Buildings in Sofia and Bucharest; 100l. Projected Danube Bridge.

252 Botev's House, Kalofer

253 Botev

1948. Birth Centenary of Khristo Botev (poet and revolutionary).
732 **252** 1l. green 10 10
733 **253** 4l. brown 15 10
734 4l. purple 15 10
735 – 9l. violet 40 10
736 – 15l. brown 20 10
737a – 20l. blue 20 10
738 – 40l. brown 45 20
739 – 50l. black 65 30
DESIGNS—HORIZ: 9l. River paddle-steamer "Radetski"; 15l. Village of Kalofer; 40l. Botev's mother and verse of poem. VERT: 20l. Botev in uniform; 50l. Quill, pistol and laurel wreath.

254 Lenin

255 Road Construction

1949. 25th Death Anniv of Lenin. Inscr "1924–1949".
740 **254** 4l. brown 15 10
741 – 20l. red 40 25
DESIGN—(27 × 37 mm): 20l. Lenin as an orator.

1949. National Youth Movement.
742 **255** 4l. red 20 10
743 – 5l. brown . . . . 1·10 40
744 – 9l. green . . . . 2·25 30
745 – 10l. violet 50 20
746 – 20l. blue 85 45
747 – 40l. brown . . . . 1·75 1·00
DESIGNS—HORIZ: 5l. Tunnel construction; 9l. Class 10 steam locomotive; 10l. Textile workers; 20l. Girl driving tractor; 40l. Workers in lorry.

256 Lisunov Li-2 over Pleven Mausoleum

1949. Air. 7th Philatelic Congress, Pleven.
748 **256** 50l. bistre . . . . 4·50 3·75

257 G. Dimitrov

258 G. Dimitrov

1949. Death of Georgi Dimitrov (Prime Minister 1946–49).
749 **257** 4l. red 15 10
750 **258** 20l. blue . . . . 1·00 25

259 Hydro-electric Power Station

260 Symbols of Agriculture and Industry

1949. Five Year Industrial and Agricultural Plan.
751 **259** 4l. olive (postage) 15 10
752 – 9l. red 25 15
753 – 15l. violet 40 20
754 – 20l. blue . . . . 1·25 40
755 **260** 50l. brown (air) . . . . . 2·75 1·50
DESIGNS—VERT: 9l. Cement works; 15l. Tractors in garage. HORIZ: 20l. Tractors in field.

261 Javelin and Grenade Throwing

262 Motor-cyclist and Tractor

1949. Physical Culture Campaign.
756 **261** 4l. red 30 15
757 – 9l. olive . . . . 1·40 50
758 **262** 20l. blue . . . . 2·00 1·00
759 – 50l. red . . . . 5·00 2·75
DESIGNS—HORIZ: 9l. Hurdling and leaping barbed-wire. VERT: 50l. Two athletes marching.

263 Globe

265 Guardsman with Dog

264 Guardsman and Peasant

1949. Air. 75th Anniv of Universal Postal Union.
760 **263** 50l. blue . . . . 2·40 1·10

1949. Frontier Guards.
761 **264** 4l. brown (postage) . . . 15 15
762 – 20l. blue . . . . 1·00 75
763 **265** 60l. green (air) . . . . . 2·75 2·75
DESIGN—VERT: 20l. Guardsman on coast.

266 Georgi Dimitrov (Prime Minister 1946–49)

267 "Unanimity"

268 Zosif Stalin

1949. Fatherland Front.
764 **266** 4l. brown 15 10
765 **267** 9l. violet 20 10
766 – 20l. blue 30 20
767 – 50l. red . . . . 1·00 1·00
DESIGNS: 20l. Man and woman with wheelbarrow and spade; 50l. Young people marching with banners.

1949. 70th Birthday of Stalin.
768 **268** 4l. orange 25 10
769 – 40l. red 90 70
DESIGN—VERT: (25 × 37 mm): 40l. Stalin as an orator.

269 Kharalampi Stoyanov

270 Strikers and Train

1950. 30th Anniv of Railway Strike.
770 **269** 4l. brown 15 10
771 **270** 20l. blue . . . . 1·10 40
772 – 60l. olive . . . . 2·25 1·25
DESIGN—VERT: 60l. Two workers and flag.

271 Miner

272 Class 48 Steam Shunting Locomotive

1950.
773 **271** 1l. olive 10 10
773a 1l. violet 15 10
774 **272** 2l. black . . . . 3·00 40
774a 2l. brown . . . . 2·50 25
775 – 3l. blue 45 10
776a – 4l. green 40 10
777 – 5l. red 40 10
778 – 9l. grey 20 10
779 – 10l. purple 25 10
780 – 15l. red 45 15
781 – 20l. blue 80 45
DESIGNS—VERT: 3l. Ship under construction; 10l. Power station; 15l., 20l. Woman in factory. HORIZ: 4l. Tractor; 5l., 9l. Threshing machines.

273 Kolarov

1950. Death of Vasil Kolarov (Prime Minister 1949–50). Inscr "1877–1950".
782 **273** 4l. brown 10 10
783 – 20l. blue 40 35
DESIGN—($27\frac{1}{2} \times 39\frac{1}{2}$ mm): 20l. Portrait as Type **273**, but different frame.

274 Starislas Dospevski (self-portrait)

274a "In the Field" (Khristo Storclev)

1950. Painters and paintings.
784 **274** 1l. green 30 15
785 – 4l. orange . . . . 1·60 25
786 – 9l. brown . . . . 2·10 25
787 **274a** 15l. brown . . . . . . 2·90 70
788 20l. blue . . . . 4·75 2·00
789 – 40l. brown . . . . 5·50 2·75
790 – 60l. orange . . . . . . 6·25 4·00
DESIGNS—VERT: 4l. King Kaloyan and Desislava; 9l. Nikolai Pavlovich; 40l. Statue of Debeyanov (Ivan Lazarov); 60l. "Peasant" (Vladimir Dimitrov the Master).

275 Ivan Vazov and Birthplace, Sopot

276a G. Dimitrov (statesman)

1950. Birth Centenary of Ivan Vazov (poet).
791 **275** 4l. olive 15 10

1950. 1st Death Anniv of Georgi Dimitrov.
792 – 50s. brown (postage) . . 15 10
793 – 50s. green 15 10
794 **276a** 1l. brown 20 10
795 – 2l. slate 20 10
796 – 4l. purple 75 20
797 – 9l. red . . . . 1·25 40
798 – 10l. red . . . . 1·90 85
799 – 15l. grey . . . . 1·90 85
800 – 20l. blue . . . . 3·00 1·75
801 – 40l. brown (air) . . . . 5·50 3·25
DESIGNS—HORIZ: 50s. green, Dimitrov and birthplace, Kovachevtsi; 2l. Dimitrov's house, Sofia; 15l. Dimitrov signing new constitution; 20l. Dimitrov; 40l. Mausoleum. VERT: 50s. brown, 4, 9, 10l. Dimitrov in various poses.

277 Runners

278 Workers and Tractor

1950.
802 **277** 4l. green 65 25
803 – 9l. brown (Cycling) . . . 85 40
804 – 20l. blue (Putting the shot) . . . . 1·10 85
805 – 40l. purple (Volleyball) . . 2·40 2·10

1950. 2nd National Peace Congress.
806 **278** 4l. red 10 10
807 – 20l. blue 40 25
DESIGN—VERT: 20l. Stalin on flag and three heads.

278b

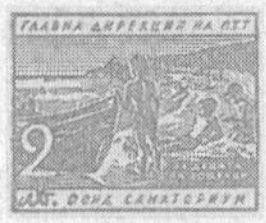

279 Children on Beach

1950. Arms designs.

807a	–	2l. brown	10	10
807b	–	3l. red	10	10
807c	**278b**	5l. red	10	10
807d	–	9l. blue	20	10

Although inscribed "OFFICIAL MAIL", the above were issued as regular postage stamps.

1950. Sunday Delivery.

808	–	1l. green (Sanatorium)	15	10
809	**279**	2l. red	20	10
810	–	5l. orange (Sunbathing)	40	15
811	**279**	10l. blue	80	35

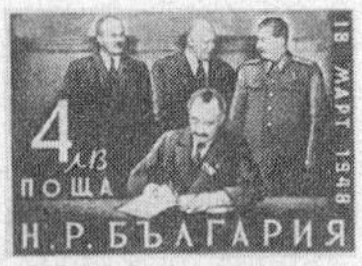

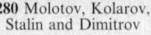

280 Molotov, Kolarov, Stalin and Dimitrov

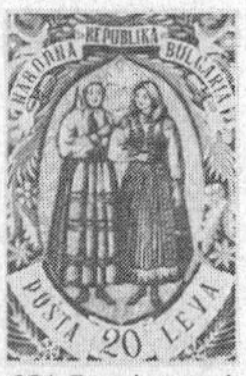

281 Russian and Bulgarian Girls

1950. 2nd Anniv of Soviet–Bulgarian Treaty of Friendship.

812	**280**	4l. brown	10	10
813	–	9l. red	15	10
814	**281**	20l. blue	30	25
815	–	50l. green	2·00	75

DESIGNS—VERT: 9l. Spassky Tower and flags; 50l. Freighter and tractor.

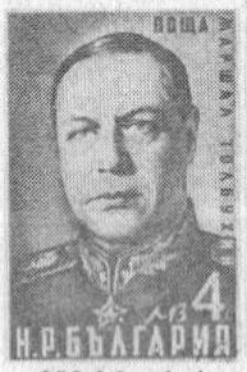

282 Marshal Tolbukhin

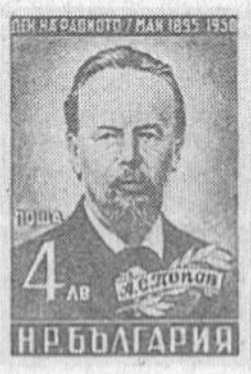

284 A. S. Popov

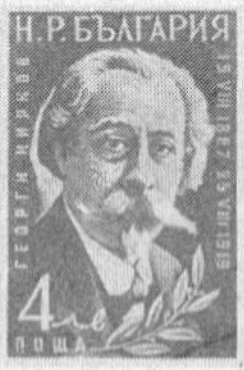

286 Georgi Kirkov

1950. Honouring Marshal Tolbukhin.

816	**282**	4l. mauve	15	10
817	–	20l. blue	1·00	30

DESIGN—HORIZ: 20l. Bulgarians greeting Tolbukhin.

1951. 45th Death Anniv of Aleksandr Popov (radio pioneer).

818	**284**	4l. brown	25	15
819		20l. blue	85	30

1951. Anti-fascist Heroes.

823	–	1l. mauve	15	10
824	–	2l. plum	20	10
825	**286**	4l. red	20	10
826	–	9l. brown	60	40
827	–	15l. olive	1·75	70
828	–	20l. blue	1·75	1·00
829	–	50l. grey	4·25	1·50

PORTRAITS: 1l. Chankova, Adalbert Antonov-Malchika, Sasho Dimitrov and Lilyana Dimitrova; 2l. Stanke Dimitrov; 9l. Anton Ivanov; 15l. Mikhailov; 20l. Georgi Dimitrov at Leipzig; 50l. Nocho Ivanov and Acram Stoyahov.

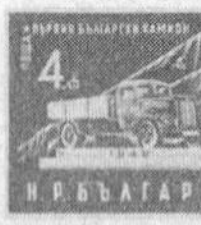

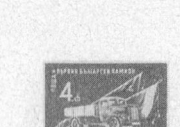

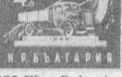

285 First Bulgarian Truck

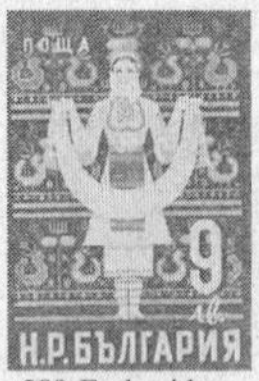

289 Embroidery

1951. National Occupations. (a) As T **285**.

820	–	1l. violet (Tractor)	15	10
821	–	2l. green (Steam-roller)	20	10
822	**285**	4l. brown	25	10

(b) As T **289**.

830	–	1l. brown (Tractor)	15	10
831	–	2l. violet (Steam-roller)	20	10
832	–	4l. brown (Truck)	45	40
833	**289**	9l. violet	85	30
834	–	15l. purple (Carpets)	1·50	1·00
835	–	20l. blue (Roses and Tobacco)	3·25	1·50
836	–	40l. green (Fruit)	5·00	2·10

The 9l. and 20l. are vert, the remainder horiz.

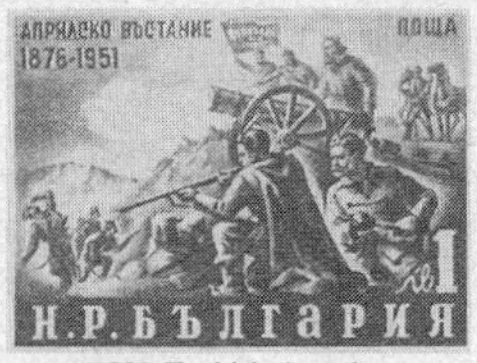

290 Turkish Attack

1951. 75th Anniv of April Uprising.

837	**290**	1l. brown	50	15
838	–	4l. green	50	15
839	–	9l. purple	85	45
840	–	20l. blue	1·25	80
841	–	40l. lake	1·90	1·50

DESIGNS—HORIZ: 4l. Proclamation of Uprising; 9l. Cannon and cavalry; 20l. Patriots in 1876 and 1944; 40l. Georgi Benkovsky and Georgi Dimitrov.

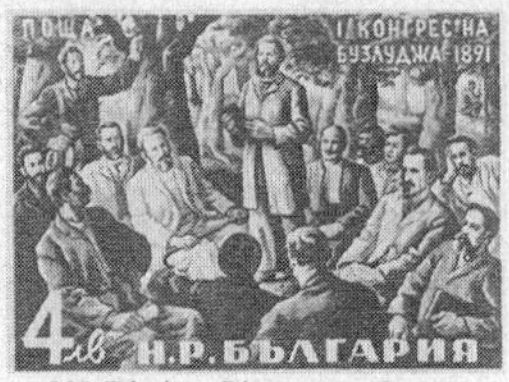

291 Dimitur Blagoev as Orator

1951. 60th Anniv of First Bulgarian Social Democratic Party Congress, Buzludzha.

842	**291**	1l. violet	20	10
843		4l. green	40	15
844		9l. purple	1·10	80

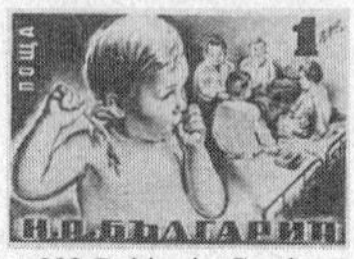

292 Babies in Creche

1951. Children's Day.

845	**292**	1l. brown	20	10
846	–	4l. purple	50	15
847	–	9l. green	1·00	35
848	–	20l. blue	2·00	1·25

DESIGNS: 4l. Children building models; 9l. Girl and children's play ground; 20l. Boy bugler and children marching.

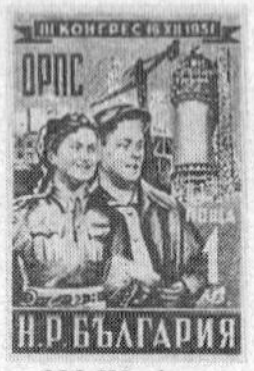

293 Workers

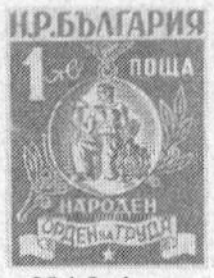

294 Labour medal (Obverse)

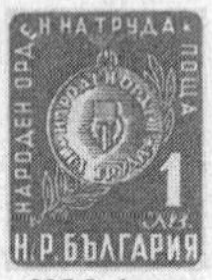

295 Labour medal (Reverse)

1951. 3rd General Workers' Union Congress.

849	**293**	1l. black	10	10
850	–	4l. brown	15	10

DESIGN inscr "16 XII 1951"; 4l. Georgi Dimitrov and Valdo Chervenkov (Prime minister).

1952. Order of Labour.

851	**294**	1l. red	10	10
852	**295**	1l. brown	10	10
853	**294**	4l. green	10	10
854	**295**	4l. green	10	10
855	**294**	9l. violet	35	15
856	**295**	9l. blue	35	15

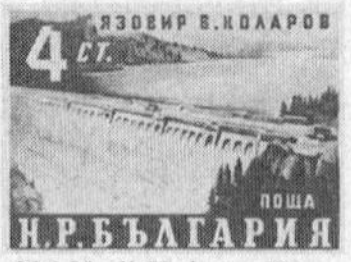

296 Vasil Kolarov Dam

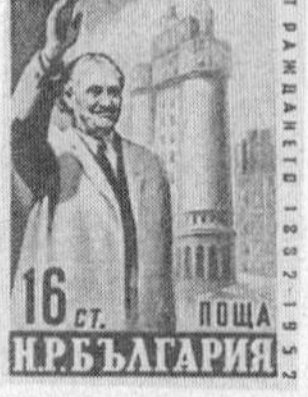

297 G. Dimitrov and Chemical Works

1952.

857	**296**	4s. green	15	10
858		12s. violet	20	10
859		16s. brown	25	10
860		44s. red	60	10
861		80s. blue	3·00	25

1952. 70th Birth Anniv of Georgi Dimitrov (statesman). Dated "1882–1952".

862	**297**	16s. brown	40	20
863	–	44s. brown	1·00	35
864	–	80s. blue	1·75	1·00

DESIGNS—HORIZ: 44s. Georgi Dimitrov (Prime minister 1946–49) and Prime minister Vulko Chervenkov. VERT: 80s. Full-face portrait of Georgi Dimitrov.

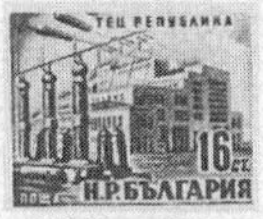

298 Republika Power Station

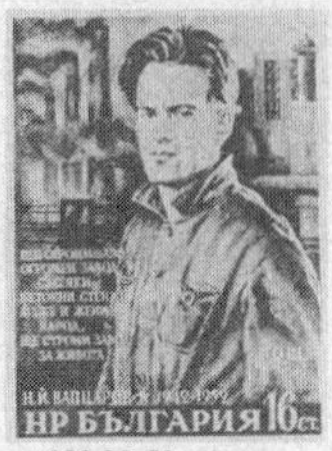

299 N. Vaptsarov (revolutionary)

1952.

866	**298**	16s. sepia	40	10
867		44s. purple	1·25	15

1952. 10th Death Anniv of Nikola Vaptsarov (poet and revolutionary).

869	**299**	16s. lake	30	25
870	–	44s. brown	1·10	90
871	–	80s. sepia	2·10	90

PORTRAITS: 44s. Facing bayonets; 80s. Full-face.

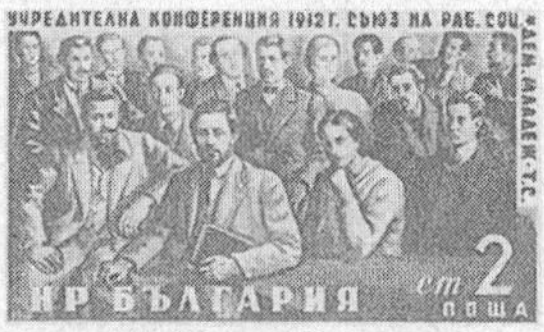

300 Congress Delegates

1952. 40th Anniv of First Workers' Social Democratic Youth League Congress.

872	**300**	2s. lake	15	10
873	–	16s. violet	25	10
874	–	44s. green	1·50	65
875	–	80s. sepia	1·90	1·40

DESIGNS: 16s. Young partisans; 44s. Factory and guards; 80s. Dimitrov addressing young workers.

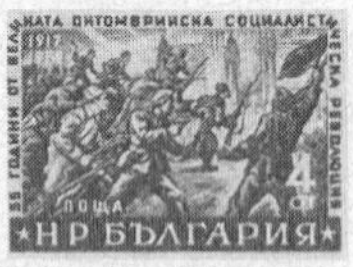

301 Attack on Winter Palace, St. Petersburg

1952. 35th Anniv of Russian Revolution. Dated "1917 1952".

876	**301**	4s. lake	10	10
877	–	8s. green	15	10
878	–	16s. blue	15	10
879	–	44s. sepia	50	20
880	–	80s. olive	1·25	40

DESIGNS: 8s. Volga–Don canal; 16s. Dove and globe; 44s. Lenin and Stalin; 80s. Lenin, Stalin and Himlay hydro-electric station.

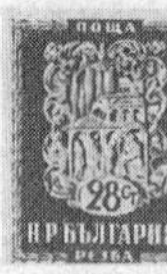

302

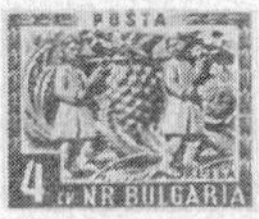

303 Vintagers and Grapes

1952. Wood Carvings depicting National Products.

881	–	2s. brown	10	10
882	–	8s. green	10	10
883	–	12s. brown	20	10
884	–	16s. purple	45	10
885	**302**	28s. green	85	15
886	–	44s. brown	90	15
887	**303**	80s. blue	1·50	15
888		1l. violet	3·25	30
889		4l. red	4·25	1·90

DESIGNS—VERT: 2s. Numeral in carved frame. HORIZ: 8s. Gift-offering to idol; 12s. Birds and grapes; 16s. Rose-gathering; 44s. "Attar of Roses".

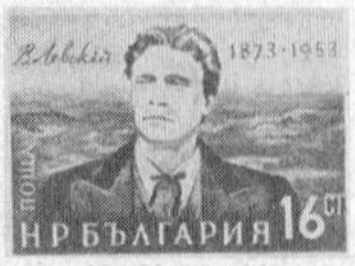

304 V. Levski

1953. 80th Anniv of Execution of Vasil Levski (revolutionary).

890	**304**	16s. brown on cream	15	10
891	–	44s. brown on cream	30	15

DESIGN: 44s. Levski addressing crowd.

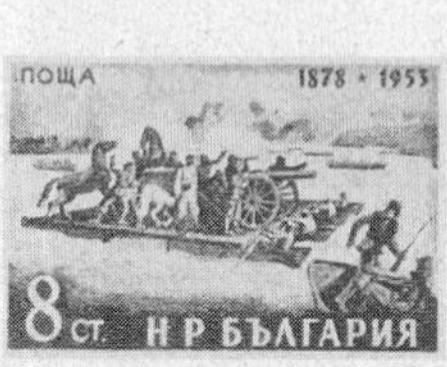

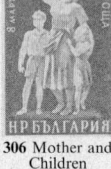

305 Russian Army Crossing R. Danube

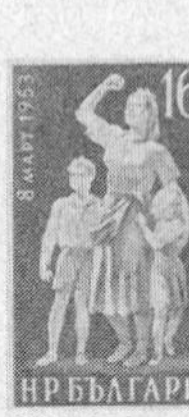

306 Mother and Children

1953. 75th Anniv of Liberation from Turkey.

892	**305**	8s. blue	30	10
893	–	16s. brown	25	10
894	–	44s. green	55	20
895	–	80s. lake	1·60	1·00
896	–	1l. black	2·00	1·60

DESIGNS—VERT: 16s. Battle of Shipka Pass. HORIZ: 44s. Peasants welcoming Russian soldiers; 80s. Bulgarians and Russians embracing; 1l. Shipka Pass memorial and Dimitrovgrad.

1953. International Women's Day.

897	**306**	16s. blue	15	10
898		16s. green	15	10

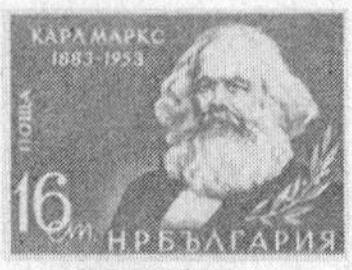

307 Karl Marx

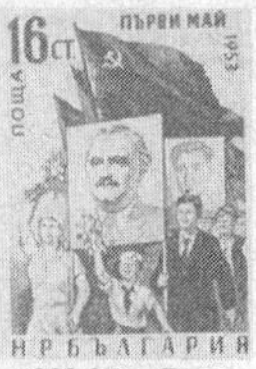

308 May Day Parade

1953. 70th Death Anniv of Karl Marx.

899	**307**	16s. blue	15	15
900	–	44s. brown	40	25

DESIGN—VERT: 44s. Book "Das Kapital".

1953. Labour Day.

901	**308**	16s. red	20	10

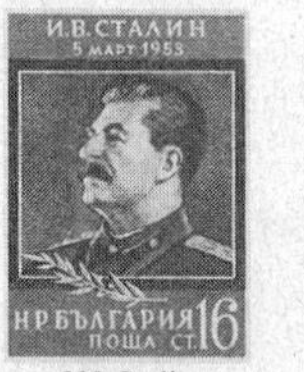

309 Stalin

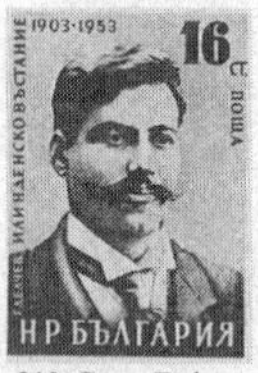

310 Goce Delcev (Macedonian revolutionary)

1953. Death of Stalin.

902	**309**	16s. brown	25	10
903		16s. black	25	15

1953. 50th Anniv of Ilinden–Preobrazhenie Rising.

904	**310**	16s. brown	10	10
905	–	44s. violet	40	25
906	–	1l. purple	55	30

DESIGNS. 44s. Insurgents and flag facing left. HORIZ: 1l. Insurgents and flag facing right.

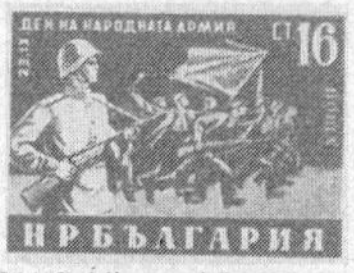

311 Soldier and Insurgents

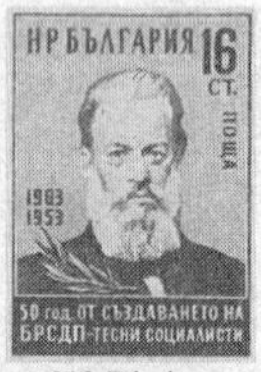

312 Dimitur Blagoev

1953. Army Day.

907	**311**	16s. red	25	10
908	–	44s. blue	65	15

DESIGN: 44s. Soldier, factories and combine-harvester.

1953. 50th Anniv of Bulgarian Workers' Social Democratic Party.

909	**312**	16s. brown	30	15
910	–	44s. red	65	20

DESIGN: 44s. Dimitrov and Blagoev.

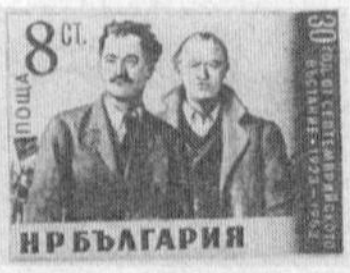

313 Georgi Dimitrov and Vasil Kolarov

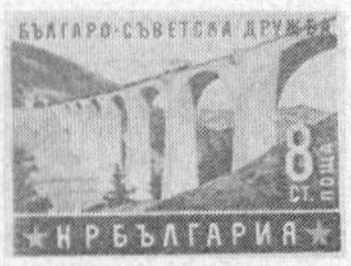

314 Railway Viaduct

1953. 30th Anniv of September Uprising.

911	**313**	8s. black	25	10
912	–	16s. brown	25	10
913	–	44s. red	80	30

DESIGNS: 16s. Insurgent and flag; 44s. Crowd of Insurgents.

1953. Bulgarian–Russian Friendship.

914	**314**	8s. blue	50	35
915	–	16s. slate	10	10
916	–	44s. brown	30	15
917	–	80s. orange	90	30

DESIGNS—HORIZ: 16s. Welder and industrial plant; 80s. Combine-harvester. VERT: 44s. Iron foundry.

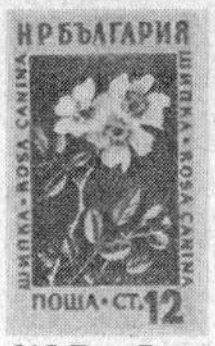
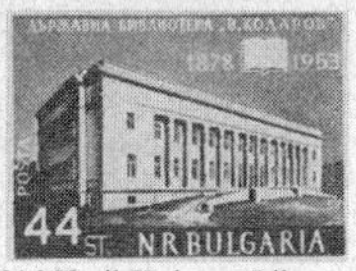

315 Dog Rose **316** Vasil Kolarov Library

1953. Medicinal Flowers.

918	–	2s. blue	10	10
919	–	4s. orange	10	10
920	–	8s. turquoise	15	10
921	**315**	12s. green	15	10
922	–	12s. red	15	10
923	–	16s. blue	25	10
924	–	16s. brown	25	10
925	–	20s. red	50	10
926	–	28s. green	50	15
927	–	40s. blue	55	25
928	–	44s. brown	75	25
929	–	80s. brown	1·50	55
930	–	1l. brown	4·00	1·00
931	–	2l. purple	6·75	2·50

FLOWERS: 2s. Deadly nightshade; 4s. Thorn-apple; 8s. Sage; 16s. Great yellow gentian; 20s. Opium poppy; 28s. Peppermint; 40s. Bear-berry; 44s. Coltsfoot; 80s. Primula; 1l. Dandelion; 2l. Foxglove.

1953. 75th Anniv of Kolarov Library, Sofia.

932	**316**	44s. brown	30	15

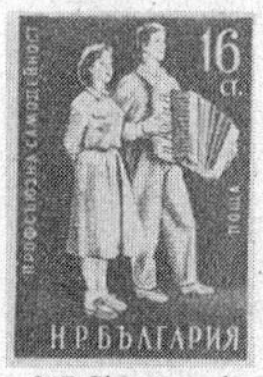
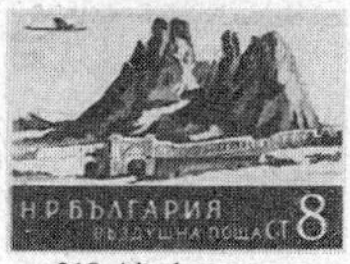

317 Singer and Musician **318** Airplane over Mountains

1953. Amateur Theatricals.

933	**317**	16s. brown	15	10
934	–	44s. green	40	20

DESIGN: 44s. Folk-dancers.

1954. Air.

935	**318**	8s. green	10	10
936	–	12s. lake	10	10
937	–	16s. brown	15	10
938	–	20s. salmon	15	10
939	–	28s. blue	20	10
940	–	44s. purple	25	10
941	–	60s. brown	45	10
942	–	80s. green	75	25
943	–	1l. green	2·25	50
944	–	4l. blue	4·50	1·75

DESIGNS—VERT: 12s. Exhibition buildings, Plovdiv; 80s. Tirnovo; 4l. Partisans' Monument. HORIZ: 16s. Seaside promenade, Varna; 20s. Combine-harvester in cornfield; 28s. Rila Monastery; 44s. Studena hydro-electric barrage; 60s. Dimitrovgrad; 1l. Sofia University and equestrian statue.

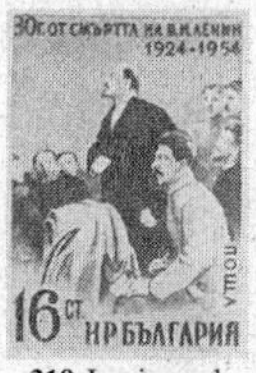
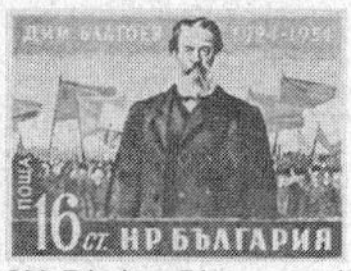

319 Lenin and Stalin **320** Dimitur Blagoev and Crowd

1954. 30th Death Anniv of Lenin.

945	**319**	16s. brown	15	10
946	–	44s. lake	30	10
947	–	80s. blue	70	20
948	–	1l. green	95	75

DESIGNS—VERT: 44s. Lenin statue; 80s. Lenin–Stalin Mausoleum and Kremlin; 1l. Lenin.

1954. 30th Death Anniv of Blagoev.

949	**320**	16s. brown	15	10
950	–	44s. sepia	40	15

DESIGN: 44s. Blagoev writing at desk.

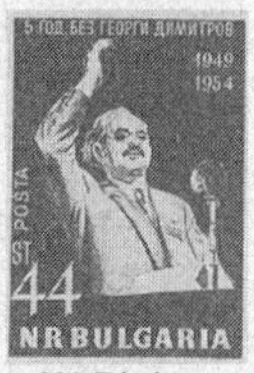
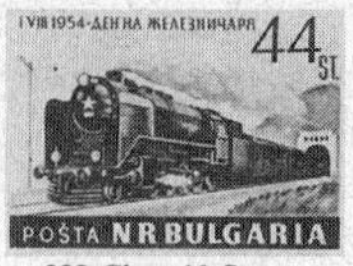

321 Dimitrov Speaking **322** Class 10 Steam Locomotive

1954. 5th Death Anniv of Dimitrov.

951	**321**	44s. lake	20	15
952	–	80s. brown	75	20

DESIGN—HORIZ: 80s. Dimitrov and blast-furnace.

1954. Railway Workers' Day.

953	**322**	44s. turquoise	1·90	20
954		44s. black	1·90	20

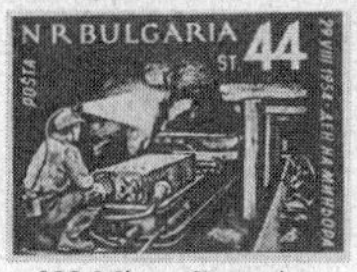
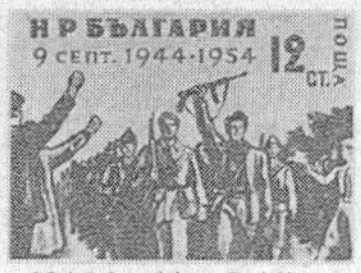

323 Miner Operating Machinery **324** Marching Soldiers

1954. Miners' Day.

955	**323**	44s. green	25	15

1954. 10th Anniv of Fatherland Front Government.

956	**324**	12s. lake	10	10
957	–	16s. red	10	10
958	–	28s. slate	20	10
959	–	44s. brown	25	10
960	–	80s. blue	70	30
961	–	1l. green	1·00	30

DESIGNS—VERT: 16s. Soldier and parents; 80s. Girl and boy pioneers; 1l. Dimitrov. HORIZ: 28s. Industrial plant; 44s. Dimitrov and workers.

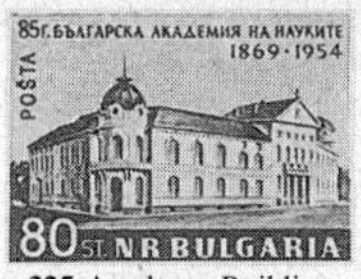
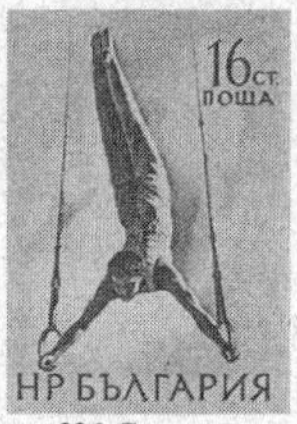

325 Academy Building **326** Gymnast

1954. 85th Anniv of Academy of Sciences.

962	**325**	80s. black	1·00	50

1954. Sports. Cream paper.

963	**326**	16s. green	1·50	20
964	–	44s. red	1·50	65
965	–	80s. brown	2·50	1·00
966	–	2l. blue	4·75	3·25

DESIGNS—VERT: 44s. Wrestlers; 2l. Ski-jumper. HORIZ: 80s. Horse-jumper.

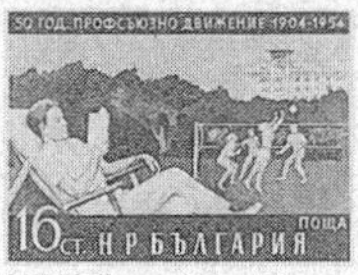

327 Velingrad Rest Home

1954. 50th Anniv of Trade Union Movement.

967	**327**	16s. green	15	10
968	–	44s. red	15	15
969	–	80s. blue	85	30

DESIGNS—VERT: 44s. Foundryman. HORIZ: 80s. Georgi Dimitrov, Dimitur Blagoev and Georgi Kirkov.

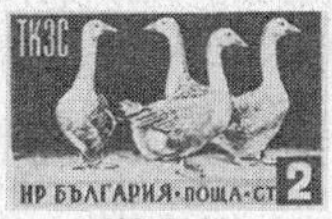
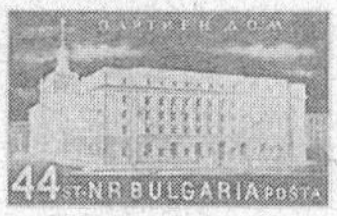

328 Geese **329** Communist Party Building

1955.

970	**328**	2s. green	10	10
971	–	4s. olive	20	10
972	–	12s. brown	35	10
973	–	16s. brown	60	10
974	–	28s. blue	30	10
975	**329**	44s. red	10·50	20
976	–	80s. brown	70	20
977	–	1l. green	1·75	30

DESIGNS: 4s. Rooster and hens; 12s. Sow and piglets; 16s. Ewe and lambs; 28s. Telephone exchange; 80s. Flats; 1l. Cellulose factory.

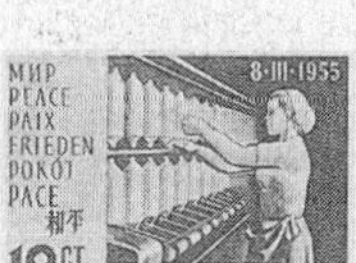
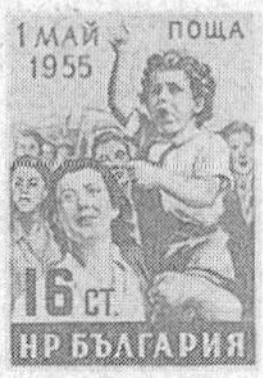

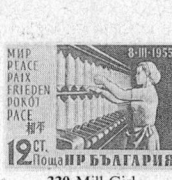

330 Mill Girl **332** Rejoicing Crowds

1955. International Women's Day.

978	**330**	12s. brown	10	10
979	–	16s. green	20	10
980	–	44s. blue	75	10
981	–	44s. red	75	10

DESIGNS—HORIZ: 16s. Girl feeding cattle. VERT: 44s. Mother and baby.

1955. As Nos. 820 and 822 surch **16 CT.**

981a	–	16s. on 1l. violet	20	10
982	**285**	16s. on 4l. brown	75	10

1955. Labour Day.

983	**332**	16s. red	15	10
984	–	44s. blue	50	10

DESIGN: 44s. Three workers and globe.

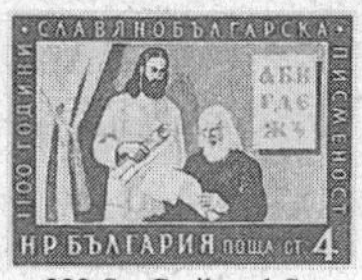
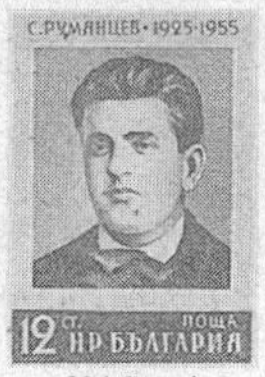

333 St. Cyril and St. Methodius **334** Sergei Rumyantsev

1955. 1100th Anniv of 1st Bulgarian Literature. On cream paper.

985	**333**	4s. blue	10	10
986	–	8s. olive	10	10
987	–	16s. black	15	10
988	–	28s. red	25	15
989	–	44s. brown	45	20
990	–	80s. red	1·00	80
991	–	2l. black	2·50	1·60

DESIGNS: 8s. Monk writing; 16s. Early printing press; 28s. Khristo Botev (poet); 44s. Ivan Vazov (poet and novelist); 80s. Dimitur Blagoev (writer and editor) and books; 2l. Dimitur Blagoev Polygraphic Complex, Sofia.

1955. 30th Death Annivs of Bulgarian Poets. On cream paper.

992	**334**	12s. brown	30	10
993	–	16s. brown	40	10
994	–	44s. green	60	25

DESIGNS: 16s. Khristo Yusenov; 44s. Geo Milev.

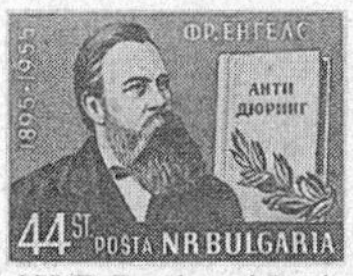
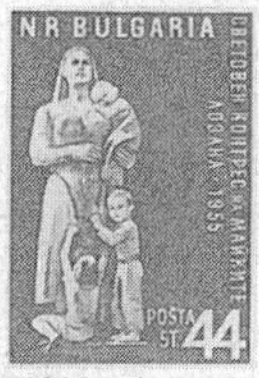

335 F. Engels and Book **336** Mother and Children

1955. 60th Death Anniv of Engels.

995	**335**	44s. brown on cream	55	20

1955. World Mothers' Congress, Lausanne.

996	**336**	44s. lake on cream	35	10

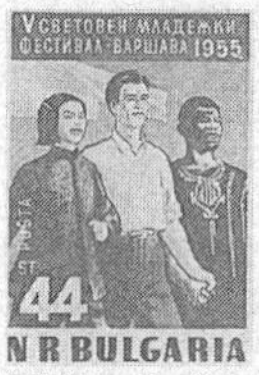
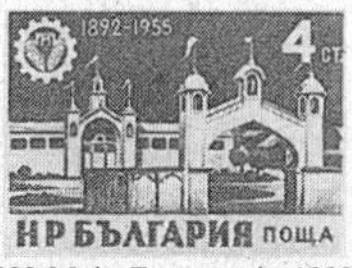

337 "Youth of the World" **338** Main Entrance in 1892

1955. 5th World Youth Festival, Warsaw.

997	**337**	44s. blue on cream	30	15

1955. 16th International Fair, Plovdiv.

998	**338**	4s. brown on cream	10	10
999	–	16s. red on cream	10	10
1000	–	44s. green on cream	20	15
1001	–	80s. cream	85	20

DESIGNS—VERT: 16s. Sculptured group; 80s. Fair poster. HORIZ: 44s. Fruit.

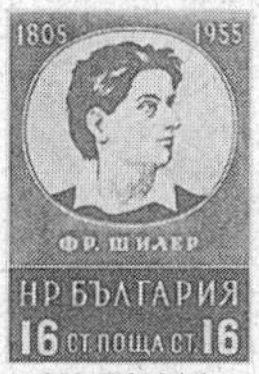
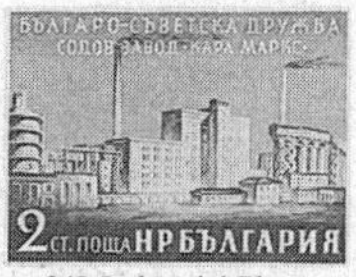

339 Friedrich Schiller (dramatist) (150th death anniv) **340** Industrial Plant

1955. Cultural Annivs. Writers. On cream paper.

1002	**339**	16s. brown	30	15
1003	–	44s. red	75	15
1004	–	60s. blue	85	15
1005	–	80s. black	1·25	15
1006	–	1l. purple	2·50	1·00
1007	–	2l. olive	3·25	2·00

PORTRAITS: 44s. Adam Mickiewicz (poet, death centenary); 60s. Hans Christian Andersen (150th birth anniv); 80s. Baron de Montesquieu (philosopher, death bicentenary); 1l. Miguel de Cervantes (350th anniv of publication of "Don Quixote"); 2l. Walt Whitman (poet) (centenary of publication of "Leaves of Grass").

1955. Bulgarian–Russian Friendship. On cream paper.

1008	**340**	2s. slate	10	10
1009	–	4s. blue	10	10
1010	–	16s. green	55	25
1011	–	44s. brown	35	10
1012	–	80s. green	70	15
1013	–	1l. black	90	30

DESIGNS—HORIZ: 4s. Dam; 16s. Friendship railway bridge over River Danube between Ruse and Giurgiu (Rumania). VERT: 44s. Monument; 80s. Ivan-Michurin (botanist); 1l. Vladimir Mayakovsky (writer).

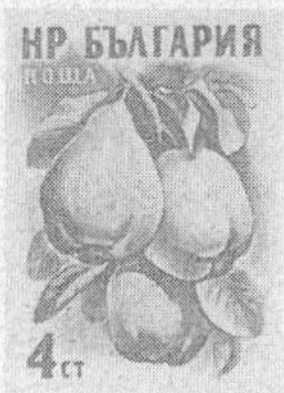

341 Emblem **342** Quinces

1956. Centenary of Library Reading Rooms. On cream paper.

1014	**341**	12s. red	10	10
1015	–	16s. brown	10	10
1016	–	44s. myrtle	50	20

DESIGNS: 16s. K. Pshourka writing; 44s. B. Kiro reading.

1956. Fruits.

1017	**342**	4s. red	1·40	10
1017a		4s. green	15	10
1018	–	8s. green (Pears)	60	15
1018a	–	8s. brown (Pears)	15	10
1019	–	16s. dark red (Apples)	1·25	15
1019a	–	16s. red (Apples)	35	10
1020	–	44s. violet (Grapes)	1·40	30
1020a	–	44s. ochre (Grapes)	70	20

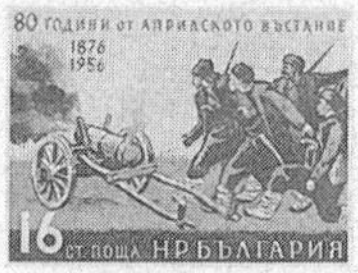

343 Artillerymen

1956. 80th Anniv of April Uprising.

1021	**343**	16s. brown	25	20
1022	–	44s. green (Cavalry charge)	30	25

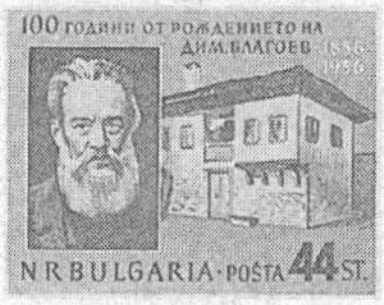

344 Blagoev and Birthplace at Zagovichane

1956. Birth Centenary of Dimitur Blagoev (socialist writer).

1023	**344**	44s. turquoise	30	15

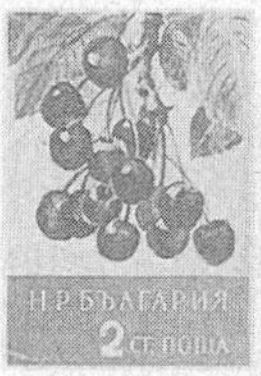
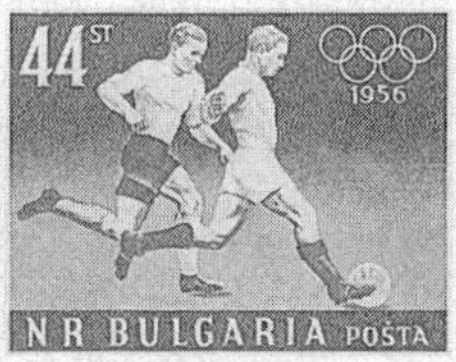

345 Cherries **346** Football

1956. Fruits.

1024	**345**	2s. lake	15	10
1025	–	12s. blue (Plums)	20	10
1026	–	28s. buff (Greengages)	35	10
1027	–	80s. red (Strawberries)	1·00	35

1956. Olympic Games.

1028	–	4s. blue	40	15
1029	–	12s. red	55	10
1030	–	16s. brown	60	10
1031	**346**	44s. green	1·10	30
1032	–	80s. brown	1·60	1·00
1033	–	1l. lake	2·40	1·40

DESIGNS—VERT: 4s. Gymnastics; 12s. Throwing the discus; 80s. Basketball. HORIZ: 16s. Pole vaulting; 1l. Boxing.

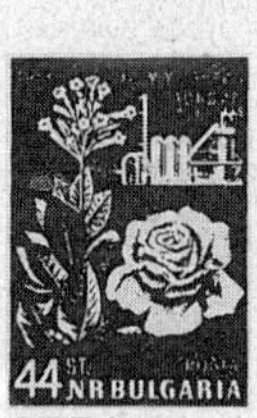
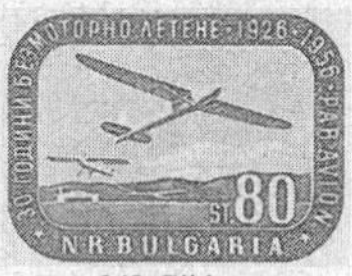

347 Tobacco and Rose **348** Gliders

1956. 17th International Fair, Plovdiv.

1034	**347**	44s. red	60	35
1035		44s. green	60	35

1956. Air. 30th Anniv of Gliding Club.

1036	–	44s. blue	30	15
1037	–	60s. violet	55	20
1038	**348**	80s. green	80	25

DESIGNS: 44s. Launching glider; 60s. Glider over hangar.

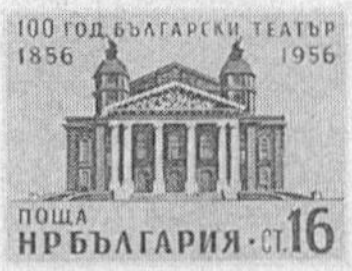
349 National Theatre

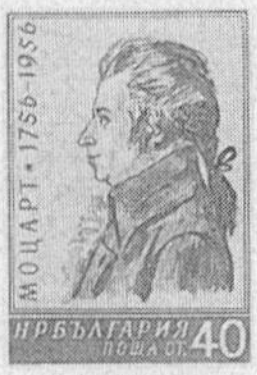
350 Wolfgang Mozart (composer, birth bicent)

1956. Centenary of National Theatre.
1039 **349** 16s. brown 15 10
1040 – 44s. turquoise 40 15
DESIGN: 44s. Dobri Voinikov and Sava Dobroplodni (dramatist).

1956. Cultural Anniversaries.
1041 – 16s. olive 20 10
1042 – 20s. brown 25 10
1043 **350** 40s. red 50 10
1044 – 44s. brown 40 15
1045 – 60s. slate 65 15
1046 – 80s. brown 75 15
1047 – 1l. green . . . . . . 1·25 60
1048 – 2l. green . . . . . . 2·40 1·25
PORTRAITS: 16s. Benjamin Franklin (journalist and statesman, 150th birth anniv); 20s. Rembrandt (artist, 350th birth anniv); 44s. Heinrich Heine (poet, death centenary); 60s. George Bernard Shaw (dramatist, birth centenary); 80s. Fyodor Dostoevsky (novelist, 75th death anniv); 1l. Henrik Ibsen (dramatist, 50th death anniv); 2l. Pierre Curie (physicist, 50th death anniv).

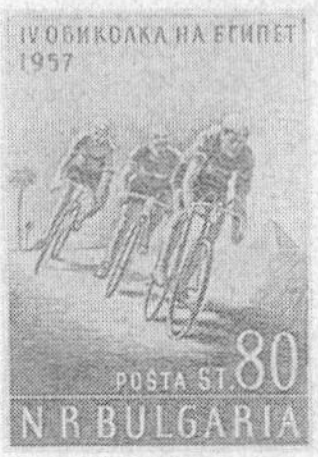
351 Cyclists

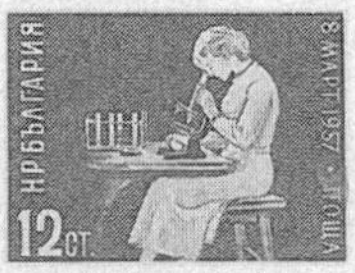
352 Woman with Microscope

1957. Tour of Egypt Cycle Race.
1049 **351** 80s. brown 90 30
1050 80s. turquoise 90 30

1957. International Women's Day. Inscr as in T **352**.
1051 **352** 12s. blue 10 10
1052 – 16s. brown 15 10
1053 – 44s. green 35 15
DESIGNS: 16s. Woman and children; 44s. Woman feeding poultry.

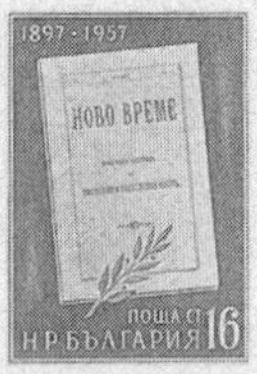
353 "New Times"

1957. 60th Anniv of "New Times" (book).
1054 **353** 16s. red 20 10

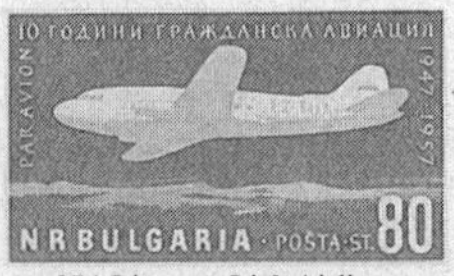
354 Lisunov Li-2 Airliner

1957. Air. 10th Anniv of Bulgarian Airways.
1055 **354** 80s. blue . . . . 1·00 30

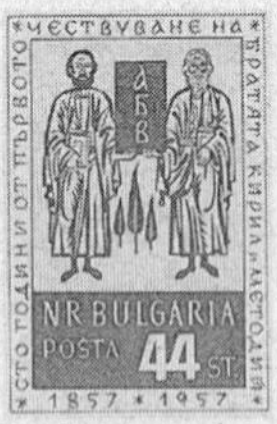
355 St. Cyril and St. Methodius

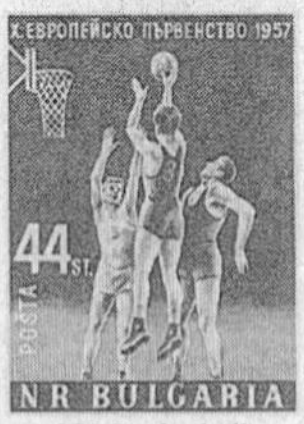
356 Basketball

1957. Centenary of Canonization of Saints Cyril and Methodius (founders of Cyrillic alphabet).
1056 **355** 44s. olive and buff . . . 85 20

1957. 10th European Basketball Championships.
1057 **356** 44s. green . . . . 1·60 30

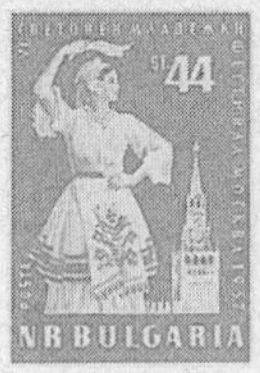
357 Girl in National Costume

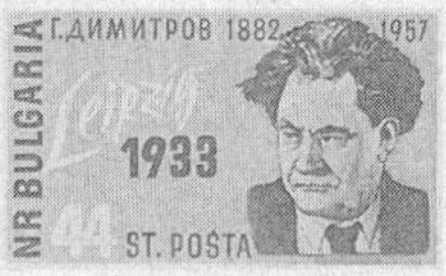
358 G. Dimitrov

1957. 6th World Youth Festival, Moscow.
1058 **357** 44s. blue 50 15

1957. 75th Birth Anniv of Georgi Dimitrov (statesman).
1059 **358** 44s. red . . . . 1·00 15

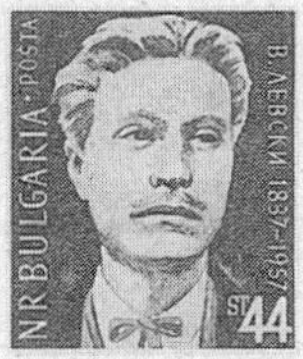
359 V. Levski

1957. 120th Birth Anniv of Vasil Levski (revolutionary).
1060 **359** 44s. green 85 15

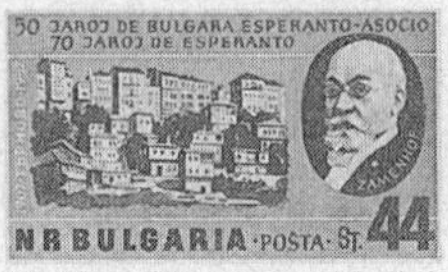
360 View of Turnovo and Ludwig Zamenhof (inventor)

1957. 70th Anniv of Esperanto (invented language) and 50th Anniv of Bulgarian Esperanto Association.
1061 **360** 44s. green . . . . 1·00 20

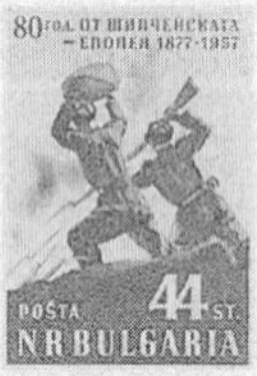
361 Soldiers in Battle

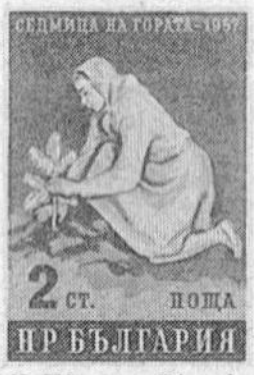
362 Woman Planting Tree

1957. 80th Anniv of Liberation from Turkey.
1062 – 16s. green 20 10
1063 **361** 44s. brown 55 15
DESIGN: 16s. Old and young soldiers.

1957. Reafforestation Campaign.
1064 **362** 2s. green 10 10
1065 – 12s. brown 10 10
1066 – 16s. blue 10 10
1067 – 44s. turquoise 40 10
1068 – 80s. green 85 25
DESIGNS—HORIZ: 12s. Red deer in forest; 16s. Dam and trees; 44s. Polikarpov Po-2 biplane over forest; 80s. Trees and cornfield.

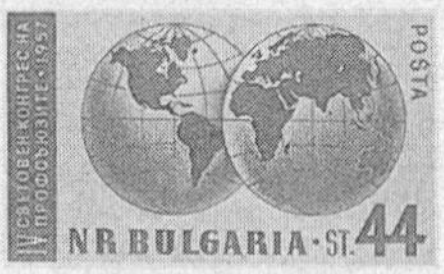
363 Two Hemispheres

1957. 4th World T.U.C., Leipzig.
1069 **363** 44s. blue 45 15

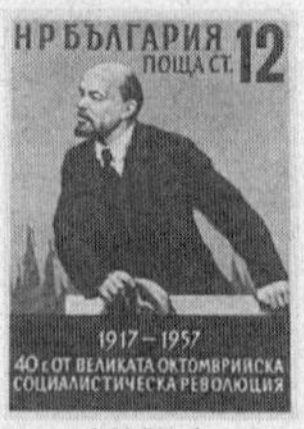
364 Lenin

1957. 40th Anniv of Russian Revolution. Inscr "1917–1957".
1070 **364** 12s. brown 30 10
1071 – 16s. turquoise . . . . . 1·10 10
1072 – 44s. blue . . . . 1·10 30
1073 – 60s. red . . . . 1·75 25
1074 – 80s. green . . . . 2·75 50
DESIGNS: 16s. Cruiser "Aurora"; 44s. Dove of Peace over Europe; 60s. Revolutionaries; 80s. Oil refinery.

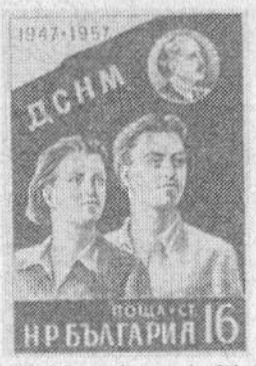
365 Youth and Girl

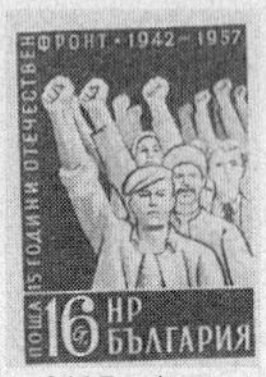
366 Partisans

1957. 10th Anniv of Dimitrov National Youth Movement.
1075 **365** 16s. red 15 10

1957. 15th Anniv of Fatherland Front.
1076 **366** 16s. brown 15 10

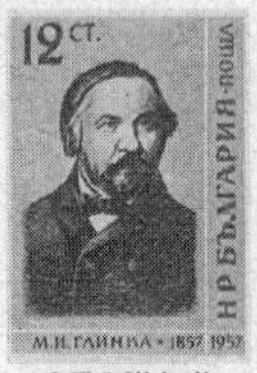
367 Mikhail Glinka (composer, death centenary)

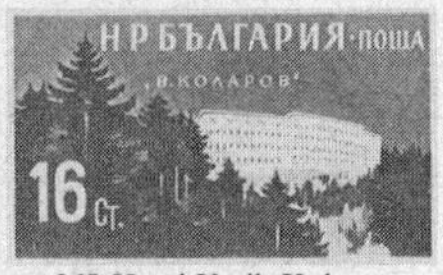
368 Hotel Vasil, Kolarov

1957. Cultural Celebrities.
1077 **367** 12s. brown 30 10
1078 – 16s. green 30 10
1079 – 40s. blue . . . . 1·00 25
1080 – 44s. brown . . . . . . 1·10 25
1081 – 60s. brown . . . . . . 1·25 50
1082 – 80s. purple . . . . . . 3·25 2·10
DESIGNS: 16s. Ion Comenius (educationist) (300th anniv of publication of "Didoetica Opera Omria"); 40s. Carl Linnaeus (botanist, 250th birth anniv); 44s. William Blake (writer, birth bicent); 60s. Carlo Goldoni (dramatist, 250th birth anniv); 80s. Auguste Comte (philosopher, death centenary).

1958. Holiday Resorts.
1083 – 4s. blue 10 10
1084 – 8s. brown 10 10
1085 – 12s. green 10 10
1086 **368** 16s. green 15 10
1087 – 44s. turquoise 30 15
1088 – 60s. blue 40 15
1089 – 80s. brown 50 25
1090 – 1l. brown 60 25
DESIGNS—HORIZ: 4s. Skis and Pirin Mts; 8s. Old house in Koprivshtita; 12s. Hostel at Yelingrad; 44s. Hotel at Momin-Prokhod; 60s. Seaside hotel and peninsula, Nesebur; 80s. Beach scene, Varna; 1l. Modern hotels, Varna.

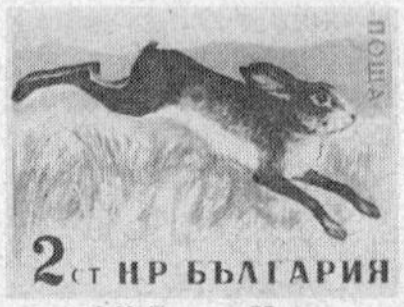
369 Brown Hare

1958. Forest Animals.
1091 **369** 2s. deep green & green 15 10
1092 – 12s. brown and green . . 40 10
1093 – 16s. brown and green . . 50 15
1094 – 44s. brown and blue . . 75 15
1095 – 80s. brown and ochre . . 1·00 40
1096 – 1l. brown and blue . . . 2·25 70
DESIGNS—VERT: 12s. Roe doe. HORIZ: 16s. Red deer; 44s. Chamois; 80s. Brown bear; 1l. Wild boar.

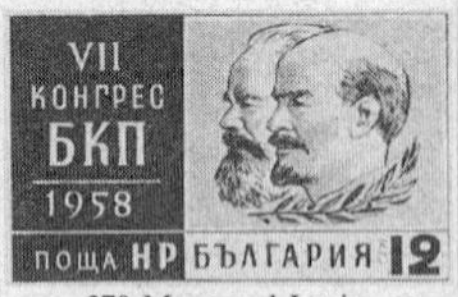
370 Marx and Lenin

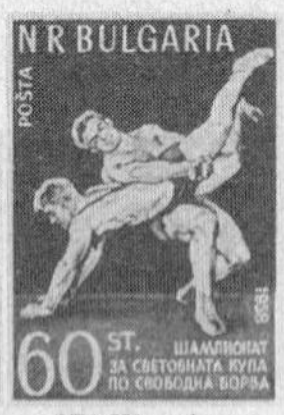
371 Wrestlers

1958. 7th Bulgarian Communist Party Congress. Inscr as in T **370**.
1097 **370** 12s. brown 30 10
1098 – 16s. red 60 15
1099 – 44s. blue . . . . 1·25 15
DESIGNS: 16s. Workers marching with banners; 44s. Lenin blast furnaces.

1958. Wrestling Championships.
1100 **371** 60s. lake . . . . 1·75 1·00
1101 80s. sepia . . . . 2·00 1·25

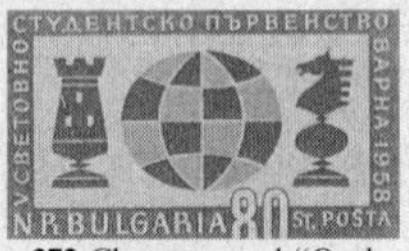
372 Chessmen and "Oval Chessboard"

1958. 5th World Students' Team Chess Championship, Varna.
1102 **372** 80s. green . . . . 7·50 7·50

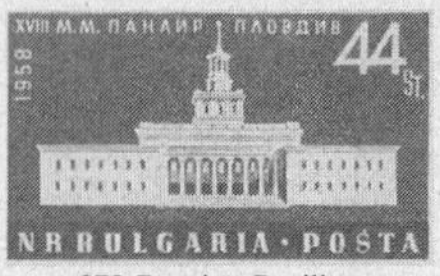
373 Russian Pavilion

1958. 18th International Fair, Plovdiv.
1103 **373** 44s. red 45 25

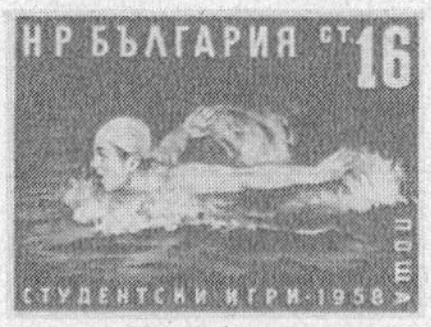
374 Swimmer

1958. Bulgarian Students' Games.
1104 **374** 16s. blue 15 10
1105 – 28s. brown 30 15
1106 – 44s. green 50 15
DESIGNS: 28s. Dancer; 44s. Volleyball players at net.

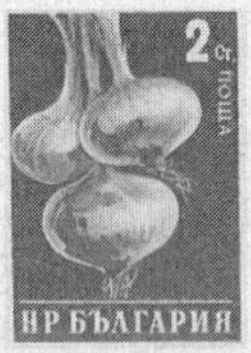
375 Onions

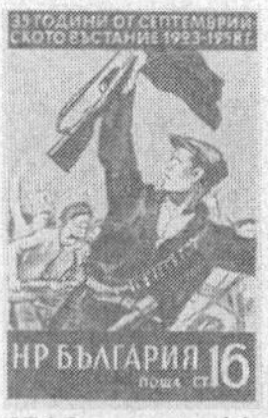
376 Insurgent with Rifle

1958. "Agricultural Propaganda".
1107 **375** 2s. brown 10 10
1108 – 12s. lake (Garlic) 10 10
1109 – 16s. myrtle (Peppers) . . 15 10
1110 – 44s. red (Tomatoes) . . 20 10
1111 – 80s. green (Cucumbers) 55 20
1112 – 1l. violet (Aubergines) 1·10 20

1958. 35th Anniv of September Uprising.
1113 **376** 16s. orange 15 10
1114 – 44s. lake 40 20
DESIGN—HORIZ: 44s. Insurgent helping wounded comrade.

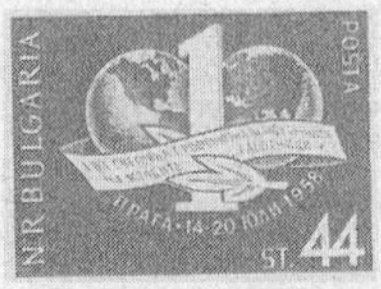
377 Conference Emblem

1958. 1st World Trade Union's Young Workers' Conference, Prague.
1115 **377** 44s. blue 65 45

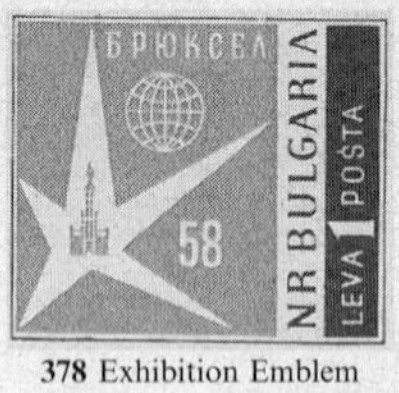
378 Exhibition Emblem

1958. Brussels International Exhibition.
1116 **378** 1l. blue and black . . . 10·50 8·50

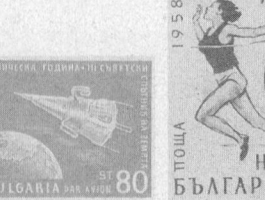

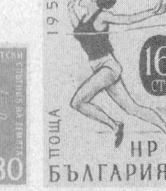

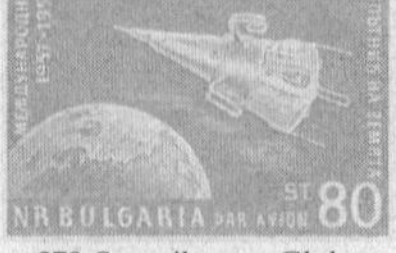
379 Sputnik over Globe

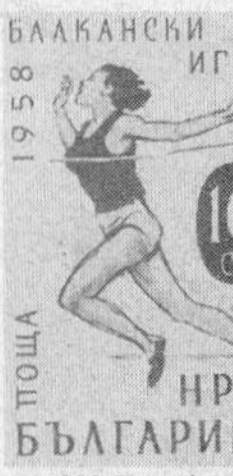
380 Running

1958. Air. I.G.Y.
1117 **379** 80s. turquoise . . . . . 6·00 3·25

1958. Balkan Games. Inscr "1958".
1118 **380** 16s. brown 60 15
1119 – 44s. olive 70 20
1120 – 60s. blue . . . . 1·10 25
1121 – 80s. green . . . . 1·75 65
1122 – 4l. lake . . . . 9·25 6·75
DESIGNS—HORIZ: 44s. Throwing the javelin; 60s. High-jumping; 80s. Hurdling. VERT: 4l. Putting the shot.

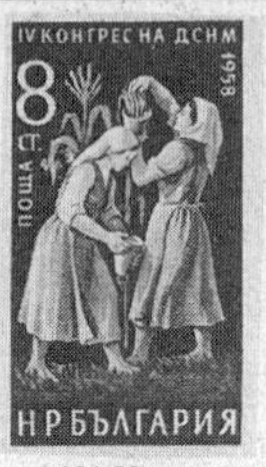

381 Young Gardeners

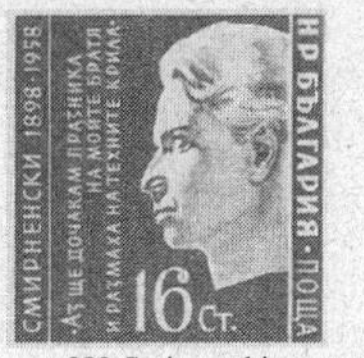

382 Smirnenski

1958. 4th Dimitrov National Youth Movement Congress. Inscr as in T **381**.
1123 **381** 8s. green 10 10
1124 – 12s. brown 10 10
1125 – 16s. purple 15 10
1126 – 40s. blue 30 15
1127 – 44s. red 75 25
DESIGNS—HORIZ: 12s. Farm girl with cattle; 40s. Youth with wheel-barrow. VERT: 16s. Youth with pickaxe and girl with spade; 44s. Communist Party Building.

1958. 60th Birth Anniv of Khristo Smirnenski (poet and revolutionary).
1128 **382** 16s. red 15 15

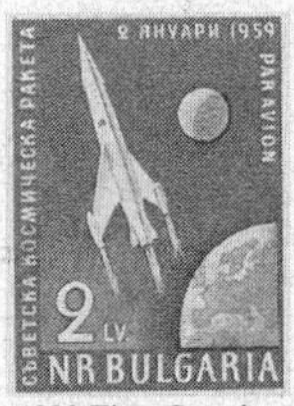

383 First Cosmic Rockets

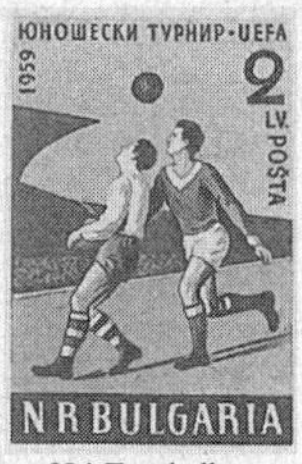

384 Footballers

1959. Air. Launching of First Cosmic Rocket.
1129 **383** 2l. brown and blue . . . 8·50 8·50

1959. Youth Football Games, Sofia.
1130 **384** 2l. brown on cream . . . 2·40 1·75

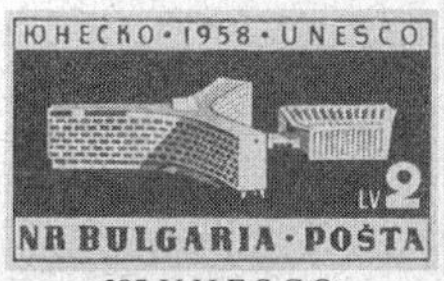

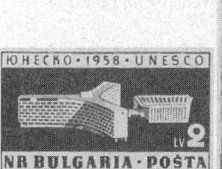

385 U.N.E.S.C.O. Headquarters, Paris

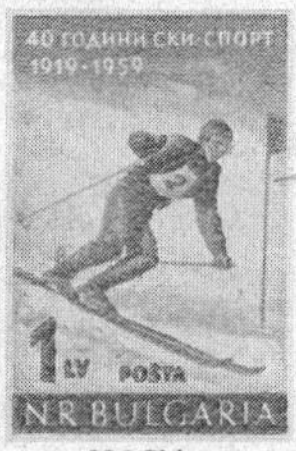

386 Skier

1959. Inauguration of U.N.E.S.C.O. Headquarters Building.
1131 **385** 2l. purple on cream . . . 2·40 1·90

1959. 40 Years of Skiing in Bulgaria.
1132 **386** 1l. blue on cream . . . 1·50 85

1959. No. 1110 surch **45 CT**.
1133 45s. on 44s. red . . . . . . 1·00 15

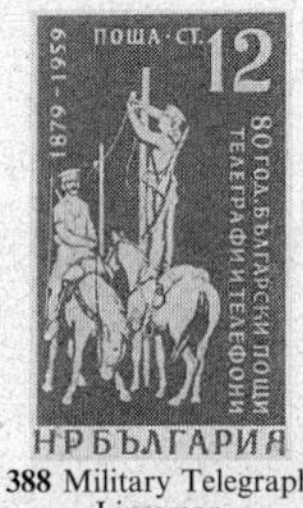

388 Military Telegraph Linesman

1959. 80th Anniv of 1st Bulgarian Postage Stamps.
1134 **388** 12s. yellow and green . . 15 10
1135 – 16s. mauve and purple 35 10
1136 – 60s. yellow and brown 85 25
1137 – 80s. salmon and red . . 95 25
1138 – 1l. blue . . . . 1·10 50
1139 – 2l. brown . . . . 3·50 1·90
DESIGNS—HORIZ: 16s. 19th-century mail-coach; 80s. Early postal car; 2l. Striking railway workers. VERT: 60s. Bulgarian 1879 stamp; 1l. Radio tower.

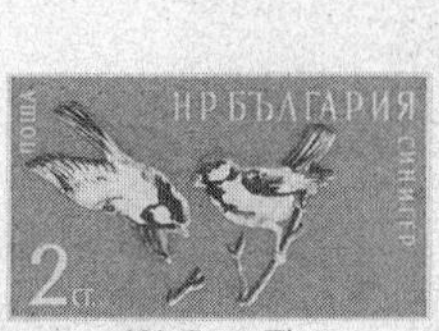

389 Great Tits

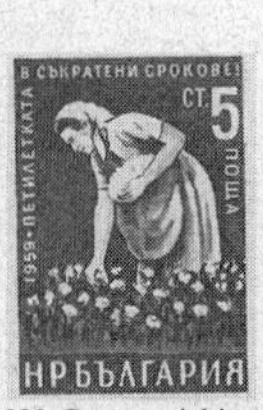

390 Cotton-picking

1959. Birds.
1140 **389** 2s. slate and yellow . . . 15 10
1141 – 8s. green and brown . . 20 15
1142 – 16s. sepia and brown . . 70 30
1143 – 45s. myrtle and brown 1·10 45
1144 – 60s. grey and blue . . . 2·50 55
1145 – 80s. drab and turquoise 4·00 65
DESIGNS—HORIZ: 8s. Hoopoe; 60s. Rock partridge; 80s. European cuckoo. VERT: 16s. Great spotted woodpecker; 45s. Grey partridge.

1959. Five Year Plan.
1146 – 2s. brown 10 10
1147 – 4s. bistre 20 10
1148 **390** 5s. green 20 10
1149 – 10s. brown 20 10
1150 – 12s. brown 15 10
1151 – 15s. mauve 20 10
1152 – 16s. violet 20 10
1153 – 20s. orange 30 10
1154 – 25s. blue 25 10
1155 – 28s. green 35 10
1156 – 40s. blue 45 10
1157 – 45s. brown 35 15
1158 – 60s. red 60 20
1159 – 80s. olive . . . . . . 1·25 20
1160 – 1l. lake 90 20
1161 – 1l.25 blue . . . . . . 2·25 75
1162 – 2l. red . . . . 1·25 35
DESIGNS—HORIZ: 2s. Children at play; 10s. Dairymaid milking cow; 16s. Industrial plant; 20s. Combine-harvester; 40s. Hydro-electric barrage; 60s. Furnaceman; 1l.25, Machinist. VERT: 4s. Woman doctor examining child; 12s. Tobacco harvesting; 15s. Machinist; 25s. Power linesman; 28s. Tending sunflowers; 45s. Miner; 80s. Fruit-picker; 1l. Workers with symbols of agriculture and industry; 2l. Worker with banner.

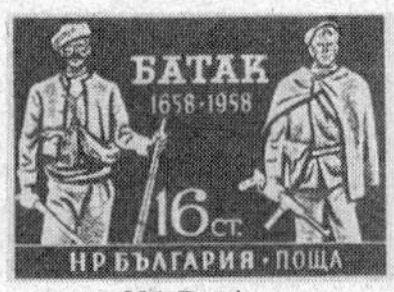

391 Patriots

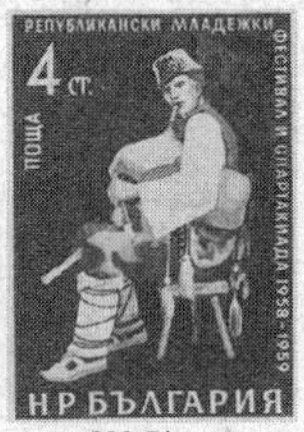

392 Piper

1959. 300th Anniv of Batak.
1163 **391** 16s. brown 25 10

1959. Spartacist Games. Inscr "1958–1959".
1164 **392** 4s. olive on cream . . . 20 10
1165 – 12s. red on yellow . . . 20 10
1166 – 16s. lake on salmon . . 20 15
1167 – 20s. blue on blue . . . 30 15
1168 – 80s. green on green . . 90 35
1169 – 1l. brown on orange . . 1·25 60
DESIGNS—VERT: 12s. Gymnastics; 1l. Urn. HORIZ: 16s. Girls exercising with hoops; 20s. Dancers leaping; 80s. Ballet dancers.

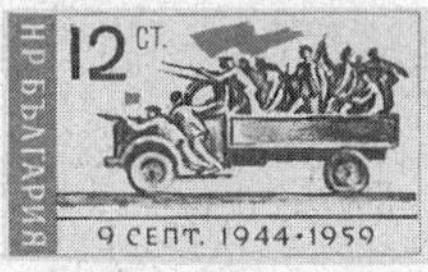

393 Soldiers in Lorry

1959. 15th Anniv of Fatherland Front Government.
1170 **393** 12s. blue and red 10 10
1171 – 16s. black and red . . . 10 10
1172 – 45s. blue and red . . . 20 10
1173 – 60s. green and red . . . 25 20
1174 – 80s. brown and red . . . 45 25
1175 – 1l.25 brown and red . . 95 45
DESIGNS—HORIZ: 16s. Partisans meeting Red Army soldiers; 45s. Blast furnaces; 60s. Tanks; 80s. Combine-harvester in cornfield. VERT: 1l.25, Pioneers with banner.

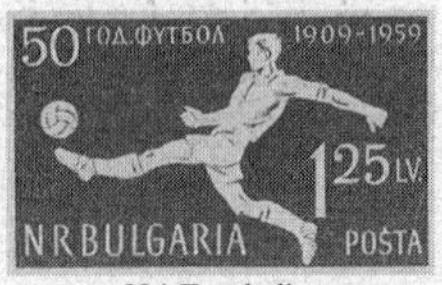

394 Footballer

1959. 50th Anniv of Football in Bulgaria.
1176 **394** 1l.25 green on yellow . . 6·75 5·00

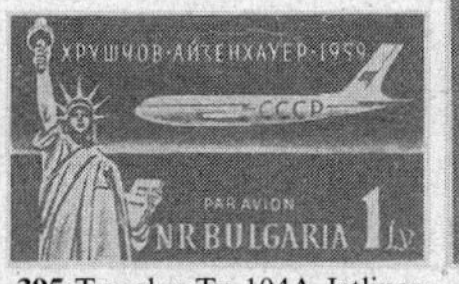

395 Tupolev Tu-104A Jetliner and Statue of Liberty

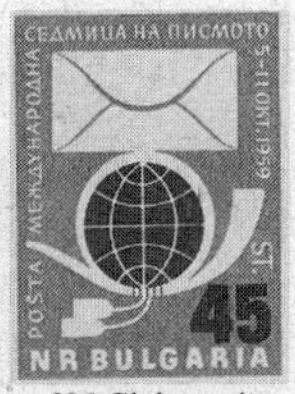

396 Globe and Letter

1959. Air. Visit of Nikita Khrushchev (Russian Prime Minister) to U.S.A.
1177 **395** 1l. pink and blue . . . . 3·00 2·75

1959. International Correspondence Week.
1178 **396** 45s. black and green . . 60 15
1179 – 1l.25 red, black & blue 85 25
DESIGN: 1l.25, Pigeon and letter.

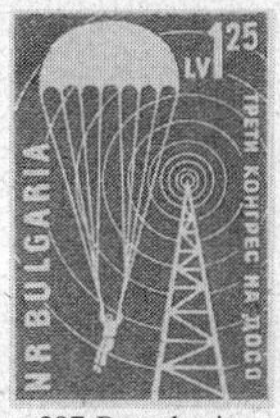

397 Parachutist

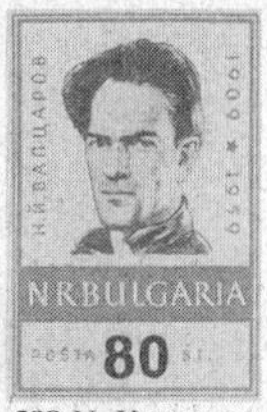

398 N. Vaptsarov

1960. 3rd Voluntary Defence Congress.
1180 **397** 1l.25 cream & turquoise 2·40 1·10

1960. 50th Birth Anniv of Nikola Vaptsarov (poet and revolutionary).
1181 **398** 80s. brown and green . . 45 15

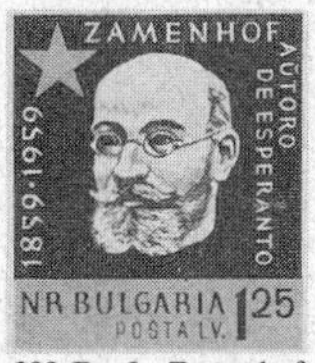

399 Dr. L. Zamenhof

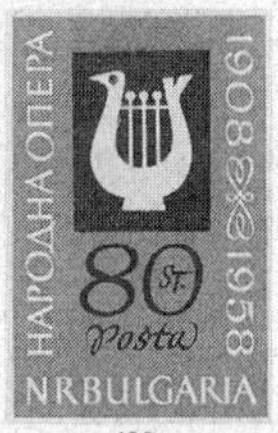

400

1960. Birth Centenary of Dr. Ludwig Zamenhof (inventor of Esperanto).
1182 **399** 1l.25 green & lt green . . 1·40 85

1960. 50th Anniv of State Opera.
1183 **400** 80s. black and green . . 85 25
1184 – 1l.25 black and red . . . 1·25 30
DESIGN: 1l.25, Lyre.

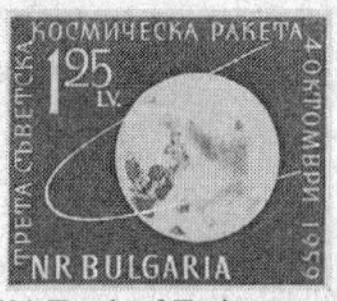

401 Track of Trajectory of "Lunik 3" around the Moon

1960. Flight of "Lunik 3".
1185 **401** 1l.25 green, yellow & bl 7·00 5·00

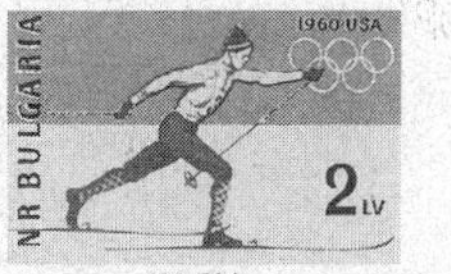

402 Skier

1960. Winter Olympic Games.
1186 **402** 2l. brown, blue & black 1·60 1·00

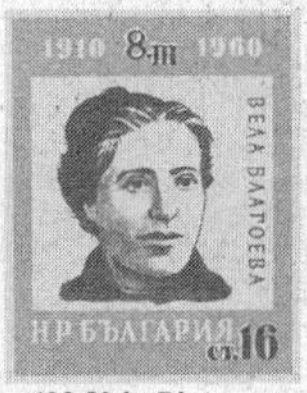

403 Vela Blagoeva

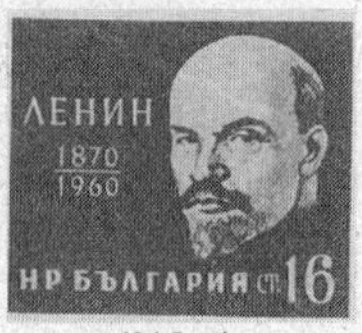

404 Lenin

1960. 50th Anniv of International Women's Day. Inscr "1910–1960".
1187 **403** 16s. brown and pink . . 10 10
1188 – 28s. olive and yellow . . 15 10
1189 – 45s. green and olive . . 20 10
1190 – 60s. blue and light blue 30 15
1191 – 80s. brown and red . . . 35 15
1192 – 1l.25 olive and ochre . . 70 30
PORTRAITS: 28s. Anna Maimunkowa; 45s. Vela Piskova; 60s. Rosa Luxemburg; 80s. Clara Zetkin; 1l.25, Nadezhda Krupskaya.

1960. 90th Birth Anniv of Lenin.
1193 **404** 16s. flesh and brown . . 1·25 25
1194 – 45s. black and pink . . . 2·00 30
DESIGN: 45s. "Lenin at Smolny" (writing in chair).

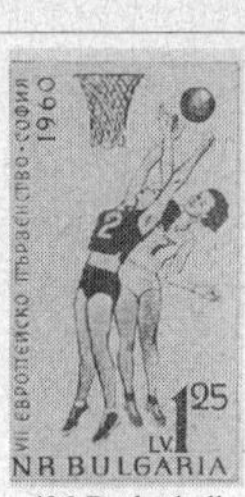

406 Basketball Players

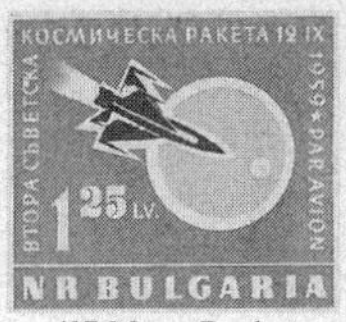

407 Moon Rocket

1960. 7th European Women's Basketball Championships.
1195 **406** 1l.25 black and yellow 1·50 45

1960. Air. Landing of Russian Rocket on Moon.
1196 **407** 1l.25 black, yellow & bl 8·25 5·00

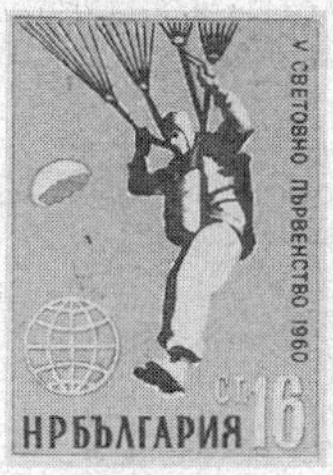

408 Parachutist

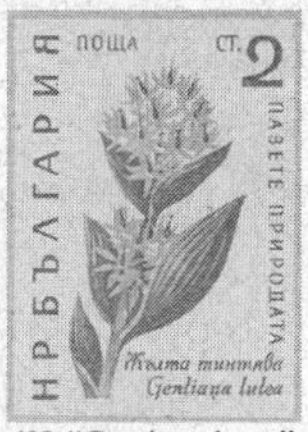

409 "Gentiana lutea"

1960. World Parachuting Championships, 1960.
1197 **408** 16s. blue and lilac . . . 60 55
1198 – 1l.25 red and blue . . . 2·75 85
DESIGN: 1l.25, Parachutes descending.

1960. Flowers.
1199 **409** 2s. orange, grn & drab 15 10
1200 – 5s. red, green and yellow 20 10
1201 – 25s. orge, grn & salmon 60 10
1202 – 45s. mauve, grn & lilac 75 15
1203 – 60s. red, green and buff 1·25 15
1204 – 80s. blue, green & drab 1·50 65
FLOWERS: 5s. "Tulipa rhodopea"; 25s. "Lilium jankae"; 45s. "Rhododendron ponticum"; 60s. "Cypripedium calceolus"; 80s. "Haberlea rhodopenis".

410 Football

1960. Olympic Games.
1205 **410** 8s. pink and brown . . . 10 10
1206 – 12s. pink and violet . . 15 10
1207 – 16s. pink & turquoise . . 25 15
1208 – 45s. pink and purple . . 50 15
1209 – 80s. pink and blue . . . 75 30
1210 – 2l. pink and green . . . 1·60 55
DESIGNS: 12s. Wrestling; 16s. Weightlifting; 45s. Gymnastics; 80s. Canoeing; 2l. Running.

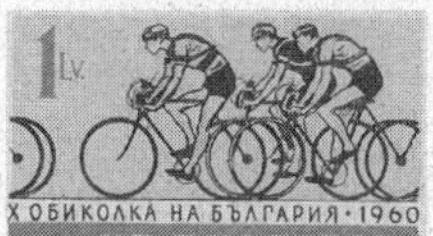

411 Racing Cyclists

1960. Tour of Bulgaria Cycle Race.
1211 **411** 1l. black, yellow & red 1·75 1·10

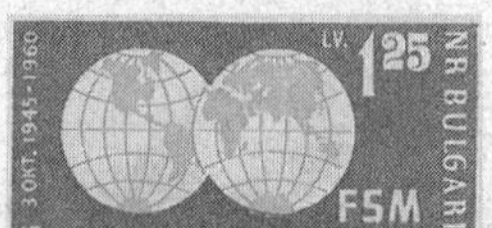

412 Globes

1960. 15th Anniv of W.F.T.U.
1212 **412** 1l.25 cobalt and blue . . 60 30

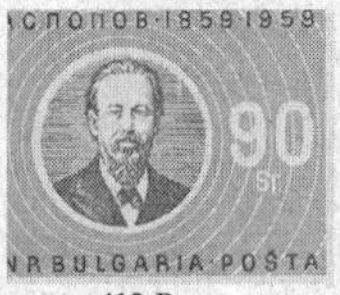

413 Popov

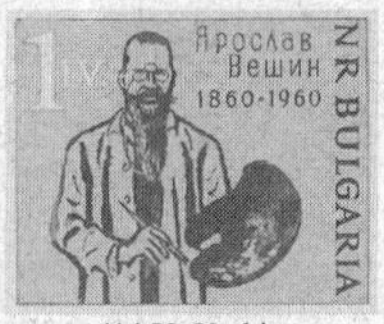

414 Y. Veshin

1960. Birth Centenary of Alexsandr Popov (Russian radio pioneer).
1213 **413** 90s. black and blue . . . 1·10 30

1960. Birth Centenary of Yavoslav Veshin (painter).
1214 **414** 1l. olive and yellow . . . 5·00 2·40

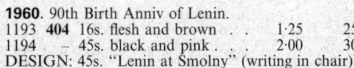

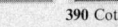

415 U.N. Headquarters, New York

416 Boyana Church

1961. 15th Anniv of U.N.O.
1215 **415** 1l. cream and brown . . 2·00 1·50

1961. 700th Anniv of Boyana Murals (1959).
1216 **416** 60s. black, emer & grn 1·00 15
1217 – 80s. grn, cream & orange 1·25 25
1218 – 1l.25 red, cream & green 2·00 65
DESIGNS (Frescoes of): 80s. Theodor Tiron; 1l.25, Desislava.

417 Cosmic Rocket and Dogs Belda and Strelka

1961. Russian Cosmic Rocket Flight of August, 1960.
1219 **417** 1l.25 blue and red . . . 8·50 6·00

419 Pleven Costume

420 Clock Tower, Vratsa

1961. Provincial Costumes.
1220 – 12s. yellow, green & orge 15 10
1221 **419** 16s. brown, buff & lilac 15 10
1222 – 28s. red, black, & green 25 10
1223 – 45s. blue and red 40 15
1224 – 60s. yellow, blue & turq 70 20
1225 – 80s. red, green & yellow 90 30
COSTUMES: 12s. Kyustendil; 28s. Sliven; 45s. Sofia; 60s. Rhodope; 80c. Karnobat.

1961. Museums and Monuments. Values and star in red.
1226 **420** 8s. green 10 10
1227 – 12s. violet 10 10
1228 – 16s. brown 15 10
1229 – 20s. blue 20 10
1230 – 28s. turquoise 25 15
1231 – 40s. brown 30 10
1232 – 45s. olive 35 15
1233 – 60s. slate 65 15
1234 – 80s. brown 85 20
1235 – 1l. turquoise . . . . . . 1·25 45
DESIGNS—As Type **420**. VERT: 12s. Clock Tower, Bansko; 20s. "Agushev" building, Mogilitsa (Smolensk). HORIZ: 28s. Oslekoff House, Koprivshtitsa; 40s. Pasha's House, Melnik. SQUARE (27×27 mm): 16s. Wine jug; 45s. Lion (bas-relief); 60s. "Horseman of Madara"; 80s. Fresco, Bachkovo Monastery; 1l. Coin of Tsar Konstantin-Asen (13th cent).

421 Dalmatian Pelican

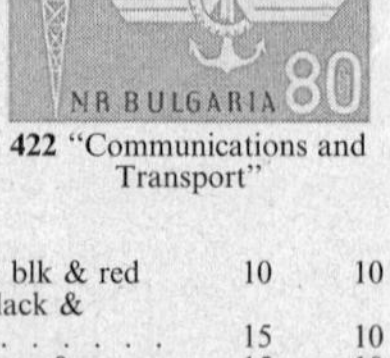

422 "Communications and Transport"

1961. Birds.
1236 – 2s. turquoise, blk & red 10 10
1237 **421** 4s. orange, black & green 15 10
1238 – 16s. orange, brn & grn 15 10
1239 – 80s. yellow, brn & turq 1·75 30
1240 – 1l. yellow, sepia and blue 1·75 75
1241 – 2l. yellow, brown & blue 2·75 80
DESIGNS: 2s. White capercaillie; 16s. Common pheasant; 80s. Great bustard; 1l. Lammergeier; 2l. Hazel grouse.

1961. 50th Anniv of Transport Workers' Union.
1242 **422** 80s. green and black . . 85 20

423 Gagarin and Rocket

1961. World's First Manned Space Flight.
1243 **423** 4l. turquoise, blk & red 5·00 3·25

424 Shevchenko (Ukrainian poet)

1961. Death Centenary of Taras Shevchenko.
1244 **424** 1l. brown and green . . 4·75 2·40

425 Throwing the Discus

1961. World Students' Games. Values and inscr in black.
1245 – 4s. blue 10 10
1246 – 5s. red 20 10
1247 – 16s. olive 30 10
1248 **425** 45s. blue 45 20
1249 – 1l.25 brown . . . . . . 1·00 35
1250 – 2l. mauve . . . . 1·25 80
DESIGNS—VERT: 4s. Water polo; 2l. Basketball. HORIZ: 5s. Tennis; 16s. Fencing; 1l.25, Sports Palace, Sofia.

426 Short-snouted Seahorse

427 "Space" Dogs

1961. Black Sea Fauna.
1251 – 2s. sepia and green . . . 10 10
1252 – 12s. pink and blue . . . 25 10
1253 – 16s. violet and blue . . . 40 10
1254 **426** 45s. brown and blue . . 1·40 50
1255 – 1l. blue and green . . . 2·75 1·00
1256 – 1l.25 brown and blue . . 4·00 1·50
DESIGNS—HORIZ: 2s. Mediterranean monk seal; 12s. Lung jellyfish; 16s. Common dolphins; 1l. Stellate sturgeons; 1l.25, Thorn-backed ray.

1961. Air. Space Exploration.
1257 **427** 2l. slate and purple . . . 4·00 3·00
1258 – 2l. blue, yellow & orange 8·25 5·00
DESIGN: No. 1258, "Venus" rocket in flight (24×41½ mm).

428 Dimitur Blagoev as Orator

1961. 70th Anniv of First Bulgarian Social Democratic Party Congress, Buzludzha.
1259 **428** 45s. red and cream . . . 25 15
1260 80s. blue and pink . . . 40 15
1261 2l. sepia and green . . . 1·40 45

429 Hotel

1961. Tourist issue. Inscr in black; designs green. Background colours given.
1262 **429** 4s. green 10 10
1263 – 12s. blue (Hikers) . . . 10 10
1264 – 16s. green (Tents) . . . 10 10
1265 – 1l.25 bistre (Climber) . . 85 15
Nos. 1263/5 are vert.

430 "The Golden Girl"

1961. Bulgarian Fables.
1266 **430** 2s. multicoloured 15 10
1267 – 8s. grey, black & purple 20 10
1268 – 12s. pink, black & green 25 10
1269 – 16s. multicoloured . . . 85 20
1270 – 45s. multicoloured . . . 1·50 30
1271 – 80s. multicoloured . . . 2·00 45
DESIGNS: 8s. Man and woman ("The Living Water"); 12s. Archer and dragon ("The Golden Apple"); 16s. Horseman ("Krali Marko", national hero); 45s. Female archer on stag ("Samovila-Vila", fairy); 80s. "Tom Thumb" and cockerel.

431 Major Titov in Space-suit

432 "Amanita caesarea"

1961. Air. 2nd Russian Manned Space Flight.
1272 **431** 75s. flesh, blue & olive 3·50 2·50
1273 – 1l.25 pink, bl & violet 4·50 3·75
DESIGN: 1l.25, "Vostok-2" in flight.

1961. Mushrooms.
1274 **432** 2s. red, bistre & black 10 10
1275 – 4s. brown, grn & blk . . 15 10
1276 – 12s. brown, bistre & blk 20 10
1277 – 16s. brown, mve & blk 20 10
1278 – 45s. multicoloured . . . 40 15
1279 – 80s. orange, sepia & blk 75 25
1280 – 1l.25 lav, brn & blk . . 90 45
1281 – 2l. brown, bistre & black 1·75 80
MUSHROOMS: 4s. "Psalliota silvatica"; 12s. "Boletus elegans"; 16s. "Boletus edulis"; 45s. "Lactarius deliciosus"; 80s. "Lepiota procera"; 1l.25, "Pleurotus ostreatus"; 2l. "Armillariella mellea".

433 Dimitur and Konstantin Miladinov (authors)

436 Isker River

1961. Publication Centenary of "Bulgarian Popular Songs".
1282 **433** 1l.25 black and olive . . 1·00 30

(Currency revaluation)

1962. Surch. (A) Surch in one line; (B) in two lines.
1283 1s. on 10s. brown (1149) . . 10 10
1284 1s. on 12s. brown (1150) . . 10 10
1285 2s. on 15s. mauve (1151) . . 10 10
1286 2s. on 16s. violet (1152) . . 10 10
1287 2s. on 20s. orange (1153) (A) 10 10
1288 2s. on 20s. orange (1153) (B) 25 10
1289 3s. on 25s. blue (1154) . . . 20 10
1290 3s. on 28s. green (1155) . . 20 10
1291 5s. on 44s. green (1087) . . 25 10
1292 5s. on 44s. red (1110) . . . 25 10
1293 5s. on 45s. brown (1157) . . 25 10
1294 10s. on 1l. red (1160) . . . 45 15
1295 20s. on 2l. red (1162) . . . 75 40
1296 40s. on 4l. red (889) . . . . 2·00 75

1962. Air.
1297 **436** 1s. blue and violet . . . 10 10
1298 – 2s. blue and pink 30 10
1299 – 3s. brown and chestnut 20 10
1300 – 10s. black and bistre . . 60 15
1301 – 40s. black and green . . 2·00 45
DESIGNS: 2s. Yacht at Varna; 3s. Melnik; 10s. Turnovo; 40s. Pirin Mountains.

437 Freighter "Varna"

438 Rila Mountains

1962. Bulgarian Merchant Navy.
1302 **437** 1s. green and blue . . . 10 10
1303 – 5s. light blue and green 60 10
1304 – 20s. violet and blue . . . 1·75 35
SHIPS: 5s. Tanker "Komsomols"; 20s. Liner "Georgi Dimitrov".

1962. Views.
1305 **438** 1s. turquoise 10 10
1306 – 2s. blue 10 10
1307 – 6s. turquoise 60 10
1308 – 8s. purple 80 20
1309 – 13s. green 65 15
1310 – 1l. deep green . . . . . 5·25 40
VIEWS: 2s. Pirin Mts; 6s. Fishing boats, Nesebur; 8s. Danube shipping; 13s. Viden Castle; 1l. Rhodope Mts.

439 Georgi Dimitrov as Typesetter

440 Pink Roses

1962. 80th Anniv of State Printing Office.
1311 **439** 2s. red, black & yellow 10 10
1312 – 13s. black, orange & yell 75 15
DESIGN: 13s. Emblem of Printing Office.

1962. Bulgarian Roses. T **440** and similar designs.
1313 1s. pink, green and violet . . 10 10
1314 2s. red, green and buff . . . 10 10
1315 3s. red, green and blue . . . 25 10
1316 4s. yellow, turquoise & grn 35 10
1317 5s. pink, green and blue . . 65 20
1318 6s. red, green and turquoise 80 40
1319 8s. red, green and yellow . . 2·75 65
1320 13s. yellow, green and blue 4·75 1·10

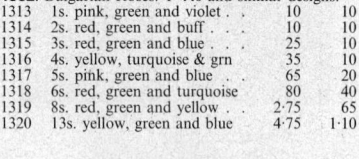

441 "The World United against Malaria"

1962. Malaria Eradication.
1321 **441** 5s. yellow, black & brn 60 15
1322 – 20s. yellow, green & blk 1·40 60
DESIGN: 20s. Campaign emblem.

442 Lenin and Front Page of "Pravda"

443 Text-book and Blackboard

1962. 50th Anniv of "Pravda" Newspaper.
1323 **442** 5s. blue, red and black 90 25

1962. Bulgarian Teachers' Congress.
1324 **443** 5s. black, yellow & blue 15 10

444 Footballer

1962. World Football Championship, Chile.
1325 **444** 13s. brown, green & blk 1·10 35

445 Dimitrov

1962. 80th Birth Anniv of Georgi Dimitrov (Prime Minister 1946–49).
1326 **445** 2s. green 15 10
1327 5s. blue 75 35

446 Bishop

448 Festival Emblem

1962. 15th Chess Olympiad, Varna. Inscr "1962". Inscr in black.
1328 **446** 1s. green and grey . . . 15 10
1329 – 2s. bistre and grey . . . 15 10
1330 – 3s. purple and grey . . . 15 10
1331 – 13s. orange and grey . . 1·50 40
1332 – 20s. blue and grey . . . 2·00 70
CHESS PIECES: 2s. Rook; 3s. Queen; 14s. Knight; 20s. Pawn.

XXXV КОНГРЕС
1962

13 =
(447)

1962. 35th Esperanto Congress, Burgas. Surch as T **447**.
1333 **360** 13s. on 44s. green . . . 4·75 3·00

1962. World Youth Festival, Helsinki. Inscr "1962".
1334 **448** 5s. blue, pink and green 20 10
1335 – 13s. blue, purple & grey 50 20
DESIGN: 13s. Girl and emblem.

449 Ilyushin Il-18 Airliner

1962. Air. 13th Anniv of TABSO Airline.
1336 **449** 13s. blue, ultram & blk 1·25 20

450 Apollo

1962. Butterflies and Moths. Multicoloured.
1337 1s. Type **450** 10 10
1338 2s. Eastern festoon 15 10
1339 3s. Meleager's blue 20 10
1340 4s. Camberwell beauty . . . 25 10
1341 5s. Crimson underwing . . 30 10
1342 6s. Hebe tiger moth 85 15
1343 10s. Danube clouded . . . 3·00 60
1344 13s. Cardinal . . . . 2·75 90

451 K. E. Tsiolkovsky (scientist)

1962. Air. 13th International Astronautics Congress. Inscr "1962".
1345 **451** 5s. drab and green . . . 4·00 1·50
1346 – 13s. blue and yellow . . 2·00 75
DESIGN: 13s. Moon rocket.

452 Combine Harvester

1962. 8th Bulgarian Communist Party Congress.
1347 **452** 1s. olive and turquoise 10 10
1348 – 2s. turquoise and blue 15 30
1349 – 3s. brown and red . . . 20 10
1350 – 13s. sepia, red & purple 1·00 30
DESIGNS: 2s. Electric train; 3s. Steel furnace; 13s. Blagoev and Dimitrov.

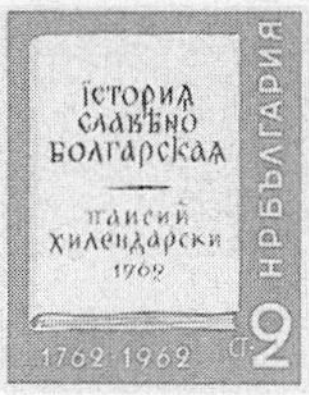

453 Cover of "History of Bulgaria"

1962. Bicentenary of Paisii Khilendarski's "History of Bulgaria".
1351 **453** 2s. black and olive . . . 10 10
1352 – 5s. sepia and brown . . 25 10
DESIGN—HORIZ: 5s. Father Paisii at work on book.

454 Andrian Nikolaev and "Vostok 3"

1962. Air. 1st "Team" Manned Space Flight.
1353 **454** 1s. olive, blue and black 15 10
1354 – 2s. olive, green & black 30 15
1355 – 40s. pink, turquoise & blk . . . . 3·25 2·10
DESIGNS: 2s. Pavel Ropovich and "Vostok 4"; 40s. "Vostoks 3" and "4" in flight.

455 Parachutist

1963.
1356 – 1s. lake 10 10
1357 – 1s. brown 10 10
1358 – 1s. turquoise 10 10
1359 – 1s. green 10 10
1360 **455** 1s. blue 10 10
DESIGNS—VERT: No. 1356, State crest. HORIZ: No. 1357, Sofia University; 1358, "Vasil Levski" Stadium, Sofia; 1359, "The Camels" (archway), Hisar.

456 Aleko Konstantinov

1963. Birth Cent of Konstantinov (author).
1361 **456** 5s. green and red 20 10

457 Mars and "Mars 1" Space Probe

1963. Air. Launching of Soviet Space Station "Mars 1".
1362 **457** 5s. multicoloured 70 30
1363 – 13s. turquoise, red & blk 1·40 75
DESIGN: 13s. Release of probe from rocket.

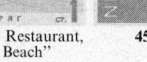

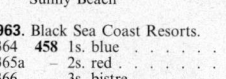

458 Orpheus Restaurant, "Sunny Beach"

459 V. Levski

1963. Black Sea Coast Resorts.
1364 **458** 1s. blue 10 10
1365a – 2s. red 80 15
1366 – 3s. bistre 25 10
1367 – 5s. purple 45 10
1368 – 13s. turquoise . . . . . 1·25 15
1369 – 20s. green . . . . . . 1·75 30
VIEWS "Sunny Beach": 5s. The Dunes Restaurant; 20s. Hotel. "Golden Sands"; 2s., 3s., 13s. Various hotels.

1963. 90th Anniv of Execution of Vasil Levski (revolutionary).
1370 **459** 13s. blue and yellow . . 75 30

460 Dimitrov, Boy and Girl

461 Eurasian Red Squirrel

1963. 10th Dimitrov Communist Youth League Congress, Sofia.
1371 **460** 2s. brown, red & black 15 10
1372 – 13s. brown, turq & blk 45 20
DESIGN: 13s. Girl and youth holding book and hammer aloft.

1963. Woodland Animals.
1373 **461** 1s. brown, red and green on turquoise 10 10
1374 – 2s. blk, red & grn on yell 15 10
1375 – 3s. sep, red & ol on drab 10 10
1376 – 5s. brown, red and blue on violet 60 10
1377 – 13s. black, red and brown on pink . . . . 2·25 25
1378 – 20s. sepia, red and blue on blue . . . . 3·50 40
ANIMALS—HORIZ: 2s. East European hedgehog; 3s. Marbled polecat; 5s. Beech marten; 13s. Eurasian badger. VERT: 20s. European otter.

462 Wrestling

1963. 15th International Open Wrestling Championships, Sofia.
1379 **462** 5s. bistre and black . . . 20 15
1380 – 20s. brown and black . . 1·25 30
DESIGN—HORIZ: 20s. As Type **462** but different hold.

463 Congress Emblem and Allegory

1963. World Women's Congress, Moscow.
1381 **463** 20s. blue and black . . . 1·00 25

464 Esperanto Star and Sofia Arms

1963. 48th World Esperanto Congress, Sofia.
1382 **464** 13s. multicoloured . . . 1·00 25

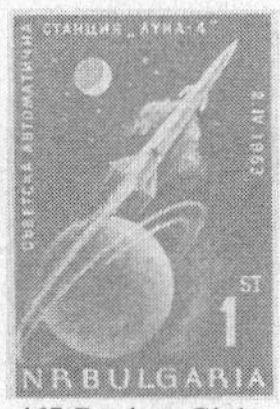

465 Rocket, Globe and Moon

466 Valery Bykovsky in Spacesuit

1963. Launching of Soviet Moon Rocket "Luna 4". Inscr "2.IV.1963".
1383 **465** 1s. blue 10 10
1384 – 2s. purple 10 10
1385 – 3s. turquoise 15 10
DESIGNS: 2s. Tracking equipment; 3s. Sputniks.

1963. Air. 2nd "Team" Manned Space Flights. Inscr "14.VI.1963".
1386 **466** 1s. turquoise and lilac 10 10
1387 – 2s. brown and yellow . . 15 10
1388 – 5s. red and light red . . 25 10
1389 – 20s.+10s. grn & lt bl . . 2·10 80

DESIGNS: 2s. Valentina Tereshkova in spacesuit; 5s. Globe; 20s. Bykovsky and Tereshkova.

1963. Europa Fair, Riccione. Nos. 1314/5 and 1318 (Roses) optd **MOSTRA EUROPEISTICA.1963 RICCIONE** and sailing boat motif or additionally surch.
1390 2s. red, green and buff . . . 30 15
1391 5s. on 3s. red, green and blue 40 15
1392 13s. on 6s. red, green & turq 1·40 40

468 Relay-racing

1963. Balkan Games. Flags in red, yellow, blue, green and black.
1393 **468** 1s. green 10 10
1394 – 2s. violet 15 10
1395 – 3s. turquoise 20 10
1396 – 5s. red 50 20
1397 – 13s. brown . . . . . . 3·00 2·25
DESIGNS: 2s. Throwing the hammer; 3s. Long jumping; 5s. High jumping; 13s. Throwing the discus. Each design includes the flags of the competing countries.

469 Slavonic Scroll

470 Insurgents

1963. 5th International Slav Congress, Sofia.
1398 **469** 5s. red, yellow & dp grn 20 10

1963. 40th Anniv of September Uprising.
1399 **470** 2s. black and red 15 10

471 "Aquilegia aurea"

472 Khristo Smirnenski

1963. Nature Protection. Flowers in natural colours; background colours given.
1400 **471** 1s. turquoise 10 10
1401 – 2s. olive 10 10
1402 – 3s. yellow 20 10
1403 – 5s. blue 40 10
1404 – 6s. purple 45 15
1405 – 8s. light grey 65 15
1406 – 10s. mauve . . . . . . 1·75 25
1407 – 13s. olive . . . . 2·75 45
FLOWERS: 2s. Edelweiss; 3s. "Primula deorum"; 5s. White water-lily; 6s. Tulip; 8s. "Viola delphinantha"; 10s. Alpine clematis; 13s. "Anemone narcissiflora".

1963. 65th Birth Anniv of Smirnenski (poet and revolutionary).
1408 **472** 13s. black and lilac . . . 75 15

473 Chariot Horses (wall-painting)

474 Hemispheres and Centenary Emblem

1963. Thracian Tombs, Kazanilk.
1409 **473** 1s. red, yellow and grey 10 10
1410 – 2s. violet, yellow & grey 15 10
1411 – 3s. turquiose, yell & grey 20 10
1412 – 5s. brown, yellow & grn 25 10
1413 – 13s. black, yellow & grn 60 15
1414 – 20s. red, yellow & green 1·40 55
DESIGNS (wall paintings on tombs): 2s. Chariot race; 3s. Flautists; 5s. Tray-bearer; 13s. Funeral feast; 20s. Seated woman.

1964. Centenary of Red Cross.
1415 **474** 1s. yellow, red & black 10 10
1416 – 2s. blue, red and black 10 10
1417 – 3s. multicoloured . . . 10 10
1418 – 5s. turq, red & black . . 25 10
1419 – 13s. black, red & orange 85 25
DESIGNS: 2s. Blood donation; 3s. Bandaging wrist; 5s. Nurse; 13s. Henri Dunant.

475 Speed-skating

1964. Winter Olympic Games, Innsbruck.
1420	475	1s. indigo, brown & blue	10	10
1421	–	2s. olive, mauve & black	10	10
1422	–	3s. green, brown & blk	15	10
1423	–	5s. multicoloured	25	15
1424	–	10s. orange, blk & grey	85	20
1425	–	13s. mauve, violet & blk	1·00	25

DESIGNS: 2s. Figure skating; 3s. Cross-country skiing; 5s. Ski jumping. Ice hockey—10s. Goalkeeper; 13s. Players.

476 Head (2nd cent)   477 "The Unborn Maid"

1964. 2500 Years of Bulgarian Art. Borders in grey.
1426	476	1s. turquoise and red	10	10
1427	–	2s. sepia and red	10	10
1428	–	3s. bistre and red	10	10
1429	–	5s. blue and red	25	10
1430	–	6s. brown and red	35	10
1431	–	8s. brown and red	50	15
1432	–	10s. olive and red	60	10
1433	–	13s. olive and red	1·10	25

DESIGNS: 2s. Horseman (1st to 4th cent); 3s. Jug (19th cent); 5s. Buckle (19th cent); 6s. Pot (19th cent); 8s. Angel (17th cent); 10s. Animals (8th to 10th cent); 13s. Peasant woman (20th cent).

1964. Folk Tales. Multicoloured.
1434	477	1s. Type 477	10	10
1435	–	2s. "Grandfather's Glove"	10	10
1436	–	3s. "The Big Turnip"	10	10
1437	–	5s. "The Wolf and the Seven Kids"	25	10
1438	–	8s. "Cunning Peter"	40	15
1439	–	13s. "The Loaf of Corn"	1·25	30

478 Turkish Lacewing ("Ascalaphus ottomanus")

1964. Insects.
1440	478	1s. black, yellow & brn	10	10
1441	–	2s. black, ochre & turq	15	10
1442	–	3s. green, black & drab	20	10
1443	–	5s. violet, black & green	65	10
1444	–	13s. brown, black & vio	1·40	25
1445	–	20s. yellow, black & bl	2·50	40

DESIGNS—VERT: 2s. Thread lacewing fly ("Nemoptera coa"); 5s. Alpine longhorn beetle ("Rosalia alpina"); 13s. Cockchafer ("Anisoplia austriaca"). HORIZ: 3s. Cricket ("Saga natalia"); 20s. Hunting wasp ("Scolia flavitrons").

479 Football

1964. 50th Anniv of Levski Physical Culture Association.
1446	479	2s. Type 479	15	10
1447	–	13s. Handball	95	30

480 Title Page and Petar Beron (author)

1964. 40th Anniv of First Bulgarian Primer.
1448	480	20s. black and brown	2·00	2·00

481 Stephenson's "Rocket", 1829

1964. Railway Transport. Multicoloured.
1449	481	1s. Type 481	10	10
1450	–	2s. Class 05 steam locomotive	15	10
1451	–	3s. German V.320.001 diesel locomotive	25	10
1452	–	5s. Electric locomotive	45	10
1453	–	8s. Class 05 steam locomotive and train on bridge	70	15
1454	–	13s. Class E41 electric train emerging from tunnel	1·10	25

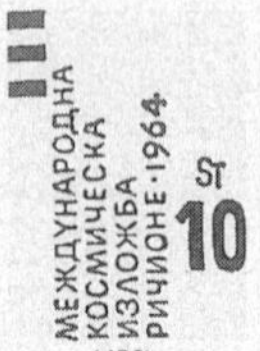

482 Alsatian   (483)

1964. Dogs. Multicoloured.
1455	482	1s. Type 482	10	10
1456	–	2s. Setter	20	10
1457	–	3s. Poodle	25	10
1458	–	4s. Pomeranian	30	10
1459	–	5s. St. Bernard	40	15
1460	–	6s. Fox terrier	85	15
1461	–	10s. Pointer	3·00	55
1462	–	13s. Dachshund	3·50	1·40

1964. Air. International Cosmic Exhibition, Riccione. No. 1386 surch with T **483** and No. 1387 surch as T **483**, but in Italian.
1463	466	10s. on 1s. turquoise and lilac	50	20
1464	–	20s. on 2s. brown & yell	1·00	30

484 Partisans and Flag

1964. 20th Anniv of Fatherland. Front Government. Flag in red.
1465	484	1s. blue and light blue	10	10
1466	–	2s. olive and bistre	10	10
1467	–	3s. lake and mauve	10	10
1468	–	4s. violet and lavender	15	10
1469	–	5s. brown and orange	20	10
1470	–	6s. blue and light blue	30	10
1471	–	8s. green and light green	70	10
1472	–	13s. brown and salmon	1·00	50

DESIGNS: Greeting Soviet troops; 3s. Soviet aid—arrival of goods; 4s. Industrial plant, Kremikovtsi; 5s. Combine-harvester; 6s. "Peace" campaigners; 8s. Soldier of National Guard; 3s. Blagoev and Dimitrov. All with flag as Type **484**.

(485)   486 Transport

1964. 21st Int Fair, Plovdiv. Surch with T **485**.
1473		20s. on 44s. ochre (No. 1020a)	1·90	35

1964. 1st National Stamp Exn, Sofia.
1474	486	20s. blue	2·75	1·00

DESIGNS: 2s. Long-jump; 3s. Swimmer on starting block; 5s. Football; 13s. Volleyball; 20s. Wrestling.

1964. Landscapes.
1481	488	1s. green	10	10
1482	–	2s. brown	10	10
1483	–	3s. blue	15	10
1484	–	4s. brown	20	10
1485	–	5s. green	30	10
1486	–	6s. violet	40	10

DESIGNS: 2s. The Ritli; 3s. Maliovitsa; 4s. Broken Rocks; 5s. Erkyupria; 6s. Rhodope mountain pass.

489 Paper and Cellulose Factory, Bukovtsi

1964. Air. Industrial Buildings.
1487	489	8s. turquoise	25	10
1488	–	10s. purple	35	10
1489	–	13s. violet	40	10
1490	–	20s. blue	1·00	15
1491	–	40s. green	1·90	60

DESIGNS: 10s. Metal works, Plovdiv; 13s. Metallurgical works, Kremikovtzi; 20s. Petrol refinery, Burgas; 40s. Fertiliser factory, Stara-Zagora.

490 Rila Monastery

1964. Philatelic Exn for Franco–Bulgarian Amity.
1492	490	5s. black and drab	30	15
1493	–	13s. black and blue	1·10	30

DESIGN: 13s. Notre-Dame, Paris (inscr in French).

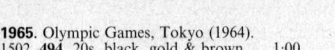

491 500-year-old Walnut   492

1964. Ancient Trees. Values and inscr in black.
1494	491	1s. brown	10	10
1495	–	2s. purple	10	10
1496	–	3s. sepia	15	10
1497	–	4s. blue	15	10
1498	–	10s. green	45	10
1499	–	13s. olive	80	25

TREES: 2s. Plane (1000 yrs.); 3s. Plane (600 yrs.); 4s. Poplar (800 yrs.); 10s. Oak (800 yrs.); 13s. Fir (1200 yrs.).

1964. 8th Congress of Int Union of Students, Sofia.
1500	492	13s. black and blue	80	15

493 Bulgarian Veteran and Soviet Soldier (Sculpture by T. Zlatarev)   494 "Gold Medal"

1965. 30 Years of Bulgarian–Russian Friendship.
1501	493	2s. red and black	20	10

1965. Olympic Games, Tokyo (1964).
1502	494	20s. black, gold & brown	1·00	30

495 Vladimir Komarov

1965. Flight of "Voskhod 1". Multicoloured.
1503		1s. Type 495	10	10
1504		2s. Konstantin Feoktistov	10	10
1505		5s. Boris Yegorov	15	10
1506		13s. The three astronauts	85	15
1507		20s. "Voskhod l"	1·40	25

496 Corn-cob   497 "Victory against Fascism"

1965. Agricultural Products.
1508	496	1s. yellow	10	10
1509	–	2s. green	10	10
1510	–	3s. orange	15	10
1511	–	4s. olive	20	10
1512	–	5s. red	30	10
1513	–	10s. blue	55	20
1514	–	13s. bistre	1·25	25

DESIGNS: 2s. Ears of Wheat; 3s. Sunflowers; 4s. Sugar beet; 5s. Clover; 10s. Cotton; 13s. Tobacco.

1965. 20th Anniv of "Victory of 9 May, 1945".
1515	497	5s. black, bistre & grey	15	10
1516	–	13s. blue, black & grey	40	20

DESIGN: 13s. Globes on dove ("Peace").

498 Northern Bullfinch   499 Transport, Globe and Whale

1965. Song Birds. Multicoloured.
1517	498	1s. Type 498	10	10
1518	–	2s. Golden oriole	15	10
1519	–	3s. Rock thrush	20	10
1520	–	5s. Barn swallows	60	10
1521	–	8s. European roller	95	15
1522	–	10s. European goldfinch	3·75	25
1523	–	13s. Rose-coloured starling	3·75	40
1524	–	20s. Nightingale	4·00	1·25

1965. 4th International Transport Conf, Sofia.
1525	499	13s. multicoloured	1·10	30

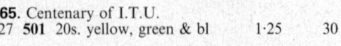

500 I.C.Y. Emblem   501 I.T.U. Emblem and Symbols

1965. International Co-operation Year.
1526	500	20s. orange, olive & blk	90	40

1965. Centenary of I.T.U.
1527	501	20s. yellow, green & bl	1·25	30

502 Pavel Belyaev and Aleksei Leonov

1965. "Voskhod 2" Space Flight.
1528	502	2s. purple, grn & drab	30	10
1529	–	20s. multicoloured	3·00	1·10

DESIGN: 20s. Leonov on space.

503 Common Stingray   504 Marx and Lenin

1965. Fishes. Borders in grey.
1530	503	1s. gold, black & orange	10	10
1531	–	2s. silver, indigo & blue	10	10
1532	–	3s. gold, black & green	20	10
1533	–	5s. gold, black and red	25	10
1534	–	10s. silver, blue & turq	1·40	20
1535	–	13s. gold, black & brown	1·75	45

FISHES: 2s. Atlantic bonito; 3s. Brown scorpionfish;

5s. Tub gurnard; 10s. Mediterranean horse-mackerel; 13s. Black Sea turbot.

1965. Organization of Socialist Countries' Postal Ministers' Conference, Peking.
1536 504 13s. brown and red . . 1·10 20

505 Film and Screen   506 Quinces

1965. Balkan Film Festival. Varna.
1537 505 13s. black, silver & blue 85 20

1965. Fruits.
1538 506 1s. orange 10 10
1539 – 2s. olive (Grapes) . . . 10 10
1540 – 3s. bistre (Pears) 10 10
1541 – 4s. orange (Plums) . . . 15 10
1542 – 5s. red (Strawberries) . 30 10
1543 – 6s. brown (Walnuts) . . 50 15

507 Ballerina   508 Dove, Emblem and Map

1965. Ballet Competitions, Varna.
1544 507 5s. black and mauve . . 85 30

1965. "Balkanphila" Stamp Exhibition, Varna.
1545 508 1s. silver, blue & yellow 10 10
1546 – 2s. silver, violet & yellow 10 10
1547 – 3s. gold, green & yellow 15 10
1548 – 13s. gold, red & yellow 85
1549 – 20s. brown, blue & silver 1·40 1·00
DESIGNS: 2s. Yacht emblem; 3s. Stylised fish and flowers; 13s. Stylised sun, planet and rocket. LARGER (45×25¼ mm): 20s. Cosmonauts Pavel Belyaev and Aleksei Leonov.

509 Escapers in Boat   511 Gymnast

2ct

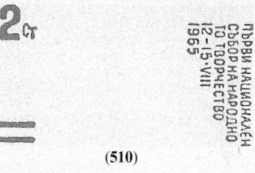

(510)

1965. 40th Anniv of Political Prisoners' Escape from "Bolshevik Island".
1551 509 2s. black and slate . . . 20 15

1965. National Folklore Competition. No. 1084 surch with T 510.
1552 2s. on 8s. brown . . . . 1·75 1·40

1965. Balkan Games.
1553 511 1s. black and red . . . 10 10
1554 – 2s. purple and black . . 10 10
1555 – 3s. purple, black & red . 10 10
1556 – 5s. brown, black & red . 25 10
1557 – 10s. purple, black & mve 1·25 20
1558 – 13s. purple and black . 1·00 25
DESIGNS: 2s. Gymnastics on bars; 3s. Weight-lifting; 5s. Rally car and building; 10s. Basketball; 13s. Rally car and map.

512 Dressage

1965. Horsemanship.
1559 512 1s. plum, black & blue 10 10
1560 – 2s. brown, black & ochre 10 10
1561 – 3s. red, black and purple 15 10
1562 – 5s. brown and green . . 55 10
1563 – 10s. brown, blk & grey 2·00 25
1564 – 13s. brown, grn & buff 3·00 35
DESIGNS: 5s. Horse-racing. Others, Horse-jumping (various).

513 Young Pioneers

1965. Dimitrov Septembrist Pioneers Organization.
1566 513 1s. green and turquoise 10 10
1567 – 2s. mauve and violet . . 10 10
1568 – 3s. bistre and olive . . . 10 10
1569 – 5s. ochre and blue . . . 15 10
1570 – 8s. orange and brown . 50 15
1571 – 13s. violet and red . . . 95 30
DESIGNS: 2s. Admitting recruit; 3s. Camp bugler; 5s. Flying model airplane; 8s. Girls singing; 13s. Young athlete.

514 Junkers Ju 52/3m over Turnovo   515 Women of N. and S. Bulgaria

1965. Bulgarian Civil Aviation. Multicoloured.
1572 1s. Type 514 . . . . . . 10 10
1573 2s. Ilyushin Il-14M over Plovdiv 10 10
1574 3s. Mil Mi-4 helicopter over Dimitrovgrad 15 10
1575 5s. Tupolev Tu-104A over Ruse 35 10
1576 13s. Ilyushin Il-18 over Varna . . . . . . 1·40 20
1577 20s. Tupolev Tu-114 over Sofia . . . . . . 1·75 50

1965. 80th Anniv of Union of North and South Bulgaria.
1578 515 13s. black and green . . 85 30

516 I.Q.S.Y. Emblem and Earth's Radiation Zones   517 "Spring Greetings"

1965. International Quiet Sun Year.
1579 516 1s. yellow, green & blue 10 10
1580 – 2s. multicoloured . . . 10 10
1581 – 13s. multicoloured . . . 90 20
DESIGNS (I.Q.S.Y. emblem and): 2s. Sun and solar flares; 13s. Total eclipse of the Sun.

1966. "Spring". National Folklore.
1582 517 1s. mauve, blue and drab 10 10
1583 – 2s. red, black and drab 10 10
1584 – 3s. violet, red and grey 10 10
1585 – 5s. red, violet and black 15 10
1586 – 8s. purple, brown & mve 35 15
1587 – 13s. mauve, black & bl 70 20
DESIGNS: 2s. Drummer; 3s. "Birds" (stylised); 5s. Folk dancer; 8s. Vase of flowers; 13s. Bagpiper.

518 Byala Bridge

1966. Ancient Monuments.
1588 518 1s. turquoise 10 10
1589 – 1s. green 10 10
1590 – 2s. green 10 10
1591 – 2s. purple 10 10
1592 – 8s. brown 40 15
1593 – 13s. blue 65 25
DESIGNS: No. 1589, Svilengrad Bridge; 1590, Fountain, Samokov; 1591, Ruins of Matochina Castle, Khaskovo; 1592, Cherven Castle, Ruse; 1593, Cafe, Bozhentsi, Gabrovo.

519 "Christ" (from fresco Boyana Church)

1966. "2,500 Years of Culture". Multicoloured.
1594 519 1s. Type 519 . . . . 5·50 4·25
1595 2s. "Destruction of the Idols" (from fresco, Boyana Church) (horiz) 30 15
1596 3s. Bachkovo Monastery . . 50 20
1597 4s. Zemen Monastery (horiz) 50 20
1598 5s. John the Baptist Church, Nesebur 60 30
1599 13s. "Nativity" (icon, Aleksandr Nevski Cathedral, Sofia) . . . 1·10 85
1600 20s. "Virgin and Child" (icon, Archaeological Museum, Sofia) . . 1·75 1·00

520 "The First Gunshot" at Koprivshtitsa

1966. 90th Anniv of April Uprising.
1601 520 1s. black, brown & gold 10 10
1602 – 2s. black, red and gold 10 10
1603 – 3s. black, green & gold 10 10
1604 – 5s. black, blue & gold 15 10
1605 – 10s. black, purple & gold 60 15
1606 – 13s. black, violet & gold 60 20
DESIGNS: 2s. Georgi Benkovski and Todor Kableskov; 3s. "Showing the Flag" (horiz); 5s. Vasil Petleshkov and Tsanko Dyustabanov; 10s. Landing of Khristo Botev's detachment at Kozlodui; 13s. Panyot Volov and Zlarion Dragostinov.

522 W.H.O. Building

1966. Inaug of W.H.O. Headquarters, Geneva.
1608 522 13s. blue and silver . . . 1·00 20

523 Worker

1966. 6th Trades Union Congress, Sofia
1609 523 20s. black and pink . . . 1·10 20

524 Indian Elephant   525 Boy and Girl holding Banners

1966. Sofia Zoo Animals. Multicoloured.
1610 1s. Type 524 . . . . 10 10
1611 2s. Tiger 10 10
1612 3s. Chimpanzee . . . 15 10
1613 4s. Ibex 20 10
1614 5s. Polar bear . . . 50 15
1615 8s. Lion 65 25
1616 13s. American bison . . 2·50 45
1617 20s. Eastern grey kangaroo 3·00 70

1966. 3rd Congress of Bulgarian Sports Federation.
1618 525 13s. blue, orge & cobalt 45 20

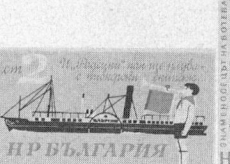

526 "Radetski" and Pioneer   527 Standard-bearer Simov-Kuruto

1966. 90th Anniv of Khristo Botev's Seizure of River Paddle-steamer "Radetski".
1619 526 2s. multicoloured 20 10

1966. 90th Death Anniv of Nikola Simov-Kuruto (hero of the Uprising against Turkey).
1620 527 5s. multicoloured 30 10

528 Federation Emblem

1966. 7th Int Youth Federation Assembly, Sofia.
1621 528 13s. blue and black . . . 65 15

529 U.N.E.S.C.O. Emblem

1966. 20th Anniv of U.N.E.S.C.O.
1622 529 20s. ochre, red & black 85 30

530 Footballer with Ball

1966. World Cup Football Championships, London. Showing players in action. Borders in grey.
1623 530 1s. black and brown . . 10 10
1624 – 2s. black and red . . 10 10
1625 – 5s. black and bistre . . 20 10
1626 – 13s. black and blue . . 65 15
1627 – 20s. black and blue . . 1·00 30

532 Wrestling

1966. 3rd Int Wrestling Championships, Sofia.
1629 532 13s. sepia, green & brn 45 20

533 Throwing the Javelin

1966. 3rd Republican Spartakiade.
1630 533 2s. green, red & yellow 10 10
1631 – 13s. green, red & yellow 65 25
DESIGN: 13s. Running.

534 Map of Balkans, Globe and U.N.E.S.C.O. Emblem

1966. Int Balkan Studies Congress, Sofia.
1632 534 13s. green, pink & blue 65 15

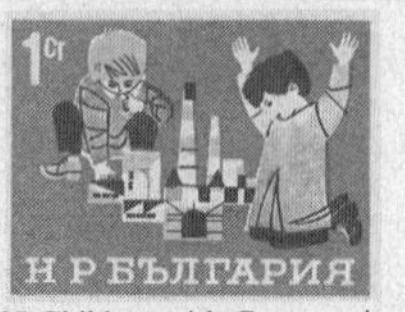

535 Children with Construction Toy

1966. Children's Day.

1633	535	1s. black, yellow & red	10	10
1634	–	2s. black, brown & grn	10	10
1635	–	3s. black, yellow & blue	15	10
1636	–	13s. black, mauve & bl	1·00	25

DESIGNS: 2s. Rabbit and Teddy Bear; 3s. Children as astronauts; 13s. Children with gardening equipment.

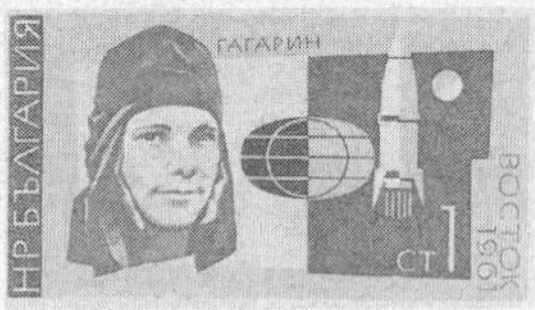

536 Yuri Gagarin and "Vostok 1"

1966. Russian Space Exploration.

1637	536	1s. slate and grey	10	10
1638	–	2s. purple and grey	10	10
1639	–	3s. brown and grey	10	10
1640	–	5s. lake and grey	20	10
1641	–	8s. blue and grey	25	15
1642	–	13s. turquoise and grey	80	25
1643	–	20s.+10s. vio & grey	1·75	55

DESIGNS: 2s. German Titov and "Vostok 2"; 3s. Andrian Nikolaev, Povel Popovich and "Vostok 3" and "4"; 5s. Valentina Tereshkova, Vallery Bykovsky and "Vostok 5" and "6"; 8s. Vladimir Komarov, Boris Yegorov, Konstantin Feoktistov and "Voskhod 1"; 13s. Povel Belyaev, Aleksei Leonov and "Voskhod 2"; 20s. Gagarin, Leonov and Tereshkova.

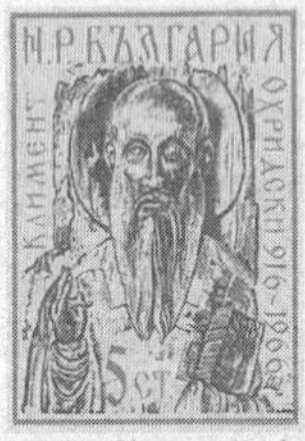

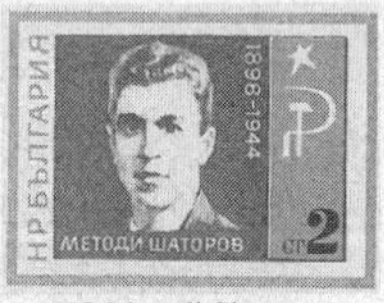

537 St. Clement (14th-cent. wood-carving)

538 Metodi Shatorov

1966. 1050th Death Anniv of St. Clement of Ohrid.

1645	537	5s. brown, red & drab	65	15

1966. Anti-fascist Fighters. Frames in gold; value in black.

1646	538	2s. violet and red	10	10
1647	–	3s. brown and mauve	10	10
1648	–	5s. blue and red	15	10
1649	–	10s. brown and orange	35	15
1650	–	13s. brown and red	70	15

PORTRAITS: 3s. Vladno Trichkov; 5s. Vulcho Ivanov; 10s. Rasko Daskalov; 13s. Gen. Vladimir Zaimov.

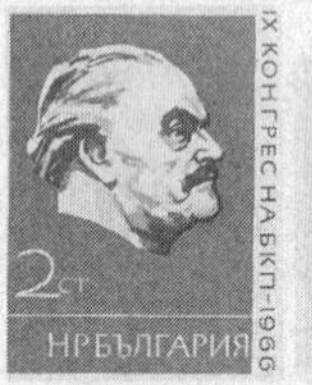

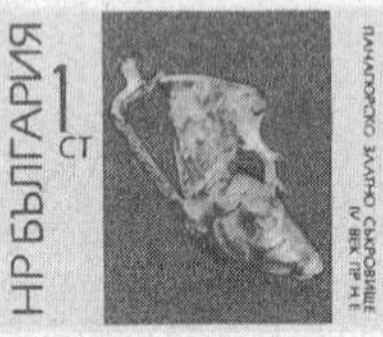

539 Georgi Dimitrov (statesman)

540 Deer's Head Vessel

1966. 9th Bulgarian Communist Party Congress, Sofia.

1651	539	2s. black and red	20	10
1652	–	20s. black, red and grey	1·10	20

DESIGN: 20s. Furnaceman and steelworks.

1966. The Gold Treasures of Panagyurishte. Multicoloured.

1653	1s. Type 540	10	10
1654	2s. Amazon	20	10
1655	3s. Ram	25	10
1656	5s. Plate	30	10
1657	6s. Venus	35	10
1658	8s. Roe-buck	1·10	15
1659	10s. Amazon (different)	1·25	15
1660	13s. Amphora	1·40	30
1661	20s. Goat	2·00	65

Except for the 5s. and 13s. the designs show vessels with animal heads.

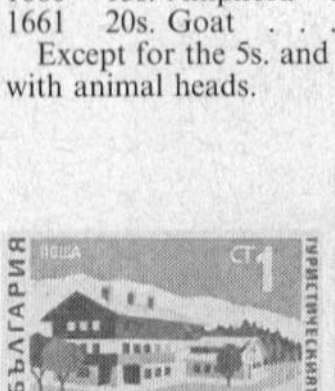

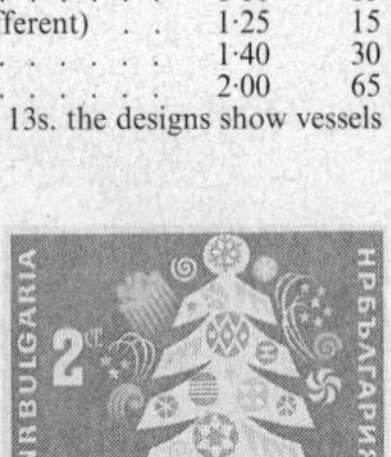

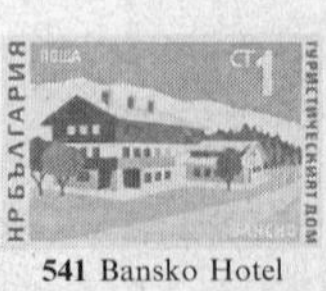

541 Bansko Hotel

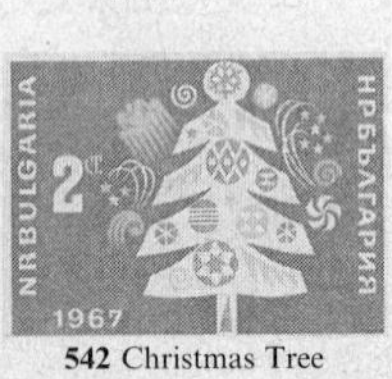

542 Christmas Tree

1966. Tourist Resorts.

1662	541	1s. blue	10	10
1663	–	2s. green (Belogradchik)	10	10
1664	–	2s. lake (Tryavna)	10	10
1665	–	20s. pur (Malovitsa, Rila)	70	15

1966. New Year. Multicoloured.

1666	2s. Type 542	10	10
1667	13s. Money-box	45	15

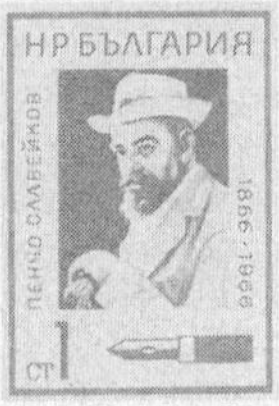

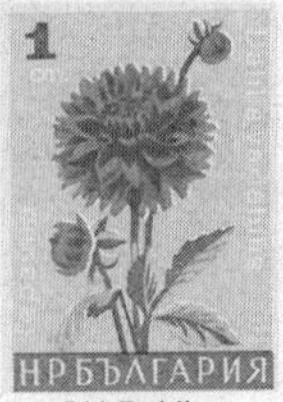

543 Percho Slaveikov (poet)

544 Dahlias

1966. Cultural Celebrities.

1668	543	1s. bistre, blue & orange	10	10
1669	–	2s. brown, orge & grey	10	10
1670	–	3s. blue, bistre & orange	10	10
1671	–	5s. purple, drab & orge	10	10
1672	–	8s. grey, purple & blue	50	15
1673	–	13s. violet, blue & purple	65	25

CELEBRITIES. Writers (with pen emblem): 2s. Dimcho Debelyanov (poet); 3s. Petko Todorov. Painters (with brush emblem): 5s. Dimitur Dobrovich; 8s. Ivan Murkvichka; 13s. Iliya Beshkov.

1966. Flowers. Multicoloured.

1674	1s. Type 544	10	10
1675	1s. Clematis	10	10
1676	2s. Poet's narcissus	15	10
1677	2s. Foxgloves	15	10
1678	3s. Snowdrops	25	10
1679	5s. Petunias	25	10
1680	13s. Tiger lilies	1·00	25
1681	20s. Canterbury bells	1·40	35

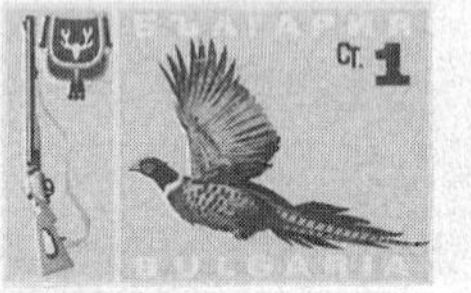

545 Common Pheasant

1967. Hunting. Multicoloured.

1682	1s. Type 545	40	10
1683	2s. Chukar partridge	40	10
1684	3s. Grey partridge	30	10
1685	5s. Brown hare	75	10
1686	8s. Roe deer	2·00	20
1687	13s. Red deer	2·25	40

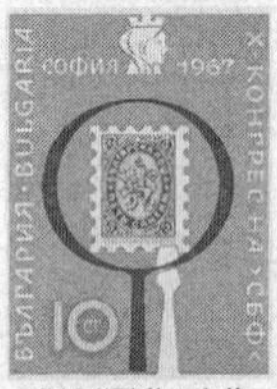

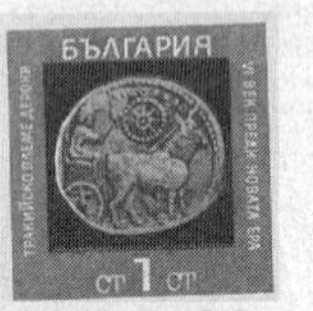

546 "Philately"

547 6th-cent. B.C. Coin of Thrace

1967. 10th Bulgarian Philatelic Federation Congress, Sofia.

1688	546	10s. yellow, black & grn	1·60	1·00

1967. Ancient Bulgarian Coins. Coins in silver on black background except 13s. (gold on black). Frame colours given.

1689	547	1s. brown	10	10
1690	–	2s. purple	10	10
1691	–	3s. green	15	10
1692	–	5s. brown	25	10
1693	–	13s. turquoise	1·40	40
1694	–	20s. violet	1·90	75

COINS—SQUARE: 2s. 2nd-cent B.C. Macedonian tetradrachm; 3s. 2nd-cent B.C. Odessos (Varna) tetradrachm; 5s. 4th-cent B.C. Macedonian coin of Philip II. HORIZ: (38 × 25 mm): 13s. Obverse and reverse of 4th cent B.C. coin of King Sevt (Thrace); 20s. Obverse and reverse of 5th-cent B.C. coin of Apollonia (Sozopol).

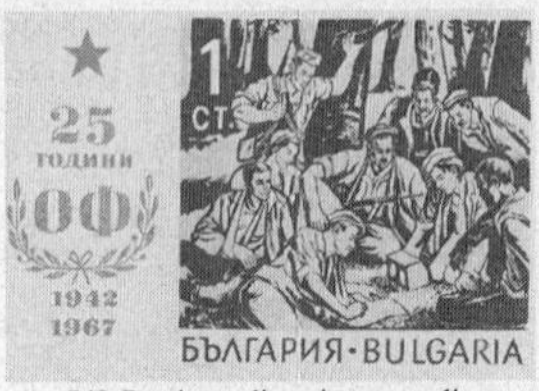

548 Partisans listening to radio

1967. 25th Anniv of Fatherland Front. Mult.

1695	1s. Type 548	10	10
1696	20s. Dimitrov speaking at rally	75	25

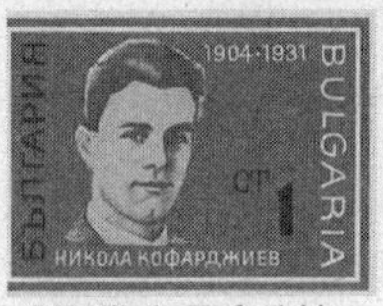

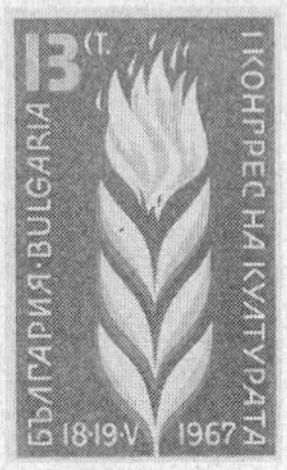

549 Nikola Kofardzhiev

550 "Cultural Development"

1967. Anti-fascist Fighters.

1697	549	1s. red, black & blue	10	10
1698	–	2s. green, black & blue	10	10
1699	–	5s. brown, black & blue	15	10
1700	–	10s. blue, black & lilac	30	10
1701	–	13s. purple, black & grey	55	15

PORTRAITS: 2s. Petko Napetov; 5s. Petko Petkov; 10s. Emil Markov; 13s. Traicho Kostov.

1967. 1st Cultural Conference, Sofia.

1702	550	13s. yellow, grn & gold	80	15

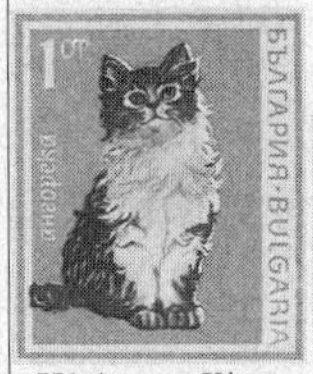

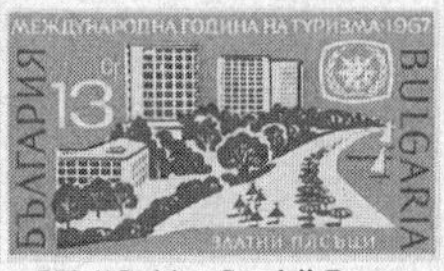

551 Angora Kitten

552 "Golden Sands" Resort

1967. Cats. Multicoloured.

1703	1s. Type 551	10	10
1704	2s. Siamese (horiz)	20	10
1705	3s. Abyssinian	25	10
1706	5s. European black and white	1·25	10
1707	13s. Persian (horiz)	1·50	25
1708	20s. European tabby	2·25	90

1967. International Tourist Year. Multicoloured.

1709	13s. Type 552	35	15
1710	20s. Pamporovo	80	20
1711	40s. Old Church, Nesebur	1·60	50

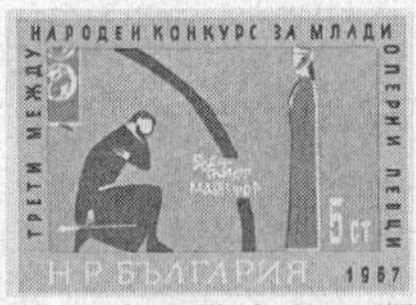

553 Scene from Iliev's Opera "The Master of Boyana"

1967. 3rd International Young Opera Singers' Competition, Sofia.

1712	553	5s. red, blue and grey	20	10
1713	–	13s. red, blue and grey	60	15

DESIGN—VERT: 13s. "Vocal Art" (song-bird on piano-keys).

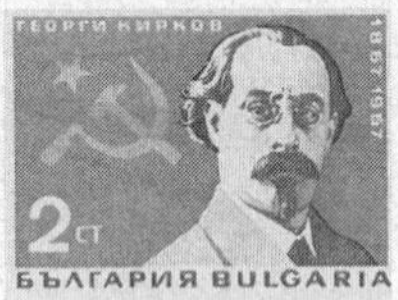

554 G. Kirkov

1967. Birth Cent of Georgi Kirkov (patriot).

1714	554	2s. bistre and red	15	10

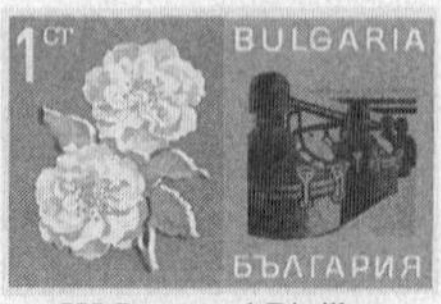

555 Roses and Distillery

1967. Economic Achievements. Multicoloured.

1715	1s. Type 555	10	10
1716	1s. Chick and incubator	10	10
1717	2s. Cucumber and glass-houses	10	10
1718	2s. Lamb and farm building	10	10
1719	3s. Sunflower and oil-extraction plant	10	10
1720	4s. Pigs and piggery	15	10
1721	5s. Hops and vines	15	10
1722	6s. Grain and irrigation canals	20	10
1723	8s. Grapes and "Bulgar" tractor	20	10
1724	10s. Apples and tree	35	10
1725	13s. Honey bees and honey	60	15
1726	20s. Honey bee on flower, and hives	1·10	25

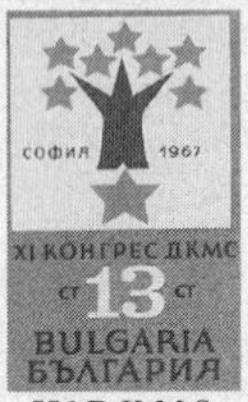

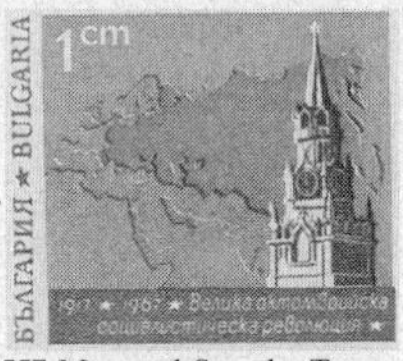

556 D.K.M.S. Emblem

557 Map and Spassky Tower, Moscow Kremlin

1967. 11th Anniv of Dimitrov Communist Youth League.

1727	556	13s. black, red and blue	70	15

1967. 50th Anniv of October Revolution.

1728	557	1s. multicoloured	10	10
1729	–	2s. olive and purple	10	10
1730	–	3s. violet and purple	10	10
1731	–	5s. red and purple	15	10
1732	–	13s. blue and purple	30	15
1733	–	20s. blue and purple	1·00	20

DESIGNS: 2s. Lenin directing revolutionaries; 3s. Revolutionaries; 5s. Marx, Engels and Lenin; 13s. Soviet oil refinery; 20s. "Molniya" satellite and Moon (Soviet space research).

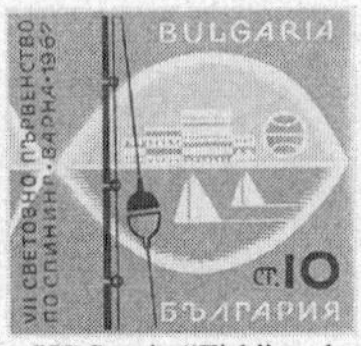

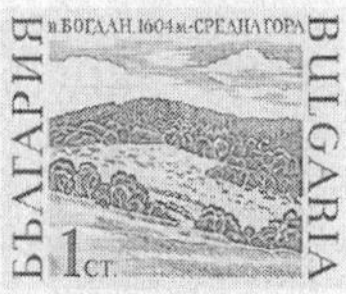

558 Scenic "Fish" and Rod

560 Bogdan Peak, Sredna Mts

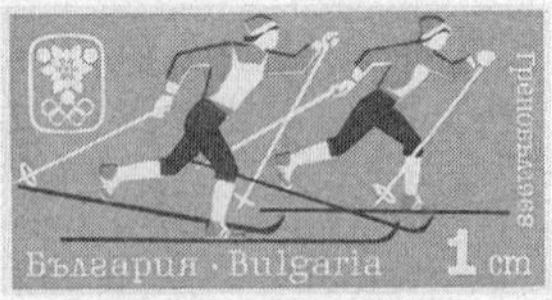

559 Cross-country Skiing

1967. 7th World Angling Championships, Varna.

1734	558	10s. multicoloured	40	15

1967. Winter Olympic Games, Grenoble (1968).

1735	559	1s. black, red & turq	10	10
1736	–	2s. black, bistre & blue	10	10
1737	–	3s. black, blue & purple	10	10
1738	–	5s. black, yellow & grn	15	10
1739	–	13s. black, buff & blue	1·00	15
1740	–	20s.+10s. mult	1·90	50

DESIGNS: 2s. Ski jumping; 3s. Biathlon; 5s. Ice hockey; 13s. Ice skating (pairs); 20s. Men's slalom.

1967. Tourism. Mountain Peaks.

1742	560	1s. green and yellow	10	10
1743	–	2s. sepia and blue	10	10
1744	–	3s. indigo and blue	10	10
1745	–	5s. green and blue	15	10
1746	–	10s. brown and blue	30	10
1747	–	13s. black and blue	40	15
1748	–	20s. blue and purple	70	25

DESIGNS—HORIZ: 2s. Cherni Vruh, Vitosha; 5s. Persenk, Rhodopes; 10s. Botev, Stara-Planina; 20s. Vikhren, Pirin. VERT: 3s. Ruen, Osogovska Planina; 13s. Musala, Rila.

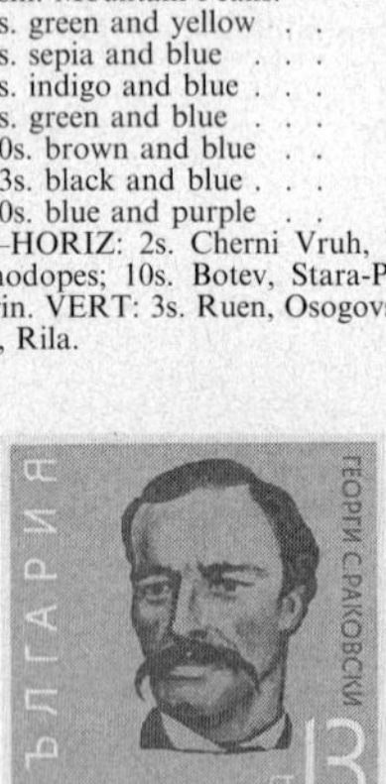

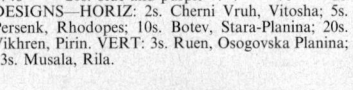

561 G. Rakovski

1967. Death Cent of G. Rakovski (revolutionary).

1749	561	13s. black and green	45	15

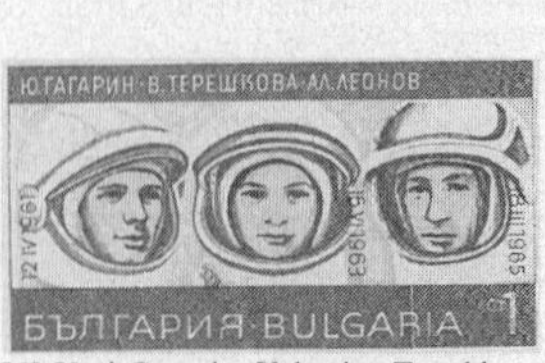

562 Yuri Gagarin, Valentina Tereshkova and Aleksei Leonov

1967. Space Exploration. Multicoloured.

1750	1s. Type 562	10	10
1751	2s. John Glenn and Edward White	15	10
1752	5s. "Molniya 1"	25	10
1753	10s. "Gemini 6" and "7"	65	15
1754	13s. "Luna 13"	85	15
1755	20s. "Gemini 10" docking with "Agena"	1·10	35

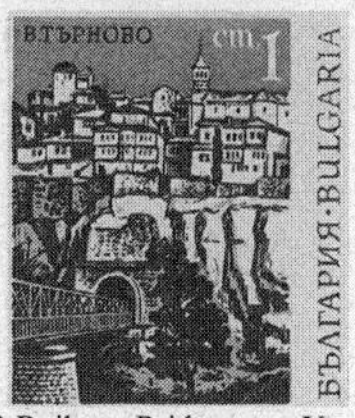

563 Railway Bridge over Yantra River

1967. Views of Turnovo (ancient capital).

1756	563	1s. black, drab and blue	15	10
1757	–	2s. multicoloured	10	10
1758	–	3s. multicoloured	10	10
1759	–	5s. black, slate and red	65	20
1760	–	13s. multicoloured	65	15
1761	–	20s. black, orange & lav	1·00	25

DESIGNS: 2s. Hadji Nikola's Inn; 3s. Houses on hillside; 5s. Town and river; 13s. "House of the Monkeys"; 20s. Gurko street.

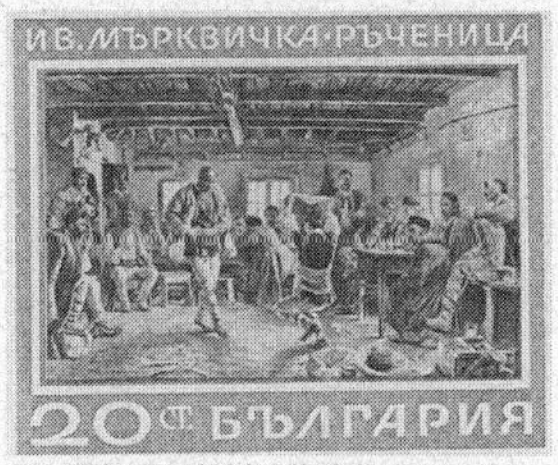

564 "The Ruchenitsa" (folk dance, from painting by Murkvichka)

1967. Belgian–Bulgarian "Painting and Philately" Exhibition, Brussels.

1762	564	20s. green and gold	1·90	1·50

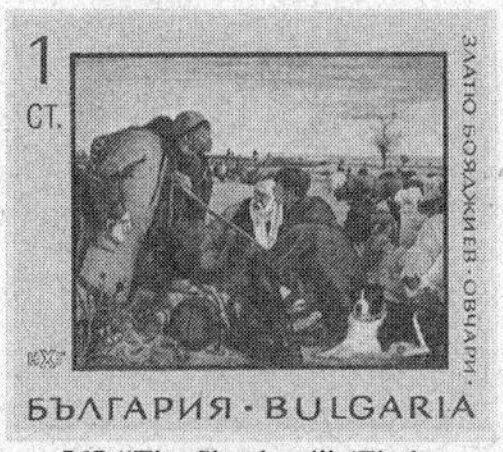

565 "The Shepherd" (Zlatko Boyadzhiev)

1967. Paintings in the National Gallery, Sofia. Multicoloured.

1763		1s. Type 565	10	10
1764		2s. "The Wedding" (Vladimir Dimitrov) (vert)	10	10
1765		3s. "The Partisans" Ilya Petrov (55 × 35 mm)	20	10
1766		5s. "Anastasia Penchovich" (Nikolai Pavlovich) (vert)	85	15
1767		13s. "Self-portrait" (Zakharii Zograf) (vert)	1·50	50
1768		20s. "Old Town of Plovdiv" (Tsanko Lavrenov)	2·00	1·00

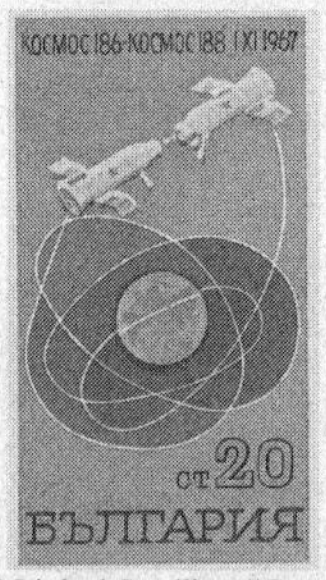

566 Linked Satellites "Cosmos 186" and "188"

1968. "Cosmic Activities". Multicoloured.

1770		20s. Type 566	1·00	25
1771		40s. "Venus 4" and orbital diagram (horiz)	1·90	50

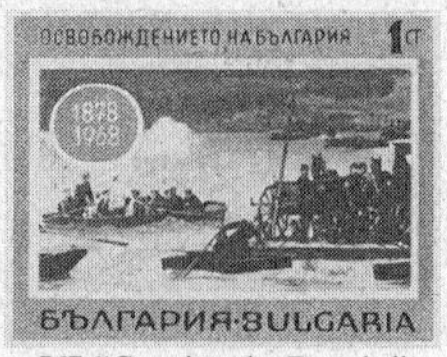

567 "Crossing the Danube" (Orenburgski)

1968. 90th Anniv of Liberation from Turkey. Paintings. Inscr and frames in black and gold; centre colours below.

1772	567	1s. green	25	10
1773	–	2s. blue	10	10
1774	–	3s. brown	15	10
1775	–	13s. blue	60	25
1776	–	20s. turquoise	1·00	40

DESIGNS—VERT: 2s. "Flag of Samara" (Veschin); 13s. "Battle of Orlovo Gnezdo" (Popov). HORIZ: 3s. "Battle of Pleven" (Orenburgski); 20s. "Greeting Russian Soldiers" (Goudienov).

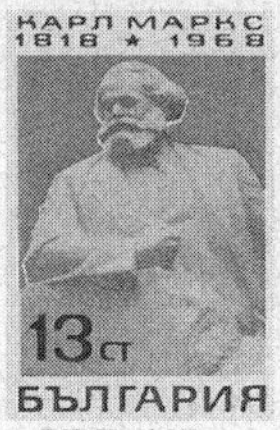

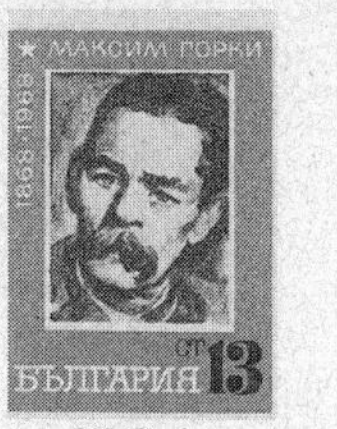

568 Karl Marx **569** Gorky

1968. 150th Birth Anniv of Karl Marx.

1777	568	13s. grey, red & black	65	15

1968. Birth Cent of Maksim Gorky (writer).

1778	569	13s. green, orange & blk	65	15

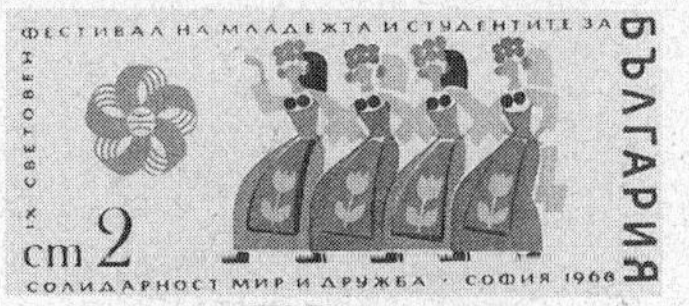

570 Dancers

1968. 9th World Youth and Students' Festival. Sofia. Multicoloured.

1779		2s. Type 570	10	10
1780		5s. Running	10	10
1781		13s. "Doves"	75	10
1782		20s. "Youth" (symbolic design)	85	25
1783		40s. Bulgarian 5c. stamp of 1879 under magnifier and Globe	1·50	55

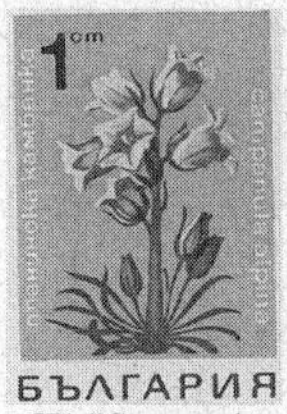

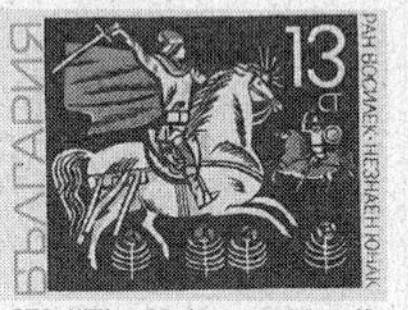

571 "Campanula alpina" **572** "The Unknown Hero" (Ran Bosilek)

1968. Wild Flowers. Multicoloured.

1784		1s. Type 571	10	10
1785		2s. Trumpet gentian	10	10
1786		3s. "Crocus veluchensis"	15	10
1787		5s. Siberian iris	20	10
1788		10s. Dog's-tooth violet	30	10
1789		13s. House leek	1·00	15
1790		20s. Burning bush	1·40	30

1968. Bulgarian–Danish Stamp Exhibition. Fairy Tales. Multicoloured.

1791		13s. Type 572	45	20
1792		20s. "The Witch and the Young Men" (Hans Andersen)	55	35

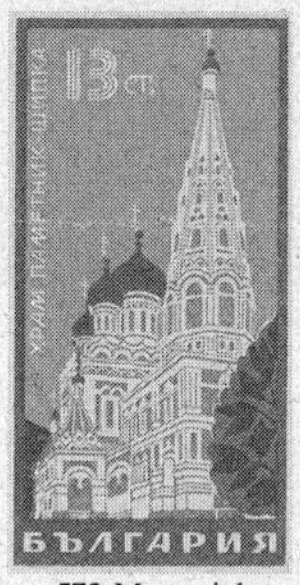

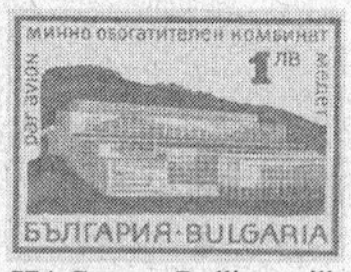

573 Memorial Temple, Shipka **574** Copper Rolling-mill, Medet

1968. Bulgarian–West Berlin Stamp Exn.

1793	573	13s. multicoloured	1·00	35

1968. Air.

1794	574	1l. red	2·75	35

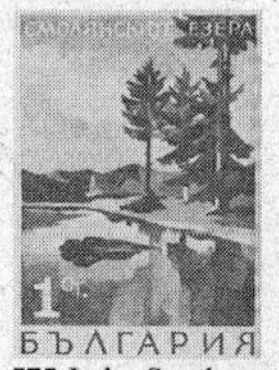

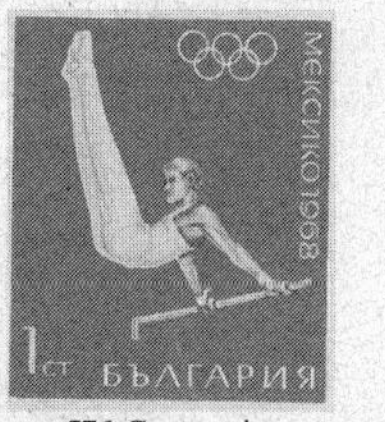

575 Lake Smolyan **576** Gymnastics

1968.

1795	575	1s. green	10	10
1796	–	2s. myrtle	10	10
1797	–	3s. sepia	10	10
1798	–	8s. green	25	10
1799	–	10s. brown	65	10
1800	–	13s. olive	45	15
1801	–	40s. blue	1·25	35
1802	–	2l. brown	6·00	1·40

DESIGNS: 2s. River Ropotamo; 3s. Lomnitza Gorge, Erma River; 8s. River Isker; 10s. Cruise ship "Die Fregatte"; 13s. Cape Kaliakra; 40s. Sozopol; 2l. Mountain road, Kamchia River.

1968. Olympic Games, Mexico.

1803	576	1s. black and red	10	10
1804	–	2s. black, brown & grey	10	10
1805	–	3s. black and mauve	15	10
1806	–	10s. black, yell & turq	50	10
1807	–	13s. black, pink & blue	1·00	20
1808	–	20s.+10s. grey, pk & bl	1·75	40

DESIGNS: 2s. Horse-jumping; 3s. Fencing; 10s. Boxing; 13s. Throwing the discus; 20s. Rowing.

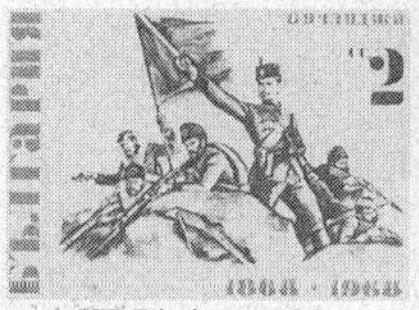

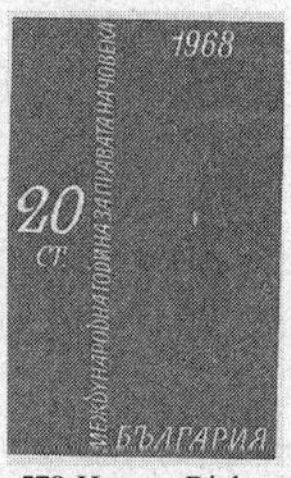

577 Dimitur on Mt. Buzludzha, 1868 **578** Human Rights Emblem

1968. Centenary of Exploits of Khadzhi Dimitur and Stefan Karadzha (revolutionaries).

1810	577	2s. brown and silver	15	10
1811	–	13s. green and gold	35	15

DESIGN: 13s. Dimitur and Karadzha.

1968. Human Rights Year.

1812	578	20s. gold and blue	1·00	15

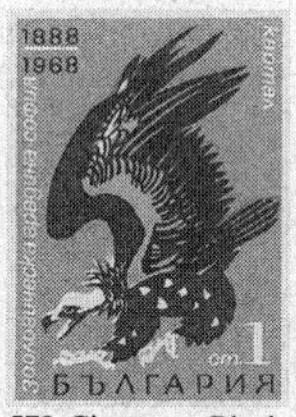

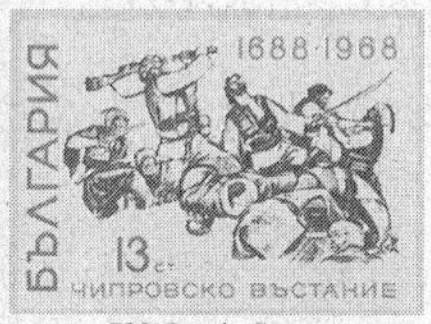

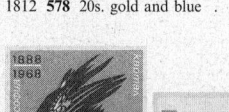

579 Cinereous Black Vulture **580** Battle Scene

1968. 80th Anniv of Sofia Zoo.

1813	579	1s. black, brown & blue	50	10
1814	–	2s. black, yellow & brn	50	10
1815	–	3s. black and green	30	10
1816	–	5s. black, yellow & red	50	10
1817	–	13s. black, bistre & grn	1·60	15
1818	–	20s. black, green & blue	2·50	55

DESIGNS: 2s. South African crowned crane; 3s. Common zebra; 5s. Leopard; 13s. Python; 20s. Crocodile.

1968. 280th Anniv of Chiprovtsi Rising.

1819	580	13s. multicoloured	80	15

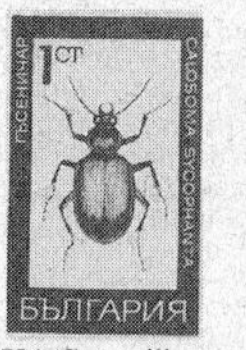

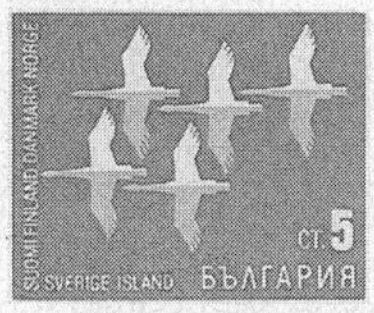

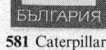

581 Caterpillar-hunter **582** Flying Swans

1968. Insects.

1820	581	1s. green	15	10
1821	–	1s. brown	15	10
1822	–	1s. blue	15	10
1823	–	1s. brown	15	10
1824	–	1s. purple	35	10

DESIGNS—VERT: No. 1821, Stag beetle ("Lucanus cervus"); 1822, "Procerus scabrosus" (ground beetle). HORIZ: No. 1823, European rhinoceros beetle ("Oryctes nasicornis"); 1824, "Perisomena caecigena" (moth).

1968. "Co-operation with Scandinavia".

1825	–	2s. ochre and green	1·25	1·25
1826	582	5s. blue, grey & black	1·25	1·25
1827	–	13s. purple and maroon	1·25	1·25
1828	–	20s. grey and violet	1·25	1·25

DESIGNS: 2s. Wooden flask; 13s. Rose; 20s. "Viking ship".

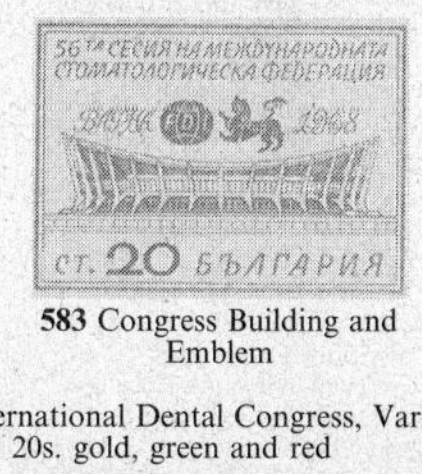

583 Congress Building and Emblem

1968. International Dental Congress, Varna.

1829	583	20s. gold, green and red	85	15

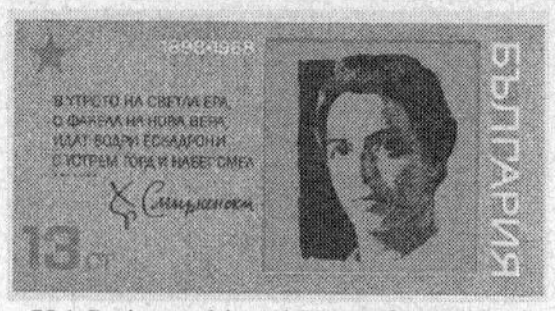

584 Smirnenski and Verse from "Red Squadrons"

1968. 70th Birth Anniv of Khristo Smirnenski (poet).

1830	584	13s. black, orange & gold	45	15

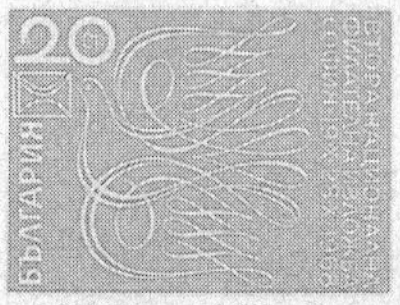

585 Dove with Letter

1968. National Stamp Exhibition, Sofia and 75th Anniv of "National Philately".

1831	585	20s. green	1·10	85

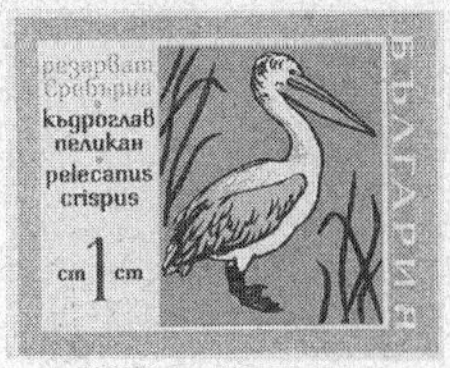

586 Dalmatian Pelican

1968. Srebirna Wildlife Reservation. Birds. Mult.

1832		1s. Type 586	10	10
1833		2s. Little egret	15	10
1834		3s. Great crested grebe	20	10
1835		5s. Common tern	50	15
1836		13s. White spoonbill	1·50	50
1837		20s. Glossy ibis	2·75	85

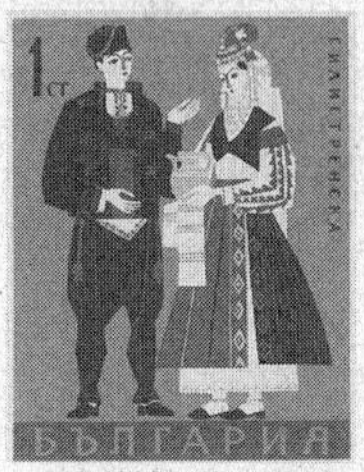

587 Silistra Costume

1968. Provincial Costumes. Multicoloured.

1838		1s. Type 587	10	10
1839		2s. Lovech	10	10
1840		3s. Yamboi	15	10
1841		13s. Chirpan	45	10
1842		20s. Razgrad	1·00	25
1843		40s. Ikhtiman	2·00	50

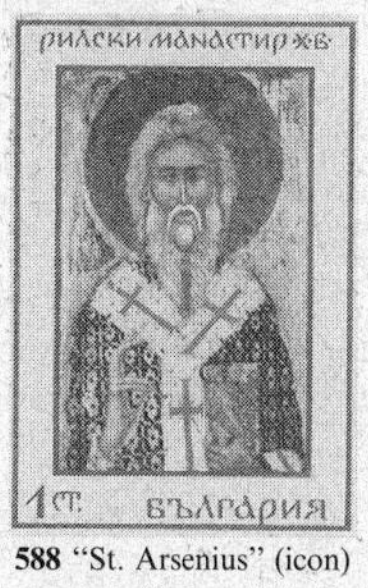

588 "St. Arsenius" (icon)

1968. Rila Monastery. Icons and murals. Mult.

1844		1s. Type 588	10	10
1845		2s. "Carrying St. Ivan Rilski's Relics" (horiz)	10	10
1846		3s. "St. Michael torments the Rich Man's Soul"	15	10
1847		13s. "St. Ivan Rilski"	1·00	15
1848		20s. "Prophet Joel"	1·40	30
1849		40s. "St. George"	2·40	1·00

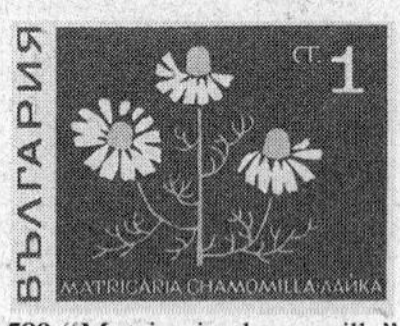

589 "Matricaria chamomilla"

1968. Medicinal Plants. Multicoloured.

1851		1s. Type 589	10	10
1852		1s. "Mespilus oxyacantha"	10	10
1853		2s. Lily of the valley	10	10
1854		3s. Deadly nightshade	10	10
1855		5s. Common mallow	15	10
1856		10s. Yellow peasant's eye	25	10
1857		13s. Common poppy	50	15
1858		20s. Wild thyme	1·00	25

590 Silkworms and Spindles

1969. Silk Industry. Multicoloured.
1859 1s. Type **590** 10 10
1860 2s. Worm, cocoons and pattern 10 10
1861 3s. Cocoons and spinning wheel 10 10
1862 5s. Cocoons and pattern . . 15 10
1863 13s. Moth, cocoon and spindles 40 15
1864 20s. Moth, eggs and shuttle 85 25

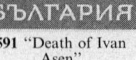

591 "Death of Ivan Asen"
592 "Saints Cyril and Methodius" (mural, Troyan Monastery)

1969. Manasses Chronicle (1st series). Mult.
1865 1s. Type **591** 10 10
1866 2s. "Emperor Nicephorus invading Bulgaria" . . . 10 10
1867 3s. "Khan Krum's Feast" 15 10
1868 13s. "Prince Sviatoslav invading Bulgaria" . . . 85 15
1869 20s. "The Russian invasion" 1·10 25
1870 40s. "Jesus Christ, Tsar Ivan Alexander and Constantine Manasses" 2·10 75
See also Nos. 1911/16.

1969. Saints Cyril and Methodius Commem.
1871 **592** 28s. multicoloured . . . 1·40 45

593 Galleon
594 Posthorn Emblem

1969. Air. "SOFIA 1969" International Stamp Exhibition. Transport. Multicoloured.
1872 1s. Type **593** 10 10
1873 2s. Mail coach 10 10
1874 3s. Steam locomotive . . . 20 10
1875 5s. Early motor-car 15 10
1876 10s. Montgolfier's balloon and Henri Giffard's steam-powered dirigible airship 20 10
1877 13s. Early flying machines 30 15
1878 20s. Modern aircraft 85 25
1879 40s. Rocket and planets . . 1·50 50

1969. 90th Anniv of Bulgarian Postal Services.
1881 **594** 2s. yellow and green . . 10 10
1882 – 13s. multicoloured . . . 65 10
1883 – 20s. blue 85 25
DESIGNS: 13s. Bulgarian Stamps of 1879 and 1946; 20s. Post Office workers' strike, 1919.

595 I.L.O. Emblem
596 "Fox" and "Rabbit"

1969. 50th Anniv of I.L.O.
1884 **595** 13s. black and green . . 35 15

1969. Children's Book Week.
1885 **596** 1s. black, orange & grn 10 10
1886 – 2s. black, blue and red 10 10
1887 – 13s. black, olive & blue 65 15
DESIGNS: 2s. Boy with "hedgehog" and "squirrel"; 13s. "The Singing Lesson".

597 Hand with Seedling

1969. "10,000,000 Hectares of New Forests".
1888 **597** 2s. black, green & purple 15 10

598 "St. George" (14th Century)

1969. Religious Art. Multicoloured.
1889 1s. Type **598** 10 10
1890 2s. "The Virgin and St. John Bogoslov" (14th century) 10 10
1891 3s. "Archangel Michael" (17th century) 15 10
1892 5s. "Three Saints" (17th century) 25 10
1893 8s. "Jesus Christ" (17th century) 30 10
1894 13s. "St. George and St. Dimitr" (19th century) . . 75 15
1895 20s. "Christ the Universal" (19th century) . . . . . 1·10 15
1896 60s. "The Forty Martyrs" (19th century) . . . . . 3·25 90
1897 80s. "The Transfiguration" (19th century) . . . . . 4·00 1·60

599 Roman Coin
600 St. George and the Dragon

1969. "SOFIA 1969" International Stamp Exhibition. "Sofia Through the Ages".
1899 **599** 1s. silver, blue and gold 10 10
1900 – 2s. silver, green & gold 10 10
1901 – 3s. silver, lake and gold 10 10
1902 – 4s. silver, violet & gold 15 10
1903 – 5s. silver, purple & gold 15 10
1904 – 13s. silver, green & gold 50 15
1905 – 20s. silver, blue & gold 1·00 15
1906 – 40s. silver, red & gold 2·00 35
DESIGNS: 2s. Roman coin showing Temple of Aesculapius; 3s. Church of St. Sophia; 4s. Boyana Church; 5s. Parliament Building; 13s. National Theatre; 20s. Aleksandr Nevski Cathedral; 40s. Sofia University.

1969. Int Philatelic Federation Congress, Sofia.
1908 **600** 40s. black, orange & sil 2·00 75

601 St. Cyril

1969. 1,100th Death Anniv of St. Cyril.
1909 **601** 2s. green & red on silver 15 10
1910 – 28s. blue & red on silver 1·40 35
DESIGN: 28s. St. Cyril and procession.

1969. Manasses Chronicle (2nd series). Designs as T **591**, but all horiz. Multicoloured.
1911 1s. "Nebuchadnezzar II and Balthasar of Babylon, Cyrus and Darius of Persia" 10 10
1912 2s. "Cambyses, Gyges and Darius of Persia" 10 10
1913 5s. "Prophet David and Tsar Ivan Alexander" . . 15 10
1914 13s. "Rout of the Byzantine Army, 811" 85 15
1915 20s. "Christening of Khan Boris" . . . . 1·60 20
1916 60s. "Tsar Simeon's attack on Constantinople" . . . 3·25 1·10

602 Partisans

1969. 25th Anniv of Fatherland Front Government.
1917 **602** 1s. lilac, red and black 10 10
1918 – 2s. brown, red & black 10 10
1919 – 3s. green, red and black 10 10
1920 – 5s. brown, red & black 20 10
1921 – 13s. blue, red & black 30 10
1922 – 20s. multicoloured . . . 75 20
DESIGNS: 2s. Combine-harvester; 3s. Dam; 5s. Folk singers; 13s. Petroleum refinery; 20s. Lenin, Dimitrov and flags.

603 Gymnastics

1969. 3rd Republican Spartakiad. Multicoloured.
1923 2s. Type **603** 10 10
1924 20s. Wrestling 85 25

604 "Construction" and soldier
605 T. Tserkovski

1969. 25th Anniv of Army Engineers.
1925 **604** 6s. black and blue . . . 15 10

1969. Birth Cent of Tsanke Tserkovski (poet).
1926 **605** 13s. multicoloured . . . 35 15

606 "Woman" (Roman Statue)
607 Skipping-rope Exercise

1969. 1,800th Anniv of Silistra.
1927 **606** 2s. grey, blue and silver 15 10
1928 – 13s. brown, grn & silver 75 15
DESIGN—HORIZ: 13s. "Wolf" (bronze statue).

1969. World Gymnastics Competition, Varna.
1929 **607** 1s. grey, blue and green 10 10
1930 – 2s. grey and blue 10 10
1931 – 3s. grey, green and emerald 10 10
1932 – 5s. grey, purple and red 10 10
1933 – 13s.+5s. grey, bl & red 85 25
1934 – 20s.+10s. grey, green and yellow . . . . 1·40 40
DESIGNS: 2s. Hoop exercise (pair); 3s. Hoop exercise (solo); 5s. Ball exercise (pair); 13s. Ball exercise (solo); 20s. Solo gymnast.

608 Marin Drinov (founder)

1969. Cent of Bulgarian Academy of Sciences.
1935 **608** 20s. black and red . . . 45 15

609 "Neophit Rilski" (Zakharii Zograf)

1969. Paintings in National Gallery, Sofia. Mult.
1936 1s. Type **609** 10 10
1937 2s. "German's Mother" (Vasil Stoilov) 10 10
1938 3s. "Workers' Family" (Neuko Balkanski) (horiz) 20 10
1939 4s. "Woman Dressing" (Ivan Nenov) 30 10
1940 5s. "Portrait of a Woman" (Nikolai Pavlovich) . . . 30 10
1941 13s. "Krustyn Sarafov as Falstaff" (Dechko Uzunov) 85 15
1942 20s. "Artist's Wife" (N. Mikhailov) (horiz) . . 1·00 25
1943 20s. "Worker's Lunch" (Stoyan Sotirov) (horiz) 1·10 30
1944 40s. "Self-portrait" (Tseno Todorov) (horiz) . . . . 1·60 80

610 Pavel Banya

1969. Sanatoria.
1945 **610** 2s. blue 10 10
1946 – 5s. blue 10 10
1947 – 6s. green 20 10
1948 – 20s. green 55 15
SANATORIA: 5s. Khisar; 6s. Kotel; 20s. Narechen Polyclinic.

611 Deep-sea Trawler

1969. Ocean Fisheries.
1949 **611** 1s. grey and blue 30 10
1950 – 1s. green and black . . . 10 10
1951 – 2s. violet and black . . . 10 10
1952 – 3s. blue and black . . . 10 10
1953 – 5s. mauve and black . . 20 10
1954 – 10s. grey and black . . . 1·00 15
1955 – 13s. flesh, orange & blk 1·50 25
1956 – 20s. brown, ochre & blk 2·00 35
DESIGNS: 1s. (No. 1950), Cape hake; 2s. Atlantic horse-mackerel; 3s. South African pilchard; 5s. Large-eyed dentex; 10s. Chub mackerel; 13s. Senegal croaker; 20s. Vadigo.

612 Trapeze Act
613 V. Kubasov, Georgi Shonin and "Soyuz 6"

1969. Circus. Multicoloured.
1957 1s. Type **612** 10 10
1958 2s. Acrobats 10 10
1959 3s. Balancing act with hoops 10 10
1960 5s. Juggler, and bear on cycle 10 10
1961 13s. Equestrian act 40 15
1962 20s. Clowns . . . . 1·00 35

1970. Space Flights of "Soyuz 6, 7 and 8".
1963 **613** 1s. multicoloured 10 10
1964 – 2s. multicoloured 10 10
1965 – 3s. multicoloured 15 10
1966 – 28s. pink and blue . . . 1·40 30
DESIGNS: 2s. Viktor Gorbacko, Vladislav Volkov, Anatoly Filipchenko and "Soyuz 7"; 3s. Aleksei Elseev, Vladimir Shatalov and "Soyuz 8"; 28s. Three "Soyuz" spacecraft in orbit.

614 Khan Asparerch and "Old-Bulgars" crossing the Danube, 679

1970. History of Bulgaria. Multicoloured.
1967	1s. Type 614	10	10
1968	2s. Khan Krum and defeat of Emperor Nicephorus, 811	10	10
1969	3s. Conversion of Khan Boris I to Christianity, 865	15	10
1970	5s. Tsar Simeon and Battle of Akhelo, 917	20	10
1971	8s. Tsar Samuel and defeat of Byzantines, 976	20	10
1972	10s. Tsar Kaloyan and victory over Emperor Baldwin, 1205	30	15
1973	13s. Tsar Ivan Assen II and defeat of Komnine of Epirus, 1230	85	15
1974	20s. Coronation of Tsar Ivailo, 1277	1·40	25

615 Bulgarian Pavilion

1970. "Expo 70" World's Fair, Osaka, Japan (1st issue).
| 1975 | 615 | 20s. silver, yellow & brn | 1·40 | 85 |

See Nos. 2009/12.

616 Footballers

1970. World Football Cup, Mexico.
1976	616	1s. multicoloured	10	10
1977	–	2s. multicoloured	10	10
1978	–	3s. multicoloured	15	10
1979	–	5s. multicoloured	20	10
1980	–	20s. multicoloured	1·25	35
1981	–	40s. multicoloured	2·40	60

DESIGNS: 2s. to 40s. Various football scenes.

 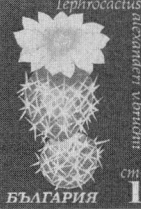

617 Lenin   618 "Tephrocactus Alexanderi v. bruchi"

1970. Birth Cent of Lenin. Multicoloured.
1983	2s. Type 617	10	10
1984	13s. Full-face portrait	40	15
1985	20s. Lenin writing	75	25

1970. Flowering Cacti. Multicoloured.
1986	1s. Type 618	10	10
1987	2s. "Opuntia drummondii"	15	10
1988	3s. "Hatiora cilindrica"	20	10
1989	5s. "Gymnocalycium vatteri"	25	10
1990	8s. "Heliantho cereus grandiflorus"	40	20
1991	10s. "Neochilenia andreaeana"	1·75	25
1992	13s. "Peireskia vargasii v. longispina"	1·90	30
1993	20s. "Neobesseya rosiflora"	2·50	45

619 Rose   620 Union Badge

1970. Bulgarian Roses.
1994	619	1s. multicoloured	10	10
1995	–	2s. multicoloured	15	10
1996	–	3s. multicoloured	25	10
1997	–	4s. multicoloured	30	10
1998	–	5s. multicoloured	35	10
1999	–	13s. multicoloured	55	10
2000	–	20s. multicoloured	1·60	45
2001	–	28s. multicoloured	2·75	85

DESIGNS: 2s. to 28s. Various roses.

1970. 70th Anniv of Agricultural Union.
| 2002 | 620 | 20s. black, gold and red | 1·00 | 25 |

621 Gold Bowl

1970. Gold Treasures of Thrace.
2003	621	1s. black, blue and gold	10	10
2004	–	2s. black, lilac and gold	10	10
2005	–	3s. black, red and gold	15	10
2006	–	5s. black, green & gold	20	10
2007	–	13s. black, orge & gold	1·00	15
2008	–	20s. black, violet & gold	1·50	30

DESIGNS: 2s. Three small bowls; 3s. Plain lid; 5s. Pear shaped ornaments; 13s. Large lid with pattern; 20s. Vase.

622 Rose and Woman with Baskets of Produce

1970. "Expo 70" World's Fair, Osaka, Japan (2nd issue). Multicoloured.
2009	1s. Type 622	10	10
2010	2s. Three Dancers	10	10
2011	3s. Girl in National costume	10	10
2012	28s. Dancing couples	1·25	35

623 U.N. Emblem

1970. 25th Anniv of United Nations.
| 2014 | 623 | 20s. gold and blue | 85 | 15 |

624 I. Vasov

1970. 120th Birth Anniv of Ivan Vasov (poet).
| 2015 | 624 | 13s. blue | 45 | 15 |

625 Edelweiss Sanatorium, Borovets

1970. Health Resorts.
2016	625	1s. green	10	10
2017	–	2s. olive	10	10
2018	–	4s. blue	20	10
2019	–	8s. blue	30	10
2020	–	10s. blue	35	10

DESIGNS: 2s. Panorama Hotel, Pamporovo; 4s. Yachts, Albena; 8s. Harbour scene, Rousalka; 10s. Shtastlivetsa Hotel, Mt. Vitosha.

626 Hungarian Retriever

1970. Dogs. Multicoloured.
2021	1s. Type 626	15	10
2022	2s. Retriever (vert)	20	10
2023	3s. Great Dane (vert)	30	10
2024	4s. Boxer (vert)	40	10
2025	5s. Cocker spaniel (vert)	50	10
2026	13s. Dobermann pinscher (vert)	1·25	25
2027	20s. Scottish terrier (vert)	2·25	50
2028	28s. Russian hound	2·75	75

627 Fireman with Hose   628 Congress Emblem

1970. Fire Protection.
| 2029 | 627 | 1s. grey, yellow & black | 10 | 10 |
| 2030 | – | 3s. red, grey and black | 15 | 10 |

DESIGN. 3s. Fire-engine.

1970. 7th World Sociological Congress, Varna.
| 2031 | 628 | 13s. multicoloured | 50 | 15 |

 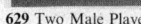

629 Two Male Players   630 Cyclists

1970. World Volleyball Championships.
2032	629	2s. black and brown	10	10
2033	–	2s. orange, black & blue	15	10
2034	–	20s. yellow, black & grn	1·00	20
2035	–	20s. multicoloured	1·00	20

DESIGNS: No. 2033, Two female players; 2034, Male player; 2035, Female player.

1970. 20th Round-Bulgaria Cycle Race.
| 2036 | 630 | 20s. mauve, yellow & grn | 75 | 20 |

631 Enrico Caruso and Scene from "Il Pagliacci"

1970. Opera Singers. Multicoloured.
2037	1s. Type 631	10	10
2038	2s. Khristina Morfova and "The Bartered Bride"	10	10
2039	3s. Petur Raichev and "Tosca"	10	10
2040	10s. Tsvetana Tabakova and "The Flying Dutchman"	40	20
2041	13s. Katya Popova and "The Masters of Nuremberg"	45	10
2042	20s. Fyodor Chaliapin and "Boris Godunov"	1·75	40

632 Beethoven

1970. Birth Bicentenary of Ludwig von Beethoven (composer).
| 2043 | 632 | 28s. blue and purple | 3·00 | 50 |

633 Ivan Asen II Coin

1970. Bulgarian Coins of the 14th century. Multicoloured.
2044	1s. Type 633	10	10
2045	2s. Theodor Svetoslav	10	10
2046	3s. Mikhail Shishman	10	10
2047	13s. Ivan Alexander and Mikhail Asen	45	10
2048	20s. Ivan Sratsimir	1·00	15
2049	28s. Ivan Shishman (initials)	1·25	20

635 Engels   636 Snow Crystal

1970. 150th Birth Anniv of Friedrich Engels.
| 2051 | 635 | 13s. brown and red | 60 | 15 |

1970. New Year.
| 2052 | 636 | 2s. multicoloured | 15 | 10 |

638 "Girl's Head" (Zheko Spiridonov)

1971. Modern Bulgarian Sculpture.
2054	638	1s. violet and gold	10	10
2055	–	2s. green and gold	35	10
2056	–	3s. brown and gold	10	10
2057	–	13s. green and gold	45	15
2058	–	20s. red and gold	1·10	20
2059	–	28s. brown and gold	1·50	45

SCULPTURES: 2s. "Third Class Carriage" (Ivan Funev); 3s. "Elin Pelin" (Marko Markov); 13s. "Nina" (Andrei Nikolov); 20s. "Kneeling Woman" (Yavorov monument, Ivan Lazarov); 28s. "Engineer" (Ivan Funev).

639 Birds and Flowers

1971. Spring.
2061	639	1s. multicoloured	10	10
2062	–	2s. multicoloured	10	10
2063	–	3s. multicoloured	10	10
2064	–	5s. multicoloured	10	10
2065	–	13s. multicoloured	25	10
2066	–	20s. multicoloured	1·00	20

DESIGNS: 2s. to 20s. Various designs of birds and flowers similar to Type 639.

640 "Khan Asparuch crossing Danube" (Boris Angelushev)

1971. Bulgarian History. Paintings. Mult.
2067	2s. Type 640	10	10
2068	3s. "Ivajlo in Turnovo" (Ilya Petrov)	15	10
2069	5s. "Cavalry Charge, Benkovski" (P. Morosov)	50	10
2070	8s. "Gen. Gzrko entering Sofia, 1878" (D. Gyudzhenov)	85	10
2071	28s. "Greeting Red Army" (Stefan Venev)	4·25	1·50

641 Running

1971. 2nd European Indoor Track and Field Championships. Multicoloured.
| 2073 | 2s. Type 641 | 15 | 10 |
| 2074 | 20s. Putting the shot | 1·60 | 25 |

642 School Building

1971. Foundation of First Bulgarian Secondary School, Bolgrad.
2075	642	2s. green, brown & sil	10	10
2076	–	20s. violet, brown & sil	95	20

DESIGN: 20s. Dimitur Mutev, Prince Bogoridi and Sava Radulov (founders).

643 Communards

1971. Centenary of Paris Commune.
2077	643	20s. black and red . . .	65	25

644 Georgi Dimitrov challenging Hermann Goering

1971. 20th Anniv of "Federation Internationale des Resistants".
2078	644	2s. multicoloured	15	10
2079		13s. multicoloured . . .	1·10	20

646 G. Rakovski   **647** Worker and Banner ("People's Progress")

1971. 150th Birth Anniv of Georgi Rakovski (politician and Revolutionary).
2081	646	13s. brown, cream & grn	35	15

1971. 10th Bulgarian Communist Party Congress. Multicoloured.
2082	1s. Type 647		10	10
2083	2s. Symbols of "Technical Progress" (horiz)		10	10
2084	12s. Men clasping hands ("Bulgarian-Soviet Friendship")		75	10

648 Pipkov and Music

1971. Birth Centenary of Panaiot Pipokov.
2085	648	13s. black, green & silver	60	20

649 "Three Races"   **650** Mammoth

1971. Racial Equality Year.
2086	649	13s. multicoloured . . .	45	15

1971. Prehistoric Animals. Multicoloured.
2087	1s. Type 650		10	10
2088	2s. Bear (vert) . . .		10	10
2089	3s. Hipparion		15	10
2090	13s. Mastodon		90	15
2091	20s. Dinotherium (vert)		1·40	20
2092	28s. Sabre-toothed tiger		1·90	35

651 Facade of Ancient Building   **652** Weights Emblem on Map of Europe

1971. Ancient Buildings of Koprivshitsa.
2093	651	1s. green, brown & grn	10	10
2094	–	2s. brown, green & buff	10	10
2095	–	6s. violet, brown & blue	20	10
2096	–	13s. red, blue & orange	65	25

DESIGNS: 1s. to 13s. Different facades.

1971. 30th European Weightlifting Championships, Sofia. Multicoloured.
2097	2s. Type 652		10	10
2098	13s. Figures supporting weights		1·25	20

653 Frontier Guard and Dog   **654** Tweezers, Magnifying Glass and "Stamp"

1971. 25th Anniv of Frontier Guards.
2099	653	2s. olive, green & turq	10	10

1971. 9th Congress of Bulgarian Philatelic Federation.
2100	654	20s.+10s. brown, black and red	1·50	50

655 Congress Meeting (sculpture)

1971. 80th Anniv of Bulgarian Social Democratic Party Congress, Buzludzha.
2101	655	2s. green, cream and red	15	10

656 "Mother" (Ivan Nenov)   **657** Factory Botevgrad

1971. Paintings from the National Art Gallery (1st series). Multicoloured.
2102	1s. Type 656		10	10
2103	2s. "Lazorova" (Stefan Ivanov)		10	10
2104	3s. "Portrait of Yu. Kh." (Kiril Tsonev) . . .		15	10
2105	13s. "Portrait of a Lady" (Dechko Uzunov) . .		75	15
2106	30s. "Young Woman from Kalotina" (Vladimir Dimitrov)		1·10	35
2107	40s. "Goryanin" (Stryan Venev)		2·00	60

See also Nos. 2145/50.

1971. Industrial Buildings.
2108	657	1s. violet	10	10
2109	–	2s. red	10	10
2110	–	10s. violet	20	10
2111	–	13s. red	25	10
2112	–	40s. brown	90	15

DESIGNS—VERT: 2s. Petro-chemical plant, Pleven. HORIZ: 10s. Chemical works, Vratsa; 13s. "Maritsa-Istok" plant, Dimitrovgrad; 40s. Electronics factory, Sofia.

658 Free Style Wrestling

1971. European Wrestling Championships, Sofia.
2113	658	2s. green, black and blue	10	10
2114	–	13s. black, red and blue	75	20

DESIGN: 13s. Greco-Roman wrestling.

659 Posthorn Emblem

1971. Organization of Socialist Countries' Postal Administrations Congress.
2115	659	20s. gold and green . . .	65	25

660 Entwined Ribbons

1971. 7th European Biochemical Congress, Varna.
2116	660	13s. red, brown & black	65	25

661 "New Republic" Statue

1971. 25th Anniv of People's Republic.
2117	661	2s. red, yellow and gold	10	10
2118	–	13s. green, red and gold	50	20

DESIGN: 13s. Bulgarian flag.

662 Cross-country Skiing

1971. Winter Olympic Games, Sapporo, Japan. Multicoloured.
2119	1s. Type 662		10	10
2120	2s. Downhill skiing . .		10	10
2121	3s. Ski jumping . . .		15	10
2122	4s. Figure skating . .		15	10
2123	13s. Ice hockey		85	75
2124	28s. Slalom skiing . . .		1·50	40

663 Brigade Members   **664** U.N.E.S.C.O. Emblem and Wreath

1971. 25th Anniv of Youth Brigades Movement.
2126	663	2s. blue	15	10

1971. 25th Anniv of U.N.E.S.C.O.
2127	664	20s. multicoloured . . .	75	25

665 "The Footballer"

1971. Paintings by Kiril Tsonev. Multicoloured.
2128	1s. Type 665		10	10
2129	2s. "Landscape" (horiz)		10	10
2130	3s. Self-portrait		15	10
2131	13s. "Lilies"		75	10
2132	20s. "Woodland Scene" (horiz)		1·10	30
2133	40s. "Portrait of a Young Woman"		2·00	40

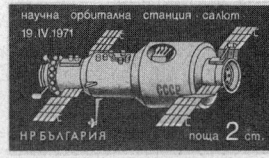

666 "Salyut" Space-station

1971. Space Flights of "Salyut" and "Soyuz 11". Multicoloured.
2134	2s. Type 666		10	10
2135	13s. "Soyuz 11"		40	15
2136	40s. "Salyut" and "Soyuz 11" joined together . . .		1·90	45

667 "Vikhren" (ore carrier)

1972. "One Million Tons of Bulgarian Shipping".
2138	667	18s. lilac, red and black	1·25	20

668 Goce Delcev

1972. Birth Centenaries of Macedonian Revolutionaries.
2139	668	2s. black and red . . .	10	10
2140	–	5s. black and green . .	10	10
2141	–	13s. black and yellow .	45	15

PATRIOTS: 5s. Jan Sandanski (1972); 13s. Dume Gruev (1971).

669 Gymnast with Ball

1972. World Gymnastics Championships, Havana (Cuba). Multicoloured.
2142	13s. Type 669		85	15
2143	18s. Gymnast with hoop .		1·00	25

1972. Paintings in Bulgarian National Gallery (2nd series). As T 656 but horiz. Multicoloured.
2145	1s. "Melnik" (Petur Mladenov)		10	10
2146	2s. "Ploughman" (Pencho Georgiev)		10	10
2147	3s. "By the Death-bed" (Aleksandur Zhendov)		15	10
2148	13s. "Family" (Vladimir Dimitrov)		75	15
2149	20s. "Family" (Neuko Balkanski)		1·25	25
2150	40s. "Father Paisii" (Koyu Denchev)		2·00	40

670 Bulgarian Worker

671 "Singing Harvesters"

1972. 7th Bulgarian Trade Unions Congress.
2151 **670** 13s. multicoloured . . . 35 15

1972. 90th Birth Anniv of Vladimir Dimitrov, the Master (painter). Multicoloured.
2152 1s. Type **671** 10 10
2153 2s. "Farm Worker" 10 10
2154 3s. "Women Cultivators"
(horiz) 10 10
2155 13s. "Peasant Girl" (horiz) 75 10
2156 20s. "My Mother" . . . . 1·10 30
2157 40s. Self-portrait . . . . . 2·00 40

672 Heart and Tree Emblem

673 St. Mark's Cathedral

1972. World Heart Month.
2158 **672** 13s. multicoloured . . . 1·10 50

1972. U.N.E.S.C.O. "Save Venice" Campaign.
2159 **673** 2s. green, turquoise & bl 10 10
2160 – 13s. brown, violet & grn 70 20
DESIGN: 13s. Doge's Palace.

674 Dimitrov at Typesetting Desk

1972. 90th Birth Anniv of Georgi Dimitrov (statesman). Multicoloured.
2161 1s. 674 . . . . 10 10
2162 2s. Dimitrov leading
uprising of 1923 . . . . 10 10
2163 3s. Dimitrov at Leipzig Trial 10 ·10
2164 5s. Dimitrov addressing
workers 15 10
2165 13s. Dimitrov with
Bulgarian crowd . . . 40 15
2166 18s. Addressing young
people . . . . . . 1·00 15
2167 28s. Dimitrov with children 1·40 20
2168 40s. Dimitrov's mausoleum 2·00 25
2169 80s. Portrait head (green
and gold) . . . . 5·75 60
2173 80s. As No. 2169 . . 10·00 10·00
No. 2173 has the centre in red and gold, and is imperforate.

675 "Lamp of Learning" and Quotation

1972. 250th Birth Anniv of Father Paisii Khilendurski (historian).
2171 **675** 2s. brown, green & gold 15 10
2172 – 13s. brown, grn & gold 75 20
DESIGN: 13s. Paisii writing.

676 Canoeing

1972. Olympic Games, Munich. Multicoloured.
2174 1s. Type **676** 10 10
2175 2s. Gymnastics 10 10
2176 3s. Swimming 10 10
2177 13s. Volleyball 35 10
2178 18s. Hurdling 85 25
2179 40s. Wrestling . . . . . 1·50 45

677 Angel Kunchev

1972. Death Cent of Angel Kunchev (patriot).
2181 **677** 2s. mauve, gold & purple 10 10

678 "Golden Sands"

1972. Black Sea Resorts. Hotels. Multicoloured.
2182 1s. Type **678** 10 10
2183 2s. Druzhba 10 10
2184 3s. "Sunny Beach" 10 10
2185 13s. Primorsko 25 10
2186 28s. Rusalka 80 25
2187 40s. Albena . . . . . . 1·25 30

679 Canoeing (Bronze Medal)

1972. Bulgarian Medal Winners, Olympic Games, Munich. Multicoloured.
2188 1s. Type **679** 10 10
2189 2s. Long jumping (Silver
Medal) 15 10
2190 3s. Boxing (Gold Medal) . 15 10
2191 18s. Wrestling (Gold Medal) 1·00 30
2192 40s. Weightlifting (Gold
Medal) . . . . . 1·60 40

680 Subi Dimitrov

682 "Lilium rhodopaeum"

681 Commemorative Text

1972. Resistance Heroes. Multicoloured.
2193 1s. Type **680** 10 10
2194 2s. Tsvyatko Radoinov . . 10 10
2195 3s. Iordan Lyutibrodski . . 10 10
2196 5s. Mito Ganev 10 10
2197 13s. Nedelcho Nikolov . . 35 10

1972. 50th Anniv of U.S.S.R.
2198 **681** 13s. red, yellow & gold 50 15

1972. Protected Flowers. Multicoloured.
2199 1s. Type **682** 10 10
2200 2s. Marsh gentian 10 10
2201 3s. Sea lily 15 10
2202 4s. Globe flower 20 10
2203 18s. "Primula frondosa" . . 70 20
2204 23s. Pale pasque flower . 1·00 30
2205 40s. "Fritillaria stribrnyi" . 2·00 50

(683)

684 Dobri Chintulov

1972. "Bulgaria, World Weightlifting Champions". No. 2192 optd with T **683**.
2206 40s. multicoloured . . . . 1·75 50

1972. 150th Birth Anniv of Dobri Chintulov (poet).
2207 **684** 2s. multicoloured 10 10

685 Forehead Ornament (19th-century)

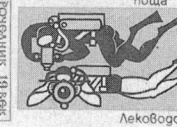
686 Divers with Cameras

1972. Antique Ornaments.
2208 **685** 1s. black and brown . . 10 10
2209 – 2s. black and green . . 10 10
2210 – 3s. black and blue . . 10 10
2211 – 8s. black and red . . 20 10
2212 – 23s. black and brown . 60 10
2213 – 40s. black and violet . 1·25 10
DESIGNS: 2s. Belt-buckle (19th-century); 3s. Amulet (18th-century); 8s. Pendant (18th-century); 23s. Earrings (14th-century); 40s. Necklace (18th-century).

1973. Underwater Research in the Black Sea.
2214 **686** 1s. black, yellow & blue 10 10
2215 – 2s. black, yellow & blue 20 10
2216 – 18s. black, yellow & blue 90 25
2217 – 40s. black, yellow & blue 1·10 20
DESIGNS—HORIZ: 2s. Divers with underwater research vessel "Shelf 1". VERT: 18s. Diver and "NIV 100" diving bell; 40s. Lifting balloon.

687 "The Hanging of Vasil Levski" (Boris Angelushev)

688 Elhovo Mask

1973. Death Cent of Vasil Levski (patriot).
2219 **687** 2s. green and red . . . 10 10
2220 – 20s. brown, cream & grn 1·50 40
DESIGN: 20s. "Vasil Levski" (Georgi Danchov).

1973. Kukeris' Festival Masks. Mult.
2221 1a. Type **688** 10 10
2222 2s. Breznik 10 10
2223 3s. Khisar 10 10
2224 13s. Radomir 40 15
2225 20s. Karnobat 50 25
2226 40s. Pernik . . . . . . 4·50 2·75

689 Copernicus

690 Vietnamese "Girl"

1973. 500th Birth Anniv of Copernicus.
2227 **689** 28s. purple, black & brn 1·50 50

1973. Vietnam Peace Treaty.
2229 **690** 18s. multicoloured . . . 20 10

691 Common Poppy   692 C. Botev (after T. Todorov)

1973. Wild Flowers. Multicoloured.
2231 1s. Type **691** 10 10
2232 2s. Ox-eye daisy 10 10
2233 3s. Peony 15 10
2234 13s. Cornflower 40 15
2235 18s. Corn cockle . . . . 4·75 2·25
2236 28s. Meadow buttercup . . 1·25 65

1973. 125th Birth Anniv of Khristo Botev (poet and revolutionary).
2237 **692** 2s. yellow, brown & grn 10 10
2238 18s. grn, lt grn & bronze 80 65

693 Asen Khalachev and Insurgents

1973. 50th Anniv of June Uprising.
2239 **693** 1s. black, red and gold 10 10
2240 – 2s. black, orange & gold 10 10
DESIGN: 2s. "Wounded Worker" (illustration by Boris Angelushev to the poem "September" by Geo Milev).

694 Stamboliiski (from sculpture by A. Nikolov)

1973. 50th Death Anniv of Aleksandur Stamboliiski (Prime Minister 1919–23).
2241 **694** 18s. lt brn, brn & orge 40 20
2242 18s. orange . . . . . 4·50 3·25

695 Muskrat

1973. Bulgarian Fauna. Multicoloured.
2243 1s. Type **695** 10 10
2244 2s. Racoon-dog 10 10
2245 2s. Mouflon (vert) 20 10
2246 12s. Fallow deer (vert) . . 50 25
2247 18s. European bison . . . 3·25 1·50
2248 40s. Elk . . . . . . 2·00 55

696 Turnovo   698 Congress Emblem

697 Insurgents on the March (Boris Angelushev)

1973. Air. Tourism. Views of Bulgarian Towns and Cities. Multicoloured.
2249 2s. Type **696** 10 10
2250 13s. Rusalka 30 10

2251 20s. Plovdiv . . . . 2·10 1·75
2252 28s. Sofia 80 50

1973. 50th Anniv of September Uprising.
2253 **697** 2s. multicoloured 10 10
2254 – 5s. violet, pink & red . 75 35
2255 – 13s. multicoloured . . . 15 10
2256 – 18s. olive, cream & red 45 25
DESIGNS—HORIZ: 5s. "Armed Train" (Boris Angelushev). VERT: 13s. Patriotic poster by N. Mirchev. HORIZ: 18s. Georgi Dimitrov and Vasil Kolarov.

1973. 8th World Trade Union Congress, Varna.
2257 **698** 2s. multicoloured 10 10

699 "Sun" Emblem   **700** "Prince Kaloyan"
and Olympic Rings

1973. Olympic Congress, Varna. Multicoloured.
2258 13s. Type **699** 40 20
2259 28s. Lion Emblem of
 Bulgarian Olympic
 Committee (vert) 70 40

1973. Fresco Portraits, Boyana Church. Mult.
2261 1s. Type **700** 10 10
2262 2s. "Desislava" 30 10
2263 3s. "Saint" 20 10
2264 5s. "St. Eustratius" . . . 25 10
2265 10s. "Tsar Constantine-
 Asen" 60 10
2266 13s. "Deacon Laurentius" 80 10
2267 18s. "Virgin Mary" . . . 1·25 30
2268 20s. "St. Ephraim" . . . 1·50 40
2269 28s. "Jesus Christ" . . . 5·00 1·00

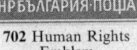
701 Smirnenski and Cavalry Charge

1973. 75th Birth Anniv of Khristo Smirnenski (poet and revolutionary).
2271 **701** 1s. blue, red and gold . . 10 10
2272 2s. blue, red and gold . . 10 10

702 Human Rights   **704** "Finn" One-man
Emblem   Dinghy

703 Tsar Todor Svetoslav meeting the
Byzantine Embassy, 1307

1973. 25th Anniv of Declaration of Human Rights.
2273 **702** 13s. gold, red and blue . . 15 10

1973. Bulgarian History. Multicoloured.
2274 1s. Type **703** 10 10
2275 2s. Tsar Mikhail Shishman
 in battle against
 Byzantines, 1328 . . . 10 10
2276 3s. Battle of Rosokastro,
 1332 and Tsar Ivan
 Aleksandur 10 10
2277 4s. Defence of Turnovo,
 1393 and Patriarch
 Evtimii 10 10
2278 5s. Tsar Ivan Shisman's
 attack on the Turks . . 10 10
2279 13s. Momchil attacks
 Turkish ships at Umur,
 1344 . . . . 15 10

2280 18s. Meeting of Tsar Ivan
 Sratsimir and Crusaders,
 1396 . . . . 25 10
2281 28s. Embassy of Empress
 Anne of Savoy meets
 Boyars Balik, Teodor and
 Dobrotitsa 75 30

1973. Sailing. Various Yachts. Multicoloured.
2282 1s. Type **704** 10 10
2283 2s. "Flying Dutchman" two-
 man dinghy 10 10
2284 3s. "Soling" yacht . . . 15 10
2285 13s. "Tempest" dinghy . . 60 35
2286 20s. "470" two-man dinghy 80 65
2287 40s. "Tornado" catamaran 3·25 1·50

705 "Balchik" (Bercho Obreshkov)

1973. 25th Anniv of National Art Gallery, Sofia and 150th Birth Anniv of Stanislav Dospevski (painter). Multicoloured.
2288 1s. Type **705** 10 10
2289 2s. "Mother and Child"
 (Stryan Venev) 10 10
2290 3s. "Rest" (Tsenko
 Boyadzhiev) 10 10
2291 13s. "Vase with Flowers"
 (Siruk Skitnik) (vert) . . 20 10
2292 18s. "Mary Kuneva" (Iliya
 Petrov) (vert) 30 10
2293 40s. "Winter in Plovdiv"
 (Zlatyn Boyadzhiev) (vert) 1·10 50

707 Old Testament Scene
(Wood-carving)

1974. Wood-Carvings from Rozhen Monastery.
2296 **707** 1s. dk brn, cream & brn 10 10
2297 – 2s. dk brn, cream & brn 10 10
2298 – 3s. dk brn, cream & brn 10 10
2299 – 5s. olive, cream & green 10 10
2300 – 8s. olive, cream & green 10 10
2301 – 13s. brown, cream and
 chestnut 25 15
2302 – 28s. brown, cream and
 chestnut 40 15
DESIGNS: Nos. 2296/8, "Passover Table"; 2299/2300, "Abraham and the Angel"; 2301/2, "The Expulsion from Eden".
 Nos. 2296/8, 2299/300 and 2301/2 form three composite designs.

708 "Lenin" (N. Mirchev)

1974. 50th Death Anniv of Lenin. Mult.
2303 2s. Type **708** 10 10
2304 18s. "Lenin with Workers"
 (W. A. Serov) 20 10

709 "Blagoev addressing Meeting"
(G. Kovachev)

1974. 50th Death Anniv of D. Blagoev (founder of Bulgarian Social Democratic Party).
2305 **709** 2s. multicoloured . . . 10 10

710 Sheep

1974. Domestic Animals.
2306 **710** 1s. brown, buff & green 10 10
2307 – 2s. purple, violet & red 10 10
2308 – 3s. brown, pink & green 10 10
2309 – 5s. brown, buff & blue 10 10
2310 – 13s. black, blue and
 brown 15 10
2311 – 20s. brown, pink & blue 1·10 25
DESIGNS: 2s. Goat; 3s. Pig; 5s. Cow; 13s. Buffalo; 20s. Horse.

711 Social Economic Integration
Emblem

1974. 25th Anniv of Council for Mutual Economic Aid.
2312 **711** 13s. multicoloured . . . 20 10

712 Footballers

1974. World Cup Football Championship.
2313 **712** 1s. multicoloured 10 10
2314 – 2s. multicoloured . . . 10 10
2315 – 3s. multicoloured . . . 10 10
2316 – 13s. multicoloured . . . 25 10
2317 – 28s. multicoloured . . . 50 10
2318 – 40s. multicoloured . . . 2·00 75
DESIGNS: Nos. 2314/18, Various designs similar to Type **712**.

713 Folk-singers   **714** "Cosmic Research"
(Penko Barnbov)

1974. Amateur Arts and Sports Festival. Multicoloured.
2320 1s. Type **713** 10 10
2321 2s. Folk-dancers 10 10
2322 3s. Piper and drummer . . 10 10
2323 5s. Wrestling 10 10
2324 13s. Athletics . . . . . 1·00 50
2325 18s. Gymnastics . . . . 1·60 20

1974. "Mladost '74" Youth Stamp Exhibition, Sofia. Multicoloured.
2326 1s. Type **714** 10 10
2327 2s. "Salt Production"
 (Mariana Bliznakaa) . . . 20 10
2328 3s. "Fire-dancer" (Detelina
 Lalova) 10 10
2329 28s. "Friendship Train"
 (Vanya Boyanova) . . . 3·00 1·75

715 Motor-cars

1974. World Automobile Federation's Spring Congress, Sofia.
2331 **715** 13s. multicoloured . . . 20 10

716 Period Architecture

1974. U.N.E.S.C.O. Executive Council's 94th Session, Varna.
2332 **716** 18s. multicoloured . . . 15 10

717 Chinese Aster

1974. Bulgarian Flowers. Multicoloured.
2333 1s. Type **717** 10 10
2334 2s. Mallow 10 10
2335 3s. Columbine 10 10
2336 18s. Tulip 40 10
2337 20s. Marigold 50 20
2338 28s. Pansy . . . . . . 1·60 50

718 19th Century Post-boy

1974. Centenary of U.P.U.
2340 **718** 2s. violet & blk on orge 10 10
2341 – 18s. green & blk on orge 25 10
DESIGN: 18s. First Bulgarian mail-coach.

719 Young Pioneer and   **720** Communist Soldiers
Komsomol Girl   with Flag

1974. 30th Anniv of Dimitrov's Septembrist Pioneers Organization. Multicoloured.
2343 1s. Type **719** 10 10
2344 2s. Pioneer with doves . . . 10 10

1974. 30th Anniv of Fatherland Front Government. Multicoloured.
2346 1s. Type **720** 10 10
2347 2s. "Soviet Liberators" . . . 10 10
2348 5s. "Industrialisation" . . . 10 10
2349 13s. "Modern Agriculture" . . 10 10
2350 18s. "Science and
 Technology" 25 15

722 Gymnast on Beam   **724** Envelope with
Arrow pointing to
Postal Code

1974. 18th World Gymnastic Championships, Varna. Multicoloured.
2352 2s. Type **722** 10 10
2353 13s. Gymnast on horse . . . 40 15

1974. Introduction of Postal Coding System (1 January 1975).
2355 **724** 2s. green, orange & blk 10 10

725 "Sourovachka" (twig decorated
with coloured ribbons)

1974. New Year.
2356 **725** 2s. multicoloured 10 10

726 Icon of St. Theodor Stratilar   727 Apricot

1974. Bulgarian History.
2357	726	1s. multicoloured . . .	10	10
2358	– 2s. grey, mauve & black		10	10
2359	– 3s. grey, blue and black		10	10
2360	– 5s. grey, lilac and black		10	10
2361	– 8s. black, buff and brown		10	10
2362	– 13s. grey, green & black		15	10
2363	– 18s. black, gold & red		20	10
2364	– 28s. grey, blue & black		75	50

DESIGNS: 2s. Bronze medallion; 3s. Carved capital; 5s. Silver bowl of Sivin Jupan; 8s. Clay goblet; 13s. Lioness (torso); 18s. Gold tray; 28s. Double-headed eagle.

1975. Fruit-tree Blossoms. Multicoloured.
2365	727	1s. Type 727	10	10
2366	2s. Apple	10	10
2367	3s. Cherry	10	10
2368	19s. Pear	25	10
2369	28s. Peach	50	15

730 Star and Arrow   731 "Weights and Measures"

1975. 30th Anniv of "Victory in Europe" Day.
2372	730	2s. red, black & brown	10	10
2373	– 13s. black, brown & bl	20	10

DESIGNS: 13s. Peace dove and broken sword.

1975. Centenary of Metre Convention.
2374 731 13s. violet, black & silver   10   10

732 Tree and open Book

1975. 50th Anniv of Forestry School.
2375 732 2s. multicoloured   10   10

733 Michelangelo   734 Festival Emblem

1975. 500th Birth Anniv of Michelangelo.
2376	733	2s. purple and blue . . .	10	10
2377	– 13s. violet and purple . .	15	10
2378	– 18s. brown and green . .	20	10

DESIGNS—HORIZ: Sculptures from Giuliano de Medici's tomb: 13s. "Night"; 18s. "Day".

1975. Festival of Humour and Satire, Gabrovo.
2380 734 2s. multicoloured   10   10

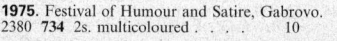

735 Women's Head and Emblem

1975. International Women's Year.
2381 735 13s. multicoloured . . .   10   10

736 Vasil and Sava Kokareshkov

1975. "Young Martyrs to Fascism".
2382	736	1s. black, green & gold	10	10
2383	– 2s. black, mauve & gold	10	10
2384	– 5s. black, red and gold	10	10
2385	– 13s. black, blue & gold	20	10

DESIGNS—HORIZ: 2s. Mitko Palauzov and Ivan Vasilev; 5s. Nikola Nakev and Stefcho Kraichev; 13s. Ivanka Pashkolouva and Detelina Mincheva.

737 "Mother feeding Child" (Jean Millet)   738 Gabrovo Costume

1975. World Graphics Exhibition, Sofia. Celebrated Drawings and Engravings. Multicoloured.
2386	1s. Type 737	10	10
2387	2s. "Mourning a Dead Daughter" (Goya)	10	10
2388	3s. "The Reunion" (Iliya Beshkov)	10	10
2389	13s. "Seated Nude" (Auguste Renoir)	10	10
2390	20s. "Man in a Fur Hat" (Rembrandt)	10	10
2391	40s. "The Dream" (Horore Daumier) (horiz) . . .	70	20

1975. Women's Regional Costumes. Mult.
2393	2s. Type 738	10	10
2394	3s. Trun costume	10	10
2395	5s. Vidin costume	10	10
2396	13s. Goce Delcev costume	15	10
2397	18s. Ruse costume	40	15

739 "Bird" (manuscript illumination)   740 Ivan Vasov

1975. Original Bulgarian Manuscripts. Mult.
2398	1s. Type 739	10	10
2399	2s. "Head"	10	10
2400	3s. Abstract design . . .	10	10
2401	8s. "Pointing finger" . . .	10	10
2402	13s. "Imaginary creature" .	10	10
2403	18s. Abstract design . . .	40	15

1975. 125th Anniv of Ivan Vasov (writer). Multicoloured.
2404	2s. Type 740	10	10
2405	13s. Vasov seated	10	10

741 "Soyuz" and Aleksei Leonov

1975. "Apollo"–"Soyuz" Space Link. Mult.
2406	741	13s. Type 741	30	10
2407	18s. "Apollo" and Thomas Stafford	50	10
2408	28s. Linking manoeuvre .	1·50	20

742 Ryukyu Sailing Boat, Map and Emblems

1975. International Exposition, Okinawa.
2410 742 13s. multicoloured . . .   30   10

743 St. Cyril and St. Methodius   744 Footballer

1975. "Balkanphila V" Stamp Exhibition, Sofia.
2411	743	2s. brown, lt brn & red	10	10
2412	– 13s. brown, lt brn & grn	10	10

DESIGN: 13s. St. Constantine and St. Helene.

1975. 8th Inter-Toto (Football Pools) Congress, Varna.
2414 744 2s. multicoloured   10   10

745 Deaths-head Hawk Moth

1975. Hawk Moths. Multicoloured.
2415	1s. Type 745	10	10
2416	2s. Oleander hawk moth .	10	10
2417	3s. Eyed hawk moth . . .	15	10
2418	10s. Mediterranean hawk moth	25	20
2419	13s. Elephant hawk moth .	50	25
2420	18s. Broad-bordered bee hawk moth	1·10	40

746 U.N. Emblem   747 Map of Europe on Peace Dove

1975. 30th Anniv of U.N.O.
2421 746 13s. red, brown & black   10   10

1975. European Security and Co-operation Conference, Helsinki.
2422 747 18s. lilac, blue & yellow   40   20

748 D. Khristov

1975. Birth Cent of Dobri Khristov (composer).
2423 748 5s. brown, yellow & grn   10   10

749 Constantine's Rebellion against the Turks

750 "First Aid"

1975. 90th Anniv of Bulgarian Red Cross.
2430	750	2s. brown, black and red	10	10
2431	– 13s. green, black and red	25	10

DESIGN: 13s. "Peace and international Co-operation".

751 Ethnographical Museum, Plovdiv

1975. European Architectural Heritage Year.
2432 751 80s. brown, yellow & grn   1·75   1·75

752 Christmas Lanterns

1975. Christmas and New Year. Multicoloured.
2433	2s. Type 752	10	10
2434	13s. Stylized peace dove . .	10	10

753 Egyptian Galley

1975. Historic Ships (1st series). Multicoloured.
2435	1s. Type 753	10	10
2436	2s. Phoenician galley . . .	10	10
2437	3s. Greek trireme	10	10
2438	5s. Roman galley	10	10
2439	13s. "Mora" (Norman ship)	50	25
2440	18s. Venetian galley . . .	90	35

See also Nos. 2597/2602, 2864/9, 3286/91 and 3372/7.

754 Modern Articulated Tramcar

1976. 75th Anniv of Sofia Tramways. Mult.
2441	2s. Type 754	30	15
2442	13s. Early 20th-century tramcar	1·10	50

755 Skiing

1976. Winter Olympic Games, Innsbruck. Mult.
2443	1s. Type 755	10	10
2444	2s. Cross-country skiing (vert)	10	10
2445	5s. Ski jumping	10	10
2446	13s. Biathlon (vert)	20	15
2447	18s. Ice hockey (vert) . . .	40	25
2448	18s. Speed skating (vert) . .	1·00	30

756 Stylized Bird

1976. 11th Bulgarian Communists Party Congress. Multicoloured.
2450	2s. Type 756	10	10
2451	5s. "1956–1976, Fulfilment of the Five Year Plans"	10	10
2452	13s. Hammer and Sickle	10	10

757 Alexander Graham Bell and early Telephone

1976. Telephone Centenary.
2454	757	18s. lt brown, brn & pur	20	10

758 Mute Swan

1976. Waterfowl. Multicoloured.
2455	1s. Type 758	20	10
2456	2s. Ruddy shelduck	25	10
2457	3s. Common shelduck	40	15
2458	5s. Garganey	60	20
2459	13s. Mallard	1·25	30
2460	18s. Red-crested pochard	1·75	80

759 Guerillas' Briefing

1976. Cent of April Uprising (1st issue). Mult.
2461	1s. Type 759	10	10
2462	2s. Peasants' briefing	10	10
2463	5s. Krishina, horse and guard	10	10
2464	13s. Rebels with cannon	20	10

See also Nos. 2529/33.

760 Kozlodui Atomic Energy Centre

1976. Modern Industrial Installations.
2465	760	5s. green	10	10
2466	–	8s. red	10	10
2467	–	10s. green	10	10
2468	–	13s. violet	10	10
2469	–	20s. green	15	10

DESIGNS: 8s. Bobaudol plant; 10s. Sviloza chemical works; 13s. Devaya chemical works; 20s. Sestvitro dam.

761 Guard with Patrol-dog

1976. 30th Anniv of Frontier Guards. Mult.
2470	2s. Type 761	10	10
2471	13s. Mounted guards	10	10

762 Worker with Spade　　**763** Botev

1976. 30th Anniv of Youth Brigades Movement.
2472	762	2s. multicoloured	10	10

1976. Death Cent of Khristo Botev (poet).
2473	763	13s. green and brown	10	10

764 "Martyrs of First　　**765** Dimitur Blagoev
Congress" (relief)

1976. 85th Anniv of 1st Bulgarian Social Democratic Party Congress, Buzludzha. Multicoloured.
2474	2s. Type 764	10	10
2475	5s. Modern memorial, Buzludzha Peak	10	10

1976. 120th Birth Anniv of Dimitur Blagoev (founder of Bulgarian Social Democratic Party).
2476	765	13s. black, red and gold	10	10

767 Children Playing

1976. Child Welfare.
2478	767	1s. multicoloured	10	10
2479	–	2s. multicoloured	10	10
2480	–	5s. multicoloured	10	10
2481	–	23s. multicoloured	25	20

DESIGNS: 2s. Girls with pram and boy on rocking horse; 5s. Playing ball; 23s. Dancing.

768 Wrestling

1976. Olympic Games, Montreal. Multicoloured.
2482	1s. Type 768	10	10
2483	2s. Boxing	10	10
2484	3s. Weight-lifting	10	10
2485	13s. Canoeing	20	10
2486	18s. Gymnastics	30	15
2487	28s. Diving	45	20
2488	40s. Athletics	65	30

Nos. 2483/8 are vert.

769 Belt Buckle, Vidin　　**772** Fish on line

1976. Thracian Art (8th–4th Centuries B.C.). Mult.
2490	1s. Type 769	10	10
2491	2s. Brooch, Durzhanitsa	10	10
2492	3s. Mirror handle, Chukarka	10	10
2493	5s. Helmet cheek guard, Gurlo	10	10
2494	13s. Gold decoration, Orizovo	10	10
2495	18s. Decorated horse-harness, Brezovo	15	15
2496	20s. Greave, Mogilanska Mogila	20	15
2497	28s. Pendant, Bukovtsi	25	25

1976. Paintings by Iliya Petrov and Tsanko Lavrenov from the National Gallery. Mult.
2498	2s. Type 770	10	10
2499	5s. "Kurshum-Khan" (Lavrenov)	10	10
2500	13s. "Seated Woman" (Petrov)	15	10
2501	18s. "Boy seated in chair" (Petrov) (vert)	25	10
2502	28s. "Old Plovdiv" (Lavrenov) (vert)	40	15

1976. World Sports Fishing Congress, Varna.
2505	772	5s. multicoloured	10	10

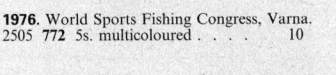

773 "The Pianist"　　**774** St. Theodor

1976. 75th Birth Anniv of Alex Jhendov (caricaturist).
2506	773	2s. dp grn, cream & grn	10	10
2507	–	5s. dp violet, vio & lilac	10	10
2508	–	13s. black, pink & red	20	10

DESIGNS: 5s. "Trick or Treat"; 13s. "The Leader".

1976. Zemen Monastery. Frescoes. Multicoloured.
2509	2s. Type 774	10	10
2510	3s. St. Paul and Apostle	10	10
2511	5s. St. Joachim	10	10
2512	13s. Prophet Melchisadek	10	10
2513	19s. St. Porphyrus	15	10
2514	28s. Queen Doya	25	15

 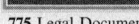

775 Legal Document　　**776** Horse Chestnut

1976. 25th Anniv of State Archives.
2516	775	5s. multicoloured	10	10

1976. Plants. Multicoloured.
2517	1s. Type 776	10	10
2518	2s. Shrubby cinquefoil	10	10
2519	5s. Holly	15	10
2520	8s. Yew	15	10
2521	13s. "Daphne pontica"	30	15
2522	23s. Judas tree	75	30

777 Cloud over Sun

1976. Protection of the Environment. Mult.
2523	2s. Cloud over tree	10	10
2524	18s. Type 777	20	10

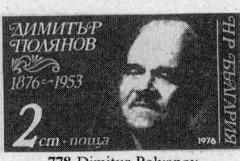

778 Dimitur Polyanov

1976. Birth Cent of Dimitur Polyanov (poet).
2525	778	2s. lilac and orange	10	10

779 Congress Emblem

1976. 33rd Bulgarian People's Agrarian Union Congress. Multicoloured.
2526	2s. Type 779	10	10
2527	13s. Flags	10	10

781 "Khristo Botev" (Zlatyu Boyadzhiev)

1976. Centenary of April Uprising (2nd issue). Multicoloured.
2529	1s. Type 781	10	10
2530	2s. "Partisan carrying Cherrywood Cannon" (Iliya Petrov)	10	10
2531	3s. "Necklace of Immortality" (Dechko Uzunov)	10	10
2532	13s. "April 1876" (Georgi Popov)	10	15
2533	18s. "Partisans" (Stoyan Venev)	25	20

782 Tobacco Workers

1976. 70th Birth Anniv of Veselin Staikov (artist). Multicoloured.
2535	1s. Type 782	10	10
2536	2s. "Melnik"	10	10
2537	13s. "Boat Builders"	20	10

783 "Snowflake"

1976. New Year.
2538	783	2s. multicoloured	10	10

784 Zakhari Stojanov

1976. 125th Birth Anniv of Zakhari Stojanov (writer).
2539	784	2s. brown, red and gold	10	10

785 Bronze Coin of Septimus Severus

1977. Roman Coins struck in Serdica. Mult.
2540	1s. Type 785	10	10
2541	2s. Bronze coin of Caracalla	10	10
2542	13s. Bronze coin of Caracalla (diff.)	10	10
2543	18s. Bronze coin of Caracalla (diff.)	15	15
2544	23s. Copper coin of Diocletian	25	20

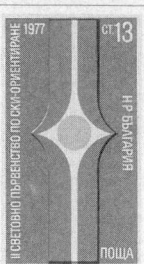

786 Championships Emblem   **787** Congress Emblem

1977. World Ski-orienteering Championships.
2545 **786** 13s. blue, red & ultram   20   10

1977. 5th Congress of Bulgarian Tourist Associations.
2546 **787** 2s. multicoloured   10   10

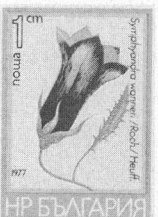

788 "Symphyandra wanneri"   **789** V. Kolarov

1977. Mountain Flowers. Multicoloured.
2547   1s. Type **788**   10   10
2548   2s. "Petcovia orphanidea"   10   10
2549   3s. "Campanula lanatre"   10   10
2550   13s. "Campanula scutellata"   15   10
2551   43s. Nettle-leaved bellflower   60   40

1977. Birth Centenary of Vasil Kolarov (Prime Minister 1949–50).
2552 **789** 2s. grey, black & blue . .   10   10

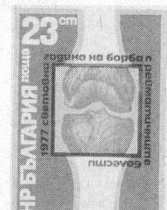

790 Congress Emblem   **791** Joint

1977. 8th Bulgarian Trade Unions Congress.
2553 **790** 2s. multicoloured   10   10

1977. World Rheumatism Year.
2554 **791** 23s. multicoloured . . .   20   10

792 Wrestling

1977. World University Games, Sofia. Mult.
2555   2s. Type **792**   10   10
2556   13s. Running   20   10
2557   23s. Handball   40   15
2558   43s. Gymnastics   70   25

793 Ivan Vazov National Theatre   **794** Congress Emblem

1977. Buildings in Sofia. Pale brown backgrounds.
2559 **793** 12s. red   10   10
2560   – 13s. brown   10   10
2561   – 23s. blue   15   10
2562   – 30s. green   20   10
2563   – 80s. violet   60   25
2564   – 1l. brown   80   80
DESIGNS: 13s. Party Building; 23s. People's Army

Building; 30s. Clement of Ohrid University; 80s. National Art Gallery; 1l. National Assembly Building.

1977. 13th Dimitrov Communist Youth League Congress.
2565 **794** 2s. red, green and gold   10   10

795 "St. Nicholas" Nesebur

1977. Bulgarian Icons. Multicoloured.
2566   1s. Type **795**   10   10
2567   2s. "Old Testament Trinity", Sofia   10   10
2568   3s. "The Royal Gates", Veliko Turnovo . .   10   10
2569   5s. "Deisis", Nesebur . . .   10   10
2570   13s. "St. Nicholas", Elena   10   10
2571   23s. "The Presentation of the Blessed Virgin", Rila Monastery   30   10
2572   35s. "The Virgin Mary with Infant", Varna . . .   40   15
2573   40s. "St. Demetrius on Horseback", Provadya . .   50   20

796 Wolf

1977. Wild Animals. Multicoloured.
2575   1s. Type **796**   10   10
2576   2s. Red fox   10   10
2577   10s. Weasel   20   10
2578   13s. Wild cat   35   15
2579   23s. Golden jackal   60   25

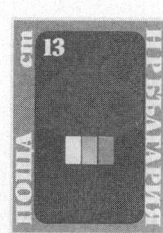

797 Congress Emblem   **798** "Crafty Peter riding a Donkey" (drawing by Iliya Beshkov)

1977. 3rd Bulgarian Culture Congress.
2580 **797** 13s. multicoloured . . .   10   10

1977. 11th Festival of Humour and Satire, Gabrovo.
2581 **798** 2s. multicoloured   10   10

799 Congress Emblem

1977. 8th Congress of the Popular Front, Sofia.
2582 **799** 2s. multicoloured   10   10

800 Newspaper Masthead

1977. Centenary of Bulgarian Daily Press.
2583 **800** 2s. multicoloured   10   10

802 Conference Emblem

1977. International Writers Conference, Sofia.
2585 **802** 23s. blue, lt blue & grn   75   40

803 Map of Europe

1977. 21st Congress of European Organization for Quality Control, Varna.
2586 **803** 23s. multicoloured . . .   25   10

804 Basketball   **805** Weightlifter

1977. Women's European Basketball Championships.
2587 **804** 23s. multicoloured . . .   40   10

1977. World Junior Weightlifting Championships.
2588 **805** 13s. multicoloured . . .   30   10

806 Georgi Dimitrov

1977. 95th Birth Anniv of Georgi Dimitrov (statesman).
2589 **806** 13s. brown and red . . .   15   10

807 Tail Section of Tupolev Tu-154

1977. Air. 30th Anniv of Bulgarian Airline "Balkanair".
2590 **807** 35s. multicoloured . . .   75   25

809 T.V. Towers, Berlin and Sofia   **810** Elin Pelin alias Dimitur Stoyanov (writer)

1977. "Sozphilex 77" Stamp Exhibition, East Berlin.
2592 **809** 25s. blue and deep blue   40   10

1977. Writers and Painters.
2593 **810** 2s. brown and gold . .   10   10
2594   – 5s. olive and gold . .   10   10
2595   – 13s. red and gold . .   10   10
2596   – 23s. blue and gold . .   20   15
DESIGNS: 5s. Peyu Yavorov (poet); 13s. Boris

Angelushev (painter and illustrator); 23s. Iseno Todorov (painter).

1977. Historic Ships (2nd series). As T **753**. Multicoloured.
2597   1s. Hansa Kogge   10   10
2598   2s. "Santa Maria".   10   10
2599   3s. Drake's "Golden Hind"   10   10
2600   12s. Carrack "Santa Catherina"   30   10
2601   13s. "La Couronne" (French galleon)   35   15
2602   43s. Mediterranean galley   1·10   40

811 Women Canoeists

1977. World Canoe Championships.
2603 **811** 2s. blue and yellow . . .   10   10
2604   – 23s. blue and turquoise   30   10
DESIGN: 23s. Men canoeists.

812 Balloon over Plovdiv   **813** Presidents Zhivkov and Brezhnev

1977. Air. 85th Anniv "Panair". International Aviation Exhibition, Plovdiv.
2605 **812** 25s. orange, yell & brn   85   20

1977. Soviet–Bulgarian Friendship.
2606 **813** 18s. brown, red & gold   10   10

814 Conference Building

1977. 64th International Parliamentary Conference, Sofia.
2607 **814** 23s. green, pink and red   15   10

815 Newspaper Mastheads   **816** "The Union of Earth and Water"

1977. 50th Anniv of Official Newspaper "Rabotnichesko Delo" (Workers' Press).
2608 **815** 2s. red, green and grey   10   10

1977. 400th Birth Anniv of Rubens. Mult.
2609   13s. Type **816**   25   10
2610   23s. "Venus and Adonis" (detail)   45   20
2611   40s. "Amorous Shepherd" (detail)   90   30

817 Cossack with Bulgarian Child (Angelushev)

818 Albena, Black Sea

1977. Centenary of Liberation from Turkey. (1978). Posters.

2613 **817** 2s. multicoloured 10 10
2614 – 13s. green, blue & red 10 10
2615 – 23s. blue, red & green 20 15
2616 – 25s. multicoloured . . . 20 15

DESIGNS: 13s. Bugler (Cheklarov); 23s. Mars (god of war) and Russian soldiers (Petrov); 25s. Flag of Russian Imperial Army.

1977. Tourism.

2617 **818** 35s. blue, turq & brn . . 75 20
2618 – 43s. yellow, grn & blue 75 20

DESIGN: 43s. Rila Monastery.

819 Dr. Nikolai Pirogov (Russian surgeon)

821 Soviet Emblems and Decree

820 Space walking

1977. Cent of Dr. Pirogov's Visit to Bulgaria.

2619 **819** 13s. brown, buff & grn 10 10

1977. Air. 20th Anniv of First Artificial Satellite. Multicoloured.

2620 12s. Type **820** 20 10
2621 25s. Space probe over Mars 40 10
2622 35s. Space probe "Venus-4" over Venus 55 10

1977. 60th Anniv of Russian Revolution.

2623 **821** 2s. red, black & stone . . 10 10
2624 – 13s. red and purple . . . 10 10
2625 – 23s. red and violet . . . 15 10

DESIGNS: 13s. Lenin; 23s. "1977" as flame.

822 Diesel Train on Bridge

1977. 50th Anniv of Transport, Bridges and Highways Organization.

2626 **822** 13s. yellow, green & olive 65 15

1977. 150th Birth Anniv of Petko Ratshev Slaveikov (poet). As T **810**.

2627 8s. brown and gold 10 10

824 Decorative Initials of New Year Greeting

1977. New Year. Multicoloured.

2628 2s. Type **824** 10 10
2629 13s. "Fireworks" 10 10

825 Footballer

1978. World Cup Football Championship, Argentina. Multicoloured.

2630 13s. Type **825** 20 10
2631 23s. Shooting the ball . . . 35 10

826 Baba Vida Fortress, Vidin

1977. Air. "The Danube — European River". Mult.

2633 25s. Type **826** 45 20
2634 35s. Friendship Bridge . . . 1·25 1·25

827 Television Mast, Moscow

829 Red Cross in Laurel Wreath

1978. 20th Anniv of Organization of Socialist Postal Administrations (O.S.S.).

2635 **827** 13s. multicoloured . . . 10 10

1978. Centenary of Bulgarian Red Cross.

2637 **829** 25s. red, brown & blue 50 10

830 "XXX" formed from Bulgarian and Russian National Colours

1978. 30th Anniv of Bulgarian–Soviet Friendship.

2638 **830** 2s. multicoloured 10 10

831 Leo Tolstoy (Russian writer)

832 Nikolai Roerich (artist)

1978. Famous Personalities.

2639 **831** 2s. green and yellow . . 10 10
2640 – 5s. brown and bistre . . 10 10
2641 – 13s. green and mauve . . 10 10
2642 – 23s. brown and grey . . 15 15
2643 – 25s. brown and green . . 15 15
2644 – 35s. violet and blue . . 25 20

DESIGNS: 5s. Fyodor Dostoevsky (Russian writer); 13s. Ivan Turgenev (Russian writer); 23s. Vassily Vereshchagin (Russian artist); 25s. Giuseppe Garibaldi (Italian patriot); 35s. Victor Hugo (French writer).

1978. Nikolai Roerich Exhibition, Sofia.

2645 **832** 8s. brown, green & red 10 10

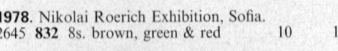

833 Bulgarian Flag and Red Star

1978. Communist Party National Conference, Sofia.

2646 **833** 2s. multicoloured 10 10

834 Goddess

835 "Spirit of Nature"

1978. "Philaserdica 79" International Stamp Exhibition (1st issue). Ancient Ceramics. Mult.

2647 2s. Type **834** 10 10
2648 5s. Mask with beard 10 10
2649 13s. Decorated vase 25 10
2650 23s. Vase with scallop design 45 15
2651 35s. Head of Silenus 60 20
2652 53s. Cockerel . . . . 1·25 30

See also Nos. 2674/9, 2714/18, 2721/5 and 2753/4.

1978. Birth Cent of Andrei Nikolov (sculptor).

2653 **835** 13s. blue, mauve & vio 10 10

836 Heart and Arrows

1978. World Hypertension Month.

2654 **836** 23s. red, orange & grey 20 10

837 "Kor Karoli" and Map of Route

1978. Georgi Georgiev's World Voyage.

2655 **837** 23s. blue, mauve & grn 55 25

838 Doves

1978. 11th World Youth and Students' Festival, Havana.

2656 **838** 13s. multicoloured . . . 10 10

839 "Portrait of a Young Man" (Durer)

840 "Fritillaria stribrnyi"

1978. Paintings. Multicoloured.

2657 13s. Type **839** 10 10
2658 23s. "Bathsheba at the Fountain" (Rubens) . . . 20 10
2659 25s. "Signor de Moret" (Hans Holbein the Younger) 20 10
2660 35s. "Self portrait with Saskia" (Rembrandt) . . 30 10
2661 43s. "Lady in Mourning" (Tintoretto) 40 15
2662 60s. "Old Man with a Beard" (Rembrandt) . . . 45 20
2663 80s. "Man in Armour" (Van Dyck) 60 25

1978. Flowers. Multicoloured.

2664 1s. Type **840** 10 10
2665 2s. "Fritillaria drenovskyi" 10 10
2666 3s. "Lilium rhodopaeum" 10 10
2667 13s. "Tulipa urumoffii" . . 25 10
2668 23s. "Lilium jankae" . . . 40 15
2669 43s. "Tulipa rhodopaea" . . 70 30

841 Varna

1978. 63rd Esperanto Congress, Varna.

2670 **841** 13s. orange, red & green 10 10

842 Delcev

1978. 75th Death Anniv of Goce Delcev (Macedonian revolutionary).

2671 **842** 13s. multicoloured . . . 10 10

843 Freedom Fighters

1978. 75th Anniv of Ilinden-Preobrazhenie Rising.

2672 **843** 5s. black and red 10 10

845 "Market" (Noiden Petkov)

1978. "Philaserdica 79" International Stamp Exhibition (2nd issue). Paintings of Sofia. Multicoloured.

2674 2s. Type **845** 10 10
2675 5s. "View of Sofia" (Euril Stoichev) 10 10
2676 13s. "View of Sofia" (Boris Ivanov) . . . . 1·10 20
2677 23s. "Tolbukhin Boulevard" (Nikola Tanev) 20 10
2678 35s. "National Theatre" (Nikola Petrov) 25 10
2679 53s. "Market" (Anton Mitov) 35 15

846 Black Woodpecker

848 "Elka 55" Computer

1978. Woodpeckers. Multicoloured.

2680 1s. Type **846** 15 10
2681 2s. Syrian woodpecker . . . 15 10
2682 3s. Three-toed woodpecker 20 10
2683 13s. Middle-spotted woodpecker 70 30
2684 23s. Lesser spotted woodpecker . . . . 1·25 50
2685 43s. Green woodpecker . . 2·25 1·00

1978. Plovdiv International Fair.

2687 **848** 2s. multicoloured 10 10

849 "September 1923" (Boris Angelushev)

1978. 55th Anniv of September Uprising.

2688 **849** 2s. red and brown . . . 10 10

850 Khristo Danov

1978. 150th Birth Anniv of Khristo Danov (first Bulgarian publisher).
2689 **850** 2s. orange and lake . . . 10 10

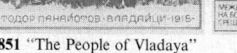

851 "The People of Vladaya" (Todor Panayotov)

852 Hands supporting Rainbow

1978. 60th Anniv of Vladaya Mutiny.
2690 **851** 2s. lilac, brown and red 10 10

1978. International Anti-apartheid Year.
2691 **852** 13s. multicoloured . . . 10 10

853 Pipeline and Flags **854** Acrobats

1978. Inauguration of Orenburg–U.S.S.R. Natural Gas Pipeline.
2692 **853** 13s. multicoloured . . . 10 10

1978. 3rd World Sports Acrobatics Championships, Sofia.
2693 **854** 13s. multicoloured . . . 25 10

855 Salvador Allende **856** Human Rights Emblem

1978. 70th Birth Anniv of Salvador Allende (Chilean politician).
2694 **855** 13s. brown and red . . . 10 10

1978. 30th Anniv of Declaration of Human Rights.
2695 **856** 23s. yellow, red & blue 40 10

857 "Levski and Matei Mitkaloto" (Kalina Taseva) **858** Tourist Home, Plovdiv

1978. History of Bulgaria. Paintings. Multicoloured.
2696 1s. Type **857** 10 10
2697 2s. "Give Strength to my Arm" (Zlatyu Boyadzhiev) . . . 10 10
2698 3s. "Rumena Voevoda" (Nikola Mirchev) (horiz) 10 10

2699 13s. "Kolya Ficheto" (Elza Goeva) 20 15
2700 23s. "A Family of the National Revival Period" (Naiden Petkov) 35 25

1978. European Architectural Heritage. Mult.
2701 43s. Type **858** 30 15
2702 43s. Tower of the Prince, Rila Monastery 30 15

859 "Geroi Plevny" and Route Map

1978. Opening of the Varna–Ilichovsk Ferry Service.
2703 **859** 13s. blue, red & green 70 10

860 Mosaic Bird (Santa Sofia Church)

1978. "Bulgaria 78" National Stamp Exhibition, Sofia.
2704 **860** 5s. multicoloured . . . 15 10

861 Monument to St. Clement of Ohrid (university patron) (Lyubemir Dalcher) **862** Nikola Karastoyanov

1978. 90th Anniv of Sofia University.
2705 **861** 2s. lilac, black & green 10 10

1978. Birth Bicentenary of Nikola Karastoyanov (first Bulgarian printer).
2706 **862** 2s. brn, yell & chestnut 10 10

863 Initial from 13th Century Bible Manuscript

1978. Centenary of Cyril and Methodius People's Library. Multicoloured.
2707 2s. Type **863** 10 10
2708 13s. Monk writing (from a 1567 manuscript) 10 10
2709 23s. Decorated page from 16th-century manuscript Bible 15 10

864 Ballet Dancers

1978. 50th Anniv of Bulgarian Ballet.
2711 **864** 13s. green, mauve & lav 15 10

865 Tree of Birds

1978. New Year, Multicoloured.
2712 2s. Type **865** 10 10
2713 13s. Posthorn 10 10

866 1961 Communist Congress Stamp

1978. "Philaserdica 79" International Stamp Exhibition (3rd issue) and Bulgarian Stamp Centenary (1st issue).
2714 – 2s. red and green 10 10
2715 – 13s. claret and blue . . . 20 10
2716 – 23s. green and mauve . . 35 15
2717 **866** 35s. grey and blue . . . 50 20
2718 – 53s. green and red . . . 75 30
DESIGNS—HORIZ: 2s. 1901 "Cherrywood Cannon" stamp; 13s. 1946 "New Republic" stamp; 23s. 1957 Canonisation of St. Cyril and St. Methodius stamp. VERT: 53s. 1962 Dimitrov stamp.

867 Council Building, Moscow and Flags

1979. 30th Anniv of Council of Mutual Economic Aid.
2720 **867** 13s. multicoloured . . . 10 10

1979. "Philaserdica 79" Int Stamp Exn (4th issue) and Bulgarian Stamp Cent (2nd issue). As Nos. 2714/18 but inscr "1979" and colours changed.
2721 – 2s. red and blue 10 10
2722 – 13s. claret and green . . 20 10
2723 – 23s. green, yellow & red 35 15
2724 **866** 35s. grey and red . . . 50 20
2725 – 53s. brown and violet . . 75 30

868 National Bank **868a**

1979. Centenary of Bulgarian National Bank.
2726 **868** 2s. grey and yellow . . . 10 10

1979. Coil stamps.
2726a **868a** 2s. blue 10 10
2726b 5s. red 10 10
The 5s. is as T **868a** but different pattern.

869 Stamboliiski **870** Child's Head as Flower

1979. Birth Centenary of Alexandur Stamboliiski (Prime Minister 1919–23).
2727 **869** 2s. brown and yellow . . 10 10

1979. International Year of the Child.
2728 **870** 23s. multicoloured . . . 20 10

871 Profiles **872** "75" and Emblem

1979. 8th World Congress for the Deaf, Varna.
2729 **871** 13s. green and blue . . . 10 10

1979. 75th Anniv of Bulgarian Trade Unions.
2730 **872** 2s. green and orange . . 10 10

874 Rocket **876** Running

875 Carrier Pigeon and Tupolev Tu-154 Jet

1979. Soviet–Bulgarian Space Flight. Multicoloured.
2732 2s. Georgi Ivanov (horiz) . . 10 10
2733 12s. Type **874** 10 10
2734 13s. Nikolai Rukavishnikov and Ivanov (horiz) . . . 10 10
2735 25s. Link-up with "Salyut" space station (horiz) . . 20 15
2736 35s. Capsule descending by parachute 30 20

1979. Centenary of Bulgarian Post and Telegraph Services. Multicoloured.
2738 2s. Type **875** 10 10
2739 5s. Old and new telephones 10 10
2740 13s. Morse key and teleprinter 10 10
2741 23s. Old radio transmitter and aerials 20 15
2742 35s. T.V. tower and satellite 30 20

1979. Olympic Games. Moscow (1980) (1st issue). Athletics. Multicoloured.
2744 2s. Type **876** 10 10
2745 13s. Pole vault (horiz) . . . 15 10
2746 25s. Discus 30 10
2747 35s. Hurdles (horiz) . . . 40 15
2748 43s. High jump (horiz) . . . 50 20
2749 1l. Long jump . . . . . . 1·10 45
See also Nos. 2773/78, 2803/8, 2816/21, 2834/9 and 2851/6.

879 Hotel Vitosha-New Otani

1979. "Philaserdica 79" International Stamp Exhibition, Sofia (5th issue) and Bulgaria Day.
2753 **879** 2s. pink and blue 10 10

880 "Good Morning, Little Brother" (illus by Kukuliev of folktale)

1979. "Philaserdica 79" International Stamp Exhibition, Sofia (6th issue) and Bulgarian–Russian Friendship Day.
2754 **880** 2s. multicoloured . . . 10 10

882 "Man on Donkey" (Boris Angelushev)

883 "Four Women"

1979. 12th Festival of Humour and Satire, Grabovo.
2756 882 2s. multicoloured 10 10

1979. 450th Death Anniv of Albrecht Durer (artist). Multicoloured.
2757 13s. Type 883 . . . . 20 10
2758 23s. "Three Peasants Talking" 55 20
2759 25s. "The Cook and his Wife" 40 20
2760 35s. "Portrait of Eobanus Hessus" 55 15

884 Clocktower, Byala Cherkva

885 Petko Todorov (birth centenary)

1979. Air. Clocktowers (1st series). Mult.
2762 13s. Type 884 . . . . . 10 10
2763 23s. Botevgrad 20 10
2764 25s. Pazardzhik 25 10
2765 35s. Gabrovo 35 15
2766 53s. Tryavna 50 20
See also Nos. 2891/5.

1979. Bulgarian Writers.
2767 885 2s. black, brown & yell 10 10
2768 – 2s. green and yellow . . 10 10
2769 – 2s. red and yellow . . . 10 10
DESIGNS: No. 2768, Dimitur Dimov (70th birth anniv); 2769, Stefan Kostov (birth cent).

886 Congress Emblem

887 House of Journalists, Varna

1979. 18th Congress of International Theatrical Institute, Sofia.
2770 886 13s. cobalt, blue & black 10 10

1979. 20th Anniv of House of Journalists (holiday home), Varna.
2771 887 8s. orange, black & blue 10 10

888 Children of Different Races

889 Parallel Bars

1979. "Banners for Peace" Children's Meeting, Sofia.
2772 888 2s. multicoloured 10 10

1979. Olympic Games, Moscow (1980) (2nd issue). Gymnastics. Multicoloured.
2773 2s. Type 889 . . . . . . 10 10
2774 13s. Horse exercise (horiz) 15 10
2775 25s. Rings exercise 30 10
2776 35s. Beam exercise 40 15
2777 43s. Uneven bars 50 20
2778 1l. Floor exercise . . . . 1·10 45

890 "Virgin and Child" (Nesebur)

1979. Icons of the Virgin and Child. Mult.
2780 13s. Type 890 . . . . . . 10 10
2781 23s. Nesebur (diff) 25 10
2782 35s. Sozopol 40 10
2783 43s. Sozopol (diff) 50 15
2784 53s. Samokov 70 20

891 Anton Bezenshek

892 Mountaineer

1979. Centenary of Bulgarian Stenography.
2785 891 2s. yellow and grey . . . 10 10

1979. 50th Anniv of Bulgarian Alpine Club.
2786 892 2s. multicoloured 10 10

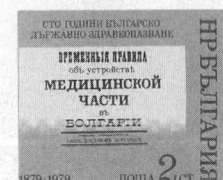

893 Commemorative Inscription

1979. Centenary of Bulgarian Public Health Services.
2787 893 2s. black, silver & green 10 10

894 Rocket and Flowers

896 Games Emblem

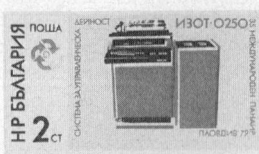

895 "IZOT–0250" Computer

1979. 35th Anniv of Fatherland Front Government. Multicoloured.
2788 2s. Type 894 . . . . . . 10 10
2789 5s. Russian and Bulgarian flags 10 10
2790 13s. "35" in national colours 10 10

1979. 35th Plovdiv Fair.
2791 895 2s. multicoloured 10 10

1979. World University Games, Mexico.
2792 896 5s. red, yellow and blue 10 10

897 Footballer

1979. 50th Anniv of DFS Lokomotiv Football Team.
2793 897 2s. red and black 40 10

898 Lyuben Karavelov

899 Cross-country Skiing

1979. Death Centenary of Lyuben Karavelov (newspaper editor and President of Bulgarian Revolutionary Committee).
2794 898 2s. green and blue 10 10

1979. Winter Olympic Games, Lake Placid (1980).
2795 899 2s. red, purple and black 10 10
2796 – 13s. orange, blue & blk 10 10
2797 – 23s. turquoise, blue & blk 20 10
2798 – 43s. purple, turq & blk 40 20
DESIGNS: 13s. Speed skating; 23s. Skiing; 43s. Luge.

900 "Woman from Thrace"

901 Canoeing (Canadian pairs)

1979. 80th Birth Anniv of Dechko Uzunov (artist). Multicoloured.
2800 12s. "Figure in Red" . . . 10 10
2801 13s. Type 900 . . . . . . 10 10
2802 23s. "Composition II" . . . 20 10

1979. Olympic Games, Moscow (1980) (3rd issue). Water Sports. Multicoloured.
2803 2s. Type 901 . . . . . . 10 10
2804 13s. Swimming (freestyle) . 15 10
2805 25s. Swimming (backstroke) (horiz) 30 10
2806 35s. Kayak (horiz) 40 15
2807 43s. Diving 50 20
2808 1l. Springboard diving . . 1·10 45

902 Nikola Vaptsarov

1979. 70th Birth Anniv of Nikola Vaptsarov (writer).
2810 902 2s. pink and red 10 10

903 "Dawn in Plovdiv" (Ioan Leviev)

1979. History of Bulgaria. Paintings. Mult.
2811 2s. "The First Socialists" (Boyan Petrov) (horiz) . 10 10
2812 13s. "Dimitur Blagoev as Editor of "Rabotnik" (Dimitur Gyvdzhenov) (horiz) 10 10
2813 25s. "Workers' Party March" (Stoyan Sotirov) 20 15
2814 35s. Type 903 . . . . . 30 20

904 Doves in a Girl's Hair

1979. New Year.
2815 904 13s. multicoloured . . . 10 10

905 Shooting

906 Procession with Relics of Saints

1979. Olympic Games, Moscow (1980) (4th issue). Multicoloured.
2816 2s. Type 905 . . . . . . 10 10
2817 13s. Judo (horiz) 15 10
2818 25s. Wrestling (horiz) . . . 30 10
2819 35s. Archery 40 15
2820 43s. Fencing (horiz) . . . 50 20
2821 1l. Fencing (different) . . 1·10 45

1979. Frescoes of Saints Cyril and Methodius in St. Clement's Basilica, Rome. Multicoloured.
2823 2s. Type 906 . . . . . . 10 10
2824 13s. Cyril and Methodius received by Pope Adrian II 10 10
2825 23s. Burial of Cyril the Philosopher 15 15
2826 25s. St. Cyril 20 15
2827 35s. St. Methodius 25 20

907 Television Screen showing Emblem

908 Puppet of Krali Marko (national hero)

1979. 25th Anniv of Bulgarian Television.
2828 907 5s. blue and deep blue . . 10 10

1980. 50th Anniv of International Puppet Theatre Organization (U.N.I.M.A.).
2829 908 2s. multicoloured 10 10

909 Thracian Rider (3rd-cent votive tablet)

910 "Meeting of Lenin and Dimitrov" (Aleksandur Poplilov)

1980. Centenary of National Archaeological Museum, Sofia.
2830 909 2s. brown, gold & purple 10 10
2831 – 13s. brown, gold & grn 10 10
DESIGN: 13s. Grave stele of Deines (5th–6th cent).

1980. 110th Birth Anniv of Lenin.
2832 910 13s. multicoloured 10 10

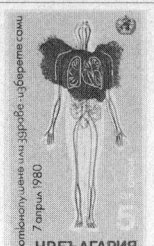

911 Diagram of Blood
Circulation and Lungs
obscured by Smoke

912 Basketball

1980. World Health Day. Anti-smoking Campaign.
2833 **911** 5s. multicoloured 10 10

1980. Olympic Games, Moscow (5th issue).
Multicoloured.
2834 2s. Type **912** 10 10
2835 13s. Football 15 10
2836 25s. Hockey 30 10
2837 35s. Cycling 40 15
2838 43s. Handball 50 10
2839 1l. Volleyball . . . . 1·10 45

914 Penyo Penev

915 Penny Black

1980. 50th Birth Anniv of Penyo Penev (poet).
2842 **914** 5s. brown, red & turq . . 10 10

1980. "London 1980" International Stamp
Exhibition.
2843 **915** 25s. black and red . . . 75 25

916 Dimitur Khv. Chorbadzhuski-
Chudomir (self-portrait)

1980. 90th Birth Anniv of Dimitur Khv.
Chorbadzhusk-Chudomir (artist).
2844 **916** 5s. pink, brown & turq 10 10
2845 – 13s. black, blue & turq 10 10
DESIGN: 13s. "Our People".

917 Nikolai Gyaurov

918 Soviet Soldiers
raising Flag on Berlin
Reichstag

1980. 50th Birth Anniv of Nikolai Gyaurov (opera
singer).
2846 **917** 5s. yellow, brown & grn 10 10

1980. 35th Anniv of "Victory in Europe" Day.
2847 **918** 5s. gold, brown & black 10 10
2848 – 13s. gold, brown & black 10 10
DESIGN: 13s. Soviet Army memorial, Berlin–
Treptow.

919 Open Book and Sun

920 Stars representing
Member Countries

1980. 75th Anniv Bulgarian Teachers' Union.
2849 **919** 5s. purple and yellow . . 10 10

1980. 25th Anniv of Warsaw Pact.
2850 **920** 13s. multicoloured . . . 10 10

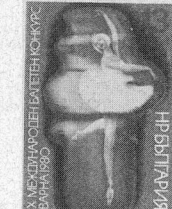

921 Greek Girl with
Olympic Flame

922 Ballerina

1980. Olympic Games, Moscow (6th issue).
Multicoloured.
2851 2s. Type **921** 10 10
2852 13s. Spartacus monument,
Sandanski 15 10
2853 25s. Liberation monument,
Sofia (detail) 30 10
2854 35s. Liberation monument,
Plovdiv 40 15
2855 43s. Liberation monument,
Shipka Pass 50 20
2856 1l. Liberation monument,
Ruse . . . . 1·10 45

1980. 10th International Ballet Competition, Varna.
2858 **922** 13s. multicoloured . . . 10 10

923 Europa Hotel, Sofia

1980. Hotels. Multicoloured.
2859 23s. Type **923** 20 10
2860 23s. Bulgaria Hotel, Burgas
(vert) 20 10
2861 23s. Plovdiv Hotel, Plovdiv 20 10
2862 23s. Riga Hotel, Ruse (vert) 20 10
2863 23s. Varna Hotel, Prazhba 20 10

1980. Historic Ships (3rd series). As T **753.**
Multicoloured.
2864 5s. Hansa kogge "Jesus of
Lubeck" 10 10
2865 8s. Roman galley 20 10
2866 13s. Galleon "Eagle" . . . 25 10
2867 23s. "Mayflower" 40 15
2868 35s. Maltese galleon . . . 55 25
2869 53s. Galleon "Royal Louis" 1·10 40

924 Parachute Descent

1980. 15th World Parachute Championships,
Kazanluk. Multicoloured.
2870 13s. Type **924** 10 10
2871 25s. Parachutist in free fall 20 10

925 Clown and Children

1980. 1st Anniv of "Banners for Peace" Children's
Meeting. Multicoloured.
2872 3s. Type **925** 10 10
2873 5s. "Cosmonauts in
Spaceship" (vert) . . 10 10
2874 8s. "Picnic" 10 10
2875 13s. "Children with Ices" . 10 10
2876 25s. "Children with Cat"
(vert) 20 10
2877 35s. "Crowd" . . . . . . 1·10 40
2878 43s. "Banners for Peace"
monument (vert) . . 40 20

926 Assembly
Emblem

927 Iordan Iovkov

1980. Assembly of Peoples' Parliament for Peace,
Sofia.
2879 **926** 25s. multicoloured . . . 15 10

1980. Birth Centenary of Iordan Iovkov (writer).
2880 **927** 5s. multicoloured 10 10

928 Yakovlev Yak-24
Helicopter, Missile Launcher
and Tank

1980. Bulgarian Armed Forces. Multicoloured.
2881 3s. Type **928** 15 10
2882 5s. Mikoyan Gurevich MiG-
21 bomber, radar
antennae and missile
transporter 25 10
2883 8s. Mil Mi-24 helicopter,
missile boat and landing
ship "Ropucha" . . 60 15

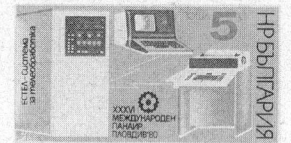

929 Computer

1980. 36th Plovdiv Fair.
2884 **929** 5s. multicoloured . . . 10 10

930 "Virgin and Child with St.
Anne"

1980. Paintings by Leonardo da Vinci. Mult.
2885 5s. Type **930** 10 10
2886 8s. Angel (detail, "The
Annunciation") . . . 10 10
2887 13s. Virgin (detail, "The
Annunciation") . . . 10 10
2888 25s. "Adoration of the
Kings" (detail) . . . 20 15
2889 35s. "Woman with Ermine" 30 20

1980. Air. Clocktowers (2nd series). As T **884.**
Multicoloured.
2891 13s. Byala 10 10
2892 23s. Razgrad 20 10
2893 25s. Karnobat 25 10
2894 35s. Sevlievo 35 15
2895 53s. Berkovitsa 50 20

931 "Parodia saint-pieana"

1980. Cacti. Multicoloured.
2896 5s. Type **931** 10 10
2897 13s. "Echinopsis bridgesii" 25 10
2898 25s. "Echinocereus
purpureus" 50 10
2899 35s. "Opuntia bispinosa" . 65 15
2900 53s. "Mamillopsis senilis" 90 20

933 Wild Horse

1980. Horses. Multicoloured.
2902 3s. Type **933** 20 10
2903 5s. Tarpan 25 10
2904 13s. Arabian 40 10
2905 23s. Anglo-Arabian . . . 60 15
2906 35s. Draught horse . . . 1·00 20

934 Vasil Stoin

1980. Birth Centenary of Vasil Stoin (collector of folk
songs).
2907 **934** 5s. violet, yellow & gold 10 10

935 Armorial Lion

936 Red Star

1980. New Year. 1300th Anniv of Bulgarian State.
Multicoloured.
2908 5s. Type **935** 10 10
2909 13s. Dish and dates "681–
1981" 10 10

1980. 12th Bulgarian Communist Party Congress (1st
issue).
2910 **936** 5s. yellow and red . . . 10 10
See also Nos. 2920/2.

937 Cross-country Skier

1981. World Ski-racing Championship, Velingrad.
2911 **937** 43s. orange, blue & blk 40 10

938 Midland Hawthorn
("Crataegus
oxpacantha")

939 Skier

1981. Useful Plants. Multicoloured.
2912 3s. Type **938** 10 10
2913 5s. Perforate St. John's wort
("Hypericum
perforatum") . . . 10 10
2914 13s. Elder ("Sambucus
nigra") 20 10
2915 25s. Dewberry ("Rubus
caesius") 40 15
2916 35s. Lime ("Tilia argentea") 50 20
2917 43s. Dog rose ("Rosa
canina") 75 25

1981. Alpine Skiing World Championships, Borovets.
2918 **939** 43s. yellow, black & blue 40 10

940 Nuclear Traces

1981. 25th Anniv of Nuclear Research Institute,
Dubna, U.S.S.R.
2919 **940** 13s. black and silver . . 10 10

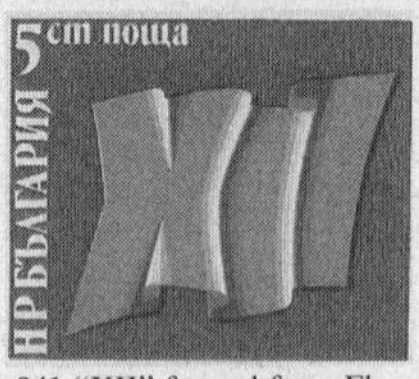

941 "XII" formed from Flag

1981. 12th Bulgarian Communist Party Congress (2nd issue).

2920	941	5s. multicoloured	10	10
2921	–	13s. red, black and blue	10	10
2922	–	23s. red, black and blue	10	10

DESIGNS: 13s. Stars; 23s. Computer tape.

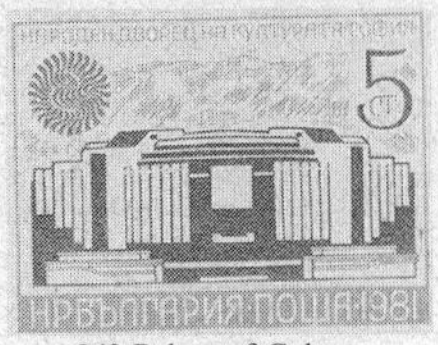

942 Palace of Culture

1981. Opening of Palace of Culture, Sofia.

2924 **942** 5s. dp green, grn & red 10 10

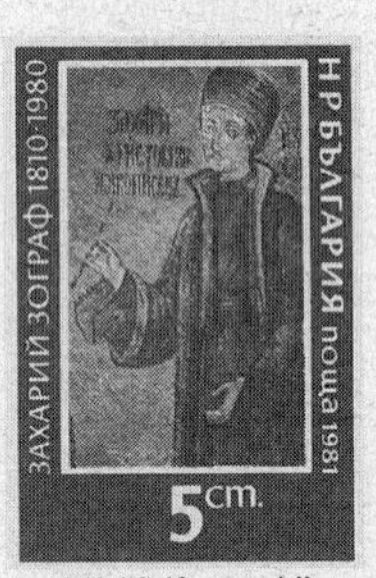

943 "Self-portrait"

1981. 170th Birth Anniv (1980) of Zakharu Zograf (artist). Multicoloured.

2925	5s. Type **943**	10	10
2926	13s. "Portrait of Khristionia Zografska"	10	10
2927	23s. "The Transfiguration" (icon from Preobrazhenie Monastery)	20	10
2928	25s. "Doomsday" (detail) (horiz)	25	15
2929	35s. "Doomsday" (detail – different) (horiz)	40	20

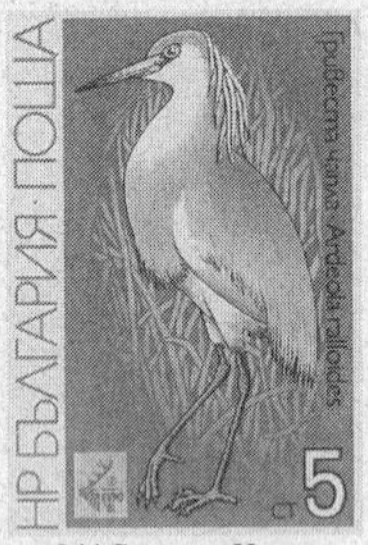

944 Squacco Heron

1981. Birds. Multicoloured.

2930	5s. Type **944**	20	10
2931	8s. Eurasian bittern	40	15
2932	13s. Cattle egret	70	20
2933	25s. Great egret	1·25	50
2934	53s. Black stork	2·50	1·00

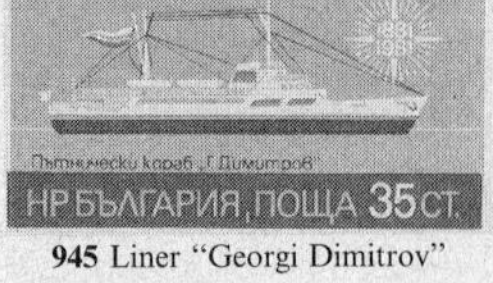

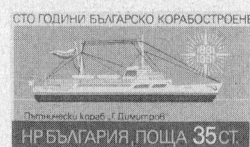

945 Liner "Georgi Dimitrov"

1981. Centenary of Bulgarian Shipbuilding. Mult.

2935	35s. Type **945**	1·00	30
2936	43s. Freighter "Petimata of RMS"	1·40	40
2937	53s. Tanker "Khan Asparuch"	2·00	70

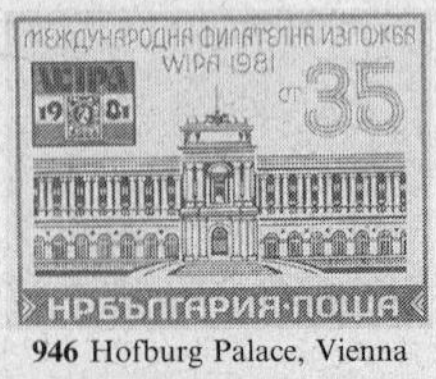

946 Hofburg Palace, Vienna

1981. "WIPA 1981" International Stamp Exhibition, Vienna.

2938 **946** 35s. crimson, red & green 20 10

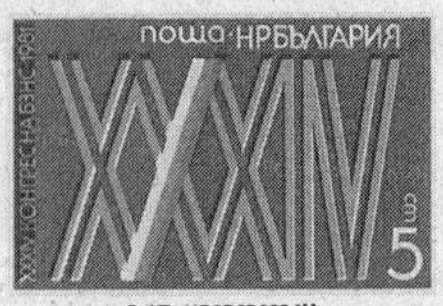

947 "XXXIV"

1981. 34th Bulgarian People's Agrarian Union Congress.

2939	947	5s. multicoloured	10	10
2940	–	8s. orange, black & blue	10	10
2941	–	13s. multicoloured . . .	10	10

DESIGNS: 8s. Flags; 13s. Bulgarian Communist Party and Agrarian Union flags.

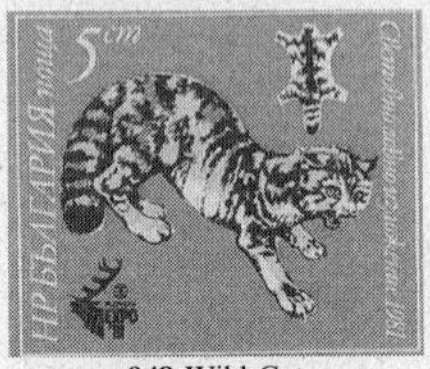

948 Wild Cat

1981. International Hunting Exhibition, Plovdiv.

2942	948	5s. stone, black & brown	15	10
2943	–	13s. black, brn & stone	40	15
2944	–	23s. brown, blk & orge	60	20
2945	–	25s. black, brown & mve	70	40
2946	–	35s. lt brown, blk & brn	95	35
2947	–	53s. brown, blk & grn	1·50	50

DESIGNS: 13s. Wild boar; 23s. Mouflon; 25s. Chamois; 35s. Roe deer; 53s. Fallow deer.

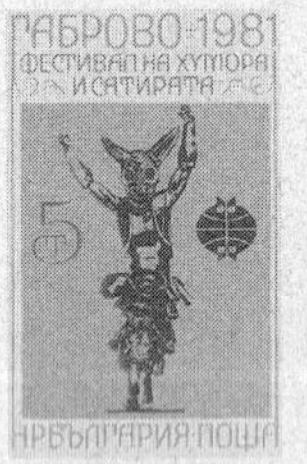

949 "Crafty Peter" (sculpture, Georgi Chapkanov)

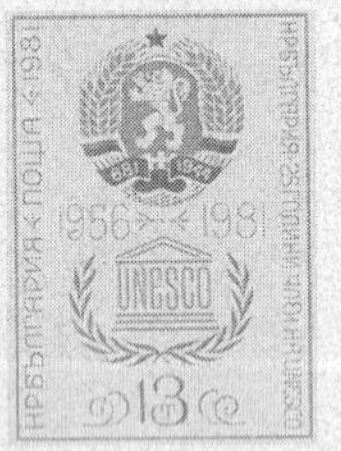

950 Bulgarian Arms and U.N.E.S.C.O. Emblem

1981. Festival of Humour and Satire, Gabrovo.

2949 **949** 5s. multicoloured 10 10

1981. 25th Anniv of U.N.E.S.C.O. Membership.

2950 **950** 13s. multicoloured . . . 10 10

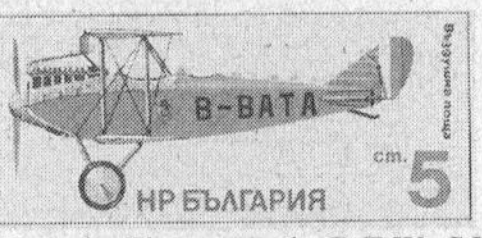

951 Deutsche Flugzeugwerke D.F.W. C.V. Biplane

1981. Air. Aircraft. Multicoloured.

2951	5s. Type **951**	10	10
2952	12s. LAS-7 monoplane . . .	35	15
2953	25s. LAS-8 monoplane . . .	70	30
2954	35s. DAR-1 biplane	85	45
2955	45s. DAR-3 biplane	1·25	55
2956	55s. DAR-9 biplane	1·75	70

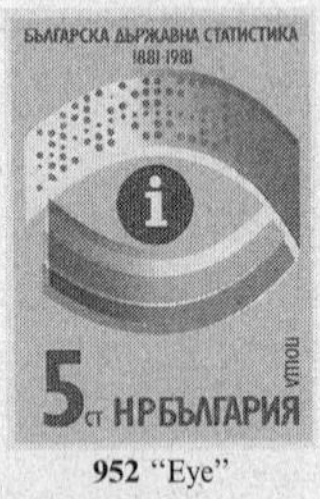

952 "Eye"

1981. Centenary of State Statistical Office.

2957 **952** 5s. multicoloured 10 10

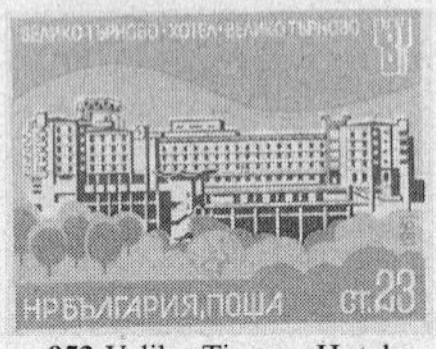

953 Veliko Tirnovo Hotel

1981. Hotels.

2958 **953** 23s. multicoloured . . . 15 10

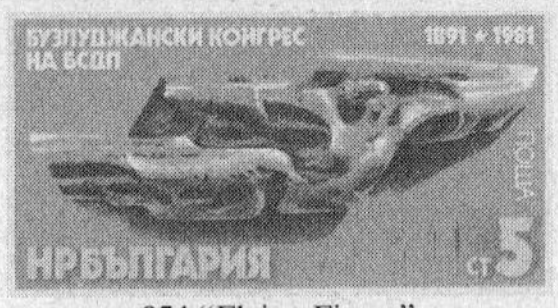

954 "Flying Figure"

1981. 90th Anniv of First Bulgarian Social Democratic Party Congress, Buzludzha. Sculptures by Velichko Minekov.

2959	954	5s. blue, black and green	10	10
2960	–	13s. brown, blk & orge	10	10

DESIGN: 13s. "Advancing Female".

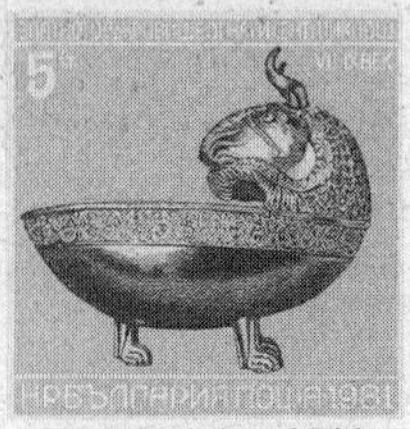

955 Animal-shaped Dish

1981. Golden Treasure of Old St. Nicholas. Multicoloured.

2961	5s. Type **955**	10	10
2962	13s. Jug with decorated neck	10	10
2963	23s. Jug with loop pattern	20	10
2964	25s. Jug with bird pattern	25	10
2965	35s. Decorated vase	35	15
2966	53s. Decorated dish	50	25

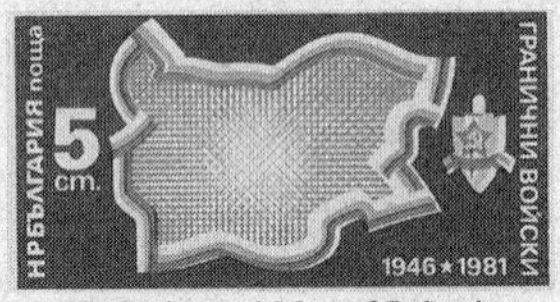

956 Badge and Map of Bulgaria

1981. 35th Anniv of Frontier Guards.

2967 **956** 5s. multicoloured 10 10

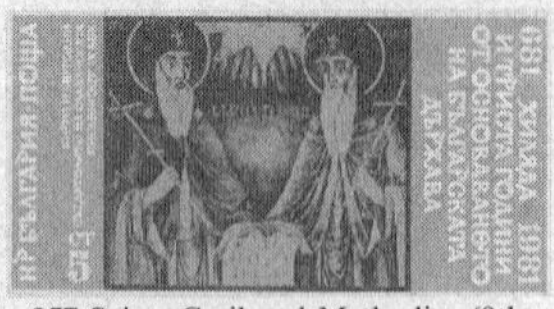

957 Saints Cyril and Methodius (9th century)

1981. 1300th Anniv of Bulgarian State.

2968	–	5s. green and grey . . .	10	10
2969	957	5s. brown and yellow . .	10	10
2970	–	8s. violet and lilac . . .	10	10
2971	–	12s. mauve and purple	10	10
2972	–	13s. purple and brown	10	10
2973	–	13s. green and black . .	10	10
2974	–	16s. green & deep green	15	10
2975	–	23s. black and blue . . .	20	10
2976	–	25s. green and light green	20	10
2977	–	35s. brown & light brown	30	15
2978	–	41s. red and pink . . .	35	20
2979	–	43s. red and pink . . .	35	20
2980	–	53s. dp brown and brown	40	25
2981	–	55s. dp green and green	40	25

DESIGNS: No. 2968, Madara horsemen (8th century); 2970, Plan of Round Church at Veliki Preslav (10th century); 2971, Four Evangelists of King Ivan, 1356; 2972, Column of Ivan Asen II (13th century); 2973, Manasiev Chronicle (14th century); 2974, Rising of April 1876; 2975, Arrival of Russian liberation troops; 2976, Foundation ceremony of Bulgarian Social Democratic Party, 1891; 2977, Rising of September 1923; 2978, Formation of Fatherland Front Government, 9 September 1944; 2979, Bulgarian Communist Party Congress, 1948; 2980, 10th Communist Party Congress, 1971; 2981, Kremikovski metallurgical combine.

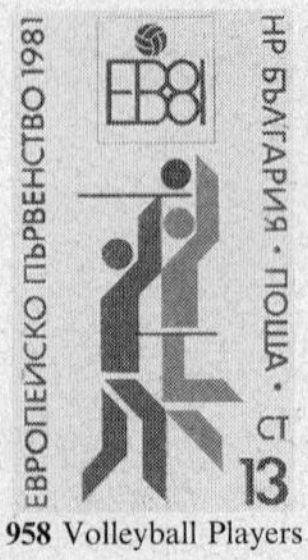

958 Volleyball Players

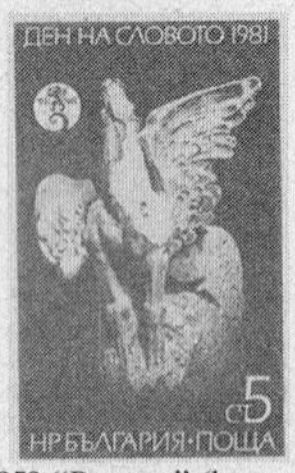

959 "Pegasus" (bronze sculpture)

1981. European Volleyball Championships.

2983 **958** 13s. red, blue and black 10 10

1981. Day of the Word.

2984 **959** 5s. green 10 10

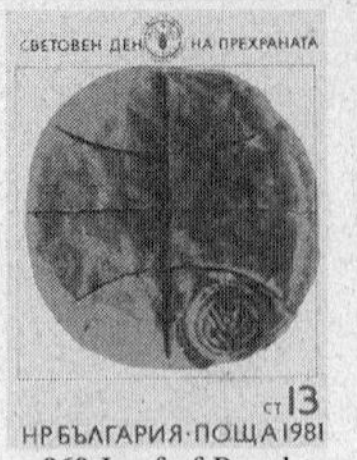

960 Loaf of Bread

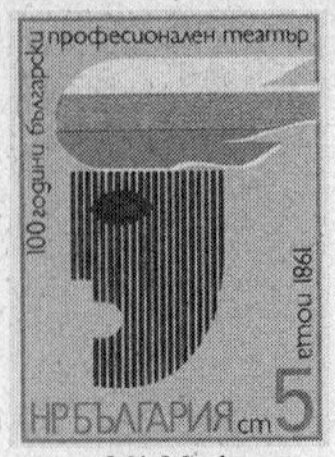

961 Mask

1981. World Food Day.

2985 **960** 13s. brown, black & grn 10 10

1981. Cent of Bulgarian Professional Theatre.

2986 **961** 5s. multicoloured 10 10

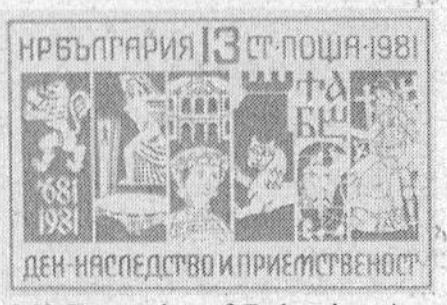

962 Examples of Bulgarian Art

1981. Cultural Heritage Day.

2987 **962** 13s. green and brown . . 10 10

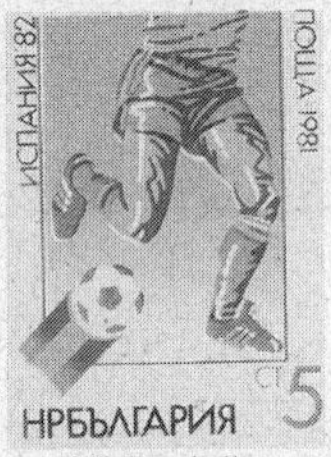

963 Footballer

1981. World Cup Football Championship, Spain (1982). Multicoloured.

2988	5s. Type **963**	10	10
2989	13s. Heading ball	25	10
2990	43s. Saving a goal	70	25
2991	53s. Running with ball . . .	90	35

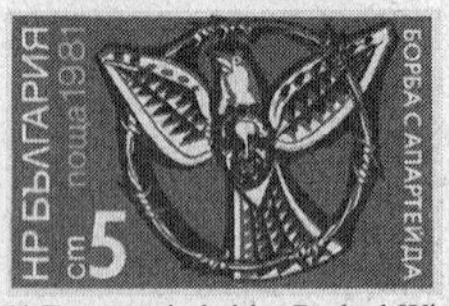

964 Dove encircled by Barbed Wire

1981. Anti-apartheid Campaign.

2992 **964** 5s. red, black and yellow 10 10

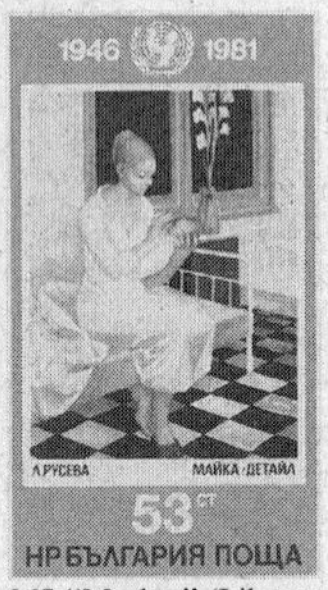

965 "Mother" (Lilyann Ruseva)

1981. 35th Anniv of U.N.I.C.E.F. Various designs showing mother and child paintings by named artists. Multicoloured.

2994	53s. Type **965**	50	20
2995	53s. "Bulgarian Madonna" (Vasil Stoilov)	50	20
2996	53s. "Village Madonna" (Ivan Milev)	50	20
2997	53s. "Mother" (Vladimir Dimitrov)	50	20

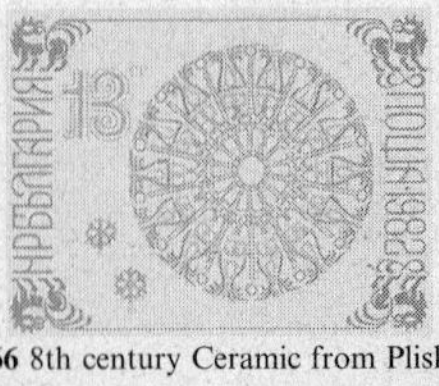

966 8th century Ceramic from Pliska

1981. New Year. Multicoloured.

2998	5s. Armorial lion	10	10
2999	13s. Type **966**	10	10

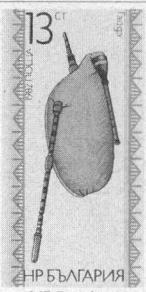

967 Bagpipes   968 Open Book

1982. Musical Instruments. Multicoloured.
3000	13s. Type 967	10	10
3001	25s. Single and double flutes	20	10
3002	30s. Rebec	25	10
3003	35s. Flute and pipe	30	15
3004	44s. Mandolin	40	15

1982. 125th Anniv of Public Libraries.
3005	968 5s. green	10	10

969 "Sofia Plains"

1982. Birth Centenary of Nikola Petrov (artist).
3006	5s. Type 969	10	10
3007	13s. "Girl Embroidering"	10	10
3008	30s. "Fields of Peshtera"	25	10

971 "Peasant Woman"

1982. Birth Centenary of Valadimir Dimitrov (artist). Multicoloured.
3010	5s. Figures in a landscape (horiz)	10	10
3011	8s. Town and harbour (horiz)	10	10
3012	13s. Town scene (horiz)	10	10
3013	25s. "Reapers"	20	10
3014	30s. Woman and child	20	15
3015	35s. Type 971	25	10

972 Georgi Dimitrov

1982. 9th Bulgarian Trade Unions Congress, Sofia.
3017	972 5s. lt brn, dp brn & brn	10	10
3018	– 5s. brown and blue	10	10

DESIGN: No. 3018, Palace of Culture, Sofia.

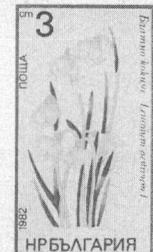

973 Summer Snowflake

1982. Medicinal Plants. Multicoloured.
3019	3s. Type 973	10	10
3020	5s. Chicory	10	10
3021	8s. Rosebay willowherb	20	10
3022	13s. Solomon's seal	25	10
3023	25s. Sweet violet	50	15
3024	35s. "Ficaria verna"	50	25

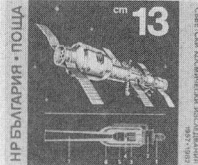

974 Russian Space Station

1982. 25th Anniv of First Soviet Artificial Satellite.
3025	974 13s. multicoloured	10	10

976 Dimitrov and Congress Emblem

1982. 14th Dimitrov Communist Youth League Congress, Sofia.
3027	976 5s. blue, red & yellow	10	10

977 First French and Bulgarian Stamps

1982. "Philexfrance 82" International Stamp Exhibition, Paris.
3028	977 42s. multicoloured	75	25

978 Abstract with Birds   980 Georgi Dimitrov

1982. Alafrangi Frescoes from 19th-century Houses.
3029	978 5s. multicoloured	10	10
3030	– 13s. multicoloured	10	10
3031	– 25s. multicoloured	20	10
3032	– 30s. multicoloured	20	10
3033	– 42s. multicoloured	30	15
3034	– 60s. multicoloured	45	25

DESIGNS: 13s. to 60s. Various flower and bird patterns.

During 1982 sets were issued for World Cup Football Championship, Spain (5, 13, 30s.), Tenth Anniv of First European Security and Co-operation Conference (5, 13, 25, 30s.), World Cup Results (5, 13, 30s.) and 10th Anniv (1983) of European Security and Co-operation Conference, Helsinki (5, 13, 25, 30s.). Supplies and distribution of these stamps were restricted and it is understood they were not available at face value.

1982. 9th Fatherland Front Congress, Sofia.
3036	980 5s. multicoloured	10	10

981 Airplane

1982. 35th Anniv of Balkanair (state airline).
3037	981 42s. blue, green & red	65	30

982 Atomic Bomb   983 Lyudmila
Mushroom-cloud   Zhivkova

1982. Nuclear Disarmament Campaign.
3038	982 13s. multicoloured	10	10

1982. 40th Birth Anniv of Lyudmila Zhivkova (founder of "Banners for Peace" Children's Meetings).
3039	983 5s. multicoloured	10	10
3040	13s. multicoloured	10	10

984 Emblem

1982. 10th Anniv of U.N. Environment Programme.
3042	984 13s. green and blue	10	10

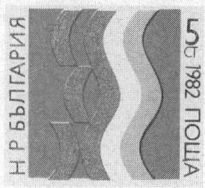

985 Wave Pattern

1982. 5th Bulgarian Painters' Association Congress.
3043	985 5s. multicoloured	10	10

986 Child Musicians

1982. 2nd "Banners for Peace" Children's Meeting (1st issue). Children's Paintings. Multicoloured.
3044	3s. Type 986	10	10
3045	5s. Children skating	10	10
3046	8s. Adults, children and flowers	10	10
3047	13s. Children with flags	20	15

See also Nos. 3057/62.

987 Moscow Park Hotel,   988 Cruiser "Aurora"
Sofia   and Satellite

1982. Hotels. Multicoloured.
3049	32s. Type 987	20	10
3050	32s. Black Sea Hotel, Varna	20	10

1982. 65th Anniv of Russian October Revolution.
3051	988 13s. red and blue	55	10

989 Hammer and Sickle

1982. 60th Anniv of U.S.S.R.
3052	989 13s. red, gold & violet	10	10

990 "The Piano"

1982. Birth Cent of Pablo Picasso (artist). Mult.
3053	13s. Type 990	20	10
3054	30s. "Portrait of Jacqueline"	55	10
3055	42s. "Maternity"	75	10

991 Boy and Girl

1982. 2nd "Banners for Peace" Children's Meeting (2nd issue). Multicoloured.
3057	3s. Type 991	10	10
3058	5s. Market place	10	10
3059	8s. Children in fancy dress (vert)	10	10
3060	13s. Chickens (vert)	15	10
3061	25s. Interlocking heads	25	15
3062	30s. Lion	30	20

992 Lions

1982. New Year. Multicoloured.
3064	5s. Type 992	10	10
3065	13s. Decorated letters	10	10

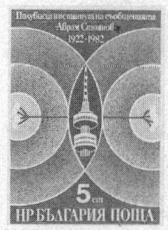

993 Broadcasting Tower   994 Dr. Robert Koch

1982. 60th Anniv of Avram Stoyanov Broadcasting Institute.
3066	993 5s. blue	10	10

1982. Cent of Discovery of Tubercle Bacillus.
3067	994 25s. brown and green	15	10

995 Simon Bolivar   996 Vasil Levski

1982. Birth Anniversaries.
3068	995 30s. green and grey	20	10
3069	30s. yellow and brown	20	10

DESIGN: No. 3068, Type 995 (bicent); 3069, Rabindranath Tagore (philosopher, 120th anniv).

1983. 110th Death Anniv of Vasil Levski (revolutionary).
3070	996 5s. brown & green	10	10

997 Skier

1983. "Universiade 83" University Games, Sofia.
3071	997 30s. multicoloured	20	10

998 Northern Pike

1983. Freshwater Fishes. Multicoloured.
3072	3s. Type 998	10	10
3073	5s. Beluga sturgeon	10	10
3074	13s. Chub	10	10
3075	25s. Zander	20	10
3076	30s. Wels	25	15
3077	42s. Brown trout	35	20

999 Karl Marx

1983. Death Centenary of Karl Marx.
3078 **999** 13s. red, purple & yellow 10 10

1000 Hasek and Illustrations from "The Good Soldier Schweik"

1983. Birth Centenary of Jaroslav Hasek (Czech writer).
3079 **1000** 13s. brown, grey & grn 10 10

1001 Martin Luther

1983. 500th Birth Anniv of Martin Luther (Protestant reformer).
3080 **1001** 13s. grey, black & brn 10 10

1002 Figures forming Initials

1983. 55th Anniv of Young Workers' Union.
3081 **1002** 5s. red, black & orange 10 10

1003 Khaskovo Costume **1004** Old Man feeding a Chicken

1983. Folk Costumes. Multicoloured.
3082 5s. Type **1003** 10 10
3083 8s. Pernik 10 10
3084 13s. Burgas 10 10
3085 25s. Tolbukhin 15 15
3086 30s. Blagoevgrad 20 15
3087 42s. Topolovgrad 30 25

1983. 6th International Festival of Humour and Satire, Gabrovo.
3088 **1004** 5s. multicoloured 10 10

During 1983 sets were issued for European Security and Co-operation Conference, Budapest (5, 13, 25, 30s.), Olympic Games, Los Angeles (5, 13, 30, 42s.), Winter Olympic Games, Sarajevo (horiz designs, 5, 13, 30, 42s.) and European Security and Co-operation Conference, Madrid (5, 13, 30, 42s.). Supplies and distribution of these stamps were restricted, and it is understood they were not available at face value.

1005 Smirnenski

1983. 85th Birth Anniv of Khristo Smirnenski (poet).
3089 **1005** 5s. red, brown & yellow 10 10

1006 Emblem

1983. 17th Int Geodesy Federation Congress.
3090 **1006** 30s. green, blue & yell 15 10

1007 Stylized Houses

1983. "Interarch 83" World Architecture Biennale, Sofia.
3091 **1007** 30s. multicoloured 15 10

1008 Staunton Chessmen on Map of Europe **1011** Television Mast, Tolbukhin

1983. 8th European Chess Team Championship, Plovdiv.
3092 **1008** 13s. multicoloured 20 10

1983. Air. World Communications Year.
3095 **1011** 5s. blue and red 10 10
3096 – 13s. mauve and red 15 10
3097 – 30s. yellow and red 20 10
DESIGNS: 13s. Postwoman; 30s. Radio tower, Mount Botev.

1012 Lenin addressing Congress

1983. 80th Anniv of 2nd Russian Social Democratic Workers' Party Congress.
3098 **1012** 5s. pur, dp pur & yell 10 10

1013 Pistol and Dagger on Book

1983. 80th Anniv of Ilinden-Preobrazhenie Rising.
3099 **1013** 5s. yellow and green 10 10

1014 Crystals and Hammers within Gearwheels

1983. 30th Anniv of Mining and Geology Institute, Sofia.
3100 **1014** 5s. grey, purple & blue 10 10

1015 Georgi Dimitrov and Revolution Scenes

1983. 60th Anniv of September Uprising. Mult.
3101 5s. Type **1015** 10 10
3102 13s. Wreath and revolution scenes 10 10

1016 Animated Drawings **1017** Angora

1983. 3rd Animated Film Festival, Varna.
3103 **1016** 5s. multicoloured 10 10

1983. Cats. Multicoloured.
3104 5s. Type **1017** 15 10
3105 13s. Siamese 35 10
3106 20s. Abyssinian (vert) 50 10
3107 25s. European 60 15
3108 30s. Persian (vert) 75 15
3109 42s. Khmer 1·00 20

1018 Richard Trevithick's Locomotive, 1803

1983. Locomotives (1st series). Multicoloured.
3110 5s. Type **1018** 20 10
3111 13s. John Blenkinsop's rack locomotive "Prince Royal", 1810 30 10
3112 42s. William Hedley's "Puffing Billy", 1813–14 2·25 50
3113 60s. Stephenson locomotive "Adler", 1835, Germany 3·75 75
See also Nos. 3159/63.

1020 Mask and Laurel as Lyre **1021** Ioan Kukuzel

1983. 75th Anniv of National Opera, Sofia.
3115 **1020** 5s. red, black & gold 10 10

1983. Bulgarian Composers.
3116 **1021** 5s. yellow, brown & grn 10 10
3117 – 8s. yellow, brown & red 10 10
3118 – 13s. yellow, brown & grn 10 10
3119 – 20s. yellow, brown & bl 15 10
3120 – 25s. yellow, brn & grey 20 15
3121 – 30s. yell, dp brn & brn 25 20
DESIGNS: 8s. Georgi Atanasov; 13s. Petko Stainov; 20s. Veselin Stoyanov; 25s. Lyubomir Pipkov; 30s. Pancho Vladigerov.

1022 Snowflake

1983. New Year.
3122 **1022** 5s. green, blue & gold 10 10

1023 "Angelo Donni"

1983. 500th Birth Anniv of Raphael (artist). Multicoloured.
3123 5s. Type **1023** 10 10
3124 13s. "Portrait of a Cardinal" 10 10
3125 30s. "Baldassare Castiglioni" 25 15
3126 42s. "Woman with a Veil" 35 25

1024 Eurasian Common Shrew

1983. Protected Mammals. Multicoloured.
3128 12s. Type **1024** 45 20
3129 13s. Greater horseshoe bat 55 20
3130 20s. Common long-eared bat 85 30
3131 30s. Forest dormouse 1·00 40
3132 42s. Fat dormouse 1·50 60

1025 Karavelov

1984. 150th Birth Anniv of Lyuben Karavelov (poet).
3133 **1025** 5s. blue, bistre & brn 10 10

During 1984 sets were issued for European Confidence- and Security-building Measures and Disarmament Conference, Stockholm (5, 13, 30, 42s.) and Winter Olympic Games, Sarajevo (vert designs, 5, 13, 30, 42s.). Supplies and distribution of these stamps were restricted and it is understood that they were not available at face value.

1026 Mendeleev and Formulae

1984. 150th Birth Anniv of Dmitry Mendeleev (chemist).
3134 **1026** 13s. multicoloured 10 10

1027 Bulk Carrier "Gen. Vl. Zaimov"

1984. Ships. Multicoloured.
3135 5s. Type **1027** 20 10
3136 13s. Tanker "Mesta" 45 10
3137 25s. Tanker "Veleka" 85 20
3138 32s. Train ferry "Geroite na Odesa" 95 45
3139 42s. Bulk carrier "Rozhen" 1·40 55

1029 Pigeon with Letter over Globe **1030** Wild Cherries

1984. "Mladost '84" Youth Stamp Exhibition, Pleven (1st issue).
3141 **1029** 5s. multicoloured . . . 15 10
See also Nos. 3171/2.

1984. Fruits. Multicoloured.
3142 5s. Type **1030** 10 10
3143 8s. Wild strawberries . . . 20 10
3144 13s. Dewberries 30 10
3145 20s. Raspberries 40 10
3146 42s. Medlars 75 20

1031 "Vitosha Conference" (K. Buyukliiski and P. Petrov)

1984. 60th Anniv of Bulgarian Communist Party Conference, Vitosha.
3147 **1031** 5s. purple, brn & red 10 10

1033 Athletes and Doves   1034 Mt. Everest

1984. 6th Republican Spartakiad.
3149 **1033** 13s. multicoloured . . . 10 10

1984. Bulgarian Expedition to Mt. Everest.
3150 **1034** 5s. multicoloured . . . 10 10

1036 Drummer

1984. 6th Amateur Performers Festival.
3152 **1036** 5s. multicoloured . . . 10 10

1037 Seal

1984. 50 Years of Bulgarian–U.S.S.R. Diplomatic Relations.
3153 **1037** 13s. multicoloured . . . 10 10

1038 Feral Rock Pigeon   1039 Production Quality Emblem

1984. Pigeons and Doves. Multicoloured.
3154 5s. Type **1038** 20 10
3155 13s. Stock pigeon 55 15
3156 20s. Wood pigeon 80 25
3157 30s. Turtle dove . . . . 1·25 45
3158 42s. Domestic pigeon . . . 1·60 60

1984. Locomotives (2nd series). As T **1018**. Multicoloured.
3159 13s. "Best Friend of Charleston", 1830, U.S.A. 30 10
3160 25s. "Saxonia", 1836, Saxony 55 10
3161 30s. "Lafayette", 1837, U.S.A. 65 15

3162 42s. "Borsig", 1841, Germany . . . . . . 1·25 20
3163 60s. "Philadelphia", 1843, U.S.A. . . . . . . 1·90 30

1984. 40th Anniv of Fatherland Front Government.
3164 **1039** 5s. red, lt green & green 10 10
3165 – 20s. red and violet . . . 10 10
3166 – 30s. red and blue . . . 15 10
DESIGNS: 20s. Monument to Soviet Army, Sofia; 30s. Figure nine and star.

1040 "Boy with Harmonica"   1041 Mausoleum of Russian Soldiers

1984. Paintings by Nenko Balkanski. Multicoloured.
3167 5s. Type **1040** 10 10
3168 30s. "Window in Paris" . . . 15 10
3169 42s. "Portrait of Two Women" (horiz) 20 10

1984. "Mladost '84" Youth Stamp Exhibition, Pleven (2nd issue).
3171 **1041** 5s. multicoloured . . . 10 10
3172 – 13s. black, grn & red 10 10
DESIGN: 13s. Panorama building.

1042 Pioneers saluting

1984. 40th Anniv of Dimitrov Septembrist Pioneers Organization.
3173 **1042** 5s. multicoloured . . . 10 10

1043 Vaptsarov (after D. Nikolov)

1984. 75th Birth Anniv of Nikola I. Vaptsarov (poet).
3174 **1043** 5s. yellow and red . . . 10 10

1044 Goalkeeper saving Goal

1984. 75th Anniv of Bulgarian Football.
3175 **1044** 42s. multicoloured . . . 50 15

1046 Devil's Bridge, R. Arda

1984. Bridges. Multicoloured.
3177 5s. Type **1046** 10 10
3178 13s. Kolo Ficheto Bridge, Byala 25 10
3179 30s. Asparukhov Bridge, Varna 50 20
3180 42s. Bebresh Bridge, Botevgrad 70 30

1047 Olympic Emblem

1984. 90th Anniv of International Olympic Committee.
3181 **1047** 13s. multicoloured . . . 10 10

1049 Dalmatian Pelican with Chicks   1050 Anton Ivanov

1984. Wildlife Protection. Dalmatian Pelican.
3183 **1049** 5s. multicoloured . . . 40 15
3184 – 13s. lav, blk & brn . . 90 25
3185 – 20s. multicoloured . . . 1·75 40
3186 – 32s. multicoloured . . . 2·50 75
DESIGNS: 13s. Two pelicans; 20s. Pelican on water; 32s. Pelican in flight.

1984. Birth Cent of Anton Ivanov (revolutionary).
3187 **1050** 5s. yell, brn & red . . . 10 10

1051 Girl's Profile with Text as Hair

1984. 70th Anniv of Bulgarian Women's Socialist Movement.
3188 **1051** 5s. multicoloured . . . 10 10

1052 Snezhanka Television Tower

1984. Television Towers.
3189 **1052** 5s. blue, green & mve 10 10
3190 – 11. brown, mauve & bis 75 20
DESIGN: 11. Orelek television tower.

1053 Birds and Posthorns

1984. New Year. Multicoloured.
3191 5s. Type **1053** 10 10
3192 13s. Decorative pattern . . 10 10

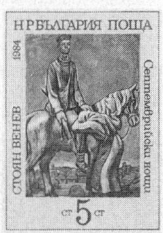

1054 "September Nights"

1984. 80th Birth Anniv of Stoyan Venev (artist). Multicoloured.
3193 5s. Type **1054** 10 10
3194 30s. "Man with Three Orders" 10 10
3195 42s. "The Hero" 15 10

1055 Peacock (butterfly)   1056 Augusto Sandino

1984. Butterflies. Multicoloured.
3196 13s. Type **1055** 30 10

3197 25s. Swallowtail 50 20
3198 30s. Great banded grayling . 60 25
3199 42s. Orange-tip 90 40
3200 60s. Red admiral . . . . 1·25 60

1984. 50th Death Anniv of Augusto Sandino (Nicaraguan revolutionary).
3202 **1056** 13s. black, red & yell 10 10

1057 Tupolev Tu-154 Jetliner

1984. 40th Anniv of I.C.A.O.
3203 **1057** 42s. multicoloured . . . 90 35

1058 "The Three Graces" (detail)

1984. 500th Birth Anniv (1983) of Raphael (artist) (2nd issue). Multicoloured.
3204 5s. Type **1058** 10 10
3205 13s. "Cupid and the Three Graces" (detail) . . . 15 10
3206 30s. "Original Sin" (detail) 35 15
3207 42s. "La Fornarina" . . . 50 20

1059 "Sofia"

1984. Maiden Voyage of Danube Cruise Ship "Sofia".
3209 **1059** 13s. dp blue, blue & yell 90 10

1060 Eastern Hog-nosed Skunk

1985. Mammals.
3210 **1060** 13s. black, blue & orge 25 10
3211 – 25s. black, brown & grn 45 20
3212 – 30s. black, brown & yell 65 20
3213 – 42s. multicoloured . . . 1·00 25
3214 – 60s. multicoloured . . . 1·25 40
DESIGNS: 25s. Banded linsang; 30s. Zorilla; 42s. Banded palm civet; 60s. Broad-striped galidia.

1061 Nikolai Liliev

1985. Birth Centenary of Nikolai Liliev (poet).
3215 **1061** 30s. lt brn, brn & gold 15 10

1062 Tsvyatko Radoinov

1985. 90th Birth Anniv of Tsvyatko Radoinov (resistance fighter).
3216 **1062** 5s. brown and red . . . 10 10

1063 Asen Zlatarov

1066 Olive Branch and Sword Blade

1985. Birth Cent. of Asen Zlatarov (biochemist).
3217 1063 5s. purple, yellow & grn   10   10

1985. 30th Anniv of Warsaw Pact.
3220 1066 13s. multicoloured . . .   20   10

1067 Bach

1069 St. Methodius

1068 Girl with Birds

1985. Composers.
3221 1067 42s. blue and red . . .   1·00   25
3222   – 42s. violet and green . .   1·00   25
3223   – 42s. yellow, brn & orge   1·00   25
3224   – 42s. yellow, brn & red   1·00   25
3225   – 42s. yellow, grn & blue   1·00   25
3226   – 42s. yellow, red & grn   1·00   25
DESIGNS: No. 3222, Mozart; 3223, Tchaikovsky; 3224, Modest Petrovich Musorgsky; 3225, Giuseppe Verdi; 3226, Filip Kutev.

1985. 3rd "Banners for Peace" Children's Meeting, Sofia. Multicoloured.
3227 5s. Type 1068   10   10
3228 8s. Children painting . . .   10   10
3229 13s. Girl among flowers . .   10   10
3230 20s. Children at market stall   15   10
3231 25s. Circle of children . . .   20   15
3232 30s. Nurse   20   15

1985. 1100th Death Anniv of St. Methodius.
3234 1069 13s. multicoloured . . .   10   10

1070 Soldiers and Nazi Flags

1985. 40th Anniv of V.E. ("Victory in Europe") Day. Multicoloured.
3235 5s. Type 1070   10   10
3236 13s. 11th Infantry parade, Sofia   15   10
3237 30s. Soviet soldier with orphan   40   10

1071 Woman carrying Child and Man on Donkey

1985. 7th International Festival of Humour and Satire, Gabrovo.
3239 1071 13s. black, yell & red   10   10

1072 Profiles and Flowers

1985. International Youth Year.
3240 1072 13s. multicoloured . . .   20   10

1073 Ivan Vazov

1985. 135th Birth Anniv of Ivan Vazov (poet).
3241 1073 5s. brown and stone . .   10   10

1074 Monument to Unknown Soldiers and City Arms

1985. Millenary of Khaskovo.
3242 1074 5s. multicoloured . . .   10   10

1075 Festival Emblem   1077 Vasil E. Aprilov (founder)

1985. 12th World Youth and Students' Festival, Moscow.
3243 1075 13s. multicoloured . . .   10   10

1985. Indira Gandhi (Indian Prime Minister) Commemoration.
3244 1076 30s. brown, orge & yell   20   10

1985. 150th Anniv of New Bulgarian School, Gabrovo.
3245 1077 5s. blue, purple & grn   10   10

1076 Indira Gandhi

1078 Congress Emblem

1985. 36th International Shorthand and Typing Federation Congress ("Intersteno"), Sofia.
3246 1078 13s. multicoloured . . .   10   10

1079 Alexandr Nevski Cathedral, Sofia

1985. Sixth General Assembly of World Tourism Organization, Sofia.
3247 1079 42s. green, blue & orge   30   15

1080 State Arms and U.N. Flag   1081 Rosa "Trakijka"

1985. 40th Anniv of U.N.O. (3248) and 30th Anniv of Bulgaria's Membership (3249). Multicoloured.
3248 13s. Dove around U.N. emblem   10   10
3249 13s. Type 1080   10   10

1985. Roses. Multicoloured.
3250 5s. "Rosa damascena" . . .   10   10
3251 13s. Type 1081   20   10
3252 20s. "Radiman"   30   10
3253 30s. "Marista"   45   15
3254 42s. "Valentina"   60   25
3255 60s. "Maria"   85   40

1082 Peace Dove

1985. 10th Anniv of European Security and Co-operation Conference, Helsinki.
3256 1082 13s. multicoloured . . .   10   10

1083 Water Polo

1985. European Swimming Championships, Sofia. Multicoloured.
3257 5s. Butterfly stroke (horiz)   10   10
3258 13s. Type 1083   20   10
3259 42s. Diving   60   15
3260 60s. Synchronized swimming (horiz)   85   20

1084 Edelweiss

1985. 90th Anniv of Bulgarian Tourist Organization.
3261 1084 5s. multicoloured . . .   10   10

1085 State Arms   1086 Footballers

1985. Cent of Union of E. Roumelia and Bulgaria.
3262 1085 5s. black, orge & green   10   10

1985. World Cup Football Championship, Mexico (1986) (1st issue).
3263 1086 5s. multicoloured . . .   10   10
3264   – 13s. multicoloured . . .   20   10
3265   – 30s. multicoloured . . .   45   15
3266   – 42s. multicoloured . . .   60   20
DESIGNS: 13s. to 42s. Various footballers. See also Nos. 3346/51.

1087 Computer Picture of Boy

1985. International Young Inventors' Exhibition, Plovdiv. Multicoloured.
3268 5s. Type 1087   10   10
3269 13s. Computer picture of youth   10   10
3270 30s. Computer picture of cosmonaut   20   10

1088 St. John's Church, Nesebur

1985. 40th Anniv of U.N.E.S.C.O. Mult.
3271 5s. Type 1088   10   10
3272 13s. Rila Monastery . . .   10   10
3273 35s. Soldier (fresco, Ivanovo Rock Church)   25   10
3274 42s. Archangel Gabriel (fresco, Boyana Church)   30   15
3275 60s. Thracian woman (fresco, Kazanlak tomb)   50   20

1090 Colosseum, Rome   1091 "Gladiolus"

1985. "Italia '85" International Stamp Exhibition, Rome.
3278 1090 42s. multicoloured . . .   25   10

1985. Flowers.
3279 1091 5s. pink and red . . .   10   10
3280   – 5s. blue and light blue   10   10
3281   – 5s. lt violet & violet . .   10   10
3282   – 8s. light blue and blue   15   10
3283   – 8s. orange and red . .   15   10
3284   – 32s. orange and brown   50   30
DESIGNS: No. 3280, Garden iris; 3281, Dwarf morning glory; 3282, Morning glory; 3283, "Anemone coronaria"; 3284, Golden-rayed lily.

1985. Historic Ships (4th series). As T 753. Multicoloured.
3286 5s. 17th-century Dutch fly   15   10
3287 12s. "Sovereign of the Seas" (English galleon)   30   10
3288 20s. Mediterranean polacca   55   20
3289 25s. "Prince Royal" (English warship)   60   25
3290 42s. Xebec   80   40
3291 60s. 17th-century English warship . . . .   1·25   60

1094 Bacho Kiro   1095 Hands, Sword and Bible

1985. Revolutionaries.
3293 1094 5s. light brown, brown and blue   10   10
3294   – 5s. green, purple & brown   10   10
DESIGN: No. 3294, Georgi S. Rakovski

1985. 150th Anniv of Turnovo Uprising.
3295 1095 13s. brown, blue & pur   10   10

1096 "1185 Revolution"
(G. Bogdanov)

1985. 800th Anniv of Liberation from Byzantine Empire. Multicoloured.
3296 **1096** 5s. Type **1096** 10 10
3297 13s. "1185 Revolution" (Al. Terziev) 10 10
3298 30s. "Battle of Klakotnitsa, 1230" (B. Grigorov and M. Ganovski) . . . 20 15
3299 42s. "Veliko Turnovo" (Ts. Lavrenov) 30 20

1098 Emblem and Globe

1985. International Development Programme for Posts and Telecommunications.
3302 **1098** 13s. multicoloured . . . 10 10

1099 Popov

1985. 70th Birth Anniv of Anton Popov (revolutionary).
3303 **1099** 5s. red 10 10

1100 Doves around Snowflake

1985. New Year. Multicoloured.
3304 **1100** 5s. Type **1100** 10 10
3305 13s. Circle of stylized doves 10 10

1101 Pointer and Chukar Partridge

1985. Hunting Dogs. Multicoloured.
3306 **1101** 5s. Type **1101** 50 20
3307 8s. Irish setter and common pochard 65 20
3308 13s. English setter and mallard 85 20
3309 20s. Cocker spaniel and Eurasian woodcock . . . 1·25 30
3310 25s. German pointer and rabbit 25 20
3311 30s. Bulgarian bloodhound and boar 30 20
3312 42s. Dachshund and fox . . 4·25 1·10

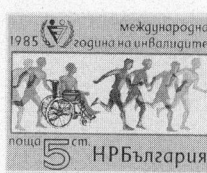

1102 Person in Wheelchair and Runners

1985. International Year of Disabled Persons (1984).
3313 **1102** 5s. multicoloured . . . 10 10

1103 Georgi Dimitrov (statesman)

1985. 50th Anniv of 7th Communist International Congress, Moscow.
3314 **1103** 13s. red 10 10

1104 Emblem within "40"

1986. 40th Anniv of U.N.I.C.E.F.
3315 **1104** 13s. blue, gold & black 10 10

1105 Blagoev   **1106** Hands and Dove within Laurel Wreath

1986. 130th Birth Anniv of Dimitur Blagoev (founder of Bulgarian Social Democratic Party).
3316 **1105** 5s. purple and orange 10 10

1986. International Peace Year.
3317 **1106** 5s. multicoloured . . . 10 10

1107 "Dactylorhiza romana"

1986. Orchids. Multicoloured.
3318 **1107** 5s. Type **1107** 10 10
3319 13s. "Epipactis palustris" . . 20 10
3320 30s. "Ophrys cornuta" . . . 40 10
3321 32s. "Limodorum abrotivum" 40 15
3322 42s. "Cypripedium calceolus" 55 20
3323 60s. "Orchis papilionacea" . 1·40 25

1108 Angora Rabbit

1986. Rabbits.
3324 – 5s. grey, black & brown 10 10
3325 **1108** 25s. red and black . . . 35 10
3326 – 30s. brown, yell & blk 40 10
3327 – 32s. orange and black 40 15
3328 – 42s. red and black . . . 55 15
3329 – 60s. blue and black . . 1·50 25
DESIGNS: 5s. French grey; 30s. English lop-eared; 32s. Belgian; 42s. English spotted; 60s. Dutch black and white rabbit.

1109 Front Page and Ivan Bogorov

1986. 140th Anniv of "Bulgarian Eagle".
3330 **1109** 5s. multicoloured . . . 10 10

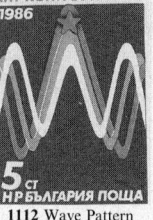

1111 Bashev   **1112** Wave Pattern

1986. 50th Birth Anniv (1985) of Vladimir Bashev (poet).
3332 **1111** 5s. blue & light blue . . 10 10

1986. 13th Bulgarian Communist Party Congress.
3333 **1112** 5s. blue, green and red 10 10
3334 – 8s. blue and red . . . 10 10
3335 – 13s. blue, red & lt blue 10 10
DESIGNS: 8s. Printed circuit as tail of shooting star; 13s. Computer picture of man.

1114 Monument, Panagyurishte   **1116** Stylized Ear of Wheat

1986. 110th Anniv of April Uprising.
3338 **1114** 5s. black, stone and green 10 10
3339 – 13s. black, stone & red 10 10
DESIGN: 13s. Statue of Khristo Botev, Vratsa.

1986. 35th Bulgarian People's Agrarian Union Congress.
3341 **1116** 5s. gold, orange & blk 10 10
3342 – 8s. gold, blue and black 10 10
3343 – 13s. multicoloured . . . 10 10
DESIGNS: 8s. Stylized ear of wheat on globe; 13s. Flags.

1117 Transport Systems   **1118** Emblem

1986. Socialist Countries' Transport Ministers Conference.
3344 **1117** 13s. multicoloured . . . 30 10

1986. 17th International Book Fair, Sofia.
3345 **1118** 13s. grey, red and black 10 10

1119 Player with Ball

1986. World Cup Football Championship, Mexico (2nd issue). Multicoloured.
3346 **1119** 5s. Type **1119** 20 10
3347 13s. Player tackling (horiz) 30 10
3348 20s. Player heading ball (horiz) 50 15
3349 30s. Player kicking ball (horiz) 75 20
3350 42s. Goalkeeper (horiz) . . 90 40
3351 60s. Player with trophy . . 1·25 40

1120 Square Brooch

1986. Treasures of Preslav. Multicoloured.
3353 **1120** 5s. Type **1120** 10 10
3354 13s. Pendant (vert) 10 10
3355 20s. Wheel-shaped pendant 15 10
3356 30s. Breast plate decorated with birds and chalice . . 20 10
3357 42s. Pear-shaped pendant (vert) 25 15
3358 60s. Enamelled cockerel on gold base 40 25

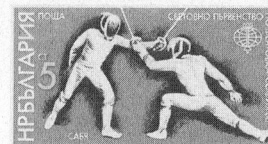

1121 Fencers with Sabres

1986. World Fencing Championships, Sofia. Mult.
3359 **1121** 5s. Type **1121** 10 10
3360 13s. Fencers 10 10
3361 25s. Fencers with rapiers . . 20 10

1122 Stockholm Town Hall

1986. "Stockholmia 86" International Stamp Exn.
3362 **1122** 42s. brn, red & dp red 60 25

1124 Arms and Parliament Building, Sofia

1986. 40th Anniv of People's Republic.
3364 **1124** 5s. green, red & lt grn 10 10

1125 Posthorn

1986. 15th Organization of Socialist Countries' Postal Administrations Session, Sofia.
3365 **1125** 13s. multicoloured . . . 10 10

1126 "All Pull Together"   **1127** Dove and Book as Pen Nib

1986. 40th Anniv of Voluntary Brigades.
3366 **1126** 5s. multicoloured . . . 10 10

1986. 10th International Journalists Association Congress, Sofia.
3367 **1127** 13s. blue & deep blue 10 10

1128 Wrestlers

1986. 75th Anniv of Levski-Spartak Sports Club.
3368 **1128** 5s. multicoloured . . . 10 10

1129 Saints Cyril and Methodius with Disciples (fresco)

1986. 1100th Anniv of Arrival in Bulgaria of Pupils of Saints Cyril and Methodius.
3369 **1129** 13s. brown and buff . . . 15 10

1130 Old and Modern Telephones

1986. Centenary of Telephone in Bulgaria.
3370 **1130** 5s. multicoloured . . . 10 10

1131 Weightlifter

1986. World Weightlifting Championships, Sofia.
3371 **1131** 13s. multicoloured . . . 15 10

1986. Historic Ships (5th series). 18th-century ships. As T 753. Multicoloured.
3372 5s. "King of Prussia" . . . 15 10
3373 13s. Indiaman 30 10
3374 25s. Xebec 55 25
3375 30s. "Sv. Paul" 70 30
3376 32s. Topsail schooner . . . 70 30
3377 42s. "Victory" 90 35

1133 Silver Jug decorated with Seated Woman

1986. 14th Congress of Bulgarian Philatelic Federation and 60th Anniv of International Philatelic Federation. Repoussé work found at Rogozen.
3379 **1133** 10s. grey, black & bl 15 15
3380 – 10s. green, blk & red 15 15
DESIGN: No. 3380, Silver jug decorated with sphinx.

1134 Doves between Pine Branches

1986. New Year.
3381 **1134** 5s. red, green and blue 10 10
3382 – 13s. mauve, blue & vio 15 10
DESIGN: 13s. Fireworks and snowflakes.

1135 Earphones as "60" on Globe

1986. 60th Anniv of Bulgarian Amateur Radio.
3383 **1135** 13s. multicoloured . . . 10 10

1137 Gen. Augusto Sandino and Flag

1988. 25th Anniv of Sandinista National Liberation Front of Nicaragua.
3385 **1137** 13s. multicoloured . . . 15 10

1138 Dimitur and Konstantin Miladinov (authors)   **1139** Pencho Slaveikov (poet)

1986. 125th Anniv of "Bulgarian Popular Songs".
3386 **1138** 10s. blue, brn & red . . 15 10

1986. Writers' Birth Annivs. Multicoloured.
3387 5s. Type **1139** (125th anniv) 10 10
3388 5s. Stoyan Mikhailovski (130th anniv) 10 10
3389 8s. Nikola Atanasov (dramatist) (centenary) . 10 10
3390 8s. Ran Bosilek (children's author) (centenary) . . . 10 10

1140 Raiko Daskalov   **1141** "Girl with Fruit"

1986. Birth Cent of Raiko Daskalov (politician).
3391 **1140** 5s. brown 10 10

1986. 500th Birth Anniv of Titian (painter). Multicoloured.
3392 5s. Type **1141** 10 10
3393 13s. "Flora" 20 10
3394 20s. "Lucretia and Tarquin" 30 10
3395 30s. Caiphas and Mary Magdalene 50 15
3396 32s. "Toilette of Venus" (detail) 50 15
3397 42s. "Self-portrait" . . . . 1·10 20

1142 Fiat, 1905

1986. Racing Cars.
3399 **1142** 5s. brown, red & black 10 10
3400 – 10s. red, orange & blk 20 10
3401 – 25s. green, red & black 45 20
3402 – 32s. brown, red & blk 60 20
3403 – 40s. violet, red & black 70 25
3404 – 42s. grey, black and red 1·25 25
DESIGNS: 10s. Bugatti, 1926; 25s. Mercedes, 1936; 32s. Ferrari, 1952; 40s. Lotus, 1985; 42s. Maclaren, 1986.

1143 Steam Locomotive

1987. 120th Anniv of Ruse–Varna Railway.
3405 **1143** 5s. multicoloured . . . 20 10

1144 Debelyanov

1987. Birth Cent of Dimcho Debelyanov (poet).
3406 **1144** 5s. dp blue, yellow & bl 10 10

1145 Lazarus Ludwig Zamenhof (inventor)

1987. Centenary of Esperanto (invented language).
3407 **1145** 13s. blue, yellow & grn 15 10

1146 The Blusher   **1147** Worker

1987. Edible Fungi. Multicoloured.
3408 5s. Type **1146** 10 10
3409 20s. Royal boletus 35 15
3410 30s. Red-capped scaber stalk 60 30
3411 32s. Shaggy ink cap . . . 70 30
3412 40s. Bare-toothed russula . 90 35
3413 60s. Chanterelle . . . . . 1·25 75

1987. 10th Trade Unions Congress, Sofia.
3414 **1147** 5s. violet and red . . . 10 10

1148 Silver-gilt Plate with Design of Hercules and Auge

1987. Treasure of Rogozen. Multicoloured.
3415 5s. Type **1148** 10 10
3416 8s. Silver-gilt jug with design of lioness attacking stag 10 10
3417 20s. Silver-gilt plate with quatrefoil design . . . 15 10
3418 30s. Silver-gilt jug with design of horse rider . . . 25 15
3419 32s. Silver-gilt pot with palm design 30 15
3420 42s. Silver jug with chariot and horses design . . . 50 20

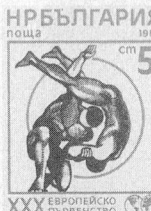

1150 Wrestlers   **1152** "X" and Flags

1151 Totem Pole

1987. 30th European Freestyle Wrestling Championships, Turnovo.
3422 **1150** 5s. lilac, red and violet 10 10
3423 – 13s. dp blue, red & blue 15 10
DESIGNS: 13st. Wrestlers (different).

1987. "Capex '87" International Stamp Exhibition, Toronto.
3424 **1151** 42s. multicoloured . . . 60 20

1987. 10th Fatherland Front Congress.
3425 **1152** 5s. green, orange & bl 10 10

1153 Georgi Dimitrov and Profiles

1987. 15th Dimitrov Communist Youth League Congress.
3426 **1153** 5s. purple, green & red 10 10

1154 Mask   **1156** Mariya Gigova

1155 Mastheads

1987. 8th International Festival of Humour and Satire, Gabrovo.
3427 **1154** 13s. multicoloured . . . 15 10

1987. 60th Anniv of "Rabotnichesko Delo" (newspaper).
3428 **1155** 5s. red and black . . . 10 10

1987. 13th World Rhythmic Gymnastics Championships, Varna.
3429 **1156** 5s. blue and yellow . . 10 10
3430 – 8s. red and yellow . . . 10 10
3431 – 13s. blue and stone . . 15 10
3432 – 25s. red and yellow . . 30 10
3433 – 30s. black and yellow . 30 10
3434 – 42s. mauve and yellow 45 20
DESIGNS: 8s. Iliana Raeva; 13s. Aneliya Ralenkova; 25s. Dilyana Georgieva; 30s. Liliya Ignatova; 42s. Bianka Panova.

1157 Man breaking Chains around Globe and Kolarov

1987. 110th Birth Anniv of Vasil Kolarov (Prime Minister 1949–50).
3436 **1157** 5s. multicoloured . . . 10 10

1158 Stela Blagoeva   **1160** Roe Deer

1159 Levski

1987. Birth Centenary of Stela Blagoeva.
3437 **1158** 5s. brown and pink . . 10 10

1987. 150th Birth Anniv of Vasil Levski (revolutionary).
3438 **1159** 5s. brown & green . . 10 10
3439 – 13s. green & brown . . 15 10
DESIGN: 13s. Levski and Bulgarian Revolutionary Central Committee emblem.

1987. Stags. Multicoloured.
3440 5s. Type **1160** 10 10
3441 10s. Elk (horiz) 15 10
3442 32s. Fallow deer 50 20
3443 40s. Sika deer 60 20
3444 42s. Red deer (horiz) . . . 60 20
3445 60s. Reindeer 90 30

1161 Barbed Wire as Dove

1987. International Namibia Day.
3446 **1161** 13s. black, red & orge   15   10

1162 Kirkov   **1163** "Phacelia tanacetifolia"

1987. 120th Birth Anniv of Georgi Kirkov (pseudonym Maistora) (politician).
3447 **1162** 5s. red and pink   10   10

1987. Flowers. Multicoloured.
3448   5s. Type **1163**   10   10
3449   10s. Sunflower   15   10
3450   30s. False acacia   45   20
3451   32s. Dutch lavender   50   20
3452   42s. Small-leaved lime   . . .   60   20
3453   60s. "Onobrychis sativa"   . . .   90   30

1164 Mil Mi-8 Helicopter, Tupolev Tu-154 and Antonov An-12 Aircraft

1987. 40th Anniv of Balkanair.
3454 **1164** 25s. multicoloured   . . .   70   30

1165 1879 5c. Stamp

1987. "Bulgaria '89" International Stamp Exhibition, Sofia (1st issue).
3455 **1165** 13s. multicoloured   . . .   20   10
See also Nos. 3569, 3579/82 and 3602/5.

1166 Copenhagen Town Hall   **1167** "Portrait of Girl" (Stefan Ivanov)

1987. "Hafnia '87" International Stamp Exhibition, Copenhagen.
3456 **1166** 42s. multicoloured   . . .   50   20

1987. Paintings in Sofia National Gallery. Mult.
3457   5s. Type **1167**   10   10
3458   8s. "Woman carrying Grapes" (Bencho Obreshkov)   10   10
3459   20s. "Portrait of a Woman wearing a Straw Hat" (David Perez)   30   10
3460   25s. "Women listening to Marimba" (Kiril Tsonev)   40   15
3461   32s. "Boy with Harmonica" (Nenko Balkanski)   . . .   50   15
3462   60s. "Rumyana" (Vasil Stoilov)   90   20

1168 Battle Scene

1987. 75th Anniv of Balkan War.
3463 **1168** 5s. black, stone and red   10   10

1169 Emblem

1987. 30th Anniv of International Atomic Energy Agency.
3464 **1169** 13s. blue, green and red   15   10

1170 Mastheads

1987. 95th Anniv of "Rabotnik", 90th Anniv of "Rabotnicheski Vestnik" and 60th Anniv of "Rabotnichesko Delo" (newspapers).
3465 **1170** 5s. red, blue and gold   10   10

1171 Winter Wren   **1174** Biathlon

1173 Lenin and Revolutionary

1987. Birds. Multicoloured.
3466   5s. Type **1171**   10   10
3467   13s. Yellowhammer   30   15
3468   20s. Eurasian nuthatch   . . .   40   20
3469   30s. Blackbird   60   35
3470   42s. Hawfinch   90   40
3471   60s. White-throated dipper   .   1·25   60

1987. 70th Anniv of Russian Revolution.
3473 **1173** 5s. purple and red   . . .   10   10
3474   – 13s. blue and red   . . .   15   10
DESIGN: 13s. Lenin and cosmonaut.

1987. Winter Olympic Games, Calgary. Mult.
3475   5s. Type **1174**   10   10
3476   13s. Slalom   20   10
3477   30s. Figure skating (women's)   45   10
3478   42s. Four-man bobsleigh   .   65   15

1175 "Socfilex" Emblem within Folk-design Ornament

1987. New Year. Multicoloured.
3480   5s. Type **1175**   10   10
3481   13s. Emblem within flower ornament   15   10

1177 Kabakchiev   **1178** "Scilla bythynica"

1988. 110th Birth Anniv of Khristo Kabakchiev (Communist Party official).
3483 **1177** 5s. multicoloured   . . .   10   10

1988. Marsh Flowers. Multicoloured.
3484   5s. Type **1178**   10   10
3485   10s. "Geum rhodopaeum"   . .   15   10
3486   13s. "Caltha polypetala"   . .   20   10
3487   25s. Fringed water-lily   . . .   35   15
3488   30s. "Cortusa matthioli"   . .   40   20
3489   42s. Water soldier   60   25

1179 Commander on Horseback

1988. 110th Anniv of Liberation from Turkey. Multicoloured.
3490   5s. Type **1179**   10   10
3491   13s. Soldiers   15   10

1180 Emblem

1988. Public Sector Workers' 8th International Congress, Sofia.
3492 **1180** 13s. multicoloured   . . .   15   10

1181 "Yantra", 1888

1988. Centenary of State Railways. Locomotives. Multicoloured.
3493   5s. Type **1181**   20   10
3494   13s. "Khristo Botev", 1905   30   10
3495   25s. Steam locomotive No. 807, 1918   40   15
3496   32s. Class 46 steam locomotive, 1943   55   20
3497   42s. Diesel locomotive, 1964   90   25
3498   60s. Electric locomotive, 1979   . . . . . .   1·25   40

1182 Ivan Nedyalkov (Shablin)   **1183** Traikov

1988. Post Office Anti-fascist Heroes.
3499 **1182** 5s. light brown and brown   10   10
3500   – 8s. grey and blue   . . .   10   10
3501   – 10s. green and olive   . .   10   10
3502   – 13s. pink and red   . . .   15   10
DESIGNS: 8s. Delcho Spasov; 10s. Nikola Ganchev (Gudzho); 13s. Ganka Rasheva (Boika).

1988. 90th Birth Anniv of Georgi Traikov (politician).
3503 **1183** 5s. orange and brown   10   10

1184 Red Cross, Red Crescent and Globe   **1185** Girl

1988. 125th Anniv of International Red Cross.
3504 **1184** 13s. multicoloured   . . .   20   10

1988. 4th "Banners for Peace" Children's Meeting, Sofia. Children's paintings. Multicoloured.
3505   5s. Type **1185**   10   10
3506   8s. Artist at work   10   10
3507   13s. Circus (horiz)   20   10
3508   20s. Kite flying (horiz)   . . .   30   15
3509   32s. Accordion player   . . .   45   20
3510   42s. Cosmonaut   60   25

1186 Marx

1988. 170th Birth Anniv of Karl Marx.
3512 **1186** 13s. red, black & yellow   15   10

1187 Herring Gull   **1189** "Soyuz TM" Spacecraft, Flags and Globe

1988. Birds. Multicoloured.
3513   5s. Type **1187**   25   10
3514   5s. White stork   25   10
3515   8s. Grey heron   45   15
3516   8s. Carrion crow   45   15
3517   10s. Northern goshawk   . . .   60   20
3518   42s. Eagle owl   . . . . .   1·25   30

1188 African Elephant

1988. Centenary of Sofia Zoo. Multicoloured.
3519   5s. Type **1188**   10   10
3520   13s. White rhinoceros   . . .   20   10
3521   25s. Hunting dog   35   15
3522   30s. Eastern white pelican   .   70   30
3523   32s. Abyssinian ground hornbill   75   35
3524   60s. Snowy owl   . . . . .   1·75   55

1988. 2nd Soviet–Bulgarian Space Flight. Mult.
3525   5s. Type **1189**   10   10
3526   13s. Rocket on globe   . . .   20   10

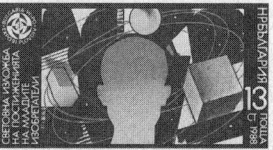

1190 Young Inventor

1988. International Young Inventors' Exhibition, Plovdiv.
3527 **1190** 13s. multicoloured   . . .   20   10

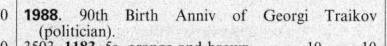

1191 1856 Handstamp of Russian Duchy of Finland

1988. "Finlandia '88" International Stamp Exhibition, Helsinki.
3528 **1191** 30s. blue and red . . . 40   20

1192 Player taking Corner Kick   **1193** "Portrait of Child"

1988. 8th European Football Championship, West Germany. Multicoloured.
3529   5s. Type **1192** 10   10
3530   13s. Goalkeeper and player   20   10
3531   30s. Referee and player . .   40   20
3532   42s. Player with trophy . .   60   25

1988. 2nd Death Anniv of Dechko Uzunov (painter). Multicoloured.
3534   5s. Type **1193** 10   10
3535   13s. "Portrait of Mariya Vasileva" 20   10
3536   30s. "Self-portrait" 40   20

1195 "St. John"   **1196** High Jumping

1988. Icons from Kurdzhali. Multicoloured.
3538   5s. Type **1195** 10   10
3539   8s. "St. George and Dragon" 10   10

1988. Olympic Games, Seoul. Multicoloured.
3540   5s. Type **1196** 10   10
3541   13s. Weightlifting 20   10
3542   30s. Wrestling 40   20
3543   42s. Gymnastics 60   25

1197 Dimitur and Karadzha

1988. 120th Death Anniv of Khadzhi Dimitur and Stefan Karadzha (revolutionaries).
3545 **1197** 5s. green, black & brn . . 10   10

1198 Magazines

1988. 30th Anniv of "Problems of Peace and Socialism" (magazine).
3546 **1198** 13s. multicoloured . . . 15   10

1199 "The Dead Tree" (Roland Udo)

1988. Paintings in Lyudmila Zhivkova Art Gallery. Multicoloured.
3547   30s. Type **1199** 45   15
3548   30s. "Algiers Harbour" (Albert Marque) 45   15
3549   30s. "Portrait of Hermine David" (Jule Pasquin) . . 45   15
3550   30s. "Madonna and Child with two Saints" (Giovanni Rosso) 45   15

1200 University Building

1988. Centenary of St. Clement of Ohrid University, Sofia.
3551 **1200** 5s. black, yellow & grn . . 10   10

1201 Czechoslovakia 1918 Stamp Design

1988. "Praga '88" International Stamp Exhibition, Prague.
3552 **1201** 25s. red and blue . . . 35   15

1202 Korea 1884 5m. Stamp

1988. "Olymphilex '88" Olympic Stamps Exhibition, Seoul.
3553 **1202** 62s. red and green . . . 90   40

1203 Anniversary Emblem   **1204** Parliament Building, Sofia, and Map

1988. 25th Anniv of Kremikovtsi Steel Mills.
3554 **1203** 5s. violet, red and blue . 10   10

1988. 80th Interparliamentary Conference, Sofia.
3555 **1204** 13s. blue and red . . . 15   10

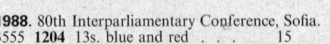

1205 Chalice, Glinena

1988. Kurdzhali Culture. Multicoloured.
3556   5s. Type **1205** 10   10
3557   8s. Part of ruined fortifications, Perperikon (vert) 10   10

1206 Soldiers

1988. 300th Anniv of Chiprovtsi Rising.
3558 **1206** 5s. multicoloured . . . 10   10

1207 Brown Bear

1988. Bears. Multicoloured.
3559   5s. Type **1207** 10   10
3560   8s. Polar bear 10   10
3561   13s. Sloth bear 25   10
3562   20s. Sun bear 35   15
3563   32s. Asiatic black bear . . 50   20
3564   42s. Spectacled bear . . . 65   25

1208 Emblem

1988. 80th Council of Mutual Economic Aid Transport Commission Meeting, Sofia.
3565 **1208** 13s. red and black . . . 15   10

1209 Emblem

1988. World Ecoforum.
3566 **1209** 20s. multicoloured . . . 25   10

1210 Amphitheatre, Plovdiv

1988. "Plovdiv '88" National Stamp Exhibition.
3567 **1210** 5s. multicoloured . . . 10   10

1211 Transmission Towers

1988. 25th Anniv of Radio and Television.
3568 **1211** 5s. green, blue & brown . 10   10

1212 1879 5c. Stamp

1988. "Bulgaria '89" International Stamp Exhibition (2nd issue).
3569 **1212** 42s. orange, blk & mve . 60   25

1214 Children and Cars

1988. Road Safety Campaign.
3571 **1214** 5s. multicoloured . . . 10   10

1215 Rila Hotel, Borovets

1988. Hotels. Multicoloured.
3572   5s. Type **1215** 10   10
3573   8s. Pirin Hotel, Bansko . . 10   10
3574   13s. Shtastlivetsa Hotel, Vitosha 15   10
3575   30s. Perelik Hotel, Pamporovo 40   15

1216 Tree Decoration

1988. New Year. Multicoloured.
3576   5s. Type **1216** 10   10
3577   13s. "Bulgaria '89" emblem, tree and decorations . . . 15   10

1218 Mail Coach

1988. "Bulgaria '89" International Stamp Exhibition, Sofia (3rd issue). Mail Transport. Multicoloured.
3579   25s. Type **1218** 35   15
3580   25s. Paddle-steamer . . . 35   15
3581   25s. Lorry 35   15
3582   25s. Biplane 45   15

1219 India 1947 1½a. Independence Stamp

1989. "India 89" International Stamp Exhibition, New Delhi.
3583 **1219** 62s. green and orange . . 1·40   60

1220 France 1850 10c. Ceres Stamp

1989. "Philexfrance '89" International Stamp Exhibition, Paris.
3584 **1220** 42s. brown and blue . . 90   40

1222 Don Quixote (sculpture, House of Humour and Satire)   **1223** "Ramonda serbica"

1989. International Festival of Humour and Satire, Gabrovo.
3586 **1222** 13s. multicoloured . . . 20   10

1989. Flowers. Multicoloured.
3587   5s. Type **1223** 10   10
3588   10s. "Paeonia maskula" . . 15   10
3589   25s. "Viola perinensis" . . 35   30

3590 30s. "Dracunculus vulgaris" 45 40
3591 42s. "Tulipa splendens" . . 60 55
3592 60s. "Rindera umbellata" 90 80

1224 Common Noctule Bat

1989. Bats. Multicoloured.
3593 5s. Type 1224 . . . . . 10 10
3594 13s. Greater horseshoe bat 25 10
3595 30s. Large mouse-eared bat 65 20
3596 42s. Particoloured frosted
bat 95 25

1225 Stamboliiski

1989. 110th Birth Anniv of Aleksandur Stamboliiski (Prime Minister 1919–23).
3597 1225 5s. black and orange . . 10 10

1227 Young Inventor

1989. International Young Inventors' Exhibition, Plovdiv.
3599 1227 5s. multicoloured . . . 10 10

1228 Stanke Dimitrov-Marek (Party activist)
1229 "John the Baptist" (Toma Vishanov)

1989. Birth Centenaries.
3600 1228 5s. red and black . . . 10 10
3601 – 5s. red and black . . . 10 10
DESIGN: No. 3601, Petko Yenev (revolutionary).

1989. "Bulgaria '89" International Stamp Exhibition, Sofia (4th issue). Icons. Multicoloured.
3602 30s. Type 1229 . . . . . . 45 15
3603 30s. "St. Dimitur" (Ivan
Terziev) . . 45 15
3604 30s. "Archangel Michael"
(Dimitur Molerov) 45 15
3605 30s. "Madonna and Child"
(Toma Vishanov) 45 15

1230 Fax Machine and Woman reading letter

1989. 110th Anniv of Bulgarian Post and Telegraph Services. Multicoloured.
3606 5s. Type 1230 . . . . . 10 10
3607 8s. Telex machine and old
telegraph machine . . . 10 10
3608 35s. Modern and old
telephones 40 15
3609 42s. Dish aerial and old
radio 50 20

1232 A. P. Aleksandrov, A. Ya. Solovov and V. P. Savinikh

1989. Air. "Soyuz TM5" Soviet-Bulgarian Space Flight.
3611 1232 13s. multicoloured . . . 20 10

1233 Party Programme
1234 Sofronii Vrachanski (250th anniv)

1989. 70th Anniv of First Bulgarian Communist Party Congress, Sofia.
3612 1233 5s. blk, red & dp red 10 10

1989. Writers' Birth Anniversaries.
3613 1234 5s. green, brown & blk 10 10
3614 – 5s. green, brown & blk 10 10
DESIGN: No. 3614, Iliya Bluskov (150th anniv).

1235 Birds

1989. Bicentenary of French Revolution. Each black, red and blue.
3615 13s. Type 1235 . . . . . 20 10
3616 30s. Jean-Paul Marat . . . 40 15
3617 42s. Robespierre 50 20

1236 Gymnastics

1989. 7th Friendly Armies Summer Spartakiad. Multicoloured.
3618 5s. Type 1236 . . . . . . 10 10
3619 8s. Show jumping 20 10
3620 30s. Long jumping 40 15
3621 42s. Shooting 50 20

1237 Aprilov
1238 Zagorchinov

1989. Birth Bicent of Vasil Aprilov (educationist).
3622 1237 8s. lt blue, blue & blk 10 10

1989. Birth Centenary of Stoyan Zagorchinov (writer).
3623 1238 10s. turq, brown & blk 15 10

1239 Woman in Kayak

1989. Canoeing and Kayak Championships, Plovdiv. Multicoloured.
3624 13s. Type 1239 . . . . . 20 10
3625 30s. Man in kayak 45 15

1240 Felix Nadar taking Photograph from his Balloon "Le Geant" (1863) and Airship "Graf Zeppelin" over Alexsandr Nevski Cathedral, Sofia

1989. 150th Anniv of Photography.
3626 1240 42s. black, stone & yell 80 30

1241 Lammergeier and Lynx

1989. Centenary of Natural History Museum.
3627 1241 13s. multicoloured . . . 1·00 20

1242 Soldiers
1243 Lyubomir Dardzhikov

1989. 45th Anniv of Fatherland Front Government. Multicoloured.
3628 5s. Type 1242 . . . . . 10 10
3629 8s. Welcoming officers . . 10 10
3630 13s. Crowd of youths . . . 15 10

1989. 48th Death Anniversaries of Post Office War Heroes. Multicoloured.
3631 5s. Type 1243 . . . . . . 10 10
3632 8s. Ivan Bankov Dobrev . . 10 10
3633 13s. Nestor Antonov . . . 10 10

1244 Yasenov
1246 Nehru

1245 Lorry leaving Weighbridge

1989. Birth Cent of Khisto Yasenov (writer).
3634 1244 8s. grey, brown & blk 10 10

1989. 21st Transport Congress, Sofia.
3635 1245 42s. blue & deep blue 50 20

1989. Birth Centenary of Jawaharlal Nehru (Indian statesman).
3636 1246 13s. yellow, brn & blk 15 10

1248 Javelin Sand Boa

1989. Snakes. Multicoloured.
3638 5s. Type 1248 . . . . . 10 10
3639 10s. Aesculapian snake . . 10 10
3640 25s. Leopard snake 35 10
3641 30s. Four-lined rat snake . . 45 15
3642 42s. Cat snake 60 25
3643 60s. Whip snake 90 40

1249 Tiger and Balloon of Flags
1251 Goalkeeper saving Ball

1989. Young Inventors' Exhibition, Plovdiv.
3644 1249 13s. multicoloured . . . 15 10

1989. World Cup Football Championship, Italy (1990) (1st issue). Multicoloured.
3646 5s. Type 1251 . . . . . 15 10
3647 13s. Player tackling . . . 25 15
3648 30s. Player heading ball . . 65 30
3649 42s. Player kicking ball . . 90 40
See also Nos. 3675/8.

1252 Gliders

1989. 82nd International Airsports Federation General Conference, Varna. Aerial Sports. Mult.
3651 5s. Type 1252 . . . . . 10 10
3652 13s. Hang gliding 20 15
3653 30s. Parachutist landing . . 40 20
3654 42s. Free falling parachutist 60 30

1253 Children on Road Crossing

1989. Road Safety.
3655 1253 5s. multicoloured . . . 10 10

1254 Santa Claus's Sleigh
1255 European Shorthair

1989. New Year. Multicoloured.
3656 5s. Type 1254 . . . . . . 10 10
3657 13s. Snowman 15 10

1989. Cats.
3658 1255 5s. black and yellow . . 15 10
3659 – 5s. black and grey . . . 15 10
3660 – 8s. black and yellow . . 20 10
3661 – 10s. black & brown . . 25 15
3662 – 10s. black and blue . . 25 15
3663 – 13s. black and red . . . 40 20
DESIGNS—HORIZ: No. 3659, Persian; 3660, European shorthair (different); 3662, Persian (different). VERT: No. 3661, Persian (different); 3663, Siamese.

1256 Christopher Columbus and "Santa Maria"

1990. Navigators and their Ships. Multicoloured.
3664 5s. Type 1256 . . . . . 20 10
3665 8s. Vasco da Gama and "Sao Gabriel" 20 10
3666 13s. Ferdinand Magellan and "Vitoria" 35 10
3667 32s. Francis Drake and "Golden Hind" 45 20
3668 42s. Henry Hudson and "Discoverie" 65 25
3669 60s. James Cook and H.M.S. "Endeavour" 90 25

1257 Banner

1990. Centenary of Esperanto (invented language) in Bulgaria.
3670 **1257** 10s. stone, green & blk   10   10

1258 "Portrait of Madeleine Rono" (Maurice Brianchon)

1990. Paintings. Multicoloured.
3671   30s. Type **1258**   45   20
3672   30s. "Still Life" (Suzanne Valadon)   45   20
3673   30s. "Portrait of a Woman" (Moise Kisling)   45   20
3674   30s. "Portrait of a Woman" (Giovanni Boltraffio)   45   20

1259 Players

1990. World Cup Football Championship, Italy.
3675 **1259** 5s. multicoloured   10   10
3676   – 13s. multicoloured   15   10
3677   – 30s. multicoloured   45   20
3678   – 42s. multicoloured   70   30
DESIGNS: 13 to 42s. Various match scenes.

1260 Bavaria 1849 1k. Stamp

1990. "Essen 90" International Stamp Fair.
3680 **1260** 42s. black and red   70   40

1262 "100" and Rainbow

1990. Centenary of Co-operative Farming.
3682 **1262** 5s. multicoloured   10   10

1263 "Elderly Couple at Rest"

1990. Birth Centenary of Dimitur Chorbadzhiiski-Chudomir (artist).
3683 **1263** 5s. multicoloured   10   10

1264 Map

1990. Centenary of Labour Day.
3684 **1264** 10s. multicoloured   15   10

1265 Emblem

1990. 125th Anniv of I.T.U.
3685 **1265** 20s. blue, red & black   25   15

1266 Belgium 1849 10c. "Epaulettes" Stamp

1990. "Belgica 90" International Stamp Exhibition, Brussels.
3686 **1266** 30s. brown and green   50   35

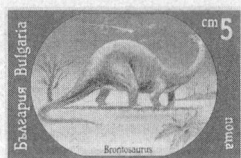
1267 Lamartine and his House

1990. Birth Bicentenary of Alphonse de Lamartine (poet).
3687 **1267** 20s. multicoloured   25   15

1268 Brontosaurus

1990. Prehistoric Animals. Multicoloured.
3688   5s. Type **1268**   10   10
3689   8s. Stegosaurus   15   10
3690   13s. Edaphosaurus   20   10
3691   25s. Rhamphorhynchus   50   20
3692   32s. Protoceratops   65   30
3693   42s. Triceratops   90   40

1269 Swimming

1990. Olympic Games, Barcelona (1992) (1st issue). Multicoloured.
3694   5s. Type **1269**   10   10
3695   13s. Handball   20   10
3696   30s. Hurdling   50   25
3697   42s. Cycling   75   35
See also Nos. 3840/3.

1270 Southern Festoon

1990. Butterflies and Moths. Multicoloured.
3699   5s. Type **1270**   10   10
3700   10s. Jersey tiger moth   15   10
3701   20s. Willow-herb hawk moth   20   10
3702   30s. Striped hawk moth   50   20
3703   42s. "Thecla betulae"   70   30
3704   60s. Cynthia's fritillary   1·00   60

1271 Airbus Industrie A310 Jetliner

1990. Aircraft. Multicoloured.
3705   5s. Type **1271**   10   10
3706   10s. Tupolev Tu-204   15   10
3707   25s. Concorde   40   20
3708   30s. Douglas DC-9   45   25
3709   42s. Ilyushin Il-86   60   35
3710   60s. Boeing 747-300/400   90   55
No. 3705 is wrongly inscribed Airbus "A300".

1272 Iosif I   **1274** Putting the Shot

1990. 150th Birth Anniv of Exarch Iosif I.
3711 **1272** 5s. mauve, black & grn   10   10

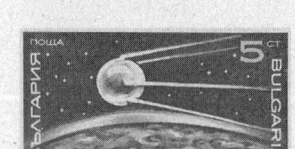
1273 Road and U.N. Emblem within Triangles

1990. International Road Safety Year.
3712 **1273** 5s. multicoloured   10   10

1990. "Olymphilex '90" Olympic Stamps Exhibition, Varna. Multicoloured.
3713   5s. Type **1274**   10   10
3714   13s. Throwing the discus   20   10
3715   42s. Throwing the hammer   70   35
3716   60s. Throwing the javelin   95   55

1275 "Sputnik" (first artificial satellite, 1957)

1990. Space Research. Multicoloured.
3717   5s. Type **1275**   10   10
3718   8s. "Vostok" and Yuri Gagarin (first manned flight, 1961)   10   10
3719   10s. Aleksei Leonov spacewalking from "Voskhod 2" (first spacewalk, 1965)   15   10
3720   20s. "Soyuz"–"Apollo" link, 1975   30   15
3721   42s. Space shuttle "Columbia", 1981   65   30
3722   60s. Space probe "Galileo"   90   45

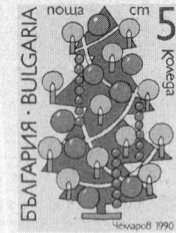
1276 St. Clement of Ohrid   **1277** Tree

1990. 1150th Birth Anniv of St. Clement of Ohrid.
3724 **1276** 5s. brown, black & grn   10   10

1990. Christmas. Multicoloured.
3725   5s. Type **1277**   10   10
3726   20s. Father Christmas   15   10

1278 Skaters

1991. European Figure Skating Championships, Sofia.
3727 **1278** 15s. multicoloured   20   10

1279 Chicken

1281 "Good Day" (Paul Gauguin)

1280 Death Cap

1991. Farm Animals.
3728   – 20s. brown and black   10   10
3729   – 25s. blue and black   10   10
3730 **1279** 30s. brown and black   10   10
3731   – 40s. brown and black   15   10
3732   – 62s. green and black   25   10
3733   – 86s. red and black   30   10
3734   – 95s. mauve and black   35   10
3735   – 1l. brown and black   40   15
3736   – 2l. green and black   60   25
3737   – 5l. violet and black   1·50   75
3738   – 10l. blue and black   1·75   75
DESIGNS: 20s. Sheep; 25s. Goose; 40s. Horse; 62, 95s. Billy goat; 86s. Sow; 1l. Donkey; 2l. Bull; 5l. Common turkey; 10l. Cow.

1991. Fungi. Multicoloured.
3746   5s. Type **1280**   10   10
3747   10s. "Amanita verna"   25   10
3748   20s. Panther cap   60   15
3749   32s. Fly agaric   90   15
3750   42s. Beefsteak morel   1·25   35
3751   60s. Satan's mushroom   1·90   60

1991. Paintings. Multicoloured.
3752   20s. Type **1281**   10   10
3753   43s. "Madame Dobini" (Edgar Degas)   10   10
3754   62s. "Peasant Woman" (Camille Pissarro)   30   15
3755   67s. "Woman with Black hair" (Edouard Manet)   40   15
3756   80s. "Blue Vase" (Paul Cezanne)   50   20
3757   2l. "Madame Samari" (Pierre Auguste Renoir)   1·10   50

1282 Map

1991. 700th Anniv of Swiss Confederation.
3759 **1282** 62s. red and violet   40   10

1283 Postman on Bicycle, Envelopes and Paper

1991. 100 Years of Philatelic Publications in Bulgaria.
3760 **1283** 30s. multicoloured   10   10

1284 "Meteosat" Weather Satellite

1991. Europa. Europe in Space. Multicoloured.

3761	43s. Type **1284**	10	10
3762	62s. "Ariane" rocket	40	10

1285 Przewalski's Horse

1991. Horses. Multicoloured.

3763	5s. Type **1285**	10	10
3764	10s. Tarpan	10	10
3765	25s. Black arab	15	10
3766	35s. White arab	20	15
3767	42s. Shetland pony	40	15
3768	60s. Draught horse	70	10

1286 "Expo 91"

1991. "Expo '91" Exhibition, Plovdiv.

3769	**1286** 30s. multicoloured	10	10

1287 Mozart

1991. Death Bicentenary of Wolfgang Amadeus Mozart (composer).

3770	**1287** 62s. multicoloured	40	10

1288 Astronaut and Rear of Space Shuttle "Columbia"

1991. Space Shuttles. Multicoloured.

3771	12s. Type **1288**	10	10
3772	32s. Satellite and "Challenger"	10	10
3773	50s. "Discovery" and satellite	30	10
3774	86s. Satellite and "Atlantis" (vert)	40	20
3775	11.50 Launch of "Buran"	75	30
3776	2l. Satellite and "Atlantis" (vert)	1·10	40

1289 Luge   **1291** Japanese Chin

1290 Sheraton Hotel Balkan, Sofia

1991. Winter Olympic Games, Albertville (1992). Multicoloured.

3778	30s. Type **1289**	10	10
3779	43s. Skiing	20	10

3780	67s. Ski jumping	30	10
3781	2l. Biathlon	80	30

1991.

3783	**1290** 62s. multicoloured	20	10

1991. Dogs. Multicoloured.

3784	30s. Type **1291**	10	10
3785	43s. Chihuahua	10	10
3786	62s. Miniature pinscher	20	10
3787	80s. Yorkshire terrier	40	10
3788	1l. Mexican hairless	50	15
3789	3l. Pug	1·50	45

1292 Arms

1991. "Philatelia '91" Stamp Fair, Cologne.

3790	**1292** 86s. multicoloured	50	10

1294 Japan 1871 48mon "Dragon" Stamp

1991. "Phila Nippon '91" International Stamp Exhibition, Tokyo.

3792	**1294** 62s. black, brown & bl	20	10

1295 Early Steam Locomotive and Tender

1991. 125th Anniv of the Railway in Bulgaria. Multicoloured.

3793	30s. Type **1295**	30	10
3794	30s. Early six-wheeled carriage	30	10

1296 Ball ascending to Basket   **1297** "Christ carrying the Cross"

1991. Centenary of Basketball. Multicoloured.

3795	43s. Type **1296**	10	10
3796	62s. Ball level with basket mouth	10	10
3797	90s. Ball entering basket	40	10
3798	1l. Ball in basket	40	15

1991. 450th Birth Anniv of El Greco (painter). Multicoloured.

3799	43s. Type **1297**	10	10
3800	50s. "Holy Family with St. Anna"	10	10
3801	60s. "St. John of the Cross and St. John the Evangelist"	15	10
3802	62s. "St. Andrew and St. Francis"	15	10
3803	1l. "Holy Family with Magdalene"	35	15
3804	2l. "Cardinal Fernando Nino de Guevara"	85	30

1298 Snowman, Moon, Candle, Bell and Heart

1991. Christmas. Multicoloured.

3806	30s. Type **1298**	10	10
3807	62s. Star, clover, angel, house and Christmas tree	10	10

1299 Small Pasque Flower

1991. Medicinal Plants. Multicoloured.

3808	30s.(+15s.) Pale pasque flower	10	10
3809	40s. Type **1299**	10	10
3810	55s. "Pulsatilla halleri"	15	10
3811	60s. "Aquilegia nigricans"	15	10
3812	1l. Sea buckthorn	35	15
3813	2l. Blackcurrant	85	30

No. 3808 includes a se-tenant premium-carrying label for 15s. inscribed "ACTION 2000. For Environment Protection".

1300 Greenland Seals

1991. Marine Mammals. Multicoloured.

3814	30s. Type **1300**	10	10
3815	43s. Killer whales	10	10
3816	62s. Walruses	15	10
3817	68s. Bottle-nosed dolphins	15	10
3818	1l. Mediterranean monk seals	35	15
3819	2l. Common porpoises	85	30

1301 Synagogue

1992. 500th Anniv of Jewish Settlement in Bulgaria.

3820	**1301** 1l. multicoloured	30	10

1302 Rossini, "The Barber of Seville" and Figaro

1992. Birth Bicentenary of Gioacchino Rossini (composer).

3821	**1302** 50s. multicoloured	30	10

1303 Plan of Fair

1992. Centenary of Plovdiv Fair.

3822	**1303** 1l. black and stone	20	10

1304 Volvo "740"

1992. Motor Cars. Multicoloured.

3823	30s. Type **1304**	10	10
3824	45s. Ford "Escort"	10	10
3825	50s. Fiat "Croma"	15	10
3826	50s. Mercedes Benz "600"	15	10
3827	1l. Peugeot "605"	35	15
3828	2l. B.M.W. "316"	85	30

1305 Amerigo Vespucci

1992. Explorers. Multicoloured.

3829	50s. Type **1305**	20	10
3830	50s. Francisco de Orellana	20	10
3831	1l. Ferdinand Magellan	40	10
3832	1l. Jimenez de Quesada	40	10
3833	2l. Sir Francis Drake	85	35
3834	3l. Pedro de Valdivia	1·25	50

1306 Granada

1992. "Granada '92" Int Stamp Exhibition.

3836	**1306** 62s. multicoloured	25	10

1307 "Santa Maria"

1992. Europa. 500th Anniv of Discovery of America by Columbus. Multicoloured.

3837	1l. Type **1307**	50	20
3838	2l. Christopher Columbus	1·00	40

Nos. 3837/8 were issued together, se-tenant, forming a composite design.

1308 House

1992. S.O.S. Children's Village.

3839	**1308** 1l. multicoloured	40	10

1309 Long Jumping

1992. Olympic Games, Barcelona (2nd issue). Multicoloured.

3840	50s. Type **1309**	15	10
3841	50s. Swimming	15	10
3842	1l. High jumping	40	15
3843	3l. Gymnastics	1·25	50

1310 1902 Laurin and Klement Motor Cycle

1992. Motor Cycles. Multicoloured.

3845	30s. Type **1310**	10	10
3846	45s. 1928 Puch "200 Luxus"	10	10
3847	50s. 1931 Norton "CS 1"	10	10
3848	70s. 1950 Harley Davidson	15	10
3849	1l. 1986 Gilera "SP 01"	35	15
3850	2l. 1990 BMW "K 1"	85	30

1311 Genoa

1992. "Genova '92" International Thematic Stamp Exhibition.
3851 **1311** 1l. multicoloured . . . 40   10

1312 Grasshopper   1313 Silhouette of Head on Town Plan

1992. Insects. Multicoloured.
3852   1l. Four-spotted libellula . 10   10
3853   2l. "Raphidia notata" . . . 20   10
3854   3l. Type **1312** 40   10
3855   4l. Stag beetle 50   10
3856   5l. Fire bug 75   10
3857   7l. Ant . . . . 1·40   25
3858   20l. Wasp . . . . 3·00   1·25
3859   50l. Praying mantis . . . . 7·50   3·00

1992. 50th Anniv of Institute of Architecture and Building.
3862 **1313** 1l. red and black . . . 35   10

1314 Oak

1992. Trees. Multicoloured.
3863   50s. Type **1314** 10   10
3864   50s. Horse chestnut . . . 10   10
3865   1l. Oak 40   10
3866   1l. Macedonian pine . . . 40   10
3867   2l. Maple 80   20
3868   3l. Pear . . . . 1·25   35

1315 Embroidered Flower

1992. Centenary of Folk Museum, Sofia.
3869 **1315** 1l. multicoloured . . . 35   10

1316 "Bulgaria" (freighter)

1992. Centenary of National Shipping Fleet. Multicoloured.
3870   30s. Type **1316** 10   10
3871   50s. "Kastor" (tanker) . . . 20   10
3872   1l. "Geroite na Sebastopol" (train ferry) 65   25
3873   2l. "Aleko Konstantinov" (tanker) 65   25
3874   2l. "Bulgaria" (tanker) . . . 85   40
3875   3l. "Varna" (container ship) 1·40   55

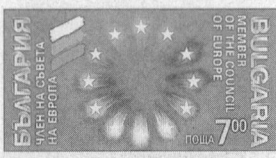

1317 Council Emblem

1992. Admission to Council of Europe.
3876 **1317** 7l. multicoloured . . . 2·75   1·00

1319 "Santa Claus" (Ani Bacheva)

1992. Christmas. Children's Drawings. Mult.
3878   1l. Type **1319** 35   10
3879   7l. "Madonna and Child" (Georgi Petkov) . . . . 2·25   75

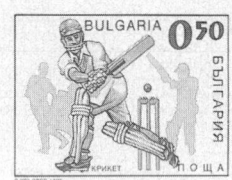

1320 Leopard   1322 Tengmalm's Owl

1321 Cricket

1992. Big Cats. Multicoloured.
3880   50s. Type **1320** 15   10
3881   50s. Cheetah 15   10
3882   1l. Jaguar 40   40
3883   2l. Puma 80   30
3884   2l. Tiger 80   30
3885   3l. Lion . . . . 1·25   45

1992. Sport. Multicoloured.
3886   50s. Type **1321** 10   10
3887   50s. Baseball 10   10
3888   1l. Pony and trap racing . . 40   10
3889   1l. Polo 40   10
3890   2l. Hockey 80   15
3891   3l. American football . . . 1·25   40

1992. Owls. Multicoloured.
3892   30s. Type **1322** 15   10
3893   50s. Tawny owl (horiz) . . . 15   10
3894   1l. Long-eared owl 40   20
3895   1l. Short-eared owl 80   35
3896   2l. Eurasian scops owl (horiz) 80   35
3897   3l. Barn owl . . . . 1·25   55

1324 Sculpted Head   1325 Shooting

1323 "Khan Kubrat" (Dimitur Gyudzhenov)

1992. Historical Paintings. Multicoloured.
3898   50s. Type **1323** 15   10
3899   1l. "Khan Asparukh (Nikolai Pavlovich) 40   15
3900   2l. "Khan Terval at Tsarigrad" (Dimitur Panchev) 80   30
3901   3l. "Prince Boris" (Nikolai Pavlovich) . . . . . 1·25   45

1993. Centenary of National Archaeological Museum, Sofia.
3903 **1324** 1l. multicoloured . . . 40   10

1993. "Borovets '93" Biathlon Championship. Multicoloured.
3904   1l. Type **1325** 40   15
3905   7l. Cross-country skiing . . 3·00   1·25

1326 Rilski   1327 "Morning" (sculpture, Georgi Chapkunov)

1993. Birth Bicentenary of Neofit Rilski (compiler of Bulgarian grammar and dictionary).
3906 **1326** 1l. bistre and red . . . 40   15

1993. Europa. Contemporary Art. Multicoloured.
3907   3l. Type **1327** 60   25
3908   8l. "Composition" (D. Buyukliiski) . . . . 1·60   65

1328 Veil-tailed Goldfish

1993. Fishes. Multicoloured.
3909   1l. Type **1328** 15   10
3910   2l. Yucatan sail-finned molly 25   10
3911   3l. Two-striped lyretail . . 50   15
3912   3l. Freshwater angelfish . . 50   15
3913   4l. Red discus 75   30
3914   8l. Pearl gourami . . . . . 1·50   55

1329 Apple   1330 Monteverdi

1993. Fruits. Multicoloured.
3915   1l. Type **1329** 15   10
3916   2l. Peach 25   10
3917   2l. Pear 25   10
3918   3l. Quince 50   15
3919   5l. Pomegranate 80   25
3920   7l. Fig . . . . 1·40   50

1993. 350th Death Anniv of Claudio Monteverdi (composer).
3921 **1330** 1l. green, yellow & red . 20   10

1331 High Jumping

1993. Int Games for the Deaf, Sofia. Mult.
3922   1l. Type **1331** 20   10
3923   2l. Swimming 40   10
3924   3l. Cycling 50   20
3925   7l. Tennis 70   25

1333 Prince Alexander   1334 Tchaikovsky

1993. Death Centenary of Prince Alexander I.
3928 **1333** 3l. multicoloured . . . 50   20

1993. Death Centenary of Pyotr Tchaikovsky (composer).
3929 **1334** 3l. multicoloured . . . 50   20

1335 Crossbow   1336 Newton

1993. Weapons. Multicoloured.
3930   1l. Type **1335** 15   10
3931   2l. 18th-century flintlock pistol 25   10
3932   3l. Revolver 50   15
3933   3l. Luger pistol 50   15
3934   5l. Mauser rifle 80   30
3935   7l. Kalashnikov assault rifle 1·40   55

1993. 350th Birth Anniv of Sir Isaac Newton (mathematician).
3936 **1336** 1l. multicoloured . . . 15   10

1337 "100" on Stamps and Globe

1993. Centenary of Bulgarian Philately.
3937 **1337** 1l. multicoloured . . . 25   10

1338 "Ecology" in Cyrillic Script

1993. Ecology. Multicoloured.
3938   1l. Type **1338** 15   10
3939   7l. "Ecology" in English . . 1·00   40

1339 Mallard

1993. Hunting. Multicoloured.
3940   1l. Type **1339** 20   10
3941   1l. Common pheasant . . . 20   10
3942   2l. Red fox 25   15
3943   3l. Roe deer 50   20
3944   6l. European brown hare . . 1·00   40
3945   8l. Wild boar . . . . . . 1·50   55

1340 "Taurus", "Gemini" and "Cancer"   1341 Sofia Costume

1993. Christmas. Signs of the Zodiac. Mult.
3946   1l. Type **1340** 15   10
3947   1l. "Leo", "Virgo" and "Libra" 15   10
3948   7l. "Aquarius", "Pisces and "Aries" . . . . . . 1·00   40
3949   7l. "Scorpio", "Sagittarius" and "Capricorn" . . . 1·00   40
Nos. 3946/7 and 3948/9 were each issued together, se-tenant; when placed together the four stamps form a composite design.

1993. Costumes. Multicoloured.
3950   1l. Type **1341** 15   10
3951   1l. Plovdiv 15   10
3952   2l. Belograd 25   15
3953   3l. Oryakhovo 35   20
3954   3l. Shumen 35   20
3955   8l. Kurdzhali . . . . . . 1·25   55

1342 Freestyle Skiing   **1343** "Self-portrait" and "Tsar Simeon"

1994. Winter Olympic Games, Lillehammer, Norway. Multicoloured.

3956	1l. Type **1342**	15	10
3957	2l. Speed skating	25	10
3958	3l. Two-man luge	50	15
3959	4l. Ice hockey	75	30

1994. Death Centenary of Nikolai Pavlovich (artist).

3961	**1343** 3l. multicoloured	20	10

1344 Plesiosaurus

1994. Prehistoric Animals. Multicoloured.

3962	2l. Type **1344**	35	10
3963	3l. Archaeopteryx	50	20
3964	3l. Iguanodon	50	15
3965	4l. Edmontonia	70	25
3966	5l. Styracosaurus	85	35
3967	7l. Tyrannosaurus	1·00	40

1345 Players (Chile, 1962)

1994. World Cup Football Championship, U.S.A. Multicoloured.

3968	3l. Type **1345**	45	10
3969	6l. Players (England, 1966)	90	30
3970	7l. Goalkeeper making save (Mexico, 1970)	1·00	40
3971	9l. Player kicking (West Germany, 1974)	1·25	50

1346 Photoelectric Analysis (Georgi Nadzhakov)

1994. Europa. Discoveries. Multicoloured.

3973	3l. Type **1346**	40	10
3974	15l. Cardiogram and heart (Prof. Ivan Mitev)	2·00	75

1347 Khristov

1994. 80th Birth Anniv of Boris Khristov (actor).

3975	**1347** 3l. multicoloured	25	10

1348 Sleeping Hamster   **1349** Space Shuttle, Satellite and Dish Aerial

1994. The Common Hamster. Multicoloured.

3976	3l. Type **1348**	45	10
3977	7l. Hamster looking out of burrow	1·00	40

3978	10l. Hamster sitting up in grass	1·25	50
3979	15l. Hamster approaching berry	2·00	75

1994. North Atlantic Co-operation Council (North Atlantic Treaty Organization and Warsaw Pact members).

3980	**1349** 3l. multicoloured	25	10

1350 Baron Pierre de Coubertin (founder of modern games)   **1351** "Christ Pantocrator"

1994. Cent of International Olympic Committee.

3981	**1350** 3l. multicoloured	50	20

1994. Icons. Multicoloured.

3982	2l. Type **1351**	30	10
3983	3l. "Raising of Lazarus"	45	10
3984	5l. "Passion of Christ"	75	25
3985	7l. "Archangel Michael"	1·00	40
3986	8l. "Sts. Cyril and Methodius"	1·10	50
3987	15l. "Madonna Enthroned"	2·00	75

1352 Vechernik

1994. Christmas. Breads. Multicoloured.

3988	3l. Type **1352**	40	10
3989	15l. Bogovitsa	2·00	75

1353 "Golden Showers"

1994. Roses. Multicoloured.

3990	2l. Type **1353**	30	10
3991	3l. "Caen Peace Monument"	45	10
3992	5l. "Theresa of Lisieux"	75	25
3993	7l. "Zambra 93"	1·00	40
3994	10l. "Gustave Courbet"	1·60	50
3995	15l. "Honore de Balzac	2·25	75

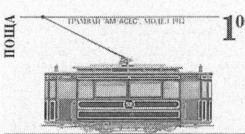

1355 "AM/ASES", 1912

1994. Trams. Multicoloured.

3997	1l. Type **1355**	15	10
3998	2l. "AM/ASES", 1928	35	15
3999	7l. "M.A.N./AEG", 1931	50	20
4000	5l. "D.T.O.", 1942	80	35
4001	8l. Republika, 1951	1·75	65
4002	10l. Kosmonavt articulated tramcar set, 1961	1·90	80

1356 Petleshkov and Flag

1995. 150th Birth Anniv of Vasil Petleshkov (leader of 1876 April uprising).

4003	**1356** 3l. multicoloured	40	15

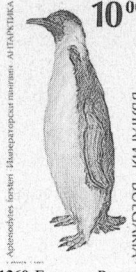

1357 Daisy growing through Cracked Helmet   **1360** Emperor Penguin

1995. Europa. Peace and Freedom. Mult.

4004	3l. Type **1357**	40	15
4005	15l. Dove with olive branch on rifle barrel	1·90	75

1995. Antarctic Animals. Multicoloured.

4008	1l. Shrimp (horiz)	15	10
4009	2l. Ice fish (horiz)	30	10
4010	3l. Sperm whale (horiz)	45	20
4011	5l. Weddell's seal (horiz)	70	30
4012	8l. South polar skua (horiz)	1·10	45
4013	10l. Type **1360**	1·40	55

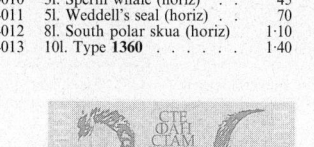

1361 Stambolov

1995. Death Cent of Stefan Stambolov (politician).

4014	**1361** 3l. multicoloured	40	15

1362 Pole Vaulting

1995. Olympic Games, Atlanta (1996) (1st issue). Multicoloured.

4015	3l. Type **1362**	45	10
4016	7l. High jumping	1·00	40
4017	10l. Long jumping	1·40	55
4018	15l. Triple jumping	2·10	85

See also Nos. 4083/6.

1363 Pea   **1365** "Ivan Nikolov-Zograf"

1995. Food Plants. Multicoloured.

4019	2l. Type **1363**	30	10
4020	3l. Chickpea	40	15
4021	3l. Soya bean	40	15
4022	4l. Spinach	55	20
4023	5l. Peanut	70	30
4024	15l. Lentil	2·10	85

1364 "100"

1995. Centenary of Organized Tourism.

4025	**1364** 1l. multicoloured	40	15

1995. Birth Centenary of Vasil Zakhariev (painter).

4026	**1365** 2l. multicoloured	30	10
4027	– 3l. multicoloured	40	15
4028	– 5l. black, brown & grn	70	30
4029	– 10l. multicoloured	1·40	55

DESIGNS:—2l. "Rila Monastery"; 5l. "Self-portrait"; 10l. "Raspberry Collectors".

1366 "Dove-Hands" holding Globe

1995. 50th Anniv of U.N.O.

4030	**1366** 3l. multicoloured	40	15

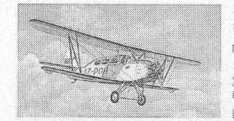

1367 Polikarpov Po-2 Biplane

1995. Aircraft. Multicoloured.

4031	3l. Type **1367**	45	20
4032	5l. Lisunov Li-2 airliner	70	30
4033	7l. Junkers Ju 52	1·00	40
4034	10l. Focke Wulf Fw 58	1·40	55

1368 Charlie Chaplin and Mickey Mouse

1995. Centenary of Motion Pictures. Mult.

4035	2l. Type **1368**	30	10
4036	3l. Marilyn Monroe and Marlene Dietrich	45	20
4037	5l. Nikolai Cherkasov and Humphrey Bogart	70	30
4038	8l. Sophia Loren and Liza Minelli	1·10	45
4039	10l. Gerard Philipe and Toshiro Mifune	1·40	55
4040	15l. Katya Paskaleva and Nevena Kokanova	2·10	85

1369 Agate

1995. Minerals. Multicoloured.

4041	1l. Type **1369**	15	10
4042	2l. Sphalerite	30	10
4043	5l. Calcite	70	30
4044	7l. Quartz	1·00	40
4045	8l. Pyromorphite	1·10	45
4046	10l. Almandine	1·40	55

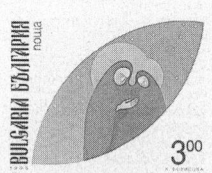

1370 Mary and Joseph

1995. Christmas. Multicoloured.

4047	3l. Type **1370**	40	15
4048	15l. Three wise men approaching stable	1·90	75

1371 "Polynesian Woman with Fruit"

1996. Birth Centenary of Kiril Tsonev (painter).

4049	**1371** 3l. multicoloured	30	10

1372 Luther (after Lucas Cranach the elder)

1996. 450th Death Anniv of Martin Luther (Protestant reformer).
4050 1372 3l. multicoloured 30   10

1373 Preobrazhenie   1374 Bulgarian National Bank

1996. Monasteries.
4051	1373	3l. green	20	10
4052		– 5l. red	35	15
4053		– 10l. blue	70	30
4054		– 20l. orange	1·40	55
4055		– 25l. brown	1·75	70
4056		– 40l. purple	2·75	1·10

DESIGNS: 5l. Arapov; 10l. Dryanovo; 20l. Bachkov; 25l. Troyan; 40l. Zograf.

1996. 5th Anniv of European Reconstruction and Development Bank.
4063 1374 7l. green, red and blue   45   20
4064   – 30l. blue, red & purple   1·90   75
DESIGN: 30l. Palace of Culture, Sofia.

1375 Yew

1996. Conifers. Multicoloured.
4065	5l. Type 1375	35	15
4066	8l. Silver fir	60	25
4067	10l. Norway spruce	70	30
4068	20l. Scots pine	1·40	55
4069	25l. "Pinus heldreichii"	1·75	70
4070	40l. Juniper	3·00	1·25

1376 Battle Scene and   1377 Modern Officer's
Mourning Women   Parade Uniform

1996. 120th Anniversaries. Multicoloured.
4071 10l. Type 1376 (April uprising) 65   25
4072 40l. Khristo Botev and script (poet, death anniv) (horiz) . . . . . 2·50   1·00

1996. Military Uniforms. Multicoloured.
4073	5l. Type 1377	35	15
4074	8l. Second World War combat uniform	60	25
4075	10l. Balkan War uniform	70	30
4076	20l. Guard officer's ceremonial uniform	1·40	55
4077	25l. Serbo-Bulgarian War officer's uniform	1·75	70
4078	40l. Russo-Turkish War soldier's uniform	3·00	1·75

1378 Monument

1996. 50th Anniv of the Republic.
4079 1378 10l. multicoloured . . . 70   30

1379 Elisaveta Bagryana (poet)

1996. Europa. Famous Women. Multicoloured.
4080 10l. Type 1379 65   25
4081 40l. Katya Popova (opera singer) . . . . 2·50   1·00

1381 Nikola Stanchev   1382 "The Letter"
(wrestling, Melbourne   (detail)
1956)

1996. Olympic Games, Atlanta (2nd issue). Bulgarian Medal Winners. Multicoloured.
4083 5l. Type 1381 20   10
4084 8l. Boris Georgiev (boxing, Helsinki 1952) 35   10
4085 10l. Ivanka Khristova (putting the shot, Montreal 1976) 40   15
4086 25l. Z. Iordanova and S. Otsetova (double sculls, Montreal 1976) . . . . 1·00   40

1996. 250th Birth Anniv of Francisco Goya (painter). Multicoloured.
4088 5l. Detail of fresco 20   10
4089 8l. Type 1382 35   10
4090 26l. "3rd of May 1808 in Madrid" (detail) . . . 1·10   45
4091 40l. "Neighbours on a Balcony" (detail) . . . 1·75   70

1383 Water Flea

1996. Aquatic Life. Multicoloured.
4093 5l. Type 1383 20   10
4094 10l. Common water louse . 45   15
4095 12l. European river crayfish . 50   20
4096 25l. Prawn . . . . . . 1·10   45
4097 30l. "Cumella limicola" . . 1·25   50
4098 40l. Mediterranean shore crab . . . . 1·75   70

1385 Tryavna

1996. Houses.
4100	1385	10l. brown and stone	30	10
4101		– 15l. red and yellow	45	15
4102		– 30l. green and yellow	90	35
4103		– 50l. violet and mauve	1·50	60
4104		– 60l. green and lt green	1·75	70
4105		– 100l. ultramarine & bl	3·00	1·25

DESIGNS: 15l. Nesebur; 30l. Tryavna (different); 50l. Koprivshtitsa; 60l. Plovdiv; 100l. Koprivshtitsa (different).

1386 "Philadelphia", 1836

1996. Steam Locomotives. Multicoloured.
4106 5l. Type 1386 15   10
4107 10l. "Jenny Lind", 1847 . . 30   10
4108 12l. "Liverpool", 1848 . . 35   15
4109 26l. "Anglet", 1876 80   30

1387 Anniversary Emblem and Academy

1996. Centenary of National Arts Academy.
4110 1387 15l. black and yellow   40   15

1388 Sword and Miniature from "Chronicle of Ivan Skilitsa"

1996. 1100th Anniv of Tsar Simeon's Victory over the Turks. Multicoloured.
4111 10l. Type 1388 25   10
4112 40l. Dagger and right-hand detail of miniature . . . . 1·00   40
Nos. 4111/12 were issued together, se-tenant, forming a composite design.

1389 Fishes and Diver (Dilyana Lokmadzhieva)

1996. 50th Anniv of U.N.I.C.E.F. Children's Paintings. Multicoloured.
4113 7l. Type 1389 20   10
4114 15l. Circus (Velislava Dimitrova) 40   15
4115 20l. Man and artist's pallet (Miglena Nikolova) . . 55   20
4116 60l. Family meal (Darena Dencheva) . . . . 1·60   65

1390 Christmas Tree   1391 "Zograf Monastery"

1996. Christmas. Multicoloured.
4117 15l. Type 1390 40   15
4118 60l. Star over basilica and Christmas tree . . . . . 1·50   60

1996. Birth Centenary of Tsanko Lavrenov (painter).
4119 1391 15l. multicoloured . . . 40   15

1392 Pointer

1997. Puppies. Multicoloured.
4120 5l. Type 1392 15   10
4121 7l. Chow chow 20   10
4122 25l. Carakachan dog . . . 70   30
4123 50l. Basset hound . . . . 1·40   55

1393 Bell

1997. 150th Birth Anniv of Alexander Graham Bell (telephone pioneer).
4124 1393 30l. multicoloured . . . 50   20

1394 Man drinking   1395 Lady March (symbol of spring)

1997. Birth Centenary of Ivan Milev (painter). Murals from Kazaluk. Multicoloured.
4125 5l. Type 1394 10   10
4126 15l. Woman praying 25   10
4127 30l. Reaper 45   20
4128 60l. Mother and child . . . 90   35

1997. Europa. Tales and Legends. Mult.
4129 120l. Type 1395 25   10
4130 600l. St. George (national symbol) 85   35

1396 Kisimov in Character

1997. Birth Cent of Konstantin Kisimov (actor).
4131 1396 120l. multicoloured . . 20   10

1397 Von Stephan   1398 Old Town, Nesebur

1997. Death Centenary of Heinrich von Stephan (founder of U.P.U.).
4132 1397 60l. multicoloured . . . 10   10

1997. Historic Sights.
4133	1398	80l. brown and black	10	10
4134		– 200l. violet and black	15	10
4135		– 300l. yellow and black	20	10
4136		– 500l. green and black	25	10
4137		– 600l. yellow and black	35	15
4138		– 1000l. orange and black	55	20

DESIGNS: 200l. Sculpture, Ivanovski Church; 300l. Christ (detail of icon), Boyana Church; 500l. Horseman (stone relief), Madara; 600l. Figure of woman (carving from sarcophagus), Sveshary; 1000l. Tomb decoration, Kazanlak.

1399 Gaetano Donizetti

1997. Composers' Anniversaries. Multicoloured.
4139 120l. Type 1399 (birth bicentenary) 20   10
4140 120l. Franz Schubert (birth bicentenary) 20   10
4141 120l. Felix Mendelssohn-Bartholdy (150th death anniv) 20   10
4142 120l. Johannes Brahms (death centenary) 20   10

1400 "Trifolium rubens"

1997. Flowers in the Red Book. Multicoloured.
4143 80l. Type 1400 15   10
4144 100l. "Tulipa hageri" . . . 25   10
4145 120l. "Inula spiraeifolia" . . 45   20
4146 200l. Thin-leafed peony . . . 60   25

1401 Anniversary Emblem   **1402** Georgiev

1997. 50th Anniv of Civil Aviation.
4147	**1401**	120l. multicoloured		20	10

1997. Death Centenary of Evlogii Georgiev.
4148	**1402**	120l. multicoloured		20	10

1403 Show Jumping and Running

1997. World Modern Pentathlon Championship, Sofia. Multicoloured.
4149	60l. Type **1403**		10	10
4150	80l. Fencing and swimming		15	10
4151	100l. Running and fencing		25	10
4152	120l. Shooting and swimming		40	15
4153	200l. Show jumping and shooting		60	25

1405 D 2500 M Boat Engine

1997. Centenary of Diesel Engine. Multicoloured.
4155	80l. Type **1405**		10	10
4156	100l. D 2900 T tractor engine		15	10
4157	120l. D 3900 A truck engine	25	10
4158	200l. D 2500 K fork-lift truck engine		35	15

1406 Goddess with Mural Crown

1997. 43rd General Assembly of Atlantic Club, Sofia.
4159	**1406**	120l. mve, bl & ultram	25	10
4160	–	120l. grn, bl & ultram	25	10
4161	–	120l. brn, bl & ultram	25	10
4162	–	120l. vio, bl & ultram	25	10

DESIGNS: No. 4160, Eagle on globe; 4161, Venue; 4162, Venue (different).

1407 Cervantes and Don Quixote with Sancho

1997. 450th Birth Anniv of Miguel de Cervantes (writer).
4163	**1407**	120l. multicoloured		30	10

1408 Raztsvetnikov

1997. Birth Centenary of Asen Raztsvetnikov (writer and translator).
4164	**1408**	120l. multicoloured		30	10

1409 Fragment of Tombstone

1997. Millenary of Coronation of Tsar Samuel. Multicoloured.
4165	120l. Type **1409**		20	10
4166	600l. Tsar Samuel and knights in battle		1·10	45

1410 Star and Houses forming Christmas Tree

1997. Christmas. Multicoloured.
4167	120l. Type **1410**		15	10
4168	600l. Stable with Christmas tree roof		1·00	40

1411 Speed Skating

1997. Winter Olympic Games, Nagano, Japan (1998). Multicoloured.
4169	60l. Type **1411**		10	10
4170	80l. Skiing		15	10
4171	120l. Shooting (biathlon)		25	10
4172	600l. Ice skating		1·25	50

1413 State Arms

1997.
4174	**1413**	120l. multicoloured		20	10

1414 Botev (after B. Petrov)   **1415** Brecht

1998. 150th Birth and 120th Death (1996) Anniv of Khristo Botev (poet and revolutionary).
4175	**1414**	120l. multicoloured		20	10

1998. Birth Cent of Bertolt Brecht (playwright).
4176	**1415**	120l. multicoloured		20	10

1416 Arrows

1998. Cent of Bulgarian Telegraph Agency.
4177	**1416**	120l. multicoloured		20	10

1417 Barn Swallow at Window

1998. 120th Birth Anniv of Aleksandur Bozhinov (children's illustrator). Multicoloured.
4178	120l. Type **1417**		25	10
4179	120l. Blackbird with backpack on branch		25	10
4180	120l. Father Frost and children		25	10
4181	120l. Maiden Rositsa in field holding hands up to rain	25	10

1418 Tsar Alexander II   **1419** Christ ascending and Hare pulling Cart of Eggs

1997. Millenary of Coronation of Tsar Samuel. Multicoloured.

1998. 120th Anniv of Liberation from Turkey. Multicoloured.
4182	120l. Type **1418**		15	10
4183	600l. Independence monument, Ruse		1·00	40

1998. Easter.
4184	**1419**	120l. multicoloured		20	10

1420 Torch Bearer

1998. 75th Anniv of Bulgarian Olympic Committee.
4185	**1420**	120l. multicoloured		20	10

1421 Map of Participating Countries

1998. Phare International Programme for Telecommunications and Post.
4186	**1421**	120l. multicoloured		20	10

1422 Girls in Folk Costumes

1998. Europa. National Festivals. Multicoloured.
4187	120l. Type **1422**		20	10
4188	600l. Boys wearing dance masks		1·00	40

(1423)   **1424** "Dante and Virgil in Hell"

1998. Winning of Gold Medal in 15km Biathlon by Ekaterina Dafovska at Winter Olympic Games, Nagano. No. 4171 optd with T **1423**.
4189	120l. multicoloured		15	10

1998. Birth Bicentenary of Eugene Delacroix (artist).
4190	**1424**	120l. multicoloured		15	10

1425 Footballer and Club Badge   **1426** European Tabby

1998. 50th Anniv of TsSKA Football Club.
4191	**1425**	120l. multicoloured		15	10

1998. Cats. Multicoloured.
4192	60l. Type **1426**		10	10
4193	80l. Siamese		15	10
4194	120l. Exotic shorthair		25	10
4195	600l. Birman		1·10	45

1427 "Oh, You are Jealous!"

1998. 150th Birth Anniv of Paul Gauguin (artist).
4196	**1427**	120l. multicoloured		15	10

1428 Khilendarski-Bozveli

1998. 150th Death Anniv of Neofit Khilendarski-Bozveli (priest and writer).
4197	**1428**	120l. multicoloured		15	10

1429 Tackling

1998. World Cup Football Championship, France. Multicoloured.
4198	60l. Type **1429**		10	10
4199	180l. Players competing for ball		15	10
4200	120l. Players and ball		25	10
4201	600l. Goalkeeper		1·10	40

1430 A. Aleksandrov

1998. 10th Anniv of Second Soviet–Bulgarian Space Flight.
4203	**1430**	120l. multicoloured		15	10

1431 Vasco da Gama

1998. "Expo '98" World's Fair, Lisbon. 500th Anniv of Vasco da Gama's Voyage to India. Multicoloured.
4204	600l. Type **1431**		80	30
4205	600l. "Sao Gabriel" (Vasco da Gama's ship)		1·00	40

Nos. 4204/5 were issued together, se-tenant, forming a composite design.

1432 Focke Wolf FW 61, 1937

1998. Helicopters. Multicoloured.
4206	80l. Type **1432**		10	10
4207	100l. Sikorsky R-4, 1943		10	10
4208	120l. Mil Mi-V12, 1970		15	10
4209	200l. McDonnell-Douglas MD-900, 1995		35	10

1434 Talev

1998. Birth Centenary of Dimitur Talev (writer).
4211 **1434** 180l. multicoloured . . 20 10

1435 Aleksandur Malinov (Prime Minister, 1931)　**1436** "Limenitis redukta" and "Ligularia sibirica"

1998. 90th Anniv of Independence.
4212 **1435** 180l. black, blue & yell 25 10

1998. Butterflies and Flowers. Multicoloured.
4213　60l. Type **1436** 10 10
4214　180l. Painted lady and "Anthemis macrantha" 25 10
4215　200l. Red admiral and "Trachelium jacquinii" 25 10
4216　600l. "Anthocharis gruneri" and "Geranium tuberosum" 95 40

1437 Smirnenski

1998. Birth Cent of Khristo Smirnenski (writer).
4217 **1437** 180l. multicoloured . . 25 10

1438 Silhouette of Man

1998. 50th Anniv of Universal Declaration of Human Rights.
4218 **1438** 180l. multicoloured . . 25 10

1439 Bruno

1998. 450th Birth Anniv of Giordano Bruno (scholar).
4219 **1439** 180l. multicoloured . . 25 10

1440 Man diving through Heart ("I Love You")

1998. Greetings Stamps. Multicoloured.
4220　180l. Type **1440** 25 10
4221　180l. Making wine (holiday) (vert) 25 10
4222　180l. Man in chalice (birthday) (vert) 25 10
4223　180l. Waiter serving wine (name day) (vert) . . . 25 10

1441 Madonna and Child

1998. Christmas.
4224 **1441** 180l. multicoloured . . 25 10

1442 Geshov

1999. 150th Birth Anniv of Ivan Evstratiev Geshov (politician).
4225 **1442** 180l. multicoloured . . 25 10

1443 National Assembly Building, Sofia

1999. 120th Anniv of Third Bulgarian State. Mult.
4226　180l. Type **1443** 25 10
4227　180l. Council of Ministers 25 10
4228　180l. Statue of Justice (Supreme Court of Appeal) 25 10
4229　180l. Coins (National Bank) 25 10
4230　180l. Army 25 10
4231　180l. Lion emblem of Sofia and lamp post 25 10

1444 Georgi Karakashev (stage designer) and Set of "Kismet"

1999. Birth Centenaries. Multicoloured.
4232　180l. Type **1444** 25 10
4233　200l. Bencho Obreshkov (artist) and "Lodki" . . . 25 10
4234　300l. Score and Asen Naidenov (conductor of Sofia Opera) 35 15
4235　600l. Pancho Vladigerov (composer) and score of "Vardar" 75 30

1446 Sun and Emblem

1999. 50th Anniv of North Atlantic Treaty Organization.
4237 **1446** 180l. multicoloured . . 25 10

1447 Decorated Eggs

1999. Easter.
4238 **1447** 180l. multicoloured . . 25 10

1448 Red-crested Pochard and Ropotamo Reserve

1449 Albrecht Durer (self-portrait) and Nuremberg

1999. "iBRA '99" International Stamp Exhibition, Nuremberg, Germany.
4241 **1449** 600l. multicoloured . . 75 30

1450 Anniversary Emblem

1999. 50th Anniv of Council of Europe.
4242 **1450** 180l. multicoloured . . 25 10

1451 Honore de Balzac (novelist)

1999. Birth Anniversaries. Multicoloured.
4243　180l. Type **1451** (bicentenary) 25 10
4244　200l. Johann Wolfgang von Goethe (poet and playwright) (250th anniv) 25 10
4245　300l. Aleksandr Pushkin (poet) (bicentenary) . . 35 15
4246　600l. Diego de Silva Velazquez (painter) (400th anniv) 75 30

1452 Penny Farthing

1999. Bicycles. Multicoloured.
4247　180l. Type **1452** 25 10
4248　200l. Road racing bicycles 25 10
4249　300l. Track racing bicycles 35 15
4250　600l. Mountain bike . . . 75 30

1454 Sopot Monastery Fountain　**1456** Cracked Green Russula

1999. Fountains.
4252 **1454** 1st. light brown . . . 10 10
4254　－ 8st. green and black . . . 10 10
4255　－ 10st. deep brown 10 10
4257　－ 18st. light blue 10 10
4258　－ 20st. bright blue 10 10
4260　－ 60st. brown and black . . 85 60
DESIGNS: 8st. Peacock Fountain, Karlovo; 10st. Peev Fountain, Kopivshtitsa; 18st. Sandanski Fountain; 20st. Eagle Owl Fountain, Karlovo; 60st. Fountain, Sokolski Monastery.

1999. Fungi. Multicoloured.
4266　10st. Type **1456** 10 10
4267　18st. Field mushroom . . . 25 20
4268　20st. "Hygrophorus russula" 30 20
4269　60st. Wood blewit 85 60

1458 Four-leaved Clover　**1460** Lesser Grey Shrike

1999. Centenary of Organized Peasant Movement.
4271 **1458** 18st. multicoloured . . . 25 20

1999. Song Birds and their Eggs. Multicoloured.
4273　8st. Type **1460** 10 10
4274　18st. Mistle thrush 25 20
4275　20st. Dunnock 30 20
4276　60st. Ortolan bunting . . . 85 60

1461 Greek Tortoise

1999. Reptiles. Multicoloured.
4277　10st. Type **1461** 10 10
4278　18st. Swamp turtle 30 20
4279　30st. Hermann's tortoise . . 35 25
4280　60st. Caspian turtle 85 60

1462 Boxing (16 medals)

1999. Bulgarian Olympic Medal Winning Sports. Multicoloured.
4281　10st. Type **1462** 10 10
4282　20st. High jumping (17 medals) 30 20
4283　30st. Weightlifting (31 medals) 35 25
4284　60st. Wrestling (60 medals) 85 60

1463 Police Light and Emblem

1999. 10th European Police Conference.
4285 **1463** 18st. multicoloured . . . 20 10

1464 Jug　**1465** Virgin and Child

1999. Gold Artefacts from Panagyurishte.
4286 **1464** 2st. brown and green . . . 10 10
4287　－ 3st. brown and green . . . 10 10
4288　－ 5st. brown and blue . . 10 10
4289　－ 30st. brown and violet . . 20 10
4290　－ 1l. brown and red . . . 90 35
DESIGNS: 3st. Human figures around top of drinking horn; 5st. Bottom of chamois-shaped drinking horn; 30st. Decorated handle and spout; 1l. Head-shaped jug.

1999. Christmas. Religious Icons. Multicoloured.
4291　18st. Type **1465** 15 10
4292　60st. Jesus Christ 85 30

1466 Scout beside Fire

1999. Europa. Parks and Gardens. Multicoloured.
4239　180l. Type **1448** 25 10
4240　600l. Central Balkan National Park 75 30

1999. Scouts. Multicoloured.
4293	10st. Type **1466**	10	10
4294	18st. Scout helping child .	15	10
4295	30st. Scout saluting . . .	30	10
4296	60st. Girl and boy scouts .	85	30

1467 Emblem

1999. "Expo 2005" World's Fair, Aichi, Japan.
| 4297 | **1467** | 18st. multicoloured | 20 | 10 |

1468 Emblem and Flag

2000. Bulgarian Membership of European Union.
| 4298 | **1468** | 18st. multicoloured . . | 10 | 10 |

1470 Peter Beron and Scientific Instruments

2000. Birth Anniversaries. Multicoloured.
4300	10st. Type **1470** (scientist, bicentenary)	10	10
4301	20st. Zakhari Stoyanov (writer, 150th anniv) . . .	15	10
4302	50st. Kolyo Ficheto (architect, bicentenary) . .	30	10

1471 Madonna and Child with Circuit Board

2000. Europa. Multicoloured.
| 4303 | 18st. Type **1471** . . . . | 10 | 10 |
| 4304 | 60st. Madonna and Child (Leonardo da Vinci) with circuit board . . . . . | 40 | 10 |

1472 Judo

2000. Olympic Games, Sydney. Multicoloured.
4305	10st. Type **1472**	10	10
4306	18st. Tennis	10	10
4307	20st. Pistol shooting	15	10
4308	60st. Long jump	40	10

1473 *Puss in Boots* (Charles Perrault)

2000. Children's Fairytales. Multicoloured.
4309	10st. Type **1473**	10	10
4310	18st. *Little Red Riding Hood* (Brothers Grimm)	10	10
4311	18st. *Thumbelina* (Hans Christian Andersen) . . .	10	10

1474 "Friends" (detail) (Assen Vasiliev)

2000. Artists Birth Centenaries. Art. Multicoloured.
4312	18st. Type **1474**	10	10
4313	18st. "All Soul's Day" (detail) (Pencho Georgiev)	10	10
4314	18st. "Veliko Tunovo" (detail) (Ivan Khristov)	10	10
4315	18st. "At the Fountain" (sculpture) (detail) (Ivan Funev)	10	10

1475 Roman Mosaic (detail), Stara Zagora

2000. "EXPO 2000" World's Fair, Hanover, Germany.
| 4316 | **1475** | 60st. multicoloured . . | 40 | 10 |

1476 Johannes Gutenberg (inventor of printing) and Printed Characters

2000. Anniversaries. Multicoloured.
4317	10st. Type **1476** (600th birth anniv)	10	10
4318	18st. Johann Sebastian Bach (composer, 250th death anniv)	10	10
4319	20st. Guy de Maupassant (writer, 150th birth anniv)	15	10
4320	60st. Antoine de Saint-Exupery (writer and aviator, birth centenary)	40	10

1477 *La Jeune* (Lebardy-Juillot airship) and Eiffel Tower, 1903

1480 St. Atanasii Church, Startsevo

2000. Centenary of First Zeppelin Flight. Airship Development. Multicoloured.
4321	10st. Type **1477**	10	10
4322	18st. LZ-13 *Hansa* (Zeppelin airship) over Cologne	10	10
4323	20st. N-1 *Norge* over Rome	15	10
4324	60st. *Graf Zeppelin* over Sofia	40	10

1478 Vazov and Text

2000. 150th Birth Anniv of Ivan Vazov (writer).
| 4325 | **1478** | 18st. multicoloured | 10 | 10 |

2000. Churches.
4327	**1480**	22st. black and blue . .	15	10
4328	–	24st. black and mauve .	15	10
4329	–	50st. black and yellow .	30	10
4330	–	65st. black and green .	40	10
4331	–	3l. black and orange .	2·00	40
4332	–	5l. black and rose . .	3·00	40

DESIGNS: 24st. St. Clement of Orhid, Sofia; 50st. Mary of the Ascension, Sofia; 65st. St. Nedelya, Nedelino, 3l. Mary of the Ascension, Sofia (different); 5l. Mary of the Ascension, Pamporovo.

1481 Ibex (*Capra ibex*)

2000. Animals. Multicoloured.
4333	10st. Type **1481**	10	10
4334	22st. Argali (*Ovis ammon*)	15	10
4335	30st. European bison (*Bison bonasus*)	20	10
4336	65st. Yak (*Bos grunniens*) . .	40	10

1482 Field Gladiolus (*Gladiolus segetum*)

1484 Order of Gallantry, 1880

2000. Spring Flowers. Multicoloured.
4337	10st. Type **1482**	10	10
4338	22st. Liverwort (*Hepatica nobilis*)	15	10
4339	30st. Pheasant's eye (*Adonis vernalis*)	20	10
4340	65st. Peacock anemone (*Anemone pavonina*) . .	40	10

1483 Crowd and Emblem

2000. 50th Anniv of European Convention on Human Rights.
| 4341 | **1483** | 65st. multicoloured . . | 40 | 10 |

2000. Medals. Multicoloured.
4342	12st. Type **1484**	10	10
4343	22st. Order of St. Aleksandu, 1882 . . .	15	10
4344	30st. Order of Merit, 1891	20	10
4345	65st. Order of Cyril and Methodius, 1909	40	10

1485 Prince Boris-Mihail

2000. Bimillenary of Christianity. Multicoloured.
4346	22st. Type **1485**	15	10
4347	22st. Sofroni Vrachanski . .	15	10
4348	65st. Mary and Child (detail)	40	10
4349	65st. Antim I	40	10

1486 Seal

2000. 120th Anniv of Supreme Audit Office.
| 4350 | **1486** | 22st. multicoloured . . | 15 | 10 |

EXPRESS STAMPS

E **137** Express Delivery Van

1939.
E429	–	5l. blue	50	25
E430	E **137**	6l. brown	30	25
E431	–	7l. brown	40	30
E432	E **137**	8l. red	65	30
E433	–	20l. red	1·25	65

DESIGNS—VERT: 5l., 20l. Bicycle messenger; 7l. Motor-cyclist and sidecar.

OFFICIAL STAMPS

O **158**

O **177**

1942.
O507	O **158**	10s. green	10	10
O508	–	30s. orange	10	10
O509	–	50s. brown	10	10
O510	–	1l. blue	10	10
O511	–	2l. green	10	10
O534	–	2l. red	20	10
O512	–	3l. mauve	10	10
O513	–	4l. pink	10	10
O514	–	5l. red	10	10

The 1l. to 5l. are larger (19 × 23 mm).

1945. Arms designs. Imperf or perf.
O580	–	1l. mauve	10	10
O581	O **177**	2l. green	10	10
O582	–	3l. brown	10	10
O583	–	4l. blue	10	10
O584	–	5l. red	10	10

PARCEL POST STAMPS

P **153** Weighing Machine

P **154** Loading Motor Lorry

1941.
P494	P **153**	1l. green	10	10
P495	A	2l. red	30	10
P496	B	3l. brown	10	10
P497	B	4l. orange	10	10
P498	P **153**	5l. blue	10	10
P506		5l. green	10	10
P499	B	6l. purple	10	10
P507		6l. brown	10	10
P500	P **153**	7l. blue	10	10
P508		7l. sepia	10	10
P501	P **154**	8l. turquoise . . .	10	10
P509		8l. green	10	10
P502	A	9l. olive	50	15
P503	B	10l. orange . . .	15	10
P504	P **154**	20l. violet	35	10
P505	A	30l. black	1·60	15

DESIGNS—HORIZ: A, Loading mail coach; B, Motor-cycle combination.

P **163**

1944. Imperf.
P532	P **163**	1l. red	10	10
P533		3l. green	10	10
P534		5l. green	10	10
P535		7l. mauve	10	10
P536		10l. blue	10	10
P537		20l. brown	10	10
P538		30l. purple	10	10
P539		50l. orange	35	10
P540		100l. blue	60	25

POSTAGE DUE STAMPS

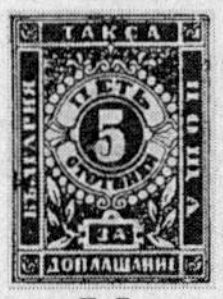
D 7

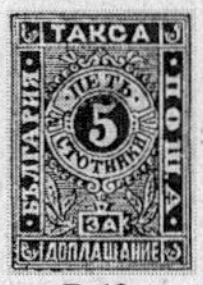
D 12

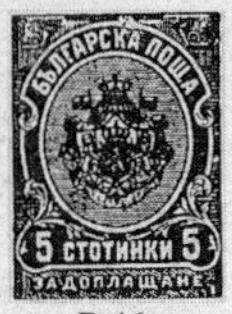
D 16

1884. Perf.
D75 D 7 5s. orange . . . . 17·00 2·50
D54 25s. lake . . . . 7·50 2·50
D55 50s. blue . . . . 3·50 2·50

1886. Imperf.
D50 D 7 5s. orange . . . . . . £150 8·50
D51 25s. lake . . . . £250 7·50
D52a 50s. blue . . . . 8·00 6·50

1893. Surch with bar and **30**.
D78d D 7 30s. on 50s. blue (perf) 13·50 5·00
D79 30s. on 50s. blue (imperf) . . . . . . 10·00 4·00

1896. Perf.
D83 D 12 5s. orange . . . . . . 6·75 1·25
D84 10s. violet . . . . . . 4·25 1·60
D85 30s. green . . . . . . 3·15 1·00

1901.
D124 D 16 5s. red 35 20
D125 10s. green 70 25
D126 20s. blue . . . . . . 5·00 25
D127 30s. red 50 30
D128 50s. orange . . . . . 7·50 4·50

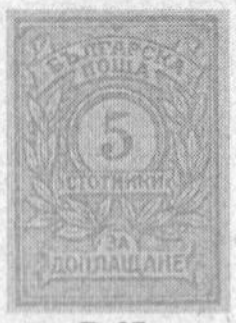
D 37

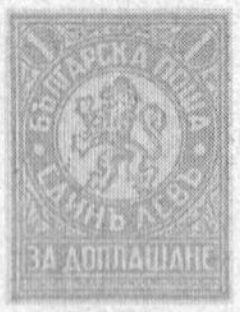
D 110

1915.
D200 D 37 5s. green 15 10
D240 10s. violet 10 10
D202 20s. red 15 10
D241 20s. orange 10 10
D203a 30s. red 15 10
D242 50s. blue 10 10
D243 1l. green 10 10
D244 2l. red 10 10
D245 3l. brown 20 10

1932.
D326 D 110 1l. bistre 50 40
D327 2l. red 50 40
D328 6l. purple . . . . . 1·50 60

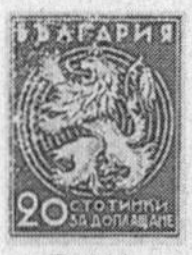
D 111

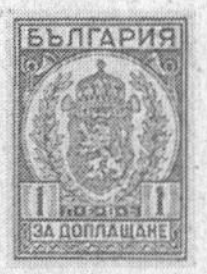
D 112

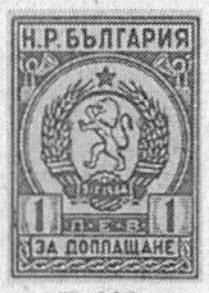
D 293

1933.
D333 D 111 20s. sepia 10 10
D334 40s. blue 10 10
D335 80s. red 10 10
D336 D 112 1l. brown 40 40
D337 2l. olive 50 50
D338 6l. violet 30 30
D339 14l. blue 40 40

1947. As Type D **112**, but larger (18 × 24 mm).
D646 1l. brown 10 10
D647 2l. red 10 10
D648 8l. orange 15 10
D649 20l. blue 35 15

1951.
D849 D 293 1l. brown 10 10
D850 2l. purple 10 10
D851 8l. orange 40 30
D852 20l. blue . . . . . . 1·10 90

BULGARIAN OCCUPATION OF RUMANIA Pt. 3

(DOBRUJA DISTRICT)

100 stotinki = 1 leva.

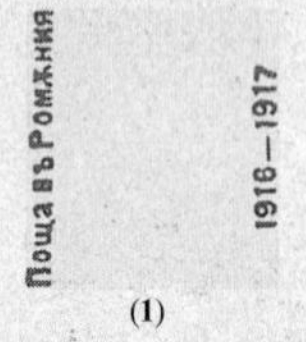

(1)

1916. Bulgarian stamps of 1911 optd with T **1**.
1 23 1s. grey 10 10
2 – 5s. brown and green . . . . 1·50 1·25
3 – 10s. sepia and brown 15 10
4 – 25s. black and blue 15 10

BUNDI Pt. 1

A state of Rajasthan, India. Now uses Indian stamps.

12 pies = 1 anna; 16 annas = 1 rupee.

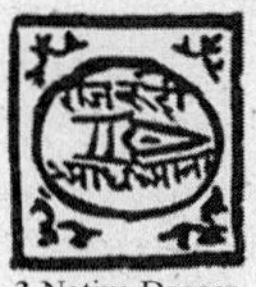
3 Native Dagger

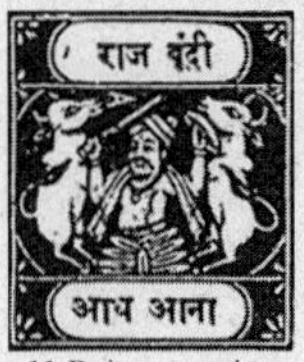
11 Raja protecting Sacred Cows

1894. Imperf.
12 3 ½a. grey . . . . 3·25 3·50
13 1a. red . . . . 2·25 2·25
14 2a. green . . . . 7·00 10·00
8 4a. green . . . . 45·00 65·00
15 8a. red . . . . 8·50 11·00
16a 1r. yellow on blue . . . . . 11·00 19·00

1898. As T **3**, but with dagger point to left.
17a 3 4a. green . . . . 10·00 15·00

1914. Roul or perf.
26 11 ¼a. blue . . . . 1·90 4·25
38 ½a. black . . . . 1·40 4·50
28 1a. red . . . . 3·25 9·50
20a 2a. green . . . . 3·00 9·00
30 2½a. yellow . . . . 5·00 21·00
31 3a. brown . . . . 4·75 30·00
32 4a. green . . . . 3·50 32·00
33 6a. blue . . . . 11·00 80·00
42 8a. orange . . . . 9·00 55·00
43 10a. olive . . . . 16·00 80·00
44 12a. green . . . . 9·50 85·00
25 1r. lilac . . . . 21·00 85·00
46 2r. brown and black . . . 60·00 £225
47 3r. blue and brown . . . . 90·00 £250
48 4r. green and red £190 £325
49 5r. red and green £190 £325

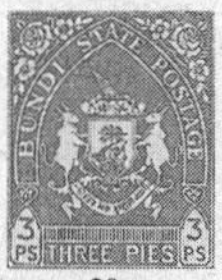
20

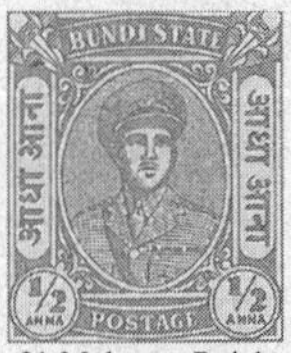
21 Maharao Rajah Bahadur Singh

1941. Perf.
79 20 3p. blue . . . . 2·00 3·00
80 6p. blue . . . . 3·50 5·00
81 1a. red . . . . 3·75 6·50
82 2a. brown . . . . 5·50 14·00
83 4a. green . . . . 11·00 40·00
84 8a. green . . . . 12·00 £140
85 1r. blue . . . . 32·00 £200

1947.
86 21 ¼a. green . . . . 1·60 28·00
87 ½a. violet . . . . 1·60 27·00
88 1a. green . . . . 1·60 26·00
89 – 2a. red . . . . 1·60 50·00
90 – 4a. orange . . . . 1·60 75·00
91 – 8a. blue . . . . 2·00
92 – 1r. brown . . . . 14·00
DESIGNS: 2, 4a. Rajah in Indian dress; 8a., 1r. View of Bundi.

OFFICIAL STAMPS

बूंदी

सरविस
(O 1)

1915. Optd as Type O **1**.
O 6A ¼a. blue . . . . 1·60
O16A ½a. black . . . . 7·50
O 8A 1a. red . . . . 4·00
O18A 2a. green . . . . 5·00
O 2A 2½a. yellow . . . . 3·75
O 3A 3a. brown . . . . 3·00
O19A 4a. green . . . . 9·00
O11A 6a. blue . . . . 13·00
O20A 8a. orange . . . . 15·00
O21A 10a. olive . . . . 45·00
O22A 12a. green . . . . 40·00
O 5A 1r. lilac . . . . 42·00
O24A 2r. brown and black £375
O25A 3r. blue and brown £350
O26A 4r green and red £300
O27A 5r. red and green £300

1915. Optd **BUNDI SERVICE**.
O 6B 11 ¼a. blue . . . . 1·75
O16B ½a. black . . . . 3·00
O 8bB 1a. red . . . . 12·00
O18 B 2a. green . . . . 14·00
O 2 B 2½a. yellow . . . . 14·00
O 3 B 3a. brown . . . . 20·00
O19 B 4a. green . . . . 65·00
O11 B 6a. blue £170
O20 B 8a. orange . . . . 24·00
O21 B 10a. olive . . . . 75·00
O22 B 12a. green . . . . 85·00
O 5 B 1r. lilac . . . . 42·00
O24 B 2r. brown and black £180
O25 B 3r. blue and brown £200
O26 B 4r. green and red £300
O27 B 5r. red and green £300
Prices for Nos. O2/27 are for unused examples. Used examples are generally worth a small premium over the prices quoted.

1941. Optd **SERVICE**.
O53 20 3p. blue . . . . 5·50 10·00
O54 6p. blue . . . . 13·00 10·00
O55 1a. red . . . . 13·00 7·50
O56 2a. brown . . . . . . 10·00 8·50
O57 4a. green . . . . . . 30·00 75·00
O58 20 8a. green £120 £375
O59 1r. blue . . . . 14·00 £400

For later issues see **RAJASTHAN**.

BURKINA FASO Pt. 12

A country in W. Africa, formerly known as Upper Volta. The name was changed in August 1984.

100 centimes = 1 franc.

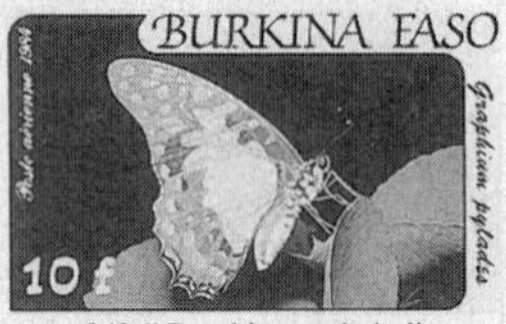

249 "Graphium pylades"

1984. Air. Butterflies. Multicoloured.
738 10f. Type **249** 10 10
739 120f. "Hyploimnas misippus" 65 40
740 400f. "Danaus chrysippus" 2·10 1·50
741 450f. "Papilio demodocus" 2·40 1·60

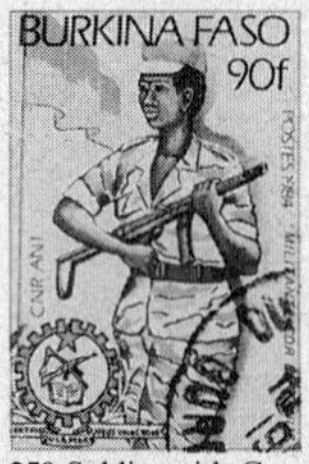

250 Soldier with Gun

1984. 1st Anniv of Captain Thomas Sankara's Presidency. Multicoloured.
742 90f. Type **250** 40 25
743 120f. Capt. Sankara and crowd 50 35

1984. Aid for the Sahel. No. 682 of Upper Volta optd **BURKINA FASO Aide au Sahel 84**.
743a 100f. multicoloured 20 15

1985. Nos. 716/21 of Upper Volta optd **BURKINA FASO**.
744 25f. Type **246** (postage) . . . 15 10
745 185f. "Pterocarpus lucens" 80 65
746 200f. "Phlebopus colossus sudanicus" . . . . 1·50 85
747 250f. "Cosmos sulphureus" 1·10 90
748 300f. "Trametes versicolor" (air) . . . . 1·75 1·25
749 400f. "Ganoderma lucidum" 2·25 1·75

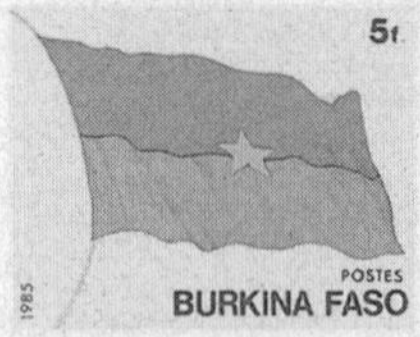

252 National Flag

1985. National Symbols. Multicoloured.
750 5f. Type **252** (postage) . . . 10 10
751 15f. National arms (vert) . . . 10 10
752 90f. Maps of Africa and Burkina Faso 40 25
753 120f. Type **252** (air) 50 35
754 150f. As No. 751 . . . . . . 65 50
755 185f. As No. 752 . . . . . . 80 65

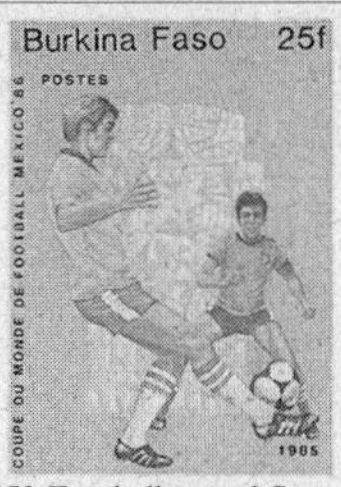

253 Footballers and Statue

1985. World Cup Football Championship, Mexico.
756 253 25f. mult. (postage) . . . 15 10
757 – 45f. multicoloured 20 15
758 – 90f. multicoloured 40 25
759 – 100f. multicoloured (air) 45 30
760 – 150f. multicoloured . . . 65 50
761 – 200f. mult (horiz) 90 75
762 – 250f. mult (horiz) . . . . 1·10 90
DESIGNS: 45f. to 250f. Mexican statues and various footballing scenes.

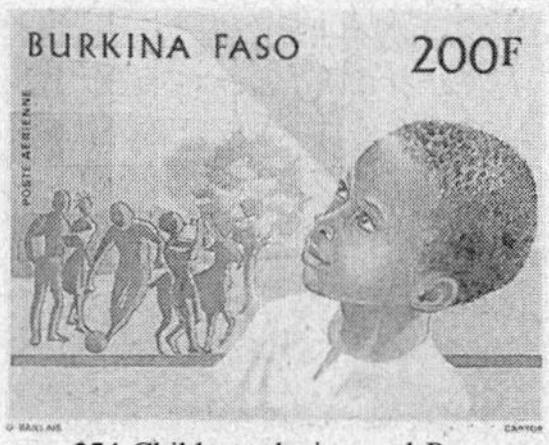

254 Children playing and Boy

1985. Air "Philexafrique" International Stamp Exhibition, Lome, Togo (1st issue). Multicoloured.
764 200f. Type **254** 90 75
765 200f. Solar panels, transmission mast, windmill, dish aerial and tree 90 75
See also Nos. 839/40.

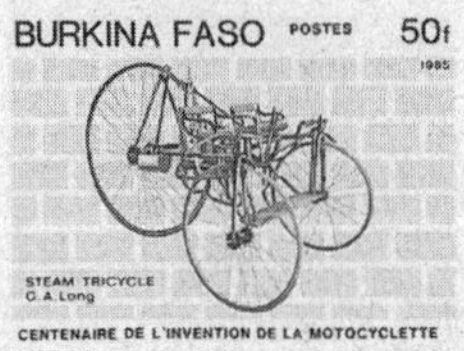

255 G. A. Long's Steam Tricycle

1985. Centenary of Motor Cycle. Multicoloured.
766 50f. Type **255** (postage) . . . 20 15
767 75f. Pope 30 20
768 80f. Manet 35 25
769 100f. Ducati (air) 45 30
770 150f. Jawa 65 50
771 200f. Honda 90 75
772 250f. B.M.W. . . . . 1·10 90

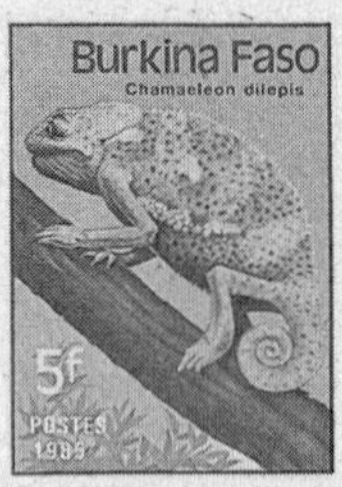

256 "Chamaeleon dilepis"

1985. Reptiles and Amphibians. Multicoloured.
773 5f. Type **256** (postage) . . . 10 10
774 15f. "Agama stellio" 10 10
775 33f. "Lacerta lepida" (horiz) 15 10
776 85f. "Hiperolius marmoratus" (horiz) 35 25
777 100f. "Echis leucogaster" (horiz) (air) 45 30
778 150f. "Kinixys erosa" (horiz) 65 50
779 250f. "Python regius" (horiz) 1·10 90

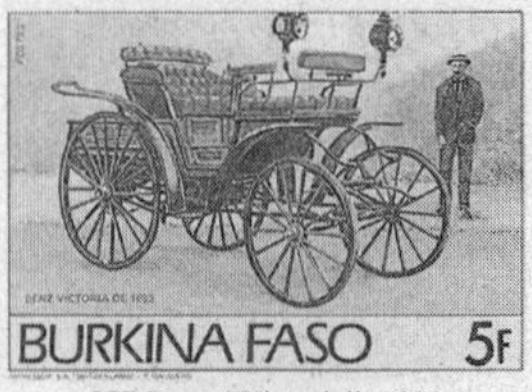

257 Benz "Victoria", 1893

1985. Motor Cars and Aircraft. Multicoloured.
780 5f. Type **257** (postage) . . . 10 10
781 25f. Peugeot "174", 1927 . . 15 10
782 45f. Bleriot XI airplane . . . 40 15
783 50f. Breguet 14T biplane . . . 40 15
784 500f. Bugatti "Napoleon T41 Royale" (air) . . . . 2·75 2·25
785 500f. Airbus Industrie A300 2·75 2·25

786 600f. Mercedes-Benz "540 K", 1938 . . . . 3·00 2·50
787 600f. Airbus Industrie A300 3·00 2·50

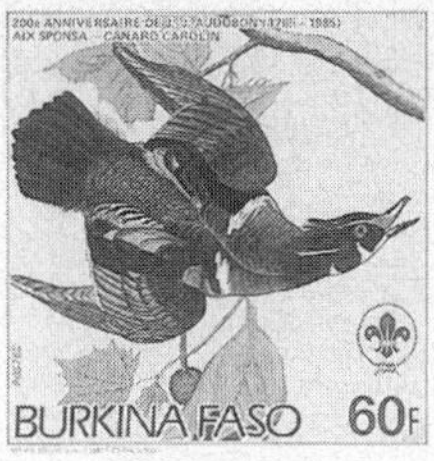
258 Wood Duck

1985. Birth Bicentenary of John J. Audubon (ornithologist). Multicoloured.
789 60f. Type **258** (postage) . . . 40 25
790 100f. Northern mockingbird 80 40
791 300f. Northern oriole . . . . 2·25 75
792 400f. White-breasted nuthatch 2·50 1·75
793 500f. Common flicker (air) 3·50 2·40
794 600f. Rough-legged buzzard 3·75 2·75

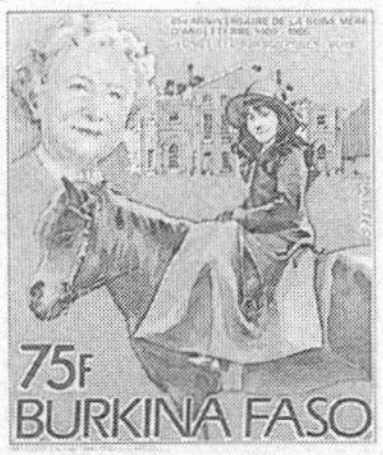
259 Young Lady Elizabeth Bowes-Lyon on Pony

1985. 85th Birthday of Queen Elizabeth the Queen Mother. Multicoloured.
796 75f. Type **259** (postage) . . . 30 20
797 85f. Marriage of Lady Elizabeth Bowes-Lyon and Albert, Duke of York . . 35 25
798 500f. Duke and Duchess of York with Princess Elizabeth (air) . . . . . . 2·25 1·90
799 600f. Royal family in Coronation robes . . . . 2·50 2·25

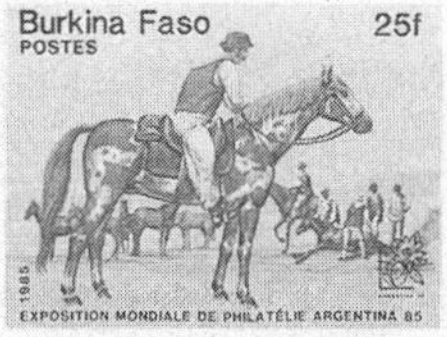
260 Gaucho on Piebald Horse

1985. "Argentina '85" International Stamp Exhibition, Buenos Aires. Horses. Multicoloured.
801 25f. Type **260** (postage) . . . 15 10
802 45f. Gaucho on horse 20 15
803 90f. Rodeo rider 45 30
804 100f. Rider hunting gazelle (air) 45 30
805 150f. Horses and gauchos at camp fire 65 50
806 200f. Horse and man sitting on steps 90 75
807 250f. Riding contest . . . . 1·10 90

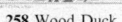

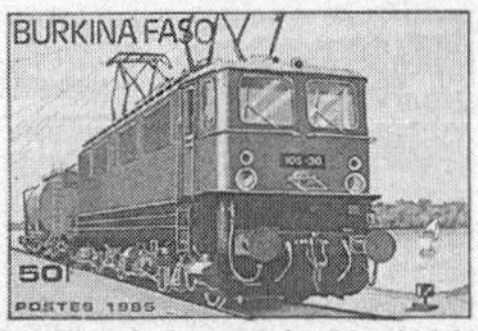
261 Electric Locomotive No. 105-30 and Tank Wagon

1985. Trains. Multicoloured.
809 50f. Type **261** (postage) . . . 50 10
810 75f. Diesel shunting locomotive 65 15
811 80f. Diesel passenger locomotive 70 20
812 100f. Diesel railcar (air) . . . 90 20
813 150f. Diesel locomotive No. 6093 . . . . 1·25 35
814 200f. Diesel railcar No. 105 1·60 50
815 250f. Diesel locomotive pulling passenger train . . 2·40 70

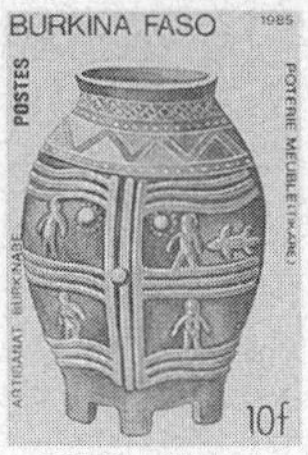
262 Pot (Tikare)

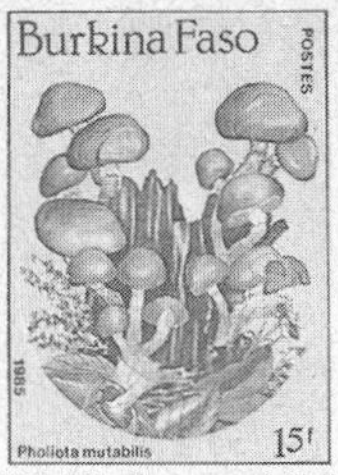
263 "Pholiota mutabilis"

1985. Handicrafts. Multicoloured.
816 10f. Type **262** (postage) . . . 10 10
817 40f. Pot with lid decorated with birds (P. Bazega) . . 20 15
818 90f. Bronze statuette of mother with child (Ouagadougou) 40 25
819 120f. Bronze statuette of drummer (Ouagadougou) (air) 50 35

1985. Fungi. Multicoloured.
820 15f. Type **263** (postage) . . . 15 10
821 20f. "Hypholoma (nematoloma) fasciculare" 20 10
822 30f. "Ixocomus granulatus" 25 10
823 60f. "Agaricus campestris" 50 20
824 80f. "Trachypus scaber" . . 70 40
825 250f. "Marasmius scorodonius" . . . . . . 2·25 1·40
826 150f. "Armillaria mellea" (air) . . . . 1·10 60

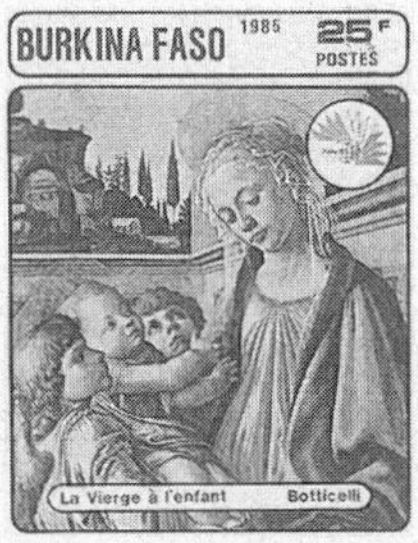
264 "Virgin and Child"

1985. "Italia '85" International Stamp Exhibition, Rome. Paintings by Botticelli.
827 25f. Type **264** (postage) . . . 15 10
828 45f. "Portrait of an Unknown Man" 20 15
829 90f. "Mars and Venus" . . . 50 30
830 100f. "Birth of Venus" (air) 55 40
831 150f. "Allegory of Calumny" 75 60
832 200f. "Pallas and the Centaur" 90 75
833 250f. "Allegory of Spring" 1·10 90

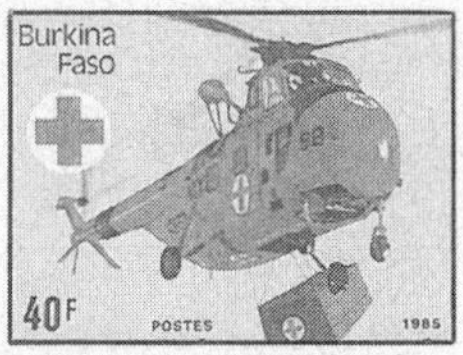
265 Sikorsky S-55 Helicopter

1985. Red Cross. Multicoloured.
835 40f. Type **265** (postage) . . . 30 15
836 85f. Ambulance 35 25
837 150f. Henri Dunant (founder) (vert) (air) 65 50
838 250f. Nurse attending patient (vert) . . . . 1·10 90

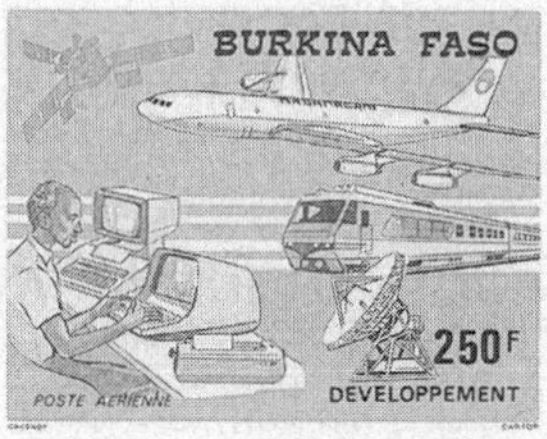
266 Transport and Communications (development)

1985. Air. "Philexafrique" International Stamp Exhibition, Lome, Togo (2nd issue). Mult.
839 250f. Type **266** . . . . 3·75 1·50
840 250f. Youth activities (youth) 1·10 90

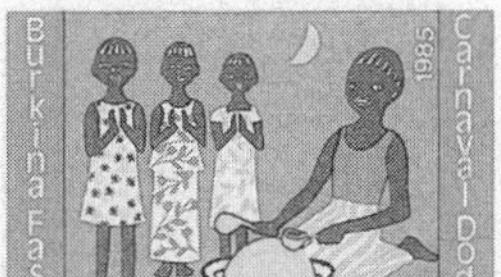
267 Girls drumming and clapping

1986. Dodo Carnival. Multicoloured.
841 20f. Type **267** 10 10
842 25f. Masked lion dancers . . 15 10
843 40f. Masked stick dancers and drummers 20 15
844 45f. Stick dancers with elaborate headdresses . . . 20 15
845 90f. Masked elephant dancer 40 25
846 90f. Animal dancers 40 25

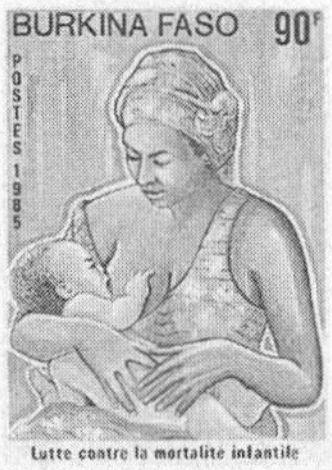
268 Mother breast-feeding Baby

1986. Child Survival Campaign.
847 **268** 90f. multicoloured 40 25

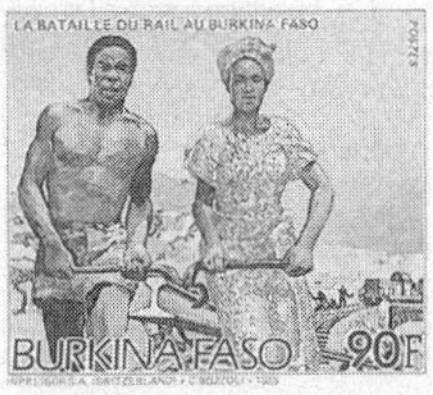
269 Couple carrying Rail

1986. Railway Construction. Multicoloured.
848 90f. Type **269** (postage) . . . 70 15
849 120f. Laying tracks 85 25
850 185f. Workers waving to passing train . . . . . . 1·60 60
851 500f. "Inauguration of First German Railway" (Heim) (air) . . . . 4·00 1·75
No. 851 commemorates the 150th anniv of German railways.

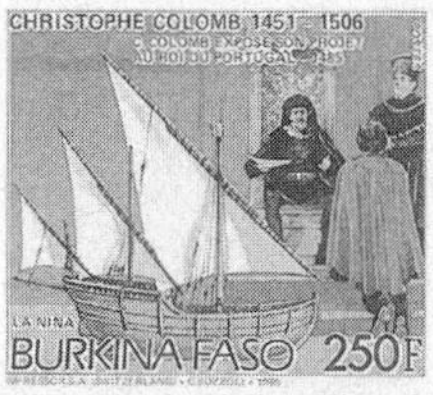
270 Columbus before King of Portugal, and "Nina"

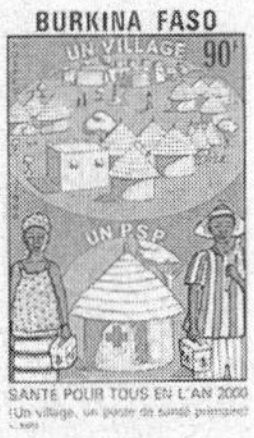
271 Village and First Aid Post

1986. 480th Death Anniv of Christopher Columbus (explorer). Multicoloured.
853 250f. Type **270** (postage) . . 1·60 90
854 300f. "Santa Maria" and Columbus with astrolabe 2·00 1·00
855 400f. Columbus imprisoned and "Santa Maria" . . . . 2·60 1·50
856 450f. Landing at San Salvador and "Pinta" (air) 3·25 1·60

1986. "Health For All by Year 2000". Mult.
858 90f. Type **271** 40 25
859 100f. Man receiving first aid (26 × 36 mm) 40 25
860 120f. People queuing for vaccinations (26 × 36 mm) 50 35

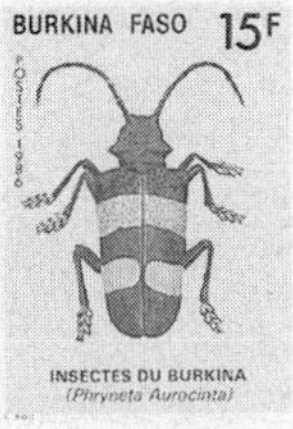
272 "Phryneta aurocinta"

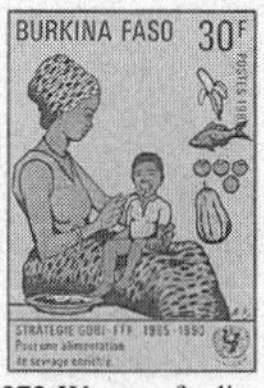
273 Woman feeding Child and Fresh Foods

1986. Insects. Multicoloured.
861 15f. Type **272** 10 10
862 20f. "Sternocera interrupta" 10 10
863 40f. "Prosoprocera lactator" 35 15
864 45f. "Gonimbrasia hecate" 40 15
865 85f. "Charaxes epijasius" . . 70 50

1986. Gobi Health Strategy. Multicoloured.
866 30f. Type **273** 15 10
867 60f. Ingredients of oral rehydration therapy . . . 25 15
868 90f. Mother holding child for vaccination 40 25
869 120f. Doctor weighing child 50 35

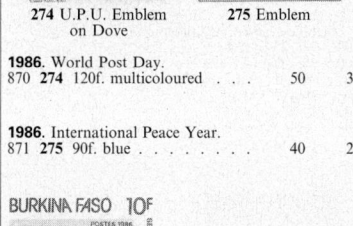

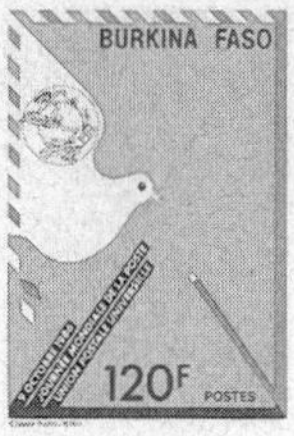
274 U.P.U. Emblem on Dove

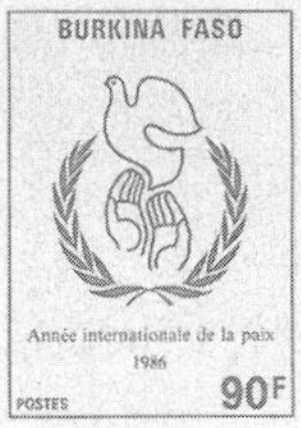
275 Emblem

1986. World Post Day.
870 **274** 120f. multicoloured . . . 50 35

1986. International Peace Year.
871 **275** 90f. blue 40 25

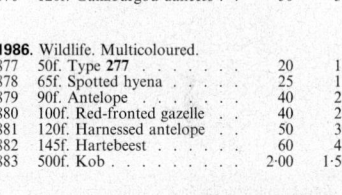

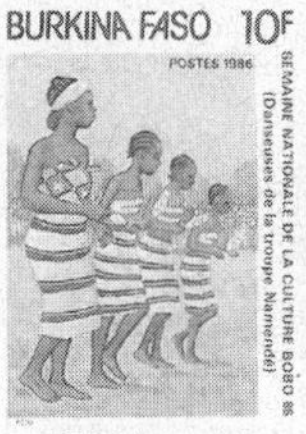
276 Namende Dancers

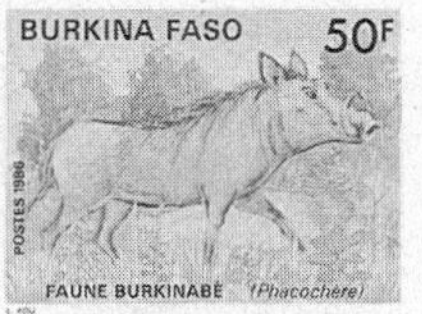
277 Warthog

1986. National Bobo Culture Week. Mult.
872 10f. Type **276** 10 10
873 25f. Mouhoun dancers . . . 10 10
874 90f. Houet dancer 40 25
875 105f. Seno musicians 40 25
876 120f. Ganzourgou dancers . . 50 35

1986. Wildlife. Multicoloured.
877 50f. Type **277** 20 15
878 65f. Spotted hyena 25 15
879 90f. Antelope 40 25
880 100f. Red-fronted gazelle . . 40 25
881 120f. Harnessed antelope . . 50 35
882 145f. Hartebeest 60 45
883 500f. Kob . . . . 2·00 1·50

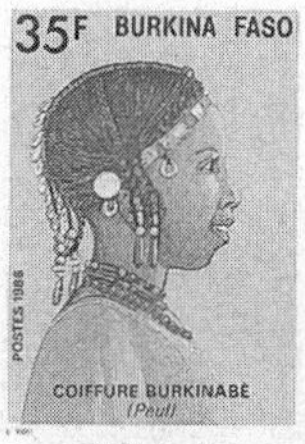
278 Peul

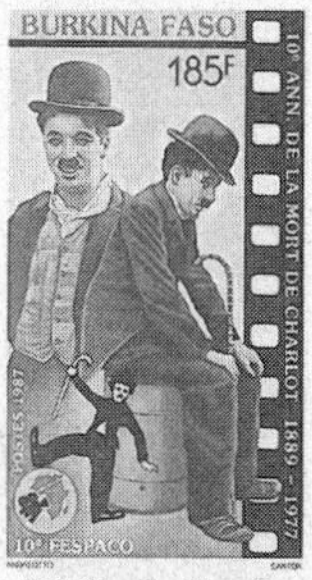
279 Charlie Chaplin within Film Frame (10th death anniv)

1986. Traditional Hairstyles. Multicoloured.
884 35f. Type **278** 25 15
885 75f. Dafing 30 20
886 90f. Peul (different) 55 30
887 120f. Mossi 60 35
888 185f. Peul (different) . . . . 1·00 80

1987. 10th Fespaco Film Festival.
889 – 90f. mauve, black & brn 40 25
890 – 120f. multicoloured . . . 50 35
891 **279** 185f. multicoloured . . . 75 60
DESIGNS: 90f. Camera on map in film frame; 120f. Cameraman and soundman (60th anniv of first talking film "The Jazz Singer").

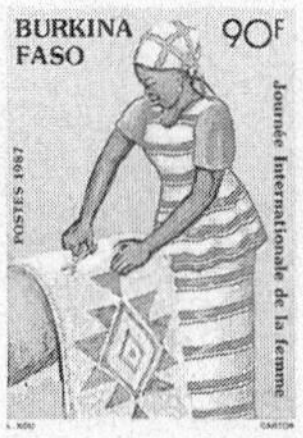
280 Woman trimming Rug

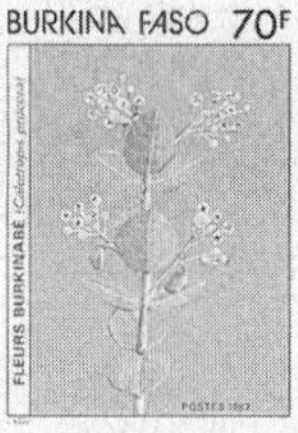
281 "Calotripis procera"

1987. International Women's Day.
892 **280** 90f. multicoloured 40 25

1987. Flowers. Multicoloured.
893 70f. Type **281** 30 20
894 75f. "Acacia seyal" 30 20
895 85f. "Parkia biglobosa" . . . 35 25
896 90f. "Sterospernum kunthianum" 40 25
897 100f. "Dichrostachys cinerea" 40 25
898 300f. "Combretum paniculatum" . . . . . . 1·25 1·00

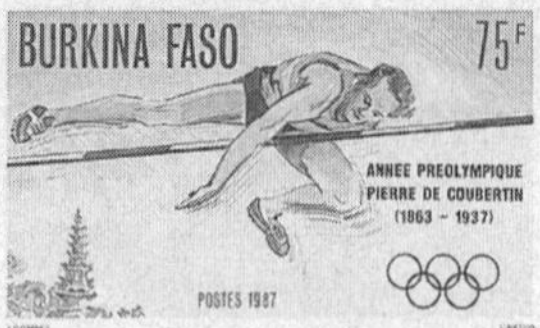

282 High Jumping

1987. Olympic Games, Seoul (1988). 50th Death Anniv of Pierre de Coubertin (founder of modern Olympic Games). Multicoloured.

899	75f. Type **282**	30	20
900	85f. Tennis (vert)	35	25
901	90f. Ski jumping	40	25
902	100f. Football	40	25
903	145f. Running	60	45
904	350f. Pierre de Coubertin and tennis game (vert)	1·50	1·25

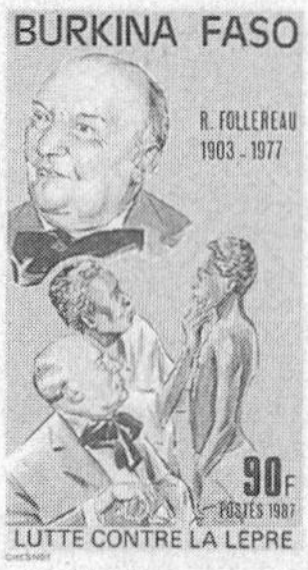

283 Follereau and Doctor treating Patient

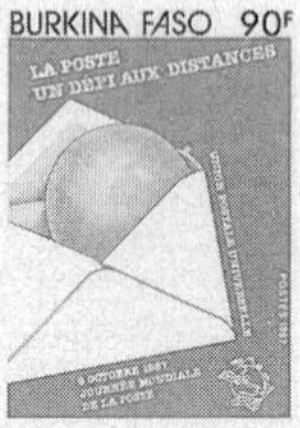

285 Globe in Envelope

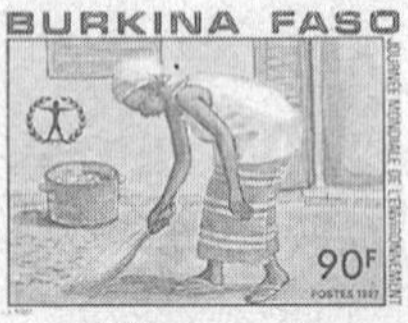

284 Woman sweeping

1987. Anti-leprosy Campaign. 10th Death Anniv of Raoul Follereau (pioneer). Multicoloured.

905	90f. Type **283**	40	25
906	100f. Laboratory technicians	40	25
907	120f. Gerhard Hansen (discoverer of bacillus)	50	35
908	300f. Follereau kissing patient	1·25	1·00

1987. World Environment Day. Multicoloured.

909	90f. Type **284**	40	25
910	145f. Emblem	60	45

1987. World Post Day.

911 **285**	90f. multicoloured	35	25

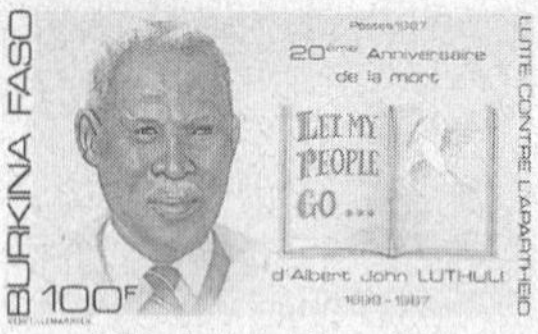

286 Luthuli and Open Book

1987. Anti-Apartheid Campaign. 20th Death Anniv of Albert John Luthuli (anti-apartheid campaigner). Multicoloured.

912	90f. Barbed wire and apartheid victims	35	25
913	100f. Type **286**	40	25

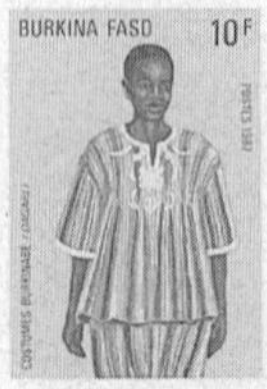

287 Dagari

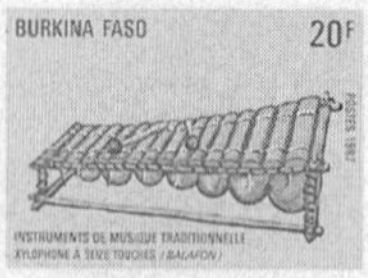

288 Balafon (16 key xylophone)

1987. Traditional Costumes. Multicoloured.

914	10f. Type **287**	10	10
915	30f. Peul	15	10
916	90f. Mossi (female)	35	25
917	200f. Senoufo	80	60
918	500f. Mossi (male)	1·90	1·40

1987. Traditional Music Instruments. Multicoloured.

919	20f. Type **288**	10	10
920	25f. Kunde en more (3 stringed lute) (vert)	10	10
921	35f. Tiahoun en bwaba (zither)	15	10
922	90f. Jembe en dioula (conical drum)	35	25
923	1000f. Bendre en more (calabash drum) (vert)	3·75	2·40

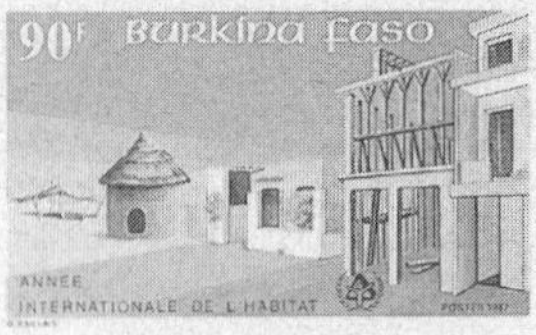

289 Dwellings

1987. International Year of Shelter for the Homeless.

924 **289**	90f. multicoloured	35	25

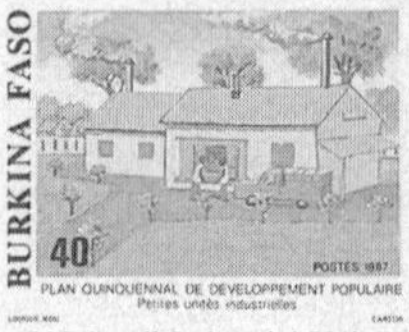

290 Small Industrial Units

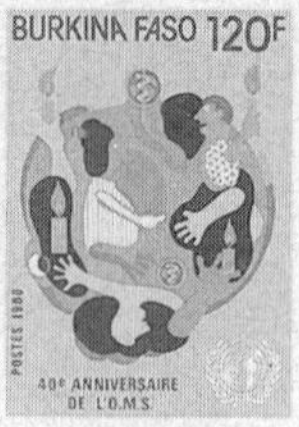

291 People with Candles

1987. Five Year Plan for Popular Development. Multicoloured.

925	40f. Type **290**	15	10
926	55f. Management of dams	20	15
927	60f. Village community building primary school	25	15
928	90f. Bus (Transport and communications)	35	25
929	100f. National education: literacy campaign	40	25
930	120f. Intensive cattle farming	45	30

1988. 40th Anniv of W.H.O.

931 **291**	120f. multicoloured	45	30

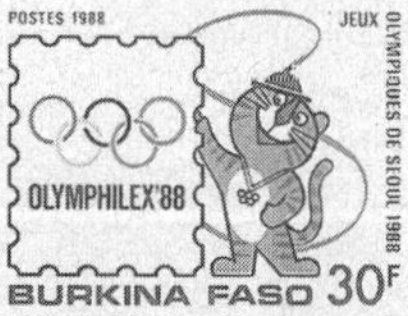

292 Exhibition Emblem and Games Mascot

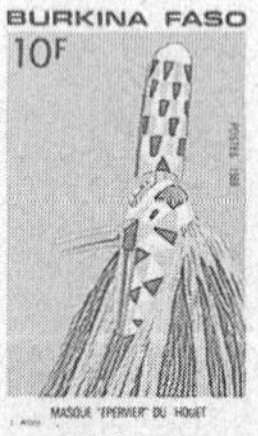

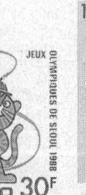

293 Houet "Sparrow Hawk" Mask

1988. Olympic Games, Seoul, and "Olymphilex '88" Olympic Stamps Exhibition, Rome (932). Multicoloured.

932	30f. Type **292**	15	10
933	160f. Olympic flame (vert)	60	45
934	175f. Football	65	45
935	235f. Volleyball (vert)	90	65
936	450f. Basketball (vert)	1·75	1·25

1988. Masks. Multicoloured.

938	10f. Type **293**	10	10
939	20f. Ouillo "Young Girls" mask	10	10
940	30f. Houet "Hartebeest" mask	15	10
941	40f. Mouhoun "Blacksmith" mask	15	10
942	120f. Ouri "Nanny" mask	45	30
943	175f. Ouri "Bat" mask (horiz)	65	45

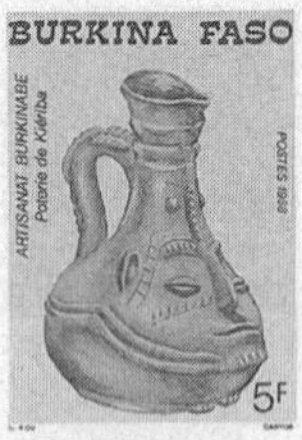

294 Kieriba Jug

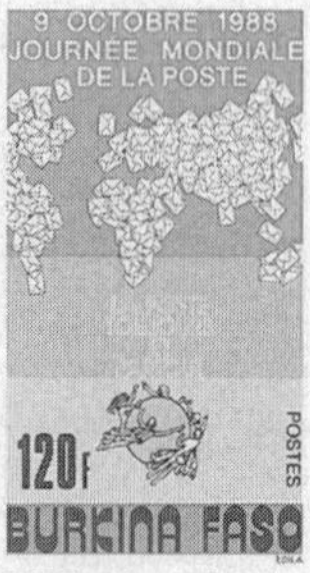

295 Envelopes forming Map

1988. Handicrafts. Multicoloured.

944	5f. Type **294**	10	10
945	15f. Mossi basket (horiz)	10	10
946	25f. Gurunsi chair (horiz)	10	10
947	30f. Bissa basket (horiz)	15	10
948	45f. Ouagadougou hide box (horiz)	15	10
949	85f. Ouagadougou bronze statuette	35	20
950	120f. Ouagadougou hide travelling bag (horiz)	45	30

1988. World Post Day.

951 **295**	120f. blue, black & yellow	45	30

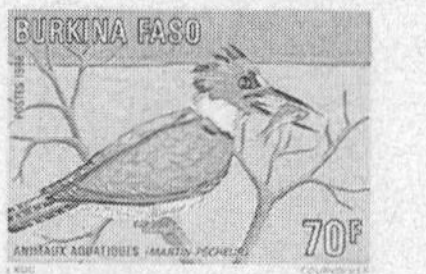

296 White-collared Kingfisher

1988. Aquatic Wildlife. Multicoloured.

952	70f. Type **296**	1·25	40
953	100f. Elephantfish	1·00	35
954	120f. Frog	55	30
955	160f. White-faced whistling duck	2·25	1·25

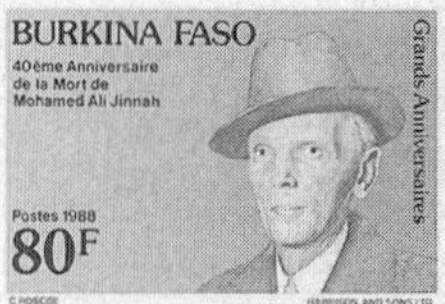

297 Mohammed Ali Jinnah (first Pakistan Governor-General)

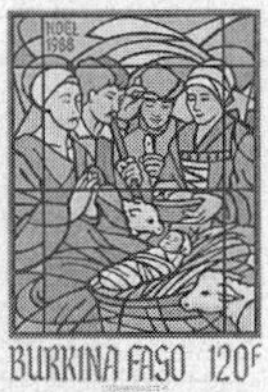

298 Shepherds adoring Child

1988. Death Anniversaries. Multicoloured.

956	80f. Type **297** (40th anniv) (postage)	30	20
957	120f. Mahatma Gandhi (Indian human rights activist, 40th anniv)	45	30
958	160f. John Fitzgerald Kennedy (U.S. President, 25th anniv)	60	45
959	235f. Martin Luther King (human rights activist, 20th anniv) (air)	90	65

1988. Christmas. Stained Glass Windows. Mult.

960	120f. Type **298**	45	30
961	160f. Wise men presenting gifts to Child	60	45
962	450f. Virgin and Child	1·75	1·25
963	1000f. Flight into Egypt	3·75	2·75

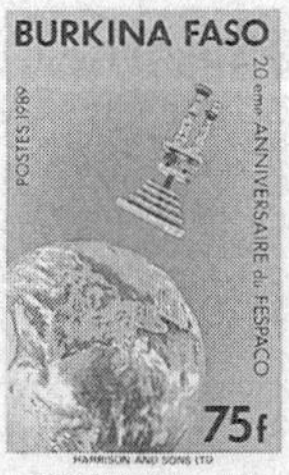

299 Satellite and Globe

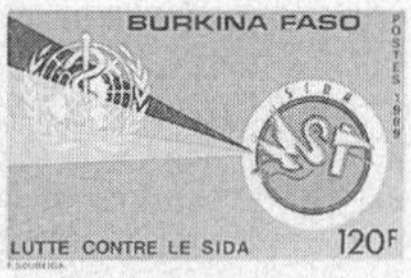

300 W.H.O. and Aids Emblems

1989. 20th Anniv of FESPACO Film Festival. Multicoloured.

964	75f. Type **299** (postage)	30	20
965	500f. Ababacar Samb Makharam (air)	1·90	1·40
966	500f. Jean Michel Tchissoukou	1·90	1·40
967	500f. Paulin Soumanou Vieyra	1·90	1·40

1989. Campaign against AIDS.

969 **300**	120f. multicoloured	45	30

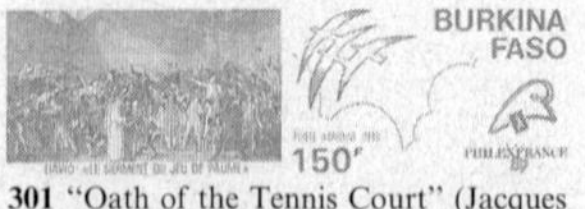

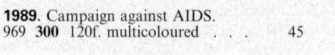

301 "Oath of the Tennis Court" (Jacques Louis David) (Illustration reduced. Actual size 80 × 36 mm)

1989. Air. "Philexfrance 89" International Stamp Exhibition, Paris, and Bicentenary of French Revolution. Multicoloured.

970	150f. Type **301**	60	45
971	200f. "Storming of the Bastille" (Thevenin)	75	50
972	600f. "Rouget de Lisle singing La Marseillaise" (Pils)	2·25	1·60

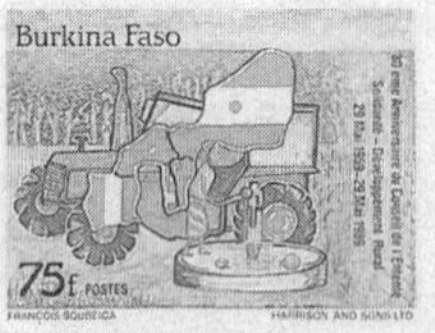

302 Map and Tractor

1989. 30th Anniv of Council of Unity.

973 **302**	75f. multicoloured	30	20

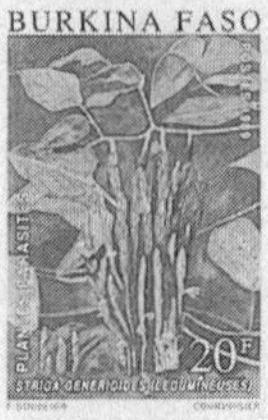

303 "Striga generioides"

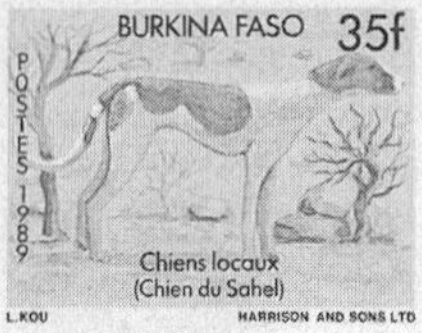

304 Sahel Dog

1989. Parasitic Plants. Multicoloured.

974	20f. Type **303**	10	10
975	50f. "Striga hermonthica"	20	15
976	235f. "Striga aspera"	90	65
977	450f. "Alectra vogelii"	1·75	1·25

1989. Dogs. Multicoloured.

978	35f. Type **304**	10	10
979	50f. Young dog	20	15
980	60f. Hunting dog	20	15
981	350f. Guard dog	1·50	1·00

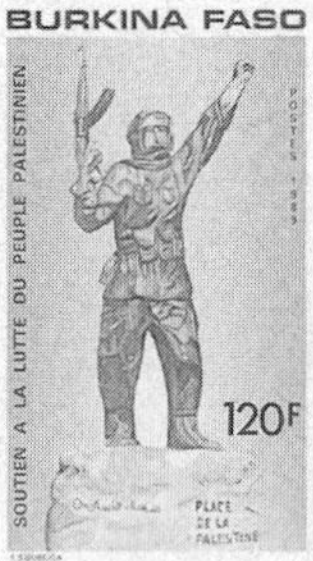

305 Statue

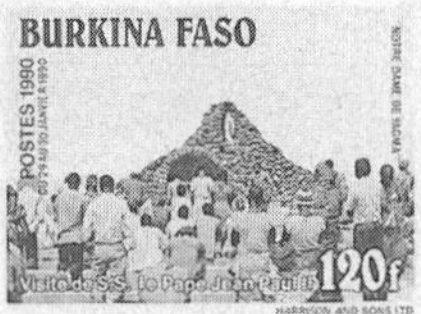

307 Pilgrims at Shrine of Our Lady of Yagma

1989. Solidarity with Palestinian People.

982 **305**	120f. multicoloured	45	30

1989. Nos. 647/9 of Upper Volta optd **BURKINA FASO**.

983 **229**	90f. multicoloured	35	20
984	120f. multicoloured	50	35
985	170f. multicoloured	70	50

1990. Visit of Pope John Paul II. Multicoloured.

986	120f. Type **307**	50	35
987	160f. Pope and crowd	65	45

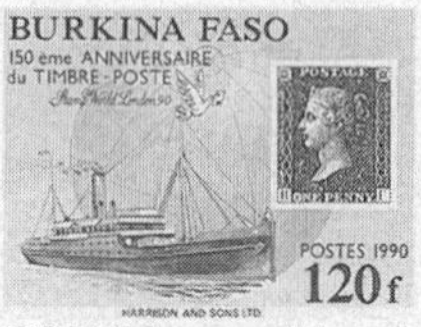

308 Mail Steamer, Globe and Penny Black

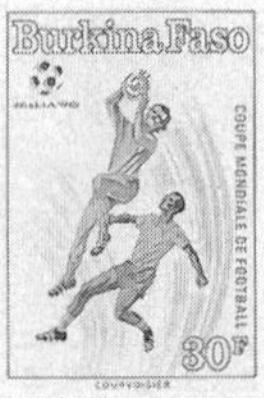

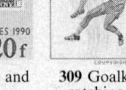

309 Goalkeeper catching Ball

1990. 150th Anniv of Penny Black and "Stamp World London 90" International Stamp Exhibition.

988 **308**	120f. multicoloured	90	45

1990. World Cup Football Championship, Italy. Multicoloured.

990	30f. Type **309**	15	10
991	150f. Footballers	60	45

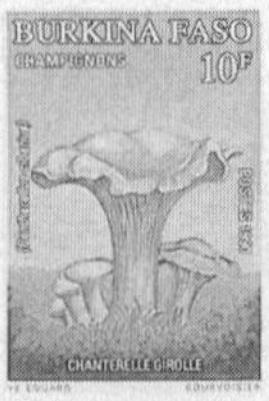

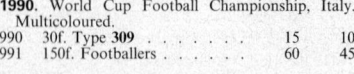

310 "Cantharellus cibarius"

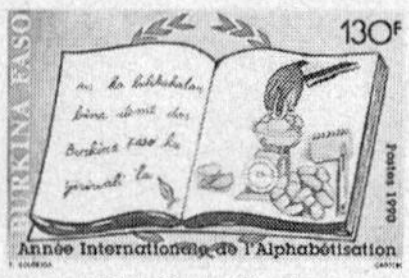

311 Open Book

1990. Fungi. Multicoloured.

993	10f. Type **310**	10	10
994	15f. "Psalliota bispora"	15	10
995	60f. "Amanita caesarea"	75	35
996	190f. "Boletus badius"	2·40	1·25

1990. International Literacy Year.

998 **311**	40f. multicoloured	15	10
999	130f. multicoloured	50	35

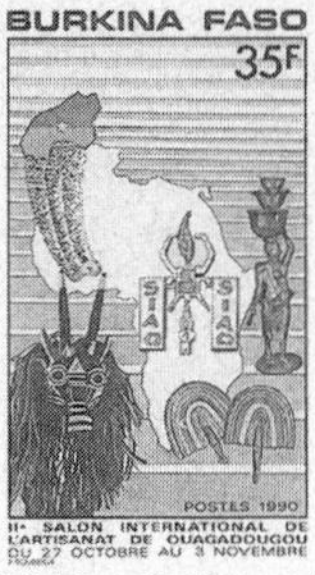

312 Maps, Emblem and Native Artefacts

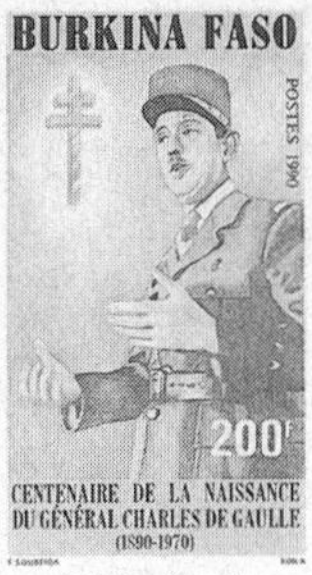

313 De Gaulle

1990. 2nd International Salon of Arts and Crafts, Ouagadougou. Multicoloured.

1000	35f. Type **312**	15	10
1001	45f. Pottery (horiz)	20	15
1002	270f. Cane chair	1·10	75

1990. Birth Centenary of Charles de Gaulle (French statesman).

1003	**313** 200f. multicoloured	80	55

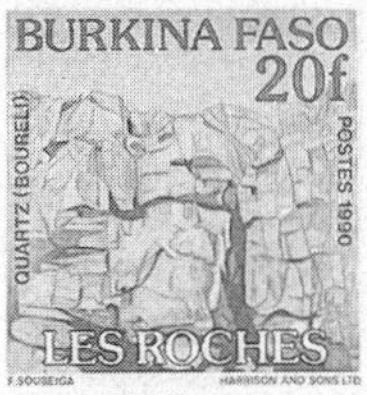

314 Quartz

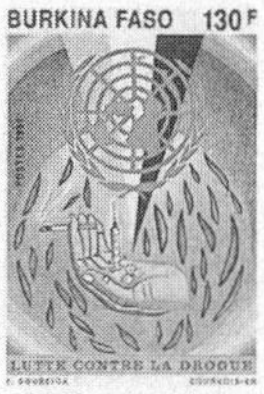

315 Hand Holding Cigarette, Syringe and Tablets

1991. Rocks. Multicoloured.

1004	20f. Type **314**	10	10
1005	50f. Granite	20	15
1006	280f. Amphibolite	1·10	75

1991. Anti-drugs Campaign.

1007	**315** 130f. multicoloured	50	35

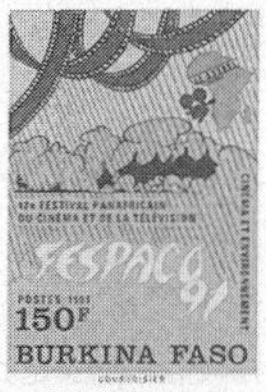

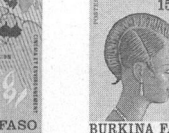

316 Film and Landscape

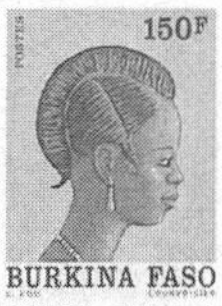

318 Traditional Hairstyle

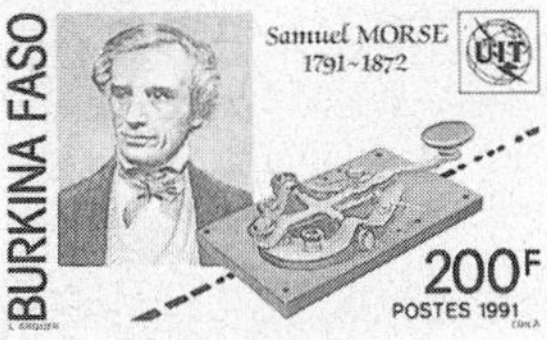

317 Morse and Key

1991. 12th "Fespaco 91" Pan-African Cinema and Television Festival. Multicoloured.

1008	**316** 150f. multicoloured	60	40

1991. Birth Bicentenary of Samuel Morse (inventor of signalling system).

1010	**317** 200f. multicoloured	80	55

1991.

1011	**318** 5f. multicoloured	10	10
1012	10f. multicoloured	10	10
1013	25f. multicoloured	10	10
1014	50f. multicoloured	10	10
1018	130f. multicoloured	30	20
1019	150f. multicoloured	60	40
1020	200f. multicoloured	80	55
1021	330f. multicoloured	80	55

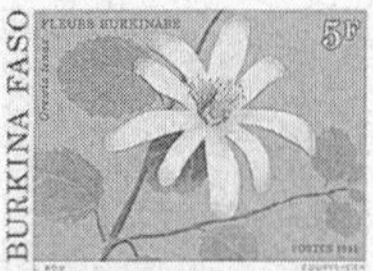

319 "Grewia tenax"

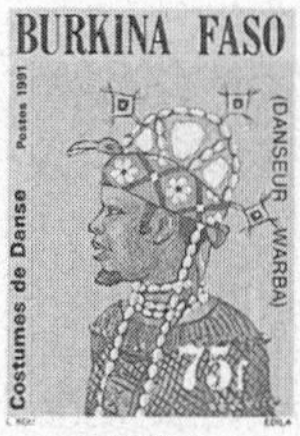

320 Warba

1991. Flowers. Multicoloured.

1025	5f. Type **319**	10	10
1026	15f. "Hymenocardia acide"	10	10
1027	60f. "Cassia sieberiana" (vert)	25	20
1028	100f. "Adenium obesum"	40	30
1029	300f. "Mitragyna inermis"	1·25	85

1991. Dance Costumes. Multicoloured.

1030	75f. Type **320**	40	25
1031	130f. Wiskamba	65	40
1032	280f. Pa-Zenin	1·40	85

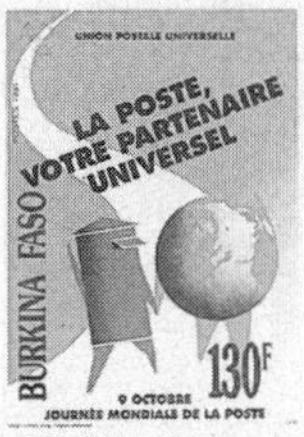

321 Pillar Box and Globe

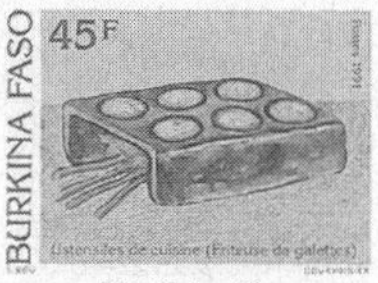

322 Cake Tin

1991. World Post Day.

1033	**321** 130f. multicoloured	50	35

1992. Cooking Utensils.

1034	45f. Type **322**	40	20
1035	130f. Cooking pot (vert)	1·00	70
1036	310f. Pestle and mortar (vert)	1·50	1·00
1037	500f. Ladle and bowl	2·40	1·60

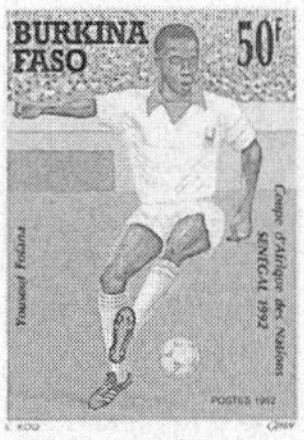

323 Yousouf Fofana

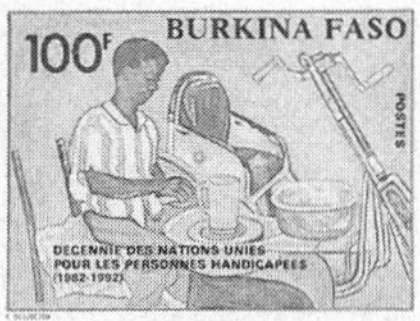

324 Disabled Man at Potter's Wheel

1992. African Nations Cup Football Championship, Senegal. Multicoloured.

1038	50f. Type **323**	25	20
1039	100f. Francois-Jules Bocande	50	35

1992. U.N. Decade of the Handicapped.

1041	**324** 100f. multicoloured	50	35

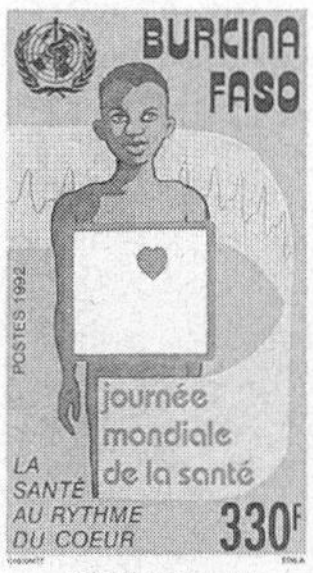

325 Child and Cardiograph

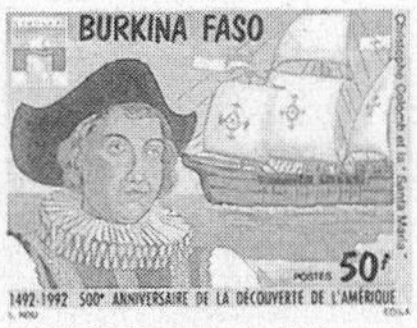

326 Columbus and "Santa Maria"

1992. World Health Day. "Health in Rhythm with the Heart".

1042	**325** 330f. multicoloured	1·60	1·10

1992. "Genova '92" International Thematic Stamp Exhibition and 500th Anniv of Discovery of America by Columbus. Multicoloured.

1043	50f. Type **326**	25	20
1044	150f. Amerindians watching Columbus's fleet off San Salvador	75	55

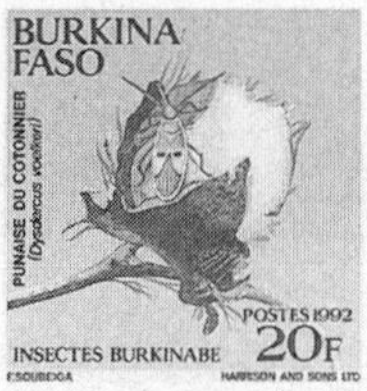

327 "Dysdercus voelkeri" (fire bug) on Cotton Boll

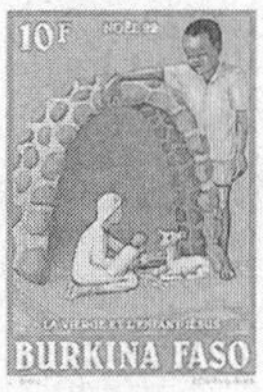

328 Crib

1992. Insects. Multicoloured.

1046	20f. Type **327**	10	10
1047	40f. "Rhizopertha dominica" (beetle) on leaf	20	15
1048	85f. "Orthetrum microstigma" (dragonfly) on stem	40	30
1049	500f. Honey bee on flower	2·40	1·60

1992. Christmas. Multicoloured.

1050	10f. Type **328**	10	10
1051	130f. Children decorating crib	60	40
1052	1000f. Boy with Christmas card	4·50	3·00

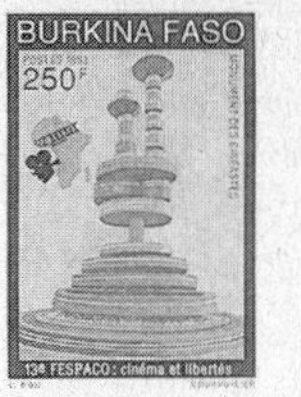

329 Film Makers' Monument

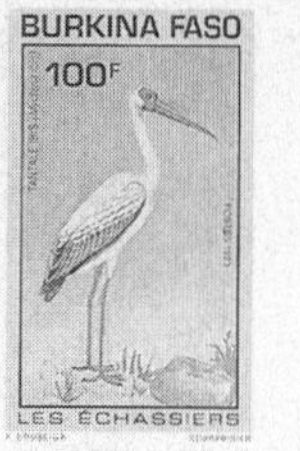

330 Yellow-billed Stork

1993. 13th "Fespaco" Pan-African Film Festival, Ouagadougou. Multicoloured.

1053	250f. Type **329**	1·10	75
1054	750f. Douta Seck (comedian) (horiz)	3·50	2·40

1993. Birds. Multicoloured.

1055	100f. Type **330**	95	60
1056	200f. Marabou stork	1·75	1·40
1057	500f. Saddle-bill stork	4·50	2·75

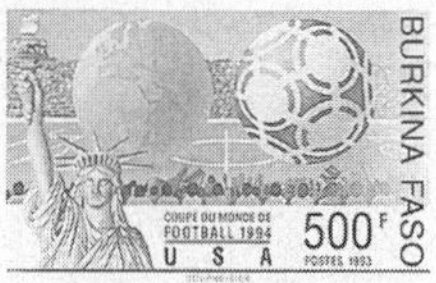

331 Statue of Liberty, Globe and Ball

1993. World Cup Football Championship, U.S.A. (1994). Multicoloured.

1059	500f. Type **331**	2·25	1·50
1060	1000f. Players, map of world and U.S. flag	4·50	3·00

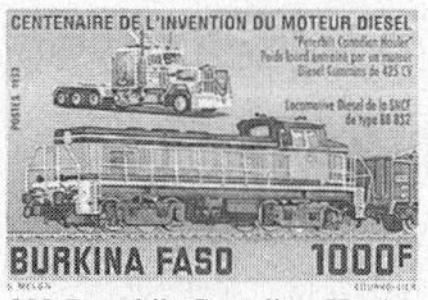

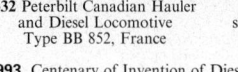

332 Peterbilt Canadian Hauler and Diesel Locomotive Type BB 852, France

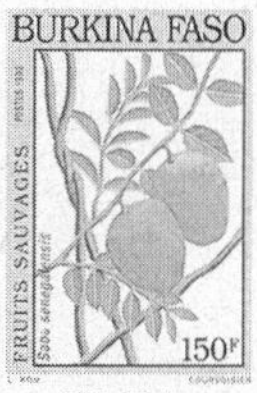

333 "Saba senegalensis"

1993. Centenary of Invention of Diesel Engine.

1061	**332** 1000f. multicoloured	5·75	3·00

1993. Wild Fruits. Multicoloured.

1062	150f. Type **333**	70	50
1063	300f. Karite (horiz)	1·40	95
1064	600f. Baobab	2·75	1·90

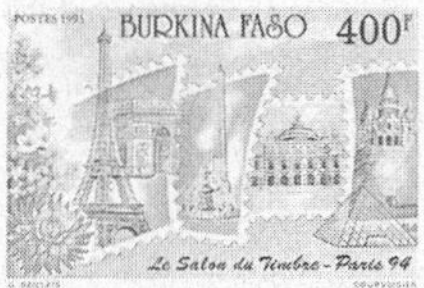

334 Flowers, "Stamps" and Sights of Paris

1993. 1st European Stamp Salon, Flower Gardens, Paris (1994). Multicoloured.

1065	400f. Type **334**	95	65
1066	650f. "Stamps", sights of Paris, daffodils and irises	1·50	1·00

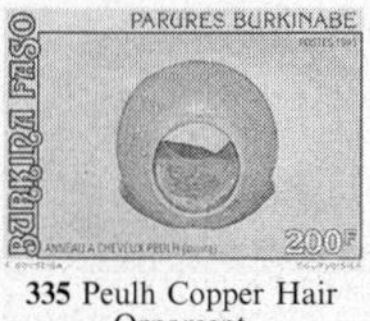

335 Peulh Copper Hair Ornament

1993. Jewellery. Multicoloured.

1067	200f. Type **335**	50	35
1068	250f. Mossi agate necklace (vert)	60	40
1069	500f. Gourounsi copper bracelet	1·25	85

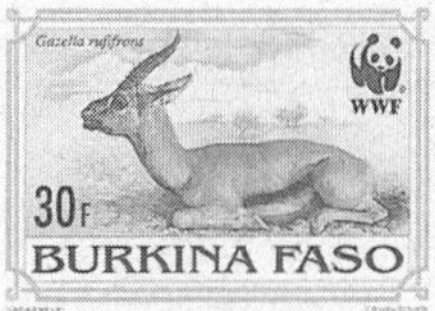

336 Gazelle

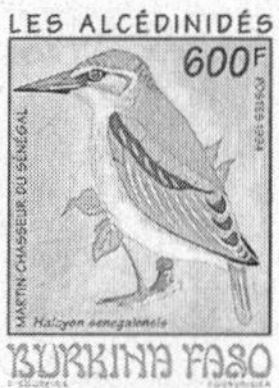

337 Woodland Kingfisher

1993. The Red-fronted Gazelle. Multicoloured.

1070	30f. Type **336**	10	10
1071	40f. Two gazelle	10	10
1072	60f. Two gazelle (different)	15	10
1073	100f. Gazelle	25	20

1994. Kingfishers.

1075	600f. Type **337**	1·50	1·00
1076	1200f. Striped kingfisher	3·00	2·00

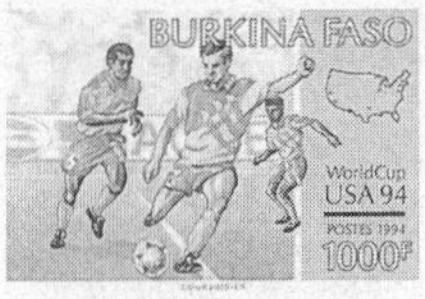

338 Players

1994. World Cup Football Championship, United States. Multicoloured.

1078	1000f. Type **338**	2·40	1·60
1079	1800f. Goalkeeper saving ball	4·25	3·00

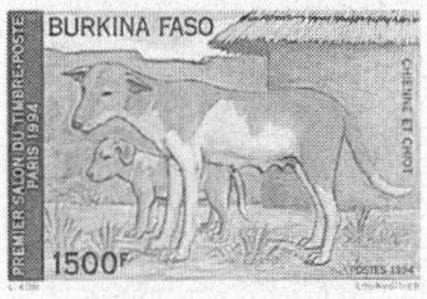

339 Dog with Puppy

1994. 1st European Stamp Salon, Flower Gardens, Paris, France.

1081	**339** 1500f. multicoloured	3·75	2·50

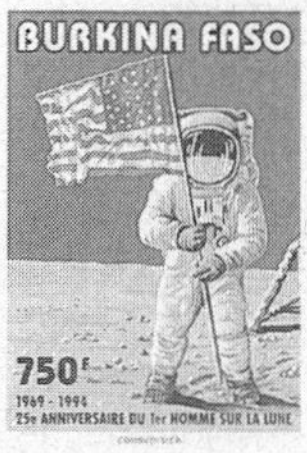

340 Astronaut planting Flag on Moon

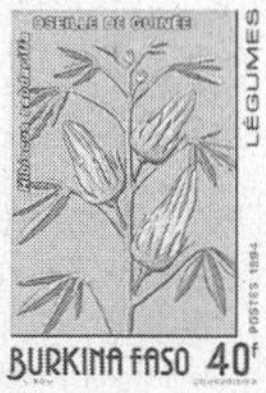

341 Guinea Sorrel

1994. 25th Anniv of First Manned Moon Landing. Multicoloured.

1083	750f. Type **340**	1·75	1·25
1084	750f. Landing module on Moon	1·75	1·25

Nos. 1083/4 were issued together, se-tenant, forming a composite design.

1994. Vegetables. Multicoloured.

1085	40f. Type **341**	10	10
1086	45f. Aubergine	10	10
1087	75f. Aubergine	20	15
1088	100f. Okra	25	20

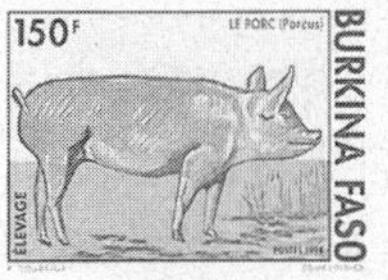

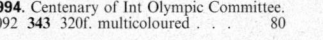

342 Pig

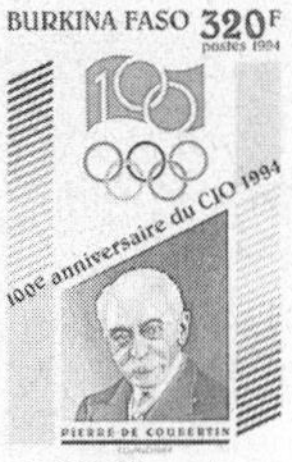

343 Pierre de Coubertin (founder) and Anniversary Emblem

1994. Domestic Animals. Multicoloured.

1089	150f. Type **342**	35	25
1090	1000f. Goat (vert)	2·40	1·60
1091	1500f. Sheep	3·75	2·50

1994. Centenary of Int Olympic Committee.

1092	**343** 320f. multicoloured	80	55

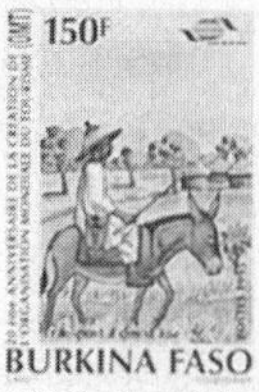

344 Donkey Rider

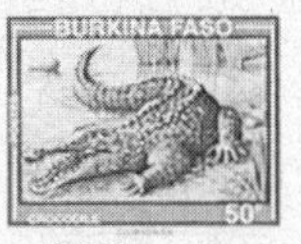

345 Crocodile

1995. 20th Anniv of World Tourism Organization. Multicoloured.

1093	150f. Type **344**	40	30
1094	350f. Bobo-Dioulasso railway station (horiz)	90	60
1095	450f. Great Mosque, Bani (horiz)	1·10	75
1096	650f. Roan antelope and map (horiz)	1·60	1·10

1995. Multicoloured, colour of frame given.

1097	**345** 10f. brown	10	10
1098	20f. mauve	10	10

1099	25f. brown	10	10
1100	30f. green	10	10
1101	40f. purple	10	10
1102	50f. grey	15	10
1103	75f. purple	20	15
1104	100f. brown	20	15
1105	150f. green	40	30
1106	175f. blue	45	30
1107	250f. brown	65	45
1108	400f. green	1·00	70

346 "Rabi" (dir. Gaston Kabore)

1995. "Fespaco 95" Pan-African Film Festival and Centenary of Motion Pictures. Multicoloured.

1109	150f. Type **346**	40	30
1110	250f. "Tila" (Idrissa Ouedraogo)	65	45

347 Elvis Presley in "Loving You"

1995. Entertainers. Multicoloured.

1111	300f. Type **347**	75	50
1112	400f. Marilyn Monroe	1·00	70
1113	500f. Elvis Presley in "Jailhouse Rock"	1·25	85
1114	650f. Marilyn Monroe in "Asphalt Jungle"	1·60	1·10
1115	750f. Marilyn Monroe in "Niagara"	1·90	1·40
1116	1000f. Elvis Presley in "Blue Hawaii"	2·50	1·75

348 Common Gonolek

1995. Birds. Multicoloured.

1118	450f. Type **348**	1·10	75
1119	600f. Red-cheeked cordon-bleu	1·50	1·10
1120	750f. Golden bishop	1·90	1·40

349 Hissing Sand Snake

1995. Reptiles. Multicoloured.

1122	450f. Type **349**	1·10	75
1123	500f. Sand python	1·25	85
1124	1500f. Tortoise	4·00	2·75

350 Basketball

1995. Olympic Games, Atlanta (1996). Mult.

1125	150f. Type **350**	40	30
1126	250f. Baseball	65	45
1127	650f. Tennis	1·60	1·10
1128	750f. Table tennis	1·90	1·40

351 Juan Manuel Fangio (racing driver)

1995. Sportsmen. Multicoloured.

1130	300f. Type **351**	75	50
1131	400f. Andre Agassi (tennis player)	1·00	70
1132	500f. Ayrton Senna (racing driver)	1·25	85
1133	1000f. Michael Schumacher (racing driver)	2·50	1·75

352 Children and Christmas Tree

1995. Christmas. Multicoloured.

1135	150f. Type **352**	40	30
1136	450f. Grotto, Yagma	1·10	75
1137	500f. Flight into Egypt	1·25	85
1138	1000f. Adoration of the Wise Men	2·50	1·75

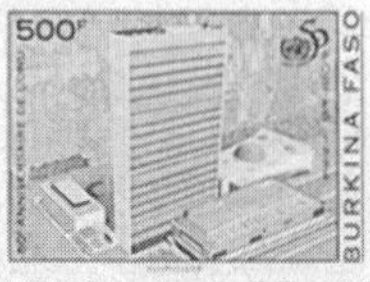

353 Headquarters Building, New York

1995. 50th Anniv of United Nations. Multicoloured.

1139	500f. Type **353**	1·25	85
1140	1000f. Village council under tree with superimposed U.N. emblem (vert)	2·50	1·75

354 Mossi Type

1995. Traditional Houses. Multicoloured.

1141	70f. Type **354**	20	15
1142	100f. Kassena type	25	15
1143	200f. Roro type	50	35
1144	250f. Peulh type	65	45

APPENDIX

The following stamps have either been issued in excess of postal needs or have not been available to the public in reasonable quantities at face value. Such stamps may later be given full listing if there is evidence of regular postal use.

1985.

85th Birthday of Queen Elizabeth the Queen Mother. 1500f.

BURMA Pt. 1, Pt. 21

A territory in the east of India, which was granted independence by the British in 1948. From May 1990 it was known as Myanmar.

1937. 12 pies = 1 anna; 16 annas = 1 rupee.
1953. 100 pyas = 1 kyat.

1937. Stamps of India (King George V) optd **BURMA**.

1	**55**	3p. grey	60	10
2	**79**	½a. green	1·00	10
3	**80**	9p. green	1·00	10
4	**81**	1a. brown	75	10
5	**59**	2a. red	75	10
6	**61**	2½a. orange	60	10
7	**62**	3a. red	1·00	30
8	**83**	3½a. blue	1·75	10
9	**63**	4a. olive	1·00	10
10	**64**	6a. bistre	75	35
11	**65**	8a. mauve	1·50	10
12	**66**	12a. red	3·50	1·00
13	**67**	1r. brown and green	17·00	2·75
14		2r. red and orange	28·00	9·50
15		5r. blue and violet	38·00	17·00
16		10r. green and red	80·00	60·00
17		15r. blue and olive	£275	£110
18		25r. orange and blue	£550	£275

2 King George VI and "Chinthes"

3 King George VI and "Nagas"

4 "Karaweik" (royal barge)

8 King George VI and Peacock

1938. King George VI.

18a	**2**	1p. orange	3·00	1·00
19		3p. violet	20	50
20		6p. blue	20	10
21		9p. green	1·00	80
22	**3**	1a. brown	20	10
23		1½a. green	20	80
24		2a. red	45	10
25	**4**	2a.6p. red	14·00	1·25
26	–	3a. mauve	14·00	1·75
27	–	3a.6p. blue	1·25	4·00
28	**3**	4a. blue	60	10
29	–	8a. green	5·00	30
30	**8**	1r. purple and blue	6·00	20
31		2r. brown and purple	16·00	1·75
32	–	5r. violet and red	48·00	23·00
33	–	10r. brown and green	55·00	50·00

DESIGNS—HORIZ: As Type **4**: 3a. Burma teak; 3a.6p. Burma rice; 8a. River Irrawaddy. VERT: As Type **3**: 5, 10r. King George VI and "Nats".

1940. Cent of First Adhesive Postage Stamp. Surch **COMMEMORATION POSTAGE STAMP 6th MAY 1840 ONE ANNA 1A** and value in native characters.

34	**4**	1a. on 2a.6p. red	3·75	1·50

For Japanese issues see "Japanese Occupation of Burma".

1945. British Military Administration. Stamps of 1938 optd **MILY ADMN**.

35	**2**	1p. orange	10	10
36		3p. violet	10	40
37		6p. blue	10	30
38		9p. green	30	50
39	**3**	1a. brown	10	10
40		1½a. green	10	15
41		2a. red	10	15
42	**4**	2a.6p. red	2·00	60
43	–	3a. mauve	1·50	20
44	–	3a.6p. blue	10	70
45	**3**	4a. blue	10	25
46	–	8a. green	10	40
47	**8**	1r. purple and blue	40	50
48		2r. brown and purple	40	1·00
49	–	5r. violet and red	40	1·00
50	–	10r. brown and green	40	1·00

1946. British Civil Administration. As 1938, but colours changed.

51	**2**	3p. brown	10	1·50
52		6p. violet	10	30
53		9p. green	15	2·00
54	**3**	1a. blue	15	20
55		1½a. orange	15	10
56		2a. red	15	40
57	**4**	2a.6p. blue	2·75	3·50
57a	–	3a. blue	6·50	3·25
57b	–	3a. 6p. black and blue	30	1·75
58	**3**	4a. purple	50	30
59	–	8a. mauve	1·75	2·50
60	**8**	1r. violet and mauve	1·25	40
61		2r. brown and orange	6·00	2·50
62	–	5r. green and brown	6·00	14·00
63	–	10r. red and violet	8·50	18·00

14 Burman

ကြားဖြတ်
အစိုးရ။

(**18** Trans. "Interim Government")

1946. Victory.

64	**14**	9p. green	20	20
65	–	1½a. violet (Burmese woman)	20	10
66	–	2a. red (Chinthe)	20	10
67	–	3a.6p. (Elephant)	50	20

1947. Stamps of 1946 opt with T **18** or with larger opt on large stamps.

68	**2**	3p. brown	70	70
69		6p. violet	10	30
70		9p. green	10	30
71	**3**	1a. blue	10	30
72		1½a. orange	1·00	10
73		2a. red	30	15
74	**4**	2a.6p. blue	1·75	1·00
75	–	3a. blue	2·50	1·75
76	–	3a.6p. black and blue	50	2·00
77	**3**	4a. purple	1·75	30
78	–	8a. mauve	1·75	1·50
79	**8**	1r. violet and mauve	4·00	50
80		2r. brown and orange	4·50	3·25
81	–	5r. green and brown	4·50	3·50
82	–	10r. red and violet	3·25	3·50

20 Gen. Aung San, Chinthe and Map of Burma

21 Martyrs' Memorial

1948. Independence Day.

83	**20**	½a. green	10	10
84		1a. pink	10	10
85		2a. red	15	15
86		3½a. blue	20	15
87		8a. brown	25	25

1948. 1st Anniv of Murder of Aung San and his Ministers.

88	**21**	3p. blue	10	10
89		6p. green	10	10
90		9p. red	10	10
91		1a. violet	10	10
92		2a. mauve	10	10
93		3½a. green	15	15
94		4a. brown	15	15
95		8a. red	20	15
96		12a. purple	25	20
97		1r. green	35	20
98		2r. blue	60	40
99		5r. brown	1·90	1·10

22 Playing Cane-ball

25 Bell, Mingun Pagoda

27 Transplanting Rice

28 Lion Throne

1949. 1st Anniv of Independence.

100	**22**	3p. blue	95	25
120		3p. orange	65	25
101	–	6p. green	10	10
121	–	6p. purple	10	10
102	–	9p. red	10	10
122	–	9p. blue	10	10
103	**25**	1a. red	15	10
123		1a. blue	10	10
104	–	2a. orange	45	10
124	–	2a. green	40	20
105	**27**	2a.6p. mauve	20	15
125		2a.6p. green	20	15
106	–	3a. violet	20	15
126	–	3a. red	20	15
107	–	3a.6p. green	25	15
127	–	3a.6p. orange	25	15
108	–	4a. brown	25	15
128	–	4a. red	25	15
109	–	8a. red	35	15
129	–	8a. blue	25	20
110	**28**	1r. green	50	15
130		1r. violet	50	35
111	–	2r. blue	1·25	40
131		2r. green	85	75
112		5r. brown	2·50	1·25
132		5r. blue	2·25	2·25
113		10r. orange	4·25	1·90
133		10r. blue	5·50	4·25

DESIGNS—As Type **22**: 6p. Dancer; 9p. Girl playing saunggaut (string instrument); 2a. Hintha (legendary bird). As Type **25**: 4a. Elephant hauling log. As Type **27**: 3a. Girl weaving; 3a.6p. Royal Palace; 8a. Ploughing paddy field with oxen.

See also Nos. 137/50.

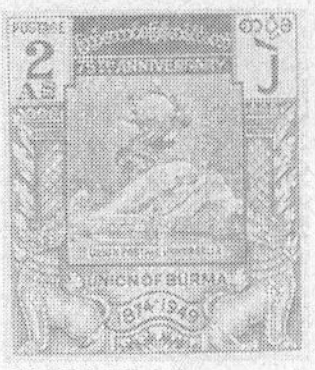

29 U.P.U. Monument, Berne

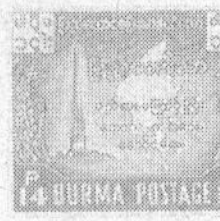

30 Independence Monument, Rangoon, and Map

1949. 75th Anniv of U.P.U.

114	**29**	2a. orange	15	15
115		3½a. green	20	15
116		6a. violet	25	25
117		8a. red	40	25
118		12½a. blue	70	40
119		1r. green	90	50

1953. 5th Anniv of Independence.

134	**30**	14p. green (22 × 18 mm)	20	10
135		20p. red (36½ × 26½ mm)	25	15
136		25p. blue (36½ × 26½ mm)	35	20

1954. New Currency. As 1949 issue but values in pyas and kyats.

137	**22**	1p. orange	65	10
138	–	2p. purple (as 6p.)	10	10
139	–	3p. blue (as 9p.)	10	10
140	**25**	5p. blue	10	10
141	**27**	10p. green	10	10
142	–	15p. green (as 2a.)	25	10
143	–	20p. red (as 3a.)	15	10
144	–	25p. orange (as 3a.6p.)	15	10
145	–	30p. red (as 4a.)	25	15
146	–	50p. blue (as 8a.)	25	15
147	**28**	1k. violet	75	25
148		2k. green	1·25	35
149		5k. blue	3·75	70
150		10k. blue	6·50	1·25

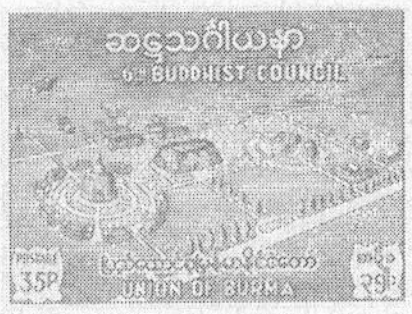

31 Sangiti Mahapasana Rock Cave in Grounds of Kaba-Aye Pagoda

1954. 6th Buddhist Council, Rangoon.

151	–	10p. blue	10	10
152	–	15p. purple	15	15
153	**31**	35p. brown	25	20
154	–	50p. green	40	25
155	–	1k. red	90	50
156	–	2k. violet	1·40	1·00

DESIGNS: 10p. Rock caves and Songha of Cambodia; 15p. Buddhist priests and Kuthodaw Pagoda, Mandalay; 50p. Rock cave and Songha of Thailand; 1k. Rock cave and Songha of Ceylon; 2k. Rock cave and Songha of Laos.

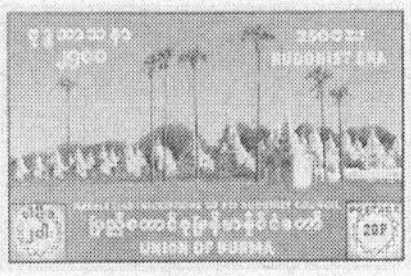

32 Fifth Buddhist Council Monuments

1956. Buddha Jayanti.

157	**32**	20p. green and blue	20	15
158	–	40p. green and blue	25	20
159	–	60p. yellow and green	45	35
160	–	1k.25 blue and yellow	85	70

DESIGNS: 40p. Thatbyinnyu Pagoda, Pagan; 60p. Shwedagan Pagoda, Rangoon; 1k.25, Sangiti Mahapasana Rock Cave and Kaba-Aye Pagoda, Rangoon (venue of 6th Buddhist Council).

မြို့မန္တလေး-နှစ်တရာ

၁၂၂၁-၁၃၂၁

15 P ၁၅ပြား

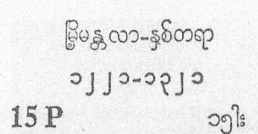

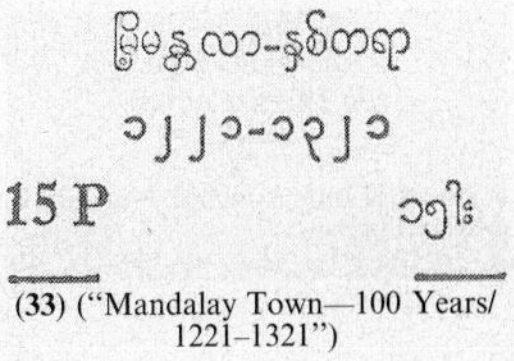

(33) ("Mandalay Town—100 Years/ 1221–1321")

1959. Centenary of Mandalay. No. 144 surch with T **33** and Nos. 147/8 with two-line opt only.

161	–	15p. on 25p. orange	15	20
162	**28**	1k. violet	70	60
163		2k. green	1·50	1·25

1961. No. 134 surch as right-hand characters in third line of T **33**.

164	**30**	15p. on 14p. green	60	25

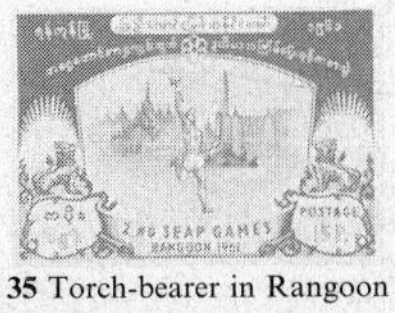

35 Torch-bearer in Rangoon

1961. 2nd South-East Asia Peninsula Games, Rangoon.

165	**35**	15p. blue and red	20	10
166	–	25p. green and brown	25	15
167	–	50p. mauve and blue	50	25
168	–	1k. yellow and green	95	75

DESIGNS—VERT: 25p. Contestants; 50p. Women sprinting in Aung San Stadium, Rangoon. HORIZ: 1k. Contestants.

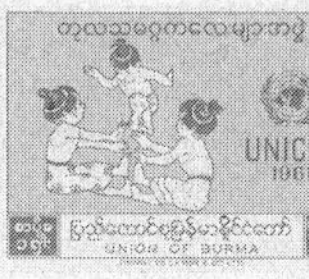

36 Children at Play

1961. 15th Anniv of U.N.I.C.E.F.

169	**36**	15p. red and pink	30	10

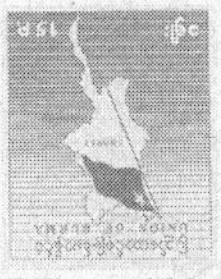

37 Flag and Map

အလုပ်သမားနေ့

၁၉၆၃

(39)

1963. 1st Anniv of Military Coup by General Ne Win.

170	**37**	15p. red	30	20

1963. Freedom from Hunger. Nos. 141 and 146 optd **FREEDOM FROM HUNGER**.

171	**27**	10p. green	40	35
172	–	50p. blue	75	65

1963. Labour Day. No. 143 optd with T **39**.

173		20p. red	35	20

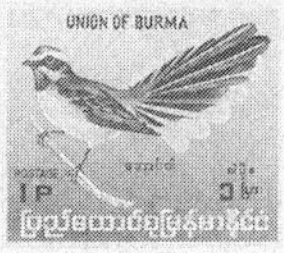

40 White-browed Fantail

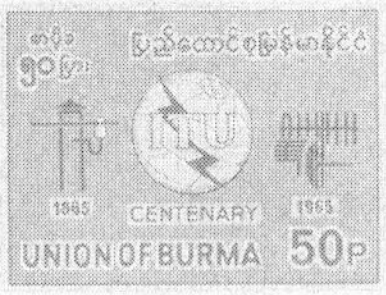

41 I.T.U. Emblem and Symbols

1964. Burmese Birds (1st series).

174	**40**	1p. black	15	15
175		2p. red	20	15
176		3p. green	20	15
177	–	5p. blue	25	20
178	–	10p. brown	25	20
179	–	15p. green	25	20
180	–	20p. brown and red	45	25
181	–	25p. brown and yellow	45	25
182	–	50p. blue and red	85	30
183	–	1k. blue, yellow & grey	2·40	70
184	–	2k. blue, green and red	4·75	1·75
185	–	5k. multicoloured	9·75	4·50

BIRDS—22 × 26 mm: 5 to 15p. Indian roller. 27 × 37 mm: 25p. Crested serpent eagle. 50p. Sarus crane. 1k. Indian pied hornbill. 5k. Green peafowl. 35½ × 25 mm: 20p. Red-whiskered bulbul. 37 × 27 mm: 2k. Kalij pheasant.

See also Nos. 195/206.

1965. Centenary of I.T.U.

186	**41**	20p. mauve	15	15
187		50p. green (34 × 24½ mm)	40	40

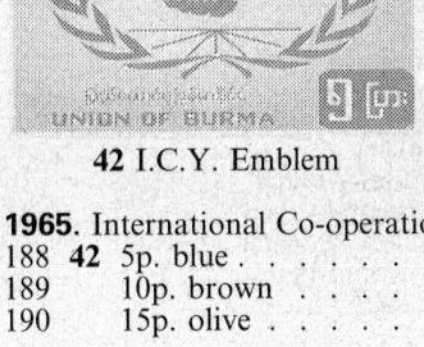

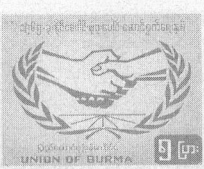

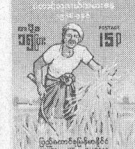

42 I.C.Y. Emblem

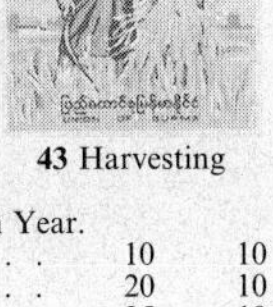

43 Harvesting

1965. International Co-operation Year.

188	**42**	5p. blue	10	10
189		10p. brown	20	10
190		15p. olive	25	10

1966. Peasants' Day

191	**43**	15p. multicoloured	25	15

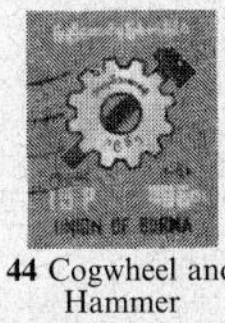

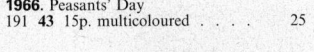

44 Cogwheel and Hammer

1967. May Day.

192	**44**	15p. yellow, black & blue	25	20

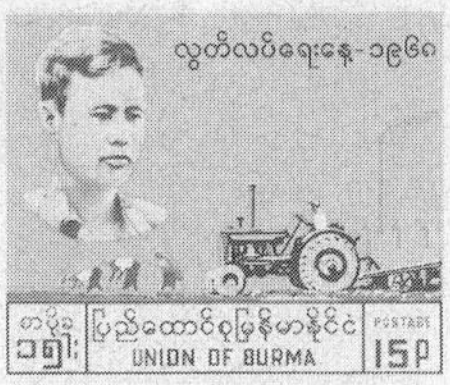

45 Aung San and Agricultural Cultivation

1968. 20th Anniv of Independence.

193	**45**	15p. multicoloured	25	20

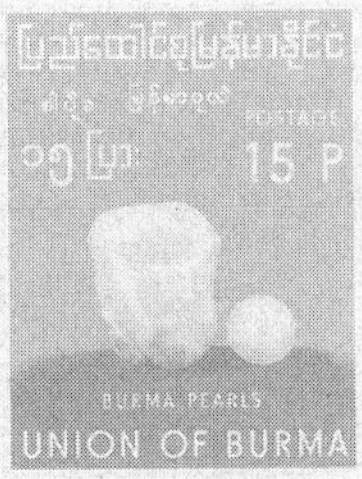

46 Burma Pearls

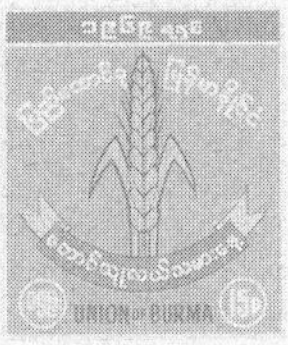

47 Spike of Paddy

1968. Burmese Gems, Jades and Pearls Emporium, Rangoon.

194	**46**	15p. ultram, blue & yell	40	15

1968. Burmese Birds (2nd series). Designs and colours as Nos. 174/85 but formats and sizes changed.

195	**40**	1p. black	15	15
196		2p. red	15	15
197		3p. green	20	15
198	–	5p. blue	20	15
199	–	10p. brown	20	15
200	–	15p. yellow	25	20
201	–	20p. brown and red	25	20
202	–	25p. brown and yellow	30	25
203	–	50p. blue and red	55	45
204	–	1k. blue, yellow & grey	1·60	45
205	–	2k. blue, green and red	4·50	1·10
206	–	5k. multicoloured	9·50	4·50

NEW SIZES—21 × 17 mm: 1, 2, 3p. 39 × 21 mm: 20p., 2k. 23 × 28 mm: 5, 10, 15p. 21 × 39 mm: 25, 50p., 1, 5k.

1969. Peasants' Day.

218	**47**	15p. yellow, blue & green	25	10

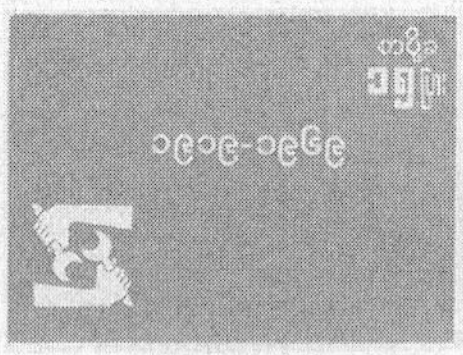

48 I.L.O. Emblem

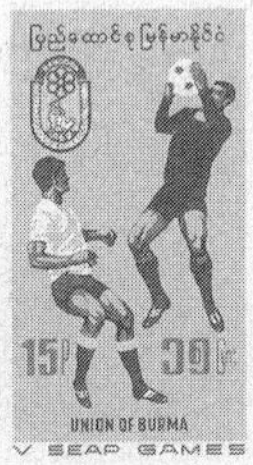

49 Football

1969. 50th Anniv of I.L.O.

219	**48**	15p. gold and green	15	10
220		50p. gold and red	40	25

1969. 5th South-East Asian Peninsula Games, Rangoon.

221	**49**	15p. multicoloured	20	10
222	–	25p. multicoloured	25	15
223	–	50p. multicoloured	50	20
224	–	1k. black, green & blue	95	50

DESIGNS—HORIZ: 25p. Running. VERT: 50p. Weightlifting; 1k. Volleyball.

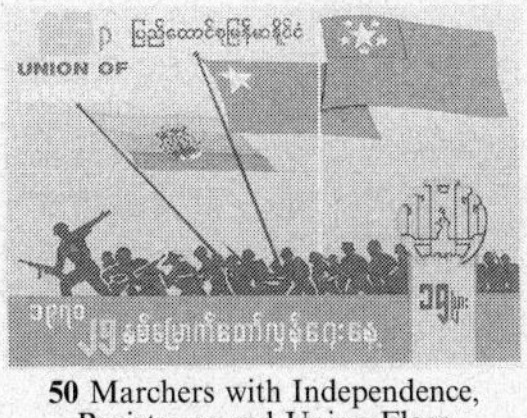

50 Marchers with Independence, Resistance and Union Flags

1970. 25th Anniv of Burmese Armed Forces.

225	**50**	15p. multicoloured	20	15

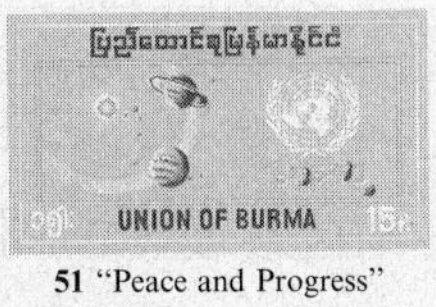

51 "Peace and Progress"

1970. 25th Anniv of United Nations.

226	**51**	15p. multicoloured	25	20

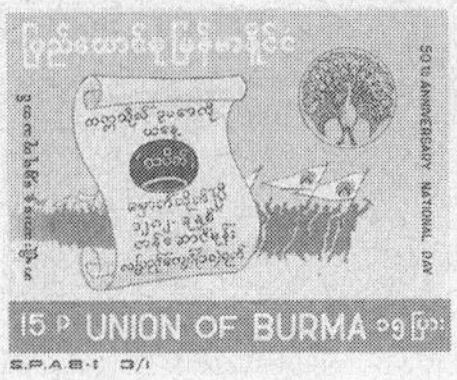

52 Boycott Declaration and Marchers

1970. National Day and 50th Anniv of University Boycott. Multicoloured.

227		15p. Type **52**	10	10
228		25p. Students on boycott march	20	10
229		50p. Banner and demonstrators	40	20

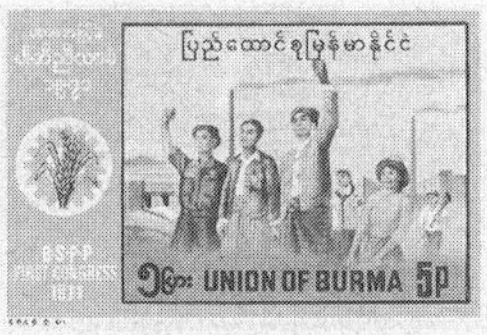

53 Burmese Workers

1971. 1st Burmese Socialist Programme Party Congress. Multicoloured.

230		5p. Type **53**	10	10
231		15p. Burmese races and flags	15	10
232		25p. Hands holding scroll	25	15
233		50p. Party flag	50	30

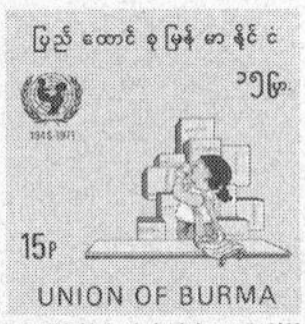

54 Child drinking Milk

1971. 25th Anniv of U.N.I.C.E.F. Multicoloured.

235		15p. Type **54**	25	15
236		50p. Marionettes	55	40

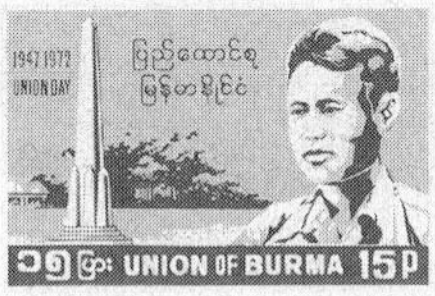

55 Aung San and Independence Monument, Panglong

1972. 25th Anniv of Independence. Multicoloured.

237		15p. Type **55**	10	10
238		50p. Aung San and Burmese in national costumes	25	20
239		1k. Flag and map (vert)	60	40

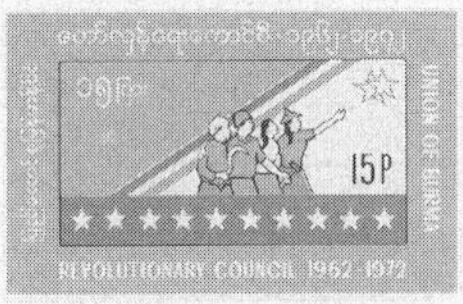

56 Burmese and Stars

1972. 10th Anniv of Revolutionary Council.

240	**56**	15p. multicoloured	20	10

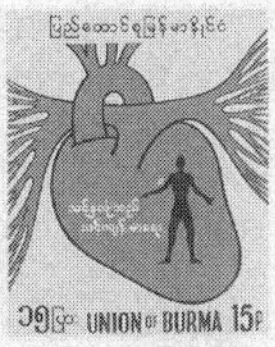

57 Human Heart

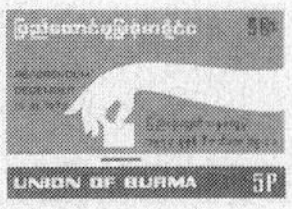

59 Casting Vote

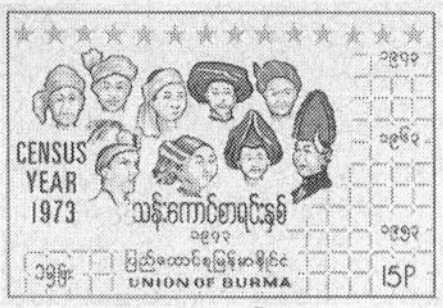

58 Ethnic Groups

1972. World Health Day.

241	**57**	15p. red, black & yellow	20	15

1973. National Census.

242	**58**	15p. multicoloured	20	10

1973. National Constitutional Referendum.

243	**59**	5p. red and black	15	10
244	–	10p. multicoloured	15	10
245	–	15p. multicoloured	15	10

DESIGNS—HORIZ: 10p. Voter supporting map. VERT: 15p. Burmese with ballot papers.

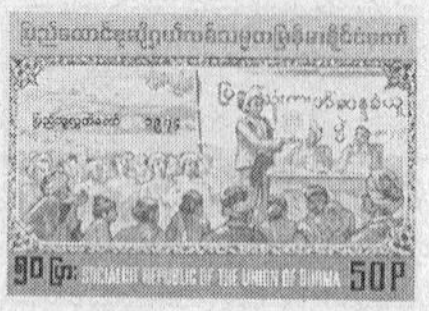

60 Open-air Meeting

1974. Opening of 1st Pyithu Hluttaw (People's Assembly). Multicoloured.

246		15p. Burmese flags, 1752–1974 (80 × 26 mm)	20	15
247		50p. Type **60**	40	25
248		1k. Burmese badge	80	55

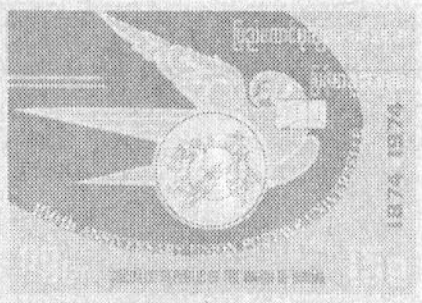

61 U.P.U. Emblem and Carrier Pigeon

1974. Centenary of Universal Postal Union. Mult.

249		15p. Type **61**	15	10
250		20p. Woman reading letter (vert)	20	10
251		50p. U.P.U. emblem on "stamps" (vert)	45	20
252		1k. Stylized doll (vert)	75	35
253		2k. Postman delivering letter to family	1·75	75

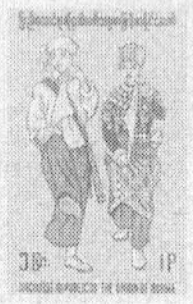

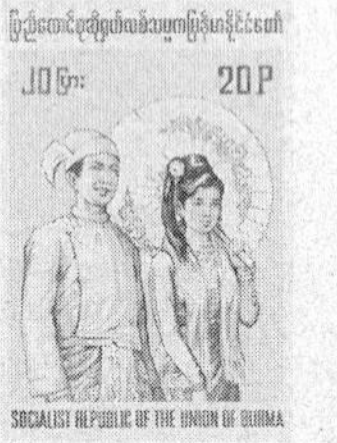

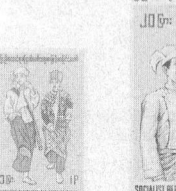

62 Kachin Couple **63** Bamar Couple

1974. Burmese Costumes. Inscr "SOCIALIST REPUBLIC OF THE UNION OF BURMA".

254	**62**	1p. mauve	10	10
255		3p. brown and mauve	10	10
256		5p. violet and mauve	10	10
257		10p. blue	10	10
258		15p. green and light green	10	10
259	**63**	20p. black, brown & blue	15	10
260	–	50p. violet, brown & ochre	40	15
261	–	1k. violet, mauve & black	1·10	60
262	–	5k. multicoloured	4·00	2·25

DESIGNS—As Type **62**: 3p. Kayah girl; 5p. Kayin couple and bronze drum; 15p. Chin couple. As Type **63**: 50p. Mon woman; 1k. Rakhine woman; 5k. Musician.

For 15, 50p. and 1k. stamps in these designs, but inscr "UNION OF BURMA", see Nos. 309/11.

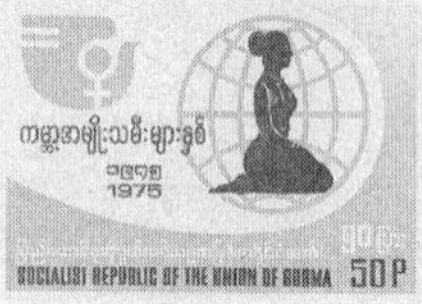

64 Woman on Globe and I.W.Y. Emblem

1975. International Women's Year

263	**64**	50p. black and green	30	20
264	–	2k. black and blue	1·25	95

DESIGN—VERT: 2k. Globe on flower and I.W.Y. emblem.

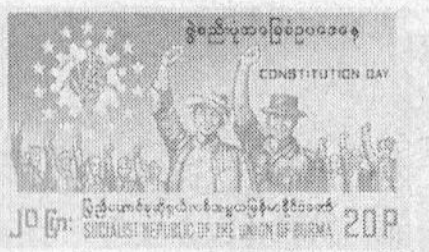

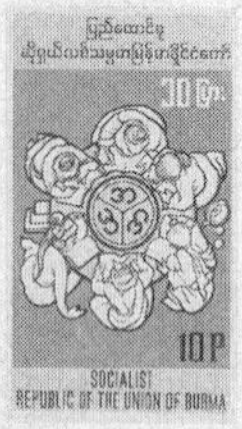

65 Burmese and Flag **66** Emblem and Burmese Learning Alphabet

1976. Constitution Day.

265	**65**	20p. black and blue	15	10
266	–	50p. brown and blue	35	30
267	–	1k. multicoloured	1·00	60

DESIGNS—As Type **65**: 50p. Burmese with banners and flag. 57 × 21 mm: 1k. Map of Burma, Burmese and flag.

1976. International Literacy Year.

268	**66**	10p. brown and red	10	10
269	–	15p. turquoise, grn & blk	10	10
270	–	50p. blue, orange & black	40	20
271	–	1k. multicoloured	75	50

DESIGNS—HORIZ: 15p. Abacus and open books. 50p. Emblem. VERT: 1k. Emblem, open book and globe.

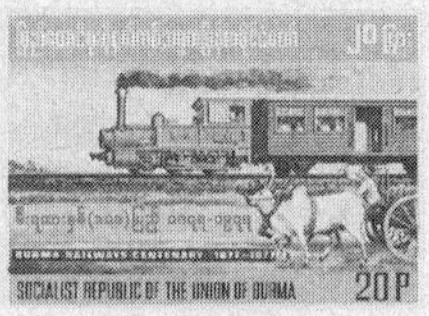

67 Early Train and Ox-cart

1977. Centenary of Railway.

272	–	15p. green, black & mauve	5·25	1·10
273	**67**	20p. multicoloured	1·75	40
274	–	25p. multicoloured	2·75	60
275	–	50p. multicoloured	3·50	1·00
276	–	1k. multicoloured	7·75	1·90

DESIGNS—26 × 17 mm: 15p. Early steam locomotive. As Type **67**—HORIZ: 25p. Diesel locomotive DD1517, steam train and railway station; 50p. Ava railway bridge over River Irrawaddy. VERT: Diesel train emerging from tunnel.

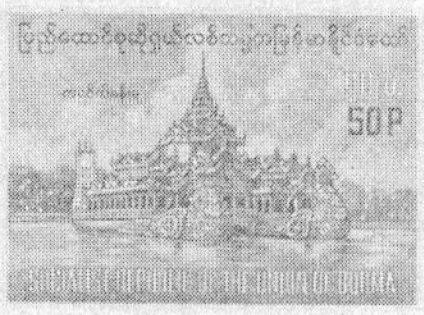

68 Karaweik Hall

1978.

277	**68**	50p. brown	35	25
278	–	1k. multicoloured	95	60

DESIGN—79½ × 25 mm: 1k. Side view of Karaweik Hall.

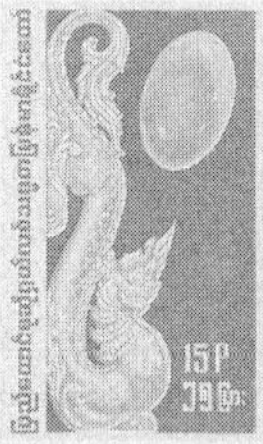

69 Jade Naga and Gem

1979. 16th Gem Emporium.

279	**69**	15p. green and turquoise	15	10
280	–	20p. blue, yellow & mauve	35	15
281	–	50p. blue, brown & green	65	40
282	–	1k. multicoloured	1·25	70

DESIGNS—As T **69**: 20p. Hintha (legendary bird) holding pearl in beak; 50p. Hand holding pearl and amethyst pendant. 55 × 20 mm: 1k. Gold jewel-studded dragon.

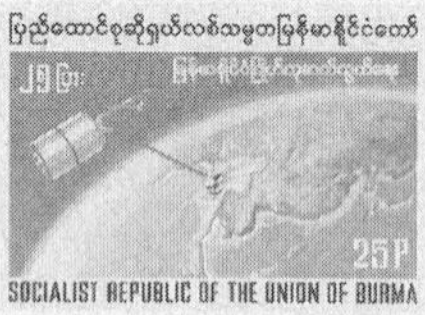

70 "Intelsat IV" Satellite over Burma

1979. Introduction of Satellite Communications System.

283	**70**	25p. multicoloured	25	15

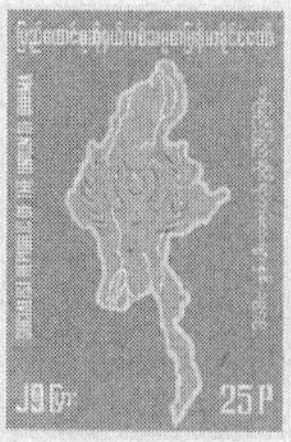

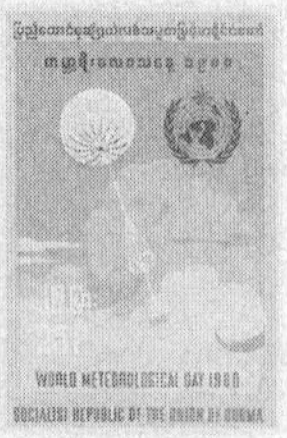

71 I.Y.C. Emblem on Map of Burma **72** Weather Balloon

1979. International Year of the Child.

284	**71**	25p. orange and blue	35	25
285		50p. red and violet	65	40

1980. World Meteorological Day.

286	**72**	25p. blue, yellow & black	25	15
287	–	50p. green, black and red	50	35

DESIGN: 50p. Meteorological satellite and W.M.O. emblem.

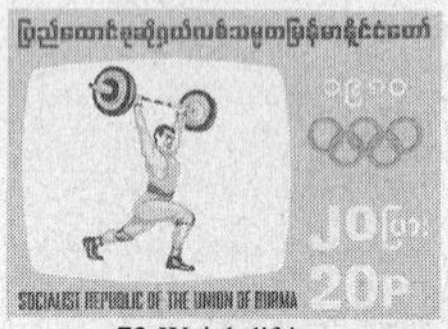

73 Weightlifting

1980. Olympic Games, Moscow.

288	**73**	20p. green, orange & blk	20	10
289	–	50p. black, orange and red	45	25
290	–	1k. black, orange and blue	90	50

DESIGNS: 50p. Boxing; 1k. Football.

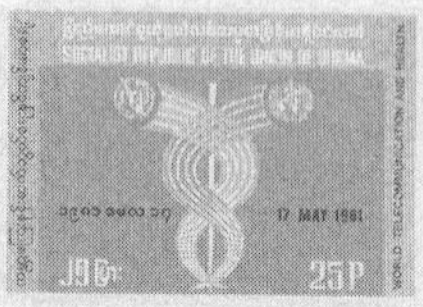

74 I.T.U. and W.H.O. Emblems with Ribbons forming Caduceus

1981. World Telecommunications Day.

291	**74**	25p. orange and black	20	10

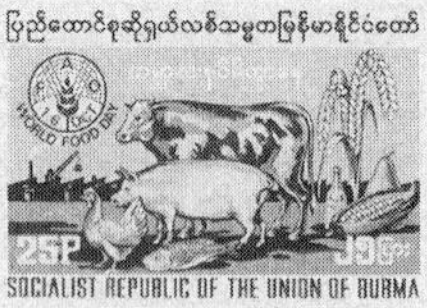

75 Livestock and Vegetables

1981. World Food Day. Multicoloured.

292		25p. Type **75**	35	10
293		50p. Farm produce and farmer holding wheat	55	20
294		1k. Globe and stylized bird	75	45

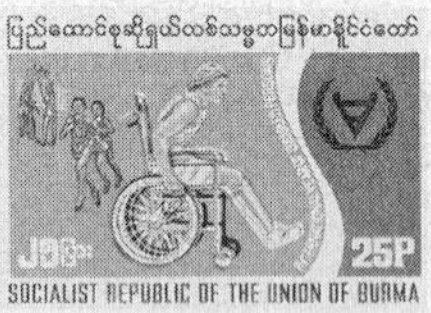

76 Athletes and Person in Wheelchair

1981. International Year of Disabled Persons.

295	**76**	25p. multicoloured	25	15

77 Telephone, Satellite and Antenna

1983. World Communications Year.

296	**77**	15p. blue and black	10	10
297		25p. mauve and black	30	15
298		50p. green, black and red	50	35
299		1k. brown, black & green	1·25	70

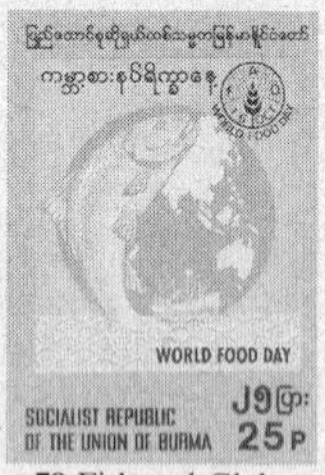

78 Fish and Globe

1983. World Food Day.

300	**78**	15p. yellow, blue & black	15	10
301		25p. orange, green & black	25	15
302		50p. green, yellow & black	60	60
303		1k. blue, yellow and black	1·75	1·40

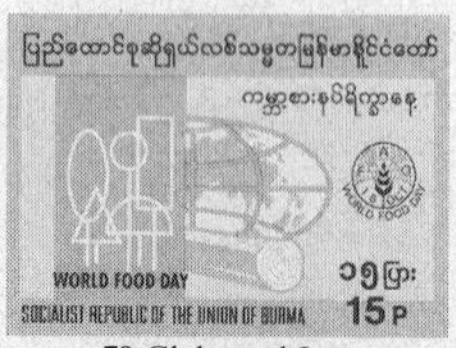

79 Globe and Log

1984. World Food Day.

304	**79**	15p. blue, yellow & black	10	10
305		25p. violet, yellow & black	15	10
306		50p. green, pink and black	50	40
307		1k. mauve, yellow & black	1·00	90

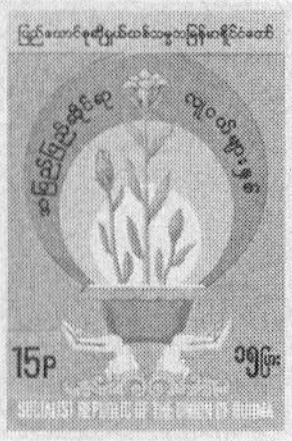

80 Potted Plant

1985. International Youth Year.

308	**80**	15p. multicoloured	25	20

1989. As Nos. 258/9 and 260/1 but inscr "UNION OF BURMA".

309	**62**	15p. dp green & green	25	20
309a	–	20p. black, brown & blue	5·00	
310	–	50p. violet and brown	50	30
311	–	1k. violet, mauve & black	85	65

OFFICIAL STAMPS

1937. Stamps of India (King George V) optd **BURMA SERVICE**.

O 1	**55**	3p. grey	1·75	10
O 2	**79**	½a. green	7·50	10
O 3	**80**	9p. green	4·00	30
O 4	**81**	1a. brown	5·00	10
O 5	**59**	2a. red	8·00	35
O 6	**61**	2½a. orange	4·25	2·00
O 7	**63**	4a. olive	5·00	10
O 8	**64**	6a. bistre	4·25	7·00
O 9	**65**	8a. mauve	4·00	80
O10	**66**	12a. red	4·00	4·25
O11	**67**	1r. brown and green	20·00	3·75
O12		2r. red and orange	48·00	38·00
O13		5r. blue and violet	95·00	48·00
O14		10r. green and red	£250	£130

1939. Stamps of 1938 optd **SERVICE**.

O15	**2**	3p. violet	15	20
O16		6p. blue	15	20
O17		9p. green	5·00	3·00
O18	**3**	1a. brown	15	15
O19		1½a. green	4·50	1·75
O20		2a. red	1·25	20
O21	**4**	2a.6p. red	26·00	12·00
O22	**3**	4a. blue	5·50	45
O23	–	8a. green (No. 29)	25·00	4·00
O24	**8**	1r. purple and blue	38·00	5·50
O25		2r. brown and purple	45·00	14·00
O26	–	5r. violet and red (No. 32)	42·00	29·00
O27	–	10r. brown and green (No. 33)	£120	38·00

1946. Stamps of 1946 optd **SERVICE**.

O28	**2**	3p. brown	1·50	3·00
O29		6p. violet	1·50	2·50
O30		9p. green	20	3·00
O31	**3**	1a. blue	20	2·00
O32		1½a. orange	20	20
O33		2a. red	20	2·00
O34	**4**	2a.6p. blue	1·40	5·50
O35	**3**	4a. purple	20	70
O36	–	8a. mauve (No. 59)	2·25	3·50
O37	**8**	1r. violet and mauve	60	3·75
O38		2r. brown and orange	7·00	40·00
O39	–	5r. green and brown (No. 62)	9·00	45·00
O40	–	10r. red and violet (No. 63)	17·00	50·00

1947. Interim Government. Nos. O28 etc., optd with T **18** or with large overprint on larger stamps.

O41	**2**	3p. brown	20	40
O42		6p. violet	1·25	10
O43		9p. green	2·00	90
O44	**3**	1a. blue	2·25	80
O45		1½a. orange	4·50	30
O46		2a. red	2·25	15
O47	**4**	2a.6p. blue	25·00	11·00
O48	**3**	4a. purple	10·00	40
O49	–	8a. mauve	8·00	4·00
O50	**8**	1r. violet and mauve	14·00	2·25
O51		2r. brown and orange	14·00	20·00
O52	–	5r. green and brown	14·00	20·00
O53	–	10r. red and violet	14·00	30·00

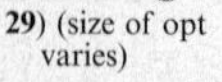

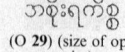

(O 29) (size of opt varies)

1949. 1st Anniv of Independence. Nos. 100/4 and 107/113 optd as Type O **29**.

O114	**22**	3p. blue	40	10
O115	–	6p. green	10	15
O116	–	9p. red	10	15
O117	**25**	1a. red	10	15
O118	–	2a. orange	15	15
O119	–	3a.6p. green	15	15
O120	–	4a. brown	15	15
O121	–	8a. red	15	15
O122	**28**	1r. green	40	25
O123		2r. blue	65	45
O124		5r. brown	2·25	1·50
O125		10r. orange	5·00	3·75

1954. Nos. 137/40 and 142/50 optd as Type O **29**.

O151	**22**	1p. orange	10	10
O152	–	2p. purple	10	10
O153	–	3p. blue	10	10
O154	**25**	5p. blue	10	10
O155	–	15p. green	10	10
O156	–	20p. red	15	10
O157	–	25p. orange	15	10
O158	–	30p. red	15	10
O159	–	50p. blue	25	20
O160	**28**	1k. violet	45	20
O161		2k. green	1·25	35

O162	5k. blue		2·50	90
O163	10k. blue		6·00	2·50

1964. No. 139 optd **Service.**

O174	– 3p. blue		9·50	6·50

1965. Nos. 174/7 and 179/85 optd as Type O **29.**

O196	**40**	1p. black	20	15
O197		2p. red	30	25
O198		3p. green	30	25
O199		– 5p. blue	35	30
O200		– 15p. green	35	30
O201		– 20p. brown and red	65	60
O202		– 25p. brown and yellow	70	65
O203		– 50p. blue and red	1·25	80
O204		– 1k. blue, yellow & grey	3·50	1·90
O205		– 2k. blue, green & red	4·75	1·75
O206		– 5k. multicoloured	14·00	12·00

1968. Nos. 195/8 and 200/6 optd as Type O **29.**

O207		1p. black	20	15
O208		2p. red	25	20
O209		3p. green	30	25
O210		– 5p. blue	30	25
O211		15p. green	30	25
O212		20p. brown and red	40	30
O213		25p. brown and yellow	30	25
O214		50p. blue and red	30	25
O215		1k. blue, yellow and grey	1·75	45
O216		2k. blue, green and red	3·50	1·10
O217		5k. multicoloured	5·00	4·50

For later issues see **MYANMAR.**

JAPANESE OCCUPATION OF BURMA

1942. 12 pies = 1 anna; 16 annas = 1 rupee.
1942. 100 cents = 1 rupee.

(1)   (3)

Note.—There are various types of the Peacock overprint. Our prices, as usual in this Catalogue, are for the cheapest type.

1942. Postage stamps of Burma of 1937 (India types) optd as T **1.**

J22	**55**	3p. grey	3·00	18·00
J23	**80**	9p. green	22·00	60·00
J24	**59**	2a. red	£100	£180
J 2	**83**	3½a. blue	50·00	

1942. Official stamp of Burma of 1937 (India type) optd as T **1.**

J3	**64**	6a. bistre	70·00

1942. Postage stamps of Burma, 1938, optd as T **1** or with T **3** (rupee values).

J25	**1**	1p. orange	£180	£275
J12		3p. violet	17·00	65·00
J27		6p. green	25·00	50·00
J14		9p. green	19·00	60·00
J29	**3**	1a. brown	9·00	40·00
J30		1½a. green	21·00	65·00
J16		2a. brown	19·00	75·00
J17		4a. blue	35·00	95·00
J18	**8**	1r. purple and blue	£250	
J19		2r. brown and purple	£150	

1942. Official stamps of Burma of 1939 optd with T **1.**

J 7	**1**	3p. violet	24·00	80·00
J 8		6p. green	16·00	55·00
J 9	**3**	1a. brown	16·00	48·00
J35		1½a. green	£160	£275
J10		2a. red	23·00	90·00
J11		4a. blue	22·00	70·00

(6a) ("Yon Thon" = "Office Use")

1942. Official stamp of Burma of 1939 optd with T **6a.**

J44		8a. green (No. O23)	85·00

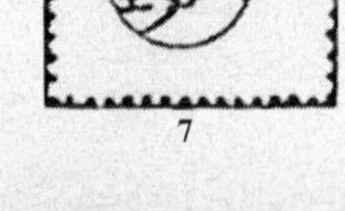

7   8 Farmer

1942. Yano Seal.

J45	**7**	(1a.) red	38·00	65·00

1942.

J46	**8**	1a. red	15·00	15·00

1942. Stamps of Japan surch in annas or rupees.

J47		– ½a. on 1s. brown (No. 314)	25·00	30·00
J48	**83**	¼a. on 2s. red	28·00	32·00
J49		– ¾ a. on 3s. green (No. 316)	60·00	65·00
J50		– 1a. on 5s. purple (No. 396)	45·00	42·00
J51		– 3a. on 7s. green (No. 320)	85·00	95·00
J52		– 4a. on 4s. green (No. 317)	42·00	45·00
J53		– 8a. on 8s. violet (No. 321)	£150	£150
J54		– 1r. on 10s. red (No. 322)	17·00	24·00
J55		– 2r. on 20s. blue (No. 325)	50·00	50·00
J56		– 5r. on 30s. blue (No. 327)	12·00	27·00

1942. No. 386 of Japan commemorating the fall of Singapore, surch in figures.

J56g		– 4a. on 4s.+2s. green and red	£150	£160

1942. Handstamped **5 C.**

J57	**5**	5c. on 1a. red (No. J46)	12·00	16·00

1942. Nos. J47/53 with anna surcharges obliterated, and handstamped with new values in figures.

J58		– 1c. on ½a. on 1s. brown	45·00	45·00
J59	**84**	– 2c. on ¼a. on 2s. red	42·00	45·00
J60		– 3c. on ¾a. on 3s. green	48·00	48·00
J61		– 5c. on 1a. on 5s. red	65·00	65·00
J62		– 10c. on 3a. on 7s. green	£110	£100
J63		– 15c. on 4a. on 4s. green	32·00	35·00
J64		– 20c. on 8a. on 8s. violet	£425	£375

1942. Stamps of Japan surch in cents.

J65		– 1c. on 1s. brown (No. 314)	21·00	20·00
J66	**83**	2c. on 2s. red	42·00	32·00
J67		– 3c. on 3s. green (No. 316)	50·00	45·00
J68		– 5c. on 5s. purple (No. 396)	55·00	42·00
J69		– 10c. on 5s. green (No. 320)	70·00	60·00
J70		– 15c. on 4s. green (No. 317)	16·00	20·00
J71		– 20c. on 8s. violet (No. 321)	£150	85·00

14 Burma State Crest   15 Farmer

1943. Perf or imperf.

J72	**14**	5c. red	17·00	20·00

1943.

J73a	**15**	1c. orange	1·50	4·25
J74		2c. green	60	1·00
J75		3c. blue	2·00	1·00
J77		5c. red	2·50	3·50
J78		10c. brown	4·50	4·00
J79		15c. mauve	30	50
J80		20c. lilac	30	80
J81		30c. green	30	1·00

16 Soldier carving word "Independence"   17 Rejoicing Peasant

18 Boy with National Flag

1943. Independence Day. Perf or roul.

J85	**16**	1c. orange	1·00	1·75
J86	**17**	3c. blue	1·75	2·00
J87	**18**	5c. red	1·50	2·00

19 Burmese Woman   20 Elephant carrying Log    21 Watch Tower Mandalay

1943.

J88	**19**	1c. orange	27·00	15·00
J89		2c. green	50	2·00
J90		3c. violet	50	2·25
J91	**20**	5c. blue	55	60
J92		10c. blue	1·25	1·10
J93		15c. orange	65	2·50
J94		20c. green	65	1·75
J95		30c. brown	65	1·75
J96	**21**	1r. orange	30	2·00
J97		2r. violet	30	2·25

22 Bullock Cart    23 Shan Woman

1943. Shan States issue.

J 98	**22**	1c. brown	25·00	32·00
J 99		2c. green	25·00	32·00
J100		3c. violet	3·50	10·00
J101		5c. blue	2·00	5·50
J102	**23**	10c. blue	12·00	17·00
J103		20c. red	26·00	17·00
J104		30c. brown	17·00	40·00

ဗမာနိုင်ငံတော်

၂၀ ဆင့်။

(24 "Burma State" and value)

1944. Optd with T **24.**

J105	**22**	1c. brown	3·00	6·00
J106		2c. green	40	2·25
J107		3c. violet	2·00	7·00
J108		5c. blue	1·00	1·25
J109	**23**	10c. blue	2·75	2·00
J110		20c. red	40	1·50
J111		30c. brown	40	1·75

BURUNDI   Pt. 12

Once part of the Belgian territory, Ruanda-Urundi. Independent on 1 July 1962, when a monarchy was established. After a revolution in 1967 Burundi became a republic.

100 centimes = 1 franc.

1962. Stamps of Ruanda-Urundi optd **Royaume du Burundi** and bar or surch also. (a) Flowers. (Nos. 178, etc.).

1		25c. multicoloured	25	20
2		40c. multicoloured	25	20
3		60c. multicoloured	35	35
4		1f.25 multicoloured	16·00	16·00
5		1f.50 multicoloured	60	60
6		5f. multicoloured	1·10	90
7		7f. multicoloured	1·75	1·40
8		10f. multicoloured	2·50	2·25

(b) Animals (Nos. 203/14).

9		10c. black, red and brown	10	10
10		20c. black and green	10	10
11		40c. black, olive and mauve	10	10
12		50c. brown, yellow & green	10	10
13		1f. black, blue and brown	10	10
14		1f.50 black and orange	10	10
15		2f. black, brown and turq	10	10
16		3f. black, red and brown	10	10
17		3f.50 on 3f. black, red & brn	10	10
18a		4f. multicoloured	20	20
19		5f. multicoloured	20	20
20		6f.50 brown, yellow and red	20	20
21		8f. black, mauve and blue	35	25
23		10f. multicoloured	50	30

(c) Animals (Nos. 229/30).

24	**25**	20f. multicoloured	1·60	60
25		– 50f. multicoloured	1·90	1·10

10 King Mwambutsa IV and Royal Drummers

1962. Independence. Inscr "1.7.1962".

26	**10**	50c. sepia and lake	10	10
27	A	1f. green, red & deep green	10	10
28	B	2f. sepia and olive	10	10
29	**10**	3f. sepia and red	10	10
30	A	4f. green, red and blue	15	10
31	B	8f. sepia and violet	30	15
32	**10**	10f. sepia and green	40	15
33	A	20f. green, red and sepia	45	20
34	B	50f. sepia and mauve	1·25	45

DESIGNS—VERT: A, Burundi flag and arms. HORIZ: B, King and outline map of Burundi.

1962. Dag Hammarskjold Commem. No. 222 of Ruanda-Urundi surch **HOMMAGE A DAG HAMMARSKJOLD ROYAUME DU BURUNDI** and new value. U.N. emblem and wavy pattern at foot. Inscr in French or Flemish.

35		3f.50 on 3f. salmon and blue	35	35
36		6f.50 on 3f. salmon and blue	65	45
37		10f. on 3f. salmon and blue	1·25	1·10

1962. Malaria Eradication. As Nos. 31 and 34 but colours changed and with campaign emblem superimposed on map.

38	B	8f. sepia, turquoise & bistre	55	35
39		50f. sepia, turquoise & olive	1·40	35

12 Prince Louis Rwagasore    13 "Sowing"

1963. Prince Rwagasore Memorial and Stadium Fund.

40	**12**	50c.+25c. violet	10	10
41		1f.+50c. blue and orange	10	10
42		1f.50+75c. vio & bistre	10	10
43	**12**	3f.50+1f.50 mauve	20	10
44		5f.+2f. blue and pink	20	10
45		6f.50+3f. violet & olive	25	10

DESIGNS—HORIZ: 1f., 5f. Prince and stadium; 1f.50, 6f.50 Prince and memorial.

1963. Freedom from Hunger.

46	**13**	4f. purple and olive	15	15
47		8f. purple and olive	20	15
48		15f. purple and green	35	15

1963. "Peaceful Uses of Outer Space" Nos. 28 and 34 optd **UTILISATIONS PACIFIQUES DE L'ESPACE** around globe encircled by rocket.

49	B	2f. sepia and olive	2·25	2·25
50		50f. sepia and mauve	3·50	3·50

1963. 1st Anniv of Independence. Nos. 30/3 but with colours changed and optd **Premier Anniversaire.**

51	A	4f. green, red and olive	20	10
52	B	8f. sepia and orange	30	10
53	**10**	10f. sepia and mauve	40	10
54	A	20f. green, red and grey	90	30

1963. Nos. 27 and 33 surch.

55	A	6f.50 on 1f. green, red and deep green	55	10
56		15f. on 20f. grn, red & sepia	85	35

17 Globe and Red Cross Flag

1963. Centenary of Red Cross.

57	**17**	4f. green, red and grey	20	10
58		8f. brown, red and grey	40	20
59		10f. blue, red and grey	50	20
60		20f. violet, red and grey	1·10	40

IMPERF STAMPS. Many Burundi stamps from No. 61 onwards exist imperf from limited printings and/or miniature sheets.

18 "1962" and U.N.E.S.C.O. Emblem

1963. 1st Anniv of Admission to U.N.O. Emblems and values in black.

61	**18**	4f. olive and yellow	15	10
62		– 8f. blue and lilac	25	10
63		– 10f. violet and blue	40	10
64		– 20f. green and yellow	65	20
65		– 50f. brown and ochre	1·75	35

EMBLEMS: 8f. I.T.U.; 10f. W.M.O.; 20f. U.P.U.; 50f. F.A.O.

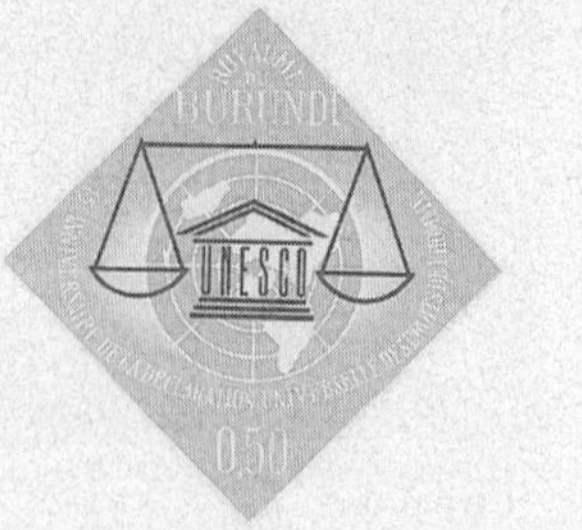

19 U.N.E.S.C.O. Emblem and Scales of Justice

1963. 15th Anniv of Declaration of Human Rights.

66 **19**	50c. blk, blue and pink	10	10
67 –	1f.50 black, blue & orange	10	10
68 –	3f.50 black, green & brown	15	10
69 –	6f.50 black, green and lilac	25	10
70 –	10f. black, bistre and blue	40	15
71 –	20f. multicoloured	70	25

DESIGNS: 3f.50, 6f.50, Scroll; 10f., 20f. Lincoln.

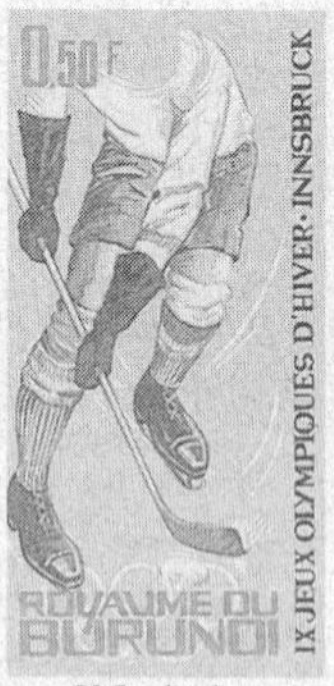

20 Ice-hockey

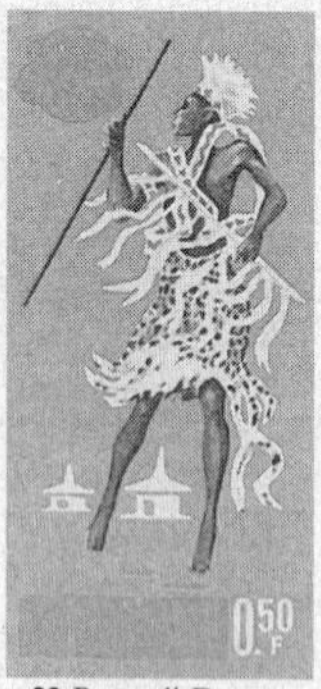

22 Burundi Dancer

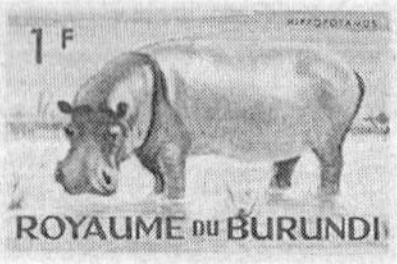

21 Hippopotamus

1964. Winter Olympic Games, Innsbruck.

72 **20**	50c. black, gold and olive	15	10
73 –	3f.50 black, gold & brown	20	10
74 –	6f.50 black, gold and grey	45	20
75 –	10f. black, gold and grey	90	35
76 –	20f. black, gold and bistre	2·10	65

DESIGNS: 3f.50, Figure-skating; 6f.50, Olympic flame; 10f. Speed-skating; 20f. Skiing (slalom).

1964. Burundi Animals. Multicoloured. (i) Postage. (a) Size as T **21**.

77	50c. Impala	10	10
78	1f. Type **21**	10	10
79	1f.50 Giraffe	10	10
80	2f. African buffalo	20	10
81	3f. Common zebra	20	10
82	3f.50 Waterbuck	20	10

(b) Size 16 × 42½ mm or 42½ × 26 mm.

83	4f. Impala	25	10
84	5f. Hippopotamus	30	10
85	6f.50 Common zebra	30	10
86	8f. African buffalo	55	20
87	10f. Giraffe	60	20
88	15f. Waterbuck	85	30

(c) Size 53½ × 33½ mm.

89	20f. Cheetah	1·50	40
90	50f. African elephant	4·00	65
91	100f. Lion	6·50	1·10

(ii) Air. Inscr "POSTE AERIENNE" and optd with gold border. (a) Size 26 × 42½ mm or 42½ × 26 mm.

92	6f. Common zebra	35	10
93	8f. African buffalo	60	10
94	10f. Impala	70	10
95	14f. Hippopotamus	85	15
96	15f. Waterbuck	1·40	35

(b) Size 53½ × 33½ mm.

97	20f. Cheetah	1·75	40
98	50f. African elephant	4·00	90

The impala, giraffe and waterbuck stamps are all vert. designs, and the remainder are horiz.

1964. World's Fair, New York (1st series). Gold backgrounds.

99 **22**	50c. multicoloured	10	10
100 –	1f. multicoloured	10	10
101 –	4f. multicoloured	15	10
102 –	6f.50 multicoloured	20	10
103 –	10f. multicoloured	40	15
104 –	15f. multicoloured	70	20
105 –	20f. multicoloured	90	30

DESIGNS: 1f. to 20f. Various dancers and drummers as Type **22**.

See also Nos. 175/81.

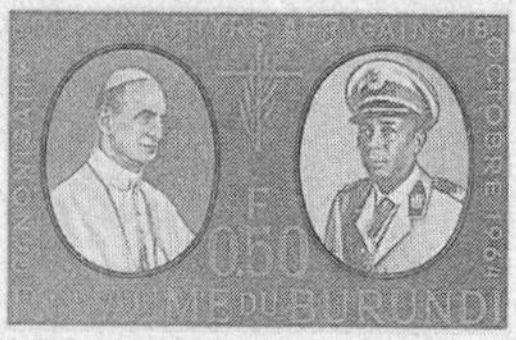

23 Pope Paul and King Mwambutsa IV

1964. Canonization of 22 African Martyrs. Inscriptions in gold.

106 **23**	50c. lake and blue	15	10
107 –	1f. blue and purple	15	10
108 –	4f. sepia and mauve	25	10
109 –	8f. brown and red	40	15
110 –	14f. brown and turquoise	40	20
111 **23**	20f. green and red	65	40

DESIGNS—VERT: 1f., 8f. Group of martyrs. HORIZ: 4f., 14f., Pope John XXIII and King Mwambutsa IV.

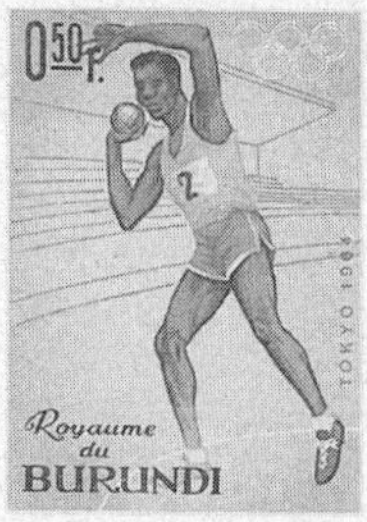

24 Putting the Shot

1964. Olympic Games, Tokyo. Inscr "TOKYO 1964". Multicoloured.

112	50c. Type **24**	10	10
113	1f. Throwing the discus	10	10
114	3f. Swimming (horiz)	10	10
115	4f. Relay-racing	10	10
116	6f.50 Throwing the javelin	30	20
117	8f. Hurdling (horiz)	35	20
118	10f. Long-jumping (horiz)	40	20
119	14f. High-diving	55	20
120	18f. High-jumping (horiz)	65	35
121	20f. Gymnastics (horiz)	85	35

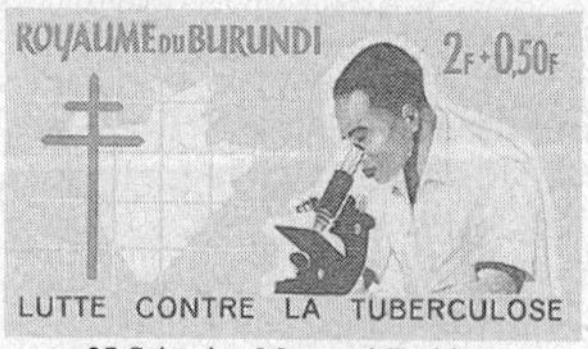

25 Scientist, Map and Emblem

1965. Anti-T.B. Campaign. Country name, values and Lorraine Cross in red.

122 **25**	2f.+50c. sepia and drab	10	10
123	4f.+1f.50 green & pink	25	10
124	5f.+2f.50 violet & buff	30	15
125	8f.+3f. blue and grey	40	20
126	10f.+5f. red and green	55	30

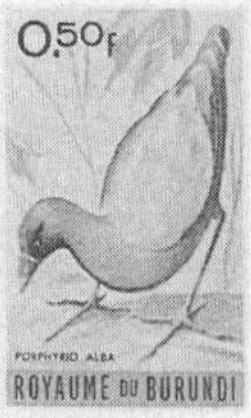

26 Purple Swamphen

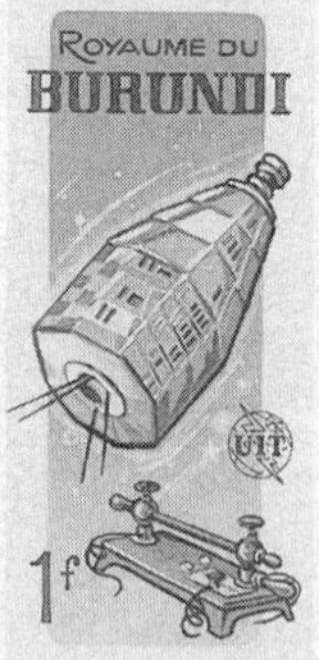

27 "Relay" Satellite and Telegraph Key

1965. Birds. Multicoloured. (i) Postage. (a) Size as T **26**.

127	50c. Type **26**	10	10
128	1f. Little bee eater	10	10
129	1f.50 Secretary bird	10	10
130	2f. Painted stork	20	10
131	3f. Congo peafowl	25	10
132	3f.50 African darter	30	10

(b) Size 26 × 42½ mm.

133	4f. Type **26**	40	10
134	5f. Little bee eater	50	15
135	6f.50 Secretary bird	60	15
136	8f. Painted stork	60	15
137	10f. Congo peafowl	70	15
138	15f. African darter	85	25

(c) Size 33½ × 53 mm.

139	20f. Saddle-bill stork	1·25	25
140	50f. Abyssinian ground hornbill	2·40	50
141	100f. South African crowned crane	4·00	90

(ii) Air. Inscr "POSTE AERIENNE". Optd with gold border. (a) Size 26 × 42½ mm.

142	6f. Secretary bird	50	10
143	8f. African darter	60	15
144	10f. Congo peafowl	70	15
145	14f. Little bee eater	75	20
146	15f. Painted stork	85	20

(b) Size 33½ × 53 mm.

147	20f. Saddle-bill stork	1·25	30
148	50f. Abyssinian ground hornbill	2·25	80
149	75f. Martial eagle	2·50	1·00
150	130f. Lesser flamingo	4·75	1·60

1965. Centenary of I.T.U. Multicoloured.

151	1f. Type **27**	10	10
152	3f. "Telstar 1" and hand telephone	10	10
153	4f. "Lunik 3" and wall telephone	10	10
154	6f.50 Weather satellite and tracking station	15	10
155	8f. "Telstar 2" and headphones	15	15
156	10f. "Sputnik" and radar scanner	20	15
157	14f. "Syncom" and aerial	30	20
158	20f. "Pioneer 5" space probe and radio aerial	35	30

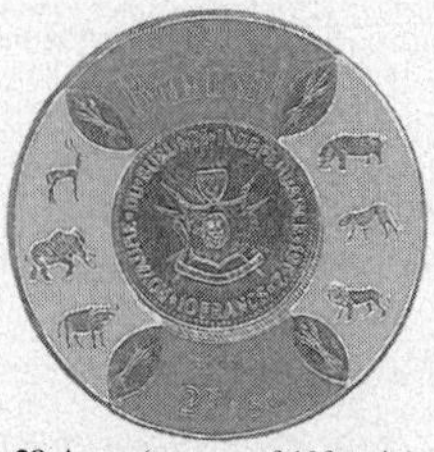

28 Arms (reverse of 10f. coin)

1956. 1st Independence Anniv Gold Coinage Commem. Circular designs on gold foil, backed with multicoloured patterned paper. Imperf. (i) Postage. (a) 10f. coin. Diameter 1½ in.

159 **28**	2f.+50c. red & yellow	15	15
160 –	4f.+50c. blue & red	20	20

(b) 25f. coin. Diameter 1¾ in.

161 **28**	6f.+50c. orange & grey	50	30
162 –	8f.+50c. blue & purple	60	60

(c) 50f. coin. Diameter 2¼ in.

163 **28**	12f.+50c. green & purple	60	60
164 –	15f.+50c. green & lilac	65	65

(d) 100f. coin. Diameter 2 in.

165 **28**	25f.+50c. blue and flesh	1·25	1·25
166 –	40f.+50c. mauve & brn	1·75	1·75

(ii) Air. (a) 10f. coin. Diameter 1½ in.

167 **28**	3f.+1f. violet & lavender	30	30
168 –	5f.+1f. red & turquoise	40	40

(b) 25f. coin. Diameter 1¾ in.

169 **28**	11f.+1f. purple & yellow	60	60
170 –	14f.+1f. green and red	60	60

(c) 50f. coin. Diameter 2¼ in.

171 **28**	20f.+1f. black and blue	85	85
172 –	30f.+1f. red and orange	1·10	1·10

(d) 100f. coin. Diameter 2¾ in.

173 **28**	50f.+1f. violet and blue	1·25	1·25
174 –	100f.+1f. purple & mve	3·00	3·00

DESIGNS: The 4, 5, 8, 14, 15, 30, 40 and 100f. each show the obverse side of the coin (King Mwambutsa IV).

1965. Worlds Fair, New York (2nd series). As Nos. 99/105, but with silver backgrounds.

175 **22**	50c. multicoloured	10	10
176 –	1f. multicoloured	10	10
177 –	4f. multicoloured	15	10
178 –	6f.50 multicoloured	25	10
179 –	10f. multicoloured	45	20
180 –	15f. multicoloured	55	30
181 –	20f. multicoloured	70	35

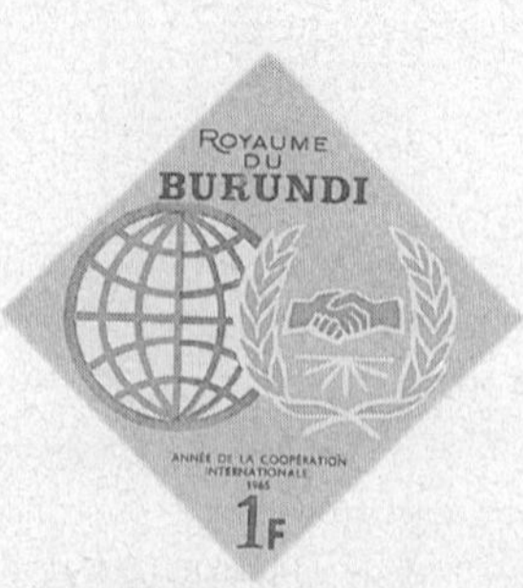

29 Globe and I.C.Y. Emblem

1965. International Co-operation Year. Mult.

182	1f. Type **29**	10	10
183	4f. Map of Africa and cogwheel emblem of U.N. Science and Technology Conference	15	10
184	8f. Map of South-East Asia and Colombo Plan emblem	20	10
185	10f. Globe and U.N. emblem	25	10
186	18f. Map of Americas and "Alliance for Progress" emblem	40	10
187	25f. Map of Europe and C.E.P.T. emblems	60	30
188	40f. Space map and satellite (U.N.—"Peaceful Uses of Outer Space")	1·00	50

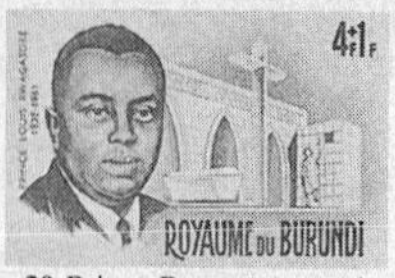

30 Prince Rwagasore and Memorial

1966. Prince Rwagasore and Pres. Kennedy Commemoration.

189 **30**	4f.+1f. brown and blue	20	10
190 –	10f.+1f. blue, brn & grn	30	10
191 –	20f.+2f. green and lilac	65	15
192 –	40f.+2f. brown & green	75	30

DESIGNS—HORIZ: 10f. Prince Rwagasore and Pres. Kennedy; 20f. Pres. Kennedy and memorial library. VERT: 40f. King Mwambutsa at Pres. Kennedy's grave.

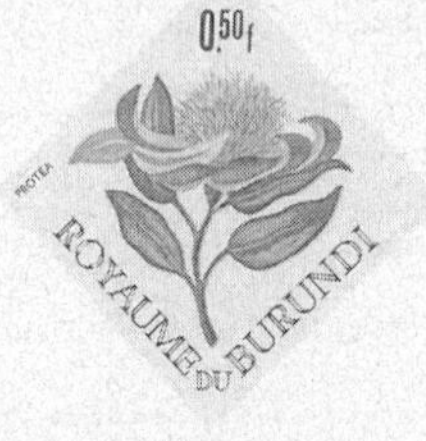

31 Protea

1966. Flowers. Multicoloured. (i) Postage. (a) Size as T **31**.

194	50c. Type **31**	15	10
195	1f. Crossandra	15	10
196	1f.50 Ansellia	15	10
197	2f. Thunbergia	15	10
198	3f. Schizoglossum	25	10
199	3f.50 Dissotis	25	10

(b) Size 41 × 41 mm.

200	4f. Type **31**	25	10
201	5f. Crossandra	35	10
202	6f.50 Ansellia	45	10
203	8f. Thunbergia	65	10
204	10f. Schizoglossum	70	10
205	15f. Dissotis	85	10

(c) Size 50 × 50 mm.

206	20f. Type **31**	1·10	15
207	50f. Gazania	2·50	35
208	100f. Hibiscus	4·00	55
209	150f. Markhamia	6·25	75

(ii) Air. (a) Size 41 × 41 mm.

210	6f. Dissotis	25	15
211	8f. Crossandra	35	15
212	10f. Ansellia	35	15
213	14f. Thunbergia	40	15
214	15f. Schizoglossum	40	15

(b) Size 50 × 50 mm.

215	20f. Gazania	65	20
216	50f. Type **31**	1·75	40
217	75f. Hibiscus	2·50	1·00
218	130f. Markhamia	3·75	1·40

1967. Various stamps optd. (i) Nos. 127, etc. (Birds) optd **REPUBLIQUE DU BURUNDI** and bar. (a) Postage.

221	50c. multicoloured	1·60	25
222	1f.50 multicoloured	35	25
223	3f.50 multicoloured	45	35
224	5f. multicoloured	60	45
225	6f.50 multicoloured	60	65
226	8f. multicoloured	70	80
227	10f. multicoloured	80	80
228	15f. multicoloured	1·10	1·25
229	20f. multicoloured	2·75	1·75
230	50f. multicoloured	5·25	3·75
231	100f. multicoloured	8·50	7·00

(b) Air.

232	6f. multicoloured	55	25
233	8f. multicoloured	70	40
234	10f. multicoloured	85	65
235	14f. multicoloured	1·10	65
236	15f. multicoloured	1·25	80
237	20f. multicoloured	1·75	95
238	50f. multicoloured	6·25	2·75
239	75f. multicoloured	8·50	3·50
240	130f. multicoloured	12·00	5·75

(ii) Nos. 194, etc. (Flowers) optd as Nos. 221, etc., but with two bars. (a) Postage.

241	50c. multicoloured	15	15
242	1f. multicoloured	15	15
243	1f.50 multicoloured	15	15
244	2f. multicoloured	15	15
245	3f. multicoloured	20	15
246	3f.50 multicoloured	30	15
247	4f. multicoloured	1·90	15
248	5f. multicoloured	50	20
249	6f.50 multicoloured	45	30
250	8f. multicoloured	45	30
251	10f. multicoloured	60	40
252	15f. multicoloured	75	45
253	50f. multicoloured	3·75	65
254	100f. multicoloured	9·00	2·50
255	150f. multicoloured	8·50	9·25

(b) Air.

256	6f. multicoloured	20	15
257	8f. multicoloured	30	15
258	10f. multicoloured	35	15
259	14f. multicoloured	45	30
260	15f. multicoloured	55	30
261	20f. multicoloured	1·75	40
262	50f. multicoloured	3·75	65
263	75f. multicoloured	5·75	90
264	130f. multicoloured	5·75	1·50

35 Sir Winston Churchill and St. Paul's Cathedral

1967. Churchill Commemoration.
265	**35**	4f.+1f. multicoloured	30	10
266	–	15f.+2f. multicoloured	50	25
267	–	20f.+3f. multicoloured	60	35

DESIGNS (Churchill and): 15f. Tower of London; 20f. Big Ben and Boadicea statue, Westminster.

36 Egyptian Mouthbrooder

1967. Fishes. Multicoloured. (a) Postage. (i) Size as T **36**.
269	50c. Type **36**	15	20
270	1f. Spotted climbing-perch	15	20
271	1f.50 Six-banded lyretail	15	20
272	2f. Congo tetra	15	20
273	3f. Jewel cichlid	15	20
274	3f.50 Spotted mouthbrooder	15	20

(ii) Size 53½ × 27 mm.
275	4f. Type **36**	50	20
276	5f. As 1f.	50	20
277	6f.50. As 1f.50	65	20
278	8f. As 2f.	65	20
279	10f. As 3f.	1·00	20
280	15f. As 3f.50	1·10	20

(iii) Size 63½ × 31½ mm.
281	20f. Type **36**	1·90	30
282	50f. Dusky snakehead	3·50	50
283	100f. Red-tailed notho	7·50	75
284	150f. African tetra	7·50	1·10

(b) Air. (i) Size 50 × 23 mm.
285	6f. Type **36**	30	20
286	8f. As 1f.	45	20
287	10f. As 1f.50	55	20
288	14f. As 2f.	65	20
289	15f. As 3f.	80	20

(ii) Size 59 × 27 mm.
290	20f. As 3f.50	95	20
291	50f. As 50f. (No. 282)	4·75	30
292	75f. As 100f.	6·00	50
293	130f. As 150f.	11·00	1·00

37 Baule Ancestral Figures

1967. "African Art". Multicoloured.
294	50c. Type **37** (postage)	10	10
295	1f. "Master of Buli's" carved seat	10	10
296	1f.50 Karumba antelope's head	10	10
297	2f. Bobo buffalo's head	10	10
298	4f. Guma-Goffa funeral figures	15	10
299	10f. Bakoutou "spirit" (carving) (air)	30	20
300	14f. Bamum sultan's throne	40	20
301	17f. Bebin bronze head	45	20
302	24f. Statue of 109th Bakouba king	55	30
303	26f. Burundi basketwork and lances	60	35

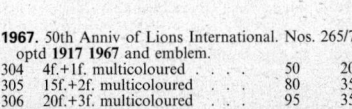

1967. 50th Anniv of Lions International. Nos. 265/7 optd **1917 1967** and emblem.
304	4f.+1f. multicoloured	50	20
305	15f.+2f. multicoloured	80	35
306	20f.+3f. multicoloured	95	35

39 Lord Baden-Powell (founder)

1967. 60th Anniv of Scout Movement and World Scout Jamboree, Idaho.
308	50c. Scouts climbing (postage)	20	10
309	1f. Scouts preparing meal	20	10
310	1f.50 Type **39**	20	10
311	2f. Two scouts	20	10
312	4f. Giving first aid	30	10
313	10f. As 50c. (air)	60	15
314	14f. As 1f.	70	15
315	17f. Type **39**	85	15
316	24f. As 2f.	1·10	35
317	26f. As 4f.	1·25	40

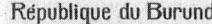

40 "The Gleaners" (Millet)

1967. World Fair, Montreal. Multicoloured.
318	4f. Type **40**	15	10
319	8f. "The Water-carrier of Seville" (Velasquez)	15	10
320	14f. "The Triumph of Neptune and Amphitrite" (Poussin)	35	15
321	18f. "Acrobat with a ball" (Picasso)	35	15
322	25f. "Margaret van Eyck" (Van Eyck)	95	25
323	40f. "St. Peter denying Christ" (Rembrandt)	1·10	50

41 Boeing 707

1967. Air. Opening of Bujumbura Airport. Aircraft and inscr in black and silver.
325	**41**	10f. green	40	10
326	–	14f. yellow	65	20
327	–	17f. blue	95	20
328	–	26f. purple	1·60	30

AIRCRAFT: 14f. Boeing 727 over lakes. 17f. Vickers Super VC-10 over lake. 26f. Boeing 727 over Bujumbura Airport.

42 Pres. Micombero and Flag

1967. 1st Anniv of Republic. Multicoloured.
329	5f. Type **42**	25	10
330	14f. Memorial and Arms	35	15
331	20f. View of Bujumbura and Arms	50	20
332	30f. "Place de la Revolution" and President Micombero	90	30

43 "The Adoration of the Shepherds" (J. B. Mayno)   **45** Downhill Skiing

1967. Christmas. Religious Paintings. Multicoloured.
333	1f. Type **43**	10	10
334	4f. "The Holy Family" (A. van Dyck)	15	10
335	14f. "The Nativity" (Maitre de Moulins)	40	20
336	26f. "Madonna and Child" (C. Crivelli)	75	30

1968. Winter Olympic Games, Grenoble. Mult.
339	5f. Type **45**	20	10
340	10f. Ice-hockey	25	10
341	14f. Figure-skating	40	10
342	17f. Bobsleighing	50	10
343	26f. Ski-jumping	65	10
344	40f. Speed-skating	1·10	25
345	60f. Olympic torch	1·75	30

46 "Portrait of a Young Man" (Botticelli)

1968. Famous Paintings. Multicoloured.
347	1f.50 Type **46** (postage)	10	10
348	2f. "La Maja Vestida" (Goya) (horiz)	10	10
349	4f. "The Lacemaker" (Vermeer)	15	10
350	17f. "Woman and Cat" (Renoir) (air)	40	20
351	24f. "The Jewish Bride" (Rembrandt) (horiz)	55	30
352	26f. "Pope Innocent X" (Velasquez)	80	40

47 Module landing on Moon

1968. Space Exploration. Multicoloured.
353	4f. Type **47** (postage)	20	10
354	6f. Russian cosmonaut in Space	30	10
355	8f. Weather satellite	30	10
356	10f. American astronaut in Space	45	15
357	14f. Type **47** (air)	40	15
358	18f. As 6f.	50	15
359	25f. As 8f.	80	25
360	40f. As 10f.	1·10	40

48 "Salamis aethiops"

1968. Butterflies. Multicoloured. (a) Postage. (i) Size 30½ × 34 mm.
362	50c. Type **48**	15	15
363	1f. "Graphium ridleyanus"	20	15
364	1f.50 "Cymothoe"	25	15
365	2f. "Charaxes eupale"	35	15
366	3f. "Papilio bromius"	40	15
367	3f.50 "Teracolus annae"	50	15

(ii) Size 34 × 38 mm.
368	4f. Type **48**	50	15
369	5f. As 1f.	50	15
370	6f.50 As 1f.50	60	15
371	8f. As 2f.	90	20
372	10f. As 3f.	1·10	20
373	15f. As 3f.50	1·40	25

(iii) Size 41 × 46 mm.
374	20f. Type **48**	2·50	30
375	50f. "Papilio zenobia"	4·50	75
376	100f. "Danais chrysippus"	8·25	1·25
377	150f. "Salamis temora"	14·00	2·10

(b) Air. With gold frames. (i) Size 33 × 37 mm.
378	6f. As 3f.50	50	15
379	8f. As 1f.	55	15
380	10f. As 1f.50	60	15
381	14f. As 2f.	70	20
382	15f. As 3f.	1·00	20

(ii) Size 39 × 44 mm.
383	20f. As 50f. (No. 375)	2·40	25
384	50f. Type **48**	5·50	50
385	75f. As 100f.	6·75	90
386	130f. As 150f.	12·50	1·10

49 "Woman by the Manzanares" (Goya)

1968. International Letter-writing Week. Mult.
387	4f. Type **49** (postage)	25	10
388	7f. "Reading a Letter" (De Hooch)	35	10
389	11f. "Woman reading a Letter" (Terborch)	40	10
390	14f. "Man writing a Letter" (Metsu)	45	10
391	17f. "The Letter" (Fragonard) (air)	60	10
392	26f. "Young Woman reading Letter" (Vermeer)	80	20
393	40f. "Folding a Letter" (Vigee-Lebrun)	90	25
394	50f. "Mademoiselle Lavergne" (Liotard)	95	35

50 Football

1968. Olympic Games, Mexico. Multicoloured.
396	4f. Type **50** (postage)	25	10
397	7f. Basketball	30	10
398	13f. High jumping	35	10
399	24f. Relay racing	55	20
400	40f. Throwing the javelin	1·25	40
401	10f. Putting the shot (air)	25	15
402	17f. Running	45	15
403	26f. Throwing the hammer	70	25
404	50f. Hurdling	1·40	45
405	75f. Long jumping	2·25	60

51 "Virgin and Child" (Lippi)

1968. Christmas. Paintings. Multicoloured.
407	3f. Type **51** (postage)	20	10
408	5f. "The Magnificat" (Botticelli)	25	10
409	6f. "Virgin and Child" (Durer)	40	10
410	11f. "Virgin and Child" (Raphael)	40	10
411	10f. "Madonna" (Correggio) (air)	25	10

412 14f. "The Nativity" (Baroccio) 35 15
413 17f. "The Holy Family" (El Greco) 55 20
414 26f. "Adoration of the Magi" (Maino) 75 35

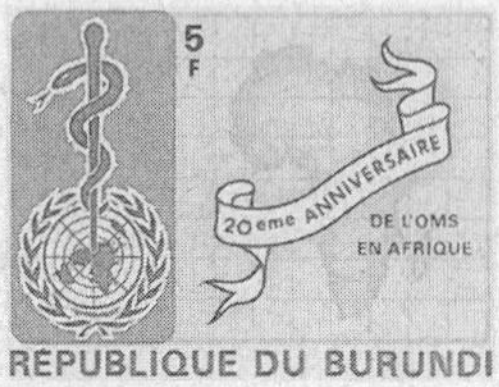

52 W.H.O. Emblem and Map

1969. 20th Anniv of World Health Organization Operation in Africa.
416 **52** 5f. multicoloured 15 10
417 6f. multicoloured 20 10
418 11f. multicoloured 25 15

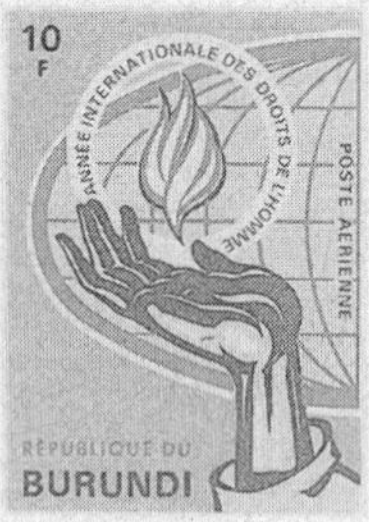

53 Hand holding Flame

1969. Air. Human Rights Year.
419 **53** 10f. multicoloured 35 10
420 14f. multicoloured 45 10
421 26f. multicoloured 65 25

1969. Space Flight of "Apollo 8". Nos. 407/14 optd ***VOL DE NOEL APOLLO 8*** and space module.
422 3f. multicoloured (postage) 15 10
423 5f. multicoloured 25 10
424 6f. multicoloured 40 10
425 11f. multicoloured 50 20
426 10f. multicoloured (air) . . . 30 15
427 14f. multicoloured 35 20
428 17f. multicoloured 55 25
429 26f. multicoloured 70 35

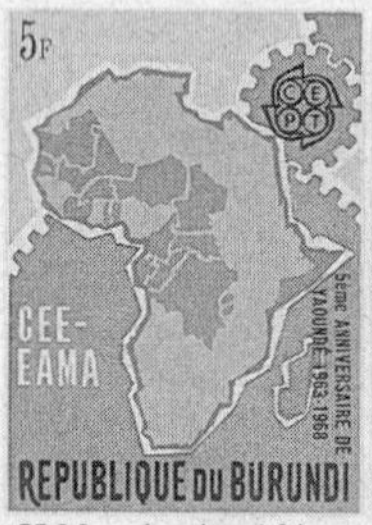

55 Map showing African Members

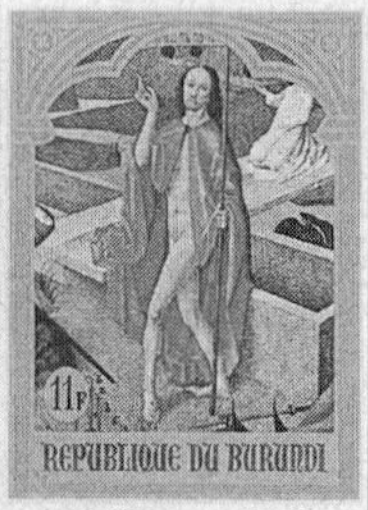

56 "Resurrection" (Isenmann)

1969. 5th Anniv of Yaounde Agreement between Common Market Countries and African-Malagasy Economic Community. Multicoloured.
430 5f. Type **55** 20 10
431 14f. Ploughing with tractor 40 15
432 17f. Teacher and pupil . . . 55 20
433 26f. Maps of Africa and Europe (horiz) 75 25

1969. Easter. Multicoloured.
434 11f. Type **56** 30 10
435 14f. "Resurrection" (Caron) 40 15
436 17f. "Noli me Tangere" (Schongauer) 45 20
437 26f. "Resurrection" (El Greco) 75 30

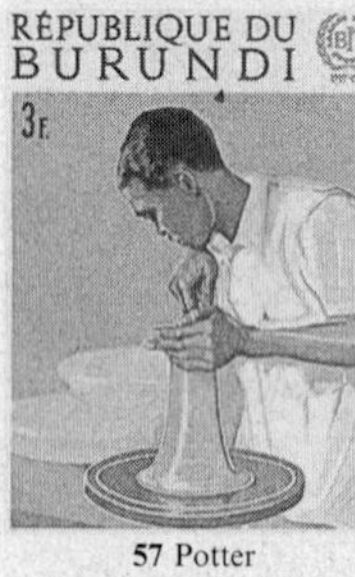

57 Potter

1969. 50th Anniv of I.L.O. Multicoloured.
439 3f. Type **57** 10 10
440 5f. Farm workers 10 10
441 7f. Foundry worker 25 10
442 10f. Harvester 25 15

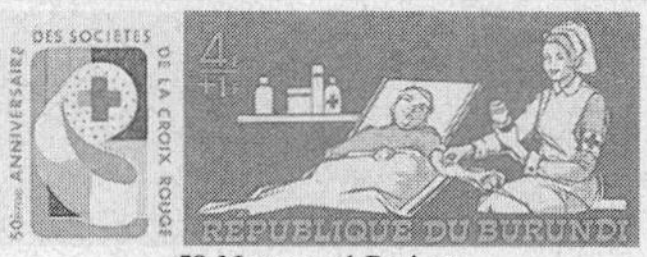

58 Nurse and Patient

1969. 50th Anniv of League of Red Cross Societies. Multicoloured.
443 4f.+1f. Type **58** (postage) . . 15 10
444 7f.+1f. Stretcher bearers . . . 35 10
445 11f.+1f. Operating theatre . . 50 15
446 17f.+1f. Blood bank 60 25
447 26f.+3f. Laboratory (air) . . 75 25
448 40f.+3f. Red Cross truck in African village . . . . . . 1·10 45
449 50f.+3f. Nurse and woman patient . . . . 1·60 50

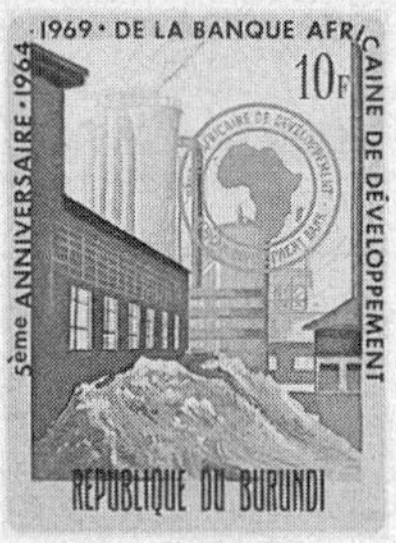

59 Steel Works

1969. 5th Anniv of African Development Bank. Multicoloured.
451 10f. Type **59** 30 30
452 17f. Broadcaster 50 50
453 30f. Language laboratory . . 70 70
454 50f. Tractor and harrow . . 1·25 1·25

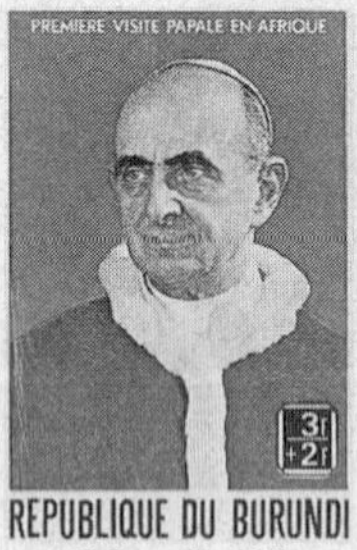

60 Pope Paul VI

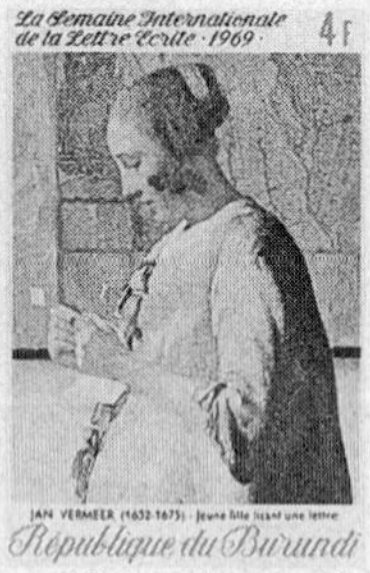

61 "Girl reading Letter" (Vermeer)

1969. 1st Papal Visit to Africa. Multicoloured.
456 3f.+2f. Type **60** 15 10
457 5f.+2f. Pope Paul and map of Africa (horiz) 30 10
458 10f.+2f. Pope Paul and African flags (horiz) . . . 30 10
459 14f.+2f. Pope Paul and the Vatican (horiz) 55 10
460 17f.+2f. Type **60** 60 10
461 40f.+2f. Pope Paul and Uganda Martyrs (horiz) . . 1·25 30
462 50f.+2f. Pope Paul enthroned (horiz) . . . . 1·60 35

1969. International Letter-writing Week. Mult.
464 4f. Type **61** 15 10
465 7f. "Graziella" (Renoir) . . . 20 10
466 14f. "Woman writing a Letter" (Terborch) 30 10
467 26f. "Galileo" (unknown painter) 55 15
468 40f. "Beethoven" (unknown painter) . . . . 1·10 35

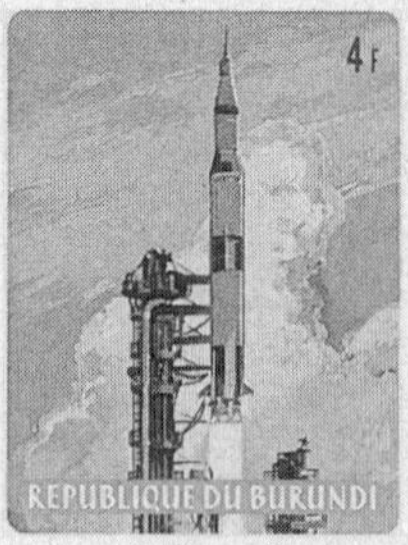

62 Blast-off

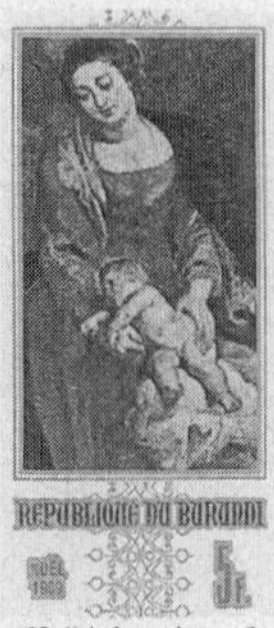

63 "Adoration of the Magi" (detail, Rubens)

1969. 1st Man on the Moon. Multicoloured.
470 4f. Type **62** (postage) . . . 30 10
471 6f.50 Rocket in Space 40 10
472 7f. Separation of lunar module 50 10
473 14f. Module landing on Moon 80 15
474 17f. Command module in orbit . . . . 1·10 25
475 26f. Astronaut descending ladder (air) . . . . . . 1·25 20
476 40f. Astronaut on Moon's surface . . . . 2·00 25
477 50f. Module in sea . . . . . 3·00 45

1969. Christmas. Multicoloured.
479 5f. Type **63** (postage) 15 10
480 6f. "Virgin and Child with St. John" (Romano) 15 10
481 10f. "Madonna of the Magnificat" (Botticelli) . . 40 15
482 17f. "Virgin and Child" (Garofalo) (horiz) (air) . . 60 15
483 26f. "Madonna and Child" (Negretti) (horiz) 80 20
484 50f. "Virgin and Child" (Barbarelli) (horiz) . . . . 1·60 35

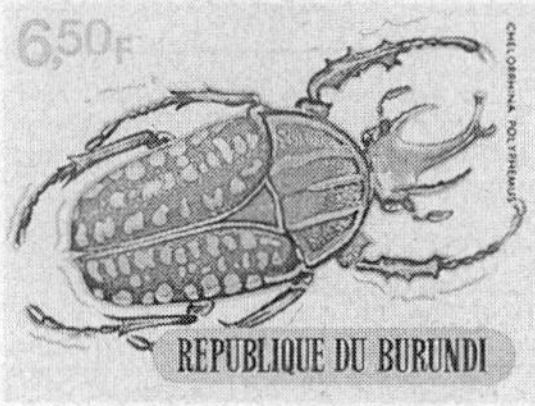

64 "Chelorrhina polyphemus"

1970. Beetles. Multicoloured. (a) Postage. (i) Size 39 × 28 mm.
486 50c. "Sternotomis bohemani" 20 10
487 1f. "Tetralobus flabellicornis" 20 10
488 1f.50 Type **64** 20 10
489 2f. "Brachytritus hieroglyphicus" 20 10
490 3f. "Goliathus goliathus" . . 20 10
491 3f.50 "Homoderus mellyi" . . 30 10

(ii) Size 46 × 32 mm.
492 4f. As 50c. 45 10
493 5f. As 1f. 65 10
494 6f. Type **64** 65 10
495 8f. As 2f. 65 10
496 10f. As 3f. 70 10
497 15f. As 3f.50 . . . . 1·10 15

(iii) Size 62 × 36 mm.
498 20f. As 50c. . . . . 1·50 30
499 50f. "Stephanorrhina guttata" 4·00 40
500 100f. "Phyllocnema viridocostata" . . . . . . 6·75 85
501 150f. "Mecynorrhina oberthueri" . . . . 8·25 1·60

(b) Air. (i) Size 46 × 32 mm.
502 6f. As 3f.50 . . . . 35 10
503 8f. As 1f. 45 10
504 10f. Type **64** 60 15
505 14f. As 2f. 70 15
506 15f. As 3f. 75 20

(ii) Size 52 × 36 mm.
507 20f. As 50f. (No. 499) . . . . 1·25 25
508 50f. As 50c. . . . . 4·00 35
509 75f. As 100f. . . . . 5·00 55
510 130f. As 150f. . . . . 8·00 80

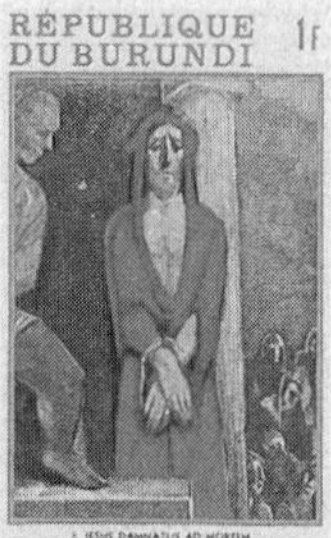

65 "Jesus Condemned to Death"

1970. Easter. "The Stations of the Cross" (Carredano). Multicoloured.
511 1f. Type **65** (postage) 10 10
512 1f.50 "Carrying the Cross" . . 10 10
513 2f. "Jesus falls for the First Time" 10 10
514 3f. "Jesus meets His Mother" 10 10
515 3f.50 "Simon of Cyrene takes the Cross" 15 10
516 4f. "Veronica wipes the face of Christ" 15 10
517 5f. "Jesus falls for the Second Time" 15 10
518 8f. "The Women of Jerusalem" (air) 20 10
519 10f. "Jesus falls for the Third Time" 25 15
520 14f. "Christ stripped" 30 25
521 15f. "Jesus nailed to the Cross" 40 25
522 18f. "The Crucifixion" . . . 40 30
523 20f. "Descent from the Cross" 50 30
524 50f. "Christ laid in the Tomb" . . . . 1·25 45

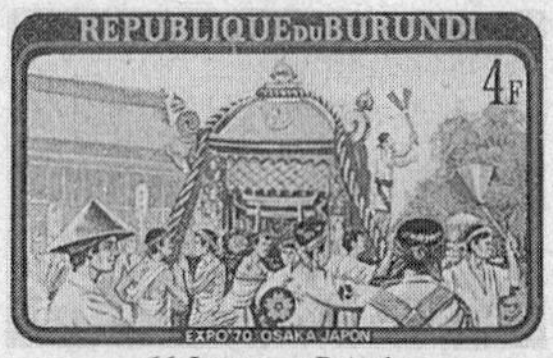

66 Japanese Parade

1970. World Fair, Osaka, Japan (EXPO '70). Multicoloured.
526 4f. Type **66** 15 10
527 6f.50 Exhibition site from the air 75 15
528 7f. African pavilions 20 10
529 14f. Pagoda (vert) 30 10
530 26f. Recording pavilion and pool 60 15
531 40f. Tower of the Sun (vert) 1·00 30
532 50f. National flags (vert) . . 1·25 35

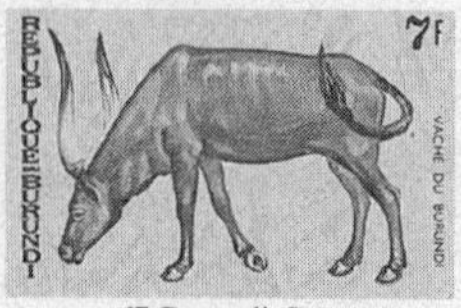

67 Burundi Cow

1970. Source of the Nile. Multicoloured.
534 7f. Any design (postage) . . 95 30
535 14f. Any design (air) . . . . 1·25 30

Nos. 534 and 535 were each issued in se-tenant sheets of 18 stamps as Type **67**, showing map sections, animals and birds, forming a map of the Nile from Cairo to Burundi.

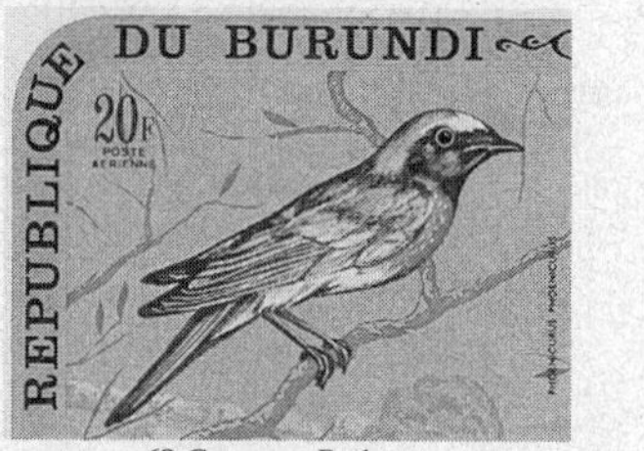

68 Common Redstart

1970. Birds. Multicoloured. (a) Postage. Size 44 × 33 mm or 33 × 44 mm.
536 2f. Great grey shrike (vert) 25 10
537 2f. Common starling (vert) 25 10
538 2f. Yellow wagtail (vert) . . . 25 10
539 2f. Sand martin (vert) 25 10
540 3f. Winter wren 60 10
541 3f. Firecrest 60 10
542 3f. Eurasian skylark 60 10
543 3f. Crested lark 60 10
544 3f.50 Woodchat shrike (vert) 65 10
545 3f.50 Rock thrush (vert) 65 10
546 3f.50 Black redstarts (vert) . . 65 10
547 3f.50 Ring ousel (vert) . . . 65 10
548 4f. Type **68** 95 10
549 4f. Dunnock 95 10
550 4f. Grey wagtail 95 10
551 4f. Meadow pipit 95 10
552 5f. Hoopoe (vert) . . . . . 1·25 15
553 5f. Pied flycatcher (vert) . . . 1·25 15
554 5f. Great reed warbler (vert) 1·25 15
555 5f. River kingfisher (vert) . . 1·25 15
556 6f.50 House martin . . . . . 1·40 20
557 6f.50 Sedge warbler . . . . . 1·40 20
558 6f.50 Fieldfare . . . . 1·40 20
559 6f.50 Golden oriole . . . . . 1·40 20

(b) Air. Size 52 × 44 mm or 44 × 52 mm.
560 8f. As No. 536 . . . . 1·50 20
561 8f. As No. 537 . . . . 1·50 20
562 8f. As No. 538 . . . . 1·50 20
563 8f. As No. 539 . . . . 1·50 20
564 10f. As No. 540 . . . . . . 1·75 25
565 10f. As No. 541 . . . . . . 1·75 25
566 10f. As No. 542 . . . . . . 1·75 25
567 10f. As No. 543 . . . . . . 1·75 25
568 14f. As No. 544 . . . . . . 1·75 25
569 14f. As No. 545 . . . . . . 1·75 25
570 14f. As No. 546 . . . . . . 1·75 25
571 14f. As No. 547 . . . . . . 1·75 25
572 20f. Type **68** . . . . 2·10 30
573 20f. As No. 549 . . . . . . 2·10 30
574 20f. As No. 550 . . . . . . 2·10 30
575 20f. As No. 551 . . . . . . 2·10 30
576 30f. As No. 552 . . . . . . 2·25 30
577 30f. As No. 553 . . . . . . 2·25 30
578 30f. As No. 554 . . . . . . 2·25 30
579 30f. As No. 555 . . . . . . 2·25 30
580 50f. As No. 556 . . . . . . 3·75 30
581 50f. As No. 557 . . . . . . 3·75 30
582 50f. As No. 558 . . . . . . 3·75 30
583 50f. As No. 559 . . . . . . 3·75 30

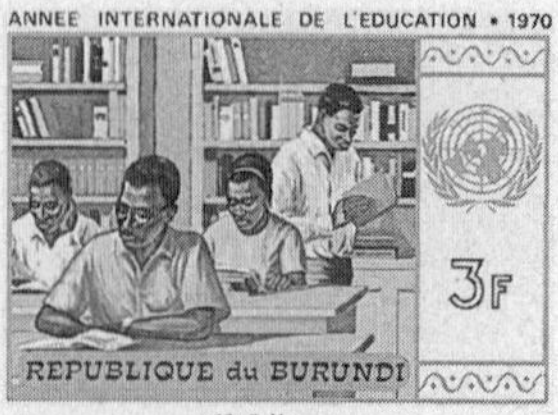

69 Library

1970. International Educational Year. Mult.
584 3f. Type **69** 10 10
585 5f. Examination 15 10
586 7f. Experiments in the laboratory 25 10
587 10f. Students with electron microscope 30 10

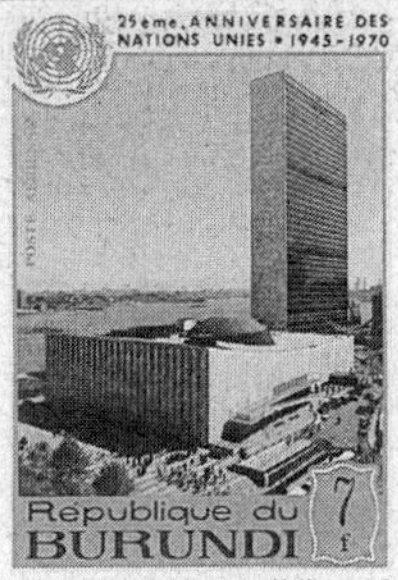

70 United Nations Building, New York

1970. Air. 25th Anniv of United Nations. Mult.
588 7f. Type **70** 25 10
589 11f. Security Council in session 30 10
590 26f. Paul VI and U Thant . . 70 20
591 40f. U.N. and National flags 1·00 30

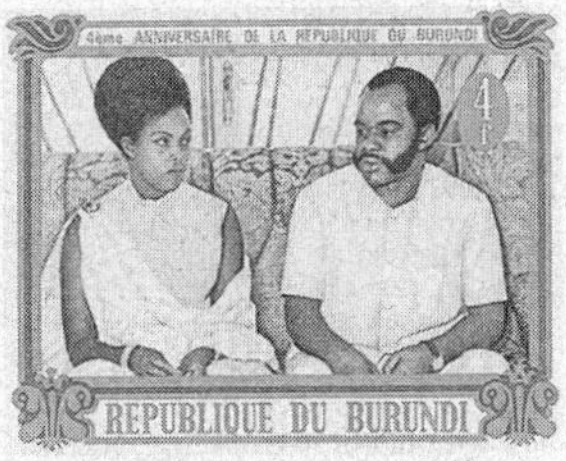

71 Pres. Micombero and Wife

1970. 4th Anniv of Republic.
593 4f. Type **71** 10 10
594 7f. Pres. Micombero and flag 25 10
595 11f. Revolution Memorial . . . 35 15

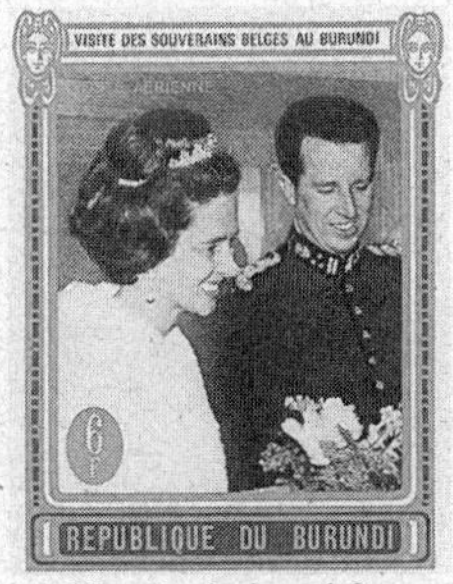

72 King Baudouin and Queen Fabiola

1970. Air. Visit of King and Queen of the Belgians. Each brown, purple and gold.
597 6f. Type **72** 65 15
598 20f. Pres. Micombero and King Baudouin . . . . . 1·50 40
599 40f. Pres. Micombero in evening dress . . . . . . 3·00 70

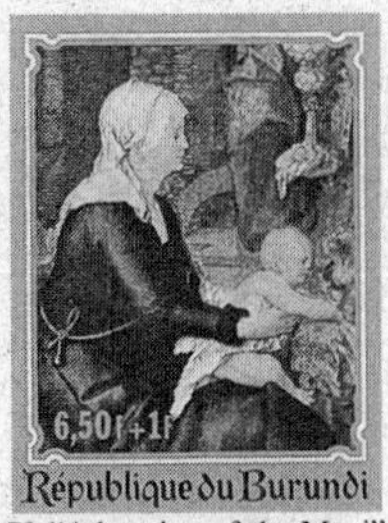

73 "Adoration of the Magi" (Durer)

1970. Christmas. Multicoloured.
601 6f.50+1f. Type **73** (postage) 50 15
602 11f.+1f. "The Virgin of the Eucharist" (Botticelli) . . . 60 25
603 20f.+1f. "The Holy Family" (El Greco) 90 30
604 14f.+3f. "The Adoration of the Magi" (Velasquez) (air) 50 25
605 26f.+3f. "The Holy Family" (Van Cleve) 85 40
606 40f.+3f. "Virgin and Child" (Van der Weyden) . . . . 1·40 60

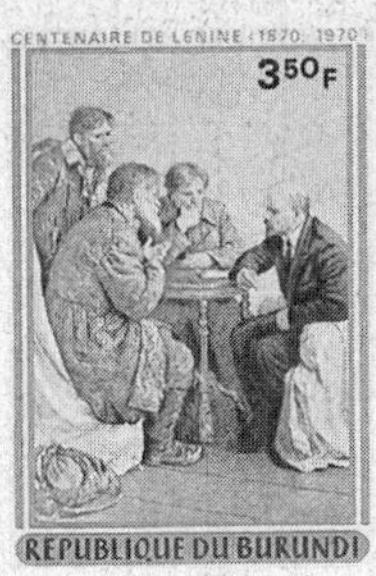

74 Lenin in Discussion

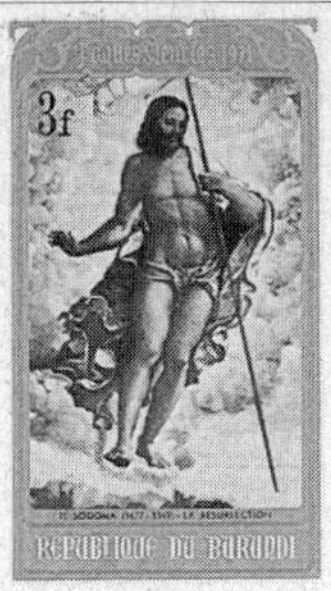

76 "The Resurrection" (Il Sodoma)

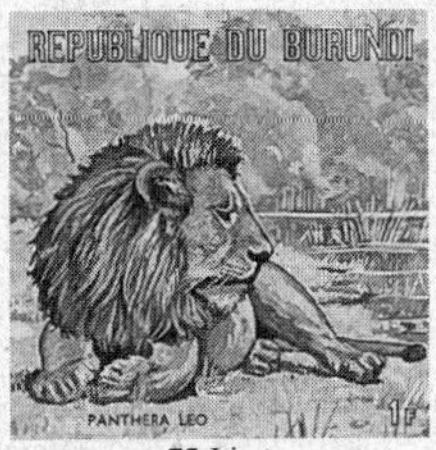

75 Lion

1970. Birth Cent of Lenin. Each brown and gold.
608 3f.50 Type **74** 20 15
609 5f. Lenin addressing Soviet 30 15
610 6f.50 Lenin with soldier and sailor 40 15
611 15f. Lenin speaking to crowd 60 25
612 50f. Lenin . . . . 2·00 55

1971. African Animals (1st series). Multicoloured.
(a) Postage. Size 38 × 38 mm.
613 1f. Type **75** 35 10
614 1f. African buffalo 35 10
615 1f. Hippopotamus 35 10
616 1f. Giraffe 35 10
617 2f. Topi 50 15
618 2f. Black rhinoceros 50 15
619 2f. Common zebra 50 15
620 2f. Leopard 50 15
621 3f. Grant's gazelle 85 25
622 3f. Cheetah 85 25
623 3f. African white-backed vultures 85 25
624 3f. Okapi 85 25
625 5f. Chimpanzee . . . . . . 1·00 25
626 5f. African elephant . . . . 1·00 25
627 5f. Spotted hyena . . . . . 1·00 25
628 5f. Gemsbok . . . . 1·00 25
629 6f. Gorilla . . . . 1·40 25
630 6f. Blue wildebeest . . . . . 1·40 25
631 6f. Warthog . . . . 1·40 25
632 6f. Hunting dog . . . . . . 1·40 25
633 11f. Sable antelope . . . . . 2·25 30
634 11f. Caracal . . . . 2·25 30
635 11f. Ostriches . . . . 2·25 30
636 11f. Bongo . . . . 2·25 30

(b) Air. Size 44 × 44 mm.
637 10f. Type **75** 70 35
638 10f. As No. 614 . . . . . . 70 35
639 10f. As No. 615 . . . . . . 70 35
640 10f. As No. 616 . . . . . . 70 35
641 14f. As No. 617 . . . . . . 80 40
642 14f. As No. 618 . . . . . . 80 40
643 14f. As No. 619 . . . . . . 80 40
644 14f. As No. 620 . . . . . . 80 40
645 17f. As No. 621 . . . . . . 90 40
646 17f. As No. 622 . . . . . . 90 40
647 17f. As No. 623 . . . . . . 90 40
648 17f. As No. 624 . . . . . . 90 40
649 24f. As No. 625 . . . . . . 1·50 55
650 24f. As No. 626 . . . . . . 1·50 55
651 24f. As No. 627 . . . . . . 1·50 55
652 24f. As No. 628 . . . . . . 1·50 55
653 26f. As No. 629 . . . . . . 1·50 55
654 26f. As No. 630 . . . . . . 1·50 55
655 26f. As No. 631 . . . . . . 1·50 55
656 26f. As No. 632 . . . . . . 1·50 55
657 31f. As No. 633 . . . . . . 1·60 70
658 31f. As No. 634 . . . . . . 1·60 70
659 31f. As No. 635 . . . . . . 1·60 70
660 31f. As No. 636 . . . . . . 1·60 70

See also Nos. 1028/75, 1178/1225 and 1385/97.

1971. Easter. Multicoloured.
661 3f. Type **76** (postage) . . . 15 10
662 6f. "The Resurrection" (Del Castagno) 30 10
663 11f. "Noli Me Tangere" (Correggio) 45 15
664 14f. "The Resurrection" (Borrassa) (air) 50 20
665 17f. "The Resurrection" (Della Francesca) 65 20
666 26f. "The Resurrection" (Pleydenwyurff) 85 30

1971. Air. United Nations Campaigns. Nos. 637/48 optd or surch. (a) Optd **LUTTE CONTRE LE RACISME ET LA DISCRIMINATION RACIALE** and Racial Equality Year emblem.
668 10f. multicoloured 90 15
669 10f. multicoloured 90 15
670 10f. multicoloured 90 15
671 10f. multicoloured 90 15

(b) Surch **LUTTE CONTRE L'ANALPHABETISME**, U.N.E.S.C.O. emblem and premium (Campaign against Illiteracy).
672 14f.+2f. multicoloured . . . 1·40 25
673 14f.+2f. multicoloured . . . 1·40 25
674 14f.+2f. multicoloured . . . 1·40 25
675 14f.+2f. multicoloured . . . 1·40 25

(c) Surch **AIDE INTERNATIONALE AUX REFUGIES**, emblem and premium (Int Help for Refugees).
676 17f.+1f. multicoloured . . . 2·25 40
677 17f.+1f. multicoloured . . . 2·25 40
678 17f.+1f. multicoloured . . . 2·25 40
679 17f.+1f. multicoloured . . . 2·25 40

1971. Air. Olympic Commems. Nos. 653/56 surch. (a) Surch **75eme ANNIVERSAIRE DES JEUX OLYMPIQUES MODERNES (1896–1971)**, Olympic rings and premium.
680 26f.+1f. multicoloured . . . 1·25 35
681 26f.+1f. multicoloured . . . 1·25 35
682 26f.+1f. multicoloured . . . 1·25 35
683 26f.+1f. multicoloured . . . 1·25 35

(b) Surch **JEUX PRE-OLYMPIQUES MUNICH 1972**, rings and premium (Olympic Games, Munich (1972)).
684 31f.+1f. multicoloured . . . 2·25 1·10
685 31f.+1f. multicoloured . . . 2·25 1·10
686 31f.+1f. multicoloured . . . 2·25 1·10
687 31f.+1f. multicoloured . . . 2·25 1·10

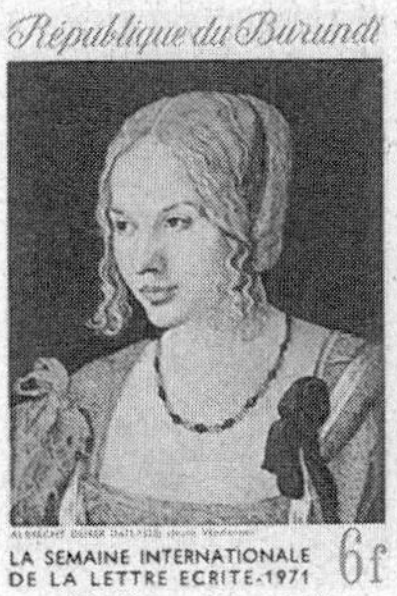

79 "Venetian Girl"

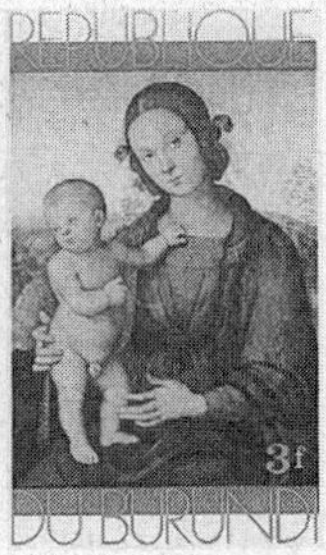

81 "The Virgin and Child" (Il Perugino)

1971. International Letter-writing Week. Paintings by Durer. Multicoloured.
688 6f. Type **79** 30 30
689 11f. "Jerome Holzschuhers" 35 35
690 14f. "Emperor Maximilian" 40 40
691 17f. Altar painting, Paumgartner 65 65
692 26f. "The Halle Madonna" 80 80
693 31f. Self-portrait . . . . . . 1·00 1·00

1971. 6th Congress of International Institute of French Law, Bujumbura. Nos. 668/693 optd **VIeme CONGRES DE L'INSTITUT INTERNATIONAL DE DROIT D'EXPRESSION FRANCAISE**.
695 6f. multicoloured 30 10
696 11f. multicoloured 35 10
697 14f. multicoloured 45 20
698 17f. multicoloured 65 20
699 26f. multicoloured 75 25
700 31f. multicoloured . . . . . 1·00 25

1971. Christmas. Paintings of "Virgin and Child" by following artists. Multicoloured.
702 3f. Type **81** (postage) 15 10
703 5f. Del Sarto 25 10
704 6f. Morales 50 10
705 14f. Da Conegliano (air) . . 55 15
706 17f. Lippi 60 20
707 31f. Leonardo da Vinci . . . 1·10 45

1971. 25th Anniv of U.N.I.C.E.F. Nos. 702/7 surch **UNICEF XXVe ANNIVERSAIRE 1946–1971**, emblem and premium.
709 3f.+1f. mult (postage) 30 10
710 5f.+1f. multicoloured 50 20
711 6f.+1f. multicoloured 60 30
712 14f.+1f. mult (air) 40 20
713 17f.+1f. multicoloured . . . 95 25
714 31f.+1f. multicoloured . . . 1·50 45

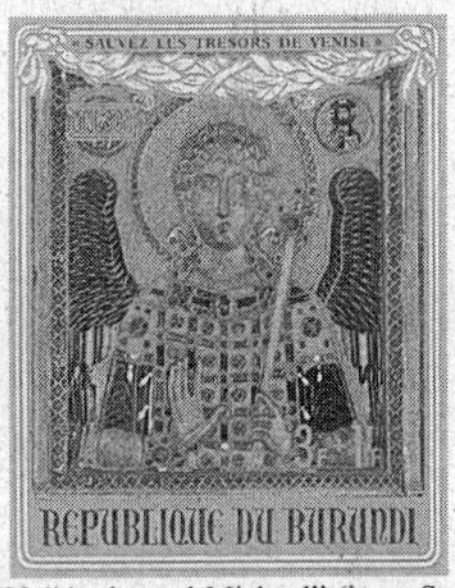

83 "Archangel Michael" (icon, St. Mark's)

1971. U.N.E.S.C.O. "Save Venice" Campaign. Multicoloured.
716 3f.+1f. Type **83** (postage) . . 25 10
717 5f.+1f. "La Polenta" (Longhi) 35 15
718 6f.+1f. "Gossip" (Longhi) . . 35 15
719 11f.+1f. "Diana's Bath" (Pittoni) 45 25
720 10f.+1f. Casa d'Oro (air) . . . 45 10
721 17f.+1f. Doge's Palace . . . 65 15
722 24f.+1f. St. John and St. Paul Church 90 25
723 31f.+1f. "Doge's Palace and Piazzetta" (Canaletto) . . . 2·00 40

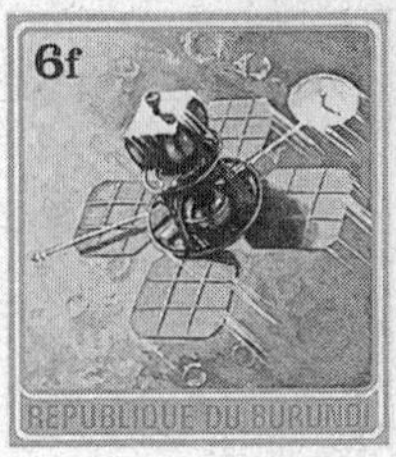

84 "Lunar Orbiter"

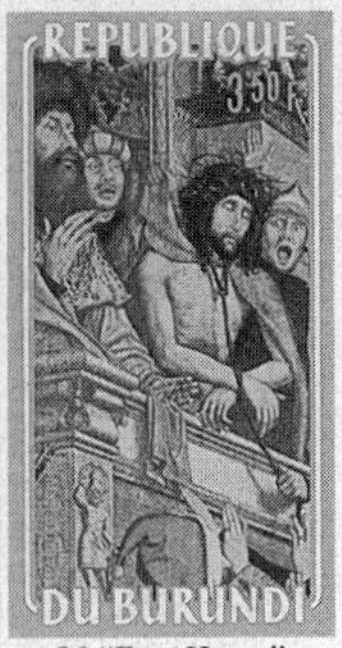

86 "Ecce Homo" (Metzys)

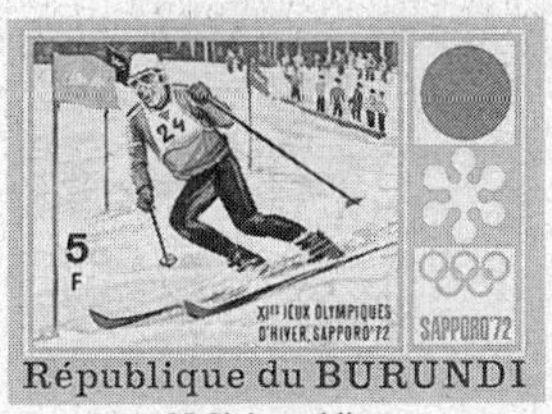

85 Slalom skiing

1972. Conquest of Space. Multicoloured.
725 6f. Type **84** 15 15
726 11f. "Vostok" spaceship . . . 40 15
727 14f. "Luna 1" 45 30
728 17f. First Man on Moon . . 65 30
729 26f. "Soyuz 11" space flight 80 40
730 40f. "Lunar Rover" . . . . 1·60 95

1972. Winter Olympic Games, Sapporo, Japan. Multicoloured.
732 5f. Type **85** 15 10
733 6f. Pair skating 20 10
734 11f. Figure-skating 35 10
735 14f. Ski-jumping 35 20
736 17f. Ice-hockey 50 20
737 24f. Speed skating 60 25
738 26f. Ski-bobbing 60 25
739 31f. Downhill skiing 75 25
740 50f. Bobsleighing . . . . . . 1·50 35

1972. Easter. Paintings. Multicoloured.
742 3f.50 Type **86** 20 10
743 6f.50 "The Crucifixion" (Rubens) 30 10
744 10f. "The Descent from the Cross" (Portormo) 40 10
745 18f. "Pieta" (Gallegos) . . . 70 15
746 27f. "The Trinity" (El Greco) 1·40 30

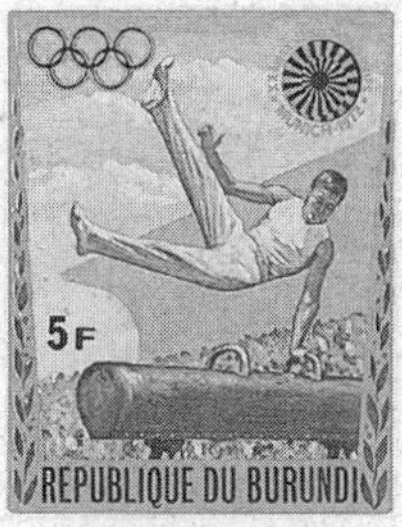

87 Gymnastics

1972. Olympic Games. Munich. Multicoloured.
748 5f. Type **87** (postage) 20 10
749 6f. Throwing the javelin . . . 20 10
750 11f. Fencing 35 15
751 14f. Cycling 50 20
752 17f. Pole-vaulting 75 20
753 24f. Weightlifting (air) . . . 65 25
754 26f. Hurdling 90 25
755 31f. Throwing the discus . . 1·40 40
756 40f. Football . . . . 1·50 50

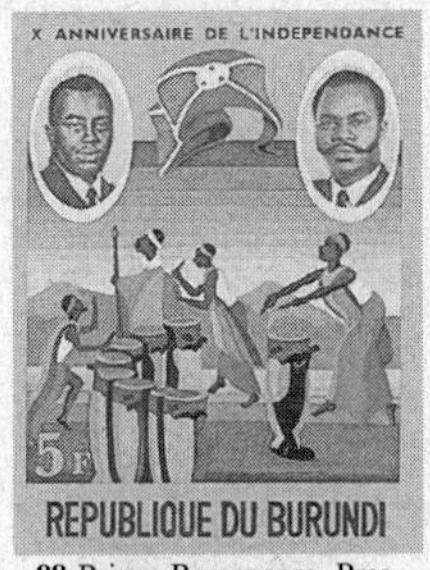

88 Prince Rwagasore, Pres. Micombero and Drummers

1972. 10th Anniv of Independence. Multicoloured.
758 5f. Type **88** (postage) 15 10
759 7f. Rwagasore, Micombero and map 25 10
760 13f. Pres. Micombero and Burundi flag 40 15
761 15f. Type **65** (air) 30 15
762 18f. As 7f. 35 15
763 27f. As 13f. 60 30

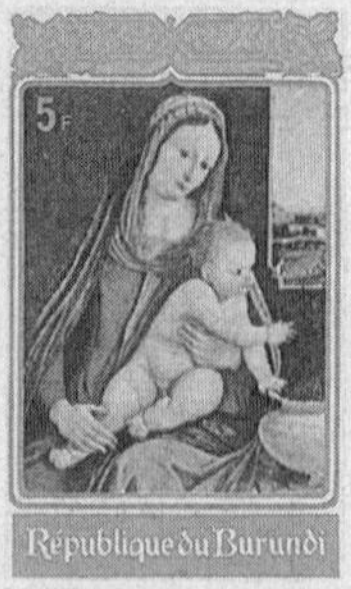

89 "Madonna and Child" (A. Solario)

1972. Christmas. "Madonna and Child" paintings by artists given below. Multicoloured.

765 5f. Type **89** (postage) 30 10
766 10f. Raphael 50 10
767 15f. Botticelli 75 15

768 18f. S. Mainardi (air) 50 15
769 27f. H. Memling . . . . . . 1·00 25
770 40f. Lotto . . . . 1·50 40

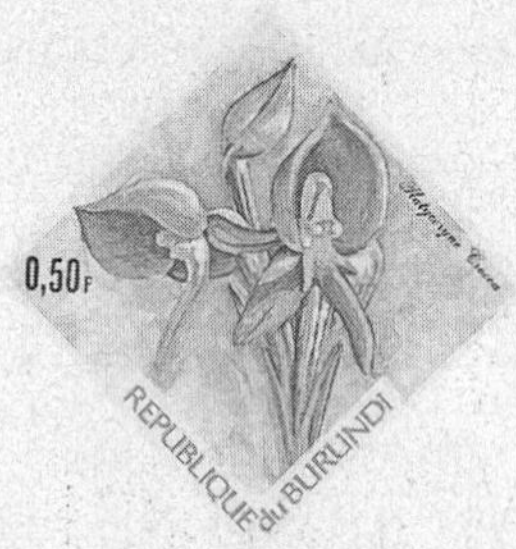

90 "Platycoryne crocea"

1972. Orchids. Multicoloured.

772 50c. Type **90** (postage) . . . 30 15
773 1f. "Cattleya trianaei" 30 15
774 2f. "Eulophia cucullata" . . . 30 15
775 3f. "Cymbidium hamsey" . . . 30 15
776 4f. "Thelymitra pauciflora" . . 30 15
777 5f. "Miltassia" 30 15
778 6f. "Miltonia" . . . . 1·25 15
779 7f. Type **90** . . . . 1·25 15
780 8f. As 1f. . . . . 1·40 15
781 9f. As 2f. . . . . 1·40 20
782 10f. As 3f. . . . . 1·90 20

783 13f. As 4f. (air) . . . . . 1·25 15
784 14f. As 5f. . . . . 1·25 15
785 15f. As 6f. . . . . 1·60 20
786 18f. Type **90** . . . . . . 1·60 20
787 20f. As 1f. . . . . 1·60 25
788 27f. As 2f. . . . . 2·75 30
789 36f. As 3f. . . . . 4·50 40

Nos. 779/89 are size 53 × 53 mm.

1972. Christmas Charity. Nos. 765/770 surch.

790 5f.+1f. mult (postage) 35 15
791 10f.+1f. multicoloured . . . 65 20
792 15f.+1f. multicoloured . . . 75 25

793 18f.+1f. multicoloured (air) 60 20
794 27f.+1f. multicoloured . . . 90 25
795 40f.+1f. multicoloured . . . 1·50 45

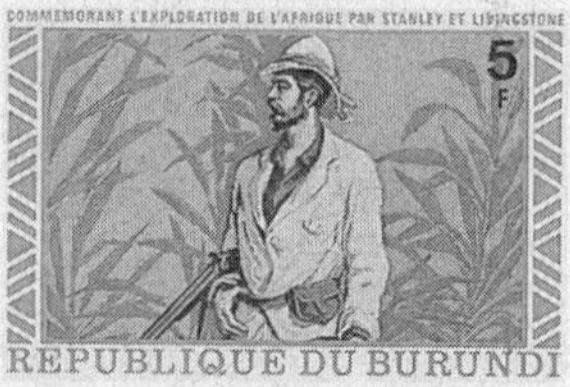

92 H. M. Stanley

1973. Centenary of Stanley/Livingstone African Exploration. Multicoloured.

797 5f. Type **92** (postage) 20 10
798 7f. Expedition bearers 25 10
799 13f. Stanley directing foray 45 15

800 15f. Dr. Livingstone (air) . . 35 20
801 18f. Stanley meets Livingstone 55 20
802 27f. Stanley conferring with Livingstone . . . . 1·00 30

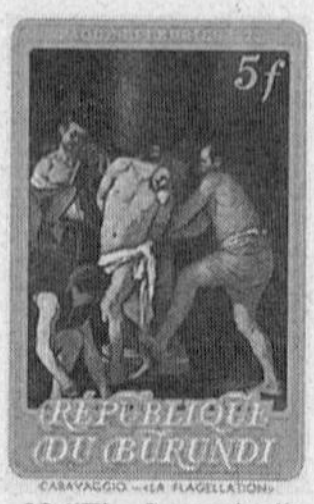

93 "The Scourging" (Caravaggio)

1973. Easter. Multicoloured.

804 5f. Type **93** (postage) 15 10
805 7f. "Crucifixion" (Van der Weyden) 25 10
806 13f. "The Deposition" (Raphael) 50 15

807 15f. "Christ bound to the Pillar" (Guido Reni) (air) 45 25
808 18f. "Crucifixion" (M. Grunewald) 70 25
809 27f. "The Descent from the Cross" (Caravaggio) . . . 1·10 30

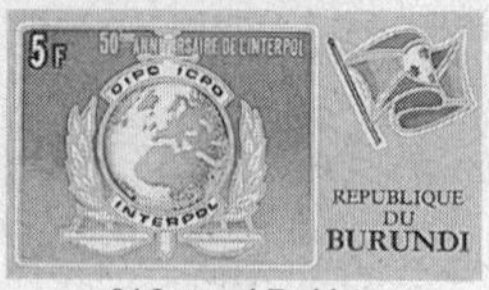

94 Interpol Emblem

1973. 50th Anniv of Interpol. Multicoloured.

811 5f. Type **94** (postage) 25 10
812 10f. Burundi flag 40 10
813 18f. Interpol H.Q., Paris . . 60 15

814 27f. As 5f. (air) 75 25
815 40f. As 10f. . . . . 1·25 35

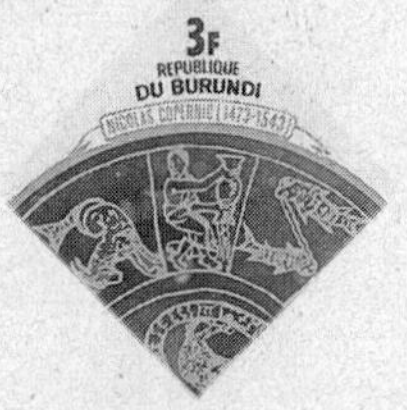

95 Capricorn, Aquarius, and Pisces

1973. 500th Birth Anniv of Copernicus.

816 **95** 3f. gold, red and black (postage) 20 10
817 – 3f. gold, red and black . . 20 10
818 – 3f. gold, red and black . . 20 10
819 – 3f. gold, red and black . . 20 10
820 – 5f. multicoloured 30 10
821 – 5f. multicoloured 30 10
822 – 5f. multicoloured 30 10
823 – 5f. multicoloured 30 10
824 – 7f. multicoloured 40 10
825 – 7f. multicoloured 40 10
826 – 7f. multicoloured 40 10
827 – 7f. multicoloured 40 10
828 – 13f. multicoloured 60 10
829 – 13f. multicoloured 60 10
830 – 13f. multicoloured 60 10
831 – 13f. multicoloured 60 10

832 – 15f. multicoloured (air) . . 40 15
833 – 15f. multicoloured 40 15
834 – 15f. multicoloured 40 15
835 – 15f. multicoloured 40 15
836 – 18f. multicoloured 55 15
837 – 18f. multicoloured 55 15
838 – 18f. multicoloured 55 15
839 – 18f. multicoloured 55 15
840 – 27f. multicoloured 95 25
841 – 27f. multicoloured 95 25
842 – 27f. multicoloured 95 25
843 – 27f. multicoloured 95 25
844 – 36f. multicoloured . . . . 2·10 40
845 – 36f. multicoloured . . . . 2·10 40
846 – 36f. multicoloured . . . . 2·10 40
847 – 36f. multicoloured . . . . 2·10 40

DESIGNS: No. 816, Type **95**. No. 817, Aries, Taurus and Gemini; No. 818, Cancer, Leo and Virgo; No. 819, Libra, Scorpio and Sagittarius; Nos. 820/23, Greek and Roman Gods; Nos. 824/7, Ptolemy and Ptolemaic System; Nos. 828/31, Copernicus and Solar System; Nos. 823/5, Copernicus, Earth, Pluto and Jupiter; Nos. 836/39, Copernicus, Venus, Saturn and Mars; Nos. 840/43, Copernicus, Uranus, Neptune and Mercury; Nos. 844/7, Earth and spacecraft.

The four designs of each value were issued se-tenant in blocks of four within the sheet, forming composite designs.

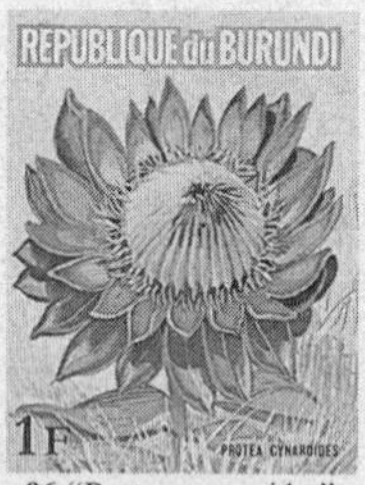

96 "Protea cynaroides"

1973. Flora and Butterflies. Multicoloured.

849 1f. Type **96** (postage) 70 15
850 1f. "Precis octavia" 70 15
851 1f. "Epiphora bauhiniae" . . 70 15
852 1f. "Gazania longiscapa" . . 70 15
853 2f. "Kniphofia" – "Royal Standard" 70 15
854 2f. "Cymothoe coccinata hew" . . . . 1·00 20
855 2f. "Nudaurelia zambesina" . 1·00 20
856 2f. "Freesia refracta" . . . . 1·00 15
857 3f. "Calotis eupompe" . . . 1·00 20
858 3f. Narcissus . . . . 1·00 15
859 3f. "Cineraria hybrida" . . . 1·00 15
860 3f. "Cyrestis camillus" . . . 1·00 20
861 5f. "Iris tingitana" . . . . . 1·40 15
862 5f. "Papilio demodocus" . . 2·10 20
863 5f. "Catopsilia avelaneda" . . 2·10 20
864 5f. "Nerine sarniensis" . . . 1·40 15
865 6f. "Hypolimnas dexithea" 2·10 20
866 6f. "Zantedeschia tropicalis" 1·40 15
867 6f. "Sandersonia aurantiaca" 1·40 15
868 6f. "Drurya antimachus" . . 2·10 20
869 11f. "Nymphaea capensis" 1·75 20
870 11f. "Pandoriana pandora" 2·75 25
871 11f. "Precis orythia" . . . . 2·75 25
872 11f. "Pelargonium domesticum"–"Aztec" . . 1·75 20

873 10f. Type **96** (air) 50 10
874 10f. As No. 850 . . . . . 90 10
875 10f. As No. 851 . . . . . 90 10
876 10f. As No. 852 . . . . . 50 10
877 14f. As No. 853 . . . . . 60 10
878 14f. As No. 854 . . . . . 1·00 20
879 14f. As No. 855 . . . . . 1·00 20
880 14f. As No. 856 . . . . . 40 15
881 17f. As No. 857 . . . . . 1·25 25
882 17f. As No. 858 . . . . . 90 20
883 17f. As No. 859 . . . . . 90 20
884 17f. As No. 860 . . . . . 1·25 25
885 24f. As No. 861 . . . . . 1·40 25
886 24f. As No. 862 . . . . . 1·75 30
887 24f. As No. 863 . . . . . 1·75 30
888 24f. As No. 864 . . . . . 1·10 25
889 26f. As No. 865 . . . . . 1·75 30
890 26f. As No. 866 . . . . . 1·10 30
891 26f. As No. 867 . . . . . 1·10 30
892 26f. As No. 868 . . . . . 1·75 30
893 31f. As No. 869 . . . . . 1·25 35
894 31f. As No. 870 . . . . . 1·90 45
895 31f. As No. 871 . . . . . 1·90 45
896 31f. As No. 872 . . . . . 1·25 35

Nos. 849, 852/3, 856, 858/9, 861, 864, 866/7, 869, 872, 876/7, 880, 882/3, 885, 888, 890/1, 893 and 896 depict flora and the remainder butterflies.

The four designs of each value were issued se-tenant in blocks of four within the sheet, forming composite designs.

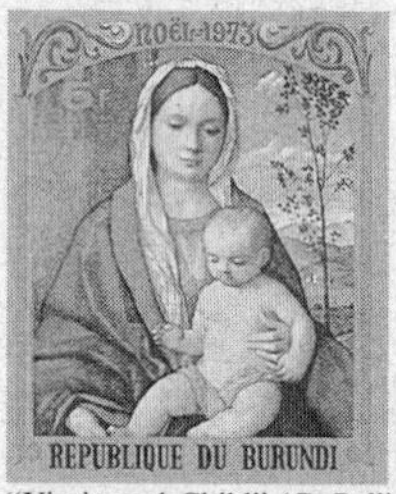

97 "Virgin and Child" (G. Bellini)

1973. Christmas. Various paintings of "The Virgin and Child" by artists listed below. Multicoloured.

897 5f. Type **97** (postage) 45 10
898 10f. Van Eyck 55 15
899 15f. G. A. Boltraffio 75 20

900 18f. Raphael (air) 35 10
901 27f. P. Perugino . . . . . . 1·10 30
902 40f. Titian . . . . 1·60 40

1973. Christmas Charity. Nos. 897/902 surch.

904 **97** 5f.+1f. mult (postage) . . . 50 15
905 – 10f.+1f. multicoloured . . 80 20
906 – 15f.+1f. multicoloured . . 95 25

907 – 18f.+1f. mult (air) 70 15
908 – 27f.+1f. multicoloured . . 1·10 35
909 – 40f.+1f. multicoloured . . 1·60 50

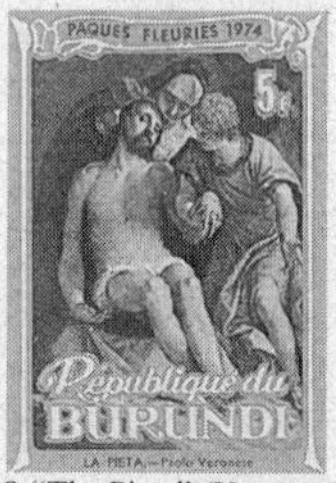

98 "The Pieta" (Veronese)

1974. Easter. Religious Paintings. Multicoloured.

911 5f. Type **98** 15 10
912 10f. "The Virgin and St. John" (Van der Weyden) 30 15
913 18f. "The Crucifixion" (Van der Weyden) 60 20
914 27f. "The Entombment" (Titian) 85 30
915 40f. "The Pieta" (El Greco) 2·10 50

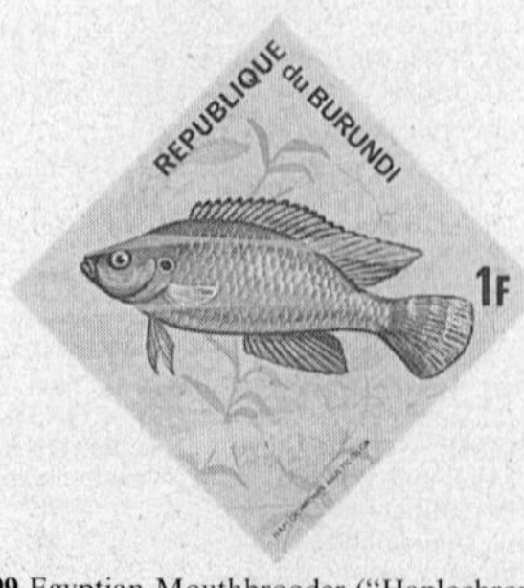

99 Egyptian Mouthbrooder ("Haplochromis multicolor")

1974. Fishes. Multicoloured.

917 1f. Type **99** (postage) 55 10
918 1f. Spotted mouthbrooder ("Tropheus duboisi") . . . 55 10
919 1f. Freshwater butterfly-fish ("Pantodon buchholzi") . . 55 10
920 1f. Six-banded distichodus ("Distichodus sexfasciatus") 55 10
921 2f. Rainbow krib ("Pelmatochromis kribensis") 55 10
922 2f. African leaf-fish ("Polycentropsis abbreviata") 55 10
923 2f. Three-lined tetra ("Nannaethiops tritaeniatus") 55 10
924 2f. Jewel cichlid ("Hemichromis bimaculatus") 55 10
925 3f. Spotted climbing-perch ("Ctenopoma acutirostre") 55 10
926 3f. African mouthbrooder ("Tilapia melanopleura") 55 10
927 3f. Angel squeaker ("Synodontis angelicus") 55 10
928 3f. Two-striped lyretail ("Aphyosemion bivittatum") 55 10
929 5f. Diamond fingerfish ("Monodactylus argenteus") 90 10
930 5f. Regal angelfish ("Pygoplites diacanthus") 90 10
931 5f. Moorish idol ("Zanclus canescens") 90 10
932 5f. Peacock hind ("Cephalopholis argus") and surgeonfish 90 10
933 6f. Bigeye ("Priacanthus arenatus") . . . . 2·75 10
934 6f. Rainbow parrotfish ("Scarus guacamaia") and French angelfish . . . . 2·75 10
935 6f. French angelfish ("Pomacanthus arcuatus") 2·75 10
936 6f. John dory ("Zeus faber") 2·75 10
937 11f. Scribbled cowfish ("Lactophrys quadricornis") . . . . . 3·00 20
938 11f. Ocean surgeonfish ("Acanthurus bahianus") 3·00 20
939 11f. Queen triggerfish ("Balistes vetula") . . . . 3·00 20
940 11f. Queen angelfish ("Holocanthus ciliaris") . . 3·00 20

941 10f. Type **99** (air) 45 10
942 10f. As No. 918 . . . . . . 45 10
943 10f. As No. 919 . . . . . . 45 10
944 10f. As No. 920 . . . . . . 45 10
945 14f. As No. 921 . . . . . . 95 10
946 14f. As No. 922 . . . . . . 95 10
947 14f. As No. 923 . . . . . . 95 10
948 14f. As No. 924 . . . . . . 95 10
949 17f. As No. 925 . . . . . . 95 10
950 17f. As No. 926 . . . . . . 95 10
951 17f. As No. 927 . . . . . . 95 10
952 17f. As No. 928 . . . . . . 95 10
953 24f. As No. 929 . . . . . . 2·10 15
954 24f. As No. 930 . . . . . . 2·10 15
955 24f. As No. 931 . . . . . . 2·10 15
956 24f. As No. 932 . . . . . . 2·10 15
957 26f. As No. 933 . . . . . . 3·00 20
958 26f. As No. 934 . . . . . . 3·00 20
959 26f. As No. 935 . . . . . . 3·00 20
960 26f. As No. 936 . . . . . . 3·00 20
961 31f. As No. 937 . . . . . . 3·75 30
962 31f. As No. 938 . . . . . . 3·75 30
963 31f. As No. 939 . . . . . . 3·75 30
964 31f. As No. 940 . . . . . . 3·75 30

The four designs of each value are arranged together in se-tenant blocks of four within the sheet, forming composite designs.

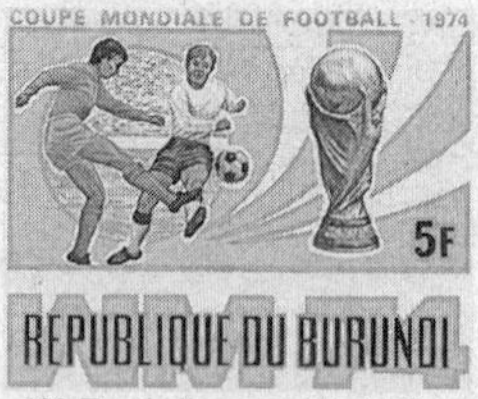

100 Footballers and World Cup Trophy

1974. World Cup Football Championships.

965 **100** 5f. mult (postage) 25 10
966 – 6f. multicoloured 30 10
967 – 11f. multicoloured 40 20
968 – 14f. multicoloured 50 25
969 – 17f. multicoloured 55 25

970 – 20f. multicoloured (air) 70 35
971 – 26f. multicoloured 90 45
972 – 40f. multicoloured . . . . 1·40 60

DESIGNS: Nos. 966/72, Football scenes as Type **100**.

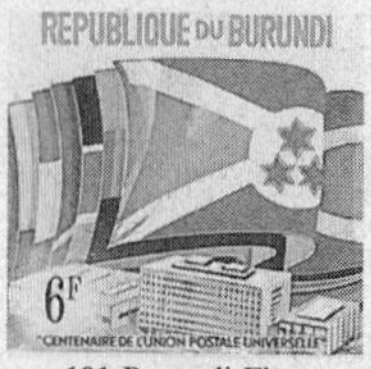

101 Burundi Flag

1974. Centenary of U.P.U. Multicoloured.

974 6f. Type **101** (postage) . . . 20 10
975 6f. Burundi P.T.T. Building 20 10
976 11f. Postmen carrying letters 30 10
977 11f. Postmen carrying letters 30 10
978 14f. U.P.U. Monument . . . 1·25 70
979 14f. Mail transport . . . . . 1·25 70

980 17f. Burundi on map 55 10
981 17f. Dove and letter 55 10

982 24f. Type **101** (air) 80 20
983 24f. As No. 975 . . . . . . 80 20
984 26f. As No. 976 . . . . . . 1·10 30
985 26f. As No. 977 . . . . . . 1·10 30
986 31f. As No. 978 . . . . . . 2·75 1·10
987 31f. As No. 979 . . . . . . 2·75 1·10
988 40f. As No. 980 . . . . . . 3·50 45
989 40f. As No. 981 . . . . . . 3·50 45

The two designs in each denomination were arranged together in se-tenant pairs within the sheet, each pair forming a composite design.

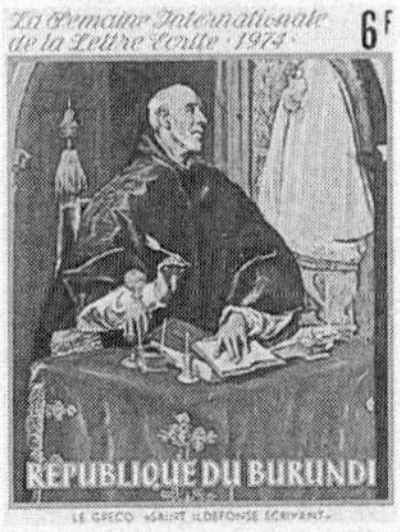

102 "St. Ildefonse writing a letter" (El Greco)

1974. International Letter-writing Week. Mult.
991 6f. Type **102** 30 15
992 11f. "Lady sealing a letter" (Chardin) 50 20
993 14f. "Titus at desk" (Rembrandt) 55 30
994 17f. "The Love-letter" (Vermeer) 60 30
995 26f. "The Merchant G. Gisze" (Holbein) 65 50
996 31f. "A. Lenoir" (David) . . 90 55

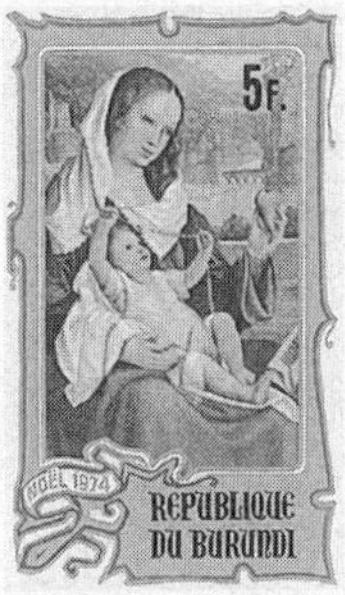

103 "Virgin and Child". (Van Orley)

1974. Christmas. Showing "Virgin and Child" paintings by artists named. Multicoloured.
998 5f. Type **103** (postage) . . . 25 10
999 10f. Hans Memling 45 15
1000 15f. Botticelli . . . . 1·00 20

1001 18f. Hans Memling (different) (air) 35 20
1002 27f. F. Lippi . . . . 1·10 35
1003 40f. L. di Gredi . . . . . . 1·50 45

1974. Christmas Charity. Nos. 998/1003 surch.
1005 **103** 5f.+1f. mult (postage) . . 30 10
1006 – 10f.+1f. multicoloured 40 25
1007 – 15f.+1f. multicoloured 1·10 30

1008 – 18f.+1f. mult (air) . . . 55 20
1009 – 27f.+1f. multicoloured 85 35
1010 – 40f.+1f. multicoloured 1·60 45

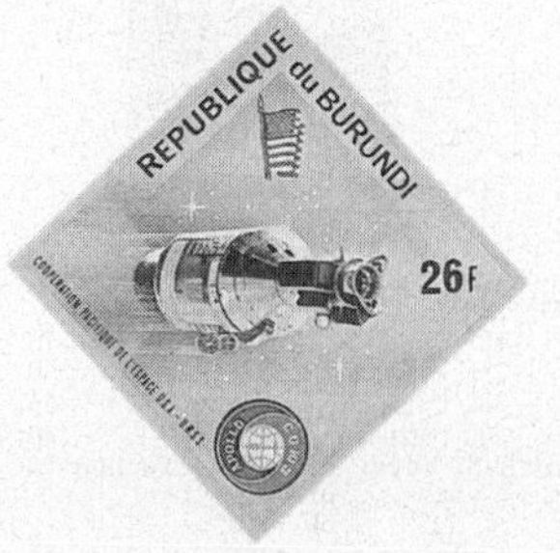

104 "Apollo" Spacecraft with Docking Tunnel

1975. "Apollo–Soyuz" Space Project.
1012 26f. Type **104** (postage) . . 45 30
1013 26f. Leonov and Kubasov 45 30
1014 26f. "Soyuz" Spacecraft . . 45 30
1015 26f. Slayton, Brand and Stafford 45 30
1016 31f. "Soyuz" launch 55 40
1017 31f. "Apollo" and "Soyuz" spacecraft 55 40
1018 31f. "Apollo" third stage separation 55 40
1019 31f. Slayton, Brand, Stafford, Leonov and Kubasov 55 40

1020 27f. Type **104** (air) 60 45
1021 27f. As No. 1012 . . . . . 60 45
1022 27f. As No. 1013 . . . . . 60 45
1023 27f. As No. 1014 . . . . . 60 45
1024 40f. As No. 1015 . . . . . 80 60
1025 40f. As No. 1016 . . . . . 80 60
1026 40f. As No. 1017 . . . . . 80 60
1027 40f. As No. 1018 . . . . . 80 60

The four designs in each value were issued together in se-tenant blocks of four within the sheet.

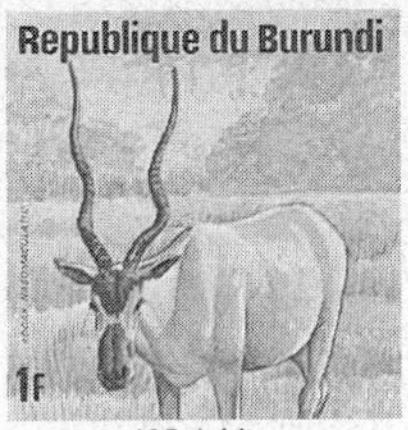

105 Addax

1975. African Animals (2nd series). Multicoloured.
1028 1f. Type **105** (postage) . . . 40 15
1029 1f. Roan antelope 40 15
1030 1f. Nyala 40 15
1031 1f. White rhinoceros 40 15
1032 2f. Mandrill 40 15
1033 2f. Eland 40 15
1034 2f. Salt's dik-dik 40 15
1035 2f. Thomson's gazelles . . . 40 15
1036 3f. African claw-less otter 55 15
1037 3f. Bohar reedbuck 55 15
1038 3f. African civet 55 15
1039 3f. African buffalo 55 15
1040 5f. Black wildebeest 55 15
1041 5f. African asses 55 15
1042 5f. Angolan black and white colobus 55 15
1043 5f. Gerenuk 55 15
1044 6f. Addra gazelle 95 20
1045 6f. Black-backed jackal . . 95 20
1046 6f. Sitatungas 95 20
1047 6f. Banded duiker 95 20
1048 11f. Fennec fox . . . . . . 1·40 20
1049 11f. Lesser kudus . . . . . 1·40 20
1050 11f. Blesbok . . . . 1·40 20
1051 11f. Serval . . . . 1·40 20

1052 10f. Type **105** (air) 60 10
1053 10f. As No. 1029 . . . . . 60 10
1054 10f. As No. 1030 . . . . . 60 10
1055 10f. As No. 1031 . . . . . 60 10
1056 14f. As No. 1032 . . . . . 70 15
1057 14f. As No. 1033 . . . . . 70 15
1058 14f. As No. 1034 . . . . . 70 15
1059 14f. As No. 1035 . . . . . 70 15
1060 17f. As No. 1036 . . . . . 1·10 15
1061 17f. As No. 1037 . . . . . 1·10 15
1062 17f. As No. 1038 . . . . . 1·10 15
1063 17f. As No. 1039 . . . . . 1·10 15
1064 24f. As No. 1040 . . . . . 1·75 20
1065 24f. As No. 1041 . . . . . 1·75 20
1066 24f. As No. 1042 . . . . . 1·75 20
1067 24f. As No. 1043 . . . . . 1·75 20
1068 26f. As No. 1044 . . . . . 1·90 20
1069 26f. As No. 1045 . . . . . 1·90 20
1070 26f. As No. 1046 . . . . . 1·90 20
1071 26f. As No. 1047 . . . . . 1·90 20
1072 31f. As No. 1048 . . . . . 2·25 25
1073 31f. As No. 1049 . . . . . 2·25 25
1074 31f. As No. 1050 . . . . . 2·25 25
1075 31f. As No. 1051 . . . . . 2·25 25

The four designs in each value were issued together in horiz. se-tenant strips within the sheet, forming composite designs.

1975. Air. International Women's Year. Nos. 1052/9 optd **ANNEE INTERNATIONALE DE LA FEMME**.
1076 **105** 10f. multicoloured . . . 80 50
1077 – 10f. multicoloured . . . 80 50
1078 – 10f. multicoloured . . . 80 50
1079 – 10f. multicoloured . . . 80 50
1080 – 14f. multicoloured . . . 1·40 60
1081 – 14f. multicoloured . . . 1·40 60
1082 – 14f. multicoloured . . . 1·40 60
1083 – 14f. multicoloured . . . 1·40 60

1975. Air. 30th Anniv of United Nations. Nos. 1068/75 optd **30eme ANNIVERSAIRE DES NATIONS UNIES**.
1084 26f. multicoloured . . . . . 1·40 1·25
1085 26f. multicoloured . . . . . 1·40 1·25
1086 26f. multicoloured . . . . . 1·40 1·25
1087 26f. multicoloured . . . . . 1·40 1·25
1088 31f. multicoloured . . . . . 2·25 2·00
1089 31f. multicoloured . . . . . 2·25 2·00
1090 31f. multicoloured . . . . . 2·25 2·00
1091 31f. multicoloured . . . . . 2·25 2·00

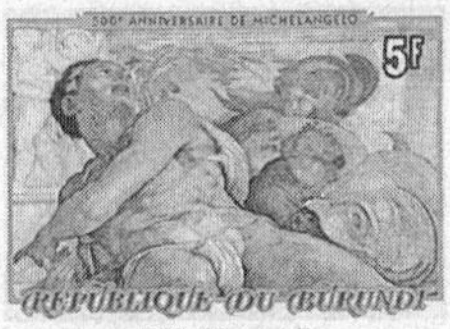

108 "Jonah"

1975. Christmas. 500th Birth Anniv of Michaelangelo. Multicoloured.
1092 5f. Type **108** (postage) . . . 25 10
1093 5f. "Libyan Sibyl" 25 10
1094 13f. "Daniel" 90 10
1095 13f. "Cumaean Sybil" . . . 90 10
1096 27f. "Isaiah" . . . . 1·25 15
1097 27f. "Delphic Sybil" (different) . . . . 1·25 15

1098 18f. "Zachariah" (air) . . . 90 10
1099 18f. "Joel" 90 10
1100 31f. "Erythraean Sybil" . . 1·60 30
1101 31f. "Ezekiel" . . . . . . 1·60 30
1102 40f. "Persian Sybil" . . . . 2·00 35
1103 40f. "Jeremiah" . . . . . . 2·00 35

1975. Christmas Charity. Nos. 1092/1103 surch **+1F**.
1105 **108** 5f.+1f. mult (postage) . . 45 10
1106 – 5f.+1f. multicoloured . . 45 10
1107 – 13f.+1f. multicoloured 75 10
1108 – 13f.+1f. multicoloured 75 10
1109 – 27f.+1f. multicoloured 1·25 15
1110 – 27f.+1f. multicoloured 1·25 15

1111 – 18f.+1f. mult (air) . . . 1·00 10
1112 – 18f.+1f. multicoloured 1·00 10
1113 – 31f.+1f. multicoloured 1·60 30
1114 – 31f.+1f. multicoloured 1·60 30
1115 – 40f.+1f. multicoloured 1·90 35
1116 – 40f.+1f. multicoloured 1·90 35

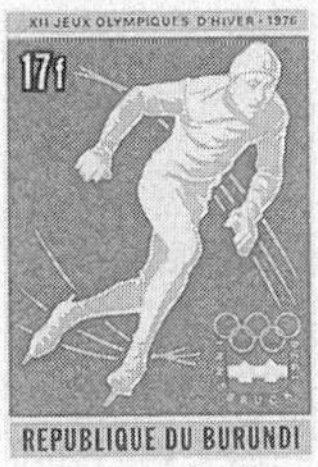

110 Speed Skating

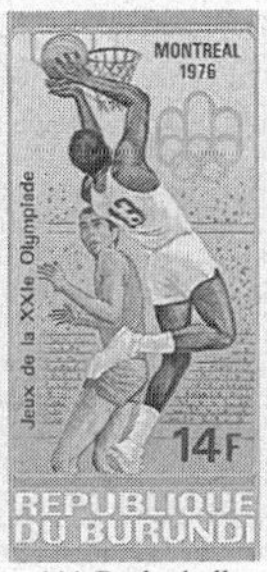

111 Basketball

1976. Winter Olympic Games, Innsbruck. Mult.
1118 17f. Type **110** (postage) . . 45 20
1119 24f. Figure-skating 50 20
1120 26f. Two-man bobsleigh . . 60 20
1121 31f. Cross-country skiing . . 70 30

1122 18f. Ski-jumping (air) . . . 40 25
1123 36f. Skiing (slalom) . . . . 1·50 40
1124 50f. Ice-hockey . . . . . . 1·60 60

1976. Olympic Games, Montreal. Multicoloured.
1126 14f. Type **111** (postage) . . 40 30
1127 14f. Pole-vaulting 40 30
1128 17f. Running 60 45
1129 17f. Football 60 45
1130 28f. As No. 1127 . . . . . 90 65
1131 28f. As No. 1128 . . . . . 90 65
1132 40f. As No. 1129 . . . . . 1·50 1·10
1133 40f. Type **111** . . . . . . 1·50 1·10

1134 27f. Hurdling (air) 90 65
1135 27f. High-jumping (horiz) 90 65
1136 31f. Gymnastics (horiz) . . 1·25 90
1137 31f. As No. 1134 (horiz) . . 1·25 90
1138 50f. As No. 1135 (horiz) . . 1·90 1·40
1139 50f. As No. 1136 (horiz) . . 1·90 1·40

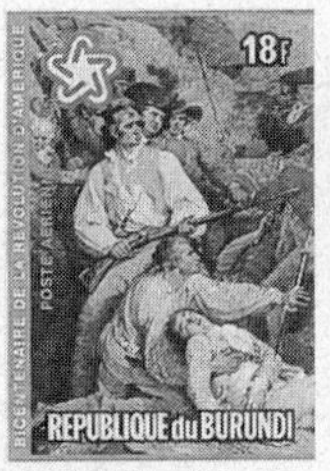

112 "Battle of Bunker Hill" (detail, John Trumbull)

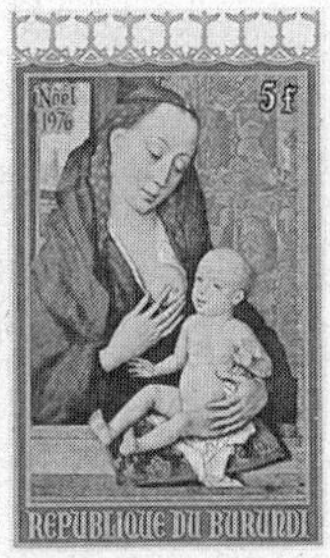

113 "Virgin and Child" (Dirk Bouts)

1976. Air. Bicent of American Revolution. Mult.
1141 18f. Type **112** 55 15
1142 18f. As Type **112** 55 15
1143 26f. Franklin, Jefferson and John Adams 75 25
1144 26f. As No. 1143 . . . . . 75 25
1145 36f. "Signing of Declaration of Independence" (Trumbull) . . . . 1·25 35
1146 36f. As No. 1145 . . . . . 1·25 35

The two designs of each value form composite pictures. Type **112** is the left-hand portion of the painting.

1976. Christmas. Multicoloured.
1148 5f. Type **113** (postage) . . . 35 10
1149 13f. "Virgin of the Trees" (Bellini) 65 10
1150 27f. "Virgin and Child" (C. Crivelli) . . . . . . 1·00 25

1151 18f. "Virgin and Child" with St. Anne" (Leonardo) (air) 80 30
1152 31f. "Holy Family with Lamb" (Raphael) . . . . 1·10 60
1153 40f. "Virgin with Basket" (Correggio) . . . . 1·60 70

1976. Christmas Charity. Nos. 1148/53 surch **+1F**.
1155 **113** 5f.+1f. mult (postage) . . 25 10
1156 – 13f.+1f. multicoloured 70 30
1157 – 27f.+1f. multicoloured 1·10 50

1158 – 18f.+1f. mult (air) . . . 60 30
1159 – 31f.+1f. multicoloured 1·00 45
1160 – 40f.+1f. multicoloured 1·90 65

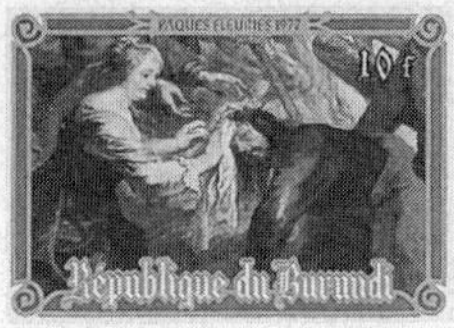

115 "The Ascent of Calvary" (Rubens)

1977. Easter. 400th Birth Anniv of Peter Paul Rubens. Multicoloured.
1162 10f. Type **115** 35 25
1163 21f. "Christ Crucified" . . . 95 70
1164 27f. "The Descent from the Cross" . . . . 1·10 80
1165 35f. "The Deposition" . . . 1·50 1·10

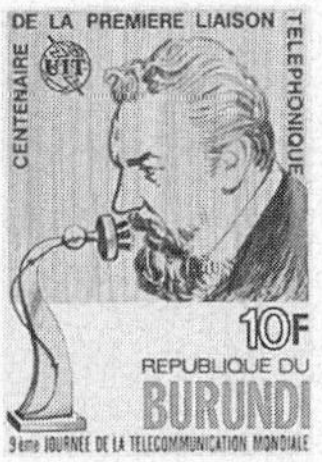

116 Alexander Graham Bell

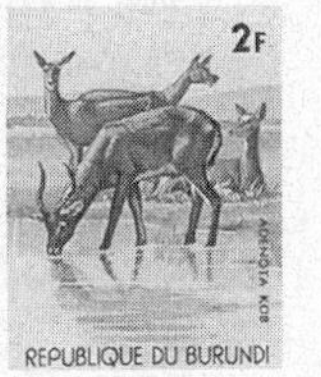

117 Kobs

1977. Telephone Centenary and World Telecommunications Day. Multicoloured.
1167 10f. Type **116** (postage) . . 25 15
1168 10f. Satellite, Globe and telephones 25 15
1169 17f. Switchboard operator and wall telephone . . . 45 30
1170 17f. Satellite transmitting to Earth 45 30
1171 26f. A. G. Bell and first telephone 80 60
1172 26f. Satellites circling Globe, and videophone 80 60

1173 18f. Type **116** (air) 40 30
1174 18f. As No. 1172 . . . . . 40 30
1175 36f. As No. 1169 . . . . . 1·10 80
1176 36f. As No. 1168 . . . . . 1·10 80

1977. African Animals (3rd series). Multicoloured.
1178 2f. Type **117** (postage) . . . 75 20
1179 2f. Marabou storks 75 20
1180 2f. Blue wildebeest 75 20
1181 2f. Bush pig 75 20
1182 5f. Grevy's zebras 85 20
1183 5f. Whale-headed stork . . 85 20
1184 5f. Striped hyenas 85 20
1185 5f. Pygmy chimpanzee . . . 85 20
1186 8f. Greater flamingoes . . . 95 20
1187 8f. Nile crocodiles 95 20
1188 8f. Green tree snake 95 20
1189 8f. Greater kudus 95 20
1190 11f. Large-toothed rock hyrax . . . . 1·00 20
1191 11f. Cobra . . . . 1·00 20
1192 11f. Golden jackals . . . . 1·00 20
1193 11f. Verreaux eagles . . . . 1·00 20
1194 21f. Ratel . . . . 1·25 30
1195 21f. Bushbuck . . . . . . 1·25 30
1196 21f. Secretary bird . . . . . 1·25 30
1197 21f. Klipspringer . . . . . 1·25 30
1198 27f. Bat-eared fox . . . . . 1·60 30
1199 27f. African elephants . . . 1·60 30
1200 27f. Vulturine guineafowl . . 1·60 30
1201 27f. Impalas . . . . 1·60 30

1202 9f. Type **117** (air) 60 25
1203 9f. As No. 1179 . . . . . . 60 25
1204 9f. As No. 1180 . . . . . . 60 25
1205 9f. As No. 1181 . . . . . . 60 25
1206 13f. As No. 1182 . . . . . 85 30
1207 13f. As No. 1183 . . . . . 85 30
1208 13f. As No. 1184 . . . . . 85 30
1209 13f. As No. 1185 . . . . . 85 30
1210 30f. As No. 1186 . . . . . 1·25 50
1211 30f. As No. 1187 . . . . . 1·25 50
1212 30f. As No. 1188 . . . . . 1·25 50
1213 30f. As No. 1189 . . . . . 1·25 50
1214 35f. As No. 1190 . . . . . 1·40 60
1215 35f. As No. 1191 . . . . . 1·40 60
1216 35f. As No. 1192 . . . . . 1·40 60
1217 35f. As No. 1193 . . . . . 1·40 60
1218 54f. As No. 1194 . . . . . 2·40 70
1219 54f. As No. 1195 . . . . . 2·40 70
1220 54f. As No. 1196 . . . . . 2·40 70
1221 54f. As No. 1197 . . . . . 2·40 70
1222 70f. As No. 1198 . . . . . 3·25 85
1223 70f. As No. 1199 . . . . . 3·25 85
1224 70f. As No. 1200 . . . . . 3·25 85
1225 70f. As No. 1201 . . . . . 3·25 85

The four designs in each value were issued together se-tenant in horizontal strips within the sheet, forming composite designs.

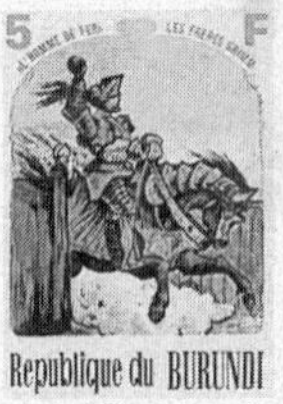

118 "The Man of Iron" (Grimm)

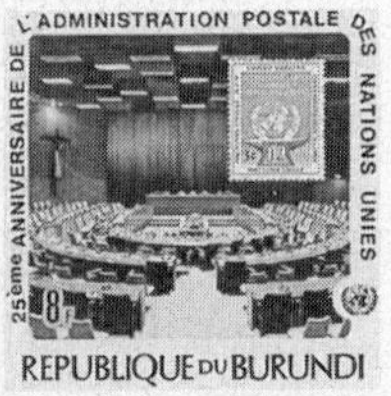

119 U.N. General Assembly and U.N. 3c. Stamp, 1954

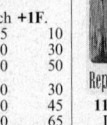

1977. Fairy Tales. Multicoloured.

1226	5f. Type **118**	20	10
1227	5f. "Snow White and Rose Red" (Grimm)	20	10
1228	5f. "The Goose Girl" (Grimm)	20	10
1229	5f. "The Two Wanderers" (Grimm)	20	10
1230	11f. "The Hermit and the Bear" (Aesop)	60	10
1231	11f. "The Fox and the Stork" (Aesop)	60	10
1232	11f. "The Litigious Cats" (Aesop)	60	10
1233	11f. "The Blind and the Lame" (Aesop)	60	10
1234	14f. "The Ice Maiden" (Andersen)	70	10
1235	14f. "The Old House" (Andersen)	70	10
1236	14f. "The Princess and the Pea" (Andersen)	70	10
1237	14f. "The Elder Tree Mother" (Andersen)	70	10
1238	17f. "Hen with the Golden Eggs" (La Fontaine)	80	15
1239	17f. "The Wolf Turned Shepherd" (La Fontaine)	80	15
1240	17f. "The Oyster and Litigants" (La Fontaine)	80	15
1241	17f. "The Wolf and the Lamb" (La Fontaine)	80	15
1242	26f. "Jack and the Beanstalk" (traditional)	1·60	25
1243	26f. "Alice in Wonderland" (Lewis Carroll)	1·60	25
1244	26f. "Three Heads in the Well" (traditional)	1·60	25
1245	26f. "Tales of Mother Goose" (traditional)	1·60	25

1977. 25th Anniv of United Nations Postal Administration. Multicoloured.

1246	8f. Type **119** (postage)	40	30
1247	8f. U.N. 4c. stamp, 1957	40	30
1248	8f. U.N. 3c. stamp, 1954 (FAO)	40	30
1249	8f. U.N. $1\frac{1}{2}$ c. stamp, 1951	40	30
1250	10f. Security Council and U.N. 8c. red, 1954	50	35
1251	10f. U.N. 8c. green, 1956	50	35
1252	10f. U.N. 8c. black, 1955	50	35
1253	10f. U.N. 7c. stamp, 1959	50	35
1254	21f. Meeting hall and U.N. 3c. grey, 1956	80	60
1255	21f. U.N. 8c. stamp, 1956	80	60
1256	21f. U.N. 3c. brown, 1953	80	60
1257	21f. U.N. 3c. green, 1952	80	60
1258	24f. Building by night and U.N. 4c. red, 1957 (air)	80	60
1259	24f. U.N. 8c. brn & grn, 1960	80	60
1260	24f. U.N. 8c. green, 1955	80	60
1261	24f. U.N. 8c. red, 1955	80	60
1262	27f. Aerial view of U.N. 8c. red, 1957	90	65
1263	27f. U.N. 3c. stamp, 1953	90	65
1264	27f. U.N. 8c. green, 1954	90	65
1265	27f. U.N. 8c. brown, 1956	90	65
1266	35f. U.N. Building by day and U.N. 5c. stamp, 1959	1·40	1·00
1267	35f. U.N. 3c. stamp, 1962	1·40	1·00
1268	35f. U.N. 3c. bl & pur, 1951	1·40	1·00
1269	35f. U.N. 1c. stamp, 1951	1·40	1·00

The four designs in each value were issued together in se-tenant blocks of four, each design in the block having the same background.

120 "Virgin and Child" (Jean Lambardos)

121 Cruiser "Aurora" and Russian 5r. Stamp, 1922

1977. Christmas. Paintings of Virgin and Child by artists named. Multicoloured.

1271	5f. Type **120** (postage)	15	10
1272	13f. Melides Toscano	65	50
1273	27f. Emmanuel Tzanes	95	70
1274	18f. Master of Moulins (air)	50	35
1275	31f. Lorenzo di Credi	1·00	75
1276	40f. Palma the Elder	1·25	90

1977. 60th Anniv of Russian Revolution. Mult.

1278	5f. Type **121**	40	10
1279	5f. Russia S.G. 455	40	10
1280	5f. Russia S.G. 1392	40	10
1281	5f. Russia S.G. 199	40	10
1282	8f. Decemberists' Square, Leningrad and Russia S.G. 983	25	10
1283	8f. Russia S.G. 2122	25	10
1284	8f. Russia S.G. 1041	25	10
1285	8f. Russia S.G. 2653	25	10
1286	11f. Pokrovski Cathedral, Moscow and Russia S.G. 3929	45	10
1287	11f. Russia S.G. 3540	45	10
1288	11f. Russia S.G. 3468	45	10
1289	11f. Russia S.G. 3921	45	10
1290	13f. May Day celebrations, Moscow and Russia S.G. 4518	60	15
1291	13f. Russia S.G. 3585	60	15
1292	13f. Russia S.G. 3024	60	15
1293	13f. Russia S.G. 2471	60	15

The four designs in each value were issued in se-tenant blocks of four, each design in the block having the same background.

122 Tanker Unloading (Commerce)

1977. 15th Anniv of Independence. Mult.

1294	1f. Type **122**	20	15
1295	5f. Assembling electric armatures (Economy)	20	15
1296	11f. Native dancers (Tourism)	30	20
1297	14f. Picking coffee (Agriculture)	45	30
1298	17f. National Palace, Bujumbura	55	40

1977. Christmas Charity. Nos. 1271/6 surch **+1F**.

1299	**120** 5f.+1f. mult (postage)	30	15
1300	– 13f.+1f. multicoloured	65	20
1301	– 27f.+1f. multicoloured	95	45
1302	– 18f.+1f. mult (air)	65	25
1303	– 31f.+1f. multicoloured	1·00	45
1304	– 40f.+1f. multicoloured	1·60	60

123 "Madonna and Child" (Solario)

124 Abyssinian Ground Hornbill

1979. Christmas (1978). Paintings of Virgin and Child by named artists. Multicoloured.

1306	13f. Rubens	85	85
1307	17f. Type **123**	90	90
1308	27f. Tiepolo	1·40	1·40
1309	31f. Gerard David	1·60	1·60
1310	40f. Bellini	2·00	2·00

1979. Christmas Charity. Nos. 1306/10 surch **+1F**.

1312	– 13f.+1f. multicoloured	85	85
1313	**123** 17f.+1f. multicoloured	90	90
1314	– 27f.+1f. multicoloured	1·40	1·40
1315	– 31f.+1f. multicoloured	1·60	1·60
1316	– 40f.+1f. multicoloured	2·00	2·00

1979. Birds. Multicoloured.

1318	1f. Type **124** (postage)	1·10	60
1319	2f. African darter	1·10	60
1320	3f. Little bee eater	1·10	60
1321	5f. Lesser flamingo	1·50	80
1322	8f. Congo peafowl	1·90	1·10
1323	10f. Purple swamphen	2·10	1·25
1324	20f. Martial eagle	2·40	1·40
1325	27f. Painted stork	3·00	1·75
1326	50f. Saddle-bill stork	4·75	2·50
1327	6f. Type **124** (air)	1·75	1·00
1328	13f. As No. 1319	2·10	1·25
1329	18f. As No. 1320	2·40	1·40
1330	26f. As No. 1321	2·75	1·60
1331	31f. As No. 1322	3·00	1·60
1332	36f. As No. 1323	3·00	1·75
1333	40f. As No. 1324	3·75	2·10
1334	54f. As No. 1325	4·00	2·40
1335	70f. As No. 1326	5·25	3·00

125 Mother and Child

1979. International Year of the Child. Mult.

1336	10f. Type **125**	90	90
1337	20f. Baby	1·40	1·40
1338	27f. Child with doll	1·50	1·50
1339	50f. S.O.S. village, Gitega	2·00	2·00

126 "Virgin and Child" (Raffaellino Del Garbo)

127 Sir Rowland Hill and Penny Black

1979. Christmas. "Virgin and Child" paintings by named artists. Multicoloured.

1341	20f. Type **126**	90	90
1342	27f. Giovanni Penni	1·10	1·10
1343	31f. Giulio Romano	1·25	1·25
1344	50f. Detail of "Adoration of the Shepherds" (Jacopo Bassano)	1·75	1·75

1979. Death Centenary of Sir Rowland Hill. Mult.

1346	20f. Type **127**	80	80
1347	27f. German East Africa 25p. stamp and Ruanda-Urundi 5c. stamp	95	95
1348	31f. Burundi 1f.25 and 50f. stamps of 1962	1·10	1·10
1349	40f. 4f. (1962) and 14f. (1969) stamps of Burundi	1·25	1·25
1350	60f. Heinrich von Stephan (founder of U.P.U.) and Burundi 14f. U.P.U. stamps of 1974	6·75	3·00

1979. Christmas Charity. Nos. 1341/4 additionally inscr with premium.

1352	20f.+1f. multicoloured	65	65
1353	27f.+1f. multicoloured	1·40	1·40
1354	31f.+1f. multicoloured	1·60	1·60
1355	50f.+1f. multicoloured	2·10	2·10

1980. As Nos. 1318/19 and 1321/3 but new values.

(a) With copper frames.

1356a	5f. Abyssinian ground hornbill		
1356b	10f. African darter		
1356c	40f. Lesser flamingo		
1356d	45f. Congo peafowl		
1356e	50f. Purple swamphen		

(b) With grey-green frames.

1356f	5f. As No. 1356a		
1356g	10f. As No. 1356b		
1356h	40f. As No. 1356c		
1356i	45f. As No. 1356d		
1356j	50f. As No. 1356e		

128 Approaching Hurdle (110 m Hurdles, Thomas Munkelt)

1980. Olympic Medal Winners. Multicoloured.

1357	20f. Type **128**	95	95
1358	20f. Jumping hurdle	95	95
1359	20f. Completing jump	95	95
1360	30f. Discus—beginning to throw	1·40	1·40
1361	30f. Continuing throw	1·40	1·40
1362	30f. Releasing discus	1·40	1·40
1363	40f. Football—running for goal (Czechoslovakia)	1·50	1·50
1364	40f. Kicking ball	1·50	1·50
1365	40f. Saving ball	1·50	1·50

129 "The Virgin and Child" (Sebastiano Mainardi)

1980. Christmas. Multicoloured.

1367	10f. Type **129**	90	90
1368	30f. "Doni Tondo" (Michelangelo)	1·50	1·50
1369	40f. "The Virgin and Child" (Piero di Cosimo)	2·10	2·10
1370	45f. "The Holy Family" (Fra Bartolomeo)	2·25	2·25

130 Congress Emblem

131 Kepler and Dish Aerial

1980. 1st National Party Congress, Uprona.

1372	**130** 10f. multicoloured	30	30
1373	40f. multicoloured	1·50	1·50
1374	45f. multicoloured	1·60	1·60

1981. Christmas Charity. Nos. 1367/70 additionally inscr with premium.

1376	10f.+1f. multicoloured	75	75
1377	30f.+1f. multicoloured	1·75	1·75
1378	40f.+1f. multicoloured	2·25	2·25
1379	50f.+1f. multicoloured	2·50	2·50

1981. 350th Death Anniv of Johannes Kepler (astronomer). First Earth Satellite Station in Burundi. Multicoloured.

1381	10f. Type **131**	60	60
1382	40f. Satellite and antenna	1·50	1·50
1383	45f. Satellite (different) and antenna	1·90	1·90

132 Giraffes

1982. African Animals (4th series). Multicoloured.

1385	2f. Lion	4·75	2·10
1386	3f. Type **132**	4·75	2·10
1387	5f. Black rhinoceros	4·75	2·10
1388	10f. African buffalo	15·00	6·75
1389	20f. African elephant	23·00	11·50
1390	25f. Hippopotamus	26·00	12·50
1391	30f. Common zebra	30·00	14·50
1392	50f. Warthog	55·00	26·00
1393	60f. Eland	70·00	32·00
1394	65f. Black-backed jackal	85·00	40·00
1395	70f. Cheetah	95·00	45·00
1396	75f. Blue Wildebeest	£100	48·00
1397	85f. Spotted hyena	£120	60·00

1983. Animal Protection Year. Nos. 1385/97 optd with World Wildlife Fund Emblem.

1398	2f. Type **131**	5·00	4·25
1399	3f. Giraffe	5·00	4·25
1400	5f. Black rhinoceros	5·00	4·25
1401	10f. African buffalo	14·00	13·00
1402	20f. African elephant	23·00	20·00
1403	25f. Hippopotamus	26·00	24·00
1404	30f. Common zebra	28·00	25·00
1405	50f. Warthog	55·00	48·00
1406	60f. Eland	70·00	60·00
1407	65f. Jackal ("Canis mesomelas")	80·00	75·00
1408	70f. Cheetah	95·00	80·00
1409	75f. Blue wildebeest	£100	90·00
1410	85f. Spotted Hyena	£120	£110

133 Flag and National Party Emblem

1983. 20th Anniv (1982) of Independence. Multicoloured.

1411	10f. Type **133**	65	65
1412	25f. Flag and arms	1·00	1·00
1413	30f. Flag and map of Africa	1·10	1·10
1414	50f. Flag and emblem	1·50	1·50
1415	65f. Flag and President Bagaza	2·00	2·00

134 "Virgin and Child" (Lucas Signorelli)

1983. Christmas. Multicoloured.

1416	10f. Type **134**	1·10	1·10
1417	25f. E. Murillo	1·50	1·50
1418	30f. Carlo Crivelli	1·75	1·75
1419	50f. Nicolas Poussin	2·40	2·40

DESIGNS: Virgin and Child paintings by named artists.

1983. Christmas Charity. Nos. 1416/19 additionally inscr with premium.

1421	10f.+1f. multicoloured	1·10	1·10
1422	25f.+1f. multicoloured	1·50	1·50
1423	30f.+1f. multicoloured	1·75	1·75
1424	50f.+1f. multicoloured	2·40	2·40

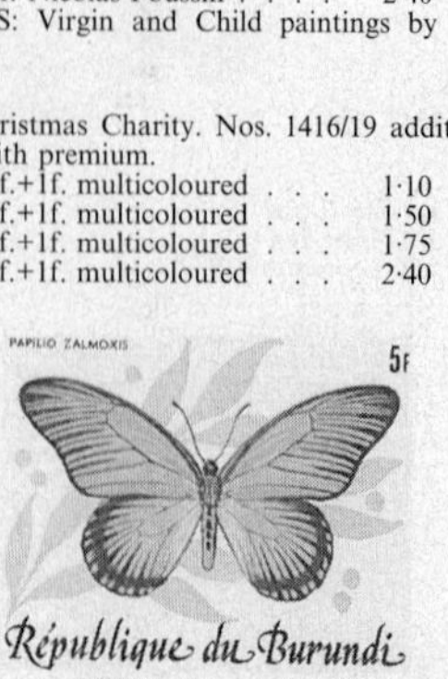

135 "Papilio zalmoxis"

1984. Butterflies. Multicoloured.

1426	5f. Type **135**	2·00	85

1427 5f. "Cymothoe coccinata" 2·00 85
1428 10f. "Papilio antimachus" 4·75 2·10
1429 10f. "Asterope pechueli" . . 4·75 2·10
1430 30f. "Bebearia mardania" 9·25 4·00
1431 30f. "Papilio hesperus" . . 9·25 4·00
1432 35f. "Euphaedra perseis" . . 12·00 5·25
1433 35f. "Euphaedra neophron" 12·00 5·25
1434 65f. "Pseudacraea striata" 22·00 9·75
1435 65f. "Euphaedra imperialis" 22·00 9·75

136 Stamps of German East Africa and Belgian Occupation

1984. 19th U.P.U. Congress, Hamburg. Mult.
1436 10f. Type **136** 65 65
1437 30f. 1962 Burundi overprinted stamps . . . 1·10 1·10
1438 35f. 1969 14f. Letter-writing Week and 1982 30f. Zebra stamps . . . . 1·25 1·25
1439 65f. Heinrich von Stephan (founder of U.P.U.) and 1974 14f. U.P.U. Centenary stamps . . . . 18·00 11·50

137 Jesse Owens (runner)

1984. Olympic Games, Los Angeles. Mult.
1441 10f. Type **137** . . . . 1·10 1·10
1442 30f. Rafer Johnson (discus thrower) . . . . 1·60 1·60
1443 35f. Bob Beamon (long jumper) . . . . 1·75 1·75
1444 65f. K. Keino (sprinter) . . 2·25 2·25

138 "Virgin and Child" (Botticelli)

1984. Christmas. Multicoloured.
1446 10f. "Rest on the Flight into Egypt" (Murillo) 30 30
1447 25f. "Virgin and Child" (R. del Garbo) . . . . 1·10 1·10
1448 30f. Type **138** . . . . 1·60 1·60
1449 50f. "Adoration of the Shepherds" (J. Bassano) 2·00 2·00

1984. Christmas Charity. As Nos. 1446/49 but with additional premium.
1451 10f.+1f. multicoloured . . . 30 30
1452 25f.+1f. multicoloured . . . 1·10 1·10
1453 30f.+1f. multicoloured . . . 1·60 1·60
1454 50f.+1f. multicoloured . . . 2·00 2·00

139 Thunbergia

140 Bombs as Flats

1986. Flowers. Multicoloured.
1456 2f. Type **139** (postage) . . . 1·40 80
1457 3f. African violets . . . . . 1·40 80
1458 5f. "Clivia" . . . . 1·40 80
1459 10f. "Cassia" . . . . 1·40 80
1460 20f. Bird of Paradise flower 2·50 1·60
1461 35f. "Gloriosa" . . . . . . 4·50 3·00

1462 70f. Type **139** (air) . . . . 2·50 2·10
1463 75f. As No. 1457 . . . . . 2·75 2·25
1464 80f. As No. 1458 . . . . . 2·75 2·40
1465 85f. As No. 1459 . . . . . 3·25 2·75
1466 100f. As No. 1460 . . . . 3·50 2·75
1467 150f. As No. 1461 . . . . . 6·00 5·00

1987. International Peace Year (1986). Mult.
1468 10f. Type **140** 20 20
1469 20f. Molecular diagrams as flower 40 40
1470 30f. Clasped hands across globe . . . . 1·10 1·10
1471 40f. Chicks in split globe . . 1·25 1·25

141 Map, Airplane and Emblem

1987. 10th Anniv of Great Lakes Countries Economic Community. Multicoloured.
1473 5f. Type **141** 55 55
1474 10f. Map, ear of wheat, cogwheel and emblem . . 65 65
1475 15f. Map, factory and emblem 75 75
1476 25f. Map, electricity pylons and emblem . . . . . . 1·60 1·60
1477 35f. Map, flags and emblem 2·25 2·25

142 Leaves and Sticks Shelter

1988. International Year of Shelter for the Homeless (1987). Multicoloured.
1479 10f. Type **142** 55 55
1480 20f. People living in concrete pipes 70 70
1481 80f. Boys mixing mortar . . 1·50 1·50
1482 150f. Boys with model house 3·00 3·00

143 Skull between Cigarettes

144 Pope John Paul II

1989. Anti-smoking Campaign. Multicoloured.
1484 5f. Type **143** 70 70
1485 20f. Cigarettes, lungs and skull . . . . 1·40 1·40
1486 80f. Cigarettes piercing skull 2·25 2·25

1989. Various stamps surch.
1487b 20f. on 3f. mult (No. 1457) 70 70
1487c 80f. on 30f. mult (No. 1430) . . . . . . 2·00 2·00
1487d 80f. on 30f. mult (No. 1431) . . . . . . 2·00 2·00
1487e 80f. on 35f. mult (No. 1432) . . . . . . 2·00 2·00
1487f 80f. on 35f. mult (No. 1433) . . . . . . 2·00 2·00
1487g 85f. on 65f. mult (No. 1435)

1990. Papal Visit.
1488 **144** 5f. multicoloured 45 45
1489 10f. multicoloured . . . 45 45
1490 20f. multicoloured . . . 70 70
1491 30f. multicoloured . . . 70 70
1492 50f. multicoloured . . . 1·40 1·40
1493 80f. multicoloured . . . 2·00 2·00

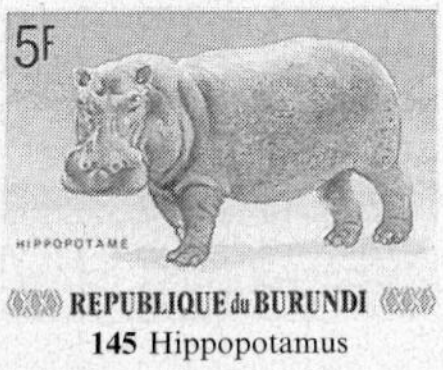

145 Hippopotamus

1991. Animals. Multicoloured.
1495 5f. Type **145** . . . . 1·10 75
1496 10f. Hen and cockerel . . . 1·10 75
1497 20f. Lion . . . . 1·10 75
1498 30f. Elephant . . . . 1·10 1·10
1499 50f. Helmet guineafowl ("Pintade") . . . . 3·00 2·25
1500 80f. Crocodile . . . . . . 4·50 3·25

146 Drummer

147 "Impatiens petersiana"

1992. Traditional Dancing. Multicoloured.
1502 15f. Type **146** 25 25
1503 30f. Men dancing 40 40
1504 115f. Group of drummers (horiz) . . . . 1·90 1·90
1505 200f. Men dancing in fields (horiz) . . . . 3·25 3·25

1992. Flowers. Multicoloured.
1507 15f. Type **147** 90 65
1508 20f. "Lachenalia aloides" "Nelsonii" 90 65
1509 30f. Egyptian lotus . . . . 1·40 1·00
1510 50f. Kaffir lily . . . . . . 3·00 2·25

148 Pigtail Macaque

1992. Air. Animals. Multicoloured.
1512 100f. Type **148** . . . . . . 2·40 1·75
1513 115f. Grevy's zebra . . . . 2·75 2·10
1514 200f. Ox . . . . 4·00 3·00
1515 220f. Eastern white pelican 5·00 3·75

149 People holding Hands and Flag

1992. 30th Anniv of Independence. Multicoloured.
1517 30f. Type **149** 20 20
1518 85f. State flag 80 80
1519 110f. Independence monument (vert) . . . . 1·10 1·10
1520 115f. As No. 1518 . . . . . 1·10 1·10
1521 120f. Map (vert) . . . . . 1·40 1·40
1522 140f. Type **149** . . . . . . 1·50 1·50
1523 200f. As No. 1519 . . . . . 2·10 2·10
1524 250f. As No. 1521 . . . . . 2·75 2·75

150 "Russula ingens"

1992. Fungi. Multicoloured.
1525 10f. Type **150** 15 15
1526 15f. "Russula brunneorigida" 20 20
1527 20f. "Amanita zambiana" 25 30
1528 30f. "Russula subfistulosa" 40 45
1529 75f. "Russula meleagris" . . 90 95
1530 85f. As No. 1529 . . . . . 1·00 1·10
1531 100f. "Russula immaculata" 1·25 1·25
1532 110f. Type **150** . . . . . . 1·40 1·40
1533 115f. As No. 1526 . . . . . 1·40 1·40
1534 120f. "Russula sejuncta" . . 1·40 1·60
1535 130f. As No. 1534 . . . . . 1·50 1·60
1536 250f. "Afroboletus luteolus" 3·00 3·25

151 Columbus's Fleet, Treasure and Globes

1992. 500th Anniv of Discovery of America by Columbus. Multicoloured.
1541 200f. Type **151** . . . . . . 2·00 2·00
1542 400f. American produce, globes and Columbus's fleet . . . . 4·25 4·25

152 Serval

1992. The Serval. Multicoloured.
1543 30f. Type **152** 60 50
1544 130f. Pair sitting and crouching . . . . 2·40 2·00
1545 200f. Pair, one standing over the other . . . . 3·75 3·00
1546 220f. Heads of pair . . . . 4·00 3·50

153 Running

154 Emblems

1992. Olympic Games, Barcelona. Multicoloured.
1547 130f. Type **153** . . . . . . 1·50 1·50
1548 500f. Hurdling . . . . . . 5·25 5·25

1992. International Nutrition Conference, Rome. Multicoloured.
1549 200f. Type **154** . . . . . . 2·00 2·00
1550 220f. Woman's face made from vegetables (G. Arcimbolo) . . . . . 2·40 2·40

155 Horsemen

156 Flags of Member Countries and European Community Emblem

1992. Christmas. Details of "Adoration of the Magi" by Gentile da Fabriano. Multicoloured.
1551 100f. Type **155** 90 90
1552 130f. Three Kings . . . . . 1·10 1·10
1553 250f. Holy family . . . . . 2·50 2·50

1993. European Single Market. Multicoloured.
1555 130f. Type **156** . . . . . . 1·25 1·25
1556 500f. Europe shaking hands with Africa . . . . 5·00 5·00

157 Indonongo

1993. Musical Instruments. Multicoloured.
1557 200f. Type **157** . . . . . . 2·00 2·00
1558 220f. Ingoma (drum) . . . 2·25 2·25
1559 250f. Ikembe (xylophone) . . 2·50 2·50
1560 300f. Umuduri (musical bow) . . . . 3·25 3·25

158 Broad Blue-banded Swallowtail

159 Players, Stadium, United States Flag and Statue of Liberty

1993. Butterflies. Multicoloured.
1561 130f. Type **158** . . . . . . 1·50 1·25
1562 200f. Green charaxes . . . 2·40 2·10
1563 250f. Migratory glider . . . 3·00 2·50
1564 300f. Red swallowtail . . . 3·75 3·50

1993. World Cup Football Championship, U.S.A. (1994). Multicoloured.
1566 130f. Type **159** . . . . . . 1·25 1·25
1567 200f. Players, stadium, United States flag and Golden Gate Bridge . . . 2·50 2·50

160 Cattle

161 Woman with Baby and Two Men

1993. Domestic Animals. Multicoloured.
1568 100f. Type **160** . . . . . . 1·00 1·00
1569 120f. Sheep . . . . 1·10 1·10
1570 130f. Pigs . . . . 1·25 1·25
1571 250f. Goats . . . . 2·50 2·50

1993. Christmas. Each orange and black.
1572 100f. Type **161** . . . . . . 1·25 1·25
1573 130f. Nativity . . . . 1·50 1·50
1574 250f. Woman with baby and three men . . . . 3·00 3·00

162 Elvis Presley

163 "The Discus Thrower" (statue)

1994. Entertainers. Multicoloured.
1576 60f. Type **162** 30 30
1577 115f. Mick Jagger 55 55
1578 120f. John Lennon 60 60
1579 200f. Michael Jackson . . . 1·00 1·00

1994. Cent of International Olympic Committee.
1581 **163** 150f. multicoloured . . . 75 75

164 Pres. Buyoya handing over Baton of Power to Pres. Ndadaye

165 Madonna, China

1994. 1st Anniv of First Multi-party Elections in Burundi. Multicoloured.
1582 30f.+10f. Type **164** 20 20
1583 110f.+10f. Pres. Ndadaye (first elected President) giving inauguration speech 60 60
1584 115f.+10f. Arms on map . . 60 60
1585 120f.+10f. Warrior on map 65 65

1994. Christmas. Multicoloured.
1586 115f. Type **165** 55 55
1587 120f. Madonna, Japan . . . 60 60
1588 250f. Black Virgin, Poland 1·25 1·25

166 Emblem and Earth

167 "Cassia didymobotrya"

1995. 50th Anniversaries. Multicoloured.
1590 115f. Type **166** (F.A.O.) . . 55 55
1591 120f. U.N.O. emblems and dove 60 60

1995. Flowers. Multicoloured.
1592 15f. Type **167** 15 15
1593 20f. "Mitragyna rubrostipulosa" 15 15
1594 30f. "Phytolacca dodecandra" 25 20
1595 85f. "Acanthus pubescens" 65 60
1596 100f. "Bulbophyllum comatum" 80 75
1597 110f. "Angraecum evrardianum" 90 80
1598 115f. "Eulophia burundiensis" 90 80
1599 120f. "Habenaria adolphii" 1·00 90

168 Otraca Bus

169 Boy with Panga

1995. Transport. Multicoloured.
1600 30f. Type **168** 15 15
1601 115f. Transintra lorry . . . 65 65
1602 120f. Lake ferry 90 70
1603 250f. Air Burundi airplane 1·40 1·40

1995. Christmas. Multicoloured.
1604 100f. Type **169** 55 55
1605 130f. Boy with sheaf of wheat 75 75
1606 250f. Mother and children 1·40 1·40

170 Venuste Niyongabo

1996. Olympic Games, Atlanta. Runners. Mult.
1608 130f. Type **170** (5000 m gold medal winner) 40 40
1609 500f. Arthemon Hatungimana . . . . . . 1·50 1·50

171 Hadada Ibis

1996. Birds. Multicoloured.
1610 15f. Type **171** 25 25
1611 20f. Egyptian goose 25 25
1612 30f. African fish eagle . . . 25 25
1613 120f. Goliath heron 75 75
1614 165f. South African crowned crane . . . . 1·00 1·00
1615 220f. African jacana . . . . 1·40 1·40

172 Marlier's Julie

1996. Fishes of Lake Tanganyika. Multicoloured.
1616 30f. Type **172** 25 20
1617 115f. "Cyphotilapia frontosa" 75 60
1618 120f. "Lamprologus brichardi" 75 60
1619 250f. Stone squeaker . . . . 1·50 1·25

173 Children

1998. 50th Anniv of S.O.S Children's Villages. Multicoloured.
1621 100f. Type **173** 25 25
1622 250f. Flags, "50" and children waving 65 65
1623 270f. Children dancing around flag 70 70

174 Madonna and Child

175 Diana, Princess of Wales

1999. Christmas (1996–98). Multicoloured.
1624 100f. Type **174** (1996) . . . 25 25
1625 130f. Madonna and Child (different) (1997) 30 30
1626 250f. Madonna and Child (different) (1998) 65 65

1999. 2nd Death Anniv of Diana, Princess of Wales.
1628 **175** 100f. multicoloured . . . 20 20
1629 250f. multicoloured . . . 20 20
1630 300f. multicoloured . . . 50 50

176 Danny Kaye (entertainer) holding African Baby

2000. New Millennium. "A World Free from Hunger".
1631 **176** 350f. multicoloured . . . 60 60

BUSHIRE Pt. 1

An Iranian seaport. Stamps issued during the British occupation in the 1914–18 War.

20 chahis = 1 kran, 10 krans = 1 toman.

1915. Portrait stamps of Iran (1911) optd **BUSHIRE Under British Occupation**.
1 **57** 1ch. orange and green . . . 38·00 40·00
2 2ch. brown and red . . . . 38·00 35·00
3 3ch. green and grey . . . . 45·00 50·00
4 5ch. red and brown £275 £275
5 6ch. lake and green . . . . 35·00 24·00
6 9ch. lilac and brown . . . . 35·00 40·00
7 10ch. brown and red . . . . 38·00 40·00
8 12ch. blue and green . . . . 45·00 48·00
9 24ch. green and purple . . . 70·00 50·00
10 1kr. red and blue . . . . . 70·00 28·00
11 2kr. red and green £190 £150
12 3kr. black and lilac £160 £170
13 5kr. blue and red . . . . . £110 95·00
14 10kr. red and brown . . . . 95·00 90·00

1915. Coronation issue of Iran optd **BUSHIRE Under British Occupation**.
15 **66** 1ch. blue and red £325 £325
16 2ch. red and blue £6000 £6500
17 3ch. green £400 £400
18 5ch. red £5000 £5000
19 6ch. red and green £4000 £4250
20 9ch. violet and brown . . . £550 £600
21 10ch. brown and green . . . £850 £900
22 12ch. blue £1000 £1100
23 24ch. black and brown . . . £400 £400
24 **67** 1kr. black, brown and silver £400 £425
25 2kr. red, blue and silver . . £350 £375
26 3kr. black, lilac and silver . £475 £500
27 5kr. slate, brown and silver £450 £475
28 – 1t. black, violet and gold . . £400 £450
29 – 3t. red, lake and gold . . . £2750 £3000

BUSSAHIR (BASHAHR) Pt. 1

A state in the Punjab, India. Now uses Indian stamps.

12 pies = 1 anna; 16 annas = 1 rupee.

1

1895. Various frames. Imperf, perf or roul.
9 **1** ¼a. pink . . . . 42·00 85·00
10 ½a. grey . . . . 18·00 90·00
11 1a. red . . . . 19·00 75·00
12 2a. yellow . . . . 28·00 80·00
13 4a. violet . . . . 19·00 85·00
14 8a. brown . . . . 20·00 90·00
15 12a. green . . . . 60·00 £110
16 1r. blue . . . . 32·00 90·00

1896. Similar types, but inscriptions on white ground and inscr "POSTAGE" instead of "STAMP".
27 **1** ¼a. violet . . . . 15·00 14·00
37 ¼a. red . . . . 3·00 7·50
25 ½a. blue . . . . 6·00 14·00
26 1a. olive . . . . 12·00 28·00
32 1a. red . . . . 3·50 10·0
41 2a. yellow . . . . 35·00 60·00
36 4a. red . . . . 38·00 90·00

CAICOS ISLANDS Pt. 1

Separate issues for these islands, part of the Turks and Caicos Islands group, appeared from 1981 to 1985.

100 cents = 1 dollar.

1981. Nos. 514, 518, 520, 523 and 525/7 of Turks and Caicos Islands optd **CAICOS ISLANDS**.
1 1c. Indigo hamlet 15 15
2 5c. Spanish grunt 20 20
3 8c. Four-eyed butterflyfish . . . 20 20
4 20c. Queen angelfish 35 30
5 50c. Royal gramma ("Fairy Basslet") . . . . 50 1·00
6 $1 Fin-spot wrasse . . . . . . 70 1·75
7 $2 Stoplight parrotfish . . . . 1·40 3·25

1981. Royal Wedding. Nos. 653/6 of Turks and Caicos Islands optd. (A) **Caicos Islands**.
8A 35c. Prince Charles and Lady Diana Spencer . . . 20 25
9A 65c. Kensington Palace . . . 30 40
10A 90c. Prince Charles as Colonel of the Welsh Guards 40 50

(B) **CAICOS ISLANDS**.
8B 35c. Prince Charles and Lady Diana Spencer 30 70
9B 65c. Kensington Palace . . . 40 1·00
10B 90c. Prince Charles as Colonel of the Welsh Guards . . . . 50 1·50

1981. Royal Wedding. As Nos. 657/9 of Turks and Caicos Islands, but each inscr "Caicos Islands". Mult. Self-adhesive.
12 20c. Lady Diana Spencer . . . 30 40
13 $1 Prince Charles . . . . . . 80 1·25
14 $2 Prince Charles and Lady Diana Spencer . . . . . . 4·00 5·50

4 Queen or Pink Conch and Lobster Fishing, South Caicos

1983. Multicoloured.
15 8c. Type **4** . . . . 1·25 75
16 10c. Hawksbill turtle, East Caicos . . . . 1·25 75
17 20c. Arawak Indians and idol, Middle Caicos . . . . . . 1·25 75
18 35c. Boat-building, North Caicos . . . . 1·50 1·00
19 50c. Marine biologist at work, Pine Cay . . . . 2·25 1·25
20 95c. Boeing 707 airliner at new airport, Providenciales . . . 4·25 2·25
21 $1.10 Columbus's "Pinta", West Caicos . . . . 4·25 2·50
22 $2 Fort George Cay . . . . . 3·50 4·00
23 $3 Pirates Anne Bonny and Calico Jack at Parrot Cay 6·00 4·75

5 Goofy and Patch

1983. Christmas. Multicoloured.
30 1c. Type **5** 10 10
31 1c. Chip and Dale 10 10
32 2c. Morty 10 10
33 2c. Morty and Ferdie 10 10
34 3c. Goofy and Louie 10 10
35 3c. Donald Duck, Huey, Dewey and Louie 10 10
36 50c. Uncle Scrooge . . . . . 3·25 2·50
37 70c. Mickey Mouse and Ferdie 3·50 3·00
38 $1.10 Pinocchio, Jiminy Cricket and Figaro . . . . 4·00 3·75

6 "Leda and the Swan"

7 High Jumping

1984. 500th Birth Anniv of Raphael. Mult.

40		35c. Type **6**	75	50
41		50c. "Study of Apollo for Parnassus"	1·00	70
42		95c. "Study of two figures for the battle of Ostia"	2·00	1·25
43		$1.10 "Study for the Madonna of the Goldfinch"	2·00	1·50

1984. Olympic Games, Los Angeles.

45	**7**	4c. multicoloured	10	10
46	–	25c. multicoloured	20	20
47	–	65c. black, deep blue and blue	1·10	50
48	–	$1.10 multicoloured	1·10	85

DESIGNS: 25c. Archery; 65c. Cycling; $1.10, Football.

8 Horace Horsecollar and Clarabelle Cow

1984. Easter. Walt Disney Cartoon Characters. Multicoloured.

50		35c. Type **8**	1·00	60
51		45c. Mickey and Minnie Mouse, and Chip	1·10	75
52		75c. Gyro Gearloose, Chip 'n Dale	1·60	1·25
53		85c. Mickey Mouse, Chip 'n Dale	1·60	1·40

1984. Universal Postal Union Congress Hamburg. Nos. 20/1 optd **UNIVERSAL POSTAL UNION 1874–1984** and emblem.

55		95c. Boeing 707 airliner at new airport, Providenciales	1·00	1·25
56		$1.10 Columbus's "Pinta", West Caicos	1·25	1·50

1984. "Ausipex" International Stamp Exhibition, Melbourne. No. 22 optd **AUSIPEX 1984**.

57	–	$2 Fort George Cay	2·40	2·50

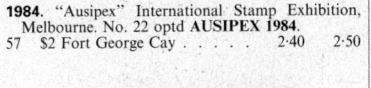

11 Seamen sighting American Manatees

1984. 492nd Anniv of Columbus's First Landfall. Multicoloured.

58		10c. Type **11**	85	60
59		70c. Columbus's fleet	3·25	2·75
60		$1 First landing in the West Indies	3·75	3·25

12 Donald Duck and Mickey Mouse with Father Christmas

1984. Christmas. Walt Disney Cartoon Characters. Multicoloured.

62		20c. Type **12**	1·00	75
63		35c. Donald Duck opening refrigerator	1·40	1·00
64		50c. Mickey Mouse, Donald Duck and toy train	1·90	1·50
65		75c. Donald Duck and parcels	2·50	2·25
66		$1.10 Donald Duck and carol singers	2·75	2·75

13 Thick-billed Vireo

1985. Birth Bicentenary of John J. Audubon (ornithologist). Multicoloured.

68		20c. Type **13**	1·75	60
69		35c. Black-faced grassquit	2·00	85
70		50c. Pearly-eyed thrasher	2·25	1·25
71		$1 Greater Antillean bullfinch	2·75	2·00

14 Two Children learning to Read and Write (Education)

16 The Queen Mother visiting Foundation for the Disabled, Leatherhead

15 Douglas DC-3 on Ground

1985. International Youth Year. 40th Anniv of United Nations. Multicoloured.

73		16c. Type **14**	20	25
74		35c. Two children on playground swings (Health)	50	55
75		70c. Boy and girl (Love)	1·00	1·10
76		90c. Three children (Peace)	1·25	1·40

1985. 40th Anniv of International Civil Aviation Organization. Multicoloured.

78		35c. Type **15**	2·50	55
79		75c. Convair CV 440 Metropolitan	3·50	1·40
80		90c. Britten Norman Islander	3·50	1·60

1985. Life and Times of Queen Elizabeth the Queen Mother. Multicoloured.

82		35c. Type **16**	1·00	55
83		65c. With Princess Anne (horiz)	1·40	95
84		95c. At Epsom, 1961	1·75	1·60

1985. 150th Birth Anniv of Mark Twain (author). Designs as T **118** of Anguilla, showing Walt Disney cartoon characters in scenes from "Tom Sawyer, Detective". Multicoloured.

86		8c. Huckleberry Finn (Goofy) and Tom Sawyer (Mickey Mouse) reading reward notice	60	20
87		35c. Huck and Tom meeting Jake Dunlap	1·75	65
88		95c. Huck and Tom spying on Jubiter Dunlap	3·25	2·00
89		$1.10 Huck and Tom with hound (Pluto)	3·25	2·25

1985. Birth Bicentenaries of Grimm Brothers (folklorists). Designs as T **119** of Anguilla, showing Walt Disney cartoon characters in scenes from "Six Soldiers of Fortune". Multicoloured.

91		16c. The Soldier (Donald Duck) with his meagre pay	1·25	30
92		25c. The Soldier meeting the Strong Man (Horace Horsecollar)	1·50	45
93		65c. The Soldier meeting the Marksman (Mickey Mouse)	3·00	1·25
94		$1.35 The Fast Runner (Goofy) winning the race against the Princess (Daisy Duck)	3·75	2·25

CAMBODIA Pt. 21

A kingdom in south-east Asia.

From 1887 Cambodia was part of the Union of Indo-China. In 1949 it became an Associated State of the French Union, in 1953 it attained sovereign independence and in 1955 it left the Union.

Following the introduction of a republican constitution in 1970 the name of the country was changed to Khmer Republic and in 1975 to Kampuchea.

In 1989 it reverted to the name of Cambodia. Under a new constitution in 1993 it became a parliamentary monarchy.

1951. 100 cents = 1 piastre.
1955. 100 cents = 1 riel.

1 "Apsara" or Dancing Nymph

2 Throne Room, Phnom-Penh

3 King Norodom Sihanouk

5 "Kinnari"

1951.

1	**1**	10c. green and deep green	85	85
2		20c. brown and red	70	55
3		30c. blue and violet	70	55
4		40c. blue and ultramarine	70	55
5	**2**	50c. green and deep green	60	55
6	**3**	80c. green and blue	85	90
7	**2**	1p. violet and blue	1·25	1·10
8	**3**	1p.10 red and lake	1·40	1·10
9	**1**	1p.50 red and lake	1·75	1·25
10	**2**	1p.50 blue and indigo	1·60	1·25
11	**3**	1p.50 brown and chocolate	1·60	1·25
12		1p.90 blue and indigo	2·75	2·25
13	**2**	2p. brown and red	2·75	1·50
14	**3**	3p. brown and red	3·25	2·75
15	**1**	5p. violet and blue	12·00	5·25
16	**2**	10p. blue and violet	24·00	12·00
17	**3**	15p. violet and deep violet	30·00	18·00

1952. Students' Aid Fund. Surch **AIDE A L'ETUDIANT** and premium.

18	**3**	1p.10+40c. red and lake	3·75	4·00
19		1p.90+60c. blue & indigo	3·75	4·00
20		3p.+1p. brown and red	3·75	4·00
21	**1**	5p.+2p. violet and blue	3·75	4·00

1953. Air.

22	**5**	50c. green	85	80
23		3p. red	95	85
24		3p.30 violet	1·40	1·25
25		4p. blue and brown	1·60	1·50
26		5p.10 ochre, red and brown	2·75	2·25
27		6p.50 purple and brown	2·75	2·75
28		9p. green and mauve	3·75	4·00
29		11p.50 multicoloured	8·00	6·50
30		30p. ochre, brown and green	15·00	11·00

6 Arms of Cambodia

7 "Postal Transport"

1954.

31	–	10c. red	30	30
32	–	20c. green	30	20
33	–	30c. blue	30	20
34	–	40c. violet	30	20
35	–	50c. purple	30	20
36	–	70c. brown	40	30
37	–	1p. violet	50	30
38	–	1p.50 red	50	30
39	**6**	2p. red	50	50
40		2p.50 green	80	70
41	**7**	2p.50 green	1·75	1·25
42	**6**	3p. blue	1·50	1·40
43	**7**	4p. sepia	2·50	2·50
44	**6**	4p.50 violet	1·90	1·40
45	**7**	5p. red	3·50	2·50
46	**6**	6p. brown	2·25	1·90
47	**7**	10p. violet	3·75	2·25
48		15p. blue	4·25	2·75
49	–	20p. blue	8·25	5·50
50	–	30p. green	13·00	9·75

DESIGNS—VERT: 10c. to 50c. View of Phnom Daun Penah. HORIZ: 70c. 1, 1p.50, 20, 30p. East Gate, Temple of Angkor.

8 King Norodom Suramarit

9 King and Queen of Cambodia

1955.

51	–	50c. blue	25	25
52	**8**	50c. violet	25	25
53		1r. red	40	25
54		2r. blue	45	40
55	–	2r.50 brown	60	50
56	–	4r. green	90	80
57	–	6r. lake	1·40	1·10
58	**8**	7r. brown	1·75	1·25
59	–	15r. lilac	2·75	2·10
60	**8**	20r. green	4·00	3·00

PORTRAIT: Nos. 51, 55/7 and 59, Queen Kossamak.

For stamps as Nos. 58 and 60, but with black border, see Nos. 101/2.

1955. Coronation (1st issue).

61	**9**	1r.50 sepia and brown	55	35
62		2r. black and blue	55	35
63		3r. red and orange	70	55
64		5r. black and green	1·10	90
65		10r. purple and violet	1·90	1·10

See Nos. 66/71.

10 King Norodom Suramarit

11 Prince Sihanouk, Flags and Globe

1956. Coronation (2nd issue).

66	**10**	2r. red	1·50	1·50
67	–	3r. blue	2·10	2·10
68	–	5r. green	4·00	4·00
69	**10**	10r. green	7·75	7·75
70		30r. violet	18·00	18·00
71	–	50r. purple	35·00	35·00

PORTRAIT—VERT: 3, 5, 50r. Queen of Cambodia.

1957. 1st Anniv of Admission of Cambodia to U.N.O.

72	**11**	2r. red, blue and green	1·00	70
73		4r.50 blue	1·00	70
74		8r.50 red	1·00	70

12

13 Mythological Bird

1957. 2,500th Anniv of Buddhism. (a) With premiums.

75	**12**	1r.50+50c. bis, red & bl	1·25	1·25
76		6r.50+1r.50 bis, red & pur	2·00	2·00
77		8r.+2r. bistre, red & blue	3·25	3·25

(b) Colours changed and premiums omitted.

78	**12**	1r.50 red	85	85
79		6r.50 violet	1·00	1·00
80		8r. green	1·00	1·00

1957. Air.

81	**13**	50c. lake	30	15
82		1r. green	40	20
83		4r. blue	1·40	95
84		50r. red	6·00	5·50
85		100r. red, green and blue	10·50	7·75

14 King Ang Duong

15 King Norodom I

1958. King Ang Duong Commemoration.

86	**14**	1r.50 brown and violet	35	35
87		5r. bistre and black	45	45
88		10r. sepia and purple	90	90

1958. King Norodom I Commemoration.

89	**15**	2r. brown and blue	30	30
90		6r. green and orange	45	45
91		15r. brown and green	90	90

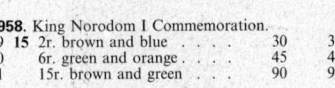

16 Children

1959. Children's World Friendship.
92	16	20c. purple	25	25
93		50c. blue	40	40
94		80c. red	90	90

1959. Red Cross Fund. Nos. 92/4 surch with red cross and premium.
95	16	20c.+20c. purple	25	25
96		50c.+30c. blue	50	50
97		80c.+50c. red	95	95

18 Prince Sihanouk, Plan of Port and Freighter **19** Sacred Plough in Procession

1960. Inauguration of Sihanoukville Port.
98	18	2r. sepia and red	50	50
99		5r. brown and blue	50	50
100		20r. blue and violet	1·75	1·75

1960. King Norodom Suramarit Mourning issue. Nos. 58 and 60 reissued with black border.
| 101 | 8 | 7r. brown and black | 3·00 | 3·00 |
| 102 | | 20r. green and black | 3·00 | 3·00 |

1960. Festival of the Sacred Furrow.
103	19	1r. purple	40	40
104		2r. brown	50	50
105		3r. green	75	75

20 Child and Book ("Education") **21** Flag and Dove of Peace

1960. "Works of the Five Year Plan".
106	20	2r. brown, blue and green	35	25
107		3r. green and brown	45	30
108		4r. violet, green and pink	45	35
109		6r. brown, orange & green	55	45
110		10r. blue, green and bistre	1·25	85
111		25r. red and lake	2·75	2·40

DESIGNS—HORIZ: 3r. Chhouksar Barrage ("Irrigation"); 6r. Carpenter and huts ("Construction"); 10r. Rice-field ("Agriculture"). VERT: 4r. Industrial scene and books ("National balance-sheet"); 25r. Anointing children ("Child welfare").

1961. Peace. Flag in red and blue.
112	21	1r.50 green and brown	35	35
113		5r. red	50	50
114		7r. blue and green	65	65

23 Frangipani **24** "Rama" (from temple door, Baphoun)

1961. Cambodian Flowers.
115	23	2r. yellow, green & mauve	45	45
116		5r. mauve, green and blue	70	70
117		10r. red, green and blue	2·00	2·00

FLOWERS: 5r. Oleander. 10r. Amaryllis.

1961. Cambodian Soldiers Commemoration.
118	24	1r. mauve	40	25
118a		2r. blue	2·50	1·50
119		3r. green	50	35
120		6r. orange	70	45

25 Prince Norodom Sihanouk and Independence Monument

1961. Independence Monument.
121	25	2r. green (postage)	65	50
122		4r. sepia	65	45
123		7r. multicoloured (air)	60	50

| 124 | | 30r. red, blue and green | 2·00 | 1·60 |
| 125 | | 50r. multicoloured | 3·00 | 2·75 |

1961. 6th World Buddhist Conference. Optd **VIe CONFERENCE MONDIALE BOUDDHIQUE 12-11-1961.**
| 126 | 6 | 2p.50 (2r.50) green | 50 | 50 |
| 127 | | 4p.50 (4r.50) violet | 70 | 70 |

27 Power Station (Czech Aid) **28** Campaign Emblem

1962. Foreign Aid Programme.
128	27	2r. lake and red	25	15
129		3r. brown, green and blue	30	15
130		4r. brown, red and blue	30	15
131		5r. purple and green	40	35
132		6r. brown and blue	80	50

DESIGNS: 3r. Motorway (American Aid); 4r. Textile Factory (Chinese Aid); 5r. Friendship Hospital (Soviet Aid); 6r. Airport (French Aid).

1962. Malaria Eradication.
133	28	2r. purple and brown	35	20
134		4r. green and brown	40	40
135		6r. violet and bistre	50	35

29 Curucmas

1962. Cambodian Fruits (1st issue).
136	29	2r. yellow and brown	45	40
137		4r. green and turquoise	65	45
138		6r. red, green and blue	80	60

FRUITS: 4r. Lychees. 6r. Mangosteens.

1962. Cambodian Fruits (2nd issue).
139		2r. brown and green	40	30
140		5r. green and brown	55	40
141		9r. brown and green	70	45

DESIGNS—VERT: 2r. Pineapples. 5r. Sugar-cane. 9r. "Bread" trees.

1962. Surch.
| 142 | 16 | 50c. on 80c. red | 60 | 35 |
| 150 | | 3r. on 2r.50 brn (No. 55) | 45 | 40 |

1962. Inauguration of Independence Monument. Surch **INAUGURATION DU MONUMENT** and new value.
| 143 | 25 | 3r. on 2r. green (postage) | 50 | 30 |
| 144 | | 12r. on 7r. mult (air) | 1·40 | 1·00 |

32 Campaign Emblem, Corn and Maize **33** Temple Preah Vihear

1963. Freedom from Hunger.
| 145 | 32 | 3r. chestnut, brown & blue | 50 | 40 |
| 146 | | 6r. chestnut, brown & blue | 50 | 40 |

1963. Reunification of Preah Vihear Temple with Cambodia.
147	33	3r. brown, purple & green	30	20
148		6r. green, orange and blue	50	40
149		15r. brown, blue & green	80	65

35 Kep sur Mer

1963. Cambodian Resorts. Multicoloured.
151		3r. Koh Tonsay (vert)	35	25
152		7r. Popokvil (waterfall) (vert)	50	30
153		20r. Type **35**	1·60	70

1963. Red Cross Centenary. Surch **1863 1963 CENTENAIRE DE LA CROIX-ROUGE** and premium.
| 154 | 28 | 4r.+40c. green & brown | 60 | 60 |
| 155 | | 6r.+60c. violet & bistre | 95 | 95 |

37 Scales of Justice

1963. 15th Anniv of Declaration of Human Rights.
156	37	1r. green, red and blue	30	30
157		3r. red, blue and green	50	50
158		12r. blue, green and red	95	95

38 Kouprey **39** Black-billed Magpie

1964. Wild Animal Protection.
159	38	50c. brown, green & chest	40	25
160		3r. brown, chestnut & grn	55	35
161		6r. brown, blue and green	85	55

1964. Birds.
162	39	3r. blue, green and indigo	60	40
163		6r. orange, purple & blue	95	65
164		12r. green and purple	1·75	95

BIRDS: 6r. River kingfisher. 12r. Grey heron.

40 "Hanuman" **42** Airline Emblem

1964. Air.
165	40	5r. mauve, brown & blue	60	40
166		10r. bistre, mauve & green	95	40
167		20r. bistre, violet and blue	1·60	75
168		40r. bistre, blue and red	3·50	1·50
169		80r. orange, green & purple	5·75	3·75

1964. Air Olympic Games, Tokyo. Surch **JEUX OLYMPIQUES TOKYO-1964**, Olympic rings and value.
170	40	3r. on 5r. mve, brn and bl	55	40
171		6r. on 10r. bis, mve & grn	85	60
172		9r. on 20r. bistre, vio & bl	95	70
173		12r. on 40r. bis, bl & red	1·90	1·10

1964. 8th Anniv of Royal Air Cambodia.
174	42	1r.50 red and violet	20	15
175		3r. red and blue	30	20
176		7r.50 red and blue	75	45

43 Prince Norodom Sihanouk **44** Weaving

1964. 10th Anniv of Foundation of Sangkum (Popular Socialist Community).
177	43	2r. violet	25	20
178		3r. brown	35	30
179		10r. blue	70	55

1965. Native Handicrafts.
180	44	1r. violet, brown & bistre	25	20
181		3r. brown, green & purple	45	35
182		5r. red, purple and green	75	50

DESIGNS: 3r. Engraving. 5r. Basket-making.

1965. Indo-Chinese People's Conference. Nos. 178/9 optd **CONFERENCE DES PEUPLES INDOCHINOIS.**
| 183 | 43 | 3r. brown | 40 | 35 |
| 184 | | 10r. blue | 60 | 45 |

46 I.T.U. Emblem and Symbols **47** Cotton

1965. Centenary of I.T.U.
185	46	3r. bistre and green	35	30
186		4r. blue and red	45	30
187		10r. purple and violet	70	60

1965. Industrial Plants. Multicoloured.
188		1r.50 Type **47**	30	20
189		3r. Groundnuts	45	25
190		7r.50 Coconut palms	70	50

48 Preah Ko

1966. Cambodian Temples.
191	48	3r. green, turquoise & brn	50	30
192		5r. brown, green & purple	60	40
193		7r. brown, green & ochre	80	50
194		9r. purple, green and blue	1·25	70
195		12r. red, green & verm	1·90	1·40

TEMPLES: 5r. Baksei Chamkrong, 7r. Banteay Srei, 9r. Angkor Vat. 12r. Bayon.

49 W.H.O. Building **50** Tree-planting

1966. Inaug of W.H.O. Headquarters, Geneva.
196	49	2r. multicoloured	30	15
197		3r. multicoloured	35	25
198		5r. multicoloured	55	35

1966. Tree Day.
199	50	1r. brown, green & dp brn	20	15
200		3r. brown, green & orange	35	25
201		7r. brown, green and grey	60	40

51 U.N.E.S.C.O. Emblem **52** Stadium

1966. 20th Anniv of U.N.E.S.C.O.
| 202 | 51 | 3r. multicoloured | 35 | 25 |
| 203 | | 7r. multicoloured | 45 | 35 |

1966. "Ganefo" Games, Phnom Penh.
204	52	3r. blue	25	20
205		4r. green	35	25
206		7r. red	50	40
207		10r. brown	70	60

DESIGNS: 4r., 7r., 10r. Various bas-reliefs of ancient sports from Angkor Vat.

53 Wild Boar **56** Ballet Dancer

1967. Fauna.
208	53	3r. black, green and blue	60	25
209		5r. multicoloured	75	30
210		7r. multicoloured	1·10	40

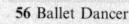

FAUNA—VERT: 5r. Hog-deer. HORIZ: 7r. Indian elephant.

1967. International Tourist Year. Nos. 191/2, 194/5 and 149 optd **ANNEE INTERNATIONALE DU TOURISME 1967**.

211 **48** 3r. green, turquoise & brn 45 35
212 5r. brown, green & purple 55 35
213 – 9r. purple, green and blue 65 55
214 – 12r. red, green & verm . . 90 70
215 **33** 15r. brown, blue & green 1·10 90

1967. Millenary of Banteay Srei Temple. No. 193 optd **MILLENAIRE DE BANTEAY SREI 967–1967**.

216 7r. brown, green and ochre 50 35

1967. Cambodian Royal Ballet. Designs showing ballet dancers.

217 **56** 1r. orange 25 20
218 – 3r. blue 40 30
219 – 5r. blue 50 35
220 – 7r. red 60 45
221 – 10r. multicoloured . . . . 1·10 60

1967. Int Literacy Day. Surch **Journee Internationale de l'Alphabetisation 8-9-67** and new value.

222 **37** 6r. on 12r. blue, grn & red 50 35
223 **15** 7r. on 15r. brown & green 60 40

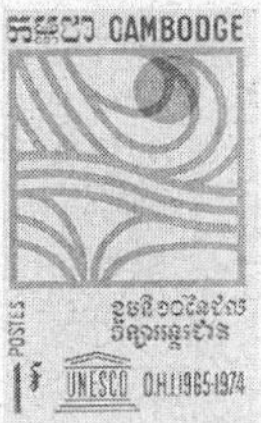

58 Decade Emblem

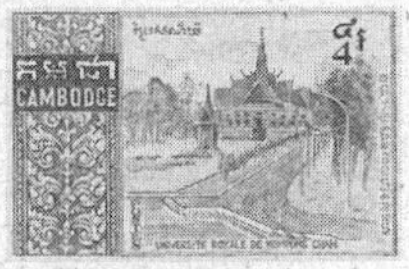

59 Royal University of Kompong-Cham

1967. International Hydrological Decade.

224 **58** 1r. orange, blue and black 20 15
225 6r. orange, blue and violet 40 30
226 10r. orange, lt green & grn 65 45

1968. Cambodian Universities and Institutes.

227 **59** 4r. purple, blue & brown 30 20
228 – 6r. brown, green and blue 45 35
229 – 9r. brown, green and blue 65 40

DESIGNS: 6r. "Khmero-Soviet Friendship" Higher Technical Institute; 9r. Sangkum Reaster Niyum University Centre.

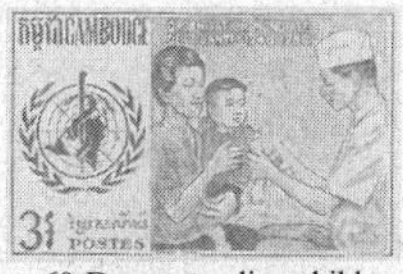

60 Doctor tending child

1968. 20th Anniv of W.H.O.

230 **60** 3r. blue 30 20
231 – 7r. blue 40 35

DESIGN: 7r. Man using insecticide.

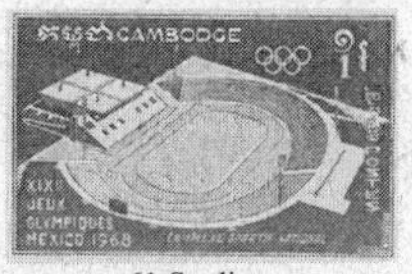

61 Stadium

1968. Olympic Games, Mexico.

232 **61** 1r. brown, green and red 25 20
233 – 2r. brown, red and blue . . 35 20
234 – 3r. brown, blue and purple 40 25
235 – 5r. violet 45 30
236 – 7r.50 brown, green & red 55 40

DESIGNS—HORIZ: 2r. Wrestling; 3r. Cycling. VERT: 5r. Boxing; 7r.50, Runner with torch.

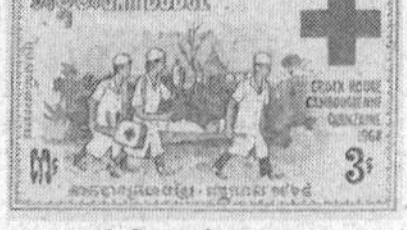

62 Stretcher-party

1968. Cambodian Red Cross Fortnight.

237 **62** 3r. red, green and blue . . 40 25

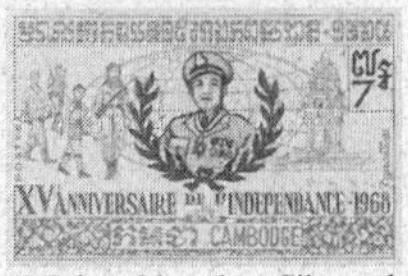

63 Prince Norodom Sihanouk

1968. 15th Anniv of Independence.

238 **63** 7r. violet, green and blue 35 35
239 – 8r. brown, green and blue 45 45

DESIGN: 8r. Soldiers wading through stream.

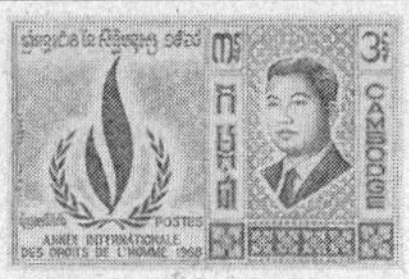

64 Human Rights Emblem and Prince Norodom Sihanouk

1968. Human Rights Year.

240 **64** 3r. blue 30 20
241 5r. purple 35 20
242 7r. black, orange & green 65 30

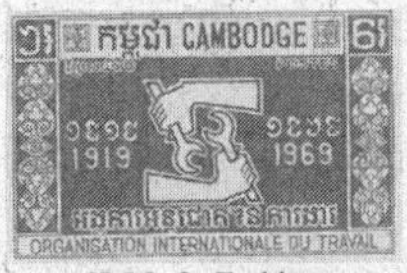

65 I.L.O. Emblem

1969. 50th Anniv of I.L.O.

243 **65** 3r. blue 25 15
244 6r. red 40 20
245 9r. green 60 35

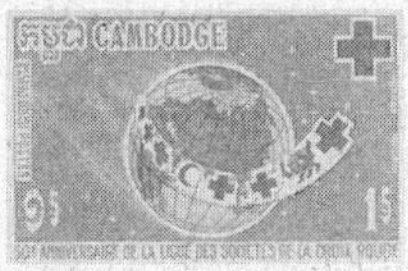

66 Red Cross Emblems around Globe

1969. 50th Anniv of League of Red Cross Societies.

246 **66** 1r. multicoloured 25 15
247 3r. multicoloured 30 20
248 10r. multicoloured 65 35

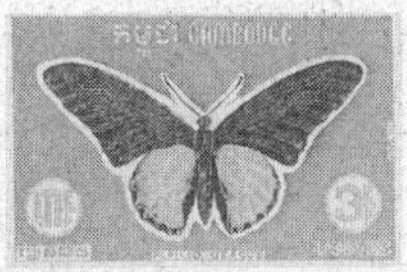

67 Golden Birdwing

1969. Butterflies.

249 **67** 3r. black, yellow & violet 1·00 45
250 – 4r. black, green & verm . . 1·00 50
251 – 8r. black, orange & green 1·50 90

DESIGNS: 4r. Tailed jay. 8r. Orange tiger.

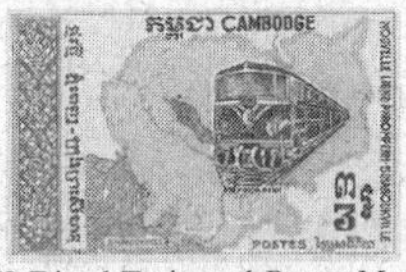

68 Diesel Train and Route Map

1969. Opening of Phnom Penh–Sihanoukville Railway.

252 **68** 3r. multicoloured . . . . . 1·25 90
253 – 6r. brown, black & green 1·50 1·10
254 – 8r. black . . . . 2·75 1·75
255 – 9r. blue, turquoise & grn 2·75 1·75

DESIGNS: 6r. Phnom Penh Station; 8r. Diesel locomotive and Kampor Station; 9r. Steam locomotive at Sihanoukville Station.

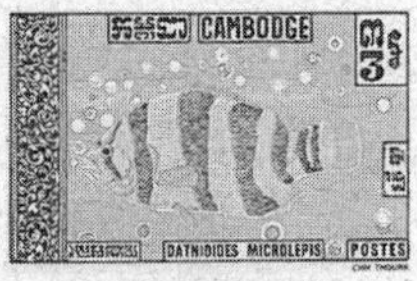

69 Siamese Tigerfish

1970. Fishes. Multicoloured.

256 3r. Type **69** 50 30
257 7r. Marbled sleeper . . . . . 1·25 75
258 9r. Chevron snakehead . . . 1·90 90

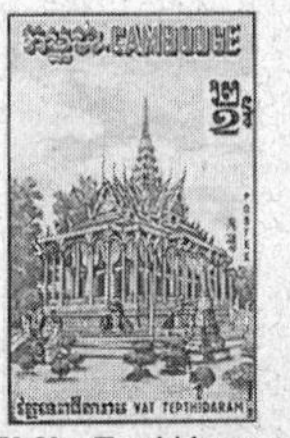

70 Vat Tepthidaram

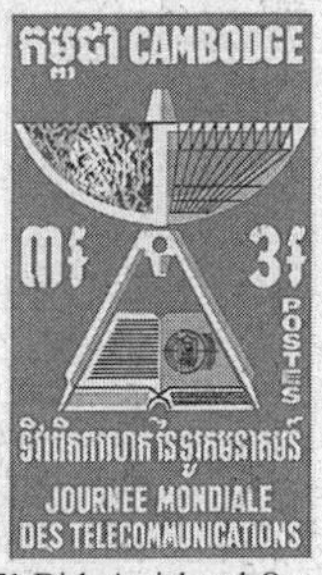

71 Dish Aerial and Open Book

1970. Buddhist Monasteries in Cambodia. Mult.

259 2r. Type **70** 20 15
260 3r. Vat Maniratanaram (horiz) 25 15
261 6r. Vat Patumavati (horiz) . . 45 20
262 8r. Vat Unnalom (horiz) . . 55 40

1970. World Telecommunications Day.

263 **71** 3r. multicoloured 20 10
264 4r. multicoloured 30 15
265 9r. multicoloured 50 30

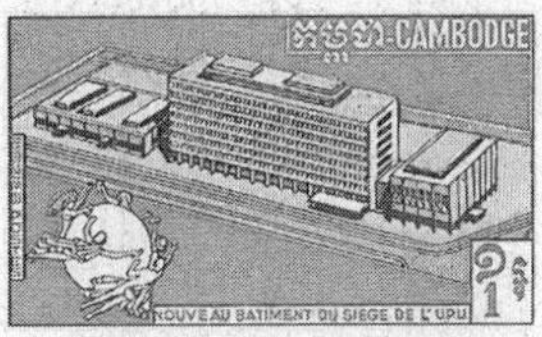

72 New Headquarters Building

1970. Opening of New U.P.U. Headquarters Building, Berne.

266 **72** 1r. multicoloured 20 10
267 3r. multicoloured 25 15
268 4r. multicoloured 40 25
269 10r. multicoloured 65 35

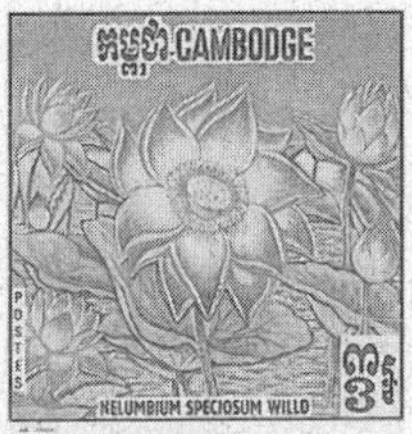

73 "Nelumbium speciosum"

1970. Aquatic Plants. Multicoloured.

270 3r. Type **73** 60 15
271 4r. "Eichhornia crassipes" . . 85 20
272 13r. "Nymphea lotus" . . . . 1·50 50

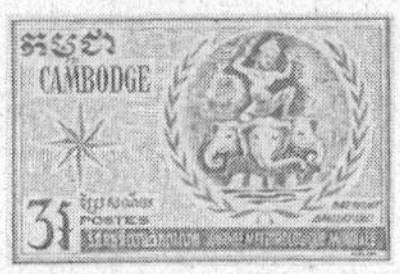

74 "Banteay-srei" (bas-relief)

1970. World Meteorological Day.

273 **74** 3r. red and green 20 10
274 4r. red, green and blue . . 30 15
275 7r. green, blue and black 40 20

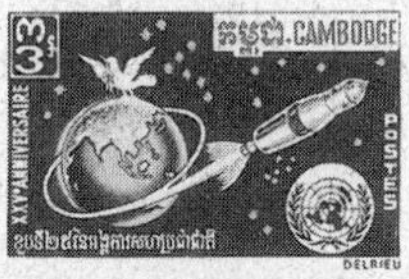

75 Rocket, Dove and Globe

1970. 25th Anniv of United Nations.

276 **75** 3r. multicoloured 20 15
277 5r. multicoloured 40 20
278 10r. multicoloured 60 40

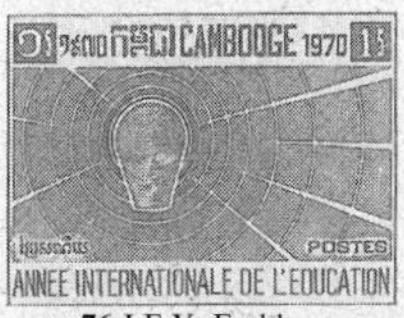

76 I.E.Y. Emblem

1970. International Education Year.

279 **76** 1r. blue 15 10
280 3r. purple 20 15
281 8r. green 45 20

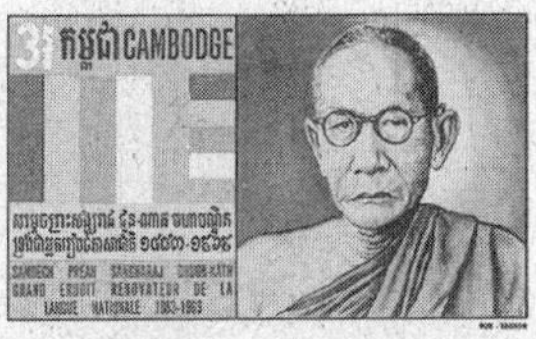

77 Samdech Chuon Nath

1971. 2nd Death Anniv of Samdech Chuon-Nath (Khmer language scholar).

282 **77** 3r. multicoloured 15 15
283 8r. multicoloured 45 20
284 9r. multicoloured 55 30

For issues between 1971 and 1989 see under KHMER REPUBLIC and KAMPUCHEA in volume 3.

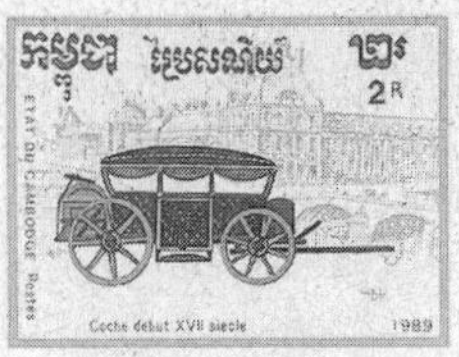

203 17th-century Coach

1989. Coaches. Multicoloured.

1020 2r. Type **203** 10 10
1021 3r. Paris–Lyon coach, 1720 20 10
1022 5r. Mail coach, 1793 . . . . 30 10
1023 10r. Light mail coach, 1805 65 20
1024 15r. Royal mail coach . . . 1·00 30
1025 20r. Russian mail coach . . 1·25 40
1026 35r. Paris–Lille coupe, 1837 (vert) . . . . 2·40 70

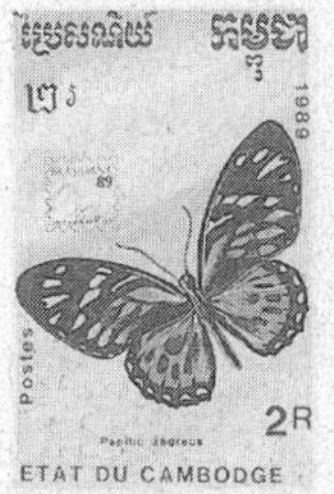

204 "Papilio zagreus"

1989. "Brasiliana 89" International Stamp Exhibition, Rio de Janeiro. Butterflies. Multicoloured.

1028 2r. Type **204** 10 10
1029 3r. "Morpho catenarius" . . 20 10
1030 5r. "Morpho aega" 30 10
1031 10r. "Callithea sapphira" ("wrongly inscr "saphhira") 65 20
1032 15r. "Catagramma sorana" 1·00 30
1033 20r. "Pierella nereis" . . . 1·25 40
1034 35r. "Papilio brasiliensis" 2·40 70

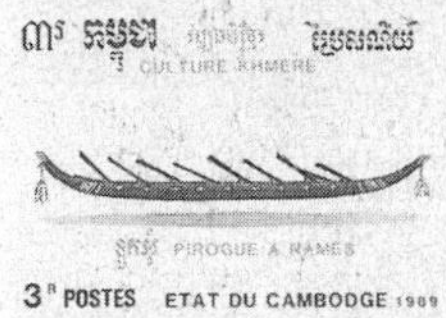

205 Pirogue

1989. Khmer Culture. Multicoloured.

1036 3r. Type **205** 30 10
1037 12r. Pirogue (two sets of oars) . . . . 1·00 30
1038 30r. Pirogue with cabin . . 2·50 70

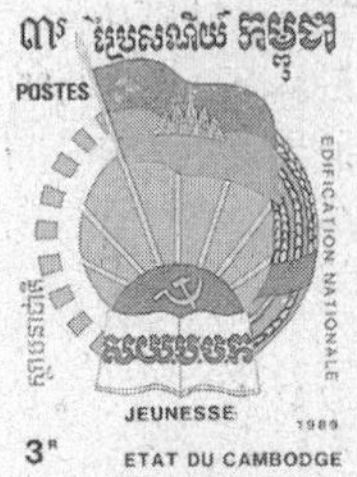

206 Youth

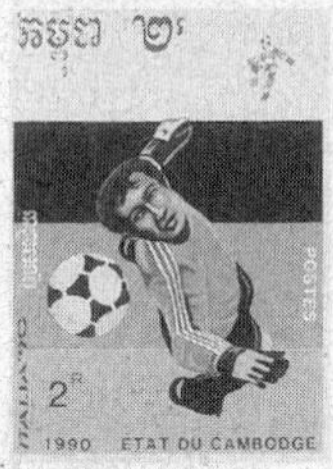

207 Goalkeeper

1989. National Development. Multicoloured.

1039 3r. Type **206** 25 10
1040 12r. Trade unions emblem (horiz) 90 30
1041 30r. National Front emblem (horiz) . . . . 2·40 70

1990. World Cup Football Championship, Italy. Multicoloured.

1042 2r. Type **207** 10 10
1043 3r. Dribbling ball 20 10
1044 5r. Controlling ball with thigh 30 10
1045 10r. Running with ball . . . 65 20
1046 15r. Shooting . . . . 1·00 30
1047 20r. Tackling . . . . 1·25 40
1048 35r. Tackling (different) . . 2·40 70

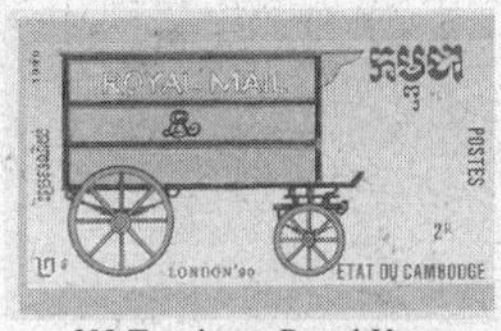

208 Two-horse Postal Van

1990. "Stamp World London 90" International Stamp Exhibition. Royal Mail Horse-drawn Transport. Multicoloured.

1050 2r. Type **208** 10 10
1051 3r. One-horse cart 20 10

1052	5r. Rural post office cart	30	10
1053	10r. Rural post office van	65	20
1054	15r. Local post office van	1·00	30
1055	20r. Parcel-post cart	1·25	40
1056	35r. Two-horse wagon	2·40	70

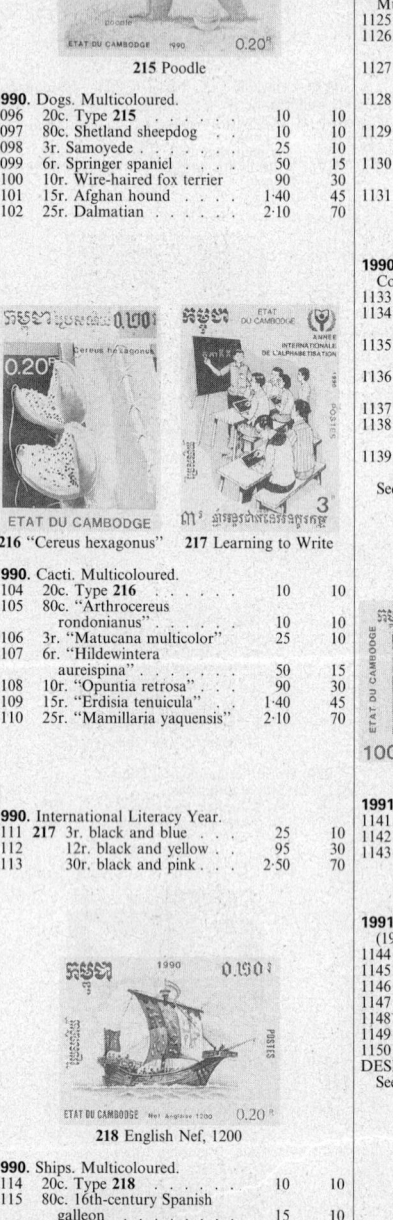

209 Rice Grains **210** Shooting

1990. Cultivation of Rice. Multicoloured.

1058	3r. Type **209**	25	10
1059	12r. Transporting rice (horiz)	90	30
1060	30r. Threshing rice	2·40	70

1990. Olympic Games, Barcelona (1992) (1st issue). Multicoloured.

1061	2r. Type **210**	10	10
1062	3r. Putting the shot	20	10
1063	5r. Weightlifting	30	10
1064	10r. Boxing	65	20
1065	15r. Pole vaulting	1·00	30
1066	20r. Basketball	1·25	40
1067	35r. Fencing	2·40	70

See also Nos. 1163/9, 1208/12 and 1241/5.

211 Four-man Bobsleighing

1990. Winter Olympic Games, Albertville (1992) (1st issue). Multicoloured.

1069	2r. Type **211**	10	10
1070	3r. Speed skating	20	10
1071	5r. Figure skating	30	10
1072	10r. Ice hockey	65	20
1073	15r. Biathlon	1·00	30
1074	20r. Lugeing	1·25	40
1075	35r. Ski jumping	2·40	70

See also Nos. 1152/8.

212 Facade of Banteay Srei

1990. Khmer Culture. Multicoloured.

1077	3r. Type **212**	25	10
1078	12r. Ox-carts (12th-century relief)	90	30
1079	30r. Banon ruins (36 × 21 mm)	2·40	70

213 "Zizina oxleyi"

1990. "New Zealand 1990" International Stamp Exhibition, Auckland. Butterflies. Multicoloured.

1080	2r. Type **213**	10	10
1081	3r. "Cupha prosope"	10	10
1082	5r. "Heteronympha merope"	25	10
1083	10r. "Dodonidia helmsi"	50	15
1084	15r. "Argirophenga antipodum"	90	30
1085	20r. "Tysonotis danis"	1·40	45
1086	35r. "Pyrameis gonnarilla"	2·10	70

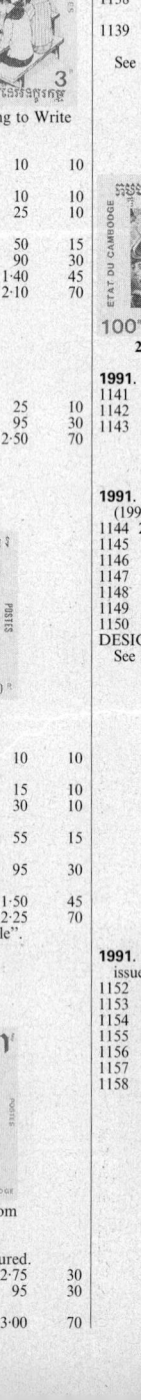

214 "Vostok"

1990. Spacecraft. Multicoloured.

1088	2r. Type **214**	15	10
1089	3r. "Soyuz"	20	10
1090	5r. Satellite	35	10
1091	10r. "Luna 10"	75	25
1092	15r. "Mars 1"	1·10	40
1093	20r. "Venus 3"	1·50	50
1094	35r. "Mir" space station	2·50	95

215 Poodle

1990. Dogs. Multicoloured.

1096	20c. Type **215**	10	10
1097	80c. Shetland sheepdog	10	10
1098	3r. Samoyede	25	10
1099	6r. Springer spaniel	50	15
1100	10r. Wire-haired fox terrier	90	30
1101	15r. Afghan hound	1·40	45
1102	25r. Dalmatian	2·10	70

216 "Cereus hexagonus" **217** Learning to Write

1990. Cacti. Multicoloured.

1104	20c. Type **216**	10	10
1105	80c. "Arthrocereus rondonianus"	10	10
1106	3r. "Matucana multicolor"	25	10
1107	6r. "Hildewintera aureispina"	50	15
1108	10r. "Opuntia retrosa"	90	30
1109	15r. "Erdisia tenuicula"	1·40	45
1110	25r. "Mamillaria yaquensis"	2·10	70

1990. International Literacy Year.

1111	**217** 3r. black and blue	25	10
1112	12r. black and yellow	95	30
1113	30r. black and pink	2·50	70

218 English Nef, 1200

1990. Ships. Multicoloured.

1114	20c. Type **218**	10	10
1115	80c. 16th-century Spanish galleon	15	10
1116	3r. Dutch jacht, 1627	30	10
1117	6r. "La Couronne" (French galleon), 1638	55	15
1118	10r. Dumont d'Urville's ship "L'Astrolabe", 1826	95	30
1119	15r. "Louisiane" (steamer), 1864	1·50	45
1120	25r. Clipper, 1900 (vert)	2·25	70

No. 1118 is wrongly inscribed "d'Uville".

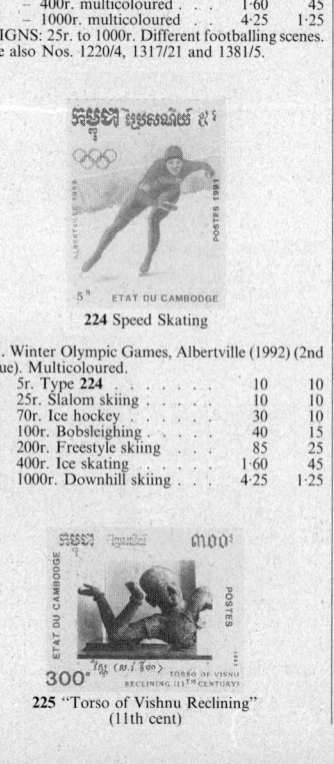

219 Phnom-Penh–Kampong Som Railway

1990. National Development. Multicoloured.

1122	3r. Type **219**	2·75	30
1123	12r. Port, Kampong Som	95	30
1124	30r. Fishing boats, Kampong Som	3·00	70

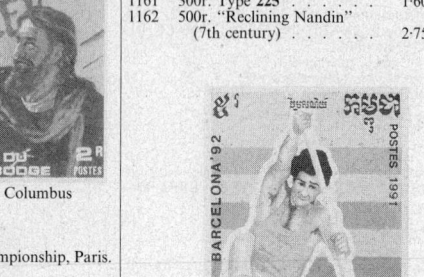

220 Sacre-Coeur de Montmartre and White Bishop

221 Columbus

1990. "Paris '90" World Chess Championship, Paris. Multicoloured.

1125	2r. Type **220**	15	10
1126	3r. "The Horse Trainer" (statue) and white knight	25	10
1127	5r. "Victory of Samothrace" (statue) and white queen	40	10
1128	10r. Azay-le-Rideau Chateau and white rook	80	25
1129	15r. "The Dance" (statue) and white pawn	1·25	40
1130	20r. Eiffel Tower and white king	1·60	50
1131	35r. Arc de Triomphe and black chessmen	2·75	95

1990. 500th Anniv (1992) of Discovery of America by Columbus (1st issue). Multicoloured.

1133	2r. Type **221**	15	10
1134	3r. Queen Isabella's jewel-chest	20	10
1135	5r. Queen Isabella the Catholic	35	10
1136	10r. "Santa Maria" (flagship)	1·40	25
1137	15r. Juan de la Cosa	1·10	40
1138	20r. Monument to Columbus	1·50	50
1139	35r. Devin Pyramid, Yucatan	2·50	95

See also Nos. 1186/92.

222 Tyre Factory **223** Tackle

1991. National Festival. Multicoloured.

1141	100r. Type **222**	55	25
1142	300r. Rural hospital	1·60	75
1143	500r. Freshwater fishing (27 × 40 mm)	2·75	1·25

1991. World Cup Football Championship, U.S.A. (1994) (1st issue).

1144	**223** 5r. multicoloured	10	10
1145	– 25r. multicoloured	10	10
1146	– 70r. multicoloured	30	10
1147	– 100r. multicoloured	40	15
1148	– 200r. multicoloured	85	25
1149	– 400r. multicoloured	1·60	45
1150	– 1000r. multicoloured	4·25	1·25

DESIGNS: 25r. to 1000r. Different footballing scenes. See also Nos. 1220/4, 1317/21 and 1381/5.

224 Speed Skating

1991. Winter Olympic Games, Albertville (1992) (2nd issue). Multicoloured.

1152	5r. Type **224**	10	10
1153	25r. Slalom skiing	10	10
1154	70r. Ice hockey	30	10
1155	100r. Bobsleighing	40	15
1156	200r. Freestyle skiing	85	25
1157	400r. Ice skating	1·60	45
1158	1000r. Downhill skiing	4·25	1·25

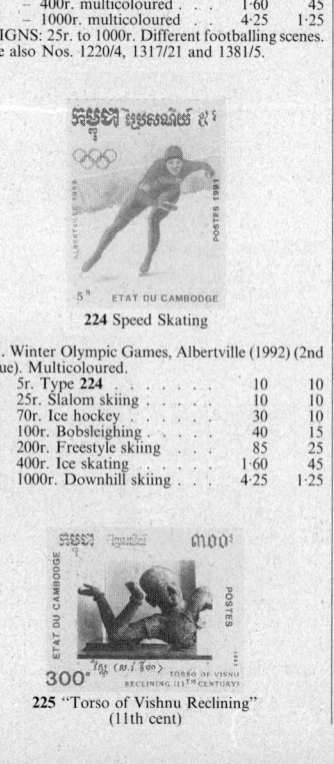

225 "Torso of Vishnu Reclining" (11th cent)

1991. Sculpture. Multicoloured.

1160	100r. "Garuda" (Koh Ker, 10th century)	55	25
1161	300r. Type **225**	1·60	75
1162	500r. "Reclining Nandin" (7th century)	2·75	1·25

226 Pole Vaulting

1991. Olympic Games, Barcelona (1992) (2nd issue). Multicoloured.

1163	5r. Type **226**	10	10
1164	25r. Table tennis	10	10
1165	70r. Running	30	10
1166	100r. Wrestling	40	15
1167	200r. Gymnastics (bars)	85	25
1168	400r. Tennis	1·60	45
1169	1000r. Boxing	4·25	1·25

227 Douglas DC-10-30

1991. Airplanes. Multicoloured.

1171	5r. Type **227**	10	10
1172	25r. McDonnell Douglas MD-11	10	10
1173	70r. Ilyushin Il-96-300	30	10
1174	100r. Airbus Industrie A310	40	15
1175	200r. Yakovlev Yak-42	85	25
1176	400r. Tupolev Tu-154	1·60	45
1177	1000r. Douglas DC-9	4·25	1·25

228 Diaguita Funerary Urn, Catamarca

1991. "Espamer '91" Iberia–Latin America Stamp Exhibition, Buenos Aires. Multicoloured.

1178	5r. Bareales glass pot, Catamarca (horiz)	10	10
1179	25r. Type **228**	10	10
1180	70r. Quiroga urn, Tucuman	30	10
1181	100r. Round glass pot, Santiago del Estero (horiz)	40	15
1182	200r. Pitcher, Santiago del Estero (horiz)	85	25
1183	400r. Diaguita funerary urn, Tucuman	1·60	45
1184	1000r. Bareales funerary urn, Catamarca (horiz)	4·25	1·25

229 "Pinta"

1991. 500th Anniv (1992) of Discovery of America by Columbus (2nd issue). Each brown, stone and black.

1186	5r. Type **229**	30	10
1187	25r. "Nina"	35	10
1188	70r. "Santa Maria"	75	20
1189	100r. Landing at Guanahani, 1492 (horiz)	1·00	25
1190	200r. Meeting of two cultures (horiz)	85	25

1191	400r. La Navidad (first European settlement in America) (horiz)	3·00	75
1192	1000r. Amerindian village (horiz)	4·25	1·25

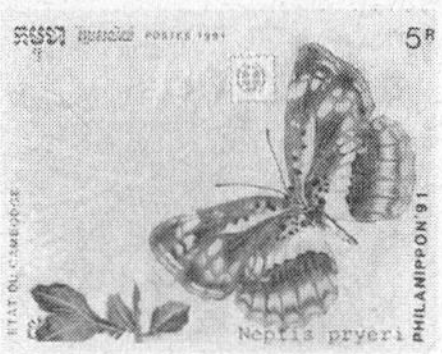

230 "Neptis pryeri"

1991. "Phila Nippon '91" International Stamp Exhibition, Tokyo. Butterflies. Multicoloured.

1194	5r. Type **230**	10	10
1195	25r. "Papilio xuthus"	10	10
1196	70r. Common map butterfly	30	10
1197	100r. "Argynnis anadiomene"	40	15
1198	200r. "Lethe marginalis"	85	25
1199	400r. "Artopoetes pryeri"	1·60	45
1200	1000r. African monarch	4·25	1·25

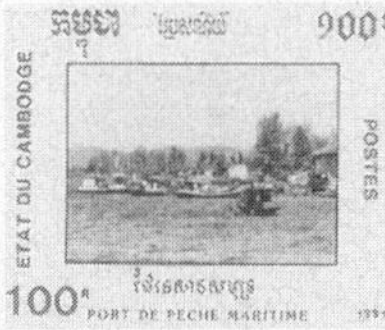

231 Coastal Fishing Port

1991. National Development. Food Industry. Multicoloured.

1202	100r. Type **231**	80	25
1203	300r. Preparing palm sugar (29 × 40 mm)	1·60	75
1204	500r. Picking peppers	2·75	1·25

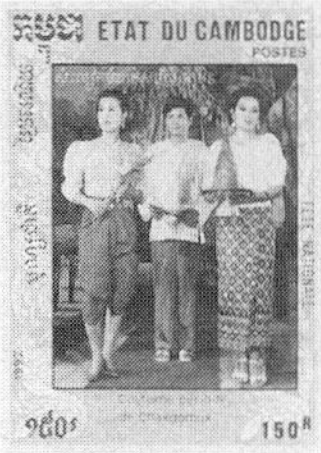

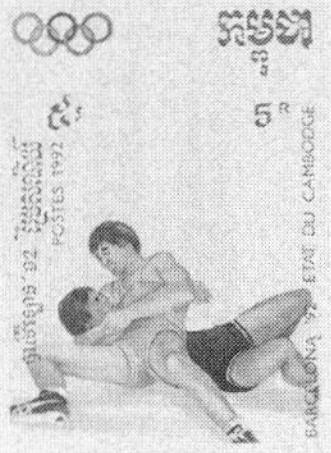

232 Chakdomuk Costumes **233** Wrestling

1992. National Festival. Traditional Costumes. Multicoloured.

1205	150r. Type **232**	55	30
1206	350r. Longvek	1·25	70
1207	1000r. Angkor	3·50	1·25

1992. Olympic Games, Barcelona (3rd issue). Multicoloured.

1208	5r. Type **233**	10	10
1209	15r. Football	10	10
1210	80r. Weightlifting	20	10
1211	400r. Archery	1·10	35
1212	1500r. Gymnastics	4·25	1·40

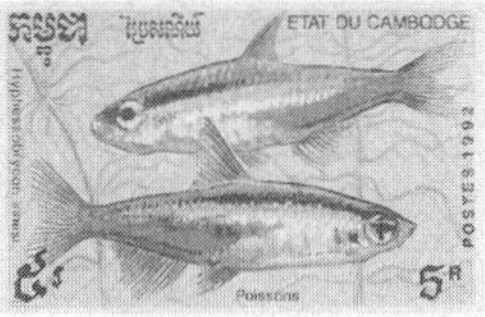

234 Neon Tetra

1992. Fishes. Multicoloured.

1214	5r. Type **234**	10	10
1215	15r. Siamese fighting fish	15	10
1216	80r. Kaiser tetra	25	10
1217	400r. Dwarf gourami	1·50	50
1218	1500r. Port hoplo	5·25	2·25

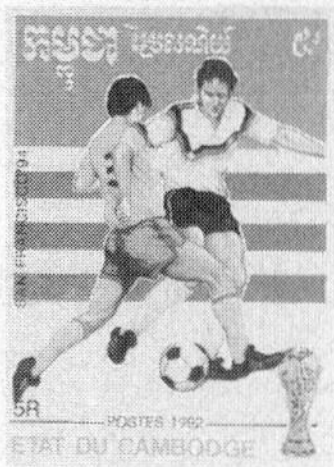

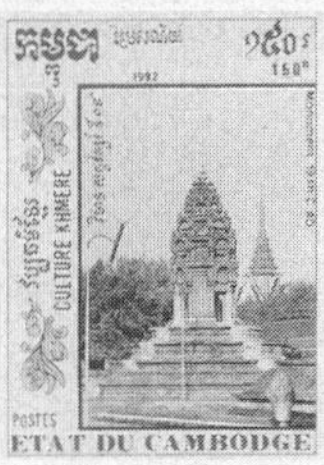

235 Germany v. Columbia **236** Monument

1992. World Cup Football Championship, U.S.A. (1994) (2nd issue). Multicoloured.

1220	5r. Type **235**	10	10
1221	15r. Netherlands player (horiz)	10	10
1222	80r. Uruguay v. C.I.S. (ex-Soviet states)	20	10
1223	400r. Cameroun v. Yugoslavia	1·10	35
1224	1500r. Italy v. Sweden	4·25	1·40

1992. Khmer Culture. 19th-century Architecture. Multicoloured.

1226	150r. Type **236**	55	30
1227	350r. Stupa	1·25	70
1228	1000r. Mandapa library	3·50	1·25

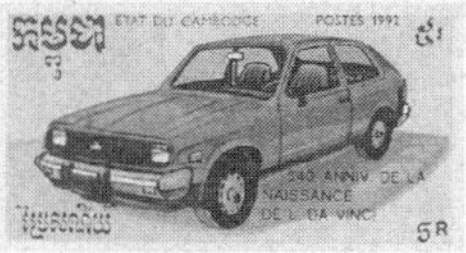

237 Motor Car

1992. 540th Birth Anniv (1992) of Leonardo da Vinci (artist and inventor). Multicoloured.

1229	5r. Type **237**	10	10
1230	15r. Container ship	30	10
1231	80r. Helicopter	20	10
1232	400r. Scuba diver	1·10	35
1233	1500r. Parachutists (vert)	4·25	1·40

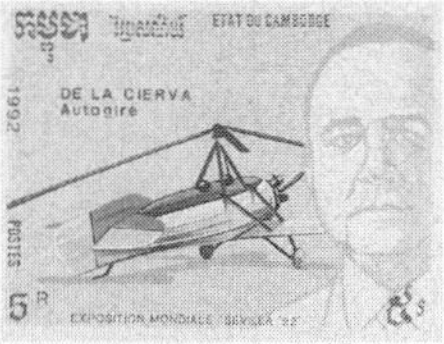

238 Juan de la Cierva and Autogyro

1992. "Expo '92" World's Fair, Seville. Inventors. Multicoloured.

1235	5r. Type **238**	10	10
1236	15r. Thomas Edison and electric light bulb	10	10
1237	80r. Samuel Morse and Morse telegraph	20	10
1238	400r. Narciso Monturiol and "Ictineo" (early submarine)	2·75	50
1239	1500r. Alexander Graham Bell and early telephone	4·25	1·40

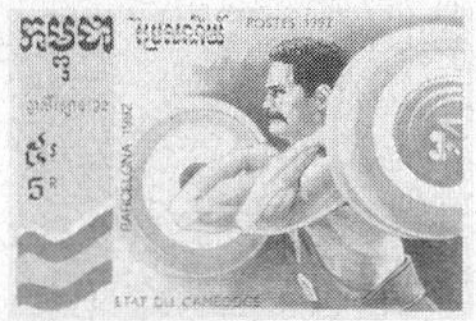

239 Weightlifting

1992. Olympic Games, Barcelona (4th issue). Multicoloured.

1241	5r. Type **239**	10	10
1242	15r. Boxing	10	10
1243	80r. Basketball	20	10
1244	400r. Running	1·00	35
1245	1500r. Water polo	4·00	1·40

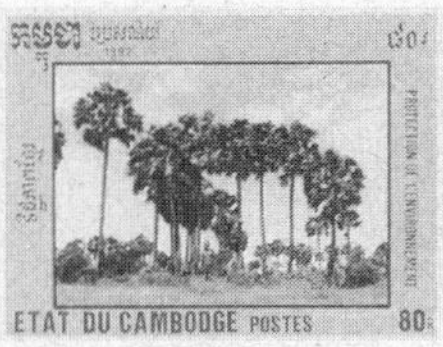

240 Palm Trees

1992. Environmental Protection. Multicoloured.

1247	5r. Couple on riverside	10	10
1248	15r. Pagoda	10	10
1249	80r. Type **240**	20	10
1250	400r. Boy riding water buffalo	1·00	35
1251	1500r. Swimming in river	4·00	1·40

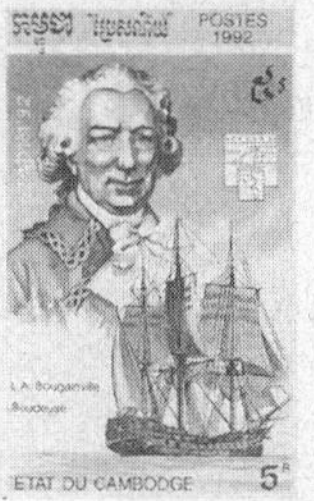

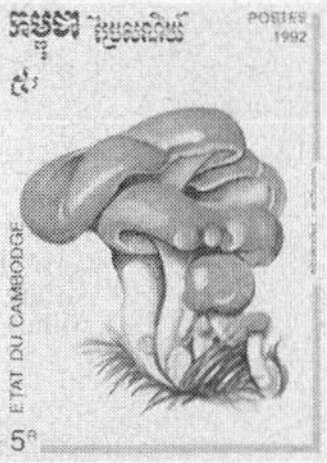

241 Louis de Bougainville and "La Boudeuse" **242** "Albatrellus confluens"

1992. "Genova '92" International Thematic Stamp Exhibition, Genoa. Multicoloured.

1253	5r. Type **241**	10	10
1254	15r. James Cook and H.M.S. "Endeavour"	15	10
1255	80r. Charles Darwin and H.M.S. "Beagle"	25	10
1256	400r. Jacques Cousteau and "Calypso"	1·10	35
1257	1500r. "Kon Tiki" (replica of balsa raft)	4·25	1·40

1992. Fungi. Multicoloured.

1259	5r. Type **242**	10	10
1260	15r. Scarlet-stemmed boletus	10	10
1261	80r. Verdigris agaric	30	10
1262	400r. "Telamonia armillata"	1·50	60
1263	1500r. Goaty smell cortinarius	6·00	2·00

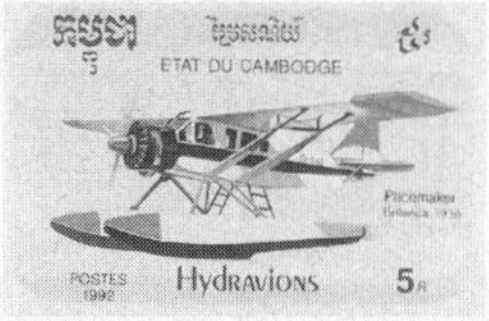

243 Bellanca Pacemaker Seaplane, 1930

1992. Aircraft. Multicoloured.

1264	5r. Type **243**	10	10
1265	15r. Canadair CL-215 fire-fighting amphibian, 1965	10	10
1266	80r. Grumman G-21 Goose amphibian, 1937	20	10
1267	400r. Grumman SA-6 Sealand flying boat, 1947	95	30
1268	1500r. Short S.23 Empire "C" Class flying boat, 1936	3·75	1·00

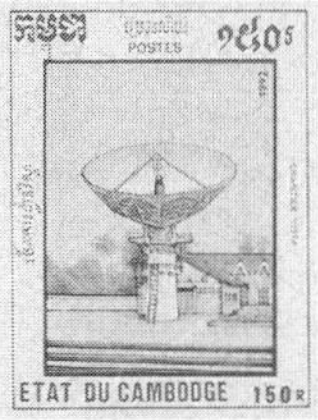

244 Dish Aerial

1992. National Development. Multicoloured.

1270	150r. Type **244**	40	20
1271	350r. Dish aerial, flags and satellite	90	45
1272	1000r. Hotel Cambodiana	2·25	1·10

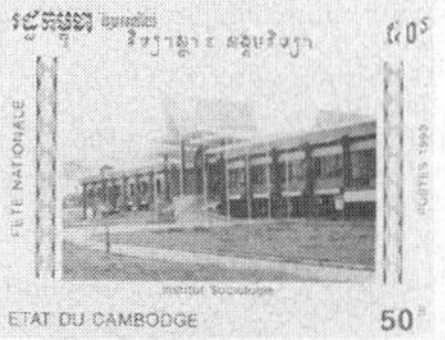

245 Sociological Institute

1993. National Festival. Multicoloured.

1273	50r. Type **245**	15	10
1274	450r. Motel Cambodiana	1·00	50
1275	1000r. Theatre, Bassac	2·25	1·10

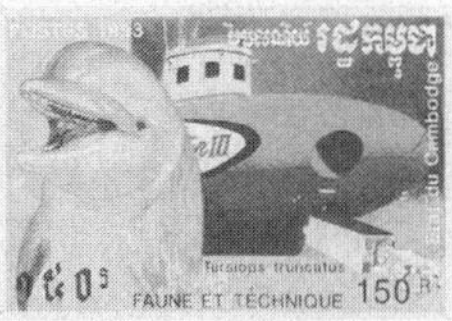

246 Bottle-nosed Dolphin and Submarine

1993. Wildlife and Technology. Multicoloured.

1276	150r. Type **246**	55	10
1277	200r. Supersonic jet airplane and Peregrine falcon	60	10
1278	250r. Eurasian beaver and dam	75	15
1279	500r. Satellite and Natterer's bat	2·25	30
1280	900r. Rufous humming-bird and helicopter	3·50	70

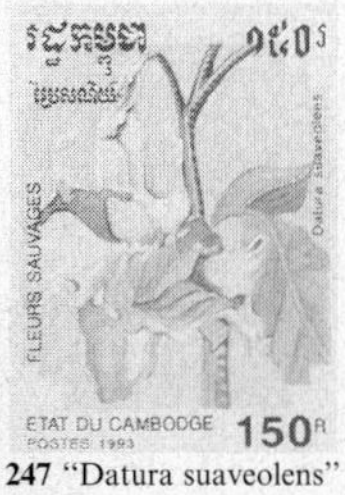

247 "Datura suaveolens"

1993. Wild Flowers. Multicoloured.

1281	150r. Type **247**	40	10
1282	200r. "Convolvulus tricolor"	50	10
1283	250r. "Hippeastrum" hybrid	65	15
1284	500r. "Camellia" hybrid	1·25	30
1285	900r. "Lilium speciosum"	2·25	55

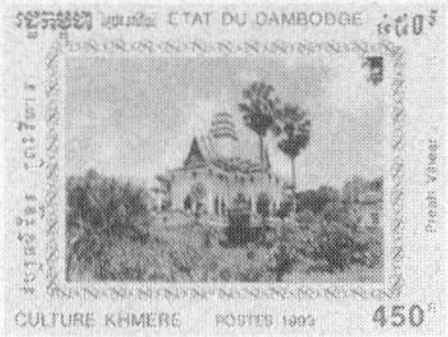

248 Vihear Temple

1993. Khmer Culture. Multicoloured.

1287	50r. Sculpture of ox	15	10
1288	450r. Type **248**	1·10	20
1289	1000r. Offering to Buddha	2·50	55

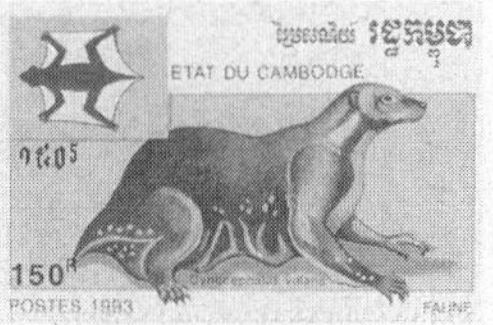

249 Philippine Flying Lemur

1993. Animals. Multicoloured.

1290	150r. Type **249**	40	10
1291	200r. Red giant flying squirrel	50	10
1292	250r. Fringed gecko	65	15
1293	500r. Wallace's flying frog	1·25	30
1294	900r. Flying lizard	2·25	55

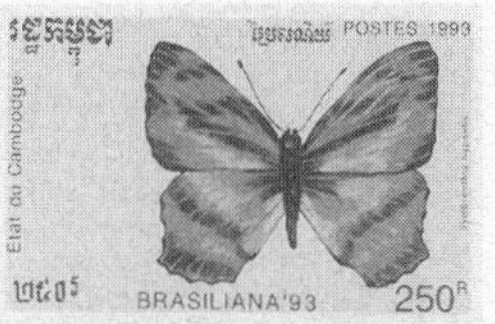

250 "Symbrenthia hypselis"

1993. "Brasiliana '93" International Stamp Exhibition, Rio de Janeiro. Butterflies. Mult.

1295	250r. Type **250**	65	15
1296	350r. "Sithon nedymond"	90	20
1297	600r. "Geitoneura minyas"	1·50	35
1298	800r. "Argyreus hyperbius"	2·00	50
1299	1000r. "Argyrophenga antipodum"	2·50	60

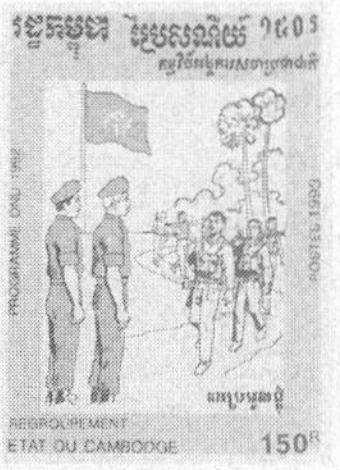

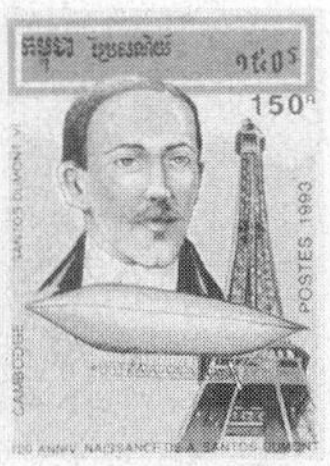

251 Armed Cambodians reporting to U.N. Base **253** Santos-Dumont, Eiffel Tower and "Ballon No. 6", 1901

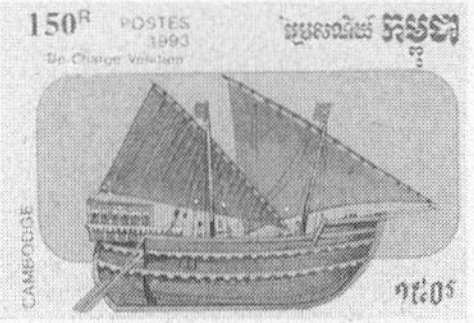

252 Venetian Felucca

1993. United Nations Transitional Authority in Cambodia Pacification Programme. Each black and blue.

1301	150r. Type **251**	40	10
1302	200r. Military camp	50	10
1303	250r. Surrender of arms	65	15
1304	500r. Vocational training	1·25	30
1305	900r. Liberation	2·25	50

1993. Sailing Ships. Multicoloured.

1307	150r. Type **252**	40	10
1308	200r. Phoenician galley	50	10
1309	250r. Egyptian merchantman	65	15
1310	500r. Genoese merchantman	1·25	30
1311	900r. English merchantman	2·25	50

1993. 120th Birth Anniv of Alberto Santos-Dumont (aviator). Multicoloured.

1312	150r. Type **253**	40	10
1313	200r. "14 bis" (biplane), 1906 (horiz)	50	10
1314	250r. "Demoiselle" (monoplane), 1909 (horiz)	65	15
1315	500r. Embraer EMB-201 A (horiz)	1·25	30
1316	900r. Embraer EMB-111 (horiz)	2·25	50

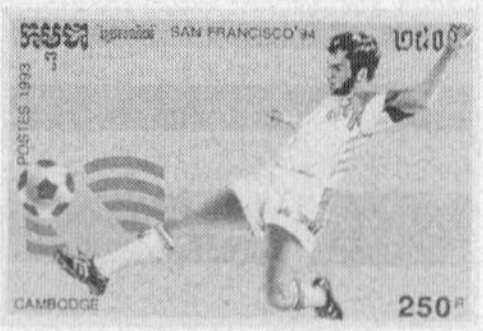

254 Footballer

1993. World Cup Football Championship, U.S.A. (1994) (3rd issue).

1317	**254** 250r. multicoloured . . .	65	10
1318	– 350r. multicoloured . . .	90	15
1319	– 600r. multicoloured . . .	1·50	30
1320	– 800r. multicoloured . . .	2·00	40
1321	– 1000r. mult (vert) . . .	2·50	50

DESIGNS: 350r. to 1000r. Various footballing scenes.

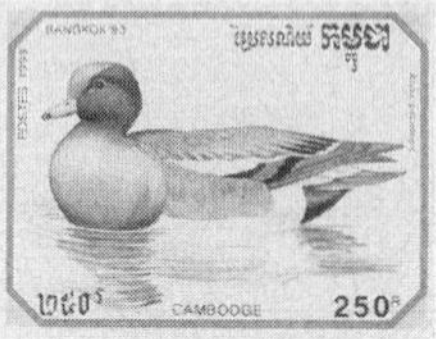

255 European Wigeon

1993. "Bangkok 1993" International Stamp Exhibition, Thailand. Ducks. Multicoloured.

1323	250r. Type **255**	65	10
1324	350r. Baikal teal	90	15
1325	600r. Mandarin	1·50	30
1326	800r. Wood duck	2·00	40
1327	1000r. Harlequin duck . . .	2·50	50

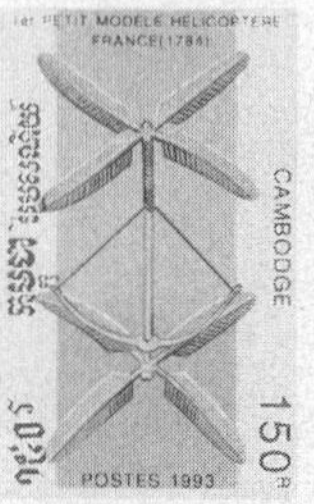

256 First Helicopter Model, France, 1784

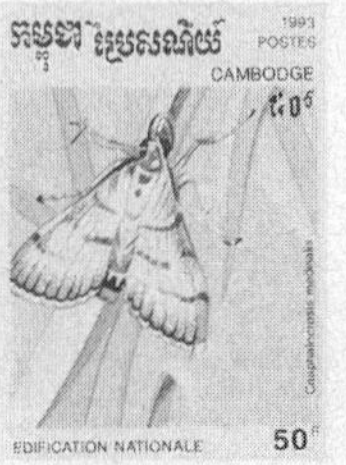

257 "Cnaphalocrosis medinalis"

1993. Vertical Take-off Aircraft. Multicoloured.

1329	150r. Type **256**	40	10
1330	200r. Model of steam helicopter, 1863	50	10
1331	250r. New York–Atlanta–Miami autogyro flight, 1927 (horiz)	65	10
1332	500r. Sikorsky helicopter, 1943 (horiz)	1·25	20
1333	900r. French vertical take-off jet	2·25	40

1993. National Development. Harmful Insects. Multicoloured.

1335	50r. Type **257**	10	10
1336	450r. Brown leaf-hopper . .	1·10	15
1337	500r. "Scirpophaga incertulas"	1·25	20
1338	1000r. Stalk-eyed fly	2·50	40

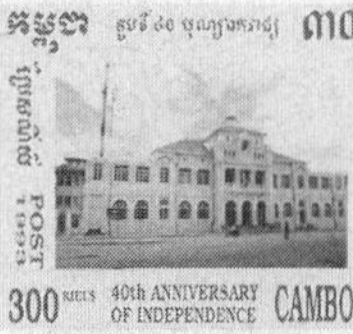

258 Ministry of Posts and Telecommunications

1993. 40th Anniv of Independence.

1340	**258** 300r. multicoloured . . .	75	15
1341	– 500r. multicoloured . . .	1·25	20
1342	– 700r. blue, red & black	1·75	30

DESIGNS—VERT: 500r. Independence monument. HORIZ: 700r. National flag.

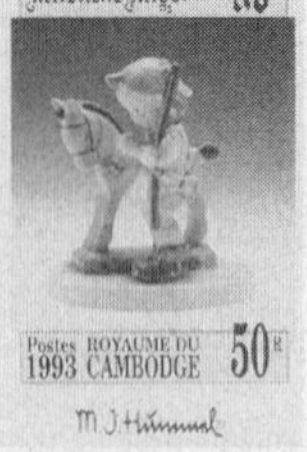

259 Boy with Pony

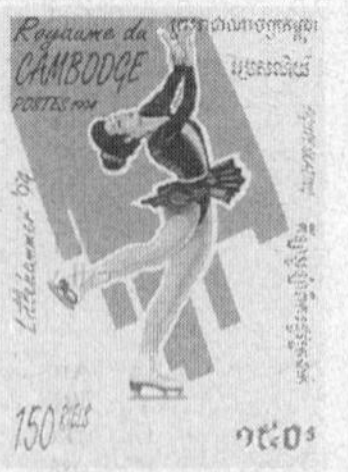

260 Figure Skating

1993. Figurines by M. J. Hummel. Multicoloured.

1343	50r. Type **259**	10	10
1344	100r. Girl and pram	25	10
1345	150r. Girl bathing doll . . .	40	10
1346	200r. Girl holding doll . . .	50	10
1347	250r. Boys playing	65	10
1348	300r. Girls pulling boy in cart	75	15
1349	350r. Girls playing ring-o-roses	90	15
1350	600r. Boys with stick and drum	1·50	25

1994. Winter Olympic Games, Lillehammer, Norway. Multicoloured.

1351	150r. Type **260**	40	10
1352	250r. Two-man luge (horiz)	65	10
1353	400r. Skiing (horiz)	1·00	15
1354	700r. Biathlon (horiz) . . .	1·75	30
1355	1000r. Speed skating	2·50	40

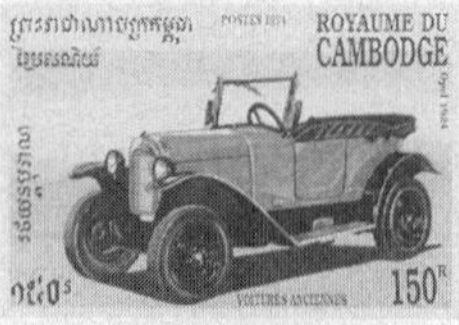

261 Opel, 1924

1994. Motor Cars. Multicoloured.

1357	150r. Type **261**	40	10
1358	200r. Mercedes, 1901 . . .	50	10
1359	250r. Ford Model "T", 1927	65	10
1360	500r. Rolls Royce, 1907 . .	1·25	20
1361	900r. Hutton, 1908	2·25	35

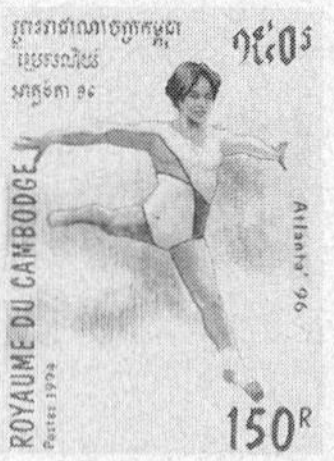

262 Gymnastics

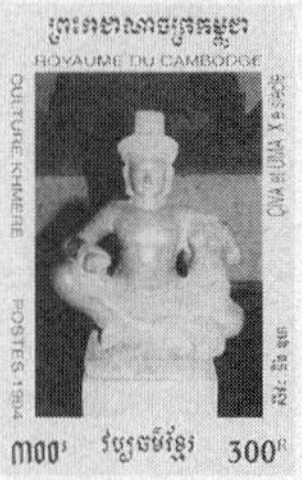

263 Siva and Uma (10th century, Banteay Srei)

1994. Olympic Games, Atlanta (1996) (1st issue). Multicoloured.

1363	150r. Type **262**	40	10
1364	200r. Football	50	10
1365	250r. Throwing the javelin	65	10
1366	300r. Canoeing	75	15
1367	600r. Running	1·50	25
1368	1000r. Diving (horiz) . . .	2·50	40

See also Nos. 1437/41 and 1495/1500.

1994. Khmer Culture. Statues. Multicoloured.

1370	300r. Type **263**	75	15
1371	500r. Vishnu (6th cent, Tvol Dai-Buon)	1·25	20
1372	700r. King Jayavarman VII (12th–13th century, Krol Romeas Angkor)	1·75	30

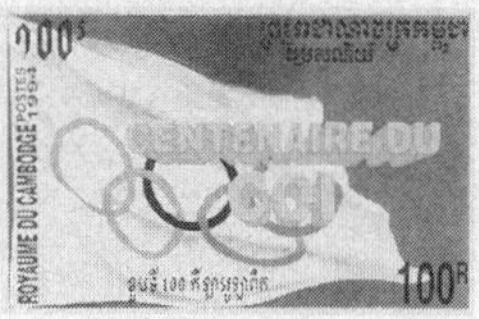

264 Olympic Flag

1994. Centenary of International Olympic Committee. Multicoloured.

1373	100r. Type **264**	30	10
1374	300r. Flag and torch	90	15
1375	600r. Flag and Pierre de Coubertin (reviver of modern Olympic Games)	1·75	25

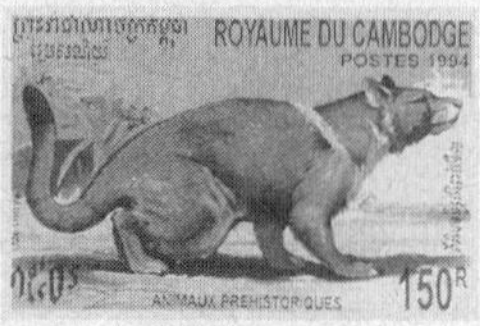

265 Mesonyx

1994. Prehistoric Animals. Multicoloured.

1376	150r. Type **265**	40	10
1377	250r. Doedicurus	65	10
1378	400r. Mylodon	1·00	15
1379	700r. Uintatherium	1·75	30
1380	1000r. Hyrachyus	2·50	40

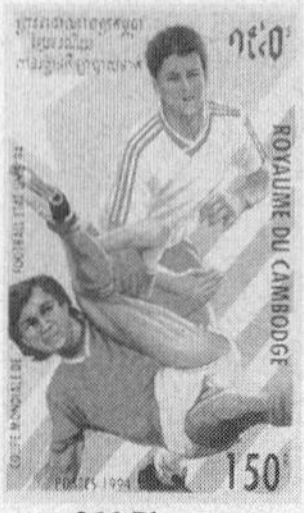

266 Players

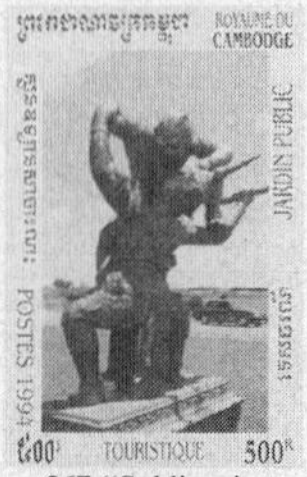

267 "Soldiers in Combat"

1994. World Cup Football Championship, U.S.A. (4th issue).

1381	**266** 150r. multicoloured . . .	40	10
1382	– 250r. multicoloured . . .	65	10
1383	– 400r. multicoloured . . .	1·00	15
1384	– 700r. multicoloured . . .	1·75	30
1385	– 1000r. multicoloured . .	2·50	40

DESIGNS: 250r. to 1000r. Different footballing scenes.

1994. Tourism. Statues in Public Gardens. Mult.

1387	300r. "Stag and Hind" . . .	75	15
1388	500r. Type **267**	1·25	20
1389	700r. "Lions"	1·75	30

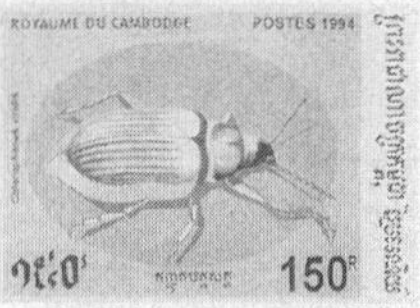

268 "Chlorophanus viridis"

1994. Beetles. Multicoloured.

1390	150r. Type **268**	40	10
1391	200r. "Chrysochroa fulgidissima"	50	10
1392	250r. "Lytta vesicatoria" . .	65	10
1393	500r. "Purpuricenus kaehleri"	1·25	20
1394	900r. Herculese beetle . . .	2·25	25

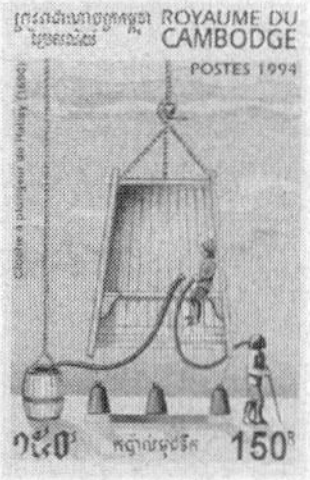

269 Halley's Diving-bell, 1690

1994. Submarines. Multicoloured.

1396	150r. Type **269**	40	10
1397	200r. "Gimnote", 1886 (horiz)	50	10
1398	250r. "Peral" (Spain), 1888 (horiz)	65	10
1399	500r. "Nautilus" (first nuclear-powered submarine), 1954 (horiz)	1·25	20
1400	900r. "Trieste" (bathyscaphe), 1953 (horiz)	2·25	35

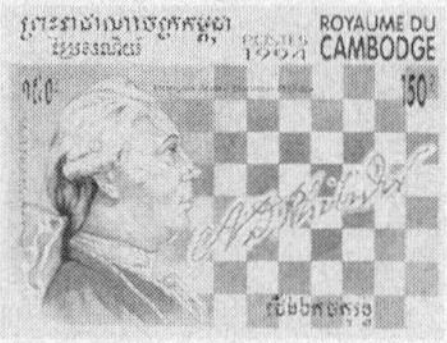

270 Francois-Andre Philidor, 1795

1994. Chess Champions. Multicoloured.

1402	150r. Type **270**	40	10
1403	200r. Mahe de la Bourdonnais, 1821 . . .	50	10
1404	250r. Karl Anderssen, 1851	65	10
1405	500r. Paul Morphy, 1858 . .	1·25	20
1406	900r. Wilhelm Steinitz, 1866	2·25	35

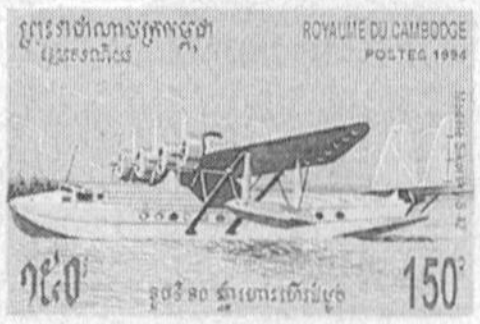

271 Sikorsky S-42 Flying Boat

1994. Aircraft. Multicoloured.

1408	150r. Type **271**	40	10
1409	200r. Vought-Sikorsky VS-300A helicopter prototype	50	10
1410	250r. Sikorsky S-37 biplane	65	10
1411	500r. Sikorsky S-35 biplane	1·25	20
1412	900r. Sikorsky S-43 amphibian	2·25	35

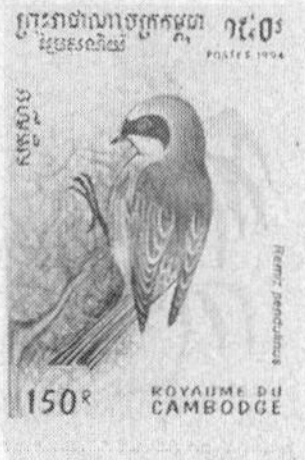

272

272 Penduline Tit

1994. Birds. Multicoloured.

1414	150r. Type **272**	40	10
1415	250r. Bearded reedling . . .	65	10
1416	400r. Little bunting	1·00	15
1417	700r. Cirl bunting	1·75	30
1418	1000r. Goldcrest	2·50	40

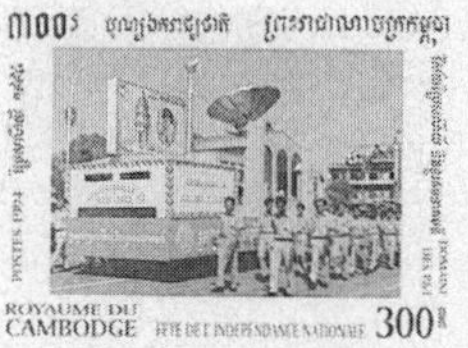

273 Postal Service Float

1994. National Independence Festival. Mult.

1420	300r. Type **273**	80	15
1421	500r. Soldiers marching . .	1·40	25
1422	700r. Women's army units on parade	2·00	35

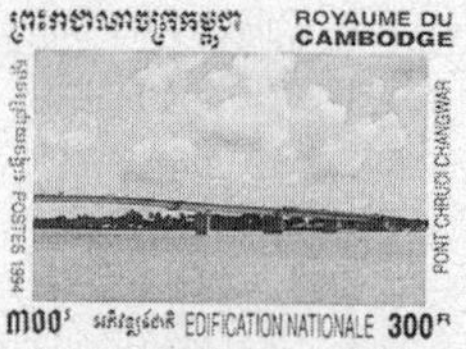

274 Chruoi Changwar Bridge

1994. National Development. Multicoloured.

1423	300r. Type **274**	80	15
1424	500r. Olympique Commercial Centre . . .	1·40	25
1425	700r. Sakyamony Chedei Temple	2·00	35

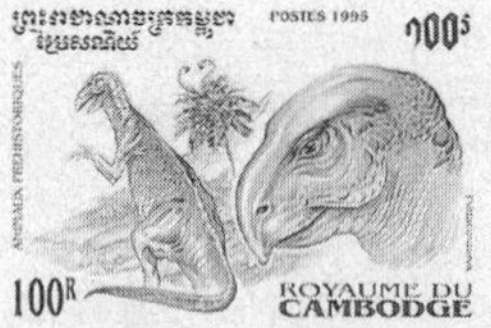

275 Psittacosaurus

1995. Prehistoric Animals. Multicoloured.

1426	100r. Type **275**	30	10
1427	200r. Protoceratops	90	10
1428	300r. Montanoceraptors . .	1·00	15
1429	400r. Centrosaurus	1·40	20
1430	700r. Styracosaurus	2·25	35
1431	800r. Triceratops	2·50	40

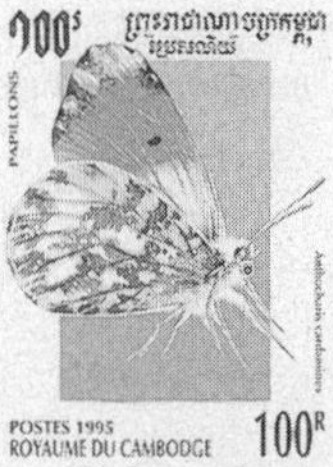

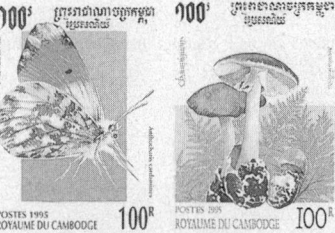

276 Orange-tip

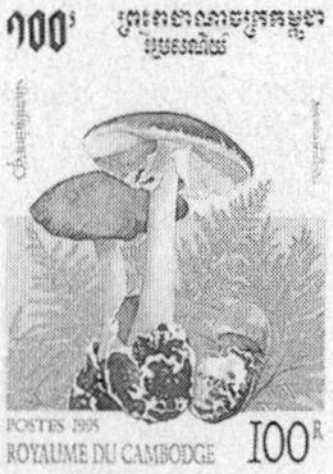

278 Death Cap

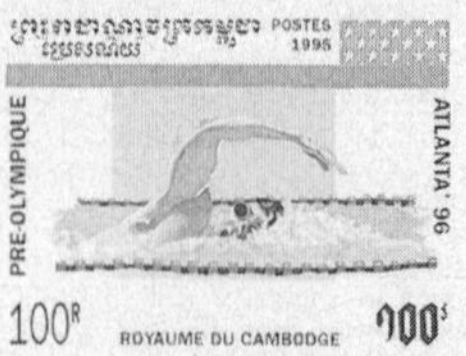

277 Swimming

1995. Butterflies. Multicoloured.

1432	100r. Type **276**	30	10
1433	200r. Scarce swallowtail . .	1·50	10
1434	300r. Dark green fritillary	2·00	15
1435	600r. Red admiral	2·50	30
1436	800r. Peacock	3·00	40

1995. Olympic Games, Atlanta (1996) (2nd issue). Multicoloured.

1437	100r. Type **277**	30	10
1438	200r. Callisthenics (vert) . .	1·50	10
1439	400r. Basketball (vert) . . .	2·00	20
1440	800r. Football (vert)	2·50	40
1441	1000r. Cycling (vert)	3·00	45

1995. Fungi. Multicoloured.

1443	100r. Type **278**	40	15
1444	200r. Chanterelle	75	20
1445	300r. Honey fungus	1·00	30
1446	600r. Field mushroom . . .	2·10	60
1447	800r. Fly agaric	3·00	80

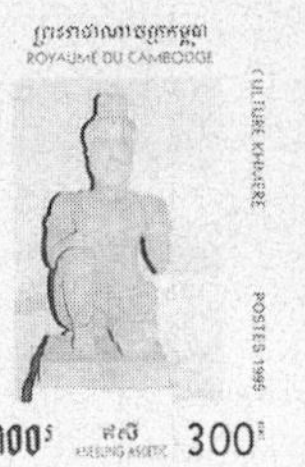
279 Kneeling Ascetic

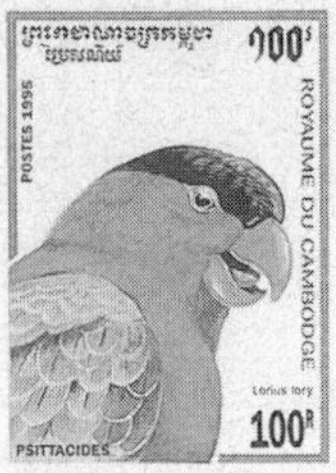
281 Black-capped Lory

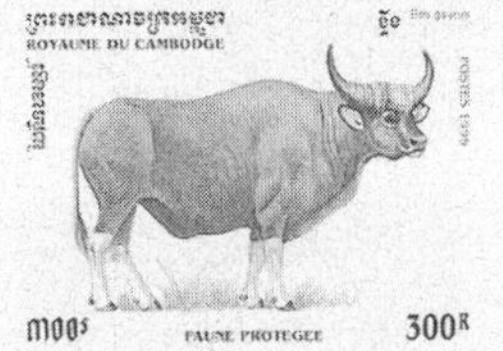
280 Gaur

1995. Khmer Culture. Statues. Multicoloured.

1448	300r. Type **279**	1·00	15
1449	500r. Parasurama	1·75	25
1450	700r. Shiva	3·00	35

1995. Protected Animals. Multicoloured.

1451	300r. Type **280**	80	15
1452	500r. Kouprey (vert)	1·75	25
1453	700r. Saurus crane (vert)	3·00	35

1995. Parrot Family. Multicoloured.

1454	100r. Type **281**	40	15
1455	200r. Princess parrot	80	15
1456	400r. Eclectus parrot	1·50	30
1457	800r. Scarlet macaw	3·00	65
1458	1000r. Budgerigar	3·50	70

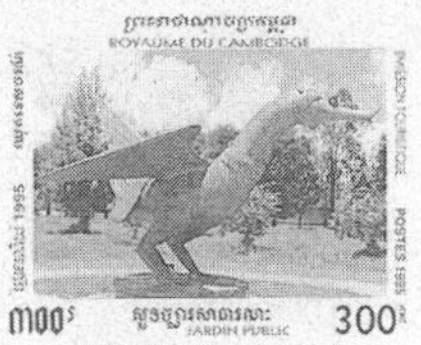
282 Bird (sculpture)

1995. Tourism. Public Gardens. Multicoloured.

1460	300r. Type **282**	80	15
1461	500r. Water feature	1·50	25
1462	700r. Mythical figures (sculpture)	2·75	35

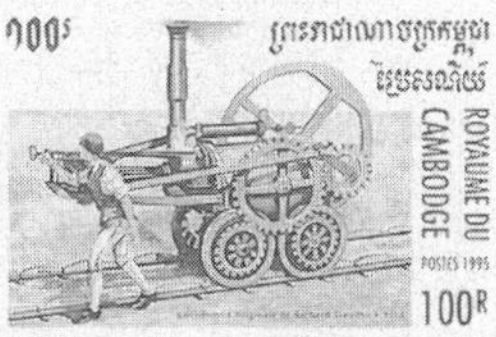
283 Richard Trevithick's Locomotive, 1804

1995. Steam Locomotives. Multicoloured.

1463	100r. Type **283**	30	25
1464	200r. G. and R. Stephenson's "Rocket", 1829	70	55
1465	300r. George Stephenson's "Locomotion", 1825	1·00	85
1466	600r. "Lafayette", 1837	2·00	1·75
1467	800r. "Best Friend of Charleston", 1830	2·40	2·25

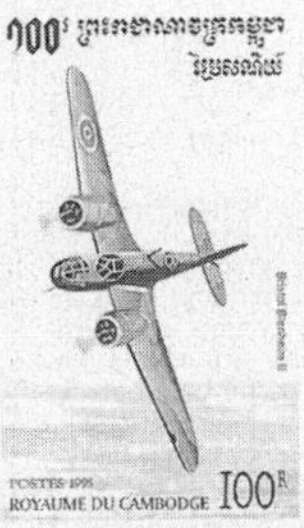
284 Bristol Type 142 Blenheim Mk II Bomber

1995. Second World War Planes. Multicoloured.

1469	100r. Type **284**	40	10
1470	200r. North American B-25B Mitchell bomber (horiz)	90	20
1471	300r. Avro Type 652 Anson Mk I general purpose plane (horiz)	1·25	30
1472	600r. Avro Manchester bomber (horiz)	2·00	55
1473	800r. Consolidated B-24 Liberator bomber (horiz)	2·50	70

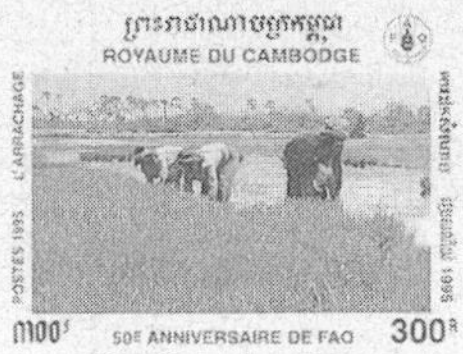
285 Gathering Crops

1995. 50th Anniv of F.A.O. Multicoloured.

1475	300r. Type **285**	1·00	30
1476	500r. Transplanting crops	1·75	50
1477	700r. Paddy field	2·75	80

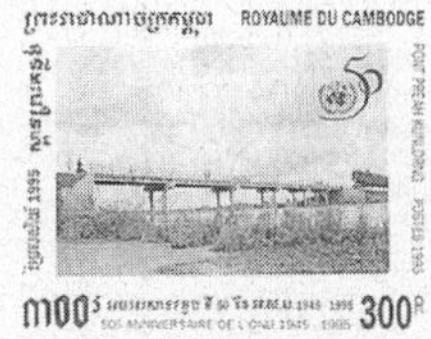
286 Bridge

1995. 50th Anniv of U.N.O. Preah Kunlorng Bridge. Multicoloured.

1478	300r. Type **286**	1·10	25
1479	500r. People on bridge	2·00	45
1480	700r. Closer view of bridge	2·50	60

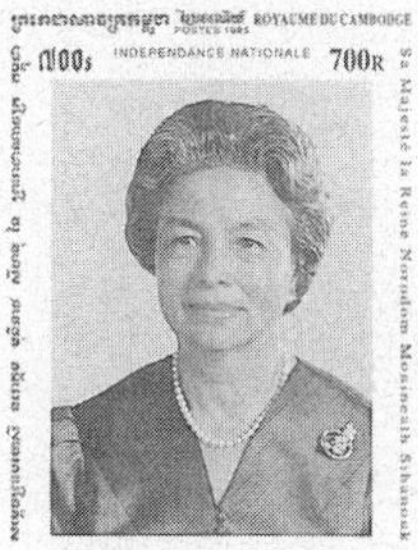
287 Queen Monineath

1995. National Independence. Multicoloured.

1481	700r. Type **287**	3·00	80
1482	800r. King Norodom Sihanouk	3·50	90

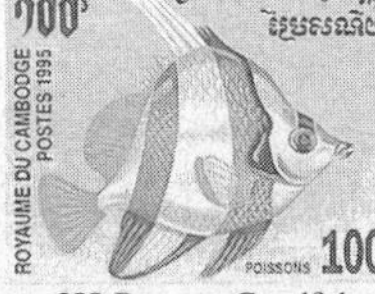
288 Pennant Coralfish

1995. Fishes. Multicoloured.

1483	100r. Type **288**	30	15
1484	200r. Copper-banded butterflyfish	70	25
1485	400r. Crown anemonefish	1·25	45
1486	800r. Palette surgeonfish	2·50	85
1487	1000r. Queen angelfish	3·00	1·10

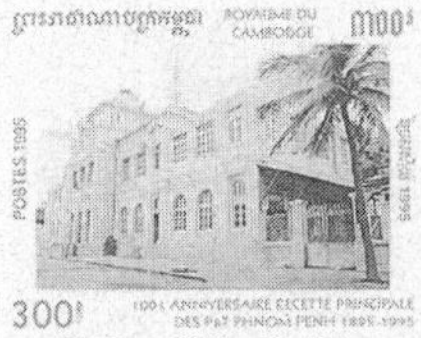
289 Post Office Building

1995. Cent of Head Post Office, Phnom Penh.

1489	**289**	300r. multicoloured	1·25	25
1490		500r. multicoloured	1·75	40
1491		700r. multicoloured	2·50	60

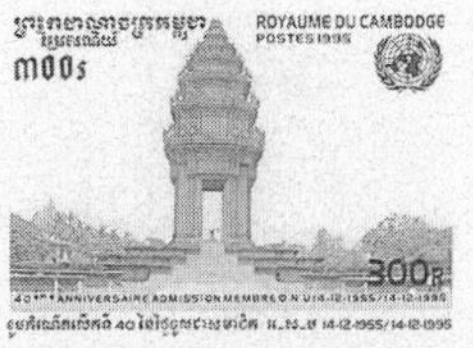
290 Independence Monument

1995. 40th Anniv of Admission of Cambodia to United Nations Organization. Multicoloured.

1492	300r. Type **290**	1·25	25
1493	400r. Angkor Wat	1·75	35
1494	800r. U.N. emblem and national flag (vert)	2·50	70

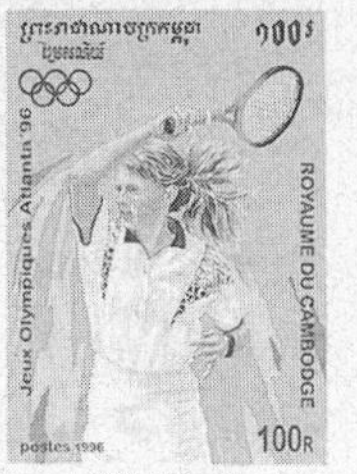
291 Tennis

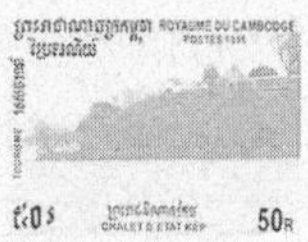
292 Kep State Chalet

1996. Olympic Games, Atlanta (3rd issue). Mult.

1495	100r. Type **291**	25	10
1496	200r. Volleyball	60	15
1497	300r. Football	1·00	20
1498	500r. Running	1·40	35
1499	900r. Baseball	2·40	70
1500	1000r. Basketball	2·50	75

1996.

1502	**292**	50r. blue and black	10	10
1503	–	100r. red and black	30	10
1504	–	200r. yellow and black	40	10
1505	–	500r. blue and black	1·00	20
1506	–	800r. mauve and black	1·40	35
1507	–	1000r. yellow and black	1·75	50
1508	–	1500r. green and black	3·00	75

DESIGNS—HORIZ: 100r. Power station; 200r. Wheelchair; 500r. Handicapped basketball team; 1000r. Kep beach; 1500r. Serpent Island. VERT: 800r. Man making crutches.

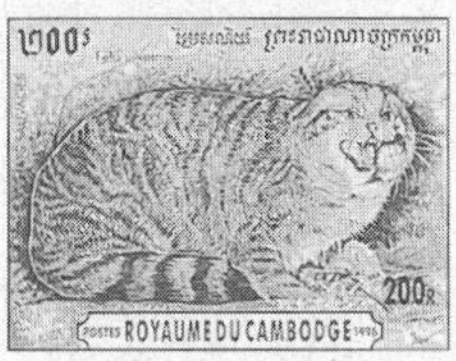
293 European Wild Cat

1996. Wild Cats. Multicoloured.

1509	100r. "Felis libyca" (vert)	40	10
1510	200r. Type **293**	75	15
1511	300r. Caracal	1·00	20
1512	500r. Geoffroy's cat	1·75	35
1513	900r. Black-footed cat	2·75	70
1514	1000r. Flat-headed cat	3·00	75

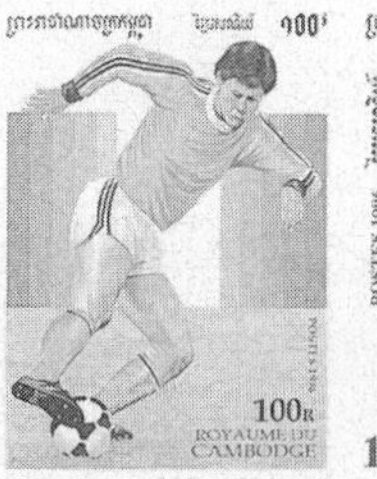
294 Player dribbling Ball

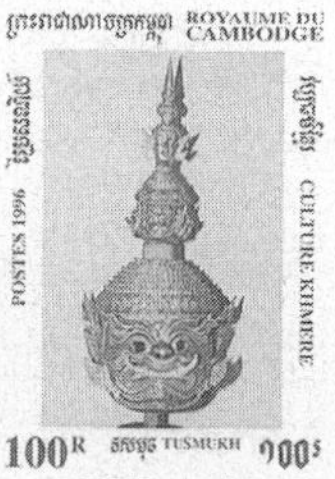
295 Tusmukh

1996. World Cup Football Championship, France (1998) (1st issue). Multicoloured.

1515	**294**	100r. multicoloured	55	10
1516	–	200r. multicoloured	75	15
1517	–	300r. multicoloured	1·10	20
1518	–	500r. multicoloured	1·75	35
1519	–	900r. multicoloured	3·00	70
1520	–	1000r. mult (horiz)	3·25	75

DESIGNS: 200r. to 1000r. Different players.

See also Nos. 1613/18 and 1726/31.

1996. Khmer Culture. Multicoloured.

1522	100r. Type **295**	30	10
1523	300r. Ream Iso	75	15
1524	900r. Isei	1·25	30

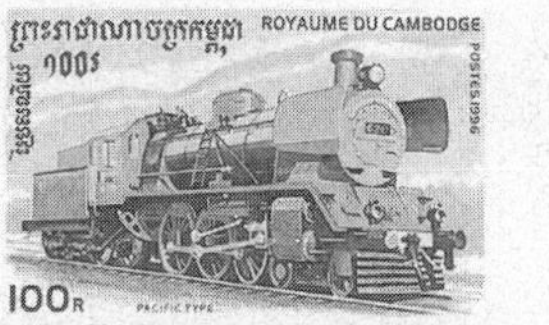
296 Pacific Steam Locomotive No. 620, Finland

1996. Railway Locomotives. Multicoloured.

1525	100r. Type **296**	20	10
1526	200r. GNR steam locomotive No. 261, Great Britain	25	15
1527	300r. Steam tank locomotive, 1930	65	20
1528	500r. Steam tank locomotive No. 1362, 1914	90	30
1529	900r. LMS Turbomotive No. 6202, 1930, Great Britain	1·25	40
1530	1000r. Locomotive "Snake", 1884, New Zealand	1·60	55

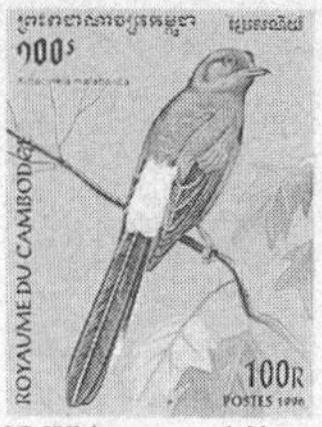
297 White-rumped Shama

1996. Birds. Multicoloured.

1532	100r. Type **297**	15	10
1533	200r. Pekin robin	20	10
1534	300r. Varied tit	50	15
1535	500r. Black-naped oriole	70	20
1536	900r. Japanese bush warbler	1·00	30
1537	1000r. Blue and white flycatcher	1·25	40

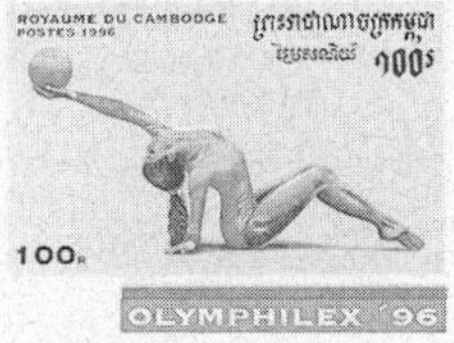
298 Rhythmic Gymnastics

1996. "Olymphilex '96" Olympic Stamps Exhibition, Atlanta, U.S.A. Multicoloured.

1538	100r. Type **298**	30	10
1539	200r. Judo	40	10
1540	300r. High jumping	75	15
1541	500r. Wrestling	1·00	20
1542	900r. Weightlifting	1·50	30
1543	1000r. Football	2·50	40

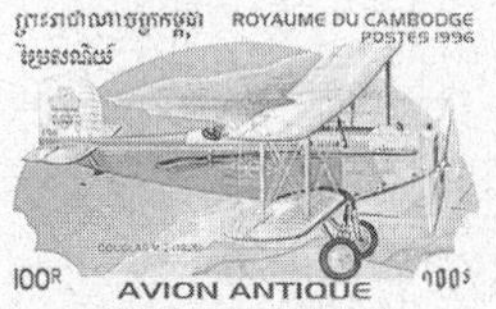
299 Douglas M-2, 1926

1996. Biplanes. Multicoloured.

1545	100r. Type **299**	30	10
1546	200r. Pitcairn PS-5 Mailwing, 1926	50	10
1547	300r. Boeing 40-B, 1928	75	15
1548	500r. Potez 25. 1925	1·50	20
1549	900r. Stearman C-3MB, 1927	2·25	30
1550	1000r. De Havilland D.H.4. 1918	2·75	40

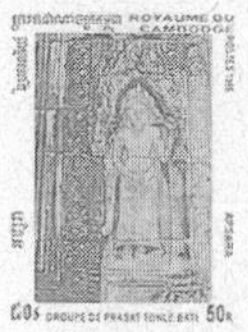
300 Aspara

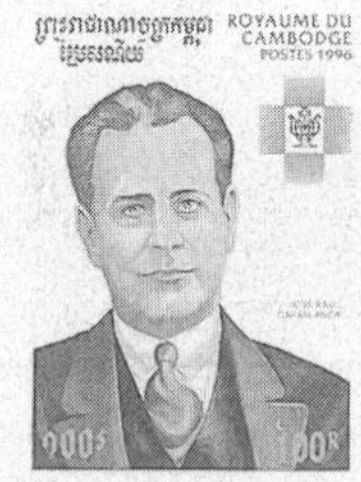
302 Jose Raul Capablanca (1921–27)

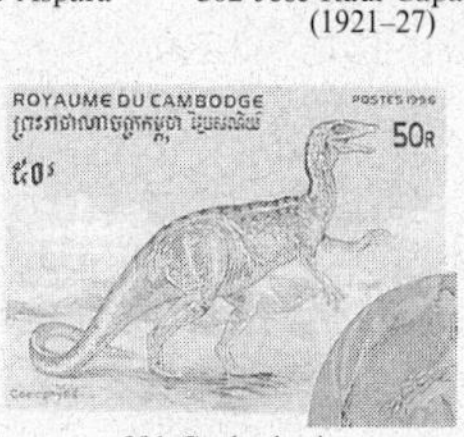
301 Coelophysis

1996. Tonle Bati Temple Ruins.

1552	**300**	50r. black and yellow	25	10
1553	–	100r. black and blue	35	10
1554	–	200r. black and brown	50	10
1555	–	500r. black and blue	1·50	20
1556	–	800r. black and green	1·75	25
1557	–	1000r. black and green	2·75	30
1558	–	1500r. black and bistre	3·00	35

DESIGNS—VERT: 100r. Aspara (different); 200r. Aspara (different); 800r. Taprum Temple; 1000r. Grandmother Peou Temple. HORIZ: 500r. Reliefs on wall; 1500r. Overall view of Tonle Bati.

1996. Prehistoric Animals. Multicoloured.

1559	50r. Type **301**	30	10
1560	100r. Euparkeria	40	10
1561	150r. Plateosaurus	50	10
1562	200r. Herrerasaurus	75	10
1563	250r. Dilophosaurus	1·00	10
1564	300r. Tuojiangosaurus	1·50	10
1565	350r. Camarasaurus	1·75	10
1566	400r. Ceratosaurus	2·00	10
1567	500r. Espinosaurio	2·25	15
1568	700r. Ouranosaurus	2·50	25
1569	800r. Avimimus	3·25	30
1570	1200r. Deinonychus	3·50	35

Nos. 1559/62, 1563/6 and 1567/70 respectively were

issued together, se-tenant, each sheetlet containing a composite design of a globe.

1996. World Chess Champions. Multicoloured.

1571	100r. Type **302**	15	10
1572	200r. Aleksandr Alekhine (1927–35, 1937–46)	20	10
1573	300r. Vasily Vasilevich Smyslov (1957–58)	50	15
1574	500r. Mikhail Nekhemyevich Tal (1960–61)	70	20
1575	900r. Robert Fischer (1972–75)	1·00	30
1576	1000r. Anatoly Karpov (1975–85)	1·25	40

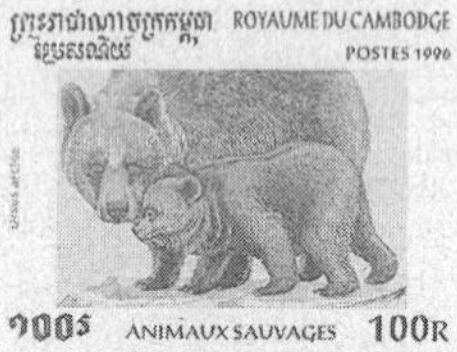

303 Brown Bear

1996. Mammals and their Young. Multicoloured.

1578	100r. Type **303**	15	10
1579	200r. Lion	20	10
1580	300r. Malayan tapir	75	15
1581	500r. Bactrian camel	1·00	20
1582	900r. Ibex (vert)	1·25	30
1583	1000r. Californian sealion (vert)	1·50	40

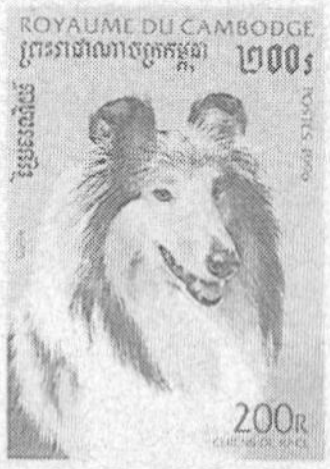

304 Rough Collie

1996. Dogs. Multicoloured.

1584	200r. Type **304**	35	10
1585	300r. Labrador retriever	75	15
1586	500r. Dobermann pinscher	1·00	20
1587	900r. German shepherd	1·50	30
1588	1000r. Boxer	1·75	40

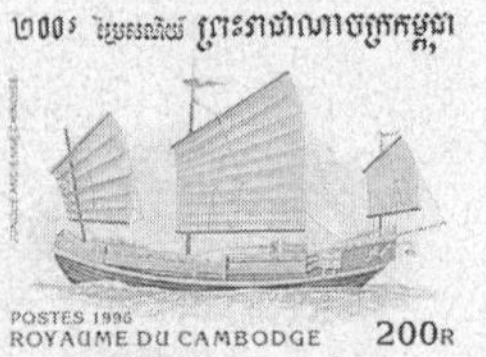

305 Chinese Junk

1996. Ships. Multicoloured.

1589	200r. Type **305**	50	15
1590	300r. Phoenician warship, 1500–1000 B.C.	75	20
1591	500r. Roman war galley, 264–241 B.C.	1·00	25
1592	900r. 19th-century full-rigged ship	1·25	35
1593	1000r. "Sirius" (paddle-steamer), 1838	1·50	45

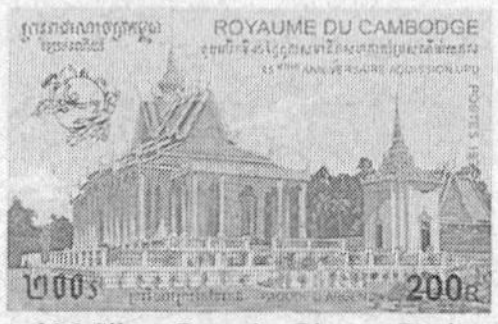

306 Silver Pagoda, Phnom Penh

1996. 45th Anniv of Cambodian Membership of Universal Postal Union.

1595	**306**	200r. multicoloured	50	10
1596		400r. multicoloured	1·00	15
1597		900r. multicoloured	2·00	30

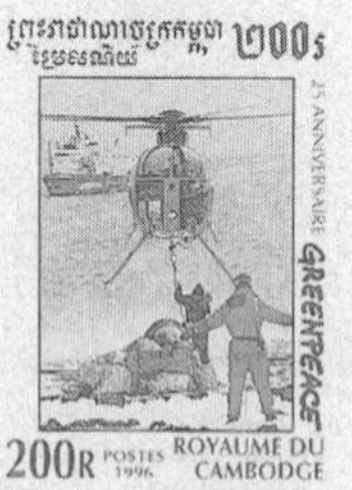

307 Environmental Vessel and Helicopter

1996. 25th Anniv of Greenpeace (environmental organization). Multicoloured.

1598	200r. Type **307**	70	10
1599	300r. Float-helicopter hovering over motor launch	2·00	15
1600	500r. Helicopter on deck and motor launches	2·50	20
1601	900r. Helicopter with two barrels suspended beneath	3·50	30

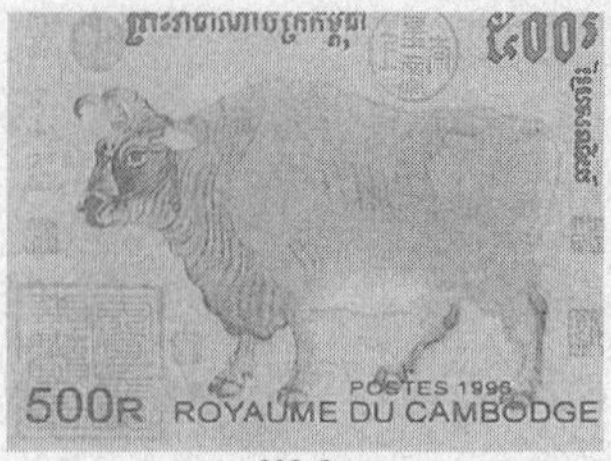

308 Ox

1996. New Year. Year of the Ox. Details of painting by Han Huang. Multicoloured.

1603	500r. Type **308**	80	20
1604	500r. Ox with head turned to right (upright horns)	80	20
1605	500r. Brown and white ox with head up ("handlebar" horns)	80	20
1606	500r. Ox with head in bush ("ram's" horns)	80	20

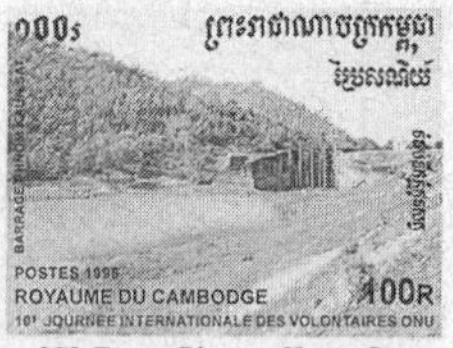

309 Dam, Phnom Kaun Sat

1996. 10th International United Nations Volunteers Day. Multicoloured.

1607	100r. Type **309**	35	10
1608	500r. Canal, O Angkrung	1·25	20
1609	900r. Canal, Chrey Krem	2·25	30

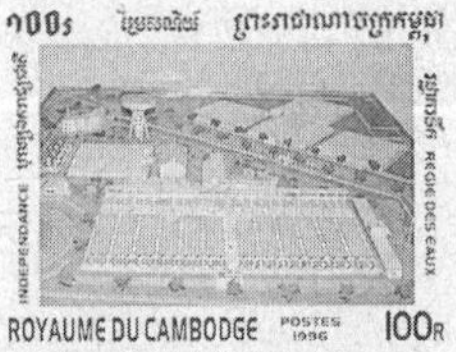

310 Architect's Model of Reservoir

1996. 43rd Anniv of Independence. Water Management. Multicoloured.

1610	100r. Type **310**	35	10
1611	500r. Reservoir	1·25	20
1612	900r. Reservoir (different)	2·25	30

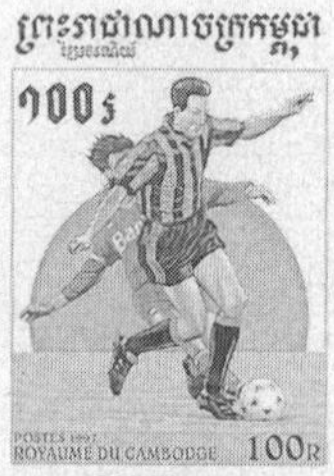

311 Players

1997. World Cup Football Championship, France (1998) (2nd issue).

1613	**311**	100r. multicoloured	50	10
1614	–	200r. multicoloured	75	10
1615	–	300r. multicoloured	1·00	10
1616	–	500r. multicoloured	1·40	10
1617	–	900r. multicoloured	2·50	20
1618	–	1000r. multicoloured	2·50	20

DESIGNS: 200r. to 1000r. Different footballing scenes.

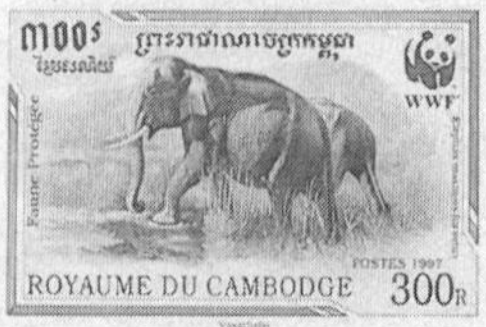

312 Two Elephants

1997. The Indian Elephant. Multicoloured.

1620	300r. Type **312**	30	10
1621	500r. Group of three	60	10
1622	900r. Elephants fighting	1·10	20
1623	1000r. Adult and calf	1·25	20

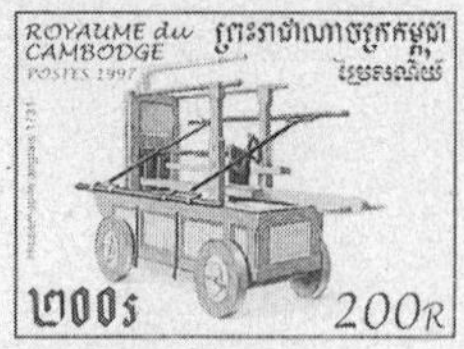

314 Horse-drawn Water Pump, 1731

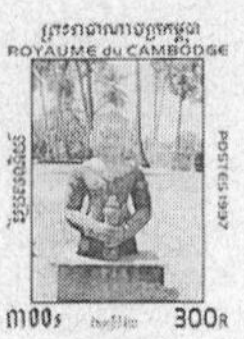

315 Statue on Plinth

1997. Fire Engines. Multicoloured.

1630	200r. Type **314**	15	10
1631	500r. Putnam horse-drawn water pump, 1863	35	10
1632	900r. Merryweather horse-drawn engine, 1894	60	20
1633	1000r. Shand Mason Co horse-drawn water pump, 1901	65	20
1634	1500r. Maxin Motor Co automatic pump, 1949	95	30
1635	4000r. Merryweather exhaust pump, 1950	3·25	90

1997. Angkor Wat.

1637	**315**	300r. black and red	20	10
1638	–	300r. black and blue	20	10
1639	–	800r. black and green	55	15
1640	–	1500r. black & brown	1·25	30
1641	–	1700r. black & orange	1·40	35
1642	–	2500r. black and blue	2·00	55
1643	–	3000r. black & green	2·50	75

DESIGNS—VERT: No. 1638, Statue in wall recess; 1639, Walled courtyard; 1640, Decorative panel with two figures. HORIZ: No. 1641, Rectangular gateway; 1642, Statues and arched gateway; 1643, Stupa and ruins.

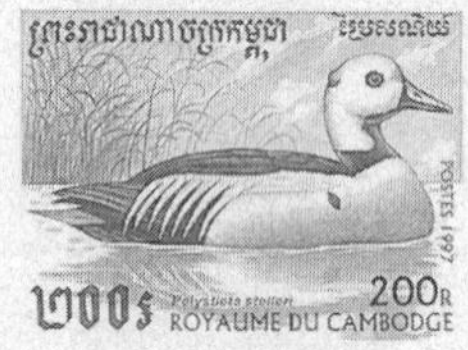

316 Steller's Eider

1997. Aquatic Birds. Multicoloured.

1644	200r. Type **316**	15	10
1645	500r. Egyptian goose	35	10
1646	900r. American wigeon	60	20
1647	1000r. Falcated teal	65	20
1648	1500r. Surf scoter	95	30
1649	4000r. Blue-winged teal	2·75	90

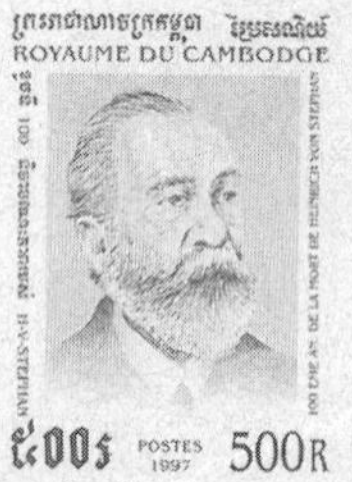

317 Von Stephan

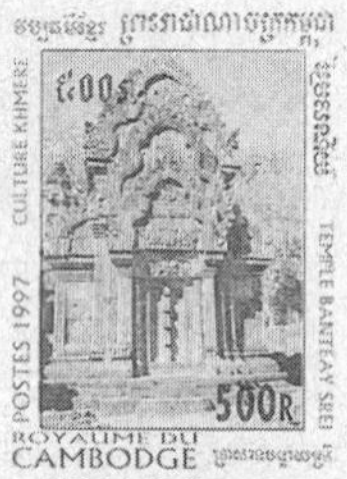

318 Main Entrance

1997. Death Centenary of Heinrich von Stephan (founder of U.P.U.).

1651	**317**	500r. blue & dp blue	35	10
1652		1500r. green and olive	1·25	30
1653		2000r. yellow & green	1·75	45

1997. Khmer Culture. Banteay Srei Temple. Multicoloured.

1654	500r. Type **318**	35	10
1655	1500r. Main and side entrances	1·25	30
1656	2000r. Courtyard	1·75	45

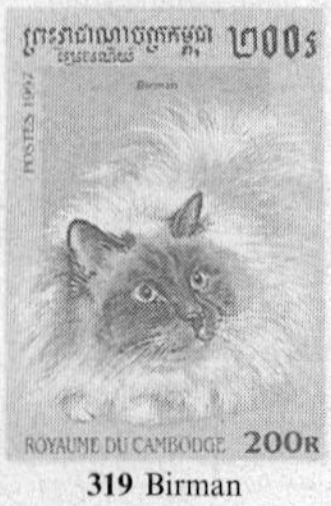

319 Birman

1997. Cats. Multicoloured.

1657	200r. Type **319**	15	10
1658	500r. Exotic shorthair	35	10
1659	900r. Persian	60	20
1660	1000r. Turkish van	65	20
1661	1500r. American shorthair	95	30
1662	4000r. Scottish fold	2·75	90

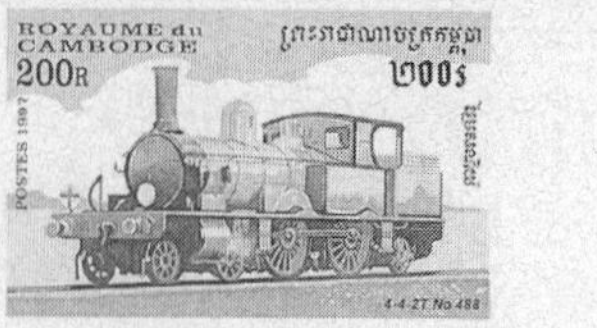

320 No. 488

1997. Steam Railway Locomotives. Multicoloured.

1664	200r. Type **320**	15	10
1665	500r. "Frederick Smith"	35	10
1666	900r. No. 3131	60	20
1667	1000r. London Transport No. L44, Great Britain	65	20
1668	1500r. LNER No. 1711, Great Britain	1·25	30
1669	4000r. No. 60523 "Chateau du Soleil"	3·25	90

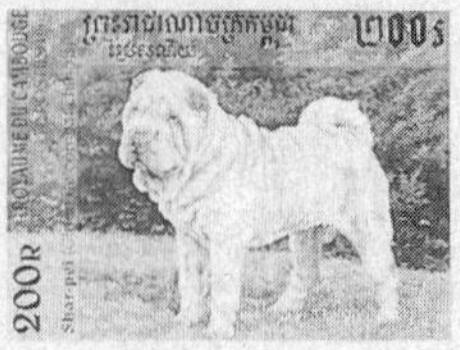

321 Shar-pei

1997. Dogs. Multicoloured.

1671	200r. Type **321**	15	10
1672	500r. Chin-chin	35	10
1673	900r. Pekingese	60	20
1674	1000r. Chow-chow (vert)	65	20
1675	1500r. Pug (vert)	1·25	30
1676	4000r. Akita (vert)	3·25	90

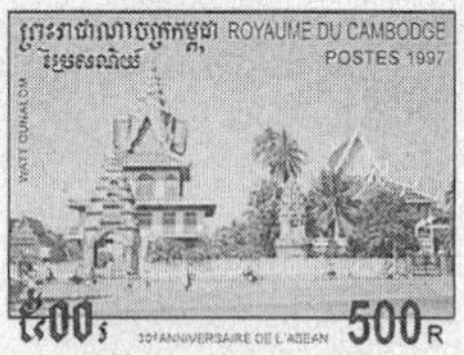

322 Qunalom Temple

1997. 30th Anniv of Association of South East Asian Nations. Multicoloured.

1678	500r. Type **322**	35	10
1679	1500r. Royal Palace	1·25	30
1680	2000r. National Museum	1·75	45

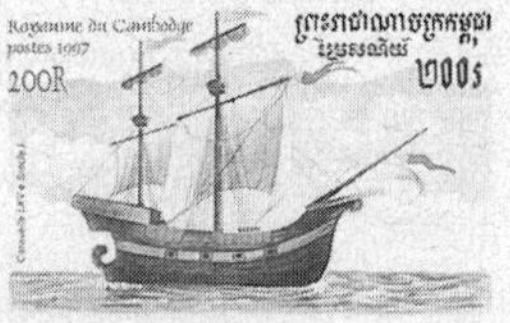

323 15th-century Caravelle

1997. Sailing Ships. Multicoloured.

1681	200r. Type **323**	20	10
1682	500r. Spanish galleon	50	15
1683	900r. "Great Harry" (British galleon)	90	25
1684	1000r. "La Couronne" (French galleon)	1·00	25
1685	1500r. 18th-century East Indiaman	1·40	35
1686	4000r. 19th-century clipper	4·25	1·00

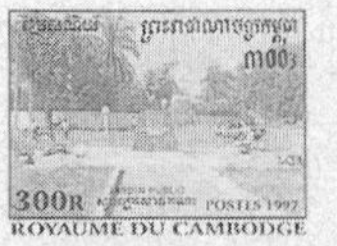

324 Public Garden

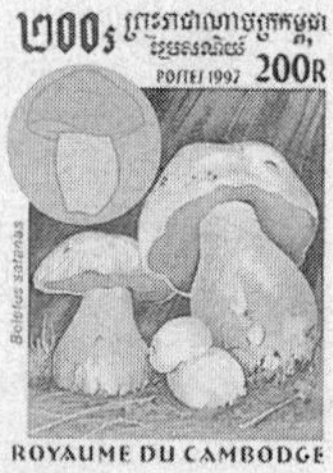

325 Satan's Mushroom

1997. Public Gardens (Nos. 1688/91) and Tuk Chha Canal (others).

1688	**324**	300r. green and black	20	10
1689	–	300r. red and black	20	10
1690	–	800r. yellow and black	55	15
1691	–	1500r. orange and black	95	30
1692	–	1700r. pink and black	1·10	35
1693	–	2500r. blue and black	1·75	55
1694	–	3000r. blue and black	2·25	75

DESIGNS—HORIZ: 300r. Statue at intersection of paths; 300r. Hedging in triangular bed; 1500r. Tree and statue of lion; 1700r. View along canal; 2500r. View across canal; 3000r. Closed lock gates. VERT: 800r. Mounted bowl.

1997. Fungi. Multicoloured.

1695	200r. Type **325**	15	10
1696	500r. "Amanita regalis"	35	10
1697	900r. "Morchella semilibera"	60	20
1698	1000r. "Gomphus clavatus"	65	20
1699	1500r. "Hygrophorus hypothejus"	2·25	75
1700	4000r. "Albatrellus confluens"	2·75	90

326 Peaceful Fightingfish ("Betta imbellis") and Siamese Fightingfish ("Betta splendens")

1997. Fishes. Multicoloured.
1702	200r.	Type 326	15	10
1703	500r.	Banded gourami	35	10
1704	900r.	Rosy barbs	60	20
1705	1000r.	Paradise fish	65	20
1706	1500r.	"Epalzeorhynchos frenatus"	2·25	75
1707	4000r.	"Capoeta tetrazona"	2·75	90

327 Kampot Post Office

1997. 44th Anniv of Independence. Multicoloured.
1709	1000r.	Type 327	65	20
1710	3000r.	Prey Veng Post Office	2·25	75

328 "Orchis militaris" 329 In black Jacket

1997. Orchids. Multicoloured.
1711	200r.	Type 328	15	10
1712	500r.	"Orchiaceras bivonae"	35	10
1713	900r.	"Orchiaceras spuria"	60	20
1714	1000r.	"Gymnadenia conopsea"	65	20
1715	1500r.	"Serapias neglecta"	2·25	30
1716	4000r.	"Pseudorhiza bruniana"	2·75	90

1997. Diana, Princess of Wales Commemoration. Multicoloured.
1718	100r.	Type 329	10	10
1719	200r.	In black dress	15	10
1720	300r.	In blue jacket	15	10
1721	500r.	Close-up of Princess in visor	35	10
1722	1000r.	In mine-protection clothing	65	20
1723	1500r.	With Elizabeth Dole	95	30
1724	2000r.	Holding landmine	1·75	60
1725	2500r.	With Mother Teresa and Sisters of Charity	2·10	70

330 Player with Ball 331 Suorprat Gateway

1998. World Cup Football Championship, France (3rd issue).
1726	330	200r. multicoloured	10	10
1727	–	500r. multicoloured	35	10
1728	–	900r. multicoloured	60	20
1729	–	1000r. multicoloured	65	20
1730	–	1500r. multicoloured	95	30
1731	–	4000r. multicoloured	2·75	90

DESIGNS: 500r. to 4000r. Different footballing scenes.

1998. Temple Ruins.
1733	331	300r. orange and black	15	10
1734	–	500r. pink and black	25	10
1735	–	1200r. orange and black	70	20
1736	–	1500r. orange and black	95	30
1737	–	1700r. blue and black	1·00	40
1738	–	2000r. green and black	1·25	40
1739	–	3000r. lilac and black	2·10	70

DESIGNS—HORIZ: No. 1734, Kumlung wall; 1735, Bapuon entrance; 1737, Prerup; 1738, Preah Khan. VERT: No. 1736, Palilai; 1739, Bayon.

332 Tiger Cub 334 Rottweiler

333 Oakland, Antioch and Eastern Electric Locomotive No. 105

1998. New Year. Year of the Tiger. Multicoloured.
1740	200r.	Type 332	10	10
1741	500r.	Tiger and cubs	35	15
1742	990r.	Tiger on alert	60	20
1743	1000r.	Tiger washing itself (horiz)	65	20
1744	1500r.	Tiger lying in grass (horiz)	95	30
1745	4000r.	Tiger snarling (horiz)	2·75	90

1998. Railway Locomotives. Multicoloured.
1747	200r.	Type 333	10	10
1748	500r.	New York, Westchester and electric locomotive No. 1	35	15
1749	900r.	Spokane and Inland electric locomotive No. MII	60	20
1750	1000r.	International Railway electric locomotive	65	20
1751	1500r.	British Columbia Electric Railway locomotive No. 823	90	30
1752	4000r.	Southern Pacific electric locomotive No. 200	2·75	90

1998. Dogs. Multicoloured.
1754	200r.	Type 334	10	10
1755	500r.	Beauceron	35	15
1756	900r.	Boxer	60	20
1757	1000r.	Siberian husky	65	20
1758	1500r.	Welsh Pembroke corgi	90	30
1759	4000r.	Basset hound	2·75	90

335 Stag Beetle

1998. Beetles. Multicoloured.
1761	200r.	Type 335	10	10
1762	500r.	"Carabus auronitens" (ground beetle)	35	15
1763	900r.	Alpine longhorn beetle	60	20
1764	1000r.	"Geotrupes" (dor beetle)	65	20
1765	1500r.	"Megasoma elephas"	90	30
1766	4000r.	"Chalcosoma"	2·75	90

336 Prerup Temple

1998. Khmer Culture. Multicoloured.
1768	500r.	Type 336	30	10
1769	1500r.	Bayon Temple	90	30
1770	2000r.	Angkor Vat	1·40	45

337 Cutter

1998. Ships. Multicoloured.
1771	200r.	Type 337	10	10
1772	500r.	"Britannia" (mail paddle-steamer, 1840)	35	10
1773	900r.	Viking longship, Gokstad	60	20
1774	1000r.	"Great Britain" (steam/sail)	65	20
1775	1500r.	Medieval coasting nau	90	30
1776	4000r.	Full-rigged ship (inscr "Fregate")	2·75	90

338 Scottish Fold

1998. Domestic Cats. Multicoloured.
1778	200r.	Type 338	10	10
1779	500r.	Ragdoll	35	10
1780	900r.	Cymric	60	20
1781	1000r.	Devon rex	65	20
1782	1500r.	American curl	90	30
1783	4000r.	Sphinx	2·75	90

339 "Petasites japonica"

1998. Flowers. Multicoloured.
1785	200r.	Type 339	10	10
1786	500r.	"Gentiana triflora"	35	10
1787	900r.	"Doronicum cordatum"	60	20
1788	1000r.	"Scabiosa japonica"	65	20
1789	1500r.	"Magnolia sieboldii"	90	30
1790	4000r.	"Erythronium japonica"	2·75	90

340 "Baptism of Christ" (Gerard David)

1998. "Italia 98" International Stamp Exhibition, Milan. Paintings. Multicoloured.
1792	200r.	Type 340	10	10
1793	500r.	"Madonna of Martin van Niuwenhoven" (Hans Memling)	35	10
1794	900r.	"Baptism of Christ" (Hendrich Holtzius)	60	20
1795	1000r.	"Christ with the Cross" (Luis de Morales)	65	20
1796	1500r.	"Elias in the Desert" (Dirk Bouts)	90	30
1797	4000r.	"The Virgin" (Petrus Christus)	2·75	90

There are errors of spelling in some of the inscriptions.

341 "Phyciodes tharos"

1998. Butterflies. Multicoloured.
1799	200r.	Type 341	10	10
1800	500r.	"Pararge megera"	35	10
1801	900r.	Monarch	60	20
1802	1000r.	Apollo	65	20
1803	1500r.	Swallowtail	90	30
1804	4000r.	"Eumenis semele"	2·75	90

342 Post Box, 1997

1998. World Post Day. Multicoloured.
1806	1000r.	Type 342	65	20
1807	3000r.	Wall-mounted post box, 1951	2·00	65

343 Big-Headed Turtle

1998. Tortoise and Turtles. Multicoloured.
1808	200r.	Type 343	10	10
1809	500r.	Green turtle	35	10
1810	900r.	American soft-shelled turtle	60	20
1811	1000r.	Hawksbill turtle	65	20
1812	1500r.	Aldabra tortoise	90	30
1813	4000r.	Leatherback sea turtle	2·75	90

344 Bayon Dance

1998. 45th Anniv of Independence. Multicoloured.
1815	500r.	Type 344	35	10
1816	1500r.	Bayon dance (different)	90	30
1817	2000r.	Bayon dance (different)	1·25	40

345 Cheetah

1998. Big Cats. Multicoloured.
1818	200r.	Type 345	10	10
1819	500r.	Snow leopard	35	10
1820	900r.	Ocelot	60	30
1821	1000r.	Leopard	65	20
1822	1500r.	Serval	90	30
1823	4000r.	Jaguar	2·75	90

346 Rabbit

1999. New Year. Year of the Rabbit. Multicoloured. Showing rabbits.
1825	200r.	Type 346	10	10
1826	500r.	Facing left	35	10
1827	900r.	Sitting in bush	60	30
1828	1000r.	Sitting on rock	65	30
1829	1500r.	Sitting upright	90	30
1830	4000r.	Head looking out from grass (vert)	2·75	90

347 Foster and Rastik's "Stourbridge Lion", 1829, U.S.A.

1999. Steam Railway Locomotives. Multicoloured.
1832	200r.	Type 347	10	10
1833	500r.	"Atlantic", 1832	30	10
1834	900r.	No. O35, 1934	60	20
1835	1000r.	Daniel Gooch's "Iron Duke", 1847, Great Britain	65	20
1836	1500r.	"4-6-0"	90	30
1837	4000r.	"4-4-2"	2·75	90

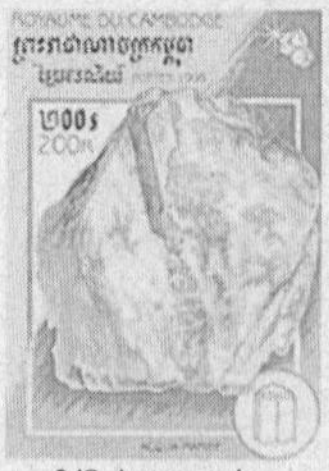

348 Aquamarine

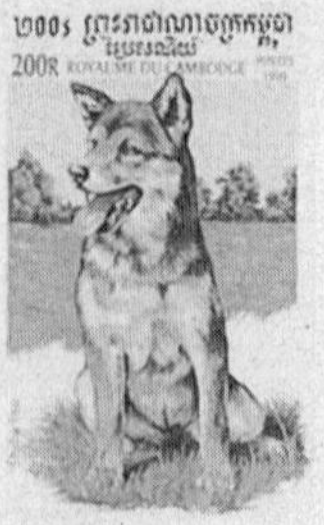

349 Alsatian

1999. Minerals. Multicoloured.

1839	200r. Type **348**	10	10
1840	500r. Cat's eye	30	10
1841	900r. Malachite	60	20
1842	1000r. Emerald	65	20
1843	1500r. Turquoise	90	30
1844	4000r. Ruby	2·75	90

1999. Dogs. Multicoloured.

1846	200r. Type **349**	10	10
1847	500r. Shih tzu (horiz)	30	10
1848	900r. Tibetan spaniel (horiz)	60	20
1849	1000r. Ainu-ken	65	20
1850	1500r. Lhassa apso (horiz)	90	30
1851	4000r. Tibetan terrier (horiz)	2·75	90

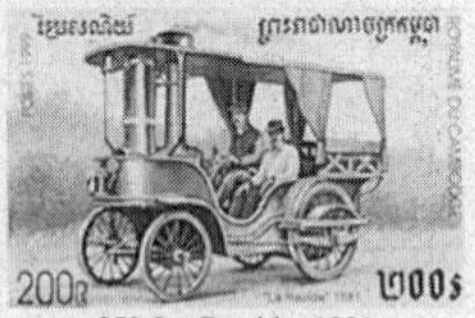

350 La Rapide, 1881

1999. Cars. Multicoloured.

1853	200r. Type **350**	10	10
1854	500r. Car designed by Frank Duryea, 1895	30	10
1855	900r. Car designed by Marius Barbarou, 1898	60	20
1856	1000r. Panhard, 1898	65	20
1857	1500r. Mercedes-Benz "Tonneau", 1901	90	30
1858	4000r. Ford, 1915	2·75	90

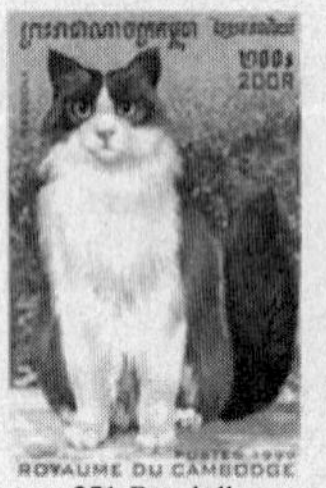

351 Ragdoll

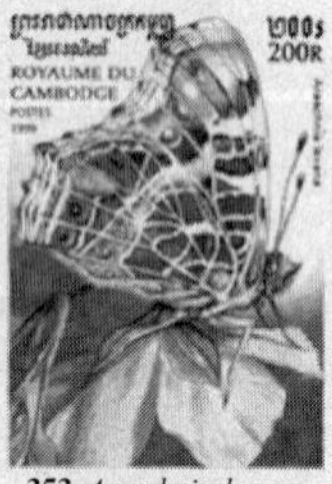

353 *Araschnia levana*

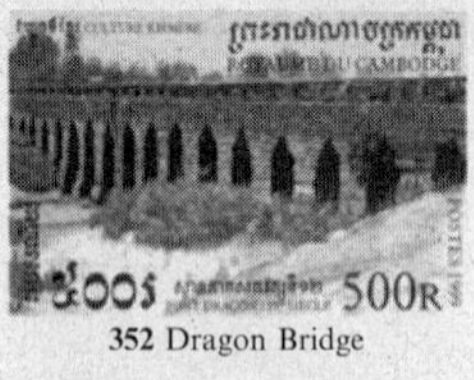

352 Dragon Bridge

1999. Cats. Multicoloured.

1860	200r. Type **351**	10	10
1861	500r. Russian blue	20	10
1862	900r. Bombay	50	15
1863	1000r. Siamese	50	15
1864	1500r. Oriental shorthair	80	25
1865	4000r. Somali	2·60	85

1999. Khmer Culture. Multicoloured.

1867	500r. Type **352**	20	10
1868	1500r. Temple of 100 Columns, Kratie	80	25
1869	2000r. Krapum Chhouk, Kratie	1·25	40

1999. Butterflies. Multicoloured.

1870	200r. Type **353**	10	10
1871	500r. Painted lady (horiz)	20	10
1872	900r. *Clossiana euphrosyne*	50	15
1873	1000r. *Coenonympha hero*	50	15
1874	1500r. Apollo (horiz)	80	25
1875	4000r. *Plebejus argus*	2·60	85

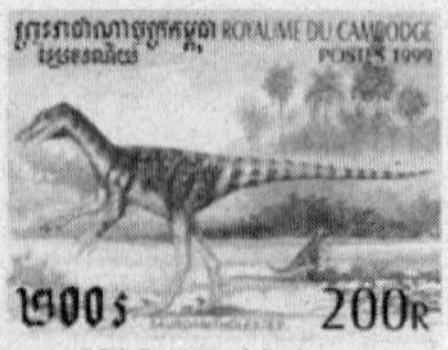

354 Saurornitholestes

1999. Prehistoric Animals. Multicoloured.

1877	200r. Type **354**	10	10
1878	500r. Prenocephale	20	10
1879	900r. Wuerhosaurus	50	15
1880	1000r. Muttaburrasaurus	50	15
1881	1500r. Shantungosaurus	80	25
1882	4000r. Microceratops	2·60	85

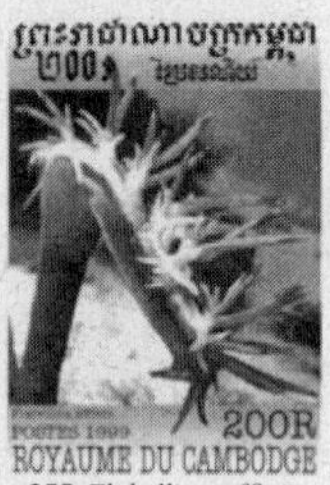

355 *Flabellina affinis*

1999. Molluscs. Multicoloured.

1884	200r. Type **355**	10	10
1885	500r. *Octopus macropus*	20	10
1886	900r. *Helix hortensis*	50	15
1887	1000r. *Lima hians*	50	15
1888	1500r. *Arion empiricorum*	80	25
1889	4000r. Swan mussel	2·60	85

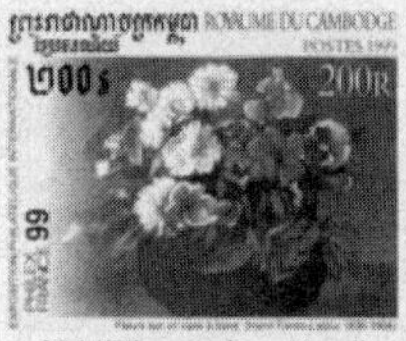

356 "Flowers in a Vase" (Henri Fantin-Latour)

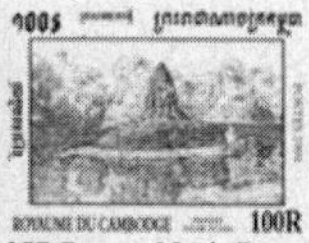

357 Prasat Neak Poan

1999. "Philexfrance 99" International Stamp Exhibition, Paris. Paintings. Multicoloured.

1891	200r. Type **356**	10	10
1892	500r. "Fruit" (Paul Cezanne)	20	10
1893	900r. "Table and Chairs" (Andre Derain)	50	15
1894	1000r. "Vase on a Table" (Henri Matisse)	50	15
1895	1500r. "Tulips and Marquerites" (Othon Friesz)	80	25
1896	4000r. "Still Life with Tapestry" (Matisse)	2·60	85

1999. Temples.

1898	**357**	100r. blue and black	10	10
1899	–	300r. red and black	10	10
1900	–	500r. grn & blk (vert)	20	10
1901	–	1400r. green and black	75	25
1902	–	1600r. mauve and black	80	25
1903	–	1800r. vio & blk (vert)	1·10	35
1904	–	1900r. brown and black	1·25	40

DESIGNS: 300r. Statue, Neak Poan; 500r. Banteay Srey; 1400r. Banteay Samre; 1600r. Banteay Srey; 1800r. Bas-relief, Angkor Vat; 1900r. Brasat Takeo.

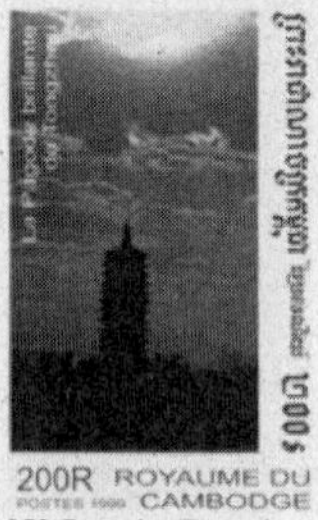

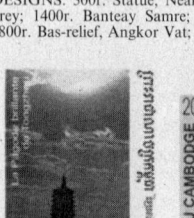

358 Pagoda, Tongzhou

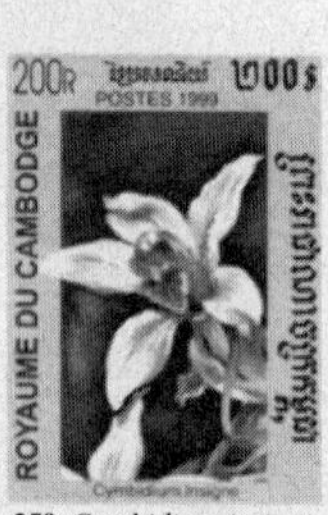

359 *Cymbidium insigne*

1999. "China 1999" International Stamp Exhibition, Peking. Multicoloured.

1905	200r. Type **358**	10	10
1906	500r. Pagoda, Tianning Temple	20	10
1907	900r. Pagoda, Summer Palace	50	15
1908	900r. Pagoda, Blue Cloud Temple	50	15
1909	1000r. White pagoda, Bei Hai	50	15
1910	1000r. Pagoda, Scented Hill	50	15
1911	1500r. Pagoda, Yunju Temple	85	25
1912	4000r. White pagoda, Miaoying Temple	2·60	85

1999. Orchids. Multicoloured.

1913	200r. Type **359**	10	10
1914	500r. *Papilionanthe teres*	20	10
1915	900r. *Panisea uniflora*	50	15
1916	1000r. *Euanthe sanderiana*	50	15
1917	1500r. *Dendrobium trigonopus*	80	25
1918	4000r. *Vanda coerulea*	2·60	85

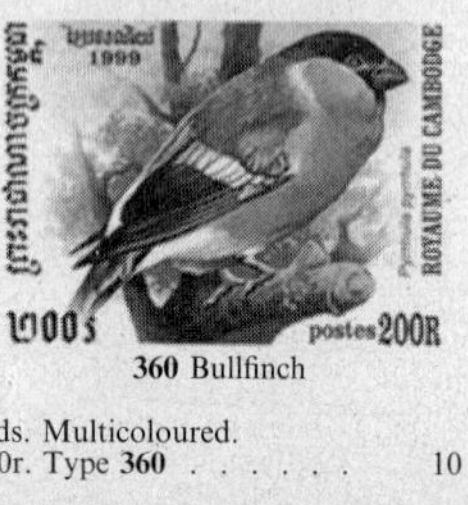

360 Bullfinch

1999. Birds. Multicoloured.

1920	200r. Type **360**	10	10
1921	500r. Hawfinch	20	10
1922	900r. Greenfinch	50	15
1923	1000r. Yellow warbler	50	15
1924	1500r. Great grey shrike	85	25
1925	4000r. Blue tit	2·60	85

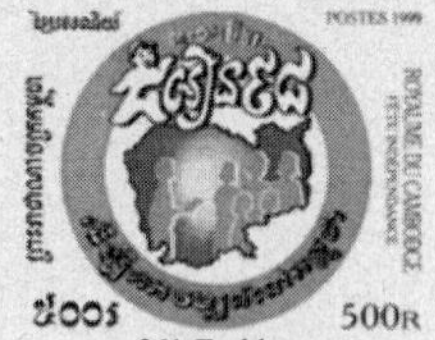

361 Emblem

1999. 46th Anniv of Independence. Multicoloured.

1927	500r. Type **361**	20	10
1928	1500r. People with symbols of transport and industry	85	25
1929	2000r. People queueing to vote	1·25	40

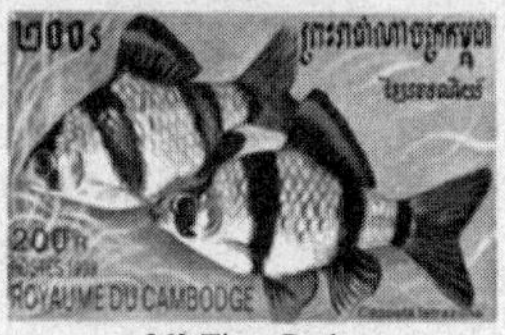

362 Tiger Barbs

1999. Fishes. Multicoloured.

1930	200r. Type **362**	10	10
1931	500r. Rainbow shark minnow	20	10
1932	900r. Clown rasbora	50	15
1933	1000r. Orange-spotted cichlid	50	15
1934	1500r. Crescent betta	85	25
1935	4000r. Honey gourami	2·60	85

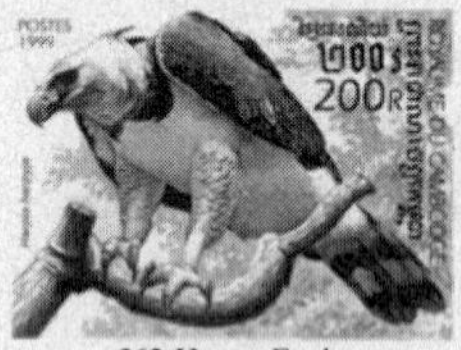

363 Harpy Eagle

1999. Birds of Prey. Multicoloured.

1937	200r. Type **363**	10	10
1938	500r. Bateleur (vert)	20	10
1939	900r. Egyptian vulture (vert)	50	15
1940	1000r. Peregrine falcon (vert)	50	15
1941	1500r. Red-tailed hawk (vert)	85	25
1942	4000r. American bald eagle	2·60	85

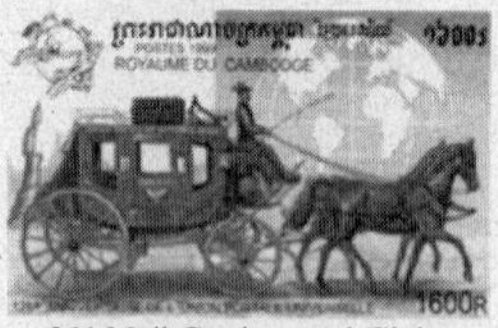

364 Mail Carriage and Globe

1999. 125th Anniv of Universal Postal Union.

1944	**364**	1600r. multicoloured	90	30

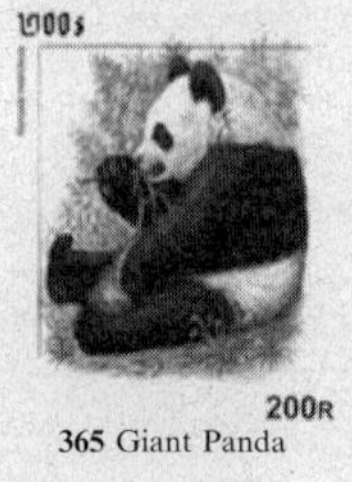

365 Giant Panda

1999. Mammals. Multicoloured.

1945	200r. Type **365**	10	10
1946	500r. Yak	20	10
1947	900r. Chinese water deer	50	10
1948	1000r. Eurasian water shrew (horiz)	50	10
1949	1500r. European otter (horiz)	85	25
1950	4000r. Tiger (horiz)	2·60	85

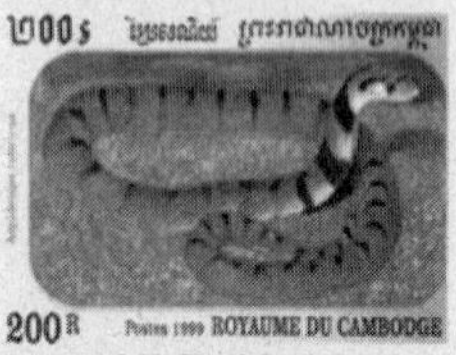

366 Coral Snake

1999. Snakes. Multicoloured.

1952	200r. Type **366**	10	10
1953	500r. Rainbow boa	20	10
1954	900r. Yellow anaconda	50	10
1955	1000r. Southern ring-necked snake	50	10
1956	1500r. Harlequin snake	85	25
1957	4000r. Eastern tiger snake	2·60	85

EXPRESS MAIL STAMPS

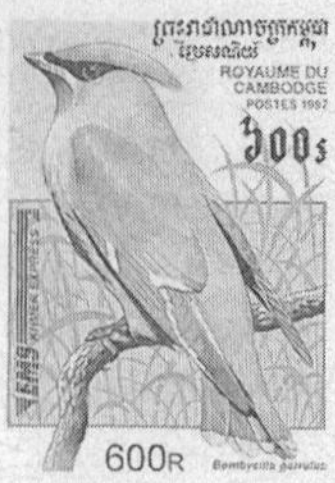

E 313 Bohemian Waxwing

1997. Birds. Multicoloured.

E1624	600r. Type E **313**	1·00	30
E1625	900r. Great grey shrike	1·40	45
E1626	1000r. Tree sparrow	1·75	55
E1627	2000r. Redstart	3·50	1·10
E1628	2500r. Reed bunting	4·50	1·50
E1629	3000r. Ortolan bunting	5·25	1·75

POSTAGE DUE STAMPS

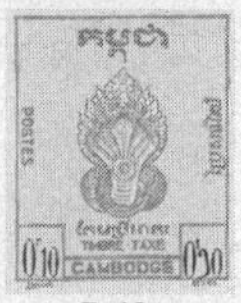

D 13

1957.

D81	D **13**	10c. red, blue & black	20	20
D82		50c. red, blue & black	40	40
D83		1r. red, blue & black	55	55
D84		3r. red, blue & black	70	70
D85		5r. red, blue & black	1·40	1·40

CAMEROON Pt. 1

12 pence = 1 shilling;
20 shillings = 1 pound.

Former German colony occupied by British and French troops during 1914–16. The territory was divided between them and the two areas were administered under League of Nations mandates from 1922, converted into United Nations trusteeships in 1946.

The British section was administered as part of Nigeria until 1960, when a plebiscite was held. The northern area voted to join Nigeria and the southern part joined the newly-independent Cameroun Republic (formerly the French trust territory). In November 1995 this republic joined the Commonwealth.

I. CAMEROONS EXPEDITIONARY FORCE

1915. "Yacht" key-types of German Kamerun surch **C.E.F.** and value in English currency.

B 1	N	½d. on 3pf. brown	13·00	29·00
B 2		½d. on 5pf. green	2·75	9·00
B 3		1d. on 10pf. red	1·25	9·50
B 4		2d. on 20pf. blue	3·50	19·00
B 5		2½d. on 25pf. black and red on yellow	12·00	42·00
B 6		3d. on 30pf. black and orange on buff	12·00	42·00
B 7		4d. on 40pf. black and red	12·00	42·00
B 8		6d. on 50pf. black and purple on buff	12·00	42·00
B 9		8d. on 80pf. black and red on rose	12·00	42·00
B10	O	1s. on 1m. red	£150	£600
B11		2s. on 2m. blue	£150	£600
B12		3s. on 3m. black	£150	£600
B13		5s. on 5m. red and black	£190	£650

II. CAMEROONS TRUST TERRITORY

Issue used in the British trusteeship from October 1960 until June 1961 in the northern area and until September 1961 in the southern area, when they joined with Nigeria and the Cameroun Republic respectively.

1960. Stamps of Nigeria of 1953 optd **CAMEROONS U.K.T.T.**

T1	**18**	½d. black and orange	10	1·25
T2	–	1d. black and green	10	70
T3	–	1½d. green	10	20
T4c	–	2d. grey	10	40
T5	–	3d. black and lilac	15	10
T6	–	4d. black and blue	10	1·25
T7	–	6d. brown and black	30	20
T8	–	1s. black and purple	15	10
T9	**26**	2s.6d. black and green	1·10	80
T10	–	5s. black and orange	1·60	3·50
T11	–	10s. black and brown	2·50	6·50
T12	**29**	£1 black and violet	8·50	20·00

III. REPUBLIC OF CAMEROON

The Republic of Cameroon joined the Commonwealth on 1 November 1995 and issues from that date will be listed below, when examples and information have been received.

CAMEROUN Pt. 7; Pt. 6; Pt. 12

Territory in western Africa which became a German Protectorate in 1884. During 1914–16 it was occupied by Allied troops and in 1922 Britain and France were granted separate United Nations mandates.

In 1960 the French trust territory became an independent republic and, following a plebiscite, in September 1961 the southern part of the area under British control joined the Cameroun Republic. In November 1995 the republic joined the Commonwealth.

A. GERMAN COLONY OF KAMERUN

100 pfennig = 1 mark.

1897. Stamps of Germany optd **Kamerun**.
K1a 8 3pf. brown 7·00 13·00
K2 5pf. green 4·00 5·00
K3 9 10pf. red 4·00 5·00
K4 20pf. blue 3·50 6·25
K5 25pf. orange 18·00 29·00
K6a 50pf. brown 13·00 22·00

1900. "Yacht" key-types inscr "KAMERUN".
K 7 N 3pf. brown 95 1·25
K21 5pf. green 55 95
K22 10pf. red 45 45
K10 20pf. blue 20·00 1·60
K11 25pf. black & red on yell 1·25 4·25
K12 30pf. black & orge on buff 1·40 3·25
K13 40pf. black and red 1·40 3·25
K14 50pf. black & pur on buff 1·75 4·00
K15 80pf. black & red on rose 2·25 8·25
K16 O 1m. red 48·00 48·00
K17 2m. blue 5·50 42·00
K18 3m. black 5·00 80·00
K19 5m. red and black £100 £400

B. FRENCH ADMINISTRATION OF CAMEROUN

100 centimes = 1 franc.

1915. Stamps of Gabon with inscription "AFRIQUE EQUATORIALE-GABON" optd **Corps Expeditionnaire Franco-Anglais CAMEROUN**.
1 7 1c. brown and orange 60·00 32·00
2 2c. black and brown £120 £120
3 4c. violet and blue £120 £120
4 5c. olive and green 27·00 23·00
5 10c. red and lake (on No. 37 of Gabon) 25·00 16·00
6 20c. brown and violet £120 £130
7 8 25c. brown and blue 48·00 32·00
8 30c. red and grey £120 £120
9 35c. green and violet 50·00 32·00
10 40c. blue and brown £120 £120
11 45c. violet and red £120 £120
12 50c. grey and green £120 £120
13 75c. brown and orange £180 £130
14 9 1f. yellow and brown £180 £130
15 2f. brown and red £200 £170

1916. Optd **Occupation Francaise du Cameroun**.
(a) On stamps of Middle Congo.
16 1 1c. olive and brown 65·00 65·00
17 2c. violet and brown 75·00 65·00
18 4c. blue and brown 75·00 65·00
19 5c. green and blue 32·00 25·00
20 2 35c. brown and blue 85·00 65·00
21 45c. violet and orange 70·00 60·00

(b) On stamps of French Congo
22 6 15c. violet and green 75·00 70·00
23 8 20c. green and red £110 75·00
24 30c. red and yellow 70·00 60·00
25 40c. brown and green 70·00 60·00
26 50c. violet and lilac 75·00 55·00
27 75c. purple and orange 80·00 55·00
28 – 1f. drab and grey (48) £100 80·00
29 – 2f. red and brown (49) £120 80·00

1916. Stamps of Middle Congo optd **CAMEROUN Occupation Francaise**.
30 1 1c. olive and brown 10 2·40
31 2c. violet and brown 10 2·40
32 4c. blue and brown 10 2·40
33 5c. green and blue 60 1·90
34 10c. red and blue 50 2·40
34a 15c. purple and red 2·50 2·75
35 20c. brown and blue 1·25 2·75
36 2 25c. blue and green 1·00 1·25
37 30c. pink and green 2·00 2·40
38 35c. brown and blue 1·75 2·75
39 40c. green and brown 1·40 3·25
40 45c. violet and orange 2·25 3·25
41 50c. green and orange 2·50 3·25
42 75c. brown and blue 2·50 3·25
43 3 1f. green and violet 1·75 3·00
44 2f. violet and green 6·50 9·50
45 5f. blue and pink 8·25 14·00

1921. Stamps of Middle Congo (colours changed) optd **CAMEROUN**.
46 1 1c. orange and green 10 2·75
47 2c. red and brown 10 2·75
48 4c. green and grey 20 2·75
49 5c. orange and red 20 2·50
50 10c. light green and green 30 2·75
51 15c. orange and blue 80 3·00
52 20c. grey and purple 1·40 3·00
53 2 25c. orange and grey 1·40 1·90
54 30c. red and carmine 1·75 3·00
55 35c. blue and grey 1·50 3·00
56 40c. orange and green 1·75 3·00
57 45c. red and brown 1·75 3·00
58 50c. ultramarine and blue 1·00 2·75
59 75c. green and purple 1·00 3·00
60 3 1f. orange and grey 3·75 4·00
61 2f. red and green 7·00 9·00
62 5f. grey and red 6·50 14·00

1924. Stamps of 1921 surch.
63 1 25c. on 15c. orange & blue 55 3·00
64 3 25c. on 2f. red and green 1·50 3·00
65 25c. on 5f. grey and red 1·25 3·50
66 2 "65" on 45c. red and brown 1·10 4·00
67 "85" on 75c. green & red 2·25 4·25

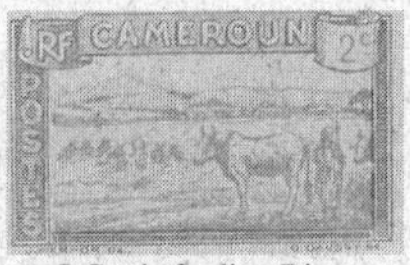
5 Cattle fording River

1925.
68 5 1c. mauve and olive 10 1·75
69 2c. green & red on green 10 1·75
70 4c. black and blue 30 2·00
71 5c. mauve and yellow 35 40
72 10c. orange & pur on yell 90 50
73 15c. green 1·90 2·75
88 15c. red and lilac 55 2·50
74 A 20c. brown and olive 1·60 3·00
89 20c. green 80 2·50
90 20c. brown and red 20 25
75 25c. black and green 55 25
76 30c. red and green 45 1·00
91 30c. green and olive 50 1·40
77 35c. black and brown 1·25 3·00
91a 35c. green 2·50 3·00
78 40c. violet and orange 2·75 3·25
79 45c. red 40 3·00
92 45c. brown and mauve 3·25 3·50
80 50c. red and green 2·25 40
93 55c. red and blue 2·75 3·75
81 60c. black and mauve 2·50 2·75
94 60c. red 1·50 2·75
82 65c. brown and blue 2·25 40
83 75c. blue 60 2·75
95 75c. mauve and brown 50 1·25
95a 80c. brown and red 90 3·50
84 85c. blue and red 80 2·50
96 90c. red 2·50 3·00
85 B 1f. brown and blue 55 3·00
97 1f. blue 75 1·40
98 1f. mauve and brown 1·00 2·25
99 1f. brown and green 2·50 1·75
100 1f.10 brown and red 2·75 6·00
100a 1f.25 blue and brown 7·75 6·00
101 1f.50 blue 2·50 75
101a 1f.75 red and brown 95 1·90
101b 1f.75 blue 7·00 7·00
86 2f. orange and olive 3·00 60
102 3f. mauve and brown 4·75 3·75
87 5f. black & brown on bl 3·75 60
103 10f. mauve and orange 9·50 9·00
104 20f. green and red 20·00 16·00
DESIGNS—VERT: A, Tapping rubber-trees. HORIZ: B, Liana suspension bridge.

1926. Surch with new value.
105 B 1f.25 on 1f. blue 60 2·75

1931. "Colonial Exhibition" key-types inscribed "CAMEROUN".
106 E 40c. green 4·25 4·50
107 F 50c. mauve 4·75 5·00
108 G 90c. orange 4·75 5·25
109 H 1f.50 blue 6·25 5·25

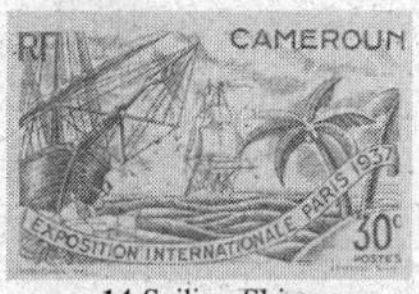
14 Sailing Ships

1937. Paris International Exhibition. Inscr "EXPOSITION INTERNATIONALE PARIS 1937".
110 – 20c. violet 2·25 4·00
111 14 30c. green 2·25 3·50
112 – 40c. red 1·10 3·75
113 – 50c. brown & deep brown 1·90 3·25
114 – 90c. red 1·25 4·00
115 – 1f.50 blue 1·50 3·75
DESIGNS—VERT: 20c. Allegory of Commerce; 50c. Allegory of Agriculture. HORIZ: 40c. Berber, Negress and Annamite; 90c. France extends torch of Civilization; 1f.50, Diane de Poitiers.

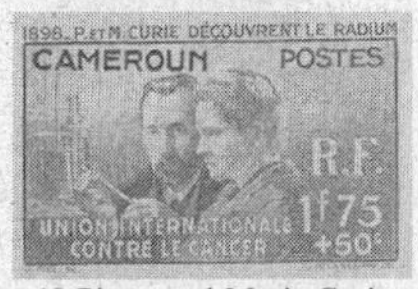
19 Pierre and Marie Curie

1938. International Anti-cancer Fund.
116 19 1f.75+50c. blue 6·00 14·00

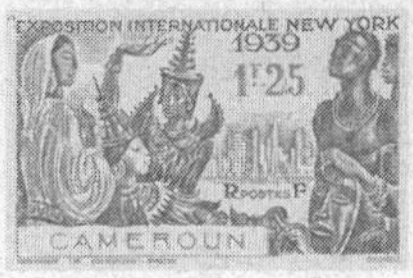
20

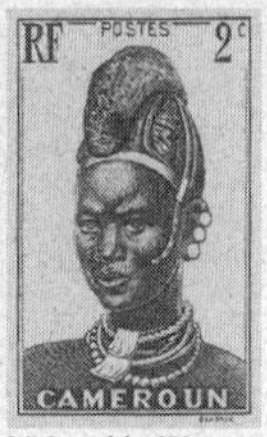
21 Lamido Woman

1939. New York World's Fair.
117 20 1f.25 red 2·00 3·25
118 2f.25 blue 2·00 3·50

1939.
119 21 2c. black 20 2·50
120 3c. mauve 15 2·00
121 4c. blue 65 2·50
122 5c. brown 45 2·50
123 10c. green 45 2·25
124 15c. red 70 2·75
125 20c. purple 55 2·75
126 A 25c. black 1·10 2·75
127 30c. orange 35 3·00
128 40c. blue 50 3·00
129 45c. green 1·40 4·50
130 50c. brown 70 3·00
131 60c. blue 1·10 3·25
132 70c. purple 2·25 4·25
133 B 80c. blue 1·25 4·50
134 90c. blue 2·75 2·00
135 1f. red 2·50 3·00
135a 1f. brown 1·75 2·25
136 1f.25 red 3·75 7·00
137 1f.40 orange 1·90 3·25
138 1f.50 brown 90 1·60
139 1f.60 brown 2·25 4·25
140 1f.75 blue 1·40 2·75
141 2f. green 1·50 1·25
142 2f.25 blue 1·90 2·75
143 2f.50 purple 2·00 2·75
144 3f. violet 1·25 2·25
145 C 5f. brown 1·75 3·00
146 10f. purple 1·50 3·75
147 20f. green 3·50 5·00
DESIGNS—VERT: A, Banyo Waterfall; C, African boatman. HORIZ: B, African elephants.

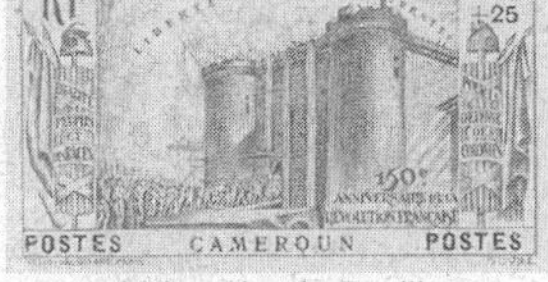
25 Storming the Bastille

1939. 150th Anniv of Revolution.
148 25 45c.+25c. green 6·25 11·50
149 70c.+30c. brown 4·75 11·50
150 90c.+35c. orange 5·50 13·00
151 1f.25+1f. red 5·50 16·00
152 2f.25+2f. blue 8·75 20·00

1940. Adherence to General de Gaulle. Optd **CAMEROUN FRANCAIS 27-8-40**.
153 21 2c. black 1·10 60
154 3c. mauve 85 1·00
155 4c. blue 65 45
156 5c. brown 3·75 4·00
157 10c. green 80 25
158 15c. red 1·25 2·75
159 20c. purple 12·00 10·50
160 A 25c. black 1·00 70
161 30c. orange 9·75 10·50
162 40c. blue 3·25 1·40
163 45c. green 2·00 1·10
164 – 50c. red & green (No. 80) 80 45
165 A 60c. blue 3·75 4·50
166 70c. purple 1·75 75
167 B 80c. blue 4·75 1·75
168 90c. blue 75 30
169 20 1f.25 red 3·75 1·40
170 B 1f.25 red 80 85
171 1f.40 orange 1·50 1·10
172 1f.50 brown 75 50
173 1f.60 brown 1·50 85
174 1f.75 blue 1·50 1·10
175 20 2f.25 blue 3·75 1·50
176 B 2f.25 blue 70 60
177 2f.50 purple 55 40
178 – 5f. black and brown on blue (No. 87) 17·00 6·25
179 C 5f. brown 16·00 6·00
180 – 10f. mve & orge (No. 103) 30·00 6·50
181 C 10f. purple 55·00 45·00
182 – 20f. green & red (No. 104) 50·00 13·00
183 C 20f. green £140 £180

1940. War Relief Fund. Nos. 100a, 101a and 86 surch **OEUVRES DE GUERRE** and premium.
184 1f.25+2f. blue and brown 19·00 22·00
185 1f.75+3f. red and brown 19·00 22·00
186 2f.+5f. orange and olive 16·00 16·00

1940. Spitfire Fund. Nos. 126, 129, 131/2 surch **+5 Frs. SPITFIRE**.
187 A 25c.+5f. black 95·00 £100
188 45c.+5f. green £110 £100
189 60c.+5f. blue £110 £110
190 70c.+5f. purple £100 £110

1941. Spitfire Fund. Surch **SPITFIRE +10 fr. General de GAULLE**.
190a 20 1f.25+10f. red £100 £100
190b 2f.25+10f. blue £100 £100

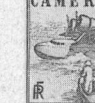

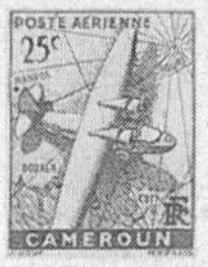
29b Sikorsky S-43 over Map

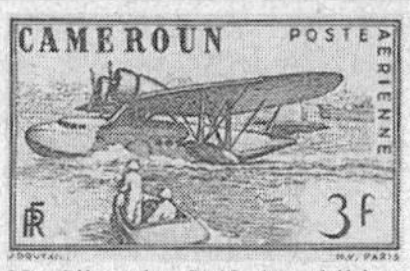
29c Sikorsky S-43 Amphibian

1941. Air.
190c 29b 25c. red 90 3·00
190d 50c. green 50 3·00
190e 1f. purple 1·75 3·00
190f 29c 2f. olive 65 2·75
190g 3f. brown 90 2·75
190h 4f. blue 55 1·75
190i 6f. myrtle 70 2·75
190j 7f. purple 55 2·75
190k 12f. orange 5·50 6·75
190l 20f. red 3·00 3·50
190m – 50f. blue 3·25 3·75
DESIGN: 50f. Latecoere 631 flying boat over harbour.

1941. Laquintinie Hospital Fund. Surch **+10 Frs. AMBULANCE LAQUINTINIE**.
191 20 1f.25+10f. red 32·00 28·00
192 2f.25+10f. blue 32·00 28·00

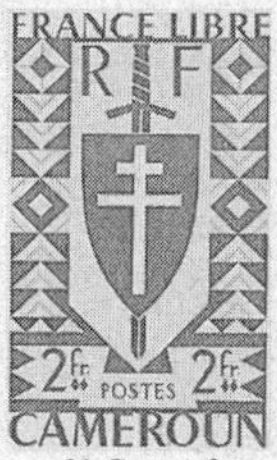
31 Cross of Lorraine, Sword and Shield

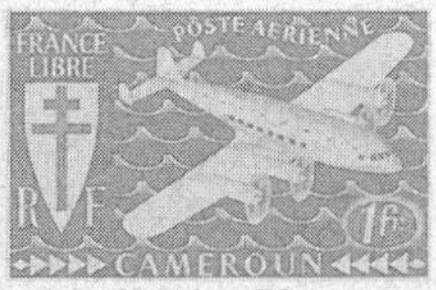
32 Fairey FC-1

1942. Free French Issue.
193 31 5c. brown (postage) 10 1·25
194 10c. blue 10 15
195 25c. green 10 40
196 30c. red 10 40
197 40c. green 10 30
198 80c. purple 10 35
199 1f. mauve 35 15
200 1f.50 red 40 15
201 2f. black 45 15
202 2f.50 blue 45 30
203 4f. violet 20 30
204 5f. yellow 40 25
205 10f. brown 30 45
206 20f. green 55 65
207 32 1f. orange (air) 1·50 2·75
208 1f.50 red 1·90 2·75
209 5f. purple 80 2·75
210 10f. black 45 3·00
211 25f. blue 1·75 3·00
212 50f. green 2·25 3·00
213 100f. red 2·00 2·75

1943. Surch **Valmy +100 frs.**
213a – 1f.25+100f. blue and brown (No. 100a) 16·00 32·00
213b 20 1f.25+100f. red 10·00 32·00
213c – 1f.25+100f. red (No. 136) 21·00 32·00
213d – 1f.50+100f. brown (No. 138) 19·00 32·00
213e 20 2f.25+100f. blue 12·00 32·00

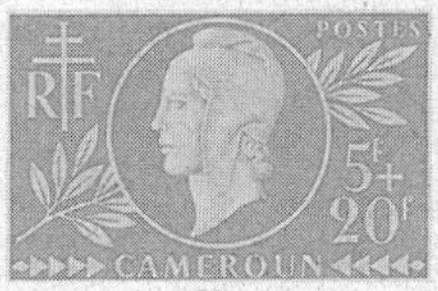
33

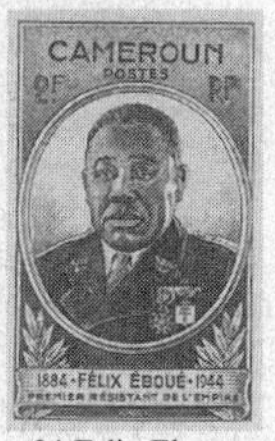
34 Felix Eboue

1944. Mutual Aid and Red Cross Funds.
214 33 5f.+20f. red 80 4·50

1945. Surch.
215 31 50c. on 5c. brown 1·40 2·75
216 60c. on 5c. brown 60 3·00
217 70c. on 5c. brown 75 30
218 1f.20 on 5c. brown 1·10 30
219 2f.40 on 25c. green 1·25 1·00
220 3f. on 25c. green 1·00 1·25
221 4f.50 on 25c. green 1·60 3·50
222 15f. on 2f.50 blue 1·75 3·50

1945.
223 34 2f. black 20 1·75
224 25f. green 1·25 3·00

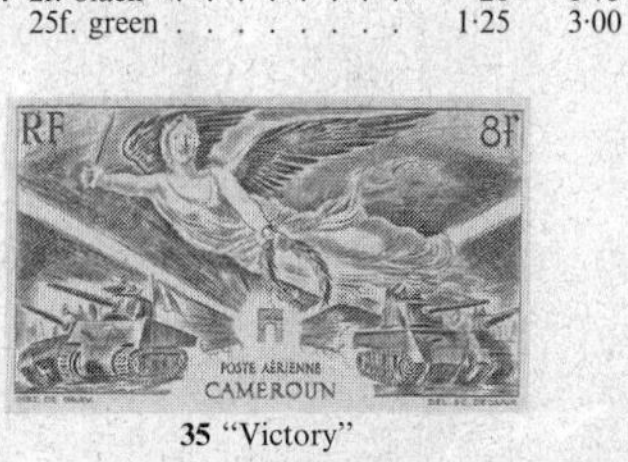
35 "Victory"

1946. Air. Victory.
225 **35** 8f. purple . . . . 25 2·00

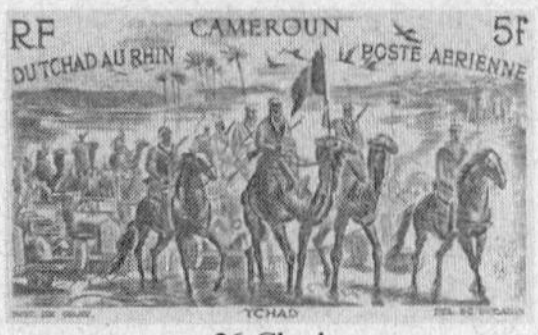

36 Chad

1946. Air. From Chad to the Rhine. Inscr "DU TCHAD AU RHIN".
226 **36** 5f. blue . . . . 2·00 3·50
227 – 10f. purple . . . . 1·40 3·50
228 – 15f. red . . . . 1·75 3·25
229 – 20f. blue . . . . 1·75 3·50
230 – 25f. brown . . . . 2·25 3·50
231 – 50f. black . . . . 1·25 3·75
DESIGNS: 10f. Koufra; 15f. Mareth; 20f. Normandy; 25f. Paris; 50f. Strasbourg.

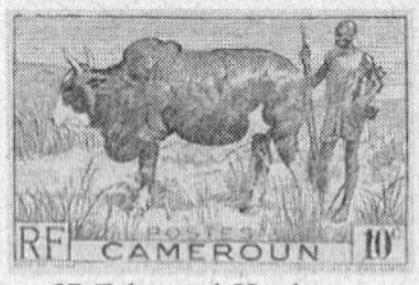

37 Zebu and Herdsman

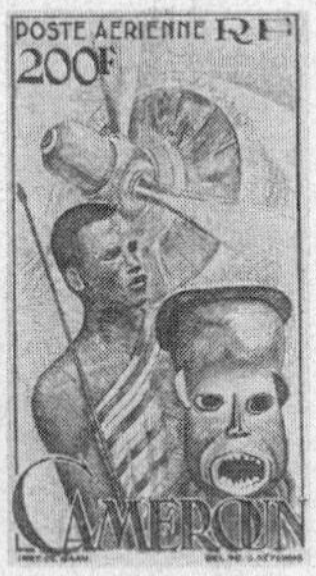

45 Aeroplane, African and Mask

1946.
232 **37** 10c. green (postage) . . . 15 60
233 30c. orange . . . . 15 2·00
234 40c. blue . . . . 15 2·75
235 – 50c. sepia . . . . 55 1·40
236 – 60c. purple . . . . 15 2·25
237 – 80c. brown . . . . 30 2·75
238 – 1f. orange 40 15
239 – 1f.20 green . . . . 35 3·00
240 – 1f.50 red . . . . 1·10 1·10
241 – 2f. black 35 10
242 – 3f. red . . . . 1·50 10
243 – 3f.60 red . . . . 1·25 3·00
244 – 4f. blue 85 15
245 – 5f. red . . . . 1·75 15
246 – 6f. blue . . . . 1·50 15
247 – 10f. green . . . . 1·25 15
248 – 15f. blue . . . . 1·25 15
249 – 20f. green . . . . 1·50 25
250 – 25f. black . . . . 1·50 60

251 – 50f. green (air) . . . . . 1·75 75
252 – 100f. brown . . . . 2·25 2·25
253 **45** 200f. olive . . . . 4·25 4·75
DESIGNS—VERT: 50c. to 80c. Tikar women; 1f. to 1f.50, Africans carrying bananas; 2f. to 4f. Bowman; 5f. to 10f. Lamido horsemen; 15f. to 25f. Native head. HORIZ: 50f. Birds over mountains; 100f. African horsemen and Dewoitine D-333 trimotor airplane.

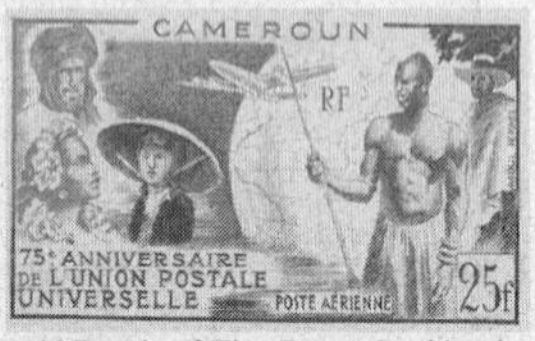

46 People of Five Races, Lockheed Constellation Airplane and Globe

1949. Air. 75th Anniv of U.P.U.
254 **46** 25f. multicoloured . . . . 2·50 6·00

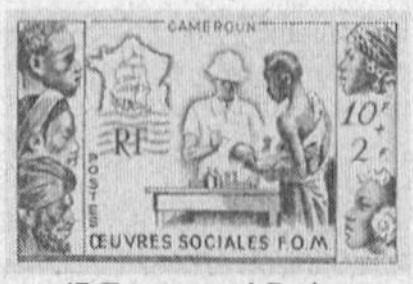

47 Doctor and Patient

1950. Colonial Welfare Fund.
255 **47** 10f.+2f. green & turq . . . 4·50 7·75

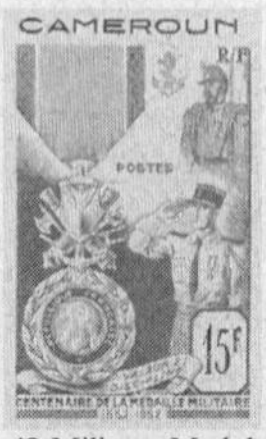

48 Military Medal

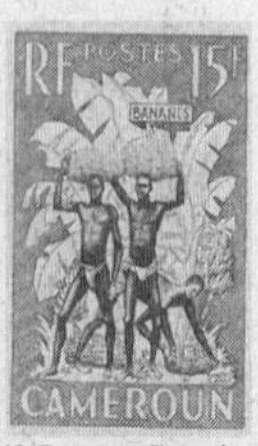

49 Porters Carrying Bananas

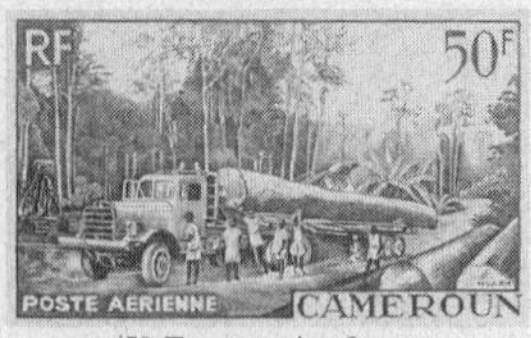

50 Transporting Logs

1952. Military Medal Centenary.
256 **48** 15f. red, yellow and green 4·50 5·00

1953.
257 **49** 8f. violet, orange and purple (postage) 35 10
258 15f. brown, yellow & red 1·50 35
259 – 40f. brown, pink & choc 1·25 30

260 **50** 50f. ol, brn & sep (air) . . 2·50 65
261 – 100f. sepia, brown & turq 5·75 1·10
262 – 200f. brown, blue & grn 8·25 7·25
262a – 500f. indigo, blue and lilac . . . . 16·00 14·50
DESIGNS—As Type **49**: 40f. Woman gathering coffee. As Type **50**: HORIZ: 100f. Airplane over giraffes; 200f. Freighters, Douala Port. VERT: 500f. Sud Ouest Corse II over Piton d'Humsiki.

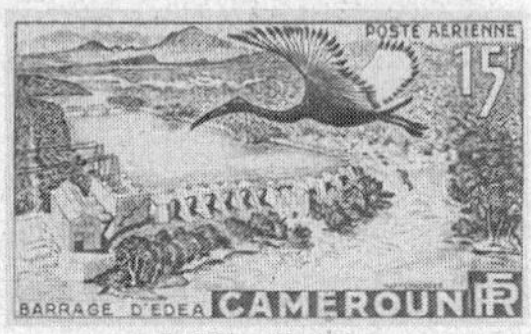

51 Edea Barrage

1953. Air. Opening of Edea Barrage.
263 **51** 15f. blue, lake and brown 2·75 1·50

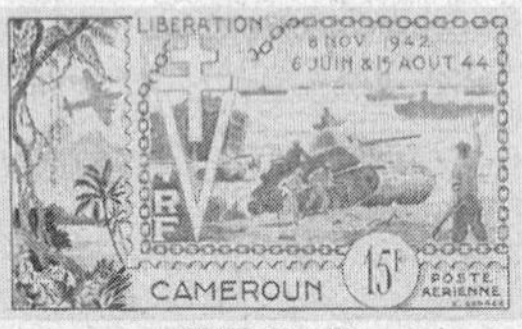

52 "D-Day"

1954. Air. 10th Anniv of Liberation.
264 **52** 15f. green and turquoise 4·00 4·00

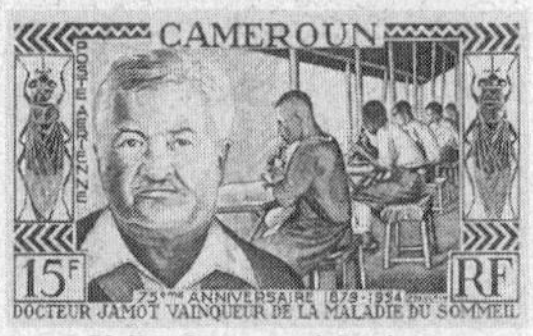

53 Dr. Jamot and Students

1954. Air. 75th Birthday of Dr. Jamot (physician).
265 **53** 15f. brown, blue & green 4·50 4·00

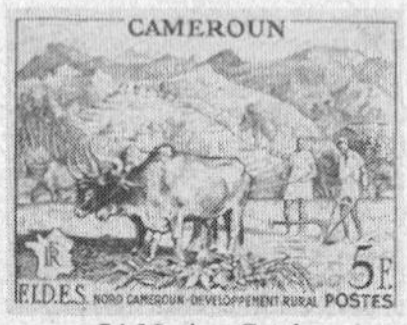

54 Native Cattle

1956. Economic and Social Development Fund. Inscr "F.I.D.E.S.".
266 **54** 5f. brown and sepia . . . 30 25
267 – 15f. turq, blue & black . . 1·25 25
268 – 20f. turquoise and blue . . 1·10 30
269 – 25f. blue . . . . 1·50 35
DESIGNS: 15f. R. Wouri bridge; 20f. Technical education; 25f. Mobile medical unit.

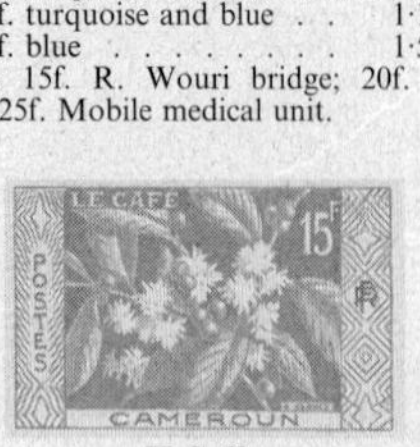

55 Coffee

1956.
270 **55** 15f. vermilion and red . . 40 15

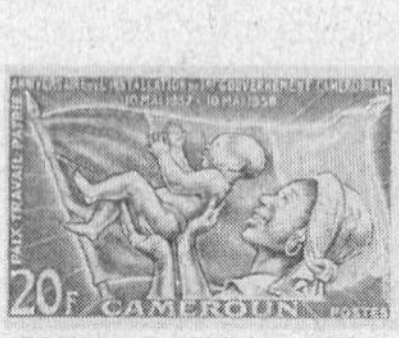

56 Woman, Child and Flag

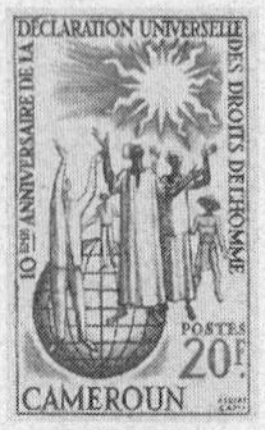

57 "Human Rights"

1958. 1st Anniv of First Cameroun Govt.
271 **56** 20f. multicoloured 35 25

1958. 30th Anniv of Declaration of Human Rights.
272 **57** 20f. brown and red . . . . 75 2·75

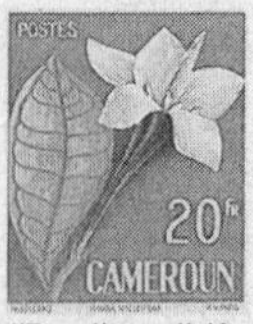

58 "Randia malleifera"

1958. Tropical Flora.
273 **58** 20f. multicoloured . . . . 1·50 45

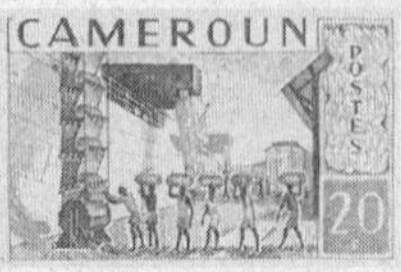

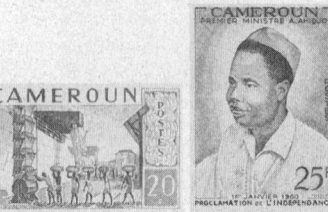

59 Loading Bananas on Ship at Douala

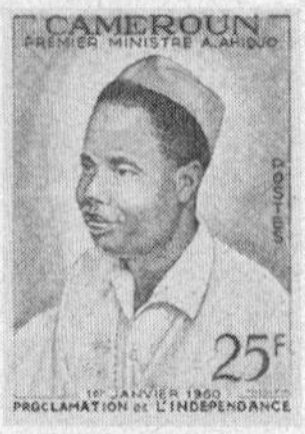

60 Prime Minister A. Ahidjo

1959.
274 **59** 20f. multicoloured 65 45
275 – 25f. green, brn & pur . . . 60 40
DESIGN—VERT: 25f. Bunch of bananas and native bearers in jungle path.

C. INDEPENDENT REPUBLIC

1960. Proclamation of Independence. Inscr "1 ER JANVIER 1960".
276 – 20f. multicoloured 55 15
277 **60** 25f. green, bistre & black 55 15
DESIGN: 20f. Cameroun flag and map.

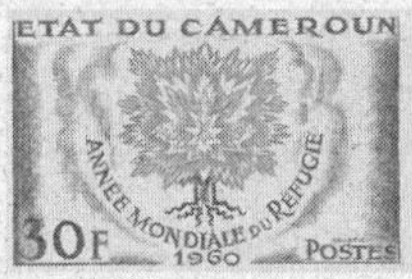

61 "Uprooted Tree"

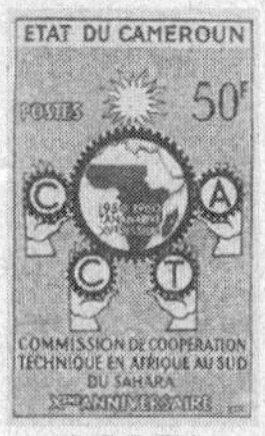

62 C.C.T.A. Emblem

1960. World Refugee Year.
278 **61** 30f. green, blue and brown 1·00 50

1960. 10th Anniv of African Technical Co-operation Commission.
279 **62** 50f. black and purple . . . 1·10 60

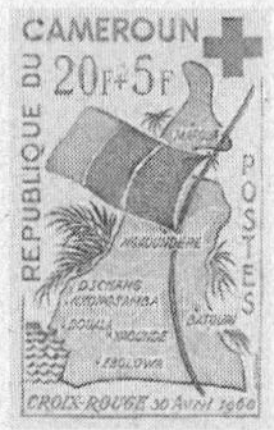

63 Map and Flag

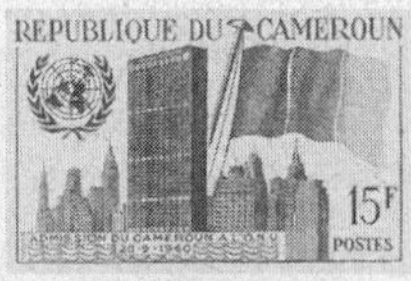

64 U.N. Headquarters, Emblem and Cameroun Flag

1961. Red Cross Fund. Flag in green, red and yellow; cross in red; background colours given.
280 **63** 20f.+5f. green and red . . 70 70
281 25f.+10f. red and green . . 95 95
282 30f.+15f. red and green . . 1·75 1·75

1961. Admission to U.N.O. Flag in green, red and yellow; emblem in blue, buildings and inscr in colours given.
283 **64** 15f. brown and green . . . 45 30
284 25f. green and blue 55 30
285 85f. purple, blue and red 2·10 1·10

1961. Surch **REPUBLIQUE FEDERALE** and value in Sterling currency.
286 – ½d. on 1f. orange (238) (postage) 35 25
287 – 1d. on 2f. black (241) . . 45 30
288 **54** 1½d. on 5f. brown & sepia 50 40
289 – 2d. on 10f. green (247) . . 95 50
290 – 3d. on 15f. turquoise, indigo and black (267) 1·25 35
291 – 4d. on 15f. vermilion and red (270) . . . . . . 1·10 85
292 – 6d. on 20f. mult (274) . . 2·25 1·25
293 **60** 1s. on 25f. grn, bis & blk 2·75 2·00
294a **61** 2s.6d. on 30f. green, blue and brown . . . . . 4·75 4·75
295a – 5s. on 100r. sepia, brown and turquoise (264) (air) . . . . 9·00 9·00
296a – 10s. on 200f. brown, blue and green (265) . . . . 18·00 18·00
297a – £1 on 500f. indigo, blue and lilac (253a) . . . . 30·00 30·00
The above were for use in the former British Cameroon Trust Territory pending the introduction of the Cameroun franc.

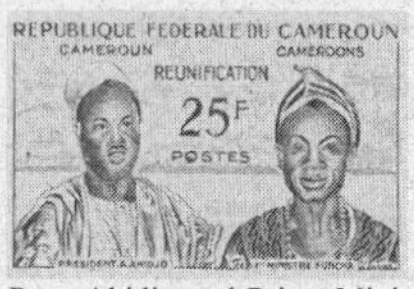

66 Pres. Ahidjo and Prime Minister Foncha

1962. Reunification. (a) T **66**.
298 20f. brown and violet . . . . 16·00 14·00
299 25f. brown and green . . . . 16·00 14·00
300 60f. green and red . . . . . 16·00 14·00

(b) T **66** surch in Sterling currency.
301 3d. on 20f. brown & violet
302 6d. on 25f. brown and green
303 2s.6d. on 60f. green and red
Set of 3 . . . . £375 £375

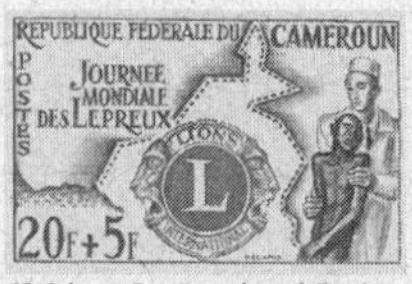

68 Lions International Badge, Doctor and Leper

1962. World Leprosy Day. Lions International Relief Fund.
304 **68** 20f.+5f. purple & brown 60 60
305 25f.+10f. purple & blue . . 70 70
306 50f.+15f. purple & green 1·40 1·40

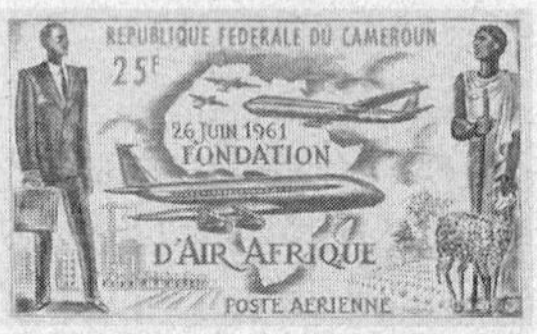

69 European, African and Boeing 707 Airliners

1962. Air. Foundation of "Air Afrique" Airline.
307 **69** 25f. purple, violet & grn 65 40

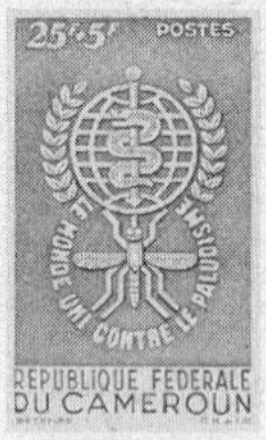

70 Campaign Emblem

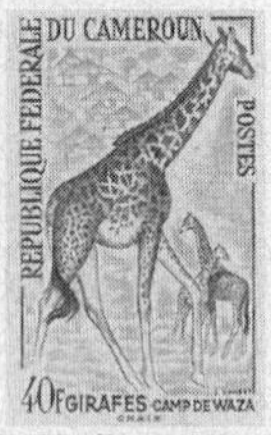

71 Giraffes and Waza Camp

1962. Malaria Eradication.
308 **70** 25f.+5f. mauve 65 60

1962. (a) Postage. Animals.
309 A 50c. sepia, blue & turquoise 10 10
310 B 1f. black, turquoise & orge 10 10
311 C 1f.50 brown, sage & blk . . 10 10
312 D 2f. black, blue and green 15 10
313 C 3f. brown, orange & purple 15 10
314 B 4f. sepia, green & turq . . 20 10
315 D 5f. purple, green & brown 20 10
316 A 6f. sepia, blue and lemon 30 15
317 E 8f. blue, red and green . . 65 45
318 F 10f. black, orange & blue 50 15
319 A 15f. brown, blue & turq . . 65 35
320 **71** 20f. brown and grey . . . 85 35
321 F 25f. brown, yellow & grn 2·10 85
322 E 30f. black, blue & brown 2·50 90
323 **71** 40f. lake and green . . . . 4·75 1·40

(b) Air.
324 – 50f. brown, myrtle & blue 90 40
325 – 100f. multicoloured . . . 2·75 85
326 – 200f. black, brn & turq . . 8·50 2·10
327 – 500f. buff, purple and blue 9·50 3·00
DESIGNS—HORIZ: As Type **71**: A, Moustached monkey; B, African elephant and Ntem Falls; C, Kob, Dschang; D, Hippopotamus, Hippo Camp; E, African manatee, Lake Ossa; F, Buffalo, Batoun Region. (48 × 27 mm): 50f. Cocotiers Hotel, Douala; 100f. "Cymothoe sangaris" (butterfly); 200f. Ostriches; 500f. Kapsikis, Mokolo (landscape).

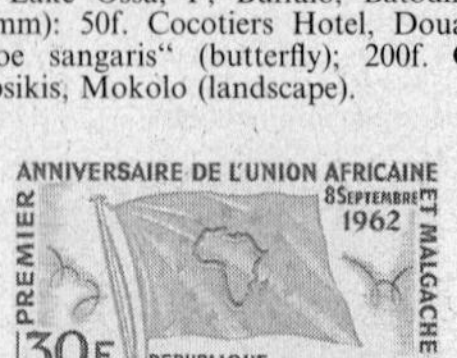

72 Union Flag

1962. 1st Anniv of Union of African and Malagasy States. Flag in green, red and gold.
328 **72** 30f. brown . . . . 1·40 65

73 Map and View

74 "The School Under the Tree"

1962. 1st Anniv of Reunification.
329 **73** 9f. bistre, violet & brown . . . 30 20
330 18f. red, green and blue . . 40 30
331 – 20f. bistre, blue and purple . . 45 30
332 – 25f. orange, sepia & blue . . 45 35
333 – 50f. blue, sepia and red . . 1·25 80
DESIGNS: 20f., 25f. Sunrise over Cameroun; 50f. Commemorative scroll.

1962. Literacy and Popular Education Plan.
334 **74** 20f. red, yellow and green . . 65 35

75 Globe and "Telstar"

1963. 1st Trans-Atlantic Television Satellite Link.
335 **75** 1f. ol, vio & blue (postage) . . 10 10
336 2f. lake, green and blue . . 15 15
337 3f. olive, purple and green . . 20 20
338 25f. blue and green 85 85
339 100f. brown and green (air)
(48 × 27 mm) . . . . . 1·90 1·10

76 Globe and Emblem

77 VHF Station, Mt. Bankolo, Yaounde

1963. Freedom from Hunger.
340 **76** 18f.+5f. blue, brn & grn . . 70 40
341 25f.+5f. green & brown . . 85 45

1963. Inauguration of Doala–Yaounde VHF Radio Service.
342 **77** 15f. mult (postage) 35 30
343 – 20f. multicoloured 45 35
344 – 100f. multicoloured (air) . . 1·90 1·10
DESIGNS: 20f. Aerials and control panel; 100f. Edea relay station (26 × 44 mm).

78 "Centre regional ..."

80 Pres. Ahidjo

1963. Inauguration of U.N.E.S.C.O. Regional Schoolbooks Production Centre, Yaounde.
345 **78** 20f. red, black and green . . 35 20
346 25f. red, black and orange . . 40 20
347 100f. red, black and gold . . 1·50 85

1963. Air. African and Malagasian Posts and Telecommunications Union. As T **18** of Central African Republic.
348 85f. multicoloured . . . . . 1·60 1·10

1963. 2nd Anniv of Reunification. Multicoloured.
349 **80** 9f. Type **80** 30 20
350 18f. Map and flag 40 20
351 20f. Type **80** 45 30

1963. Air. Inauguration of "DC-8" Service. As T **11** of Congo Republic.
352 50f. multicoloured 90 45

82 Globe and Scales of Justice

1963. 15th Anniv of Declaration of Human Rights.
353 **82** 9f. brown, black and blue . . 35 15
354 18f. red, black and green . . 40 20
355 25f. green, black & red . . 50 30
356 75f. blue, black & yellow . . 1·60 65

83 Lion

1964. Waza National Park.
357 **83** 10f. bistre green & brown . . 1·25 35
358 25f. bistre and green . . . 2·40 80

84 Football Stadium, Yaounde

1964. Tropics Cup. Inscr as in T **84**.
359 **84** 10f. brown, turquoise & grn 35 20
360 – 18f. green, red and violet . . 40 30
361 – 30f. blue, brown and black . . 70 40
DESIGNS: 18f. Sports Equipment; 30f. Stadium Entrance. Yaounde.

85 Palace of Justice, Yaounde

1964. 1st Anniv of European–African Economic Convention. Multicoloured.
362 **85** 15f. Type **85** . . . . 1·25 55
363 40f. Sun, moon and economic emblems (vert) . . . . . 2·10 1·10

86 Olympic Flame and Hurdling

1964. Olympic Games, Toyko.
364 **86** 9f. red, blk & grn (postage) . 1·75 1·40
365 – 10f. brown, violet and red . 1·90 1·40
366 – 300f. turquoise, brown and red (air) . . . . 7·75 4·25
DESIGNS—VERT: 10f. Running. HORIZ: 300f. Wrestling.

87 Ntem Falls

88 Co-operation

1964. Folklore and Tourism.
367 – 9f. red, blue & grn (postage) 45 20
368 – 18f. blue, brown and red . . 55 35
369 **87** 20f. drab, green and red . . 65 35
370 – 25f. red, brown & orange . 1·40 55
371 – 50f. brown, grn & bl (air) . . 90 55
372 – 250f. sepia, grn & brn . . 9·75 3·25
DESIGNS—As Type **87**. VERT: 9f. Bamileke dance costume; 18f. Bamenda dance mask. HORIZ: 25f. Fulani horseman. LARGER (43 × 27½ mm): 50f. View of Kribi and Longji; 250f. Black rhinoceros.

1964. French, African and Malagasy Co-operation.
373 **88** 18f. brown, green and blue . 1·25 75
374 30f. brown, turq & brn . . 2·50 1·00

89 Pres. Kennedy

1964. Air. Pres. Kennedy Commem.
375 **89** 100f. sepia, grn & apple . . 2·00 2·00

90 Inscription recording laying of First Rail

1965. Opening of Mbanga–Kumba Railway.
376 **90** 12f. indigo, green and blue . 1·00 60
377 – 20f. yellow, green and red . . 2·75 1·25
DESIGN—HORIZ: (36 × 22 mm): 20f. Series BB500 diesel locomotive.

91 Abraham Lincoln

1965. Air. Death Centenary of Abraham Lincoln.
378 **91** 100f. multicoloured . . . . 2·00 1·40

92 Ambulance and First Aid Post

1965. Cameroun Red Cross.
379 **92** 25f. yellow, green and red . . 50 30
380 – 50f. brown, red and grey . . 1·25 45
DESIGN—VERT: 50f. Nurse and child.

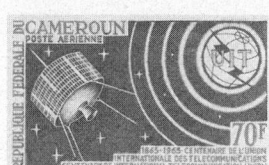

93 "Syncom" and I.T.U. Emblem

1965. Air. Centenary of I.T.U.
381 **93** 70f. black, blue and red . . 1·40 70

94 Churchill giving "V" Sign

95 "Map" Savings Bank

1965. Air. Churchill Commem. Multicoloured.
382 12f. Type **94** . . . . . . 1·00 55
383 18f. Churchill, oak spray and cruiser "De Grasse" . . . 1·40 60

1965. Federal Postal Savings Bank.
384 **95** 9f. yellow, red and green . . 30 15
385 – 15f. brown, green & blue . . 40 20
386 – 20f. brown, chest & turq . . 45 30
DESIGNS—HORIZ: (48 × 27 mm): 15f. Savings Bank building. VERT: (27 × 48 mm): 20f. "Cocoa-bean" savings bank.

96 Africa Cup and Players

1965. Winning of Africa Cup by Oryx Football Club.
387 **96** 9f. brown, yellow and red . . 55 35
388 20f. blue, yellow and red . . 1·40 45

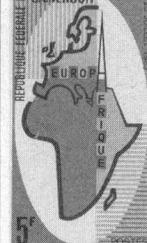

97 Map of Europe and Africa

98 U.P.U. Monument, Berne and Doves

1965. "Europafrique".
389 **97** 5f. red, lilac and black . . . 20 15
390 – 40f. multicoloured 90 60
DESIGN: 40f. Yaounde Conference.

1965. 5th Anniv of Admission to U.P.U.
391 **98** 30f. purple and red 60 45

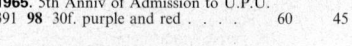

99 I.C.Y. Emblem

1965. International Co-operation Year.
392 **99** 10f. red & blue (postage) . . 35 30
393 100f. blue and red (air) . . 1·60 90

100 Pres. Ahidjo and Government House

1965. Re-election of Pres. Ahidjo. Multicoloured.
394 9f. Pres. Ahidjo wearing hat, and Government House (vert) 20 10
395 18f. Type **100** 35 15
396 20f. As 9f. 45 20
397 25f. Type **100** 55 30

101 Musgum Huts, Pouss

1965. Folklore and Tourism.
398 **101** 9f. green, brown and red (postage) 35 15
399 – 18f. brown, green & blue . . 50 30
400 – 20f. brown and blue . . 70 30
401 – 25f. grey, lake and green . . 95 30
402 – 50f. brown, blue and green (48 × 27 mm) (air) . 2·00 80
DESIGNS—HORIZ: 18f. Great Calao's dance (N. Cameroons); 25f. National Tourist office, Yaounde; 50f. Racing pirogue on Sanaga River, Edea. VERT: 20f. Sultan's palace gate Foumban.

102 "Vostok 6"

1966. Air. Spacecraft.
403 **102** 50f. green and red 80 45
404 – 100f. blue and purple . . 2·00 85
405 – 200f. violet and blue . . 3·50 2·10
406 – 500f. blue and indigo . . 8·50 4·25
DESIGNS: 100f. "Gemini 4", and White in space; 200f. "Gemini 5"; 500f. "Gemini 6" and "Gemini 7" making rendezvous.

103 Mountain's Hotel, Buea

1966. Cameroun Hotels.
407 **103** 9f. bistre, green and red (postage) 30 15
408 – 20f. black, green & blue . . 35 20

409 – 35f. red, brown & green 60 40
410 103 18f. black, grn & bl (air) 35 20
411 – 25f. indigo, red and blue 55 20
412 – 50f. brown, orange & grn 5·25 3·00
413 – 60f. brown, green & blue 1·40 55
414 – 85f. blue, red and green 1·75 65
415 – 100f. purple, blue & grn 2·40 95
416 – 150f. orange, brn & blue 3·25 1·60
HOTELS—HORIZ: 20f. Deputies, Yaounde. 25f. Akwa Palace, Douala. 35f. Dschang. 50f. Terminus, Yaounde. 60f. Imperial, Yaounde. 85f. Independence, Yaounde. 150f. Huts, Waza Camp. VERT: 100f. Hunting Lodge, Mora.

104 Foumban Bas-relief

1966. World Festival of Negro Arts, Dakar
417 104 9f. black and red 55 15
418 – 18f. purple, brn and grn 55 30
419 – 20f. brown, blue & violet 80 30
420 – 25f. brown and plum 90 30
DESIGNS—VERT: 18f. Ekoi mask; 20f. Bamileke statue. HORIZ: 25f. Bamoun stool.

105 W.H.O. Headquarters, Geneva   106 "Phaeomeria magnifica"

1966. U.N. Agency Buildings.
421 105 50f. lake, blue and yellow 90 50
422 – 50f. yellow, blue & green 90 50
DESIGN: No. 422, I.T.U. Headquarters, Geneva.

1966. Flowers. Multicoloured. (a) Postage. Size as T 106.
423 9f. Type 106 45 15
424 15f. "Strelitzia reginae" 65 15
425 18f. "Hibiscus schizopetalus x rosa-sinensis" 55 20
426 20f. "Antigonon leptopus" 55 15
(b) Air. Size 26 × 45½ mm.
427 25f. "Hibiscus mutabilis" ("Caprice des dames") 80 20
428 50f. "Delonix regia" 1·40 30
429 100f. "Bougainvillea glabra" 2·50 50
430 200f. "Thevetia peruviana" 3·75 1·50
431 250f. "Hippeastrum equestre" 4·50 1·90
For stamps as Type 106 but showing fruits, see Nos. 463/71.

107 Mobile Gendarmerie

1966. Air. Cameroun Armed Forces.
432 107 20f. blue, brown & plum 45 20
433 – 25f. green, violet & brown 45 20
434 – 60f. indigo, green & blue 1·60 80
435 – 100f. blue, red & purple 2·40 95
DESIGNS: 25f. Paratrooper; 60f. Gunboat "Vigilant"; 100f. Dassault MD-315 Flamant airplane.

108 Wembley Stadium

1966. Air. World Cup Football Championships.
436 108 50f. green, blue and red 1·40 45
437 – 200f. red, blue and green 3·75 2·10
DESIGN: 200f. Footballers.

109 Douglas DC-8F Jet Trader and "Air Afrique Emblem"

1966. Air. Inauguration of DC-8 Air Service.
438 109 25f. grey, black & purple 60 35

110 U.N. General Assembly

1966. 6th Anniv of Admission to U.N.
439 110 50f. purple, green & blue 65 20
440 – 100f. blue, brown & green 1·40 65
DESIGN—VERT: 100f. Africans encircling U.N. emblem within figure "6".

111 1st Minister's Residency, Buea (side view)

1966. 5th Anniv of Cameroun's Reunification. Multicoloured.
441 9f. Type 111 30 15
442 18f. Prime Minister's Residency, Yaounde (front view) 40 20
443 20f. As 18f. but side view 45 30
444 25f. As Type 111 but front view 55 30

112 Learning to Write

1966. 20th Anniv of U.N.E.S.C.O. and U.N.I.C.E.F.
445 112 50f. brown, purple & blue 90 45
446 – 50f. black, blue & purple 90 45
DESIGN: No. 446. Cameroun children.

113 Buea Cathedral

1966. Air. Religious Buildings.
447 113 18f. purple, blue & green 35 20
448 – 25f. violet, brown & green 45 20
449 – 30f. lake, green & purple 55 30
450 – 60f. green, red & turquoise 1·10 50
BUILDINGS: 25f. Yaounde Cathedral. 30f. Orthodox Church, Yaounde. 60f. Garoua Mosque.

114 Proclamation

1967. 7th Anniv of Independence.
451 114 20f. red, green & yellow 1·90 1·10

115 Map of Africa, Railway Lines and Signals   117 Aircraft and I.C.A.O. Emblem

116 Lions Emblem and Jungle

1967. 5th African and Malagasy Railway Technicians Conference, Yaounde. Multicoloured.
452 20f. Type 115 2·00 1·00
453 20f. Map of Africa and diesel train 3·25 1·25

1967. 50th Anniv of Lions International. Mult.
454 50f. Type 116 80 45
455 100f. Lions emblem and palms 1·75 95

1967. International Civil Aviation Organization.
456 117 50f. multicoloured 90 45

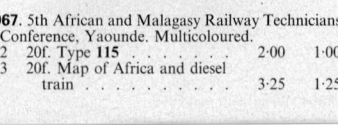
118 Dove and I.A.E.A. Emblem

1967. International Atomic Energy Agency.
457 118 50f. blue and green 90 45

119 Rotary Banner and Emblem

1967. 10th Anniv of Cameroun Branch, Rotary Int.
458 119 25f. red, gold and blue 80 45

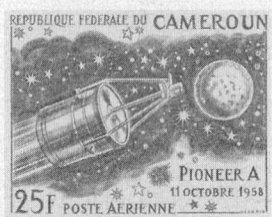
120 "Pioneer A"

1967. Air. "Conquest of the Moon".
459 120 25f. green, brown & blue 40 20
460 – 50f. violet, purple & grn 85 35
461 – 100f. purple, brown & bl 2·00 85
462 – 250f. purple, grey and brown 4·50 2·50
DESIGNS: 50f. "Ranger 6"; 100f. "Luna 9"; 250f. "Luna 10".

121 Grapefruit   122 Sanaga Waterfalls

1967. Fruits. Multicoloured.
463 1f. Type 121 10 10
464 2f. Papaw 10 10
465 3f. Custard-apple 15 15
466 4f. Breadfruit 15 15
467 5f. Coconut 30 15
468 6f. Mango 35 15
469 8f. Avocado 65 30
470 10f. Pineapple 1·10 40
471 30f. Bananas 3·00 1·25

1967. International Tourist Year.
472 122 30f. multicoloured 55 30

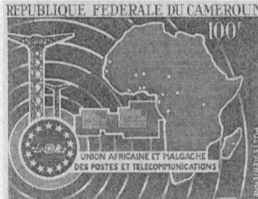
123 Map, Letters and Pylons

1967. Air. 5th Anniv of African and Malagasy Posts and Telecommunications Union (U.A.M.P.T.).
473 123 100f. pur, lake & turq 2·00 85

124 Harvesting Coconuts (carved box)   125 Crossed Skis

1967. Cameroun Art.
474 124 10f. brown, red and blue 30 15
475 – 20f. brown, green & yell 45 30
476 – 30f. brown, red & green 65 30
477 – 100f. brown, red & grn 2·00 70
DESIGNS (Carved boxes): 20f. Lion-hunting; 30f. Harvesting coconuts (different); 100f. Carved chest.

1967. Air. Winter Olympic Games, Grenoble.
478 125 30f. brown and blue 1·40 65

126 Cameroun Exhibit

1967. Air. World Fair, Montreal.
479 126 50f. brown, chest & pur 90 35
480 – 100f. brown, purple & grn 2·75 95
481 – 200f. green, purple & brn 3·75 1·90
DESIGNS: 100f. Totem poles; 200f. African pavilion.
For No. 481 optd PREMIER HOMME SUR LA LUNE 20 JUILLET 1969/FIRST MAN LANDING ON MOON 20 JULY 1969 see note below Nos. 512/17.

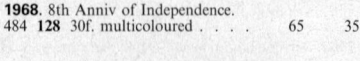
127 Chancellor Adenauer and Cologne Cathedral   128 Arms of the Republic

1967. Air. Adenauer Commem. Multicoloured.
482 30f. Type 127 80 30
483 70f. Adenauer and Chancellor's residence, Bonn 1·75 55

1968. 8th Anniv of Independence.
484 128 30f. multicoloured 65 35

129 Pres. Ahidjo and King Faisal of Saudi Arabia

1968. Air. Pres. Ahidjo's Pilgrimage to Mecca and Visit to the Vatican. Multicoloured.
485 30f. Type **129** 65 35
486 60f. Pope Paul VI greeting Pres. Ahidjo . . . . 1·60 55

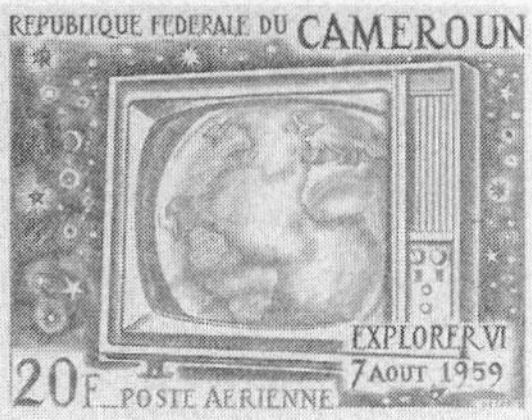

130 "Explorer VI" (televised picture of Earth)

1968. Air. Telecommunications Satellites.
487 **130** 20f. grey, red and blue . . 40 20
488 – 30f. blue, indigo and red 55 30
489 – 40f. green, red & plum . . 80 40
DESIGNS: 30f. "Molnya"; 40f. "Molnya" (televised picture of Earth).

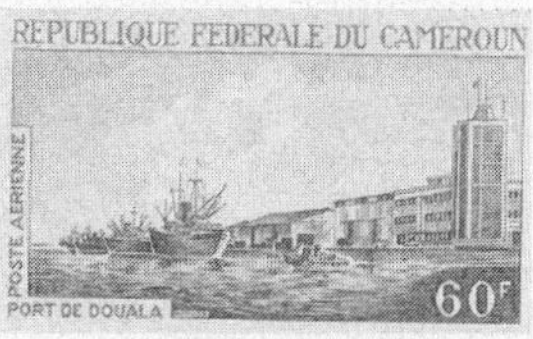

131 Douala Port

1968. Air. Five-year Development Plan.
490 – 20f. blue, red and green 35 20
491 – 30f. blue, green & brown 4·25 1·75
492 – 30f. blue, brown & green 65 30
493 – 40f. brown, green & turq 65 30
494 **131** 60f. purple, indigo & blue 1·75 70
DESIGNS—VERT: 20f. Steel forge; 30f. (No. 491), "Transcamerounais" express train leaving tunnel; 30f. (No. 492), Tea-harvesting; 40f. Rubber-tapping.

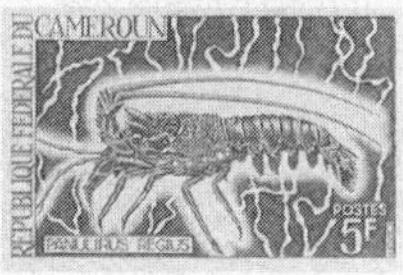

132 Spiny Lobster

1968. Fishes and Crustaceans.
495 **132** 5f. green, brown & violet 15 15
496 – 10f. slate, brown & blue 20 15
497 – 15f. brown, chest & pur 60 15
498 – 20f. brown and blue . . . 70 15
499 – 25f. blue, brown and green 80 45
500 – 30f. brown, blue and red 1·00 45
501 – 40f. blue, brown & orge 1·40 55
502 – 50f. red, slate and green 2·00 65
503 – 55f. purple, brown & blue 2·75 1·10
504 – 60f. blue, purple & green 4·25 1·40
FISHES AND CRUSTACEANS—HORIZ: 10f. Freshwater crayfish. 15f. Nile mouthbrooder. 20f. Sole. 25f. Northern pike. 30f. Swimming crab. 55f. Dusky snakehead. 60f. Capitaine threadfin. VERT: 40f. African spadefish. 50f. Prawn.

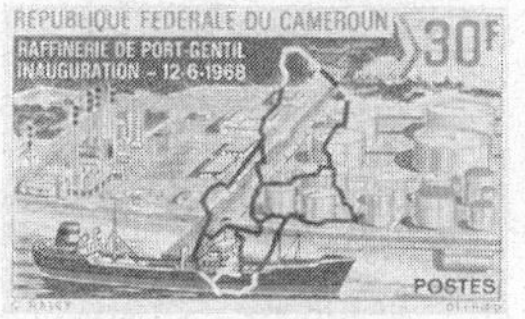

133 Refinery and Tanker

1968. Inauguration of Petroleum Refinery, Port Gentil, Gabon.
505 **133** 30f. multicoloured . . . . 1·00 40

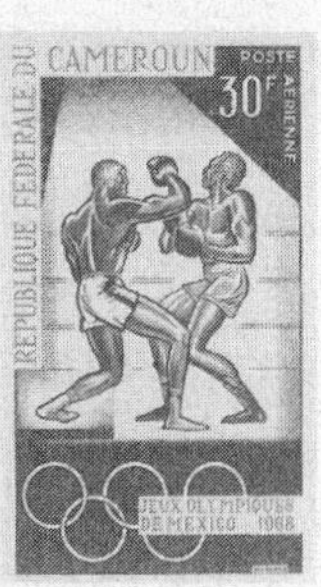

134 Boxing

1968. Air. Olympic Games, Mexico.
506 **134** 30f. brown, green & emer 60 30
507 – 50f. brown, red & green 1·25 50
508 – 60f. brown, blue & green 1·50 55
DESIGNS: 50f. Long-jumping; 60f. Gymnastics.

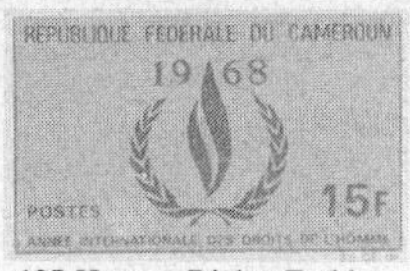

135 Human Rights Emblem

1968. Human Rights Year.
510 **135** 15f. blue & orge (postage) 45 20
511 30f. green & purple (air) 55 35

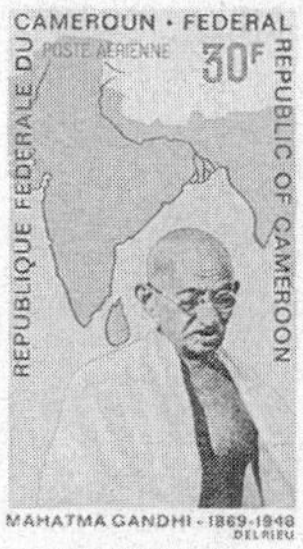

136 Mahatma Gandhi and Map of India

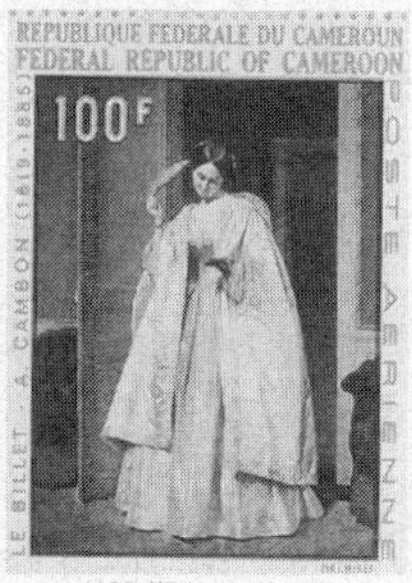

137 "The Letter" (A. Cambon)

1968. Air. "Apostles of Peace".
512 **136** 30f. black, yellow & blue 45 30
513 – 30f. black and blue . . . 45 30
514 – 40f. black and pink . . . 65 55
515 – 60f. black and lilac . . . 90 65
516 – 70f. black, blue & buff . . 1·25 80
517 – 70f. black and green . . . 1·25 80
PORTRAITS: No. 513, Martin Luther King. No. 514, J. F. Kennedy. No. 515, R. F. Kennedy. No. 516, Gandhi (full-face). No. 517, Martin Luther King (half-length).

During 1969, Nos. 481 and 512/17 were issued optd **PREMIER HOMME SUR LA LUNE 20 JUILLET 1969/FIRST MAN LANDING ON MOON 20 JULY 1969** in very limited quantities.

1968. Air. "Philexafrique" Stamp Exhibition, Abidjan (in 1969). (1st issue).
519 **137** 100f. multicoloured . . . 3·00 2·40

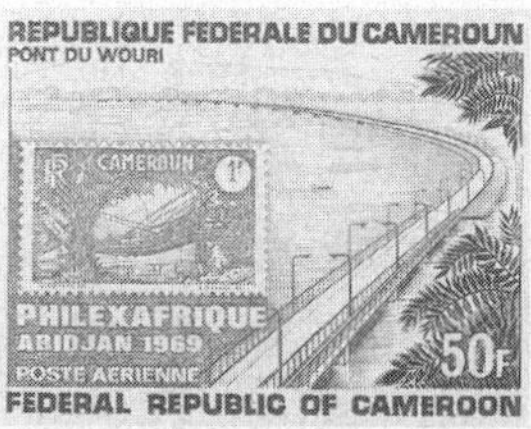

138 Wouri Bridge and 1f. stamp of 1925

1969. Air. "Philexafrique" Stamp Exhibition, Abidjan, Ivory Coast (2nd issue).
520 **138** 50f. blue, olive and green 1·50 1·10

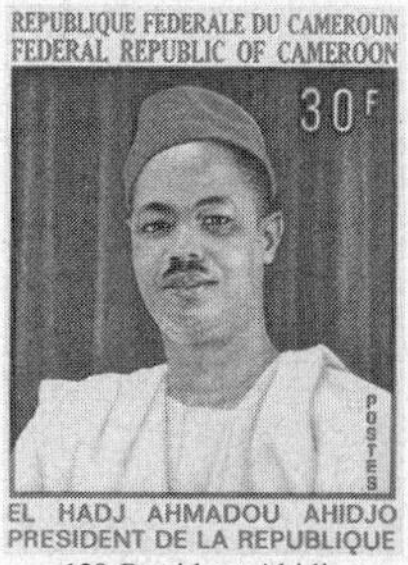

139 President Ahidjo

1969. 9th Anniv of Independence.
521 **139** 30f. multicoloured 65 25

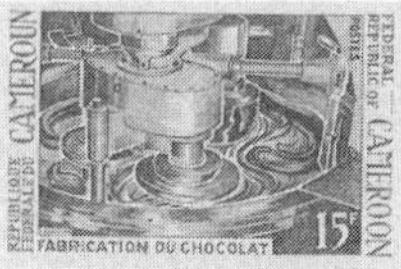

140 Vat of Chocolate

1969. Chocolate Industry Development.
522 **140** 15f. blue, brown and red 30 20
523 – 30f. brown, choc & grn 55 30
524 – 50f. red, green & bistre 80 35
DESIGNS—HORIZ: 30f. Chocolate factory. VERT: 50f. Making confectionery.

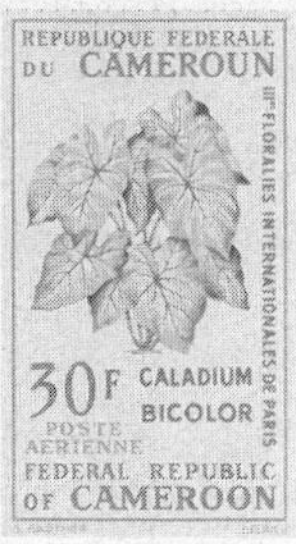

141 "Caladium bicolor"

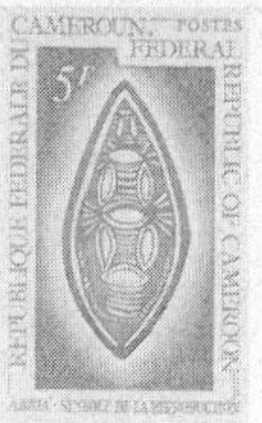

142 Reproduction Symbol

1969. Air. 3rd Int Flower Show, Paris. Mult.
525 30f. Type **141** 65 45
526 50f. "Aristolochia elegans" 1·40 65
527 100f. "Gloriosa simplex" . . 3·00 1·40

1969. Abbia Arts and Folklore.
528 **142** 5f. purple, turq & blue . . 20 15
529 – 10f. orange, olive & blue 30 15
530 – 15f. indigo, red & blue . . 40 20
531 – 30f. green, brown & blue 60 30
532 – 70f. red, green and blue 1·50 70
DESIGNS—HORIZ: 10f. "Two Toucans"; 30f. "Vulture attacking Monkey". VERT: 15f. Forest Symbol; 70f. Oliphant-player.

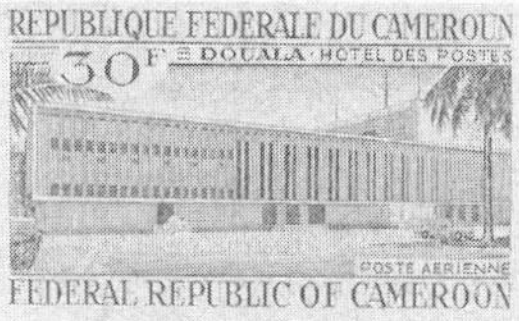

143 Post Office, Douala

1969. Air. New Post Office Buildings.
533 **143** 30f. brown, blue & green 40 20
534 – 50f. red, slate & turquoise 65 35
535 – 100f. brown and turquoise 1·40 65
DESIGNS: 50f. G.P.O., Buea; 100f. G.P.O., Bafoussam.

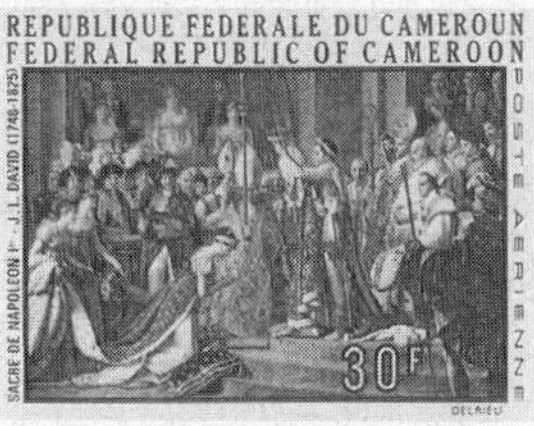

144 "Coronation of Napoleon" (David)

1969. Air. Birth Bicent of Napoleon Bonaparte.
536 **144** 30f. multicoloured 90 55
537 – 1,000f. gold . . . . . . 35·00
DESIGN: 1,000f. "Napoleon crossing the Alps". No. 537 is embossed on gold foil.

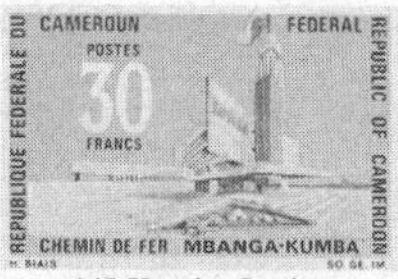

145 Kumba Station

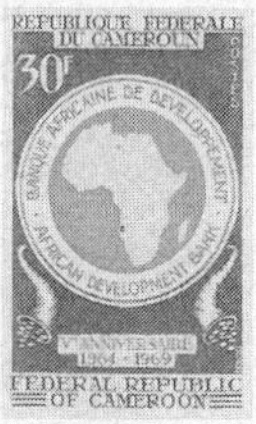

146 Bank Emblem

1969. Opening of Mbanga–Kumba Railway. Mult.
538 30f. Type **145** . . . . 1·00 75
539 50f. Diesel train on bridge over River Mungo (vert) 3·25 1·50

1969. 5th Anniv of African Development Bank.
540 **146** 30f. brown, green & vio 60 30

1969. Air. Negro Writers. Portrait designs as T **136**.
541 15f. brown and blue 40 20
542 30f. brown and purple . . . 50 20
543 30f. brown and yellow . . . 50 20
544 50f. brown and green 70 40
545 50f. brown and agate 70 40
546 100f. brown and yellow . . . 1·75 1·10
DESIGNS—VERT: No. 541, Dr. P. Mars (Haiti); No. 542, W. Dubois (U.S.A.); No. 543, A. Cesaire (Martinique); No. 544, M. Garvey (Jamaica); No. 545, L. Hughes (U.S.A.); No. 546, R. Maran (Martinique).

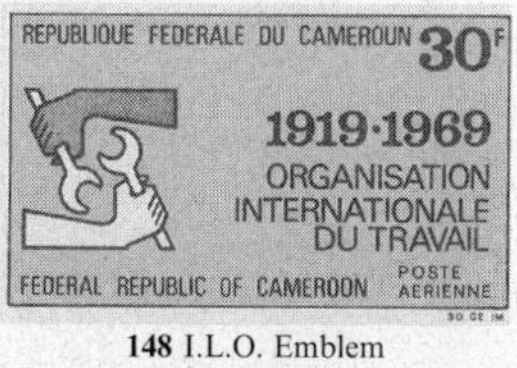

148 I.L.O. Emblem

1969. Air. 50th Anniv of I.L.O.
548 **148** 30f. black and turquoise 55 30
549 50f. black and mauve . . 90 40

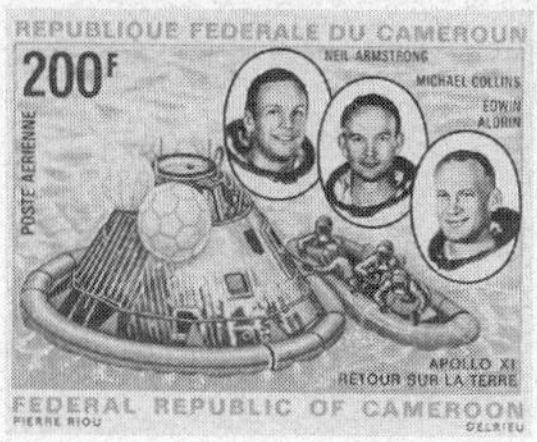

149 Astronauts and "Apollo 11" in Sea

1969. Air. 1st Man on the Moon. Multicoloured.
550 200f. Type **149** . . . . 3·25 1·75
551 500f. Astronaut and module on Moon . . . . 7·75 3·50

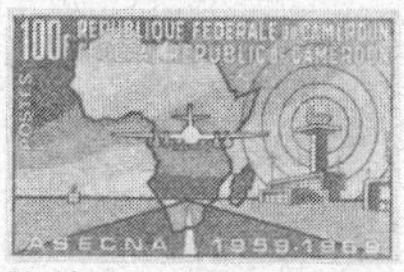

150 Airplane, Map and Airport

1969. 10th Anniv of Aerial Navigation Security Agency for Africa and Madagascar (ASECNA).
552 **150** 100f. green . . . . 1·50 70

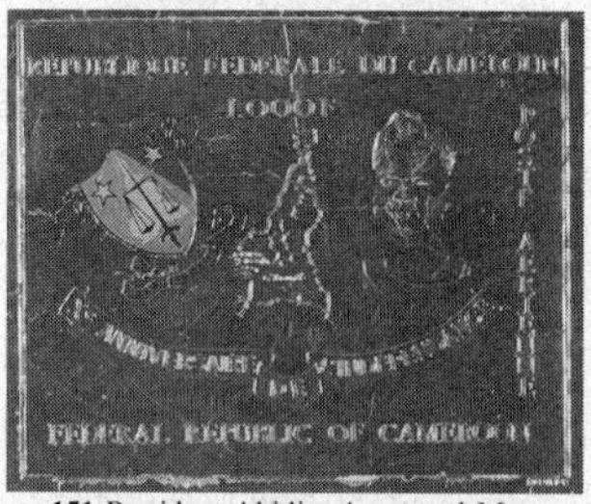

151 President Ahidjo, Arms and Map

1970. Air. 10th Anniv of Independence.
553 **151** 1,000f. gold & mult . . . 21·00
No. 553 is embossed on gold foil.

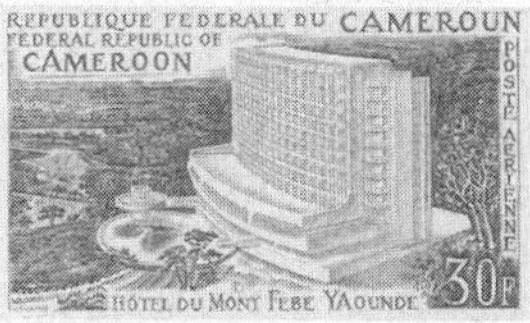

152 Mont Febe Hotel, Yaounde

1970. Air. Tourism.
554 **152** 30f. grey, green & brn . . 60 30

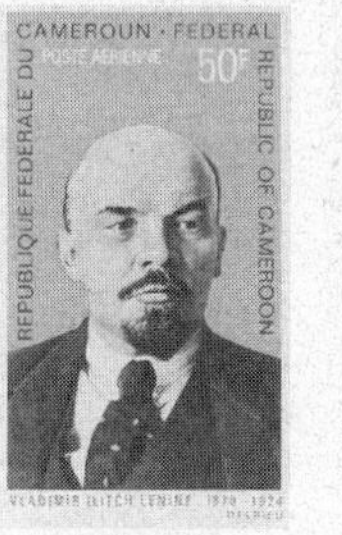

153 Lenin

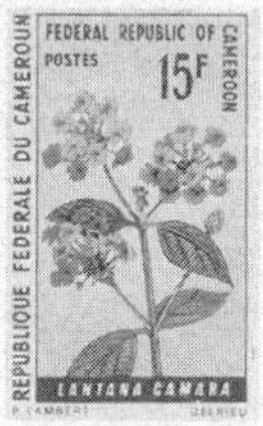

154 "Lantana camara"

1970. Air. Birth Centenary of Lenin.
555 **153** 50f. brown and yellow . . 1·40 35

1970. African Climbing Plants. Multicoloured.
556 15f. Type **154** (postage) . . . 35 15
557 30f. "Passiflora quadrangularis" 80 20
558 50f. "Cleome speciosa" (air) 1·40 55
559 100f. "Mussaenda erythrophylla" . . . . . . 2·50 1·40

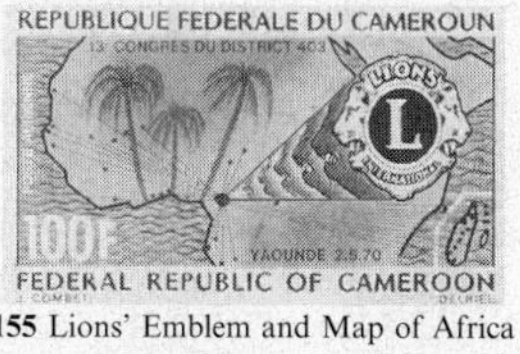

155 Lions' Emblem and Map of Africa

1970. Air. 13th Congress of Lions International District 403, Yaounde.
560 **155** 100f. multicoloured . . . 1·90 80

156 New U.P.U. H.Q

1970. New U.P.U. Headquarters Building, Berne.
561 **156** 30f. green, violet & blue 55   30
562   50f. blue, red and grey 80   30

157 U.N. Emblem and Stylized Doves

1970. Air. 25th Anniv of United Nations.
563 **157** 30f. brown and orange . .   65   30
564   50f. indigo and blue . .   90   40
DESIGN—VERT: 50f. U.N. emblem and stylized dove.

158 Fermenting Vats

1970. Brewing Industry.
565 **158** 15f. brown, green & grey   35   20
566   30f. red, brown and blue   65   30
DESIGN: 30f. Storage tanks.

159 Japanese Pavilion

1970. Air. Expo 70.
567 **159** 50f. blue, red and green   90   45
568   100f. red, blue and green   1·90   80
569   150f. brown, slate & blue   3·00   1·50
DESIGNS—VERT: 100f. Expo Emblem and Map of Japan. HORIZ: 150f. Australian Pavilion.

160 Gen. De Gaulle in   **162** Dancers
Tropical Kit

161 Aztec Stadium, Mexico City

1970. Air. "Homage to General De Gaulle".
570 **160** 100f. brown, blue & grn   2·50   1·60
571   200f. blue, green & brn   4·50   2·25
DESIGN: 200f. Gen. De Gaulle in military uniform.
Nos. 570/1 were issued together as a triptych, separated by a stamp-size label showing maps of France and Cameroun.

1970. Air. World Cup Football Championships, Mexico. Multicoloured.
572   50f. Type **161**   80   40
573   100f. Mexican team . . . . 1·75   1·00
574   200f. Pele and Brazilian team
     with World Cup (vert) . . . . 3·00   1·40

1970. Ozila Dancers.
575 **162** 30f. red, orange & grn . .   70   35
576   50f. red, brown & scar . . 1·90   80

163 Doll in National   **164** Beethoven (after
Costume   Stieler)

1970. Cameroun Dolls.
577 **163** 10f. green, black & red . .   45   35
578   15f. red, green & yellow   55   45
579   30f. brown, green & blk   1·50   55

1970. Air. Birth Bicent of Beethoven.
580 **164** 250f. multicoloured . . . . 3·75   1·90

1970. Air. Rembrandt Paintings. As T **144**. Mult.
581   70f. "Christ at Emmaus" . . 1·40   45
582   150f. "The Anatomy Lesson" 2·50   95

166 "Industry and   **167** Bust of Dickens
Agriculture"

1970. "Europafrique" Economic Community.
583 **166** 30f. multicoloured   60   30

1970. Air. Death Centenary of Charles Dickens.
584 **167** 40f. brown and red . . .   65   30
585   50f. multicoloured   80   35
586   100f. multicoloured . . . . 1·40   90
DESIGNS: 50f. Characters from David Copperfield; 100f. Dickens writing.

1971. Air. De Gaulle Memorial Issue. Nos. 570/1 optd **IN MEMORIAM 1890-1970**.
587 **160** 100f. brown, blue & grn   2·50   1·40
588   200f. blue, green & brn   4·50   2·00

169 University Buildings

1971. Inauguration of Federal University, Yaounde.
589 **169** 50f. green, blue & brown   65   30

170 Presidents Ahidjo and Pompidou

1971. Visit of Pres. Pompidou of France.
590 **170** 30f. multicoloured   90   55

171 "Cameroun Youth"

1971. 5th National Youth Festival.
591 **171** 30f. multicoloured   55   30

172 Timber Yard, Douala

1971. Air. Industrial Expansion.
592 **172** 40f. brown, green & red   40   20
593   70f. brown, green and
     blue   90   40
594   100f. red, blue & green . . 1·50   50
DESIGNS—VERT: 70f. "Alucam" aluminium plant, Edea. HORIZ: 100f. Mbakaou Dam.

173 "Gerbera hybrida"   **174** "World Races"

1971. Flowers. Multicoloured.
595   20f. Type **173**   45   35
596   40f. "Opuntia polyantha" . . 1·00   45
597   50f. "Hemerocallis hybrida" 1·40   55
    For similar designs inscr "United Republic of Cameroon" etc., see Nos. 648/52.

1971. Racial Equality Year. Multicoloured.
598   20f. Type **174**   35   15
599   30f. Hands of four races
     clasping globe   50   20

175 Crowned Cranes, Camp de
Waza

1971. Landscapes.
600 **175** 10f. blue, red and green   1·00   30
601   20f. red, brown & green   40   25
602   30f. green, blue & brown   55   25
DESIGNS: 20f. African pirogue; 30f. Sanaga River.

176 Relay-racing

1971. Air. 75th Anniv of Modern Olympic Games.
603 **176** 30f. blue, red and brown   45   30
604   50f. purple and blue . .   65   30
605   100f. black, green & red   1·40   55
DESIGNS—VERT: 50f. Olympic runner with torch. HORIZ: 100f. Throwing the discus.

177 "Villalba" (deep-sea trawler)

1971. Air. Fishing Industry.
606 **177** 30f. brown, green & blue   65   45
607   40f. purple, blue & green   80   45
608   70f. brown, red and blue   1·75   65
609   150f. multicoloured . . . 3·75   1·75
DESIGNS: 40f. Traditional fishing method, Northern Cameroun; 70f. Fish quay, Douala; 150f. Shrimp-boats, Douala.

178 Peace Palace, The Hague

1971. 25th Anniv of International Court of Justice, The Hague.
610 **178** 50f. brown, blue & green   65   30

179 1916 French Occupation 20c. and
1914-18 War Memorial, Yaounde

1971. Air. "Philatecam 71" Stamp Exhibition, Yaounde (1st issue).
611 **179** 20f. brown, ochre & grn   35   20
612   25f. brown, green & blue   40   20
613   40f. green, grey & brown   65   20
614   50f. multicoloured   85   35
615   100f. green, brown & orge   2·00   65
DESIGNS: 25f. 1954 15f. Jamot stamp and memorial; 40f. 1965 25f. Tourist Office stamp and public buildings, Yaounde; 50f. German stamp and Imperial German postal emblem; 100f. 1915 Expeditionary Force optd, error, and Expeditionary Force memorial.
See also No. 620.

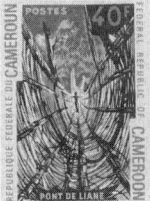 

180 Rope Bridge   **181** Bamoun Horseman
(carving)

1971. "Rural Life". Multicoloured.
616   40f. Type **180**   70   20
617   45f. Local market (horiz) . .   85   30

1971. Cameroun Carving.
618 **181** 10f. brown and yellow . .   35   15
619   15f. brown and yellow . .   35   20
DESIGN: 15f. Fetish statuette.

182 Pres. Ahidjo, Flag and "Reunification
Road

1971. Air. "Philatecam 71" Stamp Exhibition, Yaounde (2nd issue).
620 **182** 250f. multicoloured . . . 5·25   3·75

183 Satellite and Globe

1971. Pan-African Telecommunications Network.
621 **183** 40f. multicoloured   55   35

184 U.A.M.P.T. Headquarters, Brazzaville and
Carved Stool

1971. Air. 10th Anniv of African and Malagasy Posts and Telecommunications Union.
622 **184** 100f. multicoloured . . . 1·40   65

185 Children acclaiming Emblem

1971. 25th Anniv of U.N.I.C.E.F.
623 **185** 40f. purple, blue & slate   60   20
624   50f. red, green and blue   70   35
DESIGN—VERT: 50f. Ear of Wheat and Emblem.

186 "The Annunciation" (Fra
Angelico)

1971. Air. Christmas. Paintings. Multicoloured.
625 40f. Type 186 45   15
626 45f. "Virgin and Child" (Del
      Sarto) 55   30
627 150f. "The Holy Family with
      the Lamb" (detail Raphael)
      (vert) . . . . 2·75   95

187 Cabin, South-Central Region

1972. Traditional Cameroun Houses. Mult.
628 10f. Type 187 20   15
629 15f. Adamaoua round house . 35   15

188 Airline Emblem

1972. Air. Cameroun Airlines' Inaugural Flight.
630 188 50f. multicoloured 55   20

189 Giraffe and   190 Africa Cup
Palm Tree

1972. Festival of Youth. Multicoloured.
631 2f. Type 189 15   10
632 5f. Domestic scene 15   10
633 10f. Blacksmith (horiz) . . . 20   15
634 15f. Women 20   15

1972. African Football Cup Championships. Mult.
635 20f. Type 190 45   20
636 40f. Players with ball (horiz) . 65   35
637 45f. Team captains . . . . . 1·10   35

191 "St. Mark's Square and Doge's
Palace (detail–Caffi)

1972. Air. U.N.E.S.C.O. "Save Venice" Campaign,
Multicoloured.
638 40f. Type 191 55   30
639 100f. "Regatta on the Grand
      Canal" (detail – Canaletto) . 1·75   55
640 200f. "Regatta on the Grand
      Canal" (detail – Canaletto)
      (different) . . . . 3·50   1·40

192 Assembly Building, Yaounde

1972. 110th Session of Inter-Parliamentary Council,
Yaounde.
641 192 40f. multicoloured 55   30

193 Horseman, North Cameroun

1972. Traditional Life and Folklore. Mult.
642 15f. Type 193 30   15
643 20f. Bororo woman (vert) . . 35   15
644 40f. Wouri River and Mt.
      Cameroun . . . . 1·40   45

194 Pataiev, Dobrovolsky and Volkov

1972. Air. "Soyuz 11" Cosmonauts. Memorial Issue.
645 194 50f. multicoloured 65   35

195 U.N. Building, New York,
Gate of Heavenly Peace, Peking
and Chinese Flag

1972. Air. Admission of Chinese People's Republic to
U.N.
646 195 50f. multicoloured 55   20

196 Chemistry Laboratory, Federal
University

1972. Pres. Ahidjo Prize.
647 196 40f. red, green & purple . 55   35

1972. Flowers. As T 173, but inscr "UNITED
REPUBLIC OF CAMEROON", etc. Mult.
648 40f. "Solanum macranthum" . 55   20
649 40f. "Kaempferia aethiopica" . 65   20
650 45f. "Hoya carnosa" 65   35
651 45f. "Cassia alata" 65   20
652 50f. "Crinum sanderianum" . 90   35

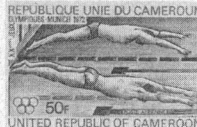

197 Swimming

1972. Air. Olympic Games, Munich.
653 197 50f. green, brown & lake . 80   35
654 – 50f. brown, blue and sepia . 80   35
655 – 200f. lake, grey & purple . 3·25   1·40
DESIGNS—HORIZ: No. 655, Horse-jumping.
VERT: No. 654, Boxing.

198 "Charaxes   201 Great Blue
ameliae"   Turacos

1972. Butterflies. Multicoloured.
657 40f. Type 198 . . . . 2·00   55
658 45f. "Papiliotyndaraeus" . . 2·50   1·10

1972. No. 471 surch.
659 40f. on 30f. multicoloured . . 60   40

1972. Air. Olympic Gold Medal Winners. Nos. 653/
5 optd as listed below.
660 50f. green, brown and red . . 80   35
661 50f. brown, blue and sepia . 80   35
662 200f. lake, grey and purple . 3·25   1·40
OVERPRINTS: No. 660, NATATION MARK
SPITZ 7 MEDAILLES D'OR. No. 661, SUPER-
WELTER KOTTYSCH MEDAILLE D'OR.

No. 662, CONCOURS COMPLET MEADE
MEDAILLE D'OR.

1972. Birds. Multicoloured.
663 10f. Type 201 . . . . 1·00   50
664 45f. Red-faced lovebirds
      (horiz) . . . . 2·25   1·00

202 "The Virgin with   203 St. Theresa
Angels" (Cimabue)

1972. Air. Christmas. Multicoloured.
665 45f. Type 202 80   35
666 140f. "The Madonna of the
      Rose Arbour" (S. Lochner) . 2·25   1·25

1973. Air. Birth Centenary of St. Theresa of Lisieux.
667 203 45f. blue, brown & violet . 55   20
668 – 100f. mauve, brown, & bl . 1·40   55
DESIGN: 100f. Lisieux Basilica.

204 Emperor Haile Selassie and "Africa
Hall", Addis Ababa

1973. Air. 80th Birthday of Emperor Haile Selassie
of Ethiopia.
669 204 45f. multicoloured 60   35

205 Cotton Cultivation,   207 Human Hearts
North Cameroun

206 "Food for All"

1973. 3rd Five Year Plan. Multicoloured.
670 5f. Type 205 10   10
671 10f. Cacao pods, South-
      central region 10   10
672 15f. Forestry, South-eastern
      area 20   10
673 20f. Coffee plant, West
      Cameroun 45   15
674 45f. Tea-picking, West
      Cameroun 95   30

1973. Air. 10th Anniv of World Food Programme.
675 206 45f. multicoloured 60   35

1973. Air. 25th Anniv of W.H.O.
676 207 50f. red and blue 60   35

208 Pres. Ahidjo, Map, Flag and
Cameroun Stamp

1973. 1st Anniv of United Republic. Mult.
677 10f. Type 208 (postage) . . . 45   20
678 20f. Pres. Ahidjo,
      proclamation and stamp . . 65   35

679 45f. Pres. Ahidjo, map of
      Cameroun rivers and
      stamp (air) 55   20
680 70f. Significant dates on
      Cameroun flag 80   50

209 Mask   210 Dr. G. A. Hansen

1973. Bamoun Masks.
681 209 5f. black, brown & green . 10   10
682 – 10f. brown, black &
      purple 20   10
683 – 45f. brown, black & red . 55   30
684 – 100f. brown, black & blue . 1·40   55
DESIGNS: 10f., 45f., 100f., as Type 209, but different
masks.

1973. Centenary of Hansen's Identification of
Leprosy Bacillus.
685 210 45f. blue, lt blue & brown . 55   30

211 Scout Emblem and   213 Folk-dancers
Flags

1973. Air. Admission of Cameroun to 24th World
Scout Conference.
686 211 40f. multicoloured 50   30
687 – 45f. multicoloured 60   35
688 – 100f. multicoloured . . . . 1·40   60

1973. African Solidarity "Drought Relief". No. 670
surch 100F. SECHERESSE SOLIDARITE
AFRICAINE.
689 205 100f. on 5f. multicoloured . 1·25   90

1973. Folklore Dances of South-west Cameroun.
Multicoloured.
690 10f. Type 213 15   10
691 25f. Dancer in plumed hat . . 45   15
692 45f. Dancers with "totem" . . 80   30

214 W.M.O. Emblem

1973. Centenary of W.M.O.
693 214 45f. blue and green . . . 55   30

215 Garoua Party H.Q. Building

1973. 7th Anniv of Cameroun National Union.
694 215 40f. multicoloured 55   30

216 Crane with Letter and
Telecommunications Emblem

1973. 12th Anniv of U.A.M.P.T.
695 216 100f. blue, lt blue & green . 1·40   55

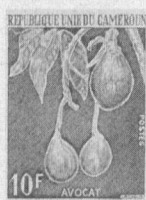

217 African Mask and Old Town Hall, Brussels   218 Avocado

1973. Air. African Fortnight, Brussels.
696   217   40f. brown and purple   55   30

1973. Cameroun Fruits. Multicoloured.
697   10f. Type **218**   30   15
698   20f. Mango   35   15
699   45f. Plum   85   20
700   50f. Custard-apple   1·25   35

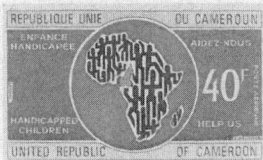

219 Map of Africa

1973. Air. Aid for Handicapped Children.
701   219   40f. red, brown & green   55   35

220 Kirdi Village

1973. Cameroun Villages.
702   220   15f. black, green & brown   20   15
703   –   45f. brown, red & orange   50   30
704   –   50f. black, green & orange   70   35
DESIGNS: 45f. Mabas village. 50f. Fishing village.

221 Earth Station

1973. Air. Inauguration of Satellite Earth Station, Zamengoe.
705   221   100f. brown, blue & grn   1·10   55

222 "The Madonna with Chancellor Rolin" (Van Eyck)   223 Handclasp on Map of Africa

1973. Air. Christmas. Multicoloured.
706   45f. Type **222**   80   40
707   140f. "The Nativity" (Federico Fiori–Il Barocci)   2·25   1·50

1974. 10th Anniv of Organization of African Unity.
708   223   40f. blue, red and green   40   20
709   –   45f. green, blue and red   50   20

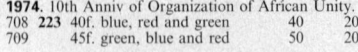

224 Mill-worker

1974. C.I.C.A.M. Industrial Complex.
710   224   45f. brown, green & red   55   20

225 Bilinga Carved Panel (detail)

1974. Cameroun Art.
711   225   10f. brown and green   20   15
712   –   40f. brown and red   50   20
713   –   45f. red and blue   70   30
DESIGNS: 40f. Tubinga carving (detail); 45f. Acajou Ngollon carved panel (detail).

1974. No. 469 surch.
714   40f. on 8f. multicoloured   60   30

227 Cameroun Cow   228 Route-map and Track

1974. Cattle-raising in North Cameroun. Mult.
715   40f. Type **227** (postage)   65   30
716   45f. Cattle in pen (air)   65   35

1974. Trans-Cameroun Railway. Inauguration of Yaounde–Ngaoundere Line.
717   228   5f. brown, blue & green   70   55
718   –   20f. brown, blue & violet   1·25   75
719   –   40f. red, blue & green   2·00   1·25
720   –   100f. green, blue & brown   3·75   2·10
DESIGNS—HORIZ: 20f. Laying track; 100f. Railway bridge over Djerem River. VERT: 40f. Welding rails.

229 Sir Winston Churchill

1974. Air. Birth Cent of Sir Winston Churchill.
721   229   100f. black, red & blue   1·10   55

230 Footballer and City Crests

1974. Air. World Cup Football Championships.
722   230   45f. orange, slate & grey   55   20
723   –   100f. orange, slate & grey   1·00   50
724   –   200f. blue, orange & grey   2·00   1·25
DESIGNS: 100f. Goalkeeper and city crests; 200f. World Cup.

1974. Air. West Germany's Victory in World Cup Football Championships. Nos. 722/4 optd **7th JULY 1974 R.F.A. 2 HOLLANDE 1 7 JUILLET 1974**.
725   230   45f. orange, slate & grey   55   20
726   –   100f. orange, slate & grey   1·25   50
727   –   200f. blue, orange & blk   2·40   1·50

232 U.P.U. Emblem and Hands with Letters

1974. Centenary of Universal Postal Union.
728   232   40f. red, blue and green (postage)   65   35
729   –   100f. green, vio & bl (air)   1·40   65
730   –   200f. green, red and blue   2·25   1·40
DESIGNS: 100f. Cameroun U.P.U. headquarters stamps of 1970; 200f. Cameroun U.P.U. 75th anniv stamps of 1949.

233 Copernicus and Solar System

1974. Air. 500th Birth Anniv (1973) of Copernicus.
731   233   250f. blue, red & brown   3·50   2·25

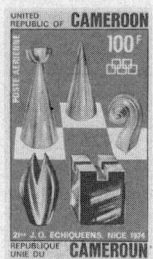

234 Modern Chess Pieces

1974. Air. Chess Olympics, Nice.
732   234   100f. multicoloured   2·75   1·10

235 African Mask and "Arphila" Emblem

1974. Air. "Arphila 75" Stamp Exhibition, Paris.
733   235   50f. brown and red   45   30

236 African Leaders, U.D.E.A.C. H.Q. and Flags

1974. 10th Anniv of Central African Customs and Economics Union.
734   236   40f. mult (postage)   55   30
735   –   100f. multicoloured (air)   1·40   50
DESIGN: 100f. Similar to Type **236**.

1974. No. 717 surch **100F 10 DECEMBRE 1974**.
736   228   100f. on 5f. brn, bl & grn   2·00   1·50

238 "Apollo" Emblem, Astronaut, Module and Astronaut's Boots

1974. Air. 5th Anniv of 1st Landing on Moon.
737   238   200f. brown, red & blue   2·75   1·40

1974. Christmas. As T **222**. Multicoloured.
738   40f. "Virgin of Autumn" (15th-century sculpture)   60   35
739   45f. "Virgin and Child" (Luis de Morales)   80   45

239 De Gaulle and Eboue

1975. Air. 30th Anniv of Felix Eboue ("Free French" leader).
740   239   45f. multicoloured   1·40   55
741   –   200f. multicoloured   4·50   2·50

240 "Celosia cristata"   242 Afo Akom Statue

1975. Flowers of North Cameroun. Mult.
742   5f. Type **240**   15   10
743   40f. "Costus spectabilis"   60   20
744   45f. "Mussaenda erythrophylla"   80   30

241 Fish and Fishing-boat

1975. Offshore Fishing.
745   241   40f. brown, blue & choc   95   30
746   –   45f. brown, bistre & blue   1·25   45
DESIGN: 45f. Fishing-boat and fish in net.

1975.
747   242   40f. multicoloured   45   20
748   –   45f. multicoloured   55   35
749   –   200f. multicoloured   2·10   1·50

243 "Polypore" (fungus)   245 Presbyterian Church, Elat

1975. Natural History. Multicoloured.
750   15f. Type **243**   3·25   1·25
751   40f. "Nymphalis Chrysalis"   2·00   55

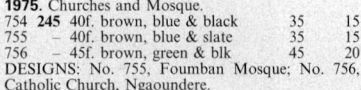

244 View of Building

1975. Inaug of New Ministry of Posts Building.
752   244   40f. blue, green & brown   45   15
753   –   45f. brown, green & blue   65   35

1975. Churches and Mosque.
754   245   40f. brown, blue & black   35   15
755   –   40f. brown, blue & slate   35   15
756   –   45f. brown, green & blk   45   20
DESIGNS: No. 755, Foumban Mosque; No. 756, Catholic Church, Ngaoundere.

246 Marquis de Lafayette (after Chappel) and Naval Battle   247 Harvesting Maize

1975. Air. Bicent (1976) of American Revolution.
757   246   100f. blue, turq & brn   1·75   85
758   –   140f. blue, brown & green   1·90   90
759   –   500f. green, brown & blue   6·00   1·25
DESIGNS: 140f. George Washington (after Stuart)

and Continental Infantry (after Ogden); 500f. Benjamin Franklin (after Peale and Nee) and Boston.

1975. "Green Revolution". Multicoloured.
760 40f. Type **247** 45 15
761 40f. Ploughing with oxen
  (horiz) 40 20

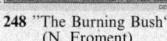

248 "The Burning Bush"
(N. Froment)

1975. Air. Christmas. Multicoloured.
762 50f. Type **248** 55 45
763 500f. "Adoration of the
  Magi" (Gentile da
  Fabriano) (horiz) . . . . . 6·50 4·75

249 Tracking Aerial

1976. Inauguration of Satellite Monitoring Station, Zamengoe. Multicoloured.
764 40f. Type **249** 35 15
765 100f. Close-up of tracking
  aerial (vert) 65 40

250 Porcelain Rose 252 Masked Dancer

251 Concorde

1976. Flowers. Multicoloured.
766 40f. Type **250** 55 15
767 50f. Flower of North
  Cameroun 85 20

1976. Air. Concorde's First Commercial Flight, Paris to Rio de Janeiro.
768 **251** 500f. multicoloured . . . 4·50 2·40

1976. Cameroun Dances. Multicoloured.
770 40f. Type **252** (postage) . . . 55 35
771 50f. Drummers and two
  dancers (air) 45 20
772 100f. Female dancer . . . 90 35

253 Telephone
Exchange

255 Dr. Adenauer and
Cologne Cathedral

254 Young Men Building House

1976. Air. Telephone Centenary.
773 **253** 50f. multicoloured 40 30

1976. 10th Anniv of National Youth Day. Multicoloured.
774 40f. Type **254** 30 15
775 45f. Gathering palm leaves . . 40 15

1976. Birth Centenary of Dr. Konrad Adenauer (Statesman).
776 **255** 100f. multicoloured 65 35

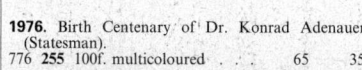

256 "Adoration of the Shepherds" (Charles Le Brun)

1976. Air. Christmas.
777 30f. Type **256** 45 15
778 60f. "Adoration of the Magi"
  (Rubens) 55 40
779 70f. "Virgin and Child"
  (Bellini) 80 40
780 500f. "The New-born" (G. de
  la Tour) . . . . . 5·75 3·50

257 Pres. Ahidjo and Douala Party H.Q.

1976. 10th Anniv of Cameroun National Union. Multicoloured.
782 50f. Type **257** 35 15
783 50f. Pres. Ahidjo and
  Yaounde Party H.Q. . . . 35 15

258 Bamoun Copper
Pipe

259 Crowned Cranes
("Crown-Cranes")

1977. 2nd World Festival of Negro Arts, Nigeria. Multicoloured.
784 50f. Type **258** (postage) . . . 55 30
785 60f. Traditional chief on
  throne (sculpture) (air) . . . 85 35

1977. Cameroun Birds. Multicoloured.
786 30f. Ostrich . . . . . 2·75 65
787 50f. Type **259** . . . . . 2·75 95

260 "Christ on the Cross" (Issenheim Altarpiece, Mathias Grunewald)

1977. Air. Easter. Multicoloured.
788 50f. Type **260** 65 30
789 125f. "Christ on the Cross"
  (Veslasquez) (vert) . . . 1·40 55
790 150f. "The Entombment"
  (Titian) . . . . . 2·25 85

261 Lions Club Emblem 262 Rotary Club
  Emblem, Mountain and
  Road

1977. Air. 19th Congress of Douala Lions Club.
792 **261** 250f. multicoloured . . . 3·25 2·00

1977. Air. 20th Anniv of Douala Rotary Club.
793 **262** 60f. red and blue . . . 50 30

263 Jean Mermoz and Seaplane "Comte de la Vaulx"

1977. Air. History of Aviation.
794 **263** 50f. blue, orange & brown 65 35
795 — 60f. purple and orange . . 70 45
796 — 80f. lake and blue . . . 85 45
797 — 100f. green and yellow . . 1·40 65
798 — 300f. blue, red & purple 4·50 2·40
799 — 500f. purple, grn & plum 6·50 3·75
DESIGNS—VERT: 60f. Antoine de Saint-Exupery and Latecoere 2b. HORIZ: 80f. Maryse Bastie and Caudron C-635 Simoun; 100f. Sikorski S-43 amphibian (1st airmail, Marignane–Douala, 1937); 300f. Concorde; 500f. Charles Lindbergh and "Spirit of St. Louis".

1977. Air. 10th Anniv of International French Language Council. As T **204** of Benin.
801 70f. multicoloured 55 30

264 Cameroun 40f. and Basle 2½r. Stamps

1977. "Jufilex" Stamp Exhibition, Berne.
802 **264** 50f. multicoloured 65 35
803 — 70f. green, black & brown 90 45
804 — 100f. multicoloured . . . 1·90 65
DESIGNS: 70f. Zurich 4r. and Kamerun 1m. stamps; 100f. Geneva 5+5c. and Cameroun 20f. stamps.

265 Stafford and "Apollo" Rocket

1977. U.S.A.–U.S.S.R. Space Co-operation. Mult.
805 40f. Type **265** (postage) . . . 35 15
806 60f. Leonov and "Soyuz"
  rocket 45 20
807 100f. Brand and "Apollo"
  space vehicle (air) 65 35
808 250f. "Apollo–Soyuz" link-up 2·00 1·10
809 350f. Kubasov and "Soyuz"
  vehicle . . . . . 2·75 1·40

266 Luge Sledging

1977. Winter Olympics. Innsbruck. Multicoloured.
811 40f. Type **266** (postage) . . . 30 15
812 50f. Ski-jumping 40 15
813 140f. Ski-marathon (air) . . . 90 45

814 200f. Ice-hockey . . . . . 1·40 65
815 350f. Figure-skating . . . . 2·75 1·10

1977. Palestinian Welfare. No. 765 optd **Au bien-etre des familles des martyrs et des combattants pour la liberte de la Palestine. To the Welfare of the families of martyrs and freedom fighters of Palestine.**
817 100f. multicoloured 65 45

268 Mao Tse-tung and Great Wall of China

1977. 1st Death Anniv of Mao Tse-tung.
818 **268** 100f. brown and green . . 1·50 65

269 Knee Joint

1977. Air. World Rheumatism Year.
819 **269** 70f. brown, red & blue . . 55 20

1977. Air. 1st Paris–New York Commercial Flight of Concorde. Nos. 798 and 768 optd **PREMIER VOL PARIS-NEW YORK FIRST FLIGHT PARIS-NEW YORK 22 nov. 1977 — 22nd Nov. 1977.**
820 — 300f. blue, red & purple 2·75 1·40
821 **251** 500f. multicoloured . . . 4·25 2·25

271 "The Nativity" (Albrecht Altdorfer)

1977. Christmas. Multicoloured.
822 30f. Type **271** (postage) . . . 40 15
823 50f. "Madonna of the Grand
  Duke" (Raphael) 70 30
824 60f. "Virgin and Child with
  Four Saints" (Bellini)
  (horiz) (air) 80 30
825 400f. "Adoration of the
  Shepherds" (G. de la Tour)
  (horiz) . . . . . 4·50 2·25

272 Club Flag and
Rotary Emblem

273 Pres. Ahidjo, Flag
and Map

1978. 20th Anniv of Yaounde Rotary Club.
826 **272** 50f. multicoloured 60 30

1978. New Cameroun Flag. Multicoloured.
827 50f. Type **273** (postage) . . . 55 20
828 60f. President, Flag and arms
  (air) 30 20

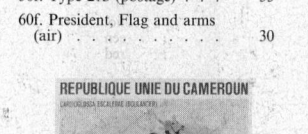

274 "Cardioglossa escalerae"

1978. Cameroun Frogs. Multicoloured.
829   50f. Type **274** (postage) . . .   50   35
830   60f. "Cardioglossa elegans"   1·00   45
831   100f. "Cardioglossa
     trifasciata" (air) . . . . .   1·25   35

275 "L'Arlesienne" (Van Gogh)

1978. Air. Paintings. Multicoloured.
832   200f. Type **275** . . . . .   3·00   1·40
833   200f. "Deposition of Christ"
     (Durer) . . . .   2·25   65

276 Raoul Follereau and Leprosy
Distribution Map

1978. Air. World Leprosy Day.
834 **276** 100f. multicoloured . . .   80   45

277 Capt. Cook and the Siege of Quebec

1978. Air. 250th Birth Anniv of Capt. James Cook.
835 **277** 100f. green, blue & lilac   1·40   55
836   –   250f. brown, red and lilac   3·25   1·40
DESIGN: 250f. Capt. Cook, H.M.S. "Adventure"
and H.M.S. "Resolution".

278 Footballers

1978. Air. World Cup Football Championship,
Argentina. Multicoloured.
837   100f. Argentinian Team
     (horiz)   70   35
838   200f. Type **278** . . . . .   1·50   65
839   1000f. Football illuminating
     globe . . . .   9·00   4·50

279 Jules Verne and scene
from "From the Earth to the
Moon"

1978. 150th Birth Anniv of Jules Verne (novelist).
Multicoloured.
840   250f. Type **279** (postage) . .   1·90   55
841   400f. Portrait and "20,000
     Leagues under the Sea"
     (horiz) (air) . . . . . .   3·25   1·40

280 "Hypolimnas salmacis"

1978. Butterflies. Multicoloured.
842   20f. Type **280**   35   20
843   25f. "Euxanthe trajanus" . .   35   20
844   30f. "Euphaedra cyparissa"   45   20

281 Planting Trees   **282** Carved Bamoun
Drum

1978. Protection against Saharan Encroachment.
845 **281** 10f. multicoloured . . .   15   10
846   15f. multicoloured   20   10

1978. Musical Instruments. Multicoloured.
847   50f. Type **282** (postage) . . .   35   20
848   60f. Gueguerou (horiz) . . .   50   30
849   100f. Mvet Zither (air) . . .   80   35

283 Presidents of Cameroun and France
with Independence Monument, Douala

1978. Visit of President Giscard d'Estaing.
850 **283** 60f. multicoloured   85   40

284 African, Human Rights Charter and
Emblem

1979. 30th Anniv of Declaration of Human Rights.
851 **284** 5f. mult (postage)   15   10

852   500f. multicoloured (air)   5·25   2·50
See also No. 1070.

285 Lions Emblem   **286** Globe, Emblem and
and Map of Cameroun   Waving Children

1979. Air. Lions International Congress.
853 **285** 60f. multicoloured   60   30

1979. International Year of the Child.
854 **286** 50f. multicoloured . . .   55   20

287 Penny Black, Rowland Hill and
German Cameroun 10pf. Stamp

1979. Air. Death Cent of Sir Rowland Hill.
855 **287** 100f. black, red & turq . .   1·10   45

288 Black Rhinoceros   **289** "Telecom 79"

1979. Endangered Animals (1st series). Mult.
856   50f. Type **288**   65   30
857   60f. Giraffe (vert)   80   45
858   60f. Gorilla   80   35
859   100f. African elephant (vert)   2·70   1·00
860   100f. Leopard . . . . .   1·75   75
     See also Nos. 891/2, 904/6, 975/7, 939/40 and
1007/8.

1979. Air. 3rd World Telecommunications
Exhibition, Geneva.
861 **289** 100f. orange, blue & grey   90   45

290 Pope John Paul   **291** Dr. Jamot, Map and
II   "Glossina palpalis"

1979. Air. Popes.
862 **290** 100f. blue, violet & grn   1·90   55
863   –   100f. brown, red & green   1·90   55
864   –   100f. chestnut, olive & grn   1·90   55
DESIGNS: No. 863, Pope John Paul I. No. 864, Pope
Paul VI.

1979. Birth Centenary of Dr. Eugene Jamot
(discoverer of sleeping sickness cure).
865 **291** 50f. brown, blue and red   60   30

292 "The Annunciation" (Fra
Filippo Lippi)

1979. Christmas. Multicoloured.
866   10f. Type **292**   10   10
867   50f. "Rest during the Flight
     into Egypt" (Antwerp
     Master)   35   10
868   60f. "The Nativity" (Kalkar)   50   15
869   60f. "The Flight into Egypt"
     (Kalkar)   50   15
870   100f. "The Nativity"
     (Boticelli) . . . .   1·25   35

293 "Double Eagle II" and
Balloonists

1979. Air. 1st Atlantic Crossing by Balloon.
Multicoloured.
871   500f. Type **293** . . . .   4·50   1·40
872   500f. "Double Eagle II" over
     Atlantic and balloonists in
     basket . . . .   4·50   1·40

294 "Piper capense"

1979. Medicinal Plants. Multicoloured.
873   50f. Type **294**   65   15
874   60f. "Pteridium aquilinum" .   70   20

295 Pres. Ahidjo, Map,
Independence Stamp and Arms

1980. 20th Anniv of Independence.
875 **295** 50f. multicoloured   45   20

296 Congress Building

1980. 3rd Ordinary Congress of Cameroun National
Union, Bafoussam.
876 **296** 50f. multicoloured   45   20

297 Globe

1980. 75th Anniv of Rotary International. Mult.
877   200f. Type **297** . . . . . .   2·00   65
878   200f. Map of Cameroun . . .   2·00   65

298 Voacanga Fruit and   **299** "Dissotis perkin-
Seeds   siae"

1980. Medicinal Plants. Multicoloured.
880   50f. Type **298**   45   10
881   60f. Voacanga tree   45   15
882   100f. Voacanga flowers . . .   80   20

1980. Flowers. Multicoloured.
883   50f. Type **299**   45   10
884   60f. "Brillantaisia" sp. . . .   65   15
885   100f. "Clerodendron
     splendens" . . . .   1·40   20

300 Ka'aba, Mecca

1980. 1350th Anniv of Mohammed's Occupation of
Mecca.
886 **300** 50f. multicoloured   65   35

301 Ice Skating

1980. Air. Olympic Games, Moscow and Lake Placid.
887   –   100f. brown and ochre . .   65   30
888 **301** 150f. brown and blue . .   1·00   45
889   –   200f. brown and green . .   1·75   55
890   –   300f. brown and red . .   2·25   95
DESIGNS: 100f. Running; 200f. Throwing the
Javelin; 300f. Wrestling.

302 Crocodile

1980. Endangered Animals (2nd series). Mult.
891 200f. Type **302** . . . . 2·50   55
892 300f. Kob . . . . 3·25   90

303 Bororo Girls and Roumsiki Peak

1980. Tourism. Multicoloured.
893 50f. Type **303** 40   15
894 60f. Dschang tourist centre 45   20

304 Banana Trees

1981. Bertona Agricultural Research Station.
Multicoloured.
895 50f. Type **304** 45   10
896 60f. Cattle in watering hole 55   15

305 Girl on Crutches

1981. Int Year of Disabled People. Multicoloured.
897 60f. Type **305** 40   20
898 150f. Boy in wheelchair . . 1·00   50

306 Camair Headquarters, Douala

1981. 20th Anniv of Cameroun Airlines. Mult.
899 100f. Type **306** 65   20
900 200f. Boeing 747 "Mount
    Cameroun" . . . . . . 1·60   45
901 300f. Douala International
    Airport . . . . 2·50   65

307 Presentation   308 African Buffalo
African Club
Champions Cup

1981. Football Victories of Cameroun Clubs.
Multicoloured.
902 60f. Type **307** 65   35
903 60f. Cup presentation
    (African Cup Winner's
    Cup) 65   35

1981. Endangered Animals (3rd series). Mult.
904 50f. Type **308** 65   20
905 50f. Cameroun tortoise . . 65   20
906 100f. Long-tailed pangolin . . 1·40   35

309 Prince Charles,   310 Bafoussam–Bamenda
Lady Diana Spencer   Road
and St. Paul's
Cathedral

1981. Wedding of Prince of Wales. Multicoloured.
907 500f. Type **309** . . . . 3·75   1·75
908 500f. Prince Charles, Lady
    Diana and Royal Coach 3·75   1·75

1981. Tourism.
910 310 50f. multicoloured 45   15

311 Yuri Gagarin and "Vostok 1"

1981. 20th Anniv of 1st Men in Space. Mult.
911 500f. Type **311** . . . . 4·50   1·40
912 500f. Alan Shepard and
    "Freedom 7" . . . . . . 4·50   1·40

312 "Cam Iroko" (freighter) in
Harbour

1981. Cameroun Shipping Lines.
913 312 60f. multicoloured 65   30

313 Scout Salute and Badge
within Knotted Rope, and
National Flag

1981. Air. 4th African Scouting Conference, Abidjan.
Multicoloured.
914 100f. Type **313** 55   30
915 500f. Saluting Girl Guide . . . 3·75   1·40

314 Unity Monument

1981. 20th Anniv of Reunification.
916 314 50f. multicoloured 45   20

315 "L'Estaque" (Cezanne)

1981. Air. Paintings. Multicoloured.
917 500f. Type **315** . . . . 5·25   1·50
918 500f. "Guernica" (detail)
    (Picasso) . . . . . . 5·25   1·50

316 "Virgin and Child" (detail of
San Zeno altarpiece, Mantegna)

1981. Air. Christmas. Paintings. Multicoloured.
919 50f. "Virgin and Child"
    (detail, "The Burning
    Bush") (Nicholas Froment) 30   10
920 60f. Type **316** 45   15
921 400f. "The Flight into Egypt"
    (Giotto) (horiz) . . . . . 3·00   1·25

317 "Voacanga thouarsii"

1981. Medicinal Plants. Multicoloured.
923 60f. Type **317** 55   15
924 70f. "Cassia alata" 65   20

318 "Descent from the Cross" (detail,
Giotto)

1982. Easter. Paintings. Multicoloured.
925 100f. "Christ in the Garden
    of Olives" (Eugene
    Delacroix) 65   20
926 200f. Type **318** . . . . 1·40   45
927 250f. "Pieta in the
    Countryside" (Bellini) . . . 2·00   55

319 Carving, Giraffes and Map

1982. "Philexfrance 82" International Stamp
Exhibition, Paris.
928 319 90f. multicoloured 80   20

320 Clay Water Jug

1982. Local Handicrafts. Multicoloured.
929 60f. Python-skin handbag . . 45   15
930 70f. Type **320** 55   20

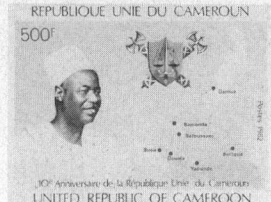

321 Pres. Ahidjo, Map and Arms

1982. 10th Anniv of United Republic.
931 321 500f. multicoloured . . . 4·50   1·40

322 Douala Town Hall

1982. Town Halls. Multicoloured.
932 40f. Type **322** 35   10
933 60f. Yaounde town hall 45   15
See also No. 1139.

323 Cameroun Football Team

1982. World Cup Football Championship, Spain.
Multicoloured.
934 100f. Type **323** . . . . 1·40   35
935 200f. Cameroun and Algerian
    teams . . . . . . 2·50   55
936 300f. Nkono Thomas,
    Cameroun goalkeeper . . 3·75   80
937 400f. Cameroun team
    (different) . . . . . . 5·25   1·40

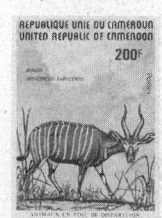

324 Bongo   325 Cameroun
                 Mountain Francolin
                 ("Perdrix")

1982. Endangered Animals (4th series). Mult.
939 200f. Type **324** . . . . 2·40   85
940 300f. Black colobus . . . . . 3·50   1·40

1982. Birds. Multicoloured.
941 10f. Type **325** 60   35
942 15f. Red-eyed dove
    ("Tourterelle") 70   50
943 20f. Barn swallow
    ("Hirondelle") . . . 1·00   90
See also No. 1071.

326 Scouts round Campfire

1982. 75th Anniv of Boy Scout Movement.
Multicoloured.
944 200f. Type **326** . . . . 2·00   55
945 400f. Lord Baden-Powell . . . 3·50   1·40

327 I.T.U. Emblem   328 Nyasoso Chapel

1982. I.T.U. Delegates' Conference, Nairobi.
946   327   70f. multicoloured   55   20

1982. 25th Anniv of Presbyterian Church. Multicoloured.
947   45f. Buea Chapel   40   15
948   60f. Type **328**   50   20

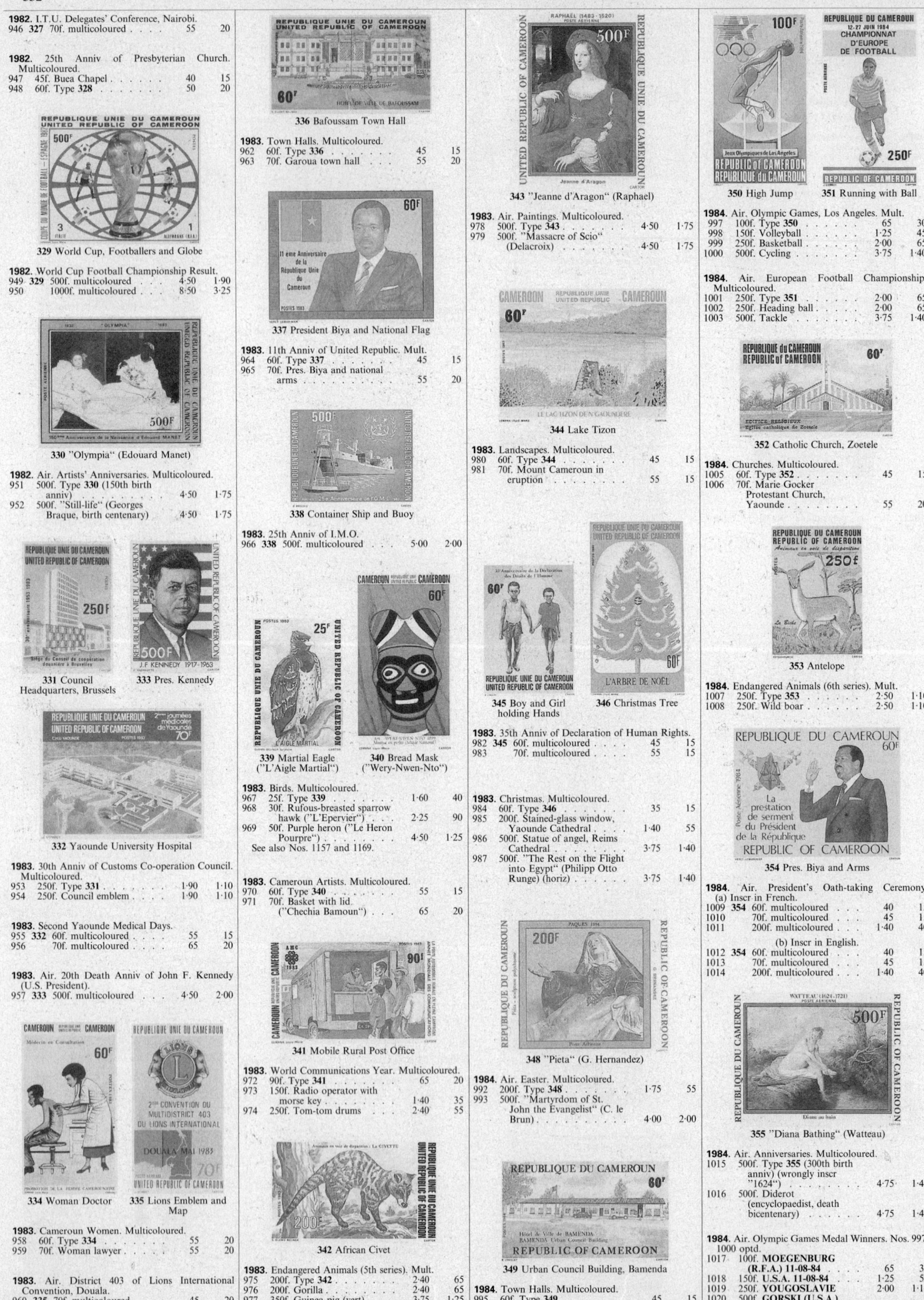

329 World Cup, Footballers and Globe

1982. World Cup Football Championship Result.
949   329   500f. multicoloured . . .   4·50   1·90
950   1000f. multicoloured . . .   8·50   3·25

330 "Olympia" (Edouard Manet)

1982. Air. Artists' Anniversaries. Multicoloured.
951   500f. Type **330** (150th birth anniv)   4·50   1·75
952   500f. "Still-life" (Georges Braque, birth centenary)   4·50   1·75

331 Council   333 Pres. Kennedy
Headquarters, Brussels

332 Yaounde University Hospital

1983. 30th Anniv of Customs Co-operation Council. Multicoloured.
953   250f. Type **331** . . . . .   1·90   1·10
954   250f. Council emblem . . . .   1·90   1·10

1983. Second Yaounde Medical Days.
955   60f. multicoloured   55   15
956   70f. multicoloured   65   20

1983. Air. 20th Death Anniv of John F. Kennedy (U.S. President).
957   333   500f. multicoloured . . .   4·50   2·00

334 Woman Doctor   335 Lions Emblem and Map

1983. Cameroun Women. Multicoloured.
958   60f. Type **334**   55   20
959   70f. Woman lawyer   55   20

1983. Air. District 403 of Lions International Convention, Douala.
960   335   70f. multicoloured . . .   45   20
961   150f. multicoloured . . .   1·25   55

336 Bafoussam Town Hall

1983. Town Halls. Multicoloured.
962   60f. Type **336**   45   15
963   70f. Garoua town hall . . .   55   20

337 President Biya and National Flag

1983. 11th Anniv of United Republic. Mult.
964   60f. Type **337**   45   15
965   70f. Pres. Biya and national arms   55   20

338 Container Ship and Buoy

1983. 25th Anniv of I.M.O.
966   338   500f. multicoloured . . .   5·00   2·00

339 Martial Eagle   340 Bread Mask
("L'Aigle Martial")   ("Wery-Nwen-Nto")

1983. Birds. Multicoloured.
967   25f. Type **339** . . . . . .   1·60   40
968   30f. Rufous-breasted sparrow hawk ("L'Epervier") . . .   2·25   90
969   50f. Purple heron ("Le Heron Pourpre") . . . .   4·50   1·25
See also Nos. 1157 and 1169.

1983. Cameroun Artists. Multicoloured.
970   60f. Type **340**   55   15
971   70f. Basket with lid ("Chechia Bamoun") . . .   65   20

341 Mobile Rural Post Office

1983. World Communications Year. Multicoloured.
972   90f. Type **341**   65   20
973   150f. Radio operator with morse key . . . .   1·40   35
974   250f. Tom-tom drums . . .   2·40   55

342 African Civet

1983. Endangered Animals (5th series). Mult.
975   200f. Type **342** . . . . .   2·40   65
976   200f. Gorilla. . . . . . .   2·40   65
977   350f. Guinea-pig (vert) . .   3·75   1·25
See also No. 1170.

343 "Jeanne d'Aragon" (Raphael)

1983. Air. Paintings. Multicoloured.
978   500f. Type **343** . . . . . .   4·50   1·75
979   500f. "Massacre of Scio" (Delacroix) . . . .   4·50   1·75

344 Lake Tizon

1983. Landscapes. Multicoloured.
980   60f. Type **344**   45   15
981   70f. Mount Cameroun in eruption   55   15

345 Boy and Girl   346 Christmas Tree
holding Hands

1983. 35th Anniv of Declaration of Human Rights.
982   345   60f. multicoloured   45   15
983   70f. multicoloured   55   15

1983. Christmas. Multicoloured.
984   60f. Type **346**   35   15
985   200f. Stained-glass window, Yaounde Cathedral . .   1·40   55
986   500f. Statue of angel, Reims Cathedral . . . . .   3·75   1·40
987   500f. "The Rest on the Flight into Egypt" (Philipp Otto Runge) (horiz) . . .   3·75   1·40

348 "Pieta" (G. Hernandez)

1984. Air. Easter. Multicoloured.
992   200f. Type **348** . . . . . .   1·75   55
993   500f. "Martyrdom of St. John the Evangelist" (C. le Brun) . . . .   4·00   2·00

349 Urban Council Building, Bamenda

1984. Town Halls. Multicoloured.
995   60f. Type **349**   45   15
996   70f. Mbalmayo   55   20

350 High Jump   351 Running with Ball

1984. Air. Olympic Games, Los Angeles. Mult.
997   100f. Type **350**   65   30
998   150f. Volleyball . . . . .   1·25   45
999   250f. Basketball . . . . .   2·00   65
1000   500f. Cycling . . . . . .   3·75   1·40

1984. Air. European Football Championship. Multicoloured.
1001   250f. Type **351** . . . . . .   2·00   65
1002   250f. Heading ball . . . . .   2·00   65
1003   500f. Tackle . . . .   3·75   1·40

352 Catholic Church, Zoetele

1984. Churches. Multicoloured.
1005   60f. Type **352**   45   15
1006   70f. Marie Gocker Protestant Church, Yaounde   55   20

353 Antelope

1984. Endangered Animals (6th series). Mult.
1007   250f. Type **353** . . . . . .   2·50   1·10
1008   250f. Wild boar . . . . . .   2·50   1·10

354 Pres. Biya and Arms

1984. Air. President's Oath-taking Ceremony.
  (a) Inscr in French.
1009   354   60f. multicoloured   40   15
1010   70f. multicoloured   45   15
1011   200f. multicoloured . . . .   1·40   40

  (b) Inscr in English.
1012   354   60f. multicoloured   40   15
1013   70f. multicoloured   45   15
1014   200f. multicoloured . . . .   1·40   40

355 "Diana Bathing" (Watteau)

1984. Air. Anniversaries. Multicoloured.
1015   500f. Type **355** (300th birth anniv) (wrongly inscr "1624") . . . .   4·75   1·40
1016   500f. Diderot (encyclopaedist, death bicentenary) . . . .   4·75   1·40

1984. Air. Olympic Games Medal Winners. Nos. 997/ 1000 optd.
1017   100f. MOEGENBURG (R.F.A.) 11-08-84 . . .   65   35
1018   150f. U.S.A. 11-08-84 . . . .   1·25   50
1019   250f. YOUGOSLAVIE . .   2·00   1·10
1020   500f. GORSKI (U.S.A.) 3-08-84 . . . .   3·75   1·90

357 Nightingale ("Le Rossignol")   358 Neil Armstrong

1984. Birds. Multicoloured.
1021   60f. Type **357** . . . . .   2·00   70
1022   60f. Ruppell's griffon ("Le Vautour") . . . . . .   2·00   70
See also No. 1158.

1984. Air. 15th Anniv of 1st Man on the Moon. Multicoloured.
1023   500f. Type **358** . . . . . .   4·50   1·75
1024   500f. Launching of "Apollo 12" . . . .   4·50   1·75

359 Maize and Young Plants

1984. Agro-pastoral Fair. Bamenda. Mult.
1025   60f. Type **359**   45   15
1026   70f. Zebus   55   20
1027   300f. Potatoes . . . . . .   2·50   85

360 Anniversary Emblem   362 Balafons (xylophone)

361 Wrestling

1984. 40th Anniv of I.C.A.O.
1028   – 200f. multicoloured . . .   1·40   55
1029   360 200f. blue & deep blue .   1·40   55
1030   – 300f. multicoloured . . .   2·40   85
1031   – 300f. multicoloured . . .   3·00   1·40
DESIGNS: No. 1028, "Icarus" (Hans Herni); 1030, Cameroun Airlines Boeing 737; 1031, "Solar Princess" (Sadiou Diouf).

1985. "Olymphilex '85" International Thematic Stamps Exhibition, Lausanne.
1032   361 150f. multicoloured . . .   1·40   55

1985. Musical Instruments. Multicoloured.
1033   60f. Type **362**   45   10
1034   70f. Mvet (stringed instrument)   55   15
1035   100f. Flute . . . .   1·10   20

363 Intelcam Headquarters, Yaounde

1985. 20th Anniv of Int Telecommunications Satellite Consortium.
1036   – 125f. black, orange & bl   1·40   45
1037   363 200f. multicoloured . . .   1·75   50
DESIGN: 125f. "Intelsat V" satellite.

365 U.N. Emblem and Headquarters

1985. 40th Anniv of U.N.O.
1038   365 250f. multicoloured . . .   2·40   65
1039   – 500f. multicoloured . . .   4·50   1·40

366 French and Cameroun Flags and Presidents

1985. President Mitterrand of France's Visit to Cameroun. (a) Inscr "Mitterand" in error.
1040   366 60f. multicoloured . . . . .
1041   – 70f. multicoloured . . . . .
         (b) Inscr corrected to "Mitterrand".
1041a   366 60f. multicoloured . . .   55   30
1041b   – 70f. multicoloured . . .   65   30

367 U.N.I.C.E.F. Emblem

1985. Child Survival Campaign.
1042   367 60f. black, blue & yell   45   15
1043   – 300f. multicoloured . . .   2·40   80
DESIGN: Doctor inoculating babies.

368 Lake Barumbi, Kumba

1985. Landscapes. Multicoloured.
1044   60f. Type **368**   55   10
1045   70f. Pygmy village, Bonando   55   15
1046   150f. River Cameroun . . .   1·40   35

369 Ebolowa Town Hall

1985. Town Halls. Multicoloured.
1047   60f. Type **369**   45   15
1048   60f. Ngaoundere town hall .   45   15

370 Pope John Paul II   371 Porcupine

1985. Papal Visit to Cameroun. Multicoloured.
1049   60f. Type **370**   60   30
1050   70f. Pope John Paul II holding crucifix   80   30
1051   200f. Pres. Biya and Pope John Paul II . . . . .   2·25   1·25

1985. Animals. Multicoloured.
1053   125f. Type **371** . . . . . .   1·25   35
1054   200f. Squirrel . . . .   1·75   55
1055   350f. Greater cane rat . . .   2·75   90

372 Wooden Mask   373 "Tomb of Henri Claude d'Harcourt" (detail)

1985. Cameroun Art (1st series). Multicoloured.
1056   60f. Type **372**   45   15
1057   70f. Wooden mask (different)   55   20
1058   100f. Men using pestle and mortar (wooden bas-relief)   80   30
See also Nos. 1081/3.

1985. Air. Death Anniversaries. Multicoloured.
1059   500f. Type **373** (bicentenary Jean Baptiste Pigalle (sculptor)) . . . . . .   4·75   1·40
1060   500f. Louis Pasteur (bacteriologist, 90th anniv) (after Edelfelt) . . .   4·75   1·40

374 Yellow-casqued Hornbill ("Le Toucan")   375 Child's Toys

1985. Birds. Multicoloured.
1061   140f. Type **374** . . . . . .   2·10   70
1062   150f. Cock . . . .   1·75   60
1063   200f. European robins ("Le Rouge-gorge") . . . . .   3·25   1·10
See also No. 1156.

1985. Air. Christmas. Multicoloured.
1064   250f. Type **375** . . . . . .   1·90   65
1065   300f. Akono church . . . .   2·25   80
1066   400f. Christmas crib . . . .   2·75   1·10
1067   500f. "The Virgin of the Blue Diadem" (Raphael) .   4·50   1·40

376 Emblem, Flag and Volunteers

1986. 25th Anniv of American Peace Corps in Cameroun.
1068   376 70f. multicoloured . . .   55   20
1069   – 100f. multicoloured . . .   80   35

1986. As Nos. 851 and 941 but inscr "Republique du Cameroun/Republic of Cameroun".
1070   284 5f. multicoloured . . .   10   10
1071   325 10f. multicoloured . . .   80   40

377 "Virgin Mary" (Pierre Prud'hon)

1986. Easter. Multicoloured.
1072   210f. Type **377** . . . . . .   1·40   65
1073   350f. "Stoning of St. Stephen" (Van Scorel) .   2·50   1·25

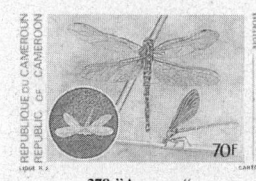

378 "Anax sp."

1986. Insects. Multicoloured.
1074   70f. Type **378**   60   40
1075   70f. Bee on flower (vert) . .   60   40
1076   100f. Grasshopper   90   55

379 Map of Africa

1986. Economic Commission for Africa Ministers' Conference. Multicoloured.
1077   100f. Type **379**   80   45
1078   175f. Members' flags . . . .   1·40   65

380 Azteca Stadium

1986. Air. World Cup Football Championship, Mexico. Multicoloured.
1079   300f. Type **380** . . . . . .   2·25   1·10
1080   400f. Mexico team . . . .   3·00   1·40

1986. Cameroun Art (2nd series). As T **372**. Multicoloured.
1081   70f. Copper Statuette . . .   45   15
1082   100f. Wooden ash-tray . . .   70   20
1083   130f. Wooden horseman . .   1·40   35

381 Queen Elizabeth

1986. 60th Birthday of Queen Elizabeth II. Multicoloured.
1084   100f. Type **381**   80   35
1085   175f. Queen and President Biya . . . .   1·40   55
1086   210f. Queen Elizabeth (different) . . . . . .   1·75   80

382 President Biya

1986. 1st Anniv of Cameroun Republic Democratic Party. Multicoloured.
1087	70f. Type **382**	. . . .	50	20
1088	70f. Bamenda Party headquarters (horiz)	. . .	50	20
1089	100f. President Biya making speech	. . . .	65	30

383 Argentine Team   **384** Mask Dancer with Sword

1986. Air. World Cup Football Championship Winners.
1090	383	250f. multicoloured . . .	2·50	1·10

1986. Traditional Dances of North-west Kwem. Multicoloured.
1091	100f. Type **384**	70	45
1092	130f. Mask dancer with rattle	1·25	55

385 Cheetah   **386** Bishop Desmond Tutu (Nobel Peace Prize Winner)

1986. Endangered Animals (7th series). Mult.
1093	300f. Type **385**	2·50	1·40
1094	300f. Varan	2·50	1·40

1986. International Peace Year. Multicoloured.
1095	175f. Type **386**	1·40	55
1096	200f. Type **386**	1·75	65
1097	250f. I.P.Y. and U.N. emblems	2·00	1·10

387 Pierre Curie (physicist)

1986. Air. Death Anniversaries. Multicoloured.
1098	500f. Type **387** (80th anniv)	5·25	2·25
1099	500f. Jean Mermoz and "Arc en Ciel" (aviation pioneer, 50th anniv) . . .	5·25	2·25

388 Emblem   **389** Man holding Syringe and National Flag "Umbrella" over Woman and Child

1986. National Federation of Cameroun Handicapped Associations.
1100	**388** 70f. yellow and red . . .	50	20

1986. African Vaccination Year.
1101	70f. Type **389**	50	15
1102	100f. Flag behind woman holding child being immunised	65	30

390 Trees on Map   **391** Loading Palm Nuts onto Trailer at Dibombari

1986. National Tree Day.
1103	70f. Type **390**	50	15
1104	100f. Hands holding clump of earth and seedling . .	65	30

1986. Agricultural Development. Multicoloured.
1105	70f. Type **391**	50	20
1106	70f. Payment for produce harvested	50	20
1107	200f. Pineapple plantation	1·40	65

392 "Antestiopsis lineaticollis intricata"

1987. Harmful Insects. Multicoloured.
1108	70f. Type **392**	70	45
1109	100f. "Distantiella theobroma"	85	55

393 Millet

1987. Agricultural Show, Maroua. Multicoloured.
1110	70f. Type **393**	50	30
1111	100f. Cotton	65	40
1112	150f. Cattle	1·25	55

394 Shot-putting

1987. 4th All-Africa Games, Kenya. Mult.
1113	100f. Type **394**	65	35
1114	140f. Pole-vaulting . . .	1·25	45

395 Drill Baboon

1988. Endangered Mammals. Drill Baboon. Multicoloured.
1115	30f. Type **395**	30	15
1116	40f. Adult baboons . . .	35	15
1117	70f. Young baboon . . .	60	35
1118	100f. Mother with baby . .	1·10	55

396 National Assembly Building

1989. Centenary of Interparliamentary Union.
1119	**396** 50f. multicoloured . . .	35	15

397 Cameroun and Argentine Players

1990. World Cup Football Championship, Italy. Multicoloured.
1120	200f. Type **397**	1·50	55
1121	250f. Cameroun player and match scene . . .	2·00	1·10
1122	250f. Cameroun winning goal	2·00	1·10
1123	300f. Cameroun first eleven	2·25	1·40

1990. Nos. 1062 and 1093 surch.
1125	– 20f. on 150f. mult . .	15	10
1126	**385** 70f. on 300f. mult . . .	45	20

399 Milla and Match Scene

1990. Roger Milla, 4th Best Player in World Cup.
1127	**399** 500f. multicoloured . . .	3·75	2·50

400 Anniversary Emblem

1990. 40th Anniv of United Nations Development Programme.
1129	**400** 50f. multicoloured . . .	35	20

401 U.N.E.S.C.O. and I.L.Y. Emblems

1990. International Literacy Year.
1130	**401** 200f. black, lt blue & bl	1·40	55

402 Arms and Pres. Paul Biya

1991. 30th Anniv (1990) of Independence. Multicoloured.
1131	150f. Type **402**	1·40	55
1132	1000f. Flag, city and 1960 20f. Independence stamp	7·75	3·75

403 Treating Cacao Plantation

1991. Unissued stamps (for Ebolowa Agricultural Show) with bars over inscr and surch **125F**. Multicoloured.
1134	125f. on 70f. Type **403** . . . .
1135	125f. on 100f. Sheep . . . .

The stamps without surcharge were sold only by the Paris agency.

405 Snake on National Colours and Map

1991. Anti-AIDS Campaign. Multicoloured.
1137	15f. Type **405**	10	10
1138	25f. Youth pushing back "AIDS" in French and English (horiz)	15	10

See also Nos. 1171/2.

1991. As No. 932 but inscr "Republic du Cameroun / Republic of Cameroon".
1139	**322** 40f. multicoloured . . .	30	15

406 Oribi

1991. Sovereign Military Order of Malta Child Survival Project. Antelopes. Multicoloured.
1140	125f.+10f. Type **406**	1·25	95
1141	250f.+20f. Waterbucks . . .	2·25	2·25

407 Serle's Bush Shrike ("La Pie Grieche du Mont-kupe")   **408** African Elephant

1991. Birds. Multicoloured.
1143	70f. Type **407**	60	45
1144	70f. Grey-necked bald crow ("Le Picathartes Chauve") (horiz)	60	45
1145	300f. As No. 1144	2·50	1·50
1146	350f. Type **407**	3·00	1·75

1991. Animals. Multicoloured.
1148	125f. Type **408**	1·10	55
1149	250f. Buffalo	2·00	1·40

409 Mvolye Church

1991. Centenary (1990) of Catholic Church in Cameroun. Multicoloured.
1151	125f. Type **409**	1·10	55
1152	250f. Akono church	2·00	1·40

410 Emblems

1991. 7th African Group Meeting of Int Savings Banks Institute, Yaounde.
1154	**410** 250f. multicoloured . . .	2·00	1·10

1992. Birds. As previous designs but with values changed. Multicoloured.
1156	125f. As No. 1063	1·40	50
1157	200f. As No. 968	1·60	60
1158	350f. Type **357**	2·75	1·50

411 Columbus's Fleet

412 Mbappe Lepe (footballer)

1992. 500th Anniv of Discovery of America by Columbus. Multicoloured.

1159	125f. Type **411**	1·40	50
1160	250f. Columbus kneeling on beach	2·10	1·40
1161	400f. Meeting Amerindians	3·00	1·90
1162	500f. Fleet crossing the Atlantic	4·75	3·00

1992. Cameroun Football. Multicoloured.

1163	125f. Type **412**	1·10	40
1164	250f. League emblem	2·10	1·40
1165	400f. National Football Federation emblem (horiz)	3·00	1·90
1166	500f. Ahmadou Ahidjo Stadium, Yaounde (horiz)	4·25	4·75

See also Nos. 1173/5.

413 Crocodile

1993. Endangered Animals. Mult. Self-adhesive.

1167	125f. Type **413**	1·00	65
1168	250f. Kob (vert)	2·00	1·40

1993. As Nos. 967 and 975 but inscr "REPUBLIQUE DU CAMEROUN REPUBLIC OF CAMEROON" and with values changed.

1169	**339** 370f. multicoloured	2·50	1·60
1170	**342** 410f. multicoloured	3·25	2·00

1993. Anti-AIDS Campaign. As Nos. 1137/8 but values changed. Multicoloured.

1171	100f. Type **405**	80	55
1172	175f. As No. 1138	1·40	80

1993. As Nos. 1163/5 but values changed.

1173	10f. As No. 1165	10	10
1174	25f. As No. 1164	10	10
1175	50f. Type **412**	15	10

414 President Biya holding Football and Lion (national team mascot)

1994. World Cup Football Championship, United States. Multicoloured.

1176	125f. Type **414**	50	40
1177	250f. Emblem, lion, player and map of Cameroun	90	65
1178	450f. Players, ball showing world map, national flag and trophy	1·75	1·25
1179	500f. Eagle and lion supporting ball	1·90	1·50

415 Grey Parrot

417 Anniversary Emblem and Dove carrying Branch

416 Chi-rho, Cross and Pope John Paul II

1995.

1181	**415** 125f. multicoloured	50	35

1995. 2nd Papal Visit.

1182	**416** 55f. black, pink & yell	25	20
1183	– 125f. multicoloured	50	35

DESIGN: 125f. Pope and open book.

1995. 50th Anniv of U.N.O. Multicoloured.

1184	200f. Type **417**	55	40
1185	250f. Anniversary emblem and figures joining hands	65	45

Cameroun joined the Commonwealth on 1 November 1995.

MILITARY FRANK STAMP

M 78 Arms and Crossed Swords

1963. No value indicated.

M1	**M 78** (–) lake	3·25	3·25

POSTAGE DUE STAMPS

D 8 Felling Mahogany Tree

D 25 African Idols

1925.

D 88	**D 8**	2c. black and blue	10	2·00
D 89		4c. purple and olive	10	1·60
D 90		5c. black and lilac	20	1·90
D 91		10c. black and red	45	2·75
D 92		15c. black and grey	85	2·50
D 93		20c. black and olive	1·75	2·75
D 94		25c. black and yellow	80	3·25
D 95		30c. orange and blue	1·60	3·50
D 96		50c. black and brown	1·25	3·50
D 97		60c. red and green	1·40	4·00
D 98		1f. green & red on grn	1·25	95
D 99		2f. mauve and red	1·90	5·75
D100		3f. blue and brown	4·25	7·75

1939.

D148	**D 25**	5c. purple	10	2·50
D149		10c. blue	20	3·00
D150		15c. red	10	8·50
D151		20c. brown	20	2·50
D152		30c. blue	20	1·90
D153		50c. green	25	2·75
D154		60c. purple	25	2·75
D155		1f. violet	45	1·75
D156		2f. orange	40	3·00
D157		3f. blue	50	3·50

D 46

1947.

D254	**D 46**	10c. red	10	2·75
D255		30c. orange	10	2·75
D256		50c. black	10	2·75
D257		1f. red	15	2·75
D258		2f. green	1·75	3·00
D259		3f. mauve	2·00	3·25
D260		4f. blue	2·00	2·75
D261		5f. brown	1·75	3·00
D262		10f. blue	1·75	1·60
D263		20f. sepia	1·90	4·00

D 77 "Hibiscus rosa sinensis"

1963. Flowers. Multicoloured.

D342	50c. Type **D 77**	10	10
D343	50c. "Erythrine"	10	10
D344	1f. "Plumeria lutea"	10	10
D345	1f. "Ipomoea sp."	10	10
D346	1f.50 "Grinum sp."	10	10
D347	1f.50 "Hoodia gordonii"	10	10
D348	2f. "Ochna"	10	10
D349	2f. "Gloriosa"	10	10
D350	5f. "Costus spectabilis"	15	15
D351	5f. "Bougainvillea spectabilis"	15	15
D352	10f. "Delonix regia"	40	40
D353	10f. "Haemanthus"	40	40
D354	20f. "Titanopsis"	1·25	1·25
D355	20f. "Ophthalmophyllum"	1·25	1·25
D356	40f. "Zingiberacee"	1·75	1·75
D357	40f. "Amorphophalus"	1·75	1·75

CANADA Pt. 1

A British dominion consisting of the former province of Canada with British Columbia, New Brunswick, Newfoundland, Nova Scotia and Prince Edward Island.

1851. 12 pence = 1 shilling (Canadian).
1859. 100 cents = 1 dollar.

COLONY OF CANADA

1 Beaver

2 Prince Albert

3

4

5

6 Jacques Cartier

1851. Imperf.

17	**4**	½d. red	£700	£400
5	**1**	3d. red	£1100	£160
2	**2**	6d. purple	£14000	£900
12	**5**	7½d. green	£7000	£1500
14	**6**	10d. blue	£6500	£1100
4	**3**	12d. black	£60000	£40000

1858. Perf.

25	**4**	½d. red	£1800	£600
26	**1**	3d. red	£2500	£300
27a	**2**	6d. purple	£6500	£2250

1859. Values in cents. Perf.

29	**4**	1c. red	£225	27·00
44		2c. red	£400	£140
31	**1**	5c. red	£250	11·00
38	**2**	10c. purple	£800	42·00
36		10c. brown	£750	42·00
40	**5**	12½c. green	£550	40·00
42	**6**	17c. blue	£750	60·00

DOMINION OF CANADA

13

14

1868. Various frames.

54	**13**	½c. black	50·00	50·00
55	**14**	1c. brown	£300	40·00
56a		1c. yellow	£650	60·00
57		2c. green	£325	28·00
49		3c. red	£600	21·00
63		5c. green	£700	65·00
59b		6c. brown	£650	38·00
60		12½c. blue	£450	40·00
70		15c. purple	65·00	17·00
69		15c. blue	£140	28·00

27

21

28

1870. Various frames.

101	**27**	½c. black	10·00	6·50
75	**21**	1c. yellow	24·00	1·00
104		2c. green	32·00	1·50
105		3c. red	28·00	80
106		5c. grey	60·00	1·75
107		6c. brown	30·00	8·50
117	–	8c. grey	90·00	4·25
120	–	8c. purple	75·00	4·25
111	**21**	10c. pink	£160	23·00

On 8c. head is to left.

1893.

115	**28**	20c. red	£160	42·00
116		50c. blue	£225	24·00

30

31

1897. Jubilee.

121	**30**	½c. black	48·00	48·00
122		1c. orange	10·00	4·50
124		2c. green	15·00	9·00
126		3c. red	12·00	2·25
128		5c. blue	40·00	14·00
129		6c. brown	85·00	85·00
130		8c. violet	32·00	29·00
131		10c. purple	50·00	42·00
132		15c. slate	85·00	85·00
133		20c. red	85·00	85·00
134		50c. blue	£120	95·00
136		$1 red	£400	£400
137		$2 violet	£700	£350
138		$3 bistre	£800	£650
139		$4 violet	£800	£600
140		$5 green	£800	£600

1897. Maple-leaves in four corners.

141	**31**	½c. black	6·00	4·75
143		1c. green	18·00	90
144		2c. violet	18·00	1·50
145		3c. red	24·00	40
146		5c. blue	60·00	2·75
147		6c. brown	55·00	21·00
148		8c. orange	75·00	7·00
149		10c. purple	£130	55·00

1898. As T **31** but figures in lower corners.

150	½c. black	3·25	1·10
151	1c. green	22·00	40
154	2c. purple	22·00	30
155	2c. red	30·00	30
156	3c. red	42·00	1·00
157	5c. blue	95·00	1·60
159	6c. brown	85·00	48·00
160	7c. yellow	55·00	13·00
162	8c. orange	£100	25·00
163	10c. purple	£160	14·00
165	20c. green	£300	48·00

33

35 King Edward VII

1898. Imperial Penny Postage.

168	**33**	2c. black, red and blue	25·00	4·75

1899. Surch **2 CENTS**.

171	2c. on 3c. red (No. 145)	12·00	8·00
172	2c. on 3c. red (No. 156)	17·00	4·25

1903.

175	**35**	1c. green	20·00	50
176		2c. red	20·00	50
178		5c. blue	70·00	2·50
180		7c. olive	55·00	2·75
182		10c. purple	£110	9·50
185		20c. olive	£200	23·00
187		50c. violet	£350	85·00

36 King George V and Queen Mary, when Prince and Princess of Wales

44

1908. Tercentenary of Quebec. Dated "1608 1908".

188	**36**	½c. brown	3·50	3·25
189	–	1c. green	13·00	2·75
190	–	2c. red	18·00	1·00
191	–	5c. blue	45·00	20·00
192	–	7c. olive	50·00	40·00
193	–	10c. violet	55·00	45·00

194 – 15c. orange . . . . 75·00 65·00
195 – 20c. brown . . . . £100 80·00
DESIGNS: 1c. Cartier and Champlain; 2c. King Edward VII and Queen Alexandra; 5c. Champlain's House in Quebec; 7c. Generals Montcalm and Wolfe; 10c. Quebec in 1700; 15c. Champlain's departure for the West; 20c. Cartier's arrival before Quebec.

1912.

196 **44** 1c. green . . . . 5·50 50
200 2c. red . . . . 4·50 50
205 3c. brown . . . . 5·00 50
205b 5c. blue . . . . 60·00 75
209 7c. yellow . . . . 20·00 3·00
210 10c. purple . . . . 90·00 2·75
212 20c. olive . . . . 29·00 1·50
215 50c. brown . . . . 48·00 3·75
See also Nos. 246/55.

1915. Optd **WAR TAX** diagonally.
225 **44** 5c. blue £110 £190
226 20c. olive . . . . 55·00 95·00
227 50c. brown £110 £150

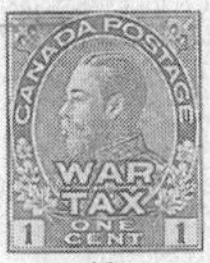
46

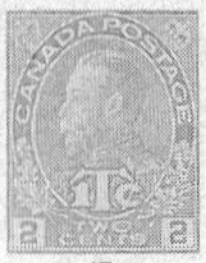
47

1915.

228 **46** 1c. green . . . . 8·00 50
229 2c. red . . . . 12·00 70

1916.

233 **47** 2c.+1c. red . . . . 21·00 1·25
239 2c.+1c. brown . . . . . . 4·00 50

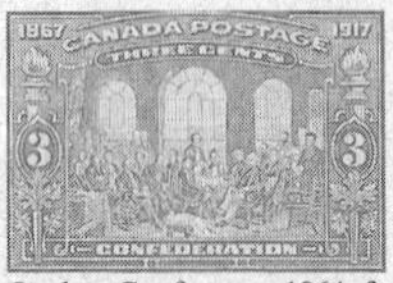
48 Quebec Conference, 1864, from painting "The Fathers of the Confederation" by Robert Harris

1917. 50th Anniv of Confederation.
244 **48** 3c. brown . . . . 18·00 1·75

1922.

246 **44** 1c. yellow . . . . 2·50 60
247 2c. green . . . . 2·25 10
248 3c. red . . . . 3·75 10
249 4c. yellow . . . . 8·00 3·50
250 5c. violet . . . . 5·00 1·75
251 7c. brown . . . . 12·00 7·00
252 8c. blue . . . . 19·00 10·00
253 10c. blue . . . . 20·00 3·25
254a 10c. brown . . . . 18·00 3·00
255 $1 orange . . . . 50·00 8·00

1926. Surch **2 CENTS** in one line.
264 **44** 2c. on 3c. red . . . . . . 42·00 50·00

1926. Surch **2 CENTS** in two lines.
265 **44** 2c. on 3c. red . . . . . . 16·00 20·00

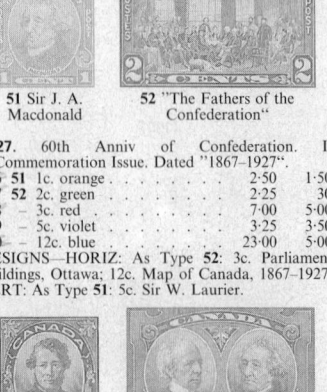

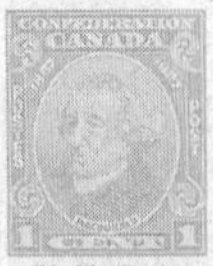
51 Sir J. A. Macdonald

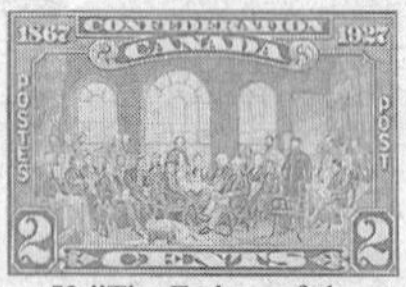
52 "The Fathers of the Confederation"

1927. 60th Anniv of Confederation. I. Commemoration Issue. Dated "1867–1927".
266 **51** 1c. orange . . . . 2·50 1·50
267 **52** 2c. green . . . . 2·25 30
268 – 3c. red . . . . 7·00 5·00
269 – 5c. violet . . . . 3·25 3·50
270 – 12c. blue . . . . 23·00 5·00
DESIGNS—HORIZ: As Type **52**: 3c. Parliament Buildings, Ottawa; 12c. Map of Canada, 1867–1927. VERT: As Type **51**: 5c. Sir W. Laurier.

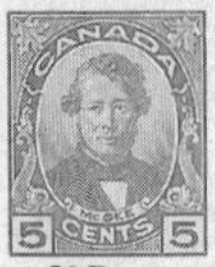
56 Darcy McGee

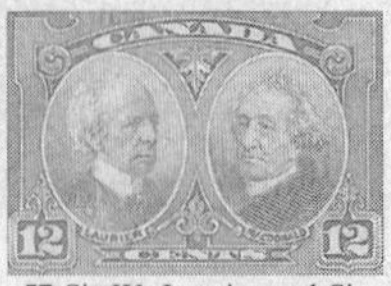
57 Sir W. Laurier and Sir J. A. Macdonald

II. Historical Issue.
271 **56** 5c. violet . . . . 3·00 2·50
272 **57** 12c. green . . . . 15·00 4·50
273 – 20c. red . . . . 17·00 12·00
DESIGN—As Type **57**: 20c. R. Baldwin and L. H. Lafontaine.

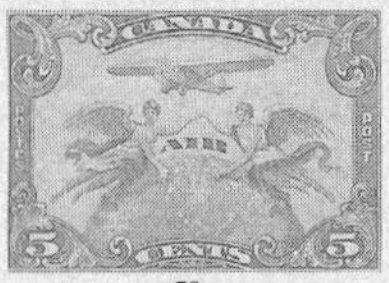
59

1928. Air.
274 **59** 5c. brown . . . . 6·00 3·50

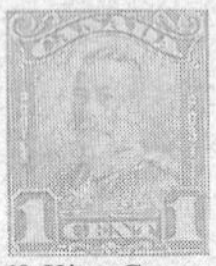
60 King George V

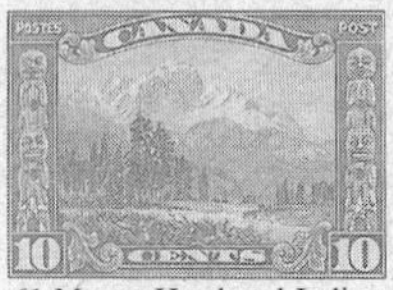
61 Mount Hurd and Indian Totem Poles

1928.

275 **60** 1c. orange . . . . 2·75 60
276 2c. green . . . . 1·25 20
277 3c. red . . . . 17·00 15·00
278 4c. yellow . . . . 13·00 6·50
279 5c. violet . . . . 6·50 3·25
280 8c. blue . . . . 7·50 4·75
281 **61** 10c. green . . . . 8·50 1·25
282 – 12c. black . . . . 22·00 10·00
283 – 20c. red . . . . 27·00 12·00
284 – 50c. blue . . . . £100 38·00
285 – $1 olive . . . . £110 60·00
DESIGNS—HORIZ: 12c. Quebec Bridge; 20c. Harvesting with horses; 50c. "Bluenose" (fishing schooner); $1 Parliament Buildings, Ottawa.

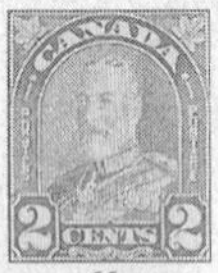
66

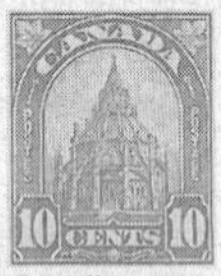
67 Parliamentary Library, Ottawa

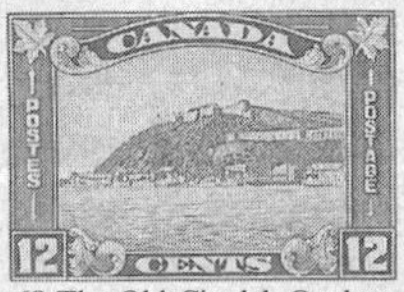
68 The Old Citadel, Quebec

1930.

288 **66** 1c. orange . . . . 1·75 1·00
289 1c. green . . . . 1·50 10
290 2c. green . . . . 1·75 10
291 2c. red 70 75
292b 2c. brown . . . . 1·25 10
293 3c. red 90 10
294 4c. yellow . . . . 6·50 4·50
295 5c. violet . . . . 2·75 4·50
296 5c. blue . . . . 5·00 20
297 8c. blue . . . . 11·00 16·00
298 8c. red . . . . 7·00 5·50
299 **67** 10c. olive . . . . 14·00 1·00
300 **68** 12c. black . . . . 14·00 5·50
325 13c. violet . . . . 32·00 2·25
301 – 20c. red . . . . 22·00 1·00
302 – 50c. blue . . . . 80·00 17·00
303 – $1 olive . . . . 95·00 23·00
DESIGNS—HORIZ: 20c. Harvesting with tractor; 50c. Acadian Memorial Church, Grand Pre, Nova Scotia; $1 Mount Edith Cavell.

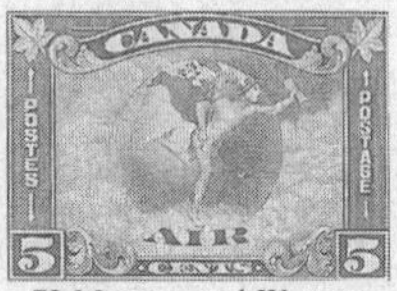
72 Mercury and Western Hemisphere

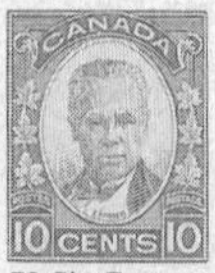
73 Sir Georges Etienne Cartier

1930. Air.
310 **72** 5c. brown . . . . 18·00 18·00

1931.

312 **73** 10c. green . . . . 5·00 20

1932. Air. Surch **6** and bars.
313 **59** 6c. on 5c. brown . . . . . 3·00 2·50

1932. Surch **3** between bars.
314a **66** 3c. on 2c. red . . . . . . 1·00 60

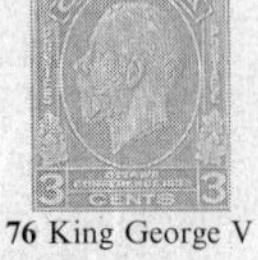
76 King George V

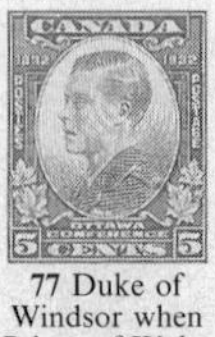
77 Duke of Windsor when Prince of Wales

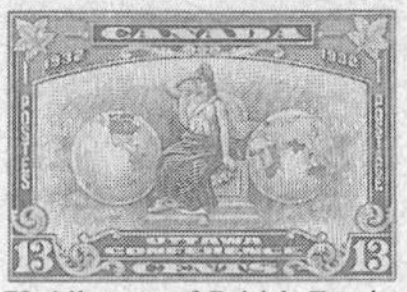
78 Allegory of British Empire

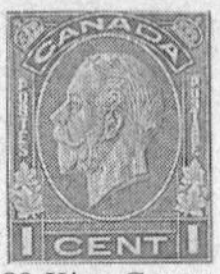
80 King George V

1932. Ottawa Conference. (a) Postage.
315 **76** 3c. red 70 80
316 **77** 5c. blue . . . . 8·50 4·75
317 **78** 13c. green . . . . 9·00 6·00

(b) Air. Surch **6 6 OTTAWA CONFERENCE 1932**.
318 **72** 6c. on 5c. brown . . . . . 10·00 12·00

1932.

319 **80** 1c. green 60 10
320 2c. brown 70 10
321b 3c. red 85 10
322 4c. brown . . . . 35·00 9·00
323 5c. blue . . . . 10·00 10
324 8c. orange . . . . 23·00 4·25

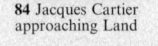

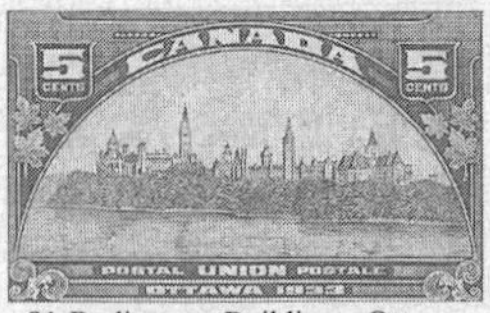
81 Parliament Buildings, Ottawa

1933. U.P.U. Congress (Preliminary Meeting).
329 **81** 5c. blue . . . . 6·00 2·75

1933. Optd **WORLD'S GRAIN EXHIBITION & CONFERENCE REGINA 1933**.
330 – 20c. red (No. 295) . . . . . 16·00 7·00

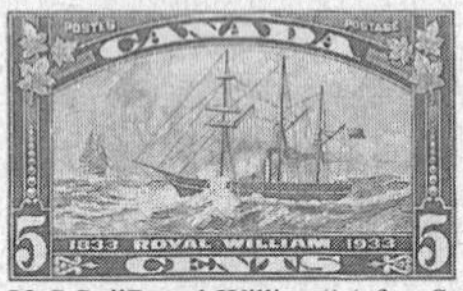
83 S.S. "Royal William" (after S. Skillett)

1933. Cent of 1st Transatlantic Steamboat Crossing.
331 **83** 5c. blue . . . . 9·50 3·00

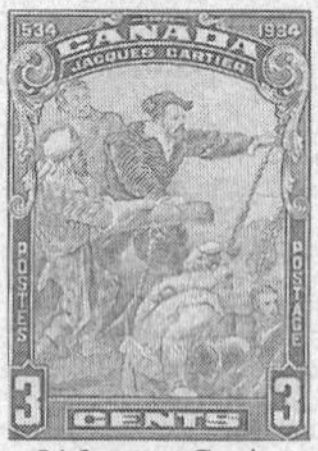
84 Jacques Cartier approaching Land

1934. 4th-century of Discovery of Canada.
332 **84** 3c. blue . . . . 2·50 1·50

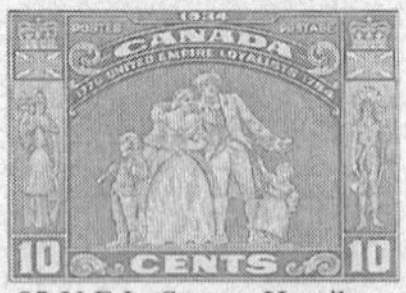
85 U.E.L. Statue, Hamilton

1934. 150th Anniv of Arrival of United Empire Loyalists.
333 **85** 10c. olive . . . . 8·50 4·75

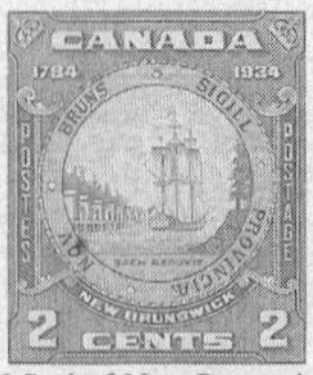
86 Seal of New Brunswick

1934. 150th Anniv of New Brunswick.
334 **86** 2c. brown . . . . 1·50 2·25

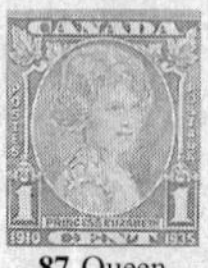
87 Queen Elizabeth II when Princess

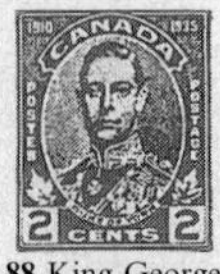
88 King George VI when Duke of York

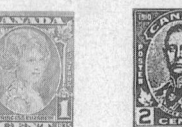

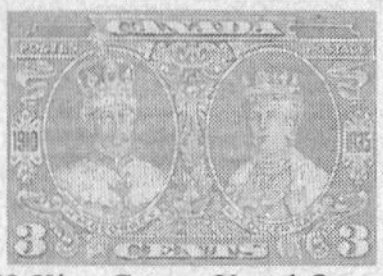
89 King George V and Queen Mary

1935. Silver Jubilee. Dated "1910–1935".
335 **87** 1c. green 55 55
336 **88** 2c. brown 60 50
337 **89** 3c. red . . . . 1·75 50
338 – 5c. blue . . . . 5·50 5·50
339 – 10c. green . . . . 3·25 3·75
340 – 13c. blue . . . . 6·50 6·00
DESIGNS—VERT: 5c. Duke of Windsor when Prince of Wales. HORIZ: 10c. Windsor Castle; 13c. Royal Yacht "Britannia".

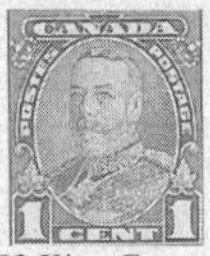
93 King George V

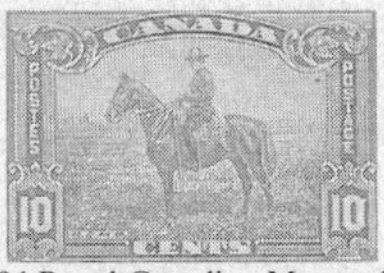
94 Royal Canadian Mounted Policeman

1935.

341 **93** 1c. green 70 10
342 2c. brown 75 10
343 3c. red 80 10
344 4c. yellow . . . . 3·00 1·75
345 5c. blue . . . . 2·00 10
346 8c. orange . . . . 3·25 3·50
347 **94** 10c. red . . . . 6·00 50
348 – 13c. violet . . . . 6·00 65
349 – 20c. green . . . . 17·00 70
350 – 50c. violet . . . . 25·00 4·75
351 – $1 blue . . . . 40·00 11·00
DESIGNS—HORIZ: 13c. Confederation, Charlottetown, 1864; 20c. Niagara Falls; 50c. Parliament Buildings, Victoria, B.C.; $1 Champlain Monument, Quebec.

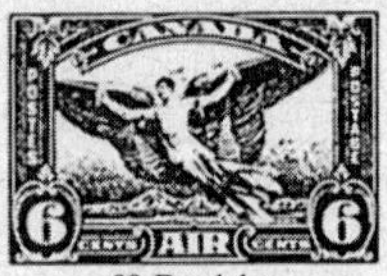
99 Daedalus

1935. Air.
355 **99** 6c. brown . . . . 2·75 1·00

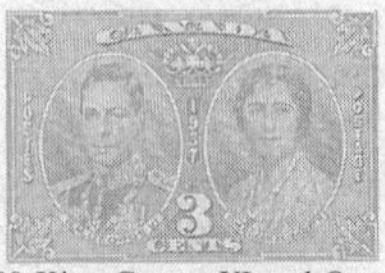
100 King George VI and Queen Elizabeth

1937. Coronation.
356 **100** 3c. red 85 30

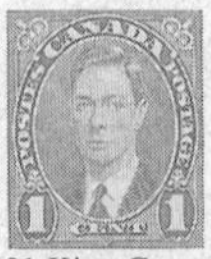
101 King George VI

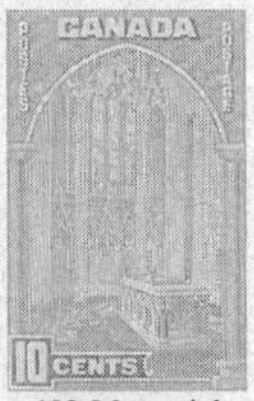
102 Memorial Chamber Parliament Buildings, Ottawa

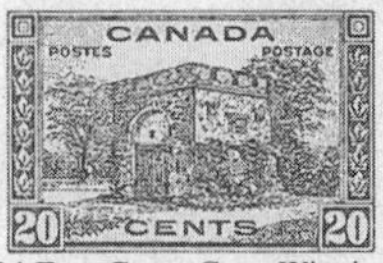
104 Fort Garry Gate, Winnipeg

1937.

357 **101** 1c. green . . . . 1·50 10
358 2c. brown . . . . 1·75 10
359 3c. red . . . . 1·75 10
360 4c. yellow . . . . 4·00 1·75
361 5c. blue . . . . 4·00 10
362 8c. orange . . . . 3·75 1·75
363 **102** 10c. red . . . . 5·00 10
364 – 13c. blue . . . . 14·00 1·25
365 **104** 20c. brown . . . . 22·00 70
366 – 50c. green . . . . 45·00 8·00
367 – $1 violet . . . . 60·00 9·00
DESIGNS—HORIZ: 13c. Halifax Harbour; 50c. Vancouver Harbour; $1 Chateau de Ramezay, Montreal.

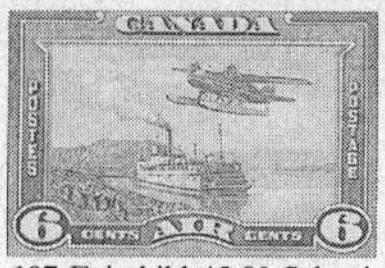

107 Fairchild 45-80 Sekani Seaplane over "Distributor" on Mackenzie River

1938. Air.
371 **107** 6c. blue . . . . 11·00 60

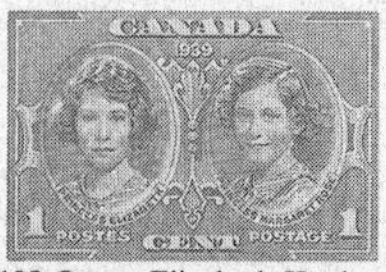

108 Queen Elizabeth II when Princess and Princess Margaret

1939. Royal Visit.
372 **108** 1c. black and green . . . 1·75 10
373 – 2c. black and brown . . . 60 50
374 – 3c. black and red 60 10
DESIGNS—HORIZ: 3c. King George VI and Queen Elizabeth. VERT: 2c. National War Memorial, Ottawa.

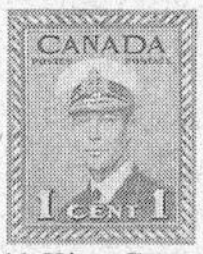

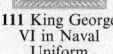

111 King George VI in Naval Uniform

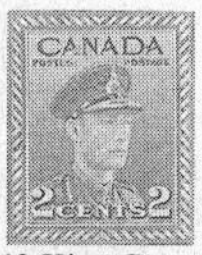

112 King George VI in Military Uniform

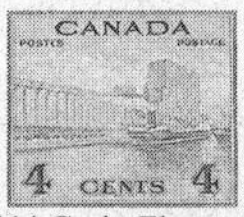

114 Grain Elevator

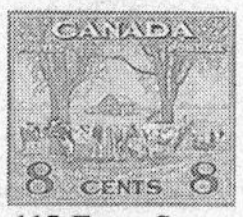

115 Farm Scene

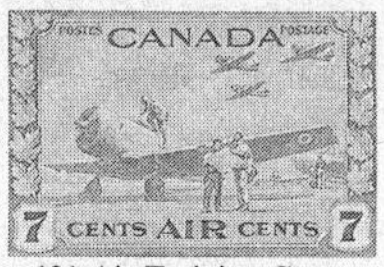

121 Air Training Camp

1942. War Effort.
375 **111** 1c. green (postage) . . . 1·50 10
376 **112** 2c. brown . . . . 1·75 10
377 – 3c. red . . . . 1·25 60
378 – 3c. purple 90 10
379 **114** 4c. grey . . . . 5·50 1·00
380 **112** 4c. red 70 10
381 **111** 5c. blue . . . . 3·00 10
382 **115** 8c. sepia . . . . 5·50 75
383 – 10c. brown . . . . 5·50 10
384 – 13c. green . . . . 6·50 6·50
385 – 14c. green . . . . 15·00 1·00
386 – 20c. brown . . . . 14·00 20
387 – 50c. violet . . . . 26·00 3·00
388 – $1 blue . . . . 42·00 5·50
399 **121** 6c. blue (air) . . . . . . 17·00 4·75
400 7c. blue . . . . 3·00 10
DESIGNS—As Type **112**: 3c. King George VI. As Type **121**. VERT: 10c. Parliament Buildings. HORIZ: 13, 14c. Ram tank; 20c. Corvette; 50c. Munitions factory; $1 H.M.S. "Cossack" (destroyer).

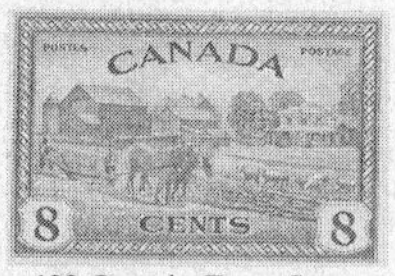

122 Ontario Farm Scene

1946. Re-conversion to Peace.
401 **122** 8c. brown (postage) . . . 1·25 2·00
402 – 10c. green . . . . 1·75 10
403 – 14c. brown . . . . 4·00 1·00
404 – 20c. grey . . . . 3·00 10
405 – 50c. green . . . . 17·00 2·75
406 – $1 purple . . . . 27·00 3·00
407 – 7c. blue (air) . . . . . . 4·00 10
DESIGNS: 10c. Great Bear Lake; 14c. St. Maurice River power station; 20c. Combine harvester; 50c. Lumbering in British Columbia; $1 "Abegweit" (train ferry); 7c. Canada geese in flight.

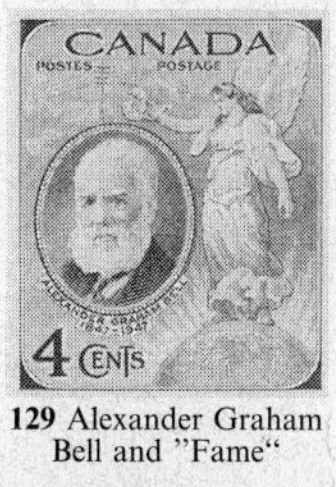

129 Alexander Graham Bell and "Fame"

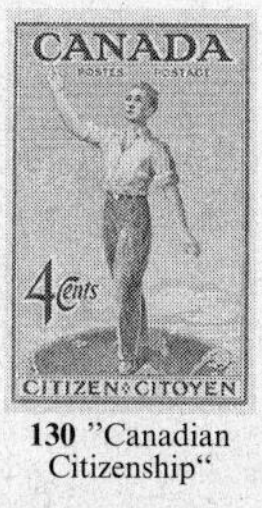

130 "Canadian Citizenship"

1947. Birth Centenary of Graham Bell (inventor of the telephone).
408 **129** 4c. blue 15 10

1947. Advent of Canadian Citizenship and 80th Anniv of Confederation.
409 **130** 4c. blue 10 10

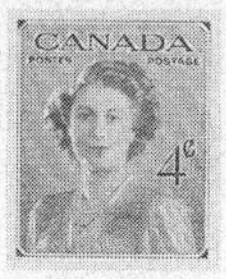

131 Queen Elizabeth II when Princess

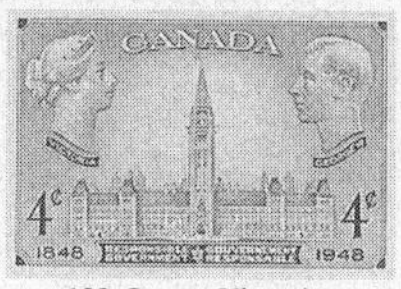

132 Queen Victoria. Parliament Building, Ottawa, and King George VI

1948. Princess Elizabeth's Wedding.
410 **131** 4c. blue 10 10

1948. Centenary of Responsible Government.
411 **132** 4c. grey 10 10

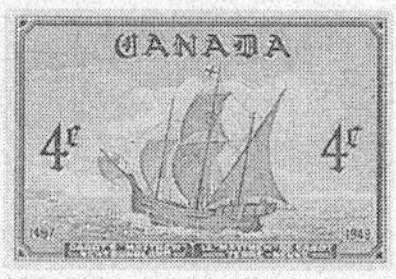

133 Cabot's Ship "Matthew"

1949. Entry of Newfoundland into Canadian Confederation.
412 **133** 4c. green 30 10

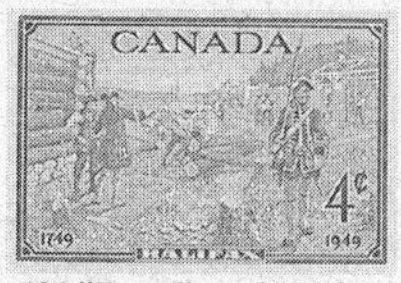

134 "Founding of Halifax, 1749" (after C. W. Jeffries)

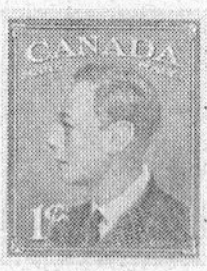

135 King George VI

1949. Halifax Bicentenary.
413 **134** 4c. violet 30 10

1949. Portraits of King George VI.
414 **135** 1c. green 10 10
415 – 2c. brown 60 30
415a – 2c. green 30 10
416 – 3c. purple 30 10
417 – 4c. red 20 10
418 – 5c. blue . . . . 2·00 10

1950. As Nos. 414 and 416/18 but without "POSTES POSTAGE".
424 1c. green 10 50
425 2c. brown . . . . 10 1·25
426 3c. purple 10 65
427 4c. red 10 20
428 5c. blue . . . . 30 1·25

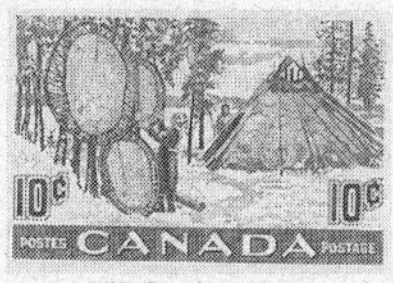

142 Drying Furs

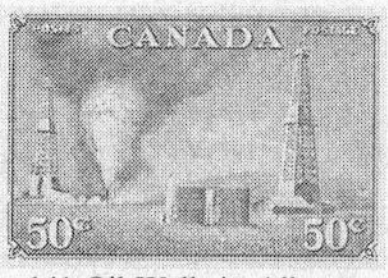

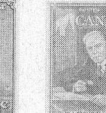

141 Oil Wells in Alberta

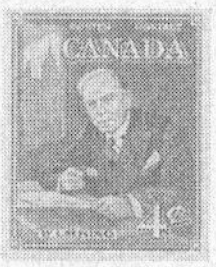

145 Mackenzie King

1950.
432 **142** 10c. purple . . . . 1·60 10
441 – 20c. grey . . . . 1·50 10
431 **141** 50c. green . . . . 6·00 1·00
433 – $1 blue . . . . 38·00 5·00
DESIGNS: 20c. Forestry products; $1 Fisherman.

1951. Canadian Prime Ministers.
434 – 3c. green (Borden) 10 50
444 – 3c. purple (Abbott) . . . 15 20
435 **145** 4c. red 10 10
445 – 4c. red (A. Mackenzie) . . 20 10
475 – 4c. violet (Thompson) . . 15 20
483 – 4c. violet (Bennett) . . . 10 20
476 – 5c. blue (Bowell) 15 10
484 – 5c. blue (Tupper) 10 10

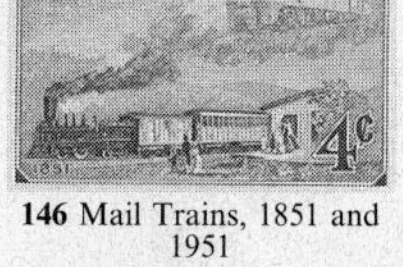

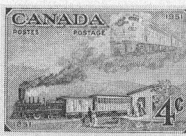

146 Mail Trains, 1851 and 1951

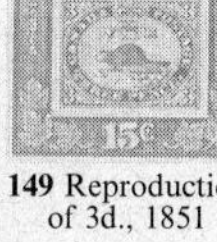

149 Reproduction of 3d., 1851

1951. Centenary of First Canadian Postage Stamp. Dated "1851 1951".
436 **146** 4c. black 35 10
437 – 5c. violet . . . . 65 1·75
438 – 7c. blue . . . . 35 1·00
439 **149** 15c. red . . . . 1·40 10
DESIGNS—As Type **146**: 5c. "City of Toronto" and S.S. "Prince George"; 7c. Mail coach and Canadair DC-4M North Star airplane.

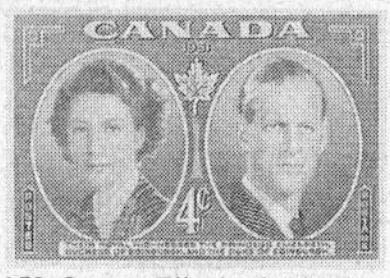

150 Queen Elizabeth II when Princess and Duke of Edinburgh

1951. Royal Visit.
440 **150** 4c. violet 10 10

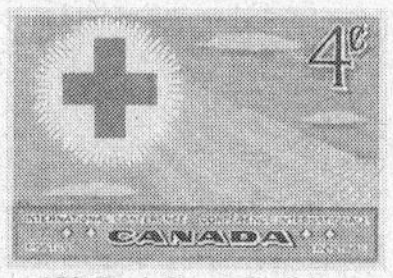

152 Red Cross Emblem

1952. 18th Int Red Cross Conf, Toronto.
442 **152** 4c. red and blue 15 10

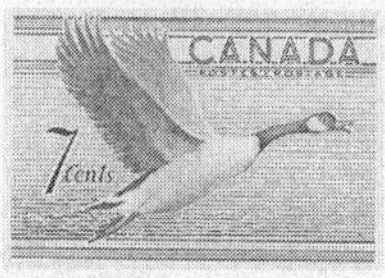

153 Canada Goose

1952.
443 **153** 7c. blue 75 10

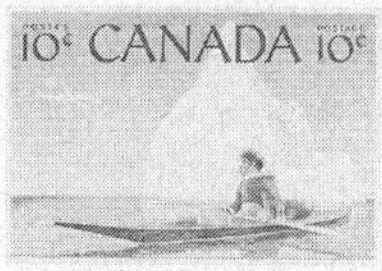

165 Eskimo Hunter

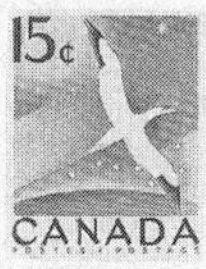

164 Northern Gannet

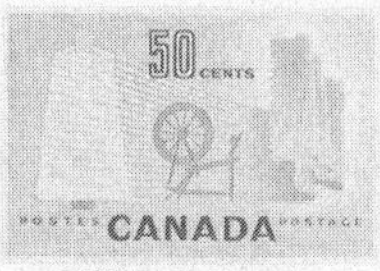

160 Textile Industry

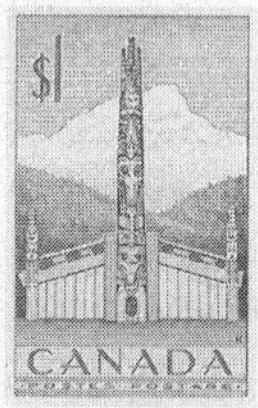

154 Pacific Coast Indian House and Totem Pole

1953.
477 **165** 10c. brown 30 10
474 **164** 15c. black . . . . 1·00 10
488 – 20c. green 55 10
489 – 25c. red 55 10
462 **160** 50c. green . . . . 1·25 10
446 **154** $1 black . . . . 3·75 20
DESIGNS (As Type **160**)—HORIZ: 20c. Pulp and paper industry. VERT: 25c. Chemical industry.

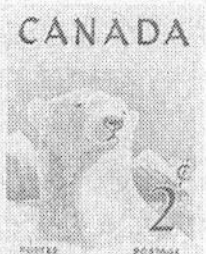

155 Polar Bear

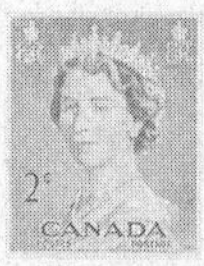

158 Queen Elizabeth II

1953. National Wild Life Week.
447 **155** 2c. blue 10 10
448 – 3c. sepia (Elk) 10 40
449 – 4c. slate (American bighorn) 15 10

1953.
450 **158** 1c. brown 10 10
451 2c. green 15 10
452 3c. red 15 15
453 4c. violet 20 10
454 5c. blue 20 10

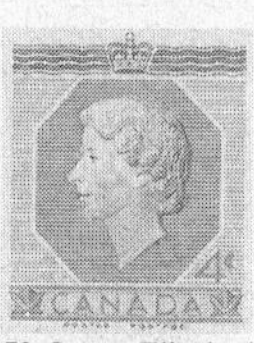

159 Queen Elizabeth II

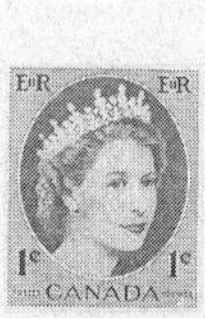

161

1953. Coronation.
461 **159** 4c. violet 10 10

1954.
463 **161** 1c. brown 10 10
464 2c. green 20 10
465 3c. red 70 10
466 4c. violet 30 10
467 5c. blue 30 10
468 6c. orange . . . . 1·00 45

1954. National Wild Life Week. As T **155**.
472 4c. slate (Walrus) 35 10
473 5c. blue (American beaver) 35 10

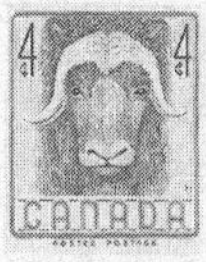

166 Musk-ox

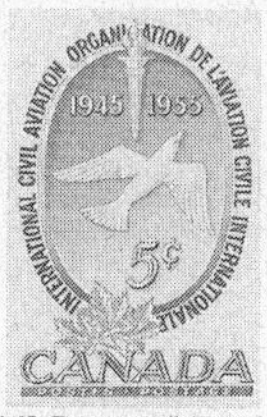

168 Dove and Torch

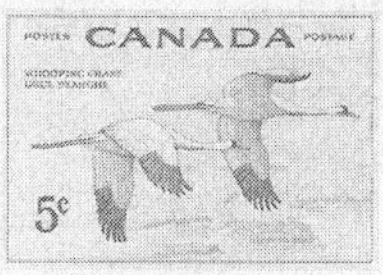

167 Whooping Cranes

1955. National Wild Life Week.
478 **166** 4c. violet 30 10
479 **167** 5c. blue . . . . 1·00 20

1955. 10th Anniv of I.C.A.O.
480 **168** 5c. blue 20 20

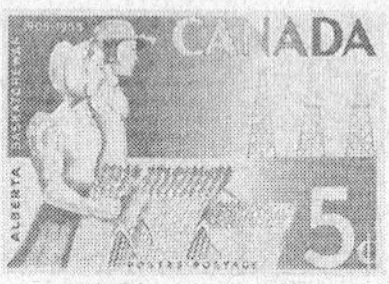

169 Pioneer Settlers

1955. 50th Anniv of Alberta and Saskatchewan Provinces.
481 **169** 5c. blue 15 20

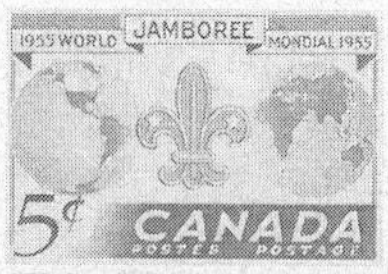

170 Scout Badge and Globe

1955. 8th World Scout Jamboree.
482 **170** 5c. brown and green . . . 20 10

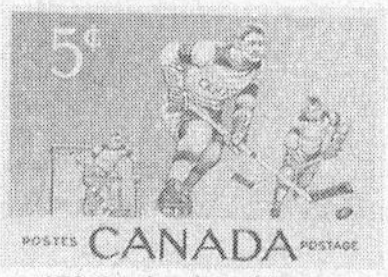

173 Ice-hockey Players

1956. Ice-hockey Commemoration.
485 **173** 5c. blue 20 20

1956. National Wild Life Week. As T **155**.
486 4c. violet (Reindeer) 20 15
487 5c. blue (Mountain goat) . . 20 10

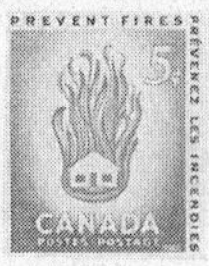

178

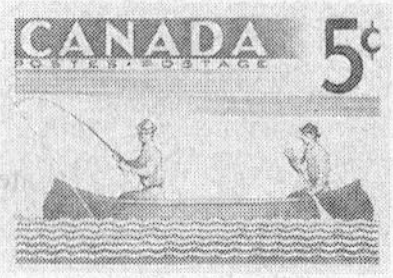

179 Fishing

1956. Fire Prevention Week.
490 **178** 5c. red and black 30 10

1957. Outdoor Recreation.
491 **179** 5c. blue 25 10
492 – 5c. blue 25 10
493 – 5c. blue 25 10
494 – 5c. blue 25 10
DESIGNS: No. 492, Swimming; 493, Hunting; 494, Skiing.

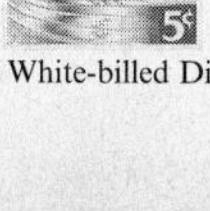

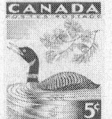

183 White-billed Diver

1957. National Wild Life Week.
495   183   5c. black 50   20

184 Thompson with Sextant, and North American Map

185 Parliament Buildings, Ottawa

1957. Death Cent of David Thompson (explorer).
496   184   5c. blue 15   30

1957. 14th U.P.U. Congress, Ottawa.
497   185   5c. slate 15   10
498   –   15c. slate 55   1·75
DESIGNS—HORIZ (33½×22 mm): 15c. Globe within posthorn.

187 Miner

188 Queen Elizabeth II and Duke of Edinburgh

1957. Mining Industry.
499   187   5c. black 35

1957. Royal Visit.
500   188   5c. black 30   10

189 "A Free Press"

190 Microscope

1958. The Canadian Press.
501   189   5c. black 15   40

1958. International Geophysical Year.
502   190   5c. blue 20   10

191 Miner panning for Gold

1958. Centenary of British Columbia.
503   191   5c. turquoise 20   10

192 La Verendrye statue

1958. La Verendrye (explorer) Commemoration.
504   192   5c. blue 15   10

193 Samuel de Champlain and Heights of Quebec

194 Nurse

1958. 350th Anniv of Founding of Quebec by Samuel de Champlain.
505   193   5c. brown and green . . . 30   10

1958. National Health.
506   194   5c. purple 30   10

195 "Petroleum 1858–1958"

196 Speaker's Chair and Mace

1958. Centenary of Canadian Oil Industry.
507   195   5c. red and olive 30   10

1958. Bicentenary of First Elected Assembly.
508   196   5c. slate 30   10

197 John McCurdy's Biplane "Silver Dart"

198 Globe showing N.A.T.O. Countries

1959. 50th Anniv of First Flight of the "Silver Dart" in Canada.
509   197   5c. black and blue 30   10

1959. 10th Anniv of N.A.T.O.
510   198   5c. blue 40   10

199

200 Queen Elizabeth II

1959. "Associated Country Women of the World" Commemoration.
511   199   5c. black and olive . . . 15   10

1959. Royal Visit.
512   200   5c. red 30   10

201 Maple Leaf linked with American Eagle

1959. Opening of St. Lawrence Seaway.
513   201   5c. blue and red 20   10

202 Maple Leaves

203 Girl Guides Badge

1959. Bicentenary of Battle of Quebec.
514   202   5c. green and red . . . 30   10

1960. Golden Jubilee of Canadian Girl Guides Movement.
515   203   5c. blue and brown . . . 20   10

204 Dollard des Ormeaux

205 Surveyor, Bulldozer and Compass Rose

1960. Tercent of Battle of Long Sault.
516   204   5c. blue and brown . . . 20   10

1961. Northern Development.
517   205   5c. green and red 15   10

206 E. Pauline Johnson

207 Arthur Meighen (statesman)

1961. Birth Centenary of E. Pauline Johnson (Mohawk poetess).
518   206   5c. green and red . . . 15   10

1961. Arthur Meighen Commemoration.
519   207   5c. blue 15   10

208 Engineers and Dam

1961. Colombo Plan.
520   208   5c. brown and blue . . . 30   10

209 "Resources for Tomorrow"

210 "Education"

1961. Natural Resources.
521   209   5c. green and brown . . . 15   10

1962. Education Year.
522   210   5c. black and brown . . . 15   10

211 Lord Selkirk and Farmer

212 Talon bestowing Gifts on Married Couple

1962. 150th Anniv of Red River Settlement.
523   211   5c. brown and green . . . 20   10

1962. Jean Talon Commemoration.
524   212   5c. blue 20   10

213 British Columbia and Vancouver Island 2½d. Stamp of 1860, and Parliament Buildings, B.C.

214 Highway (map version) and Provincial Arms

1962. Centenary of Victoria, B.C.
525   213   5c. red and black 30   10

1962. Opening of Trans-Canada Highway.
526   214   5c. black and brown . . . 15   10

215 Queen Elizabeth II and Wheat (agriculture) Symbol

216 Sir Casimir Gzowski

1962. Different symbols in top left corner.
527   215   1c. brown 10   10
528   2c. green 10   10
529   3c. violet 15   10
530   4c. red 15   10
531   5c. blue 15   10
SYMBOLS: 1c. Crystals (Mining); 2c. Tree (Forestry); 3c. Fish (Fisheries); 4c. Electricity pylon (Industrial power); 5c. Wheat (Agriculture).

1963. 150th Birth Anniv of Sir Casimir Gzowski (engineer).
535   216   5c. purple 10   10

217 "Export Trade"

218 Frobisher and barque "Gabriel"

1963.
536   217 $1 red . . . . 4·75   2·00

1963. Sir Martin Frobisher Commemoration.
537   218   5c. blue 20   10

219 Horseman and Map

1963. Bicent of Quebec–Trois-Rivieres–Montreal Postal Service.
538   219   5c. brown and green . . . 15   10

220 Canada Geese

221 Douglas DC-9 Airliner and Uplands Airport, Ottawa

1963.
540   221   7c. black 35   70
540a   8c. blue 50   50
539   220   15c. blue . . . . 1·00   10

222 "Peace on Earth"

223 Maple Leaves

1964. "Peace".
541   222   5c. ochre, blue & turq . . . 15   10

1964. "Canadian Unity".
542   223   5c. lake and blue 10   10

224 White Trillium and Arms of Ontario

1964. Provincial Badges.
543   224   5c. green, brown and orange . . . 40   20
544   –   5c. green, brown and yellow . . . 40   20
545   5c. red, green and violet . . . 30   20
546   5c. blue, red and green . . . 30   20
547   5c. purple, green and brown . . . 30   20
548   5c. brown, green and mauve . . . 30   20
549   5c. lilac, green and purple . . . 50   20
550   5c. green, yellow and red . . . 30   20
551   5c. sepia, orange and green . . . 30   20
552   5c. black, red and green . . . 30   20
553   5c. drab, green and yellow . . . 30   20
554   5c. blue, green and red . . . 30   20
555   5c. red and blue . . . 30   20

FLOWERS AND ARMS OF: No. 544, Madonna Lily, Quebec; 545, Purple Violet, New Brunswick; 546, Mayflower, Nova Scotia; 547, Dogwood, British Columbia; 548, Prairie Crocus, Manitoba; 549, Lady's Slipper, Prince Edward Island; 550, Wild Rose, Alberta; 551, Prairie Lily, Saskatchewan; 552, Pitcher Plant, Newfoundland; 553, Mountain Avens, Northwest Territories; 554, Fireweed, Yukon Territory; 555, Maple Leaf, Canada.

1964. Surch 8.
556   221   8c. on 7c. blue 15   15

238 Fathers of the Confederation Memorial, Charlottetown

1964. Centenary of Charlottetown Conference.
557   238   5c. black 10   10

239 Maple Leaf and Hand with Quill Pen

1964. Centenary of Quebec Conference.
558   239   5c. red and brown 15   10

240 Queen Elizabeth II

241 "Canadian Family"

1964. Royal Visit.
559 240 5c. purple 15 10

1964. Christmas.
560 241 3c. red 10 10
561   5c. blue 10 10

242 "Co-operation"

1965. International Co-operation Year.
562 242 5c. green 35 10

243 Sir W. Grenfell

1965. Birth Centenary of Sir Wilfred Grenfell (missionary).
563 243 5c. green 20 10

244 National Flag

1965. Inauguration of National Flag.
564 244 5c. red and blue 15 10

245 Sir Winston Churchill

246 Peace Tower, Parliament Buildings, Ottawa

1965. Churchill Commemoration.
565 245 5c. brown 15 10

1965. Inter-Parliamentary Union Conference, Ottawa.
566 246 5c. green 10 10

247 Parliament Buildings, Ottawa, 1865

248 "Gold, Frankincense and Myrrh"

1965. Centenary of Proclamation of Ottawa as Capital.
567 247 5c. brown 10 10

1965. Christmas.
568 248 3c. green 10 10
569   5c. blue 10 10

249 "Alouette 2" over Canada

250 La Salle

1966. Launching of Canadian Satellite, "Alouette 2".
570 249 5c. blue 15 10

1966. 300th Anniv of La Salle's Arrival in Canada.
571 250 5c. green 15 10

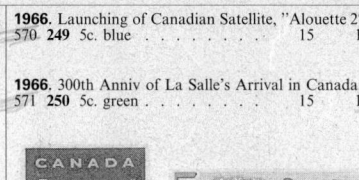

251 Road Signs   252 Canadian Delegation and Houses of Parliament

1966. Highway Safety.
572 251 5c. yellow, blue and black 15 10

1966. Centenary of London Conference.
573 252 5c. brown 10 10

253 Douglas Point Nuclear Power Station

254 Parliamentary Library, Ottawa

1966. Peaceful Uses of Atomic Energy.
574 253 5c. blue 10 10

1966. Commonwealth Parliamentary Association Conference, Ottawa.
575 254 5c. purple 10 10

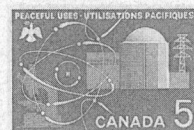

255 "Praying Hands", after Durer

256 Flags and Canada on Globe

1966. Christmas.
576 255 3c. red 10 10
577   5c. orange 10 10

1967. Canadian Centennial.
578 256 5c. red and blue 10 10

257 Queen Elizabeth, Northern Lights and Dog-team

262 "Alaska Highway" (A. Y. Jackson)

1967.
579 257 1c. brown 10 10
580 – 2c. green 10 10
581 – 3c. purple 30 10
582 – 4c. red 20 10
583 – 5c. blue 20 10
601 – 6c. red 45 10
607 – 6c. black 30 10
609 – 6c. green 30 10
584 262 8c. purple 35 30
610 – 8c. black 30 10
585 – 10c. olive 30 10
586 – 15c. purple 30 10
587 – 20c. blue . . . . . 1·00 10
588 – 25c. green 75 10
589 – 50c. brown . . . . . 1·25 10
590 – $1 red . . . . . . 1·75 65
DESIGNS—As Type 257: 2c. Totem pole; 3c. Combine-harvester and oil derrick; 4c. Ship in lock; 5c., Harbour scene; 6c., 7c. "Transport"; 8c. (No. 610), Library of Parliament. As Type 262: 10c. "The Jack Pine" (T. Thomson); 15c. "Bylot Island" (L. Harris); 20c. "Quebec Ferry" (J. W. Morrice); 25c. "The Solemn Land" (J. E. H. MacDonald); 50c. "Summer's Stores" (Grain elevators, J. Ensor); $1 "Oilfield" (near Edmonton, H. G. Glyde).

269 Canadian Pavilion

270 Allegory of "Womanhood" on Ballot-box

271 Queen Elizabeth II and Centennial Emblem

272 Athlete

1967. World Fair, Montreal.
611 269 5c. blue and red 10 10

1967. 50th Anniv of Women's Franchise.
612 270 5c. purple and black . . . 10 10

1967. Royal Visit.
613 271 5c. plum and brown . . . 15 10

1967. Pan-American Games, Winnipeg.
614 272 5c. red 10 10

273 "World News"

1967. 50th Anniv of Canadian Press.
615 273 5c. blue 10 10

274 Governor-General Vanier

1967. Vanier Commemoration.
616 274 5c. black 10 10

275 People of 1867, and Toronto, 1967

276 Carol Singers

1967. Cent of Toronto as Capital City of Ontario.
617 275 5c. green and red 10 10

1967. Christmas.
618 276 3c. red 10 10
619   5c. green 10 10

277 Grey Jays

278 Weather Map and Instruments

1968. Wild Life.
620 277 5c. multicoloured 30 10
See also Nos. 638/40.

1968. 20th Anniv of First Meteorological Readings.
621 278 5c. multicoloured 15 10

279 Narwhal

1968. Wild Life.
622 279 5c. multicoloured 15 10

280 Globe, Maple Leaf and Rain Gauge

1968. International Hydrological Decade.
623 280 5c. multicoloured 15 10

281 The "Nonsuch"

1968. 300th Anniv of Voyage of the "Nonsuch".
624 281 5c. multicoloured 20 10

282 Lacrosse Players

283 Front Page of "The Globe", George Brown and Legislative Building

1968. Lacrosse.
625 282 5c. multicoloured 15 10

1968. 150th Birth Anniv of George Brown (politician and journalist).
626 283 5c. multicoloured 10 10

284 H. Bourassa (politician and journalist)

286 Armistice Monument, Vimy

285 John McCrae, Battlefield and First Lines of "In Flanders Fields"

1968. Birth Centenary of Henri Bourassa.
627 284 5c. black, red and cream . . 10 10

1968. 50th Death Anniv of John McCrae (soldier and poet).
628 285 5c. multicoloured 10 10

1968. 50th Anniv of 1918 Armistice.
629 286 15c. black 30 40

287 Eskimo Family (carving)

289 Curling

1968. Christmas.
630 287 5c. black and blue 10 10
631 – 6c. black and ochre . . . 10 10
DESIGN: 6c. "Mother and Child" (carving).

1969. Curling.
632 289 6c. black, blue and red . . 15 10

290 Vincent Massey

292 Globe and Tools

291 "Return from the Harvest Field" (Suzor-Cote)

1969. Vincent Massey, First Canadian-born Governor-General.

633 **290** 6c. sepia and ochre . . . 　10　10

1969. Birth Centenary of Marc Aurele de Foy Suzor-Cote (painter).

634 **291** 50c. multicoloured . . . . 　70　2·00

1969. 50th Anniv of I.L.O.

635 **292** 6c. green . . . . 　10　10

293 Vickers Vimy Aircraft over Atlantic Ocean

1969. 50th Anniv of 1st Non-stop Transatlantic Flight.

636 **293** 15c. brown, green and blue . . . . 　40　55

294 "Sir William Osler" (J. S. Sargent)　**295** White-throated Sparrow

1969. 50th Death Anniv of Sir William Osler (physician).

637 **294** 6c. blue and brown . . . . 　20　10

1969. Birds. Multicoloured.

638　6c. Type **295** . . . . 　25　10
639　10c. Savannah sparrow ("Ipswich Sparrow") (horiz) . . . . 　35　1·10
640　25c. Hermit thrush (horiz) . . 　1·10　3·50

298 Flags of Winter and Summer Games　**300** Sir Isaac Brock and Memorial Column

299 Outline of Prince Edward Island showing Charlottetown

1969. Canadian Games.

641 **298** 6c. green, red and blue . . 　10　10

1969. Bicentenary of Charlottetown as Capital of Prince Edward Island.

642 **299** 6c. brown, black and blue 　20　10

1969. Birth Bicentenary of Sir Isaac Brock.

643 **300** 6c. orange, bistre and brown . . . . 　10　10

301 Children of the World in Prayer　**302** Stephen Butler Leacock, Mask and "Mariposa"

1969. Christmas.

644 **301** 5c. multicoloured . . . . 　10　10
645　6c. multicoloured . . . . 　10　10

1969. Birth Centenary of Stephen Butler Leacock (humorist).

646 **302** 6c. multicoloured . . . . 　10　10

303 Symbolic Cross-roads

1970. Centenary of Manitoba.

647 **303** 6c. blue, yellow and red 　15　10

304 "Enchanted Owl" (Kenojuak)

1970. Centenary of Northwest Territories.

648 **304** 6c. red and black . . . . 　10　10

305 Microscopic View of Inside of Leaf

1970. International Biological Programme.

649 **305** 6c. green, yellow and blue 　15　10

306 Expo 67 Emblem and stylized Cherry Blossom

1970. World Fair, Osaka. Multicoloured.

650　25c. Type **306** (red) . . . . 　1·50　2·25
651　25c. Dogwood (violet) . . . 　1·50　2·25
652　25c. White trillium (green) . 　1·50　2·25
653　25c. White garden lily (blue) 　1·50　2·25

NOTE: Each stamp shows a stylized cherry blossom, in a different colour, given above in brackets.

310 Henry Kelsey

1970. 300th Birth Anniv of Henry Kelsey (explorer).

654 **310** 6c. multicoloured . . . . 　10　10

311 "Towards Unification"

1970. 25th Anniv of U.N.O.

655 **311** 10c. blue . . . . 　40　30
656　15c. mauve and lilac . . . . 　40　35

312 Louis Riel (Metis leader)　**313** Mackenzie's Inscription, Dean Channel

1970. Louis Riel Commemoration.

657 **312** 6c. blue and red . . . . 　10　10

1970. Sir Alexander Mackenzie (explorer).

658 **313** 6c. brown . . . . . . 　15　10

314 Sir Oliver Mowat (statesman)

1970. Sir Oliver Mowat Commemoration.

659 **314** 6c. red and black . . . . 　10　10

315 "Isles of Spruce" (A. Lismer)

1970. 50th Anniv of "Group of Seven" (artists).

660 **315** 6c. multicoloured . . . . 　10　10

316 "Horse-drawn Sleigh" (D. Niskala)　**328** Sir Donald A. Smith

1970. Christmas. Children's Drawings. Mult.

661　5c. Type **316** . . . . . . 　50　20
662　5c. "Stable and Star of Bethlehem" (L. Wilson) . . 　50　20
663　5c. "Snowmen" (M. Lecompte) . . . . . 　50　20
664　5c. "Skiing" (D. Durham) . . 　50　20
665　5c. "Santa Claus" (A. Martin) . . . . . . 　50　20
666　6c. "Santa Claus" (E. Bhattacharya) . . . . 　50　20
667　6c. "Christ in Manger" (J. McKinney) . . . . . 　50　20
668　6c. "Toy Shop" (N. Whateley) . . . . . 　50　20
669　6c. "Christmas Tree" (J. Pomperleau) . . . . 　50　20
670　6c. "Church" (J. McMillan) 　50　20
671　10c. "Christ in Manger" (C. Fortier) (37 × 20 mm) 　30　30
672　15c. "Trees and Sledge" (J. Dojcak) (37 × 20 mm) 　45　60

1970. 150th Birth Anniv of Sir Donald Alexander Smith.

673 **328** 6c. yellow, brown and green . . . . 　15　10

329 "Big Raven" (E. Carr)

1971. Birth Centenary of Emily Carr (painter).

674 **329** 6c. multicoloured . . . . 　20　30

330 Laboratory Equipment　**332** Maple "Keys"

331 "The Atom"

1971. 50th Anniv of Discovery of Insulin.

675 **330** 6c. multicoloured . . . . 　30　30

1971. Birth Centenary of Lord Rutherford (scientist).

676 **331** 6c. yellow, red and brown 　20　20

1971. "The Maple Leaf in Four Seasons". Mult.

677　6c. Type **332** (spring) . . . 　20　20
678　7c. Green leaves (summer) . , 　20　20
679　7c. Autumn leaves . . . . 　20　20
680　7c. Withered leaves and snow (winter) . . . . 　20　20

333 Louis Papineau　**334** Chart of Coppermine River

1971. Death Centenary of Louis-Joseph Papineau (politician).

681 **333** 6c. multicoloured . . . . 　15　20

1971. Bicentenary of Samuel Hearne's Expedition to the Coppermine River.

682 **334** 6c. red, brown and buff 　40　40

335 "People" and Computer Tapes

1971. Centenary of 1st Canadian Census.

683 **335** 6c. blue, red and black . . 　30　20

336 Maple Leaves

1971. Radio Canada International.

684 **336** 15c. red, yellow and black 　50　1·50

337 "B. C."

1971. Centenary of British Columbia's Entry into the Confederation.

685 **337** 7c. multicoloured . . . . 　15　10

338 "Indian Encampment on Lake Huron" (Kane)　**339** "Snowflake"

1971. Death Centenary of Paul Kane (painter).

686 **338** 7c. multicoloured . . . . 　20　20

1971. Christmas.

687 **339** 6c. blue . . . . 　10　10
688　7c. green . . . . 　15　10
689　10c. silver and red . . . . 　50　1·25
690　15c. silver, purple and lavender . . . . . . 　65　2·00

DESIGN: 10c., 15c. "Snowflake" design similar to Type **339** but square (26 × 26 mm).

340 Pierre Laporte (Quebec Cabinet Minister)　**341** Skaters

1971. 1st Anniv of Assassination of Pierre Laporte.

691 **340** 7c. black on buff . . . . 　15　10

1972. World Figure Skating Championships, Calgary.

692 **341** 8c. purple . . . . . . 　15　10

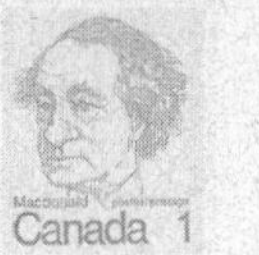

342 J. A. MacDonald

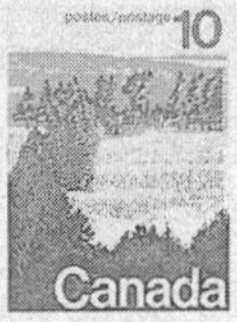

343 Forest, Central Canada

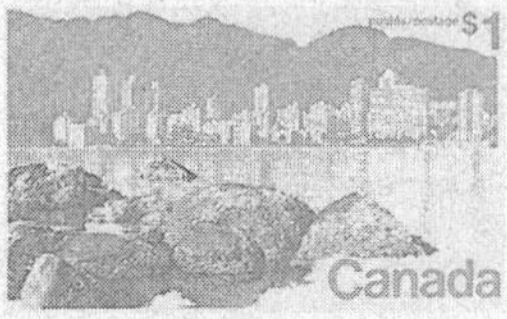

344 Vancouver

1972.

693	342	1c. orange	10	20
694	–	2c. green	10	10
695	–	3c. brown	10	40
696	–	4c. black	10	40
697	–	5c. mauve	10	10
698	–	6c. red	10	30
699	–	7c. brown	40	40
700	–	8c. blue	15	10
701	–	10c. red	75	10
702a	343	10c. green, turquoise and orange	40	15
703b	–	15c. blue and brown	1·00	10
704a	–	20c. orange, violet and blue	65	10
705b	–	25c. ultram and blue	1·00	10
706	–	50c. green, blue and brown	80	30
709a	344	$1 multicoloured	85	70
708	–	$2 multicoloured	1·50	2·00

DESIGNS—As Type **342** (1 to 7c. show Canadian Prime Ministers): 2c. W. Laurier; 3c. R. Borden; 4c. W. L. Mackenzie King; 5c. R. B. Bennett; 6c. L. B. Pearson; 7c. Louis St. Laurent; 8, 10c. Queen Elizabeth II. As Type **343**: 15c. American bighorn; 20c. Prairie landscape from the air; 25c. Polar bears; 50c. Seashore, Eastern Canada. As Type **344**: $2 Quebec.

345 Heart

1972. World Health Day.

719	345	8c. red	30	10

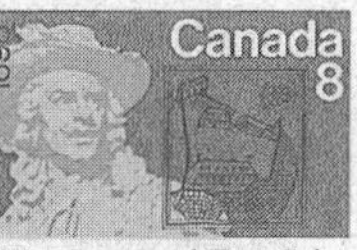

346 Frontenac and Fort Saint-Louis, Quebec

1972. 300th Anniv of Governor Frontenac's Appointment to New France.

720	346	8c. red, brown and blue	15	15

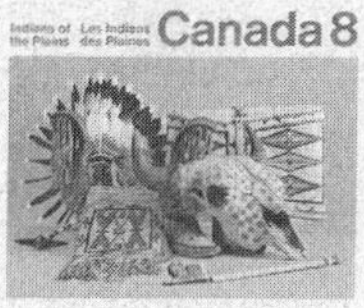

347 Plains Indians' Artefacts

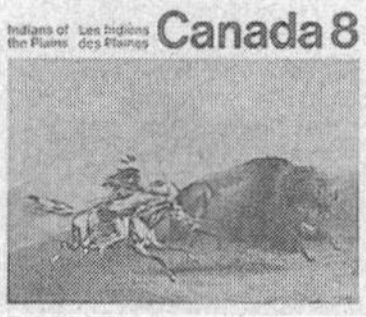

347a Buffalo Chase

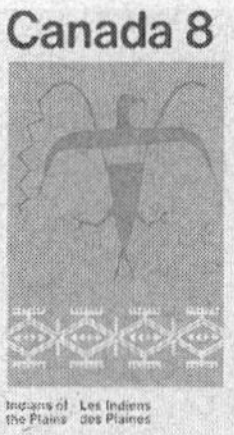

348 Thunderbird and Tribal Pattern

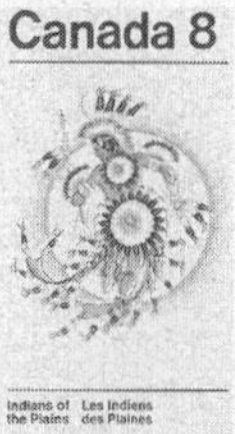

348a Dancer in Ceremonial Costume

1972. Canadian Indians. (a) Horiz designs showing Artefacts as T **347** or Scenes from Indian Life as T **347a**.

721	347	8c. multicoloured	40	10
722	347a	8c. brown, yellow & blk	40	10
723	–	8c. multicoloured	40	10
724	–	8c. multicoloured	40	10
725	–	8c. multicoloured	40	10
726	–	8c. brown, yellow & blk	40	10
727	–	8c. multicoloured	40	10
728	–	8c. multicoloured	40	10
729	–	10c. multicoloured	40	20
730	–	10c. red, brown and black	40	20

TRIBES: Nos. 721/2, Plains Indians; Nos. 723/4, Algonkians; Nos. 725/6, Pacific Coast Indians; Nos. 727/8, Subarctic Indians; Nos. 729/30, Iroquoians.

(b) Vert designs showing Thunderbird and pattern as T **348** or Costumes as T **348a**.

731	348	8c. orange, red and black	40	15
732	348a	8c. multicoloured	40	15
733	–	8c. red, violet and black	40	10
734	–	8c. green, brown and black	40	10
735	–	8c. red and black	40	10
736	–	8c. multicoloured	40	10
737	–	8c. green, brown and black	40	10
738	–	8c. multicoloured	40	10
739	–	10c. brown, orange & blk	40	20
740	–	10c. multicoloured	40	20

TRIBES: Nos. 731/2, Plains Indians; Nos. 733/4, Algonkians; Nos. 735/6, Pacific Coast Indians; Nos. 737/8, Subarctic Indians; Nos. 739/40, Iroquoians.

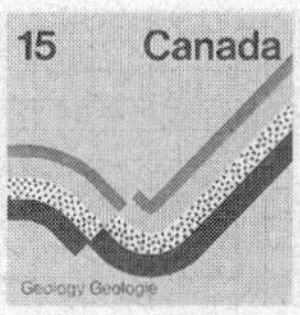

349 Earth's Crust

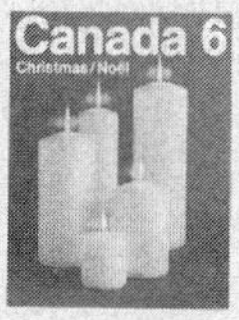

350 Candles

1972. Earth Sciences.

741	–	15c. multicoloured	1·10	1·90
742	–	15c. grey, blue and black	1·10	1·90
743	349	15c. multicoloured	1·10	1·90
744	–	15c. green, orange and black	1·10	1·90

DESIGNS AND EVENTS: No. 741 Photogrammetric surveying (12th Congress of International Society of Photogrammetry); No. 742 "Siegfried" lines (6th Conference of Int Cartographic Association); No. 743 (24th International Geological Congress); No. 744 Diagram of village at road-intersection (22nd Int Geographical Congress).

1972. Christmas. Multicoloured.

745		6c. Type **350**	15	10
746		8c. Type **350**	15	10
747		10c. Candles with fruits and pine boughs (horiz)	50	1·00
748		15c. Candles with prayer-book, caskets and vase (horiz)	60	1·40

Nos. 747/8 are size 36 × 20 mm.

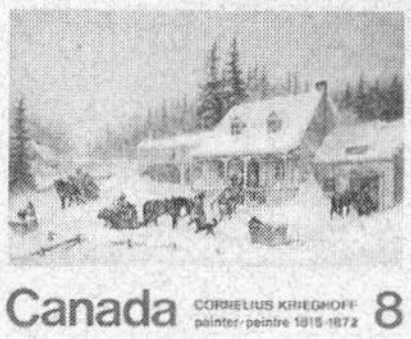

351 "The Blacksmith's Shop" (Krieghoff)

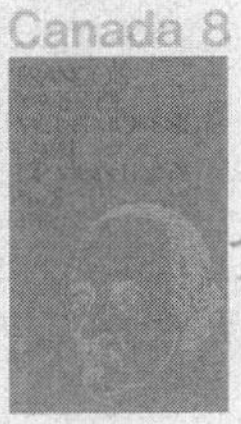

352 F. de Montmorency-Laval

1972. Death Centenary of Cornelius Krieghoff (painter).

749	351	8c. multicoloured	30	15

1973. 350th Birth Anniv of Monsignor de Laval (1st Bishop of Quebec).

750	352	8c. blue, gold and silver	20	40

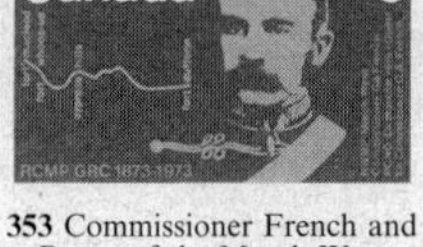

353 Commissioner French and Route of the March West

1973. Centenary of Royal Canadian Mounted Police.

751	353	8c. brown, orange and red	35	20
752	–	10c. multicoloured	1·00	1·25
753	–	15c. multicoloured	1·75	2·00

DESIGNS: 10c. Spectrograph; 15c. Mounted policeman.

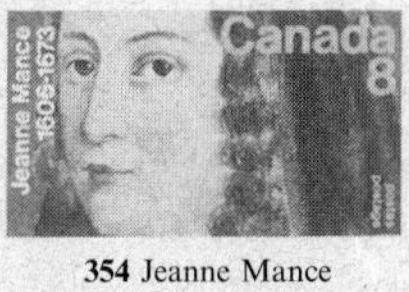

354 Jeanne Mance

1973. 300th Death Anniv of Jeanne Mance (nurse).

754	354	8c. multicoloured	20	40

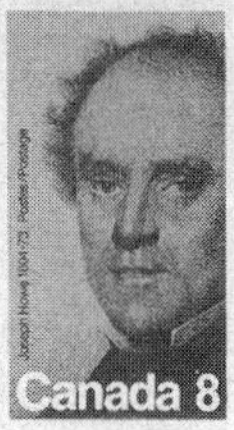

355 Joseph Howe

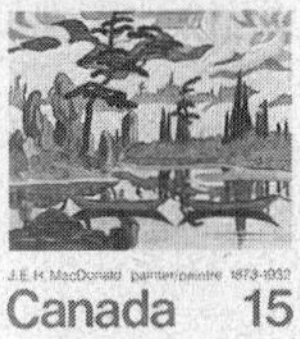

356 "Mist Fantasy" (MacDonald)

1973. Death Centenary of Joseph Howe (Nova Scotian politician).

755	355	8c. gold and black	20	40

1973. Birth Cent of J. E. H. MacDonald (artist).

756	356	15c. multicoloured	30	55

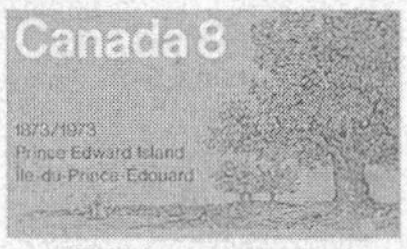

357 Oaks and Harbour

1973. Centenary of Prince Edward Island's Entry into the Confederation.

757	357	8c. orange and red	20	30

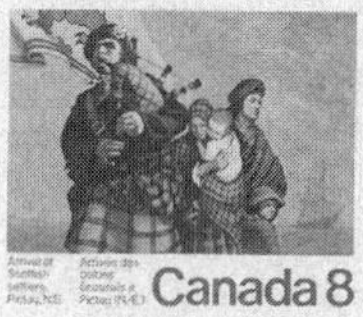

358 Scottish Settlers

1973. Bicentenary of Arrival of Scottish Settlers at Pictou, Nova Scotia.

758	358	8c. multicoloured	25	20

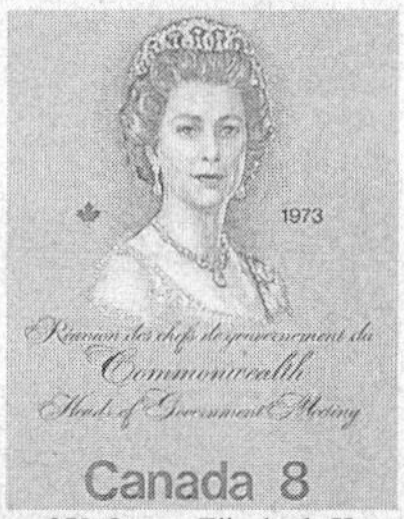

359 Queen Elizabeth II

1973. Royal Visit and Commonwealth Heads of Government Meeting, Ottawa.

759	359	8c. multicoloured	25	20
760		15c. multicoloured	80	1·50

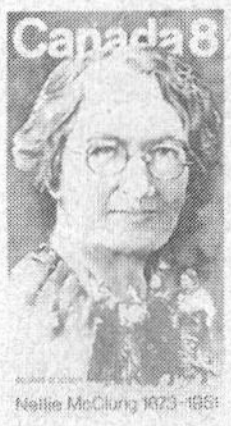

360 Nellie McClung

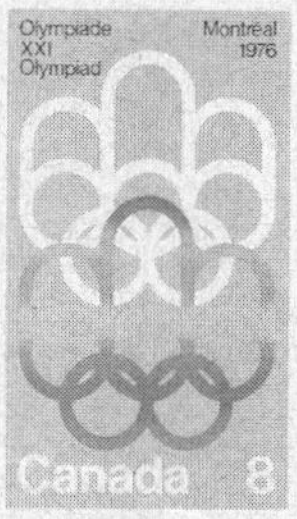

361 Emblem of 1976 Olympics

1973. Birth Centenary of Nellie McClung (feminist).

761	360	8c. multicoloured	20	50

1973. 1976 Olympic Games, Montreal (1st issue).

762	361	8c. multicoloured	25	15
763		15c. multicoloured	45	1·25

See also Nos. 768/71, 772/4, 786/9, 798/802, 809/11, 814/16, 829/32, 833/7 and 842/4.

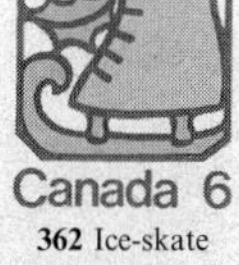

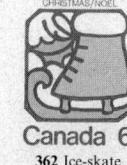

362 Ice-skate

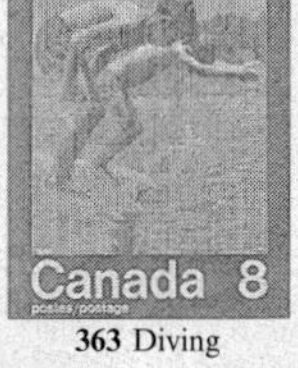

363 Diving

1973. Christmas. Multicoloured.

764		6c. Type **362**	15	10
765		8c. Bird decoration	20	10
766		10c. Santa Claus (20 × 36 mm)	70	1·40
767		15c. Shepherd (20 × 36 mm)	80	1·75

1974. 1976 Olympic Games, Montreal. (2nd issue). "Summer Activities". Each blue.

768		8c. Type **363**	30	50
769		8c. "Jogging"	30	50
770		8c. Cycling	30	50
771		8c. Hiking	30	50

1974. 1976 Olympic Games, Montreal. (3rd issue). As T **361** but smaller (20 × 36½ mm).

772	361	8c.+2c. multicoloured	25	45
773		10c.+5c. multicoloured	40	1·00
774		15c.+5c. multicoloured	45	1·40

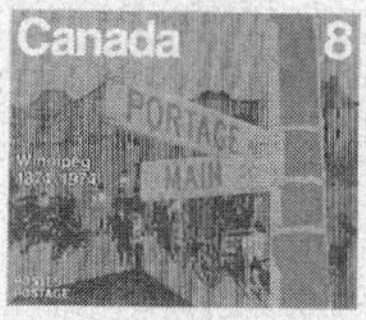

364 Winnipeg Signpost, 1872

1974. Winnipeg Centennial.

775	364	8c. multicoloured	20	15

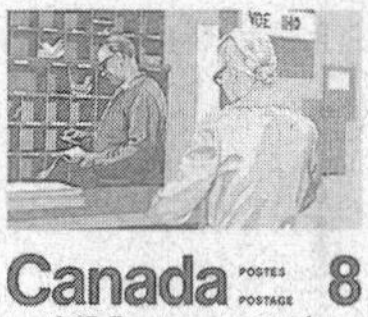

365 Postmaster and Customer

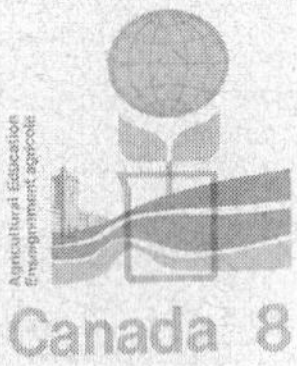

366 "Canada's Contribution to Agriculture"

1974. Centenary of Canadian Letter Carrier Delivery Service. Multicoloured.

776		8c. Type **365**	50	80
777		8c. Postman collecting mail	50	80
778		8c. Mail handler	50	80
779		8c. Mail sorters	50	80
780		8c. Postman making delivery	50	80
781		8c. Rural delivery by car	50	80

1974. Centenary of "Agricultural Education". Ontario Agricultural College.

782	366	8c. multicoloured	20	20

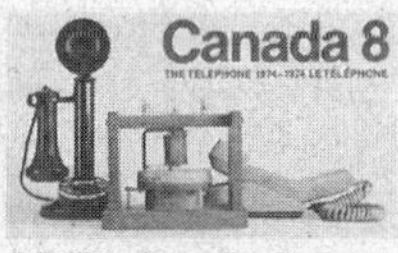

367 Telephone Development

1974. Centenary of Invention of Telephone by Alexander Graham Bell.

783	367	8c. multicoloured	20	20

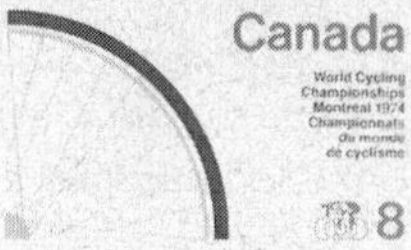

368 Bicycle Wheel

1974. World Cycling Championships, Montreal.

784	368	8c. black, red and silver	20	30

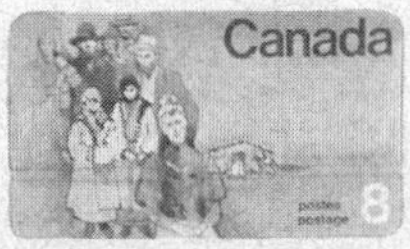

369 Mennonite Settlers

1974. Centenary of Arrival of Mennonites in Manitoba.

785	369	8c. multicoloured	20	20

1974. 1976 Olympic Games, Montreal (4th issue). "Winter Activities". As T **363**. Each red.

786		8c. Snow-shoeing	55	60
787		8c. Skiing	55	60
788		8c. Skating	55	60
789		8c. Curling	55	60

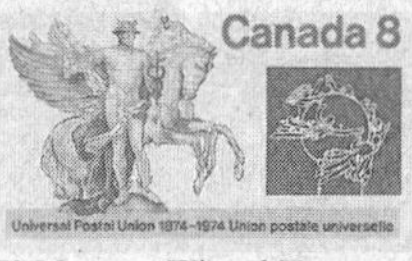

370 Mercury, Winged Horses and U.P.U. Emblem

1974. Centenary of U.P.U.

790	370	8c. violet, red and blue	15	15
791		15c. red, violet and blue	50	1·50

Canada 6

371 "The Nativity" (J. P. Lemieux)

1974. Christmas. Multicoloured.
792 6c. Type 371 . . . . 10 10
793 8c. "Skaters in Hull"
(H. Masson) (34 × 31 mm) 10 10
794 10c. "The Ice Cone,
Montmorency Falls"
(R. C. Todd) 30 75
795 15c. "Village in the
Laurentian Mountains"
(C. A. Gagnon) . . . . 35 1·10

372 Marconi and St. John's Harbour, Newfoundland

1974. Birth Centenary of Guglielmo Marconi (radio pioneer).
796 372 8c. multicoloured 20 20

373 Merritt and Welland Canal

1974. William Merritt Commemoration.
797 373 8c. multicoloured 20 30

374 Swimming   376 "Anne of Green Gables" (Lucy Maud Montgomery)

375 "The Sprinter"

1975. 1976 Olympic Games, Montreal (5th issue). Multicoloured.
798 8c.+2c. Type 374 . . . . . 35 60
799 10c.+5c. Rowing . . . . . 50 1·10
800 15c.+5c. Sailing . . . . . 55 1·25

1975. 1976 Olympic Games, Montreal (6th issue). Multicoloured.
801 $1 Type 375 . . . . 1·50 2·25
802 $2 "The Diver" (vert) . . . 2·25 4·25

1975. Canadian Writers (1st series). Multicoloured.
803 8c. Type 376 . . . . . . 30 10
804 8c. "Maria Chapdelaine"
(Louis Hemon) 30 10
See also Nos. 846/7, 940/1 and 1085/6.

377 Marguerite Bourgeoys (founder of the Order of Notre Dame)   378 S. D. Chown (founder of United Church of Canada)

1975. Canadian Celebrities.
805 377 8c. multicoloured 60 40
806 — 8c. multicoloured 60 40
807 378 8c. multicoloured 30 75
808 — 8c. multicoloured 30 75

DESIGNS—As Type 377: No. 806, Alphonse Desjardins (leader of Credit Union movement). As Type 378: No. 808, Dr. J. Cook (first moderator of Presbyterian Church in Canada).

379 Pole-vaulting   380 "Untamed" (photo by Walt Petrigo)

1975. 1976 Olympics (7th issue). Multicoloured.
809 20c. Type 379 . . . . . . 40 50
810 25c. Marathon-running . . . 55 80
811 50c. Hurdling . . . . . 70 1·25

1975. Centenary of Calgary.
812 380 8c. multicoloured 30 30

381 I. W. Y. Symbol   382 Fencing

1975. International Women's Year.
813 381 8c. grey, brown and black 30 30

1975. Olympic Games, Montreal (1976) (8th issue). Multicoloured.
814 8c.+2c. Type 382 . . . . 35 55
815 10c.+5c. Boxing . . . . . 45 1·25
816 15c.+5c. Judo . . . . . . 55 1·50

383 "Justice-Justitia" (statue by W. S. Allward)   385 "Santa Claus" (G. Kelly)

384 "William D. Lawrence" (full-rigged ship)

1975. Centenary of Canadian Supreme Court.
817 383 8c. multicoloured 20 30

1975. Canadian Ships (1st series). Coastal Vessels.
818 384 8c. brown and black . . . 70 75
819 — 8c. green and black . . . 70 75
820 — 8c. green and black . . . 70 75
821 — 8c. brown and black . . . 70 75
DESIGNS: No. 819, "Neptune" (steamer); 820, "Beaver" (paddle-steamer); 821, "Quadra" (steamer). See also Nos. 851/4, 902/5 and 931/4.

1975. Christmas. Multicoloured.
822 6c. Type 385 . . . . . . 15 10
823 6c. "Skater" (B. Cawsey) . . 15 10
824 8c. "Child" (D. Hebert) . . 15 10
825 8c. "Family" (L. Caldwell) . 15 10
826 10c. "Gift" (D. Lovely) . . 30 50
827 15c. "Trees" (R. Kowalski)
(horiz) 40 75

386 Text, Badge and Bugle   387 Basketball

1975. 50th Anniv of Royal Canadian Legion.
828 386 8c. multicoloured 20 20

1976. Olympic Games, Montreal (9th issue). Mult.
829 8c.+2c. Type 387 . . . . . 1·25 85
830 10c.+5c. Gymnastics . . . . 50 1·25
831 20c.+5c. Soccer . . . . 70 1·50

388 Games Symbol and Snow Crystal   389 "Communications Arts"

1976. 12th Winter Olympic Games, Innsbruck.
832 388 20c. multicoloured 20 40

1976. Olympic Games, Montreal (10th issue). Multicoloured.
833 20c. Type 389 . . . . . 40 25
834 25c. Handicrafts 65 75
835 50c. Performing Arts . . . . 95 1·60

390 Place Ville Marie and Notre-Dame Church

1976. Olympic Games, Montreal (11th issue). Multicoloured.
836 $1 Type 390 . . . . . . 2·25 4·50
837 $2 Olympic stadium and flags 2·75 5·50

391 Flower and Urban Sprawl

1976. HABITAT. U.N. Conference on Human Settlements, Vancouver.
838 391 20c. multicoloured 20 30

392 Benjamin Franklin and Map

1976. Bicentenary of American Revolution.
839 392 10c. multicoloured 20 35

393 Wing Parade before Mackenzie Building   394 Transfer of Olympic Flame by Satellite

1976. Centenary of Royal Military College. Mult.
840 8c. Colour party and
Memorial Arch 15 20
841 8c. Type 393 . . . . . . 15 20

1976. Olympic Games, Montreal (12th issue). Multicoloured.
842 8c. Type 394 . . . . . . 20 10
843 20c. Carrying the Olympic
flag 45 60
844 25c. Athletes with medals . . 45 85

395 Archer

1976. Disabled Olympics.
845 395 20c. multicoloured 20 30

396 "Sam McGee" (Robert W. Service)   397 "Nativity" (F. Mayer)

1976. Canadian Writers (2nd series). Mult.
846 8c. Type 396 . . . . . . 15 40
847 8c. "Le Survenant"
(Germaine Guevremont) . . 15 40

1976. Christmas. Stained-glass Windows. Multi.
848 8c. Type 397 . . . . . . 10 10
849 10c. "Nativity" (G. Maile &
Son) 10 10
850 20c. "Nativity" (Yvonne
Williams) 20 60

398 "Northcote" (paddle-steamer)

1976. Canadian Ships (2nd series). Inland Vessels.
851 398 10c. lt brown, brn & blk 45 60
852 — 10c. blue and black . . . 45 60
853 — 10c. blue and black . . . 45 60
854 — 10c. lt green, green & blk 45 60
DESIGNS: No. 852, "Passport" (paddle-steamer); 853, "Chicora" (paddle-steamer); 854, "Athabasca" (steamer).

399 Queen Elizabeth II

1977. Silver Jubilee.
855 399 25c. multicoloured 30 50

400 Bottle Gentian   401 Queen Elizabeth II (bas-relief by J. Huta)   402 Houses of Parliament

403 Trembling Aspen   404 Prairie Town Main Street

405 Fundy National Park

1977.
856 400 1c. multicoloured 10 10
870 402 1c. blue . . . . . . 1·25 2·50
857 — 2c. multicoloured 10 10
858 — 3c. multicoloured 10 10
859 — 4c. multicoloured 10 10
860 — 5c. multicoloured 10 10
871 402 5c. lilac 60 90
861 — 10c. multicoloured 15 10
867 401 12c. blue, grey and black 15 10
872 402 12c. blue 50 20
866 — 12c. multicoloured 15 50
868 401 14c. red, grey and black 20 10
873 402 14c. red 15 10
875 403 15c. multicoloured 15 10
866a — 15c. multicoloured 15 15
869 401 17c. black, grey and
green 50 10
874 402 17c. green 30 10
876 — 25c. multicoloured 15 10
877 — 25c. multicoloured 15 10
878 — 30c. multicoloured 15 10
869b 401 30c. dp pur, grey & pur 70 70
869c — 32c. black, grey and blue 45 60
879 — 35c. multicoloured 25 10
883 404 50c. multicoloured 85 60
883a — 60c. multicoloured 65 50

881 – 75c. multicoloured . . . 85 1·00
882 – 80c. multicoloured . . . 85 90
884 405 $1 multicoloured 90 50
884b – $1 multicoloured 85 45
884c – $1.50 multicoloured . . 2·00 2·50
885 – $2 multicoloured . . . . 1·50 45
885c – $2 multicoloured . . . . 3·75 1·50
885d – $5 multicoloured . . . . 4·00 2·50
885e – $5 multicoloured . . . . 7·00 4·00
DESIGN—As Type **400**: 2c. Red columbine; 3c. Canada lily; 4c. Hepatica; 5c. Shooting star; 10c. Franklin's lady's slipper orchid. 12c. Jewel-weed; 15c. (No. 866a) Canada violet. As Type **403**: 20c. Douglas fir; 25c. Sugar maple; 30c. Red oak; 35c. White pine. As Type **404**: 60c. Ontario City street; 75c. Eastern City street; 80c. Maritimes street. As Type **405**: $1 Glacier; $1.50, Waterton Lakes; $2 (No. 885) Kluane; $2 (No. 885c) Banff; $5 (No. 885d) Point Pelee; $5 (No. 885e) La Maurice.

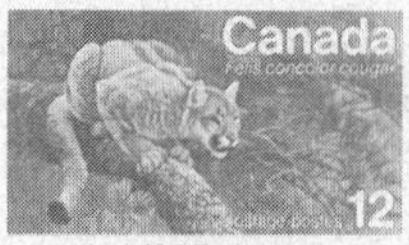

406 Puma

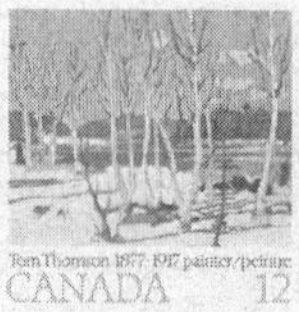

407 "April in Algonquin Park"

1977. Endangered Wildlife (1st series).
886 **406** 12c. multicoloured 20 20
See also Nos. 906, 936/7, 976/7 and 1006/7.

1977. Birth Centenary of Tom Thomson (painter). Multicoloured.
887 12c. Type **407** 15 20
888 12c. "Autumn Birches" . . . 15 20

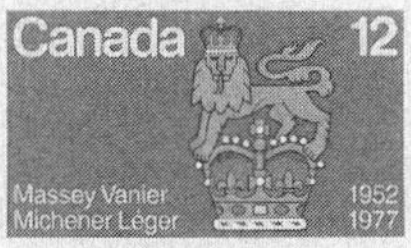

408 Crown and Lion

1977. Anniversaries. Multicoloured.
889 12c. Type **408** 15 20
890 12c. Order of Canada 15 20
EVENTS: No. 889, 25th anniv of First Canadian-born Governor-General; No. 890, 10th anniv of Order of Canada.

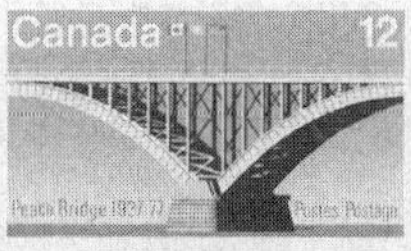

409 Peace Bridge, Niagara River

1977. 50th Anniv of Opening of Peace Bridge.
891 **409** 12c. multicoloured 15 15

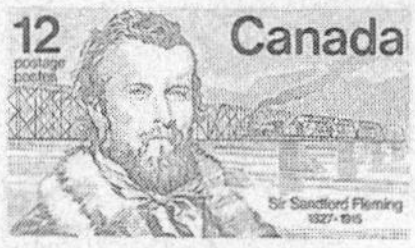

410 Sir Sandford Fleming (engineer)

1977. Famous Canadians.
892 **410** 12c. blue 30 20
893 – 12c. brown 30 20
DESIGN: No. 893, Joseph E. Bernier (explorer) and "Arctic" (survey ship).

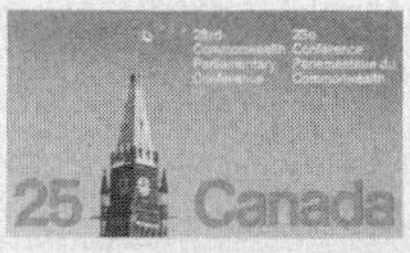

411 Peace Tower, Parliament Buildings, Ottawa

1977. 23rd Commonwealth Parliamentary Conference
894 **411** 25c. multicoloured 20 30

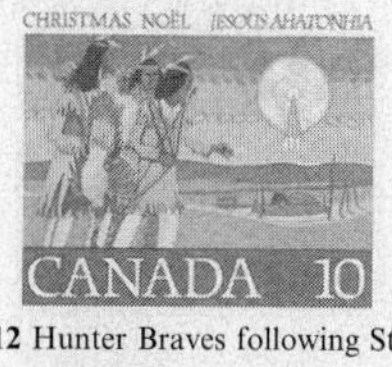

412 Hunter Braves following Star

1977. Christmas. Canada's first carol "Jesous Ahatonhia". Multicoloured.
895 10c. Type **412** 10 10
896 12c. Angelic choir 10 10
897 25c. Christ Child and "Chiefs from afar" 20 45

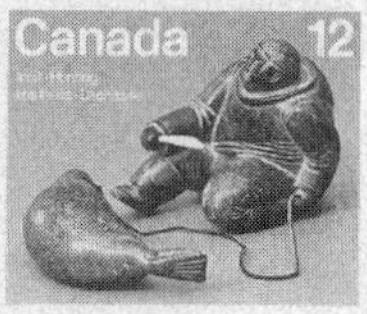

413 Seal Hunter (soapstone sculpture)

1977. Canadian Eskimos ("Inuits") (1st series). Hunting. Multicoloured.
898 12c. Type **413** 35 35
899 12c. Fishing with spear . . . 35 35
900 12c. Disguised archer 35 35
901 12c. Walrus hunting 35 35
See also Nos. 924/7, 958/61 and 989/92.

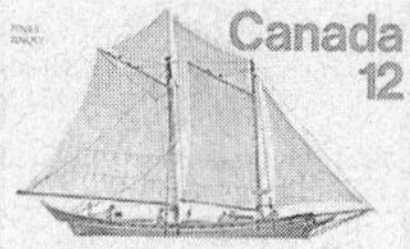

414 Pinky (fishing boat)

1977. Canadian Ships (3rd series). Sailing Craft. Multicoloured.
902 12c. Type **414** 20 35
903 12c. "Malahat" (schooner) 20 35
904 12c. Tern schooner 20 35
905 12c. Mackinaw boat 20 35

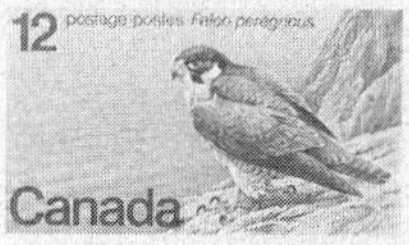

415 Peregrine Falcon

1978. Endangered Wildlife (2nd series).
906 **415** 12c. multicoloured 30 20

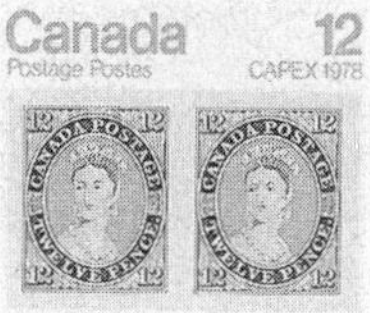

416 Pair of 1851 12d. Black Stamps

1978. "CAPEX '78" International Philatelic Exhibition, Toronto.
907 **416** 12c. black and sepia . . . 10 10
914 – 14c. blue, lt grey & grey 15 10
915 – 30c. red, lt grey and grey 25 40
916 – $1.25 violet, lt grey & grey . . . . 70 1·50
DESIGNS: 14c. Pair of 1855 10d. Cartier stamps; 30c. Pair of 1857 $\frac{1}{2}$d. red stamps; $1.25, Pair of 1851 6d. Prince Albert stamps.

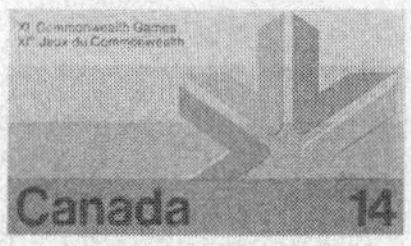

417 Games Emblem

1978. 11th Commonwealth Games, Edmonton (1st issue). Multicoloured.
908 14c. Type **417** 10 10
909 30c. Badminton 20 60
See also Nos. 918/21.

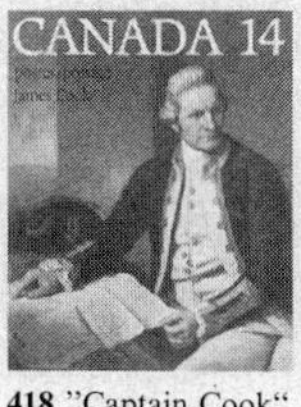

418 "Captain Cook" (Nathaniel Dance)

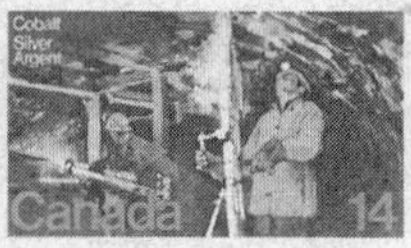

419 Hardrock Silver Mine, Cobalt, Ontario

1978. Bicentenary of Cook's 3rd Voyage. Mult.
910 14c. Type **418** 20 20
911 14c. "Nootka Sound" (J. Webber) 20 20

1978. Resources Development. Multicoloured.
912 14c. Type **419** 15 20
913 14c. Giant excavators, Athabasca Tar Sands . . . 15 20

1978. 11th Commonwealth Games, Edmonton (2nd issue). As T **417**. Multicoloured.
918 14c. Games stadium 20 20
919 14c. Running 20 20
920 30c. Alberta legislature building 50 50
921 30c. Bowls 50 50

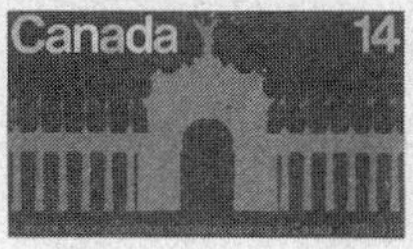

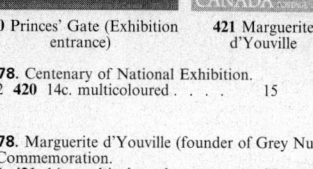

420 Princes' Gate (Exhibition entrance)

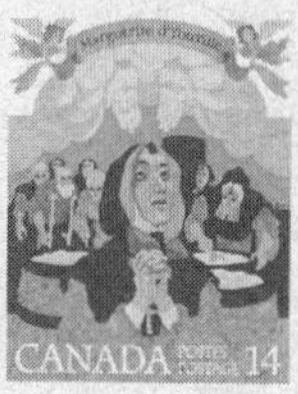

421 Marguerite d'Youville

1978. Centenary of National Exhibition.
922 **420** 14c. multicoloured 15 30

1978. Marguerite d'Youville (founder of Grey Nuns) Commemoration.
923 **421** 14c. multicoloured 15 30

1978. Canadian Eskimos ("Inuits") (2nd series). Travel. As T **413**. Multicoloured.
924 14c. Woman on foot (painting by Pitseolak) . . 30 30
925 14c. "Migration" (soapstone sculpture of sailing umiak by Joe Talurinili) 30 30
926 14c. Aeroplane (stonecut and stencil print by Pudlo) . . 30 30
927 14c. Dogteam and dogsled (ivory sculpture by Abraham Kingmeatook) 30 30

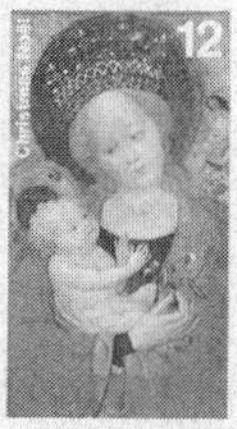

422 "Madonna of the Flowering Pea" (Cologne School)

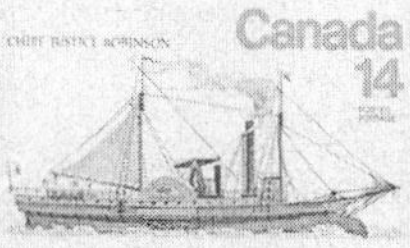

423 "Chief Justice Robinson" (paddle-steamer)

1978. Christmas. Paintings. Multicoloured.
928 12c. Type **422** 10 10
929 14c. "The Virgin and Child with St. Anthony and Donor" (detail, Hans Memling) 10 10
930 30c. "The Virgin and Child" (Jacopo di Cione) 25 90

1978. Canadian Ships (4th series). Ice Vessels. Multicoloured.
931 14c. Type **423** 45 65
932 14c. "St. Roch" (steamer) . . 45 65
933 14c. "Northern Light" (steamer) 45 65
934 14c. "Labrador" (steamer) . . 45 65

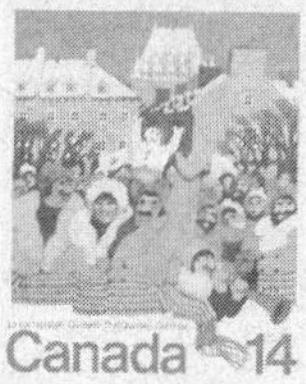

424 Carnival Revellers

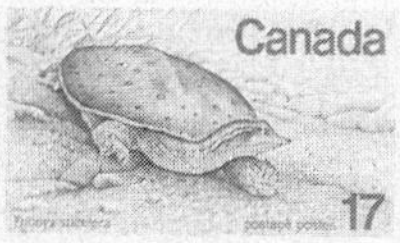

425 Eastern Spiny Soft-shelled Turtle

1978. Quebec Carnival.
935 **424** 14c. multicoloured 20 20

1979. Endangered Wildlife (3rd series). Multicoloured.
936 17c. Type **425** 20 10
937 35c. Bowhead whale 90 90

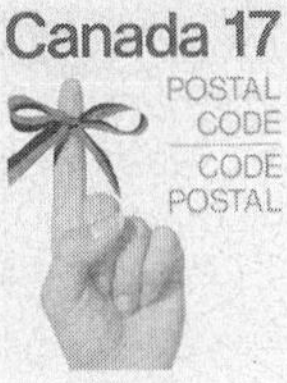

426 Knotted Ribbon round Woman's Finger

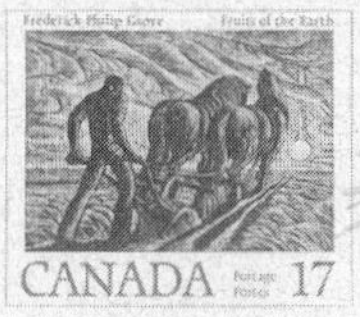

427 Scene from "Fruits of the Earth" by Frederick Philip Grove

1979. Postal Code Publicity. Multicoloured.
938 17c. Type **426** 20 15
939 17c. Knotted string around man's finger 20 15

1979. Canadian Writers (3rd series). Multicoloured.
940 17c. Type **427** 15 15
941 17c. Scene from "Le Vaisseau d'Or" by Emile Nelligan 15 15

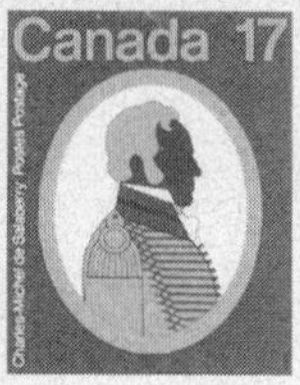

428 Charles-Michel de Salaberry (military hero)

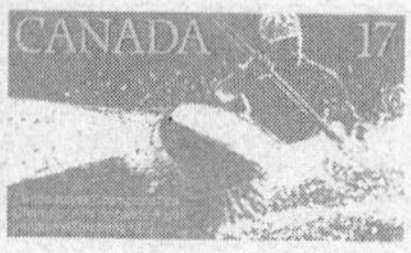

430 Paddling Kayak

1979. Famous Canadians. Multicoloured.
942 17c. Type **428** 25 15
943 17c. John By (engineer) . . . 25 15

1979. Canoe-Kayak Championships.
956 **430** 17c. multicoloured 15 30

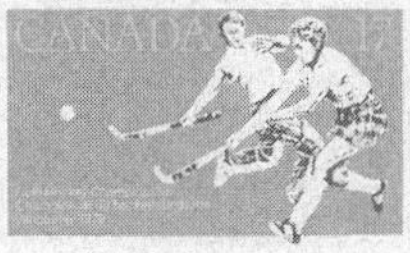

431 Hockey Players

1979. Women's Field Hockey Championships, Vancouver.
957 **431** 17c. black, yellow and green 15 30

1979. Canadian Eskimos (3rd series). Shelter and the Community. As T **413**. Multicoloured.
958 17c. "Summer Tent" (print by Kiakshuk" 15 20
959 17c. "Five Eskimos building an Igloo" (soapstone sculpture by Abraham) . . 15 20
960 17c. "The Dance" (print by Kalvak) 15 20
961 17c. "Inuit drum dance" (soapstone sculptures by Madeleine Isserkut and Jean Mapsalak) 15 20

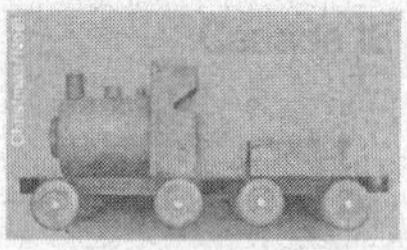

432 Toy Train

1979. Christmas. Multicoloured.
962 15c. Type **432** 10 10
963 17c. Hobby-horse 10 10
964 35c. Rag doll (vert) 25 80

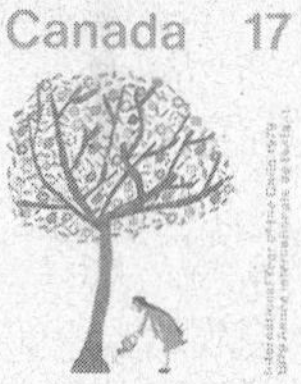

433 Child watering Tree of Life (painting by Marie-Annick Viatour)

1979. International Year of the Child.
965 **433** 17c. multicoloured 15 30

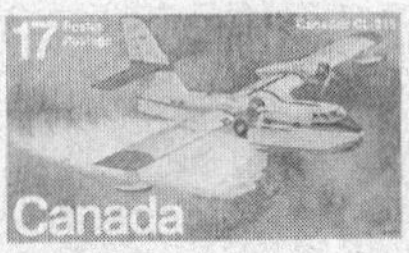

434 Canadair CL-215

1979. Canadian Aircraft (1st series). Flying Boats. Multicoloured.
966 17c. Type **434** 25 15
967 17c. Curtiss HS-2L 25 15
968 35c. Vickers Vedette 65 55
969 35c. Consolidated Canso . . 65 55
See also Nos. 996/9, 1050/3 and 1026/9.

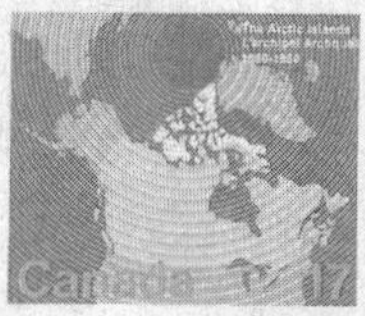

435 Map of Arctic Islands

1980. Centenary of Arctic Islands Acquisition.
970 **435** 17c. multicoloured 15 30

436 Skier

1980. Winter Olympic Games, Lake Placid.
971 436 35c. multicoloured 55 85

437 "A Meeting of the School Trustees" (Robert Harris)

1980. Centenary of Royal Canadian Academy of Arts. Multicoloured.
972 17c. Type 437 . . . . 25 20
973 17c. "Inspiration" (Philippe Hebert) 25 20
974 35c. "Sunrise on the Saguenay" (Lucius O'Brien) 50 55
975 35c. Thomas Fuller's design sketch for the original Parliament Buildings . . . 50 55

438 Canadian Whitefish   **439** Garden Flowers

1980. Endangered Wildlife (4th series). Multicoloured.
976 17c. Type 438 . . . . 30 15
977 17c. Prairie chicken 30 15

1980. International Flower Show, Montreal.
978 439 17c. multicoloured . . . 15 20

440 "Helping Hand"   **441** Opening Bars of "O Canada"

1980. Rehabilitation.
979 440 17c. gold and blue 15 20

1980. Centenary of "O Canada" (national song). Multicoloured.
980 17c. Type 441 . . . . 15 15
981 17c. Calixa Lavallee (composer), Adolphe-Basile Routhier (original writer) and Robert Stanley Weir (writer of English version) . 15 15

442 John G. Diefenbaker (statesman)   **443** Emma Albani (singer)

1980. John G. Diefenbaker Commemoration.
982 442 17c. blue 15 20

1980. Famous Canadians. Multicoloured.
983 17c. Type 443 . . . . 15 25
984 17c. Healey Willan (composer) 15 25
985 17c. Ned Hanlan (oarsman) (horiz) 15 15

444 Alberta

1980. 75th Anniv of Alberta and Saskatchewan Provinces. Multicoloured.
986 17c. Type 444 . . . . 15 15
987 17c. Saskatchewan 15 15

445 Uraninite Molecular Structure   **446** "Christmas Morning" (J. S. Hallam)

1980. Uranium Resources.
988 445 35c. multicoloured 30 30

1980. Canadian Eskimos ("Inuits") (4th series). Spirits. As T 413. Multicoloured.
989 17c. "Return of the Sun" (print, Kenojouak) 20 15
990 17c. "Sedna" (sculpture, Ashoona Kiawak) 20 15
991 35c. "Shaman" (print, Simon Tookoome) 35 40
992 35c. "Bird Spirit" (sculpture, Doris Hagiolok) 35 40

1980. Christmas. Multicoloured.
993 15c. Type 446 . . . . 10 10
994 17c. "Sleigh Ride" (Frank Hennessy) 15 10
995 35c. "McGill Cab Stand" (Kathleen Morris) . . . . 30 1·40

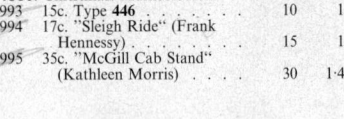

447 Avro (Canada) CF-100 Canuck Mk 5

1980. Canadian Aircraft (2nd series). Multicoloured.
996 17c. Type 447 . . . . 30 15
997 17c. Avro Type 683 Lancaster 30 15
998 35c. Curtiss JN-4 Canuck biplane 50 50
999 35c. Hawker Hurricane Mk I 50 50

448 Emmanuel-Persillier Lachapelle   **449** Mandora (18th century)

1980. Dr. E.-P. Lachapelle (founder, Notre-Dame Hospital, Montreal) Commemoration.
1000 448 17c. brown, deep brown and blue 15 15

1981. "The Look of Music" Exhibition, Vancouver.
1001 449 17c. multicoloured . . . 15 15

450 Henrietta Edwards

1981. Feminists. Multicoloured.
1002 17c. Type 450 . . . . 30 30
1003 17c. Louise McKinney . . . 30 30
1004 17c. Idola Saint-Jean 30 30
1005 17c. Emily Stowe 30 30

451 Vancouver Marmot

1981. Endangered Wildlife (5th series). Multicoloured.
1006 17c. Type 451 . . . . 15 10
1007 35c. American bison 35 30

452 Kateri Tekakwitha   **453** "Self Portrait" (Frederick H. Varley)

1981. 17th-century Canadian Women. Statues by Emile Brunet.
1008 452 17c. brown and green . . 15 15
1009 – 17c. deep blue and blue 15 15
DESIGN: No. 1009, Marie de L'Incarnation.

1981. Canadian Paintings. Multicoloured.
1010 17c. Type 453 . . . . 20 10
1011 17c. "At Baie Saint-Paul" (Marc-Aurele Fortin) (horiz) 20 10
1012 35c. "Untitled No 6" (Paul-Emile Borduas) 40 45

454 Canada in 1867

1981. Canada Day. Maps showing evolution of Canada from Confederation to present day. Multicoloured.
1013 17c. Type 454 . . . . 15 20
1014 17c. Canada in 1873 . . . . 15 20
1015 17c. Canada in 1905 . . . . 15 20
1016 17c. Canada since 1949 . . . 15 20

455 Frere Marie-Victorin   **456** The Montreal Rose

1981. Canadian Botanists. Multicoloured.
1017 17c. Type 455 . . . . 20 25
1018 17c. John Macoun 20 25

1981. Montreal Flower Show.
1019 456 17c. multicoloured . . . 15 20

457 Drawing of Niagara-on-the-Lake   **458** Acadian Community

1981. Bicentenary of Niagara-on-the-Lake (town).
1020 457 17c. multicoloured . . . 15 20

1981. Centenary of First Acadia (community) Convention.
1021 458 17c. multicoloured . . . 15 20

459 Aaron R. Mosher   **460** Christmas Tree, 1781

1981. Birth Centenary of Aaron R. Mosher (founder of Canadian Labour Congress).
1022 459 17c. multicoloured . . . 15 20

1981. Christmas. Bicentenary of First Illuminated Christmas Tree in Canada.
1023 15c. Type 460 . . . . 20 15
1024 15c. Christmas Tree, 1881 . . 20 15
1025 15c. Christmas Tree, 1981 . . 20 15

461 De Havilland Tiger Moth   **462** Canadian Maple Leaf Emblem

1981. Canadian Aircraft (3rd series). Multicoloured.
1026 17c. Type 461 . . . . 20 15
1027 17c. Canadair CL-41 Tutor jet trainer 20 15
1028 35c. Avro (Canada) CF-102 jet airliner 35 40
1029 35c. De Havilland D.H.C.7 Dash 7 . . . . 35 40

1981.
1030a 462 A (30c.) red 20 25
No. 1030a was printed before a new first class domestic letter rate had been agreed, "A" representing the face value of the stamp, later decided to be 30c.

1982. As T 462 but including face values.
1033 462 5c. purple 10 20
1033d 8c. blue . . . . 1·50 2·25
1034 10c. green . . . . . . 1·25 2·00
1036 30c. red 35 30
1032 30c. red, grey and blue 30 40
1036b 32c. red . . . . 1·50 2·00
1032b 32c. red, brown and stone 45 45

463 1851 3d. Stamp

1982. "Canada 82" International Philatelic Youth Exhibition, Toronto. Stamps on Stamps. Mult.
1037 30c. Type 463 . . . . . . 30 30
1038 30c. 1908 Centenary of Quebec 15c. commemorative 30 30
1039 35c. 1935 10c. R.C.M.P . . . 30 50
1040 35c. 1928 10c. 30 50
1041 60c. 1929 50c. . . . . . . 60 1·00

464 Jules Leger   **465** Stylized drawing of Terry Fox

1982. Jules Leger (politician) Commemoration.
1043 464 30c. multicoloured 20 20

1982. Cancer victim Terry Fox's "Marathon of Hope" (Trans-Canada fund-raising run) Commemoration.
1044 465 30c. multicoloured 20 20

466 Stylized Open Book

1982. Patriation of Constitution.
1045 466 30c. multicoloured . . . 20 20

467 Male and Female Salvationists with Street Scene

1982. Centenary of Salvation Army in Canada.
1046 467 30c. multicoloured 20 20

469 Regina Legislative Building

1982. Centenary of Regina.
1048 **469** 30c. multicoloured . . . 20 20

470 Finish of Race

1982. Centenary of Royal Canadian Henley Regatta.
1049 **470** 30c. multicoloured . . . 20 25

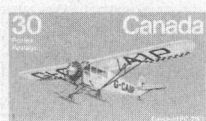

471 Fairchild FC-2W1

1982. Canadian Aircraft (4th series). Bush Aircraft.
Multicoloured.
1050 30c. Type **471** 35 20
1051 30c. De Havilland D.H.C.2
    Beaver 35 20
1052 60c. Fokker Super Universal 65 85
1053 60c. Noorduyn Norseman 65 85

472 Decoy

475 Mary, Joseph and Baby Jesus

1982. Heritage Artefacts.
1054 **472** 1c. black, lt brn and brn 10 10
1055 — 2c. black, blue and green 10 10
1056 — 3c. black and deep blue 10 10
1057 — 5c. black, pink and
    brown 10 10
1058 — 10c. black, blue & turq 10 10
1059 — 20c. black, lt brn & brn 20 10
1060 — 25c. multicoloured . . 35 10
1061 — 37c. black, grn & dp grn 60 40
1062 — 39c. black, grey and
    violet . . . . 1·75 1·25
1063 — 42c. multicoloured . . 1·00 15
1064 — 48c. dp brn, brn & pink 70 40
1065 — 50c. black, lt blue & blue 1·75 20
1066 — 55c. multicoloured . . 1·00 30
1067 — 64c. dp grey, blk & grey 80 35
1068 — 68c. black, lt brn & brn 1·75 50
1069 — 72c. multicoloured . . 85 35
DESIGNS—VERT: 2c. Fishing spear; 3c. Stable
lantern; 5c. Bucket; 10c. Weathercock; 20c. Skates;
25c. Butter stamp. HORIZ: 37c. Plough; 39c. Settle-
bed; 42c. Linen chest; 48c. Cradle; 50c. Sleigh; 55c.
Iron kettle; 64c. Kitchen stove; 68c. Spinning wheel;
72c. Hand-drawn cart.

1982. Christmas. Nativity Scenes.
1080 30c. Type **475** 20 10
1081 35c. The Shepherds 25 60
1082 60c. The Three Wise Men 45 1·50

476 Globes forming
Symbolic Designs

478 Scene from Novel
"Angeline de Montbrun"
by "Laure Conan" (Felicite
Angers)

477 Map of World showing Canada

1983. World Communications Year.
1083 **476** 32c. multicoloured . . . 30 30

1983. Commonwealth Day.
1084 **477** $2 multicoloured . . . . 2·00 3·25

1983. Canadian Writers (4th series).
1085 32c. Type **478** 40 90
1086 32c. Woodcut illustrating
    "Sea-gulls" (poem by
    E. J. Pratt) 40 90

479 St. John Ambulance
Badge and "100"

480 Victory Pictogram

1983. Centenary of St. John Ambulance in Canada.
1087 **479** 32c. red, yellow and
    brown 30 30

1983. "Universiade 83" World University Games,
Edmonton.
1088 **480** 32c. multicoloured . . . 25 15
1089 64c. multicoloured . . . 50 70

481 Fort William, Ontario

1983. Canada Day. Forts (1st series). Multicoloured.
1090 32c. Fort Henry, Ontario
    (44 × 22 mm) 55 75
1091 32c. Type **481** 55 75
1092 32c. Fort Rodd Hill, British
    Columbia 55 75
1093 32c. Fort Wellington,
    Ontario (28 × 22 mm) . . 55 75
1094 32c. Fort Prince of Wales,
    Manitoba (28 × 22 mm) 55 75
1095 32c. Halifax Citadel, Nova
    Scotia (44 × 22 mm) . . 55 75
1096 32c. Fort Chambly, Quebec 55 75
1097 32c. Fort No. 1, Point
    Levis, Quebec 55 75
1098 32c. Coteau-du-Lac Fort,
    Quebec (28 × 22 mm) . . 55 75
1099 32c. Fort Beausejour, New
    Brunswick (28 × 22 mm) 55 75
See also Nos. 1163/72.

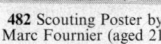

482 Scouting Poster by
Marc Fournier (aged 21)

483 Cross Symbol

1983. Scouting in Canada (75th Anniv) and 15th
World Scout Jamboree, Alberta.
1100 **482** 32c. multicoloured . . . 30 30

1983. 6th Assembly of the World Council of
Churches, Vancouver.
1101 **483** 32c. green and lilac . . . 30 20

484 Sir Humphrey
Gilbert (founder)

485 "NICKEL" Deposits

1983. 400th Anniv of Newfoundland.
1102 **484** 32c. multicoloured . . . 30 30

1983. Cent of Discovery of Sudbury Nickel Deposits.
1103 **485** 32c. multicoloured . . . 30 30

486 Josiah Henson and Escaping
Slaves

1983. 19th-century Social Reformers. Multicoloured.
1104 32c. Type **486** 35 35
1105 32c. Father Antoine Labelle
    and rural village
    (32 × 26 mm) 35 35

487 Robert Stephenson's Locomotive
"Dorchester", 1836

1983. Railway Locomotives (1st series). Mult.
1106 32c. Type **487** . . . . 90 1·00
1107 32c. Locomotive "Toronto",
    1853 . . . . . 90 1·00
1108 37c. Timothy Hackworth's
    locomotive "Samson",
    1838 . . . . . 90 1·00
1109 64c. Western Canadian
    Railway locomotive
    "Adam Brown", 1855 . . 1·40 2·25
See also Nos. 1132/5, 1185/8 and 1223/6.

488 School Coat of Arms

1983. Centenary of Dalhousie Law School.
1110 **488** 32c. multicoloured . . . 30 40

489 City Church

1983. Christmas. Churches. Multicoloured.
1111 32c. Type **489** 30 10
1112 37c. Family walking to
    church 40 90
1113 64c. Country chapel . . . . 1·00 2·00

490 Royal Canadian
Regiment and British
Columbia Regiment

491 Gold Mine in
Prospecting Pan

1983. Canadian Army Regiments. Multicoloured.
1114 32c. Type **490** . . . . 75 1·25
1115 32c. Royal Winnipeg Rifles
    and Royal Canadian
    Dragoons . . . . 75 1·25

1984. 50th Anniv of Yellowknife.
1116 **491** 32c. multicoloured . . . 30 30

492 Montreal Symphony Orchestra

1983. 50th Anniv of Montreal Symphony Orchestra.
1117 **492** 32c. multicoloured . . . 35 30

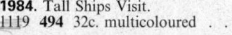

493 Jacques Cartier

494 U.S.C.S. "Eagle"

1984. 450th Anniv of Jacques Cartier's Voyage to
Canada.
1118 **493** 32c. multicoloured . . . 40 30

1984. Tall Ships Visit.
1119 **494** 32c. multicoloured . . . 35 30

495 Service Medal

496 Oared Galleys

1984. 75th Anniv of Canadian Red Cross Society.
1120 **495** 32c. multicoloured . . . 35 40

1984. Bicentenary of New Brunswick.
1121 **496** 32c. multicoloured . . . 35 30

497 St. Lawrence Seaway

1984. 25th Anniv of St. Lawrence Seaway.
1122 **497** 32c. multicoloured . . . 45 30

499 Loyalists of 1784

1984. Bicentenary of Arrival of United Empire
Loyalists.
1124 **499** 32c. multicoloured . . . 30 30

500 St. John's Basilica

501 Coat of Arms of Pope
John Paul II

1984. Bicentenary of Roman Catholic Church in
Newfoundland.
1125 **500** 32c. multicoloured . . . 30 25

1984. Papal Visit.
1126 **501** 32c. multicoloured . . . 40 20
1127 64c. multicoloured . . . 85 1·10

502 Louisbourg Lighthouse, 1734

1984. Canadian Lighthouse (1st series). Mult.
1128 32c. Type **502** . . . . 1·50 1·50
1129 32c. Fisgard Lighthouse,
    1860 . . . . 1·50 1·50
1130 32c. Ile Verte Lighthouse,
    1809 . . . . 1·50 1·50
1131 32c. Gibraltar Point
    Lighthouse, 1808 . . . . 1·50 1·50
See also Nos. 1176/9.

503 Great Western Railway Locomotive
"Scotia", 1860

1984. Railway Locomotives (2nd series). Mult.
1132 32c. Type **503** . . . . 1·25 1·25
1133 32c. Northern Pacific
    Railroad locomotive
    "Countess of Dufferin",
    1872 . . . . 1·25 1·25
1134 37c. Grand Trunk Railway
    Class E3 locomotive, 1886 1·25 1·50
1135 64c. Canadian Pacific Class
    D10a steam locomotive 1·75 2·50
See also Nos. 1185/8 and 1223/6.

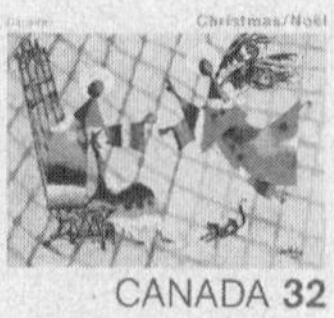

504 "The Annunciation" (Jean Dallaire)

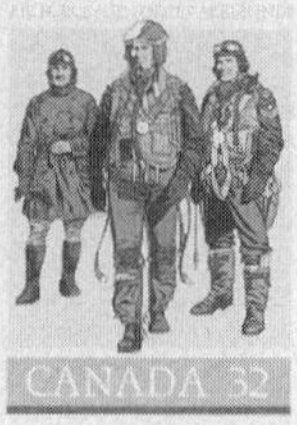

505 Pilots of 1914–18, 1939–45 and 1984

1984. Christmas. Religious Paintings. Multicoloured.
1137 32c. Type **504** 40 10
1138 37c. "The Three Kings" (Simone Bouchard) . . . 70 1·00
1139 64c. "Snow in Bethlehem" (David Milne) . . . . . 90 1·75

1984. 60th Anniv of Royal Canadian Air Force.
1140 **505** 32c. multicoloured . . . 35 30

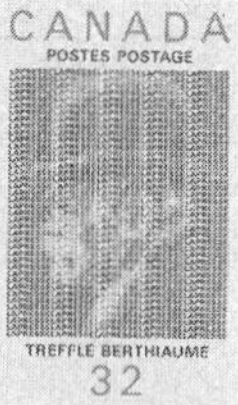

506 Treffle Berthiaume (editor)

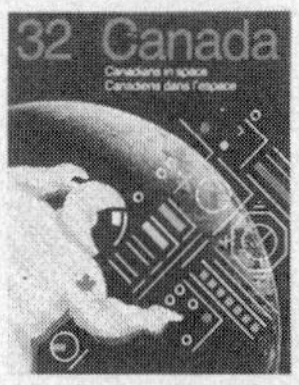

508 Astronaut in Space, and Planet Earth

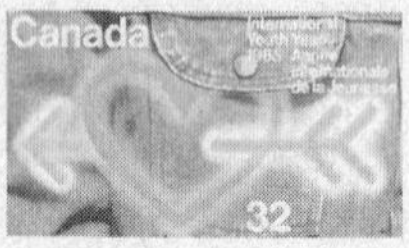

507 Heart and Arrow

1984. Centenary of "La Presse" (newspaper).
1141 **506** 32c. brown, red & lt brn 35 30

1985. International Youth Year.
1142 **507** 32c. multicoloured . . . 30 30

1985. Canadian Space Programme.
1143 **508** 32c. multicoloured . . . 40 30

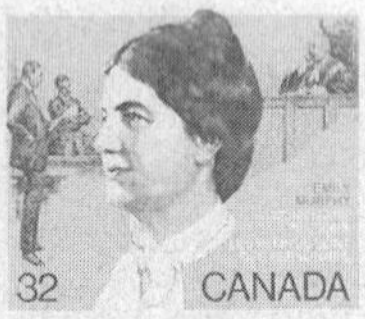

509 Emily Murphy

1985. Women's Rights Activists. Multicoloured.
1144 32c. Type **509** 40 90
1145 32c. Therese Casgrain . . . 40 90

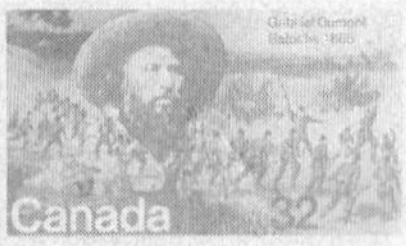

510 Gabriel Dumont (Metis leader) and Battle of Batoche, 1885

1985. Centenary of the North-West Rebellion.
1146 **510** 32c. blue, red and grey 30 30

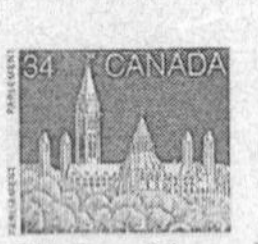

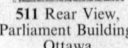

511 Rear View, Parliament Building, Ottawa

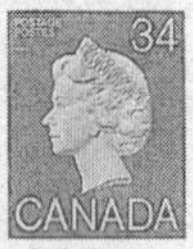

512 Queen Elizabeth II

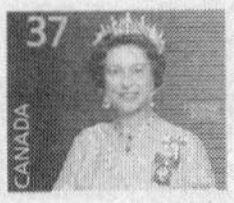

512a Queen Elizabeth II in 1984 (from photo by Karsh)

1985.
1147b – 1c. green 70 80
1148 – 2c. green 20 65
1149 – 5c. brown 40 85
1150a – 6c. brown 50 30
1150b – 6c. purple . . . . . 1·50 1·00
1151 **511** 34c. black . . . . . 1·50 1·75
1155 34c. multicoloured . . 50 10
1158 34c. brown . . . . . 2·25 2·75
1161 **512** 34c. black and blue . . 45 30
1152 **511** 36c. purple . . . . . 3·25 3·50
1156 36c. multicoloured . . 60 30
1159 36c. red . . . . 1·25 55
1162 **512** 36c. purple . . . . . 2·75 1·10
1153 **511** 37c. blue . . . . . . 1·25 30
1157 – 37c. multicoloured . . 85 10
1162a **512a** 37c. multicoloured . . 2·25 10
1154 **511** 38c. blue . . . . . . 2·00 1·25
1157c – 38c. multicoloured . . 35 10
1160b **511** 38c. green 50 30
1162b **512a** 38c. multicoloured . . 55 20
1162c 39c. multicoloured . . 1·00 20
1162d 40c. multicoloured . . 80 20
1162e 42c. multicoloured . . 90 40
1162f 43c. multicoloured . . 1·25 65
1162g 45c. multicoloured . . 1·00 80
1162h 46c. multicoloured . . 50 45
1162i 47c. multicoloured . . 40 45
DESIGNS: 1, 5, 6c. (1150b) East Block, Parliament Building; 2, 6c. (1150a) West Block, Parliament Building; 37c. (1157) Front view, Parliament Building; 38c. (1157c) Side view, Parliament Building.

1985. Canada Day. Forts (2nd series). As T **481**. Multicoloured.
1163 34c. Lower Fort Garry, Manitoba 50 60
1164 34c. Fort Anne, Nova Scotia 50 60
1165 34c. Fort York, Ontario . . 50 60
1166 34c. Castle Hill, Newfoundland 50 60
1167 34c. Fort Whoop Up, Alberta 50 60
1168 34c. Fort Erie, Ontario . . 50 60
1169 34c. Fort Walsh, Saskatchewan 50 60
1170 34c. Fort Lennox, Quebec 50 60
1171 34c. York Redoubt, Nova Scotia 50 60
1172 34c. Fort Frederick, Ontario 50 60
Nos. 1163 and 1168 measure 44 × 22 mm and Nos. 1166/7 and 1171/2 28 × 22 mm.

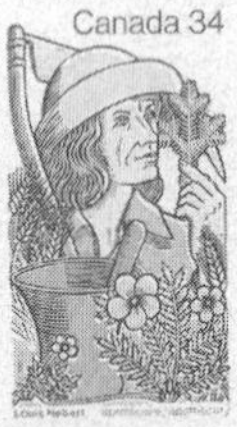

513 Louis Hebert (apothecary)

514 Parliament Buildings and Map of World

1985. 45th International Pharmaceutical Sciences Congress of Pharmaceutical Federation, Montreal.
1173 **513** 34c. multicoloured . . . 45 35

1985. 74th Conference of Inter-Parliamentary Union, Ottawa.
1174 **514** 34c. multicoloured . . . 45 35

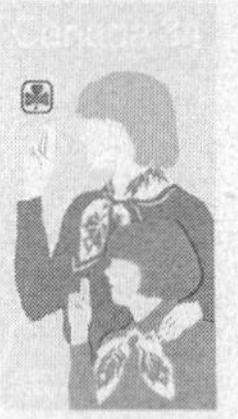

515 Guide and Brownie Saluting

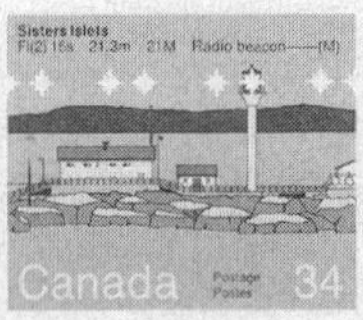

516 Sisters Islets Lighthouse

1985. 75th Anniv of Girl Guide Movement.
1175 **515** 34c. multicoloured . . . 45 35

1985. Canadian Lighthouses (2nd series). Multicoloured.
1176 34c. Type **516** . . . . . . 1·75 1·75
1177 34c. Pelee Passage Lighthouse . . . . . . 1·75 1·75
1178 34c. Haut-fond Prince Lighthouse . . . . 1·75 1·75
1179 34c. Rose Blanche Lighthouse, Cains Island 1·75 1·75

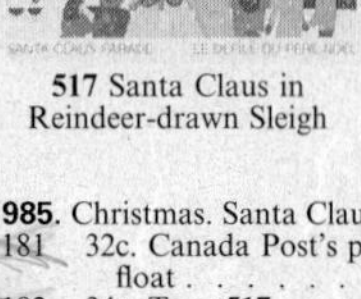

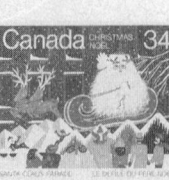

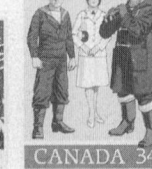

517 Santa Claus in Reindeer-drawn Sleigh

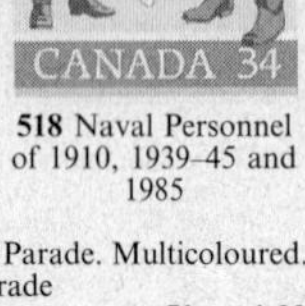

518 Naval Personnel of 1910, 1939–45 and 1985

1985. Christmas. Santa Claus Parade. Multicoloured.
1181 32c. Canada Post's parade float . . . . 70 1·00
1182 34c. Type **517** 60 20
1183 39c. Acrobats and horse-drawn carriage . . . . . 70 1·25
1184 68c. Christmas tree, pudding and goose on float . . . 1·50 2·00

1985. Steam Railway Locomotives (3rd series). As T **503**. Multicoloured.
1185 34c. Grand Trunk Railway Class K2 . . . . 1·00 1·25
1186 34c. Canadian Pacific Class P2a . . . . 1·00 1·25
1187 39c. Canadian Northern Class O10a . . . . . . 1·25 1·50
1188 68c. Canadian Govt Railway Class H4D . . . 2·00 2·25

1985. 75th Anniv of Royal Canadian Navy.
1189 **518** 34c. multicoloured . . . 65 65

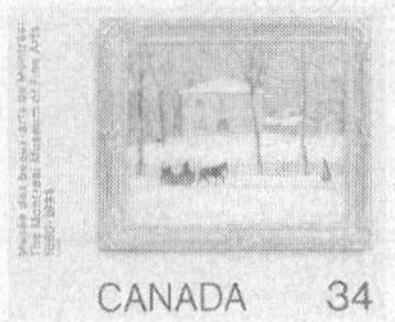

519 "The Old Holton House, Montreal" (James Wilson Morrice)

1985. 125th Anniv of Montreal Museum of Fine Arts.
1190 **519** 34c. multicoloured . . . 40 50

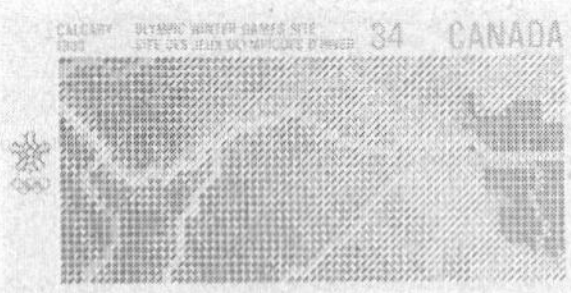

520 Map of Alberta showing Olympic Sites

1986. Winter Olympic Games, Calgary (1988) (1st issue).
1191 **520** 34c. multicoloured . . . 40 50
See also Nos. 1216/17, 1236/7, 1258/9 and 1281/4.

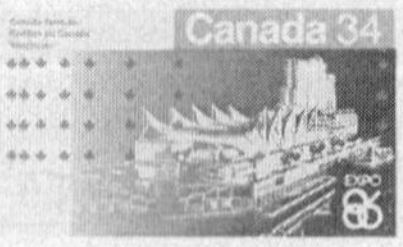

521 Canada Pavilion

1986. "Expo '86" World Fair, Vancouver (1st issue). Multicoloured.
1192 34p. Type **521** . . . . . . 1·00 50
1193 39p. Early telephone, dish aerial and satellite . . . . 1·75 2·50
See also Nos. 1196/7.

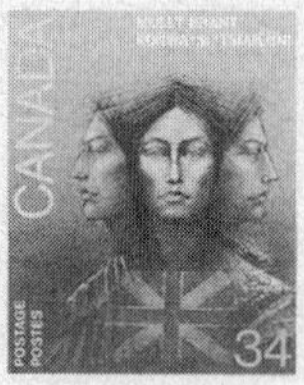

522 Molly Brant

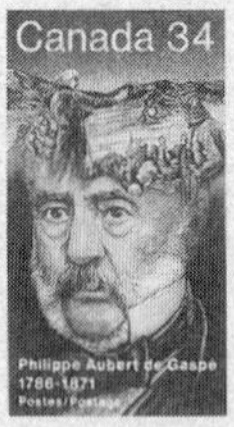

523 Aubert de Gaspe and Scene from "Les Anciens Canadiens"

1986. 250th Birth Anniv of Molly Brant (Iroquois leader)
1194 **522** 34c. multicoloured . . . 40 50

1986. Birth Bicentenary of Philippe Aubert de Gaspe (author).
1195 **523** 34c. multicoloured . . . 40 50

1986. "Expo '86" World Fair, Vancouver (2nd issue). As T **521**. Multicoloured.
1196 34c. Expo Centre, Vancouver (vert) 70 50
1197 68c. Early and modern trains . . . . 1·40 2·75

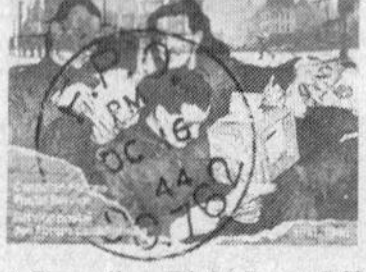

524 Canadian Field Post Office and Cancellation, 1944

1986. 75th Anniv of Canadian Forces Postal Service.
1198 **524** 34c. multicoloured . . . 85 50

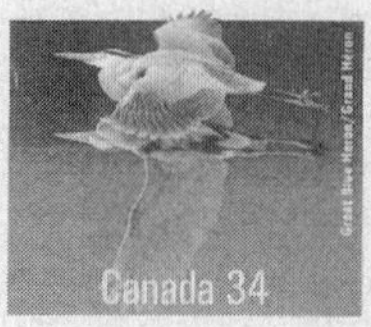

525 Great Blue Heron

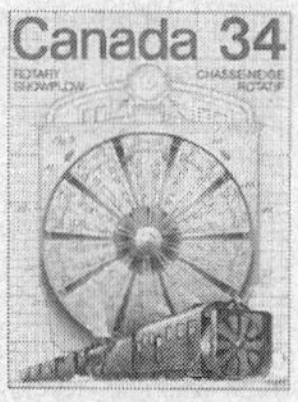

526 Railway Rotary Snowplough

1986. Birds of Canada. Multicoloured.
1199 34c. Type **525** . . . . . . 1·50 1·75
1200 34c. Snow goose . . . . . 1·50 1·75
1201 34c. Great horned owl . . . 1·50 1·75
1202 34c. Spruce grouse . . . . 1·50 1·75

1986. Canada Day. Science and Technology. Canadian Inventions (1st series). Multicoloured.
1203 34c. Type **526** . . . . . . 1·10 1·50
1204 34c. Space shuttle "Challenger" launching satellite with Canadarm 1·10 1·50
1205 34c. Pilot wearing anti-gravity flight suit and Supermarine Spitfire . . . 1·10 1·50
1206 34c. Variable-pitch propeller and Avro 504 airplane . . 1·10 1·50
See also Nos. 1241/4 and 1292/5.

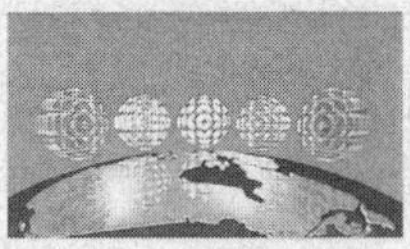

527 C.B.C. Logos over Map of Canada

1986. 50th Anniv of Canadian Broadcasting Corporation.
1207 **527** 34c. multicoloured . . . 40 50

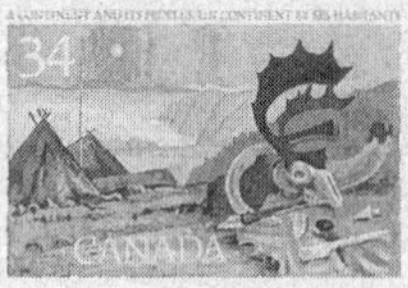

528 Ice Age Artefacts, Tools and Settlement

1986. Exploration of Canada (1st series). Discoverers. Multicoloured.
1208 34c. Type **528** . . . . . . 1·00 1·50
1209 34c. Viking ships . . . . . 1·00 1·50
1210 34c. John Cabot's "Matthew", 1497, compass and Arctic char (fish) . . . . 1·00 1·50
1211 34c. Henry Hudson cast adrift, 1611 . . . . . . 1·00 1·50
See also Nos. 1232/5, 1285/8 and 1319/22.

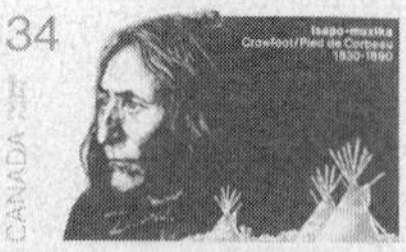

529 Crowfoot (Blackfoot Chief) and Indian Village

1986. Founders of the Canadian West. Multicoloured.
1213 34c. Type **529** 60 85
1214 34c. James Macleod of the North West Mounted Police and Fort Macleod 60 85

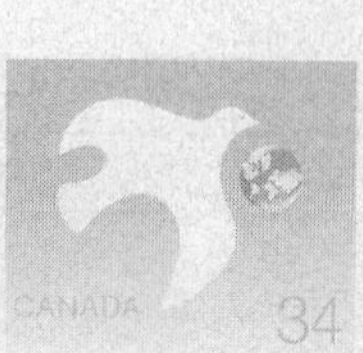

530 Peace Dove and Globe

1986. International Peace Year.
1215 **530** 34c. multicoloured . . . 40 45

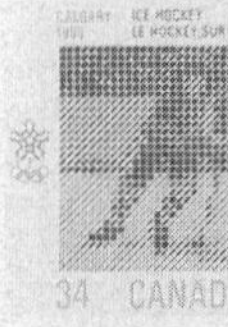

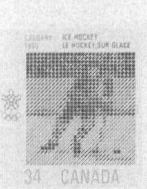

531 Ice Hockey

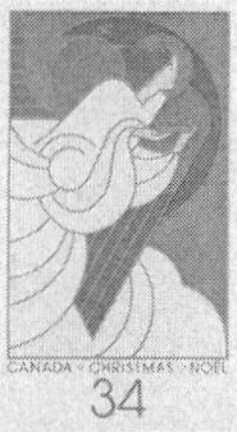

532 Angel with Crown

1986. Winter Olympic Games, Calgary (1988) (2nd issue). Multicoloured.
1216 34c. Type **531** . . . . 1·40 1·40
1217 34c. Biathlon . . . . 1·40 1·40

1986. Christmas. Multicoloured.
1218 29c. Angel singing carol
 (36 × 22 mm) 65 30
1219 34c. Type **532** 60 25
1220 39c. Angel playing lute . . . 1·00 1·00
1221 68c. Angel with ribbon . . . 1·50 2·50

533 John Molson with Theatre Royal, Montreal, "Accomodation" (paddle-steamer) and Railway Train

1986. 150th Death Anniv of John Molson (businessman).
1222 **533** 34c. multicoloured . . . 60 50

1986. Railway Locomotives (4th series). As T **503** but size 60 × 22 mm. Multicoloured.
1223 34c. Canadian National
 Class V-1-a diesel
 locomotive No. 9000 . . 1·50 1·50
1224 34c. Canadian Pacific Class
 T1a steam locomotive
 No. 9000 . . . . 1·50 1·50
1225 39c. Canadian National
 Class U-2-a steam
 locomotive . . . . . . 1·50 1·00
1226 68c. Canadian Pacific Class
 H1c steam locomotive
 No. 2850 . . . . 2·25 3·00

534 Toronto's First Post Office

1987. "Capex '87" International Stamp Exhibition, Toronto. Post Offices.
1227 34c. Type **534** 60 20
1228 36c. Nelson-Miramichi, New
 Brunswick 65 45
1229 42c. Saint-Ours, Quebec . . 70 65
1230 72c. Battleford,
 Saskatchewan . . . . . 1·00 1·25

535 Etienne Brule exploring Lake Superior

1987. Exploration of Canada (2nd series). Pioneers of New France. Multicoloured.
1232 34c. Type **535** . . . . . . 1·00 1·25
1233 34c. Radisson and Des
 – Groseilliers with British
 and French flags . . . . 1·00 1·25
1234 34c. Jolliet and Father
 Marquette on the
 Mississippi . . . . . . 1·00 1·25
1235 34c. Jesuit missionary
 preaching to Indians . . 1·00 1·25

1987. Winter Olympic Games, Calgary (1988) (3rd issue). As T **531**. Multicoloured.
1236 36c. Speed skating 50 40
1237 42c. Bobsleighing 75 60

536 Volunteer Activities

1987. National Volunteer Week.
1238 **536** 36c. multicoloured . . . 30 35

537 Canadian Coat of Arms

539 R. A. Fessenden (AM Radio)

538 Steel Girder, Gear Wheel and Microchip

1987. 5th Anniv of Canadian Charter of Rights and Freedoms.
1239 **537** 36c. multicoloured . . . 50 35

1987. Centenary of Engineering Institute of Canada.
1240 **538** 36c. multicoloured . . . 50 40

1987. Canada Day. Science and Technology. Canadian Inventors (2nd series). Multicoloured.
1241 36c. Type **539** . . . . . . 95 1·25
1242 36c. C. Fenerty (newsprint
 pulp) . . . . 95 1·25
1243 36c. G.-E. Desbarats and W.
 Leggo (half-tone
 engraving) . . . . . . 95 1·25
1244 36c. F. N. Gisborne (first
 North American undersea
 telegraph) . . . . . . 95 1·25

540 "Segwun"

1987. Canadian Steamships. Multicoloured.
1245 36c. Type **540** . . . . . . 1·50 2·25
1246 36c. "Princess Marguerite"
 (52 × 22 mm) . . . . . 1·50 2·25

541 Figurehead from "Hamilton", 1813

1987. Historic Shipwrecks. Multicoloured.
1247 36c. Type **541** . . . . . . 70 1·00
1248 36c. Hull of "San Juan",
 1565 . . . . 70 1·00
1249 36c. Wheel from
 "Breadalbane", 1853 . . . 70 1·00
1250 36c. Bell from "Ericsson",
 1892 . . . . 70 1·00

542 Air Canada Boeing 767-200 and Globe

543 Summit Symbol

1987. 50th Anniv of Air Canada.
1251 **542** 36c. multicoloured . . . 75 35

1987. 2nd Int Francophone Summit, Quebec.
1252 **543** 36c. multicoloured . . . 30 35

544 Commonwealth Symbol

545 Poinsettia

1987. Commonwealth Heads of Government Meeting, Vancouver.
1253 **544** 36c. multicoloured . . . 35 40

1987. Christmas. Christmas Plants. Multicoloured.
1254 31c. Decorated Christmas
 tree and presents
 (36 × 20 mm) 50 35
1255 36c. Type **545** 40 40
1256 42c. Holly wreath 75 50
1257 72c. Mistletoe and decorated
 tree 90 80

1987. Winter Olympic Games, Calgary (1988) (4th issue). As T **531**. Multicoloured.
1258 36c. Cross-country skiing . . 65 50
1259 36c. Ski-jumping 65 50

546 Football, Grey Cup and Spectators

547 Flying Squirrel

548a Runnymede Library, Toronto

1987. 75th Grey Cup Final (Canadian football championship), Vancouver.
1260 **546** 36c. multicoloured . . . 35 40

1988. Canadian Mammals and Architecture. Multicoloured. (a) As T **547**.
1261 1c. Type **547** 10 10
1262 2c. Porcupine 10 10
1263 3c. Muskrat 10 10
1264 5c. Varying hare 10 10
1265 6c. Red fox 10 10
1266 10c. Striped skunk 10 10
1267 25c. American beaver . . . 30 15
1268 43c. Lynx (26 × 20 mm) . . 1·40 30
1269 44c. Walrus (27 × 21 mm) . 1·00 20
1270 45c. Pronghorn
 (27 × 21 mm) 40 40
1270c 46c. Wolverine
 (27 × 21 mm) 80 50
1271 57c. Killer whale
 (26 × 20 mm) . . . . . 2·00 55
1272 59c. Musk ox (27 × 21 mm) 2·25 1·00
1273 61c. Wolf (27 × 21 mm) . . 60 1·00
1273b 63c. Harbour porpoise
 (27 × 21 mm) . . . . . 1·00 1·25
1274 74c. Wapiti (26 × 20 mm) . 1·60 50
1275 76c. Brown bear
 (27 × 21 mm) . . . . . 1·00 50
1276 78c. White whale
 (27 × 21 mm) 90 55
1276c 80c. Peary caribou
 (27 × 21 mm) . . . . . 1·00 60

 (b) As T **548a**.
1277 $1 Type **548a** . . . . . . 1·25 30
1278 $2 McAdam Railway
 Station, New Brunswick . 2·00 50
1279 $5 Bonsecours Market,
 Montreal . . . . 4·75 4·00

1988. Winter Olympic Games, Calgary (5th issue). As T **531**. Multicoloured.
1281 37c. Slalom skiing 75 50
1282 37c. Curling 75 50
1283 43c. Figure skating 75 45
1284 74c. Luge . . . . 1·25 80

549 Trade Goods, Blackfoot Encampment and Page from Anthony Henday's Journal

1988. Exploration of Canada (3rd series). Explorers of the West. Multicoloured.
1285 37c. Type **549** 85 60
1286 37c. Discovery and map of
 George Vancouver's
 voyage 85 60
1287 37c. Simon Fraser's
 expedition portaging
 canoes 85 60
1288 37c. John Palliser's
 surveying equipment and
 view of prairie 85 60

550 "The Young Reader" (Ozias Leduc)

1988. Canadian Art (1st series).
1289 **550** 50c. multicoloured . . . 70 70
See also Nos. 1327, 1384, 1421, 1504, 1539, 1589, 1629, 1681, 1721, 1825, 1912, 2011 and 2097.

551 Mallard landing on Marsh

552 Kerosene Lamp and Diagram of Distillation Plant

1988. Wildlife and Habitat Conservation. Mult.
1290 37c. Type **551** 90 50
1291 37c. Moose feeding in marsh 90 50

1988. Canada Day. Science and Technology. Canadian Inventions (3rd series). Multicoloured.
1292 37c. Type **552** . . . . . . 75 1·00
1293 37c. Ears of Marquis wheat . 75 1·00
1294 37c. Electron microscope
 and magnified image . . . 75 1·00
1295 37c. Patient under "Cobalt
 60" cancer therapy . . . 75 1·00

553 "Papilio brevicauda"

1988. Canadian Butterflies. Multicoloured.
1296 37c. Type **553** 80 80
1297 37c. "Lycaeides idas" 80 80
1298 37c. "Oeneis macounii" . . . 80 80
1299 37c. "Papilio glaucus" . . . 80 80

554 St. John's Harbour Entrance and Skyline

1988. Centenary of Incorporation of St. John's, Newfoundland.
1300 **554** 37c. multicoloured . . . 35 40

555 Club Members working on Forestry Project and Rural Scene

1988. 75th Anniv of 4-H Clubs.
1301 **555** 37c. multicoloured . . . 35 40

556 Saint-Maurice Ironworks

557 Tahltan Bear Dog

1988. 250th Anniv of Saint-Maurice Ironworks, Quebec.
1302 **556** 37c. black, orange & brn 40 40

1988. Canadian Dogs. Multicoloured.
1303 37c. Type **557** . . . . . . 1·00 1·25
1304 37c. Nova Scotia duck
 tolling retriever . . . . 1·00 1·25
1305 37c. Canadian eskimo dog . 1·00 1·25
1306 37c. Newfoundland . . . . 1·00 1·25

558 Baseball, Glove and Pitch

559 Virgin with Inset of Holy Child

1988. 150th Anniv of Baseball in Canada. Multicoloured.
1307 **558** 37c. multicoloured . . . 35 40

1988. Christmas. Icons. Multicoloured.
1308 32c. Holy Family (36 × 21 mm) 35 35
1309 37c. Type **559** 35 40
1310 43c. Virgin and Child . . . 40 45
1311 74c. Virgin and Child (different) 70 75

On No. 1308 the left-hand third of the design area is taken up by the bar code.

No. 1309 also commemorates the millennium of Ukrainian Christianity.

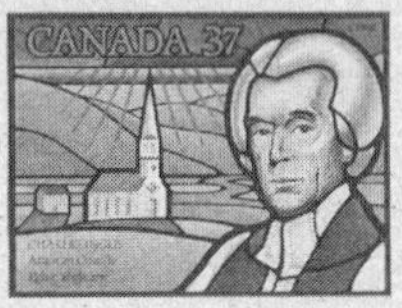

560 Bishop Inglis and Nova Scotia Church

1988. Bicentenary of Consecration of Charles Inglis (first Canadian Anglican bishop) (1987).
1312 **560** 37c. multicoloured . . . 35 40

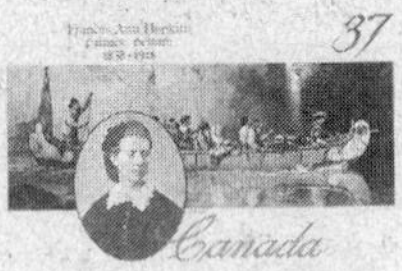

561 Frances Ann Hopkins and "Canoe manned by Voyageurs"

1988. 150th Birth Anniv of Frances Anne Hopkins (artist).
1313 **561** 37c. multicoloured . . . 35 40

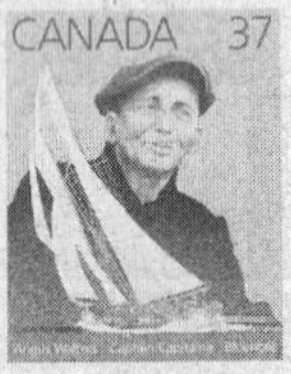

562 Angus Walters and "Bluenose" (yacht)

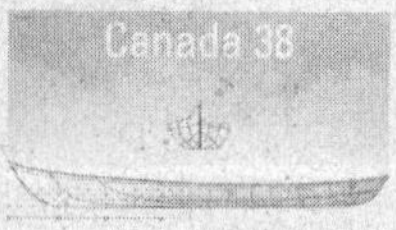

563 Chipewyan Canoe

1988. 20th Death Anniv of Angus Walters (yachtsman).
1314 **562** 37c. multicoloured . . . 40 40

1989. Small Craft of Canada (1st series). Native Canoes. Multicoloured.
1315 38c. Type **563** 85 70
1316 38c. Haida canoe 85 70
1317 38c. Inuit kayak 85 70
1318 38c. Micmac canoe 85 70

See also Nos. 1377/80 and 1428/31.

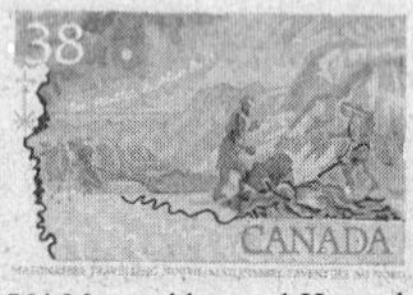

564 Matonabbee and Hearne's Expedition

1989. Exploration of Canada (4th issue). Explorers of the North. Multicoloured.
1319 38c. Type **564** . . . . . . 1·00 70
1320 38c. Relics of Franklin's expedition and White Ensign . . . . 1·00 70
1321 38c. Joseph Tyrell's compass, hammer and fossil . . . . 1·00 70
1322 38c. Vilhjalmur Stefansson, camera on tripod and sledge dog team . . . . . 1·00 70

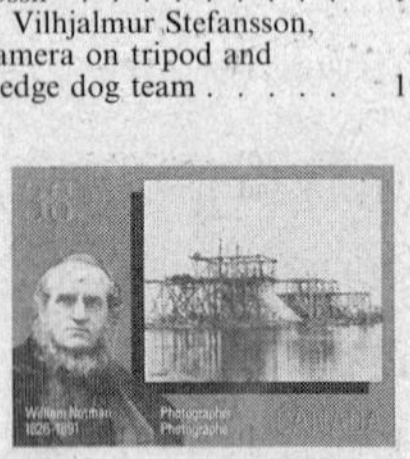

565 Construction of Victoria Bridge, Montreal and William Notman

1989. Canada Day. "150 Years of Canadian Photography". Designs showing early photographs and photographers. Multicoloured.
1323 38c. Type **565** 60 60
1324 38c. Plains Indian village and W. Hanson Boorne . . 60 60
1325 38c. Horse-drawn sleigh and Alexander Henderson . . 60 60
1326 38c. Quebec street scene and Jules-Ernest Livernois . . 60 60

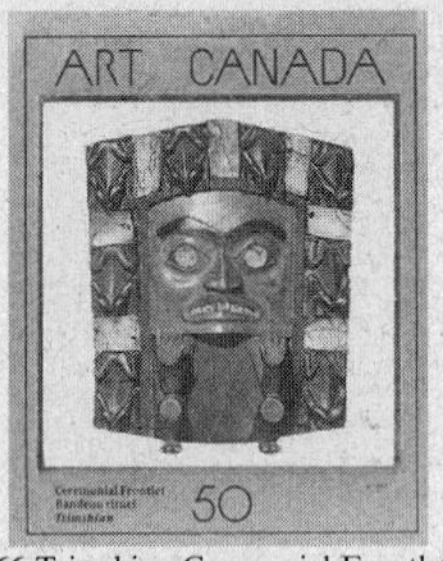

566 Tsimshian Ceremonial Frontlet, c. 1900

1989. Canadian Art (2nd series).
1327 **566** 50c. multicoloured . . . 55 60

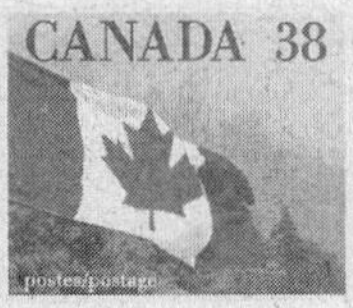

567 Canadian Flag and Forest

1989. Self-adhesive. Multicoloured.
1328 38c. Type **567** . . . . . . 1·25 1·75
1328b 39c. Canadian flag and prairie . . . . 1·25 2·00
1328c 40c. Canadian flag and sea 1·00 1·25
1328d 42c. Canadian flag over mountains . . . . . . 1·50 2·00
1328e 43c. Canadian flag over lake . . . . 80 1·50

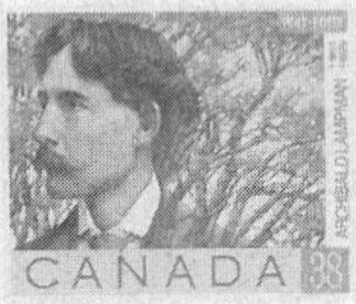

568 Archibald Lampman

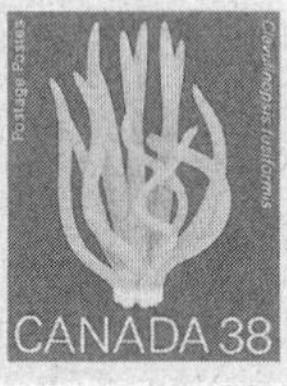

569 "Clavulinopsis fusiformis"

1989. Canadian Poets. Multicoloured.
1329 38c. Type **568** 50 50
1330 38c. Louis-Honore Frechette 50 50

1989. Mushrooms. Multicoloured.
1331 38c. Type **569** 70 80
1332 38c. "Boletus mirabilis" . . 70 80
1333 38c. "Cantharellus cinnabarinus" 70 80
1334 38c. "Morchella esculenta" 70 80

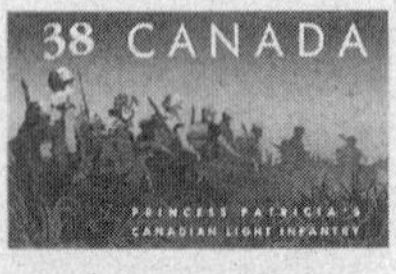

570 Night Patrol, Korea

1989. 75th Anniv of Canadian Regiments. Mult.
1335 38c. Type **570** (Princess Patricia's Canadian Light Infantry) . . . . 1·25 1·40
1336 38c. Trench raid, France, 1914–18 (Royal 22e Regiment) . . . . 1·25 1·40

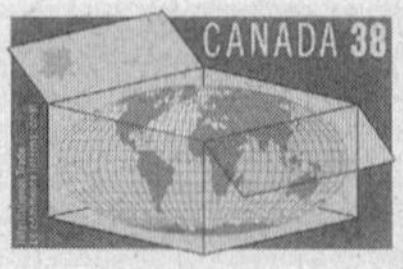

571 Globe in Box

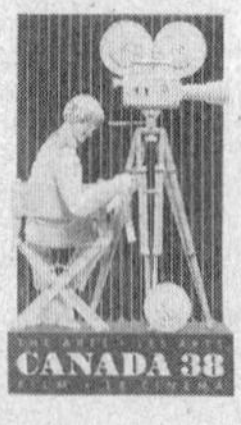

572 Film Director

1989. Canada Export Trade Month.
1337 **571** 38c. multicoloured . . . 40 45

1989. Arts and Entertainment.
1338 **572** 38c. brown, dp brn & vio 65 55
1339 – 38c. brown, dp brn & grn 65 55
1340 – 38c. brown, dp brn & mve 65 55
1341 – 38c. brown, dp brn & bl 65 55

DESIGNS: No. 1339, Actors; No. 1340, Dancers; No. 1341, Musicians.

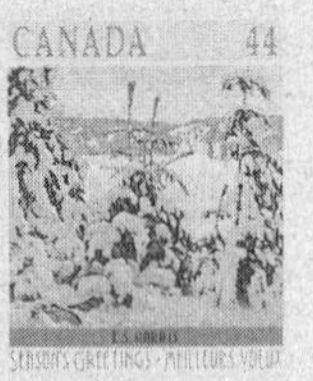

573 "Snow II" (Lawren S. Harris)

1989. Christmas. Paintings of Winter Landscapes. Multicoloured.
1342 33c. "Champ-de-Mars, Winter" (William Brymner) (35 × 21 mm) 90 55
1343 38c. "Bend in the Gosselin River" (Marc-Aurele Suzor-Cote) (21 × 35 mm) 40 35
1344 44c. Type **573** 60 50
1345 76c. "Ste. Agnes" (A. H. Robinson) . . . . 1·10 85

On No. 1342 the left-hand third of the design area is taken up by a bar code.

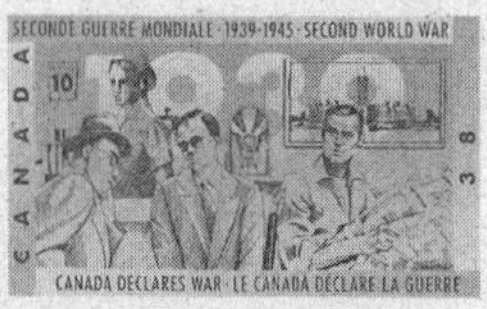

574 Canadians listening to Declaration of War, 1939

1989. 50th Anniv of Outbreak of Second World War (1st issue).
1346 **574** 38c. black, silver & pur 1·00 65
1347 – 38c. black, silver and grey . . . . 1·00 65
1348 – 38c. black, silver and green . . . . 1·00 65
1349 – 38c. black, silver and blue . . . . 1·00 65

DESIGNS: No. 1347, Army mobilization; No. 1348, British Commonwealth air crew training; No. 1349, North Atlantic convoy.

See also Nos. 1409/12, 1456/9, 1521/4, 1576/9, 1621/4, and 1625/8.

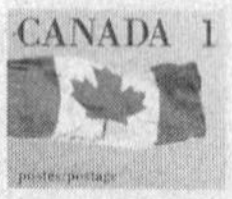

575 Canadian Flag

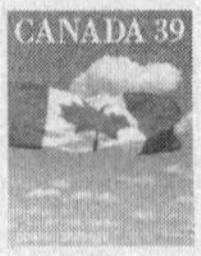

576

1989.
1350 **575** 1c. multicoloured . . . 20 1·00
1351 – 5c. multicoloured . . . 20 30
1352 – 39c. multicoloured . . . 1·75 2·25
1354 **576** 39c. multicoloured . . . 50 10
1360 – 39c. purple 60 75
1353 – 40c. multicoloured . . . 1·75 2·00
1355 – 40c. multicoloured . . . 60 10
1361 – 40c. blue 40 45
1356 – 42c. multicoloured . . . 60 15
1362 – 42c. red 40 45
1357 – 43c. multicoloured . . . 80 60
1363 – 43c. green . . . . 1·00 1·50
1358c – 45c. multicoloured . . . 45 55
1364 – 45c. green 55 40
1359 – 46c. multicoloured . . . 40 45
1365 – 46c. red 40 45
1367 – 46c. multicoloured . . . 40 45
1368 – 48c. multicoloured . . . 40 45

DESIGNS: Nos. 1351/3, 1360/5, As T **575** but different folds in flag. As T **576**: No. 1355, Flag over forest; 1356, Flag over mountains; 1357c, Flag over prairie; 1358, Flag and skyscraper; 1359, Flag and iceberg; 1367, Flag and inukshuk (Inuit cairn); 1368 Flag in front of Canada Post Headquarters, Ottawa.

No. 1359 comes with ordinary or self-adhesive gum and 1367/8 are self-adhesive.

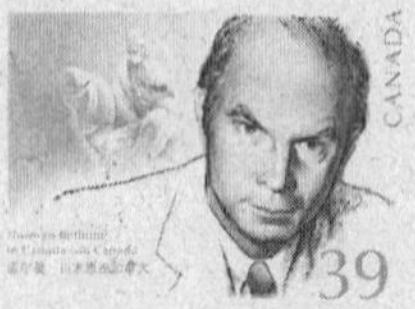

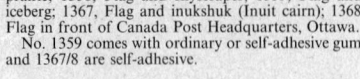

577 Norman Bethune in 1937 and performing Operation, Montreal

1990. Birth Centenary of Dr. Norman Bethune (surgeon). Multicoloured.
1375 39c. Type **577** . . . . . . 1·00 1·25
1376 39c. Bethune in 1939, and treating wounded Chinese soldiers . . . . 1·00 1·25

1990. Small Craft of Canada (2nd series). Early Work Boats. As T **563**. Multicoloured.
1377 39c. Fishing dory . . . . . 90 1·10
1378 39c. Logging pointer . . . . 90 1·10
1379 39c. York boat . . . . . . 90 1·10
1380 39c. North canoe . . . . . 90 1·10

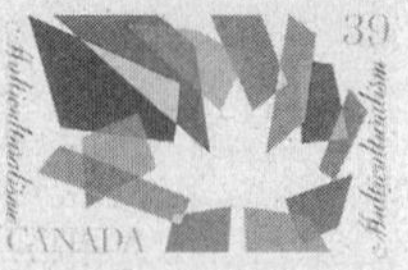

578 Maple Leaf Mosaic

1990. Multiculturalism.
1381 **578** 39c. multicoloured . . . 35 40

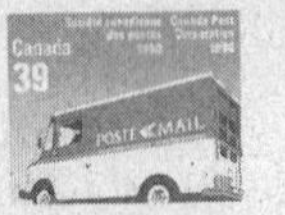

579 Mail Van (facing left)

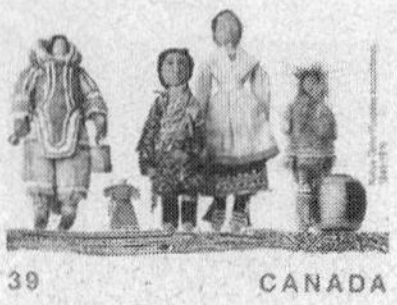

580 Amerindian and Inuit Dolls

1990. "Moving the Mail". Multicoloured.
1382 39c. Type **579** 45 55
1383 39c. Mail van (facing right) 45 55

1990. Canadian Art (3rd series). As T **550**. Multicoloured.
1384 50c. "The West Wind" (Tom Thomson) 55 65

1990. Dolls. Multicoloured.
1385 39c. Type **580** . . . . . . 90 1·00
1386 39c. 19th-century settlers' dolls . . . . 90 1·00
1387 39c. Commerical dolls, 1917–36 . . . . 90 1·00
1388 39c. Commercial dolls, 1940–60 . . . . 90 1·00

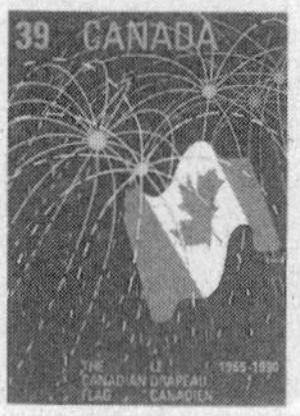

581 Canadian Flag and Fireworks

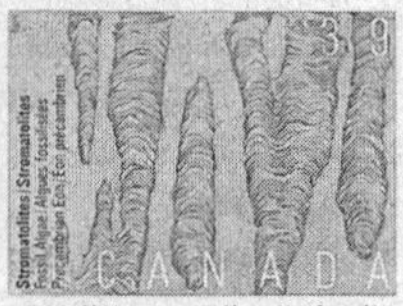

582 "Stromatolites" (fossil algae)

1990. Canada Day.
1389 **581** 39c. multicoloured . . . 45 50

1990. Prehistoric Canada (1st series). Primitive Life. Multicoloured.
1390 39c. Type **582** 90 75
1391 39c. "Opabinia regalis" (soft invertebrate) 90 75
1392 39c. "Paradoxides davidis" (trilobite) 90 75
1393 39c. "Eurypterus remipes" (sea scorpion) 90 75

See also Nos. 1417/20, 1568/71 and 1613/16.

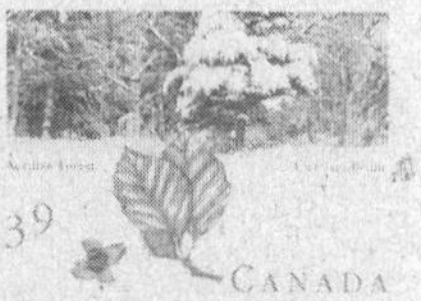

583 Acadian Forest

1990. Canadian Forests. Multicoloured.
1394 39c. Type **583** 60 70
1395 39c. Great Lakes–St. Lawrence forest 60 70
1396 39c. Pacific Coast forest . . 60 70
1397 39c. Boreal forest 60 70

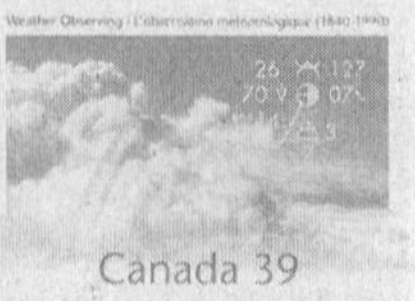

584 Clouds and Rainbow

1990. 150th Anniv of Weather Observing in Canada.
1398 **584** 39c. multicoloured . . . 40 50

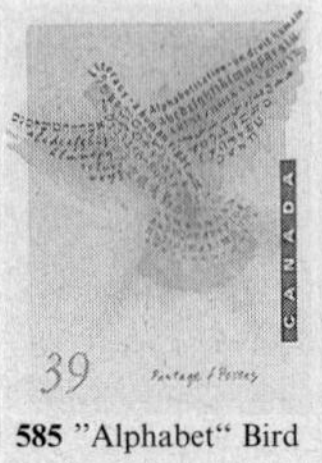

585 "Alphabet" Bird

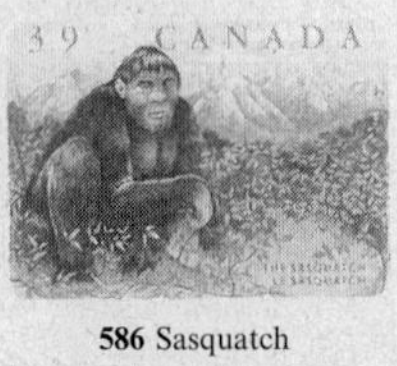

586 Sasquatch

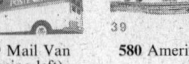

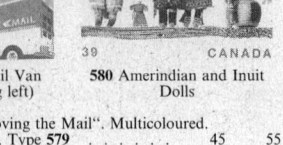

1990. International Literacy Year.
1399 **585** 39c. multicoloured . . . 40 50

1990. Legendary Creatures. Multicoloured.
1400 39c. Type **586** . . . . . . 1·00 1·10
1401 39c. Kraken . . . . . . 1·00 1·10
1402 39c. Werewolf . . . . . . 1·00 1·10
1403 39c. Ogopogo . . . . . . 1·00 1·10

587 Agnes Macphail   **588** "Virgin Mary with Christ Child and St. John the Baptist" (Norval Morrisseau)

1990. Birth Centenary of Agnes Macphail (first woman elected to Parliament).
1404 **587** 39c. multicoloured . . . 40 50

1990. Christmas. Native Art.
1405 – 34c. multicoloured . . . 40 35
1406 **588** 39c. multicoloured . . . 40 40
1407 – 45c. multicoloured . . . 40 45
1408 – 78c. black, red and grey 70 75
DESIGNS—35 × 21 mm: 34c. "Rebirth" (Jackson Beardy). As T **588**: 45c. "Mother and Child" (Inuit sculpture, Cape Dorset); 78c. "Children of the Raven" (Bill Reid).
No. 1405 includes a bar code in the design.

1990. 50th Anniv of Second World War (2nd issue). As T **574**.
1409 39c. black, silver and green 1·40 1·40
1410 39c. black, silver and brown 1·40 1·40
1411 39c. black, silver and brown 1·40 1·40
1412 39c. black, silver and mauve 1·40 1·40
DESIGNS: No. 1409, Canadian family at home, 1940; 1410, Packing parcels for the troops; 1411, Harvesting; 1412, Testing anti-gravity flying suit.

589 Jennie Trout (first woman physician) and Women's Medical College, Kingston   **590** Blue Poppies and Butchart Gardens, Victoria

1991. Medical Pioneers. Multicoloured.
1413 40c. Type **589** 90 90
1414 40c. Wilder Penfield (neurosurgeon) and Montreal Neurological Institute 90 90
1415 40c. Frederick Banting (discoverer of insulin) and University of Toronto medical faculty 90 90
1416 40c. Harold Griffith (anesthesiologist) and Queen Elizabeth Hospital, Montreal 90 90

1991. Prehistoric Canada (2nd series). Primitive Vertebrates. As T **582**. Multicoloured.
1417 40c. Foord's crossopt ("Eusthenopteron foordi") (fish fossil) . . . . 1·25 1·40
1418 40c. "Hylonomus lyelli" (land reptile) . . . . 1·25 1·40
1419 40c. Fossil conodonts (fossil teeth) . . . . . 1·25 1·40
1420 40c. "Archaeopteris halliana" (early tree) . . 1·25 1·40

1991. Canadian Art (4th series). As T **550**. Multicoloured.
1421 50c. "Forest, British Columbia" (Emily Carr) 1·00 1·25

1991. Public Gardens. Multicoloured.
1422 40c. Type **590** 55 55
1423 40c. Marigolds and International Peace Garden, Boissevain . . 55 55
1424 40c. Lilac and Royal Botanical Gardens, Hamilton 55 55
1425 40c. Roses and Montreal Botanical Gardens . . 55 55
1426 40c. Rhododendrons and Halifax Public Gardens 55 55

591 Maple Leaf   **592** South Nahanni River

1991. Canada Day.
1427 **591** 40c. multicoloured . . . 50 60

1991. Small Craft of Canada (3rd series). As T **563**. Multicoloured.
1428 40c. Verchere rowboat . . 1·25 1·25
1429 40c. Touring kayak . . . . 1·25 1·25
1430 40c. Sailing dinghy . . . 1·25 1·25
1431 40c. Cedar strip canoe . . . 1·25 1·25

1991. Canadian Rivers (1st series). Multicoloured.
1432 40c. Type **592** . . . . . 1·00 1·40
1433 40c. Athabasca River . . . 1·00 1·40
1434 40c. Boundary Waters, Voyageur Waterway . . 1·00 1·40
1435 40c. Jacques-Cartier River 1·00 1·40
1436 40c. Main River . . . . 1·00 1·40
See also Nos. 1492/6, 1558/62 and 1584/8.

593 "Leaving Europe"   **594** Ski Patrol rescuing Climber

1991. Centenary of Ukrainian Immigration. Panels from "The Ukrainian Pioneer" by William Kurelek. Multicoloured.
1437 40c. Type **593** 80 85
1438 40c. "Canadian Winter" . . 80 85
1439 40c. "Clearing the Land" . . 80 85
1440 40c. "Harvest" 80 85

1991. Emergency Services. Multicoloured.
1441 40c. Type **594** . . . . . 1·50 1·50
1442 40c. Police at road traffic accident . . . . . . 1·50 1·50
1443 40c. Firemen on extending ladder . . . . . . 1·50 1·50
1444 40c. Boeing-Vertol Chinook rescue helicopter and "Spindrift" (lifeboat) . . 1·50 1·50

595 "The Witched Canoe"   **596** Grant Hall Tower

1991. Canadian Folktales. Multicoloured.
1445 40c. Type **595** 95 95
1446 40c. "The Orphan Boy" . . 95 95
1447 40c. "Chinook" 95 95
1448 40c. "Buried Treasure" . . 95 95

1991. 150th Anniv of Queen's University, Kingston.
1449 **596** 40c. multicoloured . . 80 1·00

597 North American Santa Claus   **598** Players jumping for Ball

1991. Christmas. Multicoloured.
1450 35c. British Father Christmas (35 × 21 mm) 80 40
1451 40c. Type **597** 70 20

1452 46c. French Bonhomme Noel . . . . . . 85 1·25
1453 80c. Dutch Sinterklaas . . . 1·60 2·75

1991. Basketball Centenary. Multicoloured.
1454 **598** 40c. multicoloured . . . 1·25 75

1991. 50th Anniv of Second World War (3rd issue). As T **574**.
1456 40c. black, silver and blue 1·25 1·25
1457 40c. black, silver and brown 1·25 1·25
1458 40c. black, silver and lilac 1·25 1·25
1459 40c. black, silver and brown 1·25 1·25
DESIGNS: No. 1456, Women's services, 1941; 1457, Armament factory; 1458, Cadets and veterans, 1459, Defence of Hong Kong.

599 Blueberry   **600** McIntosh Apple

600a Court House, Yorktown

1991. Multicoloured. (a) Edible Berries. As T **599**.
1460 1c. Type **599** 10 10
1461 2c. Wild strawberry . . . 10 10
1462 3c. Black crowberry . . . 30 10
1463 5c. Rose hip 10 10
1464 6c. Black raspberry . . . 10 10
1465 10c. Kinnikinnick 10 10
1466 25c. Saskatoon berry . . . 20 25
   (b) Fruit and Nut Trees. As T **600**
1467 48c. Type **600** 50 35
1468 49c. Delicious apple . . . 1·50 1·00
1469 50c. Snow apple . . . . 1·00 1·00
1470b 52c. Grauenstein apple . . 60 45
1471 65c. Black walnut 70 50
1472 67c. Beaked hazelnut . . . 1·00 1·25
1473 69c. Shagbark hickory . . 1·25 1·25
1474 71c. American chestnut . . 1·50 1·00
1475 84c. Stanley plum . . . . 1·00 75
1476 86c. Bartlett pear . . . . 1·00 1·00
1477 88c. Westcot apricot . . . 1·60 1·60
1478 90c. Elberta peach . . . . 1·00 1·00
   (c) Architecture. As T **600a**
1479 $1 Type **600a** . . . . 1·75 1·00
1480a $2 Provincial Normal School, Truro . . . 2·25 1·60
1481 $5 Public Library, Victoria 4·50 4·75

601 Ski Jumping

1992. Winter Olympic Games, Albertville. Mult.
1482 42c. Type **601** 80 90
1483 42c. Figure skating 80 90
1484 42c. Ice hockey 80 90
1485 42c. Bobsleighing 80 90
1486 42c. Alpine skiing 80 90

602 Ville-Marie in 17th Century

1992. "CANADA 92" International Youth Stamp Exhibition, Montreal. Multicoloured.
1487 42c. Type **602** . . . . . 1·00 1·25
1488 42c. Modern Montreal . . . 1·00 1·25
1489 48c. Compass rose, snow shoe and crow's nest of Cartier's ship "Grande Hermine" . . . . . 1·50 1·00
1490 84c. Atlantic map, Aztec "calendar stone" and navigational instrument 2·25 2·50

1992. Canadian Rivers (2nd series). As T **592** but horiz. Multicoloured.
1492 42c. Margaree River . . . 95 1·00
1493 42c. West (Eliot) River . . . 95 1·00
1494 42c. Ottawa River . . . . 95 1·00
1495 42c. Niagara River . . . . 95 1·00
1496 42c. South Saskatchewan River . . . . . . 95 1·00

603 Road Bed Construction and Route Map   **605** Jerry Potts (scout)

1992. 50th Anniv of Alaska Highway.
1497 **603** 42c. multicoloured . . . 85 70

1992. Olympic Games, Barcelona. As T **601**. Multicoloured.
1498 42c. Gymnastics . . . . . 1·00 1·10
1499 42c. Athletics . . . . . 1·00 1·10
1500 42c. Diving . . . . . . 1·00 1·10
1501 42c. Cycling . . . . . . 1·00 1·10
1502 42c. Swimming . . . . . 1·00 1·10

1992. Canadian Art (5th series). As T **550**. Multicoloured.
1504 50c. "Red Nasturtiums" (David Milne) . . . . . 1·40 1·10

1992. Folk Heroes. Multicoloured.
1505 42c. Type **605** . . . . . 90 1·10
1506 42c. Capt. William Jackman and wreck of "Sea Clipper", 1867 . . . . 90 1·10
1507 42c. Laura Secord (messenger) . . . . 90 1·10
1508 42c. Jos Montferrand (lumberjack) . . . . 90 1·10

606 Copper

1992. 150th Anniv of Geological Survey of Canada. Minerals. Multicoloured.
1509 42c. Type **606** . . . . . . 1·25 1·50
1510 42c. Sodalite . . . . . . 1·25 1·50
1511 42c. Gold . . . . 1·25 1·50
1512 42c. Galena . . . . . . 1·25 1·50
1513 42c. Grossular . . . . . 1·25 1·50

607 Satellite and Photographs from Space

1992. Canadian Space Programme. Multicoloured.
1514 42c. Type **607** . . . . . . 1·25 1·50
1515 42c. Space shuttle over Canada (hologram) (32 × 26 mm) . . . . 1·25 1·50

608 Babe Siebert, Skates and Stick   **609** Companion of the Order of Canada Insignia

1992. 75th Anniv of National Ice Hockey League. Multicoloured.
1516 42c. Type **608** . . . . . . 1·25 1·50
1517 42c. Claude Provost, Terry Sawchuck and team badges . . . . . . 1·25 1·50
1518 42c. Hockey mask, gloves and modern player . . . 1·25 1·50

1992. 25th Anniv of the Order of Canada and Daniel Roland Michener (former Governor-General) Commemoration. Multicoloured.
1519 42c. Type **609** . . . . . . 1·25 1·50
1520 42c. Daniel Roland Michener . . . . . . 1·25 1·50

1992. 50th Anniv of Second World War (4th issue). As T **574**.
1521 42c. black, silver & brown 1·40 1·50
1522 42c. black, silver & green . . 1·40 1·50
1523 42c. black, silver & brown 1·40 1·50
1524 42c. black, silver and blue 1·40 1·50
DESIGNS: No. 1521, Reporters and soldier, 1942; 1522, Consolidated Liberator bombers over Newfoundland; 1523 Dieppe raid; 1524, U-boat sinking merchant ship.

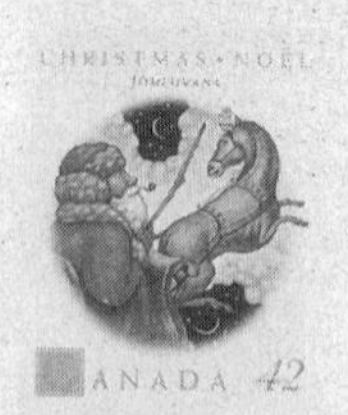

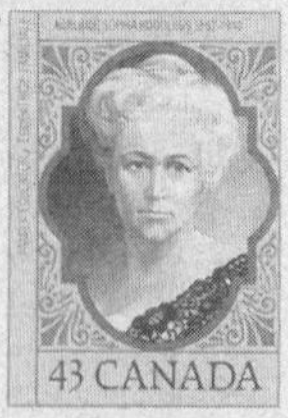

610 Estonian Jouluvana **611** Adelaide Hoodless (women's movement pioneer)

1992. Christmas. Multicoloured.

1525	37c. North American Santa Claus (35 × 21 mm)	80	80
1526	42c. Type **610**	40	20
1527	48c. Italian La Befana	80	1·25
1528	84c. German Weihnachtsmann	1·75	2·50

1993. Prominent Canadian Women. Multicoloured.

1529	43c. Type **611**	85	1·10
1530	43c. Marie-Josephine Gerin-Lajoie (social reformer)	85	1·10
1531	43c. Pitseolak Ashoona (Inuit artist)	85	1·10
1532	43c. Helen Kinnear (lawyer)	85	1·10

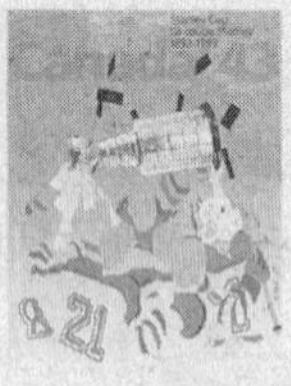

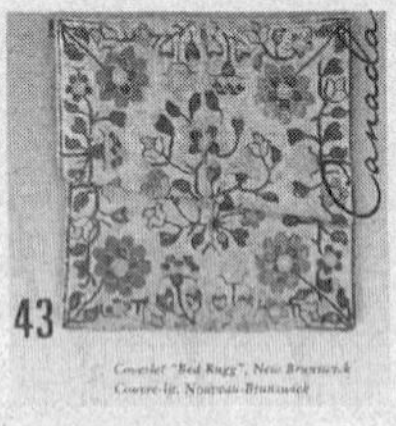

612 Ice Hockey Players with Cup **613** Coverlet, New Brunswick

1993. Centenary of Stanley Cup.

1533	**612** 43c. multicoloured	75	60

1993. Hand-crafted Textiles. Multicoloured.

1534	43c. Type **613**	1·00	1·25
1535	43c. Pieced quilt, Ontario	1·00	1·25
1536	43c. Doukhobor bedcover, Saskatchewan	1·00	1·25
1537	43c. Ceremonial robe, Kwakwaka'wakw	1·00	1·25
1538	43c. Boutonne coverlet, Quebec	1·00	1·25

1993. Canadian Art (6th series). As T **550**. Multicoloured.

1539	86c. "The Owl" (Kenojuak Ashevak)	2·00	2·50

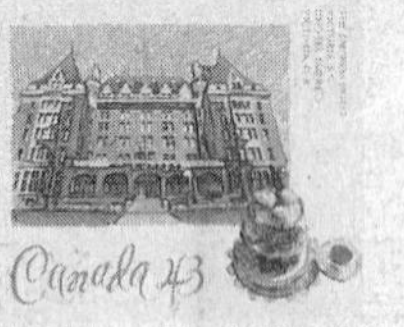

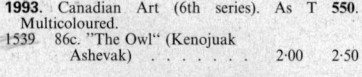

614 Empress Hotel, Victoria

1993. Historic Hotels. Multicoloured.

1540	43c. Type **614**	70	1·00
1541	43c. Banff Springs Hotel	70	1·00
1542	43c. Royal York Hotel, Toronto	70	1·00
1543	43c. Le Chateau Frontenac, Quebec	70	1·00
1544	43c. Algonquin Hotel, St. Andrews	70	1·00

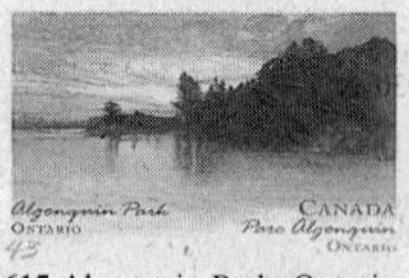

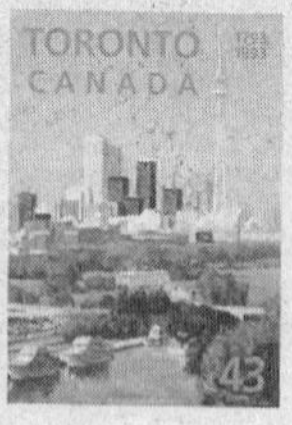

615 Algonquin Park, Ontario **616** Toronto Skyscrapers

1993. Canada Day. Provincial and Territorial Parks. Multicoloured.

1545	43c. Type **615**	70	80
1546	43c. De La Gaspesie Park, Quebec	70	80
1547	43c. Cedar Dunes Park, Prince Edward Island	70	80
1548	43c. Cape St. Mary's Seabird Reserve, Newfoundland	70	80
1549	43c. Mount Robson Park, British Columbia	70	80
1550	43c. Writing-on-Stone Park, Alberta	70	80
1551	43c. Spruce Woods Park, Manitoba	70	80
1552	43c. Herschel Island Park, Yukon	70	80
1553	43c. Cypress Hills Park, Saskatchewan	70	80
1554	43c. The Rocks Park, New Brunswick	70	80
1555	43c. Blomidon Park, Nova Scotia	70	80
1556	43c. Katannilik Park, Northwest Territories	70	80

1993. Bicentenary of Toronto.

1557	**616** 43c. multicoloured	80	60

1993. Canadian Rivers (3rd series). As T **592**. Multicoloured.

1558	43c. Fraser River	70	90
1559	43c. Yukon River	70	90
1560	43c. Red River	70	90
1561	43c. St. Lawrence River	70	90
1562	43c. St. John River	70	90

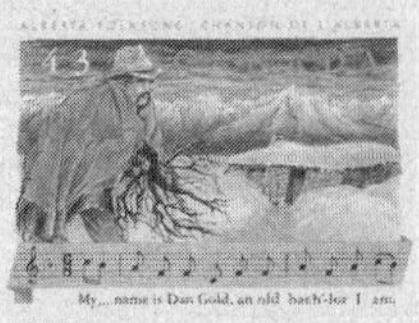

618 "The Alberta Homesteader"

1993. Folk Songs. Multicoloured.

1564	43c. Type **618**	70	90
1565	43c. "Les Raftmans" (Quebec)	70	90
1566	43c. "I'se the B'y that Builds the Boat" (Newfoundland)	70	90
1567	43c. "Onkwa:ri Tenhanonniahkwe" (Mohawk Indian)	70	90

1993. Prehistoric Canada (3rd series). Dinosaurs. As T **582** but 40 × 28 mm. Multicoloured.

1568	43c. Massospondylus	80	80
1569	43c. Stryacosaurus	80	80
1570	43c. Albertosaurus	80	80
1571	43c. Platecarpus	80	80

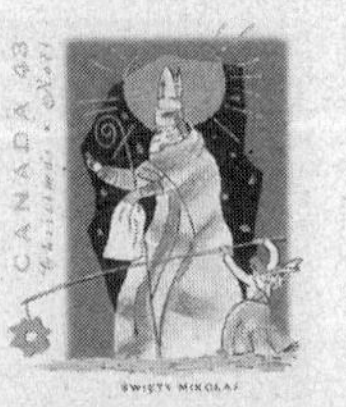

619 Polish Swiety Mikolaj

1993. Christmas. Multicoloured.

1572	38c. North American Santa Claus (35 × 22 mm)	80	80
1573	43c. Type **619**	50	20
1574	49c. Russian Ded Moroz	80	1·00
1575	86c. Australian Father Christmas	1·40	2·50

1993. 50th Anniv of Second World War (5th issue). As T **574**.

1576	43c. black, silver and green	1·25	1·50
1577	43c. black, silver and blue	1·25	1·50
1578	43c. black, silver and blue	1·25	1·50
1579	43c. black, silver and brown	1·25	1·50

DESIGNS: No. 1576, Loading munitions for Russia, 1943; No. 1577, Loading bombs on Avro Lancaster; No. 1578, Escorts attacking U-boat; No. 1579, Infantry advancing, Italy.

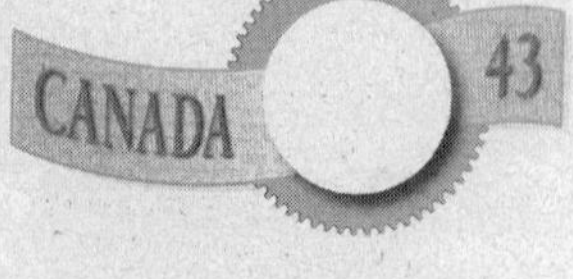

620 (face value at right)

1994. Self-adhesive Greetings stamps. Mult.

1580	43c. Type **620**	70	90
1581	43c. As Type **620** but face value at left	70	90

It was intended that the sender should insert an appropriate greetings label into the circular space on each stamp before use.

For 45c. values in this design see Nos. 1654/5.

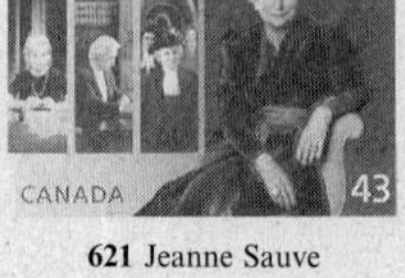

621 Jeanne Sauve

1994. Jeanne Sauve (former Governor-General) Commemoration.

1582	**621** 43c. multicoloured	60	60

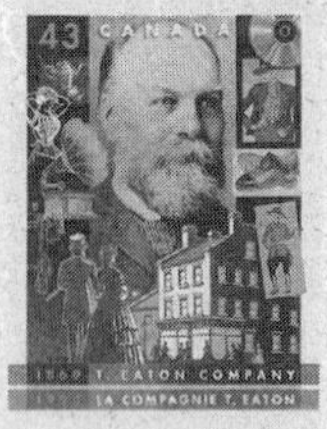

622 Timothy Eaton, Toronto Store of 1869 and Merchandise

1994. 125th Anniv of T. Eaton Company Ltd (department store group).

1583	**622** 43c. multicoloured	55	75

1994. Canadian Rivers (4th series). As T **592**, but horiz. Multicoloured.

1584	43c. Saguenay River	60	75
1585	43c. French River	60	75
1586	43c. Mackenzie River	60	75
1587	43c. Churchill River	60	75
1588	43c. Columbia River	60	75

1994. Canadian Art (7th series). As T **550**. Multicoloured.

1589	88c. "Vera" (detail) (Frederick Varley)	1·50	2·00

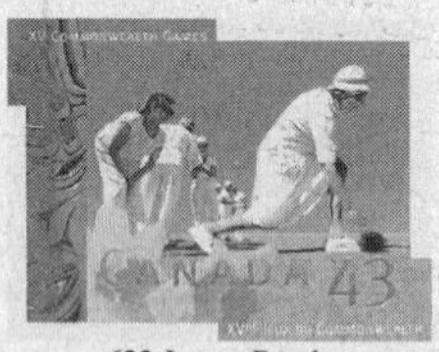

623 Lawn Bowls

1994. 15th Commonwealth Games, Victoria. Multicoloured.

1590	43c. Type **623**	40	50
1591	43c. Lacrosse	40	50
1592	43c. Wheelchair race	40	50
1593	43c. High jumping	40	50
1594	50c. Diving	45	65
1595	88c. Cycling	80	1·25

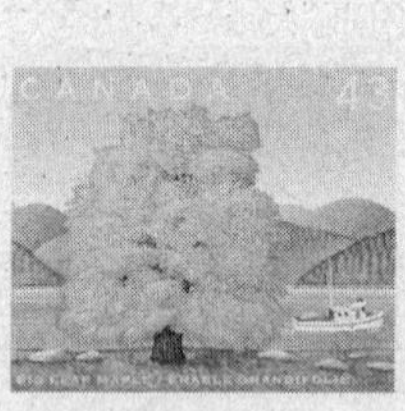

625 Big Leaf Maple Tree

1994. Canada Day. Maple Trees. Multicoloured.

1597	43c. Type **625**	70	80
1598	43c. Sugar maple	70	80
1599	43c. Silver maple	70	80
1600	43c. Striped maple	70	80
1601	43c. Norway maple	70	80
1602	43c. Manitoba maple	70	80
1603	43c. Black maple	70	80
1604	43c. Douglas maple	70	80
1605	43c. Mountain maple	70	80
1606	43c. Vine maple	70	80
1607	43c. Hedge maple	70	80
1608	43c. Red maple	70	80

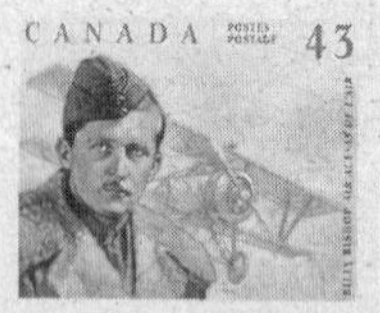

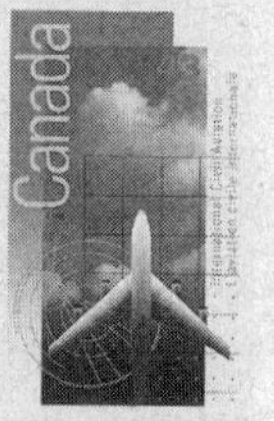

626 Billy Bishop (fighter ace) and Nieuport 17 **627** Symbolic Aircraft, Radar Screen and Clouds

1994. Birth Centenaries. Multicoloured.

1609	43c. Type **626**	75	1·00
1610	43c. Mary Travers ("La Bolduc") (singer) and musicians	75	1·00

1994. 50th Anniv of I.C.A.O.

1612	**627** 43c. multicoloured	60	60

1994. Prehistoric Canada (4th series). Mammals. As T **582**, but 40 × 28 mm. Multicoloured.

1613	43c. Coryphodon	1·40	1·50
1614	43c. Megacerops	1·40	1·50
1615	43c. Arctodus simus (bear)	1·40	1·50
1616	43c. Mammuthus primigenius (mammoth)	1·40	1·50

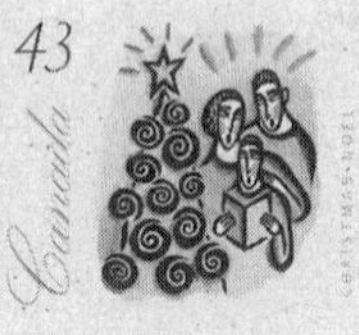

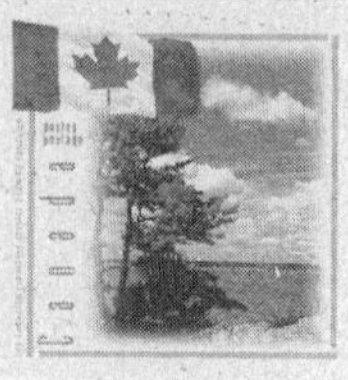

628 Carol Singing around Christmas Tree **629** Flag and Lake

1994. Christmas. Multicoloured.

1617	(–)c. Carol singer (35 × 21 mm)	70	80
1618	43c. Type **628**	45	20
1619	50c. Choir (vert)	85	1·25
1620	88c. Couple carol singing in snow (vert)	2·00	2·75

No. 1617 is without face value, but was intended for use as a 38c. on internal greetings cards posted before 31 January 1995. The design shows a barcode at left.

1994. 50th Anniv of Second World War (6th issue). As T **574**.

1621	43c. black, silver and green	1·40	1·50
1622	43c. black, silver and red	1·40	1·50
1623	43c. black, silver and blue	1·40	1·50
1624	43c. black, silver and grey	1·40	1·50

DESIGNS: No. 1621, D-Day landings, Normandy; No. 1622, Canadian artillery, Normandy; No. 1623, Hawker Typhoons on patrol; No. 1624, Canadian infantry and disabled German self-propelled gun, Walcheren.

1995. 50th Anniv of Second World War (7th issue). As T **574**.

1625	43c. black, silver and purple	1·40	1·50
1626	43c. black, silver and brown	1·40	1·50
1627	43c. black, silver and green	1·40	1·50
1628	43c. black, silver and blue	1·40	1·50

DESIGNS: No. 1625, Returning troop ship; 1626, Canadian P.O.W.s celebrating freedom; 1627, Canadian tank liberating Dutch town; 1628, Parachute drop in support of Rhine Crossing.

1995. Canadian Art (8th series). As T **550**. Multicoloured

1629	88c. "Floraison" (Alfred Pellan)	1·25	1·75

1995. 30th Anniv of National Flag. No face value.

1630	**629** (43c.) multicoloured	50	50

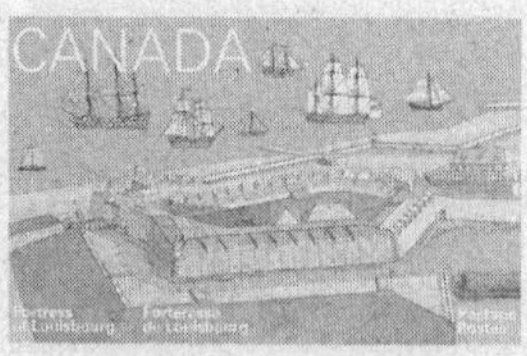

630 Louisbourg Harbour

1995. 275th Anniv of Fortress of Louisbourg. Multicoloured.

1631	(43c.) Type **630**	40	60
1632	(43c.) Barracks (32 × 29 mm)	40	60
1633	(43c.) King's Bastion (40 × 29 mm)	40	60
1634	(43c.) Site of King's Garden, convent and hospital (56 × 29 mm)	40	60
1635	(43c.) Site of coastal fortifications	40	60

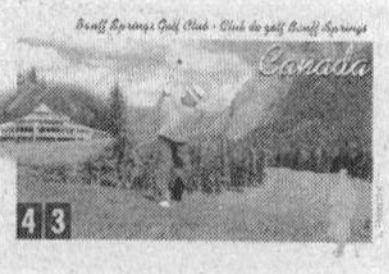

631 Banff Springs Golf Club, Alberta

1995. Centenaries of Canadian Amateur Golf Championship and of the Royal Canadian Golf Association. Multicoloured.

1637	43c. Type **631**	50	60
1638	43c. Riverside Country Club, New Brunswick	50	60
1639	43c. Glen Abbey Golf Club, Ontario	50	60
1640	43c. Victoria Golf Club, British Columbia	50	60
1641	43c. Royal Montreal Golf Club, Quebec	50	60

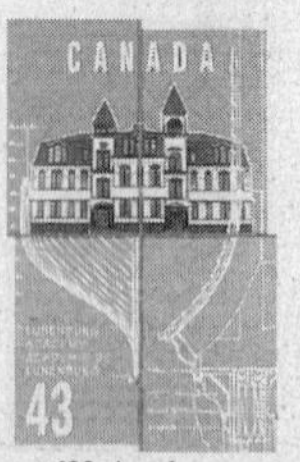

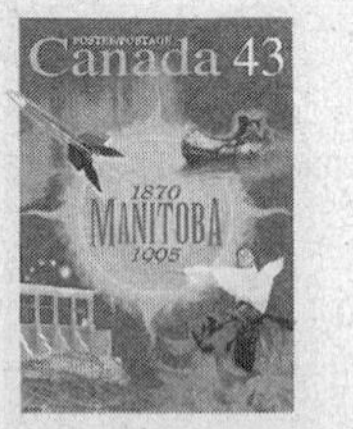

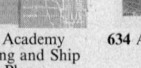

633 Academy Building and Ship Plan **634** Aspects of Manitoba

1995. Centenary of Lunenburg Academy.
1643 **633** 43c. multicoloured . . . 50 45

1995. 125th Anniv of Manitoba as Canadian Province.
1644 **634** 43c. multicoloured . . . 50 45

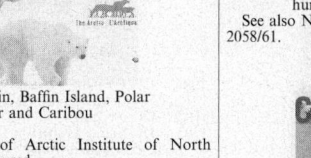

635 Monarch Butterfly

1995. Migratory Wildlife. Multicoloured.
1645 45c. Type **635** . . . . . . 90 1·25
1646 45c. Belted kingfisher* . . . 90 1·25
1647 45c. Belted kingfisher* . . . 90 1·25
1648 45c. Pintail . . . . 90 1·25
1649 45c. Hoary bat . . . . . . 90 1·25
*No. 1646: Inscr "aune migratrice" in error.
No. 1647: Inscr corrected to "faune migratrice".

636 Quebec Railway Bridge

1995. 20th World Road Congress, Montreal. Bridges. Multicoloured.
1650 45c. Type **636** . . . . . . 1·25 1·40
1651 45c. 401-403-410 Interchange, Mississauga 1·25 1·40
1652 45c. Hartland Bridge, New Brunswick . . . . . 1·25 1·40
1653 45c. Alex Fraser Bridge, British Columbia . . . . 1·25 1·40

1995. Self-adhesive Greetings stamps. As T **620**. Multicoloured. Imperf.
1654 45c. Face value at right . . 60 75
1655 45c. Face value at left . . . 60 75
It is intended the sender should insert an appropriate greetings label into the circular space on each stamp before use.

637 Mountain, Baffin Island, Polar Bear and Caribou

1995. 50th Anniv of Arctic Institute of North America. Multicoloured.
1656 45c. Type **637** . . . . . . 1·00 1·25
1657 45c. Arctic poppy, Auyuittuq National Park and cargo canoe . . . . 1·00 1·25
1658 45c. Inuk man and igloo . . 1·00 1·25
1659 45c. Ogilvie Mountains, dog team and ski-equipped airplane . . . . . 1·00 1·25
1660 45c. Inuit children . . . . 1·00 1·25

638 Superman   **640** "The Nativity"

639 Prime Minister MacKenzie King signing U.N. Charter, 1945

1995. Comic Book Superheroes. Multicoloured.
1661 45c. Type **638** 75 85
1662 45c. Johnny Canuck 75 85
1663 45c. Nelvana 75 85

1664 45c. Captain Canuck . . . 75 85
1665 45c. Fleur de Lys 75 85

1995. 50th Anniv of United Nations.
1666 **639** 45c. multicoloured . . . 60 50

1995. Christmas. Sculptured Capitals from Ste.-Anne-de-Beaupre Basilica designed by Emile Brunet (Nos. 1668/70). Multicoloured.
1667 40c. Sprig of holly (35 × 22 mm) 65 65
1668 45c. Type **640** 50 20
1669 52c. "The Annunciation" . . 1·00 1·25
1670 90c. "The Flight to Egypt" . 1·50 2·25

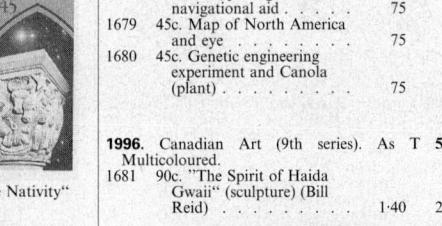

641 World Map and Emblem

1995. 25th Anniv of La Francophonie and The Agency for Cultural and Technical Co-operation.
1671 **641** 45c. multicoloured . . . 50 50

642 Concentration Camp Victims, Uniform and Identity Card

1995. 50th Anniv of the End of The Holocaust.
1672 **642** 45c. multicoloured . . . 50 50

643 American Kestrel

1996. Birds (1st series). Multicoloured.
1673 45c. Type **643** . . . . . 1·10 1·10
1674 45c. Atlantic puffin . . . . 1·10 1·10
1675 45c. Pileated woodpecker . . 1·10 1·10
1676 45c. Ruby-throated hummingbird . . . . . 1·10 1·10
See also Nos. 1717/20, 1779/82, 1865/8, 1974/7 and 2058/61.

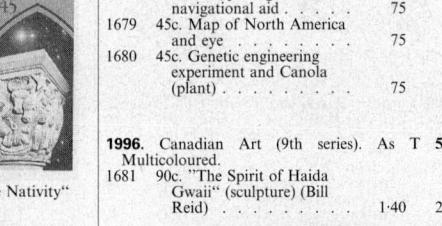

644 "Louis R. Desmarais" (tanker), Three-dimensional Map and Radar Screen

1996. High Technology Industries. Multicoloured.
1677 45c. Type **644** 75 90
1678 45c. Canadair Challenger 601-3R, jet engine and navigational aid 75 90
1679 45c. Map of North America and eye 75 90
1680 45c. Genetic engineering experiment and Canola (plant) 75 90

1996. Canadian Art (9th series). As T **550**. Multicoloured.
1681 90c. "The Spirit of Haida Gwaii" (sculpture) (Bill Reid) . . . . . . 1·40 2·00

645 "One World, One Hope" (Joe Average)

1996. 11th International Conference on AIDS, Vancouver.
1682 **645** 45c. multicoloured . . . 70 70

646 Skookum Jim Mason and Bonanza Creek

1996. Centenary of Yukon Gold Rush. Multicoloured.
1685 45c. Type **646** . . . . . 80 1·00
1686 45c. Prospector and boats on Lake Laberge . . . 80 1·00
1687 45c. Superintendent Sam Steele (N.W.M.P.) and U.S.A.-Canada border . . 80 1·00
1688 45c. Dawson saloon . . . . 80 1·00
1689 45c. Miner with rocker box and sluice . . . . . . 80 1·00

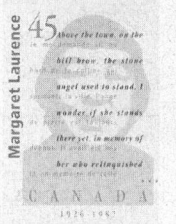

647 Patchwork Quilt Maple Leaf   **648** Ethel Catherwood (high jump), 1928

1996. Canada Day. Self-adhesive. Imperf.
1690 **647** 45c. multicoloured . . . 50 50

1996. Canadian Olympic Gold Medal Winners. Multicoloured.
1691 45c. Type **648** 80 85
1692 45c. Etienne Desmarteau (56lb weight throw), 1904 80 85
1693 45c. Fanny Rosenfeld (400 m relay), 1928 . . 80 85
1694 45c. Gerald Ouellette (small bore rifle, prone), 1956 . . 80 85
1695 45c. Percy Williams (100 and 200 m), 1928 . . 80 85

649 Indian Totems, City Skyline, Forest and Mountains   **650** Canadian Heraldic Symbols

1996. 125th Anniv of British Columbia.
1696 **649** 45c. multicoloured . . . 50 50

1996. 22nd International Congress of Genealogical and Heraldic Sciences, Ottawa.
1697 **650** 45c. multicoloured . . . 50 50

652 Interlocking Jigsaw Pieces and Hands

1996. Literacy Campaign.
1699 **652** 45c.+5c. mult 60 65

653 Edouard Montpetit and Montreal University

1996. Edouard Montpetit (academic) Commem.
1700 **653** 45c. multicoloured . . . 50 50

654 Winnie and Lt. Colebourn, 1914

1996. Stamp Collecting Month. Winnie the Pooh. Multicoloured.
1701 45c. Type **654** . . . . . 90 1·10
1702 45c. Christopher Robin Milne and teddy bear, 1925 . . . . 90 1·10
1703 45c. Illustration from "Winnie the Pooh", 1926 90 1·10
1704 45c. Winnie the Pooh at Walt Disney World, 1996 90 1·10

655 Margaret Laurence   **656** Children tobogganing

1996. Canadian Authors.
1706 **655** 45c. multicoloured . . . 60 75
1707 – 45c. black, grey and red 60 75
1708 – 45c. multicoloured . . . 60 75
1709 – 45c. multicoloured . . . 60 75
1710 – 45c. multicoloured . . . 60 75
DESIGNS: No. 1707, Donald G. Creighton; 1708, Gabrielle Roy; 1709, Felix-Antoine Savard; 1710, Thomas C. Haliburton.

1996. Christmas. 50th Anniv of U.N.I.C.E.F. Multicoloured.
1711 45c. Type **656** 50 20
1712 52c. Father Christmas skiing 80 1·00
1713 90c. Couple ice-skating . . . 1·40 2·00

657 Head of Ox   **659** Abbe Charles-Emile Gadbois

658 Man and Boy with Bike, and A. J. and J. W. Billes (company founders)

1997. Chinese New Year ("Year of the Ox").
1714 **657** 45c. multicoloured . . . 85 90

1997. Birds (2nd series). As T **643**. Multicoloured.
1717 45c. Mountain bluebird . . . 80 85
1718 45c. Western grebe 80 85
1719 45c. Northern gannet 80 85
1720 45c. Scarlet tanager 80 85

1997. Canadian Art (10th series). As T **550**. Multicoloured.
1721 90c. "York Boat on Lake Winnipeg, 1930" (Walter Phillips) . . . . 1·50 2·00

1997. 75th Anniv of the Canadian Tire Corporation.
1722 **658** 45c. multicoloured . . . 80 50

1997. Abbe Charles-Emile Gadbois (musicologist) Commemoration.
1723 **659** 45c. multicoloured . . . 50 50

660 Blue Poppy   **662** Osgoode Hall and Seal of Law School

661 Nurse attending Patient

1997. "Quebec in Bloom" International Floral Festival.
1724 **660** 45c. multicoloured . . . 55 55

1997. Centenary of Victorian Order of Nurses.
1725 **661** 45c. multicoloured . . . 60 50

1997. Bicentenary of Law Society of Upper Canada.
1726 **662** 45c. multicoloured . . . 60 50

663 Great White Shark

1997. Ocean Fishes. Multicoloured.
1727 45c. Type **663** . . . . . . 1·00 1·25
1728 45c. Pacific halibut . . . 1·00 1·25
1729 45c. Common sturgeon . . . 1·00 1·25
1730 45c. Blue-finned tuna . . . 1·00 1·25

664 Lighthouse and Confederation Bridge

1997. Opening of Confederation Bridge, Northumberland Strait. Multicoloured.
1731 45c. Type **664** 90 90
1732 45c. Confederation Bridge and great blue heron . . . 90 90

665 Gilles Villeneuve in Ferrari T-3

1997. 15th Death Anniv of Gilles Villeneuve (racing car driver). Multicoloured.
1733 45c. Type **665** . . . . . . 1·00 60
1734 90c. Villeneuve in Ferrari T-4 . . . . . . 1·75 2·00

666 Globe and the "Matthew"

1997. 500th Anniv of John Cabot's Discovery of North America.
1736 **666** 45c. multicoloured . . . 75 55

667 Sea to Sky Highway, British Columbia, and Skier

1997. Scenic Highways (1st series). Multicoloured.
1737 45c. Type **667** . . . . . . 1·00 1·10
1738 45c. Cabot Trail, Nova Scotia, and rug-making 1·00 1·10
1739 45c. Wine route, Ontario, and glasses of wine . . . 1·00 1·10
1740 45c. Highway 34, Saskatchewan, and cowboy . . . . . . 1·00 1·10
See also Nos. 1810/13 and 1876/9.

668 Kettle, Ski-bike, Lounger and Plastic Cases

1997. 20th Congress of International Council of Societies for Industrial Design.
1741 **668** 45c. multicoloured . . . 60 50

669 Caber Thrower, Bagpiper, Drummer and Highland Dancer

1997. 50th Anniv of Glengarry Highland Games, Ontario.
1742 **669** 45c. multicoloured . . . 75 50

670 Knights of Columbus Emblem

1997. Centenary of Knights of Columbus (welfare charity) in Canada.
1743 **670** 45c. multicoloured . . . 50 50

671 Postal and Telephone Workers with P.T.T.I. Emblem

1997. 28th World Congress of Postal, Telegraph and Telephone International Staff Federation, Montreal.
1744 **671** 45c. multicoloured . . . 50 50

672 C.Y.A.P. Logo

1997. Canada's Year of Asia Pacific.
1745 **672** 45c. multicoloured . . . 70 50

673 Paul Henderson celebrating Goal

1997. 25th Anniv of Canada–U.S.S.R. Ice Hockey Series. Multicoloured.
1746 45c. Type **673** 55 60
1747 45c. Canadian team celebrating 55 60

674 Martha Black

1997. Federal Politicians. Multicoloured.
1748 45c. Type **674** 70 90
1749 45c. Lionel Chevrier 70 90
1750 45c. Judy LaMarsh 70 90
1751 45c. Real Caouette 70 90

675 Vampire and Bat

1997. The Supernatural. Centenary of Publication of Bram Stoker's "Dracula". Multicoloured.
1752 45c. Type **675** 60 75
1753 45c. Werewolf 60 75
1754 45c. Ghost 60 75
1755 45c. Goblin 60 75

676 Grizzly Bear

1997. Mammals. Multicoloured.
1756 $1 Loon (47 × 39 mm) . . . 90 95
1757 $2 Polar bear (47 × 39 mm) . . . 1·75 1·90
1758 $8 Type **676** . . . . . . 7·50 8·00

677 "Our Lady of the Rosary" (detail, Holy Rosary Cathedral, Vancouver)

1997. Christmas. Stained Glass Windows. Multicoloured.
1763a 45c. Type **677** 40 45
1764a 52c. "Nativity" (detail, Leith United Church, Ontario) . . . 50 70
1765a 90c. "Life of the Blessed Virgin" (detail, St. Stephen's Ukrainian Catholic Church, Calgary) . . . . . . 85 1·25

678 Livestock and Produce

1997. 75th Anniv of Royal Agricultural Winter Fair, Toronto.
1766 **678** 45c. multicoloured . . . 75 55

679 Tiger

1998. Chinese New Year ("Year of the Tiger").
1767 **679** 45c. multicoloured . . . 60 50

680 John Robarts (Ontario, 1961–71)   **681** Maple Leaf

1998. Canadian Provincial Premiers. Multicoloured.
1769 45c. Type **680** 50 60
1770 45c. Jean Lesage (Quebec, 1960–66) . . . 50 60
1771 45c. John McNair (New Brunswick, 1940–52) . . . 50 60
1772 45c. Tommy Douglas (Saskatchewan, 1944–61) 50 60
1773 45c. Joseph Smallwood (Newfoundland, 1949–72) 50 60
1774 45c. Angus MacDonald (Nova Scotia, 1933–40, 1945–54) . . . 50 60
1775 45c. W. A. C. Bennett (British Columbia, 1960–66) . . . 50 60
1776 45c. Ernest Manning (Alberta, 1943–68) . . . 50 60
1777 45c. John Bracken (Manitoba, 1922–43) . . . 50 60
1778 45c. J. Walter Jones (Prince Edward Island, 1943–53) 50 60

1998. Birds (3rd series). As T **643**. Multicoloured.
1779 45c. Hairy woodpecker . . . 80 85
1780 45c. Great crested flycatcher 80 85
1781 45c. Eastern screech-owl . . 80 85
1782 45c. Gray-crowned rosy-finch 80 85

1998. Self-adhesive Automatic Cash Machine Stamps. Imperf.
1783 **681** 45c. multicoloured . . . 45 40
For stamps in this design, but without "POSTAGE POSTES" at top left see Nos. 1836/40.

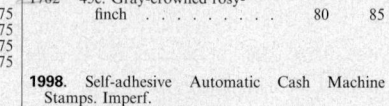

682 Coquihalla Orange Fly

1998. Fishing Flies. Multicoloured.
1784 45c. Type **682** 80 80
1785 45c. Steelhead Bee 80 80
1786 45c. Dark Montreal 80 80
1787 45c. Lady Amherst 80 80
1788 45c. Coho Blue 80 80
1789 45c. Cosseboom Special . . 80 80

683 Mineral Excavation, Oil Rig and Pickaxe   **684** 1898 2c. Imperial Penny Postage Stamp and Postmaster General Sir William Mulock

1998. Centenary of Canadian Institute of Mining, Metallurgy and Petroleum.
1790 **683** 45c. multicoloured . . . 60 50

1998. Centenary of Imperial Penny Postage.
1791 **684** 45c. multicoloured . . . 75 55

685 Two Sumo Wrestlers

1998. 1st Canadian Sumo Basho (tournament), Vancouver. Multicoloured.
1792 45c. Type **685** 65 75
1793 45c. Sumo wrestler in ceremonial ritual 65 75

686 St. Peters Canal, Nova Scotia   **687** Staff of Aesculapius and Cross

1998. Canadian Canals. Multicoloured.
1795 45c. Type **686** 90 90
1796 45c. St. Ours Canal, Quebec 90 90
1797 45c. Port Carling Lock, Ontario . . . 90 90
1798 45c. Lock on Rideau Canal, Ontario . . . 90 90
1799 45c. Towers and platform of Peterborough Lift Lock, Trent–Severn Waterway, Ontario . . . 90 90
1800 45c. Chambly Canal, Quebec . . . 90 90
1801 45c. Lachine Canal, Quebec 90 90
1802 45c. Rideau Canal in winter, Ontario . . . 90 90
1803 45c. Boat on Big Chute incline railway, Trent–Severn Waterway, Ontario 90 90
1804 45c. Sault Ste. Marie Canal, Ontario . . . 90 90

1998. Canadian Health Professionals.
1805 **687** 45c. multicoloured . . . 75 55

688 Policeman of 1873 and Visit to Indian Village

1998. 125th Anniv of Royal Canadian Mounted Police. Multicoloured.
1806   45c. Type **688** 60   75
1807   45c. Policewoman of 1998 and aspects of modern law enforcement 60   75

689 William J. Roue (designer) and "Bluenose" (schooner)

1998. William James Roue (naval architect) Commemoration.
1809 **689** 45c. multicoloured . . . 50   50

1998. Scenic Highways (2nd series). As T **667**. Multicoloured.
1810   45c. Dempster Highway, Yukon, and caribou . . . 55   65
1811   45c. Dinosaur Trail, Alberta, and skeleton . . . 55   65
1812   45c. River Valley Drive, New Brunswick, and fern . . . 55   65
1813   45c. Blue Heron Route, Prince Edward Island, and lobster 55   65

Peinture
690 "Painting" (Jean-Paul Riopelle)

1998. 50th Anniv of "Refus Global" (manifesto of The Automatistes group of artists). Multicoloured. Self-adhesive. Imperf.
1814   45c. Type **690** 90   90
1815   45c. "La derniere campagne de Napoleon" (Fernand Leduc) (37 × 31½ mm) . . 90   90
1816   45c. "Jet fuligineux sur noir torture" (Jean-Paul Mousseau) 90   90
1817   45c. "Le fond du garde-robe" (Pierre Gauvreau) (29½ × 42 mm) 90   90
1818   45c. "Joie lacustre" (Paul-Emile Borduas) 90   90
1819   45c. "Seafarers Union" (Marcelle Ferron) (36 × 34 mm) 90   90
1820   45c. "Le tumulte a la machoire crispee" (Marcel Barbeau) (36 × 34 mm) . . 90   90

691 Napoleon- Alexandre Comeau (naturalist)

1998. Legendary Canadians. Multicoloured.
1821   45c. Type **691** 55   65
1822   45c. Phyllis Munday (mountaineer) 55   65
1823   45c. Bill Mason (film-maker) 55   65
1824   45c. Harry Red Foster (sports commentator) . . 55   65

1998. Canadian Art (11th series). As T **550**. Multicoloured.
1825   90c. "The Farmer's Family" (Bruno Bobak) 80   1·10

692 Indian Wigwam

1998. Canadian Houses. Multicoloured.
1826   45c. Type **692** 50   60
1827   45c. Settler sod hut . . . 50   60
1828   45c. Maison Saint-Gabriel (17th-century farmhouse), Quebec 50   60
1829   45c. Queen Anne style brick house, Ontario 50   60
1830   45c. Terrace of town houses 50   60
1831   45c. Prefabricated house . 50   60
1832   45c. Veterans' houses . . 50   60
1833   45c. Modern bungalow . . 50   60
1834   45c. Healthy House, Toronto 50   60

693 University of Ottawa

1998. 150th Anniv of University of Ottawa.
1835 **693** 45c. multicoloured . . . 50   50

1998. As T **681**, but without "POSTAGE POSTES" at top left. Self-adhesive gum, imperf (46c.) or ordinary gum, perf (others).
1839 **681** 45c. multicoloured . . . 65   75
1840   46c. multicoloured . . . 70   80
1836   55c. multicoloured . . . 50   55
1837   73c. multicoloured . . . 65   70
1838   95c. multicoloured . . . 85   90

694 Performing Animals

1998. Canadian Circus. Multicoloured.
1851   45c. Type **694** 90   90
1852   45c. Flying trapeze and acrobat on horseback . . 90   90
1853   45c. Lion tamer 90   90
1854   45c. Acrobats and trapeze artists 90   90

695 John Peters Humphrey (author of original Declaration draft)

1998. 50th Anniv of Universal Declaration of Human Rights.
1856 **695** 45c. multicoloured . . . 50   50

696 H.M.C.S. "Sackville" (corvette)

1998. 75th Anniv of Canadian Naval Reserve. Multicoloured.
1857   45c. Type **696** 50   65
1858   45c. H.M.C.S. "Shawinigan" (coastal defence vessel) . . 50   65

697 Angel blowing Trumpet   **698** Rabbit

1998. Christmas. Statues of Angels. Multicoloured.
1859   45c. Type **697** 40   40
1860   52c. Adoring Angel . . . 60   55
1861   90c. Angel at prayer 70   1·00

1999. Chinese New Year ("Year of the Rabbit").
1862 **698** 46c. multicoloured . . . 50   50

699 Stylized Mask and Curtain   **701** "Marco Polo" (full-rigged ship)

1999. 50th Anniv of Le Theatre du Rideau Vert.
1864 **699** 46c. multicoloured . . . 50   50

1999. Birds (4th series). As T **643**. Multicoloured. Ordinary or self-adhesive gum.
1865   46c. Northern goshawk . . 60   70
1866   46c. Red-winged blackbird . 60   70
1867   46c. American goldfinch . . 60   70
1868   46c. Sandhill crane . . . 60   70

700 "The Raven and the First Men" (B. Reid) and The Great Hall

1999. 50th Anniv of University of British Columbia Museum of Anthropology.
1873 **700** 46c. multicoloured . . . 50   50

1999. Canada–Australia Joint Issue. "Marco Polo" (emigrant ship).
1874 **701** 46c. multicoloured . . . 50   50

1999. Scenic Highways (3rd series). As T **667**. Multicoloured.
1876   46c. Route 132, Quebec, and hang-glider 55   60
1877   46c. Yellowhead Highway, Manitoba, and bison . . 55   60
1878   46c. Dempster Highway, Northwest Territories, and Indian village elder . . 55   60
1879   46c. The Discovery Trail, Newfoundland, and whale's tailfin 55   60

702 Inuit Children and Landscape

1999. Creation of Nunavut Territory.
1880 **702** 46c. multicoloured . . . 50   50

703 Elderly Couple on Country Path

1999. International Year of Older Persons.
1881 **703** 46c. multicoloured . . . 50   50

704 Khanda (Sikh symbol)   **705** "Arethusa bulbosa" (orchid)

1999. Centenary of Sikhs in Canada.
1882 **704** 46c. multicoloured . . . 50   50

1999. 16th World Orchid Conference, Vancouver. Multicoloured.
1883   46c. Type **705** 60   60

1884   46c. "Amerorchis rotundifolia" 60   60
1885   46c. "Cypripedium pubescens" 60   60
1886   46c. "Platanthera psycodes" 60   60

706 Bookbinding   **707** "Northern Dancer" (racehorse)

1999. Traditional Trades. Multicoloured.
(a) Ordinary gum.
1887   1c. Type **706** 10   10
1888   2c. Decorative ironwork . . 10   10
1889   3c. Glass-blowing 10   10
1890   4c. Oyster farming 10   10
1891   5c. Weaving 10   10
1892   9c. Quilting 10   10
1893   10c. Wood carving 10   15
1894   25c. Leatherworking . . . 20   25
(b) Self-adhesive.
1895   65c. Jewellery making (horiz) 60   65
1896   77c. Basket weaving (horiz) 70   75
1897 $1.25 Wood-carving (horiz) 1·10   1·25

1999. Canadian Horses. Multicoloured. Ordinary or self-adhesive gum.
1903   46c. Type **707** 60   70
1904   46c. "Kingsway Skoal" (rodeo horse) 60   70
1905   46c. "Big Ben" (show jumper) 60   70
1906   46c. "Armbro Flight" (trotter) 60   70

708 Logo engraved on Limestone   **709** Athletics

1999. 150th Anniv of Barreau du Quebec (Quebec lawyers' association).
1911 **708** 46c. multicoloured . . . 50   50

1999. Canadian Art (12th series). As T **550**. Mult.
1912   95c. "Coq licorne" (Jean Dallaire) . . . . . . 1·00   1·25

1999. 13th Pan-American Games, Winnipeg. Mult.
1913   46c. Type **709** 60   70
1914   46c. Cycling 60   70
1915   46c. Swimming 60   70
1916   46c. Football 60   70

710 Female Rower

1999. 23rd World Rowing Championships, St. Catharines.
1918 **710** 46c. multicoloured . . . 50   50

711 U.P.U. Emblem and World Map

1999. 125th Anniv of Universal Postal Union.
1919 **711** 46c. multicoloured . . . 50   50

712 De Havilland Mosquito F.B. VI

1999. 75th Anniv of Canadian Air Force. Mult.
1920   46c. Type **712** 50   55
1921   46c. Sopwith F.1 Camel . . 50   55
1922   46c. De Havilland Canada DHC-3 Otter 50   55
1923   46c. De Havilland Canada CC-108 Caribou . . . 50   55
1924   46c. Canadair CL-28 Argus Mk 2 50   55
1925   46c. Canadair (North American) F-86 Sabre 6 50   55

1926	46c. McDonnell Douglas CF-18	50	55
1927	46c. Sopwith 5.F.1 Dolphin	50	55
1928	46c. Armstrong Whitworth Siskin IIIA	50	55
1929	46c. Canadian Vickers (Northrop) Delta II	50	55
1930	46c. Sikorsky CH-124A Sea King helicopter	50	55
1931	46c. Vickers-Armstrong Wellington Mk II	50	55
1932	46c. Avro Anson Mk I	50	55
1933	46c. Canadair (Lockheed) CF-104G Starfighter	50	55
1934	46c. Burgess-Dunne	50	55
1935	46c. Avro 504K	50	55

713 Fokker DR-1

1999. 50th Anniv of Canadian International Air Show. Multicoloured.

1936	46c. Type 713	60	70
1937	46c. H101 Salto glider	60	70
1938	46c. De Havilland DH100 Vampire Mk III	60	70
1939	46c. Wing walker on Stearman A-75	60	70

Nos. 1936/9 were printed together, se-tenant, forming a composite design which includes a nine-plane Snowbird formation of Canadair CT114 Tutor in the background.

714 N.A.T.O. Emblem and National Flags

1999. 50th Anniv of North Atlantic Treaty Organization.
1940 714 46c. multicoloured . . . 50 50

715 Man ploughing on Book

1999. Centenary of Frontier College (workers' education organization).
1941 715 46c. multicoloured . . . 50 50

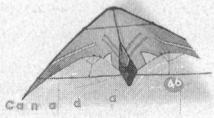

716 Master Control Sports Kite

1999. Stamp Collecting Month. Kites. Mult.

1942	46c. Type 716	50	55
1943	46c. Indian Garden Flying Carpet (irregular rectangle, 35½ × 32 mm)	50	55
1944	46c. Gibson Girl box kite (horiz, 38½ × 25 mm)	50	55
1945	46c. Dragon Centipede (oval, 39 × 29 mm)	50	55

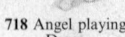

718 Angel playing Drum   720 Millennium Partnership Programme Logo

1999. Christmas. Victorian Angels. Multicoloured.

1949	46c. Type 718	50	20
1950	55c. Angel with toys	65	60
1951	95c. Angel with star	1·40	1·75

2000. Canada Millennium Partnership Programme.
1956 720 46c. red, green and blue 50 50

721 Chinese Dragon

2000. Chinese New Year ("Year of the Dragon"). Multicoloured.
1957 721 46c. multicoloured . . . 50 50

722 Wayne Gretzky (ice-hockey player)

2000. 50th National Hockey League All-Star Game. Multicoloured.

1963	46c. Type 722	55	60
1964	46c. Gordie Howe (No. 9 in white jersey)	55	60
1965	46c. Maurice Richard (No. 9 in blue and red jersey)	55	60
1966	46c. Doug Harvey (No. 2)	55	60
1967	46c. Bobby Orr (No. 4)	55	60
1968	46c. Jacques Plante (No. 1)	55	60

See also Nos. 2052/7 and 2118/23.

2000. Birds (5th series). As T 643. Multicoloured. Ordinary or self-adhesive gum.

1974	46c. Canadian warbler	55	60
1975	46c. Osprey	55	60
1976	46c. Pacific loon	55	60
1977	46c. Blue jay	55	60

723 Judges and Supreme Court Building

2000. 125th Anniv of Supreme Court of Canada.
1986 723 46c. multicoloured . . . 50 50

724 Lethbridge Bridge, Synthetic Rubber Plant, X-ray of Heart Pacemaker and Microwave Radio System

2000. 75th Anniv of Ceremony for Calling of an Engineer.
1987 724 46c. multicoloured . . . 50 50
Each vertical pair completes the engineer's ring as shown on Type 274.

725

2000. "Picture Postage" Greetings Stamps. Self-adhesive.
1988 725 46c. multicoloured . . . 40 45
No. 1988 was issued to include appropriate greetings labels which could be inserted into the rectangular space on each stamp.
See also Nos. 2045 and 2099.

726 Coastal-style Mailboxes in Autumn

2000. Traditional Rural Mailboxes. Multicoloured.

1989	46c. Type 726	50	55
1990	46c. House and cow-shaped mailboxes in springtime	50	55
1991	46c. Tractor-shaped mailbox in summertime	50	55
1992	46c. Barn and duck-shaped mailboxes in winter	50	55

727 Gorge and Fir Tree

2000. Canadian Rivers and Lakes. Multicoloured. Self-adhesive.

1993	55c. Type 727	60	65
1994	55c. Lake and water lilies	60	65
1995	55c. Glacier and reflected mountains	60	65
1996	55c. Estuary and aerial view	60	65
1997	55c. Waterfall and forest edge	60	65
1998	95c. Iceberg and mountain river	95	1·10
1999	95c. Rapids and waterfall	95	1·10
2000	95c. Moraine and river	95	1·10
2001	95c. Shallows and waves on lake	95	1·10
2002	95c. Forest sloping to waters edge and tree	95	1·10

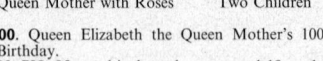

728 Queen Elizabeth the   729 Teenager with
Queen Mother with Roses   Two Children

2000. Queen Elizabeth the Queen Mother's 100th Birthday.
2003 728 95c. multicoloured . . . 1·10 1·25

2000. Centenary of Boys and Girls Clubs of Canada.
2004 729 46c. multicoloured . . . 50 50

730 Clouds over Rockies and Symbol

2000. 57th General Conference Session of Seventh-day Adventist Church, Toronto.
2005 730 46c. multicoloured . . . 50 50

731 "Space Travellers and Canadian Flag" (Rosalie Anne Nardelli)

2000. "Stampin' the Future" (children's stamp design competition). Multicoloured.

2006	46c. Type 731	60	60
2007	46c. "Travelling to the Moon" (Sarah Lutgen)	60	60
2008	46c. "Astronauts in shuttle" (Andrew Wright)	60	60
2009	46c. "Children completing Canada as jigsaw" (Christine Weera)	60	60

2000. Canadian Art (13th series). As T 550. Mult.
2011 95c. "The Artist at Niagara, 1858" (Cornelius Krieghoff) . . . . . 1·10 1·25

732 Tall Ships, Halifax Harbour

2000. Tall Ships Race. Multicoloured. Self-adhesive.

2012	46c. Type 732	55	65
2013	46c. Tall ships, Halifax Harbour (face value top right)	55	65

Nos. 2012/13 are arranged as five se-tenant pairs on a background photograph of Halifax Harbour.

733 Workers, Factory and Transport

2000. Centenary of Department of Labour.
2014 733 46c. multicoloured . . . 50 50

734 Petro-Canada Sign, Oil Rig and Consumers

2000. 25th Anniv of Petro-Canada (oil company). Self-adhesive.
2015 734 46c. multicoloured . . . 50 50

735 Narwhal

2000. Whales. Multicoloured.

2016	46c. Type 735	60	60
2017	46c. Blue whale (Balaenoptera musculus)	60	60
2018	46c. Bowhead whale (Balaena mysticetus)	60	60
2019	46c. White whales (Delphinapterus leucas)	60	60

Nos. 2016/19 were printed together, se-tenant, with the backgrounds forming an overall composite design.

736

2000. "Picture Postage" Christmas Greetings. Self-adhesive.
2020 736 46c. multicoloured . . . 40 45
See also Nos. 2045/9 and 2099/103.

737 "The Nativity"   738 Lieut.-Col. Sam
(Susie Matthias)   Steele, Lord Strathcona's Horse

2000. Christmas. Religious Paintings by Mouth and Foot Artists. Multicoloured.

2021	46c. Type 737	50	20
2022	55c. "The Nativity and Christmas Star" (Michael Guillemette)	65	60
2023	95c. "Mary and Joseph journeying to Bethlehem" (David Allan Carter)	1·25	1·50

2000. Canadian Regiments. Multicoloured.

2024	46c. Type 738	55	60
2025	46c. Drummer, Voltigeurs de Quebec	55	60

739 Red Fox   740 Maple Leaves

2000. Wildlife. Multicoloured.

2026	60c. Type 739	55	60
2027	75c. Grey wolf	70	75
2028	$1.05 White-tailed deer	95	1·00

2000. Self-adhesive coil stamp.

2029	**740**	47c. multicoloured	40	45
2030		48c. multicoloured	40	45

2000. "Picture Postage" Greetings Stamps. As T **725** and **736**. Multicoloured. Self-adhesive.

2045	47c. Type **725**	40	45
2046	47c. Type **736**	40	45
2047	47c. Roses frame	40	45
2048	47c. Mahogany frame	40	45
2049	47c. Silver frame	40	45

741 Green Jade Snake

2001. Chinese New Year. ("Year of the Snake").

2050	**741**	47c. multicoloured	50	50

2001. National Hockey League. All-Star Game Players (1st series). As T **722**. Multicoloured.

2052	47c. Jean Beliveau (wearing No. 4)	55	55
2053	47c. Terry Sawchuk (on one knee)	55	55
2054	47c. Eddie Shore (wearing No. 2)	55	55
2055	47c. Denis Potvin (wearing No. 5)	55	55
2056	47c. Bobby Hull (wearing No. 9)	55	55
2057	47c. Syl Apps (in Toronto jersey)	55	55

See also Nos. 2118/23.

2001. Birds (6th series). As T **643**. Multicoloured. Ordinary or self-adhesive gum.

2058	47c. Golden eagle	55	55
2059	47c. Arctic tern	55	55
2060	47c. Rock ptarmigan	55	55
2061	47c. Lapland longspur	55	55

742 Highjumping

2001. 4th Francophonie Games. Multicoloured.

2066	47c. Type **742**	55	55
2067	47c. Folk dancing	55	55

743 Ice Dancing

2001. World Figure Skating Championships, Vancouver. Multicoloured.

2068	47c. Type **743**	55	55
2069	47c. Pairs	55	55
2070	47c. Men's singles	55	55
2071	47c. Women's singles	55	55

744 3d. Beaver Stamp of 1851

2001. 150th Anniv of the Canadian Postal Service.

2072	**744**	47c. multicoloured	50	50

745 Toronto Blue Jay Emblem, Maple Leaf and Baseball

2001. 25th Season of the Toronto Blue Jays (baseball team). Self-adhesive.

2073	**745**	47c. multicoloured	50	50

746 North and South America on Globe | 748 Christ on Palm Sunday and Khachkar (stone cross)

747 Butchart Gardens, British Columbia

2001. Summit of the Americas, Quebec.

2074	**746**	47c. multicoloured	50	50

2001. Tourist Attractions. Multicoloured. Self-adhesive.

2075	60c. Type **747**	60	65
2076	60c. Apple Blossom Festival, Nova Scotia	60	65
2077	60c. White Pass and Yukon Route	60	65
2078	60c. Sugar Bushes, Quebec	60	65
2079	60c. Court House, Niagra-on-the-Lake, Ontario	60	65
2080	$1.05 The Forks, Winnipeg, Manitoba	1·10	1·25
2081	$1.05 Barkerville, British Colombia	1·10	1·25
2082	$1.05 Canadian Tulip Festival, Ontario	1·10	1·25
2083	$1.05 Auyuittuq National Park, Nunavut	1·10	1·25
2084	$1.05 Signal Hill, St. John's, Newfoundland	1·10	1·25

2001. 1700th Anniv of Armenian Church.

2085	**748**	47c. multicoloured	40	45

749 Cadets, Mackenzie Building and Military Equipment

2001. 125th Anniv of Royal Military College of Canada.

2086	**749**	47c. multicoloured	40	45

750 Pole-vaulting | 751 "Pierre Trudeau" (Myfanwy Pavelic)

2001. 8th International Amateur Athletic Federation World Championships, Edmonton. Multicoloured.

2087	47c. Type **750**	40	45
2088	47c. Sprinting	40	45

2001. Pierre Trudeau (former Prime Minister) Commemoration.

2089	**751**	47c. multicoloured	40	45

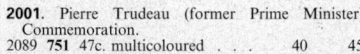

752 "Morden Centennial" Rose (⅔-size illustration)

2001. Canadian Roses. Multicoloured. Self-adhesive.

2091	47c. Type **752**	40	45
2092	47c. "Agnes"	40	45
2093	47c. "Champlain"	40	45
2094	47c. "Canadian White Star"	40	45

753 Ottawa Chief Hassaki addressing Peace Delegates

2001. 300th Anniv of Great Peace Treaty of Montreal between American Indians and New France.

2096	**753**	47c. multicoloured	40	45

2001. Canadian Art (14th series). As T **550**. Multicoloured.

2097	$1.05 "The Space Between Columns 21 (Italian)" (Jack Shadbolt)	95	1·00

754 Clown juggling with Crutches and Handicapped Boy

2001. The Shriners (charitable organization) Commemoration.

2098	**754**	47c. multicoloured		

755 Toys and Flowers

2001. "Picture Postage" Greetings Stamps. Frames as Nos. 2045/7 and 2049, but each inscr "Domestic Lettermail Postes-lettres du regime interieur". Multicoloured. Self-adhesive.

2099	– As Type **725**	40	45
2100	– As Type **736**	40	45
2101	– Type **755**	40	45
2102	– Roses frame	40	45
2103	– Silver frame	40	45

756 Jean Gascon and Jean-Louis Roux (founders of Theatre du Nouveau Monde, Montreal)

2001. Theatre Anniversaries. Multicoloured.

2104	47c. Type **756** (50th anniv)	40	45
2105	47c. Ambrose Small (founder of Grand Theatre, London, Ontario) (centenary)	40	45

757 Hot Air Balloons

2001. Stamp Collecting Month. Hot Air Balloons. Multicoloured, background colours given below. Self-adhesive.

2106	47c. Type **757** (green background)	40	45
2107	47c. Balloons with lavender background	40	45
2108	47c. Balloons with mauve background	40	45
2109	47c. Balloons with bistre background	40	45

758 Horse-drawn Sleigh and Christmas Lights

2001. Christmas. Festive Lights. Multicoloured.

2110	47c. Type **758**	40	45
2111	60c. Ice skaters and Christmas lights	55	60
2112	$1.05 Children with snowman and Christmas lights	95	1·00

759 Pattern of Ys Logo

2001. 150th Anniv of Y.M.C.A. in Canada.

2113	**759**	47c. multicoloured	40	45

760 Statues from Canadian War Memorial, Ottawa and Badge

2001. 75th Anniv of Royal Canadian Legion.

2114	**760**	47c. multicoloured	40	45

761 Queen Elizabeth and Maple Leaf

2002. Golden Jubilee.

2115	**761**	48c. multicoloured	40	45

762 Horse and Bamboo Leaves | 763 Speed Skating

2002. Chinese New Year ("Year of the Horse"). Multicoloured.

2116	**762**	48c. multicoloured	40	45

2002. National Hockey League. All-Star Game Players (2nd series). As T **722**. Multicoloured.

2118	48c. Tim Horton (wearing Maple Leaf No. 7 jersey)	40	45
2119	48c. Guy Lafleur (wearing Canadiens No. 10 jersey)	40	45
2120	48c. Howie Morenz (wearing Canadiens jersey and brown gloves)	40	45
2121	48c. Glenn Hall (wearing Chicago Blackhawks jersey)	40	45
2122	48c. Red Kelly (wearing Maple Leaf No. 4 jersey)	40	45
2123	48c. Phil Esposito (wearing Boston Bruins No. 7 jersey)	40	45

2002. Winter Olympic Games, Salt Lake City. Multicoloured.

2124	48c. Type **763**	40	45
2125	48c. Curling	40	45
2126	48c. Aerial skiing	40	45
2127	48c. Women's ice hockey	40	45

764 Lion Symbol of Governor General and Rideau Hall, Ottawa

2002. 50th Anniv of First Canadian Governor-General.

2128	**764**	48c. multicoloured	40	45

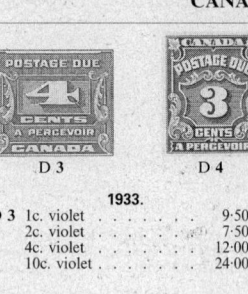

765 University of Manitoba (125th Anniv)

2002. Canadian Universities' Anniversaries.

2129	**765**	48c. multicoloured	40	45

2002. Canadian Art (15th series). As T **550**. Multicoloured.

2133		$1.25 "Church and Horse" (Alex Colville)	1·25	1·40

OFFICIAL STAMPS

1949. Optd **O.H.M.S.**

O162	**111**	1c. green (postage)	1·75	2·25
O163	**112**	2c. brown	12·00	12·00
O164	–	3c. purple (No. 378)	1·25	1·40
O165	**112**	4c. red	2·00	1·40
O166	–	10c. green (No. 402)	3·75	15
O167	–	14c. brown (No. 403)	4·50	2·00
O168	–	20c. grey (No. 404)	12·00	60
O169	–	50c. green (No. 405)	£160	£120
O170	–	$1 purple (No. 406)	45·00	48·00
O171	–	7c. blue (No. 407) (air)	24·00	7·00

1949. Optd **O.H.M.S.**

O172	**135**	1c. green	1·25	1·00
O173	–	2c. brown (No. 415)	2·25	1·50
O174	–	3c. purple (No. 416)	1·50	1·00
O175	–	4c. red (No. 417)	1·75	15
O176	–	5c. blue (No. 418)	3·00	2·00
O177	**141**	50c. green	32·00	28·00

1950. Optd **G**.

O178	**135**	1c. green (postage)	80	10
O179	–	2c. brown (No. 415)	1·75	1·75
O180	–	2c. green (No. 415a)	1·75	10
O181	–	3c. purple (No. 416)	1·50	10
O183	–	4c. red (No. 417)	1·90	10
O184	–	5c. blue (No. 418)	2·50	60
O193	**153**	7c. blue	1·75	2·00
O185	–	10c. green (No. 402)	3·00	10
O191	**142**	10c. purple	2·75	10
O186	–	14c. brown (No. 403)	12·00	3·50
O187	–	20c. grey (No. 404)	20·00	20
O194	–	20c. grey (No. 441)	2·00	10
O188	**141**	50c. green	11·00	10·00
O189	–	$1 purple (No. 406)	65·00	65·00
O192	–	$1 blue (No. 433)	60·00	65·00
O190	–	7c. blue (No. 407) (air)	24·00	13·00

1953. First Queen Elizabeth II stamps optd **G**.

O196	**158**	1c. brown	15	10
O197		2c. green	20	10
O198		3c. red	20	10
O199		4c. violet	30	10
O200		5c. blue	30	10

1953. Pictorial stamps optd **G**.

O206	**165**	10c. brown	40	10
O207	–	20c. green (No. 488)	2·25	10
O201	**160**	50c. green	3·00	2·00
O195	**154**	$1 black	10·00	11·00

1955. Second Queen Elizabeth II stamps optd **G**.

O202	**161**	1c. brown	40	20
O203		2c. green	15	10
O204		4c. violet	40	10
O205		5c. blue	15	10

1963. Third Queen Elizabeth II stamps optd **G**.

O208	**215**	1c. brown	40	3·75
O209		2c. green	40	3·50
O210		4c. red	40	2·00
O211		5c. blue	40	1·00

OFFICIAL SPECIAL DELIVERY STAMPS

1950. Optd **O.H.M.S.**

OS20	10c. green (No. S15)	17·00	22·00

1950. Optd **G**.

OS21	10c. green (No. S15)	26·00	27·00

POSTAGE DUE STAMPS

D 1

D 2

1906.

D1	**D 1**	1c. violet	8·50	2·75
D3		2c. violet	18·00	1·00
D5		4c. violet	45·00	50·00
D7		5c. violet	24·00	3·00
D8		10c. violet	32·00	17·00

1930.

D 9	**D 2**	1c. violet	8·50	10·00
D10		2c. violet	7·50	1·90
D11		4c. violet	15·00	6·50
D12		5c. violet	16·00	27·00
D13		10c. violet	65·00	65·00

D 3

D 4

1933.

D14	**D 3**	1c. violet	9·50	14·00
D15		2c. violet	7·50	4·50
D16		4c. violet	12·00	14·00
D17		10c. violet	24·00	29·00

1935.

D18	**D 4**	1c. violet	80	10
D19		2c. violet	1·00	10
D20		3c. violet	4·50	5·00
D21		4c. violet	1·50	10
D22		5c. violet	3·50	1·75
D23		6c. violet	2·25	3·00
D24		10c. violet	70	10

D 5

1967. (a) Size 21 × 17½ mm.

D25	**D 5**	1c. red	1·75	4·00
D26		2c. red	1·00	1·00
D27		3c. red	1·00	4·25
D28		4c. red	2·75	1·25
D29		5c. red	4·25	4·50
D30		6c. red	1·60	3·75
D31		10c. red	2·00	2·50

(b) Size 19½ × 16 mm.

D32	**D 5**	1c. red	30	30
D33		2c. red	1·00	2·75
D34		3c. red	2·50	3·00
D35		4c. red	30	60
D36a		5c. red	30	1·75
D37		6c. red	2·75	3·75
D38		8c. red	30	45
D39		10c. red	30	45
D40		12c. red	30	50
D41		16c. red	1·75	3·25
D42		20c. red	30	1·25
D43		24c. red	30	1·75
D44		50c. red	40	2·25

REGISTRATION STAMPS

R 1

1875.

R1	**R 1**	2c. orange	60·00	1·00
R6		5c. green	80·00	1·25
R8		8c. blue	£325	£225

SPECIAL DELIVERY STAMPS

S 1

1898.

S2	**S 1**	10c. green	45·00	6·00

S 2

1922.

S4	**S 2**	20c. red	35·00	6·50

S 3 Mail-carrying, 1867 and 1927

1927. 60th Anniv of Confederation.

S5	**S 3**	20c. orange	11·00	10·00

S 4

1930.

S6	**S 4**	20c. red	42·00	7·00

1932. As Type S **4**, but inscr "CENTS" instead of "TWENTY CENTS".

S7		20c. red	45·00	15·00

S 5 Allegory of Progress

1935.

S8	**S 5**	20c. red	3·50	2·75

S 6 Canadian Coat of Arms

1938.

S 9	**S 6**	10c. green	18·00	3·00
S10		20c. red	40·00	24·00

1939. Surch **10 10** and bars.

S11	**S 6**	10c. on 20c. red	10·00	8·00

S 8 Coat of Arms and Flags

S 9 Lockheed L.18 Lodestar

1942.

S12	**S 8**	10c. green (postage)	5·00	30
S13	**S 9**	16c. blue (air)	5·50	45
S14		17c. blue	4·25	55

1946.

S15	10c. green (postage)	2·75	30
S16	17c. blue (air)	4·50	4·00

DESIGNS: 10c. As Type S **8** but with wreath of leaves; 17c. As Type S **9** but with Canadair DC-4M North Star airplane.

CANAL ZONE Pt. 22

Territory adjacent to the Panama Canal leased by the U.S.A. from the Republic of Panama. The U.S. Canal Zone postal service closed on 30 September 1979.

1904. 100 centavos = 1 peso.
1906. 100 centesimos = 1 balboa.
1924. 100 cents = 1 dollar (U.S.).

1904. Stamps of Panama (with **PANAMA** optd twice) optd **CANAL ZONE** horiz in one line.

1	**5**	2c. red (No. 54)	£375	£300
2		5c. blue (No. 55)	£160	£120
3		10c. orange (No. 56)	£275	£160

1904. Stamps of the United States of 1902 optd **CANAL ZONE PANAMA**.

4	**103**	1c. green	22·00	16·00
5	**117**	2c. red	20·00	17·00
6	**107**	5c. blue	70·00	45·00
7	**109**	8c. violet	£120	60·00
8	**110**	10c. brown	£100	65·00

Stamps of Panama overprinted.

1904. 1905 stamps optd **CANAL ZONE** in two lines.

9	**38**	1c. green	1·90	1·60
10		2c. red	3·25	1·75

1904. Stamps with **PANAMA** optd twice, optd **CANAL ZONE** in two lines or surch also.

11	**5**	2c. red (No. 54)	5·00	3·50
12		5c. blue (No. 55)	5·50	2·50
14		8c. on 50c. brown (No. 65)	22·00	16·00
13		10c. orange (No. 56)	15·00	8·50

1906. 1892 stamps surch **PANAMA** on both sides and **CANAL ZONE** and new value in centre between bars.

21	**5**	1c. on 20c. violet (No. 64)	1·25	1·10
22		2c. on 1p. red (No. 66)	1·90	1·90

1906. 1906 stamps optd **CANAL ZONE** vert.

26	**42**	1c. black and green	1·60	85
27	**43**	2c. black and red	2·25	95
28	**45**	5c. black and blue	4·50	1·50
29	**46**	8c. black and purple	15·00	5·50
30	**47**	10c. black and violet	14·00	5·50

1909. 1909 stamps optd **CANAL ZONE** vert.

35	**48**	1c. black and green	3·00	1·25
36	**49**	2c. black and red	3·00	1·25
37	**51**	5c. black and blue	11·50	3·00
38	**52**	8c. black and purple	8·50	4·00
43	**53**	10c. black and purple	38·00	6·75

1911. Surch **CANAL ZONE 10 cts.**

53	**38**	10c. on 13c. grey	4·50	1·75

1914. Optd **CANAL ZONE** vert.

54	**38**	10c. grey	42·00	9·75

1915. 1915 and 1918 stamps optd **CANAL ZONE** vert.

55	1c. black and green (No. 162)	6·75	5·00
56	2c. black and red (No. 163)	7·75	3·25
57	5c. black and blue (No. 166)	9·00	5·00
58	10c. black & orange (No. 167)	18·00	11·00
59	12c. black & violet (No. 178)	13·50	4·75
60	15c. black & blue (No. 179)	42·00	18·00
61	24c. black & brown (No. 180)	60·00	16·00
62	50c. black & orange (No. 181)	£375	£190
63	1b. black & violet (No. 182)	£160	65·00

1921. 1921 stamps optd **CANAL ZONE** vert.

64	**65**	1c. green	3·00	1·00
65	–	2c. red (No. 186)	2·25	1·10
66	**68**	5c. blue	8·50	3·50
67	–	10c. violet (No. 191)	14·00	5·75
68	–	15c. blue (No. 192)	38·00	13·50
69	–	24c. sepia (No. 194)	55·00	17·00
70	–	50c. black (No. 195)	£120	80·00

1924. 1924 stamps optd **CANAL ZONE** vert.

72	**72**	1c. green	8·50	3·50
73		2c. red	6·50	2·25

1924. Stamps of the United States of 1922 optd **CANAL ZONE** horiz.

74	½c. sepia (No. 559)	95	60
75	1c. green (No. 602)	1·10	45
76	1½c. brown (No. 603)	1·50	1·00
103	2c. red (No. 604)	2·00	75
87	3c. violet (No. 638a)	3·00	2·25
88	5c. blue (No. 640)	3·00	1·75
106	10c. orange (No. 645)	14·00	5·00
90	12c. purple (No. 693)	18·00	11·50
141	14c. blue (No. 695)	3·75	2·25
92	15c. grey (No. 696)	5·50	3·50
93	17c. black (No. 697)	3·00	2·40
94	20c. red (No. 698)	6·00	2·50
95	30c. sepia (No. 700)	4·00	3·00
84	50c. mauve (No. 701)	60·00	35·00
97	$1 brown (No. 579)	£100	45·00

1926. Liberty Bell stamp of United States optd **CANAL ZONE**.

101	**177**	2c. red	3·50	3·00

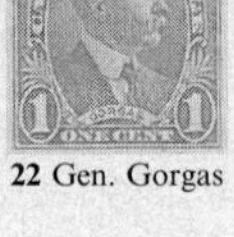

22 Gen. Gorgas

24 Panama Canal under Construction

1928.

107	**22**	1c. green	10	10
108	–	2c. red	20	15
109	**24**	5c. blue	1·90	35
110	–	10c. orange	30	20
111	–	12c. purple	60	50
112	–	14c. blue	80	80
113	–	15c. grey	60	40
114	–	20c. brown	50	20
115	–	30c. black	80	80
116	–	50c. mauve	1·25	55

PORTRAITS: 2c. Gen. Goethals. 10c. H. F. Hodges. 12c. Col. Gaillard. 14c. Gen. Sibert. 15c. Jackson Smith. 20c. Admiral Rousseau. 30c. Col. S. B. Williamson. 50c. Governor Blackburn.

1929. Air. Stamps of 1928 surch **AIR MAIL** and value.

124	–	10c. on 50c. mauve	7·50	5·50
117	**22**	15c. on 1c. green	7·50	4·50
125	–	20c. on 2c. red	4·50	1·50
119	–	25c. on 2c. red	3·00	1·75

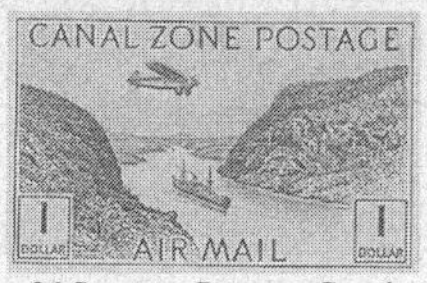

36 Steamer, Panama Canal

1931. Air.

126	36	4c. purple	55	65
127		5c. green	45	30
128		6c. brown	60	35
129		10c. orange	70	30
130		15c. blue	1·00	25
131		20c. violet	2·00	25
132		30c. red	2·75	1·00
133		40c. yellow	2·50	1·00
134		$1 black	8·50	1·75

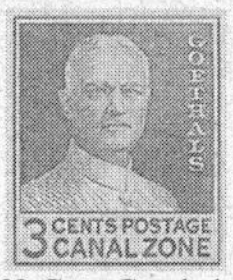

38 Gen. Goethals

1933. No. 720 of United States optd **CANAL ZONE**.

140		3c. violet	2·25	25

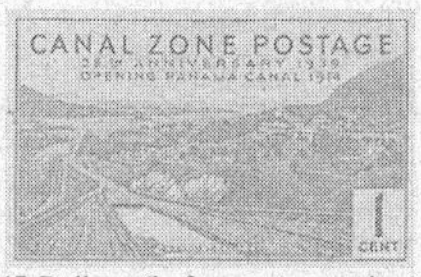

45 Balboa (before construction)

1934. 20th Anniv of Opening of Panama Canal.

142	38	3c. violet	15	10

1939. 25th Anniv of Opening of Panama Canal and 10th Anniv of Canal Zone Airmail Service. (a) Postage. As T **45**. Inscr "25TH ANNIVERSARY 1939 OPENING PANAMA CANAL 1914".

149	45	1c. green	1·25	75
150	–	2c. red	50	40
151	–	3c. violet	1·25	50
152	–	5c. blue	1·40	95
153	–	6c. orange	4·25	2·75
154	–	7c. black	2·75	1·40
155	–	8c. green	5·00	3·00
156	–	10c. blue	5·00	2·25
157	–	11c. green	14·00	10·00
158	–	12c. purple	7·00	5·50
159	–	14c. violet	16·00	10·00
160	–	15c. olive	22·00	11·00
161	–	18c. red	16·00	16·00
162	–	20c. brown	20·00	9·50
163	–	25c. orange	14·00	14·00
164	–	50c. purple	18·00	3·75

DESIGNS: 2c. Balboa (after construction); 3c., 5c. Gaillard Cut; 6c., 7c. Bas Obispo; 8c., 10c. Gatun Locks; 11c., 12c. Canal Channel; 14c., 15c. Gamboa; 18c., 20c. Pedro Miguel Locks; 25c.50c. Gatun Spillway.

(b) Air. Inscr "TENTH ANNIVERSARY AIR MAIL" and "25TH ANNIVERSARY OPENING PANAMA CANAL".

143		5c. black	3·25	3·00
144		10c. violet	3·25	2·25
145		15c. brown	3·25	1·10
146		25c. blue	16·00	11·00
147		30c. red	12·00	8·00
148		$1 green	30·00	30·00

DESIGNS—HORIZ: As Type **45**: 5c. Douglas DC-3 airplane over Sosa Hill; 10c. Douglas DC-3 airplane, Sikorsky S-42A flying boat and map of Central America; 15c. Sikorsky S-42A and Fort Amador; 25c. Sikorsky S-42A at Cristobal Harbour, Manzanillo Island; 30c. Sikorsky S-42A over Culebra Cut. $1 Sikorsky S-42A and palm trees.

1939. Stamps of United States (1938) optd **CANAL ZONE**.

165	276	½c. orange	15	10
166	–	1½c. brown (No. 801)	15	10

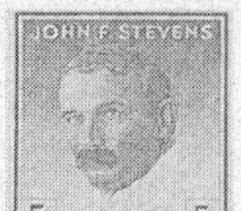

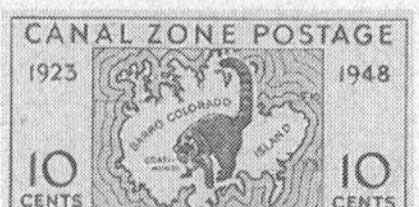

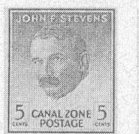

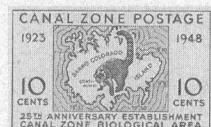

67 John F. Stevens

69 Northern Coati and Barro Colorado Island

1946. Portraits.

188	–	½c. red (Davis)	30	15
189	–	1½c. brown (Magoon)	30	15
190	–	2c. red (Theodore Roosevelt)	15	10
191	67	5c. blue	30	10
192	–	25c. green (Wallace)	1·10	60

1948. 25th Anniv of Establishment of Canal Zone Biological Area.

194	69	10c. black	1·40	80

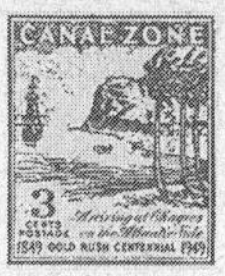

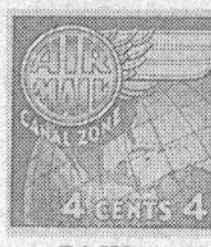

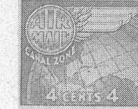

70 "Arriving at Chagres on the Atlantic Side."

74 Western Hemisphere

1949. Centenary of the Gold Rush.

195	70	3c. blue	60	30
196	–	6c. violet	80	50
197	–	12c. green	1·40	1·00
198	–	18c. mauve	2·75	2·00

DESIGNS: 6c. "Up the Chagres River to Las Cruces"; 12c. "Las Cruces Trail to Panama"; 18c. "Leaving Panama for San Francisco".

1951. Air.

199	74	4c. purple	75	25
200		5c. green	1·00	60
201		6c. brown	50	15
202		7c. olive	1·00	35
210		8c. red	40	20
203		10c. orange	1·00	35
204		15c. purple	3·50	1·75
205		21c. blue	7·00	2·75
206		25c. yellow	9·50	2·25
207		31c. red	7·25	3·25
208		35c. blue	6·00	2·50
209		80c. black	4·50	90

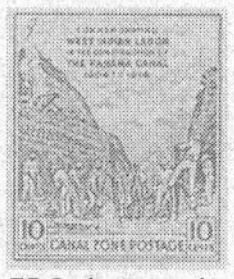

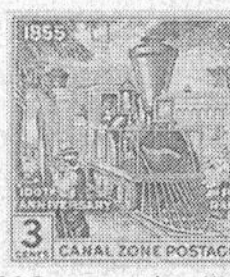

75 Labourers in Gaillard Cut

76 Locomotive "Nueva Granada", 1852

1951. West Indian Panama Canal Labourers.

211	75	10c. red	6·75	2·75

1955. Centenary of Panama Railway.

212	76	3c. violet	2·75	90

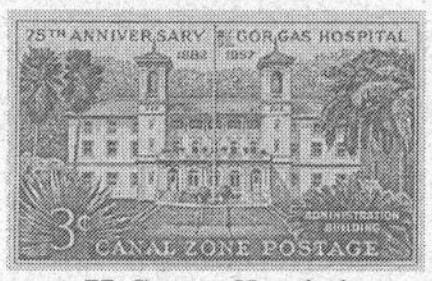

77 Gorgas Hospital

1957. 75th Anniv of Gorgas Hospital.

213	77	3c. black on green	40	30

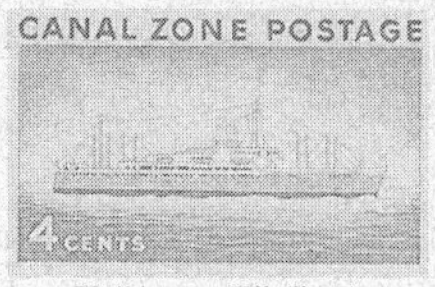

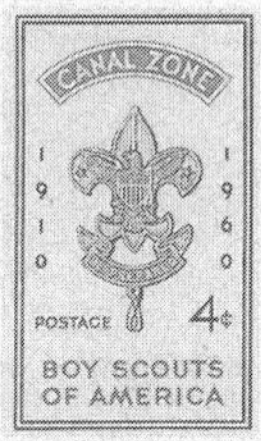

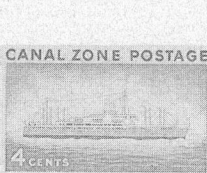

78 "Ancon II" (liner)

80 "First Class" Scout Badge

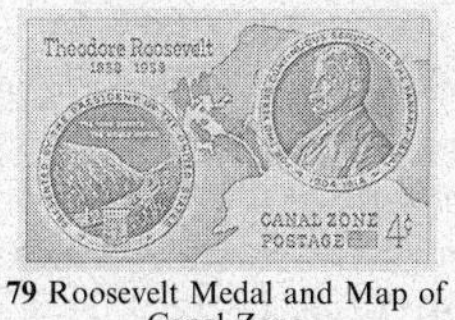

79 Roosevelt Medal and Map of Canal Zone

1958.

214	78	4c. turquoise	45	20

1958. Birth Centenary of Theodore Roosevelt.

215	79	4c. brown	40	25

1960. 50th Anniv of American Boy Scout Movement.

216	80	4c. ochre, red and blue	50	30

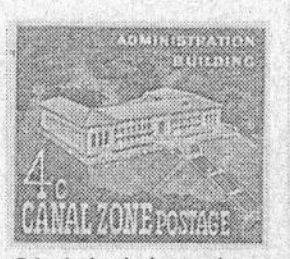

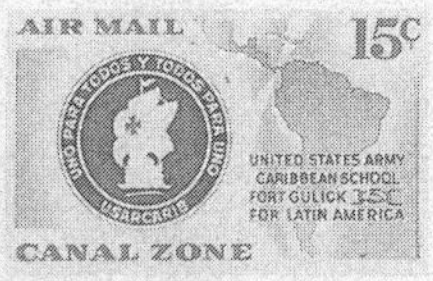

81 Administration Building, Balboa

82 U.S. Army Caribbean School Crest

1960.

217	81	4c. purple	20	15

1961. Air.

221	82	15c. blue and red	1·40	60

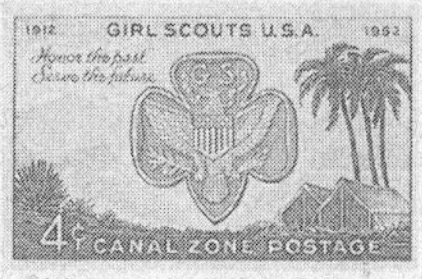

83 Girl Scout Badge and Camp on Lake Gatun

1962. 50th Anniv of U.S. Girl Scout Movement.

222	83	4c. ochre, green and blue	40	25

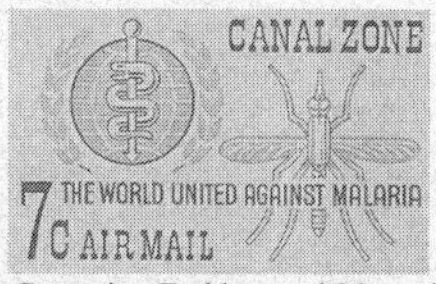

84 Campaign Emblem and Mosquito

1962. Air. Malaria Eradication.

223	84	7c. black on yellow	45	40

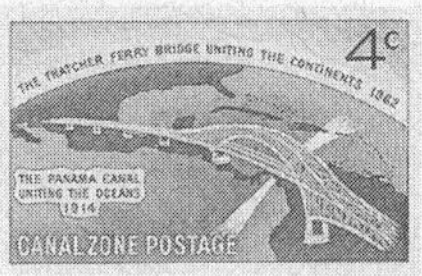

85 Thatcher Ferry Bridge

1962. Opening of Thatcher Ferry Bridge.

224	85	4c. black and silver	30	20

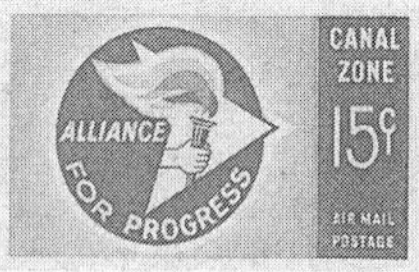

86 Torch of Progress

1963. Air. "Alliance for Progress".

225	86	15c. blue, green and black	1·10	75

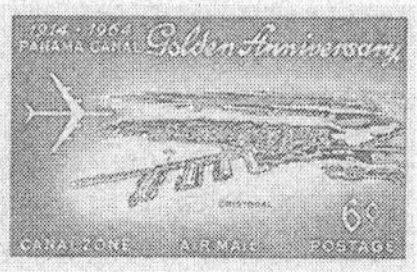

87 Cristobal

1964. Air. 50th Anniv of Panama Canal.

226	87	6c. black and green	45	30
227	–	8c. black and red	1·75	75
228	–	15c. black and blue	1·25	45
229	–	20c. black and purple	2·00	85
230	–	30c. black and brown	5·75	2·25
231	–	80c. black and bistre	5·00	2·50

DESIGNS: 8c. Gatun Locks; 15c. Madden Dam; 20c. Gaillard Cut; 30c. Miraflores Locks; 80c. Balboa.

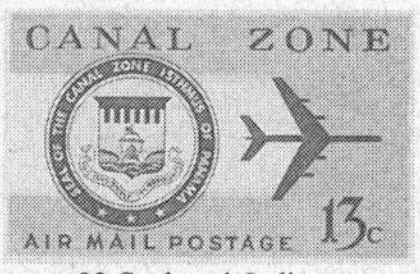

93 Seal and Jetliner

1965. Air.

232	93	6c. black and green	35	20
233		8c. black and red	30	10
234		10c. black and orange	30	10
235		11c. black and green	40	15
236		13c. black and green	95	20
237		15c. black and blue	50	15
238		20c. black and violet	55	25
239		22c. black and violet	75	55
240		25c. black and green	60	40
241		30c. black and brown	80	30
242		35c. black and red	90	65
243		80c. black and ochre	2·00	85

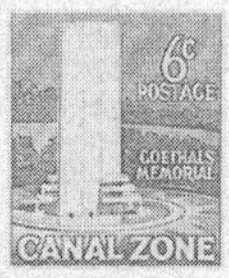

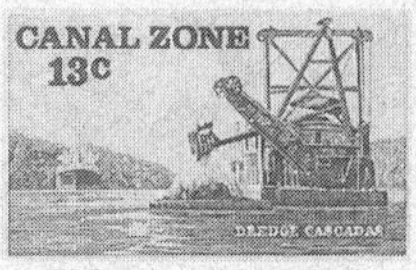

94 Goethal's Memorial, Balboa

96 Dredger "Cascadas"

1968.

244	94	6c. blue and green	20	20
245	–	8c. multicoloured	35	15

DESIGN: 8c. Fort San Lorenzo.

1976.

249	96	13c. black, green & blue	60	20

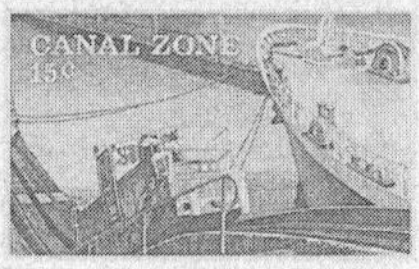

97 Electric Towing Locomotive

1978.

251	97	15c. green and deep green	3·00	75

OFFICIAL STAMPS

1941. Air. Optd **OFFICIAL PANAMA CANAL**.

O167	36	5c. green	4·25	1·25
O168		6c. brown	9·75	3·75
O169		10c. orange	8·00	1·75
O170		15c. blue	12·00	3·00
O171		20c. violet	13·00	4·00
O172		30c. red	15·00	4·00
O173		40c. yellow	17·00	7·50
O174		$1 black	20·00	10·00

1941. Optd **OFFICIAL PANAMA CANAL**.

O180	22	1c. green	1·50	40
O181	38	3c. violet	3·25	70
O182	24	5c. blue	–	38·00
O183	–	10c. orange	4·25	1·75
O184	–	15c. grey (No. 113)	9·00	2·00
O185	–	20c. brown (No. 114)	12·00	2·75
O186	–	50c. mauve (No. 116)	30·00	4·50

1947. No. 192 optd **OFFICIAL PANAMA CANAL**.

O193	67	5c. blue	7·50	3·00

POSTAGE DUE STAMPS

1914. Postage Due stamps of United States of 1894 optd **CANAL ZONE** diag.

D55	D 87	1c. red	55·00	13·00
D56		2c. red	£180	38·00
D57		10c. red	£475	38·00

1915. Postage Due stamps of Panama of 1915 optd **CANAL ZONE** vert.

D59	D 58	1c. brown	9·75	3·75
D60	–	2c. brown	£150	13·50
D61	–	10c. brown	38·00	8·00

1915. Postage Due stamps of Panama of 1915 surch **CANAL ZONE** vert and value in figures.

D62	D 58	1c. on 1c. brown	80·00	11·00
D63	–	2c. on 2c. brown	20·00	5·75
D66	–	4c. on 4c. brown	27·00	11·50
D64	–	10c. on 10c. brown	17·00	3·75

1925. Postage Due stamps of United States of 1894 optd **CANAL ZONE** horiz in two lines.

D92	D 87	1c. red	6·25	2·50
D93		2c. red	12·00	3·25
D94		10c. red	£110	17·00

1925. Stamps of Canal Zone of 1924 optd **POSTAGE DUE**.

D89		1c. green (No. 75)	70·00	11·00
D90		2c. red (No. 103)	18·00	5·50
D91		10c. orange (No. 106)	40·00	8·75

1929. No. 109 surch **POSTAGE DUE** and value and bars.

D120	24	1c. on 5c. blue	5·75	3·75
D121		2c. on 5c. blue	11·00	5·00
D122		5c. on 5c. blue	11·00	5·75
D123		10c. on 5c. blue	11·00	5·50

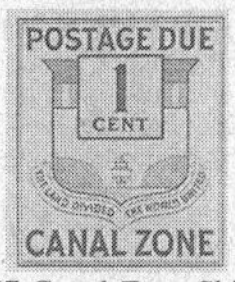

D 37 Canal Zone Shield

1932.

D135	D 37	1c. red	15	20
D136		2c. red	15	20
D137		5c. red	40	25
D138		10c. red	1·60	1·50
D139		15c. red	1·25	1·10

CANTON Pt. 17

A treaty port in S. China. Stamps issued at the French Indo-Chinese P.O., which was closed in 1922.

1901. 100 centimes = 1 franc.
1919. 100 cents = 1 piastre.

Stamps of Indo-China overprinted or surcharged.

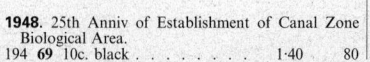

CANTON
州廣

(1)

1901. "Tablet" key-type, optd with T **1**. The Chinese characters represent "Canton" and are therefore the same on every value.

1	D	1c. black and blue	65	1·00
2		2c. brown on yellow	1·25	2·25
3		4c. brown on grey	2·50	2·50
4		5c. green	95	1·40

6 10c. black on lilac . . . . . 3·25 7·00
7 15c. blue . . . . 3·00 3·50
8 15c. grey . . . . 5·25 4·50
9 20c. red on green . . . . . 10·00 12·00
10 25c. black on pink . . . . . 10·00 10·00
11 30c. brown on drab . . . . 19·00 29·00
12 40c. red on yellow . . . . . 30·00 35·00
13 50c. red on rose . . . . . . 26·00 35·00
14 75c. brown on orange . . . 35·00 50·00
15 1f. green . . . . 42·00 45·00
16 5f. mauve on lilac £190 £200

1903. "Tablet" key-type, surch. as T **1**. The Chinese characters indicate the value and therefore differ for each value.
17 D 1c. black on blue . . . . . 2·50 2·40
18 2c. brown on yellow . . . . 3·25 3·75
19 4c. brown on grey . . . . . 2·25 3·75
20 5c. green . . . . 2·25 3·75
21 10c. red . . . . 2·50 3·75
22 15c. grey . . . . 2·75 4·25
23 20c. red on green . . . . . 12·00 19·00
24 25c. blue . . . . 7·00 6·75
25 25c. black on pink . . . . . 8·50 6·75
26 30c. brown on drab . . . . 22·00 24·00
27 40c. red on yellow . . . . . 60·00 50·00
28 50c. red on rose £275 £250
29 50c. brown on blue . . . . 65·00 60·00
30 75c. brown on orange . . . 70·00 60·00
31 1f. green . . . . 55·00 55·00
32 5f. mauve on lilac . . . . . 50·00 60·00

1906. Surch **CANTON** (letters without serifs) and value in Chinese.
33 **8** 1c. green . . . . 1·10 3·00
34 2c. purple on yellow . . . . 1·25 2·75
35 4c. mauve on blue . . . . . 95 2·25
36 5c. green . . . . 2·25 3·00
37 10c. red . . . . 2·75 3·25
38 15c. brown on blue . . . . 3·00 4·50
39 20c. red on green . . . . . 3·00 4·00
40 25c. blue . . . . 2·75 3·00
41 30c. brown on cream . . . . 4·25 4·50
42 35c. black on yellow . . . . 2·50 3·50
43 40c. black on grey . . . . . 4·50 6·50
44 50c. brown on cream . . . . 6·75 7·25
45 D 75c. brown on orange . . . 55·00 60·00
46 **8** 1f. green . . . . 13·00 15·00
47 2f. brown on yellow . . . . 35·00 40·00
48 D 5f. mauve on lilac . . . . . 65·00 85·00
49 **8** 10f. red on green . . . . . 75·00 85·00

1908. 1907 stamps surch **CANTON** and value in Chinese.
50 **10** 1c. black and brown 70 50
51 2c. black and brown 55 85
52 4c. black and blue . . . . . 75 1·75
53 5c. black and green . . . . 1·25 1·40
54 10c. black and red . . . . . 2·50 75
55 15c. black and violet . . . . 2·75 2·50
56 **11** 20c. black and violet . . . . 3·50 3·25
57 25c. black and blue . . . . 4·00 50
58 30c. black and brown . . . 6·75 6·75
59 35c. black and green . . . . 8·25 6·25
60 40c. black and brown . . . 12·00 6·50
61 50c. black and red . . . . . 12·50 5·50
62 **12** 75c. black and orange . . . 11·50 8·50
63 – 1f. black and red . . . . . 17·00 13·00
64 – 2f. black and green . . . . 45·00 38·00
65 – 5f. black and blue . . . . . 55·00 45·00
66 – 10f. black and violet . . . . 90·00 70·00

1919. As last, but additionally surch.
67 **10** 2/5c. on 1c. black and brown 75 2·50
68 4/5c. on 2c. black and brown 60 1·75
69 1 3/5c. on 4c. black and blue 1·25 1·25
70 2c. on 5c. black and green 1·60 1·10
71 4c. on 10c. black and red 2·50 1·90
72 6c. on 15c. black & violet 1·90 1·90
73 **11** 8c. on 20c. black & violet 2·75 2·50
74 10c. on 25c. black & blue 3·00 50
75 12c. on 30c. black & brown 3·50 2·25
76 14c. on 35c. black & green 1·75 1·50
77 16c. on 40c. black & brown 2·75 1·60
78 20c. on 50c. black and red 3·25 65
79 **12** 30c. on 75c. black & orange 3·50 1·25
80 – 40c. on 1f. black and red . . 1·50 8·00
81 – 80c. on 2f. black and green 13·50 12·50
82 – 2p. on 5f. black and blue . . 14·00 16·00
83 – 4p. on 10f. black & violet 15·00 19·00

CAPE JUBY Pt. 9

Former Spanish possession on the N.W. coast of Africa, ceded to Morocco in 1958.

100 centimos = 1 peseta.

1916. Stamps of Rio de Oro surch **CABO JUBI** and value.
1a **12** 5c. on 4p. red . . . . . . 75·00 24·00
2 10c. on 10p. violet . . . . 32·00 16·00
3 15c. on 50c. brown . . . . 32·00 16·00
4 40c. on 1p. lilac . . . . . . 55·00 22·00

1919. Stamps of Spain optd **CABO JUBY**.
5 **38a** ¼c. green 15 10
18 **66** 1c. green (imperf) . . . . 17·00 11·00
6 **64** 2c. brown 15 10
7 5c. green 40 10
8 10c. red 45 10
9 15c. yellow . . . . 2·25 15
10 20c. green . . . . 13·50 4·00
19 20c. violet . . . . 75·00 28·00
11 25c. blue . . . . 2·00 30
12 30c. green . . . . 2·00 40
13 40c. orange . . . . 2·00 40
14 50c. blue . . . . 2·50 40
15 1p. red . . . . 7·00 4·00
16 4p. purple . . . . 28·00 20·00
17 10p. orange . . . . 38·00 24·00

1925. Stamps of Spain optd **CABO JUBY**.
19a **68** 2c. green . . . . £200 55·00
20 5c. purple . . . . 3·50 2·75
21 10c. green . . . . 9·25 2·75
22 20c. violet . . . . 19·00 8·50

1926. As Red Cross stamps of Spain of 1926 optd **CABO-JUBY**.
23 **70** 1c. orange . . . . 9·75 9·75
24 – 2c. red . . . . 9·75 9·75
25 – 5c. brown . . . . 2·50 2·50
26 – 10c. green . . . . 1·25 1·25
27 **70** 15c. violet 85 85
28 – 20c. purple 85 85
29 **71** 25c. red 85 85
30 **70** 30c. green 85 85
31 – 40c. blue 30 30
32 – 50c. red 30 30
33 – 1p. red 30 30
34 – 4p. bistre . . . . 1·10 1·10
35 **71** 10p. violet . . . . 2·75 2·75

1929. Seville and Barcelona Exhibition stamps of Spain (Nos. 504/14) optd **CABO JUBY**.
36 – 5c. red 30 40
37 – 10c. green 30 40
38 **83** 15c. blue 30 40
39 **84** 20c. violet 30 40
40 **83** 25c. red 30 40
41 – 30c. brown 30 40
42 – 40c. blue 30 40
43 **84** 50c. orange 35 55
44 – 1p. grey . . . . 14·00 21·00
45 – 4p. red . . . . 21·00 32·00
46 – 10p. brown . . . . 21·00 32·00

1934. Stamps of Spanish Morocco optd **Cabo Juby**.
(a) Stamps of 1928
47 **11** 1c. red . . . . 1·50 85
48 2c. violet . . . . 3·00 55
49 5c. blue . . . . 3·00 55
50 10c. green . . . . 7·00 1·40
51 15c. brown . . . . 16·00 9·00
52 **12** 25c. red . . . . 3·00 3·25
53 – 1p. green . . . . 29·00 18·00
54 – 2p.50 purple . . . . . . 65·00 38·00
55 – 4p. blue . . . . 85·00 48·00

(b) Stamps of 1933.
56 **14** 1c. red 35 35
57 – 10c. green . . . . 2·25 2·25
58 **14** 20c. black . . . . 6·25 5·00
59 – 30c. red . . . . 6·25 5·00
60 **15** 40c. blue . . . . 22·00 19·00
61 50c. orange . . . . 42·00 30·00

1935. Stamps of Spanish Morocco of 1933 optd **CABO JUBY**.
62 **14** 1c. red 15 15
63 – 2c. green 50 15
64 – 5c. mauve . . . . 1·90 15
65 – 10c. green . . . . 11·00 3·00
66 – 15c. yellow . . . . 4·25 1·90
67 **14** 20c. black . . . . 4·00 3·00
68 – 25c. red . . . . 48·00 30·00
73 – 25c. violet . . . . 3·00 1·90
74 – 30c. red . . . . 3·00 1·60
75 – 40c. orange . . . . 4·00 1·90
76 – 50c. blue . . . . 8·00 1·90
77 – 60c. green . . . . 10·00 4·25
69 – 1p. grey . . . . 6·75 6·00
78 – 2p. brown . . . . 55·00 30·00
70 – 2p.50 brown . . . . . . 27·00 16·00
71 – 4p. green . . . . 45·00 22·00
72 – 5p. black . . . . 35·00 30·00

1937. 1st Anniv of Civil War. Nos. 184/99 of Spanish Morocco optd **CABO JUBY**.
79 1c. blue 30 30
80 2c. brown 30 30
81 5c. mauve 30 30
82 10c. green 30 30
83 15c. blue 30 30
84 20c. purple 30 30
85 25c. mauve 30 30
86 30c. red 30 30
87 40c. orange 85 85
88 50c. blue 85 85
89 60c. green 85 85
90 1p. violet 85 85
91 2p. blue . . . . 60·00 60·00
92 2p.50 black . . . . 60·00 60·00
93 4p. brown . . . . 60·00 60·00
94 10p. black . . . . 60·00 60·00

1938. Air. Nos. 203/12 of Spanish Morocco optd **CABO JUBY**.
95 5c. brown 15 15
96 10c. green . . . . 1·00 50
97 25c. red 15 15
98 40c. blue . . . . 1·50 1·25
99 50c. mauve 15 15
100 75c. blue 15 20
101 1p. brown 15 20
102 1p.50 violet . . . . 4·00 1·50
103 2p. red . . . . 2·10 1·75
104 3p. black . . . . 5·50 6·00

1939. As Nos. 213/16 of Spanish Morocco optd **CABO JUBY**.
105 5c. red 35 35
106 10c. green 35 35
107 15c. purple 35 35
108 20c. blue 35 35

1940. Nos. 217/32 of Spanish Morocco, but without "ZONA" on back, optd **CABO JUBY**.
109 1c. brown 15 15
110 2c. green 15 15
111 5c. blue 15 15
112 10c. mauve 15 15
113 15c. green 15 15
114 20c. violet 15 15
115 25c. brown 15 15
116 30c. green 15 15
117 40c. green 40 15
118 45c. red 40 15
119 50c. brown 40 15
120 75c. blue . . . . 1·40 60
121 1p. brown and blue . . . . 2·75 60
122 2p.50 green and brown . . 7·50 4·00
123 5p. brown and purple . . . 7·50 4·00
124 10p. brown & deep brown . . 22·00 15·00

1942. Air. Nos. 258/62 of Spanish Morocco, but without "Z" opt and inscr "CABO JUBY".
125 5c. blue 15 15
126 10c. brown 15 15
127 15c. green 15 15
128 90c. pink 35 30
129 5p. black . . . . 1·40 95

1944. Nos. 269/82 (agricultural scenes) of Spanish Morocco optd **CABO JUBY**.
130 – 1c. blue and brown . . . . 1·00 50
131 – 2c. light green & green . . 15 15
132 **26** 5c. green and brown . . . 15 15
133 – 10c. orange and blue . . . 15 15
134 – 15c. light green & green . . 15 15
135 – 20c. black and purple . . . 15 15
136 – 25c. brown and blue . . . 15 15
137 – 30c. blue and green . . . 1·50 50
138 – 40c. purple and brown . . 15 15
139 **26** 50c. brown and blue . . . 15 15
140 – 75c. blue and green . . . 90 40
141 – 1p. brown and blue . . . 90 40
142 – 2p.50 blue and black . . 2·75 2·00
143 – 10p. black and orange . . 18·00 13·00

1946. Nos. 285/94 (craftsmen) of Spanish Morocco optd **CABO JUBY**.
144 – 1c. brown and purple . . . 15 15
145 **27** 2c. violet and green . . . 15 15
146 – 10c. blue and orange . . . 15 15
147 **27** 15c. green and blue . . . 15 15
148 – 25c. blue and green . . . 15 15
149 – 40c. brown and blue . . . 15 15
150 **27** 45c. red and black 15 15
151 – 1p. blue and green . . . . 1·10 45
152 – 2p.50 green and orange . . 3·25 2·10
153 – 10p. grey and blue . . . . 10·00 7·00

1948. Nos. 307/17 (transport and commerce) of Spanish Morocco, but without "Z" on back, optd **CABO JUBY**.
154 **30** 2c. brown and violet . . . 35 1·00
155 – 5c. violet and purple . . . 15 10
156 – 15c. green and blue . . . 15 10
157 – 25c. green and black . . . 15 10
158 – 35c. black and blue . . . 15 10
159 – 50c. violet and red 15 10
160 – 70c. blue and green . . . 15 10
161 – 90c. green and mauve . . . 15 10
162 – 1p. violet and blue 25 25
163 **30** 2p.50 green and purple . . 8·50 8·50
164 – 10p. blue and black . . . 3·00 3·25

EXPRESS LETTER STAMPS

1919. Express letter stamp of Spain optd **CABO JUBY**.
E18 E **53** 20c. red . . . . 1·10 1·10

1926. Red Cross stamp. As Express letter stamp of Spain optd **CABO-JUBY**.
E36 E **77** 20c. black and blue . . 2·75 2·75

1934. Stamp of Spanish Morocco optd **Cabo Juby**.
E62 E **12** 20c. black . . . . . . 7·00 7·50

1935. Stamp of Spanish Morocco optd **CABO JUBY**.
E79 E **16** 20c. red . . . . 3·00 1·10

1937. No. E200 of Spanish Morocco optd **CABO JUBY**.
E95 E **19** 20c. red 85 85

1940. No. E233 of Spanish Morocco optd **CABO JUBY**.
E125 E **21** 25c. red 30 30

CAPE OF GOOD HOPE Pt. 1

Formerly a British Colony, later the southern most province of the Union of South Africa.

12 pence = 1 shilling;
20 shillings = 1 pound.

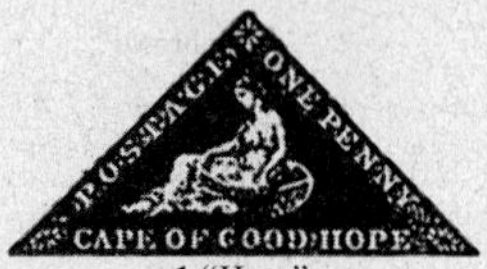

1 "Hope"

1853. Imperf.
18 **1** 1d. red £120 £225
19 4d. blue . . . . £120 48·00
20 6d. lilac £160 £450
8b 1s. green £225 £500

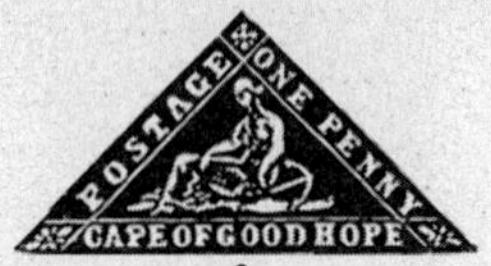

3

1861. Imperf.
13 **3** 1d. red £14000 £2250
14 4d. blue £10000 £1600

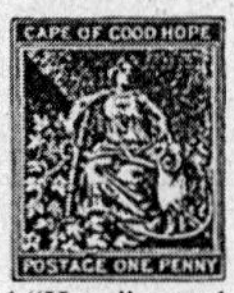

4 "Hope" seated, with vine and ram (with outer frameline)

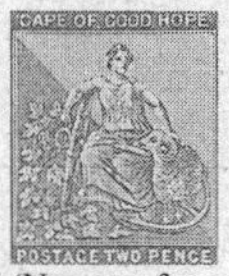

6 (No outer frameline)

1864. With outer frame line. Perf.
23a **4** 1d. red . . . . 80·00 19·00
24 4d. blue . . . . 95·00 2·50
52a 6d. purple . . . . 7·00 20
53a 1s. green . . . . 70·00 40

1868. Surch.
32 **4** 1d. on 6d. violet . . . . . £450 85·00
33 1d. on 1s. green . . . . . 60·00 40·00
34 **6** 3d. on 4d. blue . . . . . 90·00 1·75
27 **4** 4d. on 6d. violet . . . . . £200 16·00

1880. No outer frame line.
48 **6** ½d. black . . . . 3·00 10
49 1d. red . . . . 3·00 10
36 3d. pink . . . . £170 21·00
43 3d. purple . . . . 6·50 90
51 4d. blue . . . . 9·00 50
54 5s. orange . . . . 75·00 4·75

1880. Surch **THREEPENCE**.
35 **6** 3d. on 4d. pink . . . . . . 60·00 1·75

1880. Surch **3**.
37 **6** "3" on 3d. pink . . . . . . 65·00 1·50

1882. Surch **One Half-penny**.
47 **6** ½d. on 3d. purple . . . . . 22·00 3·00

1882.
61 **6** ½d. green . . . . 1·50 50
62 2d. brown . . . . 2·00 30
56 2½d. olive . . . . 6·00 10
63a 2½d. blue . . . . 3·50 10
64 3d. mauve . . . . 5·50 85
65 4d. olive . . . . 4·00 1·00
66 1s. green . . . . 55·00 3·00
67 1s. yellow . . . . 7·50 1·00
On the 2½d. stamps the value is in a white square at upper right-hand corner as well as at foot.

1891. Surch **2½d**.
55a **6** 2½d. on 3d. mauve . . . . 3·00 20

1893. Surch **ONE PENNY**.
57a **6** 1d. on 2d. brown . . . . . 1·75 50

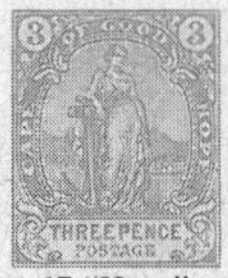

17 "Hope" standing. Table Bay in background

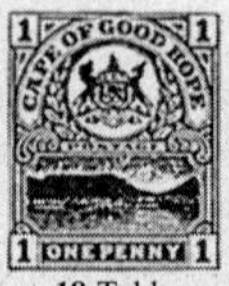

18 Table Mountain and Bay and Arms of the Colony

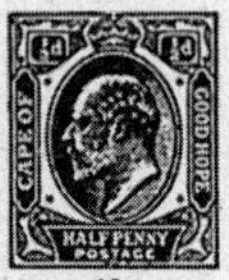

19

1893.
58 **17** ½d. green . . . . 1·50 10
59a 1d. red . . . . 1·25 10
60 3d. mauve . . . . 4·00 1·50

1900.
69 **18** 1d. red . . . . 2·25 10

1902. Various frames.
70 **19** ½d. green . . . . 2·00 10
71 1d. red . . . . 2·00 10
72 2d. brown . . . . 8·50 80
73 2½d. blue . . . . 2·75 6·50
74 3d. purple . . . . 7·00 75
75 4d. green . . . . 7·50 65
76 6d. mauve . . . . 15·00 30
77 1s. yellow . . . . 12·00 80
78 5s. orange . . . . 65·00 10·00

CAPE VERDE ISLANDS Pt. 9; Pt. 12

Islands in the Atlantic. Formerly Portuguese; became independent on 5 July 1975.

1877. 1000 reis = 1 milreis.
1913. 100 centavos = 1 escudo.

1877. "Crown" key-type inscr "CABO VERDE".
1 P 5r. black . . . . 1·25 95
2a 10r. yellow . . . . 6·75 4·00

18 10r. green 1·00 80
3 20r. bistre 90 75
19 20r. red 1·90 1·40
4 25r. pink 90 60
20 25r. lilac 1·60 1·10
5 40r. blue 30·00 20·00
21 40r. yellow 90 85
15 50r. green 30·00 20·00
22 50r. blue 2·50 1·90
7b 100r. lilac 3·00 1·40
8 200r. orange 1·60 1·10
9b 300r. brown 2·10 1·90

1886. "Embossed" key-type inscr "PROVINCIA DE CABO-VERDE".
33 Q 5r. black 1·50 1·00
34 10r. green 1·50 1·00
35 20r. red 2·75 1·90
26 25r. mauve 2·10 1·40
27 40r. brown 2·50 1·50
28 50r. blue 2·50 1·50
29 100r. brown 2·75 1·60
30 200r. lilac 6·00 3·75
31 300r. orange 6·50 4·25

1894. "Figures" key-type inscr "CABO-VERDE".
37 R 5r. orange 55 45
38 10r. mauve 60 50
39 15r. brown 1·50 1·00
40 20r. lilac 1·50 1·00
41 25r. green 1·10 85
42 50r. blue 1·10 85
51 75r. red 3·75 2·50
43 80r. green 4·00 3·50
44 100r. brown on buff 3·25 1·25
58 150r. red on rose 5·25 4·00
59 200r. blue on blue 5·25 3·00
46 300r. blue on buff 8·50 4·75

1898. "King Carlos" key-type inscr "CABO VERDE".
60 S 2½r. grey 20 15
61 5r. orange 20 15
62 10r. green 20 15
63 15r. brown 1·75 80
111 15r. green 55 40
64 20r. lilac 50 30
65 25r. green 1·10 50
112 25r. red 40 20
66 50r. blue 1·25 50
113 50r. brown 1·10 80
114 65r. blue 5·75 3·75
67 75r. red 2·10 1·10
115 75r. purple 95 75
68 80r. mauve 2·50 1·40
69 100r. blue on blue 1·10 65
116 115r. brown on pink 3·75 3·00
117 130r. brown on yellow 3·75 3·00
70 150r. brown on yellow 2·75 1·50
71 200r. purple on pink 1·25 90
72 300r. blue on pink 3·25 1·75
118 400r. blue on yellow 3·75 3·00
73 500r. black on blue 3·25 1·75
74 700r. mauve on yellow 8·50 7·00

1902. Key-types of Cape Verde Is. surch.
119 S 50r. on 65r. blue 1·10 1·00
75 Q 65r. on 5r. black 2·00 1·60
78 R 65r. on 10r. mauve 2·50 1·50
79 65r. on 20r. lilac 2·50 1·50
80 65r. on 100r. brn on buff 2·50 1·50
76 Q 65r. on 200r. lilac 2·00 1·60
77 65r. on 300r. orange 2·00 1·60
85 R 115r. on 5r. orange 1·50 1·25
82 Q 115r. on 10r. green 2·00 1·60
83 115r. on 20r. red 2·10 1·60
87 R 115r. on 25r. green 1·50 1·10
88 115r. on 150r. red on rose 2·75 2·40
90 Q 130r. on 50r. blue 2·00 1·60
93 R 130r. on 75r. red 1·00 1·00
96 130r. on 80r. green 1·10 95
92 Q 130r. on 100r. brown 2·00 1·60
97 R 130r. on 200r. blue on blue 1·25 1·25
106 V 400r. on 2½r. brown 55 45
98 Q 400r. on 25r. mauve 1·10 95
99 400r. on 40r. brown 1·50 1·40
101 R 400r. on 50r. blue 1·75 1·60
103 400r. on 300r. blue on buff 1·00 75

1902. "King Carlos" key-type of Cape Verde Is. optd **PROVISORIO**.
107 S 15r. brown 75 55
108 25r. green 75 55
109 50r. blue 75 55
110 75r. red 1·25 85

1911. "King Carlos" key-type of Cape Verde Is. optd **REPUBLICA**.
120 S 2½r. grey 15 15
121 5r. orange 15 15
122 10r. green 40 30
123 15r. green 25 15
124 20r. lilac 40 30
125 25r. red 30 20
126 50r. brown 3·00 2·25
127 75r. purple 45 30
128 100r. blue on blue 45 30
129 115r. brown on pink 40 35
130 130r. brown on yellow 40 35
131 200r. purple on pink 2·25 1·40
132 400r. blue on yellow 1·10 40
133 500r. black on blue 1·10 40
134 700r. mauve on yellow 1·10 65

1912. "King Manoel" key-type inscr "CABO VERDE" and optd **REPUBLICA**.
135 T 2½r. lilac 10 10
136 5r. black 10 10
137 10r. green 10 10
138 20r. red 90 60
139 25r. brown 15 10
140 50r. blue 1·40 1·25
141 75r. brown 40 35
142 100r. brown on green 40 35
143 200r. green on pink 60 35
144 300r. black on blue 60 35
145 400r. blue and black 1·25 1·10
146 500r. brown and olive 1·25 1·10

1913. Surch. **REPUBLICA CABO VERDE** and new value on "Vasco da Gama" issues of (a) Portuguese Colonies.
147 ¼c. on 2½r. green 50 30
148 ½c. on 5r. red 50 30
149 1c. on 10r. purple 35 30
150 2½c. on 25r. green 35 30
151 5c. on 50r. blue 70 60
152 7½c. on 75r. brown 85 75
153 10c. on 100r. brown 70 70
154 15c. on 150r. bistre 90 75

(b) Macao.
155 ¼c. on ½a. green 50 40
156 ½c. on 1a. red 50 40
157 1c. on 2a. purple 45 40
158 2½c. on 4a. green 45 40
159 5c. on 8a. blue 2·50 1·90
160 7½c. on 12a. brown 1·60 90
161 10c. on 16a. brown 80 70
162 15c. on 24a. bistre 1·75 1·25

(c) Timor.
163 ¼c. on ½a. green 50 40
164 ½c. on 1a. red 50 40
165 1c. on 2a. purple 45 40
166 2½c. on 4a. green 45 40
167 5c. on 8a. blue 2·50 1·90
168 7½c. on 12a. brown 2·00 1·40
169 10c. on 16a. brown 80 70
170 15c. on 24a. bistre 1·00 80

1913. Stamps of 1902 optd **REPUBLICA**.
171 S 75r. red (No. 110) 1·50 1·40
192 R 115r. on 5r. (No. 85) 30 20
193 Q 115r. on 10r. (No. 82) 50 40
195 115r. on 20r. (No. 83) 60 50
198 R 115r. on 25r. (No. 87) 40 30
200 115r. on 150r. (No. 88) 25 20
201 Q 130r. on 50r. (No. 90) 50 50
202 R 130r. on 75r. (No. 93) 40 30
204 130r. on 80r. (No. 96) 40 30
206 Q 130r. on 100r. (No. 92) 40 30
208 R 130r. on 200r. (No. 97) 40 30

1914. "Ceres" key-type inscr "CABO VERDE". Name and value in black.
219 U ¼c. green 10 10
220 ½c. black 10 10
221 1c. green 10 10
222 1½c. brown 10 10
223 2c. red 10 10
224 2c. grey 15 15
180 2½c. violet 25 20
214 2½c. mauve 10 10
215 3c. orange 10 10
216 4c. red 10 15
228 4½c. grey 15 15
229 5c. blue 15 15
230 6c. mauve 15 15
231 7c. blue 15 15
232 7½c. brown 10 10
233 8c. grey 20 15
234 10c. red 10 10
235 12c. green 20 20
236 15c. pink 10 10
237 20c. green 15 10
238 24c. blue 40 35
239 25c. brown 40 35
188 30c. brown on green 1·50 1·25
240 30c. green 15 15
189 40c. brown on pink 90 80
241 40c. turquoise 15 15
190 50c. orange on orange 1·10 85
242 50c. mauve 30 20
243 60c. blue 40 30
244 60c. red 40 30
245 80c. red 1·50 55
191 1e. green on blue 1·10 85
246 1e. pink 1·90 1·00
247 1e. blue 1·75 1·10
248 2e. purple 1·90 1·10
249 5e. brown 4·00 3·50
250 10e. pink 7·00 6·25
251 20e. green 17·00 16·00

1921. Nos. 153/4 surch.
252 2c. on 15c. on 150r. brown 60 55
253 4c. on 10c. on 100r. brown 80 80

1921. No. 69 surch **6 c. REPUBLICA**.
254 S 6c. on 100r. blue on blue 80 80

1921. Charity Tax stamp of Portuguese Colonies (General issues) optd **CABO VERDE CORREIOS** or surch also.
255 ¼ on 1c. green 15 15
256 ½c. on 1c. green 15 15
257 1c. green 20 15

1922. Provisionals of 1913 surch **$04**.
260 R 4c. on 130r. on 75r. red (No. 202) 35 30
262 4c. on 130r. on 80r. green (No. 204) 45 40
265 4c. on 130r. on 200r. blue (No. 208) 35 30

1925. Provisional stamps of 1902 surch **Republica 40 C.**
267 V 40c. on 400r. on 2½r. brown (No. 106) 20 20
268 R 40c. on 400r. on 300r. blue on buff (No. 103) 30 30

1931. No. 245 surch **70 C.**
269 U 70c. on 80c. red 1·40 1·10

1934. As T **17** of Angola (new "Ceres" type).
270 **17** 1c. brown 10 10
271 5c. sepia 10 10
272 10c. mauve 10 10
273 15c. black 10 10
274 20c. grey 10 10
275 30c. green 10 10
276 40c. red 10 10
277 45c. blue 40 25
278 50c. brown 30 15
279 60c. olive 30 15
280 70c. brown 30 15
281 80c. green 30 15
282 85c. red 1·40 85
283 1e. red 95 15
284 1e.40 blue 1·00 75
285 2e. mauve 1·60 75
286 5e. green 7·00 1·75
287 10e. brown 12·50 6·25
288 20e. orange 25·00 11·00

1938. As Nos. 383/409 of Angola.
289 1c. olive (postage) 10 10
290 5c. brown 10 10
291 10c. red 10 10
292 15c. purple 35 25
293 20c. slate 20 15
294 30c. purple 20 15
295 35c. green 20 15
296 40c. brown 20 15
297 50c. mauve 20 15
298 60c. black 20 15
299 70c. violet 20 15
300 80c. orange 20 15
301 1e. red 25 15
302 1e.75 blue 60 40
303 2e. green 1·10 65
304 5e. olive 3·00 85
305 10e. blue 5·25 1·00
306 20e. brown 13·00 2·00
307 10c. red (air) 30 20
308 20c. violet 30 20
309 50c. orange 30 20
310 1e. blue 35 20
311 2e. red 65 30
312 3e. green 90 45
313 5e. brown 2·00 70
314 9e. red 4·75 1·50
315 10e. mauve 6·00 1·75

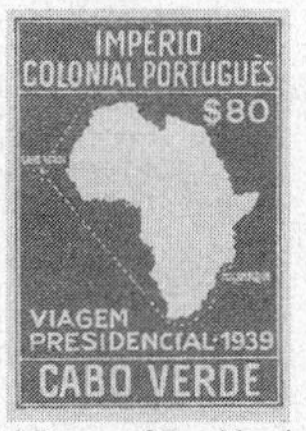

14 Route of President's Tour

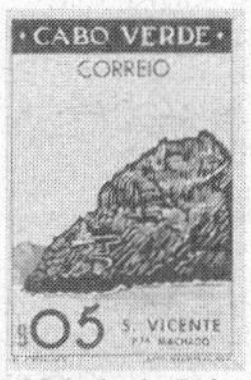

16 Machado Point, Sao Vicente

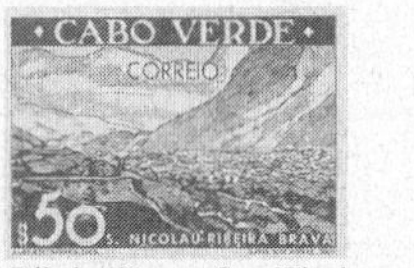

17 Ribeira Brava, Sao Nicolau

1939. Pres. Carmona's 2nd Colonial Tour.
316 **14** 80c. violet on mauve 4·00 3·75
317 1e.75 blue on blue 26·00 22·00
318 20e. brown on cream 70·00 22·00

1948. Nos. 276 and 294 surch.
319 10c. on 30c. purple 50 40
320 25c. on 40c. red 65 40

1948.
321 **16** 5c. purple and bistre 50 30
322 – 10c. green and light green 50 30
323 **17** 50c. purple and lilac 95 30
324 – 1e. purple 3·50 1·00
325 – 1e.75 blue and green 4·00 1·40
326 – 2e. brown and ochre 9·50 1·60
327 – 5e. green and yellow 19·00 2·50
328 – 10e. red and orange 30·00 12·50
329 – 20e. violet and buff 75·00 21·00
DESIGNS—VERT: 10c. Ribeira Grande. HORIZ: 1e. Porto Grande, Sao Vicente; 1e.75, 5e. Mindelo, Sao Vicente; 2e. Joao de Evora beach, Sao Vicente; 10e. Volcano, Fogo; 20e. Paul.

1948. Honouring the Statue of Our Lady of Fatima. As T **33** of Angola.
330 50c. blue 6·75 3·25

1949. 75th Anniv of U.P.U. As T **39** of Angola.
331 1e. mauve 4·75 2·75

1950. Holy Year. As T **41/2** of Angola.
332 1e. brown 55 40
333 2e. blue 2·50 1·25

1951. Surch with figures and bars over old value.
334 10c. on 35c. (No. 295) 40 40
335 20c. on 70c. (No. 299) 55 50
336 40c. on 70c. (No. 299) 60 50
337 50c. on 80c. (No. 300) 60 50
338 1e. on 1e.75 (No. 302) 60 50
339 2e. on 10e. (No. 305) 3·50 1·25

1951. Termination of Holy Year. As T **44** of Angola.
340 2e. violet and mauve 1·00 70

1952. No. 302 surch with figures and cross over old values.
341 10c. on 1e.75 blue 85 85
342 20c. on 1e.75 blue 85 85
343 50c. on 1e.75 blue 3·75 3·50
344 1e. on 1e.75 blue 45 15
345 1e.50 on 1e.75 blue 45 15

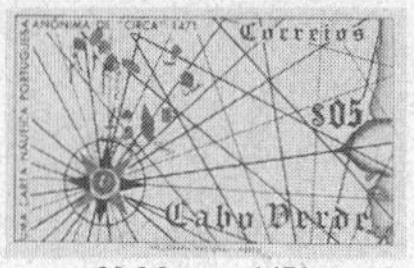

20 Map, c. 1471

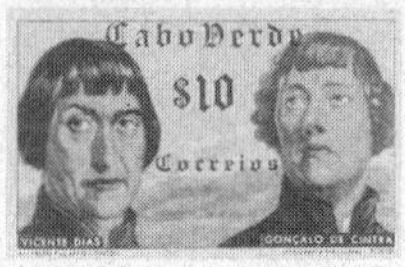

21 V. Dias and G. de Cintra

1962. Portuguese Navigators as T **20/21**. Mult.
346 5c. Type **20** 10 10
347 10c. Type **21** 10 10
348 30c. D. Afonso and A. Fernandes 10 10
349 50c. Lancarote and S. da Costa 10 10
350 1e. D. Gomes and A. da Nola 15 10
351 2e. Princes Fernando and Henry the Navigator 55 10
352 3e. A. Goncalves and D. Dias 5·50 80
353 5e. A. Goncalves Baldaia and J. Fernandes 1·75 40
354 10e. D. Fanes da Gra and A. de Freitas 3·75 1·10
355 20e. Map, 1502 6·50 1·25

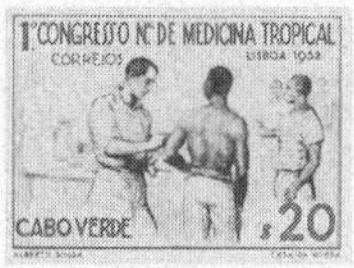

22 Doctor giving Injection

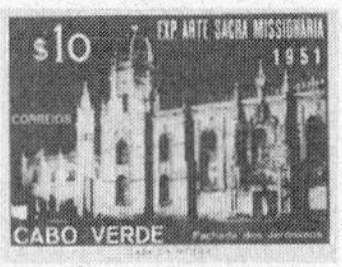

23 Facade of Monastery

1952. 1st Tropical Medicine Congress, Lisbon.
356 **22** 20c. black and green 35 30

1953. Missionary Art Exhibition.
357 **23** 10c. brown and olive 10 10
358 50c. violet and salmon 35 25
359 1e. green and orange 1·00 55

1953. Portuguese Stamp Centenary. As T **48** of Angola.
360 50c. multicoloured 1·00 55

1954. 4th Cent of Sao Paulo. As T **49** of Angola.
361 1e. black, green and buff 30 25

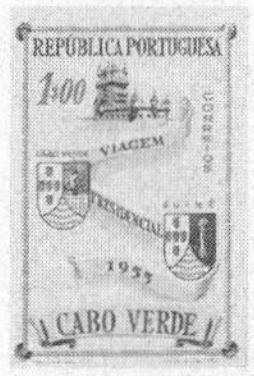

24 Arms of Cape Verde Is. and Portuguese Guinea

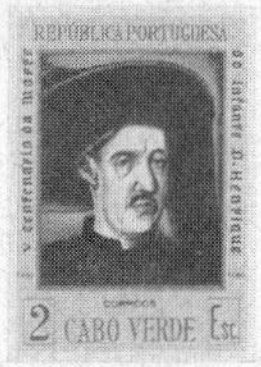

26 Prince Henry the Navigator

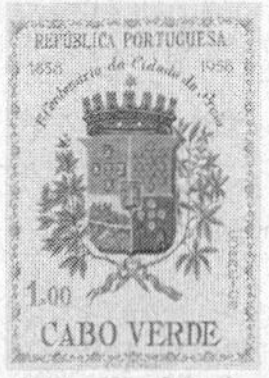

25 Arms of Praia

1955. Presidential Visit.
362 **24** 1e. multicoloured 30 25
363 1e.60c. multicoloured 50 40

1958. Centenary of City of Praia. Multicoloured.
364 **25** 1e. on yellow 30 20
365 2e.50 on salmon 45 50

1958. Brussels International Exn. As T **55** of Angola.
366 2e. multicoloured 40 20

1958. 6th International Congress of Tropical Medicine. As T **56** of Angola. Multicoloured.
367 3c. "Aloe vera" (plant) 2·75 1·25

1960. 500th Death Anniv of Prince Henry the Navigator.
368 **26** 2e. multicoloured 20 15

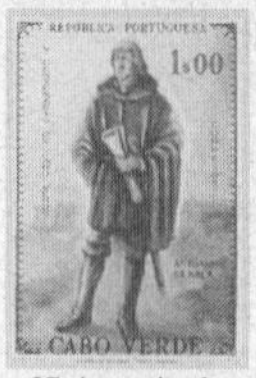
27 Antonio da Nola

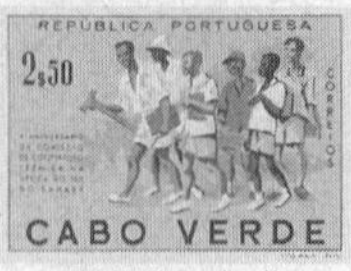
28 "Education"

1960. 500th Anniv of Colonization of Cape Verde Islands. Multicoloured.

369 1e. Type **27** 30 25
370 2e.50 Diogo Gomes 80 60

1960. 10th Anniv of African Technical Co-operation Commission.

371 **28** 2e.50 multicoloured 55 30

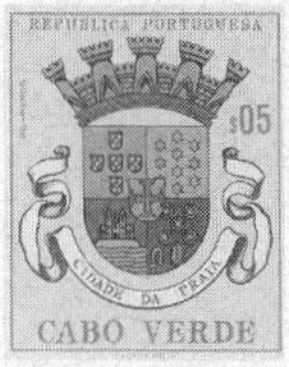
29 Arms of Praia

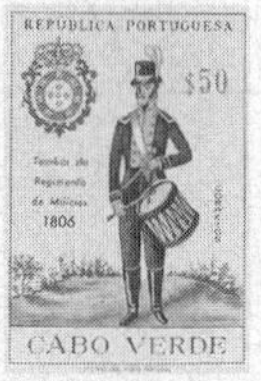
30 Militia Regiment Drummer, 1806

1961. Urban Arms. As T **29**. Arms multicoloured; inscriptions in red and green; background colours given.

372 5c. buff 15 15
373 15c. blue 15 15
374 20c. yellow 15 15
375 30c. lilac 15 15
376 1e. green 35 15
377 2e. lemon 35 15
378 2e.50 pink 50 15
379 3e. brown 75 25
380 5e. blue 75 25
381 7e.50 olive 85 40
382 15e. mauve . . . . 1·40 60
383 30e. yellow . . . . 2·75 1·60

ARMS: 15c. Nova Sintra. 20c. Ribeira Brava. 30c. Assomada. 1e. Maio. 2e. Mindelo. 2e.50 Santa Maria. 3e. Pombas. 5e. Sal-Rei. 7e.50, Tarrafal. 15e. Maria Pia. 30e. San Felipe.

1962. Sports. As T **62** of Angola. Multicoloured.

384 50c. Throwing the javelin . . 15 15
385 1e. Discus thrower 50 15
386 1e.50 Batsman (cricket) . . . 1·25 30
387 2e.50 Boxing 50 25
388 4e.50 Hurdler 80 55
389 12e.50 Golfers . . . . 1·60 1·00

1962. Malaria Eradication. Mosquito design as T **63** of Angola. Multicoloured.

390 2e.50 "Anopheles pretoriensis" 75 55

1963. 10th Anniv of T.A.P. Airline. As T **69** of Angola.

391 2e.50 multicoloured 45 30

1964. Centenary of National Overseas Bank. As T **71** of Angola but portrait of J. da S. M. Leal.

392 1e.50 multicoloured 50 40

1965. Centenary of I.T.U. As T **73** of Angola.

393 2e.50 multicoloured . . . . . 1·00 80

1965. Portuguese Military Uniforms. Mult.

394 50c. Type **30** 15 15
395 1e. Militiaman, 1806 . . . . 25 15
396 1e.50 Infantry Grenadiers officers, 1833 . . . . 40 25
397 2e.50 Infantry grenadier, 1833 70 20
398 3e. Cavalry officer, 1834 . . 1·00 30
399 4e. Infantry grenadier, 1835 70 40
400 5e. Artillery officer, 1848 . . 70 40
401 10e. Infantry drum-major, 1856 . . . . 1·40 1·10

1966. 40th Anniv of National Revolution. As T **77** of Angola, but showing different building. Multicoloured.

402 1e. Dr A. Moreira's Academy and Public Assistance Building 30 20

1967. Centenary of Military Naval Association. As T **79** of Angola. Multicoloured.

403 1e. F. da Costa and gunboat "Mandovy" 55 25
404 1e. 50 C. Araujo and minesweeper "Augusto Castilho" 85 40

1967. 50th Anniv of Fatima Apparitions. As T **80** of Angola. Multicoloured.

405 1e. Image of Virgin Mary . . 15 15

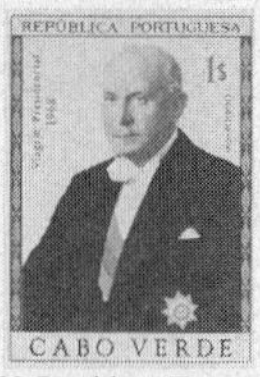
33 President Tomas

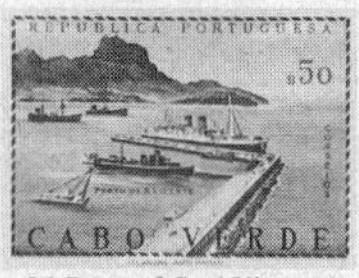
34 Port of Sao Vicente

1968. Visit of President Tomas of Portugal.

406 **33** 1e. multicoloured 15 15

1968. 500th Birth Anniv of Pedro Cabral (explorer). As T **84** of Angola. Multicoloured.

407 1e. Cantino's map, 1502 . . . 40 25
408 1e.50 Pedro Alvares Cabral (vert) 60 40

1968. "Produce of Cape Verde Islands". Mult.

409 50c. Type **34** 30 15
410 1e. "Purgueira" (Tatrophus curcus) 20 15
411 1e.50 Groundnuts 20 15
412 2e.50 Castor-oil plant 20 15
413 3e.50 "Inhame" (Dioscorea alata) 25 15
414 4e. Date palm 25 15
415 4e.50 "Goiabeira" (Psidium guajava) 35 20
416 5e. Tamarind 50 20
417 10e. Manioc 65 40
418 30e. Girl of Cape Verde . . . 1·60 1·25

The 1e. to 30e. values are vert.

1969. Birth Centenary of Admiral Gago Coutinho. As T **86** of Angola. Multicoloured.

419 30c. Fairey IIID seaplane "Lusitania" and map of Lisbon-Rio flight (vert) . . 15 15

1969. 500th Birth Anniv of Vasco da Gama (explorer). Multicoloured. As T **87** of Angola.

420 1e.50 Vasco da Gama (vert) 15 15

1969. Centenary of Overseas Administrative Reforms. As T **88** of Angola.

421 2e. multicoloured 15 15

1969. 500th Birth Anniv of King Manoel I. As T **89** of Angola. Multicoloured.

422 3e. Manoel I 20 15

1970. Birth Centenary of Marshal Carmona. As T **91** of Angola. Multicoloured.

423 2e.50 Half-length portrait . . 25 20

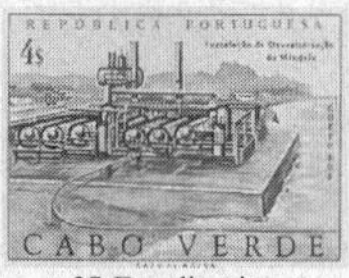
35 Desalination Installation

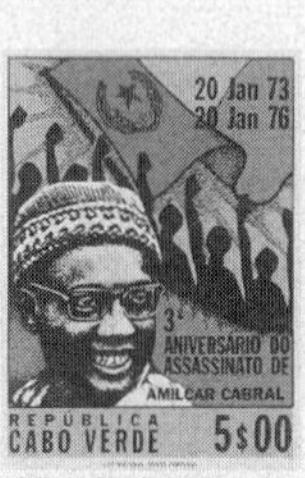
37 Cabral, Flag and People

1971. Inauguration of Desalination Plant, Mindelo.

424 **35** 4e. multicoloured 55 45

1972. 400th Anniv of Camoens' "Lusiad" (epic poem). As T **96** of Angola. Multicoloured.

425 5e. Galleons at Cape Verde 75 20

1972. Olympic Games, Munich. As T **97** of Angola. Multicoloured.

426 4e. Basketball and boxing . . 30 20

1972. 50th Anniv of 1st Flight Lisbon–Rio de Janeiro. As T **98** of Angola. Multicoloured.

427 3e.50 Fairey IIID seaplane "Lusitania" near Sao Vicente 30 20

1973. Centenary of I.M.O./W.M.O. As Type **99** of Angola.

428 2e.50 multicoloured 30 20

1975. Independence. No. 407 optd **INDEPENDENCIA 5-Julho-75.**

430 1e. multicoloured 15 10

1975. 3rd Anniv of Amilcar Cabral's Assassination.

431 **37** 5e. multicoloured 20 15

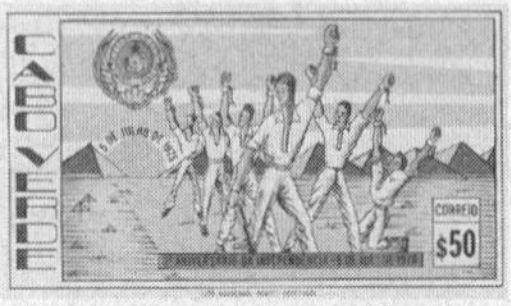
38 Islanders with Broken Shackles

1976. 1st Anniv of Independence.

432 **38** 50c. multicoloured 10 10
433 3e. multicoloured 15 10
434 15e. multicoloured 40 20
435 50e. multicoloured . . . . 1·25 65

1976. Nos. 428, 424 and 415 optd **REPUBLICA DE.**

437 2e.50 multicoloured (No. 428) 15 10
438 4e. multicoloured (No. 424) 11·00 1·75
439 4e.50 multicoloured (No. 415) 1·00 1·00

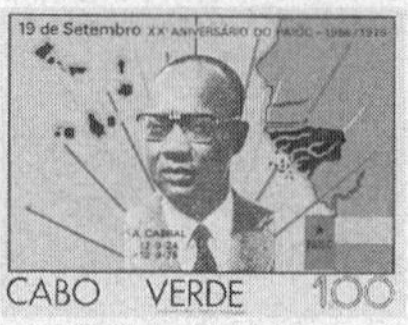
40 Cabral and Map

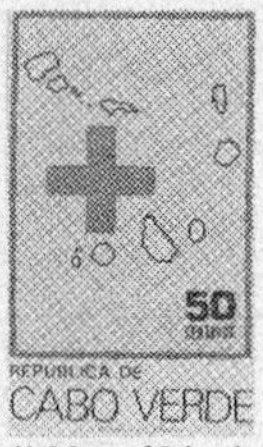
41 Map of Islands

1976. 20th Anniv of PAIGC (Revolutionary Party).

440 **40** 1e. multicoloured 10 10

1977. Red Cross.

441 **41** 50c. multicoloured 10 10

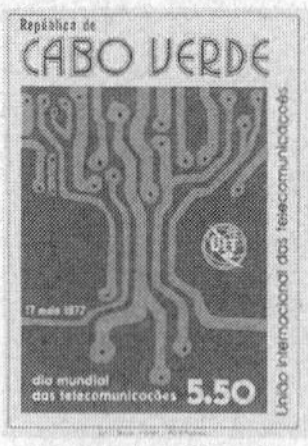
42 Printed Circuit

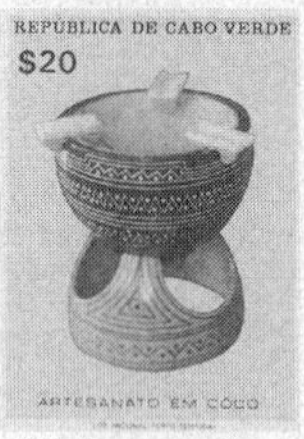
43 Ashtray on Stand

1977. International Telecommunications Day.

442 **42** 5e.50 orange, brown & blk 15 10

1977. Craftsmanship in Coconut. Multicoloured.

443 20c. Type **43** 10 10
444 30c. Ornamental bell 10 10
445 50c. Lamp 10 10
446 1e. Nativity 10 10
447 1e.50 Desk lamp 10 10
448 5e. Storage jar 15 10
449 10e. Container with hinged lid 35 15
450 20e. Tobacco jar 65 20
451 30e. Stringed instrument . . 1·10 35

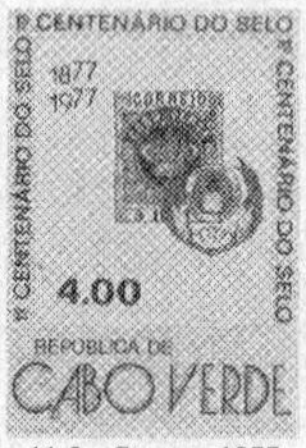
44 5r. Stamp, 1877

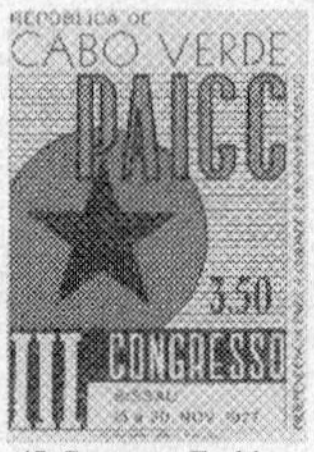
45 Congress Emblem

1977. Centenary of First Cape Verde Stamps.

452 **44** 4e. multicoloured 15 10
453 8e. multicoloured 25 10

1977. 3rd PAIGC Congress, Bissau.

454 **45** 3e.50 multicoloured 15 10

1978. No. 419 surch **3$00.**

455 3e. on 30c. multicoloured . . 15 10

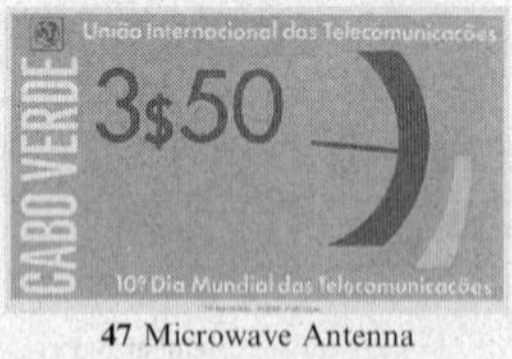
47 Microwave Antenna

1978. 10th World Telecommunications Day.

456 **47** 3e.50 multicoloured 15 10

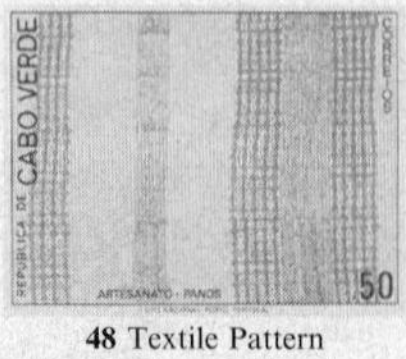
48 Textile Pattern

1978. Handicrafts. Multicoloured.

457 50c. Type **48** 10 10
458 1e.50 Carpet runner and map of Islands 10 10
459 2e. Woven ribbon and map of Islands 10 10
460 3e. Shoulder bag and map of Islands 10 10
461 10e. Woven Cushions (vert) 30 20

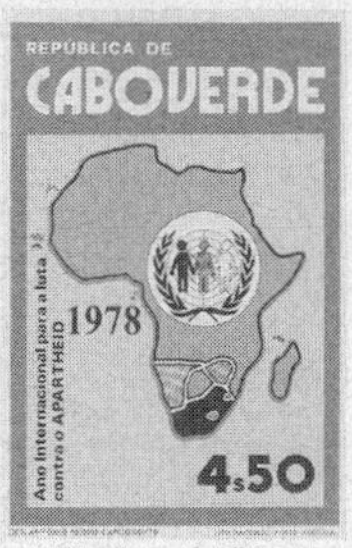
49 Map of Africa

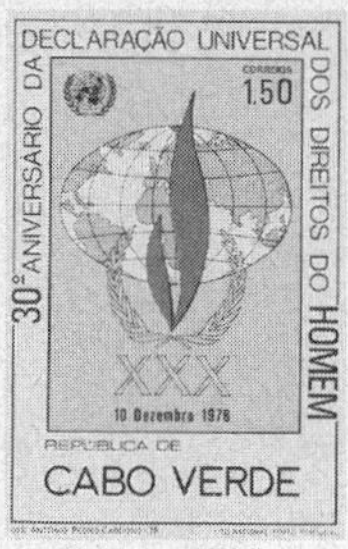
51 Human Rights Emblem

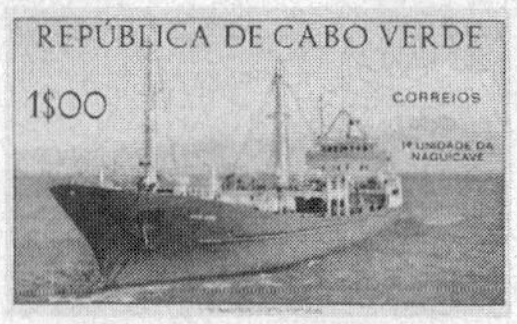
50 Freighter "Cabo Verde"

1978. International Anti-Apartheid Year.

462 **49** 4e.50 multicoloured 15 10

1978. 1st Cape Verde Merchant Ship.

463 **50** 1e. multicoloured 50 10

1978. 30th Anniv of Declaration of Human Rights.

464 **51** 1e.50 multicoloured 10 10
465 2e. multicoloured 10 10

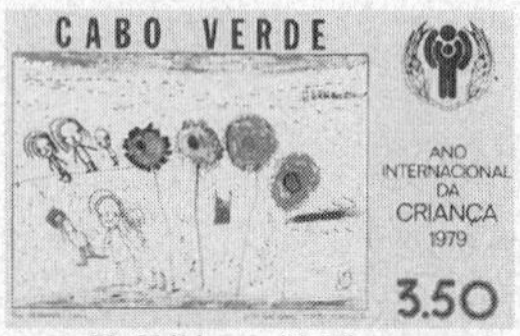
52 Children with Flowers

1979. International Year of the Child. Mult.

466 1e.50 Children with balloons and flags 10 10
467 3e.50 Type **52** 10 10

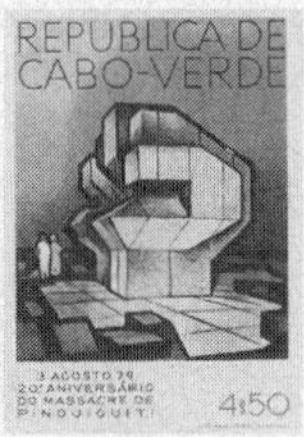
53 Monument

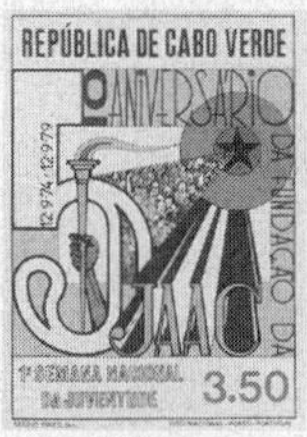
54 Poster

1979. 20th Anniv of Pindjiguiti Massacre.

468 **53** 4e.50 multicoloured 15 10

1979. 1st National Youth Week.

469 **54** 3e.50 multicoloured 15 10

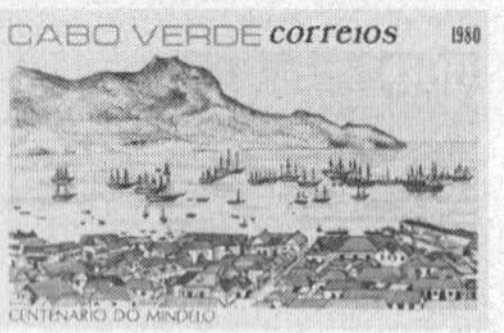
55 Mindelo

1980. Centenary of Mindelo City.

470 **55** 4e. multicoloured 55 15

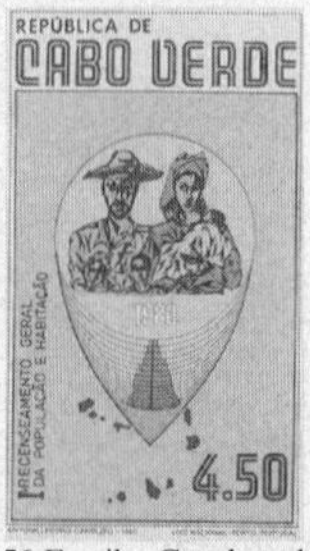
56 Family, Graph and Map

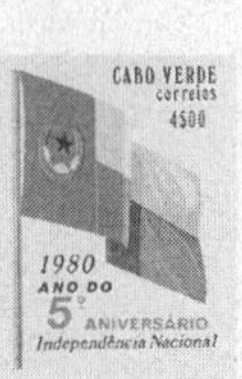
57 National Flag

1980. 1st Population and Housing Census.

471 **56** 3e.50 multicoloured 10 10
472 4e.50 multicoloured 15 10

1980. 5th Anniv of Independence (1st issue).

473 **57** 4e. multicoloured 10 10

See also Nos. 481/3.

58 Running   **59 Stylized Bird**

1980. Olympic Games, Moscow. Multicoloured.
474	1e. Type **58**	10	10
475	2e.50 Boxing	10	10
476	3e. Basketball	10	10
477	4e. Volleyball	10	10
478	20e. Swimming	55	25
479	50e. Tennis	1·25	50

1980. 5th Anniv of Independence (2nd issue).
481 **59**	4e. multicoloured	10	10
482	7e. multicoloured	15	10
483	11e. multicoloured	25	15

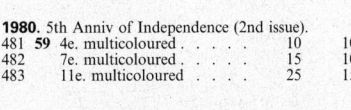

60 Cigarette, Cigar, Pipe and Diseased Heart

1980. World Health Day. Anti-smoking Campaign. Multicoloured.
484	4e. Type **60**	10	10
485	7e. Healthy lungs plus smoking equals diseased lungs	20	10

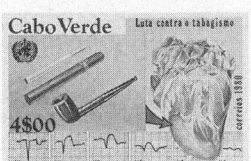

61 Albacore

1980. Marine Life. Multicoloured.
486	50c. Type **61**	10	10
487	4e.50 Atlantic horse-mackerel	15	10
488	8e. Mediterranean moray	40	15
489	10e. Brown meagre	40	15
490	12e. Skipjack tuna	50	20
491	50e. Blue shark	1·50	70

62 "Area Verdel"

1980. Freighters. Multicoloured.
492	3e. Type **62**	25	15
493	5e.50 "Ilha do Maio"	30	20
494	7e.50 "Ilha de Komo"	65	25
495	9e. "Boa Vista"	65	25
496	12e. "Santo Antao"	75	35
497	30e. "Santiago"	1·75	75

63 "Lochnera rosea"

1980. Flowers. Multicoloured.
498	50c. Type **63**	10	10
499	2e.50 "Poinciana regia Bojer"	10	10
500	8e. "Mirabilis jalapa"	25	10
501	10e. "Nerium oleander"	25	10
502	12e. "Bougainvillea litoralis"	30	10
503	30e. "Hibiscus rosa sinensis"	70	30

64 Desert Scene and Hands holding plant

1981. Desert Erosion Prevention. Multicoloured.
504	4e.50 Type **64**	15	10
505	10e.50 Hands caring for plant and river scene	25	15

65 Map, Flag, and "Official Bulletin" announcing Constitution   **67 Antenna**

1981. 6th Anniv of Constitution.
506 **65**	4e.50 multicoloured	15	10

1981. Telecommunications. Multicoloured.
508	4e.50 Type **67**	10	10
509	8e. Dish antenna	25	10
510	20e. Dish antenna and satellite	50	30

68 Disabled Person in Wheelchair and I.Y.D.P. Emblem

1981. International Year of Disabled Persons.
511 **68**	4e.50 multicoloured	15	10

69 Moorhens

1981. Birds. Multicoloured.
512	1e. Little egret (vert)	25	10
513	4e.50 Barn owl (vert)	40	20
514	8e. Grey-headed kingfisher (vert)	90	30
515	10e. Type **69**	1·90	40
516	12e. Helmet guineafowls	2·60	40

70 Map showing Member States

1982. CILSS Congress, Praia.
518 **70**	11e.50 multicoloured	30	10

71 Tackle

1982. "Amilcar Cabral" Football Cup Competition. Multicoloured.
519	4e.50 Type **71**	15	10
520	7e.50 Running with ball	20	10
521	11e.50 Goalmouth scene	30	10

72 Militiawomen

1982. 1st Anniv of Cape Verde Women's Organization. Multicoloured.
522	4e.50 Type **72**	15	10
523	8e. Women farmers	20	10
524	12e. Nursery teacher	30	10

73 Footballers

1982. World Cup Football Championship, Spain.
525 **73**	1e.50 multicoloured	10	10
526	4e.50 multicoloured	15	10
527	8e. multicoloured	20	10
528	10e.50 multicoloured	25	10
529	12e. multicoloured	30	10
530	20e. multicoloured	50	30

DESIGNS: 4e.50 to 20e. Various football scenes.

74 "Morrissey-Ernestina"

1982. Return of Schooner "Morrissey-Ernestina".
532 **74**	12e. multicoloured	1·50	45

75 San Vicente Shipyard

1982. 7th Anniv of Independence.
533 **75**	10e.50 multicoloured	1·25	45

76 "Hypolimnas misippus"

1982. Butterflies. Multicoloured.
534	2e. Type **76**	15	10
535	4e.50 "Melanitis lede"	25	15
536	8e. "Catopsilia florella"	40	20
537	10e.50 "Colias electo"	55	20
538	11e.50 "Danaus chrysippus"	65	20
539	12e. "Papilio demodecus"	65	20

77 Amilcar Cabral

1983. Amilcar Cabral Symposium.
540 **77**	7e. multicoloured	15	10
541	10e.50 multicoloured	20	10

78 Francisco Xavier de Cruz (composer)

1983. Composers and Poets. Multicoloured.
543	7e. Type **78**	15	10
544	14e. Eugenio Tavares (poet)	30	10

79 "World Communications Network"   **80 Cape Verde Cone**

1983. World Communications Year.
545 **79**	13e. multicoloured	20	10

1983. Shells. Multicoloured.
546	50c. Type **80**	10	10
547	1e. "Conus decoratus"	10	10
548	3e. "Conus salreiensis"	15	10
549	10e. "Conus verdensis"	30	20
550	50e. "Conus cuneolus"	1·40	90

81 Arch and Cross   **82 Auster D5/160 Husky**

1983. 450th Anniv of Christianity in Cape Verde Islands.
551 **81**	7e. multicoloured	15	10

1984. 40th Anniv of I.C.A.O. Multicoloured.
552	50c. Type **82**	10	10
553	2e. De Havilland Dove	10	10
554	10e. Hawker Siddeley HS748	25	15
555	13e. De Havilland Dragon Rapide	25	15
556	20e. De Havilland Twin Otter	50	30
557	50e. Britten-Norman Islander	1·10	65

83 Families, Houses and Emblems as Balloons   **84 Figure rising from Nautilus Shell**

1984. National Solidarity Campaign.
558 **83**	6e.50 multicoloured	10	10
559	13e.50 multicoloured	20	10

1985. 2nd Cape Verde Womens' Organization Conference.
560 **84**	8e. multicoloured	25	15

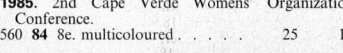

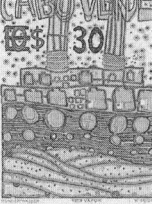

85 Emblem   **87 "Steamer"**

1985. 10th Anniv of Independence.
561 **85**	8e. multicoloured	15	10
562	12e. multicoloured	20	10

1985.
564 **87**	30e. on 10c. multicoloured	40	40

88 "Mabuya vaillanti"   **89** Food in Pot over Fire

1986. Endangered Reptiles. Multicoloured.
566   8e. Type **88**   30   10
567   10e. "Tarentola gigas brancoensis"   35   10
568   15e. "Tarentola gigas gigas"   45   10
569   30e. "Hemidactylus bouvieri"   90   20

1986. World Food Day. Multicoloured.
571   8e. Type **89**   15   10
572   12e. Women pounding food in mortar   15   10
573   15e. Woman rolling flat bread with stone   20   10

90 Dove and Olive Branch

1986. International Peace Year.
574   **90** 12e. multicoloured   15   10
575   30e. multicoloured   40   20

91 Family Planning and Child Health Centre, Praia, and Woman breast-feeding Baby

1987. Child Survival Campaign. Multicoloured.
576   8e. Type **91**   15   10
577   10e. Assomada SOS children's village   15   10
578   12e. Family planning clinic, Mindelo, and nurse with child   15   10
579   16e. Children's home, Mindelo, and nurse with baby   25   10
580   100e. Calouste Gulbenkian kindergarten, Praia, and child writing . . . . . .   1·40   1·25

92 Mindelo City

1987. Tourism. Multicoloured.
581   1e. Type **92**   10   10
582   2e.50 Santo Antao island . .   10   10
583   5e. Fogo island   10   10
584   8e. Pillory, Velha City . .   15   10
585   10e. Boa Entrada valley, Santiago island   15   10
586   12e. Fishing boats, Santiago   50   15
587   100e. Furna harbour, Brava island . . . .   1·40   65

93 "Carvalho" (schooner)

1987. Sailing Ships. Multicoloured.
588   **93** 12e. black, mauve & blue   45   20
589   – 16e. black, blue & mauve   45   20
590   – 50e. black, blue & dp blue   1·90   70
DESIGNS: 16e. "Nauta" (cutter); 50e. "Maria Sony" (schooner).

94 Emblem

1987. 2nd National Development Plan.
592   **94** 8e. multicoloured   15   10

95 Moths on Stem

1988. Crop Protection. Multicoloured.
593   50c. Type **95**   10   10
594   2e. Caterpillars on plant treated with bio-insecticides   10   10
595   9e. Use of imported predators   20   10
596   13e. Use of imported predatorial insects   30   15
597   16e. Locust on stem   35   15
598   19e. Damaged wood   45   20

96 17th-century Dutch Map

1988. Antique Maps of Cape Verde Islands. Multicoloured.
600   1e.50 Type **96**   10   10
601   2e.50 18th-cent Belgian map   10   10
602   4e.50 18th-cent French map   10   10
603   9e.50 18th-cent English map   15   10
604   19e.50 19th-cent English map   30   15
605   20e. 18th-cent French map (vert)   30   15

97 Church of the Abbot of the Holy Shelter, Tarrafal, Santiago

1988. Churches. Multicoloured.
606   5e. Type **97**   10   10
607   8e. Church of Our Lady of Light, Maio   15   10
608   10e. Church of the Nazarene, Praia, Santiago   15   10
609   12e. Church of Our Lady of the Rosary, Sao Nicolau   20   10
610   15e. Church of the Nazarene, Mindelo, Sao Vicente . . .   25   15
611   20e. Church of Our Lady of Grace, Praia, Santiago . .   30   15

98 Boy filling Tin with Water

1988. Water Economy Campaign.
612   **98** 12e. multicoloured   20   10

99 Red Cross Workers

1988. 125th Anniv of Red Cross Movement.
613   **99** 7e. multicoloured   10   10

100 Group of Youths and Pres. Pereira

1988. 3rd Congress of African Party for the Independence of Cape Verde. Multicoloured.
614   7e. Type **100**   10   10
615   10e.50 Pres. Pereira and Perez de Cuellar (U.N. Secretary-General)   15   10
616   30e. Emblem and Pres. Pereira   50   25

101 Handball

1988. Olympic Games, Seoul. Multicoloured.
618   12e. Type **101**   20   10
619   15e. Tennis   25   15
620   20e. Football   30   15
621   30e. Boxing   50   25

102 Hot-air Balloon "Pro Juventute"

1989. 2nd Pro Juventute Congress.
623   **102** 30e. multicoloured   45   25

103 Silva

1989. Death Centenary of Roberto Duarte Silva (chemist).
624   **103** 12e.50 multicoloured . . .   20   10

104 "Liberty guiding the People" (Eugene Delacroix)

1989. Bicentenary of French Revolution.
625   **104** 20e. multicoloured   30   15
626   24e. multicoloured   35   20
627   25e. multicoloured   40   20

105 Anniversary Emblem

1989. Centenary of Interparliamentary Union. Mult.
629   2e. Type **105**   10   10
630   4e. Dove   10   10
631   13e. National Assembly building   20   10

106 Fonte Lima Women firing Pots

1989. Traditional Pottery. Multicoloured.
632   13e. Type **106**   20   10
633   20e. Terra di Monti women and children arranging pots to bake in sun (vert) . . .   30   15
634   24e. Terra di Monti woman shaping pot   35   20
635   25e. Fonte Lima women kneading clay (vert) . . .   40   20

107 Boy and Truck   **108** Pope John Paul II

1989. Christmas. Home-made Toys. Mult.
636   1e. Type **107**   10   10
637   6e. Boy with car on waste ground   10   10
638   8e. Boy with truck on pavement   15   10
639   11e.50 Boys with various vehicles   15   10
640   18e. Boys and sit-on scooter   30   15
641   100e. Boy with boat . . . .   1·50   75

1990. Papal Visit.
642   **108** 13e. multicoloured   20   10
643   20e. multicoloured   30   15

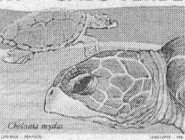

109 Green Turtles

1990. Turtles. Multicoloured.
645   50c. Type **109**   10   10
646   1e. Leatherback turtles . .   10   10
647   5e. Olive ridley turtles . . .   10   10
648   10e. Loggerhead turtles . . .   15   10
649   42e. Hawksbill turtles . . .   65   35

110 Footballers

1990. World Cup Football Championship, Italy.
650   **110** 4e. multicoloured   10   10
651   – 7e.50 multicoloured   15   10
652   – 8e. multicoloured   15   10
653   – 100e. multicoloured . . .   1·60   80
DESIGNS: 7e.50 to 100e. Different footballing scenes.

111 Face

1990. 1st Congress of Cape Verde Women's Movement.
655   **111** 9e. multicoloured   15   10

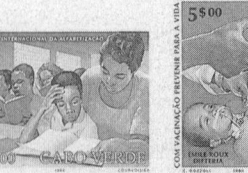

112 Teacher helping Boy to Read   **113** Diphtheria Treatment and Emile Roux (pioneer of antitoxic method)

1990. International Literacy Year. Multicoloured.
656   2e. Type **112**   10   10
657   3e. Teacher with adult class   10   10
658   15e. Teacher with flash-card   25   15
659   19e. Adult student pointing to letters on blackboard . .   30   10

1990. Vaccination Campaign. Multicoloured.
660   5e. Type **113**   10   10
661   13e. Tuberculosis vaccination and Robert Koch (discoverer of tubercle bacillus)   20   10

662	20e. Tetanus vaccination and Gaston Ramon	30	15
663	24e. Poliomyelitis oral vaccination and Jonas Edward Salk (discoverer of vaccine)	40	20

114 Musician on Bull's Back

1990. Traditional Stories. Multicoloured.

664	50c. Type **114**	10	10
665	2e.50 Fisherman and mermaid ("Joao Piquinote")	10	10
666	12e. Girl and snake	20	10
667	25e. Couple and eggs ("Ti Lobo, Ti Lobo")	40	20

115 World Map and Beam destroying AIDS Virus

1991. Anti-AIDS Campaign. Multicoloured.

668	13e. Type **115**	20	10
669	24e. Beam, AIDS virus and "SIDA"	40	20

116 Fishing Boat at Sea and Fishermen on Shore

1991. Fishing Industry. Multicoloured.

670	10e. Type **116**	20	15
671	24e. Fisherman removing hook from fish	70	30
672	25e. Fishing boats	55	30
673	50e. Fishermen taking in lines	1·10	65

117 Our Lady of the Rosary Church

1991. Tourism. Ruins of Ribeira Grande, Santiago Island. Multicoloured.

674	12e.50 Type **117**	20	10
675	15e. Se Cathedral	25	15
676	20e. Sao Filipe fortress	30	15
677	30e. St. Francis's Convent	45	20

118 "Lavandula rotundifolia"

119 Guitar

1991. Medicinal Plants. Multicoloured.

679	10e. Type **118**	15	10
680	15e. "Micromeria forbesii"	25	15
681	21e. "Sarcostemma daltonii"	30	15
682	24e. "Periploca chevalieri"	40	20
683	30e. "Echium hypertropicum"	45	20
684	35e. "Erysimum caboverdeanum"	55	25

1991. Musical Instruments. Multicoloured.

685	10e. Type **119**	25	15
686	20e. Violin	50	35
687	29e. Guitar with five double strings	80	40
688	47e. Cimboa	1·25	75

120 Crib (Tito Livio Goncalves)

1991. Christmas. Multicoloured.

690	31e. Type **120**	50	25
691	50e. Fonte-Lima crib	80	40

121 Rose Apples

1992. Tropical Fruits. Multicoloured.

692	16e. Type **121**	35	15
693	25e. Mangoes	50	25
694	31e. Cashews	65	30
695	32e. Avocados	70	35

122 Ships anchored in Bay

1992. 500th Anniv of Discovery of America by Columbus. Columbus's Landings in Cape Verde Islands. Multicoloured.

696	40e. Type **122**	1·10	70
697	40e. Caravel	1·10	70

124 Throwing the Javelin

1992. Olympic Games, Barcelona. Multicoloured.

700	16e. Type **124**	35	15
701	20e. Weightlifting	40	20
702	32e. Pole vaulting	70	35
703	40e. Putting the shot	85	40

125 Oxen and Sugar Cane

1992. Production of Molasses. Multicoloured.

705	19e. Type **125**	35	15
706	20e. Crushing cane	35	15
707	37e. Feeding cane into mill	70	35
708	38e. Cooking molasses	70	35

126 Cat

1992. Domestic Animals. Multicoloured.

709	16e. Type **126**	30	15
710	31e. Chickens	55	25
711	32e. Dog (vert)	60	30
712	50e. Horse	90	45

127 "Tubastrea aurea"

1993. Corals. Multicoloured.

713	5e. Type **127**	10	10
714	31e. "Corallium rubrum"	55	25
715	37e. "Porites porites"	65	30
716	50e. "Millepora alcicornis"	90	45

129 King Ferdinand and Queen Isabella of Spain and Pope Alexander VI

130 "Palinurus charlestoni"

1993. 500th Anniv of Pope Alexander VI's Bulls (on Portuguese and Spanish spheres of influence) and of Treaty of Tordesillas. Multicoloured.

718	37e. Type **129**	65	30
719	37e. King Joao II of Portugal and Pope Julius II	65	30
720	38e. Astrolabe, quill and left-half of globe	70	35
721	38e. Map of Iberian Peninsula and right-half of globe with Cape Verde Islands highlighted	70	35

Stamps of the same value were issued together in se-tenant pairs, each pair forming a composite design.

1993. Lobsters. Multicoloured.

722	2e. Type **130**	10	10
723	10e. Brown lobster	20	10
724	17e. Royal lobster	30	15
725	38e. Stone lobster	70	35

131 Cory's Shearwater

1993. Nature Reserves. Multicoloured.

727	10e. Type **131** (Branco and Raso Islets)	25	15
728	30e. Brown booby (De Cima and Raso Islets)	80	25
729	40e. Magnificent frigate bird (Curral Velho and Baluarte Islets)	1·50	35
730	41e. Red-billed tropic bird (Raso and De Cima Islets)	1·90	40

132 Rose

1993. Flowers. Multicoloured.

731	5e. Type **132**	10	10
732	30e. Bird of Paradise flower	55	25
733	37e. Sweet William	65	30
734	50e. Cactus dahlia	90	45

133 Map and Prince Henry (½-size illustration)

1994. 600th Birth Anniv of Prince Henry the Navigator.

736 **133**	37e. multicoloured	55	25

134 Players and Giants Stadium, New York

1994. World Cup Football Championship, U.S.A. Multicoloured.

737	1e. Type **134**	10	10
738	20e. Referee showing red card and Rose Bowl, Los Angeles	30	15
739	37e. Scoring goal and Foxboro Stadium, Boston	55	25
740	38e. Linesman raising flag and Silverdome, Detroit	55	25

135 Sand Tiger

136 "Prata" Bananas

1994. Sharks. Multicoloured.

742	21e. Type **135**	45	15
743	27e. Black-tipped shark	60	25
744	37e. Whale shark	1·00	50
745	38e. Velvet belly	1·00	50

1994. Bananas. Multicoloured.

746	12e. Type **136**	20	10
747	16e. "Pao" bananas (horiz)	25	10
748	30e. "Ana roberta" bananas	45	20
749	40e. "Roxa" bananas	60	30

137 Fontes Pereira de Melo

1994. Lighthouses. Multicoloured.

751	2e. Type **137**	10	10
752	37e. Morro Negro	60	30
753	38e. D. Amelia (vert)	60	30
754	50e. D. Maria Pia (vert)	80	40

138 X-Ray Tube and Dates

139 Child with Tuna

1995. Centenary of Discovery of X-Rays by Wilhelm Rontgen.

755 **138**	20e. multicoloured	30	15
756	37e. multicoloured	60	30

1995. 50th Anniv of F.A.O. Multicoloured.

758	37e. Type **139**	70	30
759	38e. Globe and wheat ear	60	30

140 Wire-haired Fox Terrier and "Two Foxhounds and Fox Terrier" (John Emms)

141 Communications

1995. Dogs. Heads of dogs and paintings. Mult.

760	1e. Type **140**	10	10
761	10e. Cavalier King Charles and "Shooting Over Dogs" (Richard Ansdell)	15	10
762	40e. German shepherd and rough collies	65	30
763	50e. Bearded collie and "Hounds at Full Cry" (Thomas Blinks)	80	40

1995. 20th Anniv of Independence.

764 **141**	37e. multicoloured	1·00	40

143 Horse Race

1995. St. Philip's Flag Festival, Fogo. Mult.

766	2e. Type **143**	10	10
767	10e. Preparing for horse race	15	10
768	37e. Preparing food and clapping to music	55	25
769	40e. Crowd watching final horse race	60	30

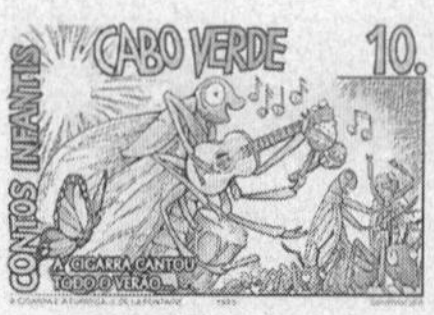

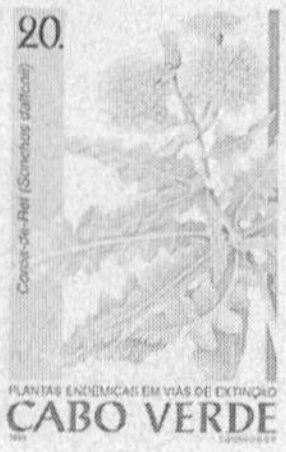

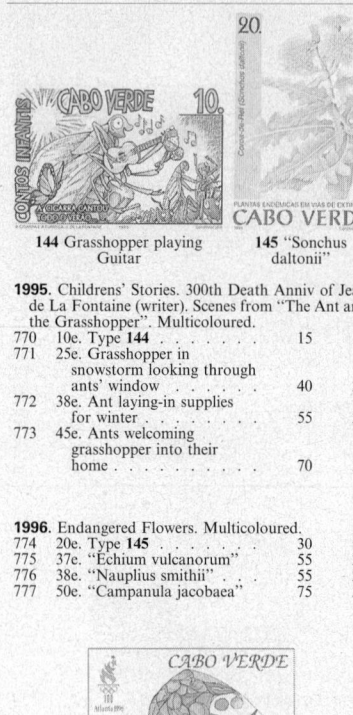

144 Grasshopper playing Guitar **145** "Sonchus daltonii"

1995. Childrens' Stories. 300th Death Anniv of Jean de La Fontaine (writer). Scenes from "The Ant and the Grasshopper". Multicoloured.

770	10e. Type **144**	15	10
771	25e. Grasshopper in snowstorm looking through ants' window	40	20
772	38e. Ant laying-in supplies for winter	55	25
773	45e. Ants welcoming grasshopper into their home	70	35

1996. Endangered Flowers. Multicoloured.

774	20e. Type **145**	30	15
775	37e. "Echium vulcanorum"	55	25
776	38e. "Nauplius smithii"	55	25
777	50e. "Campanula jacobaea"	75	35

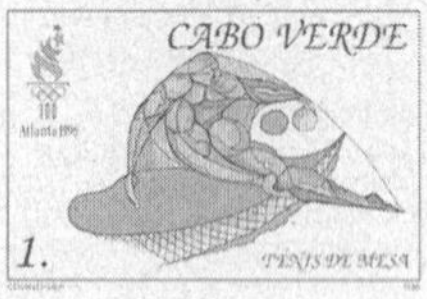

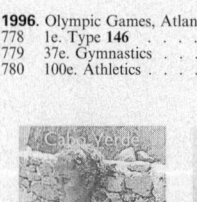

146 Table Tennis

1996. Olympic Games, Atlanta. Multicoloured.

778	1e. Type **146**	10	10
779	37e. Gymnastics	55	25
780	100e. Athletics	1·50	75

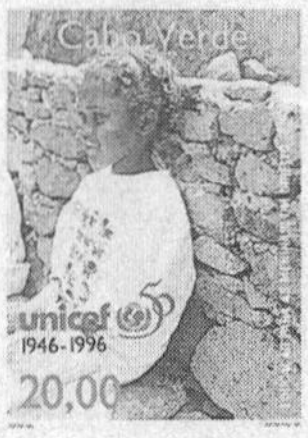

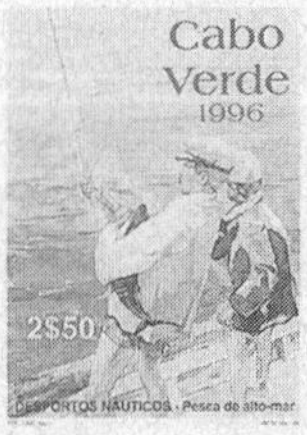

147 Student (Education of Girls) **148** Deep Sea Fishing

1996. 50th Anniv of U.N.I.C.E.F. Multicoloured.

781	20e. Type **147**	25	10
782	40e. Mother kissing child (Right to Love)	50	25

1996. Water Sports. Multicoloured.

783	2e.50 Type **148**	10	10
784	10e. Sailboard	20	10
785	22e.50 Jet skiing	30	15
786	100e. Surfing (horiz)	1·25	60

1997. Nos. 582 and 650/1 surch.

788	3e. on 2e.50 multicoloured	10	10
789	37e. on 4e. multicoloured	50	25
790	38e. on 7e.50 multicoloured	55	25

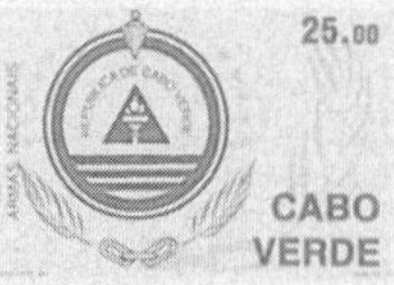

150 State Arms

1997. National Symbols. Multicoloured.

791	25e. Type **150**	30	15
792	37e. National anthem	40	20
793	50e. State flag	60	30

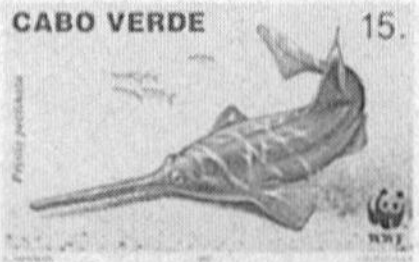

151 Small-toothed Sawfish

1997. The Small-toothed Sawfish. Multicoloured.

794	15e. Type **151**	20	10
795	15e. Underside of sawfish	20	10
796	15e. Sawfish and school of fishes	20	10
797	15e. Two sawfishes	20	10

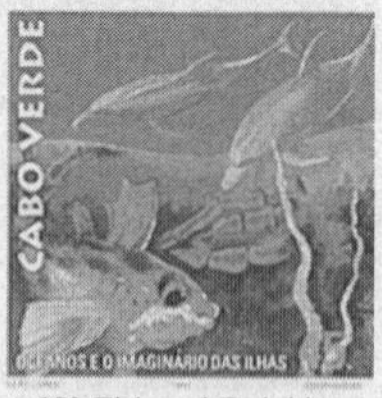

152 Fish and Dolphins

1997. Oceans. Multicoloured.

798	45e. Type **152**	55	25
799	45e. Mermaid and merman	55	25
800	45e. Fishes, eel, coral and sunken gate	55	25

Nos. 798/800 were issued together, se-tenant, forming a composite design.

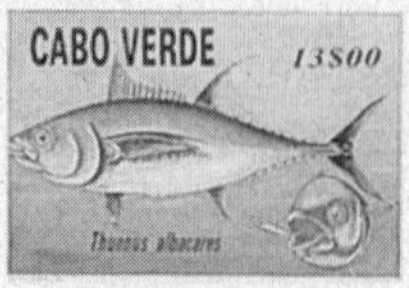

153 Yellow-finned Tuna

1997. Tuna. Multicoloured.

801	13e. Type **153**	15	10
802	21e. Big-eyed tuna	25	10
803	41e. Little tuna	50	25
804	45e. Skipjack tuna	55	25

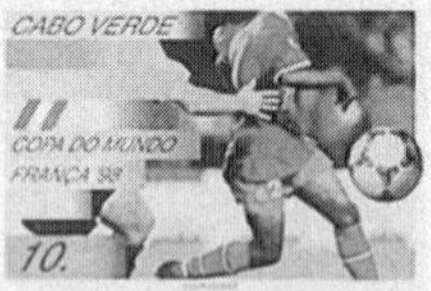

154 Players chasing Ball

1998. World Cup Football Championship, France. Multicoloured.

805	10e. Type **154**	10	10
806	30e. Ball in net (vert)	45	20
807	45e. Player with ball (vert)	55	25
808	50e. Globe, football and trophy	60	30

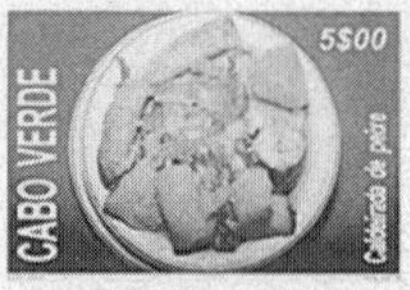

155 Fish Dish

1998. Local Cuisine.

809	**155** 5e. multicoloured	10	10
810	– 25e. multicoloured	30	15
811	– 35e. multicoloured	40	20
812	– 40e. multicoloured	45	20

DESIGNS: 25e. to 40e. Different food dishes.

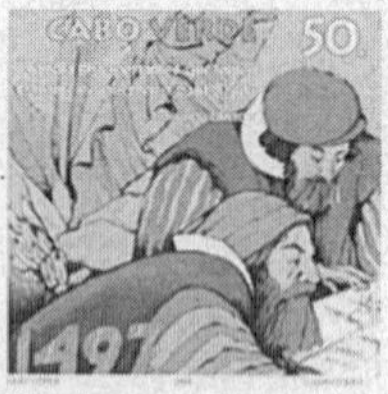

156 Navigators reading Books and Banana Tree

1998. 500th Anniv (1997) of Vasco da Gama's Expedition to India. Multicoloured.

813	50e. Type **156**	60	30
814	50e. Seaman with sword and couple	60	30
815	50e. Compass rose and Portuguese galleon in harbour	1·00	40

Nos. 813/15 were issued together, se-tenant, forming a composite design.

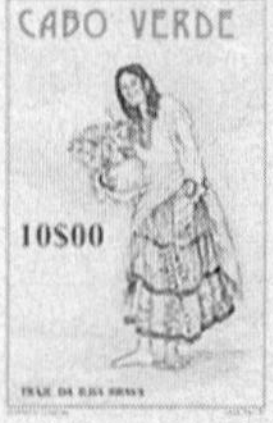

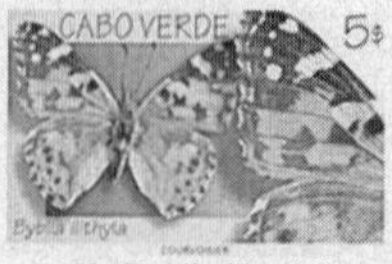

157 Brava Island Costume **158** "Byblia ilithyia"

1998. Local Women's Costumes. Multicoloured.

816	10e. Type **157**	10	10
817	18e. Fogo Island	20	10
818	30e. Boa Vista Island	35	15
819	50e. Santiago Island	60	30

1999. Butterflies and Moths. Multicoloured.

820	5e. Type **158**	10	10
821	10e. "Aganais speciosa"	10	10
822	20e. Crimson-speckled moth	25	10
823	30e. Painted lady	35	15
824	50e. Cabbage looper	60	30
825	100e. "Grammodes congenita"	1·25	60

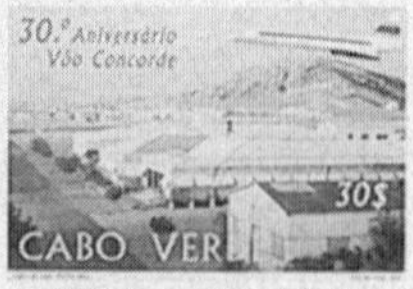

159 Concorde in Flight

1999. 30th Anniv of Concorde (supersonic airplane). Multicoloured.

827	30e. Type **159**	35	15
828	50e. Concorde on airport apron	60	30

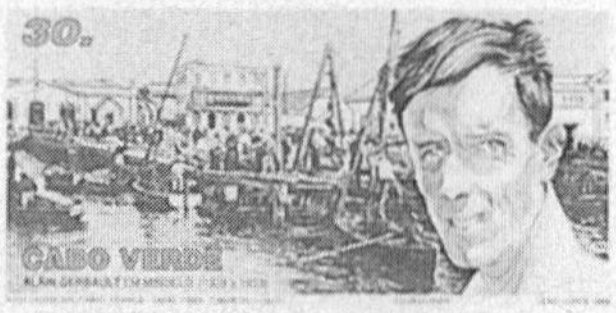

160 Alain Gerbault (solo yachtsman) and Mindelo Harbour

1999. "Philexfrance 99" International Stamp Exhibition, Paris, France. Multicoloured.

829	30e. Type **160**	40	20
830	50e. Roberto Duarte Silva (chemist) and Eiffel Tower, Paris	60	30

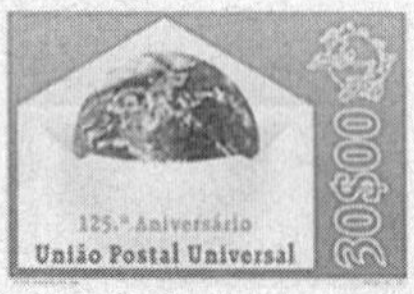

161 Globe in Envelope and U.P.U. Emblem

1999. 125th Anniv of Universal Postal Union. Mult.

832	30e. Type **161**	40	20
833	50e. Paper airplanes	60	30

Nos. 832/3 are not inscribed with the country name.

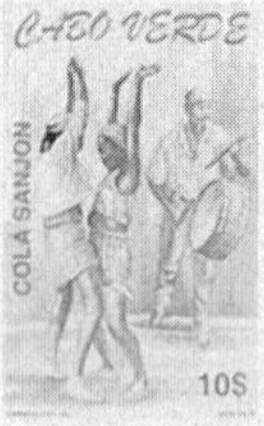

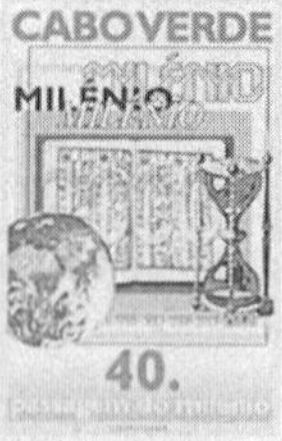

162 Cola Sanjon Dance **163** Globe, Open Book and Hourglass

1999. Local Dances. Multicoloured.

834	10e. Type **162**	10	10
835	30e. Contradanca	30	15
836	50e. Desfile de Tabanca (horiz)	50	25
837	100e. Batuque (horiz)	1·00	50

2000. New Millennium. Multicoloured.

838	40e. Type **163**	40	20
839	50e. "2000" (horiz)	50	25

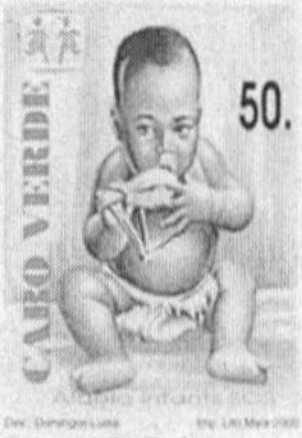

164 Baby

2000. 50th Anniv (1999) of S.O.S. Children's Villages. Multicoloured.

840	50e. Type **164**	50	25
841	100e. Child and emblem (horiz)	1·00	50

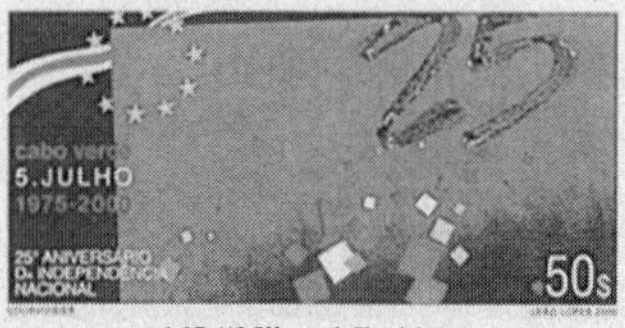

165 "25" and Emblem

2000. 25th Anniv of Independence.

842	**165** 50e. multicoloured	50	25

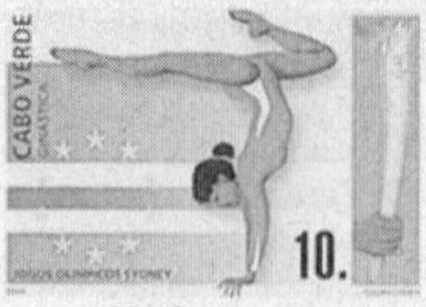

166 Gymnastics

2000. Olympic Games, Sydney. Multicoloured.

843	10e. Type **166**	10	10
844	40e. Taekwondo	40	20
845	50e. Athletics	50	25

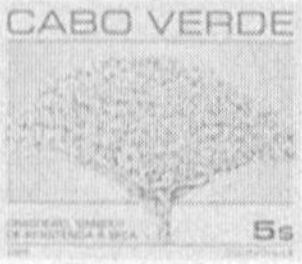

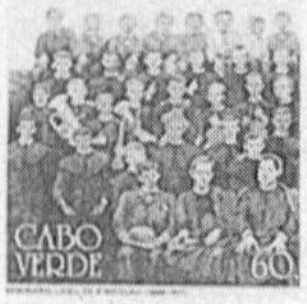

167 Dragon Tree **168** Students (left-hand detail)

2000. Dragon Tree.

847	**167** 5e. green	10	10
848	40e. red	50	25
849	60e. brown	70	35

2000. 134th Anniv of the Liceu de Sao Nicolau Seminary. Multicoloured.

850	60e. Type **168**	70	35
851	60e. Students (right-hand detail)	70	35
852	60e. Jose Alves Feio, Jose Julio Dias (co-founders) and Antonio Jose de Oliveira Boucas (Principal) (56 × 26 mm)	70	35

Nos. 850/2 were issued together, se-tenant, forming a composite design.

CHARITY TAX STAMPS

Used on certain days of the year as an additional postal tax on internal letters. Other values in some of the types were for use on telegrams only. The proceeds were devoted to public charities. If one was not affixed in addition to the ordinary postage, postage due stamps were used to collect the deficiency and the fine.

1925. As Marquis de Pombal issue of Portugal but inscr "CABO VERDE".

C266	C **73** 15c. violet	25	25
C267	– 15c. violet	25	25
C268	C **75** 15c. violet	25	25

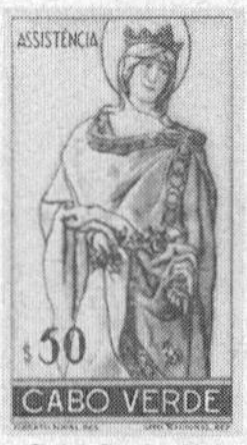

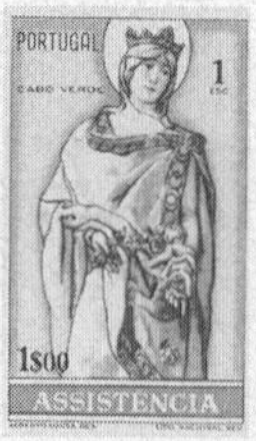

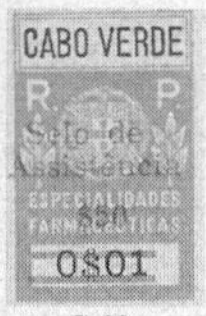

C **16** St. Isabel C **31** C **32**

1948.

C321	C **16** 50c. green	1·25	85
C322	1e. red	2·50	1·00

1959. Surch.

C368	C **16** 50c. on 1e. red	50	30

1959. Colours changed.

C369	C **16** 50c. mauve	1·10	65
C370	1e. blue	1·10	65

1967.

C406	C **31** 30c. multicoloured	15	15
C407	50c. mult (purple panel)	30	30
C408	50c. mult (red panel)	15	15
C409	1e. mult (brown panel)	45	45
C410	1e. mult (purple panel)	45	45

1968. Pharmaceutical Tax stamps surch as in Type C **32**.

C411a	C **32** 50c. on 1c. black, orange and green	80	60
C412c	50c. on 2c. black, orange and green	40	25
C413	50c. on 3c. black, orange and green	55	40
C414	50c. on 5c. black, orange and green	55	40
C415	50c. on 10c. black, orange and green	65	55
C416	1e. on 1c. black, orange and green	1·50	1·00
C417a	1e. on 2c. black, orange and green	1·00	85

NEWSPAPER STAMP

1893. "Newspaper" key-type inscr "CABO VERDE".

N37	V $2\frac{1}{2}$r. brown	55	35

POSTAGE DUE STAMPS

1904. "Due" key-type inscr "CABO VERDE".

D119	W	5r. green	15	15
D120		10r. grey	15	15
D121		20r. brown	15	15
D122		30r. orange	40	20
D123		50r. brown	20	15
D124		60r. brown	3·00	1·75
D125		100r. mauve	80	50
D126		130r. blue	80	50
D127		200r. red	85	75
D128		500r. lilac	2·10	1·50

1911. Nos. D119/28 optd **REPUBLICA**.

D135	W	5r. green	10	10
D136		10r. grey	10	10
D137		20r. brown	15	10
D138		30r. orange	15	10
D139		50r. brown	15	10
D140		60r. brown	30	20
D141		100r. mauve	30	20
D142		130r. blue	35	25
D143		200r. red	75	60
D144		500r. lilac	90	75

1921. "Due" key-type inscr "CABO VERDE" with currency in centavos.

D252	W	½c. green	10	10
D253		1c. slate	10	10
D254		2c. brown	10	10
D255		3c. orange	10	10
D256		5c. brown	10	10
D257		6c. brown	10	10
D258		10c. mauve	15	15
D259		13c. blue	30	25
D260		20c. red	30	25
D261		50c. grey	60	45

1925. As Nos. C266/8, optd **MULTA**.

D266	C 73	30c. violet	25	25
D267	–	30c. violet	25	25
D268	C 75	30c. violet	25	25

1952. As Type D **45** of Angola, but inscr "CABO VERDE". Numerals in red; name in black.

D356		10c. brown and grey	10	10
D357		30c. black, blue & mauve	10	10
D358		50c. blue, green & yellow	10	10
D359		1e. blue and pale blue	10	10
D360		2e. brown and orange	20	20
D361		5e. green and grey	45	45

CAROLINE ISLANDS Pt. 7

A group of islands in the Pacific Ocean, formerly a German protectorate; under Japanese mandate after 1918. Now under United States trusteeship.

100 pfennig = 1 mark.

1899. Stamps of Germany optd **Karolinen**.

7	8	3pf. brown	9·50	10·50
8		5pf. green	10·50	11·00
9	9	10pf. red	17·00	13·00
10		20pf. blue	17·00	19·00
11		25pf. orange	38·00	48·00
12		50pf. brown	42·00	42·00

1901. "Yacht" key-types inscr "KAROLINEN".

13	N	3pf. brown	65	1·40
14		5pf. green	65	1·40
15		10pf. red	80	3·50
16		20pf. blue	95	5·00
17		25f. black & red on yellow	1·25	10·00
18		30pf. black & orge on buff	1·25	10·00
19		40pf. black and red	1·10	11·00
20		50pf. black & pur on buff	1·40	14·00
21		80pf. black & red on rose	2·10	17·00
22	O	1m. red	3·50	42·00
23		2m. blue	6·00	60·00
24		3m. black	10·00	£110
25		5m. red and black	£140	£425

1910. No. 13 surch **5 Pf.**

26	N	5pf. on 3pf. brown	—	£4250

CASTELROSSO Pt. 3

One of the Aegean Is. Occupied by the French Navy on 27 December 1915. The French withdrew in August 1921 and, after a period of Italian Naval administration, the island was included in the Dodecanese territory.

A. FRENCH OCCUPATION

100 centimes = 1 franc = 4 piastres.

1920. Stamps of 1902–20 of French Post Offices in Turkish Empire optd **B. N. F. CASTELLORIZO.**

F 1	A	1c. grey	29·00	29·00
F 2		2c. purple	29·00	29·00
F 3		3c. red	29·00	29·00
F 4		5c. green	35·00	35·00
F 5	B	10c. red	40·00	40·00
F 6		15c. red	60·00	60·00
F 7		20c. brown	65·00	65·00
F 8		1pi. on 20c. blue	65·00	65·00
F 9		30c. lilac	70·00	70·00
F10	C	40c. red and blue	£120	£120
F11		2pi. on 50c. brown & lilac	£130	£130
F12		4pi. on 1f. red & green	£170	£170
F13		20pi. on 5f. blue & brown	£475	£475

1920. Optd **O. N. F. Castellorizo.** (a) On stamps of 1902–20 of French Post Offices in Turkish Empire.

F14	A	1c. grey	16·00	16·00
F15		2c. purple	16·00	16·00
F16		3c. red	19·00	19·00
F17		5c. green	19·00	19·00
F18	B	10c. red	19·00	19·00
F19		15c. red	25·00	25·00
F20		20c. brown	45·00	45·00
F21		1pi. on 25c. blue	45·00	45·00
F22		30c. lilac	42·00	42·00
F23	C	40c. red and blue	40·00	40·00
F24		2pi. on 50c. brown & lilac	42·00	42·00
F25		4pi. on 1f. red and green	50·00	50·00
F26		20pi. on 5f. blue & brown	£275	£275

(b) On Nos. 334 and 341 of France.

F27	18	10c. red	22·00	14·00
F28		25c. blue	22·00	14·00

1920. Stamps of France optd **O F CASTELLORISO.**

F29	18	5c. green	£120	£120
F30		10c. red	£120	£120
F31		20c. red	£120	£120
F32		25c. blue	£120	£120
F33	13	50c. brown and lilac	£700	£700
F34		1f. red and green	£700	£700

B. ITALIAN OCCUPATION

100 centesimi = 1 lira.

1922. Stamps of Italy optd **CASTELROSSO.**

15	37	5c. green	1·00	15·00
16		10c. red	1·00	16·00
17		15c. grey	1·00	21·00
18	41	20c. orange	1·00	21·00
19	39	25c. blue	1·00	16·00
20		40c. brown	1·00	16·00
21		50c. violet	1·00	17·00
22		60c. red	1·00	24·00
23		85c. brown	1·00	30·00
24	34	1l. brown and green	1·00	30·00

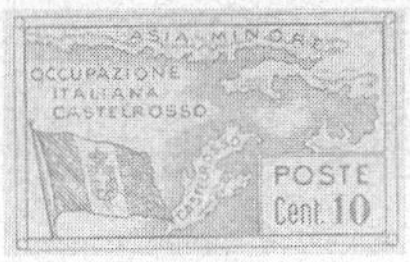

2

1923.

10	2	5c. green	2·00	11·00
11		10c. red	1·50	11·00
12		25c. blue	1·50	11·00
13		50c. purple	1·50	11·00
14		1l. brown	1·50	11·00

1930. Ferrucci stamps of Italy optd **CASTELROSSO.**

25	114	20c. violet	3·00	3·50
26	–	25c. green (No. 283)	3·00	5·00
27	–	50c. black (as No. 284)	3·00	3·50
28	–	1l.25 blue (No. 285)	3·00	6·50
29	–	5l.+2l. red (as No. 286)	13·00	29·00

1932. Garibaldi stamps of Italy optd **CASTELROSSO.**

30	–	10c. brown	13·00	24·00
31	128	20c. brown	13·00	24·00
32	–	25c. green	13·00	24·00
33	128	30c. blue	13·00	24·00
34	–	50c. purple	13·00	24·00
35	–	75c. red	13·00	24·00
36	–	1l.25 blue	13·00	24·00
37	–	1l.75+25c. brown	13·00	24·00
38	–	2l.55+50c. red	13·00	26·00
39	–	5l.+1l. violet	13·00	26·00

CAUCA Pt. 20

A State of Colombia, reduced to a Department in 1886, now uses Colombian stamps.

100 centavos = 1 peso.

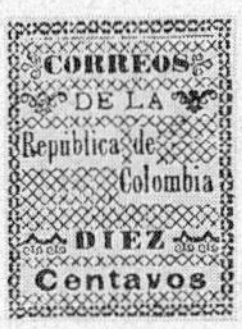

2

1902. Imperf.

2	2	10c. black on red	1·00	1·00
3		20c. black on orange	85	85

CAVALLA (KAVALLA) Pt. 16

French P.O. in a former Turkish port, now closed.

100 centimes = 1 franc.
40 paras = 1 piastre.

1893. Stamps of France optd **Cavalle** or surch also in figures and words.

41	10	5c. green	4·50	2·50
43		10c. black on lilac	6·50	3·25
45		15c. blue	6·50	3·75
46		1pi. on 25c. black on pink	8·50	4·25
47		2pi. on 50c. red	22·00	15·00
48a		4pi. on 1f. green	28·00	25·00
49		8pi. on 2f. brown on blue	32·00	30·00

1902. "Blanc", "Mouchon" and "Merson" key-types inscr "CAVALLE". The four higher values surch also.

50	A	5c. green	25	20
51	B	10c. red	30	25
52		15c. red	2·25	1·50
53		15c. orange	50	25
54		1pi. on 25c. blue	1·00	50
55	C	2pi. on 50c. brown & lilac	2·25	1·00
56		4pi. on 1f. red and green	2·50	3·00
57		8pi. on 2f. lilac and brown	6·50	5·75

CAYES OF BELIZE Pt. 1

A chain of several hundred islands, coral atolls, reefs and sandbanks stretching along the eastern seaboard of Belize.

The following issues for the Cayes of Belize fall outside the criteria for full listing as detailed on page viii.

100 cents = 1 dollar.

APPENDIX

1984.

Marine Life, Map and Views, 1, 2, 5, 10, 15, 25, 75c., $3, $5.

250th Anniv of "Lloyd's List" (newspaper). 25, 75c., $1, $2.

Olympic Games, Los Angeles. 10, 15, 75c., $2.

90th Anniv of "Caye Service" Local Stamps. 10, 15, 75c., $2.

1985.

Birth Bicent of John J. Audubon (ornithologist). 25, 75c., $1, $3.

Shipwrecks. $1 × 4.

CAYMAN ISLANDS Pt. 1

A group of islands in the British West Indies. A dependency of Jamaica until August 1962, when it became a Crown Colony.

1900. 12 pence = 1 shilling;
20 shillings = 1 pound.
1969. 100 cents = 1 Jamaican dollar.

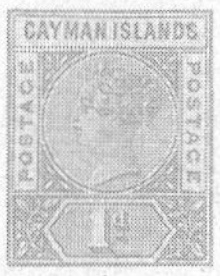

1

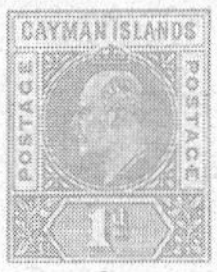

2

1900.

1a	1	½d. green	4·25	15·00
2		1d. red	3·50	2·25

1902.

8	2	½d. green	6·50	7·50
4		1d. red	10·00	9·00
10		2½d. blue	6·50	3·25
11		4d. brown and blue	32·00	55·00
13		6d. brown	16·00	38·00
14		6d. olive and red	32·00	65·00
12		1s. orange	32·00	48·00
15		1s. violet and green	55·00	75·00
16		5s. orange and green	£170	£275

1907. Surch **One Halfpenny.**

17	2	½d. on 1d. red	42·00	65·00

1907. Surch.

18	2	½d. on 5s. orange and green	£225	£325
19		1d. on 5s. orange and green	£225	£300
35		2½d. on 4d. brown and blue	£1500	£2250

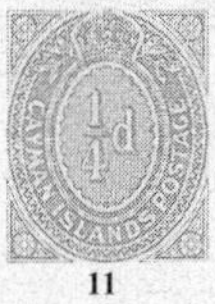

11

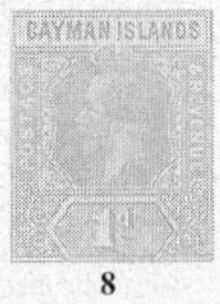

8

1907.

38	11	¼d. brown	1·75	50
25	8	½d. green	2·00	4·00
26		1d. red	1·50	75
27		2½d. blue	3·50	3·50
28		3d. purple on yellow	3·25	6·50
29		4d. black and red on yellow	50·00	70·00
30		6d. purple	9·50	35·00
31		1s. black on green	7·50	22·00
32		5s. green and red on yellow	38·00	60·00
34		10s. green and red on green	£160	£225

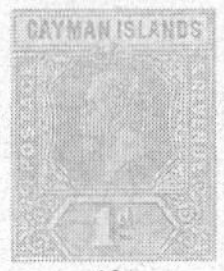

12

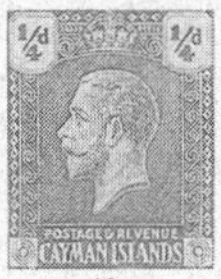

19

1912.

40	12	¼d. brown	1·00	40
41		½d. green	2·75	5·00
42		1d. red	3·25	2·50
43		2d. grey	1·00	10·00
44		2½d. blue	7·00	11·00
45a		3d. purple on yellow	3·50	8·00
46		4d. black and red on yellow	1·00	10·00
47		6d. purple	3·75	7·50
48b		1s. black on green	3·50	3·50
49		2s. purple and blue on blue	12·00	48·00
50		3s. green and violet	19·00	65·00
51		5s. green and red on yellow	75·00	£160
52b		10s. green and red on green	80·00	£140

1917. Surch **1½d** with **WAR STAMP.** in two lines.

54	12	1½d. on 2½d. blue	1·75	6·00

1917. Optd or surch as last, but with **WAR STAMP** in one line and without full point.

57	12	½d. green	60	2·50
58		1½d. on 2d. grey	1·50	7·00
56		1½d. on 2½d. blue	30	60
59		1½d. on 2½d. orange	80	1·25

1921.

69	19	¼d. brown	50	1·50
70		½d. green	50	30
71		1d. red	1·40	85
72		1½d. brown	1·75	30
73		2d. grey	1·75	4·00
74		2½d. blue	50	50
75		3d. purple on yellow	75	4·00
62		4d. red on yellow	1·00	4·00
76		4½d. green	2·25	3·00
77		6d. red	5·50	32·00
63		1s. black on green	1·25	9·50
80		2s. violet on blue	14·00	24·00
81		3s. violet	23·00	16·00
82		5s. green on yellow	24·00	45·00
83		10s. red on green	60·00	85·00

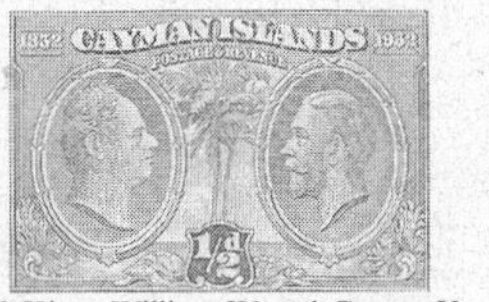

20 Kings William IV and George V

1932. Centenary of "Assembly of Justices and Vestry".

84	20	¼d. brown	1·50	1·00
85		½d. green	2·75	7·50
86		1d. red	2·75	6·50
87		1½d. orange	2·75	2·75
88		2d. grey	2·75	3·25
89		2½d. blue	2·75	1·50
90		3d. green	3·00	5·00
91		6d. purple	9·50	23·00
92		1s. black and brown	17·00	32·00
93		2s. black and blue	45·00	75·00
94		5s. black and green	80·00	£120
95		10s. black and red	£250	£350

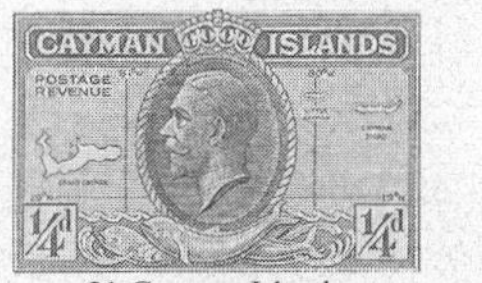

21 Cayman Islands

1935.

96	21	¼d. black and brown	50	1·00
97	–	½d. blue and green	1·00	1·00
98	–	1d. blue and red	4·00	2·25
99	–	1½d. black and orange	1·50	1·75
100	–	2d. blue and purple	3·75	1·10
101	–	2½d. blue and black	3·25	1·25
102	21	3d. black and green	2·50	3·00
103	–	6d. purple and black	8·50	4·00
104	–	1s. blue and orange	6·00	6·50
105	–	2s. blue and black	45·00	35·00
106	–	5s. green and black	50·00	50·00
107	–	10s. black and red	70·00	85·00

DESIGNS—HORIZ: ½, 2d., 1s. Cat boat; 1d., 2s. Red-footed boobys ("Booby-birds"); 2½, 6d., 5s. Hawksbill turtles. VERT: 1½d., 10s. Queen or pink conch shells and coconut palms.

1935. Silver Jubilee. As T **13** of Antigua.

108		½d. black and green	15	1·00
109		2½d. brown and blue	1·00	1·00

110 6d. blue and olive . . . . . 1·00 3·25
111 1s. grey and purple . . . . . 7·00 7·00

1937. Coronation. As T **2** of Aden.
112 ½d. green . . . . 30 1·10
113 1d. red 50 20
114 2½d. blue 95 40

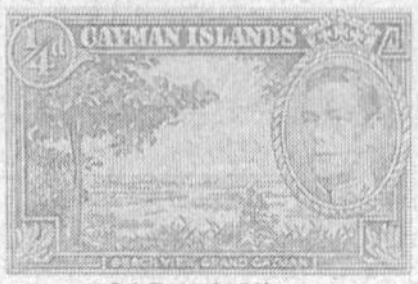

26 Beach View

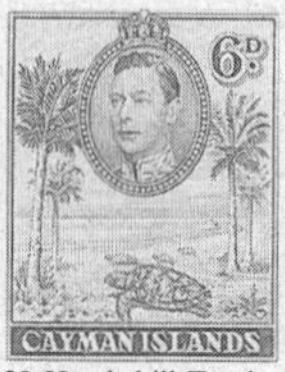

30 Hawksbill Turtles

1938.
115a **26** ¼d. orange 10 65
116 – ½d. green 75 55
117 – 1d. red 30 75
118 **26** 1½d. black 30 10
119a **30** 2d. violet 60 30
120 – 2½d. blue 40 20
120a – 2½d. orange . . . . 2·25 50
121 – 3d. orange 40 15
121a – 3d. blue . . . . 2·25 30
122a **30** 6d. olive . . . . 2·00 1·25
123a – 1s. brown . . . . 4·50 2·00
124a **26** 2s. green . . . . 25·00 9·00
125 – 5s. red . . . . 32·00 15·00
126a **30** 10s. brown . . . . 21·00 9·00
DESIGNS—HORIZ: ½d., 1s. Caribbean dolphin; 1d., 3d. Map of Islands; 2½d., 5s. "Rembro" (schooner).

1946. Victory. As T **9** of Aden.
127 1½d. black 20 10
128 3d. yellow 20 10

1948. Silver Wedding. As T **10/11** of Aden.
129 ½d. green 10 10
130 10s. blue . . . . 13·00 13·00

1949. U.P.U. As T **20/25** of Antigua.
131 2½d. orange 30 50
132 3d. blue . . . . 1·50 1·75
133 6d. olive . . . . 60 1·75
134 1s. brown 60 30

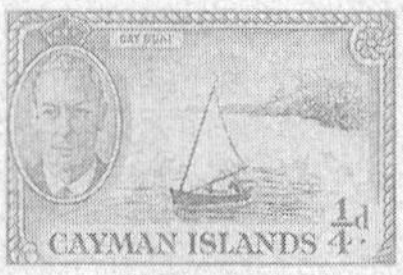

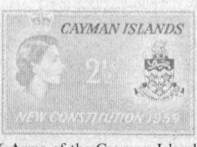

31 Cat Boat

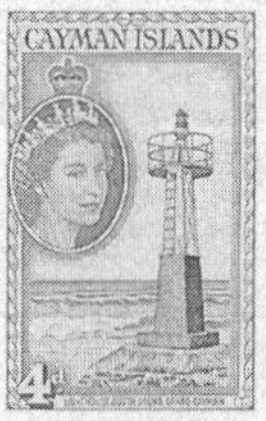

44 South Sound Lighthouse, Grand Cayman

1950.
135 **31** ¼d. blue and red 15 60
136 – ½d. violet and green . . . 15 1·25
137 – 1d. olive and blue . . . 60 75
138 – 1½d. green and brown . . . 30 75
139 – 2d. violet and red . . . 1·25 1·50
140 – 2½d. blue and black . . . 1·25 60
141 – 3d. green and blue . . . 1·40 1·50
142 – 6d. brown and blue . . . 2·00 1·25
143 – 9d. red and green . . . 5·50 2·00
144 – 1s. brown and orange . . . 3·25 2·75
145 – 2s. violet and purple . . . 8·50 9·00
146 – 5s. olive and violet . . . 13·00 7·00
147 – 10s. black and red . . . 15·00 14·00
DESIGNS: ½d. Coconut grove, Cayman Brac; 1d. Green turtle; 1½d. Making thatch rope; 2d. Cayman seamen; 2½d. Map; 3d. Parrotfish; 6d. Bluff, Cayman Brac; 9d. Georgetown Harbour. 1s. Turtle in "crawl"; 2s. "Ziroma" (schooner); 5s. Boat-building; 10s. Government offices, Grand Cayman.

1953. As 1950 issue but with portrait of Queen Elizabeth II as in T **44**.
148 ¼d. blue and red . . . . 1·00 50
149 ½d. violet and green . . . 60 50
150 1d. olive and blue 70 40
151 1½d. green and brown . . . 50 20
152 2d. violet and red . . . . 3·00 85
153 2½d. blue and black . . . 3·50 80
154 3d. green and blue . . . . 4·00 60
155 4d. black and blue . . . . 2·00 40
156 6d. brown and blue . . . . 1·75 30
157 9d. red and green . . . . 5·50 30
158 1s. brown and orange . . . 3·25 20
159 2s. violet and purple . . . 13·00 8·00
160 5s. olive and violet . . . 15·00 7·00
161 10s. black and red . . . . 15·00 7·50
161a £1 blue . . . . 32·00 10·00
Portrait faces right on ½d., 2d., 2½d., 4d., 1s. and 10s. values and left on others. The £1 shows a larger portrait of the Queen (vert).

1953. Coronation. As T **13** of Aden.
162 1d. black and green . . . . 30 1·50

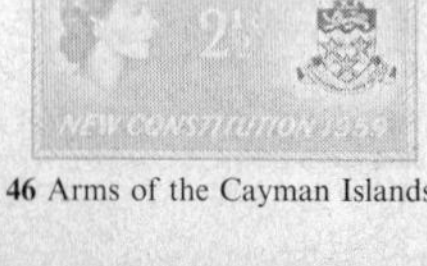

46 Arms of the Cayman Islands

1959. New Constitution.
163 **46** 2½d. black and blue . . . 45 2·00
164 1s. black and orange . . . 55 50

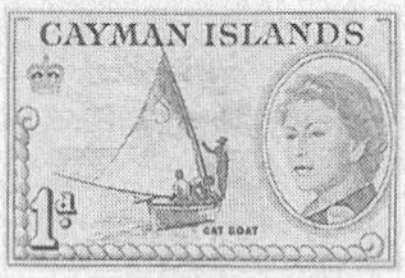

48 Cat Boat

1962. Portraits as in T **48**.
165 – ¼d. green and red . . . . 55 1·00
166 **48** 1d. black and olive 80 20
167 – 1½d. yellow and purple . . 2·75 80
168 – 2d. blue and brown . . . . 1·00 30
169 – 2½d. violet and turquoise . 85 1·00
170 – 3d. blue and red 30 10
171 – 4d. green and purple . . . 1·25 60
172 – 6d. turquoise and sepia . . 3·25 30
173 **48** 9d. blue and purple . . . . 2·25 40
174 – 1s. sepia and red 80 10
175 – 1s.3d. turquoise and brown 3·75 1·75
176 – 1s.9d. turquoise and violet 15·00 1·25
177 – 5s. plum and green . . . . 9·00 6·50
178 – 10s. olive and blue . . . . 17·00 8·00
179 – £1 red and black . . . . . 19·00 16·00
DESIGNS—VERT: ¼d. Cuban amazon ("Cayman Parrot"); 9d. Angler with king mackerel; 10s. Arms; £1 Queen Elizabeth II. HORIZ: 1½d. "Schomburgkia thomsoniana" (orchid); 2d. Cayman Islands map; 2½d. Fisherman casting net; 3d. West Bay Beach; 4d. Green turtle; 6d. "Lydia E. Wilson" (schooner), 1s Iguana; 1s.3d. Swimming pool, Cayman Brac; 1s.9d. Water sports; 5s. Fort George.

1963. Freedom from Hunger. As T **28** of Aden.
180 1s.9d. red 30 15

1963. Centenary of Red Cross. As T **33** of Antigua.
181 1d. red and black 30 75
182 1s.9d. red and blue . . . . . 70 1·75

1964. 400th Birth Anniv of Shakespeare. As T **34** of Antigua.
183 6d. purple 20 10

1965. Centenary of I.T.U. As T **36** of Antigua.
184 1d. blue and purple 15 10
185 1s.3d. purple and green . . . 55 45

1965. I.C.Y. As T **37** of Antigua.
186 1d. purple and turquoise . . 15 10
187 1s. green and lavender . . . 50 25

1966. Churchill Commemoration. As T **38** of Antigua.
188 ¼d. blue . . . . 10 1·50
189 1d. green 30 10
190 1s. brown 90 10
191 1s.9d. violet 95 75

1966. Royal Visit. As T **39** of Antigua.
192 1d. black and blue 60 30
193 1s.9d. black and mauve . . . 2·25 1·25

1966. World Cup Football Championship. As T **40** of Antigua.
194 1½d. multicoloured 15 10
195 1s.9d. multicoloured 50 25

1966. Inauguration of W.H.O. Headquarters, Geneva. As T **41** of Antigua.
196 2d. black, green and blue . . 60 15
197 1s.3d. black, purple and ochre . . . . 1·40 60

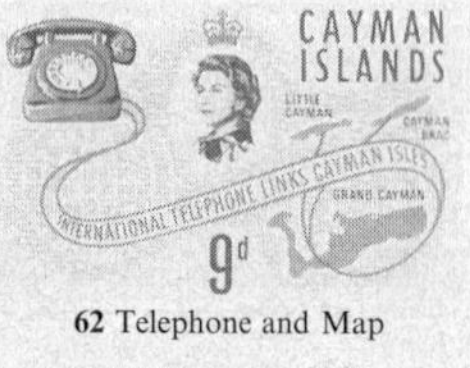

62 Telephone and Map

1966. International Telephone Links.
198 **62** 4d. multicoloured 20 20
199 9d. multicoloured 20 30

1966. 20th Anniv of U.N.E.S.C.O. As T **54/6** of Antigua.
200 1d. multicoloured 15 10
201 1s.9d. yellow, violet and olive 60 10
202 5s. black, purple and orange 1·50 70

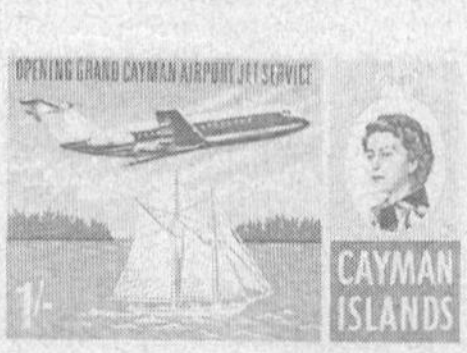

63 B.A.C One Eleven 200/400 Airliner over "Ziroma" (Cayman schooner)

1966. Opening of Cayman Jet Service.
203 **63** 1s. black, blue and green . . 35 30
204 1s.9d. purple, blue and green 40 35

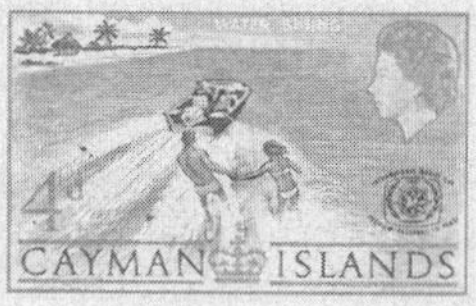

64 Water-skiing

1967. International Tourist Year. Multicoloured.
205 4d. Type **64** 35 10
206 6d. Skin diving 35 30
207 1s. Sport fishing 35 30
208 1s.9d. Sailing 40 75

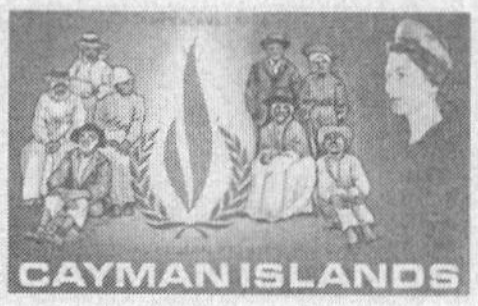

68 Former Slaves and Emblem

1968. Human Rights Year.
209 **68** 3d. green, black and gold 10 10
210 9d. brown, gold and green 10 10
211 5s. ultram, gold and green 30 90

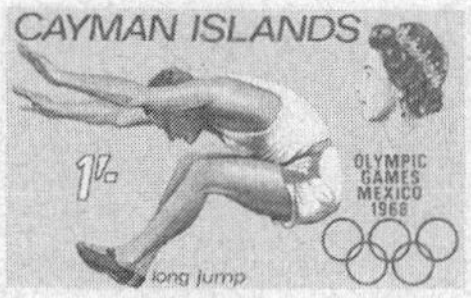

69 Long-jumping

1968. Olympic Games, Mexico. Multicoloured.
212 1s. Type **69** 15 10
213 1s.3d. High-jumping 20 25
214 2s. Pole-vaulting 20 75

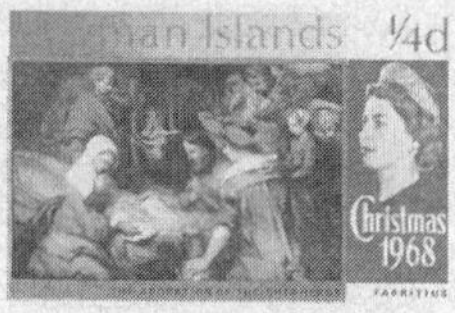

72 "The Adoration of the Shepherds" (Fabritius)

1968. Christmas. Multicoloured.
215 ¼d. Type **72*** 10 20
221 ¼d. Type **72*** 10 20
216 1d. "The Adoration of the Shepherds" (Rembrandt) 10 10
217 6d. Type **72** 15 10
218 8d. As 1d. 15 15
219 1s.3d. Type **72** 20 25
220 2s. As 1d. 25 35
*No. 215 has a brown background and No. 221 a bright purple one.

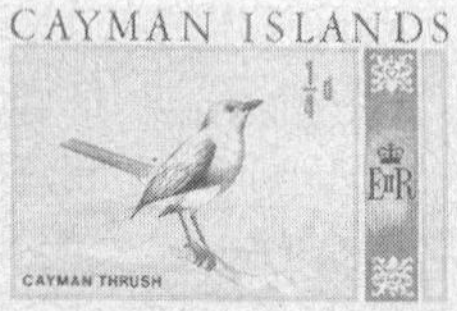

74 Grand Cayman Thrush ("Cayman Thrush")

1969. Multicoloured.
222 ¼d. Type **74** 10 75
223 1d. Brahmin cattle 10 10
224 2d. Blowholes on the coast . . 10 10
225 2½d. Map of Grand Cayman 15 10
226 3d. Georgetown scene . . . 10 10
227 4d. Royal "Poinciana" . . . 15 10
228 6d. Cayman Brac and Little Cayman on chart . . . 20 10
229 8d. Motor vessels at berth . . 25 10
230 1s. Basket-making 15 10
231 1s.3d. Beach scene . . . . . 35 1·00
232 1s.6d. Straw-rope making . . 35 1·00
233 2s. Great barracuda . . . . 1·25 80
234 4s. Government House . . . 35 80
235 10s. Arms of the Cayman Islands . . . . 1·00 1·50
236 £1 black, ochre and red (Queen Elizabeth II) . . . 1·25 2·00
Nos. 235/6 are vert.

1969. Decimal Currency. Nos. 222/36 surch **C-DAY 8th September 1969**. Multicoloured.
238 **74** ¼c. on ¼d. 10 75
239 – 1c. on 1d. 10 10
240 – 2c. on 2d. 10 10
241 – 3c. on 4d. 10 10
242 – 4c. on 2½d. 10 10
243 – 5c. on 6d. 10 10
244 – 7c. on 8d. 10 10
245 – 8c. on 3d. 15 10
246 – 10c. on 1s. 25 10
247 – 12c. on 1s.3d. . . . . . . 35 1·50
248 – 15c. on 1s.6d. . . . . . . 45 1·25
249 – 20c. on 2s. . . . . 1·25 1·50
250 – 40c. on 4s. 45 85
251 – $1 on 10s. . . . . 1·00 2·50
252 – $2 on £1 . . . . 1·50 3·25

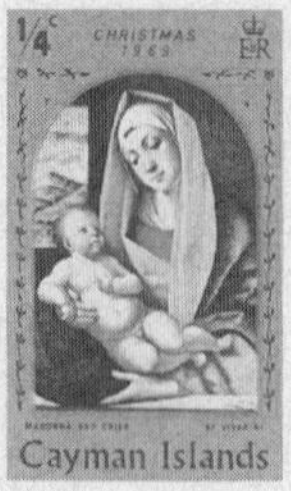

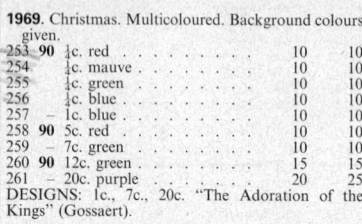

90 "Madonna and Child" (Vivarini)

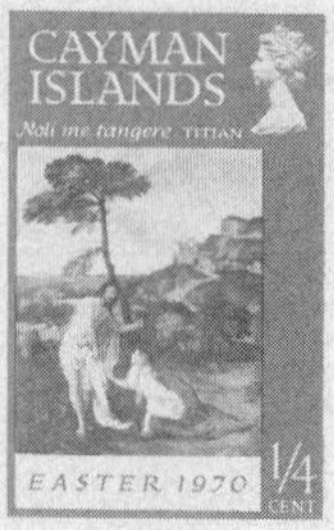

92 "Noli me tangere" (Titian)

1969. Christmas. Multicoloured. Background colours given.
253 **90** ¼c. red 10 10
254 ¼c. mauve 10 10
255 ¼c. green 10 10
256 ¼c. blue 10 10
257 – 1c. blue 10 10
258 **90** 5c. red 10 10
259 – 7c. green 10 10
260 **90** 12c. green 15 15
261 – 20c. purple 20 25
DESIGNS: 1c., 7c., 20c. "The Adoration of the Kings" (Gossaert).

1970. Easter. Multicoloured; frame colours given.
262 **92** ¼c. red 10 10
263 ¼c. green 10 10
264 ¼c. brown 10 10
265 ¼c. violet 10 10
266 10c. blue 35 10
267 12c. brown 40 10
268 40c. plum 55 60

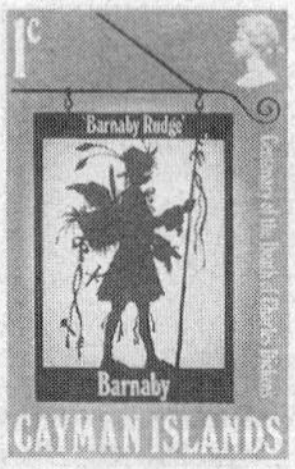

93 Barnaby ("Barnaby Rudge")

1970. Death Centenary of Charles Dickens.
269 **93** 1c. black, green and yellow 10 10
270 – 12c. black, brown and red 25 10
271 – 20c. black, brown and gold 30 10
272 – 40c. black, ultram & blue 35 25
DESIGNS: 12c. Sairey Gamp ("Martin Chuzzlewit"); 20c. Mr. Micawber and David ("David Copperfield"); 40c. The "Marchioness" ("The Old Curiosity Shop").

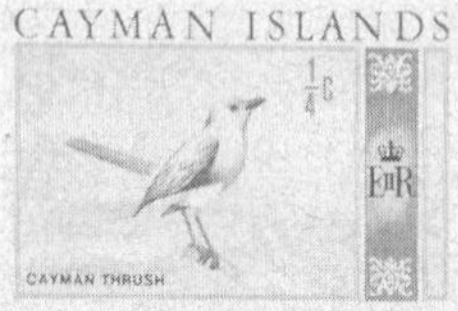

97 Grand Cayman Thrush ("Cayman Thrush")

1970. Decimal Currency. Designs as Nos. 222/36, but with values inscribed in decimal currency as in T **97**.
273 ¼c. multicoloured 50 30
274 1c. multicoloured 10 10
275 2c. multicoloured 10 10
276 3c. multicoloured 20 10
277 4c. multicoloured 20 10
278 5c. multicoloured 35 10
279 7c. multicoloured 30 10
280 8c. multicoloured 30 10
281 10c. multicoloured 30 10
282 12c. multicoloured 90 75
283 15c. multicoloured . . . . . 1·25 3·25
284 20c. multicoloured . . . . . 3·25 1·25
285 40c. multicoloured 85 75
286 $1 multicoloured . . . . . . 1·25 4·75
287 $2 black, ochre and red . . . 2·00 4·75

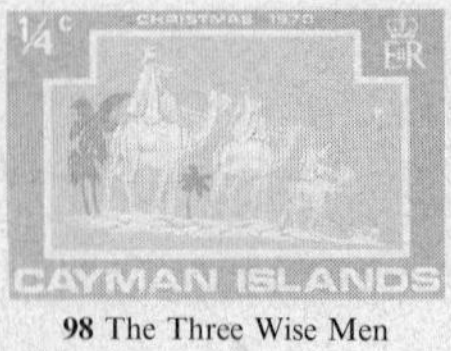

98 The Three Wise Men

1970. Christmas.
288 **98** ¼c. green, grey and emerald 10 10
289 – 1c. black, yellow and green 10 10
290 **98** 5c. grey, orange and red 10 10
291 – 10c. black, yellow and red 10 10
292 **98** 12c. grey, green and blue 15 10
293 – 20c. black, yellow and green 20 15
DESIGN: 1, 10, 20c. Nativity scene and Globe.

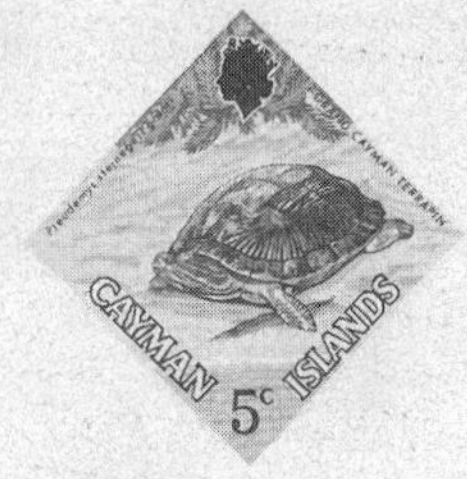

100 Grand Cayman Terrapin

1971. Turtles. Multicoloured.
294 5c. Type **100** 30 25
295 7c. Green turtle 35 25
296 12c. Hawksbill turtle 55 30
297 20c. Turtle farm . . . . . . 1·00 1·40

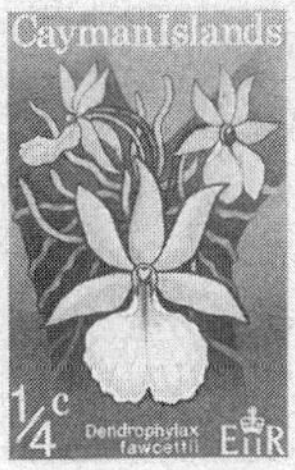

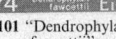

101 "Dendrophylax fawcettii"

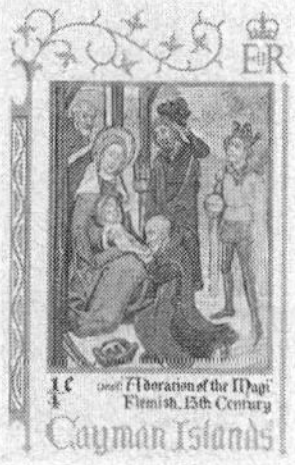

102 "Adoration of the Kings" (French 15th century)

1971. Orchids. Multicoloured.
298 $\frac{1}{4}$c. Type **101** 10 90
299 2c. "Schomburgkia thomsoniana" 50 70
300 10c. "Vanilla claviculata" . . 1·75 50
301 40c. "Oncidium variegatum" 3·75 3·50

1971. Christmas. Multicoloured.
302 $\frac{1}{4}$c. Type **102** 10 10
303 1c. "The Nativity" (Parisian, 14th century) 10 10
304 5c. "Adoration of the Magi" (Burgundian, 15th century) 10 10
305 12c. Type **102** 20 15
306 15c. As 1c. 20 25
307 20c. As 5c. 25 35

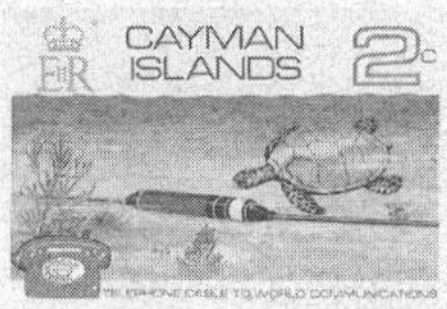

103 Turtle and Telephone Cable

1972. Co-axial Telephone Cable.
309 **103** 2c. multicoloured 10 10
310 10c. multicoloured 15 10
311 40c. multicoloured 30 40

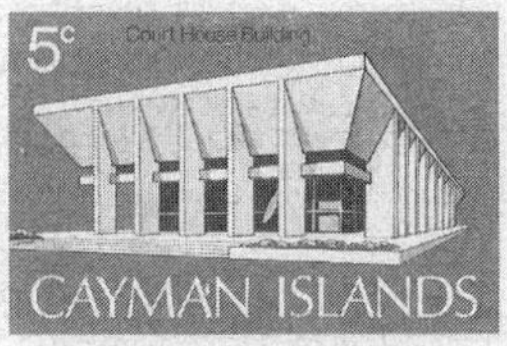

104 Court House Building

1972. New Government Buildings. Multicoloured.
312 5c. Type **104** 10 10
313 15c. Legislative Assembly Building 10 10
314 25c. Type **104** 15 15
315 40c. As 15c. 20 30

1972. Royal Silver Wedding. As T **52** of Ascension but with Hawksbill Turtle and Queen or Pink Conch in background.
317 12c. violet 15 10
318 30c. green 15 20

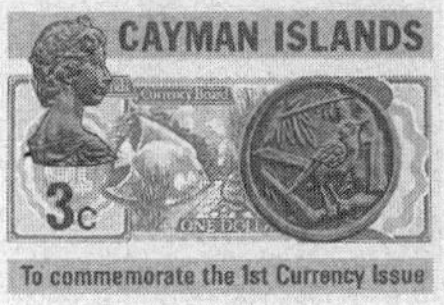

106 $1 Coin and Note

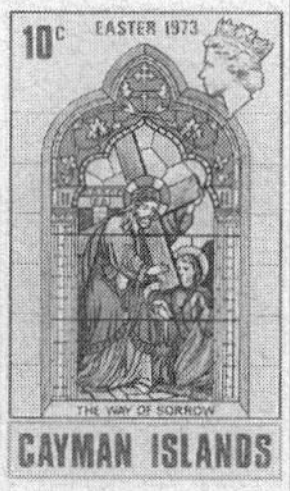

107 "The Way of Sorrow"

1972. First Issue of Currency. Multicoloured.
319 3c. Type **106** 20 10
320 6c. $5 Coin and note 20 55
321 15c. $10 Coin and note . . . 60 30
322 25c. $25 Coin and note . . . 80 45

1973. Easter. Stained-glass Windows. Multicoloured.
324 10c. Type **107** 15 10
325 12c. "Christ Resurrected" . . 20 10
326 20c. "The Last Supper" (horiz) 25 15
327 30c. "Christ on the Cross" (horiz) 30 25

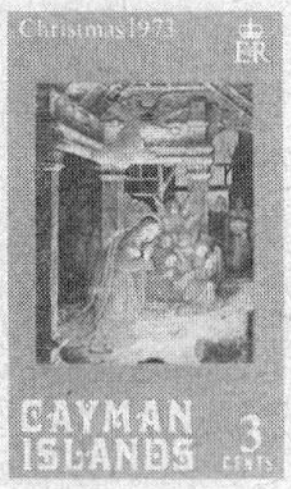

108 "The Nativity" (Sforza Book of Hours)

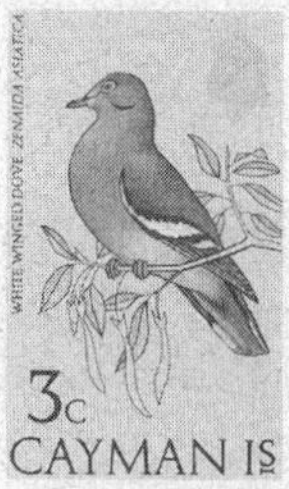

109 White-winged Dove

1973. Christmas.
329 **108** 3c. multicoloured 10 10
330 – 5c. multicoloured 10 10
331 **108** 9c. multicoloured 15 10
332 – 12c. multicoloured 15 10
333 **108** 15c. multicoloured 15 15
334 – 25c. multicoloured 20 25
DESIGN: 5, 12, 25c. "The Adoration of the Magi" (Breviary of Queen Isabella).

1973. Royal Wedding. As T **47** of Anguilla. Background colour given. Multicoloured.
335 10c. green 10 10
336 30c. mauve 15 10

1974. Birds (1st series). Multicoloured.
337 3c. Type **109** . . . . 2·00 30
338 10c. Vitelline warbler . . . . 2·75 30
339 12c. Antillean grackle ("Greater Antillean Grackle") . . . . 2·75 30
340 20c. Great red-bellied woodpecker ("West Indian Red-bellied Woodpecker") 4·25 80
341 30c. Stripe-headed tanager . . 5·50 1·50
342 50c. Yucatan vireo . . . . . 7·00 5·00
See also Nos. 383/8.

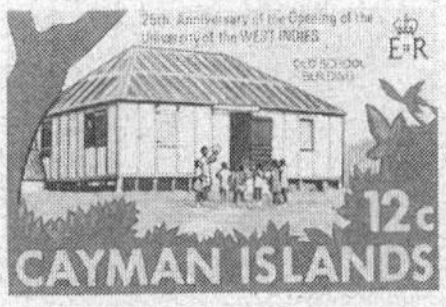

110 Old School Building

1974. 25th Anniv of University of West Indies. Multicoloured.
343 12c. Type **110** 10 10
344 20c. New Comprehensive School 15 15
345 30c. Creative Arts Centre, Mona 15 55

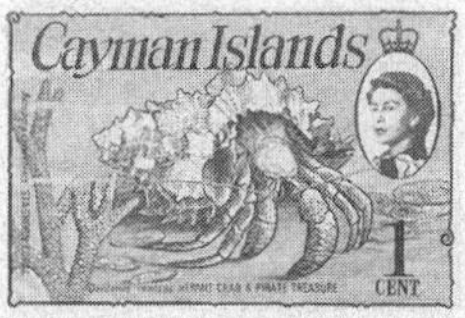

111 Hermit Crab and Staghorn Coral

1974. Size 41$\frac{1}{2}$ × 27 mm or 27 × 41$\frac{1}{2}$ mm. Mult.
346 1c. Type **111** . . . . 3·50 1·25
347 3c. Treasure-chest and lion's paw . . . . 3·50 75
348 4c. Treasure and spotted scorpionfish 50 70
349 5c. Flintlock pistol and brain coral . . . . 3·00 75
350 6c. Blackbeard and green turtle . . . . 35 2·25
366 8c. As 9c. . . . . 2·50 8·50
351 9c. Jewelled pomander and porkfish . . . . 3·75 9·00
352 10c. Spiny lobster and treasure . . . . 4·50 80
353 12c. Jewelled sword and dagger and sea-fan . . . . 35 1·60
354 15c. Cabrit's murex and treasure . . . . 45 1·25
417 20c. Queen or pink conch and treasure . . . . 3·50 3·00
356 25c. Hogfish and treasure . . 45 70
357 40c. Gold chalice and seawhip . . . . 4·00 1·25
358 $1 Coat of arms (vert) . . . 2·75 3·25
419 $2 Queen Elizabeth II (vert) 7·50 6·50
For smaller designs see Nos. 445/52.

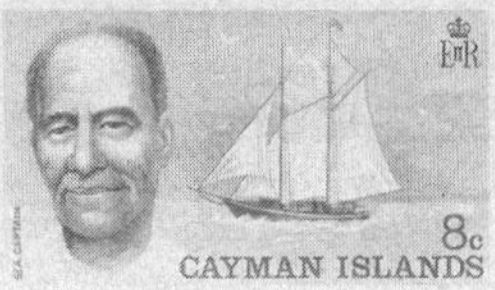

112 Sea Captain and Ship (Shipbuilding)

1974. Local Industries. Multicoloured.
360 8c. Type **112** 30 10
361 12c. Thatcher and cottage . . 25 10
362 20c. Farmer and plantation 25 20

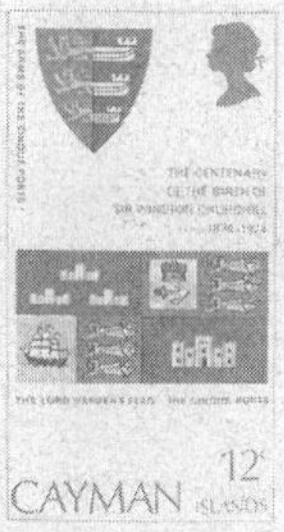

113 Arms of Cinque Ports and Lord Warden's Flag

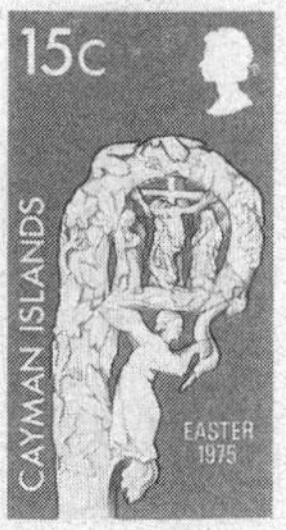

114 "The Crucifixion"

1974. Birth Centenary of Sir Winston Churchill. Multicoloured.
380 12c. Type **113** 15 10
381 50c. Churchill's coat of arms 45 70

1975. Birds (2nd series). As T **109**. Multicoloured.
383 3c. Common flicker ("Yellow-shafted Flicker") 70 45
384 10c. Black-billed whistling duck ("West Indian Tree Duck") . . . . 1·25 45
385 12c. Yellow warbler . . . . 1·40 65
386 20c. White-bellied dove . . . 2·00 2·00
387 30c. Magnificent frigate bird 3·25 4·25
388 50c. Cuban amazon ("Cayman Amazon") . . . 3·75 11·00

1975. Easter. French Pastoral Staffs.
389 **114** 15c. multicoloured 10 20
390 – 35c. multicoloured 20 45
DESIGN: 35c. Pastoral staff similar to Type **114**.

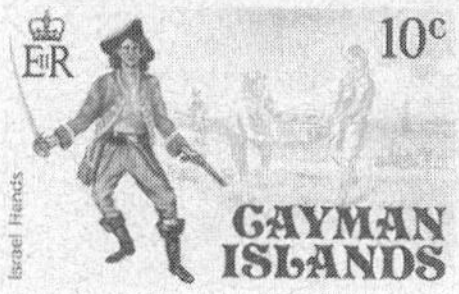

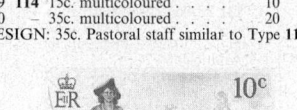

115 Israel Hands

1975. Pirates. Multicoloured.
392 10c. Type **115** 30 15
393 12c. John Fenn 30 15
394 20c. Thomas Anstis 50 40
395 30c. Edward Low . . . . . 60 1·50

1975. Christmas. "Virgin and Child with Angels". As T **114**.
396 12c. multicoloured 10 10
397 50c. multicoloured 30 30

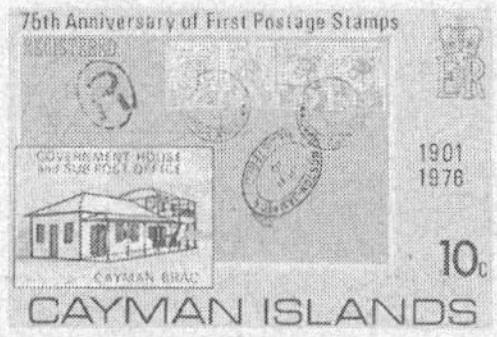

116 Registered Cover, Government House and Sub-Post Office

1975. 75th Anniv of First Cayman Islands Postage Stamp. Multicoloured.
399 10c. Type **116** 15 10
400 20c. $\frac{1}{2}$d. stamp and 1890–94 postmark 20 15
401 30c. 1d. stamp and 1908 surcharge 30 25
402 50c. $\frac{1}{2}$d. and 1d. stamps . . . 45 65

117 Seals of Georgia, Delaware and New Hampshire

1976. Bicentenary of American Revolution. Mult.
404 10c. Type **117** 40 15
405 15c. Carolina, New Jersey and Maryland seals 55 20
406 20c. Virginia, Rhode Island and Massachusetts seals . . 65 25
407 25c. New York, Connecticut and North Carolina seals 65 35
408 30c. Pennsylvania seal, Liberty Bell and U.S. Great Seal 70 40

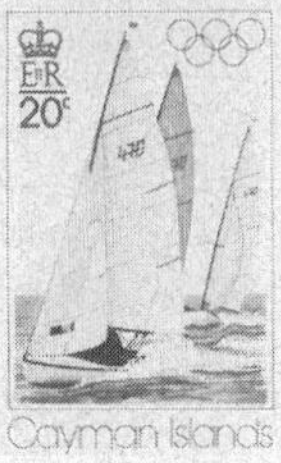

118 "470" Dinghies

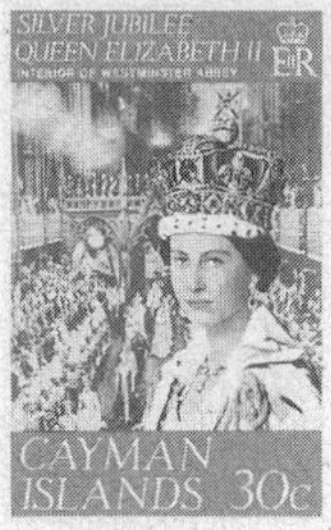

119 Queen Elizabeth II and Westminster Abbey

1976. Olympic Games, Montreal. Multicoloured.
410 20c. Type **118** 40 10
411 50c. Racing dinghy 70 50

1977. Silver Jubilee. Multicoloured.
427 8c. The Prince of Wales' visit, 1973 . . . . 10 20
428 30c. Type **119** 15 40
429 50c. Preparation for the Anointing (horiz) 30 75

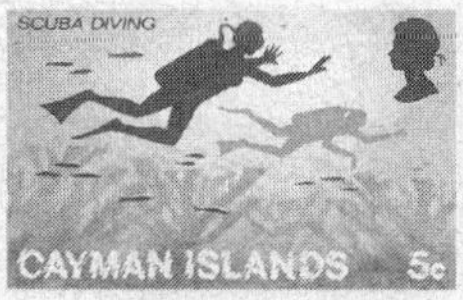

120 Scuba Diving

1977. Tourism. Multicoloured.
430 5c. Type **120** 10 10
431 10c. Exploring a wreck . . . 15 10
432 20c. Royal gramma ("Fairy basslet") (fish) 45 20
433 25c. Sergeant major (fish) . . 55 35

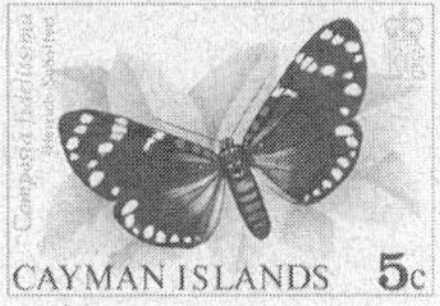

121 "Composia fidelissima" (moth)

1977. Butterflies and Moth. Multicoloured.
435 5c. Type **121** 75 20
436 8c. "Heliconius charithonia" 85 20
437 10c. "Danaus gilippus" . . . 85 20
438 15c. "Agraulis vanillae" . . . 1·25 45
439 20c. "Junonia evarete" . . . 1·25 45
440 30c. "Anartia jatrophae" . . 1·50 70

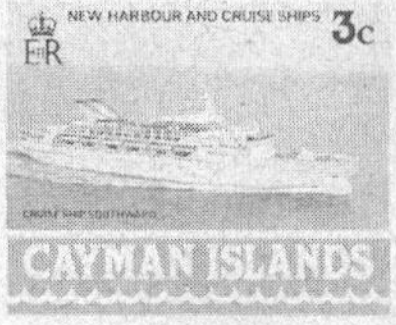

122 Cruise Liner "Southward"

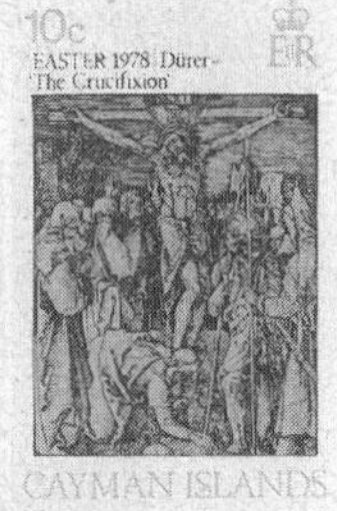

123 "The Crucifixion" (Durer)

1978. New Harbour and Cruise Ships. Multicoloured.
441 3c. Type **122** 30 10
442 5c. Cruise liner "Renaissance" 30 10
443 30c. New harbour (vert) . . . 80 25
444 50c. Cruise liner "Daphne" (vert) . . . . 1·10 65

1978. As Nos. 346/7, 349, 352, 417, 357/8 and 419, but designs smaller, 40 × 26 mm or 26 × 40 mm.
445 1c. Type **111** . . . . 1·00 1·25
446 3c. Treasure chest and lion's paw 80 50
447 5c. Flintlock pistol and brain coral . . . . 1·50 2·00
448 10c. Spiny lobster and treasure . . . . 1·25 60
449 20c. Queen or pink conch and treasure . . . . 2·25 1·00
450 40c. Gold chalice and seawhip . . . . 13·00 15·00
451 $1 Coat of arms (vert) . . . 18·00 5·50
452 $2 Queen Elizabeth II (vert) 4·00 18·00

1978. Easter and 450th Death Anniv of Durer.
459 **123** 10c. mauve and black . . 30 10
460 – 15c. yellow and black . . 40 15
461 – 20c. turquoise and black 50 20
462 – 30c. lilac and black . . . 60 35
DESIGNS: 15c. "Christ at Emmaus"; 20c. "The Entry into Jerusalem"; 30c. "Christ washing Peter's Feet".

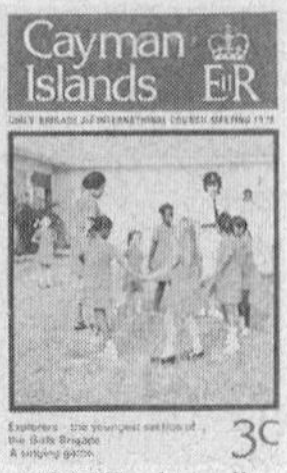

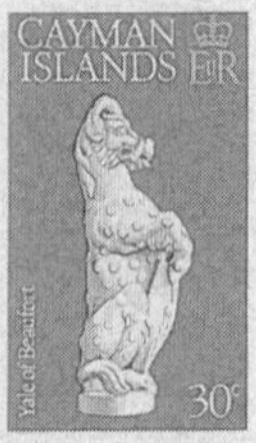

124 "Explorers" Singing Game **125** Yale of Beaufort

1978. 3rd International Council Meeting of Girls' Brigade. Multicoloured.

464	3c. Type **124**	20	10
465	10c. Colour party	30	10
466	20c. Girls and Duke of Edinburgh Award interests	60	20
467	50c. Girls using domestic skills	1·10	80

1978. 25th Anniv of Coronation.

468 **125**	30c. green, mauve and silver	20	25
469 –	30c. multicoloured	20	25
470 –	30c. green, mauve and silver	20	25

DESIGNS: No. 469, Queen Elizabeth II; 470, Barn owl.

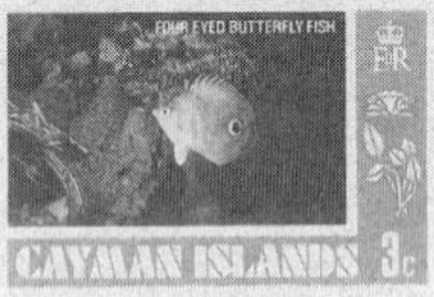

126 Four-eyed Butterflyfish

1978. Fish (1st series). Multicoloured.

471	3c. Type **126**	25	10
472	5c. Grey angelfish	30	10
473	10c. Squirrelfish	45	10
474	15c. Queen parrotfish	60	30
475	20c. Spanish hogfish	70	35
476	30c. Queen angelfish	80	50

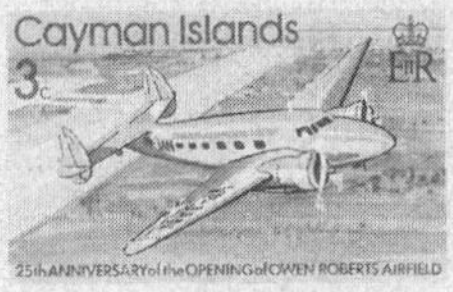

127 Lockheed L.18 Lodestar

1979. 25th Anniv of Owen Roberts Airfield. Mult.

477	3c. Type **127**	30	15
478	5c. Consolidated PBY-5A Catalina amphibian	30	15
479	10c. Vickers Viking 1B	35	15
480	15c. B.A.C. One Eleven 455 on tarmac	65	25
481	20c. Piper PA-31 Cheyenne II, Bell 47G Trooper helicopter and Hawker Siddeley H.S.125	75	35
482	30c. B.A.C. One Eleven 475 over airfield	1·00	50

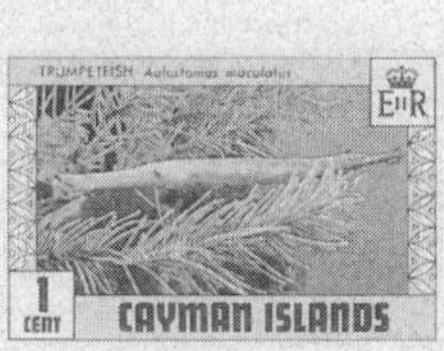

128 Trumpetfish

1979. Fishes (2nd series). Multicoloured.

483	1c. Type **128**	10	10
484	3c. Nassau grouper	25	10
485	5c. French angelfish	25	10
486	10c. Schoolmaster snapper	35	10
487	20c. Banded butterflyfish	55	25
488	50c. Black-barred soldierfish	1·00	70

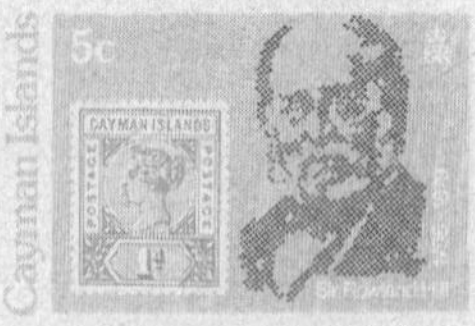

129 1900 1d. Stamp

1979. Death Centenary of Sir Rowland Hill.

489 **129**	5c. black, carmine and blue	10	10
490 –	10c. multicoloured	15	10
491 –	20c. multicoloured	20	25

DESIGNS: 10c. Great Britain 1902 3d. purple on lemon; 20c. 1955 £1 blue.

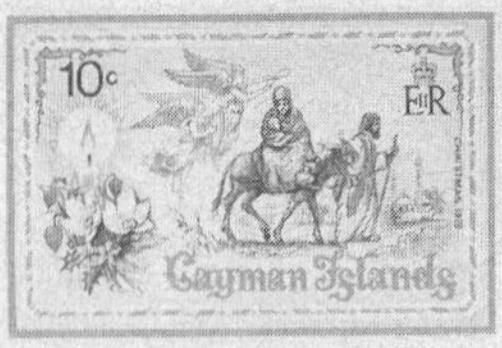

130 The Holy Family and Angels

1979. Christmas. Multicoloured.

493	10c. Type **130**	15	10
494	20c. Angels appearing to Shepherds	25	10
495	30c. Nativity	30	20
496	40c. The Magi	40	30

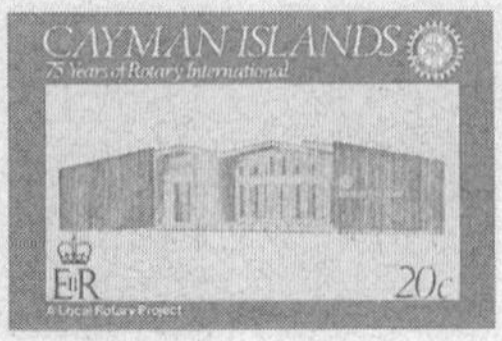

131 Local Rotary Project

1980. 75th Anniv of Rotary International.

497 **131**	20c. blue, black and yellow	20	15
498 –	30c. blue, black and yellow	25	20
499 –	50c. blue, yellow and black	35	30

DESIGNS—VERT: 30c. Paul P. Harris (founder); 50c. Rotary anniversary emblem.

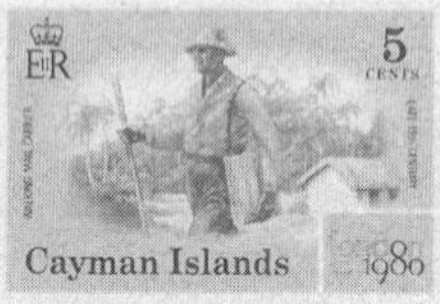

132 Walking Mail Carrier

1980. "London 1980" International Stamp Exhibition. Multicoloured.

500	5c. Type **132**	10	10
501	10c. Delivering mail by cat boat	15	10
502	15c. Mounted mail carrier	20	10
503	30c. Horse-drawn wagonette	25	15
504	40c. Postman on bicycle	35	15
505	$1 Motor transport	45	55

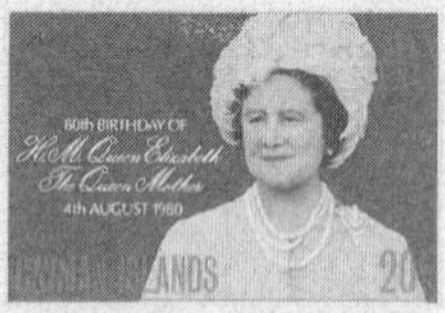

133 Queen Elizabeth the Queen Mother at the Derby, 1976

1980. 80th Birthday of the Queen Mother.

506 **133**	20c. multicoloured	20	25

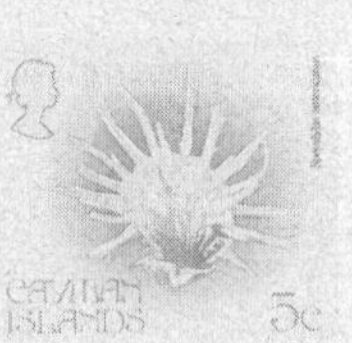

134 American Thorny Oyster

1980. Shells (1st series). Multicoloured.

507	5c. Type **134**	40	10
508	10c. West Indian murex	40	10
509	30c. Angular triton	80	40
510	50c. Caribbean vase	90	80

See also Nos. 565/8 and 582/5.

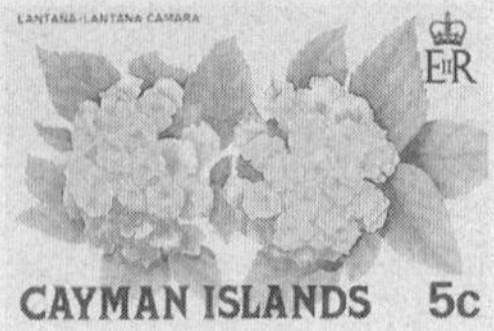

135 Lantana

1980. Flowers (1st series). Multicoloured.

511	5c. Type **135**	15	10
512	15c. "Bauhinia"	20	10
513	30c. "Hibiscus Rosa"	30	10
514	$1 "Milk and Wine Lily"	70	90

See also Nos. 541/4.

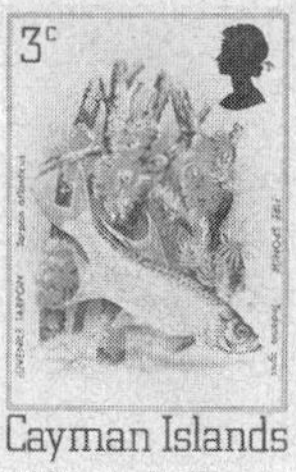

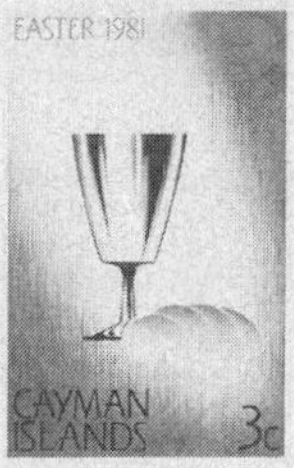

136 Juvenile Tarpon and Fire Sponge **137** Eucharist

1980. Multicoloured.

515A	3c. Type **136**	80	1·50
516B	5c. Flat tree or mangrove-root oyster	1·25	80
517A	10c. Mangrove crab	50	80
518A	15c. Lizard and "Phyciodes phaon" (butterfly)	1·00	1·50
519A	20c. Louisiana heron ("Tricoloured Heron")	1·50	2·00
520A	30c. Red mangrove flower	70	1·00
521A	40c. Red mangrove seeds	75	1·00
522A	50c. Waterhouse's leaf-nosed bat	1·25	1·50
523A	$1 Black-crowned night heron	5·50	5·00
524A	$2 Coat of arms	1·50	3·75
525A	$4 Queen Elizabeth II	2·25	4·75

1981. Easter. Multicoloured.

526	3c. Type **137**	10	10
527	10c. Crown of thorns	10	10
528	20c. Crucifix	15	10
529	$1 Lord Jesus Christ	50	60

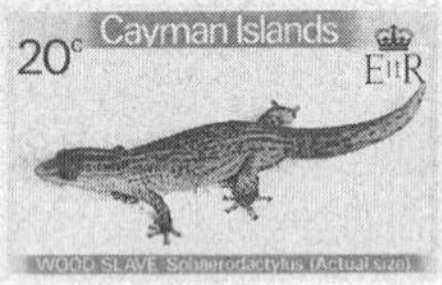

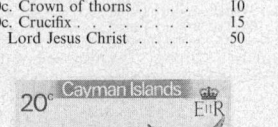

138 Wood Slave

1981. Reptiles and Amphibians. Multicoloured.

530	20c. Type **138**	25	20
531	30c. Cayman iguana	30	35
532	40c. Lion lizard	40	45
533	50c. Terrapin ("Hickatee")	45	55

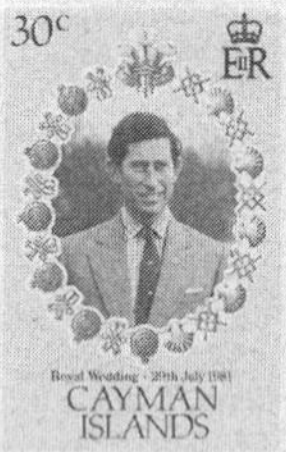

139 Prince Charles

1981. Royal Wedding. Multicoloured.

534	20c. Wedding bouquet from Cayman Islands	15	10
535	30c. Type **139**	20	10
536	$1 Prince Charles and Lady Diana Spencer	50	75

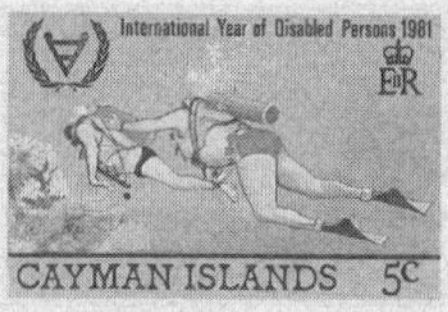

140 Disabled Scuba Divers

1981. Int Year for Disabled Persons. Mult.

537	5c. Type **140**	10	10
538	15c. Old school for the handicapped	25	20
539	20c. New school for the handicapped	30	25
540	$1 Disabled people in wheelchairs by the sea	1·25	85

1981. Flowers (2nd series). As T **135**. Multicoloured.

541	3c. Bougainvillea	10	10
542	10c. Morning Glory	15	10
543	20c. Wild amaryllis	25	25
544	$1 Cordia	70	1·75

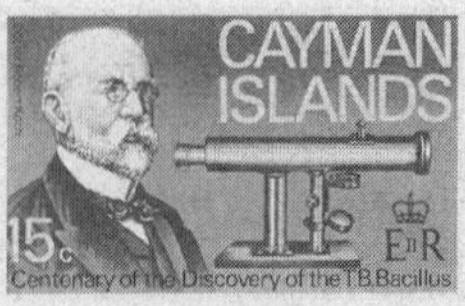

141 Dr. Robert Koch and Microscope

1982. Centenary of Robert Koch's Discovery of Tubercle Bacillus. Multicoloured.

545	15c. Type **141**	25	25
546	30c. Koch looking through microscope (vert)	45	45
547	40c. Microscope (vert)	70	70
548	50c. Dr. Robert Koch (vert)	80	80

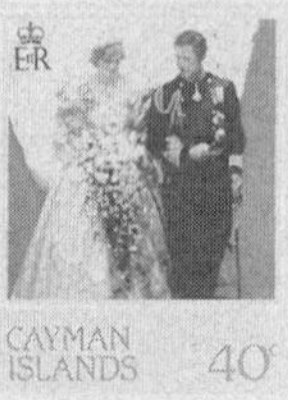

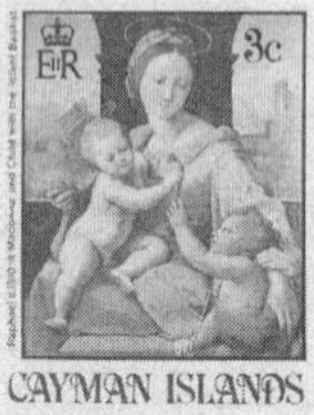

142 Bride and Groom walking down Aisle **144** "Madonna and Child with the Infant Baptist"

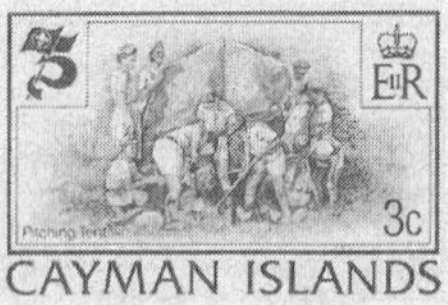

143 Pitching Tent

1982. 21st Birthday of Princess of Wales. Mult.

549	20c. Cayman Islands coat of arms	30	35
550	30c. Lady Diana Spencer in London, June, 1981	70	45
551	40c. Type **142**	70	65
552	50c. Formal portrait	2·50	90

1982. 75th Anniv of Boy Scout Movement. Mult.

553	3c. Type **143**	15	10
554	20c. Scouts camping	40	40
555	30c. Cub Scouts and Leaders	60	55
556	50c. Boating skills	80	85

1982. Christmas. Raphael Paintings. Multicoloured.

557	3c. Type **144**	10	10
558	10c. "Madonna of the Tower"	20	20
559	20c. "Ansidei Madonna"	35	35
560	30c. "Madonna and Child"	50	50

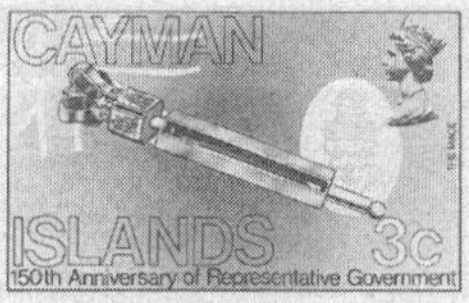

145 Mace

1982. 150th Anniv of Representative Government. Multicoloured.

561	3c. Type **145**	10	30
562	10c. Old Courthouse	20	30
563	20c. Commonwealth Parliamentary Association coat of arms	35	50
564	30c. Legislative Assembly building	50	90

1983. Shells (2nd series). As T **134**. Multicoloured.

565	5c. Colourful Atlantic moon	15	30
566	10c. King helmet	25	30
567	20c. Rooster-tail conch	30	40
568	$1 Reticulated cowrie-helmet	1·00	4·00

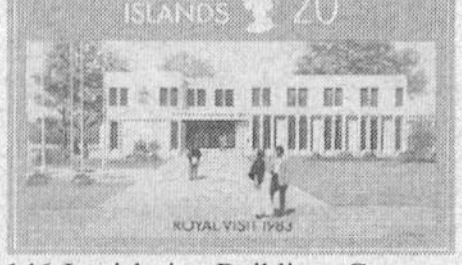

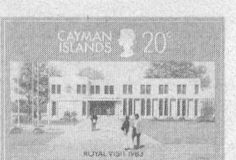

146 Legislative Building, Cayman Brac

1983. Royal Visit. Multicoloured.

569	20c. Type **146**	45	35
570	30c. Legislative Building, Grand Cayman	60	50
571	50c. Duke of Edinburgh (vert)	1·25	90
572	$1 Queen Elizabeth II (vert)	2·00	2·00

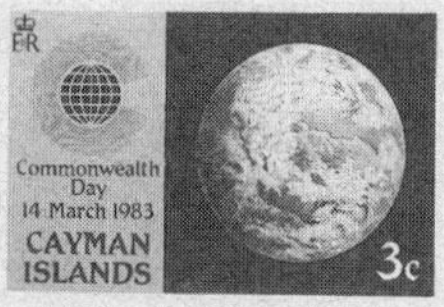

147 Satellite View of Earth

1983. Commonwealth Day. Multicoloured

574	3c. Type **147**	15	10
575	15c. Cayman Islands and Commonwealth flags	35	30
576	20c. Fishing	40	35
577	40c. Portrait of Queen Elizabeth II	65	65

148 MRCU Cessna Ag Wagon

1983. Bicentenary of Manned Flight. Multicoloured.

578	3c. Type **148**	60	40
579	10c. Consolidated PBY-5A Catalina amphibian	65	40
580	20c. Boeing 727-200	1·25	1·50
581	40c. Hawker Siddeley H.S.748	1·75	3·50

1984. Shells (3rd series). As T **134**. Multicoloured.

582	3c. Florida moon	70	35
583	10c. Austin's cone	80	35
584	30c. Leaning dwarf triton	2·25	2·75
585	50c. Filose or threaded turban	2·50	4·25

149 "Song of Norway" (cruise liner) **152** Couple on Beach at Sunset

151 Snowy Egret

1984. 250th Anniv of "Lloyd's List" (newspaper). Multicoloured.

586	5c. Type **149**	45	20
587	10c. View of old harbour	50	25
588	25c. Wreck of "Ridgefield" (freighter)	1·00	1·00
589	50c. "Goldfield" (schooner)	2·00	2·25

1984. Universal Postal Union Congress, Hamburg. No. 589 optd **U.P.U. CONGRESS HAMBURG 1984**.

591	50c. Schooner "Goldfield"	1·00	1·50

1984. Birds of the Cayman Islands (1st series). Multicoloured.

592	5c. Type **151**	1·00	65
593	10c. Bananaquit	1·00	65
594	35c. Belted kingfisher ("Kingfisher")	3·25	2·50
595	$1 Brown booby	6·00	9·50

See also Nos. 627/30.

1984. Christmas. Local Festivities. Multicoloured.

596	5c. Type **152**	60	1·00
597	5c. Family and schooner	60	1·00
598	5c. Carol singers	60	1·00
599	5c. East End bonfire	60	1·00
600	25c. Yachts	80	1·10
601	25c. Father Christmas in power-boat	80	1·10
602	25c. Children on beach	80	1·10
603	25c. Beach party	80	1·10

Nos. 596/9 and 600/3 were each printed together, se-tenant, the four designs of each value forming a composite picture of a beach scene at night (5c.) or in the daytime (25c.).

153 "Schomburgkia thomsoniana" (var. minor) **154** Freighter Aground

1985. Orchids. Multicoloured.

605	5c. Type **153**	1·00	30
606	10c. "Schomburgkia thomsoniana"	1·00	30
607	25c. "Encyclia plicata"	2·50	1·00
608	50c. "Dendrophylax fawcettii"	3·75	3·00

1985. Shipwrecks. Multicoloured.

609	5c. Type **154**	90	50
610	25c. Submerged sailing ship	2·75	1·25
611	35c. Wrecked trawler	3·00	2·50
612	40c. Submerged wreck on its side	3·25	3·50

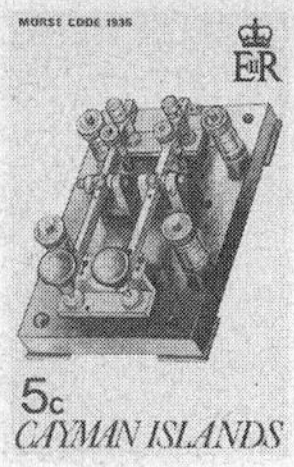

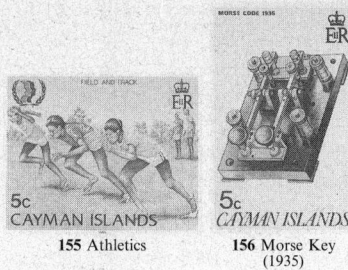

155 Athletics **156** Morse Key (1935)

1985. International Youth Year. Multicoloured.

613	5c. Type **155**	20	20
614	15c. Students in library	35	30
615	25c. Football (vert)	65	55
616	50c. Netball (vert)	1·25	2·00

1985. 50th Anniv of Telecommunications System. Multicoloured.

617	5c. Type **156**	40	40
618	10c. Hand cranked telephone	45	40
619	25c. Tropospheric scatter dish (1966)	1·25	80
620	50c. Earth station dish aerial (1979)	2·00	3·375

1986. 60th Birthday of Queen Elizabeth II. As T **110** of Ascension. Multicoloured.

621	5c. Princess Elizabeth at wedding of Lady May Cambridge, 1931	10	20
622	10c. In Norway, 1955	15	20
623	25c. Queen inspecting Royal Cayman Islands Police, 1983	1·50	75
624	50c. During Gulf tour, 1979	75	1·75
625	$1 At Crown Agents Head Office, London, 1983	1·10	2·50

157 Magnificent Frigate Bird

1986. Birds of the Cayman Islands (2nd series). Multicoloured.

627	10c. Type **157**	1·50	75
628	25c. Black-billed whistling duck ("West Indian Whistling Duck") (vert)	2·00	1·40
629	35c. La Sagra's flycatcher (vert)	2·25	2·50
630	40c. Yellow-faced grassquit	2·50	4·00

1986. Royal Wedding. As T **112** of Ascension. Multicoloured.

633	5c. Prince Andrew and Miss Sarah Ferguson	25	15
634	50c. Prince Andrew aboard H.M.S. "Brazen"	1·25	1·75

158 Red Coral Shrimp **159** Golf

1986. Marine Life. Multicoloured.

635	5c. Type **158**	40	50
636	10c. Yellow crinoid	40	50
637	15c. Hermit crab	35	60
638	20c. Tube dwelling anemone	35	80
639	25c. Christmas tree worm	45	2·25
640	35c. Porcupinefish	70	2·50
641	50c. Orangeball anenome	80	4·00
642	60c. Basket starfish	3·50	7·50
643	75c. Flamingo tongue	9·50	9·50
644	$1 Sea anenome	1·10	2·50
645	$2 Diamond blenny	1·25	4·25
646	$4 Rough file shell	2·50	6·50

1987. Tourism. Multicoloured.

647	10c. Type **159**	2·00	1·00
648	15c. Sailing	2·25	1·00
649	25c. Snorkelling	2·25	1·50
650	35c. Paragliding	2·25	2·00
651	$1 Game fishing	4·50	9·00

160 Ackee **162** Poinsettia

161 Lion Lizard

1987. Cayman Islands Fruits. Multicoloured.

652	5c. Type **160**	55	55
653	25c. Breadfruit	1·25	55
654	35c. Pawpaw	1·25	70
655	$1 Soursop	3·25	5·50

1987. Lizards. Multicoloured.

656	10c. Type **161**	1·25	50
657	50c. Iguana	2·75	2·25
658	$1 Anole	3·75	4·00

1987. Flowers. Multicoloured.

659	5c. Type **162**	75	55
660	25c. Periwinkle	2·00	75
661	35c. Yellow allamanda	2·00	1·10
662	75c. Blood lily	3·75	5·50

163 "Hemiargus ammon" and "Strymon martialis" **164** Green-backed Heron

1988. Butterflies. Multicoloured.

663	5c. Type **163**	1·25	65
664	25c. "Phocides pigmalion"	2·50	85
665	50c. "Anaea troglodyta"	4·00	3·75
666	$1 "Papilio andraemon"	5·00	5·00

1988. Herons. Multicoloured.

667	5c. Type **164**	1·25	65
668	25c. Louisiana heron	2·25	85
669	50c. Yellow-crowned night heron	3·00	3·00
670	$1 Little blue heron	3·50	4·25

165 Cycling **166** Princess Alexandra

1988. Olympic Games, Seoul. Multicoloured.

671	10c. Type **165**	1·75	70
672	50c. Cayman Airways Boeing 727 airliner and national team	2·75	2·50
673	$1 "470" dinghy	3·00	3·50

1988. Visit of Princess Alexandra. Multicoloured.

675	5c. Type **166**	1·25	75
676	$1 Princess Alexandra in evening dress	4·75	4·50

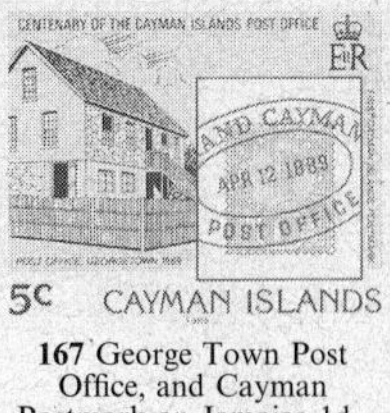

167 George Town Post Office, and Cayman Postmark on Jamaica 1d., 1889 **168** Captain Bligh ashore in West Indies

1989. Centenary of Cayman Islands Postal Service. Multicoloured.

677	**167** 5c. multicoloured	75	75
678	– 25c. green, black and blue	1·75	80
679	– 35c. multicoloured	1·75	1·10
680	– $1 multicoloured	7·50	7·50

DESIGNS: 25c. "Orinoco" (mail steamer) and 1900 ½d. stamp; 35c. G.P.O., Grand Cayman and "London 1980" $1 stamp; $1 Cayman Airways B.A.C. One Eleven 200/400 airplane and 1966 1s. Jet Service stamp.

1989. Captain Bligh's Second Breadfruit Voyage, 1791–93. Multicoloured.

681	50c. Type **168**	3·25	3·37
682	50c. H.M.S. "Providence" (sloop) at anchor	3·25	3·37
683	50c. Breadfruit in tubs and H.M.S. "Assistant" (transport)	3·25	3·37
684	50c. Sailors moving tubs of breadfruit	3·25	3·37
685	50c. Midshipman and stores	3·25	3·37

Nos. 681/5 were printed together, se-tenant, forming a composite design.

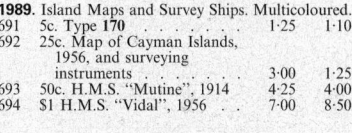

169 Panton House **170** Map of Grand Cayman, 1773, and Surveying Instruments

1989. Architecture. Designs showing George Town buildings. Multicoloured.

686	5c. Type **169**	45	45
687	10c. Town hall and clock tower	45	45
688	25c. Old Court House	90	55
689	35c. Elmslie Memorial Church	1·00	75
690	$1 Post Office	2·50	4·00

1989. Island Maps and Survey Ships. Multicoloured.

691	5c. Type **170**	1·25	1·10
692	25c. Map of Cayman Islands, 1956, and surveying instruments	3·00	1·25
693	50c. H.M.S. "Mutine", 1914	4·25	4·00
694	$1 H.M.S. "Vidal", 1956	7·00	8·50

171 French Angelfish

1990. Angelfishes. Multicoloured.

707	10c. Type **171**	1·25	60
708	25c. Grey angelfish	2·25	90
709	50c. Queen angelfish	3·50	3·75
710	$1 Rock beauty	5·50	7·50

1990. 90th Birthday of Queen Elizabeth the Queen Mother. As T **134** of Ascension.

711	50c. multicoloured	1·25	2·25
712	$1 black and blue	2·75	4·00

DESIGNS—21 × 36 mm: 50c. Silver Wedding photograph, 1948. 29 × 37 mm: $1 King George VI and Queen Elizabeth with Winston Churchill, 1940.

172 "Danaus eresimus"

1990. "Expo 90" International Garden and Greenery Exhibition, Osaka. Butterflies. Multicoloured.

713	5c. Type **172**	65	60
714	25c. "Brephidium exilis"	1·50	1·10
715	35c. "Phyciodes phaon"	1·75	1·25
716	$1 "Agraulis vanillae"	4·00	6·50

173 Goes Weather Satellite

1991. International Decade for Natural Disaster Reduction. Multicoloured.

717	5c. Type **173**	80	60
718	30c. Meteorologist tracking hurricane	2·00	1·10
719	40c. Damaged buildings	2·25	1·25
720	$1 U.S. Dept of Commerce weather reconnaisance Lockheed WP-3D Orion	5·00	7·50

174 Angels and "Datura candida"

1991. Christmas. Multicoloured.

721	5c. Type **174**	50	50
722	30c. Mary and Joseph going to Bethlehem and "Allamanda cathartica"	1·40	60
723	40c. Adoration of the Kings and "Euphorbia pulcherrima"	1·60	1·10
724	60c. Holy Family and "Guaiacum officinale"	2·00	3·75

175 Coconut Palm

177 Woman and Donkey with Panniers

176 Single Cyclist

1991. Island Scenes. Multicoloured.

725	5c. Type **175**	50	30
726	15c. Beach scene (horiz)	1·25	30
727	20c. Poincianas in bloom (horiz)	70	35
728	30c. Blowholes (horiz)	1·25	50
729	40c. Police band (horiz)	2·50	1·40
730	50c. "Song of Norway" (liner) at George Town	2·00	1·40
731	60c. The Bluff, Cayman Brac (horiz)	1·75	2·00
732	80c. Coat of arms	1·50	2·25
733	90c. View of Hell (horiz)	1·60	2·25
734	$1 Game fishing (horiz)	3·25	2·25
735	$2 "Nieuw Amsterdam" (1983) and "Holiday" (liners) in harbour	7·00	6·00
736	$8 Queen Elizabeth II	15·00	17·00

1992. 40th Anniv of Queen Elizabeth II's Accession. As T **143** of Ascension. Multicoloured.

737	5c. Caymans' house	30	30
738	20c. Sunset over islands	1·00	50
739	30c. Beach	1·10	65
740	40c. Three portraits of Queen Elizabeth	1·10	1·00
741	$1 Queen Elizabeth II	2·00	3·50

1992. Olympic Games, Barcelona. Cycling. Mult.

742	15c. Type **176**	1·50	65
743	40c. Two cyclists	2·25	1·50
744	60c. Cyclist's legs	2·75	3·00
745	$1 Two pursuit cyclists	3·50	4·25

1992. Island Heritage. Multicoloured.

746	5c. Type **177**	50	50
747	30c. Fisherman weaving net	1·25	85
748	40c. Maypole dancing	1·50	1·10
749	60c. Basket making	2·50	3·50
750	$1 Cooking on caboose	3·00	4·50

178 Yellow Stingray

1993. Rays. Multicoloured.

751	5c. Type **178**	70	60
752	30c. Southern stingray	1·75	1·25
753	40c. Spotted eagle-ray	2·00	1·50
754	$1 Manta	4·25	5·50

179 Turtle and Sailing Dinghies

180 Cuban Amazon with Wings spread

1993. Tourism. Multicoloured.

755	15c. Type **179**	1·25	1·40
756	15c. Tourist boat, fishing launch and scuba diver	1·25	1·40
757	15c. Golf	1·25	1·40
758	15c. Tennis	1·25	1·40
759	15c. Pirates and ship	1·25	1·40
760	30c. Liner, tourist launch and yacht	1·40	1·60
761	30c. George Town street	1·40	1·60
762	30c. Tourist submarine	1·40	1·60
763	30c. Motor scooter riders and cyclist	1·40	1·60
764	30c. Cayman Airways Boeing 737 airliners	1·40	1·60

1993. Endangered Species. Cuban Amazon ("Grand Cayman Parrot"). Multicoloured.

765	5c. Type **180**	85	1·25
766	5c. On branch with wings folded	85	1·25
767	30c. Head of parrot	2·25	2·50
768	30c. Pair of parrots	2·25	2·50

181 "Ionopsis utricularioides" and Manger

1993. Christmas. Orchids. Multicoloured.

769	5c. Type **181**	80	65
770	40c. "Encyclia cochleata" and shepherd	2·00	85
771	60c. "Vanilla pompona" and wise men	2·75	3·25
772	$1 "Oncidium caymanense" and Virgin Mary	3·75	5·00

183 Flags of Great Britain and Cayman Islands

184 Black-billed Whistling Duck

1994. Royal Visit. Multicoloured.

774	5c. Type **183**	1·00	65
775	15c. Royal Yacht "Britannia"	2·00	1·00
776	30c. Queen Elizabeth II	2·00	1·10
777	$2 Queen Elizabeth and Prince Philip disembarking	6·00	8·00

1994. Black-billed Whistling Duck ("West Indian Whistling Duck"). Multicoloured.

778	5c. Type **184**	90	70
779	15c. Duck landing on water (horiz)	1·60	75
780	20c. Duck preening (horiz)	1·60	80
781	80c. Duck flapping wings	3·50	4·50
782	$1 Adult and duckling	4·00	5·00

185 "Electrostrymon angelia"

186 H.M.S. "Convert" (frigate)

1994. Butterflies. Multicoloured.

784	10c. Type **185**	1·00	1·40
785	10c. "Eumaeus atala"	1·00	1·40
786	$1 "Eurema daira"	4·75	5·00
787	$1 "Urbanus dorantes"	4·75	5·00

1994. Bicentenary of Wreck of Ten Sail off Grand Cayman. Multicoloured.

788	10c. Type **186**	45	45
789	10c. Merchant brig and full-rigged ship	45	45
790	15c. Full-rigged ship near rock	65	45
791	20c. Long boat leaving full-rigged ship	75	55
792	$2 Merchant brig	4·25	6·75

187 Young Green Turtles

1995. Sea Turtles. Multicoloured.

793	10c. Type **187**	55	45
794	20c. Kemp's ridley turtle	80	55
795	25c. Hawksbill turtle	90	60
796	30c. Leatherback turtle	95	70
797	$1.30 Loggerhead turtle	3·50	4·50
798	$2 Pacific ridley turtles	4·50	5·50

188 Running

1995. C.A.R.I.F.T.A. and I.A.A.F. Games, George Town. Multicoloured.

800	10c. Type **188**	60	40
801	20c. High jumping	90	70
802	30c. Javelin throwing	1·25	80
803	$1.30 Yachting	4·25	6·00

1995. 50th Anniv of End of Second World War. As T **161** of Ascension. Multicoloured.

805	10c. Members of Cayman Home Guard	70	55
806	25c. "Comayagua" (freighter)	1·75	85
807	40c. U-boat "U125"	2·00	1·50
808	$1 U.S. Navy L-3 airship	3·75	5·50

190 Ox and Christ Child

191 Sea Grape

1995. Christmas. Nativity Animals. Multicoloured.

811	10c. Type **190**	60	30
812	20c. Sheep and lamb	1·00	45
813	30c. Donkey	1·50	60
814	$2 Camels	6·00	8·50

1996. Wild Fruit. Multicoloured.

816	10c. Type **191**	40	30
817	25c. Guava	85	50
818	40c. West Indian cherry	1·25	80
819	$1 Tamarind	2·50	3·00

192 "Laser" Dinghy

193 Guitar and Score of National Song

1996. Centenary of Modern Olympic Games. Multicoloured.

820	10c. Type **192**	40	30
821	20c. Sailboarding	70	60
822	30c. "Finn" dinghy	90	80
823	$2 Running	4·00	6·50

1996. National Identity. Multicoloured.

824	10c. Type **193**	35	30
825	20c. Cayman Airways Boeing 737-200	70	55
826	25c. Queen Elizabeth opening Legislative Assembly	75	50
827	30c. Seven Mile Beach	75	55
828	40c. Scuba diver and stingrays	1·00	75
829	60c. Children at turtle farm	1·50	1·10
830	80c. Cuban amazon ("Cayman Parrot") (national bird)	2·50	2·00
831	90c. Silver thatch palm (national tree)	1·75	2·00
832	$1 Cayman Islands flag	2·75	2·25
833	$2 Wild Banana Orchid (national flower)	4·75	5·00
834	$4 Cayman Islands coat of arms	9·00	11·00
835	$6 Cayman Islands currency	11·00	13·00

194 "Christmas Time on North Church Street" (Joanne Sibley)

1996. Christmas. Paintings. Multicoloured.

836	10c. Type **194**	40	30
837	25c. "Gone Fishing" (Lois Brezinsky)	70	50
838	30c. "Claus Encounters" (John Doak)	80	70
839	$2 "A Caymanian Christmas" (Debbie van der Bol)	4·00	6·50

1997. Golden Wedding of Queen Elizabeth and Prince Philip. As T **173** of Ascension. Multicoloured.

841	10c. Queen Elizabeth	70	80
842	10c. Prince Philip and Prince Charles at Trooping the Colour	70	80
843	30c. Prince William horse riding, 1989	1·25	1·40
844	30c. Queen Elizabeth and Prince Philip at Royal Ascot	1·25	1·40
845	40c. Prince Philip at the Brighton Driving Trials	1·40	1·50
846	40c. Queen Elizabeth at Windsor Horse Show, 1993	1·40	1·50

195 Children accessing Internet

196 Santa in Hammock

1997. Telecommunications. Multicoloured.

848	10c. Type **195**	35	25
849	25c. Cable & Wireless cable ship	70	45
850	30c. New area code "345" on children's T-shirts	75	60
851	60c. Satellite dish	1·50	2·25

1997. Christmas. Multicoloured.

852	10c. Type **196**	35	25
853	30c. Santa with children on the Bluff	65	45
854	40c. Santa playing golf	1·50	80
855	$1 Santa scuba diving	2·00	3·00

1998. Diana, Princess of Wales Commemoration. As T **91** of Kiribati. Multicoloured.

856	10c. Wearing gold earrings, 1997	40	40
857	20c. Wearing black hat	70	70

1998. 80th Anniv of the Royal Air Force. As T **178** of Ascension. Multicoloured.

859	10c. Hawker Horsley	50	50
860	20c. Fairey Hendon	65	65
861	25c. Hawker Siddeley Gnat	75	75
862	30c. Hawker Siddeley Dominie	85	85

197 West Indian Whistling Duck

198 Santa at the Blowholes

1998. Birds. Multicoloured.

864	10c. Type **197**	55	40
865	20c. Magnificent frigate bird	90	45
866	60c. Red-footed booby	1·75	1·75
867	$1 Grand cayman parrot	2·10	2·75

1998. Christmas. Multicoloured.

868	10c. Type **198**	30	25
869	30c. Santa diving on wreck of "Capt. Keith Tibbetts"	75	60
870	40c. Santa at Pedro Castle	90	75
871	60c. Santa arriving on Little Cayman	1·75	2·00

199 "They Rolled the Stone Away" (Miss Lassie)

1999. Easter. Paintings by Miss Lassie (Gladwyn Bush). Multicoloured.

884	10c. Type **199**	25	25
885	20c. "Ascension" (vert)	50	50
886	30c. "The World Praying for Peace"	65	65
887	40c. "Calvary" (vert)	85	85

200 "Cayman House" (Jessica Cranston)

1999. Vision 2008 Project. Children's Paintings. Multicoloured.
888 10c. Type **200** 30 20
889 30c. "Coral Reef" (Sarah Hetley) 80 55
890 40c. "Fisherman on North Sound" (Sarah Cuff) . . . 90 70
891 $2 "Three Fish and a Turtle" (Ryan Martinez) . . . . . 4·00 5·00

1999. Royal Wedding. As T **185** of Ascension. Multicoloured.
892 10c. Photographs of Prince Edward and Miss Sophie Rhys-Jones 50 30
893 $2 Engagement photograph 3·75 4·50

1999. 30th Anniv of First Manned Landing on Moon. As T **186** of Ascension. Multicoloured.
894 10c. Coastguard cutter on patrol during launch . . . 35 25
895 25c. Firing of third stage rockets 70 60
896 30c. Buzz Aldrin descending to Moon's surface 75 65
897 60c. Jettisoning of lunar module . . . . 1·25 1·50

1999. "Queen Elizabeth the Queen Mother's Century". As T **187** of Ascension. Multicoloured.
899 10c. Visiting anti-aircraft battery, London, 1940 . . 45 30
900 20c. With children on her 94th birthday, 1994 . . . . 65 55
901 30c. With Prince Charles and Prince William, 1997 . . . 80 80
902 40c. Reviewing Chelsea Pensioners, 1986 . . . . . 90 90

201 1969 Christmas ¼c. Stamp

1999. Christmas. Designs showing previous Christmas stamps. Multicoloured.
904 10c. Type **201** 30 25
905 30c. 1984 Christmas 5c. . . . 60 50
906 40c. 1997 Christmas 10c. . . . 75 65
907 $1 1979 Christmas 20c. (horiz) . . . . 1·75 2·25

2000. "Stamp Show 2000" International Stamp Exhibition, London. Kings and Queens of England. As T **223** of British Virgin Islands. Multicoloured.
909 10c. King Henry VII 35 35
910 40c. King Henry VIII . . . . 90 1·10
911 40c. Queen Mary I . . . . . 90 1·10
912 40c. King Charles II . . . . 90 1·10
913 40c. Queen Anne . . . . . . 90 1·10
914 40c. King George IV . . . . 90 1·10
915 40c. King George V . . . . 90 1·10

202 Ernie fishing from Rubber Ring

2000. "Sesame Street" (children's T.V. programme). Multicoloured.
916 10c. Type **202** 25 25
917 20c. Grover flying 40 50
918 20c. Zoe in airplane 40 50
919 20c. Oscar the Grouch in balloon 40 50
920 20c. The Count on motorbike 40 50
921 20c. Big Bird rollerskating . . 40 50
922 20c. Cookie Monster heading for Cookie Factory 40 50
923 20c. Type **202** 40 50
924 20c. Bert in rowing boat . . 40 50
925 20c. Elmo snorkeling 40 50
926 30c. As No. 920 . . . . . . 55 55

Nos. 917/25 were printed together, se-tenant, with the backgrounds forming a composite design.

2000. 18th Birthday of Prince William. As T **191** of Ascension. Multicoloured.
928 10c. Prince William in 1999 (horiz) 30 25
929 20c. In evening dress, 1997 (horiz) 55 45
930 30c. At Muick Falls, 1997 . . 70 70
931 40c. In uniform of Parachute Regiment, 1986 . . . . . 90 95

203 Green Turtle

2000. Marine Life. Multicoloured.
932 10c. Type **203** 30 25
933 20c. Queen angel fish 55 45
934 30c. Sleeping parrotfish . . . 75 65
935 $1 Green moray eel . . . . 2·75 2·75

204 Boy thinking about Drugs and Fitness

2000. National Drugs Council. Multicoloured.
936 10c. Type **204** 35 25
937 15c. Rainbow, sun, clouds and "ez2B Drug Free" . . . 50 35
938 30c. Musicians dancing . . . 80 65
939 $2 Hammock between two palm trees . . . . 4·50 5·00

205 Children on Beach ("Backing Sand") **206** Woman on Beach

2000. Christmas. Traditional Customs. Mult.
941 10c. Type **205** 35 25
942 30c. Christmas dinner 80 60
943 40c. Yard dance 90 80
944 60c. Conch shell borders . . 1·40 1·50

2001. United Nations Women's Human Rights Campaign.
945 **206** 10c. multicoloured 25 25

207 Red Mangrove Cay

2001. Cayman Brac Tourism Project. Mult.
946 15c. Type **207** 35 35
947 20c. Peter's Cave (vert) . . . 45 45
948 25c. Bight Road steps (vert) 55 55
949 30c. Westerly Ponds 65 65
950 40c. Aerial view of Spot Bay 80 80
951 60c. The Marshes . . . . . 1·25 1·50

208 Work of National Council of Voluntary Organizations

2001. Non-Profit Organizations. Multicoloured.
952 15c. Type **208** 25 30
953 20c. Pet welfare (Cayman Humane Society) 35 40
954 25c. Stick figures (Red Cross and Red Crescent) 45 50
955 30c. Pink flowers (Cayman Islands Cancer Society) (vert) 50 55
956 40c. Women's silhouettes and insignia (Lions Club Breast Cancer Awareness Campaign) (vert) 70 80

209 Children walking Home

2001. Transportation. Multicoloured.
958 15c. Type **209** 25 30
959 15c. Boy on donkey 25 30
960 20c. Bananas by canoe . . . 35 40
961 25c. Horse and buggy 45 50
962 30c. Catboats fishing 50 55
963 40c. Schooner 70 75
964 60c. Police cyclist (vert) . . 1·00 1·10
965 80c. Lady drivers . . . . . 1·40 1·50
966 90c. Launching *Cimboco* (motor coaster) (vert) . . 1·50 1·60
967 $1 Amphibian aircraft . . . 1·75 1·90
968 $4 Container ship . . . . . 7·00 7·50
969 $10 Boeing 767 airliner . . . 17·00 18·00

210 Father Christmas on Scooter with Children, Cayman Brac

2001. Christmas. Multicoloured.
970 15c. Type **210** 25 30
971 30c. Father Christmas on eagle ray, Little Cayman 50 55
972 40c. Father Christmas in catboat, Grand Cayman 70 75
973 60c. Father Christmas parasailing over Grand Cayman . . . . 1·00 1·10

211 Statue of Liberty, U.S. and Cayman Flags

2002. In Remembrance. Victims of Terrorist Attacks on U.S.A. (11 September 2001).
974 **211** $1 multicoloured . . . . 1·75 1·90

2002. Golden Jubilee. As T **200** of Ascension.
975 15c. grey, blue and gold . . . 25 30
976 20c. multicoloured 35 40
977 30c. black, blue and gold . . 50 55
978 80c. multicoloured . . . . . 1·40 1·50
DESIGNS: 15c. Princess Elizabeth as young child; 20c. Queen Elizabeth in evening dress, 1976; 30c. Princess Elizabeth and Princess Margaret as Girl Guides, 1942; 80c. Queen Elizabeth at Newbury, 1996.

212 Snoopy painting Woodstock at Cayman Brac Bluff

2002. "A Cayman Vacation". Peanuts (cartoon characters by Charles Schulz). Multicoloured.
980 15c. Type **212** 25 30
981 20c. Charlie Brown and Sally at Hell Post Office, Grand Cayman 35 40
982 25c. Peppermint Patty and Marcie on beach, Little Cayman 45 50
983 30c. Snoopy as Red Baron and Boeing 737-200 over Grand Cayman 50 55
984 40c. Linus and Snoopy at Point of Sand, Little Cayman 70 75
985 60c. Charlie Brown, playing golf at The Links, Grand Cayman . . . . 1·00 1·10

CENTRAL AFRICAN EMPIRE

Pt. 12

Central African Republic was renamed Central African Empire on 4 December 1976, when Pres. Bokassa became Emperor.
The country reverted to Central African Republic on his overthrow in 1979.

100 centimes = 1 franc.

1977. Various stamps of Central African Republic optd **EMPIRE CENTRAFRICAIN**.
439 **150** 3f. mult (postage) 40 35
444 **167** 10f. multicoloured 25 25
457 – 10f. red and blue (386) . . 25 25
459 **172** 10f. multicoloured 35 35
460 – 15f. multicoloured (391) 45 45
465 – 15f. brown, grn & bl (397) 25 25
445 – 20f. multicoloured (366) 25 25
461 – 20f. multicoloured (392) 40 40
446 – 25f. multicoloured (367) 25 25
451 – 25f. multicoloured (376) 25 25
449 **168** 30f. multicoloured 40 40
452 – 30f. multicoloured (377) 40 40
462 – 30f. multicoloured (393) 45 45
447 – 40f. multicoloured (370) 40 40
450 – 40f. multicoloured (373) 45 45
453 – 40f. multicoloured (378) 40 40
454 – 40f. multicoloured (380) 45 45
455 **170** 40f. multicoloured 40 40
456 – 40f. multicoloured (384) 40 40
458 – 40f. multicoloured (389) 40 35
482 – 40f. multicoloured (423) 65 55
466 – 50f. blue, brn & grn (398) 55 55
440 **163** 100f. multicoloured . . . 13·00 13·00
441 **164** 100f. grn, red & brn . . . 1·25 1·25
442 **165** 100f. brn, grn & blue . . 1·60 1·60
468 **179** 100f. black and yellow . . 1·25 1·25
469 **180** 100f. purple, blue & grn 1·25 1·25
491 **185** 100f. multicoloured . . . 1·25 1·25

483 – 50f. mult (424) (air) . . . 45 30
448 – 100f. multicoloured (371) 85 85
463 **173** 100f. red and blue 90 90
467 **178** 100f. multicoloured . . . 85 85
484 – 100f. multicoloured (425) 85 85
464 **174** 200f. multicoloured . . . 1·90 1·90
443 **166** 500f. red, green & brown 6·25 6·25

1977. "Apollo–Soyuz" Space Link. Nos. 410/14 of Central African Republic optd **EMPIRE CENTRAFRICAIN**.
470 **181** 40f. mult (postage) . . . 50 50
471 – 50f. multicoloured 60 60

472 – 100f. multicoloured (air) 85 85
473 – 200f. multicoloured . . . 1·90 1·90
474 – 300f. multicoloured . . . 2·50 2·50

1977. Air. Bicentenary of American Revolution. Nos. 416/20 of Central African Republic optd **EMPIRE CENTRAFRICAIN**.
476 **182** 100f. multicoloured . . . 75 45
477 – 125f. multicoloured . . . 95 60
478 – 150f. multicoloured . . . 1·25 70
479 – 200f. multicoloured . . . 1·60 95
480 – 250f. multicoloured . . . 1·90 1·25

1977. Winners of Winter Olympic Games, Innsbruck. Nos. 426/30 of Central African Republic optd **EMPIRE CENTRAFRICAIN**.
485 – 40f. mult (postage) . . . 40 35
486 – 60f. multicoloured 50 35

487 **184** 100f. multicoloured (air) 65 45
488 – 200f. multicoloured . . . 1·50 85
489 – 300f. multicoloured . . . 2·25 1·25

1977. "Viking" Space Mission. Nos. 433/7 of Central African Republic optd **EMPIRE CENTRAFRICAIN**.
492 **186** 40f. mult (postage) . . . 40 30
493 – 60f. multicoloured 50 35

494 – 100f. multicoloured (air) 65 45
495 – 200f. multicoloured . . . 1·50 85
496 – 300f. multicoloured . . . 2·25 1·25

189 Pierre and Marie Curie (Physics, 1903)

1977. Nobel Prize-winners. Multicoloured.
503 40f. Type **189** (postage) . . . 60 25
504 60f. W. C. Rontgen (Physics, 1901) 60 35
505 100f. Rudyard Kipling (Literature, 1907) (air) . . 75 35
506 200f. Ernest Hemingway (Literature, 1954) . . . . 1·50 65
507 300f. L. Pirandello (Literature, 1934) . . . . . 2·25 75

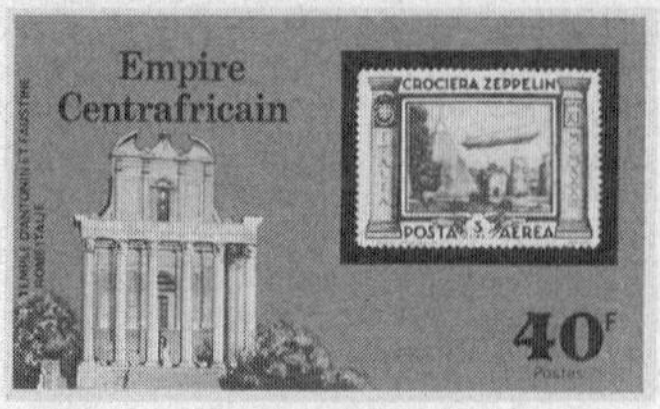

190 Roman Temple and Italy 1933 3l. stamp

1977. "Graf Zeppelin" Flights. Multicoloured.

509 40f. Type **190** (postage) . . . 60 25
510 60f. St. Basil's Cathedral, Moscow, and Russia 1930 40k. stamp 70 40
511 100f. North Pole and Germany 1931 "Polarfahrt" stamp (air) 1·10 45
512 200f. Museum of Science and Industry, Chicago, and Germany 1933 "Chicagofahrt" stamp . . 2·10 65
513 300f. Brandenburg Gate, Berlin, and German 1931 stamp . . . . 3·25 95

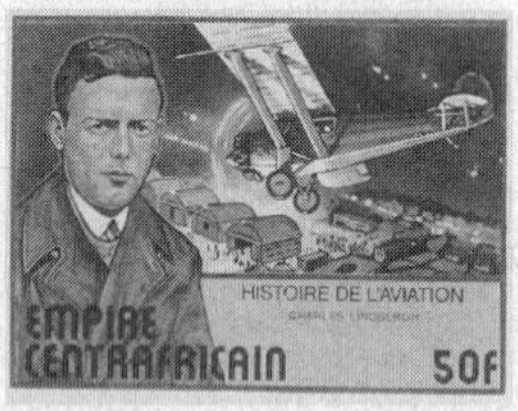

191 Charles Lindbergh and "Spirit of St. Louis"

1977. History of Aviation. Multicoloured.

515 50f. Type **191** 45 20
516 60f. Alberto Santos-Dumont and "14 bis" biplane . . . 55 25
517 100f. Louis Bleriot and Bleriot XI 95 40
518 200f. Roald Amundsen and Dornier Wal flying boat . . 1·60 60
519 300f. Concorde . . . . . . 3·00 1·25

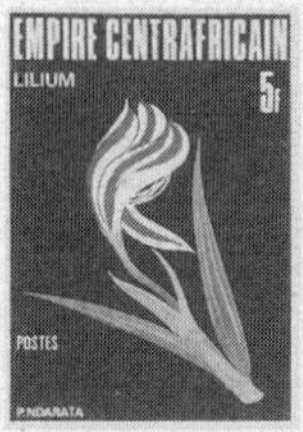

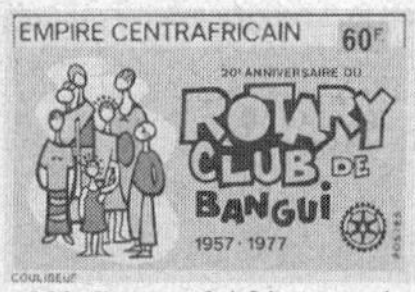

192 Lily **193** Group of Africans and Rotary Emblem

1977. Flowers. Multicoloured.

521 5f. Type **192** 50 35
522 10f. Hibiscus . . . . 1·00 60

1977. 20th Anniv of Bangui Rotary Club.

523 **193** 60f. multicoloured . . . . 1·90 1·25

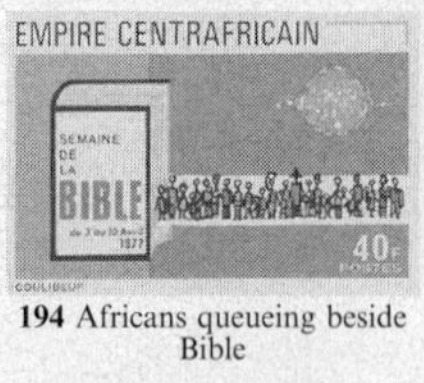

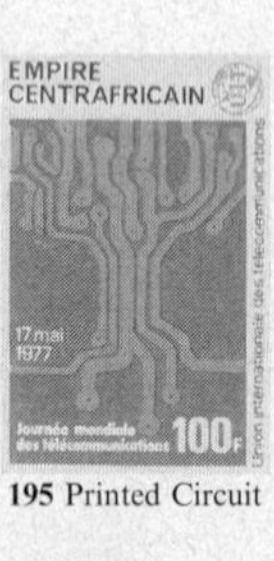

194 Africans queueing beside Bible **195** Printed Circuit

1977. Bible Week.

524 **194** 40f. multicoloured . . . . 1·50 95

1977. World Telecommunications Day.

525 **195** 100f. orange, brown & blk 2·25 1·90

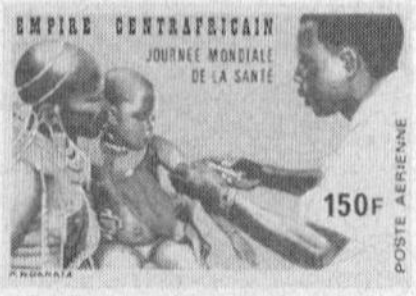

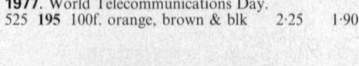

196 Doctor inoculating Child

1977. Air. World Health Day.

526 **196** 150f. multicoloured . . . 1·00 70

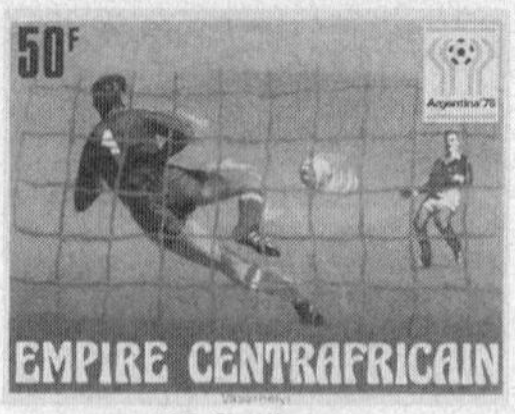

197 Goalkeeper

1977. World Cup Football Championship (1978). Multicoloured.

527 50f. Type **197** 40 20
528 60f. Goalmouth melee . . . 45 25
529 100f. Mid-field play 75 30
530 200f. World Cup poster . . . 1·60 50
531 300f. Mario Jorge Lobo Zagalo (Argentine trainer) and Buenos Aires stadium 2·50 90

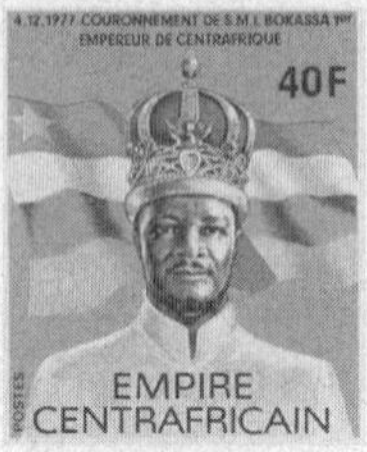

198 Emperor Bokassa I

1977. Coronation of Emperor Bokassa.

533 **198** 40f. mult (postage) . . . 25 20
534 60f. multicoloured 40 25
535 100f. multicoloured . . . 75 45
536 150f. multicoloured . . . 1·25 70
537 200f. mult (air) . . . . . 1·50 75
538 300f. multicoloured . . . 2·25 1·25

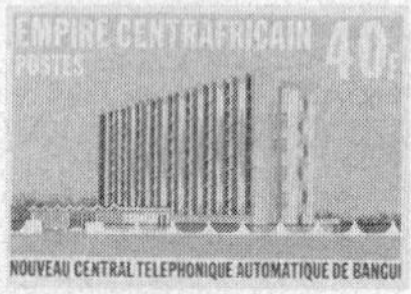

199 Bangui Telephone Exchange

1978. Opening of Automatic Telephone Exchange, Bangui. Multicoloured.

541 40f. Type **199** 40 25
542 60f. Bangui Telephone Exchange (different) . . . 50 35

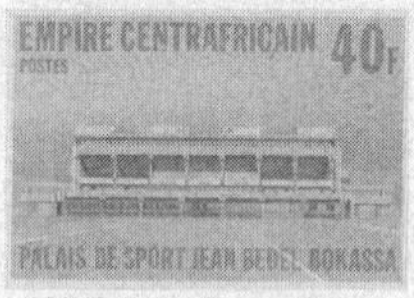

200 Bokassa Sports Palace

1978. Bokassa Sports Palace. Multicoloured.

543 40f. Type **200** 40 25
544 60f. Sports Palace (different) 50 35

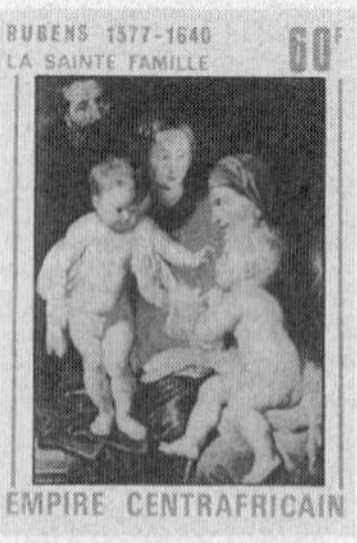

201 "The Holy Family"

1978. 400th Birth Anniv of Rubens. Mult.

545 60f. Type **201** 50 20
546 150f. "Marie de Medici" . . 1·10 40
547 200f. "The Artist's Sons" . . 1·60 60
548 300f. "Neptune" (horiz) . . . 2·50 75

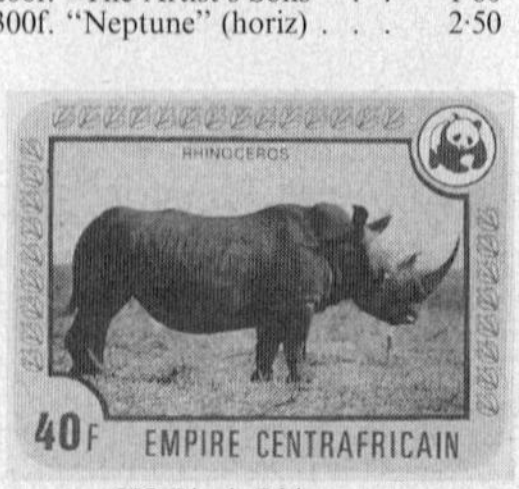

202 Black Rhinoceros

1978. Endangered Animals. Multicoloured.

550 40f. Type **202** 50 15
551 50f. Crocodile 65 20
552 60f. Leopard (vert) 75 25
553 100f. Giraffe (vert) . . . . . 1·25 40
554 200f. African elephant . . . 3·25 60
555 300f. Gorilla (vert) . . . . . 3·75 1·00

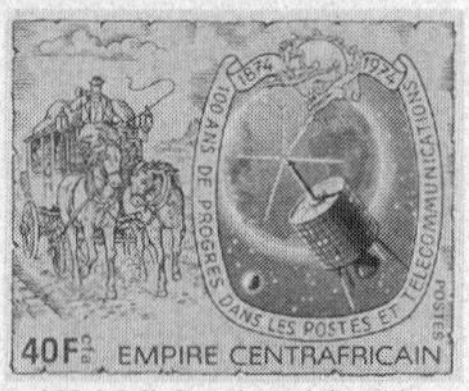

203 Mail Coach and Satellite

1978. 100 Years of Progress in Posts and Telecommunications. Multicoloured.

556 40f. Type **203** (postage) . . . 35 20
557 50f. Steam locomotive and space communications . . 5·50 2·75
558 60f. Paddle-steamer and ship-to-shore communications 45 25
559 80f. Renault car and "Pioneer" satellite 65 25
560 100f. Mail balloon and "Apollo"–"Soyuz" link-up (air) 75 40
561 200f. Seaplane "Comte da la Vaulx" and Concorde . . 1·50 65

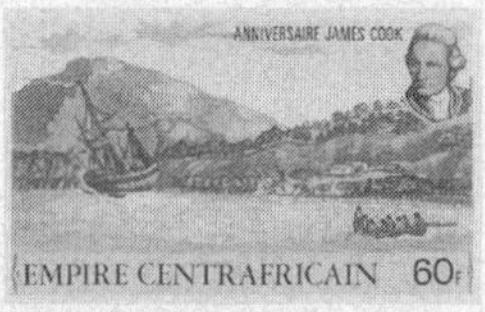

205 H.M.S. "Endeavour" under Repair (after W. Byrne)

1978. 250th Birth Anniv of Captain Cook. Mult.

578 60f. Type **205** . . . . 1·00 35
579 80f. Cook on board "Endeavour" (vert) 75 25
580 200f. Landing party in New Hebrides . . . . 1·90 65
581 350f. Masked paddlers in canoe (after Webber) . . . 3·75 1·25

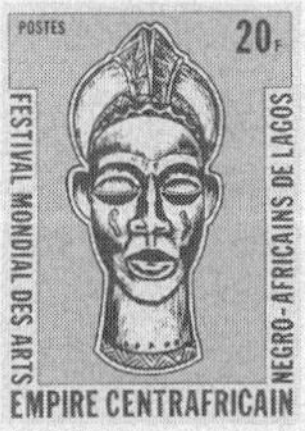

206 Ife Bronze Head

1978. 2nd World Festival of Negro Arts, Lagos.

582 **206** 20f. black and yellow . . 25 20
583 – 30f. black and blue . . . 25 20
584 – 60f. multicoloured 65 40
585 – 100f. multicoloured . . . 1·10 65

DESIGNS—VERT: 30f. Carved mask. HORIZ: 60f. Dancers; 100f. Dancers with musical instruments.

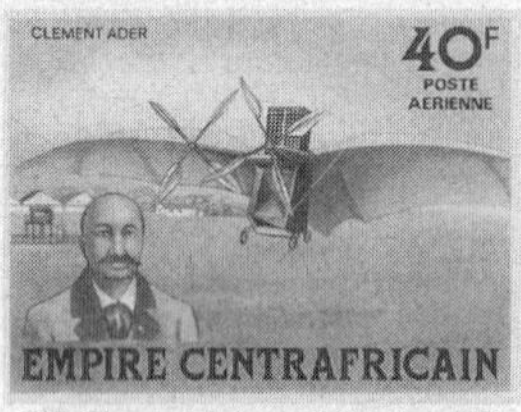

207 Clement Ader and "Avion III"

1978. Air. Aviation Pioneers. Multicoloured.

586 40f. Type **207** 40 20
587 50f. Wright Brothers and glider No. III 40 20
588 60f. Alcock, Brown and Vickers Vimy 45 30
589 100f. Sir Alan Cobham and De Havilland D.H.50 . . . 90 45
590 150f. Dr. Claude Dornier and Dornier Gs1 flying boat . . 1·40 65

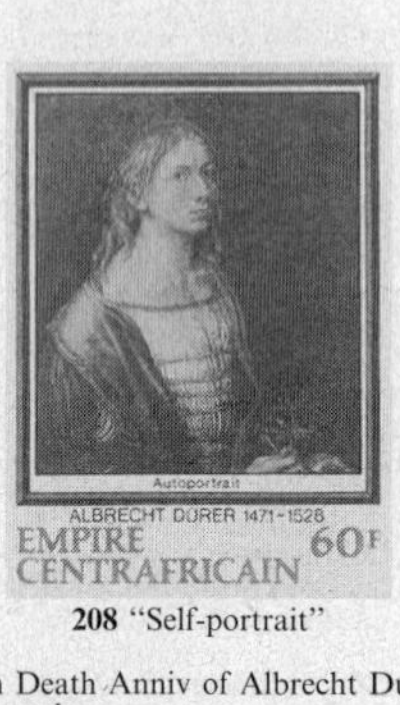

208 "Self-portrait"

1978. 450th Death Anniv of Albrecht Durer (artist). Multicoloured.

592 60f. Type **208** 50 20
593 80f. "The Four Apostles" . . 75 25
594 200f. "The Virgin and Child" 1·90 80
595 350f. "The Emperor Maxillian I" . . . . 3·25 1·25

1978. Air. "Philexafrique" Stamp Exhibition, Gabon (1st issue) and International Stamp Fair, Essen. As T **237** of Benin. Multicoloured.

596 100f. Red Crossbills and Mecklenberg-Schwerin 1856 ¼s. stamp . . . . . . 1·50 1·25
597 100f. Crocodile and Central African Republic 1960 500f. stamp . . . . 1·50 1·25

See also Nos. 647/8.

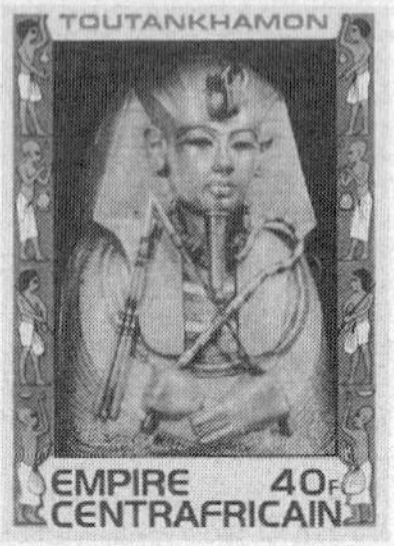

209 Third Mummiform Coffin

1978. Treasures of Tutankhamun. Mult.

598 40f. Type **209** 35 20
599 60f. Tutankhamun and Ankhesenamun (back of gilt throne) 45 25
600 80f. Ecclesiastical throne . . 65 35
601 100f. Head of Tutankhamun (wooden statuette) 75 35
602 120f. Lion's head (funerary bedhead) 95 40
603 150f. Life-size statue of Tutankhamun . . . . . . 1·25 45
604 180f. Gilt throne . . . . . . 1·50 55
605 250f. Canopic coffin . . . . 1·90 75

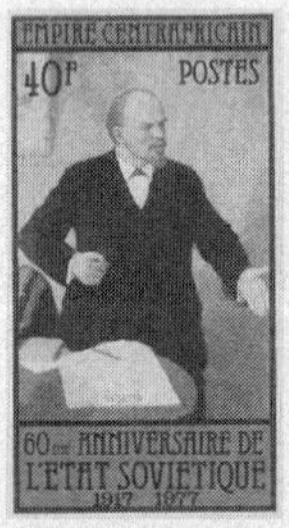

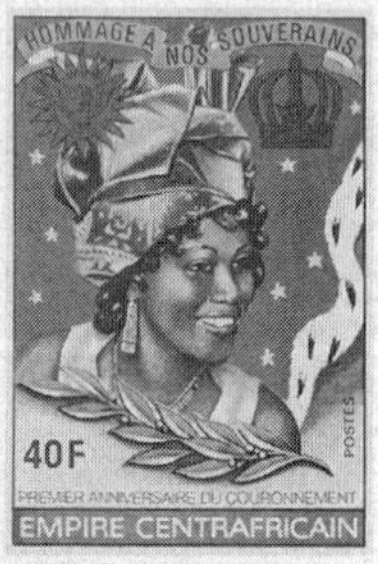

210 Lenin speaking at the Smolny Institute **211** Catherine Bokassa

1978. 60th Anniv of Russian Revolution.

606 **210** 40f. multicoloured 40 25
607 – 60f. multicoloured 50 35
608 – 100f. black, grey and gold 90 40
609 – 150f. red, black and gold 1·40 65
610 – 200f. multicoloured . . . 1·90 95
611 – 300f. multicoloured . . . 2·50 1·25

DESIGNS—VERT: 60f. Lenin addressing crowd in Red Square; 200f. Lenin at Smolny Institute; 300f. Lenin and banner. HORIZ: 100f. Lenin, Krupskaya and family; 150f. Lenin, Cruiser "Aurora" and revolutionaries.

1978. 1st Anniv of Emperor Bokassa's Coronation. Multicoloured.

613 40f. Type **211** (postage) . . . 40 20
614 60f. Emperor Bokassa . . . 50 35
615 150f. The Emperor and Empress (horiz) (air) . . . 1·25 70

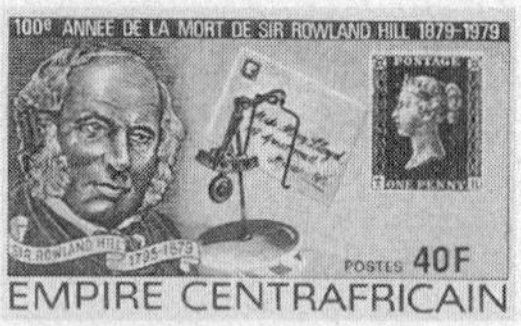

212 Rowland Hill, Letter-weighing Scale and Penny Black

1978. Death Centenary of Sir Rowland Hill (1st issue). Multicoloured.

617 40f. Type **212** (postage) . . . 35 20
618 50f. Postman on bicycle and U.S. 5c. stamp, 1847 . . . 40 25
619 60f. Danish postman and Austrian newspaper stamp, 1856 . . . . 45 30
620 80f. Postilion, mail coach and Geneva 5+5c. stamp, 1843 65 25
621 100f. Postman, mail train and Tuscan 3l. stamp, 1860 (air) . . . . 3·25 1·60
622 200f. Mail balloon and French 10c. stamp, 1850 1·50 65

See also Nos. 671/4.

1978. Argentina's Victory in World Cup Football Championship. Nos. 527/31 optd **VAINQUEUR ARGENTINE**.

625 50f. Type **197** 40 25
626 60f. Goalmouth melee . . . 45 35

627		100f. Mid-field play	75	45
628		200f. World Cup poster	1·50	95
629		300f. Mario Jorge Lobo Zagalo and Buenos Aires Stadium	2·25	1·25

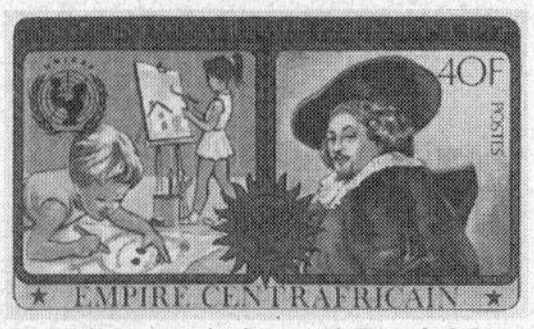

214 Children painting and Dutch Master

1979. International Year of the Child (1st issue). Multicoloured.

631		40f. Type **214** (postage)	40	15
632		50f. Eskimo children and skier	50	20
633		60f. Benz automobile and children with toy car	65	20
634		80f. Satellite and children launching rocket	90	25
635		100f. Dornier Do-X flying boat and Chinese child flying kite (air)	95	40
636		200f. Hurdler and children playing leap-frog	1·90	45

See also Nos. 666/70.

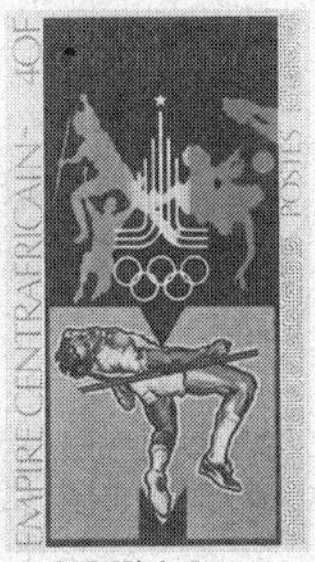

215 High Jump

1979. Pre-Olympic Year (1st issue). Mult.

639		40f. Type **215** (postage)	35	15
640		50f. Cycling	40	20
641		60f. Weightlifting	45	20
642		80f. Judo	65	30
643		100f. Hurdles (air)	75	35
644		200f. Long jump	1·50	50

See also Nos. 676/70 and 705.

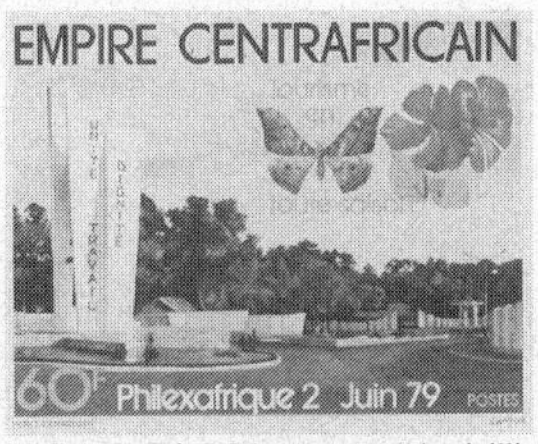

216 Co-operation Monument, "Aurivillius arata" and Hibiscus

1979. "Philexafrique" Exhibition (2nd issue). Mult.

647		60f. Type **216**	1·60	1·10
648		150f. Envelopes, van, canoeist and U.P.U. emblem	3·25	2·10

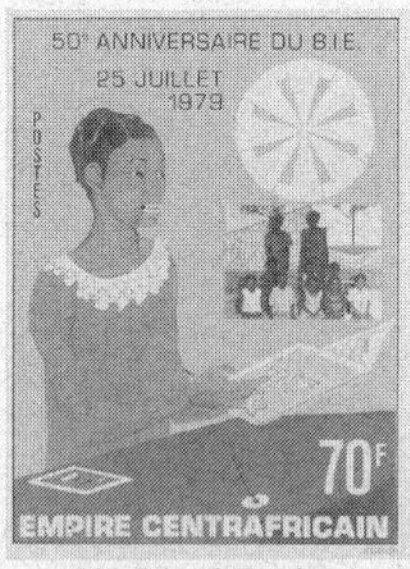

217 School Teacher

1979. 50th Anniv of International Bureau of Education.

649	**217**	70f. multicoloured	65	40

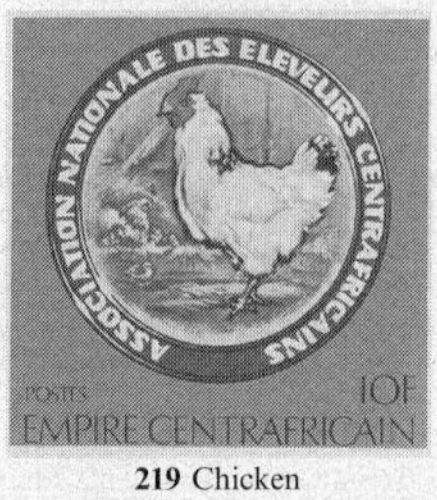

219 Chicken

1979. National Association of Farmers. Mult.

651		10f. Type **219** (postage)	1·25	90
652		20f. Bullock	1·25	90
653		40f. Sheep	2·50	1·75
654		60f. Horse (air)	3·50	1·60

OFFICIAL STAMPS

1977. Official stamps of Central African Republic optd **EMPIRE CENTRAFRICAIN**.

O498	O **109**	5f. multicoloured	25	20
O499		40f. multicoloured	40	20
O500		100f. multicoloured	1·00	45
O501		140f. multicoloured	1·25	70
O502		200f. multicoloured	2·25	1·00

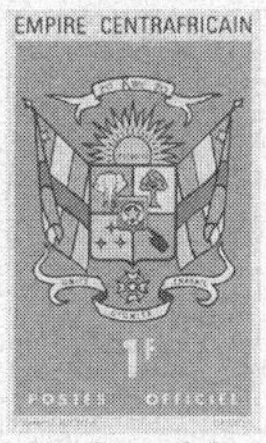

O **204** Coat of Arms

1978.

O564	O **204**	1f. multicoloured	20	15
O565		2f. multicoloured	15	15
O566		5f. multicoloured	15	15
O567		10f. multicoloured	20	15
O568		15f. multicoloured	20	15
O569		20f. multicoloured	25	20
O570		30f. multicoloured	35	25
O571		40f. multicoloured	40	30
O572		50f. multicoloured	50	35
O673		60f. multicoloured	65	45
O574		100f. multicoloured	75	60
O575		130f. multicoloured	1·25	90
O576		140f. multicoloured	1·25	90
O577		200f. multicoloured	2·50	1·25

CENTRAL AFRICAN REPUBLIC
Pt. 12

Formerly Ubangi-Shari. An independent republic within the french Community.

100 centimes = 1 franc.

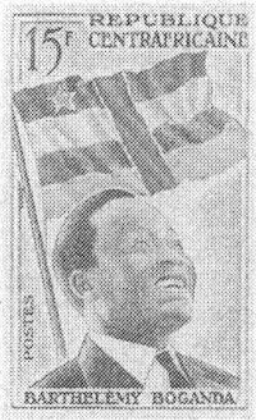

1 President Boganda

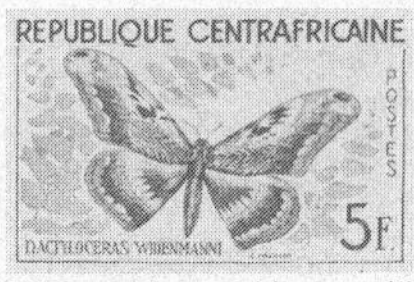

3 "Dactyloceras widenmanni"

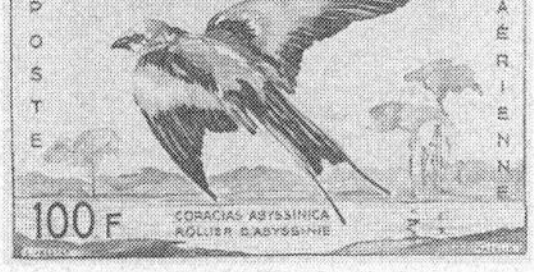

4 Abyssinian Roller

1959. Republic. 1st Anniv. Centres multicoloured. Frame colours given.

1	**1**	15f. blue	35	25
2	–	25f. red	45	25

DESIGN—HORIZ: 25f. As Type **1** but flag behind portrait.

1960. 10th Anniv of African Technical Co-operation Commission. As T **62** of Cameroun.

3		50f. blue and green	1·25	75

1960.

4	–	50c. brn, red & turq (postage)	10	10
5	–	1f. myrtle, brown & violet	10	10
6	–	2f. myrtle, brown and green	15	15
7	–	3f. brown, red and olive	25	20
8	**3**	5f. brown and green	35	25
9	–	10f. blue, black and green	70	45
10	–	20f. red, black and green	1·50	65
11	–	85f. red, black and green	5·75	1·60
12	–	50f. turq, red & green (air)	4·25	1·40
13	**4**	100f. violet, brown & green	7·00	2·00
14	–	200f. multicoloured	12·00	4·75
15	–	250f. multicoloured	12·50	5·00
16	–	500f. brown, blue and green	42·00	8·50

BUTTERFLIES—As Type **3**: 50c., 3f. "Cymothoe sangaris"; 1f., 2f. "Charaxes mobilis"; 10f. "Charaxes ameliae"; 20f. "Charaxes zingha"; 85f. "Drurya antimachus". BIRDS—As Type **4**: 50f. Great blue turaco; 200f. Green turaco; 250f. Red-faced lovebirds; 500f. African fish eagle.

See also Nos. 42/5.

1960. National Festival. No. 2 optd **FETE NATIONALE 1-12-1960.**

17		25f. multicoloured	1·25	1·25

1960. Air. Olympic Games. No. 276 of French Equatorial Africa optd with Olympic rings, **XVIIe OLYMPIADE 1960 REPUBLIQUE CENTRAFRICAINE** and surch **250F** and bars.

18		250f. on 500f. blue, blk & grn	7·75	7·50

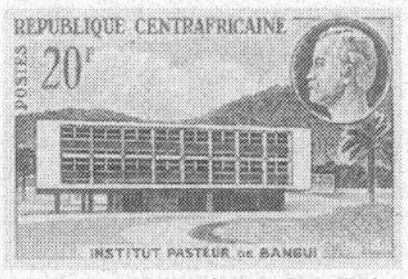

7 Pasteur Institute, Bangui

1961. Opening of Pasteur Institute, Bangui.

19	**7**	20f. multicoloured	75	65

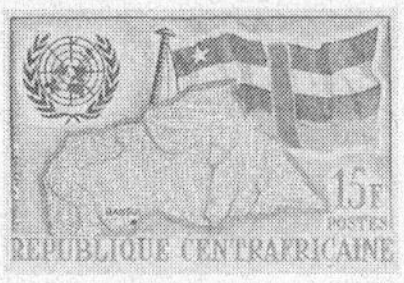

8 U.N. Emblem, Map and Flag

1961. Admission into U.N.O.

20	**8**	15f. multicoloured	40	35
21		25f. multicoloured	45	35
22		85f. multicoloured	1·40	95

1961. National Festival. Optd with star and **FETE NATIONALE 1-12-01**.

23	**8**	25f. multicoloured	1·75	1·75

1962. Air. "Air Afrique" Airline. As T **69** of Cameroun.

24		50f. violet, brown and green	95	60

1962. Union of African States and Madagascar Conference, Bangui. Surch **U.A.M. CONFERENCE DE BANGUI 25-27 MARS 1962 50F**.

25	**8**	50f. on 85f. multicoloured	1·25	1·25

1962. Malaria Eradication. As T **70** of Cameroun.

26		25f.+5f. slate	85	85

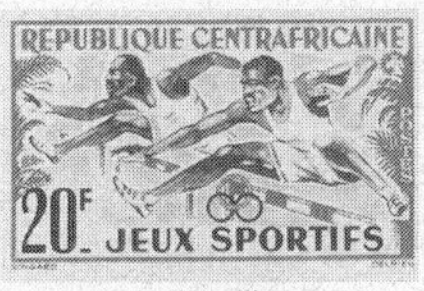

12 Hurdling

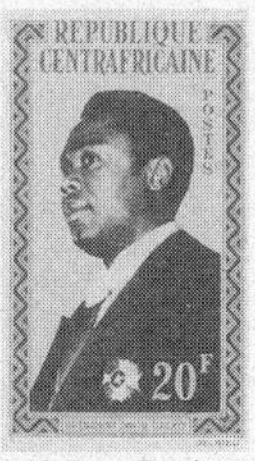

13 Pres. Dacko

1962. Sports.

27	**12**	20f. sep, yell & grn (postage)	45	35
28	–	50f. sepia, yellow and green	1·10	65
29	–	100f. sep, yell & grn (air)	2·10	1·40

DESIGNS—As Type **12**: 50f. Cycling. VERT: (26×47 mm): 100f. Pole-vaulting.

1962.

30	**13**	20f. multicoloured	35	20
31		25f. multicoloured	45	20

1962. 1st Anniv of Union of African and Malagasy States. As T **72** of Cameroun.

32		30f. green	65	45

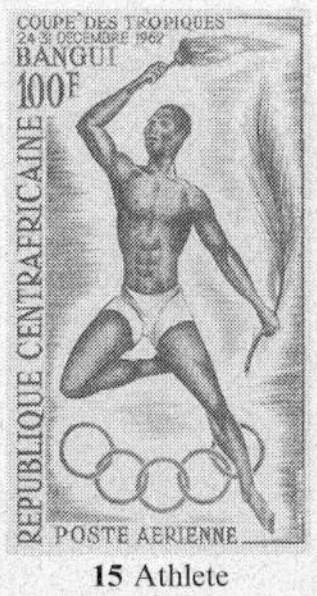

15 Athlete

18 "Posts and Telecommunications"

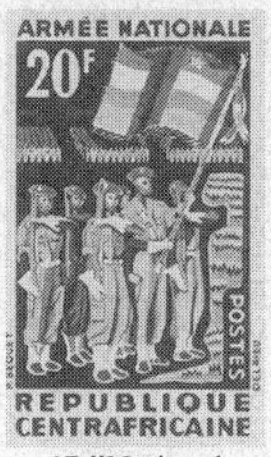

17 "National Army"

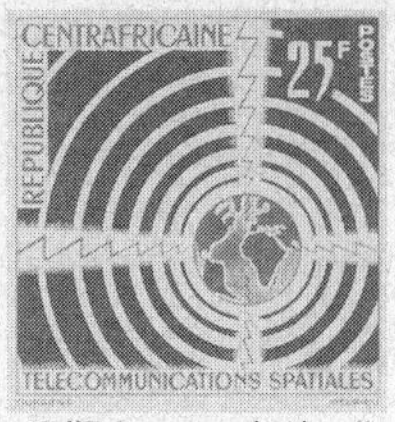

19 "Telecommunications"

1962. Air. "Coupe des Tropiques" Games, Bangui.

33	**15**	100f. brown, turquoise & red	2·25	1·40

1963. Freedom from Hunger. As T **76** of Cameroun.

34		25f.+5f. turquoise, brn & bis	75	75

1963. 3rd Anniv of Proclamation of Republic.

35	**17**	20f. multicoloured	60	40

1963. Air. African and Malagasy Posts and Telecommunications Union.

36	**18**	85f. multicoloured	1·60	80

1963. Space Telecommunications.

37	**19**	25f. green and purple	65	50
38	–	100f. green, orange & blue	1·60	1·40

DESIGN: 100f. Radio waves and globe.

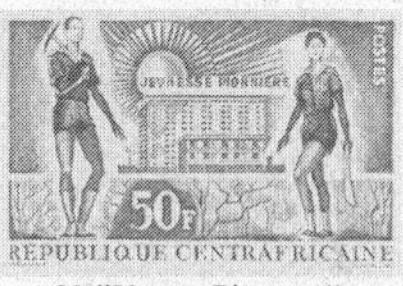

20 "Young Pioneers"

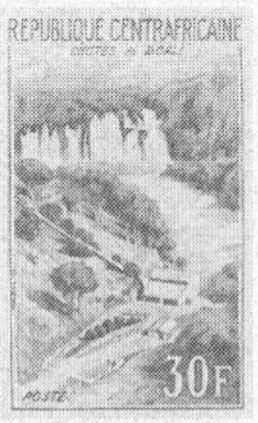

21 Boali Falls

1963. Young Pioneers.

39	**20**	30f. brown, blue & turquoise	65	45

1963.

40	**21**	30f. purple, green and blue	65	40

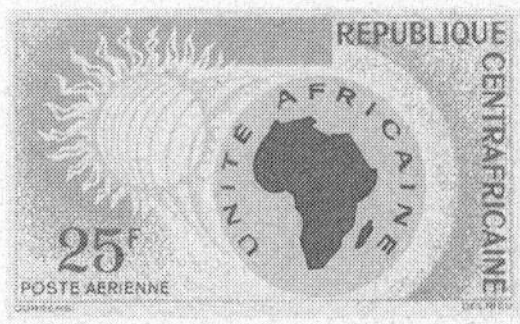

22 Map of Africa and Sun

1963. Air. "African Unity".

41	**22**	25f. ultramarine, yellow & bl	55	35

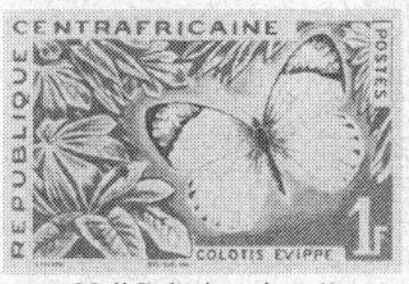

23 "Colotis evippe"

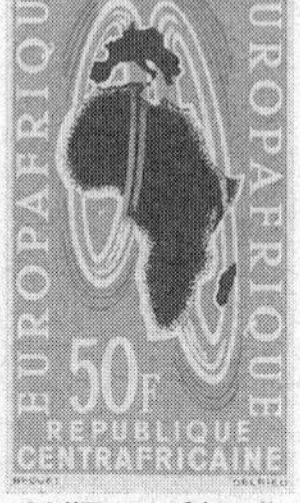

24 "Europafrique"

1963. Butterflies. Multicoloured.

42		1f. Type **23**	20	15
43		3f. "Papilio dardanus"	30	25
44		4f. "Papilio lormieri"	50	30
45		60f. "Papilio zalmoxis"	3·50	2·25

1963. Air. European–African Economic Convention.

46	**24**	50f. multicoloured	2·25	1·75

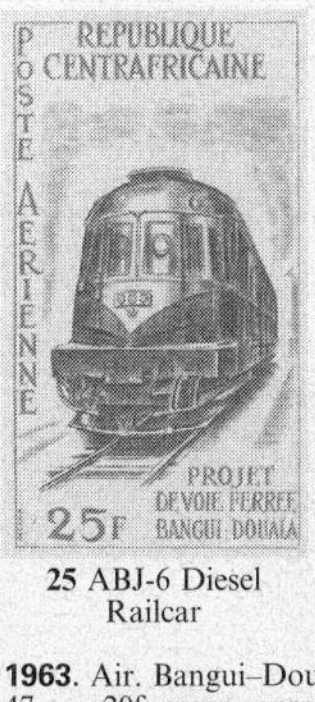

25 ABJ-6 Diesel Railcar

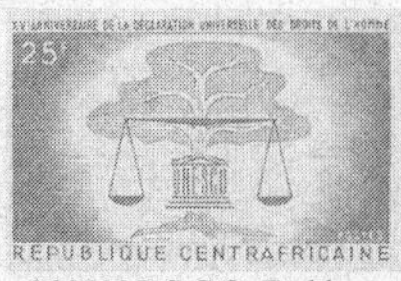

26 U.N.E.S.C.O. Emblem, Scales of Justice and Tree

1963. Air. Bangui–Douala Railway Project.

47	–	20f. green, purple & brown	75	80
48	**25**	25f. chocolate, blue & brn	90	1·00

49 – 50f. violet, purple & brown   3·00   3·25
50 – 100f. purple, turquoise and
         brown . . . .   3·75   3·75
DESIGNS: (Diesel rolling stock)—HORIZ: 20f. ABJ-
6 railcar; 100f. Diesel locomotive. VERT: 50f. Series
BB500 diesel shunter.

1963. 15th Anniv of Declaration of Human Rights.
51 **26** 25f. bistre, green and brown   70   50

27 Bangui Cathedral

1964. Air.
52 **27** 100f. brown, green & blue   1·50   85

28 Cleopatra, Temple   30 "Tree" and Sun Emblem
of Kalabsha

29 Radar Scanner

1964. Air. Nubian Monuments Preservation.
53 **28** 25f.+10f. mauve, bl & grn   1·10   1·10
54 – 50f.+10f. brn, grn & turq . .   1·90   1·90
55 – 100f.+10f. pur, vio & grn   3·00   3·00

1964. Air. World Meteorological Day.
56 **29** 50f. violet, brown and blue   95   95

1964. International Quiet Sun Years.
57 **30** 25f. orange, ochre & turq   1·00   75

31 Map and African Heads   33 Pres. Kennedy
of State

32 Throwing the Javelin

1964. Air. 5th Anniv of Equatorial African Heads of
State Conference.
58 **31** 100f. multicoloured . . . .   1·60   85

1964. Air. Olympic Games, Tokyo.
59 **32** 25f. brown, green and blue   40   30
60 – 50f. red, black and green . .   85   40
61 – 100f. brown, blue and green   1·90   85
62 – 250f. black, green and red   5·00   2·50
DESIGNS: 50f. Basketball; 100f. Running; 250f.
Diving and swimming.

1964. Air. Pres. Kennedy Memorial Issue.
63 **33** 100f. brown, black & violet   1·90   1·40

34 African Child   35 Silhouettes of
European and
African

1964. Child Welfare. Different portraits of children.
As T **34**.
64 **34** 20f. brown, green & purple   35   25
65 – 25f. brown, blue and red . .   40   35
66 – 40f. brown, purple & green   60   45
67 – 50f. brown, green and red   70   50

1964. French, African and Malagasy Co-operation.
As T **88** of Cameroun.
68 – 25f. brown, red and green . .   60   40

1964. National Unity.
69 **35** 25f. multicoloured   65   40

36 "Economic Co-operation"

1964. Air. "Europafrique".
70 **36** 50f. green, red and yellow   95   65

37 Handclasp

1965. Air. International Co-operation Year.
71 **37** 100f. multicoloured . . . .   1·60   85

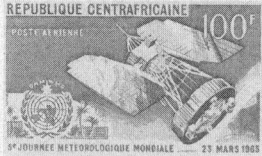
38 Weather Satellite

1965. Air. World Meteorological Day.
72 **38** 100f. blue and brown . .   1·60   85

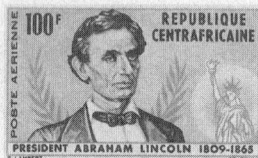
39 Abraham Lincoln

1965. Air. Death Centenary of Abraham Lincoln.
73 **39** 100f. flesh, blue & green . .   1·60   85

40 Team of Oxen

1965. Harnessed Animals in Agriculture.
74 **40** 25f. red, brown and green   50   35
75 – 50f. purple, green and blue   85   45
76 – 85f. brown, green and blue   1·25   70
77 – 100f. multicoloured . . . .   1·60   90
DESIGNS: 50f. Ploughing with bullock; 85f.
Ploughing with oxen; 100f. Oxen with hay cart.

41 Pouget-Maisonneuve Telegraph
Instrument

1965. Centenary of I.T.U.
78 **41** 25f. blue, red & grn (post)   50   40
79 – 30f. lake and green   60   45
80 – 50f. red and violet   90   65

81 – 85f. blue and purple . . . .   1·60   95
82 – 100f. brown, blue & green
         (48½ × 27 mm) (air) . . .   1·90   1·10
DESIGNS—VERT: 30f. Chappe's telegraph
instrument; 50f. Doignon regulator for Hughes
telegraph. HORIZ: 85f. Pouillet's telegraph
apparatus; 100f. "Relay" satellite and I.T.U. emblem.

42 Women and Loom ("To   43 Coffee Plant,
Clothe")   Hammer Grubs
and
"Epicampoptera
strandi"

1965. "M.E.S.A.N." Welfare Campaign. Designs
depicting "Five Aims".
83 **42** 25f. green, brown and blue
         (postage)   45   35
84 – 50f. brown, blue and green   75   45
85 – 60f. brown, blue and green   85   60
86 – 85f. multicoloured . . . . .   1·25   65
87 – 100f. blue, brown and green
         (48 × 27 mm) (air) . . . .   1·25   70
DESIGNS: 50f. Doctor examining child, and hospital
("To care for"); 60f. Student and school ("To
instruct"); 85f. Women and child, and harvesting
scene ("To nourish"); 100f. Village houses ("To
house"). "M.E.S.A.N.—Mouvement Evolution Social
Afrique Noire".

1965. Plant Protection.
88 **43** 2f. purple, red and green . .   10   10
89 – 3f. red, green and black . .   25   15
90 – 30f. purple, green and red   1·50   65
DESIGNS—HORIZ: 3f. Coffee plant, caterpillar and
hawk-moth. VERT: 30f. Cotton plant caterpillar and
rose-moth.

1965. Surch.
91 – 2f. on 3f. (No. 43) . . . . .   2·50   2·50
92 **1** 5f. on 15f. . . . .   2·50   2·50
93 – 5f. on 85f. (No. 76)   35   35
94 **13** 10f. on 20f. . . . .   3·25   3·25
95 – 10f. on 100f. (No. 77) . . .   45   45

45 Camp Fire   47 "Industry and
Agriculture"

46 U.N. and Campaign Emblems

1965. Scouting.
96 **45** 25f. red, purple and blue . .   75   25
97 – 50f. brown and blue (Boy
         Scout) . . . .   1·00   60

1965. Freedom from Hunger.
98 **46** 50f. brown, blue and green   90   65

1965. Air. "Europafrique".
99 **47** 50f. multicoloured   80   50

48 Mercury (statue after   49 Father and Child
Coysevox)

1965. Air. 5th Anniv of Admission to U.P.U.
100 **48** 100f. black, blue & red . .   1·90   1·10

1965. Air. Red Cross.
101 **49** 50f. black, blue and red . .   1·00   50
102 – 100f. brown, green and red
         (Mother and Child) . .   2·10   1·00

50 Grading Diamonds   51 Mbaka Porter

1966. National Diamond Industry.
103 **50** 25f. brown, violet and red   75   40

1966. World Festival of Negro Arts, Dakar.
104 **51** 25f. multicoloured   65   40

52 W.H.O. Building   53 "Eulophia
cucullata"

1966. W.H.O. Headquarters, Geneva. Inaug.
105 **52** 25f. violet, blue & yellow   65   40

1966. Flowers. Multicoloured.
106 – 2f. Type **53**   10   10
107 – 5f. "Lissochilus horsfalii" . .   20   10
108 – 10f. "Tridactyle bicaudata"   25   20
109 – 15f. "Polystachya"   50   25
110 – 20f. "Eulophia alta"   75   40
111 – 25f. "Microcelia
         macrorrhynchium" . . . .   1·00   50

54 Douglas DC-8F Aircraft and "Air
Afrique" Emblem

1966. Air. Inaug of "DC-8" Air Services.
112 **54** 25f. multicoloured   60   30

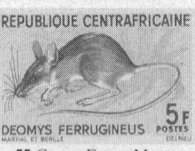
55 Congo Forest Mouse

1966. Rodents. Multicoloured.
113 – 5f. Type **55**   50   25
114 – 10f. Black-striped mouse . .   85   40
115 – 20f. Dollman's tree mouse . .   1·75   70

56 "Luna 9"

1966. Air. "Conquest of the Moon". Mult.
116 – 130f. Type **56** . . . .   1·60   95
117 – 130f. "Surveyor" . . . . . .   1·60   95
118 – 200f. "From the Earth to the
         Moon" (Jules Verne) . . .   2·75   1·60

57 Cernan

59 U.N.E.S.C.O.
Emblem

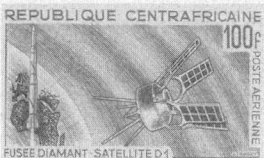

58 Satellite "D 1" and Rocket "Diamant"

1966. Air. Astronauts. Multicoloured.
120 50f. Type **57**   85   50
121 50f. Popovich   85   50

1966. Air. Launching of Satellite "D 1".
122 **58** 100f. purple and brown . .   1·60   80

1966. 20th Anniv of U.N.E.S.C.O.
123 **59** 30f. multicoloured   65   40

60 Symbols of Industry
and Agriculture

61 Pres. Bokassa

1966. Air. Europafrique.
124 **60** 50f. multicoloured . . . .   1·10   75

1967.
125 **61** 30f. black, ochre & green   60   35

1967. Provisional Stamps. (a) Postage. No. 111 surch **XX** and value.
126 10f. on 25f. multicoloured . .   45   20

(b) Air. No. 112 with face value altered by obliteration of figure "2" in "25".
127 **54** 5f. multicoloured   25   20

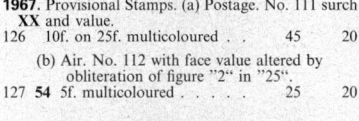

63 Douglas DC-8 over Bangui M'Poko
Airport

1967. Air.
128 **63** 100f. blue, green & brown   2·10   1·00

64 Aerial View of Fair

1967. Air. World Fair, Montreal.
129 **64** 100f. brown, ultram & bl   2·75   1·25

65 Central Market, Bangui

1967. Multicoloured.
130 30f. Type **65**   65   35
131 30f. Safari Hotel, Bangui . .   65   35

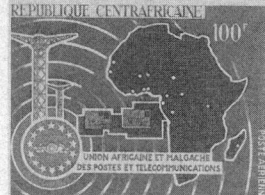

66 Map, Letters and Pylons

1967. Air. 5th Anniv of African and Malagasy Posts and Telecommunications Union (U.A.M.P.T.).
132 **66** 100f. purple, grn & red . . .   1·50   70

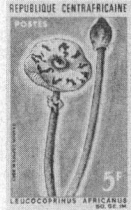

67 "Leucocoprinus africanus"

68 Projector, Africans and Map

1967. Mushrooms. Multicoloured.
133   5f. Type **67**   95   30
134 10f. "Synpodia arborescens"   1·25   60
135 15f. "Phlebopus sudanicus"   1·40   90
136 30f. "Termitomyces schimperi" . . . .   4·75   1·50
137 50f. "Psalliota sebedulis" . .   7·25   2·75

1967. "Radiovision" Service.
138 **68** 30f. blue, green and brown   65   40

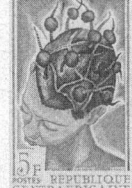

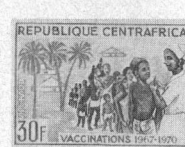

69 Coiffure

70 Inoculation Session

1967. Female Coiffures. Showing different hairstyles.
139 **69** 5f. brown and blue   25   20
140 10f. brown, choc & red . .   40   25
141 15f. brown, choc & grn . .   65   45
142 20f. brown, choc & orge   75   45
143 30f. brown, choc & purple   1·25   60

1967. Vaccination Programme, 1967–70.
144 **70** 30f. brown, green & red . .   65   45

71 Douglas DC-3

1967. Aircraft.
145 **71** 1f. grey, grn & brn (post)   20   10
146   2f. black, blue and purple   20   10
147   5f. black, green and blue   25   15
148 100f. brown, grn & bl (air)   1·75   80
149 200f. blue, brown and green . . . . . .   3·75   1·75
150 500f. slate, red and blue . .   11·00   4·50
DESIGNS—As T **71**: 2f. Beechcraft Baron; 5f. Douglas DC-4. 48×27 mm: 100f. Potez 25-TOE; 200f. Junkers 52/3m; 500f. Sud Aviation Caravelle.

72 Presidents Boganda and Bokassa

1967. Air. 9th Anniv of Republic.
151 **72** 130f. multicoloured . . . .   1·60   1·10

73 Primitive Shelter, Toulou

1967. 6th Pan-African Prehistory Congress, Dakar.
152 **73** 30f. blue, purple and red   65   25
153 50f. bistre, ochre & green   1·25   65
154 100f. purple, brown & blue   2·50   95
155 130f. red, green & brown   2·50   95
DESIGNS—VERT: 50f. Kwe perforated stone; 100f. Megaliths, Bouar. HORIZ: 130f. Rock drawings, Toulou.

74 Pres. Bokassa

1968. Air.
156 **74** 30f. multicoloured   60   35

75 Human Rights Emblem, Human Figures and Globe

1968. Air. Human Rights Year.
157 **75** 200f. red, green and violet   3·25   1·50

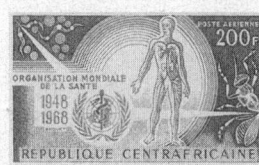

76 Human Figure and W.H.O. Emblem

1968. Air. 20th Anniv of W.H.O.
158 **76** 200f. red, blue & brown . .   3·50   1·90

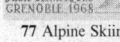

77 Alpine Skiing

78 Parachute-landing on Venus

1968. Air. Olympic Games, Grenoble and Mexico.
159 **77** 200f. brown, blue and red   4·25   2·50
160 200f. brown, blue and red   4·25   2·50
DESIGN: No. 160, Throwing the javelin.

1968. Air. "Venus 4". Exploration of planet Venus.
161 **78** 100f. blue, turquoise & grn   1·60   80

79 Marie Curie and impaled Crab (of Cancer)

1968. Air. Marie Curie Commem.
162 **79** 100f. brown, violet & blue   1·90   1·00

80 Refinery and Tanker

1968. Inauguration of Petroleum Refinery, Port Gentil, Gabon.
163 **80** 30f. multicoloured   90   30

1968. Air. Surch. Nos. 165/6 are obliterated with digit.
164 **56** 5f. on 130f. (No. 116) . .   15   10
165 10f. (100f. No. 148)   20   15
166 20f. (200f. No. 149)   35   25
167 50f. on 130f. (No. 117) . .   75   50

82 "CD-8" Bulldozer

1968. Bokassa Project.
168 **82** 5f. brown, black & green   25   15
169 10f. black, brown & green   40   25
170 20f. green, yellow & brown   65   25
171 30f. blue, drab and brown   95   45
172 30f. red, blue and green . .   95   50
DESIGNS: 10f. Baoule cattle; 20f. Spinning-machine; 30f. (No. 171), Automatic looms; 30f. (No. 172), "D4-C" bulldozer.

83 Bangui Mosque

1968. 2nd Anniv of Bangui Mosque.
173 **83** 30f. flesh, green and blue   70   40

84 Za Throwing-knife

1968. Hunting Weapons.
174 **84** 10f. blue and bistre   45   25
175 20f. green, brown & blue   60   35
176 30f. green, orange & blue   65   45
DESIGNS: 20f. Kpinga-Gbengue throwing-knife; 30f. Mbano cross-bow.

85 "Ville de Bangui" (1958)

1968. River Craft.
177 **85** 10f. blue, green and purple (postage)   50   40
178 30f. brown, blue & green   90   50
179 50f. black, brown & grn . .   1·40   65
180 100f. brown, grn & bl (air)   2·10   95
181 130f. blue, green & purple   2·10   1·25
DESIGNS: 30f. "J. B. Gouandjia" (1968); 50f. "Lamblin" (1944). LARGER (48×27 mm): 100f. "Pie X" (Bangui, 1894); 130f. "Ballay" (Bangui, 1891).

86 "Madame de Sevigne" (French School, 17th century)

1968. Air. "Philexafrique" Stamp Exhibition, Abidjan, Ivory Coast (1969) (1st issue).
182 **86** 100f. multicoloured . . . .   2·25   2·00

87 President Bokassa, Cotton Plantation, and Ubangui Chari stamp of 1930

1969. Air. "Philexafrique" Stamp Exhibition, Abidjan, Ivory Coast (2nd issue).
183 **87** 50f. black, green & brown   1·75   1·75

88 "Holocerina angulata"

1969. Air. Butterflies. Multicoloured.
184	10f. Type **88**		50	25
185	20f. "Nudaurelia dione"		75	35
186	30f. "Eustera troglophylla"			
	(vert)		1·90	60
187	50f. "Aurivillius aratus"		3·00	1·60
188	100f. "Epiphora albida"		5·00	2·50

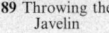

89 Throwing the Javelin   90 Miner and Emblems

1969. Sports. Multicoloured.
189	5f. Type **89** (postage)		20	10
190	10f. Start of race		25	15
191	15f. Football		40	20
192	50f. Boxing (air)		80	30
193	100f. Basketball		1·75	65

Nos. 192/3 are 48 × 28 mm.

1969. 50th Anniv of I.L.O.
194	**90** 30f. multicoloured		50	25
195	50f. multicoloured		75	40

91 "Apollo 8" over Moon's Surface

1969. Air. Flight of "Apollo 8" Around Moon.
196	**91** 200f. multicoloured		3·00	1·60

92 Nuremberg Spire and Toys

1969. Air. International Toy Fair, Nuremberg.
197	**92** 100f. black, purple & grn		3·25	1·75

1969. Air. Birth Bicentenary of Napoleon Bonaparte. As T **144** of Cameroun. Multicoloured.
198	100f. "Napoleon as First Consul" (Girodet-Trioson) (vert)		1·90	1·25
199	130f. "Meeting of Napoleon and Francis II of Austria" (Gros)		2·50	1·40
200	200f. "Marriage of Napoleon and Marie-Louise" (Rouget)		3·75	2·50

93 President Bokassa in Military Uniform   94 Pres. Bokassa, Flag and Map

1969.
201	**93** 30f. multicoloured		50	25

1969. 10th Anniv of A.S.E.C.N.A. As T **151** of Cameroun.
202	100f. blue		1·75	75

1970. Air. Die-stamped on gold foil.
203	**94** 2000f. gold		32·00	32·00

95 Garayah   97 F. D. Roosevelt (25th Death Anniv)

96 Flour Storage Depot

1970. Musical Instruments.
204	**95** 10f. brown, sepia & green		40	15
205	– 15f. brown and green		45	20
206	– 30f. brown, lake & yellow		70	35
207	– 50f. blue and red		1·00	40
208	– 130f. brown, olive & blue		3·25	1·00

DESIGNS—VERT: 130f. Gatta and Babylon. HORIZ: 15f. Ngombi; 30f. Xylophone; 50f. Nadla.

1970. Societie Industrielle Centrafricaine des Produits Alimentaires et Derives (S.I.C.P.A.D.) Project. Multicoloured.
209	25f. Type **96**		45	25
210	50f. Mill machinery		90	70
211	100f. View of flour mill		1·40	1·00

1970. Air. World Leaders. Multicoloured.
212	100f. Lenin (birth centenary)		2·50	1·10
213	100f. Type **97**		1·50	85

1970. New U.P.U. Headquarters Building, Berne. As T **156** of Cameroun.
214	100f. vermilion, red and blue		1·40	65

1970. Air. Moon Landing of "Apollo 12". No. 196 optd **ATTERRISSAGE d'APOLLO 12 19 novembre 1969**.
215	**91** 200f. multicoloured		12·50	9·25

99 Pres. Bokassa   101 Silkworm

100 Cheese Factory, Sarki

1970.
216	**99** 30f. multicoloured		5·00	3·75
217	40f. multicoloured		6·25	4·50

1970. "Operation Bokassa" Development Projects. Multicoloured.
218	5f. Type **100** (postage)		35	20
219	10f. M'Bali Ranch		4·75	3·75
220	20f. Zebu bull and herdsman (vert)		65	45
221	40f. Type **101**		1·90	65
222	140f. Type **101** (air)		3·00	1·25

102 African Dancer

1970. Air. "Knokphila 70" Stamp Exhibition, Knokke, Belgium. Multicoloured.
223	100f. Type **102**		1·50	50
224	100f. African produce		1·50	50

103 Footballer

1970. Air. World Cup Football Championship, Mexico.
225	**103** 200f. multicoloured		3·00	1·60

104 Central African Republic's Pavilion

1970. Air. "EXPO 70", Osaka, Japan.
226	**104** 200f. multicoloured		3·50	1·75

105 Dove and Cogwheel

1970. Air. 25th Anniv of U.N.O.
227	**105** 200f. black, yellow & bl		3·00	1·50

106 Presidents Mobutu, Bokassa and Tombalbaye

1970. Air. Reconciliation with Chad and Zaire.
228	**106** 140f. multicoloured		1·90	80

107 Scaly Francolin and Helmet Guineafowl

1971. Wildlife. Multicoloured.
229	5f.+5f. Type **107**		4·00	2·25
230	10f.+5f. Common duiker and true achatina (snail)		4·75	2·75
231	20f.+5f. Hippopotamus, African elephant and tortoise in tug-of-war		5·75	3·00
232	30f.+10f. Tortoise and Senegal coucal		8·50	7·50
233	50f.+20f. Monkey and leopard		12·50	10·50

108 Lengue Dancer

1971. Traditional Dances. Multicoloured.
234	20f.+5f. Type **108**		50	25
235	40f.+10f. Lengue (diff)		75	40

236	100f.+40f. Teke		2·25	1·25
237	140f.+40f. Englabolo		3·00	1·40

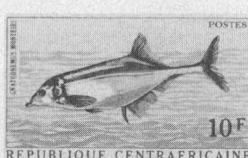

110 Monteir's Mormyrid

1971. Fishes. Multicoloured.
244	10f. Type **110**		40	30
245	20f. Trunk-nosed mormyrid		75	40
246	30f. Wilverth's mormyrid		1·10	70
247	40f. Elephant-nosed mormyrid		2·25	80
248	50f. Curve-nosed mormyrid		2·75	1·40

111 Satellite and Globe

1971. Air. World Telecommunications Day.
249	**111** 100f. multicoloured		1·50	75

112 Berberati Cathedral   113 Gen. De Gaulle

1971. Consecration of Roman Catholic Cathedral, Berberati.
250	**112** 5f. multicoloured		25	15

1971. 1st Death Anniv of De Gaulle.
251	**113** 100f. multicoloured		3·25	1·90

114 Lesser Bushbaby

1971. Animals: Primates. Multicoloured.
252	30f. Type **114**		65	60
253	40f. Western needle-clawed bushbaby		95	65
254	100f. Angwantibo (horiz)		2·25	1·40
255	150f. Potto (horiz)		3·75	2·40
256	200f. Red colobus (horiz)		5·00	3·25

1971. Air. 10th Anniv of African and Malagasy Posts and Telecommunications Union. Similar to T **184** of Cameroun. Multicoloured.
257	100f. Headquarters and carved head		1·50	75

115 Shepard in Capsule

1971. Space Achievements. Multicoloured.
258	40f. Type **115**		45	30
259	40f. Gagarin in helmet		45	30
260	100f. Aldrin in Space		1·10	45
261	100f. Leonov in Space		1·10	45

262 200f. Armstrong on Moon 2·25 1·00
263 200f. "Lunokhod 1" on
     Moon . . . . 2·25 1·00

116 Crab Emblem

117 "Operation Bokassa"

1971. Air. Anti-cancer Campaign.
264 116 100f. multicoloured . . . 1·90 95

1971. 12th Year of Independence.
265 117 40f. multicoloured 65 40

118 Racial Equality Year Emblem

1971. Racial Equality Year.
266 118 50f. multicoloured 65 40

119 I.E.Y. Emblem and Child with Toy Bricks

1971. Air. 25th Anniv of U.N.E.S.C.O.
267 119 140f. multicoloured . . . . 1·50 70

120 African Children

1971. Air. 25th Anniv of U.N.I.C.E.F.
268 120 140f.+50f. mult . . . . . 2·50 1·60

121 Arms and Parade

122 Pres. G. Nasser

1972. Bokassa Military School.
269 121 30f. multicoloured 65 45

1972. Air. Nasser Commemoration.
270 122 100f. ochre, brown & red 1·60 80

123 Book Year Emblem

124 Heart Emblem

1972. International Book Year.
271 123 100f. gold, yellow & brn 1·60 95

1972. World Heart Month.
272 124 100f. red, black & yellow 1·40 80

125 First-Aid Post

126 Global Emblem

1972. Red Cross Day.
273 125 150f. multicoloured . . . 2·25 1·25

1972. World Telecommunications Day.
274 126 50f. black, yellow & red 75 50

127 Boxing

1972. Air. Olympic Games, Munich.
275 127 100f. bistre and brown . . 1·60 95
276 – 100f. violet and green . . 1·60 1·10
DESIGN—VERT: No. 276, Long-jumping.

128 Pres. Bokassa and Family

1972. Mothers' Day.
278 128 30f. multicoloured 75 40

129 Pres. Bokassa planting Cotton Bush

130 Savings Bank Building

1972. "Operation Bokassa" Cotton Development.
279 129 40f. multicoloured 55 35

1972. Opening of New Postal Cheques and Savings Bank Building.
280 130 30f. multicoloured 50 35

131 "Le Pacifique" Hotel

1972. "Operation Bokassa" Completion of "Le Pacifique" Hotel.
281 131 30f. blue, red and green 35 25

132 Giraffe and Monkeys

133 Postal Runner

134 Tiling's Postal Rocket, 1931

1972. Clock-faces from Central African HORCEN Factory. Multicoloured.
282 5f. Rhinoceros chasing
     African 20 20
283 10f. Camp fire and Native
     warriors 25 20
284 20f. Fishermen 60 30
285 30f. Type **132** 65 45
286 40f. Warriors fighting 90 65

1972. "CENTRAPHILEX" Stamp Exhibition, Bangui.
287 133 10f. mult (postage) . . . 25 20
288 – 20f. multicoloured 40 30
289 134 40f. orange, blue and slate
     (air) 55 45
290 – 50f. blue, slate & orange 70 50
291 – 150f. grey, orange & brn 1·90 1·25
292 – 200f. blue, orange & brn 2·75 1·90
DESIGNS—AS Type **133**: HORIZ: Protestant Youth Centre. As Type **134**: VERT: 50f. Douglas DC-3 and camel postman; 150f. "Sirio" satellite and rocket. HORIZ: 200f. "Intelsat 4" satellite and rocket.

135 University Buildings

1972. Inauguration of Bokassa University.
294 135 40f. grey, blue and red . . 55 35

136 Mail Van

1972. World U.P.U. Day.
295 136 100f. multicoloured . . . 1·75 85

137 Paddy Field

1972. Bokassa Plan. State Farms. Multicoloured.
296 5f. Type **137** 20 15
297 25f. Rice cultivation 35 20

138 Four Linked Arrows

140 Hotel Swimming Pool

1972. Air. "Europafrique".
298 138 100f. multicoloured . . . 1·25 75

1972. Air. Munich Olympic Gold Medal Winners. Nos. 275/6 optd as listed below.
299 127 100f. bistre and brown . . 1·25 80
300 – 100f. violet and green . . 1·25 80
OVERPRINTS: No. 299, **POIDS-MOYEN LEMECHEV MEDAILLE D'OR.** No. 300, **LONGUEUR WILLIAMS MEDAILLE D'OR.**

1972. Opening of Hotel St. Sylvestre.
302 140 30f. brown, turq & blue 40 30
303 – 40f. purple, green & blue 40 30
DESIGN: 40f. Facade of Hotel.

141 Landing Module and Lunar Rover on Moon

1972. Air. Moon Flight of "Apollo 16".
304 141 100f. green, blue & grey 1·25 60

142 "Virgin and Child" (F. Pesellino)

1972. Air. Christmas. Multicoloured.
305 100f. Type **142** . . . . . . 1·60 95
306 150f. "Adoration of the
     Child" (F. Lippi) . . . . . 2·25 1·25

143 Learning to Write

1972. "Central African Mothers". Multicoloured.
307 5f. Type **143** 15 10
308 10f. Baby-care 25 20
309 15f. Dressing hair 25 20
310 20f. Learning to read 40 25
311 180f. Suckling baby . . . . 2·40 1·25
312 190f. Learning to walk . . . 2·40 1·25

144 Louys (marathon), Athens, 1896

1972. Air. 75th Anniv of Revival of Olympic Games.
313 144 30f. purple, brown & grn 30 25
314 – 40f. green, blue & brown 35 25
315 – 50f. violet, blue and red 50 40
316 – 100f. purple, brn & grey 1·00 50
317 – 150f. black, blue & purple 1·60 1·10
DESIGNS: 40f. Barrelet (sculling), Paris, 1900; 50f. Prinstein (triple-jump), St. Louis, U.S.A., 1904; 100f. Taylor (400 m freestyle swimming), London, 1908; 150f. Johansson (Greco-Roman wrestling), Stockholm, 1912.

145 W.H.O. Emblem, Doctor and Nurse

1973. Air. 25th Anniv of W.H.O.
318 145 100f. multicoloured . . . 1·25 70

146 "Telecommunications"

1973. World Telecommunications Day.
319 146 200f. orange, blue & black 1·90 1·00

147 Harvesting

1973. 10th Anniv of World Food Programme.
320 **147** 50f. multicoloured   65   40

148 "Garcinia punctata"

1973. "Flora". Multicoloured.
321   10f. Type **148**   25   15
322   20f. "Bertiera racemosa" . . .   35   20
323   30f. "Coryanthe pachyceras" . .   50   30
324   40f. "Combretodendron
        africanum"   70   30
325   50f. "Xylopia villosa"   85   45

149 Pygmy Chameleon

1973.
326 **149** 15f. multicoloured   60   25

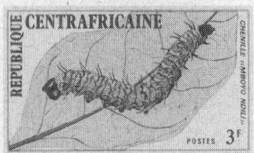
150 "Mboyo Ndili"

1973. Caterpillars. Multicoloured.
327   3f. Type **150**   25   20
328   5f. "Piwili"   40   25
329   25f. "Loulia Konga"   90   40

1973. African Solidarity "Drought Relief". No. 321
surch **SECHERESSE SOLIDARITE AFRICAINE**
and value.
330 **148** 100f. on 10f. mult . . . .   1·25   95

1973. U.A.M.P.T. As Type **216** of Cameroun.
331   100f. red, brown and olive . .   1·10   70

1973. Air. African Fortnight, Brussels. As T **217** of
Cameroun.
332   100f. brown and violet . . .   1·00   60

152 African and Symbolic Map

1973. Air. Europafrique.
333 **152** 100f. red, green & brown   1·25   75

153 Bird with Letter

1973. Air. World U.P.U. Day.
334 **153** 200f. multicoloured . . . .   2·25   1·40

154 Weather Map

1973. Air. Centenary of I.M.O./W.M.O.
335 **154** 150f. multicoloured . . . .   1·90   85

155 Copernicus

1973. Air. 500th Birth Anniv of Copernicus.
336 **155** 100f. multicoloured . . . .   2·25   1·50

156 Pres. Bokassa   **158** Launch

1973.
337 **156** 1f. mult (postage)   10   10
338   2f. multicoloured   10   10
339   3f. multicoloured   15   10
340   5f. multicoloured   15   10
341   10f. multicoloured   25   15
342   15f. multicoloured   25   20
343   20f. multicoloured   35   20
344   30f. multicoloured   35   25
345   40f. multicoloured   45   35
346   – 50f. multicoloured (air)   50   35
347   – 100f. multicoloured . . . .   1·00   50
DESIGNS—SQUARE (35 × 35 mm): 50f. Pres.
Bokassa facing left. VERT (26 × 47 mm): 100f. Pres.
Bokassa in military uniform.

1973. Air. Moon Flight of "Apollo 17".
348 **158** 50f. red, green & brown   50   30
349   – 65f. green, red & purple   60   35
350   – 100f. blue, brown & red   1·00   50
351   – 150f. green, brown & red   1·50   70
352   – 200f. green, red and blue   2·00   1·10
DESIGNS—HORIZ: 65f. Surveying lunar surfaces;
100f. Descent on Moon. VERT: 150f. Astronauts on
Moon's surface; 200f. Splashdown.

159 Interpol Emblem within "Eye"

1973. 50th Anniv of Interpol.
353 **159** 50f. multicoloured   70   50

160 St. Theresa

1973. Air. Birth Centenary of St. Theresa of Lisieux.
354 **160** 500f. blue and light blue   5·00   3·50

161 Main Entrance

1974. Opening of "Catherine Bokassa" Mother-and-
Child Centre.
355 **161** 30f. brown, red and blue   35   25
356   – 40f. brown, blue and red   45   35
DESIGN: 40f. General view of Centre.

162 Cigarette-packing   **163** "Tele-
     Machine   communications"

1974. "Centra" Cigarette Factory.
357 **162** 5f. purple, green & red . .   10   10
358   – 10f. blue, green & brown   25   15
359   – 30f. blue, green and red   30   20
DESIGNS: 10f. Administration block and factory
building; 30f. Tobacco warehouse.

1974. World Telecommunications Day.
360 **163** 100f. multicoloured . . .   6·50   4·00

164 "Peoples of the World" **165** Mother and Baby

1974. World Population Year.
361 **164** 100f. green, red & brown   1·10   65

1974. 26th Anniv of W.H.O.
362 **165** 100f. brown, blue & grn   1·25   65

166 Letter and U.P.U.   **168** Modern Building
     Emblem

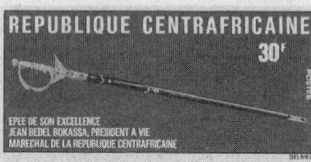
167 Battle Scene

1974. Centenary of U.P.U.
363 **166** 500f. red, green & brown   4·00   3·00

1974. "Activities of Forces' Veterans". Mult.
364   10f. Type **167**   15   10
365   15f. "Today" (Peace-time
        activities)   20   15
366   20f. Planting rice   20   15
367   25f. Cattle-shed   25   20
368   30f. Workers hoeing   25   20
369   40f. Veterans' houses   40   20

1974. 10th Anniv of Central African Customs and
Economics Union. As Nos. 734/5 of Cameroun.
370   40f. multicoloured (postage)   50   35
371   100f. multicoloured (air) . . .   1·00   65

1975. "OCAM City" Project.
372 **168** 30f. multicoloured   25   20
373   – 40f. multicoloured   35   25
374   – 50f. multicoloured   40   30
375   – 100f. multicoloured   75   50
DESIGNS: Nos. 373/5, Various views similar to
Type **150**.

1975. "J. B. Bokassa Pilot Village Project". As T **168**,
but inscr "VILLAGE PILOTE J. B. BOKASSA".
376   25f. multicoloured   20   15
377   30f. multicoloured   30   20
378   40f. multicoloured   35   25
DESIGNS: Nos. 376/8, Various views similar to
Type **168**.

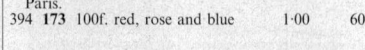
169 President Bokassa's Sword

1975. "Homage to President Bokassa". Mult.
379   30f. Type **169** (postage) . . . 45   25
380   40f. President Bokassa's
        baton   45   30
381   50f. Pres. Bokassa in uniform
        (vert, 36 × 49 mm) (air)   50   35
382   100f. Pres. Bokassa in cap
        and cape (vert,
        36 × 49 mm) . . . .   1·00   45

170 Foreign Minister and Ministry

1975. Government Buildings. Multicoloured.
383   40f. Type **170**   50   35
384   40f. Television Centre
        (36 × 23 mm)   50   35

171 "No Entry"

1975. Road Signs.
385 **171** 5f. red and blue   10   10
386   – 10f. red and blue   15   10
387   – 20f. red and blue   20   15
388   – 30f. multicoloured   35   20
389   – 40f. multicoloured   50   25
SIGNS: 10f. "Stop"; 20f. "No stopping"; 30f.
"School"; 40f. "Crossroads".

172 Kob   **173** Carved Wooden
                          Mask

1975. Wild Animals. Multicoloured.
390   10f. Type **172**   25   20
391   15f. Warthog   50   20
392   20f. Waterbuck   75   25
393   30f. Lion   75   35

1975. Air. "Arphila" International Stamp Exhibition.
Paris.
394 **173** 100f. red, rose and blue   1·00   60

174 Dr. Schweitzer and   **175** Forest Scene
     Dug-out Canoe

1975. Air. Birth Centenary of Dr. Albert Schweitzer.
395 **174** 200f. black, blue & brown   2·50   1·60

1975. Central African Woods.
396 **175** 10f. brown, green & red   20   15
397   – 15f. brown, green & blue   25   15
398   – 50f. blue, brown & green   45   20
399   – 100f. brown, blue & grn   95   55
400   – 150f. blue, brown & grn   1·25   95
401   – 200f. brown, red & green   1·75   1·25
DESIGNS—VERT: 15f. Cutting sapeles. HORIZ:
50f. Mobile crane; 100f. Log stack; 150f. Floating
logs; 200f. Timber-sorting yard.

176 Women's Heads and Women Working

1975. International Women's Year.
402 **176** 40f. multicoloured 45 25
403 100f. multicoloured . . . 1·25 65

177 River Vessel "Jean Bedel Bokassa"

1976. Air. Multicoloured.
404 30f. Type **177** 50 25
405 40f. Frontal view of "Jean
Bedel Bokassa" 60 40

178 Co-operation Monument

1976. Air. Central African–French Co-operation and
Visit of President Giscard d'Estaing. Mult.
406 100f. Type **178** . . . . 1·00 75
407 200f. Flags and Presidents
Giscard d'Estaing and
Bokassa . . . . 2·10 1·25

179 Alexander Graham Bell

1976. Telephone Centenary.
408 **179** 100f. black and yellow . . 1·25 75

180 Telecommunications Satellite

1976. World Telecommunications Day.
409 **180** 100f. purple, blue & grn 1·40 95

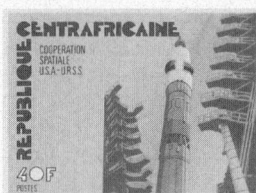

181 Rocket on Launch-pad

1976. Apollo–Soyuz Space Link. Multicoloured.
410 40f. Type **181** (postage) . . . 45 25
411 50f. Blast-off 55 25
412 100f. "Soyuz" in flight (air) 75 25
413 200f. "Apollo" in flight . . 1·50 50
414 300f. Crew meeting in space 2·25 85

182 French Hussar

1976. Air. American Revolution Bicent. Mult.
416 100f. Type **182** 75 30
417 125f. Black Watch soldier . . 95 45
418 150f. German Dragoons'
officer . . . . . 1·10 50
419 200f. British Grenadiers'
officer . . . . . 1·90 55
420 250f. American Ranger . . 2·25 75

183 "Drurya antimachus"

1976. Butterflies. Multicoloured.
422 30f. Type **183** (postage) . . . 1·25 75
423 40f. "Argema mittrei" (vert) 1·90 75
424 50f. "Acherontia atropos"
and "Saturnia pyri" (air) 1·25 75
425 100f. "Papilio nireus" and
"Heniocha marnois" . . . 2·50 1·10

184 Dorothy Hamill of U.S.A.
(figure skating)

1976. Medal Winners, Winter Olympic Games,
Innsbruck. Multicoloured.
426 40f. Piero Gros of Italy
(slalom) (horiz) (postage) 45 25
427 60f. Karl Schnabl and Toni
Innauer of Austria (ski-
jumping) (horiz) . . . 55 35
428 100f. Type **184** (air) 70 35
429 200f. Alexandre Gorshkov
and Ludmilla Pakhomova
(figure-skating, pairs)
(horiz) . . . . . . 1·25 60
430 300f. John Curry of Great
Britain (figure-skating) . 2·25 95

185 U.P.U. Emblem, Letters, and Types of
Mail Transport

1976. World U.P.U. Day.
432 **185** 100f. multicoloured . . . 1·60 95

186 Assembly of "Viking"

1976. "Viking" Space Mission to Mars.
Multicoloured.
433 40f. Type **186** (postage) . . . 45 25
434 60f. Launch of "Viking" . . 55 35
435 100f. Parachute descent on
Mars (air) 70 35

436 200f. "Viking" on Mars
(horiz) . . . . . 1·25 60
437 300f. "Viking" operating
gravel scoop . . . . 2·25 75

Issues between 1977 and 1979 are listed under
CENTRAL AFRICAN EMPIRE.

220 Ski Jump

1979. Air. Winter Olympic Games, Lake Placid
(1980). Multicoloured.
655 60f. Type **220** 45 20
656 100f. Downhill skiing 75 35
657 200f. Ice hockey . . . . 1·60 80
658 300f. Skiing (slalom) . . . 2·25 1·10

1979. "Apollo 11" Moon Landing. 10th Anniv.
Nos. 433/7 optd **ALUNISSAGE APOLLO XI
JUILLET 1969** and lunar module.
660 **186** 40f. mult (postage) . . . 40 35
661 – 60f. multicoloured 45 40
662 – 100f. multicoloured (air) 75 50
663 – 200f. multicoloured . . . 1·25 85
664 – 300f. multicoloured . . . 2·25 1·10

222 Thumbellina   **224** Basketball
(Andersen)

1979. International Year of the Child (2nd issue).
Multicoloured.
666 30f. Type **222** 25 15
667 40f. Sleeping Beauty (horiz) 35 20
668 60f. Hansel and Gretel . . 50 25
669 200f. The Match Girl (horiz) 1·25 60
670 250f. The Little Mermaid . . 1·90 70

223 Steam Locomotive, U.S.A. Stamp
and Hill

1979. Death Centenary of Sir Rowland Hill (2nd
issue). Multicoloured.
671 60f. Type **223** 90 20
672 100f. Locomotive
"Champion" (1882,
U.S.A.), French stamp and
Hill . . . . . . 1·25 35
673 150f. Steam locomotive,
German stamp and Hill . 1·75 45
674 250f. Steam locomotive,
British stamp and Hill . 3·25 95

1979. Olympic Games, Moscow (2nd issue).
Basketball.
676 **224** 50f. multicoloured 40 20
677 – 125f. multicoloured 90 35
678 – 200f. multicoloured . . . 1·50 60
679 – 300f. multicoloured . . . 2·25 85
680 – 500f. multicoloured . . . 3·75 1·25
DESIGNS: 125f. to 500f. Views of different basketball
matches.

1980. Various stamps, including one unissued, of
Central African Empire optd **REPUBLIQUE
CENTRAFRICAINE.**
681 **192** 5f. multicoloured 10 10
682 – 10f. mult (No. 522) 10 10
683 – 20f. multicoloured
(Balambo (stand)) . . 15 10
684 **206** 20f. black and yellow . . 15 10
685 – 30f. black and blue
(No. 583) 25 15

226 "Viking"

1980. Space Exploration. Multicoloured.
686 40f. Type **226** (postage) . . 35 15
687 50f. "Apollo"–"Soyuz" link 40 20
688 60f. "Voyager" 45 20
689 100f. European Space Agency 75 25
690 150f. Early satellites (air) . . 1·25 30
691 200f. Space shuttle . . . 1·60 45

1980. Air. Winter Olympic Medal Winners. Nos. 655/
8 optd as listed below.
693 **220** 60f. multicoloured 45 20
694 – 100f. multicoloured 75 35
695 – 200f. multicoloured . . . 1·60 80
696 – 300f. multicoloured . . . 2·25 1·10
OVERPRINTS: 60f. **VAINQUEUR INNAVER
AUTRICHE**; 100f. **VAINQUEUR MOSER-
PROELL AUTRICHE**; 200f. **VAINQUEUR ETATS-
UNIS**; 300f. **VAINQUEUR STENMARK SUEDE.**

228 Telephone and Sun

1980. World Telecommunications Day. Mult.
698 100f. Type **228** 90 50
699 150f. Telephone and sun
(different) . . . . . . 1·25 65

229 Walking

1980. Olympic Games, Moscow (3rd issue). Mult.
700 30f. Type **229** (postage) . . . 35 15
701 40f. Women's relay 40 20
702 70f. Running 60 20
703 80f. Women's high jump . . 65 30
704 100f. Boxing (air) 75 25
705 150f. Hurdles . . . . . . 1·10 30

229a Fruit

1980.
706a **229a** 40f. multicoloured . . . .

230 Agriculture   **232** "Foligne
Madonna" (detail)

1980. European-African Co-operation. Mult.
707 30f. Type **230** (postage) . . . 25 15
708 40f. Industry 40 15
709 70f. Communications . . . 65 20
710 100f. Building construction
and rocket 95 45
711 150f. Meteorological satellite
(air) . . . . . . 1·25 30
712 200f. Space shuttle . . . . 1·50 45

1980. Olympic Medal Winners. Nos. 676/80 optd.
717 50f. **MEDAILLE OR
YOUGOSLAVIE** 40 20
718 125f. **MEDAILLE OR URSS** 90 45
719 200f. **MEDAILLE OR URSS** 1·50 65
720 300f. **MEDAILLE ARGENT
ITALIE** . . . . . 2·25 1·00
721 500f. **MEDAILLE BRONZE
URSS** . . . . . 3·75 1·50

1980. Christmas. Multicoloured.
722 60f. Type **232** 50 20
723 150f. Virgin and Saints . . 1·25 50
724 250f. "Conestabile Madonna" 2·00 85

1980. 5th Anniv of African Posts and
Telecommunications Union. As T **269** of Benin.
725 70f. multicoloured 65 40

233 Peruvian Football Team

1981. World Cup Football Championship, Spain (1982). Multicoloured.

726	10f. Type **233** (postage)	15	10
727	15f. Scottish team	20	15
728	20f. Mexican team	25	15
729	25f. Swedish team	25	15
730	30f. Austrian team	30	15
731	40f. Polish team	35	20
732	50f. French team	50	20
733	60f. Italian team	55	25
734	70f. West German team	75	30
735	80f. Brazilian team	75	30
736	100f. Dutch team (air)	75	25
737	200f. Spanish team	1·25	35

234 "Fight between Jacob and the Angel"

236 I.T.U. and W.H.O. Emblems and Ribbons forming Caduceus

1981. Air. 375th Birth Anniv of Rembrandt. Multicoloured.

739	60f. Type **234**	50	20
740	90f. "Christ in the Tempest"	75	25
741	150f. "Jeremiah mourning the Destruction of Jerusalem"	1·25	50
742	250f. "Anna accused by Tobit of Theft of a Goat"	2·25	60

1981. Olympic Games Winners. Nos. 701/5 optd with events and names of winners.

744	30f. Type **229** (postage)	25	15
745	40f. Women's relay	30	20
746	70f. Running	50	30
747	80f. Women's high jump	55	35
748	100f. Boxing (air)	45	30
749	150f. Hurdles	70	45

OPTS—30f. **50 KM. MARCHE HARTWIG GAUDER – G.D.R.**; 40f. **4 × 400 M. DAMES – U.R.S.S.**; 70f. **100 M. COURSE HOMMES ALAN WELLS – G.B.R.**; 80f. **SAUT EN HAUTEUR DAMES SARA SIMEONI – ITALIE**; 100f. **BOXE 71 KG ARMANDO MARTINEZ – CUBA**; 150f. **110 M. HAIES HOMMES THOMAS MUNKELT – G.D.R.**

1981. World Telecommunications Day.

751	**236** 150f. multicoloured	1·10	65

237 Boeing 747 carrying Space Shuttle "Enterprise"

1981. Conquest of Space. Multicoloured.

752	100f. "Apollo 15" and jeep on the Moon	75	30
753	150f. Type **237**	1·10	50
754	200f. Space Shuttle launch	1·60	55
755	300f. Space Shuttle performing experiment in space	2·50	90

238 "Family of Acrobats with a Monkey"

1981. Birth Bicentenary of Pablo Picasso. Mult.

757	40f. Type **238** (postage)	35	15
758	50f. "The Balcony"	50	20
759	80f. "The Artist's Son as Pierrot"	90	25
760	100f. "The Three Dancers"	1·10	35
761	150f. "Woman and Mirror with Self-portrait" (air)	1·75	40
762	200f. "Sleeping Woman, the Dream"	1·90	45

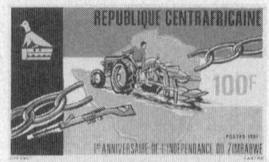

239 Tractor and Plough breaking Chain

1981. 1st Anniv of Zimbabwe's Independence.

764	**239** 100f. multicoloured	75	45
765	150f. multicoloured	1·10	50
766	200f. multicoloured	1·60	65

240 Prince Charles

1981. Royal Wedding (1st issue). Multicoloured.

767	75f. Type **240**	55	20
768	100f. Lady Diana Spencer	70	30
769	150f. St. Paul's Cathedral	1·10	45
770	175f. Couple and Prince's personal Standard	1·40	55

See also Nos. 772/7.

241 Lady Diana Spencer with Children

1981. Royal Wedding (2nd issue). Multicoloured.

772	40f. Type **241** (postage)	30	15
773	50f. Investiture of the Prince of Wales	35	20
774	80f. Lady Diana Spencer at Althorp House	60	25
775	100f. Prince Charles in naval uniform	75	30
776	150f. Prince of Wales's feathers (air)	1·10	35
777	200f. Highgrove House	1·40	45

242 C. V. Rietschoten

1981. Navigators. Multicoloured.

779	40f. Type **242** (postage)	35	25
780	50f. M. Pajot	45	40
781	60f. L. Jaworski	55	50
782	80f. M. Birch	75	55
783	100f. O. Kersauson (air)	80	65
784	200f. Sir Francis Chichester	1·75	1·25

243 Renault, 1906

1981. 75th Anniv of French Grand Prix Motor Race. Multicoloured.

786	20f. Type **243**	25	10
787	40f. Mercedes-Benz, 1937	45	15
788	50f. Matra-Ford, 1969	50	25
789	110f. Tazio Nuvolari	1·10	45
790	150f. Jackie Stewart	1·25	65

244 Emperor's Crown pierced by Bayonet

1981. Overthrow of the Empire. Multicoloured.

792	5f. Type **244**	10	10
793	10f. Type **244**	15	10
794	25f. Axe splitting crown, and angel holding map	20	15
795	60f. As 25f.	45	25
796	90f. Emperor Bokassa's statue being toppled and map of Republic	70	30
797	500f. As 90f.	3·75	1·60

245 F.A.O. Emblem

1981. World Food Day.

798	**245** 90f. green, brown & yell	75	25
799	110f. green, brown & bl	90	30

246 Lizard   **247** Plumed Guineafowl ("Komba")

1981. Air. Reptiles. Multicoloured.

800	30f. Type **246**	50	15
801	60f. Snake	55	20
802	110f. Crocodile	1·10	30

1981. Birds. Multicoloured.

803	50f. Type **247**	90	50
804	90f. Schlegel's francolin ("Dodoro")	1·40	60
805	140f. Black-headed bunting and ortolan bunting ("Kaya")	2·40	1·10

248 Bank Building

1981. Central African States' Bank.

806	**248** 90f. multicoloured	75	25
807	110f. multicoloured	90	30

249 "Madonna and Child" (Fra Angelico)

1981. Christmas. Various paintings showing Virgin and Child by named artists. Multicoloured.

808	50f. Type **249** (postage)	35	20
809	60f. Cosme-Tura	45	25
810	90f. Bramantino	65	30
811	110f. Memling	80	45
812	140f. Correge (air)	95	30
813	200f. Gentileschi	1·60	45

250 Scouts with Packs

1982. 75th Anniv of Boy Scout Movement. Mult.

815	100f. Type **250**	75	35
816	150f. Three scouts (horiz)	1·10	55
817	200f. Scouts admiring mountain view (horiz)	1·25	75
818	300f. Scouts taking oath	2·25	1·10

251 African Elephant

1982. Animals. Multicoloured.

820	60f. Type **251** (postage)	50	35
821	90f. Giraffe	70	40
822	100f. Addax	75	45
823	110f. Okapi	85	50
824	300f. Mandrill (air)	2·25	1·25
825	500f. Lion	3·75	2·10

252 "Grandfather Snowman"

1982. Norman Rockwell Illustrations. Mult.

827	30f. Type **252**	25	15
828	60f. "Croquet Players"	55	25
829	110f. "Women talking"	1·00	35
830	150f. "Searching"	1·25	50

253 Vickers Valentia biplane, 1928

1982. Transport. Multicoloured.

831	5f. Astra Torres AT-16 airship, 1919 (postage)	15	15
832	10f. Beyer-Garrat 1 locomotive	2·50	1·60
833	20f. Bugatti "Royale" car, 1926	20	15
834	110f. Type **253**	80	40
835	300f. Nuclear-powered freighter "Savannah" (air)	3·50	1·75
836	500f. Space shuttle	4·25	1·25

254 George Washington

1982. Anniversaries. Multicoloured.
838	200f. "Le Jardin de Bellevue" (E. Manet) (150th birth anniv) (horiz)	2·25	60
839	300f. Type **254** (250th birth anniv)	2·25	85
840	400f. Goethe (150th death anniv)	3·00	1·25
841	500f. Princess of Wales (21st Birthday)	3·75	1·90

255 Edward VII and Lady Diana Spencer with her Brother

1982. 21st Birthday of Princess of Wales. Mult.
843	5f. George II and portrait of Lady Diana as child (postage)	10	10
844	10f. Type **255**	15	10
845	20f. Charles I and Lady Diana with guinea pig	20	15
846	110f. George V and Lady Diana as student in Switzerland	80	25
847	300f. Charles II and Lady Diana in skiing clothes (air)	2·25	65
848	500f. George IV and Lady Diana as nursery teacher	3·75	1·25

256 Football

1982. Olympic Games, Los Angeles. (1984). Multicoloured.
850	5f. Type **256** (postage)	10	10
851	10f. Boxing	15	10
852	20f. Running	20	15
853	110f. Hurdling	80	25
854	300f. Diving (air)	2·25	65
855	500f. Show jumping	3·75	1·25

257 Weather Satellite   259 Pestle and Mortar, Chopping Board and Dish

1982. Space Resources. Multicoloured.
857	5f. Space shuttle and scientist (Food resources) (postage)	10	10
858	10f. Type **257**	15	10
859	20f. Space laboratory (Industrial use)	20	15
860	110f. Astronaut on Moon (Lunar resources)	80	25
861	300f. Satellite and energy map (Planetary energy) (air)	2·25	65
862	500f. Satellite and solar panels (Solar energy)	3·75	1·25

1982. Birth of Prince William of Wales. Nos. 767/70 optd **NAISSANCE ROYALE 1982.**
864	**240** 75f. multicoloured	50	25
865	– 100f. multicoloured	60	35
866	– 150f. multicoloured	1·10	50
867	– 175f. multicoloured	1·50	75

1982. Utensils. Multicoloured.
869	5f. Basket of vegetables (horiz)	10	10
870	10f. As No. 869	15	10
871	25f. Flagon made from decorated gourd	20	15
872	60f. As No. 871	40	20
873	120f. Clay jars (horiz)	1·00	35
874	175f. Decorated bowls (horiz)	1·25	50
875	300f. Type **259**	2·50	1·10

260 Footballers

1982. World Cup Football Championship Results. Unissued stamps optd as T **260.** Multicoloured.
876	60f. ITALIE 1er ALLEMAGNE 2e (R.F.A.)	50	25
877	150f. POLOGNE 3e	1·10	50
878	300f. FRANCE 4e	2·50	1·10

261 Jean Tubind   262 Globe and U.P.U. Emblem

1982. Painters. Multicoloured.
880	40f. Type **261**	35	15
881	70f. Pierre Ndarata and 10f. stamp	55	25
882	90f. As No. 881	75	30
883	140f. Type **261**	1·10	45

1982. U.P.U. Day.
884	**262** 60f. violet, blue and red	50	25
885	120f. violet, yellow & red	1·00	45

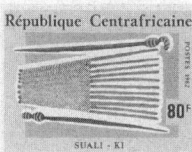

263 Hairpins and Comb

1983. Hair Accessories.
886	**263** 20f. multicoloured	10	10
887	30f. multicoloured	25	15
888	70f. multicoloured	50	25
889	80f. multicoloured	70	30
890	120f. multicoloured	95	35

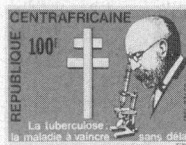

264 Koch and Microscope

1982. Centenary of Discovery of Tubercle Bacillus by Dr. Robert Koch.
891	**264** 100f. mauve and black	85	30
892	120f. red and black	1·00	45
893	175f. blue and black	1·60	60

265 Emblem

1982. 10th Anniv of United Nations Environment Programme.
894	**265** 120f. blue, orange & blk	1·00	35
895	150f. blue, yellow & blk	1·10	50
896	300f. blue, green & black	2·25	1·00

266 Granary

1982.
897	**266** 60f. multicoloured	50	25
898	80f. multicoloured	75	35
899	120f. multicoloured	1·00	50
900	200f. multicoloured	1·75	85

267 "The Beautiful Gardener"   268 Stylized Transmitter

1982. Air. Christmas. Paintings by Raphael. Multicoloured.
901	150f. Type **267**	1·60	35
902	500f. "The Holy Family"	4·00	1·25

1983. I.T.U. Delegates' Conference, Nairobi (1982).
903	**268** 100f. multicoloured	75	30
904	120f. multicoloured	1·00	45

269 Steinitz

1983. Chess Masters. Multicoloured.
905	5f. Type **269** (postage)	10	10
906	10f. Aaron Niemsovich	10	10
907	20f. Aleksandr Alekhine	15	10
908	110f. Botvinnik	1·10	30
909	300f. Boris Spassky (air)	2·50	75
910	500f. Bobby Fischer	4·00	1·40

270 George Washington

1983. Celebrities. Multicoloured.
912	20f. Type **270** (postage)	15	10
913	110f. Pres. Tito of Yugoslavia	90	25
914	500f. Princess of Wales with Prince William (air)	3·75	1·00

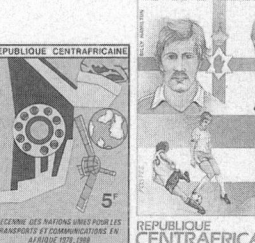

271 Telephone, Satellite and Globe   272 Billy Hamilton and Bruno Pezzey

1983. U.N. Decade for African Transport and Communications. Multicoloured.
916	5f. Type **271**	15	15
917	60f. Type **271**	50	20
918	120f. Radar screen and map of Africa	95	40
919	175f. As No. 918	1·25	60

1983. World Cup Football Championship, Spain. Multicoloured.
920	5f. Type **272** (postage)	10	10
921	10f. Sergeij Borovski and Zbigniew Boniek	10	10
922	20f. Pierre Littbarski and Jesus Maria Zamora	15	10
923	110f. Zico and Alberto Pajsarella	85	25
924	300f. Paolo Rossi and Smolarek (air)	2·25	60
925	500f. Rummenigge and Alain Giresse	3·75	95

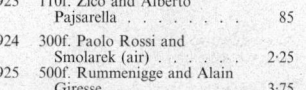

273 "Entombment"

1983. Easter. Paintings by Rembrandt. Mult.
927	100f. Type **273**	75	35
928	300f. "Christ on the Cross"	2·25	1·10
929	400f. "Descent from the Cross"	3·00	1·50

274 J. and L. Robert and Colin Hullin's Balloon, 1784

1983. Air. Bicentenary of Manned Flight. Mult.
930	65f. Type **274**	60	30
931	130f. John Wise and "Atlantic", 1859	1·10	55
932	350f. "Ville d'Orleans", Paris, 1870	3·00	1·50
933	400f. Modern advertising balloon	3·50	1·60

275 Emile Levassor, Rene Panhard and Panhard-Levassor Car, 1895   276 I.M.O. Emblem

1983. Car Manufacturers. Multicoloured.
935	10f. Type **275** (postage)	10	10
936	20f. Henry Ford and first Ford car, 1896	15	10
937	30f. Louis Renault and first Renault car, 1899	20	15
938	80f. Ettore Bugatti and Bugatti "Type 37", 1925	70	25
939	400f. Enzo Ferrari and Ferrari "815 Sport", 1940 (air)	3·25	85
940	500f. Ferdinand Porsche and Porsche "356 Coupe", 1951	3·75	1·00

1983. 25th Anniv of Int Maritime Organization.
942	**276** 40f. blue, lt blue & turq	35	15
943	100f. multicoloured	85	35

277 Gymnastics

1983. Olympic Games, Los Angeles. Mult.
944	5f. Type **277** (postage)	15	15
945	40f. Javelin	25	15
946	60f. High jump	45	20
947	120f. Fencing	95	25
948	200f. Cycling (air)	1·50	45
949	300f. Sailing	2·25	60

278 W.C.Y. Emblem and Satellite

1983. World Communications Year. Mult.
951 50f. Type **278** 40 20
952 130f. W.C.Y. emblem and
satellite (different) . . . 1·00 45

279 Horse Jumping

1983. Air. Pre-Olympic Year. Multicoloured.
953 100f. Type **279** 80 40
954 200f. Dressage 80 65
955 300f. Jumping double jump 2·50 75
956 400f. Trotting . . . . . 3·00 1·00

280 Andre Kolingba

281 Antenna, Bangui
M'Poko Earth
Station

1983. 2nd Anniv of Military Committee for National
Recovery.
958 **280** 65f. multicoloured 55 20
959 130f. multicoloured . . . 1·10 40

1983. Bangui M'Poko Earth Station.
960 **281** 130f. multicoloured . . . 1·10 50

282 Flower and Broken Chain
on Map of Africa

1983. Namibia Day.
961 **282** 100f. green, lt grn & red 75 35
962 200f. multicoloured . . . 1·50 75

283 J. Montgolfier and Balloon

1983. Bicentenary of Manned Flight. Mult.
963 50f. Type **283** (postage) . . 35 15
964 100f. J. Blanchard and
Channel crossing, 1785 . . 75 35
965 200f. Joseph Gay-Lussac and
ascent to 4000 m, 1804 . . 1·60 65
966 300f. Henri Giffard and
steam-powered dirigible
airship, 1852 . . . . . 2·25 1·00
967 400f. Santos-Dumont and
airship "Ballon No. 6",
Paris, 1901 (air) . . . . 3·00 1·25
968 500f. A. Laquot and captive
observation balloon, 1914 3·75 1·50

284 "Global
Communications"

1983. World Communications Year. U.P.U. Day.
970 **284** 205f. multicoloured . . . 1·75 90

285 Black Rhinoceros

1983. Endangered Animals. Multicoloured.
971 10f. Type **285** (postage) . . 10 10
972 40f. Two rhinoceros . . . 65 20
973 70f. Black rhinoceros
(different) 75 20
974 180f. Black rhinoceros and
young . . . . . . 3·50 1·25
975 400f. Rangers attending sick
rhinoceros (air) . . . 6·50 3·25
976 500f. Wild animals and flag 7·50 3·75

286 Handicapped Person and Old
Man

1983. National Day of the Handicapped and Old.
978 **286** 65f. orange and mauve . . 50 25
979 130f. orange and blue . . . 1·00 50
980 250f. orange and green . . . 1·50 75

287 Fish Pond

1983. Fishery Resources. Multicoloured.
981 25f. Type **287** 15 10
982 65f. Net fishing 70 25
983 100f. Traditional fishing . . . 80 35
984 130f. Butter catfish, eel and
cichlids on plate . . . 1·60 70
985 205f. Weir basket . . . . 1·60 70

288 "The Annunciation" (Leonardo
da Vinci)

1984. Air. Christmas. Multicoloured.
986 130f. Type **288** 95 25
987 205f. "The Virgin of the
Rocks" (Leonardo da
Vinci) . . . . . . 1·60 45
988 350f. "Adoration of the
Shepherds" (Rubens) . . 2·50 80
989 500f. "A. Goubeau before the
Virgin" (Rubens) . . . . . 3·75 1·00

289 Bush Fire

1984. Nature Protection. Multicoloured.
990 30f. Type **289** 75 25
991 130f. Soldiers protecting
wildlife from hunters . . . 1·10 70

290 Goethe and Scene from "Faust"

1984. Celebrities. Multicoloured.
992 50f. Type **290** (postage) . . . 40 15
993 100f. Henri Dunant and
battle scene . . . 75 35
994 200f. Alfred Nobel . . . . 1·60 55
995 300f. Lord Baden-Powell and
scout camp . . . . . 2·25 90
996 400f. President Kennedy and
first foot-print on Moon
(air) . . . . . . 3·00 90
997 500f. Prince and Princess of
Wales . . . . . . 3·75 1·00

291 Fixed Bar

1984. Air. Olympic Games, Los Angeles. Gymnastics.
Multicoloured.
999 65f. Type **291** 50 20
1000 100f. Parallel bars 85 25
1001 130f. Ribbon (horiz.) . . . 1·10 30
1002 205f. Cord . . . . . 1·90 45
1003 350f. Hoop . . . . . . 3·00 85

292 "Madonna and Child"
(Raphael)

1984. Paintings. Multicoloured.
1005 50f. Type **292** (postage) . . . 35 15
1006 100f. "The Madonna of the
Pear" (Durer) . . . 75 20
1007 200f. "Aldobrandini
Madonna" (Raphael) . . 1·60 35
1008 300f. "Madonna of the
Pink" (Durer) . . . 2·25 70
1009 400f. "Virgin and Child"
(Correggio) (air) . . 3·00 1·50
1010 500f. "The Bohemian"
(Modigliani) . . . 3·75 2·10

293 "Le Pericles" (mail ship)

1984. Transport. Multicoloured. (a) Ships.
1012 65f. Type **293** 50 25
1013 120f. "Pereire" (steamer) . . 90 50
1014 250f. "Admella" (passenger
steamer) . . . . 1·75 85
1015 400f. "Royal William"
(paddle-steamer) . . . 3·00 1·50
1016 500f. "Great Britain"
(steam/sail) . . . . 3·75 2·10

(b) Locomotives.
1017 110f. CC-1500 ch 85 20
1018 240f. Series 210, 1968 . . 1·90 40
1019 350f. 231-726, 1937 . . 2·75 60
1020 440f. Pacific Series S3/6,
1908 . . . . . 3·50 75
1021 500f. Henschel 151 Series
45, 1937 . . . . 4·00 85
Nos. 1017/21 each include an inset portrait of
George Stephenson in the design.

294 Forest

295 Weighing Baby
and Emblem

1984. Forest Resources. Multicoloured.
1022 70f. Type **294** 65 25
1023 130f. Log cabin and timber . 1·25 50

1984. Infant Survival Campaign. Multicoloured.
1024 10f. Type **295** 15 10
1025 30f. Vaccinating baby . . . 30 25
1026 65f. Feeding dehydrated
baby 50 30
1027 100f. Mother, healthy baby
and foodstuffs 95 50

296 Bangui-Kette Conical Trap

1984. Fish Traps. Multicoloured.
1028 50f. Type **296** 60 30
1029 80f. Mbres fish trap . . . 85 50
1030 150f. Bangui-Kette round
fish trap . . . . . 1·60 50

297 Galileo and
"Ariane" Rocket

298 "Leptoporus lignosus"

1984. Space Technology. Multicoloured.
1031 20f. Type **297** (postage) . . 15 10
1032 70f. Auguste Piccard and
stratosphere balloon
"F.N.R.S." . . . 50 20
1033 150f. Hermann Oberth and
satellite . . . . 1·10 45
1034 205f. Albert Einstein and
"Giotto" satellite . . 1·50 55
1035 300f. Marie Curie and
"Viking I" and "II" (air) 2·50 65
1036 500f. Dr. U. Merbold and
"Navette" space
laboratory . . . . . 3·75 95

1984. Fungi. Multicoloured.
1038 5f. Type **298** (postage) . . 10 10
1039 10f. "Phlebopus sudanicus" . 20 10
1040 40f. "Termitomyces letestui" . 45 20
1041 130f. "Lepiota esculenta" . . 1·25 60
1042 300f. "Termitomyces
aurantiacus" (air) . . 3·25 1·40
1043 500f. "Termitomyces
robustus" . . . . . 5·75 2·25

299 Hibiscus

300 G. Boucher (speed skating)

1984. Flowers. Multicoloured.
1045 65f. Type **299** 60 35
1046 130f. Canna . . . . . 1·10 50
1047 205f. Water Hyacinth . . . 1·75 85

1984. Winter Olympic Gold Medallists. Mult.
1048 30f. Type **300** (postage) . . 20 15
1049 90f. W. Hoppe, R. Wetzig,
D. Schauerhammer and
A. Kirchner (bobsleigh) . 70 25
1050 140f. P. Magoni (ladies'
slalom) . . . . . 1·10 35
1051 200f. J. Torvill and C. Dean
(ice skating) . . . 1·50 50
1052 400f. M. Nykanen (90 m ski
jump) (air) . . . 3·00 90
1053 400f. Russia (ice hockey) . . 3·75 1·00

301 Workers sowing Cotton Seeds

1984. Economic Campaign. Multicoloured.
1055 25f. Type **301** 25 20
1056 40f. Selling cotton . . . 45 30
1057 130f. Cotton market . . . . 1·25 50

302 Woman picking corn

1984. World Food Day.
1058 **302** 205f. multicoloured . . . 1·75 85

303 Abraham Lincoln

1984. Celebrities. Multicoloured.
1059 50f. Type **303** (postage) . . 45 15
1060 90f. Auguste Piccard
(undersea explorer) . . . 80 30
1061 120f. Gottlieb Daimler
(automobile designer) . . . 1·25 35
1062 200f. Louis Bleriot (pilot) 1·90 55
1063 350f. A. Karpov (chess
champion) (air) . . . . 3·00 75
1064 400f. Henri Dunant (founder
of Red Cross) . . . . . 3·00 85

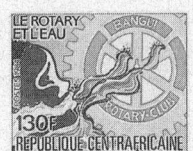

304 Profile, Water and Emblem

1984. Bangui Rotary Club and Water.
1066 **304** 130f. multicoloured . . . 1·25 35
1067 205f. multicoloured . . . 1·90 60

305 United States (4 × 400 m relay)

1985. Air Olympic Games Gold Medallists.
Multicoloured.
1068 60f. Type **305** 45 20
1069 140f. E. Moses (400 m
hurdles) . . . . . 1·10 30
1070 300f. S. Aouita (5000 m) . 2·50 75
1071 440f. D. Thompson
(decathlon) . . . . . . 3·50 1·00

306 "Virgin and Infant Jesus" (Titian)

1985. Air. Christmas (1984). Multicoloured.
1073 130f. Type **306** 95 45
1074 350f. "Virgin with Rabbit"
(Titian) . . . . . 2·50 1·10
1075 400f. "Virgin and Child"
(Titian) . . . . . 3·00 1·25

307 Eastern Screech Owls

1985. Air. Birth Bicentenary of John J. Audubon
(ornithologist) (1st issue). Multicoloured.
1076 60f. Type **307** . . . . 1·25 70
1077 110f. Mangrove cuckoo
(vert) . . . . . 1·90 1·10

1078 200f. Mourning doves (vert) 3·25 1·75
1079 500f. Wood ducks . . . . . 8·00 4·50
See also Nos. 1099/1104.

1985. International Exhibitions. Nos. 1014/15 and
1019/20 overprinted as listed below.
1083 250f. multicoloured . . . 1·90 95
1084 350f. multicoloured . . . 2·50 1·10
1085 400f. multicoloured . . . 3·75 1·90
1086 440f. multicoloured . . . 3·00 1·40
OVERPRINTS: 250f. **ARGENTINA '85 BUENOS
AIRES** and emblem; 350f. **TSUKUBA EXPO '85**;
400f. **Italia '85 ROME** and emblem; 440f. **MOPHILA
'85 HAMBOURG.**

310 "Chelorrhina
polyphemus"

312 Blue Jay

1985. Beetles. Multicoloured.
1088 15f. Type **310** 20 15
1089 20f. "Fornasinius russus" 25 15
1090 25f. "Goliathus giganteus" 30 15
1091 65f. "Goliathus meleagris" 80 50

311 Olympic Games Poster and
Stockholm

1985. "Olymphilex '85" Olympic Stamps Exhibition,
Lausanne. Multicoloured.
1092 5f. Type **311** (postage) 15 10
1093 10f. Olympic Games poster
and Paris 20 15
1094 20f. Olympic Games poster
and London 20 15
1095 100f. Olympic Games poster
and Tokyo . . . . . 7·50 1·75
1096 400f. Olympic Games poster
and Mexico (air) . . . 3·25 85
1097 500f. Olympic Games poster
and Munich . . . . 3·75 1·00

1985. Birth Bicentenary of John J. Audubon
(ornithologist) (2nd issue). Multicoloured.
1099 40f. Type **312** (postage) . . 45 25
1100 80f. Chuck Will's widow . 85 55
1101 130f. Ivory-billed
woodpecker . . . . . 1·10 80
1102 250f. Collie's magpie-jay . 2·50 1·75
1103 300f. Mangrove cuckoo
(horiz) (air) . . . . 2·75 1·90
1104 500f. Barn swallow (horiz) 5·50 3·75

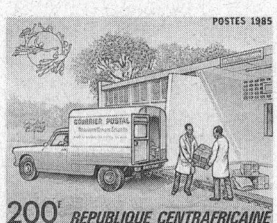

313 Delivering Post by Van

1985. "Philexafrique" Stamp Exhibition, Lome, Togo
(1st issue). Multicoloured.
1106 200f. Type **313** . . . . 1·90 1·00
1107 200f. Scouts and flag . . 1·90 1·00
See also Nos. 1154/5.

314 Tiger and Rudyard Kipling

1985. Int Youth Year (1st issue). Multicoloured.
1108 100f. Type **314** . . . . 1·00 30
1109 200f. Men on horseback and
Joseph Kessel . . . . 1·90 55
1110 300f. Submarine gripped by
octopus and Jules Verne 2·25 1·10
1111 400f. Mississippi stern-
wheeler, Huckleberry Finn
and Mark Twain . . . 3·00 1·75
See also Nos. 1163/68.

315 Louis Pasteur

1985. Anniversaries. Multicoloured.
1112 150f. Type **315** (centenary of
discovery of anti-rabies
vaccine) (postage) . . . . 1·75 40
1113 200f. Henri Dunant (founder
of Red Cross) and 125th
anniv of Battle of
Solferino (horiz) . . . 1·90 50
1114 300f. Girl guides (75th anniv
of Girl Guide Movement)
(air) . . . . . 1·90 75
1115 450f. Queen Elizabeth the
Queen Mother (85th
birthday) . . . . . 3·25 1·25
1116 500f. Statue of Liberty (cent) 3·75 1·50

316 Pele and Footballers

1985. World Cup Football Championship, Mexico.
Multicoloured.
1117 5f. Type **316** (postage) . . . 10 10
1118 10f. Harald "Tony"
Schumacher 15 10
1119 20f. Paolo Rossi 15 15
1120 350f. Kevin Keegan
(wrongly inscr "Kervin") 2·75 90
1121 400f. Michel Platini (air) . . 3·00 90
1122 500f. Karl Heinz
Rummenigge . . . . 3·75 1·00

317 La Kotto Waterfalls

318 Pope with Hand
raised in Blessing

1985.
1124 **317** 65f. multicoloured . . . 60 25
1125 90f. multicoloured . . . 75 30
1126 130f. multicoloured . . . 1·10 50

1985. Papal Visit. Multicoloured.
1127 65f. Type **318** 55 25
1128 130f. Pope John Paul II in
Communion robes . . . 1·10 50

319 Soldier using Ox-drawn Plough

1985. Economic Campaign. Multicoloured.
1129 5f. Type **319** 15 10
1130 60f. Soldier sowing cotton 35 20
1131 130f. Soldier sowing cotton
(different) . . . . . 1·00 35

320 As Young Girl with her Brother

1985. 85th Birthday of Queen Elizabeth the Queen
Mother. Multicoloured.
1132 100f. Type **320** (postage) . . 60 20
1133 200f. Queen Mary with
Duke and Duchess of
York . . . . . 1·50 35
1134 300f. Duchess of York
inspecting Irish Guards 2·25 70
1135 350f. Duke and Duchess of
York with the young
Princesses . . . . 2·50 80
1136 400f. In the Golden State
Coach at Coronation of
King George VI (air) . . 3·00 90
1137 500f. At the service for her
Silver Wedding . . . . 3·75 1·00

321 Dr. Labusquiere and Map of
Republic

1985. 8th Death Anniv of General Doctor
Labusquiere. Multicoloured.
1139 **321** 10f. multicoloured . . . 15 10
1140 45f. multicoloured . . . 35 20
1141 110f. multicoloured . . . 1·00 35

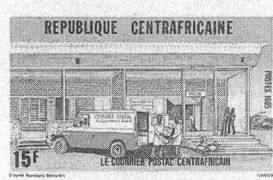

322 Mail Van delivering Parcels to Local
Post Office

1985. Postal Service. Multicoloured.
1142 15f. Type **322** 15 10
1143 60f. Van collecting mail
from local post office . . 45 20
1144 150f. Vans at main post
office . . . . . 1·10 50

323 Gagarin, Korolev and Space Station
Complex

1985. Space Research. Multicoloured.
1145 40f. Type **323** (postage) . . 20 10
1146 110f. Copernicus and
"Cassini" space probe . . 75 25
1147 240f. Galileo and "Viking"
orbiter . . . . . 1·75 50
1148 300f. T. von Karman and
astronaut recovering
satellite . . . . . 2·25 70
1149 450f. Percival Lowell and
"Viking" space probe (air) 3·50 90
1150 500f. Dr. U. Merbold and
"Columbus" space station 3·75 1·00

324 Damara Solar Energy Plant

1985.
1152 **324** 65f. multicoloured . . . 55 25
1153 130f. multicoloured . . . 1·10 50

325 Ouaka Sugar Refinery

1985. "Philexafrique" Stamp Exhibition, Lome, Togo (2nd issue). Multicoloured.
1154　250f. Nature studies . . . . .　3·25　1·60
1155　250f. Type **325** . . . .　2·10　1·40

326 Pres. Mitterrand, Gen. Kolingba and Flags

1985. Visit of President Mitterrand of France.
1156　**326**　65f. multicoloured . . . .　50　20
1157　130f. multicoloured . . . .　1·00　45
1158　160f. multicoloured . . . .　1·40　60

327 Map and U.N. Emblem
328 "Virgin and Angels" (Master of Burgo de Osma)

1985. 40th Anniv of U.N.O. and 25th Anniv of Central African Republic Membership.
1159　**327**　140f. multicoloured . . .　1·10　50

1985. Air. Christmas. Multicoloured.
1160　100f. Type **328** . . . . .　80　25
1161　200f. "Nativity" (Louis Le Nain) . . . .　1·75　1·00
1162　400f. "Virgin and Child with Dove" (Piero di Cosimo) . . .　3·25　1·00

329 Leonardo da Vinci and "Madonna of the Eyelet"

1985. Int Youth Year (2nd issue). Multicoloured.
1163　40f. Type **329** (postage) . .　30　15
1164　80f. Johann Sebastian Bach　75　20
1165　100f. Diego Velasquez and "St. John of Patmos" . .　1·00　20
1166　250f. Franz Schubert and illustration of "King of Aulnes" . . . .　2·00　50
1167　400f. Francisco Goya and "Vicente Osario de Moscoso" (air) . . . . .　3·50　90
1168　500f. Wolfang Amadeus Mozart . . . .　4·00　1·00

330 Halley and "Comet"

1985. Appearance of Halley's Comet (1st issue). Multicoloured.
1170　100f. Type **330** (postage) . .　60　20
1171　200f. Newton's telescope . .　1·50　35
1172　300f. Halley and Newton observing comet . . . . .　2·25　45
1173　350f. American space probe and comet . . . .　2·50　80

1174　400f. Sun, Russian space probe and diagram of comet trajectory (air)　3·00　90
1175　500f. Infra-red picture of comet . . . .　3·75　1·00
See also Nos. 1184/8.

331 Columbus with Globe

1986. 480th Death Anniv of Christopher Columbus (explorer). Multicoloured.
1177　90f. Type **331** (postage) . .　70　20
1178　110f. Receiving blessing . .　85　25
1179　240f. Crew going ashore in rowing boat . . . . .　2·00　1·25
1180　300f. Columbus with American Indians . . . .　2·50　60
1181　400f. Ships at sea in storm (air) . . . .　3·50　2·00
1182　500f. Sun breaking through clouds over fleet . . . .　4·00　2·25

332 Halley and Comet

1986. Air. Appearance of Halley's Comet (2nd issue). Multicoloured.
1184　110f. Type **332** . . . . .　80　25
1185　130f. "Giotto" space probe　1·00　25
1186　200f. Comet and globe . . .　1·50　45
1187　300f. "Vega" space probe . .　2·25　60
1188　400f. Space shuttle . . . .　3·25　95

1986. Nos. 874/5 surch.
1188a　－　30f. on 175f. mult . . . . . .
1188b　**259**　65f. on 300f. mult . . . . . .

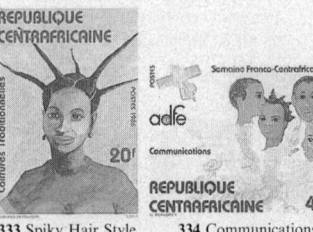

333 Spiky Hair Style
334 Communications

1986. Traditional Hair Styles. Multicoloured.
1189　20f. Type **333** . . . .　20　10
1190　30f. Braids around head . .　25　15
1191　65f. Plaits . . . .　30　25
1192　160f. Braids from front to back of head . . . .　1·50　50

1986. Franco-Central African Week. Mult.
1193　40f. Type **334** . . . .　30　15
1194　60f. Youth . . . .　50　20
1195　100f. Basket weaver (craft)　75　30
1196　130f. Cyclists (sport) . . .　1·25　50

335 "Allamanda neriifolia"

1986. Flora and Fauna. Multicoloured.
1197　25f. Type **335** (postage) . .　20　15
1198　65f. Bongo (horiz) . . . . .　50　20
1199　160f. "Plumieria acuminata"　1·10　40
1200　300f. Cheetah (horiz) . . . .　2·25　1·00
1201　400f. "Eulophia erthoplata" (air) . . . .　2·75　90
1202　500f. Leopard (horiz) . . .　3·75　1·75

336 Palm Tree and Bossongo Oil Refinery

1986. Centrapalm. Multicoloured.
1204　25f. Type **336** . . . .　20　15
1205　65f. Type **336** . . . .　50　30
1206　120f. Palm tree and Bossongo agro-industrial complex . . . .　85　60
1207　160f. As No. 1206 . . . . .　1·25　50

337 Pointer

1986. Dogs and Cats. Multicoloured.
1208　10f. Type **337** (postage) . .　15　10
1209　20f. Egyptian mau . . . . .　25　15
1210　200f. Newfoundland . . . .　1·75　50
1211　300f. Borzoi (air) . . . . .　2·50　60
1212　400f. Persian red . . . . .　3·50　80

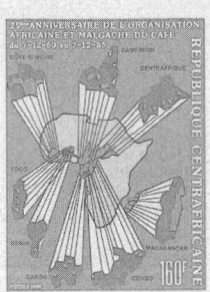

338 Map of Africa showing Member Countries

1986. 25th Anniv of African and Malagasy Coffee Producers Organization.
1214　**338**　160f. multicoloured . . .　1·40　60

339 Trophy, Brazilian flag, L.-A. Muller and Socrates

1986. World Cup Football Championship, Mexico. Multicoloured.
1215　30f. Type **339** (postage) . .　20　15
1216　110f. Trophy, Belgian flag, V. Scifo and F. Ceulemans . . . .　70　20
1217　160f. Trophy, French flag. Y. Stopyra and M. Platini　1·00　25
1218　350f. Trophy, West German flag, A. Brehme and H. Schumacher . . . .　2·50　70
1219　450f. Trophy, Argentinian flag and Diego Maradona (air) . . . .　3·00　1·00

340 Judith Resnik and Astronaut
341 People around Globe within Emblem

1986. Anniversaries and "Challenger" Astronauts Commemoration. Multicoloured.
1221　15f. Type **340** (postage) . .　15　10
1222　25f. Frederic Bartholdi and torch (centenary of Statue of Liberty) . . . .　25　15
1223　70f. Elvis Presley (9th death anniv) . . . .　95　20

1224　300f. Ronald MacNair and man watching astronaut on screen . . . .　2·10　65
1225　485f. on 70f. No. 1223 . . .　5·25　1·00
1226　450f. Christa McAulife and Shuttle lifting off (air) . . .　3·25　1·10

1986. International Peace Year.
1228　**341**　160f. multicoloured . . .　1·40　65

342 Globe, Douglas DC-10 and "25"
343 Emblem and Flag as Map

1986. 25th Anniv of Air Afrique.
1229　**342**　200f. multicoloured . . .　1·50　85

1986. U.N.I.C.E.F. Child Survival Campaign. Multicoloured.
1230　15f. Type **343** . . . .　15　10
1231　130f. Doctor vaccinating child . . . .　1·10　50
1232　160f. Basket of fruit and boy holding fish on map . .　2·25　1·00

344 "Nativity" (detail, Giotto)

1986. Air. Christmas. Multicoloured.
1233　250f. Type **344** . . . . .　1·90　60
1234　440f. "Adoration of the Magi" (detail, Sandro Botticelli) (vert) . . . .　3·25　1·10
1235　500f. "Nativity" (detail, Giotto) (different) . . . .　4·00　1·10

345 Transmission Mast, People with Radios and Baskets of Produce

1986. African Telecommunications Day. Telecommunications and Agriculture. Mult.
1236　170f. Type **345** (Rural Radio Agriculture Project) . . .　1·40　75
1237　265f. Lorry, satellite, men using telephones and sacks of produce . . . .　2·10　1·10

346 Steam Locomotive Class "DH 2 Green Elephant" and Alfred de Glehn

1986. 150th Anniv of German Railways. Mult.
1238　40f. Type **346** (postage) . .　50　15
1239　70f. Rudolf Diesel (engineer) and steam locomotive No. 1829 Rheingold . . .　80　15
1240　160f. Electric locomotive Type 103 Rapide and Carl Golsdorf . . . . . .　2·00　40
1241　300f. Wilhelm Schmidt and Beyer-Garratt type steam locomotive . . . . . .　3·50　95
1242　400f. De Bousquet and compound locomotive Class 3500 (air) . . . . .　4·75　1·10

347 Player returning Ball

1986. Air. Olympic Games, Seoul (1988) (1st issue). Tennis. Multicoloured.
1244	150f. Type **347**		1·25	45
1245	500f. Player serving (vert)		2·25	60
1246	440f. Right-handed player returning to left-handed player (vert)		3·00	1·10
1247	600f. Left-handed player returning to right-handed player		4·50	1·25

See also Nos. 1261/4, 1310/13 and 1315/18.

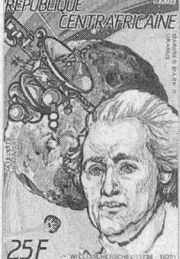

348 "Miranda" Satellite, Uranus, "Mariner II" and William Herschel (astronomer)

349 Footballer and "Woman with Umbrella" Fountain

1987. Space Research. Multicoloured.
1248	25f. Type **348** (postage)		20	15
1249	65f. Mars Rover vehicle and Werner von Braun (rocket pioneer)		45	20
1250	160f. "Mariner II", Titan and Rudolf Hanel		1·25	35
1251	300f. Space ship "Hermes", space platform "Eureka" and Patrick Baudry		2·25	70
1252	400f. Halley's Comet, "Giotto" space probe and Dr. U. Keller (air)		2·75	85
1253	500f. European space station "Columbus", Wubbo Ockels and Ulf Merbold		3·25	1·00

1987. Olympic Games, Barcelona (1992). Mult.
1255	30f. Type **349** (postage)		25	15
1256	150f. Judo competitors and Barcelona Cathedral		1·00	40
1257	265f. Cyclist and Church of the Holy Family		1·90	65
1258	350f. Diver and Christopher Columbus's tomb (air)		2·50	85
1259	495f. Runner and human tower		3·75	1·10

350 Triple Jumping

1987. Air. Olympic Games, Seoul (1988) (2nd issue). Multicoloured.
1261	100f. Type **350**		75	25
1262	200f. High jumping (horiz)		1·50	50
1263	300f. Long jumping (horiz)		2·25	75
1264	400f. Pole vaulting		3·00	1·00

351 Two-man Luge   **352** Peace Medal

1987. Winter Olympic Games, Calgary (1988) (1st issue). Multicoloured.
1266	20f. Type **351** (postage)		20	15
1267	140f. Cross-country skiing		1·10	40
1268	250f. Figure skating		1·90	65
1269	300f. Ice hockey (air)		2·25	75
1270	400f. Slalom		2·75	1·00

See also Nos. 1320/3.

1987. International Peace Year (1986).
1272	**352** 50f. brown, blue & blk		35	25
1273	160f. brown, grn & blk		1·25	65

1987. 10th Death Anniv of Elvis Presley (singer). Nos. 1223 and 1225 optd **Elvis Presley 1977–1987**.
1274	70f. multicoloured		75	50
1275	485f. on 70f. multicoloured		5·00	1·75

354 Woman at Village Pump

1987. International Decade of Drinkable Water. Multicoloured.
1276	5f. Type **354**			
1277	10f. Woman at village pump (different)			
1278	200f. Three women at village pump			

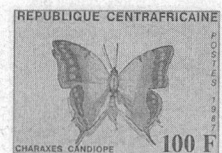

355 "Charaxes candiope"

1987. Butterflies. Multicoloured.
1279	100f. Type **355**		75	55
1280	120f. "Graphium leonidas"		95	60
1281	130f. "Charaxes brutus"		1·10	60
1282	160f. "Salamis aetiops"		1·25	70

356 Nola Football Team

1987. Campaign for Integration of Pygmies.
1283	**356** 90f. multicoloured		1·10	75
1284	160f. multicoloured		1·75	1·10

357 James Madison (U.S. President, 1809–17)

1987. Anniversaries and Celebrities. Mult.
1285	40f. Type **357** (bicent of U.S. constitution) (postage)		30	15
1286	160f. Queen Elizabeth II and Prince Philip (40th wedding anniv)		1·25	25
1287	200f. Steffi Graf (tennis player)		1·60	45
1288	300f. Gary Kasparov (chess champion) and "The Chess Players" (after Honoré Daumier) (air)		2·50	75
1289	400f. Boris Becker (tennis player)		3·00	1·00

358 Brontosaurus

1988. Prehistoric Animals. Multicoloured.
1291	50f. Type **358**		35	15
1292	65f. Triceratops		50	15
1293	100f. Ankylosaurus		75	25
1294	160f. Stegosaurus		1·25	45
1295	200f. Tyrannosaurus rex		1·50	50
1296	240f. Corythosaurus		1·90	65
1297	300f. Allosaurus		2·25	75
1298	350f. Brachiosaurus		2·75	95

Nos. 1295/8 are vert.

359 Pres. Kolingba vaccinating Baby   **360** Carmine Bee Eater

1988. 40th Anniv of W.H.O.
1299	**359** 70f. multicoloured		60	40
1300	120f. multicoloured		1·60	45

1988. Scouts and Birds. Multicoloured.
1301	25f. Type **360** (postage)		15	10
1302	170f. Red-crowned bishop		1·10	80
1303	300f. Lesser pied kingfisher		3·25	2·25
1304	400f. Red-cheeked cordon-bleu (air)		2·75	2·40
1305	450f. Lizard buzzard		3·50	2·75

361 Schools replanting Campaign

1988. National Tree Day. Multicoloured.
1307	50f. Type **361**		35	25
1308	100f. Type **361**		75	50
1309	130f. Felling tree and planting saplings		1·10	60

362 1972 100f. Stamp and Beam Exercise

1988. Air. Olympic Games, Seoul (3rd issue). Gymnastics. Multicoloured.
1310	90f. Type **362**		75	25
1311	200f. 1964 50f. stamp and beam exercise (horiz)		1·50	35
1312	300f. 1964 100f. stamp and vault exercise (horiz)		2·25	75
1313	400f. 1964 250f. stamp and parallel bars exercise (horiz)		3·00	1·10

363 Running   **364** Cross-country Skiing

1988. Olympic Games, Seoul (4th issue). Mult.
1315	150f. Type **363** (postage)		1·10	25
1316	300f. Judo		2·25	60
1317	400f. Football (air)		2·75	85
1318	450f. Tennis		3·00	1·00

1988. Winter Olympic Games, Calgary (2nd issue). Multicoloured.
1320	170f. Type **364** (postage)		1·25	30
1321	350f. Ice hockey		2·25	60
1322	400f. Downhill skiing (air)		2·75	85
1323	450f. Slalom		3·00	1·00

1988. Nos. 1302/5 surch.
1325	30f. on 170f. mult (postage)		40	20
1326	70f. on 300f. mult		1·50	85
1327	160f. on 400f. mult (air)		2·50	1·40
1328	200f. on 450f. mult		3·00	1·90

366 Hospital and Grounds

1988. 1st Anniv of L'Amitie Hospital. Mult.
1329	5f. Type **366**		15	10
1330	60f. Aerial view of hospital complex		50	35
1331	160f. Hospital entrance		1·25	75

367 Buildings Complex

1988. 30th Anniv of Republic. Multicoloured.
1332	65f. Family on map, flags and dove			
1334	240f. Type **367**			

368 Kristine Otto (East Germany)   **369** Hebmuller and Volkswagen Cabriolet, 1953

1989. Olympic Games, Seoul, Gold Medal Winners. Multicoloured.
1335	150f. Type **368** (100 m butterfly and 100 m backstroke) (postage)		1·00	35
1336	240f. Matt Biondi (100 m freestyle)		1·50	50
1337	300f. Florence Griffith-Joyner (U.S.A.) (100 and 200 m sprints)		1·90	75
1338	450f. Pierre Durand (France) (show jumping) (air)		3·00	1·10

1989. Transport. Multicoloured.
1340	20f. Type **369** (postage)		20	15
1341	205f. Werner von Siemens and his first electric locomotive, 1879		2·25	75
1342	300f. Dennis Conner and "Stars and Stripes" (winner of Americas Cup yacht races)		2·25	65
1343	400f. Andre Citroen and "16 Six" car, 1955		3·00	1·00
1344	450f. Mare Seguin and Decauville Mallet locomotive, 1895 (air)		3·75	75

370 Allegory in Honour of Liberty

1989. Bicentenary of French Revolution and "Philexfrance 89" International Stamp Exhibition, Paris (1st issue). Multicoloured.
1346	200f. Type **370**		1·75	60
1347	300f. Declaration of Rights of Man		2·50	1·25

See also Nos. 1366/9.

371 Statue of Liberty at Night

1989. Centenary of Statue of Liberty. Mult.
1349	150f. Type **371**	1·10	60
1350	150f. Maintenance worker	1·10	60
1351	150f. Close-up of face	1·10	60
1352	200f. Maintenance worker (different)	1·40	95
1353	200f. Colour party in front of statue	1·40	95
1354	200f. Close-up of head at night	1·40	95

373 ''Apollo 11'' Astronaut on Moon

1989. Air. 20th Anniv of First Manned Landing on Moon. Multicoloured.
1355	40f. Type **373**	30	20
1356	80f. ''Apollo 15'' astronaut and moon buggy	55	25
1357	130f. ''Apollo 16'' module landing in sea	1·00	50
1358	1000f. ''Apollo 17'' astronaut on Moon	7·50	2·25

374 Champagnat, Map and ''Madonna and Child''

1989. Birth Bicentenary of Marcelino Champagnat (founder of Marist Brothers). Multicoloured.
1359	15f. Type **374**	15	15
1360	50f. Champagnat, cross, globe and emblem	35	25
1361	160f. Champagnat and flags (horiz)	1·40	1·00

375 Food Products

1989. Bambari Harvest Festival. Multicoloured.
1362	100f. Type **375**	1·25	65
1363	160f. Ploughing with oxen	1·25	60

376 Raising of Livestock

1989. World Food Day. Multicoloured.
1364	60f. Type **376**	50	35
1365	240f. Soldiers catching poachers	2·00	1·10

377 Gen. Kellermann and Battle of Valmy

1989. Bicentenary of French Revolution and ''Philexfrance 89'' International Stamp Exhibition, Paris (2nd issue). Multicoloured.
1366	160f. Type **377** (postage)	1·25	35

1367	200f. Gen. Dumouriez and Battle of Jemappes (wrongly inscr ''JEMMAPES'')	1·60	50
1368	500f. Gen. Pichegru and capture of Dutch fleet (air)	4·50	1·25
1369	600f. Gen. Hoche and Royalist landing at Quiberon	4·25	1·00

378 Players and Trophy

1989. Victory in 1987 African Basketball Championships, Tunis (1st issue). Multicoloured.
1371	160f. Type **378**	1·25	60
1372	240f. National team with medals and trophy (horiz)	1·60	80
1373	500f. Type **378**	4·00	1·75
	See also Nos. 1383/4.		

379 Governor's Palace, 1906

1989. Centenary of Bangui. Multicoloured.
1374	100f. Type **379**	75	35
1375	160f. Bangui post office	1·10	90
1376	200f. A. Dosilie (founder of Bangui post office) (vert)	1·50	85
1377	1000f. Michel Dolisie and Chief Gbembo agreeing peace pact (vert)	7·25	3·75

380 Footballer and Palermo Cathedral Belltower　**381** Trophy and Map of Africa

1989. World Cup Football Championship, Italy (1990) (1st issue). Multicoloured.
1378	20f. Type **380** (postage)	20	15
1379	160f. Footballer and St. Francis's church, Bologna	1·10	35
1380	200f. Footballer and Old Palace, Florence	1·50	50
1381	120f. Footballer and Church of Trinita dei Monti, Rome (air)	90	35
	See also Nos. 1405/8.		

1990. Victory in 1987 African Basketball Championships, Tunis (2nd issue).
1383	**381** 100f. multicoloured	80	35
1384	130f. multicoloured	1·10	60

382 Tree with Map as Foliage　**383** Speed Skating

1990. Inauguration (1989) of Forest Conservation Organization.
1385	**382** 160f. multicoloured	1·40	65

1990. Winter Olympic Games, Albertville (1992). Multicoloured.
1386	10f. Type **383** (postage)	15	15
1387	60f. Cross-country skiing	45	25
1388	500f. Slalom skiing (air)	3·75	95
1389	750f. Ice dancing	5·50	1·25

384 ''Euphaera eusemoides''

1990. Scouts and Butterflies. Multicoloured.
1391	25f. Type **384**	20	15
1392	65f. Becker's glider	45	15
1393	160f. ''Pseudacraea clarki''	1·10	25
1394	250f. Giant charaxes	1·75	50
1395	300f. ''Euphaedra gausape''	2·25	60
1396	500f. Red swallowtail	3·75	85

385 Throwing the Javelin

1990. Olympic Games, Barcelona (1992). Mult.
1398	10f. Type **385** (postage)	15	15
1399	40f. Running	35	15
1400	130f. Tennis	95	25
1401	240f. Hurdling (horiz)	1·75	50
1402	400f. Yachting (horiz) (air)	3·00	85
1403	500f. Football (horiz)	3·75	1·00

386 Footballers and Globe

1990. Air. World Cup Football Championship, Italy (2nd issue).
1405	**386** 5f. multicoloured	10	10
1406	– 30f. multicoloured	20	15
1407	– 500f. multicoloured	3·25	1·00
1408	– 1000f. multicoloured	7·50	1·60
	DESIGNS: 30 to 1000f. Various footballing scenes.		

387 Pres. Gorbachev of U.S.S.R., Map of Malta and Pres. Bush of U.S.A.

1990. Anniversaries and Events. Multicoloured.
1409	120f. Type **387** (summit conference, Malta) (postage)	85	20
1410	130f. Sir Rowland Hill and Penny Black (150th anniv of first postage stamps)	85	20
1411	160f. Galileo space probe and planet Jupiter	1·10	25
1412	200f. Pres. Gorbachev meeting Pope John Paul II, statue of Saturn and dove	1·50	35
1413	240f. Neil Armstrong and eagle (21st anniv of first manned landing on Moon)	1·90	45
1414	250f. Concorde, German experimental Maglev train and Rotary International emblem	3·75	50
1415	300f. Don Mattingly (baseball player) and New York Yankees club badge (air)	2·25	60
1416	500f. Charles de Gaulle (French statesman, birth centenary)	3·75	85

388 AIDS Information on Radio, Television and Leaflets

1991. Anti-AIDS Campaign. Multicoloured.
1418	5f. Type **388**	15	10
1419	70f. Type **388**	55	35
1420	120f. Lecture on AIDS (vert)	85	50

389 Demonstrators

1991. Protection of Animals. Multicoloured.
1421	15f. Type **389**	15	10
1422	60f. Type **389**	50	25
1423	100f. Decrease in elephant population, 1945–2045 (vert)	75	35

390 Butter Catfish

1991. Fishes. Multicoloured.
1424	50f. Type **390**	50	35
1425	160f. Type **390**	2·10	1·00
1426	240f. Distichodus	3·50	1·90

391 President Kolingba

1992. 10th Anniv (1991) of Assumption of Power by Military Committee under Andre Kolingba.
1427	**391** 160f. multicoloured	1·25	50

392 Count Ferdinand von Zeppelin (airship pioneer)

1992. Celebrities, Anniversaries and Events. Multicoloured.
1428	80f. Type **392** (75th death anniv) (postage)	40	10
1429	140f. Henri Dunant (founder of Red Cross)	95	15
1430	160f. Michael Schumacher (racing driver)	1·10	25
1431	350f. Brandenburg Gate (bicent) and Konrad Adenauer (German Federal Republic Chancellor) signing 1949 constitution	2·50	75
1432	500f. Pope John Paul II (tour of West Africa) (air)	3·50	90
1433	600f. Wolfgang Amadeus Mozart (composer, death bicent (1991))	4·50	1·00

393 Dam　　**395** Breastfeeding

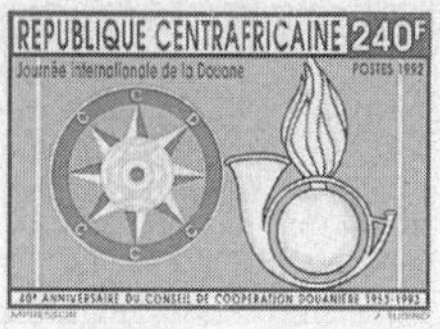

394 Compass Rose and Organization Emblem

1993. River M'Bali Dam. Multicoloured.

1435	160f. Type **393**	80	15
1436	200f. People fishing near dam (self-sufficiency in food)	1·00	25

1993. International Customs Day and 40th Anniv of Customs Co-operation Council.

1437 **394**	240f. multicoloured	1·10	25

1993. International Nutrition Conference, Rome (1992). Multicoloured.

1438	90f. Type **395**	40	10
1439	140f. Foodstuffs	70	15

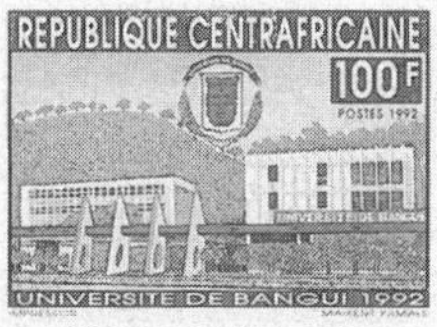

396 Bangui University

1993.

1440 **396**	100f. multicoloured	50	15

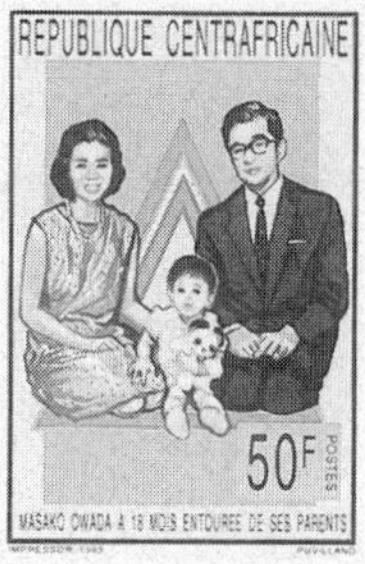

397 Masako Owada as Baby

1993. Wedding of Crown Prince Naruhito of Japan and Masako Owada. Multicoloured.

1441	50f. Type **397** (postage)	10	10
1442	65f. Prince Naruhito as child with parents	25	10
1443	160f. Masako Owada at Harvard University, U.S.A.	70	15
1444	450f. Prince Naruhito at Oxford University (air)	1·75	50

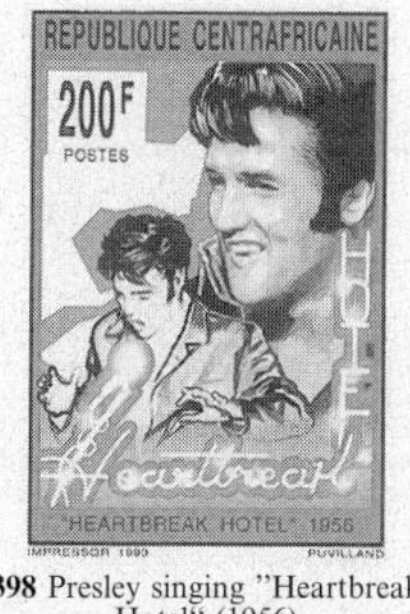

398 Presley singing "Heartbreak Hotel" (1956)

1993. 16th Death Anniv of Elvis Presley (entertainer). Multicoloured.

1446	200f. Type **398**	1·00	15
1447	300f. "Love Me Tender", 1957	1·50	25
1448	400f. "Jailhouse Rock", 1957	1·75	30
1449	600f. "Harum Scarum", 1965 (air)	2·50	50

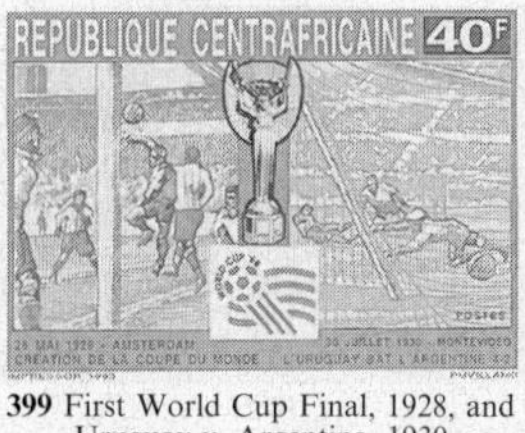

399 First World Cup Final, 1928, and Uruguay v. Argentina, 1930

1993. World Cup Football Championship, U.S.A. (1994). History of the World Cup. Multicoloured.

1451	40f. Type **399**	10	10
1452	50f. Italy v. Czechoslovakia, 1934, and Italy v. Hungary, 1938	10	10
1453	60f. Uruguay v. Brazil, 1950, and Germany v. Hungary, 1954	15	10
1454	80f. Brazil v. Sweden, 1958, and Brazil v. Czechoslovakia, 1962	20	10
1455	160f. England v. West Germany, 1966, and Brazil v. Italy, 1970	40	15
1456	200f. West Germany v. The Netherlands, 1974, and Argentina v. The Netherlands, 1978	55	20
1457	400f. Italy v. West Germany, 1982, and Argentina v. West Germany, 1986	1·00	35
1458	500f. West Germany v. Argentina, 1990, and 1994 Championship emblem and player	1·40	45

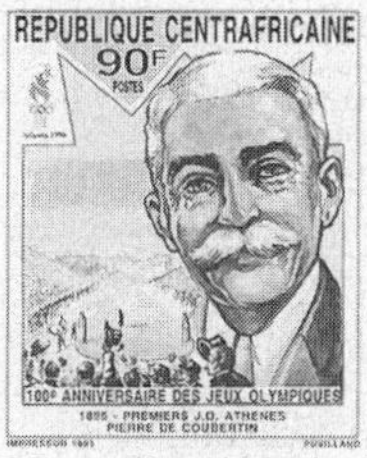

400 Baron Pierre de Coubertin (founder of modern games)

1993. Centenary (1996) of Modern Olympic Games. Multicoloured.

1460	90f. Ancient Greek athlete	25	10
1461	90f. Type **400**	25	10
1462	90f. Charles Bennett (running), Paris, 1900	25	10
1463	90f. Etienne Desmarteau (stone throwing), St. Louis, 1904	25	10
1464	90f. Harry Porter (high jump), London, 1908	25	10
1465	90f. Patrick MacDonald (putting the shot), Stockholm, 1912	25	10
1466	90f. Coloured and black Olympic rings (1916)	25	10
1467	90f. Frank Loomis (400 m hurdles), Antwerp, 1920	25	10
1468	90f. Albert White (diving), Paris, 1924	25	10
1469	100f. El Ouafi (marathon), Amsterdam, 1928	25	10
1470	100f. Eddie Tolan (100 m), Los Angeles, 1932	25	10
1471	100f. Jesse Owens (100 m, long jump and 200 m hurdles), Berlin, 1936	25	10
1472	100f. Coloured and black Olympic rings (1940)	25	10
1473	100f. Coloured and black Olympic rings (1944)	25	10
1474	100f. Tapio Rautavaara (throwing the javelin), London, 1948	25	10
1475	100f. Jean Boiteux (400 m freestyle swimming), Helsinki, 1952	25	10
1476	100f. Petrus Kasterman (three-day equestrian event), Melbourne, 1956	25	10
1477	100f. Sante Gaiardoni (cycling), Rome, 1960	25	10
1478	160f. Anton Geesink (judo), Tokyo, 1964	40	15
1479	160f. Bob Beamon (long jump), Mexico, 1968	40	15
1480	160f. Mark Spitz (swimming), Munich, 1972	40	15
1481	160f. Nadia Comaneci (gymnastics (beam)), Montreal, 1976	40	15
1482	160f. Aleksandre Ditjatin (gymnastics (rings) and dressage), Moscow, 1980	40	15
1483	160f. J. F. Lamour (sabre), Los Angeles, 1984	40	15
1484	160f. Pierre Durand (show jumping), Seoul, 1988	40	15
1485	160f. Michael Jordan (basketball), Barcelona, 1992	40	15
1486	160f. Footballer and Games emblem, Atlanta, 1996	40	15

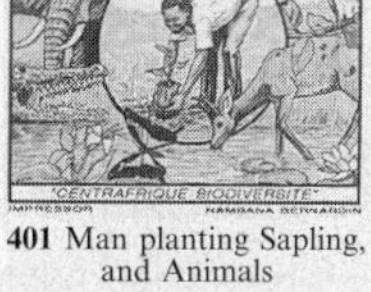

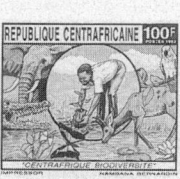

401 Man planting Sapling, and Animals

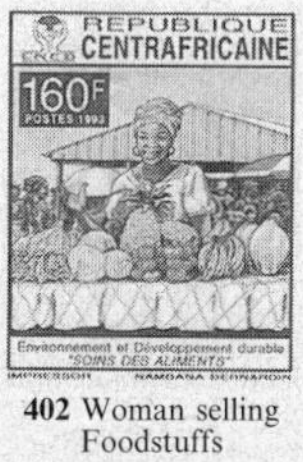

402 Woman selling Foodstuffs

1993. Biodiversity. Multicoloured.

1487	100f. Type **401**	25	10
1488	130f. Man amongst flora and fauna (vert)	35	15

1993. The Environment and Sustainable Development. Multicoloured.

1489	160f. Type **402**	40	15
1490	240f. Woman tending cooking pot	60	20

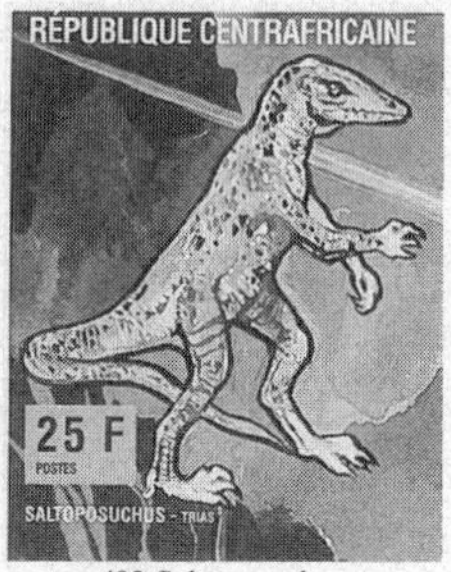

403 Saltoposuchus

1993. Prehistoric Animals. Multicoloured.

1491	25f. Type **403**	10	10
1492	25f. Rhamphorhynchus	10	10
1493	25f. Dimorphodon	10	10
1494	25f. Archaeopteryx	10	10
1495	30f. "Compsognathos longipes"	10	10
1496	30f. "Cryptocleidus oxoniensis"	10	10
1497	30f. Stegosaurus	10	10
1498	30f. Cetiosaurus	10	10
1499	50f. Brontosaurus	10	10
1500	50f. "Corythosaurus casuarius"	10	10
1501	50f. Styracosaurus	10	10
1502	50f. Gorgosaurus	10	10
1503	500f. Scolosaurus	1·40	45
1504	500f. Trachodon	1·40	45
1505	500f. Struthiomimus	1·40	45
1506	500f. "Tarbosaurus bataar"	1·40	45

Nos. 1491/1506 were issued together, se-tenant, forming a composite design of a volcanic landscape.

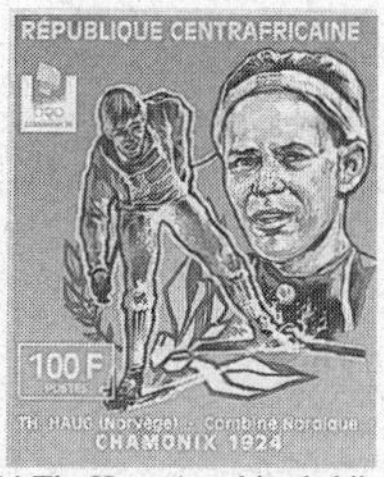

404 Th. Haug (combined skiing, Chamonix, 1924)

1994. Winter Olympic Games, Lillehammer, Norway. Previous Medal Winners. Multicoloured.

1508	100f. Type **404**	25	10
1509	100f. J. Heaton (luge, St. Moritz, 1928)	25	10
1510	100f. B. Ruud (ski jumping, Lake Placid, 1932)	25	10
1511	100f. I. Ballangrud (speed skating, Garmisch-Partenkirchen, 1936)	25	10
1512	100f. G. Fraser (slalom, St. Moritz, 1948)	25	10
1513	100f. West German 4-man bobsleigh team (Oslo, 1952)	25	10
1514	100f. U.S.S.R. ice hockey team (Cortina d'Ampezzo, 1956)	25	10
1515	100f. J. Vuarnet (downhill skiing, Squaw Valley, 1960)	25	10
1516	200f. M. Goitschel (giant slalom, Innsbruck, 1964)	50	15
1517	200f. Jean-Claud Killy (special slalom, Grenoble, 1968)	50	15
1518	200f. U. Wehling (cross-country skiing, Sapporo, 1972)	50	15
1519	200f. Irina Rodnina and Aleksandr Zaitsev (figure skating, Innsbruck, 1976)	50	15
1520	200f. E. Heiden (speed skating, Lake Placid, 1980)	50	15
1521	200f. Katarina Witt (figure skating, Sarajevo, 1984)	50	15
1522	200f. J. Mueller (single luge, Calgary, 1988)	50	15
1523	200f. E. Grospiron (acrobatic skiing, Albertville, 1992)	50	15
1524	200f. Speed skiing, Lillehammer, 1994	50	15

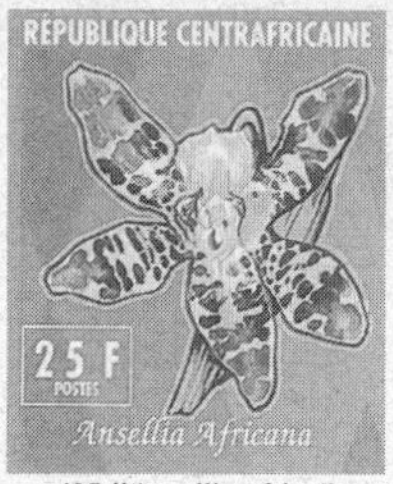

405 "Ansellia africa"

1994. Flowers, Vegetables, Fruit and Fungi. Multicoloured.

1525	25f. Type **405**	10	10
1526	30f. Yams	10	10
1527	40f. Oranges	10	10
1528	50f. Termite mushroom	10	10
1529	60f. "Polystachia bella" (flower)	15	10
1530	65f. Manioc	15	10
1531	70f. Banana	15	10
1532	80f. "Synpodia arborescens" (wrongly inscr "Sympodia") (fungi)	20	10
1533	90f. "Aerangis rhodosticta" (flower)	20	10
1534	100f. Maize	25	10
1535	160f. Mango	40	15
1536	200f. "Phlebopus sudanicus" (fungi)	50	15
1537	300f. Coffee beans	75	25
1538	400f. Sweet potato	95	30
1539	500f. "Angraecum eburneum" (flower)	1·25	40
1540	600f. "Leucocoprinus africanus" (fungi)	1·50	50

Nos. 1525/40 were issued together, se-tenant, the backgrounds forming a composite design.

MILITARY FRANK STAMPS

1963. Optd **FM**. No. M1 also has the value obliterated with two bars. Centre multicoloured; frame colour given.

M35 **1**	(–) on 15f. blue	4·50	
M36	15f. blue	3·00	

OFFICIAL STAMPS

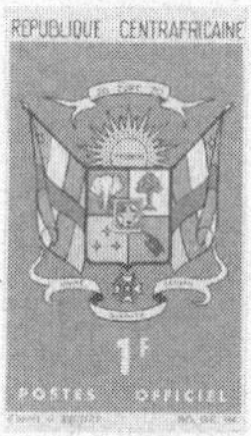

O 41 Arms

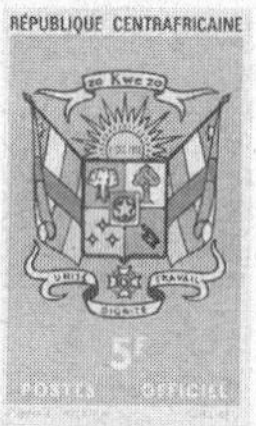

O 109 Arms

1965.

O78 **O 41**	1f. multicoloured	15	10
O79	2f. multicoloured	10	10
O80	5f. multicoloured	10	10
O81	10f. multicoloured	25	10
O82	20f. multicoloured	35	30
O83	30f. multicoloured	70	50
O84	50f. multicoloured	80	70
O85	100f. multicoloured	2·10	1·00
O86	130f. multicoloured	3·00	1·90
O87	200f. multicoloured	4·75	2·25

1971.

O238 **O 109**	5f. multicoloured	10	10
O239	30f. multicoloured	30	20
O240	40f. multicoloured	50	25
O241	100f. multicoloured	1·25	55
O242	140f. multicoloured	2·25	75
O243	200f. multicoloured	2·75	1·25

POSTAGE DUE STAMPS

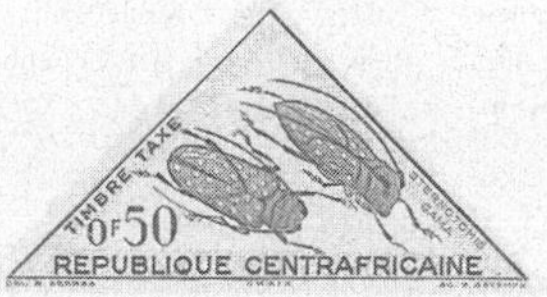

D 15 "Sternotomis gama" (Beetle)

1962. Beetles.

D33	50c. brown and turquoise	10	10
D34	50c. turquoise and brown	10	10
D35	1f. brown and green	10	10
D36	1f. green and brown	10	10
D37	2f. pink and black	10	10
D38	2f. green, black and pink	10	10
D39	5f. green and brown	25	25
D40	5f. green and brown	25	25
D41	10f. green, black and drab	50	50
D42	10f. drab, black and green	50	50
D43	25f. brown, black and green	1·40	1·40
D44	25f. brown, green and black	1·40	1·40

DESIGNS: No. D33, Type D **15**; D34, "Sternotomis virescens"; D35, "Augosoma centaurus"; D36, "Phosphorus virescens" and "Ceroplesis carabarica"; D37, "Ceroplesis S.P."; D38, "Cetoine scaraboidae"; D39, "Cetoine scaraboidae"; D40, "Macrorhina S.P."; D41, "Taurina longiceps"; D42, "Phryneta

leprosa"; D43, "Monohamus griseoplagiatus"; D44, "Jambonus trifasciatus".

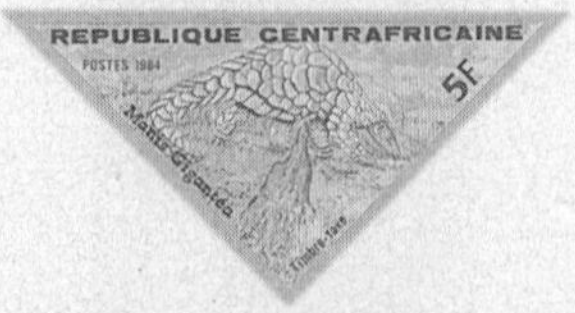

D 308 Giant Pangolin ("Manis gigantea")

1985.

D1080	D 308	5f. multicoloured . .	10	10
D1081		20f. multicoloured	20	20
D1082		30f. multicoloured	25	25

APPENDIX

The following stamps have either been issued in excess of postal needs or have not been availble to the public in reasonable quantities at face value. Such stamps may later be given full listing if there is evidence of regular postal use.

All the stamps listed below are embossed on gold foil.

1977.

Coronation of Emperor Bokassa. Air 2500f.

1978.

100 Years of Progress in Posts and Telecommunications. Air 1500f.

Death Centenary of Sir Rowland Hill. Air 1500f.

1979.

International Year of the Child. Air 1500f.

Olympic Games, Moscow. Air 1500f. ("The Discus-thrower")

Space Exploration. Air 1500f.

1980.

Olympic Games, Moscow. Air 1500f. (Relay)

European-African Co-operation. Air 1500f.

World Cup Football Championship, Spain. Air 1500f.

1981.

Olympic Games Medal Winners. 1980 Olympic Games issue optd. Air 1500f.

Birth Centenary of Pablo Picasso. Air 1500f.

Wedding of Prince of Wales. Air 1500f.

Navigators. Air 1500f.

Christmas. Air 1500f.

1982.

Animals and Rotary International. Air 1500f.

Transport. Air 1500f.

21st Birthday of Princess of Wales. Air 1500f.

Olympic Games, Los Angeles.Air 1500f. (horiz)

Space Resources. Air 1500f.

1983.

Chess Masters. Air 1500f.

World Cup Football Championship, Spain. Air 1500f.

Car Manufacturers. Air 1500f.

Olympic Games, Los Angeles. Air 1500f. (vert)

Bicentenary of manned flight. Air 1500f.

1984.

Winter Olympic Gold Medalists. Air 1500f.

Celebrities. Air 1500f.

1985.

85th Birthday of Queen Elizabeth the Queen Mother. Air 1500f.

Appearence of Halley's Comet. Air 1500f.

480th Death Anniv of Christopher Columbus. Air 1500f.

1988.

Olympic Games, Seoul. Air 1500f.

Scouts and Birds. Air 1500f.

1989.

Olympic Games, Seoul, Gold Medal Winner. Air 1500f.

Bicentenary of French Revolution. Air 1500f.

World Cup Football Championship, Italy. Air 1500f.

1990.

Winter Olympic Games, Albertville (1992). Air 1500f.

Scouts and Butterflies. Air 1500f.

Birth Centenary of Charles de Gaulle. Air 1500f.

1993.

Wedding of Crown Prince Naruhito of Japan and Masako Owada. Air 1500f.

16th Death Anniv of Elvis Presley. Air 1500f.

World Cup Football Championship, U.S.A. (1994). Air 1500f.

Visit of Pope John Paul II to Africa. Air 1500f.

1994.

Winter Olympic Games, Lillehammer. Air 1500f.

CENTRAL LITHUANIA Pt. 10

Became temporarily independent in 1918 and was subsequently absorbed by Poland.

100 fenigi = 1 mark.

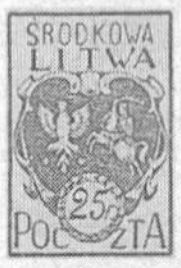

1

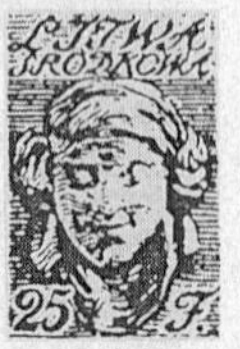

3 Girl

1920. Imperf or perf.

1	1	25f. red	10	10
20		25f. green	20	30
2		1m. blue	10	10
21		1m. brown	20	30
3		2m. violet	15	15
22		2m. yellow	20	30

1920. Stamps of Lithuania of 1919 surch **SRODKOWA LITWA POCZTA**, new value and Arms of Poland and Lithuania. Perf.

4	5	2m. on 15s. violet	6·50	8·00
5		4m. on 10s. red	4·00	5·00
6		4m. on 20s. blue	6·00	8·00
7		4m. on 30s. orange	5·00	6·00
8	6	6m. on 50s. green	6·00	7·00
9		6m. on 60s. red and violet	6·00	7·00
10		6m. on 75s. red & yellow	6·00	8·00
11	7	10m. on 1a. red & grey	12·00	14·00
12		10m. on 3a. red & brown	£450	£550
13		10m. on 5a. red and green	£450	£550

1920. Imperf or perf. Inscr "LITWA SRODKOWA".

14	3	25f. grey	15	15
15	–	1m. orange	20	15
16	–	2m. red	40	50
17	–	4m. olive and yellow	60	75
18	–	6m. grey and red	1·00	1·25
19	–	10m. yellow and brown	1·50	2·00

DESIGNS: 1m. Warrior; 2m. Ostrabrama Gate, Vilnius; 4m. St. Stanislaus Cathedral and Tower, Vilnius; 6m. Rector's insignia; 10m. Gen. Zeligowski.

1921. Fund for Polish Participation in Plebiscite for Upper Silesia. Surch **NA SLASK** and new value. Imperf or perf.

23	1	25f.+2m. red	50	60
24		25f.+2m. green	50	60
25		1m.+2m. blue	60	80
26		1m.+2m. brown	60	80
27		2m.+2m. violet	70	1·10
28		2m.+2m. yellow	70	1·10

1921. Red Cross Fund. Nos. 16/17 surch with cross and value. Imperf or perf.

29	2m.+1m. red	50	65
30	4m.+1m. green and yellow	50	65

1921. White Cross Fund. As Nos. 16, 17 and 19, but with cross and value in white added. Imperf or perf.

31	2m.+1m. purple	30	30
32	4m.+1m. green and buff	30	30
33	10m.+2m. yellow and brown	30	30

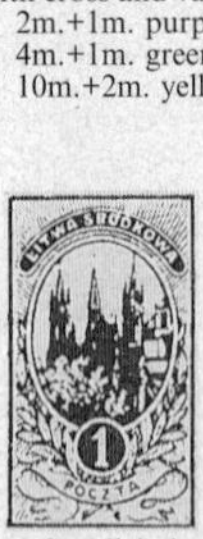

13 St. Nicholas Cathedral

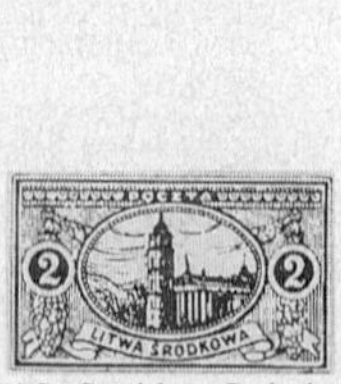

14 St. Stanislaus Cathedral

1921. Imperf or perf.

34	13	1m. yellow and slate	30	40
35	14	2m. green and red	30	40
36	–	3m. green	40	50
37	–	4m. brown	40	60
38	–	5m. brown	40	60
39	–	6m. buff and green	40	60
40	–	10m. buff and purple	60	80
41	–	20m. buff and brown	60	90

DESIGNS—HORIZ: 4m. Queen Jadwiga and King Wladislaw Jagiello; 6m. Poczobut Observatory, Vilnius University; 10m. Union of Lithuania and Poland, 1569; 20m. Kosciuszko and Mickiewicz. VERT: 3m. Arms (Eagle); 5m. Arms (Shield).

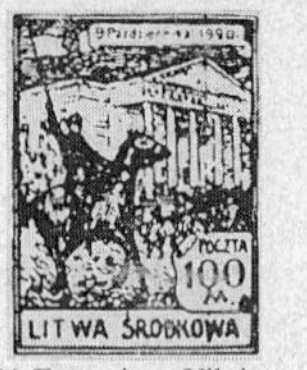

21 Entry into Vilnius

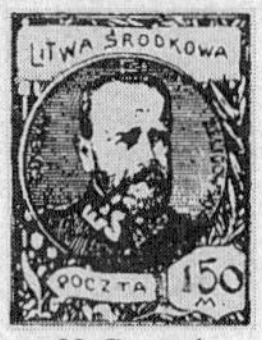

22 General Zeligowski

1921. 1st Anniv of Entry of Gen. Zeligowski into Vilnius. Imperf or perf.

42	21	100m. blue and bistre	1·75	1·75
43	22	150m. green and brown	2·25	2·25

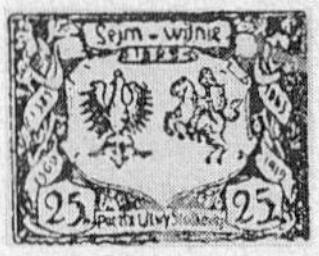

24 Arms

1922. Opening of National Parliament. Inscr "SEJM—WILNIE". Imperf or perf.

44	–	10m. brown	1·50	1·75
45	24	25m. red and buff	1·75	1·90
46	–	50m. blue	2·75	3·00
47	–	75m. lilac	4·00	4·50

DESIGNS—HORIZ: 50m. National Assembly, Vilnius. VERT: 10m. Agriculture; 75m. Industry.

POSTAGE DUE STAMPS

D 9 Government Offices

1921. Inscr "DOPLATA". Imperf or perf.

D23	D 9	50f. red	50	60
D24	–	1m. green	50	60
D25	–	2m. purple	50	60
D26	–	3m. purple	75	90
D27	–	5m. purple	75	90
D28	–	20m. red	1·00	1·25

DESIGNS—HORIZ: 2m. Castle on Troki Island. VERT: 1m. Castle Hill, Vilnius; 3m. Ostrabrama Gate, Vilnius; 5m. St. Stanislaus Cathedral; 20m. (larger) St. Nicholas Cathedral.

CEYLON Pt. 1

An island to the south of India formerly under British administration, then a self-governing Dominion. The island became a Republic within the Commonwealth on 22 May 1972 and was renamed Sri Lanka (q.v.).

1857. 12 pence = 1 shilling;
20 shillings = 1 pound.
1872. 100 cents = 1 rupee.

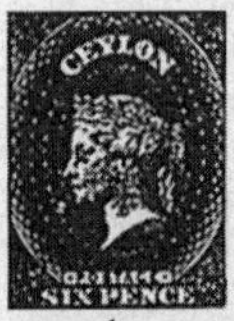

1

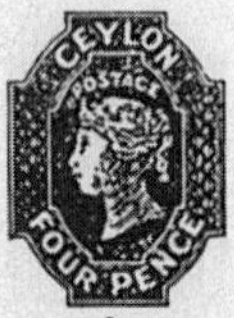

2

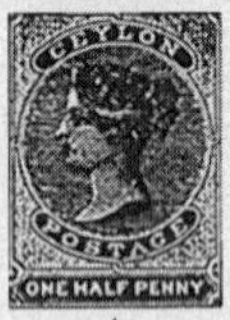

4

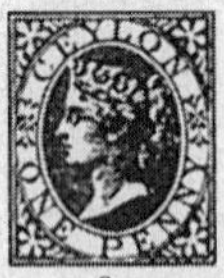

8

1857. Imperf.

17	4	½d. lilac	£170	£180
2	1	1d. blue	£650	26·00
3		2d. green	£150	55·00
4	2	4d. red	£50000	£4500
5	1	5d. brown	£1500	£150
6		6d. brown	£1800	£140
7	2	8d. brown	£22000	£1500
8		9d. brown	£32000	£900
9	1	10d. orange	£800	£300
10		1s. violet	£4500	£200
11	2	1s.9d. green	£700	£800
12		2s. blue	£5500	£1200

The prices of these imperf stamps vary greatly according to condition. The above prices are for fine copies with four margins. Poor to medium specimens are worth much less.

1861. Perf.

48c	4	½d. lilac	25·00	26·00
49	1	1d. blue	95·00	4·00
50		2d. green	60·00	9·00
64b		2d. yellow	45·00	7·00
65b	2	4d. red	48·00	13·00
22	1	5d. brown	80·00	8·00
66c		5d. green	28·00	42·00
67b		6d. brown	28·00	32·00
56	2	8d. brown	80·00	40·00
69b		9d. brown	40·00	6·00
70b	1	10d. orange	42·00	11·00
71b		1s. violet	80·00	5·50
72b	2	2s. blue	£100	12·00

1866. The 3d. has portrait in circle.

61	8	1d. blue	18·00	7·50
62	–	3d. red	60·00	35·00

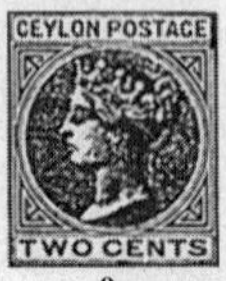

9

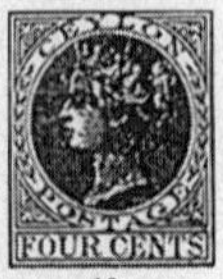

10

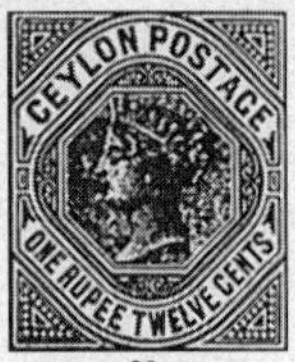

30

1872. Various frames.

256	9	2c. brown	2·25	30
147		2c. green	2·50	15
122	10	4c. grey	30·00	1·50
148		4c. purple	3·00	30
149		4c. red	3·75	11·00
258		4c. yellow	3·00	2·75
150a	–	8c. yellow	3·50	7·00
126	–	16c. violet	75·00	2·75
127	–	24c. green	48·00	2·00
128	–	32c. grey	£140	15·00
129	–	36c. blue	£130	17·00
130	–	48c. red	65·00	5·00
131	–	64c. brown	£250	60·00
132	–	90c. grey	£180	26·00
201	30	1r.12 red	22·00	20·00
138		2r.50 red	£450	£300
249		2r.50 purple on red	28·00	48·00

1882. Nos. 127 and 131 surch in words and figures.

142	16c. on 24c. green	22·00	6·50
143	20c. on 64c. brown	9·00	5·00

1885. As Nos. 148/132 surch **Postage & Revenue** and value in words.

178	5c. on 4c. red	18·00	3·50
179	5c. on 8c. yellow	55·00	6·50
180	5c. on 16c. violet	85·00	10·00
154	5c. on 24c. green	£2250	£100
182	5c. on 24c. purple	–	£500
155	5c. on 32c. grey	55·00	15·00
156	5c. on 36c. blue	£225	8·00
157	5c. on 48c. red	£950	50·00
158	5c. on 64c. brown	85·00	4·50
159	5c. on 96c. grey	£400	60·00

1885. As Nos. 126/249 surch with new value in words.

184	10c. on 16c. violet	£4500	£950
162	10c. on 24c. green	£400	£100
185	10c. on 24c. purple	12·00	5·50
163	10c. on 36c. blue	£375	£160
174	10c. on 64c. brown	55·00	90·00
186	15c. on 16c. violet	9·50	6·50
165	20c. on 24c. green	50·00	18·00
166a	20c. on 32c. grey	55·00	42·00
167	25c. on 32c. grey	13·00	4·50
168	28c. on 48c. red	35·00	6·00
169x	30c. on 36c. blue	10·00	8·50
170	56c. on 96c. grey	22·00	18·00
176	1r.12 on 2r.50 red	85·00	42·00

1885. Surch **REVENUE AND POSTAGE 5 CENTS**.

187	5c. on 8c. lilac (as No. 150a)	14·00	1·40

1885. As Nos. 126/32 surch in words and figures.

188	10c. on 24c. purple	8·50	6·50
189	15c. on 16c. yellow	50·00	8·50
190	28c. on 32c. grey	20·00	2·50
191	30c. on 36c. olive	28·00	14·00
192	56c. on 96c. grey	45·00	13·00

1885. Surch **1 R. 12 C.**

193	30	1r.12 on 2r.50 red	38·00	80·00

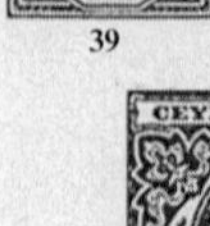

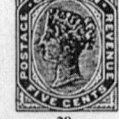

39

28

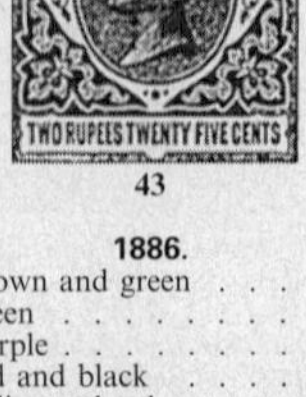

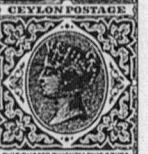

43

1886.

245	39	3c. brown and green	3·25	45
257		3c. green	2·25	55
195	28	5c. purple	2·25	10
259	39	6c. red and black	1·25	45
260		12c. olive and red	4·00	7·00

196		15c. olive	4·50	1·25
261		15c. blue	5·50	1·25
198		25c. brown	3·50	1·00
199		28c. grey	16·00	1·40
247		30c. mauve and brown	4·25	2·00
262		75c. black and brown	4·75	6·00
263	43	1r.50 red	19·00	35·00
264		2r.25 blue	30·00	35·00

1887. Nos. 148/9 surch. A. Surch **TWO CENTS**.
202	10	2c. on 4c. purple		1·40	80
203		2c. on 4c. red		2·25	30

B. Surch **TWO**.
204	10	2c. on 4c. purple		75	30
205		2c. on 4c. red		4·50	20

C. Surch **2 Cents** and bar.
206	10	2c. on 4c. purple		55·00	28·00
207		2c. on 4c. red		2·25	75

D. Surch **Two Cents** and bar.
208	10	2c. on 4c. purple		42·00	16·00
209		2c. on 4c. red		2·50	1·10

E. Surch **2 Cents** without bar.
210	10	2c. on 4c. purple		42·00	24·00
211		2c. on 4c. red		9·50	1·00

1890. Surch **POSTAGE Five Cents REVENUE**.
233	39	5c. on 15c. olive	2·00	1·90

1891. Surch **FIFTEEN CENTS**.
239	39	15c. on 25c. brown	9·00	10·00
240		15c. on 28c. grey	14·00	8·50

1892. Surch **3 Cents** and bar.
241	10	3c. on 4c. purple	1·00	3·25
242		3c. on 4c. red	3·00	6·00
243	39	3c. on 28c. grey	3·50	3·00

1898. Surch **Six Cents**.
250	39	6c. on 15c. green	70	75

1898. Surch with new value.
254	30	1r.50 on 2r.50 grey	20·00	42·00
255		2r.25 on 2r.50 yellow	35·00	75·00

44   45

1903. Various frames.
277	44	2c. brown	1·25	10
278	45	3c. green (A)	1·25	15
293		3c. green (B)	1·00	75
279		4c. orange and blue	1·50	1·50
268	–	5c. purple	1·50	60
289	–	5c. purple	2·00	10
281	–	6c. red	1·10	15
291	–	6c. red	1·00	10
294	45	10c. olive and red	2·00	2·00
282		12c. olive and red	1·50	1·75
283		15c. blue	1·50	60
284		25c. brown	6·00	3·75
295		25c. grey	2·50	1·50
285		30c. violet and green	2·50	2·75
296		50c. brown	4·00	7·50
286		75c. blue and orange	5·25	8·00
297		1r. purple on yellow	7·50	10·00
287		1r.50 grey	24·00	10·00
298		2r. red on yellow	15·00	27·00
288		2r.25 brown and green	20·00	29·00
299		5r. black on green	38·00	65·00
300		10r. black on red	75·00	£170

(A) has value in shaded tablet; (B) in white tablet as in Type **45**.
Nos. 268 and 281 have the value in words; Nos. 289 and 291 in figures.

52   57

1912.
301	52	1c. brown	1·00	10
307a		2c. orange	30	20
339		3c. green	2·75	75
340		3c. grey	75	20
341		5c. purple	50	15
342		6c. red	2·00	75
343		6c. violet	90	15
345		9c. red on yellow	80	30
346		10c. olive	1·40	40
347a		12c. red	1·00	2·25
311a		15c. blue	1·75	1·25
349a		15c. green on yellow	1·50	1·00
350b		20c. blue	3·50	45
351		25c. yellow and blue	1·40	1·90
352a		30c. green and violet	2·50	1·25
353		50c. black and red	1·40	80
315		1r. purple on yellow	2·50	3·50
355		2r. black and red on yellow	7·00	7·50
317		5r. black on green	17·00	28·00

318		10r. purple & blk on red	60·00	80·00
319		20r. black and red on blue	£100	£110

Large type, As Bermuda T **15**.
358		50r. purple	£350	
359		100r. black	£1400	
360		100r. purple and blue	£1300	

1918. Optd **WAR STAMP**, No. 335 surch **ONE CENT** and bar also.
335	52	1c. on 5c. purple	50	40
330		1c. orange	20	40
332		3c. green	20	50
333		5c. purple	50	30

1918. Surch **ONE CENT** and bar.
337	52	1c. on 5c. purple	15	25

1926. Surch with new value and bar.
361	52	1c. on 3c. grey	80	1·00
362		5c. on 3c. violet	50	40

1927.
363	57	1r. purple	2·50	1·25
364		2r. green and red	3·75	2·75
365		5r. green and purple	13·00	19·00
366		10r. green and orange	30·00	80·00
367		20r. purple and blue	90·00	£180

60 Adam's Peak

1935. King George V.
368	–	2c. black and red	30	40
369	60	3c. black and green	35	40
370	–	6c. black and blue	30	30
371	–	9c. green and orange	1·00	65
372	–	10c. black and purple	1·25	2·25
373	–	15c. brown and green	1·00	50
374	–	20c. black and blue	1·75	2·50
375	–	25c. blue and brown	1·40	1·25
376	–	30c. red and green	2·00	2·75
377	–	50c. black and violet	8·50	1·75
378	–	1r. violet and brown	17·00	16·00

DESIGNS—VERT: 2c. Tapping rubber; 6c. Colombo Harbour; 9c. Plucking tea; 20c. Coconut palms. HORIZ: 10c. Hill paddy (rice); 15c. River scene; 25c. Temple of the Tooth, Kandy; 30c. Ancient irrigation tank; 50c. Indian elephants; 1r. Trincomalee.

1935. Silver Jubilee. As T **13** of Antigua.
379		6c. blue and grey	65	30
380		9c. green and blue	70	1·25
381		20c. brown and blue	4·25	2·75
382		50c. grey and purple	5·25	9·00

1937. Coronation. As T **2** of Aden.
383		6c. red	65	15
384		9c. green	2·50	3·25
385		20c. blue	3·50	3·00

70 Sigiriya (Lion Rock)

1938. As 1935 issue but with portrait of King George VI, and "POSTAGE & REVENUE" omitted.
386b	–	2c. black and green	2·00	10
387d	60	3c. black and green	80	10
387f	–	5c. green and orange	30	10
388	–	6c. black and blue	30	10
389	70	10c. black and blue	2·25	10
390	–	15c. green and brown	2·00	10
391	–	20c. black and blue	3·25	10
392a	–	25c. blue and brown	4·25	10
393	–	30c. red and green	11·00	1·75
394e	–	50c. black and violet	3·75	20
395	–	1r. blue and brown	16·00	1·75
396	–	2r. black and red	13·00	2·50
396b	–	2r. black and green	1·00	1·60

DESIGNS—VERT: 5c. Coconut palms; 20c. Plucking tea; 2r. Ancient guard-stone, Anuradhapura. Others, same as for corresponding values of 1935 issue.

1938. As T **57**, but head of King George VI to right.
397a		5r. green and purple	14·00	2·75

1940. Surch with new value and bars.
398	–	3c. on 6c. blk & bl (No. 388)	10	10
399	–	3c. on 20c. blk & bl (No. 391)	2·00	1·50

1946. Victory. As T **9** of Aden.
400		6c. blue	10	10
401		15c. brown	10	40

75 Parliament Building

1947. New Constitution.
402	75	6c. black and blue	10	15
403	–	10c. black, orange and red	15	20
404	–	15c. green and purple	15	80
405	–	25c. yellow and green	15	20

DESIGNS—VERT: 10c. Adam's Peak; 25c. Anuradhapura. HORIZ: 15c. Temple of the Tooth.

79 Lion Flag of Dominion   80 D. S. Senanayake

1949. 1st Anniv of Independence.
406	79	4c. red, yellow and brown	15	20
407	80	5c. brown and green	10	10
408	79	15c. red, yellow and orange	30	15
409	80	25c. brown and blue	15	65

No. 408 is larger, 28 × 22 mm.

82 Globe and Forms of Transport

1949. 75th Anniv of U.P.U. Inscr as in T **82**. Designs showing globe.
410	82	5c. brown and green	75	10
411	–	15c. black and red (horiz)	1·10	1·75
412	–	25c. black and blue (vert)	1·10	1·10

85 Kandyan Dancer   88 Sigiriya (Lion Rock)

90 Ruins at Madirigiriya

1950.
413	85	4c. purple and red	10	10
414	–	5c. green	10	10
415	–	15c. green and violet	1·50	30
416	88	30c. red and yellow	30	40
417	–	75c. blue and orange	3·50	10
418	90	1r. blue and brown	1·75	30

DESIGNS—VERT (As Types **85** and **88**): 5c. Kiri Vehera, Polonnaruwa; 15c. Vesak orchid. (As Type **90**): 75c. Octagon Library, Temple of the Tooth.

94 Coconut Trees   99 Tea Plantation

1951.
419	–	2c. brown and turquoise	10	75
420	–	3c. black and violet	10	75
421	–	6c. sepia and green	10	30
422	94	10c. green and grey	75	65
423	–	25c. orange and blue	10	30
424	–	35c. red and green	1·50	1·50
425	–	40c. brown	4·50	90
426	–	50c. slate	30	10
427	99	85c. black and turquoise	60	20
428	–	2r. blue and brown	6·50	1·00
429	–	5r. brown and orange	4·75	1·25
430	–	10r. brown and buff	35·00	9·00

DESIGNS—VERT (As Type **94**): 2c. Sambars, Ruhuna National Park; 3c. Ancient guardstone, Anuradhapura; 6c. Harvesting rice; 25c. Sigiriya fresco; 35c. Star orchid. (As Type **99**): 5r. Bas-relief, Anuradhapura; 10r. Harvesting rice. HORIZ (As Type **94**): 40c. Rubber plantation; 50c. Outrigger canoe. (As Type **99**): 2r. River Gal Dam.

103 Ceylon, Mace and Symbols of Progress   104 Queen Elizabeth II

1952. Colombo Plan Exhibition.
431	103	5c. green	10	10
432		15c. blue	30	60

1953. Coronation.
433	104	5c. green	1·00	

105 Ceremonial Procession   106 King Coconuts

1954. Royal Visit.
434	105	10c. blue	30	10

1954.
435	106	10c. orange, brown and buff	10	10

107 Farm Produce

1955. Royal Agricultural and Food Exhibition.
436	107	10c. brown and orange	10	10

108 Sir John Kotelawala and House of Representatives

1956. Prime Minister's 25 Years of Public Service.
437	108	10c. green	10	10

109 Arrival of Vijaya in Ceylon   110 Lampstand and Dharmachakra

1956. Buddha Jayanti. Inscr "2500".
438	109	3c. blue and grey	15	15
439	110	4c.+2c. yellow and blue	20	75
440	–	10c.+5c. red, yell & grey	20	75
441	–	15c. brown	25	10

DESIGNS—VERT: 10c. Hand of Peace and Dharmachakra. HORIZ: 15c. Dharmachakra encircling the globe.

113 Mail Transport   114 Stamp of 1857

1957. Stamp Centenary.
442	113	4c. red and turquoise	75	40
443	–	15c. red and blue	75	10
444	114	35c. brown, yellow and blue	30	50
445	–	85c. brown, yellow & grn	80	1·60

1958. Nos. 439/40 with premium obliterated with bars.
446	110	4c. yellow and blue	10	10
447	–	10c. red, yellow and grey	10	10

117 Kandyan Dancer   118 "Human Rights"

1958. As Nos. 413 and 419 etc, and 435, but with inscriptions changed as in T **117**.
448		2c. brown and turquoise	10	50
449		3c. black and violet	10	70
450		4c. purple and red	10	10
451		5c. green	10	1·40

452	6c. sepia and green	. . . .	10	65
453	10c. orange, brown and buff	.	10	10
454	15c. green and violet	. . . .	3·50	80
455	25c. orange and blue	. . . .	10	10
456	30c. red and yellow	. . . .	15	1·40
457	35c. red and green	. . . .	6·50	30
459	50c. slate	. . . .	30	10
460a	75c. blue and orange	. . . .	9·00	2·25
461	85c. black and turquoise	. .	3·75	4·50
462	1r. blue and brown	. . . .	60	10
463	2r. blue and brown	. . . .	1·00	30
464	5r. brown and orange	. . .	4·00	30
465	10r. brown and buff	. . . .	9·50	1·00

1958. 10th Anniv of Declaration of Human Rights.

466	**118**	10c. red, brown and purple	. . . .	10	10
467		85c. red, turq & grn	. .	30	55

119 Portraits of Founders and University Buildings

1959. Institution of Pirivena Universities.

468	**119**	10c. orange and blue	. . .	10	10

120 "Uprooted Tree"   **121** S.W.R.D. Bandaranaike

1960. World Refugee Year.

469	**120**	4c. brown and gold	. . .	10	60
470		25c. violet and gold	. . .	10	15

1961. Prime Minister Bandaranaike Commemoration.

471	**121**	10c. blue and turquoise	. . .	10	10

See also Nos. 479 and 481.

122 Ceylon Scout Badge   **123** Campaign Emblem

1962. Golden Jubilee of Ceylon Boy Scouts Association

472	**122**	35.c buff and blue	. . . .	15	10

1962. Malaria Eradication.

473	**123**	25c. red and drab	. . . .	10	10

124 De Havilland Leopard Moth and Hawker Siddeley Comet 4

1963. 25th Anniv of Airmail Services.

474	**124**	50c. black and blue	. . .	40	50

125 "Produce" and Campaign Emblem   (126)

1963. Freedom from Hunger.

475	**125**	5c. red and blue	. . . .	30	2·00
476		25c. brown and olive	. . .	1·50	30

1963. No. 450 surch with T **126**.

477		2c. on 4c. purple and red	. .	10	10

---

127 "Rural Life"   **131** Anagarika Dharmapala (Buddhist missionary)

129 Terrain, Indian Elephant and Tree

1963. Golden Jubilee of Ceylon Co-operative Movement (1962).

478	**127**	60c. red and black	. . . .	80	60

1963. Design as T **121**, but smaller (21 × 26 mm) and with inscription rearranged at top.

479		10c. blue	. . . .	10	10
481		10c. violet and grey	. . . .	10	10

No. 481 has a decorative pattern at foot instead of the inscription.

1963. National Conservation Week.

480	**129**	5c. sepia and blue	. . .	60	40

1964. Birth Centenary of A. Dharmapala (founder of Maha Bodhi Society)

482	**131**	25c. sepia and yellow	. . .	10	10

135 D. S. Senanayake   **143** Ceylon Jungle Fowl

138 Ruins at Madirigiriya

1964.

485	– 5c. multicoloured	. . .	2·00	1·50
486	**135** 10c. green	. . .	80	10
487	– 10c. green	. . .	10	10
488	– 15c. multicoloured	. . .	3·00	30
489	**138** 20c. purple and buff	. .	20	25
494	**143** 60c. multicoloured	. . .	4·00	1·25
495	– 75c. multicoloured	. . .	2·75	70
497	– 1r. brown and green	. . .	1·00	30
499	– 5r. multicoloured	. . .	5·00	4·00
500	– 10r. multicoloured	. . .	19·00	3·50

DESIGNS—HORIZ (As Type **143**): 5c. Southern grackle ("Grackle"); 15c. Common peafowl ("Peacock"); 75c. Asian black-headed oriole ("Oriole"). (As Type **138**): 5r. Girls transplanting rice. VERT (As Type **135**): 10c. (No. 487) Similar portrait, but large head and smaller inscriptions. (21 × 35 mm): 1r. Tea plantation. (23 × 36 mm): 10r. Map of Ceylon.

150 Exhibition Buildings and Cogwheels

1964. Industrial Exhibition.

501		– 5c. multicoloured	. . . .	10	75
502	**150**	5c. multicoloured	. . . .	10	75

No. 501 is inscribed "INDUSTRIAL EXHIBITION" in Sinhala and Tamil, No. 502 in Sinhala and English.

151 Trains of 1864 and 1964

1964. Centenary of Ceylon Railways.

503		– 60c. blue, purple and green	. . .	2·75	40
504	**151**	60c. blue, purple and green	. . .	2·75	40

No. 503 is inscribed "RAILWAY CENTENARY" in Sinhala and Tamil, No. 504 in Sinhala and English.

---

152 I.T.U. Emblem and Symbols

1965. Centenary of I.T.U.

505	**152**	2c. blue and red	. . . .	1·00	1·10
506		30c. brown and red	. . . .	3·00	45

153 I.C.Y. Emblem

1965. International Co-operation Year.

507	**153**	3c. blue and red	. . . .	1·25	1·00
508		50c. black, red and gold	. .	3·25	50

154 Town Hall, Colombo

1965. Centenary of Colombo Municipal Council.

509	**154**	25c. green and sepia	. . .	20	20

1965. No. 481 surch **5**.

510		5c. on 10c. violet and grey	. .	10	40

157 Kandy and Council Crest

1966. Centenary of Kandy Municipal Council.

512	**157**	25c. multicoloured	. . . .	20	20

158 W.H.O. Building   **159** Rice Paddy and Map of Ceylon

1966. Inauguration of W.H.O. Headquarters, Geneva.

513	**158**	4c. multicoloured	. . .	1·75	3·00
514		1r. multicoloured	. . . .	6·75	1·50

1966. International Rice Year. Multicoloured.

515	6c. Type **159**	. . . .	20	75
516	30c. Rice paddy and globe	. .	30	15

161 U.N.E.S.C.O. Emblem   **162** Water-resources Map

1966. 20th Anniv of U.N.E.S.C.O.

517	**161**	3c. multicoloured	. . . .	2·00	2·25
518		50c. multicoloured	. . . .	5·50	30

1966. International Hydrological Decade.

519	**162**	2c. brown, yellow and blue	. . .	30	85
520		2r. multicoloured	. . .	1·50	2·25

163 Devotees at Buddhist Temple

1967. Poya Holiday System. Multicoloured.

521	5c. Type **163**	. . . . . .	15	60
522	20c. Mihintale	. . . . . .	15	10

523	**35c.** Sacred Bo-tree, Anuradhapura	. . . . . .	15	15
524	60c. Adam's Peak	. . . . . .	15	10

167 Galle Fort and Clock Tower

1967. Centenary of Galle Municipal Council.

525	**167**	25c. multicoloured	. . . .	70	20

168 Field Research

1967. Centenary of Ceylon Tea Industry. Mult.

526	4c. Type **168**	. . . . . .	60	10
527	40c. Tea-tasting equipment	. .	1·75	1·50
528	50c. Leaves and bud	. . . .	1·75	20
529	1r. Shipping tea	. . . . . .	1·75	10

172 Elephant Ride

1967. International Tourist Year.

530	**172**	45c. multicoloured	. . . .	2·25	80

173 Ranger, Jubilee Emblem and Flag

1967. Golden Jubilee of Ceylon Girl Guides' Association.

532	**173**	3c. multicoloured	. . . .	50	20
533		25c. multicoloured	. . . .	75	20

174 Colonel Olcott and Buddhist Flag

1967. 60th Death Anniv of Colonel Olcott (theosophist).

534	**174**	15c. multicoloured	. . . .	30	20

175 Independence Hall   **177** Sir D. B. Jayatilleke

1968. 20th Anniv of Independence. Multicoloured.

535	5c. Type **175**	. . . . . .	10	55
536	1r. Lion flag and sceptre	. . .	50	10

1968. Birth Centenary of Sir Baron Jayatilleke (scholar and statesman).

537	**177**	25c. brown	. . . . . .	10	10

178 Institute of Hygiene

1968. 20th Anniv of World Health Organization.

538	**178**	50c. multicoloured	. . . .	10	10

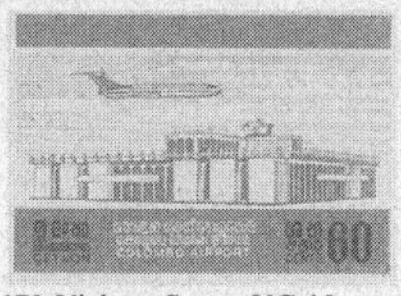
179 Vickers Super VC-10 over Terminal Building

1968. Opening of Colombo Airport.
539 **179** 60c. multicoloured 60 10

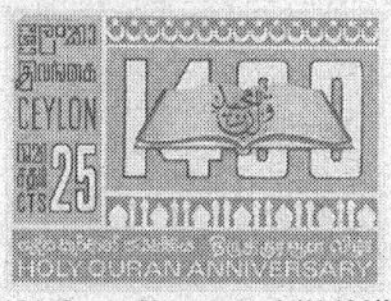
181 Open Koran and "1400"

1968. 1400th Anniv of Koran.
541 **181** 25c. multicoloured 10 10

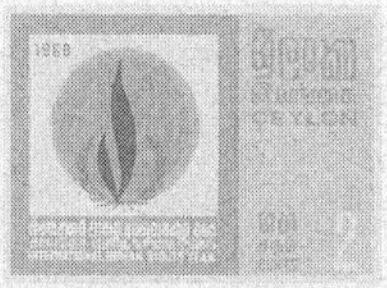
182 Human Rights Emblem

1968. Human Rights Year.
542 **182** 2c. multicoloured 10 15
543 20c. multicoloured 10 10
544 40c. multicoloured 10 10
545 2r. multicoloured 1·00 3·25

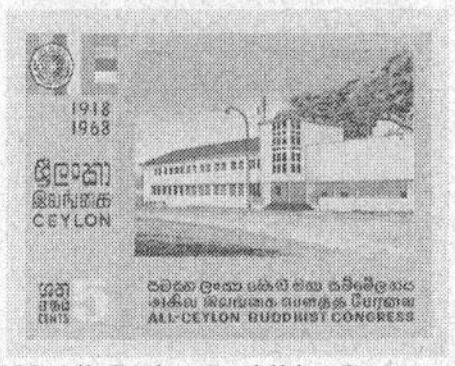
183 All-Ceylon Buddhist Congress Headquarters

1968. Golden Jubilee of All-Ceylon Buddhist Congress.
546 **183** 5c. multicoloured 10 40

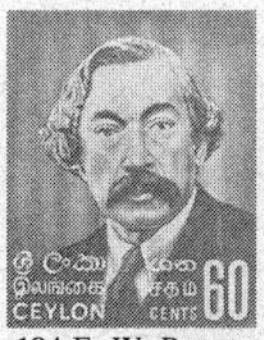
184 E. W. Perera (patriot)

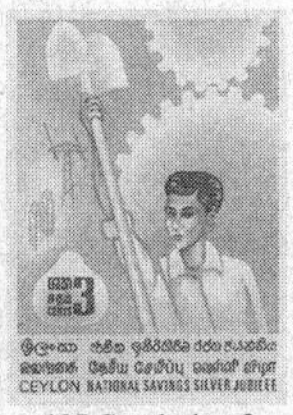
185 Symbols of Strength in Savings

1969. Perera Commemoration.
547 **184** 60c. brown 10 30

1969. Silver Jubilee of National Savings Movement.
548 **185** 3c. multicoloured 10 10

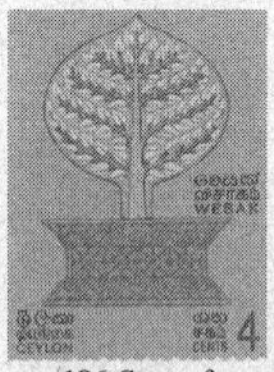
186 Seat of Enlightenment under Sacred Bodhi Tree

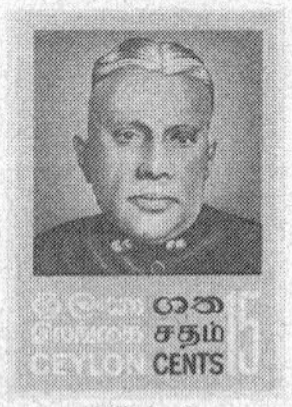
188 A. E. Goonesinghe

1969. Vesak Day. Inscr "Wesak".
549 **186** 4c. multicoloured 10 40
550 – 6c. multicoloured 10 40
551 **186** 35c. multicoloured 10 10
DESIGN: 6c. Buduresmala (six-fold Buddha-rays).

1969. Goonesinghe Commemoration.
552 **188** 15c. multicoloured 10 10

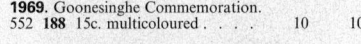

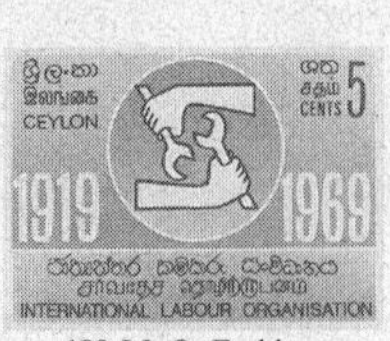
189 I.L.O. Emblem

1969. 50th Anniv of I.L.O.
553 **189** 5c. black and blue 10 10
554 25c. black and red 10 10

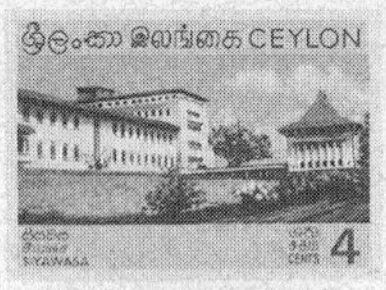
190 Convocation Hall, University of Ceylon

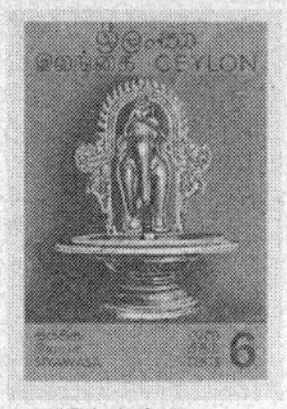
194 Ath Pana (Elephant Lamp)

1969. Educational Centenary. Multicoloured.
555 4c. Type **190** 10 80
556 35c. Lamp of learning, globe and flags (horiz) 20 10
557 50c. Uranium atom 20 10
558 60c. Symbols of scientific education 30 10

1969. Archaeological Centenary. Multicoloured.
559 6c. Type **194** 25 1·50
560 1r. Rock fortress of Sigiriya 25 10

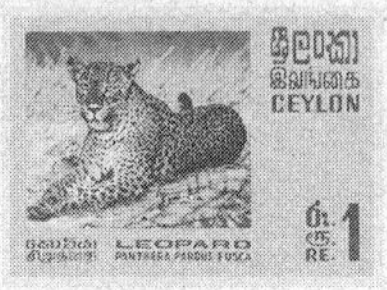
196 Leopard

1970. Wild Life Conservation. Multicoloured.
561 5c. Water buffalo 50 1·25
562 15c. Slender loris 1·00 30
563 50c. Spotted deer 1·00 1·25
564 1r. Type **196** 1·00 1·75

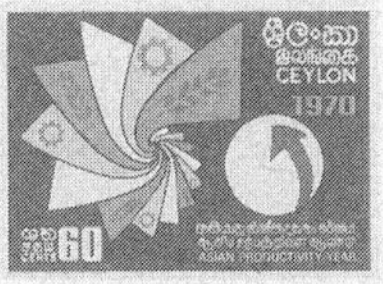
197 Emblem and Symbols

1970. Asian Productivity Year.
565 **197** 60c. multicoloured 10 10

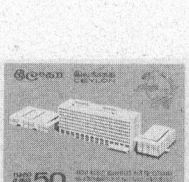

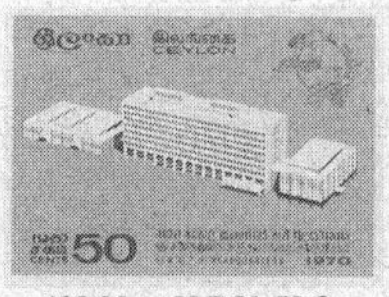
198 New U.P.U. H.Q. Building

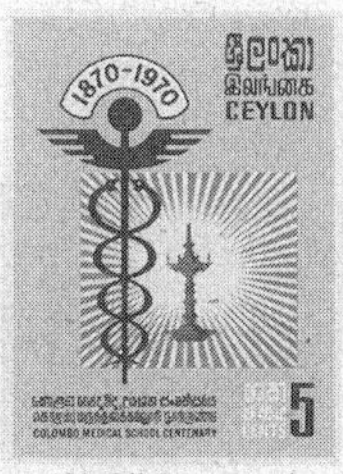
199 Oil Lamp and Caduceus

1970. New U.P.U. Headquarters Building.
566 **198** 50c. orange, black and blue 20 10
567 1r.10 red, black and blue 2·75 30

1970. Centenary of Colombo Medical School.
568 **199** 5c. multicoloured 40 80
569 45c. multicoloured 40 60

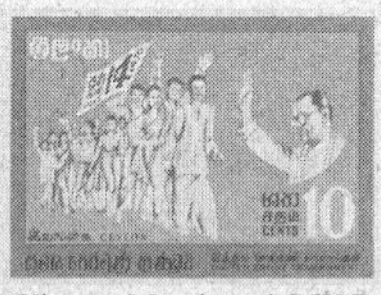
200 Victory March and S.W.R.D. Bandaranaike

1970. Establishment of United Front Government.
570 **200** 10c. multicoloured 10 10

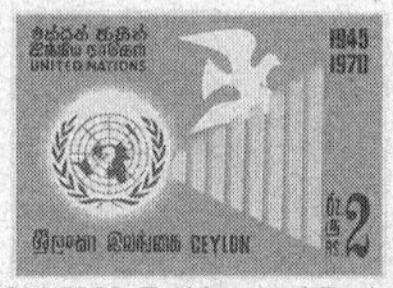
201 U.N. Emblem and Dove of Peace

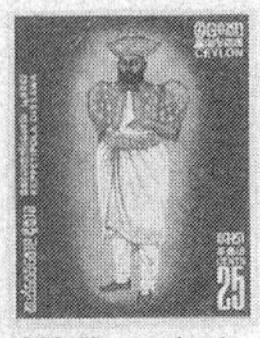
202 Keppetipola Dissawa

1970. 25th Anniv of United Nations.
571 **201** 2r. multicoloured 2·00 3·00

1970. 152nd Death Anniv of Keppetipola Dissawa (Kandyan patriot).
572 **202** 25c. multicoloured 10 10

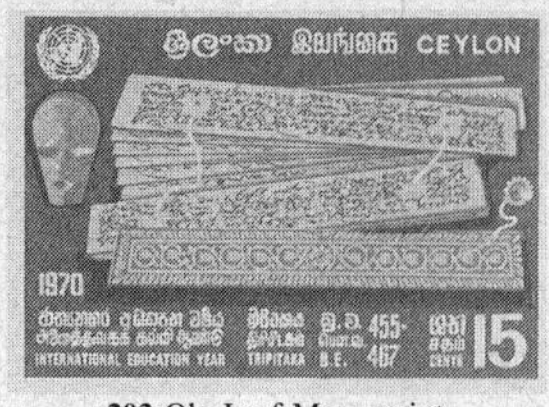
203 Ola Leaf Manuscript

1970. International Education Year.
573 **203** 15c. multicoloured 1·75 1·25

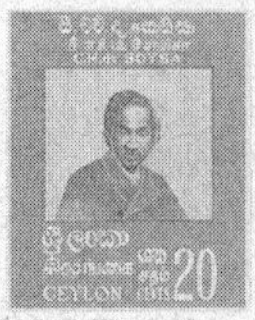
204 C. H. de Soysa

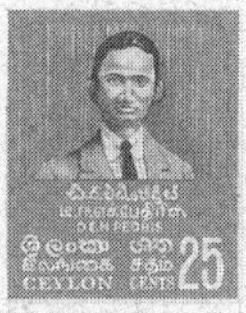
205 D. E. H. Pedris (patriot)

1971. 135th Birth Anniv of C. H. de Soysa (philanthropist)
574 **204** 20c. multicoloured 15 40

1971. D. E. H. Pedris Commemoration.
575 **205** 25c. multicoloured 15 50

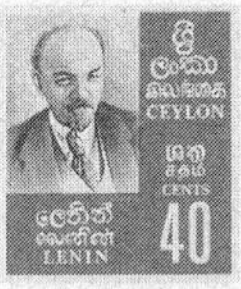
206 Lenin

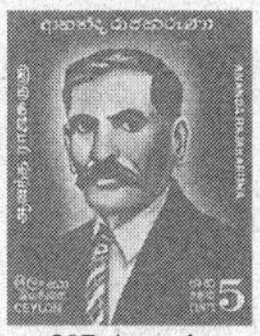
207 Ananda Rajakaruna

1971. Lenin Commemoration.
576 **206** 40c. multicoloured 15 40

1971. Poets and Philosophers.
577 **207** 5c. blue 10 15
578 – 5c. brown 10 15
579 – 5c. orange 10 15
580 – 5c. blue 10 15
581 – 5c. brown 10 15
PORTRAITS: No. 578, Arumuga Navalar; 579, Rev. S. Mahinda; 580, Ananda Coomaraswamy; 581, Cumaratunga Munidasa.

1971. Surch in figures.
582 **186** 5c. on 4c. multicoloured 6·00 1·75
583 **190** 5c. on 4c. multicoloured 10 1·25
584 **200** 15c. on 10c. multicoloured 10 30
585 – 25c. on 6c. mult (No. 550) 30 60
586 **194** 25c. on 6c. multicoloured 30 1·25

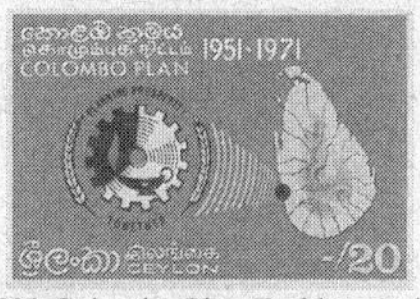
209 Colombo Plan Emblem and Ceylon

1971. 20th Anniv of Colombo Plan.
587 **209** 20c. multicoloured 15 30

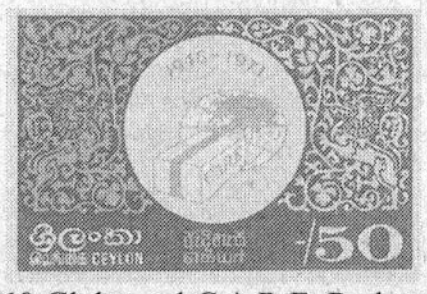
210 Globe and C.A.R.E. Package

1971. 20th Anniv of Co-operative for American Relief Everywhere.
588 **210** 50c. blue, violet and lilac 35 30

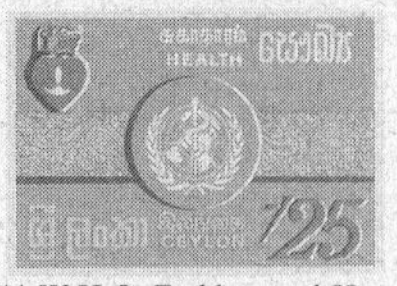
211 W.H.O. Emblem and Heart

1972. World Health Day.
589 **211** 25c. multicoloured 2·00 60

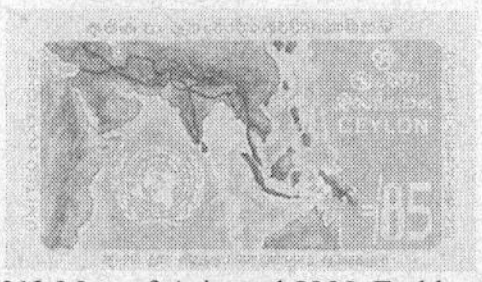
212 Map of Asia and U.N. Emblem

1972. 25th Anniv of E.C.A.F.E.
590 **212** 85c. multicoloured 4·25 2·75

OFFICIAL STAMPS

1895. Stamps of Queen Victoria optd **On Service**.
O 1 **9** 2c. green 8·00 45
O 8 2c. brown 7·00 60
O 2 **39** 3c. brown and green 10·00 80
O 9 3c. green 8·00 2·00
O 3 **28** 5c. purple 3·25 30
O 4 **39** 15c. olive 12·00 50
O10 15c. blue 16·00 60
O 5 25c. brown 10·00 1·75
O 6 30c. mauve and brown 13·00 60
O11 75c. black and brown 5·50 6·50
O 7 **30** 1r.12 red 70·00 55·00

1903. Stamps of King Edward VII optd **On Service**.
O12 **44** 2c. brown 12·00 1·00
O13 **45** 3c. green 7·00 2·00
O14 – 5c. purple (No. 268) 18·00 1·50
O15 **45** 15c. blue 27·00 2·50
O16 25c. brown 21·00 18·00
O17 30c. violet and green 11·00 1·50

For later issues see **SRI LANKA**.

CHAD Pt. 6; Pt. 12

Formerly a dependency of Ubangi-Shari. Became one of the separate colonies of Fr. Equatorial Africa in 1937. In 1958 became a republic within the French Community.

100 centimes = 1 franc.

1922. Stamps of Middle Congo, colours changed, optd **TCHAD**.
1 **1** 1c. pink and violet 50 2·75
2 2c. brown and pink 90 2·75
3 4c. blue and violet 1·75 3·00
4 5c. brown and green 1·90 3·25
5 10c. green and turquoise 3·25 3·75
6 15c. violet and pink 3·25 4·00
7 20c. green and violet 5·75 7·50
8 **2** 25c. brown and chocolate 10·00 13·50
9 30c. red 2·50 3·25
10 35c. blue and pink 3·25 4·25
11 40c. brown and green 3·50 4·50
12 45c. violet and green 3·75 4·50
13 50c. blue and light blue 2·50 4·50
14 60 on 75c. violet on pink 4·75 6·50
15 75c. pink and violet 3·75 4·25
16 **3** 1f. blue and pink 13·50 16·00
17 2f. blue and violet 19·00 24·00
18 5f. blue and brown 16·00 22·00

1924. Stamps of 1922 and similar stamps further optd **AFRIQUE EQUATORIALE FRANCAISE**.
19 **1** 1c. pink and violet 25 2·50
20 2c. brown and pink 15 2·25
21 4c. blue and violet 15 2·25
22 5c. brown and green 50 2·50
23 10c. green and turquoise 2·00 2·75
24 10c. red and grey 80 2·50
25 15c. violet and red 60 2·25
26 20c. green and violet 1·75 2·50
27 **2** 25c. brown and chocolate 1·60 2·50
28 30c. red 85 2·50
29 30c. grey and blue 65 2·25
30 30c. olive and green 2·00 3·00
31 35c. blue and pink 75 2·50
32 40c. brown and green 2·00 2·50
33 45c. violet and green 1·60 2·75
34 50c. blue and light blue 85 2·75
35 50c. green and purple 2·50 1·75
36 60 on 75c. violet on pink 40 2·75
37 65c. brown and blue 3·50 4·25
38 75c. pink and violet 1·00 2·75
39 75c. blue and light blue 2·00 2·50
40 75c. purple and brown 3·25 4·00
41 90c. carmine and red 5·00 10·00
42 **3** 1f. blue and pink 2·50 2·50
43 1f.10 green and blue 3·00 4·25
44 1f.25 brown and blue 7·75 11·50
45 1f.50 ultramarine and blue 4·75 11·50
46 1f.75 brown and mauve 50·00 60·00
47 2f. blue and violet 3·25 3·75
48 3f. mauve on pink 7·50 15·00
49 5f. blue and brown 3·75 4·25

1925. Stamps of Middle Congo optd **TCHAD** and **AFRIQUE EQUATORIALE FRANCAISE** and surch also.
50 **3** 65 on 1f. brown and green 2·25 3·50
51 85 on 1f. brown and green 2·50 3·50
52 **2** 90 on 75c. red and pink 2·75 3·50
53 **3** 1f.25 on 1f. blue & ultram 1·50 3·00
54 1f.50 on 1f. blue & ultram 2·75 3·50
55 3f. on 5f. brown and red 5·75 6·00
56 10f. on 5f. green and red 12·00 14·50
57a 20f. on 5f. violet & orange 19·00 19·00

1931. "Colonial Exhibition" key-types inscr "TCHAD".
58 E 40c. green 4·00 7·00
59 F 50c. mauve 4·50 7·00
60 G 90c. red 3·50 5·50
61 H 1f.50 blue 4·50 6·50

2 "Birth of the Republic" **3** Flag, Map and U.N. Emblem

1959. Ist Anniv of Republic.
62 **2** 15f. multicoloured . . . . 3·00 1·10
63 – 25f. lake and myrtle 80 75
DESIGN: 25f. Map and birds.

1960. 10th African Technical Co-operation Commission. As T **62** of Cameroun.
64 50f. violet and purple . . . 1·60 1·75

1960. Air. Olympic Games. No. 276 of French Equatorial Africa surch with Olympic rings and **XVIIe OLYMPIADE 1960 REPUBLIQUE DU TCHAD 250F.**
65 250f. on 500f. blue, black & grn . . . . 9·50 9·50

1961. Admission into U.N.
66 **3** 15f. multicoloured 45 20
67 – 25f. multicoloured 50 25
68 – 85f. multicoloured . . . . 1·60 80

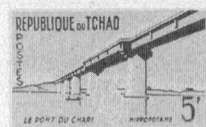

4 Shari Bridge and Hippopotamus

1961.
69 – 50c. green and black 10 10
70 – 1f. green and black 10 10
71 – 2f. brown and black 10 10
72 – 3f. orange and green 10 10
73 – 4f. red and black 10 10
74 **4** 5f. lemon and black 20 15
75 – 10f. pink and black 20 20
76 – 15f. violet and black 45 20
77 – 20f. red and black 55 30
78 – 25f. blue and black 60 30
79 – 30f. blue and black 70 45
80 – 60f. yellow and black . . . . 1·40 65
81 – 85f. orange and black . . . . 1·60 80
DESIGNS (with animal silhouettes)—VERT: 50c. Biltine and Dorcas gazelle; 1f. Logone and elephant; 2f. Batha and lion; 3f. Salamat and buffalo; 4f. Ouaddai and greater kudu; 10f. Abtouyour and bullock; 15f. Bessada and Derby's eland; 20f. Tibesti and moufflon; 25f. Tikem Rocks and hartebeest; 30f. Kanem and cheetah; 60f. Borkou and oryx; 85f. Guelta D'Archei and addax.

5 Red Bishops

1961. Air.
82 **5** 50f. black, red and green . . 3·00 1·10
83 – 100f. multicoloured . . . . 6·75 2·00
84 – 200f. multicoloured . . . . 12·00 3·75
85 – 250f. blue, orange and green 15·00 5·25
86 – 500f. multicoloured . . . . 30·00 11·00
BIRDS: 100f. Scarlet-chested sunbird; 200f. African paradise flycatcher; 250f. Malachite kingfisher; 500f. Carmine bee eater.

1962. Air. "Air Afrique" Airline. As T **69** of Cameroun.
87 25f. blue, brown and black . . 60 25

1962. Malaria Eradication. As T **70** of Cameroun.
88 25f.+5f. orange 75 75

1962. Sports. As T **12** of Central African Republic. Multicoloured.
89 20f. Relay-racing (horiz) (postage) 45 30
90 50f. High-jumping (horiz) . . 1·10 55
91 100f. Throwing the discus (air) 2·50 1·25
The 100f. is 26 × 47 mm.

1962. Ist Anniv of Union of African and Malagasy States. As No. 328 of Cameroun.
92 **72** 30f. blue 70 40

1963. Freedom from Hunger. As T **76** of Cameroun.
93 25f.+5f. blue, brown & green 80 80

 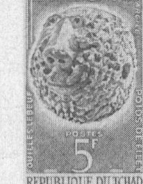

6 Pres. Tombalbaye **7** Carved Thread-weight

1963.
94 **6** 20f. multicoloured 45 20
95 – 85f. multicoloured . . . . 1·10 55

1963. Air. African and Malagasy Posts and Telecommunications Union. As T **11** of Central African Republic.
96 85f. multicoloured . . . . . 1·25 55

1963. Space Telecommunications, As Nos. 37/8 of Central African Republic.
97 25f. violet, emerald and green 50 35
98 100f. blue and pink . . . . . 2·00 1·25

1963. Air. Ist Anniv of "Air Afrique" and Inauguration of "DC-8" Service. As T **11** of Congo Republic.
99 50f. multicoloured . . . . . . 1·50 75

1963. Air. European–African Economic Convention. As T **24** of Central African Republic.
100 50f. multicoloured . . . . . 1·00 60

1963. Sao Art.
101 **7** 5f. orange and turquoise . . 10 10
102 – 15f. purple, slate and red . . 30 25
103 – 25f. brown and blue . . . 60 35
104 – 60f. bronze and brown . . 1·40 60
105 – 80f. bronze and brown . . . 1·60 80
DESIGNS: 15f. Ancestral mask; 25f. Ancestral statuette; 60f. Gazelle's-head pendant; 80f. Pectoral.

1963. 15th Anniv of Declaration of Human Rights. As Central African Republic T **26**.
106 25f. purple and green 65 35

8 Broussard Monoplane

1963. Air.
107 **8** 100f. blue, green & brown 2·25 1·25

9 Pottery

1964. Sao Handicrafts.
108 **9** 10f. black, orange & blue 30 20
109 – 30f. red, black and yellow 55 30
110 – 50f. black, red and green . 1·00 45
111 – 85f. black, yellow & purple 1·25 65
DESIGNS: 30f. Canoe-building; 50f. Carpet-weaving; 85f. Blacksmith working iron.

10 Rameses II in War Chariot, Abu Simbel

1964. Air. Nubian Monuments Preservation Fund.
112 **10** 10f.+5f. violet, grn & red 60 35
113 – 25f.+5f. purple, grn & red 95 50
114 – 50f.+5f. turq, grn & red . . 1·90 1·40

1964. World Meteorological Day. As T **14** of Congo Republic.
115 50f. violet, blue and purple 1·00 50

11 Cotton

1964. Multicoloured.
116 20f. Type **11** 95 50
117 25f. Flamboyant tree . . . . 1·10 55

1964. Air. 5th Anniv of Equatorial African Heads of State Conf. As T **31** of Central African Republic.
118 100f. multicoloured . . . . . 1·50 75

12 Globe, Chimneys and Ears of Wheat

1964. Air. Europafrique.
119 **12** 50f. orange, purple & brn 1·00 55

13 Football

1964. Air. Olympic Games. Tokyo.
120 **13** 25f. green, lt green & brn 75 45
121 – 50f. brown, indigo & blue 1·00 55
122 – 100f. black, green and red 2·00 1·10
123 – 200f. black, bistre and red 4·25 2·10
DESIGNS—VERT: 50f. Throwing the javelin; 100f. High-jumping. HORIZ: 200f. Running.

1964. Air. Pan-African and Malagasy Post and Telecommunications Congress, Cairo. As T **23** of Congo Republic.
124 25f. sepia, red and mauve . . 60 25

1964. French, African and Malagasy Co-operation. As T **88** of Cameroun.
125 25f. brown, blue and red . . 60 30

14 Pres. Kennedy **15** National Guard

1964. Air. Pres. Kennedy Commem.
126 **14** 100f. multicoloured . . . . 1·75 1·10

1964. Chad Army. Multicoloured.
127 20f. Type **15** 50 20
128 25f. Standard-bearer and troops of Land Forces . . 55 25

16 Barbary Sheep

1964. Fauna. Protection. Multicoloured.
129 **16** 5f. Type **16** 25 15
130 10f. Addax 35 20
131 20f. Scimitar oryx 65 30
132 25f. Giant eland (vert) . . . 95 35
133 30f. Giraffe, African buffalo and lion (Zakouma Park)(vert) . . . . . . 1·25 50
134 85f. Greater kudu (vert) . . . 3·00 1·10

17 Perforator of Olsen's Telegraph Apparatus

1965. I.T.U. Centenary.
135 **17** 30f. brown, red and green 55 25
136 – 60f. green, red and brown 1·00 45
137 – 100f. green, brown & red 1·90 80
DESIGNS—VERT: 60f. Milde's telephone. HORIZ: 100f. Distributor of Baudot's telegraph apparatus.

18 Badge and Mobile Gendarmes

1965. National Gendarmerie.
138 **18** 25f. multicoloured 60 35

19 I.C.Y. Emblem

1965. Air. International Co-operation Year.
139 **19** 100f. multicoloured . . . . 1·25 70

20 Abraham Lincoln

1965. Air. Death Centenary of Abraham Lincoln.
140 **20** 100f. multicoloured . . . . 1·75 75

21 Guitar

1965. Native Musical Instruments.
141 – 1f. brown & grn (postage) 10 10
142 **21** 2f. brown, purple and red 10 10
143 – 3f. lake, black and brown 20 15
144 – 15f. green, orange and red 50 25
145 – 60f. green and lake . . . 1·60 80
146 – 100f. ultram, brn & bl (48¼ × 27 mm) (air) . . . 1·90 1·25
DESIGNS—VERT: 1f. Drum and seat; 3f. Shoulder drum; 60f. Harp. HORIZ: 15f. Viol; 100f. Xylophone.

22 Sir Winston Churchill

1965. Air. Churchill Commemoration.
147 **22** 50f. black and green . . . 1·00 50

23 Dr. Albert Schweitzer (philosopher and missionary) and "Appealing Hands"

1966. Air. Schweitzer Commemoration.
148 **23** 100f. multicoloured . . . . 1·90 95

24 Mask in Mortar **26** W.H.O. Building

1966. World Festival of Negro Arts, Dakar.
149 **24** 15f. purple, bistre & blue 35 20
150 – 20f. brown, red and green 50 25
151 – 60f. purple, blue and red 1·40 55
152 – 80f. green, brown & violet 2·10 85
DESIGNS—Sao Art: 20f. Mask; 60f. Mask (different)

(All from J. Courtin's excavations at Bouta Kebira);
80f. Armband (from I.N.T.S.H. excavations, Gawi).

1966. No. 94 surch.
153 **6** 25f. on 20f. multicoloured   60   30

1966. Inaug of W.H.O. Headquarters, Geneva.
154 **26** 25f. blue, yellow and red   45   20
155   32f. blue, yellow & green   50   25

27 Caduceus and Map of Africa   **28** Footballer

1966. Central African Customs and Economic Union.
156 **27** 30f. multicoloured   60   30

1966. World Cup Football Championship.
157 **28** 30f. red, green and emerald   50   25
158   60f. red, black and blue   .   1·25   50
DESIGN—VERT: 60f. Footballer (different).

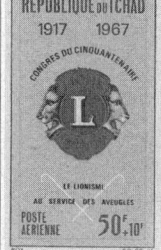

29 Youths, Flag and Arms

1966. Youth Movement.
159 **29** 25f. multicoloured   60   30

30 Columns   **31** Skull of Lake Chad Man
("Tchadanthropus uxoris")

1966. 20th Anniv of U.N.E.S.C.O.
160 **30** 32f. blue, violet and red   . .   65   50

1966. Air. Inauguration of "DC-8" Air Services.
As T **54** of Central African Republic.
161   30f. grey, black and green   . .   60   25

1966. Archaeological Excavation.
162 **31** 30f. slate, yellow and red   1·60   75

32 White-throated Bee Eater

1966. Air. Birds. Multicoloured.
163   50f. Greater blue-eared glossy
      starling   . . . . . .   3·50   1·40
164   100f. Type **32**   . . . . .   4·50   2·40
165   200f. African pigmy
      kingfisher   . . . .   8·50   2·50
166   250f. Red-throated bee eater   12·50   3·25
167   500f. Little green bee eater   18·00   7·00

33 Battle-axe   **35** Sportsmen and
Dais on Map

34 Congress Palace

1966. Prehistoric Implements.
168 **33** 25f. brown, blue and red   35   25
169 – 30f. black, brown & blue   45   25
170 – 85f. brown, red and blue   1·50   60
171 – 100f. brown, turq & sepia   1·75   85
DESIGNS: 30f. Arrowhead; 85f. Harpoon; 100f.
Sandstone grindstone and pounder. From Tchad
National Museum.

1967. Air.
173 **34** 25f. multicoloured   55   25

1967. Sports Day.
174 **35** 25f. multicoloured   60   35

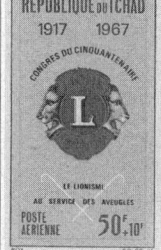

36 "Colotis protomedia klug"

1967. Butterflies. Multicoloured.
175   5f. Type **36**   20   15
176   10f. "Charaxes jasius
      epijasius L"   35   20
177   20f. "Junonia cebrene trim"   1·00   50
178   130f. "Danaida petiverana
      H.D."   . . . .   3·25   1·40

37 Lions Emblem   **39** H.Q. Building

1967. Air. 50th Anniv of Lions International.
179 **37** 50f.+10f. multicoloured   . .   1·25   65

38 Dagnaux's Breguet "19" Aircraft

1967. Air. 1st Anniv of Air Chad Airline.
180 **38** 25f. green, blue & brown   55   40
181 – 30f. indigo, green and blue   75   40
182 – 50f. brown, green & blue   1·25   75
183 – 100f. red, blue and green   2·50   1·10
DESIGNS: 30f. Latecoere "631" flying-boat; 50f.
Douglas "DC-3"; 100f. Piper Cherokee "6".

1967. Air. 5th Anniv of U.A.M.P.T. As T **66** of
Central African Republic.
184   100f. brown, bistre & mve   . .   1·25   75

1967. Opening of W.H.O. Regional Headquarters,
Brazzaville.
185 **39** 30f. multicoloured   60   30

40 Scouts and Jamboree Emblem

1967. World Scout Jamboree, Idaho. Multicoloured.
186   25f. Type **40**   45   20
187   32f. Scout and Jamboree
      emblem   65   25

41 Flour Mills

1967. Economic Development.
188 **41** 25f. slate, brown and blue   45   20
189 – 30f. blue, brown & green   55   30
DESIGN: 30f. Land reclamation, Lake Bol.

42 Woman and Harpist   **43** Emblem of
Rotary
International

1967. Bailloud Mission in the Ennedi. Rock
paintings.
190 – 2f. choc, brn & red (post)   20   15
191 – 10f. red, brown and violet   45   25
192 **42** 15f. lake, brown and blue   55   25
193 – 20f. red, brown and green   1·25   50
194 – 25f. red, brown and blue   1·60   60
195 – 30f. lake, brown and blue   1·00   50
196 – 50f. lake, brown and green   1·90   80
197 – 100f. red, brn & grn (air)   3·00   1·40
198 – 125f. lake, brown & blue   4·25   2·10
DESIGNS: 2f. Archers; 10f. Male and female
costumes; 20f. Funeral vigil; 25f. "Dispute"; 30f.
Giraffes; 50f. Cameleer pursuing ostrich.
(48 × 27 mm): 100f. Masked dancers; 125f. Hunters
and hare.

1968. 10th Anniv of Rotary Club, Fort Lamy.
199 **43** 50f. multicoloured   95   45

44 Downhill Skiing

1968. Air. Winter Olympic Games, Grenoble.
200 **44** 30f. brown, green & purple   95   35
201 – 100f. blue, green & turq   . .   2·50   1·10
DESIGN—VERT: 100f. Ski-jumping.

45 Chancellor Adenauer   **46** "Health Services"

1968. Air. Adenauer Commemoration.
202 **45** 52f. brown, lilac and green   1·00   50

1968. Air. Anniv of W.H.O.
204 **46** 25f. multicoloured   45   20
205   32f. multicoloured   55   25

47 Allegory of Irrigation

1968. International Hydrological Decade.
206 **47** 50f. blue, brown & green   75   30

48 "The Snake-charmer"

1968. Air. Paintings by Henri Rousseau. Mult.
207   100f. Type **48**   . . . . . .   2·50   1·60
208   130f. "The War"
      (49 × 35 mm)   . . . . .   3·75   2·25

49 College Building, Student and
Emblem

1968. National College of Administration.
209 **49** 25f. purple, blue and red   45   25

50 Child writing and
Blackboard   **52** "Utetheisa
pulchella"

51 Harvesting Cotton

1968. Literacy Day.
210 **50** 60f. black, blue & brown   80   35

1968. Cotton Industry.
211 **51** 25f. purple, green & blue   50   20
212 – 30f. brown, blue & green   50   20
DESIGN—VERT: 30f. Loom, Fort Archambault
Mill.

1968. Butterflies and Moths. Multicoloured.
213   25f. Type **52**   . . . . .   1·10   35
214   30f. "Ophideres materna"   .   1·40   35
215   50f. "Gynanisa maja"   . . .   2·75   70
216   100f. "Epiphora bauhiniae"   3·75   1·25

53 Hurdling

1968. Air. Olympic Games, Mexico.
217 **53** 32f. chocolate, grn & brn   80   50
218 – 80f. purple, blue and red   1·75   75
DESIGN: 80f. Relay-racing.

54 Human Rights Emblem
within Man

1968. Human Rights Year.
219 **54** 32f. red, green and blue   . .   60   25

1969. Air. "Philexafrique" Stamp Exn, Abidjan,
Ivory Coast (1st issue). As T **137** of Cameroun.
Multicoloured.
220   100f. "The actor Wolf, called
      Bernard" (J. L. David)   . .   2·75   2·75

1969. Air. "Philexafrique" Stamp Exn, Abidjan,
Ivory Coast (2nd issue). As T **138** of Cameroun.
Multicoloured.
221   50f. Moundangs dancers and
      Chad postage due stamp of
      1930   . . . .   1·90   1·90

55 G. Nachtigal and Tibesti landscape,
1869

1969. Air. Chad Explorers.
222 – 100f. violet, green & blue   1·75   75
223 **55** 100f. purple, blue & brown   1·75   75
DESIGN: No. 222, H. Barth (portrait) and aboard
canoe, Lake Region, 1851.

56 "Apollo 8" circling Moon

1969. Air. Flight of "Apollo 8" around the Moon.
224 **56** 100f. black, blue & orange . . . 1·75　75

57 St. Bartholomew

1969. Jubilee Year of Catholic Church. Mult.
225　50c. St. Paul . . . . 　10　10
226　1f. St. Peter . . . . 　10　10
227　2f. St. Thomas . . . . 　10　10
228　5f. St. John the Evangelist . . 　10　10
229　10f. Type **57** . . . . 　10　10
230　20f. St. Matthew . . . . . . 　25　15
231　25f. St. James the Less . . . 　25　15
232　30f. St. Andrew . . . . . . 　30　20
233　40f. St. Jude . . . . 　35　20
234　50f. St. James the Greater . . 　45　25
235　85f. St. Philip . . . . 　70　45
236　100f. St. Simon . . . . . . 　80　55

58 Mahatma Gandhi　　59 Motor Vehicles
　　　　　　　　　　　　　and I.L.O. Emblem

1969. Air. "Apostles of Peace".
237 **58** 50f. brown and green . . . 　95　45
238　– 50f. sepia and agate . . . 　95　45
239　– 50f. brown and pink . . . 　95　45
240　– 50f. brown and blue . . . 　95　45
DESIGNS: No. 238, President Kennedy; No. 239, Martin Luther King; No. 240, Robert F. Kennedy.

1969. 50th Anniv of I.L.O.
242 **59** 32f. blue, purple & green . . 　60　30

60 Cipolla, Baran and　　61 "African Woman"
　　Sambo (pair with cox)　　(Bezombes)

1969. "World Solidarity". Multicoloured. (a) Gold Medal Winners, Mexico Olympics.
243　1f. Type **60** . . . . . . 　25　25
244　1f. R. Beamon (long-jump) . . 　25　25
245　1f. I. Becker (women's pentathlon) . . . . . . 　25　25
246　1f. C. Besson (women's 400 m) . . . . . . 　25　25
247　1f. W. Davenport (110 m hurdles) . . . . . . 　25　25
248　1f. K. Dibiasi (diving) . . . 　25　25
249　1f. R. Fosbury (high-jump) . . 　25　25
250　1f. M. Gamoudi (5000 m) . . 　25　25
251　1f. Great Britain (sailing) . . 　25　25
252　1f. J. Guyon (cross-country riding) . . . . . . 　25　25
253　1f. D. Hemery (200 m hurdles) . . . . . . 　25　25
254　1f. S. Kato (gymnastics) . . 　25　25
255　1f. B. Klinger (small bore rifle shooting) . . . . . 　25　25
256　1f. R. Matson (shot put) . . 　25　25
257　1f. R. Matthes (100 m backstroke) . . . . . 　25　25
258　1f. D. Meyer (women's 200 m freestyle) . . . . . 　25　25
259　1f. Morelon and Trentin (tandem cycle) . . . 　25　25
260　1f. D. Rebillard (4000 m cycle pursuit) . . . 　25　25
261　1f. T. Smith (200 m) . . . 　25　25
262　1f. P. Trentin (1000 m cycle) 　25　25
263　1f. F. Vianelli (196 km cycle race) . . . . . . 　25　25

264　1f. West Germany (dressage) 　25　25
265　1f. M. Wolke (welterweight boxing) . . . . . 　25　25
266　1f. Zimmermann and Esser (women's kayak pair) . . . 　25　25

(b) Paintings.
267　1f. Type **61** . . . . . . 　25　25
268　1f. "Mother and Child" (Gauguin) . . . . . 　25　25
269　1f. "Holy Family" (Murillo) (horiz) . . . . . 　25　25
270　1f. "Adoration of the Kings" (Rubens) . . . . . 　25　25
271　1f. "Three Negroes" (Rubens) 　25　25
272　1f. "Woman with Flowers" (Veneto) . . . . . 　25　25

62 Presidents Tombalbaye and Mobutu

1969. Air. 1st Anniv of Central African States Union.
273 **62** 1000f. gold, red and blue 　20·00　20·00
This stamp is embossed in gold foil; colours of flags enamelled.

63 "Cochlospermum tinctorium"

1969. Flowers. Multicoloured.
274　1f. Type **63** . . . . . . 　10　10
275　4f. "Parkia biglobosa" . . . 　20　15
276　10f. "Pancratium trianthum" . 　30　20
277　15f. "Ipomoea aquatica" . . 　45　20

1969. Air. Birth Bicentenary of Napoleon Bonaparte. Multicoloured. As T **144** of Cameroun.
278　30f. "Napoleon visiting the Hotel des Invalides" (Veron-Bellecourt) . . . 　95　50
279　85f. "The Battle of Wagram" (H. Vernet) . . . . 　1·90　1·00
280　130f. "The Battle of Austerlitz" (Gerard) . . 　3·50　1·90

64 Frozen Carcases

1969. Frozen Meat Industry.
281 **64** 25f. red, green and orange 　35　20
282　– 30f. brown, slate & green 　50　25
DESIGN: 30f. Cattle and refrigerated abattoir, Farcha.

1969. 5th Anniv of African Development Bank. As T **146** of Cameroun.
283　30f. brown, green and red . . 　45　25

66 Astronaut and Lunar Module

1969. Air. 1st Man on the Moon. Embossed on gold foil.
289 **66** 1000f. gold . . . . . 　22·00　22·00

67 Nile Mouthbrooder　　68 President
　　　　　　　　　　　　　Tombalbaye

1969. Fishes.
290 **67** 2f. purple, grey and green 　20　10
291　– 3f. grey, red and blue . . 　30　25
292　– 5f. blue, yellow and ochre 　55　25
293　– 20f. blue, green and red . . 　1·75　60

FISHES: 3f. Deep-sided citharinid; 5f. Nile pufferfish; 20f. Lesser tigerfish.

1969. 10th Anniv of A.S.E.C.N.A. As T **150** of Cameroun.
294　30f. orange . . . . 　55　30

1970. President Tombalbaye.
295 **68** 25f. multicoloured . . . . 　45　20

69 "Village Life" (G. Narcisse)

1970. Air. African Paintings. Multicoloured.
296　100f. Type **69** . . . . . . 　2·10　1·00
297　250f. "Market Woman" (I. N'Diaye) . . . . 　4·00　1·60
298　250f. "Flower-seller" (I. N'Diaye) (vert) . . . . 　4·00　1·60

70 Lenin　　　　72 Osaka Print

71 Class and Torchbearers

1970. Birth Centenary of Lenin.
299 **70** 150f. black, cream & gold 　2·50　1·25

1970. New U.P.U. Headquarters Building, Berne, As T **156** of Cameroun.
300　30f. brown, violet and red . . 　55　30

1970. International Education Year.
301 **71** 100f. multicoloured . . . . 　1·50　80

1970. Air. World Fair "EXPO 70", Osaka, Japan.
302 **72** 50f. green, blue and red . . 　45　30
303　– 100f. blue, green and red . . 　75　45
304　– 125f. slate. brown & red . 　1·00　55
DESIGNS: 100f. Tower of the Sun; 125f. Osaka print (different).

1970. Air. "Apollo" Moon Flights. Nos. 164/6 surch with new value, and optd with various inscriptions and diagrams concerning space flights.
305 **32** 50f. on 100f. mult ("Apollo 11") . . . . 　1·50　1·00
306　– 100f. on 200f. mult ("Apollo 12") . . . . 　2·75　1·40
307　– 125f. on 250f. mult ("Apollo 13") . . . . 　4·25　2·25

 (left)

74 Meteorological　　76 Ahmed Mangue
　　Equipment and　　(Minister of Education)
　　"Agriculture"

75 "DC-8-63" over Airport

1970. World Meteorological Day.
308 **74** 50f. grey, green & orange 　75　30

1970. Air. "Air Afrique" DC-8 "Fort Lamy".
309 **75** 30f. multicoloured . . . . 　75　35

1970. Ahmed Mangue (air crash victim) Commem.
310 **76** 100f. black, red and gold . 　1·10　50

77 Tanning

1970. Trades and Handicrafts.
311 **77** 1f. bistre, brown and blue 　10　10
312　– 2f. brown, blue and green 　15　10
313　– 3f. violet, brown & mauve 　20　15
314　– 4f. brown, bistre & green 　25　15
315　– 5f. brown, green and red 　35　35
DESIGNS—VERT: 2f. Dyeing; 4f. Water-carrying. HORIZ: 3f. Milling palm-nuts for oil; 5f. Copper-founding.

78 U.N. Emblem　　79 "The Visitation" (Venetian
　　and Dove　　　　School, 15th cent)

1970. 25th Anniv of United Nations.
316 **78** 32f. multicoloured . . . . 　60　35

1970. Air. Christmas. Multicoloured.
317　20f. Type **79** . . . . . . 　50　30
318　25f. "The Nativity" (Venetian School, 15th cent) . . 　75　35
319　30f. "Virgin and Child" (Veneziano) . . . . 　95　45

80 Map and O.C.A.M. Building

1971. O.C.A.M. (Organization Commune Africane et Malgache) Conference, Fort Lamy.
320 **80** 30f. multicoloured . . . . 　60　30

81 Maritius "Post Office" 2d. of 1847

1971. Air. "PHILEXOCAM" Stamp Exhibition, Fort-Lamy.
321 **81** 10f. slate, brown & turq . . 　30　20
322　– 20f. brown, black & turq 　45　20
323　– 30f. brown, black and red 　55　30
324　– 60f. black, brown & purple 　80　50
325　– 80f. slate, brown and blue 　1·25　70
326　– 100f. brown, slate & blue 　1·60　95
DESIGNS—20f. Tuscany 3 lire of 1860; 30f. France 1f. of 1849; 60f. U.S.A. 10c. of 1847; 80f. Japan 5 sen of 1872; 100f. Saxony 3pf. of 1850.

82 Pres. Nasser   **83** "Racial Harmony" Tree

1971. Air. 1st Death Anniv of Gamal Abdel Nasser (Egypt).
328 **82** 75f. multicoloured   80   35

1971. Racial Equality Year.
329 **83** 40f. red, green and blue . .   75   30

1971. Air. Reconciliation with Central African Republic and Zaire. As T **106** of Central African Republic.
330   100f. multicoloured . . .   1·50   75

84 Map and Dish Aerial

1971. World Telecommunications Day.
331 **84** 5f. orge, red & bl (postage)   20   15
332   – 40f. green, brown & pur   55   25
333   – 50f. black, brown & red . .   75   30
334   – 125f. red, green & blue
     (air) . . . .   1·90   85
DESIGNS: 40f. Map and communications tower; 50f. Map and satellite. (48×27 mm): 125f. Map and telecommunications symbols.

85 Scouts by Camp-fire

1971. Air. World Scout Jamboree, Asagiri, Japan.
335 **85** 250f. multicoloured . . . .   3·75   1·90

86 Great Egret

1971. Air.
336 **86** 1000f. multicoloured . . .   29·00   16·00

87 Ancient Marathon Race

1971. Air. 75th Anniv of Modern Olympic Games. Multicoloured.
337   40f. Type **87**   55   30
338   45f. Ancient stadium,
     Olympia   80   35
339   75f. Ancient wrestling . .   1·00   50
340   130f. Athens Stadium, 1896
     Games . . . .   1·75   85

88 Sidney Bechet   **89** Gen. de Gaulle

1971. Air. Famous American Black Musicians. Multicoloured.
341   50f. Type **88** . . . .   1·25   50
342   75f. Duke Ellington . . . .   1·60   75
343   100f. Louis Armstrong . . .   2·50   1·25

1971. Air. 1st Death Anniv of De Gaulle.
344   – 200f. gold, blue and light
     blue . . . .   6·25   6·25
345 **89** 200f. gold, green & yellow   6·25   6·25
DESIGN: No. 344, Governor-General Felix Eboue.

1971. Air. 10th Anniv of African and Malagasy Posts and Telecommunications Union. As T **184** of Cameroun. Multicoloured.
347   100f. Headquarters building
     and Sao carved animal
     head . . . .   1·25   60

90 Children's Heads

1971. 25th Anniv of U.N.I.C.E.F.
348 **90** 50f. blue, green & purple   85   35
On the above stamp, "24e" has been obliterated and "25e" inserted in the commemorative inscription.

91 Gorane Nangara Dancers

1971. Chad Dancers. Multicoloured.
349   10f. Type **91**   30   20
350   15f. Yondo initiates   45   25
351   30f. M'Boum (vert)   80   35
352   40f. Sara Kaba (vert) . . .   1·25   55

93 Presidents Pompidou and Tombalbaye

1972. Visit of French President.
354 **93** 40f. multicoloured . . . .   1·25   60

94 Bobsleighing

1972. Air. Winter Olympic Games, Sapporo, Japan.
355 **94** 50f. red and blue   70   40
356   – 100f. green and purple . . .   1·50   60
DESIGN: 100f. Slalom.

95 Human Heart   **96** "Gorrizia dubiosa"

1972. World Heart Month.
357 **95** 100f. red, blue and violet   1·50   75

1972. Insects. Multicoloured.
358   1f. Type **96**   10   10
359   2f. "Argiope sector"   20   15
360   3f. "Nephila senegalense" . .   25   15
361   4f. "Oryctes boas"   35   25
362   5f. "Hemistigma
     albipunctata"   45   25
363   25f. "Dinothrombium
     tinctorium"   45   30
364   30f. "Bupreste sternocera H."   50   30
365   40f. "Hyperechia bomboides"   60   35
366   50f. "Chrysis" (Hymenoptere)   95   50

367   100f. "Tithoes confinis"
     (Longicore) . . . . . .   2·50   85
368   130f. "Galeodes araba"
     (Solifuge) . . . .   3·75   1·40

1972. Air. U.N.E.S.C.O. "Save Venice" Campaign. As T **191** of Cameroun. Multicoloured.
369   40f. "Harbour Panorama"
     (detail, Caffi)   95   50
370   45f. "Venice Panorama"
     (detail, Caffi) (horiz) . .   1·25   60
371   140f. "Grand Canal" (detail,
     Caffi) . . . .   3·00   1·40

97 Hurdling

1972. Olympic Games, Munich. Multicoloured.
372   50f. Type **97**   75   35
373   130f. Gymnastics . . . . .   1·50   75
374   150f. Swimming . . . . .   1·90   85

98 Alphonse Daudet and Scene from "Tartarin de Tarascon"

1972. Air. International Book Year.
376 **98** 100f. brown, red & purple   1·50   75

99 Dromedary

1972. Domestic Animals.
377 **99** 25f. brown and violet . . .   45   20
378   – 30f. blue and mauve . . .   50   25
379   – 40f. brown and green . . .   70   30
380   – 45f. brown and blue . . .   85   35
DESIGNS: 30f. Horse; 40f. Saluki hound; 45f. Goat.

100 "Luna 16" and   **101** Tobacco Production
Moon Probe

1972. Air. Russian Moon Exploration.
381 **100** 100f. violet, brown & blue   1·40   70
382   – 150f. brown, blue &
     purple . . . .   2·10   80
DESIGN—HORIZ: 150f. "Lunokhod 1" Moon vehicle.

1972. Economic Development.
383 **101** 40f. green, red & brown   50   25
384   – 50f. brown, green & blue   75   35
DESIGN: 50f. Ploughing with oxen.

102 Microscope, Cattle and Laboratory

1972. Air. 20th Anniv of Farcha Veterinary Laboratory.
385 **102** 75f. multicoloured   80   35

103 Massa Warrior

1972. Chad Warriors. Multicoloured.
386   15f. Type **103**   55   25
387   20f. Moudang archer . . .   70   35

104 King Faisal and Pres. Tombalbaye

1972. Visit of King Faisal of Saudi Arabia. Multicoloured.
388   100f. Type **104** (postage) . .   1·90   95
389   75f. King Faisal and Ka'aba,
     Mecca (air) . . . . . .   1·00   50

105 Gen. Gowon, Pres. Tombalbaye and Map

1972. Visit of Gen. Gowon, Nigerian Head-of-State.
390 **105** 70f. multicoloured   75   30

106 "Madonna and Child" (G. Bellini)

1972. Air. Christmas. Paintings. Multicoloured.
391   40f. Type **106**   45   25
392   75f. "Virgin and Child" (bas-
     relief, Da Santivo, Dall'
     Occhio)   80   45
393   80f. "Nativity" (B. Angelico)
     (horiz) . . . .   1·25   65
394   90f. "Adoration of the Magi"
     (P. Perugino) . . . . .   1·60   80

107 Commemorative Scroll

1972. 50th Anniv of U.S.S.R.
395 **107** 150f. multicoloured . . .   1·50   55

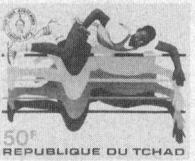

108 High-jumping

1973. 2nd African Games, Lagos. Multicoloured.
396　50f. Type **108** . . . .　75　35
397　125f. Running . . . . .　1·40　60
398　200f. Putting the shot . . . .　2·00　1·00

109 Copernicus and Planetary System Diagram

1973. Air. 500th Birth Anniv of Nicholas Copernicus.
400　**109**　250f. grey, brown & mve　4·00　1·90

1973. African Solidarity. "Drought Relief". No. 377 surch **SECHERESSE SOLIDARITE AFRICAINE 100F.**
401　**99**　100f. on 25f. brown & vio　1·60　90

1973. U.A.M.P.T. As Type **216** of Cameroun.
402　100f. green, red & brown . .　1·50　75

111 "Skylab" over Globe

1974. Air. "Skylab" Exploits.
403　**111**　100f. brown, red & blue　1·25　55
404　–　150f. turquoise, blue & brn　1·90　80
DESIGN: 150f. Close-up of "Skylab".

112 Chad Mother and Children

1974. 1st Anniv of Chad Red Cross.
405　**112**　30f.+10f. multicoloured　60　60

113 Football Players

1974. Air. World Cup Football Championship, West Germany.
406　**113**　50f. brown and red　50　30
407　–　125f. green and red (vert)　1·40　60
408　–　150f. red and green . . .　1·90　95
DESIGNS: Nos. 407/8, Footballers in action similar to Type **113**.

114 Chad Family　　**116** Rotary Emblem

115 U.P.C. Emblem and Mail Canoe

1974. Air. World Population Year.
409　**114**　250f. brown, green & bl　3·00　1·60

1974. Air. Centenary of U.P.U.
410　**115**　30f. brown, red & green　50　25
411　–　40f. black and blue　2·75　1·50

412　–　100f. blue, brown & blk　1·60　70
413　–　150f. violet, green & turq　2·25　75
DESIGNS—U.P.U. Emblem and: 40f. Electric train; 100f. Jet airliner; 150f. Satellite.

1975. 70th Anniv of Rotary International.
414　**116**　50f. multicoloured . . .　75　35

117 Heads of Women of Four Races

1975. Air. International Women's Year.
415　**117**　250f. multicoloured . . .　3·75　1·90

118 "Apollo" and "Soyuz" Spacecraft about to dock

1975. Air. "Apollo–Soyuz" Test Project.
416　**118**　100f. brown, blue & green　1·10　50
417　–　130f. brown, blue & green　1·40　75
DESIGN: 130f. "Apollo" and "Soyuz" spacecraft docked.

119 "Craterostigma plantagineum"

1975. Flowers. Multicoloured.
418　5f. Type **119** . . . . . .　10　10
419　10f. "Tapinanthus globiferus"　20　15
420　15f. "Commelina forsalaei" (vert) . . . .　30　15
421　20f. "Adenium obasum" . .　35　15
422　25f. "Hibiscus esulenus" . .　60　20
423　30f. "Hibiscus sabdariffa" .　75　25
424　40f. "Kigelia africana" . .　1·10　30

120 Football

1975. Air. Olympic Games, Montreal (1976).
425　**120**　75f. green and red . . . .　80　30
426　–　100f. brown, blue & red　1·25　55
427　–　125f. blue and brown . .　1·40　80
DESIGNS: 100f. Throwing the discus; 125f. Running.

1975. Air. Successful Rendezvous of "Apollo–Soyuz" Mission. Optd **JONCTION 17 JUILLET 1975.**
428　**118**　100f. brown, blue & grn　1·10　70
429　–　130f. brown, blue & grn　1·40　90

122 Stylized British and American Flags

1975. Air. Bicentenary of American Revolution.
430　**122**　150f. blue, red & brown　1·90　95

123 "Adoration of the Shepherds" (Murillo)

1975. Air. Christmas. Religious Paintings. Mult.
431　**123**　40f. Type **123** . . . . .　55　35
432　75f. "Adoration of the Shepherds" (G. de la Tour)　1·00　55
433　80f. "Virgin of the Bible" (R. van der Weyden) (vert) .　1·25　60
434　100f. "Holy Family with the Lamb" (attrib. Raphael) (vert) . . . .　1·90　95

124 Alexander Graham Bell and Satellite

1976. Telephone Centenary.
435　**124**　100f. multicoloured . . .　1·00　50
436　125f. multicoloured . . .　1·50　75

125 U.S.S.R. (ice hockey)

1976. Winter Olympics. Medal-winners, Innsbruck. Multicoloured.
437　**125**　60f. Type **125** (postage) .　75　35
438　90f. Ski-jumping (K. Schnabl, Austria) . . . .　95　40
439　250f. Bobsleighing (West Germany) (air) . . . .　2·25　75
440　300f. Speed-skating (J. E. Storholt, Norway) . .　2·75　1·10
These stamps were not issued without overprints.

126 Paul Revere (after Copley) and his Night Ride

1976. Air. Bicentenary of American Revolution.
442　**126**　100f. Type **126** . . . . .　80　25
443　125f. Washington (after Stuart) and "Washington crossing the Delaware" (detail, Leutze) . . . .　95　35
444　150f. Lafayette offering his services to America . . . .　1·25　45
445　200f. Rochambeau and detail "Siege of Yorktown" (Couder) . . . .　1·60　70
446　250f. Franklin (after Duplessis) and "Declaration of Independence" (detail, Trumball) . . . .　2·25　80

127 Hurdles

1976. Olympic Games, Montreal. Multicoloured.
448　**127**　45f. Type **127** (postage) . .　60　25
449　100f. Boxing (air) . . . .　95　35
450　200f. Pole vaulting . . . .　1·90　55
451　300f. Putting the shot . . .　2·75　95

128 Launch of "Viking"

1976. "Viking" landing on Mars. Mult.
453　**128**　45f. Type **128** (postage) . .　45　20
454　90f. Trajectory of flight . . .　80　30
455　100f. Descent to Mars (air) .　85　35
456　200f. "Viking" in flight . . .　1·60　50
457　250f. "Viking" on landing approach . . . .　1·90　75

129 Flag and Clasped Hands on Map of Chad

1976. National Reconciliation. Mult.
459　**129**　30f. Type **129** . . . .　35　25
460　60f. Type **129** . . . .　85　30
461　120f. Map, people and various occupations . . .　1·60　70

130 Release of Political Prisoners

1976. 1st Anniv of April 1st Revolution. Mult.
462　**130**　30f. Type **130** . . . . . .　25　20
463　60f. Officer-cadets on parade　50　30
464　120f. Type **130** . . . .　1·10　55

131 Concorde

1976. Air. Concorde's First Commercial Flight.
465　**131**　250f. blue, red & black .　4·25　2·75

132 Gourd and Ladle

1976. Pyrograved Gourds.
466　**132**　30f. multicoloured . . . .　30　20
467　–　60f. multicoloured . . . .　60　25
468　–　120f. multicoloured . . . .　1·25　60
DESIGNS: 60f., 120f. Gourds with different decorations.

1976. Nobel Prizewinners. As T **189** of Central African Empire. Multicoloured.
469　45f. Robert Koch (Medicine, 1905) . . . .　95　35
470　90f. Anatole France (Literature, 1921) . . . . .　1·25　60
471　100f. Albert Einstein (Physics, 1921) (air) . . . .　1·25　60
472　200f. Dag Hammarskjold (Peace, 1961) . . . . . .　1·90　50
473　300f. Dr. S. Tomonaga (Physics, 1965) . . . . . .　2·75　75

133 "The Nativity" (Hans Holbein)

1976. Air. Christmas. Multicoloured.
475 30f. "The Nativity"
(Altdorfer) 30 20
476 60f. Type **133** 55 30
477 120f. "Adoration of the
Shepherds" (Honthorst)
(horiz) . . . . 1·00 60
478 150f. "Adoration of the
Magi" (David) (horiz) . . 1·60 95

134 "Lesdiguieres Bridge"

1976. Air. Centenary of Impressionism. Paintings by Johan Bathold Jongkind. Multicoloured.
479 100f. Type **134** . . . . . 1·40 70
480 120f. "Warship" . . . . . 3·00 1·10

1977. Zeppelin Flights. As T **190** of Central African Empire. Multicoloured.
481 100f. Friedrichshafen and
German 50pf. stamp, 1936
(postage) . . . . 1·25 50
482 125f. Polar scene and
German 1m. stamp, 1931
(air) . . . . 1·10 30
483 150f. Chicago store and
German 4m. stamp, 1933 2·00 45
484 175f. New York, London and
German 2m. stamp, 1928 4·00 75
485 200f. New York and U.S.
$2.60 stamp, 1930 . . . 2·75 85

1977. Air. 10th Anniv of International French Language Council. As T **204** of Benin.
487 100f. multicoloured 85 50

135 Simon Bolivar

1977. Great Personalities. Multicoloured.
488 150f. Type **135** . . . . . . 1·25 50
489 175f. Joseph J. Roberts . . 1·50 50
490 200f. Queen Wilhelmina . . 1·75 60
491 200f. General de Gaulle . . . 2·50 85
493 250f. Coronation of Queen
Elizabeth II (horiz) . . . 2·50 90
492 325f. King Baudouin and
Queen Fabiola . . . . 2·75 95

137 Lafayette and Arrival in America

1977. Air. Bicentenary of American Independence. Multicoloured.
495 100f. Type **137** . . . . . 1·10 50
496 120f. Abraham Lincoln . . 1·25 60
497 150f. F. J. Madison . . . 1·75 75

138 Radio Aerial, Sound
Waves and Map

1977. Posts and Telecommunications Emblems.
498 – 30f. black and yellow . . 35 20
499 **138** 60f. multicoloured 70 25
500 – 120f. multicoloured . . . 1·25 60
DESIGNS—HORIZ (47 × 26 mm): 30f. Posthorn and initials "ONPT". VERT (26 × 36 mm): 120f. Telecommunications skyline and initials "TIT".

139 Concorde

1977. Air. "North Atlantic"—Concorde and Lindbergh Commemorations.
501 **139** 100f. blue, red & lt blue 75 45
502 – 120f. brown, blue & grn 85 50
503 – 150f. violet, red & green 1·10 65
504 – 200f. orange, pur & brn 1·60 85
505 – 300f. blue, purple & blk 2·50 1·25
DESIGNS: 120f. to 300f. Various portraits of Lindbergh with "Spirit of St. Louis" against different backgrounds.

140 "Mariner 10"

1977. Air. Space Research.
506 **140** 100f. blue, olive & green 80 50
507 – 200f. brown, green & red 1·75 1·00
508 – 300f. brown, grn & bistre 2·50 1·25
DESIGNS: 200f. "Luna 21"; 300f. "Viking".

141 Running **142** "Back Pain"

1977. Air. Sports.
509 **141** 30f. brown, red & blue . . 30 20
510 – 60f. brown, blue & orge 55 30
511 – 120f. multicoloured . . 1·00 50
512 – 125f. mauve, violet & grn 1·25 60
DESIGNS: 60f. Volleyball; 120f. Football; 125f. Basketball.

1977. World Rheumatism Year.
513 **142** 30f. red, green and violet 35 20
514 – 60f. red, violet and green 55 25
515 – 120f. blue, red & lt blue 1·25 60
DESIGNS—HORIZ: 60f. "Neck pain". VERT: 120f. "Knee pain".

1977. Air. 1st Commercial Paris–New York Flight of Concorde. Optd **PARIS NEW-YORK 22.11.77.**
516 **139** 100f. blue, red & lt blue 2·25 1·25

144 Saving a Goal

1977. World Football Cup Championship. Mult.
517 40f. Type **144** 35 15
518 60f. Heading the ball 55 20
519 100f. Referee 95 30
520 200f. Foot kicking ball . . . 1·90 60
521 300f. Pele (Brazilian player) . 3·00 95

145 "Christ in the Manger" (detail)

1977. Air. Christmas. Paintings by Rubens. Mult.
523 30f. Type **145** 45 25
524 60f. "Virgin and Child with
Two Donors" 75 35
525 100f. "The Adoration of the
Shepherds" . . . . . . 1·25 60
526 125f. "The Adoration of the
Magi" (detail) . . . . . 1·60 80

1978. Coronation of Queen Elizabeth II. No. 493 optd **ANNIVERSAIRE DU COURONNEMENT 1953–1978.**
527 250f. multicoloured . . . . 2·50 1·50

147 Antoine de Saint-Exupery

1978. Air. History of Aviation. Multicoloured.
529 40f. Type **147** 50 20
530 50f. Wright Brothers and
aircraft in flight 60 25
531 80f. Hugo Junkers 85 45
532 100f. Italo Balbo . . . . . 1·10 55
533 120f. "Concorde" . . . . . 1·25 75

1978. Air. "Philexafrique" Stamp Exhibition, Gabon (1st issue), and International Stamp Fair, Essen. As T **237** of Benin. Multicoloured.
535 100f. Grey heron and
Mecklenburg-Strelitz, ½sgr.
stamp, 1864 . . . . . 2·75 1·90
536 100f. Black rhinoceros and
Chad 500f. stamp, 1961 . 2·75 1·90

148 "Portrait" **150** Head and
Unhealthy and
Healthy Villages

1978. 450th Death Anniv of Albrecht Durer (artist). Multicoloured.
537 60f. Type **148** 50 15
538 150f. "Jacob Muffel" . . . . 1·40 30
539 250f. "Young Girl" . . . . 2·25 60
540 350f. "Oswolt Krel" . . . . 3·50 80

149 "Helene Fourment"

1978. 400th Birth Anniv of Peter Paul Rubens (artist). Multicoloured.
541 60f. "Abraham and
Melchisedek" (horiz) . . 60 15
542 120f. Type **149** . . . . . 1·10 25

543 200f. "David and the Elders
of Israel" (horiz) . . . . 1·90 60
544 300f. "Anne of Austria" . . . 3·25 85

1978. National Health Day.
546 **150** 60f. multicoloured 60 35

1978. World Cup Football Championship Finalists. Nos. 517/21 optd with teams and scores of past finals.
547 **144** 40f. multicoloured 35 20
548 – 60f. multicoloured . . . 50 30
549 – 100f. multicoloured . . . 85 50
550 – 200f. multicoloured . . . 1·90 95
551 – 300f. multicoloured . . . 3·00 1·50
OPTS: 40f. **1962 BRESIL-TCHECOSLOVAQUIE 3-1**;. 60f. **1966 GRAND BRETAGNE-ALLEMAGNE (RFA) 4-2**;. 100f. **1970 BRESIL-ITALIE 4-1**; 200f. **1974 ALLEMAGNE (RFA)-PAYS BAS 2-1**;. 300f. **1978 ARGENTINE-PAYS BAS 3-1.**

152 Camel Riders, Satellites and U.P.U. Emblem

1978. "Philexafrique 2" Exhibition, Libreville, Gabon (2nd issue).
553 **152** 60f. red, mauve & blue . . 1·60 95
554 – 150f. multicoloured . . . 3·00 2·25
DESIGN: 150f. Mother and child, native village and hibiscus.

153 Sand Gazelle

1979. Endangered Animals. Multicoloured.
555 40f. Type **153** 45 15
556 50f. Addax 50 15
557 60f. Scimitar oryx 60 20
558 100f. Cheetah . . . . . . 1·00 40
559 150f. African ass . . . . . 1·60 50
560 300f. Black rhinoceros . . . 3·25 90

154 African Boy and Wall Painting

1979. International Year of the Child. Mult.
561 65f. Type **154** 50 20
562 75f. Asian girl 55 25
563 100f. European child and
doves 80 30
564 150f. African boys and
drawing of boats . . . . . 1·25 50

1979. 10th Anniv of "Apollo 11" Moon Landing. Nos. 453/7 optd with lunar module and **ALUNISSAGE APOLLO XI JUILLET 1969.**
567 45f. Type **128** (postage) . . . 35 25
568 90f. Trajectory of flight . . . 80 35
569 100f. Descent on Mars (air) . 75 50
570 200f. "Viking" in flight . . . 1·50 85
571 250f. "Viking" on landing
approach . . . . . . 1·90 1·10

157 Hurdles

1979. Air. Olympic Games, Moscow 1980. Mult.
573 15f. Type **157** 20 15
574 30f. Hockey 30 20
575 250f. Swimming . . . . . 1·90 70
576 350f. Running . . . . . 2·50 90

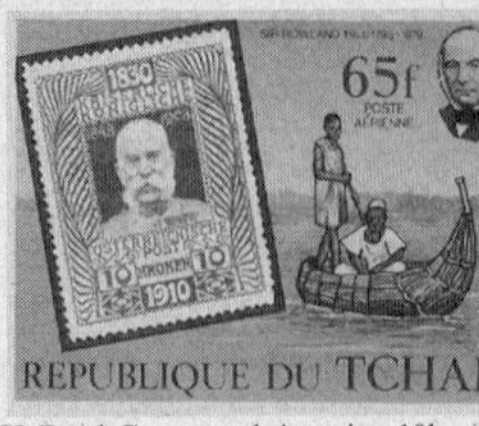

158 Reed Canoe and Austrian 10k. stamp, 1910

1979. Air. Death Centenary of Sir Rowland Hill. Multicoloured.

578 65f. Type **158** 50 15
579 100f. Sailing canoe and U.S. $1 stamp of 1894 85 30
580 200f. "Curacao" (paddle-steamer) and French 1f. stamp of 1853 1·75 60
581 300f. "Calypso" (liner) and Holstein 1⅓s. stamp of 1864 2·25 1·10

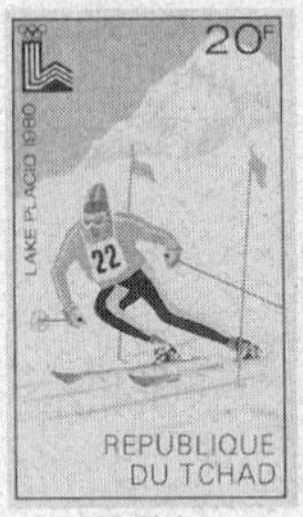

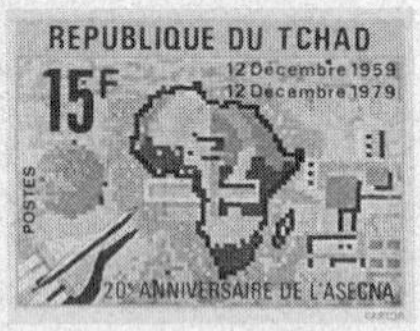

159 Slalom **160** "Concorde" and Map of Africa

1979. Winter Olympic Games, Lake Placid (1980). Multicoloured.

583 20f. Type **159** 20 15
584 40f. Biathlon 35 15
585 60f. Ski jump (horiz) 40 15
586 150f. Women's giant slalom 1·10 35
587 350f. Cross-country skiing (horiz) 2·50 80
588 500f. Downhill skiing (horiz) 3·75 1·25

1980. 20th Anniv of African Air Safety Organization (ASECNA).

589 **160** 15f. multicoloured 30 10
590 30f. multicoloured 45 25
591 60f. multicoloured 90 50

1981. Various stamps optd **POSTES 1981** or surch also.

592 **157** 30f. on 15f. multicoloured 75 60
593 – 30f. mult (No. 574) 75 60
594 **158** 60f. on 65f. multicoloured 1·50 1·00
595 – 60f. on 100f. mult (No. 579) 1·50 1·00

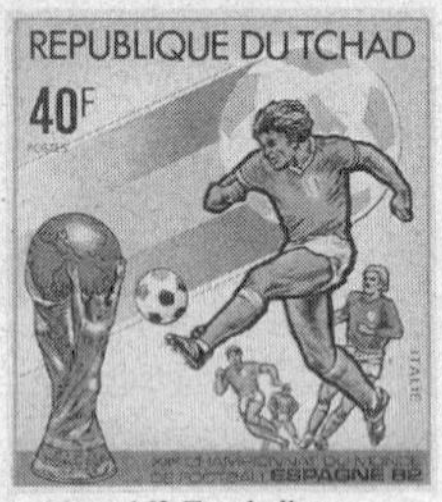

162 Footballer

1982. World Cup Football Championship, Spain. Multicoloured.

596 30f. Hungary (postage) 25 15
597 40f. Type **162** 30 15
598 50f. Algeria 35 20
599 60f. Argentina 45 20
600 80f. Brazil (air) 55 20
601 300f. West Germany 2·25 70

DESIGNS: As T **162** but each value showing different team's footballer.

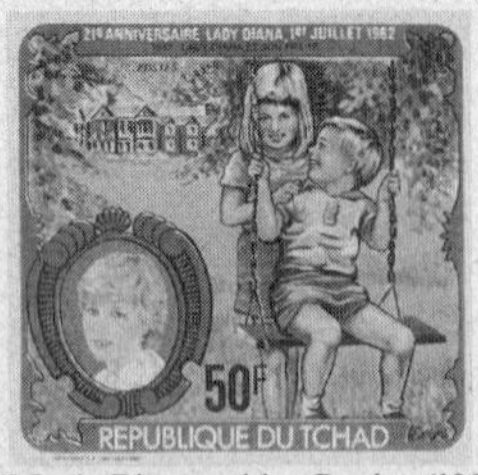

163 Lady Diana and her Brother (1967)

1982. 21st Birthday of Princess of Wales. Mult.

603 30f. Lady Diana in christening robe (1961) (postage) 30 15
604 40f. Portrait of Lady Diana (1965) 35 15
605 50f. Type **163** 45 20
606 60f. Lady Diana and her pony (1975) 55 20
607 80f. Lady Diana in Switzerland (1977) (air) 60 20
608 300f. Lady Diana as nursery teacher (1980) 2·50 70

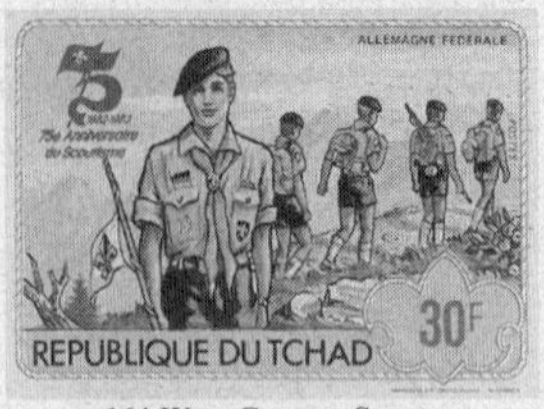

164 West German Scouts

1982. 75th Anniv of Scout Movement. Mult.

610 30f. Type **164** (postage) 35 15
611 40f. Upper Volta scouts 35 15
612 50f. Mali scouts and African dancers 50 20
613 60f. Scottish scout, piper and dancer 60 20
614 80f. Kuwait scouts (air) 55 20
615 300f. Chad cub scout 2·25 70

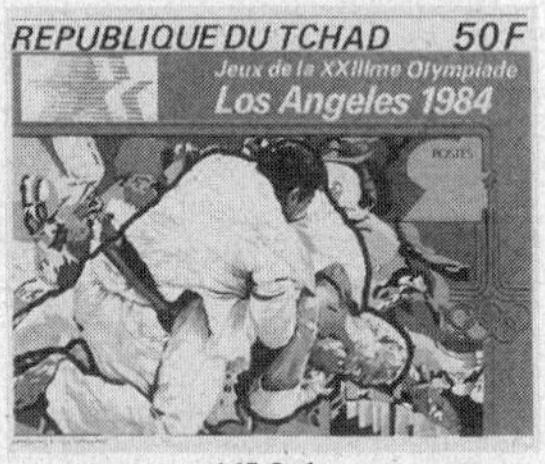

165 Judo

1982. Olympic Games, Los Angeles (1984) (1st issue). Multicoloured.

617 30f. Gymnastics (horse exercise) (postage) 30 15
618 40f. Show jumping 30 15
619 50f. Type **165** 35 20
620 60f. High jumping 60 20
621 80f. Hurdling (air) 55 20
622 300f. Gymnastics (floor exercise) 2·25 70

See also Nos. 678/83 and 735/8.

1982. Birth of Prince William of Wales. Nos. 603/8 optd **21 JUIN 1982 WILLIAM ARTHUR PHILIP LOUIS PRINCE DE GALLES**.

624 30f. Type **163** (postage) 30 15
625 40f. Portrait of Lady Diana as a young girl 35 15
626 50f. Lady Diana and her brother 45 20
627 60f. Lady Diana with her pony 50 20
628 80f. Lady Diana in Switzerland (air) 60 20
629 300f. Lady Diana with children 2·50 70

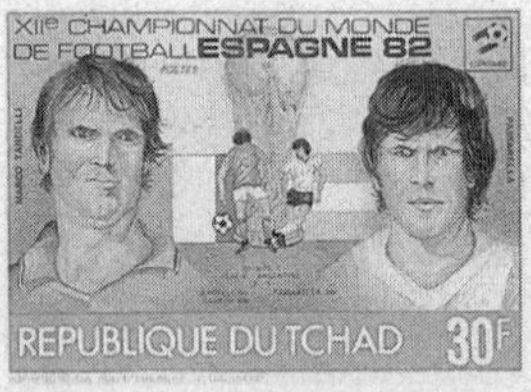

167 Marco Tardelli (Italy) and Passarella (Argentine)

1983. World Cup Football Championship Results. Multicoloured.

631 30f. Type **167** (postage) 25 10
632 40f. Paolo Rossi (Italy) and Zico (Brazil) 30 15
633 50f. Pierre Littbarski (West Germany) and Platini (France) 35 20
634 60f. Gabriele Oriali (Italy) and Smolarek (Poland) 45 20
635 70f. Boniek (Poland) and Alain Giresse (France) (air) 55 20
636 300f. Bruno Conti (Italy) and Paul Breitner (West Germany) 2·25 70

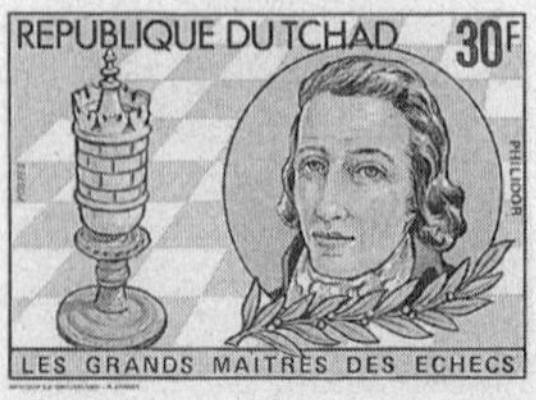

168 Philidor and 19th-century European Rook

1982. Chess Grand Masters. Multicoloured.

638 30f. Type **168** (postage) 35 15
639 40f. Paul Morphy and 19th-century Chinese knight 50 15
640 50f. Howard Staunton and Lewis knight 60 25
641 60f. Jean-Paul Capablanca and African knight 75 25
642 80f. Boris Spassky and Staunton knight (air) 1·25 25
643 300f. Anatoly Karpov and 19th-century Chinese knight 3·00 1·00

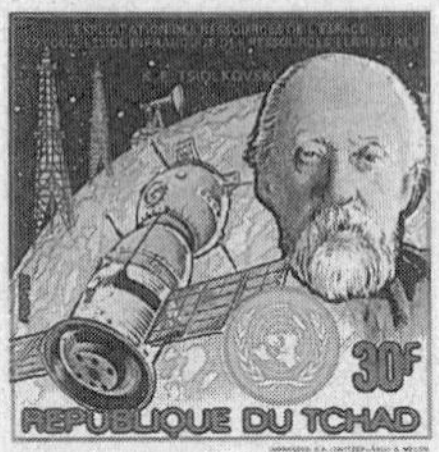

169 K. E. Tsiolkovski and "Soyuz"

1983. Exploitation of Space. Multicoloured.

645 30f. Type **169** (postage) 25 10
646 40f. R. H. Goddard and space telescope 30 15
647 50f. Korolev and ultra-violet telescope 35 20
648 60f. Von Braun and Space Shuttle 45 20
649 80f. Esnault Pelterie and "Ariane" rocket and "Symphonie" satellite (air) 55 25
650 300f. H. Oberth and construction of orbiting space station 2·25 70

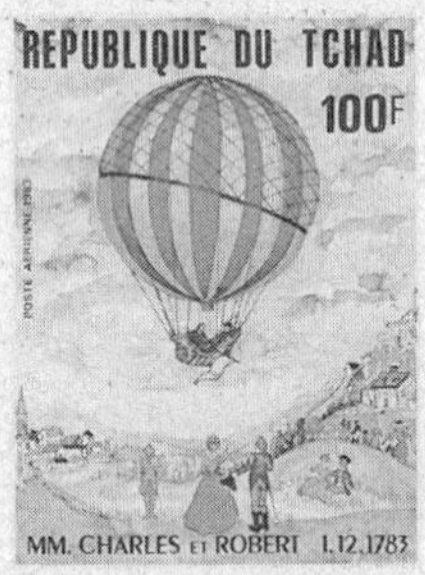

170 Charles and Robert Balloon, 1783

1983. Air. Balloons. Multicoloured.

652 100f. Type **170** 95 50
653 200f. Blanchard balloon, Berlin, 1788 1·90 95
654 300f. Charles Green balloon, London, 1837 (horiz) 2·50 1·75
655 400f. Modern advertising airship (horiz) 3·25 1·75

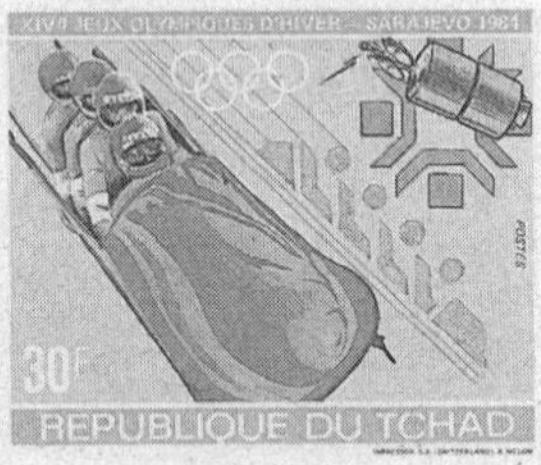

171 Bobsleigh

1983. Winter Olympic Games, Sarajevo. Mult.

657 30f. Type **171** (postage) 25 10
658 40f. Speed skating 30 15
659 50f. Cross-country skiing 30 20
660 60f. Ice hockey 35 20
661 80f. Ski jump (air) 55 20
662 300f. Downhill skiing 2·25 70

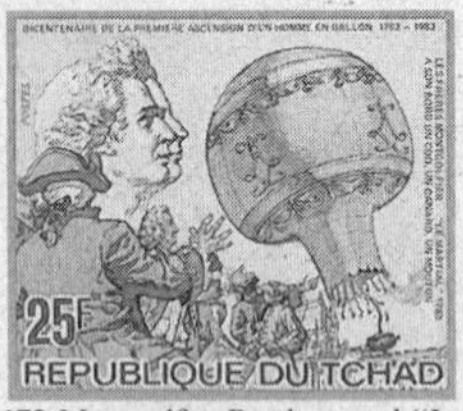

172 Montgolfier Brothers and "Le Martial" Balloon, 1783

1983. Bicentenary of Manned Flight. Multicoloured.

664 25f. Type **172** (postage) 20 15
665 45f. Pilatre de Rozier and first manned flight, 1783 35 20
666 50f. Jacques Garnerin and balloon (first parachute descent, 1797) 35 20
667 60f. J. P. Blanchard and balloon at Chelsea, 1784 45 30
668 80f. H. Giffard and steam-powered dirigible, 1852 (air) 75 40
669 250f. Zeppelin and airship "L 21", 1900 2·10 1·25

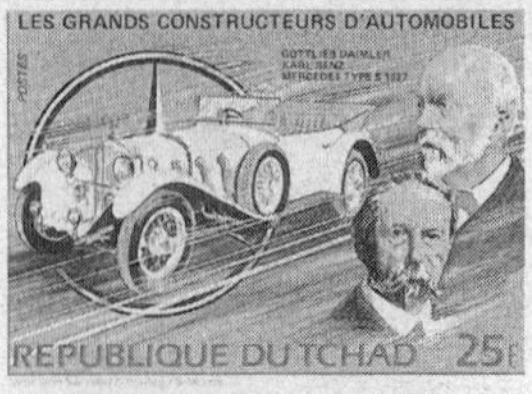

173 Gottlieb Daimler, Karl Benz and Mercedes "Type S," 1927

1983. Car Manufacturers. Multicoloured.

671 25f. Type **173** (postage) 30 10
672 35f. Friedrich von Martini and Torpedo, Martini "Type GC 32", 1913 45 15
673 50f. Walter P. Chrysler and Chrysler "70", 1926 70 20
674 60f. Nicola Romeo and Alfa Romeo "6 C 1750 Grand Sport", 1929 75 20
675 80f. Stewart Rolls, Henry Royce and "Phantom II Continental", 1934 (air) 95 20
676 250f. Lord Shrewsbury and Talbot-Lago "Record", 1948 2·50 70

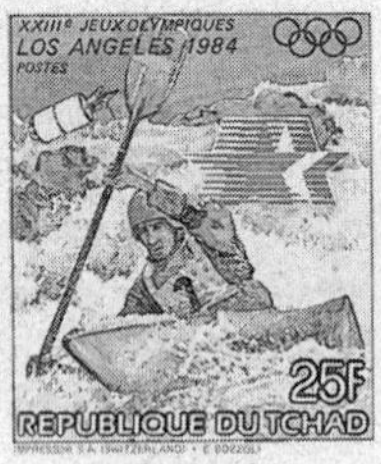

174 Kayak

1983. Olympic Games, Los Angeles (2nd issue). Multicoloured.

678 25f. Type **174** (postage) 20 10
679 45f. Long jumping 30 15
680 50f. Boxing 35 15
681 60f. Discus-throwing 45 20
682 80f. Relay race (air) 60 20
683 350f. Horse jumping 2·50 70

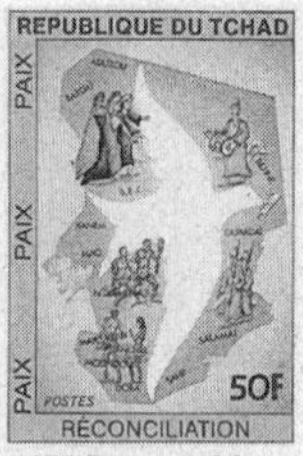

175 Dove on Map

1983. Peace and Reconciliation. Multicoloured.

685 50f. Type **175** (postage) 35 15
686 50f. Foodstuffs on map 45 20
687 50f. President Habre 35 15
688 60f. As No. 687 45 15
689 80f. Type **175** 65 25
690 80f. As No. 686 80 30
691 80f. As No. 687 65 25
692 100f. As No. 687 75 25
693 150f. Type **175** (air) 1·00 30
694 150f. As No. 686 1·40 50
695 200f. Type **175** 1·25 45
696 200f. As No. 686 1·75 65

1983. 15th World Scout Jamboree, Canada. Nos. 610/15 optd **XV WORLD JAMBOREE MONDIAL ALBERTA CANADA 1983**.

697 30f. multicoloured (postage) 25 15
698 40f. multicoloured 30 15
699 50f. multicoloured 35 20
700 60f. multicoloured 45 20
701 80f. multicoloured (air) 55 20
702 300f. multicoloured 2·25 70

1983. 60th Anniv of Int Chess Federation. Nos. 638/43 optd **60e ANNIVERSAIRE FEDERATION MONDIAL D'ECHECS 1924–1984**.

704 30f. multicoloured (postage) 50 20
705 40f. multicoloured 60 20
706 50f. multicoloured 60 25
707 60f. multicoloured 75 25
708 80f. multicoloured (air) 1·25 45
709 300f. multicoloured 3·75 1·25

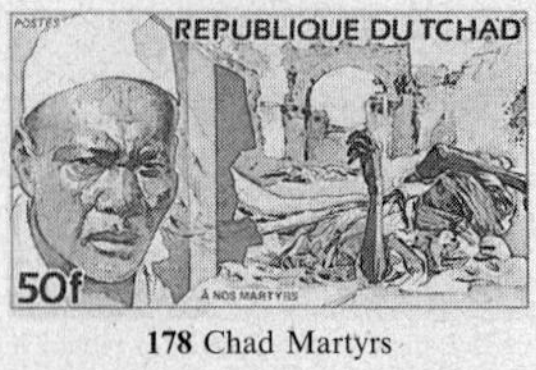

178 Chad Martyrs

1984. Celebrities. Multicoloured.

711 50f. Type **178** 35 15
712 200f. P. Harris and Rotary Headquarters, U.S.A. 1·50 35
713 300f. Alfred Nobel and will 2·50 60

714		350f. Raphael and "Virgin with the Infant and St. John the Baptist"	3·75	75
715		400f. Rembrandt and "The Holy Family" (air)	3·75	85
716		500f. Goethe and Scenes from "Faust"	4·25	1·00

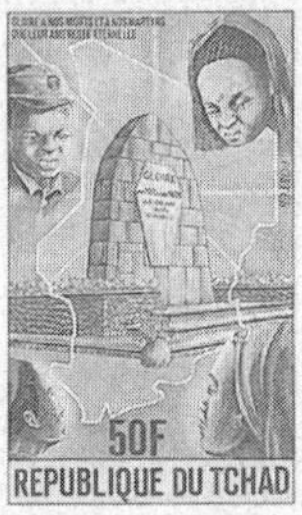

179 Martyrs Memorial

1984. Martyrs Memorial.

718	**179**	50f. mult (postage)	35	15
719		80f. multicoloured	60	25
720		120f. multicoloured	85	25
721		200f. multicoloured (air)	1·60	50
722		250f. multicoloured	2·25	75

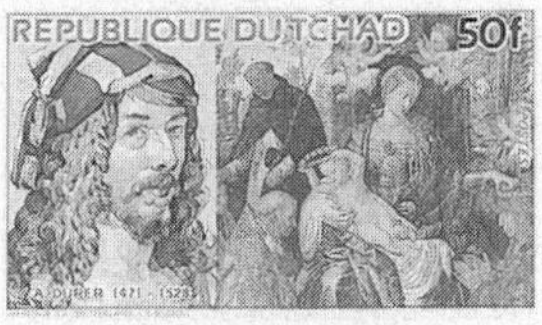

180 Durer and Painting

1984. Celebrities and Events. Multicoloured.

723		50f. Type **180** (postage)	75	15
724		200f. Henri Dunant and battle scene	1·75	35
725		300f. Early telephone and satellite receiving station, Goonhilly Downs	2·25	60
726		350f. President Kennedy and first foot-print on Moon	2·75	75
727		400f. Infra-red satellite picture (Europe–Africa co-operation) (air)	2·50	75
728		500f. Prince and Princess of Wales	3·75	1·00

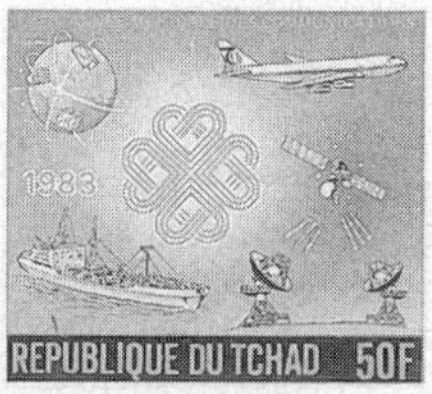

181 "Communications"

1984. World Communications Year.

730	**181**	50f. mult (postage)	45	15
731		60f. multicoloured	50	35
732		70f. multicoloured	50	35
733		125f. multicoloured (air)	1·00	55
734		250f. multicoloured	1·90	1·10

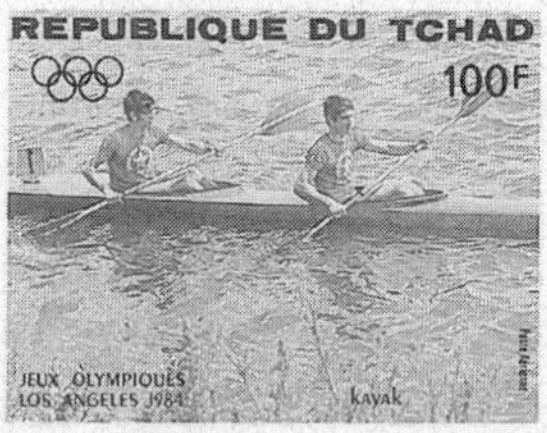

182 Two-man Kayak

1984. Air. Olympic Games, Los Angeles (3rd issue). Multicoloured.

735		100f. Type **182**	75	25
736		200f. Kayaks (close-up)	1·50	50
737		300f. One-man kayak	2·25	75
738		400f. Coxed fours	3·00	1·00

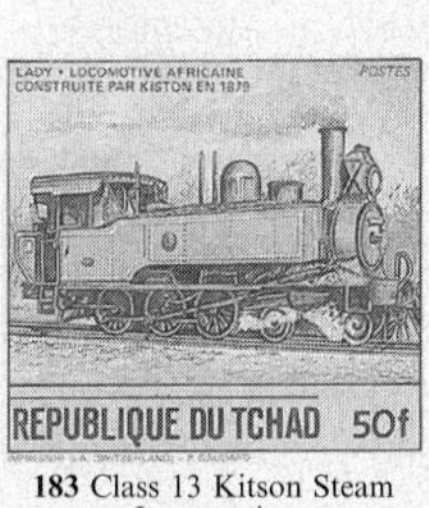

183 Class 13 Kitson Steam Locomotive

1984. Historic Transport. Multicoloured.

740		50f. Type **183** (postage)	1·50	1·00
741		200f. Sailing boat on Lake Chad	1·75	65
742		300f. Graf Zeppelin (airship)	3·00	1·25
743		350f. Six-wheel Renault automobile, 1930	2·75	1·25
744		400f. Bloch "120" airplane (air)	2·50	1·50
745		500f. Douglas "DC-8" airplane	3·75	2·00

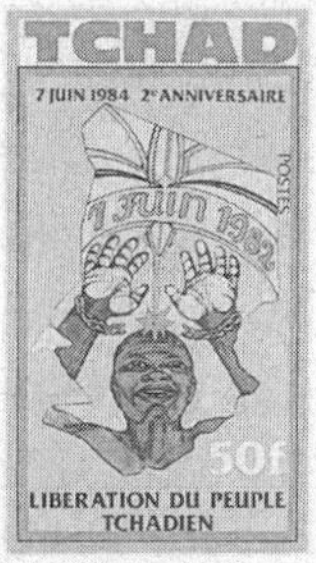

184 African with broken Manacles

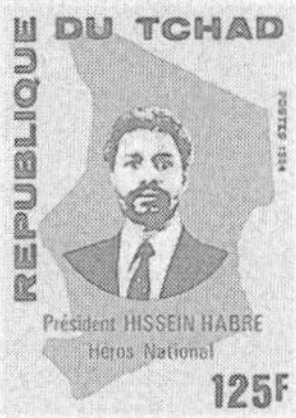

185 Pres. Hissein Habre

1984. 2nd Anniv of Entrance of Government Forces in N'Djamena.

747	**184**	50f. multicoloured	50	25

1984.

748	**185**	125f. black, blue & yellow	1·25	50

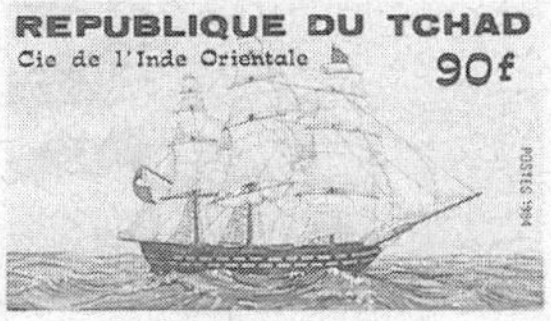

186 British East Indiaman

1984. Transport. Multicoloured. (a) Ships.

749		90f. Type **186**	95	45
750		125f. "Vera Cruz" (steamer)	1·25	55
751		200f. "Carlisle Castle" (sail merchantman)	2·25	75
752		300f. "Britannia" (steamer)	2·75	1·25
		(b) Locomotives.		
753		100f. Series 701, 1885, France	1·25	15
754		150f. "Columbia", 1888, Belgium	1·90	25
755		250f. Mediterranean locomotive, 1900, Italy	3·00	40
756		350f. MAV 114	4·50	55

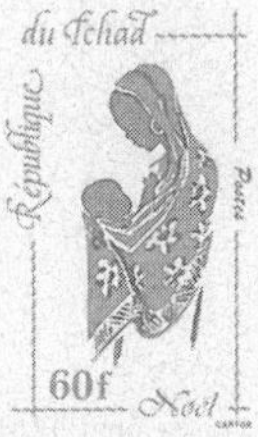

187 Virgin and Child

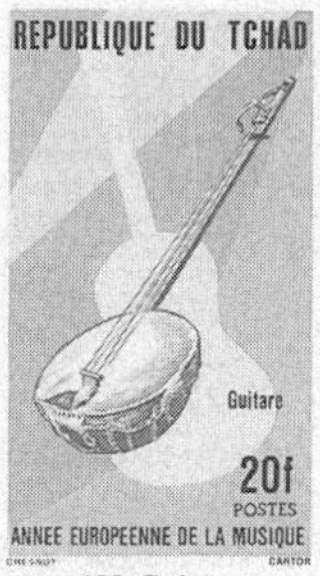

188 Guitars

1984. Christmas.

757	**187**	50f. brown and blue	45	15
758		60f. brown and orange	50	20
759		80f. brown and green	65	25
760		85f. brown and purple	70	25
761		100f. brown and orange	85	30
762		135f. brown and blue	1·25	45

1985. European Music Year. Multicoloured.

763		20f. Type **188**	20	10
764		25f. Harps	25	15
765		30f. Xylophones	30	15
766		50f. Drums	45	20
767		70f. As No. 766	55	20
768		80f. As No. 764	75	30
769		100f. Type **188**	90	45
770		250f. As No. 765	2·25	85

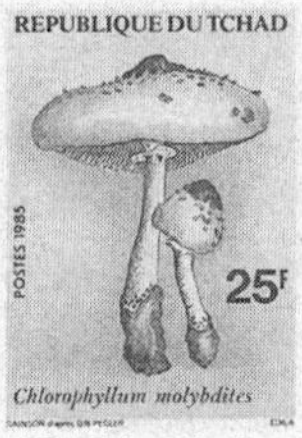

189 "Chlorophyllum molybdites"

1985. Fungi. Multicoloured.

771		25f. Type **189**	55	30
772		30f. "Tulostoma volvulatum"	70	35
773		50f. "Lentinus tuberregium"	1·00	45
774		70f. As No. 773	1·40	60
775		80f. "Podaxis pistillaris"	1·75	65
776		100f. Type **189**	2·50	1·00

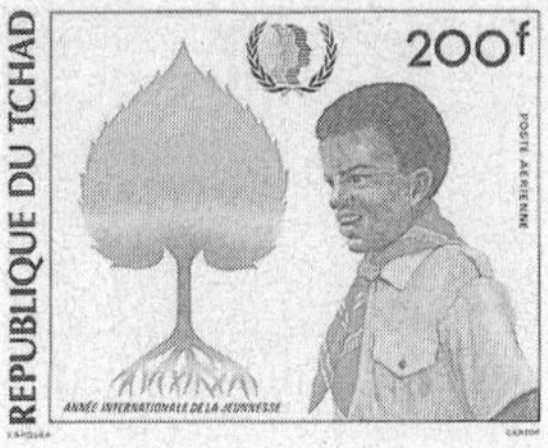

190 Stylized Tree and Scout

1985. Air. "Philexafrique" Stamp Exhibition, Lome, Togo (1st issue). Multicoloured.

777		200f. Type **190**	1·90	1·50
778		200f. Fokker "27" airplane	1·90	1·50

See also Nos. 808/9.

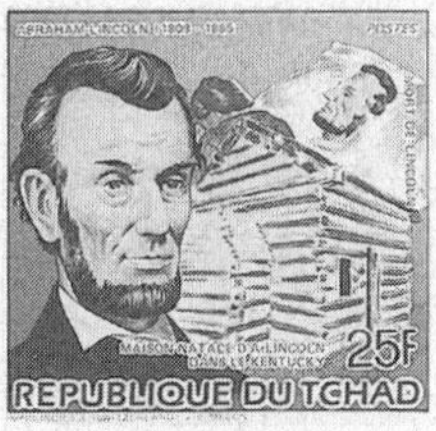

191 Abraham Lincoln

1985. Celebrities. Multicoloured.

779		25f. Type **191** (postage)	20	10
780		45f. Henri Dunant (founder of Red Cross)	45	15
781		50f. Gottlieb Daimler (automobile designer)	60	15
782		60f. Louis Bleriot (pilot) (air)	55	30
783		80f. Paul Harris (founder of Rotary International)	55	20
784		350f. Auguste Piccard (undersea explorer)	3·75	1·60

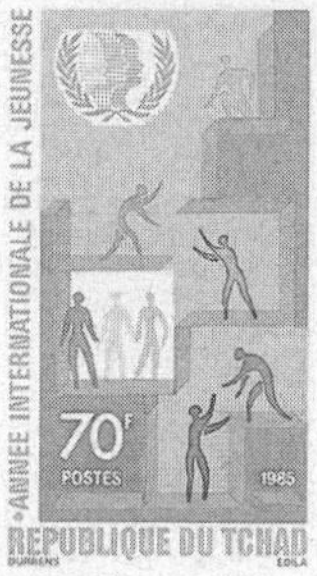

192 Figures within Geometric Pattern

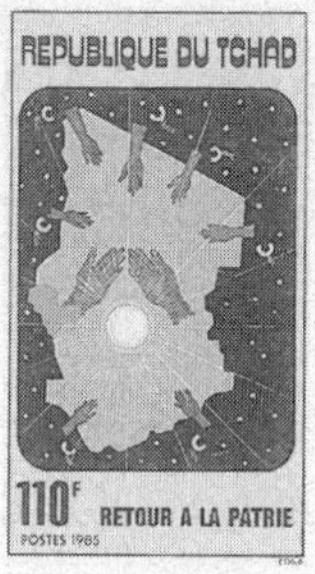

193 Sun and Hands breaking through Darkness

1985. International Youth Year. Multicoloured.

786		70f. Type **192**	50	25
787		200f. Figures on ribbon around globe	1·50	75

1985. 3rd Anniv of Entrance of Government Forces in N'DJamena. Multicoloured.

788		70f. Type **193**	55	25
789		70f. Claw attacking hand	55	25
790		70f. Pres. Hissein Habre (36×48 mm)	25	20
791		110f. Type **193**	80	35
792		110f. As No. 789	80	35
793		110f. As No. 790	1·10	35

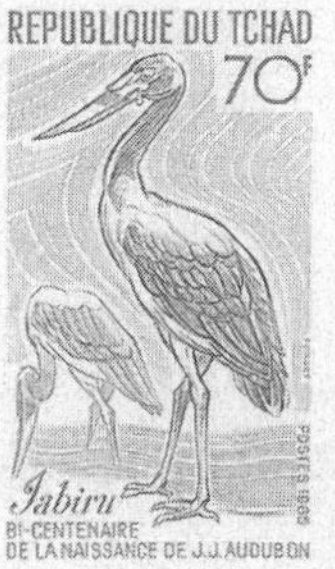

194 Saddle-bill Stork ("Jabiru")

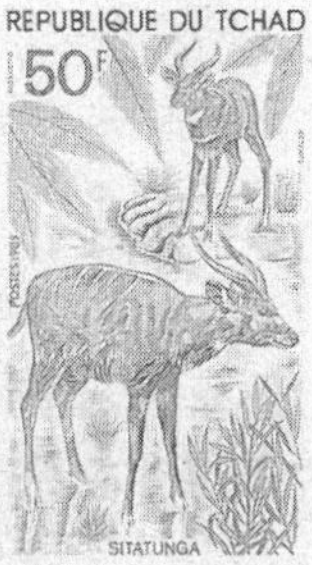

196 Sitatunga

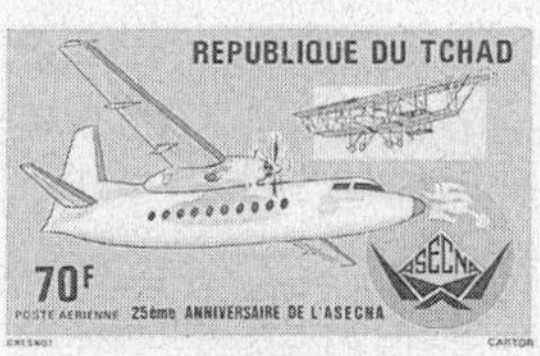

195 Fokker Friendship, Farman M.F.11 and Emblem

1985. Birth Bicentenary of John J. Audubon (ornithologist).

794	**194**	70f. black, blue & brown	1·40	85
795	–	110f. olive, green & brown	2·00	1·25
796	–	150f. blue, red and olive	3·00	1·90
797	–	200f. dp blue, mauve & bl	3·50	2·10

DESIGNS: 110f. Ostrich ("Autruche"); 150f. Marabou stork ("Marabout"); 200f. Secretary bird ("Messager Serpentaire").

1985. Air. 25th Anniv of ASECNA (navigation agency). Multicoloured.

799		70f. Type **195**	50	30
800		110f. Fokker "F.27" "Friendship" and "Spirit of St. Louis"	75	50
801		250f. Fokker "F.27" "Friendship" and Vickers Vimy	1·90	1·25

1985. Mammals.

802	**196**	50f. brown, bl & dp brn	55	35
803	–	70f. brown, green and red	70	50
804	–	250f. multicoloured	2·50	1·60

DESIGNS—HORIZ: 70f. Greater kudus. VERT: 250f. Bearded mouflons.

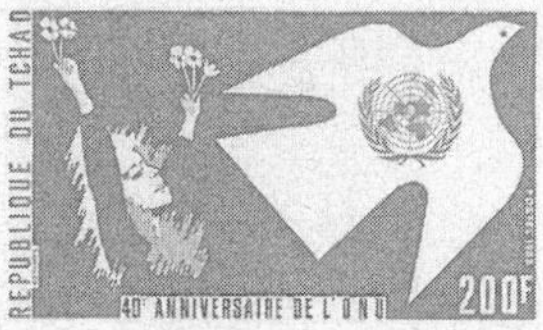

197 U.N. Emblem on Peace Dove and Girl with Flowers

1985. 40th Anniv of U.N.O. and 25th Anniv of U.N. Membership.

806	**197**	200f. blue, red & brown	1·50	1·00
807	–	300f. blue, red & yellow	2·25	1·50

DESIGN: 300f. U.N. emblem as flower with peace doves forming stalk.

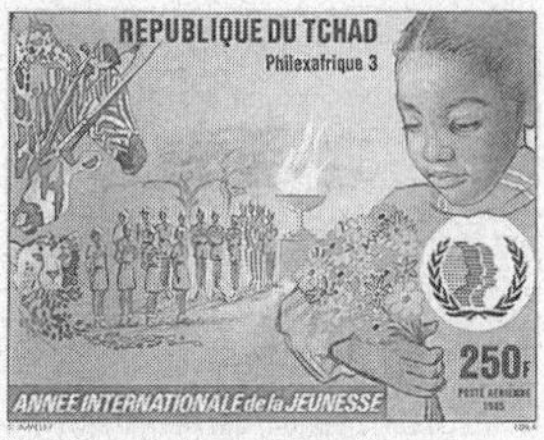

198 Girl with Posy, Youth Ceremony and I.Y.Y. Emblem

1985. Air. "Philexafrique" Stamp Exhibition, Lome, Togo (2nd issue). Multicoloured.

808		250f. Type **198** (International Youth Year)	2·25	1·90
809		250f. Computer terminal, liner, airplane, diesel freight train, rocket and U.P.U. emblem	4·25	1·00

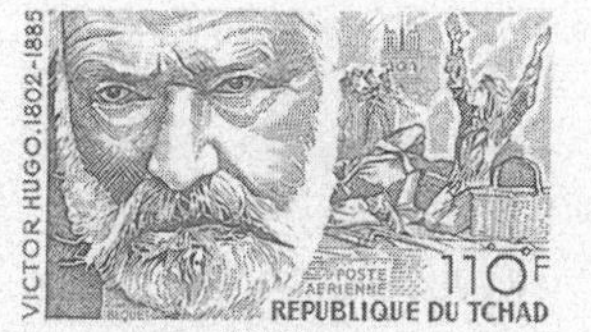

199 Hugo

1985. Air. Death Centenary of Victor Hugo (writer).

810	**199**	70f. blue, sepia and brown	50	35
811		110f. brown, green & red	75	50
812		250f. black, red & orange	1·90	1·00
813		300f. purple, blue and red	2·25	1·25

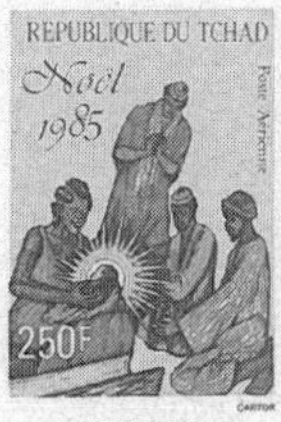

200 Nativity

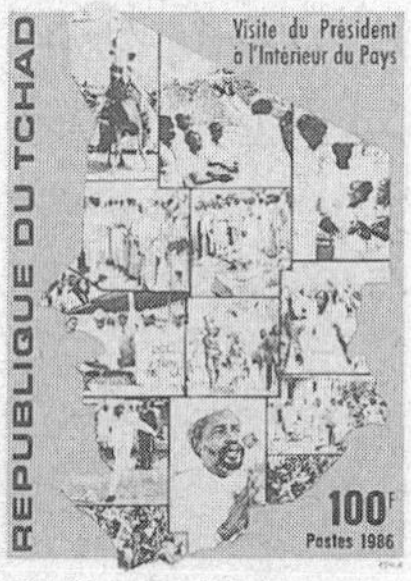

201 Pictures of Visit on Map

1985. Air. Christmas.

814	**200**	250f. multicoloured	1·90	75

1986. Visit of President to Interior.

815	**201**	100f. yellow, black & grn	95	50
816		170f. yellow, black & pink	1·90	75
817		200f. yellow, black & grn	2·25	1·25

1987. Various stamps surch.

818	–	170f. on 300f. mult (725) (postage)	70	60
819	–	230f. on 300f. blue, red and yellow (807)	1·00	85
820	–	240f. on 300f. mult (742)	1·00	85
822	**175**	100f. on 200f. mult (air)	70	55
823	–	100f. on 200f. mult (696)	60	60
824	–	100f. on 250f. mult (669)	70	55
825	–	100f. on 300f. mult (643)	40	30
826	–	100f. on 300f. mult (662)	40	30
827	**179**	170f. on 200f. mult	70	60

828	181	170f. on 250f. mult	1·10	90
829	–	170f. on 300f. mult (601)	70	60
830	–	170f. on 300f. mult (622)	70	60
831	–	240f. on 300f. mult (636)	1·00	90

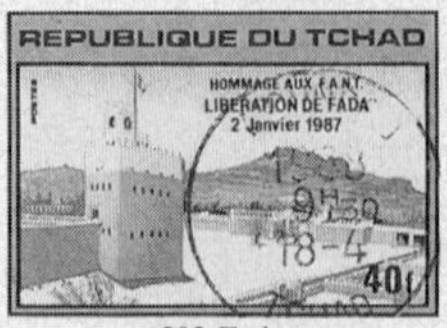

203 Fada

1987. Liberation of Fada.
832 **203** 40f. multicoloured . . . .

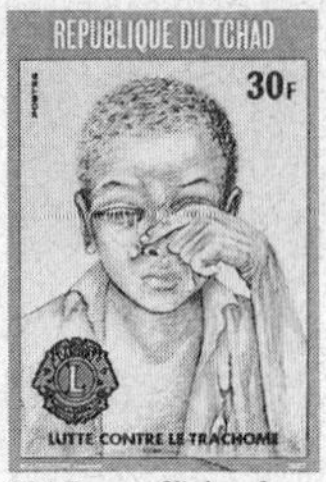

204 Boy suffering from Trachoma

1987. Lions Club Anti-trachoma Campaign. Mult.

835	30f. Type **204** . . . .
837	100f. Type **204** . . . .
838	120f. Healthy boy and afflicted boys (horiz) . . .
840	200f. Doctor examining boy (horiz) . . . .

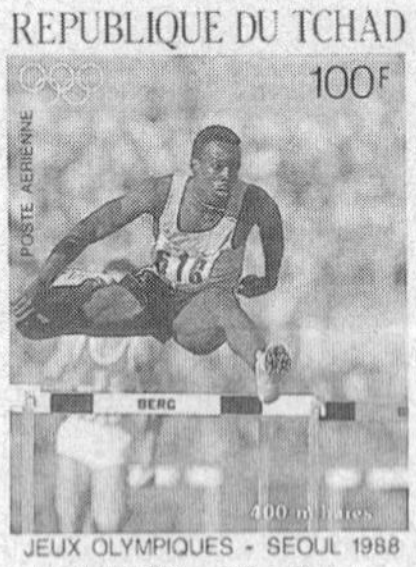

205 400 m Hurdles

1988. Air. Olympic Games, Seoul. Multicoloured.

841	100f. Type **205**	75	25
842	170f. 5000 m (horiz)	1·25	35
843	200f. Long jump (horiz) . . .	1·50	50
844	600f. Triple jump	4·50	1·40

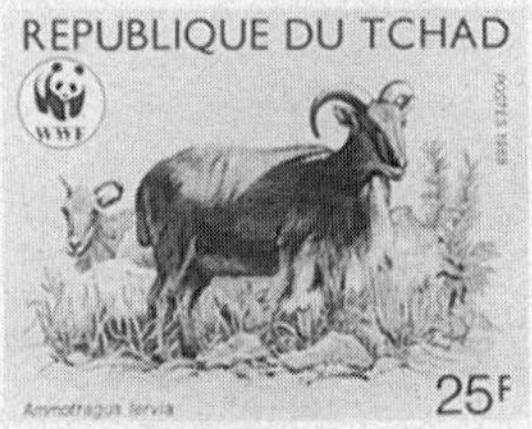

206 Barbary Sheep

1988. Endangered Animals. Barbary Sheep. Mult.

846	25f. Type **206**	25	20
847	45f. Mother and lamb . . .	50	25
848	70f. Two sheep	75	30
849	100f. Two adults with lamb	1·00	50

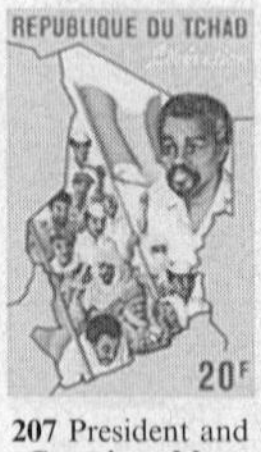

207 President and Crowd on Map

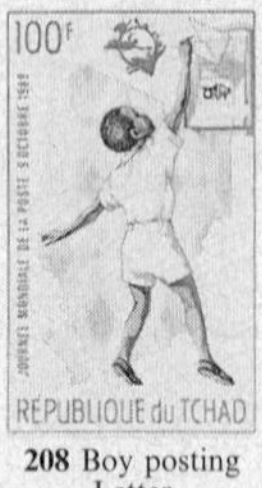

208 Boy posting Letter

1989. "Liberation".

850	207	20f. multicoloured	25	15
851		25f. multicoloured	25	15
852		40f. multicoloured	35	20
853		100f. multicoloured . . .	1·00	30
854		170f. multicoloured . . .	1·60	50

1989. World Post Day.

855	208	100f. multicoloured . . .
856		120f. multicoloured . . .
857		170f. multicoloured . . .
858		250f. multicoloured . . .

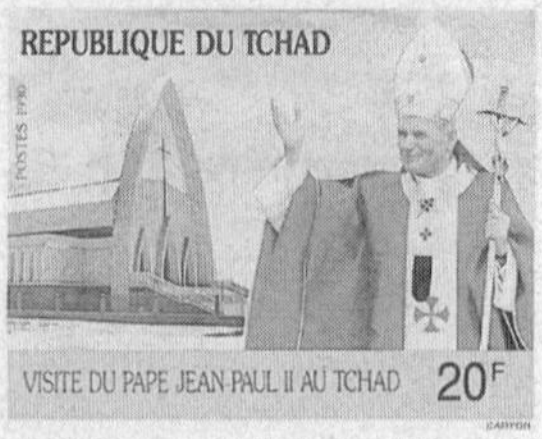

209 N'Djamena Cathedral and Pope with Crucifix

1990. Visit of Pope John Paul II. Multicoloured.

859	20f. Type **209**	25	10
860	80f. Cathedral and Pope (different)	70	35
861	100f. Type **209**	95	60
862	170f. As No. 860	1·60	1·10

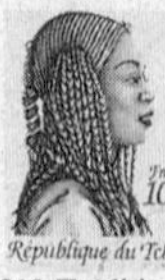

210 Traditional Hairstyle

1990.

863	210	100f. multicoloured . . .	45	25
864		120f. multicoloured . . .	55	30
865		170f. multicoloured . . .	80	45
866		250f. multicoloured . . .	1·10	65

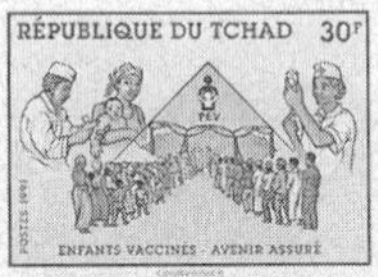

215 Queues and Nurse vaccinating Child

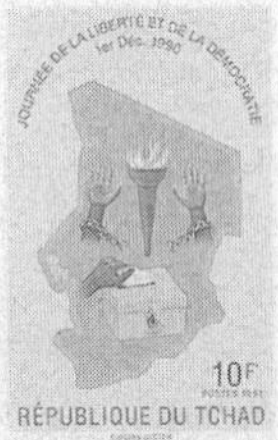

216 Torch, Hands with Broken Manacles and Ballot Box

1991. "Child Vaccination—Assured Future".

880	215	30f. multicoloured	25	20
881		100f. multicoloured . . .	75	45
882		170f. multicoloured . . .	1·25	75
883		180f. multicoloured . . .	1·25	75
884		200f. multicoloured . . .	1·50	1·00

1991. Day of Freedom and Democracy.

885	216	10f. multicoloured	10	10
886		20f. multicoloured	20	15
887		40f. multicoloured	30	20
888		70f. multicoloured	50	30
889		130f. multicoloured . . .	95	60
890		200f. multicoloured . . .	1·50	80

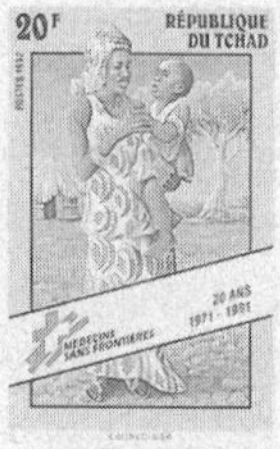

217 Mother and Child

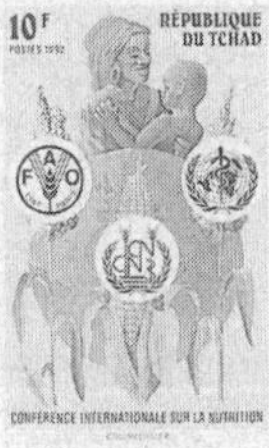

219 Mother and Child, Globe and Cereals

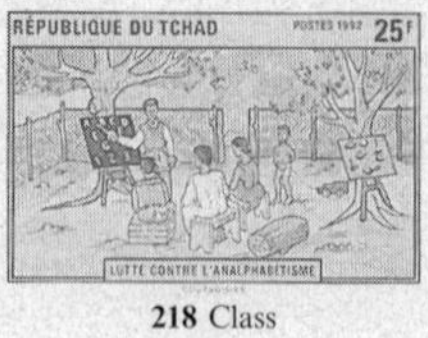

218 Class

1992. 20th Anniv of Medecins sans Frontieres (medical relief organization).

891	217	20f. multicoloured	20	10
892		45f. multicoloured	30	20
893		85f. multicoloured	70	35
894		170f. multicoloured . . .	1·25	70
895		300f. multicoloured . . .	2·25	1·10

1992. Literacy Campaign.

896	218	25f. multicoloured	20	10
897		40f. multicoloured	30	20
898		70f. multicoloured	50	25
899		100f. multicoloured . . .	75	35
900		180f. multicoloured . . .	1·25	60
901		200f. multicoloured . . .	1·50	95

1992. International Nutrition Conference, Rome.

902	219	10f. multicoloured	15	10
903		60f. multicoloured	45	25
904		120f. multicoloured . . .	95	55
905		500f. multicoloured . . .	3·50	1·60

MILITARY FRANK STAMPS

1965. No. 77 optd **F.M.**
M148 20f. red and black £250 £250

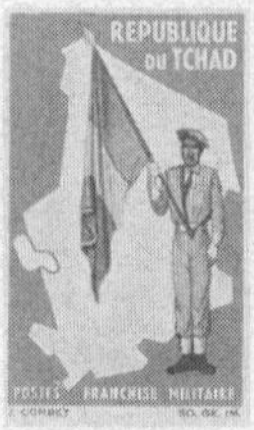

M **24** Soldier with Standard

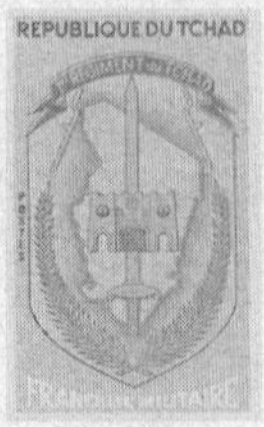

M **92** Shoulder Flash of 1st Regiment

1966. No value indicated.
M149 M **24** (–) multicoloured . . 1·50 1·00

1972. No value indicated.
M353 M **92** (–) multicoloured . . 75 35

OFFICIAL STAMPS

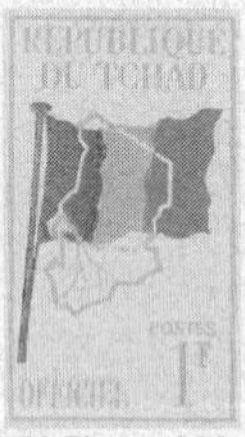

O **23** Flag and Map

1966. Flag in blue, yellow and red.

O148	O 23	1f. blue	10	10
O149		2f. grey	10	10
O150		5f. black	15	10
O151		10f. blue	25	10
O152		25f. orange	25	15
O153		30f. turquoise	40	20
O154		40f. red	45	20
O155		50f. purple	55	25
O156		85f. green	85	45
O157		100f. brown	1·40	50
O158		200f. red	2·50	95

POSTAGE DUE STAMPS

1928. Postage Due type of France optd **TCHAD A. E. F.**

D58	D 11	5c. blue	10	2·50
D59		10c. brown	35	2·50
D60		20c. olive	35	2·50
D61		25c. red	40	2·75
D62		30c. red	50	2·75
D63		45c. green	55	3·00
D64		50c. purple	40	3·25
D65		60c. brown on cream	90	4·00
D66		1f. red on cream . . .	90	4·00
D67		2f. red	1·60	7·00
D68		3f. violet	90	4·25

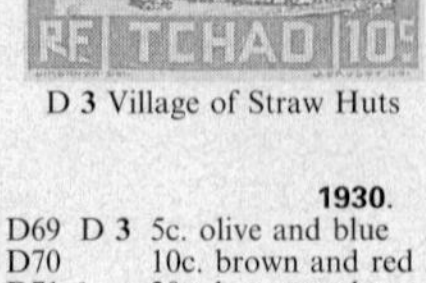

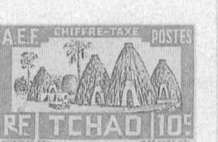

D **3** Village of Straw Huts

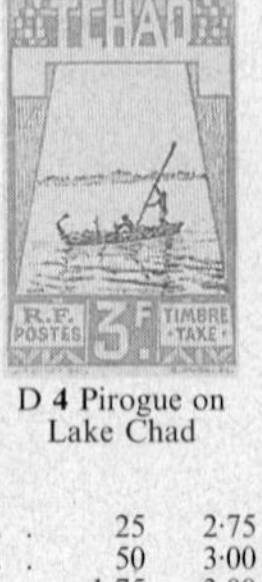

D **4** Pirogue on Lake Chad

1930.

D69	D 3	5c. olive and blue . . .	25	2·75
D70		10c. brown and red . . .	50	3·00
D71		20c. brown and green . .	1·75	3·00
D72		25c. brown and blue . .	1·90	3·25
D73		30c. green and brown . .	1·75	3·25
D74		45c. olive and green . .	2·25	3·50
D75		50c. brown & mauve . .	2·50	4·00
D76		60c. black and lilac . .	3·25	5·00
D77	D 4	1f. black and brown . .	4·00	5·25
D78		2f. brown and mauve . .	4·00	8·50
D79		3f. brown and red . . .	20·00	55·00

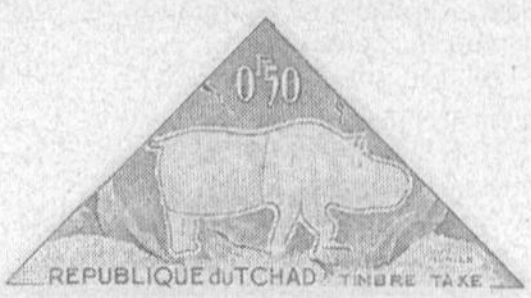

D **6** Gonoa Hippopotamus

1962.

D 89	50c. bistre	10	10
D 90	50c. brown	10	10
D 91	1f. blue	10	10
D 92	1f. green	10	10
D 93	2f. red	15	15
D 94	2f. red	15	15
D 95	5f. myrtle	30	30
D 96	5f. violet	30	30
D 97	10f. brown	75	75
D 98	10f. brown	75	75
D 99	25f. purple	1·75	1·75
D100	25f. violet	1·75	1·75

DESIGNS (rock-paintings): No. D89, Type D **6**; D90, Gonoa kudu; D91, Two Gonoa antelopes; D92, Three Gonoa antelopes; D93, Gonoa antelope; D94, Tibestiram; D95, Tibestiox; D96, Oudingueur boar; D97, Gonoa elephant; D98, Gira-Gira rhinoceros; D99, Bardai warrior; D100, Gonoa masked archer. The two designs in each value are arranged in tete-beche pairs throughout the sheet.

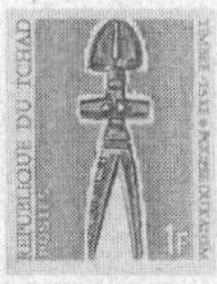

D **65** Kanem Puppet

1969. Native Puppets.

D284	D 65	1f. brown, red & grn	10	10
D285	–	2f. brown, grn & red	10	10
D286	–	5f. green and brown	10	10
D287	–	10f. brown, pur & grn	20	20
D288	–	25f. brown, pur & grn	45	25

DESIGNS: 2f. Kotoko doll; 5f. Copper doll; 10f. Kotoko (diff); 25f. Guera doll.

APPENDIX

The following stamps have either been issued in excess of postal needs or have not been available to the public in reasonable quantities at face value. Such stamps may later be given full listing if there is evidence of regular postal use.

1970.

"Apollo programme". Postage 40f.; Air 15, 25f.

Birth Bicent of Napoleon. Air. 10, 25, 32f.

World Cup Football Championship, Mexico. Air 5f.

World Cup. Previous Winners. 1, 4f., 5f. × 2.

"Expo 70" World Fair, Osaka, Japan. Japanese Paintings. 50c., 1, 2f.

Christmas. Paintings. Postage 3, 25f.; Air 32f.

Past Olympic Venues. Postage 3, 8, 20f.; Air 10, 35f.

1971.

Space Exploration. 8, 10, 35f.

Winter Olympic Games, Sapporo, Japan. Japanese Paintings. 50c., 1, 2f.

Kings and Queens of France. Postage 25f. × 2, 30, 32, 35f., 40f. × 2, 50f. × 4, 60f.; Air 40, 50, 60, 70, 75, 80f., 100f. × 5, 150f., 200f. × 4.

150th Death Anniv of Napoleon. Air. 10f.

Famous Paintings. 1, 4, 5f.

Past Olympic Venues. Postage 15, 20f.; Air 25, 50f.

Winter Olympic Games, Sapporo, Japan. Optd on 1970 "Expo 70" issue 50c., 1, 2f.

Olympic Games Munich. World Cup Previous Winners issue (1970) optd **1f.**

1972.

Moon Flight of "Apollo 15". Air 40, 80, 150, 250, 300, 500f.

"Soyuz 11" Disaster. Air 30, 50, 100, 200, 300, 400f.

Pres. Tombalbaye. Postage 30, 40f.; Air 70, 80f.

Winter Olympic Games, Sapporo, Japan. Postage 25, 75, 150f.; Air 130, 200f.

13th World Scout Jamboree, Asagiri, Japan (1971). Postage 30, 70, 80f.; Air 100, 200f.

Medal Winners, Sapporo Winter Olympics. Postage 25, 75, 100, 130f.; Air 150, 200f.

Olympic Games, Munich. Postage 20, 40, 60f.; Air 100, 120, 150f.

African Animals. Air 20, 30, 100, 130, 150f.

Medal Winners, Munich Olympics (1st series). Postage 10, 20, 40, 60f.; Air 150, 250f.

Medal Winners, Munich Olympics (2nd series). Gold frames, Postage 20, 30, 50f.; Air 150, 250f.

1973.

Locomotives. 10, 40, 50, 150, 200f.

Domestic Animals (2nd issue). Postage 20, 30f.; Air 100, 130, 150f.

Horses. 20, 60, 100, 120f.

Airplanes. Air 5, 25, 70, 150, 200f.

Christmas. Postage 30, 40, 55f.; Air 60, 250f.

Other issues exist which were prepared by various agencies, but it is uncertain whether these were placed on sale in Chad. They include further values in the "Kings and Queens of France" series.

All the stamps below are on gold foil.

1982.

World Cup Football Championship, Spain. Air 1500f.

21st Birthday of Princess of Wales. Air 1500f.

75th Anniv of Scout Movement. Air 1500f.

Olympic Games, Los Angeles. Air 1500f.

Birth of Prince William of Wales. 21st Birthday of Princess of Wales stamp optd. Air 1500f.

1983.

World Cup Football Championship Results. Air 1500f.

Chess Grand Masters. Air 1500f.

Exploitation of Space. Air 1500f.

Winter Olympic Games, Sarajevo. Air 1500f.

Bicentary of Manned Flight. Air 1500f.

Olympic Games, Los Angeles. Air 1500f.

CHAMBA Pt. 1

An Indian "convention" state of the Punjab.

Stamps of India overprinted.

12 pies = 1 anna; 16 annas = 1 rupee.

1886. Queen Victoria. Optd **CHAMBA STATE** in two lines.

1	23	½a. turquoise	15	45
2	–	1a. purple	90	1·10
4	–	1a.6p. brown	1·00	9·00
6	–	2a. blue	1·40	1·50
7	–	2a.6p. green	28·00	70·00
9	–	3a. orange	1·00	3·75
11	–	4a. green (No. 96)	3·75	4·75
12	–	6a. brown (No. 80)	2·75	13·00
14	–	8a. mauve	5·50	7·00
16	–	12a. purple on red	4·25	10·00
17	–	1r. grey (No. 101)	32·00	£100
18	37	1r. green and red	5·50	11·00
19	38	2r. red and brown	80·00	£250
20		3r. brown and green	80·00	£200
21		5r. blue and violet	90·00	£375

1900. Queen Victoria. Optd **CHAMBA STATE** in two lines.

22	40	3p. red	10	50
23		3p. grey	15	1·60
25	23	½a. green	25	70
26	–	1a. red	10	30
27	–	2a. lilac	6·50	22·00

1903. King Edward VII. Optd **CHAMBA STATE** in two lines.

28	41	3p. grey	10	85
30	–	½a. green (No. 122)	20	20
31	–	1a. red (No. 123)	85	35
33	–	2a. lilac	85	2·00
34	–	3a. orange	2·25	3·25
35	–	4a. olive	3·50	13·00
36	–	6a. bistre	2·75	16·00
37	–	8a. mauve	3·50	15·00
39	–	12a. purple on red	5·00	20·00
40	–	1r. green and red	5·50	18·00

1907. King Edward VII. Optd **CHAMBA STATE** in two lines.

41	–	½a. green (No. 149)	60	2·75
42	–	1a. red (No. 150)	75	3·00

1913. King George V. Optd **CHAMBA STATE** in two lines.

43	55	3p. grey	10	50
44	56	½a. green	30	55
45a	57	1a. red	60	2·25
55		1a. brown	1·40	3·25
56	58	1½a. brown (No. 163)	21·00	95·00
57		1½a. brown (No. 165)	1·10	4·25
58		1½a. red	75	15·00
47	59	2a. purple	2·00	7·00
59	61	2a.6p. blue	60	3·00
60		2a.6p. orange	1·25	13·00
48	62	3a. orange	2·25	5·50
61		3a. blue	2·25	16·00
49	63	4a. olive	1·60	3·00
50	64	6a. bistre	1·75	4·00
51	65	8a. mauve	3·50	8·50
52	66	12a. red	2·75	10·00
53	67	1r. brown and green	11·00	20·00

1921. No. 192 of India optd **CHAMBA**.

54	57	9p. on 1a. red	1·00	17·00

1927. Stamps of India (King George V) optd **CHAMBA STATE** in one line.

62	55	3p. grey	10	1·00
63	56	½a. green	20	1·40
76	79	½a. green	1·00	7·00
64	80	9p. green	2·00	11·00
65	57	1a. brown	1·60	50
77	81	1a. brown	1·25	60
66	82	1a.3p. mauve	1·10	4·25
67w	58	1½a. red	4·25	4·75
68	70	2a. lilac	1·25	1·75
78	59	2a. red	85	19·00
69	61	2a.6p. orange	1·25	12·00
70	62	3a. blue	1·00	14·00
80		3a. red	1·90	8·00
71	71	4a. green	80	3·75
81	63	4a. olive	2·25	11·00
72	64	6a. bistre	26·00	£140
73	65	8a. mauve	1·40	8·00
74	66	12a. red	1·40	9·50
75	67	1r. brown and green	4·50	20·00

1938. Stamps of India (King George VI Nos. 247/64) optd **CHAMBA STATE**.

82	91	3p. slate	5·00	9·50
83		½a. brown	1·00	5·50
84		9p. green	5·50	24·00
85		1a. red	1·00	1·75
86	92	2a. red	3·75	8·50
87	–	2a.6p. violet	4·50	18·00
88	–	3a. green	5·00	18·00
89	–	3a.6p. blue	5·00	21·00
90	–	4a. brown	16·00	15·00
91	–	6a. green	15·00	45·00
92	–	8a. violet	16·00	38·00
93	–	12a. red	10·00	42·00
94	93	1r. slate and brown	25·00	50·00
95		2r. purple and brown	48·00	£225
96		5r. green and blue	80·00	£350
97		10r. purple and red	£130	£500
98		15r. brown and green	£160	£750
99		25r. slate and purple	£225	£800

1942. Stamps of India (King George VI) optd **CHAMBA**. (a) On issue of 1938

100	91	½a. brown	28·00	20·00
101		1a. red	32·00	24·00
102	93	1r. slate and brown	18·00	15·00
103		2r. purple and brown	24·00	£190
104		5r. green and blue	45·00	£200
105		10r. purple and red	65·00	£400
106		15r. brown and green	£140	£600
107		25r. slate and purple	£140	£600

(b) On issue of 1940.

108	100a	3p. slate	70	3·75
109		½a. mauve	70	3·50
110		9p. green	1·00	11·00
111		1a. red	1·00	3·00
112	101	1½a. violet	1·00	7·00
113		2a. red	3·75	7·50
114		3a. violet	12·00	25·00
115		3½a. blue	6·50	28·00
116	102	4a. brown	8·00	8·50
117		6a. green	12·00	35·00
118		8a. violet	12·00	42·00
119		12a. purple	18·00	55·00
120	–	14a. purple (No. 277)	9·50	3·00

OFFICIAL STAMPS

Stamps of India overprinted.

1886. Queen Victoria. Optd **SERVICE CHAMBA STATE**.

O 1	23	½a. turquoise	10	10
O 3	–	1a. purple	90	10
O 5	–	2a. blue	1·00	1·40
O 7	–	3a. orange	1·90	9·00
O 8	–	4a. green (No. 96)	2·00	3·75
O10	–	6a. brown (No. 80)	4·00	9·00
O13	–	8a. mauve	1·00	1·75
O14	–	12a. purple on red	7·50	32·00
O15	–	1r. grey (No. 101)	13·00	95·00
O16	37	1r. green and red	6·00	28·00

1902. Queen Victoria. Optd **SERVICE CHAMBA STATE**.

O17	40	3p. grey	15	50
O18	23	½a. green	20	2·75
O20	–	1a. red	40	40
O21	–	2a. lilac	9·00	25·00

1903. King Edward VII. Optd **SERVICE CHAMBA STATE**.

O22	41	3p. grey	15	15
O24	–	½a. green (No. 122)	25	10
O25	–	1a. red (No. 123)	65	30
O27	–	2a. lilac	90	50
O28	–	4a. olive	3·50	14·00
O29	–	8a. mauve	4·00	13·00
O31	–	1r. green and red	1·75	8·50

1907. King Edward VII. Optd **SERVICE CHAMBA STATE**.

O32	–	½a. green (No. 149)	25	75
O33	–	1a. red (No. 150)	2·00	1·40

1913. King George V Official stamps optd **CHAMBA STATE**.

O34	55	3p. grey	20	40
O36	56	½a. green	10	10
O38	57	1a. red	10	10
O47		1a. brown	1·90	50
O40	59	2a. lilac (No. O83)	1·10	10·00
O41	63	4a. olive (No. O86)	1·10	13·00
O42	65	8a. mauve	1·75	14·00
O43	67	1r. brown and green	4·00	23·00

1914. King George V Postage stamps optd **SERVICE CHAMBA STATE**.

O44	59	2a. lilac (No. 166)		13·00
O45	63	4a. olive (No. 210)		10·00

1921. No O97 of India optd **CHAMBA**.

O46	57	9p. on 1a. red	15	6·00

1927. King George V Postage stamps optd **CHAMBA STATE SERVICE**.

O48	55	3p. grey	50	30
O49	56	½a. green	35	15
O61	79	½a. green	2·50	50
O50	80	9p. green	2·00	7·50
O51	57	1a. brown	20	10
O62	81	1a. brown	2·50	45
O52	82	1¼a. mauve	5·00	60
O53	70	2a. lilac	1·25	60
O63	59	2a. red	3·50	1·00
O54	71	4a. olive	1·10	1·50
O65	63	4a. green	5·00	4·25
O55	65	8a. mauve	3·75	7·00
O56	66	12a. red	2·50	18·00
O57	67	1r. brown and green	11·00	32·00
O58		2r. red and orange	21·00	£180
O59		5r. blue and violet	40·00	£250
O60		1r. green and red	60·00	£250

1938. King George VI Postage stamps of India optd **CHAMBA STATE SERVICE**.

O66	91	9p. green	9·50	42·00
O67		1a. red	8·00	2·00
O68	93	1r. slate and brown	£350	£800
O69		2r. purple and brown	38·00	£275
O70		5r. green and blue	60·00	£350
O71		10r. purple and red	90·00	£600

1940. Official stamps of India optd **CHAMBA**.

O72	O 20	3p. grey	70	70
O73		½a. brown	13·00	1·75
O74		½a. purple	70	2·00
O75		9p. green	4·00	6·50
O76		1a. red	70	1·50
O77		1a.3p. brown	45·00	14·00
O78		1½a. violet	4·25	5·50
O79		2a. orange	4·25	5·00
O80		2½a. violet	2·25	17·00
O81		4a. brown	3·50	8·00
O82		8a. violet	11·00	45·00

1942. King George VI Postage stamps of India optd **CHAMBA SERVICE**.

O83	93	1r. slate and brown	20·00	£160
O84		2r. purple and brown	35·00	£225
O85		5r. green and blue	60·00	£350
O86		10r. purple and red	80·00	£600

CHARKHARI Pt. 1

A state of Central India. Now uses Indian stamps.

12 pies = 1 anna; 16 annas = 1 rupee.

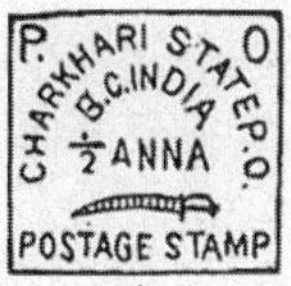

1

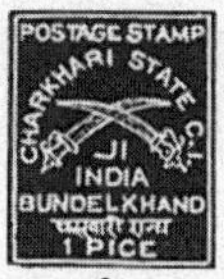

2

1894. Imperf. No gum.

10	1	¼a. purple	1·75	2·50
6a		½a. purple	2·50	3·00
7a		1a. green	4·00	4·50
8a		2a. green	7·00	8·00
9a		4a. green	6·00	9·50

1909. Perf or imperf.

15a	2	1p. brown	3·25	38·00
16		1p. blue	60	45
33		1p. violet	16·00	£120
32		1p. green	45·00	£160
25		½a. red	1·25	1·50
34		½a. olive	1·25	13·00
35		½a. brown	5·00	22·00
36		½a. black	50·00	£140
18a		1a. green	1·75	1·60
40		1a. brown	7·00	22·00
41		1a. red	85·00	55·00
19		2a. blue	3·00	3·25
43		2a. grey	42·00	50·00
20		4a. green	3·50	4·75
44		4a. red	3·00	19·00
21		8a. red	7·50	16·00
22		1r. brown	13·00	30·00

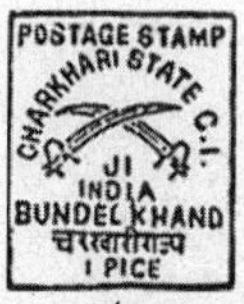

4

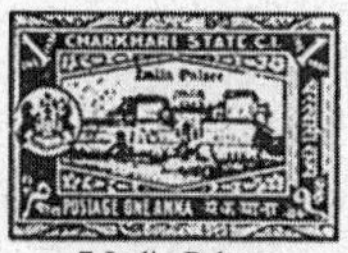
7 Imlia Palace

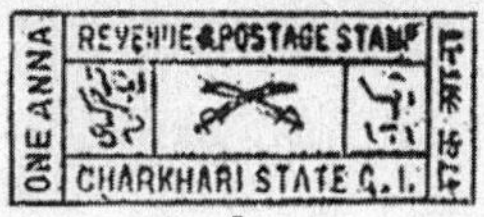

5

1912. Imperf.

28	4	1p. violet	7·00	5·00

1922. Imperf.

29	5	1a. violet	70·00	80·00

1931. Perf.

45	–	½a. green	1·10	10
46	7	1a. sepia	1·40	10
47	–	2a. violet	1·00	10
48	–	4a. olive	1·10	15
49	–	8a. mauve	1·40	10
50	–	1r. green and red	2·00	20
51	–	2r. red and brown	3·50	25
52	–	3r. brown and green	9·00	40
53	–	5r. blue and lilac	8·50	50

DESIGNS—HORIZ: ½a. The Lake; 2a. Industrial school; 4a. Bird's-eye view of city; 8a. Fort; 1r. Guest House; 2r. Palace Gate; 3r. Temples at Rainpur; 5r. Goverdhan Temple.

1940. Nos. 21/2 surch.

54	2	½a. on 8a. red	26·00	£110
55		1a. on 1r. brown	80·00	£350
56		"1 ANNA" on 1r. brown	£550	£600

CHILE Pt. 20

A republic on the W. coast of S. America.

1853. 100 centavos = 1 peso.
1960. 10 milesimos = 1 centesimo; 100 centesimos = 1 escudo.
1975. 100 centavos = 1 peso.

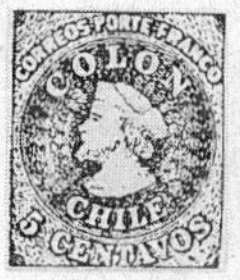
1 Columbus

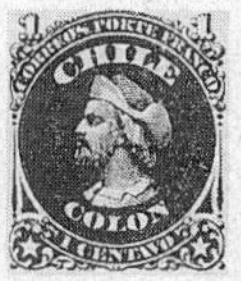
9

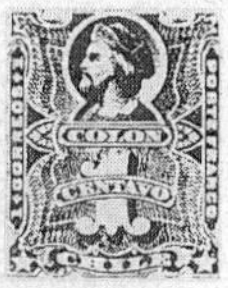
10

1853. Imperf.

29	1	1c. yellow	18·00	20·00
17		5c. brown	£100	11·00
37		5c. red	23·00	6·50
32		10c. blue	32·00	5·00
33		20c. green	35·00	28·00

1867. Perf.

41	9	1c. orange	12·50	1·25
43		2c. black	17·00	2·75
45		5c. red	13·00	90
46		10c. blue	13·00	1·10
48		20c. green	22·00	2·00

1877. Roul.

49	10	1c. slate	2·00	75
50		2c. orange	9·00	1·50
51		5c. lake	11·50	50
52		10c. blue	10·00	1·60
53		20c. green	13·00	2·50

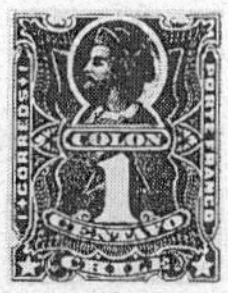
12

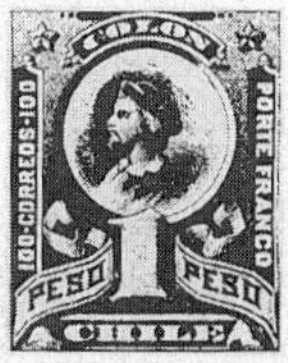
15

1878. Roul.

55	12	1c. green	1·00	15
57		2c. red	1·00	15
58		5c. red	5·00	25
59a		5c. blue	1·50	50
60a		10c. orange	2·25	10
61		15c. green	2·50	15
62		20c. grey	2·50	35
63		25c. brown	2·50	15
64		30c. red	5·00	2·00
65a		50c. violet	2·50	1·00
66	15	1p. black and brown	13·50	2·00

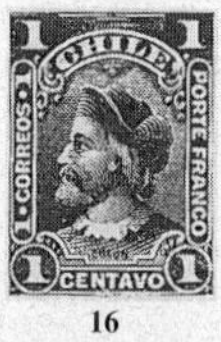
16

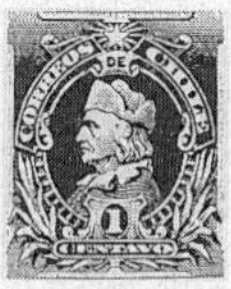
18

1900. Roul.

82	16	1c. green	75	10
83		2c. red	75	10
84a		5c. blue	3·50	25
85		10c. lilac	4·00	35
79		20c. grey	4·00	1·25
80		30c. brown	4·50	1·25
81		50c. brown	5·50	1·50

1900. Surch 5.

86	12	5c. on 30c. red	1·00	20

1901. Perf.

87	18	1c. green	25	15
88		2c. red	35	15
89		5c. blue	1·10	15
90		10c. black and red	2·10	25
91		30c. black and violet	6·75	65
92		50c. black and red	6·50	1·75

1903. Surch **Diez CENTAVOS**.

93	16	10c. on 30c. red	1·60	95

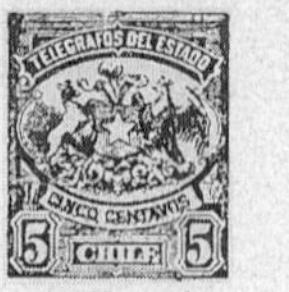
20 Huemul (mountain deer)

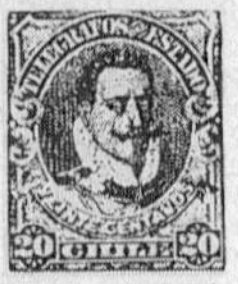
24 Pedro Valdivia

1904. Animal supporting shield at left without mane and tail. Optd **CORREOS** in frame.
94 **20** 2c. brown 25 15
95 5c. red 40 15
96 10c. olive . . . . 1·40 40

1904. As T **20**, but animal with mane and tail optd **CORREOS** in frame and the 1p. also surch **CENTAVOS 3 3**.
97 **20** 2c. brown . . . . 5·00
98 3c. on 1p. brown 35 20
99 5c. red . . . . 6·00
100 10c. green . . . . 12·00

1904. Surch **CORREOS** in frame and new value.
101 **24** 1c. on 20c. blue 25 15
102 3c. on 5c. red . . . . . . 40·00 40·00
103 12c. on 5c. red 85 35

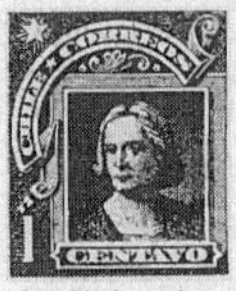
26 Christopher Columbus

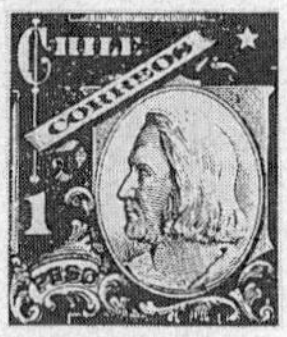
28 Christopher Columbus

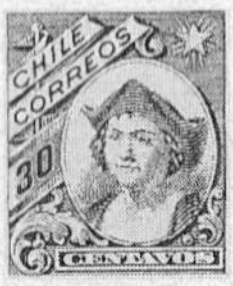
27 Christopher Columbus

1905.
104 **26** 1c. green 25 15
105 2c. red 25 15
106 3c. brown 60 25
107 5c. blue 60 15
108 **27** 10c. black and grey . . . . 1·25 15
109 12c. black and lake . . . . 5·25 2·00
110 15c. black and lilac . . . . 1·25 15
111 20c. black and brown . . . 2·50 15
112 30c. black and green . . . 3·50 25
113 50c. black and blue . . . . 3·50 25
114 **28** 1p. grey and green . . . . 12·50 8·50

1910. Optd **ISLAS DE JUAN FERNANDEZ** or surch also.
115 **27** 5c. on 12c. black & red . . 40 30
116 **28** 10c. on 1p. grey & green . 1·10 65
117 20c. on 1p. grey & green . 1·75 1·00
118 1p. grey and green . . . . 3·50 2·40

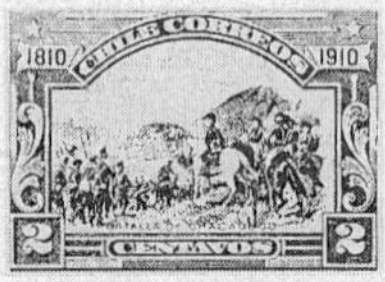
31 Battle of Chacabuco

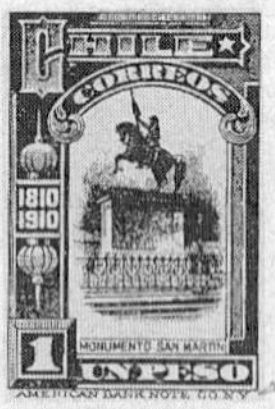
33 San Martin Monument

1910. Centenary of Independence. Centres in black.
119 – 1c. green 25 15
120 **31** 2c. lake 25 15
121 – 3c. brown . . . . 1·00 65
122 – 5c. blue 35 10
123 – 10c. brown . . . . 1·50 25
124 – 12c. red . . . . 3·00 90
125 – 15c. slate . . . . 1·60 65
126 – 20c. orange . . . . 2·50 1·00
127 – 25c. blue . . . . 3·50 2·40
128 – 30c. mauve . . . . 3·25 1·40
129 – 50c. olive . . . . 6·75 1·50
130 **33** 1p. yellow . . . . 13·50 4·50
131 – 2p. red . . . . 13·50 3·75
132 – 5p. green . . . . 35·00 17·00
133 – 10p. purple . . . . 30·00 13·50
DESIGNS—HORIZ: 1c. Oath of Independence; 3c. Battle of Roble; 5c. Battle of Maipu; 10c. Fight between frigates "Lautaro" and "Esmeralda"; 12c. Capture of the "Maria Isabella"; 15c. First sortie of the liberating forces; 20c. Abdication of O'Higgins; 25c. First Chilean Congress. VERT: 30c. O'Higgins Monument; 50c. Carrera Monument; 2p. General Blanco; 5p. General Zenteno; 10p. Admiral Cochrane.

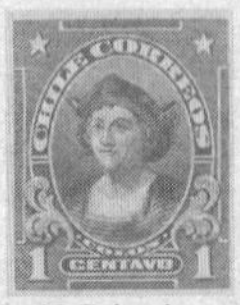
46 Columbus

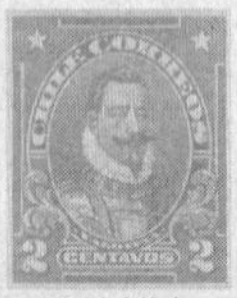
47 Valdivia

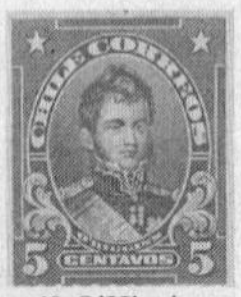
49 O'Higgins

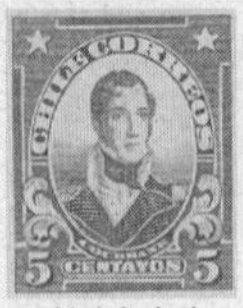
64 Admiral Cochrane

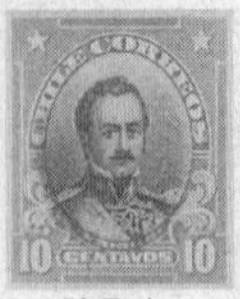
50 Freire

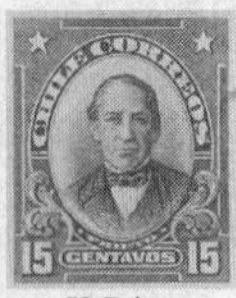
52 Prieto

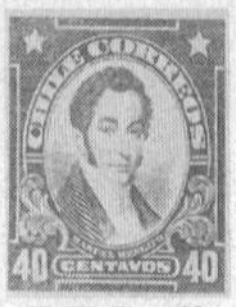
65 M. Rengifo

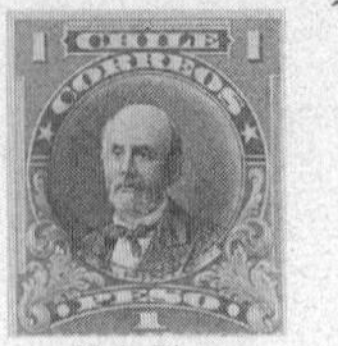
57 A. Pinto

1911. Inscr "CHILE CORREOS".
135 **46** 1c. green 15 10
136 **47** 2c. red 15 10
150 **46** 2c. red 15 10
137 – 3c. sepia 50 35
151 – 4c. sepia 20 10
138 **49** 5c. blue 15 10
161 **64** 5c. blue 35 15
152 – 8c. grey 70 30
139 **50** 10c. black and grey . . . 50 30
153 **49** 10c. black and blue . . . 70 10
140 – 12c. black and red 85 30
154 – 14c. black and red 70 10
141 **52** 15c. black and purple . . 70 30
142 – 20c. black and orange . . 1·40 15
167 – 25c. black and blue . . . 50 15
168 – 30c. black and brown . . 1·50 15
155 **52** 40c. black and purple . . 4·50 65
186 **65** 40c. black and violet . . . 40 15
170 – 50c. black and green . . . 1·50 15
156 – 60c. black and blue . . . 8·50 1·60
171 – 80c. black and sepia . . . 1·90 55
188 **57** 1p. black and green . . . 70 10
189 – 2p. black and red . . . . 3·25 30
190 – 5p. black and olive . . . 8·00 70
190a – 10p. black and orange . . 8·00 1·00
PORTRAITS: 3c., 4c. Toro Z. 8c. Freire. 12, 14c. F. A. Pinto. 20c. Bulnes. 25c., 60c. Montt. 30c. Perez. 50c. Errazuriz Z. 80c. Admiral Latorre. 2p. Santa Maria. 5p. Balmaceda. 10p. Errazuriz E.

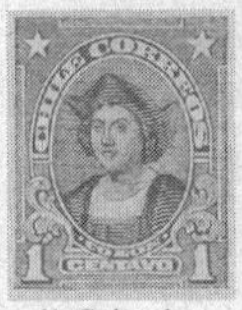
61 Columbus

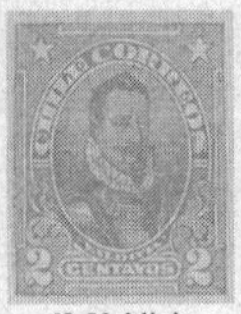
62 Valdivia

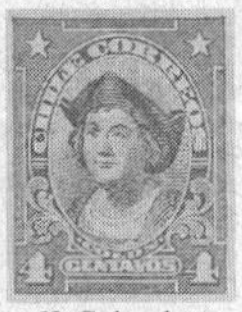
63 Columbus

1915. Larger Stars.
157 **61** 1c. green 20 10
158 **62** 2c. red 20 10
160 **61** 4c. brown (small head) . . 30 10
159 **63** 4c. brown (large head) . . 25 10

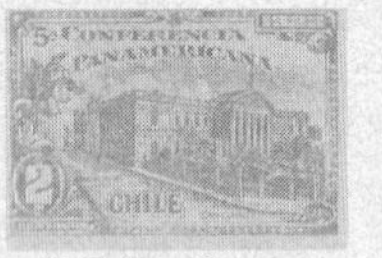
67 Chilean Congress Building

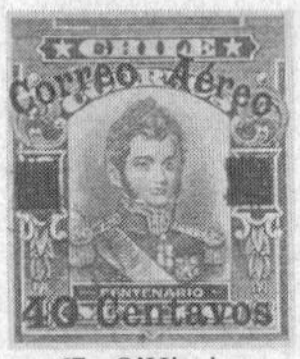
67a O'Higgins

1923. Pan-American Conference.
176 **67** 2c. red 15 10
177 4c. brown 15 10
178 10c. black and blue 15 10
179 20c. black and orange . . . 40 15
180 40c. black and mauve . . . 70 20
181 1p. black and green . . . 85 35
182 2p. black and red . . . . 3·00 40
183 5p. black and green . . . 10·00 2·25

1927. Air. Unissued stamp surch **Correo Aereo** and value.
184 **67a** 40c. on 10c. blue & brn £200 30·00
184a 80c. on 10c. blue & brn £200 42·00
184b 1p.20 on 10c. bl & brn £200 50·00
184c 1p.60 on 10c. bl & brn £200 50·00
184d 2p. on 10c. blue & brn £200 50·00

1928. Air. Optd **CORREO AEREO** and bird or surch also.
191 – 20c. blk & orge (No. 141) 35 15
199 **65** 40c. black and violet . . . 40 20
200 **57** 1p. black and green . . . 1·10 35
194 – 2p. black & red (No. 189) 1·60 25
201 **64** 3p. on 5c. blue . . . . . 40·00 30·00
195 – 5p. black & ol (No. 190) 2·75 70
196 **49** 6p. on 10c. black & blue 50·00 30·00
198 – 10p. blk & orge (No. 190a) 9·00 2·75

1928. As Types of 1911, but inscr "CORREOS DE CHILE".
205 **64** 5c. blue 50 10
206 5c. green 50 10
204 **49** 10c. black and blue 75 25
208 **52** 15c. black and purple . . . 1·75 10
209 – 20c. black and orange (As No. 142) . . . . 4·00 15
210 – 25c. black and blue (As No. 167) 75 10
211 – 30c. black and brown (As No. 168) 55 20
212 – 50c. black and green (As No. 170) 50 10

1929. Air. Nos. 209/12 optd **CORREO AEREO** and bird.
213a 20c. black and orange . . . 25 15
214 25c. black and blue 40 15
215 30c. black and brown . . . 25 15
216 50c. black and green 35 15

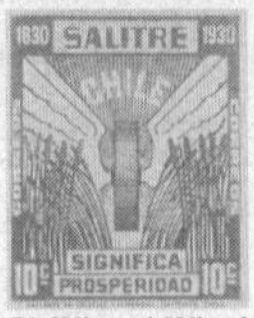
71 Winged Wheel

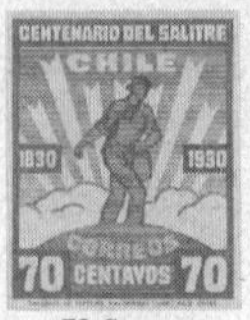
72 Sower

1930. Centenary of Nitrate Industry.
217 **71** 5c. green 35 15
218 10c. brown 35 15
219 15c. violet 35 15
220 – 25c. slate (Girl harvester) 1·40 15
221 **72** 70c. blue . . . . 3·25 1·00
222 1p. green (24½ × 30 mm) . . 2·50 50

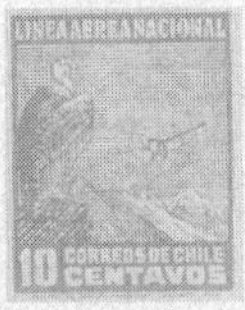
73 Andean Condor and Fokker Super Universal Airplane

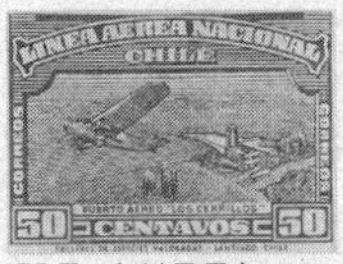
75 Ford 4AT Trimotor over Los Cerrillos Airport

1931. Air. Inscr "LINEA AEREA NACIONAL".
223 **73** 5c. green 40 25
224 10c. brown 40 25
225 20c. red 40 10
226a – 50c. sepia 40 25
227 **75** 50c. blue . . . . 1·75 85
228 – 1p. violet 55 30
229 – 2p. slate . . . . 1·50 25
230 **75** 5p. red . . . . 3·50 60
DESIGN: 50c. (No. 226a), 1p., 2p. Fokker Super Universal airplane.

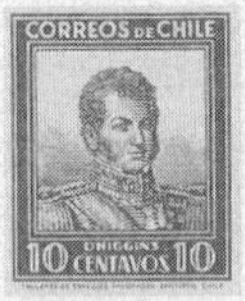
76 O'Higgins

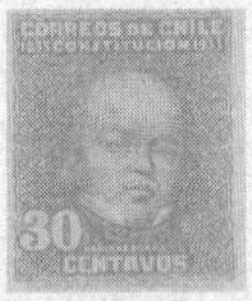
79 Mariano Egana

1931.
231 **76** 10c. blue . . . . 1·00 10
232 – 20c. brown (Bulnes) . . . 85 10
233 – 30c. mauve (Perez) . . . . 1·40 10

1934. Centenary of Constitution of 1833.
234 **79** 30c. mauve 50 25
235 – 1p.20 blue 90 25
PORTRAIT: 1p.20, Joaquin Tocornal (24½ × 29 mm).

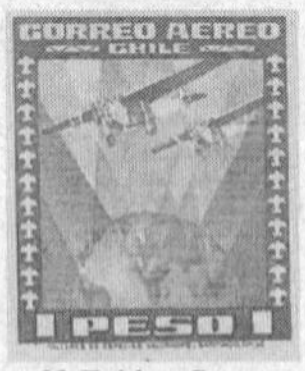
83 Fokker Super Universal Aircraft over Globe

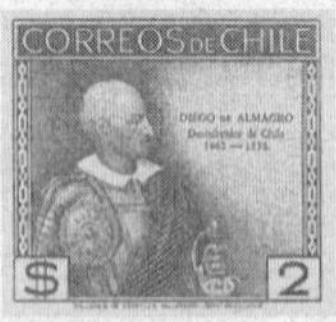
87 Diego de Almagro

1934. Air. As T **83**.
236 10c. green 15 10
237 15c. green 25 20
238 20c. blue 20 15
239 30c. black 20 15
239a 40c. blue 20 15
240 50c. brown 20 15
241 60c. black 20 15
356a 70c. blue 30 20
243 80c. green 20 15
244 1p. grey 20 15
245 2p. blue 20 15
360 3p. brown 25 15
361 4p. brown 25 15
248 5p. red 20 10
249 6p. brown 35 15
250 8p. green 30 10
251 10p. purple 35 15
252 20p. olive 35 15
253 30p. grey 35 10
254 40p. violet 70 40
255a 50p. purple 85 40
DESIGNS—21 × 25 mm: 10, 15, 20c. Fokker Super Universal over Santiago; 30, 40, 50c. Junkers G.24 over landscape; 60c. Condor in flight; 70c. Airplane and star; 80c. Condor and statue of Caupolican; 25 × 29 mm: 1, 2p. Type **83**; 3, 4, 5p. Stinson Faucett F.19 seaplane in flight; 6, 8, 10p. Northrop Alpha monoplane and rainbow; 20, 30p. Stylized Dornier Wal flying boat and compass; 40, 50p. Airplane riding a storm.

1936. 400th Anniv of Discovery of Chile.
256 – 5c. red 35 15
257 – 10c. violet 15 10
258 – 20c. mauve 20 10
259 – 25c. blue . . . . 2·00 55
260 – 30c. green 20 10
261 – 40c. black . . . . 2·00 50
262 – 50c. blue . . . . 1·10 20
263 – 1p. green . . . . 1·50 35
264 – 1p.20 blue . . . . 1·25 45
265 **87** 2p. brown . . . . 1·25 55
266 – 5p. red . . . . 3·50 1·40
267 – 10p. purple . . . . 9·00 7·00
DESIGNS: 5c. Atacama desert; 10c. Fishing boats; 20c. Coquito palms; 25c. Sheep. 30c. Coal mines; 40c. Lonquimay forests; 50c. Lota coal port; 1p. "Orduna" (liner), Valparaiso; 1p.20. Mt. Puntiaguda; 5p. Cattle; 10p. Shovelling nitrate.

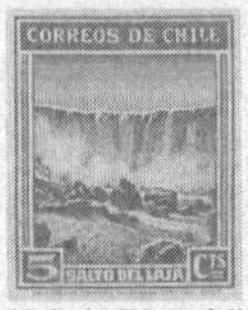
88 Laja Waterfall

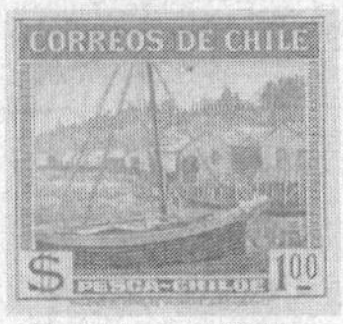
90 "Calbuco" (fishing boat)

1938.
268 **88** 5c. purple 15 10
269 – 10c. red 15 10
269a – 15c. red 15 10
270 – 20c. blue 45 10
271 – 30c. pink 15 10
272 – 40c. green 15 10
273 – 50c. violet 15 10
274 **90** 1p. orange 15 10
275 – 1p.80 blue 85 20
338h – 2p. red 50 10
278 – 5p. green 35 10
338j – 10p. purple . . . . 1·10 10
DESIGNS—As Type **88**: 10c. Rural landscape; 15c. Boldo tree; 20c. Nitrate works; 30c. Mineral spas; 40c. Copper mine; 50c. Petroleum tanks. As Type **90**: 1p.80, Osorno Volcano; 2p. "Conte de Biancamano" (freighter) and "Ponderoso" (tug); 5p. Lake Villarrica; 10p. Steam locomotive No. 908.

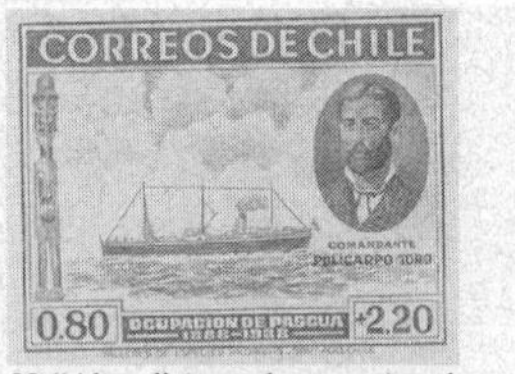
92 "Abtao" (armed steamer) and Policarpo Toro

1940. 50th Anniv of Occupation of Easter Island and Local Hospital Fund.
279 **92** 80c.+2p.20 red & green . . 2·00 1·40
280 – 3p.60+6p.40 green and red 2·00 1·40
DESIGN: 3p.60, "Abtao" and E. Eyraud.

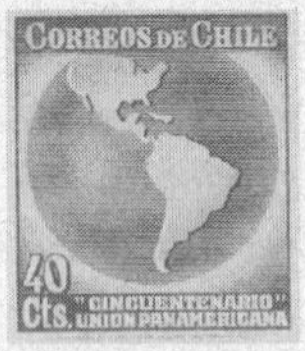
93 Western Hemisphere

1940. 50th Anniv of Pan-American Union.
281 **93** 40c. green 20 10

1940. Air. Surch with winged device above new values.
282 **73** 80c. on 20c. red 45 25
283 **75** 1p.60 on 5p. red . . . . . 3·25 85
284 – 5p.10 on 2p. slate (No. 229) . . . . . . 2·50 1·00

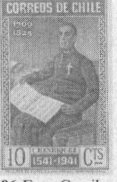

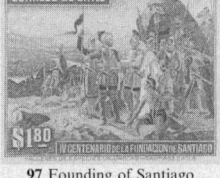

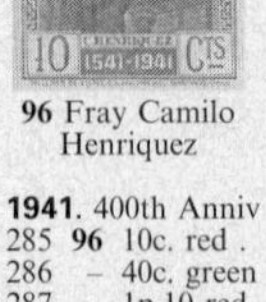
96 Fray Camilo Henriquez

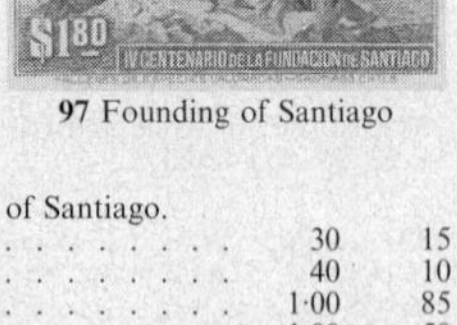
97 Founding of Santiago

1941. 400th Anniv of Santiago.
285 **96** 10c. red 30 15
286 – 40c. green 40 10
287 – 1p.10 red . . . . 1·00 85
288 **97** 1p.80 blue . . . . 1·00 50
289 – 3p.60 blue . . . . 3·25 1·60
PORTRAITS—As Type **96**: 40c. P. Valdivia. 1p.10, B. V. MacKenna. 3p.60, D. B. Arana.

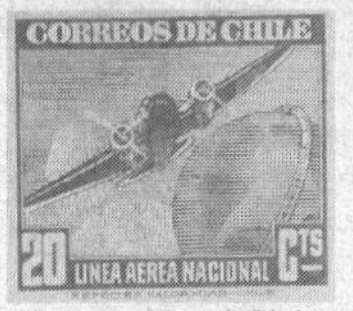

98 Potez 56 and Globe

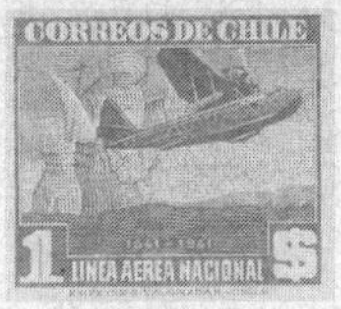

99 Sikorsky S-43 Amphibian and Galleon

1941. Air. No. 304 is dated "1541–1941" and commemorates the 4th Centenary of Santiago.

290	–	10c. olive	30	10
291	–	10c. mauve	30	10
316	–	10c. blue	20	10
292	**98**	20c. red	30	10
318		20c. green	20	10
294		20c. brown	20	10
295	–	30c. violet	30	10
295a	–	30c. olive	20	10
296	–	40c. brown	30	10
297	–	40c. blue	20	10
324	–	50c. red	30	10
325	–	50c. orange	30	10
299a	–	60c. green	20	15
326	–	60c. orange	30	10
300	–	70c. red	60	20
301	–	80c. blue	3·00	35
302	–	80c. olive	20	15
303a	–	90c. brown	30	10
304	**99**	1p. blue	60	20
304a		1p. green and blue	30	10
305	–	1p.60 violet	30	15
306	–	1p.80 violet	30	10
307	–	2p. lake	85	25
308	–	2p. brown	60	10
309	–	3p. green	1·25	45
310a	–	3p. violet and yellow	2·50	25
334	–	3p. violet and orange	85	15
311	–	4p. violet and brown	2·00	55
335	–	4p. green	85	30
336a	–	5p. brown	35	20
336	–	5p. red	35	25
314	–	10p. green and blue	9·50	4·00
337	–	10p. blue	85	25

DESIGNS: (each incorporating a different type of airplane): 10c. Steeple; 30c. Flag; 40c. Stars; 50c. Mountains; 60c. Tree; 70c. Estuary; 80c. Shore; 90c. Sun rays; 1p.60, 1p.80, Wireless mast; 2p. Compass; 3p. Telegraph wires; 4p. Rainbow; 5p. Factory; 10p. Snow-capped mountain.

See also Nos. 395 etc.

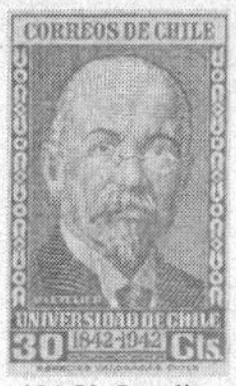

101 V. Letelier

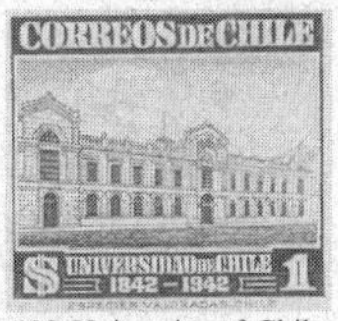

102 University of Chile

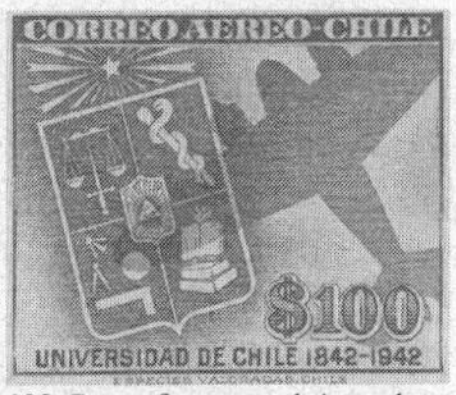

103 Coat of arms and Aeroplane

1942. Centenary of Santiago de Chile University.

339	**101**	30c. red (postage)	20	10
340	–	40c. green	20	10
341	–	90c. violet	1·50	70
342	**102**	1p. brown	1·00	40
343	–	1p.80 blue	2·50	1·40
344	**103**	100p. red (air)	30·00	20·00

DESIGNS—As Type **101**: 40c. A. Bello; 90c. M. Bulnes; 1p.80, M. Montt.

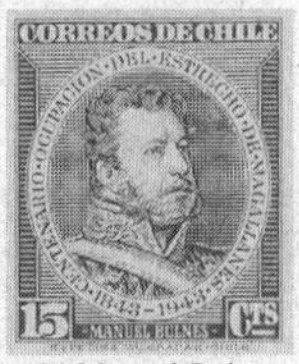

104 Manuel Bulnes

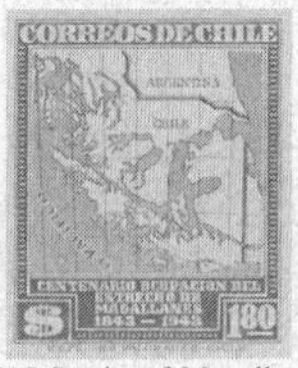

105 Straits of Magellan

1944. Centenary of Occupation of Magellan Straits.

345	**104**	15c. black	15	10
346	–	30c. red	15	10
347	–	40c. green	15	10
348	–	1p. brown	85	25
349	**105**	1p.80 blue	1·25	70

PORTRAITS: 30c. J. W. Wilson. 40c. D. D. Almeida. 1p. Jose de los Santos Mardones.

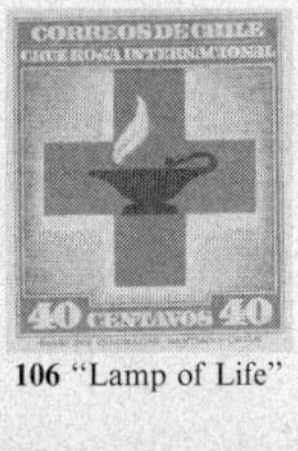

106 "Lamp of Life"

1944. International Red Cross.

350	**106**	40c. black, red and green	50	10
351	–	1p.80 red and blue	1·00	50

DESIGN: 1p.80, Serpent and chalice symbol of Hygiene.

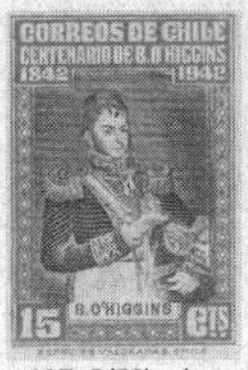

107 O'Higgins (after J. G. de Castro)

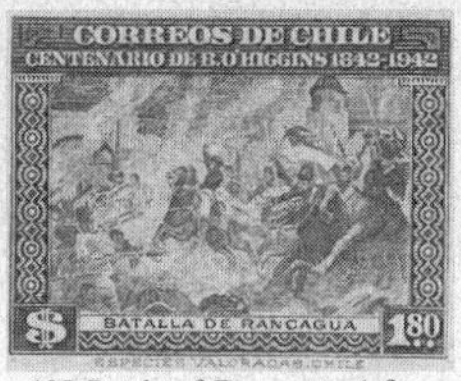

108 Battle of Rancagua (after Subercaseaux)

1944. Death Centenary of Bernardo O'Higgins.

367	**107**	15c. black and red	15	10
368	–	30c. black and brown	25	10
369	–	40c. black and green	25	10
370	**108**	1p.80 black and blue	1·25	80

DESIGNS—As Type **108**: 30c. Battle of the Maipu; 40c. Abdication of O'Higgins.

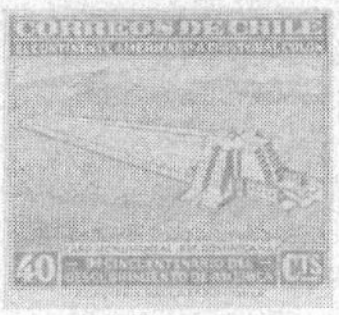

109 Columbus Lighthouse, Dominican Republic

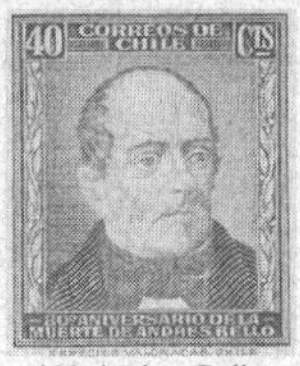

110 Andres Bello

1945. 450th Anniv of Discovery of America by Columbus.

371	**109**	40c. green	30	15

1946. 80th Death Anniv of Andres Bello (educationist).

372	**110**	40c. green	15	10
373		1p.80 blue	15	10

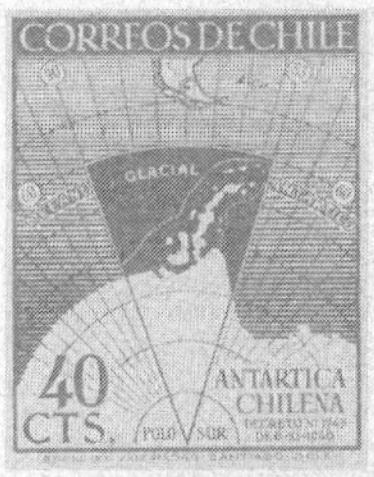

111 Antarctic Territory

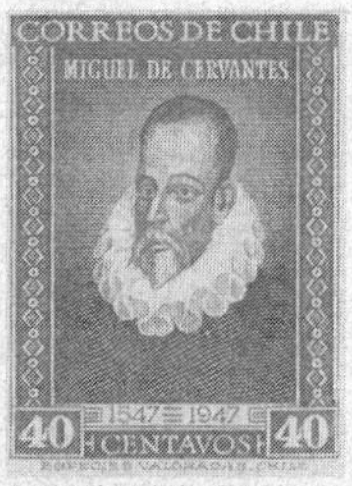

113 Miguel de Cervantes

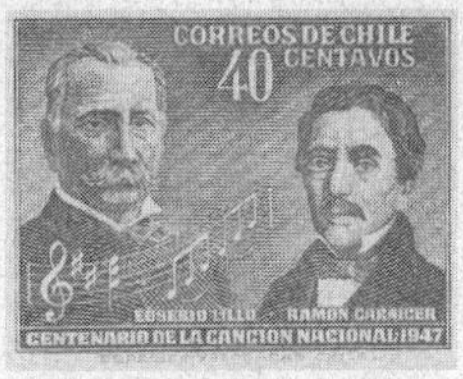

112 Eusebio Lillo and Ramon Carnicer

1947.

374	**111**	40c. red	40	15
375		2p.50 blue	1·25	30

1947. Centenary of National Anthem.

376	**112**	40c. green	15	10

1947. 400th Birth Anniv of Cervantes.

377	**113**	40c. red	15	10

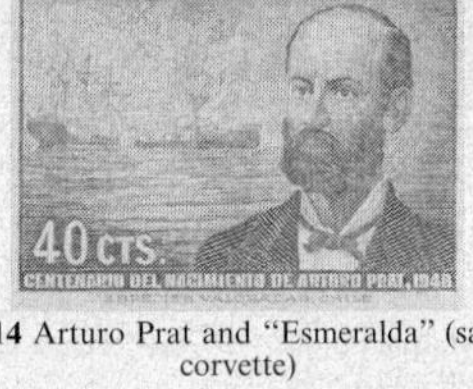

114 Arturo Prat and "Esmeralda" (sail corvette)

1948. Birth Centenary of Arturo Prat.

378	**114**	40c. blue	35	10

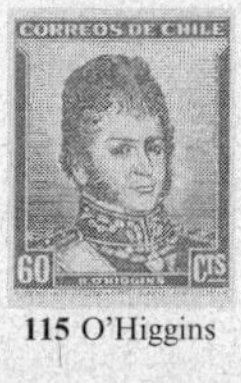

115 O'Higgins

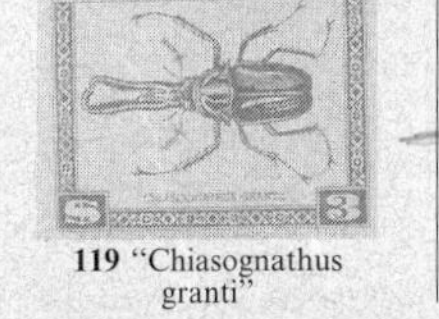

119 "Chiasognathus granti"

1948.

379	**115**	60c. black	10	10

1948. No. 272 surch **VEINTE CTS.** and bar.

380		20c. on 40c. green	10	10

1948. Centenary of Publication on Chilean Flora and Fauna. Botanical and zoological designs, as T **119** inscr "CENTENARIO DEL LIBRO DE GAY 1844–1944".

381a/y	60c. blue (postage)	80	35
382a/y	2p.60 green	1·50	90
383a/y	3p. red (air)	1·60	1·10

Each value in 25 different designs. Prices are for individual stamps.

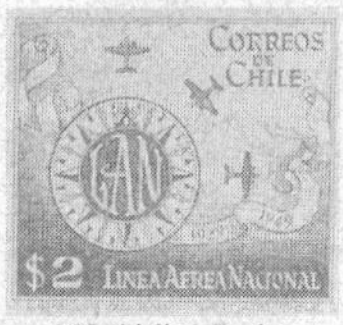

120 Airline Badge

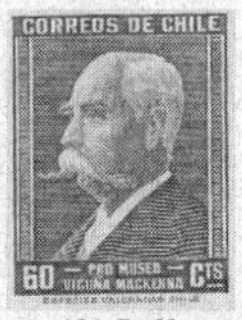

121 B. V. Mackenna

1949. Air. 20th Anniv of National Airline.

384	**120**	2p. blue	15	25

1949. Vicuna Mackenna Museum.

385	**121**	60c. blue (postage)	10	10
386		3p. red (air)	15	10

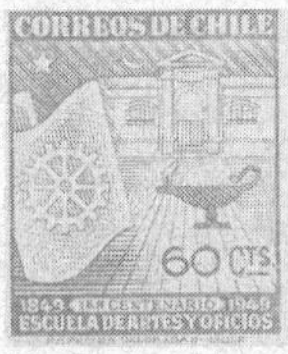

122 Wheel and Lamp

1949. Cent of School of Arts and Crafts, Santiago.

387	**122**	60c. mauve (postage)	15	10
388	–	2p.60 blue	30	20
389	–	5p. green (air)	45	30
390	–	10p. brown	75	40

DESIGNS: 2p.60, Shield and book; 5p. Shield, book and factory; 10p. Wheel and column.

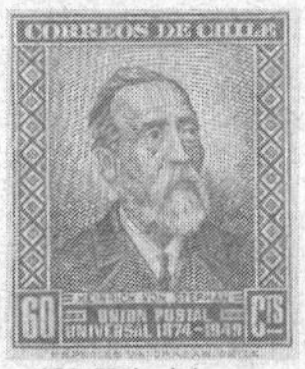

123 Heinrich von Stephan

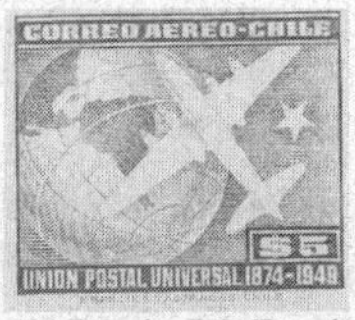

124 Douglas DC-6B and Globe

1950. 75th Anniv of U.P.U.

391	**123**	60c. red (postage)	10	10
392		2p.50 blue	45	20
393	**124**	5p. green (air)	30	20
394		10p. brown	60	35

1950. Air. As T **98/99**.

395	20c. brown	15	10
396	40c. violet	15	10
404c	60c. blue	25	10
398	1p. green	15	10
399	2p. brown	15	10
404f	3p. blue	15	10
401	4p. orange	30	10
402	5p. violet	15	10
403	10p. green	20	10
480	20p. brown	30	10
481	50p. green	35	10
482	100p. red	75	10
483	200p. blue	80	10

DESIGNS (each including an aeroplane): 20c. Mountains; 40c. Coastline; 60c. Fishing vessel; 1p. Araucanian pine tree; 2p. Chilean flag; 3p. Dock crane; 4p. River; 5p. Industrial plant; 10p. Landscape; 20p. Aerial railway; 50p. Mountainous coastline; 100p. Antarctic map; 200p. Rock "bridge" in sea.

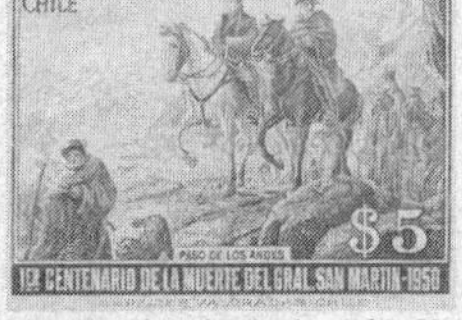

126 Crossing the Andes (after Y. Prades)

1951. Death Centenary of Gen. San Martin.

405	–	60c. blue (postage)	10	10
406	**126**	5p. purple (air)	50	15

PORTRAIT (25 × 29 mm): 60c. San Martin.

1951. Air. No. 303a surch **UN PESO**.

407	1p. on 90c. brown	15	10

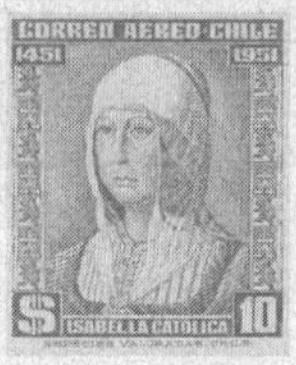

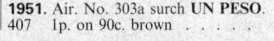

128 Issabella the Catholic

1952. 500th Birth Anniv of Issabella the Catholic.

408	**128**	60c. blue (postage)	10	10
409		10p. red (air)	40	20

1952. Surch **40 Ctvs.**

410	**115**	40c. on 60c. black	10	10

1952. Air. No. 302 surch **40 Centavos.**

411	40c. on 80c. olive	15	10

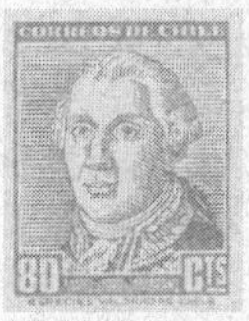

116 M. de Toro y Zambrano

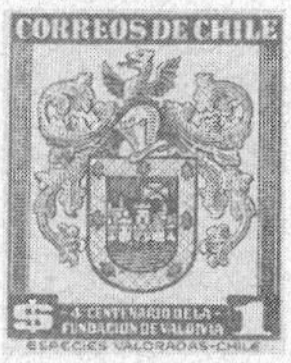

131 Arms of Valdivia

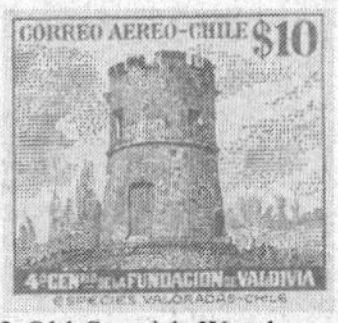

132 Old Spanish Watch-tower

1952.

379b	**116**	80c. green	15	10
379c	–	1p. turquoise (O'Higgins)	10	10
446	–	2p. lilac (Carrera)	10	10
447	–	3p. blue (R. Freire)	10	10
448	–	5p. sepia (M. Bulnes)	10	10
449	–	10p. violet (F. A. Pinto)	10	10
450	–	50p. red (M. Montt)	35	10

1953. 400th Anniv of Valdivia.

414	**131**	1p. blue (postage)	15	10
415	–	2p. violet	15	10
416	–	3p. green	35	10
417	–	5p. brown	45	10
418	**132**	10p. red (air)	1·25	20

DESIGNS—As Type **132**: 2p. Ancient cannons, Corral Fort; 3p. Valdivia from the river; 5p. Street scene (after old engraving).

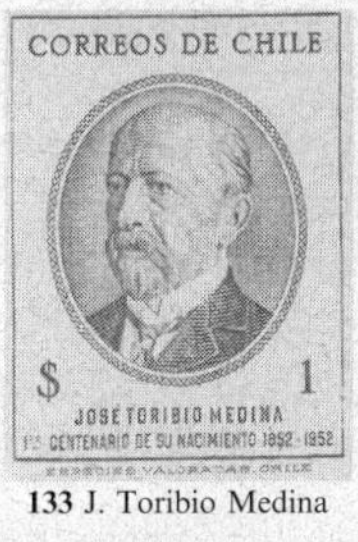

133 J. Toribio Medina

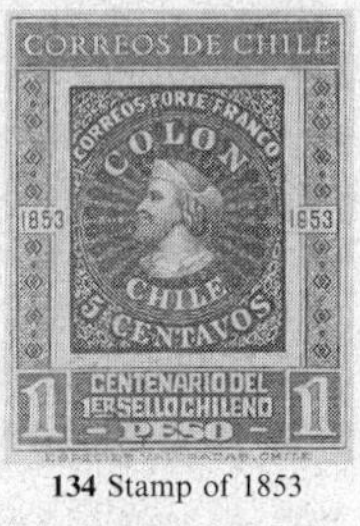

134 Stamp of 1853

1953. Birth Centenary of Toribio Medina.

419	**133**	1p. brown	15	10
420		2p.50 blue	25	10

1953. Chilean Stamp Centenary.

421	**134**	1p. brown (postage)	15	10
422		100p. turquoise (air)	3·00	1·75

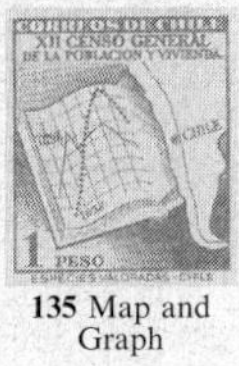

135 Map and Graph

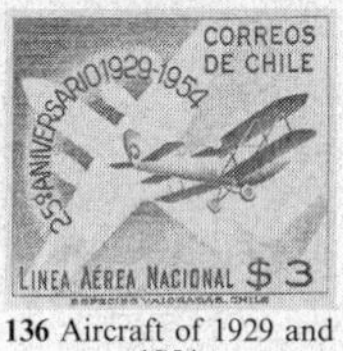

136 Aircraft of 1929 and 1954

1953. 12th National Census.

423	**135**	1p. green	10	10
424		2p.50 blue	15	10
425		3p. brown	25	15
426		4p. red	35	15

1954. Air. 25th Anniv of National Air Line.

427	**136**	3p. blue	10	10

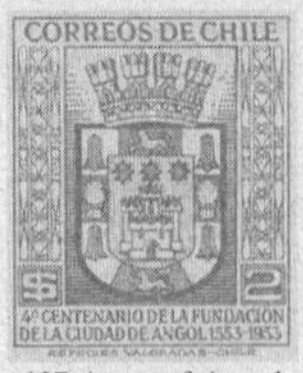

137 Arms of Angol

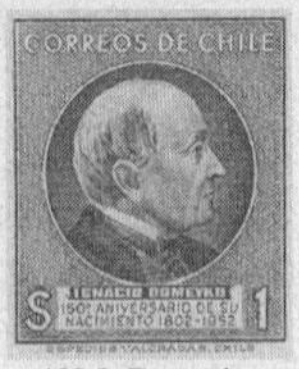

138 I. Domeyko

1954. 400th Anniv of Angol City.

428	**137**	2p. red	10	15

1954. 150th Birth Anniv of Domeyko (educationist and mineralogist).

429	**138**	1p. blue (postage)	15	10
430		5p. brown (air)	15	10

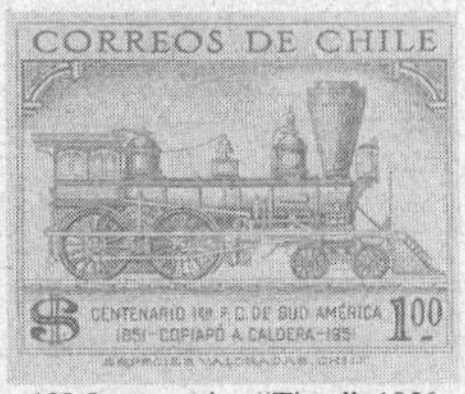

139 Locomotive "Tiger", 1856

1954. Centenary of Chilean Railways.

431	**139**	1p. red (postage)	20	25
432		10p. purple (air)	90	1·25

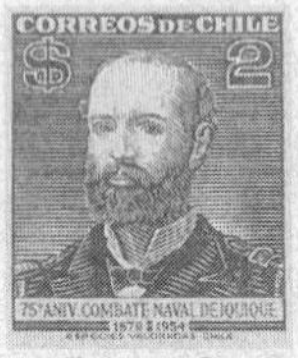

140 Arturo Prat

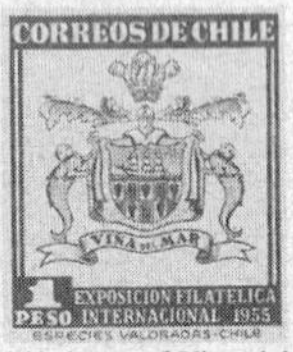

141 Arms of Vina del Mar

1954. 75th Anniv of Naval Battle of Iquique.

433	**140**	2p. violet	15	10

1955. Int Philatelic Exhibition, Valparaiso.

434	**141**	1p. blue	15	10
435	–	2p. red	15	10

DESIGN: 2p. Arms of Valparaiso.

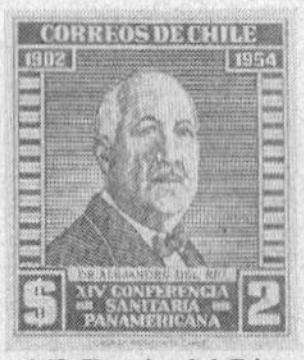

142 Dr. A. del Rio

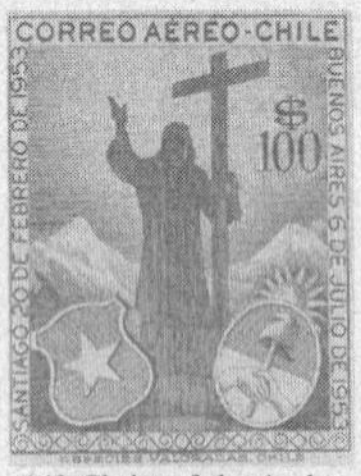

143 Christ of the Andes

1955. 14th Pan-American Sanitary Conference.

436	**142**	2p. blue	10	10

1955. Exchange of Visits between Argentine and Chilean Presidents.

437	**143**	1p. blue (postage)	15	10
438		100p. red (air)	1·90	75

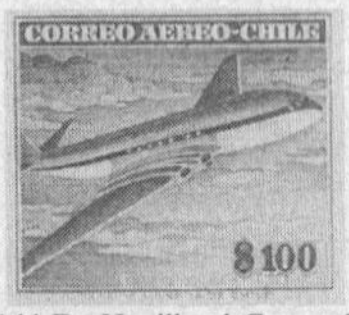

144 De Havilland Comet 1

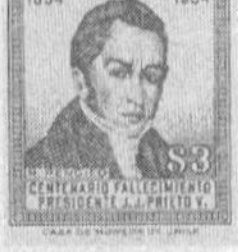

145 M. Rengifo

1955. Air.

441a	**144**	100p. green	75	15
441b	–	200p. blue	4·50	75
441c	–	500p. red	6·00	75

AIRCRAFT: 200p. Morane Saulnier Paris I. 500p. Douglas DC-6B.

1955. Death Centenary of Joaquin Prieto (President, 1833–41).

442	**145**	3p. blue	10	10
443	–	5p. red (Egana)	10	10
444	–	50p. purple (Portales)	1·40	25

For 15p. in similar design see under Compulsory Tax Stamps.

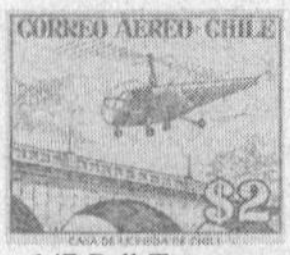

147 Bell Trooper Helicopter and Bridge

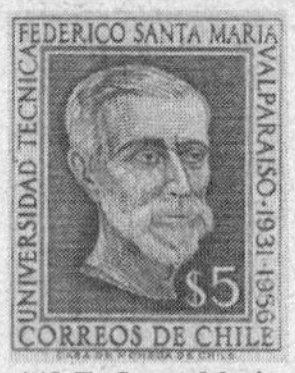

148 F. Santa Maria

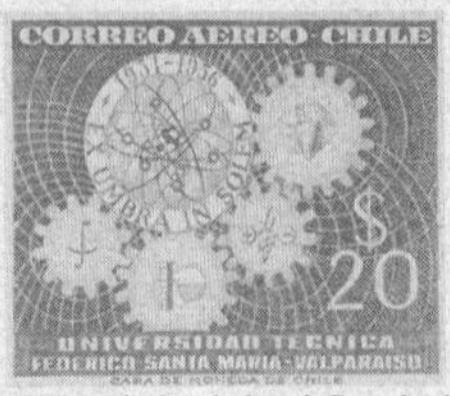

149 Atomic Symbol and Cogwheels

1956. Air.

451	–	1p. red	20	10
452	**147**	2p. sepia	20	10
455	–	5p. violet	20	10
456	–	10p. green	15	10
456a	–	20p. blue	15	10
456b	–	50p. red	20	10

DESIGNS: 1p. De Havilland Venom FB.4; 5p. Diesel locomotive and Douglas DC-6B; 10p. Oil derricks and Douglas DC-6B; 20p. De Havilland Venom FB.4 and Easter Island monolith; 50p. Douglas DC-2 and control tower.

See also Nos. 524/7.

1956. 25th Anniv of Santa Maria Technical University, Valparaiso.

457	**148**	5p. brown (postage)	15	10
458	**149**	20p. green (air)	25	15
459	–	100p. violet	70	40

DESIGN—As Type **149**: 100p. Aerial view of University.

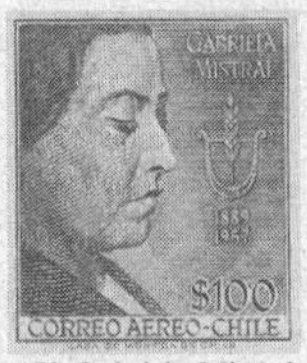

150 Gabriela Mistral

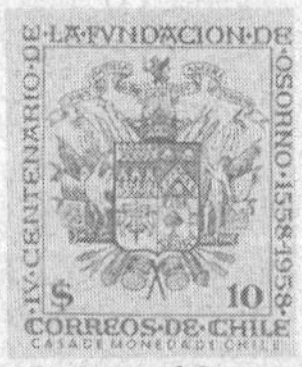

151 Arms of Osorno

1958. Gabriela Mistral (poetess, Nobel Prize Winner).

460	**150**	10p. brown (postage)	15	10
461		100p. green (air)	30	10

1958. 400th Anniv of Osorno.

462	**151**	10p. red (postage)	15	10
463	–	50p. green	35	10
464	–	100p. blue (air)	65	25

PORTRAITS: 50p. G. H. de Mendoza. 100p. O'Higgins.

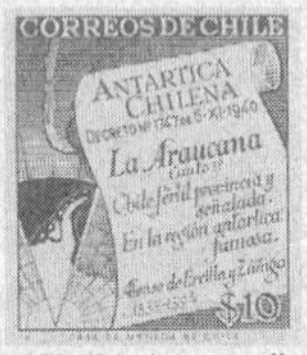

152 "La Araucana" (poem) and Antarctic Map

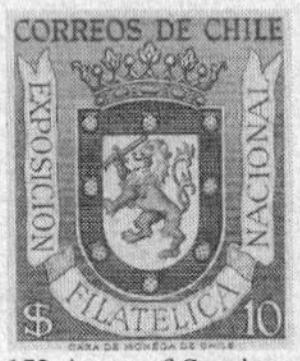

153 Arms of Santiago de Chile

1958. Antarctic issue.

465	**152**	10p. blue (postage)	20	10
466	–	200p. purple	3·25	1·25
467	**152**	20p. violet (air)	45	10
468	–	500p. blue	5·50	1·75

DESIGN: 200p., 500p. Chilean map of 1588.

1958. National Philatelic Exhibition, Santiago.

469	**153**	10p. purple (postage)	15	10
470		50p. green (air)	25	10

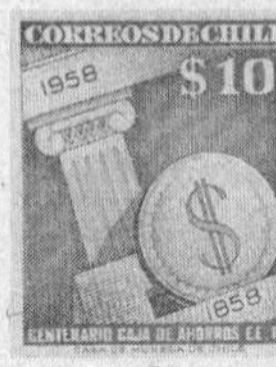

154

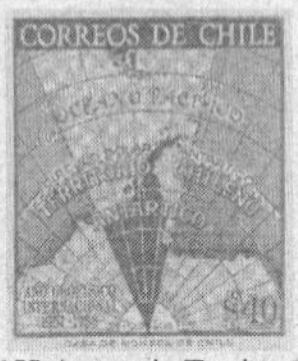

155 Antarctic Territory

1958. Cent of Chilean Civil Servants' Savings Bank.

471	**154**	10p. blue (postage)	10	10
472		50p. brown (air)	25	10

1958. I.G.Y.

473	**155**	40p. red (postage)	40	10
474		50p. green (air)	50	15

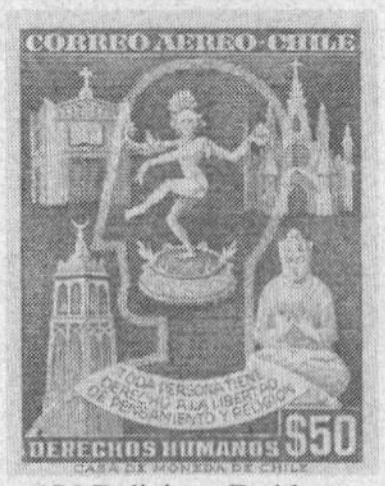

156 Religious Emblems

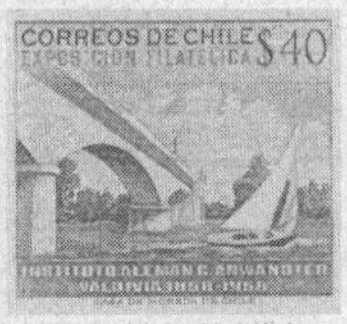

157 Bridge, Valdivia

1959. Air. Human Rights Day.

475	**156**	50p. red	65	1·00

1959. Centenary of German School, Valdivia and Philatelic Exhibition.

476	**157**	40p. green (postage)	20	10
477	–	20p. red (air)	15	15

DESIGN—VERT: 20p. A. C. Anwandter (founder).

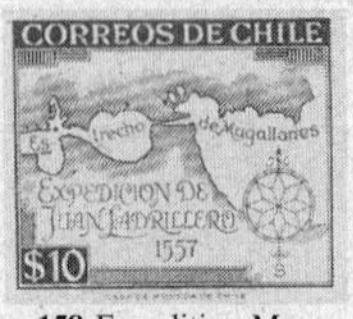

158 Expedition Map

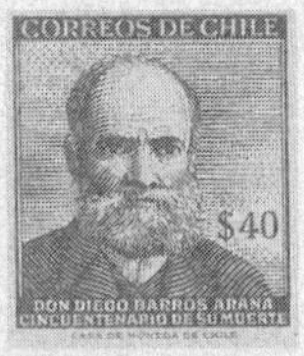

159 D. Barros-Arana

1959. 400th Anniv of Juan Ladrillero's Expedition of 1557.

484	**158**	10p. violet (postage)	25	10
485		50p. green (air)	35	10

1959. 50th Death Anniv of D. Barros-Arana (historian).

486	**159**	40p. blue (postage)	15	10
487		100p. lilac (air)	40	20

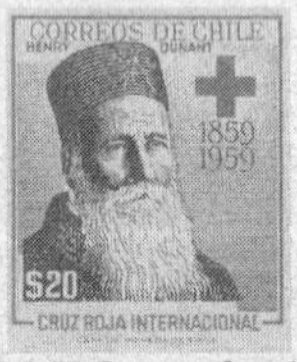

160 J. H. Dunant (founder)

1959. Red Cross Commemoration.

488	**160**	20p. lake & red (postage)	20	10
489		50p. black & red (air)	25	10

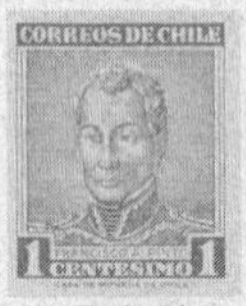

161 F. A. Pinto

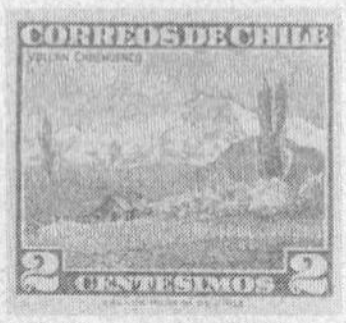

162 Choshuenco Volcano

1960. (a) Portraits as T **161**.

490	–	5m. turquoise	10	10
491	**161**	1c. red	10	10
493	–	5c. blue	10	10

(b) Views as T **162**.

492	**162**	2c. blue	10	10
492a		2c. blue ($23\frac{1}{2} \times 18$ mm)	10	10
494	–	10c. green	20	10
495	–	20c. blue	35	10
496	–	1E. turquoise	40	15

DESIGNS—As Type **161**: 5m. M. Bulnes; 5c. M. Montt. As Type **162**: 10c. R. Maule Valley; 20c., 1E. Inca Lake.

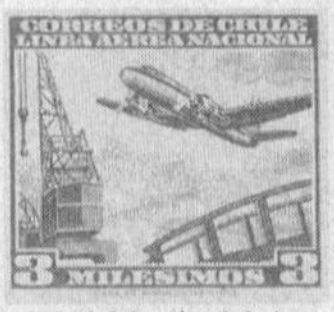

163 Martin 4-0-4 Airplane and Dock Crane

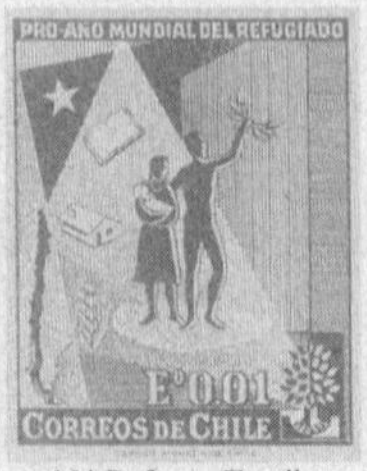

164 Refugee Family

1960. Air (Inland).

497	–	1m. orange	10	10
498	–	2m. green	10	10
499	**163**	3m. violet	10	10
500	–	4m. olive	10	10
501	–	5m. turquoise	10	10
502	–	1c. blue	10	10
503	–	2c. brown	25	10
504	–	5c. green	1·90	15
505	–	10c. red	45	10
506	–	20c. blue	60	10

DESIGNS: Airplane over—1m. Araucanian pine; 2m. Chilean flag; 4m. River; 5m. Industrial plant; 1c. Landscape; 2c. Aerial railway; 5c. Mountainous coastline; 10c. Antarctic map; 20c. Rock "bridge" in sea.

1960. World Refugee Year.

507	**164**	1c. green (postage)	35	10
508		10c. violet (air)	60	10

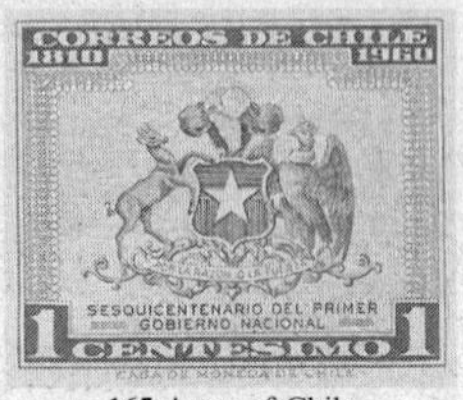

165 Arms of Chile

1960. 150th Anniv of 1st National Government (1st issue).

509	**165**	1c. brn & red (postage)	15	10
510		10c. chestnut & brn (air)	20	10

See also Nos. 512/23.

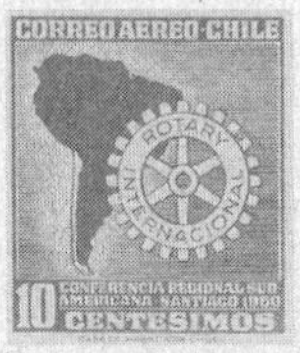

166 Rotary Emblem and Map

1960. Air. Rotary International S. American Regional Conference, Santiago.

511	**166**	10c. blue	25	10

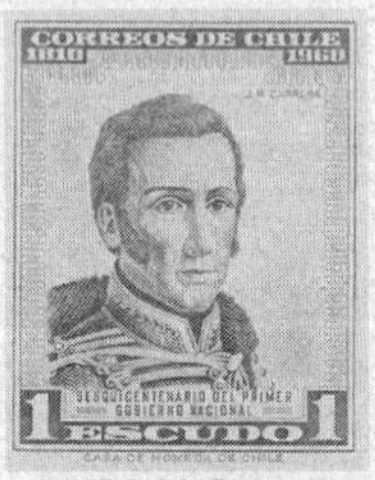

167 J. M. Carrera

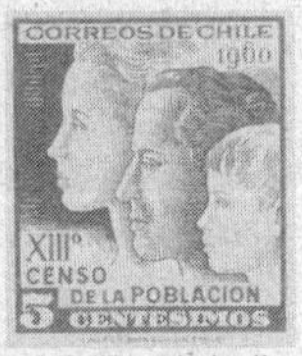

168 "Population"

1960. 150th Anniv of 1st National Government (2nd issue). (a) Postage.

512	–	1c. red and brown	15	10
513	–	5c. turquoise & green	15	10
514	–	10c. purple and brown	15	10
515	–	20c. green and blue	15	10
516	–	50c. red and brown	50	10
517	**167**	1E. brown and green	1·40	40

DESIGNS—HORIZ: 1c. Palace of Justice; 10c. M. de Toro y Zambrano and M. de Rozas; 20c. M. de Salas and Juan Egana; 50c. M. Rodriguez and J. Mackenna. VERT: 5c. Temple of the National Vow.

(b) Air.

518	–	2c. violet and red	10	10
519	–	5c. purple and blue	15	10
520	–	10c. bistre and brown	15	10
521	–	20c. violet and blue	25	10
522	–	50c. blue and green	45	20
523	–	1E. brown and red	1·40	40

DESIGNS—HORIZ: 2c. Palace of Justice; 10c. J. G. Martin and J. G. Argomedo; 20c. J. A. Eyzaguirre and J. M. Infante; 50c. Bishop J. I. Cienfuegos and Fray C. Henriquez. VERT: 5c. Temple of the National Vow. 1E. O'Higgins.

1961. Air (Foreign). As T **147** or **144** (10c. and 50c.), but values in new currency.

524	5m. brown	15	10
525	1c. blue	10	10
526	2c. blue	10	10
527	5c. red	10	10
528	10c. blue	10	10
529	20c. red	10	10
530	50c. turquoise	10	10

DESIGNS: 5m. Diesel locomotive and Douglas DC-6B; 1c. Oil derricks and Douglas DC-6B; 2c. De Havilland Venom FB.4 and monolith; 5c. Douglas DC-2 and control tower; 10c. De Havilland Comet 1; 20c. Morane Saulnier Paris I; 50c. Douglas DC-6B.

1961. National Census. 13th Population Census (5c.); 2nd Housing Census (10c.).

531	**168**	5c. green	40	10
532	–	10c. violet (buildings)	40	10

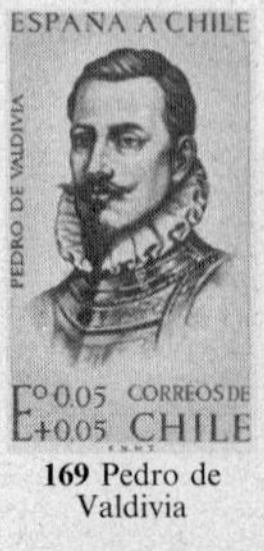

169 Pedro de Valdivia

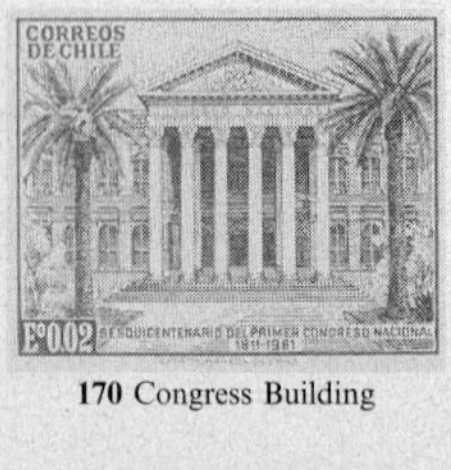

170 Congress Building

1961. Earthquake Relief Fund. Inscr "ESPANA A CHILE".

533	169	5c.+5c. green and pink (postage)	1·00	15
534	–	10c.+10c. violet & buff . .	1·00	15
535	–	10c.+10c. brown and orange (air)	1·00	20
536	–	20c.+20c. red and blue . .	1·00	20

PORTRAITS: No. 534, J. T. Medina. No. 535, A. de Ercilla. No. 536, Gabriela Mistral.

1961. 150th Anniv of 1st National Congress.

537	170	2c. brown (postage)	40	10
538		10c. green (air)	1·10	70

171 Footballers and Globe

1962. World Football Championships, Chile.

539	171	2c. blue (postage)	10	10
540	–	5c. green	15	10
541	–	5c. purple (air)	15	10
542	171	10c. lake	25	10

DESIGN—HORIZ: Nos. 540/1, Goalkeeper and stadium.

172 Mother and Child

1963. Freedom from Hunger.

543	172	3c. purple (postage) . . .	10	10
544	–	20c. green (air)	15	10

DESIGN—HORIZ: 20c. Mother holding out food bowl.

173 Centenary Emblem **174** Fire Brigade Monument

1963. Red Cross Centenary.

545	173	3c. red & grey (postage)	10	10
546	–	20c. red and grey (air) . .	15	10

DESIGN—HORIZ: 20c. Centenary emblem and silhouette of aircraft.

1963. Centenary of Santiago Fire Brigade.

547	174	3c. violet (postage) . . .	10	10
548	–	30c. red (air)	30	15

DESIGN—HORIZ: (39 × 30 mm): 30c. Fire engine of 1863.

175 Band encircling Globe **176** Enrique Molina

1964. Air. "Alliance for Progress" and Pres. Kennedy Commemoration.

549	175	4c. blue	10	10

1964. Molina Commemoration (founder of Concepcion University).

550	176	4c. bistre (postage) . . .	10	10
551		60c. violet (air)	10	10

1965. Casanueva Commemoration. As T **176** but portrait of Mons. Carlos Casanueva, Rector of Catholic University.

552		4c. purple (postage) . . .	10	10
553		60c. green (air)	10	10

177 Battle Scene (after Subercaseaux)

1965. Air. 150th Anniv of Battle of Rancagua.

554	177	5c. brown and green . . .	10	10

178 Monolith **179** I.T.U. Emblem and Symbols

1965. Easter Island Discoveries.

555	178	6c. purple	10	10
556		10c. mauve	15	10

1965. Air. Centenary of I.T.U.

557	179	40c. purple and red . . .	15	10

180 Crusoe on Juan Fernandez **181** Skier descending slope

1965. Robinson Crusoe Commemoration.

558	180	30c. red	15	10

1965. World Skiing Championships.

559	181	4c. green (postage) . . .	15	10
560	–	20c. blue (air)	10	10

DESIGN—HORIZ: 20c. Skier crossing slope.

182 Angelmo Harbour **183** Aviators, Monument

1965. Air.

561	182	40c. brown	30	10
562	183	1E. red	20	10

184 Copihue (National Flower) **185** A. Bello

1965.

563	184	15c. red and green . . .	15	10
563a		20c. red and green . . .	15	10

1965. Air. Death Centenary of Andres Bello (poet).

564	185	10c. red	10	10

186 Dr. L. Sazie **187** Skiers

1966. Death Centenary of Dr. L. Sazie.

565	186	1E. green	1·25	10

1966. Air. World Skiing Championships.

566	–	75c. red and lilac . . .	20	10
567	–	3E. ultramarine and blue	40	10
568	187	4E. brown and blue . .	85	25

DESIGN—HORIZ: (38 × 25 mm): 75c., 3E. Skier in slalom race.

188 Ball and Basket **189** J. Montt

1966. Air. World Basketball Championships.

569	188	13c. red	15	10

1966.

570	189	30c. violet	10	10
571	–	50c. brown (G. Riesco)	10	10

190 W. Wheelwright and Paddle-steamers "Chile" and "Peru"

1966. 125th Anniv (1965) of Arrival of Paddle-steamers "Chile" and "Peru".

572	190	10c. ultram & bl (postage)	40	10
573		70c. blue and green (air)	60	10

191 "Learning" **193** Chilean Flag and Ships

192 I.C.Y. Emblem

1966. Education Campaign.

574	191	10c. purple	10	10

1966. International Co-operation Year (1965).

575	192	1E. brn & green (postage)	1·75	10
576		3E. red and blue (air) . .	60	20

1966. Air. Antofagasta Centenary.

577	193	13c. purple	10	10

194 Capt. Pardo and "Yelcho" (coastguard vessel)

1967. 50th Anniv of Pardo's Rescue of Shackleton Expedition.

578	194	20c. turquoise (postage)	1·40	10
579		40c. blue (air)	30	15

DESIGN: 40c. Capt. Pardo and Antarctic sectoral map.

195 Chilean Family **197** Pine Forest

196 R. Dario (poet)

1967. 8th International Family Planning Congress.

580	195	10c. black and purple (postage)	10	10
581		80c. black and blue (air)	20	10

1967. Air. Birth Centenary of Ruben Dario (Nicaraguan poet).

582	196	10c. blue	15	10

1967. National Afforestation Campaign.

583	197	10c. green & bl (postage)	10	10
584		75c. green & brown (air)	20	10

198 Lions Emblem

1967. 50th Anniv of Lions International.

585	198	20c. blue & brn (postage)	15	10
586		1E. violet & yellow (air)	15	10
587		5E. blue and yellow . . .	1·40	50

199 Chilean Flag

1967. 150th Anniv of National Flag.

588	199	80c. red & blue (post) . .	20	10
589		50c. red and blue (air) . .	15	10

200 I.T.Y. Emblem

1967. Air. International Tourist Year.

590	200	30c. black and blue . .	10	10

201 Cardinal Caro **203** Farmer and Wife

202 San Martin and O'Higgins

1967. Birth Centenary of Cardinal Caro.

591	201	20c. lake (postage) . . .	35	20
592		40c. violet (air)	75	15

1968. 150th Anniv of Battles of Chacabuco and Maipu.

593	202	3E. blue (postage) . . .	10	10
594		2E. violet (air)	10	10

1968. Agrarian Reform.

595	203	20c. black, green and orange (postage) . . .	15	10
596		50c. black, green and orange (air)	15	10

204 Juan I. Molina (scientist) and "Lamp of Learning" **205** Hand supporting Cogwheel

1968. Molina Commemoration.
597 204 2E. purple (postage) . . . 10 10
598 – 1E. green (air) 10 10
DESIGN: 1E. Molina and books.

1968. 4th Manufacturing Census.
599 205 30c. red 15 10

206 Map, "San Sebastian" (galleon) and "Alonso de Erckla" (ferry)

1968. "Five Towns" Centenaries.
600 206 30c. blue (postage) . . . 50 10
601 – 1E. purple (air) 15 10
DESIGN—VERT: 1E. Map of Chiloe Province.

207 Club Emblem

1968. 40th Anniv of Chilean Automobile Club.
602 207 1E. red (postage) 20 10
603 5E. blue (air) 15 15

208 Chilean Arms

1968. Air. State Visit of Queen Elizabeth II.
604 208 50c. brown and green . . 15 10
605 – 3E. brown and blue . . . 15 10
606 – 5E. purple and plum . . . 25 15
DESIGN—HORIZ: 3E. Royal arms of Great Britain.
VERT: 5E. St. Edward's Crown on map of South America.

209 Don Francisco Garcia Huidobro (founder)

1968. 225th Anniv of Chilean Mint.
608 209 2E. blue & red (postage) 10 10
609 – 5E. brown and green . . . 20 · 10
610 – 50c. purple & yell (air) 10 10
611 – 1E. red and blue 15 15
DESIGNS: 50c. First Chilean coin and press; 1E. First Chilean stamp printed by the mint (1915); 5E. Philip V of Spain.

210 Satellite and Dish Aerial

1969. Inauguration of "ENTEL-CHILE" Satellite Communications Ground Station, Longovilo (1st issue).
613 210 30c. blue (postage) . . . 10 10
614 2E. purple (air) . . . 20 10
See also Nos. 668/9.

211 Red Cross Symbols

1969. 50th Anniv of League of Red Cross Societies.
615 211 2E. red & violet (postage) 15 10
616 5E. red and black (air) . . 15 10

212 Rapel Dam

1969. Rapel Hydro-electric Project.
617 212 40c. green (postage) . . . 10 10
618 3E. blue (air) 15 10

213 Rodriguez Memorial

1969. 150th Death Anniv of Col. Manuel Rodriguez.
619 213 2E. red (postage) 10 10
620 30c. brown (air) 10 10

214 Open Bible

1969. 400th Anniv of Spanish Translation of Bible.
621 214 40c. brown (postage) . . 10 10
622 1E. green (air) 15 10

215 Hemispheres and I.L.O. Emblem

1969. 50th Anniv of I.L.O.
623 215 1E. grn & blk (postage) 10 10
624 2E. purple & black (air) 10 10

216 Human Rights Emblem **217** "EXPO" Emblem

1969. Human Rights Year (1968).
625 216 4E. red and blue (postage) 35 25
626 4E. red and brown (air) 45 25

1969. World Fair "EXPO 70", Osaka, Japan.
628 217 3E. blue (postage) 10 10
629 5E. red (air) 15 10

218 Mint, Santiago (18th cent.)

1970. Spanish Colonization of Chile.
630 218 2E. purple 20 10
631 – 3E. red 15 10
632 – 4E. blue 15 10
633 – 5E. brown 15 10
634 – 10E. green 15 10
DESIGNS—HORIZ: 5E. Cal y Canto Bridge. VERT: 3E. Pedro de Valdivia; 4E. Santo Domingo Church, Santiago; 10E. Ambrosio O'Higgins.

219 Policarpo Toro and Map

1970. 80th Anniv of Seizure of Easter Island.
636 219 5E. violet (postage) . . . 25 10
637 50c. turquoise (air) . . . 35 10

221 Chilean Schooner and Arms

1970. 150th Anniv of Capture of Valdivia by Lord Cochrane.
640 221 40c. lake (postage) . . . 45 10
641 2E. blue (air) 90 10

222 Paul Harris **223** Mahatma Gandhi

1970. Birth Centenary of Paul Harris (founder of Rotary International).
642 222 10E. blue (postage) . . . 90 20
643 1E. red (air) 30 15

1970. Birth Centenary of Gandhi.
644 223 40c. green (postage) . . . 2·50 20
645 1E. brown (air) 30 15

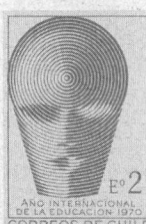

225 Education Year Emblem **226** "Virgin and Child"

1970. International Education Year.
648 225 2E. red (postage) 10 10
649 4E. brown (air) 15 10

1970. O'Higgins National Shrine, Maipu.
650 226 40c. green (postage) . . . 10 10
651 1E. blue (air) 15 15

227 Snake and Torch Emblem **228** Chilean Arms and Copper Symbol

1970. 10th Int Cancer Congress, Houston, U.S.A.
652 227 40c. purple & bl (postage) 80 10
653 2E. brown and green (air) 50 10

1970. Copper Mines Nationalization.
654 228 40c. red & brn (postage) 15 10
655 3E. green & brown (air) 25 10

229 Globe, Dove and Cogwheel

1970. 25th Anniv of United Nations.
656 229 3E. vio & red (postage) 10 10
657 5E. green and red (air) . . 20 10

1970. Nos. 613/14 surch.
658 210 52c. on 30c. blue (postage) 30 10
659 52c. on 2E. purple (air) 50 15

231 Freighter "Lago Maihue" and Ship's Wheel **233** Scout Badge

232 Bernardo O'Higgins and Fleet

1971. State Maritime Corporation.
660 231 52c. red (postage) 30 10
661 5E. brown (air) 50 10

1971. 150th Anniv of Peruvian Liberation Expedition.
662 232 5E. grn & blue (postage) 35 10
663 1E. purple & blue (air) . . 50 10

1971. 60th Anniv of Chilean Scouting Association.
664 233 1E. brn & grn (postage) 20 10
665 5c. green & lake (air) . . 20 10

234 Young People and U.N. Emblem

1971. 1st Latin-American Meeting of U.N.I.C.E.F. Executive Council, Santiago (1969).
666 234 52c. brn & blue (postage) 10 10
667 2E. green & blue (air) . . 15 10

1971. Longovilo Satellite Communications Ground Station (2nd issue). As T 210, but with "LONGOVILO" added to centre inscr and wording at foot of design changed to "PRIMERA ESTACION LATINOAMERICANA".
668 40c. green (postage) . . . 30 10
669 2E. brown (air) 50 15

235 Diver with Harpoon Gun

1971. 10th World Underwater Fishing Championships, Iquique.
670 235 1E.15 myrtle and green 65 10
671 2E.35 ultramarine & blue 15 10

239 Magellan and Caravel

1971. 450th Anniv of Discovery of Magellan Straits.
676 239 35c. plum and blue . . . 30 10

240 Dagoberto Godoy and Bristol Monoplane over Andes

1971. 1st Trans-Andes Flight (1918) Commem.
677 **240** 1E.15 green and blue 20 10

241 Statue of the Virgin, San Cristobal

1971. 10th Postal Union of the Americas and Spain Congress, Santiago.
678 **241** 1E.15 blue 75 10
679 – 2E.35 blue and red . . . 45 10
680 – 4E.35 red 45 10
681 – 9E.35 lilac 45 10
682 – 18E.35 mauve 60 10
DESIGNS—VERT: 4E.35, St. Francis's Church, Santiago. HORIZ: 2E.35, U.P.A.E. emblem; 9E.35, Central Post Office, Santiago; 18E.35, Corregidor Inn.

242 Cerro el Tololo Observatory

1972. Inauguration of Astronomical Observatory, Cerro el Tololo.
683 **242** 1E.95 blue & dp blue . . . 20 10

243 Boeing 707 over Tahiti

1972. 1st Air Service Santiago–Easter Island–Tahiti.
684 **243** 2E.35 purple and ochre . . 30 10

244 Alonso de Ercilla y Zuniga   **246** Human Heart

245 Antarctic Map and Dog-sledge

1972. 400th Anniv (1969) of "La Araucana" (epic poem by de Ercilla y Zungia).
685 **244** 1E. brown (postage) . . . 15 10
686 2E. blue (air) 20 15

1972. 10th Anniv of Antarctic Treaty.
687 **245** 1E.15 black and blue . . . 80 15
688 3E.50 blue and green . . . 55 10

1972. World Heart Month.
689 **246** 1E.15 red and black . . . 20 10

247 Text of Speech by Pres. Allende

1972. 3rd United Nations Conference on Trade and Development, Santiago.
690 **247** 35c. green and brown . . 25 15
691 – 1E.15 violet and blue . . 10 10
692 **247** 4E. violet and pink . . . 50 25
693 – 6E. blue and orange 20 10
DESIGNS: 1E.15, 6E. Conference Hall Santiago.
Nos. 690 and 692 each include a se-tenant label showing Chilean workers and inscr "CORREOS DE CHILE". The stamp was only valid for postage with the label attached.

248 Soldier and Crest

1972. 150th Anniv of O'Higgins Military Academy.
694 **248** 1E.15 yellow and blue . . 15 10

249 Copper Miner   **250** Barquentine "Esmeralda"

1972. Copper Mines Nationalization Law (1971).
695 **249** 1E.15 blue and red . . . 15 10
696 5E. black, blue and red 30 10

1972. 150th Anniv of Arturo Prat Naval College.
697 **250** 1E.15 purple . . . . . . 1·00 20

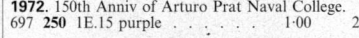

251 Observatory and Telescope

1972. Inauguration of Cerro Calan Observatory.
698 **251** 50c. blue 20 10

252 Dove with Letter

1972. International Correspondence Week.
699 **252** 1E.15 violet & mauve . . 15 10

253 Gen. Schneider, Flag and Quotation

1972. 2nd Death Anniv of General Rene Schneider.
700 **253** 2E.30 multicoloured . . . 30 20

254 Book and Students

1972. International Book Year.
701 **254** 50c. black and red . . . 15 10

255 Folklore and Handicrafts

1972. Tourist Year of the Americas.
702 **255** 1E.15 black and red . . . 15 10
703 – 2E.65 purple and blue . . 40 10
704 – 3E.50 brown and red . . 15 10
DESIGNS—HORIZ: 2E.65, Natural produce.
VERT: 3E.50, Stove and rug.

256 Carrera in Prison   **257** Antarctic Map

1973. 150th Death Anniv of General J. M. Carrera.
705 **256** 2E.30 blue 20 10

1973. 25th Anniv of General Bernardo O'Higgins Antarctic Base.
706 **257** 10E. red and blue 35 15

258 "Latorre" (cruiser) and Emblem   **259** Telescope

1973. 50 Years of Chilean Naval Aviation.
707 **258** 20E. blue and brown . . 55 10

1973. Inaug of La Silla Astronomical Observatory.
708 **259** 2E.30 black and blue . . 10

260 Interpol Emblem   **261** Bunch of Grapes

1973. 50th Anniv of Interpol.
709 **260** 30E. blue, black & brown 1·40 20
710 – 50E. black and red . . 1·40 25
DESIGN: 50E. Fingerprint superimposed on globe.

1973. Chilean Wine Exports. Multicoloured.
711 20E. Type **261** 50 10
712 100E. Inscribed globe . . . 1·00 20

1974. Centenary of World Meteorological Organization. No. 668 surch **"Centenario de la Organizacion Meteorologica Mundial IMO-W-MO 1973"** and value.
713 27E.+3E. on 40c. green . . . 15 10

263 U.P.U. Headquarters Building, Berne

1974. Centenary of U.P.U. Unissued stamp surch.
714 **263** 500E. on 45c. green . . . 85 20

264 Bernardo O'Higgins and Emblems

1974. Chilean Armed Forces.
715 **264** 30E. yellow and red . . . 20 10
716 – 30E. lake and red . . . 20 10
717 – 30E. blue and light blue 20 10
718 – 30E. blue and lilac . . 20 10
719 – 30E. emerald and green . 20 10
DESIGNS: No. 716, Soldiers with mortar; No. 717, Naval gunners; No. 718, Air Force pilot; No. 719, Mounted policeman.

1974. 500th Birth Anniv (1973) of Copernicus. No. 683 surch **"V Centenario del Nacimiento de Copernico 1473 - 1973"** and value.
720 **242** 27E.+3E. on 1E.95 blue and deep blue . . . 30 10

1974. Centenary of Vina del Mar. No. 496 surch **"Centenario de la ciudad de Vina del Mar 1874 - 1974"** and value.
721 27E.+3E. on 1E. turquoise 15 10

267 Football and Globe   **269** Police and Gloved Hand

1974. World Cup Football Championships, West Germany.
722 **267** 500E. orange and red . . 20 10
723 – 1000E. blue & dp blue . . 1·00 15
DESIGN—HORIZ: 1000E. Football on stylized stadium.

1974. Various stamps surch.
724 **212** 47E.+3E. on 40c. green 15 10
725 **228** 67E.+3E. on 40c. red and brown 15 10
726 **214** 97E.+3E. on 40c. brown 15 10
727 **223** 100E. on 40c. green . . 20 10
728 – 300E. on 50c. brown (No. 571) 20 10

1974. Campaign for Prevention of Traffic Accidents.
729 **269** 30E. brown and green . . 25 10

270 Manutara and Part of Globe   **271** Core of Globe

1974. Inaugural LAN Flight to Tahiti, Fiji and Australia. Each green and brown.
730 200E. Type **270** 40 15
731 200E. Tahitian dancer and part of Globe 40 15
732 200E. Map of Fiji and part of Globe 40 15
733 200E. Eastern grey kangaroo and part of Globe . . . 40 15

1974. International Symposium of Volcanology, Santiago de Chile.
734 **271** 500E. orange & brown . . 60 10

1974. Inauguration of Votive Temple. No. 650 surch **24 OCTUBRE 1974 INAUGURACION TEMPLO VOTIVO** and value.
735 **226** 100E. on 40c. green . . 15 10

273 Map of Robinson Crusoe Island   **275** F. Vidal Gormaz and Seal

274 O'Higgins and Bolivar

1974. 400th Anniv of Discovery of Juan Fernandez Archipelago. Each brown and blue.
736   200E. Type **273** 85   20
737   200E. Chontas (hardwood
     palm-trees)   40   20
738   200E. Mountain goat   40   20
739   200E. Spiny lobster   40   20

1974. 150th Anniv of Battles of Junin and Ayacucho.
740   **274** 100E. brown and buff . .   20   10

1975. Centenary of Naval Hydrographic Institute.
741   **275** 100E. blue and mauve . .   20   10

1975. Surch **Revalorizada 1975** and value.
742   **228** 70c. on 40c. red & brown   15   10

277 Dr. Schweitzer   **278** Lighthouse

1975. Birth Centenary of Dr. Albert Schweitzer (missionary).
743   **277** 500E. brown and yellow   35   10

1975. 50th Anniv of Valparaiso Lifeboat Service. Each blue and green.
744   150E. Type **278** 55   20
745   150E. Wreck of
     "Teotopoulis"   75   25
746   150E. "Cap Christiansen"
     (lifeboat)   75   25
747   150E. Survivor in water . .   55   20

279 Sail/steam Corvette "Baquedano"

1975. 30th Anniv of Shipwreck of Sail Frigate "Lautaro".
749   **279** 500E. black and green . .   75   20
750   — 500E. black and green . .   75   20
751   — 500E. black and green . .   75   20
752   — 500E. black and green . .   75   20
753   **279** 800E. black and brown   1·00   25
754   — 800E. black and brown   1·00   25
755   — 800E. black and brown   1·00   25
756   — 800E. black and brown   1·00   25
757   **279** 1000E. black and blue . .   1·25   25
758   — 1000E. black and blue . .   1·25   25
759   — 1000E. black and blue . .   1·25   25
760   — 1000E. black and blue . .   1·25   25
DESIGNS: Nos. 750, 754, 758, Sail frigate "Lautaro"; Nos. 751, 755, 759, Cruiser "Chacabuco"; Nos. 752, 756, 760, Cadet barquentine "Esmeralda".

280 "The Happy   **281** Diego Portales
Mother" (A. Valenzuela)   (politician)

1975. International Women's Year. Chilean Paintings. Multicoloured.
761   50c. Type **280** 65   15
762   50c. "Girl" (F. J. Mandiola)   65   15
763   50c. "Lucia Guzman" (P. L.
     Rencoret) 65   15
764   50c. "Unknown Woman"
     (Magdalena M. Mena) . . 65   15

1975. Inscr "D. PORTALES".
765   **281** 10c. green 20   10
765a   20c. lilac 10   10
765b   30c. orange 10   10
766   50c. brown 15   10
767   1p. blue 15   10
767a   1p.50 brown 15   10
767b   2p. black 15   10
767c   2p.50 brown 15   10
767d   3p.50 red 15   10
768   5p. mauve 15   15
For this design inscr "DIEGO PORTALES", see Nos. 901 etc.

282 Lord Cochrane and Fleet, 1820

1975. Birth Bicentenary of Lord Thomas Cochrane. Multicoloured.
769   1p. Type **282** 80   25
770   1p. Cochrane's capture of
     Valdivia, 1820 80   25
771   1p. Capture of "Esmeralda",
     1820 80   25
772   1p. Cruiser "Cochrane", 1874   80   25
773   1p. Destroyer "Cochrane",
     1962 80   25

283 Flags of Chile and Bolivia

1976. 150th Anniv of Bolivia's Independence.
774   **283** 1p.50 multicoloured . . . 1·75   10

284 Lake of the Incas

1976. 6th General Assembly of Organization of American States.
775   **284** 1p.50 multicoloured . . . 1·40   10

285 George Washington

1976. Bicentenary of American Revolution.
776   **285** 5p. multicoloured . . . . 1·50   15

286 Minerva and Academy Emblem

1976. 50th Anniv of Polytechnic Military Academy.
777   **286** 2p.50 multicoloured . . . 1·00   10

287 Indian Warrior

1976. 3rd Anniv of Military Junta. Multicoloured.
778   1p. Type **287** 25   15
779   2p. Andean condor with
     broken chain . . . . . 2·50   1·00
780   3p. Winged woman ("Rebirth
     of the Country") 25   15

288 Chilean Base, Antarctica

1977. Presidential Visit to Antarctica.
781   **288** 2p. multicoloured . . . . 5·25   25

289 College Emblem and   **290** Statue of Justice
Cultivated Field

1977. Cent of Advanced Agricultural Education.
782   **289** 2p. multicoloured . . . . 1·40   15

1977. 150th Anniv of Supreme Court.
783   **290** 2p. brown and grey . . . 1·40   10

291 Globe within "Eye"

1977. 11th Pan-American Ophthalmological Congress.
784   **291** 2p. multicoloured . . . . 2·00   10

292 Police Emblem and Activities

1977. 50th Anniv of Chilean Police Force. Multicoloured.
785   2p. Type **292** 60   10
786   2p. Mounted carabinero
     (vert) 25   10
787   2p. Policewoman with
     children (vert) 25   10
788   2p. Torres del Paine and
     Osorno Volcano (vert) . . 25   10

293 "Intelsat" Satellite and Globe

1977. World Telecommunications Day.
789   **293** 2p. multicoloured 25   10

294 Front Page, Press and Schooner

1977. 150th Anniv of Newspaper "El Mercurio de Valparaiso".
790   **294** 2p. multicoloured 20   15

295 St. Francis of Assisi   **296** "Science and Technology"

1977. 750th Death Anniv of St. Francis of Assisi.
791   **295** 5p. multicoloured . . . . 1·00   15

1977. Council for Science and Technology.
792   **296** 4p. multicoloured 40   15

297 Weaving (Mothers'   **298** Diego de Almagro
Centres)   (discoverer of Chile)

1977. 4th Anniv of Government Junta. Welfare Facilities. Multicoloured.
793   5p. Type **297** 55   10
794   5p. Nurse with cripple (Care
     of the Disabled) 55   10
795   10p. Children dancing
     (Protection of Minors)
     (horiz) . . . . 1·00   15
796   10p. Elderly man (Care for
     the Aged) (horiz) . . . . 1·00   15

1977. Columbus Day.
797   **298** 5p. brown 45   10

299 Boy, Christmas Bell and Post Box

1977. Christmas.
798   **299** 2p.50 multicoloured 15   15

300 Freighter loading Timber

1978. Timber Export. Multicoloured.
799   10p. Type **300** . . . . 1·00   25
800   20p. As T **300** but inscr
     "CORREOS" and with
     ship flying Chilean flag . . 1·50   35

301 Papal Arms and Globe

1978. World Peace Day.
801   **301** 10p. multicoloured . . . 80   15

302 University

1978. 50th Anniv of Catholic University, Valparaiso.
802   **302** 25p. multicoloured . . . 2·50   60

303 "Bernardo O'Higgins" (Gil de Castro)

1978. Birth Bicentenary of Bernardo O'Higgins (1st issue).
803   **303** 10p. multicoloured . . . 1·00   15
See also Nos. 804, 806/8 and 816.

304 Chacabuco Victory Monument

1978. Birth Bicentenary of Bernardo O'Higgins (2nd issue), and 5th Anniv of Military Junta.
804 **304** 10p. multicoloured . . . 1·00 15

305 Teacher writing on Blackboard

1978. 10th Anniv and 9th Meeting of Inter-American Council for Education, Science and Culture.
805 **305** 15p. multicoloured 60 15

306 "The Last Moments at Rancagua" (Pedro Subercaseaux)

1978. Birth Bicentenary of Bernardo O'Higgins (3rd issue).
806 **306** 30p. multicoloured . . . 2·00 65

307 "First National Naval Squadron" (Thomas Somerscales)

1978. Birth Bicentenary of Bernardo O'Higgins (4th issue).
807 **307** 20p. multicoloured . . . 1·75 80

308 Medallion

1978. Birth Bicentenaries of O'Higgins (5th issue) and San Martin.
808 **308** 7p. multicoloured 30 10

309 Council Emblem **310** Three Kings

1978. 30th Anniv of International Council of Military Sports.
809 **309** 50p. multicoloured . . . 3·50 1·00

1978. Christmas. Multicoloured.
810 3p. Type **310** 65 15
811 11p. Virgin and Child . . . . 1·25 20

311 Bernardo and Rodulfo Philippi

1978. The Philippi Brothers (scientists and travellers).
812 **311** 3p.50 multicoloured . . . 20 10

1979. No. 765 surch **$ 3.50**.
813 **281** 3p.50 on 10c. green . . . 15 10

313 Flowers and Flags of Chile and Salvation Army

1979. 70th Anniv of Salvation Army in Chile.
814 **313** 10p. multicoloured . . . 55 25

314 Pope Paul VI

1979. Pope Paul VI Commemoration.
815 **314** 11p. multicoloured . . . 80 25

315 Battle of Maipu Monument

1979. Birth Bicentenary of Bernardo O'Higgins (6th issue).
816 **315** 8p.50 multicoloured . . . 55 20

316 "Battle of Iquique" (Thomas Somerscales)

1979. Naval Battle Centenaries. Multicoloured.
817 3p.50 Type **316** 75 25
818 3p.50 "Battle of Punta Gruesa" (Alvaro Casanova Zenteno) 75 25
819 3p.50 "Battle of Angamos" (Alvaro Casanova Zenteno) 75 25

317 Diego Portales **319** Monument at Puntas Arenas (Miodrag Zivkovic)

318 Horse-drawn Ambulance

1979.
820 **317** 1p.50 brown 15 10

821 2p. grey 10 10
822 3p.50 red 10 10
823 4p.50 blue 20 10
824 5p. red 20 10
825 6p. green 20 10
826 7p. yellow 20 10
827 10p. blue 25 10
828 12p. orange 10 10
The 1p.50, 3p.50, 5p. and 6p. are inscribed "D. PORTALES" and have the imprint "CAMONEDA CHILE". The 2p., 4p.50, 7p. and 10p. are inscribed "DIEGO PORTALES" and have the imprint "CASA DE MONEDA DE CHILE".

1979. 75th Anniv of Chilean Red Cross.
831 **318** 25p. multicoloured . . . 2·75 60

1979. Centenary of Yugoslav Immigration.
832 **319** 10p. multicoloured . . . 45 15

320 Children in Playground (Kiochi Kayano Gomez)

1979. International Year of the Child. Mult.
833 9p.50 Type **320** 45 30
834 11p. Running girl (Carmed Pizarro Toto) (vert) . . 55 35
835 12p. Children dancing in circle (Ana Pizarro Munizaga) . . . . 1·00 50

321 Laveredo and Arms of Coyhaique

1979. 50th Anniv of Coyhaique.
836 **321** 20p. multicoloured . . . 80 40

322 Exhibition Emblem and Posthorn

1979. 3rd World Telecommunications Exhibition, Geneva.
837 **322** 15p. grey, blue & orange 70 30

323 Canal

1979. 25th Anniv of Puerto Williams, Navirino Island.
838 **323** 3p.50 multicoloured . . . 70 15

324 Chileans adoring Child Jesus **325** Rafael Sotomayor (Minister of War)

1979. Christmas.
839 **324** 3p.50 multicoloured . . . 1·10 20

1979. Military Heroes. Each ochre and brown.
840 3p.50 Type **325** 50 10
841 3p.50 General Erasmo Escala (Commander in Chief of Army) 50 10
842 3p.50 Colonel (later General) Emilio Sotomayor (Commander of troops at Battle of Dolores) . . . 50 10
843 3p.50 Colonel Eleuterio Ramirez (Commander of 2nd Line Regiment) . . . 50 10

326 Bell Model 205 Iroquois Rescue Helicopter at Tinguiririca Volcano

1980. 50th Anniv of Chilean Air Force. Mult.
844 3p.50 Type **326** 40 15
845 3p.50 Consolidated Catalina Skua amphibian in Antarctic 40 15
846 3p.50 Northrop Tiger II jet fighter in Andes 40 15

327 Rotary Emblem and Globe

1980. 75th Anniv of Rotary International.
847 **327** 10p. multicoloured . . . 80 25

328 "The Death of Bueras" (Pedro Leon Carmona) **329** "Gen. Manuel Gaquedano" (after Pedro Subercaseaux)

1980. Cavalry Charge led by Colonel Santiago Bueras at Battle of Maipu, 1818.
848 **328** 12p. multicoloured . . . 65 30

1980. Centenary of Battle of Arica Head. Mult.
849 3p.50 Type **329** 25 10
850 3p.50 Gen. Pedro Largos (43 × 26 mm) . . . 25 10
851 3p.50 Col. Juan Jose San Martin (43 × 26 mm) 25 10

330 Freire and Bars of "Ay, Ay, Ay!"

1980. Birth Centenary of Osman Perez Freire (composer).
852 **330** 6p. multicoloured 35 15

331 Mt. Gasherbrum II, Chilean flag and Ice-pick

1980. Chilean Himalayan Expedition (1979).
853 **331** 15p. multicoloured . . . . 1·00 35

332 "St Vincent de Paul" (stained glass window, former Mother House) **334** Mummy of Inca Child

333 Andean Condor

1980. 125th Anniv of Sisters of Charity in Chile.
854 332 10p. multicoloured . . . 50 25

1980. 7th Anniv of Military Government.
855 333 3p.50 multicoloured . . . 40 20

1980. 150th Anniv of National History Museum. Multicoloured.
856 5p. Type 334 . . . . . 55 15
857 5p. Claudio Gay (founder)
(after Alejandro Laemlein) 55 15

335 "Pablo Burchard"   336 Emblem and
(Pedro Lira)   Buildings

1980. Centenary of National Museum of Fine Arts.
858 335 3p.50 multicoloured . . . 20 10

1980. "Fisa '80" International Fair, Santiago.
859 336 3p.50 multicoloured . . . 20 10

337 "Family and Angels"   338 Infantryman
(Sara Hinojosa Orellana)

1980. Christmas. Multicoloured.
860 3p.50 Type 337 . . . . . 85 10
861 10p.50 "The Holy Family"
(Catalina Imboden
Fernandez) . . . . 1·10 20

1980. Army Uniforms of 1879 (1st series). Multicoloured.
862 3p.50 Type 338 . . . . . 55 15
863 3p.50 Cavalry officer (parade
uniform) 55 15
864 3p.50 Artillery officer 55 15
865 3p.50 Colonel of Engineers
(parade uniform) 55 15
See also Nos. 887/90.

339 Congress Emblem   340 Cattle

1980. 23rd International Congress of Military Medicine and Pharmacy, Santiago.
866 339 11p.50 multicoloured . . 55 30

1981. Eradication of Foot and Mouth Disease from Chile.
867 340 9p.50 multicoloured . . . 45 20

341 Robinson Crusoe Island

1981. Tourism. Multicoloured.
868 3p.50 Type 341 . . . . . 25 15
869 3p.50 Easter Island monoliths 60 15
870 10p.50 Gentoo penguins,
Antarctica . . . . 1·75 50

342 "Javiera Carrera" (after D. M.
Pizarro) and Flag

1981. Birth Bicentenary of Javiera Carrera (creator of first national flag).
871 342 3p.50 multicoloured . . . 20 10

343 U.P.U. Emblem

1981. Centenary of U.P.U. Membership.
872 343 3p. multicoloured 25 15

344 Unloading Cargo from Lockheed
Hercules

1981. 1st Anniv of Lieutenant Marsh Antarctic Air Force Base.
873 344 3p.50 multicoloured . . . 50 15

345 I.T.U. and W.H.O. Emblems
and Ribbons forming Caduceus

1981. World Telecommunications Day.
874 345 3p.50 multicoloured . . . 20 15

346 Arturo Prat Antarctic Naval Base

1981. 20th Anniv of Antarctic Treaty.
875 346 3p.50 multicoloured . . . 1·00 20

347 Capt. Jose Luis Araneda

1981. Centenary of Battle of Sangrar.
876 347 3p.50 multicoloured . . . 25 15

348 Philatelic Society Yearbook
and Medal

1981. 92nd Anniv of Philatelic Society of Chile.
877 348 4p.50 multicoloured . . . 25 15

349 "Exchange of Speeches between
Minister Recabarren and Indian Chief
Conuepan at the Nielol Hill" (Hector
Robles Acuna)

1981. Centenary of Temuco City.
878 349 4p.50 multicoloured . . . 25 15

350 Exports (embroidery by J.L.
Gutierrez)

1981. Exports.
879 350 14p. multicoloured . . . 65 20

351 Moneda Palace (seat of Government)

1981. 8th Anniv of Military Government.
880 351 4p.50 multicoloured . . . 25 15

352 St. Vincent de Paul

1981. 400th Birth Anniv of St. Vincent de Paul (founder of Sisters of Charity).
881 352 4p.50 multicoloured . . . 25 15

353 Medallion by Rene Thenot,
Quill and Law Code

1981. Birth Bicentenary of Andres Bello (statesman, lawyer, and founder of Chile University). Multicoloured.
882 4p.50 Type 353 . . . . . . 25 15
883 9p.50 Profile of Bello and
three of his books 40 20
884 11p.50 University of Chile
arms and Nicanor Plaza's
statue of Bello 45 20

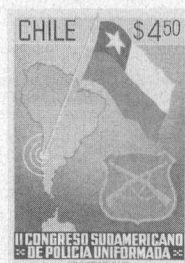

354 Flag on Map of South
America and Police Badge

1981. 2nd South American Uniformed Police Congress, Santiago.
885 354 4p.50 multicoloured . . . 30 15

355 F.A.O. and U.N. Emblems

1981. World Food Day.
886 355 5p.50 multicoloured . . . 30 15

1981. Army Uniforms of 1879 (2nd series). As T 338. Multicoloured.
887 5p.50 Infantryman 55 20
888 5p.50 Military School cadet 55 20
889 5p.50 Cavalryman 55 20
890 5p.50 Artilleryman 55 20

356 Mother and Child

1981. International Year of Disabled Persons.
891 356 5p.50 multicoloured . . . 30 15

357 "Nativity" (Ruth Tatiana Aguero
Eguiliz)

1981. Christmas. Multicoloured.
892 5p.50 Type 357 . . . . . 75 10
893 11p.50 "The Three Kings"
(Ignacio Jorge Manriquez
Gonzalez) 95 20

358 Dario Salas

1981. Birth Cent of Dario Salas (educationist).
894 **358** 5p.50 multicoloured . . . 25 15

359 Main Buildings of University

1981. 50th Anniv of Federico Santa Maria Technical University, Valparaiso.
895 **359** 5p.50 multicoloured . . . 25 15

360 Fair Emblem

1982. "Fida '82" International Air Fair.
896 **360** 4p.50 multicoloured . . . 30 15

361 Cardinal Caro and Chilean Family

1982. 1st Anniv of New Constitution. Mult.
897 4p.50 Type **361** 25 15
898 11p. Diego Portales and
national arms 45 20
899 30p. Bernardo O'Higgins and
national arms 65 40

362 Globe on Chilean Flag **363** Pedro Montt (President, 1906–10)

1982. 12th Panamerican Institute of Geography and History General Assembly.
900 **362** 4p.50 multicoloured . . . 25 15

1982. As T 281 but inscr "DIEGO PORTALES" and designs as T **363**.
901 **281** 1p. blue 60 10
902 – 1p. blue 10 10
903 **281** 1p.50 orange 10 10
904 – 2p. grey 10 10
905 – 2p. lilac 10 10
906 **281** 2p.50 yellow 10 10
907 **363** 3p. mauve 30 10
908 – 5p. red 10 10
909 **281** 5p. mauve 60 10
910 – 7p. blue 25 10
911 – 10p. black 15 10
DESIGNS: Nos. 902, 905, 908, 910, 911, Ramon Barros Luco (President, 1911–15).

364 Dassault Mirage IIIC Airplane and Chilean Air Force and American Air Forces Co-operation System Badges

1982. American Air Forces Co-operation System.
916 **364** 4p.50 multicoloured . . . 50 15

365 Trawler and Map **367** Capt. Ignacio Carrera Pinto

366 Scout Emblems and Brownsea Island

1982. Fisheries Exports.
917 **365** 20p. multicoloured . . . 2·00 80

1982. 75th Anniv of Boy Scout Movement and 125th Birth Anniv of Lord Baden-Powell (founder). Multicoloured.
918 4p.50 Type **366** 75 15
919 4p.50 Lord Baden-Powell and Brownsea Island 75 15
Nos. 918/19 were printed together, se-tenant, forming a composite design.

1982. Centenary of Battle of Concepcion. Mult.
920 4p.50 Type **367** 25 20
921 4p.50 Sub-lieutenant Arturo Perez Canto 25 20
922 4p.50 Sub-lieutenant Julio Montt Salamanca 25 20
923 4p.50 Sub-lieutenant Luis Cruz Martinez 25 20

368 Old Man at Window

1982. World Assembly on Ageing, Vienna.
924 **368** 4p.50 multicoloured . . . 25 15

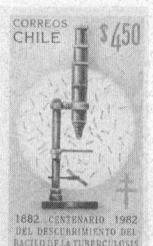

369 Microscope and Bacillus

1982. Centenary of Discovery of Tubercle Bacillus.
925 **369** 4p.50 multicoloured . . . 30 15

370 National Flag and Flame of Freedom

1982. 9th Anniv of Military Government.
926 **370** 4p.50 multicoloured . . . 25 15

1982. Nos. 688/9 surch.
927 **245** 1p. on 3E.50 blue & grn 30 10
928 **246** 1p. on 1E.15 red & black 35 10

372 "Nativity" (Mariela Espinoza Fuetes)

1982. Christmas. Multicoloured.
929 10p. Type **372** 25 10
930 25p. "Adoration of the Shepherds" (Jared Jeria Abarca) (vert) . . . . . . 1·25 40

373 "Virgin Mary and Marcellus" (stained-glass window, Sacred Heart of Jesus Church, Barcelona) **374** "El Sur", Quill and Printing Press

1982. 9th World Union of Former Marist Alumni Congress.
931 **373** 7p. multicoloured . . . . 1·60 40

1982. Cent of Concepcion's Newspaper "El Sur".
932 **374** 7p. multicoloured . . . 25 15

375 "Steamship Copiapo" (W. Yorke)

1982. 110th Anniv of South American Steamship Company.
933 **375** 7p. multicoloured . . . . 1·50 30

376 Club Badge, Radio Aerial, Dove and Globe

1982. 60th Anniv of Radio Club of Chile.
934 **376** 7p. multicoloured 25 15

377 Arms of Sovereign Military Order

1983. Postal Agreement with Sovereign Military Order of Malta. Multicoloured.
935 25p. Type **377** 65 40
936 50p. Arms of Chile . . . . . 1·00 55

378 Badge **380** Child watching Railway

379 Cardinal Samore

1983. 50th Anniv of Criminal Investigation Bureau.
937 **378** 20p. multicoloured . . . 65 20

1983. Cardinal Antonio Samore Commem.
938 **379** 30p. multicoloured . . . 80 25

1983. Centenary of Valparaiso Incline Railway.
939 **380** 40p. multicoloured . . . 1·25 65

381 Puoko Tangata (carved head from Easter Island) **383** General Francisco Morazan

382 Winged Girl with Broken Chains

1983. Tourism. Multicoloured.
940 7p. Type **381** 25 15
941 7p. Ruins of Pucar de Quitor, San Pedro de Atacama . . 25 15
942 7p. Rock painting, Rio Ibanez, Aisen 25 15
943 7p. Diaguita pot 25 15

1983. 10th Anniv of Military Government. Mult.
944 7p. Type **382** 50 15
945 7p. Young couple with flag . . 50 15
946 10p. Family with torch 55 15
947 40p. National arms . . . . . 1·10 40

1983. Famous Hondurans. Multicoloured.
948 7p. Type **383** 20 10
949 7p. Sabio Jose Cecilio del Valle 20 10

384 Central Post Office, Santiago **385** "Holy Family" (Lucrecia Cardenas Gomez)

1983. World Communications Year. Mult.
950 7p. Type **384** 55 10
951 7p. Space Shuttle "Challenger" 55 10
Nos. 950/1 were printed together in se-tenant pairs within the sheet forming a composite design.

1983. Christmas. Children's Paintings. Mult.
952 10p. "Nativity" (Hanny Chacon Scheel) 25 10
953 30p. Type **385** 90 25

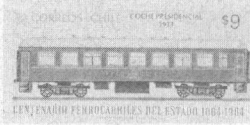

386 Presidential Coach, 1911

1984. Railway Centenary. Multicoloured.
954 9p. Type **386** . . . . . . 1·40 60
955 9p. Service car and tender . . 1·40 60
956 9p. Class 80 steam locomotive, 1929 . . . . . 1·40 60
Nos. 954/6 were printed together, se-tenant, forming a composite design.

387 Juan Luis Sanfuentes

1984. (a) Inscr "CORREOS CHILE".

989	387	5p. red	10	10
958		9p. green	15	10
959		10p. grey	15	10
960		15p. blue	15	10

(b) Inscr "D.S. No. 20 CHILE".

961	387	9p. brown	15	10
962		15p. blue	15	10
963		20p. yellow	20	10

388 Piper Pillan Trainer and Flags

1984. 3rd International Aeronautical Fair.

966	388	9p. multicoloured	85	10

389 Agriculture, Industry and Science

1984. 20th Anniv of Chilean Nuclear Energy Commission.

967	389	9p. multicoloured	25	10

1984. Nos. 944/5 surch.

968		9p. on 7p. Type 382	65	10
969		9p. on 7p. Young couple with flag	65	10

391 Chilean Women's Antarctic Expedition

1984. Chile's Antarctic Territories. Mult.

970	391	15p. Type 391	90	50
971		15p. Villa Las Estrellas Antarctic settlement	75	30
972		15p. Scouts visiting Antarctic, 1983	75	30

392 Parinacota Church (Tarapaca Region)

1984. 10th Anniv of Regionalization. Mult.

973	392	9p. Type 392	50	20
974		9p. El Tatio geyser (Antofagasta Region)	50	20
975		9p. Copper miners (Atacama Region)	50	20
976		9p. El Tololo observatory (Coquimbo Region)	50	20
977		9p. Valparaiso harbour (Valparaiso Region)	75	20
978		9p. Stone images (Easter Island Province)	50	20
979		9p. St. Francis's Church (Santiago Metropolitan Region)	50	20
980		9p. El Huique Hacienda (Libertador General Bernardo O'Higgins Region)	50	20
981		9p. Hydro-electric dam and reservoir, Machicura (Maule Region)	50	20
982		9p. Sta. Juana de Guadalcazar Fort (Bio Bio Region)	50	20
983		9p. Araucana woman (Araucania Region)	50	20
984		9p. Church, Guar Island (Los Lagos Region)	50	20
985		9p. South Highway (Aisen del General Carlos Ibanez del Campo Region)	50	20
986		9p. Shepherd (Magallanes Region)	50	20
987		9p. Villa Las Estrellas (Chile Antarctic Territories)	75	30

393 Pedro Sarmiento de Gamboa and Map

1984. 400th Anniv of Spanish Settlements on Straits of Magellan.

988	393	100p. multicoloured	2·25	80

394 Antonio Varas de la Barra (founder) and Coin

1984. Centenary of State Savings Bank.

990	394	35p. multicoloured	50	20

395 Flame and Bernardo O'Higgins Monument

1984. 11th Anniv of Military Government.

991	395	20p. multicoloured	30	15

396 Clown

1984. Centenary of Circus in Chile.

992	396	45p. multicoloured	80	25

397 Blue Whale

1984. Endangered Animals. Multicoloured.

993		9p. Type 397	70	20
994		9p. Juan Fernandez fur seal	70	20
995		9p. Chilean guemal	70	20
996		9p. Long-tailed chinchilla	70	20

398 "Shepherds following Star" (Ruth M. Flores Rival)

1984. Christmas. Multicoloured.

997		9p. Type 398	15	10
998		40p. "Bethlehem" (Vianka Pastrian Navea)	95	30

399 Satellite and Planetarium

1984. Inaug of Santiago University Planetarium.

999	399	10p. multicoloured	30	15

400 Andean Hog-nosed Skunk   401 Flags and Emblem

1985. Flora and Fauna. Multicoloured.

1000	401	10p. Type 400	60	25
1001		10p. "Leucocoryne purpurea"	60	25
1002		10p. Black-winged stilt	90	30
1003		10p. Marine otter	60	25
1004		10p. "Balbisia peduncularis"	60	25
1005		10p. Patagonian conure	90	30
1006		10p. Southern pudu	60	25
1007		10p. "Fuchsia magellanica"	60	25
1008		10p. Common diuca finch	90	30
1009		10p. Argentine grey fox	60	25
1010		10p. "Alstroemeria sierrae"	60	25
1011		10p. Austral pygmy owl	90	30

1985. 25th Anniv (1986) of American Air forces Co-operation System.

1012	401	45p. multicoloured	1·50	1·00

402 Chile and Argentina Flags and Papal Arms

1985. Chilean–Argentinian Peace Treaty.

1013	402	20p. multicoloured	45	25

403 Kentenich and Schoenstatt Sanctuary, La Florida

1985. Birth Centenary of Father Jose Kentenich (founder of Schoenstatt Movement).

1014	403	40p. multicoloured	75	40

404 Landscape and Shrimp

1985. Antarctic Territories and 25th Anniv of Antarctic Treaty. Multicoloured.

1015		15p. Type 404	50	30
1016		20p. Seismological Station, O'Higgins Base	65	40
1017		35p. Earth receiving station, Anvers Island	1·10	70

405 "Canis fulvipes"

1985. Endangered Animals. Multicoloured.

1018		20p. Type 405	70	30
1019		20p. James's flamingo	1·90	40
1020		20p. Giant coot	1·90	40
1021		20p. Huidobria otter	70	30

406 Doves and "J"

1985. International Youth Year (1022) and 40th Anniv of U.N.O. (1023). Multicoloured.

1022		15p. Type 406	20	15
1023		15p. U.N. emblem	20	15

407 Farmer with Haycart

1985. Occupations. Each in brown.

1024		10p. Type 407	10	15
1025		10p. Photographer with plate camera	10	15
1026		10p. Street entertainer	10	15
1027		10p. Basket maker	10	15

408 Carrera and Statue

1985. Birth Bicentenary of Gen. Jose Miguel Carrera (Independence leader and first President).

1028	408	40p. multicoloured	75	30

409 "Holy Family"   411 Escort of Light Infantry, 1818

1985. Chilean Art.

1029	409	10p. brown and ochre	10	15

410 "Nativity" (Jennifer Gomez)

1985. Christmas. Multicoloured.

1030		15p. Type 410	20	10
1031		100p. Man with donkey (Esteban Morales Medina) (vert)	2·00	90

1985. 16th American Armies Conference. Mult.

1032		20p. Type 411	35	20
1033		35p. Officer of the Hussars of the Grand Guard, 1813	75	30

412 Moon, Earth and Comet

1985. Appearance of Halley's Comet.

1034	412	45p. multicoloured	35	20

413 Living Trees and Flame   414 Saltpetre

1985. Forest Fires Prevention. Multicoloured.

1036		40p. Type 413	65	20
1037		40p. Burnt trees and flame	70	20

1986. Exports. Each brown and blue.

1038		12p. Type 414	15	10
1039		12p. Iron	15	10
1040		12p. Copper	15	10
1041		12p. Molybdenum	15	10

415 Dungeness Point Lighthouse

1986. Chilean Lighthouses. Multicoloured.
1042	45p. Type **415**		45	25
1043	45p. Evangelistas lighthouse in storm		45	25

416 St. Lucia Hill, Santiago

1986. Death Centenary of Benjamin Vicuna Mackenna (Municipal Superintendent).
1044	**416**	30p. multicoloured	30	20

417 Diego Portales

1986. Unissued stamp surch.
1045	**417**	12p. on 3p.50 mult	70	10

418 National Stadium, Chile, 1962

1986. World Cup Football Championship, Mexico. Multicoloured.
1046	15p. Type **418**		15	10
1047	20p. Azteca Stadium, Mexico, 1970		20	15
1048	35p. Maracana Stadium, Brazil, 1950		35	25
1049	50p. Wembley Stadium, England, 1966		50	40

419 Birds flying above City

1986. Environmental Protection. Mult.
1050	20p. Type **419**		20	10
1051	20p. Fish		30	10
1052	20p. Full litter bin in forest		20	10

420 "Santiaguillo" (caravel) and flags   **421** Emblem

1986. 450th Anniv of Valparaiso.
1053	**420**	40p. multicoloured	85	30

1986. 25th Anniv of Inter-American Development Bank.
1054	**421**	45p. multicoloured	40	20

422 St. Rosa and Pelequen Sanctuary

1986. 400th Birth Anniv of St. Rosa of Lima.
1055	**422**	15p. multicoloured	15	10

423 Stone Head on Raraku Volcano

1986. Easter Island. Multicoloured.
1056	60p. Type **423**		1·00	25
1057	100p. Tongariki ruins		1·60	45

424 Flags, Stamps in Album, Magnifying Glass and Tweezers

1986. "Ameripex '86" International Stamp Exhibition, Chicago.
1059	**424**	100p. multicoloured	1·40	50

425 Schooner "Ancud"

1986. Naval Traditions. Multicoloured.
1060	35p. Type **425**		80	45
1061	35p. Brigantine "Aguila"		80	45
1062	35p. Sail corvette "Esmeralda"		80	45
1063	35p. Sail frigate "O'Higgins"		80	45

426 "Gate of Serenity"

1986. Paintings by Juan F. Gonzalez. Mult.
1064	30p. "Rushes and Chrysanthemums"		25	15
1065	30p. Type **426**		25	15

427 Antarctic Terns

1986. Antarctic Fauna. Sea Birds. Mult.
1066	40p. Type **427**		1·40	55
1067	40p. Blue-eyed cormorants		1·40	55
1068	40p. Emperor penguins		1·40	55
1069	40p. Antarctic skuas		1·40	55

428 Pedro de Ona (poet)

1986. Chilean Literature. Multicoloured.
1070	20p. Type **428**		15	15
1071	20p. Vicente Huidobro		15	15

429 Major-General, 1878

1986. Centenary of Military Academy. Mult.
1072	45p. Type **429**		65	20
1073	45p. Major, 1950		65	20

430 Diaguita Art

1986. Indian Art. Multicoloured.
1074	30p. Type **430**		20	15
1075	30p. Mapuche art		20	15

431 "Nativity" (Begona Andrea Orrego Castro)

1986. Christmas. Multicoloured.
1076	15p. Type **431**		15	10
1077	105p. "Shrine and Mountains" (Andrea Maribel Riquelme Labarde)		1·60	80

432 Shepherds looking at   **433** Emblem and Globe Hill Town

1986. Christmas.
1078	**432**	12p. multicoloured	20	10

1986. International Peace Year.
1079	**433**	85p. multicoloured	1·00	50

1986. No. 1029 surch.
1080	**409**	12p. on 10p. brown and ochre	15	10

1986. Nos. 1024/7 surch.
1081	12p. on 10p. Farmer with haycart		25	10
1082	12p. on 10p. Photographer with plate camera		25	10
1083	12p. on 10p. Street entertainer		25	10
1084	12p. on 10p. Basket maker		25	10
1085	15p. on 10p. Farmer with haycart		25	10
1086	15p. on 10p. Photographer with plate camera		25	10
1087	15p. on 10p. Street entertainer		25	10
1088	15p. on 10p. Basket maker		25	10

436 Profiles and Flag

1986. Women's Voluntary Organization.
1089	**436**	15p. multicoloured	15	10

437 Virgin of Carmelites   **439** "The Guitarist of Quinchamali"

438 Kitson Meyer Steam Locomotive No. 59

1986. 60th Anniv of Coronation of Virgin of the Carmelites.
1090	**437**	25p. multicoloured	40	15

1987. Railways.
1091	**438**	95p. multicoloured	1·75	80

1987. Folk Tales. (a) As T **439**.
1092	**439**	15p. green	20	10
1093	–	15p. blue	40	10
1094	–	15p. brown	20	10
1095	–	15p. mauve	20	10

(b) Discount stamps. Inscr "D/S No 20" in colour of stamp in right-hand margin and dated "1992".
1092C	15p. As Type **439**		10	10
1093C	15p. As No. 1093		10	10
1094C	15p. As No. 1094		10	10
1095C	15p. As No. 1095		10	10

DESIGNS: No. 1093, "El Caleuche"; 1094, "El Pihuychen"; 1095, "La Lola".

440 Rowing Boat and Storage Tanks

1987. 40th Anniv of Capt. Arturo Prat Antarctic Naval Base. Multicoloured.
1096	100p. Type **440**		2·50	1·10
1097	100p. Buildings and rowing boat at jetty		2·50	1·10

Nos. 1096/7 were printed together, se-tenant, forming a composite design.

441 Pope and "Christ the Redeemer" Statue

1987. Visit of Pope John Paul II. Mult.
1098	20p. Type **441**		10	10
1099	25p. Votive Temple, Maipu		35	10
1100	90p. "Cross of the Seas", Magellan Straits		1·10	50
1101	115p. "Virgin of the Hill" statue, Santiago		1·60	80

442 Horse-riding Display   **443** Players and Ball

1987. 60th Anniv of Carabineers. Mult.
1103   50p. Type **442**   65   15
1104   50p. Sea rescue by Air
      Police   65   15

1987. World Youth Football Cup. Mult.
1105   45p. Type **443**   50   15
1106   45p. Player and Concepcion
      stadium   50   15
1107   45p. Player and Antofagasta
      stadium   50   15
1108   45p. Player and Valparaiso
      stadium   50   15

444 Battleship "Almirante Latorre"

1987. Naval Tradition. Multicoloured.
1110   60p. Type **444**   95   45
1111   60p. Cruiser "O'Higgins" . .   95   45

445 Portales and "El Vigia" Newspaper

1987. 150th Death Anniv of Diego Portales
(statesman).
1112   **445** 30p. multicoloured . . .   40   10

446 Works Projects

1987. Centenary of Ministry of Public Works.
1113   **446** 25p. multicoloured . . .   1·00   30

447 School Entrance

1987. Centenary of Infantry School. Mult.
1114   50p. Type **447**   25   10
1115   100p. Soldiers and national
      flag   80   40

448 "Chiasognathus   **449** Family
granti"

1987. Flora and Fauna. Multicoloured.
1116   25p. Type **448**   40   25
1117   25p. Sanderling   50   30
1118   25p. Peruvian guemal   40   25
1119   25p. Chilean palm   40   25
1120   25p. "Colias vauthieri"
      (butterfly)   50   25
1121   25p. Osprey   50   30
1122   25p. Commerson's dolphin . .   50   25
1123   25p. Mountain cypress . . .   40   25
1124   25p. San Fernandez Island
      spiny lobster   40   25
1125   25p. Fernandez firecrown . .   50   30
1126   25p. Vicuna   40   25
1127   25p. Arboreal fern   40   25
1128   25p. Spider-crab   45   25
1129   25p. Lesser rhea   50   30
1130   25p. Mountain viscacha . . .   50   25
1131   25p. Giant cactus   40   25

1987. International Year of Shelter for the Homeless.
1132   **449** 40p. multicoloured . . .   45   10

450 Emblem   **452** "Holy Family"
                (Ximena Soledad
                Rosales Opazo)

451 Condell, Battle of Iquique and
Statue

1987. "fisa'87", 25th International Santiago Fair.
1133   **450** 20p. multicoloured . . .   10   15

1987. Death Centenary of Admiral Carlos Condell.
1134   **451** 50p. multicoloured . . .   1·00   60

1987. Christmas. Multicoloured.
1135   30p. Type **452**   35   10
1136   100p. "Star over Bethlehem"
      (Marcelo Bordones
      Meneses) . . . .   1·00   60

453 Casting   **454** "Nativity"

1987. "Cobre '87" International Copper Conference,
Vina del Mar.
1137   **453** 40p. multicoloured . . .   20   10

1987. Christmas. (a) Non-discount.
1139   **454** 15p. blue and orange . .   20   10
     (b) Discount stamps. Additionally inscr "D.S.
          No. 20".
1140   **454** 15p. blue and orange . .   20   10

455 Non-smokers   **457** Freire
inhaling Smoke

456 "Capitan Luis Alcazar" (supply ship)
and Antarctic Landscape

1987. Anti-smoking Campaign.
1141   **455** 15p. blue and orange . .   20   10

1987. 25th Anniv of National Antarctic Research
Commission.
1142   **456** 45p. multicoloured . . .   1·25   40

1987. Birth Bicentenary of General Ramon Freire
Serrano (Director, 1823–27).
1143   **457** 20p. red and purple . . .   25   20

458 Violin and Frutillar Church and
Lake

1988. 20th Music Weeks, Frutillar.
1144   **458** 30p. multicoloured . . .   15   10

459 St. John with Boy   **460** Bird, Da Vinci's Glider,
(after C. Di Girolamo)   Wright's Flyer 1, Junkers Ju
                       52/3m, De Havilland
                       Vampire and Grumman
                       Tomcat

1988. Death Centenary of St. John Bosco (founder of
Salesian Brothers).
1145   **459** 40p. multicoloured . . .   45   10

1988. "Fida'88" 5th International Air Fair.
1146   **460** 60p. blue and deep blue   75   25

461 Shot Putting, Pole Vaulting and
Javelin Throwing

1988. Olympic Games, Seoul. Multicoloured.
1147   50p. Type **461**   60   45
1148   100p. Swimming, cycling
      and running . . . . . .   1·25   1·00

1988. Discount stamp. No. 958 surch **$20 D.S.No 20**.
1150   **387** 20p. on 9p. green   10   20

463 Kava-Kava Head

1988. Easter Island. (a) Inscr "CORREOS" only.
1151   **463** 20p. black and pink . .   25   15
1152   – 20p. black and pink . .   25   15
     (b) Discount stamps. As T **463** but additionally inscr
           "D.S.No 20".
1153   **463** 20p. black and yellow . .   25   15
1154   – 20p. black and yellow . .   25   15
DESIGN: Nos. 1152, 1154, Tangata Manu bird-man
(petroglyph).

464 Medal, Scientist, Bull and Farm
Workers

1988. 150th Anniv of National Agricultural Society.
1155   **464** 45p. multicoloured . . .   25   15

465 Tending Accident Victim

1988. 125th Anniv of Red Cross.
1156   **465** 150p. multicoloured . . .   2·25   2·00

466 Gipsy Moth, Boeing 767, Mirage 50
and Merino

1988. Birth Centenary of Commodore Arturo Merino
Benitez (air pioneer).
1157   **466** 35p. multicoloured . . .   45   10

467 Cadet Barquentine
"Esmeralda"

1988. Naval Tradition. Multicoloured.
1158   50p. Type **467**   75   45
1159   50p. "Capt. Arturo Prat"
      (stained glass window,
      Valparaiso Naval
      Museum)   75   45

468 Vatican City and University Arms

1988. Centenary of Pontifical Catholic University of
Chile.
1160   **468** 40p. multicoloured . . .   45   10

469 Esslingen Locomotive No. 3331

1988. Railway Anniversaries. Multicoloured.
1161   60p. Type **469** (75th anniv
      of Arica–La Paz railway)   2·40   1·25
1162   60p. North British
      locomotive No. 45 (cent
      of Antofagasta–Bolivia
      railway)   35   25

470 Chemistry Student

1988. 175th Anniv of Jose Miguel Carrera National
Institute.
1164   **470** 45p. multicoloured . . .   25   15

471 "Chloraea chrysantha"

1988. Flowers. Multicoloured.
1165   30p. Type **471**   45   10
1166   30p. "Lapogeria rosea" . . .   45   10
1167   30p. "Nolana paradoxa" . . .   45   10
1168   30p. "Rhodophiala advena" . .   45   10
1169   30p. "Schizanthus hookeri" . .   45   10
1170   30p. "Acacia caven"   45   10
1171   30p. "Cordia decanda" . . .   45   10
1172   30p. "Leontochir ovallei" . .   45   10
1173   30p. "Alstroemeria
      pelegrina"   45   10
1174   30p. "Copiapoa cinerea" . . .   45   10
1175   30p. "Salpiglossis sinuata" . .   45   10
1176   30p. "Leucocoryne
      coquimbensis"   45   10
1177   30p. "Eucryphia glutinosa" . .   45   10

1178	30p. "Calandrinia longiscapa"	45	10
1179	30p. "Desfontainia spinosa"	45	10
1180	30p. "Sophora macrocarpa"	45	10

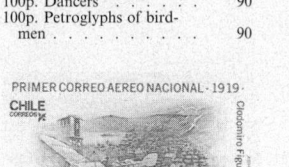

472 Commander Policarpo Toro and "Angamos"

1988. Centenary of Incorporation of Easter Island into Chile. Multicoloured.
1181 50p. Type 472 . . . . . . 75 20
1182 50p. Map of Easter Island and globe 55 20
1183 100p. Dancers 90 50
1184 100p. Petroglyphs of bird-men 90 50

473 Bleriot XI over Town

1988. 70th Anniv of First National Airmail Service.
1186 473 150p. multicoloured . . 90 60

474 Pottery

1988. 15th Anniv of Centre for Education of Women. Traditional Crafts. Multicoloured.
1187 25p. Type 474 . . . . . 10 10
1188 25p. Embroidery 10 10

475 Policeman and Brigade Members

1988. Schools' Security Brigade.
1189 475 45p. multicoloured . . 20 10

476 "Nativity"   477 Cancelled 1881 2c.
(Paulette Thiers)   Stamp

1988. Christmas. Multicoloured.
1190 35p. Type 476 . . . . 15 10
1191 100p. "Family going to church" (Jose M. Lamas) 70 35

1988. Centenary of Chile Philatelic Society.
1192 477 40p. multicoloured . . . 45 10

478 Child in   479 Manuel Bulnes and Battle
Manger   of Yungay, 1839

1988. Christmas. (a) Non-discount.
1193 478 20p. purple and yellow 10 10
(b) Discount stamps. As T 478 but additionally inscr "D.S. No. 20".
1194 478 20p. purple and yellow 10 10

1989. Historic Heroes. Multicoloured.
1195 50p. Type 479 . . . . . 20 10
1196 50p. Soldier and battle scene 20 10

| 1197 | 100p. Roberto Simpson and Battle of Casma, 1839 . . | 1·25 | 55 |
| 1198 | 100p. Sailor and battle scene | 1·25 | 55 |

480 St. Ambrose's Church,   483 Sister Teresa of the
Vallenar (bicentenary)   Andes

1989. Town Anniversaries. Multicoloured.
1199 30p. Type 480 . . . . . 10 10
1200 35p. Craftsman, Combarbala (bicent) . . 15 10
1201 45p. Laja Falls, Los Angeles (250th anniv) . . . 20 10
See also No. 1306.

1989. Various stamps surch. (a) Surch $25 only.
1202 25p. on 15p. green (1092) 10 10
1203 25p. on 15p. blue (1093) . . 30 10
1204 25p. on 15p. brown (1094) 10 10
1205 25p. on 15p. mauve (1095) 10 10
1206 25p. on 20p. black and pink (1151) 10 10
1207 25p. on 20p. black and pink (1152) 10 10
1208 25p. on 20p. black and yellow (1153) 10 10
1209 25p. on 20p. black and yellow (1154) 10 10

(b) Surch D.S. No 20 $25.
1210 25p. on 20p. black and pink (1151) 10 10
1211 25p. on 20p. black and pink (1152) 10 10

1989. Beatifications. Multicoloured.
1212 40p. Type 483 . . . . . 20 10
1213 40p. Laura Vicuna 20 10

484 Christopher Columbus

1989. "Exfina '89" Stamp Exhibition, Santiago. Multicoloured.
1214 100p. Type 484 . . . . . 70 35
1215 100p. "Nina", "Santa Maria" and "Pinta" . . 95 40

485 Container Ship and Trawler

1989. 50th Anniv of Energy Production Corporation. Multicoloured.
1217 60p. Type 485 . . . . . 90 20
1218 60p. Tree trunks on trailer and factory 25 15
1219 60p. Telephone tower and pylon 25 15
1220 60p. Coal wagons and colliery 25 15

486 Town and Sketch

1989. Birth Centenary of Gabriela Mistral (writer). Multicoloured.
1221 30p. Type 486 . . . . . 15 10
1222 30p. Mistral with children 15 10
1223 30p. Mistral writing . . . 15 10
1224 30p. Mistral receiving Nobel Prize 15 10

487 Grapes

1989. Exports. (a) Inscr as T 487.
1225 487 5p. blue 15 10
1226 – 5p. red and blue . . . 15 10
1227 487 10p. deep blue & blue . . 15 10
1228 – 10p. red and blue . . . 15 10
1229 487 25p. blue and green . . 10 10
1230 – 25p. red and green . . 10 10
1350 487 45p. blue and mauve . . 15 10
1351 – 45p. red and mauve . . 15 10

(b) Discount stamps. As T 487 but additionally inscr "D.S. No. 20".
1231 487 25p. blue and yellow . 10 10
1232 – 25p. red and yellow . 10 10
1352 487 45p. blue and yellow . 15 15
1353 – 45p. red and yellow . 15 15

DESIGNS: Nos. 1226, 1228, 1230, 1232, 1351, 1353, Apple.

488 Battle Scene, Soldiers and "Justice"

1989. 150th Anniv of Army Court of Justice.
1233 488 50p. multicoloured . . . 20 10

489 Monument   490 Victoria, Vina del
                               Mar

1989. Frontier Guards' Martyrs' Monument.
1234 489 35p. multicoloured . . . 15 10

1989. Transport.
1235 490 30p. black and orange 15 10
1236 – 30p. black and blue . . 35 10
1237 – 40p. black and green . . 20 10
1238 – 45p. black and green . . 55 10
1239 – 50p. black and red . . 55 10
1240 – 60p. black and bistre . . 45 15
1241 – 100p. black and green 65 35

DESIGNS—VERT: 35p. Scow, Chiloe Archipelago. HORIZ: 40p. Ox-cart, Cautin; 45p. Raft ferry, Rio Palena; 50p. Lighters, Gen. Carrera Lake; 60p. Valparaiso incline railway; 100p. Santiago funicular.
See also Nos. 1346 and 1458.

491 Scientist and Bearded Penguins

1989. 25th Anniv of Chilean Antarctic Institute.
1245 491 150p. multicoloured . . 2·10 1·00

492 Present Naval Engineers School and "Chacabuco" (first school)

1989. Centenary of Naval Engineering. Mult.
1246 45p. Type 492 . . . . . 40 10
1247 45p. Sailors in engine room 40 10
1248 45p. Destroyer, Aerospatiale Dauphin 2 helicopter and submarine 40 10
1249 45p. Launch of "Aquiles" (patrol boat) 40 10

493 Globes, Polar Bear   494 Atacamena
and Gentoo Penguins   Culture

1989. "World Stamp Expo '89" International Stamp Exhibition, Washington D.C.
1250 493 250p. multicoloured . . 3·00 1·75

1989. America. Pre-Columbian Cultures. Mult.
1252 30p. Type 494 . . . . . 40 10
1253 150p. Selk'nam and Onas cultures . . . . . . 1·25 60

495 Balls   497 Vicuna, Lauca

496 "Rowing to Church" (Cristina Lopez)

1989. Christmas. (a) As T 495.
1254 495 25p. yellow and green . . 10 10
1255 – 25p. yellow and green . . 10 10

(b) Discount stamps. Additionally inscr "D.S. No 20".
1256 495 25p. red and green . . . 10 10
1257 – 25p. red and green . . . 10 10

DESIGN: Nos. 1255, 1257, Bells.

1989. Christmas.
1258 496 100p. multicoloured . . 80 40

1990. National Parks. Multicoloured.
1259 35p. Type 497 . . . . . 30 10
1260 35p. Chilian flamingo, Salar de Surire 50 20
1261 35p. Cactus, La Chimba . . 30 10
1262 35p. Guanaco, Pan de Azucar 30 10
1263 35p. Long-tailed meadowlark, Fray Jorge 50 20
1264 35p. Sooty tern, Rapa Nui 50 20
1265 35p. Lesser grison, La Campana 30 10
1266 35p. Torrent duck, Rio Clarillo 50 20
1267 35p. Mountain cypress, Rio de los Cipreses 30 10
1268 35p. Black-necked swan, Laguna de Torca . . 50 20
1269 35p. Puma, Laguna del Laja 40 20
1270 35p. Araucaria, Villarrica 30 10
1271 35p. "Philesia magellanica", Vicente Perez Rosales . 30 10
1272 35p. "Nothofagus pumilio", Dos Lagunas 30 10
1273 35p. Leopard seal, Laguna San Rafael 40 20
1274 35p. Lesser rhea, Torres del Paine 50 20

498 Boot

1990. World Cup Football Championship, Italy. Multicoloured.
1275 50p. Type 498 . . . . . 20 10
1276 50p. Hand 20 10
1277 50p. Ball in net 20 10
1278 50p. Player 20 10

499 Vickers Wibault I Biplane, 1927–37

1990. Chilean Airforce Airplanes. Multicoloured.
1279	40p. Type **499**	25	10
1280	40p. Curtiss O1E Falcon, 1928–40	25	10
1281	40p. Pitts S-2A (Falcons aerobatic team, 1981–90)	25	10
1282	40p. Extra 33 (Falcons aerobatic team, 1990)	25	10

No. 1282 is inscribed "EXTRA 300".

500 Inca

1990. 500th Anniv of Discovery of America by Columbus. Multicoloured.
1284	60p. Type **500**	20	10
1285	60p. Spanish officer	20	10

501 Valparaiso

1990. Ports. Multicoloured.
1286	40p. Type **501**	15	10
1287	40p. San Vicente	15	10

502 "Piloto Pardo" (Antarctic supply ship)

1990. Naval Tradition. Multicoloured.
1288	50p. Type **502**	70	30
1289	50p. "Yelcho" (survey ship)	70	30

503 "Sunrise in Chile"

1990. "Democracy in Chile". Multicoloured.
1290	20p. Type **503**	10	10
1291	30p. Dove ("Peace in Chile")	10	10
1292	60p. "ChiLe" ("Rejoicing in Chile")	45	10
1293	100p. Star ("Thus Chile pleases me")	70	25

504 Child and Slogan

1990. "One Chile for All Chileans".
1295	**504** 45p. multicoloured	15	10

505 Sir Rowland Hill   **506** Flags

1990. 150th Anniv of the Penny Black.
1297	**505** 250p. multicoloured	1·50	75

1990. Centenary of Organization of American States.
1299	**506** 150p. multicoloured	95	40

507 Purplish Scallop and Diver with Net

1990. Fishing. Multicoloured.
1300	40p. Type **507**	25	15
1301	40p. Giant wedge clam and man with net	25	15
1302	40p. Swordfish ("Albacora") and harpooner on "San Antonio" (fishing boat)	40	15
1303	40p. Marine spider crab and fishing boat raising catch	40	15
1304	40p. Chilean hake ("Merluza") and trawler	40	15
1305	40p. Women baiting hooks	40	15

1990. Town Anniversaries. 250th Anniv of San Felipe. As T **480**. Multicoloured.
1306	50p. Curimon Convent	20	10

508 Aerosol   **509** Salvador Allende

1990. Environmental Protection. Each red and black.
(a) As T **508**.
1307	35p. Type **508**	15	10
1308	35p. Tree and tree stumps	15	10
1309	35p. Factory chimneys emitting smoke	15	10
1310	35p. Oil tanker polluting wildlife and sea	40	10
1311	35p. Deer escaping from burning forest	15	10

(b) Discount stamps. Additionally inscr "D.S. No 20".
1312	35p. Type **508**	15	10
1313	35p. As No. 1308	15	10
1314	35p. As No. 1309	15	10
1315	35p. As No. 1310	40	10
1316	35p. As No. 1311	15	10

See also Nos. 1421/30.

1990. Presidents.
1317	**509**	35p. black and blue	15	10
1318	–	35p. black and blue	15	10
1319	–	40p. black and green	15	10
1320	–	45p. black and green	15	10
1321	–	50p. black and red	20	10
1322	–	60p. black and red	20	10
1323	–	70p. black and blue	25	15
1324	–	80p. black and blue	30	20
1325	–	90p. black and brown	30	20
1326	–	100p. black & brown	35	25

DESIGNS: No. 1318, Eduardo Frei; 1319, Jorge Alessandri; 1320, Gabriel Gonzalez; 1321, Juan Antonio Rios; 1322, Pedro Aguirre Cerda; 1323, Juan E. Montero; 1324, Carlos Ibanez; 1325, Emiliano Figueroa; 1326, Arturo Alessandri.

510 Opening Ceremony

1990. Rodeo. Multicoloured.
1327	45p. Type **510**	15	10
1328	45p. Riders saluting crowd	15	10
1329	45p. Rider reining in	15	10
1330	45p. Two riders cornering steer	15	10

511 Chilean Flamingoes

1990. America. The Natural World. Mult.
1331	30p. Type **511**	85	20
1332	150p. South American fur seals	1·40	40

512 Chilean State Arms and Spanish Royal Arms

1990. State Visit by King Juan Carlos and Queen Sofia of Spain. Multicoloured.
1333	100p. Type **512**	70	25
1334	100p. Spanish and Chilean (at right) State Arms	70	25

513 Construction Diagram of Viaduct

1990. Centenary of Malleco Viaduct. Mult.
1335	60p. Type **513**	55	20
1336	60p. Boy waving to steam train on completed viaduct	55	20

Nos. 1335/6 were printed together, se-tenant, forming a composite design.

514 Antarctic Skua, Whale and Supply Ship

1990. 50th Anniv of Chilean Antarctic Territory. Multicoloured.
1337	250p. Type **514**	1·25	85
1338	250p. Adelie penguins, Bell Model 206 jet helicopters and tents	2·00	80

515 Children decorating Tree

1990. Christmas. (a) As T **515**.
1340	515 35p. green & emerald	10	10

(b) Discount stamps. Additionally inscr "D.S. No 20".
1341	515 35p. green and orange	10	10

516 Santa Claus in Space (Carla Levill)

1990. Christmas. Children's drawings. Mult.
1342	35p. Type **516**	10	10
1343	150p. Television on sea bed (Jose M. Lamas)	70	35

517 Assembly Hall

1990. National Congress. Multicoloured.
1344	100p. Type **517**	75	25
1345	100p. Painting above dais	75	25

1991. Discount stamp. As No. 1238 but colour changed and additionally inscr "D.S. No 20".
1346	45p. black and yellow	40	10

518 Casa Colorada

1991. 450th Anniv of Santiago. Multicoloured.
1347	100p. Type **518**	75	25
1348	100p. City landmarks	75	25

519 Voisin "Boxkite"

1991. Aviation History. Multicoloured.
1354	150p. Type **519**	90	45
1355	150p. Royal Aircraft Factory S.E.5A	90	45
1356	150p. Morane Saulnier MS 35	90	45
1357	150p. Consolidated PBY-5A/ OA-10 Catalina amphibian	90	45

520 Map, Player and Left Half of Ball

1991. America Cup Football Championship. Mult.
1358	100p. Type **520**	75	25
1359	100p. Right half of ball and goalkeeper	75	25

Nos. 1358/9 were printed together, se-tenant, forming a composite design.

521 Drill and Miner

1991. Coal Mining. Multicoloured.
1360	200p. Type **521**	1·60	45
1361	200p. Miners emptying truck	1·90	45

522 Youths and Emblem   **525** Santiago Cathedral

1991. Centenary of Scientific Society.
1362	**522** 45p. black and green	15	10

1991. Traditional Crafts. Multicoloured.
1363	90p. Type **523**	55	25
1364	90p. Carvings and ceramics	55	25

523 Dish and Hanging Ornaments

1991. Various stamps surch.
1365	**463**	45p. on 20p. black and yellow	15	10
1366	–	45p. on 20p. black and yellow (1154)	15	10
1367	**487**	45p. on 25p. blue & yell	15	10
1368	–	45p. on 25p. red and yellow (1232)	15	10

1991. National Monuments.
1369	**525**	300p. black, pink & brn	1·90	70

526 Dish Aerial and Transmission Masts

1991. World Telecommunications Day.
1370	**526**	90p. multicoloured	65	25

527 Pope Leo XIII and Factory Line **528** Capt. L. Pardo and Sir Ernest Shackleton

1991. Centenary of "Rerum Novarum" (papal encyclical on workers' rights).
1371 **527** 100p. multicoloured . . 65 25

1991. Naval Tradition. 75th Anniv of Pardo's Rescue of Shackleton Expedition. Multicoloured.
1372 50p. Type **528** 40 10
1373 50p. "Yelcho" (coast-guard vessel) 75 25
1374 50p. Chilean sailor sighting stranded men on Elephant Island 40 10
1375 50p. "Endurance" 75 25

529 Flags and Globe **531** "Maipo" (container ship)

530 Building and Police Officers

1991. 21st General Assembly of Organization of American States, Santiago.
1377 **529** 70p. multicoloured . . . 80 15

1991. Opening of New Police School.
1378 **530** 50p. Multicoloured . . . 15 10

1991. National Merchant Navy Day.
1379 **531** 45p. black and red . . . 45 10

532 Opening Ceremony

1991. 11th Pan-American Games, Havana. Mult.
1380 100p. Type **532** 60 25
1381 100p. Cycling, running and basketball competitors . . 60 25

533 Carriage and Building

1991. Bicentenary of Los Andes.
1382 **533** 100p. multicoloured . . 60 25

534 Common Octopus **536** "Woman in Red" (Pedro Reszka)

535 Nitrate Processing and Jose Balmaceda (President, 1886–91)

1991. Marine Life. Multicoloured.
1383 50p. Type **534** 30 15
1384 50p. "Durvillaea antarctica" 30 15
1385 50p. Lenguado 45 15
1386 50p. "Austromegabalanus psittacus" 30 15
1387 50p. Barnacle rock shell ("Concholepas concholepas") 30 15
1388 50p. Crab ("Cancer setosus") 30 15
1389 50p. "Lessonia nigrescens" 30 15
1390 50p. Sea-urchin 30 15
1391 50p. Crab ("Homalaspis plana") 30 15
1392 50p. "Porphyra columbina" 30 15
1393 50p. Loro knife-jaw . . . 45 15
1394 50p. "Chorus giganteus" . 30 15
1395 50p. Rock shrimp 30 15
1396 50p. Peruvian anchovy . . 45 15
1397 50p. "Gracilaria sp." . . . 30 15
1398 50p. "Pyura chilensis" . . . 30 15

1991. Centenary of 1891 Revolution. Pre-Revolution Events. Multicoloured.
1399 100p. Type **535** 90 25
1400 100p. Education and Balmaceda 60 25

1991. Paintings. Multicoloured.
1401 50p. Type **536** 40 10
1402 70p. "The Traveller" (Camilo Mori) . . . . 1·25 30
1403 200p. "Head of Child" (Benito Rebolledo) . . 90 45
1404 300p. "Child in Fez" (A. Valenzuela Puelma) 2·00 70

537 Map of South American Interests in Antarctica

1991. 30th Anniv of Antarctic Treaty. Mult.
1405 80p. Type **537** 70 20
1406 80p. Wildlife 90 45

538 Glove in Envelope (Guillermo Suarez)

1991. International Letter Writing Week. Children's drawings. Multicoloured.
1407 45p. Type **538** 45 10
1408 70p. Human figures in envelope (Jorge Vargas) 60 15

539 Amerindians watching Columbus's Fleet

1991. America. Voyages of Discovery. Mult.
1409 50p. Type **539** 30 15
1410 150p. Columbus's fleet and navigator . . . . . . 1·40 65

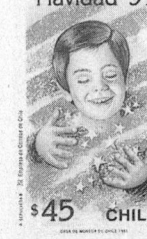

540 Line Drawing of Neruda **541** Boy and Stars

1991. 20th Anniv of Award of Nobel Prize for Literature to Pablo Neruda. Multicoloured, colour of cap given.
1411 **540** 45p. blue 15 10
1412 45p. red 15 10
Nos. 1411/12 were issued together, se-tenant, the backgrounds of the stamps forming a composite design of one of Neruda's manuscripts.

1991. Christmas. Multicoloured.
1414 45p. Type **541** 15 10
1415 100p. Girl and stars 30 25

542 Postman making Delivery **544** Houses and Figures

1991. Christmas. (a) As T **542**.
1416 **542** 45p. mauve and violet 15 10
1417 – 45p. mauve and violet 30 10
(b) Discount stamps. Additionally inscr "D.S. No 20" in left-hand margin.
1418 **542** 45p. mauve and violet 15 10
1419 – 45p. mauve and violet 30 20
DESIGN: Nos. 1417, 1419, Starlit town.

1992. No. 1238 surch **$60**.
1420 60p. on 45p. black & green 40 15

1992. Environmental Protection. As Nos. 1307/16 but values and colours changed. (a) As T **508**, each yellow and green.
1421 60p. Type **508** 20 15
1422 60p. As No. 1308 . . . . 20 15
1423 60p. As No. 1309 . . . . 20 15
1424 60p. As No. 1310 . . . . 40 15
1425 60p. As No. 1311 . . . . 20 15
(b) Discount stamps. Additionally inscr "D.S. No 20". Each orange and green.
1426 60p. Type **508** 20 15
1427 60p. As No. 1308 . . . . 20 15
1428 60p. As No. 1309 . . . . 20 15
1429 60p. As No. 1310 . . . . 40 15
1430 60p. As No. 1311 . . . . 20 15

1992. 16th Population and Housing Census.
1431 **544** 60p. blue, orange & blk 20 15

545 Score and Mozart

1992. Death Bicentenary of Wolfgang Amadeus Mozart (composer). Multicoloured.
1432 60p. Type **545** 50 15
1433 200p. Mozart playing harpsichord . . . . . . 1·10 50

546 Stylized Jet Fighter

1992. "Fidae '92" International Air and Space Fair.
1435 **546** 60p. multicoloured . . 20 15

547 Arms and Church, San Jose de Maipo

1992. 200th (80p.) or 250th (others) Anniversaries of Cities. Multicoloured.
1436 80p. Type **547** 50 20
1437 90p. Pottery (Melipilla) . . 55 25
1438 100p. Lircunlauta House (San Fernando) . . . 60 25
1439 150p. Fruits and woodsman (Cauquenes) 75 35
1440 250p. Huilquilemu Cultural Villa (Talca) . . . . . 1·25 60

548 Chilean Pavilion

1992. "Expo '92" World's Fair, Seville. Mult.
1441 150p. Type **548** 90 35
1442 200p. Iceberg . . . . . . 1·10 50

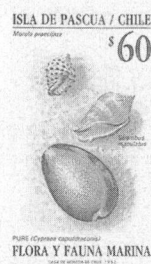

549 "Morula praecipua", Maculated Conch and Dragon's-head Cowrie

1992. Marine Flora and Fauna of Easter Island. Multicoloured.
1444 60p. Type **549** 35 20
1445 60p. "Codium pocockiae" 35 20
1446 60p. Easter Island swordfish ("Myripristis tiki") . . . 50 20
1447 60p. Seaweed 35 20
1448 60p. Fuentes' wrasse ("Pseudolabrus fuentesi") 50 20
1449 60p. Coral 35 20
1450 60p. Spiny lobster 35 20
1451 60p. Sea urchin 35 20

550 Statues, Liner and Launch

1992. Easter Island Tourism. Multicoloured.
1452 200p. Type **550** 85 50
1453 200p. Airplane, dancers and hill-carving 85 50
Nos. 1452/3 were issued together, se-tenant, forming a composite design.

551 Sun shining through Doorway and Handicapped People **552** Flags and Emblem

1992. National Council for the Handicapped.
1454 **551** 60p. multicoloured . . . 20 15

1992. 50th Anniv of National Defence Staff.
1455 **552** 60p. multicoloured . . . 45 15

553 "Simpson" (submarine)

1992. 75th Anniv of Chilean Submarine Fleet. Multicoloured.
1456 150p. Type **553** 90 35
1457 250p. Officer using periscope 1·40 60

1992. Discount stamp. As No. 1240 but additionally inscr "D/S No 20".
1458 60p. black and bistre . . . 1·10 30

1992. Nos. 1350/3 surch **$60**.
1459 **487** 60p. on 45p. blue & mve 20 15
1460 – 60p. on 45p. red & mve 20 15
1461 **487** 60p. on 45p. blue & yell 20 15
1462 – 60p. on 45p. red & yell 20 15

1992. Nos. 1416/19 surch **$60**.
1463 **542** 60p. on 45p. mauve and violet (1416) 20 15

1464	– 60p. on 45p. mauve and violet (1417)	35	15
1465 **542**	60p. on 45p. mauve and violet (1418)	20	15
1466	– 60p. on 45p. mauve and violet (1419)	35	15

556 Emperor Penguin

1992. The Emperor Penguin. Multicoloured.
1467	200p. Type **556**	1·40	50
1468	250p. Adult and chick	1·75	60

557 Santiago Central Post Office

1992. National Monuments.
1470 **557**	200p. multicoloured	1·25	50

558 Columbus and Navigation Instruments

1992. America. 500th Anniv of Discovery of America by Columbus. Multicoloured.
1471	200p. Type **558**	1·25	50
1472	250p. Church, map of Americas and "Santa Maria"	1·10	70

559 Presenter at Microphone   **560** O'Higgins, Flag and Monument

1992. 70th Anniv of Chilean Radio.
1473 **559**	250p. multicoloured	1·40	60

1992. 150th Death Anniv of Bernardo O'Higgins.
1474 **560**	60p. multicoloured	20	15

561 Arrau as a Child

1992. Claudio Arrau (pianist). Multicoloured.
1475	150p. Type **561**	80	35
1476	200p. Arrau playing piano	1·10	50

562 Statue   **563** Nativity

1992. 150th Anniv of University of Chile. Mult.
1478	200p. Type **562**	1·00	50
1479	200p. Coat of arms, statues and clock	1·00	50

Nos. 1478/9 were issued together, se-tenant, forming a composite design.

1992. Christmas. (a) As T **563**.
1480 **563**	60p. brown and stone	20	15
1481	– 60p. brown and stone	20	15

(b) Discount stamps. Additionally inscr "DS/20" in right-hand margin.
1482 **563**	60p. red and stone	20	15
1483	– 60p. red and stone	20	15

DESIGN: Nos. 1481, 1483, Nativity (different).

564 Dam

1992. 23rd Ministerial Meeting of Latin-American Energy Organization.
1484 **564**	70p. black and yellow	25	20

565 Hands and Stars

1992. National Human Rights Day.
1485 **565**	100p. multicoloured	55	25

566 Achao Church   **567** St. Ignatius de Loyola (founder)

1993. Churches. (a) As T **566**.
1487 **566**	70p. black and pink	25	20
1488	– 70p. black and pink	25	20

(b) Discount stamps. Additionally inscr "DS/20" in left-hand margin.
1489 **566**	70p. black and yellow	25	20
1490	– 70p. black and yellow	25	20

DESIGN: Nos. 1488, 1490, Castro church.
See also Nos. 1507/15.

1993. 400th Anniv of Jesuits' Arrival in Chile.
1491 **567**	200p. multicoloured	1·25	75

568 St. Teresa   **569** Finger-Puppets

1993. Canonization of St. Teresa of the Andes.
1493 **568**	300p. multicoloured	1·50	70

1993. International Theatre Festival.
1494 **569**	250p. multicoloured	1·10	60

---

570 Satellite in Orbit

1993. 2nd Pan-American Space Conference.
1495 **570**	150p. multicoloured	80	35

571 Clotario Blest (Trade Union leader)   **572** Drawing of Huidobro by Picasso

1993. Labour Day.
1497 **571**	70p. multicoloured	50	20

1993. Birth Centenary of Vicente Huidobro (poet). Each black, stone and red.
1498	100p. Type **572**	30	25
1499	100p. Drawing of Huidobro by Juan Gris	30	25

573 Watterous, 1902

1993. Fire Engines (1st series). Multicoloured.
1500	100p. Type **573**	60	25
1501	100p. Merryweather, 1872	60	25

See also Nos. 1568/71.

574 Douglas B-26 Invader

1993. Aviation and Space. Multicoloured.
1503	100p. Type **574**	60	25
1504	100p. Mirage M 50 Pantera	60	25
1505	100p. Sanchez Besa biplane	60	25
1506	100p. Bell-47 Dl helicopter	60	25

1993. Churches. (a) As T **566**.
1507	10p. black and green	10	10
1508	20p. black and brown	10	10
1509	30p. black and orange	10	10
1510	40p. black and blue	10	10
1511	50p. black and rose	15	10
1512	80p. black and buff	25	20
1513	90p. black and green	25	20
1514	100p. black and grey	30	25

(b) Discount stamp. Additionally inscr "DS/20" at left.
1515	80p. black and lilac	25	20
1516	90p. black and red	25	20
1517	100p. black and yellow	30	25

CHURCHES: 10p. Chonchi; 20p. Vilupulli; 30p. Llau-Llao; 40p. Dalcahue; 50p. Tenaun; 80p. Quinchao; 90p. Quehui; 100p. Nercon.

575 Nortina   **577** Early Coin Production

---

576 "Late Dawn" (Mario Carreno)

1993. Regional Variations of La Cueca (national dance). Multicoloured.
1525	70p. Type **575**	45	15
1526	70p. Central	45	15
1527	70p. Chilota	45	15

1993. Santiago, Iberian-American City of Culture 1993. Paintings. Multicoloured.
1528	80p. Type **576**	50	20
1529	90p. "Summer" (Gracia Barrios)	50	20
1530	150p. "Protection" (Roser Bru) (vert)	70	35
1531	200p. "Tango, Valparaiso" (Nemesio Antunez)	1·00	45

1993. 250th Anniv of Chilean Mint.
1532 **577**	250p. multicoloured	1·25	55

578 Patagonian Conure   **579** Underground Train

1993. America. Endangered Animals. Mult.
1534	150p. Type **578**	90	35
1535	200p. Chilean guemal	1·40	45

1993. 25th Anniv of Chilean Metro.
1536 **579**	80p. multicoloured	45	20

580 "Ancud" (schooner) off Santa Ana Point

1993. 150th Anniv of Chilean Possession of Strait of Magellan.
1537 **580**	100p. multicoloured	40	25

581 Marines in Inflatable Assault Boats

1993. Naval Tradition. Multicoloured.
1538	80p. Type **581** (175th anniv of Marines)	25	20
1539	80p. Sailors making fast patrol boat (125th anniv of Alejandro Navarette Training School)	25	20
1540	80p. "Esmeralda" (cadet barquentine) and cadets in traditional "unloading the cannon" exercise (175th anniv of Arturo Prat Naval College)	25	20
1541	80p. "Sailing of First Squadron" (175th anniv) (painting, Alvaro Casanova Zenteno)	25	20

582 Carved Figures

1993. International Year of Indigenous Peoples.
1542 **582**	100p. multicoloured	60	25

583 Holy Family   584 Adelie Penguins

1993. Christmas. (a) Sold at face value.
1543 583 70p. lilac and stone . . . 20 15
(b) Discount stamp. Additionally inscribed "DS/20" in right-hand margin.
1544 583 70p. blue and green . . . 20 15

1993. Chilean Antarctic Territory. Mult.
1545 200p. Type 584 . . . . . . 1·40 45
1546 250p. Adelie penguin with young . . . . 1·60 55

585 Plaza de Armas, Ancud

1993. City Anniversaries. Multicoloured.
1548 80p. Type 585 (225th) . . . 35 20
1549 80p. Matriz church, Curico (250th) 35 20
1550 80p. Corner Pillar House, Rancagua (250th) 35 20

586 Hands

1994. International Year of the Family.
1551 586 100p. multicoloured . . 55 25

587 Violin

1994. 26th Music Weeks, Frutillar. Mult.
1552 150p. Type 587 . . . . . . 90 35
1553 150p. Cello 90 35
Nos. 1552/3 were issued together, se-tenant, forming a composite design.

588 Sukhoi Su-30 Flanker

1994. "Fidae '94" International Air and Space Fair. Multicoloured.
1554 300p. Type 588 . . . . . . 1·60 65
1555 300p. Vought Sikorsky OS2U3 Kingfisher seaplane . . . . 1·60 65
1556 300p. Lockheed F-117A Stealth . . . . 1·60 65
1557 300p. Northrop F-5E Tiger III . . . . 1·60 65

589 Ears of Grain

1994. 50th Anniv of Chile Agronomical Engineers' College.
1558 589 220p. multicoloured . . 1·50 45

1994. Nos. 1092/5 surch $80.
1559 80p. on 15p. green 25 20
1560 80p. on 15p. blue 35 20
1561 80p. on 15p. brown 25 20
1562 80p. on 15p. mauve 25 20

591 Skeletons buried under Cactus

1994. 75th Anniv of Concepcion University. Details of "Latin American Presence" (mural by Jorge Gonzalez Camarena). Multicoloured.
1563 250p. Type 591 . . . . . . 1·50 55
1564 250p. Faces . . . . 1·50 55
1565 250p. Building pyramid from spare parts . . . . 1·50 55
1566 250p. Cablework in building 1·50 55
Nos. 1563/6 were issued together, se-tenant, forming a composite design.

592 Gentoo Penguins and Harbour

1994. 30th Anniv of Chilean Antarctic Institute. Multicoloured.
1567 300p. Type 592 . . . . . . 1·90 65
1568 300p. Antarctic base . . . . 1·90 65
Nos. 1567/8 were issued together, se-tenant, forming a composite design.

593 "Vanessa terpsichore"

1994. Butterflies. Multicoloured.
1569 100p. Type 593 . . . . . . 60 25
1570 100p. "Hypsochila wagenknechti" 60 25
1571 100p. Polydamas swallowtail ("Battus polydamas") . . 60 25
1572 100p. "Polythysana apollina" 60 25
1573 100p. "Satyridae" 60 25
1574 100p. "Tetraphloebia stellygera" 60 25
1575 100p. "Eroessa chilensis" . . 60 25
1576 100p. Cloudless sulphur ("Phoebis sennae") . . . 60 25

594 Merryweather Steam Fire Engine, 1869

1994. Fire Engines (2nd series). Mult.
1577 150p. Type 594 . . . . . . 80 35
1578 150p. Poniente steam fire engine, 1863 . . . . . . 80 35
1579 150p. Mieusset steam fire engine, 1905 . . . . . . 80 35
1580 150p. Merryweather motor fire engine, 1903 . . . . 80 35

595 Bust and Banner

1994. Centenary of Javiera Carrera School for Girls, Santiago.
1581 595 200p. multicoloured . . 85 45

596 Door Panels, Porvenir (centenary)

1994. Town Anniversaries. Multicoloured.
1582 90p. Type 596 . . . . . . 50 20
1583 100p. Railway station, Villa Alemana (cent) . . . . 1·00 25
1584 150p. Church, Constitucion (bicentenary) 70 35
1585 200p. Fountain and church, Linares (bicent) 90 45
1586 250p. Steam locomotive and statue, Copiapo (250th) 2·25 55
1587 300p. La Serena (450th) . . 1·60 65

597 Painting by Carlos Maturana   600 Fr. Hurtado

1994. 20th International Very Large Data Bases Conference, Santiago.
1588 597 100p. multicoloured . . 30 25

599 First Chilean Mail Van

1994. Nos. 1487/8 and 1544 surch $80.
1589 566 80p. on 70p. blk & pink 25 20
1590 – 80p. on 70p. blk & pink 25 20
1591 583 80p. on 70p. blue & grn 25 20

1994. America. Postal Transport. Mult.
1592 80p. Type 599 . . . . . . 50 20
1593 220p. De Havilland D.H.60G Gipsy Moth (first Chilean mail plane) 1·10 50

1994. Beatification of Fr. Alberto Hurtado.
1594 600 300p. blue, green & blk 1·40 70

601 Madonna and Child   603 "Almirante Williams" (destroyer)

602 Star

1994. Christmas. (a) Sold at face value.
1595 601 80p. multicoloured . . . 25 20
(b) Discount stamp. Additionally inscribed "DS/20" at foot.
1596 601 80p. multicoloured . . . 25 20

1995. International Women's Day. Mult.
1597 90p. Type 602 . . . . . . 55 25
1598 90p. Moon and sun 55 25
1599 90p. Dove 55 25
1600 90p. Earth 55 25

1995. Naval Tradition.
1601 603 100p. multicoloured . . . 30 25

604 Emblem   605 Arms

1995. United Nations World Summit for Social Development, Copenhagen.
1602 604 150p. multicoloured . . . 75 35

1995. 150th Anniv of Conciliar Seminary of Ancud.
1603 605 200p. multicoloured . . . 90 45

606 Stained Glass Window, Santiago Cathedral

1995. 400th Anniv of Augustinian Order in Chile.
1604 606 250p. multicoloured . . . 1·10 60

607 Religious Mask, Limari

1995. Rock Paintings. Multicoloured.
1605 150p. Type 607 . . . . . . 75 35
1606 150p. Herdsmen and llamas, Taira 75 35
1607 150p. Whale, Tal-tal 75 35
1608 150p. Masks, Encanto Valley 75 35

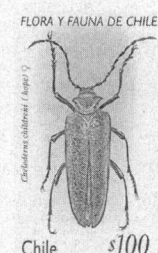

608 Camera and Director's Chair   610 "Cheloderus childreni"

609 Arms and Express Steam Train

1995. Centenary of Motion Pictures. Mult.
1609 100p. Type 608 . . . . . . 55 25
1610 100p. Advertising poster for "The Kid" 55 25
1611 100p. Early cinema advertising poster . . . 55 25
1612 100p. Advertising poster for "Valparaiso Mi Amor" . . 55 25

1995. Bicentenary of Parral.
1613 609 200p. multicoloured . . 1·00 50

1995. Flora and Fauna. Multicoloured.
1614 100p. Type 610 . . . . . . 55 25
1615 100p. "Eulychnia acida" (cactus) 55 25

1616 100p. "Chiasognathus grantii" (stag beetle) . . . 55 25
1617 100p. "Browningia candelaris" (cactus) . . . 55 25
1618 100p. "Capiapoa dealbata" (cactus) 55 25
1619 100p. "Acanthinodera cummingi" (beetle) . . . 55 25
1620 100p. "Neoporteria subgibbosa" (cactus) . . . 55 25
1621 100p. "Semiotus luteipennis" (beetle) 55 25

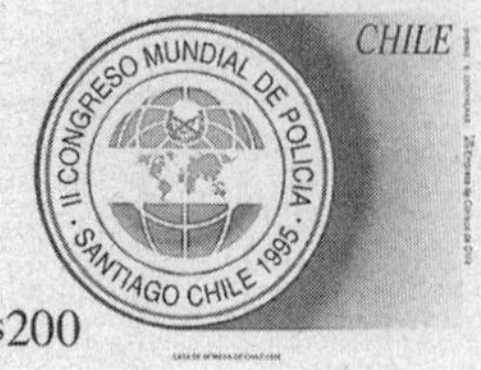

611 Congress Emblem

1995. 2nd World Police Congress, Santiago.
1622 **611** 200p. multicoloured . . 90 45

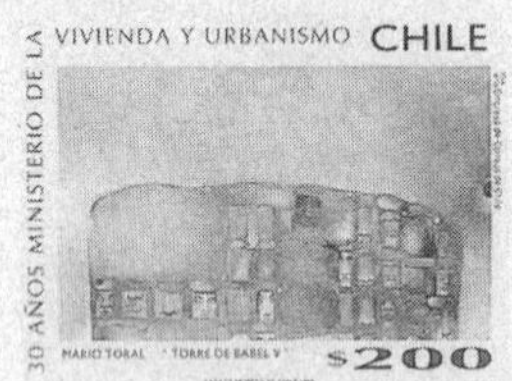

612 "Tower of Babel V" (Mario Toral)

1995. 30th Anniv of Ministry of Housing and Town-planning.
1623 **612** 200p. multicoloured . . . 90 45

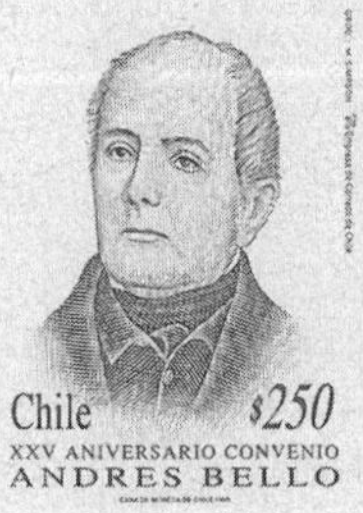

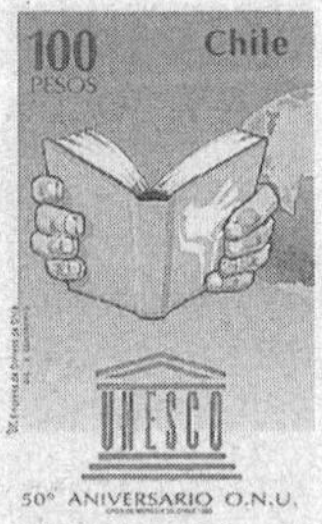

613 Bello **614** Open Book and Emblem

1995. 25th Anniv of Andres Bello Agreement (South American co-operation in education. science and culture).
1624 **613** 250p. purple and black 1·10 60

1995. 50th Anniversaries. Multicoloured.
1625 100p. Type **614** (U.N.E.S.C.O.) 30 25
1626 100p. Globes and handshake (U.N.O.) 30 25
1627 100p. Seedling in hand (F.A.O.) 30 25
Nos. 1625/7 were issued together, se-tenant, forming a composite design.

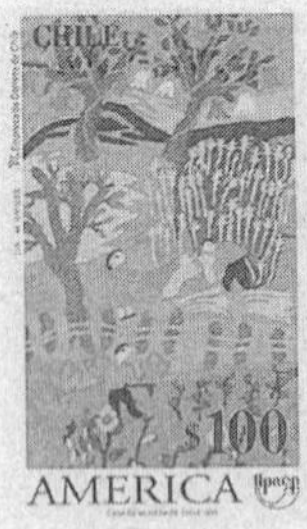

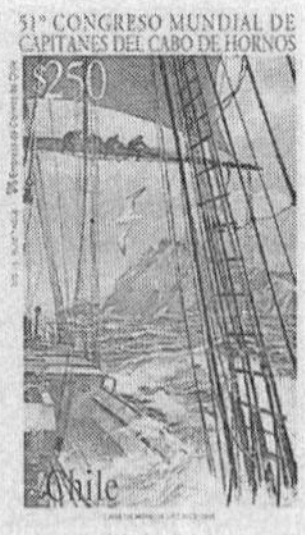

615 Farming (M. Cruces) **616** Sailing Ship and Cape Horn

1995. America. Environmental Protection. Children's Paintings. Multicoloured.
1628 100p. Type **615** 55 25
1629 250p. Forestry (E. Munoz) (horiz) . . . . 1·00 55

1995. 51st World Congress of Cape Horn Captains.
1630 **616** 250p. multicoloured . . 90 55

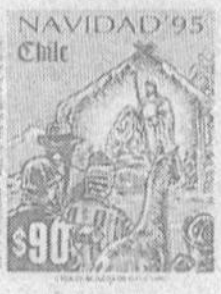

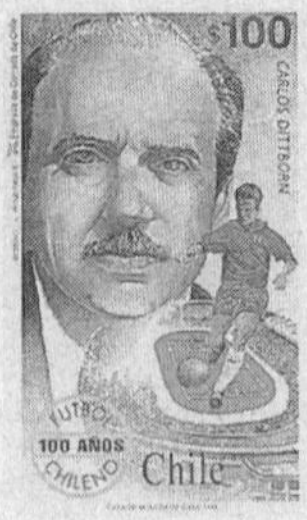

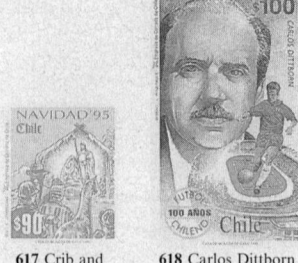

617 Crib and Inhabitants of North Chile **618** Carlos Dittborn (trainer) and Arica Stadium

1995. Christmas. (a) Sold at face value.
1631 **617** 90p. blue and violet . . 25 20
1632 – 90p. blue and violet . . 25 20

(b) Discount stamps. Additionally inscr "DS/20".
1633 **617** 90p. green and purple . . 25 20
1634 – 90p. green and purple . . 25 20
DESIGNS: Nos. 1632, 1634, Crib and people of South Chile.

1995. Centenary of Chile Football Federation. Mult.
1635 100p. Type **618** 55 25
1636 100p. Hugo Lepe (player) 55 25
1637 100p. Eladio Rojas (player) 55 25
1638 100p. Honorino Landa (player) 55 25

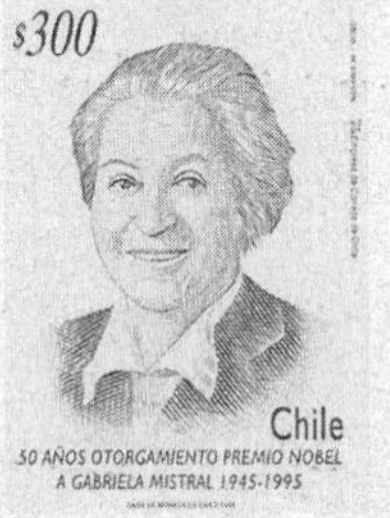

619 Mistral

1995. 50th Anniv of Award of Nobel Prize for Literature to Gabriela Mistral.
1639 **619** 300p. blue and black . . 1·25 65

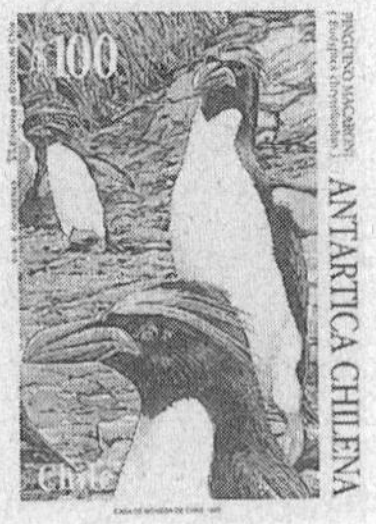

620 Penguins

1995. Chilean Antarctic Territory. The Macaroni Penguin. Multicoloured.
1640 100p. Type **620** 60 25
1641 250p. Penguins (different) 1·50 55

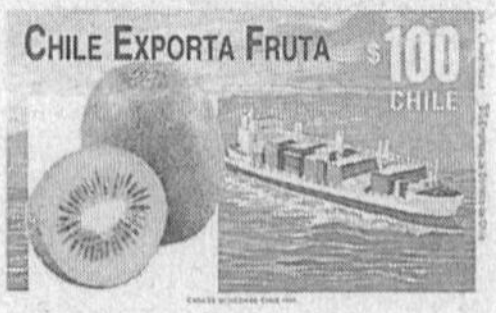

621 Kiwi Fruit and Container Ship

1995. 60th Anniv of Chilean Exports Association. Fruit. Multicoloured.
1643 100p. Type **621** 40 25
1644 100p. Grapes and container ship 40 25
1645 100p. Peaches and container ship 40 25
1646 100p. Apples and container ship 40 25
1647 100p. Soft fruit and airplane 40 25

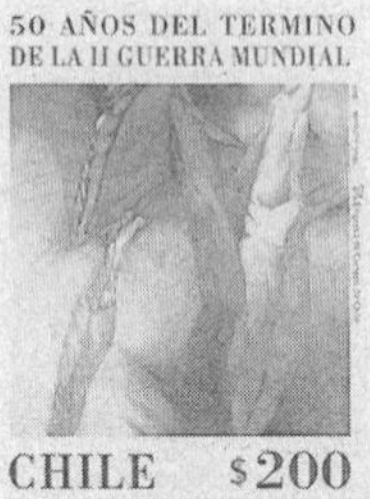

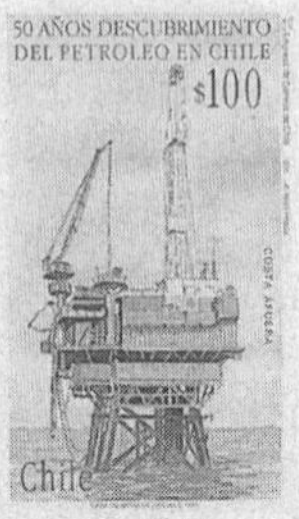

622 "Reunion" (Mario Toral) **623** Oil Rig

1995. 50th Anniv of End of Second World War.
1648 **622** 200p. multicoloured . . 90 45

1995. 50th Anniv of Discovery of Oil in Chile. Multicoloured.
1649 100p. Type **623** 40 25
1650 100p. Concon Refinery (grass in foreground) . . 40 25
1651 100p. Concepcion Refinery 40 25
1652 100p. Rig (different) 40 25

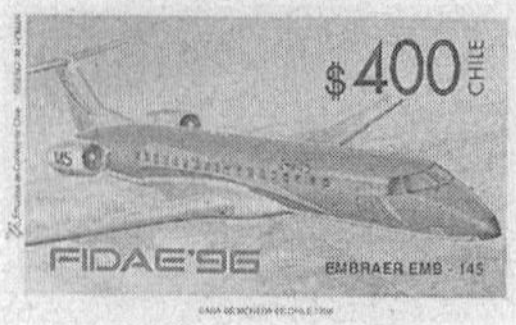

624 Embraer EMB-145

1996. "FIDAE '96" International Air and Space Fair, Santiago. Aircraft. Multicoloured.
1653 400p. Type **624** . . . . . . 2·50 90
1654 400p. Mirage M5M Elkan 2·50 90
1655 400p. De Havilland D.H.C. 6 Twin Otter . . 2·50 90
1656 400p. Saab JAS-39 Gripen 2·50 90

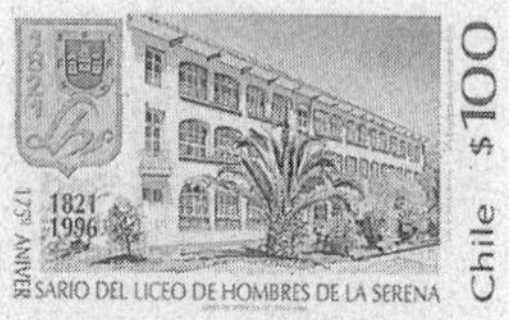

625 School

1996. 175th Anniv of Serena Boys' School.
1657 **625** 100p. multicoloured . . 75 25

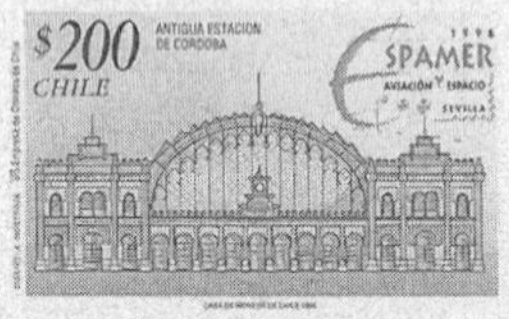

626 Old Cordoba Rail Station, Seville

1996. "Espamer" and "Aviation and Space" Spanish and Latin American Stamp Exhibitions, Seville, Spain. Multicoloured.
1658 200p. Type **626** . . . . . . 1·10 25
1659 200p. Lope de Vega Theatre, Seville 85 45

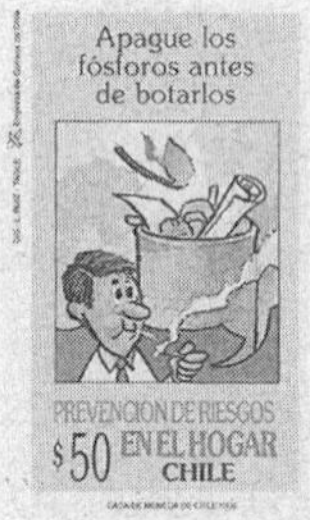

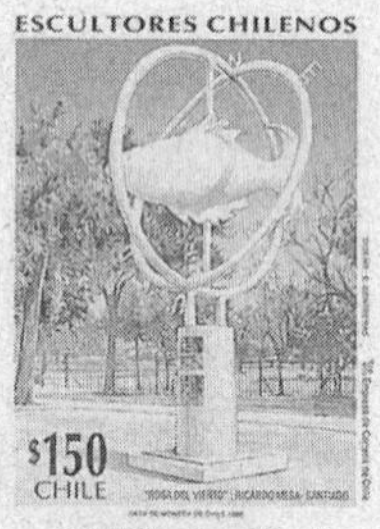

627 Extinguish Matches Properly **629** "Weather Rose" (Ricardo Mesa)

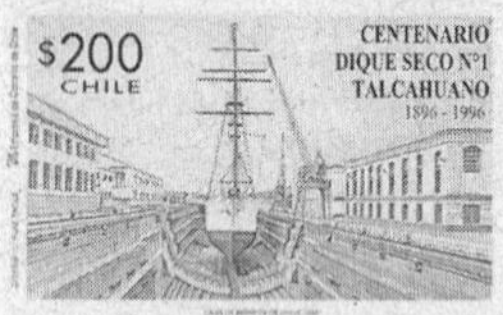

628 "Esmeralda" (cadet barquentine) in Dry-dock

1996. Safety Precautions. Multicoloured.
(a) Accidents in the Home.
1660 50p. Type **627** 15 10
1661 50p. Do not leave boiling water unattended . . . 15 10
1662 50p. Keep sharp objects away from children . . . 15 10
1663 50p. Protect electrical sockets 15 10
1664 50p. Do not improvise electrical connections . . 15 10
1665 50p. Do not play the television or radio too loud 15 10
1666 50p. Check gas connections regularly 15 10
1667 50p. Do not overload electrical circuits 15 10
1668 50p. Keep inflammable materials away from fire 15 10
1669 50p. Do not leave toys lying around on the floor . . . 15 10

(b) Road Safety.
1670 50p. Use crossings 15 10
1671 50p. Obey the instructions of the traffic police . . . 15 10
1672 50p. Only cross on the green light 15 10
1673 50p. Wait on the pavement for buses 15 10
1674 50p. Do not cross the road between vehicles 15 10
1675 50p. Do not travel on the step of buses 15 10
1676 50p. Walk on the side of the road facing on-coming traffic 15 10
1677 50p. Look out for drains . . 15 10
1678 50p. Do not play ball in the road 15 10
1679 50p. Bicyclists should obey the Highway Code . . . 15 10

(c) Safety at School.
1680 50p. Do not panic in emergencies 15 10
1681 50p. Do not run around corners 15 10
1682 50p. Do not play practical jokes 15 10
1683 50p. Do not sit on banisters or railings 15 10
1684 50p. Do not run on the stairs 15 10
1685 50p. Do not drink while walking 15 10
1686 50p. Do not swing on your chair 15 10
1687 50p. Do not play with pointed or sharp objects 15 10
1688 50p. Do not open doors sharply 15 10
1689 50p. Go straight home after school and do not stop to talk to strangers 15 10

(d) Safety in the Workplace.
1690 50p. Wear protective clothing 15 10
1691 50p. Do not work with tools in bad condition 15 10
1692 50p. Keep your attention on your work (man at lathe) 15 10
1693 50p. Always use the proper tools 15 10
1694 50p. Work carefully (man at filing cabinet) 15 10
1695 50p. Do not leave objects on the stairs 15 10
1696 50p. Do not carry so much that you cannot see where you are going 15 10
1697 50p. Check ladders are safe 15 10
1698 50p. Always keep the workplace clean and tidy 15 10
1699 50p. Remove old nails first 15 10

(e) Enjoy Leisure Safely.
1700 50p. Only swim in the permitted areas 15 10
1701 50p. Do not put any part of the body out of the window of a moving vehicle 15 10
1702 50p. Avoid excessive exposure to the sun . . . 15 10
1703 50p. Do not contaminate swimming water with detergents 15 10
1704 50p. Do not throw litter . . 15 10
1705 50p. Always put out fires before leaving them . . . 15 10
1706 50p. Do not play pranks in water 15 10
1707 50p. Check safety precautions 15 10
1708 50p. Do not fly kites near overhead electrical lines 15 10
1709 50p. Do not run by the side of swimming pools . . . 15 10

(f) Alcohol and Drugs Awareness.
1710 50p. Do not drink and drive 15 10
1711 50p. Do not drink if you are pregnant 15 10
1712 50p. Do not give in to peer pressure 15 10
1713 50p. Being under the influence of alcohol is irresponsible in the workplace 15 10
1714 50p. Do not destroy your family through alcohol . . 15 10
1715 50p. You do not need drugs to have a good time . . . 15 10
1716 50p. You do not need drugs to succeed 15 10
1717 50p. You do not need drugs to entertain 15 10
1718 50p. Do not abandon your friends and family for drugs 15 10
1719 50p. Without drugs you are free and safe 15 10

1996. Centenary of Dry-dock No. 1, Talcahuano.
1720 **628** 200p. multicoloured . . 70 45

1996. Modern Sculpture. Multicoloured.
1721 150p. Type **629** 70 35
1722 150p. "Friendship" (Francisca Cerda) 70 35
1723 200p. "Memory" (Fernando Undurraga) (horiz) . . . 70 35
1724 200p. "Andean Airs" (Benito Rojo) (horiz) . . 70 35

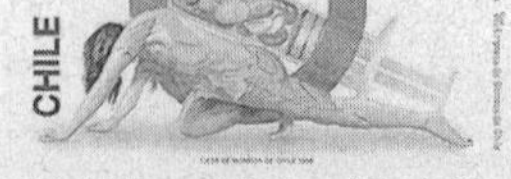

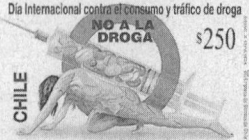

630 Addict and Syringe full of Pills

1996. International Day against Drug Abuse.
1725 **630** 250p. multicoloured . . 75 55

631 Boxing Glove

1996. Centenary of National Olympic Committee and Modern Olympic Games. Olympic Games, Atlanta. Multicoloured.
1726 450p. Type **631** . . . . 2·25 1·00
1727 450p. Running shoe . . . . 2·25 1·00
1728 450p. Rollerblade . . . . . 2·25 1·00
1729 450p. Ball . . . . 2·25 1·00

632 School

1996. 150th Anniv of San Fernando School.
1730 **632** 200p. multicoloured . . 85 45

633 Polluted Forest

1996. 4th International Congress on Earth Sciences. Multicoloured.
1731 200p. Type **633** 95 45
1732 200p. Industrial pollution . . 95 45
1733 200p. Deforestation 95 45
1734 200p. Map, camera and cracked earth 95 45
Nos. 1731/4 were issued together, se-tenant, forming a composite design.

634 Crookesite and Open-cast Mine

1996. Mining. Multicoloured.
1735 150p. Type **634** 70 35
1736 150p. Lapis lazuli and pendant 70 35
1737 150p. Bornite and calcium and crates 70 35
1738 150p. Azurite and atacamite . 70 35

635 St. John Leonardi (founder)

1996. 50th Anniv of Order of Mother of God in Chile.
1739 **635** 200p. multicoloured . . 90 45

636 German-style Wooden house and Mt. Osorno

1996. 150th Anniv of German Immigration. Multicoloured.
1740 200p. Type **636** . . . . . 1·00 50
1741 300p. "German Fountain" (monument) . . . . . . 1·10 60

637 King Penguins

1996. Chilean Antarctic Territory. Mult.
1742 250p. Type **637** . . . . . 1·40 50
1743 300p. Adult and young king penguins . . . . 1·75 60

638 Lancia Fire Engine, 1937

1996. Centenary of Castro Fire Service. Mult.
1745 200p. Type **638** 90 40
1746 200p. Ford V8 fire engine, 1940 . . . . 90 40
1747 200p. Gorlitz G. A. Fischer 4-speed motor pump, 1930s 90 40
1748 200p. Lever-action pump, 1907 . . . . 90 40

639 Rafting, Vicente Perez Rosales National Park

1996. National Parks. Multicoloured.
1749 100p. Type **639** 55 25
1750 100p. Horse riding, Torres del Paine National Park 55 25
1751 100p. Cross-country skiing, Puyehue National Park 55 25
1752 100p. Walking, Pan de Azucar National Park . . 55 25

640 Latorre and "Almirante Latorre" (destroyer)

641 Women with Child

1996. 150th Birth Anniv of Admiral Juan Jose Latorre.
1753 **640** 200p. multicoloured . . 70 40

1996. America. Costumes. Multicoloured.
1754 100p. Type **641** 55 25
1755 100p. Men with horse . . . 55 25
1756 250p. Men on horseback . . 95 50

642 "Visual History of a Nation" (Mario Toral) (left-hand detail)

643 Beach, Arms and Cathedral, Arica

1996. 6th Ibero-Latin American Heads of State Summit, Santiago. Multicoloured.
1757 110p. Type **642** 55 25
1758 110p. Right-hand detail of painting 55 25
Nos. 1757/8 were issued together, se-tenant, forming a composite design.

1996. Cities. 1st Anniv of Arica Law. Multicoloured.
1759 100p. Type **643** 55 25
1760 150p. Llamas and flamingoes, Parinacota Province 65 30

1996. Christmas. (a) Face value in black.
1761 **644** 100p. multicoloured . . 30 25

(b) Discount stamp. Additionally inscribed "DS/20" at foot and with face value in orange.
1762 **644** 100p. multicoloured . . 30 25

645 Pablo Neruda (poet), Gabriela Mistral (writer) and Nobel Prize Medal

1996. Visit of King and Queen of Sweden.
1763 **645** 300p. multicoloured . . 1·40 60

646 Children, Star and Globe

1996. 50th Anniv of U.N.I.C.E.F.
1764 **646** 200p. multicoloured . . 80 40

647 Church

1997. Centenary of Frontera Region. Mult.
1765 110p. Type **647** (centenary of Christian and Missionary Church Alliance) 60 25
1766 110p. Mountain valley (cent of Lonquimay Municipality) 60 25

648 Base Camp **649** La Pincoya

1997. 50th Anniv of Arturo Prat Antarctic Naval Base.
1767 250p. Type **648** . . . . . . 1·00 50
1768 300p. Monument and flags (horiz) . . . . 1·25 60

1997. Mythology. (a) As T **649**.
1769 40p. black and blue 10 10
1770 110p. black and orange . . . 30 25
(b) Discount stamp. Additionally inscr "DS/20".
1778 110p. black and green . . . 30 25
DESIGN: Nos. 1770, 1778, La Fiura.

650 "Justice" and National Flag

1997. 70th Anniv of Controller General.
1781 **650** 110p. multicoloured . . 55 25

651 Underground Train in Station

1997. Inauguration of Metro Line No. 5.
1782 **651** 200p. multicoloured . . 1·25 60

652 Masonic Symbols and Flags

1997. 50th Anniv of Interamerican Masonic Confederation and 17th Grand General Assembly, Santiago.
1783 **652** 250p. multicoloured . . 1·00 50

653 Von Stephan

1997. Death Centenary of Heinrich von Stephan (founder of Universal Postal Union).
1785 **653** 250p. multicoloured . . 1·00 50

654 Books

1997. World Books and Copyright Day.
1786 **654** 110p. multicoloured . . 55 25

655 "Death to the Invader, Chile"

1997. Birth Centenary of David Alfaro Siqueiros (painter). Designs showing details of his murals in the Mexican School, Chillan, Chile. Multicoloured.
1787 150p. Type **655** 70   30
1788 200p. "Death to the
       Invader, Mexico" 95   40

656 Arms and Town Hall

1997. Centenary of Providencia.
1790 **656** 250p. multicoloured . . . 1·10   50

657 Pacific Ocean and Mt. Osorno (after Hokusai Katsushika)
658 Award, National Flag and "Thumbs-up" Sign

1997. Centenary of Chile–Japan Relations.
1791 **657** 300p. multicoloured . . . 1·10   60

1997. National Centre for Productivity and Quality.
1792 **658** 110p. multicoloured . . 75   25

659 Transmission from University of Chile to "El Mercurio" (newspaper) Offices

1997. 75th Anniv of First Radio Broadcast in Chile.
1793 **659** 110p. multicoloured . . 80   25

660 Postman on Bicycle, 1997

1997. America. The Postman. Multicoloured.
1794 110p. Type **660** 55   25
1795 250p. Late 19th-century
       mounted postman 95   50

661 Carlo Morelli in "Rigoletto"
662 Jack-in-a-Box and Baubles on Tree

1997. Opera Singers. Multicoloured.
1796 120p. Type **661** 35   25
1797 200p. Pedro Navia in "La
       Boheme" 55   40
1798 250p. Renato Zanelli in
       "Faust" 70   50

1799 300p. Rayen Quitral in "The
       Magic Flute" . . . . . . 1·10   60
1800 500p. Ramon Vinay in
       "Othello" . . . . 1·60   70

1997. Christmas. (a) "NAVIDAD '97" in blue.
1801 **662** 110p. multicoloured 30   25

  (b) Discount stamp. "NAVIDAD '97" in orange and additionally inscr "D/S 20" below face value.
1802 **662** 110p. multicoloured . . . 30   25

663 Cancelling Letters
664 Great Dane

1997. 250th Anniv of Postal Service in Chile. Multicoloured.
1803 120p. Type **663** 85   25
1804 300p. Man posting letter . . 1·60   60

1998. Dogs. Multicoloured. (a) As T **664**.
1805 120p. Type **664** 25   20
1806 120p. Dalmatian 25   20

  (b) Discount stamps. Additionally inscr "DS/20".
1807 120p. Type **664** 25   20
1808 120p. As No. 1806 25   20

665 Prat and "Esmeralda" (sail corvette)
666 Summit Emblem

1998. 150th Birth Anniv of Captain Arturo Prat Chacon.
1809 **665** 120p. multicoloured . . . 40   25

1998. 2nd Summit of the Americas, Santiago.
1810 **666** 150p. multicoloured . . . 35   25

667 Vets treating Horse

1998. Centenary of Army Veterinary Service. Mult.
1812 250p. Type **667** 55   40
1813 350p. Vet using stethoscope
       on horse 80   55

668 "Los Zambos de Calama" (Mauricio Moran)

1998. Paintings. Multicoloured.
1814 350p. Type **668** 80   55
1815 400p. "Soaking
       Watermelon" (Roser Bru) . 90   65

669 Monk writing in Book

1998. 150th Anniv of Capuchin Order in Chile. Multicoloured.
1816 150p. Type **669** 35   25
1817 250p. Monk treating man's
       leg 55   40

670 Players

1998. World Cup Football Championship, France. Multicoloured.
1818 250p. Type **670** 55   40
1819 350p. Players and trophy . . 80   55
1820 500p. Players and map of
       France . . . . 1·10   75
1821 700p. Attacker and
       goalkeeper . . . . . . 1·50   1·10

671 Penguin and Emblem

1998. 25th Meeting of Scientific Committee on Antarctic Research (1823) and 10th Meeting of Council of Managers of National Antarctic Programmes (1824), Concepcion. Multicoloured.
1823 250p. Type **671** 55   40
1824 350p. Two penguins on map
       of Antarctica and emblem . 80   55

672 Lighthouse

1998. International Year of the Ocean (1st issue). 150th Anniv of General Office for Territorial Waters and the Merchant Navy.
1825 **672** 500p. multicoloured . . 1·10   85

673 Iceberg and Ocean

1998. International Year of the Ocean (2nd issue).
1826 **673** 400p. blue, violet and
       black 90   60
1827 – 400p. blue, violet and
       black 90   60
1828 – 500p. multicoloured . . 1·10   75
DESIGNS: No. 1827, Compass rose, map of South Chile and ocean; 1828, Easter Island monolith and ocean.

674 Clara Solovera

1998. Composers and Folk Singers. Multicoloured.
1829 200p. Type **674** 45   30
1830 250p. Francisco Flores del
       Campo 55   40
1831 300p. Victor Jara 65   45
1832 350p. Violeta Parra 80   55

675 Delivery to Letter Box and Dog

1998. World Stamp Day.
1833 **675** 250p. multicoloured . . . 55   40

676 Bilbao

1998. 175th Birth Anniv of Francisco Bilbao (writer).
1834 **676** 250p. purple, blue and
       orange 55   40

677 Amanda Labarca (educationist)

1998. America. Famous Women.
1835 **677** 120p. mauve, blue and
       black 25   20
1836 – 250p. yellow, mauve and
       black 55   40
DESIGN: 250 p, Marta Brunet (writer).

678 "Self-portrait" (Augusto Eguiluz)

1998. Paintings. Multicoloured.
1837 300p. Type **678** 65   45
1838 450p. "Solitary Tree"
       (Agustin Abarca) (horiz) . 1·00   70

679 Arms and University
680 Rufous-collared Sparrow

1998. 70th Anniv of Valparaiso Catholic University.
1840 **679** 130p. multicoloured . . 30   20

1998. Birds. Multicoloured.
1841 10p. Type **680** 10   10
1842 20p. Austral blackbird . . . 10   10
1845 50p. Magellanic woodpecker
       (vert) 10   10
1849 100p. Peregrine falcon (vert) . 25   20

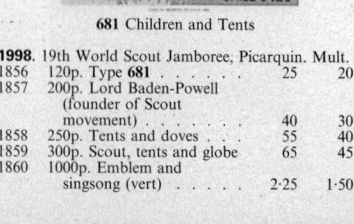

681 Children and Tents

1998. 19th World Scout Jamboree, Picarquin. Mult.
1856 120p. Type **681** 25   20
1857 200p. Lord Baden-Powell
       (founder of Scout
       movement) 40   30
1858 250p. Tents and doves . . . 55   40
1859 300p. Scout, tents and globe . 65   45
1860 1000p. Emblem and
       singsong (vert) . . . . 2·25   1·50

682 Capt. Alberto Larraguibel and Horse

1999. 50th Anniv of World Equestrian High Jump Record.
1862 **682** 200p. multicoloured . . 45 35

683 Fire Engine, 1990

1999. Centenary of Temuco Fire Department. Mult.
1863 140p. Type **683** 35 25
1864 200p. Ford fire engine, 1929 45 35
1865 300p. Ford K 1800 fire engine, 1955 . . . . . 70 50
1866 350p. Mercedes Benz fire engine, 1967 . . . . . 75 55

684 Chamber

1999. 1000th Session of Chilean Chamber of Deputies.
1868 **684** 140p. multicoloured . . 35 25

685 Facade

1999. 150th Anniv of Sagrados College.
1869 **685** 250p. multicoloured . . 60 45

686 Pedro Aguirre Cerda (Chilean President, 1938–41)   **689** Weddell Seal

687 Man with Sphere on Shoulder

1999. 60th Anniv of Economic Development Corporation.
1870 **686** 140p. multicoloured . . 35 25

1999. Centenary of Chilean Insurance Association.
1871 **687** 140p. multicoloured . . 35 25

1999. Antarctica. Multicoloured.
1873 360p. Type **689** 85 60
1874 450p. Chinstrap penguin . . 1·10 80

690 Easter Island, Dancers, Ship and Figures

1999. Easter Island.
1876 **690** 360p. multicoloured . . 85 60

691 Business and Arts School

1999. 150th Anniv of Santiago University. Mult.
1877 140p. Type **691** 35 25
1878 250p. State Technical University 60 45
1879 300p. Woman using microscope, computer and building 70 50

692 J. L. Molina (naturalist), Statue of Humboldt, Mountains and Llamas

1999. Bicentenary of Alexander von Humboldt's Exploration of South America. Multicoloured.
1880 300p. Type **692** 70 50
1881 360p. Rodulfo A. Philippi (medical doctor and naturalist), statue of Humboldt and penguins 85 60

693 Cardinal Silva and Crucifix

1999. Cardinal Raul Silva Henrique Commemoration. Multicoloured.
1882 140p. Type **693** 35 25
1883 200p. Silva and image of Christ 45 35

694 Chinese and Chilean Flags with Pagoda

1999. "China 1999" International Stamp Exhibition, Peking. Multicoloured.
1884 140p. Type **694** 35 25
1885 450p. Chinese and Chilean Flags with junk . . . . . 1·10 80

695 Our Lady of the Rosary Church Tower, Train and Arms   **696** Nurse and Donor

1999. Centenary of Quilpue City.
1887 **695** 250p. multicoloured . . 60 45

1999. Red Cross Blood Donation Campaign.
1888 **696** 140p. multicoloured . . 35 25

697 People in Glass Ball

1999. 75th Anniv of Employment Legislation.
1889 **697** 320p. multicoloured . . 75 55

698 Emblem

1999. 42nd International Congress of Confederation of Authors' and Composers' Societies, Santiago.
1890 **698** 170p. multicoloured . . 40 30

699 Elderly Couple watching Children

1999. International Year of Elderly Persons.
1891 **699** 250p. multicoloured . . 60 45

700 Post Box, 1854

1999. 125th Anniv of Universal Postal Union. Multicoloured.
1892 300p. Type **700** 70 50
1893 360p. Gold coloured post box, 1900 . . . . 85 60

701 Bomb releasing Doves

1999. America. A New Millennium without Arms. Multicoloured.
1894 140p. Type **701** 35 25
1895 320p. Broken bomb 75 55

702 Felipe Herrera Lane (first President, 1960–71) and Projects

1999. 40th Anniv of Inter-American Development Bank.
1896 **702** 360p. multicoloured . . 85 60

703 Globe and Chilean Flag

1999. Holy Year 2000.
1897 **703** 450p. multicoloured . . 1·10 80

704 Clock Face, "2000" and Fireworks (⅓-size illustration)

1999. New Millennium. Multicoloured. (a) As T **704**.
1898 170p. Type **704** 40 30
(b) Discount stamps. Additionally inscr "D.S. 20".
1899 170p. Type **704** 40 30
Nos. 1898/9 each include the prize draw coupons shown in T **704**.

705 Recabarren and Blest

1999. Trade Union Leaders. Multicoloured.
1900 200p. Type **705** 45 35
1901 200p. Jimenez and Bustos 45 35
Nos. 1900/1 were issued together, se-tenant, forming a composite design.

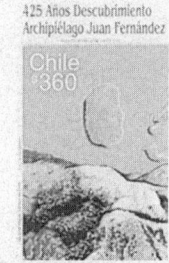

706 Mountains and Map of Islands

2000. Discovery of Juan Fernandez Archipelago. Multicoloured.
1902 360p. Type **706** 85 60
1903 360p. Mountains and map of islands (different) . . . 85 60
1904 360p. Hummingbird and mountains 85 60
1905 360p. *Rhaphythamnus venustus* (plant) 85 60
1906 360p. Lobster 85 60
1907 360p. Antennae of lobster and anchored boat . . . 85 60
1908 360p. Plant and boat . . . 85 60
1909 360p. *Gavilea insularis* (orchid) 85 60
Nos. 1902/9 were issued together, se-tenant, forming a composite design.

707 Condorito celebrating

2000. 50th Anniv (1999) of Condorito (cartoon character) by Rene Rios. Multicoloured.
1910 150p. Type **707** 35 25
1911 260p. Playing football . . . 60 45
1912 480p. As a fireman . . . . 1·10 80
1913 980p. On horseback . . . 2·40 1·75

708 Dancer and Local Crafts

2000. Easter Island. Multicoloured.

1915	200p. Type **708**	50	45
1916	260p. Statue and rock carving	60	45
1917	340p. Statue and man wearing headdress	80	60
1918	480p. Dancer and text	1·10	80

709 Steam Locomotive and Pot

2000. Centenary of Carahue. Multicoloured.

1919	220p. Type **709**	55	40
1920	220p. Potato tubers and plant	55	40

Nos. 1919/20 were issued together, se-tenant, forming a composite design.

710 Iguanodon

2000. Discount stamps. Prehistoric Animals. Mult.

1921	150p. Type **710**	35	25
1922	150p. Plesiosaur	35	25
1923	150p. Titanosaurus	35	25
1924	150p. Milodon	35	25

711 Emblem, Printing Press and Office

2000. Centenary of *El Mercurio* (newspaper).

1925	**711** 370p. multicoloured	90	65

712 Emblems

2000. 4th National Masonic Lodge Congress.

1926	**712** 460p. multicoloured	1·10	80

713 *Quillaja saponaria*

2000. Medicinal Plants. Multicoloured.

1927	200p. Type **713**	40	25
1928	360p. *Fabiana imbricata*	70	45

714 Map and Butterfly

2000. 500th Anniv of Discovery of Brazil.

1929	**714** 260p. multicoloured	50	30

715 Man wearing Costume (Bailarin de Diablada Festival, La Tirana)

2000. Religious Festivals. Multicoloured.

1931	150p. Type **715**	30	20
1932	200p. Girl wearing costume (San Pedro de Atacama fiesta)	40	25
1933	370p. Men dancing (La Candelaria Copiapo fiesta)	75	45
1934	460p. Drummer (Chinese Dance of Andacollo)	90	55

716 San Martin

2000. 150th Death Anniv of General Jose de San Martin.

1935	**716** 320p. multicoloured	65	40

717 Emblem, Globe and Weather Symbols

718 Magellanic Penguin (*Spheniscus magellanicus*)

2000. 50th Anniv of World Meteorological Organization.

1936	**717** 320p. multicoloured	65	40

2000. Antarctica. Multicoloured.

1937	450p. Type **718**	90	55
1938	650p. Humpback whales (*Megaptera novaeangliae*) (horiz)	1·25	1·40
1939	940p. Killer whale (*Orcinus orca*) (horiz)	1·90	2·00

No. 1937 is inscribed "Sphenis" in error.

719 Tennis, Football, Athletics and Sydney Opera House

2000. Olympic Games, Sydney. Multicoloured.

1941	290p. Type **719**	60	40
1942	290p. Archery, high jumping, cycling and Australian flag	60	40

Nos. 1941/2 were issued together, se-tenant, forming a composite design.

720 Native Chileans with Axe and Bow

2000. 450th Anniv of City of Concepcion. Depicting paintings by G. de la Fuente Riojas. Multicoloured.

1943	250p. Type **720**	50	30
1944	250p. Chileans and Spanish Conquistadors	50	30
1945	250p. Hand and scenes of destruction	50	30
1946	250p. Seated woman with shield	50	30
1947	250p. Horse, locomotive and coal truck	50	30
1948	250p. Modern Chileans and child	50	30

Nos. 1943/8 were issued together, se-tenant, forming a composite design.

721 Child's Hand holding Adult's Hand

2000. America. A.I.D.S. Awareness Campaign. Multicoloured.

1949	150p. Type **721**	30	20
1950	220p. Joined hands showing bones	45	30

722 Documents and Courtroom

2000. Penal Reform.

1951	**722** 150p. multicoloured	30	20

723 Star

2000. Christmas. Multicoloured. (a) As T **723**.

1953	150p. Type **723**	30	20
1954	150p. Silhouette of sleigh and reindeer above church	30	20
1955	150p. The Three Wise Men	30	20
1956	150p. Star on Christmas tree	30	20
1957	150p. Boy posting letter	30	20
1958	150p. Boy asleep	30	20
1959	150p. Man with bowl of fish and hindquarters of oxen	30	20
1960	150p. Jesus in manger	30	20
1961	150p. Mary and Joseph	30	20
1962	150p. Girl decorating tree	30	20

(b) Discount stamps. As Nos. 1953/62 additionally inscr "D S/20" above (Nos. 1963/7) or below (Nos. 1968/72) face value.

1963	150p. As No. 1953	30	20
1964	150p. As No. 1954	30	20
1965	150p. As No. 1955	30	20
1966	150p. As No. 1956	30	20
1967	150p. As No. 1957	30	20
1968	150p. As No. 1958	30	20
1969	150p. As No. 1959	30	20
1970	150p. As No. 1960	30	20
1971	150p. As No. 1961	30	20
1972	150p. As No. 1962	30	20

Nos. 1953/62 and Nos. 1963/72 respectively were issued together, se-tenant, forming a composite design.

ACKNOWLEDGEMENT OF RECEIPT STAMP

1894. Portrait of Columbus. Inscr "A.R.". Perf or Imperf.

AR77	5c. brown	1·40	1·40

COMPULSORY TAX STAMPS

T **100** Arms of Talca

T **224** Chilean Arms

1942. Talca Bicentenary.

T338	T **100** 10c. blue	10	10

1955. Death Centenary of Pres. Prieto. As T **145**.

T445	15p. green	15	10

PORTRAIT: 15p. Pres. Prieto.

1970. Postal Tax. No. 492a and 555 surch **E° O,10 Art. 77 LEY 17272.**

T638	**162** 10c. on 2c. blue	10	10
T639	**178** 10c. on 6c. purple	10	10

1971. Postal Modernization.

T646	T **224** 10c. blue	15	10
T647	15c. red	15	10

1971. Postal Modernization. Nos. T646/7 surch.

T673	T **224** 15c. on 10c. blue	10	10
T674	20c. on 15c. red	10	10
T675	50c. on 15c. red	10	10

OFFICIAL STAMPS

1928. Stamps of 1911 inscr "CHILE CORREOS" optd **Servicio del ESTADO**.

O190	**49** 10c. black and blue	3·75	1·00
O191	– 20c. (No. 142)	1·60	50
O192	– 25c. (No. 167)	4·25	50
O193	– 50c. (No. 170)	1·75	50
O194	**57** 1p. black and green	2·75	70

1930. Stamps inscr "CORREOS DE CHILE" optd **Servicio del ESTADO**.

O217	**49** 10c. (No. 204)	2·00	70
O234	**76** 10c. blue	1·60	35
O219	– 20c. (No. 209)	90	25
O235	– 20c. brown (No. 232)	1·10	25
O220	– 25c. (No. 210)	90	25
O221	– 50c. (No. 212)	1·10	35

1934. Stamps inscr "CORREOS DE CHILE" optd **OFICIAL**.

O236	**64** 5c. green (No. 206)	70	35
O237	**76** 10c. blue	70	35
O238	– 20c. brown (No. 232)	4·50	35

1939. Optd **Servicio del ESTADO**.

O279	– 50c. violet (No. 273)	4·50	2·00
O280	**90** 1p. orange	3·75	2·50

1941. Nos. 269/338j optd **OFICIAL**.

O281	– 10c. red	1·75	1·00
O282	– 15c. red	95	25
O283	– 20c. blue	4·50	2·75
O284	– 30c. red	45	25
O285	– 40c. green	45	25
O286	– 50c. violet	3·00	50
O339	**90** 1p. orange	2·00	80
O288	– 1p.80 blue	8·00	4·75
O442	– 2p. red	1·60	1·00
O383	– 5p. green	3·00	1·25
O443	– 10p. purple	10·00	5·00

1953. No. 379c optd **OFICIAL**.

O386	1p. turquoise	85	35

1956. Nos. 446/450 optd **OFICIAL**.

O451	2p. lilac	2·40	50
O452	3p. blue	8·00	4·00
O453	5p. sepia	1·50	40
O454a	10p. violet	1·25	40
O455	50p. red	5·00	1·40

1958. Optd **OFICIAL**.

O469	**152** 10p. blue	£140	35·00

1960. No. 493 optd **OFICIAL**.

O507	5c. blue	3·75	1·25

POSTAGE DUE STAMPS

D **18** D **19** D **68**

1895.

D 98	D **18** 1c. red on yellow	1·25	40
D 99	2c. red on yellow	1·25	40
D100	4c. red on yellow	1·25	40
D101	6c. red on yellow	1·25	40
D102	8c. red on yellow	1·25	40
D103	10c. red on yellow	1·25	40
D104	20c. red on yellow	1·25	40
D 93	40c. red on yellow	3·00	90
D 94	50c. red on yellow	4·00	1·00
D 95	60c. red on yellow	6·00	1·50
D 96	80c. red on yellow	7·00	3·00

D109		100c. red on yellow	20·00	11·50
D 97		1p. red on yellow	12·00	6·00

1898.

D110	D 19	1c. red	60	50
D111		2c. red	75	60
D112		4c. red	1·75	1·25
D113		10c. red	60	60
D114		20c. red	60	60

1924.

D184	D 68	2c. red and blue	1·25	1·00
D185		4c. red and blue	1·25	1·00
D186		8c. red and blue	1·25	1·00
D187		10c. red and blue	1·25	1·00
D188		20c. red and blue	1·25	1·00
D189		40c. red and blue	1·25	1·00
D190		60c. red and blue	1·25	1·00
D191		80c. red and blue	1·25	1·00
D192		1p. red and blue	1·40	2·50
D193		2p. red and blue	2·00	4·00
D194		5p. red and blue	2·50	4·00

CHINA — Pt. 17

People's Republic in Eastern Asia, formerly an Empire.

CHINESE CHARACTERS

Simple	Formal	
半	半	= ½
一	壹	= 1
二	貳	= 2
三	叁	= 3
四	肆	= 4
五	伍	= 5
六	陸	= 6
七	柒	= 7
八	捌	= 8
九	玖	= 9
十	拾	= 10
百	佰	= 100
千	仟	= 1,000
萬	萬	= 10,000
	分	= cent
	圓	= dollar

Examples:

十五	= 15
五十	= 50
叁佰圓	= 300 dollars
伍仟圓	= 5,000 dollars

CHINESE EMPIRE

1878. 100 candarins = 1 tael.
1897. 100 cents = 1 dollar.

1 Dragon

2

1878.

7	1	1ca. green	£120	90·00
2		3ca. red	£180	60·00
3		5ca. orange	£300	70·00

1885.

13	2	1ca. green	8·00	7·50
14		3ca. mauve	40·00	5·00
15		5ca. yellow	50·00	7·50

4

10

1894. Dowager Empress's 60th Birthday.

16	4	1ca. orange	12·00	7·50
17	–	2ca. green	12·00	10·00
18	–	3ca. yellow	12·00	3·50
19	–	4ca. pink	30·00	18·00
20	4	5ca. orange	65·00	45·00
21	–	6ca. brown	18·00	8·00
22	10	9ca. green	35·00	10·00
23		12ca. orange	85·00	40·00
24	–	24ca. red	£100	50·00

DESIGNS—VERT: (as Type **4**): 2ca. to 4ca. and 6ca. Dragon. HORIZ: (as Type **10**): 24ca. Junks.

1897. Surch in English and Chinese characters.

78	–	½c. on 3ca. yellow (No. 18)	5·00	4·00
34	2	1c. on 1ca. green	25·00	16·00
79	4	1c. on 1ca. orange	7·00	5·00
80	–	2c. on 2ca. green (No. 17)	8·00	2·50
35	2	2c. on 3ca. mauve	65·00	45·00
40	–	4c. on 4ca. pink (No. 19)	10·00	5·00
36	2	5c. on 5ca. yellow	60·00	25·00
41	–	5c. on 5ca. orange (No. 20)	12·00	5·00
42	–	8c. on 6ca. brown (No. 21)	14·00	5·00
43	–	10c. on 6ca. brown (No. 21)	60·00	60·00
63	10	10c. on 9ca. green	48·00	30·00
64		10c. on 12ca. orange	75·00	60·00
46	–	30c. on 24ca. red (No. 24)	80·00	40·00

17

24

30 Carp

31 Bean Goose

1897. Surch in English and Chinese characters.

88	17	1c. on 3c. red	45·00	30·00
89		2c. on 3c. red	55·00	30·00
90		4c. on 3c. red	£200	80·00
91		$1 on 3c. red	£900	£600
92		$5 on 3c. red	£5000	£3250

1897. Inscr "IMPERIAL CHINESE POST".

96	24	½c. purple	1·75	3·00
97		1c. yellow	2·50	1·00
98		2c. orange	2·50	50
99		4c. brown	3·00	75
100		5c. red	5·00	2·00
101		10c. green	8·50	1·75
102	30	20c. lake	20·00	6·50
103		30c. red	35·00	15·00
104		50c. green	40·00	24·00
105	31	$1 red	£170	£130
106		$2 orange and yellow	£900	£950
107		$5 green and red	£500	£650

32 Dragon

33 Carp

34 Bean Goose

1898. Inscr "CHINESE IMPERIAL POST".

121	32	½c. brown	1·00	10
122		1c. buff	1·00	10
123		2c. red	1·50	15
151		2c. green	2·00	20
152		3c. green	2·00	25
124		4c. brown	3·00	55
153a		4c. red	4·00	90
112		5c. pink	8·00	1·50
126		5c. orange	15·00	5·00
154		5c. mauve	4·00	15
155		7c. red	5·00	3·50
127		10c. green	6·00	15
156		10c. blue	7·00	20
157	33	16c. green	15·00	5·75
128		20c. purple	8·00	80
115		30c. red	11·00	4·00
130		50c. green	18·00	2·75
131	34	$1 red and orange	£160	12·00
132		$2 purple and yellow	£270	48·00
119		$5 green and orange	£475	£150

36 Temple of Heaven

1909. 1st Year of Reign of Emperor Hsuan T'ung.

165	36	2c. green and orange	1·25	80
166		3c. blue and orange	1·50	90
167		7c. purple and orange	1·25	1·50

POSTAGE DUE STAMPS

1904. Stamps of 1898 optd **POSTAGE DUE** in English and Chinese characters.

D137	32	½c. brown	3·00	4·00
D138		1c. buff	3·00	2·00
D139a		2c. red	5·50	2·75
D140		4c. brown	5·50	3·75
D141		5c. red	11·00	5·00
D142		10c. green	20·00	4·00

D 37

1904.

D143	D 37	½c. blue	2·00	85
D144		1c. blue	5·00	75
D168		1c. brown	4·00	3·00
D145		2c. blue	5·00	75
D169		2c. brown	9·00	12·00
D146		4c. blue	5·25	85
D170		4c. brown	£2000	
D147		5c. blue	5·75	1·25
D171		5c. brown	£900	£750
D148		10c. blue	6·00	1·75
D149		20c. blue	14·00	3·50
D150		30c. blue	18·00	5·25

CHINESE REPUBLIC

1912. 100 cents = 1 dollar.
1948. 100 cents = 1 gold yuan.
1949. 100 cents = 1 silver yuan.

1912. Optd vert with four Chinese characters signifying "Republic of China".

192	32	½c. brown	50	25
193		1c. buff	65	20
194		2c. green	1·25	25
221		3c. green	1·25	20
196		4c. red	2·50	40
197		5c. mauve	4·00	20
198		7c. lake	5·00	2·50
225		10c. blue	4·00	15·00
200	33	16c. olive	10·00	4·50
227		20c. red	10·00	1·00
202		30c. red	13·00	2·50
203		50c. green	18·00	2·50
204	34	$1 red and salmon	£160	12·50
205		$2 red and yellow	£130	35·00
232		$5 green and salmon	£350	£325

41 Dr. Sun Yat-sen

1912. Revolution Commemoration.

242	41	1c. orange	1·25	1·00
243		2c. green	1·25	1·00
244		3c. blue	1·25	40
245		5c. mauve	1·25	85
246		8c. sepia	1·75	1·75
247		10c. blue	1·75	1·00
248		16c. olive	7·50	8·00
249		20c. lake	6·50	5·00
250		50c. green	30·00	14·00
251		$1 red	75·00	25·00
252		$2 brown	£250	£180
253		$5 slate	75·00	£110

1912. As T **41** but portrait of Pres. Yuan Shih-kai, inscr "Commemoration of the Republic".

254		1c. orange	1·25	1·00
255		2c. green	1·25	1·00
256		3c. blue	1·25	30
257		5c. mauve	1·25	1·00
258		8c. sepia	3·50	4·00
259		10c. blue	2·75	1·00
260		16c. olive	6·00	5·00
261		20c. lake	5·75	2·50
262		50c. green	18·00	10·00
263		$1 red	42·00	18·00
264		$2 brown	45·00	14·00
265		$5 slate	£140	£110

43 Junk

44 Reaper

45 Entrance Hall of Classics, Peking

1913.

287	43	½c. sepia	20	10
269		1c. orange	35	10
289a		1½c. purple	85	75
270		2c. green	1·00	10
271		3c. green	1·40	10
292		4c. red	1·75	10
314		4c. grey	11·00	40
315		4c. olive	2·00	20
293		5c. mauve	1·50	10
294		6c. grey	2·25	45
317		6c. red	2·75	25
318		6c. brown	25·00	4·00
295		7c. violet	5·00	2·00
296		8c. orange	4·00	20
297		10c. blue	4·00	10
298	44	13c. brown	3·75	65
278		15c. brown	9·00	4·00
323		15c. blue	5·00	30
324		16c. olive	5·00	30
325		20c. lake	5·00	30
326		30c. purple	5·00	30
282		50c. green	10·00	1·50
304	45	$1 black and yellow	30·00	65
328		$1 sepia and brown	16·00	65
305		$2 black and blue	48·00	1·75
329		$2 brown and blue	32·00	1·25
306		$5 black and red	£150	24·00
330		$5 green and red	70·00	7·00
307		$10 black and green	£475	£140
331		$10 mauve and green	£200	30·00
308		$20 black and orange	£2000	£1800
332		$20 blue and purple	£325	60·00

1920. Flood Relief Fund. Surch with new value in English and Chinese characters.

349	43	1c. on 2c. green	5·00	2·00
361		2c. on 3c. green	4·00	20
350		3c. on 4c. red	7·50	1·75
351		5c. on 6c. grey	10·00	6·00

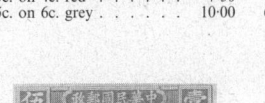

47 Curtiss JN-4 "Jenny" over Great Wall of China

I

II

1921. Air. Tail fin of aeroplane as Type I.

352	47	15c. black and green	16·00	14·00
353		30c. black and red	16·00	14·00
354		45c. black and purple	18·00	18·00
355		60c. black and blue	20·00	18·00
356		90c. black and olive	28·00	24·00

For similar stamps in this type but with tail fin as Type II, see Nos. 384a/8.

48 Yen Kung-cho, Pres. Hsu Shih-chang and Chin Yung-peng

53 Temple of Heaven

1921. 25th Anniv of Chinese National Postal Service.

357	48	1c. orange	3·50	1·00
358		3c. turquoise	3·50	40
359		6c. grey	5·00	3·50
360		10c. blue	5·75	2·75

1923. Adoption of the Constitution.

362	53	1c. orange	2·00	60
363		3c. turquoise	2·00	50
364		4c. red	4·00	1·75
365		10c. blue	7·50	1·50

1925. Surch in English and Chinese characters.

366	43	1c. on 2c. green	1·00	10
367		1c. on 3c. green	30	10
369		1c. on 4c. olive	1·25	10
370		3c. on 4c. grey	3·00	10

The figures in this surcharge are at the top and are smaller than for the 1920 provisionals.

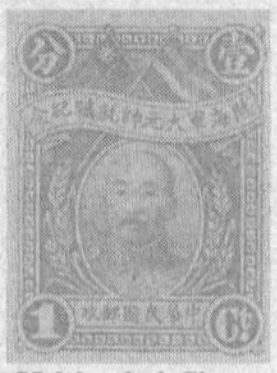
55 Marshal Chang Tso-lin

56 General Chiang Kai-shek

1928. Assumption of Title of Marshal of the Army and Navy by Chang Tso-lin.

372	55	1c. orange	1·00	1·00
373		4c. olive	1·00	1·00
374		10c. blue	5·00	4·00
375		$1 red	38·00	45·00

1929. Unification of China under Gen. Chiang Kai-shek.

376	56	1c. orange	3·00	40
377		4c. olive	4·50	45
378		10c. blue	10·00	1·50
379		$1 red	95·00	40·00

57 Mausoleum at Nanking

58 Dr. Sun Yat-sen

1929. State Burial of Dr. Sun Yat-sen.

380	57	1c. orange	1·00	50
381		4c. olive	1·00	50
382		10c. blue	5·00	1·00
383		$1 red	42·00	22·00

1929. Air. As T **47**, but tail fin of airplane as Type II.

384a	47	15c. black and green	4·00	20
385		30c. black and red	4·50	35
386		45c. black and purple	5·00	5·00
387		60c. black and blue	7·00	5·00
388		90c. black and olive	11·00	10·00

1931.

389	58	1c. orange	40	20
396		2c. olive	30	10
391		4c. green	85	10
398		5c. green	40	10
399		15c. green	65	40
400		15c. red	60	10
401		20c. blue	90	15
402		25c. blue	1·00	10
403a		$1 sepia and brown	3·75	15
735		$1 violet	30	2·00
404a		$2 brown and blue	6·50	50
736		$2 olive	30	4·00
405a		$5 black and red	12·00	2·00
737		$20 green	1·50	75
738		$30 brown	30	65
739		$50 orange	60	65

59 "Nomads of the Desert"

60 General Teng K'eng

1932. North-West China Scientific Expedition.

406	59	1c. orange	25·00	30·00
407		4c. olive	25·00	30·00
408		5c. red	25·00	30·00
409		10c. blue	25·00	30·00

1932. Martyrs of the Revolution.

410	60	½c. brown	15	10
508	–	1c. orange	10	10
509	–	2c. blue	10	15
412	60	2½c. purple	30	15
511	–	3c. brown	10	10
512	60	4c. lilac	10	20
513	–	5c. orange	10	50
514	–	8c. orange	10	10
515	–	10c. purple	10	15
516	–	13c. green	10	50
517	–	15c. purple	30	45
417	–	17c. green	60	10
418	–	20c. red	60	10
519	–	20c. blue	25	10
520	–	21c. brown	40	30
521	–	25c. purple	25	40
541	–	28c. green	30	75
542	–	30c. purple	20	25
543	–	40c. orange	20	25
544	–	50c. green	20	10

DESIGNS: 1, 25, 50c. Ch'en Ying-shih; 2, 10, 17, 28c. Shung Chiao-jen; 3, 5, 15, 30c. Liao Chung-k'ai; 8, 13, 21c. Chu Chih-hsin; 20, 40c. Gen. Huang Hsing.

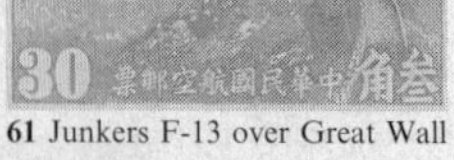
61 Junkers F-13 over Great Wall

1932. Air.

422	61	15c. green	30	15
556		25c. orange	20	60
557		30c. red	20	60
558		45c. purple	30	1·00
559		50c. brown	20	60
560		60c. blue	20	95
561		90c. green	20	1·00
562		$1 green	30	60
563		$2 brown	25	60
564		$5 red	30	50

62 Tan Yen-kai

63

1933. Tan Yen-kai Memorial.

440	62	2c. olive	1·50	85
441		5c. green	2·50	15
442		25c. blue	6·00	60
443		$1 red	42·00	20·00

1936. "New Life" Movement. Symbolic designs as T **63**.

444	63	2c. olive	1·25	25
445		5c. green	1·40	15
446	–	20c. blue (various emblems)	3·75	40
447	–	$1 red (Lighthouse)	24·00	7·00

66 "Postal Communications."

72 Dr. Sun Yat-sen

1936. 40th Anniv of Chinese National Postal Service.

448	66	2c. orange	2·25	60
449	–	5c. green	1·25	15
450	–	25c. blue	3·00	25
451	–	100c. red	18·00	6·50

DESIGNS: 5c. The Bund, Shanghai; 25c. G.P.O., Shanghai; 100c. Ministry of Communications, Nanking.

1936. Surch in figures and Chinese characters.

452	44	5c. on 15c. blue	1·50	20
453		5c. on 16c. olive	2·50	35

1937. Surch in figures and Chinese characters.

454	58	1 on 4c. green	50	20
455	–	8 on 40c. orange (No. 543)	65	40
456	58	10 on 25c. blue	50	10

1938.

462	72	2c. green	10	10
464		3c. red	10	10
489		5c. green	10	10
492		8c. green	10	10
469		10c. green	10	10
470		15c. red	85	1·25
471		16c. brown	40	50
472		25c. blue	75	75
494		30c. red	50	25
495		50c. blue	75	20
496		$1 sepia and brown	3·00	40
497		$2 brown and blue	2·25	40
498		$5 green and red	3·00	50
499		$10 violet and green	5·00	2·50
500		$20 blue and purple	10·00	4·25

For dollar values in single colours, see Nos. 666 etc.
For 15c. brown see Japanese Occupation of China: IV Shanghai and Nanking No. 12.

74 Chinese and U.S. Flags and Map of China

1939. 150th Anniv of U.S. Constitution. Flags in red and blue.

501	74	5c. green	70	30
502		25c. blue	1·00	85
503		50c. brown	2·00	2·00
504		$1 red	3·50	3·50

肆　　暫

分 4 作

(76)

1940. Surch as T **76**.

577	72	3c. on 5c. green	1·00	2·00
582		4c. on 5c. green	75	20
619		7c. on 8c. green	1·25	1·25

77 Dr. Sun Yat-sen

78 Industry

1941.

583	77	½c. brown	15	15
584		1c. orange	20	10
585		2c. blue	20	15
586		5c. green	20	15
587		8c. orange	60	1·00
588		8c. green	40	20
589		10c. green	15	10
590		17c. green	4·00	5·00
591		25c. purple	30	30
592		30c. red	30	25
593		50c. blue	40	15
594		$1 black and brown	50	10
595		$2 black and blue	65	20
596		$5 black and red	1·00	40
597		$10 black and green	2·75	2·25
598		$20 black and purple	3·00	2·50

1941. Thrift Movement.

599	78	8c. green	40	65
600		21c. brown	50	80
601		28c. olive	65	90
602		33c. red	90	1·00
603		50c. blue	1·00	1·10
604		$1 purple	1·25	1·40

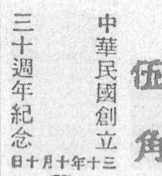

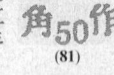

中華民國創立
三十週年紀念
日十月十年十三

(79)

改　伍
作　角 50

(81)

82 Dr. Sun Yat-sen

1941. 30th Anniv of Republic. Optd with T **79**.

606	–	1c. orange (No. 508)	1·25	1·50
607	72	2c. green	1·25	1·50
608	60	4c. lilac	1·25	1·50
609	72	8c. green	1·25	1·50
610		10c. green	1·25	1·50
611		16c. brown	1·25	1·50
612	–	21c. brown (No. 520)	1·25	1·50
613	–	28c. green (No. 541)	1·25	1·50
614	72	30c. red	1·25	1·50
615		$1 sepia and brown	1·50	1·50

1942. Provincial surcharges. Surch as T **81**.

622	60	1c. on ½c. brown	75	1·50
624	77	1c. on ½c. brown	80	2·00
690g	–	20c. on 13c. green (516)	1·00	5·00
691i	72	20c. on 16c. brown	1·00	5·00
693e	–	20c. on 17c. green (417)	1·50	5·50
694f	–	20c. on 21c. brown (520)	50	6·50
695e	–	20c. on 28c. green (541)	75	7·50
625	72	40c. on 50c. blue	2·75	4·25
627	77	40c. on 50c. blue	4·00	6·00
626	–	40c. on 50c. green (544)	5·00	6·00
689a		50c. on 16c. brown	2·25	1·40

1942.

628	82	10c. green	10	1·25
629		16c. olive	15·00	24·00
630		20c. olive	10	1·25
631		25c. purple	10	1·75
632		30c. red	10	95
642		30c. brown	20	9·00
633		40c. brown	10	1·25
634		50c. green	10	10
635		$1 red	75	10
636		$1 olive	10	20
637		$1.50 blue	10	40
638		$2 green	10	10
645		$2 blue	4·75	7·50
646		$2 purple	10	15
639		$3 yellow	20	20
640		$4 brown	30	30
641		$5 red	20	20
650		$6 violet	60	60
651		$10 brown	15	10
652		$20 blue	15	10
653		$50 green	4·50	15
654		$70 violet	5·50	35
655		$100 brown	60	45

1942. As T **72** but emblem at top redrawn with solid background. Perf, imperf or roul.

666	72	$4 blue	60	1·00
667		$5 grey	1·40	1·25
656		$10 brown	1·40	1·00
657		$20 green	1·40	75
658		$20 red	12·50	6·75
659		$30 purple	1·00	45
660		$40 red	1·25	50
661		$50 blue	1·50	1·00
662		$100 brown	6·00	4·00

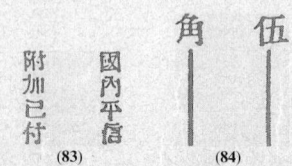

國內平信
附加已付

(83)

伍
角

(84)

(T **83** Trans. "Surcharge for Domestic Postage Paid")

1942. Surch as T **83**.

688e	82	16c. olive	30·00	30·00

1943. No 688e surch as T **84**.

701e	82	50c. on 16c. olive	4·00	4·00

89 Dr. Sun Yat-sen

91 Savings Bank and Money Box

90 War Refugees

1944.

702	89	40c. red	30	5·50
703		$2 brown	30	10
704		$3 red	15	10
705		$3 brown	75	45
706		$6 grey	15	25
707		$10 red	10	10
708		$20 pink	10	10
709		$50 brown	4·25	20
710		$70 violet	35	20

1944. War Refugees' Relief Fund. Various frames.

724	90	$2+$2 on 50c.+50c. blue	1·00	3·00
725		$4+$4 on 8c.+8c. green	1·00	3·00
726		$5+$5 on 21c.+21c. brn	1·50	3·00
727		$6+$6 on 28c.+28c. olive	2·50	3·00
728		$10+$10 on 33c.+33c. red	3·00	3·00
729		$20+$20 on $1+$1 violet	4·00	4·00

1944.

731	91	$40 slate	30	80
732		$50 green	30	30
733		$100 brown	30	25
734		$200 green	30	25

92 Dr. Sun Yat-sen

93 Dr. Sun Yat-sen

1944. 50th Anniv of Kuomintang.

740	92	$2 green	1·50	2·50
741		$5 brown	1·75	2·75
742		$6 purple	2·50	5·00
743		$10 blue	3·25	5·50
744		$20 red	3·75	7·50

1945. 20th Death Anniv of Dr. Sun Yat-sen.

746	93	$2 green	75	1·50
747		$5 brown	75	1·50
748		$6 blue	1·00	2·00
749		$10 blue	1·50	1·40
750		$20 red	2·00	3·50
751		$30 buff	2·50	4·50

94 Dr. Sun Yat-sen

96 Pres. Lin Sen

95 Gen. Chiang Kai-shek

1945.

758	94	$2 green	25	60
759		$5 green	20	35
760		$10 blue	10	10
761		$20 red	10	10

1945. Equal Treaties with Great Britain and U.S.A., abolishing Foreign Concessions. Flags in national colours.

762	95	$1 blue	75	1·50
763		$2 green	75	1·50
764		$5 olive	75	1·50

765 $6 brown . . . . . . 75 1·50
766 $10 red . . . . . . 3·25 6·00
767 $20 red . . . . . . 4·00 7·00

1945. In Memory of President Lin Sen.
768 96 $1 black and blue . . . 1·00 2·00
769 $2 black and green . . . 1·00 2·00
770 $5 black and red . . . 1·00 2·00
771 $6 black and violet . . . 1·25 2·00
772 $10 black and brown . . . 2·50 4·00
773 $20 black and olive . . . 3·50 6·00

(97) (98) (99)

1945. Chinese National Currency (C.N.C.). Various issues surch as T 97 (for Japanese controlled Government at Shanghai and Nanking) and further surch as T 98.
774 72 10c. on $20 on 3c. red . . 10 1·50
775 – 15c. on $30 on 2c. blue (509) . . 1·50
776 77 25c. on $50 on 1c. orange . . 10 1·25
777 72 50c. on $100 on 3c. red . . 10 50
778 60 $1 on $200 on 1c. orange (508) . . 10 15
779 72 $2 on 3c. red . . . 10 35
780 77 $5 on $1000 on 1c. orange . . 10 10

1945. Kaifeng provisionals. C.N.C. surcharges. Stamps of Japanese Occupation of North China surch as T 99.
781 60 $10 on 20c. lake (No. 166) 10·00 12·00
782 – $20 on 40c. orge (No. 168) 11·00 15·00
783 $50 on 30c. red (No. 167) 10·00 14·00

100 Pres. Chiang Kai-shek   101 Pres. Chiang Kai-shek

1945. Inauguration of Pres. Chiang Kai-shek. Flag in blue and red.
784 100 $2 green . . . . . 45 1·00
785 $4 blue . . . . . 75 1·00
786 $5 olive . . . . . 75 1·25
787 $6 brown . . . . . 1·50 2·00
788 $10 grey . . . . . 4·00 6·50
789 $20 red . . . . . 4·50 6·50

1945. Victory. Flag in red.
790 101 $20 green and blue . . . 10 15
791 $50 brown and blue . . . 60 60
792 $100 blue 20 25
793 $300 red and blue . . . 30 15

(102)   103 Dr. Sun Yat-sen

1945. C.N.C. surcharges. Nos. 410, 412, 514, 516/17, 519/20 and 541 surch as T 102 (value tablet at top).
794 $3 on 2½c. purple . . . 14·00 16·00
795 $10 on 15c. purple . . . 10 15
796 $20 on 8c. orange . . . 10 10
797 $20 on 20c. blue . . . 30 10
798 $30 on ½c. brown . . . 10 1·00
799 $50 on 21c. brown . . . 15 10
806 $70 on 13c. green . . . 10 10
802 $100 on 28c. green . . . 15 10

1945. No gum.
808 103 $20 red 10 10
809 $30 blue 10 15
810 $40 orange . . . . . 60 1·00
811 $50 green . . . . . 1·00 25
812 $100 brown 15 10
813 $200 brown 15 10

(104)   (108)

1946. Air. C.N.C. surcharges. Surch as T 104.
820 61 $23 on 30c. red . . . 10 1·00
821 $53 on 15c. green . . . 10 90
822 $73 on 25c. orange . . . 10 1·25
823 $100 on $2 brown . . . 10 35
824 $200 on $5 red . . . 10 15

1946. C.N.C. surcharges. Surch as T 108 (octagonal value tablet at bottom).
898 – $10 on 1c. orange (508) . . 10 65
903 77 $10 on 1c. orange . . 30 1·50
896 72 $20 on 2c. green . . 10 1·25
904 77 $20 on 2c. blue . . 10 10

899 – $20 on 3c. brown (511) . . 10 1·00
897 72 $20 on 3c. red . . . 10 1·00
879 – $20 on 8c. orange (514) . . 10 1·40
869 72 $20 on 8c. green . . 1·50 1·50
882 77 $20 on 8c. orange . . 80 4·00
883 77 $20 on 8c. green . . 10 80
900 60 $30 on 4c. lilac . . 10 50
880 – $50 on 3c. orange (513) . . 10 10
876 72 $50 on 5c. green . . 20 10
884 77 $50 on 5c. green . . 80 10

(105)   107 Dr. Sun Yat-sen

1946. C.N.C. surcharges. Surch as T 105 (rectangular value tablet at bottom). (a) Box with chequered pattern.
831 72 $20 on 3c. red . . . 10 1·40
846 – $20 on 8c. orange (514) . . 10 1·00
832 72 $20 on 3c. red . . . 10 50
833 – $50 on 5c. green . . 15 60
847 – $50 on 5c. orange (513) . . 10 30
851 77 $50 on 5c. green . . 65 1·25
854 82 $50 on $1 green . . 10 25
848 – $100 on 1c. orange (508) . . 10 10
834 77 $100 on 3c. red . . 10 10
842 $100 on 8c. green . . 25 15
852 77 $100 on 8c. green . . 10 10
860 58 $100 on $1 purple . . 50 10
868 107 $100 on $20 red . . 50 10
837 72 $200 on 10c. green . . 10 10
861 58 $200 on $4 blue . . 30 10
855 82 $250 on $1.50 blue . . 50 2·00
862 58 $250 on $2 green . . 30 30
863 $250 on $5 red . . 40 10
838 72 $300 on 10c. green . . 10 15
853 77 $300 on 10c. green . . 10 95
839 72 $500 on 3c. red . . 20 15
864 58 $500 on $20 green . . 15 10
865 $800 on $30 brown . . 10 3·00
830 $1000 on 2c. green . . 1·00 10
856 82 $1000 on $2 green . . 50 25
857 $1000 on $2 blue . . 25 2·00
858 $1000 on $2 brown . . 30 25
866 94 $1000 on $2 green . . 10 2·50
859 82 $2000 on $5 red . . 50 60
867 94 $2000 on $5 green . . 15 45

(b) Box with diamond pattern.
978 58 $500 on $20 green . . 10 10
979 107 $1250 on $70 orange . . 10 4·50
980 118 $1800 on $350 buff . . 10 5·00
974 82 $2000 on $3 yellow . . 50 40
976 89 $2000 on $3 red . . 10 15
975 82 $3000 on $3 yellow . . 15 15
977 89 $3000 on $3 brown . . 15 95

1946.
885 107 $20 red . . . . . 7·50 20
886 $30 blue 30 20
887 $50 violet 25 15
888 $70 orange . . . . . 12·00 2·00
889 $100 red 10 10
890 $200 green 10 10
891 $500 green 30 15
892 $700 brown . . . . . 15 1·50
893 $10000 purple 25 15
894 $3000 blue 30 10
895 $5000 red and green . . . 75 10

109 Douglas DC-4 over Mausoleum of Dr. Sun Yat-sen   110 Pres. Chiang Kai-sen

1946. Air. No gum.
905 109 $27 blue 10 75

1946. President's 60th Birthday.
906 110 $20 red 30 50
907 $30 blue 30 70
908 $50 orange 30 60
909 $100 green 50 90
910 $200 yellow 75 80
911 $300 red 75 50
For stamps of this type, but additionally inscribed with four characters around head, see Taiwan Nos. 30/5, or North Eastern Provinces, Nos. 48/53.

111 National Assembly House, Nanking   112 Entrance to Dr. Sun Yat-sen Mausoleum

1946. Opening of National Assembly, Nanking. No gum.
912 111 $20 green 30 40
913 $30 blue 20 40

914 $50 brown 30 40
915 $100 Hd 30 30

1947. 1st Anniv of Return of Government to Nanking.
942 112 $100 green 20 40
943 $200 blue 30 40
944 $250 red 30 75
945 $350 brown 30 75
946 $400 purple 50 55
For stamps of this type but additionally inscribed with four characters above numeral of value, see Taiwan, Nos. 36/40, or North Eastern Provinces, Nos. 65/70.

113 Dr. Sun Yat-sen   114 Confucius

115 Confucius's Lecture School   116 Tomb of Confucius

118 Dr. Sun Yat-sen and Plum Blossoms

1947.
947 113 $500 olive 30 20
948 $1,000 red and green . . 40 20
949 $2,000 lake and blue . . 45 20
950 $5,000 black and orange . . 50 20

1947. Confucius Commem. No gum.
951 114 $500 red 50 60
952 115 $800 brown 40 80
953 116 $1,250 green . . . . 40 1·10
954 $1,800 blue . . . . . 40 1·50
DESIGN—HORIZ: $1,800, Confucian Temple.

1947. (a) With noughts for cents. No gum.
955 118 $150 blue . . . . . 20 15·00
956 $250 violet . . . . . 20 4·50
957 $500 green 20 10
958 $1,000 red 20 10
959 $2,000 orange 20 10
960 $3,000 blue 20 10
961 $4,000 grey 20 10
962 $5,000 brown 20 10
963 $6,000 purple 20 20
964 $7,000 green 20 20
965 $10,000 red and blue . . 40 10
966 $20,000 green and red . . 1·00 10
967 $50,000 blue and green . . 1·10 10
968 $100,000 green & orange . . 4·00 15
969 $200,000 blue and purple . . 4·00 15
970 $300,000 orange & brown . . 5·00 40
971 $500,000 brown & green . . 5·50 40

(b) Without noughts for cents.
1032 118 $20,000 red 40 30
1033 $30,000 brown 10 10
1034 $40,000 green 10 15
1035 $50,000 blue 10 10
1036 $100,000 olive 10 10
1037 $200,000 purple 20 10
1038 $300,000 green . . . . 2·25 90
1039 $500,000 mauve 20 10
1040 $1,000,000 red 10 10
1041 $2,000,000 orange . . . 10 10
1042 $3,000,000 bistre . . . 10 50
1043 $5,000,000 blue . . . . 5·00 75

119 Map of Taiwan and Chinese Flag   122 Postal Kiosk

1947. Restoration of Taiwan (Formosa) (1st issue).
972 119 $500 red . . . . . 25 1·00
973 $1,250 green . . . . 25 1·00
See also Nos. 1003/4.

1947. Progress of the Postal Service.
981 – $500 red 30 50
982 122 $1,000 violet 30 50
983 $1,250 green 30 75
984 – $1,800 blue . . . . 30 1·00
DESIGN: $500, $1,800, Mobile Post Office.

123 Air, Sea and Rail Transport   124 Postboy and Motor Van

1947. 50th Anniv of Directorate General of Posts.
985 123 $100 violet 30 90
986 124 $200 green 30 90
987 $300 lake 30 90
988 – $400 red 30 90
989 – $500 green 30 90
DESIGN—As T 123: $400, $500, Junk and airplane.

126 Book of the Constitution and National Assembly Building

1947. Adoption of the Constitution.
990 126 $2,000 red 50 60
991 $3,000 blue 50 60
992 $5,000 green 50 60

127 Reproductions of 1947 and 1912 Stamps

1948. Perf or imperf. (a) Nanking Philatelic Exn.
1001 127 $5,000 red . . . . . 75 3·00

(b) Shanghai Philatelic Exhibition.
1002 127 $5,000 green . . . . 75 3·00

128 Sun Yat-sen Memorial Hall

1948. Restoration of Taiwan (Formosa) to Chinese Rule (2nd issue).
1003 128 $5,000 lilac . . . . 50 1·00
1004 $10,000 red . . . . 50 1·00

(130)   (129)

(133)

1948. "Re-valuation" surcharges. (a) Surch as T 130.
1012 118 $4,000 on $100 red . . . 20 20·00
1013 $5,000 on $100 red . . . 15 10
1014 $8,000 on $800 brown . . 30 1·00

(b) Surch as T 129.
1005 82 $5,000 on $1 green . . . 10 15
1007 $5,000 on $2 green . . . 15 10
1008 103 $10,000 on $20 red . . . 20 10
1018 82 $15,000 on 50c. green . . 20 50
1015 $15,000 on 50c. green . . 20 75
1019 $15,000 on $4 purple . . 20 50
1020 $15,000 on $6 blue . . 30 50
1009 $20,000 on 10c. green . . 10 15
1011 $20,000 on 30c. red . . 10 35
1010 $30,000 on 30c. red . . 10 40
1016 $40,000 on 20c. olive . . 20 75
1017 $60,000 on $4 brown . . 25 30

(c) Air. Surch as T 133.
1022 61 $10,000 on 30c. red . . 10 75
1028 109 $10,000 on $27 blue . . 10 1·50
1023 61 $20,000 on 25c. orange . . 10 75
1024 $30 on 90c. olive . . 10 1·00
1025 $50,000 on 60c. blue . . 10 1·00
1026 $50,000 on $1 green . . 10 90
On No. 1028 the Chinese characters read vertically.

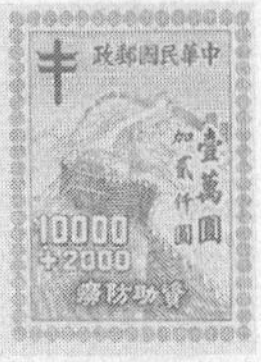

135 Great Wall of China

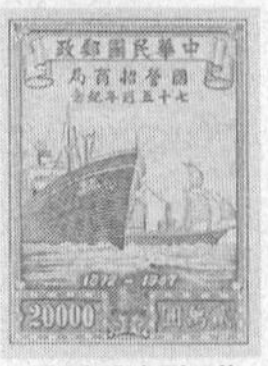

137 "Hai Tien" (freighter) and "Eton" (steamer) of 1872

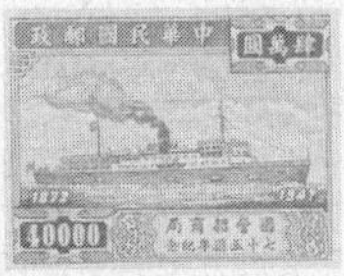

138 "Kiang Ya" (freighter)

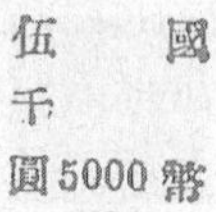

(**138a**)

1948. Tuberculosis Relief Fund. Cross in red. Perf or imperf. No gum.

1029	**135**	$5,000+$2,000 violet . .	15	2·50
1030		$10,000+$2,000 brown	15	2·50
1031		$15,000+$2,000 grey . .	15	2·50

1948. 75th Anniv of China Merchants' Steam Navigation Company. No gum.

1044	**137**	$20,000 blue	50	2·00
1045		$30,000 mauve	50	2·00
1046	**138**	$40,000 brown	50	2·75
1047		$60,000 red	50	2·75

1948. C.N.C. surcharge. Surch with T **138a**.

1048	**107**	$5,000 on $100 claret . .	9·00	40·00

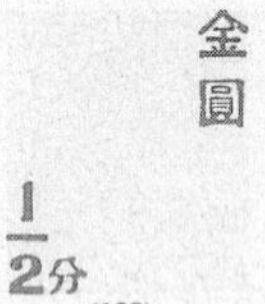

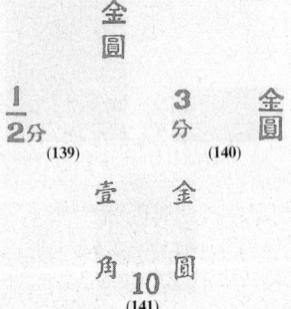

(**139**)

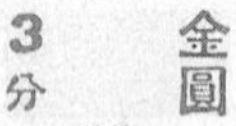

(**140**)

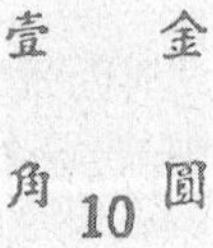

(**141**)

1948. Gold Yuan surcharges. (a) Surch as T **139** or **140**.

1049	**82**	½c. on 30c. brown . . .	10	4·00
1050	**118**	½c. on $500 green . . .	10	25
1051	**107**	1c. on $20 red	10	2·00
1052	**82**	2c. on $1.50 blue	25	3·00
1053		3c. on $5 red	10	3·00
1054		4c. on $1 red	10	3·00
1055		5c. on 50c. green	10	40

(b) Surch as T **141**.

1056	**89**	5c. on $20 red	10	1·00
1057	**103**	5c. on $30 blue	10	1·25
1058	**72**	10c. on 2c. green . . .	20	1·50
1059	**60**	10c. on 2½c. purple . .	25	1·00
1061	**82**	10c. on 25c. brown . .	10	1·10
1062	**89**	10c. on 40c. red . . .	10	1·25
1063	**82**	10c. on $1 green . . .	10	15
1065	**89**	10c. on $2 brown . . .	10	20
1066	**82**	10c. on $20 blue . . .	10	20
1067	**89**	10c. on $20 red	£250	£180
1068	**94**	10c. on $20 red	10	60
1069	**107**	10c. on $20 red	75	3·00
1070	**103**	10c. on $30 blue . . .	10	1·50
1071	**89**	10c. on $70 violet . . .	10	35
1072	**118**	10c. on $7,000 brown	2·00	1·25
1073		10c. on $20,000 red . .	15	4·00
1074	**89**	20c. on $6 purple . . .	10	35
1075	**58**	20c. on $30 brown . .	15	4·00
1076	**107**	20c. on $30 blue . . .	60	3·25
1077		20c. on $100 red . . .	15	3·25
1079	**60**	50c. on ½c. brown . . .	10	60
1081	**82**	50c. on 20c. green . . .	15	50
1082		50c. on 30c. red	10	1·25
1083		50c. on 40c. brown . .	10	80
1084	**89**	50c. on 40c. red	10	1·00
1085a	**82**	50c. on $4 purple . . .	25	1·90
1086		50c. on $20 blue . . .	10	20
1087	**94**	50c. on $20 red	50	1·50
1088	**107**	50c. on $20 red	10	1·25
1089	**82**	50c. on $70 lilac . . .	30	30
1090a	**118**	50c. on $6,000 purple	15	1·25
1091	**82**	$1 on 30c. brown . . .	10	20
1092		$1 on 40c. brown . . .	10	10
1093		$1 on $1 red	50	1·75
1094		$1 on $5 red	60	35
1095	**89**	$2 on $2 brown	10	25
1096	**102**	$2 on $20 red	10	20
1097	**107**	$2 on $100 red	15	20
1098	–	$5 on 17c. green (417)	75	75
1099	**89**	$5 on $2 brown	20	25
1100	**118**	$5 on $30,000 blue . .	10	1·25
1101	–	$8 on 20c. blue (519)	50	50
1102	**118**	$8 on $30,000 brown	10	2·00
1103	–	$10 on 40c. orange (543)	1·25	1·00
1104	**89**	$10 on $2 brown . . .	20	15
1105		$20 on $2 brown . . .	25	15
1106	**107**	$20 on $20 red	5·00	3·00
1107	**82**	$50 on 30c. red	20	30
1108	**89**	$50 on $2 brown . . .	30	15
1109	**107**	$80 on $20 red	10	1·00
1110	**82**	$100 on $1 green . . .	25	1·00
1111	**89**	$100 on $2 brown . . .	35	30
1112	**118**	$20,000 on $40,000 green	5·00	6·00
1113		$50,000 on $20,000 red	1·25	25
1114		$50,000 on $30,000 brown	10·00	5·00
1115		$100,000 on $20,000 red	5·00	4·00
1116		$100,000 on $30,000 brown	1·75	10
1117		$200,000 on $40,000 green	5·00	6·50
1118		$200,000 on $50,000 blue	5·00	8·00

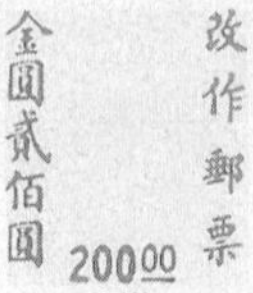

(**142**)

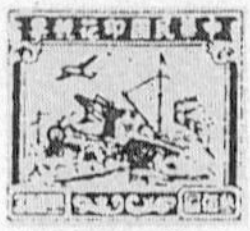

143 Liner, Train and Airplane

(**144**)

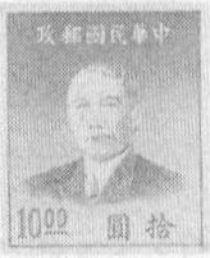

145 Dr. Sun Yat-sen

1949. Gold Yuan surcharges. Parcels Post stamps surch as T **142**.

1119	P **104**	$200 on $3,000 orange	1·00	60
1120		$500 on $5,000 blue	1·25	40
1121		$1,000 on $10,000 vio	2·00	55

1949. Gold Yuan surcharges. Revenue stamps surch. (a) As T **144**.

1136	**143**	50c. on $20 brown . . .	10	60
1137		$1 on $15 orange . . .	10	5·50
1127		$2 on $50 blue	10	1·25
1144		$3 on $50 blue	10	50
1138		$5 on $500 brown . . .	10	35
1129		$10 on $30 mauve . . .	10	55
1140		$15 on $20 brown . . .	10	45
1141		$25 on $20 brown . . .	10	20
1145		$50 on $50 blue	10	40
1147		$50 on $300 green . . .	25	60
1130		$80 on $50 blue	20	1·25
1146		$100 on $50 blue	35	50
1124		$200 on $50 blue	80	1·00
1142		$200 on $500 brown . .	50	65
1125		$300 on $50 blue	1·10	1·25
1143		$500 on $15 orange . .	1·40	4·00
1134		$500 on $30 mauve . . .	65	3·00
1135		$1,000 on $50 blue . . .	8·00	8·00
1148		$1,000 on $100 olive . .	2·75	5·00
1126		$1,500 on $50 blue . . .	65	1·75
1151		$2,000 on $300 green . .	35	30

(b) As T **144** but with key pattern inverted at top and bottom.

1183	**143**	$50 on $10 green	8·00	10·00
1184		$100 on $10 green . . .	1·50	4·50
1185		$500 on $10 green . . .	75	4·00
1186		$1,000 on $10 green . .	75	4·50
1187		$5,000 on $20 brown . .	20·00	12·00
1188		$10,000 on $20 brown	8·00	4·50
1189		$50,000 on $20 brown	12·00	6·00
1190		$100,000 on $20 brown	12·00	6·00
1191		$500,000 on $20 brown	£275	£110
1192		$2,000,000 on $20 brn	£500	£300
1193		$5,000,000 on $20 brn	£600	£375

1949.

1152	**145**	$1 orange	30	40
1153		$10 green	30	30
1154		$20 purple	10	40
1155		$50 green	10	30
1156		$100 brown	10	10
1157		$200 red	10	10
1158		$500 mauve	10	15
1159		$800 red	10	2·75
1160		$1,000 blue	15	10
1168		$2,000 violet	10	1·50
1169		$5,000 blue	10	20
1177		$5,000 red	40	50
1170		$10,000 brown	10	10
1171		$20,000 green	10	1·50
1179		$20,000 orange	40	75
1172		$50,000 pink	10	40
1180		$50,000 blue	1·25	2·00
1173		$80,000 brown	10	4·00
1174		$100,000 green	40	20
1181		$200,000 blue	1·75	2·00
1182		$500,000 purple	1·75	1·75

For stamps of Type **145** in Silver Yuan currency see Nos. 1348/56.

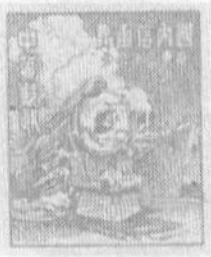

146 Steam Locomotive

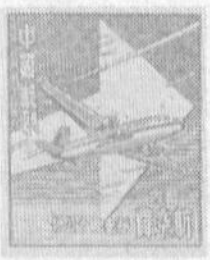

147 Douglas DC-4

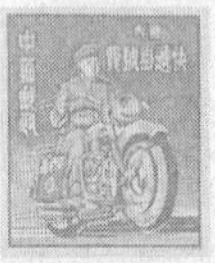

148 Postman on Motor Cycle

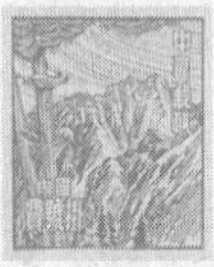

149 Mountains

1949. No value indicated. Perf or roul.

1211	**146**	Orange (Ord. postage)	4·00	1·50
1212	**147**	Green (Air Mail)	6·00	6·00
1213	**148**	Mauve (Express)	6·50	7·00
1214	**149**	Red (Registration) . . .	7·00	7·00

Owing to the collapse of the Gold Yuan the above were sold at the rate for the day for the service indicated.

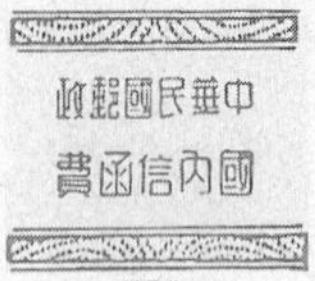

(**154**)

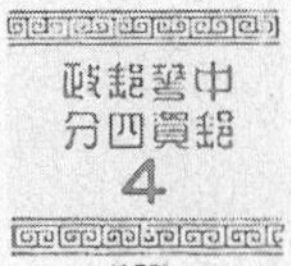

(**159**)

1949. Gold Yuan currency. Revenue stamps optd as T **154**. No gum.

1232	**143**	$10 green (B)	25·00	24·00
1233		$30 mauve (A)	£100	50·00
1234		$50 blue (C)	24·00	24·00
1235		$100 olive (D)	45·00	40·00
1236		$200 purple (A)	10·00	8·00
1237		$500 green (A)	10·00	8·00

Opt. translation: (A) Domestic Letter Fee. (B) Express Letter Fee. (C) Registered Letter Fee. (D) Air Mail Fee.

1949. Silver Yuan surcharges. Revenue stamps surch as T **159**. No gum.

1312	**143**	1c. on $20 brown . . .	40·00	45·00
1284		1c. on $5,000 brown . .	6·00	4·75
1285		4c. on $100 olive	5·00	3·25
1286		4c. on $3,000 orange . .	5·00	1·10
1313		10c. on $20 brown . . .	40·00	45·00
1287		10c. on $50 blue	6·75	2·50
1288		10c. on $1,000 red . . .	7·00	3·00
1289		20c. on $1,000 red . . .	7·00	4·50
1290		50c. on $30 mauve . . .	7·50	4·75
1291		50c. on $50 blue	18·00	2·00
1292		$1 on $50 blue	13·00	5·25

On Nos. 1312 and 1313 the key pattern is inverted at top and bottom.

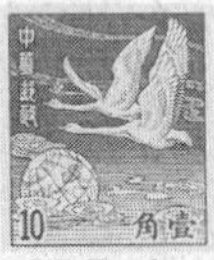

169 Tundra Swans over Globe

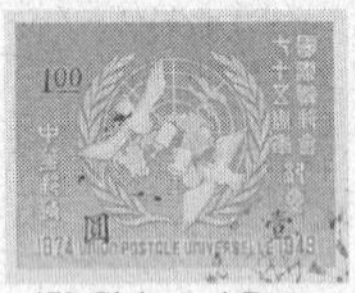

170 Globe and Doves

1949. No gum.

1344	**169**	$1 orange	10·00	10·50
1345		$2 blue	24·00	14·50
1346		$5 red	40·00	21·00
1347		$10 green	50·00	26·00

1949. Silver Yuan currency.

1348	**145**	1c. green	15·00	10·00
1349		2c. orange	4·00	15·00
1350		4c. green	10	50
1351		10c. lilac	10	20
1352		16c. red	10	15·00
1353		20c. blue	10	5·00
1354		50c. brown	50	30·00
1355		100c. blue	£175	£225
1356		500c. red	£275	£250

1949. 75th Anniv of U.P.U. Value optd in black. Imperf. No gum.

1357	**170**	$1 orange	5·00	9·00

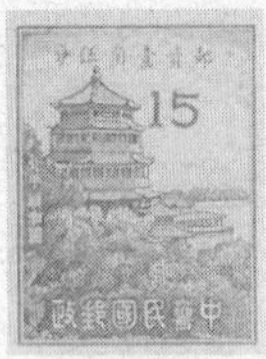

171 Buddha's Tower, Peking

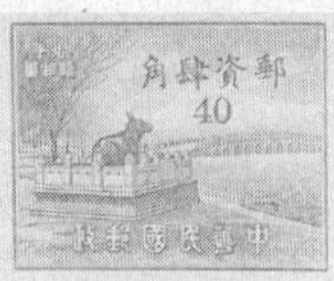

172 Bronze Bull

1949. Value optd. Roul.

1358	**171**	15c. green and brown . .	6·50	8·00
1359	**172**	40c. red and green . . .	7·50	8·00

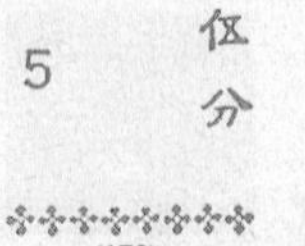

(**173**)

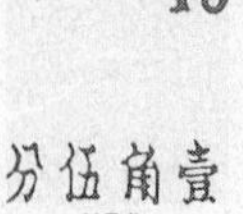

(**174**)

1949. Silver Yuan surcharges. (a) Chungking issue. Surch as T **173**.

1360	**145**	2½c. on $50 green . . .	2·25	3·25
1361		2½c. on $50,000 blue . .	4·00	3·25
1362		5c. on $1,000 blue . . .	4·00	3·00
1363		5c. on $20,000 orange	75	1·25
1364		5c. on $200,000 blue . .	4·50	3·00
1365		5c. on $500,000 purple	4·50	3·00
1366		10c. on $5,000 red . . .	4·50	3·25
1367		10c. on $10,000 brown	4·75	3·25
1368		15c. on $200 red	5·00	14·00
1369		25c. on $100 brown . .	9·50	20·00

(b) Canton issue. Surch as T **174**.

1371	**145**	1c. on $100 brown . . .	4·00	6·50
1372		2½c. on $500 mauve . .	6·50	7·50
1374		15c. on $10 green . . .	9·00	10·00
1375		15c. on $20 purple . . .	15·00	11·00

EXPRESS DELIVERY STAMP

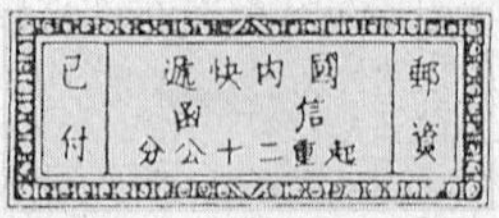

E 80

1941. Perf. No gum.

E617	E **80**	(No value) red & yellow	25·00	18·00

This stamp was sold at $2, which included ordinary postage.

MILITARY POST STAMPS

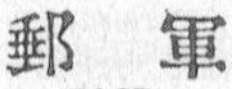

(M **85**)

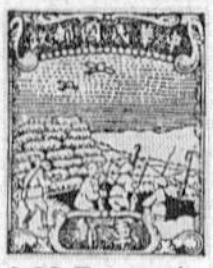

M **93** Entrenched Soldiers

1942. Optd variously as Type M **85**.

M682	**72**	8c. olive	6·50	9·00
M684	**77**	8c. green	6·00	11·00
M676		8c. orange	£425	
M683	**72**	16c. olive	20·00	24·00
M677	**82**	16c. olive	6·50	12·00
M678		50c. green	6·50	10·00
M679		$1 red	5·25	9·00
M680		$1 olive	5·50	9·00
M681		$2 green	5·75	11·00
M687		$2 purple	30·00	38·00

1945.

M745	M **93**	(No value) red . . .	1·00	12·00

PARCELS POST STAMPS

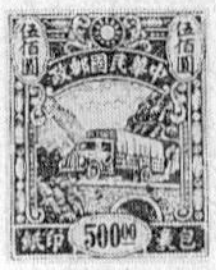

P **90**

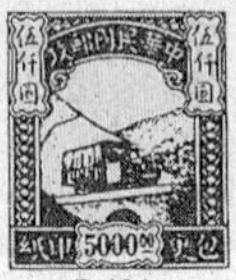

P **104**

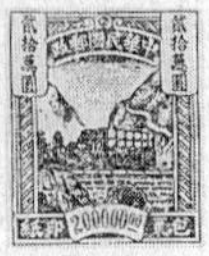

P **112**

1944.

P711	P **90**	$500 green	—	50
P712		$1,000 blue	—	60
P713		$3,000 red	—	70
P714		$5,000 brown	—	16·00
P715		$10,000 purple	—	30·00

1946.

P814	P **104**	$3,000 orange	—	50
P815		$5,000 blue	—	50
P816		$10,000 violet	—	2·25
P817		$20,000 red	—	4·25

1947. Type P **112** and similar design.

P925	$1,000 yellow	—	40
P926	$3,000 green	—	40
P927	$5,000 red	—	40
P928	$7,000 blue	—	40
P929	$10,000 red	—	40
P930	$30,000 olive	—	1·50
P931	$50,000 black	—	1·50
P932	$70,000 brown	—	1·75
P933	$100,000 purple	—	1·75
P934	$200,000 green	—	1·90
P935	$300,000 pink	—	2·00
P936	$500,000 plum	—	2·00
P937	$3,000,000 blue	—	2·50
P938	$5,000,000 lilac	—	3·75
P939	$6,000,000 grey	—	4·00
P940	$8,000,000 red	—	4·50
P941	$10,000,000 olive	—	5·00

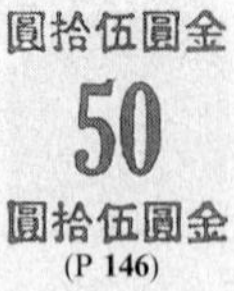

(P **146**)

1949. Gold Yuan surcharges. 1947 issue surch as Type P **146**.

P1194	$10 on $3,000 green . . .	—	2·00
P1195	$20 on $5,000 red	—	2·00
P1196	$50 on $10,000 red	—	2·00
P1197	$100 on $3,000,000 blue	—	2·50
P1198	$200 on $5,000,000 lilac	—	2·50
P1199	$500 on $1,000 yellow . .	—	3·00
P1200	$1,000 on $7,000 blue . .	—	3·00

Parcels post stamps were not on sale in unused condition; those now on the market were probably stocks seized by the Communists.

POSTAGE DUE STAMPS

1912. Chinese Empire Postage Due Stamps optd with vertical row of Chinese characters.

D207	D **37**	½c. blue	1·00	55
D208		1c. brown	1·25	50
D209		2c. brown	2·00	70
D210		4c. blue	4·00	1·75
D211		5c. blue	£110	£110
D212		5c. brown	6·00	2·25
D213		10c. blue	8·50	3·50

D214	20c. blue	9·00	9·00
D215	30c. blue	16·00	16·00

(D 41)   D 46   D 62

民 中
國 華

1912. Optd with Type D **41**.

D233	D 37	¼c. blue	8·00	5·00
D234		½c. brown	1·75	70
D235		1c. brown	1·75	60
D236		2c. brown	2·00	1·00
D237		4c. blue	6·00	1·50
D238		5c. brown	9·50	4·00
D239		10c. blue	16·00	8·00
D240		20c. brown	19·00	30·00
D241		30c. blue	22·00	40·00

1913.

D341	D 46	¼c. blue	50	20
D342		1c. blue	70	20
D343		2c. blue	85	20
D344		4c. blue	1·00	40
D345		5c. blue	1·75	40
D346		10c. blue	4·25	75
D347		20c. blue	6·25	2·75
D340		30c. blue	11·00	10·00

1932.

D432	D 62	1c. orange	25	10
D433		1c. orange	25	10
D434		2c. orange	35	15
D435		4c. orange	45	25
D569		5c. orange	15	40
D570		10c. orange	15	30
D571		20c. orange	20	30
D572		30c. orange	25	35
D573		50c. orange	25	30
D574		$1 orange	35	40
D575		$2 orange	60	50

欠 暫
資 作

(D 75) ("Temporary-use Postage Due")

1940. Optd with Type D **75**.

D545	72	$1 brown and red	4·00	10·00
D546		$2 brown and blue	5·00	10·00

D 90   D 94   D 112

1944. No gum.

D717	D 90	10c. green	10	2·00
D718		20c. blue	10	2·00
D719		40c. red	10	2·00
D720		50c. green	10	2·00
D721		60c. blue	15	4·00
D722		$1 red	10	2·00
D723		$2 purple	10	2·00

1945.

D752	D 94	$2 red	10	1·25
D753		$6 red	10	1·25
D754		$8 red	10	1·60
D755		$10 red	10	1·25
D756		$20 red	10	1·00
D757		$30 red	10	60

1947.

D916	D 112	$50 purple	10	2·00
D917		$80 purple	10	2·00
D918		$100 purple	10	2·00
D919		$160 purple	10	2·00
D920		$200 purple	10	2·00
D921		$400 purple	10	2·00
D922		$500 purple	10	2·00
D923		$800 purple	10	2·00
D924		$2,000 purple	10	2·00

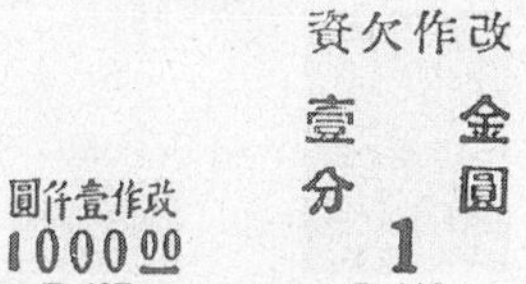

資 欠 作 改
壹 金
分 圓
1000 00 1

(D 127)   (D 146)

1948. Surch as Type D **127**.

D 993	D 94	$1,000 on $20 purple	10	3·00
D 994		$2,000 on $30 purple	10	2·00
D 995		$3,000 on $50 purple	10	2·00
D 996		$4,000 on $100 pur	10	3·00
D 997		$5,000 on $200 pur	10	1·75
D 998		$10,000 on $300 pur	10	80
D 999		$20,000 on $500 pur	10	80
D1000		$30,000 on $1,000 pur	10	50

1949. Gold Yuan surcharges. Surch as Type D **146**.

D1201	102	1c. on $40 orange	30	10·00
D1202		2c. on $40 orange	10	10·00
D1203		5c. on $40 orange	30	10·00

D1204		10c. on $40 orange	30	10·00
D1205		20c. on $40 orange	30	10·00
D1206		50c. on $40 orange	30	10·00
D1207		$1 on $40 orange	30	8·00
D1208		$2 on $40 orange	30	8·00
D1209		$5 on $40 orange	40	8·00
D1210		$10 on $40 orange	50	5·00

REGISTRATION STAMP

1941. Roul. No gum.

R617	E 80	(No value) grn & buff	25·00	18·00

This stamp was sold at $1.50 which included ordinary postage.

CHINESE PROVINCES

Manchuria

A. KIRIN AND HEILUNGKIANG

貼 吉
用貼黑吉限 用 黑
(1) (2)

Stamps of China optd

1927. Stamps of 1913 optd with T **1**.

1	43	1c. sepia	45	25
2		1c. orange	60	10
3		1½c. purple	1·75	1·50
4		2c. green	1·75	45
5		3c. green	1·50	75
6		4c. olive	1·50	10
7		5c. mauve	2·00	30
8		6c. red	1·75	90
9		7c. violet	3·00	2·25
10		8c. orange	3·50	1·75
11		10c. blue	3·00	10
12	44	13c. brown	4·25	3·50
13		15c. blue	4·00	1·50
14		16c. olive	4·75	2·25
15		20c. lake	5·00	2·25
16		30c. purple	7·00	2·75
17		50c. green	12·00	3·25
18	45	$1 sepia and brown	30·00	5·00
19		$2 brown and blue	50·00	10·00
20		$5 green and red	£160	£140

1928. Chang Tso-lin stamps optd with T **2**.

21	55	1c. orange	1·25	1·50
22		4c. olive	1·75	1·50
23		10c. blue	4·00	4·50
24		$1 red	32·00	32·00

1929. Unification stamps optd as T **2**.

25	56	1c. orange	1·25	1·40
26		4c. olive	2·00	2·00
27		10c. blue	11·00	5·00
28		$1 red	60·00	65·00

1929. Sun Yat-sen Memorial stamps optd as T **2**.

29	57	1c. orange	1·00	1·00
30		4c. olive	1·00	1·00
31		10c. blue	7·00	3·00
32		$1 red	38·00	38·00

B. NORTH-EASTERN PROVINCES

Issues made by the Chinese Nationalist Government of Chiang Kai-shek.

伍 改
角 作
用貼北東限
1 Dr. Sun Yat-sen (2)

1946. Surch as T **2**.

1	1	50c. on $5 red	20	3·00
2		50c. on $10 green	20	3·00
3		$1 on $10 green	20	2·00
4		$2 on $20 purple	20	1·50
5		$4 on $50 brown	20	1·25

拾 改
圓 作
用貼北東限 用貼北東限
(3) (4)

1946. Stamps of China optd with T **3** (= "Limited for use in North East").

6		1c. orange (508)	10	4·00
7		3c. brown (511)	25	3·50
8		5c. orange (513)	10	2·50
9	72	10c. green	25	3·25
11		20c. blue	20	3·50

1946. Stamps of China surch as T **4** but larger.

14		$5 on $50 on 21c. brown (No. 799)	50·00	55·00
15		$10 on $100 on 28c. green (No. 802)	60·00	70·00
16	91	$20 on $200 green	50·00	55·00

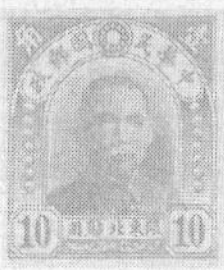

5 Dr. Sun Yat-sen

限東北貼用
10 00 圓拾
(6)

1946.

17	5	5c. lake	10	2·50
18		10c. red	10	2·50
19		20c. green	15	2·50
20		25c. brown	10	2·75
21		50c. orange	10	2·25
22		$1 blue	15	1·75
23		$2 green	15	2·00
24		$2.50 blue	10	2·75
25		$3 brown	15	2·25
26		$4 brown	15	2·75
27		$5 green	10	2·25
28		$10 red	10	1·25
29		$20 olive	10	1·00
34		$22 black	60·00	65·00
35		$44 red	12·00	20·00
36		$50 violet	10	50
37		$65 green	60·00	75·00
38		$100 green	10	50
39		$109 green	65·00	75·00
40		$200 brown	10	1·00
41		$300 green	10	2·00
42		$500 red	10	50
43		$1,000 orange	10	20

1946. Nanking National Assembly stamps of China surch as T **6**.

44	111	$2 on $20 green	40	2·50
45		$3 on $30 blue	40	2·50
46		$5 on $50 brown	40	2·50
47		$10 on $100 red	40	2·50

用貼北東限
壹 改
伍
圓 作
(8)

7 Pres. Chiang Kai-shek (note characters to right of head)

1947. President's 60th Birthday.

54	7	$2 red	50	3·00
55		$3 green	80	3·00
56		$5 red	80	3·00
57		$10 green	80	3·00
58		$20 orange	1·00	3·00
59		$30 red	1·00	3·00

For other stamps as Types **7** and **9** but with different Chinese characters, see China-Taiwan Types **4** and **5**.

1947. Stamps of China surch as T **8**.

60	107	$100 on $1,000 purple	80	3·25
61		$300 on $3,000 blue	80	3·25
62	58	$500 on $30 brown	45	3·75
63	107	$500 on $5,000 red & green	75	3·25

改
捌 作
仟
圓 8000
(10)

9 Entrance to Dr. Sun Yat-sen Mausoleum (note characters above face value)

1947. 1st Anniv of Return of Govt. to Nanking.

64	9	$2 green	50	1·50
65		$4 blue	50	1·50
66		$6 red	50	1·50
67		$10 brown	50	1·50
68		$20 purple	50	1·50

1948. Surch as T **10**.

70	5	$1,500 on 20c. green	15	3·50
71		$3,000 on $1 blue	15	3·75
72		$4,000 on 25c. brown	15	3·00
73		$8,000 on 50c. orange	10	2·50
74		$10,000 on 10c. orange	10	2·50
75		$50,000 on $109 green	25	2·75
76		$100,000 on $65 green	35	2·50
77		$500,000 on $22 black	50	2·75

No. 70 has five characters on the left side of the surcharge and No. 77 four characters.

MILITARY POST STAMPS

1946. Military Post stamp of China optd as T **3** but larger.

M13	M 93	(No value) red	2·00	14·00

郵 軍
作暫
圓肆拾肆
(M 10)

1947. Surch with Type M **10**.

M69	5	$44 on 50c. orange	8·00	32·00

PARCELS POST STAMPS

用貼北東限
伍 改
拾萬
圓 作
P 11 (P 12)

1948.

P78	P 11	$500 red	30·00
P79		$1,000 red	60·00
P80		$3,000 olive	75·00
P81		$5,000 blue	£120
P82		$10,000 green	£150
P83		$20,000 blue	£150

1948. Parcels Post stamp of China surch with Type P **12**.

P84		$500,000 on $5,000,000 lilac (No. P938)	£140

Parcels Post stamps were not on sale unused.

POSTAGE DUE STAMPS

拾 改
圓 作
D 7 (D 13)

1947.

D48	D 7	10c. blue	40	6·00
D49		20c. blue	40	6·00
D50		50c. blue	40	4·50
D51		$1 blue	10	3·25
D52		$2 blue	10	4·25
D53		$5 blue	10	4·25

1948. Surch as Type D **13**.

D85	D 7	$10 on 10c. blue	10	7·00
D86		$20 on 20c. blue	10	7·00
D87		$50 on 50c. blue	10	7·00

Sinkiang

(Chinese Turkestan)

A province between Tibet and Mongolia. Issued distinguishing stamps because of its debased currency. The following are all optd on stamps of China.

限
新
省
貼
用 用貼省新限
(1) (3)

1915. 1913 issue optd with T **1**.

17	43	½c. sepia	30	25
2		1c. orange	75	10
49		1½c. purple	1·50	2·00
3		2c. green	1·25	50
4		3c. green	1·25	10
5		4c. red	1·40	60
52		4c. grey	7·50	3·50
53		4c. olive	4·50	1·50
6		5c. mauve	1·25	40
7		6c. grey	1·40	70
55		6c. red	3·50	1·00
56		6c. brown	15·00	14·00
8		7c. violet	2·00	2·00
9		8c. orange	2·75	1·40
10		10c. blue	3·00	25
60	44	13c. brown	5·50	4·50
11		15c. brown	3·50	2·50
61		15c. blue	6·00	2·50
12		16c. olive	4·00	2·75
63		20c. lake	6·00	1·50
14		30c. purple	6·50	2·50
65		50c. green	10·00	3·50
34	45	$1 black and yellow	20·00	3·75
66		$1 sepia and brown	22·00	3·50
35		$2 black and blue	35·00	12·00
67		$2 brown and blue	26·00	8·50
36		$5 black and red	75·00	22·00
68		$5 green and red	50·00	17·00
37		$10 black and green	£225	£150
69		$10 mauve and green	£140	£120
38		$20 black and yellow	£550	£425
70		$20 blue and purple	£160	£140

1921. 25th Anniv of Chinese National Postal Service stamps optd with T **3**.

39	48	1c. orange	1·25	1·50
40		3c. turquoise	1·25	1·50
41		6c. grey	2·75	2·50
42		10c. blue	32·00	32·00

貼 新
新疆
月 省
(4)

1923. Adoption of the Constitution stamps optd with T **4**.

43	53	1c. orange	3·25	3·25
44		3c. turquoise	3·25	3·25
45		4c. red	4·00	4·00
46		10c. blue	4·75	4·25

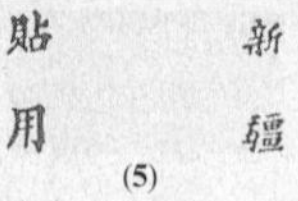
(5)

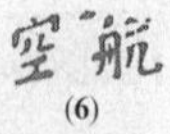
航空
(6)

1928. Assumption of Title of Marshal of the Army and Navy by Chang Tso-lin. Optd with T **5**.

71	**55**	1c. orange	1·40	1·25
72		4c. olive	2·25	2·25
73		10c. blue	5·50	5·00
74		$1 red	35·00	38·00

1929. Unification of China. Optd as T **5**.

75	**56**	1c. orange	3·00	2·50
76		4c. olive	3·00	2·75
77		10c. blue	8·50	3·50
78		$1 red	60·00	50·00

1929. Sun Yat-sen State Burial. Optd as T **5**.

79	**57**	1c. orange	1·50	1·25
80		4c. olive	2·50	2·25
81		10c. blue	6·00	3·25
82		$1 red	35·00	28·00

1932. Air. Handstamped on Sinkiang issues as T **6** ("By Air Mail").

83	**43**	5c. mauve (No. 6)	£300	£225
84		10c. blue (No. 10)	£300	£170
85	**44**	15c. blue (No. 61)	£2000	£600
86		30c. purple (No. 14)	£900	£750

1932. Dr. Sun Yat-sen stamps optd as T **3**.

87	**58**	1c. orange	1·25	2·25
95		2c. olive	1·25	1·25
103		4c. green	1·00	2·25
104		5c. green	1·25	1·50
105		15c. green	1·75	3·50
114		15c. red	2·50	2·50
115		20c. blue	2·00	75
107		25c. blue	2·00	75
108		$1 sepia and brown	6·50	5·50
100		$2 brown and blue	18·00	13·00
101		$5 black and red	24·00	25·00

1933. Tan Yen-kai Memorial. Optd as T **5**.

117	**62**	2c. olive	2·25	2·25
118		5c. green	2·75	1·25
119		25c. blue	7·00	3·50
120		$1 red	45·00	42·00

1933. Martyrs' issue optd as T **3**.

121	**60**	½c. sepia	10	1·00
122	–	1c. orange	10	85
167	–	2c. blue	30	2·25
123	**60**	2½c. mauve	20	1·75
124	–	3c. brown	20	2·00
169	**60**	4c. lilac	40	2·50
125	–	8c. orange	20	2·00
126	–	10c. purple	20	2·00
171	–	13c. green	60	3·25
172	–	15c. purple	60	3·25
173	–	17c. olive	75	3·25
137	–	20c. lake	20	4·25
174	–	20c. blue	75	3·00
175	–	21c. sepia	60	3·50
185	–	25c. purple	1·00	5·00
176	–	28c. olive	75	3·25
130	–	30c. red	25	3·25
131	–	40c. orange	25	3·50
132	–	50c. green	25	3·25

1940. Dr. Sun Yat-sen stamps optd as T **3**.

139	**72**	2c. olive	30	1·50
140		3c. red	30	2·25
141		5c. green	30	1·25
143		8c. olive	40	1·10
144		10c. green	40	1·25
145		15c. red	1·00	3·25
146		16c. olive	1·00	3·50
147		25c. blue	1·40	3·25
156		30c. red	1·00	2·75
158		50c. blue	1·50	3·00
160		$1 brown and red	1·75	5·00
161		$2 brown and blue	1·75	6·00
162		$5 green and red	1·75	7·50
163		$10 violet and green	2·00	7·50
164		$20 blue and red	3·00	11·00

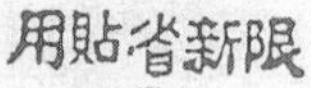
用貼省新限
(8)

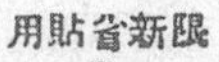
用貼省新限
(9)

1942. Air. Air stamps optd with T **8** or larger.

187	**61**	15c. green	4·00	7·00
197		25c. orange	5·00	10·00
198		30c. red	5·00	10·00
190		45c. purple	6·00	10·00
199		50c. brown	6·00	12·00
192		60c. blue	6·00	12·00
193		90c. olive	25·00	27·00
194		$1 green	7·50	13·00
200		$2 brown	25·00	24·00
201		$5 red	32·00	24·00

1942. Thrift stamps optd as T **8**.

221	**78**	8c. green	5·00	10·00
215		21c. brown	5·00	10·00
216		28c. olive	5·00	10·00
223		33c. red	6·50	10·00
218		50c. blue	7·50	10·00
225		$1 purple	10·00	15·00

1943. Dr. Sun Yat-sen stamps optd as T **3**.

227	**82**	10c. green	15	6·00
228		20c. olive	15	5·50
229		25c. purple	30	10·00
230		30c. red	15	6·50
231		40c. brown	15	6·00
232		50c. green	15	6·00
233		$1 red	35	5·50
234		$1 olive	25	5·00
235		$1.50 blue	25	8·00
236		$2 green	75	6·50
237		$3 yellow	35	6·50
238		$5 red	45	6·50

1943. Stamps optd with T **9**.

239	**72**	10c. green	7·50	15·00
240	–	20c. blue (No. 519)	7·50	14·00
241	**72**	50c. blue	7·50	12·00

1944. Dr. Sun Yat-sen stamps optd as T **3**.

248	**77**	$4 blue	1·50	10·00
249		$5 grey	2·75	10·00
250		$10 brown	2·75	10·00
251		$20 green	1·40	11·00
243		$20 red	5·00	13·00
253		$30 purple	3·00	13·00
245		$40 red	3·75	13·00
255		$50 blue	3·50	14·00
247		$100 brown	11·00	17·00

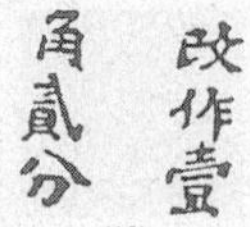
改作壹
角貳分
(10)

1944. Nos. 227 and 229 of Sinkiang surch as T **10**.

257	**82**	12c. on 10c. green	7·00	20·00
258		24c. on 25c. purple	7·00	20·00

1945. Stamps optd as T **3**.

259	**89**	40c. red	35	16·00
260		$3 red	35	14·00

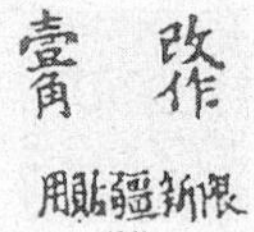
用貼疆新限
(11)

1949. Silver Yuan surcharges. Sun Yat-sen issues of China surch as T **11**.

261	**107**	1c. on $100 red (No. 889)	6·00	11·00
262		3c. on $200 green (No. 890)	6·00	14·00
263		5c. on $500 green (No. 891)	6·00	10·00
264	**136**	10c. on $20,000 red (No. 1032)	9·00	10·00
265		50c. on $4,000 grey (No. 961)	26·00	20·00
266		$1 on $6,000 purple (No. 963)	30·00	25·00

Szechwan

A province of China. Issued distinguishing stamps because of its debased currency.

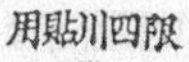
用貼川四限
(1)

Stamps of China optd with T **1**.

1933. Issue of 1913.

1	**43**	1c. orange	3·00	75
2		5c. mauve	6·00	20
3	**44**	50c. green	20·00	50

1933. Dr. Sun Yat-sen issue.

4	**58**	2c. olive	1·50	50
5		5c. green	1·50	10
6		15c. green	3·50	2·75
7		15c. red	7·00	7·50
8		25c. blue	6·00	40
9		$1 sepia and brown	18·00	2·75
10		$2 brown and blue	40·00	3·75
11		$5 black and red	80·00	12·00

1933. Martyrs issue (Nos. 410 etc).

12	**60**	½c. sepia	30	20
13	–	1c. orange	40	10
14	**60**	2½c. mauve	95	50
15	–	3c. brown	1·25	55
16	–	8c. orange	1·40	75
17	–	10c. purple	1·90	15
18	–	13c. green	2·75	60
19	–	17c. olive	2·25	1·10
20	–	20c. lake	3·00	50
21	–	30c. red	3·50	45
22	–	40c. orange	14·00	85
23	–	50c. green	16·00	1·10

Yunnan

A province of China which issued distinguishing stamps because of its debased currency.

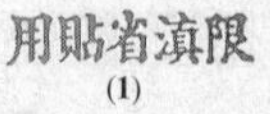
用貼省滇限
(1)

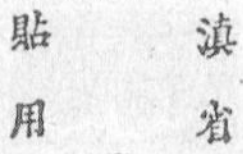
(2)

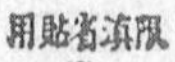
用貼省滇限
(3)

Stamps of China optd.

1926. Issue of 1913, optd with T **1**.

1	**43**	½c. sepia	30	45
2		1c. orange	1·25	10
3		1½c. purple	1·25	1·25
4		2c. green	2·00	55
5		3c. green	1·75	40
6		4c. olive	1·75	10
7		5c. mauve	3·00	35
8		6c. red	3·75	1·25
9		7c. violet	4·75	2·50
10		8c. orange	5·50	2·00
11		10c. blue	3·75	20
12	**44**	13c. brown	5·50	4·25
13		15c. blue	5·00	1·50
14		16c. olive	6·00	3·25
15		20c. lake	5·50	1·75
16		30c. purple	16·00	11·00
17		50c. green	8·50	5·00
18	**45**	$1 sepia and brown	22·00	8·50
19		$2 brown and blue	45·00	14·00
20		$5 green and red	£140	£150

1929. Unification of China. Optd with T **2**.

21	**56**	1c. orange	1·75	1·50
22		4c. olive	2·50	1·25
23		10c. blue	9·00	2·00
24		$1 red	70·00	55·00

1929. Sun Yat-sen State Burial. Optd as T **2**.

25	**57**	1c. orange	1·75	1·50
26		4c. olive	1·75	1·00
27		10c. blue	7·00	1·50
28		$1 red	45·00	40·00

1932. Dr. Sun Yat-sen stamps optd with T **3**.

29	**58**	1c. orange	80	75
30		2c. olive	95	1·10
44		4c. green	1·75	1·50
45		5c. green	2·00	75
46		15c. green	4·50	4·75
47		15c. red	5·00	7·00
32		20c. blue	3·00	85
48		25c. blue	7·50	3·50
33		$1 sepia and brown	20·00	16·00
34		$2 brown and blue	45·00	30·00
35		$5 black and red	£100	85·00

1933. Tan Yen-kai Memorial. Optd with T **2**.

52	**62**	2c. olive	1·75	2·25
53		5c. green	2·00	1·00
54		25c. blue	5·75	2·25
55		$1 red	48·00	48·00

1933. Martyrs issue optd as T **3**.

56	**60**	½c. sepia	65	1·00
57	–	1c. orange	1·25	20
58	**60**	2½c. mauve	1·50	2·50
59	–	3c. brown	3·25	3·25
60	–	8c. orange	8·50	8·00
61	–	10c. purple	3·75	3·50
62	–	13c. green	3·75	3·75
63	–	17c. olive	3·75	3·75
64	–	20c. lake	4·00	2·00
65	–	30c. red	8·50	7·00
66	–	40c. orange	14·00	15·00
67	–	50c. green	16·00	7·50

COMMUNIST CHINA

Issues were made by various Communist administrations from 1930 onwards. These had limited local availability and are outside the scope of this catalogue. For details of such issues see Part 17.

In 1946 (North East China) and 1949 these local issues were consolidated into Regional People's Post stamps for those local administrations listed below.

A. East China People's Post

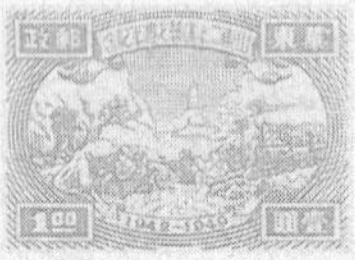
EC **105** Methods of Transport

1949. 7th Anniv of Shandong Communist Postal Administration.

EC322	EC **105**	$1 green	60	1·25
EC323		$2 green	20	85
EC324		$3 red	20	45
EC325		$5 brown	20	35
EC326		$10 blue	35	1·00
EC327		$13 violet	20	80
EC328		$18 blue	20	80
EC329		$21 red	30	1·00
EC330		$30 green	20	65
EC331		$50 red	70	80
EC332		$100 green	12·00	11·00

The $5 has an overprinted character obliterating a Japanese flag on the tower.

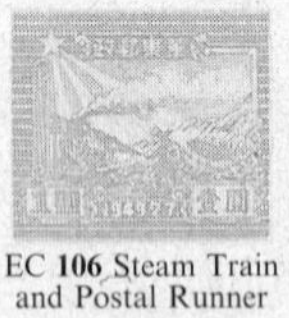
EC **106** Steam Train and Postal Runner

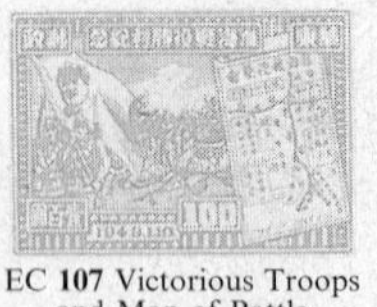
EC **107** Victorious Troops and Map of Battle

1949. Dated "1949.2.7".

EC333	EC **106**	$1 green	20	85
EC334		$2 green	30	65
EC335		$3 red	20	65
EC336		$5 brown	20	55
EC337		$10 blue	75	1·10
EC338		$13 violet	25	90
EC339		$18 blue	20	1·10
EC340		$21 red	20	1·75
EC341		$30 green	2·50	1·90
EC342		$50 red	35	2·75
EC343		$100 green	1·00	55

For stamps as Type EC **106**, but dated "1949", see Nos. EC364/71.

1949. Victory in Huaihai Campaign.

EC344	EC **107**	$1 green	20	80
EC345		$2 green	35	70
EC346		$3 red	20	70
EC347		$5 brown	20	40
EC348		$10 blue	60	60
EC349		$13 violet	20	80
EC350		$18 blue	20	80
EC351		$21 red	20	90
EC352		$30 green	1·00	75
EC353		$50 red	50	1·00
EC354		$100 green	4·00	2·00

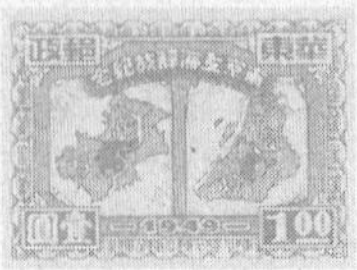
EC **108** Maps of Shanghai and Nanjing

1949. Liberation of Nanjing and Shanghai.

EC355	EC **108**	$1 red	20	1·25
EC356		$2 green	20	1·00
EC357		$3 violet	20	75
EC358		$5 brown	20	50
EC359		$10 blue	20	75
EC360		$30 green	40	1·00
EC361		$50 red	85	75
EC362		$100 green	1·25	15
EC363		$500 orange	3·50	75

1949. As Type EC **106** but dated "1949".

EC364	$10 blue	20	25
EC365a	$15 red	20	25
EC366	$30 green	20	10
EC367	$50 red	20	10
EC368	$60 green	20	1·60
EC369	$100 green	6·00	80
EC370	$1,600 violet	2·00	4·25
EC371	$2,000 purple	2·00	3·75

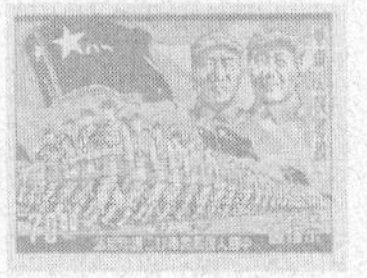
EC **111** Zhu De, Mao Tse-tung and Troops

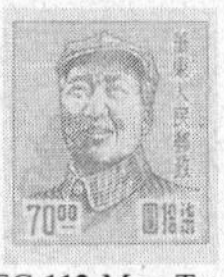
EC **112** Mao Tse-tung

1949. 22nd Anniv of Chinese People's Liberation Army.

EC378	EC **111**	$70 orange	20	10
EC379		$270 red	20	15
EC380		$370 green	20	40
EC381		$470 purple	35	60
EC382		$570 blue	30	45

For other values in this design with only three characters in bottom panel, see South West China Nos. SW9/19.

1949.

EC383	EC **112**	$10 blue	3·00	3·25
EC384		$15 red	3·00	3·50
EC385		$70 brown	20	35
EC386		$100 purple	20	20
EC387		$150 orange	20	30
EC388		$200 green	20	10
EC389		$500 blue	20	10
EC390		$1,000 red	20	15
EC391		$2,000 green	20	3·50

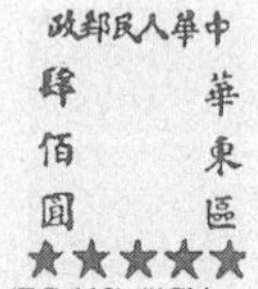
政郵民人華中
肆 華
佰 東
圓 區
(EC **113**) ("Chinese People's Postal Service East China Region")

1949. Stamps of Nationalist China surch as Type EC **113**.

EC392	**145**	$400 on $200 red	18·00	30
EC393		$1,000 on $50 green	60	25
EC394		$1,200 on $100 brown	25	1·75
EC395		$1,600 on $20,000 grn	25	2·25
EC396		$2,000 on $1,000 blue	25	15

PARCELS POST STAMPS

Stamps of Nationalist China surch.

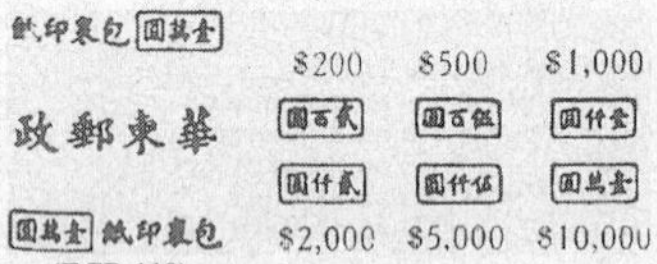
政郵東華
$200 $500 $1,000
$2,000 $5,000 $10,000
(ECP **110**)

1949. No. 1347 surch as Type ECP **110**.

ECP372	**169**	$200 on $10 green	16·00	8·00
ECP373		$500 on $10 green	16·00	3·75
ECP374		$1,000 on $10 green	18·00	7·00
ECP375		$2,000 on $10 green	26·00	13·00
ECP376		$5,000 on $10 green	40·00	21·00
ECP377		$10,000 on $10 green	75·00	29·00

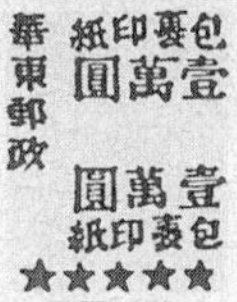
(ECP 114)

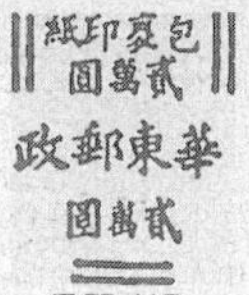
(ECP 115)

1949. Nos. 1344/6 and unissued 10c. surch as Type ECP **114**.

ECP397	**169**	$5,000 on 10c. blue	30·00	19·00
ECP398		$10,000 on $1 orange	48·00	30·00
ECP399		$20,000 on $2 blue	90·00	65·00
ECP400		$50,000 on $5 red	£300	85·00

1949. Nos. P711/2 and P926/7 surch as Type ECP **115**.

ECP401	P **90**	$5,000 on $500 green	20	10·00
ECP402		$10,000 on $1 blue	80·00	40·00
ECP403	P **112**	$20,000 on $3 green	£120	75·00
ECP404		$50,000 on $5 red	2·00	50·00

B. North China People's Post

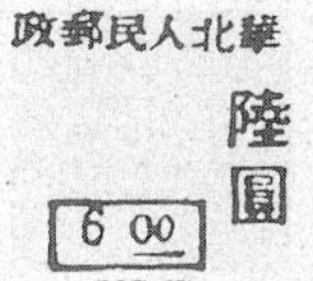
(NC **68**)

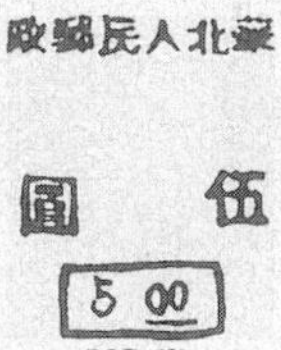
(NC **69**)

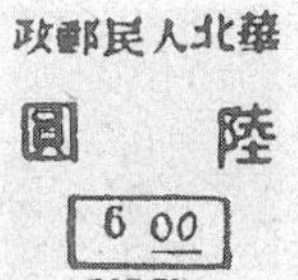
(NC **70**)

1949. Surch "North China People's Postal Administration". (a) Surch as Type NC **68**.

NC258	$5 on $500 orange	20·00	15·00
NC259	$6 on $500 orange	24·00	20·00
NC260	$12 on $200 red	4·00	5·00

(b) Surch as Type NC **69**.

NC261	$3 on 2 (20c.) brown	£200	£120
NC262	$3 on 5 (50c.) blue	15·00	10·00
NC263	$5 on 2 (20c.) brown	15·00	10·00
NC264	$5 on 5 (50c.) blue	£250	£150

(c) Surch as Type NC **70**.

NC265	$1 on $60 red	18·00	16·00
NC266	$5 on $80 purple	14·00	12·00
NC267	$6 on $2 brown	65·00	15·00
NC268	$6 on $40 brown	15·00	10·00
NC269	$6 on $80 purple	£325	£250

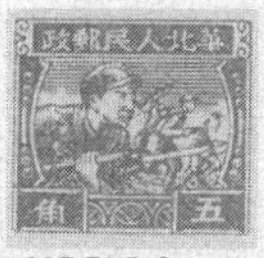
NC **71** Infantry

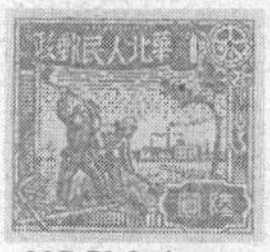
NC **72** Industry

1948. Imperf.

NC270	NC **71**	50c. purple	60	80
NC271		$1 blue	7·50	7·00
NC272		$2 green	1·00	1·50
NC273		$3 violet	30	1·10
NC274		$5 brown	90	1·25
NC275	NC **72**	$6 purple	50	1·00
NC276	NC **71**	$10 green	1·00	1·75
NC277		$12 red	2·00	1·50

The 50c. and $6 have value in Chinese characters only.

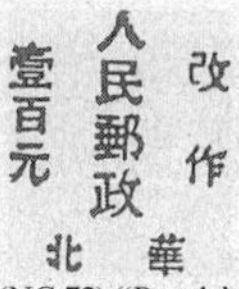
(NC **73**) "People's Postal Service North China"

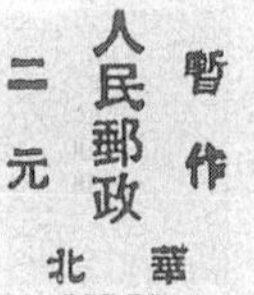
(NC **74**)

1949. Surch as Type NC **73**. (a) On stamp of Nationalist China.

NC278	$100* on $100 red	14·00	50

(b) On stamps of North Eastern Provinces.

NC279	**5**	50c. on 5c. red	60	3·50
NC280		$1 on 10c. orange	75	1·00
NC281		$2 on 20c. green	30·00	2·50
NC282		$3 on 50c. orange	30	3·00
NC283		$4 on $5 green	4·00	2·75
NC284		$6 on $10 red	60	1·00
NC285		$10 on $300 green	2·75	2·50
NC286		$12 on $1 blue	1·40	1·50
NC287		$18 on $3 brown	1·75	1·00
NC288		$20* on 50c. orange	1·25	75
NC290		$20 on $20 green	1·50	80
NC291		$30 on $2.50 blue	1·75	1·50
NC292		$40 on 25c. brown	2·00	1·50
NC293		$50 on $109 green	4·00	1·50
NC294		$80* on $1 blue	7·00	1·00
NC295		$100 on $65 green	8·00	1·75

1949. Surch as Type NC **74**. (a) On stamps of Nationalist China.

NC296	**107**	$100* on $100 red	25·00	7·50
NC297		$300* on $700 brown	8·00	2·50
NC298	**118**	$500* on $500 green	7·50	1·00
NC299		$3,000* on $3,000 blue	8·50	2·00

(b) On stamps of North Eastern Provinces.

NC300a	**5**	$1* on 25c. brown	25	1·00
NC301		$2 on 20c. green	1·75	1·25
NC302		$3 on 50c. orange	25	1·00
NC303		$4 on $5 green	1·90	1·75
NC305		$6 on $10 red	2·00	1·00
NC306		$10* on $300 green	9·00	2·25
NC307		$12 on $1 blue	95	70
NC308		$20* on 50c. orange	10·00	1·90
NC309		$20* on $20 green	5·00	60
NC310		$40* on 25c. brown	6·75	90
NC311		$50* on $109 green	10·00	1·00
NC312		$80* on $1 blue	7·50	1·00

*On these stamps the bottom character in the left-hand column of overprints is square in shape.

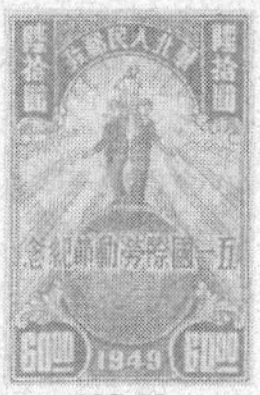
NC **75**

1949. Labour Day. Perf or imperf.

NC313	NC **75**	$20 red	2·00	1·75
NC314		$40 blue	2·00	1·75
NC315		$60 brown	2·00	2·25
NC316		$80 green	2·75	2·25
NC317		$100 violet	3·50	2·25

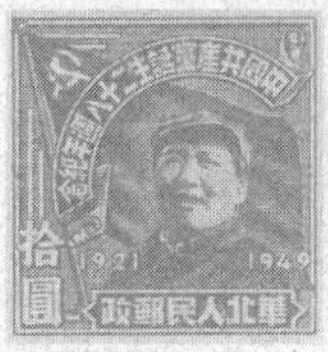
NC **79** Mao Tse-tung

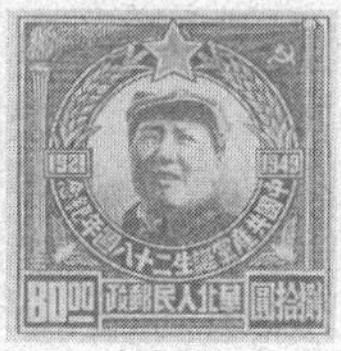
NC **80**

1949. 28th Anniv of Chinese Communist Party. Perf or imperf.

NC327A	NC **79**	$10 red	1·00	1·00
NC328A	NC **80**	$20 blue	50	75
NC329A	NC **79**	$50 orange	2·00	1·50
NC330A	NC **80**	$80 green	50	75
NC331A	NC **79**	$100 violet	2·50	1·50
NC332A	NC **80**	$120 green	50	1·00
NC333A	NC **79**	$140 purple	3·50	1·75

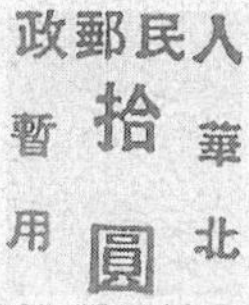
(NC **81**) ("People's Postal Service North China")

1949. Surch as Type NC **81**. (a) On stamp of Nationalist China.

NC334	**118**	$10 on $7,000 brown	15·00	7·50

(b) On stamps of North Eastern Provinces.

NC336	**5**	$10 on $10 red	5·00	1·25
NC337		$30 on 20c. green	4·00	1·50
NC338		$50 on $44 red	3·75	25
NC339		$100 on $3 brown	8·00	1·50
NC341		$200 on $4 brown	20·00	7·00

NC **83** Gate of Heavenly Peace, Peking

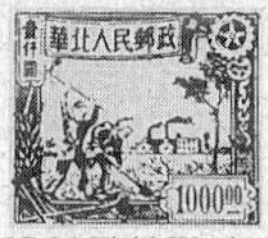
NC **84** Field Workers and Factory

1949.

NC349	NC **83**	$50 orange	2·50	6·50
NC350		$100 red	20	30
NC351		$200 green	1·00	35
NC352		$300 purple	5·00	70
NC353		$400 blue	5·00	70
NC354		$500 brown	7·00	60
NC355		$700 violet	3·00	2·50

1949.

NC356	NC **84**	$1,000 orange	4·00	60
NC357		$3,000 blue	20	90
NC358		$5,000 red	20	10
NC359		$10,000 brown	30	1·75

PARCELS POST STAMPS

Stamps of Nationalist China surch.

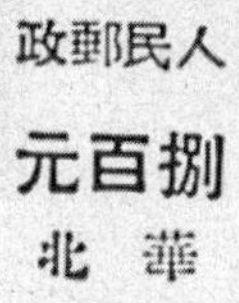
(NCP **76**)

1949. Surch as Type NCP **76**.

NCP318	P **112**	$300 on $6,000,000 grey	–	32·00
NCP319		$400 on $8,000,000 red	–	32·00
NCP320		$500 on $10,000,000 green	–	35·00
NCP321		$800 on $5,000,000 lilac	–	35·00
NCP322		$1 on $3,000,000 blue	–	40·00

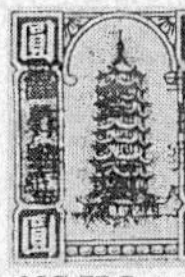
NC **77** Pagoda

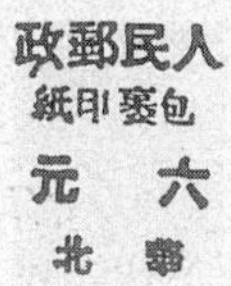
(NCP **78**)

1949. Money Order stamps. Type NC **77** surch as Type NCP **78**. No gum.

NCP323	$6 on $5 red	6·00	2·25
NCP324	$6 on $50 grey	6·00	2·25
NCP325	$50 on $20 purple	7·00	2·00
NCP326	$100 on $10 green	10·00	4·25

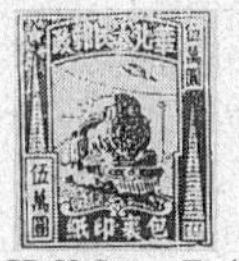
NCP **82** Steam Train

1949.

NCP342	NCP **82**	$500 red	2·00	4·50
NCP343		$1,000 blue	48·00	23·00
NCP344		$2,000 green	48·00	23·00
NCP345		$5,000 green	70·00	45·00
NCP346		$10,000 orange	£150	90·00
NCP347		$20,000 red	£250	£180
NCP348		$50,000 purple	£300	£350

C. Port Arthur and Dairen

The Soviet Union obtained facilities in these two ports by treaty in 1945. The Chinese Communists retained the civil administration, but a separate postal authority was established.

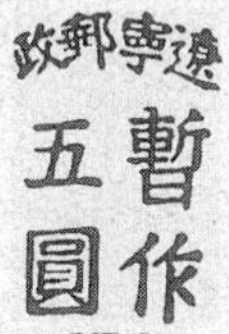
(NE **6**)

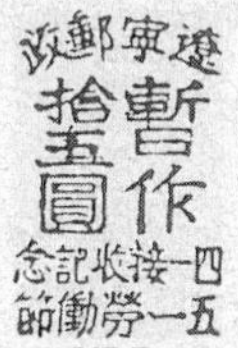
(NE **7**)

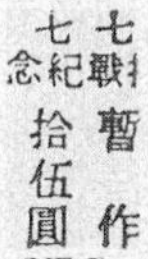
(NE **8**)

1946. Stamps of Japan handstamped "Liaoning Posts" and new value at Type NE **6**.

NE 8	20c. on 3s. green (No. 316)	6·00	8·00
NE 9	$1 on 17s. violet (No. 402)	6·00	7·00
NE11	$5 on 6s. red (No. 242)	7·00	12·00
NE12	$5 on 6s. orange (No. 319)	6·50	7·00
NE13	$15 on 40s. purple (No. 406)	32·00	30·00

1946. Transfer of Administration on 1 April and Labour Day. Stamps of Manchukuo handstamped as Type NE **7**.

NE14	**19**	$1 on 1f. red	5·00	5·00
NE15	–	$5 on 4f. green (No. 84)	7·00	9·00
NE16	**20**	$15 on 30f. brown	16·00	20·00

1946. 9th Anniv of Outbreak of War with Japan. Stamps of Manchukuo surch as Type NE **8**.

NE17	$1 on 6f. red (No. 86)	4·50	7·50
NE18	$5 on 2f. green (No. 82)	15·00	20·00
NE19	$15 on 12f. orange (No. 90)	25·00	30·00

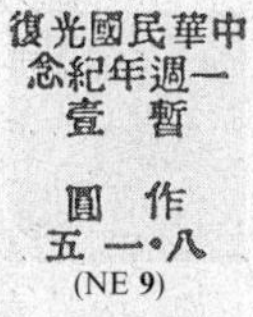
(NE **9**)

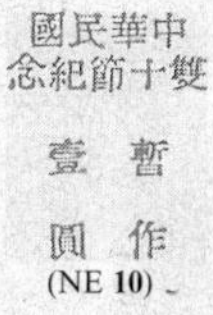
(NE **10**)

1946. 1st Anniv of Japanese Surrender. Stamps of Manchukuo surch as Type NE **9**.

NE20	–	$1 on 12f. orange (No. 90)	8·00	9·00
NE21	**19**	$5 on 1f. red	16·00	18·00
NE22	**13**	$15 on 5f. black	32·00	30·00

1946. 35th Anniv of Chinese Revolution. Stamps of Manchukuo surch as Type NE **10**.

NE23	$1 on 6f. red (No. 86)	7·00	8·00
NE24	$5 on 12f. orange (No. 90)	16·00	16·00
NE25	$15 on 2f. green (No. 82)	32·00	32·00

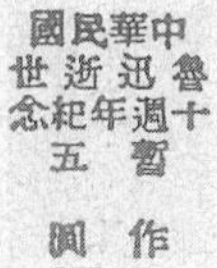
(NE **11**)

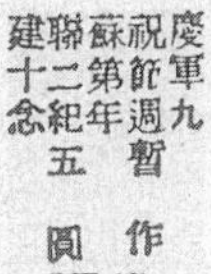
(NE **12**)

1946. 10th Death Anniv of Lu Xun (author). Stamps of Manchukuo surch as Type NE **11**.

NE26	**19**	$1 on 1f. red	18·00	15·00
NE27	–	$5 on 6f. red (No. 86)	25·00	30·00
NE28	–	$15 on 12f. orange (No. 90)	40·00	45·00

1947. 29th Anniv of Red Army. Stamps of Manchukuo surch as Type NE **12**.

NE29	–	$1 on 2f. green (No. 82)	20·00	20·00
NE30	–	$5 on 6f. red (No. 86)	35·00	35·00
NE31	**13**	$15 on 13f. brown	£110	£130

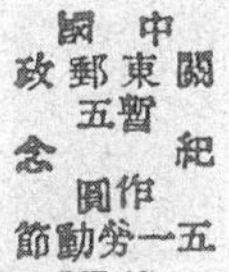
(NE **13**)

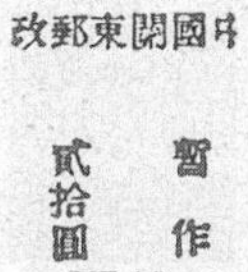
(NE **14**)

1947. Labour Day. Stamps of Manchukuo surch as Type NE **13**.

NE32	–	$1 on 2f. green (No. 82)	8·00	8·00
NE33	–	$5 on 6f. red (No. 86)	20·00	20·00
NE34	**20**	$15 on 30f. brown	40·00	45·00

1947. Stamps of Manchukuo surch. "Guandong Postal Service, China" and new value as Type NE **14**.

NE35	–	$5 on 2f. green (No. 82)	20·00	20·00
NE36	–	$15 on 4f. green (No. 84)	30·00	20·00
NE37	**20**	$20 on 30f. brown	38·00	38·00

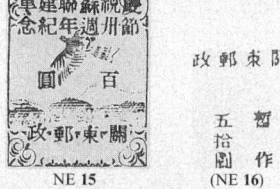

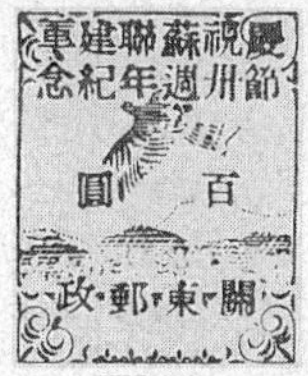
NE **15**

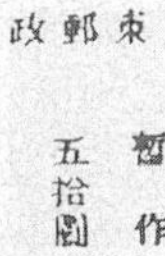
(NE **16**)

1948. 30th Anniv of Red Army. Surch as on Type NE **15**. (a) On stamps of Manchukuo.

NE39	$10 on 2f. green (No. 82)	70·00	50·00
NE40	$20 on 6f. red (No. 86)	90·00	75·00

(b) On label (Type NE **15**) commemorating 2,600th Anniv of Japanese Empire.

NE41	$100 on (no value) blue and brown	£400	£350

1948. Stamps of Manchukuo surch "Guangdong Postal Administration" and new value as Type NE **16**.

NE42	$20 on 2f. green (No. 82)	£100	£100
NE43	$50 on 4f. green (No. 84)	£200	£180
NE44	$100 on 20f. brown (No. 152)	£275	£225

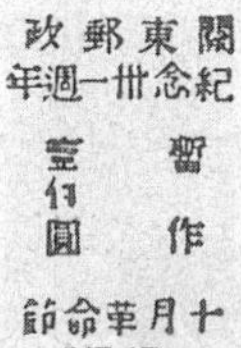
(NE **17**)

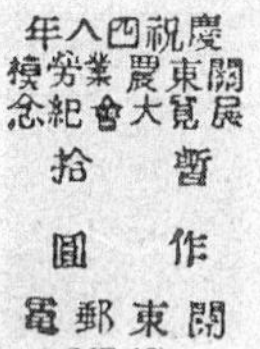
(NE **18**)

1948. 31st Anniv of Russian October Revolution. Stamps of Manchukuo surch as Type NE **17**.

NE45	**19**	$10 on 1f. red	£120	£120
NE46	–	$50 on 2f. green (No. 82)	£225	£225
NE47	–	$100 on 4f. green (No. 84)	£325	£325

1948. Guangdong Agricultural and Industrial Exhibition Stamps of Manchukuo surch as Type NE **18**.

NE48	$10 on 2f. green (No. 82)	£180	£150
NE49	$50 on 20f. brown (No. 95)	£750	£550

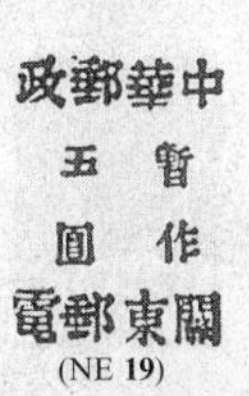
(NE **19**)

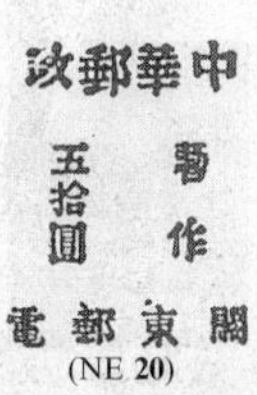
(NE **20**)

1948. Stamps of Japan and Manchukuo surch "Chinese Postal Administration: Guangdong Posts and Telegraphs" and new values. (a) No. 316 of Japan surch with Type NE 19.
NE50 $5 on 3s. green . . . . .   32·00   20·00

(b) Stamps of Manchukuo surch as Type NE 19.
NE51 $10 on 1f. red (No. 80) . .   75·00   50·00
NE52 $50 on 2f. green (No. 82)   £200   £130
NE53 $100 on 4f. green (No. 84)   £300   £225

(c) Stamps of Manchukuo surch as Type NE 20.
NE54 $10 on 2f. green (No. 82)   85·00   50·00
NE55 $50 on 1f. red (No. 80) . .   £100   70·00

NE 21 Peasant and Artisan    NE 23 Dalian Port

1949.
NE56   NE 21 $5 green . . . . .   2·00   8·00
NE57   — $10 orange . . . . .   25·00   25·00
NE58   NE 23 $50 red . . . . .   14·00   12·00
DESIGN—VERT: $10, "Transport".
For designs as Type NE 23 but with different character in bottom panel, see No. NE62.

NE 24 "Labour"    NE 25 Mao Tse-tung

1949. Labour Day.
NE59   NE 24 $10 red . . . . . .   15·00   18·00

1949. 28th Anniv of Chinese Communist Party.
NE61   NE 25 $50 red . . . . .   25·00   22·00

1949. Bottom panel inscr "Lushuan and Dalian Post and Telegraphic Administration".
NE62   NE 23 $50 red . . . . .   24·00   18·00

NE 27 Heroes' Monument, Dalian

1949. 4th Anniv of Victory over Japan and Opening of Dalian Industrial Fair.
NE63   NE 27 $10 red, blue & lt bl   32·00   35·00
NE64 $10 red, blue & green . . . . .   10·00   12·00

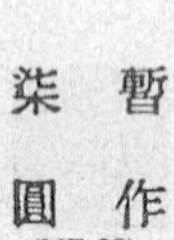

(NE 28) 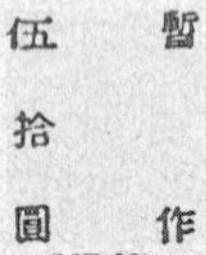   (NE 29)    (NE 30)

1949. Nos. NE56/7 surch as Types NE 28/30.
NE65   NE 28 $7 on $5 green . . .   13·00   10·00
NE66   NE 29 $50 on $5 green . .   38·00   35·00
NE67 $100 on $10 orange   £250   £250
NE68   NE 30 $500 on $5 green . .   £500
NE69   NE 29 $500 on $10 orge . .   £1000   £1100
NE70   NE 30 $500 on $10 orge . .   £450   £425

NE 31 Acclamation of Mao Tse-tung

1949. Founding of Chinese People's Republic.
NE71   NE 31 $35 red, yellow & bl   14·00   14·00

NE 32 Stalin and Lenin

1949. 32nd Anniv of Russian October Revolution.
NE72   NE 32 $10 green . . . . .   9·00   9·00

NE 33 Josef Stalin    NE 34 Gate of Heavenly Peace, Peking

1949. Stalin's 70th Birthday.
NE73   NE 33 $20 purple . . . . .   16·00   18·00
NE74 $35 green . . . . .   16·00   18·00

1950.
NE75   NE 34 $10 blue . . . . .   6·50   4·50
NE76 $20 green . . . . .   30·00   14·00
NE77 $35 red . . . . .   1·25   3·50
NE78 $50 lilac . . . . .   2·00   3·50
NE79 $100 mauve . . . .   1·25   9·50

All Soviet forces were withdrawn by 26 May 1955 and the stamps of the Chinese People's Republic are now in use.

D. North-East China People's Post

NE 48 Mao Tse-tung    NE 49 Mao Tse-tung

1946.
NE133   NE 48 $1 violet . . . . .   5·00   6·00
NE134   NE 49 $2 red . . . . .   1·75   2·75
NE135 $5 orange . . . .   2·25   2·75
NE136 $10 blue . . . . .   1·75   2·75

NE 50 Map of China with Communist Lion, Japanese Wolf and Chiang Kai-shek   NE 51 Railwaymen

1946. 10th Anniv of Seizure of Chiang Kai-shek at Xi'an.
NE137   NE 50 $1 violet   50   3·50
NE138 $2 orange   50   3·50
NE139 $5 brown . . . .   3·50   5·50
NE140 $10 green . . . .   10·00   8·00

1947. 24th Anniv of Massacre of Strikers at Zhengzhou Station.
NE141   NE 51 $1 red . . . . .   1·25   3·25
NE142 $2 green . . . .   1·50   3·25
NE143 $5 red . . . . .   1·50   3·25
NE144 $10 green . . . .   4·50   6·75

郵 東

政 北

NE 52 Women Cheering   (NE 53)

1947. International Women's Day.
NE145   NE 52 $5 red   50   3·50
NE146 $10 brown   50   3·50

1947. Optd with Type NE 53 ("North East Postal Service").
NE147   NE 53 $5 red . . . . .   5·00   4·50
NE148 $10 brown . . . .   5·00   4·50

NE 54 Children's Troop-comforts Unit   NE 55 Peasant and Workman

1947. Children's Day.
NE149   NE 54 $5 red . . . . . .   3·00   3·50
NE150 $10 green . . . .   3·00   3·75
NE151 $30 orange . . . .   4·00   4·75

1947. Labour Day.
NE152   NE 55 $10 red . . . . .   1·00   2·50
NE153 $30 blue . . . .   2·00   2·50
NE154 $50 green . . . .   2·75   2·50

伍 改
拾 作
圓 5000

NE 56 "Freedom"   (NE 57)

1947. 28th Anniv of Students' Rebellion, Peking University.
NE155   NE 56 $10 green . . . .   3·00   3·25
NE156 $30 brown . . . .   3·00   3·25
NE157 $50 violet . . . .   3·00   3·25

1947. Surch as Type NE 57.
NE158   NE 48 $50 on $1 violet   15·00   14·00
NE159   NE 49 $50 on $2 red . .   15·00   14·00
NE160b   NE 48 $100 on $1 violet   15·00   15·00
NE161   NE 49 $100 on $2 red . .   15·00   15·00

NE 58 Youths with Banner

1947. 22nd Anniv of Nanjing Road Incident, Shanghai.
NE162   NE 58 $2 red and mauve   1·50   2·50
NE163 $5 red and green   1·50   2·50
NE164 $10 red & yellow   2·00   2·50
NE165 $20 red & violet . .   2·00   2·50
NE166 $30 red & brown   3·00   3·00
NE167 $50 red and blue   5·00   3·50
NE168 $100 red & brown   7·50   5·00

NE 59 Mao Tse-tung

1947. 26th Anniv of Chinese Communist Party.
NE170   NE 59 $10 red . . . . .   5·00   6·50
NE171 $30 mauve . . . .   5·00   6·75
NE172 $50 purple . . . .   8·00   7·00
NE173 $100 green . . . .   12·00   9·00

NE 60 Hand grasping rifle   NE 61 Mountains and River

1947. 10th Anniv of Outbreak of War with Japan.
NE174   NE 60 $10 orange . . . .   5·00   5·50
NE175 $30 green . . . .   5·00   5·50
NE176 $50 blue . . . .   6·00   5·50
NE177 $100 brown . . . .   7·50   5·50

1947. 2nd Anniv of Japanese Surrender.
NE179   NE 61 $10 brown . . . .   7·50   8·00
NE180 $30 green . . . .   7·50   8·00
NE181 $50 green . . . .   5·00   8·00
NE182 $100 brown . . . .   12·00   8·00

拾 改
作
圓 1000

(NE 62)   NE 63 Map of Manchuria

1947. Surch as Type NE 62.
NE183   NE 48 $5 on $1 violet . . .   20·00   20·00
NE184   NE 49 $10 on $2 red . . .   20·00   20·00

1947. 16th Anniv of Japanese Attack on Manchuria.
NE185   NE 63 $10 green . . . .   6·00   7·50
NE186 $20 mauve . . . .   4·00   7·50
NE187 $30 brown . . . .   2·00   7·50
NE188 $50 red . . . . .   10·00   7·50

NE 64 Mao Tse-tung    NE 65 Offices of N.E. Political Council

1947.
NE189   NE 64 $1 purple . . . .   2·50   6·00
NE190 $5 green . . . .   3·00   6·00
NE191 $10 green . . . .   10·00   12·00
NE192 $15 violet . . . .   5·00   10·00
NE193 $20 red   40   3·50
NE194 $30 green   20   3·50
NE195 $50 brown . . . .   15·00   13·00
NE213 $50 green . . . .   1·00   3·00
NE196 $90 blue   75   10·00
NE197 $100 red   30   5·00
NE215 $150 red . . . .   2·00   4·50
NE214 $250 lilac   75   4·25
NE228 $300 green . . . .   32·00   32·00
NE198 $500 orange . . . .   10·00   6·50
NE229 $1,000 yellow . . .   60   7·50
For stamps as Type NE 64 but with "YUAN" in top right tablet, see Nos. NE236/40.

1947. 35th Anniv of Chinese Republic.
NE199   NE 65 $10 yellow . . . .   15·00   22·00
NE200 $20 red . . . . .   15·00   22·00
NE201 $100 brown . . . .   50·00   35·00

NE 66   NE 67 Tomb of Gen. Li Zhaolin

1947. 11th Anniv of Seizure of Chiang Kai-shek at Xi'an.
NE202   NE 66 $30 red . . . . .   5·00   10·00
NE203 $90 blue . . . .   6·50   12·00
NE204 $150 green . . . .   8·50   12·00

1948. 2nd Death Anniv of Gen. Li Zhaolin.
NE205   NE 67 $30 green . . . .   10·00   12·00
NE206 $150 lilac . . . .   10·00   12·00

NE 68 Flag and Globe   NE 69 Youth with Torch

1948. Labour Day.
NE207   NE 68 $50 red . . . . .   4·00   10·00
NE208 $150 green . . . .   4·00   10·00
NE209 $250 violet . . . .   1·00   20·00

1948. Youth Day.
NE210   NE 69 $50 green . . . .   10·00   10·00
NE211 $150 brown . . . .   10·00   10·00
NE212 $250 red . . . .   15·00   13·00

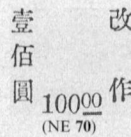 

壹 改
佰 作
圓 10000

(NE 70)   NE 71 Crane Operator

1948. Surch as Type NE 70.
NE217a   NE 64 $100 on $1 purple   18·00   18·00
NE218 $100 on $15 violet   15·00   15·00
NE219 $300 on $5 green   20·00   20·00
NE220 $300 on $30 green   7·50   12·00
NE221 $300 on $90 blue   7·50   12·00
NE230   NE 49 $500 on $2 red . .   6·00   7·50
NE222   NE 64 $500 on $50 green   8·50   13·00
NE231   NE 49 $1,500 on $5 orge   6·00   7·50
NE223   NE 64 $1,500 on $150 red . . . . .   7·50   15·00
NE232   NE 49 $2,500 on $10 blue   6·00   15·00
NE224   NE 64 $2,500 on $300 grn . . . .   7·50   15·00

1948. All-China Labour Conference.
NE225   NE 71 $100 red & pink . .   50   2·50
NE226 $300 brown & yell   3·00   4·50
NE227 $500 blue & green   1·25   4·50

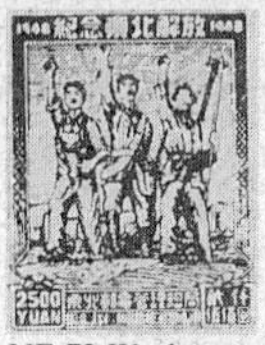

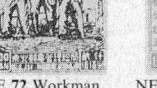

NE 72 Workman, Soldier and Peasant

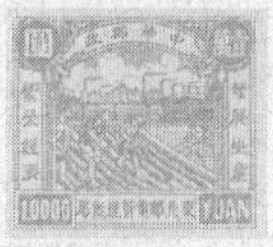

NE 74 "Production in Field and Industry"

1948. Liberation of the North East.

NE233	NE 72	$500 red	5·00	5·50
NE234		$1,500 green	7·00	7·50
NE235		$2,500 brown	11·00	10·00

1949. As Type NE **64** but "YUAN" at top right.

NE236		$300 green	1·50	3·50
NE237		$500 orange	2·00	2·50
NE238		$1,500 green	20	2·50
NE239		$4,500 brown	20	2·75
NE240		$6,500 blue	20	3·25

1949.

NE241	NE 74	$5,000 blue	3·75	5·50
NE242		$10,000 orange	20	4·25
NE243		$50,000 green	20	5·00
NE244		$100,000 violet	20	11·00

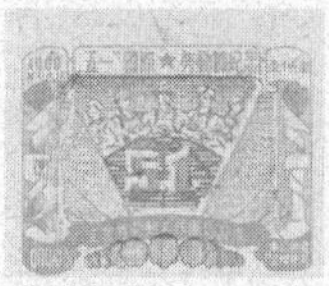

NE 75 Workers and Banners

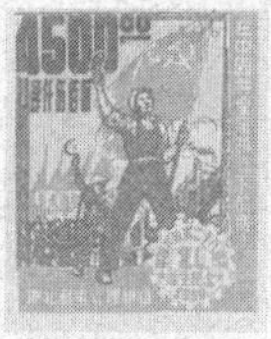

NE 76 Workers' Procession

1949. Labour Day.

NE245	NE 75	$1,000 red and blue	30	1·50
NE246		$1,500 red and blue	30	1·50
NE247		$4,500 red & brown	30	1·50
NE248		$6,500 brown & grn	30	1·50
NE249		$10,000 purple & bl	1·00	1·50

1949. 28th Anniv of Chinese Communist Party.

NE250	NE 76	$1,500 red, vio & bl	30	1·50
NE251		$4,500 red, brn & bl	40	1·50
NE252		$6,500 red, pink & bl	1·25	1·50

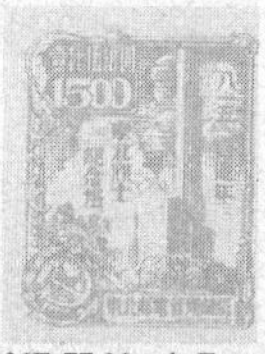

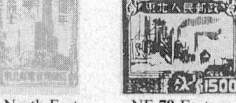

NE 77 North-East Heroes, Monument

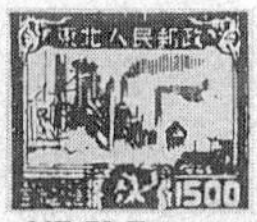

NE 78 Factory

1949. 4th Anniv of Japanese Surrender.

NE253	NE 77	$1,500 red	20	1·50
NE254		$4,500 green	75	1·50
NE255		$6,500 blue	85	1·50

REPRINTS. The note above No. 1401 of China also refers here to Nos. NE257/60, 261/3, 271/4, 286/89 and 312/4.

1949.

NE256	NE 78	$1,500 red	35	1·75

1949. 1st Session of Chinese People's Political Conference. As T **181** of People's Republic but with additional inscr.

NE257		$1,000 blue	5·00	7·50
NE258		$1,500 red	5·00	7·50
NE259		$3,000 green	5·00	7·50
NE260		$4,500 purple	5·00	8·50

1949. World Federation of Trade Unions, Asiatic and Australasian Conference, Peking. As T **182** of People's Republic but with additional inscr.

NE261		$5,000 red	60·00	40·00
NE262		$20,000 green	60·00	40·00
NE263		$35,000 blue	£100	50·00

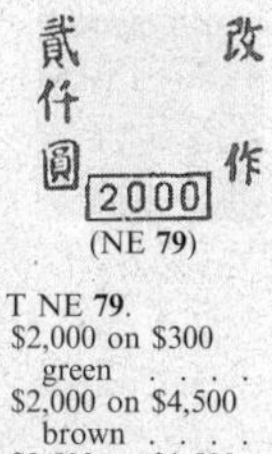

貳仟圓
改作
2000

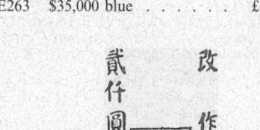

(NE 79)

1949. Surch as T NE **79**.

NE264	NE 64	$2,000 on $300 green	5·00	6·50
NE265		$2,000 on $4,500 brown	32·00	28·00
NE266		$2,500 on $1,500 green	30	5·00
NE267		$2,500 on $6,500 blue	16·00	15·00
NE268	NE 78	$5,000 on $1,500 red	75	2·50
NE269	NE 64	$20,000 on $4,500 brown	20	3·50
NE270		$35,000 on $300 green	20	3·50

1950. Chinese People's Political Conference. As T **183/4** of People's Republic but with additional inscr.

NE271		$1,000 red	7·50	8·00
NE272		$1,500 blue	7·50	8·00
NE273		$5,000 purple	8·50	8·00
NE274		$20,000 green	10·00	8·00

1950. As T **185** of People's Republic but with additional four-character inscr.

NE303	185	$250 brown	10	5·00
NE275		$500 green	10	2·00
NE276		$1,000 orange	10	1·25
NE277		$1,000 mauve	10	2·00
NE306		$2,000 green	10	2·00
NE307		$2,500 yellow	20	2·00
NE300		$5,000 orange	1·50	1·25
NE309		$10,000 brown	30	2·00
NE310		$12,500 purple	50	6·00
NE283		$20,000 purple	40	2·00
NE301		$30,000 red	2·50	4·50
NE284		$35,000 blue	60	4·50
NE285		$50,000 green	2·50	4·50
NE302		$100,000 violet	1·00	4·50

1950. Foundation of People's Republic. Additional inscr at left.

NE286	188	$5,000 red, yell & grn	40·00	40·00
NE287		$10,000 red, yell & brn	40·00	40·00
NE288		$20,000 red, yell & pur	50·00	40·00
NE289		$30,000 red, yell & bl	60·00	55·00

1950. Peace Campaign. Additional characters below olive branch.

NE290	191	$2,500 brown	10·00	10·00
NE291		$5,000 green	10·00	10·00
NE292		$20,000 blue	12·00	12·00

1950. 1st Anniv of People's Republic. Additional characters at left. Flag in red, yellow and brown.

NE293	193	$1,000 violet	26·00	30·00
NE294		$2,500 brown	28·00	30·00
NE295		$5,000 green (44 × 53 mm)	40·00	30·00
NE296		$10,000 green	50·00	35·00
NE297		$20,000 blue	60·00	40·00

1950. 1st All-China Postal Conference. Additional characters at left.

NE298	194	$2,500 brown & green	5·00	5·00
NE299		$5,000 green and red	5·00	5·00

1950. Sino-Soviet Treaty. Additional characters in top right-hand coner.

NE312	195	$2,500 red	8·00	8·00
NE313		$5,000 green	8·00	8·00
NE314		$20,000 blue	12·00	12·00

PARCELS POST STAMPS

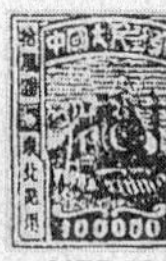

NEP 82

1951.

NEP315	NEP 82	$1,000,000 violet	40·00
NEP316		$300,000 purple	£100
NEP317		$500,000 green	£170
NEP318		$1,000,000 red	£300

E. North-West China People's Post

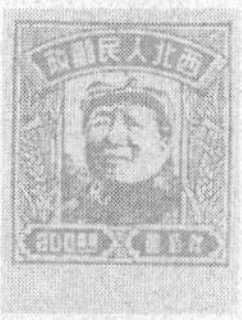

NW 25 Mao Tse-tung

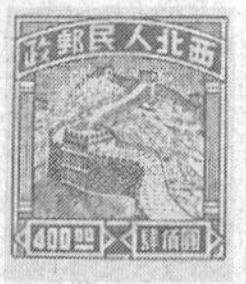

NW 26 Great Wall

1949. Imperf.

NW 97	NW 25	$50 pink	2·50	3·25
NW 98	NW 26	$100 blue	20	50
NW 99	NW 25	$200 orange	4·00	3·75
NW100	NW 26	$400 brown	3·00	2·00

F. South-West China People's Post

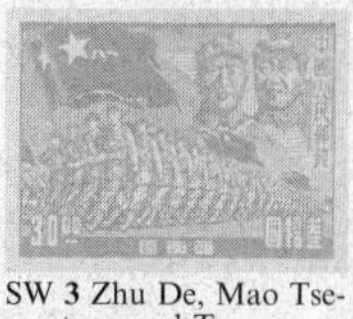

SW 3 Zhu De, Mao Tse-tung and Troops

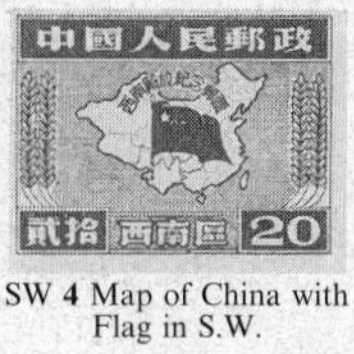

SW 4 Map of China with Flag in S.W.

1949.

SW 9	SW 3	$10 blue	5·00	3·50
SW10		$20 purple	20	2·25
SW11		$30 orange	20	1·00
SW12		$50 green	50	75
SW13		$100 red	25	60
SW14		$200 blue	1·75	75
SW15		$300 violet	5·00	1·25
SW16		$500 grey	7·50	3·25
SW17		$1,000 purple	10·00	6·00
SW18		$2,000 green	18·00	15·00
SW19		$5,000 orange	20·00	20·00

For other values in this design see East China, Nos. EC378/82.

1950. Liberation of the South West.

SW20	SW 4	$20 blue	25	1·00
SW21		$30 green	1·60	2·25
SW22		$50 red	35	1·25
SW23		$100 brown	75	1·25

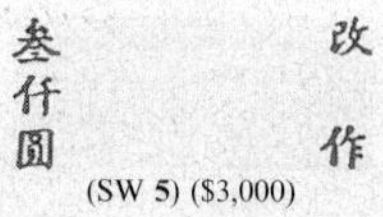

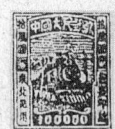

叁仟圓
改作

(SW 5) ($3,000)

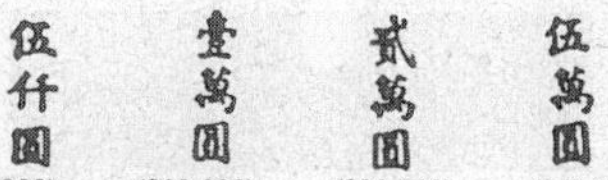

伍仟圓
壹萬圓
貳萬圓
伍萬圓

($5,000) ($10,000) ($20,000) ($50,000)

1950. Surch as Type SW **5** (characters in left-hand column of surcharge differ as indicated in illustrations and footnote).

SW24	SW 4	$60 on $30 green	15·00	12·00
SW25		$150 on $30 green	14·00	10·00
SW26		$300 on $20 blue	1·25	2·25
SW27		$300 on $100 brown	15·00	6·00
SW28		$1,500 on $100 brown	15·00	10·00
SW29		$3,000 on $50 red	8·50	7·00
SW30		$5,000 on $50 red	4·00	5·50
SW31		$10,000 on $50 red	40·00	20·00
SW32		$20,000 on $50 red	5·00	20·00
SW33		$50,000 on $50 red	4·00	40·00

Nos. SW24 and SW26/7 have three characters in left-hand column; Nos. SW25 and SW28 have five.

G. Chinese People's Republic

1949. Yuans.
1955. 100 fen = 1 yuan.

GUM or NO GUM. Nos. 1401/1891 were issued without gum (except Nos. 1843/5 and 1850/7). From No. 1892 onwards all postage stamps were issued with gum, unless otherwise stated. From 1965 some issues seem to have no gum, though in fact they bear an adhesive substance.

SERIAL MARKINGS. Issues other than definitive issues are divided into two categories: "commemorative" and "special". Figures below the design of each stamp of such issues indicate: (a) serial number of the issue; (b) number of stamps in the issue; (c) number of stamps within the issue; and (d) year of issue (from No. 1557 on). Neither chronological order of issue nor sequence of value is always strictly followed. From No. 2343 these serial markings were omitted until No. 2433.

REPRINTS were later made in replacement of exhausted stocks by the Chinese Postal Administration for sale to stamp collectors and were not available for postal purposes. Nos. 1401/11, 1432/5, 1456/8, 1464/73, 1507/9, 1524/37 and 1543/52.

Our prices are for originals. For notes describing the distinguishing features of the reprints, see Stanley Gibbons Part 17 (China) Catalogue.

For other values in the following types see North East China.

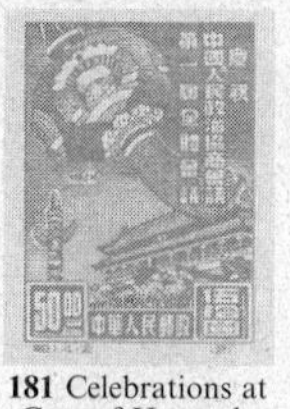

181 Celebrations at Gate of Heavenly Peace, Peking

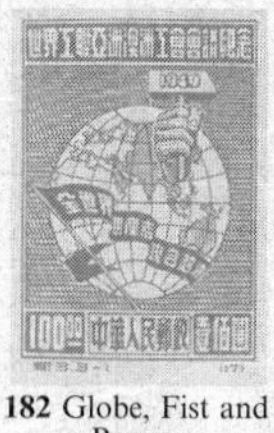

182 Globe, Fist and Banner

1949. Celebration of First Session of Chinese People's Political Conference.

1401	181	$30 blue	1·75	1·50
1402		$50 red	1·90	1·50
1403		$100 green	1·90	1·50
1404		$200 purple	2·00	1·50

1949. World Federation of Trade Unions. Asiatic and Australasian Congress, Peking.

1405	182	$100 red	4·50	3·50
1406		$300 green	4·50	2·50
1407		$500 blue	4·50	3·50

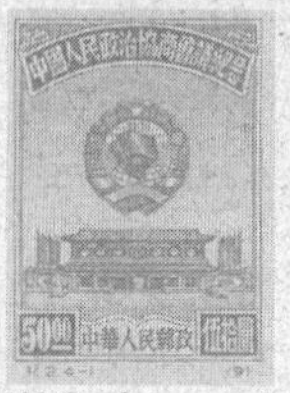

183 Conference Hall

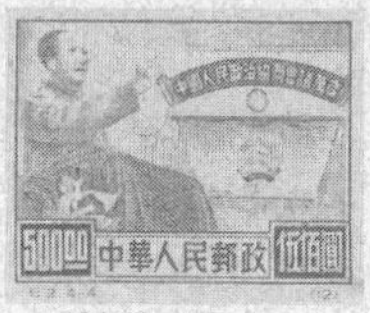

184 Mao Tse-tung

1950. Chinese People's Political Conference.

1408	183	$50 red	3·50	2·50
1409		$100 blue	3·50	2·50
1410	184	$300 purple	3·50	2·50
1411		$500 green	3·50	2·50

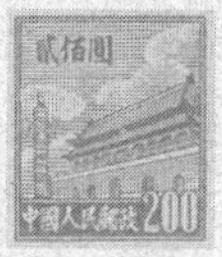

185 Gate of Heavenly Peace, Peking

1950.

1412	185	$200 green	8·00	50
1413		$300 lake	20	80
1414		$500 red	20	20
1415		$800 orange	60·00	30
1420a		$1,000 lilac	1·00	20
1417		$2,000 olive	7·00	15
1420b		$3,000 brown	1·00	40
1418		$5,000 pink	10	60
1419		$8,000 blue	10	12·00
1420c		$10,000 brown	1·00	30

See also Nos. 1481a/7 and 1493/8.

中國人民郵政
壹佰圓
100

(186)

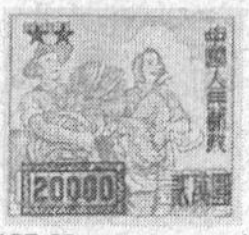

187 Harvesters and Ox

1950. Surch as T **186**. Perf or roul.

1427	148	$100 on (–) mauve	40	1·25
1428	149	$200 on (–) red	1·75	1·00
1429	147	$300 on (–) green	15	1·50
1424	146	$500 on (–) orange	30	15
1430		$800 on (–) orange	3·25	30
1426		$1,000 on (–) orange	20	20

1950. Unissued stamp of East China surch.

1431	187	$20,000 on $10,000 red	£400	32·00

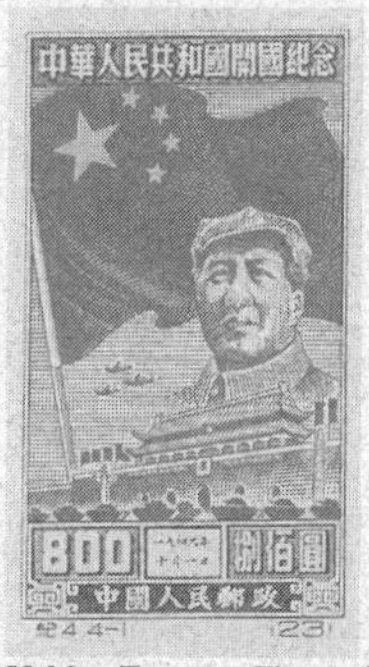

188 Mao Tse-tung, Flag and Parade

1950. Foundation of People's Republic on 1 October 1949.

1432	188	$800 red, yellow & green	25·00	7·75
1433		$1,000 red, yellow & brn	25·00	7·75
1434		$2,000 red, yellow & pur	30·00	7·25
1435		$3,000 red, yellow & blue	30·00	9·25

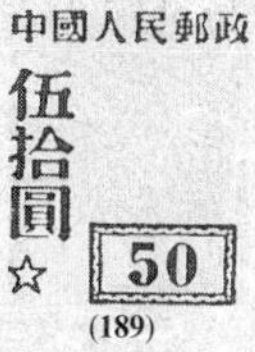

中國人民郵政
伍拾圓
☆
50

(189)

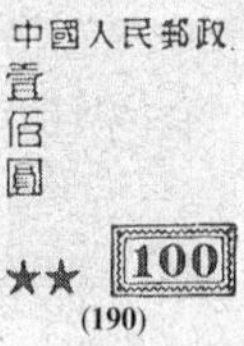

中國人民郵政
壹佰圓
★★
100

(190)

1950. Stamps of North Eastern Provinces surch as T **189**.

1436	5	$50 on 20c. green	4·00	5·00
1437		$50 on 25c. brown	2·25	3·00
1438		$50 on 50c. orange	50	50
1439		$100 on $2.50 blue	50	50
1440		$100 on $3 brown	3·25	3·00
1441		$100 on $4 brown	3·25	5·00
1442		$100 on $5 green	3·25	2·75
1443		$100 on $10 red	11·50	7·50
1444		$400 on $20 green	70·00	32·00
1445		$400 on $44 red	2·00	3·00
1446		$400 on $65 green	£110	60·00
1447		$400 on $100 green	30·00	7·50

1448	$400 on $200 brown	60·00	14·00
1449	$400 on $300 green	60·00	15·00

1950. Nos. 1344/7 and unissued values of Nationalist China (Whistling Swans) surch as T **190.**

1450	**169**	$50 on 10c. blue	10	50
1451		$100 on 16c. green	10	35
1452		$100 on 50c. green	20	20
1453		$200 on $1 orange	20	20
1453a		$200 on $2 blue	6·00	50
1454		$400 on $5 red	20	30
1455		$400 on $10 green	40	65
1455a		$400 on $20 purple	50	95

Nos. 1451/2 are imperf.

191 "Peace" (after Picasso)   **192** Gate of Heavenly Peace, Peking

1950. Peace Campaign (1st issue).

1456	**191**	$400 brown	12·00	4·50
1457		$800 green	12·00	4·50
1458		$2,000 blue	12·00	5·00

See also Nos. 1510/12 and 1590/2.

1950. Clouds redrawn.

1481a	**192**	$100 blue	20	20
1482		$200 green	7·50	1·25
1483		$300 lake	20	80
1483a		$400 green	7·50	20
1484		$500 red	30	20
1462		$800 orange	12·00	10
1485a		$1,000 violet	30	25
1463		$2,000 olive	4·00	30
1486a		$3,000 brown	40	1·00
1487		$5,000 pink	40	1·25

193 Flag of People's Republic   **194** "Communications"

1950. 1st Anniv of People's Republic. Flag in red, yellow and brown.

1464	**193**	$100 violet	15·00	4·00
1465		$400 brown	15·00	4·00
1466		$800 green (44 × 53 mm)	15·00	4·00
1467		$1,000 olive	20·00	8·00
1468		$2,000 blue	35·00	10·00

1950. 1st All-China Postal Conference.

1469	**194**	$400 brown and green	7·25	3·50
1470		$800 green and red	7·25	1·75

195 Stalin greets Mao Tse-tung

1950. Sino-Soviet Treaty.

1471	**195**	$400 red	8·00	6·00
1472		$800 green	10·00	2·75
1473		$2,000 blue	14·00	5·00

中國人民郵政 壹佰圓 ★★ (100) (196)   中國人民郵政 肆佰圓 (400) (197)

1950. Nos. EC364/5a, EC367 and EC370/1 of East China People's Post surch as T **196.**

1474	$50 on $10 blue	15	40
1475	$100 on $15 red	10	25
1476	$300 on $50 red	10	25
1477	$400 on $1,600 purple	2·75	1·25
1478	$400 on $2,000 lilac	1·00	70

1950. Stamps of East China surch as T **197.**

1479	EC 112	$50 on $10 blue	10	45
1480	$400 on $15 red	10	35
1481	$400 on $2,000 green	2·50	50

198 Temple of Heaven and Ilyushin Il-18

1951. Air.

1488	**198**	$1,000 red	35	1·00
1489		$3,000 green	40	75
1490		$5,000 orange	80	75
1491		$10,000 green and purple	1·60	1·40
1492		$30,000 brn and blue	3·50	3·50

1951. Pink network background.

1493	**185**	$10,000 brown	75	75
1494		$20,000 olive	1·40	2·25
1495		$30,000 green	60·00	35·00
1496		$50,000 violet	60·00	22·00
1497		$100,000 red	£3000	£120
1498		$200,000 blue	£2500	£200

中國人民郵政 貳拾伍圓 25 (200)   **201** Mao Tse-tung

1951. Surch as T **200.** Perf or roul.

1503	**148**	$5 on (–) mauve	3·25	1·00
1500	**147**	$10 on (–) green	25	75
1501	**149**	$15 on (–) red	20	75
1506	**146**	$25 on (–) orange	70	75

1951. 30th Anniv of Chinese Communist Party.

1507	**201**	$400 brown	3·75	2·50
1508		$500 green	4·25	2·50
1509		$800 red	5·00	1·50

202 Dove of Peace, after Picasso

1951. Peace Campaign (2nd issue).

1510	**202**	$400 brown	10·00	4·00
1511		$800 green	10·00	2·50
1512		$1,000 violet	10·00	2·75

伍拾圓 50 (203)   中國人民郵政 100 圓 **204** National Emblem

1951. Money Order stamps as North China, Type NC 77, surch with T **203.** Perf or roul.

1513	$50 on $2 green	75	2·00
1515	$50 on $5 orange	30	70
1517	$50 on $50 grey	20	15

1951. National Emblem Issue. Yellow network background.

1519	**204**	$100 blue	4·00	2·25
1520		$200 brown	4·00	2·40
1521		$400 orange	5·00	1·60
1522		$500 green	5·25	1·60
1523		$800 red	5·25	1·60

205 Lu Hsun

1951. 15th Death Anniv of Lu Hsun (author).

1524	**205**	$400 violet	3·50	2·00
1525		$800 green	3·50	1·00

206 Rebels at Chintien

1951. Centenary of Taiping Rebellion.

1526	**206**	$400 green	5·50	3·25
1527		$800 red	5·50	2·50
1528		– $800 orange	5·50	2·50
1529		– $1,000 blue	5·50	2·75

DESIGN: Nos. 1528/9, Coin and Documents of Taiping "Heavenly Kingdom of Great Peace".

207 Peasants and Tractor

1952. Agrarian Reform.

1530	**207**	$100 red	4·00	2·25
1531		$200 blue	4·00	2·25
1532		$400 brown	4·50	2·00
1533		$800 green	4·50	1·25

208 The Potala, Lhasa   **209** "Child Protection"

1952. Liberation of Tibet.

1534	**208**	$400 red	5·50	1·60
1535		– $800 green	5·50	1·60
1536	**208**	$800 red	5·50	1·60
1537		– $1,000 violet	5·50	1·60

DESIGN: Nos. 1535, 1537 Tibetan ploughing with yaks.

1952. Int Child Protection Conference, Vienna.

1538	**209**	$400 green	60	10
1539		$800 blue	60	10

210 Hammer and Sickle   **211** Gymnast

1952. Labour Day. Dated "1952".

1540	**210**	$800 red	20	10
1541		$800 green	20	10
1542		$800 brown	20	10

DESIGNS: No. 1541, Hand and dove; No. 1542, Hammer, dove and ear of corn.

1952. Gymnastics by Radio. As T **211.**

1543	$400 red (14–17)	3·00	1·00
1544	$400 deep blue (18–21)	3·00	1·00
1545	$400 purple (22–25)	3·00	1·00
1546	$400 green (26–29)	3·00	1·00
1547	$400 red (30–33)	3·00	1·00
1548	$400 blue (34–37)	3·00	1·00
1549	$400 orange (38–41)	3·00	1·00
1550	$400 violet (42–45)	3·00	1·00
1551	$400 bistre (46–49)	3·00	1·00
1552	$400 pale blue (50–53)	3·00	1·00

DESIGNS: Various gymnastic exercises, the stamps in each colour being arranged in blocks of four throughout the sheet, each block showing four stages of the exercise depicted. Where two stages are the same, the stamps differ only in the serial number in brackets, in the right-hand corner of the bottom margin of the stamp. The serial numbers are shown above after the colours of the stamps.

Prices are for single stamps.

212 "A Winter Hunt" (A.D. 386–580)

1952. "Glorious Mother Country" (1st issue). Tun Huang Mural Paintings.

1553	**212**	$800 sepia	50	30
1554		$800 brown	50	30
1555		$800 slate	50	30
1556		$800 purple	50	30

PAINTINGS: No. 1554, "Benefactor" (A.D. 581–617). No. 1555, "Celestial Flight" (A.D. 618–906). No. 1556, "Tiger" (A.D. 618–906).

See also Nos. 1565/8, 1593/96, 1601/4 and 1628/31.

213 Marco Polo Bridge, Lukouchiao

1952. 15th Anniv of War with Japan.

1557	**213**	$800 blue	75	30
1558		$800 green	75	30
1559		$800 plum	75	30
1560		$800 brown	75	30

DESIGNS (dated "1937–1952"): No. 1558, Victory at Pinghsingkwan; No. 1559, Departure of New Fourth Army from Central China; No. 1560, Mao Tse-tung and Chu The.

214 Airman, Sailor and Soldier   **217** Dove of Peace over Pacific Ocean

216 Huai River Barrage

1952. 25th Anniv of People's Liberation Army.

1561	**214**	$800 red	30	25
1562		– $800 green	30	25
1563		– $800 violet	50	30
1564		– $800 brown	50	30

DESIGNS—HORIZ: No. 1562, Soldier, tanks and guns; 1563, Sailor and destroyers; 1564, Pilot, Ilyushin Il-4 DB-3 bomber and Mikoyan Gurevich MiG-15 jet fighters.

1952. "Glorious Mother Country" (2nd issue).

1565	**216**	$800 violet	25	10
1566		– $800 red	25	10
1567		– $800 purple	30	10
1568		– $800 green	30	10

DESIGNS: No. 1566, Chungking-Chengtu railway viaduct; 1567, Oil refinery; 1568, Tractor, disc harrows and combine drill.

1952. Asia and Pacific Ocean Peace Conference.

1569	**217**	$400 purple	50	25
1570		– $800 orange	50	25
1571	**217**	$800 red	60	30
1572		– $2,500 green	60	30

DESIGNS—HORIZ: Nos. 1570 and 1572, Doves and globe.

218 Peasants collecting food for the Front

1952. 2nd Anniv of Chinese Volunteer Force in Korea.

1573		$800 blue	50	25
1574	**218**	$800 red	50	25
1575		– $800 violet	50	30
1576		– $800 brown	60	30

DESIGNS (dated "1950–1952"): HORIZ: No. 1573, Marching troops. No. 1575, Infantry attack. No. 1576, Meeting of Chinese and North Korean soldiers.

220 Textile Worker

1953. International Women's Day.

1578	**220**	$800 red	30	25
1579		– $800 green	30	25

DESIGN: No. 1579, Woman harvesting grain.

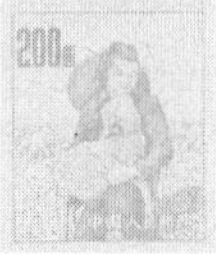
221 Shepherdess

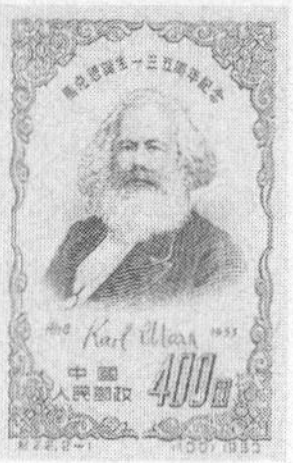
222 Karl Marx

1953.

1580	–	$50 purple	70	15
1581	221	$200 green	1·40	35
1582	–	$250 blue	5·00	2·00
1583	–	$800 turquoise	75	10
1584	–	$1,600 grey	70	25
1585	–	$2,000 orange	2·25	10

DESIGNS: $50, Mill girl; $250, Carved lion; $800, Lathe-operator; $1,600, Miners; $2, Old Palace, Peking.

1953. 135th Birth Anniv of Karl Marx.

1586	222	$400 brown	70	25
1587		$800 green	70	25

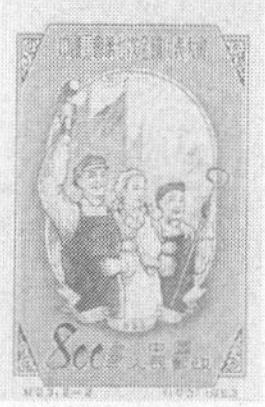
223 Workers and Flags

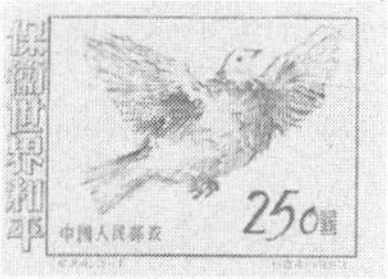
224 Dove of Peace

1953. 7th National Labour Union Conference.

1588	223	$400 blue	25	20
1589		$800 red	25	20

1953. Peace Campaign (3rd issue).

1590	224	$250 green	50	30
1591		$400 brown	50	30
1592		$800 violet	60	30

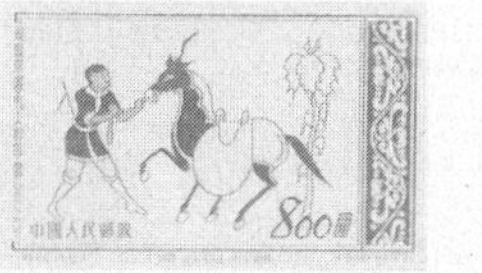
225 Horseman and Steed (A.D. 386–580)

1953. "Glorious Mother Country" (3rd issue).

1593	225	$800 green	50	10
1594	–	$800 orange	50	10
1595	–	$800 blue	50	10
1596	–	$800 red	50	10

PAINTINGS: No. 1594, Court players (A.D. 386–580). No. 1595, Battle scene (A.D. 581–617). No. 1596, Ox-drawn palanquin (A.D. 618–906).

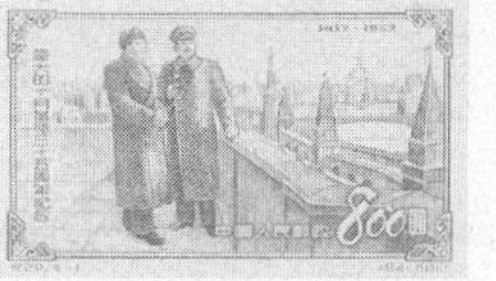
226 Mao Tse-tung and Stalin at Kremlin

1953. 35th Anniv of Russian Revolution.

1597	226	$800 green	25	10
1598	–	$800 red	25	10
1599	–	$800 blue	75	10
1600	–	$800 brown	75	10

DESIGNS—HORIZ: No. 1598, Lenin addressing revolutionaries. VERT: No. 1599, Statue of Stalin; No. 1600, Stalin making speech.

227 Compass (300 B.C.)

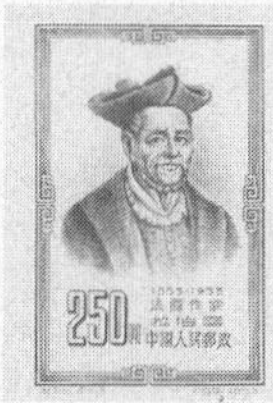
228 Rabelais (writer)

1953. "Glorious Mother Country" (4th issue). Scientific instruments.

1601	227	$800 black	25	10
1602	–	$800 green	25	10
1603	–	$800 slate	30	10
1604	–	$800 brown	30	10

DESIGNS: No. 1602, Seismoscope (A.D. 132); 1603, Drum cart for measuring distances (A.D. 300); 1604, Armillary sphere (A.D. 1437).

1953. Famous Men.

1605	228	$250 green	40	25
1606	–	$400 purple	40	25
1607	–	$800 blue	40	30
1608	–	$2,200 brown	40	30

PORTRAITS: $400, Jose Marti (Cuban revolutionary). $800, Chu Yuan (poet). $2,200, Copernicus (astronomer).

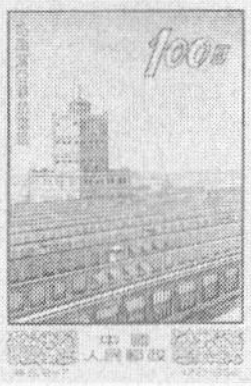
229 Flax Mill, Harbin

1954. Industrial Development.

1609	229	$100 brown	25	15
1610	–	$200 green	30	15
1611	–	$250 violet	25	15
1612	–	$400 sepia	25	15
1613	–	$800 purple	25	15
1614	–	$800 blue	25	15
1615	–	$2,000 red	25	15
1616	–	$3,200 brown	25	15

DESIGNS: No. 1610, Tangku Harbour; 1611, Tienshui–Lanchow Railway; 1612, Heavy machine works; 1613, Blast furnace; 1614, Open-cast mines, Fuhsin; 1615, North-East Electric power station; 1616, Geological survey team.

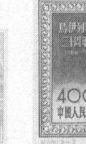

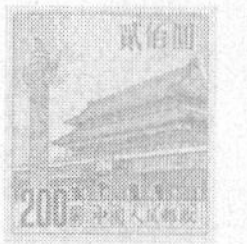
230 Gate of Heavenly Peace, Peking

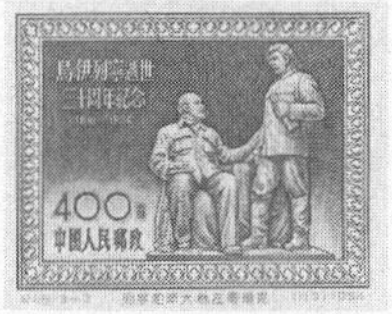
231 Statue of Lenin and Stalin at Gorki

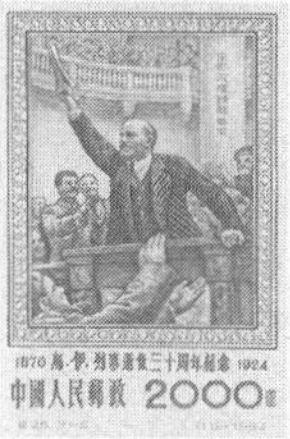
232 Lenin Speaking

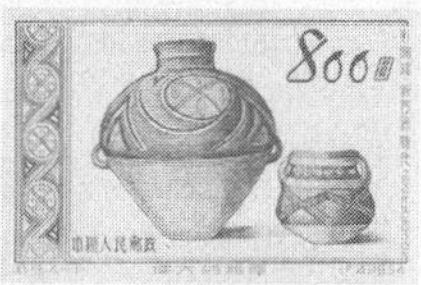
233 Painted Pottery (c. 2000 B.C.)

1954.

1617	230	$50 red	10	10
1618		$100 blue	10	10
1619		$200 green	10	10
1620		$250 blue	2·25	50
1621		$400 green	45	10
1622		$800 orange	10	10
1623		$1,600 grey	10	10
1624		$2,000 olive	10	10

1954. 30th Death Anniv of Lenin.

1625	231	$400 green	90	45
1626	–	$800 brown	1·75	40
1627	232	$2,000 red	90	30

DESIGN: (25 × 37 mm) $800, Lenin (full-face portrait).

1954. "Glorious Mother Country" (5th issue).

1628	233	$800 brown	25	20
1629	–	$800 black	25	20
1630	–	$800 turquoise	30	20
1631	–	$800 lake	30	20

DESIGNS—As Type 233: No. 1629, Musical stone (1200 B.C.); 1630, Bronze basin (816 B.C.); 1631, Lacquered wine cup and cosmetic tray (403–221 B.C.).

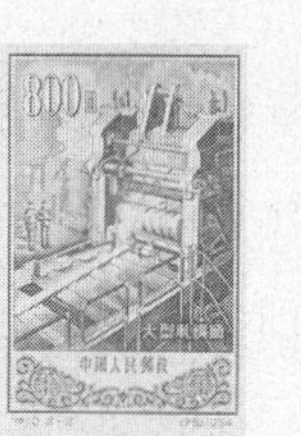
234 Heavy Rolling Mill

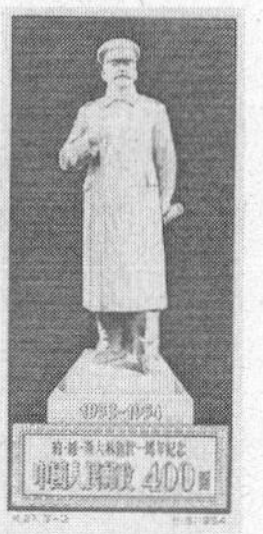
235 Statue of Stalin

1954. Anshan Steel Works.

1632	–	$400 turquoise	55	25
1633	234	$800 purple	55	25

DESIGN: $400, Seamless steel-tubing mill.

1954. 1st Death Anniv of Stalin.

1634	235	$400 black	1·60	30
1635	–	$800 sepia	75	30
1636	–	$2,000 red	1·10	45

DESIGNS—VERT: $800, Full-face portrait of Stalin (26 × 37 mm). HORIZ: $2, Stalin and hydro-electric station (42½ × 25 mm).

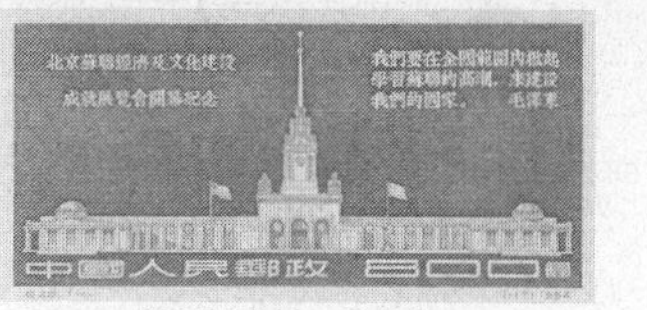
236 Exhibition Building

1954. Russian Economic and Cultural Exn, Peking.

1637	236	$800 brown on yellow	8·50	2·00

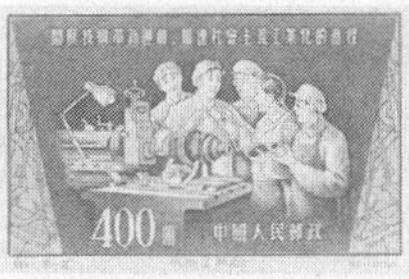
237 The Universal Fixture

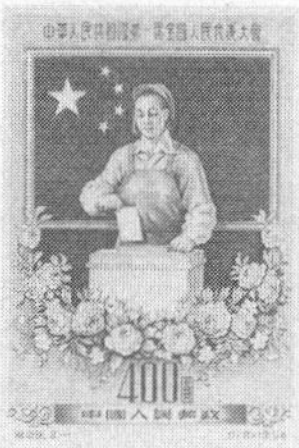
238 Woman Worker

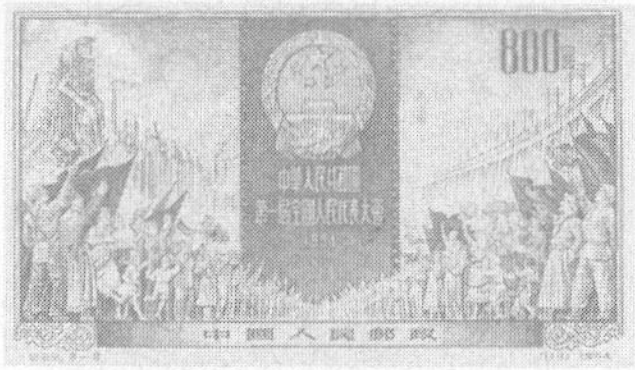
239 Rejoicing Crowds

1954. Workers' Inventions.

1638	237	$400 green	50	40
1639	–	$800 red	50	30

DESIGN: $800, The reverse repeater.

1954. 1st Session of National Congress.

1640	238	$400 purple	30	20
1641	239	$800 red	30	20

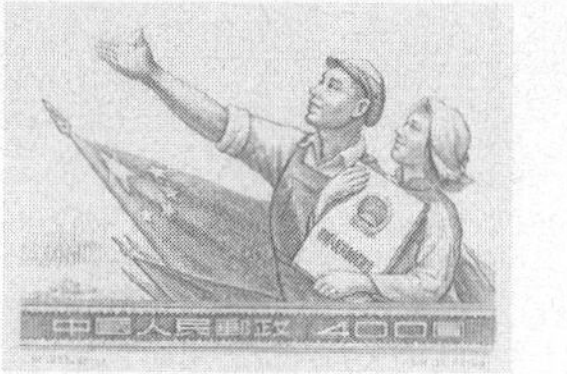
240 "New Constitution"

1954. Constitution Commemoration.

1642	240	$400 brown on buff	20	15
1643		$800 red on yellow	20	15

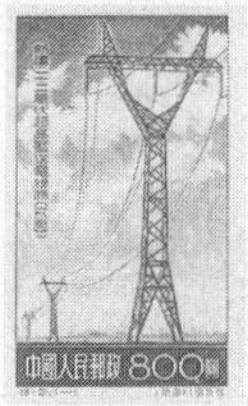
241 Pylons

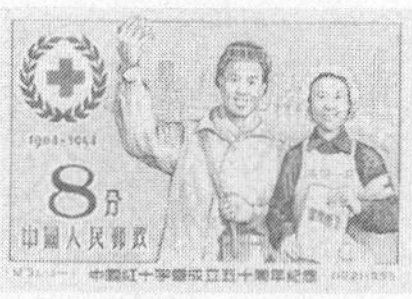
242 Nurse and Red Cross Worker

1955. Development of Overhead Transmission of Electricity.

1644	241	$800 blue	1·50	50

1955. 50th Anniv of Chinese Red Cross.

1645	242	8f. red and green	8·50	1·40

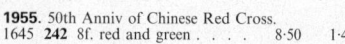

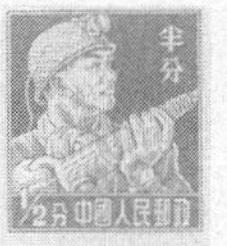
243 Miner

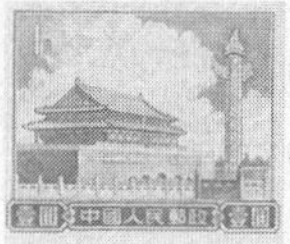
244 Gate of Heavenly Peace, Peking

1955.

1646	243	½f. brown	85	10
1647	–	1f. purple	85	10
1648	–	2f. green	3·00	10
1648a	–	2½f. blue	1·75	10
1649	–	4f. green	2·40	10
1650	–	8f. red	6·00	10
1650b	–	10f. red	11·00	35
1651	–	20f. blue	11·00	40
1652	–	50f. grey	9·75	55
1653	244	1y. red	1·25	10
1654		2y. brown	1·40	10
1655		5y. grey	2·75	35
1656		10y. red	4·75	1·50
1657		20y. violet	10·00	4·50

DESIGNS—As Type 243: 1f. Lathe operator; 2f. Airman; 2½ f. Nurse; 4f. Soldier; 8f. Foundry worker; 10f. Chemist; 20f. Farm girl; 50f. Sailor.

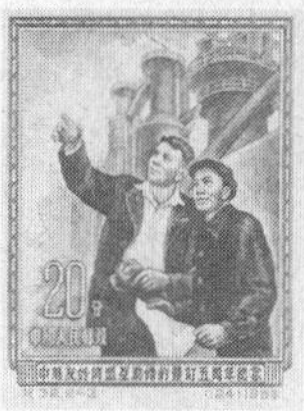
246 Workmen and Industrial Plant

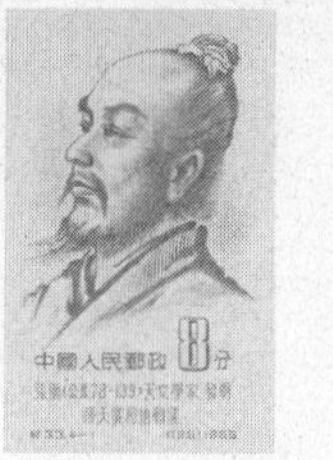
247 Chang-Heng (A.D. 78–139, astronomer)

1955. 5th Anniv of Sino–Russian Treaty.

1658	–	8f. brown	5·00	1·00
1659	246	20f. olive	7·00	1·00

DESIGN—HORIZ: (37 × 32 mm): 8f. Stalin and Mao Tse-tung.

1955. Scientists of Ancient China.

1660	247	8f. sepia on buff	2·25	25
1661	–	8f. blue on buff	2·25	25
1662	–	8f. black on buff	2·25	25
1663	–	8f. purple on buff	2·25	25

PORTRAITS: No. 1661, Tsu Chung-chi (429–500, mathematician). No. 1662, Chang-Sui (683–727, astronomer). No. 1663, Li-Shih-chen (1518–1593, pharmacologist).

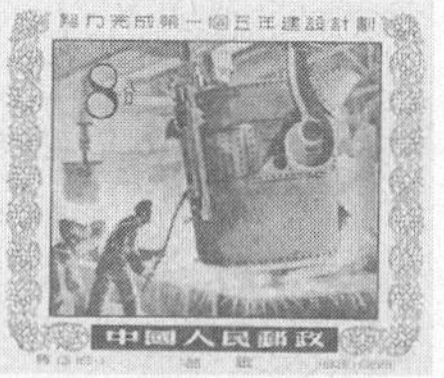
248 Foundry

1955. Five Year Plan. Frames in black.

1664	248	8f. red and orange	40	10
1665	–	8f. brown and yellow	40	10
1666	–	8f. yellow and black	40	10
1667	–	8f. violet and blue	40	10
1668	–	8f. yellow and brown	40	10
1669	–	8f. yellow and red	40	10
1670	–	8f. grey and blue	40	10
1671	–	8f. orange and black	40	10
1672	–	8f. yellow and brown	40	10
1673	–	8f. red and orange	40	10
1674	–	8f. yellow and green	40	10
1675	–	8f. red and yellow	40	10
1676	–	8f. yellow and grey	40	15
1677	–	8f. yellow and blue	40	10
1678	–	8f. orange and blue	40	10
1679	–	8f. yellow and brown	40	10
1680	–	8f. red and brown	40	10
1681	–	8f. yellow and brown	40	10

DESIGNS—No. 1665, Electricity pylons; No. 1666, Mining machinery; No. 1667, Oil tankers and derricks; No. 1668, Heavy machinery workshop; No. 1669, Factory guard and industrial plant; No. 1670, Textile machinery; No. 1671, Factory workers; No. 1672, Combine-harvester; No. 1673, Dairy herd and farm girl; No. 1674, Dam; No. 1675, Artists decorating pottery; No. 1676, Lorry; No. 1677, Freighter and wharf; No. 1678, Surveyors; No. 1679, Students; No. 1680, Man, woman and child; No. 1681, Workers', rest home.

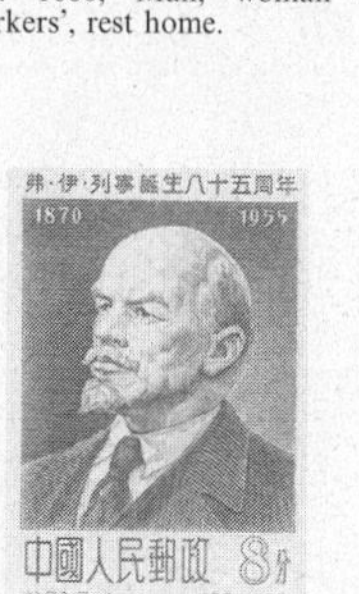
249 Lenin

1955. 85th Birth Anniv of Lenin.

1682	249	8f. blue	7·50	25
1683		20f. lake	7·50	1·40

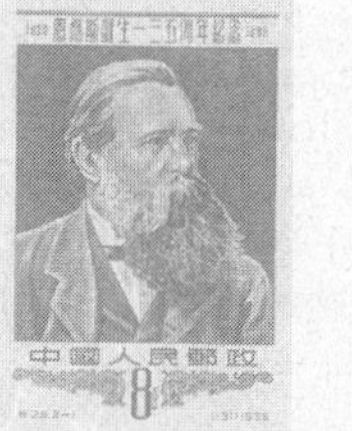
250 Engels

1955. 60th Death Anniv of Engels.

1684	250	8f. red	7·00	25
1685		20f. sepia	7·00	1·25

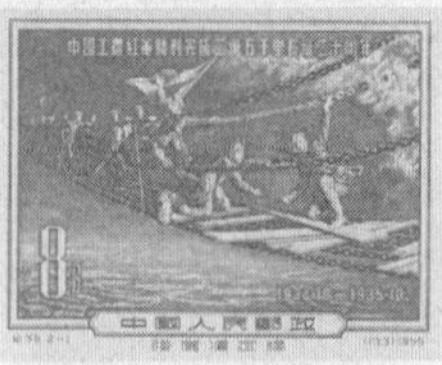

251 Capture of Lu Ting Bridge

1955. 20th Anniv of Long March by Communist Army.
1686 **251** 8f. red . . . . 5·00 60
1687 – 8f. blue . . . . 8·00 1·25
DESIGN—VERT: (28 × 46 mm): No. 1687, Crossing the Ta Hsueh Mountains.

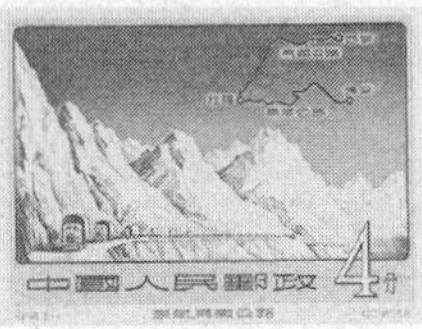

252 Convoy of Lorries

1956. Opening of Sikang–Tibet and Tsinghai–Tibet Highways.
1688 **252** 4f. blue 50 35
1689 – 8f. brown 50 20
1690 – 8f. red 50 20
DESIGNS—VERT: (21 × 42 mm): No. 1689, Suspension bridge: Tatu River. HORIZ: As T **252**: No. 1690, Opening ceremony, Lhasa.

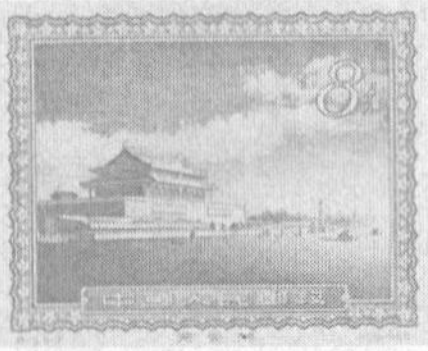

254 Gate of Heavenly Peace

1956. Views of Peking.
1691 – 4f. red . . . . 3·00 10
1692 – 4f. green . . . . 3·00 10
1693 **254** 8f. red . . . . 3·00 10
1694 – 8f. blue . . . . 3·00 10
1695 – 8f. brown . . . . 3·00 10
VIEWS: No. 1691, Summer Palace; 1692, Peihai Park; 1694, Temple of Heaven; 1695, Great Throne Hall, Tai Ho Palace.

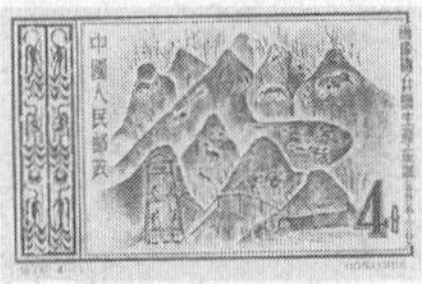

255 Salt Production

1956. Archaeological Discoveries at Chengtu.
1696 **255** 4f. green 40 10
1697 – 4f. black 40 10
1698 – 8f. sepia 50 10
1699 – 8f. sepia 40 10
DESIGNS—HORIZ: (Brick carvings of Tung Han Dynasty, A.D. 25–200): No. 1697, Residence; No. 1698, Hunting and farming; No. 1699, Carriage crossing bridge.

256

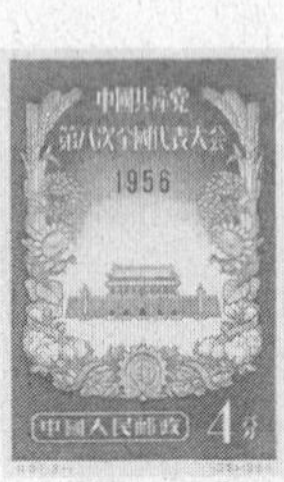

257 Gate of Heavenly Peace, Peking

1956. National Savings.
1700 **256** 4f. buff . . . . 4·50 30
1701 8f. red . . . . 5·50 25

1956. 8th National Communist Party Congress.
1702 **257** 4f. green . . . . 3·00 30
1703 8f. red . . . . 4·50 30
1704 16f. red . . . . 5·50 65

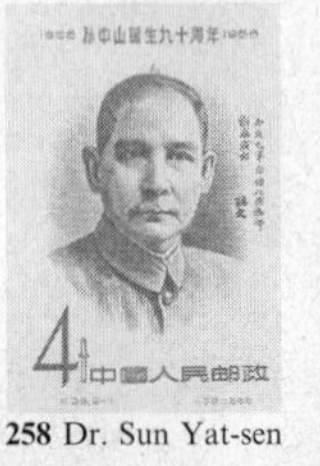

258 Dr. Sun Yat-sen

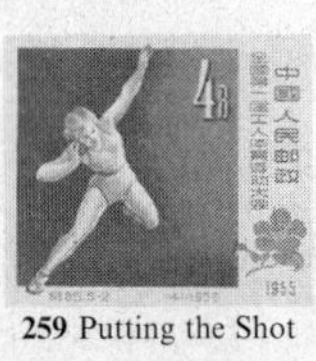

259 Putting the Shot

1956. 90th Birth Anniv of Dr. Sun Yat-sen.
1705 **258** 4f. brown . . . . 7·00 25
1706 8f. blue . . . . 6·00 1·40

1955. 1st Chinese Workers' Athletic Meeting, 1955. Inscr "1955". Flower in red and green; inscr in brown.
1707 **259** 4f. lake . . . . 1·10 10
1708 – 4f. purple (Weightlifting) 1·10 35
1709 – 8f. green (Sprinting) . . 1·50 10
1710 – 8f. blue (Football) . . . 2·00 40
1711 – 8f. brown (Cycling) . . . 1·50 10

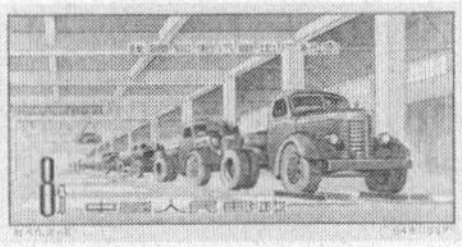

260 Assembly Line

1957. Lorry Production.
1712 – 4f. brown 25 10
1713 **260** 8f. blue 40 10
DESIGN: 4f. Changchun motor plant.

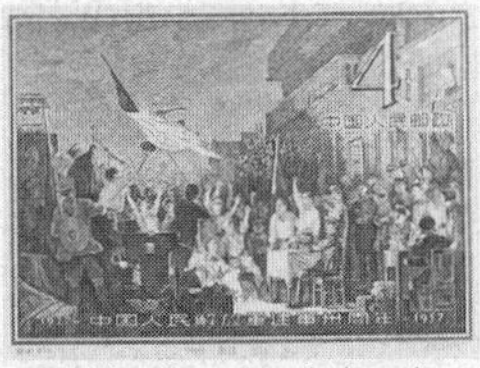

261 Nanchang Revolutionaries

1957. 30th Anniv of People's Liberation Army.
1714 **261** 4f. violet . . . . 7·75 60
1715 – 4f. green . . . . 7·75 60
1716 – 8f. brown . . . . 7·75 50
1717 – 8f. blue . . . . 7·75 50
DESIGNS: No. 1715, Meeting of Red Armies at Chinkangshan; No. 1716, Liberation Army crossing the Yellow River; No. 1717, Liberation of Nanking.

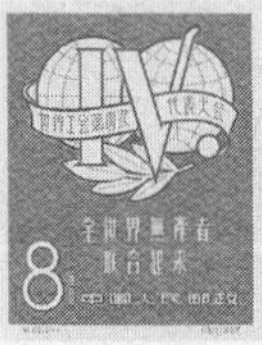

262 Congress Emblem

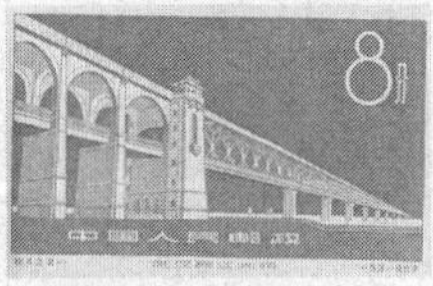

263 Yangtse River Bridge

1957. 4th W.F.T.U. Congress, Leipzig.
1718 **262** 8f. brown . . . . 4·00 50
1719 22f. blue . . . . 3·00 50

1957. Opening of Yangtse River Bridge, Wuhan.
1720 **263** 8f. red 50 10
1721 – 20f. blue . . . . 1·00 15
DESIGN: 20f. Aerial view of bridge.

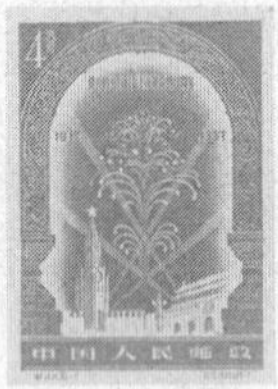

264 Fireworks over Kremlin

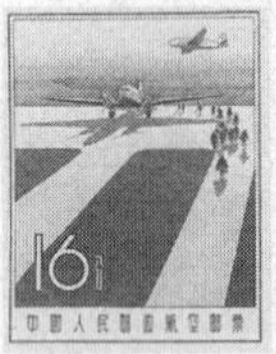

265 Airport Scene

1957. 40th Anniv of Russian Revolution.
1722 **264** 4f. red . . . . 4·25 20
1723 – 8f. sepia . . . . 4·25 20
1724 – 20f. green . . . . 5·50 30
1725 – 22f. brown . . . . 5·50 50
1726 – 32f. blue . . . . 9·25 1·25
DESIGNS: 8f. Soviet emblem, globe and broken chains; 20f. Dove of Peace and plant; 22f. Hands supporting book bearing portraits of Marx and Lenin; 32f. Electricity power pylon.

1957. Air.
1727 **265** 16f. blue . . . . 4·50 30
1728 – 28f. olive . . . . 10·00 2·00
1729 – 35f. black . . . . 13·00 1·75
1730 – 52f. blue . . . . 15·00 75
DESIGNS—Lisunov Li-2 over: 28f. mountain highway; 35f. railway tracks; 52f. collier at station.

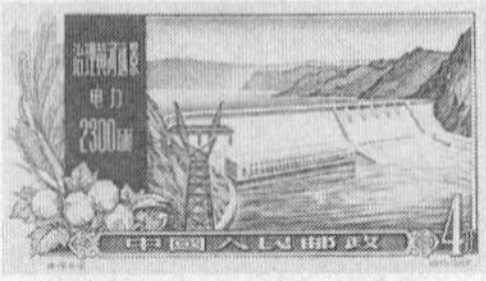

266 Yellow River Dam and Power Station

1957. Harnessing of the Yellow River.
1731 – 4f. orange . . . . 7·75 30
1732 **266** 4f. blue . . . . 7·75 1·00
1733 – 8f. lake . . . . 7·75 70
1734 – 8f. green . . . . 7·75 30
DESIGNS: No. 1731, Map of Yellow River; No. 1733, Yellow River ferry; No. 1734, Aerial view of irrigation on Yellow River.

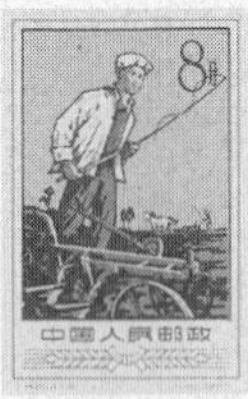

267 Ploughing

1957. Co-operative Agriculture. Multicoloured.
1735 8f. Farmer enrolling for farm 50 10
1736 8f. Type **267** 50 10
1737 8f. Tree-planting 50 10
1738 8f. Harvesting 50 10

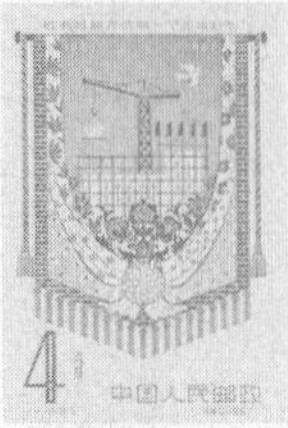

268 "Peaceful Construction"

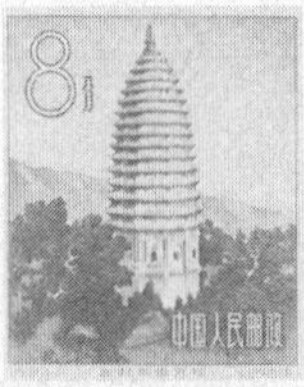

269 High Peak Pagoda, Tenfeng

1958. Completion of First Five Year Plan.
1739 **268** 4f. green and cream . . 50 10
1740 – 8f. red and cream . . . 50 10
1741 – 16f. blue and cream . . 50 10
DESIGNS: 8f. "Industry and Agriculture" (grapple and wheat-sheaves); 16f. "Communications and Transport" (steam train on viaduct and ship).

1958. Ancient Chinese Pagodas.
1742 **269** 8f. brown . . . . 1·40 25
1743 – 8f. blue . . . . 1·40 10
1744 – 8f. brown . . . . 1·40 15
1745 – 8f. green . . . . 1·40 10
DESIGNS: No. 1743, One Thousand League Pagoda, Tali; No. 1744, Buddha Pagoda, Yinghsien; No. 1745, Flying Rainbow Pagoda, Hungchao.

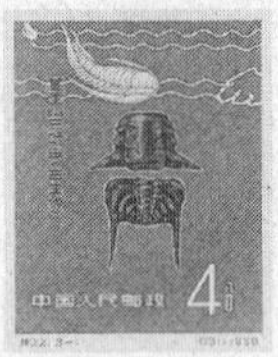

270 Trilobite of Hao Li Shan

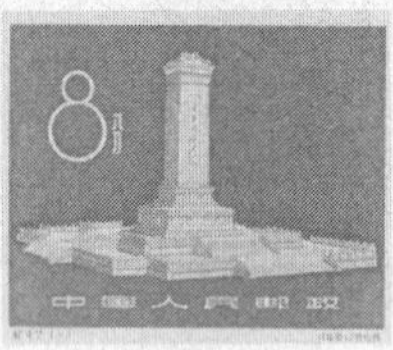

271

1958. Chinese Fossils.
1746 **270** 4f. blue 85 10
1747 – 8f. sepia 85 10
1748 – 16f. green 85 35
DESIGNS: 8f. Dinosaur of Lufeng; 16f. "Sinomegaceros pachyospeus" (deer).

1958. Unveiling of People's Heroes Monument, Peking.
1749 **271** 8f. red . . . . 12·00 1·40

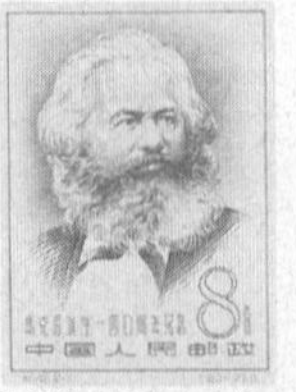

272 Karl Marx (after Zhukov)

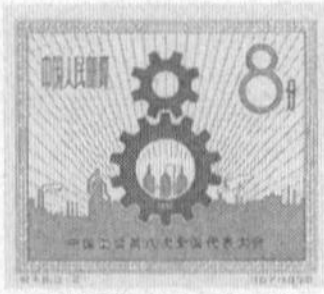

273 Cogwheels of Industry

1958. 140th Birth Anniv of Karl Marx.
1750 **272** 8f. brown . . . . 7·50 1·40
1751 – 22f. myrtle . . . . . . 7·50 1·00
DESIGN: 22f. Marx addressing German workers' Educational Association, London.

1958. 8th All-China Trade Union Congress, Peking.
1752 **273** 4f. blue . . . . 6·50 1·75
1753 8f. purple . . . . 6·50 50

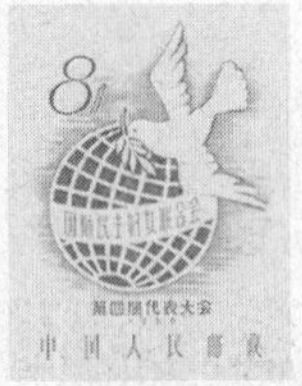

274 Federation Emblem

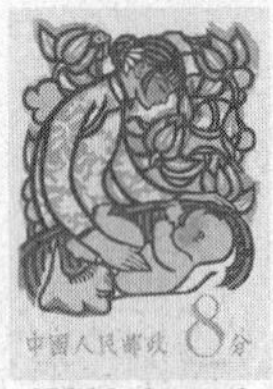

275 Mother and Child

1958. 4th International Democratic Women's Federation Congress, Vienna.
1754 **274** 8f. blue . . . . 8·50 40
1755 20f. green . . . . 8·50 2·00

1958. Chinese Children. Multicoloured.
1756 8f. Type **275** . . . . 9·75 1·10
1757 8f. Watering sunflowers . . 9·75 1·10
1758 8f. "Hide and seek" . . . . 9·75 1·10
1759 8f. Children sailing boat . . 9·75 1·10

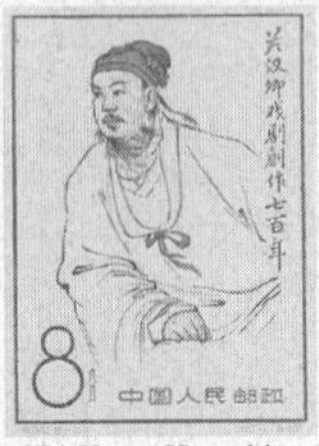

276 Kuan Han-ching (playwright)

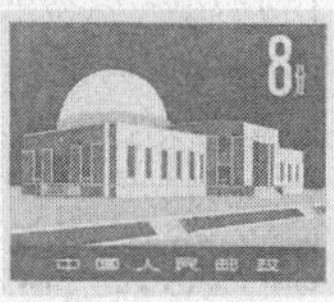

277 Peking Planetarium

1958. 700th Anniv of Works of Kuan Han-ching.
1760 – 4f. green on cream . . . 6·00 2·50
1761 **276** 8f. purple on cream . . 8·00 1·00
1762 – 20f. black on cream . . 12·00 1·25
DESIGNS: Scenes from Han-ching's comedies: 4f. "The Butterfly Dream"; 20f. "The Riverside Pavilion".

1958. Peking Planetarium.
1763 **277** 8f. green . . . . 3·50 80
1764 – 20f. blue . . . . 5·00 40
DESIGN: 20f. Planetarium in operation.

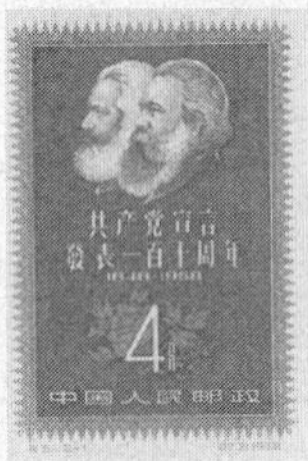

278 Marx and Engels

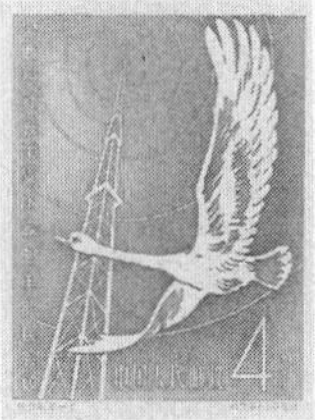

279 Tundra Swan and Radio Pylon

1958. 110th Anniv of "Communist Manifesto".
1765 **278** 4f. purple . . . . 6·00 1·75
1766 – 8f. blue . . . . 6·00 40
DESIGN: 8f. Front cover of first German "Communist Manifesto".

1958. Organization of Socialist Countries' Postal Administrations Conference, Moscow.
1767 **279** 4f. blue . . . . 7·50 1·00
1768 8f. green . . . . 7·50 75

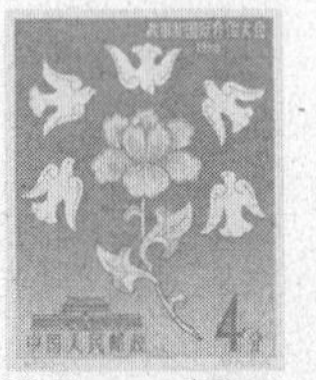

280 Peony and Doves

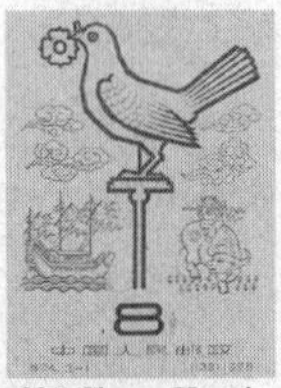

281 Chang Heng's Weather-cock

1958. International Disarmament Conf, Stockholm.
1769 **280** 4f. red . . . . 10·00 2·00
1770 – 8f. green . . . . 10·00 2·00
1771 – 22f. brown . . . . . . 7·50 1·75
DESIGNS: 8f. Olive branch; 22f. Atomic symbol and factory plant.

1958. Chinese Meteorology.
1772 **281** 8f. black on yellow . . . 80 10
1773 – 8f. black on blue 80 10
1774 – 8f. black on green . . . 80 10
DESIGNS: No. 1773. Meteorological balloon; No. 1774, Typhoon signal-tower.

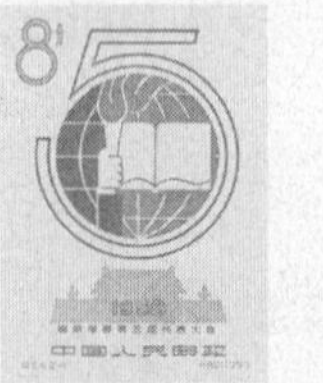

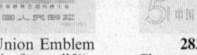

282 Union Emblem within figure "5"

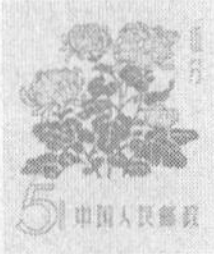

283 Chrysanthemum

1958. 5th International Students' Union Congress, Peking.
1775 **282** 8f. purple . . . . 7·50 50
1776 22f. green . . . . 5·50 1·00

1958. Flowers.
1777 – 1½f. mauve (Peony) . . . . 4·00 35
1778 – 3f. green (Lotus) . . . . 14·00 1·40
1779 **283** 5f. orange . . . . 2·00 35

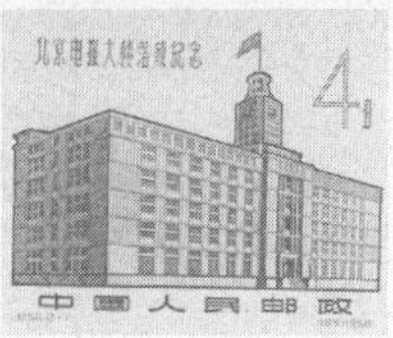

284 Telegraph Building, Peking

1958. Opening of Peking Telegraph Building.
1780 **284** 4f. olive . . . . 1·50 30
1781 8f. red . . . . 2·75 20

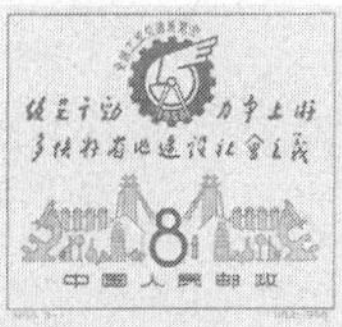

285 Exhibition Emblem and Symbols

1958. National Exhibition of Industry and Communications.
1782 **285** 8f. green . . . . 6·75 80
1783 – 8f. red . . . . 6·75 80
1784 – 8f. brown . . . . 6·75 80
DESIGNS: No. 1783, Chinese dragon riding the waves; No. 1784, Horses in the sky.

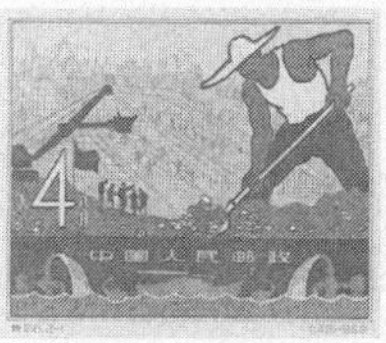
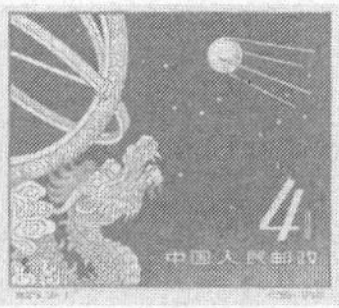

286 Labourer on Reservoir Site **287** Sputnik and ancient Theodolite

1958. Inauguration of Ming Tombs Reservoir.
1785 **286** 4f. brown 50 10
1786 – 8f. blue 50 10
DESIGN: 8f. Ming Tombs Reservoir.

1958. Russian Sputnik Commemoration.
1787 **287** 4f. red . . . . 3·25 20
1788 – 8f. violet . . . . 3·25 20
1789 – 10f. green . . . . 3·50 1·10
DESIGNS: 8f. Third Russian sputnik encircling globe; 10f. Three Russian sputniks encircling globe.

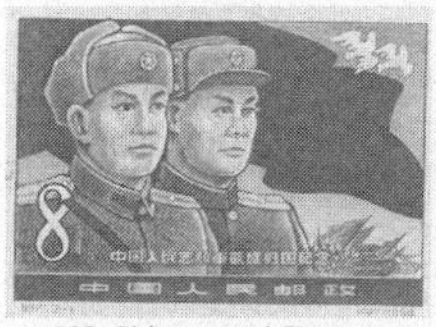
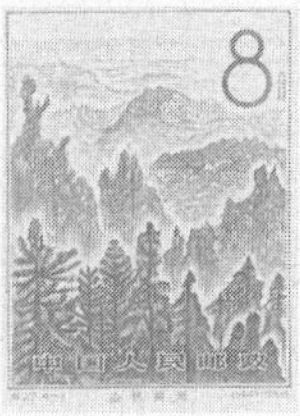

288 Chinese and Korean Soldiers **289** Forest Landscape

1958. Return of Chinese People's Volunteers from Korea.
1790 **288** 8f. purple . . . . 1·10 10
1791 – 8f. brown . . . . 1·10 10
1792 – 8f. red . . . . 1·10 10
DESIGNS: No. 1791, Chinese soldier embracing Korean woman; No. 1792, Girl presenting bouquet to Chinese soldier.

1958. Afforestation Campaign.
1793 **289** 8f. green . . . . 3·00 75
1794 – 8f. slate . . . . 3·00 20
1795 – 8f. violet . . . . 3·00 20
1796 – 8f. blue . . . . 3·00 20
DESIGNS—VERT: No. 1794, Forest patrol. HORIZ: No. 1795, Tree-felling by power-saw. No. 1796, Tree planting.

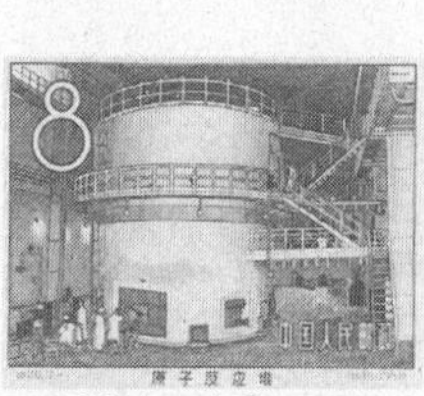

290 Atomic Reactor

1958. Inauguration of China's First Atomic Reactor.
1797 **290** 8f. blue . . . . 4·50 40
1798 – 20f. brown . . . . . . 7·50 2·00
DESIGN: 20f. Cyclotron in action.

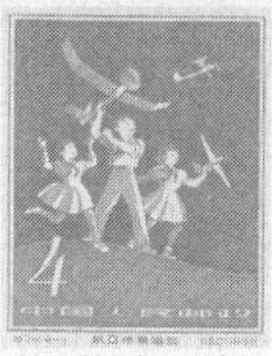
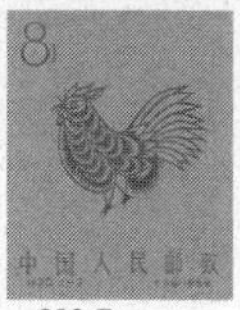

291 Children with Model Aircraft **292** Rooster

1958. Aviation Sports.
1799 **291** 4f. red 60 10
1800 – 8f. myrtle 60 10
1801 – 10f. sepia 60 10
1802 – 20f. slate . . . . 1·75 15
DESIGNS: 8f. Gliders. 10f. Parachutists; 20f. Yakovlev Yak-18U trainers.

1959. Chinese Folk Paper-cuts.
1803 – 8f. black on violet . . . 7·00 50
1804 – 8f. black on green . . . 7·00 50
1805 **292** 8f. black on red . . . . 7·00 50
1806 – 8f. black on blue . . . . 7·00 50
DESIGNS: No. 1803, Camel. 1804, Pomegranate; 1806, Actress on stage.

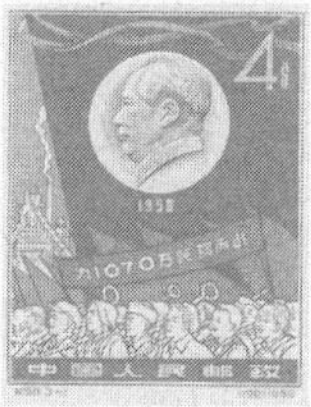
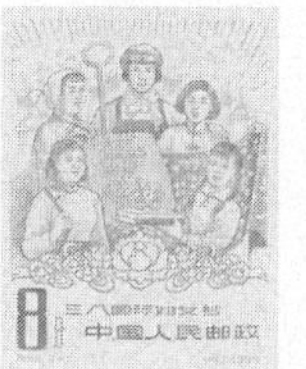

293 Mao Tse-tung and Steel Workers **294** Chinese Women

1959. Steel Production Progress. Inscr "1958".
1807 **293** 4f. red . . . . 3·50 1·00
1808 – 8f. purple . . . . 4·50 80
1809 – 10f. red . . . . 6·00 1·00
DESIGNS: 8f. Battery of steel furnaces; 10f. Steel "blowers" and workers.

1959. International Women's Day.
1810 **294** 8f. green on cream . . . 1·00 35
1811 – 22f. mauve on cream . . 1·50 10
DESIGN: 22f. Russian and Chinese women.

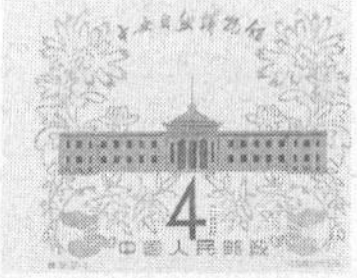
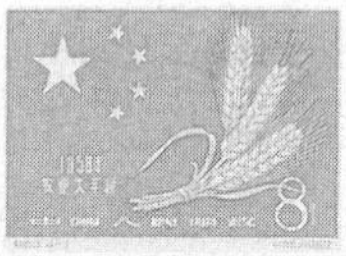

295 Natural History Museum, Peking **296** Barley

1959. Opening of Natural History Museum, Peking.
1812 **295** 4f. turquoise 80 10
1813 8f. sepia 80 10

1959. Successful Harvest, 1958.
1814 8f. red (Type **296**) . . . . . 1·90 10
1815 8f. red (Rice) . . . . 1·90 10
1816 8f. red (Cotton) . . . . . . 1·90 10
1817 8f. red (Soya beans, groundnuts and rape) . . 1·90 10

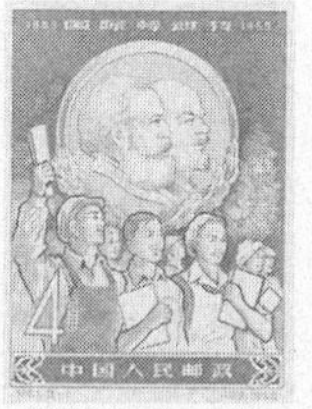
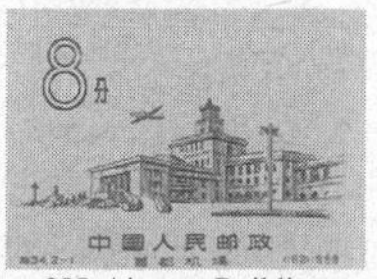

297 Workers with Marx–Lenin Banner **298** Airport Building

1959. Labour Day. Inscr "1889–1959".
1818 **297** 4f. blue . . . . 4·00 80
1819 – 8f. red . . . . 6·00 70
1820 – 22f. green . . . . 5·00 30
DESIGNS: 8f. Hands clasping Red Flag; 22f. "5.1" and workers.

1959. Inauguration of Peking Airport.
1821 **298** 8f. black on lilac . . . . 6·50 95
1822 – 10f. black on green . . . 9·00 30
DESIGN: 10f. Ilyushin Il-14P at airport.

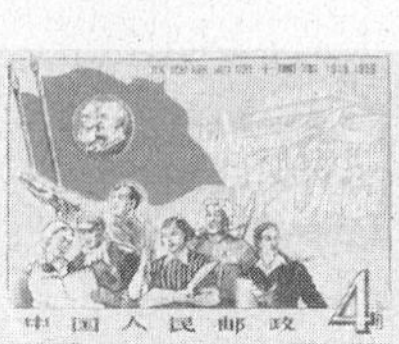
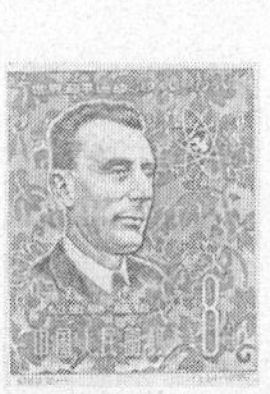

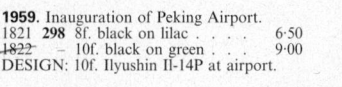

299 Students with Banners **300** F. Joliot-Curie (first President)

1959. 40th Anniv of "May 4th" Students' Rising.
1823 **299** 4f. red, brown and olive 12·00 7·00
1824 – 8f. red, brown & bistre 22·00 2·25
DESIGN: 8f. Workers with banners.

1959. 10th Anniv of World Peace Council.
1825 **300** 8f. purple . . . . 4·50 2·00
1826 – 22f. violet . . . . 7·50 50
DESIGN: 22f. Silhouettes of European, Chinese and Negro.

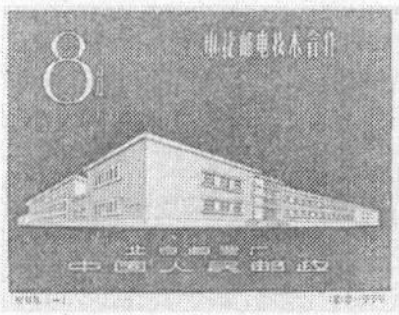

301 Stamp Printing Works, Peking

1959. Sino-Czech Co-operation in Postage Stamp Production.
1827 **301** 8f. myrtle . . . . 8·50 1·50

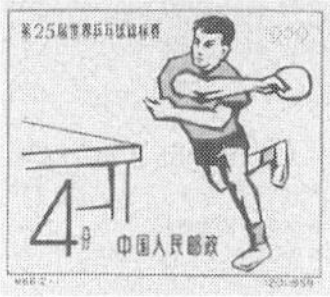

302

1959. World Table Tennis Championships, Dortmund.
1828 **302** 4f. blue and black . . . 2·50 30
1829 8f. red and black . . . . 4·00 70

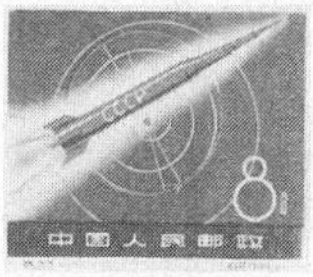
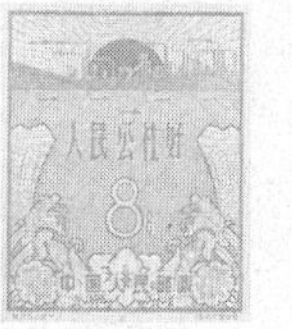

303 Moon Rocket **304** "Prologue"

1959. Launching of First Lunar Rocket.
1830 **303** 8f. red, blue & black . . 13·00 1·75

1959. 1st Anniv of People's Communes.
1831 **304** 8f. red 70 20
1832 – 8f. dull purple 70 20
1833 – 8f. orange 70 20
1834 – 8f. green 70 20
1835 – 8f. blue 70 20
1836 – 8f. olive 70 20
1837 – 8f. blue 70 20
1838 – 8f. mauve 70 20
1839 – 8f. black 70 20
1840 – 8f. green 70 20
1841 – 8f. violet 70 20
1842 – 8f. red 70 20
DESIGNS: No. 1832, Steel worker ("Rural Industries"); No. 1833, Farm girl ("Agriculture"); No. 1834, Salesgirl ("Trade"); No. 1835, Peasant ("Study"); No. 1836, Militiaman ("Militia"); No. 1837, Cook with tray of food ("Community Meals"); No. 1838, Child watering flowers ("Nursery"); No. 1839, Old man with pipe ("Old People's Homes"); No. 1840, Health worker ("Public Health"); No. 1841, Young flautist ("Recreation and Entertainment"); No. 1842, Star-shaped flower ("Epilogue").

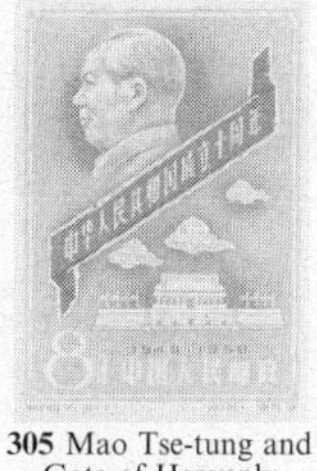

305 Mao Tse-tung and Gate of Heavenly Peace, Peking **306** Republican Emblem

1959. 10th Anniv of People's Republic. (a) 1st issue. Inscr "1949–1959". With gum.
1843 **305** 8f. red and brown . . . 10·00 1·75
1844 – 8f. red and blue . . . . 7·00 1·75
1845 – 22f. red and green . . . 7·00 1·50
DESIGNS: No. 1844, Marx, Lenin and Kremlin; No. 1845, Dove of peace and globe.

(b) 2nd issue. Emblem in red and yellow; inscriptions in yellow; background colours given.
1846 **306** 4f. turquoise . . . . . . 4·50 2·75
1847 8f. lilac . . . . 4·50 40
1848 10f. blue . . . . 5·50 50
1849 20f. buff . . . . 8·00 1·75

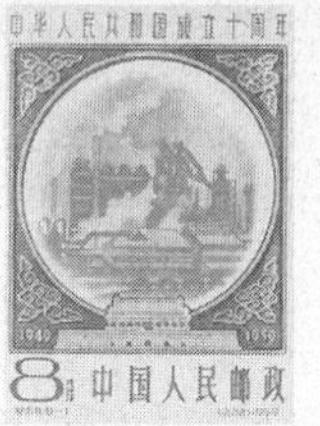

307 Steel Plant

(c) 3rd issue. Inscr "1949–1959". Frames in purple; centre colours given. With gum.
1850 **307** 8f. red . . . . 1·25 20
1851 – 8f. drab . . . . 1·25 50
1852 – 8f. bistre . . . . 1·25 30
1853 – 8f. blue . . . . 1·25 30
1854 – 8f. salmon . . . . 1·25 30
1855 – 8f. green . . . . 1·25 40
1856 – 8f. turquoise . . . . . . 1·25 30
1857 – 8f. lilac . . . . 1·25 30
DESIGNS: No. 1851, Coal-mine. No. 1852, Steelmill; No. 1853, Double-decked bridge; No. 1854, Combine-harvester; No. 1855, Dam construction; No. 1856, Textile mill; No. 1857, Chemical works.

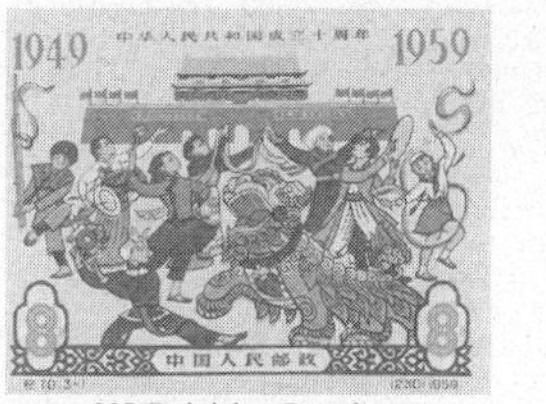

308 Rejoicing Populace

(d) 4th Issue. Multicoloured.
1858 8f. Type **308** . . . . 2·50 1·00
1859 10f. Rejoicing people and industrial plant (vert) . . 5·00 40
1860 20f. Tree, banners and people carrying wheat and flowers (vert) . . . . . . 5·00 1·00

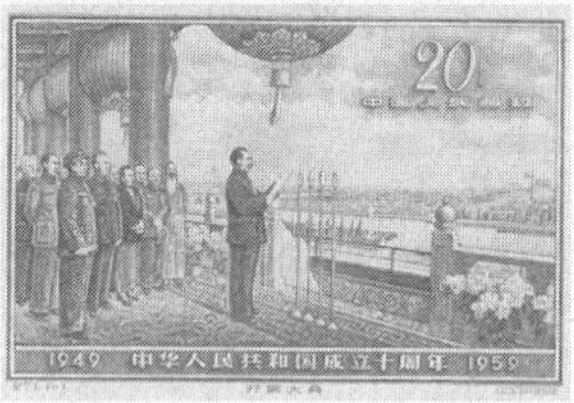

309 Mao Tse-tung proclaiming Republic

(e) 5th issue.
1861 **309** 20f. lake . . . . 22·00 7·25

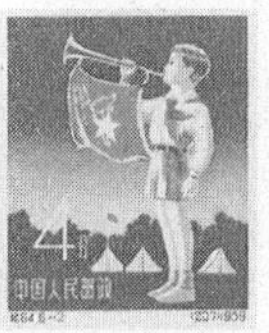
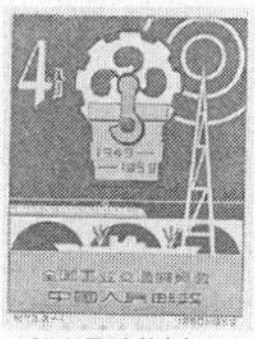

310 Boy Bugler ("Summer Camps") **311** Exhibition Emblem and Symbols of Communication

1959. 10th Anniv of Chinese Youth Pioneers.
1862 – 4f. yellow, red & black 3·50 10
1863 **310** 4f. red and blue . . . . 3·50 10
1864 – 8f. red and brown . . . 3·50 10
1865 – 8f. red and blue . . . . 3·50 10
1866 – 8f. red and green . . . 4·50 10
1867 – 8f. red and purple . . . 4·50 75
DESIGNS: No. 1862, Pioneers' emblem; No. 1864, Schoolgirl with flowers and satchel ("Study"); No. 1865, Girl with rain gauge ("Science"); No. 1866, Boy with sapling ("Forestry"); No. 1867, Girl skater ("Athletic Sports").

1959. National Exhibition of Industry and Communications, Peking. Inscr "1949–1959".
1868 **311** 4f. blue 45 15
1869 – 8f. red 30 15
DESIGN: 8f. Exn emblem and symbols of industry.

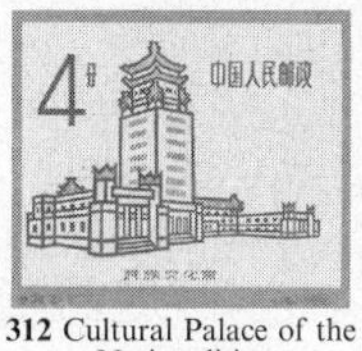
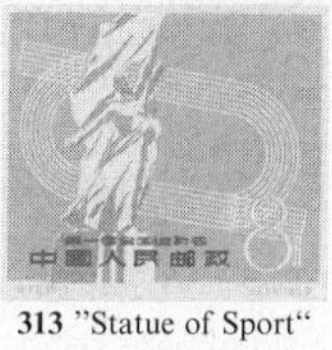

312 Cultural Palace of the Nationalities **313** "Statue of Sport"

1959. Inauguration of Cultural Palace of the Nationalities. Peking.
1870 **312** 4f. black and red . . . . 4·25 50
1871 8f. black and green . . . 4·25 50

1959. 1st National Games, Peking. Multicoloured.
1872 8f. Type **313** . . . . 1·40 30
1873 8f. Parachuting . . . . . . 1·40 30
1874 8f. Pistol-shooting . . . . . 1·40 30
1875 8f. Diving . . . . 1·40 30
1876 8f. Table tennis . . . . . . 1·40 30

1877		8f. Weightlifting	1·40	30
1878		8f. High jumping	1·40	30
1879		8f. Rowing	1·40	30
1880		8f. Running	1·40	30
1881		8f. Basketball	1·40	30
1882		8f. Fencing	1·40	30
1883		8f. Motor cycling	1·40	30
1884		8f. Gymnastics	1·40	30
1885		8f. Cycling	1·40	30
1886		8f. Horse-racing	1·40	30
1887		8f. Football	3·50	1·40

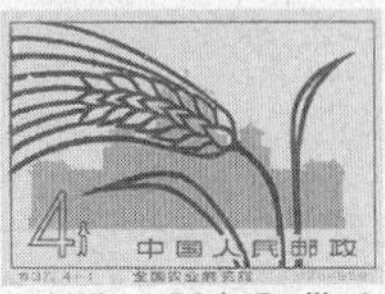

314 Wheat (Main Pavilion)

1960. Opening of National Agricultural Exhibition Hall, Peking.

1888	**314**	4f. black, red & orange	40	20
1889	–	8f. black and blue	40	20
1890	–	10f. black and brown	50	30
1891	–	20f. black and turquoise	1·50	30

DESIGNS: 8f. Meteorological symbols (Meteorological Pavilion); 10f. Cattle (Animal Husbandry Pavilion); 20f. Fishes (Aquatic Products Pavilion).

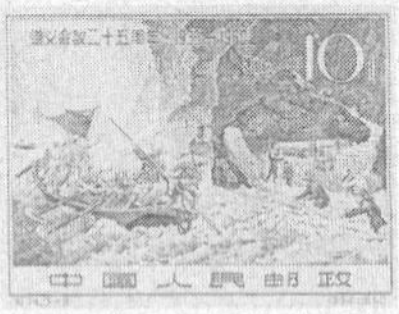

315 Crossing the Chinsha River

1960. 25th Anniv of Conference during the Long March, Tsunyi, Kweichow.

1892	–	4f. blue	9·00	1·50
1893	–	8f. turquoise	9·00	3·50
1894	**315**	10f. green	18·00	1·50

DESIGNS: 4f. Conference Hall, Tsunyi; 8f. Mao Tse-tung and flags.

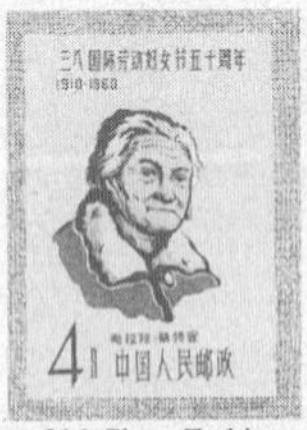

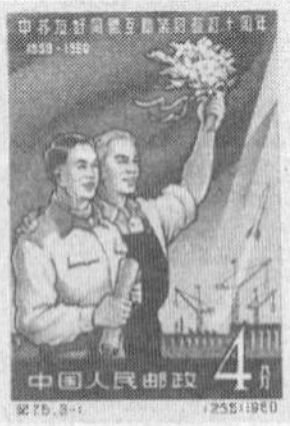

316 Clara Zetkin (founder) **317** Chinese and Soviet Workers

1960. 50th Anniv of International Women's Day. Frame and inscriptions black. Centre colours given.

1895	**316**	4f. blue, black & flesh	1·50	40
1896	–	8f. multicoloured	1·50	10
1897	–	10f. multicoloured	1·50	20
1898	–	22f. multicoloured	5·00	40

DESIGNS: 8f. Mother, child and dove; 10f. Woman tractor-driver; 22f. Women of three races.

1960. 10th Anniv of Sino-Soviet Treaty.

1899	**317**	4f. brown	7·00	1·00
1900	–	8f. black, yellow & red	7·00	1·00
1901	–	10f. blue	8·00	3·00

DESIGNS: 8f. Flowers and Sino-Soviet emblems; 10f. Chinese and Soviet soldiers.

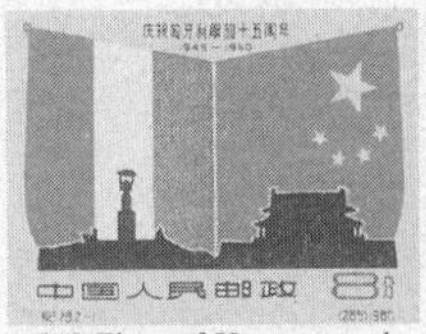

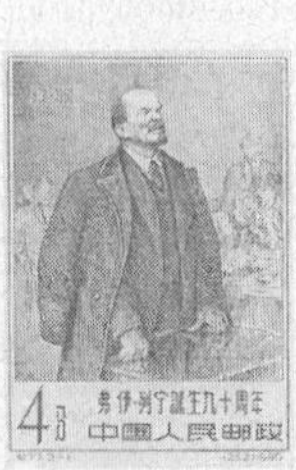

318 Flags of Hungary and China **319** Lenin Speaking

1960. 15th Anniv of Hungarian Liberation.

1902	**318**	8f. multicoloured	9·50	1·75
1903	–	8f. red, black and blue	9·50	3·25

DESIGN: No. 1903, Parliament Building, Budapest.

1960. 90th Birth Anniv of Lenin.

1904	**319**	4f. lilac	4·50	75
1905	–	8f. black and red	5·50	2·25
1906	–	20f. brown	11·00	2·00

DESIGNS: 8f. Lenin (portrait); 20f. Lenin talking with Red Guards (after Vasilyev).

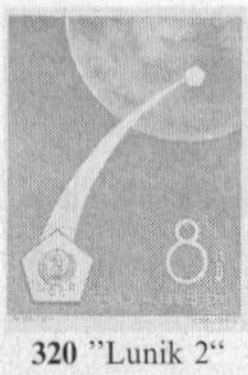

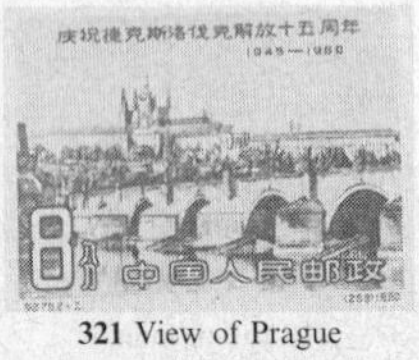

320 "Lunik 2" **321** View of Prague

1960. Lunar Rocket Flights.

1907	**320**	8f. red	4·25	75
1908	–	10f. green ("Lunik 3")	4·25	75

1960. 15th Anniv of Liberation of Czechoslovakia.

1909	–	8f. multicoloured	8·50	1·50
1910	**321**	8f. green	8·50	2·50

DESIGN—VERT: No. 1909, Child pioneers and flags of China and Czechoslovakia.

SERIAL NUMBERS. In this and many later multicoloured sets containing several stamps of the same denomination, the serial number is quoted in brackets to assist identification. This is the last figure in the bottom left corner of the stamp.

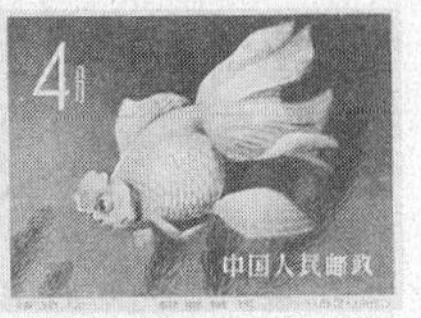

322 Narial Bouquet Goldfish

1960. Chinese Goldfish. Multicoloured.

1911	4f. (1) Type **322**	23·00	4·00
1912	4f. (2) Black-backed telescopic-eyed goldfish	27·00	4·00
1913	4f. (3) Bubble-eyed goldfish	27·00	5·00
1914	4f. (4) Ranchu goldfish	8·00	3·00
1915	8f. (5) Pearl-scaled goldfish	40·00	6·00
1916	8f. (6) Black moor goldfish	40·00	6·00
1917	8f. (7) Celestial goldfish	8·00	2·50
1918	8f. (8) Oranda goldfish	8·00	2·50
1919	8f. (9) Purple oranda goldfish	8·00	2·50
1920	8f. (10) Red-capped goldfish	8·00	2·50
1921	8f. (11) Red-capped oranda goldfish	27·00	6·00
1922	8f. (12) Red veil-tailed goldfish	27·00	6·00

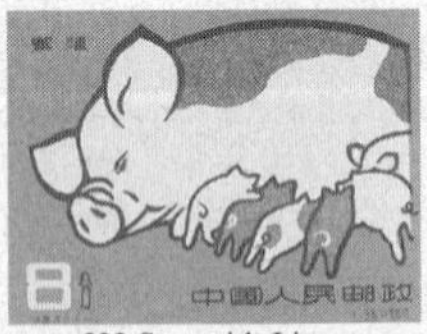

323 Sow with Litter

1960. Pig-breeding.

1923	**323**	8f. black and red	15·00	1·50
1924	–	8f. black and green	15·00	1·50
1925	–	8f. black and mauve	15·00	5·00
1926	–	8f. black and olive	19·00	1·50
1927	–	8f. black and orange	19·00	5·00

DESIGNS: No. 1924, Pig being inoculated; No. 1925, Group of pigs; No. 1926, Pig and feeding pens; No. 1927, Pig and crop-bales.

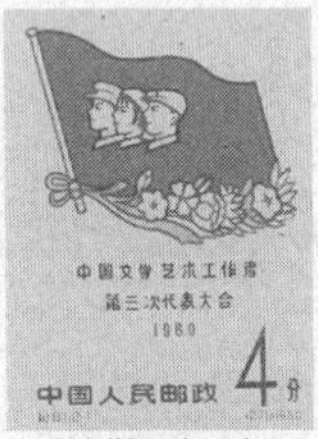

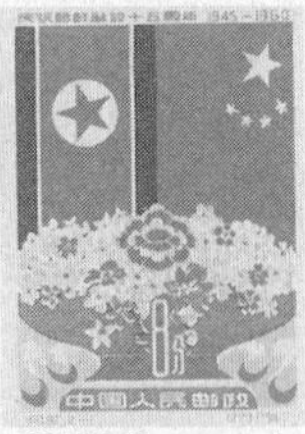

324 "Serving the Workers" **325** N. Korean and Chinese Flags, and Flowers

1960. 3rd National Literary and Art Workers' Congress, Peking. Inscr "1960".

1928	**324**	4f. red, sepia and green	7·00	1·50
1929	–	8f. red, bistre & turq	10·00	2·00

DESIGN: 8f. Inscribed stone seal.

1960. 15th Anniv of Liberation of Korea.

1930	**325**	8f. red, yellow and green	13·00	3·00
1931	–	8f. red, indigo and blue	13·00	3·00

DESIGN: No. 1931, "Flying Horse" of Korea.

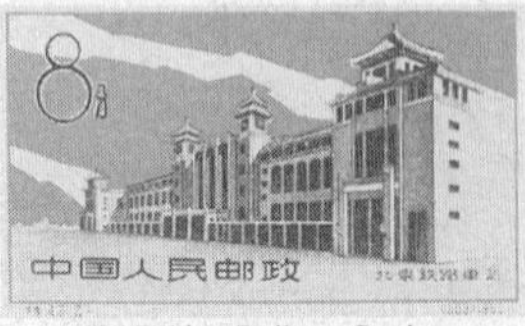

326 Peking Railway Station

1960. Opening of New Peking Railway Station.

1932	**326**	8f. multicoloured	11·00	3·50
1933	–	10f. blue, cream & turq	16·00	4·25

DESIGN: 10f. Steam train arriving at station.

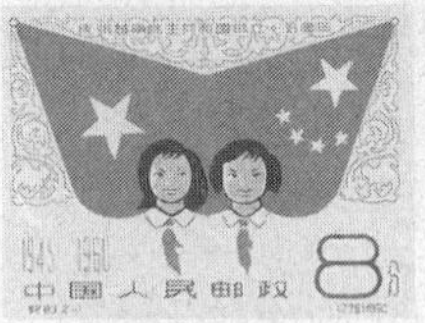

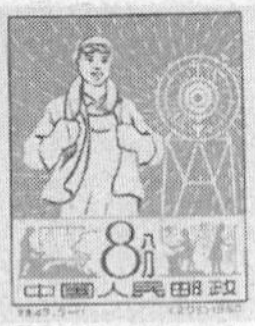

327 Chinese and N. Vietnamese Flags, and Children **328** Worker and Spray Fan

1960. 15th Anniv of N. Vietnam Republic.

1934	**327**	8f. red, yellow & black	5·50	1·00
1935	–	8f. multicoloured	5·50	2·00

DESIGN—VERT: No. 1935, "Lake of the Returning Sword", Hanoi.

1960. Public Health Campaign.

1936	**328**	8f. black and orange	2·10	10
1937	–	8f. green and blue	2·10	10
1938	–	8f. brown and blue	2·10	20
1939	–	8f. lake and brown	2·10	20
1940	–	8f. blue and turquoise	2·10	65

DESIGNS: No. 1937, Spraying insecticide; No. 1938, Cleaning windows; No. 1939, Medical examination of child; No. 1940, "Tai Chi Chuan" (Chinese physical drill).

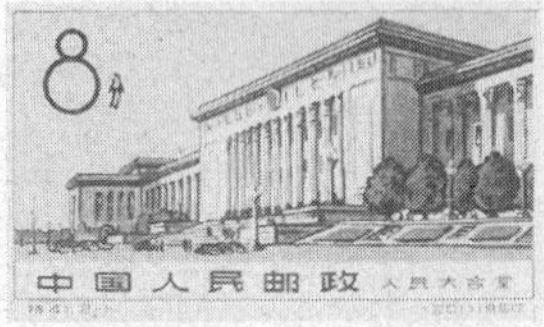

329 Facade of Great Hall

1960. Completion of "Great Hall of the People". Multicoloured.

1941	8f. Type **329**	10·00	2·50
1942	10f. Interior of Great Hall	16·00	4·00

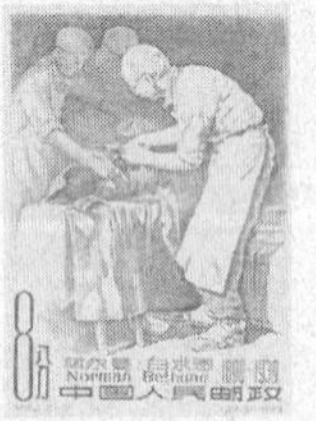

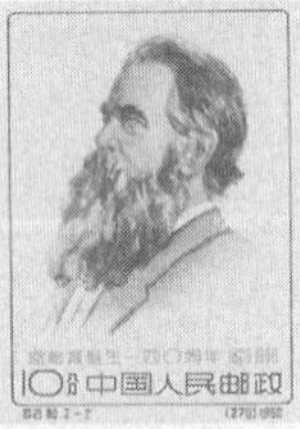

330 Dr. N. Bethune operating on Soldier **331** Friedrich Engels

1960. 70th Birth Anniv of Dr. Norman Bethune (Canadian surgeon with 8th Route Army).

1943	**330**	8f. grey, black and red	4·25	1·00
1944	–	8f. brown	4·25	30

PORTRAIT. No. 1943 Dr. N. Bethune.

1960. 140th Birth Anniv of Engels.

1945	–	8f. brown	7·00	1·75
1946	**331**	10f. orange and blue	10·00	2·25

DESIGN: 8f. Engels addressing congress at The Hague.

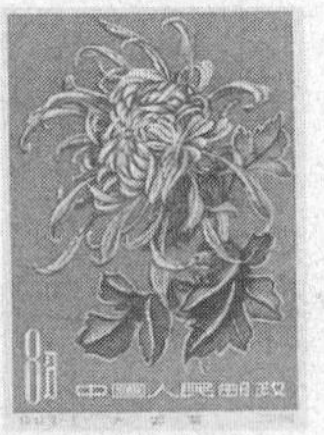

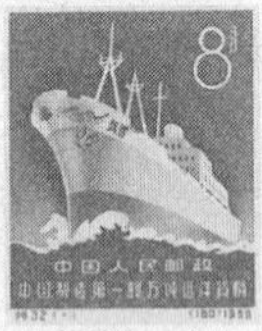

332 Big "Ju-I" **333** "Yue Jin"

1960. Chrysanthemums. Background colours given. Multicoloured.

1947	–	4f. blue	10·50	1·10
1948	–	4f. pink	21·00	1·10
1949	–	8f. grey	10·50	1·10
1950	**332**	8f. blue	10·50	1·10
1951	–	8f. green	10·50	1·10
1952	–	8f. violet	10·50	1·10
1953	–	8f. olive	10·50	1·10
1954	–	8f. turquoise	35·00	1·10
1955	–	10f. grey	10·50	1·10
1956	–	10f. brown	10·50	1·10
1957	–	20f. blue	10·50	1·10
1958	–	20f. red	28·00	3·50
1959	–	22f. brown	17·00	7·75
1960	–	22f. red	35·00	12·00
1961	–	30f. green	10·50	5·50
1962	–	30f. mauve	10·50	5·50
1963	–	35f. green	13·00	5·50
1964	–	52f. purple	13·00	9·25

CHRYSANTHEMUMS: No. 1947, "Hwang Shih Pa". No. 1948, "Green Peony". No. 1949, "Er Chiao". No. 1951, "Ju-I" with Golden Hooks. No. 1952, "Golden Peony". No. 1953, "Generalissimo's Banner". No. 1954, "Willow Thread". No. 1955, "Cassia on Salver of Hibiscus". No. 1956, "Pearls on Jade Salver". No. 1957, "Red Gold Lion". No. 1958, "Milky White Jade". No. 1959, "Purple Jade with Fragrant Beads". No. 1960, "Cassia on Ice Salver". No. 1961, "Inky Black Lotus". No. 1962, "Jade Bamboo Shoot of Superior Class". No. 1963, "Smiling Face". No. 1964, "Swan Ballet".

1960. 1st Chinese-built Freighter. Launching. No gum.

1965	**333**	8f. blue	3·75	1·00

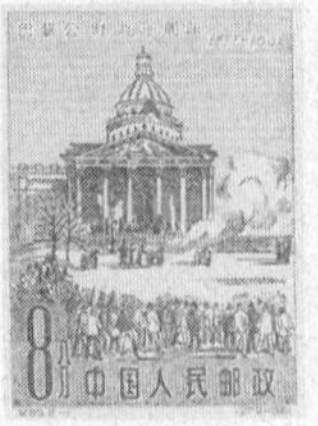

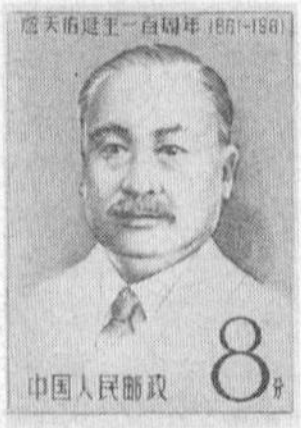

334 Pantheon, Paris **336** Chan Tien-yu

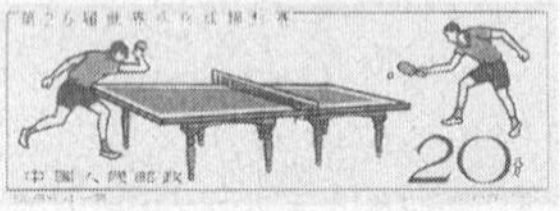

335 Table Tennis Match

1961. 90th Anniv of Paris Commune.

1966	**334**	8f. black and red	9·50	1·25
1967	–	8f. sepia and red	9·50	1·25

DESIGN: No. 1967, Proclamation of Commune.

1961. 26th World Table Tennis Championships, Peking. Multicoloured.

1968	8f. Championship emblem and jasmine	2·25	20
1969	10f. Table tennis bat and ball and Temple of Heaven	2·50	55
1970	20f. Type **335**	2·75	55
1971	22f. Peking Workers Gymnasium	3·00	30

1961. Birth Centenary of Chan Tien-yu (railway construction engineer).

1972	**336**	8f. black and sage	3·50	30
1973	–	10f. brown and sepia	6·50	1·10

DESIGN: 10f. Steam train on Peking-Changchow Railway.

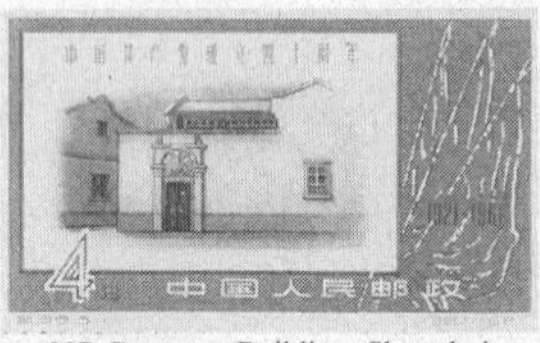

337 Congress Building, Shanghai

1961. 40th Anniv of Chinese Communist Party. Flags, red; frames, gold.

1974	**337**	4f. purple	11·00	55
1975	–	8f. green	11·00	1·50
1976	–	10f. brown	11·00	5·25
1977	–	20f. blue	16·00	1·25
1978	–	30f. red	22·00	2·00

DESIGNS: 8f. "August 1" Building, Nanchang; 10f. Provisional Central Govt. Building, Juichin; 20f. Pagoda Hill, Yenan; 30f. Gate of Heavenly Peace, Peking.

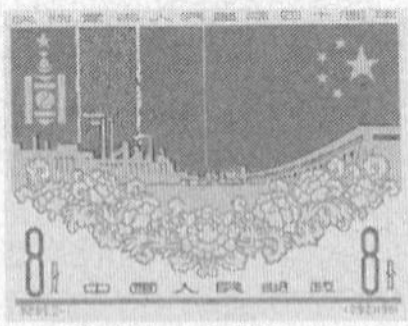

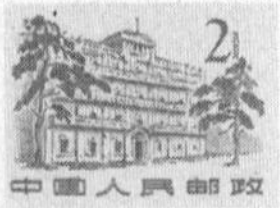

338 Flags of China and Mongolia **339** "August 1" Building, Nanchang

1961. 40th Anniv of Mongolian People's Revolution.

1979	**338**	8f. red, blue & yellow	10·00	1·40
1980	–	10f. orange, yellow & grn	17·00	6·50

DESIGN: 10f. Mongolian Government Building.

1961. Size 24 × 16½ mm. No gum.

1981	**339**	1f. blue	8·25	35
1982		1½f. red	14·00	35
1983		2f. green	8·75	1·40
1984	A	3f. violet	28·00	1·75
1985		4f. green	2·25	10
1986		5f. green	1·75	10
1987	B	8f. green	1·50	10
1988		10f. purple	3·50	10
1989		20f. blue	1·00	10
1990	C	22f. brown	1·00	10
1991		30f. blue	1·00	10
1992		50f. red	1·40	10

DESIGNS: A, Tree and Sha Chow Pa Building, Juichin; B, Yenan Pagoda; C, Gate of Heavenly Peace, Peking.

For redrawn, smaller, designs see Nos. 2010/21.

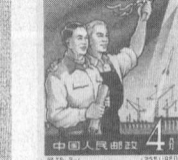

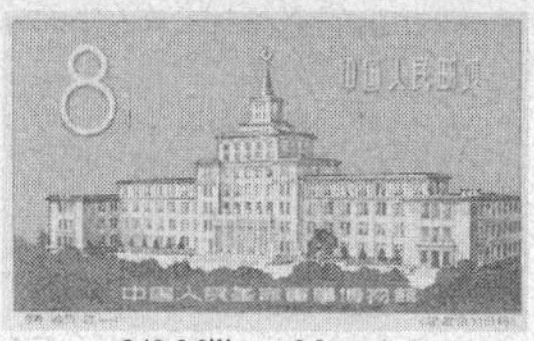
340 Military Museum

1961. People's Revolutionary Military Museum.
1993 **340** 8f. brown, green & blue 17·00 1·50
1994 10f. black, green & brn 17·00 1·50

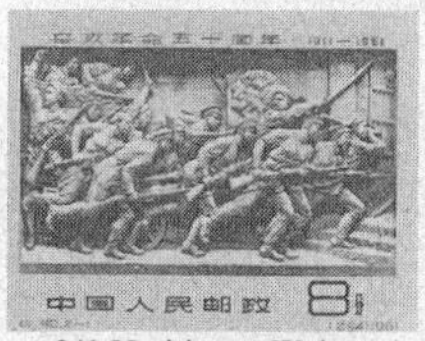
341 Uprising at Wuhan

1961. 50th Anniv of Revolution of 1911.
1995 **341** 8f. black and grey . . . 10·00 2·25
1996 – 10f. black and brown . . 15·00 1·00
DESIGN—VERT: 10f. Dr. Sun Yat-sen.

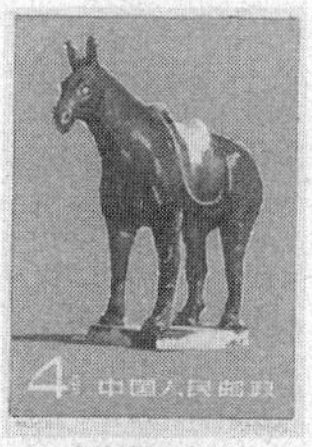
342 Donkey

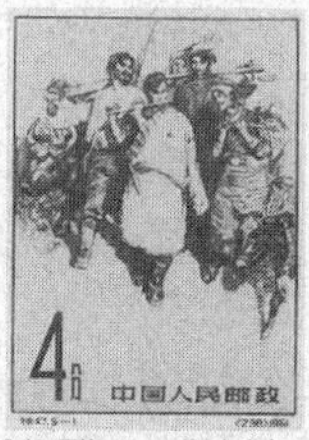
343 Tibetans Rejoicing

1961. Tang Dynasty Pottery (618–907 A.D.). Centres multicoloured. Background colours given.
1997 **342** 4f. blue . . . . 8·25 50
1998 – 8f. green . . . . 8·50 50
1999 – 8f. purple . . . . 8·50 50
2000 – 10f. blue . . . . 10·00 75
2001 – 20f. olive . . . . 10·50 2·50
2002 – 22f. turquoise . . . . . 11·50 4·00
2003 – 30f. red . . . . 13·00 10·00
2004 – 50f. slate . . . . 13·00 5·00
DESIGNS: No. 1998, Donkey; Nos. 1999/2002, Various horses; Nos. 2003/4, Various camels.

1961. "Rebirth of the Tibetan People".
2005 **343** 4f. brown and buff . . . 5·50 55
2006 – 8f. brown and turquoise 6·50 75
2007 – 10f. brown and yellow 9·50 1·25
2008 – 20f. brown and pink . . 19·00 2·25
2009 – 30f. brown and blue . . 32·00 3·50
DESIGNS: 8f. Sower; 10f. Tibetan celebrating "bumper crop"; 20f. "Responsible Citizens"; 30f. Tibetan children.

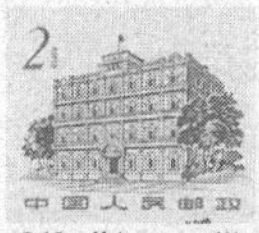
343a "August 1" Building, Nanchang

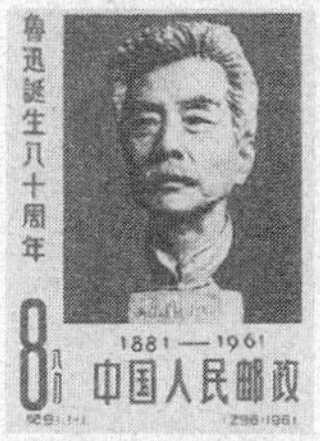
344 Lu Hsun (after Hsieh Chia-seng)

1962. Size $20\frac{1}{2} \times 16\frac{1}{2}$ mm. No gum.
2010 **343a** 1f. blue 50 10
2011 2f. green 50 10
2013 A 3f. violet 50 10
2014 **343a** 3f. brown . . . . . . 1·75 75
2015 A 4f. green 50 10
2016 B 4f. red . . . . 2·00 75
2017 C 8f. green 80 10
2018 10f. purple . . . . . . 1·00 10
2019 20f. blue . . . . 1·00 10
2020 B 30f. blue . . . . 1·75 10
2021 52f. red . . . . 1·90 1·00
DESIGNS: A, Tree and Sha Chow Pa Building, Juichin; B, Gate of Heavenly Peace, Peking; C, Yenan Pagoda.

1962. 80th Birth Anniv of Lu Hsun (writer).
2022 **344** 8f. black and red . . . . 1·75 50

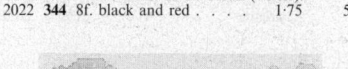

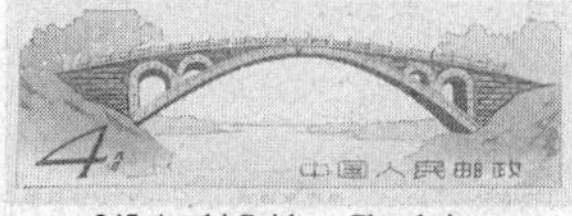
345 Anchi Bridge, Chaohsien

1962. Ancient Chinese Bridges.
2023 **345** 4f. violet and lavender 1·75 30
2024 – 8f. slate and green . . 1·75 30
2025 – 10f. sepia and bistre . . 2·50 65
2026 – 20f. blue and turquoise 3·50 1·25
BRIDGES: 8f. Paotai, Soochow. 10f. Chupu, Kuanhsien. 20f. Chenyang, Sankiang.

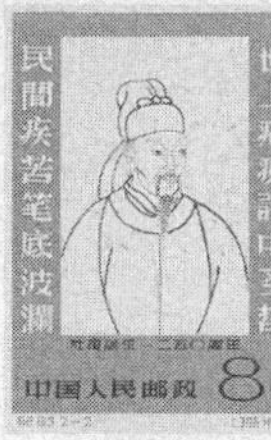
346 Tu Fu

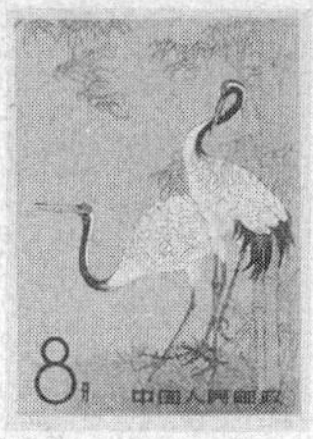
347 Manchurian Cranes and Trees

1962. 1250th Birth Anniv of Tu Fu (poet).
2027 – 4f. black and bistre . . . 11·00 70
2028 **346** 8f. black and turquoise 11·00 1·50
DESIGN: 4f. Tu Fu's Memorial, Chengtu.

1962. "The Sacred Crane". Paintings by Chen Chi-fo. Multicoloured.
2029 8f. Type **347** . . . . 20·00 3·25
2030 10f. Two cranes in flight . . 20·00 3·75
2031 20f. Crane on rock . . . . 20·00 4·75

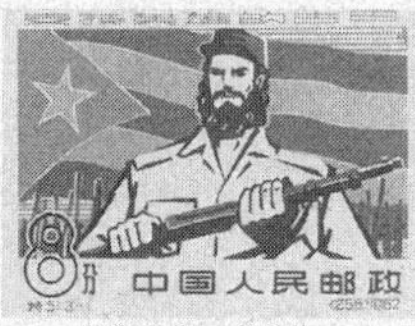
348 Cuban Soldier

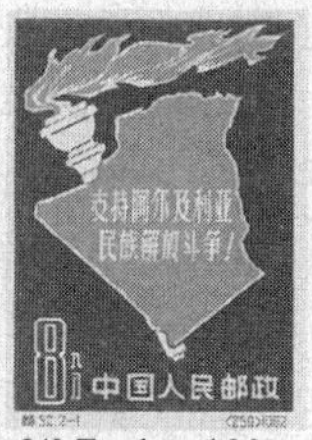
349 Torch and Map

1962. "Support for Cuba".
2032 **348** 8f. black and lake . . . 23·00 7·00
2033 – 10f. black and green . . 23·00 2·50
2034 – 22f. black and blue . . . 50·00 17·00
DESIGNS: 10f. Sugar-cane planter; 22f. Militiaman and woman.

1961. "Support for Algeria".
2035 **349** 8f. orange and brown . . 75 15
2036 – 22f. brown and ochre . . 75 20
DESIGN: 22f. Algerian patriots.

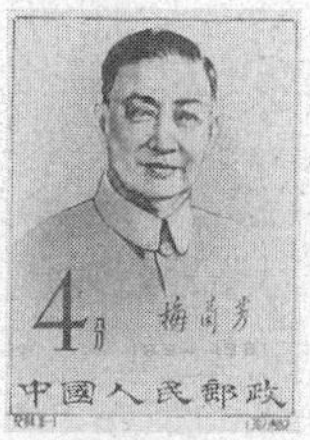
350 Mei Lan-fang (actor)

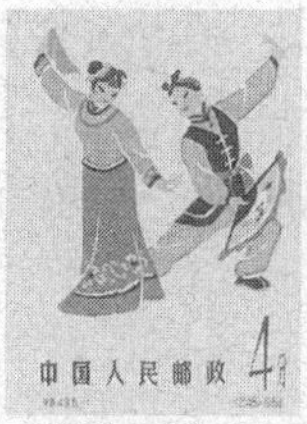
351 Han "Flower Drum" Dance

1962. "Stage Art of Mei Lan-fang". Multicoloured. Each showing Lan-fang in stage costume with items given below.
2037 4f. Type **350** . . . . 70·00 10·00
2038 8f. Drum . . . . 20·00 3·00
2039 8f. Fan . . . . 20·00 2·50
2040 10f. Swords . . . . 20·00 3·00
2041 20f. Bag . . . . 20·00 4·00
2042 22f. Ribbons (horiz) . . . . 40·00 8·00
2043 30f. Loom (horiz) . . . . . 80·00 25·00
2044 50f. Long sleeves (horiz) . . 65·00 20·00

1962. Chinese Folk Dances (1st issue). Multicoloured. No gum.
2045 4f. Type **351** 85 35
2046 8f. Mongolian "Ordos" . . 85 35
2047 10f. Chuang "Catching shrimp" . . . . 1·00 35
2048 20f. Tibetan "Fiddle" . . . 1·25 35
2049 30f. Yi "Friend" . . . . . 2·00 75
2050 50f. Uighur "Tambourine" 5·25 1·40
See also Nos. 2104/15.

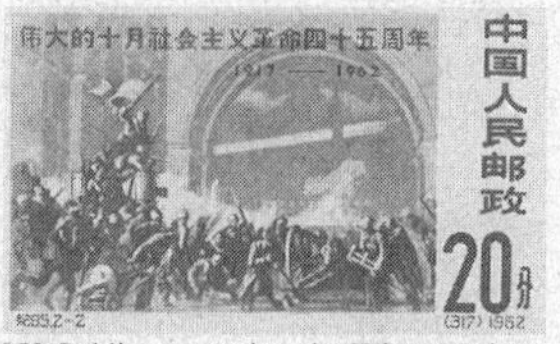
352 Soldiers storming the Winter Palace, Petrograd

1962. 45th Anniv of Russian Revolution.
2051 – 8f. brown and red . . . 18·00 1·00
2052 **352** 20f. bronze and red . . . 25·00 2·00
DESIGN—VERT: 8f. Lenin leading soldiers.

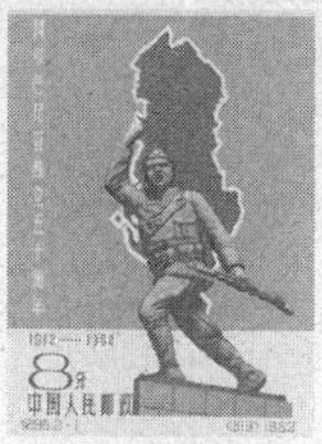
353 Revolutionary Statue and Map

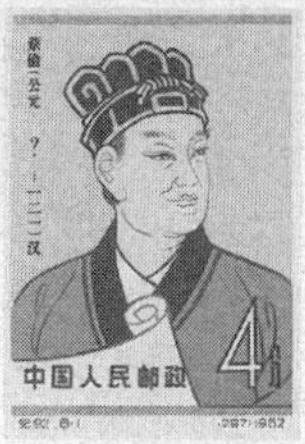
354 Tsai Lun (A.D. ?–121, inventor of paper making process)

1962. 50th Anniv of Albanian Independence.
2053 **353** 8f. sepia and blue . . . 1·75 40
2054 – 10f. multicoloured . . . 2·50 60
DESIGN: 10f. Albanian flag and girl pioneer.

1962. Scientists of Ancient China. Multicoloured.
2055 4f. Type **354** . . . . 6·25 30
2056 4f. Paper-making . . . . . 3·25 30
2057 8f. Sun Szu-miao (581–682, physician) . . . . 3·25 30
2058 8f. Preparing medical treatise . . . . 3·25 30
2059 10f. Shen Ko (1031–1095, geologist) . . . . 3·25 40
2060 10f. Making field notes . . 4·00 50
2061 20f. Ku Shou-chin (1231–1316, astronomer) . . . 7·75 2·75
2062 20f. Astronomical equipment 7·75 2·75

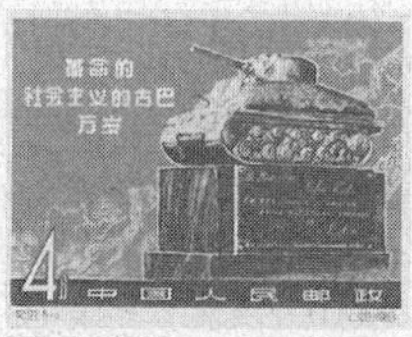
355 Tank Monument, Havana

1963. 4th Anniv of Cuban Revolution.
2063 **355** 4f. sepia and red . . . . 24·00 1·50
2064 – 4f. black and green . . . 17·00 1·50
2065 – 8f. lake and brown . . . 17·00 1·50
2066 – 8f. lake and brown . . . 55·00 4·50
2067 – 10f. black and buff . . . 55·00 6·00
2068 – 10f. sepia, red and blue 55·00 16·00
DESIGNS—As Type **355**: No. 2064, Cuban revolutionaries; No. 2067, Cuban soldier; No. 2068, Castro and Cuban flag. LARGER ($48\frac{1}{2} \times 27$ mm) No. 2065, Crowd in Havana (value on left); No. 2066, Crowd in Peking (value on right).

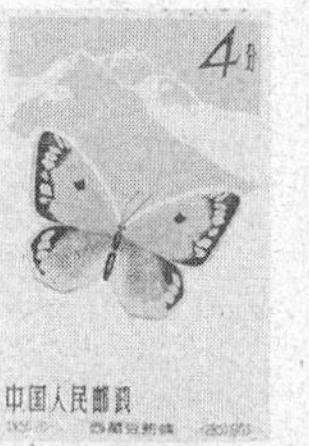
356 Tibetan Clouded Yellow

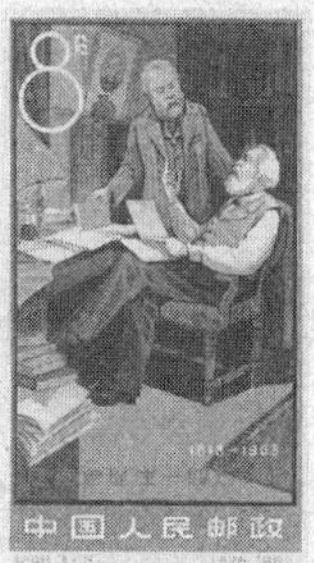
357 Marx and Engels

1963. Butterflies. Multicoloured. No gum.
2069 4f. (1) Type **356** . . . . . 6·25 50
2070 4f. (2) Tritailed glory . . . 6·25 50
2071 4f. (3) Neumogeni jungle queen . . . . 6·25 50
2072 4f. (4) Washan swordtail . . 6·25 50
2073 4f. (5) Striped ringlet . . . 6·25 50
2074 8f. (6) Green dragontail . . 12·50 50
2075 8f. (7) Dilunuleted peacock 12·50 50
2076 8f. (8) Yamfly . . . . . . 12·50 50
2077 8f. (9) Golden kaiser-i-hind 12·50 50
2078 8f. (10) Mushaell hair-streak 12·50 50
2079 10f. (11) Yellow orange-tip 12·50 75
2080 10f. (12) Great jay . . . . 12·50 75
2081 10f. (13) Striped punch . . . 12·50 75
2082 10f. (14) Beck butterfly . . . 12·50 75
2083 10f. (15) Omei skipper . . . 12·50 75
2084 20f. (16) Philippine birdwing 7·50 1·50
2085 20f. (17) Keeled apollo . . . 7·50 1·50
2086 22f. (18) Blue-banded king crow . . . . 7·50 4·00
2087 30f. (19) Solskyi copper . . 7·50 7·50
2088 50f. (20) Clipper . . . . . 15·00 15·00

1983. 145th Birth Anniv of Karl Marx. No. gum.
2089 – 8f. black, pink & gold 5·50 1·50
2090 – 8f. red and gold . . . . 5·50 1·50
2091 **357** 8f. brown and gold . . . 5·50 1·50
DESIGNS: No. 2089, Marx; No. 2090, Slogan "Workers of the World Unite" over cover of 1st edition of "Communist Manifesto".

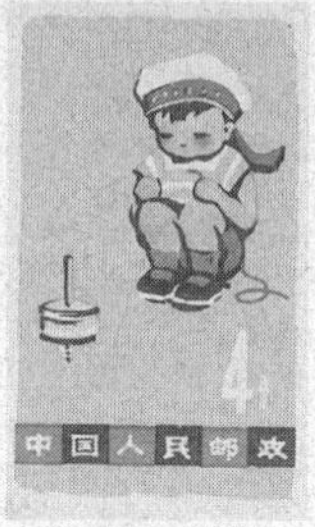
358 Child with Top

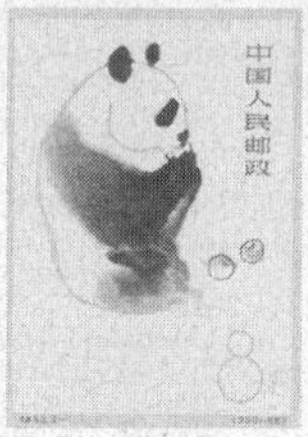
359 Giant Panda eating Apples

1963. Children. Multicoloured, background colours given. No gum.
2092 **358** 4f. turquoise 70 10
2093 – 4f. brown 70 10
2094 – 8f. grey 70 10
2095 – 8f. blue 70 10
2096 – 8f. beige 70 10
2097 – 8f. slate 70 10
2098 – 8f. green 70 10
2099 – 8f. grey 70 10
2100 – 10f. green . . . . 1·60 80
2101 – 10f. violet . . . . 1·60 80
2102 – 20f. drab . . . . 5·00 1·50
2103 – 20f. green . . . . 5·00 1·50
DESIGNS (each shows a child): No. 2093, Eating candied hawberries; No. 2094, As "traffic policeman"; No. 2095, With toy windmill; No. 2096, Listening to caged cricket; No. 2097, With toy sword; No 2098, Embroidering; No. 2099, With umbrella; No. 2100, Playing with sand; No. 2101, Playing table tennis; No. 2102, Doing sums; No. 2103, Flying kite.

1963. Chinese Folk Dances (2nd issue). As T **351** but inscr "(261) 1962" to "(266) 1962" in bottom right corner. Multicoloured. No gum.
2104 4f. Puyi "Weaving Cloth" 1·00 10
2105 8f. Kazakh . . . . 1·00 10
2106 10f. Olunchun . . . . 1·00 10
2107 20f. Kaochan "Labour" . . 1·00 35
2108 30f. Miao "Reed-pipe" . . . 1·75 60
2109 50f. Korean "Fan" . . . . 5·25 85

1963. Chinese Folk Dances (3rd issue). As T **351** but inscr "(279) 1963" to "(284) 1963" in bottom right corner. Multicoloured. No gum.
2110 4f. Yu "Wedding Ceremony" . . . . 1·40 20
2111 8f. Pai "Encircling Mountain Forest" . . . . 1·40 20
2112 10f. Yao "Long Drum" . . . 1·60 20
2113 20f. Li "Third Day of Third Month" . . . . 1·60 40
2114 30f. Kava "Knife" . . . . 2·75 50
2115 50f. Tai "Peacock" . . . . 4·25 85

1963. Giant Panda. Perf or imperf.
2116 **359** 8f. black and blue . . . 25·00 2·00
2117 – 8f. black and green . . . 25·00 5·00
2118 – 10f. black and drab . . 25·00 3·00
DESIGNS—As Type **278**. No. 2117, Giant panda eating bamboo shoots. HORIZ: (52 × 31 mm): No. 2118, Two giant pandas.

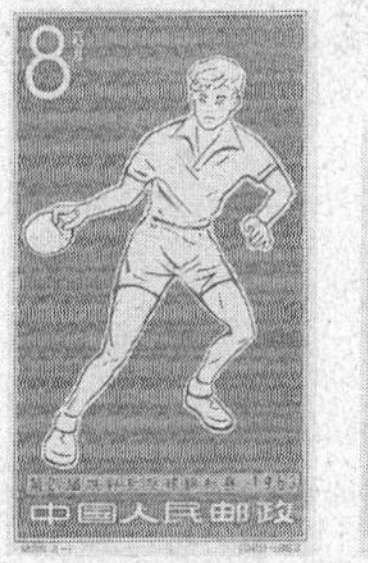
360 Table Tennis Player

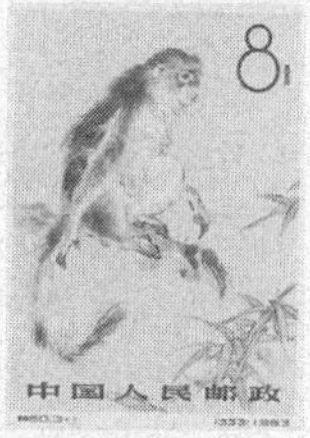
361 Snub-nosed Monkey

1963. 27th World Table-Tennis Championships.
2119 **360** 8f. grey . . . . 11·00 1·00
2120 – 8f. brown . . . . 11·00 1·50
DESIGN: No. 2120, Trophies won by Chinese team.

1963. Snub-nosed Monkeys. Multicoloured.
2121 8f. Type **361** . . . . 8·00 1·50
2122 10f. Two monkeys . . . . . 8·00 1·50
2123 22f. Two monkeys on branch of tree . . . . . 12·00 5·00

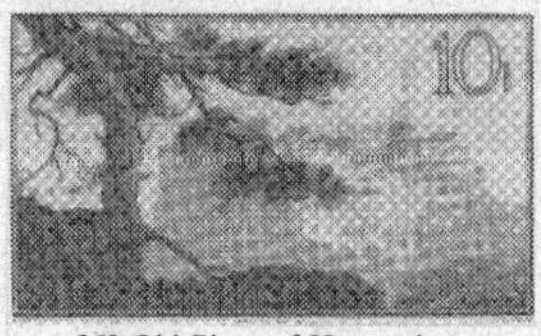
362 Old Pines of Hwangshan

1963. Hwangshan Landscapes. Multicoloured.
2124 4f. (1) Mount of The Green Jade Screen . . . . . . 11·50 1·00
2125 4f. (2) The Guest-welcoming Pines . . . . 11·50 1·00
2126 4f. (3) Pines and rocks behind the lake . . . . . 11·50 1·00
2127 4f. (4) Terrace of Keeping Cool . . . . 11·50 1·00
2128 8f. (5) Mount of the Heavenly Capital . . . . 16·00 1·00

2129 8f. (6) Mount of Scissors . . 16·00 1·00
2130 8f. (7) Forest of Ten Thousand Pines . . . . . . 16·00 1·00
2131 8f. (8) The Flowering Bush in a Dream . . . . . . 16·00 1·00
2132 10f. (9) Mount of the Lotus Flower . . . . 21·00 1·00
2133 10f. (10) Cumulus Flood Wave of the Eastern Lake 21·00 1·00
2134 10f. (11) Type **362** . . . . . 21·00 1·00
2135 10f. (12) Cumulus on the Eastern Lake . . . . . . 21·00 1·00
2136 20f. (13) The Stalagmite Mountain Range . . . . 28·00 7·50
2137 22f. (14) The Apes of the Stone watch the lake below . . . . 38·00 10·00
2138 30f. (15) The Forest of Lions . . . . £100 40·00
2139 50f. (16) The Fairy Isles of Peng Lai . . . . 85·00 20·00
The 4f. and 8f. values are vert.

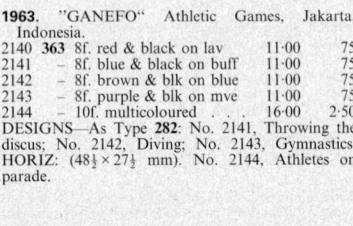

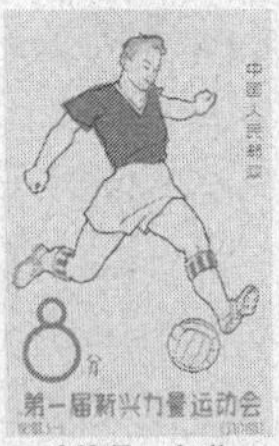
363 Football

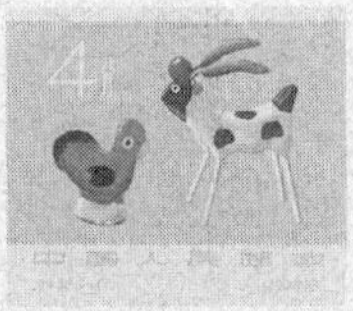
364 Clay Rooster and Goat

1963. "GANEFO" Athletic Games, Jakarta, Indonesia.
2140 **363** 8f. red & black on lav 11·00 75
2141 – 8f. blue & black on buff 11·00 75
2142 – 8f. brown & blk on blue 11·00 75
2143 – 8f. purple & blk on mve 11·00 75
2144 – 10f. multicoloured . . . 16·00 2·50
DESIGNS—As Type **282**: No. 2141, Throwing the discus; No. 2142, Diving; No. 2143, Gymnastics. HORIZ: (48½ × 27½ mm). No. 2144, Athletes on parade.

1963. Chinese Folk Toys. Multicoloured. No. gum.
2145 4f. (1) Type **364** 85 20
2146 4f. (4) Cloth camel 85 20
2147 4f. (7) Cloth tigers 85 20
2148 8f. (2) Clay ox and rider . . 85 20
2149 8f. (5) Cloth rabbit, wooden figure and clay cock . . . 85 20
2150 8f. (8) Straw cock 85 20
2151 10f. (3) Cloth donkey and clay bird 85 20
2152 10f. (6) Clay lion 85 20
2153 10f. (9) Clay-paper tumbler and cloth tiger 85 20

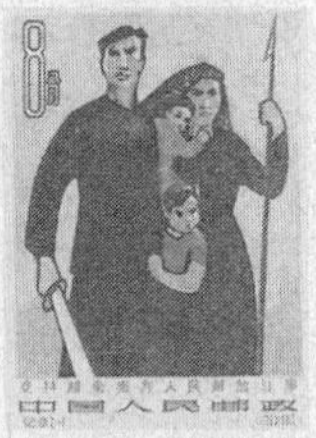
365 Vietnamese Family

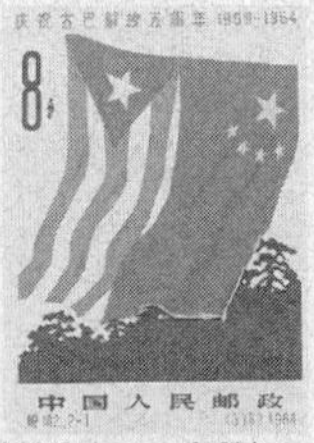
366 Cuban and Chinese Flags

1963. "Liberation of South Vietnam". Mult.
2154 8f. Type **365** . . . . 4·50 1·00
2155 8f. Vietnamese with flag . . 4·50 1·00

1964. 5th Anniv of Cuban Revolution. Mult.
2156 8f. Type **366** . . . . 8·00 1·00
2157 8f. Boy waving flag . . . . 14·00 4·00

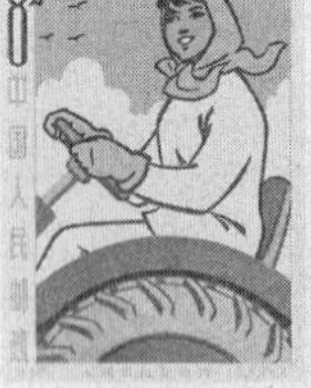
367 Woman driving Tractor

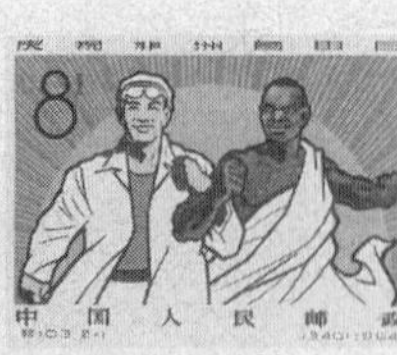
368 "Sino-African Friendship"

1964. "Women of the People's Commune". Multicoloured.
2158 8f. (1) Type **367** . . . . . 1·10 20
2159 8f. (2) Harvesting . . . . . 1·10 20
2160 8f. (3) Picking cotton . . . 1·10 20
2161 8f. (4) Picking fruit . . . . 1·10 20
2162 8f. (5) Reading book . . . 1·10 30
2163 8f. (6) Holding rifle . . . . 1·10 40

1964. African Freedom Day.
2164 **368** 8f. multicoloured 75 25
2165 – 8f. brown and black . . 75 25
DESIGN: No. 2165, African beating drum.

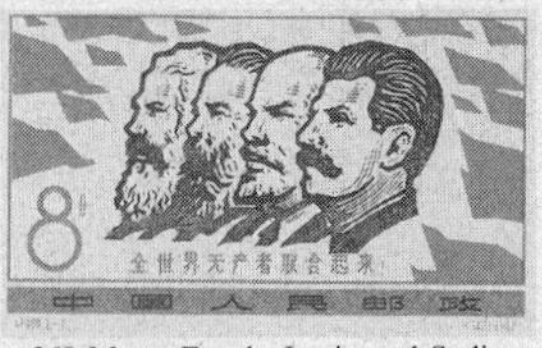
369 Marx, Engels, Lenin and Stalin

1964. Labour Day.
2166 **369** 8f. black, red & gold . . 16·00 3·50
2167 – 8f. black, red & gold . . 9·00 2·00
DESIGN: No. 2167, Workers and banners.

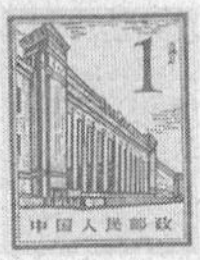
370 History Museum

1964. No gum.
2168 **370** 1f. brown 10 10
2169 A 1½f. purple 10 10
2170 B 2f. green 10 10
2171 C 3f. green 15 10
2172 **370** 4f. blue 15 10
2172a A 5f. purple 50 10
2173 B 8f. red 50 10
2174 C 10f. drab 75 10
2175 **370** 20f. violet 75 10
2176 A 22f. orange . . . . . . 1·40 10
2177 B 30f. green . . . . . . 2·10 40
2177a C 50f. blue . . . . 5·00 2·00
DESIGNS: A, Gate of Heavenly Peace; B, Great Hall of the People; C, Military Museum.

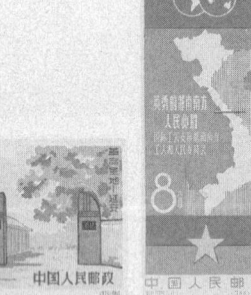

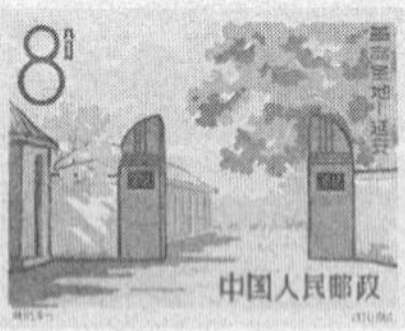
371 Date Orchard, Yenan

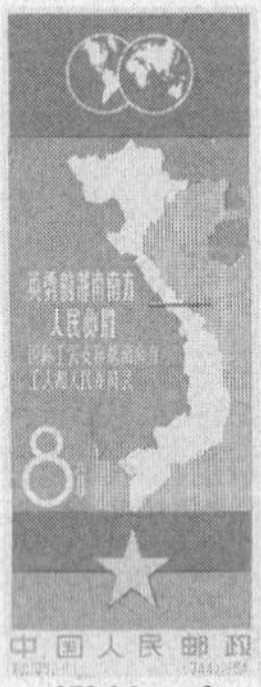
372 Map of Vietnam and Flag

1964. "Yenan-Shrine of the Chinese Revolution". Yenan buildings. Multicoloured.
2178 8f. (1) Type **371** . . . . . . 15·00 45
2179 8f. (2) Central Auditorium, Yang Chia Ling . . . . . . 3·75 25
2180 8f. (3) Mao Tse-tung's Office and Residence at Date Orchard, Yenan . . . . . 3·75 25
2181 8f. (4) Auditorium, Wang Chia Ping . . . . 3·75 30
2182 8f. (5) Border Region Assembly Hall . . . . . 22·00 75
2183 52f. (6) Pagoda Hill . . . . . 12·50 5·00

1964. South Vietnam Victory Campaign.
2184 **372** 8f. multicoloured . . . . 12·50 2·50

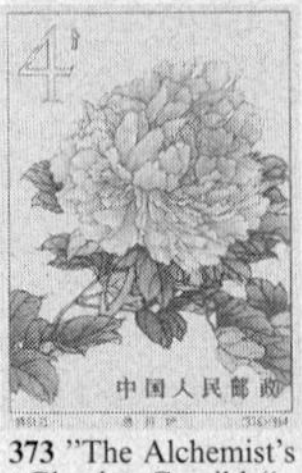
373 "The Alchemist's Glowing Crucible" (peony)

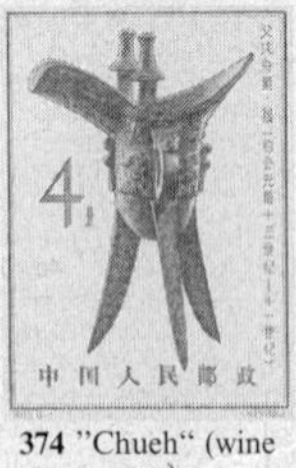
374 "Chueh" (wine cup)

1964. Chinese Peonies. Multicoloured.
2185 4f. (1) Type **373** . . . . . . 5·75 1·00
2186 4f. (2) Night-shining Jade 5·75 1·00
2187 8f. (3) Purple Kuo's Cap . . 9·50 1·00
2188 8f. (4) Chao Pinks . . . . . 9·50 1·00
2189 8f. (5) Yao Yellows . . . . . 9·50 1·00
2190 8f. (6) Twin Beauties . . . 9·50 1·00
2191 8f. (7) Ice-veiled Rubies . . 9·50 1·00
2192 10f. (8) Gold-sprinkled Chinese Ink . . . . . . 12·00 1·00
2193 10f. (9) Cinnabar Jar . . . 12·00 1·00
2194 10f. (10) Lantien Jade . . . 13·50 1·00
2195 10f. (11) Imperial Robe Yellow . . . . 14·50 2·00
2196 10f. (12) Hu Reds . . . . . 14·50 2·00
2197 20f. (13) Pea Green . . . . 29·00 5·00
2198 43f. (14) Wei Purples . . . 35·00 20·00
2199 52f. (15) Intoxicated Celestial Peach . . . . . 60·00 15·00

1964. Bronze Vessels of the Yin Dynasty (before 1050 B.C.).
2200 **374** 4f. (1) black, grn & yell 6·00 20
2201 – 4f. (2) black, grn & yell 6·00 20
2202 – 8f. (3) black, grn & yell 7·50 30
2203 – 8f. (4) black, blue & grn 7·50 30
2204 – 10f. (5) black and drab 9·00 40
2205 – 10f. (6) black, grn & yell 9·00 40
2206 – 20f. (7) black and grey 11·00 3·50
2207 – 20f. (8) black, bl & yell 11·00 3·50
DESIGNS: No. 2201, "Ku" (beaker); 2202, "Kuang" (wine urn); 2203, "Chia" (wine cup); 2204, "Tsun" (wine vessel); 2205, "Yu" (wine urn); 2206, "Tsun" (wine vessel); 2207, "Ting" (ceremonial cauldron).

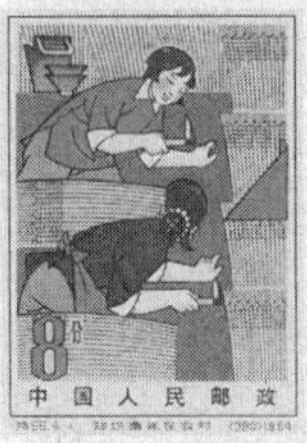
375 "Harvesting"

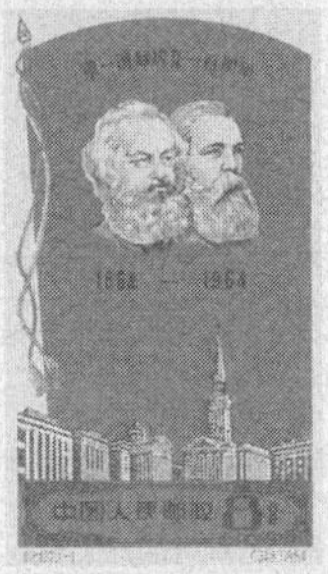
376 Marx, Engels and Trafalgar Square, London (vicinity of old St. Martin's Hall)

1964. Agricultural Students. Multicoloured.
2208 8f. (1) Type **375** . . . . . . 1·60 30
2209 8f. (2) "Sapling planting" 1·60 30
2210 8f. (3) "Study" . . . . . . 1·60 30
2211 8f. (4) "Scientific experiment" . . . . . . 1·60 30

1964. Centenary of "First International".
2212 **376** 8f. red, brown and gold 35·00 7·50

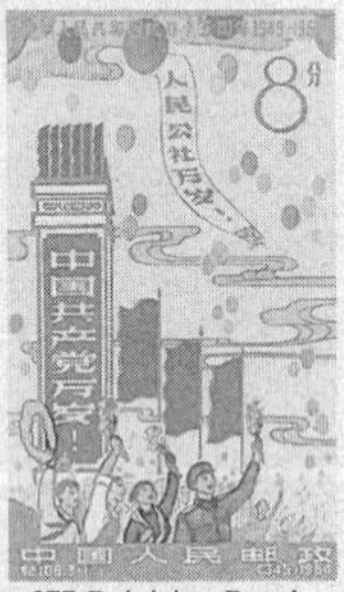
377 Rejoicing People

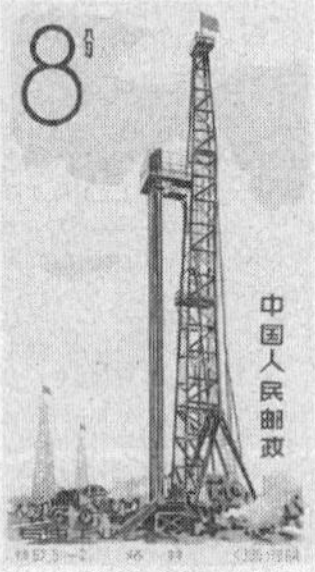
378 Oil Derrick

1964. 15th Anniv of People's Republic. Mult.
2213 8f. (1) Type **377** . . . . . . 14·00 1·75
2214 8f. (2) Chinese flag . . . . 14·00 1·75
2215 8f. (3) As T **377** in reverse 14·00 1·75
Nos. 2213/5 were issued in the form of a triptych, in sheets.

1964. Petroleum Industry. Multicoloured.
2216 4f. Geological surveyors and van (horiz) . . . . 48·00 3·00
2217 8f. Type **378** . . . . 22·00 1·00
2218 8f. Oil-extraction equipment 22·00 1·00
2219 10f. Refinery . . . . 38·00 1·00
2220 20f. Railway petroleum trucks (horiz) . . . . . . 90·00 8·00

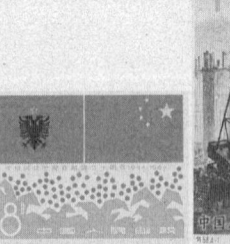

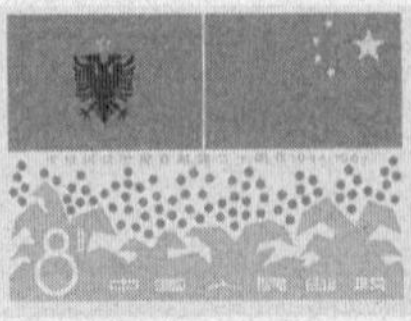
379 Albanian and Chinese Flags and Plants

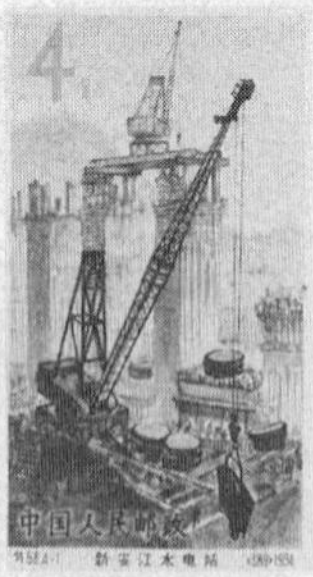
380 Dam under Construction

1964. 20th Anniv of Liberation of Albania.
2221 **379** 8f. multicoloured . . . . 10·00 1·25
2222 – 10f. black, red & yellow 12·00 5·75
DESIGN: 10f. Enver Hoxha and Albanian arms.

1964. Hsinankiang Hydro-electric Power Station. Multicoloured.
2223 4f. Type **380** . . . . 60·00 2·25
2224 8f. Installation of turbo-generator rotor . . . . . 14·50 1·00
2225 8f. Main dam . . . . 45·00 1·40
2226 20f. Pylon . . . . 70·00 7·50

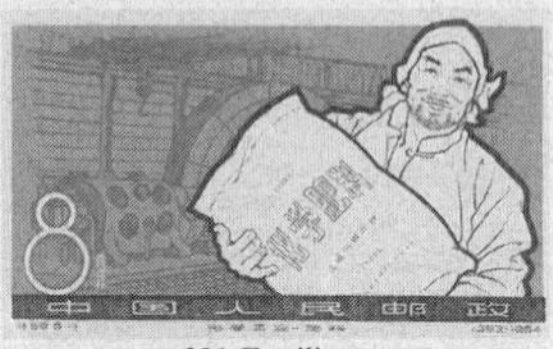
381 Fertilisers

1964. Chemical Industry. Main design and inscr in black; background colours given.
2227 **381** 8f. (1) red . . . . 2·00 20
2228 – 8f. (2) green . . . . . . 2·00 20
2229 – 8f. (3) brown . . . . . 2·00 20
2230 – 8f. (4) mauve . . . . . 2·00 20
2231 – 8f. (5) blue . . . . . . 2·00 20
2232 – 8f. (6) orange . . . . . 2·00 20
2233 – 8f. (7) violet . . . . . 2·00 20
2234 – 8f. (8) turquoise . . . . 2·00 20
DESIGNS: (2), Plastics; (3), Medicinal drugs; (4), Rubber; (5), Insecticides; (6), Acids; (7), Alkalis; (8), Synthetic fibres.

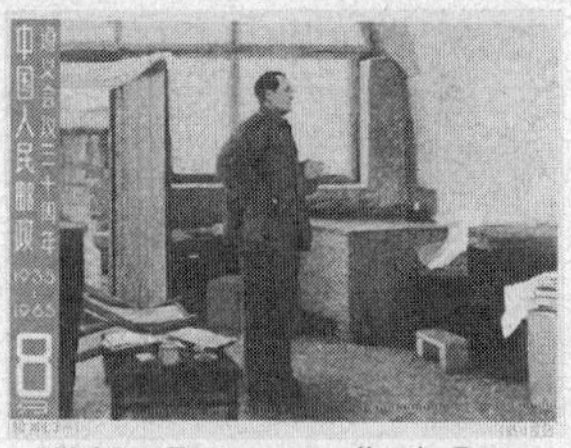
382 Mao Tse-tung standing in Room

1965. 30th Anniv of Tsunyi Conference. Mult.
2235 8f. (1) Type **382** . . . . . . 30·00 7·50
2236 8f. (2) Mao Tse-tung . . . 15·00 10·00
2237 8f. (3) "Victory at Loushan Pass" . . . . 25·00 14·00
No. 2236 is vert (26½ × 36 mm).

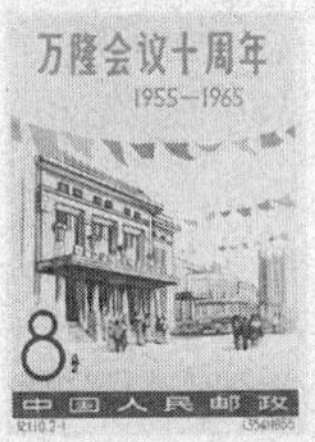

383 Conference Hall

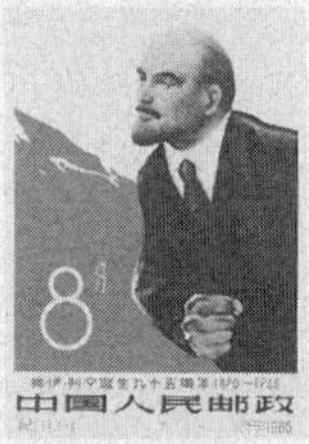
384 Lenin

1965. 10th Anniv of Bandung Conference. Mult.
2238 8f. Type **383** . . . . 1·00 30
2239 8f. Rejoicing Africans and Asians . . . . 1·00 30

1965. 95th Birth Anniv of Lenin.
2240 **384** 8f. multicoloured . . . . 10·50 4·00

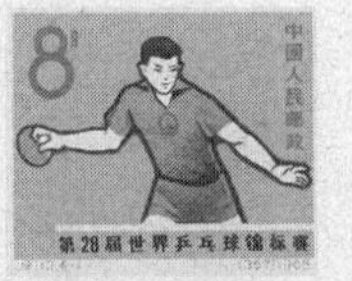
385 Table Tennis Player

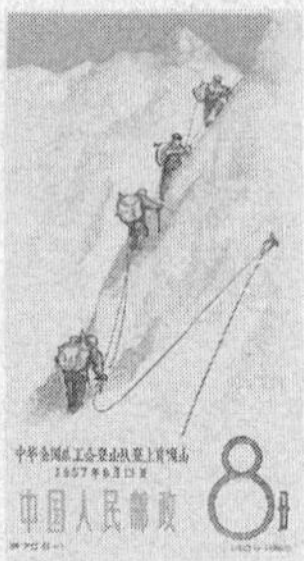
386 All China T.U. Federation Team scaling Mt. Minya Konka

1965. World Table Tennis Championships, Peking.
2241 **385** 8f. (1) multicoloured . . 20 10
2242 – 8f. (2) multicoloured . . 20 10
2243 – 8f. (3) multicoloured . . 20 10
2244 – 8f. (4) multicoloured . . 20 10
DESIGNS: Nos. 2242/4 each show different views of table tennis players.

1965. Chinese Mountaineering Achievements. Each black, yellow and blue.
2245 8f. (1) Type **386** . . . . . . 4·00 50
2246 8f. (2) Men and women's mixed team on slopes of Muztagh Ata . . . . . . 5·00 50
2247 8f. (3) Climbers on Mt. Jolmo Lungma . . . . . 5·00 50
2248 8f. (4) Women's team camping on Kongur Tiubie Tagh . . . . 5·00 50
2249 8f. (5) Climbers on Shishma Pangma . . . . 6·00 2·00

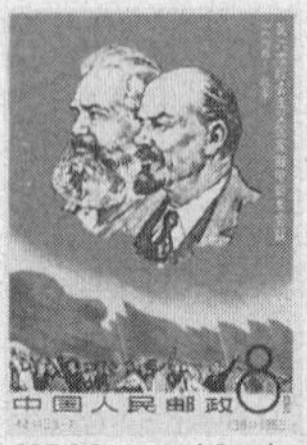
387 Marx and Lenin

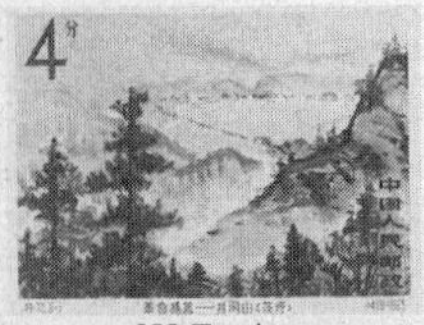
388 Tseping

1965. Organization of Socialist Countries' Postal Administrations Conference, Peking.
2250 **387** 8f. multicoloured . . . . 12·00 4·00

1965. "Chingkang Mountains – Cradle of the Chinese Revolution". Multicoloured.
2251 4f. (1) Type **388** . . . . . . 7·00 40
2252 8f. (2) Sanwantsun . . . . 7·00 40
2253 8f. (3) Octagonal Building, Maoping . . . . 28·00 40
2254 8f. (4) River and bridge at Lungshih . . . . 21·00 75
2255 8f. (5) Tachingtsun . . . . 14·00 75
2256 10f. (6) Bridge at Lungyuankou . . . . . . 14·00 40
2257 10f. (7) Hwangyangchieh . . 10·00 75
2258 52f. (8) Chingkang peaks . . 10·00 6·00

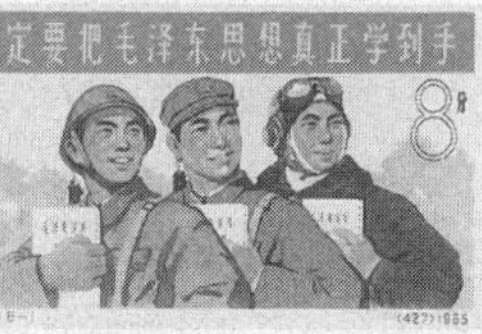

389 Soldiers with Texts

1965. People's Liberation Army. Mult.
2259 8f. (1) Type **389** . . . . . . 18·00 3·25
2260 8f. (2) Soldiers reading book 18·00 3·25
2261 8f. (3) Soldier with grenade-thrower . . . . 18·00 1·50
2262 8f. (4) Giving tuition in firing rifle . . . . 18·00 1·50
2263 8f. (5) Soldiers at rest . . . 9·50 1·50
2264 8f. (6) Bayonet charge . . . 9·50 1·50
2265 8f. (7) Soldier with banners 9·50 4·00
2266 8f. (8) Military band . . . . 9·50 2·25
Nos. 2263/6 are vert.

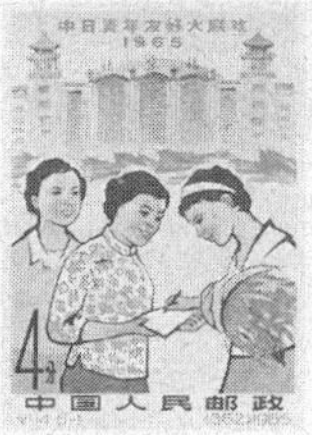

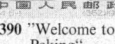

390 "Welcome to Peking"

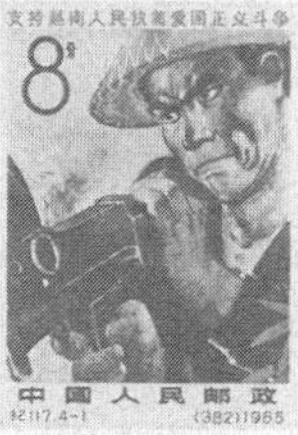

391 Soldier firing Weapon

1965. Chinese–Japanese. Youth Meeting, Peking. Multicoloured.
2267 4f. (1) Type **390** 60 30
2268 8f. (2) Chinese and Japanese youths with linked arms 60 30
2269 8f. (3) Chinese and Japanese girls 60 30
2270 10f. (4) Musical entertainment . . . . . . 1·00 30
2271 22f. (5) Emblem of Meeting 3·00 1·00

1965. "Vietnamese People's Struggle".
2272 **391** 8f. (1) brown and red . . 1·90 50
2273 – 8f. (2) olive and red . . 1·90 50
2274 – 8f. (3) purple and red . . 1·90 50
2275 – 8f. (4) black and red . . 1·90 50
DESIGNS—VERT: (2) Soldier with captured weapons; (3) Soldier giving victory salute. HORIZ: (48½ × 26 mm): (4) "Peoples of the world".

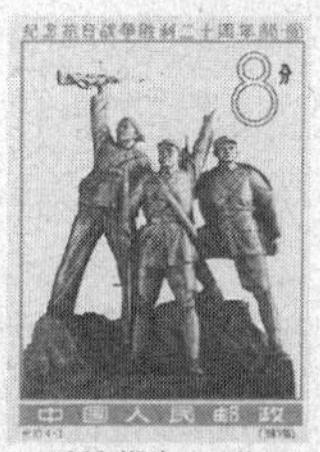

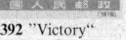

392 "Victory"

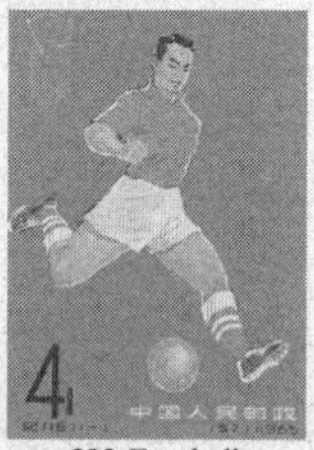

393 Football

1965. 20th Anniv of Victory over Japanese.
2276 – 8f. (1) multicoloured . . 15·00 5·00
2277 – 8f. (2) green and red . . 8·00 80
2278 **392** 8f. (3) sepia and red . . 8·00 80
2279 – 8f. (4) green and red . . 8·00 80
DESIGNS—HORIZ: (50½ × 36 mm): (1) Mao Tse-tung writing. As Type **392**—HORIZ: (2) Soldiers crossing Yellow River. (4) Recruits in cart.

1965. 2nd National Games. Multicoloured.
2280 4f. (1) Type **393** . . . . . . 6·00 30
2281 4f. (2) Archery . . . . . . 6·00 30
2282 8f. (3) Throwing the javelin 6·00 30
2283 8f. (4) Gymnastics . . . . . 6·00 30
2284 8f. (5) Volleyball . . . . . . 6·00 30
2285 10f. (6) Opening ceremony 29·00 30
2286 10f. (7) Cycling . . . . . . 60·00 30
2287 20f. (8) Diving . . . . . . 26·00 2·50
2288 22f. (9) Hurdling . . . . . 10·00 2·75
2289 30f. (10) Weightlifting . . . 10·00 6·00
2290 43f. (11) Basketball . . . . 13·00 10·00
The 10f. (6) is larger, 56 × 35½ mm.

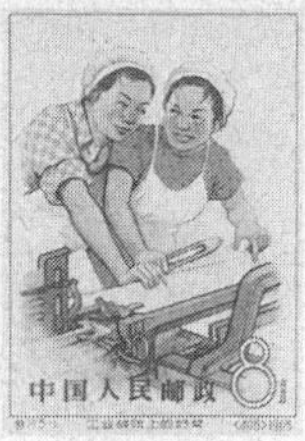

394 Textile Workers

1965. Women in Industry. Multicoloured.
2291 8f. (1) Type **394** . . . . . . 6·50 40
2292 8f. (2) Machine building . . 6·50 40
2293 8f. (3) Building construction 6·50 40
2294 8f. (4) Studying . . . . . . 6·50 60
2295 8f. (5) Militia guard . . . . 6·50 3·00

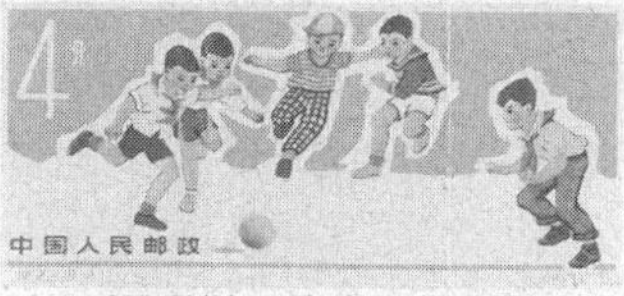

395 Children playing with Ball

1966. Children's Games. Multicoloured.
2296 4f. (1) Type **395** 50 30
2297 4f. (2) Racing 50 30
2298 8f. (3) Tobogganing 50 30
2299 8f. (4) Exercising 50 30
2300 8f. (5) Swimming 50 30
2301 8f. (6) Shooting 50 30
2302 10f. (7) Jumping with rope 80 30
2303 52f. (8) Playing table tennis 1·25 50

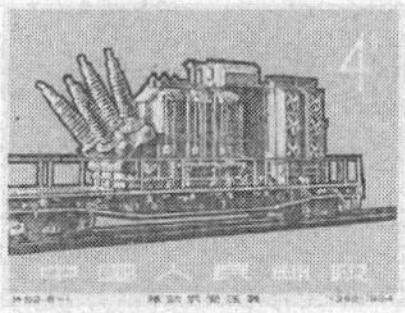
396 Mobile Transformer

1966. New Industrial Machines.
2304 **396** 4f. (1) black and yellow 6·25 50
2305 – 8f. (2) black and blue . . 9·50 30
2306 – 8f. (3) black and pink . . 9·50 30
2307 – 8f. (4) black and olive 9·50 30
2308 – 8f. (5) black and purple 9·50 30
2309 – 10f. (6) black and grey 12·50 30
2310 – 10f. (7) black & turq . . 12·50 2·00
2311 – 22f. (8) black and lilac 25·00 5·00
DESIGNS—VERT: (2), Electron microscope; (4), Vertical boring and turning machine; (6), Hydraulic press; (8), Electron accelerator. HORIZ: (3), Lathe; (5), Gear-grinding machine; (7), Milling machine.

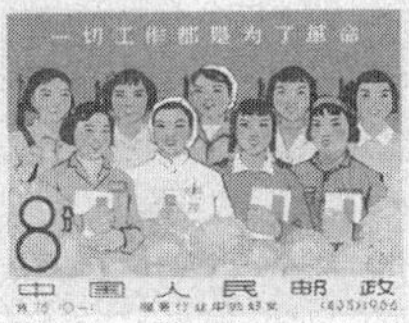

397 Women of Military and Other Services

1966. Women in Public Service. Mult.
2312 8f. (1) Type **397** 70 25
2313 8f. (2) Train conductress . . 70 25
2314 8f. (3) Red Cross worker . . 70 25
2315 8f. (4) Kindergarten teacher 70 25
2316 8f. (5) Roadsweeper 70 25
2317 8f. (6) Hairdresser 70 25
2318 8f. (7) Bus conductress . . . 70 25
2319 8f. (8) Travelling saleswoman 70 25
2320 8f. (9) Canteen worker . . . 70 25
2321 8f. (10) Rural postwoman 70 25

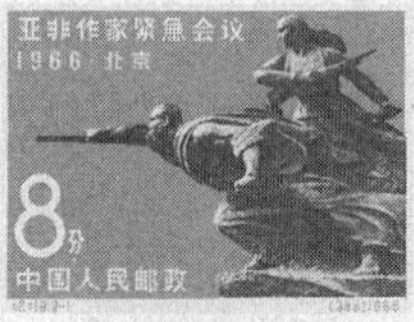

398 "Thunderstorm" (sculpture)

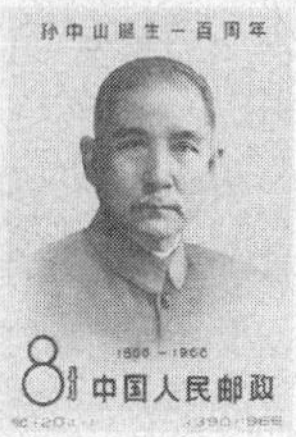

399 Dr. Sun Yat-sen

1966. Afro-Asian Writers' Meeting.
2322 **398** 8f. black and red . . . . 2·00 50
2323 – 22f. gold, yellow & red 4·00 1·60
DESIGN: 22f. Meeting emblem.

1966. Birth Centenary of Dr. Sun Yat-sen.
2324 **399** 8f. sepia and buff . . . 25·00 7·00

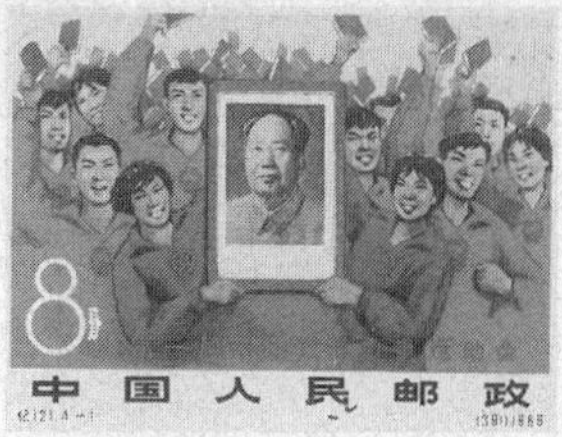

400 Athletes with Mao Tse-tung's Portrait

1966. "Cultural Revolution" Games. Multicoloured.
2325 8f. (1) Type **400** . . . . . . 21·00 6·00
2326 8f. (2) Athletes with linked arms hold Mao texts . . 21·00 6·00
2327 8f. (3) Two women athletes with Mao texts . . . . . 21·00 5·00
2328 8f. (4) Athletes reading Mao texts . . . . 21·00 5·00
SIZES: No. 2326, As Type **400**, but vert. Nos. 2327/8, 36½ × 25 mm.

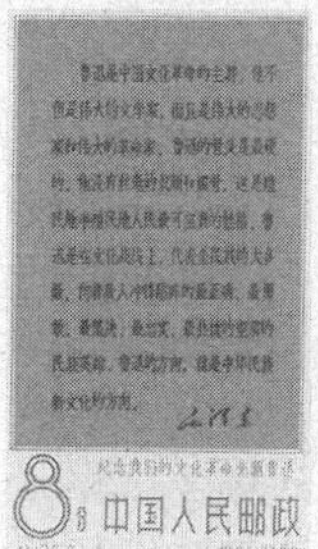

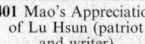

401 Mao's Appreciation of Lu Hsun (patriot and writer)

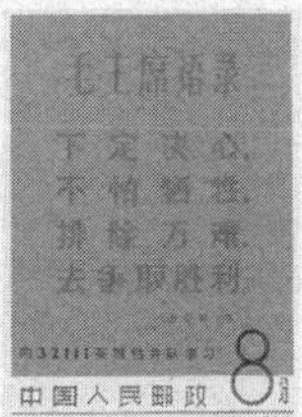

402 "Be Resolute ..." (Mao Tse-tung)

1966. 30th Death Anniv of Lu Hsun.
2329 **401** 8f. (1) black & orange 40·00 15·00
2330 – 8f. (2) black, flesh & red 40·00 15·00
2331 – 8f. (3) black & orange 40·00 15·00
DESIGNS: (2) Lu Hsun; (3) Lu Hsun's manuscript.

1967. Heroic Oilwell Firefighters.
2332 **402** 8f. (1) gold, red & black 22·00 12·00
2333 – 8f. (2) black and red . . 25·00 9·00
2334 – 8f. (3) black and red . . 25·00 9·00
DESIGNS—HORIZ: (48 × 27 mm): (2) Drilling Team No. 32111 fighting flames. VERT: (3) Smothering flames with tarpaulins.

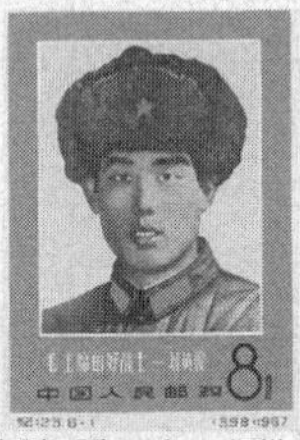

403 Liu Ying-chun (military hero)

1967. Liu Ying-chun Commem. Multicoloured.
2335 8f. (1) Type **403** . . . . . . 22·00 6·50
2336 8f. (2) Liu Ying-chun holding book of Mao texts . . . . 22·00 6·50
2337 8f. (3) Liu Ying-chun holding horse's bridle . . 22·00 6·50
2338 8f. (4) Liu Ying-chun looking at film slide . . . 22·00 6·50
2339 8f. (5) Liu Ying-chun lecturing . . . . 22·00 6·50
2340 8f. (6) Liu Ying-chun making fatal attempt to stop bolting horse . . . . 22·00 6·50

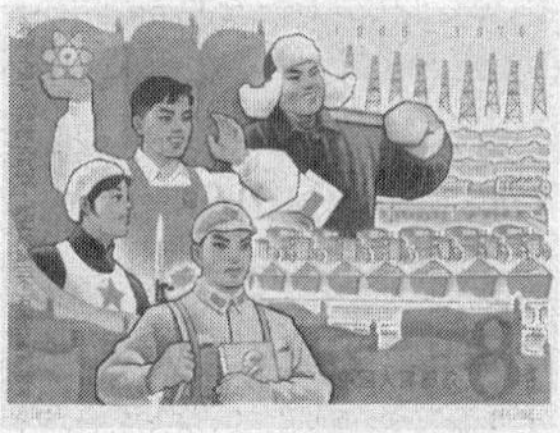
404 Soldier, Nurse, Workers and Banners

1967. 3rd Five-Year Plan. Multicoloured.
2341 8f. (1) Type **404** . . . . . . 30·00 7·50
2342 8f. (2) Armed woman, peasants and banners . . 30·00 7·50

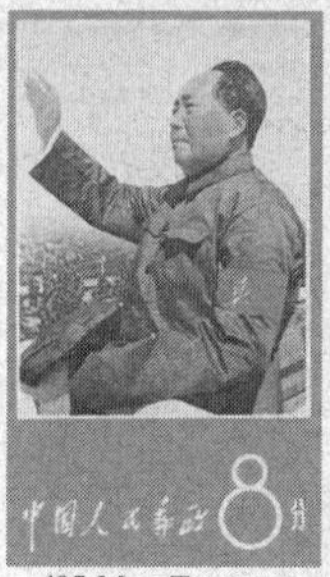

405 Mao Tse-tung

406 Mao Text (39 characters)

1967. "Thoughts of Mao Tse-tung" (1st issue). Similar designs showing Mao texts each gold and red. To assist identification of Nos. 2344/53 the total number of Chinese characters within the frames are given. (a) Type **405**.
2343 8f. multicoloured . . . . . 85·00 15·00

(b) As Type **406**. Red outer frames.
2344 8f. Type **406** . . . . 75·00 12·00
2345 8f. (50 characters) . . . . . 75·00 12·00
2346 8f. (39–in six lines) . . . . 75·00 12·00
2347 8f. (53) . . . . 75·00 12·00
2348 8f. (46) . . . . 75·00 12·00

(c) As Type **406**. Gold outer frames.
2349 8f. (41) . . . . 75·00 12·00
2350 8f. (49) . . . . 75·00 12·00
2351 8f. (35) . . . . 75·00 12·00
2352 8f. (22) . . . . 75·00 12·00
2353 8f. (29) . . . . 75·00 12·00
See also No. 2405.

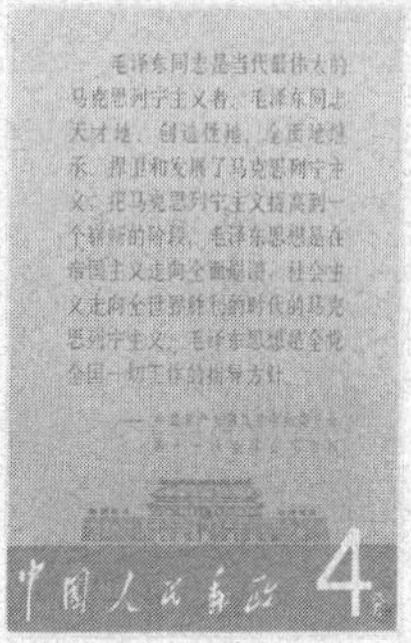

407 Text praising Mao

1967. Labour Day.
2354 **407** 4f. multicoloured . . . . 50·00 14·00
2355 – 8f. multicoloured . . . . 40·00 14·00
2356 – 8f. multicoloured . . . . 50·00 14·00
2357 – 8f. multicoloured . . . . 40·00 14·00
2358 – 8f. multicoloured . . . . 40·00 14·00
DESIGNS (Mao Tse-tung and): No. 2355, Poem; No. 2356, Multi-racial crowd with texts; No. 2357, Red Guards. (36 × 50½ mm): Mao with hand raised in greeting.
For stamps similar to No. 2358, see Nos. 2367/9.

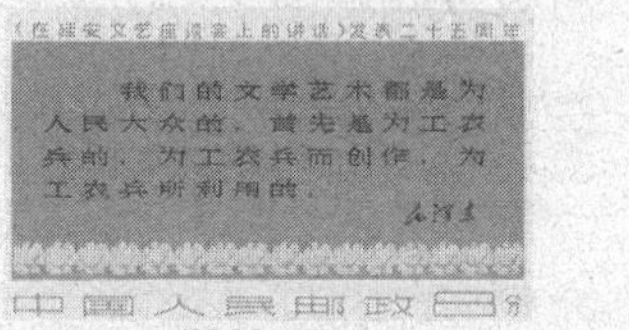

408 Mao Text

1967. 25th Anniv of Mao Tse-tung's "Talks on Literature and Art".
2359 **408** 8f. black, red & yellow £130 25·00
2360 – 8f. black, red & yellow £150 30·00
2361 – 8f. multicoloured . . . £150 30·00
DESIGNS: No. 2360, As Type **408** but different text. (50 × 36½ mm): No. 2361, Mao supporters in procession.

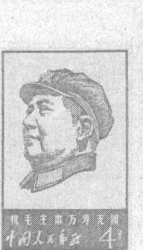

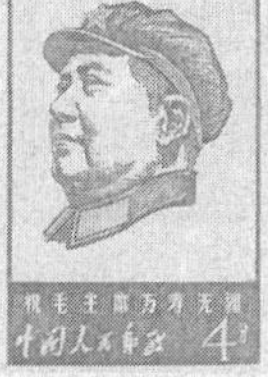
409 Mao Tse-tung

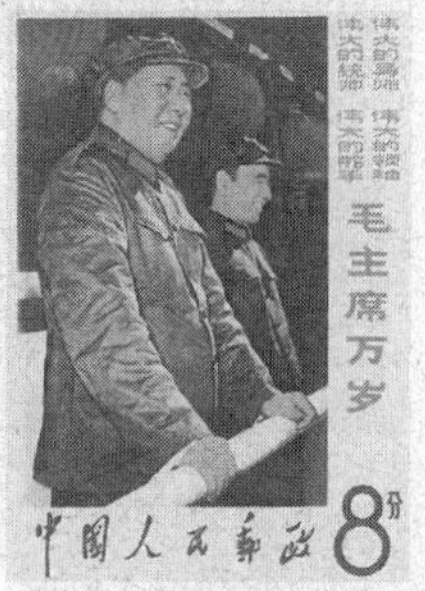

410 Mao Tse-tung and Lin Piao

1967. 46th Anniv of Chinese Communist Party.
2362 **409** 4f. red . . . . 12·00 7·50
2363 8f. red . . . . 50·00 7·50
2364 35f. brown . . . . . . 35·00 25·00

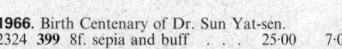

2365 43f. red . . . . 40·00 25·00
2366 52f. red . . . . 75·00 20·00

1967. "Our Great Teacher". Multicoloured.
2367 8f. Type 410 . . . . £120 30·00
2368 8f. Mao Tse-tung (horiz) . . 50·00 18·00
2369 10f. Mao Tse-tung
      conferring with Lin Piao
      (horiz) . . . . £150 30·00
For 8f. stamp showing Mao with hand raised in
greeting, see No. 2358.

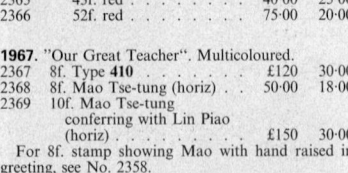

411 Mao Tse-tung as "Sun"

1967. 18th Anniv of People's Republic. Mult.
2370 8f. Type 411 . . . . 48·00 8·50
2371 8f. Mao Tse-tung with
      representatives of
      Communist countries . . . 29·00 8·50

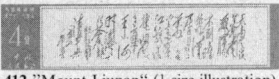

412 "Mount Liupan" (½-size illustration)

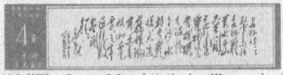

413 "The Long March" (½-size illustration)

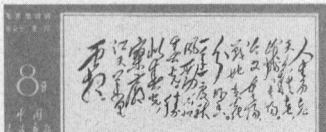

414 "Double Ninth"

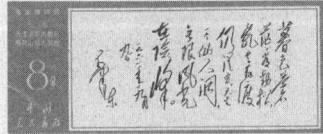

415 "Fairy Cave"

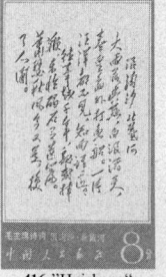

416 "Huichang"   417 "Yellow Crane
                        Pavilion"

418 "Beidahe"   419 "Swimming"

1967. Poems of Mao Tse-tung.
2372 412 4f. black, yellow & red 50·00 14·00
2373 413 4f. black, yellow & red 65·00 14·00
2374 414 8f. black, yellow & red 65·00 12·00
2375 415 8f. black, yellow & red 70·00 12·00
2376 416 8f. black, yellow & red £190 12·00
2377 417 8f. black, yellow & red £120 20·00
2378 418 8f. black, yellow & red £225 20·00
2379 419 8f. black, yellow & red 80·00 20·00
2380 420 8f. black, yellow & red 80·00 20·00
2381 421 8f. black, yellow & red 80·00 20·00
2382 422 8f. black, yellow & red 80·00 12·00
2383 423 10f. multicoloured . . . 32·00 12·00
2384 424 10f. black, yellow & red 32·00 12·00
2385 425 10f. black, yellow & red 32·00 12·00

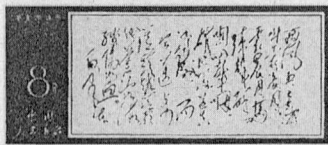

420 "Loushanguan Pass"

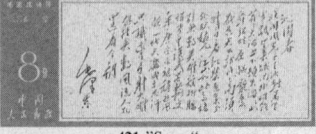

421 "Snow"

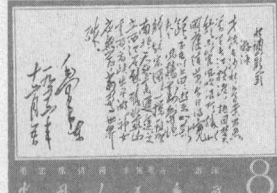

422 "Capture of Nanjing"

423 Mao Writing Poems at Desk

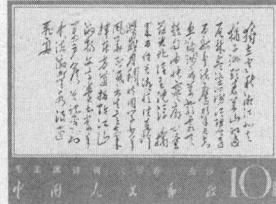

424 "Changsha"

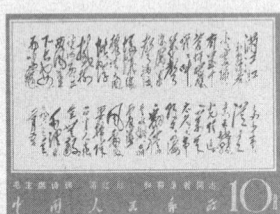

425 "Reply to Guo Moro"

426 Epigram on Chairman Mao by
    Lin Piao

1967. Fleet Expansionists' Congress.
2386 426 8f. gold and red . . . . 26·00 8·50

427 Mao Tse-tung and Procession

1968. "Revolutionary Literature and Art" (1st issue).
Multicoloured designs showing scenes from
People's Operas.
2387 8f. Type 427 . . . . 50·00 9·00
2388 8f. "Raid on the White
      Tiger Regiment" . . . . 40·00 9·00
2389 8f. "Taking Tiger
      Mountain" . . . . 50·00 8·00
2390 8f. "On the Docks" . . . 35·00 8·00
2391 8f. "Shachiapang" . . . . 40·00 8·00
2392 8f. "The Red Lantern"
      (vert) . . . . 35·00 8·00

428 "Red Detachment of Women" (ballet)

1968. "Revolutionary Literature and Art" (2nd
issue). Multicoloured.
2393 8f. Type 428 . . . . 40·00 9·00
2394 8f. "The White-haired Girl"
      (ballet) . . . . 40·00 9·00
2395 8f. Mao Tse-tung,
      Symphony Orchestra and
      Chorus (50 × 36 mm) . . 80·00 11·00

429 Mao Tse-tung ("Unite still more
    closely")

1968. Mao's Anti-American Declaration.
2396 429 8f. brown, gold and red 45·00 12·00

430   431

   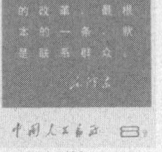

432   433

434

1968. "Directives of Mao Tse-tung".
2397 430 8f. brown, red & yellow £190 40·00
2398 431 8f. brown, red & yellow £190 40·00
2399 432 8f. brown, red & yellow £190 40·00
2400 433 8f. brown, red & yellow £190 40·00
2401 434 8f. brown, red & yellow £190 40·00

435 Inscription by Lin Piao. 26 July, 1965

1968. 41st Anniv of People's Liberation Army.
2402 435 8f. black, gold and red 12·00 5·00

436 "Chairman Mao goes to
    Anyuan" (Liu Chunhua)

1968. Mao's Youth.
2403 436 8f. multicoloured . . . . 26·00 8·00

438 Mao Tse-tung and Text

1968. "Thoughts of Mao Tse-tung" (2nd issue)
2405 438 8f. brown and red . . . 48·00 14·00

439 Displaying "The Words of Mao
    Tse-tung"

1968. "The Words of Mao Tse-tung". No gum.
2406 439 8f. multicoloured . . . . 15·00 3·00

440 Yangtse Bridge

1968. Completion of Yangtse Bridge, Nanking.
Multicoloured. No gum.
2407 4f. Type 440 . . . . 3·75 90
2408 8f. Buses on bridge . . . . 9·75 4·00
2409 8f. View of end portals . . . 7·25 2·50
2410 10f. Aerial view . . . . . . 2·50 1·25
Nos. 2408/9 are larger, size 49 × 27 mm.

441 Li Yu-ho singing "I am filled
    with Courage and Strength"

1969. Songs from "The Red Lantern" Opera.
Multicoloured. No gum.
2411 8f. Type 441 . . . . 15·00 7·50
2412 8f. Li Ti-mei singing
      "Hatred in my Heart" . . 30·00 7·50

442 Communist Party Building,
    Shanghai

1969. No gum.
2413 442 1½f. red, brown & lilac 60 50
2414 – 8f. brown, grn & cream 2·00 75
2415 – 8f. red and purple . . . 60 15
2416 – 8f. brown and blue . . . 1·50 40
2417 – 20f. blue, purple & red 2·10 1·00
2418 – 50f. brown and green . 1·75 40
DESIGNS: "Historic Sites of the Revolution"; Size
27 × 22 mm—No. 2414, Pagoda Hill, Yenan;
No. 2415, Gate of Heavenly Peace, Peking; No. 2418.
Mao Tse-tung's house, Yenan. Size as T 442—
No. 2416, People's Heroes Monument, Peking;
No. 2417, Conference Hall, Tsunyi.
See also Nos. 2455/65.

443 Rice Harvesters

1969. Agricultural Workers. Mult. No gum.

2419	4f. Type **443**	4·00	2·00
2420	8f. Grain harvest	9·00	1·75
2421	8f. Study Group with "Thoughts of Mao"	55·00	7·50
2422	10f. Red Cross worker with mother and child	4·00	1·50

444 Snow Patrol

445 Farm Worker

1969. Defence of Chen Pao Tao in the Ussur River. Multicoloured. No gum.

2423	8f. Type **444**	6·00	2·50
2424	8f. Guards by river (horiz)	5·00	2·50
2425	8f. Servicemen and Militia (horiz)	20·00	3·00
2426	35f. As No. 2424	5·00	2·75
2427	43f. Type **444**	6·00	2·75

1969. "The Chinese People" (woodcuts). No gum.

2428	**445** 4f. purple and orange	20	20
2429	– 8f. purple and orange	60	25
2430	– 10f. green and orange	90	60

DESIGNS: 8f. Foundryman. 10f. Soldier.

446 Chin Hsun-hua in Water

447 Tractor-driver

1970. Heroic Death of Chin Hsun-hua in Kirin Border Floods. No gum.

2431	**446** 8f. black and red	17·00	5·00

1970. No gum.

2432	**447** 5f. black, red & orange	60	40
2433	– 1y. black and red	4·00	1·10

DESIGN—HORIZ: 1y. Foundryman.

448 Cavalry Patrol

449 "Yang Tse-jung, Army Scout"

1970. 43rd Anniv of People's Liberation Army. No gum.

2434	**448** 8f. multicoloured	6·75	3·25

1970. "Taking Tiger Mountain" (Revolutionary opera). Multicoloured. No gum.

2435	8f. (1) Type **449**	15·00	2·50
2436	8f. (2) "The patrol sets out" (horiz)	15·00	2·50
2437	8f. (3) "Leaping through the forest"	15·00	2·50
2438	8f. (4) "Li Yung-chi's farewell" (27 × 48 mm)	15·00	2·50
2439	8f. (5) "Yang Tse-jung in disguise" (27 × 48 mm)	15·00	2·50
2440	8f. (6) "Congratulating Yang Tse-jung" (horiz)	40·00	2·50

450 Soldiers in Snow

1970. 2nd Anniv of Defence of Chen Pao Tao. No gum.

2441	**450** 4f. multicoloured	1·75	1·00

451 Communard Standard

453 Workers and Great Hall of the People, Peking

452 Communist Party Building, Shanghai

1971. Cent of Paris Commune. Mult. No gum.

2442	**451** 4f. multicoloured	40·00	10·00
2443	– 8f. brown, pink and red	80·00	20·00
2444	– 10f. red, brn and pink	40·00	10·00
2445	– 22f. brown, red & pink	40·00	10·00

DESIGNS—HORIZ: 8f. Fighting in Paris, March 1871; 22f. Communards in Place Vendome. VERT: 10f. Commune proclaimed at the Hotel de Ville.

1971. 50th Anniv of Chinese Communist Party. Multicoloured. No gum.

2446	4f. (12) Type **452**	9·00	1·25
2447	4f. (13) National Peasant Movement Inst., Canton	9·00	1·25
2448	8f. (14) Chingkang Mountains	7·50	1·25
2449	8f. (15) Conference Building, Tsunyi	7·50	1·25
2450	8f. (16) Pagoda Hill, Yenan	7·50	1·25
2452	8f. (18) Workers and Industry	16·00	3·00
2453	8f. (19) Type **453**	16·00	3·00
2454	8f. (20) Workers and Agriculture	16·00	3·00
2451	22f. (17) Gate of Heavenly Peace, Peking	6·00	1·25

SIZES: As Type **452**. Nos. 2447/2450 and 2451. As Type **453**. Nos. 2452/4.

454 National Peasant Movement Institute, Canton

455 Welcoming Bouquets

1971. Revolutionary Sites. Multicoloured. No gum.

2455	1f. Communist Party Building, Shanghai (vert)	10	10
2456	2f. Type **454**	10	10
2457	3f. Site of 1929 Congress, Kutien	10	10
2458	4f. Mao Tse-tung's house, Yenan	15	10
2459	8f. Gate of Heavenly Peace, Peking	15	10
2460	10f. Monument, Chingkang Mountains	25	10
2461	20f. River bridge, Yenan	40	15
2462	22f. Mao's birthplace, Shaoshan	70	20
2463	35f. Conference Building, Tsunyi	1·00	20
2464	43f. Start of the Long March, Chingkang Mountains	1·40	35
2465	52f. People's Palace, Peking	1·75	55

1971. "Afro-Asian Friendship" Table Tennis Tournament, Peking. Multicoloured. No gum.

2466	8f. (22) Type **455**	4·00	1·00
2467	8f. (23) Group of players	4·00	1·00
2468	8f. (24) Asian and African players	4·00	1·00
2469	43f. (21) Tournament badge	14·50	2·50

456 Enver Hoxha making speech

457 Conference Hall, Yenan

1971. 30th Anniv of Albanian Worker's Party. Multicoloured. No gum.

2470	8f. (25) Type **456**	7·25	4·00
2471	8f. (26) Party Headquarters	6·00	1·50
2472	8f. (27) Albanian flag, rifle and pick	6·00	1·50
2473	52f. (28) Soldier and Worker's Militia (horiz)	6·50	4·00

1972. 30th Anniv of Publication of "Yenan Forum's Discussions on Literature and Art". Multicoloured. No gum.

2474	8f. (33) Type **457**	5·50	1·60
2475	8f. (34) Army choir	5·50	1·60
2476	8f. (35) "Brother and Sister"	7·00	1·60
2477	8f. (36) "Open-air Theatre"	7·00	1·60
2478	8f. (37) "The Red Lantern" (opera)	7·00	1·60
2479	8f. (38) "Red Detachment of Women" (ballet)	7·00	1·60

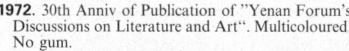

458 Ball Games

1972. 10th Anniv of Mao Tse-tungs's Edict on Physical Culture. Multicoloured. No gum.

2480	8f. (39) Type **458**	7·00	1·50
2481	8f. (40) Gymnastics	7·00	1·50
2482	8f. (41) Tug-of-War	7·00	1·50
2483	8f. (42) Rock-climbing	7·00	1·50
2484	8f. (43) High-diving	7·00	1·50

Nos. 2481/4 are size 26 × 36 mm.

460 Freighter "Fenglei"

1972. Chinese Merchant Shipping. Multicoloured. No gum.

2485	8f. (29) Type **460**	8·00	1·75
2486	8f. (30) Tanker "Taching No. 30"	8·00	1·75
2487	8f. (31) Cargo-liner "Chang Seng"	8·00	1·75
2488	8f. (32) Dredger "Hsienfeng"	8·00	1·75

461 Championship Badge

462 Wang Chin-hsi, the "Iron Man"

1972. 1st Asian Table Tennis Championships, Peking. Multicoloured. No gum.

2489	8f. (45) Type **461**	4·00	75
2490	8f. (46) Welcoming crowd (horiz)	4·00	75
2491	8f. (47) Game in progress (horiz)	4·00	75
2492	22f. (48) Players from three countries	2·50	1·50

1972. Wang Chin-hsi (workers' hero) Commem. No gum.

2493	**462** 8f. multicoloured	4·25	1·50

463 Cliff-edge Construction

464 Giant Panda eating Bamboo Shoots

1972. Construction of Red Flag Canal. Mult.

2494	8f. (49) Type **463**	2·10	80
2495	8f. (50) "Youth" tunnel	2·10	80
2496	8f. (51) "Taoguan bridge"	2·10	80
2497	8f. (52) Cliff-edge canal	2·10	80

1973. China's Giant Pandas.

2498	**464** 4f. (61) multicoloured	2·00	3·50
2499	– 8f. (59) mult (horiz)	2·00	3·50
2500	– 8f. (60) mult (horiz)	2·00	3·50
2501	– 10f. (58) multicoloured	£100	15·00
2502	– 20f. (57) multicoloured	85·00	15·00
2503	– 43f. (62) multicoloured	9·00	6·00

DESIGNS: 8f. to 43f. Different brush and ink drawings of pandas.

465 "New Power in the Mines" (Yang Shi-guang)

466 Girl dancing

1973. International Working Women's Day. Mult.

2504	8f. (63) Type **465**	3·00	1·50
2505	8f. (64) "Woman Committee Member" (Tang Hsiaoming)	3·00	1·50
2506	8f. (65) "I am a Sea-gull" (Army telegraph line woman) (Pan Jiajun)	3·00	1·50

1973. Children's Day. Multicoloured.

2507	8f. (86) Type **466**	1·90	50
2508	8f. (87) Boy musician	1·90	50
2509	8f. (88) Boy with scarf	1·90	50
2510	8f. (89) Boy with tambourine	1·90	50
2511	8f. (90) Girl with drum	1·90	50

467 Badge of Championships

468 "Hsi-erh"

1973. Asian. African and Latin-American Table Tennis Invitation Championships. Multicoloured.

2512	8f. (91) Type **467**	2·50	50
2513	8f. (92) Visitors	2·50	50
2514	8f. (93) Player	2·50	50
2515	22f. (94) Guest players	1·50	50

1973. Revolutionary Ballet "Hsi-erh" ("The White-haired Girl"). Multicoloured.

2516	8f. (53) Type **468**	4·75	1·10
2517	8f. (54) Hsi-erh escapes from Huang (horiz)	4·75	1·10
2518	8f. (55) Hsi-erh meets Tachun (horiz)	4·75	1·10
2519	8f. (56) Hsi-erh becomes a soldier	4·75	1·10

469 Fair Building

1973. Chinese Exports Fair, Canton.

2520	**469** 8f. multicoloured	3·50	1·25

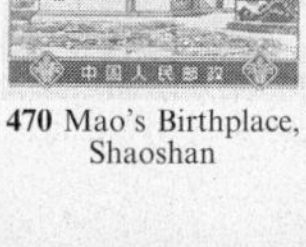

470 Mao's Birthplace, Shaoshan

471 Steam and Diesel Trains

1973. No gum.

2521	**470**	1f. green & light green	35	10
2522	–	1½f. red and yellow	35	20
2523	–	2f. blue and green	35	10
2524	–	3f. green and yellow	35	10
2525	–	4f. red and yellow	35	10
2526	–	5f. brown and yellow	35	10
2527	–	8f. purple and flesh	35	10
2528	–	10f. blue and flesh	35	10
2529	–	20f. red and buff	65	10
2530	–	22f. violet and yellow	90	10
2531	–	35f. purple and yellow	1·25	15
2532	–	43f. brown and buff	1·60	25
2533	–	50f. blue and mauve	2·10	70
2534	–	52f. brown and yellow	2·75	90
2535	**471**	1y. multicoloured	2·00	25
2536	–	2y. multicoloured	1·60	40

DESIGNS—As Type **470**: 1½ f. National Peasant Movement Institute, Shanghai. 2f. National Institute, Kwangchow. 3f. Headquarters Building, Nanching uprising. 4f. Great Hall of the People, Peking. 5f. Wen Chia Shih. 8f. Gate of Heavenly Peace, Peking. 10f. Chingkang Mountains. 20f. Kutien Congress building. 22f. Tsunyi Congress building. 35f. Bridge, Yenan. 43f. Hsi Pai Po. 50f. "Fairy Gate", Lushan. 52f. People's Heroes Monument, Peking. As Type **471**: 2y. Trucks on mountain road.

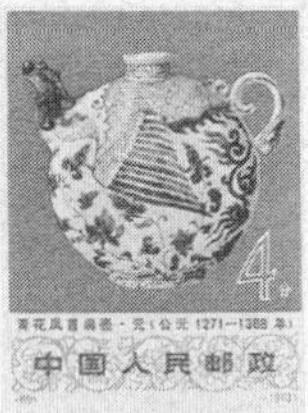

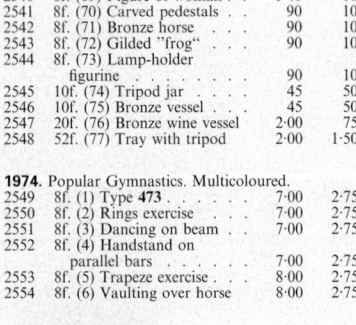

472 "Phoenix" Pot

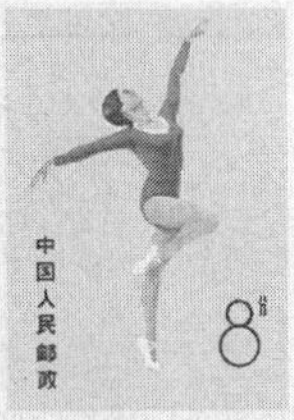

473 Dance Routine

1973. Archaeological Treasures. Multicoloured.

2537	4f. (66) Type **472**	1·75	20
2538	4f. (67) Silver pot	1·75	20
2539	8f. (68) Porcelain horse and groom	1·40	10
2540	8f. (69) Figure of woman	1·40	10
2541	8f. (70) Carved pedestals	90	10
2542	8f. (71) Bronze horse	90	10
2543	8f. (72) Gilded "frog"	90	10
2544	8f. (73) Lamp-holder figurine	90	10
2545	10f. (74) Tripod jar	45	50
2546	10f. (75) Bronze vessel	45	50
2547	20f. (76) Bronze wine vessel	2·00	75
2548	52f. (77) Tray with tripod	2·00	1·50

1974. Popular Gymnastics. Multicoloured.

2549	8f. (1) Type **473**	7·00	2·75
2550	8f. (2) Rings exercise	7·00	2·75
2551	8f. (3) Dancing on beam	7·00	2·75
2552	8f. (4) Handstand on parallel bars	7·00	2·75
2553	8f. (5) Trapeze exercise	8·00	2·75
2554	8f. (6) Vaulting over horse	8·00	2·75

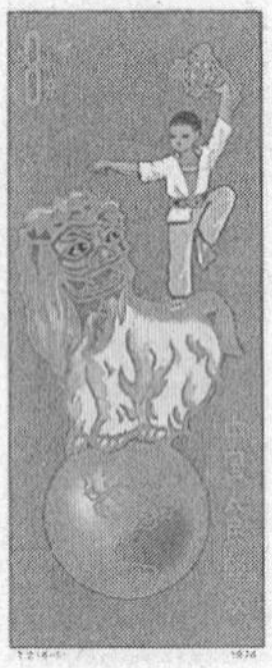

474 Lion Dance

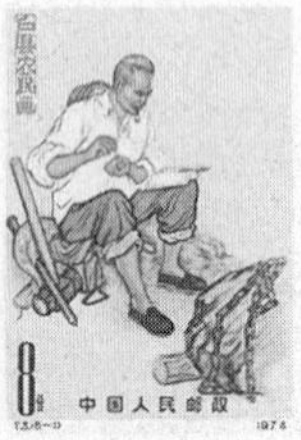

475 Man reading Book

1974. Acrobatics. Multicoloured.

2555	8f. (1) Type **474**	6·00	2·25
2556	8f. (2) Handstand on chairs	6·00	2·25
2557	8f. (3) Diabolo team (horiz)	6·00	2·25
2558	8f. Revolving jar (horiz)	7·00	2·25
2559	8f. (5) Spinning plates	7·00	2·25
2560	8f. (6) Foot-juggling with parasol	7·00	2·25

1974. Huhsien Paintings. Multicoloured.

2561	8f. (1) Type **475**	2·25	1·00
2562	8f. (2) Mineshaft (23 × 57 mm)	2·25	1·00
2563	8f. (3) Workers hoeing field (horiz)	2·25	1·00
2564	8f. (4) Workers eating (horiz)	2·25	1·00
2565	8f. (5) Wheatfield landscape (57 × 23 mm)	2·25	1·00
2566	8f. (6) Harvesting (horiz)	2·25	1·00

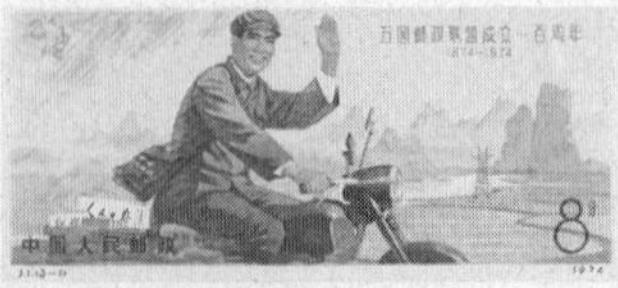

476 Postman

1974. Centenary of U.P.U. Multicoloured.

2567	8f. (1) Type **476**	6·00	2·50
2568	8f. (2) People of five races	6·00	2·50
2569	8f. (3) Great Wall of China	6·00	2·50

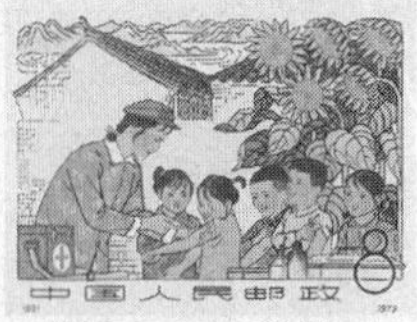

477 Inoculating Children

1974. Country Doctors. Multicoloured.

2570	8f. (1) Type **477**	1·75	90
2571	8f. (2) On country visit (vert)	1·75	90
2572	8f. (3) Gathering herbs (vert)	1·75	90
2573	8f. (4) Giving acupuncture	1·75	90

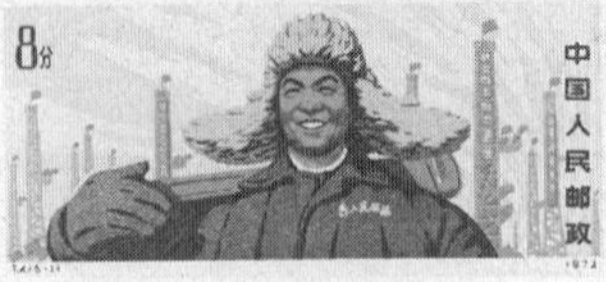

478 Wang Chin-hsi, "The Iron Man"

1974. Chairman Mao's Directives on Industrial and Agricultural Teaching. Multicoloured. (a) "Learning Industry from Taching".

2574	8f. (1) Type **478**	2·00	90
2575	8f. (2) Pupils studying Mao's works	2·00	90
2576	8f. (3) Oil-workers sinking well	2·00	90
2577	8f. (4) Consultation with management	2·00	90
2578	8f. (5) Taching oilfield as development site	2·00	90

(b) "Learning Agriculture from Tachai".

2579	8f. (1) Tachai workers looking to future	2·25	90
2580	8f. (2) Construction workers	1·40	90
2581	8f. (3) Agricultural workers making field tests	2·25	90
2582	8f. (4) Trucks delivering grain to State granaries	1·40	90
2583	8f. (5) Workers going to fields	1·40	90

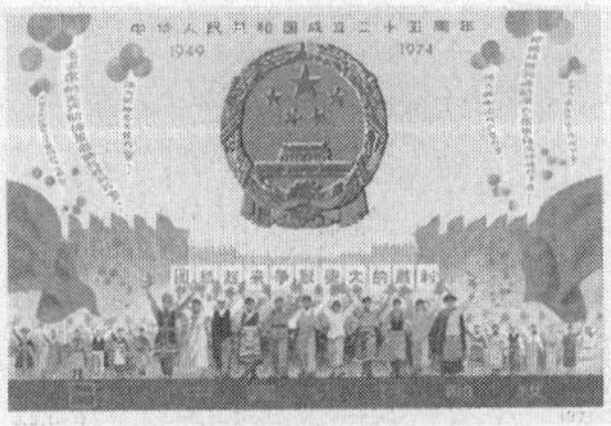

479 National Day Celebrations

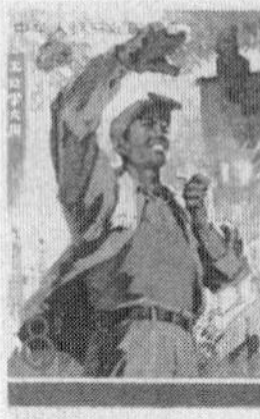

480 Steel Worker, Taching

1974. 25th Anniv of Chinese People's Republic. Multicoloured. (a) National Day.

2584	8f. Type **479**	5·50	2·50

(b) Chairman Mao's Directives.

2585	8f. (1) Type **480**	1·50	80
2586	8f. (2) Agricultural worker, Tachai	1·50	80
2587	8f. (3) Coastal guard	1·50	80

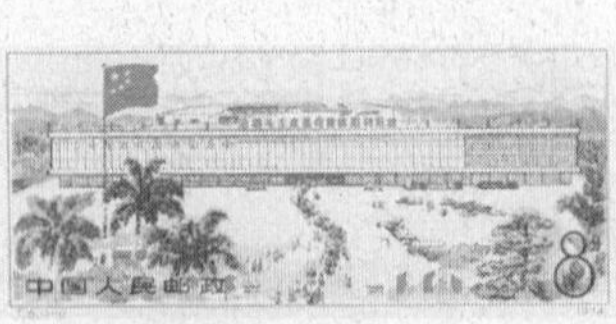

481 Fair Building

1974. Chinese Exports Fair, Canton.

2588	**481**	8f. multicoloured	3·25	1·25

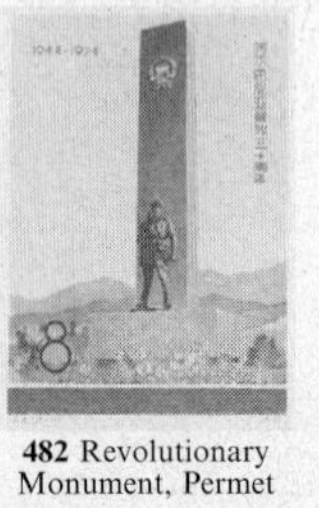

482 Revolutionary Monument, Permet

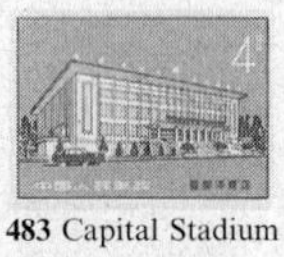

483 Capital Stadium

1974. 30th Anniv of Albania's Liberation. Mult.

2589	8f. Type **482**	2·75	1·25
2590	8f. Albanian patriots	2·75	1·25

1974. Peking Buildings. No gum.

2591	**483**	4f. black and green	15	15
2592	–	8f. black and blue	15	10

DESIGN: 8f. Hotel Peking.

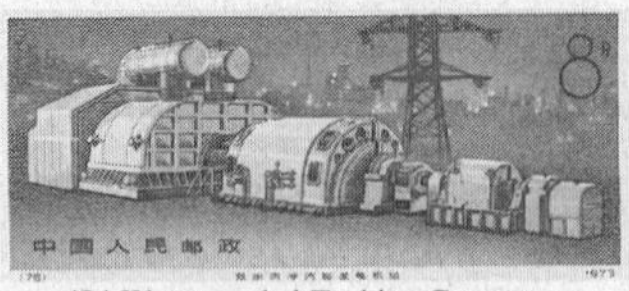

484 Water-cooled Turbine Generator

1974. Industrial Production. Multicoloured.

2593	8f. (78) Type **484**	19·00	4·00
2594	8f. (79) Mechanical rice sprouts transplanter	20·00	4·00
2595	8f. (80) Universal cylindrical grinding machine	19·00	4·00
2596	8f. (81) Mobile rock drill (vert)	19·00	4·00

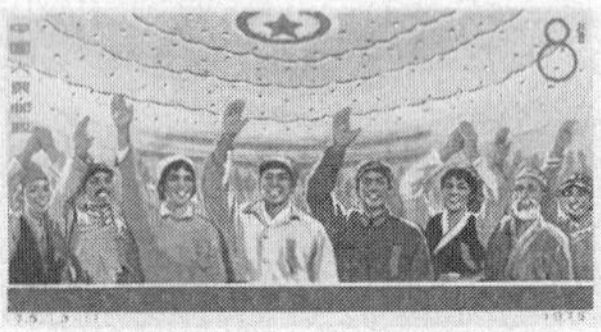

485 Congress Delegates

1975. 4th National People's Congress, Peking. Multicoloured.

2597	8f. (1) Type **485**	4·00	1·50
2598	8f. (2) Flower-decked rostrum	4·00	1·50
2599	8f. (3) Farmer, worker, soldier and steel mill	4·00	1·50

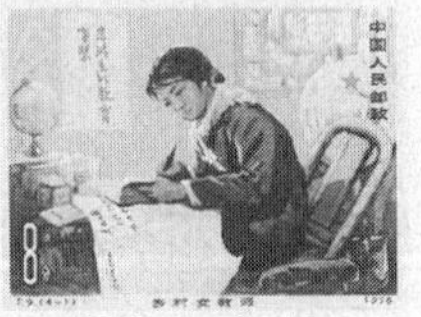

486 Teacher Studying

1975. Country Women Teachers. Multicoloured.

2600	8f. (1) Type **486**	9·75	2·00
2601	8f. (2) Teacher on rounds	9·75	2·00
2602	8f. (3) Open-air class	9·75	2·00
2603	8f. (4) Primary class aboard boat	9·75	2·00

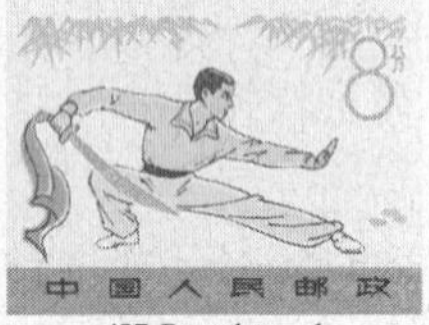

487 Broadsword

1975. "Wushu" (popular sport). Mult.

2604	8f. (1) Type **487**	4·25	1·75
2605	8f. (2) Sword exercises	4·25	1·75
2606	8f. (3) "Boxing"	4·25	1·75
2607	8f. (4) Leaping with spear	4·25	1·75
2608	8f. (5) Cudgel exercise	4·25	1·75
2609	43f. (6) Cudgel versus spears (60 × 30 mm)	5·00	3·50

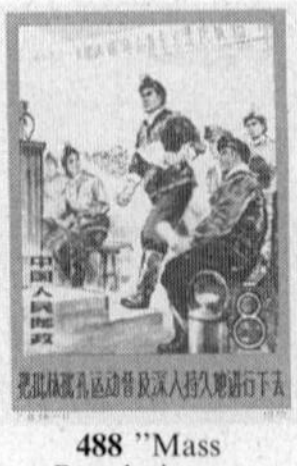

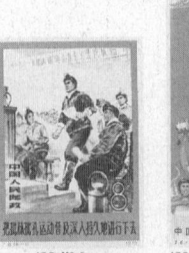

488 "Mass Revolutionary Criticism"

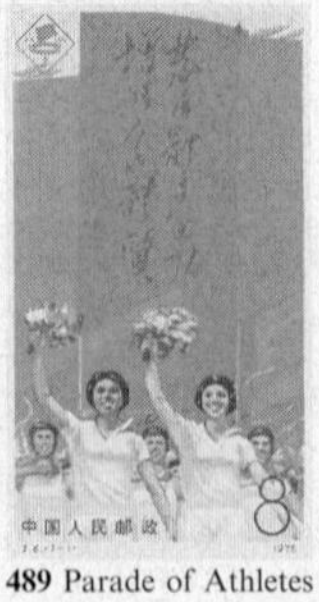

489 Parade of Athletes

1975. Criticism of Confucius and Liu Piao. Multicoloured.

2610	8f. (1) Type **488**	6·00	1·50
2611	8f. (2) "Leaders of the production brigade"	6·00	1·50
2612	8f. (3) "The battle continues" (horiz)	6·00	1·50
2613	8f. (4) "Liberated slave – pioneer critic" (horiz)	6·00	1·50

1975. 3rd National Games, Peking. Mult.

2614	8f. (1) Type **489**	1·50	30
2615	8f. (2) Athletes studying (horiz)	1·50	30
2616	8f. (3) Volleyball players (horiz)	1·50	30
2617	8f. (4) Athlete, soldier, farmer and worker	1·50	30
2618	8f. (5) Various sports (horiz)	1·50	30
2619	8f. (6) Ethnic types and horse racing (horiz)	1·50	30
2620	35f. (7) Children and divers	4·00	2·00

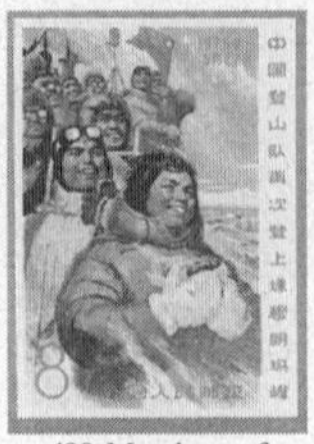

490 Members of Expedition

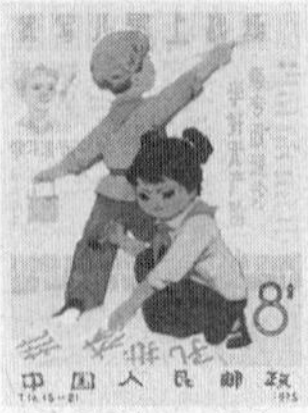

492 Children sticking Posters

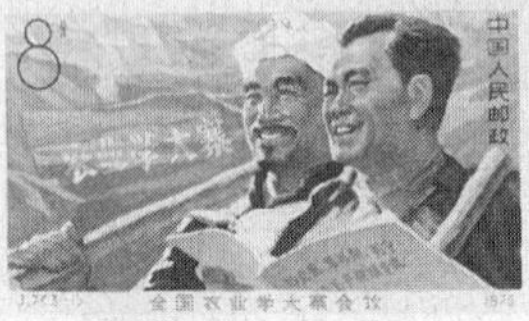

491 "Studying Together"

1975. Chinese Ascent of Mount Everest. Mult.

2621	8f. (2) Type **490**	80	25
2622	8f. (3) Mountaineers with flag (horiz)	80	25
2623	43f. (1) View of Mount Everest (horiz)	1·50	50

1975. National Conference "Learning Agriculture from Tachai". Multicoloured.

2624	8f. (1) Type **491**	3·00	1·00
2625	8f. (2) "Promote Hard Work"	3·00	1·00
2626	8f. (3) Chinese combine-harvester	3·00	1·00

1975. "Children's Progress". Multicoloured.

2627	8f. (1) Girl and young boy	1·25	50
2628	8f. (2) Type **492**	1·25	50
2629	8f. (3) Studying	1·25	50
2630	8f. (4) Harvesting	1·25	50
2631	52f. (5) Tug-of-war	6·75	2·25

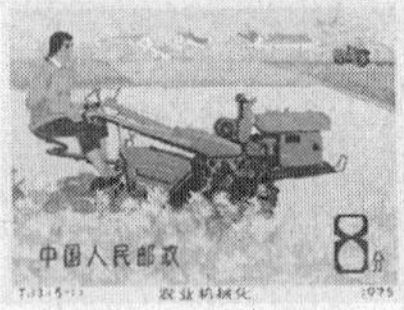

493 Ploughing Paddy Field

1975. Mechanised Farming. Multicoloured.

2632	8f. (1) Type **493**	2·40	90
2633	8f. (2) Mechanical rice seedlings transplanter	2·40	90
2634	8f. (3) Irrigation pump	2·40	90
2635	8f. (4) Spraying cotton field	2·40	90
2636	8f. (5) Combine harvester	2·40	90

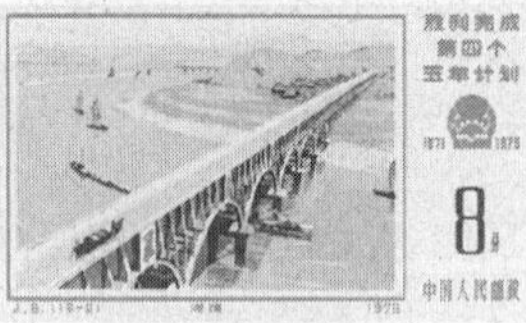

494 Bridge over Canal

1976. Completion of 4th Five-year Plan. Mult.

2637	8f. (1) Harvest scene	3·00	80
2638	8f. (2) Type **494**	3·00	80
2639	8f. (3) Fertilizer plant	3·00	80
2640	8f. (4) Textile factory	3·00	80
2641	8f. (5) Iron foundry	3·00	80
2642	8f. (6) Steam coal train	3·00	1·00
2643	8f. (7) Hydro-electric power station	3·00	80
2644	8f. (8) Shipbuilding	3·00	80
2645	8f. (9) Oil industry	3·00	80
2646	8f. (10) Pipe-line and harbour	3·00	80
2647	8f. (11) Diesel train on viaduct	5·00	1·00
2648	8f. (12) Crystal formation (scientific research)	5·00	80
2649	8f. (13) Classroom (rural education)	5·00	80
2650	8f. (14) Workers' health centre	5·00	80
2651	8f. (15) Workers' flats	5·00	80
2652	8f. (16) Department store	5·00	80

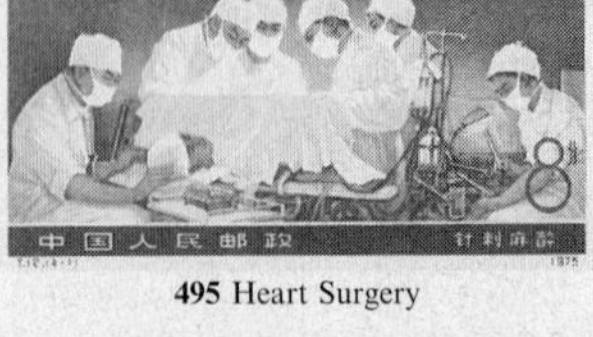

495 Heart Surgery

1976. Medical Services' Achievements. Mult.
2653 8f. (1) Type **495** . . . . . . 3·00 80
2654 8f. (2) Restoration of tractor-driver's severed arm . . . . 3·00 80
2655 8f. (3) Exercise of fractured arm . . . . 3·00 80
2656 8f. (4) Cataract operation – patient threading needle 3·00 80

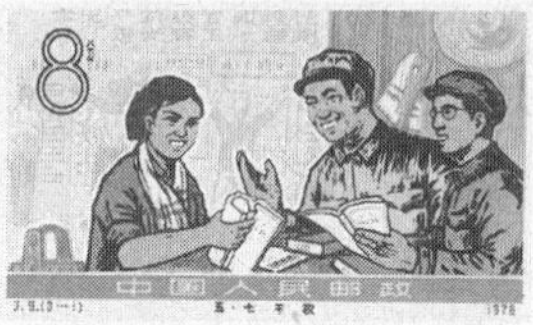

496 Students studying at "May 7" School

1976. 10th Anniv of Mao's "May 7 Directive". Multicoloured.
2657 8f. (1) Type **496** . . . . . . 2·50 80
2658 8f. (2) Students in agriculture . . . . 2·50 80
2659 8f. (3) Students in production team . . . . 2·50 80

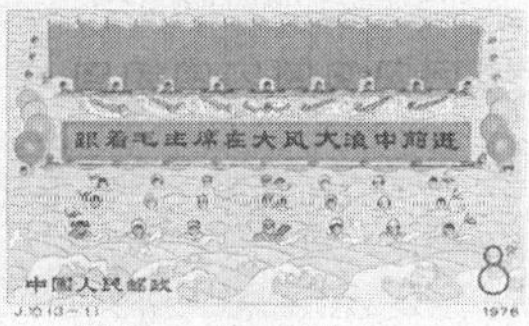

497 Formation of Swimmers

1976. 10th Anniv of Chairman Mao's Swim in Yangtse River. Multicoloured.
2660 8f. (1) Type **497** . . . . . . 2·50 80
2661 8f. (2) Swimmers crossing Yangtse . . . . 2·50 90
2662 8f. (3) Swimmers in surf . . 2·50 80
Nos. 2661/2 are smaller, 35 × 27 mm.

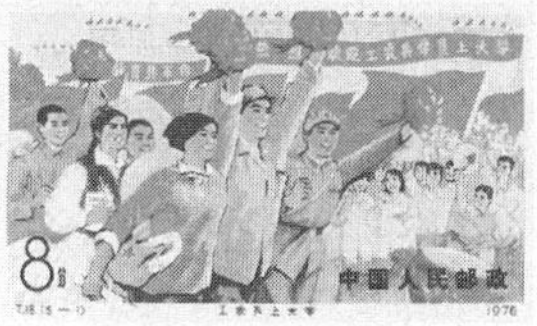

498 Students with Rosettes

1976. "Going to College". Multicoloured.
2663 8f. (1) Type **498** . . . . . 2·40 70
2664 8f. (2) Study group . . . . 2·40 70
2665 8f. (3) On-site instructions 2·40 70
2666 8f. (4) Students operating computer . . . . 2·40 70
2667 8f. (5) Return of graduates from college . . . . . 2·40 70

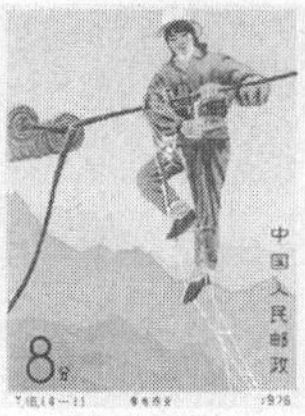

499 Electricity Lineswoman

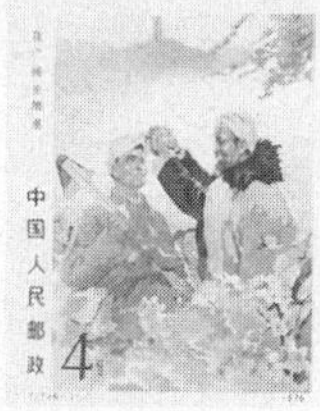

501 Peasant arranging Student's Headband

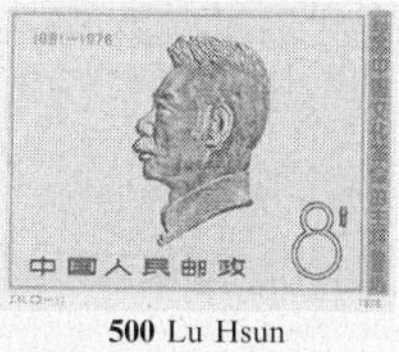

500 Lu Hsun

1976. Maintenance of Electric Power Lines. Multicoloured.
2668 8f. (1) Type **499** . . . . . . 2·50 70
2669 8f. (2) Linesman replacing insulator . . . . 2·50 70
2670 8f. (3) Linesman using hydraulic lift . . . . . . 2·50 70
2671 8f. (4) Technician inspecting transformer . . . . . . 2·50 70

1976. 95th Birth Anniv of Lu Hsun (revolutionary leader). Multicoloured.
2672 8f. (1) Type **500** . . . . . . 4·25 1·40
2673 8f. (2) Lu Hsun sick, writing in bed . . . . 4·25 1·40
2674 8f. (3) Lu Hsun, workers and soldiers . . . . 4·25 1·40

1976. Students and Country Life. Multicoloured.
2675 4f. (1) Type **501** . . . . . . 1·25 30
2676 8f. (2) Student teaching farm woman (horiz) . . . . . 1·25 30
2677 8f. (3) Irrigation survey . . 1·25 30
2678 8f. (4) Agricultural student testing wheat (horiz) . . . 1·25 30
2679 10f. (5) Student feeding lamb . . . . 2·00 1·00
2680 20f. (6) Frontier guards (horiz) . . . . 4·00 1·50

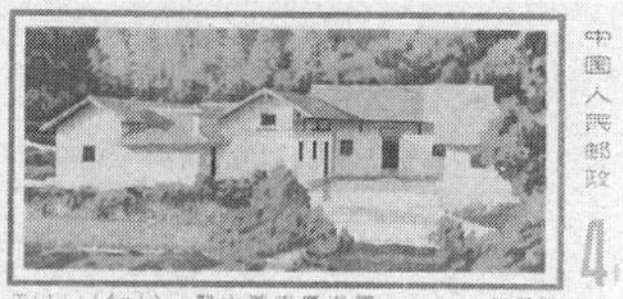

502 Mao Tse-tung's Birthplace

1976. Shaoshan Revolutionary Sites. Mult.
2681 4f. (1) Type **502** . . . . . . 1·40 60
2682 8f. (2) School building . . . 1·40 50
2683 8f. (3) Peasants' Association building . . . . 1·40 50
2684 10f. (4) Railway station . . 1·40 60

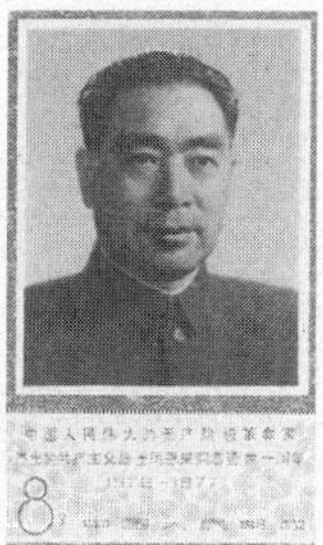

503 Chou En-lai

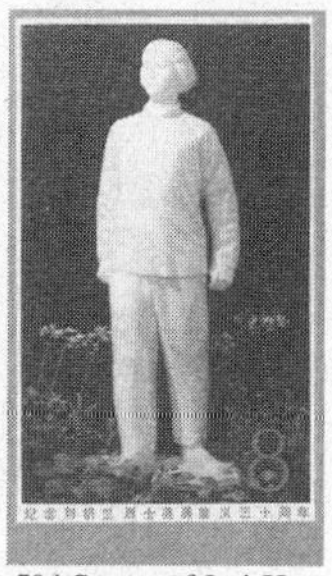

504 Statue of Lui Hu-lan

1977. 1st Death Anniv of Chou En-lai. Mult.
2685 8f. (1) Type **503** . . . . . . 2·00 80
2686 8f. (2) Chou En-lai making report . . . . 2·00 80
2687 8f. (3) Chou meeting "Iron Man" Wang Chin-hsi (horiz) . . . . 2·00 80
2688 8f. (4) Chou with provincial representatives (horiz) . . 2·00 80

1977. 30th Death Anniv of Lin Hu-lan (heroine and martyr). Multicoloured.
2689 8f. (1) Type **504** . . . . . 6·00 1·25
2690 8f. (2) Text by Mao Tse-tung . . . . 2·50 1·25
2691 8f. (3) Lin Hu-lan and people . . . . 2·50 1·25

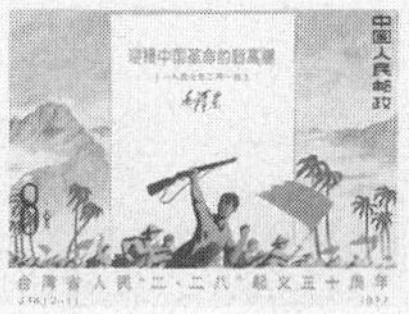

505 Revolutionaries and Text

1977. 30th Anniv of 1947 Taiwan Rising. Mult.
2692 8f. Type **505** . . . . 1·50 75
2693 10f. Three Taiwanese with banner . . . . 2·50 1·00

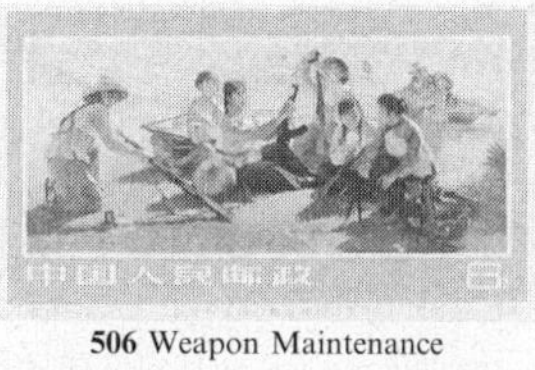

506 Weapon Maintenance

1977. Chinese Militiawomen. Multicoloured.
2694 8f. (1) Type **506** . . . . . . 4·00 1·25
2695 8f. (2) On horseback . . . . 4·00 1·25
2696 8f. (3) Directing traffic in tunnel . . . . 4·00 1·25

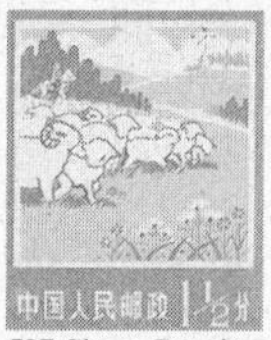

507 Sheep Rearing

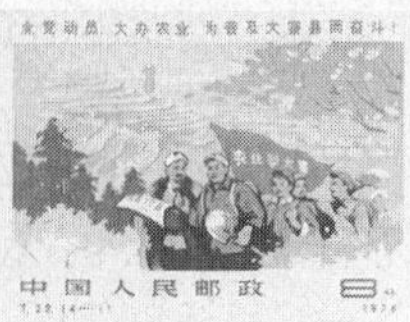

508 Cadre Members

1977. Multicoloured.
2697 1f. Coal mining 20 10
2698 1½f. Type **507** 10 20
2699 2f. Exports 20 10
2700 3f. Forest and diesel-train 20 10
2701 4f. Hydro-electric power . . 10 10
2702 5f. Fishing 50 10
2703 8f. Agriculture 10 10
2704 10f. Radio tower and mail-vans 15 10
2705 20f. Steel production 20 10
2706 30f. Road transport 20 10
2707 40f. Textile manufacture . . 25 15
2708 50f. Tractor assembly . . . 40 10
2709 60f. Oil-rigs and setting sun 45 15
2710 70f. Railway viaduct, Yangtse Gorge 85 35

1977. Promoting Tachai-type Developments. Mult.
2711 8f. (1) Type **508** . . . . . . 1·25 75
2712 8f. (2) Modern cultivation 1·25 75
2713 8f. (3) Reading wall newspaper . . . . 1·25 75
2714 8f. (4) Reclaiming land for agriculture . . . . 1·25 75

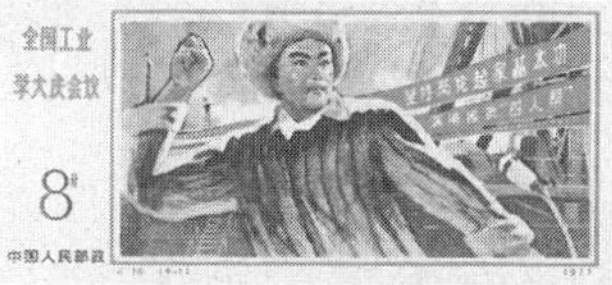

509 Party Leader addressing Workers

1977. "Taching-type" Industrial Conference. Mult.
2715 8f. (1) Type **509** . . . . . . 1·75 85
2716 8f. (2) Drilling for oil in snowstorm . . . . 1·75 85
2717 8f. (3) Man with banner over mass formation of workers . . . . 1·75 85
2718 8f. (4) Smiling workers and industrial scene . . . . . 1·75 85

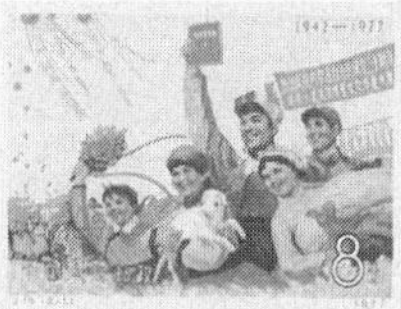

510 Mongolians Rejoicing

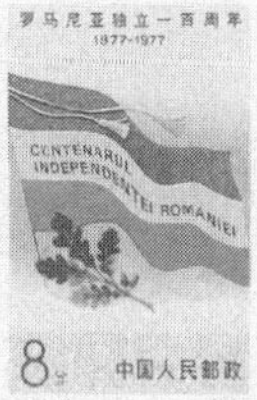

511 Rumanian Flag

1977. 30th Anniv of Inner Mongolian Autonomous Region. Multicoloured.
2719 8f. Type **510** 50 30
2720 10f. Mongolian industrial scene and iron ore train 85 40
2721 20f. Mongolian pasture . . 1·50 75

1977. Centenary of Rumanian Independence. Mult.
2722 8f. Type **511** . . . . 1·00 25
2723 10f. "The Battle of Smirdan" (Grigorescu) . . 1·50 75
2724 20f. Mihai Viteazu Memorial . . . . 2·00 75

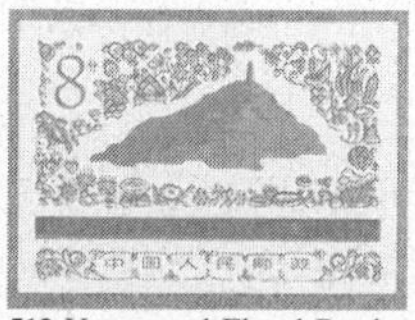

512 Yenan and Floral Border

1977. 35th Anniv of Yenan Forum on Literature and Art. Multicoloured.
2725 8f. (1) Type **512** 75 35
2726 8f. (2) Hammer, sickle and gun 75 35

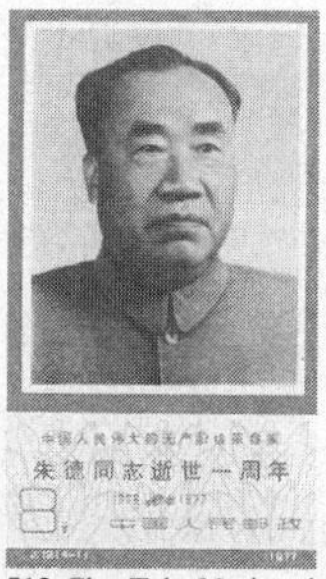

513 Chu Teh, National People's Congress Chairman

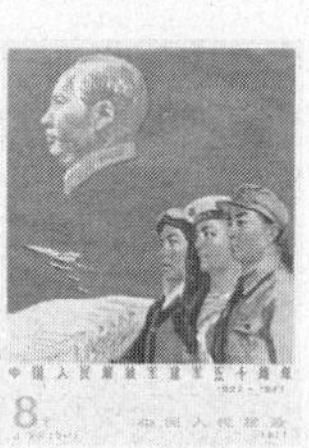

514 Soldier, Sailor and Airman under Banner of Mao Tse-tung

1977. 1st Death Anniv of Chu Teh.
2727 **513** 8f. (1) multicoloured . . 75 30
2728 – 8f. (2) multicoloured . . 75 30
2729 – 8f. (3) black, bl & gold 75 30
2730 – 8f. (4) black, bl & gold 75 30
DESIGNS—VERT: No. 2728, Chu Teh during his last session of Congress. HORIZ: No. 2729, Chu Teh at his desk. No. 2730, Chu Teh on horseback as Commander of People's Liberation Army.

1977. People's Liberation Army Day. Mult.
2731 8f. (1) Type **514** . . . . . 1·60 60
2732 8f. (2) Soldiers in Ching-kang Mountains . . . . 1·60 60
2733 8f. (3) Guerrilla fighters returning to base . . . . 1·60 60
2734 8f. (4) Chinese forces crossing Yangtse River . . 1·60 60
2735 8f. (5) "The Steel Wall" (National Defence Forces) 1·60 60

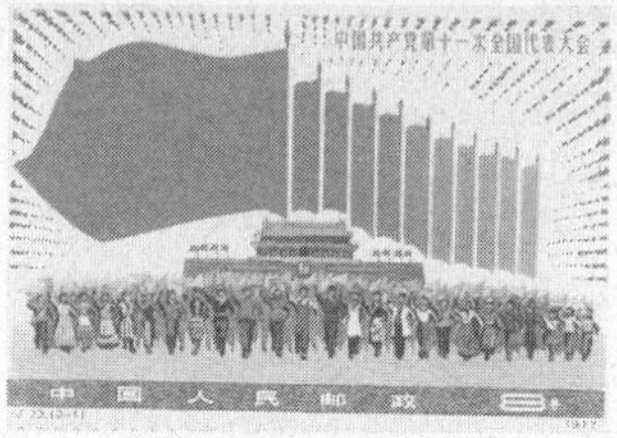

515 Red Flags and Crowd

1977. 11th National Communist Party Congress. Multicoloured.
2736 8f. (1) Type **515** . . . . . . 4·00 1·00
2737 8f. (2) Mao banner and procession . . . . 4·00 1·00
2738 8f. (3) Hammer and sickle banner and procession . . 4·00 1·00

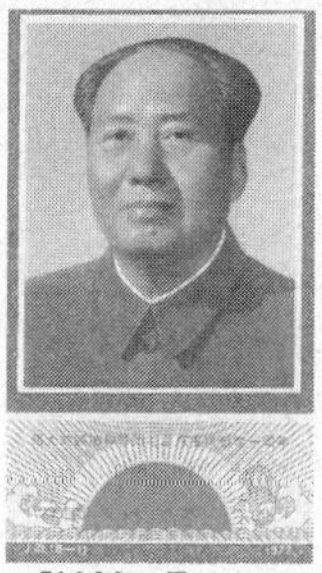

516 Mao Tse-tung

1977. 1st Death Anniv of Mao Tse-tung. Mult.
2739 8f. (1) Type **516** . . . . . . 1·00 45
2740 8f. (2) Mao as young man 1·00 45
2741 8f. (3) Making speech . . . 1·00 45
2742 8f. (4) Mao broadcasting . . 1·00 45
2743 8f. (5) Mao with Chou En-lai and Chu Teh (horiz) 1·25 45
2744 8f. (6) Reviewing the army 1·25 45

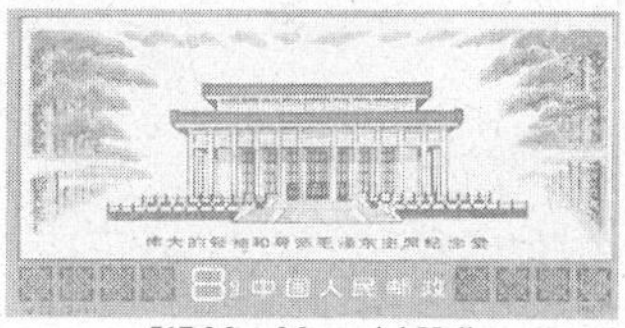

517 Mao Memorial Hall

1977. Completion of Mao Memorial Hall, Peking. Multicoloured.
2745 8f. (1) Type **517** . . . . . . 2·50 1·10
2746 8f. (2) Commemoration text 2·50 1·10

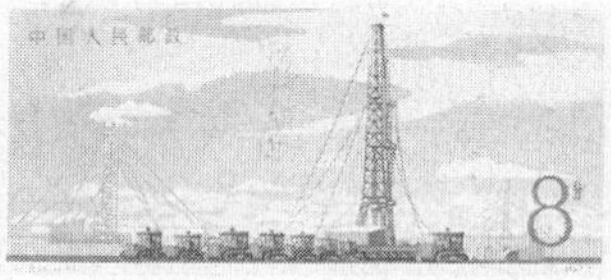

518 Tractors transporting Oil-rig

1978. Development of Petroleum Industry. Mult.
2747 8f. (1) Type **518** 50 10
2748 8f. (2) Clearing wax from oil well 50 10
2749 8f. (3) Laying pipe-line . . . 50 10
2750 8f. (4) Tung Fang Hung oil refinery, Peking 65 20
2751 8f. (5) Loading a tanker, Taching 75 20
2752 20f. (6) Oil-rig and drilling ship "Exploration" . . . 2·75 80

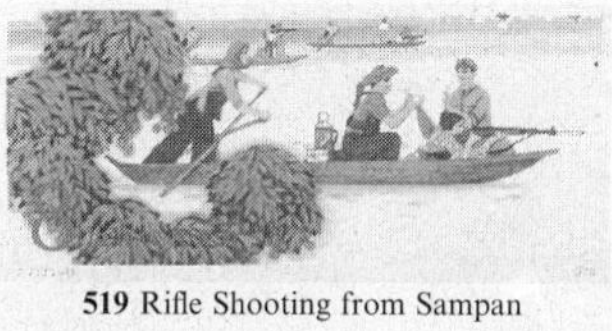

519 Rifle Shooting from Sampan

1978. "Army and People are One Family". Multicoloured.
2753 8f. (1) Type **519** . . . . . . 1·25 75
2754 8f. (2) Helping with rice harvest . . . . 1·25 75

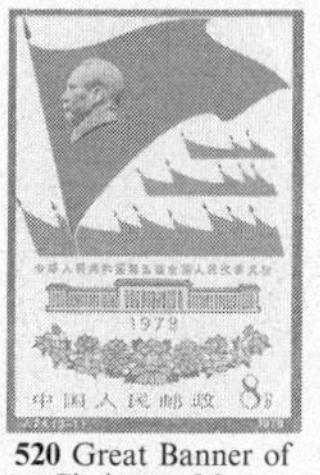

520 Great Banner of Chairman Mao

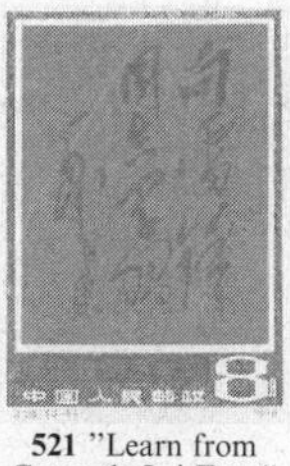

521 "Learn from Comrade Lei Feng" (Inscription by Mao Tse-tung)

1978. 5th National People's Congress. Mult.
2755	8f.	(1) Type **520**	80	40
2756	8f.	(2) Constitution	80	40
2757	8f.	(3) Emblems of modernization	80	40

1978. Lei Feng (Communist fighter) Commem.
2758	**521**	8f. (1) gold and red	1·50	50
2759	–	8f. (2) gold and red	1·50	50
2760	–	8f. (3) multicoloured	1·50	50

DESIGNS: No. 2759, Inscription by Chairman Hua; No. 2760, Lei Feng reading Mao's works.

522 Hsiang Ching-yu (Women's Movement Pioneer)   **523** Conference Emblem and Tien on Men Gate, Peking

1978. International Working Women's Day.
2761	**522**	8f. (1) black, red & gold	75	35
2762	–	8f. (2) black, red & gold	75	35

DESIGN: No. 2762, Yang Kai-hui (communist fighter).

1978. National Science Conference. Mult.
2763	8f.	(1) Type **523**	75	40
2764	8f.	(2) Flags	75	40
2765	8f.	(3) Emblem, flag and globe	75	40

524 Launching a Radio-sonde   **525** Galloping Horse

1978. Meteorological Services. Multicoloured.
2766	8f.	(1) Type **524**	60	20
2767	8f.	(2) Radar station	60	20
2768	8f.	(3) Weather forecasting with computers	60	20
2769	8f.	(4) Commune group observing sky	60	20
2770	8f.	(5) Cloud-dispersing rockets	60	20

1978. Galloping Horses.
2771	**525**	4f. (1) multicoloured	1·00	50
2772	–	8f. (2) multicoloured	1·00	50
2773	–	8f. (3) multicoloured	1·00	55
2774	–	10f. (4) multicoloured	1·00	55
2775	–	20f. (5) multicoloured	4·00	65
2776	–	30f. (6) multicoloured	3·00	75
2777	–	40f. (7) mult (horiz)	3·00	1·00
2778	–	50f. (8) mult (horiz)	4·00	1·00
2779	–	60f. (9) mult (horiz)	3·00	2·00
2780	–	70f. (10) mult (horiz)	4·00	3·00

DESIGNS: No. 2772/80, various paintings of horses by Hsu Pei-hung.

526 Football   **527** Material Feeder

1978. "Building up Strength for the Revolution". Multicoloured.
2782	8f.	(2) Type **526**	40	10
2783	8f.	(3) Swimming	40	10
2784	8f.	(4) Gymnastics	40	10
2785	8f.	(5) Running	40	10
2786	20f.	(1) Group exercises	1·10	20

The 20f. is larger, 48 × 27 mm.

1978. Chemical Industry Development. Fabric Production. Multicoloured.
2787	8f.	(1) Type **527**	80	20
2788	8f.	(2) Drawing-out threads	80	20
2789	8f.	(3) Weaving	80	20
2790	8f.	(4) Dyeing and printing	80	20
2791	8f.	(5) Finished products	80	20

528 Conference Emblem   **529** Grassland Improvement, Mongolia

1978. National Finance and Trade Conference. Multicoloured.
2792	8f.	(1) Type **528**	75	20
2793	8f.	(2) Inscription by Mao Tse-tung	75	20

1978. Progress in Animal Husbandry. Mult.
2794	8f.	(1) Type **529**	1·00	25
2795	8f.	(2) Sheep rearing by the Kazakhs	1·00	25
2796	8f.	(3) Shearing sheep, Tibet	1·00	25

530 Automated loading of Burning Coke

1978. Iron and Steel Industry. Mult.
2797	8f.	(1) Type **530**	1·00	25
2798	8f.	(2) Checking molten iron	50	25
2799	8f.	(3) Pouring molten steel	50	25
2800	8f.	(4) Steel-rolling mill	50	25
2801	8f.	(5) Loading steel train	1·00	25

531 Soldier   **532** Cloth Toy Lion

1978. Army Modernization. Multicoloured.
2802	8f.	(1) Type **531**	85	30
2803	8f.	(2) Soldier firing missile	85	30
2804	8f.	(3) Amphibious landing	85	30

1978. Arts and Crafts. Multicoloured.
2805	8f.	(1) Type **532**	45	15
2806	8f.	(2) Three-legged pot (vert)	45	10
2807	8f.	(3) Lacquerware rhinoceros	55	10
2808	10f.	(4) Embroidered kitten (vert)	55	15
2809	20f.	(5) Basketware	65	20
2810	30f.	(6) Cloisonne pot (vert)	70	30
2811	40f.	(7) Lacquerware plate and swan	85	40
2812	50f.	(8) Boxwood carving (vert)	1·00	50
2813	60f.	(9) Jade carving	1·25	40
2814	70f.	(10) Ivory carving (vert)	1·40	70

533 Worker, Peasant and Intellectual   **534** "Panax ginseng"

1978. 4th National Women's Congress.
2816	**533**	8f. multicoloured	1·50	50

1978. Medicinal Plants. Multicoloured.
2817	8f.	(1) Type **534**	60	15
2818	8f.	(2) "Datura metel"	60	15
2819	8f.	(3) "Belamcanda chinensis"	60	15
2820	8f.	(4) "Platycodon grandiflorum"	60	15
2821	55f.	(5) "Rhododendron dauricum"	2·40	75

535 Cogwheel, Grain,   **536** Emblem, Open Book and Rocket and Flag   Flowers

1978. 9th National Trades Union Congress.
2822	**535**	8f. multicoloured	2·10	75

1978. 10th National Congress of Communist Youth League.
2823	**536**	8f. multicoloured	2·10	75

537 Chinese and Japanese Children exchanging Gifts   **538** Hui, Han and Mongolian

1978. Signing of Chinese–Japanese Treaty of Peace and Friendship. Multicoloured.
2824	8f.	Type **537**	30	15
2825	55f.	Great Wall of China and Mt. Fuji	1·75	65

1978. 20th Anniv of Ningsia Hui Autonomous Region. Multicoloured.
2826	8f.	(1) Type **538**	85	30
2827	8f.	(2) Coal loading machine, Holan colliery	85	30
2828	10f.	(3) Irrigation and Chingtunghsia power station	85	30

539 Chinsha River Bridge, West Szechuan   **540** Transplanting Rice Seedlings by Machine

1978. Highway Bridges. Multicoloured.
2829	8f.	(1) Type **539**	70	30
2830	8f.	(2) Hsinghong Bridge, Wuhsi	70	30
2831	8f.	(3) Chiuhsikou Bridge, Fengdu	70	30
2832	8f.	(4) Chinsha Bridge	70	30
2833	60f.	(5) Shangyeh Bridge, Sanmen	1·90	90

1978. Water Country Modernization. Mult.
2835	8f.	(1) Type **540**	2·25	1·00
2836	8f.	(2) Crop spraying	2·25	1·00
2837	8f.	(3) Selecting seeds	2·25	1·00
2838	8f.	(4) Canal-side village	2·25	1·00
2839	8f.	(5) Delivering and storing grain	2·25	1·00

Nos. 2835/9 were issued together, se-tenant, forming a composite design.

541 Festivities

1978. 20th Anniv of Kwangsi Chuang Autonomous Region. Multicoloured.
2840	8f.	(1) Type **541**	2·25	40
2841	8f.	(2) Industrial complexes (vert)	2·25	40
2842	10f.	(3) River scene (vert)	1·50	1·00

542 Tibetan Peasant reporting Mineralogical Discovery   **543** Pair of Golden Pheasants on Rock

1979. Mining Development. Multicoloured.
2843	4f.	Type **542**	50	25
2844	8f.	Miners with pneumatic drill	50	15
2845	10f.	Open-cast mining	1·25	25
2846	20f.	Electric mine train	1·50	40

1979. Golden Pheasants. Multicoloured.
2847	4f.	Type **543**	1·25	70
2848	8f.	Pheasant in flight	3·75	1·25
2849	45f.	Pheasant looking for food	3·00	3·00

544 Einstein   **545** Woman, Monster and Phoenix

1979. Birth Centenary of Albert Einstein (physicist).
2850	**544**	8f. brown, gold & slate	1·40	40

1979. Silk Paintings from a Tomb of the Warring States Period (475–221 B.C.). Multicoloured.
2851	8f.	Type **545**	2·10	20
2852	60f.	Man riding dragon	1·40	1·25

546 Jing Shan   **547** Hammer and Sickle

1979. Peking Scenes. Multicoloured.
2853	1y.	Type **546**	75	10
2854	2y.	Summer Palace	1·50	40
2855	5y.	Beihai Park	4·00	85

1979. 90th Anniv of International Labour Day.
2856	**547**	8f. multicoloured	1·25	50

548 Memorial Frieze

1979. 60th Anniv of May 4th Movement. Mult.
2857	8f.	(1) Type **548**	70	20
2858	8f.	(2) Girl and symbols of progress	70	20

549 Children of Different Races

1979. International Year of the Child. Mult.
2859 8f. I.Y.C. emblem and
children with balloons . . . 1·50 50
2860 60f. Type 549 . . . . 8·75 3·00

550 Spring over Great Wall

1979. The Great Wall. Multicoloured.
2861 8f. (1) Type 550 . . . . . . 1·50 75
2862 8f. (2) Summer over Great
Wall . . . . 1·50 75
2863 8f. (3) Autumn over Great
Wall . . . . 1·50 75
2864 60f. (4) Winter over Great
Wall . . . . 11·00 5·00

551 Roaring Tiger

1979. Manchurian Tiger. Paintings by Liu Jiyou.
Multicoloured.
2866 4f. Type 551 . . . . . . 1·00 50
2867 8f. Two young tigers . . . . 1·00 50
2868 60f. Tiger at rest . . . . . 3·25 1·10

552 Mechanical Harvester

1979. Trades of the People's Communes. Mult.
2869 4f. (1) Type 552
(Agriculture) 75 30
2870 8f. (2) Planting a sapling
(Forestry) . . . . . . 1·00 30
2871 8f. (3) Herding ducks (Stock
raising) . . . . 1·00 30
2872 8f. (4) Basket weaving . . . 1·00 30
2873 10f. (5) Fishermen with
handcarts of fish (Fishing) . 2·00 50

554 Games' Emblem, Running, Volleyball and
Weightlifting

1979. 4th National Games.
2875 554 8f. (1) multicoloured . . 30 30
2876 – 8f. (2) multicoloured . . 30 30
2877 – 8f. (3) black, grn & red 30 30
2878 – 8f. (4) black, red & grn 30 30
DESIGNS: No. 2876, Football, badminton, high
jumping and ice skating. No. 2877, Fencing, skiing,
gymnastics and diving. No. 2878, Motor cycling, table
tennis, basketball and archery.

555 National Flag and Mountains

556 National Emblem

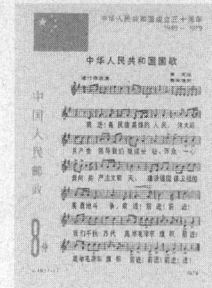
557 National Anthem

558 Dancers and
Drummer

559 Tractor and Crop-
spraying Antonov An-2

1979. 30th Anniv of People's Republic of China.
Multicoloured.
2880 8f. (1) National flag and
rainbow . . . . 1·90 70
2881 8f. (2) Type 555 . . . . . 1·90 70
2882 8f. Type 556 . . . . . . 1·25 25
2884 8f. Type 557 . . . . . . 3·00 1·00
2885 8f. (1) Type 558 . . . . . 75 15
2886 8f. (2) Dancers and
tambourine player . . . 75 15
2887 8f. (3) Dancers and banjo
player 75 15
2888 8f. (4) Dancers and
drummer 75 15
2889 8f. (1) Type 559 . . . . . 85 15
2890 8f. (2) Computer and
cogwheels 85 15
2891 8f. (3) Rocket, jet fighter
and submarine 85 15
2892 8f. (4) Atomic symbols . . . 85 15

560 Exhibition
Emblem

561 Children with
Model Aircraft

1979. National Exhibition of Juniors' Scientific and
Technological Works.
2893 560 8f. multicoloured . . . . 1·25 50

1979. Study of Science from Childhood. Mult.
2894 8f. (1) Type 561 . . . . . 65 20
2895 8f. (2) Girls with microscope
and test tube 65 20
2896 8f. (3) Children with
telescope 65 20
2897 8f. (4) Boy catching
butterflies 65 20
2898 8f. (5) Girl noting weather
readings 65 20
2899 60f. (6) Boys with model
boat . . . . 2·50 75

562 Yu Shan

1979. Taiwan Views. Multicoloured.
2901 8f. (1) Type 562 . . . . . 85 45
2902 8f. (2) Sun Moon Lake . . . 85 45
2903 8f. (3) Chikan Tower . . . 85 45
2904 8f. (4) Suao-Hualien
highway 85 45
2905 55f. (5) Tian Xiang Falls . . 2·50 1·00
2906 60f. (6) Moonlight over
Banping Mountain . . . 3·50 1·60

563 Symbols of Literature and Art

1979. 4th National Congress of Literary and Art
Workers. Multicoloured.
2907 4f. Type 563 . . . . . . 50 30
2908 8f. Seals, hammer, sickle,
rifle, atomic symbol and
flowers . . . . 1·10 30

564 "Shaoshan" Type Electric
Locomotive

1979. Railway Construction. Multicoloured.
2909 8f. (1) Type 564 . . . . . 1·50 40
2910 8f. (2) Modern railway
viaduct . . . . 1·50 40
2911 8f. (3) Goods train crossing
bridge . . . . 1·50 40

565 "Chrysanthemum Petal"

1979. Camellias of Yunnan. Multicoloured.
2912 4f. (1) Type 565 . . . . . 70 30
2913 8f. (2) "Lion Head" . . . 70 30
2914 8f. (3) Camellia "Chrysantha
(Hu) Tuyama" 70 30
2915 10f. (4) "Small Osmanthus
Leaf" 70 30
2916 20f. (5) "Baby Face" . . . 1·75 55
2917 30f. (6) "Cornelian" . . . 3·25 65
2918 40f. (7) Peony Camellia . . 2·50 65
2919 50f. (8) "Purple Gown" . . 2·50 75
2920 60f. (9) "Dwarf Rose" . . 1·90 75
2921 70f. (10) "Willow Leaf
Spinel Pink" . . . . . 1·90 75

567 Dr. Bethune
attending Wounded
Soldier

568 Central Archives Hall

1979. 40th Death Anniv of Dr. Norman Bethune.
Multicoloured.
2924 8f. Type 567 . . . . . . 55 10
2925 70f. Bethune Memorial,
Mausoleum of Martyrs,
Shijiazhuang . . . . . 2·75 75

1979. International Archives Weeks. Mult.
2926 8f. (1) Type 568 . . . . . 85 20
2927 8f. (2) Gold cabinet
containing documents of
Ming and Ching dynasties
(vert) 85 20
2928 60f. (3) Imperial Archives
Main Hall . . . . . . 7·75 1·75

569 Waterfall Cave,
Home of Monkey King

570 Stalin

1979. Scenes from "Pilgrimage to the West" (Chinese
classical novel). Multicoloured.
2929 8f. (1) Type 569 . . . . . 1·50 75
2930 8f. (2) Necha, son of Li,
fighting Monkey . . . . 1·50 75
2931 8f. (3) Monkey in Mother
Queen's peach orchard . . 1·50 75
2932 8f. (4) Monkey in alchemy
furnace . . . . 1·50 75
2933 10f. (5) Monkey fighting
White Bone Demon . . . 4·25 75
2934 20f. (6) Monkey
extinguishing fire with
palm-leaf fan . . . . . 4·25 75

2935 60f. (7) Monkey fighting
Spider Demon in Cobweb
Cave . . . . 3·25 3·00
2936 70f. (8) Monkey on
scripture-seeking route to
India . . . . 7·25 3·00

1979. Birth Centenary of Stalin.
2937 570 8f. (1) brown . . . . . 1·25 40
2938 – 8f. (2) black . . . . . 1·25 40
DESIGN: No. 2038, Stalin appealing for unity
against Germany.

571 Peony

572 Meng Liang,
"Hongyang Cave"

1980. Paintings of Qi Baishi.
2939 571 4f. (1) multicoloured . . 75 15
2940 – 4f. (2) multicoloured . . 75 15
2941 – 8f. (3) multicoloured . . 75 10
2942 – 8f. (4) black, blue & red 75 10
2943 – 8f. (5) multicoloured . . 75 10
2944 – 8f. (6) black, grey & red 75 10
2945 – 8f. (7) multicoloured . . 75 10
2946 – 8f. (8) multicoloured . . 75 50
2947 – 10f. (9) blk, yell and red 1·50 15
2948 – 20f. (10) grey, brn & blk 1·50 20
2949 – 30f. (11) multicoloured . 1·50 30
2950 – 40f. (12) multicoloured . 1·50 50
2951 – 50f. (13) blk, grey & red 3·00 75
2952 – 55f. (14) multicoloured . 3·75 75
2953 – 60f. (15) blk, grey & red 5·00 1·50
2954 – 70f. (16) multicoloured . 6·25 2·25
DESIGNS: No. 2940, Squirrels and grapes; 2941,
Crabs and wine; 2942, Tadpoles in mountain spring;
2943, Chicks; 2944, Lotus; 2945, Red plum; 2946,
River kingfisher; 2947, Bottle gourds; 2948, "The
Voice of Autumn"; 2949, Wisteria; 2950,
Chrysanthemums; 2951, Shrimps; 2952, Litchi; 2953,
Cabbages and mushrooms; 2954, Peaches.

1980. Facial Make-up in Peking Operas. Mult.
2956 4f. (1) Type 572 . . . . . 1·25 40
2957 4f. (2) Li Kui, "Black
Whirlwind" . . . . . 1·25 40
2958 8f. (3) Huang Gai, "Meeting
of Heroes" . . . . . . 1·75 60
2959 8f. (4) Monkey King,
"Havoc in Heaven" . . . 1·75 60
2960 10f. (5) Lu Zhishen, "Wild
Boar Forest" . . . . . 2·25 80
2961 20f. (6) Lian Po,
"Reconciliation between
the General and the
Minister" . . . . . . 4·50 1·50
2962 60f. (7) Zhang Fei, "Reed
Marsh" . . . . 8·25 3·00
2963 70f. (8) Dou Erdun,
"Stealing the Emperor's
Horse" . . . . 9·00 3·25

573 Chinese Olympic
Committee Emblem

574 Bear Macaque

1980. Winter Olympic Games, Lake Placid.
Multicoloured.
2964 8f. (1) Type 573 . . . . . 50 35
2965 8f. (2) Speed skating . . . 50 35
2966 8f. (3) Figure skating . . . 50 35
2967 60f. (4) Skiing . . . . . 3·50 1·25

1980. New Year. Year of the Monkey.
2968 574 8f. red, black and gold . £170 50·00

575 Klara Zetkin (journalist
and politician)

1980. 70th Anniv of International Working Women's Day.

| 2969 | 575 | 8f. black, yellow & brn | 1·25 | 65 |

576 Orchard

1980. Afforestation. Multicoloured.

2970		4f. Type **576**	70	15
2971		8f. Highway lined with trees	70	20
2972		10f. Aerial sowing by Antonov An-2 biplane	1·40	25
2973		20f. Factory amongst trees	1·40	60

577 Apsaras (celestial beings)

1980. 2nd National Conference of Chinese Scientific and Technical Association.

| 2974 | 577 | 8f. multicoloured | 1·25 | 55 |

578 Freighter

1980. Mail Transport. Multicoloured.

2975		2f. Type **578**	1·00	75
2976		4f. Mail bus	1·25	75
2977		8f. Travelling post office coach	2·50	1·00
2978		10f. Tupolev Tu-154 airplane	3·00	1·40

579 Cigarette damaging Heart and Lungs

1980. Anti-smoking Campaign. Multicoloured.

| 2979 | | 8f. Type **579** | 1·75 | 40 |
| 2980 | | 60f. Face smoking and face holding flower in mouth, symbolising choice of smoking or health | 5·00 | 2·25 |

580 Jian Zhen Memorial Hall, Yangzhou

1980. Return of High Monk Jian Zhen's Statue. Multicoloured.

2981		8f. (1) Type **580**	2·50	50
2982		8f. (2) Statue of Jian Zhen (vert)	2·50	50
2983		60f. (3) Junk in which Jian Zhen travelled to Japan	16·00	5·75

581 Lenin   **582** "Swallow Chick" Kite

1980. 110th Birth Anniv of Lenin.

| 2984 | 581 | 8f. brown, pink & green | 1·60 | 65 |

1980. Kites. Multicoloured.

| 2985 | | 8f. (1) Type **582** | 1·50 | 45 |
| 2986 | | 8f. (2) "Slender swallow" kite | 1·50 | 45 |

| 2987 | | 8f. (3) "Semi-slender swallow" kite | 1·50 | 45 |
| 2988 | | 70f. (4) "Dual swallows" kite | 12·00 | 4·50 |

583 Hare running in Fright

1980. Scenes from "Gu Dong" (Chinese fairy tale). Multicoloured.

2989		8f. (1) Type **583**	1·00	55
2990		8f. (2) Hare tells other animals "Gu Dong is coming"	1·00	55
2991		8f. (3) Lion asks "What is Gu Dong?"	1·00	55
2992		8f. (4) Animals discover sound of "Gu Dong" is made by falling papaya	1·00	55

584 Silhouette of Ilyushin Il-86 Jetliner and Plan of Terminal Building   **585** Stag

1980. Peking International Airport. Multicoloured.

| 2993 | | 8f. Type **584** | 1·00 | 30 |
| 2994 | | 10f. Airplane and runway lights | 1·50 | 50 |

1980. Sika Deer. Multicoloured.

2995		4f. Type **585**	80	65
2996		8f. Doe and fawn	80	65
2997		60f. Herd	5·25	2·10

586 "White Lotus"

1980. Lotus Paintings by Yu Zhizhen. Mult.

2998		8f. (1) Type **586**	2·00	90
2999		8f. (2) "Rose-tipped Snow"	2·00	90
3000		8f. (3) "Buddha's Seat"	2·00	90
3001		70f. (4) "Variable Charming Face"	17·00	6·00

587 Returned Pearl Cave and Sword-cut Stone

1980. Guilin Landscapes. Multicoloured.

3003		8f. (1) Type **587**	1·50	45
3004		8f. (2) Distant view of three mountains	1·50	45
3005		8f. (3) Nine-horse Fresco Hill	1·50	45
3006		8f. (4) Egrets around the aged banyan	1·50	45
3007		8f. (5) Western Hills at sunset (vert)	1·50	45
3008		8f. (6) Moonlight on the Lijiang River (vert)	1·50	45
3009		60f. (7) Springhead and ferry (vert)	9·50	3·00
3010		70f. (8) Scenic path at Yangshuo (vert)	10·50	3·00

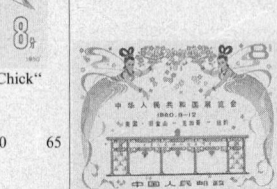

588 Exhibition Gateway   **589** Burebista (founder-king) and Rumanian Flag

1980. China Exhibition in United States. Mult.

| 3011 | | 8f. Type **588** | 75 | 40 |
| 3012 | | 70f. Great Wall and emblems of San Francisco, Chicago and New York | 4·25 | 2·25 |

1980. 2050th Anniv of Dacian State.

| 3013 | 589 | 8f. multicoloured | 1·60 | 65 |

590 "Sea of Clouds" (Liu Haisu)

1980. U.N.E.S.C.O. Exhibition of Chinese Paintings and Drawings. Multicoloured.

3014		8f. (1) Type **590**	1·10	40
3015		8f. (2) "Black-naped Oriole and Magnolia" (Yu Feian) (vert)	1·50	70
3016		8f. (3) "Tending Bactrian Camels" (Wu Zuoren)	1·10	40

591 Quzi Tower in Spring

1980. Liu Yuan (Tarrying Garden), Suzhou. Mult.

3017		8f. (1) Type **591**	5·75	2·10
3018		8f. (2) Yuancui Pavilion in Summer	5·75	2·10
3019		10f. (3) Hanbi Shanfang in Autumn	5·75	2·40
3020		60f. (4) Guanyun Peak in Winter	32·00	10·00

592 Xu Guangqi   **593** Pistol-shooting

1980. Scientists of Ancient China. Multicoloured.

3021		8f. (1) Type **592** (agriculturalist and astronomer)	2·25	65
3022		8f. (2) Li Bing (hydraulic engineer)	2·25	65
3023		8f. (3) Jia Sixie (agronomist)	2·25	65
3024		60f. (4) Huang Daopo (textile expert)	10·00	3·00

1980. 1st Anniv of Return to International Olympic Committee. Multicoloured.

3025	593	4f. (1) brown, yell & mve	50	10
3026		8f. (2) brown, yell & grn	75	15
3027		8f. (3) brown, yell & blue	75	15
3028		10f. (4) brown, yell & orge	1·10	35
3029		60f. (5) multicoloured	3·75	1·00

DESIGNS: No. 3026, Gymnastics; No. 3027, Diving; No. 3028, Volleyball; No. 3029, Archery.

594 White Flag Dolphin   **595** Cock

1980. White Flag Dolphin. Multicoloured.

| 3030 | | 8f. Type **594** | 1·25 | 25 |
| 3031 | | 60f. Two dolphins | 6·00 | 1·00 |

1981. New Year. Year of the Cock.

| 3032 | 595 | 8f. multicoloured | 8·50 | 2·00 |

596 Early Morning

1981. Scenes of Xishuang Banna. Multicoloured.

3033		4f. (1) Type **596**	60	20
3034		4f. (2) Mountain village of Dai nationality	60	20
3035		8f. (3) Rainbow over Lanchang River	1·25	25
3036		8f. (4) Ancient Temple (vert)	1·25	25

| 3037 | | 8f. (5) Moonlit night (vert) | 1·25 | 25 |
| 3038 | | 60f. (6) Phoenix tree in bloom (vert) | 7·00 | 2·50 |

597 Flower Basket Lantern

1981. Palace Lanterns. Multicoloured.

3039		4f. (1) Type **597**	95	45
3040		8f. (2) Dragons playing with a pearl	1·50	40
3041		8f. (3) Dragon and phoenix	1·50	40
3042		8f. (4) Treasure bowl	1·50	40
3043		20f. (5) Flower and birds	4·25	1·00
3044		60f. (6) Peony lantern painted with fishes	11·50	4·00

598 Crossing the River

1981. Marking the Gunwale (Chinese fable). Multicoloured.

3045		8f. (1) Chinese text of story	70	35
3046		8f. (2) Type **598**	70	35
3047		8f. (3) The sword drops in the water	70	35
3048		8f. (4) Making mark on gunwale	70	35
3049		8f. (5) Diving into river to recover sword	70	35

599 Chinese Elm   **600** Vase with Two Tigers (Song Dynasty)

1981. Miniature Landscapes (dwarf trees). Mult.

3050		4f. (1) Type **599**	45	35
3051		8f. (2) Juniper	70	30
3052		8f. (3) Maidenhair tree	70	30
3053		10f. (4) Chinese Juniper (horiz)	1·10	30
3054		20f. (5) Wild Kaki persimmon (horiz)	2·00	1·00
3055		60f. (6) Single-seed juniper (horiz)	6·25	1·40

1981. Ceramics from Cizhou Kilns. Multicoloured.

3056		4f. (1) Type **600**	35	30
3057		8f. (2) Carved black glazed vase (Jin dynasty) (horiz)	55	25
3058		8f. (3) Amphora with apricot blossoms (modern)	55	25
3059		8f. (4) Jar with two phoenixes (Yuan dynasty) (horiz)	55	25
3060		10f. (5) Flat flask with dragon and phoenix (Yuan dynasty) (horiz)	1·25	30
3061		60f. (6) Vessel with tiger-shaped handles (modern) (horiz)	4·00	1·40

601 Giant Panda "Stamp"

1981. People's Republic of China Stamp Exhibition, Japan. Multicoloured.

| 3062 | | 8f. Type **601** | 75 | 15 |
| 3063 | | 60f. Cockerel and junk "stamps" | 1·90 | 85 |

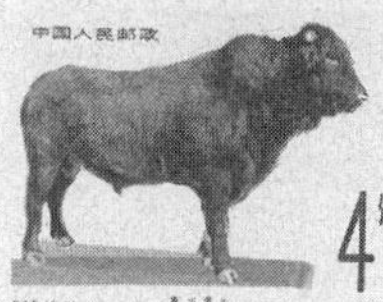

602 Qinchuan Bull

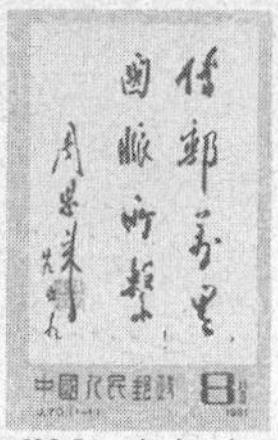

603 Inscription by Chou En-lai

1981. Cattle. Multicoloured.
3064 4f. (1) Type **602** 50 15
3065 8f. (2) Binhu buffalo 50 10
3066 8f. (3) Yak 50 10
3067 8f. (4) Black and white dairy cattle 50 10
3068 10f. (5) Red pasture bull . . 75 25
3069 55f. (6) Simmental crossbreed bull . . . . . 5·00 1·25

1981. "To Deliver Mail for Ten Thousand Li, Has Bearing on Arteries and Veins of the Country".
3070 **603** 8f. multicoloured 50 15

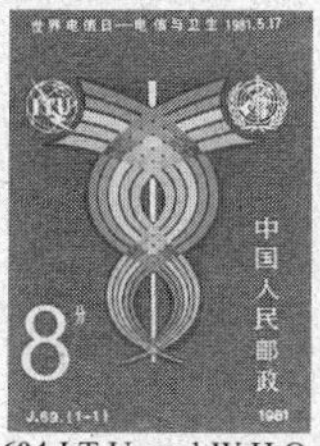

604 I.T.U. and W.H.O. Emblems and Ribbons forming Caduceus

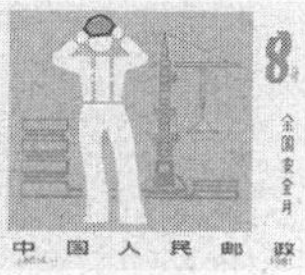

605 Safety in Building Construction

1981. World Telecommunications Day.
3071 **604** 8f. multicoloured 50 15

1981. National Safety Month. Multicoloured.
3072 8f. (1) Type **605** 40 15
3073 8f. (2) Mining safety 40 15
3074 8f. (3) Road safety 40 15
3075 8f. (4) Farming and forestry safety 40 15

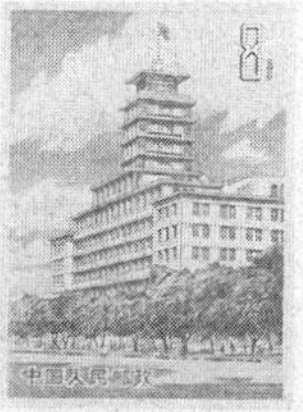

606 Trunk Call Building

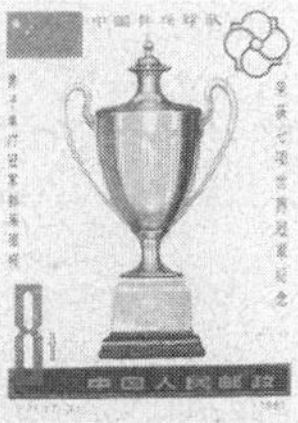

607 St. Bride Vase (Men's singles)

1981.
3076 **606** 8f. brown . . . . 1·60 40

1981. Chinese Team's Victories at World Table Tennis Championships. Multicoloured.
3077 8f. (3) Type **607** 25 15
3078 8f. (4) Iran Cup (Men's doubles) 25 15
3079 8f. (5) G. Geist Prize (Women's singles) 25 15
3080 8f. (6) W. J. Pope Trophy (Women's doubles) . . . 25 15
3081 8f. (7) Heydusek Prize (Mixed doubles) 25 15
3082 20f. (1) Swathling Cup (Men's team) 80 15
3083 20f. (2) Marcel Corbillon Cup (Women's team) . . 80 15

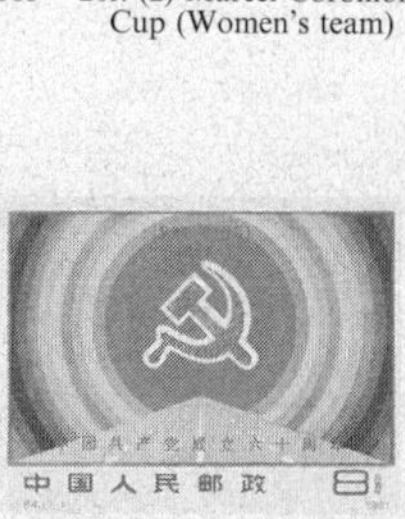

608 Hammer and Sickle

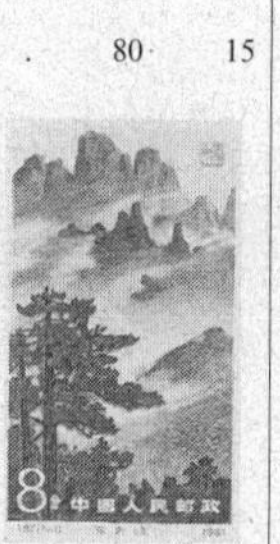

609 Five Veterans Peak

1981. 60th Anniv of Chinese Communist Party.
3084 **608** 8f. multicoloured 75 25

1981. Lushan Mountains. Multicoloured.
3085 8f. (1) Type **609** 70 20
3086 8f. (2) Hanpo Pass (horiz) 70 20
3087 8f. (3) Yellow Dragon Pool and Waterfall 70 20
3088 8f. (4) Sunlit Peak (horiz) 70 20
3089 8f. (5) Three-layer Spring . . 70 20
3090 8f. (6) Stone and pines (horiz) 70 20
3091 60f. (7) Dragon Head Cliff 7·50 2·50

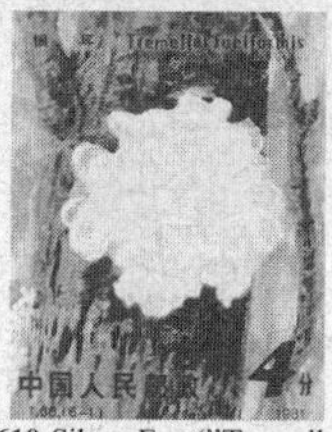

610 Silver Ear ("Tremella fuciformis")

1981. Edible Mushrooms. Multicoloured.
3092 4f. (1) Type **610** 60 15
3093 8f. (2) Veiled stinkhorn ("Dictyophora indusiata") 80 15
3094 8f. (3) "Hericium erinaceus" 80 15
3095 8f. (4) "Russula rubra" . . 80 15
3096 10f. (5) Shii-take mushroom ("Lentinus edodes") . . . 1·25 20
3097 70f. (6) White button mushroom ("Agaricus bisporus") . . . . 3·00 75

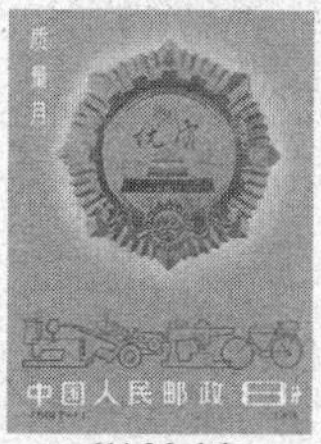

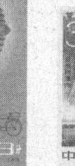

611 Medal

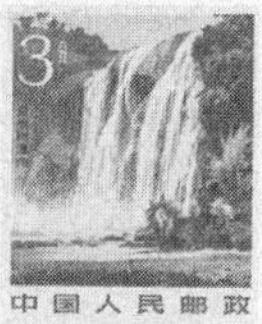

612 Huangguoshu Waterfall

1981. Quality Month.
3098 **611** 8f. (1) silver, black and red 75 20
3099 8f. (2) gold, brown and red 75 20

1981.
3100 – 1f. green 10 10
3101 – 1½f. red 10 10
3102 – 2f. green 10 10
3103 **612** 3f. brown 10 10
3118 – 3f. dp brn, brn & lt brn 10 10
3104 – 4f. violet 10 10
3119 – 4f. mauve and lilac . . . 10 10
3105 – 5f. brown 10 10
3106 – 8f. blue 10 10
3107 – 10f. purple 10 10
3121 – 10f. brown 20 10
3108 – 20f. green 55 10
3122 – 20f. blue 25 10
3109 – 30f. brown 25 10
3110 – 40f. black 35 10
3111 – 50f. mauve 35 10
3112 – 70f. black 55 10
3113 – 80f. red 55 10
3114 – 1y. lilac 65 10
3115 – 2y. green 85 15
3116 – 5y. blue . . . . 1·75 25

DESIGNS—VERT: 1f. Xishuang Banna. 1½f. Huashan Mountain. 2f. Taishan Mountain. 4f. Palm trees, Hainan. 5f. Pagoda, Huqiu Hill, Suzhou. 8f. Great Wall. 10f. North-east Forest. HORIZ: 20f. Herding sheep on Tianshan Mountain. 30f. Sheep on grassland, Inner Mongolia. 40f. Stone Forest. 50f. Pagodas, Ban Pingshan Mountain, Taiwan. 70f. Mt. Zhumulangma. 80f. Seven Star Grotto, Guangdong. 1y. Gorge, Yangtze River. 2y. Guilin. 5y. Mt. Huangshan.

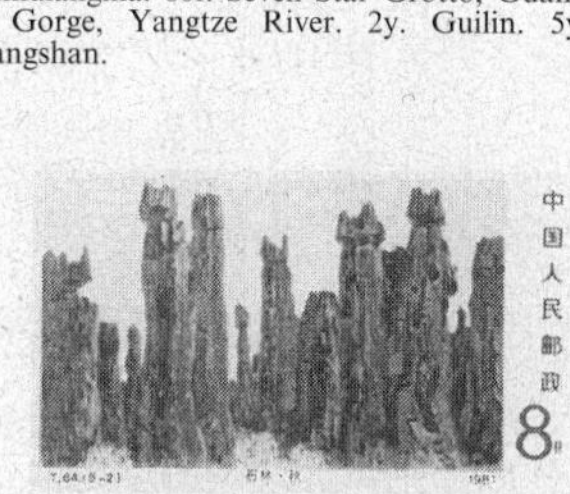

613 Stone Forest in Autumn

1981. Stone Forest. Multicoloured.
3125 8f. (1) Stone Forest in a mist 45 15
3126 8f. (2) Type **613** 45 15
3127 8f. (3) Pool in Stone Forest 45 15
3128 10f. (4) Dawn over Stone Forest (vert) 60 15
3129 70f. (5) Stone Forest by starlight (vert) . . . . 5·50 1·50

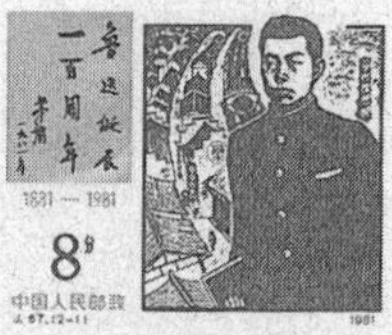

614 Lu Xun as Youth

1981. Birth Centenary of Lu Xun (writer).
3130 **614** 8f. black, green & yell 50 15
3131 – 20f. blk, brn & dp brn 1·00 50
DESIGN: 20f. Lu Xun in later life.

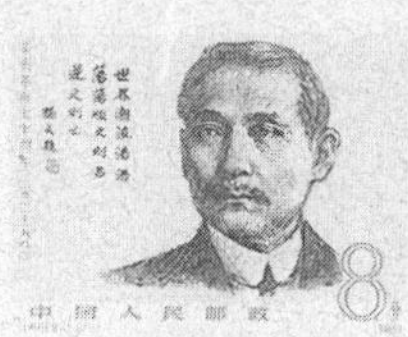

615 Dr. Sun Yat-sen

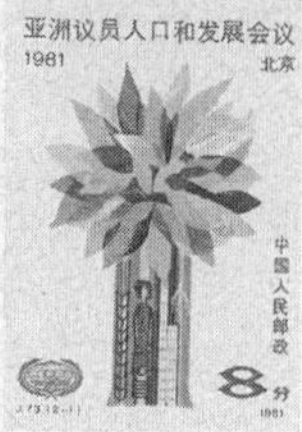

616 "Tree" symbolizing Co-ordination

1981. 70th Anniv of 1911 Revolution.
3132 **615** 8f. (1) multicoloured . . 40 15
3133 – 8f. (2) black, grn & yell 40 15
3134 – 8f. (3) black, pk & yell 40 15
DESIGNS: No. 3133, Grave of 72 Martyrs, Huang Hua Gate; No. 3134, Headquarters of Military Government of Hubei Province.

1981. Asian Conference of Parliamentarians on Population and Development. Multicoloured.
3135 8f. Type **616** 15 10
3136 70f. Design symbolizing Enlightenment 90 35

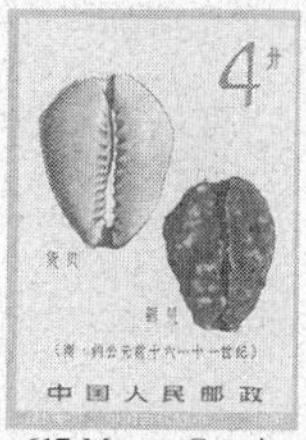

617 Money Cowrie and Cowrie-shaped Bronze Coin

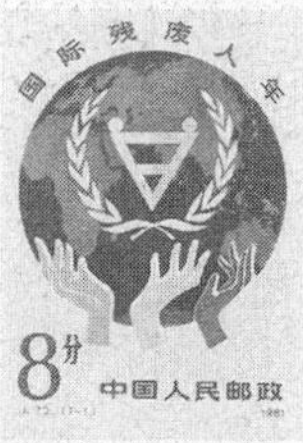

618 Hands and Globe with I.Y.D.P. Emblem

1981. Ancient Chinese Coins (1st series). Minted before 221 B.C. Multicoloured.
3137 4f. (1) Type **617** 40 15
3138 4f. (2) Shovel coin 40 15
3139 8f. (3) Shovel coin inscribed "Li" 50 10
3140 8f. (4) Shovel coin inscribed "An Yi Er Jin" 50 10
3141 8f. (5) Knife coin inscribed "Qi Fa Ha" 50 10
3142 8f. (6) Knife coin inscribed "Jie Mo Zhi Fa Hua" . . 50 10
3143 60f. (7) Knife coin inscribed "Cheng Bai" . . . . . . 3·00 70
3144 70f. (8) Circular coin with hole inscribed "Gong" . . 4·25 1·40
See also Nos. 3162/69.

1981. International Year of Disabled Persons.
3145 **618** 8f. multicoloured 25 15

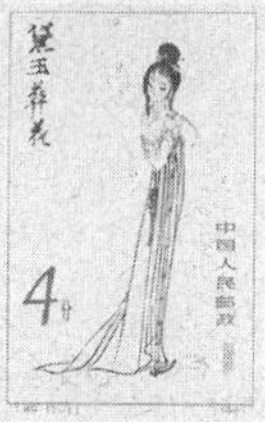

619 Daiyu

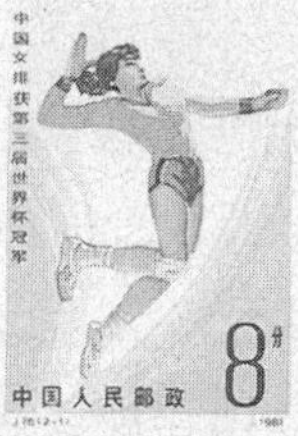

620 Volleyball Player

1981. The Twelve Beauties of Jinling from "A Dream of Red Mansions" by Cao Xueqin. Multicoloured. Designs showing paintings by Liu Danzhai.
3146 4f. (1) Type **619** 80 15
3147 4f. (2) Baochai chases butterfly 80 15
3148 8f. (3) Yuanchun visits parents 95 20
3149 8f. (4) Yingchun reading Buddhist sutras 95 20
3150 8f. (5) Tanchun forms poetry society 95 20
3151 8f. (6) Xichun painting . . . 95 20
3152 8f. (7) Xiangyun picking up necklace 95 20
3153 10f. (8) Liwan lectures her son . . . . 1·40 25
3154 20f. (9) Xifeng hatches plot 1·60 65
3155 30f. (10) Sister Qiao escapes 1·90 80
3156 40f. (11) Keqing relaxing . . 2·10 2·25
3157 80f. (12) Miaoyu serves tea 8·00 2·50

1981. Victory of Chinese Women's Team in World Cup Volleyball Championships. Multicoloured.
3159 8f. Type **620** 15 10
3160 20f. Player holding Cup . . 65 30

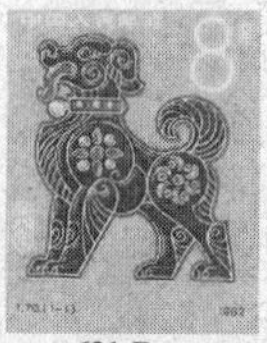

621 Dog

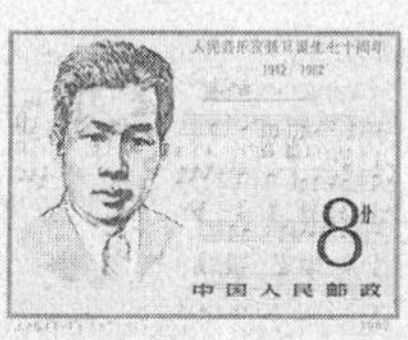

622 Nie Er and Score of "March of the Volunteers"

1982. New Year. Year of the Dog.
3161 **621** 8f. multicoloured . . . . 3·00 75

1982. Ancient Chinese Coins (2nd series). As T **617**. Multicoloured.
3162 4f. (1) Guilian ("Monster Mask") 15 15
3163 4f. (2) Shu shovel coin . . . 15 15
3164 8f. (3) Xia Zhuan shovel coin 20 10
3165 8f. (4) Han Dan shovel coin 20 10
3166 8f. (5) Pointed-head knife coin 20 10
3167 8f. (6) Ming knife coin . . . 20 10
3168 70f. (7) Jin Hua knife coin 2·00 50
3169 80f. (8) Yi Liu Hua circular coin . . . . 2·40 70

1982. 70th Anniv of Nie Er (composer).
3170 **622** 8f. multicoloured 30 15

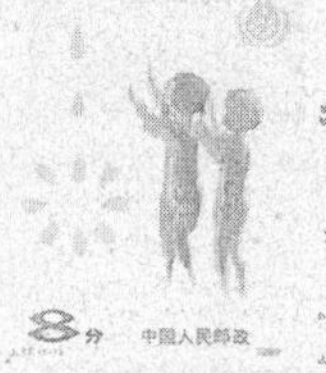

623 Dripping Water and Children

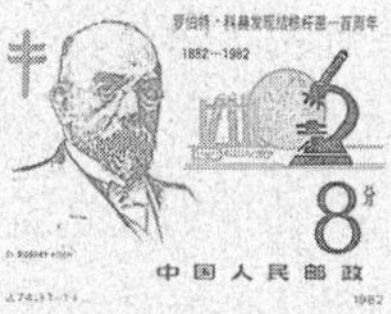

624 Dr. Robert Koch and Laboratory Equipment

1982. Int Drinking Water and Sanitation Decade.
3171 **623** 8f. grey, orange & blue 30 15

1982. Centenary of Discovery of Tubercle Bacillus.
3172 **624** 8f. multicoloured 30 15

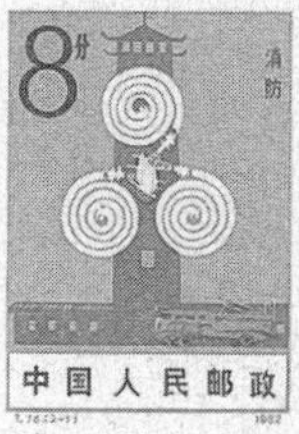

625 Building on Fire, Hoses and Fire Engine

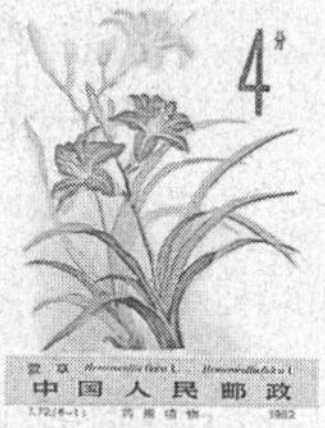

627 "Hemerocallis flava" and "H. fulva"

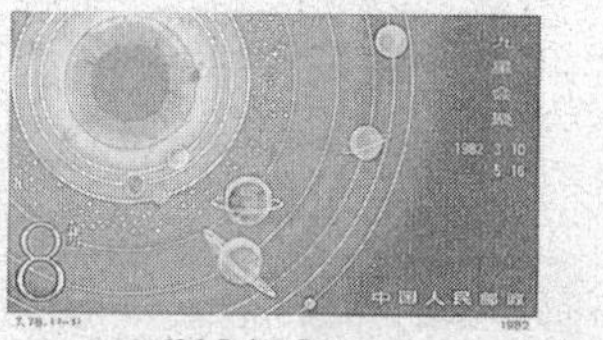

626 Solar System

1982. Fire Control. Multicoloured.
3173 8f. (1) Type **625** 60 15
3174 8f. (2) Chemical fire extinguisher 60 15

1982. "Cluster of Nine Planets" (planetary conjunction).
3175 **626** 8f. multicoloured 45 20

1982. Medicinal Plants. Multicoloured.
3176 4f. (1) Type **627** 20 10
3177 8f. (2) "Fritillaria unibracteata" 40 10
3178 8f. (3) "Aconitum carmichaeli" 40 10
3179 10f. (4) "Lilium brownii" . . 45 20
3180 20f. (5) "Arisaema consanguineum" . . . . . 1·10 25
3181 70f. (6) "Paeonia lactiflora" 1·60 80

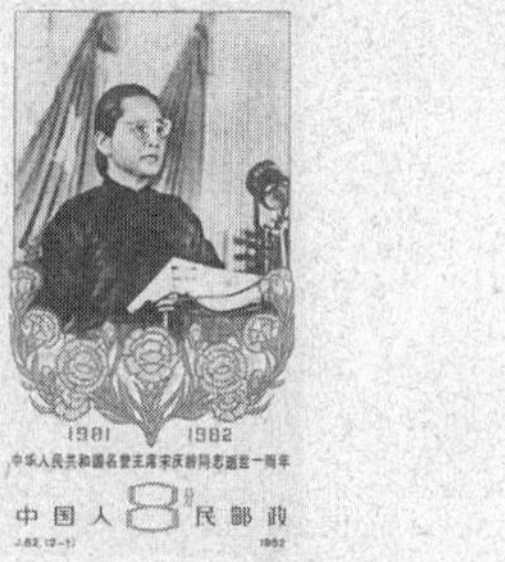

628 Soong Ching Ling addressing First Plenary Session

1982. 1st Death Anniv of Soong Ching Ling (former Head of State). Multicoloured.
3183 8f. Type **628** 30 15
3184 20f. Portrait of Soong Ching Ling 65 30

629 Sable

1982. The Sable. Multicoloured.
3185 8f. Type **629** 70 20
3186 80f. Sable running . . . . 3·50 1·75

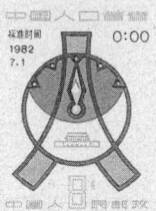

630 Census Emblem

631 Text, Emblem and Globe

1982. National Census.
3187 **630** 8f. multicoloured 25 10

1982. Second U.N. Conference on the Exploration and Peaceful Uses of Outer Space, Vienna.
3188 **631** 8f. multicoloured 25 10

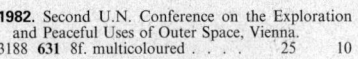

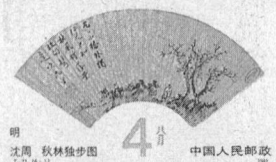

632 "Strolling Alone in Autumn Woods" (Shen Zhou)

1982. Fan Paintings of the Ming and Qing Dynasties. Multicoloured.
3189 4f. (1) Type **632** 35 10
3190 8f. (2) "Jackdaw on withered Tree" (Tang Yin) 75 30
3191 8f. (3) "Bamboos and Sparrows" (Zhou Zhimian) 75 30
3192 10f. (4) "Writing Poem under Pine" (Chen Hongshou and Bai Han) 1·00 15
3193 20f. (5) "Chrysanthemums" (Yun Shouping) . . . . 1·25 30
3194 70f. (6) "Masked Hawfinch, Grape Myrtle and Chinese Parasol" (Wang Wu) . . 4·25 2·25

634 Society Emblem

635 Orpiment

1982. 60th Anniv of Chinese Geological Society.
3196 **634** 8f. gold, stone & black 25 10

1982. Minerals. Multicoloured.
3197 4f. Type **635** 15 10
3198 8f. Stibnite 20 10
3199 10f. Cinnabar 25 10
3200 20f. Wolframite 40 20

636 "12", Hammer and Sickle and Great Hall of the People

637 Hoopoe

1982. 12th National Communist Party Congress.
3201 **636** 8f. multicoloured 60 10

1982. Birds. Multicoloured.
3202 8f. (1) Type **637** 75 60
3203 8f. (2) Barn swallow . . . 75 60
3204 8f. (3) Black-naped oriole . 75 60

3205 20f. (4) Great tit . . . . 1·75 1·25
3206 70f. (5) Great spotted woodpecker . . . . . . 3·50 3·00

638 "Plum Blossom" (Guan Shanyue)

1982. 10th Anniv of Normalization of Diplomatic Relations with Japan. Multicoloured.
3208 8f. Type **638** 25 10
3209 70f. "Hibiscus" (Xiao Shufang) . . . . . . 1·50 35

639 Globe, Profiles and Ear of Wheat

640 Guo Moruo

1982. World Food Day.
3210 **639** 8f. multicoloured 45 10

1982. 90th Birth Anniv of Guo Moruo (writer). Multicoloured.
3211 8f. Type **640** 15 10
3212 20f. Guo Moruo writing . . 30 10

641 Head of Bodhisattva

642 Dr. D. S. Kotnis

1982. Sculptures of Liao Dynasty. Mult.
3213 8f. (1) Type **641** 60 10
3214 8f. (2) Bust of Bodhisattva 60 10
3215 8f. (3) Boy on lotus flower 60 10
3216 70f. (4) Bodhisattva . . . 3·00 1·10

1982. 40th Death Anniv of Dr. D. S. Kotnis.
3218 **642** 8f. green and black . . . 40 10
3219 – 70f. lilac and black . . . . 1·60 70
DESIGN: Dr. Kotnis in army uniform.

643 Couple holding Flaming Torch

644 Wine Container

1982. 11th National Communist Youth League Congress.
3220 **643** 8f. multicoloured 25 10

1982. Bronzes of Western Zhou Dynasty. Mult.
3221 4f. (1) Type **644** 50 20
3222 4f. (2) Cooking vessel . . . 50 20
3223 8f. (3) Food container . . . 60 20
3224 8f. (4) Cooking vessel with ox head and dragon design 60 20

3225 8f. (5) Ram-shaped wine container 60 20
3226 10f. (6) Wine jar . . . . 1·00 25
3227 20f. (7) Food bowl . . . . 2·50 35
3228 70f. (8) Wine container . . . 7·25 1·75

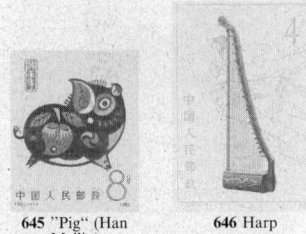

645 "Pig" (Han Meilin)

646 Harp

1983. New Year. Year of the Pig.
3229 **645** 8f. multicoloured . . . . 3·00 80

1983. Stringed Musical Instruments.
3230 **646** 4f. (1) green and brown 1·00 20
3231 8f. (2) purple, grn & brn 1·75 40
3232 – 8f. (3) multicoloured . . 1·75 40
3233 10f. (4) multicoloured . . 2·50 70
3234 – 70f. (5) multicoloured . . 12·00 3·00
DESIGNS—VERT: 8f. (3231), Four string guitar; 10f. Four string lute; 70f. Three string lute. HORIZ: 8f. (3232), Qin.

647 "February 7" Monument, Jiangan

648 Zhang Gong attracted by Yingying's Beauty

1983. 60th Anniv of Peking–Hankow Railway Workers' Strike.
3235 **647** 8f. (1) yellow, blk & grey 50 15
3236 – 8f. (2) stone, brown and lilac 50 15
DESIGN: No. 3236, "February 7" Memorial tower, Zhengzhou.

1983. Scenes from "The Western Chamber" (musical drama by Wang Shifu). Multicoloured.
3237 8f. (1) Type **648** . . . . 1·75 50
3238 8f. (2) Zhang Gong and Yingying listening to music . . . . 1·75 50
3239 10f. (3) Zhang Gong and Yingying's wedding . . . 2·75 1·40
3240 80f. (4) Zhang Gong and Yingying parting at Chanting Pavilion . . . . 12·50 4·00

649 Karl Marx

650 Tomb, Mt. Qiaoshan, Huangling

1983. Death Centenary of Karl Marx.
3242 **649** 8f. grey and black 15 10
3243 – 20f. lilac and black 70 15
DESIGN: 20f. "Marx making Speech" (Wen Guozhang).

1983. Tomb of the Yellow Emperor. Mult.
3244 8f. Type **650** 50 30
3245 10f. Hall of Founder of Chinese Culture (horiz) 1·25 30
3246 20f. Xuanyuan cypress . . . 2·25 80

651 Messengers and Globe

1983. World Communications Year.
3247 **651** 8f. multicoloured 30 15

652 Chinese Alligator

1983. Chinese Alligator. Multicoloured.
3248 8f. Type **652** 50 10
3249 20f. Alligator and hatching eggs . . . . 2·10 30

653 "Scratching" (Wang Yani)

1983. Children's Paintings. Multicoloured.
3250 8f. (1) type **653** 25 10
3251 8f. (2) "I Love the Great Wall" (Liu Zhong) . . . 25 10
3252 8f. (3) "Kitten" (Tang Axi) 25 10
3253 8f. (4) "The Sun, Birds, Flowers and Me" (Bu Hua) 25 10

654 Congress Hall

1983. 6th National People's Congress. Mult.
3254 8f. Type **654** 25 10
3255 20f. Score of National Anthem 40 15

655 Terracotta Soldiers

656 Sun Yujiao

1983. Terracotta Figures from Qin Shi Huang's Tomb. Multicoloured.
3256 8f. (1) Type **655** 40 20
3257 8f. (2) Heads figures 40 20
3258 10f. (3) Soldiers and horses 75 30
3259 70f. (4) Aerial view of excavation . . . . . . 4·25 1·25

1983. Female Roles in Peking Opera. Mult.
3261 4f. (1) Type **656** 40 10
3262 8f. (2) Chen Miaochang . . 60 15
3263 8f. (3) Bai Suzhen 60 15
3264 8f. (4) Sister Thirteen 60 15
3265 10f. (5) Qin Xianglian . . . 80 20
3266 20f. (6) Yang Yuhuan . . . 1·50 25
3267 50f. (7) Cui Yingying . . . . 4·50 55
3268 80f. (8) Mu Guiying . . . . 8·75 95

657 Li Bai (poet)

659 Games Emblem

658 Woman and Women working

1983. Poets and Philosophers of Ancient China. Paintings by Liu Lingcang. Multicoloured.
3269	8f. (1) Type **657**	55	20
3270	8f. (2) Du Fu (poet)	55	20
3271	8f. (3) Han Yu (philosopher)	55	20
3272	70f. (4) Liu Zongyuan (philosopher)	6·00	2·00

1983. 5th National Women's Congress.
3273	**658** 8f. multicoloured	20	10

1983. 5th National Games. Multicoloured.
3274	4f. (1) Type **659**	35	10
3275	8f. (2) Gymnastics	40	20
3276	8f. (3) Badminton	40	20
3277	8f. (4) Diving	40	20
3278	20f. (5) High jump	80	40
3279	70f. (6) Windsurfing	2·10	1·00

660 "One Child per Couple"

1983. Family Planning. Multicoloured.
3280	8f. (1) Type **660**	15	10
3281	8f. (2) "Population, cultivated fields and grain"	15	10

661 Hammer and Cogwheel as "10"

1983. 10th National Trade Union Congress.
3282	**661** 8f. multicoloured	30	10

662 Mute Swan

1983. Swans. Multicoloured.
3283	8f. (1) Type **662**	30	30
3284	8f. (2) Mute swans	30	30
3285	10f. (3) Tundra swans	75	1·00
3286	80f. (4) Whooper swans in flight	2·25	2·00

663 Liu Shaoqi

1983. 85th Birth Anniv of Liu Shaoqi (former Head of State).
3287	**663** 8f. (1) multicoloured . .	55	10
3288	– 8f. (2) multicoloured . .	55	10
3289	– 8f. (3) brown, bl & gold	55	10
3290	– 8f. (4) brown, bl & gold	55	10
DESIGNS: No. 3288, Liu reading a speech; 3289, Liu making a speech; 3290, Liu meeting model worker Shi Chuanxiang.

664 $100 National Emblem Stamp, 1951   **665** Mao Tse-tung in 1925

1983. National Stamp Exhibition, Peking. Mult.
3291	8f. Type **664**	20	10
3292	20f. North West China $1 Yanan Pagoda stamp, 1946	80	40

1983. 90th Birth Anniv of Mao Tse-tung.
3293	**665** 8f. (1) multicoloured . .	20	10
3294	– 8f. (2) stone, brn & gold	20	10
3295	– 10f. (3) grey, brn & gold	50	15
3296	– 20f. (4) multicoloured . .	1·25	20
DESIGNS: No. 3294, Mao Tse-tung in Yanan, 1945. 3295, Mao Tse-tung inspecting Yellow River, 1952. 3296, Mao Tse-tung in library, 1961.

666 "Rat" (Zhan Tong)   **667** Young Girl with Ball

1984. New Year. Year of the Rat.
3297	**666** 8f. black, yellow & red	2·50	70

1984. Child Welfare. Multicoloured.
3298	8f.+2f. Type **667**	20	15
3299	8f.+2f. Young boy with toy panda	20	15

668 Women with Dog

1984. Tang Dynasty Painting "Beauties wearing Flowers" by Zhou Fang. Details of scroll. Mult.
3300	8f. Type **668**	1·00	20
3301	10f. Women and Manchurian crane	1·00	50
3302	70f. Women, dog and Manchurian crane	6·25	3·00

669 "The Spring of Shanghai"   **670** Ren Bishi

1984. Chinese Roses. Multicoloured.
3304	4f. (1) Type **669**	25	10
3305	8f. (2) "Rosy Dawn of the Pujiang River"	30	10
3306	8f. (3) "Pearl"	30	10
3307	10f. (4) "Black Whirlwind"	65	10
3308	20f. (5) "Yellow Flower in the Battlefield"	90	20
3309	70f. (6) "Blue Phoenix" . .	2·25	50

1984. 80th Birth Anniv of Ren Bishi (member of Communist Party Secretariat) (1st issue).
3310	**670** 8f. brown, black & pur	20	10
See also Nos. 3361/3.

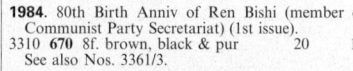

671 Japanese Crested Ibis

1984. Japanese Crested Ibis. Multicoloured.
3311	8f. (1) Type **671**	35	25
3312	8f. (2) Ibis wading	35	25
3313	80f. (3) Ibis perching . . .	2·40	1·75

672 Red Cross Activities

1984. 80th Anniv of Chinese Red Cross Society.
3314	**672** 8f. multicoloured	35	15

673 Building Dam

1984. Gezhou Dam Project. Multicoloured.
3315	8f. Type **673**	10	10
3316	10f. View of dam and lock gates (vert)	40	10
3317	20f. Freighter in lock . . .	70	15

674 Inverted Image Tower and Yilang Pavilion

1984. Zhuo Zheng Garden, Suzhou. Mult.
3318	8f. (1) Type **674**	20	10
3319	8f. (2) Loquat Garden . . .	20	10
3320	10f. (3) Water court of Xiao Cang Lang	25	15
3321	70f. (4) Yuanxiang Hall and Yiyu Study	2·10	60

675 Pistol Shooting

1984. Olympic Games, Los Angeles. Multicoloured.
3322	4f. Type **675**	10	10
3323	8f. High jumping	10	10
3324	8f. Weightlifting	10	10
3325	10f. Gymnastics	10	10
3326	20f. Volley ball	25	15
3327	80f. Diving	85	50

676 Calligraphy   **677** Tianjin

1984. Art Works by Wu Changshuo. Mult.
3329	4f. (1) Type **676**	10	10
3330	4f. (2) "Pair of Peaches" . .	10	10
3331	8f. (3) "Lotus"	45	15
3332	8f. (4) "Wisteria"	45	15
3333	8f. (5) "Peony"	45	15
3334	10f. (6) "Autumn Chrysanthemum"	55	15
3335	20f. (7) "Plum Blossom" . .	1·25	25
3336	70f. (8) Seal and impression	3·25	65

1984. Luanhe River–Tianjin Water Diversion Project. Multicoloured.
3337	8f. Type **677**	10	10
3338	10f. Locks and canal (horiz)	10	10
3339	20f. Tunnel and sculpture .	50	15

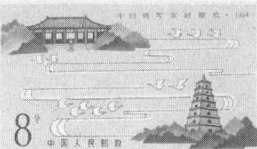

678 Chinese and Japanese Pagodas

1984. Chinese–Japanese Youth Friendship Festival. Multicoloured.
3340	8f. Type **678**	10	10
3341	20f. Girls watering shrub . .	25	15
3342	80f. Young people dancing	85	80

679 Factory Worker

1984. 35th Anniv of People's Republic. Mult.
3343	8f. (1) Type **679**	10	10
3344	8f. (2) Girl and rainbow . .	10	10
3345	8f. (4) Girl and symbols of science	10	10
3346	8f. (5) Soldier	10	10
3347	20f. (3) Flag and Manchurian cranes (36 × 50 mm)	40	25

680 Chen Jiageng

1984. 110th Birth Anniv of Chen Jiageng (educationist and patriot). Multicoloured.
3348	8f. Type **680**	15	10
3349	80f. Jimei School	65	30

681 The Maiden's Study

1984. Scenes from "Peony Pavilion" (drama) by Tang Xianzu. Paintings by Dai Dunbang. Multicoloured.
3350	8f. (1) Type **681**	50	15
3351	8f. (2) Du Liniang dreaming	50	15
3352	20f. (3) Du Liniang drawing self-portrait	1·10	25
3353	70f. (4) Du Liniang and Liu Mengmei married	3·50	1·10

682 Baoguo Temple

1984. Landscapes of Mt. Emei Shan. Mult.
3355	4f. (1) Type **682**	45	10
3356	8f. (2) Leiyin Temple . . .	55	10
3357	8f. (3) Hongchun Lawn . .	55	10
3358	10f. (4) Elephant Bath Pool	70	15
3359	20f. (5) Woyun Temple . .	1·25	25
3360	80f. (6) Shining Cloud Sea, Jinding	3·25	1·10

683 Ren Bishi

684 Flowers in Chinese Vase

1984. 80th Birth Anniv of Ren Bishi (2nd issue).
3361	**683**	8f. brown and purple	10	10
3362	–	10f. black and lilac	15	10
3363	–	20f. black and brown	40	20

DESIGNS: 10f. Ren Bishi reading speech at Communist Party Congress; 20f. Ren Bishi saluting.

1984. Chinese Insurance Industry.
| 3364 | **684** | 8f. multicoloured | 15 | 10 |

685 "Ox" (Yao Zhonghua)

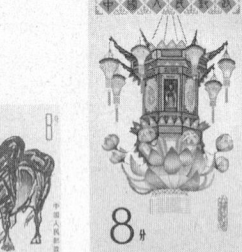
687 Lotus of Good Luck

1985. New Year. Year of the Ox.
| 3365 | **685** | 8f. multicoloured | 30 | 15 |

686 "Zunyi Meeting" (Liu Xiangping)

1985. 50th Anniv of Zunyi Meeting. Mult.
| 3366 | | 8f. Type **686** | 10 | 10 |
| 3367 | | 20f. "Arrival of the Red Army in Northern Shaanxi" (Zhao Yu) | 60 | 15 |

1985. Festival Lanterns. Multicoloured.
3368		8f. (1) Type **687**	50	15
3369		8f. (2) Auspicious dragon and phoenix	50	15
3370		8f. (3) A hundred flowers blossoming	50	15
3371		70f. (4) Prosperity and affluence	1·75	60

688 Stylized Dove and Women's Open Hands

689 Hands reading Braille

1985. United Nations Decade for Women.
| 3372 | **688** | 20f. multicoloured | 25 | 10 |

1985. Welfare Fund for the Handicapped. Multicoloured.
3373		8f.+2f. (1) Type **689**	40	15
3374		8f.+2f. (2) Lips and sign language	40	15
3375		8f.+2f. (3) Learning to use artificial limb	40	15
3376		8f.+2f. (4) Stylized figure in wheelchair	40	15

690 "Green Calyx" Mei

691 Headquarters

1985. Mei Flowers. Multicoloured.
3377		8f. (1) Type **690**	15	10
3378		8f. (2) "Pendant" mei	15	10
3379		8f. (3) "Contorted dragon" mei	15	10
3380		10f. (4) "Cinnabar" mei	20	10
3381		20f. (5) "Versicolor" mei	75	15
3382		80f. (6) "Apricot" mei	2·50	65

1985. 60th Anniv of All-China Trade Unions Federation.
| 3384 | **691** | 8f. multicoloured | 20 | 10 |

692 Bird and Children

1985. International Youth Year.
| 3385 | **692** | 20f. multicoloured | 30 | 15 |

693 Giant Panda

694 Xian Xinghai (bust, Cao Chongen)

1985. Giant Panda. Multicoloured.
3386		8f. Type **693**	10	10
3387		20f. Giant panda (different) (horiz)	40	15
3388		50f. Giant panda (different) (horiz)	60	30
3389		80f. Two giant pandas (horiz)	85	40

1985. 80th Birth Anniv of Xian Xianghai (composer).
| 3391 | **694** | 8f. multicoloured | 25 | 10 |

695 Agnes Smedley

696 Zheng He (navigator)

1985. American Journalists in China.
3392	**695**	8f. brown, stone and ochre	10	10
3393	–	20f. olive, grey and stone	15	10
3394	–	80f. purple, lilac and cream	50	10

DESIGNS: 20f. Anna Louise Strong; 80f. Edgar Snow.

1985. 580th Anniv of Zheng He's First Voyage to Western Seas. Multicoloured.
3395		8f. (1) Type **696**	10	10
3396		8f. (2) Zheng He on elephant	10	10
3397		20f. (3) Exchanging goods	20	10
3398		80f. (4) Bidding farewell	75	45

697 "Self-portrait"

1985. 90th Birth Anniv of Xu Beihong (artist). Multicoloured.
| 3399 | | 8f. Type **697** | 10 | 10 |
| 3400 | | 20f. Xu Beihong at work | 20 | 15 |

698 Lin Zexu

699 "Prosperity"

1985. Birth Bicentenary of Lin Zexu (statesman).
| 3401 | **698** | 8f. multicoloured | 15 | 10 |
| 3402 | – | 80f. brown and black | 55 | 25 |

DESIGN—55×23 mm. 80f. "Burning opium at Humen" (relief).

1985. 20th Anniv of Tibet Autonomous Region. Multicoloured.
3403		8f. Type **699**	10	10
3404		10f. "Celebration"	15	10
3405		20f. "Harvest"	35	10

700 Chinese Army at Lugouqiao

1985. 40th Anniv of Victory over Japan.
| 3406 | **700** | 8f. black, brown & red | 10 | 10 |
| 3407 | – | 80f. black, brown & red | 75 | 40 |

DESIGN: 80f. Defending the Great Wall.

701 Cycling

1985. 2nd National Workers' Games, Peking. Multicoloured.
| 3408 | | 8f. Type **701** | 10 | 10 |
| 3409 | | 20f. Hurdling | 25 | 15 |

702 Gobi Oasis

703 Athletes and Silhouette of Woman

1985. 30th Anniv of Xinjiang Uygur Autonomous Region. Multicoloured.
3410		8f. Type **702**	10	10
3411		10f. Oilfield and Lake Tianchi (54×26 mm)	15	10
3412		20f. Tianshan pasture	35	15

1985. 1st National Youth Games, Zhengzhou.
| 3413 | **703** | 8f. multicoloured | 10 | 10 |
| 3414 | – | 20f. red, blue and black | 25 | 10 |

DESIGN: 20f. Basketball players and silhouette of man.

704 Forbidden City (½-size illustration)

1985. 60th Anniv of Imperial Palace Museum.
3415	**704**	8f. (1) multicoloured	10	10
3416	–	8f. (2) multicoloured	10	10
3417	–	20f. (3) multicoloured	20	10
3418	–	80f. (4) multicoloured	70	30

DESIGNS: Nos. 3416/18, Different parts of Forbidden City.

705 Zou Taofen

706 Memorial Pavilion

1985. 90th Anniv of Zou Taofen (journalist).
| 3419 | **705** | 8f. black, brown & silver | 10 | 10 |
| 3420 | – | 20f. black, green & silver | 30 | 10 |

DESIGN: 20f. Premier Chou En-lai's inscription in memory of Zou Taofen.

1985. 50th Anniv of December 9th Movement.
| 3421 | **706** | 8f. multicoloured | 15 | 10 |

707 "Tiger"

708 First Experimental Satellite

1986. New Year. Year of the Tiger.
| 3422 | **707** | 8f. multicoloured | 45 | 15 |

1986. Space Research. Multicoloured.
3423		4f. (1) Type **708**	10	10
3424		8f. (2) Mil-Mi8 helicopters recovering satellites	10	10
3425		8f. (3) Underwater launched rocket	10	10
3426		10f. (4) Rocket launched from land	15	10
3427		20f. (5) Dish aerial	30	15
3428		70f. (6) Satellite and diagram of orbit	60	45

709 Dong Biwu

710 Lin Boqu

1986. Birth Centenary of Dong Biwu (founder of Chinese Communist Party).
| 3429 | **709** | 8f. black and brown | 10 | 10 |
| 3430 | – | 20f. black and brown | 20 | 10 |

DESIGN: 20f. At meeting for ratification of U.N. Charter, Los Angeles, 1945.

1986. Birth Centenary of Lin Boqu (politician).
| 3431 | **710** | 8f. brown and black | 10 | 10 |
| 3432 | – | 20f. brown and black | 20 | 10 |

DESIGN: 20f. At Yanan.

711 He Long

1986. 90th Birth Anniv of He Long (politician).
| 3433 | **711** | 8f. black and brown | 10 | 10 |
| 3434 | – | 20f. black and brown | 20 | 10 |

DESIGN: 20f. On horse.

712 Skin Tents, Inner Mongolia

713 Comet and Earth

1986. Traditional Houses.
3435	**712**	1f. green, brown & grey	10	10
3436	–	1½f. brown, red & blue	10	10
3437	–	2f. brown and bistre	10	10
3438	–	3f. black and brown	10	10
3439	–	4f. red and black	10	10
3439a	–	5f. black, grey & green	10	10
3440	–	8f. grey, red and black	10	10

3441	– 10f. black and orange	15	10
3441b	– 15f. black, grey & grn	15	10
3442	– 20f. grey, green & blk	65	10
3442b	– 25f. black, grey & pink	25	15
3443	– 30f. lilac, blue & brown	15	10
3444	– 40f. brn, pur & stone	30	15
3445	– 50f. blue, mve & dp bl	15	15
3445b	– 80f. black, grey & blue	70	25
3446	– 90f. black and red	70	25
3447	– 1y. brown and grey	35	20
3448	– 1y.10 blue, blk & brn	40	25
3448a	– 1y.30 blk, grey & red	40	25
3448b	– 1y.60 blue & black	40	25
3448c	– 2y. black, grey & brown	60	25

DESIGNS: 1½f. Tibet. 2f. North-East China. 3f. Hunan. 4f. Jiangsu. 5f. Shandong. 8f. Peking. 10f. Yunnan. 15f. Guangxi. 20f. Shanghai. 25f. Ningxia. 30f. Anhui. 40f. North Shaanxi. 50f. Sichuan. 80f. Shanxi. 90f. Taiwan. 1y. Fujian. 1y.10, Zhejiang, 1y.30, Qinghai. 1y.60, Guizhou. 2y. Jiangxi.

1988. Appearance of Halley's Comet.

3449	713	20f. grey and blue	20	10

714 Cranes

1986. Great White Crane. Multicoloured.

3450	8f. Type **714**	10	10
3451	10f. Crane flying (vert)	25	20
3452	70f. Four cranes (vert)	75	45

715 Li Weihan

1986. 90th Birth Anniv of Li Weihan (politician). Each green and black.

3454	8f. Type **715**	10	10
3455	20f. Li Weihan at work	20	10

716 Stylized People on Dove

1986. International Peace Year.

3456	**716**	8f. multicoloured	20	10

717 Mao Dun

1986. 90th Birth Anniv of Mao Dun (writer). Each grey, black and brown.

3457	8f. Type **717**	10	10
3458	20f. Mao Dun and manuscript	20	10

718 Wang Jiaxiang

1986. 80th Birth Anniv of Wang Jiaxiang (first People's Republic ambassador to U.S.S.R.). Multicoloured.

3459	8f. Type **718**	10	10
3460	20f. Wang Jiaxiang at Yan'an	20	10

719 Flowers on Desk

1986. Teachers' Day.

3461	**719**	8f. multicoloured	15	10

720 "Magnolia sinensis"

1986. Magnolias. Multicoloured.

3462	8f. (1) Type **720**	40	10
3463	8f. (2) "Manglietia patungensis"	40	10
3464	70f. (3) "Alcimandra cathcartii"	2·50	70

721 Sun Yat-sen (120th birth anniv)   **724** Zhu De

1986. 75th Anniv of 1911 Revolution. Leaders. Multicoloured.

3466	8f. Type **721**	10	10
3467	10f. Huang Xing (70th death anniv)	40	10
3468	40f. Zhang Taiyan (50th death anniv)	90	15

1986. Birth Centenary of Marshal Zhu De.

3471	**724**	8f. brown	35	10
3472	–	20f. green	65	10

DESIGN: 20f. Making speech, 1950.

725 Archery   **726** "Rabbit"

1986. Sport in Ancient China. Each grey, black and red.

3473	8f. (1) Type **725**	90	10
3474	8f. (2) Weiqi (horiz)	90	10
3475	10f. (3) Golf (horiz)	1·25	40
3476	50f. (4) Football	3·50	85

1987. New Year. Year of the Rabbit.

3477	**726**	8f. multicoloured	50	15

727 Xu Xiake   **728** Steller's Sea Eagle

1987. 400th Birth Anniv of Xu Xiake (explorer). Multicoloured.

3478	8f. Type **727**	1·00	20
3479	20f. Recording observations in cave	2·25	60
3480	40f. Climbing mountain	4·50	1·25

1987. Birds of Prey. Multicoloured.

3481	8f. (1) Black kite (horiz)	70	25
3482	8f. (2) Type **728**	70	30
3483	10f. (3) Himalayan griffon	1·40	30
3484	90f. (4) Upland buzzard (horiz)	5·00	1·75

729 Hawk Kite

1987. Kites. Multicoloured.

3485	8f. (1) Type **729**	20	10
3486	8f. (2) Centipede	20	10
3487	30f. (3) The Eight Diagrams	1·00	15
3488	30f. (4) Phoenix	1·00	15

730 Liao Zhongkai   **731** "Eventful Years"

1987. 110th Birth Anniv of Liao Zhongkai (politician). Multicoloured.

3489	8f. Type **730**	10	10
3490	20f. Liao Zhongkai with wife	15	10

1987. 90th Birth Anniv of Ye Jianying (revolutionary and co-founder of People's Army). Portraits. Multicoloured.

3491	8f. Type **731**	45	10
3492	10f. "Founder of the State"	55	10
3493	30f. "Everywhere Green Hills"	1·50	15

732 Worshipping Bodhisattvas (Northern Liang Dynasty)

1987. Dunhuang Cave Murals (1st series). Mult.

3494	8f. Type **732**	50	10
3495	10f. Deer King Jataka (Northern Wei dynasty)	60	15
3496	20f. Heavenly musicians (Northern Wei dynasty)	2·00	50
3497	40f. Flying Devata (Northern Wei dynasty)	3·00	1·25

See also Nos. 3553/6, 3682/5, 3811/14, 3910/13 and 4131/4.

733 "Happy Holiday" (Yan Qinghu)   **734** Town

1987. Children's Day. Childrens' drawings. Mult.

3499	8f. (1) Type **733**	10	10
3500	8f. (2) Children with doves and balloons (Liu Yuan)	10	10

1987. Improvements in Rural Areas. Multicoloured.

3501	8f. (1) Type **734**	40	10
3502	8f. (2) Fresh foods (horiz)	40	10
3503	10f. (3) Feeding cattle (horiz)	60	10
3504	20f. (4) Outdoor cinema	90	20

735 Emblem   **736** Globe

1987. Postal Savings.

3505	**735**	8f. turquoise, yell & red	15	10

1987. Centenary of Esperanto (invented language).

3506	**736**	8f. blue, black & green	15	10

737 Flag over Great Wall

1987. 60th Anniv of People's Liberation Army. Multicoloured.

3507	8f. (1) Type **737**	35	10
3508	8f. (2) Soldier and rocket launcher	35	10
3509	10f. (3) Sailor and submarine	1·00	15
3510	30f. (4) Pilot and jet fighters	1·00	15

738 Dove above Houses

1987. Int Year of Shelter for the Homeless.

3511	**738**	8f. multicoloured	15	10

739 Chinese Character   **740** Pan Gu inventing the Universe

1987. China Art Festival, Peking.

3512	**739**	8f. black, red and gold	15	10

1987. Folk Tales. Multicoloured.

3513	4f. (1) Type **740**	35	10
3514	8f. (2) Nu Wa creating human being	50	10
3515	8f. (3) Yi shooting nine suns	50	10
3516	10f. (4) Chang'e flying to the moon	60	10
3517	20f. (5) Kua Fu chasing the sun	90	15
3518	90f. (6) Jing Wei filling the sea	2·75	95

741 Sun rising behind Party Flag

1987. 13th National Communist Party Congress.

3519	**741**	8f. multicoloured	10	10

742 Yellow Crane Tower, Wuhan

1987. Ancient Buildings. Multicoloured.

3520	8f. (1) Type **742**	40	10
3521	8f. (2) Yue Yang Tower	40	10
3522	10f. (3) Teng Wang Pavilion	70	10
3523	90f. (4) Peng Lai Pavilion	3·25	1·40

743 Pole Vaulting

1987. 6th National Games, Guangdong Province. Multicoloured.

3525	8f. (1) Type **743**	40	10
3526	8f. (2) Women's softball	40	10
3527	30f. (3) Weightlifting	70	15
3528	50f. (4) Diving	1·25	20

745 Shi Jin practising Martial Arts

1987. Literature. "Outlaws of the Marsh" (1st series). Multicoloured.

3530	8f. Type **745**	30	10
3531	10f. Sagacious Lu uprooting willow tree	50	10

3532	30f. Lin Chon sheltering in temple of mountain spirit	1·50	50
3533	50f. Song Jian helping Chao Gai to escape	3·25	1·10

See also Nos. 3614/17, 3778/81, 3854/7 and 4248/51.

746 Dragon   **747** Cai Yuanpri

1988. New Year. Year of the Dragon.

3535	**746** 8f. multicoloured	25	15

1988. 120th Birth Anniv of Cai Yuanpei (educationist). Multicoloured.

3536	8f. Type **747**	10	10
3537	20f. Cai Yuanpei seated in chair	15	10

748 Tao Zhu

1988. 80th Birth Anniv of Tao Zhu (Communist Party official). Multicoloured.

3538	8f. Type **748**	10	10
3539	20f. Tao Zhu (half-length portrait)	15	10

749 Harvest Festival

1988. Flourishing Rural Areas of China. Mult.

3540	8f. Type **749**	45	10
3541	10f. Couple with fish, flowers and chickens	55	10
3542	20f. Couple making scientific study	75	40
3543	30f. Happy family	1·00	65

750 Flag and Rainbow   **751** Wuzhi Mountain

1988. 7th National People's Congress.

3544	**750** 8f. multicoloured	15	10

1988. Establishment of Hainan Province. Mult.

3545	8f. Type **751**	10	10
3546	10f. Wanquan River	10	10
3547	30f. Beach	20	10
3548	1y.10 Bay and deer	60	30

752 Li Siguang (geologist)

1988. Scientists (1st series). Multicoloured.

3549	8f. Type **752**	10	10
3550	10f. Zhu Kezhen (meteorologist)	10	10
3551	20f. Wu Youxun (physicist)	15	10
3552	30f. Hua Luogeng (mathematician)	20	10

See also Nos. 3702/5 and 3821/4.

1988. Dunhuang Cave Murals (2nd series). As T **732**. Multicoloured.

3553	8f. (1) Hunting (Western Wei dynasty)	35	10
3554	8f. (2) Fighting (Western Wei dynasty)	35	10

3555	10f. (3) Farming (Northern Zhou dynasty)	50	35
3556	90f. (4) Building pagoda (Northern Zhou dynasty)	1·60	80

753 Healthy Trees and Hand holding back polluted Soil

1988. Environmental Protection. Multicoloured.

3557	8f. (1) Type **753**	10	10
3558	8f. (2) Doves in clean air and hand holding back polluted air	10	10
3559	8f. (3) Fishes in clean water and hand holding back polluted water	25	10
3560	8f. (4) Peaceful landscape and hand holding back noise waves	10	10

755 Games Emblem

1988. 11th Asian Games, Peking (1990) (1st issue). Multicoloured.

3562	8f. Type **755**	10	10
3563	30f. Games mascot	15	10

See also Nos. 3653/6 and 3695/3700.

756 Warrior, Longmen Grotto, Henan   **757** Peony

1988. Art of Chinese Grottoes.

3564	– 2y. brown & light brown	40	10
3565	**756** 5y. black and brown	75	15
3566	– 10y. brown and stone	1·50	35
3567	– 20y. black and brown	3·00	1·50

DESIGNS: 2y. Buddha, Yungang Grotto, Shanxi. 10y. Bodhisattva, Maijishan Grotto, Gansu. 20y. Woman with chickens, Dazu Grotto, Sichuan.

1988. 10th Anniv of Chinese–Japanese Treaty of Peace and Friendship. Multicoloured.

3568	8f. Type **757**	10	10
3569	1y.60 Cherry blossom	60	30

758 Coal Wharf, Quinghuangdao

1988. Achievements of Socialist Construction (1st series). Multicoloured.

3570	8f. Type **758**	30	15
3571	10f. Ethylene works, Shangdong	10	10
3572	20f. Baoshan steel works, Shanghai	10	10
3573	30f. Television centre, Peking	15	10

See also Nos. 3691/22, 3678/81 and 3759/62.

759 Taishan Temple

1988. Mount Taishan Views. Multicoloured.

3574	8f. Type **759**	40	10
3575	10f. Ladder to Heaven	45	10
3576	20f. Daguang Park	60	10
3577	90f. Sun Watching Peak	2·75	1·25

760 Liao Chengzhi   **761** Cycling

1988. 80th Birth Anniv of Liao Chengzhi (Communist Party leader). Multicoloured.

3578	8f. Type **760**	10	10
3579	20f. Liao Chengzhi at work	15	10

1988. 1st National Peasant Games. Multicoloured.

3580	8f. Type **761**	10	10
3581	20f. Wushu	15	10

762 Peng Dehuai

1988. 90th Birth Anniv of General Peng Dehuai. Multicoloured.

3582	8f. Type **762**	10	10
3583	20f. In uniform	15	10

763 Battle against Lu Bu

1988. Literature. "Romance of the Three Kingdoms" by Luo Guanzhong (1st series). Multicoloured.

3584	8f. (1) Heroes become sworn brothers (horiz)	45	10
3585	8f. (2) Type **763**	45	10
3586	30f. (3) Fengyi Pavilion (horiz)	1·25	55
3587	50f. (4) Discussing heroes over wine	2·00	95

See also Nos. 3711/14, 3807/10, 3944/7 and 4315/18.

764 People in Heart   **765** Stag's Head

1988. International Volunteers' Day.

3589	**764** 20f. multicoloured	15	10

1988. Pere David's Deer. Multicoloured.

3590	8f. Type **765**	45	10
3591	40f. Herd	85	15

766 Da Yi Pin

1988. Orchids. Multicoloured.

3592	8f. Type **766**	50	10
3593	10f. Dragon	50	10
3594	20f. Large phoenix tail	1·10	45
3595	50f. Silver-edged black orchid	2·10	70

767 Snake   **768** Qu Quibai

1989. New Year. Year of the Snake.

3597	**767** 8f. multicoloured	25	15

1989. 90th Birth Anniv of Qu Qiubai (writer). Multicoloured.

3598	8f. Type **768**	10	10
3599	20f. Qu Qiubai (half-length portrait)	15	10

769 Pheasant

1989. Brown Eared-pheasant. Multicoloured.

3600	8f. Type **769**	10	10
3601	50f. Two pheasants	30	20

770 "Heaven" (top section)

1989. Silk Painting from Han Tomb, Mawangdui, Changsha. Multicoloured.

3602	8f. Type **770**	25	10
3603	20f. "Earth" (central section)	25	10
3604	30f. "Underworld" (bottom section)	25	10

771 Diagnosis by Thermography   **773** Children

772 Memorial Frieze

1989. Anti-cancer Campaign.

3606	**771** 8f. grey, red & black	10	10
3607	– 20f. multicoloured	10	10

DESIGN: 8f. Crab and red crosses.

1989. 70th Anniv of May 4th Movement.

3608	**772** 8f. multicoloured	15	10

1989. 40th International Children's Day. Children's paintings. Multicoloured.

3609	8f.+4f. (1) Type **773**	10	10
3610	8f.+4f. (2) Child and penguins	10	10
3611	8f.+4f. (3) Child flying on bird	10	10
3612	8f.+4f. (4) Boy and girl playing ball	10	10

774 Globe, Doves and Lectern

1989. Cent of Interparliamentary Union.

3613	**774** 20f. multicoloured	15	10

1989. Literature. "Outlaws of the Marsh" (2nd series). As T **745**. Multicoloured.

3614	8f. Wu Song killing tiger on Jingyang Ridge	10	10
3615	10f. Qin Ming riding through hail of arrows	15	10
3616	20f. Hua Rong shooting wild goose	50	10
3617	1y.30 Li Kui fighting Zhang Shun on sampan	1·60	60

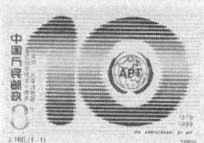

775 Anniversary Emblem

1989. 10th Anniv of Asia–Pacific Telecommunity.
3618 775 8f. multicoloured 10 10

1989. Achievements of Socialist Construction (2nd series). As T 758. Multicoloured.
3619 8f. International telecommunications building, Peking (vert) 10 10
3620 10f. Xi Qu coal mine, Gu Jiao 10 10
3621 20f. Long Yang Gorge hydro-electric power station, Qinghai . . . 15 10
3622 30f. Da Yao Shan tunnel on Guangzhou–Heng Yang railway 35 20

776 Five Peaks of Mt. Huashan

1989. Mount Huashan. Multicoloured.
3623 8f. Type 776 . . . . . 10 10
3624 10f. View from top of Mt. Huashan 15 10
3625 20f. Thousand Foot Precipice 20 15
3626 90f. Blue Dragon Ridge . . 65 35

777 "Fable of the White Snake" (stage design, Ye Qianyu)

1989. Contemporary Art. Multicoloured.
3627 8f. Type 777 . . . . . 10 10
3628 20f. "Lijiang River in Fine Rain" (Li Keran) . . . 20 10
3629 50f. "Marching Together" (oxen) (Wu Zuoren) . . . 90 40

778 Doves and 1949 $50 Stamp
780 Ribbons and Gate of Heavenly Peace, Peking

779 Lecturing in Temple of Apricot, Qufu

1989. 40th Anniv of Chinese People's Political Conference.
3630 778 8f. red, blue and black 15 10

1989. 2540th Birth Anniv of Confucius (philosopher). Multicoloured.
3631 8f. Type 779 . . . . . 10 10
3632 1y.60 Confucius in ox-drawn cart 50 25

1989. 40th Anniv of People's Republic. Mult.
3634 8f. Type 780 . . . . . 10 10
3635 10f. Flowers and ribbons . . 10 10
3636 20f. Stars and ribbons . . 10 10
3637 40f. Buildings and ribbons 25 15

781 Woman using Camera

1989. 150th Anniv of Photography.
3640 781 8f. multicoloured 15 10

782 Li Dazhao

1989. Birth Centenary of Li Dazhao (co-founder of Chinese Communist Party). Multicoloured.
3641 8f. Type 782 . . . . . 10 10
3642 20f. Li Dazhao and script 15 10

783 Diagram of Collider in Action

1989. Peking Electron-Positron Collider.
3643 783 8f. multicoloured 10 10

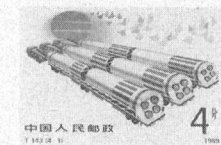

784 Rockets

1989. National Defence. Multicoloured.
3644 4f. Type 784 . . . . . 10 10
3645 8f. Rocket on transporter 10 10
3646 10f. Rocket launch (vert) . . 15 10
3647 20f. Jettison of fuel tank . 25 10

785 Spring Morning, Su Causeway

1989. West Lake, Hangzhou. Multicoloured.
3648 8f. Type 785 . . . . . 10 10
3649 10f. Crooked Courtyard . . 10 10
3650 30f. Moon over Three Pools 45 20
3651 40f. Snow on Broken Bridge 90 25

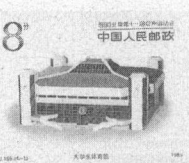

786 Peking College Gymnasium
787 Horse

1989. 11th Asian Games, Peking (1990) (2nd issue). Multicoloured.
3653 8f. Type 786 . . . . . 10 10
3654 10f. Northern Suburbs swimming pool . . . 10 10
3655 30f. Workers' Stadium . . 10 10
3656 1y.60 Chaoyang Gymnasium 50 25

1990. New Year. Year of the Horse.
3657 787 8f. multicoloured . . . 25 15

788 Narcissi
789 Bethune and Medical Team in Canada

1990. Narcissi. Multicoloured.
3658 8f. Type 788 . . . . . 10 10
3659 20f. Natural group of narcissi 10 10

3660 30f. Arrangement of narcissi 20 10
3661 1y.60 Arrangement (different) 75 35

1990. Birth Centenary of Norman Bethune (surgeon). Multicoloured.
3662 8f. Type 789 . . . . . 10 10
3663 1y.60 Bethune and medical team in China . . . 50 20

790 Emblem
791 Birds flying above Trees

1990. 80th International Women's Day.
3664 790 20f. red, green and black 15 10

1990. Tree Planting Day. Multicoloured.
3665 8f. Type 791 . . . . . 10 10
3666 10f. Trees in city 10 10
3667 20f. Great Wall and trees . 15 10
3668 30f. Forest and field of wheat 25 15

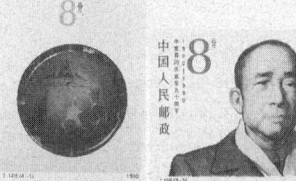

792 Ban Po Plate
793 Li Fuchun

1990. Pottery. Multicoloured.
3669 8f. Type 792 . . . . . 10 10
3670 20f. Miao Di Gou dish . . 10 10
3671 30f. Ma Jia Yao jar . . . 20 10
3672 50f. Ma Chang jar . . . 30 20

1990. 90th Birth Anniv of Li Fuchun (politician). Multicoloured.
3673 8f. Type 793 . . . . . 10 10
3674 20f. Li Fuchun (different) . 40 10

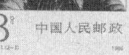

794 Charioteer
795 Snow Leopard

1990. 10th Anniv of Discovery of Bronze Chariots in Emperor Qin Shi Huang's Tomb. Multicoloured.
3675 8f. Type 794 . . . . . 15 10
3676 50f. Horse's head 35 15

1990. Achievements of Socialist Construction (3rd series). As T 758. Multicoloured.
3678 8f. Second automobile factory 10 10
3679 10f. Yizheng chemical and fibre company 10 10
3680 20f. Shengli oil field . . . 15 10
3681 30f. Qinshan nuclear power station 20 15

1990. Dunhuang Cave Murals (3rd series). Sui Dynasty. As T 732. Multicoloured.
3682 8f. Flying Devatas . . . 10 10
3683 10f. Worshipping Bodhisattva (vert) . . 10 10
3684 30f. Saviour Avalokitesvara (vert) 50 15
3685 50f. Indra 70 20

1990. The Snow Leopard. Multicoloured.
3686 8f. Type 795 . . . . . 10 10
3687 50f. Leopard stalking . . . 25 10

796 West Fujian Communications Bureau (Red Posts) 4p. Stamp

1990. 60th Anniv of Communist China Stamp Issues. Multicoloured.
3688 8f. Type 796 . . . . . 10 10
3689 20f. Chinese Soviet Republic 1c. stamp 15 10

797 Zhang Wentian
798 Emblem

1990. 90th Birth Anniv of Zhang Wentian (revolutionary).
3690 8f. Type 797 . . . . . 10 10
3691 20f. Zhang Wentian and Zunyi Meeting venue . 15 10

1990. International Literacy Year.
3692 798 20f. multicoloured . . . 10 10

799 Great Wall, Film and Screen
801 Athletics

1990. 85th Anniv of Chinese Films.
3693 799 20f. multicoloured . . . 10 10

1990. 11th Asian Games, Peking (3rd issue). Multicoloured.
3695 4f. Type 801 . . . . . 10 10
3696 8f. Gymnastics 10 10
3697 10f. Martial arts 10 10
3698 20f. Volleyball 10 10
3699 30f. Swimming 45 10
3700 1y.60 Shooting . . . . 1·00 50

802 Zhang Yuzhe (astronomer)

1990. Scientists (2nd series). Multicoloured.
3702 8f. Lin Qiaozhi (gynaecologist) 10 10
3703 10f. Type 802 . . . . . 10 10
3704 20f. Hou Debang (chemist) 15 10
3705 30f. Ding Ying (agronomist) 20 15

803 Towering Temple

1990. Mount Hengshan, Hunan Province. Mult.
3706 8f. Type 803 . . . . . 10 10
3707 10f. Aerial view of mountain 15 10
3708 20f. Trees and buildings on slopes 30 20
3709 50f. Zhurong Peak 85 20

1990. Literature. "Romance of the Three Kingdoms" by Luo Guanzhong (2nd series). As T 763. Multicoloured.
3711 20f. (1) Cao Cao leading night attack on Wuchao (horiz) 15 10
3712 20f. (2) Liu Bei calling at Zhuge Liang's thatched cottage 15 10
3713 30f. (3) General Zhao rescuing A Dou single-handedly (horiz) . . . 60 15
3714 50f. (4) Zhang Fei repulsing attackers at Changban Bridge 75 25

805 Revellers listening to Music

1990. Painting "Han Xizai's Night Revels" by Gu Hongzhong. Multicoloured.
3715 50f. (1) Type 805 . . . . 60 20

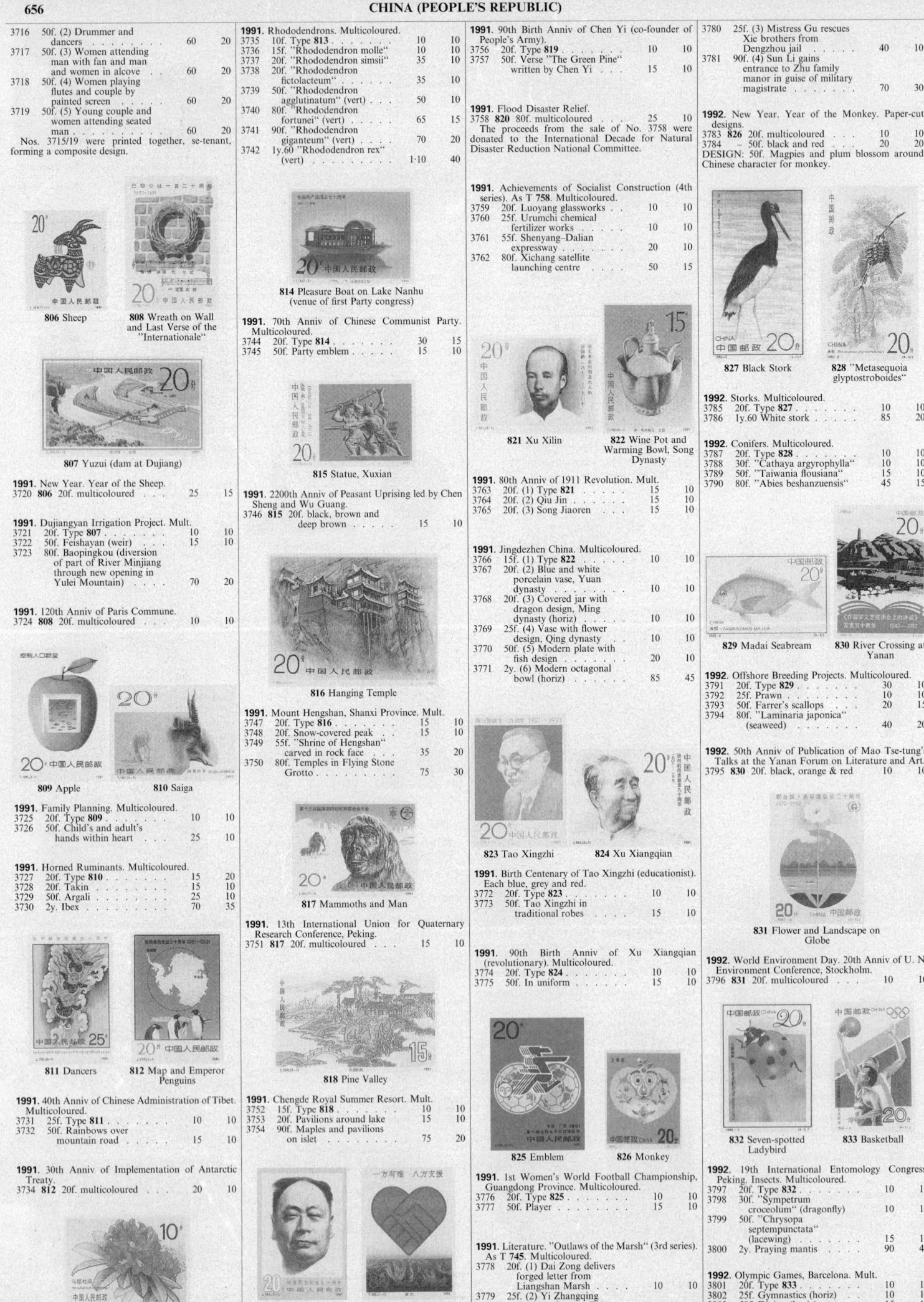

3716	50f. (2) Drummer and dancers	60	20
3717	50f. (3) Women attending man with fan and man and women in alcove	60	20
3718	50f. (4) Women playing flutes and couple by painted screen	60	20
3719	50f. (5) Young couple and women attending seated man	60	20

Nos. 3715/19 were printed together, se-tenant, forming a composite design.

806 Sheep　　**808** Wreath on Wall and Last Verse of the "Internationale"

807 Yuzui (dam at Dujiang)

1991. New Year. Year of the Sheep.
| 3720 | 806 | 20f. multicoloured | 25 | 15 |

1991. Dujiangyan Irrigation Project. Mult.
3721	20f. Type 807	10	10
3722	50f. Feishayan (weir)	15	10
3723	80f. Baopingkou (diversion of part of River Minjiang through new opening in Yulei Mountain)	70	20

1991. 120th Anniv of Paris Commune.
| 3724 | 808 | 20f. multicoloured | 10 | 10 |

809 Apple　　**810** Saiga

1991. Family Planning. Multicoloured.
| 3725 | 20f. Type 809 | 10 | 10 |
| 3726 | 50f. Child's and adult's hands within heart | 25 | 10 |

1991. Horned Ruminants. Multicoloured.
3727	20f. Type 810	15	20
3728	20f. Takin	15	10
3729	50f. Argali	25	10
3730	2y. Ibex	70	35

811 Dancers　　**812** Map and Emperor Penguins

1991. 40th Anniv of Chinese Administration of Tibet. Multicoloured.
| 3731 | 25f. Type 811 | 10 | 10 |
| 3732 | 50f. Rainbows over mountain road | 15 | 10 |

1991. 30th Anniv of Implementation of Antarctic Treaty.
| 3734 | 812 | 20f. multicoloured | 20 | 10 |

813 "Rhododendron delavayi"

1991. Rhododendrons. Multicoloured.
3735	10f. Type 813	10	10
3736	15f. "Rhododendron molle"	10	10
3737	15f. "Rhododendron simsii"	35	10
3738	20f. "Rhododendron fictolacteum"	35	10
3739	50f. "Rhododendron agglutinatum" (vert)	50	10
3740	80f. "Rhododendron fortunei" (vert)	65	15
3741	90f. "Rhododendron giganteum" (vert)	70	20
3742	1y.60 "Rhododendron rex" (vert)	1·10	40

814 Pleasure Boat on Lake Nanhu (venue of first Party congress)

1991. 70th Anniv of Chinese Communist Party. Multicoloured.
| 3744 | 20f. Type 814 | 30 | 15 |
| 3745 | 50f. Party emblem | 15 | 10 |

815 Statue, Xuxian

1991. 2200th Anniv of Peasant Uprising led by Chen Sheng and Wu Guang.
| 3746 | 815 | 20f. black, brown and deep brown | 15 | 10 |

816 Hanging Temple

1991. Mount Hengshan, Shanxi Province. Mult.
3747	20f. Type 816	15	10
3748	20f. Snow-covered peak	15	10
3749	55f. "Shrine of Hengshan" carved in rock face	35	10
3750	80f. Temples in Flying Stone Grotto	75	30

817 Mammoths and Man

1991. 13th International Union for Quaternary Research Conference, Peking.
| 3751 | 817 | 20f. multicoloured | 15 | 10 |

818 Pine Valley

1991. Chengde Royal Summer Resort. Mult.
3752	15f. Type 818	10	10
3753	20f. Pavilions around lake	15	10
3754	90f. Maples and pavilions on islet	75	20

819 Chen Yi　　**820** Clasped Hands forming Heart

1991. 90th Birth Anniv of Chen Yi (co-founder of People's Army).
| 3756 | 20f. Type 819 | 10 | 10 |
| 3757 | 50f. Verse "The Green Pine" written by Chen Yi | 15 | 10 |

1991. Flood Disaster Relief.
| 3758 | 820 | 80f. multicoloured | 25 | 10 |

The proceeds from the sale of No. 3758 were donated to the International Decade for Natural Disaster Reduction National Committee.

1991. Achievements of Socialist Construction (4th series). As T 758. Multicoloured.
3759	20f. Luoyang glassworks	10	10
3760	25f. Urumchi chemical fertilizer works	10	10
3761	55f. Shenyang–Dalian expressway	20	10
3762	80f. Xichang satellite launching centre	50	15

821 Xu Xilin　　**822** Wine Pot and Warming Bowl, Song Dynasty

1991. 80th Anniv of 1911 Revolution. Mult.
3763	20f. (1) Type 821	15	10
3764	20f. (2) Qiu Jin	15	10
3765	20f. (3) Song Jiaoren	15	10

1991. Jingdezhen China. Multicoloured.
3766	15f. (1) Type 822	10	10
3767	20f. (2) Blue and white porcelain vase, Yuan dynasty	10	10
3768	20f. (3) Covered jar with dragon design, Ming dynasty (horiz)	10	10
3769	25f. (4) Vase with flower design, Qing dynasty	10	10
3770	50f. (5) Modern plate with fish design	20	10
3771	2y. (6) Modern octagonal bowl (horiz)	85	45

823 Tao Xingzhi　　**824** Xu Xiangqian

1991. Birth Centenary of Tao Xingzhi (educationist). Each blue, grey and red.
| 3772 | 20f. Type 823 | 10 | 10 |
| 3773 | 50f. Tao Xingzhi in traditional robes | 15 | 10 |

1991. 90th Birth Anniv of Xu Xiangqian (revolutionary). Multicoloured.
| 3774 | 20f. Type 824 | 10 | 10 |
| 3775 | 50f. In uniform | 15 | 10 |

825 Emblem　　**826** Monkey

1991. 1st Women's World Football Championship, Guangdong Province. Multicoloured.
| 3776 | 20f. Type 825 | 10 | 10 |
| 3777 | 50f. Player | 15 | 10 |

1991. Literature. "Outlaws of the Marsh" (3rd series). As T 745. Multicoloured.
| 3778 | 20f. (1) Dai Zong delivers forged letter from Liangshan Marsh | 10 | 10 |
| 3779 | 25f. (2) Yi Zhangqing captures Stumpy Tiger Wang | 40 | 10 |

| 3780 | 25f. (3) Mistress Gu rescues Xie brothers from Dengzhou jail | 40 | 10 |
| 3781 | 90f. (4) Sun Li gains entrance to Zhu family manor in guise of military magistrate | 70 | 30 |

1992. New Year. Year of the Monkey. Paper-cut designs.
| 3783 | 826 | 20f. multicoloured | 10 | 10 |
| 3784 | – | 50f. black and red | 20 | 20 |

DESIGN: 50f. Magpies and plum blossom around Chinese character for monkey.

827 Black Stork　　**828** "Metasequoia glyptostroboides"

1992. Storks. Multicoloured.
| 3785 | 20f. Type 827 | 10 | 10 |
| 3786 | 1y.60 White stork | 85 | 20 |

1992. Conifers. Multicoloured.
3787	20f. Type 828	10	10
3788	30f. "Cathaya argyrophylla"	10	10
3789	50f. "Taiwania flousiana"	15	10
3790	80f. "Abies beshanzuensis"	45	15

829 Madai Seabream　　**830** River Crossing at Yanan

1992. Offshore Breeding Projects. Multicoloured.
3791	20f. Type 829	30	10
3792	25f. Prawn	10	10
3793	50f. Farrer's scallops	20	15
3794	80f. "Laminaria japonica" (seaweed)	40	20

1992. 50th Anniv of Publication of Mao Tse-tung's Talks at the Yanan Forum on Literature and Art.
| 3795 | 830 | 20f. black, orange & red | 10 | 10 |

831 Flower and Landscape on Globe

1992. World Environment Day. 20th Anniv of U. N. Environment Conference, Stockholm.
| 3796 | 831 | 20f. multicoloured | 10 | 10 |

832 Seven-spotted Ladybird　　**833** Basketball

1992. 19th International Entomology Congress, Peking. Insects. Multicoloured.
3797	20f. Type 832	10	10
3798	30f. "Sympetrum croceolum" (dragonfly)	10	10
3799	50f. "Chrysopa septempunctata" (lacewing)	15	10
3800	2y. Praying mantis	90	40

1992. Olympic Games, Barcelona. Mult.
3801	20f. Type 833	10	10
3802	25f. Gymnastics (horiz)	10	10
3803	50f. Diving (horiz)	15	10
3804	80f. Weightlifting	30	15

834 Emblem **835** Manchurian Cranes over Great Wall

1992. International Space Year.
3806 **834** 20f. multicoloured . . . 10 10

1992. Literature. "Romance of the Three Kingdoms" by Luo Guanzhong (3rd series). As T **763**. Multicoloured.
3807 20f. Zhuge Liang urging Zhang Zhao to join fight against Cao Cao (horiz) 10 10
3808 30f. Zhuge Liang's sarcastic goading of Sun Quan . . 10 10
3809 50f. Jiang Gan stealing forged letter from Zhou Yu (horiz) 35 10
3810 1y.60 Zhuge Liang and Lu Su in straw-covered boat under arrow attack . . . 85 30

1992. Dunhuang Cave Murals (4th series). Tang Dynasty. As T **732**. Multicoloured.
3811 20f. Bodhisattva (vert) . . . 10 10
3812 25f. Musical performance (vert) 10 10
3813 55f. Flight on a dragon . . 20 10
3814 80f. Emperor Wudi dispatching his envoy Zhang Qian to the western regions 55 15

1992. 20th Anniv of Normalization of Diplomatic Relations with Japan. Multicoloured.
3816 20f. Type **835** 20 20
3817 2y. Japanese and Chinese girls and dove 45 25

836 Statue of Mazu, Meizhou Islet **837** Party Emblem

1992. Mazu, Sea Goddess.
3818 **836** 20f. brown and blue . . 10 10

1992. 14th National Communist Party Congress.
3819 **837** 20f. multicoloured . . . 10 10

838 Jiao Yulu **839** Xiong Qinglai (mathematician) and Formula

1992. 70th Birth Anniv of Jiao Yulu (Party worker).
3820 **838** 20f. multicoloured . . . 10 10

1992. Scientists (3rd series). Multicoloured.
3821 20f. Type **839** 10 10
3822 30f. Tang Feifan (microbiologist) and medal 10 10
3823 50f. Zhang Xiaoqian (doctor) and hospital scene 15 10
3824 1y. Liang Sicheng (architect) and plan 25 30

840 Luo Ronghuan in Officer's Uniform **841** State Arms

1992. 90th Birth Anniv of Luo Ronghuan (army leader). Multicoloured.
3825 20f. Type **840** 10 10
3826 50f. Luo Ronghuan as young man 10 10

1992. 10th Anniv of Constitution.
3827 **841** 20f. multicoloured . . . 10 10

842 Liu Bocheng in Officer's Uniform **843** "Spring" (Zhou Baiqi)

1992. Birth Centenary of Liu Bocheng (army leader).
3828 **842** 20f. multicoloured . . . 10 10
3829 – 50f. deep green & green 10 10
DESIGN—VERT: 50f. Liu Bocheng as young man.

1992. Qingtian Stone Carvings. Multicoloured.
3830 10f. Type **843** 10 10
3831 20f. "Chinese Sorghum" (Lin Rukui) 10 10
3832 40f. "Harvest" (Zhang Aiting) 15 10
3833 2y. "Blooming Flowers and Full Moon" (Ni Dongfang) 65 40

844 Cock **845** Song Qing-ling

1993. New Year. Year of the Cock. Paper-cut designs by Cai Lanying.
3834 **844** 20f. red and black . . . 15 10
3835 – 50f. white, red & black 50 10
DESIGN: 50f. Flowers around Chinese character for rooster.

1993. Birth Centenary of Song Qing-ling (Sun Yat-sen's wife). Multicoloured.
3836 20f. Type **845** 10 10
3837 1y. Song Qing-ling with children 20 10

846 Bactrian Camel

1993. Bactrian Camel. Multicoloured.
3838 20f. Type **846** 15 10
3839 1y.60 Adult with young . . 40 15

847 Flag, Basket of Flowers and Streamers

1993. 8th National People's Congress, Peking.
3840 **847** 20f. multicoloured . . . 10 10

848 Players **849** Sportswomen

1993. Go.
3841 **848** 20f. multicoloured . . . 10 10
3842 – 1y.60 red, black & gold 30 15
DESIGN: 1y.60, "China Vogue" (black) and "linked stars" (white) formations on board.

1993. 1st East Asian Games, Shanghai. Mult.
3843 50f. Type **849** 10 10
3844 50f. Dong dong (mascot) . . 10 10
Nos. 3843/4 were printed together, se-tenant, forming a composite design of Shanghai Stadium.

850 Li Jishen

1993. Revolutionaries (1st series). Each brown and black.
3845 20f. Type **850** 10 10
3846 30f. Zhang Lan (vert) . . . 10 10
3847 50f. Shan Junru (vert) . . . 15 10
3848 1y. Huang Yanpei 35 20
See also Nos. 3888/91.

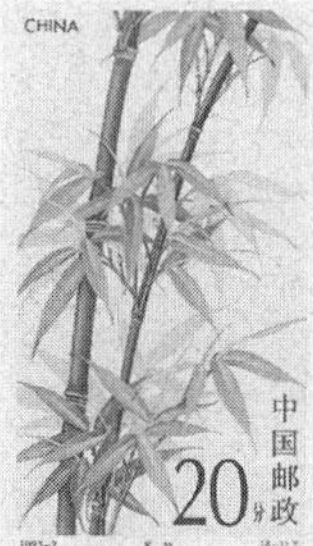

851 "Phyllostachys nigra"

1993. Bamboo. Multicoloured.
3849 20f. Type **851** 10 10
3850 30f. "Phyllostachys aureosulcata spectabilis" 10 10
3851 40f. "Bambusa ventricosa" 15 10
3852 1y. "Pseudosasa amabilis" 35 25

1993. Literature. "Outlaws of the Marsh" (4th series). As T **745**. Multicoloured.
3854 20f. Yin Tianxi and gang capturing Chai Jin . . . 10 10
3855 30f. Shi Qian stealing Xu Ning's armour 10 10
3856 50f. Xu Ning teaching use of barbed lance 40 10
3857 2y. Shi Xiu saving Lu Junyi from execution 95 35

852 Crater Lake in Winter

1993. Changbai Mountains. Multicoloured.
3858 20f. Type **852** 10 10
3859 30f. Mountain tundra in autumn 10 10
3860 50f. Waterfall in summer . . 20 10
3861 1y. Forest in spring 40 20

853 Games Emblem and Temple of Heaven **854** "Losana", Temple of Ancestors

1993. 7th National Games, Peking.
3862 **853** 20f. multicoloured . . . 10 10

1993. 1500th Anniv of Longmen Grottoes, Luoyang. Multicoloured.
3863 20f. Type **854** 10 10
3864 30f. "Sakyamuni", Middle Binyang Cave 10 10
3865 50f. "King of Northern Heavens" standing on Yaksha 20 10
3866 1y. "Bodhisattva", Guyang Cave 35 20

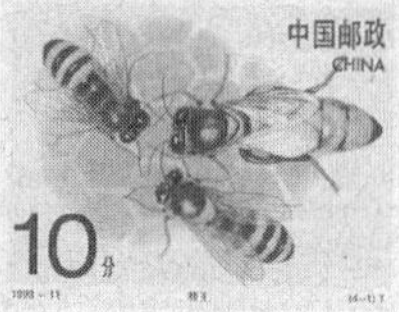

855 Queen Bee and Workers on Comb

1993. The Honey Bee. Multicoloured.
3868 10f. Type **855** 10 10
3869 15f. Bee extracting nectar . . 10 10
3870 20f. Two bees on blossom 10 10
3871 2y. Two bees among flowers 85 35

856 Bowl, New Stone Age

1993. Lacquer Work. Multicoloured.
3872 20f. Type **856** 10 10
3873 30f. Duck-shaped container (from Marquis Yi's tomb), Warring States Period 10 10
3874 50f. Plate decorated with foliage (Zhang Cheng), Yuan Dynasty 15 10
3875 1y. Chrysanthemum-shaped container, Qing Dynasty 35 20

857 Mao Tse-tung in North Shaanxi

1993. Birth Centenary of Mao Tse-tung. Mult.
3876 20f. Type **857** 10 10
3877 1y. Mao in library 20 10

858 Fan Painting of Bamboo and Rock

1993. 300th Birth Anniv of Zheng Banqiao (artist). Multicoloured.
3879 10f. Type **858** 10 10
3880 20f. Orchids 10 10
3881 20f. Orchids, bamboo and rock (scroll) (vert) . . . 10 10
3882 30f. Bamboo (scroll) (vert) 35 10
3883 50f. Chrysanthemum in vase 45 10
3884 1y.60 Calligraphy on fan . . 1·25 25

859 Yang Hucheng **860** Dog (folk toy, Hebei)

1993. Birth Centenary of General Yang Hucheng.
3885 **859** 20f. multicoloured . . . 10 10

1994. New Year. Year of The Dog.
3886 **860** 20f. multicoloured . . . 15 10
3887 – 50f. black, red & yellow 50 10
DESIGN: 50f. Dogs and flowers around Chinese character for dog.

861 Ma Xulun

1994. Revolutionaries (2nd series). Each brown and black.
3888 20f. Chen Qiyou (horiz) . . 10 10
3889 20f. Chen Shutong 10 10
3890 50f. Type **861** 20 10
3891 50f. Xu Deheng (horiz) . . 20 10

862 Great Siberian Sturgeon

1994. Sturgeons. Multicoloured.
3892	20f. Type **862**	10	10
3893	40f. Chinese sturgeon	20	10
3894	50f. Chinese paddlefish	25	10
3895	1y. Yangtze sturgeon	55	25

863 Tree in Dunes

864 Ming Dynasty Three-legged Round Teapot

1994. "Making the Desert Green". Multicoloured.
3896	15f. Type **863**	10	10
3897	20f. Flower-covered dune	10	10
3898	40f. Forest of poplars	40	10
3899	50f. Oasis	50	10

1994. Yixing Unglazed Teapots. Multicoloured.
3900	20f. Type **864**	10	10
3901	30f. Qing dynasty four-legged square teapot	10	10
3902	50f. Qing dynasty patterned teapot	15	10
3903	1y. Modern teapot	55	20

865 Entrance Gate

1994. 70th Anniv of Huang-pu Military Academy.
3904	**865** 20f. multicoloured	10	10

866 "100" and Olympic Rings

1994. Centenary of Int Olympic Committee.
3905	**866** 20f. multicoloured	10	10

867 Tao Yuanming (poet)

1994. Writers. Each black, brown and red.
3906	20f. Type **867**	10	10
3907	30f. Cao Zhi (poet)	10	10
3908	50f. Sima Qian (historian)	20	15
3909	1y. Qu Yuan (poet)	35	25

1994. Dunhuang Cave Murals (5th series). Tang Dynasty Frescoes in Mogao Caves. As T **732**. Multicoloured.
3910	10f. Flying Devata	10	10
3911	20f. Vimalakirti on dais	10	10
3912	50f. Zhang Yichao's forces	40	10
3913	1y.60 Sorceresses	75	35

868 Zhaojun

1994. Marriage of Zhaojun (from Han court) and Monarch of Xiongnu. Multicoloured.
3914	20f. Type **868**	10	10
3915	50f. Journey to Xiongnu	40	10

869 Emblem

870 Heaven's South Gate

1994. 6th Far East and South Pacific Games for the Disabled, Peking.
3917	**869** 20f. multicoloured	10	10

1994. U.N.E.S.C.O. World Heritage Site. Wulingyuan. Multicoloured.
3918	20f. Type **870**	10	10
3919	30f. Shentangwan	10	10
3920	50f. No. One Bridge (horiz)	15	15
3921	1y. Writing Brush Peak (horiz)	55	25

871 Jade Maiden Peak

1994. Mt. Wuyi. Multicoloured.
3923	50f. (1) Type **871**	35	10
3924	50f. (2) Nine Turns Brook	35	10
3925	50f. (3) Hanging Block	35	10
3926	50f. (4) Elevated Meadow	35	10

Nos. 3923/6 were issued together, se-tenant, forming a composite design.

872 Examining Scroll

873 Whooping Crane

1994. Paintings by Fu Baoshi. Multicoloured.
3927	10f. Waterfall and river	10	10
3928	20f. Type **872**	10	10
3929	20f. Tree	10	10
3930	40f. Musicians	20	15
3931	50f. Wooded landscape	25	15
3932	1y. Scholars	45	30

1994. Cranes. Multicoloured.
3933	20f. Type **873**	20	10
3934	2y. Black-necked crane	65	30

875 White Emperor's City

1994. Gorges of Yangtse River. Mult.
3936	10f. (1) Type **875**	10	10
3937	20f. (2) River steamer in Qutang Gorge	10	10
3938	20f. (3) Small boat in Wuxia Gorge	10	10
3939	20f. (4) Goddess Peak	10	10
3940	50f. (5) Boats in Xiling Gorge	25	15
3941	1y. (6) Qu Yuan Memorial Hall	40	30

1994. Literature. "Romance of the Three Kingdoms" by Luo Guanzhong (4th series). As T **763**. Multicoloured.
3944	20f. Cao Cao composing poem with lance in hand (horiz)	10	10
3945	30f. Liu Bei's wedding to sister of Sun Quan	10	10
3946	50f. Ambush at Xiaoyaojin (horiz)	20	10
3947	1y. Lu Xun's forces destroying Liu Bei's camps	35	20

877 Shenzhen

1994. Special Economic Zones. Multicoloured.
3949	50f. (1) Type **877**	15	10
3950	50f. (2) Zhuhai	15	10
3951	50f. (3) Shantou	15	10
3952	50f. (4) Xiamen	15	10
3953	50f. (5) Hainan	15	10

878 Dayan Pagoda, Cien Temple, Xian

879 Pig

1994. Pagodas. Each black, lightt brown and brown.
3954	20f. (1) Type **878**	10	10
3955	20f. (2) Zhenguo Pagoda, Kaiyuan Temple, Quanzhou	10	10
3956	50f. (3) Liuhe Pagoda, Kaihua Temple, Hangzhou	15	10
3957	2y. (4) Youguo Temple, Kaifeng	60	30

1995. New Year. Year of the Pig.
3959	**879** 20f. multicoloured	15	10
3960	– 50f. black and red	15	10

DESIGN: 50f. Chinese character ("pig") and pigs.

880 Willows beside River Songhua

1995. Winter in Jilin. Multicoloured.
3961	20f. Type **880**	15	10
3962	50f. Jade tree on hillside (vert)	15	10

881 Relief Map and Tropic of Cancer

1995. Mt. Dinghu. Multicoloured.
3963	15f. (1) Type **881**	10	10
3964	20f. (2) Ravine	10	10
3965	20f. (3) Monastery on hillside and forest-covered slopes	10	10
3966	2y.30 (4) Pair of silver pheasants in forest	65	35

882 Summit Emblem

1995. United Nations World Summit for Social Development, Copenhagen.
3967	**882** 20f. multicoloured	10	10

883 Snowy Owl

1995. Owls. Multicoloured.
3968	10f. Eagle owl	15	10
3969	20f. Long-eared owl	20	10
3970	50f. Type **883**	30	10
3971	1y. Eastern grass owls	60	20

884 "Osmanthus fragrans thunbergii"

1995. Sweet Osmanthus. Multicoloured.
3972	20f. (1) Type **884**	10	10
3973	20f. (2) "Osmanthus fragrans latifolius"	10	10
3974	50f. (3) "Osmanthus fragrans aurantiacus"	25	10
3975	1y. (4) "Osmanthus fragrans semperflorens"	45	20

885 Player

1995. World Table Tennis Championships, Tianjin. Multicoloured.
3976	20f. Type **885**	10	10
3977	50f. Stadium	10	10

886 Ladies and Courtiers

1995. "Spring Outing" by Zhang Xuan. Details of the painting. Multicoloured.
3979	50f. (1) Type **886**	50	10
3980	50f. (2) Courtiers on horseback	50	10

Nos. 3979/80 were issued together, se-tenant, forming a composite design.

887 Donglu Play, Shanxi

1995. Shadow Play. Regional characters. Mult.
3981	20f. (1) Type **887**	10	10
3982	40f. (2) Luanxain play, Hebei	10	10
3983	50f. (3) Xiaoyi play, Shanxi	15	10
3984	50f. (4) Dayi play, Sichuan	15	10

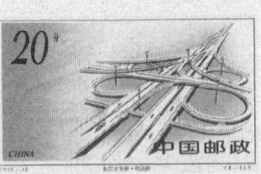

888 Siyuan

1995. Motorway Interchanges, Peking. Mult.
3985	20f. Type **888**	10	10
3986	30f. Tianningsi	10	10
3987	50f. Yuting	10	10
3988	1y. Anhui	25	15

890 Asian Elephants at River

1995. 20th Anniv of China–Thailand Diplomatic Relations. Multicoloured.
3990	1y. (1) Type **890**	25	10
3991	1y. (2) Asian elephants at river (face value at left)	25	10

Nos. 3990/1 were issued together, se-tenant, forming a composite design.

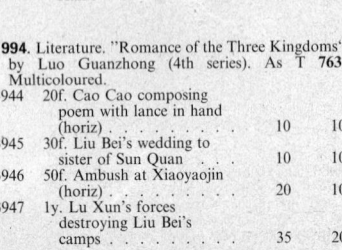

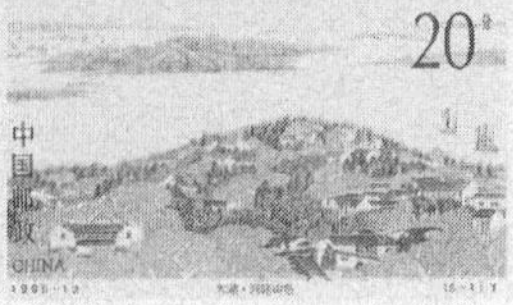

891 East and West Dongting Hills

1995. Lake Taihu. Multicoloured.

3992	20f. (1) Type **891**	10	10
3993	20f. (2) Tortoise Islet in spring	10	10
3994	50f. (3) Li Garden in summer	15	10
3995	50f. (4) Jichang Garden in autumn	15	10
3996	230f. (5) Plum Garden in winter	90	35

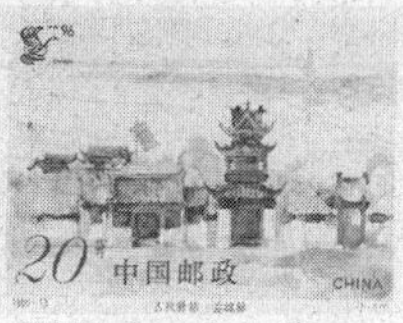

893 Yucheng Post, Jiangsu

1995. "China'96" International Stamp Exhibition, Peking. Ancient Chinese Post Offices. Mult.

3999	20f. Type **893**	10	10
4000	50f. Jimingshan Post, Hebei	15	10

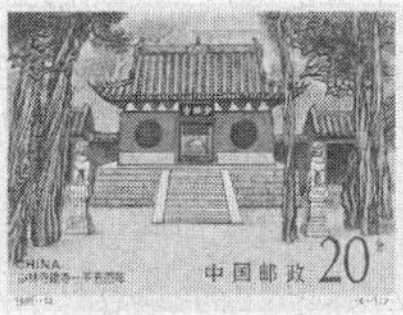

894 Hill Gate

1995. 1500th Anniv of Shaolin Temple, Henan. Multicoloured.

4001	20f. Type **894**	10	10
4002	20f. Pagoda Forest	10	10
4003	50f. Martial arts practice (detail of fresco, White Robe Hall)	15	10
4004	100f. Thirteen monks rescue the Prince of Qin (detail of fresco)	30	15

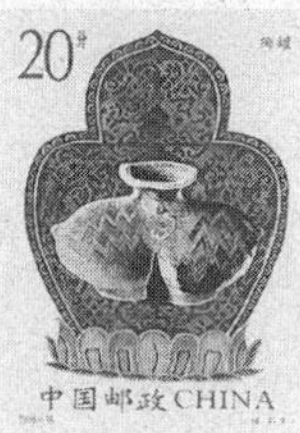

895 New Stone Age Jar

1995. Tibetan Culture. Multicoloured.

4005	20f. Type **895**	10	10
4006	30f. Helmet (7th century)	10	10
4007	50f. Celestial chart	15	10
4008	100f. Pearl and coral mandala	30	15

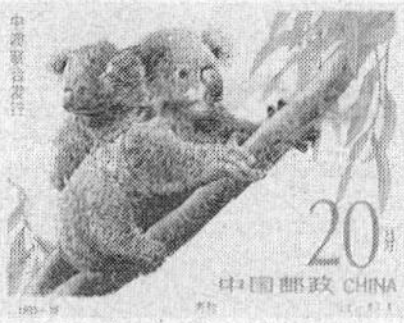

896 Koalas in Eucalyptus Tree

1995. Endangered Animals. Multicoloured.

4009	20f. Type **896**	10	10
4010	2y.90 Giant pandas amongst bamboo	90	25

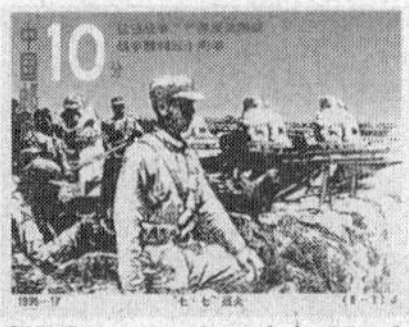

897 Japanese Attack in North China, 7 July 1937

1995. 50th Anniv of End of Second World War and of War against Japan. Multicoloured.

4011	10f. (1) Type **897**	10	10
4012	20f. (2) Battle of Taier Village	10	10
4013	20f. (3) Battle at Great Wall	10	10
4014	50f. (4) Guerrillas	15	10
4015	50f. (5) Forces at Mangyo, Burma	15	10
4016	60f. (6) Airplane donated by overseas Chinese	15	10
4017	100f. (7) Liberation of Taiwan, October 1945	25	15
4018	100f. (8) Crew on deck of battleship	25	15

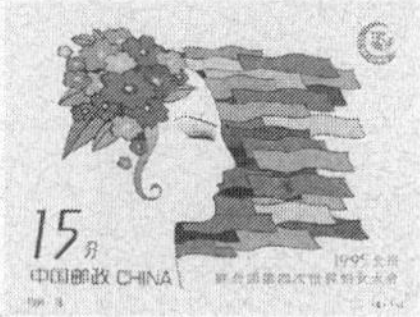

898 Woman's Profile and Flags (equality)

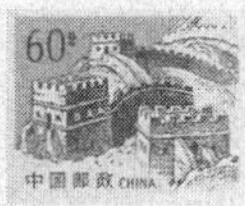

899 Great Wall at Jinshanling Hill

1995. 4th World Conference on Women, Peking. Multicoloured.

4019	15f. Type **898**	10	10
4020	20f. Woman's profile and wheel of colours (development)	10	10
4021	50f. Woman's profile and dove (peace)	15	10
4022	60f. Dove and flower (friendship)	20	15

1995. The Great Wall of China.

4024	–	5f. turquoise, bl & blk	10	10
4024a	–	10f. black and green	10	10
4024b	–	20f. black and lavender	10	10
4025	–	30f. black and yellow	10	10
4025a	–	40f. black and pink	10	10
4026	–	50f. black, brn & yell	10	10
4027	**899**	60f. black and brown	15	10
4027a	–	60f. black and yellow	15	10
4027b	–	80f. multicoloured	15	10
4028	–	100f. black and red	15	10
4029	–	150f. black and green	20	10
4031	–	200f. black and pink	30	15
4032	–	230f. black and green	45	30
4032a	–	270f. mauve, blk & grn	50	35
4035	–	290f. black and blue	50	35
4036	–	300f. black and green	40	25
4036a	–	320f. mve, blk & lav	45	25
4037	–	420f. black and orange	60	35
4037a	–	440f. light brown, black and brown	60	35
4038	–	500f. black, brn & bl	70	40
4038a	–	540f. black and blue	80	45
4038b	–	10y. multicoloured	1·75	80
4038c	–	20y. multicoloured	3·25	1·60
4038d	–	50y. grey, blk & grn	8·75	4·25

DESIGNS: 5f. Hushan section of wall; 10f. Wall at Jiumenkou Pass; 20f. Wall at Shanhaiguan; 30f. Wall at Huangya Pass; 40f. Jinshanling section of wall; 50f. Wall seen from Gubeikou; 60f. (4027a), Huanghua Tower and wall; 80f. Mutianyu section of wall; 100f. Wall seen from Badaling; 150f. Wall at Jurong Pass; 200f. Wall at Zijing Pass; 230f. Wall at Shanhaiguan Pass; 270f. Wall at Pingxingguan Pass; 290f. Laolongtou (end of wall); 300f. Wall at Niangziguan Pass; 320f. Wall at Desheng Pass; 420f. Wall at Pianguan Pass; 440f. Wall at Yanmen Pass; 500f. Bianjing Tower; 540f. Zhenbei Tower; 10y. Huama section; 20y. Wall at Sanguankou Pass; 50y. Wall at Jiayuguan Pass.

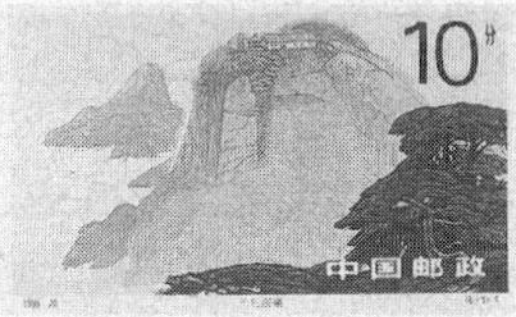

900 Dawn on Heavenly Terrace Peak

1995. The Jiuhua Mountains, Anhui. Mult.

4039	10f. (1) Type **900**	10	10
4040	20f. (2) Hall of Meditation (vert)	10	10
4041	20f. (3) Hall of the Mortal Body	10	10
4042	50f. (4) Sunset at Zhiyuan Temple	20	10
4043	50f. (5) Roc listening to Scriptures (rock formation) (vert)	20	10
4044	290f. (6) Phoenix pine	70	40

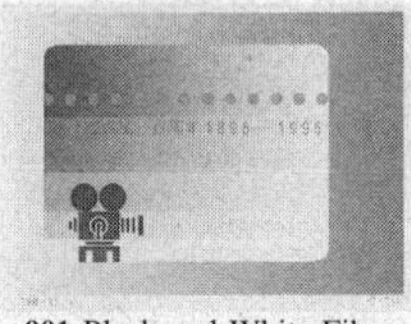

901 Black and White Film

1995. Centenary of Motion Pictures. Mult.

4045	20f. Type **901**	10	10
4046	50f. Colour film	10	10

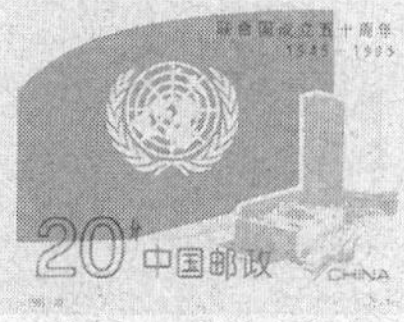

902 Flag and New York Headquarters

1995. 50th Anniv of U.N.O. Multicoloured.

4047	20f. Type **902**	10	10
4048	50f. Anniversary emblem and "flags"	10	10

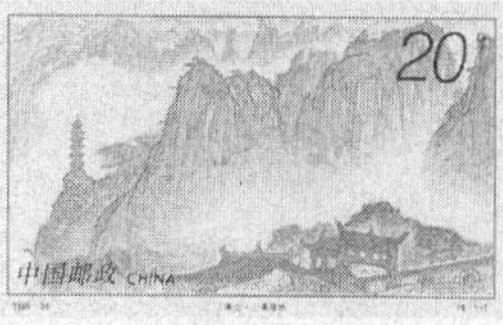

903 Blessing Spot

1995. Sanqing Mountain. Multicoloured.

4049	20f. Type **903**	10	10
4050	20f. Spring Goddess	10	10
4051	50f. Music charm (vert)	15	10
4052	100f. Supernatural python (rock formation) (vert)	60	20

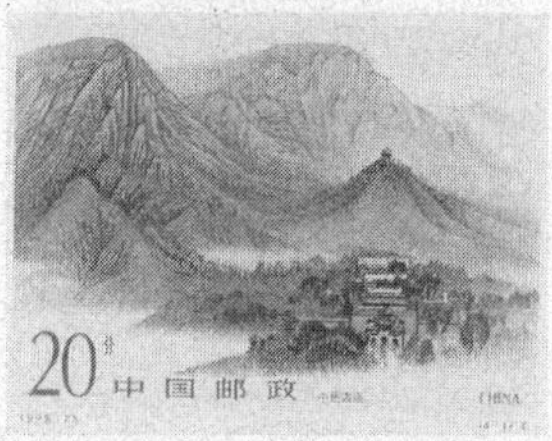

904 Central Mountain Temple and Huang Gai Peak

1995. Mount Song. Multicoloured.

4053	20f. Type **904**	10	10
4054	50f. Moonrise over Fawang Temple	15	10
4055	60f. Shaolin Temple in snow	15	10
4056	1y. Mountain ridge	55	20

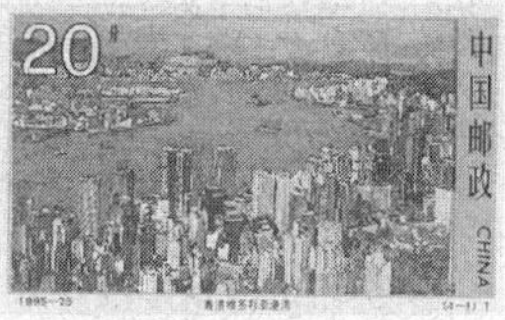

905 Victoria Harbour

1995. Hong Kong. Multicoloured.

4057	20f. Type **905**	10	10
4058	50f. Central Plaza	15	10
4059	60f. Hong Kong Cultural Centre	15	10
4060	290f. Repulse Bay	1·10	35

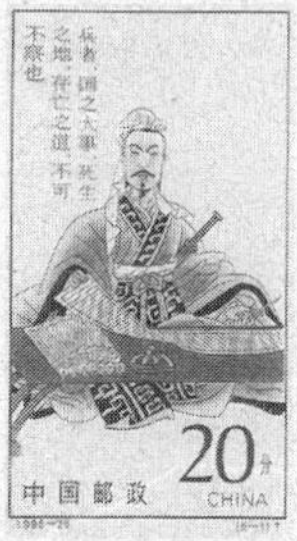

906 Sun Zi

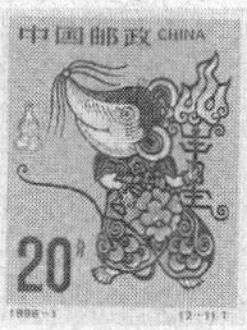

907 Rat

1995. "Art of War" (book) by Sun Zi. Mult.

4061	20f. Type **906**	10	10
4062	20f. Elaborating strategies	10	10
4063	30f. Capturing Ying	10	10
4064	50f. Battle at Ailing	15	10
4065	100f. Conference at Huangchi	55	20

1996. New Year. Year of the Rat. Mult.

4066	20f. Type **907**	40	10
4067	50f. Pattern and Chinese character	40	10

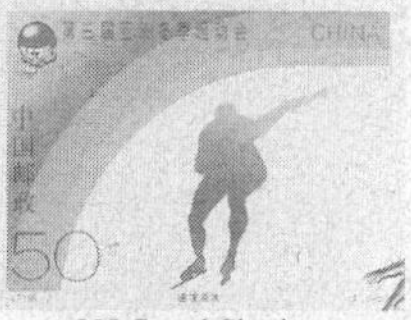

908 Speed Skating

1996. 3rd Asian Winter Games, Harbin. Mult.

4068	50f. Type **908**	15	10
4069	50f. Ice hockey	15	10
4070	50f. Figure skating	15	10
4071	50f. Skiing	15	10

Nos. 4068/71 were issued together, se-tenant, forming a composite design.

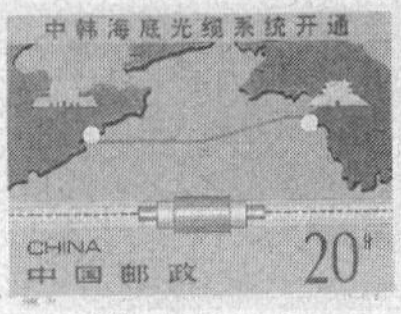

909 Cable Route

1996. Inaug of Korea–China Submarine Cable.

4072	**909**	20f. multicoloured	10	10

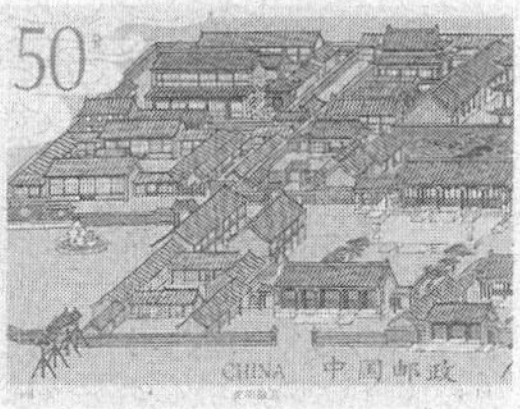

910 Palace Complex

1996. Shenyang Imperial Palace. Multicoloured.

4073	50f. Type **910**	45	10
4074	50f. Pagoda and buildings	45	10

Nos. 4073/4 were issued together, se-tenant, forming a composite design.

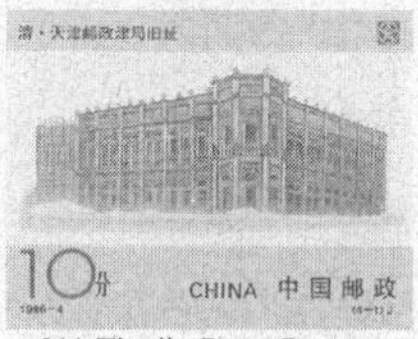

911 Tianjin Posts Bureau

1996. Cent of Chinese State Postal Service. Mult.

4075	10f. Type **911**	10	10
4076	20f. Former Directorate General of North China Posts building, Peking	10	10
4077	50f. Postal headquarters of Chinese Soviet Republic, Zhongshi, Jiangxi	20	10
4078	100f. Present Peking postal complex	35	20

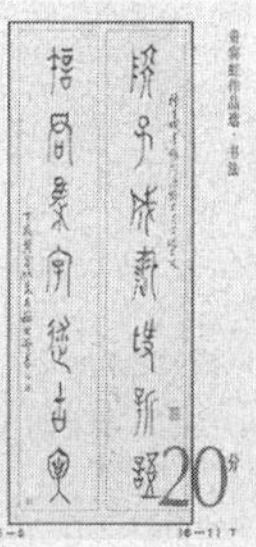

912 Calligraphy

1996. Paintings by Huang Binhong. Mult.

4080	20f. (1) Type **912**	10	10
4081	20f. (2) Mountain landscape	10	10
4082	40f. (3) Mount Qingcheng in rain	40	10
4083	50f. (4) View from Xiling	50	10
4084	50f. (5) Landscape	50	10
4085	230f. (6) Flowers	1·10	45

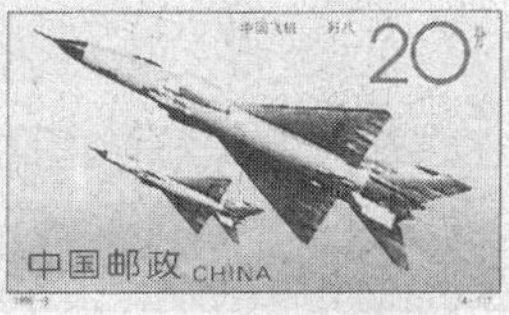

913 Shenyang F-8 Jet Fighter

1996. Chinese Aircraft. Multicoloured.

4086	20f. (1) Type **913**	10	10
4087	50f. (2) Nanchang A-5 jet fighter	15	10
4088	50f. (3) Xian Y-7 transport	15	10
4089	100f. (4) Harbin Y-12 utility plane	60	15

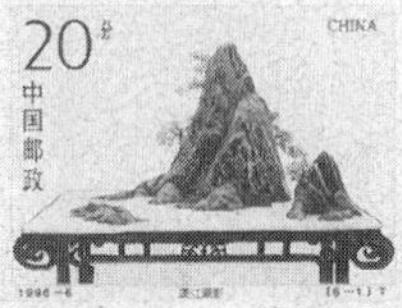

914 Green Scenery of Lijing River

1996. Bonsai Landscapes. Multicoloured.

4090	20f. (1) Type **914**	10	10
4091	20f. (2) Glistening Divine Peak	10	10
4092	50f. (3) Melting snow fills the river	15	10
4093	50f. (4) Eagle Beak Rock	15	10

4094	100f. (5) Memorable Years	60	15
4095	100f. (6) Peaks rising in Rosy Clouds	60	15

915 Sago Cycad ("Cycas revoluta")

1996. Cycads. Multicoloured.

4096	20f. Type **915**	10	10
4097	20f. Panzhihua cycad ("Cycas panzhihuaensis")	10	10
4098	50f. Nepal cycad	15	10
4099	230f. Polytomous cycad	55	30

916 Great Wall of China at Jinshan Ridge

1996. 25th Anniv of China–San Marino Diplomatic Relations. Multicoloured.

4100	100f. Type **916**	40	10
4101	100f. Walled rampart, San Marino	40	10

Nos. 4100/1 were issued together, se-tenant, forming a composite design.

919 Paddy Agricultural Tool

1996. Hemudu Archaeological Site, Yuyao, Zhejiang. Multicoloured.

4104	20f. Type **919**	10	10
4105	50f. Building supports	10	10
4106	100f. Paddles	45	10
4107	230f. Dish engraved with two birds and sun	70	25

921 Children rejoicing   **922** "The Discus Thrower" (Miron)

1996. Children. Multicoloured.

4109	20f. Type **921**	10	10
4110	30f. Girls pushing child in wheelchair in rain	10	10
4111	50f. Expedition to Antarctica	10	10
4112	100f. Planting sapling	50	10

1996. Centenary of Modern Olympic Games.

4113	**922** 20f. multicoloured	10	10

923 "Land"

1996. Preserve Land. Designs showing Chinese characters. Multicoloured.

4114	20f. Type **923**	10	10
4115	50f. "Cultivation"	10	10

924 Jinglue Terrace

1996. Jinglue Terrace, Guangxi Zhuang. Mult.

4116	20f. Type **924**	10	10
4117	50f. Structure of Zhenwu Pavilion	10	10

925 Red Flag Car

1996. Motor Vehicles. Multicoloured.

4118	20f. Type **925**	10	10
4119	20f. Dongfeng two-door truck	10	10
4120	50f. Jiefang four-door truck	10	10
4121	100f. Peking four-wheel drive	50	15

926 Banbidian Village, Kaiping District

1996. 20th Anniv of Tangshan Earthquake. Development of New City. Multicoloured.

4122	20f. (1) Type **926**	10	10
4123	50f. (2) East Hebei Cement Works	20	10
4124	50f. (3) Earthquake memorials, Xinhua Road	10	10
4125	100f. (4) Bulk carrier in Jingtang Harbour	45	15

927 Emblem, Globe and "30"

1996. 30th Int Geological Conference, Peking.

4126	**927** 20f. multicoloured	10	10

928 Tianchi Lake

1996. Tianshan Mountains, Xinjiang.

4127	**928** 20f. (1) multicoloured	10	10
4128	– 50f. (2) multicoloured	10	10
4129	– 50f. (3) blue, mve & blk	10	10
4130	– 100f. (4) multicoloured	50	15

DESIGNS—VERT: No. 4128, Waterfalls; 4129, Snow-capped mountain peaks. HORIZ: No. 4130. Mountains and landscape.

1996. Dunhuang Cave Murals (6th series). As T **732**. Multicoloured.

4131	10f. Mount Wutai (Five Dynasties) (vert)	10	10
4132	20f. Li Shengtian, King of Khotan (Five Dynasties) (vert)	10	10
4133	50f. Guanyin, Goddess of Mercy, saves boat (Northern Song period)	10	10
4134	100f. Worshipping Bodhisattvas (Western Xia)	50	15

929 Tombs

1996. Emperors' Tombs of Western Xia Dynasty, Yinchuan, Ningxia Hui. Multicoloured.

4136	20f. Type **929**	10	10
4137	20f. Divine Gate ornament	10	10
4138	50f. Stone base from Stele Pavilion	10	10
4139	100f. Piece of stele from Shouling Tomb	50	10

930 Datong–Qinhuangdao Line

1996. Railways. Multicoloured.

4140	15f. Type **930**	10	10
4141	20f. Lanzhou–Xinjiang line	10	10
4142	50f. Peking–Kowloon line	25	20
4143	100f. Peking West railway station	45	35

931 Shang Dynasty Tortoise Shell   **932** Ye Ting

1996. Ancient Archives. Multicoloured.

4144	20f. Type **931**	10	10
4145	20f. Han Dynasty wood slip inscribed with divinations on a marriage	10	10
4146	50f. Ming dynasty iron scroll conferring merit on General Li Wen	10	10
4147	100f. Qing dynasty diplomatic credentials (1905)	25	15

1996. Birth Cent of Ye Ting (revolutionary). Mult.

4148	20f. Type **932**	10	10
4149	50f. Ye Ting in uniform	10	10

933 Emblem

1996. 96th Interparliamentary Union Conference, Peking.

4150	**933** 20f. multicoloured	10	10

934 Transport and Telecommunications

1996. Pudong Area of Shanghai. Mult.

4151	10f. (1) Type **934**	10	10
4152	20f. (2) People's Bank of China branch, Lujiazui finance and business area	10	10
4153	20f. (3) Jinqiao export centre	10	10
4154	50f. (4) Garden of Advance Science and Technology, Zhangjiang	40	10
4155	60f. (5) Customs House, Waigaoqiao bonded area	40	10
4156	100f. (6) Apartment blocks	50	15

935 Chinese Rocket "Long March"

1996. 47th Congress of International Astronautical Federation. Multicoloured.

4158	20f. Type **935**	10	10
4159	100f. Communications satellite	20	10

936 Singapore

1996. City Scenes. Multicoloured.

4160	20f. Type **936**	10	10
4161	290f. Panmen Gate, Suzhou	90	15

937 Red Army in Marshland

1996. 60th Anniv of Long March by Communist Army. Multicoloured.

4162	20f. Type **937**	35	10
4163	50f. Reunion of three armies	50	10

938 Two Gods

1996. Tianjin Clay Statuettes. Multicoloured.

4164	20f. (1) Type **938**	10	10
4165	50f. (2) Seated man blowing sugar figure	10	10
4166	50f. (3) Woman and child returning from fishing	10	10
4167	100f. (4) Women painting at table	50	15

939 Bank of China

1996. Economic Growth in Hong Kong. Mult.

4168	20f. Type **939**	10	10
4169	40f. Container terminal	10	10
4170	60f. Airplane taking off from Kai Tak Airport	40	10
4171	290f. Stock exchange	95	25

940 Emblem over Farmland   **941** "Horse treading on Flying Swallow" (bronze) and Great Wall of China

1997. 1st National Agricultural Census.

4172	**940** 50f. multicoloured	10	10

1997. Tourist Year.

4173	**941** 50f. multicoloured	10	10

942 Chinese Lantern   **943** "Pine on Mount Huangshan"

1997. New Year. Year of the Ox. Mult.

4174	50f. Type **942**	35	10
4175	150f. Ox	65	15

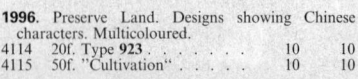

1997. Birth Centenary of Pan Tianshou (artist). Multicoloured.

4176	50f. (1) Type **943**	40	10
4177	50f. (2) "Rosy Clouds of Dawn"	40	10
4178	100f. (3) "Clearing Up after Mould Rains"	80	35
4179	100f. (4) "Chrysanthemum and Bamboo"	80	35
4180	150f. (5) "Sleeping Cat" . .	1·60	70
4181	150f. (6) "Corner of Lingyan Brook"	1·60	70

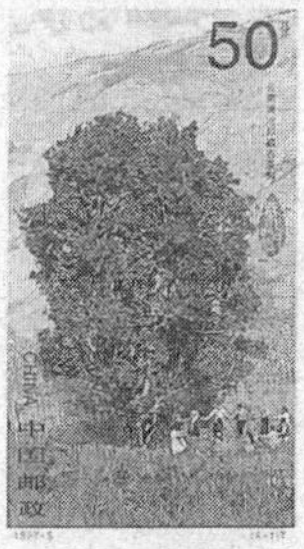

944 Tea Tree at Lancang, Yunnan

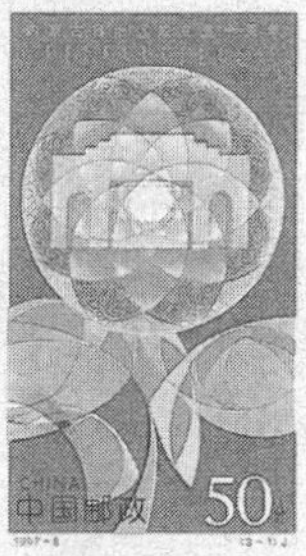

945 Celebration

1997. Tea. Multicoloured.

4182	50f. (1) Type **944**	10	10
4183	50f. (2) Statue of Lu Yu (author of "Classic of Tea")	10	10
4184	150f. (3) Tea grinder (Tang dynasty) (horiz)	60	15
4185	150f. (4) "Tea Party at Huishan" (Wen Zhenming) (horiz)	60	15

1997. 50th Anniv of Autonomous Region of Inner Mongolia. Multicoloured.

4186	50f. (1) Type **945**	10	10
4187	50f. (2) People of different cultures ("Unity") (horiz)	10	10
4188	200f. (3) Galloping horses ("Advance") (horiz) . . .	80	15

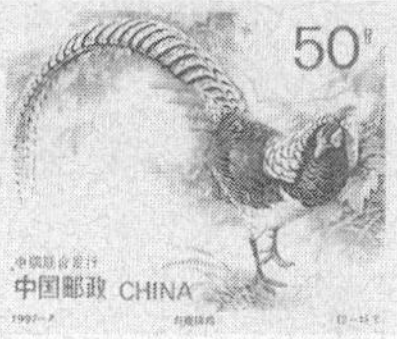

946 Lady Amherst's Pheasant

1997. Rare Pheasants. Multicoloured.

4189	50f. Type **946**	10	10
4190	540f. Ring-necked pheasant	1·25	40

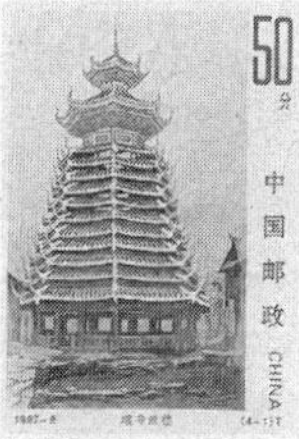

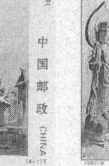

947 Zengchong Drum Tower

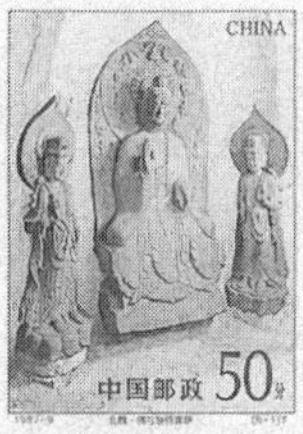

948 Buddha and Attendant Bodhisattva (Northern Wei dynasty)

1997. Dong Architecture. Multicoloured.

4191	50f. (1) Type **947**	10	10
4192	50f. (2) Baier drum tower	10	10
4193	150f. (3) Wind and rain bridge over River Nanjiang (horiz)	60	10
4194	150f. (4) Wind and rain shelter in field (horiz) . .	60	10

1997. Maiji Grottoes, Gansu Province. Mult.

4195	50f. (1) Type **948**	10	10
4196	50f. (2) Attendant Bodhisattva and disciple (Northern Wei dynasty)	10	10
4197	100f. (3) Maid servant (Western Wei dynasty) . .	15	10
4198	150f. (4) Buddha (Western Wei dynasty)	50	10
4199	150f. (5) Attendant Bodhisattva (Northern Zhou dynasty)	50	10
4200	200f. (6) Provider (Song dynasty)	55	15

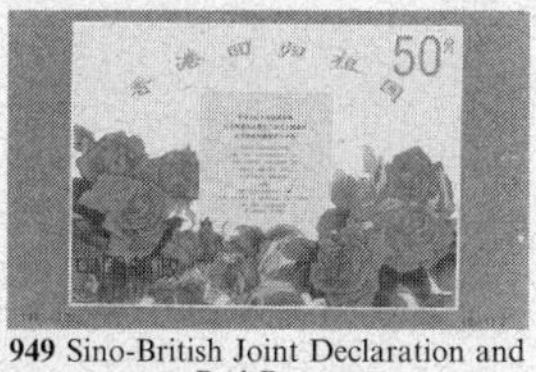

949 Sino-British Joint Declaration and Red Roses

1997. Return of Hong Kong to China. Mult.

4201	50f. Type **949**	35	10
4202	150f. Basic Law and mixed roses	50	10

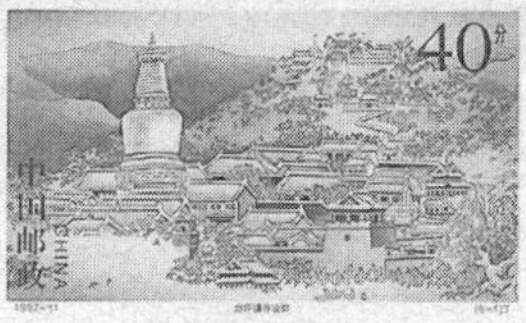

950 Taihuai Temple

1997. Ancient Temples, Wutai Mountain. Mult.

4205	40f. (1) Type **950**	10	10
4206	50f. (2) Great Hall, Nanchan Temple	10	10
4207	50f. (3) Eastern Hall, Foguang ("Buddhist Light") Temple	10	10
4208	150f. (4) Bronze Hall, Xiantong ("Revelation") Temple	60	10
4209	150f. (5) Bodhisattva Summit	60	10
4210	200f. (6) Zhenhai Temple . .	85	15

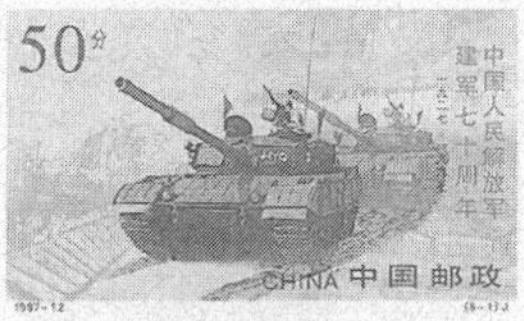

951 Tanks

1997. 70th Anniv of People's Liberation Army. Multicoloured.

4211	50f. (1) Type **951**	10	10
4212	50f. (2) Frigate flotilla . . .	10	10
4213	50f. (3) Jet fighter	10	10
4214	50f. (4) Ballistic missile . . .	10	10
4215	200f. (5) Tank, destroyer and jet fighters	90	15

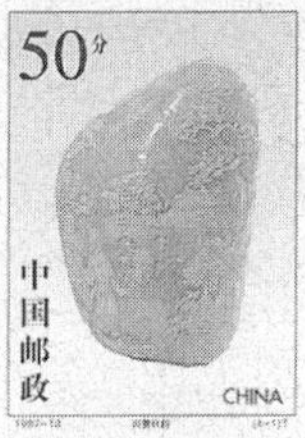

952 Scene from "A Dream of Red Mansions" (carved by Jiang Yilin)

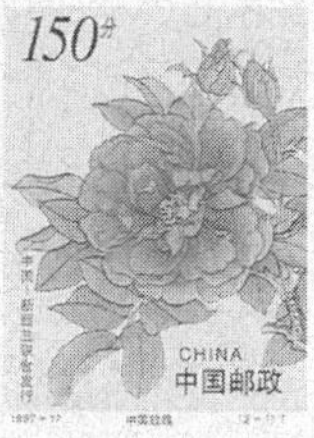

954 "Rosa rugosa"

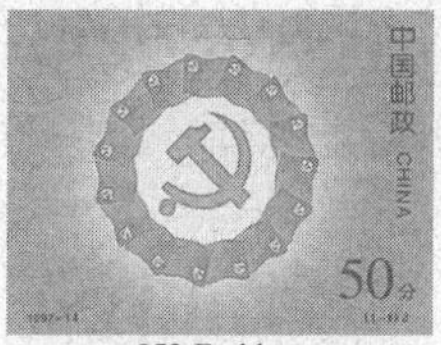

953 Emblem

1997. Shoushan Stone Carvings. Mult.

4216	50f. (1) Type **952**	10	10
4217	50f. (2) "Rhinoceros basking in Sunshine" (Zhou Jinting)	10	10
4218	150f. (3) "Fragrance and Jade"	60	10
4219	150f. (4) "Li the Cripple, Han Zhongli and Lu Dongbin in drunken Joy" (Lin Fada)	60	10

1997. 15th National Communist Party Congress.

4221	**953** 50f. multicoloured . . .	10	10

1997. Roses. Multicoloured.

4222	150f. Type **954**	50	10
4223	150f. "Aotearoa" of New Zealand	50	10

Nos. 4222/3 were issued together, se-tenant, forming a composite design.

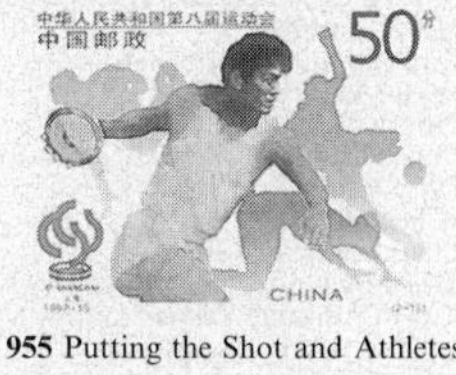

955 Putting the Shot and Athletes

1997. 8th National Games, Shanghai. Mult.

4224	50f. Type **955**	35	10
4225	150f. Mascot and stadium	45	10

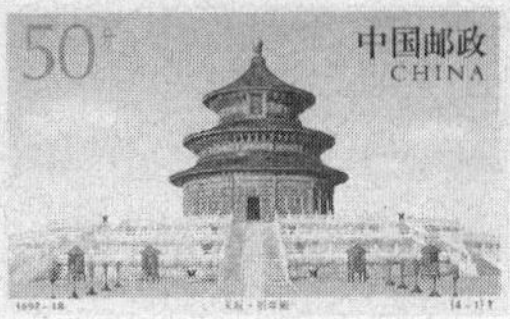

956 Hall of Prayer for Good Harvests

1997. Temple of Heaven, Peking. Mult.

4227	50f. (1) Type **956**	10	10
4228	50f. (2) Imperial Vault of Heaven	10	10
4229	150f. (3) Circular mound altar	60	10
4230	150f. (4) Hall of Abstinence	60	10

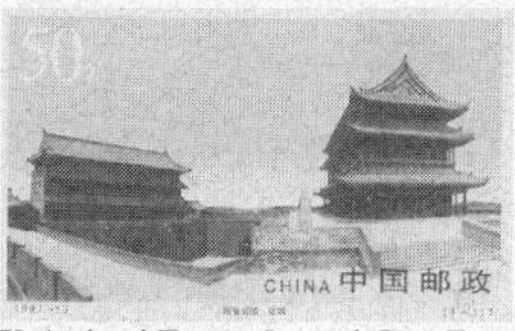

958 Archers' Tower, Jar and Gate Tower

1997. Xi'an City Walls. Multicoloured.

4232	50f. (1) Type **958**	10	10
4233	50f. (2) Archers' Tower . .	10	10
4234	150f. (3) Watchtower	45	10
4235	150f. (4) South-west corner tower	45	10

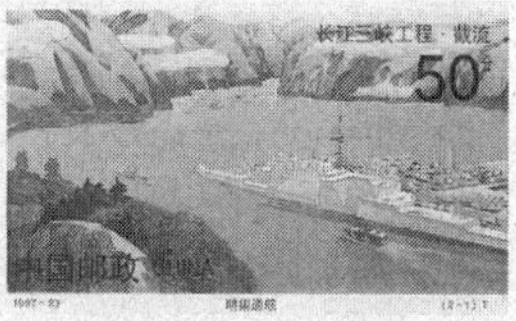

959 Diversion Canal

1997. Three Gorges Project (damming of Yangtse River). Multicoloured.

4236	50f. Type **959**	10	10
4237	50f. Dam under construction	10	10

Nos. 4236/7 were issued together, se-tenant, forming a composite design.

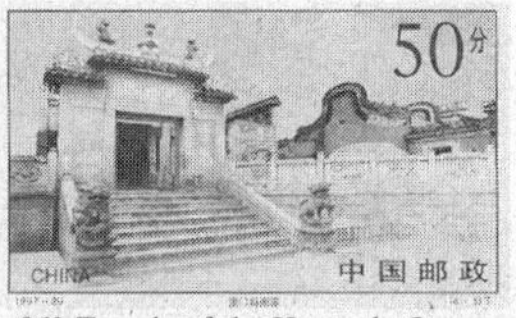

960 Temple of the Heavenly Queen

1997. Macao. Multicoloured.

4238	50f. Type **960**	10	10
4239	100f. Lianfeng (Lotus Peak) Temple	35	10
4240	150f. Great Sanba Archway (former facade of St. Paul's Church)	55	10
4241	200f. Songshan (Pine Hill) Lighthouse	70	10

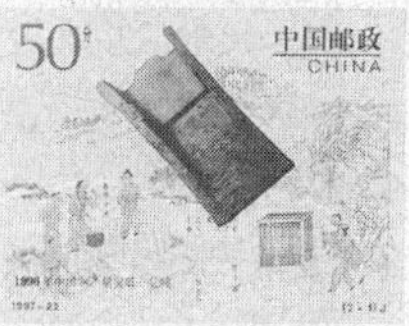

961 Metallurgy in Ancient China

1997. Achievement in 1996 of Production of over 100,000,000 Tons of Steel a Year. Multicoloured.

4242	50f. Type **961**	10	10
4243	150f. Modern steel works	55	10

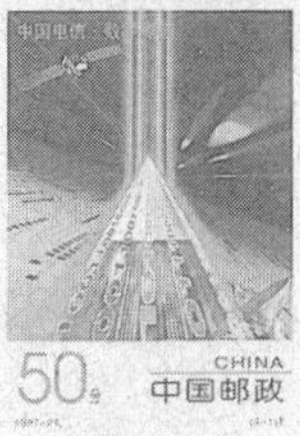

962 Digital Transmission

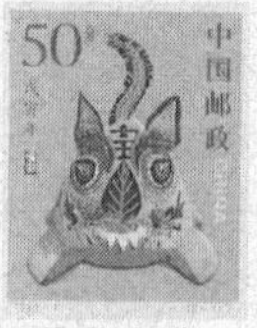

963 Cloth Tiger (Guo Qiuying)

1997. Telecommunications. Multicoloured.

4244	50f. (1) Type **962**	10	10
4245	50f. (2) Program-controlled switch and computer . . .	10	10
4246	150f. (3) Digital communication	60	10
4247	150f. (4) Mobile communication	60	10

1997. Literature. "Outlaws of the Marsh" (5th series). As T **745**. Multicoloured.

4248	40f. (1) Hu Yanzhuo tricks Guan Sheng	10	10
4249	50f. (2) Lu Junyi captures Shi Wengong	10	10
4250	50f. (3) Yan Qing wrestles with Qing Tianzhu . . .	10	10
4251	150f. (4) Hong Tianlei defeats government troops	80	10

1998. New Year. Year of the Tiger. Mult.

4253	50f. Type **963**	10	10
4254	150f. Chinese character . .	60	10

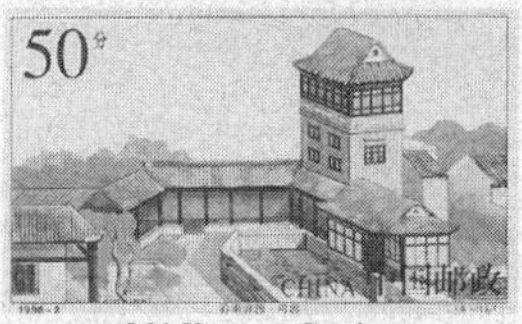

964 Keyuan Garden

1998. Villas and Gardens in Guangdong. Mult.

4255	50f. Type **964**	10	10
4256	50f. Liangyuan Garden . .	10	10
4257	100f. Qinghiu Garden . . .	40	10
4258	200f. Yuyin Villa	45	10

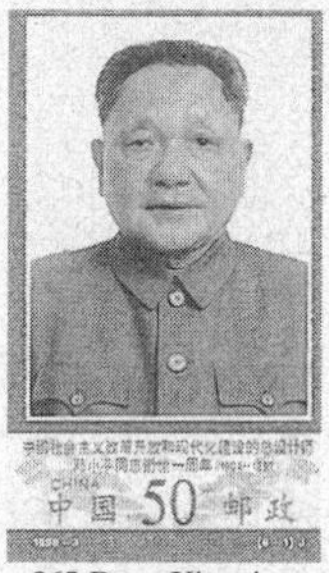

965 Deng Xiaoping

1998. 1st Death Anniv of Deng Xiaoping. Mult.

4259	50f. (1) Type **965**	10	10
4260	50f. (2) During Liberation War	10	10
4261	50f. (3) With Mao Tse-tung	10	10
4262	100f. (4) As Chairman of Military Commission . .	15	10
4263	150f. (5) Making speech . .	45	10
4264	200f. (6) In south China . .	55	20

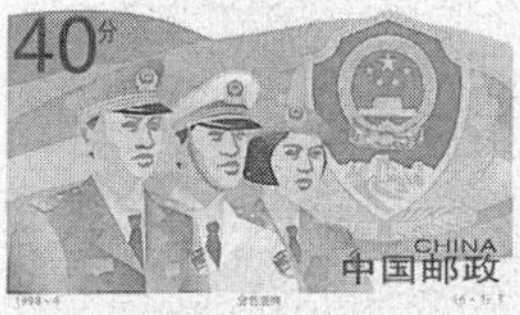

966 Officers and Badge

1998. People's Police. Multicoloured.

4265	40f. (1) Type **966**	10	10
4266	50f. (2) Officers using computer and patrol officers using radio . . .	10	10
4267	50f. (3) Officer and elderly woman	10	10
4268	100f. (4) Officer on traffic control duty	15	10
4269	150f. (5) Officers on fire duty	45	10
4270	200f. (6) Border guards . .	55	15

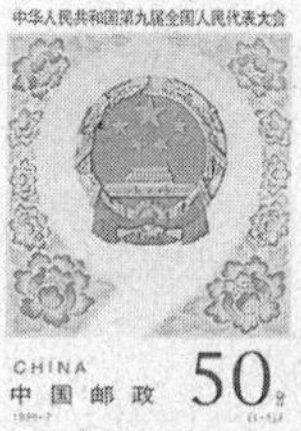

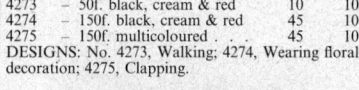

967 State Arms

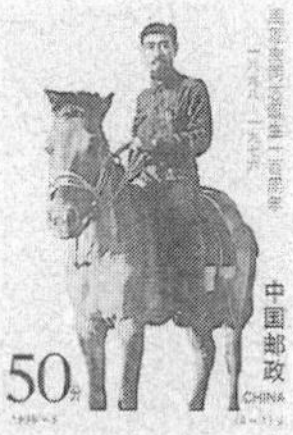

968 Chou En-lai on Horseback

1998. 9th National People's Congress, Peking.

4271	**967** 50f. multicoloured . . .	10	10

1998. Birth Centenary of Chou En-lai.

4272	**968** 50f. black, cream & red	10	10
4273	– 50f. black, cream & red	10	10
4274	– 150f. black, cream & red	45	10
4275	– 150f. multicoloured . . .	45	10

DESIGNS: No. 4273, Walking; 4274, Wearing floral decoration; 4275, Clapping.

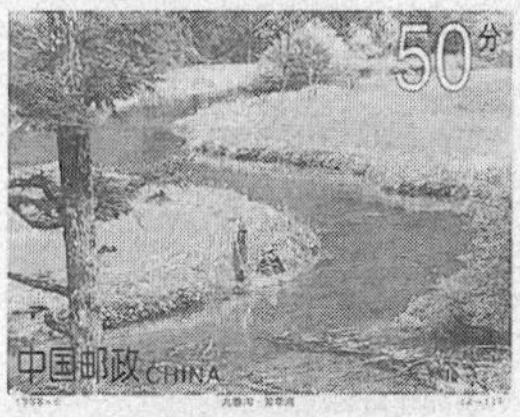

969 Fangcao Lake

1997. World Heritage Site. Jiuzhaigou (nine-village valley). Multicoloured.

4276	50f. (1) Type **969**	. . . . .	10	10
4277	50f. (2) Wuhua Lake	. . . .	10	10
4278	150f. (3) Shuzheng Falls	. .	45	10
4279	150f. (4) Nuorilang Falls	. .	45	10

970 House on Stilts

1998. Dai Architecture, Xishuangbanna. Mult.

4281	50f. (1) Type **970**	. . . . .	10	10
4282	50f. (2) Ornamental well	. .	10	10
4283	150f. (3) Pavilion and streamers	. .	60	10
4284	150f. (4) Pagoda	. . . .	60	10

971 Haikou

1998. Hainan Special Economic Zone. Mult.

4285	50f. (1) Type **971**	. . . . .	10	10
4286	50f. (2) Yangpu	. . . .	10	10
4287	150f. (3) Sanya Phoenix International Airport	. .	60	10
4288	150f. (4) Monument, Yalongwan	. .	60	10

972 Yingtian Academy

1998. Ancient Academies. Multicoloured.

4289	50f. (1) Type **972**	. . . . .	10	10
4290	50f. (2) Songyang Academy	. .	10	10
4291	150f. (3) Yuelu Academy	. .	60	10
4292	150f. (4) Bailu Academy	. .	60	10

973 University Buildings

1998. Centenary of Peking University.

4293	**973** 50f. multicoloured	. . .	10	10

974 Congress Emblem

1998. 22nd U.P.U. Congress, Peking (1999). Mult.

4294	50f. Type **974**	. . . . .	10	10
4295	540f. Emblem (vert)	. . . .	1·10	45

975 Mountain Peaks

1998. Shennongjia (primitive forest). Mult.

4296	50f. (1) Type **975**	. . . .	10	10
4297	50f. (2) River gorge	. . . .	10	10
4298	150f. (3) Forest	. . . . .	45	10
4299	150f. (4) Grasslands	. . .	45	10

976 Great Hall of the People of Chongqing

1998. Chongqing. Multicoloured.

4300	50f. Type **976**	. . . . .	10	10
4301	150f. Chongqing port	. . .	20	10

977 "Tiger"

1998. Paintings by He Xiangning. Mult.

4302	50f. Type **977**	. . . . .	10	10
4303	100f. "Lion" (vert)	. . . .	15	10
4304	150f. "Plum Blossom" (vert)	. .	45	15

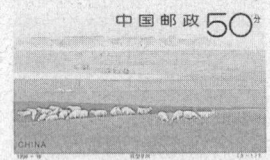

978 Grasslands

1998. Xilingguole Grasslands, Inner Mongolia. Multicoloured.

4305	50f. (1) Type **978**	. . . .	10	10
4306	50f. (2) Meadow steppe	. .	10	10
4307	150f. (3) Forest of poplars and birches	. .	60	10

979 Baishilazi

1998. Jingpo Lake, Heilonjiang. Multicoloured.

4309	50f. (1) Type **979**	. . . .	10	10
4310	50f. (2) Pearl Gate	. . . .	10	10
4311	50f. (3) Mt. Xiaogushan	. .	10	10
4312	50f. (4) Diaoshuilou waterfall	. . .	10	10

Nos. 4309/12 were issued together, se-tenant, forming a composite design.

980 Wurzburg Palace, Germany

1998. World Heritage Sites. Multicoloured.

4313	50f. Type **980**	. . . . .	35	10
4314	540f. Puning Temple, Chengde	. . . . . .	1·25	45

1998. Literature. "The Romance of the Three Kingdoms" by Luo Guanzhong (5th series). As T **763.** Multicoloured.

4315	50f. (1) Liu Bei appoints a Guardian for his Heir at Baidi City (horiz)	. . .	10	10
4316	50f. (2) Zhuge Liang leads his army home	. . . .	10	10
4317	100f. (3) Funeral of Zhuge Liang (horiz)	. . .	15	10
4318	150f. (4) Three Kingdoms united under the reign of Jin	. . . .	45	10

981 Wave and Houses

1998. Flood Relief Fund.

4320	**981** 50f. (+50f.) mult		15	10

No. 4320 includes the se-tenant premium-carrying tab shown in Type **981**. The premium was used to help the victims of floods in the Yangtse and Songhuajiang River areas.

982 Louvre Palace, Paris

1998. Ancient Palaces. Multicoloured.

4321	50f. Type **982**	. . . . .	10	10
4322	200f. Imperial Palace, Peking	. . . . . .	55	10

983 Face

1998. Rock Paintings, Helan Mountains. Mult.

4323	50f. Type **983**	. . . . .	10	10
4324	100f. Hunting	. . . . . .	15	10
4325	150f. Ox	. . . . . .	55	10

984 Vase with Five Spouts (Northern Song Dynasty)

1998. Longquan Pottery. Multicoloured.

4326	50f. (1) Type **984**	. . . .	10	10
4327	50f. (2) Vase with phoenix ears (Southern Song dynasty)	. .	10	10
4328	50f. (3) Double gourd vase (Yuan dynasty)	. .	10	10
4329	150f. (4) Ewer decorated with three fruits (Ming dynasty)	. .	50	10

985 Meridian Gate

1998. Mausoleum of King Yandi, Yanling County, Hunan. Multicoloured.

4330	50f. Type **985**	. . . . .	10	10
4331	100f. Saluting Pavilion	. .	15	10
4332	150f. Tomb	. . . . . .	55	10

986 Men discussing Campaign (Yi Rongsheng)

1998. 50th Anniv of Liberation War. Multicoloured.

4334	50f. (1) Type **986**	. . . . .	10	10
4335	50f. (2) Conquering Jinzhou (Ren Mengzhan, Zhang Hongzan, Li Shuji and Guang Tingbo)	. .	10	10
4336	50f. (3) Battle of Huaihai (Chen Qi, Zhao Guangtao, Chen Jian and Wei Chuyu)	. .	10	10
4337	50f. (4) Liberating Peking (Zhang Ruwei, Deng Jiaju, Wu Changjiang and Shen Yaoyi)	. .	10	10
4338	150f. (5) Supporting the Front (Cui Kaixi)	. . . .	60	10

987 Liu Shaoqi

1998. Birth Centenary of Liu Shaoqi (Chairman of the Republic, 1959–68).

4339	**987** 50f. (1) multicoloured	. .	10	10
4340	– 50f. (2) black, buff and red	. . . . . .	10	10
4341	– 50f. (3) multicoloured	. .	10	10
4342	– 150f. (4) multicoloured		50	10

DESIGNS—VERT: No. 4340, Shaoqi at Seventh National Communist Party Congress. HORIZ: No. 4341, Presented with necklace of flowers while on diplomatic mission; 4342, Working at desk.

988 Chillon Castle, Lake Geneva, Switzerland

1998. Lakes. Multicoloured.

4343	50f. Type **988**	. . . . .	35	10
4344	540f. Bridge 24, Slender West Lake, Yangzhou	. . .	1·25	45

989 Canal Fork

1998. Lingqu Canal. Multicoloured.

4345	50f. Type **989**	. . . . .	10	10
4346	50f. Bridge over canal (vert)	. .	10	10
4347	150f. Lock (vert)	. . . . .	45	10

990 Road into Macao

1998. Macao. Multicoloured.

4348	50f. Type **990**	. . . . .	10	10
4349	100f. Bridge and buildings	.	15	10
4350	150f. Macao Stadium	. . .	50	10
4351	200f. Airport	. . . . .	65	15

991 Deng Xiaoping at Third Plenary Session

1998. 20th Anniv of Third Plenary Session of 11th Central Committee of Chinese Communist Party. Multicoloured.

4352	50f. Type **991**	. . . . .	10	10
4353	150f. Deng Xiaoping Theory and buildings	. . . . .	45	10

993 Ceramic Rabbit (Zhang Chang)

1999. New Year. Year of the Rabbit. Multicoloured.

4355	50f. Type **993**	. . . .	10	10
4356	150f. Chinese character ("Good Luck")	. . . . .	45	10

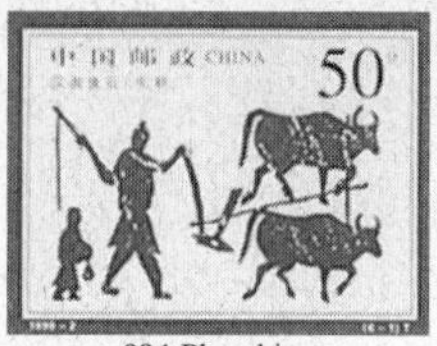

994 Ploughing

1999. Stone Carvings of Han Dynasty.
4357 **994** 50f. (1) green, cream and black 10 10
4358 – 50f. (2) brown, cream and black 10 10
4359 – 50f. (3) blue, cream and black 10 10
4360 – 50f. (4) brown, cream and black 10 10
4361 – 150f. (5) green, cream and black 50 10
4362 – 150f. (6) lilac, cream and black 50 10

DESIGNS: No. 4358, Weaving; 4359, Dancing; 4360, Carriage and outriders; 4361, Jing Ke's attempted assassination of Emperor Qinshihuang; 4362, Goddess Chang'e flying to moon.

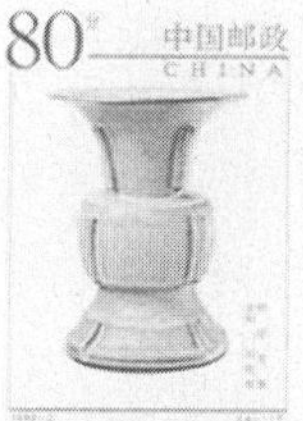

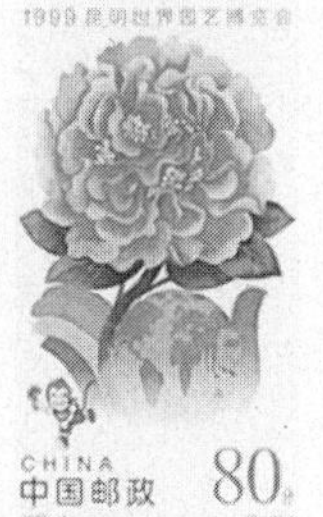

995 Wine Vessel, Northern Song Dynasty

996 Peony and Globe

1999. Ceramics from the Jun Kiln, Henan. Multicoloured.
4363 80f. Type **995** 10 10
4364 100f. Wine vessel, Northern Song Dynasty (different) 15 10
4365 150f. Double-handled stove, Yuan Dynasty 55 10
4366 200f. Double-handled vase, Yuan Dynasty 65 15

1999. World Horticulture Fair, Kunming. Mult.
4367 80f. Type **996** 10 10
4368 200f. Exhibition halls and tree 30 15

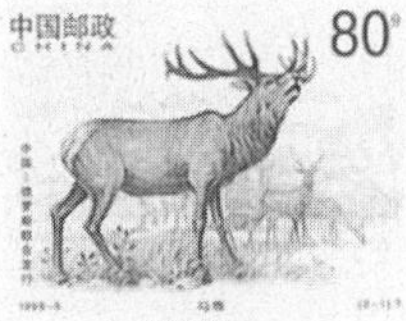

997 Stag

1999. Red Deer. Multicoloured.
4369 80f. (1) Type **997** 10 10
4370 80f. (2) Doe and fawns . . . 10 10

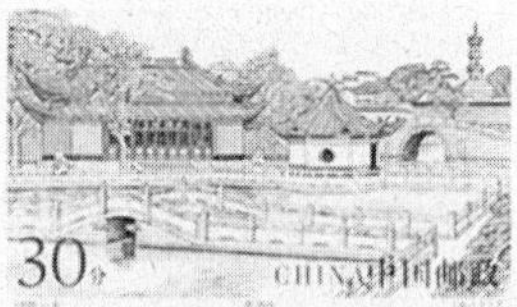

998 Puji Temple

1999. Putuo Mountain, Lianhuayang. Mult.
4371 30f. Type **998** 10 10
4372 60f. Nantian Gate (vert) . . 10 10
4373 60f. Step beach 10 10
4374 80f. Pantuo Rock 10 10
4375 80f. Fanyin Cave (vert) . . 10 10
4376 280f. Fayu Temple 40 20

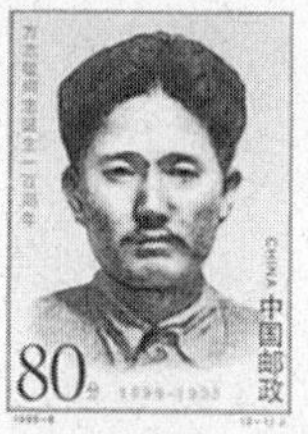

1000 Fang Zhimin (sculpture)

1999. Birth Centenary of Fang Zhimin (revolutionary). Multicoloured.
4378 80y. Type **1000** 10 10
4379 80y. Full-length portrait of Fang Zhimin 10 10

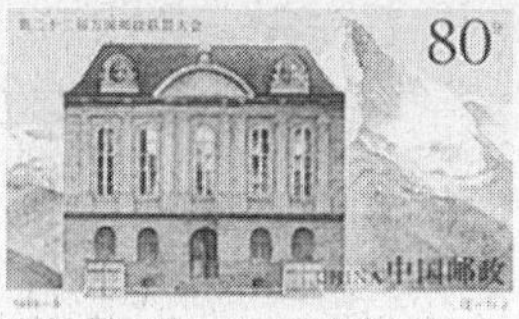

1001 First Congress Building, Berne, Switzerland (1874)

1999. 22nd Universal Postal Union Congress, Peking. Multicoloured.
4380 80f. Type **1001** 10 10
4381 540f. 22nd Congress building, Peking . . . . 1·10 45

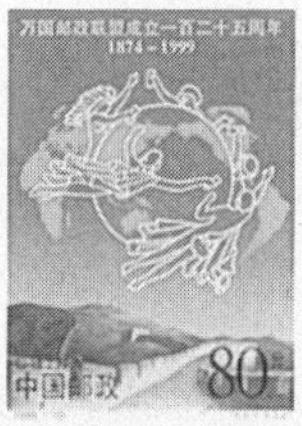

1002 U.P.U. Emblem and Great Wall

1003 Emblem

1999. 125th Anniv of Universal Postal Union.
4383 **1002** 80f. multicoloured . . . 10 10

1999. International Year of the Elderly.
4384 **1003** 80f. multicoloured . . . 10 10

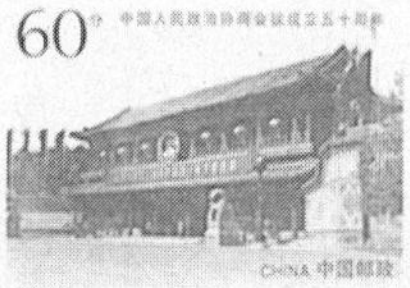

1004 Conference Hall

1999. 50th Anniv of Chinese People's Political Conference. Multicoloured.
4385 60f. Type **1004** 10 10
4386 80f. Mao Tse-tung and emblem (vert) 10 10

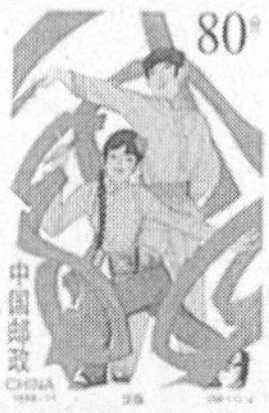

1005 Han Couple

1999. 50th Anniv of People's Republic. Ethnic Groups. Couples from different ethnic groups. Multicoloured.
4387 80f. (1) Type **1005** 10 10
4388 80f. (2) Mongolian 10 10
4389 80f. (3) Hui 10 10
4390 80f. (4) Tibetan 10 10
4391 80f. (5) Uygur 10 10
4392 80f. (6) Miao 10 10
4393 80f. (7) Yi 10 10
4394 80f. (8) Zhuang 10 10
4395 80f. (9) Bouyei 10 10
4396 80f. (10) Korean 10 10
4397 80f. (11) Manchu 10 10
4398 80f. (12) Dong 10 10
4399 80f. (13) Yao 10 10
4400 80f. (14) Bai 10 10
4401 80f. (15) Tujia 10 10
4402 80f. (16) Hani 10 10
4403 80f. (17) Kazak 10 10
4404 80f. (18) Dai 10 10
4405 80f. (19) Li 10 10
4406 80f. (20) Lisu 10 10
4407 80f. (21) Va 10 10
4408 80f. (22) She 10 10
4409 80f. (23) Gaoshan 10 10
4410 80f. (24) Lahu 10 10
4411 80f. (25) Sui 10 10
4412 80f. (26) Dongxiang 10 10
4413 80f. (27) Naxi 10 10
4414 80f. (28) Jingpo 10 10
4415 80f. (29) Kirgiz 10 10
4416 80f. (30) Tu 10 10
4417 80f. (31) Daur 10 10
4418 80f. (32) Mulam 10 10
4419 80f. (33) Qiang 10 10
4420 80f. (34) Blang 10 10
4421 80f. (35) Salar 10 10
4422 80f. (36) Maonan 10 10
4423 80f. (37) Gelao 10 10
4424 80f. (38) Xibe 10 10
4425 80f. (39) Achang 10 10
4426 80f. (40) Primi 10 10
4427 80f. (41) Tajik 10 10
4428 80f. (42) Nu 10 10
4429 80f. (43) Uzbek 10 10
4430 80f. (44) Russian 10 10
4431 80f. (45) Ewenki 10 10
4432 80f. (46) De'ang 10 10
4433 80f. (47) Bonan 10 10
4434 80f. (48) Yugur 10 10
4435 80f. (49) Gin 10 10
4436 80f. (50) Tatar 10 10
4437 80f. (51) Derung 10 10
4438 80f. (52) Oroqen 10 10
4439 80f. (53) Hezhen 10 10
4440 80f. (54) Monba 10 10
4441 80f. (55) Lhoba 10 10
4442 80f. (56) Jino 10 10

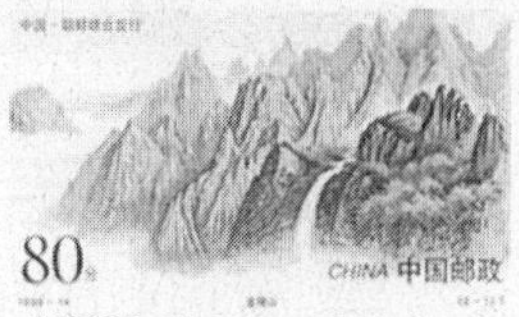

1006 Mt. Kumgang, North Korea

1999. 50th Anniv of China–North Korea Diplomatic Relations. Multicoloured.
4443 80f. (1) Type **1006** 10 10
4444 80f. (2) Mt. Lushan, China 10 10

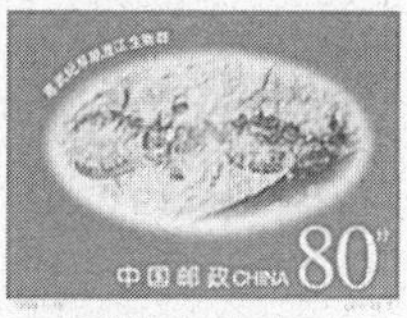

1007 Children reading

1008 Early Cambrian Chengjiang Biota Fossil

1999. 10th Anniv of Project Hope (promotion of rural education).
4445 **1007** 80f. multicoloured . . . 10 10

1999. 50th Anniv of Chinese Academy of Sciences. Multicoloured.
4446 80f. (1) Type **1008** 10 10
4447 80f. (2) Underwater robot 10 10
4448 80f. (3) Head and mathematical equation (vert) 10 10
4449 80f. (4) Astronomical telescope (vert) 10 10

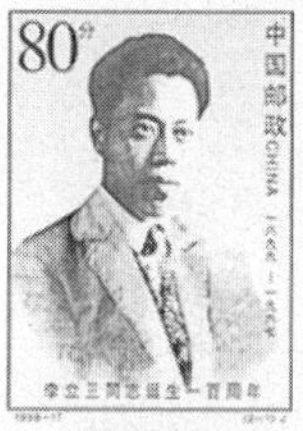

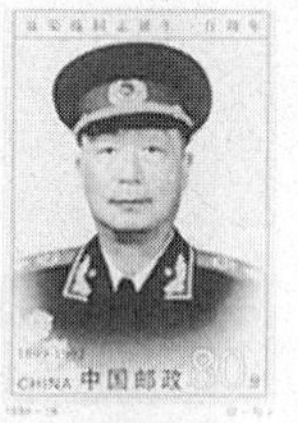

1009 Li Lisan

1011 Rongzhen in Uniform

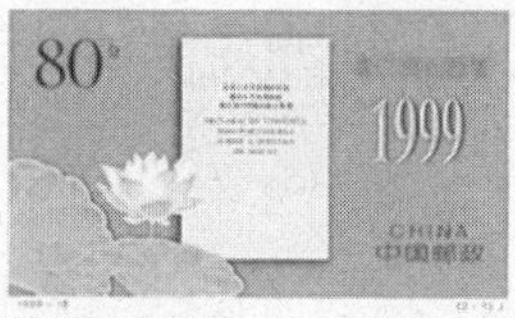

1010 Sino-Portuguese Joint Declaration

1999. Birth Centenary of Li Lisan (trade unionist). Multicoloured.
4450 80f. Type **1009** 10 10
4451 80f. Li Lisan (different) . . 10 10

1999. Return of Macao to China. Multicoloured.
4452 80f. Type **1010** 10 10
4453 150f. Basic Law of Macao Special Region and Great Wall of China 20 10

1999. Birth Centenary of Nie Rongzhen (revolutionary). Multicoloured.
4456 80f. Type **1011** 10 10
4457 80f. Rongzhen in chair . . . 10 10

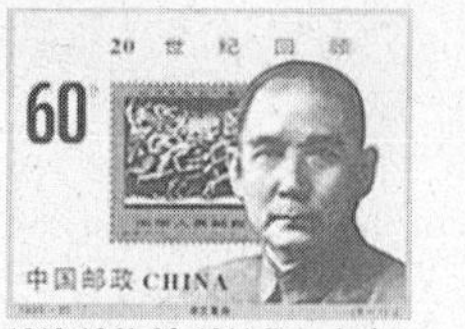

1012 1961 8f. 1911 Revolution Stamp and Dr. Sun Yat-sen

1999. The Twentieth Century. Multicoloured.
4458 60f. (1) Type **1012** 10 10
4459 60f. (2) 1989 8f. May 4th Movement stamp 10 10
4460 80f. (3) 1991 20f. Chinese Communist Party stamp 10 10
4461 80f. (4) 1995 20f. (No. 4013) End of Second World War and of War against Japan stamp 10 10
4462 80f. (5) 1959 20f. People's Republic anniversary stamp and Mao Tse-tung 10 10
4463 200f. (6) 1989 20f. National Defence stamp 35 15
4464 260f. (7) 1996 500f. Pudong Area of Shanghai stamp 35 20
4465 280f. (8) Deng Xiaoping and fireworks (based on 1997 800f. Return of Hong Kong to China stamp) . . 40 25

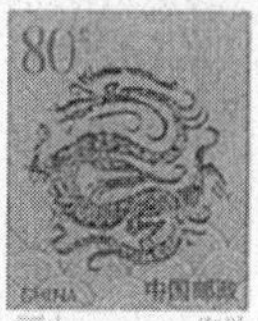

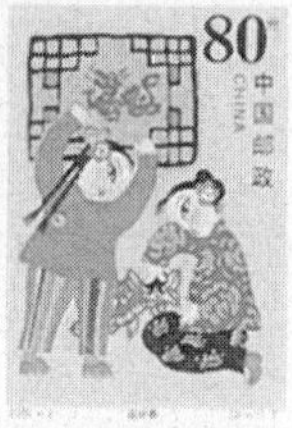

1013 Chinese Dragon

1014 Welcoming the Spring Festival

2000. New Year. Year of the Dragon. Each black, gold and red.
4466 80f. Type **1013** 10 10
4467 2y.80 "The Sun Rising in the Eastern Sky" and Chinese character for dragon 40 25

2000. Spring Festival. Multicoloured.
4468 80f. Type **1014** 10 10
4469 80f. Bidding farewell to the outgoing year 10 10
4470 2y.80 Offering sacrifices to the God of Land 40 25

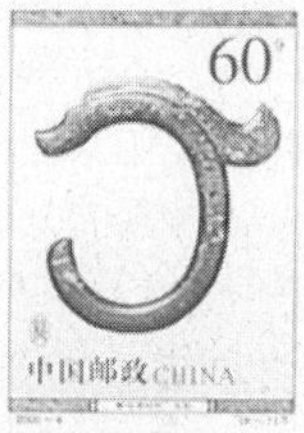

1016 Neolithic Jade Dragon

2000. Chinese Dragon Artefacts. Multicoloured.
4473 60f. (1) Type **1016** 10 10
4474 80f. (2) Dragon-shaped brooch, Warring States 15 10
4475 80f. (3) Eaves tile with carved dragon, Han Dynasty 15 10
4476 80f. (4) Coiled dragon on copper mirror, Tang Dynasty 15 10
4477 80f. (5) Bronze dragon, Jin Dynasty 15 10
4478 2y.80 (6) Dragon decoration from Qing Dynasty Red Sandalwood Throne . . . 45 25

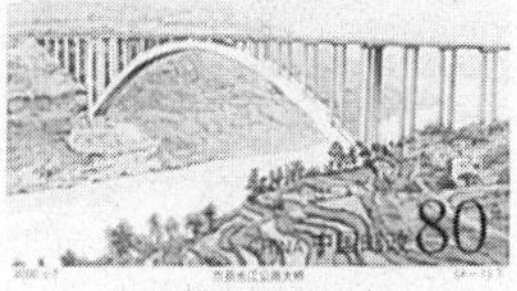

1017 Wanxian Bridge

2000. Road Bridges over the Yangtze River. Mult.
4479 80f. (1) Type **1017** 15 10
4480 80f. (2) Huangshi 15 10
4481 80f. (3) Tongling 15 10
4482 2y.80 (4) Jiangyin 45 25

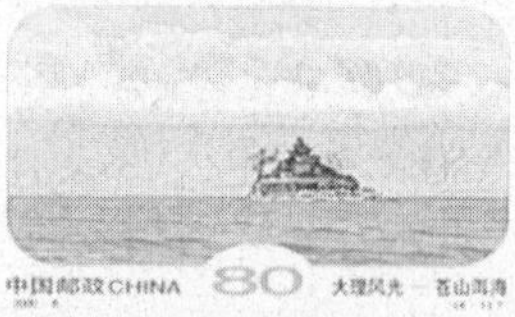

1018 Cangshan Mountain and Erhai Lake

2000. Landscapes of Dali, Yunnan Province. Mult.
4483 80f. (1) Type **1018** 15 10
4484 80f. (2) Three Pagodas, Chongsheng Temple . . . 15 10
4485 80f. (3) Jizu Mountain . . . 15 10
4486 2y.80 (4) Shibao Mountain 45 25

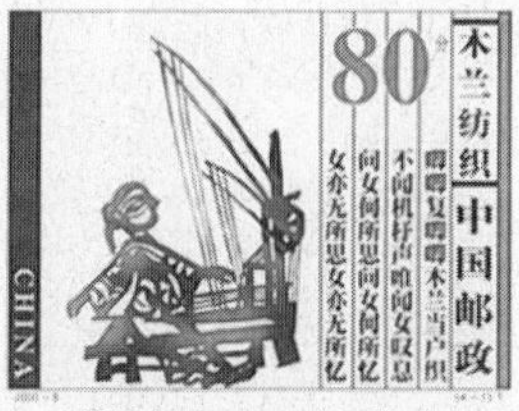

1019 Mulan weaving Cloth

2000. Literature. *Mulan* (folk tale). Multicoloured.
4487 80f. (1) Type **1019** 15 10
4488 80f. (2) Mulan dressed as male soldier 15 10

4489	80f. (3) Mulan on horseback	15	10
4490	80f. (4) Mulan resuming her female identity	15	10

1020 Good Luck Treasure Pagoda

2000. Taer Lamasery, Qinghai Province. Mult.

4491	80f. (1) Type **1020**	15	10
4492	80f. (2) Big Golden Tile Palace	15	10
4493	80f. (3) Big Scripture Hall	15	10
4494	2y.80 (4) Banqen Residence	45	25

1021 Li Fuchan and Cai Chang

2000. Birth Centenaries of Li Fuchan and Cai Chang (revolutionary couple).

4495	**1021** 80f. black, buff and brown	15	10

1022 "Entering a New Century" (Ling Lifei)

2000. New Millennium. Winning Entries in National Children's "Prospects in the New Century" Stamp Design Competition. Mult.

4496	30f. (1) Type **1022**	10	10
4497	60f. (2) "I Build a Bridge to Connect the Mainland with Taiwan" (Wang Yumeng)	10	10
4498	60f. (3) "Palace in a Tree" (Li Zhao)	10	10
4499	80f. (4) "Protecting the Earth" (Chen Zhuo) . .	15	10
4500	80f. (5) "Communications in the New Century" (Qin Tian)	15	10
4501	80f. (6) "Space Travel" (Wang Yiru)	15	10
4502	2y.60 (7) "The Earth gets Younger" (Tian Yuan) .	40	15
4503	2y.80 (8) "World Peace" (Song Zhili)	45	25

1023 Chen Yun

2000. 95th Birth Anniv of Chen Yun (revolutionary). Multicoloured.

4504	80f. (1) Type **1023**	15	10
4505	80f. (2) Chen Yun wearing white jacket and hat (vert)	15	10
4506	80f. (3) Chen Yun wearing black jacket (vert) . . .	15	10
4507	2y.80 (4) Chen Yun . . .	45	25

1024 He-Pot (Chinese wine vessel)

2000. Pots. Multicoloured.

4508	80f. (1) Type **1024** . . .	15	10
4509	80f. (2) Horse milk pot, Kazakhstan	15	10

1025 Great Peak

2000. Laoshan Mountain. Multicoloured.

4510	80f. (1) Type **1025** . . .	15	10
4511	80f. (2) Yangkou Bay	15	10

4512	80f. (3) Beijiu Lake . . .	15	10
4513	2y.80 (4) Taiqing Palace .	45	25

1027 Grandma Carp telling a Story

2000. Small Carp Leap Through Dragon Gate (children's story). Multicoloured.

4516	80f. (1) Type **1027**	15	10
4517	80f. (2) Searching for Dragon Gate	15	10
4518	80f. (3) Uncle Crab helping Carp	15	10
4519	80f. (4) Carp leaping through Dragon Gate . .	15	10
4520	80f. (5) Aunt Swallow delivering a letter	15	10

1028 Financial Central District

2000. Shenzhen Special Economic Zone. Mult.

4526	80f. (1) Type **1028**	15	10
4527	80f. (2) China International New and Hi-Tech Achievement Fair Exhibition Centre	15	10
4528	80f. (3) Yantian Harbour .	15	10
4529	80f. (4) Shenzhen Bay . . .	15	10
4530	2y.80 (5) Shekou Industrial District	15	10

1030 Coconut Forest Bay, Hainan

2000. Beaches. Multicoloured.

4532	80f. (1) Type **1030**	15	10
4533	80f. (2) Paradero seashore, Matanzas, Cuba . . .	15	10

1031 Puppets

2000. Masks and Puppets. Multicoloured.

4534	80f. (1) Type **1031**	15	10
4535	80f. (2) Carnival masks . .	15	10

1032 "Eternal Fidelity" Palace Lamp   **1033** Confucius

2000. Relics from Tomb of Liu Sheng. Multicoloured.

4536	80f. (1) Type **1032** . . .	15	10
4537	80f. (2) Bronze pot with dragon design . . .	15	10
4538	80f. (3) Boshan incense burner with gold inlay .	15	10
4539	2y.80 (4) Rosefinch-shaped cup	15	10

2000. Ancient Thinkers. Each black, red and brown.

4540	60f. (1) Type **1033** . . .	15	10
4541	80f. (2) Mencius	15	10
4542	80f. (3) Lao Zi	15	10
4543	80f. (4) Zhuang Zi . . .	15	10
4544	80f. (5) Mo Zi	15	10
4545	2y.80 (6) Xun Zi	15	10

1034 Launch of *Shenzhou*

2000. Test Flight of *Shenzhou* (spacecraft). Mult.

4546	80f. Type **1034**	15	10
4547	80f. Orbiting Earth	15	10

1035 Meteorological Satellite

2000. 50th Anniv of World Meteorological Organization. Multicoloured.

4548	80f. (1) Type **1035**	15	10
4549	80f. (2) Meteorological equipment and Qinghai–Tibet plateau	15	10
4550	80f. (3) Computers and numbers	15	10
4551	2y.80 (4) Airplane and wind flow diagram	15	10

1036 Scarlet Kaffir Lily   **1037** Jingshu Bell, Western Zhou Dynasty

2000. Flowers. Multicoloured.

4552	80f. (1) Type **1036**	15	10
4553	80f. (2) Noble clivia . . .	15	10
4554	80f. (3) Golden striat kaffir lily	15	10
4555	2y.80 (4) White kaffir lily . .	15	10

2000. Ancient Bells. Multicoloured.

4557	80f. (1) Type **1037**	15	10
4558	80f. (2) Su chime bell, Spring and Autumn Period	15	10
4559	80f. (3) Jingyun bell, Tang Dynasty	15	10
4560	2y.80 (4) Qianlong bell, Qing Dynasty	15	10

1038 Sun, Moon and Observatory   **1039** Snake

2001. New Millennium. Multicoloured.

4561	60f. (1) Type **1038**	10	10
4562	80f. (2) Globe and white dove	15	10
4563	80f. (3) Child's hands, leaf and World map (horiz)	15	10
4564	80f. (4) Silhouette of head and circuit board (horiz)	15	10
4565	2y.80 (5) Sun, stars and sundial	50	30

2001. New Year. Year of the Snake. Multicoloured.

4566	80f. (1) Type **1039**	15	10
4567	2y.80 "Fortune Illuminates all Things" and Chinese character for snake . . .	50	30

1040 Tang Qin

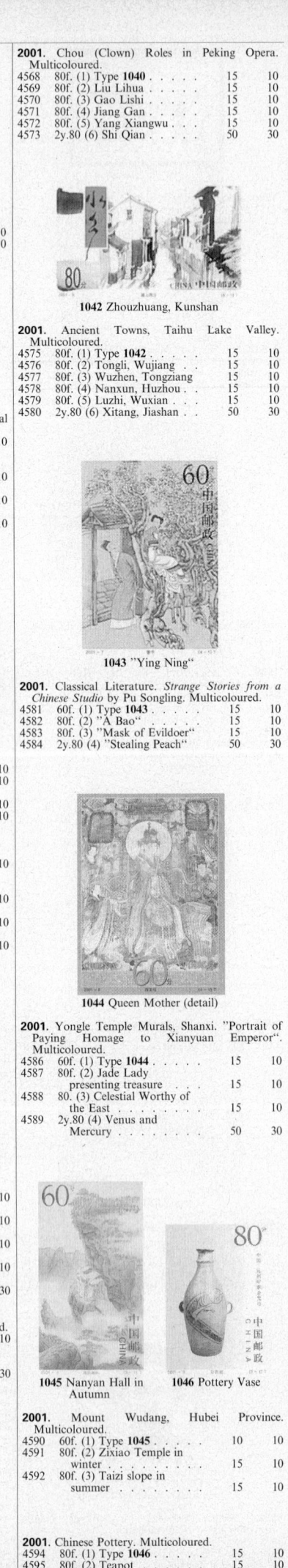

2001. Chou (Clown) Roles in Peking Opera. Multicoloured.

4568	80f. (1) Type **1040**	15	10
4569	80f. (2) Liu Lihua	15	10
4570	80f. (3) Gao Lishi	15	10
4571	80f. (4) Jiang Gan	15	10
4572	80f. (5) Yang Xiangwu . . .	15	10
4573	2y.80 (6) Shi Qian	50	30

1042 Zhouzhuang, Kunshan

2001. Ancient Towns, Taihu Lake Valley. Multicoloured.

4575	80f. (1) Type **1042**	15	10
4576	80f. (2) Tongli, Wujiang . .	15	10
4577	80f. (3) Wuzhen, Tongziang	15	10
4578	80f. (4) Nanxun, Huzhou . .	15	10
4579	80f. (5) Luzhi, Wuxian . . .	15	10
4580	2y.80 (6) Xitang, Jiashan . .	50	30

1043 "Ying Ning"

2001. Classical Literature. *Strange Stories from a Chinese Studio* by Pu Songling. Multicoloured.

4581	60f. (1) Type **1043**	15	10
4582	80f. (2) "A Bao"	15	10
4583	80f. (3) "Mask of Evildoer"	15	10
4584	2y.80 (4) "Stealing Peach" .	50	30

1044 Queen Mother (detail)

2001. Yongle Temple Murals, Shanxi. "Portrait of Paying Homage to Xianyuan Emperor". Multicoloured.

4586	60f. (1) Type **1044**	15	10
4587	80f. (2) Jade Lady presenting treasure . .	15	10
4588	80. (3) Celestial Worthy of the East	15	10
4589	2y.80 (4) Venus and Mercury	50	30

1045 Nanyan Hall in Autumn   **1046** Pottery Vase

2001. Mount Wudang, Hubei Province. Multicoloured.

4590	60f. (1) Type **1045** . . .	10	10
4591	80f. (2) Zixiao Temple in winter	15	10
4592	80f. (3) Taizi slope in summer	15	10

2001. Chinese Pottery. Multicoloured.

4594	80f. (1) Type **1046**	15	10
4595	80f. (2) Teapot	15	10

1047 Dragon Boat Race

2001. Duanwu Dragon Boat Festival. Multicoloured.
4596 80f. (1) Type **1047** 15 10
4597 80f. (2) Vase, mobile and
flowers 15 10
4598 2y.80 (3) Dragon's head and
expulsion of five poisons 50 30

1048 Wang Jinmei

2001. Leaders of the Chinese Communist Party. Multicoloured.
4599 80f. (1) Type **1048** 15 10
4600 80f. (2) Zhao Shiyan . . . 15 10
4601 80f. (3) Deng Enming . . . 15 10
4602 80f. (4) Cai Hesen 15 10
4603 80f. (5) He Shuheng 15 10

1049 Party Flag

2001. 80th Anniv of Chinese Communist Party.
4604 **1049** 80f. red, yellow and
black 15 10

1050 Emblem

2001. Choice of Beijing as 2008 Olympic Host City.
4605 **1050** 80f. multicoloured . . . 15 10

1051 Yinlianzhuitan Waterfall

2001. Waterfalls. Multicoloured.
4606 80f. (1) Type **1051** 15 10
4607 80f. (2) Doupotang
Waterfall (horiz) . . . 15 10
4608 80f. (3) Dishuitan Waterfall 15 10

1052 Pigeon Nest

2001. Beidaihe Summer Resort. Multicoloured.
4610 60f. (1) Type **1052** 10 10
4611 80f. (2) Umbrellas,
Zhonghai Beach . . . 15 10
4612 80f. (3) Sailing dinghies,
Lianfeng Hill . . . 15 10
4613 2y.80 Windsurfers, Tiger
Stone 50 30

1053 "2001" and Emblem

2001. 21st World University Games, Beijing. Multicoloured.
4614 60f. Type **1053** 10 10
4615 80f. "2001" and sports
pictograms 15 10
4616 2y.80 "2001" and globes . . 50 30

1054 Water Diversion Canal

2001. Datong River Diversion Project. Mult.
4617 80f. (1) Type **1054** 15 10
4618 80f. (2) Overland pipes,
Xianming Gorge . . . 15 10
4619 80f. (3) Canal tunnel 15 10
4620 2y.80 (4) Aqueduct,
Zhuanglang River 50 30

1055 Wuhu Bridge over Yangtze River

2001. Wuhu Bridge. Multicoloured.
4621 80f. Type **1055** 15 10
4622 2y.80 Road section of Wuhu
Bridge 50 30

1056 *Paphiopedilum malipoense*

2001. Orchids. Multicoloured.
4623 80f. (1) Type **1056** 15 10
4624 80f. (2) *Paphiopedilum
dianthum* 15 10
4625 80f. (3) *Paphiopedilum
markianum* 15 10
4626 2y.80 (4) *Paphiopedilum
appletonianum* 50 30

MILITARY POST STAMPS

M 225 **M 892 Armed Forces**

1953.
M1593 M **225** $800 yellow, red
and orange . . 85·00 40·00
M1594 $800 yellow, red
and purple . . £500
M1595 $800 yellow, red
and blue . . £28000
Nos. M1593/5 were issued for the use of the Army, Air Force and Navy respectively.

1995. No gum.
M3998 M **892** 20f. multicoloured . . 10 10

POSTAGE DUE STAMPS

D 192 **D 233**

1950.
D1459 D **192** $100 blue 10 85
D1460 $200 blue 10 85
D1461 $500 blue 10 75
D4462 $800 blue . . . . 11·00 30
D1463 $1,000 blue 10 50
D1464 $2,000 blue 10 75
D1465 $5,000 blue 10 80
D1466 $8,000 blue . . . . 15 1·50
D1467 $10,000 blue . . . . 15 2·50

1954.
D1628 D **233** $100 red 80 25
D1629 $200 red 50 25
D1630 $500 red 40 25
D1631 $800 red 25 25
D1632 $1,600 red 25 25

CHINA—TAIWAN (FORMOSA)

A. CHINESE PROVINCE

The island of Taiwan was ceded by China to Japan in 1895 and was returned to China in 1945 after the defeat of Japan. From 1949 Taiwan was controlled by the remnants of the Nationalist Government under Chiang Kai-shek.

1945. 100 sen = 1 yen.
1947. 100 cents = 1 yuan (C.N.C.).

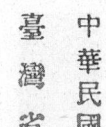

(1) "Taiwan Province,
Chinese Republic"

1945. Optd as Type **1**. (a) On stamps as Nos. J1/3 of Japanese Taiwan. Imperf.
1 J **1** 3s. red . . . . 1·00 4·50
2 5s. green . . . . . 1·00 75
3 10s. blue . . . . . 1·00 75
4 30s. blue . . . . . 5·00 4·50
5 40s. purple . . . . 5·00 3·25
6 50s. grey . . . . . 4·00 2·25
7 1y. green . . . . . 5·00 2·25

(b) On stamps of Japan. Imperf.
8 87 5y. olive (No. 424) . . . 9·00 7·50
9 88 10y. purple (No. 334) . . 15·00 12·00

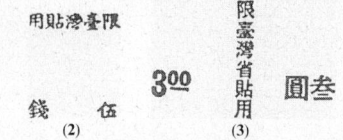

(2) (3)

1946. Stamps of China surch as T **2** with two to four characters in lower line denoting value.
10 – 2s. on 2c. blue (No. 509) 10 1·25
11 – 5s. on 5c. orange (No. 513) 10 50
12 60 10s. on 4c. lilac 10 60
13 – 30s. on 15c. pur (No. 517) 10 75
19 107 50s. on $20 red . . . . 10 1·00
16 58 65s. on $20 green . . . 30 1·00
15 – $1 on 20c. blue (No. 519) 15 1·00
17 58 $1 on $30 brown . . . 30 85
65 60 $2 on 2½c. red 40 75
18 58 $2 on $50 orange . . . 50 80
20 107 $3 on $100 red 10 75
77 103 $5 on $40 orange . . . 30 90
78 107 $5 on $50 violet . . . 40 45
79 $5 on $70 orange . . . 10 1·00
80 $5 on $100 red . . . 40 25
21 $5 on $200 green . . . 10 60
67 82 $10 on $3 yellow . . . 2·00 1·50
82 118 $10 on $150 red . . . 10 65
22 107 $10 on $500 green . . 10 40
66 72 $20 on 2c. green . . . 40 75
71 89 $20 on $3 red . . . . 1·50 1·00
83 118 $20 on $250 violet . . 25 50
23 107 $20 on $700 brown . . 20 50
68 82 $50 on 50c. green . . . 1·25 85
24 107 $100 on $1,000 red . . 85 60
72 89 $100 on $20 pink . . . 40 25
73 94 $100 on $20 red . . . £500
25 107 $100 on $3,000 blue . . 1·00 70
74 94 $200 on $10 blue . . . 2·10 75
70 72 $500 on $30 purple . . 8·00 2·25
81 107 $600 on $100 red . . . 7·50 1·25
69 82 $800 on $4 brown . . . 6·00 2·50
85 118 $1,000 on $20,000 red . 3·25 1·50
75 94 $5,000 on $10 blue . . . 5·25 2·25
76 $10,000 on $20 red . . 5·25 1·75
84 118 $200,000 on $3,000 blue . £425 14·00

1946. Opening of National Assembly, Nanking. Issue of China surch as Type **3**.
26 111 70s. on $20 green . . . 1·50 2·25
27 $1 on $30 blue . . . . 1·50 2·25
28 $2 on $50 brown . . . 1·50 2·25
29 $3 on $100 red . . . . 1·50 2·25

4 President Chiang   **5** Entrance to Dr. Sun
Kai-shek (note   Yat-sen Mausoleum (note
characters to right of   characters above face
head)   value)

1947. President's 60th Birthday.
30 **4** 70s. red . . . . . . 1·50 2·00
31 $1 green . . . . . 1·50 2·00
32 $2 red . . . . . . 1·50 2·00
33 $3 green . . . . . 1·50 2·00
34 $7 orange . . . . . 1·50 2·00
35 $10 red . . . . . . 1·50 2·00

1947. 1st Anniv of Return of Government to Nanking.
36 **5** 50s. green . . . . . 2·00 2·75
37 $3 blue . . . . . 2·00 2·75
38 $7.50 red . . . . . 2·00 2·75
39 $10 brown . . . . . 2·00 2·75
40 $20 purple . . . . . 2·00 2·75
For other stamps as Types **4** and **5**, but with different Chinese characters, see N.E. Provinces Types **7** and **9**.

1947. No gum.
41 169 $1 brown . . . . . 30 1·50
42 $2 brown . . . . . 40 1·25
43 $3 green 40 75
44 $5 orange 40 60
45 $9 blue . . . . . 1·50 2·50
46 $10 red 30 75
47 $20 green 30 50
59 $25 green 50 35
48 $50 purple 40 35
49 $100 blue 40 35
50 $200 brown 40 35
60 $5,000 orange . . . . . 5·50 85
61 $10,000 green . . . . . 5·50 2·25
62 $20,000 brown . . . . . 5·50 2·25
63 $30,000 blue . . . . . 5·50 1·00
64 $40,000 brown . . . . . 4·50 80

6 Sun Yat-sen and   **(7)**
Palms

1948. "Re-valuation" surcharges. Surch as T **7**.
51 **6** $25 on $100 blue . . . 1·00 1·75
52 $300 on $3 green . . . 75 45
53 $500 on $7.50 orange . . 2·75 1·50
54 $1,000 on 30c. grey . . 7·00 3·75
55 $1,000 on $3 green . . 1·25 35
56 $2,000 on $3 green . . 90 45
57 $3,000 on $3 green . . 1·00 1·75
58 $3,000 on $7.50 orange . 65·00 3·00

1949. No value indicated. Stamps of China optd with five Chinese characters, similar to top line of T **2**.
86 146 (–) Orange (Ord. postage) 3·50 75
87 147 (–) Green (Air Mail) . . . 4·00 95
88 148 (–) Mauve (Express) . . . 4·00 1·10
89 149 (–) Red (Registration) . . . 4·00 1·10

PARCELS POST STAMPS

1948. As Type P **112** of China, with six Chinese characters in the sky above the lorry.
P65 $100 green . . . . – 50
P66 $300 red . . . . – 50
P67 $500 olive . . . . – 50
P68 $1,000 black . . . . . . – 50
P69 $3,000 purple . . . . . . – 50
Parcels Post stamps were not on sale in unused condition.

POSTAGE DUE STAMPS

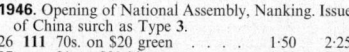

D 7   **(D 8)**   **(D 9)**

1948.
D51 D **7** $1 blue . . . . 2·10 3·00
D52 $3 blue . . . . 2·10 3·25
D53 $5 blue . . . . 2·10 3·00
D54 $10 blue . . . . 2·10 3·25
D55 $20 blue . . . . 2·10 3·00

1949. "Re-valuation" surcharges. Surch as Type D **8**.
D65 D **7** $50 on $1 blue . . . . 5·00 3·50
D66 $100 on $3 blue . . . . 5·00 2·50
D67 $300 on $5 blue . . . . 5·00 2·00
D68 $500 on $10 blue . . . . 5·00 2·00

1949. Handstamped with Type D **9**.
D86 **6** $1,000 on $3 green (No. 55) 42·00 8·00
D87 $3,000 on $3 green (No. 57) 27·00 17·00
D88 $5,000 orange (No. 60) . . 45·00 22·00

B. CHINESE NATIONALIST REPUBLIC

1949. 100 cents = 1 silver yuan (or New Taiwan Yuan).

Silver Yuan Surcharges.

(8) Small figures   **(9)** Large figures

1949. Stamps of Taiwan Province surch. (a) With T **8**.
90	**6**	10c. on $50 purple	32·00	4·50

(b) As T **9** (figures at right).
91	**6**	2c. on $30,000 blue	32·00	11·00
92		10c. on $40,000 brown	70·00	11·00

(10)   **(11)**

1949. Stamps of North Eastern Provinces (Manchuria), surch. as T **10**.
93	**5**	2c. on $44 red	£100	9·00
95		5c. on $44 red	£100	3·00
96		10c. on $44 red	£120	1·90
97		20c. on $44 red	£160	20
98		30c. on $44 red	£200	7·50
99		50c. on $44 red	£240	5·00

1950. Surch. as T **11** on stamp of China but with no indication of value.
100	**169**	$1 on (–) green	£160	14·00
101		$2 on (–) green	£160	13·00
102		$5 on (–) green	£1200	55·00
103		$10 on (–) green	£1500	50·00
104		$20 on (–) green	£3250	£400

1950. Stamps of China surch. (a) As T **8** (figure "5" at left).
105	**118**	5c. on $200,000 purple	4·50	2·25

(b) As T **9** (figures at left).
106	**118**	3c. on $30,000 brown	3·75	4·00
107		3c. on $40,000 green	3·75	3·75
108		3c. on $50,000 blue	4·50	4·50
108a		10c. on $4,000 grey	8·00	6·00
109		10c. on $6,000 purple	13·50	6·75
110		10c. on $20,000 red	13·50	6·75
110a		10c. on $2,000,000 orge	13·50	6·75
110b		20c. on $500,000 mauve	32·00	10·00
110c		20c. on $1,000,000 red	42·00	7·00
110d		30c. on $3,000,000 bistre	50·00	10·00
110e		50c. on $5,000,000 blue	95·00	10·50

> **GUM.** All the following stamps to No. 616 were issued without gum except where otherwise stated.

12 Koxinga

1950. Rouletted. (a) Postage.
111	**12**	3c. grey	2·00	1·00
112		10c. brown	2·00	10
113		15c. yellow	18·00	2·50
114		20c. green	2·00	10
115		30c. red	40·00	9·00
116		40c. orange	4·75	10
117		50c. brown	9·50	10
118		80c. red	4·75	3·00
119		$1 violet	16·00	20
120		$1.50 green	65·00	8·00
121		$1.60 blue	80·00	75
122		$2 mauve	19·00	75
123		$5 turquoise	95·00	4·00

(b) Air. With character at each side of head.
124	**12**	60c. blue	12·00	7·50

13 Peasant and Ballot Box   **15** Peasant and Scroll

1951. Division of Country into Self-governing Districts. Perf or imperf.
125	**13**	40c. red	22·00	10

126		$1 blue	38·00	90
127		$1.60 purple	50·00	75
128		$2 brown	£100	8·50

1951. Silver Yuan surcharges. As T **169** of China but without value, surch as T **14**.
129		$5 on (–) green	42·00	7·00
130		$10 on (–) green	£180	5·00
131		$20 on (–) green	£400	25·00
132		$50 on (–) green	£500	75·00

1952. Land Tax Reduction. Perf or imperf.
133	**15**	20c. orange	35·00	50
134		40c. green	48·00	30
135		$1 brown	75·00	4·00
136		$1.40 blue	£150	2·00
137		$2 grey	£225	38·00
138		$5 red	£375	5·00

16 President and Rejoicing crowds   **(17)**

1952. 2nd Anniv of Re-election of Pres. Chiang Kai-shek. Flag in red and blue. Eight characters in scroll. Perf or imperf.
139	**16**	40c. red	9·50	30
140		$1 green	29·00	2·00
141		$1.60 orange	50·00	1·50
142		$2 blue	£110	38·00
143		$5 purple	£140	2·00

See also Nos. 151/6.

1952. Stamps of China surch. with T **17**.
144	**145**	3c. on 4c. grn (No. 1350)	4·00	2·50
145		3c. on 10c. lilac (No. 1351)	7·50	3·75
146		3c. on 20c. bl (No. 1353)	4·00	2·00
147		3c. on 50c. brown (No. 1354)	12·00	7·50

(18)   **(19)**

1953. T **169** of China, but without value, surch as T **18**.
148		$10 on (–) green	£140	12·00
149		$20 on (–) green	£425	24·00
150		$50 on (–) green	£1400	£600

1953. 3rd Anniv of Re-election of Pres. Chiang Kai-shek. As T **16** but eleven characters in scroll. Flag in red and blue. Perf or imperf.
151		10c. orange	22·00	2·00
152		20c. green	22·00	2·00
153		40c. red	22·00	1·00
154		$1.40 blue	45·00	4·00
155		$2 sepia	£100	6·00
156		$5 purple	£170	15·00

1953. Surch as T **19**.
157	**12**	3c. on $1 violet	85	1·00
158		10c. on 15c. yellow	10·00	1·00
159		10c. on 30c. red	2·75	50
160		20c. on $1.60 blue	2·75	30

20 Doctor, Nurses and Patients   **21** Pres. Chiang Kai-shek

1953. Establishment of Anti-tuberculosis Assn. Cross of Lorraine in red. On paper with coloured network.
161	**20**	40c. brown on stone	4·25	20
162		$1.60 blue on turquoise	20·00	1·00
163		$2 green on yellow	32·00	85
164		$5 red on flesh	80·00	13·50

1953.
165	**21**	10c. brown	1·60	10
166		20c. purple	1·50	10
167		40c. green	1·50	10
168		50c. purple	4·00	10
169		80c. brown	11·00	4·00
170		$1 green	6·00	10
171		$1.40 blue	8·00	60
172		$1.60 red	8·00	10
173		$1.70 green	14·00	7·50
174		$2 brown	8·00	10
175		$3 blue	£140	14·00
176		$4 turquoise	12·00	1·50
177		$5 red	8·00	50
178		$10 green	14·00	4·00
179		$20 purple	48·00	6·00

---

22 Silo Bridge over River Cho-Shui-Chi   **23** Sapling, Tree and Plantation

1954. Completion of Silo Bridge. Various frames.
180	**22**	40c. red	7·00	30
181		$1.60 blue	£100	65
182	**22**	$3.60 black	32·00	3·00
183		$5 mauve	£110	8·00

DESIGN: $1.60, $5, Silo Bridge.

1954. Afforestation Day.
184	**23**	40c. green	12·50	40
185		$10 violet	£100	9·00
186		$20 red	42·00	1·60
187		$50 blue	65·00	5·00

DESIGNS: $10, Tree plantation and houses; $20, Planting seedling; $50, Map of Taiwan and tree.

24 Runner   **25** Douglas DC-6 over City Gate, Taipeh

1954. Youth Day.
188	**24**	40c. blue	14·00	60
189		$5 red	50·00	7·50

1954. Air. 15th Anniv of Air Force Day.
190	**25**	$1 brown	20·00	60
191		$1.60 black	10·00	10
192		$5 blue	20·00	60

DESIGNS: $1.60, Republic F-84G Thunderjets over Chung Shang Bridge, Taipeh. $5, Doves over Chi Kan Lee (Fort Zeelandia) in Tainan City.

26 Refugees crossing Pontoon Bridge   **27** Junk and Bridge

1954. Relief Fund for Chinese Refugees from North Vietnam.
193	**26**	40c.+10c. blue	14·50	1·50
194		$1.60+40c. purple	45·00	20·00
195		$5+$1 green	£100	£100

1954. 2nd Anniv of Overseas Chinese League.
196	**27**	40c. orange	20·00	10
197		$5 blue	10·00	1·75

28 "Chainbreaker"   **(29)**

1955. Freedom Day.
198	**28**	40c. green	4·00	10
199		$1 olive	15·00	3·00
200		$1.60 red	11·00	1·50

DESIGNS: $1, Soldier with torch and flag; $1.60, Torch and figures "1.23".

1955. Surch. as T **29**.
201	**12**	3c. on $1 violet	4·50	1·25
202		20c. on 40c. orange	4·50	15

31 Pres. Chiang Kai-shek and Sun Yat-sen Memorial Building

1955. 1st Anniv of President Chiang Kai-shek's Second Re-election.
203	**31**	20c. olive	3·25	10
204		40c. green	3·25	10
205		$2 red	8·50	40
206		$7 blue	14·50	65

---

(32)   **33** Air Force Badge

1955. Nos. 116/18, 120 and 124 surch. as T **32**. Nos. 212/14 have additional floral ornament below two characters at top.
207	**12**	10c. on 80c. red	4·50	40
208		10c. on $1.50 green	4·50	75
212		20c. on 40c. orange	5·00	10
213		20c. on 50c. brown	5·50	10
214		20c. on 60c. blue	7·50	1·75

1955. Armed Forces' Day.
209	**33**	40c. blue	5·00	10
210		$2 red	19·00	1·00
211		$7 green	16·00	70

35 Flags of U.N. and Taiwan   **36** Pres. Chiang Kai-shek

1955. 10th Anniv of U.N.O.
215	**35**	40c. blue	3·00	10
216		$2 red	7·50	75
217		$7 green	7·50	1·75

1955. President's 69th Birthday. With gum.
218	**36**	40c. brown, blue and red	6·00	30
219		$2 blue, green and red	11·00	1·25
220		$7 green, brown and red	22·00	3·25

37 Sun Yat-sen's Birthplace   **(38)**

1955. 90th Birth Anniv (1956) of Dr. Sun Yat-sen.
221	**37**	40c. blue	4·00	10
222		$2 brown	8·00	1·00
223		$7 red	10·50	1·75

1956. Nos. 1213 and 1211 of China surch. as T **38**.
232	**148**	3c. on (–) mauve	75	40
224	**146**	20c. on (–) orange I	2·25	10
304		20c. on (–) orange II	1·75	10

On No. 232 the characters are smaller and there are leaves on either side of the "3".
(I) Surch. with Type **38**. (II) The characters are below the figures.

39 Old and Modern Postal Transport   **40** Children at Play

1956. 60th Anniv of Postal Service.
225	**39**	40c. red	2·00	15
226		$1 blue	4·00	1·60
227		$1.60 brown	6·00	1·10
228		$2 green	10·00	2·00

1956. Children's Day.
229	**40**	40c. red	1·25	20
230		$1.60 blue	2·75	40
231		$2 red	6·00	1·00

42 Earliest and Latest Steam Locomotives   **43** Pres. Chiang Kai-shek

1956. 75th Anniv of Chinese Railways.
233	**42**	40c. red	5·00	25
234		$2 blue	6·50	55
235		$8 green	10·00	2·00

1956. 70th Birthday of President Chiang Kai-shek. Various portraits of President. With gum.
236	**43**	20c. orange	3·00	10
237		40c. red	3·00	10
238		$1 blue	8·00	20
239		$1.60 purple	10·00	10
240		$2 brown	18·00	20
241		$8 turquoise	42·00	50

SIZES—$21\frac{1}{2}\times30$ mm: 20c., 40c.; $26\frac{1}{2}\times26\frac{1}{2}$ mm: $1, $1.60; $30\times21\frac{1}{2}$ mm: $2, $8.

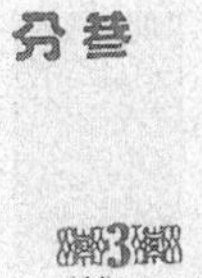

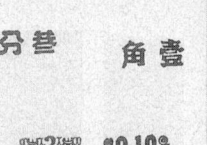

(44)

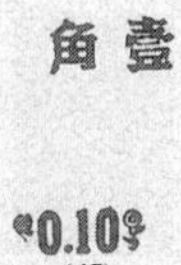

(45)

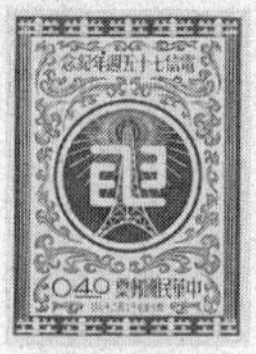
46 Telecommunications Symbols

1956. No. 1212 of China surch with T **44**.
242 **147** 3c. on (–) green 75 15

1956. No. 1214 of China surch with T **45**.
243 **149** 10c. on (–) red 75 15

1956. 75th Anniv of Chinese Telegraph Service.
244 **46** 40c. blue . . . . 1·00 10
245 $1.40 red . . . . 2·00 10
246 $1.60 green . . . . 3·00 10
247 $2 brown . . . . 7·00 20

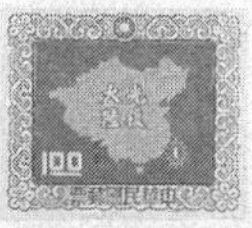
47 Map of China

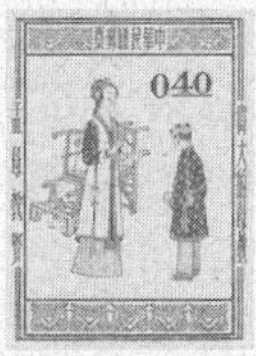
48 Mencius with his Mother

1957. (a) Printed in one colour.
248 **47** 3c. blue 20 10
249 10c. violet . . . . 1·50 15
250 20c. orange . . . . 1·50 10
251 40c. red . . . . 1·50 10
252 $1 brown . . . . 3·00 10
253 $1.60 green . . . . 6·00 15

(b) With frames in blue.
268 **47** 3c. blue 10 10
269 10c. violet 50 10
270 20c. orange 60 10
271 40c. red . . . . 2·00 10
272 $1 brown . . . . 3·75 20
273 $1.60 green . . . . 4·50 10

1957. Mothers' Teaching.
254 **48** 40c. green . . . . 3·00 10
255 – $3 brown . . . . 10·00 50
DESIGN: $3, Marshal Yueh Fei with his mother.

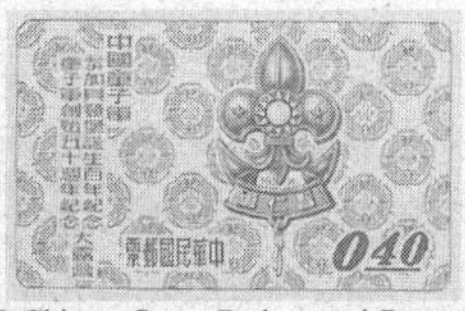
49 Chinese Scout Badges and Rosettes

1957. 50th Anniv of Boy Scout Movement, Jubilee Jamboree and Birth Centenary of Lord Baden-Powell (Founder).
256 **49** 40c. violet 50 10
257 $1 green . . . . 1·75 15
258 $1.60 blue . . . . 2·00 10

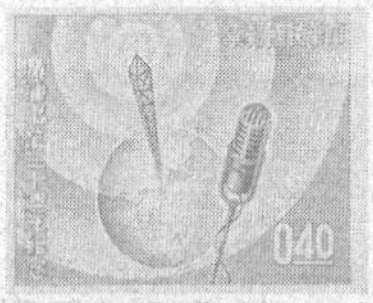
50 Globe, Radio Mast and Microphone

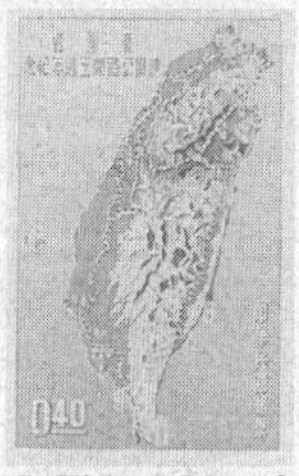
51 Highway Map of Taiwan

1957. 30th Anniv of Chinese Broadcasting Service.
259 **50** 40c. salmon 30 10
260 50c. mauve 75 15
261 $3.50 blue . . . . 1·75 30

1957. 1st Anniv of Taiwan Cross-Island Highway Project.
262 **51** 40c. green . . . . 2·50 10
263 $1.40 blue . . . . 6·25 50
264 $2 sepia . . . . 7·25 50

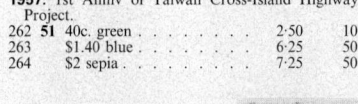

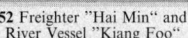

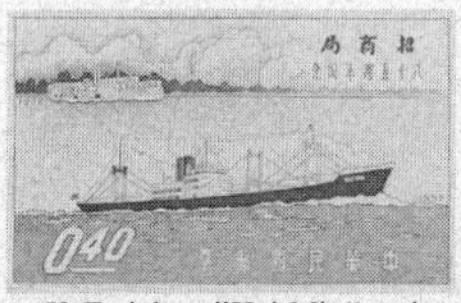
52 Freighter "Hai Min" and River Vessel "Kiang Foo"

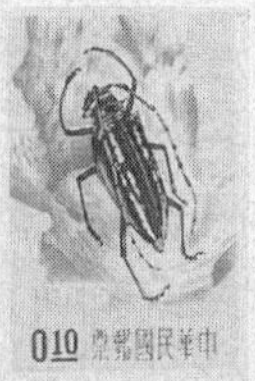
53 "Batocera lineolata" (longhorn beetle)

1957. 85th Anniv of China Merchants' Steam Navigation Co.
265 **52** 40c. blue 80 10
266 80c. purple . . . . 2·00 25
267 $2.80 red . . . . 3·00 40

1958. Insects. Multicoloured. With gum.
274 10c. Type **53** 80 25
275 40c. "Papilio maraho" (butterfly) . . . . 1·00 10
276 $1 Atlas moth . . . . 1·75 20
277 $1.40 "Erasmia pulchella" (moth) . . . . 4·00 40
278 $1.60 "Cheirotonus macleayi" (beetle) . . . . 5·00 20
279 $2 Great mormon (butterfly) 6·00 60

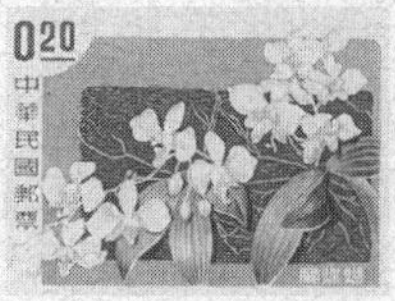
54 "Phalaenopsis amabilis"

1958. Taiwan Orchids. Orchids in natural colours; backgrounds in colours given. With gum.
280 **54** 20c. brown . . . . 1·75 10
281 – 40c. violet . . . . 1·75 10
282 – $1.40 purple . . . . . . 3·75 20
283 – $3 blue . . . . 6·00 35
ORCHIDS—VERT: 40c. "Laeliacattleya"; $1.40, "Cycnoches chlorochilon klotzsch". HORIZ: $3, "Dendrobium phalaenopsis".

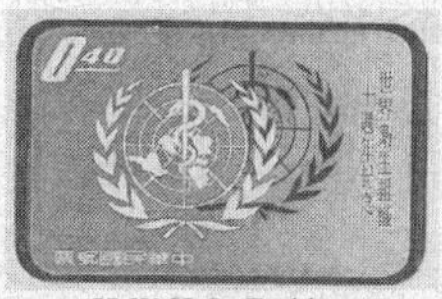
55 W.H.O. Emblem

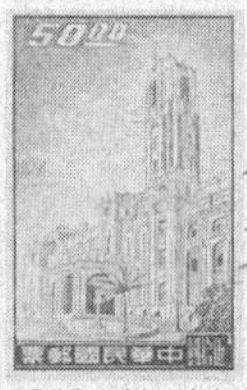
56 Presidential Mansion, Taipeh

1958. 10th Anniv of W.H.O.
284 **55** 40c. blue 20 10
285 $1.60 red 70 15
286 $2 purple . . . . 1·10 20

1958.
290a **56** $5 green . . . . 8·00 10
290b $5.60 violet . . . . 8·00 30
290c $6 orange . . . . 8·00 10
290d $10 green . . . . 7·50 10
290e $20 red . . . . 13·50 10
289 $50 brown . . . . 60·00 8·00
290 $100 blue . . . . £120 10·00

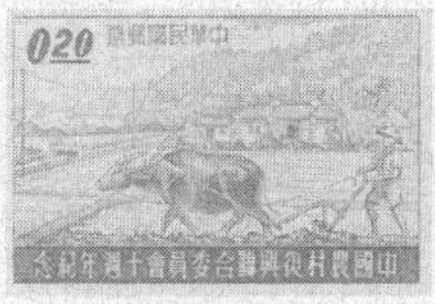
58 Ploughman

1958. 10th Anniv of Joint Commission on Chinese Rural Reconstruction.
291 **58** 20c. green 60 10
292 40c. black 75 10
293 $1.40 purple . . . . 2·25 10
294 $3 blue . . . . 3·75 30

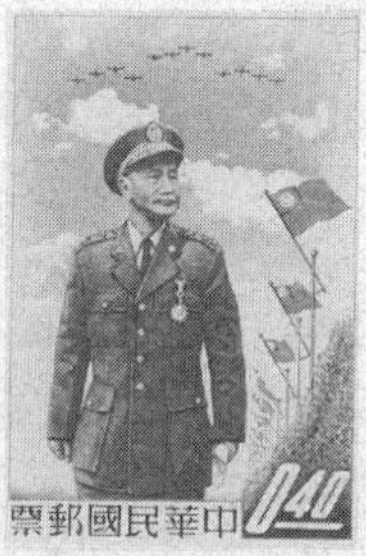
59 President Chiang Kai-shek Reviewing Troops

1958. 72nd Birthday of President Chiang Kai-shek and National Day Review. With gum.
295 **59** 40c. multicoloured . . . . 1·25 10

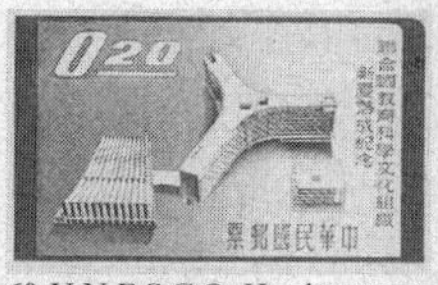
60 U.N.E.S.C.O. Headquarters, Paris

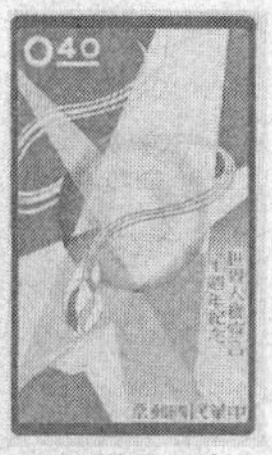
61 Flame of Freedom encircling Globe

1958. Inaug of U.N.E.S.C.O. Headquarters.
296 **60** 20c. blue 30 10
297 40c. green 80 10
298 $1.40 red 80 10
299 $3 purple . . . . 1·25 25

1958. 10th Anniv of Declaration of Human Rights.
300 **61** 40c. green 35 10
301 60c. sepia 35 10
302 $1 red 80 10
303 $3 blue . . . . 1·10 25

1958. No. 192 surch **350**.
305 $3.50 on $5 blue . . . . . . 7·00 2·00

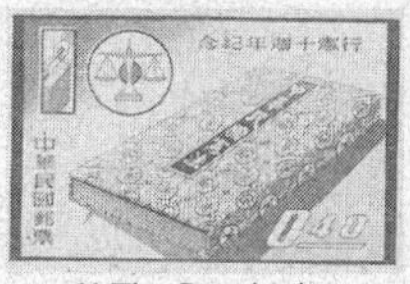
64 The Constitution

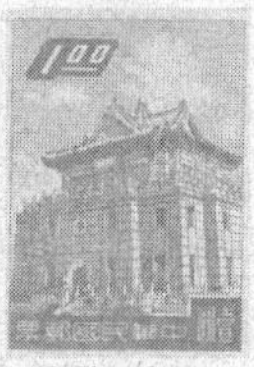
65 Chu Kwang Tower, Quemoy

1958. 10th Anniv of Constitution.
306 **64** 40c. green . . . . 1·10 10
307 50c. purple . . . . 1·25 10
308 $1.40 red . . . . 4·00 10
309 $3.50 blue . . . . 4·00 30

1959.
310 **65** 3c. orange 10 10
311 5c. olive 50 10
312 10c. lilac 10 10
313 20c. blue 10 10
314 40c. brown 10 10
315 50c. turquoise 80 10
316 $1 red 80 10
317 $1.40 green . . . . 3·00 10
318 $2 myrtle . . . . 3·00 10
319 $2.80 mauve . . . . 9·00 60
320 $3 slate . . . . 5·00 10
See also Nos. 367/82f.

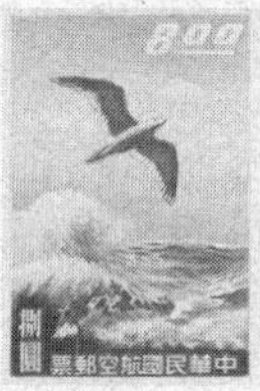
66 Slaty-backed Gull

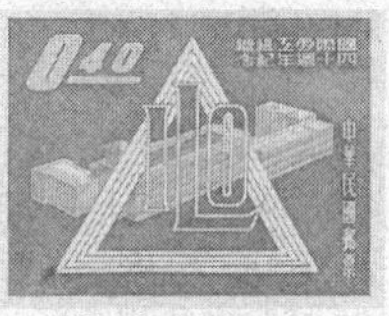
67 I.L.O. Emblem and Headquarters, Geneva

1959. Air. With gum.
321 **66** $8 black, blue and green 5·50 50

1959. 40th Anniv of I.L.O.
322 **67** 40c. blue 60 10
323 $1.60 brown 65 10
324 $3 green 75 10
325 $5 red 80 25

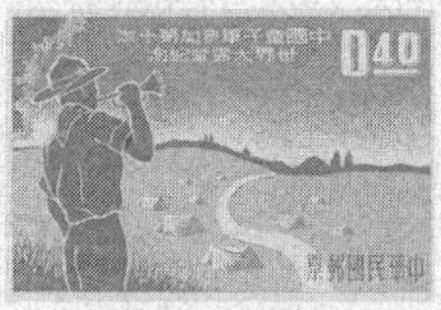
68 Scout Bugler

1959. 10th World Scout Jamboree, Manila.
326 **68** 40c. red 65 10
327 50c. blue . . . . 1·50 30
328 $5 green . . . . 3·00 75

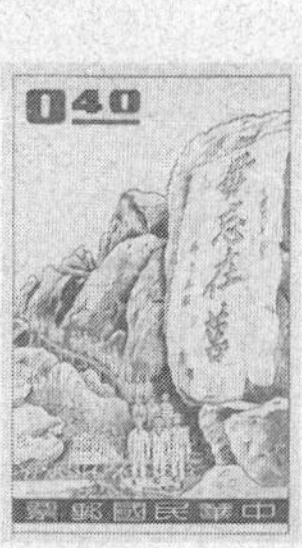
69 Inscribed Rock on Mt. Tai-wu, Quemoy

1959. Defence of Quemoy (Kinmen) and Matsu Islands, 1958.
329 **69** 40c. brown 40 10
330 – $1.40 blue . . . . 1·00 15
331 – $2 green . . . . 2·00 50
332 **69** $3 blue . . . . 3·00 50
DESIGN—($41\times23\frac{1}{2}$ mm): $1.40, $2, Map of Taiwan, Quemoy and Matsu Islands.

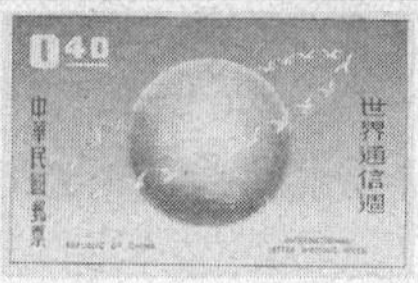
70

1959. International Correspondence Week.
333 **70** 40c. blue 85 10
334 $1 red 85 15
335 $2 sepia 85 10
336 $3.50 red . . . . 1·25 30

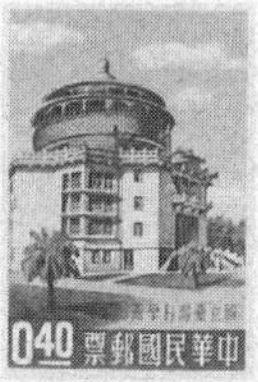
71 National Science Hall

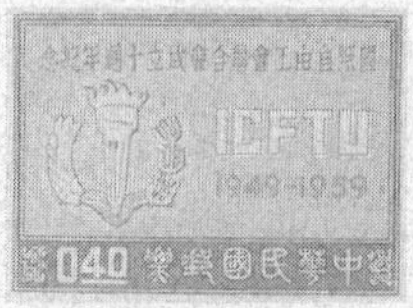
72 Confederation Emblem

1959. Inauguration of Taiwan National Science Hall. With gum.
337 **71** 40c. multicoloured . . . . 1·50 10
338 – $3 mult (different view) . . 2·75 35

1959. 10th Anniv of International Confederation of Free Trade Unions.
339 **72** 40c. green . . . . 1·10 10
340 $1.60 purple . . . . 1·25 10
341 $3 orange . . . . 1·50 20

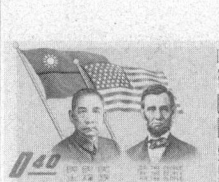

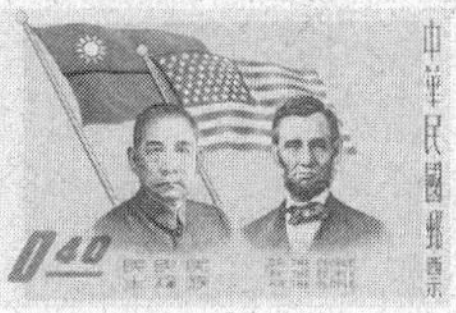
73 Sun Yat-sen and Abraham Lincoln

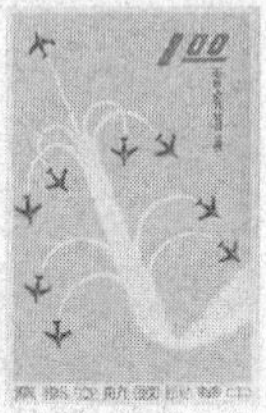
74 "Bomb Burst" by Thunder Tiger Aerobatic Squadron

1959. 150th Birth Anniv of Lincoln. With gum.
342 **73** 40c. multicoloured . . . 30 10
343 $3 multicoloured 50 25

1960. Air. Chinese Air Force Commem. With gum.
344 **74** $1 multicoloured . . . . . 7·00 75
345 – $2 multicoloured . . . . . 6·00 30
346 – $5 multicoloured . . . . . 8·00 1·10
DESIGNS—HORIZ: (Various aerobatics): $2, Loop; $5, Diamond formation flying over jet fighter.

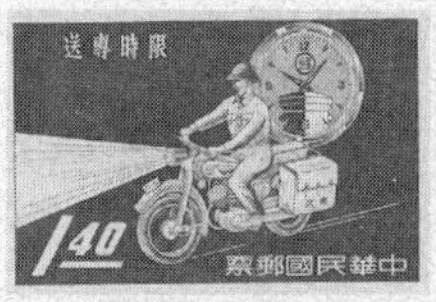
75 Night Delivery

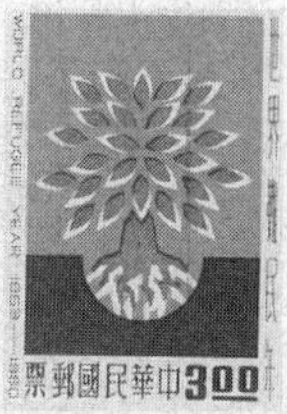
76 "Uprooted Tree"

1960. Introduction of "Prompt Delivery" and "Postal Launch" Services.
347 **75** $1.40 purple . . . . . . 1·75 30
348 $1.60 blue "Yu-Khi" (postal launch) . . . . . 1·75 50

1960. World Refugee Year. With gum.
349 **76** 40c. green, brown & black 30 10
350 $3 green, orange & black 40 25

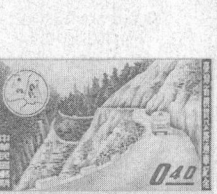

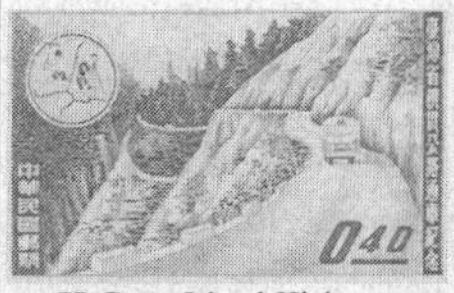
77 Cross-Island Highway

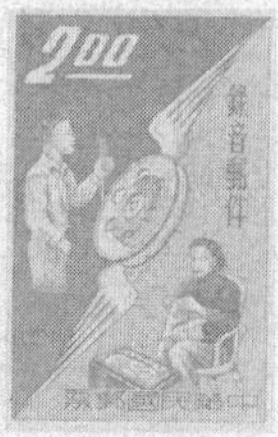
79 Winged Tape-reel

1960. Inaug of Taiwan Cross-Island Highway.
351 **77** 40c. green 60 10
352 – $1 blue . . . . 3·00 20

353   – $2 purple . . . . 1·75   15
354 **77** $3 brown . . . . 3·00   25
DESIGN—VERT: $1, $2, Tunnels on the Highway.

1960. Visit of Pres. Eisenhower. Nos. 331/2 optd
**WELCOME U.S. PRESIDENT DWIGHT D.
EISENHOWER 1960** in English and Chinese.
355   – $2 green . . . . 1·75   1·00
356 **69** $3 blue . . . . 2·00   1·00

1960. Phonopost (tape-recordings) Service.
357 **79** $2 red . . . . 1·75   20

80 "Flowers and Red-billed Blue Magpies" (after Hsiao Yung)
81 Youth Corps Flag and Summer Activities

1960. Ancient Chinese Paintings from Palace Museum Collection (1st series). With gum.
358   – $1 multicoloured . . . . 5·50   40
359   – $1.40 multicoloured . . . 9·50   75
360 **80** $1.60 multicoloured . . . 13·00   1·90
361   – $2 multicoloured . . . 17·00   2·10
PAINTINGS—HORIZ: $1, "Two Riders" (after Wei Yen). $1.40, "Two Horses and Groom" (after Han Kan). $2, "A Pair of Green-winged Teals in a Rivulet" (after Monk Hui Ch'ung).
See also Nos. 451/4, 577/80 and 716/19.

1960. Youth Summer Activities.
362 **81** 50c. green . . . . 1·10   10
363   – $3 brown . . . . 1·40   30
DESIGN—HORIZ: $3, Youth Corps Flag and other summer activities.

82 "Forest Cultivation"
83 Chu Kwang Tower, Quemoy

1960. 5th World Forestry Congress, Seattle. Multicoloured. With gum.
364 **82** $1 Type 82 . . . . 2·50   10
365   – $2 "Forest Protection" (trees and sika deer) . . . . . 3·75   65
366   – $3 "Lumber Production" (cable railway) . . . . 4·50   30

1960. As T **65** but redrawn.
367 **83** 3c. brown 10   10
382   – 10c. green . . . . . . 1·25   15
368   – 40c. violet 10   10
369   – 50c. orange 25   10
370   – 60c. purple 15   10
371   – 80c. green 10   10
372   – $1 green . . . . . . 2·00   10
373   – $1.20 green . . . . . 1·00   10
374   – $1.50 blue . . . . . 1·25   10
375   – $2 red 90   10
376   – $2.50 blue 90   15
377   – $3 green . . . . . 1·50   10
378   – $3.20 brown . . . . 5·00   10
379   – $3.60 blue . . . . 4·00   20
382f   – $4 green . . . . . 6·00   15
380   – $4.50 red . . . . . 5·00   10

84 Diving
85 Bronze Wine Vase (Shang Dynasty)

1960. Sports. With gum.
383 **84** 50c. brown, yellow & blue . 60   10
384   – 80c. violet, yellow & purple . 60   10
385   – $2 multicoloured . . . . . 1·40   10
386   – $2.50 black and orange . . 1·60   25
387   – $3 multicoloured . . . . 2·50   35
388   – $3.20 multicoloured . . . 4·50   40
DESIGNS: 80c. Discus-throwing. $2, Basketball. $2.50, Football. $3, Hurdling. $3.20, Sprinting.

1961. Ancient Chinese Art Treasures (1st series). With gum.
389 **85** 80c. multicoloured . . . . 1·75   10
390   – $1 indigo, blue and red . . 3·50   20

391   – $1.20 blue, brown & yellow . 3·50   25
392   – $1.50 brown, blue & mauve . 4·00   70
393   – $2 brown, violet and green . 4·00   40
394   – $2.50 black, lilac and blue . 5·00   60
DESIGNS: $1, Bronze cauldron (Chou); $1.20, Porcelain vase (Sung); $1.50, Jade perforated tube (Chou); $2, Porcelain jug (Ming); $2.50, Jade flower vase (Ming).
See also Nos. 408/13 and 429/34.

86 Farmer and Mechanical Plough
87 Mme. Chiang Kai-shek

1961. Agricultural Census.
395 **86** 80c. purple 60   10
396   – $2 green . . . . 3·00   75
397   – $3.20 red . . . . 4·50   50

1961. 10th Anniv (1960) of Chinese Women's Anti-Aggression League. With gum.
398 **87** 80c. black, red & turquoise . 1·00   10
399   – $1 black, red and green . . 2·75   15
400   – $2 black, red and brown . . 2·75   15
401   – $3.20 black, red and purple . 4·50   1·10

88 Taiwan Lobster
89 Jeme Tien-yao and Locomotive

1961. Mail Order Service.
402 **88** $3 myrtle . . . . 5·50   75

1961. Birth Centenary of Jeme Tien-yao (railway engineer).
403   – 80c. violet . . . . 2·00   15
404 **89** $2 black . . . . 5·00   60
DESIGN: 80c. As Type **89** but locomotive heading right.

90 Pres. Chiang Kai-shek
91 Convair 880 Jetliner ("The Mandarin Jet"), Biplane and Flag

1961. 1st Anniv of Chiang Kai-shek's Third Term Inauguration. With gum.
405   – 80c. multicoloured . . . . 1·25   10
406 **90** $2 multicoloured . . . . . 5·75   1·00
DESIGN—HORIZ: 80c. Map of China inscr (in Chinese) "Recovery of the Mainland".

1961. 40th Anniv of Chinese Civil Air Service. With gum.
407 **91** $10 multicoloured . . . . 5·50   30

1961. Ancient Chinese Art Treasures (2nd issue). As T **85**. With gum.
408   – 80c. multicoloured . . . . 2·00   10
409   – $1 blue, brown and bistre . . 4·00   20
410   – $1.50 blue and salmon . . 6·25   75
411   – $2 red, black and blue . . 9·25   25
412   – $4 blue, sepia and red . . 11·00   45
413   – $4.50 brown, sepia and blue . 11·00   1·75
DESIGNS—VERT: 80c. Palace perfumer (Ching); $1, Corn vase (Warring States); $2, Jade tankard (Sung). HORIZ: $1.50, Bronze bowl (Chou); $4, Porcelain bowl (Southern Sung); $4.50, Jade chimera (Han).

92 Sun Yat-sen and Chiang Kai-shek
93 Lotus Lake

1961. 50th National Day. With gum.
414 **92** 80c. brown, blue and grey . 1·50   10
415   – $5 multicoloured . . . . 4·50   1·00
DESIGN—HORIZ: $5, Map and flag.

1961. Taiwan Scenery. Multicoloured. With gum.
416   80c. Pitan (Green Lake) (vert) . 6·75   10
417   $1 Type **93** . . . . . . 11·00   50
418   $2 Sun-Moon Lake . . . . . 13·00   30
419   $3.20 Wulai Waterfall (vert) . 17·00   75

94 Steel Furnace
95 Atomic Reactor, National Tsing Hwa University

1961. Taiwan Industries. With gum.
420   – 80c. indigo, brown & blue . 1·75   10
421 **94** $1.50 multicoloured . . . 3·00   60
422   – $2.50 multicoloured . . 4·75   55
423   – $3.20 indigo, brown & blue 7·00   50
DESIGNS—VERT: 80c. Oil refinery. $2.50, Aluminium manufacture. HORIZ: $3.20, Fertilizer plant.

1961. 1st Taiwan Atomic Reactor Inauguration. Multicoloured. With gum.
424   80c. Type **95** . . . . . . 1·10   10
425   $2 Interior of reactor . . . 4·00   1·00
426   $3.20 Reactor building (horiz) 4·50   75

96 Telegraph Wires and Microwave Reflector Pylons
97 Postal Segregating, Facing and Cancelling Machine

1961. 80th Anniv of Chinese Telecommunications. Multicoloured. With gum.
427   80c. Type **96** . . . . . . 1·00   10
428   $3.20 Microwave parabolic antenna (horiz) . . . . 2·75   70

1962. Ancient Chinese Art Treasures (3rd issue). As T **85**. With gum.
429   80c. brown, violet and red . . 7·00   10
430   $1 purple, brown and blue . 9·50   15
431   $2.40 blue, brown and red . . 24·00   40
432   $3 multicoloured . . . . . 60·00   1·50
433   $3.20 red, green and blue . . 65·00   15
434   $3.60 multicoloured . . . . 60·00   1·50
DESIGNS—VERT: 80c. Jade topaz twin wine vessel (Chiang). $1, Bronze pouring vase (Warring States). $2.40, Porcelain vase (Ming). $3, Tsun bronze wine vase (Shang). $3.20, Porcelain jar (Ching). $3.60, Jade perforated disc (Han).

1962.
435 **97** 80c. purple . . . . 1·60   10

98 Mt. Yu Weather Station
99 Distribution of Milk and U.N. Emblem

1962. World Meteorological Day.
436 **98** 80c. brown 75   10
437   – $1 blue . . . . 1·50   40
438   – $2 green . . . . 1·75   75
DESIGNS—HORIZ: $1, Route-map of Typhoon Pamela. VERT: $2, Weather balloon passing globe.

1962. 15th Anniv of U.N.I.C.E.F.
439 **99** 80c. red 40   10
440   – $3.20 green . . . . . . 1·75   60

100 Campaign Emblem
101 Yu Yu-jen (journalist)

1962. Malaria Eradication. With gum.
441 **100** 80c. red, green and blue . . 1·10   10
442   – $3.60 brown, grn & dp brn . . . . 1·60   25

1962. "Elder Reporter" Yu Yu-jen Commemoration. With gum.
443 **101** 80c. sepia and pink . . . 1·60   25

102 Koxinga
103 Co-operative Emblem

1962. Tercentenary of Koxinga's Recovery of Taiwan. With gum.
444 **102** 80c. purple . . . . 3·25   10
445   – $2 green . . . . 6·00   35

1962. 40th International Co-operative Day.
446 **103** 80c. brown 75   10
447   – $2 lilac . . . . 2·00   35
DESIGN: $2, Global handclasp.

104 U.N.E.S.C.O. Symbols
105 Emperor T'ai Tsu (Ming Dynasty)

1962. U.N.E.S.C.O. Activities Commem.
448 **104** 80c. mauve 50   10
449   – $2 lake . . . . 1·50   35
450   – $3.20 green . . . . . . 1·50   25
DESIGNS—HORIZ: $2, U.N.E.S.C.O. emblem on open book. $3.20, Emblem linking hemispheres.

1962. Ancient Chinese Paintings from Palace Museum Collection (2nd series). Emperors. Multicoloured. With gum.
451   80c. T'ai Tsung (Tang) . . . 12·50   10
452   $2 T'ai Tsu (Sung) . . . . 42·00   4·75
453   $3.20 Genghis Khan (Yuan) . 55·00   5·00
454   $4 Type **105** . . . . . 60·00   9·25

106 "Lions" Emblem and Activities
107 Pole Vaulting

1962. 45th Anniv of Lions International With gum.
455 **106** 80c. multicoloured . . . . 1·50   10
456   – $3.60 multicoloured . . . 2·50   60

1962. Sports. With gum.
457 **107** 80c. brown, black & blue . 1·25   10
458   – $3.20 multicoloured . . . 3·00   40
DESIGN—HORIZ: $3.20, Rifle shooting.

108 Young Farmers
109 Liner

1962. 10th Anniv of Chinese 4-H Clubs.
459 **108** 80c. red . . . . 1·00   10
460   – $3.20 green . . . . . . 1·75   30
DESIGN: $3.20, 4-H Clubs emblem.

1962. 90th Anniv of China Merchants' Steam Navigation Co. Multicoloured. With gum.
461   80c. Type **109** . . . . . 1·75   10
462   $3.60 Freighter "Hai Min" and Pacific route-map (horiz) . . . . 4·50   70

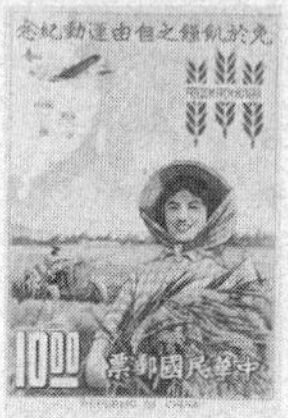
110 Harvesting

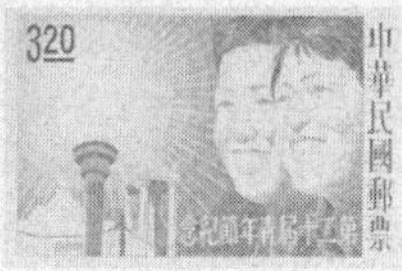
111 Youth, Girl, Torch and Martyrs Monument, Huang Hua Kang

1963. Freedom from Hunger. With gum.
463 **110** $10 multicoloured . . . . 4·50 1·00

1963. 20th Youth Day.
464 **111** 80c. purple 75 10
465 $3.20 green . . . . 2·00 60

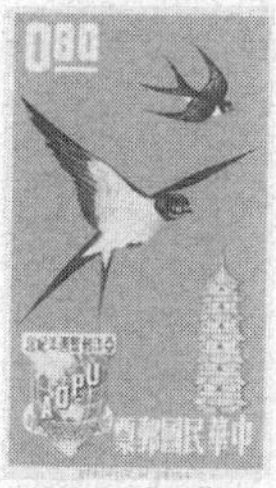
112 Barn Swallows and Pagoda

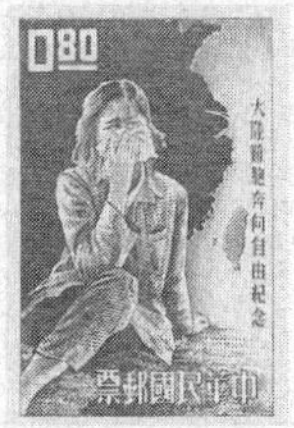
113 Refugee in Tears

1963. 1st Anniv of Asian-Oceanic Postal Union. With gum. Multicoloured.
466 80c. Type **112** . . . . 5·00 30
467 $2 Northern gannet . . . . 6·00 1·00
468 $6 Manchurian crane and pine tree (vert) . . . . . . 14·00 3·75

1963. Refugees' Flight from Mainland.
469 **113** 80c. black . . . . 1·50 10
470 – $3.20 red . . . . 3·00 40
DESIGN—HORIZ: $3.20, Refugees on march.

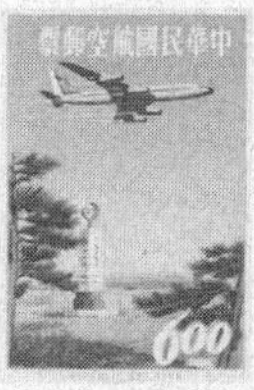
114 Convair 880 over Tropic of Cancer Monument, Kiai

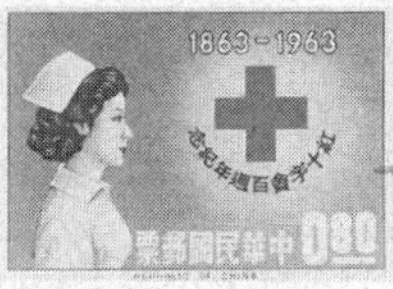
115 Red Cross Nurse and Emblem

1963. Air. Multicoloured. With gum.
471 $2.50 Suspension Bridge, Pitan (horiz) . . . . 6·00 30
472 $6 Type **114** . . . . 10·00 1·00
473 $10 Lion-head Mountain, Sinchu . . . . 14·00 2·00

1963. Red Cross Centenary. With gum.
474 **115** 80c. red and black . . . . 3·50 30
475 – $10 red, green and blue 12·00 2·50
DESIGN: $10, Globe and scroll.

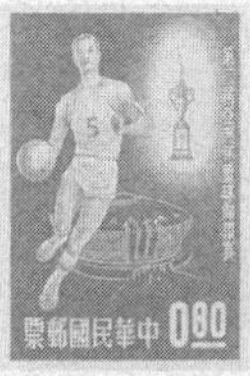
116 Basketball

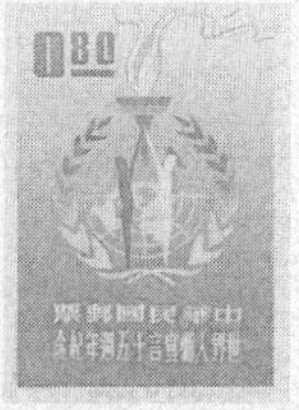
117 Freedom Torch

1963. 2nd Asian Basketball Championships, Taipeh.
476 **116** 80c. mauve . . . . 1·00 10
477 – $2 violet . . . . 2·00 60
DESIGN: $2, Hands reaching for inscribed ball.

1963. 15th Anniv of Declaration of Human Rights.
478 **117** 80c. green 60 10
479 – $3.20 red . . . . 1·25 20
DESIGN—HORIZ: $3.20, Human figures and scales of justice.

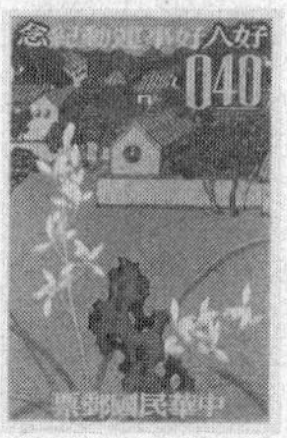
118 Country Scene

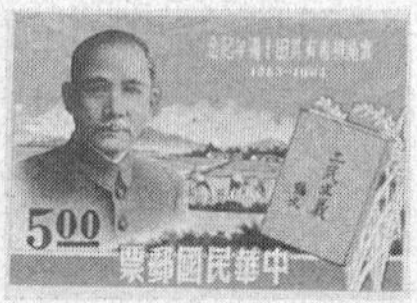
119 Dr. Sun Yat-sen and his Book "Three Principles of the People"

1963. "Good-People, Good-Deeds" Campaign. Multicoloured. With gum.
480 40c. Type **118** . . . . 3·00 10
481 $4.50 Lighting candle . . . . 7·00 1·00

1963. 10th Anniv of Land-to-Tillers Programme. With gum.
482 **119** $5 multicoloured . . . . 12·00 1·00

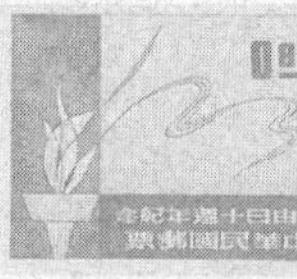
120 Torch of Liberty

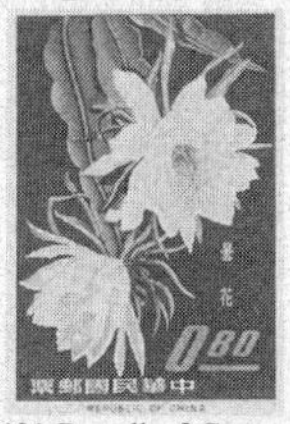
121 Broadleaf Cactus

1964. 10th Anniv of Liberty Day.
483 **120** 80c. orange 50 10
484 – $3.20 blue . . . . 2·00 50
DESIGN—VERT: $3.20, Hands with broken manacles.

1964. Taiwan Cacti. Multicoloured. With gum.
485 80c. Type **121** . . . . 1·25 10
486 $1 Crab cactus . . . . 7·00 60
487 $3.20 Nopalxochia . . . . . 5·00 30
488 $5 Grizzly-Bear cactus . . . 12·00 1·00

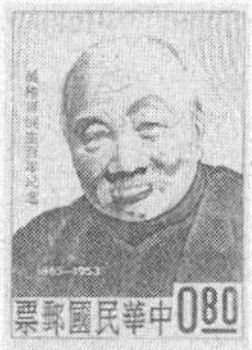
122 Wu Chih-hwei (politician)

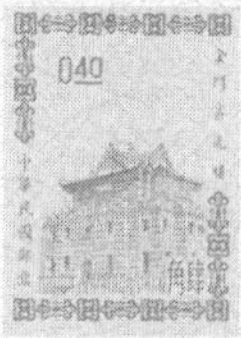
123 Chu Kwang Tower, Quemoy

1964. 99th Birth Anniv of Wu Chih-hwei (politician).
489 **122** 80c. brown . . . . 1·75 10

1964.
490 **123** 3c. purple 10 10
491 5c. green 10 10
492 10c. green 40 10
493 20c. green 15 10
494 40c. red 15 10
495 50c. purple 40 10
496 80c. orange 60 10
497 $1 violet 30 10
498 $1.50 purple . . . . . . 10·00 50
499 $2 purple . . . . 1·25 10
500 $2.50 blue . . . . 1·40 10
501 $3 grey . . . . 2·00 10
502 $3.20 blue . . . . 2·00 10
504 $4 green . . . . 3·00 10

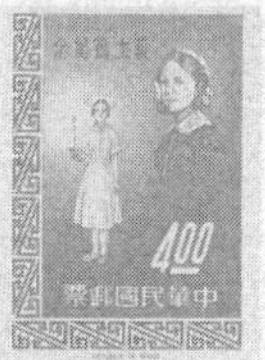
124 Nurse and Florence Nightingale

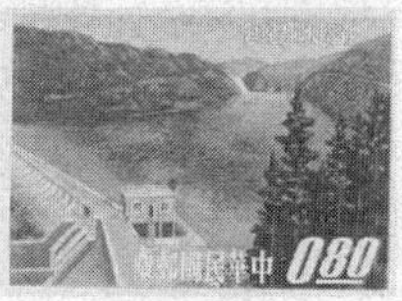
125 Weir

1964. Nurses Day.
506 – 80c. violet . . . . 1·60 10
507 **124** $4 red . . . . 4·25 40
DESIGN—HORIZ: 80c. Nurses holding candlelight ceremony.

1964. Inaug of Shihmen Reservoir. With gum. Mult.
508 80c. Type **125** . . . . 3·00 10
509 $1 Irrigation channel . . . . 4·00 10
510 $3.20 Dam and powerhouse 8·50 10
511 $5 Main spillway . . . . . . 12·50 3·00

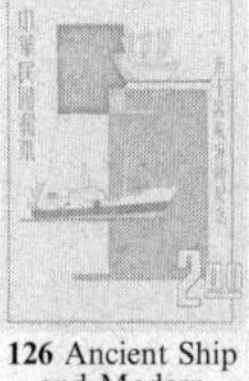
126 Ancient Ship and Modern Freighter

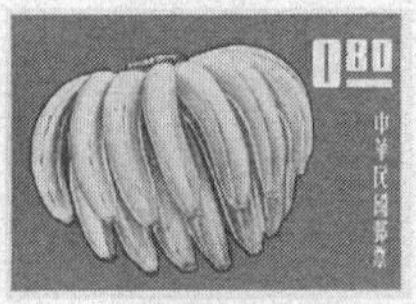
127 Bananas

1964. Navigation Day.
512 **126** $2 orange . . . . 1·00 10
513 $3.60 green . . . . 3·00 50

1964. Taiwan Fruits. Multicoloured. With gum.
514 80c. Type **127** . . . . 7·00 20
515 $1 Oranges . . . . 14·00 1·50
516 $3.20 Pineapples . . . . . . 23·00 70
517 $4 Water-melons . . . . . . 35·00 2·00

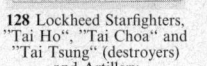

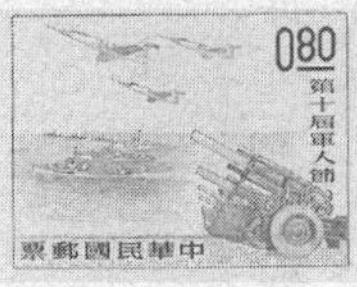
128 Lockheed Starfighters, "Tai Ho", "Tai Choa" and "Tai Tsung" (destroyers) and Artillery

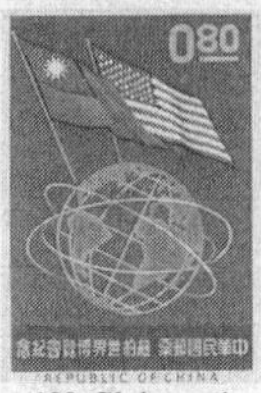
129 Globe and Flags of Formosa and U.S.A.

1964. Armed Forces Day.
518 **128** 80c. blue . . . . 1·00 10
519 $6 purple . . . . 3·50 75

1964. New York World's Fair (1st issue). With gum.
520 **129** 80c. multicoloured . . . . 5·00 30
521 – $5 multicoloured . . . . 7·00 75
DESIGN—HORIZ: $5, Taiwan Pavilion at Fair.
See also Nos. 550/1.

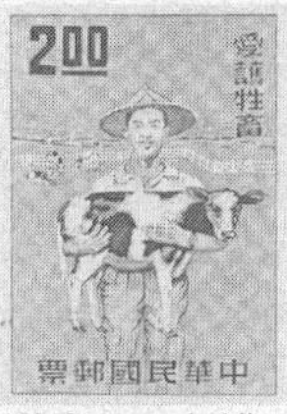
130 Cowman holding Calf

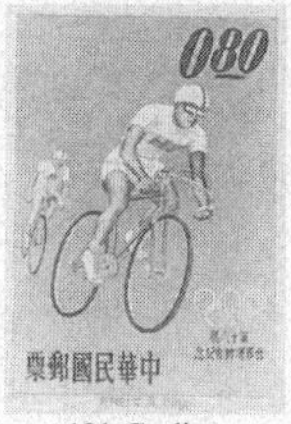
131 Cycling

1964. Animal Protection.
522 **130** $2 purple . . . . 1·00 60
523 $4 blue . . . . 5·25 1·25

1964. Olympic Games, Tokyo.
524 **131** 80c. blue 75 10
525 – $1 red . . . . 1·75 10
526 – $3.20 green . . . . 2·50 10
527 – $10 violet . . . . 3·75 1·25
DESIGNS: $1, Runner breasting tape; $3.20, Gymnastics; $10, High jumping.

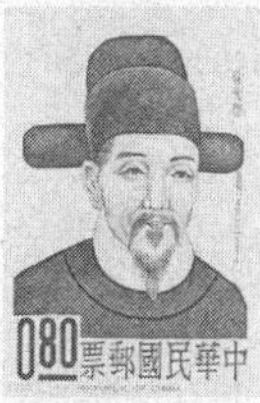
132 Hsu Kuang-chi (statesman)

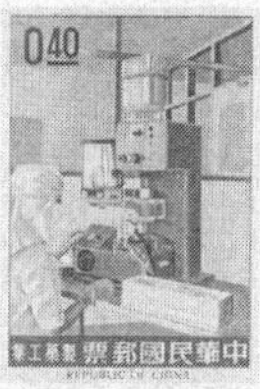
133 Factory-bench ("Pharmaceutics")

1964. Famous Chinese.
528 **132** 80c. blue . . . . 2·50 10
See also Nos. 558/9, 586/7, 599, 606/9, 610, 738/40, 960 and 1072/7.

1964. Taiwan Industries. Multicoloured. With gum.
529 40c. Type **133** . . . . 2·50 20
530 $1.50 Loom ("Textiles") . . 4·50 1·75
531 $2 Refinery ("Chemicals") . . 7·00 20
532 $3.60 Cement-mixer ("Cement") . . . . 9·50 1·25
The $1.50 and $3.60 are horiz.

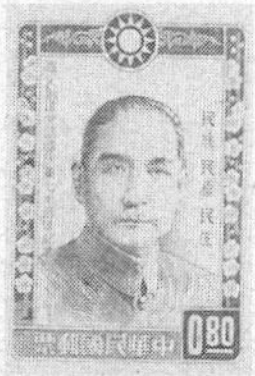
134 Dr. Sun Yat-sen (founder)

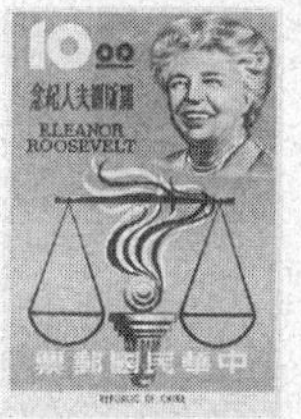
135 Mrs. Eleanor Roosevelt and "Human Rights" Emblem

1964. 70th Anniv of Kuomintang.
533 **134** 80c. green . . . . 2·50 10
534 $3.60 purple . . . . . . 5·50 60

1964. 16th Anniv of Declaration of Human Rights.
535 **135** $10 brown and violet . . 2·25 45

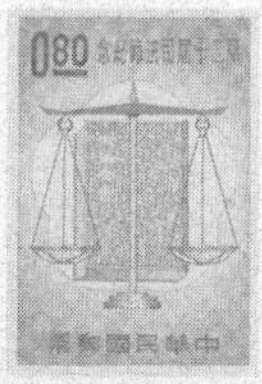
136 Law Code and Scales of Justice

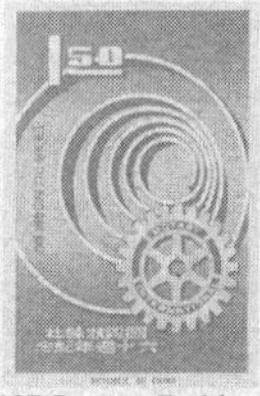
137 Rotary Emblem and Mainspring

1965. 20th Judicial Day.
536 **136** 80c. red . . . . 1·00 10
537 $3.20 green . . . . 2·00 20

1965. 60th Anniv of Rotary International.
538 **137** $1.50 red 60 10
539 $2 green 60 10
540 $2.50 blue . . . . 2·00 25

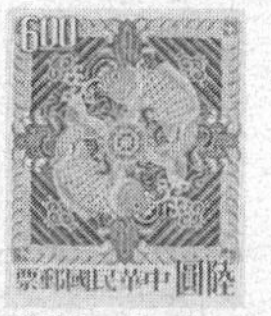
138 "Double Carp"

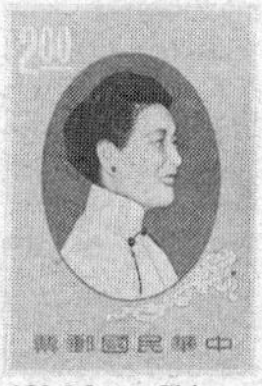
139 Mme. Chiang Kai-shek

1965.
541 **138** $5 violet . . . . 4·00 10
542 $5.60 blue . . . . 5·50 70
543 $6 brown . . . . 5·50 10
544 $10 mauve . . . . 27·00 10
545 $20 red . . . . 38·00 1·50
546 $50 green . . . . 38·00 1·50
547 $100 red . . . . 55·00 2·40
See also Nos. 695/698ab.

1965. 15th Anniv of Chinese Women's Anti-Aggression League. With gum.
548 **139** $2 multicoloured . . . . 15·00 70
549 $6 multicoloured . . . . 26·00 6·00

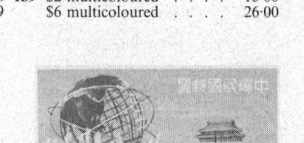

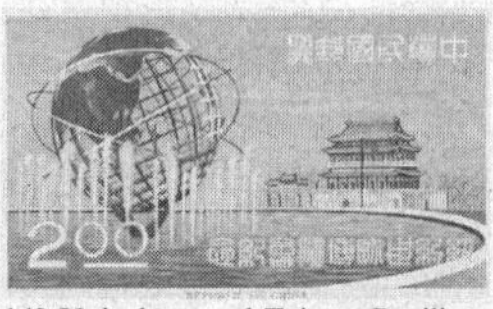
140 Unisphere and Taiwan Pavilion, N.Y. Fair

1965. New York World's Fair (2nd issue). Multicoloured. With gum.
550 $2 Type **140** . . . . 8·00 40
551 $10 Peacock and various birds ("100 birds paying tribute to Queen Phoenix") 32·00 3·00

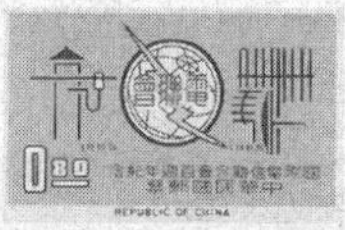
141 I.T.U. Emblem and Symbols

1965. Centenary of I.T.U. Multicoloured. With gum.
552 80c. Type **141** . . . . 1·10 10
553 $5 I.T.U. emblem and symbols (vert) . . . . . . 2·75 50

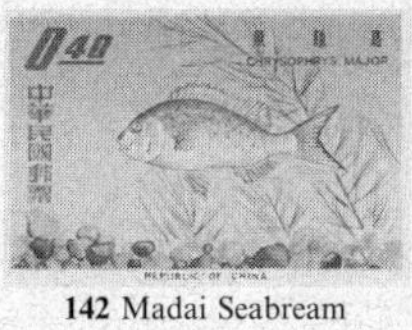
142 Madai Seabream

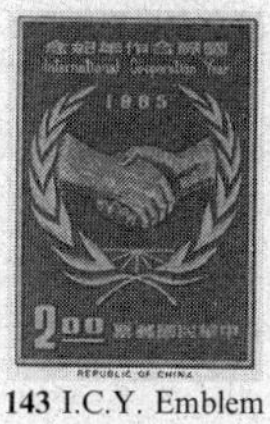
143 I.C.Y. Emblem

1965. Taiwan Fishes. Mult. With gum.
554 40c. Type **142** . . . . 3·00 30
555 80c. Silver pomfret . . . . . 5·00 30
556 $2 Skipjack tuna (vert) . . . 7·50 75
557 $4 Moonfish . . . . 12·50 1·00

1965. Famous Chinese. Portraits as T **132**.
558 $1 red (Confucius) . . . . . 4·75 10
559 $3.60 blue (Mencius) . . . . 6·00 50

1965. Int Co-operation Year. Mult. With gum.
560 $2 Type **143** . . . . 3·00 10
561 $6 I.C.Y. emblem (horiz) . . 3·00 80

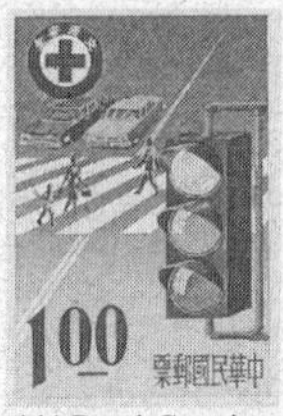
144 Road Crossing

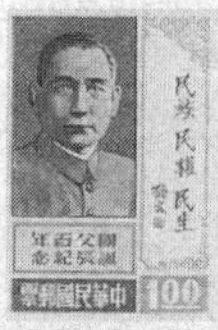
145 Dr. Sun Yat-sen

1965. Road Safety.
562 **144** $1 purple . . . . 1·40 10
563 $4 red . . . . 2·50 50

1965. Birth Centenary of Dr. Sun Yat-sen. Multicoloured. With gum.
564 $1 Type **145** . . . . . . 4·00 15
565 $4 As T **145** but with portrait, etc., on right . . . 8·00 40
566 $5 Dr. Sun Yat-sen and flags (horiz) . . . . 14·00 1·00

146 Children with Firework

147 Lien Po, "Marshal and Prime Minister Reconciled"

1965. Chinese Folklore (1st Series). Multicoloured. With gum.
567 $1 Type **146** . . . . 7·50 70
568 $4.50 Dragon dance . . . . 7·50 2·40
See also Nos. 581/3 and 617.

1966. Painted Faces of Chinese Opera. Multicoloured. With gum.
569 $1 Type **147** . . . . 16·00 40
570 $3 Kuan Yu, "Reunion at Ku City" . . . . 16·00 75
571 $4 Chang Fei, "Long Board Slope" . . . . 16·00 90
572 $6 Buddha, "The Flower-scattering Angel" . . . . . 32·00 3·00

148 Pigeon holding Postal Emblem

149 "Fishing on a Snowy Day" (After artist of the "Five Dynasties")

1966. 70th Anniv of Chinese Postal Services. Multicoloured. With gum.
573 $1 Type **148** . . . . 2·50 10
574 $2 Postman by Chu memorial stone (horiz) . . . . . . 3·50 10
575 $3 Postal Museum (horiz) . . 3·50 45
576 $4 "Postman climbing" . . . 7·00 1·50

1966. Ancient Chinese Paintings from Palace Museum Collection (3rd series). With gum. Multicoloured.
577 $2.50 Type **149** . . . . . . 7·00 70
578 $3.50 "Calves on the Plain" 10·50 70
579 $4.50 "Snowscape" . . . . . 16·00 1·75
580 $5 "Magpies" (after Lin Ch'un) . . . . 20·00 1·75
Nos. 578/9 both after Sung artists.

1966. Chinese Folklore (2nd series). As T **146**. With gum. Multicoloured.
581 $2.50 Dragon boat racing (horiz) . . . . 17·00 70
582 $4 "Lady Chang O Flying to the Moon" (horiz) . . . . 8·00 10
583 $6 Lion Dance . . . . 3·00 15

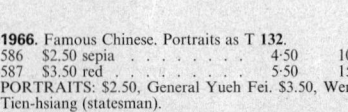

150 Flags of Argentine and Chinese Republics

151 Lin Sen

1966. 150th Anniv of Argentine Republic's Independence. With gum.
584 **150** $10 multicoloured . . . . 3·00 50

1966. Birth Centenary of Lin Sen (statesman).
585 **151** $1 sepia . . . . 2·10 10

1966. Famous Chinese. Portraits as T **132**.
586 $2.50 sepia . . . . 4·50 10
587 $3.50 red . . . . 5·50 15
PORTRAITS: $2.50, General Yueh Fei. $3.50, Wen Tien-hsiang (statesman).

153 Bean Geese

154 Pres. Chiang Kai-shek

1966.
588 **153** $3.50 brown . . . . . . 1·25 25
589 $4 red 75 10
590 $4.50 green . . . . 2·00 15
591 $5 purple 75 10
592 $5.50 green . . . . 1·25 20
593 $6 blue . . . . 6·00 1·75
594 $6.50 violet . . . . 1·75 30
595 $7 black . . . . 1·25 10
596 $8 red . . . . 1·75 10

1966. President Chiang Kai-shek's re-election for 4th Term. With gum. Multicoloured.
597 $1 Type **154** . . . . 2·10 10
598 $5 President in Uniform . . . 4·50 50

1966. Famous Chinese. Portrait as T **132**.
599 $1 blue (Tsai Yuan-Pei, scholar) . . . . 2·50 10

155 Various means of Transport

156 Boeing 727-100 over Chilin Pavilion, Grand Hotel, Taipeh

1967. Development of Taiwan Communications. Multicoloured. With gum.
600 $1 Mobile postman and microwave station (vert) . . 1·25 10
601 $5 Type **155** . . . . 2·50 30

1967. Air. Multicoloured. With gum.
602 $5 Type **156** . . . . 5·00 10
603 $8 Boeing 727-100 over Palace Museum, Taipeh . . 5·00 50

157 Pres. Chiang Kai-shek

158 "God of Happiness" (wood carving)

1967. Chiang Kai-shek's 4th Presidential Term. With gum.
604 **157** $1 multicoloured . . . . 2·00 10
605 $4 multicoloured . . . . 2·00 50

1967. Famous Chinese. Poets. Portraits. As T **132**.
606 $1 black (Chu Yuan) . . . . 2·75 20
607 $2 brown (Li Po) . . . . . 4·25 50
608 $2.50 brown (Tu Fu) . . . . 5·50 50
609 $3 green (Po Chu-i) . . . . 6·00 50

1967. Famous Chinese. Portrait as T **132**.
610 $1 black (Chiu Ching, female revolutionary) . . . . . . 4·00 10

1967. Chinese Handicrafts. Multicoloured. With gum.
611 $1 Type **158** . . . . 3·25 10
612 $2.50 Vase and dish . . . . 4·25 15
613 $3 Chinese dolls . . . . . 5·50 30
614 $5 Palace lanterns . . . . . 9·00 75

159 "WACL" on World Map

160 Muller's Barbet

1967. 1st World Anti-Communist League Conference, Taipei.
615 **159** $1 red 40 10
616 $5 blue 75 15

GUM. From No. 617 all stamps were issued with gum unless otherwise stated.

1967. Chinese Folklore (3rd series). Stilts Pastime. As T **146**.
617 $4.50 multicoloured . . . . 1·75 15
DESIGN: "The Fisherman and the Wood-cutter" (Chinese play on stilts).

1967. Taiwan Birds. Multicoloured.
618 $1 Type **160** . . . . 3·50 15
619 $2 Maroon oriole (horiz) . . 8·50 35
620 $2.50 Japanese green pigeon (horiz) . . . . 11·00 60
621 $3 Formosan blue magpie (horiz) . . . . 11·00 60
622 $5 Crested serpent eagle . . . 13·00 1·00
623 $8 Mikado pheasant (horiz) 13·00 1·00

161 Chung Hsing Pagoda

162 Flags and China Park, Manila

1967. International Tourist Year. Multicoloured.
624 $1 Type **161** . . . . 1·75 10
625 $2.50 Yeh Liu National Park (coastal scene) (horiz) . . . 5·00 40
626 $4 Statue of Buddha (horiz) 5·50 40
627 $5 National Palace Museum, Taipei (horiz) . . . . . . 7·00 50

1967. China–Philippines Friendship.
628 **162** $1 multicoloured 50 10
629 $5 multicoloured . . . . 1·50 40

163 Chungshan Building, Yangmingshan

164 Taroko Gorge

1968.
630 **163** 5c. brown 10 10
631 10c. green 15 15
632 50c. purple 10 10
633 $1 red 15 10
634 $1.50 green . . . . 4·50 20
635 $2 purple . . . . 1·40 10
636 $2.50 blue . . . . 1·40 10
637 $3 blue . . . . 1·50 10
For redrawn design see Nos. 791/8.

1968. 17th Pacific Area Travel Association Conference, Taipei. Multicoloured.
638 $5 Type **164** . . . . 3·50 60
689 $8 Chungshan Building, Yangmingshan . . . . . . 2·75 60

165 Harvesting Sugar-cane

166 Vice-Pres. Cheng

1968. Sugar-cane Technologists Congress, Taiwan.
640 **165** $1 multicoloured . . . . 1·60 10
641 $4 multicoloured . . . . 3·25 50

1968. 3rd Death Anniv of Vice-Pres. Chen Cheng.
642 **166** $1 multicoloured . . . . 1·00 10

167 Bean Geese

168 Jade Cabbage (Ching Dynasty)

1968. 90th Anniv of Chinese Postage Stamps.
643 **167** $1 red . . . . 1·00 25

1968. Chinese Art Treasures, National Palace Museum (1st series). Multicoloured.
645 $1 Type **168** . . . . 1·50 10
646 $1.50 Jade battle-axe (Warring States period) . . 3·50 35
647 $2 Lung-ch'uan porcelain flower bowl (Sung dynasty) 3·50 10
648 $2.50 Yung Cheng enamelled vase (Ching dynasty) . . . 4·00 50
649 $4 Agate "fingered" flower-holder (Ching dynasty) . . 4·50 50
650 $5 Sacrificial vessel (Western Chou) . . . . 5·00 75
The $2 and $4 are horiz.
See also Nos. 682/7 and 732/7.

169 W.H.O. Emblem on "20"

170 Sun, Planets and "Rainfall"

1968. 20th Anniv of W.H.O.
651 **169** $1 green 30 10
652 $5 red 85 30

1968. International Hydrological Decade.
653 **170** $1 green and orange . . . 30 10
654 $4 blue and orange . . . 85 10

171 "A City of Cathay" (Section of hand-scroll painting)

1968. "A City of Cathay" (Scroll, Palace Museum) (1st series).
655 **171** $1 (1) multicoloured . . . 2·00 10
656 – $1 (2) multicoloured . . . 2·00 10
657 – $1 (3) multicoloured . . . 2·00 10
658 – $1 (4) multicoloured . . . 2·00 10
659 – $1 (5) multicoloured . . . 2·00 10
660 – $5 multicoloured . . . . 15·00 2·50
661 – $8 multicoloured . . . . 17·00 2·50
DESIGNS—As Type **171**: Nos. 655/9 together show panorama of the city ending with the palace. LARGER (61 × 32 mm). $5, City wall and gate; $8, Great bridge.
The five $1 stamps were issued together se-tenant in horiz. strips, representing the last 11 feet of the 37 foot scroll, which is viewed from right to left as it is unrolled.
The stamps may be identified by the numbers given in brackets, which correspond to the numbers in the bottom right-hand corners of the stamps.
See also Nos. 699/703.

172 Map and Radio "Waves"

173 Human Rights Emblem

1968. 40th Anniv of Chinese Broadcasting Service.
662 **172** $1 grey, ultram & blue . . 40 10
663 – $4 red and blue . . . . . 1·00 10
DESIGN—VERT: $4, Stereo broadcast "waves".

1968. Human Rights Year.
664 **173** $1 multicoloured 40 10
665 $5 multicoloured . . . . 1·00 10

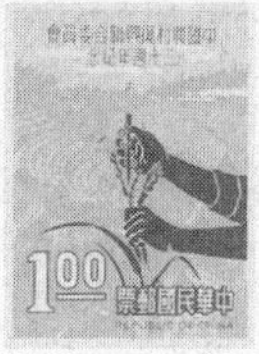
174 Harvesting Rice

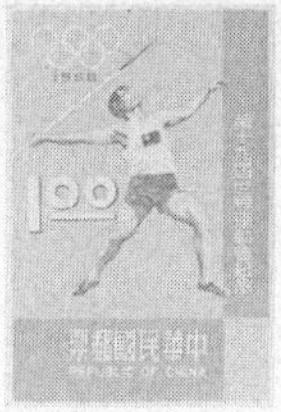
175 Throwing the Javelin

1968. Rural Reconstruction.
666 **174** $1 brown, ochre & yellow 40 10
667 $5 bronze, green & yellow 1·00 30

1968. Olympic Games, Mexico. Multicoloured.
668 $1 Type **175** 50 10
669 $2.50 Weightlifting 75 10
670 $5 Pole-vaulting (horiz) . . . 1·00 20
671 $8 Hurdling (horiz) . . . . . 1·50 40

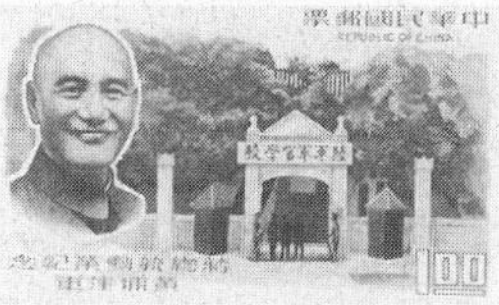
176 President Chiang Kai-shek and Main Gate, Whampoa Military Academy

1968. "President Chiang Kai-shek's Meritorious Services". Multicoloured.
672 $1 Type **176** 50 10
673 $2 Reviewing Northern Expedition Forces . . . . 1·25 20
674 $2.50 Suppression of bandits 4·00 60
675 $3.50 Marco Polo Bridge and Victory Parade, Nanking, 1945 . . . . 1·50 25
676 $4 Chinese Constitution . . . 1·75 25
677 $5 National flag . . . . . . 2·25 30
Each stamp bears the portrait of President Chiang Kai-shek as in Type **176**.

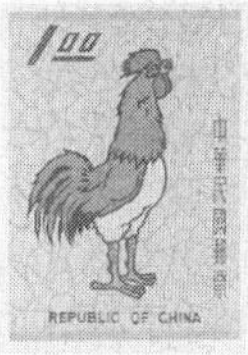
177 Cockerel

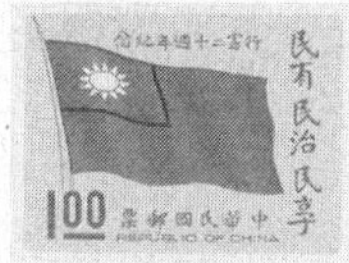
178 National Flag

1968. New Year Greetings. "Year of the Cock".
678 **177** $1 multicoloured . . . . 20·00 10
679 $4.50 multicoloured . . . 26·00 5·00

1968. 20th Anniv of Chinese Constitution.
680 **178** $1 multicoloured 75 10
681 $5 multicoloured . . . . 1·00 15

1969. Chinese Art Treasures, National Palace Museum (2nd series). Multicoloured as T **168**.
682 $1 Jade buckle (Ching dynasty) (horiz) 75 10
683 $1.50 Jade vase (Sung dynasty) . . . . 1·75 25
684 $2 Cloisonne enamel teapot (Ching dynasty) (horiz) . . 1·00 10
685 $2.50 Bronze sacrificial vessel (Kuei) (horiz) . . . . . . 1·75 40
686 $4 Hsuan-te "heavenly ball" vase (Ming dynasty) . . . 2·75 60
687 $5 "Gourd" vase (Ching dynasty) . . . . 4·00 60

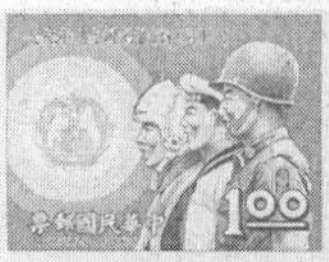
179 Servicemen and Savings Emblem

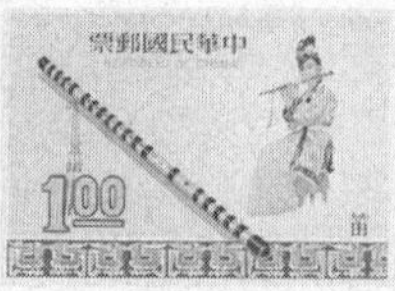
180 Ti (flute)

1969. 10th Anniv of Forces' Savings Services.
688 **179** $1 brown 40 10
689 $4 blue . . . . 1·00 15

1969. Chinese Musical Instruments. Mult.
690 $1 Type **180** . . . . 1·00 10
691 $2.50 Sheng (pipes) . . . . . 1·50 15
692 $4 P'i-p'a (lute) . . . . . . 2·00 30
693 $5 Cheng (zither) . . . . . . 2·00 15

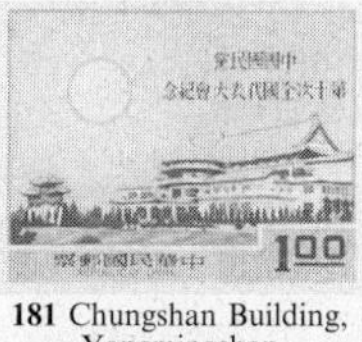
181 Chungshan Building, Yangmingshan

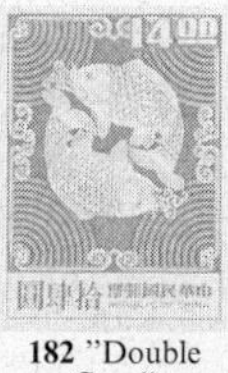
182 "Double Carp"

1969. 10th Kuomintang Congress.
694 **181** $1 multicoloured 55 10

1969.
695ab **182** $10 blue . . . . 2·50 10
695c $14 red . . . . 2·50 10
696ab $20 brown . . . . . . 2·50 10
697ab $50 green . . . . . . 5·00 15
698ab $100 red . . . . 6·50 35
Type **182** is a redrawn version of Type **138**.

1969. "A City of Cathay" (scroll) (2nd series). As T **171**. Multicoloured.
699 $1 "Musicians" . . . . . . 1·00 10
700 $1 "Bridal chair" . . . . . 1·00 10
701 $2.50 Emigrants with ox-cart 1·00 60
702 $5 "Scroll gallery" . . . . . 5·25 45
703 $8 "Roadside cafe" . . . . . 8·50 60
Nos. 699/70 form a composite picture of a bridal procession.

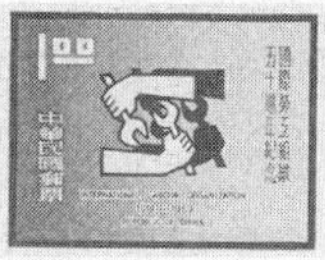
184 I.L.O. Emblem

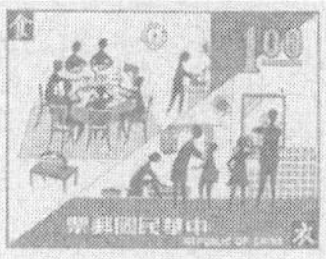
185 "Food and Clothing"

1969. 50th Anniv of I.L.O.
704 **184** $1 blue 50 10
705 $8 red . . . . 1·00 20

1969. "Model Citizen's Life" Movement.
706 **185** $1 red 20 10
707 – $2.50 blue 70 15
708 – $4 green 70 15
DESIGNS: $2.50, "Housekeeping and Road Safety"; $4, "Schooling and Recreation".

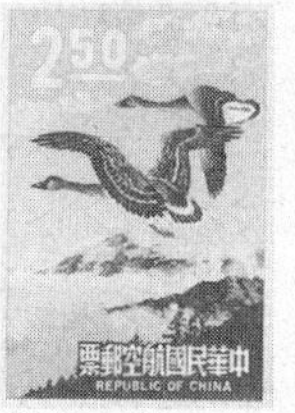
186 Bean Geese over Mountains

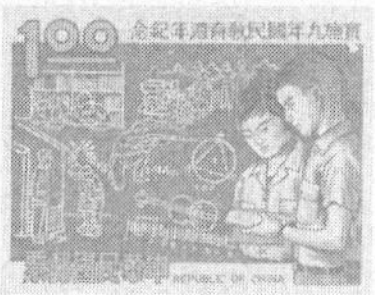
187 Children and Symbols of Learning

1969. Air. Multicoloured.
709 $2.50 Type **186** . . . . . . 4·25 75
710 $5 Bean geese over sea . . . 4·25 50
711 $8 Bean geese over land (horiz) . . . . 4·25 50

1969. 1st Anniv of Nine-year Free Education System.
712 **187** $1 red 30 10
713 – $2.50 green 50 15
714 – $4 blue . . . . 1·00 15
715 **187** $5 brown . . . . 1·25 20
DESIGNS—VERT: $2.50 and $4, Children and school.

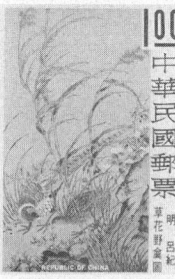

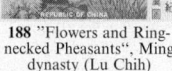

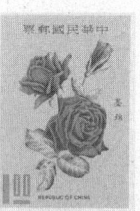

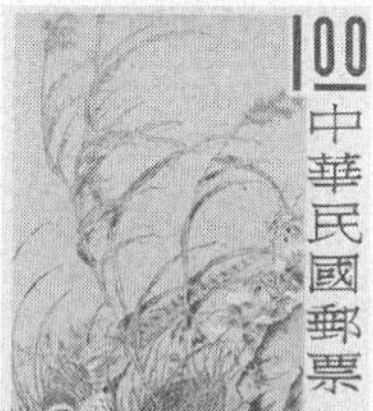
188 "Flowers and Ring-necked Pheasants", Ming dynasty (Lu Chih)

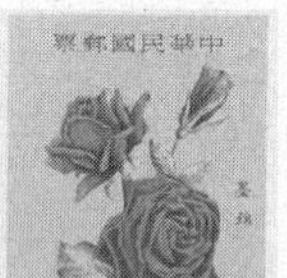
189 "Charles Mallerin" Rose

1969. Ancient Chinese Paintings from Palace Museum Collection (4th series). "Birds and Flowers". Multicoloured.
716 $1 Type **188** . . . . 1·75 20
717 $2.50 "Bamboos and Ring-necked Pheasants" (Sung dynasty) . . . . 3·75 30
718 $5 "Flowers and Birds" (Sung dynasty) . . . . . . 9·25 60
719 $8 "Twin Manchurian Cranes and Flowers" (G. Castiglione, Ching dynasty) . . . . 9·25 1·00

1969. Roses. Multicoloured.
720 $1 Type **189** . . . . 1·60 10
721 $2.50 "Golden Sceptre" . . . 2·50 20
722 $5 "Peace" . . . . 3·25 30
723 $8 "Josephine Bruce" . . . . 5·25 25

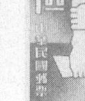

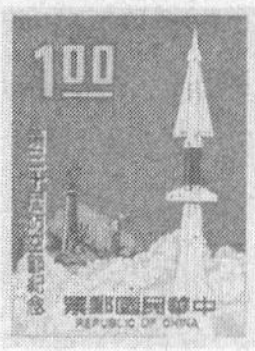
190 Launching Missile

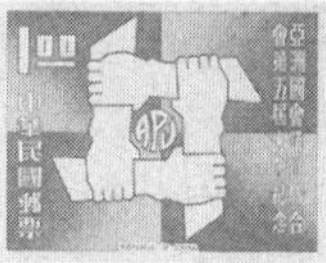
191 A.P.U. Emblem

1969. 30th Air Defence Day.
724 **190** $1 purple 80 10

1969. 5th Asian Parliamentarians' Union General Assembly. Taipeh.
725 **191** $1 red 40 10
726 $5 green 75 15

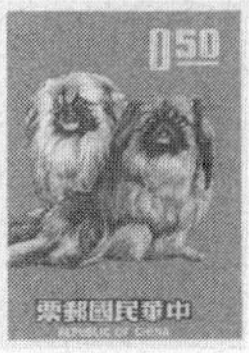
192 Pekingese Dogs

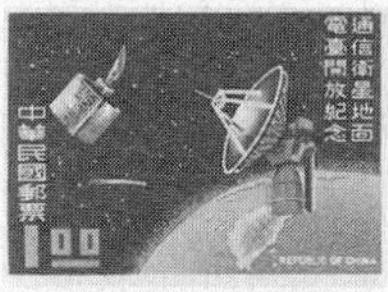
193 Satellite and Earth Station

1969. New Year Greetings. "Year of the Dog".
727 **192** 50c. multicoloured . . . . 2·00 10
728 $4.50 multicoloured . . . 5·00 1·00

1969. Inauguration of Satellite Earth Station, Yangmingshan.
729 **193** $1 multicoloured 90 10
730 $5 multicoloured . . . . 1·90 30
731 $8 multicoloured . . . . 2·60 50

1970. Chinese Art Treasures, National Palace Museum (3rd series). As T **168**. Multicoloured.
732 $1 Lacquer vase (Ching dynasty) . . . . 1·00 10
733 $1.50 Agate grinding-stone (Ching dynasty) (horiz) . . 1·75 15
734 $2 Jade carving (Ching dynasty) (horiz) . . . . . 1·75 10
735 $2.50 "Shepherd and Ram" jade carving (Han dynasty) (horiz) . . . . 2·00 30
736 $4 Porcelain jar (Ching dynasty) . . . . 2·00 30
737 $5 "Bull" porcelain urn (Northern Sung dynasty) 4·25 60

1970. Famous Chinese. Portraits as T **132**.
738 $1 red . . . . 2·00 10
739 $2.50 green . . . . 1·90 15
740 $4 blue . . . . 2·00 35
PORTRAITS: $1, Hsuan Chuang (traveller). $2.50, Hua To (physician). $4, Chu Hsi (philosopher).

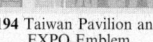

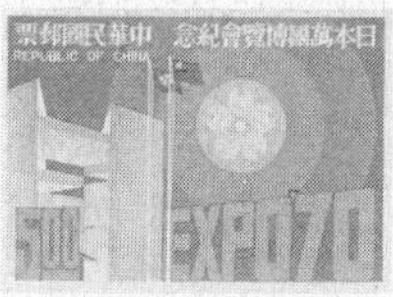
194 Taiwan Pavilion and EXPO Emblem

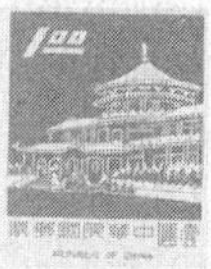
195 Chungshan Building, Yangmingshan

1970. World Fair "EXPO 70", Osaka, Japan. Multicoloured.
741 $5 Type **194** 40 15
742 $8 Pavilion encircled by national flags 90 40

1970.
743 **195** $1 red 50 20
For redrawn design see No. 1039.

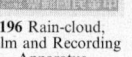

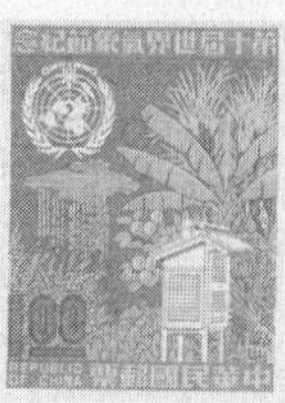
196 Rain-cloud, Palm and Recording Apparatus

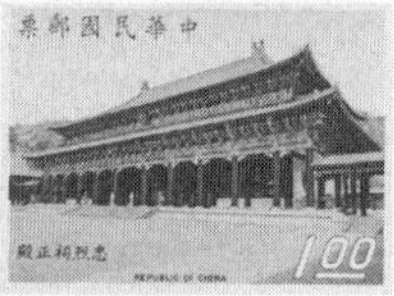
197 Martyrs' Shrine

1970. World Meteorological Day. Mult.
744 $1 Type **196** 50 10
745 $8 "Nimbus 3" satellite (horiz) . . . . 1·00 35

1970. Revolutionary Martyrs' Shrine. Mult.
746 $1 Type **197** 75 10
747 $8 Shrine gateway . . . . . 1·25 40

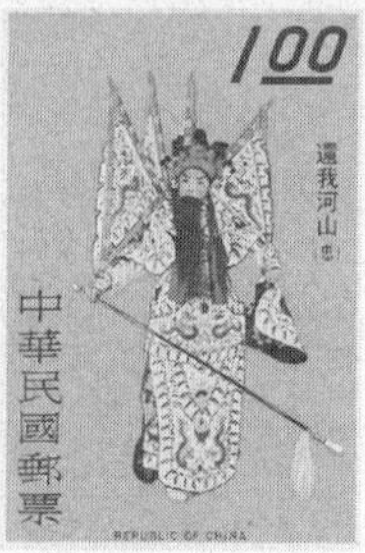
198 General Yueh Fei ("Loyalty")

1970. Chinese Opera. "The Virtues". Opera characters. Multicoloured.
748 $1 Type **198** 75 20
749 $2.50 Emperor Shun tortured by stepmother ("Filial Piety") . . . . 2·50 35
750 $5 Chin Liang-yu "The Lady General" ("Chastity") . . 4·00 35
751 $8 Kuan Yu and groom ("Fidelity") . . . . 5·00 50

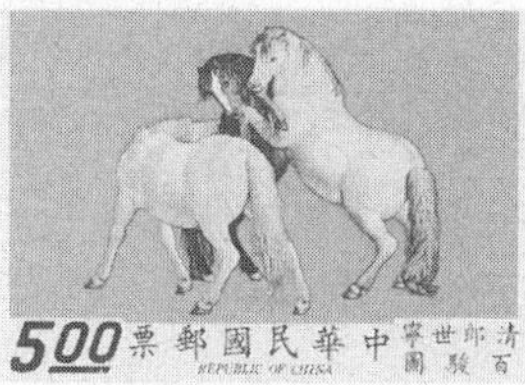
199 Three Horses at Play

1970. "One Hundred Horses" (handscroll by Lang Shih-ning (G. Castiglione)). Multicoloured.
752 $1 (1) Horses on plain . . . 50 10
753 $1 (2) Horses on plain (different) 50 10
754 $1 (3) Horses playing 50 10
755 $1 (4) Horses on river bank 50 10
756 $1 (5) Horses crossing river 50 10
757 $5 Type **199** . . . . 5·00 75
758 $8 Groom roping horses . . 6·50 50

SERIAL NUMBERS. are indicated to aid identification of the above and certain other sets. For key to Chinese numerals see table at the beginning of CHINA.

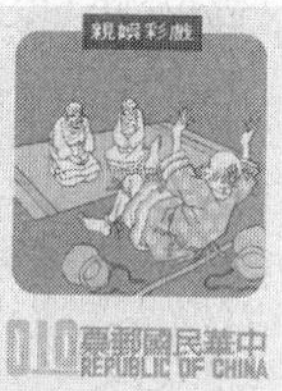
200 Old Lai-tsu dropping Buckets

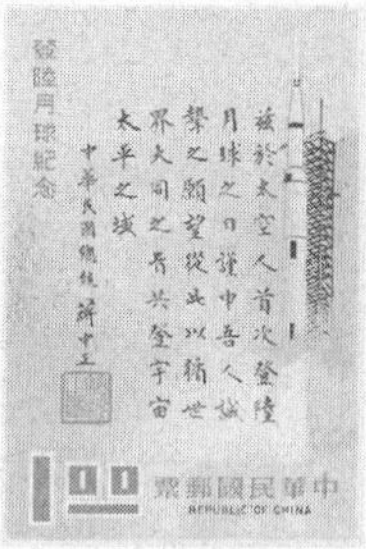
201 Chiang Kai-shek's Moon Message

1970. Chinese Folk-tales (1st series). Mult.
759 10c. Type **200** 20 10
760 10c. Yien-tsu disguised as a deer 20 10
761 10c. Hwang Hsiang with fan 20 10
762 10c. Wang Shiang fishing . . 25 10
763 10c. Chu Hsiu-chang reunited with mother 20 10
764 50c. Emperor Wen tasting mother's medicine 40 15
765 $1 Lu Chi dropping oranges 60 15
766 $1 Yang Hsiang fighting tiger 60 15
See also Nos. 817/24, 1000/7, 1064/7, 1210/13 and 1312/15.

1970. 1st Man on the Moon. Multicoloured.
767 $1 Type **201** 60 10
768 $5 "Apollo 11" astronauts (horiz) . . . . 1·00 30
769 $8 "First step on the Moon" 2·00 50

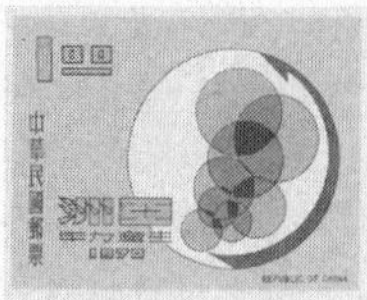
202 Productivity Symbol

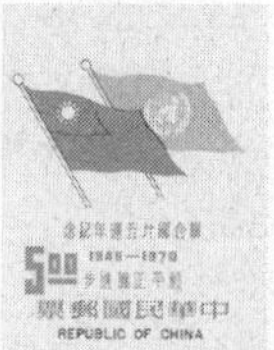
203 Flags of Taiwan and United Nations

1970. Asian Productivity Year.
770 **202** $1 multicoloured 50 10
771 $5 multicoloured . . . . 1·00 35

1970. 25th Anniv of United Nations.
772 **203** $5 multicoloured . . . . 1·25 40

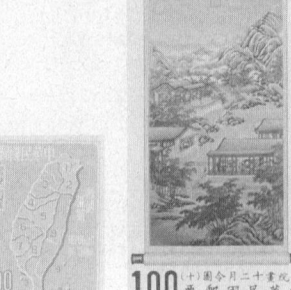

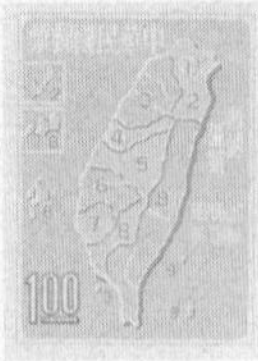
204 Postal Zone Map

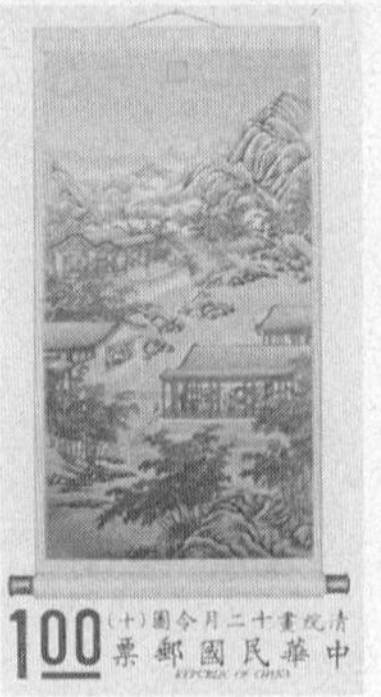
205 "Cultural Activities" (10th month)

1970. Postal Zone Numbers Campaign. Mult.
773 $1 Type **204** 90 10
774 $2.50 Postal Zone emblem (horiz) . . . . 1·00 35

1970. "Occupations of the Twelve Months" Hanging Scrolls. Multicoloured. (a) "Winter".
775 $1 Type **205** . . . . 2·40 10
776 $2.50 "School Buildings" (11th month) . . . . . . 6·00 1·00
777 $5 "Games in the Snow" (12th month) . . . . . . 8·50 75

(b) "Spring".
778 $1 "Lantern Festival" (1st month) . . . . 2·75 10
779 $2.50 "Apricots in Blossom" (2nd month) . . . . 3·50 1·00
780 $5 "Purification Ceremony" (3rd month) . . . . 4·25 60

(c) "Summer".
781 $1 "Summer Shower" (4th month) . . . . 2·75 10
782 $2.50 "Dragon boat Festival" (5th month) . . . . 4·00 1·00
783 $5 "Lotus Pond" (6th month) 4·00 50

(d) "Autumn".
784 $1 "Weaver Festival" (7th month) . . . . 3·00 10
785 $2.50 "Moon Festival" (8th month) . . . . 4·25 1·00
786 $5 "Chrysanthemum Blossom" (9th month) . . 6·25 35

The month numbers are given by the Chinese characters in brackets, which follow the face value on the stamps.

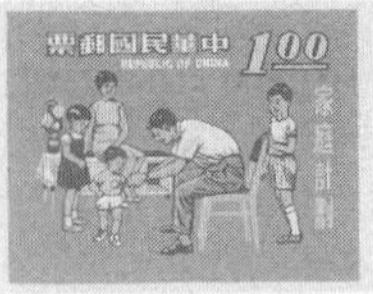
206 "Planned Family"

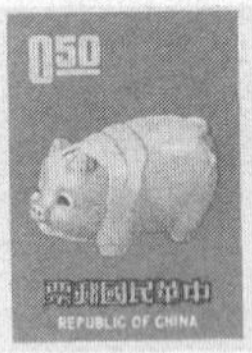
207 Toy Pig

1970. Family Planning. Multicoloured.
787 $1 Type **206** 60 10
788 $4 "Family excursion" (vert) 1·25 35

1970. New Year Greetings. "Year of the Boar".
789 **207** 50c. multicoloured . . . . 2·25 30
790 $4.50 multicoloured . . . 3·00 1·00

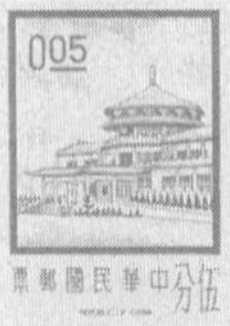
208 Chungshan Building, Yangmingshan

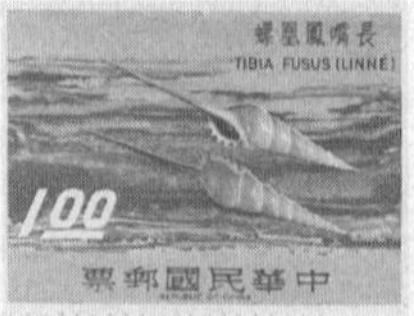
209 Shin-bone Tibia

1971.
791 **208** 5c. brown 15 10
792 10c. green 15 10
793 50c. red 25 10
794 $1 red 25 10
795 $1.50 blue . . . . 1·10 10
796 $2 purple . . . . 3·00 10
797 $2.50 green . . . . 4·25 10
798 $3 blue . . . . 4·25 10
Type **208** is a redrawn version of Type **163**.

1971. Taiwan Shells. Multicoloured.
799 $1 Type **209** 90 10
800 $2.50 Kuroda's lyria . . . . 1·10 30
801 $5 "Conus stupa kuroda" . . 1·75 50
802 $8 Rumphius's slit shell . . . 3·00 25

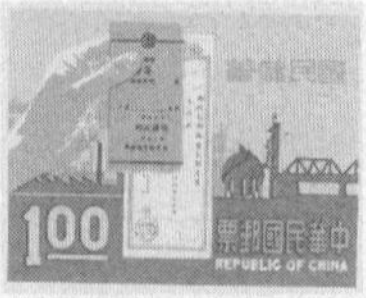
210 Savings Book and Certificate

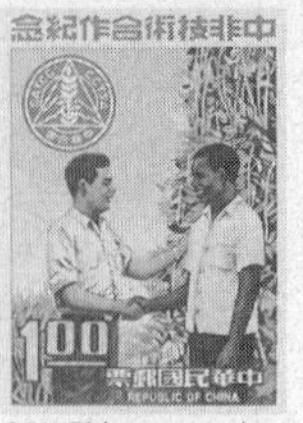
211 Chinese greeting African Farmer

1971. National Savings Campaign. Mult.
803 $1 Type **210** 45 10
804 $4 Hand dropping coin in savings bank . . . . . . 1·00 20

1971. 10th Anniv of Sino-African Technical Co-operation Committee. Multicoloured.
805 $1 Type **211** 40 10
806 $8 Rice-growing (horiz) . . . 80 35

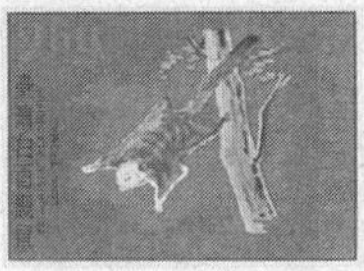
212 Red and White Flying Squirrel

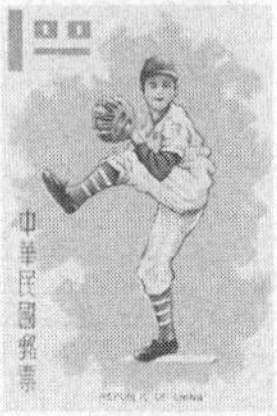
213 Pitcher delivering ball

1971. Taiwan Animals. Multicoloured.
807 $1 Taiwan macaque (vert) . . 70 10
808 $2 Type **212** . . . . 1·50 50
809 $3 Chinese pangolin . . . . 2·00 65
810 $5 Sika deer . . . . 2·50 75

1971. World Little League Baseball Championships, Taiwan. Multicoloured.
811 $1 Type **213** 30 10
812 $2.50 Players at base (horiz) 40 15
813 $4 Striker and catcher . . . 75 15

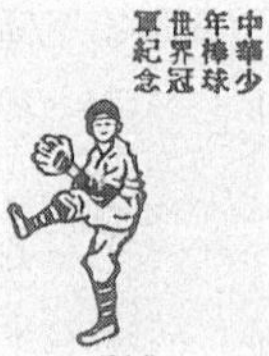
(214)

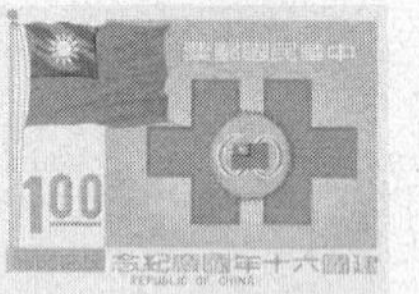
215 60th Anniv Emblem and flag

1971. Victory of "Tainan Giants" in World Little League Baseball Championships, Williamsport (U.S.A.). Optd with T **214**.
814 **163** $1 red 60 10
815 $2.50 blue . . . . 1·25 20
816 $3 blue . . . . 1·25 20

1971. Chinese Folk-tales (2nd series). As T **200**. Multicoloured.
817 10c. Yu Hsun and elephant 15 10
818 10c. Tsai Hsun with mulberries 15 10
819 10c. Tseng Sun with firewood 15 10
820 10c. Kiang Keh and bandits 15 10
821 10c. Tsu Lu with sack of rice 15 10
822 50c. Meng Chung gathering bamboo shoots 40 10
823 $1 Tung Yung and wife . . . 1·25 35
824 $1 Tzu Chien shivering with cold . . . . 1·25 35

1971. 60th National Day. Multicoloured.
825 $1 Type **215** 45 10
826 $2.50 National anthem, map and flag 60 10
827 $5 Pres. Chiang Kai-shek, constitution and flag . . . 75 35
828 $8 Dr. Sun Yat-sen, "Three Principles" and flag . . . 1·00 40

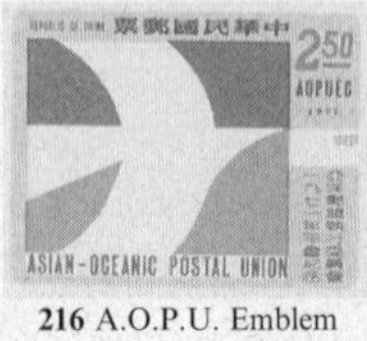
216 A.O.P.U. Emblem

1971. Asian-Oceanic Postal Union Executive Committee Session, Taipeh.
829 **216** $2.50 multicoloured . . . 50 30
830 $5 multicoloured 60 15

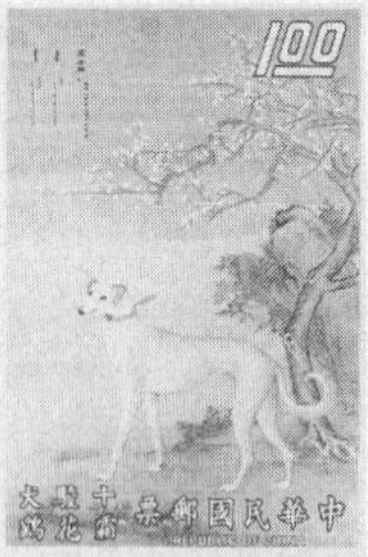
217 "White Frost Hawk"

1971. "Ten Prized Dogs" (paintings on silk by Lang Shih-ning (G. Castiglione)). Multicoloured.
831 $1 Type **217** . . . . 1·10 10
832 $1 "Black Dog with Snow-white Claws" . . . . . . 3·25 10
833 $2 "Star-glancing Wolf" . . 3·50 10
834 $2 "Yellow Leopard" . . . . 4·50 10
835 $2.50 "Golden-winged Face" 3·00 85
836 $2.50 "Flying Magpie" . . . 10·50 85
837 $5 "Young Black Dragon" 4·25 75
838 $5 "Heavenly Lion" . . . . 10·50 75
839 $8 "Young Grey Dragon" . . 4·25 65
840 $8 "Mottle-coated Tiger" . . 12·00 65

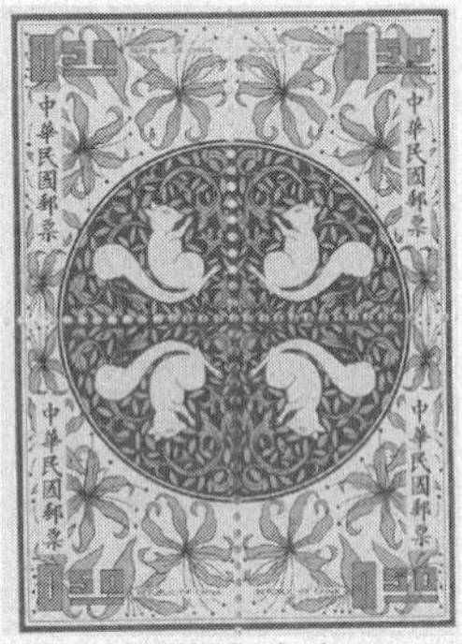
218/221 Squirrels

1971. New Year Greetings. "Year of the Rat".
841 **218** 50c. multicoloured 80 10
842 **219** 50c. multicoloured 80 10
843 **220** 50c. multicoloured 80 10
844 **221** 50c. multicoloured 80 10
845 **218** $4.50 multicoloured . . . 4·00 40
846 **219** $4.50 multicoloured . . . 4·00 40
847 **220** $4.50 multicoloured . . . 4·00 40
848 **221** $4.50 multicoloured . . . 4·00 40
The four designs in each value were issued together, se-tenant, forming a composite design.

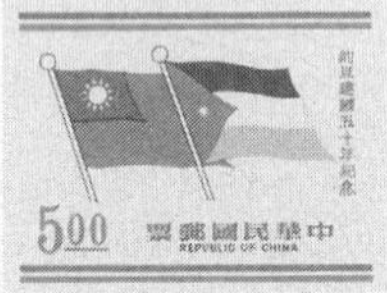
222 Flags of Taiwan and Jordan

1971. 50th Anniv of Hashemite Kingdom of Jordan.
849 **222** $5 multicoloured . . . . 1·00 30

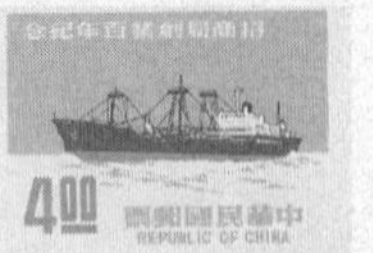
223 Freighter "Hai King"

1971. Centenary of China Merchants Steam Navigation Company. Multicoloured.
850 **223** $4 blue, red and green . . 75 40
851 – $7 multicoloured . . . . 1·25 25
DESIGN—VERT: $7. Liner on Pacific.

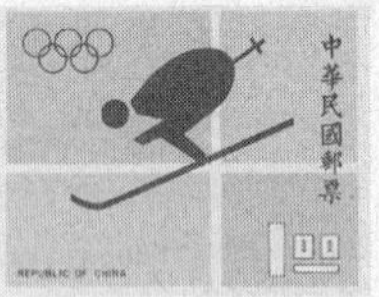
224 Downhill Skiing

1972. Winter Olympic Games, Sapporo, Japan.
852 **224** $1 black, yellow and blue 25 10
853 – $5 black, orange & green 65 20
854 – $8 black, red and grey . . 75 30
DESIGNS: $5, Cross-country skiing; $8, Giant slalom.

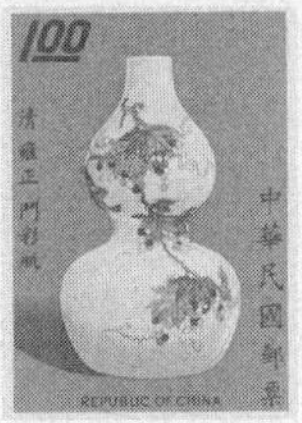
225 Yung Cheng Vase

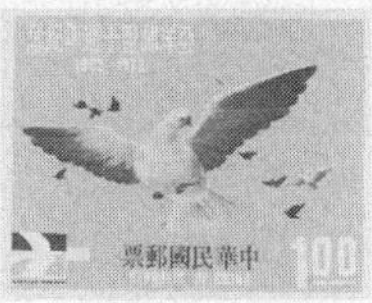
226 Doves

1972. Chinese Porcelain. (1st series). Ch'ing Dynasty. Multicoloured.
855 $1 Type **225** 75 10
856 $2 Kang Hsi jar . . . . . . 1·25 30
857 $2.50 Yung Cheng jug . . . 1·50 40
858 $5 Chien Lung vase . . . . 1·75 20
859 $8 Chien Lung jar . . . . . 3·25 40
See also Nos. 914/18, 927/31 and 977/81.

1972. 10th Anniv of Asian-Oceanic Postal Union.
860 **226** $1 black and blue 80 10
861 $5 black and violet . . . 1·25 40

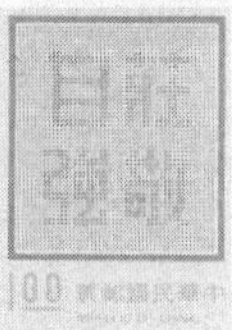
227 "Dignity with Self-Reliance" (Pres. Chiang Kai-shek)

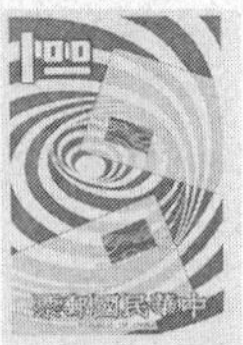
229 First Day Covers

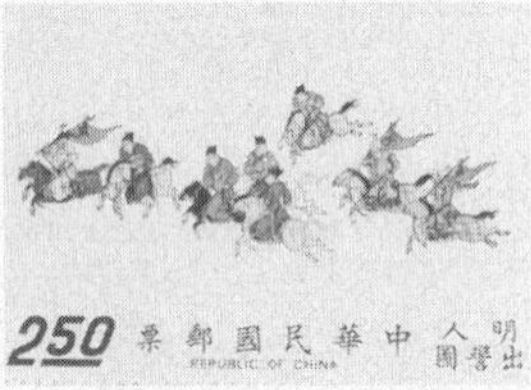
228 Mounted Messengers

1972.
862 **227** 5c. brown and yellow . . 15 10
863 10c. blue and orange . . 10 10
863b 20c. purple and green . . 20 10
864 50c. lilac and purple . . 20 10
865 $1 red and blue 10 10
866 $1.50 yellow and blue . . 20 10
867 $2 violet, purple & orge 30 10
868 $2.50 green and red . . 75 10
869 $3 red and green 50 10

1972. "The Emperor's Procession" (Ming dynasty handscrolls). Multicoloured. (a) First issue.
870 $1 (1) Pagoda and crowds . . 40 10
871 $1 (2) Seven carriages 40 10
872 $1 (3) Emperor's coach . . . 40 10
873 $1 (4) Horsemen with flags 40 10
874 $1 (5) Horsemen and Emperor 40 10
875 $2.50 Type **228** . . . . . . 5·00 25
876 $5 Guards . . . . 5·00 25
877 $8 Imperial sedan chair . . . 5·00 20

(b) Second issue.
878 $1 (1) Three ceremonial barges 40 10
879 $1 (2) Sedan chairs 40 10
880 $1 (3) Two ceremonial barges 40 10
881 $1 (4) Horsemen and mounted orchestra 40 10
882 $1 (5) Two carriages 40 10
883 $2.50 City gate . . . . . . 5·00 25
884 $5 Mounted orchestra . . . 5·00 25
885 $8 Ceremonial barge . . . . 7·00 30
Nos. 870/4 are numbered from right to left and Nos. 878/82 are numbered from left to right. They were each issued together, se-tenant, forming composite designs showing the departure of the procession from the palace and its return.
Nos. 875/7 and 883/5 show enlarged details from the scrolls.
See also Nos. 937/50 and 1040/7.

1972. Philately Day.
886 **229** $1 blue 25 10
887 $2.50 green 25 15
888 $8 red . . . . 1·25 15
DESIGNS—VERT: $2.50, Magnifying glass and stamps. HORIZ: $8, Magnifying glass, perforation-gauge and tweezers.

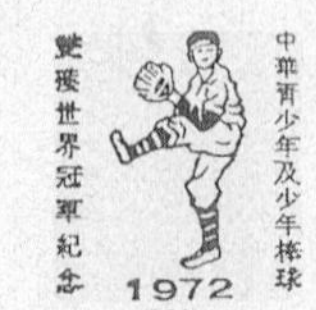
(230)

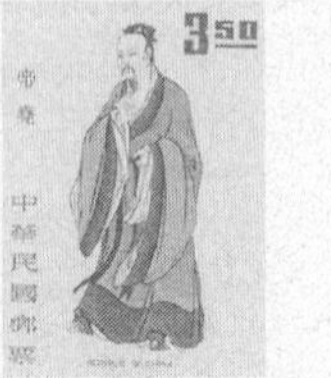
231 Emperor Yao

1972. Taiwan's Victories in Senior and Little World Baseball Leagues. Nos. 865/7 and 869 optd with T **230**.
889 **227** $1 red and blue 25 10
890 $1.50 yellow and blue . . 40 20

891 $2 violet, purple & orange 40 15
892 $3 red and green 40 20

1972. Chinese Cultural Heroes.
893 **231** $3.50 blue 50 30
894 – $4 red 50 10
895 – $4.50 violet 60 20
896 – $5 green 60 10
897 – $5.50 purple . . . . . . 1·40 35
898 – $6 orange . . . . 1·40 30
899 – $7 brown . . . . 2·00 10
900 – $8 blue . . . . 2·25 15
DESIGNS: $4, Emperor Shun; $4.50, Yu the Great; $5, King T'ang; $5.50, King Weng; $6, King Wu; $7, Chou Kung; $8, Confucius.

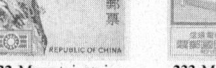

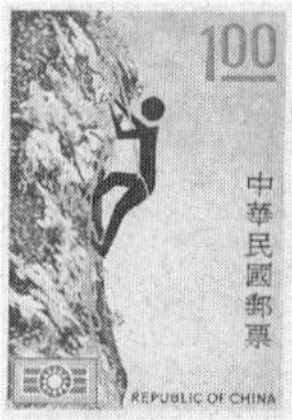
232 Mountaineering

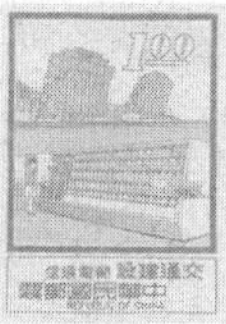
233 Microwave Systems and Electronic Sorting Machine

1972. 20th Anniv of China Youth Corps. Multicoloured.
902 $1 Type **232** 35 10
903 $2.50 Winter sport 50 10
904 $4 Diving 65 15
905 $8 Parachuting . . . . . . 1·00 45

1972. Improvement of Communications.
906 **233** $1 red 30 10
907 – $2.50 blue 50 20
908 – $5 purple 90 30
DESIGNS—HORIZ: $2.50, Boeing 721-100 airliner and "Hai Mou" (container ship); $5, Diesel railcar and motorway.

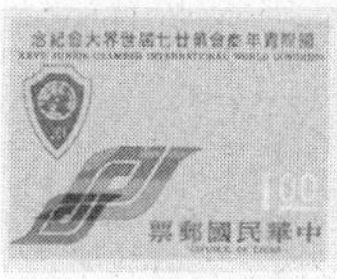
234 "Eyes" and J.C.I. Emblem

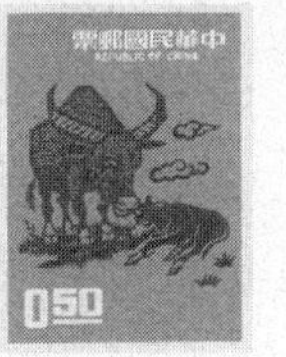
235 Cow and Calf

1972. 27th World Congress of Junior Chamber International, Taipeh.
909 **234** $1 multicoloured 30 10
910 $5 multicoloured 60 20
911 $8 multicoloured 60 30

1972. New Year Greetings. "Year of the Ox".
912 **235** 50c. black and red . . . . 1·40 25
913 $4.50 brown, red & yellow 2·00 75

1973. Chinese Porcelain (2nd series). Ming Dynasty. As T **225**. Multicoloured.
914 $1 Fu vase . . . . 1·00 10
915 $2 Floral vase . . . . 1·50 10
916 $2.50 Ku vase . . . . 1·75 20
917 $5 Hu flask . . . . 2·50 30
918 $8 Garlic-head vase . . . . 3·75 30

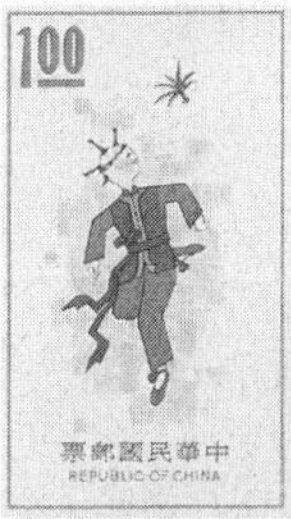
236 "Kicking the Shuttlecock"

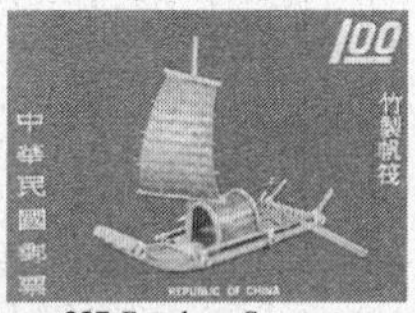
237 Bamboo Sampan

1973. Chinese Folklore (1st series). Mult.
919 $1 Type **236** 40 10
920 $4 "The Fisherman and the Oyster-fairy" (horiz) . . . 90 15
921 $5 "Lady in a Boat" (horiz) 90 15
922 $8 "The Old Man and the Lady" . . . . 1·25 35
See also Nos. 982/3 and 1037/8.

1973. Taiwan Handicrafts (1st series). Mult.
923 $1 Type **237** 60 10
924 $2.50 Marble vase (vert) . . 75 10
925 $5 Glass plate 85 15
926 $8 Aborigine Doll (vert) . . . 90 25
See also Nos. 988/91.

1973. Chinese Porcelain (3rd series). Ming Dynasty. Horiz. designs as T **225**. Multicoloured.
927 $1 Dragon stem-bowl 60 10
928 $2 Dragon pot 85 10
929 $2.50 Covered jar with lotus decor . . . . 1·50 10
930 $5 Covered jar showing horses . . . . 1·50 15
931 $8 "Immortals" bowl . . . . 2·25 15

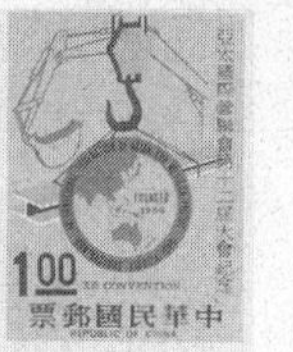
238 Contractors' Equipment

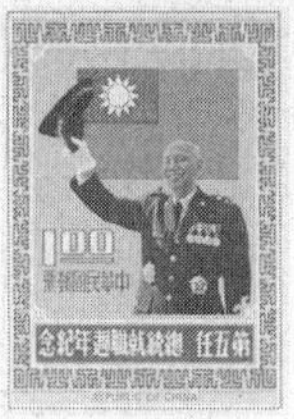
239 Pres. Chiang Kai-shek and Flag

1973. 12th Convention of International Federation of Asian and Western Pacific Contractors' Association.
932 **238** $1 multicoloured 30 10
933 – $5 blue and black 50 15
DESIGN—HORIZ: $5, Bulldozer.

1973. Inauguration of Pres. Chiang Kai-shek's 5th Term of Office.
934 **239** $1 multicoloured 50 10
935 $4 multicoloured 80 15

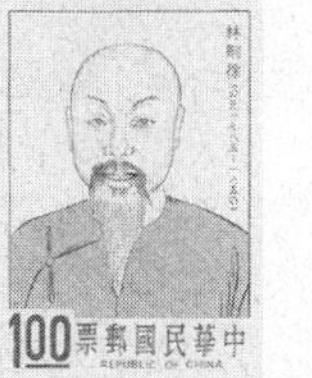
240 Lin Tse-hsu (statesman)

1973. Lin Tse-hsu Commemoration.
936 **240** $1 purple 35 10

1973. "Spring Morning in the Han Palace" (Ming dynasty handscroll). As T **228**. Mult. (a) First issue.
937 $1 (1) Palace gate 20 10
938 $1 (2) Feeding green peafowl 40 10
939 $1 (3) Emperor's wife 20 10
940 $1 (4) Ladies and pear tree 20 10
941 $1 (5) Music pavilion 20 10
942 $5 Giant rock (vert) . . . . 4·75 50
943 $8 Lady musicians (vert) . . 6·00 20

(b) Second issue.
944 $1 (6) Game with flowers . . 20 10
945 $1 (7) Leisure room 20 10
946 $1 (8) Ladies with teapots . . 20 10
947 $1 (9) Artist at work 20 10
948 $1 (10) Palace wall and guards 20 10
949 $5 Playing game at table (vert) . . . . 4·75 50
950 $8 Swatting insect (vert) . . . 6·00 20
Nos. 937/41 and 944/8 are numbered from right to left and were each issued together, se-tenant. When the two strips are placed side by side, they form a composite design showing the complete handscroll.
Nos. 942/3 and 949/50 show enlarged details from the scroll.

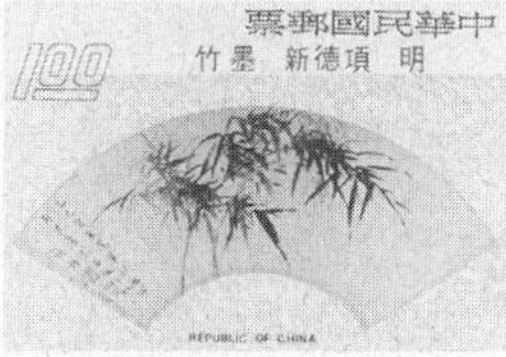
241 "Bamboo" (Hsiang Te-hsin)

1973. Ancient Chinese Fan Paintings (1st series). Multicoloured.
951 $1 Type **241** 80 10
952 $2.50 "Flowers" (Sun K'O-hung) . . . . 2·00 10
953 $5 "Landscape" (Ch'iu Ying) 3·25 20
954 $8 "Seated Figure and Tree" (Shen Chou) . . . . 3·00 20
See also Nos. 1052/5.

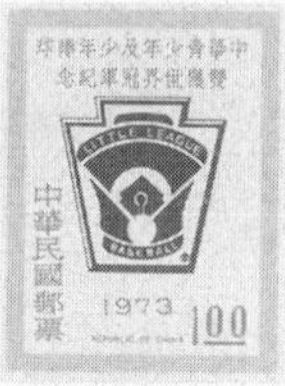
243 Emblem of World Series

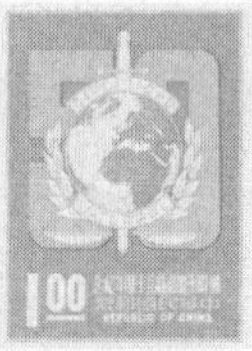
245 Interpol Emblem

1973. Little League World Baseball Series. Taiwan Victory in Twin Championships.
955 **243** $1 blue, red and yellow 45 10
956 $4 blue, green & yellow 75 15

1973. 50th Anniv of International Criminal Police Organization (Interpol).
957 **245** $1 blue and orange . . . 30 10
958 $5 green and orange . . . 60 15
959 $8 purple and orange . . 80 25

1973. Famous Chinese. Portrait as T **132**.
960 $1 violet (Ch'iu Feng-chia (poet)) 55 10

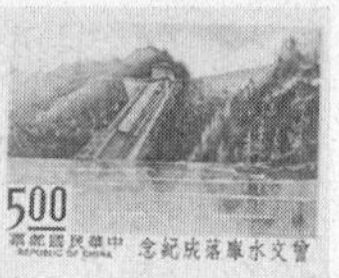
246 Dam and Power Station

1973. Opening of Tsengwen Reservoir. Mult.
961 $1 Upper section of reservoir 10 10
962 $1 Middle section of reservoir 10 10
963 $1 Lower section of reservoir 10 10
964 $5 Type **246** (30 × 22 mm) . . 1·50 25
965 $8 Spillway (50 × 22 mm) . . 1·90 15
The $1 values together show complete map of reservoir (each 38 × 26 mm).

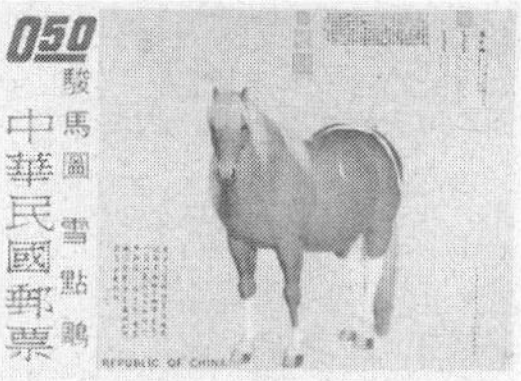
247 "Snow-dotted Eagle"

1973. Paintings of Horses. Multicoloured.
966 50c. Type **247** 10 10
967 $1 "Comfortable Ride" . . . 20 10
968 $1 "Red Flower Eagle" . . . 20 10
969 $1 "Cloud-running Steed" . . 20 10
970 $1 "Sky-running Steed" . . . 20 10
971 $2.50 "Red Jade Steed" . . . 4·50 25
972 $5 "Thunder-clap Steed" . . 6·50 25
973 $8 "Arabian Champion" . . 9·00 20

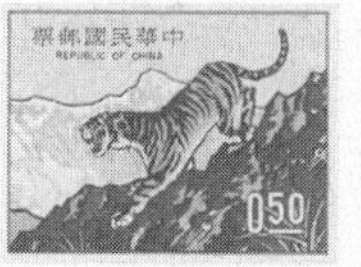
248 Tiger

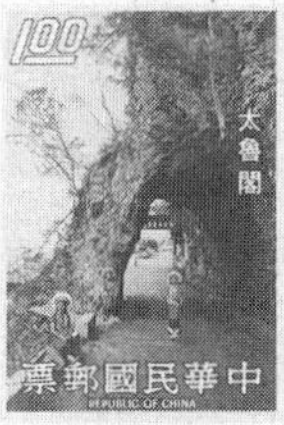
249 Road Tunnel Taroko Gorge

1973. New Year Greetings. "Year of the Tiger".
975 **248** 50c. multicoloured 60 10
976 $4.50 multicoloured . . . 1·00 30

1974. Chinese Porcelain (4th series). Sung Dynasty. As T **225**. Multicoloured.
977 $1 Ko vase 75 10
978 $2 Kuan vase (horiz) 75 10
979 $2.50 Ju bowl (horiz) . . . . 1·00 20
980 $5 Kuan incense burner (horiz) . . . . 1·10 20
981 $8 Chun incense burner (horiz) . . . . 1·40 20

1974. Chinese Folklore (2nd series). As T **236**. Multicoloured.
982 $1 Balancing pot 50 10
983 $8 Magicians (horiz) . . . . 1·00 20

1974. Taiwan Scenery (1st series). Mult.
984 $1 Type **249** 60 10
985 $2.50 Luce Chapel, Tungai University 70 10
986 $5 Tzu En Pagoda, Sun Moon Lake . . . . 1·25 15
987 $8 Goddess of Mercy Statue, Keelung . . . . 1·50 15
See also Nos. 992/5.

1974. Taiwan Handicrafts (2nd series). As T **237**. Multicoloured.
988 $1 "Fighting Cocks" (brass) 40 10
989 $2.50 "Fruits" (jade) 50 15
990 $5 "Fisherman" (wood-carving) (vert) 70 15
991 $8 "Bouquet of Flowers" (plastic) (vert) . . . . . 1·00 15

1974. Taiwan Scenery (2nd series). As T **249** but all horiz. Multicoloured.
992 $1 Dr. Sun Yat-Sen Memorial Hall. Taipeh . . 40 10
993 $2.50 Reaching-Moon Tower, Cheng Ching Lake 55 10
994 $5 Seashore, Lanyu . . . . 1·00 15
995 $8 Inter-island bridge, Penghu . . . . 1·40 15

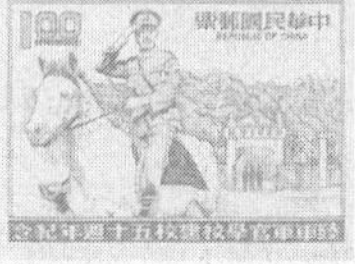
250 Pres. Chiang Kai-shek

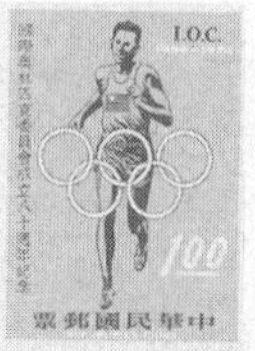
251 Long-distance Runner

1974. 50th Anniv of Chinese Military Academy.
996 **250** $1 mauve 40 10
997 – $14 blue 85 30
DESIGN—VERT: $14, Cadets on parade.

1974. 80th Anniv of International Olympic Committee.
998 **251** $1 blue, black & red . . . 20 10
999 – $8 multicoloured 60 15
DESIGN: $8, Female relay runner.

1974. Chinese Folk tales (3rd series). As T **200**. Multicoloured.
1000 50c. Wen Yen-po retrieving ball 45 10
1001 50c. T'i Ying pleading for mercy 45 10
1002 50c. Wang Ch'i in battle . . 45 10
1003 50c. Wang Hua returning gold 45 10
1004 $1 Pu Shih offering sheep to the emperor 50 10
1005 $1 Szu Ma Kuang saving playmate from water-jar 50 10
1006 $1 Tung Yu at study . . . 50 10
1007 $1 K'ung Yung selecting the smallest pear 50 10

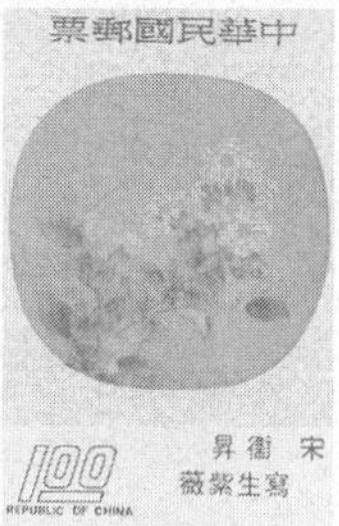
252 "Crape Myrtle" (Wei Sheng)

1974. Ancient Chinese Moon-shaped Fan-paintings (1st series). Multicoloured.
1008 $1 Type **252** 85 10
1009 $2.50 "White Cabbage and Insects" (Hsu Ti) . . . . 1·00 20
1010 $5 "Hibiscus and Rock" (Li Ti) . . . . 1·50 20
1011 $8 "Pomegranates and Narcissus Fly-catcher" (Wu Ping) . . . . 2·25 40
See also Nos. 1068/71 and 1115/1118.

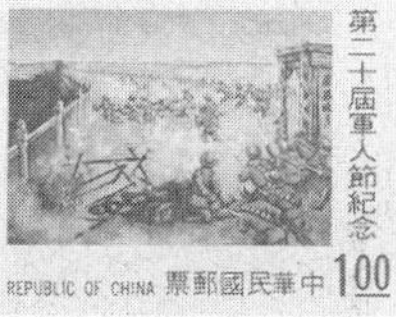
253 "The Battle of Marco Polo Bridge"

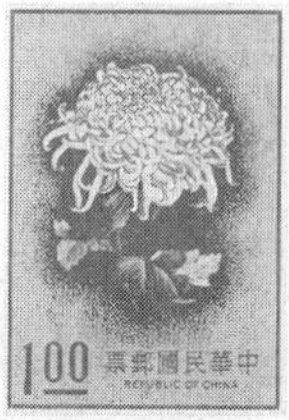
254 Chrysanthemum

1974. Armed Forces' Day.
1012 **253** $1 multicoloured 35 10

1974. Chrysanthemums.
1014 **254** $1 multicoloured 40 10
1015 – $2.50 multicoloured . . 85 20
1016 – $5 multicoloured . . . . 1·25 20
1017 – $8 multicoloured . . . . 1·75 15
DESIGNS: Nos. 1015/17, various chrysanthemums.

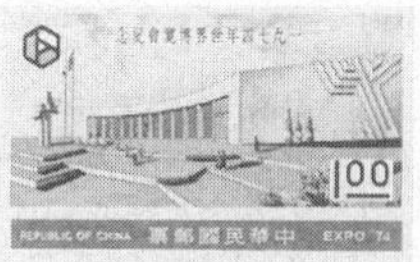
255 Chinese Pavilion

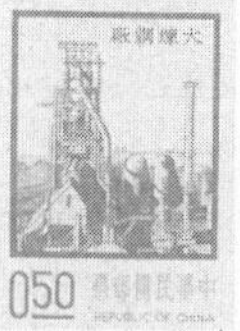
256 Steel Mill, Kaohsiung

1974. "Expo 74" World Fair, Spokane, Washington. Multicoloured.
1018 $1 Type **255** 20 10
1019 $8 Fairground map 50 15

1974. Major Construction Projects (1st series). Chinese inscr in single-line characters, figures of value solid.* Multicoloured.
1020 50c. Type **256** 10 10
1021 $1 Taiwan North link railway 30 10
1022 $2 Petrochemical works, Kaohsiung 15 10
1023 $2.50 TRA trunk line electrification 50 10
1024 $3 Taichung harbour (horiz) 30 10
1025 $3.50 Taoyuan international airport (horiz) 30 10
1026 $4 Taiwan North–south motorway (horiz) 30 10
1027 $4.50 Giant shipyard, Kaohsiung (horiz) . . . 50 25
1028 $5 Su-ao port (horiz) . . . 50 10
*The first series can also be distinguished by the Chinese and English inscr at the foot being in different

colours; in the second and third series only one colour is used.

See also Nos. 1122a/1122i and 1145/1153.

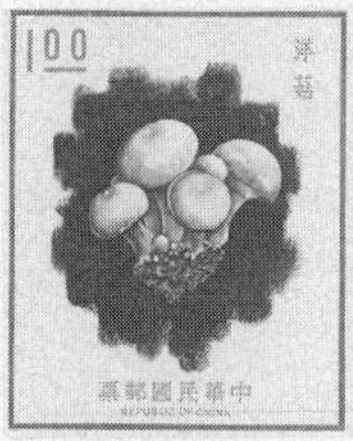

257 White Button Mushrooms

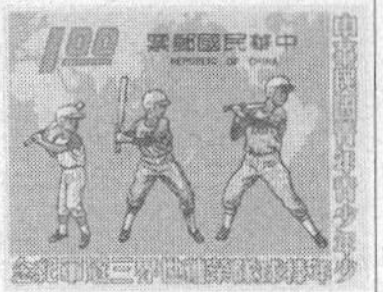

258 Baseball Strikers

1974. Edible Fungi. Multicoloured.

1029	$1 Type **257**	55	10
1030	$2.50 Oyster fungus	90	20
1031	$5 Veiled stinkhorn	1·40	25
1032	$8 Golden mushrooms . . .	1·40	30

1974. Taiwan Triple Championship Victories in World Little League Baseball Series, U.S.A. Multicoloured.

1033	$1 Type **258**	25	10
1034	$8 Player and banners . . .	50	15

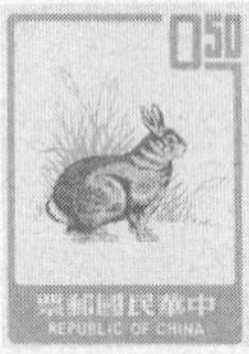

259 Chinese Hare

1974. New Year Greetings. "Year of the Hare".

1035 **259**	50c. multicoloured . . .	35	10
1036	$4.50 multicoloured . .	1·25	25

1975. Chinese Folklore (3rd series). As T **236**. Multicoloured.

1037	$4 Acrobat	50	15
1038	$5 Jugglers with diabolo . .	1·00	20

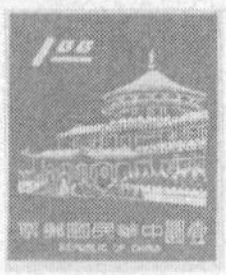

260 Chungshan Building, Yangmingshan

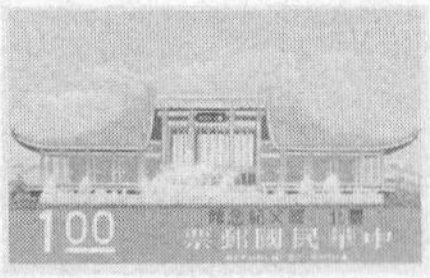

261 Sun Yat-sen Memorial Hall, Taipeh

1975.

1039 **260**	$1 red	25	15

Type **260** is a redrawn version of Type **195**.

1975. "New Year Festivals" (handscroll by Ting Kuan-p'eng). As T **228**. Multicoloured.

1040	$1 (1) Greetings	20	10
1041	$1 (2) Entertainer	20	10
1042	$1 (3) Crowd and musicians	20	10
1043	$1 (4) Picnic	20	10
1044	$1 (5) Puppet show	20	10
1045	$2.50 New Year greetings	2·50	30
1046	$5 Children buying fireworks	4·25	30
1047	$8 Entertainer with monkey and dog	5·25	45

Nos. 1040/4 were issued together, se-tenant, forming a composite design.

1975. 50th Death Anniv of Dr. Sun Yat-sen.

1048	$1 Type **261**	25	10
1049	$4 Sun Yat-sen's handwriting	40	15
1050	$5 Bronze statue of Sun Yat-sen (vert)	50	15
1051	$8 Sun Yat-sen Memorial Hall, St. John's University, U.S.A	75	15

1975. Ancient Chinese Fan Paintings (2nd series). As T **241**. Multicoloured.

1052	$1 "Landscape" (Li Liu-fang)	75	10
1053	$2.50 "Landscape" (Wen Cheng-ming)	75	20
1054	$5 "Landscape" (Chou Ch'en)	1·60	20
1055	$8 "Landscape" (T'ang Yin)	2·00	15

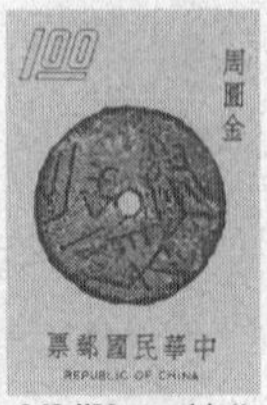

262 "Yuan-chin" Coin (Chou dynasty)

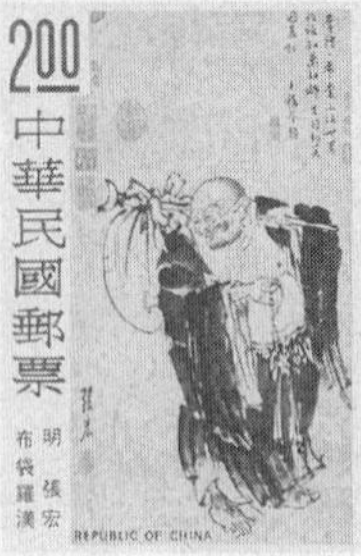

263 "Lohan, the Cloth-bag Monk" (Chang Hung)

1975. Ancient Chinese Coins (1st series). Mult.

1056	$1 Type **262**	50	10
1057	$4 "Pan-liang" coin (Chin dynasty)	85	15
1058	$5 "Five chu" coin (Han dynasty)	1·00	15
1059	$8 "Five chu" coin (Liang dynasty)	1·25	10

See also Nos. 1111/14 and 1184/7.

1975. Ancient Chinese Figure Paintings. Mult.

1060	$2 Type **263**	75	10
1061	$4 "Lao-tzu on buffalo" (Chao Pu-chih)	1·75	15
1062	$5 "Shih-te" (Wang-wen) . .	3·00	15
1063	$8 "Splashed-ink Immortal" (Liang K'ai)	3·00	15

1975. Chinese Folk-tales (4th series). As T **200**. Multicoloured.

1064	$1 Chu-Yin reading by light of fireflies	20	10
1065	$2 Hua Mu-lan going to battle disguised as a man	35	10
1066	$2 Ling Kou Chien living a humble life	40	10
1067	$5 Chou Ch'u defeating the tiger	1·00	25

1975. Ancient Chinese Moon-shaped Fan Paintings (2nd series). As T **252**. Multicoloured.

1068	$1 "Cherry-apple blossoms" (Lin Ch'un)	75	10
1069	$2 "Spring blossoms and a colourful butterfly" (Ma K'uei)	90	10
1070	$5 "Monkeys and deer" (I Yuan-chi)	1·10	20
1071	$8 "Tree sparrows among bamboo" (anon.)	2·40	40

1975. Famous Chinese. Martyrs of War against Japan. Portraits as T **132**.

1072	$2 red (Gen. Chang Tzu-chung)	25	10
1073	$2 brown (Maj.-Gen. Kao Chih-hang)	25	10
1074	$2 green (Capt. Sha Shih-chiun)	25	10
1075	$5 brown (Maj-Gen. Hsieh Chin-yuan)	40	15
1076	$5 blue (Lt. Yen Hai-wen)	40	15
1077	$5 blue (Lt.-Gen. Tai An-lan)	40	15

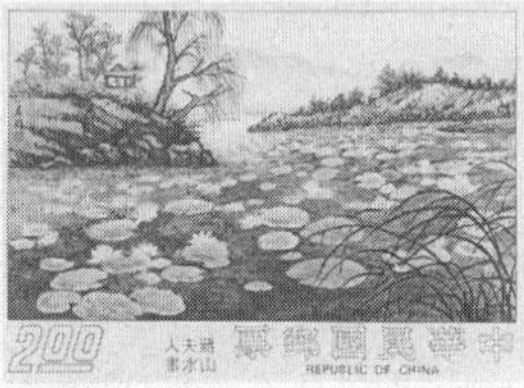

264 "Lotus Pond with Willows"

1975. Madame Chiang Kai-shek's Landscape Paintings (1st series). Multicoloured.

1078	$2 Type **264**	1·00	10
1079	$5 "Sun breaks through Mountain Clouds" . . .	1·50	30
1080	$8 "A Pair of Pine Trees"	3·75	40
1081	$10 "Fishing and Farming"	4·75	55

See also Nos. 1139/1142 and 1727/30.

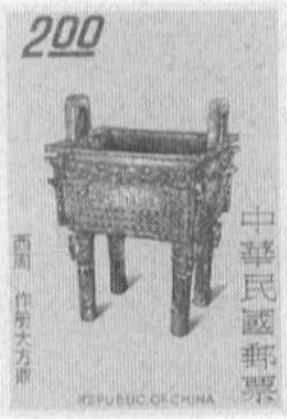

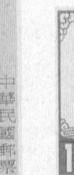

265 Rectangular Cauldron

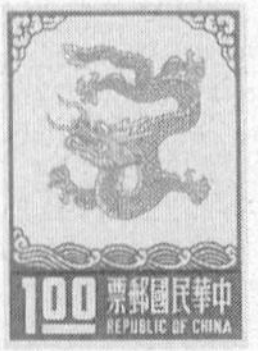

266 Dragon, Nine-Dragon Wall, Peihai

1975. Ancient Bronzes (1st series). Mult.

1082	$2 Type **265**	50	10
1083	$5 Cauldron with "Phoenix" handles (horiz)	75	15
1084	$8 Flat jar (horiz)	1·50	25
1085	$10 Wine vessel	2·00	30

See also Nos. 1119/22.

1975. New Year Greetings. "Year of the Dragon".

1086 **266**	$1 multicoloured	50	10
1087	$5 multicoloured	1·00	20

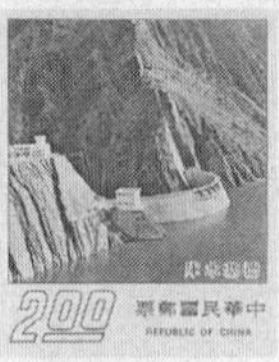

267 Techi Dam

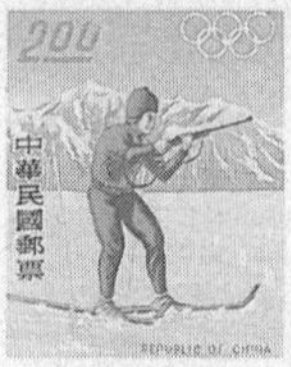

268 Biathlon

1975. Completion of Techi Reservoir. Mult.

1088	$2 Type **267**	25	10
1089	$10 Dam and reservoir . . .	50	30

1976. Winter Olympic Games, Innsbruck. Mult.

1090	$2 Type **268**	30	10
1091	$5 Luge	40	15
1092	$8 Skiing	60	15

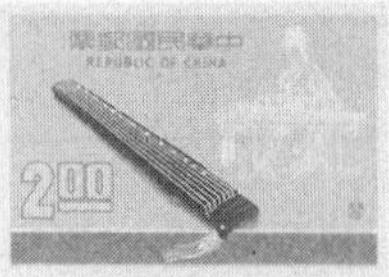

269 "Chin"

1976. Chinese Musical Instruments (1st series). Multicoloured.

1093	$2 Type **269**	40	10
1094	$5 "Se" (string instrument)	60	10
1095	$8 "Standing Kong-ho" (harp)	70	15
1096	$10 "Sleeping Kong-ho" (harp)	85	20

See also Nos. 1156/9.

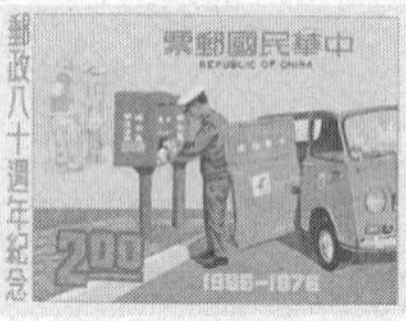

270 Postman collecting Mail

1976. 80th Anniv of Chinese Postal Service. Multicoloured.

1097	$2 Type **270**	20	10
1098	$5 Mail-sorting systems (vert)	30	15
1099	$8 Mail transport (vert) . .	1·00	15
1100	$10 Traditional and modern post deliveries	70	20

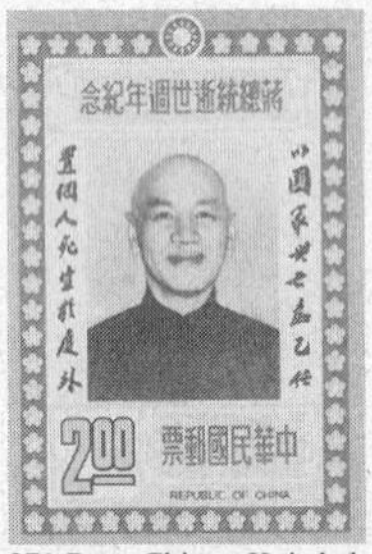

271 Pres. Chiang Kai-shek

1976. 1st Death Anniv of President Chiang Kai-shek. Multicoloured.

1102	$2 Type **271**	30	10
1103	$2 People paying homage (horiz)	30	10
1104	$2 Lying-in-state (horiz) . .	30	10
1105	$2 Start of funeral procession (horiz)	30	10
1106	$5 Roadside obeisance (horiz)	40	15
1107	$8 Altar, Tzuhu Guest-house (horiz)	50	20
1108	$10 Tzuhu Guest-house (horiz)	75	25

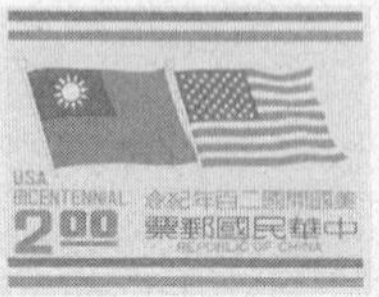

272 Chinese and U.S. Flags

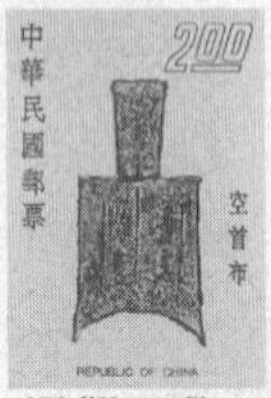

273 "Kung Shou Pu" Coin (Shang/Chou Dynasties)

1976. Bicentenary of American Revolution.

1109 **272**	$2 multicoloured	20	10
1110	$10 multicoloured . . .	50	25

1976. Ancient Chinese Coins (2nd series). Mult.

1111	$2 Type **273**	50	10
1112	$5 "Chien Tsu Pu" coin (Chao Kingdom)	75	15
1113	$8 "Yuan Tsu Pu" coin (Tsin Kingdom)	90	20
1114	$10 "Fang Tsu Pu" coin (Chin/Han Dynasties) . .	1·25	25

1976. Ancient Chinese Moon-shaped Fan-paintings (3rd series) As T **252**. Multicoloured.

1115	$2 "Hibiscus" (Li Tung) . .	50	10
1116	$5 "Lilies" (Lin Chun) . . .	1·25	15
1117	$8 "Two Sika Deer, Mushrooms and Pine" (Mou Chung-fu)	1·75	30
1118	$10 "Wild Flowers and Japanese Quail" (Li An-chung)	4·75	45

1976. Ancient Bronzes (2nd series). As T **265**. Multicoloured.

1119	$2 Square cauldron	50	10
1120	$5 Round cauldron	80	10
1121	$8 Wine vessel	1·00	15
1122	$10 Wine vessel with legs . .	1·25	20

No. 1119 is similar to Type **265**, but has four characters at left only.

1976. Major Construction Projects (2nd series). Designs as Nos. 1020/8, but Chinese inscr in double-lined characters. Figures of value solid. Multicoloured.

1122a	$1 As No. 1021	50	10
1122b	$2 As No. 1023	50	10
1122c	$3 As No. 1024	30	10
1122d	$4 As No. 1026	30	10
1122e	$5 As Type **256**	30	10
1122f	$6 As No. 1025	40	10
1122g	$7 As No. 1027	45	10
1122h	$8 As No. 1022	50	15
1122i	$9 As No. 1028	50	20

See also Nos. 1145/53.

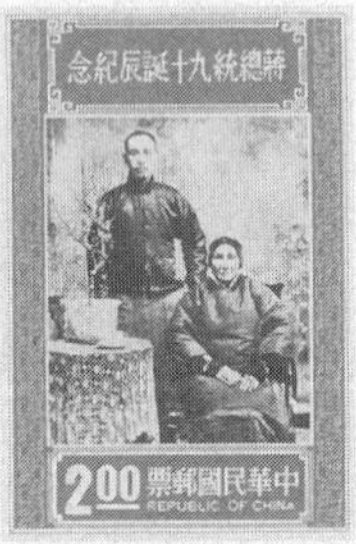

274 Chiang Kai-shek and Mother

1976. 90th Birth Anniv of President Chiang Kai-shek. Multicoloured.

1123	$2 Type **274**	30	10
1124	$5 Chiang Kai-shek	30	15
1125	$10 Chiang Kai-shek and Dr. Sun Yat-sen in railway carriage (horiz)	85	50

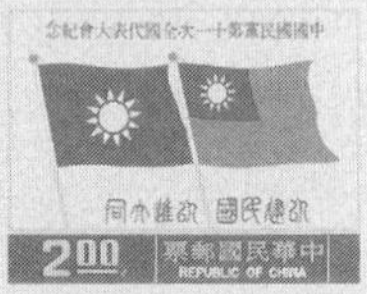

275 Chinese and KMT Flags

1976. 11th Kuomintang National Congress. Mult.

1126	$2 Type **275**	20	10
1127	$10 President Chiang Kai-shek and Dr. Sun Yat-sen	40	25

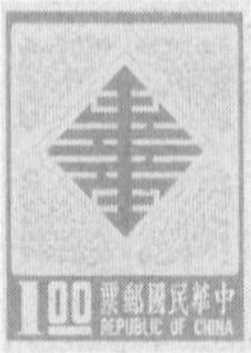

276 Brazen Serpent

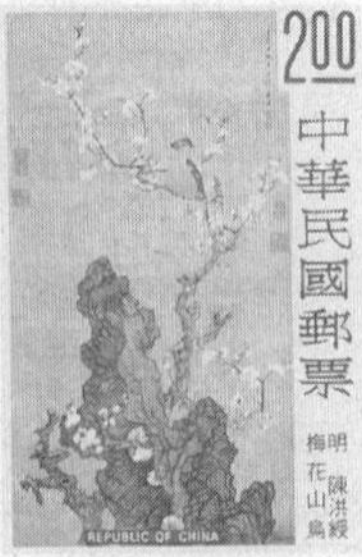

277 "Bird and Plum Blossom" (Ch'en Hung-shou)

1976. New Year Greetings. "Year of the Snake".

1129 **276**	$1 multicoloured	60	10
1130	$5 multicoloured	1·10	10

1977. Ancient Chinese Paintings. "Three Friends of Winter".

1131	$2 Type **277**	1·00	10
1132	$8 "Wintry Days" (Yang Wei-chen)	2·25	25
1133	$10 "Rock and Bamboo" (Hsia Ch'ang)	2·50	20

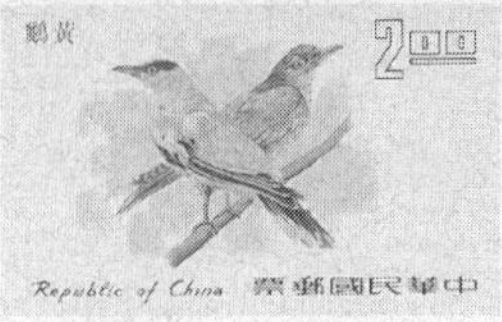
278 Black-naped Orioles

1977. Taiwan Birds. Multicoloured.
1134 $2 Type **278** . . . . 1·00 10
1135 $8 River kingfisher . . . . 1·25 50
1136 $10 Pheasant-tailed jacana 2·00 50

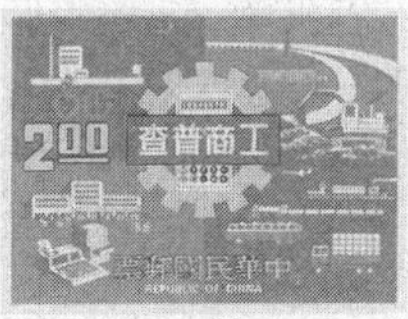
279 Emblems of Industry and Commerce

1977. Industry and Commerce Census.
1137 **279** $2 multicoloured 35 15
1138 $10 multicoloured . . . 90 35

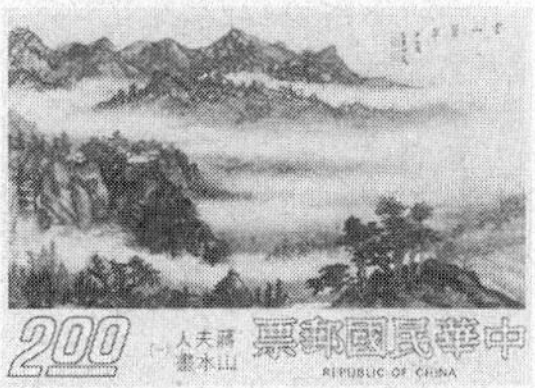
280 "Green Mountains rising into Clouds"

1977. Madame Chiang Kai-shek's Landscape Paintings (2nd series). Multicoloured.
1139 $2 Type **280** 80 10
1140 $5 "Boat amidst Spring's Beauty" . . . . 1·00 20
1141 $8 "Scholar beside the Rivulet" . . . . 2·25 15
1142 $10 "Green Water rising to meet the Bridge" . . . . 3·00 30

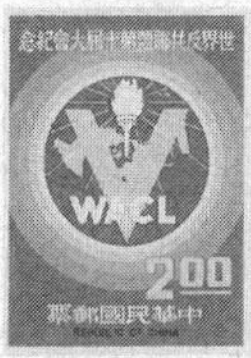
281 W.A.C.L. Emblem

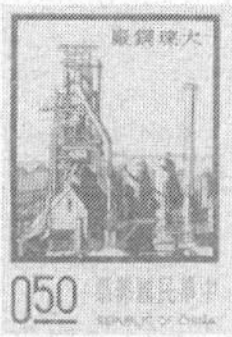
282 Steel Mill, Kaohsiung

1977. 10th World Anti-Communist League Conf.
1143 **281** $2 multicoloured 20 10
1144 $10 multicoloured . . . 50 15

1977. Major Construction Projects (3rd series). Designs as Nos. 1122a/i, but redrawn with double lined figures of value as in T **282**. Multicoloured.
1145 $1 Taiwan North link railway 50 10
1146 $2 TRA trunk line electrification 50 10
1147 $3 Taichung harbour (horiz) 30 10
1148 $4 Taiwan North–south highway (horiz) 25 10
1149 $5 Type **282** 35 10
1150 $6 Taoyuan international airport (horiz) 35 10
1151 $7 Giant shipyard, Kaohsiung (horiz) 40 10
1152 $8 Petrochemical works, Kaohsiung 50 10
1153 $9 Su-ao port (horiz) . . . 60 10

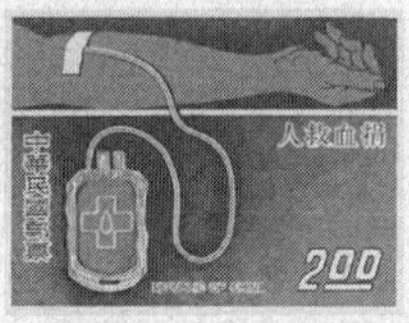
283 "Blood Donation"

1977. Blood Donation Movement.
1154 **283** $2 red, black and yellow 20 10
1155 – $10 red and black . . . 50 15
DESIGN—VERT: $10, "Blood Transfusion".

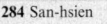

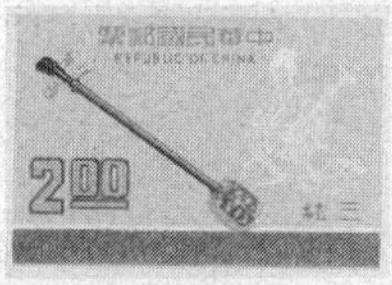
284 San-hsien

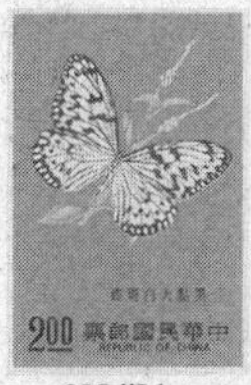
285 "Idea leuconoe"

1977. Chinese Musical Instruments (2nd series). Multicoloured.
1156 $2 Type **284** 40 10
1157 $5 Tung-hsiao (wind instrument) 70 10
1158 $8 Yang-chin (xylophone) 80 12
1159 $10 Pai-hsiao (pipes) 90 15

1977. Taiwan Butterflies. Multicoloured.
1160 $2 Type **285** 60 10
1161 $4 Great orange-tip 80 20
1162 $6 "Stichophthalma howqua" . . . . 1·00 25
1163 $10 "Atrophaneura horishanus" . . . . . . 1·75 15

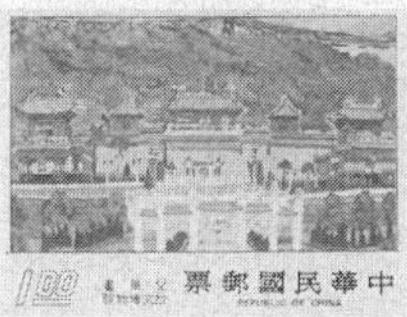
286 "National Palace Museum"

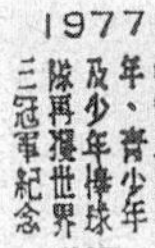
(287)

1977. Children's Drawings. Multicoloured.
1164 $1 Type **286** 15 10
1165 $2 "Festival of Sea Goddess" 25 10
1166 $4 "Boats on Lan-yu" . . . 35 10
1167 $5 "Temple" (vert) 45 10

1977. Triple Championships of the 1977 Little League World Baseball Series. Nos. 1146 and 1152 optd with Type **287**.
1168 $2 multicoloured 50 15
1169 $8 multicoloured 50 15

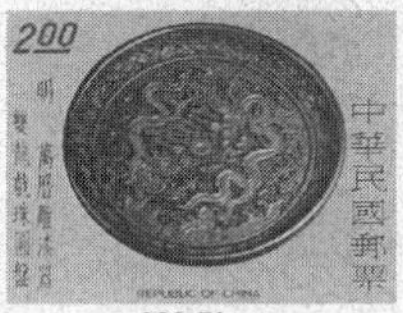
288 Plate

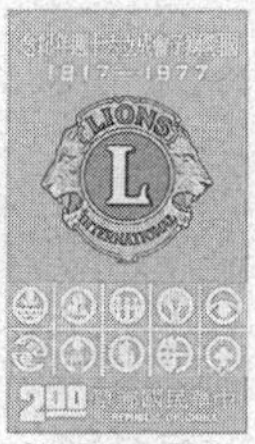
289 Lions Club Emblem

1977. Ancient Chinese Carved Lacquer Ware (1st series). Multicoloured.
1170 $2 Type **288** 60 10
1171 $5 Bowl 85 10
1172 $8 Box 85 10
1173 $10 Three-tiered box . . . . 1·00 15
See also Nos. 1206/1209.

1977. 60th Anniv of Lions International.
1174 **289** $2 multicoloured 20 10
1175 $10 multicoloured . . . 50 15

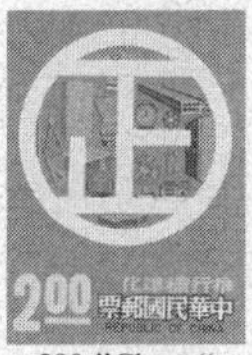
290 "Cheng" Government Standard Mark

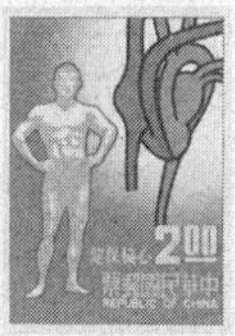
291 Human Figure and Diagram of Heart

1977. Standardization Movement.
1176 **290** $2 multicoloured 35 10
1177 $10 multicoloured . . . 90 15

1977. Prevention of Heart Disease Campaign.
1178 **291** $2 multicoloured 20 10
1179 $10 multicoloured . . . 50 15

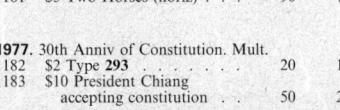

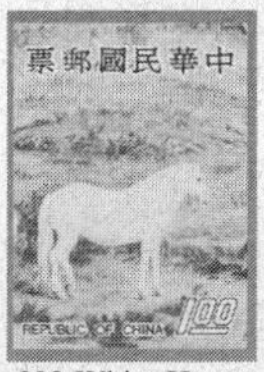
292 White Horse

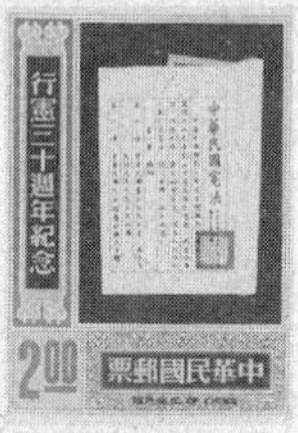
293 First Page of Constitution

1977. New Year Greetings. "Year of the Horse". Details from "One Hundred Horses" by Lang Shih-ning (Giuseppe Castiglione). Multicoloured.
1180 $1 Type **292** 35 10
1181 $5 Two Horses (horiz) . . . 90 15

1977. 30th Anniv of Constitution. Mult.
1182 $2 Type **293** 20 10
1183 $10 President Chiang accepting constitution . . 50 20

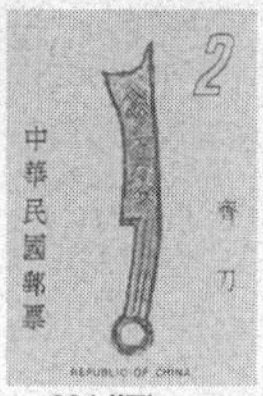
294 "Three-character" Knife (Chi State)

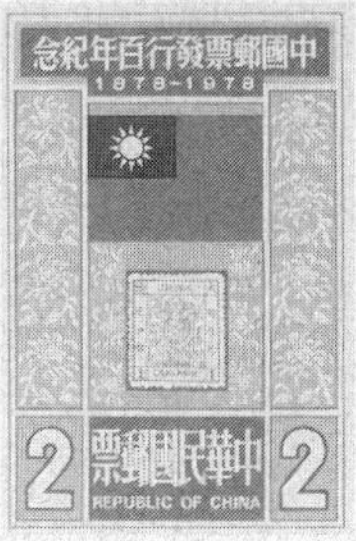
295 "Dragon" Stamp, 1878

1978. Ancient Chinese Coins (3rd series). Mult.
1184 $2 Type **294** 50 10
1185 $5 Longer sharp-headed knife (Yen State) 90 10
1186 $8 Sharp-headed knife (Yet State) . . . . 1·00 15
1187 $10 Chao or Ming knife . . 1·25 20

1978. Cent of Chinese Postage Stamp. Mult.
1188 $2 Type **295** 40 10
1189 $5 "Dr. Sun Yat-sen" stamp, 1941 . . . . . . 50 10
1190 $10 "Chiang Kai-shek" stamp, 1958 . . . . . . 75 20

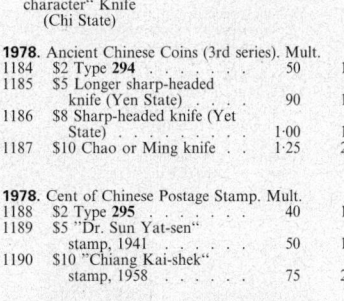

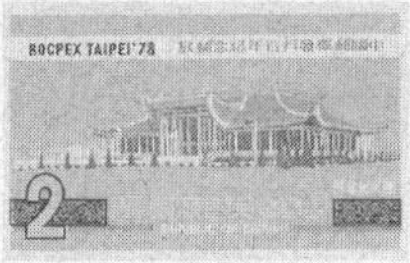
296 Dr. Sun Yat-sen Memorial Hall

1978. "Rocpex" Taipeh 1978 Philatelic Exhibition. Multicoloured.
1192 $2 Type **296** 20 10
1193 $10 "Dragon" and 1977 "New Year" stamps . . . 75 20

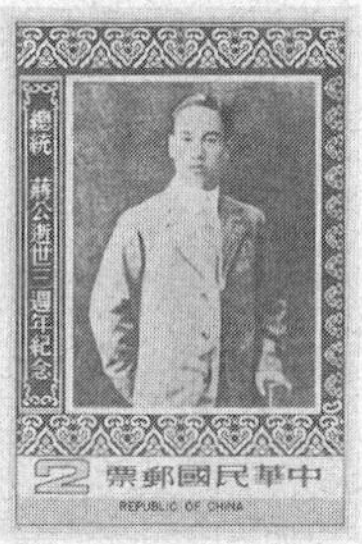
297 Chiang Kai-shek as a Young Man

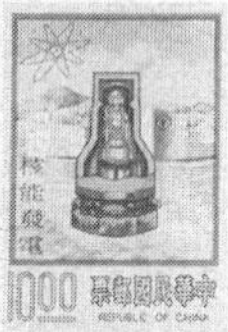
298 Section through Nuclear Reactor

1978. 3rd Death Anniv of Pres. Chiang Kai-shek. Multicoloured.
1194 $2 Type **297** 25 10
1195 $5 Chiang on horseback (horiz) 40 10
1196 $8 Chiang making speech (horiz) 60 15
1197 $10 Reviewing armed forces 80 20

1978. Nuclear Power Plant.
1198 **298** $10 multicoloured . . . 60 15

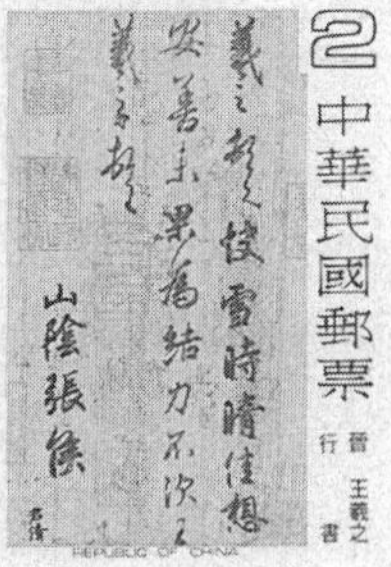
299 Letter by Wang Hsi-chih

300 Human Figure in Polluted Environment

1978. Chinese Calligraphy. Multicoloured.
1199 $2 Type **299** 60 10
1200 $4 Eulogy of Ni K'uan by Chu Sui-liang . . . . . . 1·50 15
1201 $6 Inscription on poem "Lake Tai" by Wen Cheng-ming . . . . . . 1·75 25
1202 $8 Autobiography by Huai-su . . . . 3·00 30
1203 $10 Poem by Ch'ang Piao 5·25 40

1978. Cancer Prevention.
1204 **300** $2 green, yellow & red 15 10
1205 $10 blue, green & dp blue 35 15

1978. Ancient Chinese Carved Lacquer Ware (2nd series). As T **288**. Multicoloured.
1206 $2 Square box 30 10
1207 $5 Box on legs 40 10
1208 $8 Round box 60 15
1209 $10 Vase (vert) 90 20

1978. Chinese Folk-tales (5th series). As T **200**. Multicoloured.
1210 $1 Tsu Ti brandishing sword 20 10
1211 $2 Pan Ch'ao throwing down pen 50 10
1212 $2 Tien Tan's "Fire Bull Battle" 75 10
1213 $5 Liang Hung-yu as army drummer . . . . 1·10 10

1978. Triple Championships of the Little League World Baseball Series. Nos. 1148 and 1150 optd as T **287**, but with four lines of characters and dated 1978.
1214 $4 Taiwan North–south highway 20 15
1215 $6 Taoyuan international airport 40 25

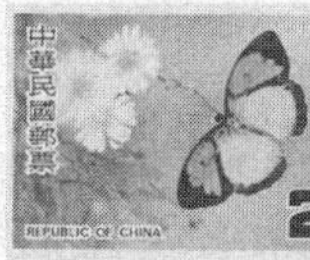
302 Yellow Orange-tip

1978. Taiwan Butterflies. Multicoloured.
1216 $2 Type **302** 30 10
1217 $4 Two-brand crow 70 10
1218 $6 Common map butterfly 1·10 15
1219 $10 "Atrophaneura polyeuctes" . . . . 1·10 25

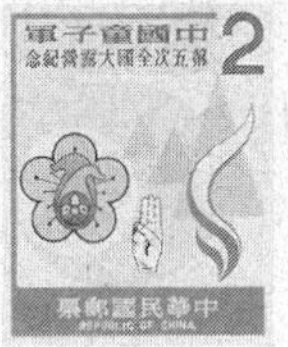
303 Jamboree Badge, Camp and Scout Salute

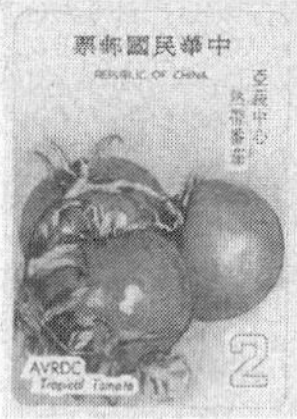
304 Tropical Tomatoes

1978. Taiwanese Boy Scouts' 5th Jamboree.
1220 **303** $2 multicoloured 40 10
1221 $10 multicoloured . . . 60 20

1978. Asian Vegetable Research and Development Centre. Multicoloured.
1222 $2 Type **304** 40 10
1223 $10 Tropical tomatoes (different) 85 25

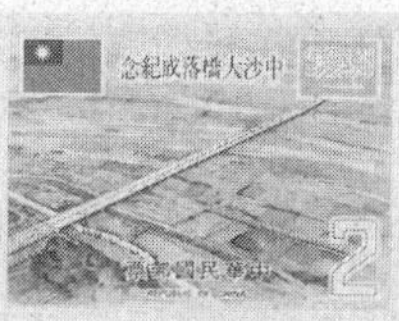
305 Aerial View of Bridge

306 National Flag

1978. Opening of the Sino-Saudi Bridge. Mult.
1224 $2 Type **305** 50 10
1225 $6 Close-up of bridge . . . 90 15

1978.
1226 **306** $1 red and blue 15 10
1377 $1 red and blue 20 10
1378 $1.50 red, blue & yellow 45 10
1227 $2 red and blue 15 10
1379 $2 red, blue and yellow 20 10
1297 $3 red, blue and green 35 10
1380 $3 red and blue 30 10
1298 $4 red, blue and brown 30 15
1381 $4 red, blue and light blue 30 10
1228 $5 red, blue and green 30 10
1382 $5 red, blue and brown 30 10
1229 $6 red, blue and orange 40 10
1300 $7 red, blue and brown 40 10
1384 $7 red, blue and green 50 10
1230 $8 red, blue and green 45 10
1385 $8 red, blue & deep red 45 10
1386 $9 red, blue and green 60 10
1231 $10 red, blue and lt blue 75 15
1387 $10 red, blue and violet 55 10
1302 $12 red, blue and mauve 60 25
1389 $14 red, blue and green 1·25 10

The $1 values differ in the face value, which is printed in colour on No. 1226, whilst on No. 1377 it is white.

Nos. 1377/8, 1379, 1380, 1381, 1382 and the $6 to $14 values are as Type **306** but have solid background panel to face value and inscr.

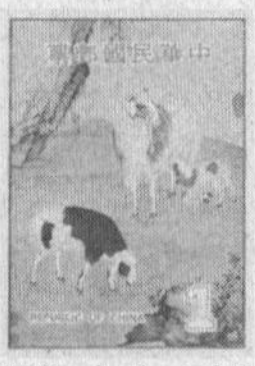
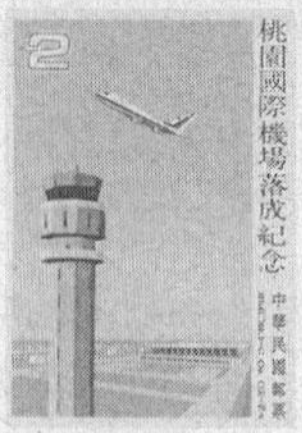

307 "Imitation of the Three Sheep by Emperor Hsuan-tsung of the Ming Dynasty" (Emperor Kao-tsung)
308 Boeing 747-100 and Control Building

1978. New Year Greetings. "Year of the Sheep".
1232 **307** $1 multicoloured 50 10
1233 $5 multicoloured 80 15

1978. Completion of Taoyuan International Airport. Multicoloured.
1234 $2 Type **308** 35 10
1235 $10 Passenger terminal building (horiz) 60 25

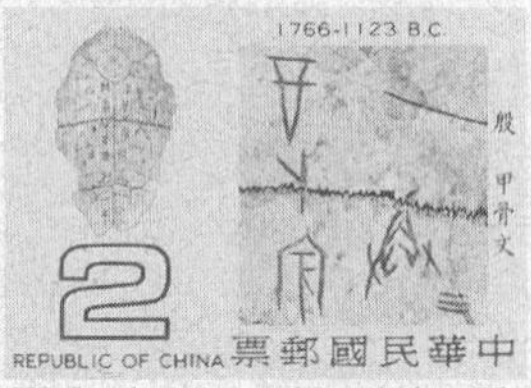

309 Oracle Bones and Inscription (Yin Dynasty)

1979. Origin and Development of Chinese Characters. Multicoloured.
1236 $2 Type **309** 60 10
1237 $5 "Leh-chi" cauldron and inscription (Spring and Autumn period) . . . . . 1·00 15
1238 $8 Engraved seal and seal-style characters (Western Han dynasty) . . . . . 1·40 25
1239 $10 Square plain-style characters inscribed on stone (Eastern Han dynasty) . . . . 2·50 45

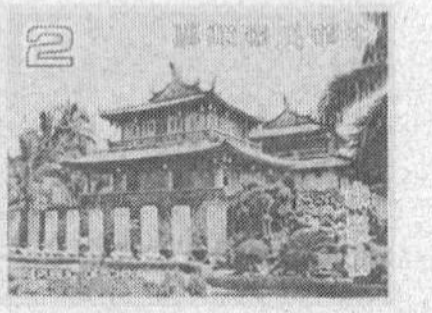

310 Chihkan Tower, Tainan

1979. Tourism. Multicoloured.
1240 $2 Type **310** 35 10
1241 $5 Confucius Temple, Tainan 35 15
1242 $8 Koxinga Shrine, Tainan 35 25
1243 $10 Eternal Castle, Tainan 1·50 30

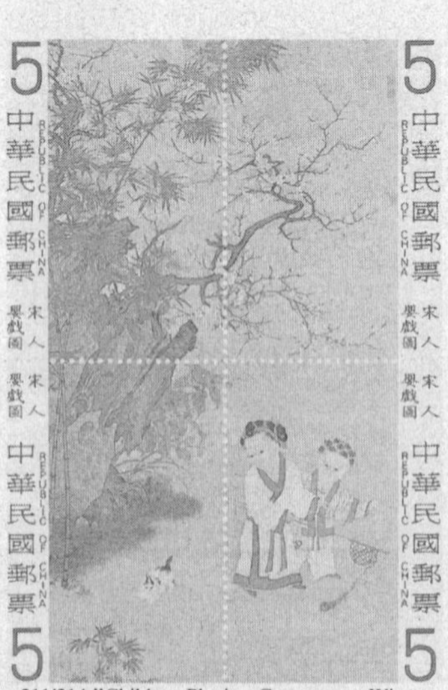

311/314 "Children Playing Games on a Winter Day". ($\frac{2}{3}$-size illustration)

1979. Sung Dynasty Painting.
1244 **311** $5 multicoloured . . . . 2·25 65
1245 **312** $5 multicoloured . . . . 2·25 65
1246 **313** $5 multicoloured . . . . 2·25 65
1247 **314** $5 multicoloured . . . . 2·25 65
Nos. 1244/7 were printed together, se-tenant, forming the composite design illustrated.

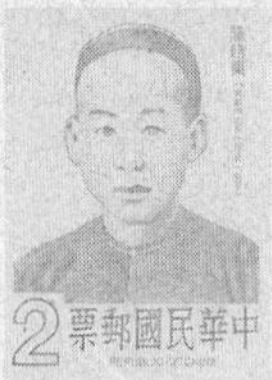
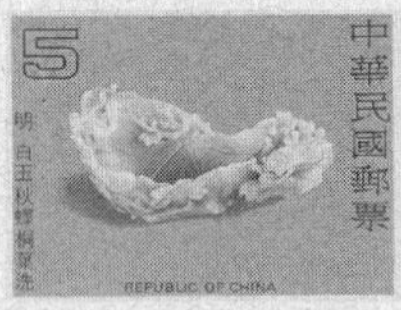

315 Lu Hao-tung (revolutionary)
316 White Jade Brush Washer (Ming dynasty)

1979. Famous Chinese.
1249 **315** $2 blue 40 10

1979. Ancient Chinese Jade (1st series). Multicoloured.
1250 $2 Yellow jade brush holder embossed with clouds and dragons (Sung dynasty) (vert) 35 10
1251 $5 Type **316** 80 15
1252 $8 Dark green jade brush washer carved with clouds and dragons (Ch'ing dynasty) 95 20
1253 $10 Bluish jade washer in shape of lotus (Ch'ing dynasty) . . . . 1·40 25
See also Nos. 1291/4.

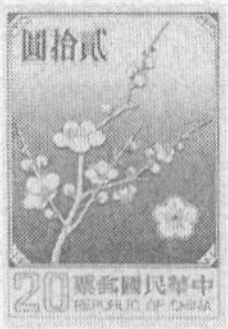
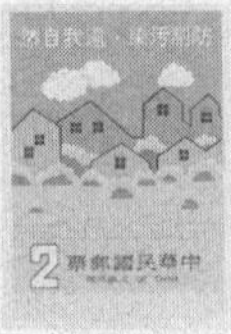

317 Plum Blossom
318 Houses

1979.
1254a **317** $10 blue 40 10
1255a $20 brown 80 10
1255ba $40 red . . . . . . 1·60 10
1256a $50 green . . . . . . 2·00 10
1257 $100 red . . . . . . 3·50 10
1257b $300 red and violet . . 14·00 2·00
1257c $500 red and brown 23·00 4·75
The $300 and $500 are size 25 × 33 mm.

1979. Environmental Protection. Mult.
1258 $2 Type **318** 15 10
1259 $10 Rural scene (horiz) . . 55 25

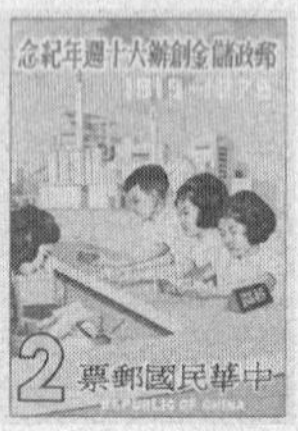

319 Savings Bank Counter

1979. 60th Anniv of Postal Savings Bank. Multicoloured.
1260 $2 Type **319** 20 10
1261 $5 Savings bank queue . . . 30 15
1262 $8 Computer and savings book (horiz) 45 20
1263 $10 Money box and "tree" emblem (horiz) 60 25

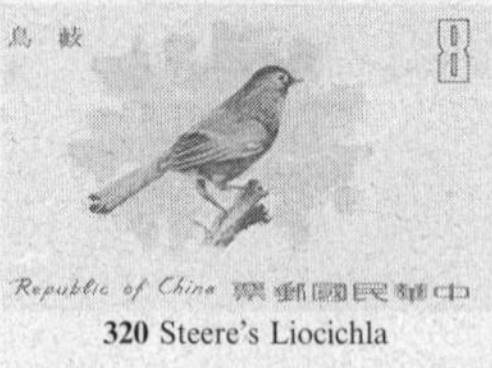

320 Steere's Liocichla

1979. Birds. Multicoloured.
1264 $2 Swinhoe's pheasant . . . 50 10
1265 $8 Type **320** . . . . 1·25 40
1266 $10 Formosan yuhina . . . 2·00 60

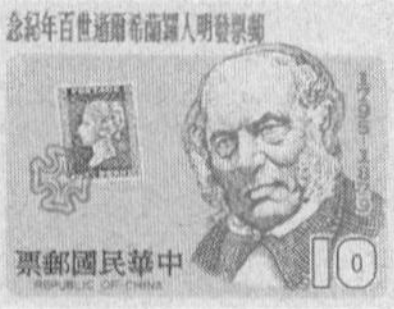
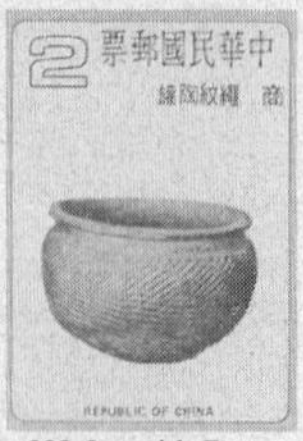

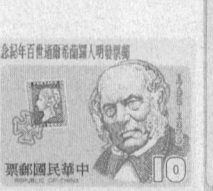

321 Sir Rowland Hill
322 Jar with Rope Pattern

1979. Death Centenary of Sir Rowland Hill.
1267 **321** $10 multicoloured . . . 75 25

1979. Ancient Chinese Pottery. Multicoloured.
1268 $2 Type **322** (Shang dynasty) 30 10
1269 $5 Two handled jar (Shang dynasty) 65 15
1270 $8 Red jar with "ears" (Han dynasty) . . . . 1·00 20
1271 $10 Green glazed jar (Han dynasty) . . . . 1·50 25

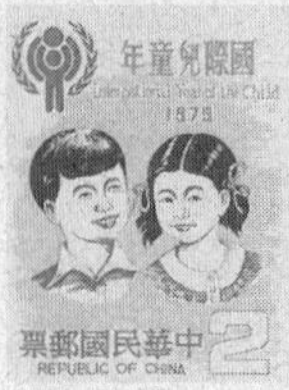
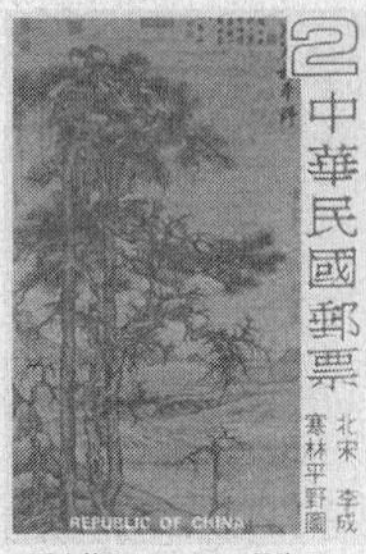

323 Children and I.Y.C. Emblem
324 "Trees on a Winter Plain" (Li Ch'eng)

1979. International Year of the Child.
1272 **323** $2 multicoloured 25 10
1273 $10 multicoloured . . . 50 25

1979. Ancient Chinese Paintings. Mult.
1274 $2 Type **324** (Sung dynasty) 60 10
1275 $5 "Bamboo" (Wen T'ung, Sung dynasty) . . . . . 1·60 15
1276 $8 "Old Tree, Bamboo and Rock" (Chao Mengfu, Yuan dynasty) . . . . . 2·40 20
1277 $10 "Twin Pines" (Li K'an, Yuan dynasty) . . . . . 3·50 25

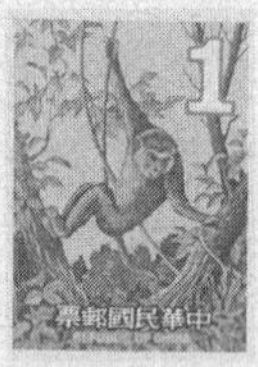
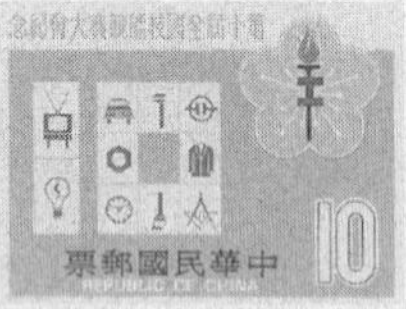

325 Taiwan Macaque
326 Competition Emblem and Symbols of Ten Trades

1979. New Year Greetings. "Year of the Monkey".
1278 **325** $1 multicoloured 75 10
1279 $6 multicoloured . . . . 1·00 25

1979. 10th National Vocational Training Competition, Taichung.
1280 **326** $2 multicoloured 20 10
1281 $10 multicoloured . . . 50 25

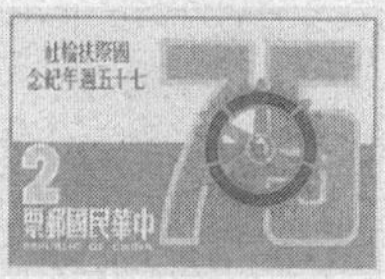
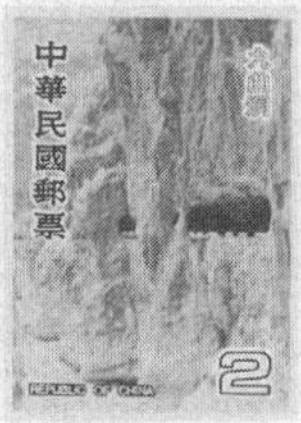

327 "75" and Rotary Emblem
328 Tunnel of Nine Turns

1980. 75th Anniv of Rotary International. Mult.
1282 $2 Type **327** 25 10
1283 $12 Anniversary emblem and symbols of Rotary's services (vert) 50 25

1980. Tourism. Scenic Spots on the East–West Cross-Island Highway. Multicoloured.
1284 $2 Type **328** 25 10
1285 $8 Mt. Hohuan (horiz) . . . 50 15
1286 $12 Bridge, Tien Hsiang . . 1·00 30

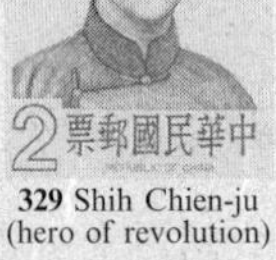
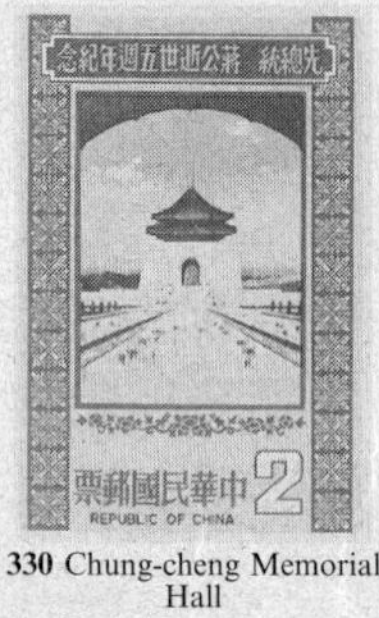

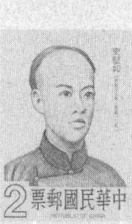

329 Shih Chien-ju (hero of revolution)
330 Chung-cheng Memorial Hall

1980. Famous Chinese.
1287 **329** $2 brown 25 10

1980. 5th Death Anniv of Chiang Kai-shek. Multicoloured.
1288 $2 Type **330** 20 10
1289 $8 Quotation of Chiang Kai-shek 40 15
1290 $12 Bronze statue of Chiang Kai-shek 50 30

1980. Ancient Chinese Jade (2nd series). As T **316**. Multicoloured.
1291 $2 Kuang (cup) decorated with dragons (Sung dynasty) (vert) 50 10
1292 $5 Dark green jade melon-shaped brush washer (Ming dynasty) 90 15
1293 $8 Bluish jade Po Monk's alms bowl (Ch'ing dynasty) . . . . 1·10 20
1294 $10 Yellow jade brush washer (Ch'ing dynasty) 1·40 25

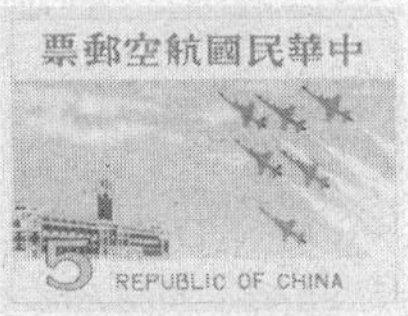

331 Tzu-Ch'iang Squadron over Presidential Mansion

1980. Air. Multicoloured.
1303 $5 Type **331** 35 10
1304 $7 Boeing 747-100 airliner and insignia of CAL (state airline) 75 20
1305 $12 National Flag and Boeing 747-100 . . . . . 90 30

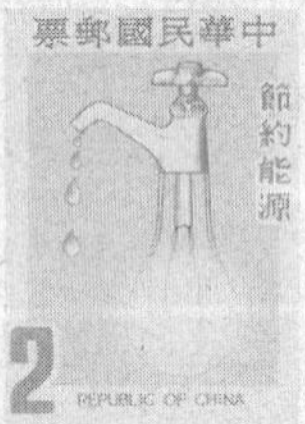
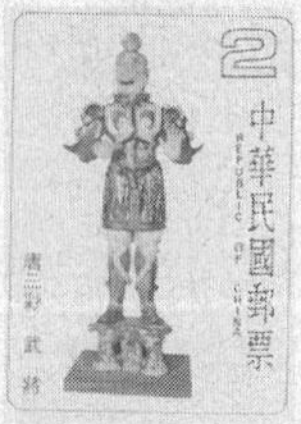

332 "Wasted Resources"
333 Military Official

1980. Energy Conservation.
1306 **332** $2 multicoloured 20 10
1307 $12 multicoloured . . . 50 30

1980. T'ang Dynasty Tri-coloured Pottery. Multicoloured.
1308 $2 Type **333** 70 10
1309 $5 Chickens . . . . 1·25 10
1310 $8 Horse . . . . 1·60 20
1311 $10 Camel . . . . 1·50 25

1980. Chinese Folk-tales (6th series). As T **200**. Multicoloured.
1312 $1 Grinding mortar into a needle 20 10
1313 $2 Returning lost articles . . 30 10
1314 $2 Wen Tien-hsiang in prison 55 10
1315 $5 Sending coal to poor during snow 75 15

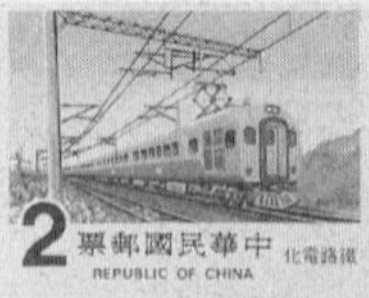
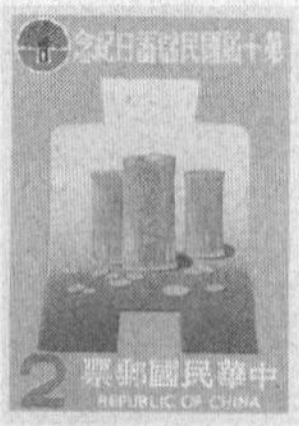

334 TRA Trunk Line Electrification
335 Money Boxes within Ancient Chinese Coin

1980. Completion of Ten Major Construction Projects. Multicoloured.
1316 $2 Type **334** 45 10
1317 $2 Taichung Harbour . . . 15 10
1318 $2 Chiang Kai-shek International Airport . . . 15 10
1319 $2 Integrated steel mill . . . 15 10
1320 $2 Sun Yat-sen National Freeway 15 10
1321 $2 Nuclear power plant . . 15 10
1322 $2 Petrochemical industrial zone in south 15 10
1323 $2 Su-ao Harbour 15 10
1324 $2 Kaohsiung Shipyard . . 40 10
1325 $2 Taiwan North Link Railway 45 10

1980. 10th National Savings Day. Mult.
1327 $2 Type **335** 20 10
1328 $12 Hand placing coin in money box 45 25

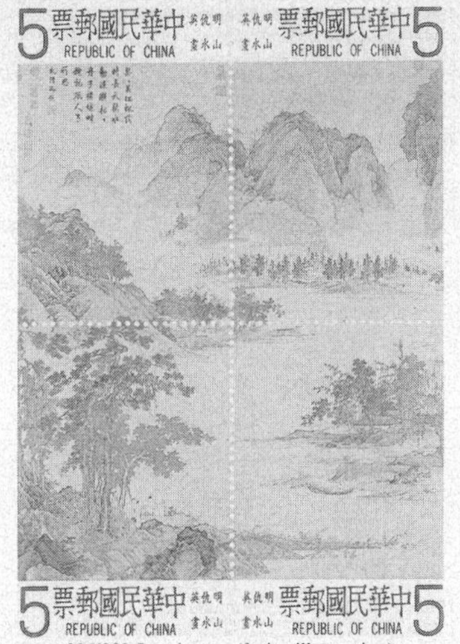

336/339 Landscape ($\frac{2}{3}$-size illustration)

1980. Painting by Ch'iu Ying.

1329	**336**	$5 multicoloured	2·25	20
1330	**337**	$5 multicoloured	2·25	20
1331	**338**	$5 multicoloured	2·25	20
1332	**339**	$5 multicoloured	2·25	20

Nos. 1329/32 were printed together, se-tenant, forming the composite design illustrated.

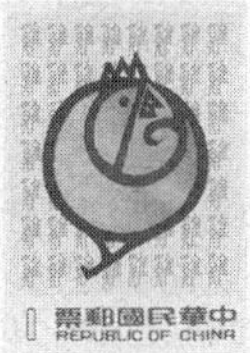

340 Cock

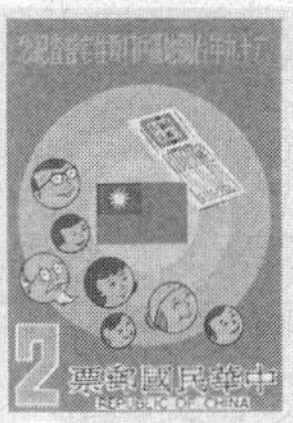

341 Heads, Flag and Census Form

1980. New Year Greetings. "Year of the Cock".

1334	**340**	$1 multicoloured	75	10
1335		$6 multicoloured	2·00	25

See also No. 2047.

1980. Population and Housing Census. Mult.

1337	$2 Type **341**	20	10
1338	$12 Flag and buildings (horiz)	50	30

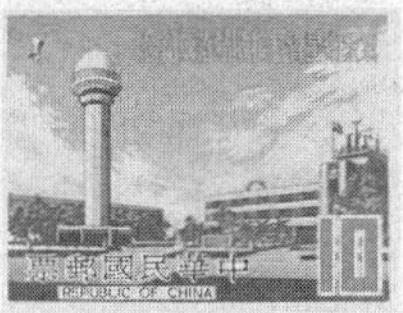

342 Central Weather Bureau

1981. Completion of Meteorological Satellite Ground Station, Taipei. Multicoloured.

1339	$2 "TIROS-N" weather satellite (vert)	20	10
1340	$10 Type **342**	50	30

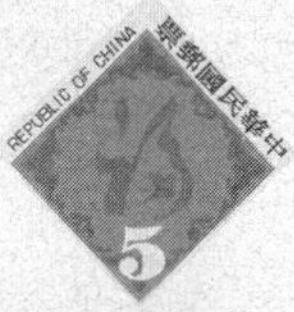

343 "Happiness"

344 "Wealth"

345 "Longevity"

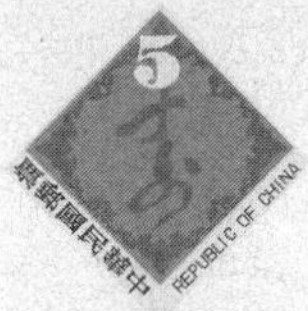

346 "Joy"

1981. New Year Calligraphy.

1341	**343**	$5 gold, red and black	90	25
1342	**344**	$5 gold, red and black	90	25
1343	**345**	$5 gold, red and black	90	25
1344	**346**	$5 gold, red and black	90	25

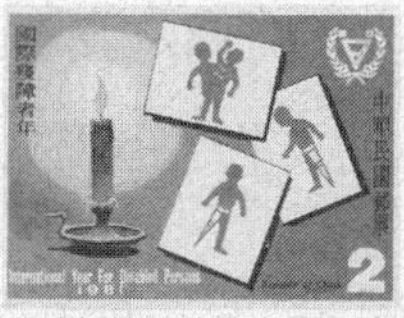

347 Candle and Siamese Twins

1981. International Year for Disabled Persons.

1345	**347**	$2 multicoloured	20	10
1346		$10 multicoloured . . .	50	30

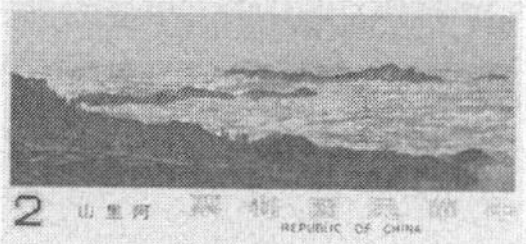

348 Mt. Ali

1981. Tourism. Multicoloured.

1347	$2 Type **348**	30	10
1348	$7 Oluanpi	55	15
1349	$12 Sun Moon Lake	1·00	25

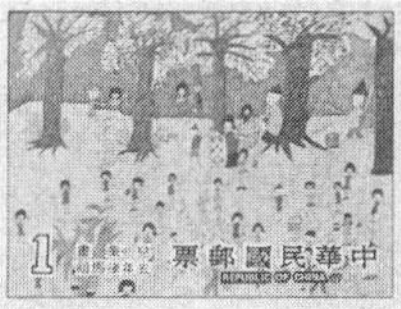

349 "Children on River Bank"

1981. Children's Day. Children's Drawings. Mult.

1350	$1 Type **349**	15	10
1351	$2 "Cable-cars"	20	10
1352	$5 "Lobsters"	30	10
1353	$7 "Village"	40	15

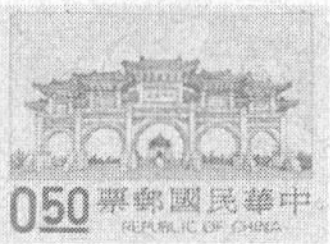

350 Main Gate Chiang Kai-shek Memorial Hall

1981. 6th Death Anniv of Chiang Kai-shek.

1712	**350**	10c. red	10	10
1354		20c. violet	10	10
1714		30c. green	10	10
1355		40c. red	10	10
1356		50c. brown	10	10
1717		60c. blue	10	10

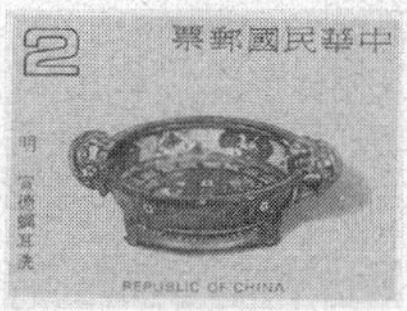

351 Brush Washer (Hsuan-te ware)

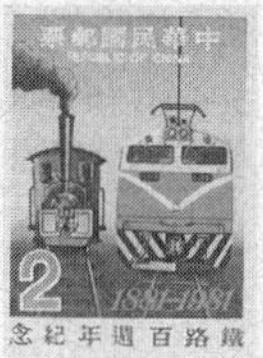

352 Electric and First Steam Locomotives

1981. Ancient Chinese Enamelware (1st series). Ming Dynasty Cloisonne Enamelware. Multicoloured.

1357	$2 Type **351**	40	10
1358	$5 Ritual vessel with ring handles (Chiang-ta'i ware) (vert)	70	10
1359	$8 Plate decorated with dragons (Wan-li ware) . .	90	10
1360	$10 Vase (vert)	1·25	25

See also Nos. 1438/41, 1472/5 and 1542/5.

1981. Centenary of Railway. Mult.

1361	$2 Type **352**	50	10
1362	$14 Side views of steam and electric locomotives (horiz)	1·50	40

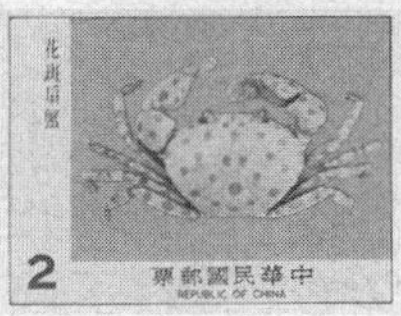

353 "Liagore rubromaculata"

1981. Crabs. Multicoloured.

1363	$2 Type **353**	20	10
1364	$5 "Ranina ranina" (vert)	40	10
1365	$8 "Platymaia wyvillethomsoni"	55	15
1366	$14 "Lambrus nummifera" (vert)	1·00	35

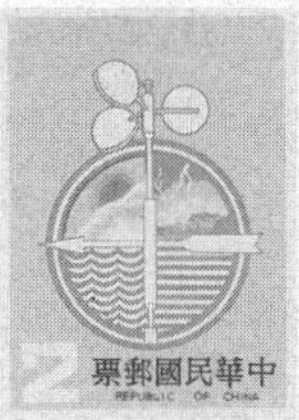

354 Bureau Emblem

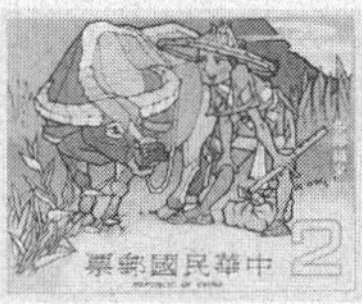

355 The Cowherd

1981. 40th Anniv of Central Weather Bureau.

1367	**354**	$2 multicoloured	20	10
1368		$14 multicoloured . . .	75	35

1981. Fairy Tales. "The Cowherd and the Weaving Maid". Multicoloured.

1369	$2 Type **355**	50	10
1370	$4 The cowherd watching the weaving maid through rushes	60	10
1371	$8 The cowherd and the weaving maid on opposite sides of Heavenly River	1·00	15
1372	$14 The cowherd and the weaving maid meeting on bridge of magpies	2·10	35

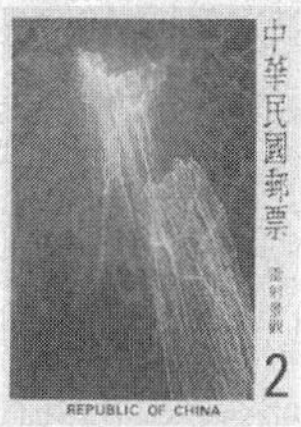

356 Laser Display

1981. Lasography Exhibition. Designs showing different laser displays.

1373	**356**	$2 multicoloured	20	10
1374	–	$5 multicoloured	30	10
1375	–	$8 multicoloured	40	15
1376	–	$14 multicoloured . . .	90	40

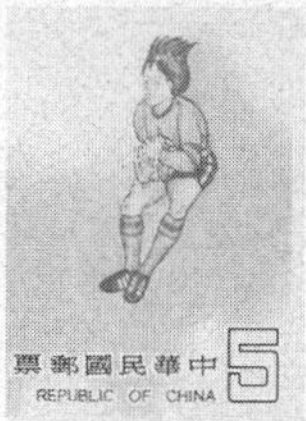

357 Goalkeeper catching Ball

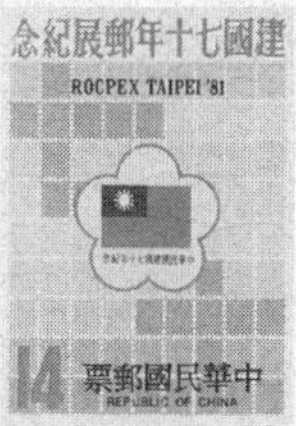

359 Chinese Republic Anniv Emblem and "Stamps"

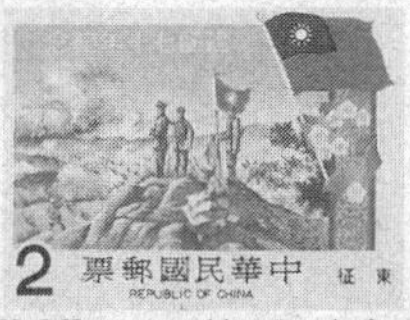

358 Officers watching Battle from Mound

1981. Athletics Day. Multicoloured.

1390	$5 Women soccer players	20	10
1391	$5 Type **357**	20	10

1981. 70th Anniv of Founding of Chinese Republic. Multicoloured.

1392	$2 Type **358**	15	10
1393	$2 Officer clenching fist and soldiers awaiting battle . .	15	10
1394	$2 Officer on horseback saluting	15	10
1395	$2 Attacking buildings . . .	15	10
1396	$3 Attacking fortifications	35	10
1397	$3 Dockside scene	60	20
1398	$8 Chiang Kai-shek	60	10
1399	$14 Sun Yat-sen	90	15

1981. "Rocpex Taipei '81" International Stamp Exhibition.

1401	**359**	$2 multicoloured	15	10
1402		$14 multicoloured . . .	50	35

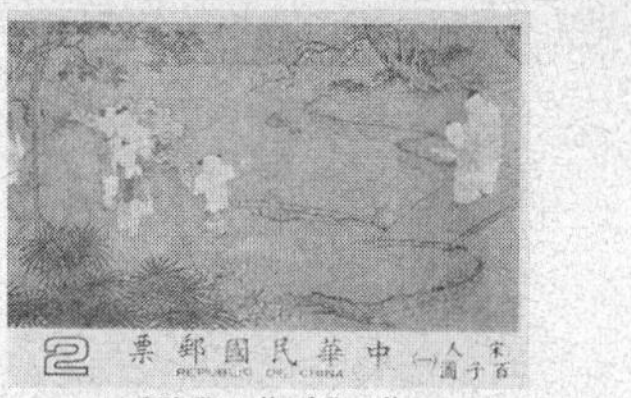

360 Detail of Scroll

1981. Sung Dynasty painting "One Hundred Young Boys". Designs showing details of Scroll.

1403	**360**	$2 (1) multicoloured . .	1·90	25
1404	–	$2 (2) multicoloured . .	1·90	25
1405	–	$2 (3) multicoloured . .	1·90	25
1406	–	$2 (4) multicoloured . .	1·90	25
1407	–	$2 (5) multicoloured . .	1·90	25
1408	–	$2 (6) multicoloured . .	1·90	25
1409	–	$2 (7) multicoloured . .	1·90	25
1410	–	$2 (8) multicoloured . .	1·90	25
1411	–	$2 (9) multicoloured . .	1·90	25
1412	–	$2 (10) multicoloured . .	1·90	25

See note below No. 661 on identification of designs.

Nos. 1403/12 were printed together in se-tenant blocks of ten (5 × 2) within the sheet, each strip of five forming a composite design.

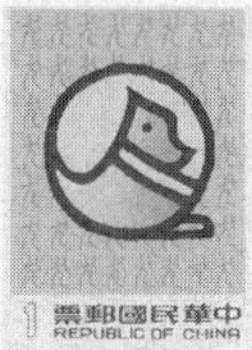

361 Dog

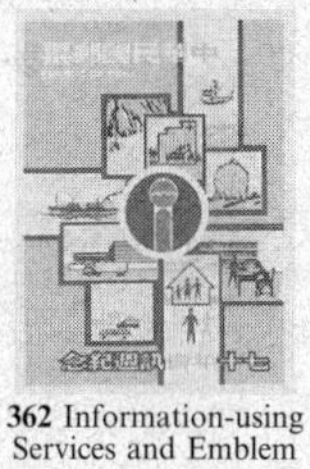

362 Information-using Services and Emblem

1981. New Year Greetings. "Year of the Dog".

1413	**361**	$1 multicoloured	1·00	10
1414		$10 multicoloured . . .	1·75	25

See also No. 2048.

1981. Information Week.

1416	**362**	$2 multicoloured	25	10

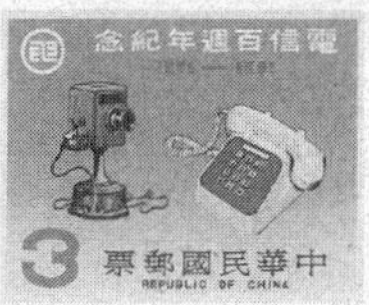

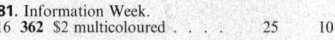

363 Telephones of 1881 and 1981

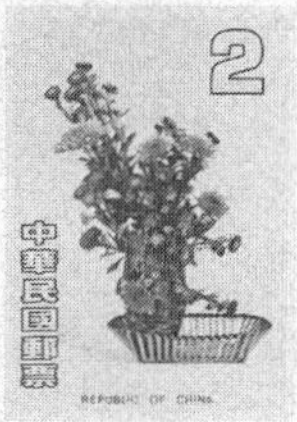

364 Arrangement in Basket

1981. Centenary of Chinese Telecommunications Service. Multicoloured.

1417	$2 Map and hand holding telephone handset (vert)	20	10
1418	$3 Type **363**	30	10
1419	$8 Submarine cable map . .	45	10
1420	$18 Computer and telecommunication units (vert)	65	20

1982. Chinese Flower Arrangements. Mult.

1421	$2 Type **364**	25	10
1422	$3 Arrangement in jug . . .	40	10
1423	$8 Arrangement in vase . .	75	10
1424	$18 Arrangement in holder	1·25	20

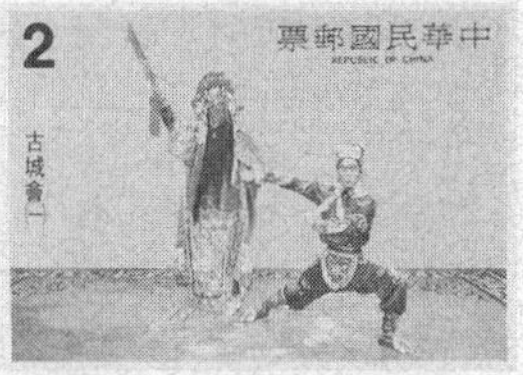

365 Kuan Yu leaves for Cheng City

1982. Scenes from "The Ku Cheng Reunion" (opera). Multicoloured.

1425	$2 Type **365**	55	10
1426	$3 Chang Fei refuses to open city gates	70	10
1427	$4 Chang Fei apologises to Kuan Yu	90	10
1428	$18 Liu Pei, Kuan Yu and Chang Fei are reunited	1·75	30

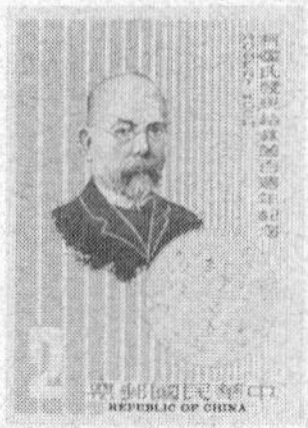

366 Dr. Robert Koch and Tubercle Bacillus

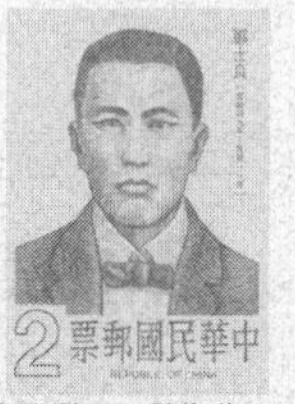

367 Chang Shih-liang (revolutionary)

1982. Centenary of Discovery of Tubercle Bacillus.
1429	366	$2 multicoloured	15	10

1982. Famous Chinese.
1430	367	$2 red	15	10

368 "Martyrs' Shrine" 369 Tooth and Child holding Toothbrush and Mug

1982. Children's Day. Children's paintings.
1431	$2 Type 368	30	10
1432	$3 "House Yard"	45	10
1433	$5 "Cattle Herd"	60	10
1434	$8 "A Sacrificial Ceremony for a Plentiful Year" . . .	90	10

1982. Dental Health. Multicoloured.
1435	$2 Type 369	25	10
1436	$3 Methods of cleaning teeth	45	10
1437	$10 Dental check-up	85	10

1982. Ancient Chinese Enamelware (2nd series). As T 351. Multicoloured.
1438	$2 Champlevé cup and plate (Ch'ien-lung ware) . . .	45	10
1439	$5 Cloisonne duck container (Ch'ien-lung ware) (vert)	60	10
1440	$8 Painted incense burner (K'ang-hsi period) . . .	1·10	10
1441	$12 Cloisonne Tibetan lama milk-tea pot (Ch'ien-lung ware) (vert)	1·75	15

370 "Spring Dawn" (Meng Hao-jan)

1982. Chinese Classical Poetry (1st series). Tang Dynasty Poems. Multicoloured.
1442	$2 Type 370	1·50	10
1443	$3 "On Looking for a Hermit and not Finding Him" (Chia Tao) . . .	3·25	10
1444	$5 "Summer Dying" (Liu Yu-hsi)	6·75	10
1445	$18 "Looking at the Snow Drifts on South Mountains" (Tsu Yung)	7·50	55

See also Nos. 1476/9, 1524/7, 1594/7, 1866/9, 1910/13 and 2074/7.

371 Softball

1982. 5th World Women's Softball Championship, Taipeh.
1446	371	$2 multicoloured	40	10
1447		$18 multicoloured . . .	85	20

372 Scouts on Rope Bridge, and Lord Baden-Powell

1982. 75th Anniv of Boy Scout Movement and 125th Birth Anniv of Lord Baden-Powell. Multicoloured.
1448	$2 Type 372	25	10
1449	$18 Emblem, scouts making frame and camp	80	15

373 Tweezers holding Stamp 374 Carved Lion

1982. Philately Day. Multicoloured.
1450	$2 Type 373	40	10
1451	$18 Examining stamp album with magnifying glass . .	80	20

1982. Tsu Shih Temple, Sanhsia. Multicoloured.
1452	$2 Type 374	40	10
1453	$3 Lion brackets (horiz) . .	50	10
1454	$5 Carved sub-lintels in passageway	75	10
1455	$18 Temple roofs (horiz) . .	1·75	20

1982. Chinese Folk-tales (7th series). Stories from "36 Examples of Filial Piety" by Wu Yen-huan, As T 200. Multicoloured.
1456	$1 Shao K'ang supporting his mother	25	10
1457	$2 Hsun Kuan leading soldier reinforcements to her father	45	10
1458	$3 Ku Yen-wu refusing to serve Ch'ing dynasty . . .	60	10
1459	$5 Ting Ch'un-liang caring for his paralysed father	1·00	10

375 Riding Horses

1982. 30th Anniv of China Youth Corps. Multicoloured.
1460	$2 Type 375	10	10
1461	$3 Flag and water sport (vert)	15	10
1462	$18 Mountaineering . . .	50	20

376 Lohan with Boy Attendant and Monkey 378 Pig

1982. Lohan (Buddhist Saint) Scroll Paintings by Liu Sung-nien. Multicoloured.
1463	$2 Type 376	1·50	10
1464	$3 Monk presenting seated Lohan with scroll . . .	2·00	10
1465	$18 Tribal king paying homage to seated Lohan	5·00	40

1982. New Year. "Year of the Pig".
1468	378	$1 multicoloured . . .	1·25	10
1469		$10 multicoloured . . .	2·25	25

See also No. 2049.

1983. Ancient Chinese Enamelware (3rd series). Ch'ing Dynasty Enamelware. As T 351. Multicoloured.
1472	$2 Square basin with rounded corners	25	10
1473	$3 Vase decorated with landscape panels (vert) .	75	10
1474	$4 Blue teapot with flower pattern	1·25	10
1475	$18 Cloisonne elephant with vase on back (vert) . . .	1·40	20

379 "Wan-hsi-sha" (Yen Shu) 380 Hsin-hsien Concealed Fall, Wawa Valley

1983. Chinese Classical Poetry (2nd series). Sung Dynasty Lyrical Poems. Multicoloured.
1476	$2 Type 379	2·50	10
1477	$3 "Ch'ing-yu-an" (Ho Chu)	3·75	10
1478	$5 "Su-mu-che" (Fan Chung-yen)	4·50	10
1479	$11 "Hsing-hsiang-tzu" (Ch'ao Pu-chih) . .	7·00	25

1983. Landscapes. Multicoloured.
1480	$2 Type 380	75	10
1481	$3 University Pond, Chitou Forest	90	10
1482	$18 Mount Jade (horiz) . .	1·10	20

381 Matteo Ricci and Astrolabe

1983. 400th Anniv of Matteo Ricci's (missionary) Arrival in China. Multicoloured.
1483	$2 Type 381	35	10
1484	$18 Matteo Ricci and Great Wall	70	20

382 Wu Ching-heng (Chairman of development committee) 383 Hsu Hsien meets Pai Su-chen

1983. 70th Anniv of Mandarin Phonetic Symbols. Multicoloured.
1485	$2 Type 382	35	10
1486	$18 Children studying symbols	70	25

1983. Fairy Tales. "Lady White Snake". Multicoloured.
1487	$2 Type 383	40	10
1488	$3 Pai Su-chen steals Tree of Life	50	10
1489	$3 Confrontation with Fahai at Chin Shan Temple .	1·00	10
1490	$18 Pai Su-chen is imprisoned beneath Thunder Peak Pagoda . .	2·25	30

384 Pot with Cord Pattern 385 Communication Emblems circling Globe

1983. Ancient Chinese Bamboo Carvings. Multicoloured.
1491	$2 Type 384	40	10
1492	$3 Vase with Tao-t'ien motif	75	10
1493	$4 Carved mountain scene with figures	75	10
1494	$18 Brush-holder with relief showing ladies . . .	1·50	20

1983. World Communications Year. Mult.
1495	$2 Type 385	75	10
1496	$18 W.C.Y. emblem . . .	90	20

386 Grouper 387 T.V. Screen, Antenna and Radio Waves

1983. Protection of Fishery Resources. Mult.
1497	$2 Type 386	40	10
1498	$18 Lizardfish	1·00	25

1983. Journalists' Day.
1499	387	$2 multicoloured	15	10

388 Yurt 389 Brown Shrike

1983. Mongolian and Tibetan Scenes.
1500	$2 Type 388	40	10
1501	$3 Potala Palace	65	10
1502	$5 Sheep on prairie . . .	80	10
1503	$11 Camel caravan	1·10	20

1983. 2nd East Asian Bird Protection Conference. Multicoloured.
1504	$2 Type 389	75	10
1505	$18 Grey-faced buzzard-eagle	1·00	40

390 Pink Plum Blossom 391 Congress Emblem

1983. Plum Blossom. Multicoloured.
1506	$2 Type 390	15	10
1507	$3 Red plum blossom . .	20	10
1508	$5 Plum blossom and pagoda	45	15
1509	$11 White plum blossom .	1·00	15

1983. 38th Jaycees International World Congress. Multicoloured.
1510	$2 Type 391	25	10
1511	$18 Emblems and globe . .	80	20

392 World Map as Heart 393 Rat

1983. 8th Asian-Pacific Cardiology Congress. Mult.
1512	$2 Type 392	25	10
1513	$18 Heart and electrocardiogram	80	20

1983. New Year. "Year of the Rat".
1514	393	$1 multicoloured	85	10
1515		$10 multicoloured . . .	2·00	20

See also No. 2038.

394 Mother and Child reading and Chin Ting Prize

1983. National Reading Week. Mult.
1517	$2 Type 394	20	10
1518	$18 Chin Ting prize (for outstanding publications) books and father and son reading (vert)	80	20

395 Boeing 737 over Chiang Kai-shek Airport 396 Soldiers with Flags

1984. Air. 37th Anniv of Civil Aeronautics Administration. Multicoloured
1519	$7 Type 395	35	15
1520	$11 Boeing 747 over Chung-cheng Memorial Hall (horiz)	50	15
1521	$18 Boeing 737 over Sun Yat-sen Memorial Hall (horiz)	65	20

1984. World Freedom Day. Multicoloured.
1522	396	$2 multicoloured	20	10
1523		$18 Globe and people of the world	80	20

397 "Hsiao-liang-chou" (Kuan Yun-shih)

1984. Chinese Classical Poetry (3rd series). Yuan Dynasty Lyric Poems. Multicoloured.

1524 $2 Type **397** . . . . 3·00 20
1525 $3 "A Lady holds a fine fan of silk", "Tien-ching-sha" (Po P'u) . . . . 4·50 25
1526 $5 "Picnic under banana leaves "Ch'ing-chiang-yin" (Chang Ko-chin) . . . . 5·00 25
1527 $18 "Plum blossoms in the snowbound wilderness "Tien-ching-sha" (Shang Cheng-shu) . . . . . . 12·50 1·40

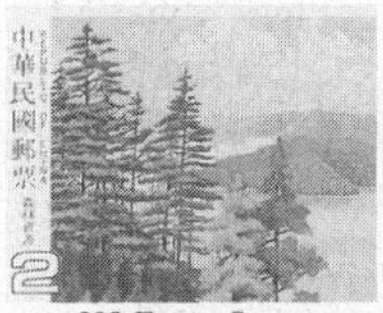

398 Forest Scene

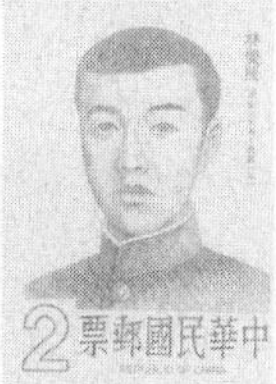

400 Lin Chueh-min (revolutionary)

1984. Forest Resources. Multicoloured.

1528 $2 Type **398** 35 10
1529 $2 Reservoir and dam . . . 35 10
1530 $2 Camp in forest 35 10
1531 $2 Wooded slopes 35 10

Nos. 1528/31 were printed together se-tenant, forming a composite design.

1984. Famous Chinese.

1536 **400** $2 green 15 10

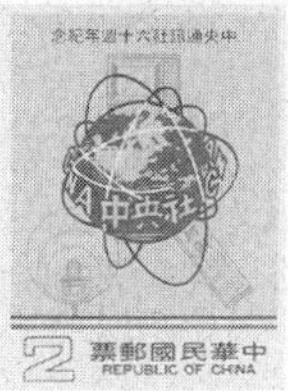

401 Agency Emblem and Broadcasting Equipment

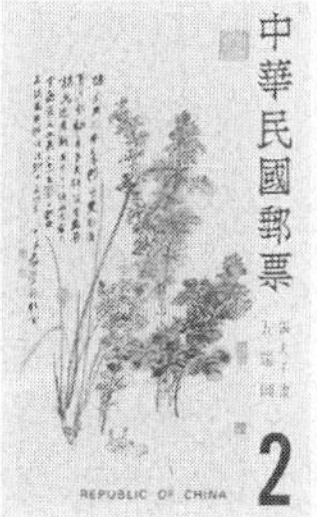

402 "Five Auspicious Tokens"

1984. 60th Anniv of Central News Agency. Multi.

1537 $2 Type **401** 15 10
1538 $10 Agency emblem and satellite communications 45 15

1984. 85th Birth Anniv of Chang Ta-chien (artist). Multicoloured.

1539 $2 Type **402** . . . . 1·75 10
1540 $5 "The God of Longevity" 2·25 15
1541 $18 "Lotus Blossoms in Ink Splash" . . . . 5·00 40

1984. Ancient Chinese Enamelware (4th series). Ch'ing Dynasty Enamelware. As T **351**. Mult.

1542 $2 Lidded cup and teapot on tray 20 10
1543 $3 Cloisonne wine vessel on phoenix (vert) 50 10
1544 $4 Yellow teapot with pink and blue chrysanthemum decoration 75 15
1545 $18 Cloisonne candle-holder on bird . . . . 1·50 40

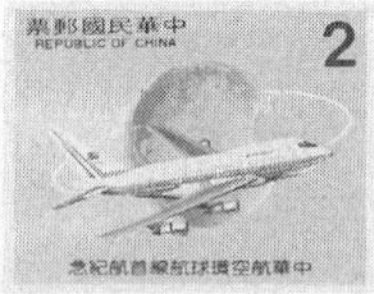

403 Boeing 747-200 circling Globe

1984. Inauguration of China Airlines Global Service. Multicoloured.

1546 $2 Type **403** 20 10
1547 $7 Globe and Boeing 747-200 . . . . 60 20
1548 $11 Boeing 747-200 over New York 85 30
1549 $18 Boeing 747-200 over Netherlands . . . . . . 1·50 55

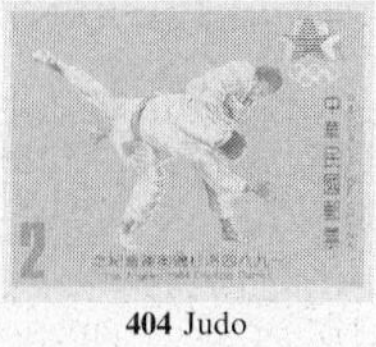

404 Judo

1984. Olympic Games, Los Angeles. Mult.

1550 $2 Type **404** 15 10
1551 $5 Archery (vert) 35 15
1552 $18 Swimming . . . . . . 1·00 60

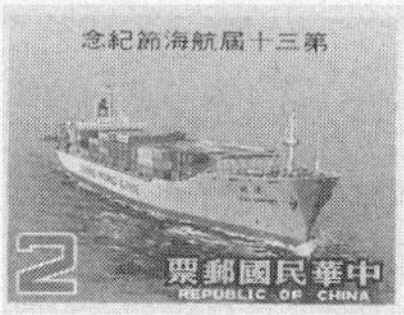

405 Container Ship "Ming Comfort"

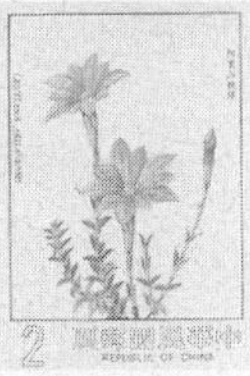

406 "Gentiana arisanensis"

1984. 30th Navigation Day. Mult.

1553 $2 Type **405** 45 10
1554 $18 "Prosperity" (tanker) 1·00 65

1984. Alpine Plants. Multicoloured.

1555 $2 Type **406** 35 10
1556 $3 "Epilobium nankotaiza nense" 55 10
1557 $5 "Adenophora uehatae" 80 15
1558 $18 "Aconitum fukutomei" 2·25 25

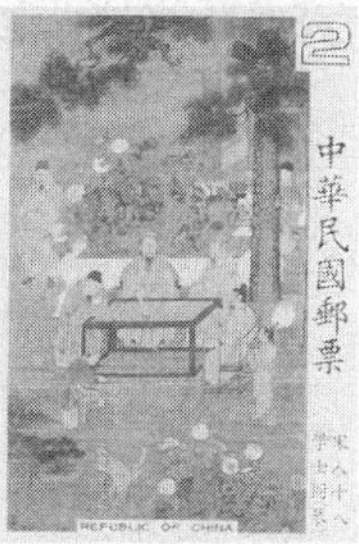

407 Scholars listening to Music

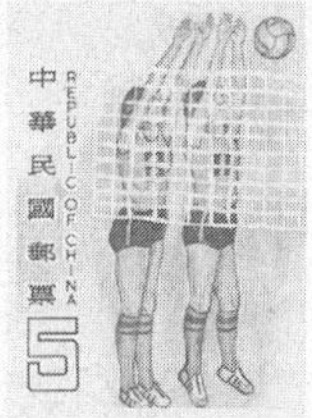

408 Volleyball Players

1984. Sung Dynasty Painting "The Eighteen Scholars". Multicoloured.

1559 $2 Type **407** . . . . 1·25 10
1560 $3 Scholars playing chess . . 2·75 10
1561 $5 Scholars writing . . . . 1·50 15
1562 $18 Scholars painting . . . 6·00 65

1984. Athletics Day. Multicoloured.

1563 $5 Type **408** 25 15
1564 $5 Volleyball player 25 15

Nos. 1563/4 were printed together, se-tenant, forming a composite design.

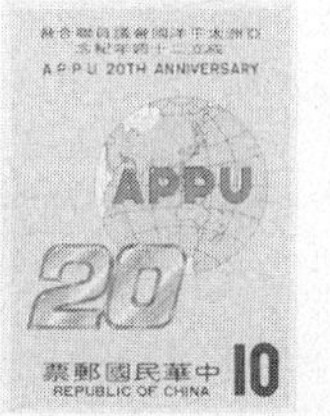

409 Union Emblem

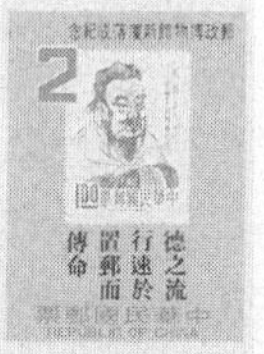

410 1965 Confucius $1 Stamp

1984. 20th Anniv of Asian-Pacific Parliamentarians' Union.

1565 **409** $10 multicoloured . . . 50 25

1984. New Postal Museum Building, Taipeh. Multicoloured.

1566 $2 Type **410** 10 10
1567 $5 1933 Sun Yat-sen 5c. stamp 25 15
1568 $18 New Postal Museum building . . . . 1·40 65

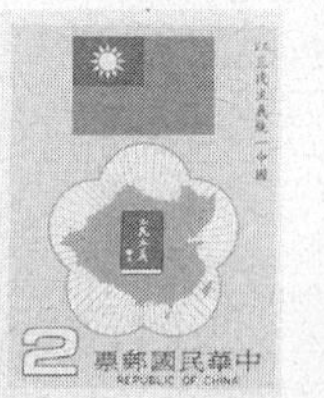

411 Flag and Emblem

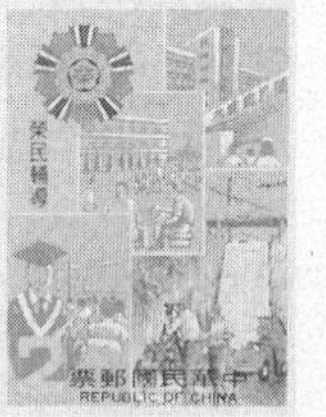

412 Commission Services

1984. Grand Alliance for China's Reunification Convention.

1570 **411** $2 multicoloured 30 10

1984. 30th Anniv of Vocational Assistance Commission for Retired Servicemen.

1571 **412** $2 multicoloured 30 10

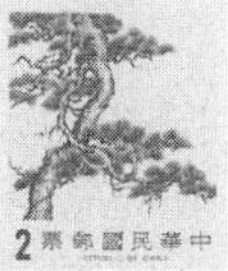

413 Pine Tree

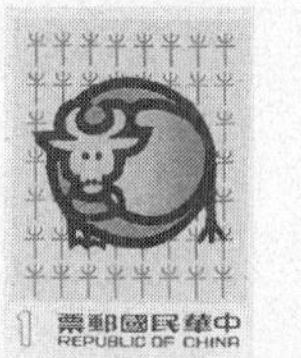

414 Ox

1984. Pine, Bamboo and Plum (1st series). Multicoloured.

1572 $2 Type **413** 20 10
1573 $8 Bamboo 60 20
1574 $10 Plum blossom 60 20

See also Nos. 1633/5, 1783/5 and 1845/7.

1984. New Year Greetings. "Year of the Ox".

1575 **414** $1 multicoloured . . . . 1·00 10
1576 $10 multicoloured . . . 2·00 20

See also No. 2039.

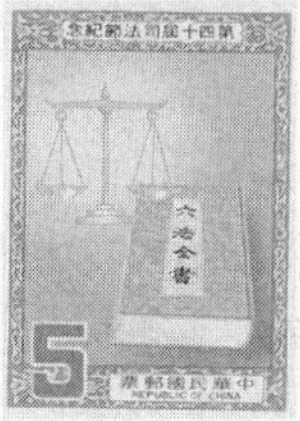

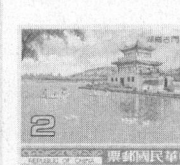

415 Legal Code Book and Scales

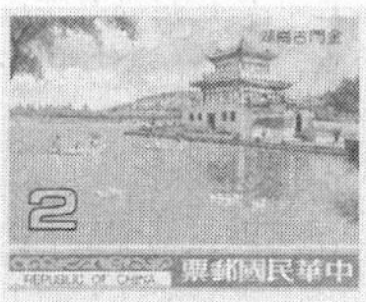

416 Ku-kang Lake and Pagoda, Quemoy

1985. Judicial Day.

1578 **415** $5 multicoloured 50 15

1985. Scenery of Quemoy and Matsu. Mult.

1579 $2 Type **416** 15 10
1580 $5 Kuang-hai stone, Quemoy 45 15
1581 $8 Sheng-li reservoir, Matsu 1·50 20
1582 $10 Tung-chu lighthouse, Matsu . . . . 1·50 20

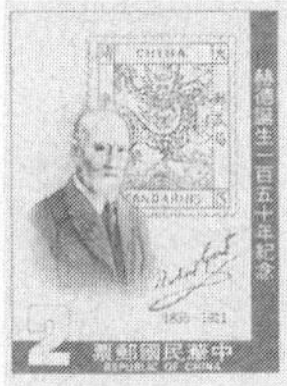

417 Sir Robert Hart and 1878 3c. Stamp

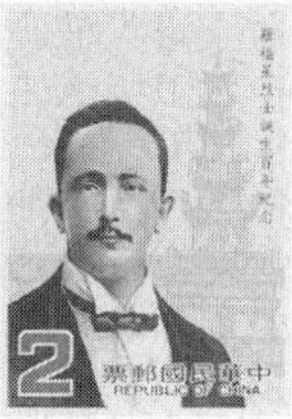

418 Lo Fu-hsing

1985. 150th Anniv of Sir Robert Hart (founder of Chinese Postal Service).

1583 **417** $2 multicoloured 30 10

1985. Birth Centenary of Lo Fu-hsing (patriot).

1584 **418** $2 multicoloured 30 10

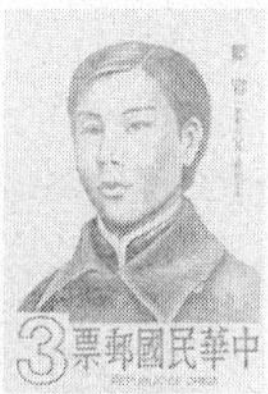

419 Tsou Jung

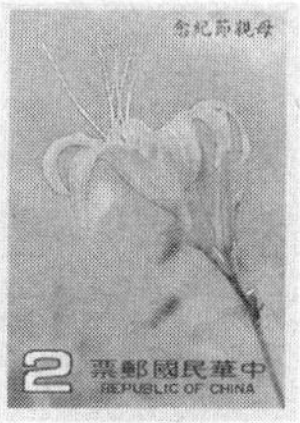

421 Lily

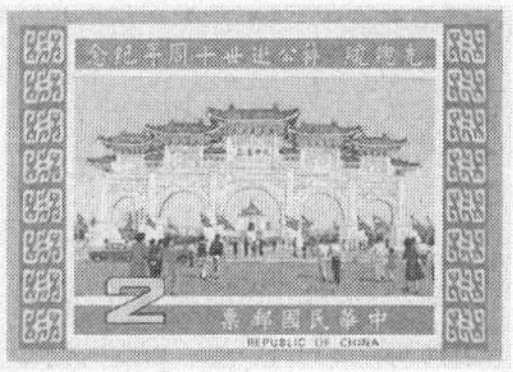

420 Main Gate, Chung-cheng Memorial Hall

1985. 80th Death Anniv of Tsou Jung (revolutionary).

1585 **419** $3 green 35 10

1985. 10th Death Anniv of President Chiang Kai-shek. Multicoloured.

1586 $2 Type **420** 15 10
1587 $8 Tzuhu, President Chiang's temporary resting place 60 20
1588 $10 President Chiang Kai-shek (vert) 80 20

1985. Mothers' Day. Multicoloured.

1589 $2 Type **421** 25 10
1590 $2 Carnation 25 10

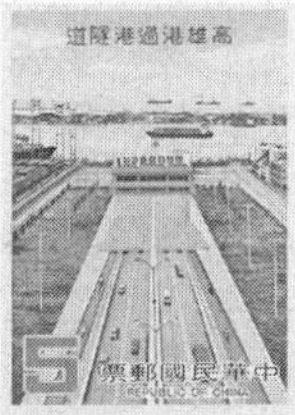

422 View of Tunnel

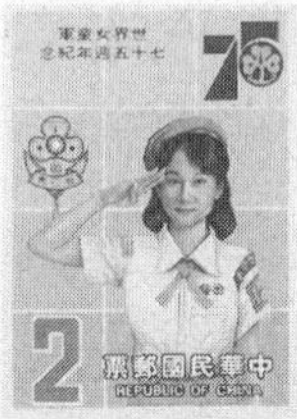

423 Girl Guide saluting

1985. 1st Anniv of Kaohsiung Cross-harbour Tunnel.

1591 **422** $5 multicoloured 60 15

1985. 75th Anniv of Girl Guide Movement.

1592 **423** $2 multicoloured 10 10
1593 $18 multicoloured . . . 80 25

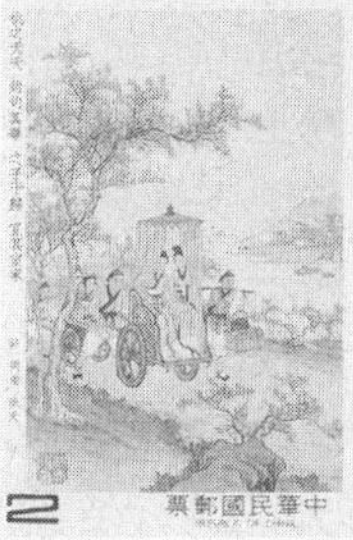

424 "Buxom is the Peach Tree..."

1985. Chinese Classical Poetry (4th series). Poems from "Book of Odes", edited by Confucius. Multicoloured.

1594 $2 Type **424** 75 10
1595 $5 "Thick grows that tarragon ..." . . . . . . 1·50 15
1596 $8 "Thick grow the rush leaves ..." . . . . 2·25 20
1597 $10 "... The snowflakes fly" 3·25 20

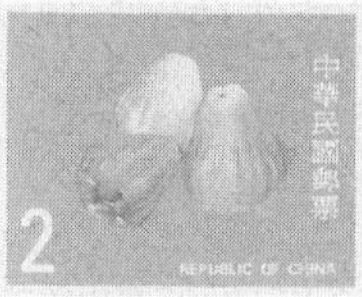

425 Wax Jambo

1985. Fruit. Multicoloured.

1598 $2 Type **425** 50 10
1599 $3 Guavas 75 10
1600 $5 Carambolas 90 15
1601 $8 Lychees . . . . 1·50 20

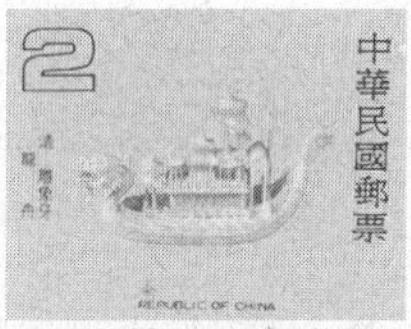

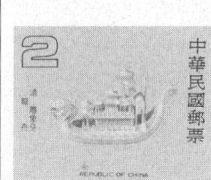

426 Dragon Boat

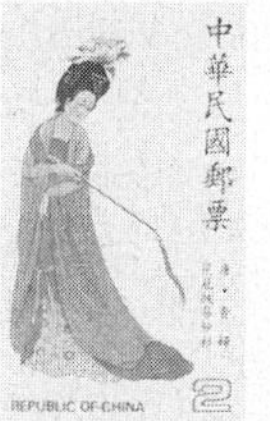

427 Lady of Rank, T'ang Dynasty

1985. Ch'ing Dynasty Ivory Carvings. Mult.

1602 $2 Type **426** 65 10
1603 $3 Carved landscape 75 10
1604 $5 Melon-shaped water container . . . . 1·25 15
1605 $18 Brush-holder (vert) . . 1·50 35

1985. 4th Asian Costume Conference. Chinese Costumes (1st series). Multicoloured.

1606 $2 Type **427** 85 10
1607 $5 Palace woman, Sung dynasty 90 10
1608 $8 Lady of rank, Yuan dynasty . . . . 1·60 20
1609 $11 Lady of rank, Ming dynasty . . . . 1·90 25

See also Nos. 1687/90, 1767/70, 1833/6, 1906/9 and 1973/6.

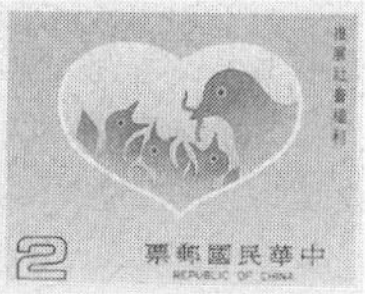

428 Bird feeding Chicks

1985. Social Welfare.

1610 **428** $2 multicoloured 25 10

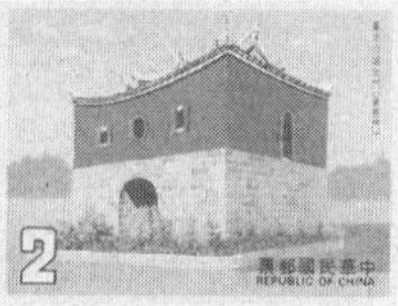

429 North Gate, Taipeh

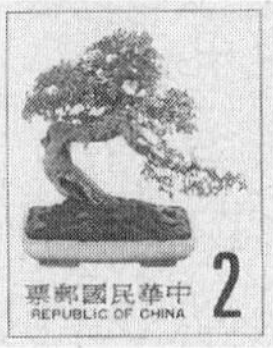

430 Oak Tree

1985. Historic Buildings (1st series). Mult.

1611 $2 Type **429** 20 10
1612 $5 San Domingo fort, Tamsui 45 15

1613	$8 Lung Shan Temple, Lukang	60	20
1614	$10 Confucius Temple, Changhua	1·00	20

See also Nos. 1700/3.

1985. Bonsai. Multicoloured.

1615	$2 Type **430**	20	10
1616	$5 Five-leaf pine	45	15
1617	$8 Lohan pine	60	20
1618	$18 Banyan	1·50	25

431 World Trade Centre and Sports Goods Logo

432 Flag, Map and Scenes of Peace

1985. Trade Shows. Multicoloured.

1619	$2 Type **431**	20	10
1620	$2 Toys and gifts logo (blue and red)	20	10
1621	$2 Electronics logo (blue)	20	10
1622	$2 Machinery logo (black and orange)	20	10

Nos. 1619/22 were printed together, se-tenant, forming a composite design depicting Taipeh World Trade Centre.

1985. 40th Anniv of Return of Taiwan to China. Multicoloured.

1623	$2 Type **432**	30	10
1624	$18 Chiang Kai-shek and triumphal arch	65	25

433 Emblem

434 Sun Yat-sen

1985. 7th Asian Federation for the Mentally Retarded Conference, Taipeh.

1625	**433** $2 multicoloured . . .	25	10
1626	$11 multicoloured . . .	60	25

1985. 120th Birth Anniv of Sun Yat-sen.

1627	**434** $2 multicoloured . . .	25	10
1628	$18 multicoloured . . .	1·25	25

435 Tiger

436 Emblem

1985. New Year Greetings. "Year of the Tiger".

1629	**435** $1 multicoloured . . .	50	10
1630	$10 multicoloured . . .	2·40	20

See also No. 2040.

1985. 50th Anniv of Postal Simple Life Insurance.

1632	**436** $2 multicoloured . . .	20	10

437 Pine Tree

1986. Pine, Bamboo and Plum (2nd series). Multicoloured.

1633	$1 Type **437**	25	10
1634	$11 Bamboo	65	20
1635	$18 Plum blossom	1·10	25

438 Detail of Scroll

1986. Painting "Hermit Anglers on a Mountain Stream" by T'ang Yin. Designs showing details of the scroll. Multicoloured.

1636	$2 (1) Type **438**	90	10
1637	$2 (2) Pavilions on bank .	90	10
1638	$2 (3) Anglers in boats near waterfall	90	10
1639	$2 (4) Pavilions on stilts .	90	10
1640	$2 (5) Anglers in boat near island	90	10

Nos. 1636/40 were printed together, forming a composite design.

See note below No. 661 on identification of designs in se-tenant strips.

439 Gladioli in Vase

440 Loading and unloading Boeing 747 Mail Plane

1986. Flower Arrangements (1st series). Mult.

1641	$2 Type **439**	10	10
1642	$5 Roses in double wicker holders	35	10
1643	$8 Roses and fern in pot on stand	65	10
1644	$10 Various flowers in large and small pots . . .	80	10

See also Nos. 1741/4.

1986. 90th Anniv of Post Office. Mult.

1645	$2 Type **440**	15	10
1646	$5 Postman on motorcycle (vert)	30	10
1647	$8 Customer at cash dispenser and clerk at savings bank computer terminal (vert)	45	10
1648	$10 Electronic sorting machine and envelopes circling globe	65	15

441 Chen Tien-hva (revolutionary writer)

442 Mountain shrouded in Mist

1986. Famous Chinese.

1650	**441** $2 violet	10	10

1986. Yushan National Park. Multicoloured.

1651	$2 Type **442**	35	10
1652	$5 People on mountain top	80	10
1653	$8 Snow covered mountain peak	1·10	10
1654	$10 Forest on mountain side	1·50	15

443 Hydro-electric Power Station

444 Taiwan Firecrest in Tree

1986. Power Stations. Multicoloured.

1655	$2 Type **443**	35	10
1656	$8 Thermo-electric power station	60	10
1657	$10 Nuclear power station .	75	15

1986. Paintings by P'u Hsin-yu. Mult.

1658	$2 Type **444**	1·50	20
1659	$8 Landscape	2·25	10
1660	$10 Woman in garden . .	2·75	15

445 Emblems

446 Green-winged Macaw

1986. 25th Anniv of Asian Productivity Organization and 30th Anniv of China Productivity Centre.

1661	**445** $2 multicoloured . . .	15	10
1662	$11 multicoloured . . .	75	20

1986. Protection of Intellectual Property.

1663	**446** $2 multicoloured . . .	90	20

447 Starck's Damselfish ("Chrysiptera starcki")

(448)

1986. Coral Reef Fishes, Multicoloured.

1664	$2 Type **447**	30	10
1665	$2 Copper-banded butterflyfish ("Chelmon rostratus")	30	10
1666	$2 Pearl-scaled butterflyfish ("Chaetodon xanthurus") . .	30	10
1667	$2 Four-spotted butterflyfish ("Chaetodon quadrimaculatus") . .	30	10
1668	$2 Meyer's butterflyfish ("Chaetodon meyeri") . .	30	10
1669	$2 Japanese swallow ("Genicanthus semifasciatus") (female)	30	10
1670	$2 Japanese swallow ("Genicanthus semifasciatus") (male) .	30	10
1671	$2 Blue-ringed angelfish ("Pomacanthus annularis")	30	10
1672	$2 Harlequin tuskfish ("Lienardella fasciata")	30	10
1673	$2 Undulate triggerfish ("Balistapus undulatus")	30	10

1986. 60th Anniv of Chiang Kai-shek's Northward Expedition. Nos. 1229 and 1386 surch as T **448**.

1674	**306** $2 on $6 red, bl & orge	15	15
1675	$8 on $9 red, bl & grn	35	25

449 Tzu Mu Bridge

450 Yingtai and Shanpo going to School

1986. Road Bridges. Multicoloured.

1676	$2 Type **449**	45	10
1677	$5 Chang Hung bridge over Hsiu-ku-luan-chi . .	70	10
1678	$8 Kuan Fu bridge over Hsintien River . . .	1·10	10
1679	$10 Kuan Tu bridge over Tanshui River . . .	1·50	15

1986. Folk Tales. "Love between Liang Shanpo and Chu Yingtai". Multicoloured.

1680	$5 Type **450**	50	10
1681	$5 Classmates	50	10
1682	$5 Yingtai and Shanpo by lake	50	10
1683	$5 Yingtai telling Shanpo she is to be married . .	50	10
1684	$5 Ascending to heaven as butterflies	50	10

451 Children playing by Lake and Rainbow

452 Lady of Warring States Period

1986. Cleanliness and Courtesy. Mult.

1685	$2 Type **451**	30	10
1686	$8 Children helping others in street	50	10

1986. Chinese Costumes (2nd series). Mult.

1687	$2 Lady of rank, Shang dynasty	70	10
1688	$5 Type **452**	1·25	10
1689	$8 Empress's assembly dress, later Han dynasty . .	2·00	10
1690	$10 Beribboned dress of lady of rank, Wei and Tsin dynasties	3·00	25

453 White Jade Ju-i Sceptre with Fish Decoration

1986. Ch'ing Dynasty Ju-i (1st series). Mult.

1691	$2 Type **453**	40	10
1692	$3 Coral ju-i sceptre with fungus motif . . .	60	10
1693	$4 Redwood ju-i sceptre inlaid with precious stones	75	10
1694	$18 Gold-painted ju-i sceptre with three abundances (fruit) . . .	1·50	25

See also Nos 1735/8.

454 Chiang Kai-shek and Books

1986. Birth Cent of Chiang Kai-shek. Mult.

1695	$2 Type **454**	55	10
1696	$5 Chiang Kai-shek, flag, map and crowd . .	45	10
1697	$8 Chiang Kai-shek, emblem and youths . . .	70	10
1698	$10 Chiang Kai-shek, flags on globe and clasped hands	80	15

455 Erh-sha-wan Gun Emplacement, Keelung

456 Hare

1986. Historic Buildings (2nd series). Mult.

1700	$2 Chin-kuang-fu House, Pei-pu	30	10
1701	$5 Type **455**	75	10
1702	$8 Hsi T'ai fort	80	10
1703	$10 Matsu Temple, Peng-hu	1·00	15

1986. New Year Greetings. "Year of the Hare".

1704	**456** $1 multicoloured . . .	45	10
1705	$10 multicoloured . .	1·90	15

See also No. 2041.

457 Shrubs on Rock Formation

458 Glove Puppet

1987. Kenting National Park. Multicoloured.

1707	$2 Type **457**	30	10
1708	$5 Rocky outcrop . . .	70	10
1709	$8 Sandy bay	1·00	10
1710	$10 Rocky bays	1·50	10

1987. Puppets. Multicoloured.

1721	$2 Type **458**	30	10
1722	$5 String puppet	85	10
1723	$18 Shadow show puppet .	1·25	25

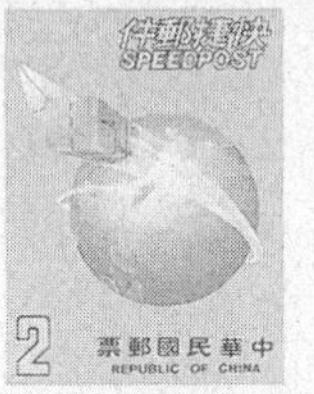

459 Envelope, Parcel and Globe

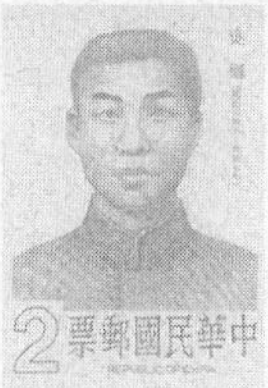

460 Wu Yueh (revolutionary)

1987. Speedpost Service.

1724	**459**	$2 multicoloured	30	10
1725		$18 multicoloured	1·00	25

1987. Famous Chinese.

1726	**460**	$2 red	30	10

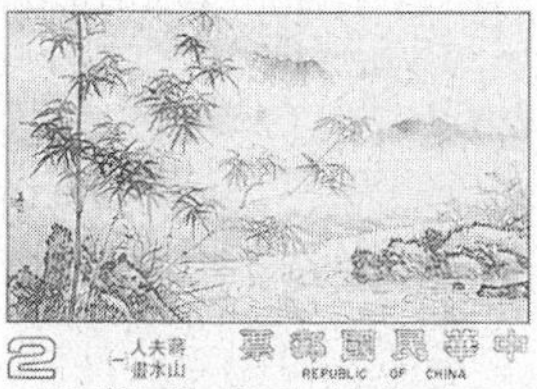

461 "Singing Creek with Bamboo Orchestra"

1987. Madame Chiang Kai-shek's Landscape Paintings (3rd series). Each black, stone and red.

1727	$2 Type **461**	50	10
1728	$5 "Mountains draped in Clouds"	1·40	10
1729	$5 "Vista of Tranquility"	1·75	10
1730	$10 "Mountains after a Snowfall"	2·10	15

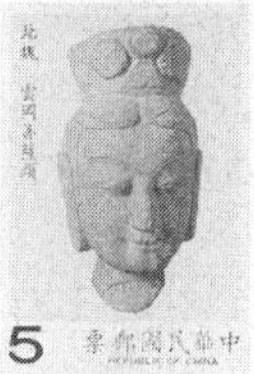

462 Bodhisattva Head, Northern Wei Dynasty

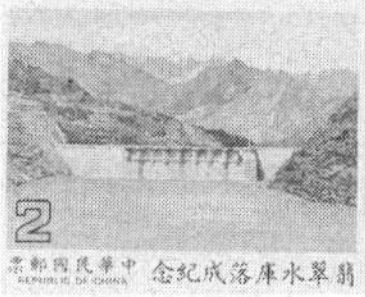

463 View of Dam

1987. Ancient Chinese Stone Carvings. Mult.

1731	$5 Type **462**	70	10
1732	$5 Standing Buddha, Northern Ch'i dynasty	70	10
1733	$5 Bodhisattva head, T'ang dynasty	70	10
1734	$5 Seated Buddha, T'ang dynasty	70	10

1987. Ch'ing Dynasty Ju-i (2nd series). As T **453**. Multicoloured.

1735	$2 Silver ju-i sceptre with fungus decoration of pearls and precious stones	30	10
1736	$3 Gold ju-i sceptre with Eight Treasures decoration of pearls and precious stones	35	10
1737	$4 Gilt ju-i sceptre inlaid with precious stones and kingfisher feather	50	10
1738	$18 Gilt ju-i sceptre with wirework and inlaid with malachite	2·00	25

1987. Feitsui Reservoir Inauguration. Multicoloured.

1739	$2 Type **463**	25	10
1740	$18 View of reservoir	80	25

1987. Flower Arrangements (2nd series). As T **439**. Multicoloured.

1741	$2 Roses and pine twig in holder	25	10
1742	$5 Flowers in pot	45	10
1743	$8 Tasselled pendant hanging from bamboo in vase	80	10
1744	$10 Pine in flask	1·00	15

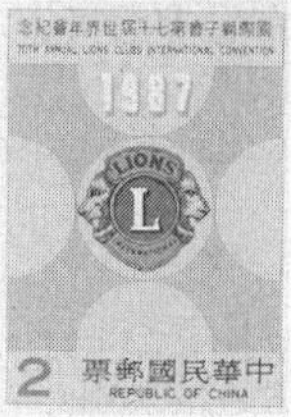

464 Emblem

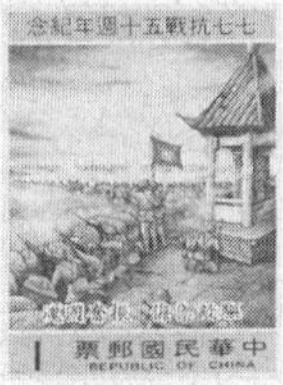

465 Soldiers firing from behind Barricades

1987. 70th Lions Clubs International Convention, Taipeh.

1745	**464**	$2 multicoloured	25	10
1746		$18 multicoloured	1·00	25

1987. 50th Anniv of Start of Sino-Japanese War. Multicoloured.

1747	$1 Type **465**	15	10
1748	$2 Chiang Kai-shek making speech from balcony	25	10
1749	$5 Crowd throwing money onto flag	40	10
1750	$6 Columns of soldiers and tanks on mountain road	50	10
1751	$8 General giving written message to Chiang Kai-shek	75	10
1752	$18 Pres. and Madame Chiang Kai-shek at front of crowd	1·10	25

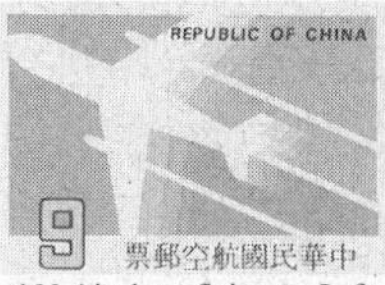

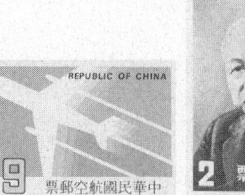

466 Airplane flying to Left

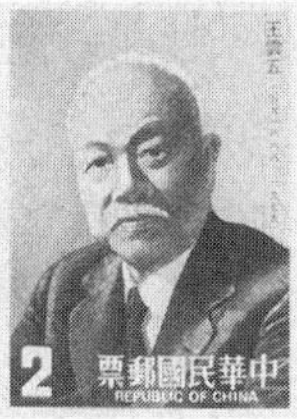

467 Wang Yun-wu

1987. Air. Multicoloured.

1753	$9 Type **466**	50	15
1754	$14 Airplane	75	20
1755	$18 Airplane flying to right	1·00	25

1987. Birth Centenary (1988) of Wang Yun-wu (lexicographer).

1756	**467**	$2 black	25	10

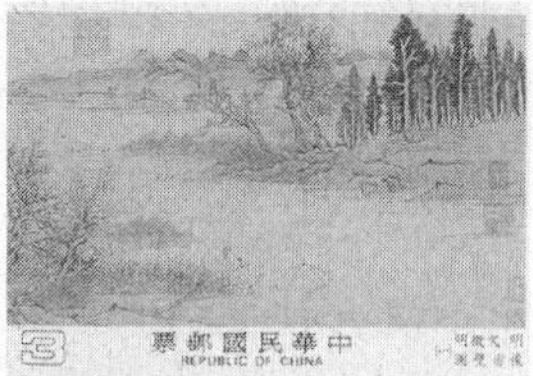

468 Trees on Islands and Fisherman

1987. Painting "After Chao Po-su's 'Red Cliff'" by Wen Cheng-ming. Designs showing details of the scroll. Multicoloured.

1757	$3 (1) Type **468**	65	10
1758	$3 (2) Tree and three figures on island	65	10
1759	$3 (3) House in walled enclosure on island	65	10
1760	$3 (4) Figures in doorway of building and horse in stable	65	10
1761	$3 (5) Cliffs and sea	65	10
1762	$3 (6) Islets, trees and figures on shore	65	10
1763	$3 (7) Trees among cliffs	65	10
1764	$3 (8) People in sampan	65	10
1765	$3 (9) Building surrounded by trees and cliffs	65	10
1766	$3 (10) Cliffs, trees and waterfall	65	10

Nos. 1757/66 were printed together, se-tenant, forming a composite design.

See note below No. 661 on identification of designs in se-tenant strips.

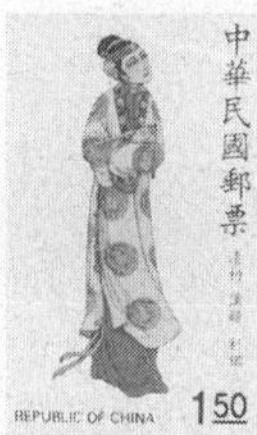

469 Han Lady of Rank, Early Ch'ing Dynasty

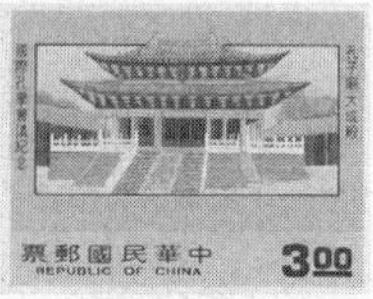

470 Ta Chen Tian, Confucius Temple, Taichung

1987. Chinese Costumes (3rd series). Mult.

1767	$1.50 Type **469**	50	10
1768	$3 Manchu bannerman's wife, Ch'ing dynasty	60	10
1769	$7.50 Woman's Manchu-style Ch'i-p'ao, early Republic period	1·40	10
1770	$18 Jacket and skirt, early Republic period	2·75	35

1987. International Confucianism and the Modern World Symposium, Taipeh. Multicoloured.

1771	$3 Type **470**	20	10
1772	$18 Confucius and fresco	80	25

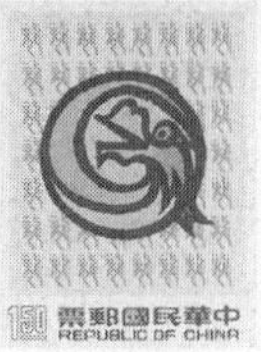

471 Dragon

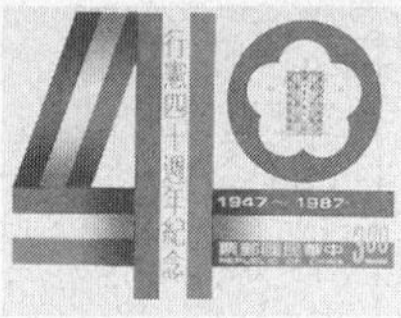

472 Flag and Emblem as "40"

1987. New Year Greetings. "Year of the Dragon".

1773	**471**	$1.50 multicoloured	60	10
1774		$12 multicoloured	2·50	20

See also No. 2042.

1987. 40th Anniv of Constitution. Mult.

1776	$3 Type **472**	20	10
1777	$16 "40" in national colours and emblem	1·00	25

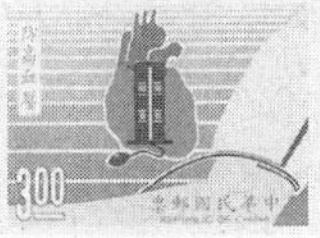

473 Sphygmomanometer

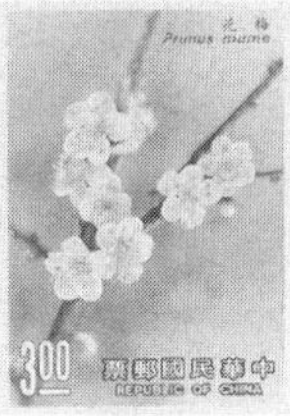

474 Plum

1988. Nat Health. Prevent Hypertension Campaign.

1778	**473**	$3 multicoloured	25	10

1988. Flowers (1st series). Multicoloured.

1779	$3 Type **474**	50	10
1780	$7.50 Apricot	1·10	10
1781	$12 Peach	1·50	20

See also Nos. 1798/1800, 1809/11 and 1829/31.

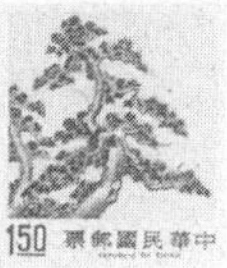

475 Pine Tree

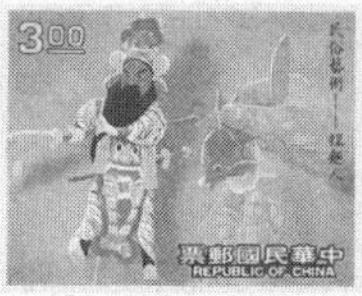

476 Modelled Dough Figurines

1988. Pine, Bamboo and Plum (3rd series). Multicoloured.

1783	$1.50 Type **475**	25	10
1784	$7.50 Bamboo	45	10
1785	$16 Plum blossom	85	25

1988. Traditional Handicrafts. Multicoloured.

1786	$3 Type **476**	50	10
1787	$7.50 Blown sugar fish	90	10
1788	$16 Sugar painting	1·25	25

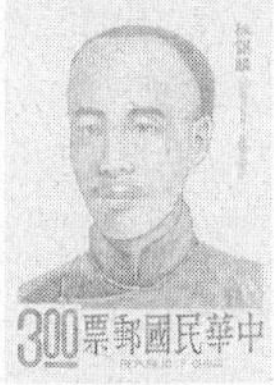

477 Hsu Hsi-lin (revolutionary)

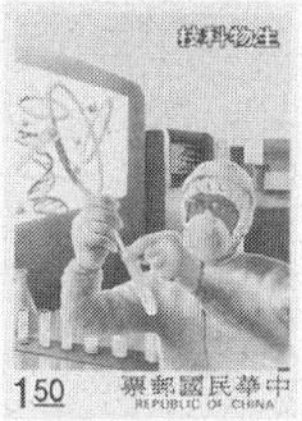

478 Bio-technology

1988. Famous Chinese.

1789	**477**	$3 brown	25	10

1988. Science and Technology. Multicoloured.

1790	$1.50 Type **478**	15	10
1791	$3 Surveyors at oil field (energy)	20	10
1792	$7 Syringe piercing letter "B" (hepatitis control)	25	10
1793	$7.50 Mechanised production line (automation)	30	10
1794	$10 Satellite and computer terminal (information)	40	15
1795	$12 Laser (electro-optics)	50	20
1796	$16 Laboratory worker (materials)	65	25
1797	$16.50 Tin of fruit and technician (food technology)	65	25

1988. Flowers (2nd series). As T **474**. Mult.

1798	$3 Tree peony	50	10
1799	$7.50 Pomegranate	1·10	10
1800	$12 East Indian lotus	1·50	20

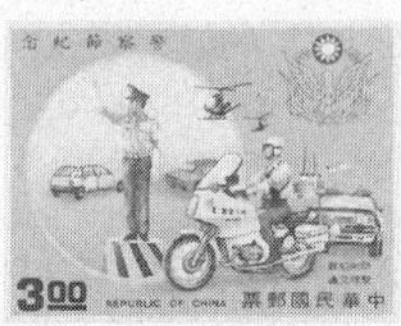

479 Policemen on Point Duty and Motor Cycle

1988. Police Day. Multicoloured.

1802	$3 Type **479**	40	10
1803	$12 Communications operator and fire-fighters	75	20

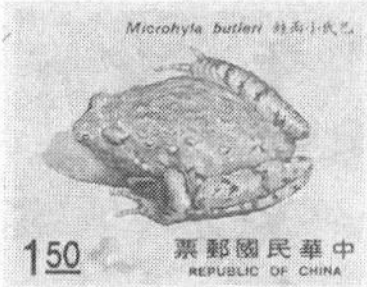

480 Butler's Pigmy Frog

1988. Amphibians. Multicoloured.

1804	$1.50 Type **480**	30	10
1805	$3 Taipeh striped slender frog	40	10
1806	$7.50 "Microhyla inornata"	1·25	10
1807	$16 Tree frog	2·50	35

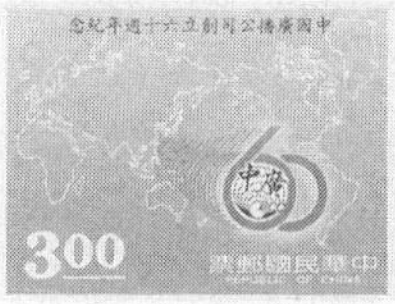

481 "60" on Map

1988. 60th Anniv of Broadcasting Corporation of China.

1808	**481**	$3 multicoloured	25	10

1988. Flowers (3rd series). As T **474**. Mult.

1809	$3 Garden balsam	50	10
1810	$7.50 Sweet osmanthus	90	10
1811	$12 Chrysanthemum	1·25	20

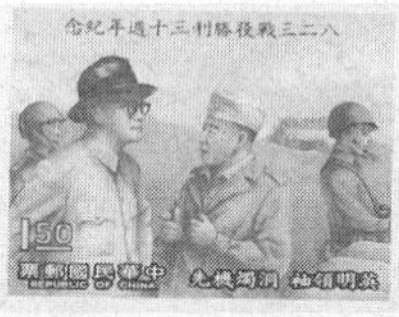

482 Chiang Kai-shek and Soldiers

1988. 30th Anniv of Kinmen Bombardment. Multicoloured.

1813	$1.50 Type **482**	25	10
1814	$3 Chiang Kai-shek and soldier reporters	25	10
1815	$7.50 Soldiers firing howitzer	65	10
1816	$12 Tank battle	75	20

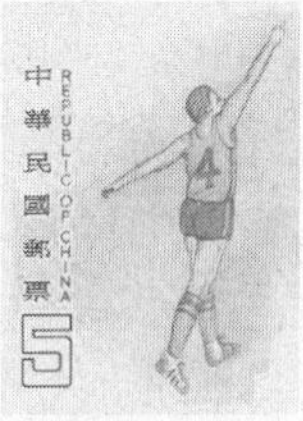

483 Basketball Player

1988. Sports Day. Multicoloured.

1817	$5 Type **483**	20	10
1818	$5 Two basketball players	20	10
1819	$5 Baseball hitter	20	10
1820	$5 Baseball catcher	20	10

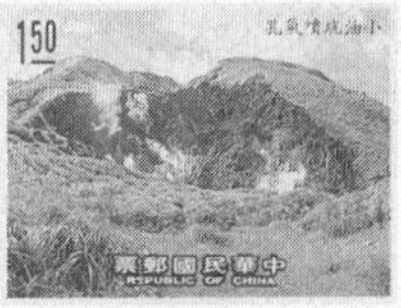

484 Crater

1988. Yangmingshan National Park. Mult.

1821	$1.50 Type **484**	50	10
1822	$3 Lake	75	10
1823	$7.50 Mountains	1·25	10
1824	$16 Lake and mountains	1·75	25

485-88 "Lofty Mount Lu"

1988. Painting by Shen Chou.
1825	**485**	$5 multicoloured	1·10	10
1826	**486**	$5 multicoloured	1·10	10
1827	**487**	$5 multicoloured	1·10	10
1828	**488**	$5 multicoloured	1·10	10

Nos. 1825/8 were printed together, se-tenant, forming the composite design illustrated.

1988. Flowers (4th series). As T **474**. Mult.
1829	$3 Cotton rose hibiscus	65	10
1830	$7.50 Camellia	90	10
1831	$12 Narcissus	1·25	20

1988. Chinese Costumes (4th series). As T **469**. Multicoloured.
1833	$2 Nobleman with tall hat, Shang dynasty	75	10
1834	$3 Ruler with topknot, Warring States period	85	10
1835	$7.50 Male official with writing brush in hair, Wei-chin dynasty	1·10	10
1836	$12 Male court official with hanging brush on hat, late Northern dynasties	2·00	20

489 Snake   **490** Tai Ch'uan-hsien

1988. New Year Greetings. "Year of the Snake".
| 1837 | **489** | $2 multicoloured | 1·25 | 10 |
| 1838 | | $13 multicoloured | 1·75 | 20 |

See also No. 2043.

1989. Birth Centenary (1990) of Tai Ch'uan-hsien (Civil Service reformer).
| 1840 | **490** | $3 black | 35 | 10 |

491 Pres. Chiang Ching-kuo

1989. 1st Death Anniv of President Chiang Ching-Kuo. Multicoloured.
1841	$3 Type **491**	15	10
1842	$6 Chiang Ching-kuo, political rally and voters	40	10
1843	$7.50 Chiang Ching-kuo at docks	85	15
1844	$16 Chiang Ching-kuo with children	1·00	25

492 Pine Tree

1989. Pine, Bamboo and Plum (4th series). Multicoloured.
1845	$3 Type **492**	10	10
1846	$16.50 Bamboo	65	25
1847	$21 Plum blossom	80	30

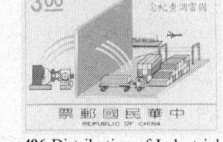

493 Ni Ying-tien   **494** Lungs smoking

1989. 79th Death Anniv of Ni Ying-tien (revolutionary).
| 1848 | **493** | $3 black | 30 | 10 |

1989. Anti-smoking Campaign.
| 1849 | **494** | $3 multicoloured | 30 | 10 |

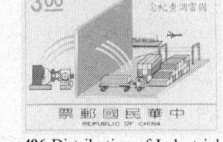

495 Mu Tou Yu Lighthouse   **496** Distribution of Industrial Goods

1989. Lighthouses. White panel at foot. Mult.
1850	75c. Type **495**	10	10
1851	$2 Lu Tao lighthouse	10	10
1852	$2.25 Pen Chia Yu lighthouse	15	10
1853	$3 Pitou Chiao lighthouse	15	10
1854	$4.50 Tungyin Tao lighthouse	25	10
1855	$6 Chilai Pi lighthouse	35	25
1856	$7 Fukwei Chiao lighthouse	45	30
1857	$7.50 Hua Yu lighthouse	50	30
1858	$9 Oluan Pi lighthouse	60	25
1859	$10 Kaohsiung lighthouse	75	40
1860	$10.50 Yuweng Tao lighthouse	75	30
1861	$12 Tungchu Tao lighthouse	80	50
1862	$13 Yeh Liu lighthouse	90	35
1863	$15 Tungchi Yu lighthouse	1·10	70
1864	$16.50 Chimei Yu lighthouse	1·25	65

For designs with blue panel at foot, see Nos. 2003/15.

1989. National Wealth Survey.
| 1865 | **496** | $3 multicoloured | 40 | 10 |

497 "I once tended nine Fields of Orchids"

1989. Chinese Classical Poetry (5th series). Poems from "Ch'u Ts'u". Multicoloured.
1866	$3 Type **497**	30	10
1867	$7.50 "No grief is greater than parting"	80	10
1868	$12 "...living remote and neglected"	1·50	20
1869	$16 "The horse will not gallop into servitude"	2·00	25

498 Underground Train

1989. Completion of Taipeh Underground Section of Western Railway Line. Multicoloured.
| 1870 | $3 Type **498** | 50 | 10 |
| 1871 | $16 Train in cutting | 1·25 | 25 |

499 Blue Triangle

1989. Butterflies (1st series). Multicoloured.
1872	$2 Type **499**	50	15
1873	$3 Great mormon	85	15
1874	$7.50 Chequered swallowtail	1·40	20
1875	$9 Common rose	2·00	20

See also Nos. 1902/5.

500 Pumpkin Teapot   **501** Fan Chung-yen

1989. Teapots (1st series). Multicoloured.
1876	$2 Type **500**	60	10
1877	$3 Clay teapot	90	10
1878	$12 "Chopped wood" teapot	1·50	10
1879	$16 Clay pear teapot	2·00	30

See also Nos. 1946/50.

1989. Birth Millenary of Fan Chung-yen (civil service reformer).
| 1880 | **501** | $12 multicoloured | 65 | 25 |

502 Trees and Right Side of Mountain

1989. Painting "Autumn Colours on the Ch'iao and Hua Mountains" by Ch'iao Mengfu. Designs showing details of the scroll. Multicoloured.
1881	$7.50 (1) Type **502**	75	15
1882	$7.50 (2) Left side of mountain and trees	75	15
1883	$7.50 (3) Trees and house	75	15
1884	$7.50 (4) Mountain, trees and house	75	15

Nos. 1872/5 were printed together, se-tenant, forming a composite design.

503 Insured Groups and Family   **504** Liwu River Gorge

1989. Social Welfare.
| 1885 | **503** | $3 multicoloured | 30 | 10 |

1989. Taroko National Park. Multicoloured.
1886	$2 Type **504**	20	10
1887	$3 North Peak of Chilai, Taroko Mountain	40	10
1888	$12 Waterfalls	80	25
1889	$16 Chingshui Cliff	1·10	30

505 Horse   **506** Yu Lu

1989. New Year Greetings. "Year of the Horse".
| 1890 | **505** | $2 multicoloured | 40 | 10 |
| 1891 | | $13 multicoloured | 1·25 | 25 |

See also No. 2044.

1990. Door Gods. Multicoloured.
1893	$3 Type **506**	50	20
1894	$3 Shen Shu	50	20
1895	$7.50 Wei-ch'ih Ching-te (facing right)	1·00	40
1896	$7.50 Ch'in Shu-pao (facing left)	1·00	40

507 Lishan   **508** Crystal containing Emblem and Industrial Symbols

1990. Tourism. Multicoloured.
| 1897 | $2 Type **507** | 25 | 10 |
| 1898 | $18 Fir tree at Tayuling (vert) | 1·00 | 25 |

1990. 40th Anniv of National Insurance.
| 1899 | **508** | $3 multicoloured | 50 | 10 |

509 Harbour and Tanks

1990. Yung-An Hsiang Liquefied Natural Gas Terminal. Multicoloured.
| 1900 | $3 Type **509** | 35 | 10 |
| 1901 | $16 Gas tanker and map showing pipeline route (vert) | 1·00 | 25 |

510 African Monarch   **511** Court Official, Northern Wei Period to T'ang Dynasty

1990. Butterflies (2nd series). Multicoloured.
1902	$2 Orange tiger	30	10
1903	$3 Type **510**	35	10
1904	$7.50 "Pieris canidia"	75	20
1905	$9 Peacock	1·10	25

1990. Chinese Costumes (5th series). Mult.
1906	$2 Type **511**	40	10
1907	$3 Civil official in winged hat and green robe, Three Kingdoms period to Ming dynasty	50	10
1908	$7.50 Royal guard in bamboo hat, Yuan dynasty	70	15
1909	$12 Highest grade civil official in robe decorated with crane bird, Ming dynasty	90	40

512 "Spring Song at Midnight"

1990. Chinese Classical Poetry (6th series). Multicoloured.
1910	$3 Type **512**	50	10
1911	$7.50 Couple on river bank ("Summer Song at Midnight")	70	15
1912	$12 Girl washing clothes in river ("Autumn Song at Midnight")	1·00	20
1913	$16 Snow-bound river scene ("Winter Song at Midnight")	1·25	25

513 Japanese Black Pine

514 Bamboo-shaped Glass Snuff Bottle

1990. Bonsai. Multicoloured.
1914 $3 Type **513** 40 10
1915 $6.50 "Ehretia microphylla" . . 60 10
1916 $12 "Buxus harlandii" . . . 90 20
1917 $16 "Celtis sinensis" . . . . 1·25 25

1990. Snuff Bottles. Multicoloured.
1918 $3 Type **514** 30 10
1919 $6 Glass bottle with peony design 60 10
1920 $9 Melon-shaped amber bottle 90 15
1921 $16 White jade bottle . . . 1·10 25

515 Taiwan Firecrest

516 Running

1990. Birds. Multicoloured.
1922 $2 Type **515** 50 25
1923 $3 Formosan barwing . . . 60 25
1924 $7.50 White-eared sibia . . 80 30
1925 $16 Formosan yellow tit . . 1·10 80

1990. Sports. Multicoloured.
1926 $2 Type **516** 20 10
1927 $3 Long jumping 35 10
1928 $7 Pole vaulting 70 10
1929 $16 Hurdling . . . . 1·00 25

517 Curtiss Tomahawk II Fighters and Air Crews

1990. 50th Anniv of Arrival of "Flying Tigers" American Volunteer Group.
1930 **517** $3 multicoloured 40 10

518 Cats

1990. Children's Drawings. Multicoloured.
1931 $2 Type **518** 30 10
1932 $3 Common peafowl . . . 40 20
1933 $7.50 Chickens 80 15
1934 $12 Cattle market . . . . . 1·25 20

519 National Theatre

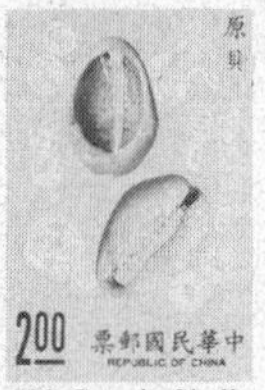
520 Cowrie Shells

1990. Cultural Buildings in Chiang Kai-shek Memorial Park, Taipeh.
1935 **519** $3 orange, dp blue & bl 30 10
1936 – $12 mauve, violet & lilac 90 20
DESIGN: $12 National Concert Hall.

1990. Ancient Coins. "Shell" Money. Mult.
1937 $2 Type **520** 20 10
1938 $3 Oyster shell 35 10
1939 $6.50 Bone 60 15
1940 $7.50 Bronze 70 15
1941 $9 Jade . . . . 1·00 20

521 Sheep

522 Hu Shih

1990. New Year Greetings. "Year of the Sheep".
1942 **521** $2 multicoloured 50 10
1943 $13 multicoloured . . . 1·00 20
See also No. 2045.

1990. Birth Centenary of Hu Shih (written Chinese reformer).
1945 **522** $3 violet 30 10

523 Teapot with Dragon Spout and Handle

524 Happiness

1991. Teapots (2nd series). Multicoloured.
1946 $2 Blue and white teapot with phoenix design . . . 25 10
1947 $3 Type **523** 40 10
1948 $9 Teapot with floral design on lid and landscape on body 70 15
1949 $12 Rectangular teapot with passion flower design . . 90 20
1950 $16 Brown rectangular teapot with floral decoration . . . . 1·10 25

1991. Greetings Stamps. Gods of Prosperity. Multicoloured.
1951 $3 Type **524** 40 10
1952 $3 Wealth 40 10
1953 $7.50 Longevity (with white beard) 60 15
1954 $7.50 Joy 60 15

525 "Petasites formosanus"

526 Hsiung Cheng-chi (revolutionary)

1991. Plants (1st series). Multicoloured.
1955 $2 Type **525** 25 10
1956 $3 "Heloniopsis acutifolia" 35 10
1957 $7.50 "Disporum shimadai" 60 15
1958 $9 "Viola nagasawai" . . . 70 15
See also Nos. 1969/72, 1995/8 and 2026/9.

1991. Famous Chinese.
1959 **526** $3 blue 35 10

527 Agriculture

528 Bamboo Hobby-horse

1991. 80th Anniv (1992) of Founding of Chinese Republic. Multicoloured.
1960 $3 Type **527** 35 10
1961 $7.50 Industry 75 10
1962 $12 Dancer and leisure equipment . . . . 1·25 20
1963 $16 Transport and communications . . . . . 1·50 30

1991. Children's Games (1st series). Mult.
1964 $3 Type **528** 25 10
1965 $3 Woven-grass grasshoppers 25 10
1966 $3 Spinning tops 25 10
1967 $3 Windmills 25 10
See also Nos. 2056/9, 2120/3 and 2184/7.

1991. Plants (2nd series). As T **525**. Mult.
1969 $2 "Gaultheria itoana" . . 30 10
1970 $3 "Lysionotus montanus" 40 10
1971 $7.50 "Leontopodium microphyllum" 75 15
1972 $9 "Gentiana flavo-maculata" . . . . 1·00 15

529 Male Official's Summer Court Dress

530 Heart, Pedestrian Crossing and Hand

1991. Chinese Costumes (6th series). Ch'ing Dynasty. Multicoloured.
1973 $2 Male official's winter court dress with dragon design 40 10
1974 $3 Type **529** 50 10
1975 $7.50 Male official's winter overcoat 95 15
1976 $12 Everyday skull-cap, jacket and travelling robe 1·75 20

1991. Road Safety. Multicoloured.
1977 $3 Type **530** 35 10
1978 $7.50 Hand, road and broken bottle ("Don't Drink and Drive") . . . 75 15

531 Ch'ing Dynasty Cloisonne Lion

532 Strawberries

1991. No value expressed. Multicoloured.
1979 (–) Type **531** 20 15
1980 (–) Cloisonne lioness 80 25
Nos. 1979/80 were sold at the prevailing rates for domestic ordinary and domestic prompt delivery letters.

1991. Fruits. Multicoloured.
1981 $3 Type **532** 50 10
1982 $7.50 Grapes 55 15
1983 $9 Mango 70 20
1984 $16 Sugar apple . . . . . . 1·10 25

533 Formosan Whistling Thrush

1991. River Birds. Multicoloured.
1985 $5 Type **533** 50 20
1986 $5 Brown dipper 50 20
1987 $5 Mandarins 50 20
1988 $5 Black-crowned night herons 50 20
1989 $5 Little egrets 50 20
1990 $5 Plumbeous redstarts . . 50 20
1991 $5 Little forktail 50 20
1992 $5 Grey wagtail 50 20
1993 $5 River kingfishers 50 20
1994 $5 Pied wagtails 50 20
Nos. 1985/94 were printed together, se-tenant, forming a composite design.

1991. Plants (3rd series). As T **525**. Mult.
1995 $3.50 "Rosa transmorrisonensis" . . . 45 10
1996 $5 "Impatiens devolii" . . . 75 10
1997 $9 "Impatiens uniflora" . . 1·00 20
1998 $12 "Impatiens taye-monii" 1·25 20

534 Rock Climbing

1991. International Camping and Caravanning Federation Rally, Fulung Beach. Multicoloured.
1999 $2 Type **534** 25 10
2000 $3 Fishing 35 10
2001 $7.50 Bird-watching 50 15
2002 $10 Boys with pail wading in water 75 20

1991. Lighthouses. As Nos. 1851/3 and 1855/64 but with blue panel at foot.
2003 50c. As No. 1863 . . . . . 10 10
2004 $1 As No. 1851 . . . . . . 10 10
2005 $3.50 As No. 1855 . . . . 25 10
2006 $5 As No. 1856 . . . . . 35 10
2007 $7 As No. 1853 . . . . . 45 10
2008 $9 As No. 1858 . . . . . 60 15
2009 $10 As No. 1859 . . . . . 70 10
2010 $12 As No. 1861 . . . . . 75 15
2011 $13 As No. 1852 . . . . . 80 15
2012 $19 As No. 1857 . . . . . 1·10 20
2013 $20 As No. 1862 . . . . . 1·25 20
2014 $26 As No. 1860 . . . . . 1·40 25
2015 $28 As No. 1864 . . . . . 1·75 30

535 Peacock

536 Monkey

1991. "Peacocks" by Giuseppe Castiglione. Designs showing details of painting. Multicoloured.
2020 $5 Type **535** 50 25
2021 $20 Peacock displaying tail 1·90 1·00

1991. New Year Greetings. "Year of the Monkey".
2023 **536** $3.50 multicoloured . . 50 10
2024 $13 multicoloured . . . 1·10 25
See also No. 2046.

1991. Plants (4th series). As T **525**. Mult.
2026 $3.50 "Kalanchoe garambiensis" 40 10
2027 $5 "Pieris taiwanensis" . . . 75 10
2028 $9 "Pleione formosana" . . 1·00 20
2029 $12 "Elaeagnus oldhamii" 1·25 20

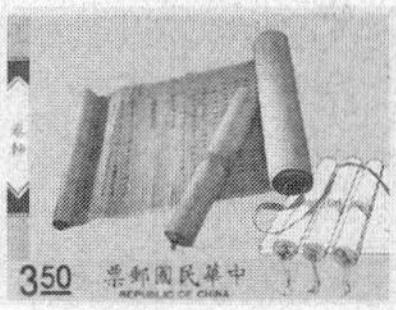
537 Scrolls

538 Peace in the Wake of Firecrackers

1992. International Book Fair, Taipeh. Mult.
2030 $3.50 Type **537** 30 10
2031 $5 Folded-leaves book . . . 40 10
2032 $9 Butterfly-bound books 75 15
2033 $15 Sewn books . . . . . 1·10 25

1992. Greetings Stamps. Nienhwas (paintings conveying wishes for the coming year). Mult.
2034 $5 Type **538** 50 10
2035 $5 Elephant with riders (Good fortune and satisfaction) 50 10
2036 $12 Children and five "birds" (Five blessings upon the house) 70 20
2037 $12 Children angling for large fish (Abundance for every year) 70 20

1992. Signs of Chinese Zodiac. As previous designs but with additional symbol in top left-hand corner.
2038 **393** $5 multicoloured 50 10
2039 **414** $5 multicoloured 50 10
2040 **435** $5 multicoloured 50 10
2041 **456** $5 multicoloured 50 10
2042 **471** $5 multicoloured 50 10
2043 **489** $5 multicoloured 50 10
2044 **505** $5 multicoloured 50 10
2045 **521** $5 multicoloured 50 10
2046 **536** $5 multicoloured 50 10
2047 **340** $5 multicoloured 50 10
2048 **361** $5 multicoloured 50 10
2049 **378** $5 multicoloured 50 10
Nos. 2038/49 were issued together in se-tenant blocks of 12 stamps within the sheet. The stamps are listed in order from right to left of the block.

5.00
REPUBLIC OF CHINA

539 Taiwan Red Cypress ("Chamaecyparis formosensis")

3.50
REPUBLIC OF CHINA

541 Mother and son (Spring)

1992. Forest Resources. Conifers. Mult.

2051	$5 Type **539**	55	10
2052	$5 Taiwan cypress ("Chamaecyparis taiwanensis")	55	10
2053	$5 Taiwan incense cedar ("Calocedrus formosana")	55	10
2054	$5 Ranta fir ("Cunninghamia konishii")	55	10
2055	$5 Taiwania ("Taiwania cryptomerioides")	55	10

Nos. 2051/5 were printed together, se-tenant, forming a composite design.

1992. Children's Games (2nd series). As T **528**. Multicoloured.

2056	$5 Walking on tin cans	40	10
2057	$5 Chopstick guns	40	10
2058	$5 Rolling hoops	40	10
2059	$5 Grass fighting	40	10

1992. Parent–Child Relationships. Mult.

2061	$3.50 Type **541**	40	10
2062	$5 Mother carrying child on back (summer)	50	10
2063	$9 Mother and child pushing toy rabbits (autumn)	75	15
2064	$10 Mother feeding child (winter)	90	15

3.50
REPUBLIC OF CHINA

542 Vase decorated with Bats and Longevity Characters

5.00
REPUBLIC OF CHINA

543 Lion and Stone Pavilion

1992. Glassware decorated with Enamel. Mult.

2066	$3.50 Type **542**	30	10
2067	$5 Gourd-shaped vase decorated with landscape and children at play	40	10
2068	$7 Vase with peony decoration	50	15
2069	$17 Vase showing mother teaching child to read	1·10	25

1992. Stone Lions from Lugouqiao Bridge.

2070	**543** $5 blue and brown	40	10
2071	– $5 green and violet	40	10
2072	– $12 orange and green	70	20
2073	– $12 violet and black	70	20

DESIGNS: No. 2071, Bridge and lioness with cub; 2070, Bridge parapet and lion; 2073, Bridge parapet and lioness with two cubs.

3.50

544 "People make Friends and are tied to Each Other as Roots to a Plant"

1992. Chinese Classical Poetry (7th series). Multicoloured.

2074	$3.50 Type **544**	30	10
2075	$5 Couple at window ("Conjugal love will last forever")	40	10
2076	$9 Couple in garden ("Man takes pains to uphold virtue/Till one's hair turns forever grey")	80	15
2077	$15 "Tartar horses lean toward the north wind"	1·25	25

5.00
REPUBLIC OF CHINA

545 Drummer and Crowd

5.00
REPUBLIC OF CHINA

546 "Two Birds perched on a Red Camellia Branch"

1992. Temple Fair. Multicoloured.

2078	$5 Type **545**	45	10
2079	$5 Man with basket dancing	45	10
2080	$5 Musicians	45	10
2081	$5 Man pushing cart	45	10
2082	$5 Women and children	45	10

Nos. 2078/82 were printed together, se-tenant, forming a composite design.

1992. Ming Dynasty Silk Tapestries. Mult.

2083	$5 Type **546**	50	10
2084	$12 "Two Birds playing on a Peach Branch"	1·00	20

3.50
中華民國郵票
REPUBLIC OF CHINA

547 Cart in "The General and the Premier"

5.00
REPUBLIC OF CHINA

548 Steam Locomotive and Train

1992. Chinese Opera Props. Multicoloured.

2086	$3.50 Type **547**	50	10
2087	$5 Ship in "The Lucky Pearl"	60	10
2088	$9 Horse in "Chao-chun serves as an Envoy"	80	15
2089	$12 Sedan chair in "Escort to the Wedding"	90	15

1992. Alishan Mountain Railway. Mult.

2090	$5 Type **548**	30	15
2091	$15 Diesel locomotive and train	1·10	35

5.00
REPUBLIC OF CHINA

549 Chinese River Otter

3.50
REPUBLIC OF CHINA

550 Cock

1992. Mammals. Multicoloured.

2092	$5 Type **549**	25	10
2093	$5 Formosan flying fox	25	10
2094	$5 Formosan clouded leopard	25	10
2095	$5 Formosan black bear	25	10

1992. New Year Greetings. "Year of the Cock". Multicoloured.

2096	$3.50 Type **550**	20	10
2097	$13 Cock (facing left)	75	15

5.00

552 Schall and Astronomical Instruments

1992. 400th Birth Anniv of Johann Adam Schall von Bell (missionary astronomer).

2100	**552** $5 multicoloured	40	10

5.00
REPUBLIC OF CHINA

553 Satisfaction for Every Year

1993. Greetings Stamps. Nienhwas (paintings conveying wishes for the coming year). Multicoloured.

2101	$5 Type **553**	50	10
2102	$5 Birds and flowers (Joy)	50	10
2103	$12 Butterfly and flowers (Happiness and longevity)	1·10	15
2104	$12 Flowers in vase (Wealth and peace)	1·10	15

3.50
REPUBLIC OF CHINA

554 Applying Enamel and Glass Decoration to Temple Roof

1992. International Traditional Crafts Exhibition, Taipeh, Multicoloured.

2105	$3.50 Type **554**	30	10
2106	$5 Ceremonial lantern	40	10
2107	$9 Pottery jars	65	10
2108	$15 Oil-paper umbrella	1·00	20

3.50
REPUBLIC OF CHINA

555 Pan Gu creating Universe

1993. The Creation. Multicoloured.

2109	$3.50 Type **555**	30	10
2110	$5 Pan Gu creating animals (horiz)	35	10
2111	$9 Nu Wa creating human beings (horiz)	70	10
2112	$19 Nu Wa mending the sky with smelted stone	1·25	20

3.50

556 Mandarins

5.00
REPUBLIC OF CHINA

557 Water Lily

1993. Lucky Animals (1st series).

2113	**556** $3.50 multicoloured	30	10
2114	– $5 multicoloured	35	10
2115	– $10 red and black	75	15
2116	– $15 multicoloured	1·00	20

DESIGNS: $5, Chinese unicorn; $10, Deer; $15, Crane.

See also Nos. 2151/4.

1993. Water Plants, Multicoloured.

2117	$5 Type **557**	40	10
2118	$9 Taiwan cow lily	75	10
2119	$12 Water hyacinth	85	15

1993. Children's Games (3rd series). As T **528**. Multicoloured.

2120	$5 Tossing sandbags	40	10
2121	$5 Bamboo dragonflies	40	10
2122	$5 Skipping	40	10
2123	$5 Duel of strength with rope passed round waists	40	10

3.50
REPUBLIC OF CHINA

560 Ching-Kang-Chang Plateau (source)

1993. Yangtze River. Multicoloured.

2127	$3.50 Type **560**	35	10
2128	$3.50 Turn in river (Chinsha River)	35	10
2129	$5 Roaring Tiger Gorge (white water in narrow ravine)	40	10
2130	$5 Chutang Gorge (calm water in wide gorge)	40	10
2131	$9 Dragon Gate, Pawu and Titsui Gorges	80	10

5.00
REPUBLIC OF CHINA

561 Noise Pollution and Music

1993. Environmental Protection. Children's Drawings. Multicoloured.

2132	$5 Type **561**	35	10
2133	$17 Family looking out over green fields (vert)	1·10	20

3.50
REPUBLIC OF CHINA

562 Cup with Tou-Ts'ai Figures

1993. Ch'eng-hua Porcelain Cups of Ming Dynasty. Multicoloured.

2134	$3.50 Type **562**	30	10
2135	$5 Chicken decoration	35	10
2136	$7 Flowers and fruits of four seasons decoration	55	10
2137	$9 Dragon decoration	75	10

3.50
REPUBLIC OF CHINA

563 Graphic Design

REPUBLIC OF CHINA
3.50

564 Child on Father's Shoulders

1993. 32nd International Vocational Training Competition, Taipeh. Multicoloured.

2138	$3.50 Type **563**	30	10
2139	$5 Computer technology	35	10
2140	$9 Carpentry	65	10
2141	$12 Welding	80	15

1993. Parent–Child Relationships. Mult.

2142	$3.50 Type **564**	30	10
2143	$5 Father playing flute to child	40	10
2144	$9 Child reading to father	75	10
2145	$10 Father pointing at bird	75	15

5.00
REPUBLIC OF CHINA

566 Persimmons

5.00
REPUBLIC OF CHINA

567 Gymnastics

1993. Fruits. Multicoloured.

2147	$5 Type **566**	40	10
2148	$5 Peaches	40	10
2149	$12 Loquats	60	15
2150	$12 Papayas	60	15

1993. Lucky Animals (2nd series). As T **556**. Mult.

2151	$1 Blue dragon (representing Spring, wood and the East)	20	10
2152	$2.50 White tiger (Autumn, metal and the West)	30	10
2153	$9 Linnet (Summer, fire and the South)	60	15
2154	$19 Black tortoise (Winter, water and the North)	1·10	20

1993. Taiwan Area Games, Taoyuan. Mult.

2155	$5 Type **567**	25	10
2156	$5 Taekwondo	25	10

REPUBLIC OF CHINA
3.50

568 Stone Lion, New Park, Taipeh

5.00
REPUBLIC OF CHINA

569 Chick

1993. Stone Lions. Multicoloured.

2157	$3.50 Type **568**	30	10
2158	$5 Hsinchu City Council building	40	10
2159	$9 Temple, Hsinchu City	70	10
2160	$12 Fort Providentia, Tainan	95	15

1993. Mikado Pheasant. Multicoloured.

2161	$5 Type **569**	55	20
2162	$5 Mother and chicks	55	20

2163 $5 Immature male and female 55 20
2164 $5 Adults 55 20
Nos. 2161/4 were issued together, se-tenant, forming a composite design.

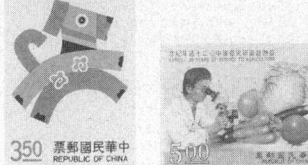

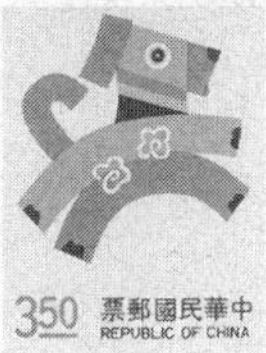
570 Dog

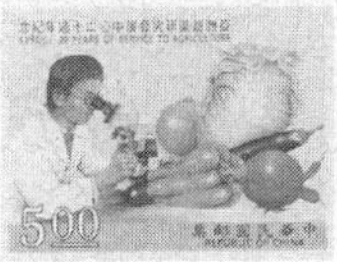
571 Scientist and Vegetables

1993. New Year Greetings. "Year of the Dog". Multicoloured.
2165 $3.50 Type **570** 15 10
2166 $13 Dog (facing left) 65 15

1993. 20th Anniv of Asian Vegetable Research and Development Centre. Multicoloured.
2168 $5 Type **571** 30 10
2169 $13 Scientists and fields of crops 75 15

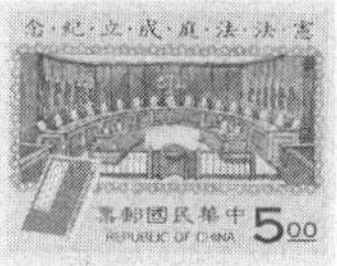
573 Courtroom

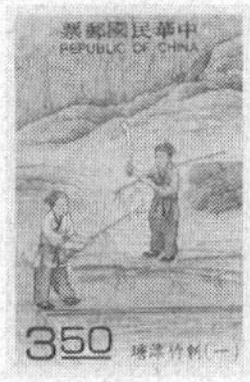
574 Cutting Bamboo

1994. Inauguration of Taiwan Constitutional Court.
2171 **573** $5 multicoloured 30 10

1994. Traditional Paper Making. Multicoloured.
2172 $3.50 Type **574** 25 10
2173 $3.50 Cooking bamboo . . 25 10
2174 $5 Moulding bamboo pulp in wooden panels 40 10
2175 $5 Stacking wet paper for pressing 40 10
2176 $12 Drying paper 80 15

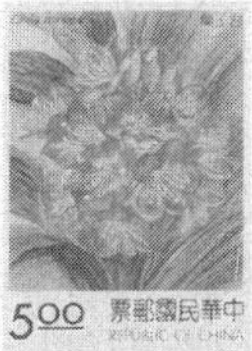
575 "Clivia miniata"

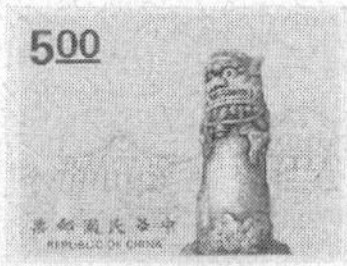
576 Wind Lion Lord

1994. Flowers. Multicoloured.
2177 $5 Type **575** 40 10
2178 $12 "Cymbidium sinense" 80 15
2179 $19 "Primula malacoides" 1·25 20

1994. Kinmen Wind Lion Lords.
2180 **576** $5 multicoloured 45 10
2181 – $9 multicoloured 80 10
2182 – $12 multicoloured . . . 1·00 15
2183 – $17 multicoloured . . . 1·25 20
DESIGNS: $9 to $17 Different Lion Lord statues.

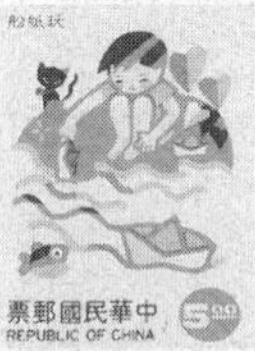
577 Sailing Paper Boats

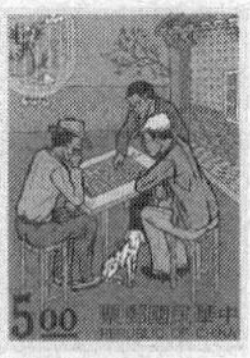
578 Playing Chess

1994. Children's Games (4th series). Mult.
2184 $5 Type **577** 40 10
2185 $5 Fighting with water-guns 40 10
2186 $5 Throwing paper plane . . 40 10
2187 $5 Human train 40 10

1994. Rural Pastimes. Multicoloured.
2189 $5 Type **578** 35 10
2190 $10 Playing the flute 60 10
2191 $12 Telling stories 85 15
2192 $19 Drinking tea . . . . . 1·25 20

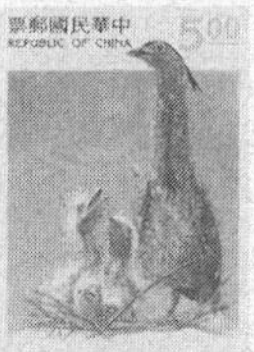
579 Tiger Bittern and Chicks

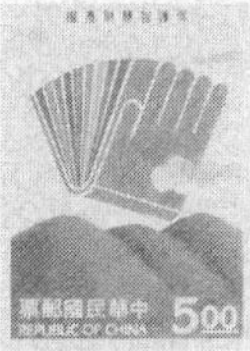
580 Book with Hand on Cover

1994. Parent–Child Relationships. Birds with their Young. Multicoloured.
2193 $5 Type **579** 30 25
2194 $7 Little tern (horiz) 50 45
2195 $10 Common noddy (horiz) 75 60
2196 $12 Muller's barbet 85 90

1994. Protection of Intellectual Property Rights. Multicoloured.
2197 $5 Type **580** 30 10
2198 $15 Head with locked computer disk as brain . . 70 15

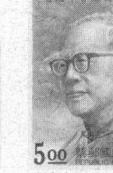

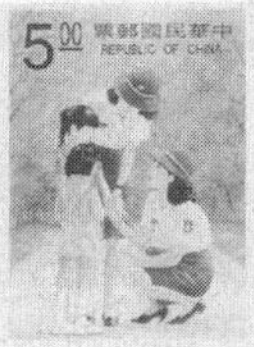
581 Caring for the Young

582 Anniversary Emblem and Olympic Rings

1994. International Rotary Clubs Convention, Taipeh. "Towards an Harmonious Society". Multicoloured.
2199 $5 Type **581** 30 10
2200 $17 Caring for the aged . . 70 20

1994. Centenary of International Olympic Committee. Multicoloured.
2201 $5 Type **582** 30 10
2202 $15 Running, high jumping and weight-lifting 70 15

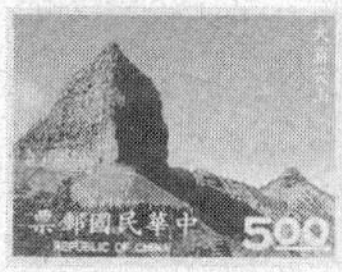
583 Summit of Dah-pa Mountain

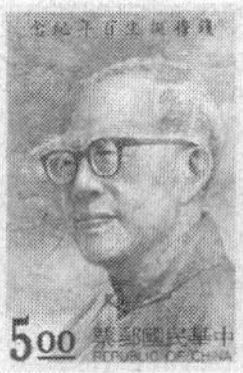
584 Chien Mu

1994. Shei-pa National Park. Multicoloured.
2203 $5 Type **583** 40 10
2204 $7 Shei-san Valley 50 10
2205 $10 Holy Ridge 70 10
2206 $17 Shiah-tsuei Pool . . . . 1·00 20

1994. Birth Centenary of Chien Mu (academic).
2207 **584** $5 multicoloured 35 10

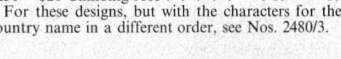

585 Window

1994. International Year of the Family. Mult.
2208 $5 Type **585** 40 10
2209 $15 Globe and house . . . 70 25

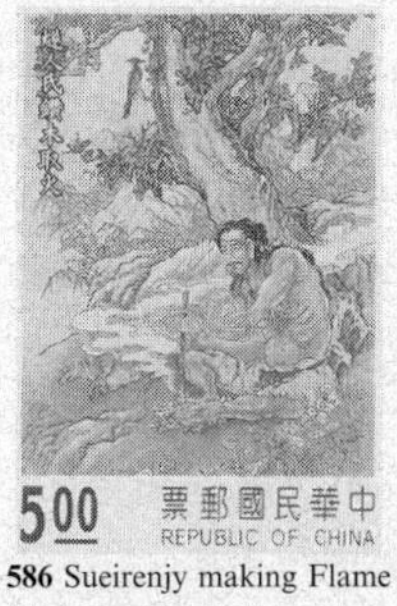
586 Sueirenjy making Flame

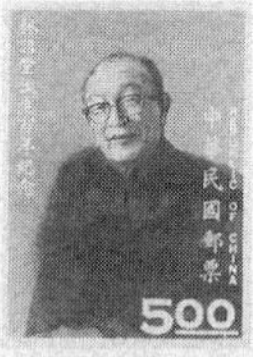
587 Lin Yutang

1994. Invention Myths. Multicoloured.
2210 $5 Type **586** 40 10
2211 $10 Fushijy drawing Pa-kua characters 75 10
2212 $12 Shennungjy making pitchfork 80 20
2213 $15 Tsangjier inventing pictorial characters . . . 1·00 25

1994. Birth Centenary of Dr. Lin Yutang (essayist and lexicographer).
2214 **587** $5 multicoloured 25 10

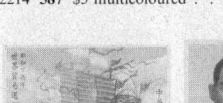

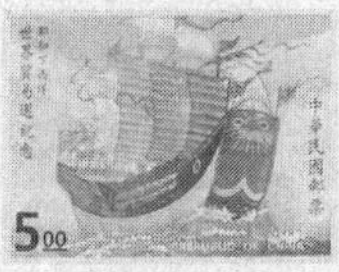
588 Cheng Ho's Junk

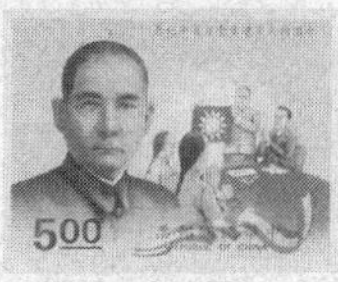
589 Dr. Sun Yat-sen (founder)

1994. World Trade Week. Multicoloured.
2215 $5 Type **588** 30 10
2216 $17 Cheng Ho and route map around South Asia 70 15

1994. Centenary of Kuomintang Party. Mult.
2217 $5 Type **589** 30 10
2218 $19 Modern developments and voter placing slip in ballot box 80 15

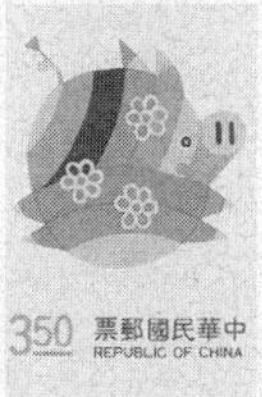
590 Pig

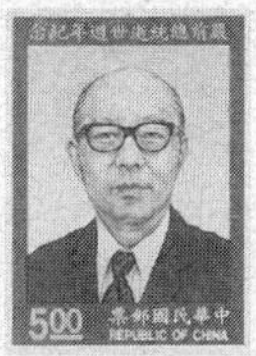
591 Yen Chia-kan

1994. New Year Greetings. "Year of the Pig". Multicoloured.
2219 $3.50 Type **590** 15 10
2220 $13 Pig (facing left) 60 15

1994. 1st Death Anniv of Yen Chia-kan (President, 1974–78). Multicoloured.
2222 $5 Type **591** 25 10
2223 $15 Visiting farmers 70 15

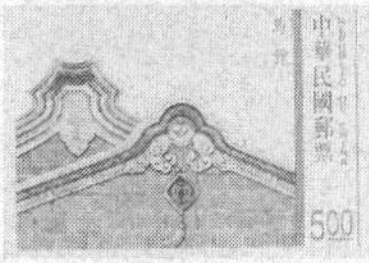
592 Horse's Back

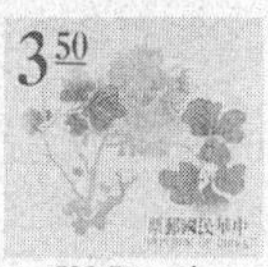
593 Begonia

1995. Traditional Architecture. Roof Styles. Mult.
2224 $5 Type **592** 35 10
2225 $5 Swallow's tail 35 10
2226 $12 Talisman (stove and bowl) 55 15
2227 $19 Cylinder-shaped brick 90 20

1995. Chinese Engravings. Flowers. Mult.
2228 $3.50 Type **593** 20 10
2229 $5 Rose 25 10
2230 $19 Flower 75 15
2231 $26 Climbing rose . . . . . 1·00 15
For these designs, but with the characters for the country name in a different order, see Nos. 2480/3.

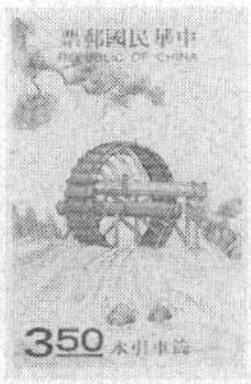
594 Rotating Wheel of Pipes

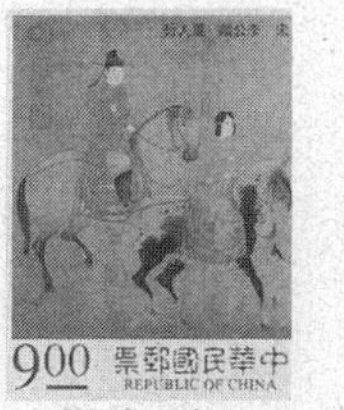
595 Courtiers

1995. Irrigation Techniques from "Tian Gong Kai Wu" (encyclopaedia) by Sung Yin-shing. Multicoloured.
2232 $3.50 Type **594** 20 10
2233 $3.50 Donkey turning wheel to raise water 20 10
2234 $5 Pedal-driven device to raise water 35 10
2235 $12 Man turning wheel to raise water 85 15
2236 $13 Well . . . . 1·00 15

1995. "Beauties on an Outing" by Lee Gong-lin. Details of the painting. Multicoloured.
2237 $9 Type **595** 45 10
2238 $9 Courtier and beauty with child 45 10
2239 $9 Courtier with two beauties 45 10
2240 $9 Courtier 45 10
Nos. 2237/40 were issued together, se-tenant, forming a composite design.

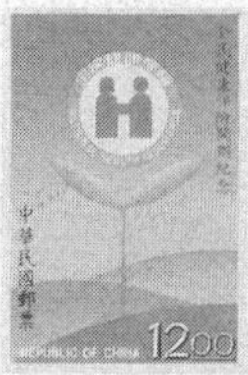
596 Emblem and Landscape

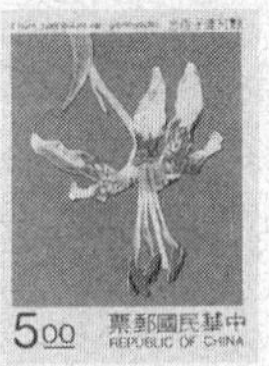
597 Chinese Showy Lily

1995. Inaug of National Health Insurance Plan.
2242 **596** $12 multicoloured . . . 55 15

1995. Bulbous Flowers. Multicoloured.
2243 $5 Type **597** 35 10
2244 $12 Blood lily 45 15
2245 $19 Hyacinth 70 20

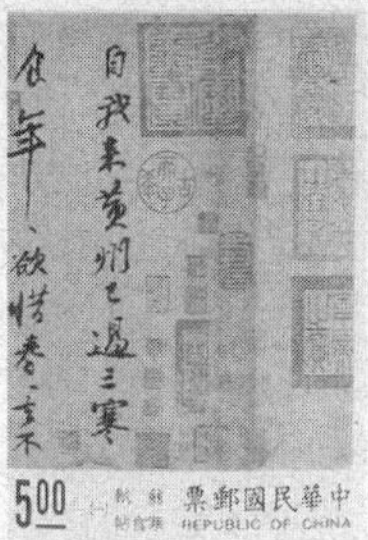
598 Opening Lines

1995. Chinese Calligraphy. "Cold Food Observance" (poem) by Su Shih.
2246 **598** $5 (1) multicoloured . . 65 10
2247 – $5 (2) multicoloured . . 65 10
2248 – $5 (3) multicoloured . . 65 10
2249 – $5 (4) multicoloured . . 65 10
Nos. 2246/9 were issued together, se-tenant, forming a composite design; the stamps are numbered in Chinese numerals to the right of the face value, from right to left.

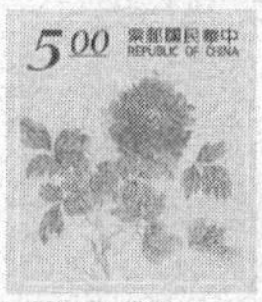
599 Red Peony

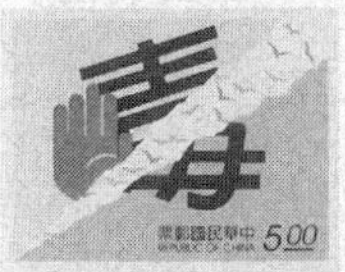
600 Hand, Birds and Cracked Symbol

1995. Peonies. Paintings by Tsou I-kuei. Self-adhesive. Imperf.
2250 $5 Type **599** . . . . 2·00 10
2251 $5 Pink peony . . . . . . 2·00 10

1995. Anti-drugs Campaign. Multicoloured.
2252 $5 Type **600** 30 10
2253 $15 Arm and syringe forming cross 65 15

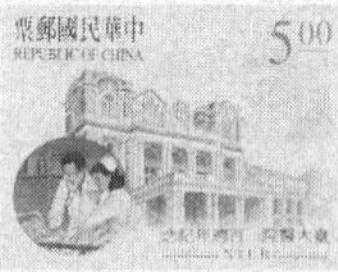
601 Old Hospital Building

1995. Centenary of National Taiwan University Hospital, Taipeh. Multicoloured.
2254 $5 Type **601** 25 10
2255 $19 New building 70 20

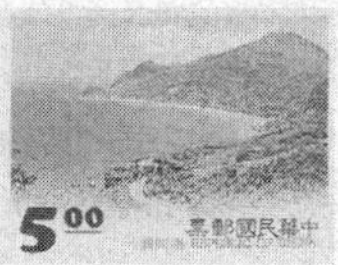
602 Chichi Bay

1995. Tourism. East Coast National Scenic Area. Multicoloured.
2256 $5 Type **602** 30 10
2257 $5 Shihyuesan (rocky promontory) 30 10
2258 $12 Hsiaoyehlieu (eroded rocks) 50 15
2259 $15 Changhong Bridge . . . 80 15

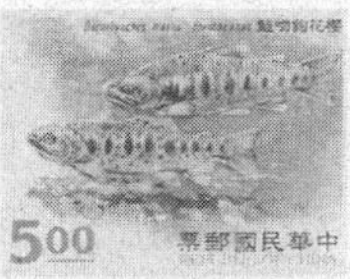
603 Mating

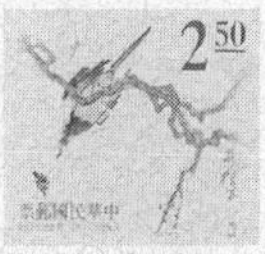
604 Bird feeding on Branch

1995. The Cherry Salmon. Multicoloured.
2260 $5 Type **603** 30 10
2261 $7 Female digging redd . . 45 10
2262 $10 Fry hatching 65 10
2263 $17 Fry swimming 80 20

1995. Chinese Engravings. Birds. Mult.
2264 $2.50 Type **604** 10 10
2265 $7 Bird on branch of peach tree 30 10
2266 $13 Bird preening 50 10
2267 $28 Yellow bird 80 20
For these designs with different face values and the order of the characters in the country name changed, see Nos. 2532/7.

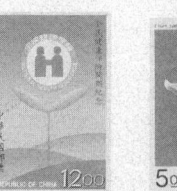

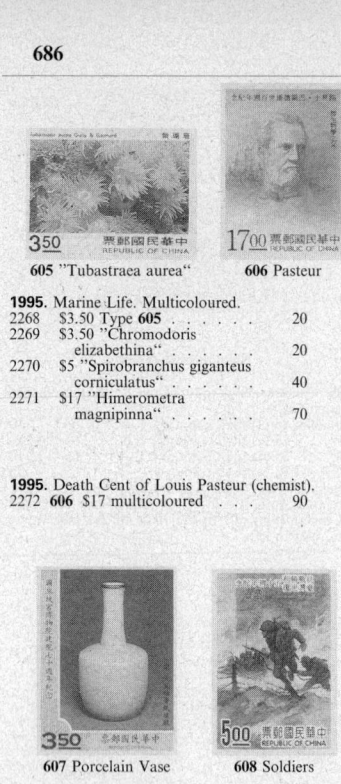

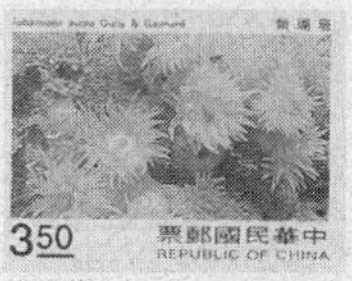
605 "Tubastraea aurea"

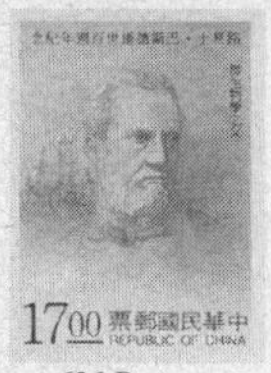
606 Pasteur

1995. Marine Life. Multicoloured.

2268	$3.50 Type **605**	20	10
2269	$3.50 "Chromodoris elizabethina"	20	10
2270	$5 "Spirobranchus giganteus corniculatus"	40	10
2271	$17 "Himerometra magnipinna"	70	20

1995. Death Cent of Louis Pasteur (chemist).

2272	**606** $17 multicoloured	90	20

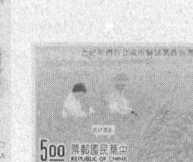

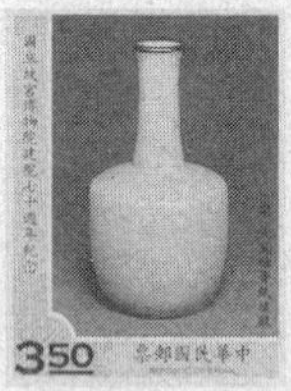
607 Porcelain Vase

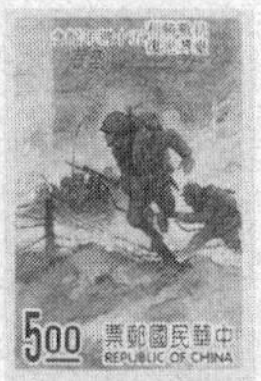
608 Soldiers

1995. 70th Anniv of National Palace Museum. Multicoloured.

2273	$3.50 "Strange Peaks and Myriad Trees" (painting) (horiz)	20	10
2274	$3.50 Type **607**	20	10
2275	$5 X Fu-K'uei Ting bronze three-fronted vessel	45	10
2276	$26 "The Fragrance of Flowers" (quatrain) (horiz)	1·00	25

1995. 50th Anniv of End of Sino-Japanese War. Multicoloured.

2277	$5 Type **608**	25	10
2278	$19 Taiwan flag, map and city	90	20

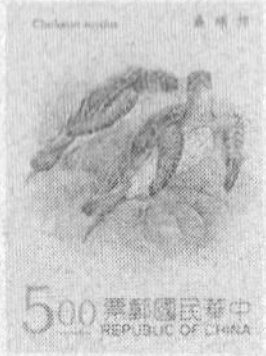
609 Common Green Turtle ("Chelonia mydas")

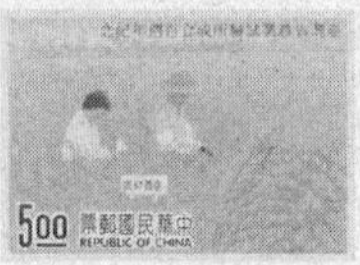
610 Scientists in Crop Field

1995. Year of the Sea Turtle. Multicoloured.

2280	$5 Type **609**	35	10
2281	$5 Loggerhead turtle ("Caretta caretta")	35	10
2282	$5 Olive ridley turtle ("Lepidochelys olivacea")	35	10
2283	$5 Hawksbill turtle ("Eretmochelys imbricata")	35	10

1995. Centenary of Taiwan Agricultural Research Institute. Multicoloured.

2284	$5 Type **610**	25	10
2285	$28 Scientists in greenhouse growing anthuriums	1·10	30

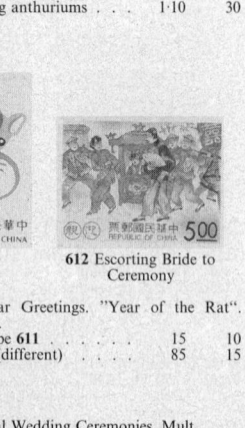

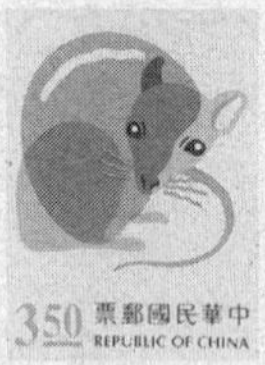
611 Rat

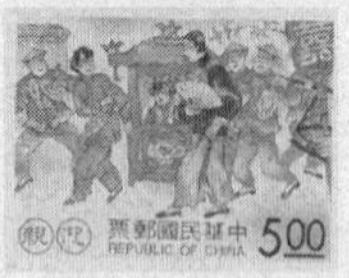
612 Escorting Bride to Ceremony

1995. New Year Greetings. "Year of the Rat". Multicoloured.

2286	$3.50 Type **611**	15	10
2287	$13 Rat (different)	85	15

1996. Traditional Wedding Ceremonies. Mult.

2289	$5 Type **612**	30	10
2290	$12 Honouring Heaven, Earth and ancestors	65	10
2291	$19 Nuptial chamber	90	15

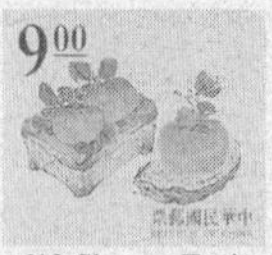
613 Sharon Fruit

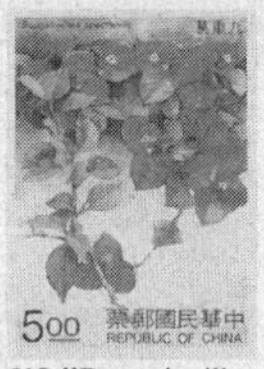
618 "Bougainvillea spectabilis"

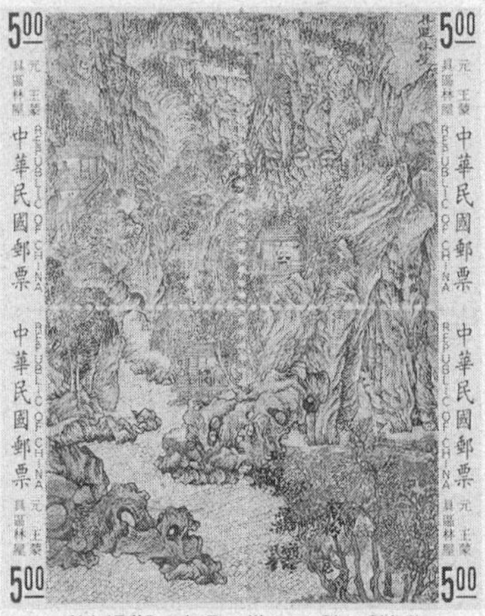
614-17 "Scenic Dwelling at Chu-Ch'u"

1996. Chinese Engravings of Fruit by Hu Chen-yan.

2292	**613** $9 multicoloured	35	10
2293	– $12 multicoloured	45	10
2294	– $15 multicoloured	55	10
2295	– $17 multicoloured	65	10

DESIGNS: $12 to $17, Different fruits.

For other values with the order of the characters in the country name reversed see Nos. 2580/2.

1996. Painting by Wang Meng.

2296	**614** $5 multicoloured	25	10
2297	**615** $5 multicoloured	25	10
2298	**616** $5 multicoloured	25	10
2299	**617** $5 multicoloured	25	10

Nos. 2296/9 were issued together, se-tenant, forming the composite design illustrated.

1996. Flowering Vines. Multicoloured.

2300	$5 Type **618**	30	10
2301	$12 Wisteria	65	10
2302	$19 Wood rose	90	15

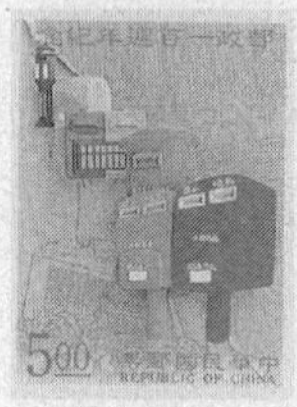
619 Postboxes

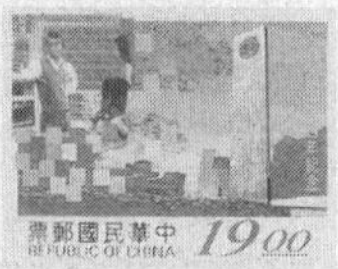
620 Lecture and University

1996. Centenary of Chinese State Postal Service. Multicoloured.

2303	$5 Type **619**	30	10
2304	$9 Weighing equipment	55	10
2305	$12 Postal transport	65	10
2306	$13 Modern technology	70	10

1996. Centenary of National Chiao Tung University.

2308	**620** $19 multicoloured	90	15

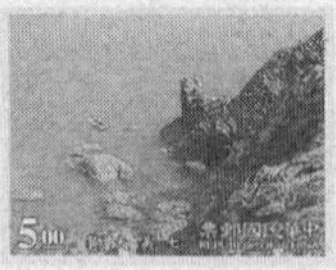
621 Chimei Giant Lion

1996. Tourism. Penghu National Scenic Area. Multicoloured.

2309	$5 Type **621**	30	10
2310	$5 Chipei beach (sand-spit)	30	10
2311	$12 Tungpan Yu	65	15
2312	$17 Tingkou Yu	85	15

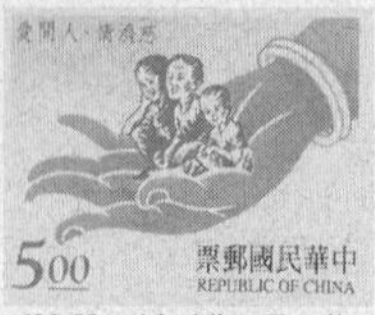
622 Hand holding Family (charity)

1996. 30th Anniv of Tzu-Chi Foundation (Buddhist relief organization). Multicoloured.

2313	$5 Type **622**	30	10
2314	$19 Hospital patient in tulip petal (medicine)	70	20

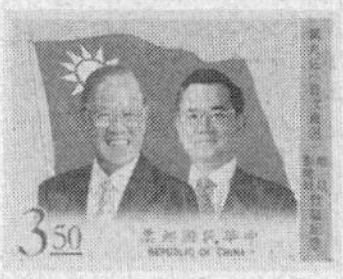
623 With National Flag

1996. Inauguration of First Directly-elected President. Designs showing President Lee Teng-Hui and Vice-President Lien Chan. Multicoloured.

2315	$3.50 Type **623**	20	10
2316	$5 Outside Presidential Office building	35	10
2317	$13 Asia-Pacific Operations Hub Project	70	10
2318	$15 Meeting public at celebrations	75	15

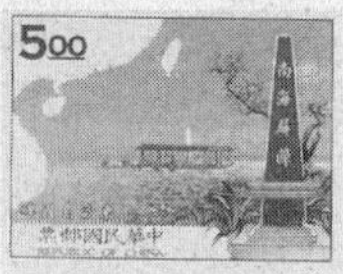
624 Monument

1996. South China Sea Archipelago. Pratas and Itu Aba Islands. Multicoloured.

2320	$5 Type **624**	30	10
2321	$12 Monument (different)	65	10

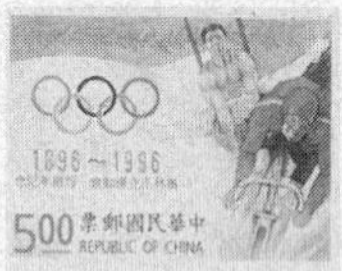
625 Modern Gymnast and Cyclist

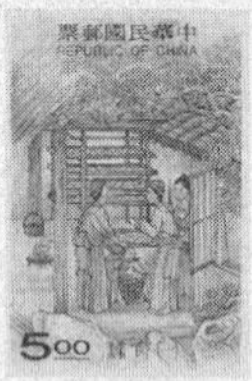
626 Feeding Silkworms

1996. Centenary of Modern Olympic Games. Multicoloured.

2323	$5 Type **625**	30	10
2324	$15 Ancient Greek athletes	75	15

1996. Silk Production Techniques from "Tian Gong Kai Wu" (encyclopaedia) by Sung Yin-shing. Multicoloured.

2325	$5 Type **626**	30	10
2326	$5 Picking out cocoons	30	10
2327	$7 Degumming raw silk	45	10
2328	$10 Reeling raw silk	60	10
2329	$13 Weaving silk	70	15

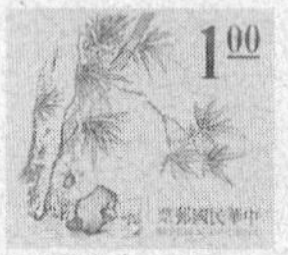
627 Bamboo

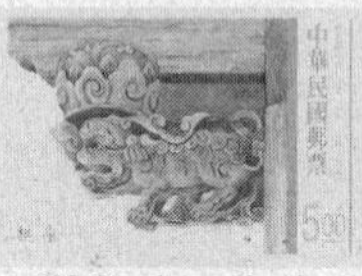
628 Tou-kung Bracket

1996. Chinese Engravings. Plants. Mult.

2330	$1 Type **627**	10	10
2331	$10 Orchid	35	10
2332	$20 Plum tree	75	15

1996. Traditional Architecture. Roof Supports. Multicoloured.

2333	$5 Type **628**	30	10
2334	$5 Chiue-ti bracket	30	10
2335	$10 Bu-tong beam	50	10
2336	$19 Dye-tou structure	85	15

629 "Princess Iron Fan" (1941)

1996. Chinese Film Production. Mult.

2337	$3.50 Type **629**	25	10
2338	$3.50 "Chin Shan Bi Xie" (1957)	25	10
2339	$5 "Oyster Girl" (1964)	40	10
2340	$19 "City of Sadness" (1989)	85	20

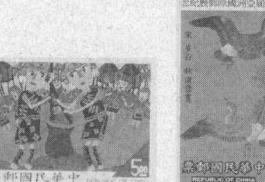

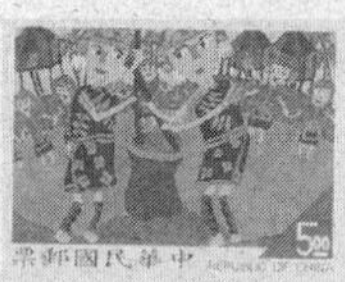
630 Children dancing

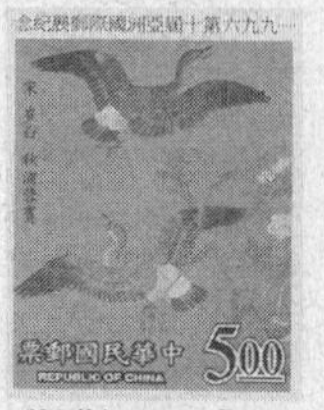
631 "Autumn Scene with Wild Geese"

1996. Winning Entries in Children's Stamp Design Competition. Multicoloured.

2341	$5 Type **630**	35	10
2342	$5 Children playing in park	35	10
2343	$5 Black and white spotted cat	35	10
2344	$5 Container ship	35	10
2345	$5 Children showering	35	10
2346	$5 Chinese gods and crowd	35	10
2347	$5 Pair of peacocks	35	10
2348	$5 Flying horse and rainbow	35	10
2349	$5 Elephant	35	10
2350	$5 Man and striped animals	35	10
2351	$5 Painting paper lampshades	35	10
2352	$5 Flock of geese	35	10
2353	$5 Children joining hands in garden	35	10
2354	$5 Archer	35	10
2355	$5 Children on ostrich's back	35	10
2356	$5 New Year celebrations	35	10
2357	$5 Butterflies on bamboo plant	35	10
2358	$5 Goatherd	35	10
2359	$5 Water-lilies on pond	35	10
2360	$5 Cats eating fish	35	10

1996. 10th Asian International Stamp Exhibition, Taipeh. Ancient Paintings from National Palace Museum. Multicoloured.

2361	$5 Type **631**	30	10
2362	$7 "Reeds and Wild Geese"	40	10
2363	$13 "Wild Geese gathering on Shore of Reeds"	65	10
2364	$15 "Wild Geese on Bank in Autumn"	70	15

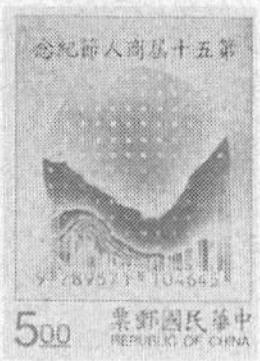
632 Bar Code and Graph

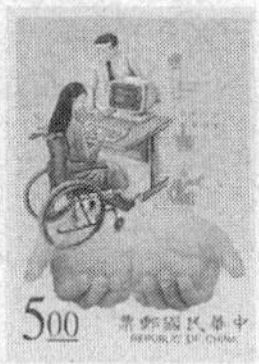
633 Disabled Worker and Open Hands

1996. 50th Anniv of Merchants' Day. Mult.

2366	$5 Type **632**	30	10
2367	$26 Line graph and globe	1·10	20

1996. Caring for the Handicapped. Mult.

2368	$5 Type **633**	30	10
2369	$19 Disabled boy painting, emblems within honeycomb and hands forming heart (employment)	85	15

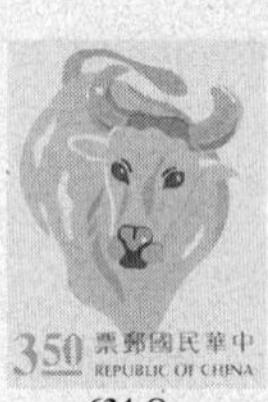
634 Ox

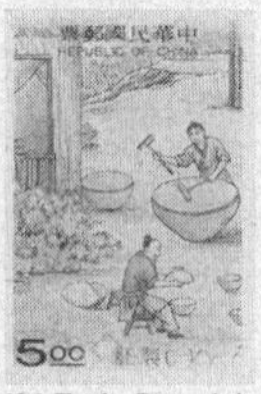
636 Early Porcelain Production

1996. New Year Greetings. "Year of the Ox". Multicoloured.

2370	$3.50 Type **634**	20	10
2371	$13 Ox (different)	65	10

1997. Porcelain Production Techniques from "Tian Gong Kai Wu" (encyclopaedia) by Sung Yin-shing. Multicoloured.

2374	$5 Type **636**	30	10
2375	$5 Improved shaping	30	10
2376	$7 Painting	35	10
2377	$10 Glazing	45	10
2378	$13 Firing	60	10

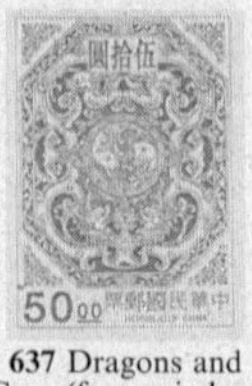
637 Dragons and Carp (from window, Longsan Temple, Lukang)

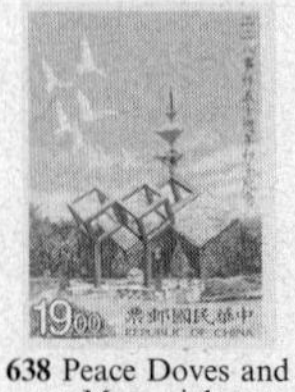
638 Peace Doves and Memorial

1997. (a) T **637**.

2379	**637**	$50 red	1·90	30
2380		$60 blue	2·25	35
2381		$70 red	2·50	40
2382		$100 green	3·75	55

(b) As T **637** but with outer decorated frame. Size 25 × 33 mm.

2386	**637**	$300 violet and blue	13·00	1·60
2387		$500 red and carmine	20·00	2·75

For $50 and $100 values in different colours and with the characters in the country name in reverse order see Nos. 2573/4.

1997. 50th Anniv of 228 Incident (civilian demonstration against government).

2390	**638** $19 multicoloured	80	15

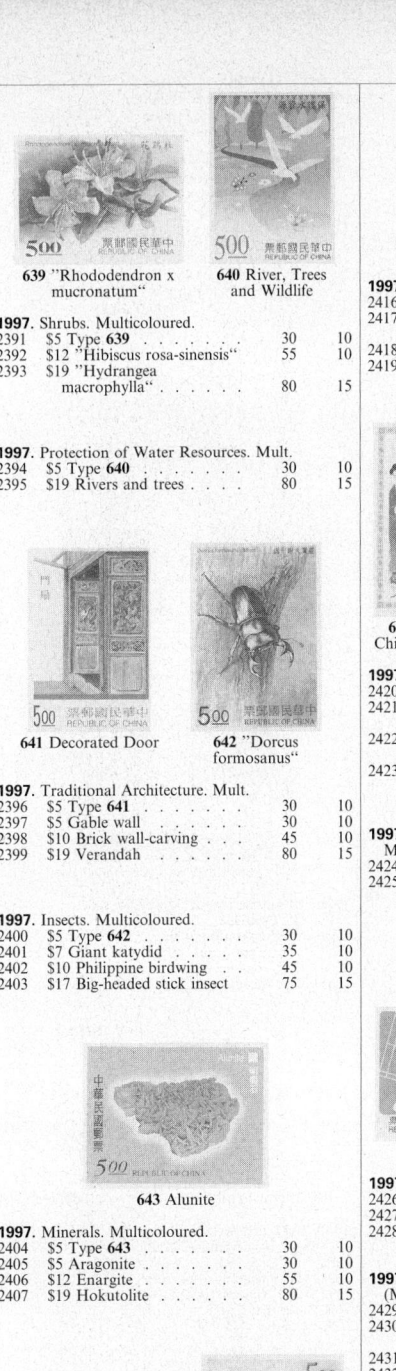

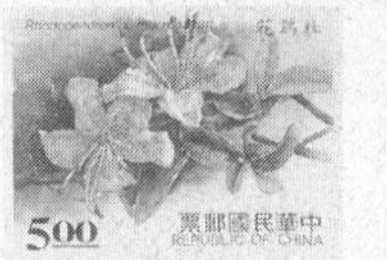
639 "Rhododendron x mucronatum"

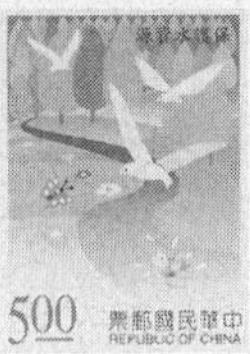
640 River, Trees and Wildlife

1997. Shrubs. Multicoloured.

2391	$5 Type **639**	30	10
2392	$12 "Hibiscus rosa-sinensis"	55	10
2393	$19 "Hydrangea macrophylla"	80	15

1997. Protection of Water Resources. Mult.

2394	$5 Type **640**	30	10
2395	$19 Rivers and trees	80	15

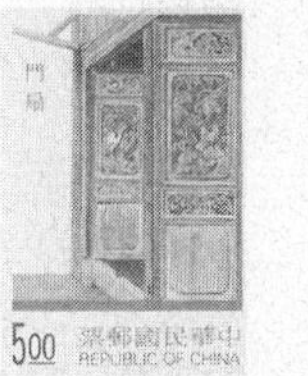
641 Decorated Door

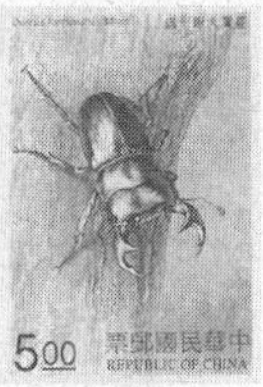
642 "Dorcus formosanus"

1997. Traditional Architecture. Mult.

2396	$5 Type **641**	30	10
2397	$5 Gable wall	30	10
2398	$10 Brick wall-carving	45	10
2399	$19 Verandah	80	15

1997. Insects. Multicoloured.

2400	$5 Type **642**	30	10
2401	$7 Giant katydid	35	10
2402	$10 Philippine birdwing	45	10
2403	$17 Big-headed stick insect	75	15

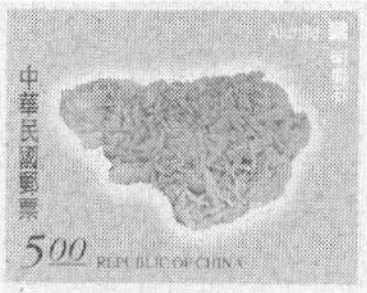
643 Alunite

1997. Minerals. Multicoloured.

2404	$5 Type **643**	30	10
2405	$5 Aragonite	30	10
2406	$12 Enargite	55	10
2407	$19 Hokutolite	80	15

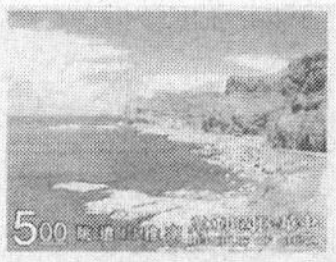
644 Nanyashan Coastline

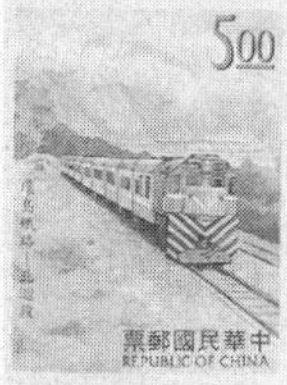
645 Train and Chingshuei Cliffs (northern loop)

1997. Tourism. North-east Coast National Scenic Area. Multicoloured.

2408	$5 Type **644**	30	10
2409	$5 Pitou Coastline (rocky shore)	30	10
2410	$12 Stone pillar, Nanya	55	10
2411	$19 Tsaoling historic trail	80	15

1997. Completion of Round-island Railway System. Multicoloured.

2412	$5 Type **645**	30	10
2413	$28 Train leaving tunnel (southern loop)	1·25	20

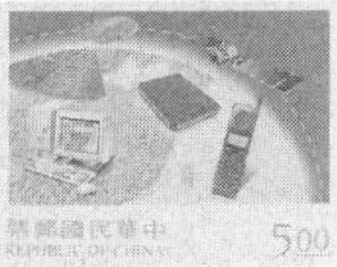
646 Integrated Circuit and Communications Equipment

1997. Electronic Industry. Multicoloured.

2414	$5 Type **646**	25	10
2415	$26 Circuit board, portable computer, mobile phone and synthesized keyboard	1·00	15

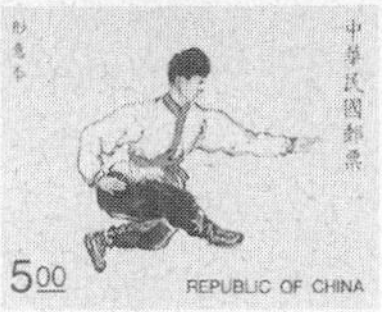
647 Shaolinquan

1997. Martial Arts. Multicoloured.

2416	$5 Type **647**	25	10
2417	$5 Form and will boxing (vert)	25	10
2418	$9 Taijiquan	40	10
2419	$19 Eight diagrams boxing (vert)	75	15

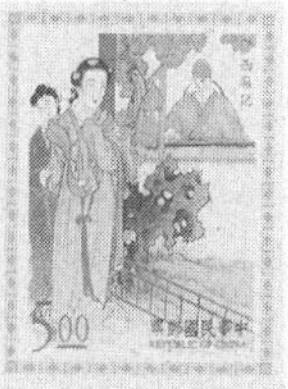
648 "Hsi Hsiang Chi" (Wang Shih-fu)

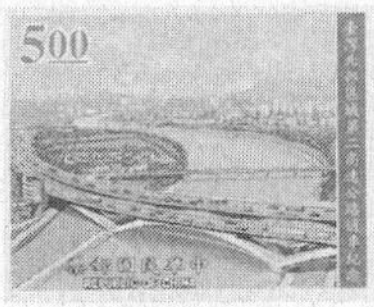
649 Bitan Bridge over River Shindian

1997. Chinese Classical Opera. Multicoloured.

2420	$5 Type **648**	25	10
2421	$5 "Dan Daw Huei" (Kuan Han-chin)	25	10
2422	$12 "Han Guong Chiou" (Ma Jyi-yuan)	50	10
2423	$15 "Wu Tong Yu" (Bai Pu)	60	10

1997. Inauguration of Second Northern Freeway. Multicoloured.

2424	$5 Type **649**	25	10
2425	$19 Hsinchu Interchange	75	15

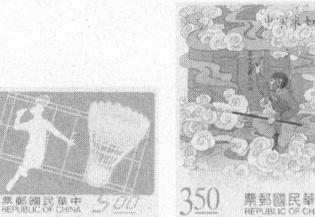

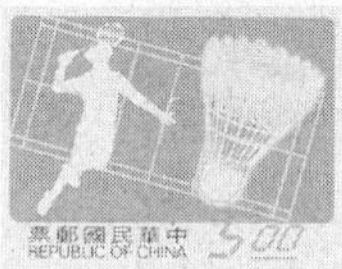
650 Badminton

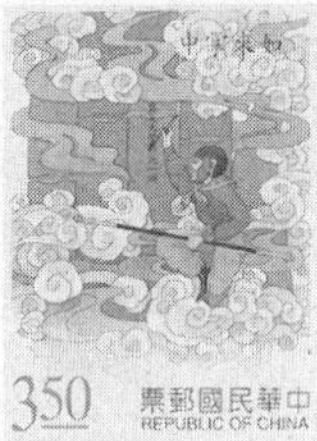
651 Palm of Buddha

1997. Sports. Multicoloured.

2426	$5 Type **650**	25	10
2427	$12 Bowling	50	10
2428	$19 Lawn tennis	75	15

1997. Classical Literature. "Journey to the West" (Ming dynasty novel). Multicoloured.

2429	$3.50 Type **651**	20	10
2430	$3.50 Pilgrimage of T'ang Monk	20	10
2431	$5 The Flaming Mountain	25	10
2432	$20 The Cobweb Cave	80	15

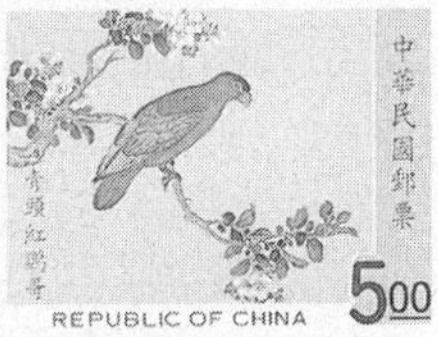
652 Purple-crowned Lorikeet

1997. Birds. Illustrations from the Ching dynasty "Bird Manual". Multicoloured.

2433	$5 Type **652**	25	10
2434	$5 Green magpie (on branch with small orange flowers)	25	10
2435	$5 Blue-crowned hanging parrot (green bird with red throat and rump)	25	10
2436	$5 Niltavas (two birds with orange breasts)	25	10
2437	$5 Red-billed blue magpie (with long blue tail)	25	10
2438	$5 Giant babax (on branch with red flowers)	25	10
2439	$5 Brambling (on branch with orange-centred white flowers)	25	10
2440	$5 Common rosefinch (on branch with yellow flowers)	25	10
2441	$5 Brandt's mountain finch (on branch with white flowers and red hips)	25	10
2442	$5 Scarlet minivets (two black and red birds)	25	10
2443	$5 Black-naped oriole (on branch with weeping leaves)	25	10
2444	$5 Yellow-throated buntings (two birds on branch with thorns and small pink flowers)	25	10
2445	$5 Bohemian waxwing (on branch with large blue flowers)	25	10
2446	$5 Brandt's mountain finches (two birds on branch with large pink flowers)	25	10
2447	$5 Brown crested mynah (with "bristles" above beak)	25	10
2448	$5 Java sparrow (with white patch on neck)	25	10
2449	$5 Long-tailed parakeet (on branch with small blue flowers)	25	10
2450	$5 Black-winged starling (by stream)	25	10
2451	$5 Hairy-footed pigeons (two green and white birds)	25	10
2452	$5 Wryneck (on ground)	25	10

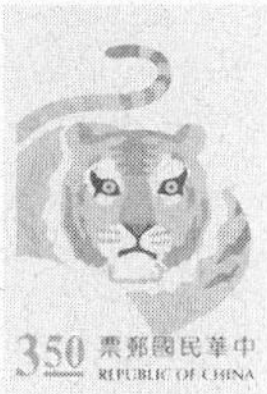
653 Tiger

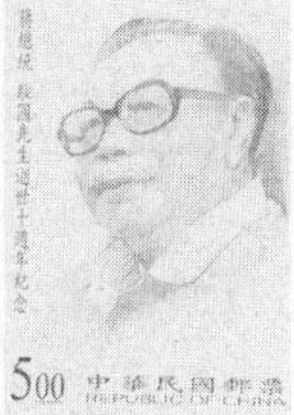
654 Pres. Chiang

1997. New Year Greetings. "Year of the Tiger".

2453	**653** $3.50 multicoloured	20	10
2454	$13 multicoloured	55	10

1998. 10th Death Anniv of Chiang Ching-kuo (President 1978–88).

2456	**654** $5 brown	20	10
2457	– $19 red	70	15

DESIGN—HORIZ: $19 Chiang and applauding crowd.

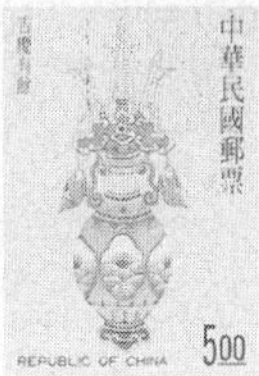
655 "Abundance"

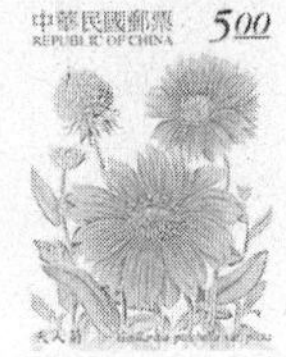
656 "Gaillardia pulchella var. picta"

1998. Wishes for the Coming Year. Mult.

2458	$5 Type **655**	20	10
2459	$5 Flowers springing from lidded bowl ("Harmony")	20	10
2460	$12 Peonies in containers ("Honour and Wealth")	45	10
2461	$12 Flowers in vase and oranges in bowl ("Luck")	45	10

1998. Herbaceous Flowers. Multicoloured.

2462	$5 Type **656**	20	10
2463	$12 "Kalanchoe blossfeldiana"	45	10
2464	$19 "Portulaca oleracea var. granatus"	70	15

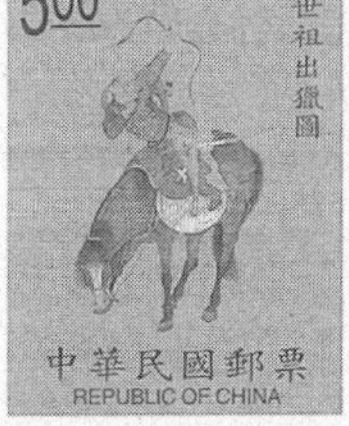
657 Horseman drawing Bow

1998. Painting by Liu Kuan-tao. Mult.

2465	$5 Type **657**	20	10
2466	$19 Kublai Khan and entourage on hunting expedition (63 × 40 mm)	70	15

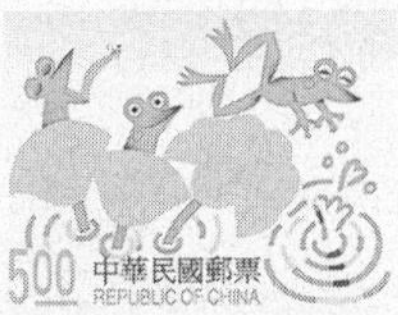
658 "A Frog has only One Mouth"

1998. Children's Nursery Rhymes. Mult.

2468	$5 Type **658**	20	10
2469	$5 Mouse and cat ("A Little Mouse climbs an Oil Lamp")	20	10
2470	$12 Children and fireflies ("Fireflies")	45	10
2471	$19 Girl and egret carrying baskets ("Egrets")	70	15

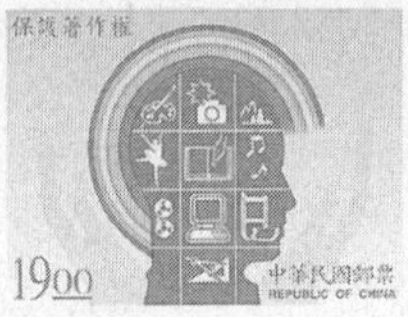
659 Cultural Symbols within Human Head

1998. 70th Anniv of Copyright Law.

2472	**659** $19 multicoloured	70	15

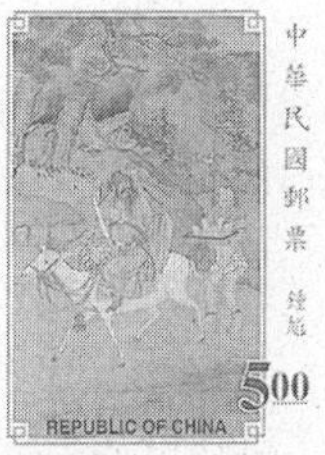
660 "Chung K'uei Moving" (Kung Kai)

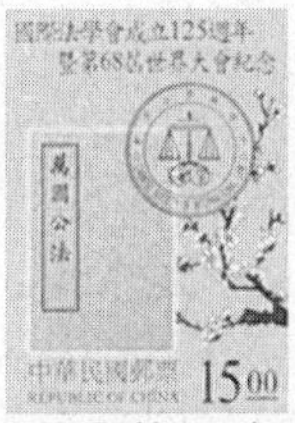
661 Emblem and Cherry Blossom

1998. Ancient Paintings of Chung K'uei (mythological figure). Multicoloured.

2473	$5 Type **660**	20	10
2474	$20 Chung K'uei dancing ("An Auspicious Occasion")	75	15

1998. 125th Anniv of International Law Association and 68th Conference, Taipeh.

2475	**661** $15 multicoloured	55	10

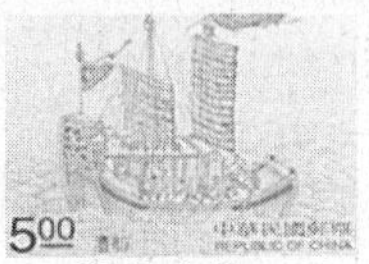
662 Grain Barge

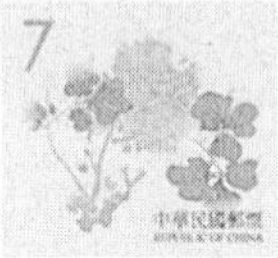
663 Begonia

1998. Ships and Vehicles from "Tian Gong Kai Wu" (encyclopaedia) by Sung Ying-shing. Multicoloured.

2476	$5 Type **662**	20	10
2477	$7 Six-oared ferry boat	25	10
2478	$10 One-wheel horse-drawn carriage	35	10
2479	$13 Man pushing one-wheel cart	50	10

1998. Chinese Engravings. Flowers. Designs as Nos. 2228/31 but with values changed and Chinese characters for the country name in reverse order as in T **663**. Multicoloured.

2480	$7 Type **663**	25	10
2481	$19 As No. 2229	70	10
2482	$20 As No. 2230	75	10
2483	$26 As No. 2231	1·00	15

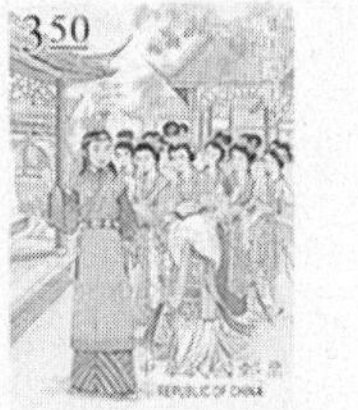
664 Pao-yu visits Garden

1998. Classical Literature. "Red Chamber Dream" (novel) by Tsao Hsueh-Chin. Multicoloured.

2484	$3.50 Type **664**	15	10
2485	$3.50 Tai-yu burying flowers	15	10
2486	$5 Pao-chai playing with butterflies	50	10
2487	$5 Hsiang-yun in drunken sleep	50	10

665 Scout Badge (⅔-size illustration)

1998. 20th Asia-Pacific and Eighth China National Scout Jamboree, Pingtung University. Multicoloured.

2488	$5 Type **665**	20	10
2489	$5 Tents	20	10

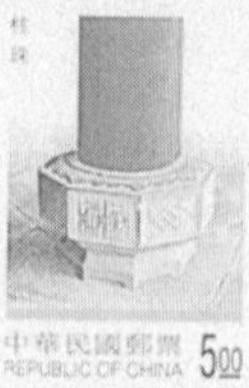
666 Carved Base of Pillar

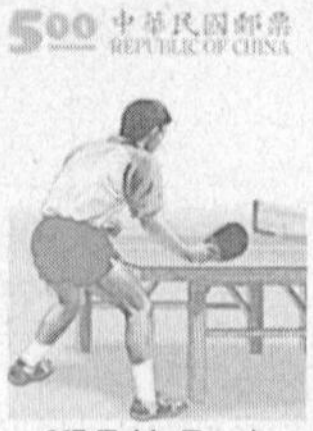
667 Table Tennis

1998. Traditional Architecture. Multicoloured.
2490 $5 Type **666** 20 10
2491 $5 Carved stone ramp ("spirit way") between staircases 20 10
2492 $10 Carved base (with fishes) of column 35 10
2493 $19 Carved stone drainage spout 70 10

1998. Sports. Multicoloured.
2494 $5 Type **667** 20 10
2495 $5 Table tennis player serving 20 10
2496 $7 Rugby player with ball 25 10
2497 $7 Rugby players 25 10
Stamps of the same value were issued together, se-tenant, forming a composite design.

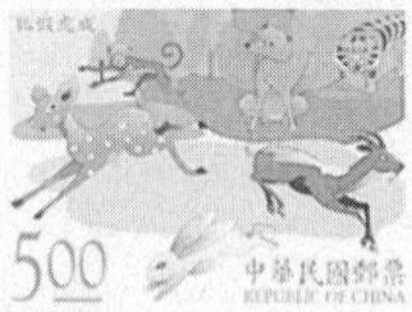
668 "The Fox borrows the Tiger's Ferocity"

1998. Chinese Fables. Multicoloured.
2498 $5 Type **668** 20 10
2499 $5 "A Frog in a Well" . . . 20 10
2500 $12 "Adding Legs to a Drawing of a Snake" . . 45 10
2501 $19 "The Snipe and the Clam at a Deadlock" . . 70 10

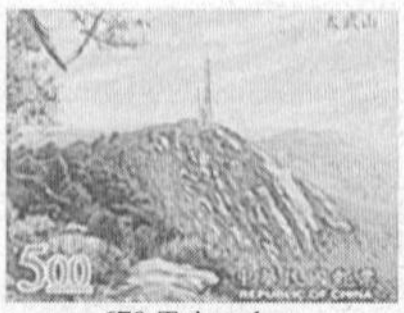
670 Taiwushan

1998. Kinmen National Park. Multicoloured.
2508 $5 Type **670** 20 10
2509 $5 Kuningtou Cliff 20 10
2510 $12 Teyueh Tower and Huang Hui-huang's House, Shuitou 45 10
2511 $19 Putou beach, Leihyu . . 70 10

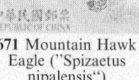

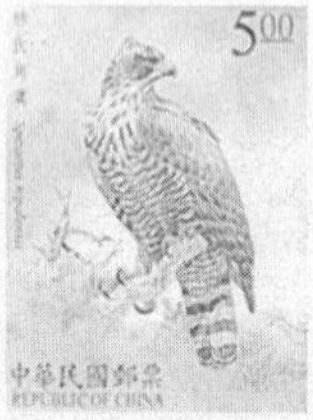
671 Mountain Hawk Eagle ("Spizaetus nipalensis")

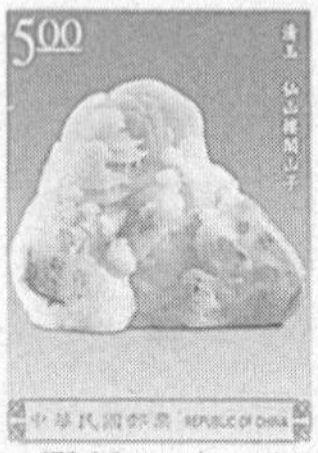
672 Mountain and Pavilions

1998. Birds. Multicoloured.
2512 $5 Type **671** 20 10
2513 $5 Mountain hawk eagle in flight 20 10
2514 $5 Crested serpent eagle ("Spilornis cheela") on branch 20 10
2515 $5 Crested serpent eagle carrying snake 20 10
2516 $10 Black kite ("Milvus migrans") on rock 35 10
2517 $10 Black kite in flight . . . 35 10
2518 $10 Indian black eagle ("Ictinaetus malayensis") on branch 35 10
2519 $10 Indian black eagle in flight 35 10
Nos. 2512/13, 2514/15, 2516/17 and 2518/19 respectively were issued together, se-tenant, each pair forming a composite design.

1998. Ching Dynasty Jade Mountain Carvings. Mult.
2520 $5 Type **672** 20 10
2521 $5 Men working in jade mine (horiz) 20 10
2522 $7 Men washing elephant (horiz) 25 10
2523 $26 Five men on a mountain . . . . 1·00 15

673 Rabbit

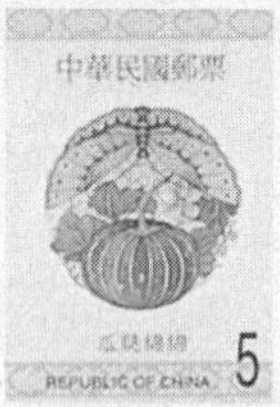
674 Butterfly and Pumpkin ("Many Descendants")

1998. New Year Greetings. "Year of the Rabbit". Multicoloured.
2525 $3.50 Type **673** 15 10
2526 $13 Rabbit (different) . . . 50 10

1999. Wishes for the Coming Year. Multicoloured.
2528 $5 Type **674** 20 10
2529 $5 Mandarins (ducks) and lotus flowers ("Good marriage that brings sons") 20 10
2530 $12 Egret ("Prosperity") . . 45 10
2531 $12 Goldfish and flowers ("Abundance") 45 10

1999. Chinese Engravings. Birds and Plants. Designs as Nos. 2264/7 and 2330/1 but with values and Chinese characters for the country name in reverse order as in T **663**. Multicoloured.
2532 $1 Type **604** 10 10
2533 $3.50 As No. 2265 . . . . 15 10
2534 $5 As No. 2266 . . . . . 20 10
2535 $10 As No. 2267 . . . . . 35 10
2536 $12 Type **627** 45 10
2536a $20 As No. 2482 . . . . . 80 35
2537 $28 As No. 2331 . . . . . 1·10 20
2537a $34 As No. 2649 . . . . . 1·40 60

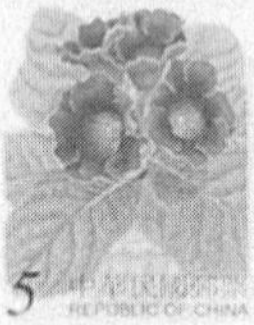
676 "Gloxinia"

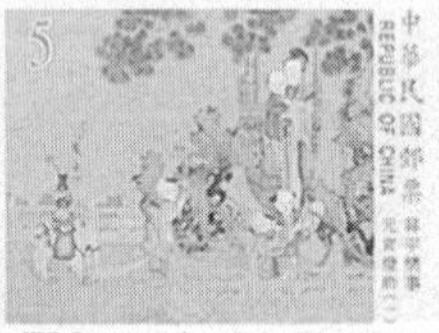
677 Boy towing Toy Elephant

1999. Indoor Flowers. Multicoloured.
2539 $5 Type **676** 20 10
2540 $12 African violet 45 10
2541 $19 Flamingo flower 70 10

1999. Illustrations from "Joy in Peacetime" (Ching Dynasty book). Lantern Festival. Multicoloured.
2542 $5 Type **677** 20 10
2543 $5 Women, children and crane 20 10
2544 $7 Children playing with toy animals 25 10
2545 $26 Children playing . . . 1·00 15

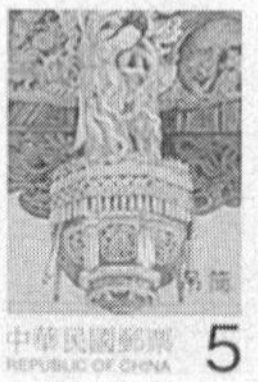
678 Hanging Cylinder

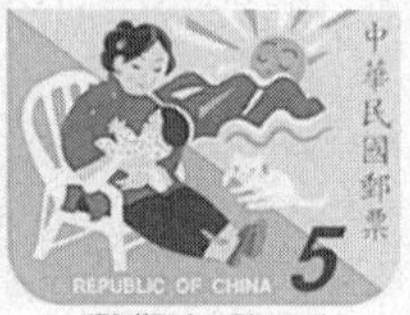
679 "Baby Sleeps"

1999. Traditional Architecture. Decorative Features. Multicoloured.
2547 $5 Type **678** 20 10
2548 $5 Taishi screen 20 10
2549 $10 Xuanyu (gable decoration) 35 10
2550 $19 Wood carving 70 10

1999. Nursery Rhymes. Multicoloured.
2551 $5 Type **679** 20 10
2552 $5 Mother comforting baby frightened by storm ("Be Brave") 20 10
2553 $12 Mother and baby rocking ("Rock, Rock, Rock") 45 10
2554 $19 Mother, baby, cat and flies ("Buggie Flies") . . . 70 10

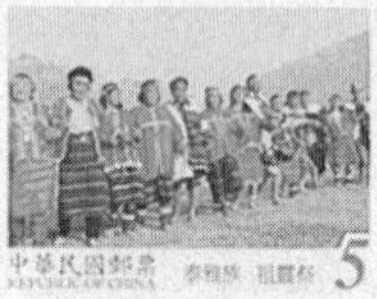
680 Atayal Ancestor Festival

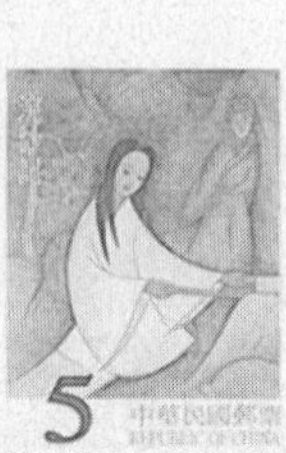
682 "Washing Cotton Yarn" (Liang Chenyu)

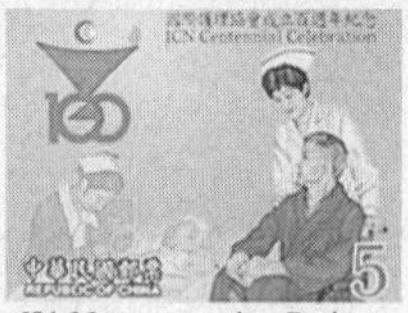
681 Nurses treating Patients

1999. Taiwan's Aboriginal Culture. Multicoloured.
2555 $5 Type **680** 20 10
2556 $5 Dancers with hip bells (Saisat Festival of the Dwarfs) 20 10
2557 $5 Circle of singers (Bunun Millet Harvest Song) . . 20 10
2558 $5 Line of singers in red coats (Tsou Victory Festival) 20 10
2559 $5 Dancers and millet biscuits mounted on board (Rukai Harvest Festival) 20 10
2560 $5 Men with bamboo poles (Paiwan Bamboo Festival) 20 10
2561 $5 Procession of men carrying yellow scarves (Puyuma Harvest Ceremony) 20 10
2562 $5 Line of women dancers with white headdresses (Ami Harvest Ceremony) 20 10
2563 $5 Launch of new fishing boat (Yami Boat Ceremony) 20 10

1999. Centenary of International Council of Nurses. Multicoloured.
2564 $5 Type **681** 60 10
2565 $17 Globe and nurse carrying tray . . . . . . 1·40 10

1999. Chinese Classical Opera (Legends of the Ming Dynasty). Multicoloured.
2566 $5 Type **682** 20 10
2567 $5 "The Story of a Pipa" (Kaoming) 20 10
2568 $12 "The Story of Hung Fu" (Chang Fengyi) . . . 45 10
2569 $15 "Paiyuch Pavilion" (Shi Hui) 55 10

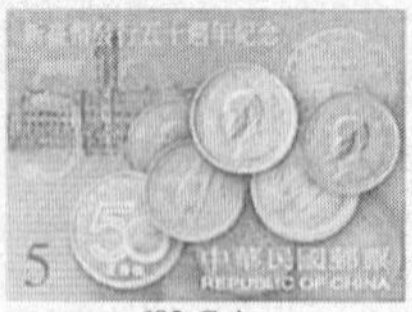
683 Coins

1999. 50th Anniv of Introduction of the Silver Yuan. Multicoloured.
2571 $5 Type **683** 20 10
2572 $25 Banknotes 95 15

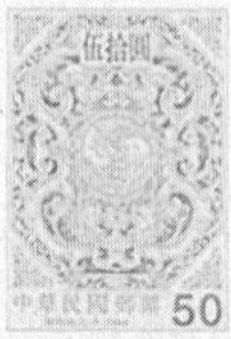
684 Dragons and Carp (from window, Longsan Temple, Lukang)

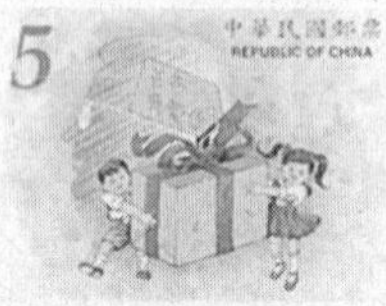
685 Childern giving Present

1999. As Nos. 2379 and 2382 but with Chinese characters for the country name in reverse order, as in T **684**, and colours changed.
2573 **684** $50 green . . . . 1·90 30
2574 $100 brown . . . . . . 4·00 60

1999. Chinese Engravings of Fruit by Hu Chen-yan. Designs as Nos. 2292/4 but with Chinese characters for the country name in reverse order, and values changed. Multicoloured.
2580 50c. As Type **613** 10 10
2581 $6 As $12 . . . . 20 10
2582 $25 As $15 . . . . 95 15

1999. Fathers' Day. Multicoloured.
2584 $5 Type **685** 20 10
2585 $25 Father teaching boy to ride bike 95 10

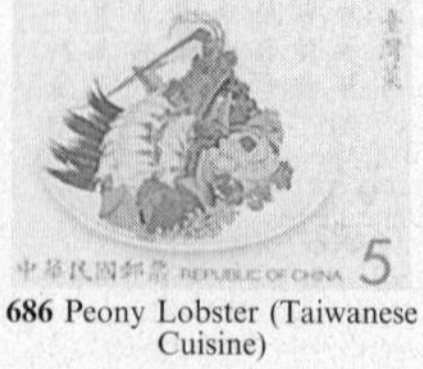
686 Peony Lobster (Taiwanese Cuisine)

1999. Chinese Regional Dishes. Multicoloured.
2586 $5 Type **686** 10 10
2587 $5 Buddha jumps the wall (Fukien) (plate, teapot, jar and cups) 10 10
2588 $5 Flower hors d'oeuvres (Cantonese) 10 10
2589 $5 Dongpo pork (Kiangsu and Chekiang) (plate, bowl and double handled jar) 10 10
2590 $5 Stewed fish jaws (Shanghai) (plate decorated with strawberries) 10 10
2591 $5 Beggar's chicken (Hunan) (with folded napkin) . . . 10 10
2592 $5 Carp jumping over dragon's gate (Szechwan) (on silver platter) 10 10
2593 $5 Peking duck (Peking) (in silver dish) 10 10

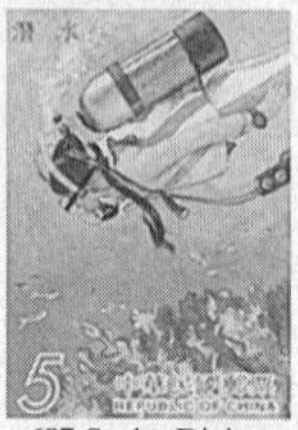
687 Scuba Diving

1999. Outdoor Activities. Multicoloured.
2594 $5 Type **687** 10 10
2595 $6 Canoeing 20 10
2596 $10 Surfing 35 10
2597 $25 Windsurfing 95 15

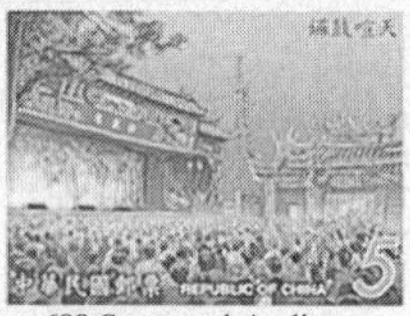
688 Stage and Audience

1999. Taiwanese Opera. Multicoloured.
2598 $5 Type **688** 10 10
2599 $6 Preparation in the dressing room 20 10
2600 $10 Two actresses 35 10
2601 $25 Actress as clown . . . 95 15

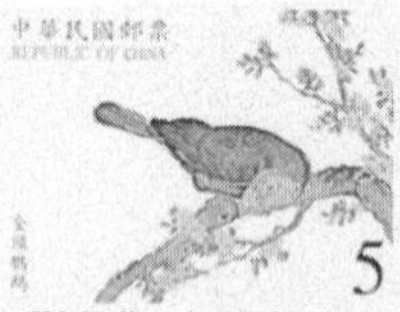
690 Yellow-headed Parrot

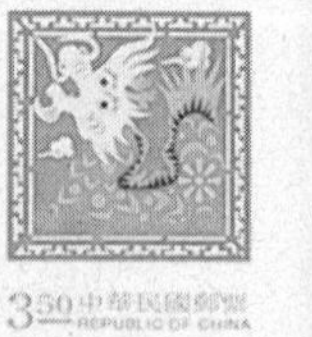
691 Dragon

1999. Birds (1st series). Illustrations from the Ching Dynasty Bird Manual. Multicoloured.
2603 $5 Type **690** 20 10
2604 $5 Blue-winged parrotlet . . 20 10
2605 $12 African grey parrot . . 50 10
2606 $25 King parrot . . . . . 1·10 20
See also Nos. 2671/4.

1999. New Year Greetings. "Year of the Dragon". Multicoloured.
2607 $3.50 Type **691** 15 10
2608 $13 Dragon (different) . . . 55 10

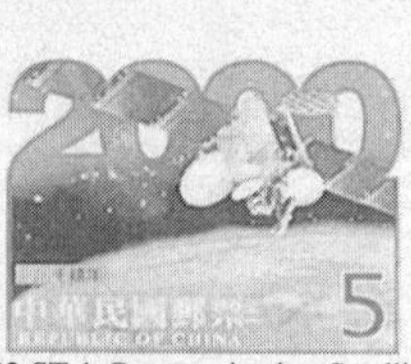
692 ST-1 Communication Satellite over Earth

1999. Year 2000. Multicoloured.
2610 $5 Type **692** (information) 20 10
2611 $5 Deer and river (environmental protection) 20 10
2612 $12 Modern buildings and high-speed train (industry and economy) 50 10
2613 $15 Dove and St. Peter's Basilica,Vatican City (peace) 65 10

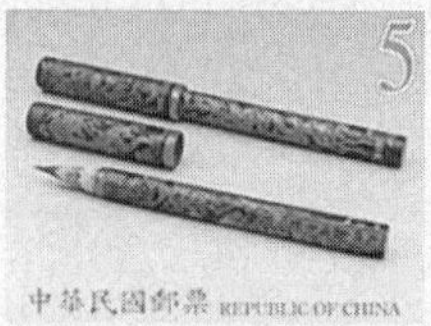
693 Emperor Chia-Ching's "Coloured Cloud Dragon" Writing Brushes (Ming Dynasty)

2000. Traditional Chinese Writing Equipment. Mult.
2616 $5 Type **693** 20 10
2617 $5 Emperor Lung Ching's "Imperial Dragon Fragrance" ink stick (Ming Dynasty) (vert) . . 20 10

2618 $7 "Clear Heart House"
(calligraphy, Tsai Hsiang)
(Sung Dynasty) (vert) . . 30 10
2619 $26 "Celadon Toad
Inkstone" (Sung Dynasty) 1·10 20

694 Kaoping River Bridge Pylon

2000. Inauguration of Second Southern Freeway.
Multicoloured.
2620 $5 Type **694** 20 10
2621 $12 Main junction, Tainan . . 50 10

695 Branch, Fields and Houses

2000. Seasonal Periods (1st series). Designs depicting
the six seasonal periods of Spring. Multicoloured.
2623 $5 Type **695**
("Commencement of
Spring") 20 10
2624 $5 Man ploughing fields in
the rain ("Rain Water") 20 10
2625 $5 Forks of lightning and
cranes ("Waking of
Insects") 20 10
2626 $5 Men transplanting rice
seedlings (Spring Equinox) 20 10
2627 $5 Basket of fruit and
houses ("Pure
Brightness") 20 10
2628 $5 Rain, farmer and river
("Grain Rain") 20 10
See also Nos. 2636/41, 2652/7 and 2675/80.

696 Shuanghsi River and
School Gates,
Waishuanghsi Campus

697 Three Heroes at
Altar.

2000. Centenary of Soochow University. Mult.
2629 $5 Type **696** 20 10
2630 $25 Justice statue, Soochow
Law School, Taipeh
campus and Ansu Hall,
Waishuanghsi campus . . 1·10 20

2000. Classical Literature. *Romance of the Three
Kingdoms* by Luo Guanzhong (1st series). Mult.
2631 $3.50 Type **697** 15 10
2632 $3.50 Guan Yu reading at
night 15 10
2633 $5 Couple in cottage
receiving guest 20 10
2634 $20 Arrows raining down on
sampans 85 10

698 Crops and Mountains

2000. Seasonal Periods (2nd series). Designs depicting
the six seasonal periods of Summer. Multicoloured.
2636 $5 Type **698**
("Commencement of
Summer") 20 10
2637 $5 Water wheel and houses
in rain ("Little Fullness") 20 10
2638 $5 Ears of grain and houses
("Husks of Grain") . . 20 10
2639 $5 Insect on plant and
houses (Summer Solstice) 20 10
2640 $5 Palm leaf fan and fields
("Lesser Heat") 20 10
2641 $5 Watermelons ("Great
Heat") 20 10
Nos. 2636/41 were issued together, se-tenant,
forming a composite design.

699 Chen Shui-bian and Lu Hsiu-
lien

2000. Inauguration of Chen Shui-bian as 10th
President and Lu Hsiu-lien as Vice-President. Mult.
2642 $5 Type **699** 20 10
2643 $5 Presidential Office
building 20 10

700 Hsialiao

701 Taiwan Giant
Sacred Tree

2000. Monuments Marking the Tropic of Cancer.
Multicoloured.
2645 $5 Type **700** 20 10
2646 $12 Wuho 55 10
2647 $25 Chingpu . . . . . . 1·10 20

2000. Chinese Engravings of Fruit by Hu Chen-yan.
As No. 2295 but with Chinese characters for the
country name in reverse order, as in T **683**, and
with value (2648) or new design changed.
2648 $32 multicoloured . . . . . 1·40 25
2649 $34 multicoloured . . . . . 1·50 25

2000. Sacred Trees. Multicoloured.
2650 $5 Type **701** 20 10
2651 $39 Sacred Sleeping Moon
Tree . . . . 1·60 25

702 Grain drying

2000. Seasonal Periods (3rd series). Depicting the six
seasonal periods of Autumn. Multicoloured.
2652 $5 Type **702**
("Commencement of
Autumn") 20 10
2653 $5 Rick and village
("Bounds of Heat") . . 20 10
2654 $5 Dew covered leaves
("White Dew") 20 10
2655 $5 Red leaves ("Autumn
Equinox") 20 10
2656 $5 Bare tree ("Cold Dew") 20 10
2657 $5 Frost on plant ("Descent
of Hoar Frost") 20 10
Nos. 2652/57 were issued together, se-tenant,
forming a composite design.

2000. No. 1784 surch **350**.
2658 $3.50 on $7.50
multicoloured 15 10

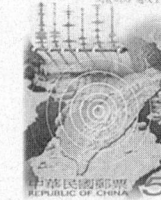

704 Red Spider Lily

705 Seismograph and
map of Taiwan

2000. Poisonous Plants. Multicoloured.
2659 $5 Type **704** 20 10
2660 $5 Odollam erberus-tree
(*Cerbera manghas*) 20 10
2661 $12 Rosary pea 55 10
2662 $20 Oleander 85 10

2000. Earthquakes. Multicoloured.
2663 $5 Type **705** 20 10
2664 $12 Rescue workers 55 10
2665 $25 Earthquake drills . . . 1·10 20

706 *Anotogaster sieboldii*

2000. Dragonflies. Multicoloured.
2666 $5 Type **706** 20 10
2667 $5 *Lamelligomphus
formosanus* (horiz) . . . 20 10
2668 $12 *Neurothemis ramburii*
(horiz) 50 20
2669 $12 *Trithemis festiva* . . . 50 20

707 Corn Bunting

2000. Birds (2nd series). Illustrations from the Ching
Dynasty Bird Manual. Multicoloured.
2671 $5 Type **707** 20 10
2672 $5 Brambling 20 10
2673 $12 Bali mynah 50 20
2674 $25 Indian grackle . . . . 1·00 40

708 Lake, Mountains and Bowl

2000. Seasonal Periods (4th series). Designs depicting
the six seasonal periods of Winter. Multicoloured.
2675 $5 Type **708**
("Commencement of
Winter") 20 10
2676 $5 Trees covered in snow
("Lesser Snow") 20 10
2677 $5 Mountains covered in
snow ("Great Snow") . . 20 10
2678 $5 Rice balls in bowl
("Winter Solstice") . . 20 10
2679 $5 Houses and tree branch
covered in snow ("Lesser
Cold") 20 10
2680 $5 Log cabin covered in
snow ("Great Cold") . . 20 10
Nos. 2675/80 were issued together, se-tenant,
forming a composite design.

709 Palace Lamp Boulevard and
Classrooms

2000. 50th Anniv of Tamkang University. Mult.
2681 $5 Type **709** 20 10
2682 $25 Maritime Museum and
"Scroll Plaza" (sculpture) 1·00 40

710 Snake

712 Cruise Ship and Buildings

2000. New Year Greetings. "Year of the Snake".
Multicoloured.
2683 $3.50 Type **710** 15 10
2684 $13 Snake (different) . . . 55 25

2001. "Three Small Links" (establishment of trade
links between Kinmen, Xiamen, Matsu and
Foochow). Multicoloured.
2687 $9 Type **712** 35 15
2688 $25 Cruise ship and
monument . . . . . . 1·00 40

713 Lotus Blossoms
("Marital Bliss")

715 Apples

714 Aquarius

2001. Wishes for the Coming Year. Multicoloured.
2689 $5 Type **713** 20 10
2690 $5 Loganberries, lichees and
walnuts ("Success in one's
career") 20 10

2691 $12 Pomegranates
("Producing many
offspring") 50 20
2692 $12 Peonies and pair of
Chinese bulbuls
("Growing old together
with wealth and high
position") 50 20

2001. Signs of the Western Zodiac (1st series). Air
Signs. Multicoloured.
2693 $5 Type **714** 20 10
2694 $12 Gemini 50 20
2695 $25 Libra . . . . 1·00 40
See also Nos. 2708/10 and 2762/8.

2001. Fruits (1st series). Multicoloured.
2696 $5 Type **715** 20 10
2697 $7 Guavas 30 15
2698 $12 Pears 50 20
2699 $25 Melons . . . . . . 1·00 40

716 Main Peak

2001. Mount Jade. Views of Mount Jade. Mult.
2700 $5 Type **716** 20 10
2701 $5 Western peak 20 10
2702 $12 Northern peak 50 20
2703 $25 Eastern peak . . . . 1·00 40

717 Girls playing with Ball ("Little
Ball")

2001. Children's Playtime Rhymes. Multicoloured.
2704 $5 Type **717** 20 10
2705 $5 Children sitting in a
circle ("Point to the
Water Vat") 20 10
2706 $12 Boys dancing
("Pangolin") 50 20
2707 $25 Children playing
("Shake and Stamp") . . 1·00 40

2001. Signs of the Western Zodiac (2nd series). Earth
Signs. As T **714**. Multicoloured.
2708 $5 Capricorn 20 10
2709 $12 Taurus 50 20
2710 $25 Virgo . . . . . . 1·00 40

718 Sakyamuni Buddha,
Northern Wei Dynasty

2001. Ancient Statues of Buddha. Multicoloured.
2711 $5 Type **718** 20 15
2712 $9 Seated Buddha, Tang
Dynasty 35 15
2713 $12 Mahavairocana Buddha,
Sung Dynasty 50 20

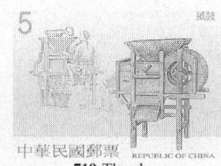

719 Thresher

2001. Early Agricultural Implements. Multicoloured.
2715 $5 Type **719** 20 10
2716 $7 Ox plough 30 15
2717 $10 Bamboo baskets and
yoke 45 10
2718 $25 Coir raincoat and hat . 1·00 80

720 Mackay

721 Girl Dancing,
Globe and Emblem

2001. Death Centenary of George Leslie Mackay (missionary and educator).

2719	**720**	$25 multicoloured	1·00	80

2001. Kiwanis International (community organization) Convention, Taipeh. Multicoloured.

2720		$5 Type **721**	20	10
2721		$25 Mother and child within heart	1·00	80

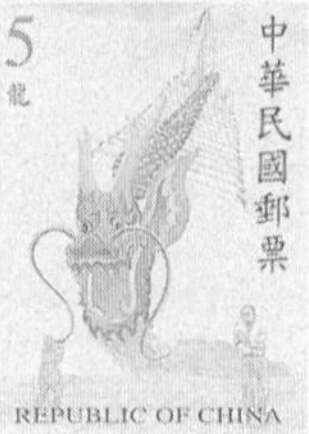

722 Dragon

2001. Kites. Multicoloured.

2722		$5 Type **722**	20	10
2723		$5 Phoenix	20	10
2724		$5 Tiger	20	10
2725		$5 Fish	20	10

2001. Signs of the Western Zodiac (3rd series). Fire Signs. As T **714**. Multicoloured.

2726		$5 Aries	20	10
2727		$12 Leo	50	20
2728		$25 Sagittarius	1·00	80

POSTAGE DUE STAMPS

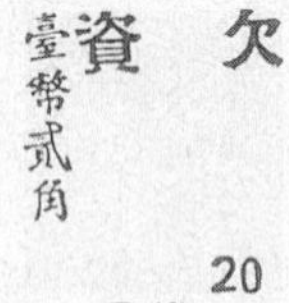

(D **12**)

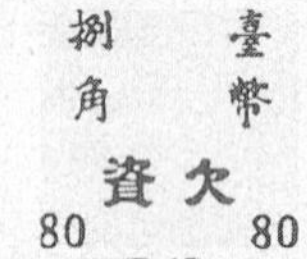

(D **15**)

1950. Surch as Type D **12**.

D105	**6**	4c. on $100 blue	11·50	9·00
D106		10c. on $100 blue	22·00	5·50
D107		20c. on $100 blue	11·50	10·00
D108		40c. on $100 blue	30·00	22·00
D109		$1 on $100 blue	30·00	40·00

1951. No. 524 of China surch as Type D **15**.

D133		40c. on 40c. orange	19·00	13·00
D134		80c. on 40c. orange	19·00	12·00

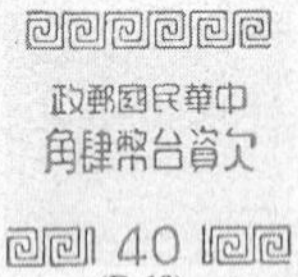

(D **19**)

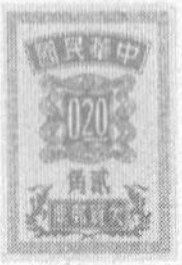

D **43**

1953. Revenue stamps as T **143** of China surch as Type D **19**.

D151		10c. on $50 blue	16·00	5·00
D152		20c. on $100 olive	16·00	5·00
D153		40c. on $20 brown	19·00	1·50
D154		80c. on $500 green	35·00	2·50
D155		100c. on $30 mauve	35·00	8·50

1956.

D236	D **43**	20c. red and blue	2·50	50
D237		40c. green and buff	2·50	50
D238		80c. brown and grey	3·75	75
D239		$1 blue and mauve	6·00	75

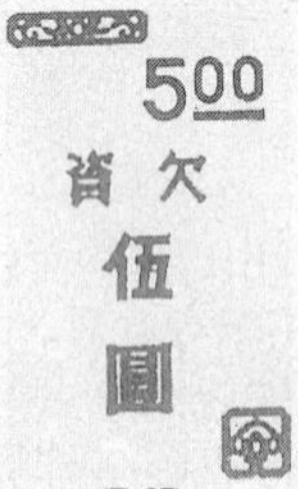

(D **97**)

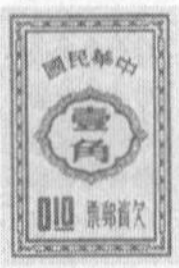

D **152**

1961. Surch with Type D **97**.

D429	**56**	$5 on $20 red	6·50	3·00

1964. Surch as Type D **97**.

D490	**83**	10c. on 80c. green	50	30
D491		20c. on $3.60 blue	50	40
D492		40c. on $4.50 red	75	35

1966.

D588	D **152**	10c. brown and lilac	10	25
D589		20c. blue and yellow	15	25
D590		50c. ultram & blue	3·00	40
D591		$1 violet and flesh	55	15
D592		$2 green and blue	55	15
D593		$5 red and buff	75	20
D594a		$10 purple & mauve	11·50	1·00

D **399**

1984.

D1532a	D **399**	$1 red and blue	40	10
D1533a		$2 yellow and blue	40	10
D1534		$3 green & mauve	40	10
D1535a		$5 blue and yellow	50	15
D1536		$5.50 mauve & bl	50	15
D1537		$7.50 yellow & vio	60	25
D1538b		$10 yellow and red	60	20
D1539		$20 blue and green	1·10	65

CHINA EXPEDITIONARY FORCE Pt. 1

Stamps used by Indian military forces in China.

12 pies = 1 anna; 16 annas = 1 rupee.

Stamps of India optd **C.E.F.**

1900. Queen Victoria.

C 1	**40**	3p. red	40	1·25
C 2	**23**	½a. green	75	30
C 3	–	1a. purple	4·00	1·50
C11	–	1a. red	28·00	8·00
C 4	–	2a. blue	3·00	9·00
C 5	–	2a.6p. green	2·75	13·00
C 6	–	3a. orange	2·75	16·00
C 7	–	4a. green (No. 96)	2·75	7·50
C 8	–	8a. mauve	2·75	18·00
C 9	–	12a. purple on red	16·00	16·00
C10	**37**	1r. green and red	21·00	21·00

1904. King Edward VII.

C12c	**41**	3p. grey	4·50	6·50
C13	–	1a. red (No. 123)	7·50	70
C14	–	2a. lilac	14·00	2·50
C15	–	2a.6p. blue	3·25	5·00
C16	–	3a. orange	3·75	4·00
C17	–	4a. olive	8·50	11·00
C18	–	8a. mauve	8·00	7·50
C19	–	12a. purple on red	11·00	19·00
C20	–	1r. green and red	13·00	28·00

1909. King Edward VII.

C21	–	½a. green (No. 149)	1·75	1·50
C22		1a. red (No. 150)	2·25	30

1913. King George V.

C23	**55**	3p. grey	4·50	26·00
C24	**56**	½a. green	3·50	6·00
C25	**57**	1a. red	4·00	4·00
C26	**58**	1½a. brown (No. 163)	23·00	70·00
C27	**59**	2a. lilac	15·00	60·00
C28	**61**	2a.6p. blue	11·00	25·00
C29	**62**	3a. orange	25·00	£190
C30	**63**	4a. olive	22·00	£150
C32	**65**	8a. mauve	25·00	£325
C33	**66**	12a. red	22·00	£110
C34	**67**	1r. brown and green	60·00	£275

BRITISH RAILWAY ADMINISTRATION

1901. No. 121 of China surch **B.R.A. 5 Five Cents.**

BR133b	**32**	5c. on ½c. brown	£275	£140

CHRISTMAS ISLAND Pt. 1

Situated in the Indian Ocean about 600 miles south of Singapore. Formerly part of the Straits Settlements and then of the Crown Colony of Singapore, Christmas Island was occupied by the Japanese from 31 March 1942 until September 1945. It reverted to Singapore after liberation but subsequently became an Australian territory on 15 October 1958.

1958. 100 cents = 1 Malayan dollar.
1968. 100 cents = 1 Australian dollar.

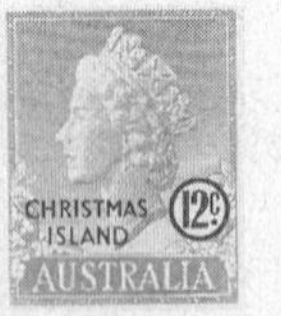

1 Queen Elizabeth II

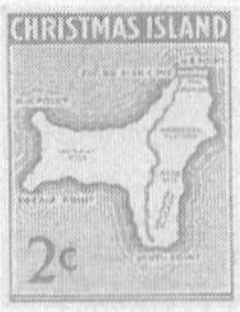

2 Map

1958. Type of Australia with opt and value in black.

1	**1**	2c. orange	55	70
2		4c. brown	60	30
3		5c. mauve	60	30
4		6c. blue	1·00	30
5		8c. sepia	2·00	50
6		10c. violet	1·00	30
7		12c. red	2·00	1·75
8		20c. blue	1·25	1·75
9		50c. green	2·00	1·75
10		$1 turquoise	2·25	1·75

1963.

11	**2**	2c. orange	90	55
12	–	4c. brown	50	20
13	–	5c. purple	50	30
14	–	6c. blue	40	50
15	–	8c. black	2·25	60
16	–	10c. violet	40	20
17	–	12c. red	40	40
18	–	20c. blue	1·00	35
19	–	50c. green	1·00	35
20	–	$1 yellow	1·75	60

DESIGNS—VERT: 4c. Moonflower; 5c. Robber crab; 8c. Phosphate train; 10c. Raising phosphate. HORIZ: 6c. Island scene; 12c. Flying Fish cove; 20c. Loading cantilever; 50c. Christmas Island frigate bird. LARGER (35 × 21 mm): $1 White-tailed tropic bird.

1965. 50th Anniv of Gallipoli Landing. As T **184** of Australia, but slightly larger (22 × 34½ mm).

21		10c. brown, black and green	30	1·00

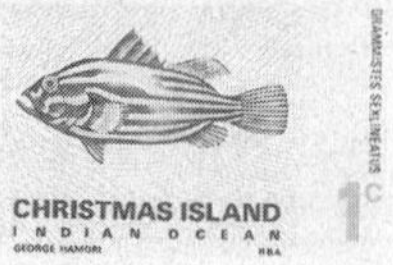

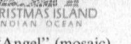

12 Golden-striped Grouper

1968. Fishes. Multicoloured.

22		1c. Type **12**	45	45
23		2c. Moorish idol	60	20
24		3c. Long-nosed butterflyfish	60	30
25		4c. Pink-tailed triggerfish	60	20
26		5c. Regal angelfish	60	20
27		9c. White-cheeked surgeonfish	60	40
28		10c. Lionfish	60	20
28a		15c. Saddle butterflyfish	7·00	3·00
29		20c. Ornate butterflyfish	1·50	55
29a		30c. Giant ghost pipefish	7·00	3·00
30		50c. Clown surgeonfish	1·75	1·75
31		$1 Meyer's butterflyfish	1·75	2·25

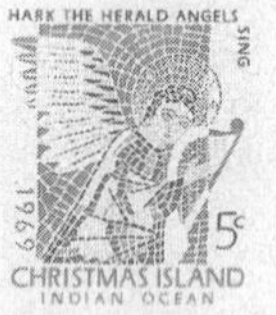

13 "Angel" (mosaic)

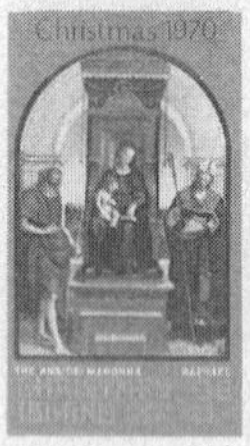

14 "The Ansidei Madonna" (Raphael)

1969. Christmas.

32	**13**	5c. multicoloured	20	30

1970. Christmas. Paintings. Multicoloured.

33		3c. Type **14**	20	15
34		5c. "The Virgin and Child, St. John the Baptist and an Angel" (Morando)	20	15

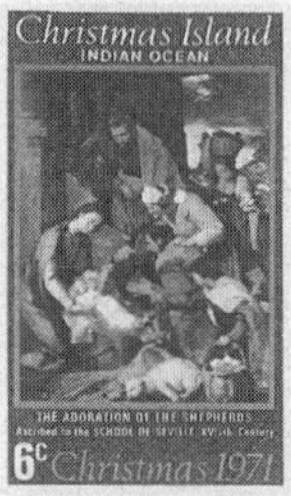

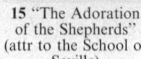

15 "The Adoration of the Shepherds" (attr to the School of Seville)

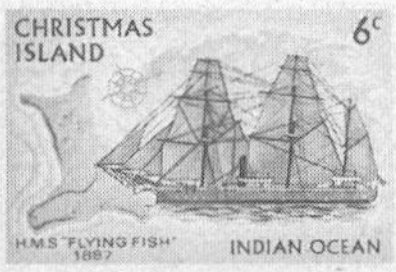

16 H.M.S. "Flying Fish" (survey ship), 1887

1971. Christmas. Multicoloured.

35		6c. Type **15**	30	50
36		20c. "The Adoration of the Shepherds" (Reni)	70	1·00

1972. Ships. Multicoloured.

37		1c. "Eagle" (merchant sailing ship), 1714	25	60
38		2c. H.M.S. "Redpole" (gunboat), 1890	30	70
39		3c. "Hoi Houw" (freighter), 1959	30	70
40		4c. "Pigot" (sailing ship), 1771	40	75
41		5c. "Valetta" (cargo-liner), 1968	40	75
42		6c. Type **16**	40	75
43		7c. "Asia" (sail merchantman), 1805	40	75
44		8c. "Islander" (freighter), 1929–60	45	80
45		9c. H.M.S. "Imperieuse" (armoured cruiser), 1888	65	70
46		10c. H.M.S. "Hecate" (coast defence turret ship), 1871	55	80
47		20c. "Thomas" (galleon), 1615	70	1·00
48		25c. Royal Navy sail sloop, 1864	80	1·50
49		30c. "Cygnet" (flute), 1688	80	1·00
50		35c. "Triadic" (freighter), 1958	80	1·00
51		50c. H.M.S. "Amethyst" (frigate), 1857	80	1·50
52		$1 "Royal Mary" (warship), 1643	1·10	1·75

No. 45 is inscribed "H.M.S. Imperious", No. 46 "H.M.S. Egeria" and No. 48 "H.M.S. Gordon", all in error.

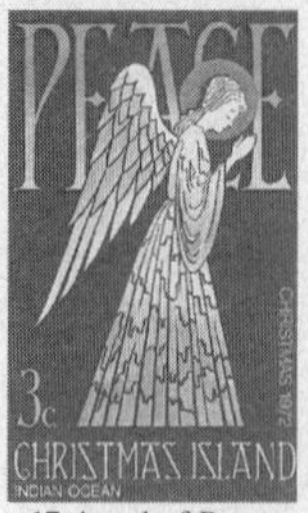

17 Angel of Peace

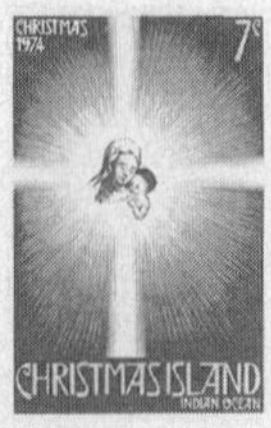

19 Mary and Holy Child within Christmas Star

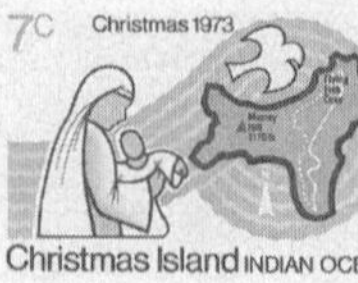

18 Virgin and Child, and Map

1972. Christmas. Multicoloured.

53		3c. Type **17**	15	40
54		3c. Angel of Joy	15	40
55		7c. Type **17**	20	50
56		7c. As No. 54	20	50

1973. Christmas.

57	**18**	7c. multicoloured	25	35
58		25c. multicoloured	75	1·00

1974. Christmas.

59	**19**	7c. mauve and grey	25	60
60		30c. orange, yellow and grey	75	2·50

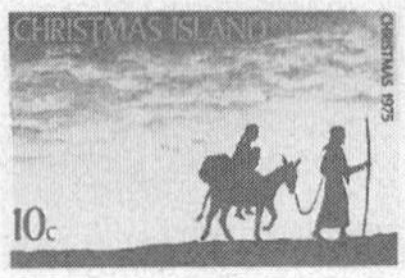

20 "The Flight into Egypt"

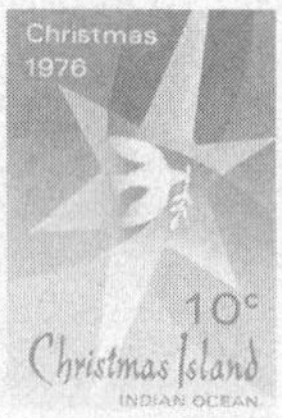

21 Dove of Peace and Star of Bethlehem

1975. Christmas.

61	**20**	10c. yellow, brown and gold	25	35
62		35c. pink, blue and gold	50	1·75

1976. Christmas.

63	**21**	10c. red, yellow and mauve	15	45
64	–	10c. red, yellow and mauve	15	45
65	**21**	35c. violet, blue and green	20	55
66	–	35c. violet, blue and green	20	55

DESIGNS: Nos. 64 and 66 are "mirror-images" of Type **21**.

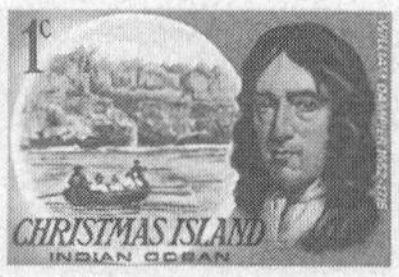

22 William Dampier (explorer)

1977. Famous Visitors. Multicoloured.

67		1c. Type **22**	15	70
68		2c. Captain de Vlamingh (explorer)	20	70
69		3c. Vice-Admiral MacLear	30	70
70		4c. Sir John Murray (oceanographer)	30	80
71		5c. Admiral Aldrich	30	40
72		6c. Andrew Clunies Ross (first settler)	30	60
73		7c. J. J. Lister (naturalist)	30	40
74		8c. Admiral of the Fleet Sir William May	35	70
75		9c. Henry Ridley (botanist)	40	1·40
76		10c. George Clunies Ross (phosphate miner)	55	55
77		20c. Captain Joshua Slocum (yachtsman)	50	75
78		45c. Charles Andrews (naturalist)	60	45
79		50c. Richard Hanitsch (biologist)	70	1·40
80		75c. Victor Purcell (scholar)	60	1·25
81		$1 Fam Choo Beng (educator)	60	1·25
82		$2 Sir Harold Spencer-Jones (astronomer)	65	2·00

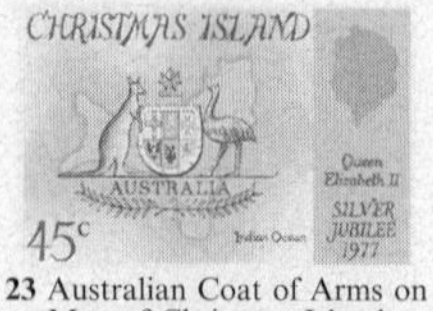

23 Australian Coat of Arms on Map of Christmas Island

1977. Silver Jubilee.

83	**23**	45c. multicoloured	45	55

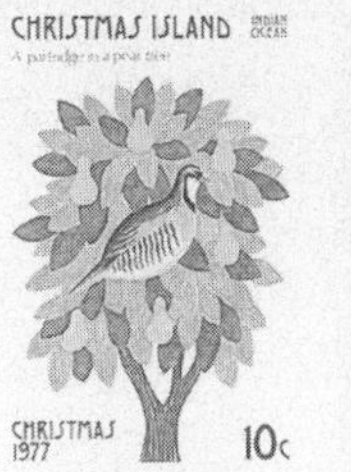

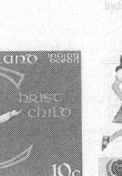

24 "A Partridge in a Pear Tree"

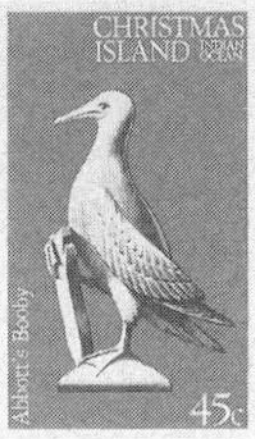

25 Abbott's Booby

1977. Christmas. "The Twelve Days of Christmas". Multicoloured.

84A	10c. Type **24**	10	20
85A	10c. "Two turtle doves"	10	20
86A	10c. "Three French hens"	10	20
87A	10c. "Four calling birds"	10	20
88A	10c. "Five gold rings"	10	20
89A	10c. "Six geese a-laying"	10	20
90A	10c. "Seven swans a-swimming"	10	20
91A	10c. "Eight maids a-milking"	10	20
92A	10c. "Nine ladies dancing"	10	20
93A	10c. "Ten lords a-leaping"	10	20
94A	10c. "Eleven pipers piping"	10	20
95A	10c. "Twelve drummers drumming"	10	20

1978. 25th Anniv of Coronation.

96	– 45c. black and blue	45	75
97	– 45c. multicoloured	45	75
98	**25** 45c. black and blue	45	75

DESIGNS: No.96, White Swan of Bohun; No. 97, Queen Elizabeth II.

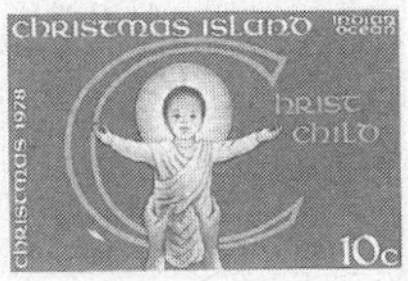

26 "Christ Child"

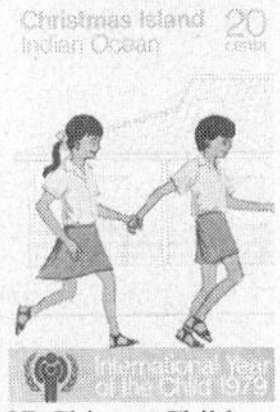

27 Chinese Children

1978. Christmas Scenes from "The Song of Christmas". Multicoloured.

99	10c. Type **26**	15	20
100	10c. "Herald Angels"	15	20
101	10c. "Redeemer"	15	20
102	10c. "Israel"	15	20
103	10c. "Star"	15	20
104	10c. "Three Wise Men"	15	20
105	10c. "Manger"	15	20
106	10c. "All He Stands For"	15	20
107	10c. "Shepherds Come"	15	20

1979. International Year of the Child. Children of different races. Multicoloured, colours of inscr given.

108	20c. green (Type **27**)	30	45
109	20c. turquoise (Malay children)	30	45
110	20c. lilac (Indian children)	30	45
111	20c. red (European children)	30	45
112	20c. yellow ("Oranges and Lemons")	30	45

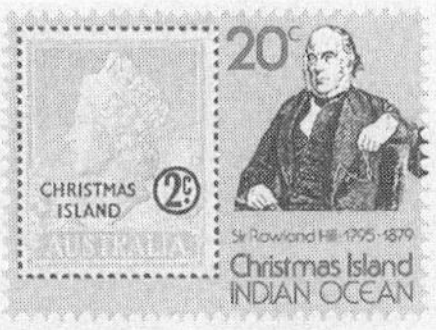

28 1958 2c. Definitive

1979. Death Centenary of Sir Rowland Hill. Multicoloured.

113	20c. Type **28**	20	40
114	20c. 1963 2c. map definitive	20	40
115	20c. 1965 50th Anniv of Gallipoli Landing 10c. commemorative	20	40
116	20c. 1964 4c. Pink-tailed triggerfish definitive	20	40
117	20c. 1969 Christmas 5c.	20	40

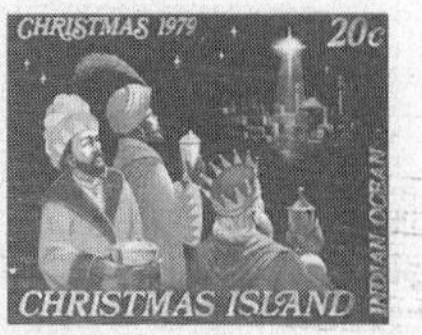

29 Wise Men following Star

1979. Christmas. Multicoloured.

118	20c. Type **29**	20	30
119	55c. Virgin and Child	45	70

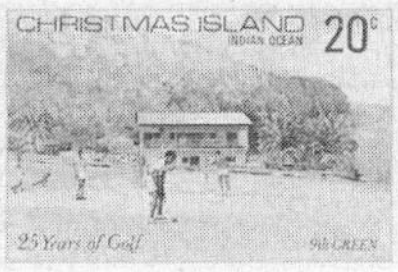

30 9th Green

1980. 25th Anniv of Christmas Island Golf Club. Multicoloured.

120	20c. Type **30**	35	50
121	55c. Clubhouse	40	1·00

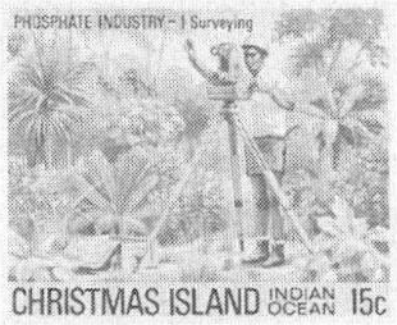

31 Surveying

1980. Phosphate Industry (1st series). Multicoloured.

122	15c. Type **31**	15	25
123	22c. Drilling for samples	15	30
124	40c. Sample analysis	20	45
125	55c. Mine planning	25	55

See also Nos. 126/9, 136/9 and 140/3.

1980. Phosphate Industry (2nd series). As T **31**. Multicoloured.

126	15c. Jungle clearing	15	15
127	22c. Overburden removal	15	20
128	40c. Open cut mining	20	25
129	55c. Restoration	20	30

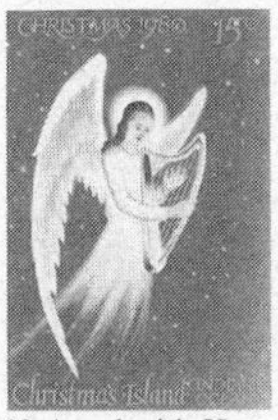
32 Angel with Harp

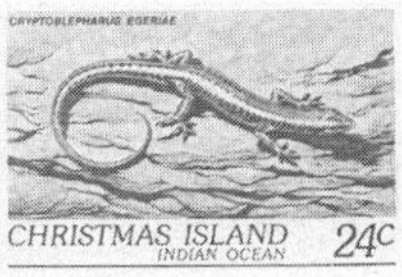

33 "Cryptoblepharus egeriae"

1980. Christmas. Multicoloured.

130	15c. Type **32**	10	25
131	15c. Angel with wounded soldier	10	25
132	22c. Virgin and Child	15	30
133	22c. Kneeling couple	15	30
134	60c. Angel with harp (different)	20	20
135	60c. Angel with children	20	30

1981. Phosphate Industry (3rd series). As T **31**. Multicoloured.

136	22c. Screening and Stockpiling	15	15
137	28c. Train loading	20	20
138	40c. Railing	25	25
139	60c. Drying	25	25

1981. Phosphate Industry (4th series). As T **31**. Multicoloured.

140	22c. Crushing	20	20
141	28c. Conveying	30	25
142	40c. Bulk storage	40	40
143	60c. "Consolidated Venture" (bulk carrier) loading	50	55

1981. Reptiles. Multicoloured.

144	24c. Type **33**	20	20
145	30c. "Emoia nativitata"	25	25
146	40c. "Lepidodactylus listeri"	30	30
147	60c. "Cyrtodactylus sp. nov."	35	35

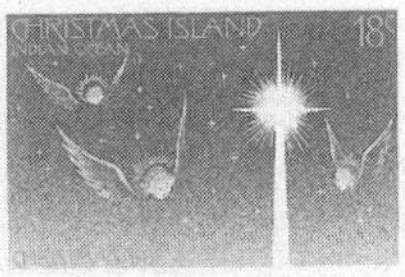

34 Scene from Carol "Away in a Manger"

1981. Christmas.

148	**34** 18c. silver, dp blue & bl	30	50
149	– 24c. multicoloured	30	55
150	– 40c. multicoloured	35	65
151	– 60c. multicoloured	40	75

DESIGNS: 24c. to 60c. show various scenes from carol "Away in a Manger".

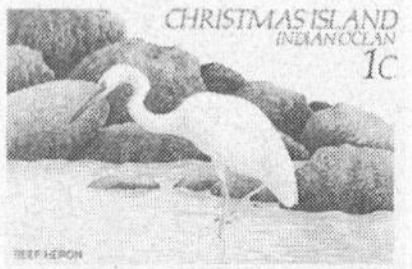

35 Reef Heron

1982. Birds. Multicoloured.

152	1c. Type **35**	70	30
153	2c. Common noddy ("Noddy")	70	30
154	3c. White-bellied swiftlet ("Glossy Swiftlet")	70	70
155	4c. Christmas Island imperial pigeon ("Imperial Pigeon")	70	70
156	5c. Christmas Island white-eye ("Silvereye")	80	70
157	10c. Island thrush ("Thrush")	70	70
158	25c. Red-tailed tropic bird ("Silver Bosunbird")	1·25	60
159	30c. Emerald dove	80	70
160	40c. Brown booby	80	55
161	50c. Red-footed booby	80	55
162	65c. Christmas Island frigate bird ("Frigatebird")	80	55
163	75c. White-tailed tropic bird ("Golden Bosunbird")	90	65
164	80c. Australian kestrel ("Nankeen Kestrel") (vert)	1·25	2·00
165	$1 Moluccan hawk owl ("Hawk-owl") (vert)	2·50	2·50
166	$2 Australian goshawk ("Goshawk")	1·75	4·00
167	$4 Abbott's booby (vert)	3·00	3·25

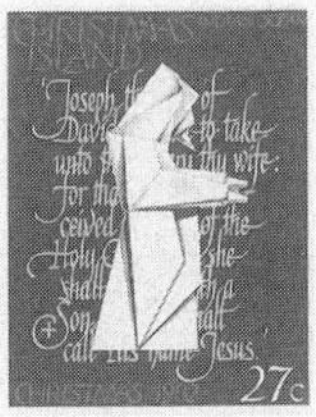

36 Joseph

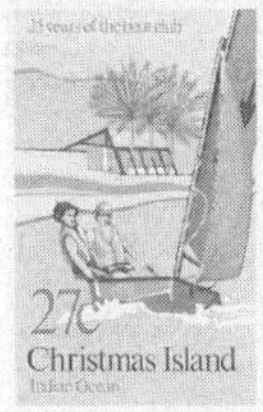

37 "Mirror" Dinghy and Club House

1982. Christmas. Origami Paper Sculptures. Mult.

168	27c. Type **36**	30	30
169	50c. Angel	45	45
170	75c. Mary and baby Jesus	65	65

1983. 25th Anniv of Christmas Island Boat Club. Multicoloured.

171	27c. Type **37**	20	30
172	35c. Ocean-going yachts	20	35
173	50c. Fishing launch and cargo ship (horiz)	25	40
174	75c. Dinghy-racing and cantilever (horiz)	25	60

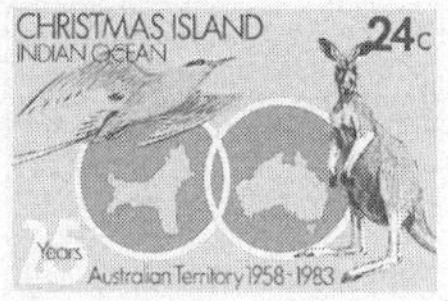

38 Maps of Christmas Island and Australia, Eastern Grey Kangaroo and White-tailed Tropic Bird

1983. 25th Anniv of Australian Territory. Mult.

175	24c. Type **38**	40	25
176	30c. Christmas Island and Australian flag	45	45
177	85c. Maps of Christmas Island and Australia, and Boeing 727	1·25	1·25

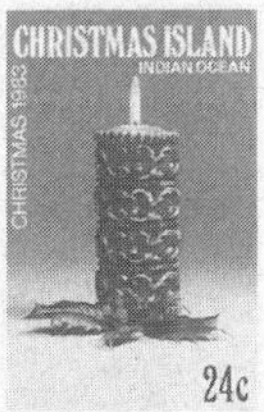

39 Candle and Holly

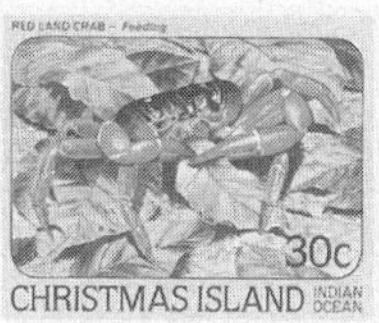

40 Feeding on Leaf

1983. Christmas. Candles. Multicoloured.

178	24c. Type **39**	20	20
179	30c. Six gold candles	30	40
180	85c. Candles	70	1·00

1984. Red Land Crab. Multicoloured.

181	30c. Type **40**	25	30
182	40c. Migration	30	40
183	55c. Development stages	30	50
184	85c. Adult females and young	45	70

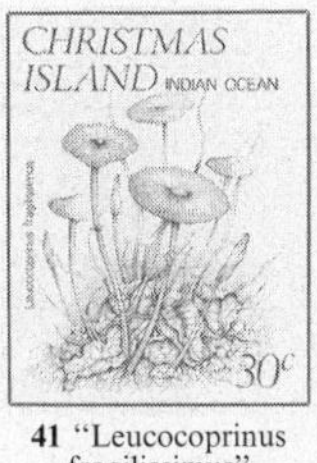

41 "Leucocoprinus fragilissimus"

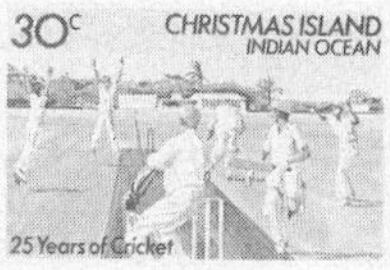

42 Run-out

1984. Fungi. Multicoloured.

185	30c. Type **41**	35	55
186	40c. "Microporus xanthopus"	40	70
187	45c. "Hydropus anthidepes" ("Trogia anthidepas")	45	80
188	55c. "Haddowia longipes"	45	90
189	85c. "Phillipsia domingensis"	55	1·25

1984. 25th Anniv of Cricket on Christmas Island. Multicoloured.

190	30c. Type **42**	40	85
191	40c. Bowled-out	40	1·10
192	50c. Batsman in action	45	1·50
193	85c. Fielder diving for catch	70	1·75

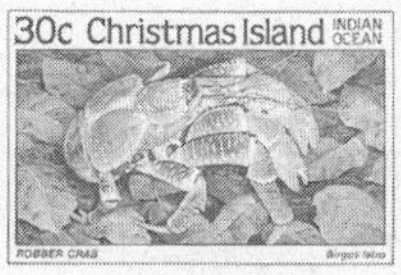

44 Robber Crab

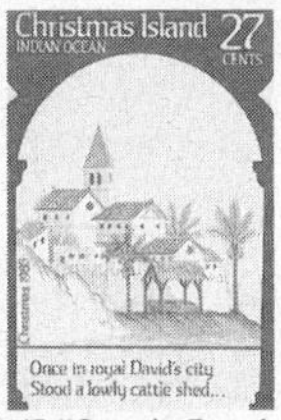

45 "Once in Royal David's City"

1985. Crabs (1st series). Multicoloured.

195	30c. Type **44**	1·00	70
196	40c. Horn-eyed ghost crab	1·10	1·10
197	55c. Purple hermit crab	1·50	1·60
198	85c. Little nipper	2·25	2·50

1985. Crabs (2nd series). As T **44**. Multicoloured.

199	33c. Blue crab	1·00	55
200	45c. Tawny hermit crab	1·10	1·10
201	60c. Red nipper	1·60	1·75
202	90c. Smooth-handed ghost crab	2·25	2·50

1985. Crabs (3rd series). As T **44**. Multicoloured.

203	33c. Red crab	1·10	60
204	45c. Mottled crab	1·50	1·40
205	60c. Rock hopper crab	2·25	2·50
206	90c. Yellow nipper	2·75	3·50

1985. Christmas Carols. Multicoloured.

207	27c. Type **45**	1·00	1·25
208	33c. "While Shepherds Watched Their Flocks by Night"	1·10	1·40
209	45c. "Away in a Manger"	1·40	1·60
210	60c. "We Three Kings of Orient Are"	1·50	1·75
211	90c. "Hark the Herald Angels Sing"	1·60	1·90

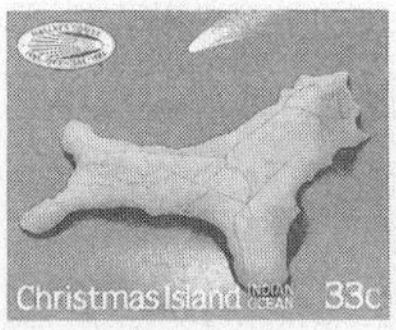

46 Halley's Comet over Christmas Island

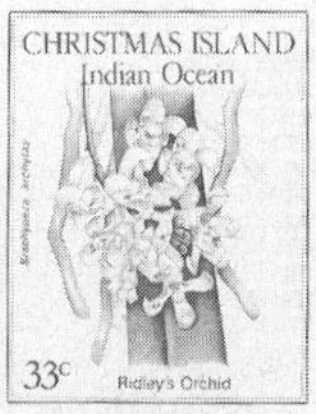

47 Ridley's Orchid

1986. Appearance of Halley's Comet. Multicoloured.

212	33c. Type **46**	45	80
213	45c. Edmond Halley	55	1·10
214	60c. Comet and "Consolidated Venture" (bulk carrier) loading phosphate	70	2·25
215	90c. Comet over Flying Fish Cove	80	2·50

1986. Native Flowers. Multicoloured.

216	33c. Type **47**	50	55
217	45c. Hanging flower	30	85
218	60c. Hoya	30	1·50
219	90c. Sea hibiscus	35	2·00

1986. Royal Wedding. As T **112** of Ascension. Multicoloured.

220	33c. Prince Andrew and Miss Sarah Ferguson	45	50
221	90c. Prince Andrew piloting helicopter, Digby, Canada, 1985	95	1·75

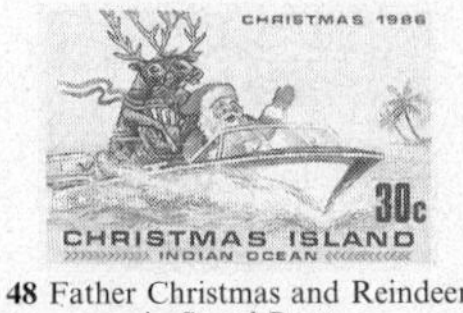

48 Father Christmas and Reindeer in Speed Boat

1986. Christmas. Multicoloured.

222	30c. Type **48**	85	60
223	36c. Father Christmas and reindeer on beach	1·00	60
224	55c. Father Christmas fishing	1·50	1·50
225	70c. Playing golf	2·50	3·25
226	$1 Sleeping in hammock	2·50	3·75

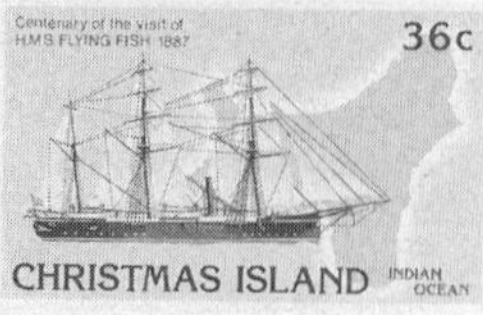

49 H.M.S. "Flying Fish" and Outline Map of Christmas Island

1987. Centenary of Visits by H.M.S. "Flying Fish" and H.M.S. "Egeria". Multicoloured.

227	36c. Type **49**	60	75
228	90c. H.M.S. "Egeria" and outline map	1·00	2·50

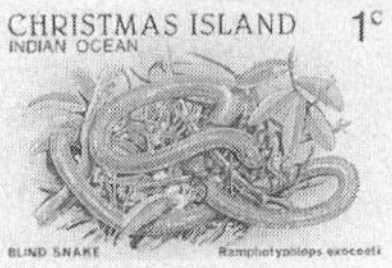

50 Blind Snake

1987. Wildlife. Multicoloured.

229	1c. Type **50**	40	90
230	2c. Blue-tailed skink	40	90
231	3c. Insectivorous bat	90	90
232	5c. Grasshopper	90	90
233	10c. Christmas Island fruit bat	90	90
234	25c. Gecko	1·00	1·00
235	30c. "Mantis religiosa" (mantid)	1·25	1·25
236	36c. Moluccan hawk owl ("Hawk-owl")	3·00	1·75
237	40c. Bull-mouth helmet	1·75	1·50
237a	41c. Nudibranch ("Phidiana" sp.)	1·25	70
238	50c. Textile or cloth of gold cone	1·75	1·50
239	65c. Brittle stars	1·40	1·25
240	75c. Regal angelfish	1·40	1·25
241	90c. "Appias paulina" (butterfly)	3·75	2·75
242	$1 "Hypolimnas misippus" (butterfly)	3·75	2·75
243	$2 Shrew	3·75	7·00
244	$5 Green turtle	4·50	7·00

1988. Bicentenary of Australian Settlement. Arrival of First Fleet. As Nos. 1105/9 of Australia, but each inscribed "CHRISTMAS ISLAND Indian Ocean" and "AUSTRALIA BICENTENARY".

246	37c. Aborigines watching arrival of Fleet, Botany Bay	1·50	1·75
247	37c. Aboriginal family and anchored ships	1·50	1·75
248	37c. Fleet arriving at Sydney Cove	1·50	1·75
249	37c. Ship's boat	1·50	1·75
250	37c. Raising the flag, Sydney Cove, 26 January 1788	1·50	1·75

Nos. 246/50 were printed together, se-tenant, forming a composite design.

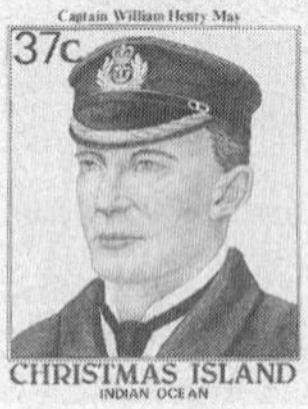

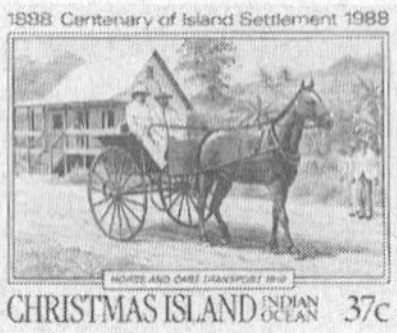

52 Captain William May **53** Pony and Trap, 1910

1988. Cent of British Annexation. Mult.

251	37c. Type **52**	35	40
252	53c. Annexation ceremony	50	55
253	95c. H.M.S. "Imperieuse" (armoured cruiser) firing salute	90	95
254	$1.50 Building commemorative cairn	1·40	1·50

1988. Cent of Permanent Settlement. Mult.

255	37c. Type **53**	60	40
256	55c. Phosphate mining, 1910	85	55
257	70c. Steam locomotive, 1914	1·25	85
258	$1 Arrival of first aircraft, 1957	1·50	1·25

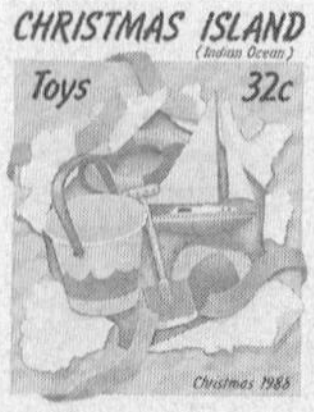

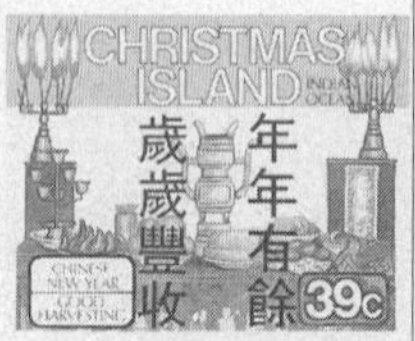

54 Beach Toys **55** Food on Table ("Good Harvesting")

1988. Christmas. Toys and Gifts. Multicoloured.

259	32c. Type **54**	40	35
260	39c. Flippers, snorkel and mask	50	40
261	90c. Model soldier, doll and soft toys	1·10	1·10
262	$1 Models of racing car, lorry and jet aircraft	1·25	1·25

1989. Chinese New Year. Multicoloured.

263	39c. Type **55**	45	40
264	70c. Decorations ("Prosperity")	80	70
265	90c. Chinese girls ("Good Fortune")	1·10	90
266	$1 Lion dance ("Progress Every Year")	1·25	1·00

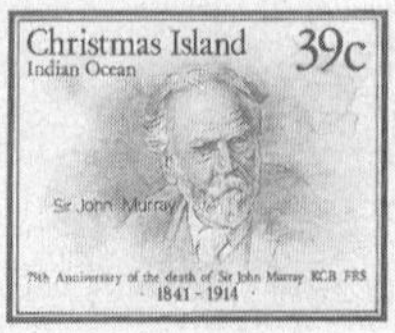

56 Sir John Murray

1989. 75th Death Anniv of Sir John Murray (oceanographer). Multicoloured.

267	39c. Type **56**	50	50
268	80c. Map of Christmas Island showing Murray Hill	1·25	95
269	$1 Oceanographic equipment	1·50	1·25
270	$1.10 H.M.S. "Challenger" (survey ship), 1872	1·75	1·50

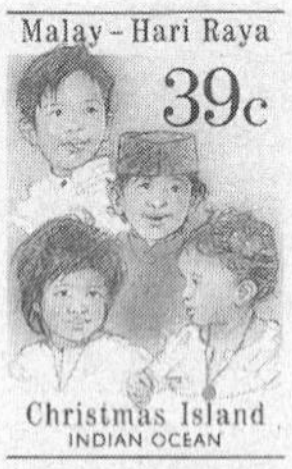

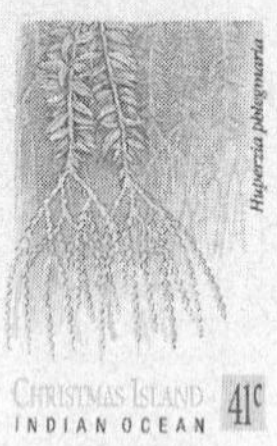

57 Four Children **58** "Huperzia phlegmaria"

1989. Malay Hari Raya Festival. Multicoloured.

271	39c. Type **57**	55	50
272	55c. Man playing tambourine	80	70
273	80c. Girl in festival costume	1·25	1·00
274	$1.10 Christmas Island Mosque	1·60	1·40

1989. Ferns. Multicoloured.

275	41c. Type **58**	75	60
276	65c. "Asplenium polydon"	1·10	85
277	80c. Common bracken	1·40	1·00
278	$1.10 Birds-nest fern	1·60	1·40

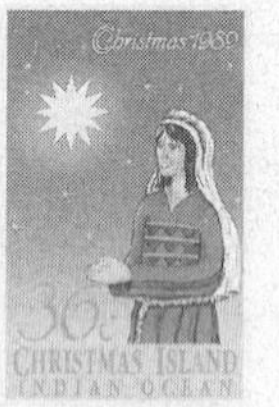

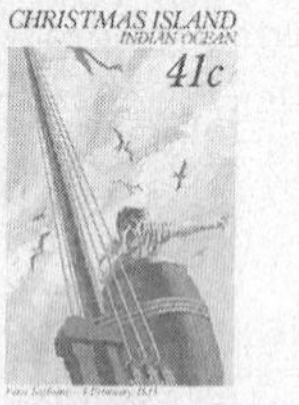

59 Virgin Mary and Star **61** First Sighting, 1615

1989. Christmas. Multicoloured.

279	36c. Type **59**	60	40
280	41c. Christ Child in manger	60	45
281	80c. Shepherds and star	1·50	80
282	$1.10 Three Wise Men following star	1·60	1·10

1989. "Melbourne Stampshow '89". Nos. 237a and 242 optd with Stampshow logo.

283	41c. Nudibranch ("Phidiana sp.")	75	45
284	$1 "Hypolimnas misippus" (butterfly)	2·25	1·00

1990. 375th Anniv of Discovery of Christmas Island. Multicoloured.

285	41c. Type **61**	1·00	50
286	$1.10 Second sighting and naming, 1643	1·25	1·40

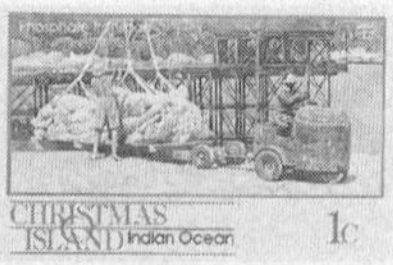

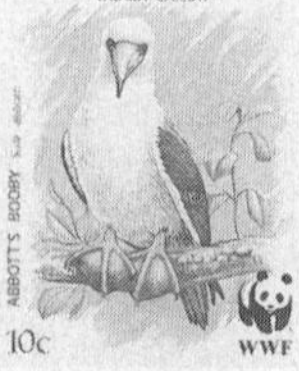

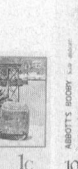

62 Miniature Tractor pulling Phosphate **63** Male Abbott's Booby

1990. Christmas Island Transport. Multicoloured.

287	1c. Type **62**	15	20
288	2c. Phosphate train	40	40
289	3c. Diesel railcar No. 8802 (vert)	20	20
290	5c. Loading road train	40	40
291	10c. Trishaw (vert)	30	30
292	15c. Terex truck	65	65
293	25c. Articulated bus	30	30
294	30c. Cable passenger carriage (vert)	30	35
295	40c. Passenger barge (vert)	35	40
296	50c. Kolek (outrigger canoe)	55	55
297	65c. Flying Doctor aircraft and ambulance	3·75	1·50
298	75c. Commercial van	1·50	1·50
299	90c. Vintage lorry	1·50	1·75
300	$1 Water tanker	1·50	1·75
301	$2 Traction engine	2·50	3·25
302	$5 Steam locomotive No. 1	3·25	4·75

1990. Abbott's Booby. Multicoloured.

303	10c. Type **63**	85	30
304	20c. Juvenile male	1·40	50
305	29c. Female with egg	1·60	55
306	41c. Pair with chick	2·25	70

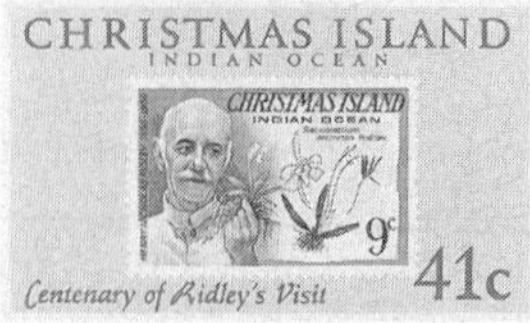

64 1977 Famous Visitors 9c. Stamp

1990. Centenary of Henry Ridley's Visit.

308	41c. Type **64**	55	65
309	75c. Ridley (botanist) in rainforest	85	1·75

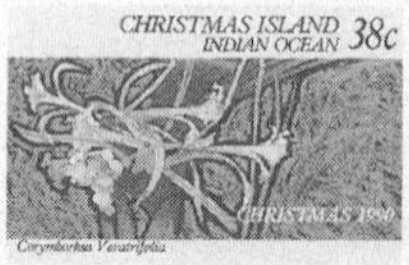

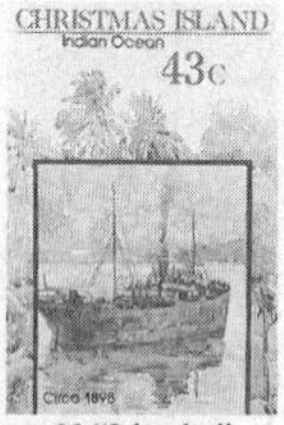

65 "Corymborkus veratrifolia" **66** "Islander" (freighter), 1898

1990. Christmas. Flowers. Multicoloured.

311	38c. Type **65**	1·10	70
312	43c. "Hoya aldrichii"	1·25	75
313	80c. "Quisqualis indica"	2·25	2·75
314	$1.20 "Barringtonia racemosa"	2·75	3·50

1991. Centenary of First Phosphate Mining Lease. Multicoloured.

316	43c. Type **66**	1·00	90
317	43c. Miners loading tipper wagons, 1908	1·00	90
318	85c. Shay steam locomotive No. 4, 1925	1·40	1·25
319	$1.20 Extracting phosphate, 1951	1·75	1·60
320	$1.70 Land reclamation, 1990	2·00	1·90

Nos. 316/20 were printed together, se-tenant, forming a composite forest design.

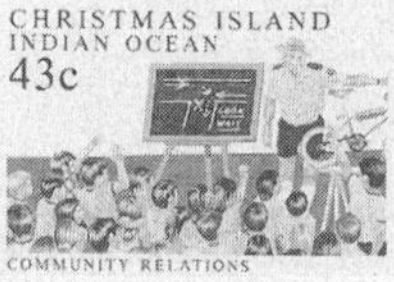

67 Teaching Children Road Safety

1991. Christmas Island Police Force. Multicoloured.

321	43c. Type **67**	1·50	1·00
322	43c. Traffic control	1·50	1·00
323	90c. Airport customs	2·25	3·25
324	$1.20 Police launch "Fregata Andrews" towing rescued boat	3·00	3·00

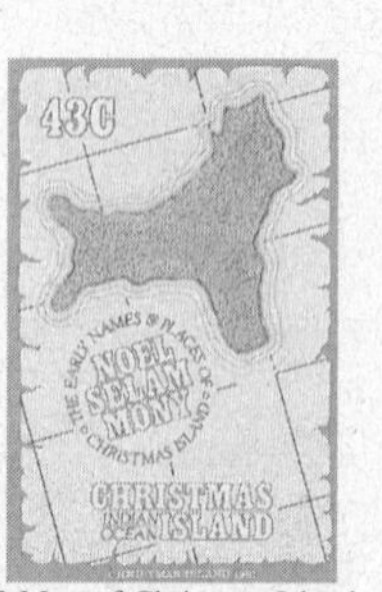

68 Map of Christmas Island, 1991

1991. Maps of Christmas Island. Multicoloured.

326	43c. Type **68**	1·00	65
327	75c. Goos Atlas, 1666	1·75	1·10
328	$1.10 De Manevillette, 1745	2·25	1·60
329	$1.20 Comberford, 1667	2·25	1·90

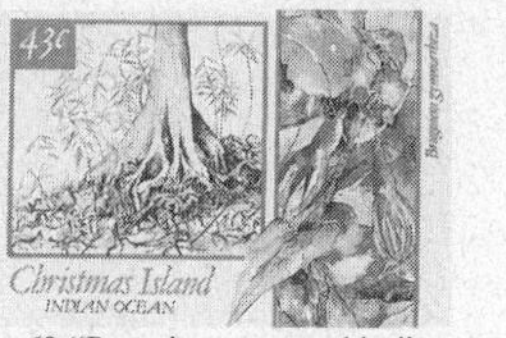

69 "Bruguiera gymnorrhiza"

1991. Local Trees. Multicoloured.

330	43c. Type **69**	1·00	65
331	70c. "Syzgium operculatum"	1·50	1·00
332	85c. "Ficus microcarpa"	1·75	1·25
333	$1.20 "Arenga listeri"	2·00	1·60

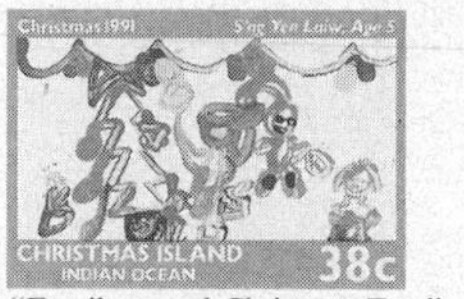

70 "Family round Christmas Tree" (S'ng Yen Luiw)

1991. Christmas. Children's Paintings. Multicoloured.

334	38c. Type **70**	75	75
335	38c. "Opening Presents" (Liew Ann Nee)	75	75
336	38c. "Beach Party" (Foo Pang Chuan)	75	75
337	38c. "Christmas Walk" (Too Lai Peng)	75	75
338	38c. "Santa Claus and Christmas Tree" (Jesamine Wheeler)	75	75
339	43c. "Santa Claus fishing" (Ho Puay Ha)	75	60
340	$1 "Santa Claus in Boat" (Ng Hooi Hua)	1·50	1·50
341	$1.20 "Santa Claus surfing" (Yani Kawi)	1·75	1·75

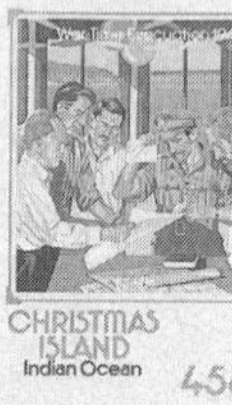

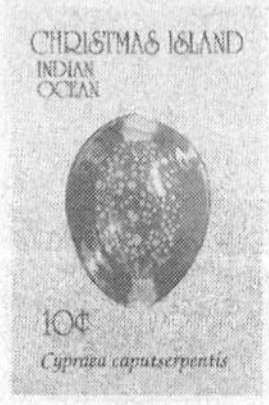

71 Discussing Evacuation, 1942 **72** Snake's-head Cowrie

1992. 50th Anniv of Partial Evacuation. Mult.

342	45c. Type **71**	1·00	1·00
343	45c. Families waiting to embark	1·00	1·00
344	$1.05 Ferrying evacuees to "Islander"	2·50	2·50
345	$1.20 Departure of "Islander" (freighter)	2·75	2·75

1992. Shells. Multicoloured.

346	5c. Tiger cowrie	50	40
347	10c. Type **72**	70	50
348	15c. Scorpion conch	1·00	50
349	20c. Royal oak scallop	1·00	50
350	25c. Striped engina	1·00	50
351	30c. Prickly Pacific drupe	1·00	50
352	40c. Reticulate distorsio	1·00	55
353	45c. Tapestry turban	1·25	60
354	50c. Beautiful goblet	1·25	55
355	60c. Captain cone	1·50	65
356	70c. Layonkaire's turban	1·50	75
357	80c. Chirage spider conch	1·75	85
358	90c. Common delphinia	1·75	1·10
359	$1 Ceramic vase	1·75	1·25
360	$2 Partridge tun	1·40	1·50
361	$5 Strawberry drupe	3·50	3·75

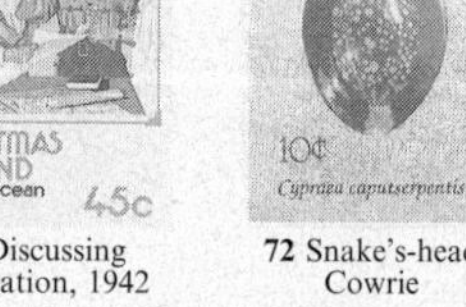

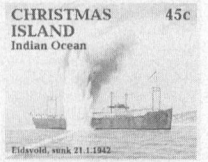

73 Torpedoing of "Eidsvold"

1992. 50th Anniv of Sinkings of "Eidsvold" and "Nissa Maru". Multicoloured.

362	45c. Type **73**	1·25	75
363	80c. "Eidsvold" sinking	2·00	1·75
364	$1.05 "Nissa Maru" under attack	2·50	3·00
365	$1.20 "Nissa Maru" beached	2·50	3·25

1992. "Kuala Lumpur '92" International Philatelic Exhibition. No. 361 optd with exhibition symbol.

366	$5 Strawberry drupe	9·00	7·00

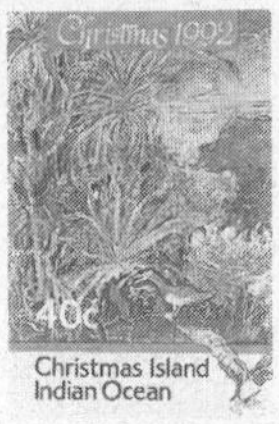

75 Jungle

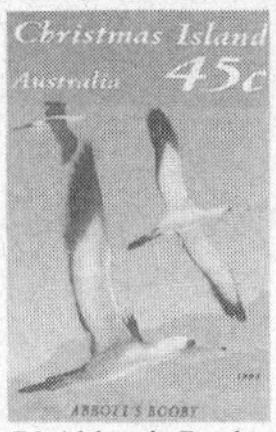

76 Abbott's Booby

1992. Christmas. Multicoloured.

367	40c. Type **75**	90	1·25
368	40c. Red-tailed tropic bird and brown booby over rock	90	1·25
369	45c. Brown boobies on headland	90	1·25
370	$1.05 Red-tailed tropic bird, brown booby and cliffs	1·60	1·75
371	$1.20 Cliffs	1·60	1·75

Nos. 367/71 were printed together, se-tenant, forming a composite coastal design.

1993. Seabirds. Multicoloured.

372	45c. Type **76**	60	85
373	45c. Christmas Island frigate bird	60	85
374	45c. Common noddy	60	85
375	45c. White-tailed ("Golden Bosunbird") tropic bird	60	85
376	45c. Brown booby	60	85

Nos. 372/6 were printed together, se-tenant, forming a composite design.

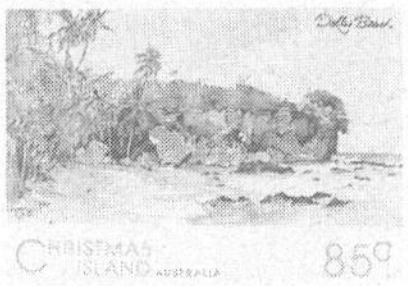

77 Dolly Beach

1993. Scenic Views of Christmas Island. Mult.

378	85c. Type **77**	1·25	1·50
379	95c. Blow Holes	1·50	2·00
380	$1.05 Merrial Beach	1·60	2·25
381	$1.20 Rainforest	1·75	2·25

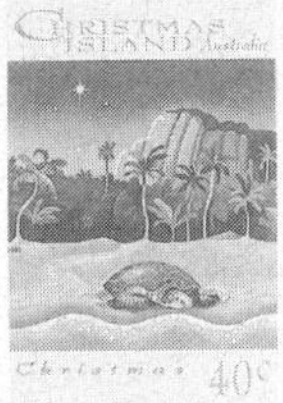

78 Turtle on Beach

1993. Christmas. Multicoloured.

382	40c. Type **78**	1·00	70
383	45c. Crabs and wave	1·00	70
384	$1 Christmas Island frigate bird and rainforest	2·25	3·25

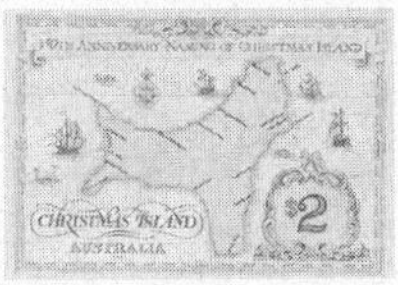

79 Map of Christmas Island

1993. 350th Anniv of Naming of Christmas Island.

385	**79** $2 multicoloured	3·00	3·50

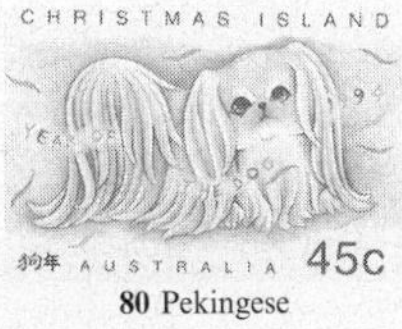

80 Pekingese

1994. Chinese New Year ("Year of the Dog"). Multicoloured.

386	45c. Type **80**	1·00	1·40
387	45c. Mickey (Christmas Island dog)	1·00	1·40

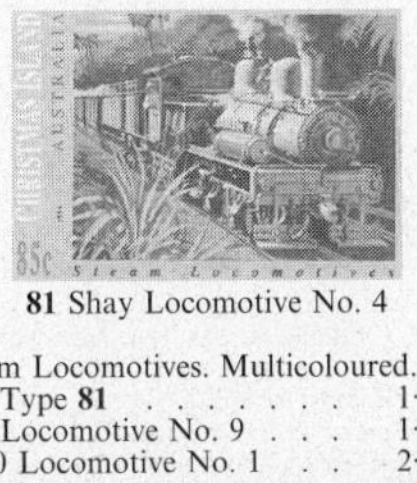

81 Shay Locomotive No. 4

1994. Steam Locomotives. Multicoloured.

389	85c. Type **81**	1·75	1·75
390	95c. Locomotive No. 9	1·75	2·00
391	$1.20 Locomotive No. 1	2·00	2·25

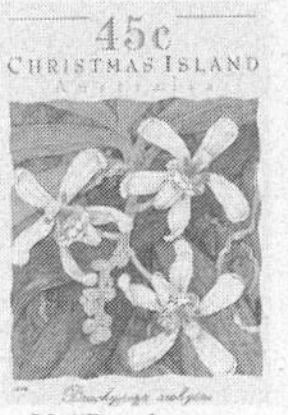

82 "Brachypeza archytas"

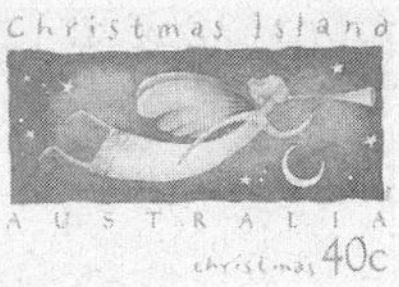

83 Angel blowing Trumpet

1994. Orchids. Multicoloured.

392	45c. Type **82**	1·10	1·40
393	45c. "Thelasis capitata"	1·10	1·40
394	45c. "Corymborkis veratrifolia"	1·10	1·40
395	45c. "Flickingeria nativitatis"	1·10	1·40
396	45c. "Dendrobium crumenatum"	1·10	1·40

1994. Christmas. Multicoloured.

397	40c. Type **83**	80	60
398	45c. Wise Man holding gift	80	60
399	80c. Star over Bethlehem	1·75	2·50

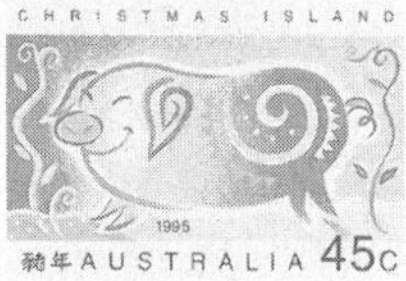

84 Pig

1995. Chinese New Year ("Year of the Pig").

400	**84** 45c. multicoloured	75	60
401	– 85c. multicoloured	1·25	1·75

DESIGN: 85c. Pig (different).

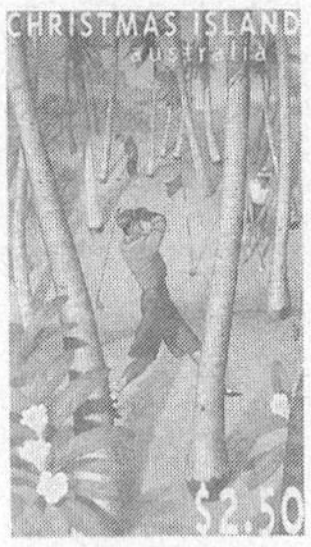

85 Golfer playing Shot

1995. 40th Anniv of Christmas Island Golf Course.

403	**85** $2.50 multicoloured	4·25	4·25

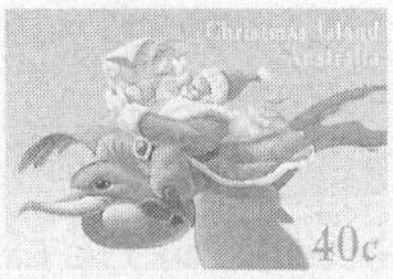

86 Father Christmas with Map on Christmas Island Frigate Bird

1995. Christmas Multicoloured

404	40c. Type **86**	80	60
405	45c. Father Christmas distributing presents	80	60
406	80c. Father Christmas waving goodbye	1·75	2·50

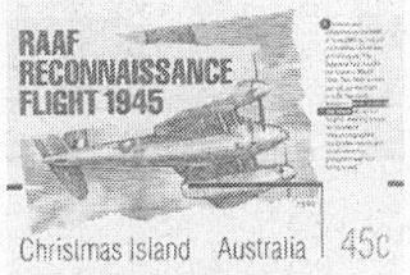

87 De Havilland D.H.98 Mosquito on Reconnaissance Mission

1995. 50th Anniv of End of Second World War. Each black, stone and red.

407	45c. Type **87**	95	95
408	45c. H.M.S. "Rother" (frigate)	95	95

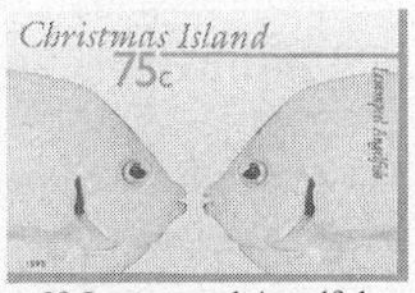

88 Lemon-peel Angelfish

1995. Marine Life. Multicoloured.

412	20c. Pink-tailed triggerfish	15	20
413	30c. Japanese inflator-filefish ("Longnose filefish")	20	25
414	45c. Princess anthias	30	35
415	75c. Type **88**	55	60
416	85c. Moon wrasse	60	65
417	90c. Spotted boxfish	65	70
418	95c. Moorish idol	65	70
419	$1 Emperor angelfish	70	75
420	$1.20 Glass-eyed snapper ("Glass bigeye")	85	90

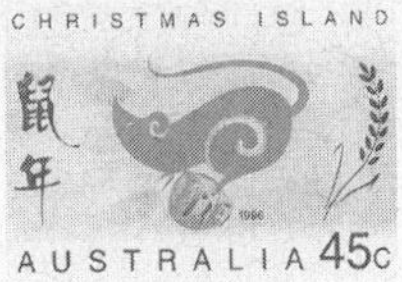

89 Rat with Drum

1996. Chinese New Year ("Year of the Rat"). Multicoloured.

425	45c. Type **89**	75	90
426	45c. Rat with tambourine	75	90

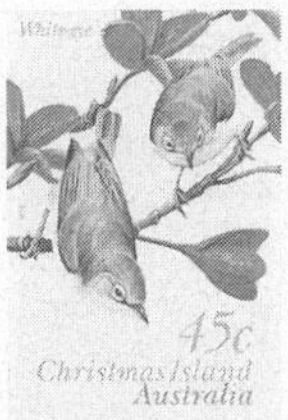

90 Christmas Island White Eye

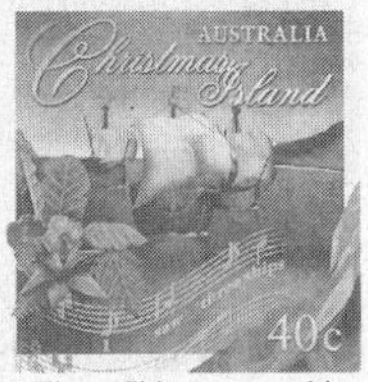

91 Three Ships approaching Island

1996. Christmas Island Land Birds. Multicoloured.

428	45c. Type **90**	75	50
429	85c. Christmas Island hawk owl	1·75	2·00

1996. Christmas. "I saw Three Ships" (carol). Multicoloured.

430	40c. Type **91**	75	60
431	45c. Madonna and Child with ships at anchor	75	60
432	80c. Ships leaving	1·60	2·10

1996. 300th Anniv of Willem de Vlamingh's Discovery of Christmas Island. As No. 1667 of Australia.

433	45c. multicoloured	75	75

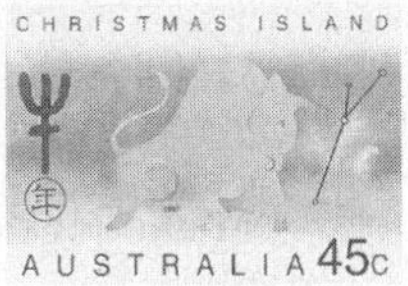

92 Ox facing Right

1997. Chinese New Year ("Year of the Ox"). Multicoloured.

434	45c. Type **92**	90	90
435	45c. Ox facing left	90	90

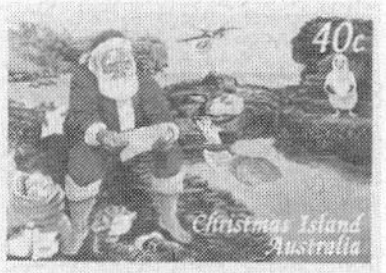

93 Father Christmas reading Letter

1997. Christmas. Multicoloured.

437	40c. Type **93**	55	50
438	45c. Father Christmas carving wooden boat	55	50
439	80c. Father Christmas in sleigh	1·10	1·50

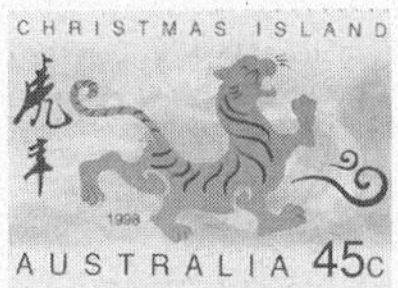

94 Tiger

1998. Chinese New Year ("Year of the Tiger"). Multicoloured.

440	45c. Type **94**	80	75
441	45c. Tiger with head facing left	80	75

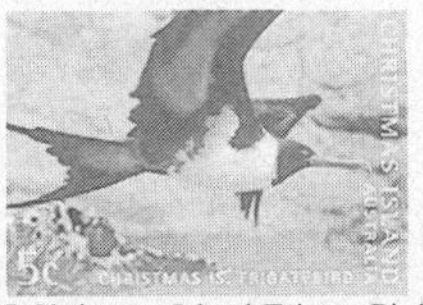

95 Christmas Island Frigate Bird

1998. Marine Life. Multicoloured.

443	5c. Type **95**	20	30
444	5c. Four ambon chromis	20	30
445	5c. Three ambon chromis	20	30
446	5c. One pink anemonefish	20	30
447	5c. Three pink anemonefish	20	30
448	10c. Eastern reef egret	25	30
449	10c. Whitelined cod	25	30
450	10c. Pyramid butterflyfish	25	30
451	10c. Dusky parrotfish	25	30
452	10c. Spotted garden eel	25	30
453	25c. Sooty tern	30	35
454	25c. Stripe-tailed damselfish ("Scissortail sergeant")	30	35
455	25c. Thicklip wrasse	30	35
456	25c. Blackaxil chromis	30	35
457	25c. Orange anthias	30	35
458	45c. Brown booby	35	40
459	45c. Green turtle	35	40
460	45c. Pink anemonefish	35	40
461	45c. Blue sea star	35	40
462	45c. Kunie's chromodoris	35	40

Nos. 443/62 were printed together, se-tenant, with the backgrounds forming a composie design.

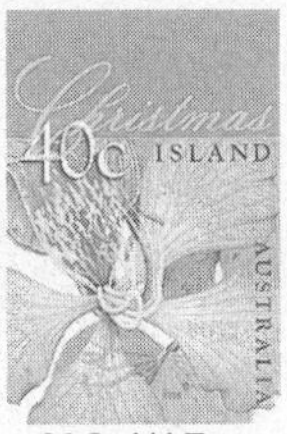

96 Orchid Tree

1998. Christmas. Flowering Trees. Multicoloured.

463	40c. Type **96**	60	50
464	80c. Flame tree	1·25	1·40
465	95c. Sea hibiscus	1·40	1·75

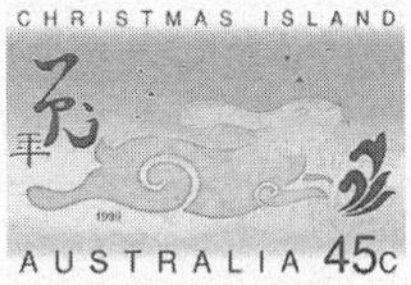

97 Leaping Rabbit

1999. Chinese New Year ("Year of the Rabbit"). Multicoloured.

466	45c. Type **97**	50	65
467	45c. Rabbit with pestle and mortar	50	65

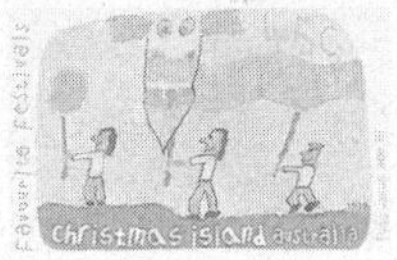

98 Carnival Dragon (Fong Jason) (Community Arts Festival)

1999. Festivals. Children's Paintings. Mult.

469	45c. Type **98**	60	60
470	45c. Red crab holding Easter egg (Community Arts Festival, Siti Zanariah Zainal)	60	60
471	85c. Ghost and child (Tan Diana) (Hungry Ghost Festival) (vert)	95	1·10
472	$1.20 Walls of Mecca (Anwar Ramlan) (Hari Raya Haji Festival) (vert)	1·25	1·40

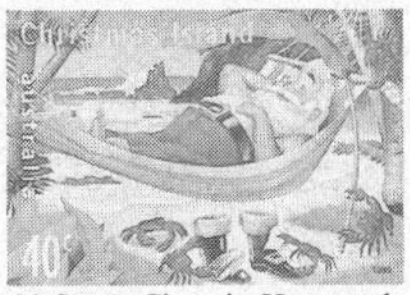

99 Santa Claus in Hammock

1999. Christmas. Multicoloured.

473	40c. Type **99**	50	50
474	45c. Santa Claus with Christmas pudding	50	50
475	95c. Santa Claus in sleigh pulled by Abbott's boobies	1·25	1·50

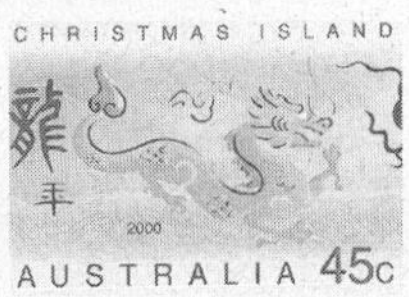

100 Chinese Dragon

2000. Chinese New Year ("Year of the Dragon"). Multicoloured.

476	45c. Type **100**	50	65
477	45c. Chinese dragon facing left	50	65

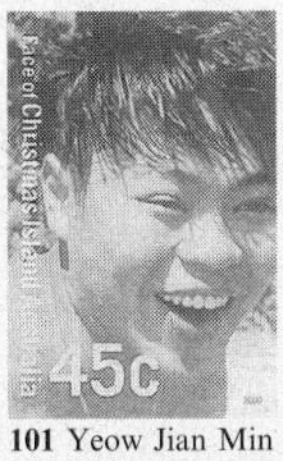

101 Yeow Jian Min

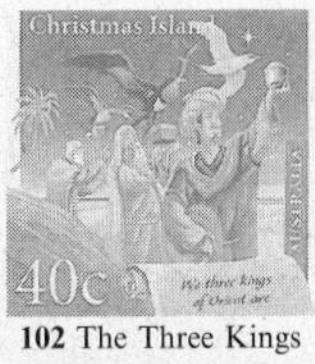

102 The Three Kings

2000. New Millennium. "Face of Christmas Island". Multicoloured.

479		45c. Type **101**	50	60
480		45c. Ida Chin (schoolgirl)	50	60
481		45c. Ho Tak Wah (elderly man)	50	60
482		45c. Thomas Faul and James Neill (young boys)	50	60
483		45c. Siti Sanniah Kawi (mother of three)	50	60

2000. Christmas. "We Three Kings" (carol). Mult.

484		40c. Type **102**	50	55
485		40c. Birds with Three Gifts	50	55
486		45c. Crabs with Three Gifts	50	55

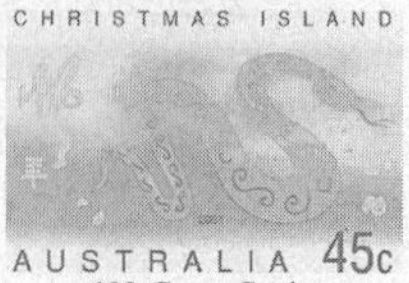

103 Green Snake

2001. Chinese New Year ("Year of the Snake"). Mult.

487		45c. Type **103**	50	50
488		$1.35 Silver snake	1·25	1·50

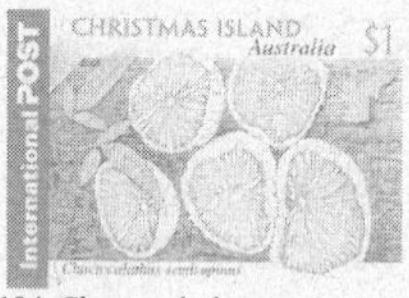

104 *Chaetocalathus semisupinus*

2001. International Stamps. Fungi. Multicoloured.

490		$1 Type **104**	70	75
491		$1.50 *Pycnoporus sanguineus*	70	75

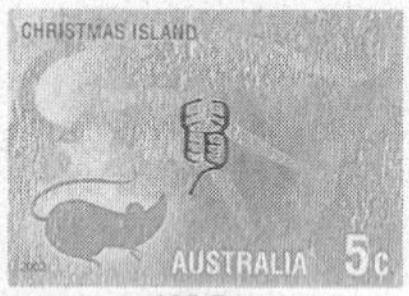

105 Rat

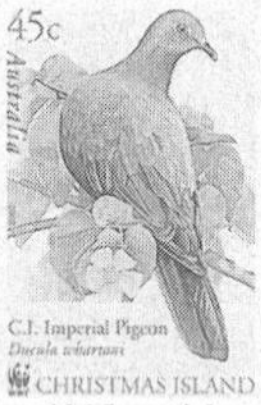

106 Imperial Pigeon

2002. Chinese New Year ("Year of the Horse"). Multicoloured.

492		5c. Type **105**	10	10
493		5c. Ox	10	10
494		5c. Tiger	10	10
495		5c. Rabbit	10	10
496		15c. Dragon	10	15
497		15c. Snake	10	15
498		15c. Horse (gold)	10	15
499		15c. Goat	10	15
500		25c. Monkey	20	25
501		25c. Cock	20	25
502		25c. Dog	20	25
503		25c. Pig	20	25
504		45c. Horse (purple)	30	35
505		$1.35 Horse (gold)	95	1·00

2002. Endangered Species. Christmas Island Birds. Multicoloured.

507		45c. Type **106**	30	35
508		45c. Christmas Island hawk owl	30	35
509		$1 Goshawk	70	75
510		$1.50 Thrush	1·10	1·25

CILICIA — Pt. 16

A district in Asia Minor, occupied and temporarily controlled by the French between 1919 and 20 October 1921. The territory was then returned to Turkey.

40 paras = 1 piastre.

1919. Various issues of Turkey optd **CILICIE**. A. On No. 726 (surch Printed Matter stamp optd with Star and Crescent).

1	**15**	5pa. on 10pa. green	75	70
		B. On 1901 issue optd with Star and Crescent.		
2	**21**	1pi. blue (No. 543)	45	45
32		1pi. blue (No. 631)	60	60
		C. On 1909 issue optd with Star and Crescent (No. 7 also optd as T **24**).		
4	**28**	20pa. red (No. 572)	55	40
35		20pa. red (No. 643)	50	50
7		1pi. blue (No. 649)	£950	£600
8		1pi. blue (No. 645)	3·75	2·75
		D. On 1913 issue.		
36	**30**	20pa. pink	45	50
		E. On Pictorial issue of 1914.		
37	**32**	2pa. purple	40	40
11	–	4pa. brown (No. 500)	1·10	1·10
12	–	6pa. blue (No. 502)	8·75	6·25
13	–	1½pi. brown and grey (No. 507)	1·60	1·40
		F. On Postal Anniv issue of 1916.		
14	**60**	5pa. green	95·00	50·00
15		20pa. blue	90	60
40		1pi. black and violet	45	50
17		5pi. black and brown	1·00	1·10
		G. On Pictorial issues of 1916 and 1917.		
18	**73**	10pa. green	1·10	1·10
19	**76**	50pa. blue	3·00	1·40
41	**69**	5pi. on 2pa. blue (No. 914)	60	60
21	**63**	25pi. red on buff	1·40	1·25
22	**64**	50pi. red	80	75
23		50pi. blue	11·50	11·00
		H. On Armistice issue of 1919 optd with T **81** of Turkey.		
24	**76**	50pa. blue	3·75	2·25
25	**77**	2pi. blue and brown	1·10	1·00
26	**78**	5pi. brown and blue	3·75	2·25

1919. Various issues of Turkey optd **Cilicie**. A. On No. 726 (surch Printed Matter stamp optd with Star and Crescent).

46	**15**	5pa. on 10pa. green	85	85
		B. On 1901 issue optd with Star and Crescent.		
47	**21**	1pi. blue (No. 543)	55	55
48		1pi. blue (No. 631)	1·50	1·50
49		1pi. blue (No. 669)	60·00	42·00
		C. On 1908 issue optd with T **24** and Star and Crescent.		
50	**25**	20pa. red	3·25	2·75
		D. On 1909 issue optd with Star and Crescent (No. 52 also optd as T **24**).		
52a	**28**	20pa. red (No. 643)	95·00	55·00
52		20pa. red (No. 647)	1·25	1·25
		E. On 1913 issue.		
53	**30**	5pa. bistre	1·90	1·75
54		20pa. pink	65	65
		F. On Pictorial issue of 1914.		
55	**32**	2pa. purple	85	75
56	–	4pa. brown (No. 500)	85	75
		G. On Postal Anniv issue of 1916.		
57	**60**	20pa. blue	90	75
58		1pi. black and violet	1·00	1·00
59		5pi. black and brown	1·00	1·00
		H. On Pictorial issues of 1916 and 1917.		
60	**72**	5pa. orange	1·75	1·50
61	**75**	1pi. blue	1·25	1·00
62	**69**	5pi. on 2pa. blue (No. 914)	3·50	2·75
63	**64**	50pi. green on yellow	19·00	10·00

1919. Various issues of Turkey optd **T.E.O. Cilicie**. A. On No. 726 (surch Printed Matter stamp optd with Star and Crescent).

69	**15**	5pa. on 10pa. green	30	30
		B. On 1892 issue optd with Star and Crescent and Arabic surch.		
70	**15**	10pa. on 20pa. red (No. 630)	25	30
		C. On 1909 issue optd with Star and Crescent.		
71	**28**	20pa. red (No. 572)	60	60
72		20pa. red (No. 643)	60	60
		D. On 1909 issue optd with Tougra and surch in Turkish.		
73	**28**	5pa. on 2pa. green (No. 938)	30	25
		E. On Pictorial stamp of 1914.		
74	–	1pi. blue (No. 505)	40	25
		F. On Postal Anniv issue of 1916.		
75	**60**	5pa. green	£120	55·00
76		20pa. blue	60	60
77		1pi. black and violet	40	30
		G. On Postal Anniv issue of 1916 optd with Star and Crescent.		
78	**60**	10pa. red (No. 654)	30	25
		H. On Pictorial issues of 1916 and 1917.		
79	**72**	5pa. orange	25	25
80	**73**	10pa. green	30	30
81	**74**	20pa. red	30	25
82	**77**	2pi. blue and brown	40	30
83	**78**	5pi. brown and blue	45	30
84	**69**	5pi. on 2pa. blue	2·50	2·50
85	**63**	25pi. red on buff	3·00	3·00
86	**64**	50pi. green on yellow	55·00	45·00
		I. On Charity stamp of 1917.		
87	**65**	10pa. purple	65	55

1920. "Mouchon" key-type of French Levant surch **T.E.O. 20 PARAS.**

88	B	20pa. on 10c. red	55	50

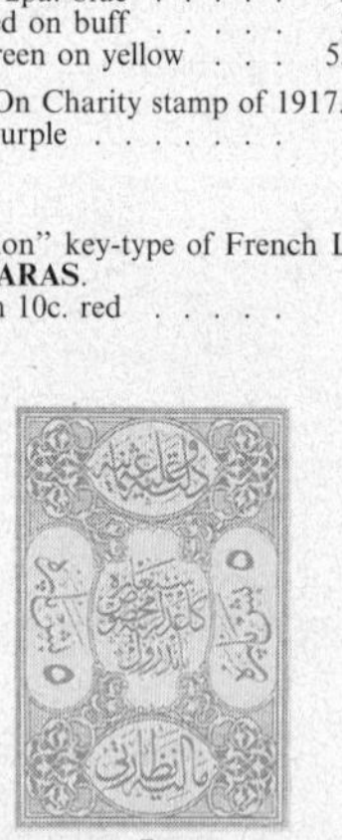
7

1920. Surch **OCCUPATION MILITAIRE Francaise CILICIE** and value.

89	**7**	70pa. on 5pa. red	35	45
90		3½pi. on 5pa. red	35	45

1920. Stamps of France surch **O.M.F. Cilicie** and new value.

100	**11**	5pa. on 2c. red	20	25
101	**18**	10pa. on 5c. green	20	25
102		20pa. on 10c. red	20	25
103		1pi. on 25c. blue	20	25
104	**15**	2pi. on 15c. green	30	35
105	**13**	5pi. on 40c. red and blue	60	60
106		10pi. on 50c. brown & lav	75	70
107		50pi. on 1f. red and green	1·25	1·25
108		100pi. on 5f. blue & yellow	10·00	11·00

1920. Stamps of France surch **O.M.F. Cilicie SAND. EST** and new value.

109	**11**	5pa. on 2c. red		1·75
110	**18**	10pa. on 5c. green		1·75
111		20pa. on 10c. red		1·10
112		1pi. on 25c. blue		1·10
113	**15**	2pi. on 15c. green		3·25
114	**13**	5pi. on 40c. red and blue		32·00
115		20pi. on 1f. red and green		40·00

1921. Air. Nos. 104/5 optd **POSTE PAR AVION** in frame.

116	**15**	2pi. on 15c. green		£6000
117	**13**	5pi. on 40c. red and blue		£6000

POSTAGE DUE STAMPS

1919. Postage Due stamps of Turkey optd **CILICIE**.

D27	D **49**	5pa. brown	1·40	1·40
D28	D **50**	20pa. red	1·40	1·40
D29	D **51**	1pi. blue	3·50	3·00
D45	D **52**	2pi. blue	2·75	2·75

1919. Postage Due stamps of Turkey optd **Cilicie**.

D64	D **49**	5pa. brown	1·40	1·40
D65	D **50**	20pa. red	1·40	1·40
D66	D **51**	1pi. blue	4·00	3·75
D67	D **52**	2pi. blue	3·00	2·75

1921. Postage Due Stamps of France surch **O.M.F. Cilicie** and value.

D118	D **11**	1pi. on 10c. brown	2·25	2·25
D119		2pi. on 20c. olive	2·25	2·25
D120		3pi. on 30c. red	2·25	2·25
D121		4pi. on 50c. purple	2·25	2·25

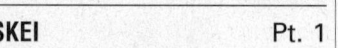

CISKEI — Pt. 1

The Republic of Ciskei was established on 4 December 1981, being constructed from tribal areas formerly part of the Republic of South Africa.

This independence did not receive international political recognition. We are satisfied, however, that the stamps had "de facto" acceptance for the carriage of mail outside Ciskei.

Ciskei was formally re-incorporated into South Africa on 27 April 1994.

100 cents = 1 rand.

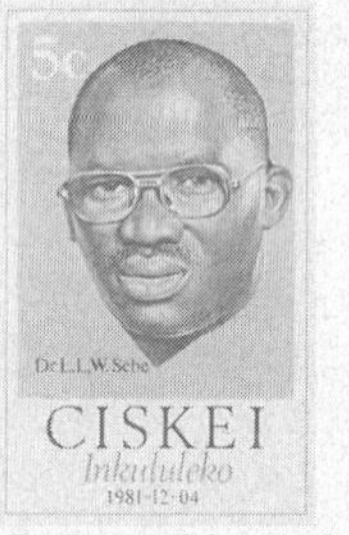

1 Dr. Lennox Sebe, Chief Minister

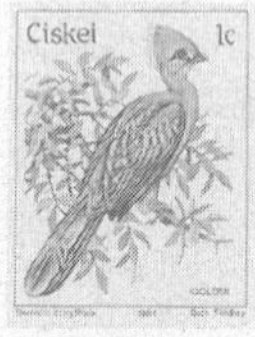

2 Green Turaco

1981. Independence. Multicoloured.

1		5c. Type **1**	10	10
2		15c. Coat of arms	20	15
3		20c. Flag	30	30
4		25c. Mace	35	25

1981. Birds. Multicoloured.

5		1c. Type **2**	20	15
6		2c. Cape wagtail	20	15
7		3c. White-browed coucal	50	15
8		4c. Yellow-tufted malachite sunbird	20	15
9		5c. Stanley crane	20	15
10		6c. African red-winged starling	20	15
11		7c. Giant kingfisher	20	15
12		8c. Hadada ibis	30	15
13		9c. Black cuckoo	30	15
14		10c. Black-collared barbet	30	15
14a		11c. African black-headed oriole	55	30
14b		12c. Malachite kingfisher	70	30
14c		14c. Hoopoe	1·00	30
15		15c. African fish eagle	30	30
15a		16c. Cape puff-back flycatcher	65	30
15b		18c. Long-tailed whydah	1·00	30
16		20c. Cape longclaw	40	30
16a		21c. Lemon dove	1·50	60
17		25c. Cape dikkop	30	30
18		30c. African green pigeon	30	40
19		50c. Brown-necked parrot	60	60
20		1r. Narina's trogon	90	1·25
21		2r. Cape eagle owl	1·75	2·50

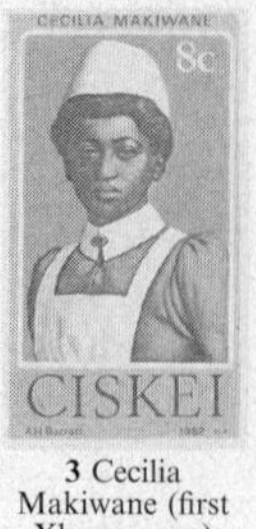

3 Cecilia Makiwane (first Xhosa nurse)

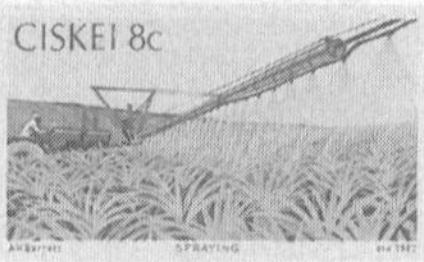

4 Boom Sprayer

1982. Nursing. Multicoloured.

22		8c. Type **3**	15	10
23		15c. Operating theatre	30	30
24		20c. Matron lighting nurse's lamp (horiz)	40	40
25		25c. Nurses and patient (horiz)	50	50

1982. Pineapple Industry. Multicoloured.

26		8c. Type **4**	10	10
27		15c. Harvesting	20	25
28		20c. Despatch to cannery	25	30
29		30c. Packing for local market	30	35

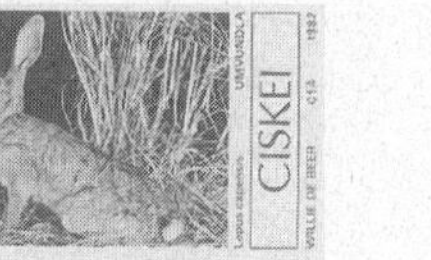

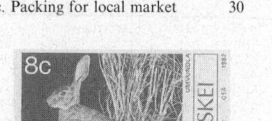

5 Brown Hare

1982. Small Mammals. Multicoloured.

30		8c. Type **5**	15	15
31		15c. Cape fox	25	25
32		20c. Cape ground squirrel	30	30
33		25c. Caracal	40	40

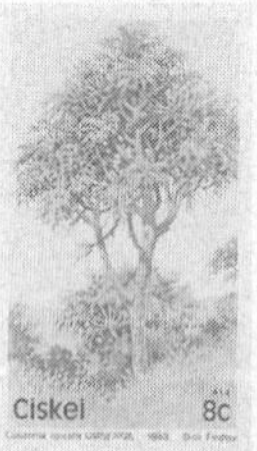

6 Assegai

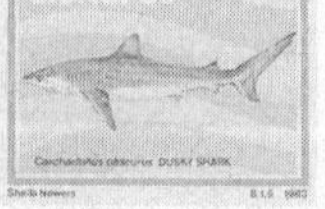

7 Dusky Shark

1983. Trees (1st series). Multicoloured.

34		8c. Cabbage tree	15	10
35		20c. Type **6**	30	30
36		25c. Cape chestnut	35	35
37		40c. Outeniqua yellowwood	50	55

See also Nos. 52/5.

1983. Sharks. Multicoloured.

38		8c. Type **7**	15	15
39		20c. Sand tiger ("Ragged-tooth shark")	30	30
40		25c. Tiger shark (57 × 21 mm)	35	35
41		30c. Scalloped hammerhead (57 × 21 mm)	40	40
42		40c. Great white shark (57 × 21 mm)	50	50

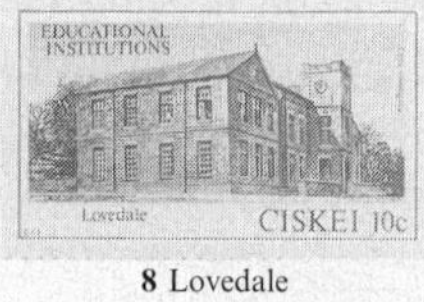

8 Lovedale

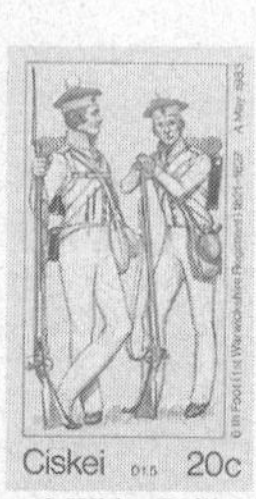

9 White Drill Uniform

1983. Educational Institutions.

43	**8**	10c. lt brown, brown & black	10	10
44	–	20c. lt brown, brown & black	20	20
45	–	25c. brown, red and black	25	25
46	–	40c. lt brown, brown & black	40	45

DESIGNS: 20c. Fort Hare; 25c. Healdtown; 40c. Lennox Sebe.

1983. British Military Uniforms (1st series). 6th Warwickshire Regiment of Foot, 1821–27. Multicoloured.

47		20c. Type **9**	40	40
48		20c. Light Company privates	40	40
49		20c. Grenadier Company sergeants	40	40
50		20c. Undress blue frock coats	40	40
51		20c. Officer and field officer in parade order	40	40

See also Nos. 64/8 and 95/8.

1984. Trees (2nd series). As T **6**. Multicoloured.

52		10c. "Rhus chirindensis"	15	15
53		20c. "Phoenix reclinata"	25	35
54		25c. "Ptaeroxyon obliquum"	30	40
55		40c. "Apodytes dimidiata"	40	55

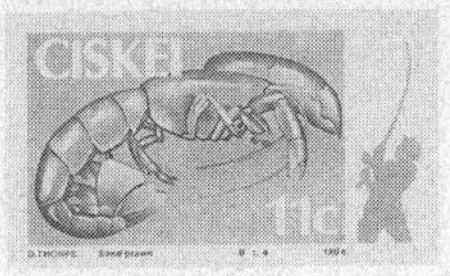

10 Sandprawn

1984. Fish-bait. Multicoloured.

56	11c. Type **10**	20	15
57	20c. Coral worm	30	30
58	25c. Bloodworm	35	35
59	30c. Red-bait	40	40

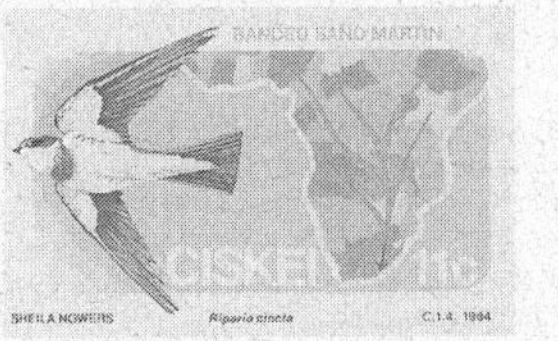

11 Banded Martin ("Banded Sand Martin")

1984. Migratory Birds. Multicoloured.

60	11c. Type **11**	25	20
61	25c. House martin	50	50
62	30c. Greater striped swallow	60	60
63	45c. Barn swallow ("European Swallow")	80	85

1984. British Military Uniforms (2nd series). Cape Mounted Rifles. As T **9**. Multicoloured.

64	25c. (1) Trooper in field and sergeant in undress uniforms, 1830	45	45
65	25c. (2) Trooper and sergeant in full dress, 1835	45	45
66	25c. (3) Officers in undress, 1830	45	45
67	25c. (4) Officers in full dress, 1827–34	45	45
68	25c. (5) Officers in full dress, 1834	45	45

The stamps are numbered as indicated in brackets.

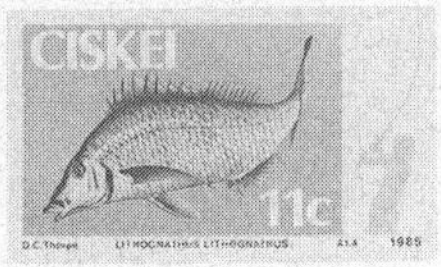

12 White Steenbras

1985. Coastal Angling. Multicoloured.

69	11c. Type **12**	20	15
70	25c. Bronze seabream	30	30
71	30c. Kob	40	45
72	50c. Spotted grunt	70	80

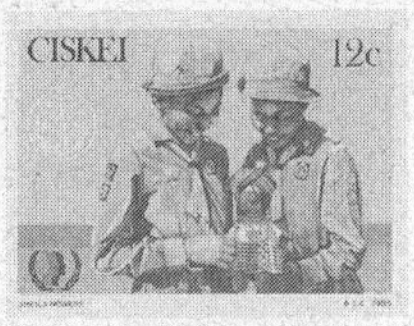

13 Brownies holding Handmade Doll

1985. International Youth Year. 75th Anniv of Girl Guide Movement. Multicoloured.

73	12c. Type **13**	15	15
74	25c. Rangers planting trees	25	25
75	30c. Guides with flag	30	30
76	50c. Guides building fire	60	65

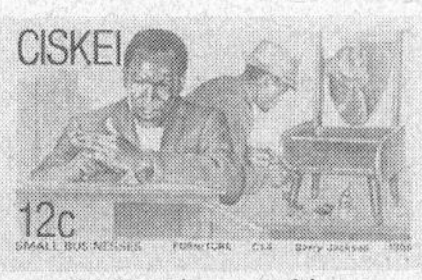

14 Furniture making

1985. Small Businesses. Multicoloured.

77	12c. Type **14**	15	10
78	25c. Dressmaking	30	30
79	30c. Welding	30	30
80	50c. Basketry	60	65

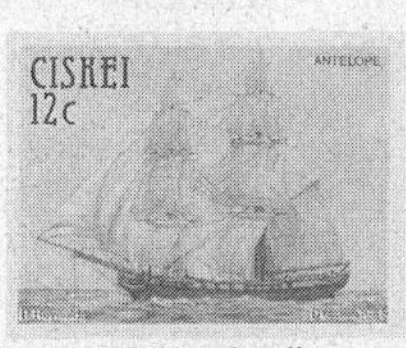

15 "Antelope"

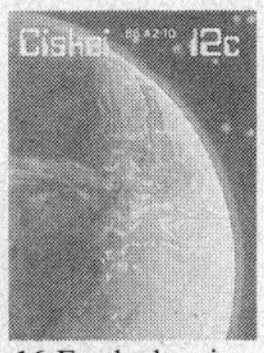

16 Earth showing Africa

1985. Sail Troopships. Multicoloured.

81	12c. Type **15**	20	15
82	25c. "Pilot"	45	45
83	30c. "Salisbury"	45	45
84	50c. "Olive Branch"	80	85

1986. Appearance of Halley's Comet. Mult.

85	12c. (1) Earth showing South America	90	70
86	12c. (2) Type **16**	90	70
87	12c. (3) Stars and Moon	90	70
88	12c. (4) Moon and Milky Way	90	70
89	12c. (5) Milky Way and stars	90	70
90	12c. (6) Earth showing Australia	90	70
91	12c. (7) Earth and meteor	90	70
92	12c. (8) Meteor, Moon and comet tail	90	70
93	12c. (9) Comet head and Moon	90	70
94	12c. (10) Sun	90	70

Nos. 85/94 were issued in sheetlets of 10 stamps forming a composite design of the southern skies in April. Each stamp is inscribed with a number from "A1-10" to "A10-10". The first number is given in brackets in the listing to aid identification.

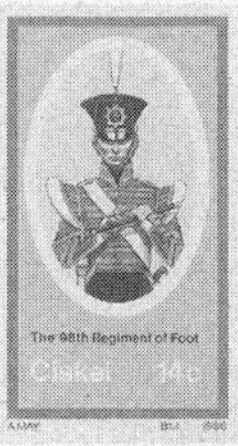

17 Fifer in Winter Dress

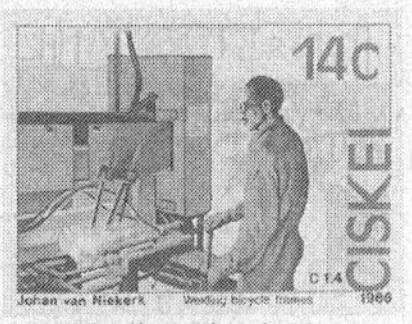

18 Welding Bicycle Frame

1986. British Military Uniforms (3rd series). 98th Regiment of Foot. Multicoloured.

95	14c. Type **17**	20	15
96	20c. Private in summer dress	30	30
97	25c. Grenadier in full summer dress	35	35
98	30c. Sergeant-major in full winter dress	50	50

1986. Bicycle Factory, Dimbaza. Multicoloured.

99	14c. Type **18**	20	15
100	20c. Spray-painting frame	30	30
101	25c. Installing wheelspokes	35	35
102	30c. Final assembly	50	50

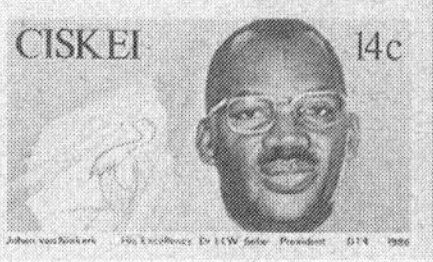

19 President Dr. Lennox Sebe

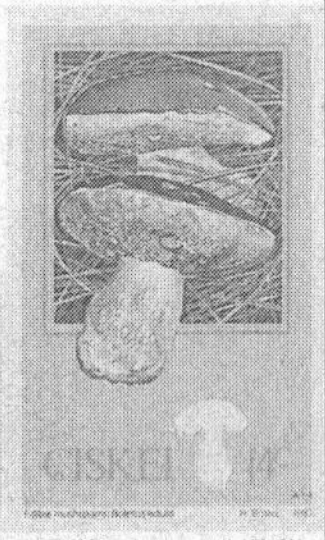

20 "Boletus edulis"

1986. 5th Anniv of Independence. Multicoloured.

103	14c. Type **19**	15	15
104	20c. National Shrine, Ntaba kaNdoda	20	30
105	25c. Legislative Assembly, Bisho	20	35
106	30c. Automatic telephone exchange, Bisho	25	50

1987. Edible Mushrooms. Multicoloured.

107	14c. Type **20**	25	15
108	20c. "Macrolepiota zeyheri"	40	40
109	25c. "Termitomyces spp"	50	50
110	30c. "Russula capensis"	60	60

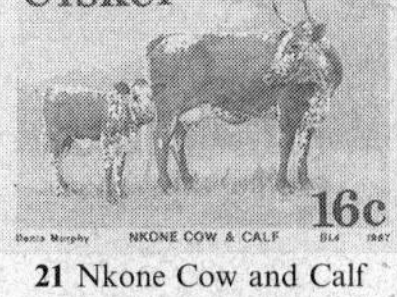

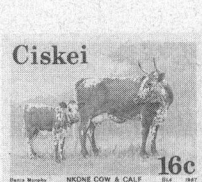

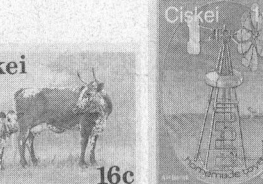

21 Nkone Cow and Calf

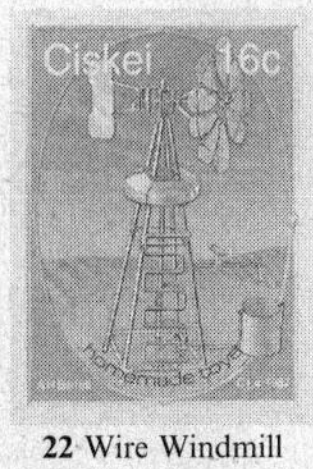

22 Wire Windmill

1987. Nkone Cattle. Multicoloured.

111	16c. Type **21**	20	15
112	20c. Nkone cow	25	30
113	25c. Nkone bull	30	35
114	30c. Herd of Nkone	40	55

1987. Homemade Toys. Multicoloured.

115	16c. Type **22**	20	15
116	20c. Rag doll	25	30
117	25c. Clay horse (horiz)	30	35
118	30c. Wire car (horiz)	40	55

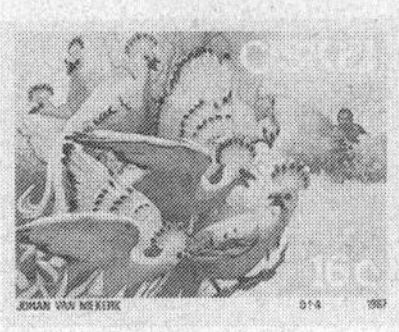

23 Seven Birds

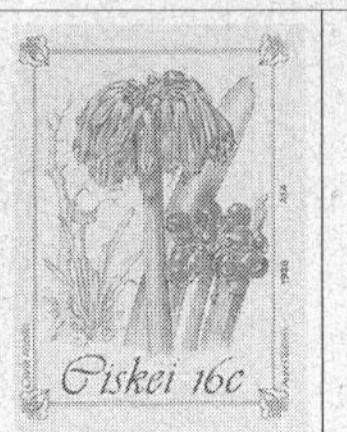

24 Bush Lily

1987. Folklore (1st series). Sikulume. Mult.

119	16c. Type **23**	20	15
120	20c. Cannibals chasing Sikulume	25	30
121	25c. Sikulume attacking the inabulele	30	35
122	30c. Chief Mangangezulu chasing Sikulume and his bride	40	55

See also Nos. 127/36, 153/6 and 161/4

1988. Protected Flowers. Multicoloured.

123	16c. Type **24**	20	15
124	30c. Harebell	35	35
125	40c. Butterfly iris	40	40
126	50c. Vlei lily	60	65

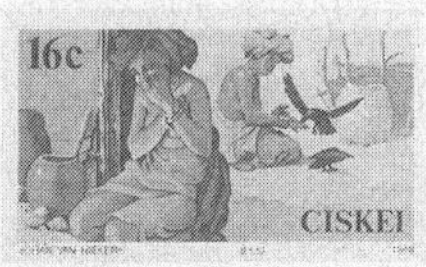

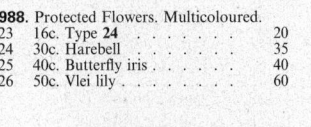

25 Numbakatali crying and Second Wife feeding Black Crows

1988. Folklore (2nd series). Mbulukazi. Mult.

127	16c. Type **25**	30	35
128	16c. Numbakatali telling speckled pigeons of her childlessness	30	35
129	16c. Numbakatali finding children in earthenware jars	30	35
130	16c. Broad Breast sees Mbulukazi and brother at river	30	35
131	16c. Broad Breast asking to marry Mbulukazi	30	35
132	16c. Broad Breast and his two wives, Mbulukazi and her half-sister Mahlunguluza	30	35
133	16c. Mahlunguluza pushing Mbulukazi from precipice to her death	30	35
134	16c. Mbulukazi's ox tearing down Mahlunguluza's hut	30	35
135	16c. Ox licking Mbulukazi back to life	30	35
136	16c. Mahlunguluza being sent back to her father in disgrace	30	35

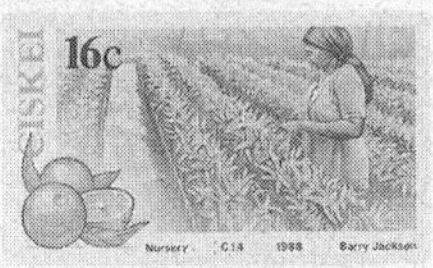

26 Oranges and Grafted Rootstocks in Nursery

1988. Citrus Farming. Multicoloured.

137	16c. Type **26**	20	15
138	30c. Lemons and inarching rootstock onto mature tree	40	40
139	40c. Tangerines and fruit being hand-picked	50	50
140	50c. Oranges and fruit being graded	60	65

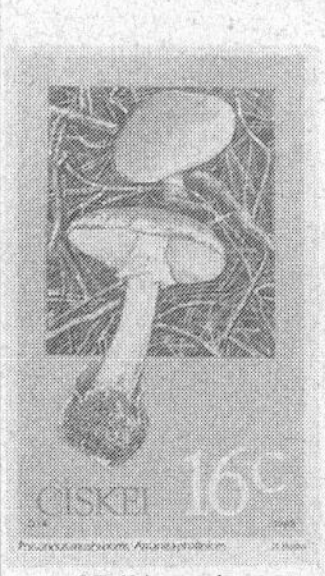

27 "Amanita phalloides"

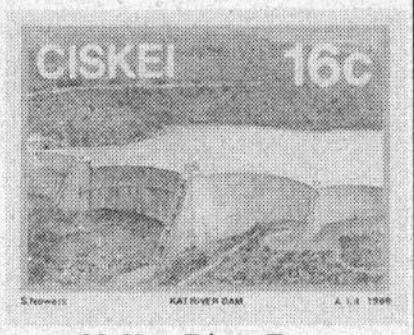

28 Kat River Dam

1988. Poisonous Fungi. Multicoloured.

141	16c. Type **27**	75	30
142	30c. "Chlorophyllum molybdites"	1·10	75
143	40c. "Amanita muscaria"	1·40	1·10
144	50c. "Amanita pantherina"	1·60	1·25

1989. Dams. Multicoloured.

145	16c. Type **28**	35	25
146	30c. Cata dam	55	50
147	40c. Binfield Park dam	65	65
148	50c. Sandile dam	70	80

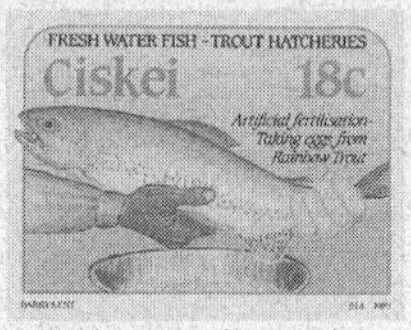

29 Taking Eggs from Rainbow Trout

1989. Trout Hatcheries. Multicoloured.

149	18c. Type **29**	25	15
150	30c. Fertilized eyed trout ova and alevins	45	45
151	40c. Five-week-old fingerlings	55	55
152	50c. Adult male	60	65

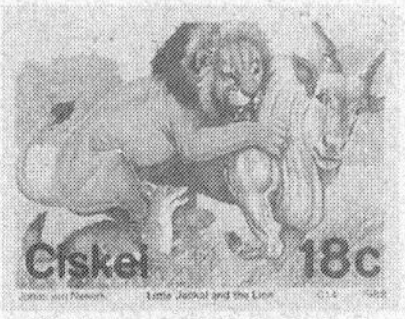

30 Lion and Little Jackal killing Eland

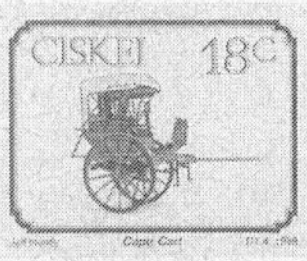

31 Cape Horse-cart

1989. Folklore (3rd series). Little Jackal and the Lion. Multicoloured.

153	18c. Type **30**	20	15
154	30c. Little Jackal's children carrying meat to clifftop home	35	35
155	40c. Little Jackal pretending to be trapped	40	40
156	50c. Lion falling down cliff face	45	50

1989. Animal-drawn Transport. Multicoloured.

157	18c. Type **31**	20	15
158	30c. Jubilee spider	35	35
159	40c. Ballantine half-tent ox-drawn wagon	40	40
160	50c. Voortrekker wagon	45	50

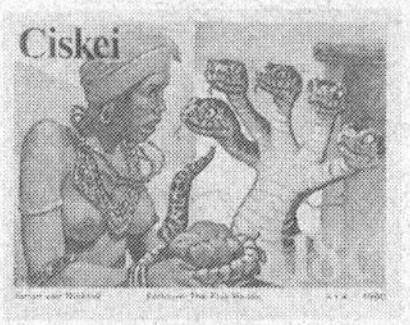

32 Mpunzikazi offering Food to Five Heads

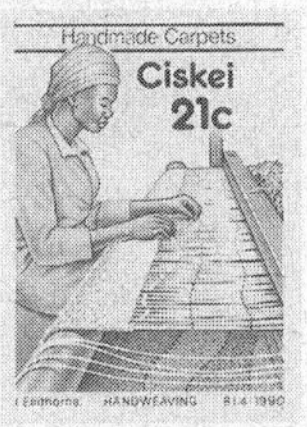

33 Handweaving on Loom

1990. Folklore (4th series). The Story of Makanda Mahlanu (Five Heads). Multicoloured.

161	18c. Type **32**	20	15
162	30c. Five Heads killing Mpunzikazi with his tail	35	35
163	40c. Mpunzanyana offering food to Five Heads	40	40
164	50c. Five Heads transformed into a man	45	50

1990. Handmade Carpets. Multicoloured.

165	21c. Type **33**	30	20
166	35c. Spinning	50	50
167	40c. Dyeing yarn	70	70
168	50c. Knotting carpet	70	70

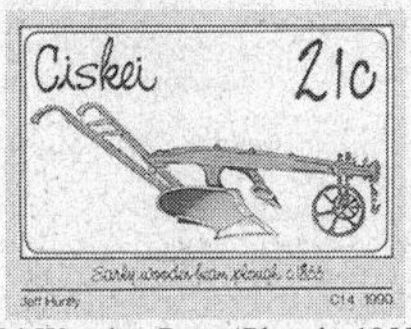

34 Wooden Beam Plough, 1855

1980. Ploughs. Multicoloured.

169	21c. Type **34**	25	20
170	35c. Triple disc plough, 1895	40	40
171	40c. Reversible disc plough, 1895	50	50
172	50c. "Het Volk" double furrow plough, 1910	60	65

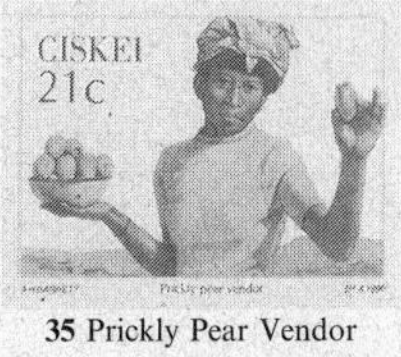

35 Prickly Pear Vendor

1990. Prickly Pear. Multicoloured.

173	21c. Type **35**	30	20
174	35c. Prickly pear bushes	50	50
175	40c. Whole and opened fruits	60	60
176	50c. Bushes in bloom	70	80

36 African Marsh Owl ("Marsh Owl")

37 Sao Bras (now Mossel Bay) on Map, 1500

1991. Owls. Multicoloured.

177		21c. Type **36**	85	40
178		35c. African scops owl ("Scops")	1·10	80
179		40c. Barn owl	1·40	1·00
180		50c. African wood owl ("Wood")	1·60	1·40

1991. Stamp Day. D'Ataide's Letter of 1501. Multicoloured.

181		25c. Type **37**	60	60
182		25c. Bartolomeo Dias's ship foundering off Cabo Tormentoso (now Cape of Good Hope) during voyage to India, 1500	60	60
183		25c. Captain Pedro d'Ataide landing at Sao Bras, 1601	60	60
184		25c. D'Ataide leaving letter relating death of Dias on tree	60	60
185		25c. Captain Joao da Nova finding letter, 1501	60	60

The inscriptions at the foot of Nos. 181 and 182 are transposed.

38 Comet Nucleus

1991. The Solar System. Multicoloured.

186		1c. Type **38**	20	15
187		2c. Trojan asteroids	20	15
188		5c. Meteoroids	20	15
189		7c. Pluto	30	15
190		10c. Neptune	30	15
191		20c. Uranus	50	20
192		25c. Saturn	60	20
193		30c. Jupiter	65	30
194		35c. Planetoids in asteroid belt	65	40
195		40c. Mars	80	50
196		50c. The Moon	80	70
197		60c. Earth	80	80
198		1r. Venus	1·00	1·25
199		2r. Mercury	1·60	2·00
200		5r. The Sun	2·75	3·75

39 Fort Armstrong and Xhosa Warrior

1991. 19th-century Frontier Forts. Multicoloured.

202		27c. Type **39**	30	30
203		45c. Keiskamma Hoek Post and Sir George Grey (governor of Cape Colony, 1854–58)	45	55
204		65c. Fort Hare and Xhosa Chief Sandile	55	70
205		85c. Peddie Cavalry Barracks and cavalryman	75	1·25

40 Cumulonimbus

1992. Cloud Formations. Multicoloured.

206		27c. Type **40**	40	25
207		45c. Altocumulus	55	65
208		65c. Cirrus	65	80
209		85c. Cumulus	75	1·10

41 "Intelsat VI" Communications Satellite

1992. International Space Year. Satellites over Southern Africa. Multicoloured.

210		35c. Type **41**	40	25
211		70c. "G P S Navstar" (navigation)	80	80
212		90c. "Meteosat" (meteorology)	1·10	1·10
213		1r.05 "Landsat VI" (Earth resources survey)	1·25	1·40

42 Universal Disc-harrow, 1914

1992. Agricultural Tools. Multicoloured.

214		35c. Type **42**	40	25
215		70c. Clod crusher and pulveriser, 1914	80	70
216		90c. Self-dump hay rake, 1910	1·10	95
217		1r.05 McCormick hay tedder, 1900	1·10	1·10

43 Mpekweni Sun Marine Resort

1992. Hotels. Multicoloured.

218		35c. Type **43**	40	25
219		70c. Katberg Protea Hotel	80	80
220		90c. Fish River Sun Hotel	1·10	1·10
221		1r.05 Amatola Sun Hotel, Amatole Mountains	1·10	1·25

44 Vasco da Gama, "Sao Gabriel" and Voyage round Cape of Good Hope, 1497

45 Island Canary

1993. Navigators. Multicoloured.

222		45c. Type **44**	55	30
223		65c. James Cook, H.M.S. "Endeavour" and first voyage, 1768–71	90	75
224		85c. Ferdinand Magellan, "Vitoria" and circumnavigation, 1519	1·10	90
225		90c. Sir Francis Drake, "Golden Hind" and circumnavigation, 1577–80	1·10	95
226		1r.05 Abel Tasman, "Heemskerk" and discovery of Tasmania, 1642	1·25	1·25

The ship on No. 222 is wrongly inscribed "San Gabriel", that on No. 224 "Victoria" and that on No. 226 "Heemskerck".

1993. Cage Birds. Multicoloured.

227		45c. Type **45**	45	30
228		65c. Budgerigar	70	60
229		85c. Peach-faced lovebirds	90	80
230		90c. Cockatiel	95	85
231		1r.05 Gouldian finch	1·00	1·10

46 Goshen Church (Moravian Mission), Whittlesea

1993. Churches and Missions.

232	**46**	45c. stone, black and red	35	20
233	–	65c. blue, black and red	60	60
234	–	85c. brown, black and red	80	80
235	–	1r.05 yellow, black and red	90	1·00

DESIGNS: 65c. Kamastone Mission Church; 85c. Richie Thompson Memorial Church (Hertzog Mission), near Seymour; 1r.05, Bryce Ross Memorial Church (Pirie Mission), near Dimbaza.

47 Jointed Cactus

48 "Losna" (steamer) (near Fish River), 1921

1993. Invader Plants. Multicoloured.

236		45c. Type **47**	40	30
237		65c. Thorn apple	70	60
238		85c. Coffee weed	90	80
239		1r.05 Poisonous wild tobacco	1·00	1·00

1994. Shipwrecks. Multicoloured.

241		45c. Type **48**	55	30
242		65c. "Catherine" (barque) (Waterloo Bay), 1846	90	60
243		85c. "Bennebroek" (East Indiaman) (near Mtana River), 1713	1·10	90
244		1r.05 "Sao Joao Baptista" (galleon) (between Fish and Kei Rivers), 1622	1·25	1·25

49 "Herman Steyn"

1994. Hybrid Roses. Multicoloured.

245		45c. Type **49**	35	30
246		70c. "Esther Geldenhuys"	60	60
247		95c. "Margaret Wasserfall"	80	80
248		1r.15 "Professor Fred Ziady"	1·00	1·00

COCHIN Pt. 1

A state of South West India. Now uses Indian stamps.

6 puttans = 5 annas.
12 pies = 1 anna; 16 annas = 1 rupee.

1 Emblems of State

1892. Value in "puttans".

5a	**1**	½put. orange	1·60	1·50
2		1put. purple	2·75	2·00
3		2put. violet	2·00	2·25

3

5

1903. Value in "pies" or "puttans". With or without gum.

16	**3**	3pies. blue	70	10
17		½put. green (smaller)	1·10	40
18	**5**	1put. red	1·75	10
19	**3**	2put. violet	2·50	50

1909. Surch **2**. No gum.

22	**3**	2 on 3 pies. mauve	15	50

8 Raja Rama Varma I

10 Raja Rama Varma II

1911. Value in "pies" or "annas".

26	**8**	2p. brown	30	10
27		3p. blue	60	10
28		4p. green	1·50	10
29		9p. red	1·10	10
30		1a. orange	2·75	10
31		1½a. purple	5·50	45
32		2a. grey	7·50	40
33		3a. red	35·00	35·00

1916. Various frames.

35b	**10**	2p. brown	1·60	10
36		4p. green	1·00	10
37		6p. brown	2·50	10
38		8p. brown	1·50	10
39		9p. red	16·00	25
40		10p. blue	2·75	10
41a		1a. orange	8·50	30
42		1½a. purple	2·25	20
43		2a. grey	4·25	10
44		2¼a. green	4·25	3·25
45		3a. red	11·00	35

1922. Surch with figure and words.

46	**8**	2p. on 3p. blue	40	30

1928. Surch **ONE ANNA ANCHAL & REVENUE** and value in native characters.

50	**10**	1a. on 2¼a. green	5·00	12·00

1932. Surch in figures and words both in English and in native characters.

51	**10**	3p. on 4p. green	1·10	90
52		3p. on 8p. brown	1·25	2·50
53		9p. on 10p. blue	1·50	3·00

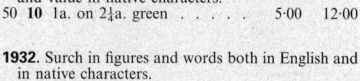

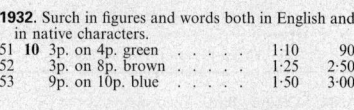

18 Maharaja Rama Varma III

26 Maharaja Kerala Varma II

1933.

54	**18**	2p. brown	60	30
55		4p. green	60	10
56		6p. red	70	10
57		1a. orange	70	10
58		1a.8p. red	3·00	4·50
59		2a. grey	4·50	75
60		2¼a. green	1·50	15
61		3a. orange	5·00	1·60
62		3a.4p. violet	1·50	1·40
63		6a.8p. sepia	1·75	10·00
64		10a. blue	3·00	12·00

1934. Surch with figure and words.

65	**10**	6p. on 8p. brown	75	60
66		6p. on 10p. blue	1·75	2·00

1939. Optd **ANCHAL**.

74	**18**	1a. orange	75	1·60

1939. Surch in words only.

75	**18**	3p. on 1a.8p. red	£160	75·00
77		6p. on 1a.8p. red	3·00	19·00

1943. Surch **SURCHARGED** and value in words.

79	**18**	3p. on 4p. green	6·00	4·00
76		3p. on 1a.8p. red	3·25	7·50
78		1a.3p. on 1a.8p. red	1·00	30

1943. Surch **ANCHAL SURCHARGED NINE PIES**.

84	**18**	9p. on 1a. orange	16·00	5·50

1943. Surch **ANCHAL** and value in words.

81a	**18**	6p. on 1a. orange	£100	55·00
82		9p. on 1a. orange	£100	£110

1943.

85	**26**	2p. brown	1·40	2·25
87a		4p. green	3·00	3·75
88		6p. brown	1·25	10
89		9p. blue	27·00	1·00
90a		1a. orange	21·00	42·00
91		2¼a. green	21·00	2·25

1944. Surch with value in words only.

93	**26**	2p. on 6p. brown	75	3·00
94		3p. on 4p. green	2·75	10
96		3p. on 6p. brown	85	20
97		4p. on 6p. brown	3·50	9·50

1944. Surch **SURCHARGED** and value in words.

95	**26**	3p. on 4p. green	4·00	10
92c		1a.3p. on 1a. orange	–	£2750

1944. Surch **ANCHAL NINE PIES**.

92a	**26**	9p. on 1a. orange	4·75	2·25

1944. Surch **ANCHAL SURCHARGED NINE PIES**.

92b	**26**	9p. on 1a. orange	4·50	2·50

28 Maharaja Ravi Varma

29 Maharaja Ravi Varma

1944.
98	**28**	9p. blue	12·00	2·25
99		1a.3p. mauve	5·00	8·50
100		1a.9p. blue	8·00	13·00

1946. No gum.
101	**29**	2p. brown	1·75	10
102		3p. red	50	15
103		4p. green	£1700	80·00
104		6p. brown	20·00	3·50
105		9p. blue	50	10
106		1a. orange	6·50	26·00
107		2a. black	85·00	8·00
108		3a. red	55·00	6·00

For No. 106, optd "U.S.T.C." or "T.-C." with or without surch, see Travancore-Cochin.

30 Maharaja Kerala Varma III

31 Chinese Nets

1948.
109	**30**	2p. brown	1·75	15
110		3p. red	75	15
111		4p. green	12·00	2·00
112		6p. brown	14·00	20
113		9p. blue	2·50	20
114		2a. black	45·00	75
115		3a. orange	55·00	75
116		3a.4p. violet	70·00	£350

1949.
117	**31**	2a. black	3·75	6·00
118	–	2¼a. green (Dutch palace)	2·75	5·50

SIX PIES
ആറു പൈ
(33)

1949. Surch as T 33.
121	**29**	3p. on 9p. blue	8·50	18·00
124a	**30**	3p. on 9p. blue	2·50	50
126		6p. on 9p. blue	1·00	40
119	**28**	6p. on 1a.3p. mauve	3·50	3·75
122	**29**	6p. on 1a.3p. mauve	12·00	13·00
120		1a. on 1a.9p. blue	90	1·10
123		1a. on 1a.9p. blue	3·00	2·00

1949. Surch **SIX PIES** or **NINE PIES** only.
127	**29**	6p. on 1a. orange	55·00	£120
128		9p. on 1a. orange	75·00	£120

OFFICIAL STAMPS

1913. Optd **ON C G S.**
O1	**8**	3p. green	£120	10
O2		4p. green	8·50	10
O3a		9p. green	15·00	10
O4		1½a. purple	38·00	10
O5		2a. grey	13·00	10
O6		3a. red	48·00	35
O7		6a. violet	40·00	2·00
O8		12a. blue	38·00	6·50
O9		1½r. green	30·00	55·00

1919. Optd **ON C G S.**
O10	**10**	4p. green	3·75	10
O11		6p. brown	7·00	10
O26		8p. brown	7·00	10
O13		9p. red	48·00	10
O27		10p. blue	6·00	10
O15		1½a. purple	5·50	10
O28		2a. grey	26·00	15
O17		2¼a. green	12·00	10
O29		3a. red	8·00	15
O19		6a. violet	32·00	50
O19a		12a. blue	15·00	3·25
O19b		1½r. green	22·00	95·00

1923. Official stamps surch in figures and words.
O32	**10**	6p. on 8p. brown	2·00	10
O33		6p. on 10p. blue	4·00	10
O20b	**8**	8p. on 9p. red	£130	20
O21	**10**	8p. on 9p. red	70·00	10
O23	**8**	10p. on 9p. red	£800	9·50
O22	**10**	10p. on 9p. red	65·00	65

1933. Optd **ON C G S.**
O34	**18**	4p. green	2·25	10
O35		6p. red	2·50	10
O52		1a. orange	1·00	10
O38		1a.8p. red	1·50	30
O37		2a. grey	11·00	10
O36		2¼a. green	4·00	10
O53		3a. orange	3·00	1·00
O41		3a.4p. violet	1·50	15
O42		6a.8p. sepia	1·50	20
O43		10a. blue	1·50	70

1943. Official stamp surch **NINE PIES**.
O57	**10**	9p. on 1½a. purple	£400	20·00

1943. Official stamps surch **SURCHARGED** and value in words.
O63	**18**	3p. on 4p. green	95·00	45·00
O58		3p. on 1a.8p. red	5·50	1·25
O66		1a.3p. on 1a. orange	£275	90·00
O61		1a.9p. on 1a.8p. red	80	30

1943. Official stamps surch in words.
O62	**18**	3p. on 4p. green	21·00	6·00
O64		3p. on 1a. orange	2·00	2·75
O65		9p. on 1a. orange	£200	45·00
O59		9p. on 1a.8p. red	£100	26·00
O60		1a.9p. on 1a.8p. red	2·50	1·60

1944. Optd **ON C G S.**
O68	**26**	4p. green	22·00	3·50
O69b		6p. brown	70	10
O70		1a. orange	£1800	45·00
O71		2a. black	3·75	45
O72		2¼a. green	2·50	70
O73a		3a. red	6·00	40

1944. Official stamps surch **SURCHARGED** and value in words.
O75	**26**	3p. on 4p. green	4·50	30
O78		9p. on 6p. brown	3·50	30
O80		1a.3p. on 1a. orange	3·25	10

1944. Official stamps surch in words.
O74	**26**	3p. on 4p. green	2·50	10
O76		3p. on 1a. orange	16·00	4·00
O77		9p. on 6p. brown	7·00	2·00
O79		1a.3p. on 1a. orange	6·00	1·25

1946. Optd **ON C G S.**
O81	**28**	9p. blue	2·75	10
O82		1a.3p. mauve	1·60	20
O83		1a.9p. blue	40	90

1948. Optd **ON C G S.**
O84	**29**	3p. red	1·00	10
O85		4p. green	25·00	4·75
O86		6p. brown	6·00	70
O87		9p. blue	75	10
O88		1a.3p. mauve	2·50	50
O89		1a.9p. blue	2·00	40
O90		2a. black	13·00	3·00
O91		2¼a. green	18·00	3·00

1949. Optd **ON C G S.**
O92	**30**	3p. red	1·25	15
O93		4p. green	1·10	30
O94		6p. brown	2·75	10
O95		9p. blue	2·50	10
O96		1a.3p. black	1·25	15
O97		2¼a. green	2·75	4·75
O98		3a. orange	1·10	50
O99		3a.4p. violet	32·00	29·00

1949. Optd **ON C G S.**
O103	**30**	3p. on 9p. red	1·00	60
O104		9p. on 4p. green	75	1·75
O100	**28**	1a. on 1a.9p. blue	60	60
O101	**29**	1a. on 1a.9p. blue	19·00	14·00

1949. Optd **SERVICE**.
O105	**30**	3p. on 9p. (No. 125)	60	65

For later issues see **TRAVANCORE-COCHIN**.

COCHIN-CHINA Pt. 6

A former French colony in the extreme S. of Indo-China, subsequently incorporated into French Indo-China.

100 centimes = 1 franc.

1886. Stamps of French Colonies surch.
1	**J**	5 on 25c. brown on yellow	£160	£110
2		5 on 2c. brown on yellow	14·50	16·00
3		5 on 25c. brown on yellow	20·00	19·00
4		5 on 25c. black on red	40·00	34·00

Nos. 1 and 4 are surcharged with numeral only; Nos. 2 and 3 are additionally optd **C. CH.**

COCOS (KEELING) ISLANDS Pt.1

Islands in the Indian Ocean formerly administered by Singapore and transferred to Australian administration on 23 November 1955.

1963. 12 pence = 1 shilling;
20 shillings = 1 pound.
1966. 100 cents = 1 dollar (Australian).

5 Jukong (sailboat)

6 White Tern

1963.
1	–	3d. brown	1·00	1·50
2	–	5d. blue	1·50	80
3	–	8d. red	1·00	1·75
4	–	1s. green	1·00	75
5	**5**	2s. purple	11·00	2·75
6	**6**	2s.3d. green	18·00	2·75

DESIGNS—HORIZ (As Type **5**): 3d. Copra industry; 1s. Palms. (As Type **6**): 5d. Lockheed Super Constellation airliner. VERT (As Type **5**): 8d. Map of islands.

1965. 50th Anniv of Gallipoli Landing. As T 184 of Australia, but slightly larger (22 × 34½ mm).
7		5d. brown, black and green	60	45

With the introduction of decimal currency on 14 February 1966, Australian stamps were used in Cocos Islands until the 1969 issue.

7 Reef Clam

9 "Dragon", 1609

1969. Decimal Currency. Multicoloured.
8		1c. Lajonkaines turbo shell (vert)	30	60
9		2c. Elongate or small giant clam (vert)	1·00	80
10		3c. Type **7**	40	20
11		4c. Floral blenny (fish)	30	50
12		5c. "Porites cocosensis" (coral)	35	30
13		6c. Atrisignis flyingfish	75	75
14		10c. Buff-banded rail	1·00	70
15		15c. Java sparrow	1·00	30
16		20c. Red-tailed tropic bird	1·00	30
17		30c. Sooty tern	1·00	30
18		50c. Reef heron (vert)	1·00	30
19		$1 Great frigate bird (vert)	2·00	1·00

1976. Ships. Multicoloured.
20		1c. Type **9**	30	40
21		2c. H.M.S. "Juno", 1857 (horiz)	30	40
22		5c. H.M.S. "Beagle", 1836 (horiz)	30	40
23		10c. H.M.A.S. "Sydney", 1914 (horiz)	35	40
24		15c. S.M.S. "Emden", 1914 (horiz)	60	55
25		20c. "Ayesha", 1907 (horiz)	60	65
26		25c. T.S.S. "Islander", 1927	60	75
27		30c. M.V. "Cheshire", 1951	60	75
28		35c. Jukong (sailboat) (horiz)	60	75
29		40c. C.S. "Scotia", 1900 (horiz)	60	75
30		50c. R.M.S. "Orontes", 1929	60	75
31		$1 Royal Yacht "Gothic", 1954	75	1·00

10 Map of Cocos (Keeling) Islands, Union Flag, Stars and Trees

1979. Inauguration of Independent Postal Service and First Statutory Council. Multicoloured.
32		20c. Type **10**	25	35
33		50c. Council seat and jukong (sailboat)	35	65

11 Forceps Fish
12 "Peace on Earth" 

1979. Fishes. Multicoloured.
34		1c. Type **11**	30	1·00
35		2c. Ornate butterflyfish	30	30
36		5c. Barbier	50	1·10
37		10c. Meyer's butterflyfish	30	1·00
38		15c. Pink wrasse	30	30
39		20c. Clark's anemonefish	45	30
39a		25c. Undulate triggerfish	45	30
40		25c. Red-breasted wrasse	45	1·00
40a		28c. Guineafowl wrasse	35	35
41		30c. Madagascar butterflyfish	50	45
42		35c. Cocos-Keeling angelfish	50	1·60
43		40c. Coral hogfish	55	90
44		50c. Clown wrasse	85	75
45		55c. Yellow-tailed tamarin	60	1·25
45a		60c. Greasy grouper	60	75
46		$1 Palette surgeonfish	75	3·50
47		$2 Melon butterflyfish	1·00	3·50

1979. Christmas. Multicoloured.
48		25c. Type **12**	25	40
49		55c. Atoll seascape ("Goodwill")	40	70

13 Star, Map of Cocos (Keeling) Islands and Island Landscape

1980. Christmas. Multicoloured.
50		15c. Type **13**	10	10
51		28c. The Three Kings	15	15
52		60c. Adoration	40	40

14 "Administered by the British Government, 1857"

15 "Eye of the Wind" and Map of Cocos (Keeling) Islands

1980. 25th Anniv of Territorial Status under Australian Administration. Multicoloured.
53		22c. Type **14**	15	15
54		22c. Arms of Ceylon	15	15
55		22c. Arms of Straits Settlements	15	15
56		22c. Arms of Singapore	15	15
57		22c. Arms and flag of Australia	15	15

1980. "Operation Drake" (round the world expedition) and 400th Anniv of Sir Francis Drake's Circumnavigation of the World. Multicoloured.
58		22c. Type **15**	25	15
59		28c. Routes map (horiz)	25	15
60		35c. Sir Francis Drake and "Golden Hind"	25	15
61		60c. Prince Charles (patron) and "Eye of the Wind" (brigantine)	45	30

16 Aerial View of Animal Quarantine Station

1981. Opening of Animal Quarantine Station. Multicoloured.
62		22c. Type **16**	15	15
63		45c. Unloading livestock	30	30
64		60c. Livestock in pen	35	35

17 Consolidated Catalina Flying Boat "Guba"

1981. Aircraft. Multicoloured.
65		22c. Type **17**	25	25
66		22c. Consolidated Liberator and Avro Lancastrian	25	25
67		22c. Douglas DC-4 and Lockheed Constellation	25	25
68		22c. Lockheed Electra	25	25
69		22c. Boeing 727-100 airliners	25	25

18 Prince Charles and Lady Diana Spencer

1981. Royal Wedding.
70	**18**	24c. multicoloured	30	20
71		60c. multicoloured	50	60

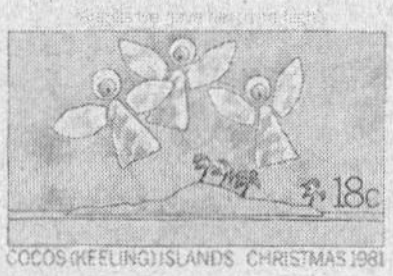

19 "Angels we have heard on High"

1981. Christmas. Scenes and Lines from Carol "Angels we have heard on High". Multicoloured.

72	18c. Type **19**	10	10
73	30c. "Shepherds why this Jubilee?"	20	20
74	60c. "Come to Bethlehem and see Him"	35	35

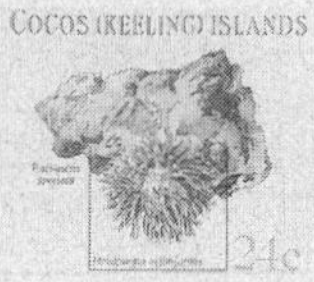

20 "Pachyseris speciosa" and "Heliofungia actiniformis" (corals)

1981. 150th Anniv of Charles Darwin's Voyage. Multicoloured.

75	24c. Type **20**	25	15
76	45c. Charles Darwin in 1853 and "Pavona cactus" (coral)	40	30
77	60c. H.M.S. "Beagle", 1832, and "Lobophyllia hemprichii" (coral)	45	35

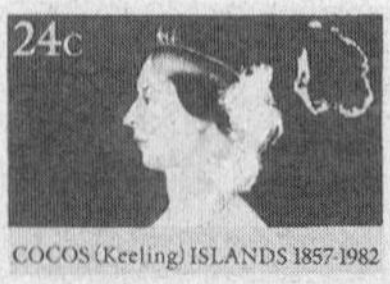

21 Queen Victoria

1982. 125th Anniv of Annexation of Cocos (Keeling) Islands to British Empire. Multicoloured.

79	24c. Type **21**	15	15
80	45c. Union flag	25	25
81	60c. Captain S. Fremantle (annexation visit, 1857)	30	35

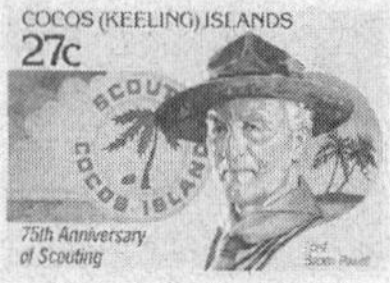

22 Lord Baden-Powell

1982. 75th Anniv of Boy Scout Movement. Multicoloured.

82	27c. Type **22**	25	25
83	75c. "75" and map of Cocos (Keeling) Islands (vert)	60	1·50

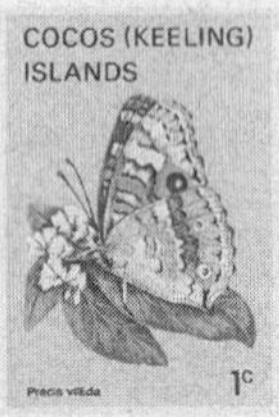

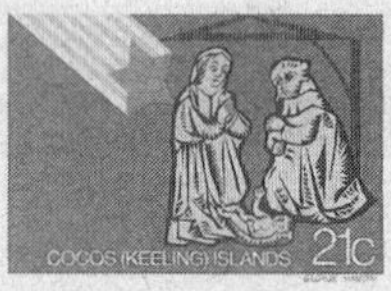

23 "Precis villida" 24 "Call His Name Immanuel"

1982. Butterflies and Moths. Multicoloured.

84	1c. Type **23**	1·00	60
85	2c. "Cephonodes picus" (horiz)	40	40
86	5c. "Macroglossom corythus" (horiz)	1·50	70
87	10c. "Chasmina candida"	40	40
88	20c. "Nagia linteola" (horiz)	40	65
89	25c. "Eublemma rivula"	40	75
90	30c. "Eurrhyparodes tricoloralis"	40	65
91	35c. "Hippotion boerhaviae" (horiz)	1·50	75
92	40c. "Euploea core"	40	80
93	45c. "Psara hipponalis" (horiz)	50	80
94	50c. "Danaus chrysippus" (horiz)	60	1·25
95	55c. "Hypolimnas misippus"	60	70
96	60c. "Spodoptera litura"	65	1·75
97	$1 "Achaea janata"	2·75	2·75
98	$2 "Panacra velox" (horiz)	2·00	2·75
99	$3 "Utetheisa pulchelloides" (horiz)	2·75	2·75

1982. Christmas. Multicoloured.

100	21c. Type **24**	25	30
101	35c. "I bring you good tidings"	40	40
102	75c. "Arise and flee into Egypt"	1·00	1·25

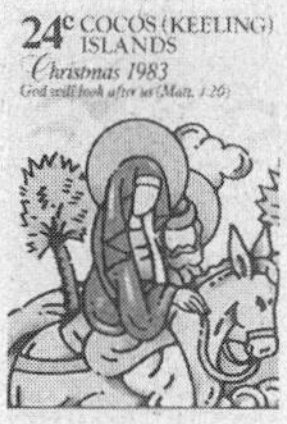

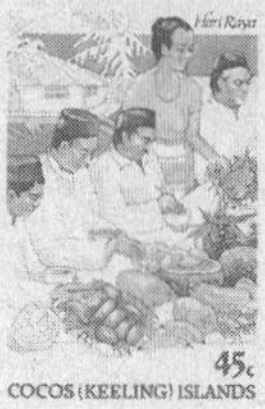

25 "God will look after us" (Matt. 1:20) 26 Hari Raya Celebration

1983. Christmas. Extracts from New Testament. Multicoloured.

103	24c. Type **25**	30	45
104	24c. "Our baby King, Jesus" (Matthew. 2:2)	30	45
105	24c. "Your Saviour is born" (Luke. 2:11)	30	45
106	24c. "Wise men followed the Star" (Matthew. 2:9–10)	30	45
107	24c. "And worship the Lord" (Matthew. 2:11)	30	45

1984. Cocos-Malay Culture (1st series). Mult.

108	45c. Type **26**	45	25
109	75c. Melenggok dancing	65	50
110	85c. Cocos-Malay wedding	75	55

See also Nos. 128/31.

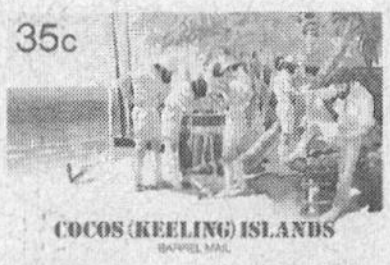

27 Unpacking Barrel

1984. 75th Anniv of Cocos Barrel Mail. Multicoloured.

111	35c. Type **27**	40	25
112	55c. Jukong awaiting mail ship	75	50
113	70c. P & O mail ship "Morea"	85	55

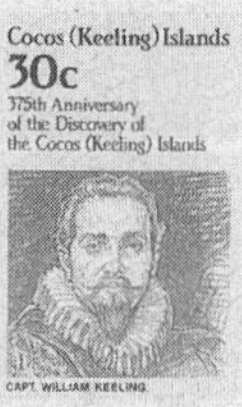

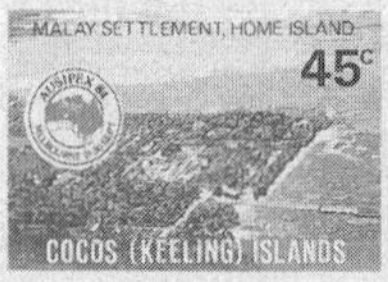

28 Captain William Keeling 29 Malay Settlement, Home Island

1984. 375th Anniv of Discovery of Cocos (Keeling) Islands. Multicoloured.

115	30c. Type **28**	60	40
116	65c. "Hector"	1·25	90
117	95c. Mariner's astrolabe	1·50	1·25
118	$1.10 Map circa 1666	1·60	1·50

1984. "Ausipex" International Stamp Exhibition, Melbourne. Multicoloured.

119	45c. Type **29**	75	50
120	55c. Airstrip, West Island	85	60

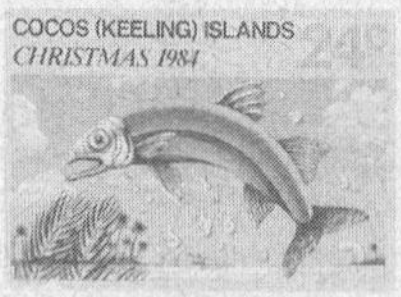

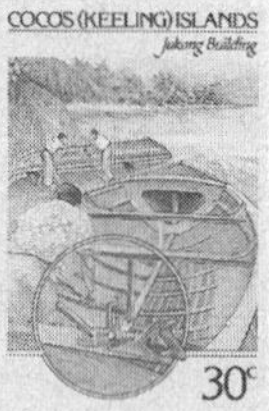

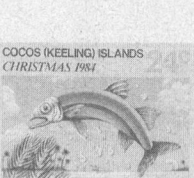

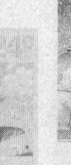

30 "Rainbow" Fish 32 Jukong-building

1984. Christmas. Multicoloured.

122	24c. Type **30**	50	60
123	35c. "Rainbow" butterfly	1·10	1·40
124	55c. "Rainbow" bird	1·25	2·00

1985. Cocos-Malay Culture (2nd series). Handicrafts. Multicoloured.

126	30c. Type **32**	75	35
127	45c. Blacksmithing	1·00	55
128	55c. Woodcarving	1·25	65

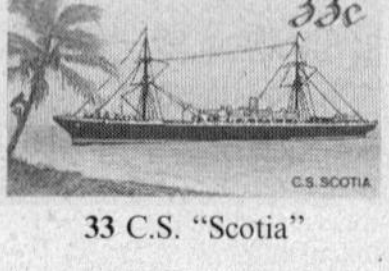

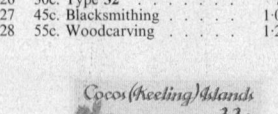

33 C.S. "Scotia"

1985. Cable-laying Ships. Multicoloured.

129	33c. Type **33**	1·50	40
130	65c. C.S. "Anglia"	2·25	1·60
131	80c. C.S. "Patrol"	2·25	2·25

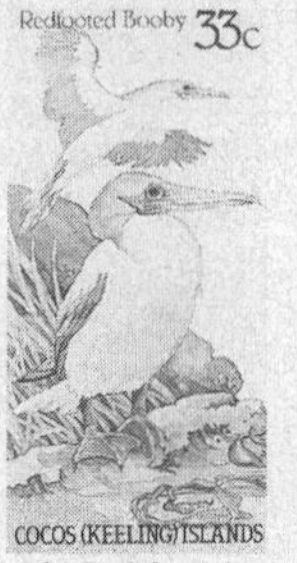

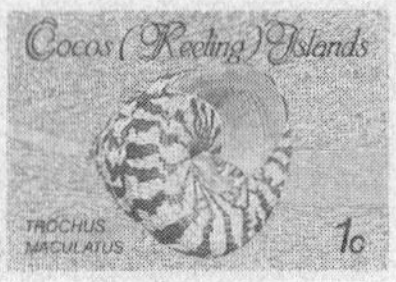

34 Red-footed Booby 35 Mantled Top

1985. Birds of Cocos (Keeling) Islands. Multicoloured.

132	33c. Type **34**	1·75	2·00
133	60c. Nankeen night heron (juvenile) (horiz)	2·00	2·50
134	$1 Buff-banded rail (horiz)	2·25	2·50

Nos. 132/4 were issued together, se-tenant, forming a composite design.

1985. Shells and Molluscs. Multicoloured.

135	1c. Type **35**	60	1·00
136	2c. Rang's nerite	60	1·00
137	3c. Jewel box	60	1·00
138	4c. Money cowrie	1·00	1·00
139	5c. Purple Pacific drupe	60	1·00
140	10c. Soldier cone	70	1·25
141	15c. Merlin-spike auger	1·75	1·00
142	20c. Pacific strawberry cockle	1·75	1·10
143	30c. Lajonkaire's turban	1·75	1·25
144	33c. Reticulate mitre	2·00	1·25
145	40c. Common spider conch	2·00	1·40
146	50c. Fluted giant clam or scaled tridacna	2·00	1·50
147	60c. Minstrel cowrie	2·25	2·00
148	$1 Varicose nudibranch	3·25	3·00
149	$2 Tesselated nudibranch	3·50	4·00
150	$3 Hamincea cymballum	4·25	4·75

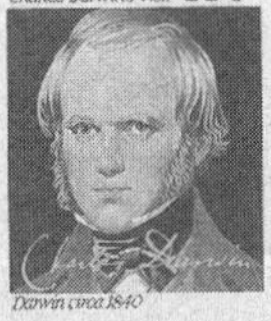

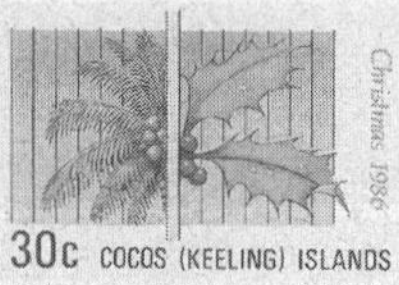

37 Charles Darwin, c. 1840 38 Coconut Palm and Holly Sprigs

1986. 150th Anniv of Charles Darwin's Visit. Multicoloured.

152	33c. Type **37**	70	60
153	60c. Map of H.M.S. "Beagle's" route, Australia to Cocos Islands	1·25	2·25
154	$1 H.M.S. "Beagle"	1·75	2·75

1986. Christmas. Multicoloured.

155	30c. Type **38**	60	60
156	90c. Nautilus shell and Christmas tree bauble	2·00	2·75
157	$1 Tropical fish and bell	2·00	2·75

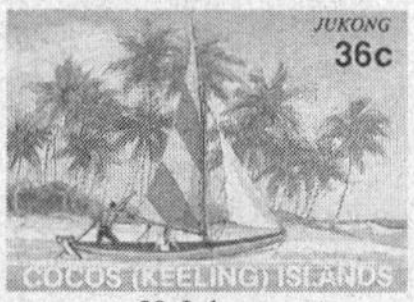

39 Jukong

1987. Sailing Craft. Multicoloured.

158	36c. Type **39**	1·10	1·50
159	36c. Ocean racing yachts	1·10	1·50
160	36c. "Sarimanok" (replica of early dhow)	1·10	1·50
161	36c. "Ayesha" (schooner)	1·10	1·50

Nos. 158/61 were printed together, se-tenant, each strip forming a composite background design.

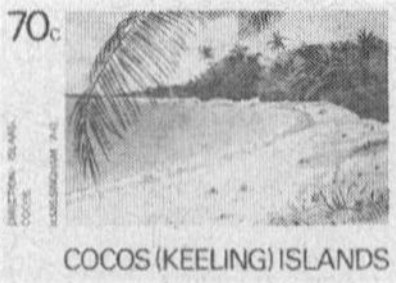

40 Beach, Direction Island

1987. Cocos Islands Scenes. Multicoloured.

162	70c. Type **40**	1·40	1·40
163	90c. Palm forest, West Island	1·75	2·00
164	$1 Golf course	2·75	3·00

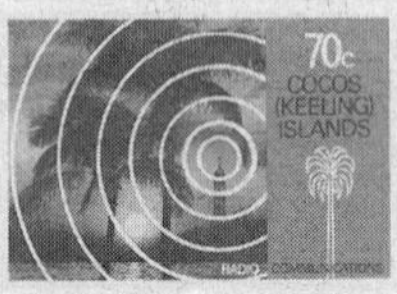

41 Radio Transmitter and Palm Trees at Sunset

1987. Communications. Multicoloured.

165	70c. Type **41**	1·25	1·50
166	75c. Boeing 727-100 airliner at terminal	1·50	1·75
167	90c. "Intelsat 5" satellite	1·75	2·25
168	$1 Airmail letter and globe	2·00	2·25

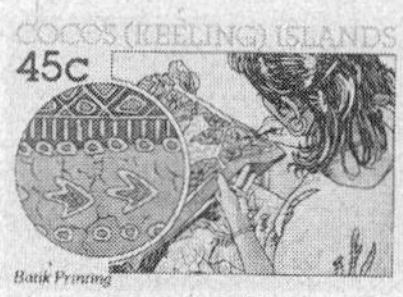

42 Batik Printing

1987. Cocos (Keeling) Islands Malay Industries. Multicoloured.

169	45c. Type **42**	1·25	1·50
170	65c. Jukong building	1·75	2·00
171	75c. Copra production	2·00	2·25

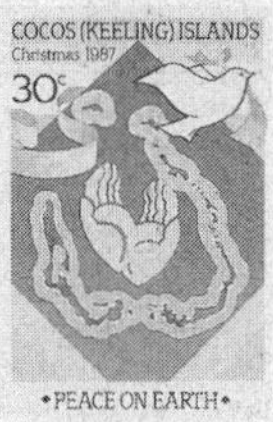

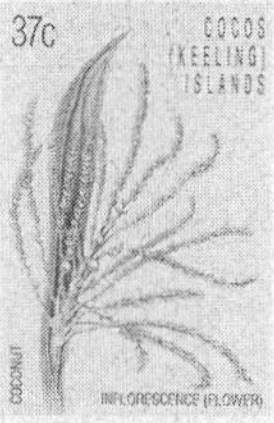

43 Hands releasing Peace Dove and Map of Islands 44 Coconut Flower

1987. Christmas. Multicoloured.

172	30c. Type **43**	40	40
173	90c. Local children at Christmas party	1·25	1·90
174	$1 Island family and Christmas star	1·50	1·90

1988. Bicentenary of Australian Settlement. Arrival of First Fleet. As Nos. 1105/9 of Australia but each inscr "COCOS (KEELING) ISLANDS" and "AUSTRALIA BICENTENARY".

175	37c. Aborigines watching arrival of Fleet, Botany Bay	1·75	1·90
176	37c. Aboriginal family and anchored ships	1·75	1·90
177	37c. Fleet arriving at Sydney Cove	1·75	1·90
178	37c. Ship's boat	1·75	1·90
179	37c. Raising the flag, Sydney Cove, 26 January 1788	1·75	1·90

Nos. 175/9 were printed together, se-tenant, forming a composite design.

1988. Life Cycle of the Coconut. Multicoloured.

180	37c. Type **44**	50	40
181	65c. Immature nuts	75	1·00
182	90c. Coconut palm and mature nuts	1·10	1·75
183	$1 Seedlings	1·25	1·75

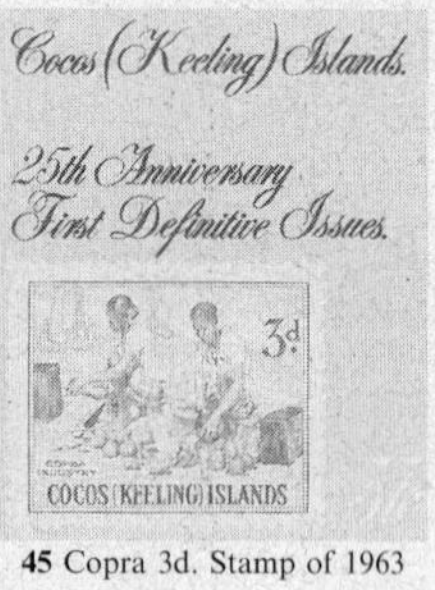

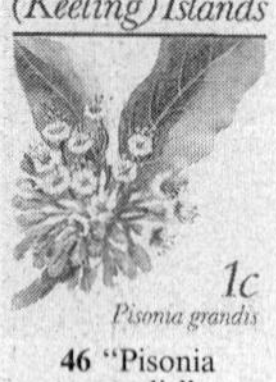

45 Copra 3d. Stamp of 1963 46 "Pisonia grandis"

1988. 25th Anniv of First Cocos (Keeling) Islands Stamps. Each showing stamp from 1963 definitive set.

185 **45**	37c. green, black and blue	1·25	1·00
186 –	55c. green, black and brown	1·75	50
187 –	65c. blue, black and lilac	1·90	2·25
188 –	70c. red, black and grey	1·90	2·25
189 –	90c. purple, black and grey	2·25	2·50
190 –	$1 green, black and brown	2·25	2·50

DESIGNS: 55c. Palms 1s.; 65c. Lockheed Super Constellation airplane 5d.; 70c. Map 8d.; 90c. "Jukong" (sailboat) 2s.; $1 White tern 2s.3d.

1988. Flora. Multicoloured.

191	1c. Type **46**	50	60
192	2c. "Cocos nucifera"	50	60
193	5c. "Morinda citrifolia"	1·00	70
194	10c. "Cordia subcordata"	70	70
195	30c. "Argusia argentea"	1·00	1·00
196	37c. "Calophyllum inophyllum"	1·50	1·00
197	40c. "Barringtonia asiatica"	1·00	1·25
198	50c. "Caesalpinia bonduc"	1·25	2·75
199	90c. "Terminalia catappa"	1·75	3·50
200	$1 "Pemphis acidula"	1·75	2·50
201	$2 "Scaevola sericea"	2·50	2·50
202	$3 "Hibiscus tiliaceus"	3·50	3·75

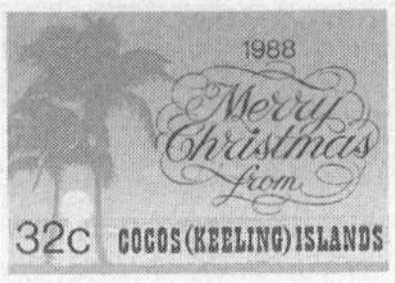

47 Beach at Sunset

1988. Christmas
204 **47** 32c. multicoloured 80 50
205 90c. multicoloured . . . . 1·75 2·50
206 $1 multicoloured . . . . . 2·00 2·50

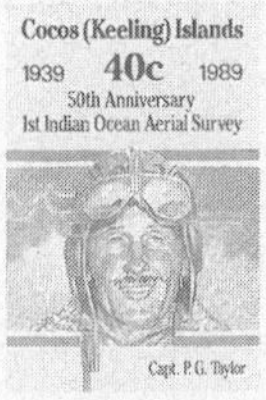

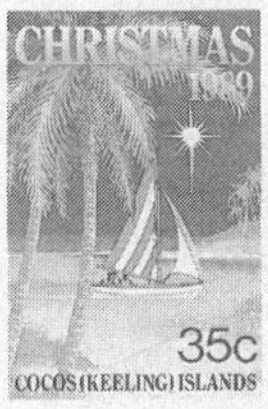

48 Captain P. G. Taylor
49 Jukong and Star

1989. 50th Anniv of First Indian Ocean Aerial Survey.
207 **48** 40c. multicoloured 80 65
208 – 70c. multicoloured . . . . 1·75 2·50
209 – $1 multicoloured . . . . 2·00 2·50
210 – $1.10 blue, lilac and black 2·25 2·75
DESIGNS: 70c. Consolidated Catalina flying boat "Guba" and crew; $1 "Guba" over Direction Islands; $1.10, Unissued Australia 5s. stamp commemorating flight.

1989. Christmas.
211 **49** 35c. multicoloured 85 60
212 80c. multicoloured . . . . 2·50 3·00
213 $1.10 multicoloured . . . 2·50 3·00

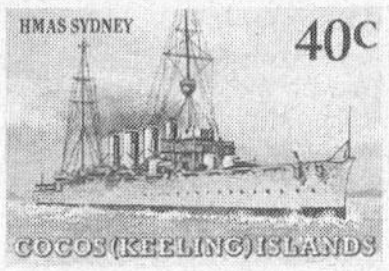

50 H.M.A.S. "Sydney" (cruiser)

1989. 75th Anniv of Destruction of German Cruiser "Emden". Multicoloured.
214 40c. Type **50** . . . . 1·75 1·75
215 70c. "Emden" . . . . 2·00 2·00
216 $1 "Emden's" steam launch 2·25 2·25
217 $1.10 H.M.A.S. "Sydney" (1914) and crest . . . . . 2·25 2·25

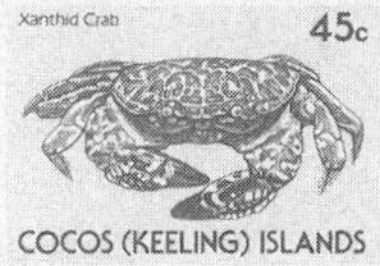

51 Xanthid Crab

1990. Cocos Islands Crabs. Multicoloured.
219 45c. Type **51** . . . . 1·50 75
220 75c. Ghost crab . . . . . . 2·00 2·00
221 $1 Red-backed mud crab . . 2·25 2·25
222 $1.30 Coconut crab (vert) . . 2·50 3·00

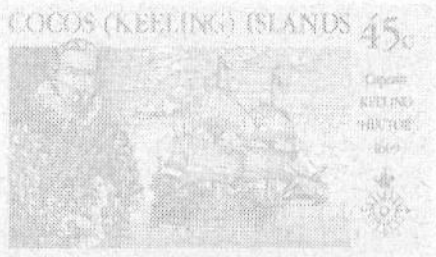

52 Captain Keeling and "Hector", 1609

1990. Navigators of the Pacific.
223 **52** 45c. mauve . . . . 2·50 1·25
224 – 75c. mauve and blue . . . 2·75 3·00
225 – $1 mauve and stone . . . 3·25 3·50
226 – $1.30 mauve and buff . . . 4·00 4·75
DESIGNS: 75c. Captain Fitzroy and H.M.S. "Beagle", 1836; $1 Captain Belcher and H.M.S. "Samarang", 1846; $1.30, Captain Fremantle and H.M.S. "Juno", 1857.

1990. "New Zealand 1990" International Stamp Exhibition, Auckland. No. 188 optd with logo and **NEW ZEALAND 1990 24 AUG 2 SEP AUCKLAND.**
228 70c. red, black and grey . . . 2·75 3·50

1990. No. 187 surch **$5**.
230 $5 on 65c. blue, black and lilac . . . . 18·00 18·00

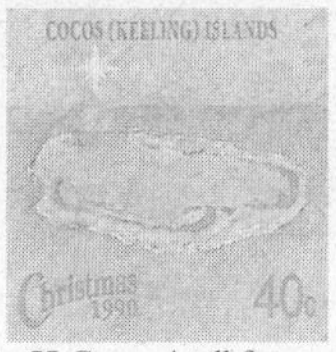

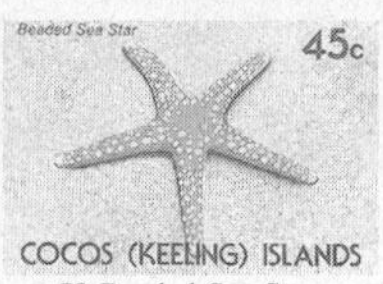

55 Cocos Atoll from West and Star
58 Beaded Sea Star

1990. Christmas. Multicoloured.
231 40c. Type **55** . . . . 70 1·00
232 70c. Cocos atoll from south 1·50 2·50
233 $1.30 Cocos atoll from east 2·75 3·00

1990. Nos. 140/1, 143 and 146/7 surch **POSTAGE PAID** plus additional words as indicated.
236 (1c.) on 30c. Lajonkaire's turban (**LOCAL**) . . . . . 1·50 2·50
235 (43c.) on 10c. Soldier cone (**MAINLAND**) . . . . . . 1·40 1·75
237 70c. on 60c. Minstrel cowrie (**ZONE 1**) . . . . 1·50 2·50
238 80c. on 50c. Fluted giant clam or scaled tridacna (**ZONE 2**) . . . . 1·75 3·25
239 $1.20 on 15c. Marlin-spike auger (**ZONE 5**) . . . . . 2·00 3·50

1991. Starfish and Sea Urchins. Multicoloured.
240 45c. Type **58** . . . . 1·25 75
241 75c. Feather star . . . . . . 2·00 2·25
242 $1 Slate pencil urchin . . . . 2·00 2·25
243 $1.30 Globose sea urchin . . 2·75 3·25

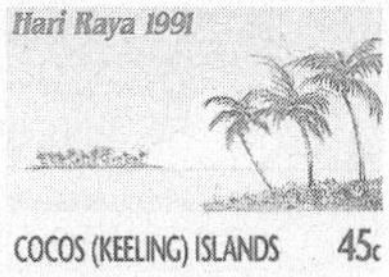

59 Cocos Islands

1991. Malay Hari Raya Festival. Multicoloured.
244 45c. Type **59** . . . . 1·00 65
245 75c. Island house . . . . . 1·75 2·25
246 $1.30 Islands scene . . . . . 2·50 3·25

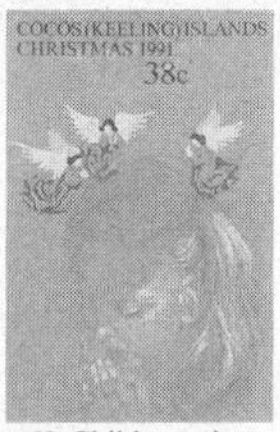

60 Child praying

1991. Christmas. Multicoloured.
247 38c. Type **60** . . . . 1·00 70
248 43c. Child dreaming of Christmas Day . . . . . . 1·00 70
249 $1 Child singing . . . . . . 2·25 2·25
250 $1.20 Child fascinated by decorations . . . . 2·75 3·50

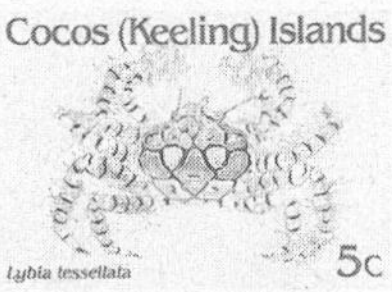

61 "Lybia tessellata"

1992. Crustaceans. Multicoloured.
252 5c. Type **61** 70 70
253 10c. "Pilodius areolatus" . . 1·00 1·00
254 20c. "Trizopagurus strigatus" 1·25 1·25
255 30c. "Lophozozymus pulchellus" . . . . 1·50 1·50
256 40c. "Thalamitoides quadridens" . . . . 1·50 1·50
257 45c. "Calcinus elegans" (vert) 1·50 1·50
258 50c. "Clibarius humilis" . . . 1·75 1·75
259 60c. "Trapezia rufopunctata" (vert) . . . . 2·00 2·00
260 80c. "Pylopaguropsis magnimanus" (vert) . . . 2·25 2·25
261 $1 "Trapezia ferruginea" (vert) . . . . 2·25 2·25
262 $2 "Trapezia guttata" (vert) 3·25 4·00
263 $3 "Trapezia cymodoce" (vert) . . . . 3·75 4·00

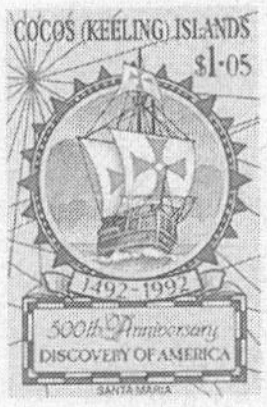

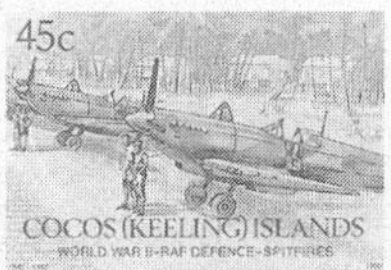

62 "Santa Maria"
64 R.A.F. Supermarine Spitfires on Island Airstrip

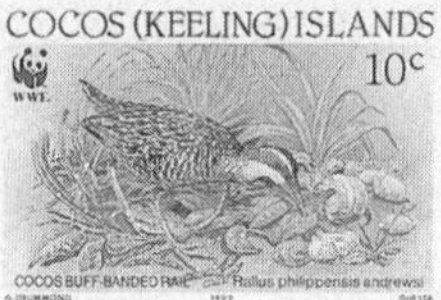

63 Buff-banded Rail searching for Food

1992. 500th Anniv of Discovery of America by Columbus.
264 **62** $1.05 multicoloured . . . 2·25 2·50

1992. Endangered Species. Buff-banded Rail. Mult.
265 10c. Type **63** 50 70
266 15c. Banded rail with chick 65 85
267 30c. Two rails drinking . . . 80 1·00
268 45c. Rail and nest . . . . . 90 1·25

1992. 50th Anniv of Second World War. Mult.
270 45c. Type **64** . . . . 1·75 1·25
271 85c. Mitsubishi A6M Zero-Sen aircraft bombing Kampong . . . . 2·50 3·25
272 $1.20 R.A.F. Short Sunderland flying boat . . 3·00 4·00

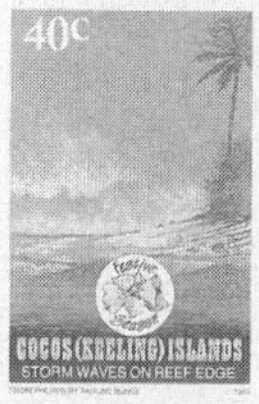

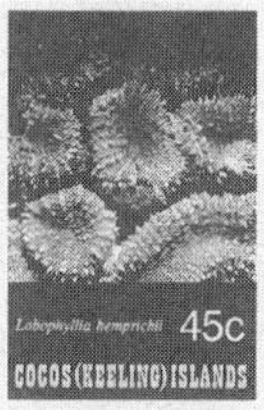

65 Waves breaking on Reef
66 "Lobophyllia hemprichii"

1992. Christmas. Multicoloured.
273 40c. Type **65** . . . . 1·00 70
274 80c. Direction Island . . . . 2·25 2·75
275 $1 Moorish idols (fish) and coral . . . . 2·25 2·75

1993. Corals. Multicoloured.
276 45c. Type **66** 75 55
277 85c. "Pocillopora eydouxi" 1·25 1·75
278 $1.05 "Fungia scutaria" . . . 1·75 2·00
279 $1.20 "Sarcophyton sp" . . . 1·75 2·25

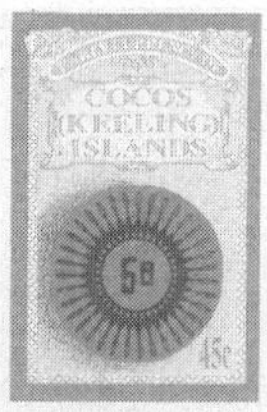

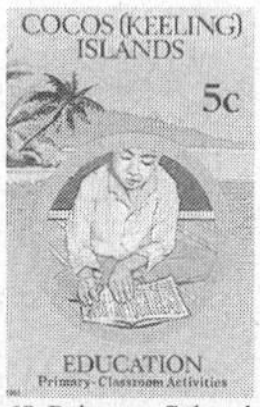

67 Plastic 5r. Token
68 Primary School Pupil

1993. Early Cocos (Keeling) Islands Currency. Multicoloured.
280 45c. Type **67** . . . . 1·25 80
281 85c. 1968 1r. plastic token . . 1·75 2·25
282 $1.05 1977 150r. commemorative gold coin 2·25 2·50
283 $1.20 1910 plastic token . . . 2·25 2·75

1993. Education. Multicoloured.
284 5c. Type **68** 40 75
285 45c. Secondary school pupil 90 60
286 85c. Learning traditional crafts . . . . 1·75 2·00
287 $1.05 Learning office skills 2·25 2·75
288 $1.20 Seaman training . . . 2·75 3·00

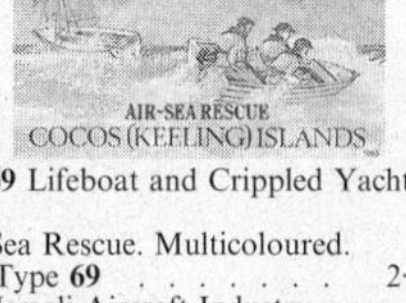

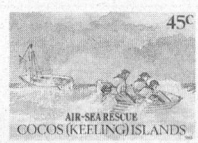

69 Lifeboat and Crippled Yacht

1993. Air-Sea Rescue. Multicoloured.
289 45c. Type **69** . . . . 2·00 1·25
290 85c. Israeli Aircraft Industry Westwind Seascan (aircraft) 3·00 3·25
291 $1.05 "R.J. Hawke" (ferry) 3·25 4·50

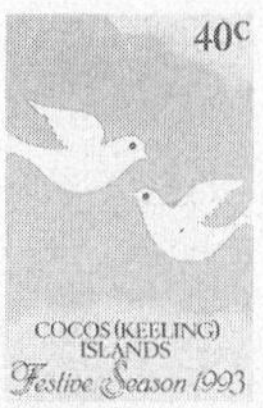

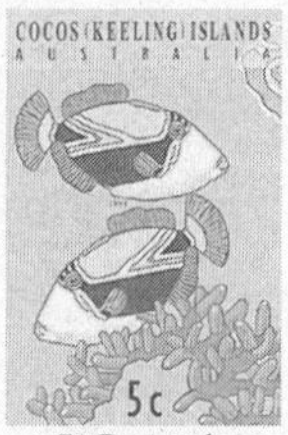

70 Peace Doves
71 Rectangle Triggerfish and Coral

1993. Christmas.
293 **70** 40c. multicoloured . . . . 1·25 80
294 80c. multicoloured . . . . 2·50 3·00
295 $1 multicoloured . . . . . 2·50 3·00

1994. Transfer of Postal Service to Australia Post. Multicoloured.
296 5c. Type **71** 25 35
297 5c. Three rectangle triggerfish and map section 25 35
298 5c. Two rectangle triggerfish and map section 25 35
299 5c. Two rectangle triggerfish, map section and red coral 25 35
300 5c. Rectangle triggerfish with red and brown corals . . . 25 35
301 10c. Green turtles on beach 25 35
302 10c. Two green turtles . . . 25 35
303 10c. Crowd of young green turtles 25 35
304 10c. Green turtle and map section 25 35
305 10c. Green turtle, pyramid butterflyfish and map section 25 35
306 20c. Three pyramid butterflyfish and map section 40 50
307 20c. Pyramid butterflyfish with brown coral 40 50
308 20c. Two pyramid butterflyfish and coral . . 40 50
309 20c. Three pyramid butterflyfish and coral . . 40 50
310 20c. Coral, pyramid butterflyfish and map section 40 50
311 45c. Jukongs with map of airport 50 60
312 45c. Two jukongs with red or blue sails and map section 50 60
313 45c. Jukong in shallows . . . 50 60
314 45c. Two jukongs with red or yellow sails and map section 50 60
315 45c. Two jukongs, one with blue jib, and map section 50 60
Nos. 296/315 were printed together, se-tenant, with the backgrounds forming a composite map.

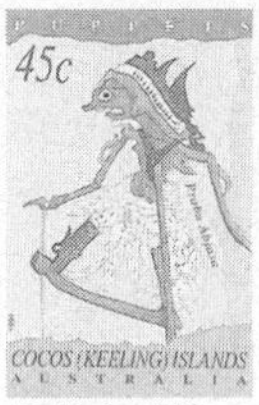

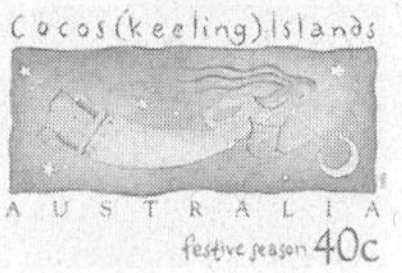

72 Prabu Abjasa Puppet
73 Angel playing Harp

1994. Shadow Puppets. Multicoloured.
316 45c. Type **72** 65 50
317 90c. Prabu Pandu . . . . . 1·25 1·50
318 $1 Judistra . . . . 1·40 1·50
319 $1.35 Abimanju . . . . . . 1·50 2·00

1994. Seasonal Festivals. Multicoloured.
320 40c. Type **73** 50 50
321 45c. Wise Man holding gift 55 50
322 80c. Mosque at night . . . . 1·00 1·75

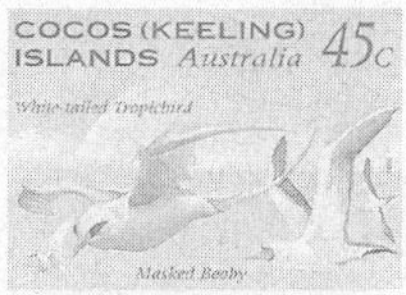

74 White-tailed Tropic Bird and Blue-faced Booby ("Masked Booby")

1995. Sea-birds of North Keeling Island. Multicoloured.
323 45c. Type **74** 75 50
324 85c. Great frigate bird and white tern . . . . 1·00 1·50

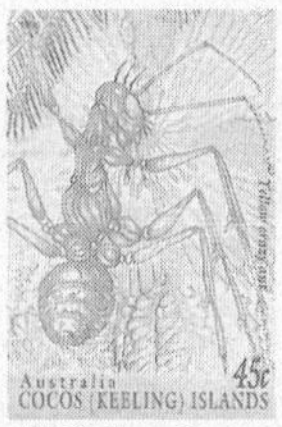

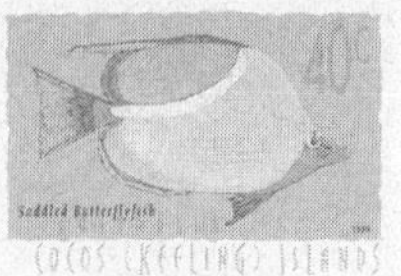

75 Yellow Crazy Ant
76 Saddle Butterflyfish

1995. Insects. Multicoloured.
326 45c. Type **75** . . . . 1·00 1·25
327 45c. Aedes mosquito . . . . 1·00 1·25
328 45c. Hawk moth . . . . . . 1·00 1·25
329 45c. Scarab beetle . . . . . 1·00 1·25
330 45c. Lauxaniid fly . . . . . 1·00 1·25
331 $1.20 Common eggfly (butterfly) . . . . 1·50 1·75
Nos. 326/30 were printed together, se-tenant, forming a composite design.

1995. Marine Life. Multicoloured.
332 5c. Redspot wrasse 10 10

333	30c. Blue-throated triggerfish ("Gilded triggerfish")	20	25
334	40c. Type **76**	30	35
335	45c. Arc-eyed hawkfish	35	40
335a	45c. Wideband fusilier	30	35
335b	45c. Striped surgeonfish	30	35
335c	45c. Orangeband surgeonfish	30	35
335d	45c. Indo-Pacific sergeant	30	35
335e	70c. Crowned squirrelfish	50	55
336	75c. Orange-pine unicornfish	55	60
337	80c. Blue tang	55	60
338	85c. Juvenile twin-spotted wrasse ("Humpback wrasse")	60	65
339	90c. Threadfin butterflyfish	65	70
339a	95c. Sixstripe wrasse	65	70
340	$1 Bluestripe snapper	70	75
341	$1.05 Longnosed butterflyfish	75	80
342	$1.20 Freckled hawkfish	85	90
343	$2 Powder-blue surgeonfish	1·40	1·50
343a	$5 Goldback anthias	3·50	3·75

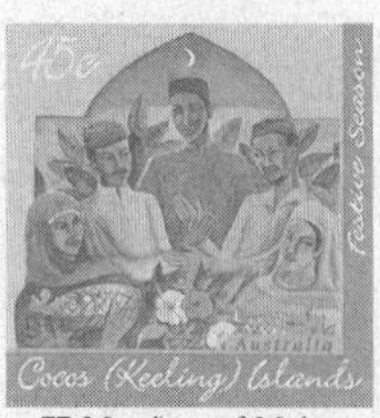

77 Members of Malay Community

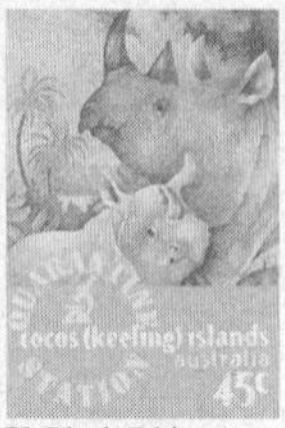

78 Black Rhinoceros with Calf

1996. Hari Raya Puasa Festival. Multicoloured.

344	45c. Type **77**	65	60
345	75c. Beating drums	1·25	1·50
346	85c. Preparing festival meal	1·25	1·75

1996. Cocos Quarantine Station. Multicoloured.

347	45c. Type **78**	1·00	1·00
348	50c. Alpacas	1·00	1·50
349	$1.05 Boran cattle	1·50	2·25
350	$1.20 Ostrich with chicks	1·75	2·25

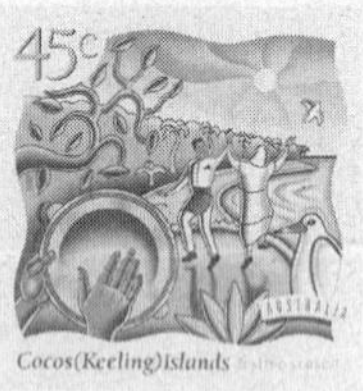

79 Dancers and Tambourine

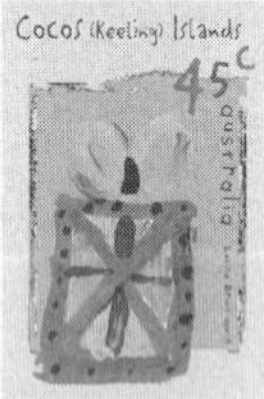

80 "Wrapped Present" (Lazina Brian)

1997. Hari Raya Puasa Festival. Multicoloured.

351	45c. Type **79**	65	60
352	75c. Girl clapping and sailing dinghies	1·00	1·60
353	85c. Dancers on beach and food	1·25	1·60

1998. Hari Raya Puasa Festival. Paintings by children. Multicoloured.

354	45c. Type **80**	70	75
355	45c. "Mosque" (Azran Jim)	70	75
356	45c. "Cocos Malay Woman" (Kate Gossage)	70	75
357	45c. "Yacht" (Matt Harber)	70	75
358	45c. "People dancing" (Rakin Chongkin)	70	75

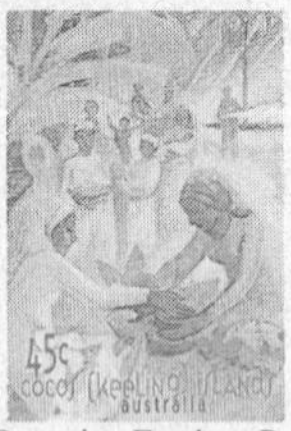

81 Preparing Food on Beach

1999. Hari Raya Puasa Festival. Multicoloured.

359	45c. Type **81**	55	65
360	45c. Woman with child and jukongs on beach	55	65
361	45c. Jukongs and palm fronds	55	65
362	45c. Two men watching jukongs	55	65
363	45c. Jukong and white flowers	55	65

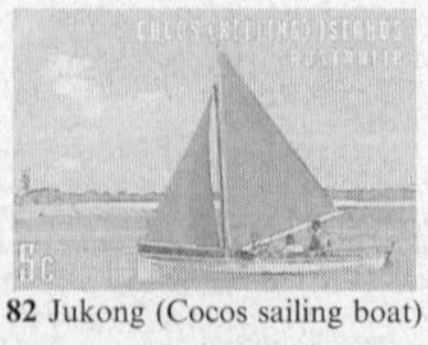

82 Jukong (Cocos sailing boat)

1999. Island Wildlife. Multicoloured.

364	5c. Type **82**	25	30
365	5c. Bennett's and ornate butterflyfish	25	30
366	5c. Green and hawksbill turtles	25	30
367	5c. Yellow-tailed anemonefish and various butterflyfish	25	30
368	5c. Hump-headed wrasse	25	30
369	10c. Yacht, Direction Island	25	30
370	10c. Black-backed butterflyfish	25	30
371	10c. Moorish idols	25	30
372	10c. "Pseudoanthias cooperi" (fish)	25	30
373	10c. Red-tailed tropic birds	25	30
374	25c. Blue-faced booby	40	45
375	25c. Lesser wanderer (butterfly)	40	45
376	25c. Lesser and greater frigate birds	40	45
377	25c. "Hippotion velox" (moth)	40	45
378	25c. Common eggfly (butterfly)	40	45
379	45c. White tern	55	60
380	45c. Red-tailed tropic bird and great frigate bird	55	60
381	45c. Chinese rose	55	60
382	45c. Meadow argus (butterfly)	55	60
383	45c. Sea hibiscus	55	60

Nos. 364/83 were printed together, se-tenant, with the backgrounds forming a composite design.

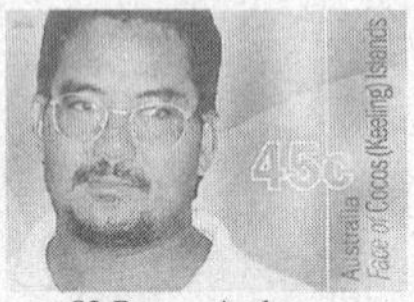

83 Ratma Anthoney

2000. New Millennium. "Face of Cocos (Keeling) Islands". Multicoloured.

384	45c. Type **83**	55	60
385	45c. Nakia Haji Dolman (schoolgirl)	55	60
386	45c. Muller Eymin (elderly man)	55	60
387	45c. Courtney Press (toddler)	55	60
388	45c. Mhd Abu-Yazid (school boy)	55	60

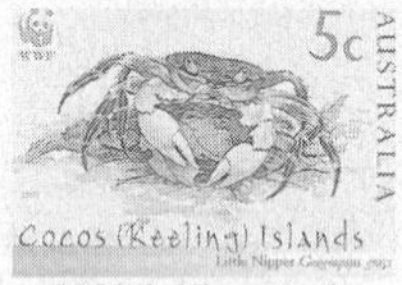

84 Little Nipper (crab)

2000. Endangered Species. Crabs of Cocos (Keeling) Islands. Multicoloured.

389	5c. Type **84**	25	30
390	5c. Purple crab	25	30
391	45c. Smooth-handed ghost crab	55	60
392	45c. Horn-eyed ghost crab	55	60

OFFICIAL STAMPS

1991. No. 182 surch **OFFICIAL PAID MAINLAND.**

O1	(43c.) on 90c. Coconut palm and mature nuts	†	90·00

No. O1 was not sold to the public in unused condition.

COLOMBIA Pt. 20

A republic in the N.W. of South America. Formerly part of the Spanish Empire, Colombia became independent in 1819. The constituent states became the Granadine Confederation in 1858. The name was changed to the United States of New Granada in 1861, and the name Colombia was adopted later the same year.

100 centavos = 1 peso.

Prices. For the early issues prices in the used column are for postmarked copies, pen-cancellations are generally worth less.

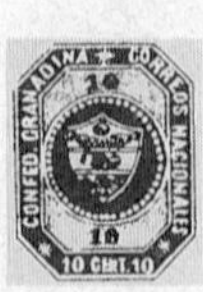

1

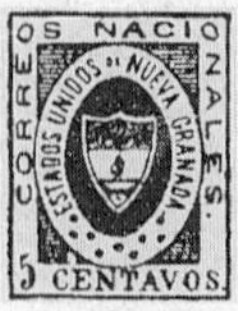

3

1859. Imperf.

1	**1**	2½c. green	70·00	80·00
2		5c. blue	70·00	70·00
8		5c. slate	55·00	45·00
9		10c. yellow	45·00	40·00
5		20c. blue	70·00	48·00
6		1p. red	48·00	80·00

1861. Imperf.

11	**3**	2½c. black	£1000	£400
12		5c. yellow	£160	£120
13		10c. blue	£650	£120
14		20c. red	£350	£150
15		1p. red	£800	£250

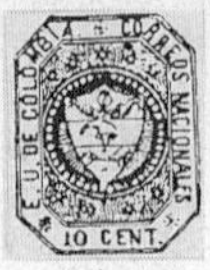

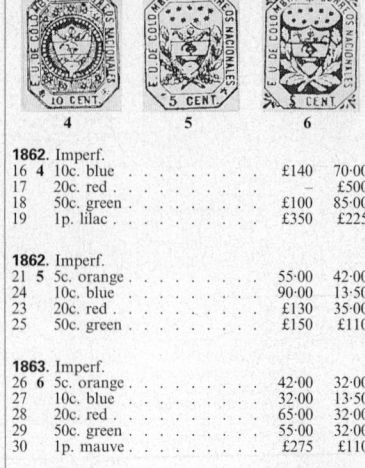

4

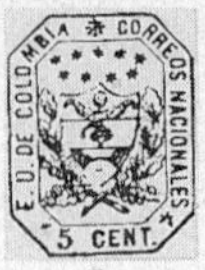

5

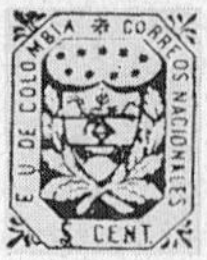

6

1862. Imperf.

16	**4**	10c. blue	£140	70·00
17		20c. red	–	£500
18		50c. green	£100	85·00
19		1p. lilac	£350	£225

1862. Imperf.

21	**5**	5c. orange	55·00	42·00
24		10c. blue	90·00	13·50
23		20c. red	£130	35·00
25		50c. green	£150	£110

1863. Imperf.

26	**6**	5c. orange	42·00	32·00
27		10c. blue	32·00	13·50
28		20c. red	65·00	32·00
29		50c. green	55·00	32·00
30		1p. mauve	£275	£110

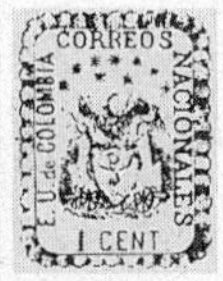

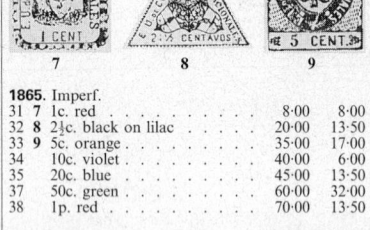

7

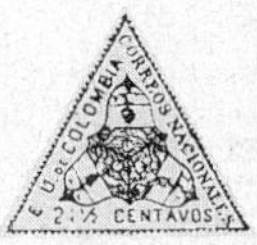

8

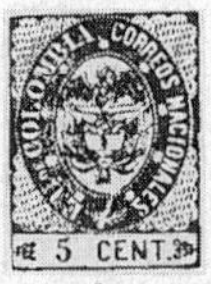

9

1865. Imperf.

31	**7**	1c. red	8·00	8·00
32	**8**	2½c. black on lilac	20·00	13·50
33	**9**	5c. orange	35·00	17·00
34		10c. violet	40·00	6·00
35		20c. blue	45·00	13·50
37		50c. green	60·00	32·00
38		1p. red	70·00	13·50

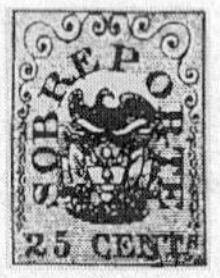

10

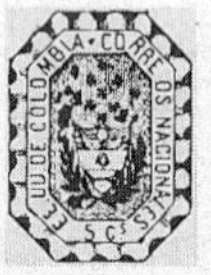

12

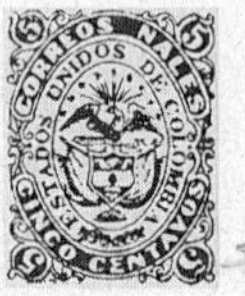

19

1865. Imperf.

39	**10**	25c. black on blue	45·00	35·00
40		50c. black on yellow	35·00	40·00
41		1p. black on red	£110	£100

1866. Imperf. Various Arms Designs.

44	**12**	5c. orange	42·00	25·00
45	–	10c. lilac	13·00	6·00
46	–	20c. blue	27·00	15·00
47	–	50c. green	10·50	10·50
48	–	1p. red	60·00	20·00
49	–	5p. black on green	–	£130
50	–	10p. black on red	£275	£120

1868. Arms (various frames) inscr "ESTADOS UNIDOS DE COLOMBIA". Imperf.

51	**19**	5c. yellow	60·00	42·00
52		10c. lilac	1·25	70
54		20c. blue	1·25	45
55		50c. green	1·25	85
57		1p. red	3·00	1·25

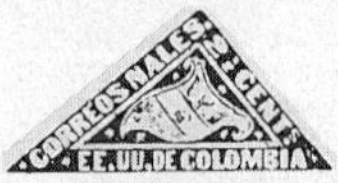

24

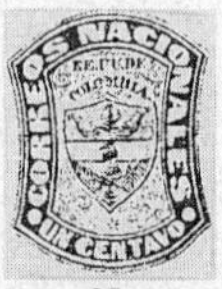

25

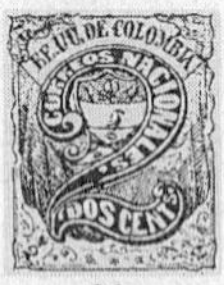

26

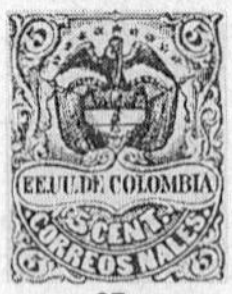

27

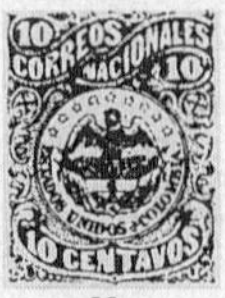

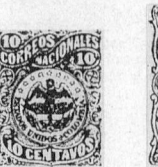

28

30

1869. Imperf.

58	**24**	2½c. black on violet	3·50	1·40

1870. Imperf.

59a	**25**	1c. green	3·00	2·10
60		1c. red	2·10	2·10
61	**26**	2c. brown	45	45
62	**27**	5c. orange	55	35
65a	**28**	10c. mauve	55	25
67		25c. black on blue	6·50	6·00
87		25c. green	15·00	15·00

1870. Different frames. Imperf.

69	**30**	5p. black on green	5·00	4·25
71		10p. black on red	5·50	3·25

See also Nos. 118/19.

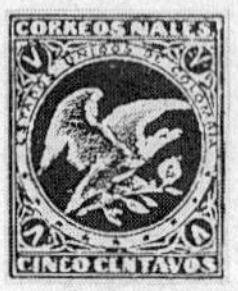

32 Andean Condor

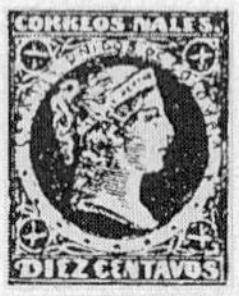

33

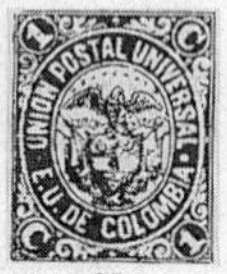

35

1876. Imperf.

84	**32**	5c. violet	5·75	1·90
85	**33**	10c. brown	90	25
86	–	20c. blue	1·10	35

DESIGN: 20c. As Type **33** but with different frame.

1881. Imperf.

93	**35**	1c. green	2·75	1·75
99		2c. red	80	65
100		5c. blue	1·75	45
101		10c. purple	1·25	85
97		20c. black	1·40	55

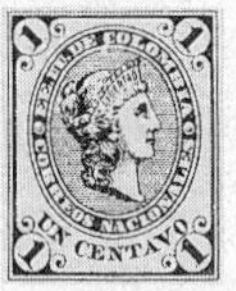

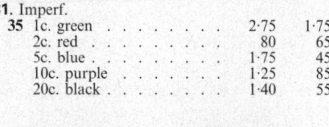

39

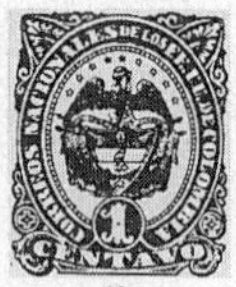

40

1881. Imperf.

102	**39**	1c. black on green	1·25	1·25
103		2c. black on rose	1·25	1·25
104		5c. black on lilac	1·75	75

1883. Inscr "CORREOS NACIONALES DE LOS E.E. U.U. DE COLOMBIA".

106a	**40**	1c. yellow on green	35	35
107		2c. red on pink	45	45
109		5c. blue on blue	45	25
111		10c. orange on yellow	25	25
112		20c. mauve on lilac	35	35
113		50c. brown on buff	90	90
114		1p. red on blue	3·00	55
115		5p. brown on yellow	2·50	2·25
116		10p. black on red	5·50	6·50

1886. Perf.

118	**30**	5p. brown	1·25	1·00
119		10p. black on lilac	1·25	1·00

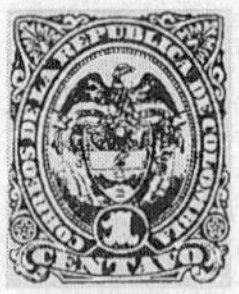

42

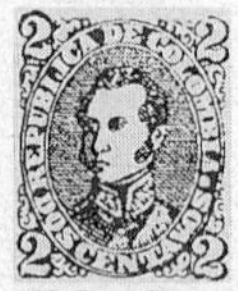

43 Gen. Sucre

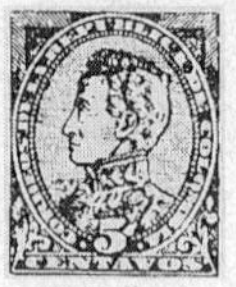

44 Bolivar

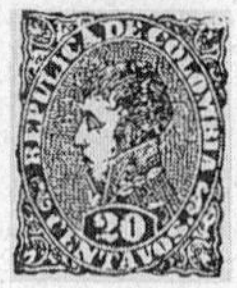

46 Gen. Nerino

1886.

120	**42**	1c. green	1·75	60
121	**43**	2c. red on pink	75	75
124	**44**	5c. blue on blue	2·10	15
125	–	10c. orange (Pres. Nunez)	1·40	25
126	**46**	20c. violet on lilac ("REPULICA")	90	35
137		20c. violet on lilac ("REPUBLICA")	1·10	50
130	**42**	50c. brown on buff	40	45
132		1p. mauve	2·10	1·00
133		5p. brown	8·50	5·00
134		5p. black	10·00	7·50
135		10p. black on pink	16·00	4·25

See also Nos. 162/4a.

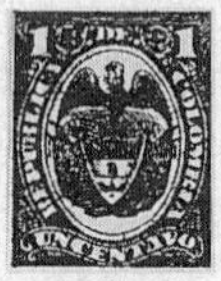

48

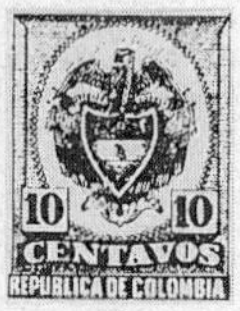

51

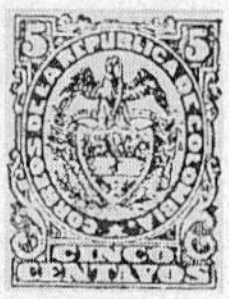

50

1890.

143	**48**	1c. green on green	2·50	85
144	**51**	2c. red on pink	70	50
145	**50**	5c. blue on blue	55	20
147	**51**	10c. brown on yellow	55	20
148		20c. violet	1·60	1·60

See also Nos. 149, etc.

53

54

55

58

61

75

1892.

149b 48 1c. red on yellow 15 10
150 53 2c. red on rose . . . . . 9·00 9·00
151a 2c. green 15 10
152a 50 5c. black on brown . . . 6·50 20
153 54 5c. brown on brown . . . 20 20
155 51 10c. brown on red . . . 20 20
156 55 20c. brown on blue . . . 20 20
159 42 50c. violet on lilac 35 20
161 58 1p. blue on green . . . 85 20
162 42 5p. red on pink . . . . . 9·00 1·25
164 10p. blue . . . . 7·50 1·25

1898.

171 61 1c. red on yellow 25 25
172 5c. brown on brown . . . 25 25
173 10c. brown on red . . . . 3·25 1·25
174 50c. blue on lilac . . . . . 1·00 75

For stamps showing map of Panama and inscr "COLOMBIA" see Panama Nos. 5/18.

For provisionals issued at Cartagena during the Civil War, 1899–1902, see list in Stanley Gibbons Stamp Catalogue Part 20 (South America).

1902. Arms in various frames. Imperf or perf.
259 75 ½c. brown 85 85
260 1c. green . . . . 2·50 2·10
192 2c. black on red 15 15
261 2c. blue 60 35
193 4c. red on green 15 15
194 4c. blue on green 20 20
195 5c. green on green 15 15
196 5c. blue on blue 10 10
262 5c. red 60 60
197 10c. black on pink 15 15
263 10c. mauve 85 25
198 20c. brown on brown 15 15
199 20c. blue on brown 20 20
200 50c. green on red 45 45
201 50c. blue on red . . . . . 1·50 1·50
202 1p. purple on brown . . . 25 25

82

85 River Magdalena

1903. Imperf or perf.
203 82 5p. green on blue . . . . 9·00 4·25
204 10p. green on green . . . 9·00 9·00
205 50p. orange on red . . . . 45·00 42·00
206 100p. blue on red . . . . 38·00 35·00
Nos. 205/6 are larger (31 × 38 mm).

1902. Imperf or perf.
212 85 2c. green 80 80
213 2c. blue 80 80
214 2c. red . . . . 10·00 10·00
215 – 10c. red 50 50
216 – 10c. pink 50 50
219 – 10c. orange . . . . 8·00 8·00
242 – 10c. blue on brown . . . . 1·75 1·75
243 – 10c. blue on green . . . . 5·00 4·25
247 – 10c. blue on red . . . . 2·50 2·50
245 – 10c. blue on lilac . . . . 13·00 13·00
220 – 20c. violet 40 40
221 – 20c. blue . . . . 3·25 3·25
224 – 20c. red . . . . 12·00 12·00
DESIGNS: 10c. Iron Quay, Savanilla, with eagle above; 20c. Hill of La Popa.

88 Gunboat "Cartagena"

89 Bolivar

90 General Pinzon

91

92

1903. Imperf or perf.
225 88 5c. blue . . . . 2·10 2·10
226 5c. brown . . . . 3·25 3·25
227 89 50c. green . . . . 5·00 5·00
228 50c. brown . . . . 4·25 4·25
230 50c. orange . . . . 4·25 4·25
231 50c. red . . . . 3·25 3·25
233 90 1p. brown 90 65
234 1p. red 90 90
235 1p. blue . . . . 3·50 3·25
237 91 5p. brown . . . . 6·00 6·00
238 5p. purple . . . . 3·75 3·75
239 5p. green . . . . 6·00 6·00
240 92 10p. green . . . . 6·50 6·00
241 10p. purple . . . . 14·00 14·00

93

96

97

98 President Marroquin

1902.

248 93 1c. green on yellow 20 20
249 2c. red on pink 20 20
250 5c. blue 20 20
251 10c. brown on yellow . . . 20 20
252 20c. mauve on pink 10 10
253 50c. red on green . . . . 1·00 1·25
254 1p. black on yellow . . . . 3·25 2·50
255 5p. blue on blue . . . . 20·00 15·00
256 10p. brown on pink . . . 14·00 11·00

1904.

270 96 ½c. yellow 55 10
274 1c. green 40 10
278 2c. red 40 10
281 5c. blue . . . . 1·00 10
283 10c. violet 45 20
284 20c. black 75 15
286 97 1p. brown . . . . 13·00 1·60
287 98 5p. black and red . . . . 38·00 30·00
288 10p. black and blue . . . 42·00 32·00

102 Camilo Torres

104 Narino demanding Liberation of Slaves

1910. Centenary of Independence.
345 102 ½c. black and purple . . . 35 20
346 – 1c. green 35 10
347 – 2c. red 35 10
348 – 5c. blue . . . . 1·00 25
349 – 10c. purple . . . . . . 6·50 5·00
350 – 20c. brown . . . . . . 12·00 7·50
351 104 1p. purple . . . . 75·00 22·00
352 – 10p. lake £300 £200
DESIGNS—As Type 102: 1c. P. Salavarrieta; 2c. Narino; 5c. Bolivar; 10c. Caldas; 20c. Santander. As Type 104: 10p. Bolivar resigning.

110 C. Torres

113 Arms

111 Boyaca Monument

123 La Sabana Station

112 Cartagena

1917. Portraits as T 110.
357 110 ½c. yellow (Caldas) . . . 10 15
358 1c. green (Torres) 10 10
393 113 1½c. brown 45 45
359 110 2c. red (Narino) 10 10
380 113 3c. red on yellow 20 10
394 3c. blue 20 15
360 110 4c. purple (Santander) . . 45 10
395 4c. blue (Santander) . . . 20 10
361 5c. blue (Bolivar) . . . . 2·50 20
396 5c. red (Bolivar) . . . . 2·50 15
397 113 8c. blue 20 15
362 110 10c. grey (Cordoba) . . . 2·50 20
398 10c. blue (Cordoba) . . . 6·50 35
363 111 20c. red . . . . 1·40 25
399 113 30c. bistre (Caldas) . . . 7·00 25
400 123 40c. brown . . . . 14·00 4·50
364 112 50c. red . . . . 1·60 25
606 50c. red (San Pedro Alejandrino) . . . . . 8·25 3·75
365a 110 1p. blue (Sucre) . . . . 10·00 40
366 2p. orange (Cuervo) . . . 12·00 25
367 5p. grey (Ricaurte) . . . 35·00 10·00
401 5p. violet (Ricaurte) . . . 3·50 35
368 113 10p. brown . . . . 35·00 8·50
402 10p. green . . . . 5·00 90
For similar 40c. see No. 541.

1918. Surch **Especie Provisional** and value.
374 96 0.00½c. on 20c. black . . . 70 10
376 0.03c. on 10c. violet . . . 1·40 35

115

124

1918.
378 115 3c. red 75 10

1918. Air. No. 359 optd **1er Servicio Postal Aereo 6-18-19.**
379 2c. red £2500 £1600

1920. As T 75, 96 and 113 but with "PROVISIONAL" added in label across design.
381 96 ½c. yellow . . . . 1·10 20
382 1c. green 55 10
383 2c. red 55 20
384 113 3c. green 40 20
385 96 5c. blue 90 25
386 10c. violet . . . . 5·00 1·25
387 10c. blue . . . . 8·50 4·00
388 20c. green . . . . 6·00 3·25
389 75 50c. red . . . . 7·50 2·50

1921. No. 360 surch **PROVICIONAL $003.**
390 $0.03 on 4c. purple 65 20

1921. No. 360 surch **PROVISIONAL $0.03.**
392 $0.03 on 4c. purple . . . . . 2·75 75

1924.
403 124 1c. red 75 25
404 3c. blue 65 25

1925. Large fiscal stamps surch **CORREOS 1 CENTAVO** or optd **CORREOS PROVISIONAL.**
405 1c. on 3c. brown 55 10
406 4c. purple 55 25

127

129 Death of Bolivar (after P. A. Quijano)

1926.
410 127 1c. green 40 10
411 4c. blue 40 10

1930. Death Centenary of Bolivar.
412 129 4c. black and blue 25 10

132

133 Galleon

1932. Air. Optd **CORREO AEREO.**
413 132 5c. yellow . . . . 3·25 3·25
414 10c. purple 80 25
415 15c. green . . . . 1·40 1·40
416 20c. red 80 45
417 30c. blue 80 25
418 40c. lilac . . . . 1·60 55
419 50c. olive . . . . 3·50 2·50
420 60c. brown . . . . 3·50 2·50
421 80c. green . . . . 10·00 8·50
422 133 1p. blue . . . . 8·50 5·00
423 2p. red . . . . 26·00 19·00
424 3p. mauve . . . . 55·00 50·00
425 5p. olive . . . . 75·00 65·00
These and similar stamps without the "CORREO AEREO" overprint were issues of a private air company and are not listed in this catalogue.

1932. Nos. 395 and 399 surch.
427 1c. on 4c. blue 20 10
428 20c. on 30c. bistre . . . . . 7·00 20

137 Oil Wells

138 Coffee Plantation

140 Gold Mining

141 Columbus

1932. 1c. is vert, 8c. is horiz.
429 – 1c. green (Emeralds) . . . 85 10
430 137 2c. red (Oil) 85 10
431 138 5c. brown (Coffee) . . . 85 10
432 – 8c. blue (Platinum) . . . 7·50 25
485 140 10c. yellow (Gold) . . . . 6·50 10
486 141 20c. blue . . . . 21·00 60

142 Coffee

143 Gold

1932. Air.
435 142 5c. brown and orange . . 45 20
436 – 10c. black and red 85 20
437 – 15c. violet and green . . . 40 15
438 – 15c. violet and red . . . 5·00 15
439 – 20c. green and red 85 10
440 – 20c. olive and green . . . 4·00 25
441 142 30c. brown and blue . . . 3·25 10
442 – 40c. bistre and violet . . 1·60 10
443 – 50c. brown and green . . 13·00 1·25
444 – 60c. violet and brown . . 2·50 25
445 142 80c. brown and green . . 15·00 65
446 143 1p. bistre and blue . . . 13·00 70
447 2p. bistre and red . . . . 14·00 1·90
448 – 3p. green and violet . . . 21·00 7·00
449 – 5p. green and olive . . . 50·00 19·00
DESIGNS—As Type 142: 10c., 50c. Cattle; 15c., 60c. Oil Wells; 20c., 40c. Bananas. As Type 143: 3p., 5p. Emeralds.

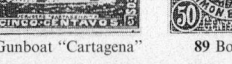

144 Pedro de Heredia

148 Coffee Plantation

147 Oil Wells

151 Allegory of 1935 Olympiad

1934. 400th Anniv of Cartagena.
451 144 1c. green . . . . 1·50 55
452 5c. brown . . . . 2·50 55
453 8c. blue . . . . 1·50 55

1934. Air. 4th Centenary of Cartagena. Surch **CARTAGENA 1533 1933** and value.
454 – 10c. on 50c. brown and green (No. 443) . . . . 3·50 3·50
455 142 15c. on 80c. brn & grn . . 3·50 3·50
456 143 20c. on 1p. bis & bl . . . 5·50 6·00
457 30c. on 2p. bistre and red 6·00 6·00

1934.
458 147 2c. red 10 10
459 148 5c. brown . . . . 3·50 10
460 – 10c. orange . . . . 17·00 10
DESIGN: 10c. Gold miner facing left.

1935. 3rd National Olympiad. Inscr "III OLIMPIADA BARRANQUILLA 1935".
461 – 2c. orange and green . . 75 25
462 – 4c. green 75 25
463 151 5c. yellow and brown . . . 75 20
464 – 7c. red . . . . 1·75 1·50
465 – 8c. mauve and black . . . 1·75 1·50
466 – 10c. blue and brown . . . 1·75 1·10
467 – 12c. blue . . . . 1·75 1·90
468 – 15c. red and blue . . . . 4·25 3·00
469 – 18c. yellow and purple . . 5·00 5·00
470 – 20c. green and violet . . . 5·00 3·25
471 – 24c. blue and green . . . 6·00 4·25
472 – 50c. orange and blue . . . 6·00 3·75
473 – 1p. blue and olive . . . . 60·00 38·00
474 – 2p. blue and green . . . £100 70·00
475 – 5p. blue and violet . . . £300 £250
476 – 10p. blue and black . . . £650 £500
DESIGNS—VERT: 2c. Footballers; 4c. Discus

thrower; 1p. G.P.O.; 2p. "Flag of the Race" Monument; 5p. Arms; 10p. Andean condor. HORIZ: 7c. Runners; 8c. Tennis player; 10c. Hurdler; 12c. Pier; 15c. Athlete; 18c. Baseball; 20c. Seashore; 24c. Swimmer; 50c. Aerial view of Barranquilla.

152 Nurse and Patients

1935. Obligatory Tax. Red Cross.
477 **152** 5c. red and green . . . . 1·75 45

1935. Surch **12 CENTAVOS**.
478 12c. on 1p. blue (No. 365a) 4·25 1·25

154 Simon Bolivar

155 Tequendama Falls

1937.
487 **154** 1c. green 10 10
488 **155** 10c. red 10 10
489 12c. blue . . . . 3·75 1·25

156 Footballer

157 Discus Thrower

1937. 4th National Olympiad.
490 **156** 3c. green 80 55
491 **157** 10c. red . . . . 3·25 1·60
492 – 1p. black . . . . 30·00 24·00
DESIGN: 1p. Runner (20½ × 27 mm).

159 Exhibition Palace

161 Mother and Child

1937. Barranquilla Industrial Exhibition.
493 **159** 5c. purple . . . . 1·60 25
494 – 15c. blue . . . . 6·00 3·25
495 – 50c. brown . . . . 17·00 6·00
DESIGNS—HORIZ: 15c. Stadium. VERT: 50c. "Flag of the Race" Monument.

1937. Obligatory Tax. Red Cross.
509 **161** 5c. red . . . . 1·40 55

1937. Surch in figures and words.
510 **156** 1c. on 3c. green 60 55
511 **155** 2c. on 12c. blue 30 30
512 – 5c. on 8c. blue (No. 432) 35 25
513 – 5c. on 8c. blue (No. 397) 35 25
514 **155** 10c. on 12c. blue . . . . 4·25 85

164 Entrance to Church of the Rosary

166 "Bochica" (Indian god)

1938. 400th Anniv of Bogota.
515 – 1c. green 15 15
516 **164** 2c. red 15 10
517 – 5c. black 20 10
518 – 10c. brown 40 25
519 **166** 15c. blue . . . . 3·25 90
520 – 20c. mauve . . . . 3·25 90
521 – 1p. brown . . . . 30·00 25·00
DESIGNS—VERT: 1c. "Calle del Arco" ("Street of the Arch") Old Bogota; 5c. Bogota Arms; 10c. G. J. de Quesada. HORIZ (larger): 20c. Convent of S. Domingo; 1p. First Mass on Site of Bogota.

168 Proposed P.O., Bogota

1939. Obligatory Tax. P.O. Rebuilding Fund.
522 **168** ½c. blue 10 10
564 ½c. purple 10 10
523 ½c. red 10 10
524 1c. violet 10 10
567 1c. orange 10 10
525 2c. green 25 10
526 20c. brown . . . . 3·25 30

1939. Air. Surch **5 cts** or **15 cts** and bar.
527 5c. on 20c. (No. 439) 25 20
528 5c. on 40c. (No. 442) 25 20
530 15c. on 30c. (No. 441) . . . 60 15
531 15c. on 40c. (No. 442) . . . 1·10 25

171 Bolivar

172 Coffee Plantation

173 Arms of Colombia

174 Columbus

175 Caldas

176 La Sabana Station

1939.
533 **171** 1c. green 10 10
535 **172** 5c. brown 10 10
536 5c. blue 10 10
538 **173** 15c. blue . . . . 1·40 10
539 **174** 20c. black . . . . 17·00 30
540 **175** 30c. olive . . . . 5·50 40
541 **176** 40c. brown . . . . 28·00 14·00
For similar 40c. see No. 400.

178 Proposed New P.O., Bogota

1940. Obligatory Tax. P.O. Rebuilding Fund.
542 **178** ½c. blue 10 10
543 ½c. red 10 10
544 1c. violet 10 10
545 2c. green 15 10
546 20c. brown . . . . 1·60 25

179 "Arms and the Law"

180 Bridge at Boyaca

1940. Death Centenary of Gen. Santander.
547 – 1c. olive 20 20
548 **179** 2c. red 25 15
549 – 5c. brown 25 20
550 – 8c. red 90 40
551 – 10c. yellow 45 40
552 – 15c. blue . . . . 1·10 55
553 – 20c. green . . . . 1·40 60
554 **180** 50c. violet . . . . 2·50 2·10
555 – 1p. red . . . . 11·00 10·00
556 – 2p. orange . . . . 35·00 32·00
DESIGNS—VERT: 1c. Gen. Santander; 5c. Medallion of Santander by David; 8c. Santander's statue, Cucuta; 15c. Church at Rosario. HORIZ: 10c. Santander's birthplace, Rosario; 20c. Battlefield at Paya; 1p. Death of Santander; 2p. Victorious Army at Zamora.

181 Tobacco Plant

182 Santander

183 Garcia Rovira

184 General Sucre

185 "Protection"

1940.
557 **181** 8c. green and red 45 30
558 **182** 15c. blue 80 25
559 **183** 20c. grey . . . . 4·00 25
560 – 40c. brown (Galan) . . . 2·50 40
561 **184** 1p. black . . . . 11·00 1·25
562 1p. violet . . . . 2·50 70

1940. Obligatory Tax. Red Cross Fund.
563 **185** 5c. red 25 15

186 Pre-Colombian Monument

187 Proclamation of Independence

1941. Air.
568 **186** 5c. grey 25 10
691 5c. yellow 20 10
742 5c. blue 35 15
747 5c. red 35 15
569 – 10c. orange 25 10
692 – 10c. red 20 10
743 – 10c. blue 35 20
570 15c. red 25 10
693 – 15c. blue 20 10
571 – 20c. green 40 10
694 – 20c. violet 20 10
745 – 20c. blue 45 25
749 – 20c. red 45 25
572 **186** 30c. blue 40 10
695 30c. green 35 10
750 30c. red 75 10
573 – 40c. purple . . . . 1·60 10
696 – 40c. grey 55 10
574 – 50c. green . . . . 1·60 10
697 – 50c. red 65 10
575 – 60c. purple . . . . 1·60 10
698 – 60c. olive 85 10
576 **186** 80c. olive . . . . 4·00 35
699 80c. brown . . . . 1·25 10
577 **187** 1p. black and blue . . . 4·00 20
700 1p. brown and olive . . . 3·00 35
578 – 2p. black and red . . . . 8·00 1·25
701 – 2p. blue and green . . . 3·75 55
579 **187** 3p. black and violet . . . 14·00 4·00
702 3p. black and red . . . . 7·00 3·50
580 – 5p. black and green . . . 35·00 17·00
703 – 5p. green and sepia . . . 20·00 8·50
DESIGNS: As Type **186**: 10c., 40c. "El Dorado" Monument; 15c., 50c. Spanish Fort, Cartagena; 20c., 60c. Street in Old Bogota. As Type **187**: 2p., 5p. National Library, Bogota.

188 Arms of Palmira

189 Home of Jorge Isaacs (author)

1942. 8th National Agricultural Exn, Palmira.
581 **188** 30c. red . . . . 5·00 70

1942. Honouring J. Isaacs.
582 **189** 50c. green . . . . 3·25 35

190 Peace Conference Delegates

1942. 40th Anniv of Wisconsin Peace Treaty ending Civil War.
583 **190** 10c. orange . . . . 3·25 45

1943. Surch **$ 0.0½ MEDIO CENTAVO**.
584 **168** ½c. on 1c. violet 10 10
585 ½c. on 2c. green 10 10
586 ½c. on 20c. brown 20 20

1944. Surch **5 Centavos**.
587 5c. on 10c. orge (No. 460) . . 20 15

193 National Shrine

194 San Pedro, Alejandrino

1944.
592 **193** 30c. olive . . . . 2·10 1·25
593 **194** 50c. red . . . . 2·10 1·25

1944. Surch with new values in figures and words.
594 **172** 1c. on 5c. brn (No. 535) 15 15
595 2c. on 5c. brn (No. 535) 15 15

195 Banner

199 Manuel Murillo Toro

196 Viceroy Solis Building

1944. 75th Anniv of General Benefit Institution of Cundinamarca.
596 **195** 2c. blue and yellow . . . 10 10
597 – 5c. blue and yellow . . . 10 10
598 – 20c. black and green . . . 95 75
599 – 40c. black and red . . . . 4·25 3·25
600 **196** 1p. black and red . . . . 8·50 6·50
DESIGNS: As T **195**: 5c. Arms of the Institution; 20c. Manuel Murillo Toro. As T **196**: 40c. St. Juan de Dios Maternity Hospital.

1944.
602 **199** 5c. olive 35 20

201 Proposed P.O., Bogota

(202 Stalin, Roosevelt and Churchill)

1945. Obligatory Tax. P.O. Rebuilding Fund.
609 **201** ½c. blue 10 10
610 ½c. brown 10 10
611 ½c. red 10 10
612 ½c. mauve 10 10
613 1c. violet 10 10
614 1c. orange 10 10
615 1c. green 10 10
616 2c. green 10 10
617a 20c. brown 80 10

1945. Victory. Optd with T **202**.
618 **172** 5c. brown 25 15

203 Clock Tower, Cartagena

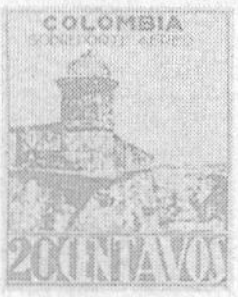

204 Fort San Sebastian Cartagena

1945.
621 **203** 50c. green . . . . 2·50 80

1945. Air.
622 **204** 5c. grey 20 10
623 – 10c. orange 20 10
624 – 15c. red 20 10
625 **204** 20c. green 25 10
626 – 30c. blue 35 10
627 – 40c. red 55 10
628 **204** 50c. green 70 15
629 – 60c. purple . . . . 3·25 80
630 – 80c. grey . . . . 5·00 55
631 – 1p. blue . . . . 5·00 55
632 – 2p. red . . . . 7·50 2·40

DESIGNS—As Type **204**: 10c., 30c., 60c. Tequendama Falls; 15c., 40c., 80c. Santa Marta. HORIZ (larger): 1p., 2p. Capitol, Bogota.

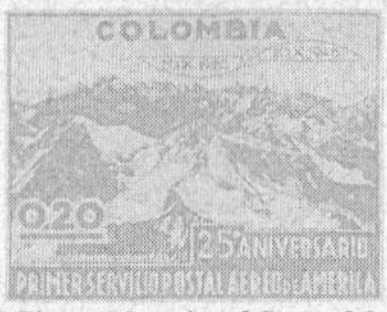

207 Sierra Nevada of Santa Maria

1945. 25th Anniv of 1st Air Mail Service in America.
633 **207** 20c. green . . . . 1·25 60
634 – 30c. blue . . . . 1·25 60
635 – 50c. red . . . . 1·25 60
DESIGNS: 30c. Junkers F-13 seaplane "Tolima"; 50c. San Sebastian Fortress, Cartagena.

1946. Surch **1** above **UN CENTAVO**.
636 **138** 1c. on 5c. brown 15 15

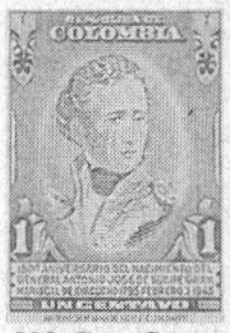
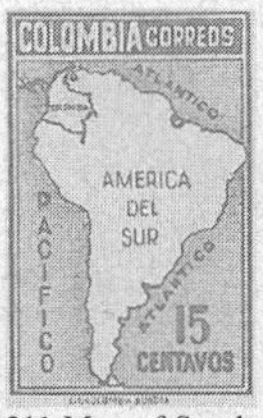

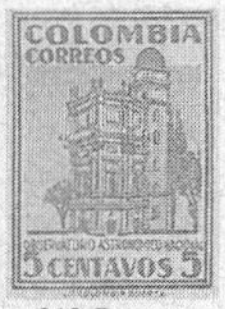

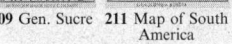

209 Gen. Sucre **211** Map of South America **212** Bogota Observatory

1946.
638 **209** 1c. blue and brown . . . 20 10
639 2c. red and violet 20 10
640 5c. blue and olive 20 10
641 9c. red and green 45 35
642 10c. orange and blue . . 35 25
643 20c. orange and black . . 45 25
644 30c. green and red 45 25
645 40c. red and green 45 25
646 50c. violet and purple . . 45 25
The 5c. to 50c. are larger (23½ × 32 mm).

1946. Obligatory Tax. Red Cross Fund. Optd with red cross.
647 **172** 5c. brown (No. 535) . . . 25 20

1946.
648 **211** 15c. blue 25 10

1946.
649 **212** 5c. brown 10 10
650 5c. blue 10 10

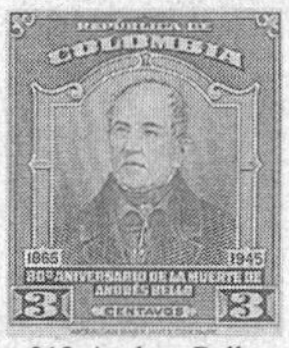

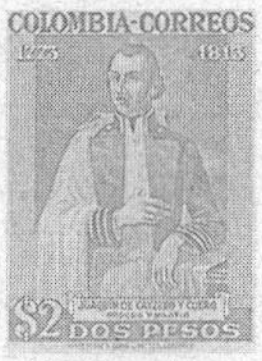

213 Andres Bello **214** Joaquin de Cayzedo y Cuero

1946. 80th Death Anniv of Andres Bello (poet and teacher).
651 **213** 3c. brown (postage) . . . 25 15
652 10c. orange 40 10
653 15c. black 55 10
654 5c. blue (air) 25 15

1946.
655 **214** 2p. turquoise . . . . . . 5·00 45
656 2p. green 65 20

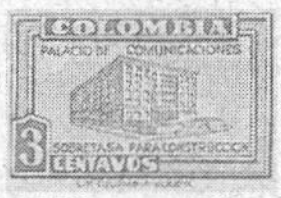

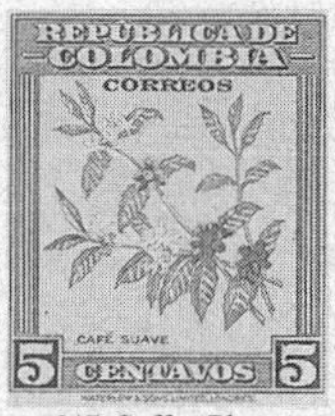

215 Proposed New P.O., Bogota **217** Coffee Plant

1946. Obligatory Tax. P.O. Rebuilding Fund.
657 **215** 3c. blue 15 10

1946. 5th Central American and Caribbean Games, Barranquilla. As No. 621 optd **V JUEGOS C. A. Y DEL C. 1946**.
658 50c. red . . . . 2·50 1·60

1947.
659 **217** 5c. multicoloured 35 10

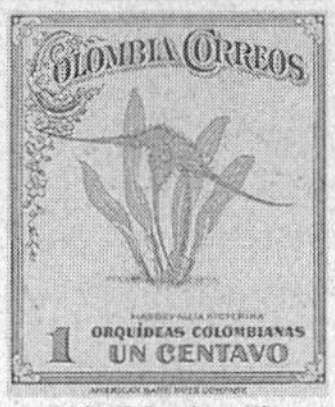

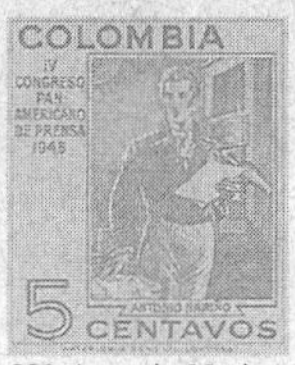

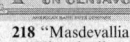

218 "Masdevallia Nicterina" **220** Antonio Narino

1947. Colombian Orchids. Multicoloured.
660 1c. Type **218** 10 10
661 2c. "Miltonia vexillaria" . . 10 10
662 5c. "Cattleya dowiana aurea" 45 20
663 5c. "Cattleya chocoensis" . . 45 20
664 5c. "Odontoglossum crispum" 45 20
665 10c. "Cattleya labiata trianae" 65 15

1947. Obligatory Tax. Optd **SOBRETASA** in fancy letters.
666 **183** 20c. grey (No. 559) . . . 4·25 1·75
676 **141** 20c. blue (No. 486) . . . 25·00 17·00

1947. 4th Pan-American Press Conf, Bogota.
667 **220** 5c. blue on blue (post) . . 25 15
668 – 10c. brown on blue . . . 35 15
669 – 5c. blue on blue (air) . . 20 10
670 – 10c. red on blue 35 20
PORTRAITS: No. 668, A. Urdaneta y Urdaneta; 669, F. J. de Caldas; 670, M. del Socorro Rodriguez.

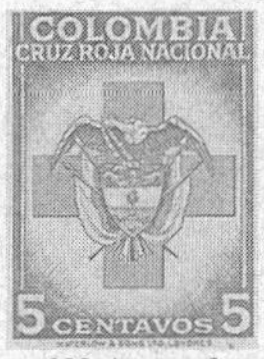

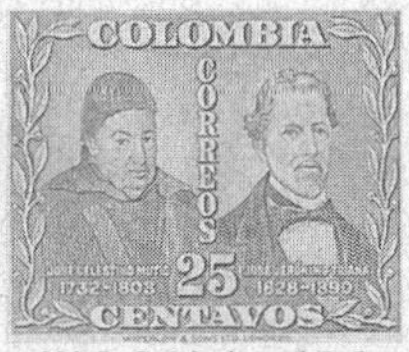

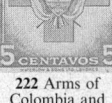

222 Arms of Colombia and Cross **223** J. C. Mutis and J. J. Triana

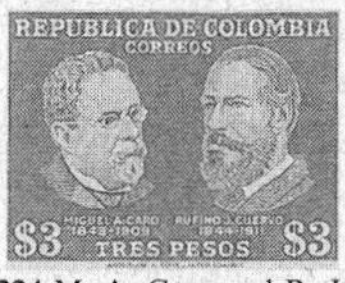

224 M. A. Caro and R. J. Cuervo

1947. Obligatory Tax. Red Cross Fund.
671 **222** 5c. lake 20 10
704 5c. red 20 10

1947.
673 **223** 25c. green 35 15
675 **224** 3p. purple 45 10

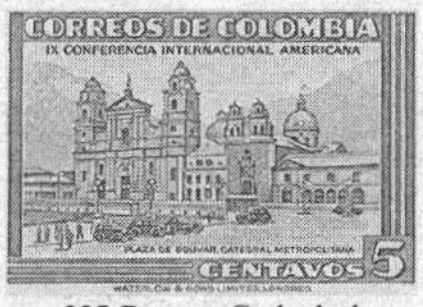

225 Bogota Cathedral

1948. 9th Pan-American Congress, Bogota. Inscr as in T **225**.
677 **225** 5c. brown (postage) 15 10
678 – 10c. orange 25 20
679 – 15c. blue 25 20
680 – 5c. brown (air) 15 10
681 – 15c. blue 35 25
DESIGNS—No. 678, National Capitol; 679, Foreign Office; 680, Chancellery; 681, Raphael Court, Capitol.

1948. Obligatory Tax. Savings Bank stamps surch **COLOMBIA SOBRETASA 1 CENTAVO**. Various designs.
682 1c. on 5c. brown 10 10
683 1c. on 10c. violet 10 10
684 1c. on 25c. red 10 10
685 1c. on 50c. blue 10 10

1948. Optd **C** (= "CORREOS"). No gum.
686 **168** 1c. orange 10 10

1948. Optd **CORREOS**.
687 **201** 1c. olive 10 10
688 2c. green 10 10
689 20c. brown 20 10

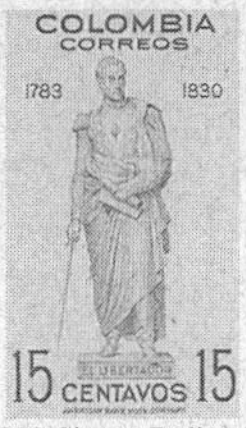

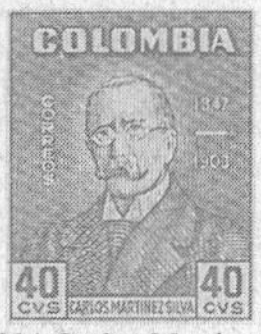

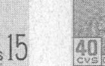

232 Simon Bolivar **234** Carlos Martinez Silva

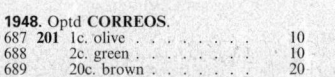

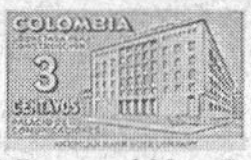
233 Proposed New P.O., Bogota

1948.
690 **232** 15c. green 35 15

1948. Obligatory Tax. P.O. Rebuilding Fund.
705 **233** 1c. red 10 10
706 2c. green 10 10
707 3c. blue 10 10
708 5c. grey 10 10
709 10c. violet 20 10
See also Nos. 756 and 758/62.

1949.
710 **234** 40c. red 35 10

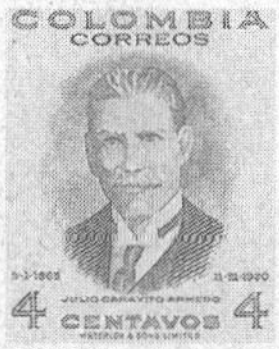

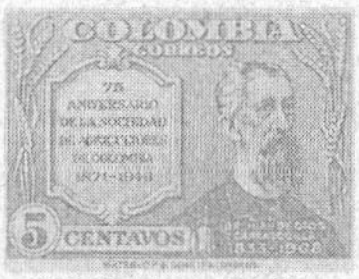

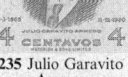

235 Julio Garavito Armero **236** Dr. Juan de Dios Carrasquilla

1949. J. G. Armero (mathematician).
711 **235** 4c. green 25 15

1949. 75th Anniv of National Agricultural Society.
712 **236** 5c. bistre 20 10

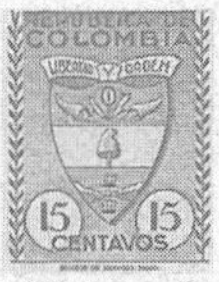

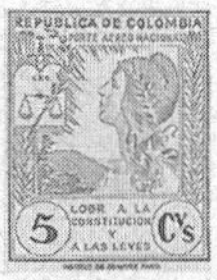

237 Arms of Colombia **238** Allegory of Justice

1949. New Constitution.
713 **237** 15c. blue (postage) . . . 20 10
714 **238** 5c. green (air) 15 10
715 – 10c. orange 15 10
DESIGN: 10c. Allegory of Constitution.

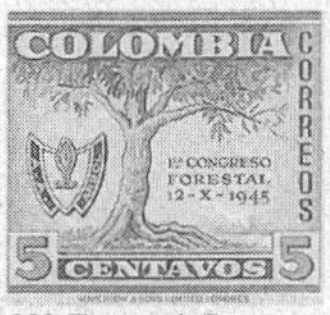

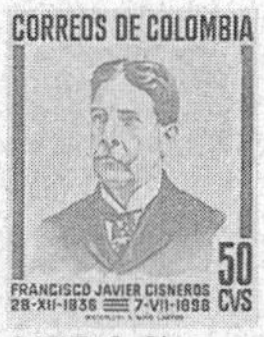

239 Tree and Congress Emblem **240** F. J. Cisneros

1949. 1st Forestry Congress, Bogota.
716 **239** 5c. olive 20 10

1949. 50th Death Anniv of Francisco Javier Cisneros (engineer).
717 **240** 50c. blue and brown . . . 1·00 50
718 50c. violet and green . . . 1·00 50
719 50c. yellow and purple . . 1·00 50

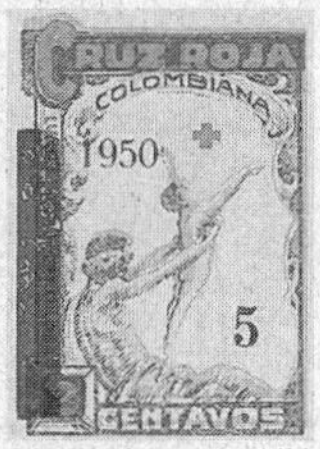

241 Mother and Child

1950. Red Cross Fund. Surch with new value and date as in T **241**.
720 **241** 5 on 2c. multicoloured . . 80 35

1950. Obligatory Tax. Optd **SOBRETASA**.
721 **172** 5c. blue 15 10

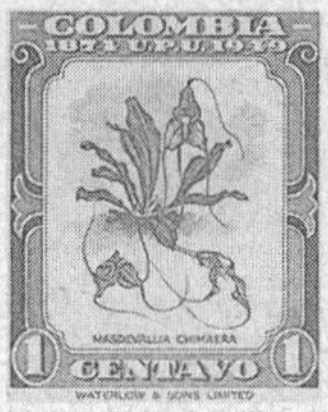

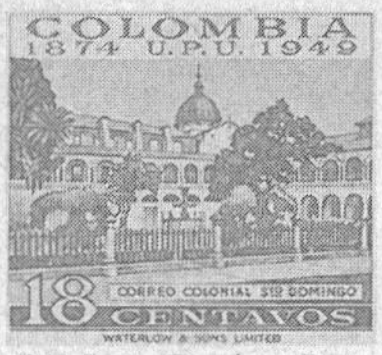

243 "Masdevallia Chimaera" **244** Santo Domingo Post Office

1950. 75th Anniv of U.P.U.
722 **243** 1c. brown 30 10
723 – 2c. violet 30 10
724 – 3c. mauve 10 10
725 – 4c. green 20 10
726 – 5c. orange 35 10
727 – 11c. red . . . . 1·60 75
728 **244** 18c. blue 80 40
DESIGNS—VERT: 3c. "Cattleya labiata trianae"; 4c. "Masdevallia nicterina"; 5c. "Cattleya dowiana aurea". HORIZ: 2c. "Odontoglossum crispum"; 11c. "Miltonia vexillaria".

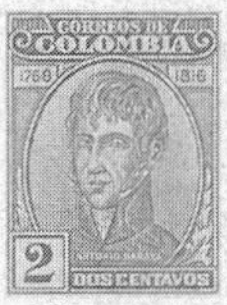

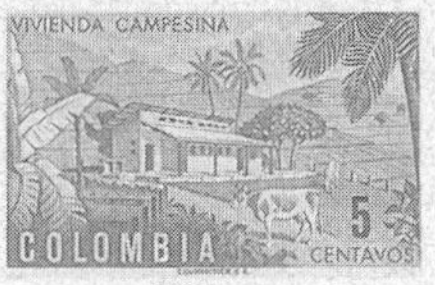

245 Antonio Baraya (patriot) **246** Farm

1950.
729 **245** 2c. red 10 10

1950.
730 **246** 5c. red and buff 30 15
731 5c. green and turquoise 30 15
732 5c. blue and light blue . . 30 15

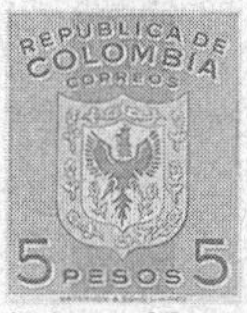

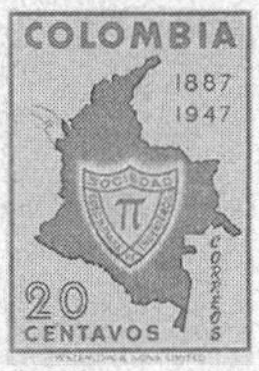

247 Arms of Bogota **248** Map and Badge

1950.
733 **247** 5p. green . . . . 1·60 10
734 – 10p. orange (Arms of Colombia) . . . . . . 2·40 15

1951. 60th Anniv of Colombian Society of Engineers.
735 **248** 20c. red, yellow and blue 35 15

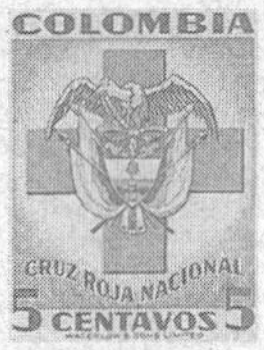

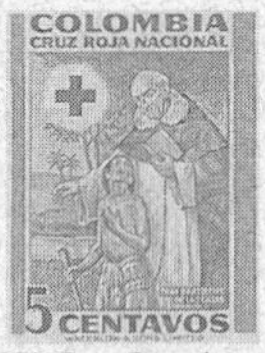

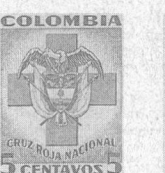

249 Arms of Colombia and Cross **250** Fray Bartolome de Las Casas

1951. Obligatory Tax. Red Cross Fund.
736 **249** 5c. red 20 15
737 **250** 5c. red 20 15
738 5c. green and red 20 10

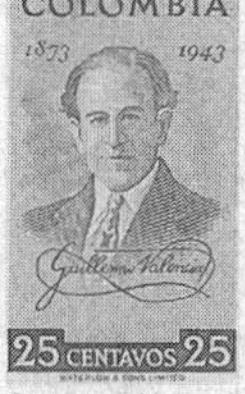

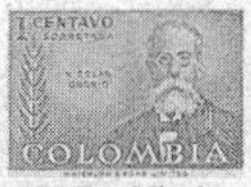

251 D. G. Valencia **254** Dr. Nicolas Osorio

1951. 8th Death Anniv of D. G. Valencia (poet and orator).
739 **251** 25c. black 40 10

1951. Surch **1 centavo**.
740 **233** 1c. on 3c. blue 10 10

1951. Nationalization of Barranca Oilfields. Optd **REVERSION CONCESION MARES 25 Agosto 1951**.
741 **147** 2c. red 10 10

1952. Colombian Doctors.
751 **254** 1c. blue 10 10
752 – 1c. blue (P. Martinez) . . 10 10
753 – 1c. bl (E. Uriocoechea) . . 10 10
754 – 1c. blue (Jose M. Lombana) 10 10

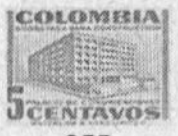

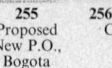

255 Proposed New P.O., Bogota

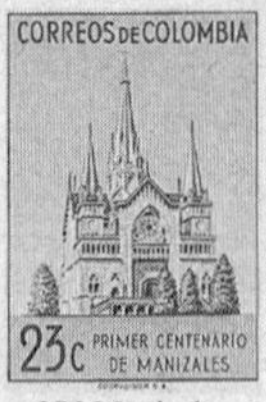

256 Manizales Cathedral

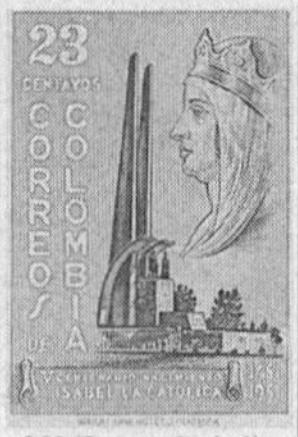

258 Queen Isabella and Columbus Monument

1952.

755	**255**	5c. blue	15	10
756	**233**	20c. brown	8·00	10
757	**201**	25c. grey	12·00	1·60
758	**233**	25c. green	20	10
759	–	50c. orange	25·00	14·00
760	–	1p. red	55	25
761	–	2p. purple	27·00	2·50
762	–	2p. violet	65	10

DESIGN: 50c. to 2p. Similar to T **233** but larger, 24½ × 19 mm.

Owing to a shortage of postage stamps the above obligatory tax types were issued for ordinary postal use.

1952. Obligatory Tax. No. 759 surch.

763		8c. on 50c. orange	15	10

1952. Centenary of Manizales.

764	**256**	23c. black and blue	25	15

1952. 1st Latin-American Congress of Iron Specialists. Surch **1952 I' CONFERENCIA SIDERURGICA LATINO-AMERICANA.** and new value

765	**223**	15c. on 25c. green (postage)	30	20
766	**186**	70c. on 80c. red (air)	75	25

1953. 500th Birth Anniv of Isabella the Catholic.

767	**258**	23c. black and blue	35	35

1953. Air. Optd **CORREO AEREO** or surch also.

768	**233**	5c. on 8c. blue	15	10
769		15c. on 20c. brown	25	10
770		15c. on 25c. green	65	10
771		25c. green	30	10

1953. Air. Optd **AEREO**.

772	**155**	10c. red	15	10

EXTRA RAPIDO. Stamps bearing this overprint or inscription were used to prepay the additional cost of air carriage of inland mail handled by the National Postal Service from 1953 to 1964. Subsequently remaining stocks of these stamps were used for other classes of correspondence. Since the 1920s regular air service for inland and foreign mail has been provided by the Air Postal Service, a separate undertaking which is administered by the Avianca airline and for which the regular air stamps are used.

1953. Air. No. 727 surch **CORREO EXTRA RAPIDO 5 5**.

773		5c. on 11c. red	20	10

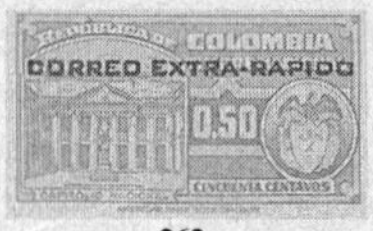

262

1953. Air. Fiscal stamps optd as in T **262** or surch also.

774	**262**	1c. on 2c. green	10	10
775		50c. red	10	10

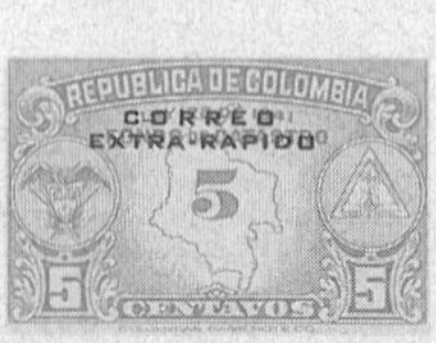

263

1953. Air. Real Estate Tax stamps optd as in T **263**.

776	**263**	5c. red	15	10
777		20c. brown	20	10

1953. Surch.

778	–	40c. on 1p. red (No. 760)	45	10
779	**214**	50c. on 2p. green	45	10

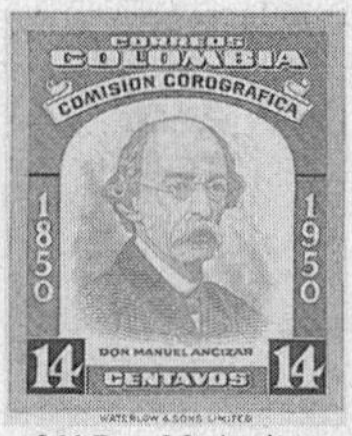

266 Don M. Ancizar

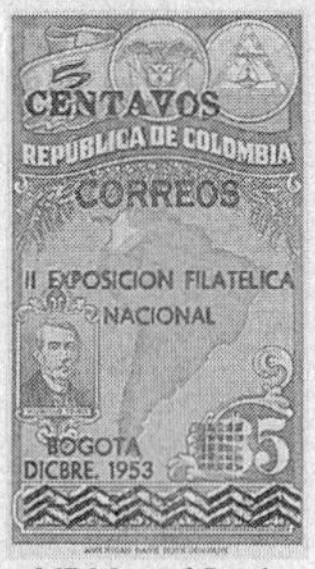

267 Map of South America

1953. Colombian Chorographical Commission Centenary. Portraits inscr as in T **266**.

780	**266**	14c. red and black	40	30
781	–	23c. blue and black	35	20
782	–	30c. sepia and black	35	15
783	–	1p. green and black	15	10

PORTRAITS: 23c. J. J. Triana; 30c. M. Ponce de Leon; 1p. A. Codazzi.

1953. 2nd National Philatelic Exhibition, Bogota. Real Estate Tax stamps surch as in T **267**.

784	**267**	5c. on 5p. mult (post)	35	15
785	–	15c. on 10p. multicoloured (air)	40	25

DESIGN: 15c. Map of Colombia.

1953. Air. Optd **CORREO EXTRA-RAPIDO** or surch also.

786	**233**	2c. on 8c. blue	10	10
787		10c. violet	15	10

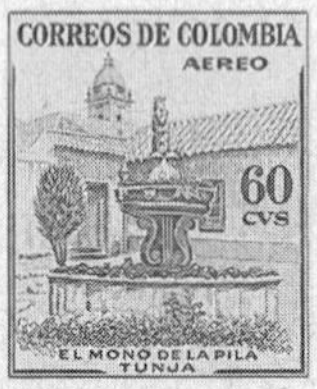

269 Fountain, Tunja

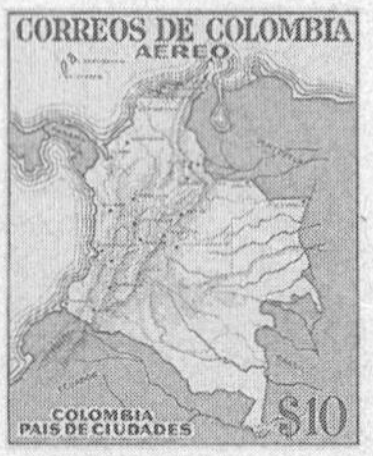

271 Map of Colombia

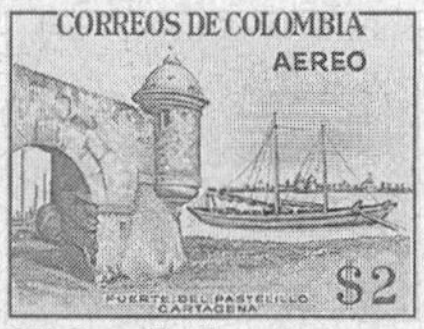

270 Pastelillo Fort, Cartagena

1954. Air.

788	–	5c. purple	30	10
789	–	10c. black	20	10
790	–	15c. red	20	10
791	–	15c. vermilion	20	10
792	–	20c. brown	30	10
793	–	25c. blue	30	10
794	–	25c. purple	30	10
795	–	30c. brown	15	10
796	–	40c. blue	25	10
797	–	50c. purple	25	10
798	**269**	60c. sepia	35	10
799	–	80c. lake	25	20
800	–	1p. black and blue	1·40	20
801	**270**	2p. black and green	3·75	25
802	–	3p. black and red	5·00	55
803	–	5p. green and brown	7·00	1·40
804	**271**	10p. olive and red	8·50	3·50

DESIGNS. As Type **269**—VERT: 5c., 30c. Galeras volcano, Pasto; 15c. red, 50c. Bolivar Monument, Boyaca; 15c. vermilion, 25c. (2) Sanctuary of the Rocks, Narino; 20c., 80c. Nevado del Ruiz Mts., Manizales; 40c. J. Isaacs Monument, Cali. HORIZ: 10c. San Diego Monastery, Bogota. As Type **270**—HORIZ: 1p. Girardot Stadium, Medellin; 3p. Santo Domingo Gateway and University, Popayan. As Type **271**—HORIZ: 5p. Sanctuary of the Rocks, Narino.

1954. Surch.

805	**266**	5c. on 14c. red & black	30	15
806	**256**	5c. on 23c. black & blue	30	15

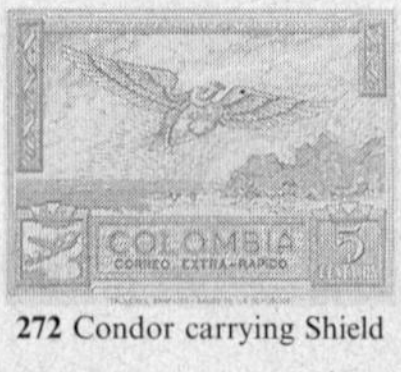

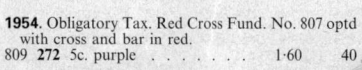

272 Condor carrying Shield

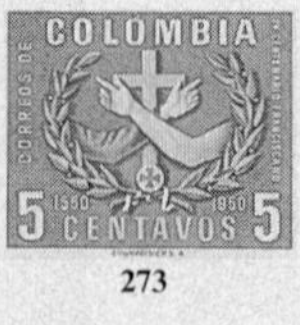

273

1954. Air.

807	**272**	5c. purple	50	20

1954. 400th Anniv of Franciscan Community in Colombia.

808	**273**	5c. brown, green & sepia	25	15

1954. Obligatory Tax. Red Cross Fund. No. 807 optd with cross and bar in red.

809	**272**	5c. purple	1·60	40

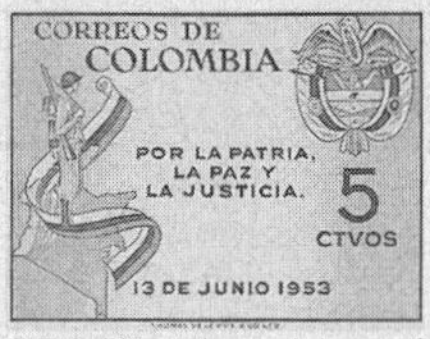

275 Soldier, Flag and Arms of Republic

1954. National Army Commemoration.

810	**275**	5c. blue (postage)	20	10
811		15c. red (air)	30	10

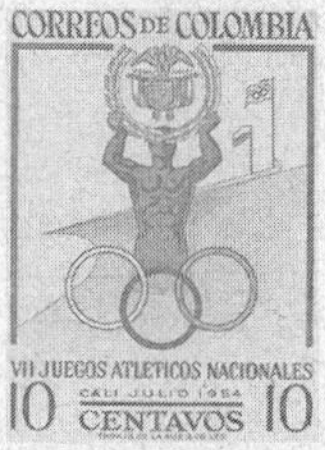

276

1954. 7th National Athletic Games, Cali. Inscr "VII JUEGOS ATLETICOS", etc.

812	–	5c. blue (postage)	15	10
813	**276**	10c. red	25	10
814	–	15c. brown (air)	25	15
815	**276**	20c. green	60	35

DESIGN: 5c., 15c. Badge of the Games.

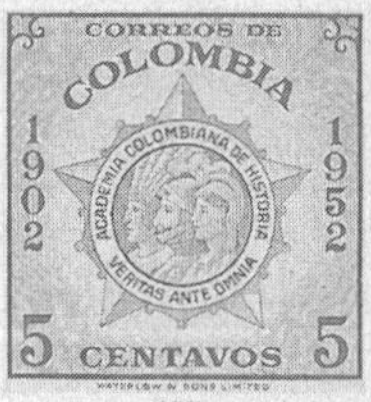

277

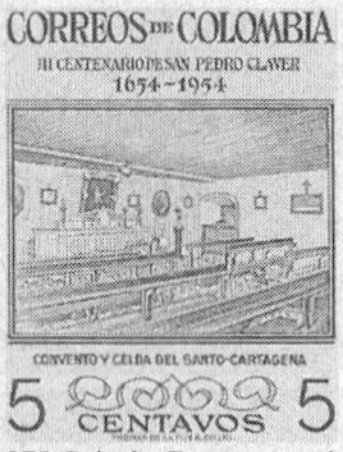

278 Saint's Convent and Cell, Cartagena

1954. 50th Anniv of Colombian Academy of History.

816	**277**	5c. green and blue	20	10

1954. Death Tercentenary of San Pedro Claver.

817	**278**	5c. green (postage)	15	10
819	–	15c. brown (air)	30	10

DESIGN: 15c. San Pedro Claver Church, Cartagena.

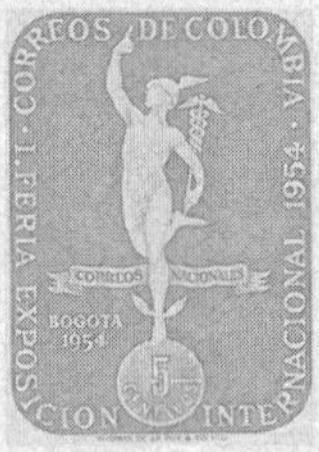

279 Mercury

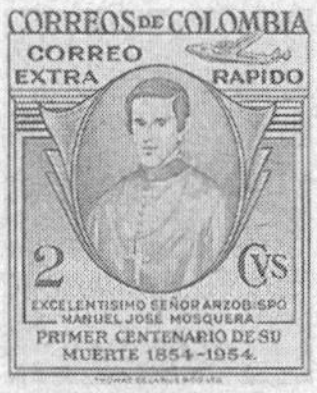

280 Archbishop Mosquera

1954. 1st International Fair, Bogota.

821	**279**	5c. orange (postage)	25	10
822		15c. blue (air)	25	10
823		50c. red ("EXTRA RAPIDO")	30	10

1954. Air. Death Cent of Archbishop Mosquera.

824	**280**	2c. green	10	10

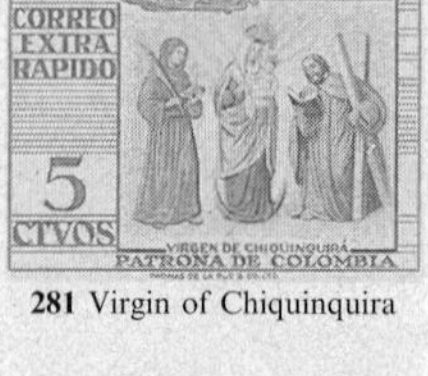

281 Virgin of Chiquinquira

1954. Air.

825	**281**	5c. mult (brown frame)	10	10
826		5c. mult (violet frame)	10	10

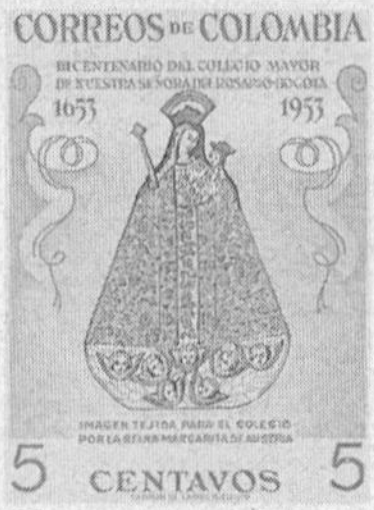

282 Tapestry presented by Queen Margaret of Austria

1954. Tercentenary of Senior College of Our Lady of the Rosary, Bogota.

827	**282**	5c. black & orge (postage)	25	15
828	–	10c. blue	25	15
829	–	15c. brown	35	15
830	–	20c. brown and black	60	25
832	**282**	15c. black & red (air)	35	15
833	–	20c. blue	55	15
834	–	25c. brown	55	15
835	–	50c. red and black	85	30

DESIGNS—VERT: Nos. 828, 833, Friar Cristobal de Torres (founder). HORIZ: Nos. 829, 834, Cloisters and statue; 830, 835, Chapel and coat of arms.

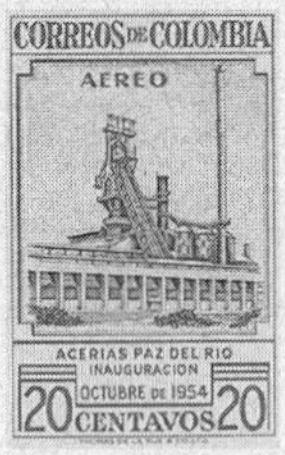

283 Paz de Rio Steel Works

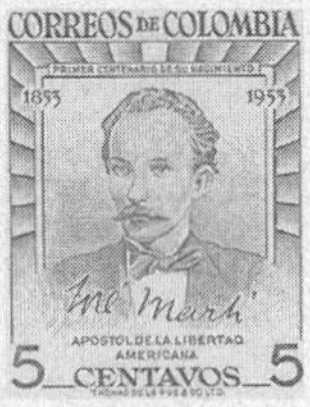

284 J. Marti

1954. Inauguration of Paz del Rio Steel Plant.

837	**283**	5c. black & bl (postage)	15	10
838		20c. black & green (air)	70	45

1955. Birth Cent of Marti (Cuban revolutionary).

839	**284**	5c. red (postage)	15	10
840	–	15c. green (air)	25	10

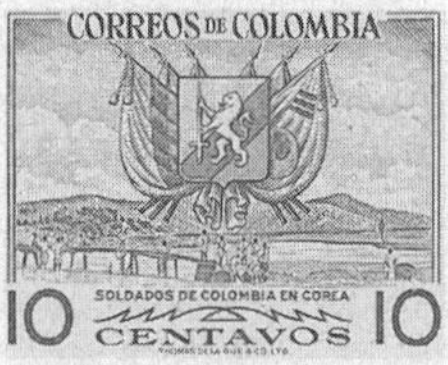

285 Badge, Flags and Korean Landscape

1955. Colombian Forces in Korea.

841	**285**	10c. purple (postage)	25	10
842		20c. green (air)	25	15

286 Merchant Marine Emblem

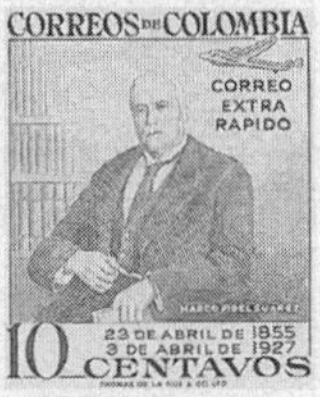

287 M. Fidel Suarez

1955. Greater Colombia Merchant Marine Commemoration. Inscr as in T **286**.

843	**286**	15c. green (postage)	20	10
844	–	20c. violet	85	15
846	**286**	25c. black (air)	35	10
847	–	50c. green	1·40	15

DESIGN—HORIZ: 20, 50c. "City of Manizales" (freighter) and skyscrapers.

1955. Air. Birth Centenary of Marco Fidel Suarez (President, 1918–21).

849	**287**	10c. blue	15	10

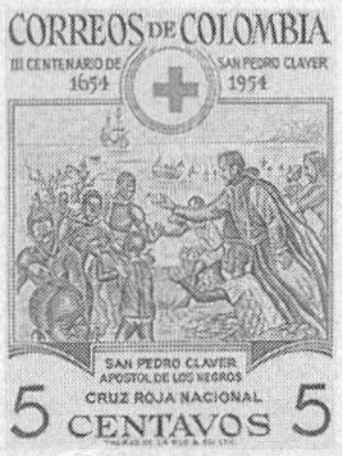

288 San Pedro Claver feeding Slaves

1955. Obligatory Tax. Red Cross Fund and 300th Anniv of San Pedro Claver.
850 **288** 5c. purple and red 25 10

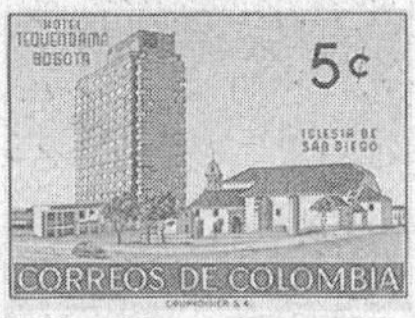
289 Hotel Tequendama and San Diego Church

1955.
851 **289** 5c. blue and light blue (postage) 15 10
852 15c. lake and pink (air) 25 10

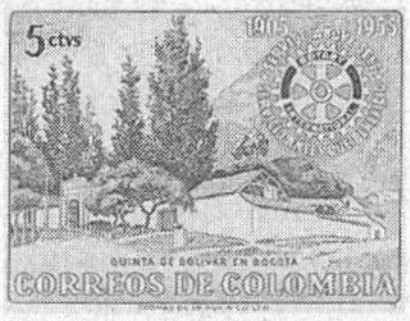
290 Bolivar's Country House

1955. 50th Anniv of Rotary International.
853 **290** 5c. blue (postage) 15 10
854 15c. red (air) 25 10

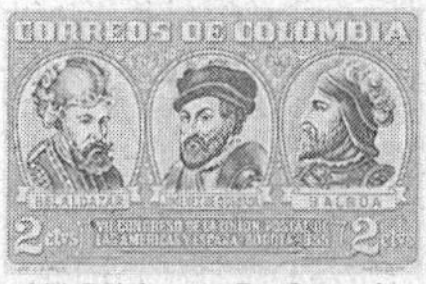
291 Belalcazar, De Quesada and Balboa

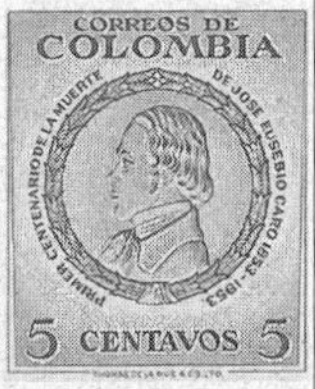
292 J. E. Caro

1955. 7th Postal Union Congress of the Americas and Spain. Inscr as in T **291**.
855 **291** 2c. brn & grn (postage) 10 10
856 – 5c. brown and blue . . . 15 10
857 – 23c. black and blue . . . 2·25 50
859 – 15c. black and red (air) 15 10
860 – 20c. black and brown . . 25 10
862 – 2c. black and brown ("EXTRA RAPIDO") 10 10
863 – 5c. sepia and yellow . . . 15 10
864 – 1p. brown and slate . . . 12·00 5·50
865 – 2p. black and violet . . . 7·50 6·50
DESIGNS—HORIZ: 2c. (No. 855), Type **291**; 2c. (No. 862), Atahualpa, Tisquesuza, Montezuma; 5c. (No. 856), San Martin, Bolivar and Washington; 5c. (No. 863), King Ferdinand, Queen Isabella and coat of arms; 15c. O'Higgins, Santander and Sucre; 20c. Marti, Hidalgo and Petion; 23c. Colombus, "Santa Maria", "Pinta" and "Nina"; 1p. Artigas, Lopez and Murillo; 2p. Calderon, Baron de Rio Branco and De La Mar.

1955. Death Cent of Jose Eusebio Caro (poet).
866 **292** 5c. brown (postage) . . . 10 10
867 15c. green (air) 25 10

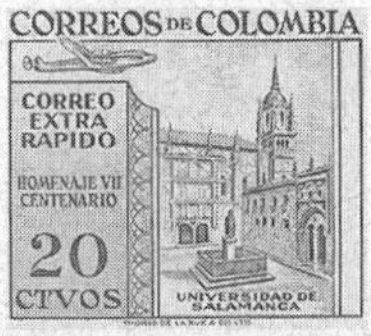
293 Salamanca University

1955. Air. 700th Anniv of Salamanca University.
868 **293** 20c. brown 15 10

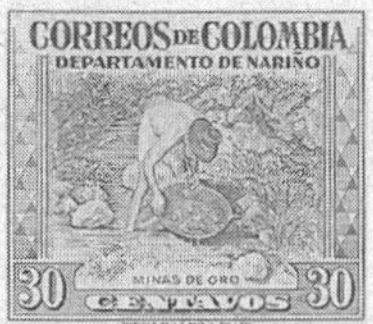
294 Gold Mining, Narino

1956. Regional Industries. Inscr "DEPARTAMENTO", "PROVIDENCIA" (No. 874), "INTENDENCIA" (2p. to 5p.) or "COMISARIA" (10p.).
869 – 2c. green and red . . . 10 10
870 – 3c. black and purple . . . 10 10
871 – 3c. brown and blue . . . 10 10
872 – 3c. violet and green . . . 10 10
873 – 4c. black and green . . . 30 10
874 – 5c. black and blue . . . 20 10
875 – 5c. slate and red . . . 30 10
876 – 5c. olive and brown . . . 30 10
877 – 5c. brown and olive . . . 25 10
878 – 5c. brown and blue . . . 30 10
879 – 10c. black and yellow . . . 25 10
880 – 10c. brown and green . . . 20 10
881 – 10c. brown and blue . . . 20 10
882 – 15c. black and blue . . . 25 10
883 – 20c. blue and brown . . . 30 10
884 – 23c. red and blue 35 15
885 – 25c. black and olive . . . 35 15
886 **294** 30c. brown and blue . . . 30 10
887 – 40c. brown and purple . . 10 10
888 – 50c. black and green . . . 30 10
889 – 60c. green and sepia . . . 25 10
890 – 1p. slate and purple . . . 90 10
891 – 2p. brown and green . . . 1·90 25
892 – 3p. black and red . . . . 1·75 35
893 – 5p. blue and brown . . . 4·00 25
894 – 10p. green and brown . . 9·50 3·00
DESIGNS—As Type **294**. HORIZ: 2c. Barranquilla naval workshops, Atlantico; 4c. Fishing, Cartagena Port, Bolivar; 5c. (No. 875) View of Port, San Andres; 5c. (No. 876) Cocoa, Cauca; 5c. (No. 877) Prize cattle, Cordoba; 23c. Rice harvesting, Huila; 25c. Bananas, Magdalena; 40c. Tobacco, Santander; 50c. Oil wells of Catatumbo, Norte de Santander; 60c. Cotton harvesting, Tolima. VERT: 3c. (3), Allegory of Industry, Antioquia; 5c. (No. 874) Map of San Andres Archipelago; 5c. (No. 878) Steel plant, Boyaca; 10c. (3), Coffee, Caldas; 15c. Cathedral at Sal Salinas de Zipaquira, Cundinamarca; 20c. Platinum and map, Choco. LARGER (37½ × 27 mm)—HORIZ: 1p. Sugar factory, Valle del Cauca; 2p. Cattle fording river, Meta; 3p. Statue and River Amazon, Leticia; 5p. Landscape, La Guajira. VERT: 10p. Rubber tapping, Vaupes.

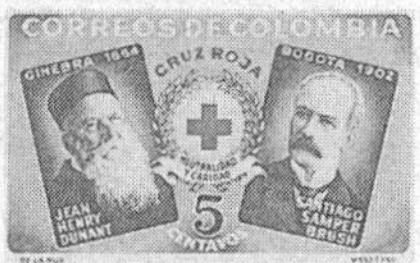
295 Henri Dunant and S. Samper Brush

1956. Obligatory Tax. Red Cross Fund.
895 **295** 5c. brown 20 10

1956. Air. No. 783 optd **EXTRA-RAPIDO**.
896 1p. green and black 25 10

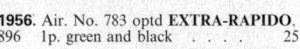

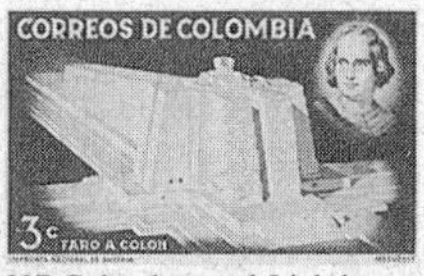
297 Columbus and Lighthouse

1956. Columbus Memorial Lighthouse.
897 **297** 3c. black (postage) . . . 15 10
898 15c. blue (air) 20 10
899 3c. green ("EXTRA RAPIDO") 15 10

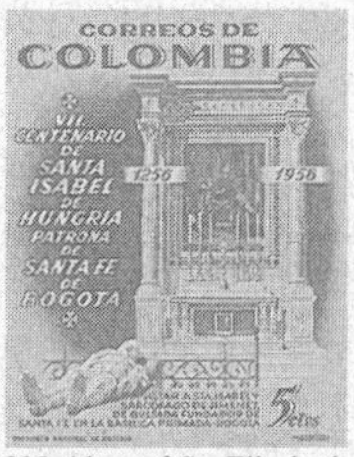
298 Altar of St. Elisabeth and Sarcophagus of Jimenez de Quesada, Primada Basilica, Bogota

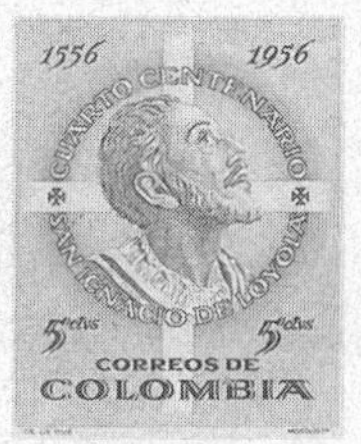
299 St. Ignatius of Loyola

1956. 700th Anniv of St. Elisabeth of Hungary.
900 **298** 5c. purple (postage) . . . 15 10
901 15c. brown (air) 30 15

1956. 400th Death Anniv of St. Ignatius of Loyola.
902 **299** 5c. blue (postage) 15 10
903 5c. brown (air) 20 10

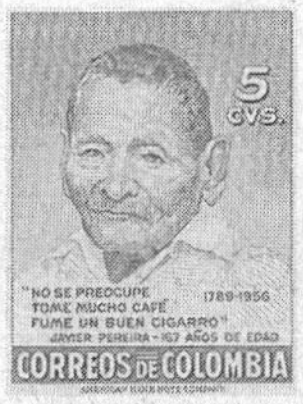
300 Javier Pereira

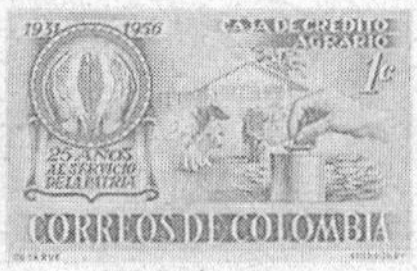
302 Dairy Farm

1956. Pereira Commemoration.
904 **300** 5c. blue (postage) 10 10
905 20c. red (air) 10 10

1957. Air. No. 874 optd **EXTRA-RAPIDO**.
906 5c. black and blue 20 10

1957. Air. As No. 580 (colours changed) optd **EXTRA-RAPIDO**.
907 5p. black and buff . . . . 6·00 3·75

1957. 25th Anniv of Agricultural Credit Bank.
908 **302** 1c. olive (postage) . . . 10 10
909 – 2c. brown 10 10
910 – 5c. blue 15 10
911 **302** 5c. orange (air) 15 10
912 – 10c. green 25 20
913 – 15c. black 25 10
914 – 20c. red 40 30
915 – 5c. brown ("EXTRA RAPIDO") 15 10
DESIGNS: 2c., 10c. Farm tractor; 5c. (No. 910), 15c. Emblem of agricultural prosperity; 5c. (No. 915), Livestock; 20c. Livestock.

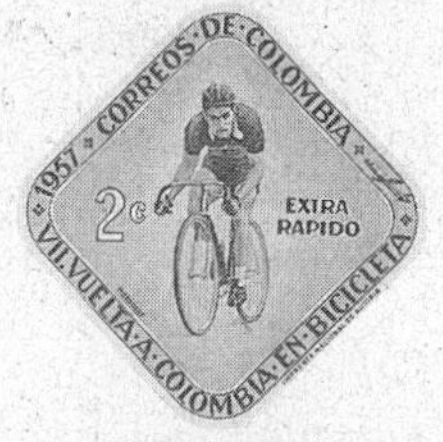
303 Racing Cyclist

1957. Air. 7th Round Colombia Cycle Race.
916 **303** 2c. brown 15 15
917 5c. blue 25 25

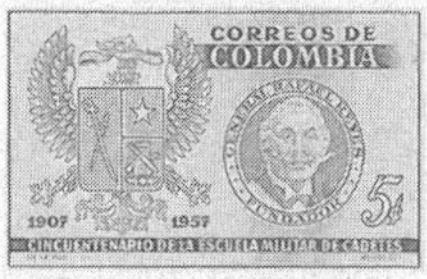
304 Arms and Gen. Rayes (founder)

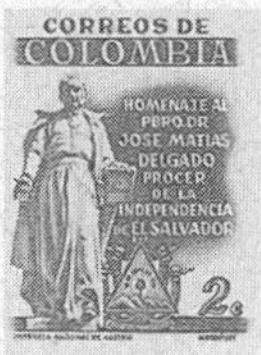
305 Father J. M. Delgado

1957. 50th Anniv of Military Cadet School.
918 **304** 5c. blue (postage) 15 10
919 – 10c. orange 20 10
921 **304** 15c. red (air) 20 10
922 – 20c. brown 30 10
DESIGN: 10c., 20c. Arms and Military Cadet School.

1957. Father Delgado Commemoration.
923 **305** 2c. lake (postage) 10 10
924 10c. blue (air) 15 10

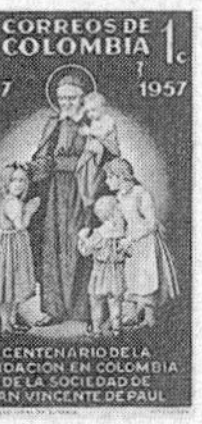
306 St. Vincent de Paul with Children

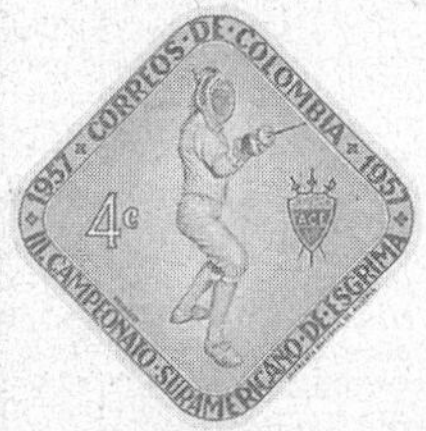
308 Fencer

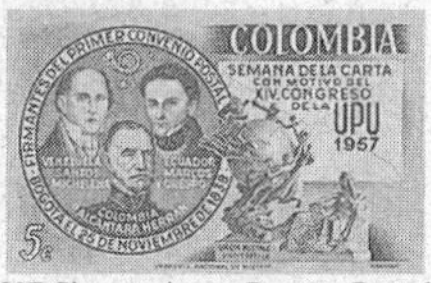
307 Signatories to Bogota Postal Convention of 1838, and U.P.U. Monument, Berne

1957. Centenary of Colombian Order of St. Vincent de Paul.
925 **306** 1c. green (postage) . . . 10 10
926 5c. red (air) 15 10

1957. 14th U.P.U. Congress, Ottawa and International Correspondence Week.
927 **307** 5c. green (postage) . . . 15 10
928 10c. grey 15 10
929 15c. brown (air) 20 10
930 25c. blue 20 10

1957. 3rd S. American Fencing Championships.
931 **308** 4c. purple (postage) . . . 20 10
932 20c. brown (air) 35 10

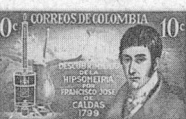

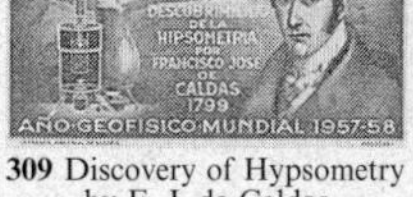
309 Discovery of Hypsometry by F. J. de Caldas

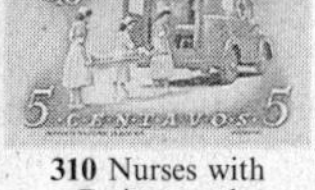
310 Nurses with Patient, and Ambulance

1958. International Geophysical Year.
933 **309** 10c. black (postage) . . . 30 10
934 25c. green (air) 45 10
935 1p. violet ("EXTRA RAPIDO") 15 10

1958. Obligatory Tax. Red Cross Fund.
936 **310** 5c. red and black 15 10

1958. Nos. 882 and 884 surch.
937 5c. on 15c. black and blue . . 10 10
938 5c. on 23c. red and blue . . 25 20

1958. Air. No. 888 optd **AEREO**.
939 50c. black and green 20 10

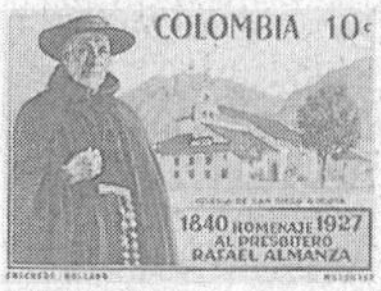
313 Father R. Almanza and San Diego Church, Bogota

1958. Father Almanza Commemoration.
940 **313** 10c. lilac (postage) . . . 10 10
941 25c. grey (air) 30 10
942 10c. green ("EXTRA RAPIDO") 10 10

1958. Nos. 780/2 surch **CINCO** (5c.) or **VEINTE** (20c.).
943 **266** 5c. on 14c. red & black 15 10
944 – 5c. on 30c. sepia & black 10 10
945 – 20c. on 23c. blue & blk 25 15

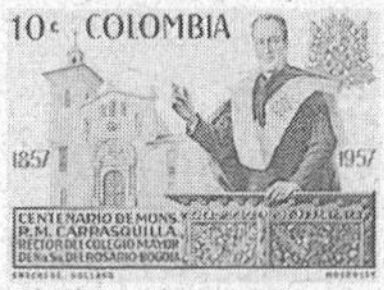
315 Msr. Carrasquilla and Rosario College, Bogota

1959. Birth Centenary of Msr. R. M. Carrasquilla.
946 **315** 10c. brown (postage) . . 15 10
947 25c. red (air) 20 10
948 1p. blue 60 20

1959. Surch **20c.** and ornament.
949 **258** 20c. on 23c. black & bl 25 15

1959. As No. 826 but with "CORREO EXTRA RAPIDO" obliterated.
950 **281** 5c. multicoloured 10 10

1959. No. 794 surch.
951 10c. on 25c. purple 15 10

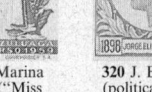

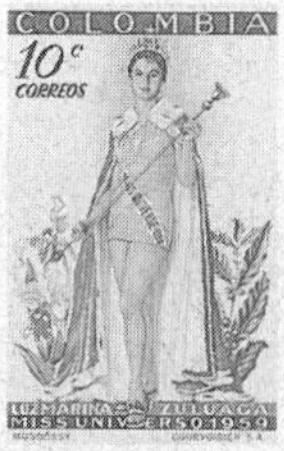
318 Luz Marina Zuluaga ("Miss Universe 1959")

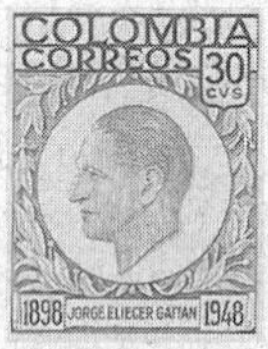
320 J. E. Gaitan (political leader)

1959. "Miss Universe 1959" Commemoration.
952 **318** 10c. mult (postage) . . . 10 10
953 1p.20 mult (air) 65 45
954 5p. mult ("EXTRA RAPIDO") . . . . . . 25·00 24·00

1959. No. 873 surch.
955 2c. on 4c. black and green . . 30 10

1959. J. E. Gaitan Commem. Nos. 956 and 958 are surch on T **320**.
956 **320** 10c. on 3c. grey 15 10
957 30c. purple 25 15
958 2p. on 1p. black ("EXTRA RAPIDO") 60 25

1959. Air. Surch.
960 **269** 50c. on 60c. sepia . . . . 5·00 30

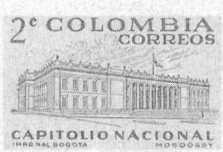

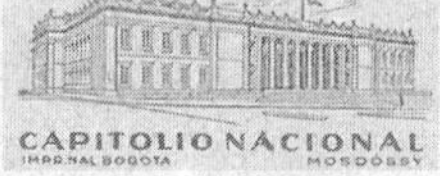
323 Capitol, Bogota

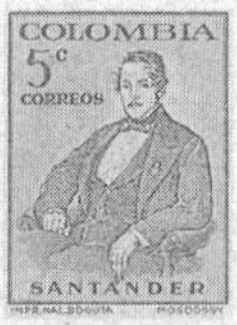
324 Santander

1959.
961 **323** 2c. brn & blue (postage) 10 10
962 3c. violet and black . . . 10 10
963 **324** 5c. brown and yellow . . 15 10
964 – 5c. ultramarine & blue . . 15 10
965 – 10c. black and red 15 10
966 **324** 10c. black and green . . . 15 10

967 – 35c. black and grey (air) 1·75 10
PORTRAIT (as Type **324**): Nos. 964/5, 967, Bolivar.

1959. Air. Unification of Airmail Rates. Optd **UNIFICADO** within outline of aeroplane.
968 **299** 5c. brown 15 10
969 **302** 5c. orange 35 35
970 **306** 5c. red 20 20
971 **155** 10c. red (No. 772) 10 10
972 – 10c. black (No. 789) 20 10
973 **304** 15c. red 30 10
974 – 20c. brown (No. 792) 20 10
975 – 20c. brown (No. 922) 10 10
976 **308** 20c. brown 25 15
977 – 25c. blue (No. 793) 25 10
978 – 25c. purple (No. 794) 25 10
979 **313** 25c. grey 25 10
980 **315** 25c. red 30 10
981 – 30c. brown (No. 795) 20 10
982 **269** 50c. on 60c. sepia (No. 960) 15 10
983 **315** 1p. blue 35 10
984 **318** 1p.20 multicoloured 45 35
985 **270** 2p. black and green 2·10 20
986 – 3p. black & red (No. 802) 7·00 45
987 – 5p. grn & brn (No. 803) 7·50 45
988 **271** 10p. olive and red 9·50 1·60

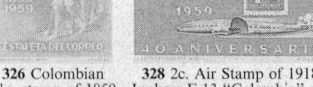

326 Colombian 2½c. stamp of 1859 and Postman with Mule

328 2c. Air Stamp of 1918, Junkers F-13 "Colombia" and Lockheed Constellation

1959. Colombian Stamp Cent. Inscr "1859 1959".
989 **326** 5c. grn & orge (postage) 20 15
990 – 10c. blue and lake 40 15
991 **326** 15c. green and red 35 10
992 – 25c. brown and blue 2·25 1·25
993 – 25c. red and brown (air) 40 20
994 – 50c. blue and red 55 20
995 – 1p.20 brown and green 2·10 1·25
996 – 10c. lilac and bistre ("EXTRA-RAPIDO") 20 10
DESIGNS—VERT: Colombian stamps of 1859 (except No. 993): No. 990, 5c. and river steamer; 992, 10c. and steam locomotive "Cordoba"; 993, Postal decree of 1859 and Pres. M. Ospina; 996, 10c. and map of Colombia. HORIZ: No. 994, 20c. and Junkers F-13 seaplane "Colombia"; 995, 1p. and Lockheed Constellation airliner over valley.

1959. Air. 40th Anniv of Colombian "AVIANCA" Air Mail Services.
998 **328** 35c. red, black and blue 15 10
999 – 60c. black and green 25 15
DESIGN: 60c. As Type **328** but without Colombian 2c. stamp.

329 Eldorado Airport, Bogota

331 A. von Humboldt (after J. K. Stieler)

1960. Air.
1002 **329** 35c. orange and black 45 20
1003 60c. red and grey 35 35
1004 1p. blue and grey ("EXTRA RAPIDO") 1·00 45

1960. Death Centenary of Alexander von Humboldt (naturalist). Animals.
1005 – 5c. brn & turq (postage) 10 10
1006 **331** 10c. sepia and red 10 10
1007 – 20c. purple and yellow 20 10
1008 – 35c. brown (air) 45 10
1009 – 1p.30 brown and red 1·25 90
1010 – 1p.45 lemon and blue 1·00 45
DESIGNS—VERT: 5c. Two-toed sloth; 20c. Long-haired spider monkey. HORIZ: 35c. Giant anteater; 1p.30, Nine-banded armadillo; 1p.45, "Blue" parrotfish.

332 "Anthurium andreanum"

333 Refugee Family

1960. Colombian Flowers.
1011 **332** 5c. mult (postage) 20 10
1012 A 20c. yellow, green & sep 10 10
1013 B 5c. multicoloured (air) 10 10
1014 5c. multicoloured 10 10
1015 A 10c. yellow, green & bl 10 10
1016 C 20c. multicoloured 10 10
1017 D 25c. multicoloured 35 10
1018 C 35c. multicoloured 25 10
1019 B 60c. multicoloured 35 20
1020 **332** 60c. multicoloured 35 10
1021 1p.45 multicoloured 90 35
1022 C 5c. multicoloured ("EXTRA RAPIDO") 10 10
1023 D 10c. multicoloured 10 10
1024 **332** 1p. multicoloured 90 55
1025 A 1p. yellow, green & sepia 90 55
1026 B 1p. multicoloured 90 55
1027 C 1p. multicoloured 90 55
1028 D 1p. multicoloured 90 55
1029 C 2p. multicoloured 1·60 80
FLOWERS: A, "Espelitia grandiflora"; B, "Passiflora mollissima"; C, Odontoglossum luteo purpureum"; D, "Stanhopea tigrina".

1960. Air. World Refugee Year.
1030a **333** 60c. grey and green 15 15

334 Lincoln Statue, Washington

335 "House of the Flower Vase"

1960. 150th Birth Anniv of Abraham Lincoln.
1032 **334** 20c. blk & mve (postage) 15 10
1033 40c. black & brown (air) 45 25
1034 60c. black and red 25 10

1960. 150th Anniv of Independence.
1035 – 5c. brn & grn (postage) 10 10
1036 **335** 20c. purple and brown 15 10
1037 – 20c. yellow, blue & mve 10 15
1038 – 5c. multicoloured (air) 15 10
1039 – 5c. sepia and violet 15 10
1040 – 35c. multicoloured 20 10
1041 – 60c. green and brown 40 10
1042 – 1p. green and red 35 20
1043 – 1p.20 indigo and blue 35 20
1044 – 1p.30 black and orange 35 20
1045 – 1p.45 multicoloured 65 55
1046 – 1p.65 brown and green 45 35
DESIGNS—VERT: No. 1035, Cartagena coins of 1811–13; 1038, Arms of Cartagena; 1037, Arms of Mompos; 1043, Statue of A. Galan. HORIZ: No. 1039, J. Camacho, J. T. Lozano and J. M. Pey; 1040, 1045, Colombian Flag; 1041, A. Rosillo, A. Villavicencio and J. Caicedo; 1042, B. Alvares and J. Gutierrez; 1044, Front page of "La Bagatela" (newspaper); 1046, A. Santos, J. A. Gomez and L. Mejia.

336 St. Luisa de Marillac and Sanctuary

337 St. Isidro Labrador (after G. Vasquez)

1960. Obligatory Tax. Red Cross Fund.
1048 **336** 5c. red and brown 20 10
1049 – 5c. red and blue 20 10
DESIGN: No. 1049, H. Dunant and battle scene.

1960. St. Isidro Labrador Commem (1st issue).
1050 **337** 10c. mult (postage) 10 10
1051 – 20c. multicoloured 15 10
1052 **337** 35c. multicoloured (air) 20 10
DESIGN: 20c. "The Nativity" (after Vasquez).
See also Nos. 1126/8.

338 U.N. Headquarters, New York

339 Highway Map of Northern Colombia

1960. U.N. Day.
1054 **338** 20c. red and black 15 10

1961. 8th Pan-American Highway Congress.
1056 **339** 20c. brn & bl (postage) 30 25
1057 10c. purple & green (air) 30 25
1058 20c. red and blue 30 25
1059 30c. black and green 30 25
1060 10c. blue and green ("EXTRA RAPIDO") 30 25

340 Alfonso Lopez (statesman)

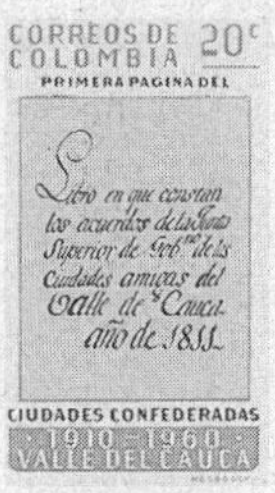

341 Text from Resolution of Confederated Cities

1961. 75th Birth Anniv of Alfonso Lopez (President, 1934–38 and 1941–45).
1061 **340** 10c. brn & red (postage) 15 10
1062 20c. brown and violet 15 10
1063 35c. brown & blue (air) 35 10
1064 10c. brown and green ("EXTRA RAPIDO") 15 10

1961. 50th Anniv of Valle del Cauca.
1066 – 10c. mult (postage) 10 10
1067 **341** 20c. brown and black 15 10
1068 – 35c. brown & olive (air) 30 10
1069 – 35c. brown and green 30 10
1070 – 1p.30 sepia and purple 35 15
1071 – 1p.45 green and brown 35 15
1072 – 10c. brown and olive ("EXTRA RAPIDO") 15 10
DESIGNS—HORIZ: 10c. (No. 1066), La Ermita Church, bridge and arms of Cali; 35c. (No. 1068), St. Francis' Church, Cali; 1p.30, Conservatoire; 1p.45, Agricultural College, Palmira. VERT: 10c. (No. 1072), Aerial view of Cali; 35c. (No. 1069), University emblem.

342 Arms and View of Cucuta

345 Arms of Barranquilla

1961. 50th Anniv of North Santander.
1073 – 20c. mult (postage) 15 10
1074 **342** 20c. multicoloured 15 10
1075 – 35c. green & bistre (air) 45 10
1076 – 10c. purple & green ("EXTRA RAPIDO") 15 10
DESIGNS—HORIZ: No. 1073, Arms of Ocana and Pamplona; 1075, Panoramic view of Cucuta. VERT: No. 1076, Villa del Rosario, Cucuta.

1961. Air. Optd **Aereo** (1077) or **AEREO** (others) and airplane or surch also.
1077 **332** 5c. multicoloured 10 10
1078 – 5c. brown & turquoise (No. 1005) 10 10
1079 – 10c. on 20c. purple and yellow (No. 1007) 10 10

1961. Atlantico Tourist Issue.
1080 – 10c. mult (postage) 10 10
1081 **345** 20c. red, blue and yellow 15 10
1082 – 20c. multicoloured 15 10
1083 – 35c. sepia and red (air) 45 10
1084 – 35c. red, yellow & green 35 10
1085 – 35c. blue and gold 65 10
1086 – 1p.45 brown and green 45 20
1088 – 10c. yellow and brown ("EXTRA RAPIDO") 15 10
DESIGNS—VERT: No. 1080, Arms of Popayan; 1082, Arms of Bucaramanga; 1083, Courtyard of Tourist Hotel; 1087, Holy Week procession, Popayan. HORIZ: No. 1084, View of San Gill; 1085, Barranquilla Port; 1086, View of Velez.

346 Nurse M. de la Cruz

347 Boxing

1961. Red Cross Fund. Cross in red.
1090 **346** 5c. brown 15 10
1091 5c. purple 15 10

1961. 4th Bolivarian Games. Inscr as in T **347**. Multicoloured.
1092 20c. Type **347** (postage) 20 10
1093 20c. Basketball 10 10
1094 20c. Running 10 10
1095 25c. Football 20 10
1096 35c. Diving (air) 25 10
1097 35c. Tennis 25 10
1098 1p.45 Baseball 35 15
1099 10c. Statue and flags ("EXTRA RAPIDO") 10 10
1100 10c. Runner with Olympic torch ("EXTRA RAPIDO") 10 10

348 "S.E.M." Emblem and Mosquito

349 Society Emblem

1962. Malaria Eradication.
1102 **348** 20c. red & ochre (post) 15 15
1103 – 50c. blue and ochre 15 15
1104 **348** 40c. red & yellow (air) 15 15
1105 – 1p.45 blue and grey 40 40
1106 – 1p. blue and green ("EXTRA RAPIDO") 2·75 2·75
DESIGN: 50c., 1p., 1p.45, Campaign emblem and mosquito.

1962. 6th National Engineers' Congress, 1961 and 75th Anniv of Colombian Society of Engineers.
1107 **349** 10c. mult (postage) 20 20
1108 – 5c. red and blue (air) 10 10
1109 – 10c. brown and green 30 15
1110 – 15c. brown and purple 25 10
1111 **349** 2p. multicoloured ("EXTRA RAPIDO") 1·60 90
DESIGNS: No. 1108, A. Ramos and Engineering Faculty, Cauca University, Popayan; 1109, M. Triana, A. Arroyo and Monserrate cable and funicular railway; 1110, D. Sanchez and first Society H.Q., Bogota.

350 O.E.A. Emblem

351 Mother Voting and Statue of Policarpa Salavarrieta

1962. 70th Anniv of Organization of American States (O.E.A.). Flags multicoloured; background colours given.
1112 **350** 25c. red & blk (postage) 15 10
1114 35c. blue & black (air) 15 10

1962. Women's Franchise.
1115 **351** 5c. black, grey and brown (postage) 10 10
1116 10c. black, grey and blue 15 10
1117 5c. blk, grey & pink (air) 10 10
1118 35c. black, grey & buff 25 10
1119 45c. black, grey & green 25 10
1120 45c. black, grey & mauve 25 10

353 Scouts in Camp

354 St. Isidro Labrador (after G. Vasquez)

1962. 30th Anniv of Colombian Boy Scouts and 25th Anniv of Colombian Girl Scouts. As T **353** but without "EXTRA RAPIDO".
1121 **353** 10c. brn & turq (postage) 10 10
1122 15c. brown & red (air) 25 10
1123 – 40c. lake and red 15 10
1124 – 1p. blue and Salmon 30 15
1125 **353** 1p. violet & yellow ("EXTRA RAPIDO") 3·50 3·25
DESIGN: 40c., 1p. Girl Scouts.

1962. St. Isidro Labrador Commem (2nd issue).
1126 **354** 10c. multicoloured 10 10
1127 – 10c. mult (air—"EXTRA RAPIDO") 15 10
1128 **354** 2p. multicoloured 2·50 1·50
DESIGN: 10c. (No. 1127), "The Nativity" (after G. Vasquez).

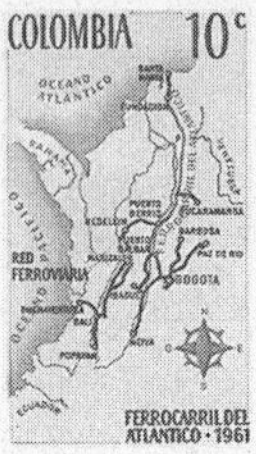
355 Railway Map

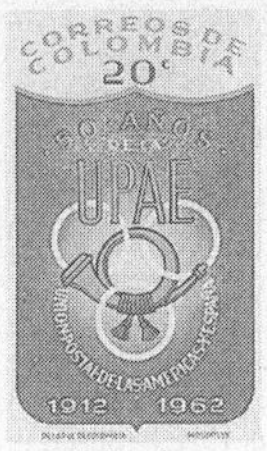
356 Posthorn

1962. Completion of Colombia Atlantic Railway.
1129 **355** 10c. red, green and olive (postage) 30 20
1130 – 5c. myrtle & sepia (air) 30 10
1131 **355** 10c. red, turq & bistre 30 20
1132 – 1p. brown and purple . . 4·50 45
1133 – 5p. brown, blue & grn ("EXTRA RAPIDO") 10·00 4·50
DESIGNS—HORIZ: 5c. 1854 steam and 1961 diesel locomotives; 1, 5p. Pres. A. Parra and R. Magdalena railway bridge.

1962. 50th Anniv of Postal Union of the Americas and Spain.
1134 **356** 20c. gold & bl (postage) 15 10
1135 – 50c. gold & green (air) 30 10
1136 **356** 60c. gold and purple . . 20 10
DESIGN: 50c. Posthorn, dove and map.

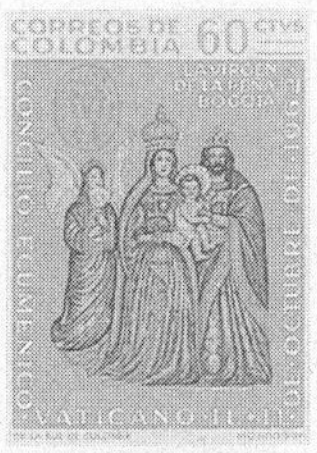
357 Virgin of the Mountain, Bogota

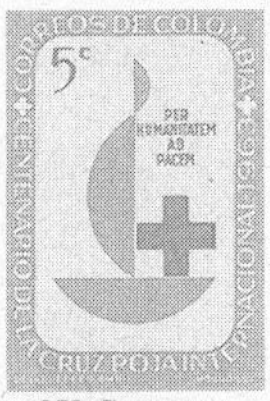
358 Centenary Emblem

1963. Ecumenical Council, Vatican City.
1137 **357** 60c. mult (postage) . . . 20 10
1138 – 60c. red, yell & gold (air) 10 10
DESIGN: No. 1138, Pope John XXIII.

1963. Obligatory Tax. Red Cross Centenary.
1139 **358** 5c. red and bistre . . . 10 10

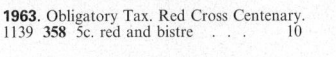

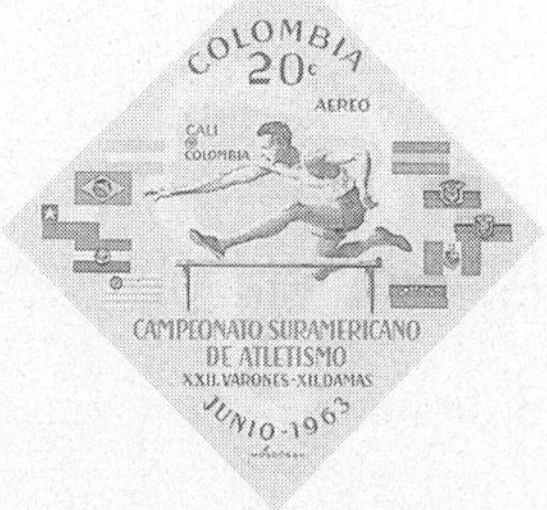
359 Hurdling and Flags

1963. Air. South American Athletic Championships, Cali.
1140 **359** 20c. multicoloured . . . 15 10
1141 80c. multicoloured . . . 15 10

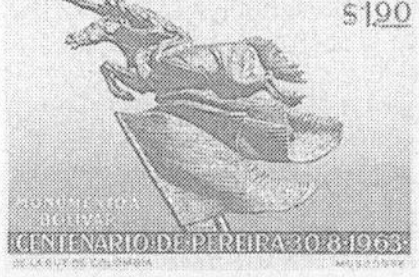
360 Bolivar Monument

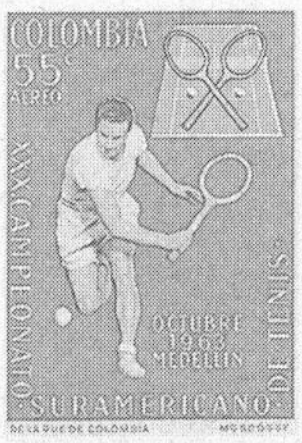
361 Tennis Player

1963. Air. Centenary of Pereira.
1142 **360** 1p.90 brown and blue . . 10 10

1963. Air. 30th South American Tennis Championships, Medellin.
1143 **361** 55c. multicoloured . . . 25 10

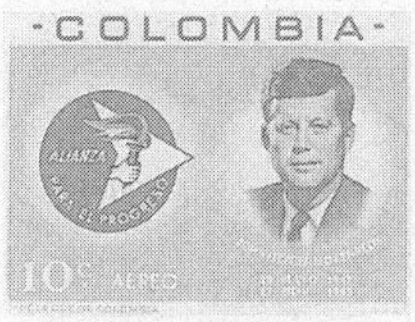
362 Pres. Kennedy and Alliance Emblem

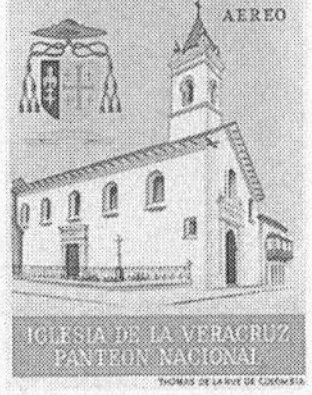
363 Veracruz Church

1963. Air. "Alliance for Progress".
1144 **362** 10c. multicoloured . . . 10 10

1964. Air. National Pantheon, Veracruz Church. Multicoloured.
1145 1p. Type **363** 25 10
1146 2p. "The Crucifixion" . . . 35 20

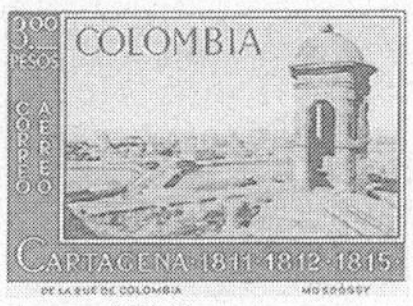
364 Cartagena

1964. Air. Cartagena Commemoration.
1147 **364** 3p. multicoloured . . . 80 55

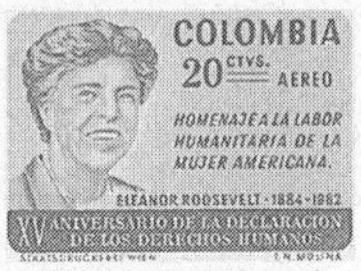
365 Eleanor Roosevelt

1964. Air. 15th Anniv of Declaration of Human Rights.
1148 **365** 20c. brown and olive . . 10 10

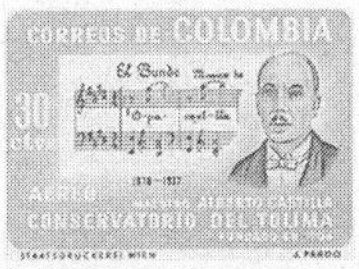
366 A. Castilla (composer and founder) and Music

1964. Air. Tolima Conservatoire Commem.
1149 **366** 30c. turquoise & bistre 20 10

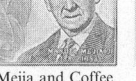

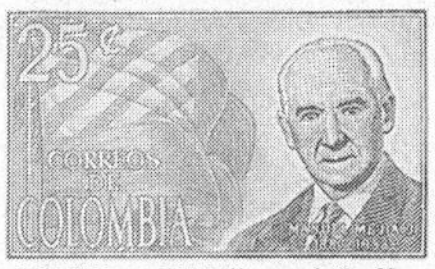
367 Manuel Mejia and Coffee Growers' Flag Emblem

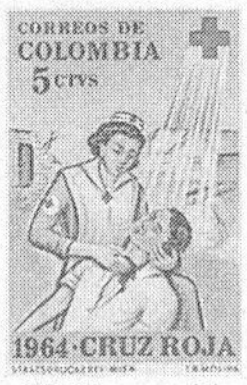
368 Nurse with Patient

1965. Manuel Mejia Commemoration.
1150 **367** 25c. brn & red (postage) 10 10
1151 – 45c. sepia & brown (air) 15 10
1152 – 5p. black and green . . 1·60 30
1153 – 10p. black and blue . . 2·10 25
DESIGNS: 45c. Gathering coffee-beans; 5p. Mule transport; 10p. Freighter "Manuel Mejia" at Buenaventura Port. Each design includes a portrait of M. Mejia, director of the National Coffee Growers' Association.

1965. Obligatory Tax. Red Cross Fund.
1154 **368** 5c. blue and red 10 10

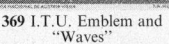

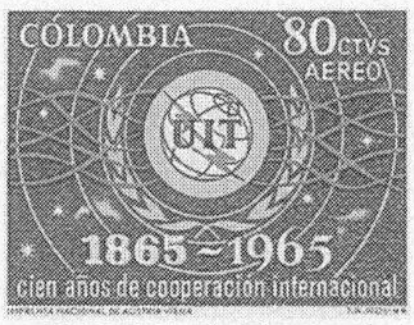
369 I.T.U. Emblem and "Waves"

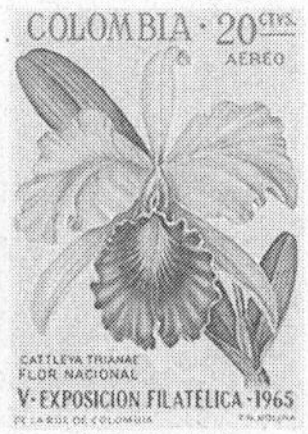
370 Orchid ("Cattleya trianae")

1965. Air. Centenary of I.T.U.
1155 **369** 80c. indigo, red and blue 15 10

1965. Air. 5th Philatelic Exhibition, Bogota.
1156 **370** 20c. multicoloured . . . 20 10

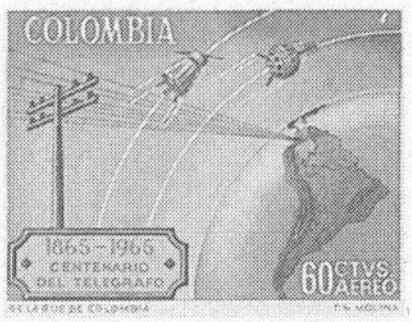
371 Satellites, Telegraph Pole and Map

1965. Air. Cent of Colombian Telegraphs. Mult.
1157 60c. Type **371** 15 10
1158 60c. Statue of Pres. Murrilo Toro, Bogota (vert) . . . 15 10

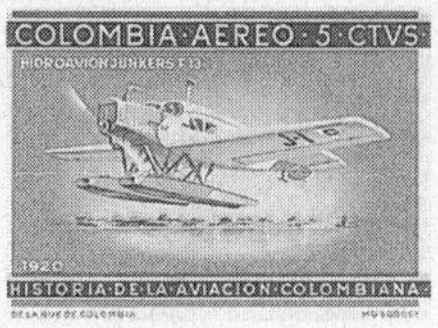
372 Junkers F-13 Seaplane "Colombia" (1920)

1965. Air. "History of Colombian Aviation". Multicoloured.
1159 5c. Type **372** 10 10
1160 10c. Dornier Wal Do-J (1924) 10 10
1161 20c. Dornier Do-B Merkur seaplane (1926) 20 10
1162 50c. Ford 5-AT Trimotor (1932) 20 10
1163 60c. De Havilland Gipsy Moth (1930) 30 10
1164 1p. Douglas DC-4 (1947) . . 35 10
1165 1p.40 Douglas DC-3 (1944) 20 15
1166 2p.80 Lockheed Constellation (1951) . . . 45 30
1167 3p. Boeing 720B jet liner (1961) 65 55
See also No. E1168.

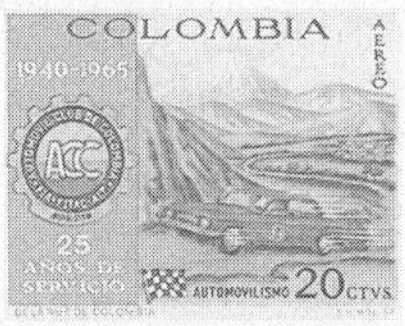
373 Badge, and Car on Mountain Road

1966. Air. 25th Anniv (1965) of Colombian Automobile Club.
1168 **373** 20c. multicoloured . . . 10 10

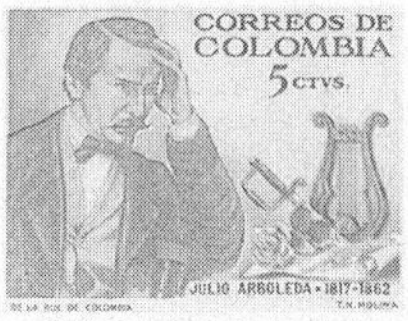
374 J. Arboleda (writer)

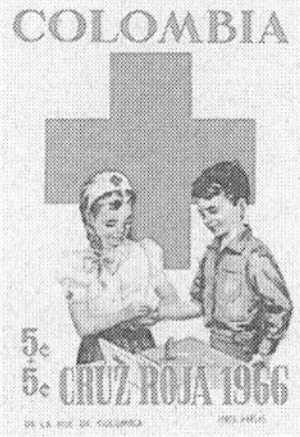
375 Red Cross and Children as Nurse and Patient

1966. Julio Arboleda Commemoration.
1169 **374** 5c. multicoloured 10 10

1966. Obligatory Tax. Red Cross Fund.
1170 **375** 5c.+5c. mult 10 10

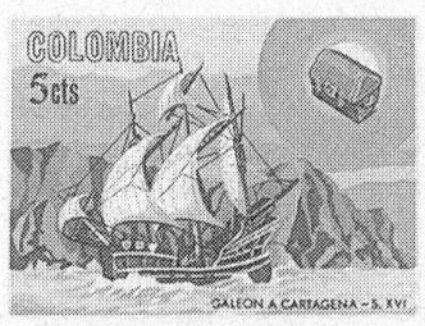
376 16th-century Galleon

1966. History of Maritime Mail. Multicoloured.
1171 5c. Type **376** 20 10
1172 15c. Riohacha brigantine (1850) 35 15
1173 20c. Uraba schooner 35 15
1174 40c. Steamer and barge, Magdalena, 1900 . . . . 65 15
1175 50c. Modern freighter . . . 1·90 1·00

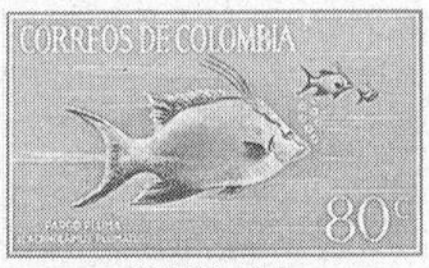
377 Hogfish

1966. Fishes. Multicoloured.
1176 80c. Type **377** (postage) . . 30 10
1177 10p. Spotted electric ray . . 4·75 3·25
1178 2p. Pacific flyingfish (air) . . 15 20
1179 2p.80 Blue angelfish 50 30
1180 20p. King mackerel . . . . 8·75 5·75

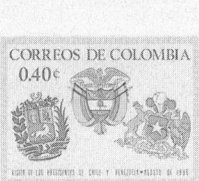

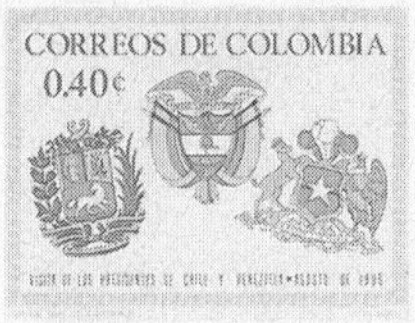
378 Arms of Colombia, Venezuela and Chile

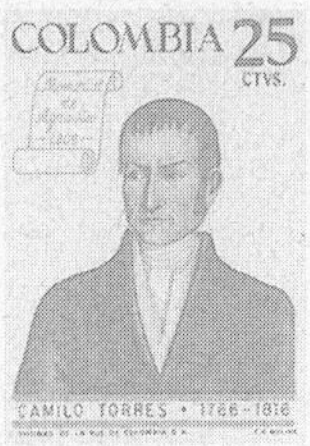
379 C. Torres (patriot)

1966. Visits of Chilean and Venezuelan Presidents.
1181 **378** 40c. mult (postage) . . . 10 10
1182 1p. multicoloured (air) 25 10
1183 1p.40 multicoloured . . 25 10

1967. Famous Colombians.
1184 **379** 25c. vio & yell (postage) 10 10
1185 – 60c. purple and yellow 10 10
1186 – 1p. green and yellow . . 35 10
1187 – 80c. blue & yellow (air) 15 10
1188 – 1p.70 black and yellow 30 10
PORTRAITS: 60c. J. T. Lozano (naturalist); 80c. Father F. R. Mejia (scholar); 1p. F. A. Zea (writer); 1p.70, J. J. Casas (diplomat).

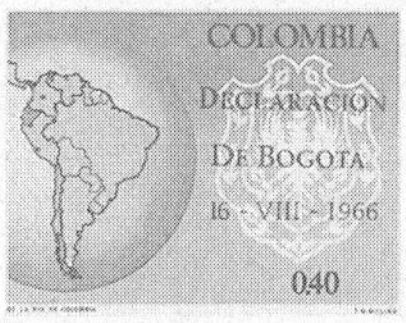
380 Map of Signatory Countries

1967. "Declaration of Bogota".
1189 **380** 40c. mult (postage) . . . 15 10
1190 60c. multicoloured . . . 15 10
1191 3p. multicoloured (air) 30 15

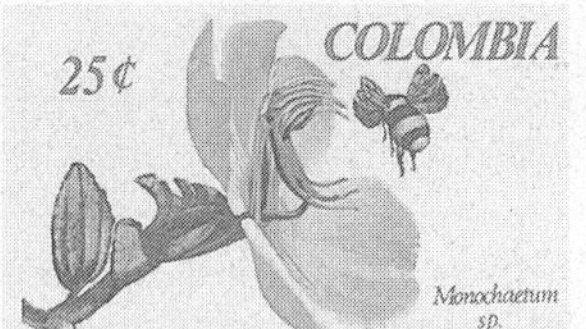
381 "Monochaetum" and Bee

1967. National Orchid Congress and Tropical Flora and Fauna Exhibition, Medellin. Multicoloured.
1192 25c. Type **381** (postage) . . 10 10
1193 2p. "Passiflora vitifolia" and butterfly 45 35
1194 1p. "Cattleya dowiana" (vert) (air) 15 10
1195 1p.20 "Masdevallia coccinea" (vert) 10 10
1196 5p. "Catasetum macrocarpum" and bee 55 10

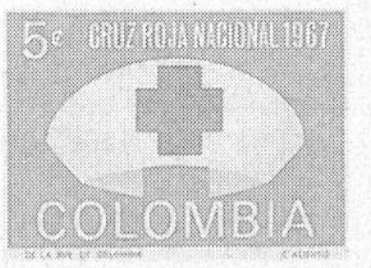
382 Nurse's Cap

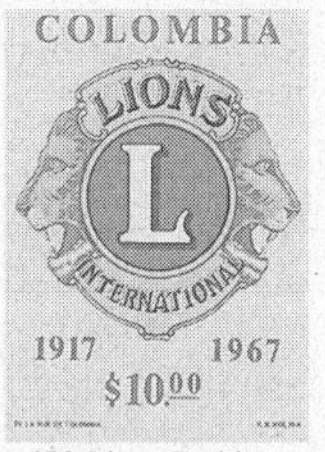
383 Lions Emblem

1967. Obligatory Tax. Red Cross Fund.
1198 **382** 5c. red and blue 10 10

1967. 50th Anniv of Lions International.
1199 **383** 10p. mult (postage) . . . 1·40 35
1200 25c. multicoloured (air) 15 10

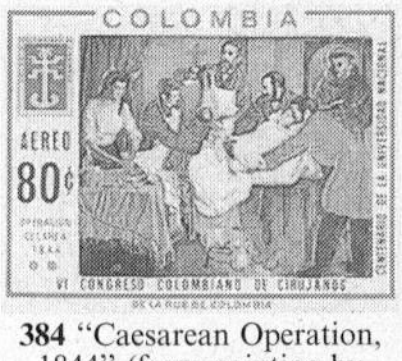
384 "Caesarean Operation, 1844" (from painting by Grau)

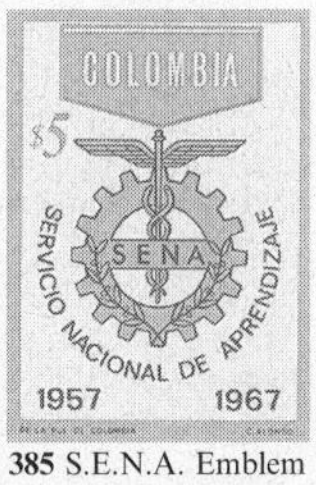
385 S.E.N.A. Emblem

1967. Air. 6th Colombian Surgeons' Congress, Bogota and Centenary of National University.
1201 **384** 80c. multicoloured . . . 15 10

1967. 10th Anniv of National Apprenticeship Service.
1202 **385** 5p. black, gold and green (postage) . . . . . . 1·25 20
1203   2p. black, gold and red (air) 20 10

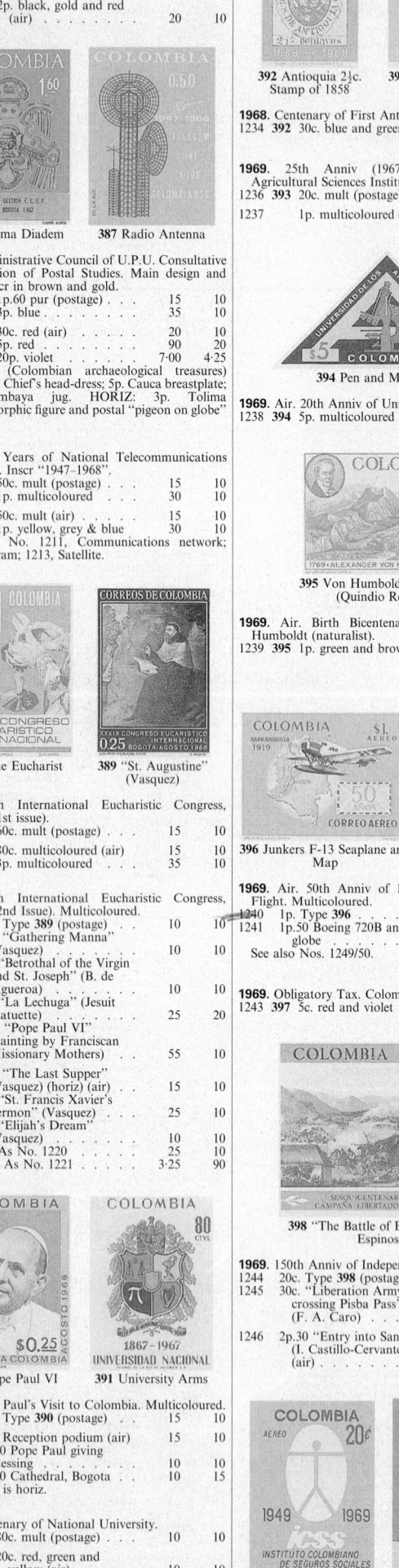
386 Calima Diadem   387 Radio Antenna

1967. Administrative Council of U.P.U. Consultative Commission of Postal Studies. Main design and lower inscr in brown and gold.
1204 **386** 1p.60 pur (postage) . . . 15 10
1205 – 3p. blue 35 10
1206 – 30c. red (air) 20 10
1207 – 5p. red 90 20
1208 – 20p. violet . . . . . . 7·00 4·25
DESIGNS (Colombian archaeological treasures) VERT: 30c. Chief's head-dress; 5p. Cauca breastplate; 20p. Quimbaya jug. HORIZ: 3p. Tolima anthropomorphic figure and postal "pigeon on globe" emblem.

1968. "21 Years of National Telecommunications Services". Inscr "1947–1968".
1210 **387** 50c. mult (postage) . . . 15 10
1211 – 1p. multicoloured . . . 30 10
1212 – 50c. mult (air) 15 10
1213 – 1p. yellow, grey & blue 30 10
DESIGNS: No. 1211, Communications network; 1212, Diagram; 1213, Satellite.

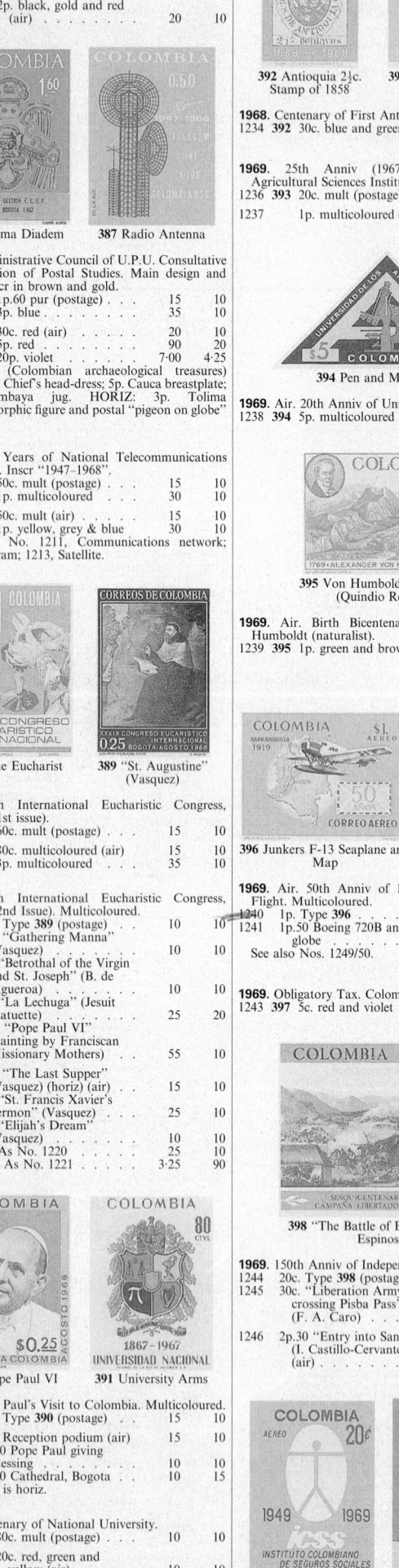
388 The Eucharist   389 "St. Augustine" (Vasquez)

1968. 39th International Eucharistic Congress, Bogota (1st issue).
1214 **388** 60c. mult (postage) . . . 15 10
1215 – 80c. multicoloured (air) 15 10
1216 – 3p. multicoloured . . . 35 10

1968. 39th International Eucharistic Congress, Bogota (2nd Issue). Multicoloured.
1217   25c. Type **389** (postage) . . 10 10
1218   60c. "Gathering Manna" (Vasquez) 10 10
1219   1p. "Betrothal of the Virgin and St. Joseph" (B. de Figueroa) 10 10
1220   5p. "La Lechuga" (Jesuit Statuette) 25 10
1221   10p. "Pope Paul VI" (painting by Franciscan Missionary Mothers) . . 55 10
1222   80c. "The Last Supper" (Vasquez) (horiz) (air) . . 15 10
1223   1p. "St. Francis Xavier's Sermon" (Vasquez) . . 25 10
1224   2p. "Elijah's Dream" (Vasquez) 10 10
1225   3p. As No. 1220 . . . . 25 10
1226   20p. As No. 1221 . . . . 3·25 90

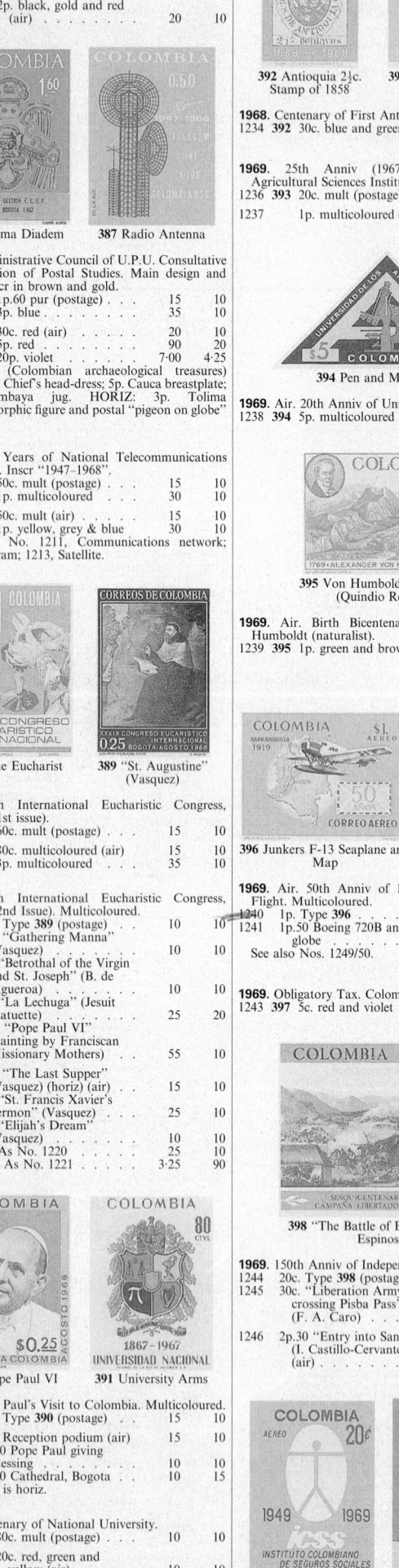
390 Pope Paul VI   391 University Arms

1968. Pope Paul's Visit to Colombia. Multicoloured.
1228   25c. Type **390** (postage) . . 15 10
1229   80c. Reception podium (air) 15 10
1230   1p.20 Pope Paul giving Blessing 10 10
1231   1p.80 Cathedral, Bogota . 10 15
No. 1229 is horiz.

1968. Centenary of National University.
1232 **391** 80c. mult (postage) . . . 10 10
1233 – 20c. red, green and yellow (air) 10 10
DESIGN: 20c. Mathematical symbols.

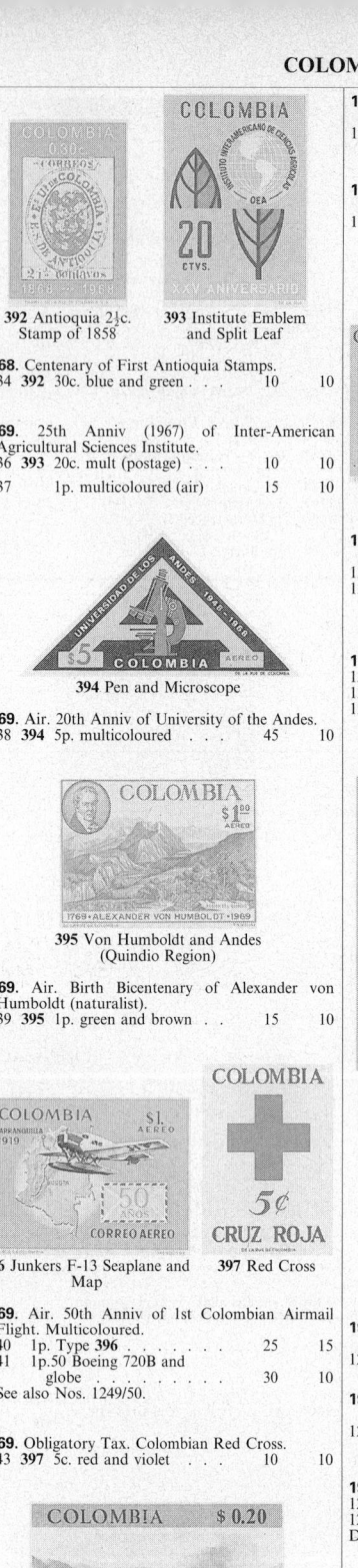
392 Antioquia 2½c. Stamp of 1858   393 Institute Emblem and Split Leaf

1968. Centenary of First Antioquia Stamps.
1234 **392** 30c. blue and green . . . 10 10

1969. 25th Anniv (1967) of Inter-American Agricultural Sciences Institute.
1236 **393** 20c. mult (postage) . . . 10 10
1237   1p. multicoloured (air) 15 10

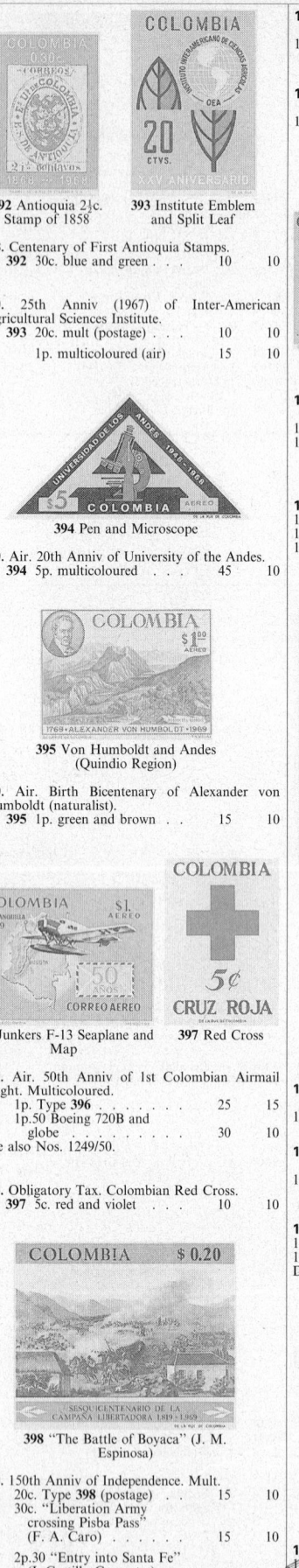
394 Pen and Microscope

1969. Air. 20th Anniv of University of the Andes.
1238 **394** 5p. multicoloured . . . 45 10

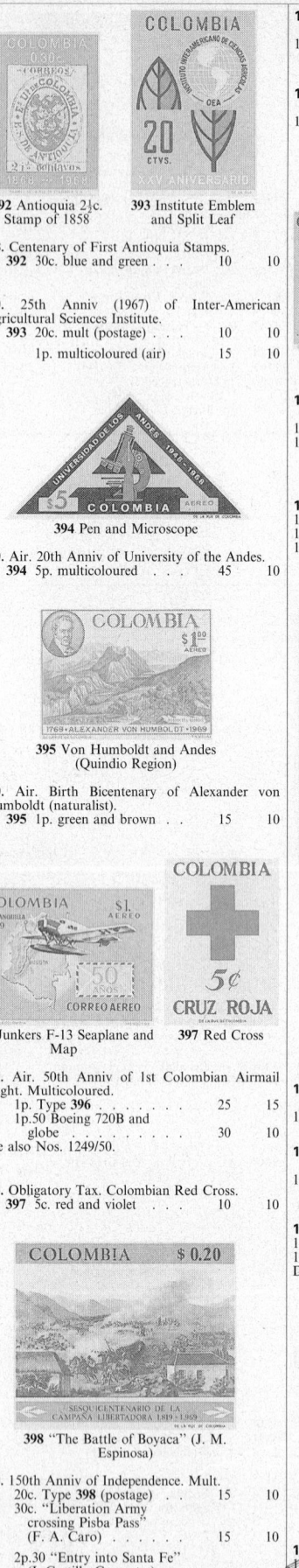
395 Von Humboldt and Andes (Quindio Region)

1969. Air. Birth Bicentenary of Alexander von Humboldt (naturalist).
1239 **395** 1p. green and brown . . 15 10

396 Junkers F-13 Seaplane and Map   397 Red Cross

1969. Air. 50th Anniv of 1st Colombian Airmail Flight. Multicoloured.
1240   1p. Type **396** 25 15
1241   1p.50 Boeing 720B and globe 30 10
See also Nos. 1249/50.

1969. Obligatory Tax. Colombian Red Cross.
1243 **397** 5c. red and violet . . . 10 10

398 "The Battle of Boyaca" (J. M. Espinosa)

1969. 150th Anniv of Independence. Mult.
1244   20c. Type **398** (postage) . . 15 10
1245   30c. "Liberation Army crossing Pisba Pass" (F. A. Caro) 15 10
1246   2p.30 "Entry into Santa Fe" (I. Castillo-Cervantes) (air) 20 20

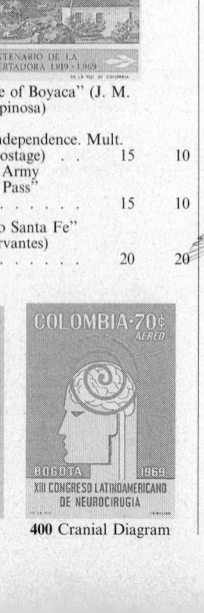
399 Institute Emblem   400 Cranial Diagram

1969. Air. 20th Anniv of Colombian Social Security Institute.
1247 **399** 20c. green and black . . 10 10

1969. Air. 13th Latin-American Neurological Congress, Bogota.
1248 **400** 70c. multicoloured . . . 20 10

401 Junkers F-13 Seaplane and Puerto Colombia   402 Child posting Christmas Card

1969. Air. 50th Anniv of "Avianca" Airline. Multicoloured.
1249   2p. Type **401** 40 10
1250   3p.50 Boeing 720B and globe 35 25

1969. Air. Christmas. Multicoloured.
1252   60c. Type **402** 15 10
1253   1p. Type **402** 15 10
1254   1p.50 Child with Christmas presents 45 10

403 "Poverty"   405 National Sports Institute Emblem

1970. Colombian Social Welfare Institute and 10th Anniv of Children's Rights Law.
1255 **403** 30c. multicoloured . . . 10 10

1970. Air. Opening of Satellite Earth Station, Choconta.
1256 **404** 1p. black, red & green 40 10

404 Dish Aerial and Ancient Head

1970. Air. 9th National Games, Ibague (1st issue).
1257 **405** 1p.50 black, yell & grn 25 15
1258 – 2p.30 multicoloured . . . 15 20
DESIGN: 2p.30, Dove and rings (Games emblem).
See also No. 1265.

406 Exhibition Emblem

1970. Air. 2nd Fine Arts Biennial, Medellin
1259 **406** 30c. multicoloured . . . 10 10

407 Dr. E. Santos (founder) and Buildings

1970. Air. 30th Anniv (1969) of Territorial Credit Institute.
1260 **407** 1p. black, yellow & grn 15 10

408 U.N. Emblem, Scales and Dove   409 Hands protecting Child

1970. Air. 25th Anniv of United Nations.
1261 **408** 1p.50 yellow, bl & ultram 20 10

1970. Obligatory Tax. Colombian Red Cross.
1262 **409** 5c. red and blue 10 10

410 Theatrical Mask

1970. Latin-American University Theatre Festival. Manizales.
1263 **410** 30c. brown, orange & blk 10 10

411 Postal Emblem, Letter and Stamps

1970. Philatelic Week.
1264 **411** 2p. multicoloured . . . 30 10

412 Discus-thrower and Ibague Arms

1970. 9th National Games, Ibague (2nd issue).
1265 **412** 80c. brown, green & yell 20 10

413 "St. Teresa" (B. de Figueroa)   414 Int Philatelic Federation Emblem

1970. St. Teresa of Avila's Elevation to Doctor of the Universal Church. No. 1267 optd **AEREO**.
1266 **413** 2p. mult (postage) . . . 10 10
1267   2p. mult (air) 30 10

1970. Air. "EXFILCA 70" Stamp Exhibition, Caracas, Venezuela.
1268 **414** 10p. multicoloured . . . 1·50 20

415 Chicha Maya Dance   416 Stylized Athlete

1970. Folklore Dances and Costumes. Mult.
1269   1p. Type **415** (postage) . . . 35 10
1270   1p.10 Currulao dance . . . 35 10
1271   60c. Napanga costume (air) 20 15
1272   1p. Joropo dance 20 10
1273   1p.30 Guabina dance 30 10

1274	1p.30 Bambuco dance . . .	20	10
1275	1p.30 Cumbia dance	20	10

1971. Air. 6th Pan-American Games, Cali (1st issue).
1277 **416** 1p.50 multicoloured . . . 35 45
1278 – 2p. orange, green & blk 35 40
DESIGN: 2p. Games emblem.

417 G. Alzate Avendano

1971. Air. 10th Anniv of Gilberto Alzate Avendano (politician).
1279 **417** 1p. multicoloured . . . 15 25

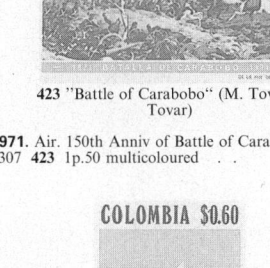
418 Priest's House, Guacari

1971. 400th Anniv of Guacari (town).
1280 **418** 1p. multicoloured . . . 25 10

419 Commemorative Medal

1971. Air. Centenary of Bank of Bogota.
1281 **419** 1p. gold, brown & green 40 20

420 Sports Centre   **421** Weightlifting

1971. Air. 6th Pan-American Games (2nd issue) and "EXFICALI 71" Stamp Exhibition, Cali. Mult.
1282 **420** 1p.30 Type **420** (yellow emblem) . . . 40 30
1283 1p.30 Football 40 30
1284 1p.30 Wrestling 40 30
1285 1p.30 Cycling 40 30
1286 1p.30 Volleyball 40 30
1287 1p.30 Diving 40 30
1288 1p.30 Fencing 40 30
1289 1p.30 Type **420** (green emblem) . . . 40 30
1290 1p.30 Sailing 40 30
1291 1p.30 Show-jumping . . . 40 30
1292 1p.30 Athletics 40 30
1293 1p.30 Rowing 40 30
1294 1p.30 Cali emblem . . . 40 30
1295 1p.30 Netball 40 30
1296 1p.30 Type **420** (blue emblem) . . . 40 30
1297 1p.30 Stadium 40 30
1298 1p.30 Baseball 40 30
1299 1p.30 Hockey 40 30
1300 1p.30 Type **421** 40 30
1301 1p.30 Medals 40 30
1302 1p.30 Boxing 40 30
1303 1p.30 Gymnastics 40 30
1304 1p.30 Rifle-shooting . . . 40 30
1305 1p.30 Type **420** (red emblem) . . . 40 30

422 "Bolivar at Congress" (after S. Martinez-Delgado)

1971. 150th Anniv of Great Colombia Constituent Assembly, Rosario del Cucuta.
1306 **422** 80c. multicoloured . . . 15 10

423 "Battle of Carabobo" (M. Tovar y Tovar)

1971. Air. 150th Anniv of Battle of Carabobo.
1307 **423** 1p.50 multicoloured . . . 15 15

424 C.I.M.E. Emblem

1972. 20th Anniv of Inter-Governmental Committee on European Migration.
1308 **424** 60c. black and grey . . . 25 10

425 I.C.E.T.E.X. Symbol

1972. 20th Anniv of Institute of Educational Credit and Technical Training Abroad.
1309 **425** 1p.10 brown and green 20 10

426 Rev. Mother Francisca del Castillo

1972. 300th Birth Anniv of Reverend Mother Francisca J. del Castillo.
1310 **426** 1p.20 multicoloured . . . 20 10

427 Soldier and Frigate "Almirante Padilla"

1972. 20th Anniv of Colombian Troops' Participation in Korean War.
1311 **427** 1p.20 multicoloured . . . 1·25 15

428 Hat and Ceramics   **429** "Maxillaria triloris" (orchid)

1972. Colombian Crafts and Products. Mult.
1312 1p.10 Type **428** (postage) . . 30 10
1313 50c. Woman in shawl (air) 30 10
1314 1p. Male doll 20 10
1315 3p. Female doll 20 25

1972. 10th National Stamp Exhibition and 7th World Orchid-growers' Congress, Medellin. Mult.
1316 20p. Type **429** (postage) . 5·00 25
1317 1p.30 "Mormodes rolfeanum" (orchid) (horiz) (air) 15 10

430 Uncut Emeralds and Pendant   **432** Congo Dance

431 Pres. Narino's House

1972. Colombian Emeralds.
1318 **430** 1p.10 multicoloured . . 30 10

1972. 400th Anniv of Leyva (town).
1319 **431** 1p.10 multicoloured . . . 30 10

1972. Air. Barranquilla International Carnival.
1320 **432** 1p.30 multicoloured . . . 30 10

433 Island Scene   **435** "Pres. Laureano Gomez" (R. Cubillos)

1972. 150th Anniv of Annexation of San Andres and Providencia Islands.
1321 **433** 60c. multicoloured . . . 20 10

1972. Air. No. 1142 surch.
1322 **360** 1p.30 on 1p.90 brn and bl 20 15

1972. Air. Pres. Gomez Commemoration.
1323 **435** 1p.30 multicoloured . . . 20 10

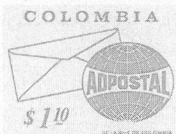
436 Postal Administration Emblem

1972. National Postal Administration.
1324 **436** 1p.10 green 15 10

437 Colombian Family

1972. "Social Front for the People" Campaign.
1325 **437** 60c. orange 10 10

438 Pres. Guillermo Valencia   **439** Benito Juarez

1972. Air. Pres. Valencia Commemoration.
1326 **438** 1p.30 multicoloured . . . 25 10

1972. Air. Death Centenary of Benito Juarez (Mexican statesman).
1327 **439** 1p.50 multicoloured . . 20 10

440 "La Rebeca" Monument   **441** "350" and Arms of Bucaramanga

1972. Air. "La Rebeca" Monument, Centenary Park, Bogota.
1328 **440** 80c. multicoloured . . . 25 30
1329 1p. multicoloured . . . 20 10

1972. Air. 350th Anniv of Bucaramanga (city).
1330 **441** 5p. multicoloured . . . 30 10

442 University Buildings   **443** League Emblems

1973. Air. 350th Anniv of Javeriana University.
1331 **442** 1p.30 brown and green 25 10
1332 1p.50 brown and blue . . 25 10

1973. 40th Anniv of Colombian Radio Amateurs League.
1333 **443** 60c. red, dp blue & blue 15 10

444 Tamalameque Vessel   **445** "Battle of Maracaibo" (M. F. Rincon)

1973. Inauguration of Museum of Pre-Colombian Antiques, Bogota. Multicoloured.
1334 60c. Type **444** (postage) . . 25 10
1335 1p. Tairona axe-head . . . 45 10
1336 1p.10 Muisca jug 30 10
1337 1p. As No. 1335 (air) . . . 40 35
1338 1p.30 Sinu vessel 20 10
1339 1p.70 Quimbaya vessel . . 25 20
1340 3p.50 Tumaco figurine . . . 50 30

1973. Air. 150th Anniv of Naval Battle of Maracaibo.
1341 **445** 10p. multicoloured . . . 3·25 30

446 Banknote Emblem

1973. Air. 50th Anniv of Republican Bank.
1342 **446** 2p. multicoloured . . . 25 10

1973. Air. No. 1306 optd **AEREO**.
1343 **422** 80c. multicoloured . . . 15 10

448 "Pres. Ospina" (after C. Leudo)   **449** Arms of Toro

1973. Air. 50th Anniv of Ministry of Communications.
1344 **448** 1p.50 multicoloured . . . 20 10

1973. Air. 400th Anniv of Toro.
1345 **449** 1p. multicoloured . . . 15 10

450 Bolivar at Bombona

1973. Air. 150th Anniv of Battle of Bombona.
1346 450 1p.30 multicoloured . . 20 10

451 "General Narino"
(after J. M. Espinosa)

452 Young Child

1973. 150th Death Anniv of General Antonio Narino.
1347 451 60c. multicoloured . . . 15 10

1973. Child Welfare Campaign.
1348 452 1p.10 multicoloured . . 20 10

453 Fiscal Emblem

1974. 50th Anniv of Republic's General Comptrollership.
1349 453 80c. black, brown & bl 15 10

454 Copernicus

455 Andes Communications and Map

1974. Air. 500th Birth Anniv of Copernicus.
1350 454 2p. multicoloured . . 20 15

1974. Air. Meeting of Communications Ministers, Andean Group, Cali.
1351 455 2p. multicoloured . . 10 15

456 Laura Montoya and Cross

457 Television Set with Inravision Emblem

1974. Birth Centenary of Revd. Mother Laura Montoya (missionary).
1352 456 1p. multicoloured . . . 15 10

1974. Air. 20th Anniv of Inravision (National Institute of Radio and Television).
1353 457 1p.30 black, brn & orge 20 10

458 Athlete

1974. 10th National Games, Pereira.
1354 458 2p. brown, red & yellow 20 10

459 Rivera and Statue

1974. 50th Anniv of Novel "La Voragine".
1355 459 10p. multicoloured . . . 35 15

460 Aquatic Emblem

1974. Air. 2nd World Swimming Championships, Cali (1975).
1356 460 4p.50 blue, turq & blk 30 15

461 Condor Emblem

1974. Air. Centenary of Bank of Colombia.
1357 461 1p.50 multicoloured . . 20 10

462 Tailplane

1974. Air.
1358 462 20c. brown 10 10

463 U.P.U. "Letter"

1974. Air. Centenary of Universal Postal Union (1st issue).
1359 463 20p. red, blue & black 1·10 30
See also Nos. 1363/6.

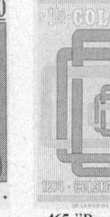

464 General Jose Maria Cordoba

465 "Progress and Expansion"

1974. Air. 150th Anniv of Battles of Junin and Ayacucho.
1360 464 1p.30 multicoloured . . 20 10

1974. Centenary of Colombian Insurance Company.
1361 465 1p.10 mult (postage) . . 20 10
1362 3p. mult (air) 35 10

466 White-tailed Trogon and U.P.U. "Letter"

467 La Quiebra Tunnel

1974. Air. Centenary of U.P.U. (2nd issue). Colombian Birds. Multicoloured.
1363 1p. Type 466 . . . . . . 75 40
1364 1p.30 Red-billed toucan (horiz) 75 50

1365 2p. Andean cock of the rock (horiz) . . . . . . 1·50 50
1366 2p.50 Scarlet macaw . . . . 1·50 60
Nos. 1364/6 also depict the U.P.U. "letter".

1974. Centenary of Antioquia Railway.
1367 467 1p.10 multicoloured . . 90 35

468 Boy with Ball

1974. Christmas. Multicoloured.
1368 80c. Type 468 . . . . . . 10 10
1369 1p. Girl with racquet . . . 10 15

469 "Protect the Trees"

1975. Air. Colombian Ecology. Multicoloured.
1370 1p. Type 469 . . . . . . 20 10
1371 6p. "Protect the Amazon" . 20 15

470 "Wood No. 1" (R. Roncancio)

1975. Air. Colombian Art. Multicoloured.
1372 2p. Type 470 . . . . . . 1·00 30
1373 3p. "The Market" (M. Diaz Vargas) . . . . . . 1·75 30
1374 4p. "Child with Thorn" (G. Vazquez) 15 10
1375 5p. "The Annunciation" (Santaferena School) . . . 45 30
Nos. 1373/5 are vert.

471 Gold Cat

1975. Pre-Colombian Archaeological Discoveries. Sinu Culture. Multicoloured.
1376 80c. Type 471 (postage) . . 20 10
1377 1p.10 Gold necklace 20 10
1378 2p. Nose pendant (air) . . . 40 10
1379 10p. "Alligator" staff ornament . . . . . . 2·10 35

472 Marconi and "Elettra" (steam yacht)

473 Santa Marta Cathedral

1975. Birth Centenary of Guglielmo Marconi (radio pioneer).
1380 472 3p. multicoloured . . . 75 10

1975. 450th Anniv of Santa Marta. Multicoloured.
1381 80c. Type 473 (postage) . . 10 10
1382 2p. "El Rodadero" (sea-front), Santa Marta (horiz) (air) 20 10

474 Maria de J. Paramo (educationalist)

475 Pres. Nunez

1975. International Women's Year.
1383 474 4p. multicoloured . . . 25 10

1975. 150th Birth Anniv of President Rafael Nunez.
1384 475 1p.10 multicoloured . . 15 10

476 Arms of Medellin

479 Sugar Cane

1975. 300th Anniv of Medellin.
1385 476 1p. multicoloured . . . 25 10
See also Nos. 1386, 1388, 1394, 1404, 1419, 1434, 1481/3, 1672/4, 1678/9, 1752, 1758, 1859 and 1876.

1976. Centenary of Reconstruction of Cucuta City. As T 476.
1386 1p.50 multicoloured 30 10

1976. Surch.
1387 471 1p.20 on 80c. mult . . . 15 10

1976. Arms of Cartagena. As T 476.
1388 1p.50 multicoloured 20 10

1976. 4th Cane Sugar Export and Production Congress, Cali.
1389 479 5p. green and black . . 45 10

480 Bogota

1976. Air. Habitat. U.N. Conference on Human Settlements. Multicoloured.
1390 10p. Type 480 . . . . . . 1·10 35
1391 10p. Barranquilla . . . . 1·10 35
1392 10p. Cali . . . . 1·10 35
1393 10p. Medellin . . . . . . 1·10 35

1976. Arms of Ibague. As T 476.
1394 1p.20 multicoloured 15 10

481 University Emblem and "90"

482 M. Samper

1976. Air. 90th Anniv of Colombia University.
1395 481 5p. multicoloured . . . 20 10

1976. Air. 150th Birth Anniv of Miguel Samper (statesman and writer).
1396 482 2p. multicoloured . . . 20 10

483 Early Telephone

484 "Callicore sp."

1976. Air. Telephone Centenary.
1397 483 3p. multicoloured . . . 20 10

1976. Colombian Fauna and Flora. Multicoloured.
1398 3p. Type 484
1399 5p. "Morpho sp." (butterfly) 1·25 20
1400 20p. Black anthurium
(plant) . . . . 1·10 25

485 Purace Indians, Cauca

486 Rotary Emblem

1976.
1401 485 1p.50 multicoloured . . 10 10

1976. 50th Anniv of Colombian Rotary Club.
1402 486 1p. multicoloured . . . 10 10

487 Boeing 747 Jumbo Jet

1976. Air. Inaug of Avianca Jumbo Jet Service.
1403 487 2p. multicoloured . . . 15 10

1976. 535th Anniv of Tunja City Arms. As T 476.
1404 1p.20 multicoloured . . . 15 10

488 "The Signing of Declaration of Independence" (left-hand detail of painting, Trumbull)

489 Police Handler and Dog

1976. Bicentenary of American Revolution.
1405 488 30p. multicoloured . . 1·75 1·10
1406 – 30p. multicoloured . . . 1·75 1·10
1407 – 30p. multicoloured . . . 1·75 1·10
DESIGNS: Nos. 1406/7 show different portions of the painting.

1976. National Police.
1408 489 1p.50 multicoloured . . 25 10

490 Franciscan Convent

1976. Air. 150th Anniv of Panama Congress.
1409 490 6p. multicoloured . . . 20 20

1977. Surch.
1411 475 2p. on 1p.10 mult
(postage) 25 10
1412 – 2p. on 1p.20 mult
(No. 1404) 20 10
1413 489 2p. on 1p.50 mult . . . 20 10
1414 487 3p. on 2p. mult (air) . . 15 10

494 Coffee Plant and Beans

495 Coffee Grower with mule

1977. Air. Coffee Production.
1416 494 3p. multicoloured . . . 15 10
1416a 3p.50 multicoloured . . 20 10

1977. Air. 50th Anniv of National Federation of Coffee Growers.
1417 495 10p. multicoloured . . . 20 15

496 Beethoven and Score of Ninth Symphony

1977. Air. 150th Anniv of Beethoven.
1418 496 8p. multicoloured . . . 25 15

1977. Arms of Popayan. As T 476.
1419 5p. multicoloured 30 15

497 Mother feeding Baby

498 Wattled Jacana and "Eichhornia crassipes"

1977. Nutrition Campaign.
1420 497 2p. multicoloured . . . 15 10
1420a 2p.50 multicoloured . . 80 10

1977. Colombian Birds and Plants. Multicoloured.
1421 10p. Type 498 (postage) . . 2·25 50
1422 20p. Plum-throated cotinga
and "Pyrostegia venusta" 2·50 60
1423 5p. Crimson-mantled
woodpecker and
"Meriania" (air) . . . . 1·50 50
1424 5p. American purple
gallinule and
"Nymphaea" . . . . . 1·50 50
1425 10p. Pampadour cotinga
and "Cochlospermum
orinocense" . . . . . 2·75 60
1426 10p. Northern royal
flycatcher and "Jacaranda
copaia" . . . . 2·75 60

499 Games Emblem

500 "La Cayetana" (E. Grau)

1977. Air. 13th Central American and Caribbean Games, Medellin (1978).
1427 499 6p. multicoloured . . . 25 10

1977. Air. 20th Anniv of Female Suffrage. Multicoloured.
1428 8p. Type 500 . . . . . 20 20
1429 8p. "Nayade" (Beatriz
Gonzalez) 20 20

501 "Judge Francisco Antonio Moreno y Escandon" (J. Gutierrez)

502 "Fidel Cano" (Francisco Cano)

1977. Air. Bicentenary of National Library. Mult.
1430 20p. Type 501 . . . . . 55 10
1431 25p. "Viceroy Manuel de
Guiror" (unknown artist) 55 20

1977. 90th Anniv of "El Espectador" Magazine by Fidel Cano.
1432 502 4p. multicoloured . . . 20 10

503 Abacus and Alphabet

1977. Popular Education.
1433 503 3p. multicoloured . . . 15 10

1977. Arms of Barranquilla. As T 476.
1434 5p. multicoloured 30 15

504 Dr. F. L. Acosta

505 Cauca University Arms

1977. Air. Birth Centenary of Dr. Federico Lleras Acosta (veterinary surgeon).
1435 504 5p. multicoloured . . . 30 10

1977. Air. 150th Anniv of Cauca University.
1436 505 5p. multicoloured . . . 25 10

506 "Cudecom" Building, Bogota

508 "Cattleya triannae"

1977. Air. 90th Anniv of Society of Colombian Engineers.
1437 506 1p.50 multicoloured . . 10 10

1977. Air. No. 1364 surch **$2.00.**
1438 2p. on 1p.30 multicoloured 90 25

1978.
1439 508 2p.50 multicoloured . . . 25 10
1439a 3p. multicoloured . . . 25 10

509 Tayronan Lost City

510 "Creator of Energy" (A. Betancourt)

1978. Air.
1440 509 3p.50 multicoloured . . 35 10

1978. Air. 150th Anniv of Antioquia University Law School.
1441 510 4p. multicoloured . . . 20 10

511 Column of the Slaves

512 "Catalina"

1978. Air. 150th Anniv of Ocana Convention.
1442 511 2p.50 multicoloured . . . 15 10

1978. Air. 150th Anniv of Cartagena University.
1443 512 4p. multicoloured . . . 20 10

513 Running

1978. 13th Central American and Caribbean Games, Medellin. Multicoloured.
1444 10p. Type 513 . . . . . 35 25
1445 10p. Basketball 35 25
1446 10p. Baseball 35 25
1447 10p. Boxing 35 25
1448 10p. Cycling 35 25
1449 10p. Fencing 35 25
1450 10p. Football 35 25
1451 10p. Gymnastics 35 25
1452 10p. Judo 35 25
1453 10p. Weightlifting 35 25
1454 10p. Wrestling 35 25
1455 10p. Swimming 35 25
1456 10p. Tennis 35 25
1457 10p. Shooting 35 25
1458 10p. Volleyball 35 25
1459 10p. Water polo 35 25

514 "Sigma 2" (A. Herran)

515 Human Figure from Gold Pendant

1978. Centenary of Bogota Chamber of Commerce.
1460 514 8p. multicoloured . . . 20 20

1978. Air. Tolima Culture.
1461 515 3p.50 multicoloured . . . 20 20

516 "Apotheosis of the Spanish Language" (Left-hand detail of mural, L. A. Acuna)

1978. Air. Millenary of Castilian Language. Multicoloured.
1462 11p. Type 516 . . . . . 55 50
1463 11p. Central detail 55 50
1464 11p. Right-hand detail . . . 55 50
Nos. 1462/4 were issued together, se-tenant, forming a composite design.

517 Presidential Guard

1978. Air. 50th Anniv of Presidential Guard Battalion.
1465 517 9p. multicoloured . . . 25 25

518 Human Figure   **519** General Tomas Cipriano de Mosquera

1978. Air. Muisca Culture.
1466 518 3p.50 multicoloured . . 20 10

1978. Death Centenary of General Tomas Cipriano de Mosquera (statesman).
1467 519 6p. multicoloured . . . 20 20

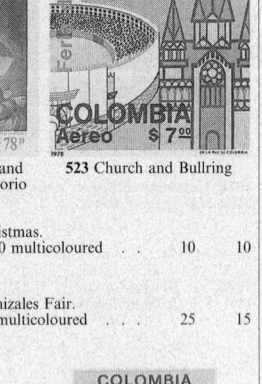

520 El Camarin de Carmen, Bogota   **521** Gold Owl Ornament

1978. Air. "Espamer '78" Stamp Exhibition, Bogota.
1468 520 30p. multicoloured . . . 1·75 20

1978. Air. Calima Culture.
1470 521 3p.50 multicoloured . . 20 10
1470a — 4p. multicoloured . . . 25 10

522 "Virgin and Child" (Gregorio Vasquez)   **523** Church and Bullring

1978. Air. Christmas.
1471 522 2p.50 multicoloured . . . 10 10

1978. Air. Manizales Fair.
1472 523 7p. multicoloured . . . 25 15

524 Frog in beaten Gold   **525** Children playing Hopscotch

1979. Air. Quimbaya Culture.
1473 524 4p. multicoloured . . . 15 10

1979. Air. International Year of the Child. Multicoloured.
1474 8p. Type 525 . . . . . . 30 10
1475 12p. Child in sou'wester and oilskins 20 20
1476 12p. Child at blackboard (horiz) 20 20

526 Anthurium   **527** Rio Prado Hydro-electric Barrage

1979. Anthurium Flowers from Narino. Multicoloured, background colours given.
1477 526 3p. light green 25 10
1478 — 3p. red 25 10

1479 — 3p. green 25 10
1480 — 3p. blue 25 10

1979. Arms. As T **476.** Multicoloured.
1481 4p. Sogamoso 45 10
1482 10p. Socorro 20 15
1483 10p. Santa Cruz y San Gil de la Nueva Baeza . . . 20 15

1979. Air. Tourism. Multicoloured.
1484 5p. Type 527 . . . . . 35 10
1485 7p. River Amazon 60 30
1486 8p. Tomb, San Agustin Archaeological Park . . . 25 20
1487 14p. San Fernando Fort, Cartagena 45 35

528 "Jimenez de Quesada" (after C. Leudo)

1979. Air. 400th Death Anniv of Gonzalo Jimenez de Quesada (conquistador).
1488 528 20p. multicoloured . . . 1·60 65

529 Hill and First Stamps of Great Britain and Colombia

1979. Air. Death Centenary of Sir Rowland Hill.
1489 529 15p. multicoloured . . . 25 25

530 "Uribe" (after Acevedo Bernal)

1979. 65th Death Anniv of General Rafael Uribe Uribe (statesman).
1490 530 8p. multicoloured . . . 30 15

531 "Village" (Leonor Alarcon)

1979. 20th Anniv of Community Works Boards.
1491 531 15p. multicoloured . . . 85 30

532 Three Kings and Soldiers

1979. Air. Christmas. Multicoloured.
1492 3p. Type 532 . . . . . 75 40
1493 3p. Nativity 75 40
1494 3p. Shepherds 75 40

533 River Magdalena Bridge and Avianca Emblem   **534** Gold Nose Pendant

1979. Air. 350th Anniv of Barranquilla and 60th Anniv of Avianca National Airline.
1495 533 15p. multicoloured . . . 25 15

1980. Air. Tairona Culture.
1496 534 3p. multicoloured . . . 25 10

535 "Boy playing Flute" (Judith Leyster)   **536** Antonio Jose de Sucre

1980. Air. 2nd International Music Competition, Ibague.
1497 535 6p. multicoloured . . . 30 10

1980. Air. 150th Death Anniv of General Antonio Jose de Sucre.
1498 536 12p. multicoloured . . . 20 15

537 "The Watchman" (Edgar Negret)

1980. Air. Modern Sculpture.
1499 537 25p. multicoloured . . . 1·40 1·25

538 Television Screen

1980. Inaug of Colour Television in Colombia.
1500 538 5p. multicoloured . . . 25 10

539 Bullfighting Poster (H. Courttin)   **540** "Learn to Write"

1980. Tourism. Festival of Cali.
1501 539 5p. multicoloured . . . 35 15

1980. The Alphabet.
1502 540 4p. black, brown & grn 25 10
1503 — 4p. multicoloured . . . 25 10
1504 — 4p. brown, blk & lt brn 25 10
1505 — 4p. multicoloured . . . 40 15
1506 — 4p. brown, black & grn 25 10
1507 — 4p. black and turquoise 25 10
1508 — 4p. black and green 25 10
1509 — 4p. mauve, black & grn 40 15
1510 — 4p. black and blue 25 10
1511 — 4p. black and green 25 10
1512 — 4p. green, black & brown 25 10
1513 — 4p. multicoloured 25 10
1514 — 4p. brown, black & grn 25 10
1515 — 4p. multicoloured 25 10
1516 — 4p. yellow, black & grn 25 10
1517 — 4p. black, brown & yell 25 10
1518 — 4p. brown, black & turq 25 10
1519 — 4p. brown, black & grn 25 10

1520 — 4p. brown, black & grn 25 10
1521 — 4p. yellow, black & turq 25 10
1522 — 4p. green, black & blue 40 15
1523 — 4p. brown, black & grn 25 10
1524 — 4p. green, black & lt grn 25 10
1525 — 4p. multicoloured . . . 25 10
1526 — 4p. multicoloured . . . 25 10
1527 — 4p. brown, black & grn 25 10
1528 — 4p. multicoloured . . . 40 15
1529 — 4p. multicoloured . . . 25 10
1530 — 4p. multicoloured . . . 25 10
1531 — 4p. brown and black . . 25 10

DESIGNS: No. 1503, "a" Eagle; 1504, "b" Buffalo; 1505, "c" Andean Condor; 1506, "ch" Chimpanzee; 1507, "d" Dolphin; 1508, "e" Elephant; 1509, "f" Greater Flamingo; 1510, "g" Seagull; 1511, "h" Hippopotamus; 1512, "i" Iguana; 1513, "j" Giraffe; 1514, "k" Koala; 1515, "l" Lion; 1516, "ll" Llama; 1517, "m" Blackbird; 1518, "n" Otter; 1519, Gnu; 1520, "o" Bear; 1521, "p" Pelican; 1522, "q" Resplendent Quetzal; 1523, "r" Rhinoceros; 1524, "s" Grasshopper; 1525, "t" Tortoise; 1526, "u" Magpie; 1527, "v" Viper; 1528, "w" Wagon with animals; 1529, "x" Fox playing xylophone; 1530, "y" Yak; 1531, "z" Fox.

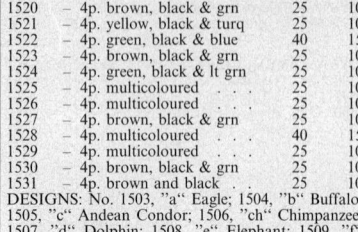

541 "Miraculous Virgin" (statue, Real del Sarte)

1980. Air. 150th Anniv of Apparition of Holy Virgin to Sister Catalina Labouri Gontard in Paris.
1532 541 12p. multicoloured . . . 45 15

542 "Country Scene, San Gil" (painting, Luis Roncancio)

1980. Air. Agriculture.
1533 542 12p. multicoloured . . . 1·00 30

543 Villavicencio Song Festival

1980. Tourism. Festivals. Multicoloured.
1534 5p. Type 543 . . . . . 30 15
1535 9p. Vallenato festival . . . 15 15

544 Gustavo Uribe Ramirez and "Samanea saman"

1980. 12th Death Anniv of Gustavo Uribe Ramirez (ecologist).
1536 544 10p. multicoloured . . . 35 15

545 Narino Palace

1980. Narino Palace (Presidential residence).
1537 545 5p. multicoloured . . . 30 10

546 Monument to First Pioneers, Armenia

1980. City of Armenia.
1538 **546** 5p. multicoloured . . . 30 10

547 Olaya Herrera (after Miguel Diaz Varges)

549 Athlete with Torch

548 "Simple Simon"

1980. Air. Birth Centenary of Dr. Enrique Olaya Herrera (President, 1930–34).
1539 **547** 20p. multicoloured . . . 45 25

1980. Air. Christmas. Illustrations to stories by Rafael Pombo. Multicoloured.
1540 4p. Type **548** . . . 25 15
1541 4p. "The Cat's Seven Lives" 25 15
1542 4p. "The Walking Tadpole" 25 15

1980. 11th National Games, Neiva.
1543 **549** 5p. multicoloured . . . 20 10

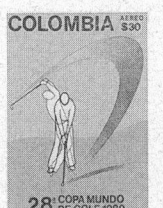

550 Golfers

551 Crab pierced by Sword

1980. Air. 28th World Golf Cup, Cajica.
1544 **550** 30p. multicoloured . . . 2·10 1·50

1980. 20th Anniv of Colombian Anti-cancer League.
1545 **551** 10p. multicoloured . . . 35 20

552 "Justice" and University Emblem

1980. 50th Anniv of Refounding of Pontifical Xavier University Law Faculty.
1546 **552** 20p. multicoloured . . . 25 30

553 "Bolivar's Last Moments" (Marcos Leon Marino)

1980. 150th Death Anniv of Simon Bolivar. Multicoloured.
1547 25p. Type **553** (postage) . . 45 35
1548 6p. Bolivar and his last proclamation (air) 25 25

554 St. Pedro Claver

555 Statue of Bird, San Agustin

1981. Air. 400th Birth Anniv of St. Pedro Claver.
1549 **554** 15p. multicoloured . . . 20 30

1981. Air. Archaeological Discoveries. Mult.
1550 7p. Type **555** 30 15
1551 7p. Hypogeum (funeral chamber), Tierradentro 30 15
1552 7p. Hypogeum, Tierradentro (different) 30 15
1553 7p. Statue of man, San Agustin 30 15

556 "Square Abstract" (Omar Rayo)

1981. Air. 4th Biennial Arts Exhibition, Medellin. Multicoloured.
1554 20p. Type **556** 30 20
1555 25p. "Flowers" (Alejandro Obregon) 40 30
1556 50p. "Child with Hobby Horse" (Fernando Botero) 1·50 1·25

557 Diver

1981. Air. 8th South American Swimming Championships, Medellin.
1557 **557** 15p. multicoloured . . . 25 30

558 Santamaria Bull Ring

1981. Air. 50th Anniv of Santamaria Bull Ring, Bogota.
1558 **558** 30p. multicoloured . . . 1·50 80

559 Mariano Ospina Perez (after Delio Ramirez)

1981. Presidents of Colombia (1st series). Multicoloured.
1559 5p. Type **559** 25 10
1560 5p. Eduardo Santos (after Ines Acevedo) . . . 25 10
1561 5p. Miguel Abadia Mendez (after Gomez Compuzano) . . . 25 10
1562 5p. Jose Vicente Concha (after Acevedo Bernal) . . 25 10
1563 5p. Carlos E. Restrepo . . . 25 10
1564 5p. Rafael Reyes (after Acevedo Bernal) . . . 25 10
1565 5p. Santiago Perez . . . 25 10
1566 5p. Manuel Murillo Toro (after Moreno Otero) . . 25 10

1567 5p. Jose Hilario Lopez . . . 25 10
1568 5p. Jose Maria Obando . . . 25 10
See also Nos. 1569/78, 1579/88, 1599/1608, 1615/24 and 1634/43.

1981. Presidents of Colombia (2nd series). Multicoloured.
1569 7p. Type **559** . . . . . 2·75 35
1570 7p. As No. 1560 . . . . 2·75 35
1571 7p. As No. 1561 . . . . 2·75 35
1572 7p. As No. 1562 . . . . 2·75 35
1573 7p. As No. 1563 . . . . 2·75 35
1574 7p. As No. 1564 . . . . 2·75 35
1575 7p. As No. 1565 . . . . 2·75 35
1576 7p. As No. 1566 . . . . 2·75 35
1577 7p. As No. 1567 . . . . 2·75 35
1578 7p. As No. 1568 . . . . 2·75 35

1981. Presidents of Colombia (3rd series). As T **559**. Multicoloured.
1579 7p. Pedro Alcantara Herran 2·10 20
1580 7p. Mariano Ospina Rodriguez (after Coriolando Leudo) . . . 2·10 20
1581 7p. Tomas Cipriano de Mosquera . . . . 2·10 20
1582 7p. Santos Gutierrez . . . 2·10 20
1583 7p. Aquileo Parra (after Constancio Franco) . . . 2·10 20
1584 7p. Rafael Nunez . . . . 2·10 20
1585 7p. Marco Fidel Suarez (after Jesus Maria Duque) 2·10 20
1586 7p. Pedro Nel Ospina (after Coriolano Leudo) . . . 2·10 20
1587 7p. Enrique Olaya Herrera (after M. Diaz Vargas) . . 2·10 20
1588 7p. Alfonso Lopez Pumarejo (after Luis F. Uscategui) 2·10 20

560 Crossed-legged Figure

1981. Air. Quimbaya Culture. Multicoloured.
1589 9p. Type **560** 40 15
1590 9p. Seated figure 40 15
1591 9p. Printing block and print 40 15
1592 9p. Clay pot 40 15

561 Fruit

1981. Air. Fruit. Designs showing fruit.
1593 **561** 25p. multicoloured . . . 2·10 1·40
1594 — 25p. multicoloured . . . 2·10 1·40
1595 — 25p. multicoloured . . . 2·10 1·40
1596 — 25p. multicoloured . . . 2·10 1·40
1597 — 25p. multicoloured . . . 2·10 1·40
1598 — 25p. multicoloured . . . 2·10 1·40
Nos. 1593/8 were issued together in se-tenant blocks of six forming a composite design.

1981. Presidents of Colombia (4th series). As T **559**. Multicoloured.
1599 7p. Manuel Maria Mallarino 1·00 15
1600 7p. Santos Acosta . . . . . 1·00 15
1601 7p. Eustorgio Salgar . . . 1·00 15
1602 7p. Julian Trujillo . . . . 1·00 15
1603 7p. Francisco Javier Zaldua (after Francisco Valles) . 1·00 15
1604 7p. Jose Eusebio Otalora (after Ricardo Moros) . . 1·00 15
1605 7p. Miguel Antonio Caro . 1·00 15
1606 7p. Manuel A. Sanclemente (after Epifanio Garay) . 1·00 15
1607 7p. Laureano Gomez (after Jose Bascones) . . . 1·00 15
1608 7p. Guillermo Leon Valencia (after Luis Angel Rengifo) . . . . . . 1·00 15

562 "Comunero tearing down Edict" (Manuela Beltran)

1981. Air. Bicentenary of Comuneros Uprising.
1609 **562** 20p. multicoloured . . . 25 30

563 Jose Maria Villa and West Bridge

564 Restrepo (after R. Acevedo Bernal)

1981. West Bridge, Santa Fe de Antioquia.
1610 **563** 60p. multicoloured . . . 65 10

1981. Air. Birth Centenary of Jose Manuel Restrepo (historian).
1611 **564** 35p. multicoloured . . . 35 15

565 Anniversary Emblem

566 Los Nevados National Park

1981. 50th Anniv of Caja Agraria (peasants' bank).
1612 **565** 15p. multicoloured . . . 15 10

1981. Los Nevados National Park.
1613 **566** 20p. multicoloured . . . 20 10

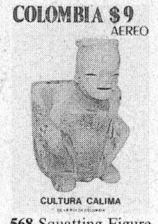

567 Andres Bello

568 Squatting Figure

1981. Birth Centenary of Andres Bello (poet).
1614 **567** 18p. multicoloured . . . 20 15

1981. Presidents of Colombia (5th series). As T **559**. Multicoloured.
1615 7p. Bartolome Calvo (after Miguel Diaz Vargas) . 60 15
1616 7p. Sergio Camargo 60 15
1617 7p. Jose Maria Rojas Garrido 60 15
1618 7p. J. M. Campo Serrano (after H. L. Brown) . . 60 15
1619 7p. Eliseo Payan (after R. Moros Urbina) . . . 60 15
1620 7p. Carlos Holguin (after Coriolano Leudo) . . . 60 15
1621 7p. Jose Manuel Marroquin (after Rafael Tavera) . 60 15
1622 7p. Ramon Gonzalez Valencia (after Jose Maria Vidal) 60 15
1623 7p. Jorge Holguin (after M. Salas Yepes) 60 15
1624 7p. Ruben Piedrahita Arango 60 15

1981. Air. Calima Culture. Multicoloured.
1625 9p. Type **568** 80 15
1626 9p. Vessel with two spouts . 80 15
1627 9p. Human-shaped vessel with two spouts 80 15
1628 9p. Pot 80 15

569 1c. Stamp of 1881

1981. Air. Centenary of Admission to U.P.U.
1629 **569** 30p. green and pink . . . 30 20

Solidaridad por Colombia

570 Girl with Water Jug

1981. Colombian Solidarity.
1631	570	30p. brown, blk & orge	70	30
1632		– 30p. brown, blk & orge	70	30
1633		– 30p. brown, blk & orge	70	30

DESIGNS: No. 1632, Baby with basket; 1633, Boy sitting on wheelbarrow.

1982. Presidents of Colombia (6th series). As T **559.** Multicoloured.
1634	7p. Simon Bolivar	50	15
1635	7p. Francisco de Paula Santander	50	15
1636	7p. Joaquin Mosquera (after C. Franco)	50	15
1637	7p. Domingo Caicedo	50	15
1638	7p. Jose Ignacio de Marquez (after C. Franco)	50	15
1639	7p. Juan de Dios Aranzazu	50	15
1640	7p. Jose de Obaldia (after Jesus M. Duque)	50	15
1641	7p. Guillermo Quintero Calderon (after Silvano Cuellar)	50	15
1642	7p. Carlos Lozano y Lozano (after Helio Ramierz)	50	15
1643	7p. Roberto Urdaneta Arbelaez (after Jose Bascones Agneto)	50	15

571 Solano Bay, Choco

1982. Air. Tourism. Multicoloured.
1644	20p. Type **571**	25	30
1645	20p. Tota Lake, Boyaca	25	30
1646	20p. Corrales, Boyaca	25	30

573 Gun Club Emblem

1982. Air. Centenary of Bogota Gun Club.
| 1648 | 573 | 20p. multicoloured | 25 | 15 |

574 Flower Arrangement in Basket

576 Capitalization Certificate

575 Zoomorphic Figure (crocodile)

1982. Country Flowers. Designs showing flower arrangements. Multicoloured.
1649	7p. Type **574**	75	15
1650	7p. Pink arrangement in basket	75	15
1651	7p. Red roses in pot	75	15
1652	7p. Lilac and white arrangement in basket	75	15
1653	7p. Orange and yellow arrangement in basket	75	15
1654	7p. Mixed arrangement in vase	75	15
1655	7p. Pink roses in vase	75	15
1656	7p. Daisies in pot	75	15
1657	7p. Bouquet of yellow roses	75	15
1658	7p. Pink and yellow arrangement	75	15

1982. Air. Tairona Culture.
1659	575	25p. gold, black & brown	90	35
1660		– 25p. gold, black & mve	90	35
1661		– 25p. gold, black & green	90	35
1662		– 25p. gold, black & mve	90	35
1663		– 25p. gold, black & blue	90	35
1664		– 25p. gold, black & red	90	35

DESIGNS—VERT: No. 1660, Anthropomorphic figure with crest; 1661, Anthropomorphic figure with two crests; 1662, Anthropozoomorphic figure; 1663, Anthropozoomorphic figure with elaborate headdress; 1664, Pectoral.

1982. 50th Anniv of Central Mortgage Bank.
| 1665 | 576 | 9p. green and black | 35 | 20 |

577 State Governor's Palace, Pereira

1982. Air. Pereira City.
| 1666 | 577 | 35p. multicoloured | 35 | 20 |

578 Biplane and Badge

1982. Air. American Air Forces Co-operation.
| 1667 | 578 | 18p. multicoloured | 25 | 15 |

579 St. Thomas Aquinas

580 St. Theresa of Avila (after Zurbaran)

1982. St. Thomas Aquinas Commemoration.
| 1668 | 579 | 5p. multicoloured | 15 | 10 |

1982. 400th Death Anniv of St. Theresa of Avila.
| 1669 | 580 | 5p. multicoloured | 15 | 10 |

581 St. Francis of Assisi (after Zurbaran)

583 Gabriel Garcia Marquez

582 Magdalena River

1982. 800th Birth Anniv of St. Francis of Assisi.
| 1670 | 581 | 5p. multicoloured | 15 | 10 |

1982. Air. Tourism.
| 1671 | 582 | 30p. multicoloured | 2·25 | 70 |

1982. Town Arms. As T **476.** Multicoloured.
1672	10p. Buga	25	10
1673	16p. Rionegro	45	15
1674	23p. Honda	25	20

1982. Award of Nobel Prize for Literature to Gabriel Garcia Marquez.
1675	583	7p. grey & grn (postage)	25	15
1676		25p. grey & blue (air)	20	10
1677		30p. grey and brown	25	

1983. Town Arms. As T **476.** Multicoloured.
| 1678 | 10p. San Juan de Pasto | 30 | 15 |
| 1679 | 20p. Santa Fe de Bogota | 25 | 10 |

584 "Liberty Fort" (drawing in National Archives)

1983. Air. San Andres Archipelago.
| 1680 | 584 | 25p. multicoloured | 25 | 10 |

585 Open Book

1983. Bicentenary of First Girls' School, Santa Fe de Bogota.
| 1681 | 585 | 9p. grey, black & gold | 25 | 15 |

586 Sunset

1983. Air. Las Gaviotas Ecological Centre.
| 1682 | 586 | 12p. multicoloured | 15 | 10 |

587 Self-portrait

588 Radio Bands

1983. Death Centenary of Jose Maria Espinosa (artist).
| 1683 | 587 | 9p. multicoloured | 20 | 10 |

1983. Air. 50th Anniv of Radio Amateurs League.
| 1684 | 588 | 12p. multicoloured | 35 | 20 |

589 "Dona Rangel de Cuellas donating Territory" (Marcos L. Marino)

590 Bolivar

1983. 250th Anniv of Cucuta.
| 1685 | 589 | 9p. multicoloured | 30 | 15 |

1983. Birth Bicentenary of Simon Bolivar.
1686	590	9p. mult (postage)	25	10
1687		– 30p. yell, bl & red (air)	35	25
1688		– 100p. multicoloured	1·25	85

DESIGNS—HORIZ: 30p. Bolivar as national flag. VERT: 100p. Bolivar and flag.

591 Porfirio Barba Jacob (after Frank Linas)

592 "Passiflora laurifolia"

1983. Birth Centenary of Porfirio Barba Jacob.
| 1689 | 591 | 9p. brown and black | 20 | 10 |

1983. Bicentenary of Royal Botanical Expedition from Spain to South America. Multicoloured.
1690	9p. Type **592** (postage)	20	10
1691	9p. "Cinchona lanceifolia"	20	10
1692	60p. "Cinchona cordifolia"	65	15
1693	12p. "Cinchona ovalifolia" (air)	30	15
1694	12p. "Begonia guaduensis"	30	15
1695	40p. "Begonia urticae"	1·10	80

593 Plaza de la Aduana

1983. Air. 450th Anniv of Cartagena. Mult.
| 1696 | 12p. Type **593** | 30 | 15 |
| 1697 | 35p. Cartagena buildings and monuments | 80 | 20 |

594 "Dawn in the Andes" (Alejandro Obregon)

595 Scout Badge

1983.
| 1698 | 594 | 20p. mult (postage) | 75 | 25 |
| 1699 | | 30p. mult (air) | 1·25 | 35 |

1983. Air. 75th Anniv of Boy Scout Movement.
| 1700 | 595 | 12p. multicoloured | 20 | 15 |

596 Santander

597 Coffee

1984. Francisco de Paula Santander (President of New Granada, 1832–37).
1701	596	12p. green	25	15
1702		12p. blue	25	15
1703		12p. red	25	15

1984. Air. Exports.
| 1704 | 597 | 14p. purple & green | 10 | 15 |

598 Admiral Jose Prudencio Padilla

1984. Anniversaries. Multicoloured.
1705	10p. Type **598** (birth bicentenary)	75	20
1706	18p. Luis A. Calvo (composer, birth cent)	35	15
1707	20p. Diego Fallon (writer, 150th birth anniv)	35	15
1708	20p. Candelario Obeso (writer, death cent)	1·00	30
1709	22p. Luis Eduardo Lopez de Mesa (writer, birth centenary)	45	15

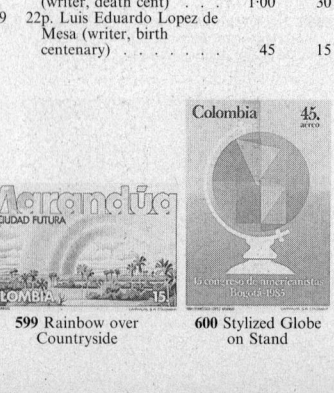

599 Rainbow over Countryside

600 Stylized Globe on Stand

1984. Marandua, City of the Future.
| 1710 | **599** | 15p. mult (postage) . . . | 30 | 15 |
| 1711 | | 30p. mult (air) . . . . . | 20 | 20 |

1984. Air. 45th Congress of Americanists, Bogota.
| 1712 | **600** | 45p. multicoloured . . . | 30 | 30 |

601 Nativity and Children playing

602 Maria Concepcion Loperena

1984. Christmas.
| 1713 | **601** | 12p. mult (postage) . . . | 25 | 10 |
| 1714 | | 14p. mult (air) . . . . . | 30 | 10 |

1985. 150th Birth Anniv of Maria Concepcion Loperena (Independence heroine).
| 1715 | **602** | 12p. multicoloured . . . | 35 | 25 |

603 Dove, Map and Members' Flags

604 Mejia and Farman F.40 Type Biplane

1985. Air. Contadora Group.
| 1716 | **603** | 40p. multicoloured . . . | 40 | 25 |

1985. Birth Centenary of Gonzalo Mejia (airport architect).
| 1717 | **604** | 12p. multicoloured . . . | 20 | 10 |

605 "Married Couple" (Pedro nel Gomez)

1985.
| 1718 | **605** | 37p. mult (postage) . . . | 25 | 10 |
| 1719 | | 40p. mult (air) . . . . . | 40 | 25 |

606 Capybara

607 Straight-billed Woodcreepers

1985. Fauna. Multicoloured. (a) Mammals.
1720	**606**	12p. Type **606** (postage) . .	15	10
1721		15p. Ocelot	35	25
1722		15p. Spectacled bear	35	25
1723		20p. Mountain tapir . . .	35	25

(b) Birds.
1724		14p. Lineated woodpeckers (air)	60	40
1725	**607**	20p. Type **607**	60	25
1726		50p. Coppery-bellied pufflegs	1·40	70
1727		55p. Blue-crowned motmots	1·60	80

608 Scenery and Gardel

609 "Gloria" (cadet ship), "Caldas" (frigate) and Naval Officer

1985. 50th Death Anniv of Carlos Gardel (singer).
| 1728 | **608** | 15p. multicoloured . . . | 20 | 10 |

1985. Air. 50th Anniv of Almirante Padilla Naval College.
| 1729 | **609** | 20p. multicoloured . . . | 1·25 | 45 |

610 Group of Colombians

611 Alphabet Tree

1985. Air. National Census.
| 1730 | **610** | 20p. multicoloured . . . | 35 | 25 |

1985. National Education Year.
| 1731 | **611** | 15p. multicoloured . . . | 30 | 15 |

612 Boy Playing Flute to Toys

613 Pumarejo

1985. Christmas. Multicoloured.
| 1732 | | 15p. Type **612** (postage) . . | 25 | 15 |
| 1733 | | 20p. Girl looking at dressed tree (air) . . . . | 30 | 20 |

1986. Air. Birth Centenary of Alfonso Lopez Pumarejo (President, 1934–38 and 1942–45).
| 1734 | **613** | 24p. multicoloured . . . | 30 | 15 |

614 Cyclists and Countryside

615 Carranza (after Carlos Dupuy)

1986. Air. "Coffee and Cycling, Pride of Colombia".
| 1735 | **614** | 60p. multicoloured . . . | 45 | 25 |

1986. Eduardo Carranza (poet) Commemoration.
| 1736 | **615** | 18p. multicoloured . . . | 20 | 15 |

616 Hand reaching for Sun

617 Northern Pudu

1986. Centenary of External University.
| 1737 | **616** | 18p. multicoloured . . . | 30 | 20 |

1986. Air.
| 1738 | **617** | 50p. multicoloured . . . | 60 | 35 |

618 Ricaurte and Birth Place, Leiva

1986. Birth Bicentenary of Gen. Antonio Ricaurte (Independence hero).
| 1739 | **618** | 18p. multicoloured . . . | 20 | 15 |

619 Pope and Arms

620 Couple and Satellite

1986. Air. Visit of Pope John Paul II (1st issue).
| 1740 | **619** | 24p. multicoloured . . . | 35 | 20 |

See also Nos. 1745/6.

1986. Air. World Communications Day.
| 1741 | **620** | 50p. multicoloured . . . | 60 | 35 |

621 Silva and Illustration of "Nocturne"

622 Girl and Doves

1986. 90th Death Anniv of Jose Asuncion Silva (poet).
| 1742 | **621** | 18p. multicoloured . . . | 20 | 15 |

1986. Air. International Peace Year.
| 1743 | **622** | 55p. multicoloured . . . | 65 | 40 |

623 Martinez

624 Pope and Medellin Cathedral

1986. 10th Death Anniv of Fernando Gomez Martinez (politician and founder of "El Colombiano" newspaper).
| 1744 | **623** | 24p. multicoloured . . . | 30 | 20 |

1986. Air. Visit of Pope John Paul II (2nd issue). Multicoloured.
| 1745 | | 55p. Type **624** . . . . . | 50 | 45 |
| 1746 | | 60p. Pope giving blessing in Bogota . . . . | 50 | 45 |

625 Montejo

626 Computer Portrait of Bach

1986. Air. Birth Centenary of Enrique Santos Montejo (journalist and editor of "El Tiempo").
| 1748 | **625** | 25p. multicoloured . . . | 30 | 20 |

1986. Air. Composers' Birth Anniversaries (1985). Multicoloured.
| 1749 | **626** | 70p. Type **626** (300th anniv) | 65 | 60 |
| 1750 | | 100p. "The Permanency of Baroque" (300th annivs of Handel and Bach and 400th anniv of H. Schutz) | 75 | 55 |

627 De La Salle (founder) and National Colours

1986. Air. Centenary of Brothers of Christian Schools in Colombia.
| 1751 | **627** | 25p. multicoloured . . . | 30 | 15 |

628 Convent of Mercy

1986. 450th Anniv of Santiago de Cali.
| 1752 | | 20p. Arms (as T **476**) . . . | 15 | 10 |
| 1753 | | 25p. Type **628** . . . . . . | 15 | 10 |

629 Piece of Coal and National Colours

630 Castro Silva

1986. Air. Completion of El Cerrejon Coal Complex.
| 1754 | **629** | 55p. multicoloured . . . | 40 | 40 |

1986. Birth Centenary (1985) of Jose Vincente Castro Silva (Principal of Senior College of the Rosary).
| 1755 | **630** | 20p. multicoloured . . . | 25 | 15 |

631 "The Five Signatories" (detail, R. Vasquez)

1986. Air. Centenary of Constitution.
| 1756 | **631** | 25p. multicoloured . . . | 30 | 20 |

1986. Arms of Antioquia. As T **476**.
| 1758 | | 55p. multicoloured . . . . | 20 | 10 |

632 Garcia Lorca

1986. Air. 50th Death Anniv of Federico Garcia Lorca (poet).
| 1759 | **632** | 60p. multicoloured . . . | 35 | 25 |

633 Symbolic Prism

634 Maya

1986. Centenary of Fine Art Faculty and 50th Anniv of Architecture Faculty at National University.
| 1760 | **633** | 40p. multicoloured . . . | 20 | 30 |

1986. 6th Death Anniv of Rafael Maya (poet and critic).
| 1761 | **634** | 25p. multicoloured . . . | 30 | 20 |

635 Andean Condor　　**636** "Thanks! Friends of the World"

1986.
1762 **635** 20p. blue 35 20
1763 **635** 25p. blue 35 20

1986. Air. Thanks for Help after Devastation of Armero by Volcanic Eruption, 1985.
1767 **636** 50p. multicoloured . . . 60 35

637 Mestiza Virgin (from crib at Pasto)　　**638** Left-hand Side of Mural

1986. Air. Christmas.
1768 **637** 25p. multicoloured . . . 30 15

1987. Air. 450th Anniv of Popayan City. "The Apotheosis of Popayan" by Ephram Martinez Zambrano. Multicoloured.
1769 100p. Type **638** . . . . . 1·40 75
1770 100p. Right-hand side of mural . . . . 1·40 75
Nos. 1769/70 were printed together, se-tenant, forming a composite design.

639 Uribe Mejia　　**640** "Conversion of St. Augustine of Hippo"

1987. Birth Centenary (1986) of Pedro Uribe Mejia (coffee industry pioneer).
1771 **639** 25p. multicoloured . . . 30 15

1987. Air. 1600th Anniv of Conversion of St. Augustine.
1772 **640** 30p. multicoloured . . . 10 10

641 Atomic Diagram, Pit Props and Miner in Shaft　　**642** St. Barbara's Church

1987. Air. Centenary of National Mines Faculty of National University, Medellin.
1773 **641** 25p. multicoloured . . . 10 10

1987. 450th Anniv of Mompox City.
1774 **642** 500p. multicoloured . . . 2·50 2·50

643 Hawk-headed Parrot　　**644** White Horse

1987. Fauna.
1775 **643** 30p. green (postage) . . 90 25
1776 – 30p. purple 45 20
1777 – 30p. red (air) 90 25
1778 – 35p. brown 15 20
DESIGNS—HORIZ: No. 1776, Boutu; 1778, South

American red-lined turtle. VERT: No. 1777, Greater flamingo.
See also Nos. 1807/9, 1815/17, 1823/6 and 1855/8.

1987. Air. Pure-bred Horses. Multicoloured.
1779 60p. Type **644** 45 35
1780 70p. Black horse 45 35

645 Mastheads, Fidel Cano (founder), Luis Cano, Luis Gabriel Cano Isaza and Alfonso Cano Isaza (editors)

1987. Air. Cent of "El Espectador" (newspaper).
1781 **645** 60p. multicoloured . . . 25 15

646 Isaacs and Scene from "Maria"

1987. 150th Birth Anniv of Jorge Isaacs (writer).
1782 **646** 70p. multicoloured . . . 25 10

648 Mutis and Illustration of "Condor"

1987. 33rd Death Anniv of Aurelio Martinez Mutis (poet).
1785 **648** 90p. multicoloured . . . 1·25 55

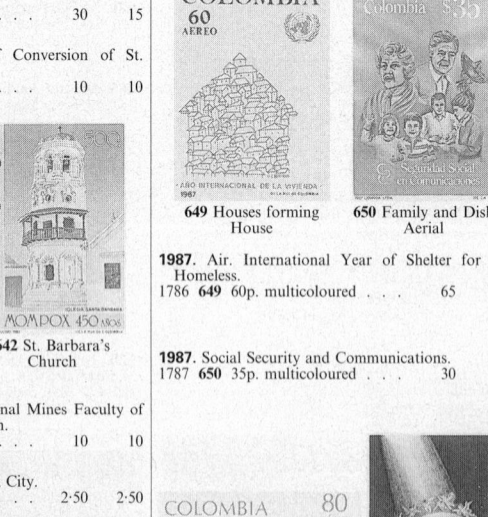

649 Houses forming House　　**650** Family and Dish Aerial

1987. Air. International Year of Shelter for the Homeless.
1786 **649** 60p. multicoloured . . . 65 35

1987. Social Security and Communications.
1787 **650** 35p. multicoloured . . . 30 20

651 Flags　　**652** Nativity Scene in Globe

1987. Air. 1st Meeting of Eight Latin-American Presidents of Contadora and Lima Groups, Acapulco, Mexico.
1788 **651** 80p. multicoloured . . . 55 55

1987. Air. Christmas.
1789 **652** 30p. multicoloured . . . 30 15

653 Houses, Telephone Wires and Dials

1987. Air. Rural Telephone Network.
1790 **653** 70p. multicoloured . . . 35 10

654 Mountain Sanctuaries　　**655** Flower (Life)

1988. Air. 450th Anniv of Bogota (1st issue).
1791 **654** 70p. multicoloured . . . 25 70
See also Nos. 1803/4.

1988. 40th Anniv of Declaration of Human Rights (1st issue).
1792 **655** 30p. green 10 10
1793 – 35p. red 10 10
1794 – 40p. lilac 15 10
1795 – 40p. blue 10 10
DESIGNS—VERT: No. 1793, Road (Freedom of choice). HORIZ: 1794, Circle of children (Freedom of association); 1795, Couple on bench (Communication).
See also Nos. 1840/1.

657 Mask

1988. Air. Gold Museum, Bogota. Multicoloured.
1796 70p. Type **657** 30 30
1797 80p. Votive figure 60 30
1798 90p. Human figure 85 65

658 Pasto Cathedral　　**659** Waterfall

1988. 450th Anniv of Pasto.
1799 **658** 60p. multicoloured . . . 40 20

1988. Centenary of Bogota Water Supply and Sewerage Organization.
1800 **659** 100p. multicoloured . . 35 10

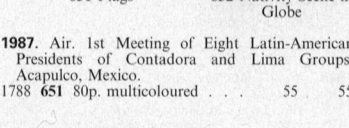

660 Score and Composers　　**661** M. Currea de Aya

1988. Centenary (1987) of National Anthem by Rafael Nunez and Oreste Sindici.
1801 **660** 70p. multicoloured . . . 25 25

1988. Birth Centenary of Maria Currea de Aya (women's rights pioneer).
1802 **661** 80p. multicoloured . . . 25 10

662 Modern Bogota　　**664** College

1988. Air. 450th Anniv of Bogota (2nd issue). Multicoloured.
1803 80p. Type **662** 55 30
1804 90p. Street in old Bogota (horiz) 60 30

1988. Fauna. As T **643**.
1807 35p. brown 25 15
1808 35p. green 25 15
1809 40p. orange 25 15
DESIGNS—HORIZ: No. 1807, Crab-eating racoon; 1808, Caribbean monk seal; 1809, Giant otter.

1988. Centenary of Return of Society of Jesus to St. Bartholomew's Senior College.
1810 **664** 120p. multicoloured . . 35 20

665 Eduardo Santos　　**666** Mother and Children

1988. Personalities. Multicoloured.
1811 80p. Type **665** (birth centenary) (postage) . . . 45 25
1812 90p. Jorge Alvarez Lleras (astronomer) 45 25
1813 80p. Zipa Tisquesusa (16th-century Indian chief) (air) 45 25

1988. Air. Christmas.
1814 **666** 40p. multicoloured . . . 15 10

1988. Fauna. As T **643**.
1815 40p. grey (postage) 15 10
1816 45p. violet 75 25
1817 45p. blue (air) 75 25
DESIGNS—HORIZ: No. 1815, American manatee; 1816, Masked trogon. VERT: No. 1817, Blue-bellied curassow.

667 Andres Bello College

1988.
1818 **667** 115p. multicoloured . . 35 20

668 Building and Nieto Caballero　　**669** Gomez

1989. Air. Birth Centenary of Agustin Nieto Caballero (educationalist).
1819 **668** 100p. multicoloured . . 30 15

1989. Air. Birth Centenary of Laureano Gomez (President, 1950–53).
1820 **669** 45p. multicoloured . . . 15 10

670 Map

1989. Air. International Coffee Organization.
1821 **670** 110p. multicoloured . . 30 15

671 Modern Flats, Recreation Area and Hands holding Brick

1989. Air. 12th Habitat U.N. Conference on Human Settlements, Cartagena.
1822 **671** 100p. multicoloured . . 20 10

1989. Fauna. As T **643**.
1823 40p. brown (postage) . . . 10 10
1824 45p. black 75 25
1825 55p. brown 15 10
1826 45p. blue (air) 10 10
DESIGNS—HORIZ: No. 1823, White-tailed deer; 1824, Harpy eagle; 1826, Blue discus. VERT: No. 1825, False anole.

672 Emblem

1989. 25th Anniv of Adpostal (postal administration).
1827 **672** 45p. multicoloured . . . 10 10

673 Hands   **675** "Simon Bolivar" (Pedro Jose Figueroa)

1989. Air. Bicentenary of French Revolution.
1828 **673** 100p. multicoloured . . 20 10

1989. 170th Anniv of Liberation Campaign. Multicoloured.
1830 40p. Type **675** 10 10
1831 40p. "Santander" (Figueroa) . 10 10
1832 45p. "Bolivar and Santander during the Campaign for the Plains" (J. M. Zamora) (46 × 37 mm) . . 10 10
1833 45p. "From Boyaca to Santa Fe" (left-hand detail) (Francisco de P. Alvarez) (29 × 36 mm) . . 10 10
1834 45p. Right-hand detail (29 × 36 mm) 10 10
1835 45p. Mounted officer and foot soldiers (left-hand detail) (31 × 51 mm) . . 35 10
1836 45p. Mounted officer (centre detail) (33 × 51 mm) . . 35 10
1837 45p. Mounted soldiers with flag (right-hand detail) (31 × 51 mm) 35 35
Nos. 1833/4 and 1835/7 (showing details of triptych by A. de Santa Maria) were issued together, se-tenant, each forming a composite design.

676 Founder's House

1989. 450th Anniv of Tunja.
1839 **676** 45p. multicoloured . . . 10 10

1989. Human Rights (2nd issue). As T **655**.
1840 45p. brown (postage) 10 10
1841 55p. green (air) 15 10
DESIGNS—HORIZ: 45p. Musicians (Culture). VERT: 55p. Family.

677 Healthy Children and Shadowy Figures   **678** Gold Ornaments of Quimbaya, Calima and Tolima

1989. Air. Anti-drugs Campaign.
1842 **677** 115p. multicoloured . . 25 15

1989. Air. America. Pre-Columbian Crafts. Multicoloured.
1843 115p. Type **678** 25 15
1844 130p. Indian making pot and Sinu ceramic figure (horiz) 25 15

679 Quimbaya Museum   **680** Mantilla

1989. Centenary of Armenia City.
1815 **679** 135p. multicoloured . . 25 15

1989. Air. 45th Death Anniv of Joaquin Quijano Mantilla (chronicler).
1846 **680** 170p. multicoloured . . 75 20

681 Boeing 767 and Globe   **682** "The Fathers of the Fatherland leaving Congress" (R. Acevedo Bernal)

1989. Air.
1847 **681** 130p. multicoloured . . 45 15

1989. Air. 170th Anniv of Creation of First Republic of Colombia (1851) and 168th Anniv of its Constitution (others). Multicoloured.
1848 130p. Type **682** 55 15
1849 130p. "Church of the Rosary, Cucuta" (Carmelo Fernandez) . 55 15
1850 130p. Republic's arms . . . 55 15
1851 130p. "Bolivar at Congress of Angostura" (46 × 36 mm) (Tito Salas) 55 15

683 Nativity (Barro-Raquira clay figures)   **684** "Plaza de la Aduana" (H. Lemaitre)

1989. Air. Christmas.
1852 **683** 55p. multicoloured . . . 40 10

1990. Air. Presidential Summit, Cartagena.
1853 **684** 130p. multicoloured . . 60 40

685 Headphones on Marble Head   **687** "Espeletia hartwegiana"

686 Cuervo Borda and National Museum

1990. Air. 50th Anniv of Colombia National Radio.
1854 **685** 150p. multicoloured . . . 30 15

1990. Fauna. As T **643**.
1855 50p. grey 10 10
1856 50p. purple 10 10
1857 60p. brown 15 10
1858 60p. brown 60 20
DESIGNS: No. 1855, Grey fox; 1856, Common poison-arrow frog; 1857, Pygmy marmoset; 1858, Sun-bittern.

1990. Air. Velez City Arms. As T **476**.
1859 60p. multicoloured 15 10

1990. Air. Birth Centenary (1989) of Teresa Cuervo Borda (artist).
1860 **686** 60p. multicoloured . . . 15 10

1990. Multicoloured.
1861 60p. Type **687** 15 10
1862 60p. "Ceiba pentandra" (horiz) 15 10
1863 70p. "Ceroxylon quindiuense" 15 10
1864 70p. "Tibouchina lepidota" . 15 10

688 Theatrical Masks   **689** Statue, Bogota

1990. Air. 2nd Iberian-American Theatre Festival, Bogota.
1865 **688** 150p. gold, brown & orge 60 15

1990. 150th Death Anniv of Francisco de Paula Santander (President of New Granada, 1832–37). Multicoloured.
1866 50p. Type **689** (postage) . . 40 10
1867 60p. Gateway of National Pantheon (air) 40 10
1868 60p. "General Santander with the Constitution" (Jose Maria Espinosa) . . 40 10
1869 70p. Santander, organizer of public education (after F. S. Guitierrez) 40 10
1870 70p. "The Postal Carrier" (Jose Maria del Castillo) (horiz) 40 10

690 Postmen

1990. Air. 150th Anniv of the Penny Black.
1872 **690** 150p. multicoloured . . . 30 15

691 Cadet, Arms and School   **693** Graph

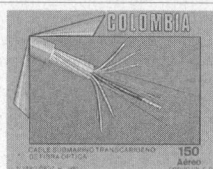

692 Cable

1990. 50th Anniv of General Santander Police Cadets School.
1873 **691** 60p. multicoloured . . . 15 10

1990. Air. Trans-Caribbean Submarine Fibre Optic Cable.
1874 **692** 150p. multicoloured . . 60 15

1990. Air. 50th Anniv of I.F.I.
1875 **693** 60p. multicoloured . . . 15 10

1990. Arms of Cartago. As T **476**.
1876 50p. multicoloured 35 10

695 Map   **696** Women on Beach

1990. Air. 10th Anniv of Organization of American States.
1878 **695** 130p. multicoloured . . 55 15

1990. La Guajira.
1879 **696** 60p. multicoloured . . . 15 10

697 Indian wearing Gold Ornaments   **698** St. John Bosco (founder) and Boys

1990. Air. 50th Anniv of Gold Museum, Bogota.
1880 **697** 170p. multicoloured . . 35 20

1990. Centenary of Salesian Brothers in Colombia.
1881 **698** 60p. multicoloured . . . 15 10

699 Brown Pelican, Roseate Spoonbills and Dolphins

1990. Air. America. Natural World. Multicoloured.
1882 150p. Type **699** . . . . . 1·00 30
1883 170p. Land animals and Salvin's curassows . . . . 1·00 30

700 Christ Child   **701** Monastery

1990. Air. Christmas.
1884 **700** 70p. multicoloured . . . 15 10

1990. Air. Monastery of Nostra Senhora de las Lajas, Ipiales.
1885 **701** 70p. multicoloured . . . 15 10

702 Titles and Abstract

703 Christ of the Miracles, Buga Church

1991. Air. Bicentenary of "La Prensa".
1886 **702** 170p. multicoloured 30 15

1991.
1887 **703** 70p. multicoloured 15 10

704 "Anaea syene"

705 Humpback Whale leaping from Water

1991. Butterflies. Multicoloured.
1888 70p. Type **704** (postage) . . 15 10
1889 70p. "Callithea philotima"
  (horiz) 15 10
1890 80p. "Thecla coronata" . . 15 10
1891 80p. "Agrias amydon"
  (horiz) (air) 15 10
1892 170p. "Morpho rhetenor"
  (horiz) 30 15
1893 190p. "Heliconius
  longarenus ernestus"
  (horiz) 35 20

1991. Air. Marine Mammals. Multicoloured.
1894 80p. Type **705** 15 10
1895 170p. Humpback whale
  diving 60 15
1896 190p. Amazon dolphins
  (horiz) 65 20

706 National Colours

1991. New Constitution.
1897 **706** 70p. multicoloured . . . 15 10
See also No. 1914.

707 Dario Echandia Olaya (after Delio Ramirez)

708 Girardot (after Jose Maria Espinosa)

1991. 2nd Death Anniv of Dario Echandia Olaya.
1898 **707** 80p. multicoloured . . . 15 10

1991. Birth Bicent of Colonel Atanasio Girardot.
1899 **708** 70p. multicoloured . . . 15 10

709 Galan

710 Stone Statue of God, San Agustin

1991. 2nd Death Anniv of Luis Carlos Galan Sarmiento (politician).
1900 **709** 80p. multicoloured . . . 15 10

1991. Pre-Columbian Art. Multicoloured.
1901 80p. Type **710** (postage) . . 15 10
1902 90p. Burial yessel,
  Tierradentro 15 10

1903 90p. Statue, San Agustin
  (air) 15 10
1904 210p. Gold flyingfish, San
  Agustin (horiz) 50 20

711 Sailfish

1991.
1905 **711** 830p. multicoloured . . 2·50 1·00

712 Cloisters of St. Augustine's, Tunja

1991. Architecture. Multicoloured.
1906 80p. Type **712** (postage) . . 15 10
1907 90p. Bridge, Chia 15 10
1908 90p. Roadside chapel,
  Pamplona (vert) (air) . . 15 10
1909 190p. Church of the
  Conception, Santa Fe de
  Bogota (vert) 60 20

713 "Santa Maria"

714 Lleras Camargo (after Rafael Salas)

1991. Air. America. Voyages of Discovery. Mult.
1910 90p. Type **713** 35 20
1911 190p. Amerindians and
  approaching ship 85 30

1991. 1st Death Anniv of Alberto Lleras Camargo (President, 1945–46 and 1958–62).
1912 **714** 80p. multicoloured . . . 15 10

715 Police Officers, Transport, Emblem and Flag

1991. Centenary of Police.
1913 **715** 80p. multicoloured . . . 30 10

1991. Air. New Constitution (2nd issue). As No. 1897 but new value and additionally inscr "SANTAFE DE BOGOTA. D.C. Julio 4 de 1991".
1914 90p. multicoloured . . . 15 10

716 Member Nations' Flags

717 First Government Building, Sogamoso

1991. Air. 5th Group of Rio Presidential Summit, Cartagena.
1915 **716** 190p. multicoloured . . 30 15

1991.
1916 **717** 80p. multicoloured . . . 10 10

718 "Adoration of the Kings" (Baltazar de Figueroa)

719 D. Turbay Quintero

1991. Air. Christmas.
1917 **718** 90p. multicoloured . . . 15 10

1992. Diana Turbay Quintero (journalist) Commemoration.
1918 **719** 80p. multicoloured . . . 15 10

720 Hand holding Posy of Flowers

721 Cut Flowers

1992. Air. 8th U.N. Conference on Trade and Development Session, Cartagena.
1919 **720** 210p. multicoloured . . 35 20

1992. Air. Exports.
1920 90p. Type **721** 15 10
1921 210p. Fruits and nuts (horiz) 35 20

722 Statue of General Santander, Barranquilla (R. Verlet)

723 Music, Book and Paint Brush

1992. Birth Bicentenary of General Francisco de Paula Santander. Multicoloured.
1922 80p. Type **722** (postage) . . 10 10
1923 190p. Francisco de Paula
  Santander (after Sergio
  Trujillo Magnenat) (air) 30 15

1992. Air. Copyright Protection.
1925 **723** 190p. multicoloured . . 30 15

725 Lievano Aguirre

726 Enrique Low Murtra (1st anniv)

1992. 10th Death Anniv of Indalecio Lievano Aguirre (ambassador to United Nations).
1928 **725** 80p. multicoloured . . . 10 10

1992. Death Anniversaries of Justice Ministers. Multicoloured.
1929 100p. Type **726** 15 10
1930 110p. Rodrigo Lara Bonilla
  (8th anniv) 20 10

727 Town Arms and Rings

1992. 14th National Games, Barranquilla.
1931 **727** 110p. multicoloured . . 20 10

728 Landscape

729 Athlete and Olympic Rings

1992. Air. 2nd U.N. Conference on Environment and Development, Rio de Janeiro. Paintings by Roberto Palomino. Multicoloured.
1932 230p. Type **728** 35 20
1933 230p. Birds in trees 35 20

1992. Air. Olympic Games, Barcelona.
1934 **729** 110p. multicoloured . . 20 10

730 "Discovery of America by C. Columbus" (Dali)

1992. Air. America. Multicoloured.
1935 230p. Type **730** 80 30
1936 260p. "America Magic,
  Myth and Legend" (Al.
  Vivero) . . . . 1·00 75

731 American Crocodile

1992. Endangered Animals. Multicoloured.
1937 100p. Type **731** 15 10
1938 100p. Andean condor (vert) . . 45 30

732 Maria Lopez de Escobar (founder)

734 Map of the Americas

1992. 50th Anniv of House of Mother and Child.
1939 **732** 100p. mult (postage) . . 15 10
1940 110p. mult (air) 20 10

1992. Air.
1941 **733** 110p. multicoloured . . 20 10

733 Avianca Colombia McDonnell Douglas MD-83

1992. Meeting of First Ladies of the Americas and the Caribbean, Cartagena.
1942 **734** 100p. multicoloured . . 15 10

735 "Zenaida" (Ana Mercedes Hoyos)

1992. 500th Anniv of Discovery of America by Columbus. Paintings.

1943	735	100p. mult (postage)	15	10
1944	–	110p. multicoloured	20	10
1946	–	110p. mult (air)	20	10
1947	–	230p. multicoloured	35	20
1948	–	260p. green and violet	40	20

DESIGNS: 110p. (1944), "Study for 1/500" (Beatriz Gonzalez); 110p. (1946), "Blue Eagle" (Alejandro Obregon); 230p. "Cantileo" (Luis Luna); 260p. "Maize" (Antonio Caro).

736 Recycling

1992.

1949	736	100p. multicoloured	15	10

737 Front Curtain

1992. Air. Columbus Theatre.

1950	737	230p. multicoloured	35	20

739 "Nativity" (Carlos Alfonso Mendez)

1992. Christmas. Children's Drawings. Mult.

1952		100p. Type 739 (postage)	15	10
1953		110p. Kings approaching stable (Catalina del Valle) (air)	20	10

740 G. Lara   748 Footballers

742 Campaign Emblem

1992. Air. 10th Death Anniv of Gloria Lara (ambassador to the United Nations).

1954	740	230p. multicoloured	40	20

1993. Lions Club International Amblyopia Prevention Campaign.

1956	742	100p. multicoloured	15	10

1993. Air. America Cup Football Championship, Ecuador.

1962	748	220p. multicoloured	35	20

749 Prisoners

1993. Bicentenary of French Declaration of Human Rights. Multicoloured.

1963		150p. Type 749 (postage)	25	15
1964		150p. The elderly	25	15
1965		200p. The infirm	35	20
1966		200p. Children	35	20
1968		220p. Women (air)	35	20
1969		220p. The poor	35	20
1970		460p. Environmental protection	1·00	40
1971		520p. Immigrants	1·10	45

750 Amerindian (Jose Luis Correal)   752 Green-winged Macaw ("Papagayo")

751 Emblem and Flags

1993. Air. International Year of Indigenous Peoples.

1972	750	460p. multicoloured	70	35

1993. Air. World Cup Football Championship, U.S.A. (1994) (1st issue).

1973	751	220p. multicoloured	35	20

See also Nos. 2006/9.

1993. The Amazon. Multicoloured.

1974		150p. Type 752 (postage)	60	40
1975		150p. Anaconda	20	10
1976		220p. Water-lilies (air)	35	20
1977		220p. Ipecacuanha flower	35	20

753 Cotton-headed Tamarin   755 Nativity

754 Alberto Pumarejo (politician)

1993. Air. America. Endangered Animals. Mult.

1979		220p. Type 753	35	20
1980		220p. American purple gallinule	60	30
1981		460p. Andean cock of the rock	90	40
1982		520p. American manatee	80	40

1993. Famous Colombians. Multicoloured.

1983		150p. Type 754	20	10
1984		150p. Lorencita Villegas de Santos (First Lady, 1938–42)	20	10
1985		150p. Meliton Rodriguez (photographer)	20	10
1986		150p. Tomas Carrasquilla (writer)	20	10

1993. Christmas. Multicoloured.

1987		200p. Type 755	30	15
1988		220p. Shepherd (air)	35	20

756 San Andres y Providencia

1993. Tourism. Multicoloured.

1989		220p. Type 756	35	20
1990		220p. Cocuy National Park	35	20
1991		220p. La Cocha Lake	35	20
1992		220p. Waterfall, La Macarena mountains	35	20
1993		460p. Chicamocha (vert)	70	35
1994		460p. Sierra Nevada de Santa Marta (vert)	70	35
1995		520p. Embalse de Penol (vert)	80	40

See also No. E1996.

757 Museum Entrance   759 Yellow-eared Conure

1993. 170th Anniv of National Museum.

1997	757	150p. multicoloured	20	10

1994. Birds. Multicoloured.

1999		180p. Type 759 (postage)	70	45
2000		240p. Bogota rail	90	60
2001		270p. Toucan barbets (horiz) (air)	1·10	70
2002		560p. Cinnamon teals (horiz)	2·10	1·40

760 Emblem

1994. Air. International Decade for Natural Disaster Reduction. National Disaster Prevention System.

2003	760	630p. blue, yellow & red	95	50

762 Escriva de Balaguer

1994. Air. Beatification of Josemaria Escriva de Balaguer (founder of Opus Dei).

2005	762	560p. multicoloured	85	45

763 Trophy and Player and Emblem on Flag

1994. World Cup Football Championship, U.S.A. (2nd issue). Multicoloured.

2006		180p. Type 763 (postage)	25	15
2008		270p. Match scene, trophy and emblem (air)	40	20
2009		560p. Trophy, emblem, ball and national colours (vert)	85	45

764 Flagpoles   765 "Self-portrait"

1994. Air. 4th Latin American Presidential Summit, Cartagena.

2011	764	630p. multicoloured	95	50

See also No. E2010.

1994. Birth Centenary of Ricardo Rendon (painter).

2012	765	240p. black	30	15

766 Biplane and William Knox Martin

1994. Air. 75th Anniv of First Airmail Flight.

2013	766	270p. multicoloured	35	20

767 Emblem

1994. 40th Anniv of Radio and Television Network.

2014	767	180p. multicoloured	25	15

768 Numbers, Graphs and Pie Chart   770 Horse and Bicycle

1994. 1993 Census.

2015	768	240p. multicoloured	30	15

1994. Air. America. Postal Transport. Mult.

2017	770	270p. multicoloured	35	20

See also No. E2018.

771 Founders and Pi Symbol

1994. Centenary of Colombian Society of Engineers.

2019	771	180p. multicoloured	25	15

772 Building and Scales

1994. Air. 80th Anniv of National Institute of Legal Medicine and Forensic Sciences.

2020	772	560p. multicoloured	75	40

773 Three Wise Men

1994. Air. Christmas.

2021	773	270p. multicoloured	35	20

See also No. E2022.

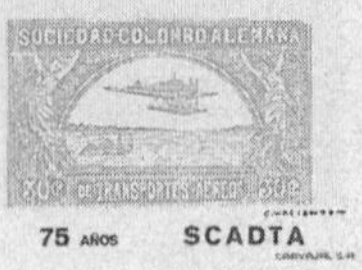
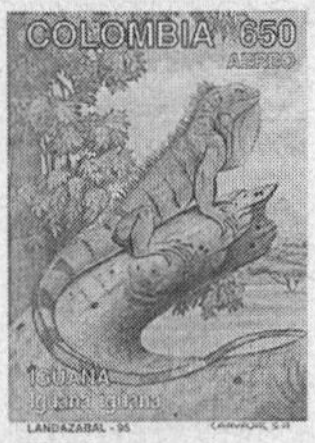

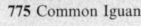

774 1921 SCADTA 30c. Stamp

775 Common Iguana

1995. Air. 75th Anniv (1994) of Sociedad Colombo-Alemana de Transportes Aereos (SCADTA) (private air company contracted to carry mail).
2023 **774** 330p. pink, brown & blk . . 60 25

1995. Air. Flora and Fauna. Multicoloured.
2024 650p. Type **775** 85 45
2025 650p. Iguana facing left . . 85 45
2026 750p. Forest (left detail) . . 1·00 50
2027 750p. Forest (right detail) . 1·00 50
Stamps of the same value were issued together in se-tenant pairs, each pair forming a composite design.

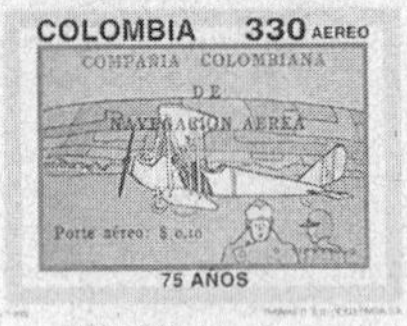

776 1920 10c, Stamp

1995. Air. 75th Anniv of Compania Colombiana de Navagacion Aerea (private air company contracted to carry mail).
2028 **776** 330p. multicoloured . . 45 25

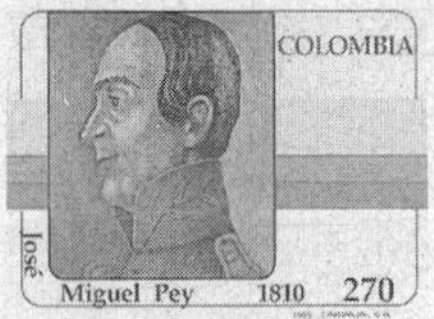

778 Jose Miguel Pey

1995. Colombian Patriots. Multicoloured.
2030 270p. Type **778** (revolutionary) 35 20
2031 270p. Jorge Tadeo Lozana (zoologist and revolutionary) 35 20
2032 270p. Antonio Narino (journalist and politician) 35 20
2033 270p. Camilo Torres (lawyer and revolutionary) . . . 35 20
2034 270p. Jose Fernandez Madrid (doctor and revolutionary) 35 20
2035 270p. Jose Maria del Castillo y Rada (lawyer) 35 20
2036 270p. Custodio Garcia Rovira (revolutionary) . . 35 20
2037 270p. Antonio Villavicencio (revolutionary) 35 20
2038 270p. Liborio Mejia (lawyer and historian) 35 20
2039 270p. Rafael Urdaneta (diplomat) 35 20
2040 270p. Juan Garcia del Rio (writer and politician) . . 35 20
2041 270p. Gen. Jose Maria Melo 35 20
2042 270p. Gen. Tomas Herrera 35 20
2043 270p. Froilan Largacha (acting President, Feb–June 1863) 35 20
2044 270p. Salvader Camacho Roldan (writer) 35 20
2045 270p. Gen. Ezequiel Hurtado (acting President, Apr–Aug 1884) 35 20
2046 270p. Dario Echandia Olaya (lawyer) 35 20
2047 270p. Alberto Lleras Camargo (President, 1945–46) 35 20
2048 270p. Gen. Gustavo Rojas Pinilla (President, 1953–57) 35 20
2049 270p. Carlos Lleras Restrepo (President, 1966–70) 35 20

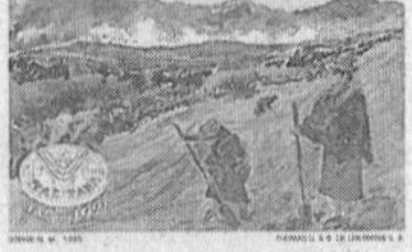

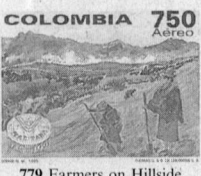

779 Farmers on Hillside

1995. Air. 50th Anniv of F.A.O.
2050 **779** 750p. multicoloured . . 1·00 50

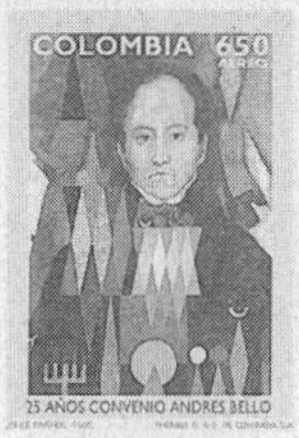
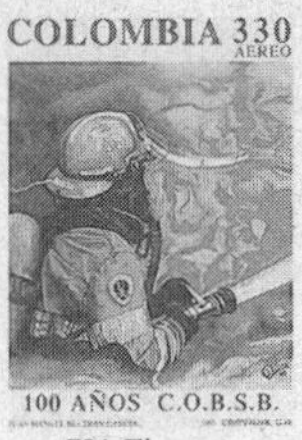

780 Bello

781 Fireman

1995. Air. 25th Anniv of Andres Bello (scholar and writer). Agreement on Intellectual Co-operation.
2051 **780** 650p. multicoloured . . 85 45

1995. Air. Centenary of Fire Brigade of Bogota.
2052 **781** 330p. multicoloured . . 45 25

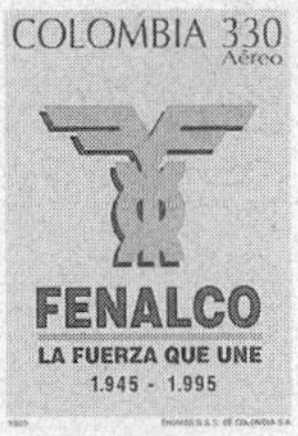
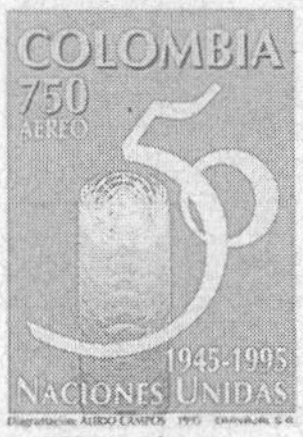

782 Emblem

783 Anniversary Emblem

1995. Air. 50th Anniv of National Chamber of Commerce.
2053 **782** 330p. multicoloured . . 45 25

1995. Air. 50th Anniv of U.N.O.
2054 **783** 750p. multicoloured . . 45 25

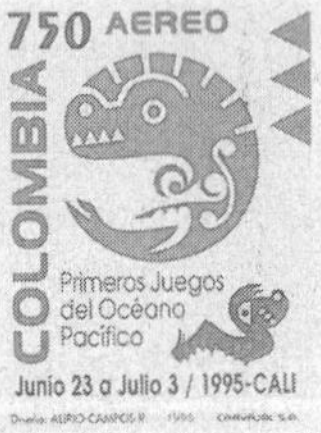
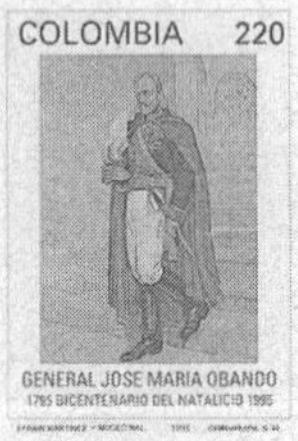

784 Emblem

786 Obando (after Efrain Martinez)

1995. Air. 1st Pacific Ocean Games, Cali.
2055 **784** 750p. multicoloured . . 1·00 50

1995. Birth Bicentenary of General Jose Maria Obando.
2057 **786** 220p. multicoloured . . 25 15

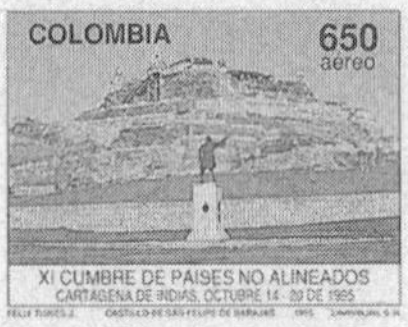

787 San Filipe de Barajas Castle

1995. Air. 11th Non-aligned Countries' Conference, Cartagena de Indias.
2058 **787** 650p. multicoloured . . 80 40

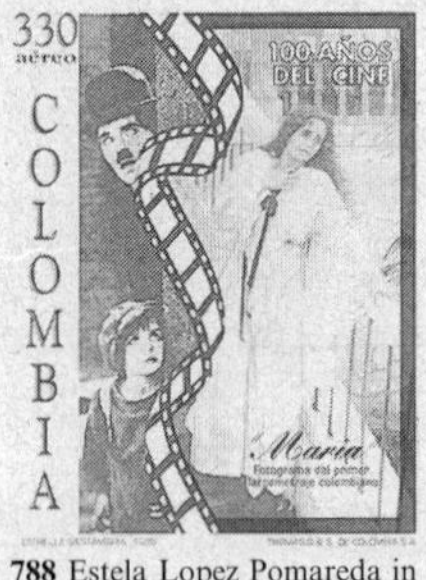

788 Estela Lopez Pomareda in "Maria", Charlie Chaplin and Jackie Coogan

1995. Air. Centenary of Motion Pictures.
2059 **788** 330p. black and brown 40 20

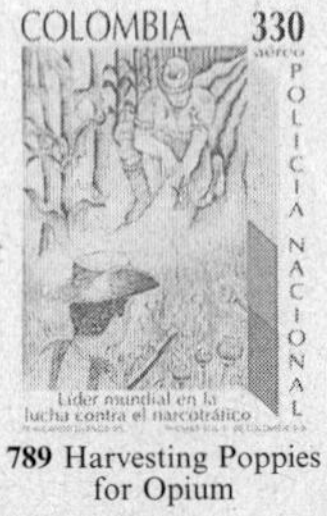
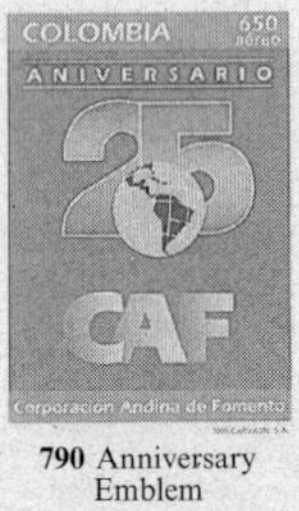

789 Harvesting Poppies for Opium

790 Anniversary Emblem

1995. Air. World Campaign against Drug Trafficking. Multicoloured.
2060 330p. Type **789** 40 20
2061 330p. Manacled hands (horiz) 40 20

1995. Air. 25th Anniv of Andean Development Corporation.
2062 **790** 650p. multicoloured . . 80 40

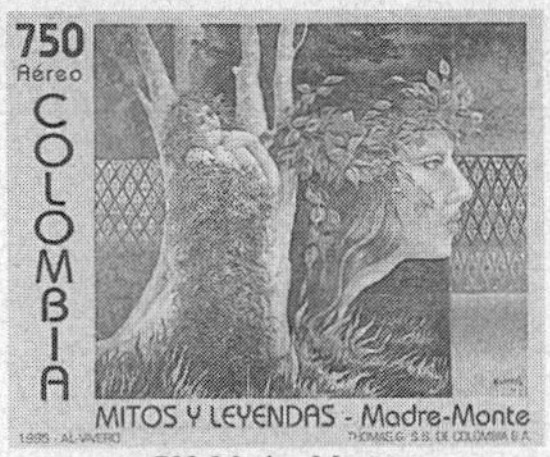

792 Madre-Monte

1995. Air. Myths and Legends (1st issue). Multicoloured.
2065 750p. Type **792** 90 45
2066 750p. La Llorana 90 45
2067 750p. El Mohan (river spirit) 90 45
2068 750p. Alligator man 90 45
Nos. 2065/8 were issued together, se-tenant, in sheetlets in which the background colour gradually changes down the sheet; each design therefore occurs in four slightly different colours.
See also Nos. 2085/8.

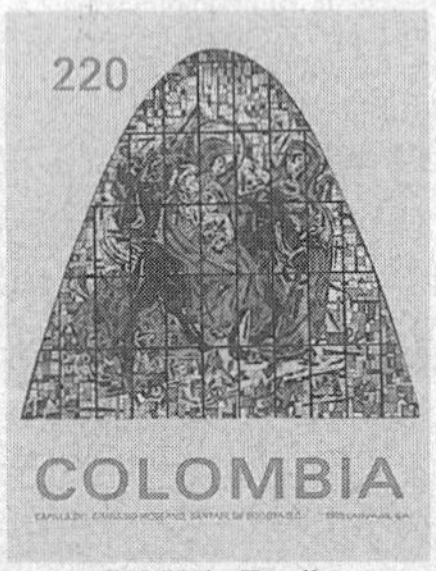

793 Holy Family

1995. Christmas. Stained Glass Windows from Chapel of the Apostles, Bogota School. Mult.
2069 220p. Type **793** (postage) . . 25 15
2070 330p. Nativity (air) 40 20

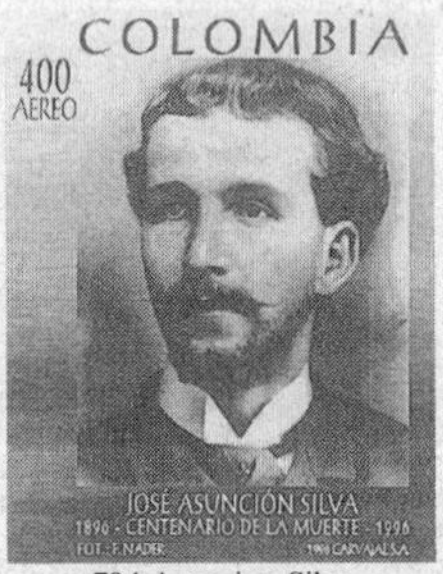

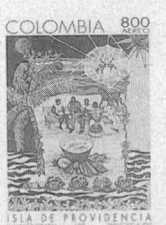

794 Asuncion Silva

1996. Air. Death Centenary of Jose Asuncion Silva (poet).
2071 **794** 400p. multicoloured . . 50 25

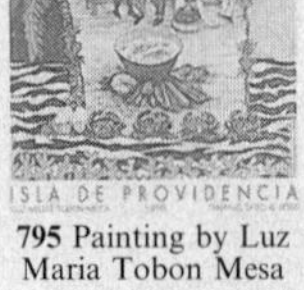
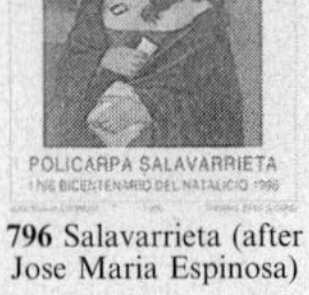

795 Painting by Luz Maria Tobon Mesa

796 Salavarrieta (after Jose Maria Espinosa)

1996. Air. Providence Island.
2072 **795** 800p. multicoloured . . 1·00 50

1996. Air. Birth Bicentenary of Policarpa Salavarrieta.
2073 **796** 900p. multicoloured . . 1·10 55

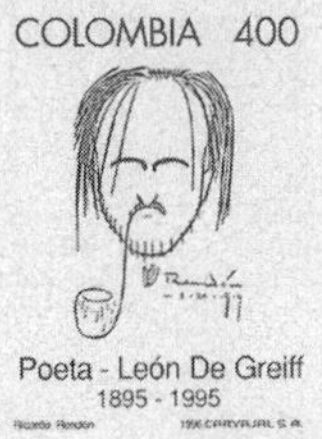
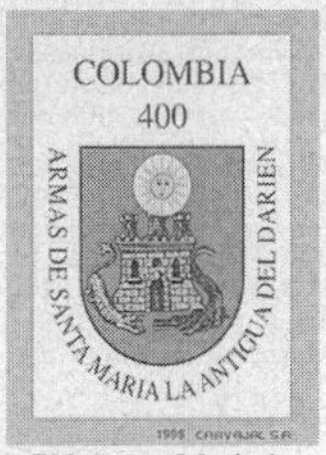

797 De Greiff (Ricardo Rendon)

799 Santa Maria la Antigua del Darien

1996. 1st Death Anniv of Leon De Greiff (poet).
2074 **797** 400p. black 50 25

1996. Town Arms. Multicoloured.
2076 400p. Type **799** 50 25
2077 400p. San Sebastian de Mariquita 50 25
2078 400p. Marinilla 50 25
2079 400p. Santa Cruz de Mompox 50 25

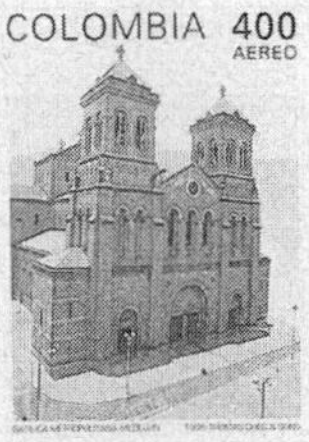

801 Medellin Cathedral

1996. Air.
2081 **801** 400p. multicoloured . . 50 25

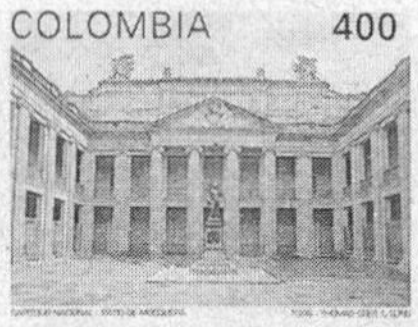

803 Mosquera Courtyard

1996. 150th Anniv of National Capitol, Bogota.
2083 **803** 400p. multicoloured . . 50 25

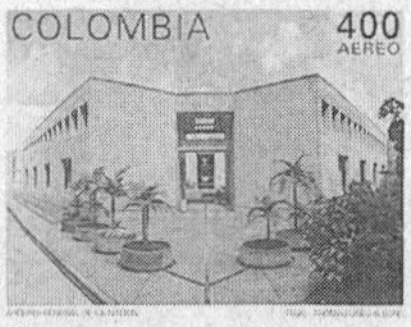

804 National Archive, Bogota

1996. Air.
2084 **804** 400p. multicoloured . . 50 25

1996. Air. Myths and Legends (2nd issue). Multicoloured.
2085 900p. The Creation of Koguin . . . . 1·10 55
2086 900p. Yonna Wayu . . . . 1·10 55
2087 900p. Jaguar-man . . . . . 1·10 55
2088 900p. Lord of the Animals 1·10 55

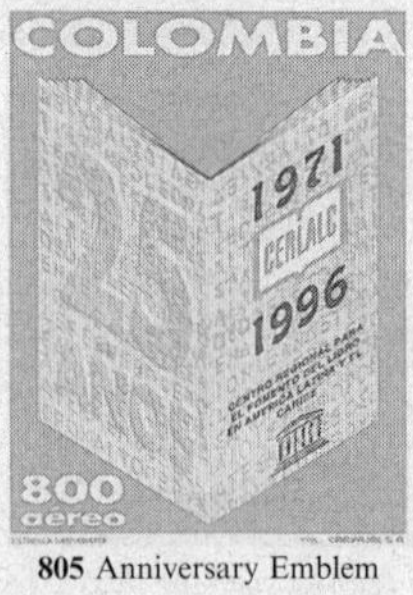

805 Anniversary Emblem

1996. Air. 25th Anniv of Regional Centre for the Development of Books in Latin America and Caribbean.
2089 **805** 800p. brn, blk & dp brn 95 50

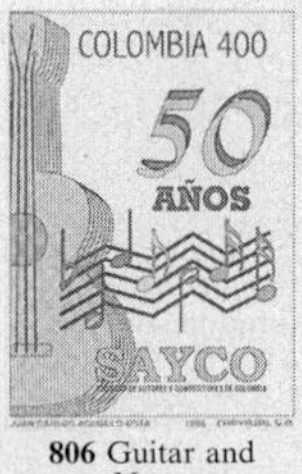
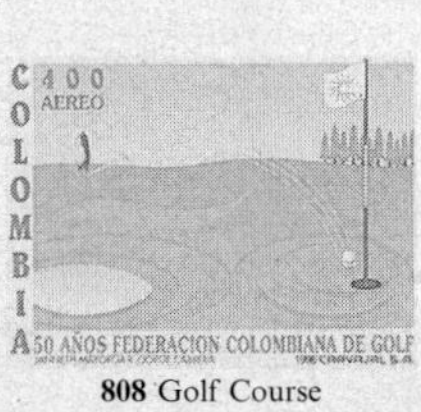

806 Guitar and Notes

808 Golf Course

807 Jorge Isaacs and Pump

1996. 50th Anniv of Society of Colombian Authors and Composers.
2090 **806** 400p. multicoloured . . . 50 25

1996. Air. Pioneers of Petroleum Industry. Multicoloured.
2091 800p. Type **807** . . . 95 50
2092 800p. Francisco Burgos Rubio and refinery (at night) . . . 95 50
2093 800p. Diego Martinez Camargo and drilling tower . . . 95 50
2094 800p. Prisciliano Cabrales Lora and drilling platform 1·25 60
2095 800p. Manuel Maria Palacio and firefighting tug . . 1·25 90
2096 800p. Roberto de Mares and refinery . . . 95 50
2097 800p. General Virgilio Barco Maldonado and workmen . 95 50
2098 800p. Workmen and Ecopetrol (state petroleum industry) emblem . . . 95 50

1996. Air. 50th Anniv of Colombian Golf Federation.
2099 **808** 400p. multicoloured . . . 50 25

809 Pre-Columban Pendant, Malagana Treasure

1996. "Exfilbo '96" National Stamp Exn, Bogota.
2100 **809** 400p. multicoloured . . . 50 25

811 Postman delivering Letter

1996. Christmas. The Annunciation. Mult.
2102 400p. Type **811** (postage) . . 50 25
2103 400p. Woman reading letter and postman (air) . . . 50 25

813 Cemetary, Mompox

1996. U.N.E.S.C.O. World Heritage Sites. Mult.
2106 400p. Type **813** . . . 50 25
2107 400p. San Agustin Archaeological Park . . 50 25
2108 400p. Palace of the Inquisition, Cartagena . . 50 25
2109 400p. Underground tomb, Tierradentro Archaeological Park . . . 50 25

814 Children holding Hands   815 Hurtado

1997. Air. Children's Rights.
2110 **814** 400p. multicoloured . . . 45 25

1997. 2nd Death Anniv of Alvaro Gomez Hurtado (lawyer and politician).
2111 **815** 400p. black and blue . . . 45 25

816 Film Reels and Harbour Tower   817 Emblem

1997. Air. Centenary of Colombian Cinema and 53rd International Union of Film Archives Congress, Cartagena de Indias.
2112 **816** 800p. multicoloured . . . 90 45

1997. Air. 50th Anniv (1996) of State Social Security.
2113 **817** 400p. multicoloured . . . 45 25

818 Hand holding Mobile Phone

1997. Air. Centenary (1996) of Ericsson Company in Colombia.
2114 **818** 900p. multicoloured . . . 90 45

819 Cattle

1997. Air. Cordoba Cattle Fair.
2115 **819** 400p. multicoloured . . . 30 15

820 "Maria Varilla in the Clouds" (William Vive)

1997. Porro National Festival, San Pelayo.
2116 **820** 400p. multicoloured . . . 30 15

821 Typewriter

1997. 50th Anniv of Bogota Journalists' Association.
2117 **821** 400p. multicoloured . . . 30 15

822 Museum Buildings

1997. Air. 1st Anniv of Numismatic Museum at State Mint, Bogota.
2118 **822** 800p. multicoloured . . . 65 35

823 Palm

1997. Air. Vegetable Ivory Palm Production Project.
2119 **823** 900p. multicoloured . . . 70 35

824 Barco

1997. Virgilio Barco (President, 1986–90) Commem.
2120 **824** 500p. multicoloured . . . 40 20

825 Straightening Contorted Tree and Healthy Couple

1997. Air. 50th Anniv of Colombian Society of Orthopaedic Surgery and Traumatology.
2121 **825** 1000p. multicoloured . . . 80 40

826 Luis Carlos Lopez (poet)

1997. Air. Personalities. Multicoloured.
2122 500p. Type **826** . . . 40 20
2123 500p. Aurelio Arturo (poet) . . 40 20
2124 500p. Enrique Perez Arbelaez (botanist and historian) . . . 40 20
2125 500p. Jose Maria Gonzalez Benito (mathematician and astronomer) . . . 40 20
2126 500p. Jose Manuel Rivas Sacconi (philologist and diplomat) . . . 40 20
2127 500p. Eduardo Lemaitre Roman (historian and journalist) . . . 40 20
2128 500p. Diojenes Arrieta (journalist and politician) . 40 20
2129 500p. Gabriel Turbay Abunader (politician and diplomat) . . . 40 20
2130 500p. Guillermo Echavarria Misas (aviation pioneer) . 40 20
2131 500p. Juan Friede Alter (historian) . . . 40 20
2132 500p. Fabio Lozano Torrijos (diplomat) . . 40 20
2133 500p. Lino de Pombo (engineer and diplomat) . 40 20
2134 500p. Cacica Gaitana (Indian resistance leader) . 40 20
2135 500p. Josefa Acevedo de Gomez (writer) . . . 40 20
2136 500p. Domingo Bioho (Black leader) . . . 40 20
2137 500p. Soledad Acosta de Samper (historian) . . . 40 20
2138 500p. Maria Cano Marquez (workers' leader) . . 55 30
2139 500p. Manuel Quintin Lame (native leader) . . . 40 20
2140 500p. Ezequiel Uricoechea (linguist and naturalist) . 40 20
2141 500p. Juan Rodriguez Freyle (chronicler) . . . 40 20
2142 500p. Gerardo Reichel-Dolmatoff (archaeologist) . 40 20
2143 500p. Ramon de Zubiria (educationist) . . . 40 20
2144 500p. Esteban Jaramillo (economist) . . . 40 20
2145 500p. Pedro Fermin de Vargas (economist) . . . 40 20

827 National Flag, Dove and Children playing

1997. Peace. Multicoloured.
2146 500p. Type **827** (postage) . . 40 20
2147 1100p. Children holding hands in ring (air) . . . 85 45

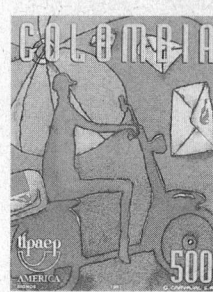

828 Postman on Moped

1997. America. The Postman. Multicoloured.
2148 500p. Type **828** (postage) . . 40 20
2149 1100p. Postman raising envelope to night sky (air) 85 45

829 Pregnant Women   830 Dove Emblem

1998. Air. 50th Anniv of W.H.O. Safe Motherhood.
2150 **829** 1100p. multicoloured . . . 65 35

1998. Air. 4th Bolivarian Stamp Exhibition, Santafe de Bogota.
2151 **830** 1000p. orange and blue . . . 60 30

831 Gaitan   832 Colombian Flag and Map of the Americas

1998. 50th Death Anniv of Jorge Eliecer Gaitan.
2152 **831** 500p. multicoloured . . . 30 15

1998. Air. 50th Anniv of Organization of American States.
2153 **832** 1000p. multicoloured . . . 60 30

833 Cogs

1998. 50th Anniv of Santander Industrial University.
2154 **833** 500p. multicoloured . . . 30 15

834 "Gloria" (cadet ship) and Dolphins

1998. Air. International Year of the Ocean.
2155 **834** 1100p. multicoloured . . 65 35

835 Football Boot

1998. Air. World Cup Football Championship, France. Multicoloured.
2156 1100p. Type **835** 65 35
2157 1100p. Ball 65 35
2158 1100p. Goalkeeper's glove   65 35
Nos. 2156/8 were issued together, se-tenant, forming a composite design.

836 University Arms

1998. 75th Anniv of Colombia Free University.
2159 **836** 500p. black and red . . . 30 15

837 "Bolivar Condor" (sculpture, R. Arenas Betancur) and Cathedral

1998. 150th Anniv of Manizales.
2160 **837** 500p. multicoloured . . . 30 15

838 Gold Coin,   **839** Borrero
Tairona Culture

1998. 75th Anniversaries. Multicoloured.
2161 500p. Type **838** (National Bank) 30 15
2162 500p. Gold sheaf of corn, Malagana Culture (Comptroller-General's Office) 30 15
2163 500p. Gold mask, Quimbaya Culture (Banking Superintendent's Office) . 30 15

1998. 1st Death Anniv of Misael Pastrana Borrero (President, 1970–74).
2164 **839** 500p. multicoloured . . . 30 15

840 The Andes and University Campus

1998. 50th Anniv of University of the Andes, Bogota.
2165 **840** 500p. black and yellow   30 15

841 Woman panning for **843** Academy of
Gold, and Cherubs   Languages Arms

842 Bochica

1998. Christmas. Multicoloured.
2166 500p. Type **841** (postage) . 30 15
2167 1000p. Three kings, camel and star (air) 60 30
2168 1000p. Nativity 60 30
Nos. 2167/8 were issued together, se-tenant, forming a composite design.

1998. Air. Muisca Mythology. Multicoloured.
2169 1000p. Type **842** 60 30
2170 1000p. Chiminigua 60 30
2171 1000p. Bachue and Huitica   60 30
Nos. 2169/71 were issued together, se-tenant, forming a composite design.

1998. Arms of Colombian Academies. Mult.
2172 500p. Type **843** 30 15
2173 500p. Medicine 30 15
2174 500p. Law 30 15
2175 500p. History 30 15
2176 500p. Physical and Natural Sciences 30 15
2177 500p. Economics 30 15
2178 500p. Ecclesiastical History   30 15

844 Soledad Roman de **845** Lopez (after
Nunez (First Lady,   G. Ricci)
1880–82 and 1884–94)

1999. America (1998). Famous Women. Mult.
2179 600p. Type **844** (postage) . 35 20
2180 1200p. Bertha Hernandez de Ospina (politician) (air)   70 35

1999. Birth Bicentenary of Jose Hilario Lopez (President, 1849–53).
2181 **845** 1000p. multicoloured . . 60 30

846 Green Turtle

1999. Turtles. Multicoloured.
2182 1300p. Type **846** 80 49
2183 1300p. Leatherback turtle ("Dermochelys coriacea")   80 40
2184 1300p. Hawksbill turtle ("Eretmochelys imbricata") 80 40
Nos. 2182/4 were issued together, se-tenant, forming a composite design.

847 Colombian and Japanese Suns across the Pacific

1999. 70 Years of Japanese Emigration to Colombia.
2185 **847** 1300p. multicoloured (yellow sun at left) . . 80 40
2186   1300p. multicoloured (red sun at left) . . . 80 40
Nos. 2185/6 were issued together, se-tenant, forming a composite design.

848 Medal   **850** Zuleta Angel

849 Crucifix above Pamplona

1999. 900th Anniv of Sovereign Military Order of Malta.
2187 **848** 1200p. multicoloured . . 70 35

1999. 450th Anniv of Pamplona.
2188 **849** 1000p. multicoloured . . 60 30

1999. Birth Centenary of Eduardo Zuleta Angel (politician and diplomat).
2189 **850** 600p. multicoloured . . . 35 20

851 Colombian Olympic Committee Emblem

1999. 13th Pan-American Games, Winnipeg. Mult.
2190 1200p. Type **851** 70 35
2191 1200p. Running (facing right) 70 35
2192 1200p. Weightlifting (facing left) 70 35
2193 1200p. Cycling (facing right)   70 35
2194 1200p. Shooting (facing left)   70 35
2195 1200p. Roller blading (facing right) 70 35
2196 1200p. Running (facing left)   70 35
2197 1200p. Weightlifting (facing right) 70 35
2198 1200p. Cycling (facing left)   70 35
2199 1200p. Shooting (facing right) 70 35
2200 1200p. Roller blading (facing left) 70 35

852 Robles   **854** Flowers leaving Hands

853 "125" and Emblem

1999. 150th Birth Anniv of Luis A. Robles.
2201 **852** 600p. multicoloured . . 35 20

1999. 125th Anniv of Universal Postal Union. Each lilac, violet and gold.
2202 1000p. Type **853** 60 30
2203 1300p. Emblem 85 45

1999. America. A New Millennium without Arms. Multicoloured.
2204 1200p. Type **854** 75 40
2205 1200p. Flowers moving towards hands 75 40
Nos. 2204/5 were issued together, se-tenant, forming a composite design.

855 Landscape

1999. 40th Anniv of International Development Bank. Multicoloured.
2206 1000p. Type **855** 60 30
2207 1000p. Landscape, sunbeams and red fruits 60 30
Nos. 2206/7 were issued together, se-tenant, forming a composite design.

856 Nativity

1999. Christmas. Multicoloured.
2208 600p. Type **856** 35 20
2209 600p. Angel and Three Wise Men 35 20
Nos. 2208/9. were issued together, se-tenant, forming a composite design.

857 Emblem   **858** Rainbow, Globe and "2000"

1999. Centenary of Invention of Aspirin (drug).
2210 **857** 600p. multicoloured . . . 35 20

2000. New Millennium. Multicoloured.
2211 1000p. Type **858** 60 30
2212 1000p. Man with Colombian flag and dove 60 30

859 University Arms

2000. 50th Anniv of Medellin University.
2213 **859** 1000p. multicoloured . . 60 30

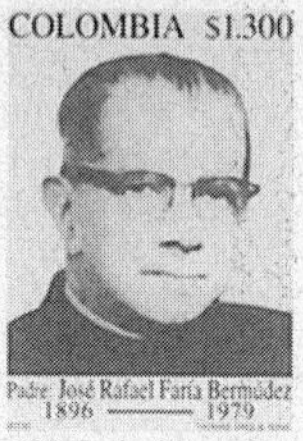
COLOMBIA $1.300
Padre José Rafael Faría Bermúdez
1896 — 1979
860 Faria Bermudez

2000. 20th Death Anniv (1999) of Father Jose Rafael Faria Bermudez.

2214	**860**	1300p. brown and black	85	45

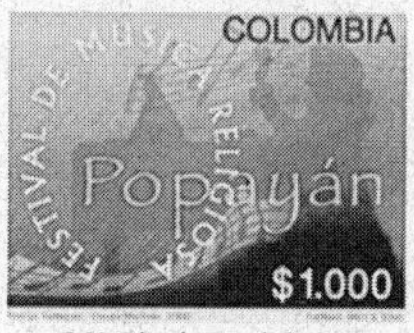
COLOMBIA
FESTIVAL DE MUSICA RELIGIOSA
Popayán
$1.000
861 Pianist and Score

2000. Religious Music Festival, Popayan.

2215	**861**	1000p. multicoloured	60	40

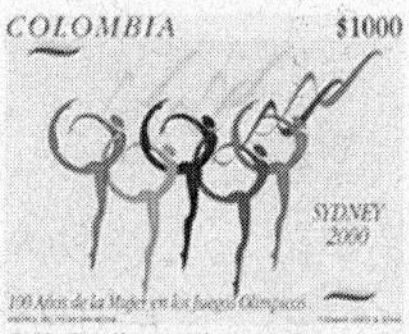
COLOMBIA
$1000
SYDNEY
2000
862 Stylized Figures forming Olympic Rings

2000. Olympic Games, Sydney.

2216	**862**	1000p. multicoloured	60	40

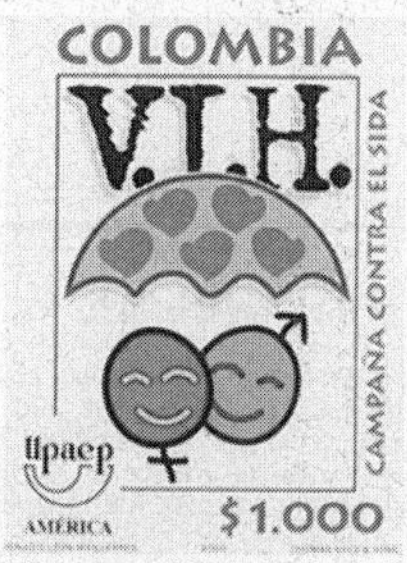
COLOMBIA
V.I.H.
CAMPAÑA CONTRA EL SIDA
$1.000
AMÉRICA
863 Male and Female Symbols under Umbrella

2000. A.I.D.S. Awareness Campaign.

2217	**863**	1000p. multicoloured	60	40

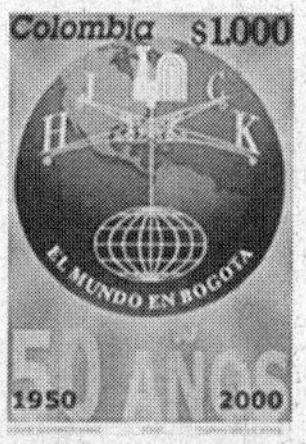
Colombia $1.000
EL MUNDO EN BOGOTA
50 AÑOS
1950
2000
864 Weather Vane

2000. 50th Anniv of World Meteorological Society.

2218	**864**	1000p. multicoloured	60	40

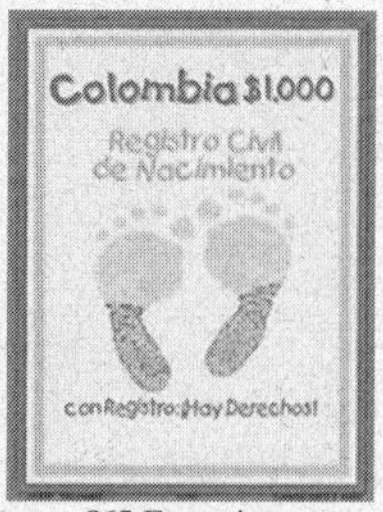
Colombia $1.000
Registro Civil de Nacimiento
con Registro ¡Hay Derechos!
865 Footprints

2000. National Birth Register

2219	**865**	1000p. multicoloured	60	40

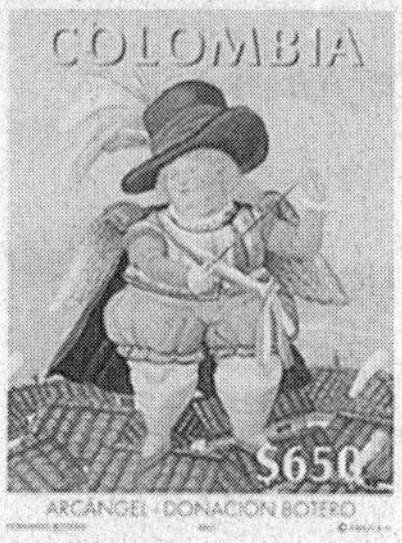
COLOMBIA
$650
ARCANGEL - DONACION BOTERO
866 "Archangel" (Fernando Botero)

2001. Botero Foundation, Bogota. Multicoloured.

2220	650p. Type **866**	40	25
2221	650p. "Gypsy with Tamborine" (Jean Baptiste Camille Corot)	40	25
2222	650p. "Vera Sergine Renoir" (Pierre-Auguste Renoir)	40	25
2223	650p. "Man on Horse" (Botero)	40	25
2224	650p. "Mother Superior" (Botero)	40	25
2225	650p. "Town" (Botero)	40	25
2226	650p. "Flowers" (Botero)	40	25
2227	650p. "Cezanne" (Botero)	40	25
2228	650p. "The Patio" (Botero)	40	25
2229	650p. "Absinthe Drinker at Grenelle" (Henri Toulouse-Lautrec)	40	25
2230	650p. "The Pequeno Valley" (Jean Baptiste Camille Corot)	40	25
2231	650p. "The Studio" (Botero)	40	25

PRIVATE AIR COMPANIES

The "LANSA" and Avianca Companies operated inland and foreign air mail services on behalf of the Government and issued the following stamps. Later only the Avianca Company performed this service and the regular air stamps were used on the mail without overprints.

Similar issues were also made by Compania Colombiana de Navegacion Aerea during 1920. These are very rare and will be found listed in the Stanley Gibbons Stamp Catalogue, Part 20 (South America).

A. "LANSA" (Lineas Aereas Nacionales Sociedad Anonima).

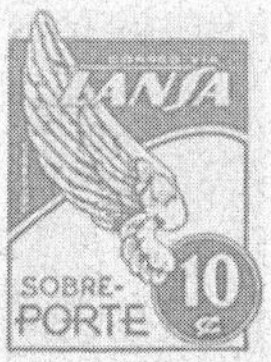
LANSA
SOBRE-PORTE
10
1 Wing

1950. Air.

1	**1**	5c. yellow	15	10
2		10c. red	25	15
3		15c. blue	25	10
4		20c. green	40	25
5		30c. purple	1·25	1·25
6		60c. brown	1·50	1·75

With background network colours in brackets.

7	**1**	1p. grey (buff)	6·00	7·50
8		2p. blue (green)	8·50	9·50
9		5p. red (red)	29·00	29·00

The 1p. was also issued without the network.

1950. Air. Nos. 691/7 and 700/3 optd **L**.

10	5c. yellow	15	10
11	10c. red	15	10
12	15c. blue	15	10
13	20c. violet	15	10
14	30c. green	15	15
15	40c. grey	3·50	15
16	50c. red	55	15
17	1p. purple and green	4·25	1·75
18	2p. blue and green	8·50	3·25
19	3p. black and red	8·50	9·50
20	5p. turquoise and sepia	28·00	28·00

1951. As Nos. 696/703 but colours changed and optd **L**.

21	40c. orange	90	55
22	50c. blue	90	55
23	60c. grey	90	45
24	80c. red	75	45
25	1p. red and vermilion	3·75	3·75
26	2p. blue and red	4·50	4·50
27	3p. green and brown	8·25	7·25
28	5p. grey and yellow	21·00	23·00

B. Avianca Company.

1950. Air. Nos. 691/703 optd **A**.

1	5c. yellow	10	10
2	10c. red	15	10
3	15c. blue	10	10
4	20c. violet	20	10
5	30c. green	15	10
6	40c. grey	45	10
7	50c. red	25	10
8	60c. olive	75	15
9	80c. brown	1·40	15
10	1p. purple and green	1·60	15
11	2p. blue and green	5·00	1·60
12	3p. black and red	8·50	7·50
13	5p. turquoise and sepia	25·00	22·00

1951. Air. As Nos. 696/703 but colours changed and optd **A**.

14	40c. orange	4·50	25
15	50c. blue	6·25	25
16	60c. grey	1·75	15
17	80c. red	60	15
18	1p. red and vermilion	2·10	15
19	1p. brown and green	2·25	35
20	2p. blue and red	2·10	35
21	3p. green and brown	4·50	90
22	5p. grey and yellow	8·25	90

The 60c. also comes with the **A** in the centre.

All values except the 2p. and 3p. exist without the overprint.

ACKNOWLEDGEMENT OF RECEIPT STAMPS

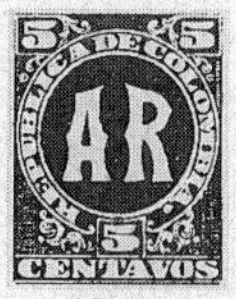
AR
5
CENTAVOS
AR **60**

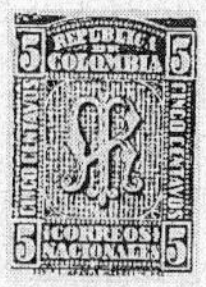
REPUBLICA DE COLOMBIA
5
CORREOS NACIONALES
AR **100**

1894.

AR169	AR **60**	5c. red	2·50	2·10

1902. Similar to Type AR **60**. Imperf or perf.

AR265	5c. blue	12·00	12·00
AR211	10c. blue on blue	90	90

1903. No. 197 optd **Habilitado Medellin A R**.

AR258	**75**	10c. black on pink	13·00	

1904. No. 262 optd **A R**.

AR266	**75**	5c. red	21·00	21·00

1904.

AR290	AR **100**	5c. blue	7·50	3·50

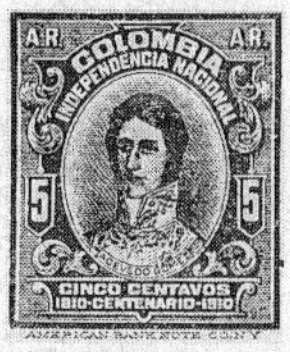
COLOMBIA
INDEPENDENCIA NACIONAL
CINCO CENTAVOS
1810-CENTENARIO-1910
AR **106** A. Gomez

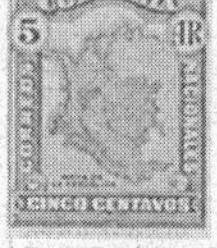
CINCO CENTAVOS
AR **117** Map of Colombia

1910.

AR354	AR **106**	5c. green & orge	6·00	15·00

1917. Inscr "AR".

AR371	**123**	4c. brown	12·50	11·00
AR372	AR **117**	5c. brown	5·00	4·00

OFFICIAL STAMPS

1937. Optd **OFICIAL**.

O496	–	1c. green (No. 429)	10	10
O497	**137**	2c. red (No. 430)	20	20
O498	–	5c. brown (No. 431)	10	10
O499	–	10c. orge (No. 485)	25	20
O500	**156**	12c. blue	90	25
O501	**141**	20c. blue	1·40	65
O502	**110**	30c. bistre	2·10	65
O503	**123**	40c. brown	22·00	14·00
O504	**112**	50c. red	1·75	80
O505	**110**	1p. blue	14·00	6·00
O506		2p. orange	15·00	6·00
O507		5p. grey	50·00	50·00
O508	**57**	10p. brown	£110	£110

REGISTRATION STAMPS

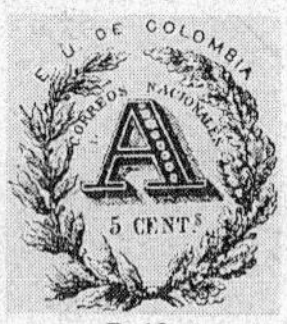
E. U. DE COLOMBIA
CORREOS NACIONALES
A
5 CENTS
R **12**

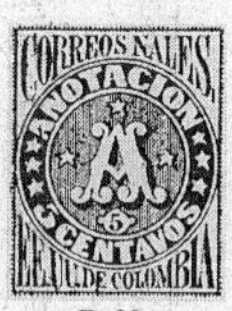
CORREOS NALES
ANOTACION
A
5 CENTAVOS
E.E.U.U. DE COLOMBIA
R **32**

1865. Imperf.

R42	R **12**	5c. black	90·00	45·00

1865. Type similar to R **12**, but letter "R" in star. Imperf.

R43	5c. black	£100	50·00

1870. Imperf.

R73	R **32**	5c. black	2·50	2·50

1870. Type similar to R **32** but with "R" in centre and inscr "REJISTRO". Imperf.

R74	5c. black	1·10	90

1881. Eagle and arms in oval frame, inscr "RECOMENDADA" at foot. Imperf or pin-perf.

R105	10c. lilac	30·00	30·00

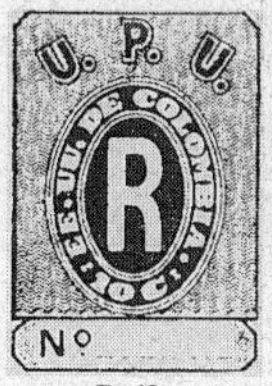
U. P. U.
R
Nº
R **42**

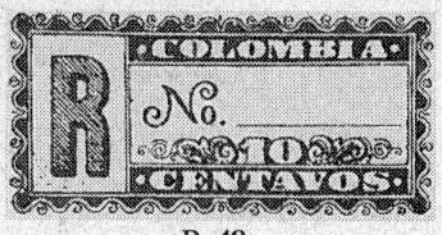
COLOMBIA
R
No.
10
CENTAVOS
R **48**

1883. Perf.

R117	R **42**	10c. red on orange	80	1·00

1899.

R141	R **48**	10c. red	5·00	3·50
R166		10c. brown	1·40	75

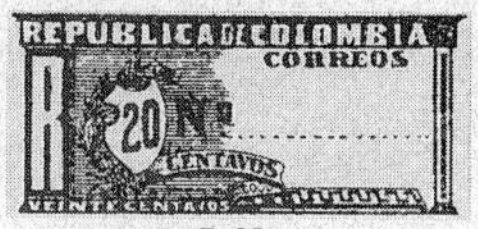
REPUBLICA DE COLOMBIA
CORREOS
R
20
R **85**

1902. Imperf or perf.

R264	R **85**	10c. purple	4·00	4·00
R207		20c. red on blue	80	80
R208		20c. blue on blue	1·25	1·25

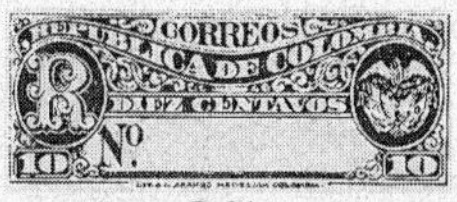
CORREOS
REPUBLICA DE COLOMBIA
R
DIEZ CENTAVOS
10
10
R **94**

1902. Perf.

R257	R **94**	10c. purple	19·00	19·00

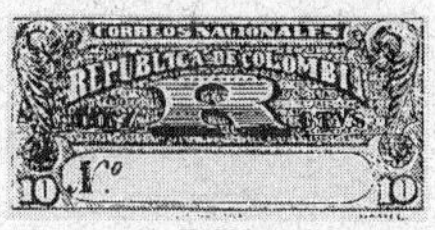
CORREOS NACIONALES
REPUBLICA DE COLOMBIA
R
10
10
R **99**

1904.

R289	R **99**	10c. purple	13·00	35

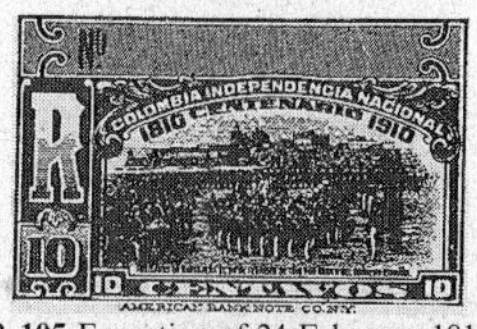
R
10
COLOMBIA INDEPENDENCIA NACIONAL
1810 CENTENARIO 1910
R **105** Execution of 24 February 1810

1910.

R353	R **105**	10c. black and red	20·00	50·00

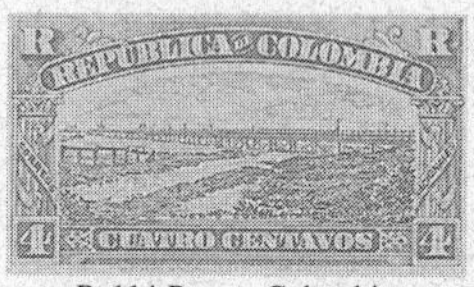
R
R
REPUBLICA DE COLOMBIA
CUATRO CENTAVOS
4
4
R **114** Puerto Colombia

1917.

R369	R **114**	4c. blue and green	35	3·25
R370	–	10c. blue	7·50	25

DESIGN: 10c. Tequendama Falls.

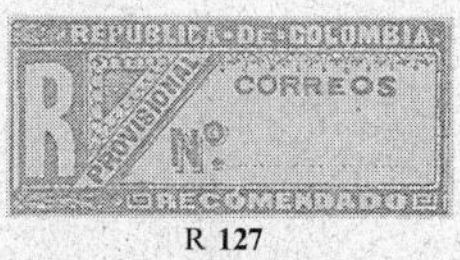
REPUBLICA DE COLOMBIA
CORREOS
R
PROVISIONAL
Nº
RECOMENDADO
R **127**

1925.

R409	R **127**	(10c.) blue	9·50	1·75

1932. Air. Air stamps of 1932 optd **R**.

R426	**132**	20c. red	6·00	4·25
R450	–	20c. green & red (439)	6·00	75

SPECIAL DELIVERY STAMPS

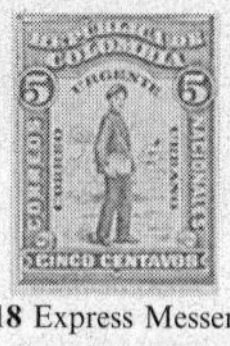
REPUBLICA DE COLOMBIA
URGENTE
5
5
CINCO CENTAVOS
E **118** Express Messenger

1917.

E373	E **118**	5c. green	5·00	4·25

E 310

1958. Air.
E936 E **310** 25c. red and blue . .   25   15

1959. Air. Unification of Air Mail Rates. Optd **UNIFICADO** within outline of airplane.
E989 E **310** 25c. red and blue . .   45   10

E **361** Boeing 720B on Back of "Express" Letter

1963. Air.
E1143 E **361** 50c. black & red . .   20   10

1966. Air. "History of Colombian Aviation". As T **372.** Inscr "EXPRESO". Multicoloured.
E1168   80c. Boeing 727 jetliner
    (1966)   10   15

E **647** Numeral

1987.
E1783 E **647** 25p. green and red   25   15
E1784   30p. green and red   25   15

E **663** Sailfish "Istiaphorus americanus"

1988. No Value expressed.
E1805 E **663** (A) blue . . . . . .   2·25   1·10
E1806   (B) blue   75   15

E **724** Black & Chestnut Eagle   E **738** Postman climbing out of Envelope

1992. No value expressed. Multicoloured.
E1926   B (200p.) Type E **724** . .   1·00   50
E1927   A (950p.) Spectacled bear   2·50   75

1992. World Post Day. No value expressed.
E1951 E **738** B (200p.) mult . . .   35   20

E **741** "Three Musicians"

1993. Fernando Botero (painter) Commemoration. No value expressed.
E1955 E **741** B multicoloured . .   35   20

E **743** Parading "Virgin of the Sorrows"

1993. Popayan Holy Week. No value expressed.
E1957 E **743** B multicoloured . .   35   20

E **744** Mother and Child   E **745** Mother House, Pasto

1993. 90th Anniv of Pan-American Health Organization. No value expressed.
E1958 E **744** B multicoloured . .   35   20

1993.
E1959 E **745** B multicoloured . .   35   20

E **746** Stamps, Magnifying Glass and Tweezers   E **747** Cano

1993. 18th National Stamp Exhibition. No value expressed.
E1960 E **746** B multicoloured . .   35   20

1993. 7th Death Anniv of Guillermo Cano (newspaper editor).
E1961 E **747** 250p. multicoloured   40   20

1993. Tourism. As T **756.** Multicoloured.
E1996   250p. Otun Lake (vert) . .   35   20

E **758** Marie Poussepin (founder)   E **761** Biplane

1994. Order of Sisters of the Presentation.
E1998 E **758** 300p. multicoloured   45   25

1994. 75th Anniv of Air Force.
E2004 E **761** 300p. multicoloured   45   25

1994. 4th Latin American Presidential Summit, Cartagena. As T **764.** Multicoloured.
E2010   300p. Setting sun over
     harbour walls   45   25

E **769** Emblem

1994. International Year of The Family.
E2016 E **769** 300p. multicoloured   40   20

1994. American Postal Transport. As T **770.** Multicoloured.
E2018   300p. Men carrying
     "stamps" depicting van,
     ship and aircraft   40   20

1994. Christmas. As T **773.** Multicoloured.
E2022   300p. Nativity   40   20

E **777** Championship Advertising Poster and Gold Ornament

1995. B.M.X. World Championship, Melgar.
E2029 E **777** 400p. multicoloured   55   30

E **785** Bicycle

1995. World Cycling Championships, Bogota and Boyaca.
E2056 E **785** 400p. multicoloured   50   25

E **791** Hands protecting Lake and Marine Angelfish   E **798** Emblem on Cross

1995. America. Environmental Protection. Multicoloured.
E2063   400p. Type E **791**   50   25
E2064   400p. Hands protecting
     tree   50   25

1996. 400th Anniv of Order of St. John of God in Colombia.
E2075 E **798** 500p. multicoloured   60   30

E **800** Trains

1996. Inauguration (1995) of Medellin Underground Railway.
E2080 E **800** 500p. multicoloured   1·50   75

E **802** Runners

1996. Olympic Games, Atlanta. Centenary of Modern Olympic Games.
E2082 E **802** 500p. multicoloured   60   30

E **812** Fruit Seller

1996. America. Traditional Costumes.
E2104   500p. Type E **812**   60   30
E2105   500p. Fisherman   60   30

TOO LATE STAMPS

L 47   L 59

1888. Perf.
L136 L **47** 2½c. black on lilac . .   4·00   1·50

1892. Perf.
L167 L **59** 2½c. blue on red . . .   4·00   3·25

L 86   L 107

1902. Imperf or perf.
L209 L **86** 5c. violet on red . . .   45   45

1914. Perf.
L355 L **107** 2c. brown . . . . . .   8·50   6·00
L356   5c. green . . . . . .   8·50   6·00

COMORO ISLANDS   Pt. 6; Pt. 12

An archipelago N.W. of Madagascar comprising Anjouan, Great Comoro, Mayotte and Moheli. A French colony from 1891, Mayotte became an Overseas Department of France in December 1974, the remaining islands forming the Independent State of Comoro.

100 centimes = 1 franc.

1 Anjouan Bay   2 Native Woman

6 Mutsamudu Village

1950.

1	1	10c. blue (postage)		15	1·00
2	–	50c. green		15	25
3	–	1f. brown		25	15
4	2	2f. green		35	20
5	–	5f. violet		50	90
6	–	6f. purple		45	1·00
7	–	7f. red		80	65
8	–	10f. green		90	60
9	–	11f. blue		80	1·60
10	–	15f. brown		75	70
11	–	20f. red		85	80
12	–	40f. indigo and blue . . .		22·00	13·00
13	6	50f. red and green (air) . . .		2·50	3·00
14	–	100f. brown and red		3·25	4·25
15	–	200f. red, green and violet . .		19·00	15·00

DESIGNS (as Type **1**)—HORIZ.: 7f., 10f., 11f. Mosque at Moroni; 40f. Coelacanth. VERT.: 15f., 20f. Ouani Mosque, Anjouan. (As Type **6**)—HORIZ.

100f. Natives and Mosque de Vendredi; 200f. Ouani Mosque, Anjouan (different).

1952. Military Medal Cent. As T **48** of Cameroun.
16 15f. blue, yellow and green . . 22·00 35·00

1954. Air. 10th Anniv of Liberation. As T **52** of Cameroun.
17 15f. red and brown . . . . . 21·00 28·00

9 Village Pump

1956. Economic and Social Development Fund.
18 **9** 9f. violet . . . . 75 3·00

10 "Human Rights"

1958. 10th Anniv of Declaration of Human Rights.
19 **10** 20f. green and blue . . . . 5·00 10·00

1959. Tropical Flora. As T **58** of Cameroun. Mult.
20 10f. "Colvillea" (horiz) . . . 1·75 3·00

11 Radio Station, Dzaoudzi

1960. Inaug of Comoro Broadcasting Service.
21 **11** 20f. green, violet and red . . 75 1·75
22 – 25f. green, brown and blue 90 1·60
DESIGN: 25f. Radio mast and map.

12 Bull-mouth Helmet **12a** Giant Clam

1962. Multicoloured. (a) Postage. Sea Shells.
23 50c. Type **12** . . . . 70 2·00
24 1f. Common harp . . . . . 1·00 1·75
25 2f. Ramose murex . . . . 1·75 3·00
26 5f. Giant green turban . . 2·75 3·75
27 20f. Scorpion conch . . . 8·50 12·50
28 25f. Trumpet triton . . . 12·00 14·50
  (b) Air. Marine Plants.
29 100f. Type **12a** . . . . . 8·50 13·50
30 500f. Stoney coral . . . . 21·00 32·00

1962. Malaria Eradication. As T **70** of Cameroun.
31 25f.+5f. red . . . . 1·50 4·75

1962. Air. 1st Trans-Atlantic T.V. Satellite Link. As Type F **23** of Andorra.
32 25f. mauve, purple and violet 2·50 1·40

14 Emblem in Hands and Globe **14a** Centenary Emblem

1963. Freedom from Hunger.
33 **14** 20f. green and brown . . 2·50 5·75

1963. Red Cross Centenary.
34 **14a** 50f. red, grey and green . 5·75 8·00

15 Globe and Scales of Justice **16** Tobacco Pouch

1963. 15th Anniv of Declaration of Human Rights.
35 **15** 15f. green and red . . . . 5·25 9·50

1963. Handicrafts. (a) Postage. As T **17**.
36 **16** 3f. ochre, red and green . . 1·00 2·25
37 – 4f. myrtle, purple & orange 1·00 2·50
38 – 10f. brown, green & chest 85 3·00
  (b) Air. Size 27×48 mm.
39 – 65f. red, brown and green . 2·75 4·25
40 – 200f. pink, red & turq . . 6·25 7·00
DESIGNS: 4f. Perfume-burner; 10f. Lamp bracket; 65f. Baskets; 200f. Filigree pendant.

16a "Philately" **17** Pirogue

1964. "PHILATEC 1964" International Stamp Exhibition, Paris.
41 **16a** 50f. red, green and blue . . 2·00 5·25

1964. Native Craft. Multicoloured.
42 15f. Type **17** (postage) . . . . 2·50 3·50
43 30f. Boutre felucca . . . . 4·50 6·50
44 50f. Mayotte pirogue (air) . . 3·50 3·50
45 85f. Schooner . . . . . . 5·25 4·25
Nos. 44/5 are larger, 27×48½ mm.

18 Boxing (Ancient bronze plaque) **19** Medal

1964. Air. Olympic Games, Tokyo.
46 **18** 100f. green, brown & choc . 6·50 10·50

1964. Air. Star of Grand Comoro.
47 **19** 500f. multicoloured . . . . 16·00 20·00

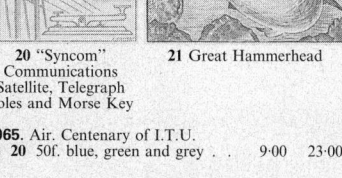
20 "Syncom" Communications Satellite, Telegraph Poles and Morse Key **21** Great Hammerhead

1965. Air. Centenary of I.T.U.
48 **20** 50f. blue, green and grey . . 9·00 23·00

1965. Marine Life.
49 – 1f. green, orange and violet 1·60 2·00
50 **21** 12f. black, blue and red . . 2·00 2·50
51 – 20f. red and green . . . . 2·50 3·00
52 – 25f. brown, red and green 5·00 3·75
DESIGNS—VERT: 1f. Spiny lobster; 25f. Spotted grouper. HORIZ: 20f. Scaly turtle.

1966. Air. Launching of 1st French Satellite. As Nos. 1696/7 of France.
53 25f. lilac, blue and violet . . 3·50 5·75
54 30f. lilac, violet and blue . . 4·50 5·75

21a Satellite "D1"

1966. Air. Launching of Satellite "D1".
55 **21a** 30f. purple, green & orange 1·90 2·25

22 Lake Sale

1966. Comoro Views. Multicoloured.
56 15f. Type **22** (postage) . . . . 75 2·00
57 25f. Itsandra Hotel, Moroni 1·25 1·50
58 50f. The Battery, Dzaoudzi (air) . . . . 2·50 4·00
59 200f. Ksar Fort, Mutsamudu (vert) . . . . 5·50 6·50
Nos. 58/9 are larger, 48×27 mm and 27×48 mm respectively.

23 Anjouan Sunbird **24** Nurse tending Child

1967. Birds. Multicoloured.
60 2f. Type **23** (postage) . . . . 3·75 3·00
61 10f. Madagascar malachite kingfisher . . . . . 4·25 4·25
62 15f. Mascarene fody . . . . 7·75 6·25
63 30f. Courol . . . . 17·00 13·50
64 75f. Madagascar paradise flycatcher (air) . . . 9·25 9·75
65 100f. Blue-cheeked bee eater 12·00 13·50
Nos. 64/5 are vert, 27×48 mm.

1967. Comoro Red Cross.
66 **24** 25f.+5f. purple, red & grn 2·25 3·50

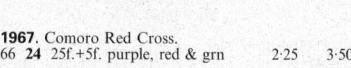

25 Slalom Skiing **26** Bouquet, Sun and W.H.O. Emblem

1968. Air. Winter Olympic Games, Grenoble.
67 **25** 70f. brown, blue and green 4·00 4·50

1968. 20th Anniv of W.H.O.
68 **26** 40f. red, violet and green . 85 1·25

27 Powder-blue Surgeonfish **28** Human Rights Emblem

1968. Fishes.
69 **27** 20f. bl, yell & red (postage) 2·75 4·25
70 – 25f. blue, orange & turq . . 3·50 5·25
71 – 60f. ochre, blue & pur (air) 5·75 4·75
72 – 90f. ochre, green & emer . 8·25 6·50
DESIGNS—As T **27**: 25f. Emperor angelfish. 48×27 mm: 50f. Moorish idol; 90f. Oriental sweetlips.

1968. Human Rights Year.
73 **28** 60f. green, brown & orange 2·75 4·75

29 Swimming

1968. Air. Olympic Games, Mexico.
74 **29** 65f. multicoloured . . . . . 3·00 4·00

30 Prayer Mat and Worshipper

1969. Msoila Prayer Mats.
75 **30** 20f. red, green and violet . . 95 2·25
76 – 30f. green, violet and red . . 1·25 2·50
77 – 45f. violet, red and green . . 2·50 3·25
DESIGNS: As Type **30**, but worshipper stooping (30f.) or kneeling upright (45f.).

31 Vanilla Flower

1969. Flowers, Multicoloured.
78 10f. Type **31** (postage) . . . . 1·60 2·50
79 15f. Ylang-ylang blossom . . 1·60 2·50
80 50f. "Heliconia" (vert) (air) . . 4·25 4·00
81 85f. Tuberose (vert) . . . . 5·50 4·75
82 200f. Orchid (vert) . . . . . 10·00 8·00

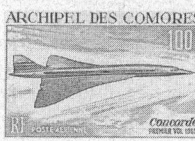
32 Concorde in Flight

1969. Air. 1st Flight of Concorde.
83 **32** 100f. purple and brown . . 11·50 18·00

33 I.L.O. Building, Geneva

1969. 50th Anniv of I.L.O.
84 **33** 5f. grey, green and orange . 1·50 2·25

34 Poinsettia **35** "EXPO" Panorama

1970. Flowers.
85 **34** 25f. multicoloured . . . . . 3·00 2·75

1970. New U.P.U. Headquarters Building, Berne. As T **156** of Cameroun.
86 65f. brown, green and violet 3·75 4·00

1970. Air. World Fair "EXPO 70", Osaka, Japan. Multicoloured.
87 60f. Type **35** . . . . 4·25 3·25
88 90f. Geisha and map of Japan 5·25 3·25

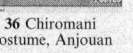

36 Chiromani Costume, Anjouan **37** Mosque de Vendredi, Moroni

1970. Comoro Costumes. Multicoloured.
89 20f. Type **36** . . . . 2·50 2·50
90 25f. Bouiboui, Great Comoro 3·00 2·50

1970.
91 **37** 5f. turquoise, green and red 2·00 2·25
92 10f. violet, green & purple 2·25 2·50
93 40f. brown, green and red 3·00 2·75

38 Great Egret

1971. Birds, Multicoloured.
94 **5f.** Type **38** . . . . 1·90 2·25
95 10f. Comoro olive pigeon . . . 1·90 2·25
96 15f. Green-backed heron . . . 2·25 2·50
97 25f. Comoro blue pigeon . . . 2·75 2·75
98 35f. Humblot's flycatcher . . 4·00 3·75
99 40f. Allen's gallinule . . . . . 6·25 4·25

39 Sunset, Moutsamoudou (Anjouan)

40 Map of Comoro Archipelago

1971. Air. Comoro Landscapes. Multicoloured.
100 **39** 15f. multicoloured . . . . 1·60 1·90
101 – 20f. multicoloured . . . . 1·75 2·25
102 – 65f. multicoloured . . . 3·00 2·75
103 – 85f. multicoloured . . . 3·75 3·25
104 **40** 100f. brown, green & bl . . 8·00 6·50
DESIGNS—(As Type **39**): 20f. Sada village
(Mayotte); 65f. Ruined palace, Iconi (Great Comoro);
85f. Offshore islands; Moumatchoua (Moheli).
See also Nos. 124/8, 132/6, 157/60 and 168/71.

41 "Pyrostegia venusta"

1971. Tropical Plants. Multicoloured.
105 **1f.** Type **41** (postage) . . . . 1·75 2·25
106 3f. "Allamanda cathartica"
        (horiz) . . . . 1·75 2·25
107 20f. "Plumeria rubra" . . . . 3·50 3·25
108 60f. "Hibiscus
        schizopetalous" (air) . . . 3·25 3·75
109 85f. "Acalypha sanderii" . . . 7·50 5·25
The 60 and 85f. are 27 × 48 mm.

42 Lithograph Cone

1971. Sea Shells. Multicoloured.
110 **5f.** Type **42** . . . . 1·75 2·25
111 10f. Lettered cone . . . . . 2·00 2·25
112 20f. Princely cone . . . . . 2·50 2·75
113 35f. Polished nerite . . . . 3·75 2·75
114 60f. Serpent's-head cowrie . . 6·00 3·25

1971. 1st Death Anniv of Charles de Gaulle. Designs
as Nos. 1937 and 1940 of France.
115 20f. black and purple . . . . 3·00 3·25
116 35f. black and purple . . . . 3·50 3·75

44 Mural, Airport Lounge

1972. Air. Inauguration of New Airport, Moroni.
117 **44** 65f. multicoloured . . . . 1·75 2·25
118 – 85f. multicoloured . . . . 2·25 2·25
119 – 100f. green, brown & blue 3·50 3·25
DESIGNS: 85f. Mural similar to T **44**; 100f. Airport
Buildings.

45 Eiffel Tower, Paris and
Telecommunications Centre, Moroni

1972. Air. Inauguration of Paris–Moroni Radio-
Telephone Link.
120 **45** 35f. red, purple & blue . . 2·50 2·25
121 – 75f. red, violet and blue . . 2·50 2·25
DESIGN: 75f. Telephone conversation.

46 Underwater Spear-fishing

1972. Air. Aquatic Sports.
122 **46** 70f. red, green and blue . . 7·25 5·25

47 Pasteur, Crucibles and
Microscope

1972. 150th Birth Anniv of Louis Pasteur.
123 **47** 65f. blue, brown & orange 4·75 4·00

1972. Air. Anjouan Landscapes. (a) As T **39**.
Multicoloured.
124 20f. Fortress wall, Cape Sima 1·60 1·90
125 35f. Bambao Palace . . . . 1·75 2·25
126 40f. Palace, Domoni . . . . 1·75 2·25
127 60f. Gomajou Island . . . . 2·75 2·75

(b) As T **40**.
128 – 100f. green, blue & brown 5·75 5·25
DESIGN: 100f. Map of Anjouan.

48 Pres. Said   **50** Bank
Mohamed Cheikh

1973. Air. Said Mohamed Cheikh, President of
Comoro Council, Commemoration.
129 **48** 20f. multicoloured . . . . 1·90 2·25
130 – 35f. multicoloured . . . . 2·25 2·50

1973. Air. International Coelacanth Study
Expedition. No. 72 surch **Mission Internationale
pour l'etude du Coelacanthe** and value.
131 120f. on 90f. brn, grn & emer 10·50 7·00

1973. Great Comoro Landscapes. (a) Postage.
As T **39**. Multicoloured.
132 10f. Goulaivoini . . . . . . 2·25 1·90
133 20f. Mitsamiouli . . . . . . 2·25 2·25
134 35f. Foumbouni . . . . . . 3·00 2·75
135 50f. Moroni . . . . 3·75 3·25

(b) Air. As Type **40**.
136 – 135f. purple, green & violet 10·50 6·25
DESIGN—VERT: 135f. Map of Great Comoro.

1973. Moroni Buildings. Multicoloured.
137 **5f.** Type **50** . . . . 2·00 2·25
138 15f. Post Office . . . . . . 2·25 2·50
139 20f. Prefecture . . . . . . 2·50 2·75

51 Volcanic Eruption

1973. Air. Karthala Volcanic Eruption (Sept 1972).
140 **51** 120f. multicoloured . . . 9·50 6·50

52 Dr. G. A. Hansen   **54** Zaouiyat Chaduli
                                     Mosque

53 Pablo Picasso (artist)

1973. Air Centenary of Hansen's Identification of
Leprosy Bacillus.
141 **52** 100f. green, purple & blue 4·75 3·75

1973. Air. 500th Birth Anniv of Nicolas Copernicus.
As T **52**.
142 150f. purple, blue & ultram 6·25 5·25
DESIGN: 150f. Copernicus and solar system.

1973. Air. Picasso Commemoration.
143 **53** 200f. multicoloured . . . . 12·00 8·00

1973. Mosques. Multicoloured.
145 20f. Type **54** . . . . 2·00 2·75
146 35f. Salimata Hamissi
        Mosque (horiz) . . . . 2·75 2·75

55 Star and Ribbon   **56** Said Omar Ben Soumeth
                                     (Grand Mufti of the
                                     Comoros)

1974. Air. Order of the Star of Anjouan.
147 **55** 500f. gold, blue & brown 16·00 13·00

1974. Air. Multicoloured.
148 135f. Type **56** . . . . 4·00 2·75
149 200f. Ben Soumeth seated
        (vert) . . . . 5·50 4·50

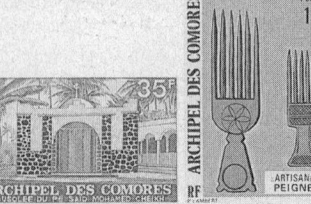
57 Doorway of Mausoleum   **58** Wooden Combs

1974. Mausoleum of Shaikh Said Mohamed.
150 **57** 35f. brown, black & green 2·75 2·75
151 – 50f. brown, black & green 3·75 2·75
DESIGN: 50f. Mausoleum.

1974. Comoro Handicrafts (1st series). Mult.
152 **15f.** Type **58** . . . . 1·90 2·25
153 20f. Three-legged table . . . 2·25 2·25

154 35f. Koran lectern (horiz) . . 3·00 2·75
155 75f. Sugar-cane press (horiz) 5·25 3·50
See also Nos. 164/7.

59 Mother and Child

1974. Comoros Red Cross Fund.
156 **59** 35f.+10f. brown & red . . 2·00 2·75

1974. Air. Mayotte Landscapes. (a) As T **39**.
Multicoloured.
157 20f. Moya beach . . . . . . 1·75 1·90
158 35f. Chiconi . . . . 1·90 1·90
159 90f. Mamutzu harbour . . . 4·00 3·25

(b) As T **40**.
160 120f. green and blue . . . . 7·25 4·75
DESIGN—VERT: 120f. Map of Mayotte.

60 U.P.U. Emblem and Globe

1974. Centenary of Universal Postal Union.
161 **60** 30f. red, brown and green 2·75 3·00

61 Boeing 707 taking off

1975. Inauguration of Direct Moroni–Hahaya–Paris
Air Service.
162 **61** 135f. blue, green and red 7·25 6·25

62 Rotary Emblem, Moroni Clubhouse
and Map

1975. Air. 70th Anniv of Rotary International and
10th Anniv of Moroni Rotary Club.
163 **62** 250f. multicoloured . . . . 9·50 8·75

63 Bracelet

1975. Comoro Handicrafts (2nd series).
164 **63** 20f. brown and purple . . 2·50 2·25
165 – 35f. brown and green . . 2·50 2·50
166 – 120f. brown and blue . . 6·00 4·50
167 – 135f. brown and red . . . 8·75 5·25
DESIGNS: 35f. Diadem; 120f. Sabre; 125f. Dagger.

1975. Moheli Landscapes. (a) Postage. As T **39**.
Multicoloured.
168 30f. Mohani Village . . . . . 2·75 2·50
169 50f. Djoezi Village . . . . . 3·25 2·75
170 55f. Chirazian tombs . . . . 4·25 3·25

(b) Air. As T **40**.
171 230f. green, blue and brown 12·00 8·00
DESIGN: 230f. Map of Moheli.

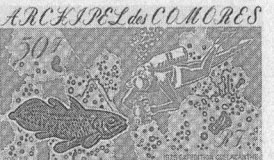
64 Coelacanth and Skin-diver

1975. Coelacanth Expedition.
172 **64** 50f. bistre, blue & brown 6·50 4·50

65 Tambourine-player

1975. Folklore Dances. Multicoloured.
173	100f. Type **65**		60·00	60·00
174	150f. Dancers with tambourines		60·00	60·00

66 Athlete and Athens, 1896 Motifs

1976. Olympic Games, Munich (1972) and Montreal (1976). Multicoloured.
175	20f. Type **66** (postage)		15	10
176	25f. Running		15	10
177	40f. Athlete and Paris, 1900 motif		25	15
178	75f. High-jumping		45	20
179	100f. Exercises and World's Fair, St. Louis, 1904 motif (air)		55	35
180	500f. Gymnast on bars		3·75	1·40

67 Government House, Flag and Map

1976. 1st Anniv of Independence. Multicoloured.
182	**67** 30f. multicoloured		25	15
183	50f. multicoloured		35	20

68 Agricultural Scene and U.N. Stamp

1976. 25th Anniv of U.N. Postal Services. Multicoloured.
184	15f. Type **68** (postage)		10	10
185	30f. Surgery scene and U.N.W.H.O. stamp		20	10
186	50f. Village scene and U.N.I.C.E.F. stamp		3·75	50
187	75f. Telecommunications satellite and U.N. I.T.U. stamp		45	20
188	200f. Concorde, airship "Graf Zeppelin" and U.N. I.C.A.O. stamp (air)		2·50	85
189	400f. Lufthansa jet airliner and U.N. U.P.U. stamp		3·00	1·40

69 Copernicus, and Rocket on Launch-pad

1976. "Success of Operation Viking", and Bicentenary of American Revolution. Multicoloured.
191	5f. Type **69** (postage)		10	10
192	10f. Einstein, Sagan and Young (horiz)		10	10
193	25f. "Viking" orbiting Mars		15	10
194	35f. Vikings' discovery of America (horiz)		50	20
195	100f. U.S. flag and Mars landing		65	30
196	500f. First colour photograph of Martian terrain (horiz) (air)		4·00	1·25

70 U.N. Headquarters, New York and Flags

1976. 1st Anniv of Comoro Islands Admission to United Nations.
198	**70** 40f. multicoloured		30	20
199	50f. multicoloured		40	25

71 President Lincoln and Bombardment of Fort Sumter

1976. Bicentenary of American Revolution. Showing various battle scenes of American Civil War. Multicoloured.
200	10f. Type **71** (postage)		10	10
201	30f. General Beauregard and Bull Run (vert)		20	10
202	50f. General Johnston and Antietam		30	15
203	100f. General Meade and Gettysburg (air)		55	30
204	200f. General Sherman and Chattanooga (vert)		1·40	45
205	400f. General Pickett and Appomattox		2·75	90

72 Andean Condor

74 Giffard's Dirigible, 1851 and French Locomotive, 1837

73 Wolf

1976. "Endangered Animals" (1st series). Multicoloured.
207	15f. Type **72** (postage)		1·75	55
208	20f. Tiger cat (horiz)		50	15
209	35f. Leopard		65	15
210	40f. White rhinoceros (horiz)		90	40
211	75f. Mountain nyala		1·60	45
212	400f. Orang-utan (horiz) (air)		4·50	1·25

1977. "Endangered Animals" (2nd series). Mult.
214	10f. Type **73** (postage)		10	10
215	30f. Aye-aye		20	10
216	40f. Banded duiker		65	15
217	50f. Giant tortoise		80	15
218	200f. Ocelot (air)		1·90	55
219	400f. Galapagos penguin ("Manchot des Galapagos")		7·00	3·00

1977. History of Communications. Airships and Railways. Multicoloured.
221	20f. Type **74** (postage)		30	10
222	25f. Santos-Dumont's airship "Ballon No. 6" (1906) and Brazilian steam locomotive (19th century)		65	15
223	50f. Russian airship "Astra" (1914) and "Trans-Siberian Express" (1905)		90	20
224	75f. British airship R-34 (1919) and "Southern Belle" pullman express (1910–25)		1·10	30
225	200f. U.S. Navy airship "Los Angeles" (1930) and Pacific locomotive (1930) (air)		4·25	50
226	500f. German airship "Hindenburg", 1933, and "Rheingold" express, 1933		7·75	1·50

75 Koch, Morgan, Fleming, Muller and Waksman (medicine)

1977. Nobel Prize Winners. Multicoloured.
228	30f. Type **75** (postage)		20	10
229	40f. Michelson, Bragg, Raman and Zernike (physics)		20	15
230	50f. Tagore, Yeats, Russell and Hemingway (literature)		30	15
231	100f. Röntgen, Becquerel, Planck, Lawrence and Einstein (physics)		80	25
232	200f. Ramsey and Marie Curie (chemistry), Banting and Hench (medicine) and Perrin (physics) (air)		1·40	45
233	400f. Dunant, Briand, Schweitzer and Martin Luther King (peace)		3·25	90

The 200f. wrongly attributes the chemistry prize to all those depicted and gives the date 1913 instead of 1911 for Marie Curie. On the 50 and 100f. names are wrongly spelt.

76 "Clara, Ruben's Daughter"

1977. 400th Birth Anniv of Peter Paul Rubens (1st issue). Multicoloured.
235	20f. Type **76** (postage)		10	10
236	25f. "Suzanne Fourment"		15	10
237	50f. "Venus in front of Mirror"		55	15
238	75f. "Ceres"		70	25
239	200f. "Young Girl with Blond Hair" (air)		1·40	95
240	500f. "Helene Fourment in Wedding Dress"		4·50	1·25

See also Nos. 407/10.

77 Queen Elizabeth II, Westminster Abbey and Guards

1977. Air. Silver Jubilee of Queen Elizabeth II.
242	**77** 500f. multicoloured		3·25	1·40

79 Swordfish

1977. Fishes. Multicoloured.
256	30f. Type **79** (postage)		20	10
257	40f. Oriental sweetlips		55	15
258	50f. Lionfish		80	15
259	100f. Racoon butterflyfish		1·60	25
260	200f. Clown anemonefish (air)		2·00	65
261	400f. Black-spotted puffer		3·50	1·75

80 Jupiter Lander

1977. Space Research. Multicoloured.
263	30f. Type **80** (postage)		20	10

264	50f. Uranus probe (vert)		35	15
265	75f. Venus probe		45	20
266	100f. Space shuttle (vert)		55	25
267	200f. "Viking 3" (air)		1·25	45
268	400f. "Apollo–Soyuz" link (vert)		2·40	90

1977. Air. First Paris–New York Commercial Flight of Concorde. No. 188 optd **Paris-New-York - 22 nov. 1977**.
270	200f. multicoloured		2·75	2·00

82 Allen's Gallinule

1978. Birds. Multicoloured.
271	15f. Type **82** (postage)		50	25
272	20f. Blue-cheeked bee eater		70	35
273	35f. Madagascar malachite kingfisher		85	45
274	40f. Madagascar paradise flycatcher		95	55
275	75f. Anjouan sunbird		1·60	80
276	400f. Great egret (air)		6·25	3·75

83 Greek Ball Game and Modern Match

1978. World Cup Football Championship, Argentina. Multicoloured.
278	30f. Type **83** (postage)		20	10
279	50f. Breton football		25	15
280	75f. 14th-century London game		45	25
281	100f. 18th-century Italian game		55	25
282	200f. 19th-century English game (air)		1·10	45
283	400f. English cup-tie, 1891		2·50	85

84 "Oswolt Krel"

1978. 450th Death Anniv of Albrecht Durer (artist) (1st issue). Multicoloured.
286	20f. Type **84** (postage)		10	10
287	25f. "Elspeth Tucher"		15	10
288	50f. "Hieronymus Holzshuher"		35	15
289	75f. "Young Girl"		50	25
290	200f. "Emperor Maximilian I" (air)		1·10	45
291	500f. "Young Girl" (detail)		3·25	1·10

See also Nos. 411/15.

85 Bach

1978. Composers. Multicoloured.
293	30f. Type **85** (postage)		20	10
294	40f. Mozart		25	15
295	50f. Berlioz		35	15
296	100f. Verdi		90	25
297	200f. Tchaikovsky (air)		1·60	45
298	400f. Gershwin		3·25	85

Following a revolution on 13 May 1978, it was announced that sets showing Butterflies or commemorating the 25th Anniversary of the

Coronation of Queen Elizabeth II, 10th World Telecommunications Day and Aviation History had not been placed on sale in the islands and were not valid for postage there.

86 Rowland Hill, Locomotive "Adler" and Saxony 3pf. Stamp, 1860

1978. Death Centenary of Sir Rowland Hill. Multicoloured.

300	20f. Type **86** (postage)	1·75	50
301	30f. Penny-farthing and Netherlands 5c. stamp, 1852	20	10
302	40f. Early letter-box and 2d. blue	25	15
303	75f. Pony Express and U.S. stamp, 1847	45	20
304	200f. Airship and French 20c. stamp, 1863 (air)	1·50	65
305	400f. Postman and Basel 2½r. stamp, 1845	2·50	85

87 Interpreting Meteorological Satellite Photographs

1978. European Space Agency. Multicoloured.

307	10f. Type **87** (postage)	10	10
308	25f. Writing weather forecast	15	10
309	35f. Aiding wrecked ship	70	20
310	50f. Telecommunications as teaching aid	35	15
311	100f. Boeing 727 landing (air)	75	40
312	500f. Space shuttle	3·25	1·10

1978. Argentina's Victory in World Cup Football Championship. Nos. 278/284 optd **REP. FED. ISLAMIQUE DES COMORES 1 ARGENTINE 2 HOLLANDE 3 BRESIL.**

314	**83** 30f. mult (postage)	20	10
315	— 50f. multicoloured	35	15
316	— 75f. multicoloured	45	20
317	— 100f. multicoloured	50	25
318	— 200f. multicoloured (air)	1·40	45
319	— 400f. multicoloured	2·50	85

89 Philidor, Anderssen and Steinitz

1979. Chess Grand Masters. Multicoloured.

321	40f. Type **89** (postage)	20	10
322	100f. Venetian players and pieces	80	20
323	500f. Alekhine, Spassky and Fischer (air)	4·00	1·10

90 Galileo and "Voyager 1"

1979. Exploration of the Solar System. Mult.

324	20f. Type **90** (postage)	10	10
325	30f. Kepler and "Voyager 2"	15	10
326	40f. Copernicus and "Voyager 1"	20	10
327	100f. Huygens and "Voyager 2"	45	20
328	200f. Herschel and "Voyager 2" (air)	1·40	35
329	400f. Leverrier and "Voyager 2"	2·50	80

91 Kayak

1979. Olympic Games, Moscow (1980). Mult.

330	10f. Type **91** (postage)	10	10
331	25f. Swimming	15	10
332	35f. Archery	20	10
333	50f. Pole vault	25	15
334	75f. Long jump	35	20
335	500f. High jump (air)	3·25	1·00

92 "Charaxes defulvata"

1979. Fauna. Multicoloured.

336	30f. Type **92**	50	15
337	50f. Courol	1·25	60
338	75f. Blue-cheeked bee eater	1·75	90

1979. Optd or surch **REPUBLIQUE FEDERALE ISLAMIQUE DES COMORES.** (a) Birds, Nos. 271/275.

339	15f. Type **82**	40	40
340	30f. on 35f. Madagascar malachite kingfisher	70	70
341	50f. on 20f. Blue-cheeked bee eater	1·10	1·10
342	50f. on 40f. Madagascar paradise flycatcher	1·25	1·25
343	200f. on 75f. Anjouan sunbird	3·25	3·25

(b) World Cup, Nos. 278/282.

344	1f. on 100f. Italian game (postage)	10	10
345	2f. on 75f. London game	10	10
346	3f. on 30f. Type **83**	10	10
347	50f. Breton football	35	35
348	200f. English game (air)	1·40	1·40

1979. Nos. 293/7 surch or optd **Republique Federale Islamique des Comores.**

349	— 5f. on 100f. Verdi (post)	10	10
350	**85** 30f. J. S. Bach	25	25
351	— 40f. Mozart	25	25
352	— 50f. Berlioz	40	40
353	— 50f. on 200f. Tchaikovsky (air)	65	65

94 State Coach

1979. 25th Anniv of Coronation of Queen Elizabeth II. Multicoloured.

354	5f. on 25f. Type **94** (postage)	10	10
355	10f. Drum Major	15	15
356	50f. on 40f. Queen carrying orb and sceptre	40	40
357	100f. St. Edward's Crown	80	80
358	50f. on 200f. Herald reading Proclamation (air)	65	65

Nos. 354/8 were only valid for postage overprinted as in Type **94.**

95 "Papilio dardanus-cenea stoll"

1979. Butterflies. Multicoloured.

359	5f. on 20f. Type **95**	10	10
360	15f. "Papilio dardanus-brown"	15	15
361	30f. "Chrysiridia croesus"	40	30
362	50f. "Precis octavia"	80	70
363	75f. "Bunaea alcinoe"	1·25	1·00

Nos. 359/63 were only valid for postage overprinted as in Type **95.**

96 Otto Lilienthal and Glider

1979. History of Aviation. Multicoloured.

364	30f. Type **96** (postage)	30	30
365	50f. Wright Brothers	50	50
366	50f. on 75f. Louis Bleriot	50	50
367	100f. Claude Dornier	1·00	1·00
368	200f. Charles Lindbergh (air)	1·25	1·25

Nos. 364/8 were only valid for postage overprinted as in Type **96.**

97 Tobogganing   98 Lychees

1979. International Year of the Child (1st issue). Multicoloured.

369	20f. Astronauts (postage)	10	10
370	30f. Type **97**	15	10
371	40f. Painting	20	10
372	100f. Locomotive "Rocket", 1829, and toy train	4·00	60
373	200f. Football (air)	1·40	35
374	400f. Canoeing	2·50	80

See also Nos. 389/90.

1979. Fruit. Multicoloured.

375	60f. Type **98**	40	15
376	70f. Papaws	45	20
377	100f. Avocado pears	80	30
378	125f. Bananas	1·00	35

101 Rotary Emblem and Village Scene

1979. Air. Rotary International.

388	**101** 400f. multicoloured	4·50	2·50

102 Mother and Child on Boat   103 Basketball

1979. Air. International Year of the Child (2nd issue). Multicoloured.

389	200f.+30f. Type **102**	2·50	2·25
390	250f. Mother and baby	2·50	1·60

1979. Indian Ocean Olympic Games.

391	**103** 200f. multicoloured	1·50	90

1979. Various stamps optd **REPUBLIQUE FEDERALE ISLAMIQUE DES COMORES.**
(a) Air. Apollo–Soyuz Space Test Project (Appendix).

392	100f. Presidents Brezhnev and Ford with astronauts	80	80
393	200f. Space link-up	1·40	1·40

(b) Bicentenary of American Revolution (Appendix).

394	25f. Fremont, Kit Carson and dancing Indian	15	15
395	35f. D. Boone, Buffalo Bill and wagon train	20	20
396	75f. H. Wells, W. Fargo and stagecoach ambush	40	40

(c) Winter Olympic Games, Innsbruck (Appendix).

397	35f. Speed skating	20	20

(d) Telephone Centenary (Appendix).

398	75f. Philip Reis	40	40

(e) Air. Olympic Games, Munich and Montreal.

399	100f. multicoloured (No. 179)	80	80

(f) U.N. Postal Services.

400	75f. mult (No. 187)	40	40

(g) Endangered Animals.

401	35f. mult (No. 209)	30	20
402	40f. mult (No. 210)	40	25

(h) Nobel Prize Winners.

403	100f. mult (No. 231)	80	80

(i) Rubens.

404	25f. mult (No. 236)	15	15

(j) Durer.

405	25f. mult (No. 287)	15	15
406	75f. mult (No. 289)	40	40

105 "Profile Head of Old Man"

1979. 400th Birth Anniv of Peter Paul Rubens (artist) (2nd issue). Multicoloured.

407	25f. Type **105**	15	15
408	35f. "Young Girl with Flag"	20	20
409	50f. "Isabelle d'Este, Margave of Mantua"	35	35
410	75f. "Philip IV, King of Spain"	40	40

106 "Portrait of Young Girl"

1979. 450th Death Anniv of Albrecht Durer (artist) (2nd issue). Multicoloured.

411	20f. "Self-portrait" (postage)	15	15
412	30f. "Young Man"	20	20
413	40f. Type **106**	25	25
414	100f. "Jerome" (air)	80	80
415	200f. "Jacob Muffel"	1·40	1·40

107 Satellite and Receiving Station

1979. 10th World Telecommunications Day. Multicoloured.

416	75f. Satellites	40	40
417	100f. Two satellites	45	45
418	200f. Type **107**	1·40	90

108 Pirogue

1980. Handicrafts. Multicoloured.
419	60f. Type **108**	65	20
420	100f. Anjouan puppet	80	25

109 Sultan Said Ali

1980. Sultans. Multicoloured.
421	40f. Type **109**	20	15
422	60f. Sultan Ahmed	30	15

110 Dimadjou Dispensary

1980. Air. 75th Anniv of Rotary International and 15th Anniv of Moroni Rotary Club (100f.).
423	100f. Type **110**	80	35
424	260f. Concorde airplane . . .	2·25	1·10

111 Sherlock Holmes and Sir Arthur Conan Doyle

1980. 50th Death Anniv of Sir Arthur Conan Doyle (writer).
425	**111** 200f. multicoloured . . .	1·50	95

112 Grand Mosque and Holy Ka'aba, Mecca

1980. 1350th Anniv of Occupation of Mecca by Mohammed.
426	**112** 75f. multicoloured	60	25

113 Dome of the Rock

1980. Year of the Holy City, Jerusalem.
427	**113** 60f. multicoloured	55	20

114 Kepler, Copernicus

1980. 50th Anniv of Discovery of Pluto.
428	**114** 400f. violet, red & mauve	3·25	2·00

115 Avicenna

1980. Birth Millenary of Avicenna (physician and philosopher).
429	**115** 60f. multicoloured	65	25

116 Mermoz, Dabry, Gimie and Seaplane "Comte da la Vaulx"

1980. 50th Anniv of First South Atlantic Flight.
430	**116** 200f. multicoloured . . .	2·25	1·40

1981. Various stamps surch.
431	15f. on 200f. multicoloured (No. 425) (postage)	10	10
432	20f. on 75f. mult (No. 426)	15	15
433	40f. on 125f. mult (No. 378)	25	25
434	60f. on 75f. mult (No. 338)	1·50	75
435	30f. on 200f. multicoloured (No. 430) (air)	30	30

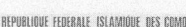

118 Team posing with Shield

1981. World Cup Football Championship, Spain (1982). Multicoloured.
436	60f. Footballers coming on Field (vert)	30	15
437	75f. Type **118**	35	20
438	90f. Captains shaking hands	40	20
439	100f. Tackle	45	25
440	150f. Players hugging after goal (vert)	1·10	30

119 "Bowls and Pot"

1981. Birth Centenary of Pablo Picasso. Mult.
442	40f. "Dove and Rainbow" . .	20	10
443	70f. "Still-life on Chest of Drawers"	55	15
444	150f. "Studio with Plaster Head"	1·10	35
445	250f. Type **119**	1·90	55
446	500f. "Red Tablecloth" . .	4·00	1·40

120 "Apollo" Launch

1981. Conquest of Space. Multicoloured.
447	50f. Type **120**	25	15
448	75f. Space Shuttle launch . .	35	20
449	100f. Space Shuttle releasing fuel tank	45	30
450	450f. Space Shuttle in orbit	3·00	1·10

121 Buckingham Palace

1981. British Royal Wedding. Multicoloured.
452	125f. Type **121**	90	25
453	200f. Highgrove House . . .	1·40	45
454	450f. Caernarvon Castle . . .	2·75	1·00

1981. Design as Type O **99** but inscr "POSTES 1981".
456	5f. green, black & brn . . .	10	10
457	15f. green, black & yell . . .	10	10
458	25f. green, black & red . . .	15	10
459	35f. green, black & lt grn . .	20	10
460	75f. green, black & blue . . .	35	20

1981. Various stamps surch.
461	114 5f. on 400f. violet, red and mauve (postage) . .	10	10
462	– 20f. on 90f. mult (No. 438)	10	10
463	– 45f. on 100f. mult (No. 377)	20	10
464	– 45f. on 100f. mult (No. 420)	20	10
465	– 10f. on 70f. mult (No. 443) (air)	10	10
466	110 10f. on 100f. mult	10	10
467	102 50f. on 200f.+30f. mult	25	15
468	– 50f. on 260f. mult (No. 424)	60	30

123 Mercedes, 1914

1981. 75th Anniv of French Grand Prix Motor Race. Multicoloured.
469	20f. Type **123**	10	10
470	50f. Delage, 1925	50	15
471	75f. Rudi Caracciola	65	20
472	90f. Stirling Moss	80	20
473	150f. Maserati, 1957	1·25	30

124 Scouts preparing to Sail

1981. 75th Anniv of Boy Scout Movement. Multicoloured.
475	50f. Type **124**	25	15
476	75f. Paddling pirogue	75	20
477	90f. Sailing felucca	1·75	80
478	350f. Scouts looking out to sea from boat	2·50	85

125 Goethe

1982. 150th Death Anniv of Goethe (poet).
480	**125** 75f. multicoloured	35	20
481	350f. multicoloured . . .	2·40	85

126 Princess of Wales

1982. 21st Birthday of Princess of Wales.
482	**126** 200f. multicoloured	1·40	45
483	– 300f. multicoloured . . .	2·00	70
DESIGN: 300f. Different portrait of Princess.

1982. Birth of Prince William of Wales. Nos. 452/4 optd **NAISSANCE ROYALE 1982**.
485	125f. Type **121**	90	25
486	200f. Highgrove House . . .	1·40	45
487	450f. Caernarvon Castle . . .	2·75	1·60

1982. World Cup Football Championship Winners. Nos. 436/40 optd.
489	60f. Type **117**	30	15
490	75f. Team posing with shield (horiz)	35	20
491	90f. Captains shaking hands (horiz)	40	20
492	100f. Tackle (horiz)	45	25
493	150f. Players hugging after goal	1·10	55
OVERPRINTS: 60f., 150f. **ITALIE - ALLEMAGNE (R.F.A.)** 3 - 1.; 75f., 90f., 100f. **ITALIE 3 ALLEMAGNE (R.F.A.)** 1.

129 Boy playing Trumpet

1982. Norman Rockwell Paintings. Multicoloured.
495	60f. Type **129**	30	15
496	75f. Sleeping porter	2·75	75
497	100f. Couple listening to early radio	80	25
498	150f. Children playing leapfrog	1·10	30
499	200f. Tramp cooking sausages	1·50	45
500	300f. Boy talking to clown . .	2·25	70

130 Sultan Said Mohamed Sidi

1982. Sultans. Multicoloured.
501	30f. Type **130**	15	10
502	60f. Sultan Ahmed Abdallah	30	15
503	75f. Sultan Salim (horiz) . .	35	20
504	300f. Sultans Said Mohamed Sidi and Ahmed Abdallah (horiz)	2·10	95

131 Montgolfier Brothers' Balloon, 1783

1983. Air. Bicentenary of Manned Flight. Mult.
505	100f. Type **131**	80	35
506	200f. Vincenzo Lunardi's balloon over London, 1784	1·40	65
507	300f. Blanchard and Jeffries crossing the Channel, 1785	2·25	1·00
508	400f. Henri Giffard's steam-powered dirigible airship, 1852 (horiz)	3·00	1·25

132 Type "470" Dinghy

1983. Air. Pre-Olympic Year. Multicoloured.
510	150f. Type **132**	1·40	65
511	200f. "Flying Dutchman" . .	1·60	80
512	300f. Type "470" (different)	2·40	1·25
513	400f. "Finn" class dinghies	3·50	1·75

133 Lake Ziani

1983. Landscapes. Multicoloured.
515	60f. Type **133**	50	20
516	100f. Sunset	65	35
517	175f. Chiromani (vert) . .	1·10	60
518	360f. Itsandra beach . . .	2·25	1·00
519	400f. Anjouan	2·75	1·25

134 Moheli

1983. Portraits. Multicoloured.
520	30f. Type **134**	15	10
521	35f. "Mask of Beauty" . .	45	15
522	50f. Mayotte	45	15

135 Pure-bred Arab

1983. Horses. Multicoloured.
523	75f. Type **135**	55	25
524	100f. Anglo-Arab	65	35
525	125f. Lipizzan	90	40
526	150f. Tennessee	1·10	50
527	200f. Appaloosa	1·40	65
528	300f. Pure-bred English . .	2·25	1·00
529	400f. Clydesdale	2·75	1·00
530	500f. Andalusian	3·50	1·25

136 "Double Portrait"　　**137** Symbols of Development

1983. 500th Birth Anniv of Raphael. Mult.
531	100f. Type **136**	65	35
532	200f. Fresco detail	1·40	65
533	300f. "St. George and the Dragon"	2·00	75
534	400f. "Balthazar Castiglione"	2·75	1·00

1984. Air. International Conference on Development of Comoros.
535	**137** 475f. multicoloured . . .	3·25	1·75

138 Basketball

1984. Air. Olympic Games, Los Angeles. Mult.
536	60f. Type **138**	25	20
537	100f. Basketball (different) .	70	35
538	165f. Basketball (different) . .	1·00	55
539	175f. Baseball (horiz) . . .	1·10	55
540	200f. Baseball (different) (horiz)	1·40	55

139 "William Fawcett"

1984. Transport. Multicoloured. (a) Ships.
542	100f. Type **139**	80	70
543	150f. "Lightning"	1·50	80
544	200f. "Rapido"	1·75	90
545	350f. "Sindia"	3·25	2·40

(b) Automobiles.
546	100f. De Dion Bouton and Trepardoux, 1885 . . .	1·10	35
547	150f. Benz "Victoria", 1893	1·50	45
548	200f. Colombia electric, 1901	2·00	55
549	350f. Fiat, 1902	3·00	80

140 Barn Swallows

1985. Air. Birth Bicentenary of John J. Audubon (ornithologist). Multicoloured.
550	100f. Type **140**	1·50	90
551	125f. Northern oriole . . .	1·60	1·10
552	150f. Red-shouldered hawk (horiz)	1·90	1·25
553	500f. Red-breasted sapsucker (horiz)	6·25	4·50

142 Harbours

1985. Air. "Philexafrique" Stamp Exhibition, Lome, Togo (1st issue). Multicoloured.
555	200f. Type **142**	2·00	1·00
556	200f. Scouts walking along road	1·50	85

See also Nos. 576/7.

143 Victor Hugo (novelist, death centenary)

1985. Anniversaries. Multicoloured.
557	100f. Type **143**	1·00	30
558	200f. Jules Verne (novelist) (80th death anniv) . . .	1·40	60
559	300f. Mark Twain (150th birth anniv)	2·25	1·00
560	450f. Queen Elizabeth, the Queen Mother (85th birth anniv) (vert)	2·75	1·00
561	500f. Statue of Liberty (centenary) (vert) . .	3·25	1·25

The 200f. and 300f. also commemorate International Youth Year.

144 Map and Flag on Sun

1985. Air. 10th Anniv of Independence.
562	**144** 10f. multicoloured . . .	10	10
563	15f. multicoloured . . .	10	10
564	125f. multicoloured . . .	1·10	40
565	300f. multicoloured . . .	2·50	1·10

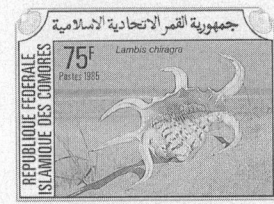

145 Arthritic Spider Conch

1985. Shells. Multicoloured.
566	75f. Type **145**	70	35
567	125f. Silver conch	1·00	45
568	200f. Costate tun	1·60	60
569	300f. Elephant's snout . . .	2·50	75
570	450f. Orange spider conch . .	3·75	1·00

146 U.N. Emblem and Map of Islands

1985. 10th Anniv of Membership of U.N.O.
571	**146** 5f. multicoloured . . .	10	10
572	30f. multicoloured . . .	15	10
573	75f. multicoloured . . .	35	30
574	125f. multicoloured . . .	90	40
575	400f. multicoloured . . .	2·50	1·50

147 Runners ("Youth")

1985. Air. "Philexafrique" Stamp Exhibition, Lome, Togo (2nd issue). Multicoloured.
576	250f. Type **147**	1·60	90
577	250f. Earth mover and road construction ("Development")	1·60	90

148 Globe, Galleon, Wright Type A Biplane and Rocket Capsule

1985. 20th Anniv of Moroni Rotary Club.
578	**148** 25f. multicoloured	25	15
579	75f. multicoloured	75	30
580	125f. multicoloured . . .	1·40	45
581	500f. multicoloured . . .	4·25	1·40

149 "Astraeus hygrometricus"

1985. Fungi. Multicoloured.
582	75f. "Boletus edulis" . . .	80	45
583	125f. "Sarcoscypha coccinea"	1·00	60
584	200f. "Hypholoma fasciculare"	1·60	90
585	350f. Type **149**	3·00	90
586	500f. "Armillariella mellea" .	4·00	1·40

150 Sikorsky S-43 Amphibian

1985. Air. 50th Anniv of Union des Transports Aeriennes. Multicoloured.
587	25f. Type **150**	10	10
588	75f. Douglas DC-9 airplane and camel	45	30
589	100f. Douglas DC-4, DC-6, Nord 2501 Noratlas and De Havilland Heron 2 aircraft	55	35
590	125f. Maintenance	90	40
591	1000f. Emblem and Latecoere 28, Sikorsky S-43, Douglas DC-10 and Boeing 747-200 aircraft (35 × 47 mm) . . .	7·75	4·25

151 Edmond Halley, Comet and "Giotto" Space Probe

1986. Air. Appearance of Halley's Comet. Multicoloured.
593	125f. Type **151**	90	40
594	150f. Giacobini-Zinner comet, 1959	1·10	55
595	225f. J. F. Encke and Encke comet, 1961	1·60	75
596	300f. Computer enhanced picture of Bradfield comet, 1980	2·10	1·10
597	450f. Halley's comet and "Planet A" space probe . .	3·00	1·50

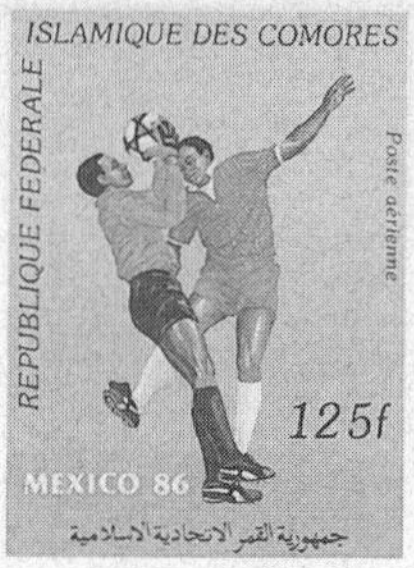

152 Footballers

1986. Air. World Cup Football Championship, Mexico. Designs showing footballers.

598 152	125f. multicoloured	90	40
599 –	210f. multicoloured	1·40	70
600 –	500f. multicoloured	3·25	1·50
601 –	600f. multicoloured	4·00	1·75

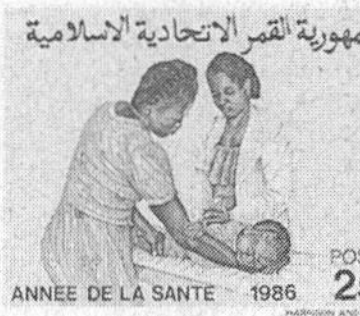

153 Doctor examining Child

1986. World Health Year. Multicoloured.

602	25f. Type **153**	10	10
603	100f. Doctor weighing child	70	35
604	200f. Nurse innoculating baby	1·40	70

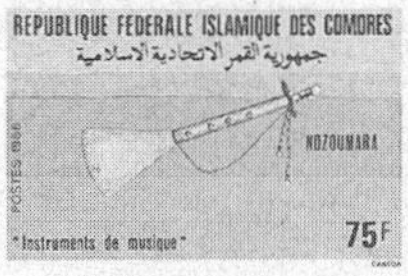

154 Ndzoumara (wind instrument)

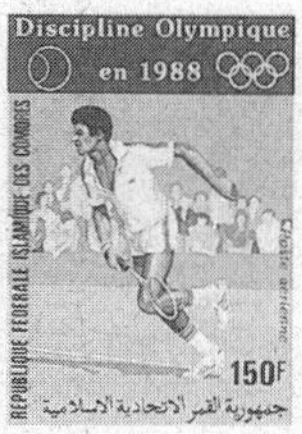

155 Server

1986. Musical Instruments. Multicoloured.

605	75f. Type **154**	55	25
606	125f. Ndzedze (string instrument)	80	40
607	210f. Gaboussi (string instrument)	1·40	70
608	500f. Ngoma (drums)	3·25	1·50

1987. Air. Tennis as 1988 Olympic Games Discipline. Multicoloured.

609	150f. Type **155**	1·10	50
610	250f. Player preparing shot	2·00	75
611	500f. Player being lobbed	3·50	1·25
612	600f. Players each side of net	4·00	1·50

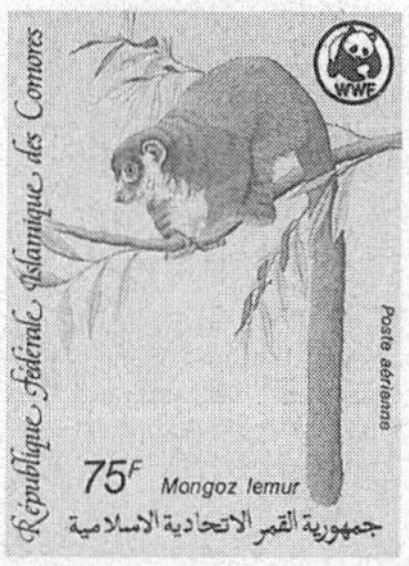

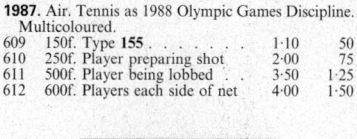

156 On Tree Branch

1987. Air. Endangered Animals. Mongoose-Lemur. Multicoloured.

613	75f. Type **156**	65	25
614	100f. Head of mongoose-lemur with ruff	90	30
615	125f. Mongoose-lemur on rock	1·40	40
616	150f. Head of mongoose-lemur without ruff	1·50	50

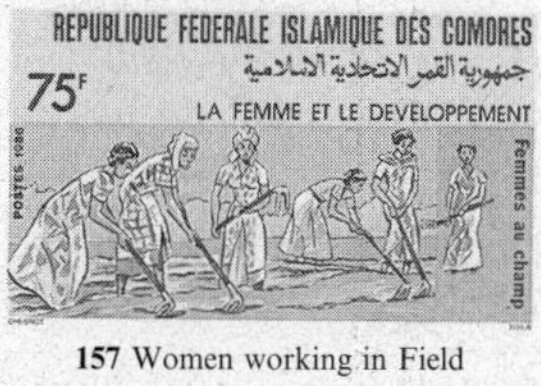

157 Women working in Field

1987. Woman and Development. Multicoloured.

617	75f. Type **157**	55	25
618	125f. Woman picking musk seeds (vert)	1·10	40
619	1000f. Woman making basket	6·75	2·25

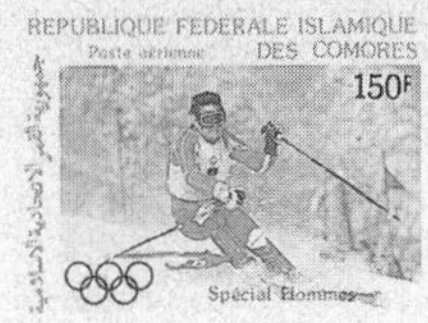

158 Men's Downhill

1987. Air. Winter Olympic Games, Calgary (1988). Multicoloured.

620	150f. Type **158**	90	50
621	225f. Ski jumping	1·40	80
622	500f. Women's slalom	3·25	1·50
623	600f. Men's luge	4·00	1·75

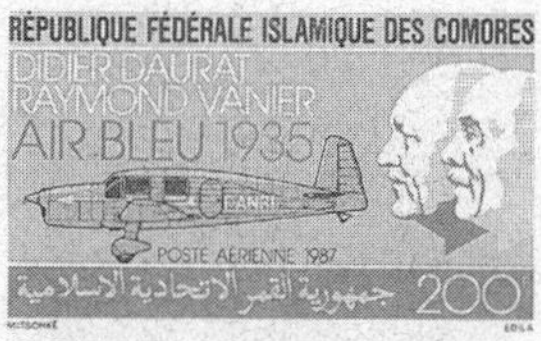

159 Didier Daurat, Raymond Vanier and "Air Bleu"

1987. Air. Aviation. Multicoloured.

624	200f. Type **159**	1·40	45
625	300f. Letord 4 Lorraine and route map (1st regular airmail service, Paris–Le Mans–St. Nazaire, 1918)	2·00	70
626	500f. Morane Saulnier Type H and route map (1st airmail flight, Villacoublay–Pauillac, 1913)	3·25	1·25
627	1000f. Henri Pequet flying Humber-Sommer biplane (1st aerophilately exn, Allahabad) (36 × 49 mm)	6·75	1·75

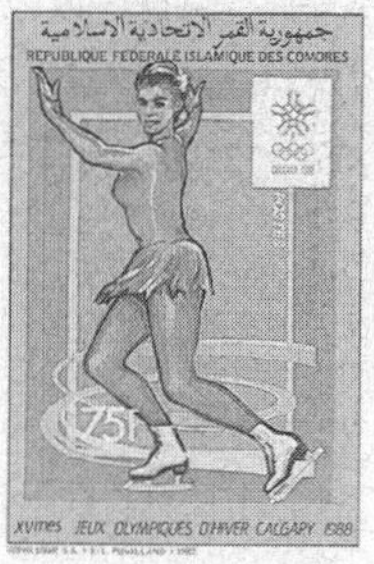

160 Ice Skating

1988. Multicoloured. (a) Winter Olympic Games, Calgary.

628	75f. Type **160** (postage)	30	25
629	125f. Speed skating	50	40
630	350f. Two-man bobsleigh	2·25	75
631	400f. Biathlon (air)	2·75	1·00
	(b) Olympic Games, Seoul.		
633	100f. Relay (postage)	65	30
634	150f. Showjumping	1·00	50
635	500f. Pole-vaulting	3·25	1·25
636	600f. Football (air)	4·00	1·25

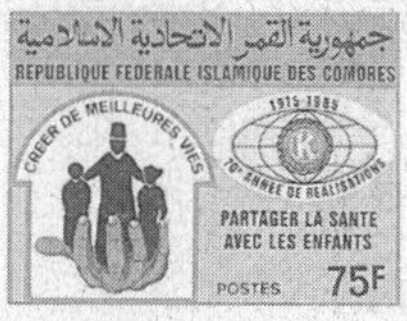

161 Kiwanis International Emblem and Hand supporting Figures

1988. Child Health Campaigns. Multicoloured.

638	75f. Type **161**	30	25
639	125f. Kiwanis emblem, wheelchair and crutch	80	40
640	210f. Kiwanis emblem and man with children (country inscr in black)	1·25	70
641	210f. As No. 640 but country inscr in white	1·25	70
642	425f. As No. 639	2·50	1·40
643	425f. As No. 639 but with Lions International emblem	2·50	1·40
644	500f. Type **161**	3·25	1·50
645	500f. As Type **161** but with Rotary emblem	3·25	1·50

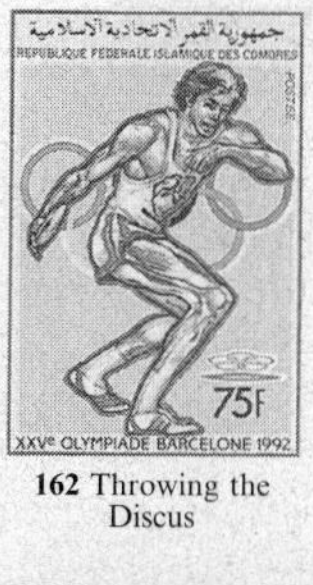

162 Throwing the Discus

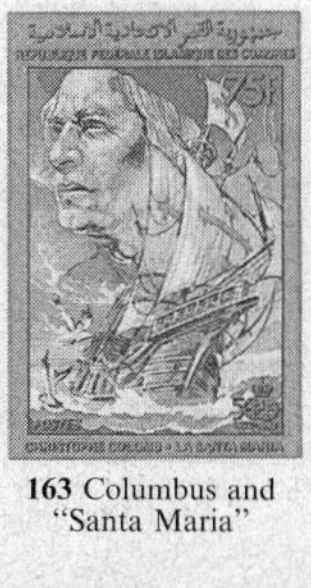

163 Columbus and "Santa Maria"

1988. Olympic Games, Barcelona (1992) (1st issue). Multicoloured.

646	75f. Type **162** (postage)	30	25
647	100f. Rowing (horiz)	65	30
648	125f. Cycling (horiz)	90	40
649	150f. Wrestling (horiz)	1·00	50
650	375f. Basketball (air)	2·75	90
651	600f. Tennis	4·00	1·10

See also Nos. 709/14.

1988. 500th Anniv (1992) of Discovery of America by Columbus. Multicoloured.

653	75f. Type **163** (postage)	75	30
654	125f. Martin Alonzo Pinzon and "Pinta"	1·00	50
655	150f. Vicente Yanez Pinzon and "Nina"	1·25	60
656	250f. Search for gold	1·60	85
657	375f. Wreck of "Santa Maria" (air)	2·50	1·00
658	450f. Preparation for fourth voyage	3·50	1·25

1988. Nos. 641, 643 and 645 (125 and 400f. with colours changed) surch.

660	75f. on 210f. multicoloured	55	25
661	125f. on 425f. multicoloured	80	40
662	200f. on 425f. multicoloured	1·40	65
663	300f. on 500f. multicoloured	1·90	1·00
664	400f. on 500f. multicoloured	2·75	1·25

1988. Olympic Games Medal Winners for Tennis. Nos. 609/12 optd.

665	150f. Optd **Medalle d'or Seoul Miloslav Mecir (Tchec.)**	1·00	50
666	250f. Optd **Medalle d'argent Seoul Tim Mayotte (U.S.A)**	1·60	1·10
667	500f. Optd **Medalle d'or Seoul Steffi Graf (R.F.A.)**	3·25	2·50
668	600f. Optd **Medalle d'argent Seoul Gabriela Sabatini (Argentine)**	4·00	2·75

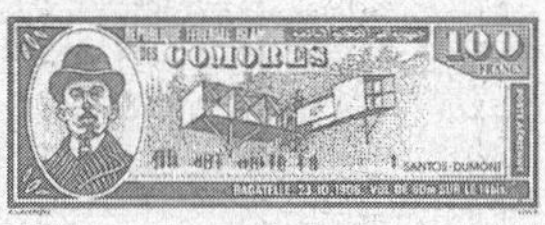

166 Alberto Santos-Dumont and "14 bis"

1988. Air. Aviation Pioneers.

669 166	100f. purple	80	30
670 –	150f. mauve	1·10	50
671 –	200f. black	1·40	65
672 –	300f. brown	2·00	1·00
673 –	500f. blue	3·25	1·75
674 –	800f. green	5·25	2·25

DESIGNS: 150f. Wright Type A and Orville and Wilbur Wright; 200f. Louis Bleriot and Bleriot XI; 300f. Farman Voisin No. 1 bis and Henri Farman; 500f. Gabriel and Charles Voisin and Voisin "Boxkite"; 800f. Roland Garros and Morane Saulnier Type I.

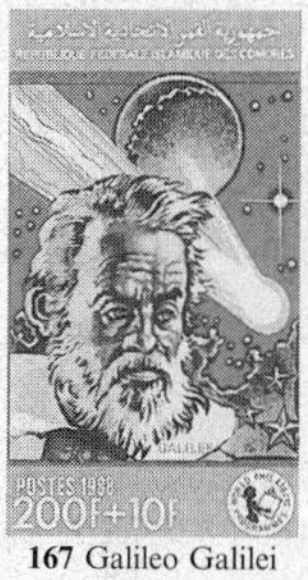

167 Galileo Galilei

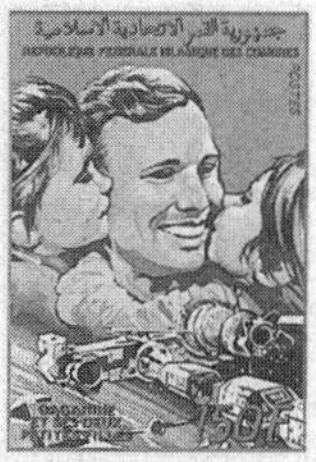
168 Yuri Gagarin (cosmonaut) and Daughters

1988. Appearance of Halley's Comet. Mult.

675	200f.+10f. Type **167**	1·40	40
676	200f.+10f. Nicolas Copernicus	1·40	40
677	200f.+10f. Johannes Kepler	1·40	40
678	200f.+10f. Edmond Halley	1·40	40
679	200f.+10f. Japanese "Planet A" space probe	1·40	40
680	200f.+10f. American "Ice" space probe	1·40	40
681	200f.+10f. "Planet A" space probe (different)	1·40	40
682	200f.+10f. Russian "Vega" space probe	1·40	40

1988. Personalities. Multicoloured.

684	150f. Type **168** (20th death anniv) (postage)	1·00	50
685	300f. Henri Dunant (founder of Red Cross) (125th anniv of Red Cross Movement)	2·00	75
686	400f. Roger Clemens (baseball player)	2·50	1·25
687	500f. Gary Kasparov (chess player) (air)	4·00	1·75
688	600f. Paul Harris (founder of Rotary International) (birth centenary)	4·00	1·25

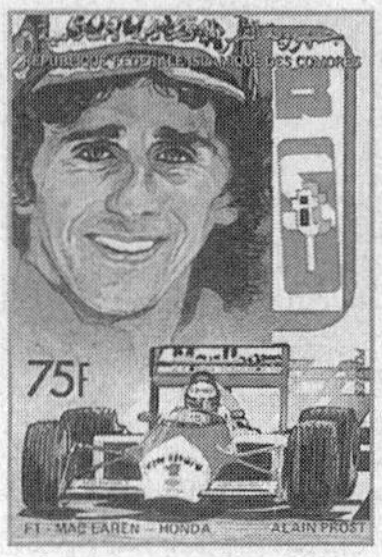

169 Alain Prost (racing driver) and Formula 1 Racing Car

1988. Cars, Trains and Yachts. Multicoloured.

690	75f. Type **169** (postage)	1·10	25
691	125f. George Stephenson (railway engineer), "Rocket" and Borsig Class 05 steam locomotive, 1935, Germany	1·25	40
692	500f. Ettore Bugatti (motor manufacturer) and Aravis "Type 57"	3·25	1·00
693	600f. Rudolph Diesel (engineer) and German Class V200 diesel locomotive	4·00	1·50
694	750f. Dennis Conner and "Stars and Stripes" (America's Cup contender) (air)	5·00	1·50
695	1000f. Michael Fay and "New Zealand" (America's Cup contender)	6·75	1·75

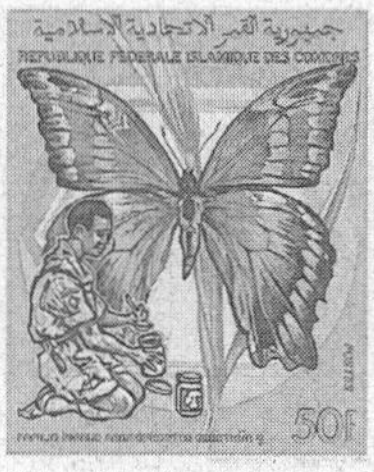

170 "Papilio nireus aristophontes" (female)

1989. Scouts, Butterflies and Birds. Multicoloured.

697	50f. Type **170** (postage)	20	10
698	75f. "Papilio nireus aristophontes" (male)	55	15
699	150f. "Charaxes fulvescens separanus"	1·10	40
700	375f. Bronze mannikin	2·75	75
701	450f. "Charaxes castor comoranus" (air)	3·00	80
702	500f. Madagascar white-eye	3·75	1·00

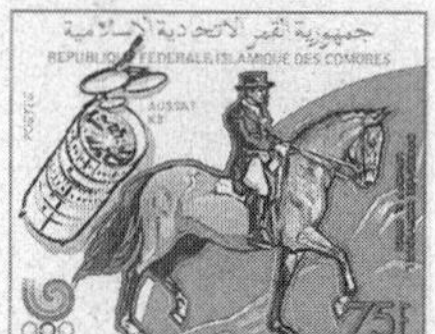

171 Aussat "K3" and N. Uphoff (individual dressage)

1989. Satellites and Olympic Games Medal Winners for Equestrian Events. Multicoloured.

704	75f. Type **171** (postage)	30	15
705	150f. "Brasil sat" and P. Durand (individual show jumping)	1·00	40
706	375f. "ECS 4" and J. Martinek (modern pentathlon)	2·50	60
707	600f. "Olympus 1" and M. Todd (cross-country) (air)	4·00	1·25

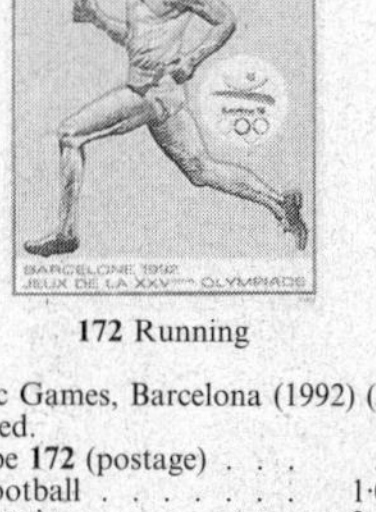

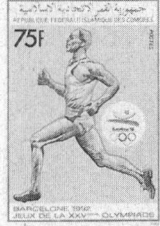

172 Running

1989. Olympic Games, Barcelona (1992) (2nd issue). Multicoloured.

709	75f. Type **172** (postage)	55	15
710	150f. Football	1·00	40
711	300f. Tennis	2·00	50
712	375f. Baseball	2·50	65
713	500f. Gymnastics (air)	3·25	85
714	600f. Table tennis	4·00	1·10

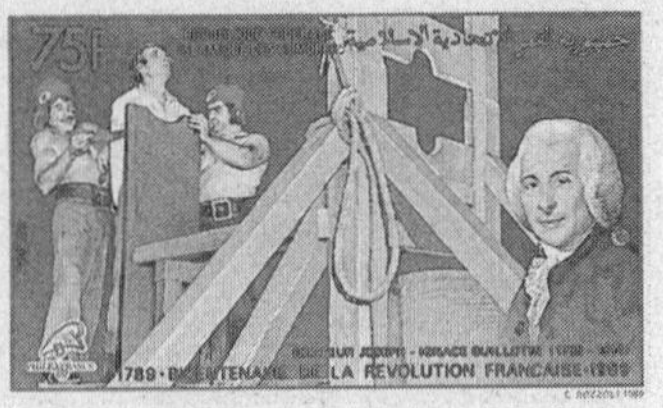

173 Dr. Joseph-Ignace Guillotin and Guillotine

1989. Bicentenary of French Revolution. Mult.

716	75f. Type **173** (postage)	55	15
717	150f. Soldiers with cannon (Battle of Valmy) and Gen. Kellermann	1·00	40
718	375f. Jean Cottereau (Chouan) and Vendeens	2·25	60
719	600f. Invasion of Les Tuileries (air)	4·00	1·00

1989. Various stamps surch.

721	25f. on 250f. mult (No. 656) (postage)	35	10
722	150f. on 200f. mult (No. 532)	1·00	40
723	150f. on 200f. mult (No. 558)	1·00	40
724	150f. on 200f. mult (No. 604)	1·00	40
725	5f. on 250f. multicoloured (No. 390) (air)	10	10
726	25f. on 250f. mult (No. 610)	10	10
727	50f. on 250f. mult (No. 576)	20	10
728	50f. on 250f. mult (No. 577)	20	10
729	150f. on 200f. mult (No. 511)	1·00	50
730	150f. on 200f. mult (No. 555)	1·00	50
731	150f. on 200f. mult (No. 556)	1·00	40
732	150f. on 200f. black (No. 671)	1·00	60

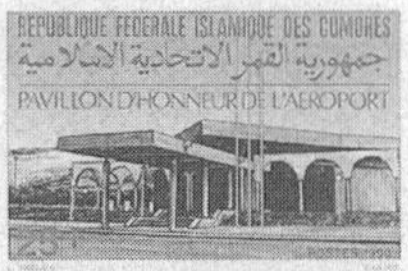

175 Airport Pavilion

1990.

733	**175**	5f. orange, brown & red	10	10
734		10f. orange, brown & bl	10	10
735		25f. orange, brown & grn	10	10
736	–	50f. black and red	20	10
737	–	75f. black and blue	35	10
738	–	150f. black and green	1·00	35

DESIGNS: 50 to 150f. Federal Assembly.

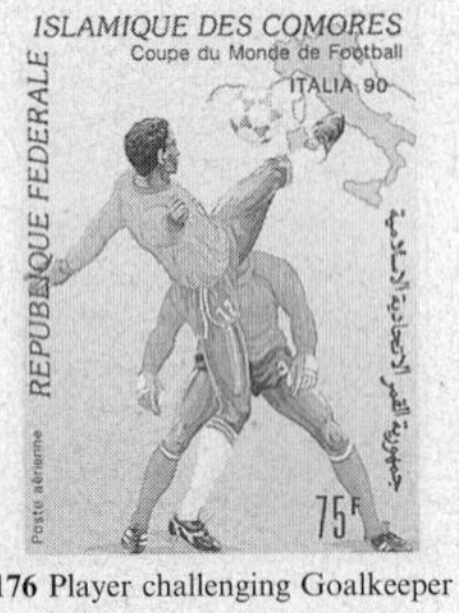

176 Player challenging Goalkeeper

1990. Air. World Cup Football Championship, Italy (1st issue). Multicoloured.

739	75f. Type **176**	65	10
740	150f. Player heading ball	1·00	35
741	500f. Overhead kick	3·25	1·25
742	1000f. Player evading tackle	6·75	1·75

See also Nos. 743/8.

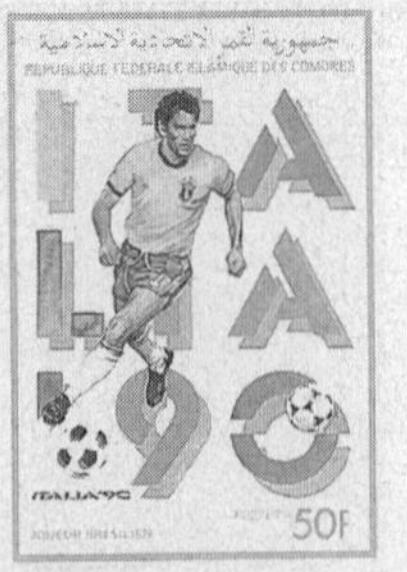

177 Brazilian Player

1990. World Cup Football Championship, Italy (2nd issue). Multicoloured.

743	50f. Type **177** (postage)	20	10
744	75f. English player	35	10
745	100f. West German player	50	25
746	150f. Belgian player	1·00	35
747	375f. Italian player (air)	2·50	85
748	600f. Argentinian player	4·00	85

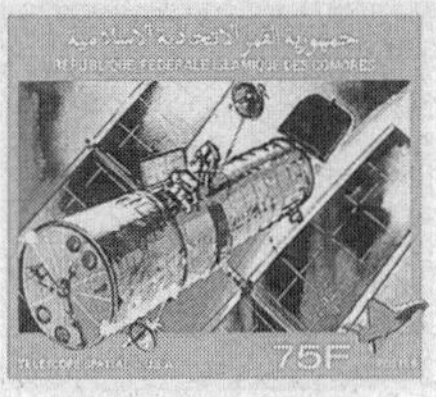

178 U.S. Space Telescope

1990. Multicoloured.

750	75f. Type **178** (postage)	60	10
751	150f. Pope John Paul II and Mikhail Gorbachev, 1989	1·00	35
752	200f. Kevin Mitchell (San Francisco Giants baseball player)	1·40	50
753	250f. De Gaulle and Adenauer, 1962	1·60	50
754	300f. "Titan 2002" space probe	2·00	70
755	375f. French TGV Atlantique express train and Concorde airplane	3·25	1·00
756	450f. Gary Kasparov (World chess champion) and Anderssen v Steinitz chess match (air)	3·25	1·00
757	500f. Paul Harris (founder of Rotary International) and symbols of health, hunger and humanity	3·25	75

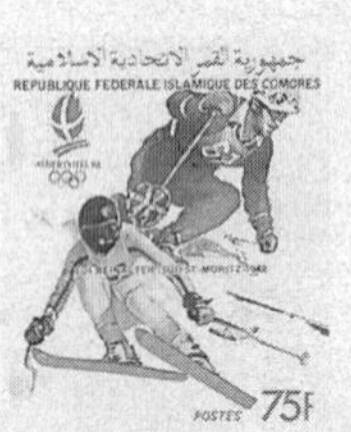

179 Edi Reinalter (skiing, 1948)

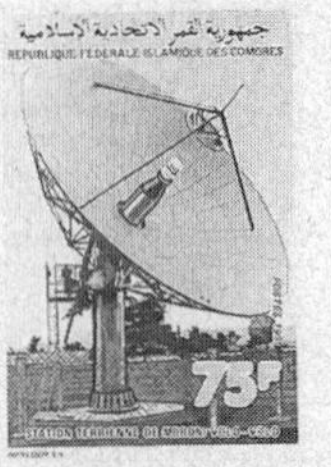

180 Dish Aerial, Moroni Volo-volo

1990. Winter Olympics, Albertville (1992). Medal Winners at previous Games. Multicoloured.

759	75f. Type **179** (postage)	35	10
760	100f. Canada (ice hockey, 1924)	50	25
761	375f. Baroness Gratia Schimmelpenninck van der Oye (skiing, 1936) (air)	2·50	85
762	600f. Hasu Haikki (ski jumping, 1948)	4·00	85

1991.

764	**180**	75f. multicoloured	60	10
765		150f. multicoloured	1·00	35
766		225f. multicoloured	1·40	55
767		300f. multicoloured	2·00	70
768		500f. multicoloured	3·25	1·25

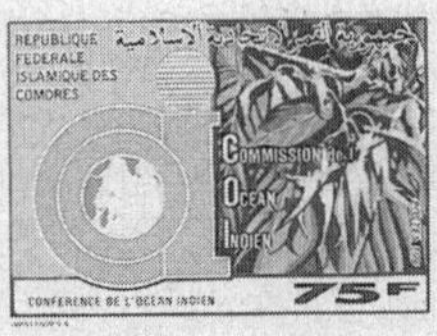

181 Emblem and Leaves

1991. Indian Ocean Commission Conference.

769	**181**	75f. multicoloured	60	10
770		150f. multicoloured	1·00	60
771		225f. multicoloured	1·40	90

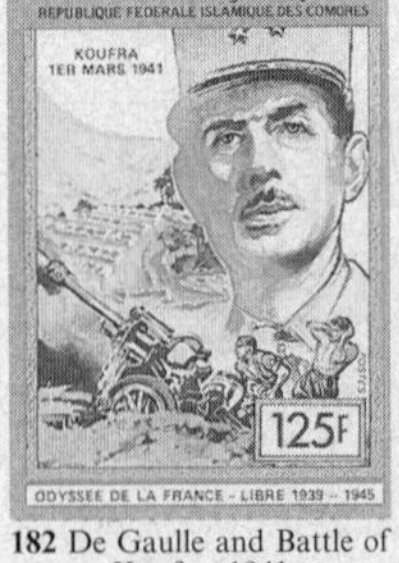

182 De Gaulle and Battle of Koufra, 1941

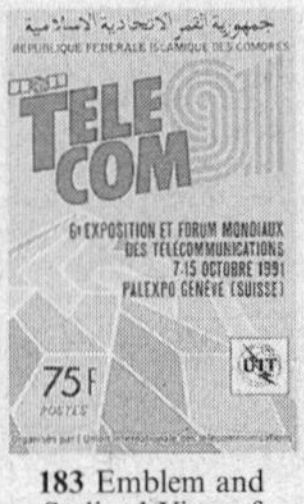

183 Emblem and Stylized View of Exhibition

1991. 50th Anniv of World War II. Multicoloured.

772	125f. Type **182** (postage)	90	30
773	150f. Errol Flynn in "Adventures in Burma"	1·00	35
774	300f. Henry Fonda in "The Longest Day"	2·00	70
775	375f. De Gaulle and Battle of Britain, 1940	2·25	70
776	450f. Humphrey Bogart in "Sahara" (air)	3·00	75
777	500f. De Gaulle and Battle of Monte Cassino, 1944	3·25	75

1991. "Telecom '91" Int Telecommunications Exhibition, Geneva. Multicoloured.

779	75f. Type **183**	60	35
780	150f. Emblem (horiz)	1·00	80

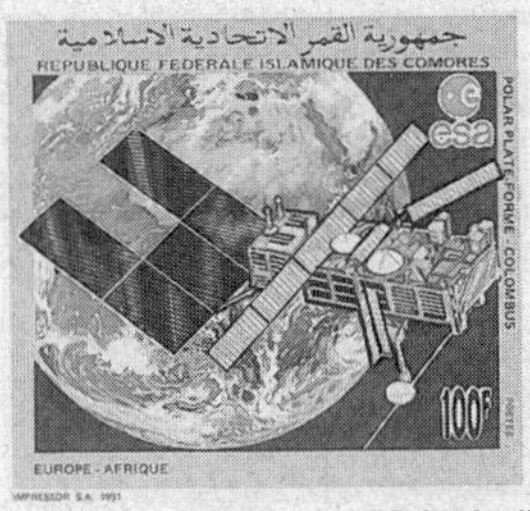

184 Weather Space Station "Columbus"

1991. Anniversaries and Events. Multicoloured.

781	100f. Type **184** (postage)	70	15
782	150f. Gandhi (43rd death anniv)	1·00	25
783	250f. Henri Dunant (founder of Red Cross) (90th anniv of award of Nobel Peace Prize)	1·60	40
784	300f. Wolfgang Amadeus Mozart (composer, death bicentenary)	2·00	55
785	375f. Brandenburg Gate (bicent and second anniv of fall of Berlin Wall)	2·50	70
786	400f. Konrad Adenauer (German Chancellor) signing new constitution (25th death anniv)	2·50	70
787	450f. Elvis Presley (entertainer, 14th death anniv) (air)	3·25	80
788	500f. Ferdinand von Zeppelin (airship pioneer, 75th death anniv)	3·25	80

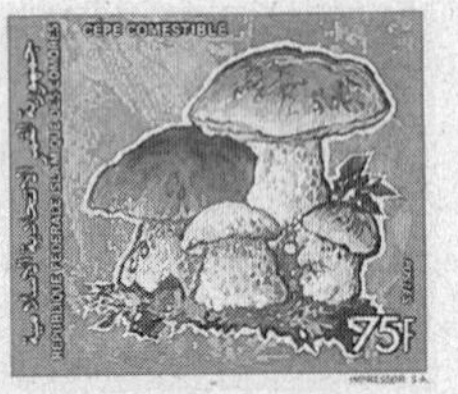

185 Cep

1992. Fungi and Shells. Multicoloured.

789	75f. Type **185** (postage)	60	15
790	125f. Textile cone	80	35
791	150f. Puff-ball	1·50	55
792	150f. Bull-mouth helmet (shell)	1·00	40
793	500f. Map cowrie (air)	3·25	1·00
794	600f. Scarlet elf cups	6·50	1·25

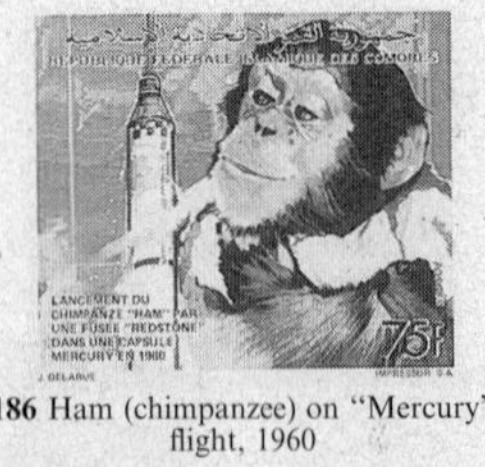

186 Ham (chimpanzee) on "Mercury" flight, 1960

1992. Space Research. Multicoloured.

796	75f. Type **186** (postage)	60	10
797	125f. "Mars Observer" space probe	90	20
798	150f. Felix (cat) and "Veronique" rocket, 1963	1·10	50
799	150f. "Mars Rover" and "Marsokod" space vehicles	1·00	50
800	500f. "Phobos" project (air)	3·25	90
801	600f. Laika (dog) and "Sputnik 2" flight, 1957	4·00	1·10

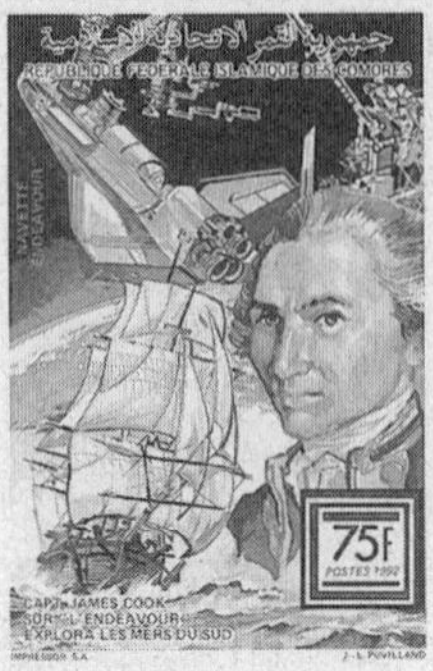

187 "Endeavour" (space shuttle), Capt. James Cook and H.M.S. "Endeavour"

1992. Space and Nautical Exploration. Mult.

803	75f. Type **187** (postage)	70	15
804	100f. "Cariane" space microphone, Sir Francis Drake and "Golden Hind"	90	20
805	150f. Infra-red astronomical observation device, John Smith and "Susan Constant"	1·40	30
806	225f. Space probe "B", Robert F. Scott and "Discovery"	1·75	45
807	375f. "Magellan" (Venus space probe), Ferdinand Magellan and ship (air)	3·25	80
808	500f. "Newton" (satellite), Vasco da Gama and "Sao Gabriel"	3·75	1·10

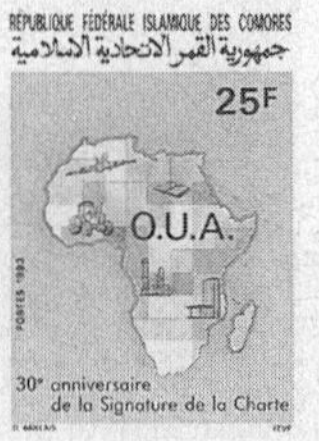

188 Map

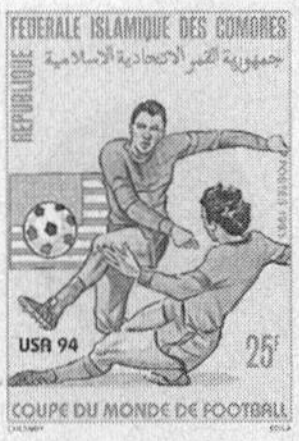

189 Footballers

1993. 30th Anniv of Organization of African Unity.

810	**188**	25f. multicoloured	10	10
811		50f. multicoloured	20	10
812		75f. multicoloured	60	35
813		150f. multicoloured	1·00	80

1993. World Cup Football Championship, U.S.A. (1994).

814	**189**	25f. multicoloured	10	10
815		75f. multicoloured	35	10
816		100f. multicoloured	70	15
817		150f. multicoloured	95	25

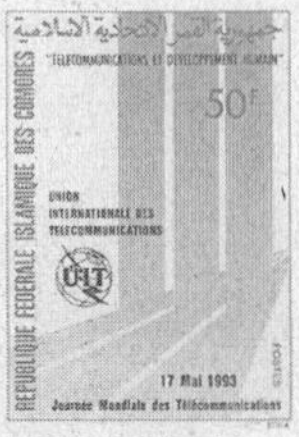

190 I.T.U. Emblem

1993. World Telecommunications Day. "Telecommunications and Human Development".

818	**190**	50f. multicoloured	20	10
819		75f. multicoloured	35	10
820		100f. multicoloured	70	15
821		150f. multicoloured	1·00	55

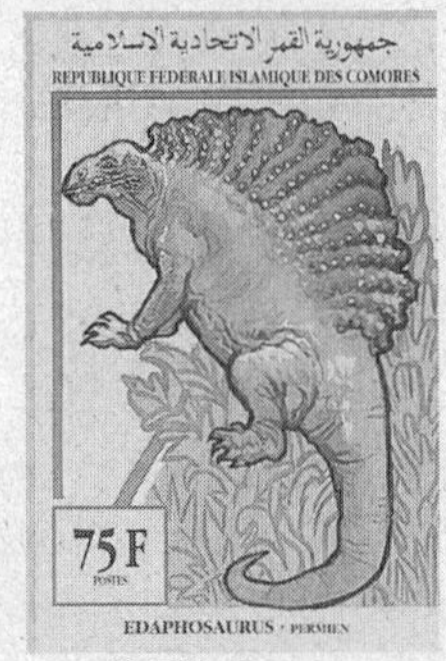

191 Edaphosaurus

1994. Prehistoric Animals. Multicoloured.

822	75f. Type **191**	25	10
823	75f. Moschops	25	10
824	75f. Kentrosaurus	25	10
825	75f. Compsognathus	25	10
826	75f. Sauroctonus	25	10
827	75f. Ornitholestes	25	10
828	75f. Styracosaurus	25	10
829	75f. Acanthopholis	25	10

830 150f. Edmontonia 50 20
831 150f. Struthiomimus 50 20
832 150f. Diatryma 50 20
833 150f. Uintatherium 50 20
834 450f. Dromiceiomimus . . . 2·10 60
835 450f. Iguanodon . . . . . . 2·10 60
836 525f. Diatryma . . . . . . 2·50 75
837 525f. Euryapteryx . . . . . 2·50 75

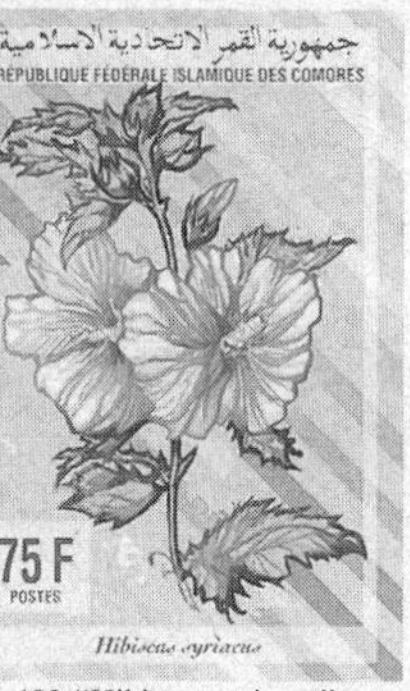

192 "Hibiscus syriacus"

1994. Plants. Multicoloured.
839 75f. Type **192** 25 10
840 75f. Cashew nut 25 10
841 75f. Butter mushroom . . . 40 15
842 150f. "Pyrostegia venusta" (flower) 50 20
843 150f. Manioc (root) 50 20
844 150f. "Lycogala epidendron" (fungus) 80 35
845 525f. "Allamanda cathartica" (flower) . . . . 2·25 75
846 525f. Cacao (nut) . . . . . 2·25 75
847 525f. "Clathrus ruber" (fungus) . . . . 3·00 1·00

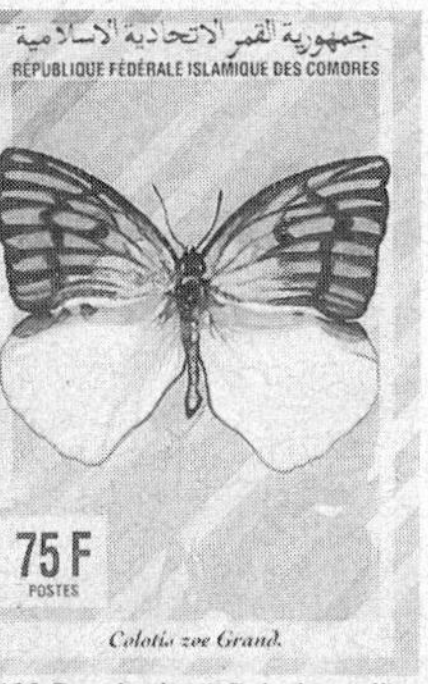

193 Purple-tip ("Colotis zoe")

1994. Insects. Multicoloured.
848 75f. Type **193** 25 10
849 75f. "Charaxes comoranus" (butterfly) 25 10
850 75f. "Hypurgus ova" (beetle) 25 10
851 150f. Death's-head hawk moth ("Acherontia atropos") 50 20
852 150f. "Verdant hawk moth ("Euchloron megaera") . . 50 20
853 150f. "Onthophagus catta" (beetle) 50 20
854 450f. African monarch ("Danaus chrysippus") (butterfly) . . . . 2·25 60
855 450f. "Papilio phorbanta" (butterfly) . . . . 2·25 60
856 450f. "Echinosoma bolivari" (beetle) . . . . 2·25 60

OFFICIAL STAMPS

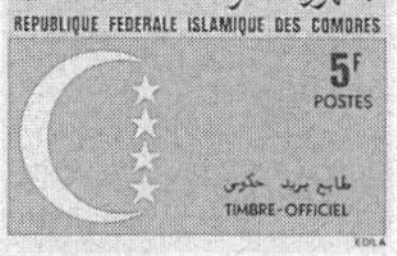

O 99 Comoro Flag

1979.
O379 O 99 5f. grn, blk & azure 10 10
O380 10f. grn, blk & grey 10 10
O381 20f. grn, blk & stone 10 10
O382 30f. green, blk & bl 20 10
O383 40f. grn, blk & yell 25 15
O384 60f. grn, blk & lt grn 30 25
O384a 75f. grn, blk & lt grn 25 15
O385 100f. grn, blk & yell 80 35
O386 – 100f. mult 70 35
O386a – 125f. mult 90 55
O387 – 400f. mult . . . . . 2·75 1·50
DESIGNS: Nos. O386, O386a, O387, Pres. Cheikh.

POSTAGE DUE STAMPS

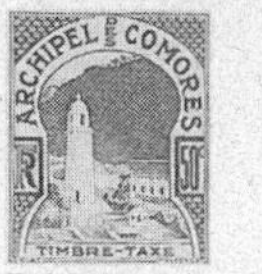

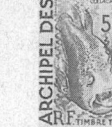

D 9 Mosque in Anjouan

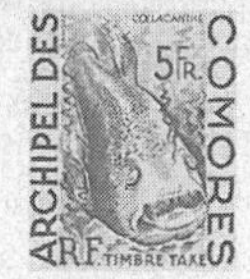

D 10 Coelacanth

1950.
D16 D 9 50c. green . . . . 15 3·25
D17 1f. brown . . . . 15 3·25

1954.
D18 D 10 5f. sepia and green . . 25 3·50
D19 10f. violet and brown 2·50 3·50
D20 20f. indigo and blue . . 70 4·00

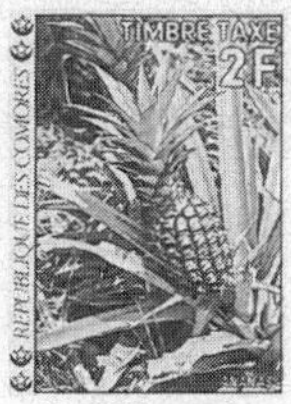

D 78 Pineapple

1977. Multicoloured.
D244 1f. Hibiscus (horiz) 10 10
D245 2f. Type D **78** 10 10
D246 5f. White butterfly (horiz) 10 10
D247 10f. Chameleon (horiz) . . 10 10
D248 15f. Banana flower (horiz) 10 10
D249 20f. Orchid (horiz) 10 10
D250 30f. "Allamanda cathartica" (horiz) . . . 20 10
D251 40f. Cashew nuts 25 15
D252 50f. Custard apple 25 15
D253 100f. Breadfruit (horiz) . . 70 25
D254 200f. Vanilla (horiz) . . . . 1·60 45
D255 500f. Ylang-ylang flower (horiz) . . . . 4·00 1·10

APPENDIX

The following stamps have either been issued in excess of postal needs or have not been available to the public in reasonable quantities at face value. Such stamps may later be given full listing if there is evidence of regular postal use.

1975.

Various stamps optd **ETAT COMORIEN** or surch also.

Birds issue (No. 60). 10f. on 2f.

Fishes issue (No. 71). Air 50f.

Birds issue (No. 99). 40f.

Comoro Landscapes issue (Nos. 102/4). Air 75f. on 65f., 100f. on 85f., 100f.

Tropical Plants issue (Nos. 105/9). Postage 5f. on 1f., 5f. on 3f.; Air 75f. on 60f., 100f. on 85f.

Seashells issue (No. 114). 75f. on 60f.

Aquatic Sports issue (No. 122). Air 75f. on 70f.

Anjouan Landscapes issue (Nos. 126/8). Air 40f., 75f. on 60f., 100f.

Said Mohamed Cheikh issue (Nos. 129/30). Air 20f., 35f.

Great Comoro Landscapes issue (Nos. 134 and 136). Postage 35f.; Air 200f. on 135f.

Moroni Buildings issue (No. 139). 20f.

Karthala Volcano issue (No. 140). Air 200f. on 120f.

Hansen issue (No. 141). Air 100f.

Copernicus issue (No. 142). Air 400f. on 150f.

Picasso issue (No. 143). Air 200f.

Mosques issue (Nos. 145/6). 15f. on 20f., 25f. on 35f.

Star of Anjouan issue (No. 147). 500f.

Said Omar Ben Soumeth issue (Nos. 148/9). Air 100f. on 135f., 200f.

Shaikh Said Mohamed issue (No. 150). 30f. on 35f.

Handicrafts issue (Nos. 153/5). 20f., 30f. on 35f., 75f.

Mayotte Landscapes issue (Nos. 157/60). Air 10f. on 20f., 30f. on 35f., 100f. on 90f., 200f. on 120f.

U.P.U. Centenary issue (No. 161). 500f. on 30f.

Air Service issue (No. 162). Air 100f. on 135f.

Rotary issue (No. 163). Air 400f. on 250f.

Handicrafts issue (Nos. 164/7). 15f. on 20f., 30f. on 35f., 100f. on 120f., 200f. on 135f.

Moheli Landscapes issue (Nos. 168/71). Postage 30f., 50f. on 55f.; Air 200f. on 230f.

Coelacanth issue (No. 172). 50f.

Folk-dances issue (Nos. 173/4). 100f., 100f. on 150f.

Apollo–Soyuz Space Test Project. Postage 10, 30, 50f.; Air 100, 200, 400f. Embossed on gold foil. Air 1500f.

1976.

Bicent of American Revolution. Postage 15, 25, 35, 40, 75f.; Air 500f. Embossed on gold foil: Air 1000f.

Winter Olympic Games, Innsbruck. Postage 5, 30, 35, 50f.; Air 200, 400f. Embossed on gold foil. Air 1000f.

Children's Stories. Postage 15, 30, 35, 40, 50f.; Air 400f.

Telephone Centenary. Postage 10, 25, 75f.; Air 100, 200, 500f.

Bicentenary of American Revolution (Early Settler and Viking Space Rocket). Embossed on gold foil. Air 1500f.

Bicent of American Revolution (J. F. Kennedy and Apollo). Embossed on gold foil. Air 1500f.

1978.

World Cup Football Championship, Argentina. Embossed on gold foil. Air 1000f.

Death Centenary of Sir Rowland Hill. Embossed on gold foil. Air 1500f.

Argentina's World Cup Victory. Optd on World Cup issue. Air 1000f.

1979.

International Year of the Child. Embossed on gold foil. Air 1500f.

1988.

Rotary International. Embossed on gold foil. Air 1500f.

1989.

Scouts, Butterflies and Birds. Embossed on gold foil. Air 1500f.

Satellites and Olympic Winners. Embossed on gold foil. Air 1500f.

Bicentenary of French Revolution. Embossed on gold foil. Air 1500f.

1990.

World Cup Football Championship. Embossed on gold foil. Air 1500f.

Winter Olympic Games, Albertville (1992). Embossed on gold foil. Air 1500f.

1991.

Birth Centenary of Charles De Gaulle (1990). Embossed on gold foil. Air 1500f.

1992.

Olympic Games, Barcelona. Boxing. Embossed on gold foil. Air 1500f.

CONFEDERATE STATES OF AMERICA — Pt. 22

Stamps issued by the seceding states in the American Civil War.

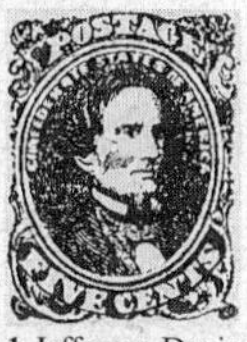

1 Jefferson Davis

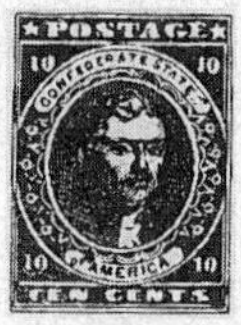

2 T. Jefferson

1861. Imperf.
1 **1** 5c. green . . . . £100 70·00
3 **2** 10c. blue . . . . £130 95·00

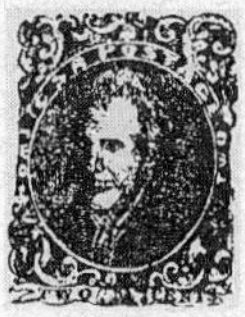
3 Jackson

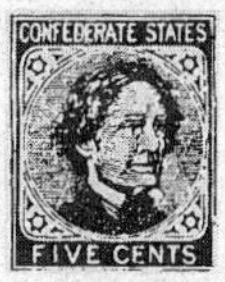

4 Jefferson Davis

1862. Imperf.
4 **3** 2c. green £350 £400
5 **1** 5c. blue . . . . 60·00 55·00
6 **2** 10c. red £600 £300

1862. Imperf.
7 **4** 5c. blue . . . . 6·00 11·00

5 Jackson

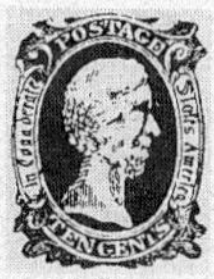

6 Jefferson Davis

9 Washington

1863. Imperf or perf (10c.).
9 **5** 2c. red . . . . 30·00 £170
10 **6** 10c. blue (TEN CENTS) . . . £475 £300
12 10c. blue (10 CENTS) . . . 5·00 9·00
14 **9** 20c. green . . . . 25·00 £200

CONGO (BRAZZAVILLE) — Pt. 6; Pt. 12

Formerly Middle Congo. An independent republic within the French Community.

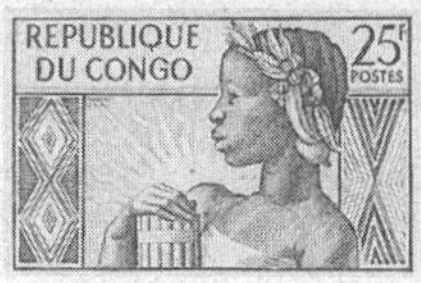

1 "Birth of the Republic"

1959. 1st Anniv of Republic.
1 **1** 25f. multicoloured 55 25

1960. 10th Anniv of African Technical Co-operation Commission. As T **62** of Cameroun.
2 50f. lake and green 65 60

1960. Air. Olympic Games. No. 276 of French Equatorial Africa optd with Olympic rings and **XVIIe OLYMPIADE 1960 REPUBLIQUE DU CONGO** 250F.
3 250f. on 500f. blue, black & grn 6·75 6·75

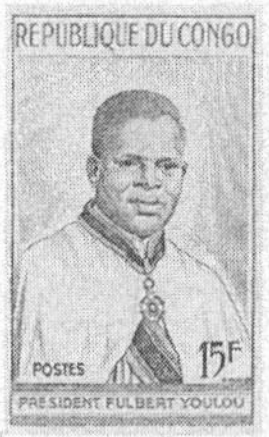

2 Pres. Youlou

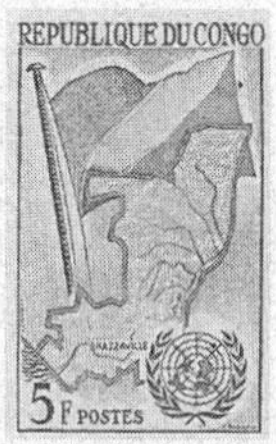

3 U.N. Emblem, map and Flag

1960.
4 **2** 15f. green, red and turquoise 25 15
5 85f. blue and red . . . . . . 1·40 50

1961. Admission into U.N.O.
6 **3** 5f. multicoloured 15 10
7 20f. multicoloured 25 20
8 100f. multicoloured . . . . . 1·40 90

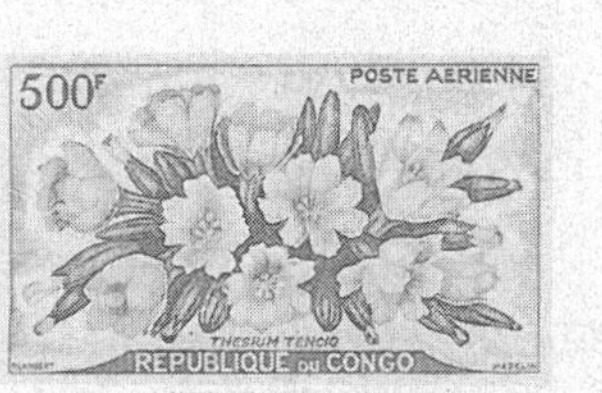

4 "Thesium tencio"

1961. Air.
9 – 100f. purple, yellow & green 2·25 1·40
10 – 200f. yellow, turq & brown 4·00 2·00
11 **4** 500f. yellow, myrtle & brown 11·00 5·00
FLOWERS: 100f. "Helicrysum mechowiam"; 200f. "Cogniauxia podolaena".

1961. Air. Foundation of "Air Afrique" Airline. As T **69** of Cameroun.
12 50f. purple, myrtle and green 1·10 45

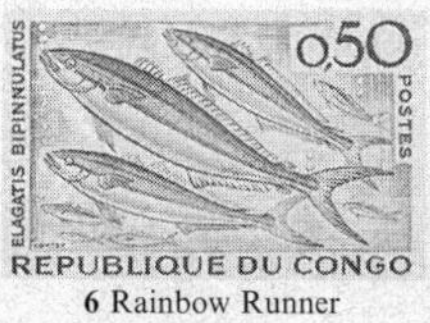

6 Rainbow Runner

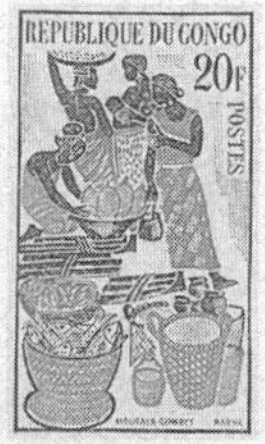

7 Brazzaville Market

1961. Tropical Fish.
13 **6** 50c. multicoloured 10 10
14 – 1f. brown and green 10 10
15 – 2f. brown and blue 10 10
15a – 2f. red, brown and green . . 45 10
16 **6** 3f. green, orange and blue 20 15
17 – 5f. sepia, brown and green 30 15
18 – 10f. brown and turquoise . . 1·00 25
18a – 15f. purple, green & violet 1·60 90
FISH: 1, 2f. (No. 15), Sloan's viperfish ("Chauliodus sloanei"); 2f. (No. 15a), Fishes pursued by squid; 5f. Giant marine hatchetfish. 10f. Long-toothed fangtooth; 15f. Johnson's deep sea angler.

1962.
19 **7** 20f. red, green and black . . 55 15

1962. Malaria Eradication. As T **70** of Cameroun.
20 25f.+5f. brown 80 80

8 "Yang-tse" (freighter) loading Timber,
Pointe Noire

1962. Air. International Fair, Pointe Noire.
21 **8** 50f. multicoloured . . . . . 2·00 90

1962. Sports. As T **12** of Central African Republic.
22 20f. sepia, red & blk (postage) 30 25
23 50f. sepia, red and black 65 50
24 100f. sepia, red and black (air) 2·00 1·00
DESIGNS—HORIZ: 20f. Boxing; 50f. Running.
VERT: (26 × 47 mm): 100f. Basketball.

1962. Union of African and Malagasy States. 1st
Anniv. As No. 328 of Cameroun.
25 **72** 30f. violet 90 50

1962. Freedom from Hunger. As T **76** of Cameroun.
26 25f.+5f. turquoise, brn & bl 80 80

9 Town Hall, Brazzaville and Pres.
Youlou

1963. Air.
27 **9** 100f. multicoloured £120 £120

9a "Costus spectabilis"   10 King Makoko's
(K. Schum)   Gold Chain

1963. Air. Flowers. Multicoloured.
28 100f. Type 9a . . . . . . 2·75 1·60
29 250f. "Acanthus montanus T.
anders" . . . . 5·50 2·75

1963. Air. African and Malagasy Posts and
Telecommunications Union. As T **18** of Central
African Republic.
30 85f. red, buff and violet . . . 1·25 75

1963. Space Telecommunications. As Nos. 37/8 of
Central African Republic.
31 25f. blue, orange and green . . 45 30
32 100f. violet, brown and blue . 1·25 1·10

1963. Folklore and Tourism.
33 **10** 10f. bistre and black 25 30
34 – 15f. multicoloured 30 25
DESIGN: 15f. Kebekebe mask.
See also Nos. 45/6 and 62/4.

11 Airline Emblem

1963. Air. 1st Anniv of "Air Afrique", and Inaug of
DC-8 Service.
35 **11** 50f. multicoloured 60 45

12 Liberty Square, Brazzaville

1963. Air.
36 **12** 25f. multicoloured 60 35
See also No. 56.

1963. Air. European-African Economic Convention.
As T **24** of Central African Republic.
37 50f. multicoloured 70 50

1963. 15th Anniv of Declaration of Human Rights.
As T **26** of Central African Republic.
38 25f. blue, turquoise & brown 45 30

13 Statue of Hathor, Abu
Simbel

1964. Air. Nubian Monuments.
39 **13** 10f.+5f. violet & brown . . . 35 20
40 25f.+5f. brown & turq 45 40
41 50f.+5f. turquoise & brn . . 1·40 90

14 Barograph

1964. World Meteorological Day.
42 **14** 50f. brown, blue & green . . 70 65

15 Machinist   16 Emblem and Implements of
Manual Labour

1964. "Technical Instruction".
43 **15** 20f. brown, mauve & turq 35 25

1964. Manual Labour Rehabilitation.
44 **16** 80f. green, red and sepia . . 1·10 45

17 Diaboua Ballet   19 Wood Carving

18 Tree-felling

1964. Folklore and Tourism. Multicoloured.
45 30f. Type 17 . . . . . . 90 30
46 60f. Kebekebe dance (vert) . . 1·40 65

1964. Air.
47 **18** 100f. brown, red and green 1·60 70

1964. Congo Sculpture.
48 **19** 50f. sepia and red . . . . 1·00 45

20 Students in Classroom

1964. Development of Education.
49 **20** 25f. red, purple and blue . . 40 30

1964. Air. 5th Anniv of Equatorial African Heads of
State Conference. As T **31** of Central African
Republic.
50 100f. multicoloured . . . . . 1·25 65

21 Sun, Ears of Wheat, and
Globe within Cogwheel

1964. Air. Europafrique.
51 **21** 50f. yellow, blue and red . . 70 50

22 Stadium, Olympic Flame and Throwing
the Hammer

1964. Air. Olympic Games, Tokyo. Sport and flame
orange.
52 **22** 25f. violet and brown . . . 35 25
53 – 50f. purple and olive 60 40
54 – 100f. green and brown . . . 1·50 85
55 – 200f. olive and red . . . . 2·75 1·75
DESIGNS—Stadium, Olympic Flame and: VERT:
50f. Weightlifting; 100f. Volleyball. HORIZ: 200f.
High-jumping.

1964. 1st Anniv of Revolution and National Festival.
As T **12** but inscr "1er ANNIVERSAIRE DE LA
REVOLUTION FETE NATIONALE 15 AOUT
1964".
56 20f. multicoloured 65 20

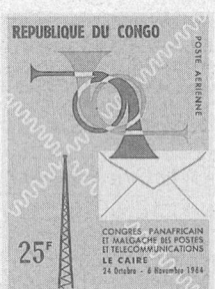

23 Posthorns, Envelope and Radio
Mast

1964. Air. Pan-African and Malagasy Posts and
Telecommunications Congress, Cairo.
57 **23** 25f. sepia and red 35 25

1964. French, African and Malagasy Co-operation.
As T **88** of Cameroun.
58 25f. brown, green and red . . 45 35

24 Dove, Envelope and Radio Mast

1965. Establishment of Posts and
Telecommunications Office, Brazzaville.
59 **24** 25f. multicoloured 35 25

25 Town Hall, Brazzaville and Arms

1965. Air.
60 **25** 100f. multicoloured . . . . 1·10 55

26 "Europafrique"

1965. Air. Europafrique.
61 **26** 50f. multicoloured 60 40

27 African Elephant   29 Pres.
Massamba-Debat

1965. Folklore and Tourism.
62 – 15f. purple, green and blue 80 25
63 **27** 20f. black, blue and green 65 30
64 – 85f. multicoloured . . . . 2·25 1·40
DESIGNS—VERT: 15f. Bushbuck; 85f. Dancer on
stilts.

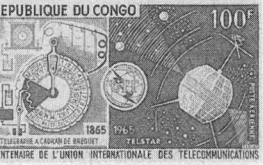

28 Cadran de Breguet's Telegraph and
"Telstar"

1965. Air. Centenary of I.T.U.
65 **28** 100f. brown and blue . . . 2·00 80

1965. Portrait in sepia.
66 **29** 20f. yellow, green & brown 25 15
66a 25f. green, turquoise & brn 35 20
66b 30f. orange, turq & brn . . 40 20

30 Sir Winston   31 Pope John XXIII
Churchill

1965. Air. Famous Men.
67 – 25f. on 50f. sepia and red 45 45
68 **30** 50f. sepia and green 90 90
69 – 80f. sepia and black . . . 1·60 1·60
70 – 100f. sepia and yellow . . 2·25 2·25
PORTRAITS: 25f. Lumumba; 80f. Pres. Boganda;
100f. Pres. Kennedy.

1965. Air. Pope John Commemoration.
71 **31** 100f. multicoloured . . . . 1·50 90

32 Athletes and Map of   33 Natives hauling Log
Africa

1965. 1st African Games, Brazzaville. Inscr
"PREMIERS JEUX AFRICAINS". Mult.
72 25f. Type **32** 40 30
73 40f. Football (34½ × 34½ mm) 55 40
74 50f. Handball (34½ × 34½ mm) 60 40
75 85f. Running (34½ × 34½ mm) 1·00 65
76 100f. Cycling (34½ × 34½ mm) 1·40 85

1965. Air. National Unity.
77 **33** 50f. brown and green . . . 60 40

34 "World Co-operation"

1965. Air. International Co-operation Year.
78 **34** 50f. multicoloured   90   55

35 Arms of Congo

37 Trench-digging

36 Lincoln

1965.
79 **35** 20f. multicoloured   30   15

1965. Air. Death Centenary of Abraham Lincoln.
80 **36** 90f. multicoloured   90   50

1966. Village Co-operative.
81 **37** 25f. multicoloured   30   20

1966. National Youth Day. As T **37** but showing youth display.
82   30f. multicoloured   40   30

38 De Gaulle and Flaming Torch

1966. Air. 22nd Anniv of Brazzaville Conference.
83 **38** 500f. brown, red & green .   24·00   19·00

39 Weaving   40 People and Clocks

1966. World Festival of Negro Arts, Dakar. Multicoloured.
84   30f. Type **39**   45   25
85   85f. Musical Instrument (horiz)   1·40   65
86   90f. Mask . . . . . .   1·40   85

1966. Establishment of Shorter Working Day.
87 **40** 70f. multicoloured   80   40

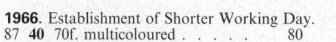

41 W.H.O. Building

1966. Inaug of W.H.O. Headquarters, Geneva.
88 **41** 50f. violet, yellow and blue   65   40

42 Satellite "D1" and Brazzaville Tracking Station

1966. Air. Launching of Satellite "D1".
89 **42** 150f. black, red and green   2·25   1·10

43 St. Pierre Claver Church

44 Volleyball

1966.
90 **43** 70f. multicoloured   80   40

1966. Sports.
91 **44** 1f. brown, bistre and blue   10   10
92   2f. brown, green and blue   15   10
93   3f. brown, lake and green   15   15
94   5f. brown, blue and green   20   15
95   10f. violet, turquoise & grn   25   20
96   15f. brown, violet and lake   35   30
DESIGNS—VERT: 2f. Basketball; 5f. Sportsmen; 10f. Athlete; 15f. Football. HORIZ: 3f. Handball.

45 Jules Rimet Cup and Globe   46 Corn, Atomic Emblem and Map

1966. World Cup Football Championship, England.
97 **45** 30f. multicoloured   45   30

1966. Air. Europafrique.
98 **46** 50f. multicoloured   55   35

47 Pres. Massamba-Debat and Presidential Palace, Brazzaville

1966. Air. 3rd Anniv of Congolese Revolution. Multicoloured.
99   25f. Type **47**   30   15
100   30f. Robespierre and Bastille, Paris   35   20
101   50f. Lenin and Winter Palace, St. Petersburg . . .   80   30

1966. Air. Inauguration of DC-8F Air Services. As T **54** of Central African Republic.
103   30f. yellow, black and violet   25

48 Dr. Albert Schweitzer

1966. Air. Schweitzer Commemoration.
104 **48** 100f. multicoloured . . . .   1·50   85

49 View of School

1966. Inaug of Savorgnan de Brazza High School.
105 **49** 30f. multicoloured   35   20

50 Pointe-Noire Railway Station   51 Silhouette of Congolese, and U.N.E.S.C.O. Emblem

1966.
106 **50** 60f. red, brown and green   1·75   75

1966. 20th Anniv of U.N.E.S.C.O.
107 **51** 90f. blue, brown & green   1·10   80

52 Balumbu Mask   53 Cancer "The Crab", Microscope and Pagoda

1966. Congolese Masks.
108 **52** 5f. sepia and red   20   15
109   10f. brown and blue . . .   25   15
110   15f. blue, sepia & brown   25   25
111   20f. multicoloured . . .   65   25
MASKS: 10f. Kuyu; 15f. Bakwele; 20f. Bateke.

1966. Air. 9th Int Cancer Congress, Tokyo.
112 **53** 100f. multicoloured . . . .   1·25   80

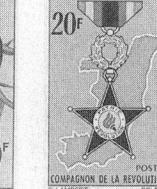

54 Sociable Weaver   55 Medal, Ribbon and Map

1967. Air. Birds. Multicoloured.
113   50f. Type **54** . . . . . .   3·75   1·10
114   75f. European bee eater . .   4·25   1·60
115   100f. Lilac-breasted roller .   6·75   2·00
116   150f. Regal sunbird . . . .   8·00   2·75
117   200f. South African crowned crane . . . .   9·00   3·00
118   250f. Secretary bird . . . .   11·00   4·50
119   300f. Black-billed turaco .   15·00   5·25

1967. "Companion of the Revolution" Order.
120 **55** 20f. multicoloured   30   25

56 Learning the Alphabet (Educational Campaign)   57 Mahatma Gandhi

1967. Education and Sugar Production Campaigns. Multicoloured.
121   25f. Type **56**   35   30
122   45f. Cutting sugar-cane . . .   90   30

1967. Gandhi Commemoration.
123 **57** 90f. black and blue . . . .   1·25   55

58 Prisoner's Hands in Chains   59 Ndumba, Lady of Fashion

1967. Air. African Liberation Day.
124 **58** 500f. multicoloured . . . .   7·75   3·25

1967. Congolese Dolls. Multicoloured.
125   5f. Type **59**   15   15
126   10f. Fruit seller   25   20
127   25f. Girl pounding saka-saka   30   20
128   30f. Mother and child . . .   35   25

60 Congo Scenery   61 "Europafrique"

1967. International Tourist Year.
129 **60** 60f. red, orange and green   65   40

1967. Europafrique.
130 **61** 50f. multicoloured   55   30

62 "Sputnik 1" and "Explorer 6"

1967. Air. Space Exploration.
131 **62** 50f. blue, violet & brown   55   30
132   75f. lake and slate . . . .   1·00   40
133   100f. blue, red & turquoise   1·40   65
134   200f. red, blue and lake . .   2·50   1·50
DESIGNS: 75f. "Ranger 6" and "Lunik 2"; 100f. "Mars 1" and "Mariner 4"; 200f. "Gemini" and "Vostok".

63 Brazzaville Arms

1967. 4th Anniv of Congo Revolution.
135 **63** 30f. multicoloured   40   20

1967. Air. 5th Anniv of African and Malagasy Posts and Telecommunications Union. As T **66** of Central African Republic.
136   100f. green, red and brown   1·10   65

64 Jamboree Emblem, Scouts and Tents

1967. Air. World Scout Jamboree, Idaho.
137 **64** 50f. blue, brown & chestnut   55   30
138   70f. red, green and blue . .   80   40

DESIGN: 70f. Saluting hand, Jamboree camp and emblem.

65 Sikorsky S-43 Amphibian and Map

1967. Air. 30th Anniv of Aeromaritime Airmail Link.
139 **65** 30f. multicoloured   40   25

66 Dove, Human Figures and U.N. Emblem

67 Young Congolese

1967. U.N. Day and Campaign in Support of U.N.
140 **66** 90f. multicoloured . . . .   1·25   65

1967. 21st Anniv of U.N.I.C.E.F.
141 **67** 90f. black, blue & brown   1·25   65

68 Albert Luthuli (winner of Nobel Peace Prize) and Dove

70 Arms of Pointe Noire

1968. Luthuli Commemoration.
142 **68** 30f. brown and green . . .   35   30

69 Global Dance

1968. Air. "Friendship of the Peoples".
143 **69** 70f. brown, green & blue   75   40

1968.
144 **70** 10f. multicoloured   35   30

71 "Old Man and His Grandson" (Ghirlandaio)

1968. Air. Paintings. Multicoloured.
145 30f. Type **71**   45   30
146 100f. "The Horatian Oath'
     (J.-L. David) (horiz)   1·60   65
147 200f. "The Negress with
     Peonies" (Bazille) (horiz)   3·25   1·60
See also Nos. 209/13.

72 "Mother and Child"

73 Diesel Train crossing Mayombe Viaduct

1968. Mothers' Festival.
148 **72** 15f. black, blue and red . . 30   25

1968.
149 **73** 45f. lake, blue and green   2·25   40

74 Beribboned Rope

1968. Air. 5th Anniv of Europafrique.
150 **74** 50f. multicoloured   55   25

75 Daimler, 1889

1968. Veteran Motor Cars. Multicoloured.
151 5f. Type **75** (postage)   20   15
152 20f. Berliet, 1897   35   20
153 60f. Peugeot, 1898 . . . . .   1·40   40
154 80f. Renault, 1900 . . . . .   2·00   90
155 85f. Fiat, 1902 . . . .   2·50   1·40
156 150f. Ford, 1915 (air) . . . .   2·50   1·40
157 200f. Citroen . . . .   3·50   1·50

1968. Inauguration of Petroleum Refinery, Port Gentil, Gabon. As T **80** of Central African Republic.
158 30f. multicoloured   60   25

76 Dr. Martin Luther King

78 Robert Kennedy

77 "The Barricade" (Delacroix)

1968. Air. Martin Luther King Commemoration.
159 **76** 50f. black, green & emerald   60   30

1968. Air. 5th Anniv of Revolution Paintings. Multicoloured.
160 25f. Type **77** . . . .   1·40   45
161 30f. "Destruction of the
     Bastille" (H. Robert) . . . .   1·40   55

1968. Air. Robert Kennedy Commemoration.
162 **78** 50f. black, green and red   55   30

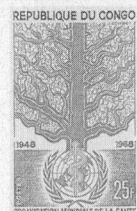

79 "Tree of Life" and W.H.O. Emblem

1968. 20th Anniv of W.H.O.
163 **79** 25f. red, purple and green   30   15

80 Start of Race

1968. Air. Olympic Games, Mexico.
164 **80** 5f. brown, blue and green   10   10
165 – 20f. green, brown & blue   30   15
166 – 60f. brown, green and red   60   35
167 – 85f. brown, red and slate   1·40   50
DESIGNS—VERT: 20f. Football; 60f. Boxing. HORIZ: 85f. High-jumping.

1968. Air. "Philexafrique" Stamp Exn, Abidjan (1969) (1st issue). As T **86** of Central African Republic.
168 100f. multicoloured . . . . .   2·25   1·60
DESIGN: 100f. "G. de Gueidan writing" (N. de Largilliere).

1969. Air. "Philexafrique" Stamp Exhibition, Abidjan, Ivory Coast (2nd issue). As T **138** of Cameroun.
169 50f. green, brown & mauve   2·50   1·00
DESIGN: 50f. Pointe-Noire harbour, lumbering and Middle Congo stamp of 1933.

1969. Air. Birth Bicentenary of Napoleon Bonaparte. As T **144** of Cameroun. Multicoloured.
170 25f. Battle of Rivoli
     (C. Vernet)   90   30
171 50f. "Battle of Marengo"
     (Pahou) . . . .   1·40   80
172 75f. "Battle of Friedland"
     (H. Vernet) . . . .   2·25   1·25
173 100f. "Battle of Jena"
     (Thevenin) . . . .   3·25   1·40

81 "Che" Guevara

1969. Air. Ernesto "Che" Guevara (Latin-American revolutionary) Commemoration.
174 **81** 90f. brown, orange & lake   80   40

82 Doll and Toys

1969. Air. International Toy Fair, Nuremberg.
175 **82** 100f. slate, mauve &
     orange . . . .   2·50   85

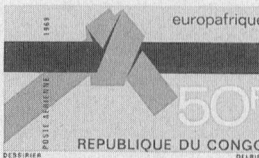

83 Beribboned Bar

1969. Air. Europafrique.
176 **83** 50f. violet, black & turq   45   25

1969. 5th Anniv of African Development Bank. As T **146** of Cameroun.
177 25f. brown, red and green   25   15
178 30f. brown, green and blue   30   15

85 Modern Bicycle

1969. Cycles and Motor-cycles.
180 **85** 50f. purple, orange & brn   80   30
181 – 75f. black, lake & orange   80   35
182 – 80f. green, blue & purple   85   45
183 – 85f. green, slate & brown   1·25   55
184 – 100f. multicoloured . . . .   1·40   65
185 – 150f. brown, red & black   2·00   80
186 – 200f. pur, dp grn & grn . .   3·25   1·40
187 – 300f. green, purple & blk   5·50   2·25
DESIGNS: 75f. "Hirondelle" cycle; 80f. Folding cycle; 85f. "Peugeot" cycle; 100f. "Excelsior Manxman" motor-cycle; 150f. "Norton" motor-cycle; 200f. "Brough Superior" motor-cycle; 300f. "Matchless and N.I.G.-J.A.P.S." motor-cycle

86 Series ZE Diesel-electric Train entering Mbamba Tunnel

1969. African International Tourist Year. Mult.
188 40f. Type **86** . . . .   2·50   40
189 60f. Series ZE diesel-electric
     train crossing the
     Mayombe (horiz) . . . . .   3·25   50

87 Mortar Tanks

1969. Loutete Cement Works.
190 **87** 10f. slate, brown and lake   10   10
191 – 15f. violet, blue & brown   25   15
192 – 25f. blue, brown and red   30   25
193 – 30f. blue, violet & ultram   35   25
DESIGNS—VERT: 15f. Mixing tower; 25f. Cableway. HORIZ: 30f. General view of works.

1969. 10th Anniv of A.S.E.C.N.A. As T **150** of Cameroun.
195 100f. brown . . . .   2·00   75

88 Harvesting Pineapples

1969. 50th Anniv of I.L.O.
196 **88** 25f. brown, green & blue   30   20
197 – 30f. slate, purple and red   35   20
DESIGN: 30f. Operating lathe.

89 Textile Plant

1970. "SOTEXCO" Textile Plant, Kinsoundi.
198 **89** 15f. black, violet & green   20   15
199 – 20f. green, red and purple   25   15
200 – 25f. brown, blue & lt blue   30   15
201 – 30f. brown, red and slate   35   15
DESIGNS: 20f. Spinning machines; 25f. Printing textiles; 30f. Checking finished cloth.

90 Linzolo Church

91 Artist at work

1970. Buildings.
202 **90** 25f. green, brown & blue 35 15
203 – 90f. brown, green & blue 80 35
DESIGN: HORIZ: 90f. Cosmos Hotel, Brazzaville.

1970. Air. "Art and Culture".
204 **91** 100f. brown, plum & grn 1·40 50
205 – 150f. plum, lake & green 2·00 75
206 – 200f. brown, choc & ochre 2·75 1·50
DESIGNS: 150f. Lesson in wood-carving; 200f. Potter at wheel.

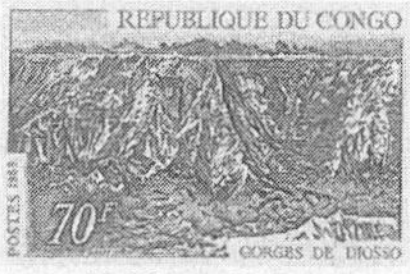

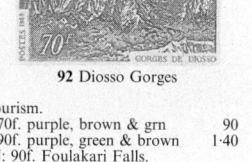

92 Diosso Gorges

1970. Tourism.
207 **92** 70f. purple, brown & grn 90 35
208 – 90f. purple, green & brown 1·40 45
DESIGN: 90f. Foulakari Falls.

1970. Air. Paintings. As T **71**. Multicoloured.
209 150f. "Child with Cherries" (J. Russell) . . . . 2·75 1·25
210 200f. "Erasmus" (Holbein the younger) . . . . 4·00 1·50
211 250f. "Silence" (Bernadino Luini) . . . . 4·00 1·90
212 300f. "Scenes from the Scio Massacre" (Delacroix) . . 5·50 2·75
213 500f. "Capture of Constantinople" (Delacroix) . . . . 8·00 3·75

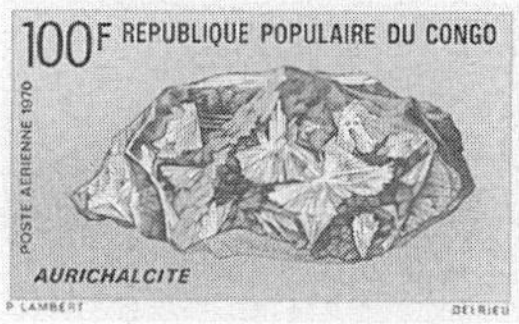

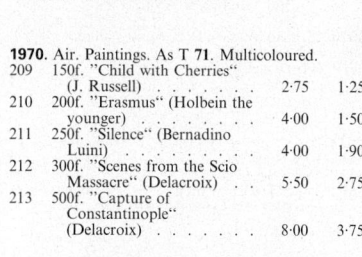

93 Aurichalcite

1970. Air. Minerals. Multicoloured.
214 100f. Type **93** . . . . 2·75 1·25
215 150f. Dioptase . . . . 3·25 1·50

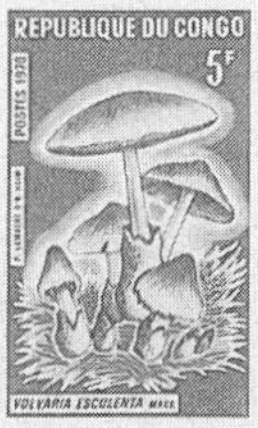

94 "Volvaria esculenta"

1970. Mushrooms. Multicoloured.
216 5f. Type **94** 50 20
217 10f. "Termitomyces entolomoides" 55 25
218 15f. "Termitomyces microcarpus" 85 35
219 25f. "Termitomyces aurantiacus" . . . . 1·75 45
220 30f. "Termitomyces mammiformis" . . . . . . 3·00 55
221 50f. "Tremella fuciformis" . . 4·50 1·25

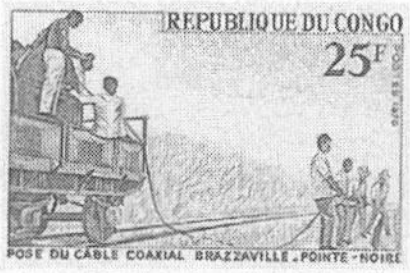

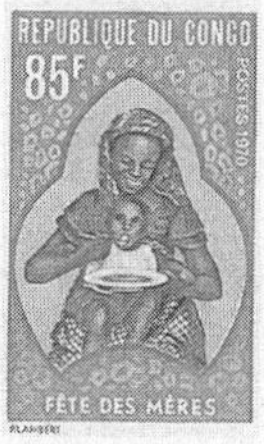

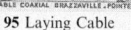

95 Laying Cable **96** Mother feeding Child

1970. Laying of Coaxial Cable, Brazzaville–Pointe Noire.
222 **95** 25f. buff, brown and blue 1·75 45
223 – 30f. brown and green . . . 2·00 55
DESIGN: 30f. Diesel locomotive and cable-laying gang.

1970. New U.P.U. Headquarters Building, Berne. As T **156** of Cameroun.
224 30f. purple, slate and plum 45 25

1970. Mothers' Day. Multicoloured.
225 85f. Type **96** 75 40
226 90f. Mother suckling baby . . 85 45

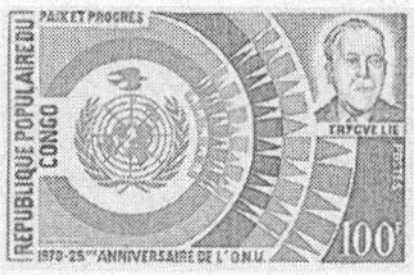
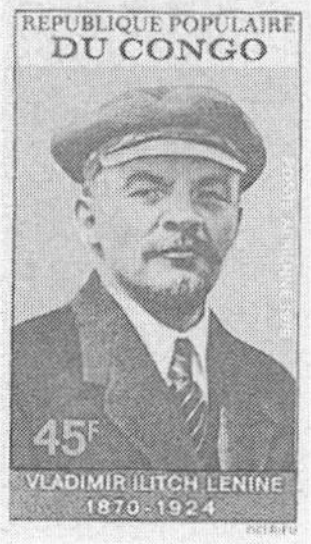

97 U.N. Emblem and Trygve Lie **98** Lenin in Cap

1970. 25th Anniv of United Nations.
227 **97** 100f. blue, indigo and lake 1·10 70
228 – 100f. lilac, red and lake . . 1·10 70
229 – 100f. green, turq & lake . . 1·10 70
DESIGNS—VERT: No. 228, as Type **97**, but with portrait of Dag Hammarskjold. HORIZ: No. 229, as Type **97**, but with portrait of U Thant and arrangement reversed.

1970. Air. Birth Centenary of Lenin.
231 **98** 45f. brown, yellow & grn 65 45
232 – 75f. brown, red and blue 1·10 65
DESIGN: 75f. Lenin seated (after Vassiliev).

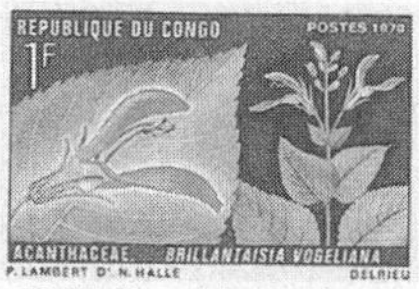

99 "Brillantaisia vogeliana"

1970. "Flora and Fauna". Multicoloured.
(a) Flowers. Horiz designs.
233 1f. Type **99** 10 10
234 2f. "Plectranthus decurrens" 10 10
235 3f. "Myrianthemum mirabile" 10 10
236 5f. "Connarus griffonianus" 15 10

(b) Insects. Vert designs.
237 10f. "Sternotomis variabilis" 30 20
238 15f. "Chelorrhina polyphemus" 80 20
239 20f. "Metopodontus savagei" 90 30

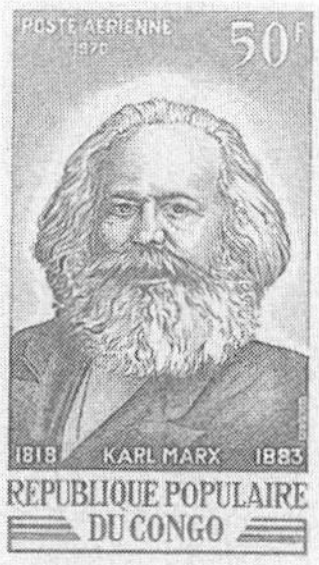

100 Karl Marx

1970. Air. Founders of Communism.
240 **100** 50f. brown, green & red 50 30
241 – 50f. brown, blue and red 50 30
DESIGN: No. 241, Friedrich Engels.

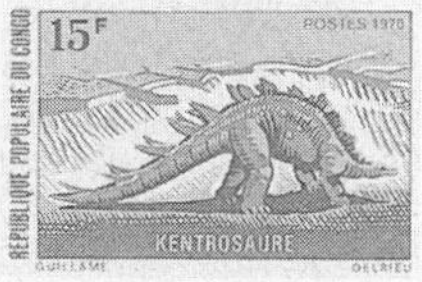

101 Kentrosaurus

1970. Prehistoric Creatures. Multicoloured.
242 15f. Type **101** 30 25
243 20f. Dinotherium (vert) . . . 1·10 55
244 60f. Brachiosaurus (vert) . . 2·25 80
245 80f. Arsinoitherium . . . . . 2·75 1·50

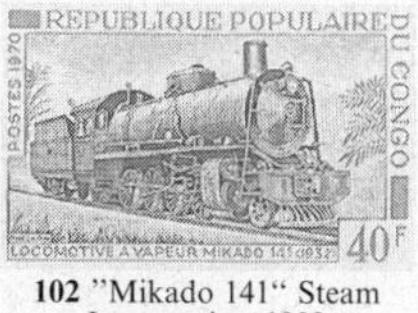

102 "Mikado 141" Steam Locomotive, 1932

1970. Locomotives of Congo Railways (1st series).
246 **102** 40f. black, green & purple 2·40 1·10
247 – 60f. black, green & blue 2·75 1·25
248 – 75f. black, red and blue 4·25 1·75
249 – 85f. red, green & orange 6·00 2·50
DESIGNS: 60f. Super-Golwe steam locomotive, 1947; 75f. Alsthom Series BB 1100 diesel locomotive, 1962; 85f. Diesel locomotive No. BB BB 302, 1969.
See also Nos. 371/4.

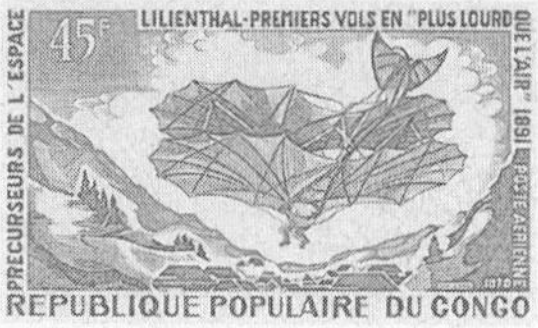

103 Lilienthal's Glider, 1891

1970. Air. History of Flight and Space Travel.
250 **103** 45f. brown, blue and red 60 25
251 – 50f. green and brown . . 60 25
252 – 70f. brown, red and blue 70 35
253 – 90f. brown, olive & blue 1·10 50
DESIGNS: 50f. Lindbergh's "Spirit of St. Louis", 1927; 70f. "Sputnik I"; 90f. First man on the Moon, 1969.

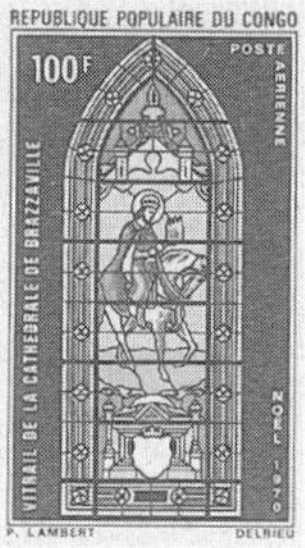

104 "Wise Man"

1970. Air. Christmas. Stained-glass Windows, Brazzaville Cathedral. Multicoloured.
254 100f. Type **104** 90 45
255 150f. "Shepherd" . . . . . . 1·60 70
256 250f. "Angels" . . . . 2·75 1·40

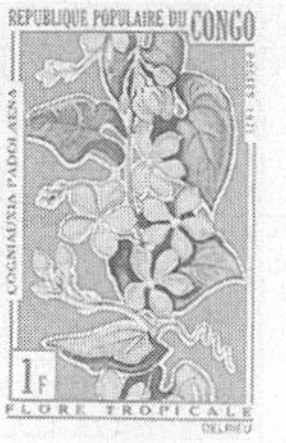

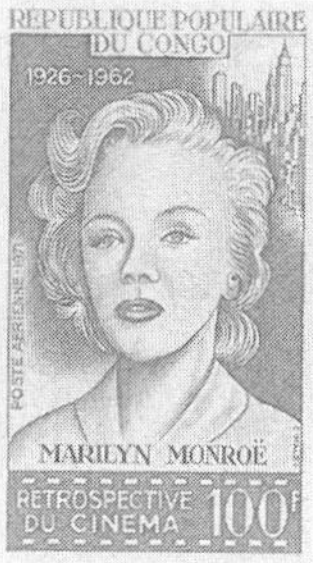

105 "Cogniauxia padolaena" **106** Marilyn Monroe

1971. Tropical Flowers. Multicoloured.
258 1f. Type **105** 10 10
259 2f. "Celosia cristata" 10 10
260 5f. "Plumeria acutifolia" . . 10 10
261 10f. "Bauhinia variegata" . . 45 15
262 15f. "Euphorbia pulcherrima 65 25
263 20f. "Thunbergia grandiflora" 1·10 25
See also D264/9.

1971. Air. Great Names of the Cinema.
270 **106** 100f. brown, blue & grn 2·75 35
271 – 150f. mauve, blue & pur 2·75 50
272 – 200f. brown and blue . . 2·75 75
273 – 250f. plum, blue & green 2·75 90
PORTRAITS: 150f. Martine Carol; 200f. Eric K. von Stroheim; 250f. Sergei Eisenstein.

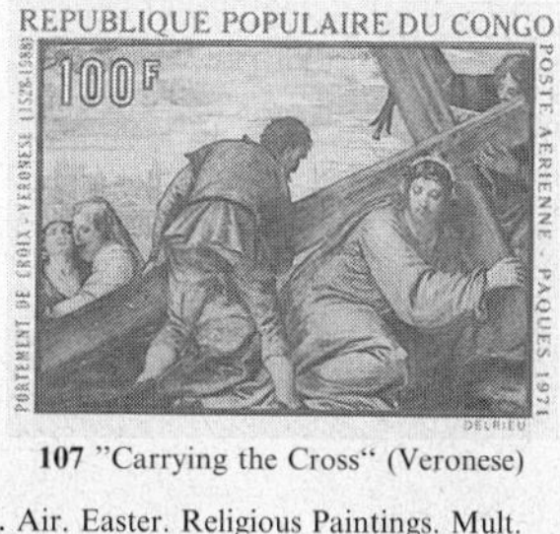

107 "Carrying the Cross" (Veronese)

1971. Air. Easter. Religious Paintings. Mult.
274 100f. Type **107** 95 55
275 150f. "Christ on the Cross" (Burgundian School c. 1500) (vert) . . . . . . 1·60 65
276 200f. "Descent from the Cross" (Van der Weyden) 2·75 90
277 250f. "The Entombment" (Flemish School c. 1500) (vert) . . . . 3·25 1·40
278 500f. "The Resurrection" (Memling) (vert) . . . . . 6·75 2·50

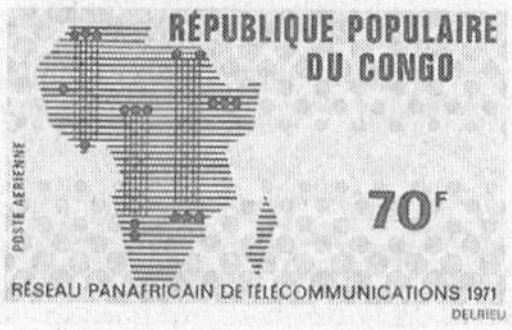

108 Telecommunications Map

1971. Air. Pan-African Telecommunications Network.
279 **108** 70f. multicoloured 60 30
280 85f. multicoloured . . . . 1·00 35
281 90f. multicoloured . . . . 1·40 45

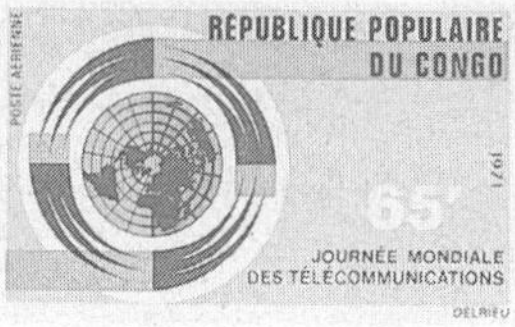

109 Global Emblem

1971. Air. World Telecommunications Day.
282 **109** 65f. multicoloured 55 25

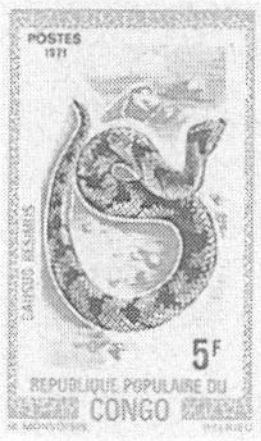

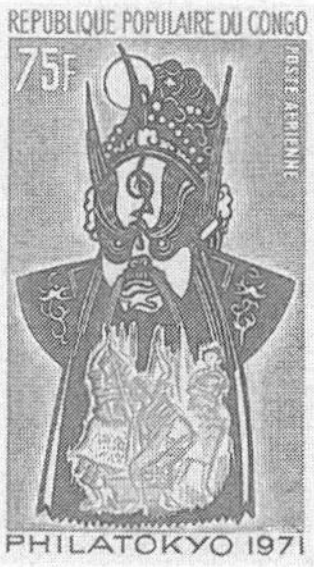

110 Green Night Adder **111** Afro-Japanese Allegory

1971. Reptiles. Multicoloured.
283 5f. Type **110** 15 10
284 10f. African egg-eating snake (horiz) 15 10
285 15f. Flap-necked chameleon 55 15
286 20f. Nile crocodile (horiz) . . 90 20
287 25f. Rock python (horiz) . . 1·10 30
288 30f. Gaboon viper . . . . . 1·40 65
289 40f. Brown house snake (horiz) . . . . 1·60 80
290 45f. Jameson's mamba . . . 2·25 90

1971. Air. "Philatokyo 1971" Stamp Exn, Tokyo.
291 **111** 75f. black, mauve & violet 90 35
292 – 150f. brown, red & purple 1·25 65
DESIGN: 150f. "Tree of Life", Japanese girl and African in mask.

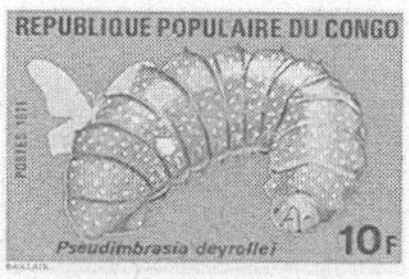

112 "Pseudimbrasia deyrollei"

1971. Caterpillars. Multicoloured.
293 10f. Type **112** 35 25
294 15f. "Bunaca alcinoe" (vert) 35 25
295 20f. "Epiphora vacuna ploetzi" 80 35
296 25f. "Imbrasia eblis" . . . . 1·40 45
297 30f. "Imbrasia dione" (vert) 2·25 1·00
298 40f. "Holocera angulata" . . 2·75 1·25

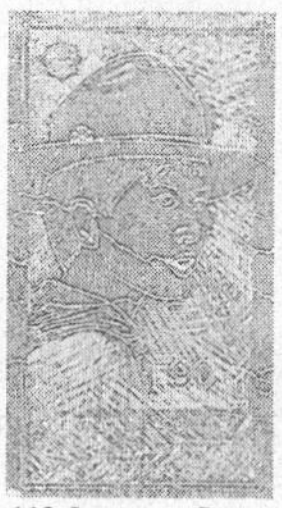
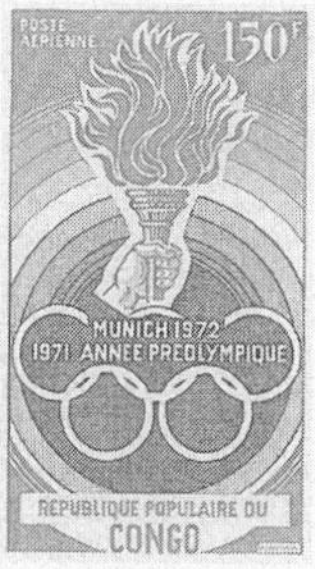

113 Japanese Scout **114** Olympic Torch

1971. World Scout Jamboree, Asagiri, Japan (1st issue). On foil.
299 **113** 90f. silver (postage) . . . 2·00 1·40
300 – 90f. silver . . . . 2·00 1·40
301 – 90f. silver . . . . 2·00 1·40
302 – 90f. silver . . . . 2·00 1·40

303 – 1000f. gold (air) . . . . . 10·00
DESIGNS—VERT: No. 300, French Scout; 301, Congolese Scout; 302, Lord Baden-Powell. HORIZ: No. 303, Scouts and Lord Baden-Powell.
See also Nos. 306/9.

1971. Air. Olympic Games, Munich.
304 **114** 150f. red, green & purple 1·40 70
305 – 350f. violet, green & brn 4·00 2·00
DESIGN—HORIZ: 350f. Sporting cameos within Olympic rings.

115 Scout Badge, Dragon and Congolese Wood-carving

1971. Air. World Scout Jamboree, Asagiri, Japan (2nd issue)
306 **115** 85f. purple, brown & grn ...... 65 ... 30
307 – 90f. brown, violet & lake ...... 70 ... 35
308 – 100f. green, red & brown ...... 90 ... 45
309 – 250f. brown, red & green ...... 2·25 ... 95
DESIGNS—HORIZ: 250f. Congolese mask, geisha and scout badge. VERT: 90f. African and Japanese mask; 100f. Japanese woman and African.

116 Running

1971. Air. 75th Anniv of Modern Olympic Games.
310 **116** 75f. brown, blue and red ...... 60 ... 30
311 – 85f. brown, blue and red ...... 65 ... 30
312 – 90f. brown and violet ...... 1·00 ... 40
313 – 100f. brown and blue ... ... 1·10 ... 45
314 – 150f. brown, red & green ...... 2·00 ... 75
DESIGNS: 85f. Hurdling; 90f. Various events; 100f. Wrestling; 150f. Boxing.

117 "Cymothae sangaris"

1971. Butterflies. Multicoloured.
315 **117** 30f. Type **117** ...... 65 ... 35
316 – 40f. "Papilio dardanus" (vert) ...... 1·25 ... 55
317 – 75f. "Iolaus timon" ...... 2·25 ... 1·10
318 – 90f. "Papilio phorcas" (vert) ...... 3·00 ... 1·60
319 – 100f. "Euchloron megaera" ...... 4·00 ... 2·25

118 African and European Workers

1971. Racial Equality Year.
320 **118** 50f. multicoloured ...... 55 ... 30

119 De Gaulle and Congo 1966 Brazzaville Conference Stamp

1971. Air. 1st Death Anniv of General De Gaulle.
321 **119** 500f. brown, green & red ...... 11·00 ... 11·00
322 – 1000f. red & grn on gold ...... 19·00
323 – 1000f. red & grn on gold ...... 19·00
DESIGNS—VERT (29 × 38 mm): No. 322, Tribute by Pres. Ngouabi; 323, De Gaulle and Cross of Lorraine.

1971. Air. 10th Anniv of African and Malagasy Posts and Telecommunications Union. Similar to T **184** of Cameroun. Multicoloured.
324 – 100f. U.A.M.P.T. H.Q. and Congolese woman ...... 1·00 ... 45

1971. Inauguration of Brazzaville–Pointe Noire Cable Link. Surch **REPUBLIQUE POPULAIRE DU CONGO INAUGURATION DE LA LIAISON COXIALE 18-11-71** and new value.
325 **95** 30f. on 25f. buff, brn & bl ...... 1·60
326 – 40f. on 30f. brown and green (No. 223) ... ... 2·00 ... 30

121 Congo Republic Flag and Allegory of Revolution

1971. Air. 8th Anniv of Revolution.
327 **121** 100f. multicoloured ...... 1·40 ... 40

122 Congolese with Flag

1971. Air. 2nd Anniv of Congolese Workers' Party, and Adoption of New National Flag. Multicoloured.
328 **122** 100f. Type **122** .... 25 ... 10
329 – 40f. National flag ...... 35 ... 20

123 Map and Emblems   **125** Book Year Emblem

1971. "Work–Democracy–Peace".
330 **123** 30f. multicoloured .... 25 ... 20
331 – 40f. multicoloured .... 30 ... 15
332 – 100f. multicoloured .... 75 ... 40

124 Lion

1972. Wild Animals.
333 **124** 1f. brown, blue & green ...... 10 ... 10
334 – 2f. brown, green and red ...... 10 ... 10
335 – 3f. brown, ogre and red ...... 15 ... 10
336 – 4f. brown, blue & violet ...... 45 ... 10
337 – 5f. brown, green and red ...... 55 ... 15
338 – 20f. brown, blue & orge ...... 1·40 ... 55
339 – 30f. green, emer & brn .. ... 2·00 ... 80
340 – 40f. black, green and blue ...... 2·75 ... 1·00
DESIGNS—HORIZ: 2f. African elephants; 3f. Leopard; 4f. Hippopotamus; 20f. Potto; 30f. De Brazza's monkey. VERT: 5f. Gorilla; 40f. Pygmy chimpanzee.

1972. Air. International Book Year.
341 **125** 50f. green, yellow & red ...... 65 ... 25

126 Team Captain with Cup   **127** Girl with Bird

1973. Air. Congolese Victory in Africa Football Cup. Multicoloured.
342 **126** 100f. Type **126** ...... 1·40 ... 50
343 – 100f. Congolese team (horiz) ...... 1·40 ... 50

1973. Air. U.N. Environmental Conservation Conference, Stockholm.
344 **127** 85f. green, blue & orange ...... 1·40 ... 90

128 Miles Davis

1973. Air. Famous Negro Musicians.
345 **128** 125f. multicoloured . . . ... 1·60 ... 65
346 – 140f. red, lilac & mauve ...... 1·60 ... 70
347 – 160f. green, emer & orge ...... 1·90 ... 1·00
348 – 175f. purple, red & blue ...... 2·00 ... 1·00
DESIGNS: 140f. Ella Fitzgerald; 160f. Count Basie; 175f. John Coltrane.

129 Hurdling

1973. Air. Olympic Games, Munich (1972).
349 **129** 100f. violet and mauve . . ... 90 ... 50
350 – 150f. violet and green ...... 1·40 ... 65
351 – 250f. red and blue . . ... 2·75 ... 1·40
DESIGNS—VERT: 150f. Pole-vaulting. HORIZ: 250f. Wrestling.

130 Oil Tanks, Djeno

1973. Air. Oil Installations, Pointe Noire.
352 **130** 180f. indigo, red & blue ...... 2·25 ... 1·40
353 – 230f. black, red and blue ...... 2·75 ... 1·40
354 – 240f. purple, blue & red ...... 3·00 ... 1·50
355 – 260f. black, red and blue ...... 4·75 ... 1·90
DESIGNS—VERT: 230f. Oil-well head; 240f. Drill in operation. HORIZ: 260f. Off-shore oil-rig.

131 Lunar Module and Astronaut on Moon

1973. Air. Moon Flight of "Apollo 17".
356 **131** 250f. multicoloured . . . ... 3·00 ... 1·75

132 "Telecommunications"

1973. Air. World Telecommunications Day.
357 **132** 120f. multicoloured . . . ... 1·40 ... 65

133 Copernicus and Solar System

1973. Air. 500th Birth Anniv of Copernicus (astronomer).
358 **133** 50f. green, blue & lt blue ...... 45 ... 35

134 Rocket and African Scenes

1973. Air. Centenary of World Meteorological Organization.
359 **134** 50f. multicoloured . . . . 1·00 ... 35

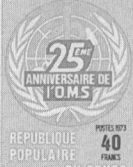 

135 W.H.O. Emblem   **137** General View of Brewery

136 "Study of a White Horse"

1973. 25th Anniv of W.H.O. Multicoloured.
360 40f. Type **135** .... 35 ... 20
361 50f. Design similar to T **135** (horiz) . . . . 45 ... 25

1973. Air. Paintings by Delacroix. Multicoloured.
362 150f. Type **136** . . . . 1·40 ... 1·25
363 250f. "Sleeping Lion" . . . . 3·25 ... 2·00
364 300f. "Tiger and Lion" . . . . 4·00 ... 2·25
See also Nos. 384/6 and 437/40.

1973. Congo Brewers' Association. Views of Kronenbourg Brewery.
365 **137** 30f. blue, red & lt blue . . ... 25 ... 20
366 – 40f. grey, orange & red ...... 30 ... 20
367 – 75f. blue, red and black ...... 55 ... 30
368 – 85f. multicoloured ...... 1·00 ... 40
369 – 100f. multicoloured ...... 1·25 ... 55
370 – 250f. green, brown & red ...... 2·25 ... 1·40
DESIGNS: 40f. Laboratory; 75f. Regulating vats; 85f. Control console; 100f. Bottling plant; 250f. Capping bottles.

1973. Locomotives of Congo Railways (2nd series). As T **102**. Multicoloured.
371 30f. Golwe steam locomotive c. 1935 . . . . 2·10 ... 85
372 40f. Diesel-electric locomotive, 1935 . . . . 3·00 ... 1·25
373 75f. Whitcomb diesel-electric locomotive, 1946 . . . . 4·75 ... 2·10
374 85f. Alsthom Series CC200 diesel-electric locomotive, 1973 . . . . 5·50 ... 2·40

138 Stamp Map, Album, Dancer and Oil Rig   **139** President Marien Ngouabi

1973. Air. International Stamp Exhibition, Brazzaville and 10th Anniv of Revolution.
375 **138** 30f. grey, lilac & brown ...... 2·50 ... 50
376 – 40f. red, brown & purple ...... 30 ... 25
377 **138** 100f. blue, brown & pur ...... 4·75 ... 1·25
378 – 100f. lilac, purple & red ...... 1·10 ... 60
DESIGNS: 40f., 100f. Map, album and Globes.

1973. Air.
379 **139** 30f. multicoloured . . . . 25 ... 10
380 – 40f. multicoloured . . . . 30 ... 15
381 – 75f. multicoloured . . . . 60 ... 35

1973. Pan-African Drought Relief. No. 236 surch **100F SECHERESSE SOLIDARITE AFRICAINE.**
382 100f. on 5f. multicoloured . . ... 1·40 ... 50

1973. 12th Anniv of African and Malagasy Posts and Telecommunications Union. As T **216** of Cameroun.
383 100f. violet, blue and purple ...... 1·10 ... 50

1973. Air. Europafrique. As T **136**. Multicoloured.
384 100f. "Wild Dog" . . . . 2·25 ... 1·10
385 100f. "Lion and Leopard" . . . ... 2·25 ... 1·10
386 100f. "Adam and Eve in Paradise" . . . . 2·25 ... 1·10
Nos. 384/6 are details taken from J. Brueghel's "Earth and Paradise".

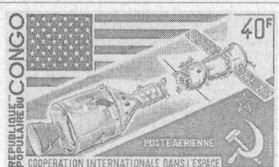

141 "Apollo" and "Soyuz" Spacecraft

1973. Air. International Co-operation in Space.
387 **141** 40f. brown, red & blue . . 30 25
388 – 80f. blue, red and green 80 40
DESIGN: 80f. Spacecraft docked.

142 U.P.U. Monument and Satellite

1973. Air. U.P.U. Day.
389 **142** 80f. blue & ultramarine 60 35

1973. Air. "Skylab" Space Laboratory. As T **141**.
390 30f. green, brown and blue 30 15
391 40f. green, red and orange . . 35 25
DESIGNS: 30f. Astronauts walking outside "Skylab"; 40f. "Skylab" and "Apollo" spacecraft docked.

143 Hive and Bees

1973. "Labour and Economy".
392 **143** 30f. green, blue and red 50 20
393 40f. green, blue & green 55 20

144 Congo Family and Emblems

1973. 10th Anniv of World Food Programme.
394 **144** 30f. brown and red . . . 25 15
395 – 40f. orange, green & blue 30 25
396 – 100f. brown, green & orge 75 45
DESIGNS—HORIZ: 40f. Ears of corn and emblems.
VERT: 100f. Ear of corn, granary and emblems.

145 Goalkeeper **146** Runners

1973. Air. World Football Cup Championship, West Germany (1974). (1st issue).
397 **145** 40f. green, dp brn & brn 35 25
398 – 100f. green, red & violet 1·25 45
DESIGN: 100f. Forward.
See also Nos. 403 and 408.

1973. Air. 2nd African Games, Lagos, Nigeria.
399 **146** 40f. red, green & brown 35 25
400 100f. green, red & brown 1·25 45

147 Pres. John F. Kennedy **148** Map and Flag

1973. Air. 10th Death Anniv of President Kennedy.
401 **147** 150f. black, gold & blue 1·40 70

1973. Air. 4th Anniv of Congo Workers' Party.
402 **148** 40f. multicoloured 30 20

149 Players seen through Goalkeeper's Legs

1974. Air. World Cup Football Championship, West Germany (2nd issue).
403 **149** 250f. green, red & brown 2·50 1·40

150 Globe, Flags and Names of Dead Astronauts

1974. Air. Conquest of Space.
404 **150** 30f. brown, blue & red . . 25 15
405 – 40f. multicoloured 35 25
406 – 100f. brown, blue & red 85 55
DESIGNS: 40f. Gagarin and Shepard; 100f. Leonov in space, and Armstrong on Moon.

151 A. Cabral **152** Spacecraft docking

1974. 1st Death Anniv of Cabral (Guinea-Bissau guerilla leader).
407 **151** 100f. purple, red & blue 70 45

1974. Air. West Germany's Victory in World Cup Football Championship. As T **149**.
408 250f. brown, pink and blue 2·75 1·40
DESIGN: Footballers within ball.

1974. Air. Soviet-American Space Co-operation.
409 **152** 200f. blue, violet and red 1·40 90
410 – 300f. blue, brown & red 2·50 1·25
DESIGN—HORIZ: 300f. Spacecraft on segments of globe.

153 "Sound and Vision"

1974. Air. Centenary of U.P.U.
411 **153** 500f. black and red . . . 5·00 2·75

154 Felix Eboue and Cross of Lorraine

1974. 30th Death Anniv of Eboue ("Free French" Leader).
412 **154** 30f. multicoloured 50 35
413 40f. multicoloured 65 45

155 Lenin

1974. Air. 30th Death Anniv of Lenin.
414 **155** 150f. orange, red & green 1·40 90

1974. Birth Centenary of Churchill. As T **154**. Multicoloured.
415 200f. Churchill and Order of the Garter . . . . 1·75 1·00

1974. Birth Centenary of Guglielmo Marconi (radio pioneer). As T **154**. Multicoloured.
416 200f. Marconi and early apparatus . . . . 1·75 85

1974. Air. Centenary of Berne Convention. No. 411 surch **9 OCTOBRE 1974 300F**.
417 **153** 300f. on 500f. blk & red 2·75 1·40

157 Pineapple

1974. Congolese Fruits. Multicoloured.
418 30f. Type **157** 35 25
419 30f. Bananas 35 25
420 30f. Safous 35 25
421 40f. Avocado pears 65 25
422 40f. Mangoes 65 25
423 40f. Papaya 65 25
424 40f. Oranges 65 25

158 Gen. Charles De Gaulle

1974. 30th Anniv of Brazzaville Conference.
425 **158** 100f. brown and green . . 2·25 1·40

1974. 10th Anniv of Central African Customs and Economic Union. As Nos. 734/5 of Cameroun.
426 40f. mult (postage) . . . 35 20
427 100f. multicoloured (air) . . . 90 45

159 George Stephenson (railway pioneer) and Early and Modern Locomotives (½-size illustration)

1974. 150th Anniv (1975) of Public Railways.
428 **159** 75f. olive and green . . . . 1·60 60

160 Irish Setter

1974. Dogs. Multicoloured.
429 30f. Type **160** 55 25
430 40f. Borzoi 65 25
431 75f. Pointer . . . . 1·40 65
432 100f. Great Dane . . . . . . 1·90 70

1974. Cats. As T **160**. Multicoloured.
433 30f. Havana chestnut 55 25
434 40f. Red Persian 65 25
435 75f. British blue . . . . . 1·40 65
436 100f. Serval . . . . 1·90 75

1974. Air. Impressionist Paintings. As T **136**. Mult.
437 30f. "The Argenteuil Regatta" (Monet) 80 50
438 40f. "Seated Dancer" (Degas) (vert) 90 55

161 National Fair

1974. Air. National Fair, Brazzaville.
441 **161** 30f. multicoloured 55 25

439 50f. "Girl on Swing" (Renoir) (vert) . . . . . . 1·40 80
440 75f. "Girl in Straw Hat" (Renoir) (vert) . . . . . 1·90 1·00

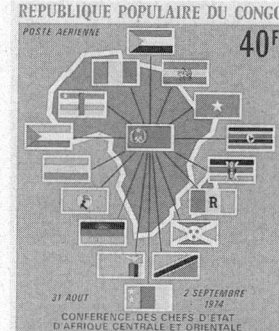

162 African Map and Flags

1974. Air. African Heads-of-State Conference, Brazzaville.
442 **162** 40f. multicoloured 60 25

163 Flags and Dove

1974. 5th Anniv of Congo Labour Party.
443 **163** 30f. red, yellow & green 25 15
444 – 40f. brown, red & yellow 80 25
DESIGN: 40f. Hands holding flowers and hammer.

164 U Thant and U.N. Headquarters Building

1975. 1st Death Anniv of U Thant (U.N. Secretary-General).
445 **164** 50f. multicoloured 40 25

1975. 1st Death Anniv of Paul G. Hoffman (U.N. Programme for Underdeveloped Countries administrator). As T **164**. Multicoloured.
446 50f. Hoffman and U.N. "Laurel Wreath" (vert) . . . 35 25

166 Workers and Development

1975. National Economic Development.
447 **166** 40f. multicoloured 30 25

167 Mao Tse-tung and Map of China

1975. 25th Anniv (1974) of Chinese People's Republic.
448 **167** 75f. red, mauve & blue . . 1·60 80

168 Woman with Hoe

1975. 10th Anniv of Revolutionary Union of Congolese Women.
449 168 40f. multicoloured 30 20

169 Paris–Brussels Line, 1890 (½-size illustration)

1975. Air. Railway History. Multicoloured.
450 50f. Type 169 . . . . 1·10 50
451 75f. Santa Fe Line, 1880 . . 2·40 60

170 "Five Weeks in a Balloon"

1975. Air. 70th Anniv of Jules Verne (novelist). Multicoloured.
452 40f. Type 170 . . . . . . 80 40
453 50f. "Around the World in
80 Days" . . . . 4·00 1·00

171 Line-up of Team

1975. Victory of Cara Football Team in Africa Cup. Multicoloured.
454 30f. Type 171 . . . . . . 30 25
455 40f. Receiving trophy (vert) 35 25

172 1935 Citroen and Notre Dame Cathedral, Paris

1975. Veteran Cars. Multicoloured.
456 30f. Type 172 . . . . 55 20
457 40f. 1911 Alfa Romeo and St.
Peter's Rome 65 20
458 50f. 1926 Rolls Royce and
Houses of Parliament,
London 80 30
459 75f. 1893 C. F. Duryea and
Manhattan skyline, New
York . . . . 1·40 35

173 "Soyuz" Spacecraft

1975. Air. "Apollo–Soyuz" Space Test Project.
460 173 95f. black, red & brown 80 35
461 — 100f. black, violet & blue 90 40
DESIGN: 100f. "Apollo" Spacecraft.

174 Tipoye Carriage

1975. Traditional Congo Transport. Multicoloured.
462 30f. Type 174 . . . . 55 20
463 40f. Pirogue 65 30

175 "Raising the Flag"

1975. 2nd Anniv of Institutions of Popular Tasks.
464 175 30f. multicoloured 25 20

176 Conference Hall

1975. 3rd Anniv of Congolese National Conference.
465 176 40f. multicoloured 35 25

177 Fishing with Wooden Baskets

1975. Traditional Fishing. Multicoloured.
466 30f. Type 177 . . . . 30 20
467 40f. Fishing with line (vert) 90 30
468 60f. Fishing with spear (vert) 80 25
469 90f. Fishing with net . . . . 1·40 80

178 Chopping Firewood

179 "Esanga"

1975. Domestic Chores. Multicoloured.
470 30f. Type 178 . . . . 25 15
471 30f. Pounding meal 25 15
472 40f. Preparing manioc (horiz) 40 20

1975. Traditional Musical Instruments. Mult.
473 30f. Type 179 . . . . 55 20
474 40f. "Kalakwa" 65 25
475 60f. "Likembe" . . . . . . 1·00 30
476 75f. "Ngongui" . . . . . . 1·10 40

180 "Dzeke" Money Cowrie

1975. Ancient Congolese Money.
477 180 30f. ochre, brown & red . . 40 25
478 — 30f. ochre, violet & brn 30 20
478a 180 35f. orange and brown 45 30
478b — 35f. red, bistre and violet 35 25
479 — 40f. brown and blue . . 45 25
480 — 50f. blue and brown . . 45 25

481 — 60f. brown and green . . 55 30
482 — 85f. green and red . . . 1·00 35
DESIGNS: 30, 35 (478b) f. "Okengo" iron money;
40f. Gallic coin (60 B.C.); 50f. Roman coin (37 B.C.);
60f. Danubian coin (2nd century B.C.); 85f. Greek
coin (4th century B.C.).

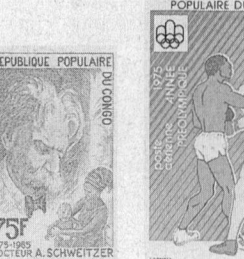

181 Dr. Schweitzer   183 Boxing

182 "Moschops"

1975. Birth Centenary of Dr. Albert Schweitzer.
483 181 75f. green, mauve & brn 1·10 40

1975. Prehistoric Animals. Multicoloured.
484 55f. Type 182 . . . . 70 25
485 75f. "Tyrannosaurus" . . . . 1·10 30
486 95f. "Cryptocleidus" . . . . 1·90 65
487 100f. "Stegosauras" . . . . 2·50 90

1975. Air. Olympic Games, Montreal (1976). Multicoloured.
488 40f. Type 183 . . . . 30 25
489 50f. Basketball 35 25
490 85f. Cycling (horiz) 80 35
491 95f. High jumping (horiz) . . 1·00 35
492 100f. Throwing the javelin
(horiz) . . . . . . 1·25 40
493 150f. Running (horiz) . . . . 1·60 65

184 Alexander Fleming (biochemist) (20th Death Anniv)

1975. Celebrities.
494 184 60f. black, green and red 65 30
495 — 95f. black, blue and red 1·25 50
496 — 95f. green, red and lilac 1·10 40
DESIGNS: No. 495, Clement Ader (aviation pioneer)
(50th death anniv); 496, Andre Marie Ampere
(physicist) (birth bicent).

185 U.N. Emblem with Laurel Wreaths

1975. 30th Anniv of U.N.O.
497 185 95f. blue, red and green 80 40

186 Map of Africa and Sportsmen

1975. Air. 10th Anniv of 1st African Games,
Brazzaville.
498 186 30f. multicoloured 30 25

187 Chained Women and Broken Link

1975. International Women's Year. Multicoloured.
499 35f. Type 187 . . . . 35 15
500 60f. Global handclasp 45 30

188 Pres. Ngouabi and Crowd with Flags

1975. 6th Anniv of Congolese Workers' Party.
Multicoloured.
501 30f. Type 188 (postage) . . . 25 20
502 35f. "Echo"–P.C.T. "man"
with roll of newsprint and
radio waves (36 × 27 mm) 30 20
503 60f. Party members with flag
(26 × 38 mm) (air) . . . 35 25

189 River Steamer "Alphonse Fondere"

1976. Air. Old-time Ships. Multicoloured.
504 5f. Type 189 . . . . 25 20
505 10f. Paddle-steamer
"Hamburg", 1839 . . . 35 20
506 15f. Paddle-steamer
"Gomer", 1831 . . . . 35 20
507 20f. Paddle-steamer "Great
Eastern", 1858 . . . . 35 20
508 30f. Type 189 . . . . 55 20
509 40f. As 10f. 60 45
510 50f. As 15f. 65 45
511 60f. As 20f. 85 60
512 95f. River steamer "J.M.
White II" 1878 . . . 1·40 90

190 "The Peasant Family" (L. le Nain)

1976. Air. Europafrique. Paintings. Multicoloured.
513 60f. Type 190 . . . . 80 15
514 80f. "Boy with spinning Top"
(Chardin) . . . . . 1·00 55
515 95f. "Venus and Aeneas"
(Poussin) . . . . . 1·10 55
516 100f. "The Sabines" (David) 1·50 80

191 Alexander Graham Bell and Early Telephone

1976. Telephone Centenary.
517 191 35f. brown, light brown
and yellow (postage) . . 30 25
518 60f. red, mve & pink (air) 40 25

192 Fruit Market

1976. Market Scenes. Multicoloured.
519 35f. Type **192** 25 20
520 60f. Laying out produce . . . 90 25

**193 Congolese
Woman**

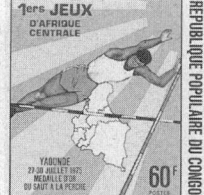
194 Pole-vaulting

1976. Congolese Women's Hair-styles.
521 **193** 35f. multicoloured 30 25
522 – 60f. multicoloured 45 25
523 – 95f. multicoloured 70 35
524 – 100f. multicoloured . . . 1·00 40
DESIGNS: 60f. to 100f. Various Congolese Women's
hair-styles.

1976. 1st Central African Games, Yaounde.
Multicoloured.
525 60f. Type **194** (postage) . . . 45 30
526 95f. Long-jumping 75 45
527 150f. Running (air) . . . . 1·25 60
528 200f. Throwing the discus . . 1·90 90

195 Kob

**196 Saddle-bill Storks
("Jabirus")**

1976. Congolese Fauna. Multicoloured.
529 5f. Type **195** 10 10
530 10f. African buffaloes 15 10
531 15f. Hippopotami 15 15
532 20f. Warthog 65 25
533 25f. African elephants . . . 80 30

1976. Birds. Multicoloured.
534 5f. Type **196** 35 30
535 10f. Shining-blue kingfisher
("Martin-Pecheur")
(37 × 37 mm) . . . . 1·75 50
536 20f. Crowned cranes ("Grues
Couronnees") (37 × 37 mm) 2·00 90

**197 O.A.U. Building
on Map**

198 Cycling

1976. Air. 13th Anniv of O.A.U.
537 **197** 60f. multicoloured 35 25

1976. Central African Games, Libreville. Mult.
538 35f. Type **198** 25 15
539 60f. Handball 35 25
540 80f. Running 55 30
541 95f. Football 90 35

**199 "Nymphaea
mierantha"**

200 Pioneers' Emblem

1976. Tropical Flowers. Multicoloured.
542 5f. Type **199** 10 10
543 10f. "Heliotrope" 10 10
544 15f. "Strelitzia reginae" . . . 20 10

1976. National Pioneers Movement.
545 **200** 35f. multicoloured 20 20

201 "Spirit of 76" (detail, A. M. Willard)

1976. Bicent of American Revolution. Mult.
546 100f. Type **201** 55 25
547 125f. Destruction of George
III's statue 90 35
548 150f. Gunners-Battle of
Princeton 90 40
549 175f. Wartime generals . . . 1·25 50
550 200f. Surrender of Gen.
Burgoyne, Saratoga . 1·40 60

202 Pirogue Race

1977. Pirogue Racing. Multicoloured.
552 35f. Type **202** 60 30
553 60f. Race in progress . . . 85 45

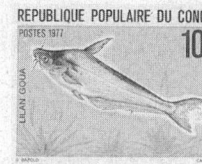
203 Butter Catfish

1977. Freshwater Fishes. Multicoloured.
554 10f. Type **203** 10 10
555 15f. Big-eyed catfish 10 10
556 25f. Citharinid 45 10
557 35f. Mbessi mormyrid . . . 65 15
558 60f. "Mongandza" . . . . . 1·25 55

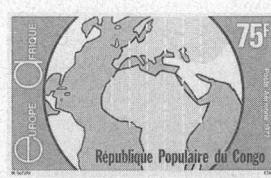
204 Map of Europe and Africa

1977. Air. Europafrique.
559 **204** 75f. multicoloured 45 35

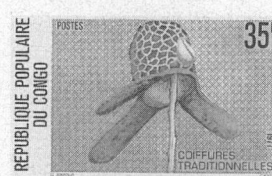
205 Headdress

1977. Traditional Headdresses. Multicoloured.
560 35f. Type **205** (postage) . . . 30 20
561 60f. Headdress with tail . . . 80 25
562 250f. Two headdresses (air) . . 2·25 1·40
563 300f. Headdresses with beads . 2·50 1·60

206 Wrestling

1977. Bondjo Wrestling.
564 – 25f. multicoloured 20 10
565 **206** 40f. multicoloured 25 15
566 – 50f. multicoloured 35 25
DESIGNS—VERT: 25f., 50f. Different wrestling
scenes.

207 "Schwaben", 1911

1977. History of the Zeppelin. Multicoloured.
567 40f. Type **207** 25 20
568 60f. "Viktoria Luise", 1913 . 35 30
569 100f. "Bodensee" 80 30
570 200f. "Graf Zeppelin" . . . 1·25 45
571 300f. "Graf Zeppelin II" . . 2·50 60

208 Rising Sun of "Revolution"

1977. 14th Anniv of Revolution.
573 **208** 40f. multicoloured 25 25

209 "Flow of Trade"

1977. Air. G.A.T.T. Trade Convention, Lome.
574 **209** 60f. black and red 45 25

**210 Hugo and Scene from "Hunchback of
Notre Dame"**

1977. 175th Birth Anniv of Victor Hugo.
575 **210** 35f. brown, red and blue . 25 15
576 – 60f. green, drab and blue . 35 25
577 – 100f. brown, blue & red . 70 45
DESIGNS: 60f. Scene from "Les Miserables"; 100f.
Scene from "The Toilers of the Sea".

211 Newton and Constellations

1977. Air. 250th Death Anniv of Isaac Newton.
578 **211** 140f. mauve, green & brn . 1·50 90

212 Mao Tse-tung

1977. 1st Death Anniv of Mao Tse-tung.
579 **212** 400f. gold and red . . . . 4·50 2·75

213 Rubens

1977. 400th Birth Anniv of Peter Paul Rubens.
580 **213** 600f. gold and blue . . . 6·75 5·50

214 Child leading Blind Person

1977. Fight Against Blindness.
581 **214** 35f. multicoloured 30 25

215 Paul Kamba and Records

1977. Paul Kamba (musician) Commemoration.
582 **215** 100f. multicoloured . . . 80 40

216 Trajan Vuia and his Vuia No. 1

1977. Aviation History. Multicoloured.
583 60f. Type **216** 35 20
584 75f. Bleriot and Bleriot XI
over Channel 40 20
585 100f. Roland Garros and
Morane Saulnier Type 1 . 80 30
586 200f. Lindbergh and "Spirit
of St. Louis" . . . . 1·50 45
587 300f. Tupolev Tu-144 . . . . 2·00 65

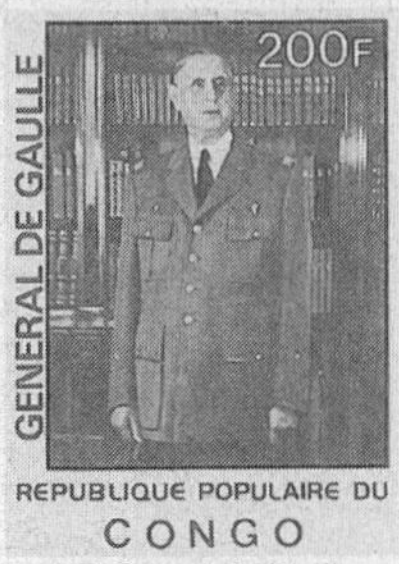

217 General de Gaulle

1977. Historic Personalities, and Silver Jubilee of Queen Elizabeth II. Multicoloured.

589	200f. Type **217**	1·90	45
590	200f. King Baudouin of Belgium	1·50	45
591	250f. Queen and Prince Philip in open car	1·50	65
592	300f. Queen Elizabeth	2·00	70

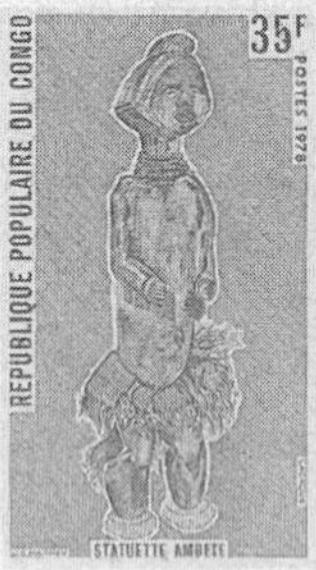

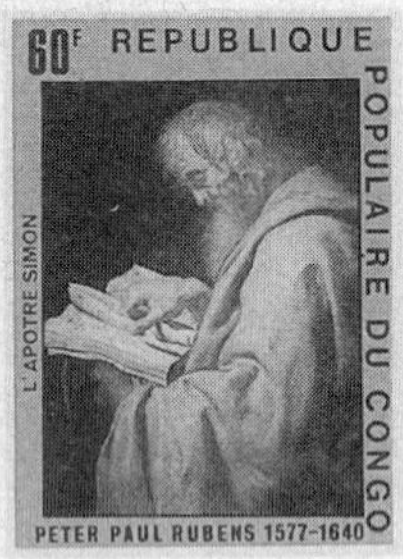

218 Ambete Statue **219** "The Apostle Simon"

1978. Congolese Sculpture.

594 **218**	35f. lake, brown & green	30	25
595 –	85f. brown, green & lake	90	35

DESIGN: 85f. Babembe statue.

1978. 400th Birth Anniv of Peter Paul Rubens (2nd issue). Multicoloured.

596	60f. Type **219**	65	20
597	140f. "The Duke of Lerma"	1·10	35
598	200f. "Madonna and Saints"	1·50	50
599	300f. "The Artist and his Wife"	2·25	65

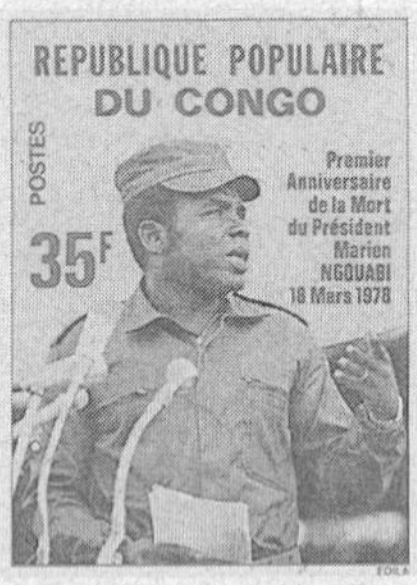

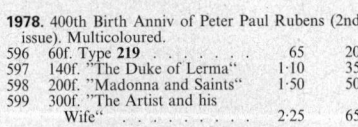

220 Pres. Ngouabi making Speech

1978. 1st Death Anniv of President Marien Ngouabi.

601 **220**	35f. black, yellow & red	15	15
602 –	60f. multicoloured	30	20
603 –	100f. black, yellow & red	45	35

DESIGNS—HORIZ: 60f. Pres. Ngouabi at his desk. VERT: 100f. Portrait of Pres. Ngouabi.

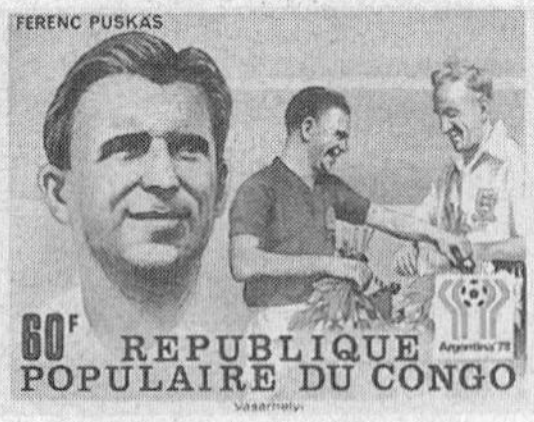

221 Ferenc Puskas (Hungary)

1978. World Cup Football Championship, Argentina. Famous Players. Multicoloured.

604	60f. Type **221**	35	20
605	75f. Giacinto Facchetti (Italy)	40	20
606	100f. Bobby Moore (England)	55	25
607	200f. Raymond Kopa (France)	1·60	50
608	300f. Pele (Brazil)	2·25	65

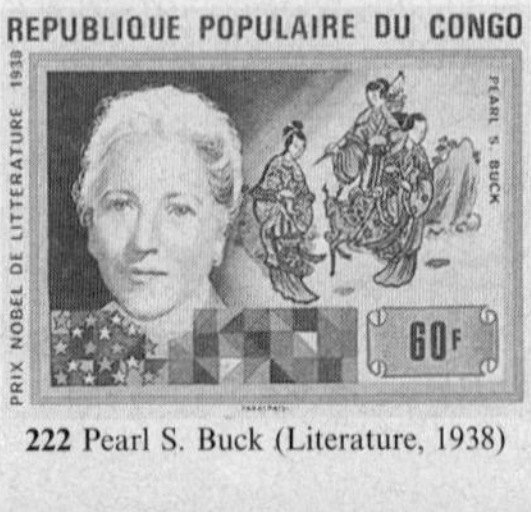

222 Pearl S. Buck (Literature, 1938)

1978. Nobel Prize Winners. Multicoloured.

610	60f. Type **222**	40	25
611	75f. Fridtjof Nansen and camp scene (Peace)	40	20
612	100f. Henri Bergson and "Elan Vita" (Literature)	55	30
613	200f. Alexander Fleming and penicillin (Medicine)	1·50	60
614	300f. Gerhart Hauptmann and hands with book (Literature)	2·00	65

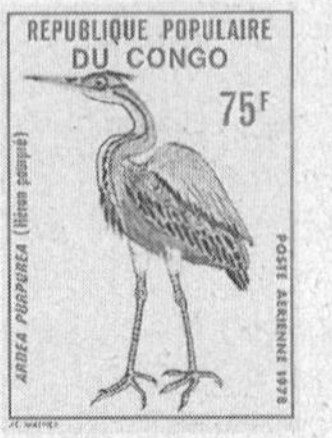

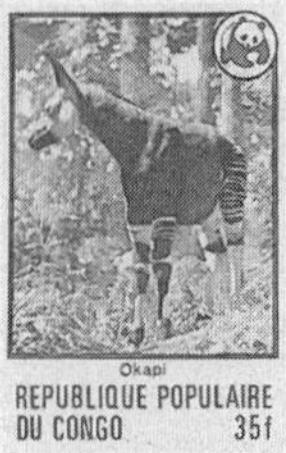

223 Purple Heron **224** Okapi

1978. Air. Birds. Multicoloured.

616	65f. Mallard	2·00	95
617	75f. Type **223**	2·00	1·10
618	150f. Great reed warbler	4·00	1·50
619	240f. Hoopoe	5·25	2·40

1978. Endangered Animals. Multicoloured.

620	35f. Type **224**	25	20
621	60f. African buffalo (horiz)	45	30
622	85f. Black rhinoceros (horiz)	1·10	40
623	150f. Chimpanzee	1·60	50
624	200f. Hippopotamus (horiz)	2·25	1·10
625	300f. Kob	4·00	1·40

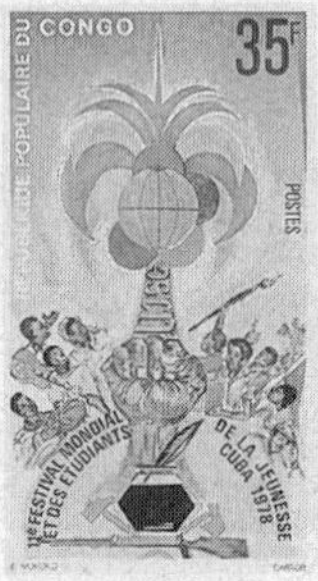

225 Clenched Fist, Emblem and Crowd

1978. 11th World Youth and Students Festival, Havana, Cuba.

626 **225**	35f. multicoloured	30	25

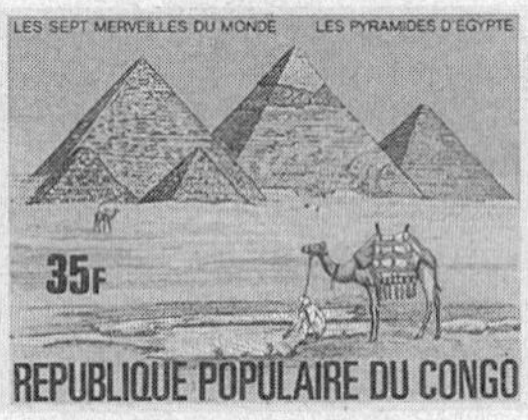

226 Pyramids, Egypt

1978. The Seven Wonders of the Ancient World. Multicoloured.

627	35f. Type **226**	20	15
628	50f. Hanging Gardens of Babylon (vert)	25	20
629	60f. Statue of Zeus, Olympia (vert)	35	20
630	95f. Colossos of Rhodes (vert)	50	25
631	125f. Mausoleum, Halicarnassus (vert)	90	30
632	150f. Temple of Artemis, Ephesus	1·10	40
633	200f. Pharos, Alexandria (vert)	2·00	65
634	300f. Map showing sites of the Seven Wonders	2·25	65

1978. 25th Anniv of Coronation of Queen Elizabeth II. Nos. 591/2 optd **ANNIVERSAIRE DU COURONNEMENT 1953 - 1978**.

635	250f. Queen Elizabeth and Prince Philip in open car	2·00	85
636	300f. Queen Elizabeth II	2·25	1·40

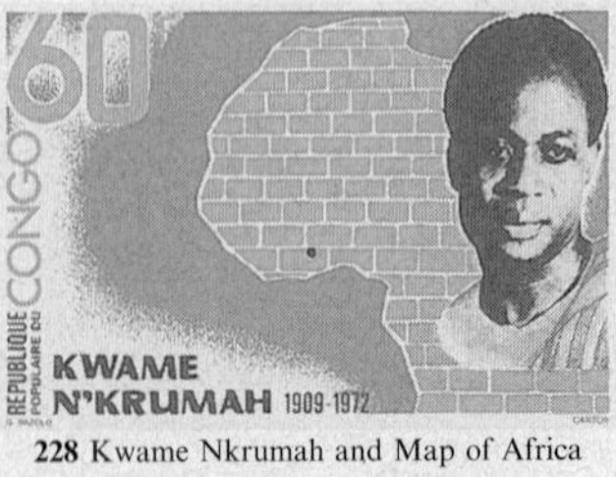

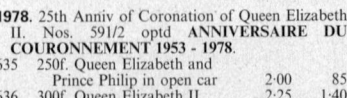

228 Kwame Nkrumah and Map of Africa

1978. Kwame Nkrumah (Ghanaian statesman) Commemoration.

638 **228**	60f. multicoloured	35	20

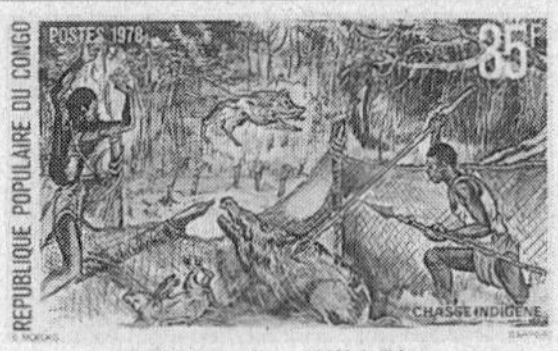

229 Hunting Wild Pigs

1978. Multicoloured.

639	35f. Type **229**	25	20
640	50f. Smoking fish	35	30
641	60f. Hunter with kill (vert)	35	20
642	140f. Woman hoeing (vert)	1·10	40

1978. Air. "Philexafrique" Stamp Exhibition, Libreville, Gabon (1st issue) and International Stamp Fair, Essen, West Germany. As T **237** of Benin. Multicoloured.

643	100f. Peregrine Falcon and Wurttemberg 1851 1k. stamp	1·50	1·10
644	100f. Leopard and Congo 1978 240f. stamp	1·50	1·10

See also Nos. 668/9.

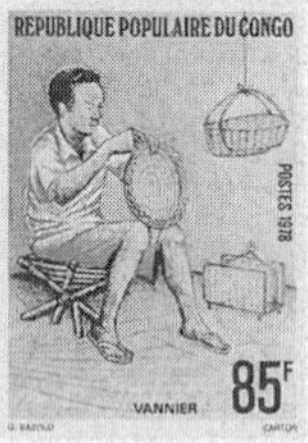

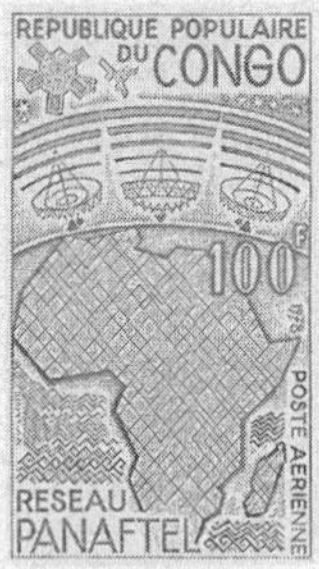

230 Basket Weaving **232** Satellites, Antennae and Map of Africa

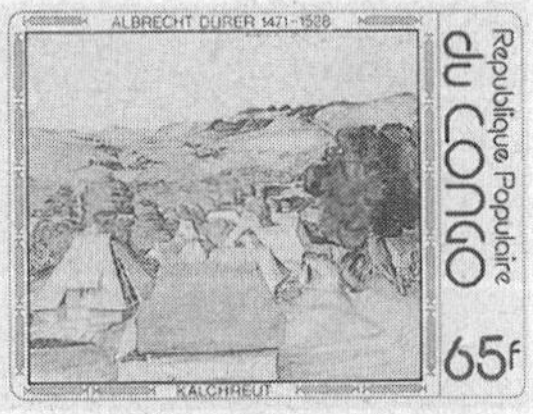

231 "Kalchreut"

1978. Occupations. Multicoloured.

645	85f. Type **230**	50	25
646	90f. Wood sculpture	50	25

1978. 450th Death Anniv of Albrecht Durer (artist). Multicoloured.

647	65f. Type **231**	35	20
648	150f. "Elspeth Tucher"	1·00	35
649	250f. "Grasses"	1·40	60
650	350f. "Self-portrait"	2·50	90

1978. Air. Pan African Telecommunications.

651 **232**	100f. red, green & orange	90	35

1978. World Cup Football Championship Winners. Nos. 604/8 optd with names of past winners.

652 **221**	60f. multicoloured	35	25
653 –	75f. multicoloured	40	30
654 –	100f. multicoloured	55	35
655 –	200f. multicoloured	1·60	60
656 –	300f. multicoloured	2·25	1·00

OPTS: 60f. **1962 VAINQUEUR BRESIL**; 75f. **1966 VAINQUEUR GRANDE BRETAGNE**; 100f. **1970 VAINQUEUR BRESIL**; 200f. **1974 VAINQUEUR ALLEMAGNE (RFA)**; 300f. **1978 VAINQUEUR ARGENTINE**.

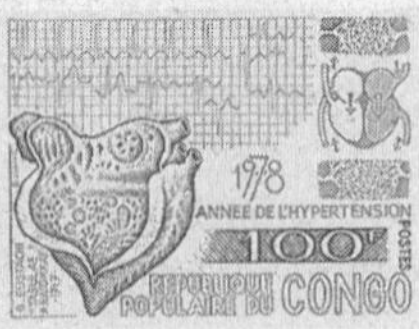

234 Diseased Heart, Blood Pressure Graph and Circulation Diagram

1978. World Hypertension Year.

658 **234**	100f. brown, red & turq	80	35

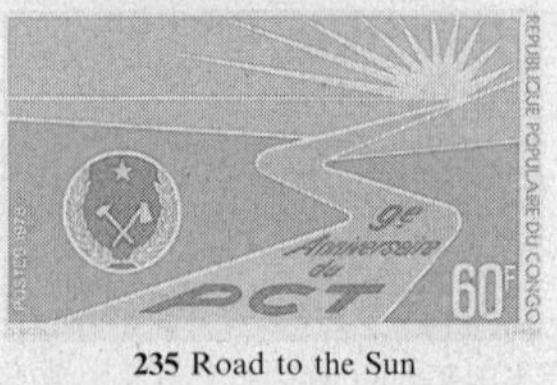

235 Road to the Sun

1978. 9th Anniv of Congolese Workers' Party.

659 **235**	60f. multicoloured	30	15

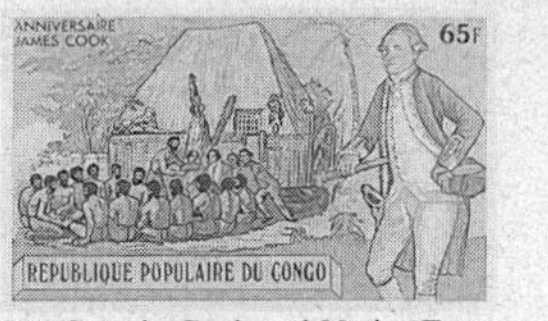

236 Captain Cook and Native Feast

1979. Death Bicentenary of Captain James Cook. Multicoloured.

660	65f. Type **236**	35	20
661	150f. Easter Island monuments	1·40	35
662	250f. Hawaiian canoes	2·00	70
663	350f. H.M.S. "Resolution" and H.M.S. "Adventure" at anchor	2·75	1·10

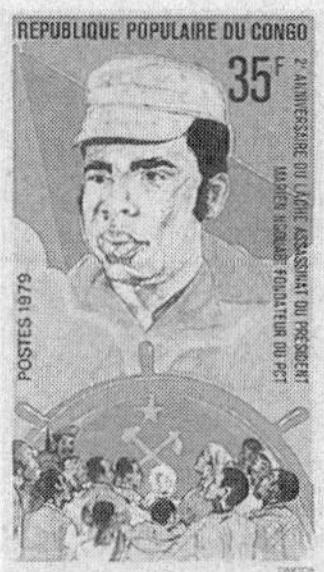

237 Pres. Ngouabi

1979. 2nd Anniv of Assassination of President Ngouabi.

664 **237**	35f. multicoloured	20	15
665	60f. multicoloured	35	20

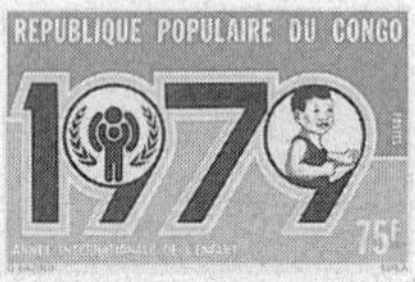

238 I.Y.C. Emblem and Child

1979. International Year of the Child.

666 **238**	45f. multicoloured	25	20
667	75f. multicoloured	30	15

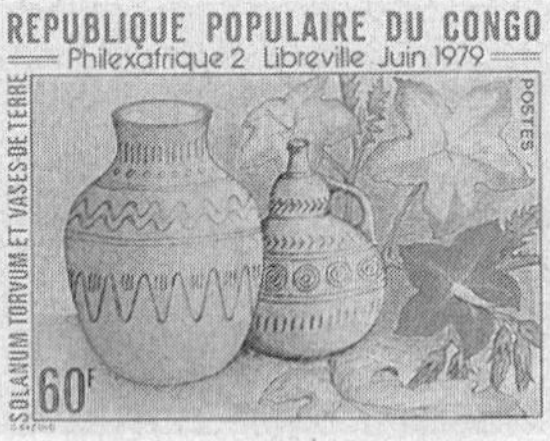

239 "Solanum torvum" and Earthenware Jars

1979. "Philexafrique" Stamp Exhibition, Libreville, Gabon (2nd issue).

668 **239**	60f. multicoloured	90	45
669 –	150f. orange, brn & grn	2·50	1·40

DESIGN: 150f. U.P.U. emblem, Concorde airplane, postal runner and diesel locomotive.

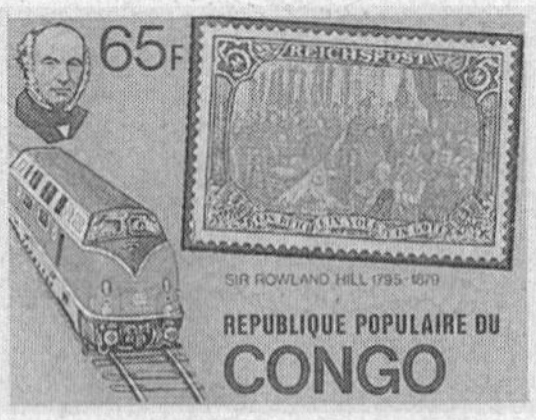

240 Rowland Hill, Diesel Locomotive and German 5m., Stamp, 1900

1979. Death Centenary of Sir Rowland Hill. Multicoloured.

670	65f. Type **240**	60	10
671	100f. Steam locomotive and French "War Orphans" stamp of 1917	80	15
672	200f. Diesel locomotive and U.S. Columbus stamp of 1893	1·75	30
673	300f. Steam locomotive and England–Australia "First Aerial Post" vignette	3·00	90

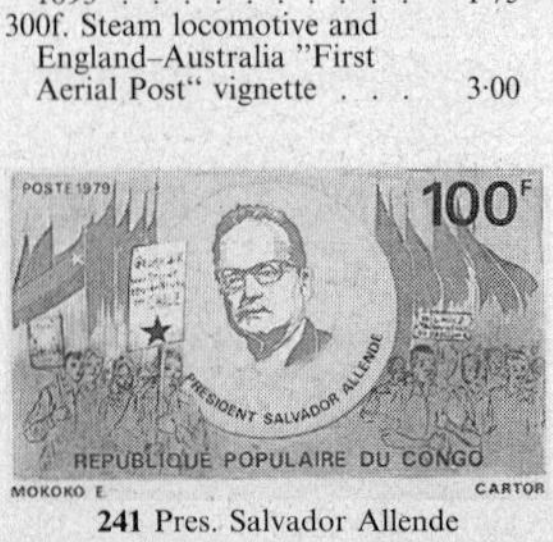

241 Pres. Salvador Allende

1979. Salvador Allende (former President of Chile) Commemoration.
675 **241** 100f. multicoloured . . . 80 25

242 "The Teller of Legends"

1979. African Folk Tales as Part of Children's Education.
676 **242** 45f. multicoloured 55 20

243 Handball Players   244 Map of Africa filled with Heads

1979. Marien Ngouabi Handball Cup. Mult.
677 45f. Type **243** 30 20
678 75f. Handball players 40 25
679 250f. Cup on map of Africa, player and Marien Ngouabi . . . . 1·75 70
No. 679 is vert, 22 × 37 mm.

1979. Air. 5th Pan-African Youth Conference, Brazzaville.
680 **244** 45f. multicoloured 30 20
681 75f. multicoloured 45 30

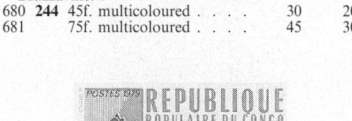

246 Congo Map and Flag

1979. 16th Anniv of Revolution.
683 **246** 50f. multicoloured 25 15

247 Abala Peasant Woman

1979. Air.
684 **247** 150f. multicoloured . . . 1·40 60

249 Bach and Musical Instruments

1979. Personalities. Multicoloured.
686 200f. Type **249** . . . . . . 1·60 50
687 200f. Albert Einstein and astronauts on the Moon . . 1·60 50

250 Yoro

1979. Yoro Fishing Port. Multicoloured.
688 45f. Type **250** 30 20
689 75f. Yoro at night 40 25

251 Moukoukoulou Dam and Power Station

1979. Moukoukoulou Hydro-electric Power Station.
690 **251** 20f. multicoloured 15 10
691 45f. multicoloured 65 20

1979. Air. 10th Anniv of "Apollo 11" Moon Landing. Optd **ALUNISSAGE APOLLO XI JUILLET 1969.**
692 – 80f. blue, red and green (No. 388) 35 35
693 **173** 95f. blk, red & crimson . . 45 45
694 – 100f. brown, blue and red (No. 406) 45 45
695 – 100f. black, violet and blue (No. 461) 45 45
696 – 300f. blue, brown and red (No. 410) . . . . . . 1·90 1·90

253 Fencer

1979. Air. Pre-Olympic Year (1st issue) Multicoloured.
697 65f. Runner, map of Africa and Olympic rings (horiz) 30 20
698 100f. Boxer (horiz) 50 25
699 200f. Type **253** . . . . . . 1·40 40
700 300f. Footballer (horiz) . . 2·00 65
701 500f. Olympic emblem . . 3·25 1·40
See also Nos. 716/9.

254 ASECNA Emblem and Douglas DC-10

1979. 20th Anniv of ASECNA (African Air Safety Organization).
702 **254** 100f. multicoloured . . . 70 45

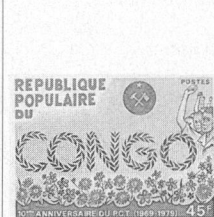   

255 Party Emblem Workers and Flowers   256 Cross-country Skiing

1979. 10th Anniv of Congolese Workers' Party.
703 **255** 45f. multicoloured . . . 25 15

1979. Air. Winter Olympic Games, Lake Placid (1980). Multicoloured.
704 40f. Type **256** 20 15
705 60f. Slalom 30 20
706 200f. Ski-jump . . . . 1·40 40
707 350f. Downhill skiing (horiz) 2·50 80
708 500f. Skier (vert, 31 × 46 mm) 1·10

257 Emblem and Globe   259 Long jump

1980. 15th Anniv of National Posts and Telecommunications Office.
709 **257** 45f. multicoloured 25 15
710 95f. multicoloured 45 25

1980. Air. Winter Olympic Games Medal Winners. Nos. 704/8 optd with names of winners.
711 40f. Cross-country skiing . . 20 15
712 60f. Slalom 30 20
713 200f. Ski jump . . . . 1·40 45
714 350f. Downhill skiing . . . . 2·50 1·00
715 500f. Skier . . . . 3·25 1·40
OVERPRINTS: 40f. **VAINQUEUR ZIMIATOV U.R.S.S.**; 60f. **VAINQUEUR MOSERPROELL Autriche**; 200f. **VAINQUEUR TOMANEN Finlande**; 350f. **VAINQUEUR STOCK AUTRICHE**; 500f. **VAINQUEURS STENMARK-WENZEL.**

1980. Air. Olympic Games, Moscow.
716 **259** 75f. multicoloured 55 10
717 – 150f. mult (horiz) . . . . 1·10 25
718 – 250f. multicoloured . . . 1·60 45
719 – 350f. multicoloured . . . 2·25 60
Nos. 717/19 show different views of the long jump.

260 Pope John Paul II

1980. Papal Visit.
721 **260** 100f. multicoloured . . . 1·10 30

261 Rotary Emblem

1980. 75th Anniv of Rotary International.
722 **261** 150f. multicoloured . . . 1·10 45

262 Glass Works

1980. Pointe Noire Glass Works. Multicoloured.
723 30f. Type **262** 15 10
724 35f. Glass works (different) . 45 10

263 Claude Chappe and Semaphore Tower

1980. Claude Chappe Commemoration.
725 **263** 200f. multicoloured . . . 1·60 1·10

264 Real Madrid Stadium

1980. Air. World Cup Football Championship, Spain (1982). Multicoloured.
726 60f. Type **264** 30 15
727 75f. Real Zaragoza 35 15
728 100f. Atletico de Madrid . . 45 20
729 150f. Valencia C.F. . . . . 1·00 30
730 175f. R.C.D. Espanol . . . 1·40 35

265 Floating Quay

1980. Port of Mossaka. Multicoloured.
732 45f. Type **265** 25 15
733 90f. Aerial view of port . . 40 20

266 "Crucifixion"

1980. Air. Paintings by Rembrandt. Multicoloured.
734 65f. "Adoration of the Shepherds" (detail) (horiz) 30 10
735 100f. "Entombment" (horiz) 45 25
736 200f. "Christ at Emmaus" (horiz) . . . . 1·40 40
737 300f. "Annunciation" . . . . 2·00 60
738 500f. Type **266** . . . . . . 4·00 1·10

267 Jacques Offenbach (composer)

1980. Air. Death Anniversaries. Multicoloured.
739 100f. Albert Camus (writer) (20th anniv) 80 35
740 150f. Type **267** (centenary) 1·40 90

268 "Papilio dardanus"

1980. Butterflies. Multicoloured.
741 5f. Type **268** 10 10
742 15f. "Kallima aethiops" . . . 10 10
743 20f. "Papilio demodocus" . . 15 10
744 60f. "Euphaedra" 55 40
745 90f. "Hypolimnas misippus" . 1·10 50

269 Hospital

1980. "31 July" Hospital.
747 **269** 45f. multicoloured 25 20

270 Man presenting Human Rights Charter

1980. 32nd Anniv of Human Rights Convention. Multicoloured.
748	350f. Type **270**		2·25	1·10
749	500f. Man breaking chains		3·25	2·00

271 Raffia Dancing Skirts

1980. Air. Traditional Dancing Costumes. Mult.
750	250f. Type **271**		2·25	70
751	300f. Tam-tam dancers (vert)		2·50	1·40
752	350f. Masks		3·00	1·60

272 Clenched Fists, Flag and Dove

273 Coffee and Cocoa Trees on Map of Congo

1980. 17th Anniv of Revolution. Multicoloured.
753	75f. Citizens and State emblem (36 × 23 mm)		35	25
754	95f. Type **272**		45	30
755	150f. Dove carrying state emblem (36 × 23 mm)		1·00	45

1980. Coffee and Cocoa Day. Multicoloured.
756	45f. Type **273**		25	20
757	95f. Coffee and cocoa beans		80	35

274 Cut Logs

1980. Forest Exploitation. Multicoloured.
758	70f. Type **274**		35	25
759	75f. Lorry with logs		35	25

275 President Neto

1980. 1st Death Anniv of President Neto.
760	275	100f. multicoloured	45	30

276 Olive-bellied Sunbird ("Souimanga Olivatre")

1980. Birds. Multicoloured.
761	45f. Type **276**		1·25	55
762	75f. Red-crowned bishop ("Travailleur a Tete Rouge")		1·75	60
763	90f. Moorhen ("Poule d'Eauafricaine")		2·10	70
764	150f. African pied wagtail ("Alouette Canelle")		3·25	1·50
765	200f. Yellow-mantled whydah (vert)		4·00	1·75
766	250f. "Geai-bleu" (vert)		2·10	85

277 Conference Emblem

1980. World Tourism Conference, Manila.
768	277	100f. multicoloured	80	45

278 Child Writing

1980. Return to School.
769	278	50f. multicoloured	25	15

279 The First House

1980. Brazzaville Centenary.
770	279	45f. ochre, grey & brown	25	15
771	–	65f. lt brown, brn & orge	55	20
772	–	75f. multicoloured	65	50
773	–	150f. multicoloured	1·25	1·00
774	–	200f. multicoloured	1·60	1·40

DESIGNS: 65f. First native village; 75f. The old Town Hall; 150f. Brazzaville from the Bacongo Promontory, 1912; 200f. Meeting between Savorgnan de Brazza (explorer) and Makoko (local chieftain).

280 Cataracts

1980. The River Congo. Multicoloured.
775	80f. Type **280**		65	50
776	150f. Bridge at Djoue		1·40	65

1980. Air. Olympic Medal Winners. Nos. 716/19 optd.
777	75f. DOMBROWSKI (RDA)		60	25
778	150f. SANEIEV (URSS)		1·00	45
779	250f. SIMEONI (IT)		1·50	80
780	350f. THOMPSON (GB)		2·25	1·40

282 Stadium and Sportsmen

1980. Revolutionary Stadium. Heroes of Congolese Sport.
782	282	60f. multicoloured	55	20

283 New Railway Bridge

1980. Realignment of Railway.
783	283	75f. multicoloured	1·00	25

284 Mangoes

1980. Loudima Fruit Station. Multicoloured.
784	10f. Type **284**		10	10
785	25f. Oranges		15	10
786	40f. Lemons		45	10
787	85f. Mandarins		65	

1980. 5th Anniv of African Posts and Telecommunications Union. As T **269** of Benin.
788	100f. multicoloured		45	35

285 Microwave Communication

1980. Communications. Multicoloured.
789	75f. Moungouni Earth Station (36 × 36 mm)		60	25
790	150f. Type **285**		1·00	45

286 Presentation of Marien Ngouabi Handball Cup

1981. African Handball Champions. Mult.
791	100f. Type **286**		90	30
792	150f. Team members		1·10	45

287 Pres. Sassou-Nguesso

1981. President Sassou-Nguesso.
793	287	45f. multicoloured	20	15
794		75f. multicoloured	40	25
795		100f. multicoloured	45	30

288 Space Shuttle

1981. Conquest of Space. Multicoloured.
796	100f. "Luna 17"		45	25
797	150f. Type **288**		1·00	35
798	200f. Satellite and space shuttle		1·40	45
799	300f. Space shuttle approaching landing strip		2·00	70

289 Head and Dove

290 Twin Palm Tree

1981. Anti-Apartheid Campaign.
801	289	100f. blue	45	30

1981. The Twin Palm Tree of Louingui.
802	290	75f. multicoloured	65	25

291 Bird approaching Snare

1981. Traditional Snares and Traps. Mult.
803	5f. Type **291**		10	10
804	10f. Bird in snare (vert)		10	10
805	15f. Rodent approaching snare		10	10
806	20f. Rodent in snare		10	10
807	30f. Sprung trap		15	10
808	35f. Deer approaching trap		20	10

292 Human Figure and Caduceus

1981. World Telecommunications Day.
809	292	120f. multicoloured	90	35

293 Sleeping Sickness and Malaria Victim

1981. Campaign against Transmissible Diseases. Multicoloured.
810	40f.+5f. Doctor, nurse, patients and mosquito		25	20
811	65f.+10f. Type **293**		45	20

294 Collecting Rubber

1981. Rubber Extraction. Multicoloured.
812	50f. Tapping rubber tree		20	15
813	70f. Type **294**		40	30

295 Helping a Disabled Person

1981. International Year of Disabled People.
814	295	45f. blue, purple & red	20	15
815	–	75f.+5f. multicoloured	65	30

DESIGN: 75f. Disabled people superimposed on globe.

296 "The Studio"

1981. Air. Birth Centenary of Pablo Picasso. Multicoloured.
816	100f. Type **296**		90	30
817	150f. "Landscape Land and Sea"		1·40	40
818	200f. "The Studio at Cannes"		1·60	50
819	300f. "Still-life with Water Melon"		2·75	85
820	500f. "Large Still-life"		4·50	1·40

297 King Maloango and Mausoleum

1981. Mausoleum of King Maloango. Mult.
821	75f. Mausoleum		60	20
822	150f. Type **297**		1·10	45

298 Prince Charles, Lady Diana Spencer and Coach

1981. Wedding of Prince of Wales. Mult.
823 100f. Type **298** 85 30
824 200f. Couple and Landau . . 1·40 25
825 300f. Couple and horses . . . 2·25 85

299 Preparing Food

1981. World Food Day.
827 **299** 150f. multicoloured . . . 1·25 45

300 Bird carrying Letter

1981. Universal Postal Union Day.
828 **300** 90f. blue, red and grey . . 65 25

301 Guardsman

1981. Royal Guard.
829 **301** 45f. multicoloured 25 15

302 Spraying Cassava

1981. Campaign for the Control of Cassava Beetle.
830 **302** 75f. multicoloured 90 20

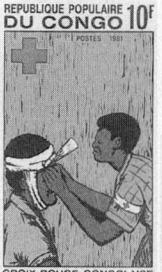 

303 Bandaging a   **304** Brazza's Tree
Patient

1981. Red Cross. Multicoloured.
831 10f. Type **303** 10 10
832 35f. Inoculating a young girl . 20 10
833 60f. Nurse and villagers . . . 30 15

1981. Tree of Brazza.
834 **304** 45f. multicoloured 25 15
835 75f. multicoloured 35 20

305 Fetish   **306** Bangou Caves

1981. Fetishes.
836 **305** 15f. multicoloured 10 10
837 – 25f. multicoloured 15 10
838 – 45f. multicoloured 20 15
839 – 50f. multicoloured 50 15
840 – 60f. multicoloured 55 20
DESIGNS: 25f. to 60f. Different fetishes.

1981. Bangou Caves.
841 **306** 20f. multicoloured 10 10
842 25f. multicoloured 15 10

307 "Congolese Coiffure"

1982. Ivory Sculptures by R. Engongodzo. Multicoloured.
843 25f. Type **307** 15 10
844 35f. "Congo Coiffure"
(different) 20 10
845 100f. "King Makoko, his
Queen and Counsellor"
(horiz) 45 25

308 "Patentee" and Inter-City 125 Express Train, Great Britain

1982. Birth Bicentenary (1981) of George Stephenson (railway engineer). Multicoloured.
846 100f. Type **308** 60 30
847 150f. "Hikari" express train,
Japan 95 45
848 200f. Advanced Passenger
Train (APT), Great Britain 1·40 60
849 300f. TGV 001 locomotive,
France . . . . 2·25 90

309 Scout with Binoculars

1982. 75th Anniv of Boy Scout Movement. Multicoloured.
850 100f. Type **309** 45 25
851 150f. Scout reading map . . 1·00 35
852 200f. Scout talking to village
woman . . . . 1·40 45
853 300f. Scouts on rope bridge . 2·00 70

310 Franklin D. Roosevelt

1982. Anniversaries. Multicoloured.
855 150f. Type **310** (birth cent) . 1·10 35
856 250f. George Washington on
horseback (250th birth
anniv) . . . . 1·90 60
857 350f. Johann von Goethe
(writer) (150th death anniv) 2·50 80

311 Princess of Wales and Candles

1982. 21st Birthday of Princess of Wales. Mult.
858 200f. Type **311** . . . . 1·40 45
859 300f. Princess and "21" . . . 2·00 70

312 Road Building

1982. Five Year Plan. Multicoloured.
861 60f. Type **312** 65 20
862 100f. Telecommunications . . 90 25
863 125f. Operating theatre
equipment . . . . 1·10 30
864 150f. Hydro-electric project . 1·50 55

313 Dish Antenna

1982. I.T.U. Delegates' Conference, Nairobi.
865 **313** 300f. multicoloured . . . 2·25 1·10

314 Mosque, Medina

1982. Air. 1350th Death Anniv of Mohammed.
866 **314** 400f. multicoloured . . . 3·00 1·40

315 W.H.O. Regional Office

1982. World Health Organization Regional Office, Brazzaville.
867 **315** 125f. multicoloured . . . 90 30

316 Mother feeding Baby

1982. Health Campaign.
868 **316** 100f. multicoloured . . . 80 25

1982. Birth of Prince William of Wales. Nos. 823/25 optd **NAISSANCE ROYALE 1982**.
869 100f. multicoloured 45 25
870 200f. multicoloured . . . . . 1·40 80
871 300f. multicoloured . . . . . 2·00 1·10

318 Dr. Robert Koch and Bacillus

1982. Centenary of Discovery of Tubercle Bacillus.
873 **318** 250f. multicoloured . . . 2·25 1·10

1982. World Cup Football Championship Results. Nos. 724/28 optd.
874 60f. **EQUIPE QUATRIEME
FRANCE** 25 20
875 75f. **EQUIPE TROISIEME
POLOGNE** 35 20
876 100f. **EQUIPE SECONDE
ALLEMAGNE (RFA)** 45 25
877 150f. **EQUIPE
VAINQUEUR/ITALIE** . . 1·00 35
878 175f. **ITALIE–ALLEMAGNE
(RFA) 3 1** . . . . 1·40 65

320 Pres. Sassou-Ngeusso and Prize

1982. Award of 1980 Simba Prize to Pres. Sassou-Nguesso.
880 **320** 100f. multicoloured . . . 45 25

321 Turtle

1982. Turtles.
881 **321** 30f. multicoloured 15 10
882 – 45f. multicoloured 55 15
883 – 55f. multicoloured 80 55
DESIGNS: 45, 55f. Different turtles.

322 Amelia Earhart and "Friendship"

1982. 50th Anniv of Amelia Earhart's Transatlantic Flight.
884 **322** 150f. lt brown, grn & brn 1·25 80

323 "La Malafoutier"   **324** Grey Parrots
nesting in Hole in Tree

1982.
885 **323** 100f. multicoloured . . . 80 25

1982. Birds' Nests. Multicoloured.
886 40f. Type **324** 90 20
887 75f. Palm tree and nest . . 1·50 20
888 100f. Nest hanging from
branch . . . . 1·75 25

325 Map of Network

1982. Hertzian Wave Network.
889 325 45f. multicoloured 20 15
890 60f. multicoloured 25 20
891 95f. multicoloured 45 25

326 Council Headquarters, Brussels

1983. 30th Anniv of Customs Co-operation Council.
892 326 100f. multicoloured . . . 45 25

327 Marien N'Gouabi Mausoleum

1983.
893 327 60f. multicoloured 25 20
894 80f. multicoloured 35 20

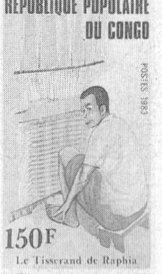

328 Raffia Weaving

1983.
895 328 150f. multicoloured . . . 1·10 35

329 Chess Pieces

1983. Chess Pieces Carved by R. Engongonzo. Multicoloured.
896 329 40f. Type 329 . . . . . . 20 10
897 60f. Close-up of white pawn, king, queen and bishop . 55 20
898 95f. Close-up of black rook, bishop, queen and king . . 1·00 55

330 Blacksmiths

1983.
899 330 45f. multicoloured 45 15

331 Study for "The Transfiguration"

1983. Easter. 500th Birth Anniv of Raphael. Multicoloured.
900 200f. Type 331 . . . . . . 1·60 45
901 300f. "Deposition from the Cross" (horiz) . . . . . 2·25 70
902 400f. "Christ in his Glory" . 2·75 90

332 Comb   333 "Pila ovata"

1983. Traditional Combs. Multicoloured.
903 30f. Type 332 . . . . . . 15 10
904 70f. Comb (different) 55 25
905 85f. Three combs 65 30

1983. Shells. Multicoloured.
906 35f. Type 333 . . . . . . 25 20
907 65f. True achatina 50 35

334 Windsurfing

1983. Air. Pre-Olympic Year.
908 334 100f. multicoloured . . . 80 40
909 — 200f. mult (horiz) . . . . 1·10 50
910 — 300f. multicoloured . . . 1·40 75
911 — 400f. multicoloured . . . 3·25 1·00
DESIGNS: 200 to 400f. Various windsurfing scenes.

335 Montgolfier Balloon, 1783   336 Hands holding Gun and Pick

1983. Air. Bicentenary of Manned Flight. Mult.
913 100f. Type 335 . . . . . . 1·10 40
914 200f. Montgolfier balloon "Le Flesselles", 1784 . . 1·60 50
915 300f. Auguste Piccard's stratosphere balloon "F.N.R.S.", 1931 . . . . 2·25 75
916 400f. Modern hot-air balloon 3·25 1·00

1983. 20th Anniv of Revolution.
918 336 60f. multicoloured 25 20
919 100f. multicoloured 65 35

337 Mgr. A. Carrie and Church of the Sacred Heart, Loango

1983. Centenary of Evangelism. Multicoloured.
920 150f. Type 337 . . . . . . 1·10 50
921 250f. Mgr. Augouard and St. Joseph's Church, Linzolo 1·75 80

338 Thunbergia   339 "Virgin and Child with St. John"

1984. Flowers. Multicoloured.
922 5f. Type 338 . . . . 10 10
923 15f. Bougainvillaea (horiz) . . 10 10
924 20f. Anthurium 15 10
925 45f. Allamanda (horiz) . . . 30 25
926 75f. Hibiscus 45 40

1984. Air. Christmas. Paintings by Botticelli. Multicoloured.
927 150f. Type 339 . . . . . . 1·10 30
928 350f. "Virgin and Child" (St. Barnabas) . . . . . . 2·50 1·00
929 500f. "Virgin and Child" . . 3·50 1·25

340 "Vase of Flowers" (Manet)

1984. Air. Paintings. Multicoloured.
930 100f. Type 340 . . . . . . 55 50
931 200f. "The Small Holy Family" (Raphael) . . . 1·40 50
932 300f. "La Belle Jardiniere" (detail) (Raphael) . . . 2·00 70
933 400f. "The Virgin of Lorette" (Raphael) . . . . . . 2·75 1·00
934 500f. "Richard Wagner" (Giuseppe Tivoli) . . . 3·25 1·25

341 Peace Dove

1984. 34th Anniv of World Peace Council.
935 341 50f. multicoloured 30 25
936 100f. multicoloured 55 50

342 Judo

1984. Air. Olympic Games, Los Angeles. Mult.
937 45f. Type 342 . . . . 30 25
938 75f. Judo (different) (horiz) . . 45 40
939 150f. Wrestling (horiz) . . . . 1·10 55
940 175f. Fencing (horiz) . . . . 1·10 60
941 350f. Fencing (different) (horiz) . . . . 2·50 1·00

343 Mushroom Cloud

1984. Campaign against Weapons of Mass Destruction.
943 343 200f. black, brown & orge 1·40 55

344 Rice

1984. Agriculture. Multicoloured.
944 10f. Type 344 . . . . 10 10
945 15f. Pineapples 10 10
946 60f. Manioc (vert) 35 30
947 100f. Palms (vert) 80 50

345 Congress Palace

1984. Chinese–Congolese Co-operation.
948 345 60f. multicoloured 35 30
949 100f. multicoloured . . . 80 50

346 Loulombo Station

1984. 50th Anniv of Congo Railways. Mult.
950 10f. Type 346 . . . . 15 15
951 25f. Chinese workers' camp at Les Bandas 45 20
952 125f. "50" forming bridge and tunnel . . . . . 2·40 65
953 200f. Headquarters building 3·50 95

347 Alsthom CC203 Diesel Locomotive

1984. Transport. Multicoloured. (a) Locomotives.
954 100f. Type 347 . . . . . . 85 15
955 150f. Alsthom BB 103 diesel 1·25 20
956 300f. Diesel locomotive No. BB BB 301 . . . . . . 2·75 45
957 500f. BB420 diesel train "L'Eclair" . . . . . . 4·50 85

(b) Ships.
958 100f. Pusher tug 80 55
959 150f. Pusher tug (different) . 1·25 65
960 300f. Buoying boat . . . . . 2·50 90
961 500f. "Saint" (freighter) . . 3·75 1·10

348 Giant Ground Pangolin

1984. Animals. Multicoloured.
962	30f. Type **348**	25	15
963	70f. Bat	50	35
964	85f. African civet	90	45

Nos. 962/4 are inscribed "1983".

349 Fish in Basket

350 Polio Victims and Hand

1984. World Fisheries Year. Multicoloured.
965	5f. Type **349**	15	10
966	20f. Casting nets	30	10
967	25f. Fishes	25	10
968	40f. Men pulling nets in . . .	40	20
969	55f. Boat net and fishes . . .	50	30

1984. Anti-polio Campaign. Multicoloured.
| 970 | 250f. Type **350** . . . . . | 2·00 | 1·10 |
| 971 | 300f. Polio victims within target . . . . | 2·50 | 1·40 |

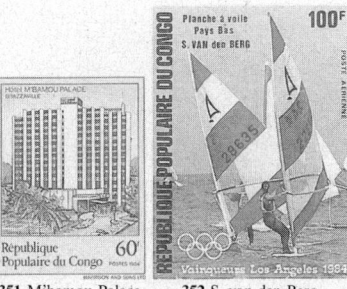

351 M'bamou Palace Hotel, Brazzaville

352 S. van den Berg, Windsurfing

1984.
| 972 | **351** | 60f. multicoloured . . . | 35 | 30 |
| 973 | | 100f. multicoloured . . . | 80 | 50 |

1984. Air. Olympic Games Yachting Gold Medal Winners. Multicoloured.
974	100f. Type **352**	75	30
975	150f. U.S.A., "Soling" class (horiz)	1·10	40
976	200f. Spain, "470" dinghy (horiz)	1·50	60
977	500f. U.S.A., "Flying Dutchman" two-man dinghy	3·75	1·25

353 Floating Logs

1984. Floating Logs on River Congo. Mult.
| 978 | 60f. Type **353** . . . . . | 25 |
| 979 | 100f. Logs and boat on river | 1·00 | 50 |

354 "The Holy Family"

355 "Zonocerus variegatus"

1985. Air. Christmas. Multicoloured.
980	100f. Type **354**	65	30
981	200f. "Virgin and Child" (G. Bellini) (horiz)	1·40	60
982	400f. "Virgin and Child with Angels" (Cimabue) . . .	2·75	1·00

1985.
| 983 | **355** | 125f. multicoloured . . . | 1·10 | 40 |

357 Black-headed Grosbeaks

1985. Air. Birth Bicentenary of John J. Audubon (ornithologist). Multicoloured.
985	100f. Type **357**	1·50	50
986	150f. Scarlet ibis	1·40	60
987	200f. Red-tailed hawk (horiz)	3·75	75
988	350f. Labrador duck	6·25	1·00

358 Funeral Procession

1985. Burial of Teke Chief.
| 989 | **358** | 225f. multicoloured . . . | 1·60 | 70 |

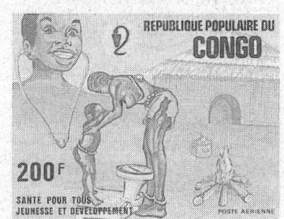

359 Mother weighing Child

1985. "Philexafrique" Stamp Exhibition, Lome, Togo (1st issue). Multicoloured.
| 990 | 200f. Type **359** . . . . . | 1·90 | 1·40 |
| 991 | 200f. Boy writing and man ploughing field . . . . | 1·90 | 1·40 |

See also Nos. 1004/5.

360 "Trichoscypha acuminata"

361 Brazzaville Lions Club Pennant

1985. Fruits. Multicoloured.
992	5f. Type **360**	10	10
993	10f. "Aframomum africanum"	10	10
994	125f. "Gambeya lacurtiana"	90	40
995	150f. "Landolphia jumelei"	1·10	65

1985. 30th Anniv of Lions Club.
| 996 | **361** | 250f. multicoloured . . . | 1·90 | 75 |

362 Moscow Kremlin, Soldier and Battlefield

1985. 40th Anniv of End of World War II.
| 997 | **362** | 60f. multicoloured . . . | 45 | 15 |

363 Doves forming Heart

1985. Air. 25th Anniv of U.N. Membership.
| 998 | **363** | 190f. multicoloured . . . | 1·40 | 60 |

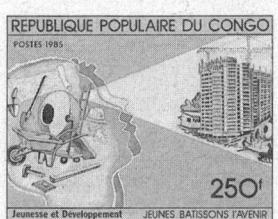

365 Girl Guide with Yellow-bellied Wattle-eye (International Youth Year)

1985. Anniversaries and Events. Multicoloured.
999	150f. Type **365**	1·75	85
1000	250f. Jacob Grimm (folklorist) and scene from "Snow White and the Seven Dwarfs" (birth bicentenary) (International Youth Year) . . .	1·60	75
1001	350f. Johann Sebastian Bach (composer) and organ (300th birth anniv) (European Music Year)	2·25	80
1002	450f. Queen Elizabeth, the Queen Mother (85th birthday) (vert) . .	2·75	90
1003	500f. Statue of Liberty (centenary) (vert) . . .	3·25	1·10

366 Construction Equipment within Heads and Building

1985. "Philexafrique" Stamp Exhibition, Lome, Togo (2nd issue). Multicoloured.
| 1004 | 250f. Type **366** . . . . . | 2·00 | 1·40 |
| 1005 | 250f. Loading mail at airport . . . . | 2·00 | 1·40 |

367 Emblem and Rainbow

368 "Coprinus"

1985. Air. 40th Anniv of U.N.O.
| 1006 | **367** | 180f. multicoloured . . . | 1·25 | 55 |

1985. Fungi. Multicoloured.
1007	100f. Type **368**	1·10	40
1008	150f. "Cortinarius"	1·60	55
1009	200f. "Armillariella mellea"	2·00	60
1010	300f. "Dictyophora"	2·50	75
1011	400f. "Crucibulum vulgare"	3·75	1·00

369 "Virgin and Child" (Gerard David)

1985. Air. Christmas. Multicoloured.
1012	100f. Type **369**	65	30
1013	200f. "Adoration of the Magi" (Hieronymus Bosch)	1·40	60
1014	400f. "Virgin and Child" (Anthony Van Dyck) (horiz)	2·75	1·10

370 Edmond Halley and Computer Picture of Comet

1986. Air. Appearance of Halley's Comet. Multicoloured.
1015	125f. Type **370**	80	40
1016	150f. West's Comet, 1976 (vert)	1·00	55
1017	225f. Ikeya-Seki Comet, 1965 (vert)	1·50	60
1018	300f. "Giotto" space probe and comet trajectory . .	2·00	70
1019	350f. Comet and "Vega" space probe	2·50	80

371 President planting Sapling

372 Boys and Hoops with Handles

1986. National Tree Day. Multicoloured.
| 1020 | 60f. Type **371** . . . . . | 25 | 20 |
| 1021 | 200f. Map, tree and production of oxygen and carbon dioxide . . . . | 1·40 | 75 |

1986. Children's Hoop Races. Multicoloured.
1022	5f. Type **372**	10	10
1023	10f. Boy with hoop on string	10	10
1024	60f. Boys racing with hoops (horiz)	25	20

373 Cosmos-Frantel Hotel

1986. Air.
| 1026 | **373** | 250f. multicoloured . . . | 1·60 | 95 |

375 Emptying Rubbish into Dustbin

376 Woman carrying Basket on Head

1986. World Environment Day. Multicoloured.
| 1030 | 60f. Type **375** . . . . . | 50 | 20 |
| 1031 | 125f. Woman dumping rubbish in street . . . . | 90 | 35 |

1986. Traditional Methods of Carrying Goods. Multicoloured.
1032	5f. Type **376**	10	10
1033	10f. Woman carrying basket at back held by rope from head	10	10
1034	60f. Man carrying wood on shoulder	50	20

377 Footballers

1986. Air. World Cup Football Championship, Mexico.
| 1035 | **377** | 150f. multicoloured . . . | 1·00 | 55 |
| 1036 | – | 250f. multicoloured . . . | 1·75 | 65 |

1037   — 440f. multicoloured . . . 3·00   90
1038   — 600f. multicoloured . . . 4·25   1·40
DESIGNS: 250f. to 600f. Various football scenes.

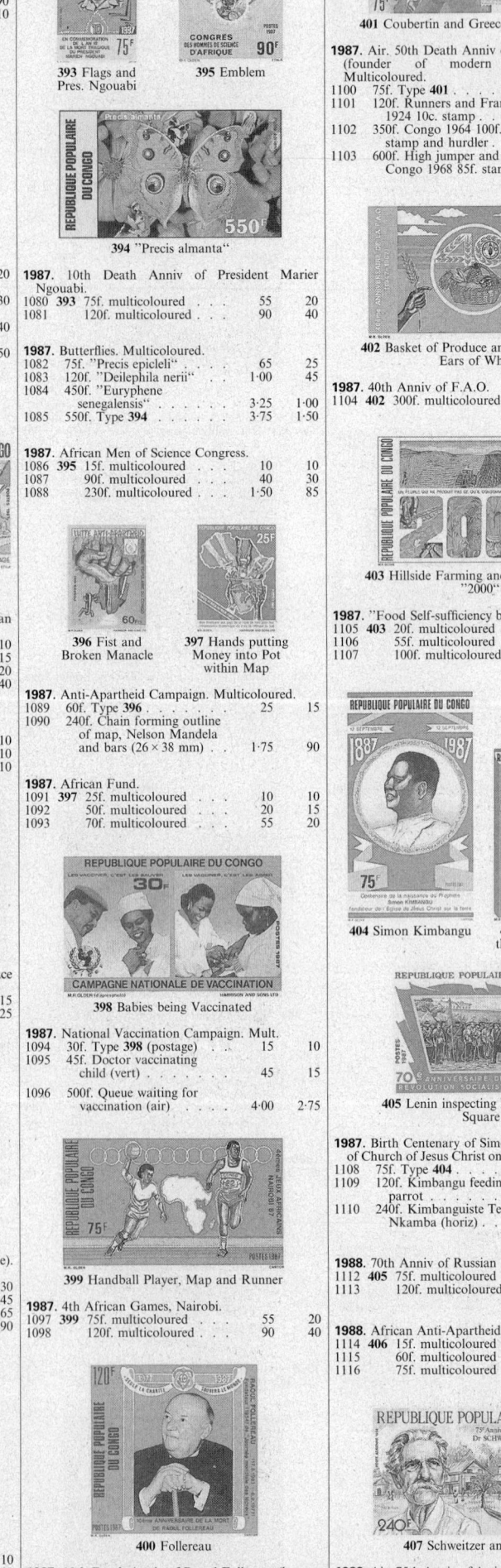

378 Sisters tending Patients   **379** Programme Emblem

1986. Centenary of Sisters of St. Joseph of Cluny Mission.
1039 **378** 230f. multicoloured . . . 1·60   90

1986. International Communications Development Programme.
1040 **379** 40f. multicoloured . . . 15   10
1041   60f. multicoloured . . . 25   20
1042   100f. multicoloured . . . 45   35

380 Emblem   **381** Foodstuffs

1986. International Peace Year.
1043 **380** 100f. blue, grn & lt grn   45   35

1986. World Food Day. Multicoloured.
1044 **381** 75f. Type **381** 60   20
1045   120f. Woman spoon-feeding child 90   40

382 Woman holding Child and Windmill with Medical Symbols   **383** Douglas DC-10 and "25" on Map

1986. U.N.I.C.E.F. Child Survival Campaign. Multicoloured.
1046 **382** 15f. Type **382** 10   10
1047   30f. Children (horiz) 15   10
1048   70f. Woman and child . . . 55   20

1986. Air. 25th Anniv of Air Afrique.
1049 **383** 200f. multicoloured . . . 1·40   65

384 Lenin   **386** "Virgin and Child"

1986. 27th U.S.S.R. Communist Party Congress.
1050 **384** 100f. multicoloured . . . 90   30

1986. Air. Winter Olympic Games, Calgary (1988). Multicoloured.
1051 **385** 150f. Type **385** . . . . 1·00   55
1052   250f. Four-man bobsleigh (vert) . . . . . . 1·75   70

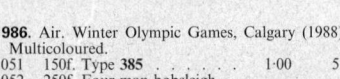
385 Men's Slalom

1053   440f. Ladies cross-country skiing (vert) . . . . . 3·00   1·00
1054   600f. Ski-jumping . . . . 4·25   1·50

1986. Air. Christmas. Paintings by Rogier van der Weyden. Multicoloured.
1055   250f. Type **386** . . . . 1·60   60
1056   440f. "Nativity" . . . . 3·00   90
1057   500f. "Virgin of the Pink"   3·25   1·10

387 "Osteolaemus tetraspis"

1987. Air. Crocodiles. Multicoloured.
1058   75f. Type **387** 90   20
1059   100f. "Crocodylus cataphractus" . . . . 1·00   30
1060   125f. "Osteolaemus tetraspis" (different) . . . 1·10   40
1061   150f. "Crocodylus cataphractus" (different)   1·40   50

388 Pres. Sassou-Nguesso and Map   **389** Traditional Marriage Ceremony

1987. Election of Pres. Sassou-Nguesso as Chairman of Organization of African Unity.
1062 **388** 30f. multicoloured . . . 15   10
1063   45f. multicoloured . . . 20   15
1064   75f. multicoloured . . . 55   20
1065   120f. multicoloured . . . 90   40

1987.
1066 **389** 5f. multicoloured . . . 10   10
1067   15f. multicoloured . . . 10   10
1068   20f. multicoloured . . . 10   10

390 "Sputnik"

1987. Air. 30th Anniv of First Artificial Space Satellite.
1069 **390** 60f. multicoloured . . . 50   15
1070   240f. multicoloured . . . 1·75   1·25

391 Starting Back-stroke Race

1987. Air. Olympic Games, Seoul (1988) (1st issue). Swimming.
1071   100f. Type **391** . . . 65   30
1072   200f. Freestyle . . . 1·40   45
1073   300f. Breast-stroke . . . 2·00   65
1074   400f. Butterfly . . . . 2·75   90
See also Nos. 1121/4.

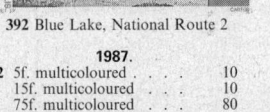
392 Blue Lake, National Route 2

1987.
1076 **392** 5f. multicoloured . . . 10   10
1077   15f. multicoloured . . . 10   10
1078   75f. multicoloured . . . 80   20
1079   120f. multicoloured . . . 1·00   40

393 Flags and Pres. Ngouabi   **395** Emblem

394 "Precis almanta"

1987. 10th Death Anniv of President Marier Ngouabi.
1080 **393** 75f. multicoloured . . . 55   20
1081   120f. multicoloured . . . 90   40

1987. Butterflies. Multicoloured.
1082   75f. "Precis epicleli" . . . 65   25
1083   120f. "Deilephila nerii" . . . 1·00   45
1084   450f. "Euryphene senegalensis" . . . . 3·25   1·00
1085   550f. Type **394** . . . . . 3·75   1·50

1987. African Men of Science Congress.
1086 **395** 15f. multicoloured . . . 10   10
1087   90f. multicoloured . . . 40   30
1088   230f. multicoloured . . . 1·50   85

396 Fist and Broken Manacle   **397** Hands putting Money into Pot within Map

1987. Anti-Apartheid Campaign. Multicoloured.
1089   60f. Type **396** 25   15
1090   240f. Chain forming outline of map, Nelson Mandela and bars (26 × 38 mm) . . 1·75   90

1987. African Fund.
1091 **397** 25f. multicoloured . . . 10   10
1092   50f. multicoloured . . . 20   15
1093   70f. multicoloured . . . 55   20

398 Babies being Vaccinated

1987. National Vaccination Campaign. Mult.
1094   30f. Type **398** (postage) . . . 15   10
1095   45f. Doctor vaccinating child (vert) 45   15
1096   500f. Queue waiting for vaccination (air) . . . 4·00   2·75

399 Handball Player, Map and Runner

1987. 4th African Games, Nairobi.
1097 **399** 75f. multicoloured . . . 55   20
1098   120f. multicoloured . . . 90   40

400 Follereau

1987. 10th Death Anniv of Raoul Follereau (leprosy pioneer).
1099 **400** 120f. multicoloured . . . 1·00   40

---

401 Coubertin and Greece 1896 1d. Stamp

1987. Air. 50th Death Anniv of Pierre de Coubertin (founder of modern Olympic games). Multicoloured.
1100   75f. Type **401** 55   20
1101   120f. Runners and France 1924 10c. stamp 90   40
1102   350f. Congo 1964 100f. stamp and hurdler . . . . 2·50   90
1103   600f. High jumper and Congo 1968 85f. stamp   4·00   1·40

402 Basket of Produce and Hands holding Ears of Wheat

1987. 40th Anniv of F.A.O.
1104 **402** 300f. multicoloured . . . 2·00   1·00

403 Hillside Farming and Produce within "2000"

1987. "Food Self-sufficiency by Year 2000".
1105 **403** 20f. multicoloured . . . 10   10
1106   55f. multicoloured . . . 50   20
1107   100f. multicoloured . . . 80   30

404 Simon Kimbangu   **406** Writer crossing through "Apartheid"

1987. Birth Centenary of Simon Kimbangu (founder of Church of Jesus Christ on Earth). Multicoloured.
1108   75f. Type **404** 55   20
1109   120f. Kimbangu feeding grey parrot . . . . . 1·50   80
1110   240f. Kimbanguiste Temple, Nkamba (horiz) . . . . 1·90   90

1988. 70th Anniv of Russian Revolution.
1112 **405** 75f. multicoloured . . . 90   55
1113   120f. multicoloured . . . 1·40   80

1988. African Anti-Apartheid Writers.
1114 **406** 15f. multicoloured . . . 10   10
1115   60f. multicoloured . . . 25   15
1116   75f. multicoloured . . . 55   20

405 Lenin inspecting Parade in Red Square

407 Schweitzer and Hospital

1988. Air. 75th Anniv of Arrival at Lambarene of Dr. Albert Schweitzer (missionary).
1117 **407** 240f. multicoloured . . . 1·90   90

408 Samuel Morse **409** Banknote and Field within "10"

1988. 150th Anniv of Morse Telegraph. Mult.
1118 90f. Type **408** 65 25
1119 120f. Morse and telegraph
equipment 90 35

1988. 10th Anniv of International Agricultural Development Fund.
1120 **409** 240f. multicoloured . . . 1·50 80

1988. Air. Olympic Games, Seoul (2nd issue). Modern Pentathlon. As T **391**. Multicoloured.
1121 75f. Swimming 55 20
1122 170f. Cross-country running
(vert) . . . . 1·25 55
1123 200f. Shooting . . . . . 1·40 65
1124 600f. Horse-riding . . . . . 4·00 1·25

411 Eucalyptus Plantation, Brazzaville **412** Hands holding Gun and Pick

1988. Anti-desertification Campaign. Mult.
1126 5f. Type **411** 10 10
1127 10f. Stop sign and man
chopping down tree . . . 10 10

1988. 25th Anniv of Revolution. Multicoloured.
1128 75f. Type **412** 55 20
1129 75f. People tending crops . . 55 20
1130 120f. Pres. Sassou-Nguesso
holding aubergine 80 35

413 Yoro Fishing Village

1988.
1131 35f. Type **413** 20 10
1132 40f. Place de la Liberte . . . 20 10

414 People on Map and Jet Fighters attacking Virus

1988. 1st International Day against A.I.D.S.
1133 **414** 60f. multicoloured 30 10
1134 – 75f. multicoloured . . . 55 20
1135 – 180f. black, red & blue 1·25 85
DESIGNS: 75f. Virus consisting of healthy and infected people; 180f. Globe and laurel branches.

415 Pres. Sassou-Nguesso addressing Crowd

1989. 10th Anniv of 5 February Movement. Multicoloured.
1136 75f. Type **415** 55 20
1137 120f. Pres. Sassou-Nguesso
and symbols of progress . 2·25 75

416 Emblems

1989. 40th Anniv of Declaration of Human Rights.
1138 **416** 120f. multicoloured . . . 80 35
1139 350f. multicoloured . . . 2·00 1·10

417 Bari

1989. Air. World Cup Football Championship, Italy (1990) (1st issue). Multicoloured.
1140 75f. Type **417** 55 20
1141 120f. Rome 90 35
1142 500f. Florence . . . . . 3·50 80
1143 550f. Naples . . . . . . 4·00 1·10
See also Nos. 1174/7.

418 "Storming of the Bastille"
(detail, J. P. Houel)

1989. Air. "Philexfrance 89" International Stamp Exhibition. Multicoloured.
1144 300f. Type **418** (bicent of
French revolution) . . . 2·25 1·00
1145 400f. "Eiffel Tower"
(G. Seurat) (centenary of
Eiffel Tower (1986)) . . . 2·75 1·25

419 Astronaut and Landing Module

1989. Air. 20th Anniv of First Manned Landing on Moon. Multicoloured.
1146 400f. Type **419** . . . . . . 2·75 1·25
1147 400f. Astronaut on lunar
surface . . . . 2·75 1·25

420 Marien Ngouabi

1989. 50th Birth Anniv (1988) of Marien Ngouabi (President, 1969–77).
1148 **420** 240f. black, yell & mve 1·60 65

421 Henri Dunant (founder), **422** Emblem on Dove
Volunteer with Child and Anniversary Emblem

1989. 125th Anniv (1988) of Red Cross.
1149 75f. Type **421** (postage) . . . 55 20
1150 120f. Emblem, Dunant and
Congolese Red Cross
station (air) 90 35

1989. 25th Anniv of Organization of African Unity.
1151 **422** 120f. multicoloured . . . 90 35

423 "Opuntia phaeacantha"

1989. Cacti. Multicoloured.
1152 35f. Type **423** 15 10
1153 40f. "Opuntia ficus-indica" . 15 10
1154 60f. "Opuntia erinacea"
(horiz) 50 15
1155 75f. "Opuntia rufida" . . . 55 20
1156 120f. "Opuntia leptocaulis"
(horiz) 90 40

424 Banknote, Coins and Woman

1989. 25th Anniv of African Development Bank.
1158 **424** 75f. multicoloured . . . 55 20
1159 120f. multicoloured . . . 90 40

425 Ice Dancing

1989. Winter Olympic Games, Albertville (1992) (1st issue). Multicoloured.
1160 75f. Type **425** 30 20
1161 80f. Cross-country skiing . . . 30 20
1162 100f. Speed skating 65 30
1163 120f. Luge 80 40
1164 200f. Slalom . . . . 1·40 45
1165 240f. Ice hockey . . . . . 1·40 50
1166 400f. Ski jumping . . . . . 2·75 70
See also Nos. 1245/6.

426 Doctor examining Patient **427** Emblem and People with raised Fists

1989. 40th Anniv of W.H.O. Multicoloured.
1168 60f. Type **426** 55 15
1169 75f. Blood donation (vert) . . 65 55

1989. 20th Anniv of Congolese Workers' Party.
1170 **427** 75f. multicoloured . . . 55 20
1171 120f. multicoloured . . . 90 40

1990. Local Health Campaigns. Nos. 1168/9 optd
NOTRE PLANETE, NOTRE SANTE PENSER GLOBALEMENT AGIR LOCALEMENT.
1172 60f. multicoloured 55 45
1173 75f. multicoloured 65 55

429 Footballers **430** Family supporting Open Book

1990. Air. World Cup Football Championship, Italy (2nd issue). Designs showing footballers.
1174 **429** 120f. multicoloured . . . 90 40
1175 – 240f. multicoloured . . . 1·75 60
1176 – 500f. multicoloured . . . 3·25 1·00
1177 – 600f. multicoloured . . . 4·00 1·25

1990. International Literacy Year.
1178 **430** 75f. black, yellow & blue 55 20

431 Ramblas, Barcelona

1990. Olympic Games, Barcelona (1992) (1st issue). Multicoloured.
1179 100f. Type **431** (postage) . . 65 30
1180 150f. Yachting (horiz) . . . 1·10 35
1181 200f. Yachting (different)
(horiz) . . . . 1·40 45
1182 240f. Market stalls,
Barcelona (horiz) . . . . 1·40 65
1183 350f. Harbour, Barcelona
(horiz) (air) . . . . . 2·50 75
1184 500f. Monument, Barcelona 3·25 1·00
See also Nos. 1322/7.

432 Turtle Dove ("Tourterelle des boris")

1990. Birds. Multicoloured.
1186 25f. Type **432** 35 30
1187 50f. Dartford warbler
("Fauvette Pitchou")
(vert) 70 40
1188 70f. Common kestrel
("Faucon Crecerelle")
(vert) . . . . 1·25 70
1189 150f. Grey parrot
("Perroquet Gris") (vert) . 2·25 1·60

433 Mondo Mask **435** Sunflower

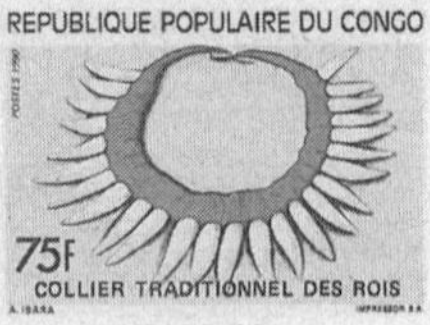

434 Necklace

1990. Dance Masks. Multicoloured.

1190	120f. Type **433**	90	40
1191	360f. Bapunu mask	2·50	1·25
1192	400f. Kwele mask	2·75	1·40

1990. Traditional Royal Necklaces. Multicoloured.

1193	75f. Type **434**	55	20
1194	100f. Money cowrie necklace	55	35

1990. Flowers. Multicoloured.

1195	30f. Type **435**	15	10
1196	45f. "Cassia alata" (horiz)	20	10
1197	75f. Opium poppy	55	20
1198	90f. "Acalypha sanderil"	65	25

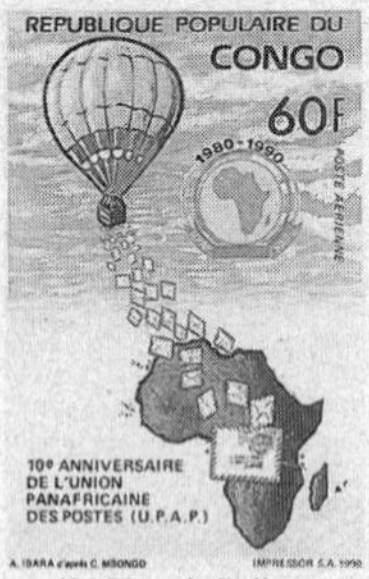

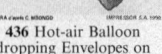

436 Hot-air Balloon dropping Envelopes on Africa

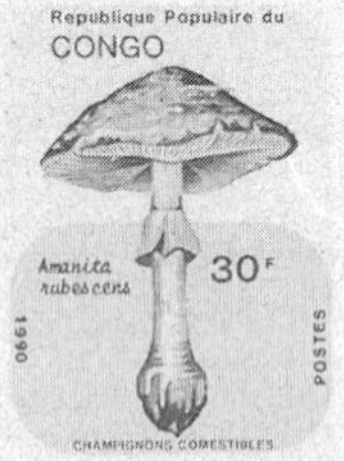

437 The Blusher

1991. Air. 10th Anniv of Pan-African Postal Union. Multicoloured.

1199	60f. Type **436**	40	20
1200	120f. Envelopes on map of Africa	90	55

1991. Fungi. Multicoloured.

1201	30f. Type **437**	25	10
1202	45f. "Catathelasma imperiale"	35	15
1203	75f. Caesar's mushroom	55	25
1204	90f. Royal boletus	65	30
1205	120f. Deer mushroom	1·00	45
1206	150f. "Boletus chrysenteron"	1·10	50
1207	200f. Horse mushroom	1·60	70

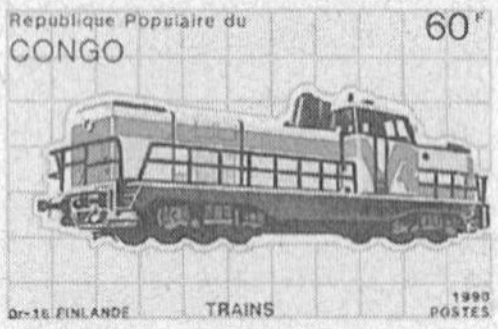

438 Type Dr-16 Diesel Locomotive, Finland

1991. Trains. Multicoloured.

1209	60f. Type **438**	90	15
1210	75f. TGV express, France	1·10	20
1211	120f. Suburban S-350 electric railcar, Italy	1·75	30
1212	200f. Type DE 24000 diesel locomotive, Turkey	3·25	55
1213	250f. DE 1024 diesel-electric locomotive, Germany	4·00	70

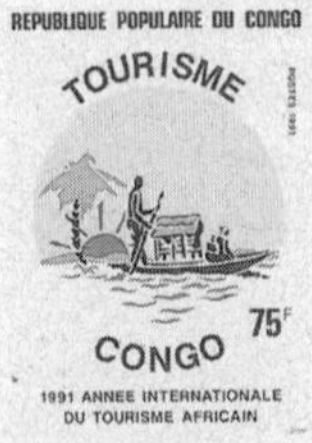

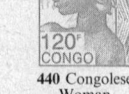

439 Canoe, Palm Tree and Setting Sun

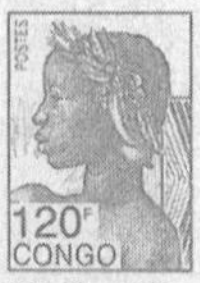

440 Congolese Woman

1991. International African Tourism Year. Multicoloured.

1215	75f. Type **439**	55	20
1216	120f. Zebra and map of Africa	90	55

1991.

1217	**440** 15f. blue	10	10
1218	30f. green	15	10
1219	60f. yellow	30	15
1220	75f. mauve	35	20
1221	120f. brown	60	30

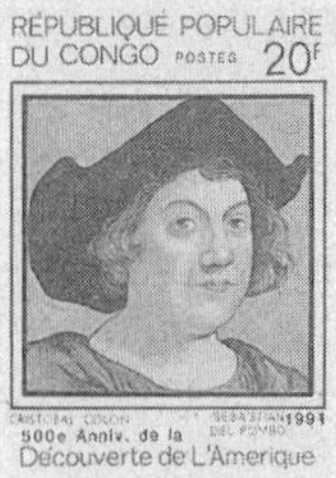

441 Christopher Columbus (after Sebastian del Pombo)

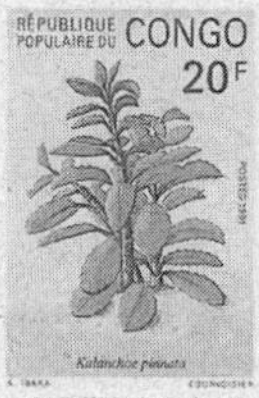

442 "Kalanchoe pinnata"

1991. 500th Anniv (1992) of Discovery of America by Columbus. Multicoloured.

1222	20f. Type **441**	10	10
1223	35f. Christopher Columbus	15	10
1224	40f. Christopher Columbus (different)	20	10
1225	55f. "Santa Maria"	60	20
1226	75f. "Nina"	80	30
1227	150f. "Pinta"	1·40	55
1228	200f. Arms and signature of Columbus	1·40	80

1991. Medicinal Plants. Multicoloured.

1229	15f. "Ocimum viride" (horiz)	10	10
1230	20f. Type **442**	10	10
1231	30f. "Euphorbia hirta" (horiz)	15	10
1232	60f. "Catharantheus roseus"	30	15
1233	75f. "Bidens pilosa"	60	20
1234	100f. "Brillantasia patula"	80	50
1235	120f. "Cassia occidentalis"	90	65

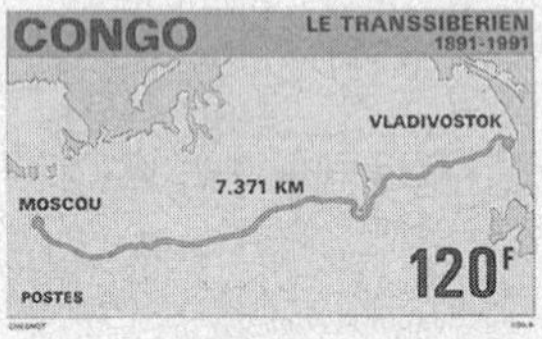

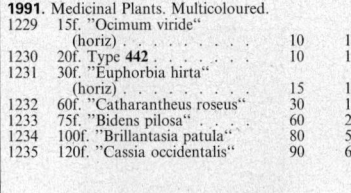

443 Route Map

1991. Centenary of Trans-Siberian Railway. Mult.

1236	120f. Type **443**	1·50	45
1237	240f. Russian Class N steam locomotive superimposed on map	2·25	80

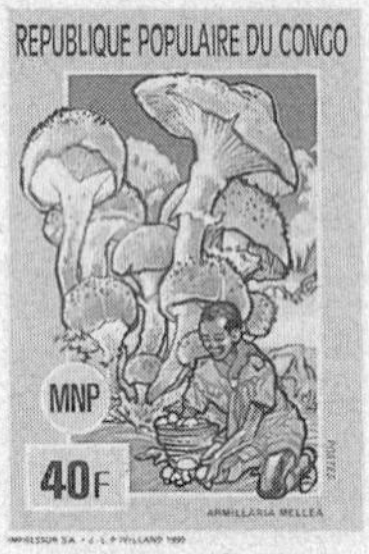

444 Honey fungus

1991. Scouts, Butterflies and Fungi. Mult.

1238	35f. "Euphaedra eusemoides" (butterfly) (postage)	15	10
1239	40f. Type **444**	40	15
1240	75f. "Palla decius" (butterfly)	60	20
1241	80f. "Kallima ansorgei" (butterfly)	65	20
1242	500f. "Cortinarius speciocissimus" (fungus) (air)	3·75	1·40
1243	600f. "Graphium illyris" (butterfly)	4·00	1·40

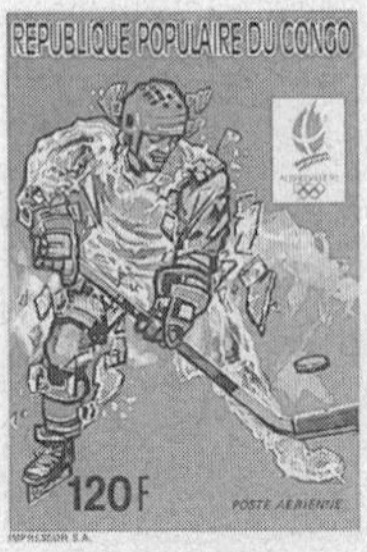

445 Ice Hockey

1991. Air. Winter Olympic Games, Albertville (1992) (2nd issue). Multicoloured.

1245	120f. Type **445**	90	30
1246	300f. Speed skating	2·00	70

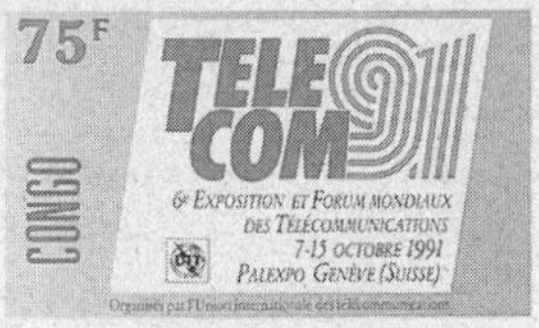

446 "Telecom 91"

1991. "Telecom 91" World Telecommunications Exhibition, Geneva. Multicoloured.

1248	75f. Type **446**	60	20
1249	120f. Stylized view of exhibition (vert)	90	55

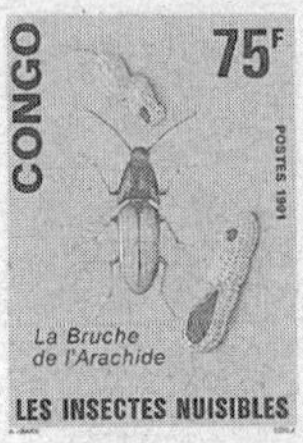

447 Beetle and Peanuts

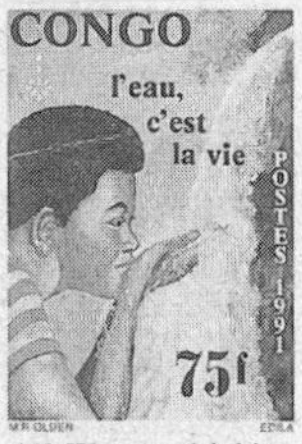

448 Woman drinking at Waterfall

1991. Harmful Insects. Multicoloured.

1250	75f. Type **447**	60	20
1251	120f. Stag beetle (horiz)	90	30
1252	200f. Beetle and coffee	1·40	50
1253	300f. Goliath beetle	2·25	70

1991. "Water is Life".

1254	**448** 75f. multicoloured	60	20

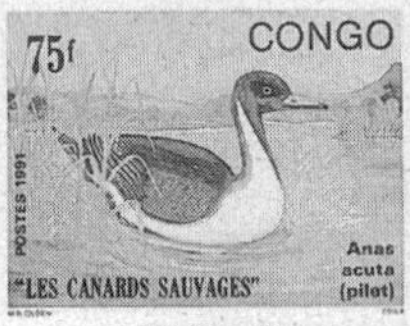

449 Pintail

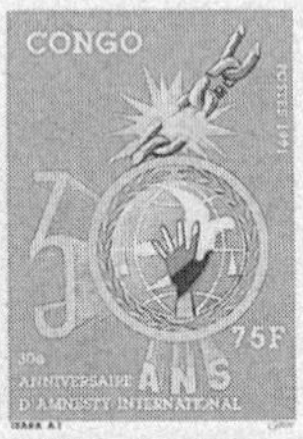

450 Breaking Chain and Hand holding Dove

1991. Wild Ducks. Multicoloured.

1255	75f. Type **449**	60	20
1256	120f. Eider (vert)	90	30
1257	200f. Common shoveler (vert)	1·40	90
1258	240f. Mallard	1·60	1·10

1991. 30th Anniv of Amnesty International. Multicoloured.

1259	40f. Candle, barbed wire and sun	20	10
1260	75f. Type **450**	35	20
1261	80f. Boy holding human rights banner and soldiers threatening boy (horiz)	65	45

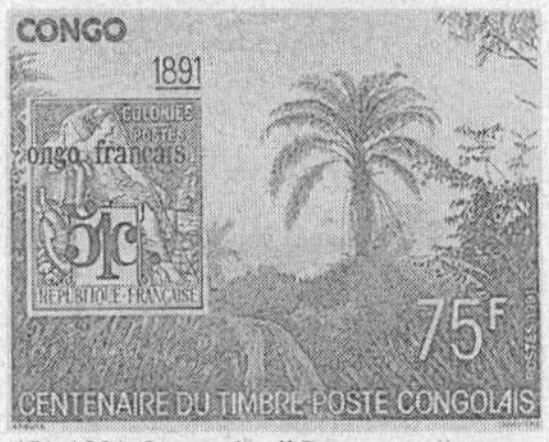

451 1891 5c. on 1c. "Commerce" stamp

1991. Centenary of Congolese Stamps.

1262	**451** 75f. green and brown	60	45
1263	– 120f. dp brn, grn & brn	1·10	90
1264	– 240f. multicoloured	2·00	1·40
1265	– 500f. multicoloured	3·50	2·75

DESIGNS: 120f. 1900 1c. "Leopard in ambush" stamp; 240f. 1959 25f. "Birth of the Republic" stamp; 500f. "Commerce", "Leopard" and "Republic" stamps.

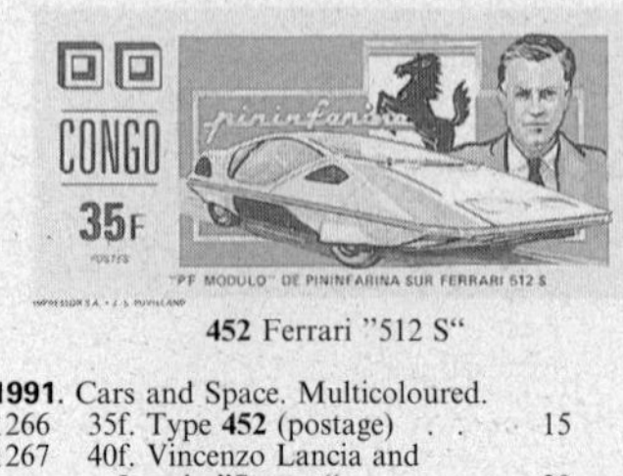

452 Ferrari "512 S"

1991. Cars and Space. Multicoloured.

1266	35f. Type **452** (postage)	15	10
1267	40f. Vincenzo Lancia and Lancia "Stratos"	20	10
1268	75f. Airship "Graf Zeppelin", Maybach "Type 12" car and Wilhelm Maybach	45	25
1269	80f. Mars space probe	40	20
1270	500f. "Magellan" space probe over Venus (air)	3·25	80
1271	600f. "Ulysses" space probe photographing sun spot	4·00	90

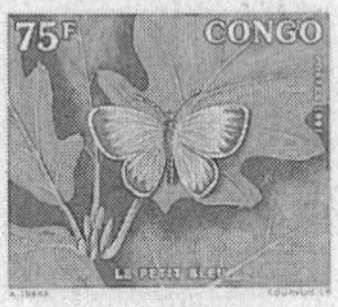

453 Small Blue

1991. Butterflies. Multicoloured.

1273	75f. Type **453**	35	20
1274	120f. Charaxes	80	30
1275	240f. Leaf butterfly (vert)	1·60	90
1276	300f. Butterfly on orange (vert)	2·00	1·40

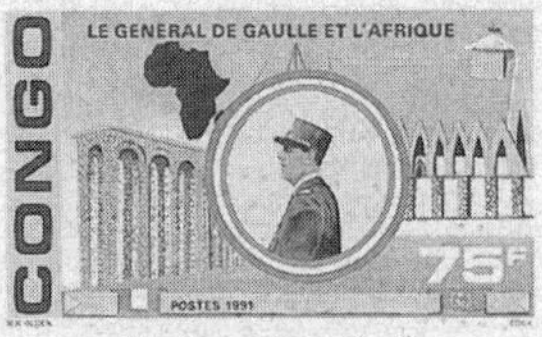

454 General De Gaulle

1991. De Gaulle and Africa. Multicoloured.

1277	75f. Type **454**	65	20
1278	120f. De Gaulle, soldiers and Free French flag (vert)	90	30
1279	240f. De Gaulle making speech, Brazzaville, 1940	1·75	1·10

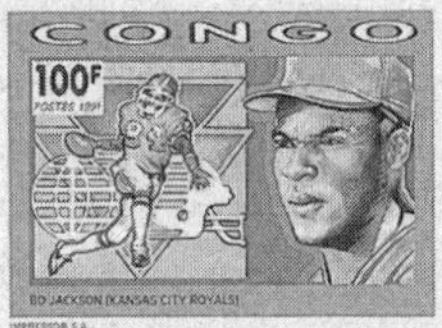

455 Bo Jackson (American footballer)

1991. Celebrities and International Organizations. Multicoloured.

1280	100f. Type **455**	50	25
1281	150f. Nick Faldo (golfer)	1·00	35
1282	200f. Rickey Henderson and Barry Bonds (baseball players)	1·40	50
1283	240f. Gary Kasparov (World chess champion)	1·75	55
1284	300f. Starving child and Lions International and Rotary International emblems	2·00	70
1285	350f. Wolfgang Amadeus Mozart (composer)	2·75	80
1286	400f. De Gaulle and Churchill visiting the Eastern Front, 1944	2·75	95
1287	500f. Henry Dunant (founder of Red Cross)	3·25	1·00

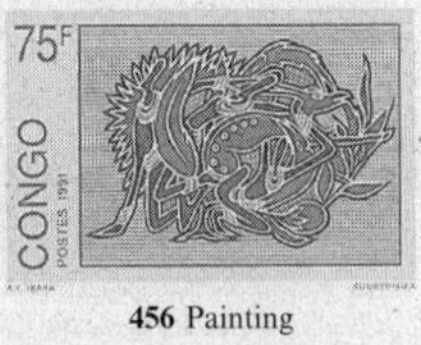

456 Painting

1991. Paintings. Multicoloured.

1289	75f. Type **456**	60	20
1290	120f. Couple in silhouette (vert)	90	30

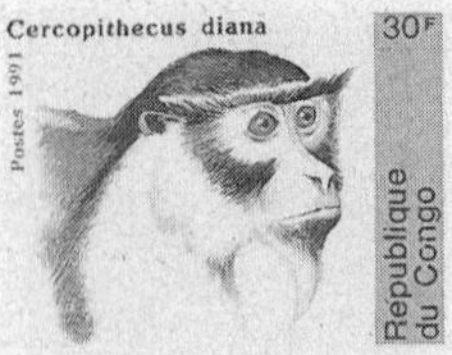

457 Diana Monkey

1991. Primates. Multicoloured.

1291	30f. Type **457**	15	10
1292	45f. Chimpanzee	20	10
1293	60f. Gelada (vert)	55	15
1294	75f. Hamadryas baboon (vert)	80	20
1295	90f. Pigtail macaque (vert)	90	20
1296	120f. Gorilla (vert)	1·10	30
1297	240f. Mandrill (vert)	2·25	55

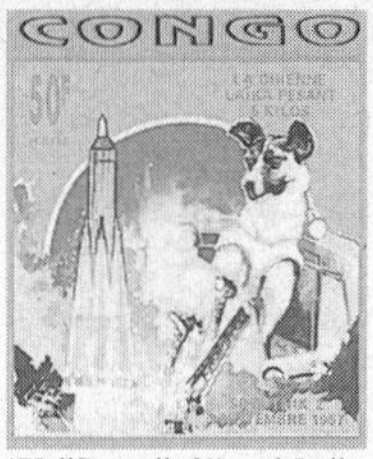

458 "Sputnik 2" and Laika (space dog)

1992. Celebrities, Anniversaries and Events. Mult.

1299	50f. Type **458** (35th anniv of space flight) (postage)	45	10
1300	75f. Martin Luther King (Nobel Peace Prize winner, 1964) and Gandhi	60	20
1301	120f. Meteosat "MOP-2" and "ERS-1" satellites, globe and stern trawler ("Europe-Africa")	1·25	40
1302	300f. Konrad Adenauer (German statesman, 25th death anniv) and crowd before Brandenburg Gate (3rd anniv of opening of Berlin Wall)	2·00	70
1303	240f. "Graf Zeppelin", Ferdinand von Zeppelin (75th death anniv) and Maybach Zeppelin motor car (air)	1·40	70
1304	500f. Pope and globe (Papal visit to Africa)	3·25	1·00

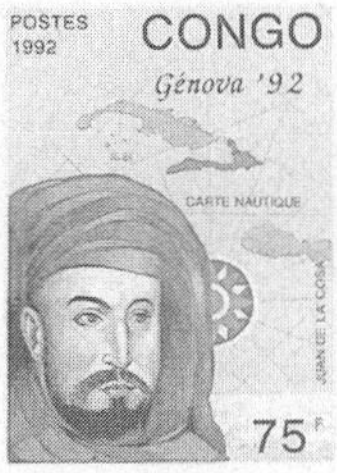

459 Juan de la Cosa and Map

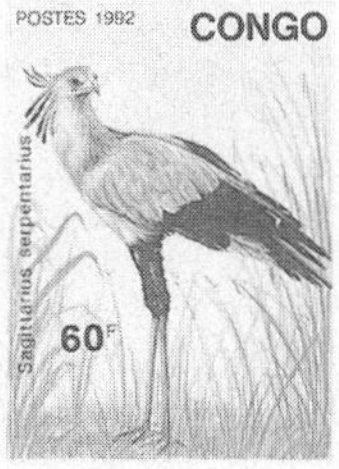

460 Secretary Bird

1992. "Genova 92" International Thematic Stamp Exhibition. Multicoloured.

1306	75f. Type **459**	80	20
1307	95f. Martin Alonso Pinzon and astrolabe	1·00	25
1308	120f. Alonso de Ojeda and hourglass	1·40	30
1309	200f. Vicente Yanez Pinzon and sun clock	2·00	45
1310	250f. Bartholomew Columbus and quadrant	2·25	55

1992. Birds. Multicoloured.

1312	60f. Type **460**	65	15
1313	75f. Saddle-bill stork	80	20
1314	120f. Wattled crane	1·10	30
1315	200f. Black-headed heron	1·90	45
1316	250f. Greater flamingo	2·75	55

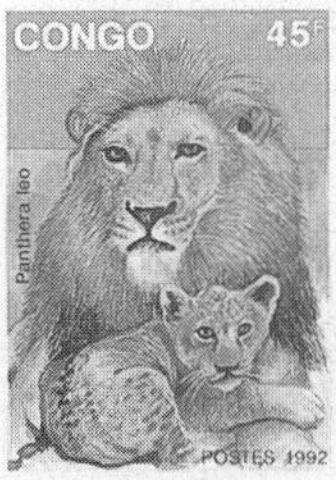

461 Lion

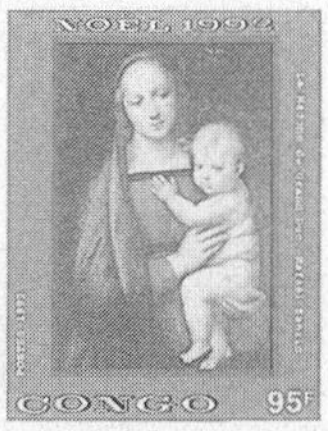

462 "Madonna of the Grand Duke" (Raphael)

1992. Big Cats. Multicoloured.

1318	45f. Type **461**	50	25
1319	60f. Tiger	70	35
1320	75f. Lynx	85	40
1321	95f. Caracal	1·10	55
1322	250f. Ocelot	2·75	1·40

1992. Christmas. Multicoloured.

1324	95f. Type **462**	70	25
1325	200f. "Madonna of the Book" (Sandro Botticelli)	1·40	50
1326	250f. "Carondelet Madonna" (Fra Bartolommeo)	1·75	1·10

No. 1325 is wrongly inscribed "Boticelli" and No. 1326 "Bartolomeo".

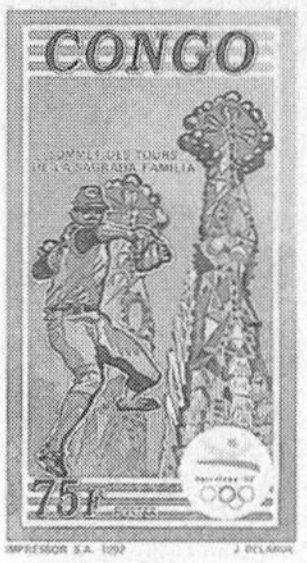

463 Baseball and Towers of Church of the Holy Family

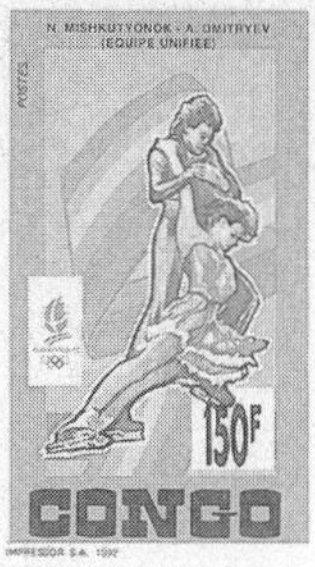

464 N. Mishkutienok and A. Dmitriev (Unified Team)

1992. Olympic Games, Barcelona (2nd issue). Multicoloured.

1328	75f. Type **463** (postage)	35	20
1329	100f. Running and "The Muses" (Eusebio Arnau)	50	25
1330	150f. Hurdling and painted dome (Miguel Barcelo) of Market Theatre	1·00	35
1331	200f. High jumping and Sant Pau hospital	1·40	50
1332	400f. Putting the shot and "Miss Barcelona" (Joan Miro) (air)	2·75	85
1333	500f. Table tennis and "Don Juan of Austria" (galley)	3·25	1·00

1992. Winter Olympic Games Gold Medal Winners. Multicoloured.

1335	150f. Type **464** (pairs figure skating) (postage)	1·00	35
1336	200f. Austrian team (four-man bobsleighing)	1·40	50
1337	500f. Gunda Niemann (Germany, women's speed skating) (air)	3·25	90
1338	600f. Bjorn Daehlie (Norway, 50 km cross-country skiing)	4·00	1·00

No. 1338 is wrongly inscribed "Blorn Daehlle".

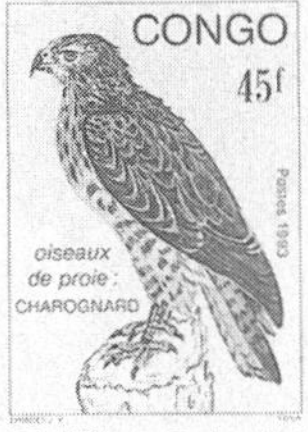

465 African Red-tailed Buzzard ("Charognard")

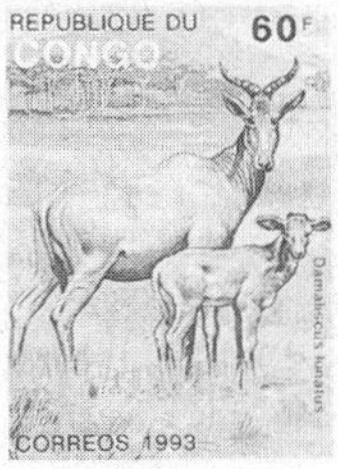

467 Topi

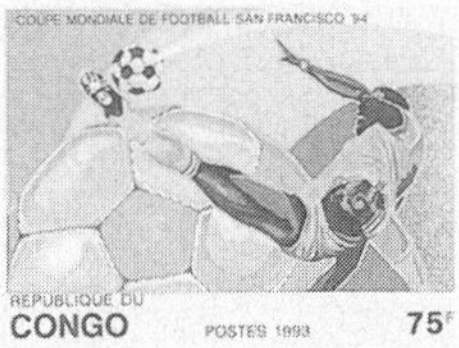

466 Overhead Volley

1993. Birds of Prey. Multicoloured.

1340	45f. Type **465**	20	10
1341	75f. Ruppell's griffon ("Vautour")	60	20
1342	120f. Verreaux's eagle ("Aigle")	80	55

1993. World Cup Football Championship, U.S.A. (1994).

1343 **466**	75f. multicoloured	80	20
1344 –	95f. multicoloured	1·00	25
1345 –	120f. multicoloured	1·40	30
1346 –	200f. multicoloured	2·00	50
1347 –	250f. multicoloured	2·75	65

DESIGNS: 95f. to 250f. Different footballing scenes.

1993. Animals. Multicoloured.

1349	60f. Type **467**	60	15
1350	75f. Grant's gazelle	80	20
1351	95f. Quagga	1·00	25
1352	120f. Leopard	1·25	25
1353	200f. African buffalo	2·00	25
1354	250f. Hippopotamus	2·50	30
1355	300f. Hooded vulture	3·00	35
1356	350f. Lioness and cub	3·25	55

Nos. 1349/56 were issued together, se-tenant, forming a composite design.

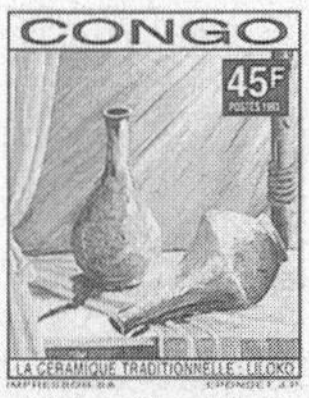

468 Jars from Liloko

1993. Traditional Pottery. Multicoloured.

1357	45f. Type **468**	20	10
1358	75f. Jug from Mbeya	35	20
1359	120f. Jar from Mbeya	60	30

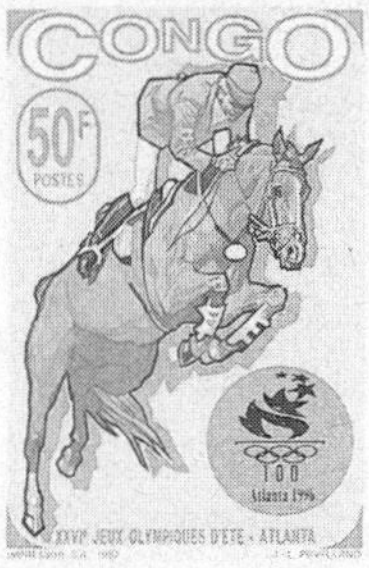

470 Show Jumping

1993. Summer Olympic Games, Atlanta (1996) and Winter Olympic Games, Lillehammer, Norway (1994). Multicoloured.

1366	50f. Type **470** (postage)	25	15
1367	75f. Cycling	35	20
1368	120f. Two-man dinghy	60	30
1369	240f. Fencing	1·40	55
1370	300f. Hurdling (air)	2·25	70
1371	400f. Figure skating	2·75	95
1372	500f. Basketball	3·25	90
1373	600f. Ice hockey	4·00	1·25

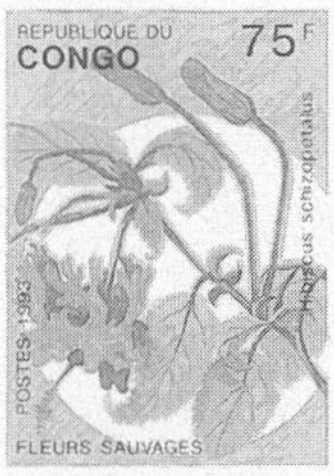

471 "Hibiscus schizopetalus"

1993. Wild Flowers. Multicoloured.

1375	75f. Type **471**	35	20
1376	95f. "Pentas lanceolata"	45	25
1377	120f. "Ricinus communis"	90	30
1378	200f. "Delonix regia"	1·50	50
1379	250f. "Stapelia gigantea"	1·90	90

OFFICIAL STAMPS

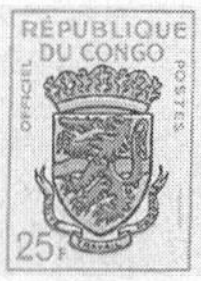

O 68 Arms

1968.

O142 **O 68**	1f. multicoloured	10	10
O143	2f. multicoloured	10	10
O144	5f. multicoloured	10	10
O145	10f. multicoloured	20	15
O146	25f. multicoloured	20	10
O147	30f. multicoloured	45	10
O148	50f. multicoloured	60	30
O149	85f. multicoloured	1·50	65
O150	100f. multicoloured	1·75	1·10
O151	200f. multicoloured	2·50	1·60

POSTAGE DUE STAMPS

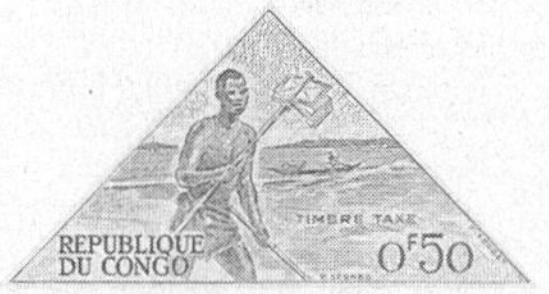

D 7 Letter-carrier

1961. Transport designs.

D19 **D 7**	50c. bistre, red & blue	10	10
D20 –	50c. bistre, purple & bl	10	10
D21 –	1f. brown, red & green	10	10
D22 –	1f. green, red and lake	10	10
D23 –	2f. brown, green & bl	10	15
D24 –	2f. brown, green & bl	10	15
D25 –	5f. sepia and violet	15	15
D26 –	5f. sepia and violet	15	15
D27 –	10f. brown, blue & grn	1·00	40
D28 –	10f. brown and green	1·00	40
D29 –	25f. brown, blue & turq	1·10	1·10
D30 –	25f. black and blue	1·10	1·10

DESIGNS: D20, Holste Broussard monoplane; D21, Hammock-bearers; D22, "Land Rover" car; D23, Pirogue; D24, River steamer of 1932; D25, Cyclist; D26, Motor lorry; D27, Steam locomotive, 1932; D28, Diesel locomotive; D29, Seaplane of 1935; D30, Boeing 707 airliner.

1971. Tropical Flowers. Similar to T **105**, but inscr "Timbre-Taxe". Multicoloured.

D264	1f. Stylized bouquet	10	10
D265	2f. "Phaeomeria magnifica"	10	10
D266	5f. "Millettia laurentii"	10	10
D267	10f. "Polianthes tuberosa"	15	15
D268	15f. "Pyrostegia venusta"	20	20
D269	20f. "Hibiscus rosa sinensis"	25	25

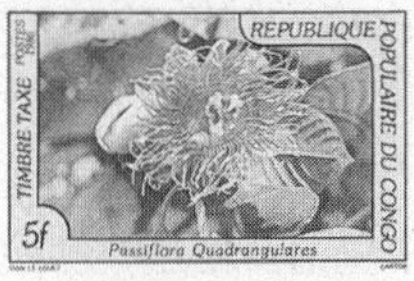

D 374 Passion Flower

1986. Flowers and Fruit. Multicoloured.

D1027	5f. Type D **374**	10	10
D1028	10f. Canna lily	10	10
D1029	15f. Pineapple	10	10

APPENDIX

The following stamps have either been issued in excess of postal needs or have not been available to the public in reasonable quantities at face value. Such stamps may later be given full listing if there is evidence of regular postal use.

All embossed on gold foil

1991.

Scout and Butterfly. Air 1500f.

Winter Olympic Games, Albertville (1992). Air 1500f.

1992.

Olympic Games, Barcelona. Air 1500f.

CONGO DEMOCRATIC REPUBLIC (EX ZAIRE) Pt. 14

In May 1997 Zaire changed its name to the Democratic Republic of Congo after President Mobutu and his Government was overthrown by a rebellion led by Laurent Kabila.

New Currency

July 1998. 100 cents = 1 congolise franc

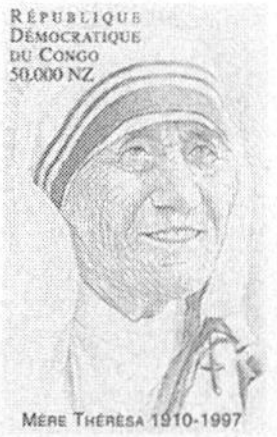

273 Mother Teresa

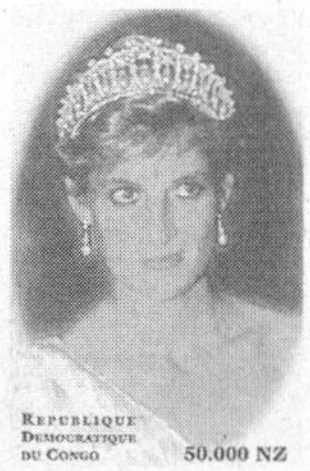

274 Diana Princess of Wales

1998. 1st Death Anniv of Mother Teresa (founder of Missionaries of Charity).

1494 **273**	50000z. multicoloured	1·25	80

1998. 1st Death Anniv of Diana, Princess of Wales. Multicoloured.

1496	50000z. Type **274**	1·10	80
1497	50000z. Wearing white jacket with blue collar	1·10	80
1498	50000z. Wearing large hat	1·10	80
1499	50000z. Wearing white top with blue dots	1·10	80
1500	50000z. Wearing neck scarf	1·10	80
1501	50000z. Wearing pearl necklace	1·10	80
1502	100000z. Wearing tiara	2·10	1·60
1503	100000z. Wearing black top	2·10	1·60
1504	100000z. Resting head on hands	2·10	1·60
1505	100000z. Wearing cream top	2·10	1·60
1506	125000z. Wearing red and black dress	2·50	2·00
1507	125000z. Wearing cream jacket	2·50	2·00
1508	125000z. Profile	2·50	2·00
1509	125000z. Wearing tiara	2·50	2·00

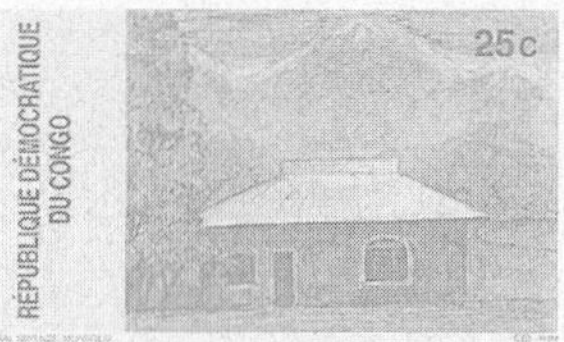

275 Building

1999. Independence. Multicoloured.

1511	25c. Type **275**	50	50
1512	50c. Coat of Arms	95	95
1513	75c. Making speech	1·40	1·40
1514	1f.25 Procession	2·40	2·40
1515	3f. Crowd and man breaking chains	5·50	5·50

No. 1511 also exists imperforate.

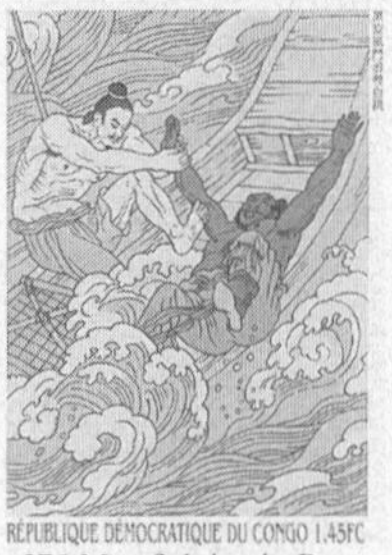

276 Men fighting in Boat

1999. *Outlaws of the Marsh* (Chinese literature). Multicoloured.
1517 1f.45 Type **276** . . . . . . 1·10 1·10
1518 1f.45 Men fighting in blacksmith's shop . . . . 1·10 1·10
1519 1f.45 Men gathered around tree . . . . 1·10 1·10
1520 1f.45 Men writing . . . . . 1·10 1·10
1521 1f.50 Crowds fighting . . . 1·10 1·25
1522 1f.50 Man pulling tree from ground . . . . 1·10 1·25
1523 1f.50 Man threatening other man with sword . . . . . 1·10 1·25
1524 1f.50 Man climbing over balcony . . . . 1·10 1·25
1525 1f.60 Men outside fort . . . 1·25 1·25
1526 1f.60 Man in snow storm . . 1·25 1·25
1527 1f.60 Man killing tiger . . . 1·25 1·25
1528 1f.60 Man reading writing on wall . . . . 1·25 1·25
1529 1f.70 Crowds fighting . . . 1·25 1·40
1530 1f.70 Man drawing sword 1·25 1·40
1531 1f.70 Man jumping from balcony . . . . 1·25 1·40
1532 1f.70 Man lifting other man 1·25 1·40
1533 1f.80 Archer on horseback 1·40 1·40
1534 1f.80 Men sitting round table eating . . . . . . 1·40 1·40
1535 1f.80 Joust . . . . 1·40 1·40
1536 1f.80 Man tearing scroll . . 1·40 1·40

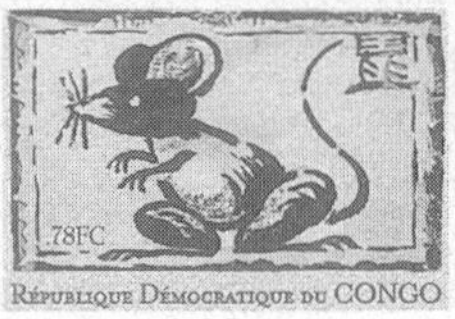

277 Rat

1999. Chinese Horoscope. Multicoloured.
1538 78c. Type **277** 85 40
1539 78c. Ox 85 40
1540 78c. Tiger 85 40
1541 78c. Rabbit 85 40
1542 78c. Dragon 85 40
1543 78c. Snake 85 40
1544 78c. Horse 85 40
1545 78c. Goat 85 40
1546 78c. Monkey 85 40
1547 78c. Cockerel 85 40
1548 78c. Dog 85 40
1549 78c. Pig 85 40

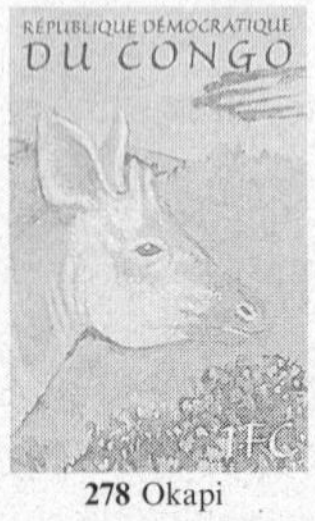

278 Okapi

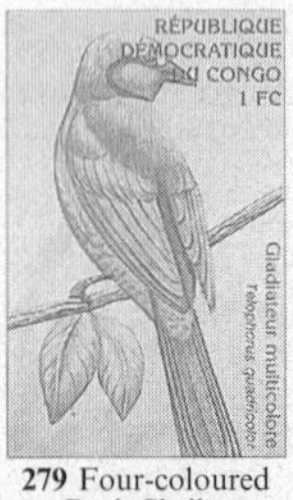

279 Four-coloured Bush Shrike (*Telophorus quadricolor*)

2000. Flora and Fauna. Multicoloured.
1550 1f. Type **278** 55 55
1551 1f. Rock kestrel 55 55
1552 1f. Giraffe and rainbow . . 55 55
1553 1f. Giraffe 55 55
1554 1f. Mandrill 55 55
1555 1f. Savannah baboon . . . 55 55
1556 1f. Leopard 55 55
1557 1f. Birdwing butterflies . . . 55 55
1558 1f. Hippopotamus 55 55
1559 1f. Wattled ibis 55 55
1560 1f. Water lilies 55 55
1561 1f. Steenbok 55 55
1562 7f.80 Lion (47 × 34 mm) . . 3·75 2·75
Nos. 1550/61 were issued together, se-tenant, forming a composite design.

2000. Flora and Fauna of Africa. Multicoloured.
1564 1f. Type **279** 45 35
1565 1f.50 Leopard (*Panthera pardus*) 70 55
1566 1f.50 Sun 80 80
1567 1f.50 *Pieris citrina* (butterfly) 80 80
1568 1f.50 European bee eater (*Merops apiaster*) 80 80
1569 1f.50 Red-backed shrike (*Lanius collurio*) 80 80
1570 1f.50 Village weaver (*Ploceus cucullatus*) 80 80
1571 1f.50 *Charaxes pelias* . . . 80 80
1572 1f.50 Green charaxes (*Charaxes eupale*) 80 80
1573 1f.50 Giraffe (*Giraffa camelopardalis*) 80 80
1574 1f.50 Bushbaby (*Galago moholi*) 80 80
1575 1f.50 *Strelitzia reginae* (flower) 80 80
1576 1f.50 Thomson's gazelle (*Gazella thomsoni*) 80 80
1577 1f.50 Hoopoe (*Upupa epops*) 80 80
1578 2f. Puku (*Kobus vardoni*) . . 95 95
1579 2f. Protomedia (*Colotis protomedia*) 95 95
1580 3f. Ground pangolin (*Smutsia temminckii*) . . . 1·40 1·40
1581 3f. *Cararina abyssinica* (flower) . . . . 1·40 1·40
Nos. 1566/1577 were issued together, se-tenant, forming a composite design.

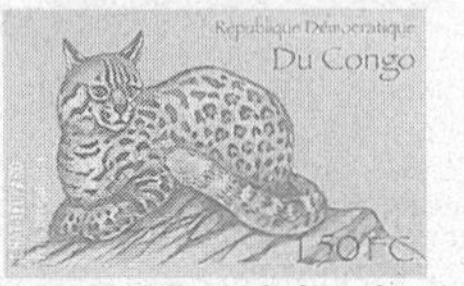

280 Leopard Cat (*Felis bengalensis*)

2000. Wild Cats and Dogs. Multicoloured.
1583 1f.50 Type **280** 80 80
1584 1f.50 African golden cat (*Felis aurata*) 80 80
1585 1f.50 Caracal (*Felis caracal*) 80 80
1586 1f.50 Puma (*Felis concolor*) 80 80
1587 1f.50 Black-footed cat (*Felis nigripes*) 80 80
1588 1f.50 Lion (*Panthera leo*) . . 80 80
1589 1f.50 Clouded leopard (*Neofelis nebulosa*) 80 80
1590 1f.50 Margay (*Felis wiedii*) 80 80
1591 1f.50 Cheetah (*Acinonyx jubatus*) 80 80
1592 1f.50 Spainsh lynx (*Felis pardina*) 80 80
1593 1f.50 Jaguarundi (*Felis yagouarundi*) 80 80
1594 1f.50 Serval (*Felis serval*) . . 80 80
1595 2f. Black-backed jackal (*Canis mesomelas*) . . . . 1·00 1·00
1596 2f. Bat-eared fox (*Otocyon megalotis*) . . . . 1·00 1·00
1597 2f. Bush dog (*Speothos venaticus*) . . . . 1·00 1·00
1598 2f. Coyote (*Canis latrans*) 1·00 1·00
1599 2f. Dhole (*Cuon alpinus*) . . 1·00 1·00
1600 2f. Fennec fox (*Fennecus zerda*) . . . . 1·00 1·00
1601 2f. Grey fox (*Urocyon cinereoargenteus*) . . . . 1·00 1·00
1602 2f. Wolf (*Canis lupus*) . . . 1·00 1·00
1603 2f. Kit fox (*Vulpes macrotis*) 1·00 1·00
1604 2f. Maned wolf (*Chrysocyon brachyurus*) . . . . . . 1·00 1·00
1605 2f. Racoon-dog (*Nyctereutes procyonoides*) . . . . . . 1·00 1·00
1606 2f. Red fox (*Vulpes vulpes*) 1·00 1·00

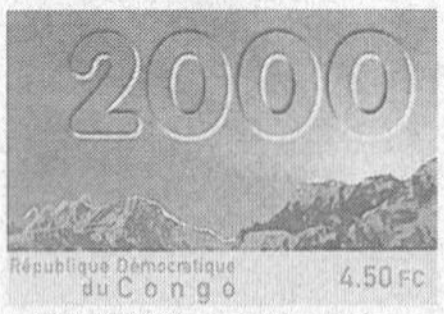

281 "2000" and Mountains

2000. New Millennium.
1608 **281** 4f.50 multicoloured . . . 1·00 1·00
1609 9f. multicoloured . . . 1·90 1·90
1610 15f. multicoloured . . . 3·25 3·25

CONGO (KINSHASA) Pt. 14

This Belgian colony in Central Africa became independent in 1960. There were separate issues for the province of Katanga (q.v.).

In 1971 the country was renamed ZAIRE and later issues will be found under that heading.

1967. 100 sengi = 1 (li)kuta;
100 (ma)kuta = 1 zaire.

1960. Various stamps of Belgian Congo optd **CONGO** or surch also. (a) Flowers issue of 1952. Multicoloured.
360 10c. "Dissotis" 20 10
361 10c. on 15c. "Protea" 20 10
362 20c. "Vellozia" 20 10
363 40c. "Ipomoea" 20 10
364 50c. on 60c. "Euphorbia" . . 20 10
365 50c. on 75c. "Ochna" . . . 20 10
366 1f. "Hibiscus" 20 10
367 1f.50 "Schizoglossum" . . . 20 10
368 2f. "Ansellia" 20 10
369 3f. "Costus" 40 10
370 4f. "Nymphaea" 40 20
371 5f. "Thunbergia" 40 10
372 6f.50 "Thonningia" 60 10
373 8f. "Gloriosa" 80 20
374 10f. "Silene" . . . . . . 1·25 20
375 20f. "Aristolochia" . . . . 2·50 55
376 50f. "Eulophia" . . . . . 14·00 3·75
377 100f. "Cryptosepalum" . . . 24·00 6·25

(b) Wild Animals issue of 1959.
378 10c. brown, sepia and blue 15 10
379 20c. blue and red 15 10
380 40c. brown and blue 15 10
381 50c. multicoloured 15 10
382 1f. black, green & brown . . 15 10
383 1f.50 black and yellow . . . 20 10
384 2f. black, brown and red . . 30 10
385 3f.50 on 3f. blk, pur & slate 35 10
386 5f. brown, green and sepia 50 15
387 6f.50 brown, yellow and blue 65 15
388 8f. bistre, violet and brown 80 30
389 10f. multicoloured . . . . . 1·00 35

(c) Madonna.
390 **102** 50c. brown, ochre & chest 50 50

(d) African Technical Co-operation Commission. Inscr in French or Flemish.
391 **103** 3f.50 on 3f. sal & slate . . 40 40

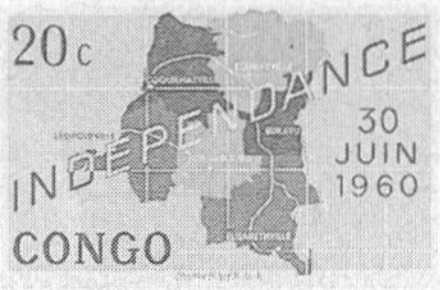

106 Congo Map

1960. Independence Commemoration.
392 **106** 20c. bistre 10 10
393 50c. red 10 10
394 1f. green 10 10
395 1f.50 brown 10 10
396 2f. mauve 10 10
397 3f.50 violet 10 10
398 5f. blue 15 10
399 6f.50 black 20 10
400 10f. orange 30 20
401 20f. blue 50 30

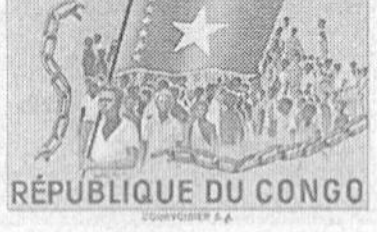

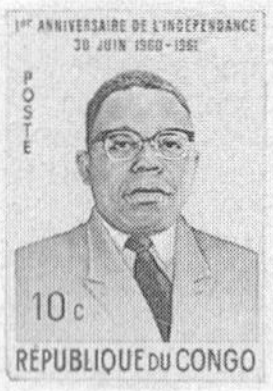

107 Congo Flag and People breaking Chain **109** Pres. Kasavubu

1961. 2nd Anniv of Congo Independence Agreement. Flag in yellow and blue.
402 **107** 2f. violet 10 10
403 3f.50 red 10 10
404 6f.50 brown 20 10
405 10f. green 25 15
406 20f. mauve 45 30

1961. Coquilhatville Conf. Optd **CONFERENCE COQUILHATVILLE AVRIL-MAI-1961.**
407 **106** 20c. bistre 60 60
408 50c. red 60 60
409 1f. green 60 60
410 1f.50 brown 60 60
411 2f. mauve 60 60
412 3f.50 violet 60 60
413 5f. blue 60 60
414 6f.50 black 60 60
415 10f. orange 60 60
416 20f. blue 60 60

1961. 1st Anniv of Independence. Inscr as in T **109**. Portraits and inscriptions in sepia.
417 **109** 10c. yellow 10 10
418 20c. red 10 10
419 40c. turquoise 10 10
420 50c. salmon 10 10
421 1f. lilac 10 10
422 1f.50 brown 10 10
423 2f. green 10 10
424 – 3f.50 mauve 15 10
425 – 5f. grey . . . . 1·75 15
426 – 6f.50 blue 30 10
427 – 8f. olive 35 10
428 – 10f. blue 75 10
429 – 20f. orange 75 15
430 – 50f. blue . . . . 1·40 30
431 – 100f. green . . . . . . 2·50 50
DESIGNS—HORIZ: 3f.50 to 8f. Pres. Kasavubu and map of Congo Republic. VERT: 10f. to 100f. Pres. Kasavubu in full uniform and outline map.

1961. Re-opening of Parliament. Optd **REOUVERTURE du PARLEMENT JUILLET 1961.**
432 **109** 10c. yellow 10 10
433 20c. red 10 10
434 40c. turquoise 10 10
435 50c. salmon 30 20
436 1f. lilac 30 20
437 1f.50 brown 80 70
438 2f. green 80 70
439 – 5f. grey (No. 425) . . . 80 70
440 – 10f. violet (No. 428) . . . 80 85

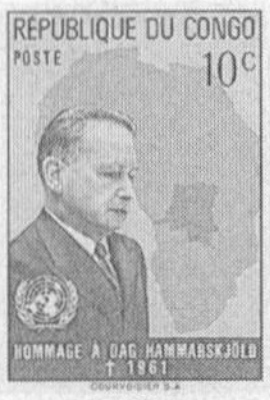

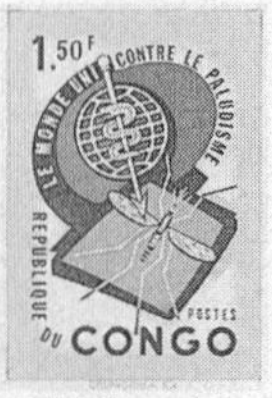

111 Dag Hammarskjold **112** Campaign Emblem

1962. Dag Hammarskjold Commemoration.
441 **111** 10c. brown and grey . . . 10 10
442 20c. blue and grey 10 10
443 30c. bistre and grey . . . 10 10
444 40c. blue and grey 10 10
445 50c. red and grey 10 10
446 3f. olive and grey . . . . 2·50 1·60
447 6f.50 violet and grey . . . 70 50
448 8f. brown and grey . . . 80 60

1962. Malaria Eradication.
449 **112** 1f.50 brown, black & yell 10 10
450 2f. turq, brown & green 30 15
451 6f.50 lake, black & blue 15 10

1962. Reorganization of Aboula Ministry. Optd **"Paix, Travail, Austerite..., C. ADOULA 11 juillet 1962.**
452 **111** 10c. brown and grey . . . 10 10
453 20c. blue and grey 10 10
454 30c. bistre and grey . . . 10 10
455 40c. blue and grey 10 10
456 50c. red and grey . . . . 1·25 50
457 3f. olive and grey 15 10
458 6f.50 violet and grey . . . 20 10
459 8f. brown and grey . . . 30 15

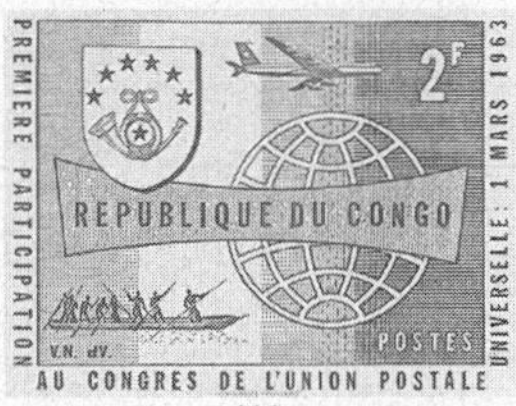

114

1963. 1st Participation in U.P.U. Congress.
460 **114** 2f. violet . . . . 1·40 1·00
461 4f. red 10 10
462 7f. blue 20 10
463 20f. green 30 15

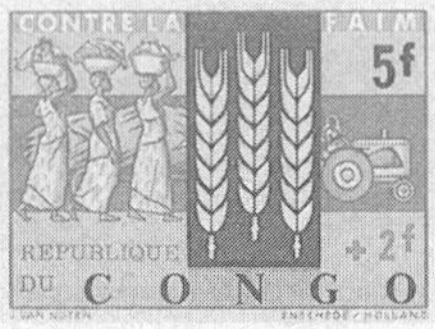

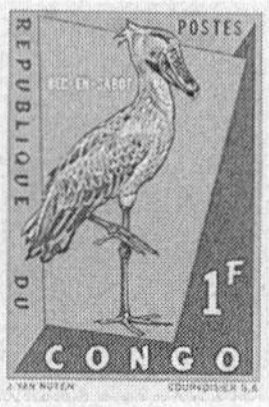

115 Emblem, Bears and Tractor **116** Whale-headed Stork

1963. Freedom from Hunger.
464 **115** 5f.+2f. violet & mauve . . 15 10
465 9f.+4f. green & yellow . . 30 20
466 12f.+6f. violet & blue . . 35 25
467 20f.+10f. green & red . . 1·75 1·60

1963. Protected Birds.
468 – 10c. multicoloured 15 10
469 – 20c. blue, black and red . . 15 10
470 – 30c. black, brown & grn . . 15 10
471 – 40c. black, orange & grey . 15 10
472 **116** 1f. black, green & brown . 30 15
473 – 2f. blue, brown and red . . 7·00 1·25
474 – 3f. black, pink and green . 55 20
475 – 4f. blue, green and red . . 55 20
476 – 5f. black, red and blue . . 85 20
477 – 6f. black, bistre & violet . 7·00 1·25
478 – 7f. indigo, blue & turq . . 1·25 20
479 – 8f. blue, yellow & orange . 1·40 20
480 – 10f. black, red and blue . . 1·40 20
481 – 20f. black, red & yellow . 2·50 30
BIRDS—VERT: 10c. Eastern white pelicans ("Pelicans"); 30c. African open-bill stork ("Bec-Duvert"); 2f. Marabou stork ("Marabout"); 4f. Congo peafowl ("Paon Congolais"); 6f. Secretary bird ("Serpentaire"); 8f. Sacred ibis ("Ibis Sacre"). HORIZ: 20c. Crested guineafowl ("Pintables de Schouteden"); 40c. Abdim's stork ("Cigoon a Ventre Blanc"); 3f. Greater flamingos ("Flamants Roses"); 5f. Hartlaub's duck ("Canards de Hartlaub"); 7f. Black-casqued hornbill ("Calaos"); 10f. South African crowned cranes ("Grue Cauronnse"); 20f. Saddle-bill stork ("Jabiru d'Afrique").

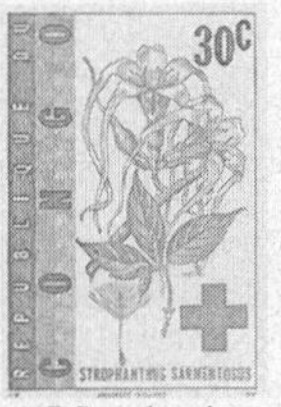

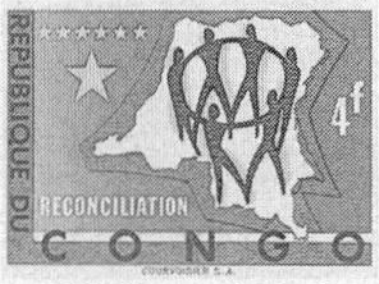

117 Strophanthus ("S. sarmentosus") **118** "Reconciliation"

1963. Red Cross Centenary. Cross in red.
482 **117** 10c. green and violet . . . 10 10
483 A 20c. blue and red 10 10
484 **117** 30c. red and green 10 10
485 A 40c. violet and blue . . . 10 10
486 **117** 5f. lake and olive 10 10
487 A 7f. purple and orange . . 10 10
488 B 9f. olive 20 10
489 20f. violet . . . . 1·60 70
DESIGNS—VERT: A, "Cinchona ledgeriana". HORIZ: B, Red Cross nurse.

1963. "National Reconciliation".
490 **118** 4f. multicoloured 90 30
491 5f. multicoloured 10 10
492 9f. multicoloured 15 10
493 12f. multicoloured 20 10

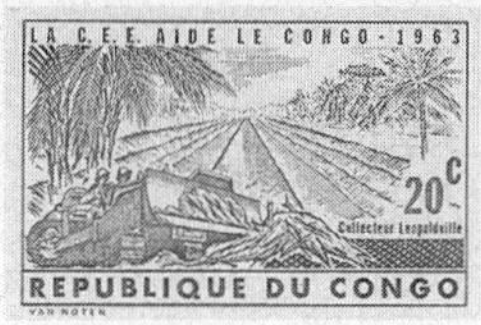

119 Kabambare Sewer, Leopoldville

1963. European Economic Community Aid.

494	119	20c. multicoloured	10	10
495	A	30c. multicoloured	10	10
496	B	50c. multicoloured	10	10
497	119	3f. multicoloured	90	35
498	A	5f. multicoloured	10	10
499	B	9f. multicoloured	15	10
500	A	12f. multicoloured	15	10

DESIGNS: A, Tractor and bridge on plan; B, Construction of Ituri Road.

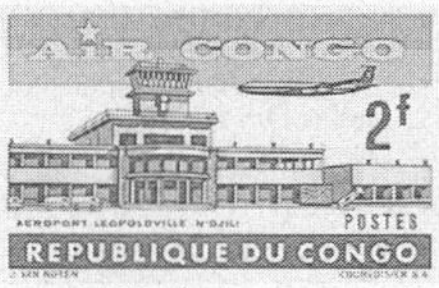

120 N'Djili Airport, Leopoldville

1963. "Air Congo" Commemoration.

501	120	2f. multicoloured	10	10
502	–	5f. multicoloured	10	10
503	120	6f. multicoloured	90	40
504	–	7f. multicoloured	10	10
505	120	30f. multicoloured	25	15
506	–	50f. multicoloured	40	25

DESIGN: 5f., 7f., 50f. Mailplane and control tower.

1963. 15th Anniv of Declaration of Human Rights. Optd **10 DECEMBRE 1948 10 DECEMBRE 1963 15e anniversaire DROITS DE L'HOMME**.

507	114	2f. violet	10	10
508		4f. red	10	10
509		7f. blue	20	20
510		20f. green	20	20

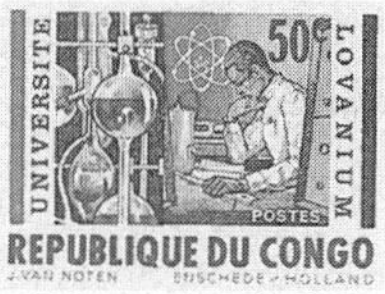

122 Student in Laboratory

1964. 10th Anniv of Lovanium University. Mult.

511	50c. Type **122**	10	10
512	1f.50 University buildings	10	10
513	8f. Atomic and nuclear reactor symbols	1·75	1·60
514	25f. University arms and buildings	20	15
515	30f. Type **122**	20	20
516	60f. As 1f.50	40	30
517	75f. As 8f.	50	50
518	100f. As 25f.	70	60

1964. Various stamps surch over coloured metallic panels. (a) Stamps of Belgian Congo surch **REPUBLIQUE DU CONGO** and value.

519	–	1f. on 20c. (No. 340)	10	10
520	–	2f. on 1f.50 (No. 306)	6·25	2·25
521	–	5f. on 6f.50 (No. 348)	15	15
522	–	8f. on 6f.50 (No. 311)	60	25

(b) Stamps of Congo (Kinshasa) surch.

523	–	1f. on 20c. (No. 379)	10	10
524	–	1f. on 6f.50 (No. 372)	10	10
525	–	2f. on 1f.50 (No. 367)	10	10
530	109	3f. on 20c.	25	20
531		4f. on 40c.	25	20
526	–	5f. on 6f.50 (No. 387)	45	20
528	106	6f. on 6f.50	30	20
529		7f. on 20c.	40	25

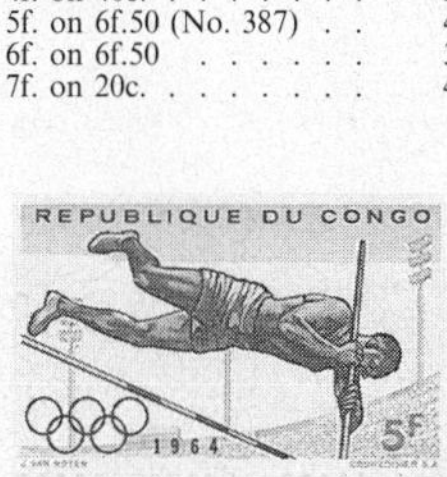

125 Pole-vaulting

1964. Olympic Games, Tokyo.

532	125	5f. sepia, grey and red	10	10
533	–	7f. violet, red and green	80	40
534	–	8f. brown, yellow & blue	10	10
535	125	10f. purple, blue & purple	10	10
536	–	20f. brown, green & orge	20	10
537	–	100f. brown, mauve & grn	80	20

DESIGNS—VERT: 7f., 20f. Throwing the javelin. HORIZ: 8f., 100f. Hurdling.

OCCUPATION OF STANLEYVILLE. During the occupation of Stanleyville from 5 August to 24 November, 1964, stocks of a number of contemporary issues were overprinted **REPUBLIQUE POPULAIRE** and issued by the rebel authorities.

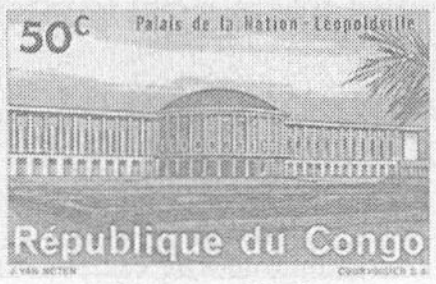

126 National Palace

1964. National Palace, Leopoldville.

538	126	50c. mauve and blue	10	10
539		1f. blue and purple	10	10
540		2f. brown and violet	10	10
541		3f. green and brown	10	10
542		4f. orange and blue	10	10
543		5f. violet and green	10	10
544		6f. brown and orange	10	10
545		7f. olive and brown	10	10
546		8f. red and blue	2·00	35
547		9f. violet and red	10	10
548		10f. brown and green	10	10
549		20f. blue and brown	10	10
550		30f. red and green	15	10
551		40f. blue and purple	25	10
552		50f. brown and green	35	10
553		100f. black and orange	65	15

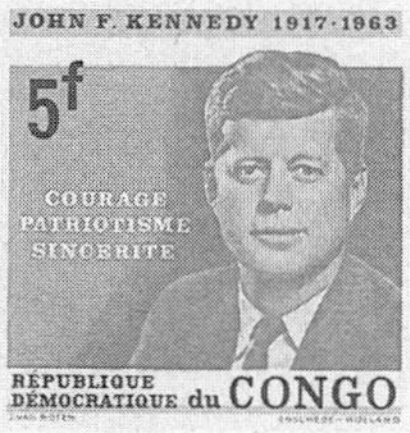

127 Pres. Kennedy

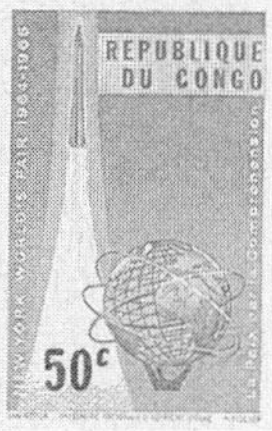

128 Rocket and Unisphere

1964. Pres. Kennedy Commemoration.

554	127	5f. blue and black	10	10
555		6f. purple and black	10	10
556		9f. brown and black	10	10
557		30f. violet and black	30	10
558		40f. green and black	2·00	60
559		60f. brown and black	50	25

1965. New York World's Fair.

560	128	50c. purple and black	10	10
561		1f.50 blue and violet	10	10
562		2f. brown and green	10	10
563		10f. green and red	70	40
564		18f. blue and brown	10	10
565		27f. red and green	25	10
566		40f. grey and red	40	15

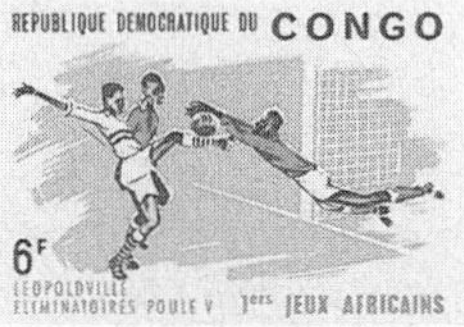

129 Football

1965. 1st African Games, Leopoldville.

567	–	5f. black, brown & blue	10	10
568	129	6f. red, black and blue	10	10
569	–	15f. black, green & orange	10	10
570	–	24f. black, green & mve	20	10
571	129	40f. blue, black & turq	1·25	45
572	–	60f. purple, black & blue	45	15

SPORTS—VERT: 5f., 24f. Basketball; 15f., 60f. Volleyball.

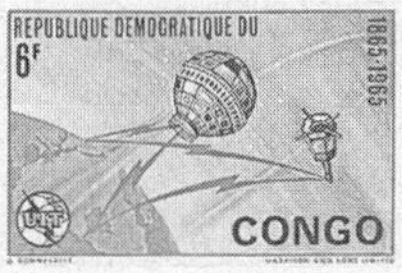

130 Telecommunications Satellites

1965. Centenary of I.T.U. Multicoloured.

573	6f. Type **130**	10	10
574	9f. Telecommunications satellites (different view)	10	10
575	12f. Type **130**	10	10
576	15f. As 9f.	10	10
577	18f. Type **130**	1·00	30
578	20f. As 9f.	15	10
579	30f. Type **130**	25	10
580	40f. As 9f.	30	10

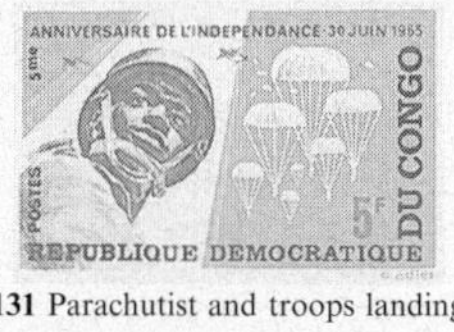

131 Parachutist and troops landing

1965. 5th Anniv of Independence.

581	131	5f. brown and blue	10	10
582		6f. brown and orange	10	10
583		7f. brown and green	45	20
584		9f. brown and mauve	10	10
585		18f. brown and yellow	15	10

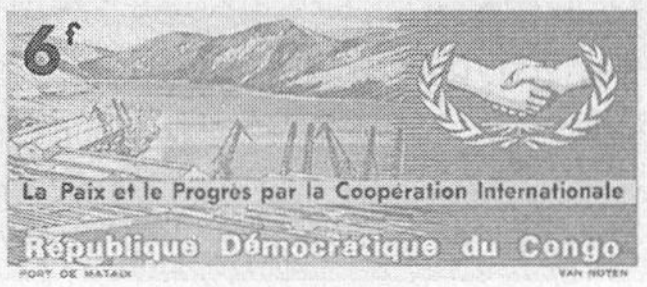

132 Matadi Port

1965. International Co-operation Year.

586	132	6f. blue, black & yellow	10	10
587	–	8f. brown, black & blue	10	10
588	–	9f. turq, black & brown	10	10
589	132	12f. mauve, black & grey	80	30
590	–	25f. olive, black and red	20	10
591	–	60f. grey, black & yellow	40	10

DESIGNS: 8f., 25f. Katanga mines; 9f., 60f. Tshopo Barrage, Stanleyville.

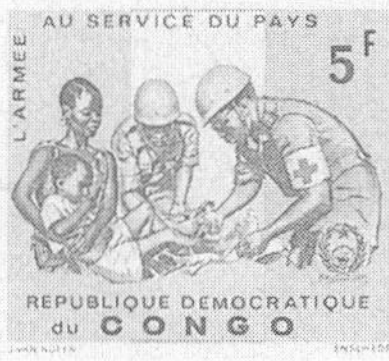

133 Medical Care

1965. Congolese Army.

592	133	2f. blue and red	10	10
593		5f. brown, red and pink	10	10
594	–	6f. brown and blue	10	10
595	–	7f. green and yellow	10	10
596	–	9f. brown and green	10	10
597	–	10f. brown and green	40	40
598	–	18f. violet and red	15	10
599	–	19f. brown & turquoise	60	40
600	–	20f. brown and blue	15	10
601	–	24f. multicoloured	20	15
602	–	30f. multicoloured	25	10

DESIGNS—HORIZ: 6f., 9f. Feeding child; 7, 18f. Bridge-building. VERT: 10f., 20f. Building construction; 19f. Telegraph line maintenance; 24f., 30f. Soldier and flag.

1966. World Meteorological Day. Nos. 590/1 optd **6e Journee Meteorologique Mondiale / 23.3.66** (on coloured metallic panel) and W.M.O. Emblem.

603	25f. olive, black and red	75	45
604	60f. grey, black and yellow	75	50

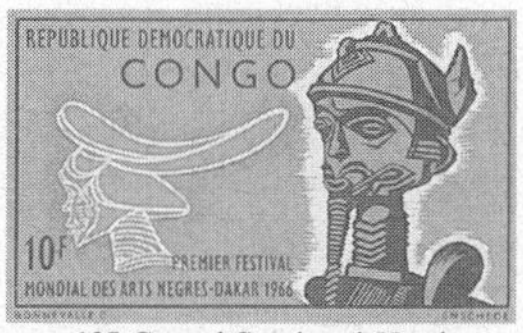

135 Carved Stool and Head

1966. World Festival of Negro Arts, Dakar.

605	135	10f. black, red and grey	10	10
606	–	12f. black, green & blue	10	10
607	–	15f. black, blue & purple	15	15
608	–	53f. black, red and blue	1·10	90

DESIGNS—VERT: 12f. Statuettes; 53f. Statuettes of women. HORIZ: 15f. Woman's head and carved goat.

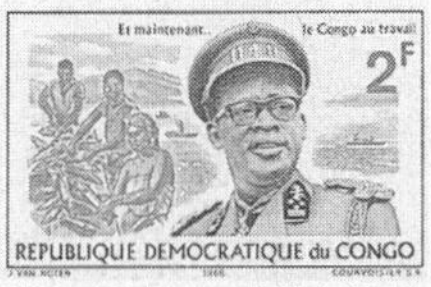

136 Pres. Mobutu and Fish Workers

1966. Pres. Mobutu Commemoration.

609	136	2f. brown and blue	10	10
610	–	4f. brown and red	10	10
611	–	6f. brown and olive	65	60
612	–	8f. brown and turquoise	10	10
613	–	10f. brown and lake	10	10
614	–	12f. brown and violet	10	10
615	–	15f. brown and green	10	10
616	–	24f. brown and mauve	20	15

DESIGNS (Pres. Mobutu and): 4f. Harvesting pyrethrum; 6f. Building construction; 8f. Winnowing maize; 10f. Cotton-picking; 12f. Harvesting fruit; 15f. Picking coffee-beans; 24f. Harvesting pineapples.

1966. Inaug of W.H.O. Headquarters, Geneva. Nos. 550/3 optd **O.M.S. Geneve 1966** and W.H.O. Emblem.

618	126	30f. red and green	70	70
619		40f. blue and purple	70	70
620		50f. brown and green	75	75
621		100f. black and orange	75	75

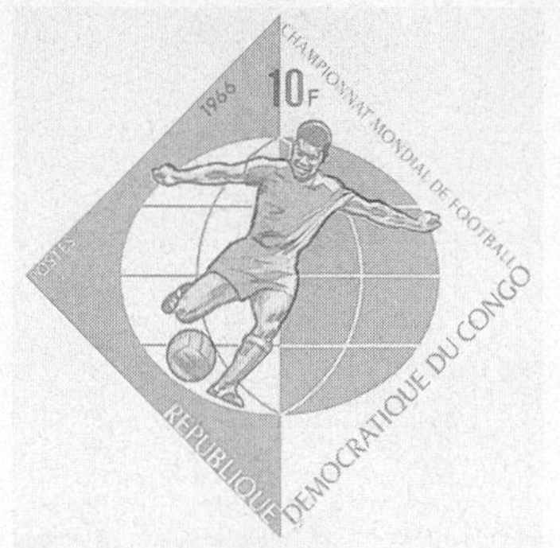

139 Footballer

1966. World Cup Football Championship.

622	139	10f. green, violet & brown	10	10
623	–	30f. green, violet & purple	25	20
624	–	50f. brown, blue & green	85	80
625	–	60f. gold, sepia & green	45	40

DESIGNS: 30f. Two footballers; 50f. Three footballers; 60f. Jules Rimet Cup and football.

1966. World Cup Football Championship Final. Nos. 622/5 optd **FINALE ANGLETERRE - ALLEMAGNE 4 - 2**.

626	139	10f. green, violet & brown	25	45
627	–	30f. green, violet & purple	80	1·40
628	–	50f. brown, blue & green	1·25	1·75
629	–	60f. gold, sepia and green	1·40	2·25

1967. 4th African Unity Organization (O.U.A.) Conf, Kinshasa. Nos. 538/43 surch **4e Sommet OUA KINSHASA du 11 au 14 - 9 - 67** and value.

631	126	1k. on 2f.	10	10
632		3k. on 5f.	10	10
633		5k. on 4f.	20	15
634		6k.60 on 1f.	25	20
635		9k.60 on 50c.	40	25
636		9k.80 on 3f.	50	40

1967. New Constitution. Nos. 609/10 and 592 surch **1967 NOUVELLE CONSTITUTION** with coloured metallic panel obliterating old value.

639	136	4k. on 2f.	20	15
640	133	5k. on 2f.	20	15
641	–	21k. on 4f.	90	70

1967. 1st Congolese Games, Kinshasa. Nos. 567 and 569 surch **1ers Jeux Congolais 25/6 au 2/7/67 Kinshasa** and value.

642	1k. on 5f.	10	10
643	9.6k. on 15f.	50	50

1967. 1st Flight by Air Congo BAC "One-Eleven". No. 504 surch **1er VOL BAC ONE ELEVEN 14/5/67** and value.

644	9.6k. on 7f.	70	20

1968. World Children's Day (8.10.67). Nos. 586 and 588 surch **JOURNEE MONDIALE DE L'ENFANCE 8 - 10 - 67** and new value.

645	132	1k. on 6f.	10	10
646		9k. on 9f.	50	50

1968. International Tourist Year (1967). Nos. 538, 541 and 544 surch **Annee Internationale du Tourisme 24-10-67** and new value.

647	126	5k. on 50c.	20	20
648		10k. on 6f.	40	40
649		15k. on 3f.	60	60

1968. (a) No. 540 surch.

650	126	1k. on 2f.	10	10

(b) Surch (coloured panel obliterating old value, and new value surch on panel. Panel colour given first, followed by colour of new value). (i) Nos. 538 and 542.

651	126	2k. on 50c. (bronze and black)	10	10
652		2k. on 50c. (blue and white)	10	10
653		9.6k. on 4f. (black and white)	50	45

(ii) No. 609.

654	136	10k. on 2f. (black and white)	55	10

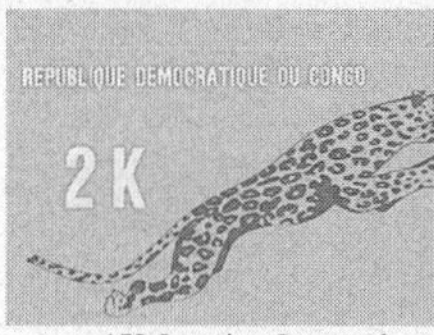

152 Leaping Leopard

1968.

655	152	2k. black on green	15	10
656		9.6k. black on red	65	15

1968. As Nos. 609, etc, but with colours changed and surch in new value.

657	136	15s. on 2f. brown & blue	10	10
658	–	1k. on 6f. brown & chest	10	10
659	–	3k. on 10f. brown & grn	10	10
660	–	5k. on 12f. brown & orge	20	15
661	–	20k. on 15f. brown & grn	70	50
662	–	50k. on 24f. brown & pur	1·90	1·25

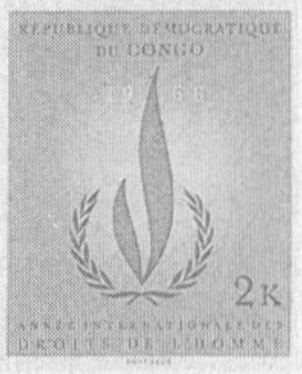

154 Human Rights Emblem

1968. Human Rights Year.

663	154	2k. green and blue	10	10
664		9.6k. red and green	40	25
665		10k. brown and lilac	40	25
666		40k. violet and brown	1·50	1·10

1969. 4th O.C.A.M. (Organization Commune Africaine et Malgache) Summit Meeting, Kinshasa. Nos. 663/6 with colours changed optd **4EME SOMMET OCAM 27-1-1969 KINSHASA** and emblem.

667	154	2k. brown and green	10	10
668		9.60k. green and pink	40	25
669		10k. blue and grey	40	25
670		40k. violet and blue	1·50	1·10

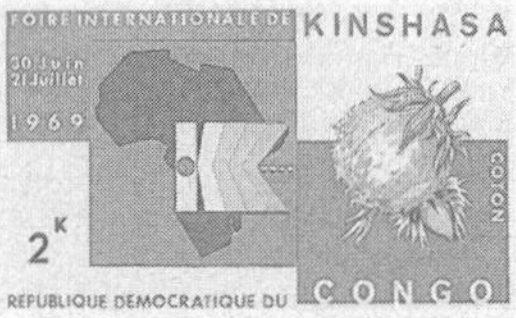

156 Map of Africa and "Cotton"

1969. International Fair, Kinshasa (1st Issue).

671	156	2k. multicoloured	10	10
672	–	6k. multicoloured	30	30
673	–	9.6k. multicoloured	40	20
674	–	9.8k. multicoloured	40	35
675	–	11.6k. multicoloured	50	50

DESIGNS: Map of Africa and: 6k. "Copper"; 9.6k. "Coffee"; 9.8k. "Diamonds"; 11.6k. "Palm-oil".

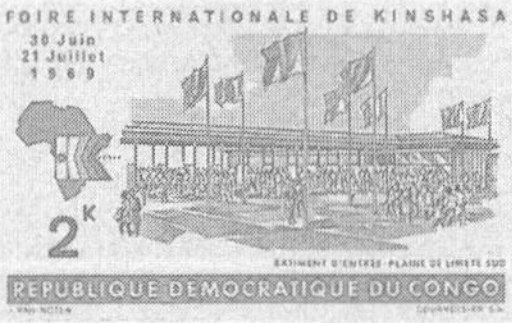

157 Fair Entrance

1969. Inaug of Int Fair, Kinshasa (2nd issue).

676	157	2k. purple and gold	10	10
677	–	3k. blue and gold	10	10
678	–	10k. green and gold	40	40
679	–	25k. red and gold	1·00	85

DESIGNS: 3k. "Gecomin" (mining company) pavilion; 10k. Administration building; 25k. African Unity Organization pavilion.

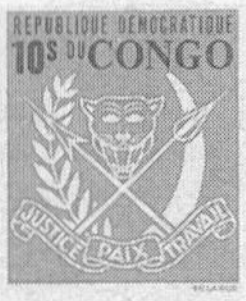

158 Congo Arms

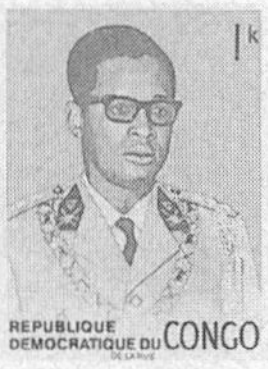

159 Pres. Mobutu

1969.

680	158	10s. red and black	10	10
681		15s. blue and black	10	10
682		30s. green and black	10	10
683		60s. purple and black	10	10
684		90s. bistre and black	10	10
685	159	1k. multicoloured	10	10
686		2k. multicoloured	10	10
687		3k. multicoloured	15	10
688		5k. multicoloured	15	15
689		6k. multicoloured	20	15
690		9.6k. multicoloured	30	25
691		10k. multicoloured	40	30
692		20k. multicoloured	80	60
693		50k. multicoloured	2·00	1·75
694		100k. multicoloured	4·00	3·50

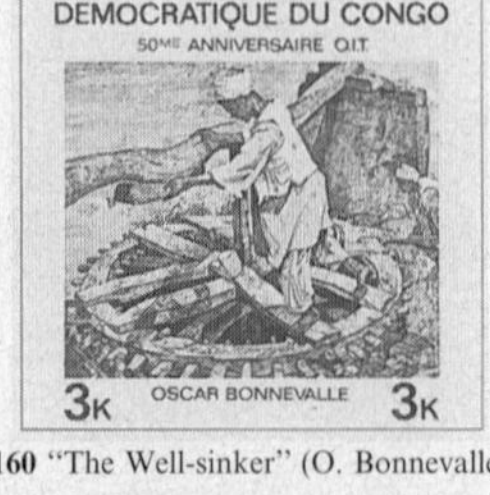

160 "The Well-sinker" (O. Bonnevalle)

1969. 50th Anniv of International Labour Organization. Paintings. Multicoloured.

695	3k. Type **160**	15	15
696	4k. "Cocoa Production" (J. van Noten)	20	15
697	8k. "The Harbour" (C. Meunier) (vert)	70	25
698	10k. "The Poulterer" (H. Evenepoel)	45	35
699	15k. "Industry" (C. Meunier)	85	50

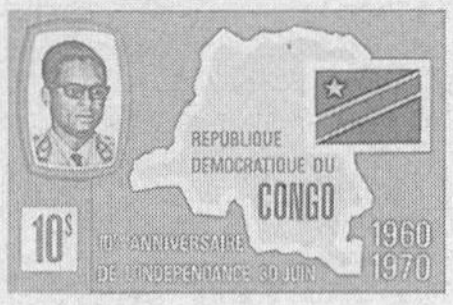

162 Pres. Mobutu, Map and Flag

1970. 10th Anniv of Independence.

701	162	10s. multicoloured	10	10
702		90s. multicoloured	10	10
703		1k. multicoloured	10	10
704		2k. multicoloured	10	10
705		7k. multicoloured	25	15
706		10k. multicoloured	40	25
707		20k. multicoloured	80	50

1970. Surch. (a) National Palace series.

708	126	10s. on 1f.	10	10
709		20s. on 2f.	10	10
710		30s. on 3f.	10	10
711		40s. on 4f.	10	10
712		60s. on 7f.	80	75
713		90s. on 9f.	80	75
714		1k. on 6f.	15	10
715		3k. on 30f.	80	75
716		4k. on 40f.	15	10
717		5k. on 50f.	2·00	1·90
718		10k. on 100f.	90	75

(b) Congolese Army series.

719		90s. on 9f. (No. 596)	15	10
720		1k. on 7f. (No. 595)	15	10
721		2k. on 24f. (No. 601)	15	10

(c) Pres. Mobutu series.

722	136	20s. on 2f.	15	10
723	–	40s. on 4f. (No. 610)	15	10
724	–	1k. on 12f. (No. 614)	80	70
725	–	2k. on 24f. (No. 616)	15	10

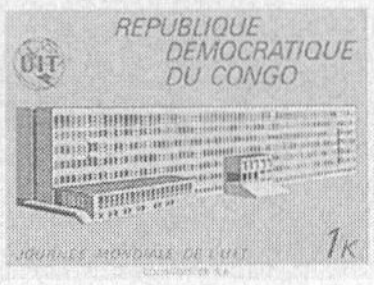

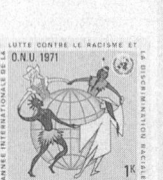

164 I.T.U. Headquarters, Geneva

1970. United Nations Commemorations.

726	164	1k. olive, green and pink	10	10
727	–	2k. grey, green and orange	10	10
728	–	6k.60 red, pink and blue	25	25
729	164	9k.60 multicoloured	30	30
730	–	9k.80 sepia, brown and bl	35	35
731	–	10k. sepia, brown and lilac	35	35
732	–	11k. sepia, brown and pink	40	40

DESIGNS AND EVENTS: 1k., 9k.60, (I.T.U. World Day); 2k., 6k.60, New U.P.U. Headquarters, Berne (Inauguration); 9k.80, 10k., 11k. U.N. Headquarters, New York (25th anniversary).

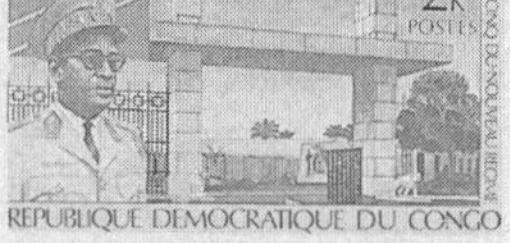

165 Pres. Mobutu and Independence Arch

1970. 5th Anniv of "New Regime".

733	165	2k. multicoloured	10	10
734		10k. multicoloured	45	35
735		20k. multicoloured	85	80

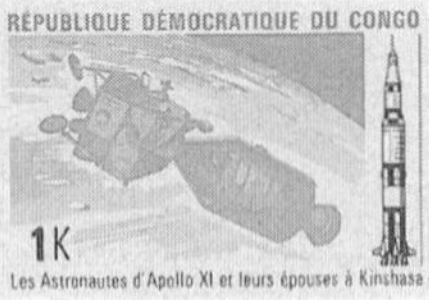

166 "Apollo 11"

1970. Visit of "Apollo 11" Astronauts to Kinshasa.

736	166	1k. blue, black and red	10	10
737	–	2k. violet, black and red	10	10
738	–	7k. black, orange and red	25	25
739	–	10k. black, pink and red	35	35
740	–	30k. black, green and red	1·00	1·00

DESIGNS: 2k. Astronauts on Moon; 7k. Pres. Mobutu decorating wives; 10k. Pres. Mobutu with astronauts; 30k. Astronauts after splashdown.

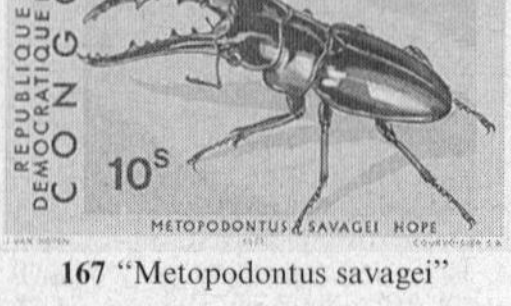

167 "Metopodontus savagei"

1971. Insects. Multicoloured.

741	10s. Type **167**	25	15
742	50s. "Cicindela regalis"	25	15
743	90s. "Magacephala catenulata"	25	15
744	1k. "Stephanorrhina guttata"	25	15
745	2k. "Pupuricenus congoanus"	25	15
746	3k. "Sagra tristis"	50	25
747	5k. "Steraspis subcalida"	1·75	80
748	10k. "Mecosaspis explanata"	2·40	1·25
749	30k. "Goliathus meleagris"	5·75	3·25
750	40k. "Sternotomis virescens"	8·25	4·75

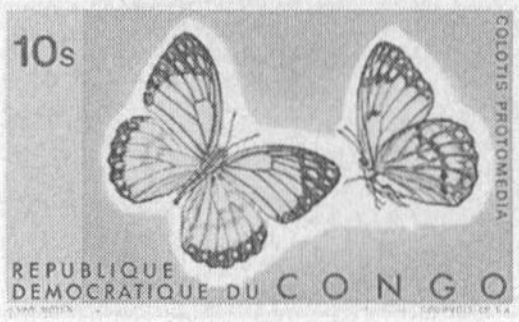

168 "Colotis protomedia"

1971. Butterflies and Moths. Multicoloured.

751	10s. Type **168**	25	15
752	20s. "Rhodophitus simplex"	25	15
753	70s. "Euphaedra overlaeti"	25	15
754	1k. "Argema bouvieri"	25	15
755	3k. "Cymothoe reginae-elisabethae"	50	25
756	5k. "Miniodes maculifera"	1·40	60
757	10k. "Salamis temora"	1·90	90
758	15k. "Eronia leda"	3·75	1·60
759	25k. "Cymothoe sangaris"	5·00	2·50
760	40k. "Euchloron megaera"	8·00	4·50

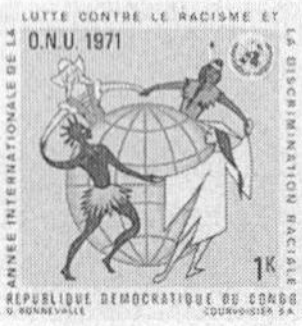

169 "Four Races" around Globe

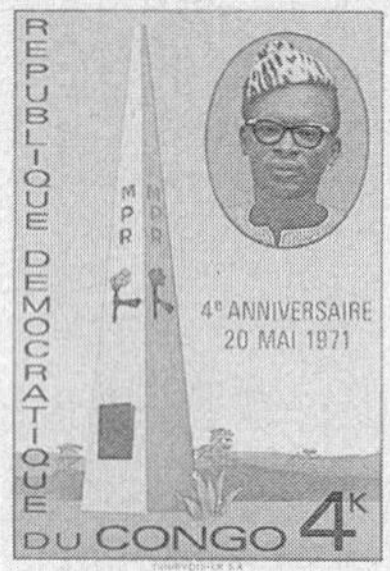

170 Pres. Mobutu and Obelisk

1971. Racial Equality Year.

761	169	1k. multicoloured	10	10
762		4k. multicoloured	15	15
763		5k. multicoloured	20	20
764		10k. multicoloured	40	40

1971. 4th Anniv of Popular Revolutionary Movement (M.P.R.).

765	170	4k. multicoloured	15	15

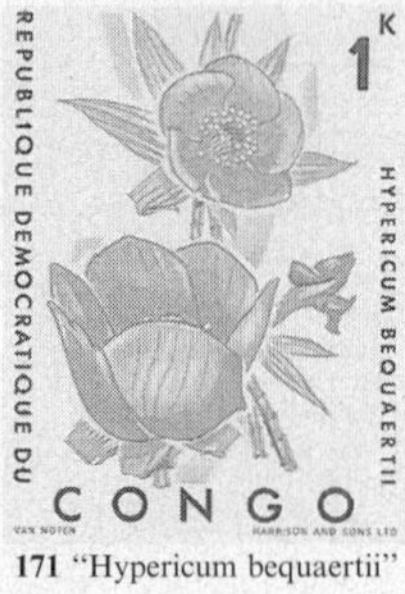

171 "Hypericum bequaertii"

1971. Tropical Plants. Multicoloured.

766	1k. Type **171**	35	15
767	4k. "Dissotis brazzae"	70	30
768	20k. "Begonia wollast"	3·50	1·50
769	25k. "Cassia alata"	4·50	1·90

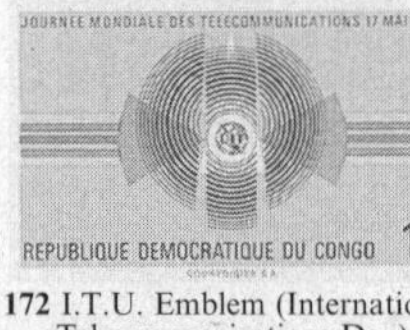

172 I.T.U. Emblem (International Telecommunications Day)

1971. "Telecommunications and Space". Mult.

770	1k. Type **172**	10	10
771	3k. Dish aerial (Satellite Earth Station, Kinshasa)	15	15
772	6k. Map of Pan-African telecommunications network	30	30

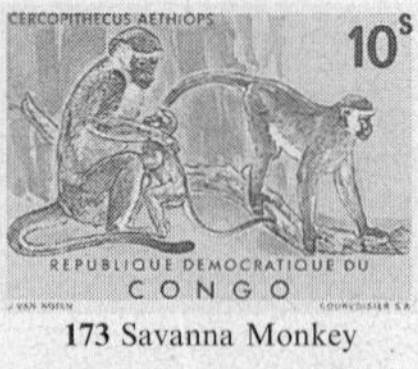

173 Savanna Monkey

1971. Congo Monkeys. Multicoloured.

773	10s. Type **173**	30	15
774	20s. Moustached monkey (vert)	30	15
775	70s. De Brazza's monkey	45	15
776	1k. Yellow baboon	45	25
777	3k. Pygmy chimpanzee (vert)	75	50
778	5k. Black mangabey (vert)	1·75	1·25
779	10k. Owl-faced monkey	3·25	2·40
780	15k. Diana monkey	5·25	3·50
781	25k. Western black-and-white colobus (vert)	9·00	6·00
782	40k. L'Hoest's monkey (vert)	12·00	8·50

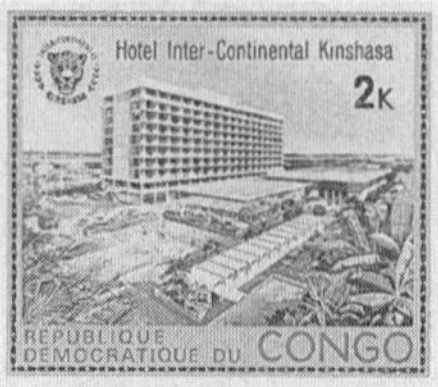

174 Hotel Inter-Continental

1971. Opening of Hotel Inter-Continental, Kinshasa.

783	174	2k. multicoloured	10	10
784		12k. multicoloured	50	50

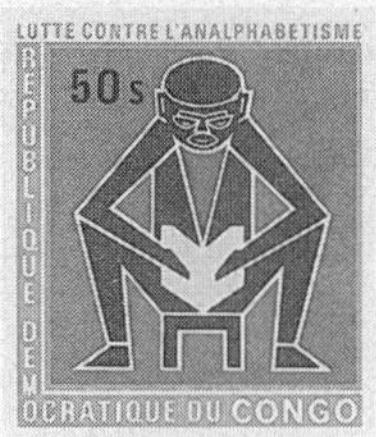

175 "Reader"

1971. Literacy Campaign. Multicoloured.

785	50s. Type **175**	10	10
786	2k.50 Open book and abacus	20	10
787	7k. Symbolic alphabet	45	35

For later issues see **ZAIRE**.

COOK ISLANDS — Pt. 1

A group of islands in the South Pacific under New Zealand control, including Aitutaki, Niue, Penrhyn and Rarotonga. Granted self-government in 1965.

See also issues for Aitutaki and Penrhyn Island.

1892. 12 pence = 1 shilling;
20 shillings = 1 pound.
1967. 100 cents = 1 dollar.

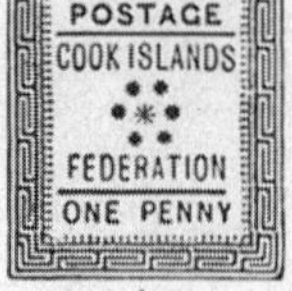

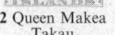

1

1892.

1b	1	1d. black	26·00	26·00
2		1½d. mauve	40·00	38·00
3		2½d. blue	40·00	38·00
4		10d. red	£140	£130

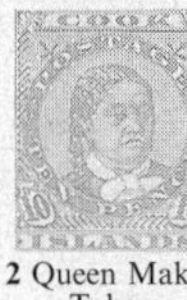

2 Queen Makea Takau

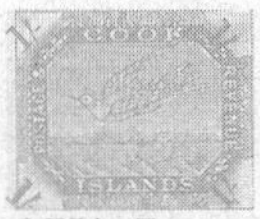

3 White Tern or Torea

1893.

11ba	3	½d. blue	4·00	5·00
28		½d. green	2·75	3·25
13	2	1d. brown	14·00	14·00
12		1d. blue	5·00	4·50
29		1d. red	4·00	3·00
43		1½d. mauve	7·50	4·00
15a	3	2d. brown	8·50	6·50
16a	2	2½d. red	15·00	9·00
32		2½d. blue	3·75	7·00
9		5d. black	15·00	13·00
18a	3	6d. purple	19·00	21·00
19	2	10d. green	18·00	48·00
46	3	1s. red	27·00	85·00

1899. Surch **ONE HALF PENNY**.

21	2	½d. on 1d. blue	32·00	42·00

1901. Optd with crown.

22	2	1d. brown	£180	£140

1919. New Zealand stamps (King George V) surch **RAROTONGA** and value in native language in words.

56	62	½d. green	40	1·00
47	53	1d. red	1·00	3·00
57	62	1½d. brown	50	75
58		2d. yellow	1·50	1·75

48a		2½d. blue	2·00	2·25
49a		3d. brown	2·25	2·00
50c		4d. violet	1·75	4·25
51a		4½d. green	1·75	8·00
52a		6d. red	1·75	5·50
53		7½d. brown	1·50	5·50
54a		9d. green	2·00	15·00
55a		1s. red	2·75	18·00

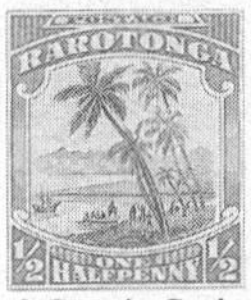

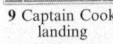

9 Captain Cook landing

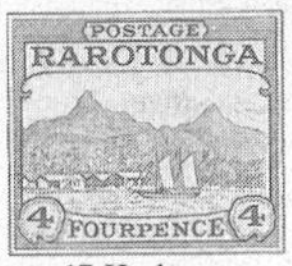

17 Harbour, Rarotonga and Mt. Ikurangi

1920. Inscr "RAROTONGA".

81	**9**	½d. black and green	4·50	8·50
82	–	1d. black and red	6·00	2·25
72	–	1½d. black and blue	8·50	8·50
83	–	2½d. brown and blue	5·00	24·00
73	–	3d. black and brown	2·25	5·50
84	**17**	4d. green and violet	8·00	16·00
74	–	6d. brown and orange	3·00	8·50
75	–	1s. black and violet	5·00	17·00

DESIGNS—VERT: 1d. Wharf at Avarua; 1½d. Captain Cook (Dance); 2½d. Te Po, Rarotongan chief; 3d. Palm tree. HORIZ: 6d. Huts at Arorangi; 1s. Avarua Harbour.

1921. New Zealand stamps optd **RAROTONGA.**

76	F **4**	2s. blue	27·00	55·00
77		2s.6d. brown	18·00	50·00
78		5s. green	27·00	65·00
79		10s. red	55·00	95·00
89		£1 red	95·00	£160

1926. "Admiral" type of New Zealand optd **RAROTONGA.**

90	**71**	2s. blue	10·00	40·00
92		3s. mauve	16·00	42·00

1931. No. 77 surch **TWO PENCE.**

93		2d. on 1½d. black and blue	9·50	2·75

1931. Arms type of New Zealand optd **RAROTONGA.**

95	F **6**	2s.6d. brown	10·00	22·00
96		5s. green	17·00	50·00
97		10s. red	35·00	90·00
98		£1 pink	85·00	£140

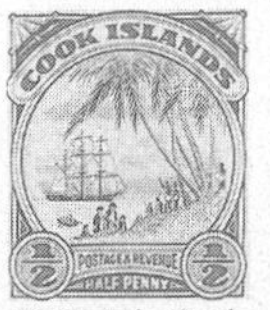

20 Captain Cook landing

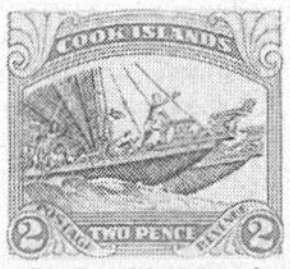

22 Double Maori Canoe

1932. Inscribed "COOK ISLANDS".

106	**20**	½d. black and green	1·00	4·50
107	–	1d. black and red	1·25	2·00
108	**22**	2d. black and brown	1·50	50
140	–	2½d. black and blue	65	1·75
110	–	4d. black and blue	1·50	50
142	–	6d. black and orange	1·50	1·75
105	–	1s. black and violet	8·50	22·00

DESIGNS—VERT: 1d. Captain Cook. HORIZ: 2½d. Natives working cargo; 4d. Port of Avarua; 6d. R.M.S. "Monowai"; 1s. King George V.

1935. Jubilee. As 1932 optd **SILVER JUBILEE OF KING GEORGE V. 1910-1935.**

113		1d. red	60	1·40
114		2½d. blue	1·00	2·50
115		6d. green and orange	3·50	6·00

1936. Stamps of New Zealand optd **COOK ISLANDS.**

116	**71**	2s. blue	13·00	45·00
131w	F **6**	2s.6d. brown	18·00	23·00
117	**71**	3s. mauve	13·00	70·00
132	F **6**	5s. green	8·50	21·00
133w		10s. red	48·00	70·00
134		£1 pink	50·00	80·00
135w		£3 green	55·00	£160
98b		£5 blue	£170	£325

1937. Coronation. T **106** of New Zealand optd **COOK IS'DS.**

124	**106**	1d. red	40	35
125		2½d. blue	80	40
126		6d. orange	80	35

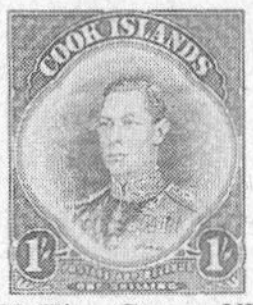

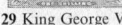

29 King George VI

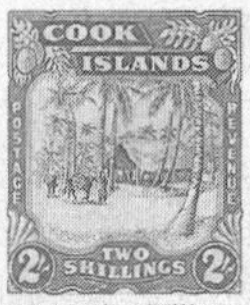

30 Native Village

1938.

143	**29**	1s. black and violet	1·50	2·25
128	**30**	2s. black and orange	18·00	13·00
145	–	3s. blue and green	30·00	30·00

DESIGN—HORIZ: 3s. Native canoe.

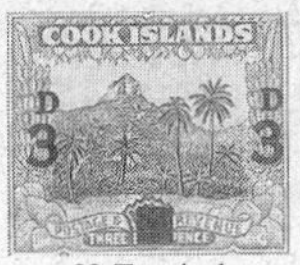

32 Tropical Landscape

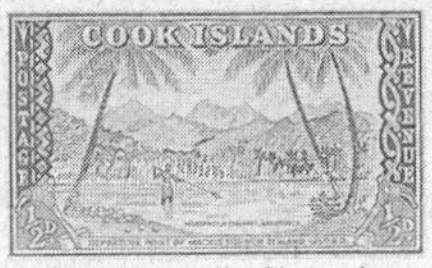

34 Ngatangiia Channel, Rarotonga

1940.

130	**32**	3d. on 1½d. black & purple	50	50

1946. Peace. Peace stamps of New Zealand of 1946 optd **COOK ISLANDS.**

146	**132**	1d. green	30	10
147	–	2d. purple	30	40
148	–	6d. brown and red	30	40
149	**139**	8d. black and red	30	40

1949.

150	**34**	½d. violet and brown	10	1·00
151	–	1d. brown and green	3·50	2·00
152	–	2d. brown and red	1·75	2·00
153	–	3d. green and blue	1·50	2·00
154	–	5d. green and violet	4·75	1·50
155	–	6d. black and red	4·75	2·75
156	–	8d. olive and orange	55	3·75
157	–	1s. blue and brown	4·25	3·75
158	–	2s. brown and red	9·00	24·00
159	–	3s. blue and green	8·50	22·00

DESIGNS—HORIZ: 1d. Captain Cook and map of Hervey Is; 2d. Rarotonga and Rev. John Williams; 3d. Aitutaki and palm trees; 5d. Rarotonga Airfield; 6d. Penrhyn village; 8d. Native hut. VERT: 1s. Map and statue of Capt. Cook; 2s. Native hut and palms; 3s. "Matua" (inter-island freighter).

1953. Coronation. As Types of New Zealand but inscr "COOK ISLANDS".

160	**164**	3d. brown	1·00	85
161	**166**	6d. grey	1·25	1·40

1960. No. 154 surch **1/6.**

162		1s.6d. on 5d. green and violet	30	30

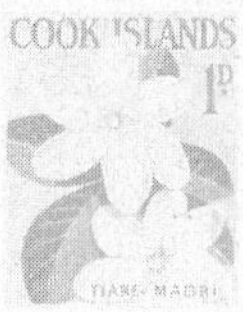

45 Tiare Maori

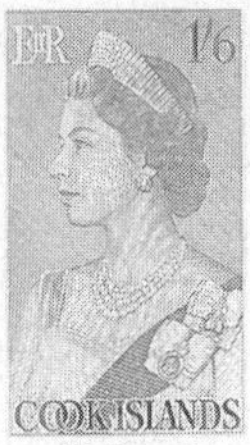

52 Queen Elizabeth II

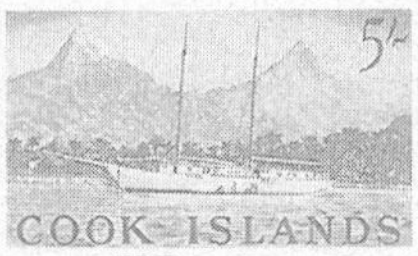

55 Rarotonga

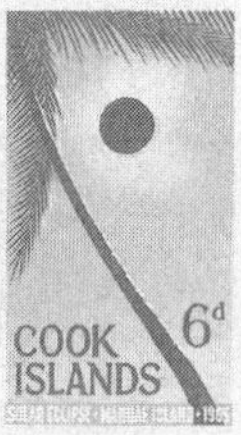

56 Eclipse and Palm

1963.

163	**45**	1d. green and yellow	45	50
164	–	2d. red and yellow	20	50
165	–	3d. yellow, green and violet	70	50
166	–	5d. blue and black	8·00	1·25
167	–	6d. red, yellow and green	1·00	50
168	–	8d. black and blue	4·25	1·50
169	–	1s. yellow and green	40	50
170	**52**	1s.6d. violet	2·75	2·00
171	–	2s. brown and blue	1·00	75
172	–	3s. black and green	1·25	1·00
173	**55**	5s. brown and blue	11·00	3·75

DESIGNS—VERT (As Type **45**): 2d. Fishing god; 8d. Long-tailed tuna. HORIZ (As Type **45**): 3d. Frangipani (plant); 5d. White tern ("Love Tern"); 6d. Hibiscus; 1s. Oranges. (As Type **55**): 2s. Island scene; 3s. Administration Centre, Mangaia.

1965. Solar Eclipse Observation, Manuae Island.

174	**56**	6d. black, yellow and blue	20	10

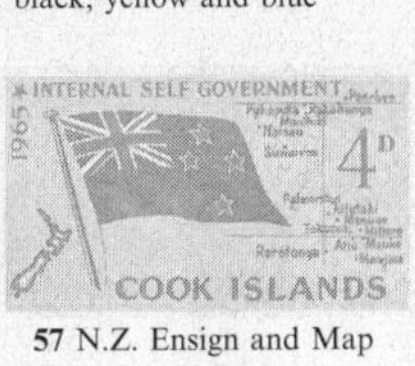

57 N.Z. Ensign and Map

1965. Internal Self-government.

175	**57**	4d. red and blue	20	10
176	–	10d. multicoloured	20	15
177	–	1s. multicoloured	20	15
178	–	1s.9d. multicoloured	50	1·25

DESIGNS: 10d. London Missionary Society Church; 1s. Proclamation of Cession, 1900; 1s.9d. Nikao School.

1966. Churchill Commemoration. Nos. 171/3 and 175/7 optd **In Memoriam SIR WINSTON CHURCHILL 1874 – 1965.**

179	**57**	4d. red and blue	75	30
180	–	10d. multicoloured	1·50	45
181	–	1s. multicoloured	1·50	65
182	–	2s. brown and blue	1·50	1·25
183	–	3s. black and green	1·50	1·25
184	**55**	5s. brown and blue	2·00	1·75

1966. Air. Various stamps optd **Airmail** and Douglas DC-3 airplane or surch in addition.

185	–	6d. red, yell & grn (No. 167)	1·25	20
186	–	7d. on 8d. blk & bl (No. 168)	2·00	25
187	–	10d. on 3d. green and violet (No. 165)	1·00	15
188	–	1s. yellow and green (No. 169)	1·00	15
189	**52**	1s.6d. violet	1·50	1·25
190	–	2s.3d. on 3s. black and green (No. 172)	1·00	65
191	**55**	5s. brown and blue	1·75	1·50
192	–	10s. on 2s. brown and blue (No. 171)	1·75	12·00
193	–	£1 pink (No. 143)	12·00	17·00

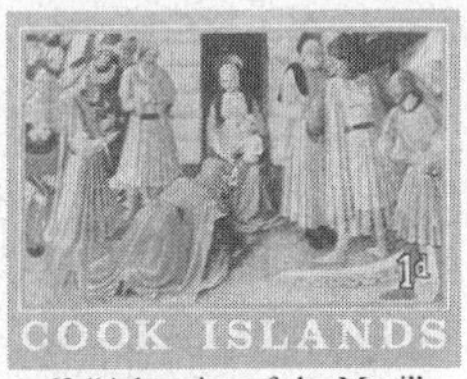

63 "Adoration of the Magi" (Fra Angelico)

1966. Christmas. Multicoloured.

194a	1d. Type **63**	10	10
195a	2d. "The Nativity" (Memling)	20	10
196a	4d. "Adoration of the Wise Men" (Velazquez)	30	15
197a	10d. "Adoration of the Wise Men" (H. Bosch)	30	20
198a	1s.6d. "Adoration of the Shepherds" (J. de Ribera)	40	35

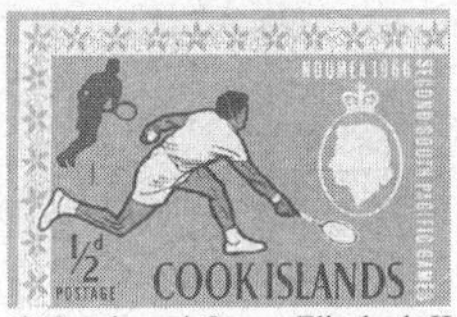

68 Tennis and Queen Elizabeth II

1967. 2nd South Pacific Games, Noumea. Mult.

199	½d. Type **68** (postage)	10	10
200	1d. Basketball and Games emblem	10	10
201	4d. Boxing and Cook Islands Team badge	10	10
202	7d. Football and Queen Elizabeth II	20	15
203	10d. Running and Games Emblem (air)	20	15
204	2s.3d. Running and Cook Islands' Team badge	25	65

1967. Decimal currency. Various stamps surch.

205	**45**	1c. on 1d.	45	1·50
206	–	2c. on 2d. (No. 164)	10	10
207	–	2½c. on 3d. (No. 165)	20	10
209	**57**	3c. on 4d.	15	10
210	–	4c. on 5d. (No. 166)	7·00	30
211	–	5c. on 6d. (No. 167)	15	10
212	**56**	5c. on 6d.	5·00	40
213	–	7c. on 8d. (No. 168)	30	10
214	–	10c. on 1s. (No. 169)	15	10
215	**52**	15c. on 1s.6d.	2·00	1·00
216	–	30c. on 3s. (No. 172)	18·00	3·75
217	**55**	50c. on 5s.	4·00	1·25
218	–	$1 and 10s. on 10d. (No. 176)	15·00	5·50
219	–	$2 on £1 (No. 134)	50·00	70·00
220	–	$6 on £3 (No. 135)	95·00	£120
221	–	$10 on £5 (No. 136)	£150	£180

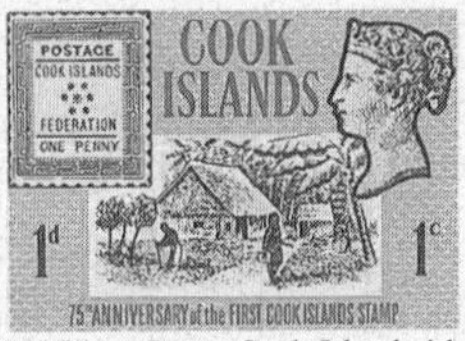

75 Village Scene, Cook Islands 1d. Stamp of 1892 and Queen Victoria

1967. 75th Anniv of First Cook Islands Stamps. Multicoloured.

222	1c. (1d.) Type **75**	10	10
223	3c. (4d.) Post Office, Avarua, Rarotonga and Queen Elizabeth II	15	10
224	8c. (10d.) Avarua, Rarotonga and Cook Islands 10d. stamp of 1892	30	15
225	18c. (1s.9d.) "Moana Roa", (inter-island ship), Douglas DC-3 aircraft, map and Captain Cook	1·40	30

The face values are expressed in decimal currency and in the Sterling equivalent.

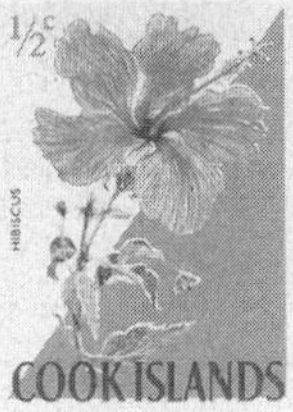

79 Hibiscus

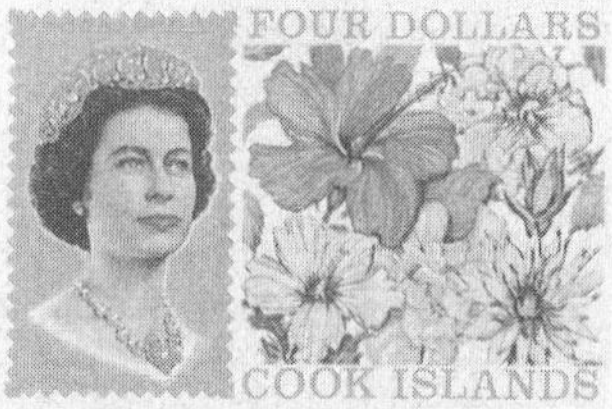

81 Queen Elizabeth and Flowers

1967. Flowers. Multicoloured.

227A	½c. Type **79**	10	10
228A	1c. "Hibiscus syriacus"	10	10
229A	2c. Frangipani	10	10
230A	2½c. "Clitoria ternatea"	20	10
231B	3c. "Suva Queen"	40	10
232A	4c. Water lily (wrongly inscribed "Walter Lily")	70	1·00
233B	4c. Water lily	2·50	10
234B	5c. "Bauhinia bipinnata rosea"	30	10
235B	6c. Yellow hibiscus	30	10
236B	8c. "Allamanda cathartica"	30	10
237B	9c. Stephanotis	30	10
238B	10c. "Poinciana regia flamboyant"	30	10
239A	15c. Frangipani	40	10
240B	20c. Thunbergia	3·50	1·25
241A	25c. Canna lily	80	30
242A	30c. "Euphorbia pulcherrima poinsettia"	65	50
243A	50c. "Gardinia taitensis"	1·00	55
244B	$1 Queen Elizabeth II	1·25	80
245B	$2 Queen Elizabeth II	2·25	1·50
246A	$4 Type **81**	1·75	4·00
247A	$6 Type **81**	2·00	5·50
247cA	$8 Type **81**	6·00	14·00
248A	$10 Type **81**	3·75	12·00

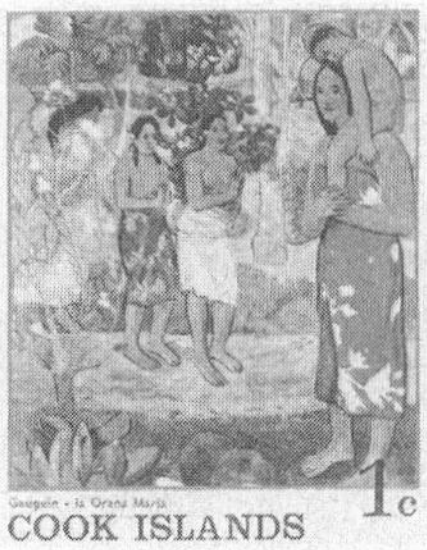

97 "Ia Orana Maria"

1967. Gauguin's Polynesian Paintings.

249	**97**	1c. multicoloured	10	10
250	–	3c. multicoloured	15	10
251	–	5c. multicoloured	20	10
252	–	8c. multicoloured	25	10
253	–	15c. multicoloured	50	15
254	–	22c. multicoloured	65	20

DESIGNS: 3c. "Riders on the Beach"; 5c. "Still Life with Flowers" and inset portrait of Queen Elizabeth; 8c. "Whispered Words"; 15c. "Maternity"; 22c. "Why are you angry?".

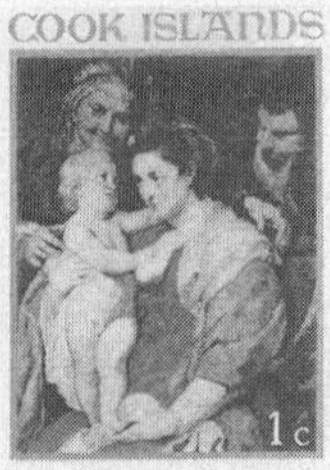

98 "The Holy Family" (Rubens)

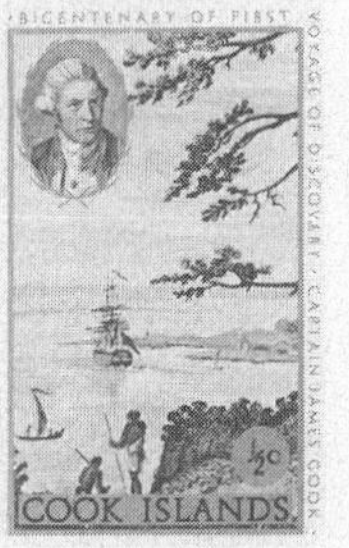

100 "Matavai Bay, Tahiti" (J. Barralet)

1967. Christmas. Renaissance Paintings.

256	**98**	1c. multicoloured	10	10
257	–	3c. multicoloured	10	10
258	–	4c. multicoloured	10	10
259	–	8c. multicoloured	20	15
260	–	15c. multicoloured	35	15
261	–	25c. multicoloured	40	15

DESIGNS: 3c. "The Epiphany" (Durer); 4c. "The Lucca Madonna" (J. van Eyck); 8c. "The Adora-tion of the Shepherds" (J. da Bassano); 15c. "The

Nativity" (El Greco); 25c. "The Madonna and Child" (Correggio).

1968. Hurricane Relief. Nos. 231, 233, 251, 238, 241 and 243/4 optd **HURRICANE RELIEF PLUS** and premium.

262	3c.+1c. multicoloured	15	15
263	4c.+1c. multicoloured	15	15
264	5c.+2c. multicoloured	15	15
265	10c.+2c. multicoloured	15	15
266	25c.+5c. multicoloured	20	20
267	50c.+10c. multicoloured	25	30
268	$1+10c. multicoloured	35	50

On No. 264 silver blocking obliterates the design area around the lettering.

1968. Bicentenary of Captain Cook's First Voyage of Discovery.

269 **100**	½c. mult (postage)	10	10
270 –	1c. multicoloured	15	10
271 –	2c. multicoloured	35	20
272 –	4c. multicoloured	50	20
273 –	6c. multicoloured (air)	60	35
274 –	10c. multicoloured	60	35
275 –	15c. multicoloured	70	50
276 –	25c. multicoloured	80	75

DESIGNS—VERT: 1c. "Island of Huaheine" (John Cleveley); 2c. "Town of St. Peter and St. Paul, Kamchatka" (J. Webber); 4c. "The Ice Islands" (Antarctica: W. Hodges). HORIZ: 6c. "Resolution" and "Discovery" (J. Webber); 10c. "The Island of Tahiti" (W. Hodges); 15c. "Karakakooa, Hawaii" (J. Webber); 25c. "The Landing at Middleburg" (J. Sherwin).

102 Dinghy-sailing

1968. Olympic Games, Mexico. Multicoloured.

277	1c. Type **102**	10	10
278	5c. Gymnastics	10	10
279	15c. High-jumping	25	10
280	20c. High-diving	25	10
281	30c. Cycling	60	20
282	50c. Hurdling	50	25

103 "Madonna and Child" (Titian)

1968. Christmas. Multicoloured.

283	1c. Type **103**	10	10
284	4c. "The Holy Family of the Lamb" (Raphael)	15	10
285	10c. "The Madonna of the Rosary" (Murillo)	25	10
286	20c. "Adoration of the Magi" (Memling)	40	10
287	30c. "Adoration of the Magi" (Ghirlandaio)	45	10

104 Campfire Cooking

1969. Diamond Jubilee of New Zealand Scout Movement and 5th National (New Zealand) Jamboree. Multicoloured.

289	½c. Type **104**	10	10
290	1c. Descent by rope	10	10
291	5c. Semaphore	15	10
292	10c. Tree-planting	20	10
293	20c. Constructing a shelter	25	15
294	30c. Lord Baden-Powell and island scene	45	25

105 High Jumping

1969. 3rd South Pacific Games, Port Moresby. Multicoloured.

295	½c. Type **105**	10	30
296	½c. Footballer	10	30
297	1c. Basketball	50	40
298	1c. Weightlifter	50	40
299	4c. Tennis-player	50	50
300	4c. Hurdler	50	50
301	10c. Javelin-thrower	55	50
302	10c. Runner	55	50
303	15c. Golfer	1·75	1·50
304	15c. Boxer	1·75	1·50

106 Flowers, Map and Captain Cook (½-size illustration)

1969. South Pacific Conference, Noumea. Mult.

306	5c. Premier Albert Henry	30	20
307	10c. Type **106**	1·00	60
308	25c. Flowers, map and arms of New Zealand	40	60
309	30c. Queen Elizabeth II, map and flowers	40	70

107 "Virgin and Child with Saints Jerome and Dominic" (Lippi)

1969. Christmas. Multicoloured.

310	1c. Type **107**	10	10
311	4c. "The Holy Family" (Fra Bartolomeo)	10	10
312	10c. "The Adoration of the Shepherds" (A. Mengs)	15	10
313	20c. "Madonna and Child with Saints" (Robert Campin)	25	20
314	30c. "The Madonna of the Basket" (Correggio)	25	30

108 "The Resurrection of Christ" (Raphael)

115 Mary, Joseph, and Christ in Manger

110 The Royal Family

1970. Easter.

316 **108**	4c. multicoloured	10	10
317 –	8c. multicoloured	10	10
318 –	20c. multicoloured	15	10
319 –	25c. multicoloured	20	10

DESIGNS: "The Resurrection of Christ" by Dirk Bouts (8c.), Altdorfer (20c.), Murillo (25c.).

1970. "Apollo 13". Nos. 233, 236, 239/40, 242 and 245/6 optd **KIA ORANA APOLLO 13 ASTRONAUTS Te Atua to Tatou Irinakianga**.

321	4c. multicoloured	10	10
322	8c. multicoloured	10	10
323	15c. multicoloured	10	10
324	20c. multicoloured	40	15
325	30c. multicoloured	20	20
326	$2 multicoloured	60	90
327a	$4 multicoloured	1·00	2·75

1970. Royal Visit to New Zealand. Multicoloured.

328	5c. Type **110**	50	30
329	30c. Captain Cook and H.M.S. "Endeavour"	2·00	1·75
330	$1 Royal Visit commemorative coin	3·00	3·00

1970. 5th Anniv of Self-Government. Nos. 328/30 optd **FIFTH ANNIVERSARY SELF-GOVERNMENT AUGUST 1970**.

332 **110**	5c. multicoloured	40	15
333 –	30c. multicoloured	80	35
334 –	$1 multicoloured	1·40	90

On No. 332, the opt is arranged in one line around the frame of the stamp.

1970. Surch **FOUR DOLLARS $4.00**.

335a **81**	$4 on $8 multicoloured	1·50	2·00
336a	$4 on $10 multicoloured	1·50	1·75

1970. Christmas. Multicoloured.

337	1c. Type **115**	10	10
338	4c. Shepherds and Apparition of the Angel	10	10
339	10c. Mary showing Child to Joseph	15	10
340	20c. The Wise Men bearing Gifts	20	20
341	30c. Parents wrapping Child in swaddling clothes	25	35

1971. Surch **PLUS 20c UNITED KINGDOM SPECIAL MAIL SERVICE**.

343	30c.+20c. (No. 242)	30	50
344	50c.+20c. (No. 243)	1·00	1·75

The premium of 20c. was to prepay a private delivery service fee in Great Britain during the postal strike. The mail was sent by air to a forwarding address in the Netherlands. No. 343 was intended for ordinary airmail ½ oz. letters, and No. 344 included registration fee.

117 Wedding of Princess Elizabeth and Prince Philip

1971. Royal Visit of Duke of Edinburgh. Multicoloured.

345	1c. Type **117**	20	50
346	4c. Queen Elizabeth, Prince Philip, Prince Charles and Princess Anne at Windsor	60	1·10
347	10c. Prince Philip sailing	1·00	1·25
348	15c. Prince Philip in polo gear	1·00	1·25
349	25c. Prince Philip in naval uniform, and Royal Yacht, "Britannia"	1·25	2·00

1971. 4th South Pacific Games, Tahiti. Nos. 238, 241 and 242 optd **Fourth South Pacific Games Papeete** and emblem or surch also.

351	10c. multicoloured	10	10
352	10c.+1c. multicoloured	10	10
353	10c.+3c. multicoloured	10	10
354	25c. multicoloured	15	10
355	25c.+1c. multicoloured	15	10
356	25c.+3c. multicoloured	15	10
357	30c. multicoloured	15	10
358	30c.+1c. multicoloured	15	10
359	30c.+3c. multicoloured	15	10

The stamps additionally surch 1c. or 3c. helped to finance the Cook Islands' team at the games.

1971. Nos. 230, 233, 236/7 and 239 surch **10c**.

360	10c. on 2½c. multicoloured	15	25
361	10c. on 4c. multicoloured	15	25
362	10c. on 8c. multicoloured	15	25
363	10c. on 9c. multicoloured	15	25
364	10c. on 15c. multicoloured	15	25

121 "Virgin and Child" (Bellini)

123 St. John

1971. Christmas.

365 **121**	1c. multicoloured	10	10
366 –	4c. multicoloured	10	10
367 –	10c. multicoloured	25	10
368 –	20c. multicoloured	50	20
369 –	30c. multicoloured	50	35

DESIGNS: Various paintings of the "Virgin and Child" by Bellini. Similar to Type **121**.

1972. 25th Anniv of South Pacific Commission. No. 244 optd **SOUTH PACIFIC COMMISSION FEB. 1947 – 1972**.

372	$1 multicoloured	40	75

1972. Easter. Multicoloured.

373	5c. Type **123**	10	10
374	10c. Christ on the Cross	10	10
375	30c. Mary, Mother of Jesus	25	40

1972. Hurricane Relief. (a) Nos. 239, 241 and 243 optd **HURRICANE RELIEF PLUS** and premium.

379	15c.+5c. multicoloured	20	20
380	25c.+5c. multicoloured	20	20
382	50c.+10c. multicoloured	25	25

(b) Nos. 373/5 optd **Hurricane Relief Plus** and premium.

377	5c.+2c. multicoloured	15	15
378	10c.+2c. multicoloured	15	15
381	30c.+5c. multicoloured	20	20

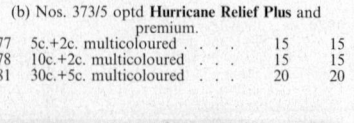

126/7 Rocket heading for Moon

1972. Apollo Moon Exploration Flights. Mult.

383	5c. Type **126**	20	15
384	5c. Type **127**	20	15
385	10c. Lunar module and astronaut	20	15
386	10c. Astronaut and experiment	20	15
387	25c. Command capsule and Earth	25	20
388	25c. Lunar Rover	25	20
389	30c. Sikorsky Sea King helicopter	75	40
390	30c. Splashdown	75	40

These were issued in horizontal se-tenant pairs of each value, forming one composite design.

1972. Hurricane Relief. Nos. 383/390 surch **HURRICANE RELIEF Plus** and premium.

392	5c.+2c. multicoloured	10	10
393	5c.+2c. multicoloured	10	10
394	10c.+2c. multicoloured	10	10
395	10c.+2c. multicoloured	10	10
396	25c.+2c. multicoloured	15	15
397	25c.+2c. multicoloured	15	15
398	30c.+2c. multicoloured	25	15
399	30c.+2c. multicoloured	25	15

129 High-jumping

130 "The Rest on the Flight into Egypt" (Caravaggio)

1972. Olympic Games, Munich. Multicoloured.

401	10c. Type **129**	20	10
402	25c. Running	40	15
403	30c. Boxing	40	20

1972. Christmas. Multicoloured.

406	1c. Type **130**	10	10
407	5c. "Madonna of the Swallow" (Guercino)	25	10
408	10c. "Madonna of the Green Cushion" (Solario)	35	10
409	20c. "Madonna and Child" (di Credi)	55	20
410	30c. "Madonna and Child" (Bellini)	85	30

131 Marriage Ceremony

133 "Noli me Tangere" (Titian)

132 Taro Leaf

1972. Royal Silver Wedding. Each black and silver.
413 5c. Type **131** 25 15
414 10c. Leaving Westminster Abbey 35 25
415 15c. Bride and bridegroom (40 × 41 mm) 45 50
416 30c. Family group (67 × 40 mm) 55 75

1973. Silver Wedding Coinage.
417 **132** 1c. gold, mauve and black 10 10
418 – 2c. gold, blue and black 10 10
419 – 5c. silver, green and black 10 10
420 – 10c. silver, blue and black 20 10
421 – 20c. silver, green and black 30 10
422 – 50c. silver, mauve and black 50 15
423 – $1 silver, blue and black 75 30
DESIGNS—HORIZ (37 × 24 mm): 2c. Pineapple; 5c. Hibiscus. (46 × 30 mm): 10c. Oranges; 20c. White tern; 50c. Striped bonito. VERT: (32 × 55 mm): $1 Tangaroa.

1973. Easter. Multicoloured.
424 5c. Type **133** 15 10
425 10c. "The Descent from the Cross" (Rubens) 20 10
426 30c. "The Lamentation of Christ" (Durer) 25 10

134 Queen Elizabeth II in Coronation Regalia

137 The Annunciation

136 Tipairua

1973. 20th Anniv of Queen Elizabeth's Coronation.
429 **134** 10c. multicoloured 50 90

1973. 10th Anniv of Treaty Banning Nuclear Testing. Nos. 234, 236, 238 and 240/2 optd **TENTH ANNIVERSARY CESSATION OF NUCLEAR TESTING TREATY.**
431 5c. multicoloured 10 10
432 8c. multicoloured 10 10
433 10c. multicoloured 10 10
434 20c. multicoloured 15 15
435 25c. multicoloured 20 15
436 30c. multicoloured 20 15

1973. Maori Exploration of the Pacific. Sailing Craft. Multicoloured.
437 ½c. Type **136** 10 10
438 1c. Wa'a Kaulua 10 10
439 1½c. Tainui 15 10
440 5c. War canoe 40 15
441 10c. Pahi 50 15
442 15c. Amatasi 75 65
443 25c. Vaka 90 80

1973. Christmas. Scene from a 15th-century Flemish "Book of Hours". Multicoloured.
444 1c. Type **137** 10 10
445 5c. The Visitation 10 10
446 10c. Annunciation to the Shepherds 10 10
447 20c. Epiphany 15 10
448 30c. The Slaughter of the Innocents 20 15

138 Princess Anne

140 "Jesus carrying the Cross" (Raphael)

139 Running

1973. Royal Wedding. Multicoloured.
450 25c. Type **138** 20 10
451 30c. Captain Mark Phillips 25 10
452 50c. Princess Anne and Captain Phillips 30 15

1974. British Commonwealth Games, Christchurch. Multicoloured.
455 1c. Diving (vert) 10 10
456 3c. Boxing (vert) 10 10
457 5c. Type 139 . . . . 10 10
458 10c. Weightlifting 10 10
459 30c. Cycling 40 25

1974. Easter. Multicoloured.
461 5c. Type **140** 10 10
462 10c. "The Holy Trinity" (El Greco) 15 10
463 30c. "The Deposition of Christ" (Caravaggio) . . . 25 20

141 Grey Bonnet

142 Queen Elizabeth II

1974. Sea Shells. Multicoloured.
466 ½c. Type **141** 30 10
467 1c. Common Pacific vase . . 30 10
468 1½c. True heart cockle . . . 30 10
469 2c. Terebellum conch 30 10
470 3c. Bat volute 45 10
471 4c. Gibbose conch 50 10
472 5c. Common hairy triton . . 50 10
473 6c. Serpent's head cowrie . . 50 1·50
474 8c. Granulate frog shell . . . 60 10
475 10c. Fly-spotted auger . . . 60 10
476 15c. Episcopan mitre 70 20
477 20c. Butterfly moon . . . . 1·00 20
478 25c. Royal oak scallop . . . 1·00 1·50
479 30c. Soldier cone . . . . . . 1·00 30
480 50c. Textile or cloth of gold cone . . . . 8·50 4·50
481 60c. Red-mouth olive . . . . 8·50 4·50
482 $1 Type **142** . . . . 3·00 4·50
483 $2 Type **142** . . . . 1·75 2·25
484 $4 Queen Elizabeth II and sea shells (60 × 39 mm) . . 2·50 6·00
485 $6 As $4 (60 × 39 mm) . . . 14·00 7·00
486 $8 As $4 (60 × 39 mm) . . . 17·00 8·50
487 $10 As $4 (60 × 39 mm) . . . 20·00 9·00

143 Footballer and Australasian Map

1974. World Cup Football Championship, West Germany. Multicoloured.
488 25c. Type **143** 20 10
489 50c. Map and Munich Stadium 35 25
490 $1 Footballer, stadium and World Cup 55 45

144 Obverse and Reverse of Commemorative $2.50 Silver Coin

146 "Madonna of the Goldfinch" (Raphael)

145 Early Stamps of Cook Islands

1974. Bicentenary of Captain Cook's Second Voyage of Discovery.
492 **144** $2.50 silver, black and violet . . . . 12·00 7·00
493 – $7.50 silver, black and green . . . . 20·00 13·00
DESIGN: $7.50, As Type **144** but showing $7.50 coin.

1974. Centenary of U.P.U. Multicoloured.
495 10c. Type **145** 20 15
496 25c. Old landing strip, Rarotonga, and stamp of 1898 . . . . 30 40
497 30c. Post Office, Rarotonga, and stamp of 1920 . . . . 30 40
498 50c. U.P.U. emblem and stamps 30 65

1974. Christmas. Multicoloured.
500 1c. Type **146** 10 10
501 5c. "The Sacred Family" (Andrea del Sarto) 20 10
502 10c. "The Virgin adoring the Child" (Correggio) 25 10
503 20c. "The Holy Family" (Rembrandt) 40 20
504 30c. "The Virgin and Child" (Rogier van der Weyden) 50 30

147 Churchill and Blenheim Palace

1974. Birth Centenary of Sir Winston Churchill. Multicoloured.
506 5c. Type **147** 15 10
507 10c. Churchill and Houses of Parliament 15 10
508 25c. Churchill and Chartwell 25 20
509 30c. Churchill and Buckingham Palace 25 25
510 50c. Churchill and St. Paul's Cathedral 30 50

148 Vasco Nunez de Balbôa and Discovery of Pacific Ocean (1513)

1975. Pacific Explorers. Multicoloured.
513 1c. Type **148** 15 10
514 5c. Fernando de Magellanes and map (1520) 65 20
515 10c. Juan Sebastian del Cano and "Vitoria" (1520) . . . 1·25 20
516 25c. Friar Andres de Urdaneta and ship (1564–67) . . . . 2·25 75
517 30c. Miguel Lopez de Legazpi and ship (1564–67) . . . . 2·25 80

149 "Apollo" Capsule

1975. "Apollo–Soyuz" Space Project. Mult.
518 25c. Type **149** 35 15
519 25c. "Soyuz" capsule 35 15
520 30c. "Soyuz" crew 40 15
521 30c. "Apollo" crew 40 15
522 50c. Cosmonaut within "Soyuz" 45 25
523 50c. Astronauts within "Apollo" 45 25
These were issued in horizontal se-tenant pairs of each value, forming one composite design.

150 $100 Commemorative Gold Coin

1975. Bicentenary of Captain Cook's 2nd Voyage.
525 **150** $2 brown, gold and violet 2·75 1·75

151 Cook Islands' Flag and Map

152 "Madonna by the Fireside" (R. Campin)

1975. 10th Anniv of Self-government.
526 5c. Type **151** 40 10
527 10c. Premier Sir Albert Henry and flag (vert) 45 10
528 25c. Rarotonga and flag . . 80 30

1975. Christmas. Multicoloured.
529 6c. Type **152** 15 10
530 10c. "Madonna in the Meadow" (Raphael) . . . 15 10
531 15c. "Madonna of the Oak" (att. Raphael) 25 10
532 20c. "Adoration of the Shepherds" (J. B. Maino) 25 15
533 35c. "The Annunciation" (Murillo) 40 20

153 "Entombment of Christ" (Raphael)

1976. Easter. Multicoloured.
536 7c. Type **153** 30 10
537 15c. "Pieta" (Veronese) . . . 50 15
538 35c. "Pieta" (El Greco) . . . 75 25

154 Benjamin Franklin and H.M.S. "Resolution"

1976. Bicent of American Revolution. Mult.
541 $1 Type **154** . . . . 6·00 1·50
542 $2 Captain Cook and H.M.S. "Resolution" . . . . . . 8·00 2·50

1976. Visit of Queen Elizabeth to U.S.A. Nos. 541/2 optd **Royal Visit July 1976.**
544 **154** $1 multicoloured . . . . 4·00 1·50
545 – $2 multicoloured . . . . 6·00 2·50

156 Hurdling

157 "The Visitation"

1976. Olympic Games, Montreal. Multicoloured.

547	7c. Type **156**	20	10
548	7c. Hurdling (value on left)	20	10
549	15c. Hockey (value on right)	40	15
550	15c. Hockey (value on left)	40	15
551	30c. Fencing (value on right)	40	15
552	30c. Fencing (value on left)	40	15
553	35c. Football (value on right)	40	20
554	35c. Football (value on left)	40	20

1976. Christmas. Renaissance Sculptures. Mult.

556	6c. Type **157**	10	10
557	10c. "Adoration of the Shepherds"	10	10
558	15c. "Adoration of the Shepherds" (different)	15	10
559	20c. "The Epiphany"	20	20
560	35c. "The Holy Family"	25	25

158 Obverse and Reverse of $5 Mangaia Kingfisher Coin

1976. National Wildlife and Conservation Day.

563	**158** $1 multicoloured	1·00	1·00

159 Imperial State Crown

1977. Silver Jubilee. Multicoloured.

564	25c. Type **159**	40	50
565	25c. The Queen with regalia	40	50
566	50c. Westminster Abbey	50	65
567	50c. Coronation coach	50	65
568	$1 The Queen and Prince Philip	80	90
569	$1 Royal Visit, 1974	80	90

160 "Christ on the Cross"

161 "Virgin and Child" (Memling)

1977. Easter. 400th Birth Anniv of Rubens. Multicoloured.

571	7c. Type **160**	35	10
572	15c. "Christ on the Cross"	55	15
573	35c. "The Deposition of Christ"	1·10	30

1977. Christmas. Multicoloured.

576	6c. Type **161**	25	10
577	10c. "Madonna and Child with Saints and Donors" (Memling)	25	10
578	15c. "Adoration of the Kings" (Geertgen)	35	10
579	20c. "Virgin and Child with Saints" (Crivelli)	45	15
580	35c. "Adoration of the Magi" (16th century Flemish school)	60	20

162 Obverse and Reverse of $5 Cook Islands Swiftlet Coin

1977. National Wildlife and Conservation Day.

583	**162** $1 multicoloured	1·00	65

163 Captain Cook and H.M.S. "Resolution" (from paintings by N. Dance and H. Roberts)

1978. Bicent of Discovery of Hawaii. Mult.

584	50c. Type **163**	1·00	60
585	$1 Earl of Sandwich and Cook landing at Owhyhee (from paintings by Thomas Gainsborough and J. Cleveley)	1·45	75
586	$2 Obverse and reverse of $200 coin and Cook monument, Hawaii	1·60	1·25

164 "Pieta" (Van der Weyden)

1978. Easter. Paintings from the National Gallery, London. Multicoloured.

588	15c. Type **164**	40	15
589	35c. "The Entombment" (Michelangelo)	50	30
590	75c. "The Supper at Emmaus" (Caravaggio)	75	55

165 Queen Elizabeth II

169 "The Virgin and Child" (Van Der Weyden)

168 Obverse and Reverse of Cook Islands Warblers $5 Coin

1978. 25th Anniv of Coronation. Multicoloured.

593	50c. Type **165**	25	30
594	50c. The Lion of England	25	30
595	50c. Imperial State Crown	25	30
596	50c. Statue of Tangaroa (god)	25	30
597	70c. Type **165**	25	30
598	70c. Sceptre with Cross	25	30
599	70c. St. Edward's Crown	25	30
600	70c. Rarotongan staff god	25	30

1978. Nos. 466, 468, 473/4 and 478/82 surch.

602	5c. on 1½c. True heart cockle	50	10
603	7c. on ½c. Type **141**	55	15
604	10c. on 6c. Serpent's-head cowrie	60	15
605	10c. on 8c. Granulate frog shell	60	15
606	15c. on ½c. Type **141**	60	20
607	15c. on 25c. Royal oak scallop	60	20
608	15c. on 30c. Soldier cone	60	20
609	15c. on 50c. Textile or cloth of gold cone	60	20
610	15c. on 60c. Red-mouth olive	60	20
611	17c. on ½c. Type **141**	80	25
612	17c. on 50c. Textile or cloth of gold cone	80	25

1978. 250th Birth Anniv of Captain James Cook. Nos. 584/6 optd **1728 250th ANNIVERSARY OF COOK'S BIRTH 1978**.

613	50c. Type **163**	2·00	75
614	$1 Earl of Sandwich and Cook landing at Owhyhee	2·25	1·00
615	$2 $200 commemorative coin and Cook monument, Hawaii	2·50	2·00

1978. National Wildlife and Conservation Day.

617	**168** $1 multicoloured	1·00	1·00

1978. Christmas. Paintings. Multicoloured.

618	15c. Type **169**	45	15
619	17c. "The Virgin and Child" (Crivelli)	45	20
620	35c. "The Virgin and Child" (Murillo)	80	35

170 Virgin with Body of Christ

171 "Captain Cook" (James Weber)

1979. Easter. Details of Painting "Descent" by Gaspar de Crayar. Multicoloured.

623	10c. Type **170**	25	10
624	12c. St. John	30	20
625	15c. Mary Magdalene	35	25
626	20c. Weeping angels	45	30

1979. Death Bicentenary of Captain Cook. Mult.

628	20c. Type **171**	40	20
629	30c. H.M.S. "Resolution"	50	35
630	35c. H.M.S. "Royal George" (ship of the line)	50	45
631	50c. "Death of Captain Cook" (George Carter)	55	60

172 Post-Rider

174 Brother and Sister

1979. Death Centenary of Sir Rowland Hill. Mult.

633	30c. Type **172**	20	20
634	30c. Mail coach	20	20
635	30c. Automobile	20	20
636	30c. Diesel train	20	20
637	35c. "Cap-Hornier" (full-rigged ship)	20	20
638	35c. River steamer	20	20
639	35c. "Deutschland" (liner)	20	20
640	35c. "United States" (liner)	20	20
641	50c. Balloon "Le Neptune"	30	25
642	50c. Junkers F13 airplane	30	25
643	50c. Airship "Graf Zeppelin"	30	25
644	50c. Concorde	30	25

1979. Nos. 466, 468 and 481 surch.

646	6c. on ½c. Type **141**	20	30
647	10c. on 1½c. Cockle shell	25	20
648	15c. on 60c. Olive shell	40	40

1979. International Year of the Child. Mult.

649	30c. Type **174**	25	25
650	50c. Boy with tree drum	40	40
651	65c. Children dancing	50	50

175 "Apollo 11" Emblem

177 Glass Christmas Tree Ornaments

176 Obverse and Reverse of $5 Rarotongan Fruit Dove Coin

1979. 10th Anniv of "Apollo 11" Moon Landing. Multicoloured.

653	30c. Type **175**	40	55
654	50c. "Apollo 11" crew	50	75
655	60c. Neil Armstrong on the Moon	65	80
656	65c. Splashdown recovery	70	90

1979. National Wildlife and Conservation Day.

658	**176** $1 multicoloured	1·60	2·50

1979. Christmas. Multicoloured.

659	6c. Type **177** (postage)	10	10
660	10c. Hibiscus and star	10	10
661	12c. Poinsettia, bells and candle	15	10
662	15c. Poinsettia leaves and Tiki (god)	15	15
663	20c. Type **177** (air)	20	15
664	25c. As No. 660	25	20
665	30c. As No. 661	30	25
666	35c. As No. 662	35	30

1980. Christmas. As Nos. 659/66 but with charity premium.

667	6c.+2c. Type **177** (postage)	10	10
668	10c.+2c. Hibiscus and star	15	15
669	12c.+2c. Poinsettia, bells and candle	15	20
670	15c.+2c. Poinsettia leaves and Tiki (god)	15	20
671	20c.+4c. Type **177** (air)	15	25
672	25c.+4c. As No. 660	15	25
673	30c.+4c. As No. 661	20	30
674	35c.+4c. As No. 662	25	35

178 "Flagellation"

181 Queen Elizabeth the Queen Mother

179 Dove with Olive Twig

1980. Easter. Illustrations by Gustav Dore. Each gold and brown.

675	20c. Type **178**	25	20
676	20c. "Crown of Thorns"	25	20
677	30c. "Jesus Insulted"	35	30
678	30c. "Jesus Falls"	35	30
679	35c. "The Crucifixion"	40	30
680	35c. "The Descent from the Cross"	40	30

1980. 75th Anniv of Rotary International. Mult.

683	30c. Type **179**	35	35
684	35c. Hibiscus flower	40	40
685	50c. Ribbons	50	50

1980. "Zeapex 80" International Stamp Exhibition, Auckland. Nos. 633/44 optd **ZEAPEX STAMP EXHIBITION—AUCKLAND 1980** and New Zealand 1865 1s. Stamp.

687	30c. Type **172**	35	25
688	30c. Mail coach	35	25
689	30c. Automobile	35	25
690	30c. Diesel train	35	25
691	35c. "Cap-Hornier" (full-rigged ship)	40	30
692	35c. River steamer	40	30
693	35c. "Deutschland" (liner)	40	30
694	35c. "United States" (liner)	40	30
695	50c. Balloon "Le Neptune"	60	35
696	50c. Junkers "F13" airplane	60	35
697	50c. Airship"Graf Zeppelin"	60	35
698	50c. Concorde	60	35

1980. 80th Birthday of the Queen Mother.

701	**181** 50c. multicoloured	1·00	1·00

182 Satellites orbiting Moon

1980. 350th Death Anniv of Johannes Kepler (astronomer). Multicoloured.

703	12c. Type **182**	50	35
704	12c. Space-craft orbiting Moon	50	35
705	50c. Space-craft orbiting Moon (different)	1·00	80
706	50c. Astronaut and Moon vehicle	1·00	80

183 Scene from novel "From the Earth to the Moon"

184 "Siphonogorgia"

1980. 75th Death Anniv of Jules Verne (author).

708	**183** 20c. multicoloured	45	35
709	– 20c. multicoloured	45	35
710	– 30c. multicoloured (mauve background)	55	45
711	– 30c. multicoloured (blue background)	55	45

DESIGNS: Showing scenes from the novel "From the Earth to the Moon".

1980. Corals (1st series). Multicoloured.

713	1c. Type **184**	30	30
714	1c. "Pavona praetorta"	30	30
715	1c. "Stylaster echinatus"	30	30
716	1c. "Tubastraea"	30	30
717	3c. "Millepora alcicornis"	30	30
718	3c. "Junceella gemmacea"	30	30
719	3c. "Fungia fungites"	30	30
720	3c. "Heliofungia actiniformis"	30	30
721	4c. "Distichopora violacea"	30	30
722	4c. "Stylaster"	30	30
723	4c. "Gonipora"	30	30
724	4c. "Caulastraea echinulata"	30	30
725	5c. "Ptilosarcus gurneyi"	30	30
726	5c. "Stylophora pistillata"	30	30
727	5c. "Melithaea squamata"	30	30
728	5c. "Porites andrewsi"	30	30
729	6c. "Lobophyllia bemprichii"	30	30
730	6c. "Palauastrea ramosa"	30	30
731	6c. "Bellonella indica"	30	30
732	6c. "Pectinia alcicornis"	30	30
733	8c. "Sarcophyton digitatum"	30	30
734	8c. "Melithaea albitincta"	30	30
735	8c. "Plerogyra sinuosa"	30	30
736	8c. "Dendropyllia gracilis"	30	30
737	10c. As Type **184**	30	30
738	10c. As No. 714	30	30
739	10c. As No. 715	30	30
740	10c. As No. 716	30	30
741	12c. As No. 717	30	30
742	12c. As No. 718	30	30
743	12c. As No. 719	30	30
744	12c. As No. 720	30	30
745	15c. As No. 721	30	30
746	15c. As No. 722	30	30
747	15c. As No. 723	30	30
748	15c. As No. 724	30	30
749	20c. As No. 725	35	30
750	20c. As No. 726	35	30
751	20c. As No. 727	35	30
752	20c. As No. 728	35	30
753	25c. As No. 729	35	30
754	25c. As No. 730	35	30
755	25c. As No. 731	35	30
756	25c. As No. 732	35	30
757	30c. As No. 733	40	30
758	30c. As No. 734	40	30
759	30c. As No. 735	40	30
760	30c. As No. 736	40	30
761	35c. Type **184**	45	35
762	35c. As No. 714	45	35
763	35c. As No. 715	45	35
764	35c. As No. 716	45	35
765	50c. As No. 717	65	75
766	50c. As No. 718	65	75
767	50c. As No. 719	65	75
768	50c. As No. 720	65	75
769	60c. As No. 721	75	75
770	60c. As No. 722	75	75
771	60c. As No. 723	75	75
772	60c. As No. 724	75	75
773	70c. As No. 725	2·50	75
774	70c. As No. 726	2·50	75
775	70c. As No. 727	2·50	75
776	70c. As No. 728	2·50	75
777	80c. As No. 729	2·50	80
778	80c. As No. 730	2·50	80
779	80c. As No. 731	2·50	80
780	80c. As No. 732	2·50	80
781	$1 As No. 733	3·75	1·00
782	$1 As No. 734	3·75	1·00
783	$1 As No. 735	3·75	1·00
784	$1 As No. 736	3·75	1·00
785	$2 As No. 723	12·00	2·25
786	$3 As No. 720	12·00	2·25
787	$4 As No. 726	4·50	12·00
788	$6 As No. 715	6·00	15·00
789	$10 As No. 734	27·00	35·00

Nos. 761/74 are 30 × 40 mm, and Nos. 785/9, which include a portrait of Queen Elizabeth II in each design, are 55 × 35 mm.

See also Nos. 966/94.

185 Annunciation

187 Prince Charles

186 "The Crucifixion" (from book of Saint-Amand)

1980. Christmas. Scenes from 13th-century French Prayer Books. Multicoloured.

801	15c. Type **185**	25	15
802	30c. The Visitation	35	25
803	40c. The Nativity	45	30
804	50c. The Epiphany	60	40

1981. Easter. Illustrations from 12th-century French Prayer Books. Multicoloured.

807	15c. Type **186**	30	30
808	25c. "Placing in Tomb" (from book of Ingeburge)	35	35
809	40c. "Mourning at the Sepulchre" (from book of Ingeburge)	45	45

1981. Royal Wedding. Multicoloured.

812	$1 Type **187**	50	1·10
813	$2 Prince Charles and Lady Diana Spencer	60	1·40

188 Footballers

1981. World Cup Football Championship, Spain (1982). Designs showing footballers. Mult.

815	20c. Type **188**	40	20
816	20c. Figures to right of stamp	40	20
817	30c. Figures to left	50	30
818	30c. Figures to right	50	30
819	35c. Figures to left	50	35
820	35c. Figures to right	50	35
821	50c. Figures to left	65	45
822	50c. Figures to right	65	45

The two designs of each value were printed together, se-tenant, in horizontal pairs throughout the sheet, forming composite designs.

1981. International Year for Disabled Persons. Nos. 812/13 surch **+5c**.

824	$1+5c. Type **187**	75	1·75
825	$2+5c. Prince Charles and Lady Diana Spencer	1·00	2·50

190 "Holy Virgin with Child"

1982. Christmas. Details of Paintings by Rubens. Multicoloured.

827	8c. Type **190**	55	20
828	15c. "Coronation of St. Catherine"	65	35
829	40c. "Adoration of the Shepherds"	90	80
830	50c. "Adoration of the Magi"	1·00	1·00

191 Princess of Wales (inscr "21st Birthday")

1982. 21st Birthday of Princess of Wales. Multicoloured.

833	$1.25 Type **191**	2·25	1·50
834	$1.25 As Type **191**, but inscr "1 July 1982"	2·25	1·50
835	$2.50 Princess (inscr "21st Birthday") (different)	3·00	2·25
836	$2.50 As No. 835, but inscr "1 July 1982"	3·00	2·25

1982. Birth of Prince William of Wales (1st issue). Nos. 812/13 optd.

838	$1 Type **187**	1·50	1·25
839	$1 Type **187**	1·50	1·25
840	$2 Prince Charles and Lady Diana Spencer	2·50	2·00
841	$2 Prince Charles and Lady Diana Spencer	2·50	2·00

OPTS: Nos. 838 and 840, **ROYAL BIRTH 21 JUNE 1982**; 839 and 841, **PRINCE WILLIAM OF WALES**.

1982. Birth of Prince William of Wales (2nd issue). As Nos. 833/6 but with changed inscriptions. Multicoloured.

843	$1.25 As Type **191**, inscribed "Royal Birth"	2·00	1·00
844	$1.25 As Type **191**, inscribed "21 June 1982"	2·00	1·00
845	$2.50 As No. 835, inscribed "Royal Birth"	2·50	1·50
846	$2.50 As No. 835, inscribed "21 June 1982"	2·50	1·50

193 "The Accordionist" (inscr "Serenade")

194 Franklin D. Roosevelt

1982. Norman Rockwell (painter) Commemoration. Multicoloured.

848	5c. Type **193**	15	10
849	10c. "Spring" (inscr "The Hikers")	20	15
850	20c. "The Doctor and the Doll"	25	25
851	30c. "Home from Camp"	25	30

1982. Air. American Anniversaries. Multicoloured.

852	60c. Type **194**	1·50	80
853	80c. Benjamin Franklin	1·75	1·00
854	$1.40 George Washington	2·00	2·00

ANNIVERSARIES: 60c. Roosevelt (birth centenary); 80c. "Articles of Peace" negotiations bicentenary; $1.40, Washington (250th birth anniv).

195 "Virgin with Garlands" (detail, Rubens) and Princess Diana with Prince William

1982. Christmas.

856	**195** 35c. multicoloured	1·50	60
857	– 48c. multicoloured	2·00	1·25
858	– 60c. multicoloured	2·25	1·75
859	– $1.70 multicoloured	3·25	4·00

DESIGNS: 48c. to $1.70, Different details from Ruben's painting "Virgin with Garlands".

197 Statue of Tangaroa

198 Scouts using Map and Compass

1983. Commonwealth Day. Multicoloured.

862	60c. Type **197**	45	50
863	60c. Rarotonga oranges	45	50
864	60c. Rarotonga Airport	45	50
865	60c. Prime Minister Sir Thomas Davis	45	50

1983. 75th Anniv of Boy Scout Movement and 125th Anniv of Lord Baden-Powell (founder). Multicoloured.

866	12c. Type **198**	55	20
867	12c. Hiking	55	20
868	36c. Campfire cooking	80	40
869	36c. Erecting tent	80	40
870	48c. Hauling on rope	1·00	55
871	48c. Using bos'n's chair	1·00	55
872	60c. Digging hole for sapling	1·00	70
873	60c. Planting sapling	1·00	70

1983. 15th World Scout Jamboree, Alberta, Canada. Nos. 866/73 optd **XV WORLD JAMBOREE** (Nos. 875, 877, 879, 881) or **ALBERTA, CANADA 1983** (others).

875	12c. Type **198**	60	20
876	12c. Hiking	60	20
877	36c. Campfire cooking	90	40
878	36c. Erecting tent	90	40
879	48c. Hauling on rope	1·10	55
880	48c. Using bos'n's chair	1·10	55
881	60c. Digging hole for sapling	1·25	70
882	60c. Planting sapling	1·25	70

1983. Various stamps surch.

884	– 18c. on 8c. mult (No. 733)	75	50
885	– 18c. on 8c. mult (No. 734)	75	50
886	– 18c. on 8c. mult (No. 735)	75	50
887	– 18c. on 8c. mult (No. 736)	75	50
888	– 36c. on 15c. mult (No. 745)	1·25	85
889	– 36c. on 15c. mult (No. 746)	1·25	85
890	– 36c. on 15c. mult (No. 747)	1·25	85
891	– 36c. on 15c. mult (No. 748)	1·25	85
892	– 36c. on 30c. mult (No. 757)	1·25	85
893	– 36c. on 30c. mult (No. 758)	1·25	85
894	– 36c. on 30c. mult (No. 759)	1·25	85
895	– 36c. on 30c. mult (No. 760)	1·25	85
896	**184** 36c. on 35c. mult	1·25	85
897	– 36c. on 35c. mult (No. 762)	1·25	85
898	– 36c. on 35c. mult (No. 763)	1·25	85
899	– 36c. on 35c. mult (No. 764)	1·25	85
900	– 48c. on 25c. mult (No. 753)	1·50	1·25
901	– 48c. on 25c. mult (No. 754)	1·50	1·25
902	– 48c. on 25c. mult (No. 755)	1·50	1·25
903	– 48c. on 25c. mult (No. 756)	1·50	1·25
904	– 72c. on 70c. mult (No. 773)	2·50	1·75
905	– 72c. on 70c. mult (No. 774)	2·50	1·75
906	– 72c. on 70c. mult (No. 775)	2·50	1·75
907	– 72c. on 70c. mult (No. 776)	2·50	1·75
908	– 96c. on $1.40 multicoloured (No. 854)	2·00	2·00
909	– 96c. on $2 mult (No. 813)	8·50	5·50
910	– 96c. on $2.50 mult (No. 835)	3·00	3·00
911	– 96c. on $2.50 mult (No. 836)	3·00	3·00
912	– $5.60 on $6 mult (No. 788)	23·00	18·00
913	– $5.60 on $10 mult (No. 789)	23·00	18·00

202 Union Flag

1983. Cook Islands Flags and Ensigns. Multicoloured.

914	6c. Type **202** (postage)	55	50
915	6c. Group Federal flag	55	50
916	12c. Rarotonga ensign	70	55
917	12c. Flag of New Zealand	70	55
918	15c. Cook Islands' flag (1973–79)	70	55
919	15c. Cook Islands' National flag	70	55
920	20c. Type **202** (air)	70	60
921	20c. Group Federal flag	70	60
922	30c. Rarotonga ensign	80	65
923	30c. Flag of New Zealand	80	65
924	35c. Cook Islands' flag (1973–1979)	85	65
925	35c. Cook Islands' National flag	85	65

203 Dish Aerial, Satellite Earth Station

204 "La Belle Jardiniere"

1983. World Communications Year.

927	– 36c. multicoloured	70	70
928	– 48c. multicoloured	85	85
929	**203** 60c. multicoloured	1·10	1·40
930	– 96c. multicoloured	1·75	2·50

DESIGNS: 36, 48, 96c. Various satellites.

1983. Christmas. 500th Birth Anniv of Raphael. Multicoloured.

932	12c. Type **204**	70	40
933	18c. "Madonna and Child with five Saints"	95	60
934	36c. "Madonna and Child with St. John"	1·60	1·60
935	48c. "Madonna of the Fish"	2·00	2·00
936	60c. "Madonna of the Baldacchino"	2·50	3·50

205 Montgolfier Balloon, 1783

1984. Bicentenary (1983) of Manned Flight. Mult.

939	36c. Type **205**	50	50
940	48c. Ascent of Adorne, Strasbourg, 1784	60	60
941	60c. Balloon driven by sails, 1785	75	90
942	72c. Ascent of man on horse, 1798	90	1·10
943	96c. Godard's aerial acrobatics, 1850	1·00	1·40

206 Cuvier's Beaked Whale

1984. Save the Whale. Multicoloured.

946	10c. Type **206**	50	50
947	18c. Risso's dolphin	75	75
948	20c. True's beaked whale	75	75
949	24c. Long-finned pilot whale	80	80
950	30c. Narwhal	90	90
951	36c. White whale	1·10	1·10
952	42c. Common dolphin	1·40	1·40
953	48c. Commerson's dolphin	1·60	1·60
954	60c. Bottle-nosed dolphin	1·90	1·90
955	72c. Sowerby's beaked whale	2·00	2·00
956	96c. Common porpoise	2·50	2·50
957	$2 Boutu	3·25	3·25

207 Athens, 1896

208 "Siphonogorgia"

1984. Olympic Games, Los Angeles. Multicoloured.

958	18c. Type **207**	50	40
959	24c. Paris, 1900	55	45
960	36c. St. Louis, 1904	65	55
961	48c. London, 1948	75	65
962	60c. Tokyo, 1964	85	75
963	72c. Berlin, 1936	1·00	90
964	96c. Rome, 1960	1·10	1·00
965	$1.20 Los Angeles, 1930	1·25	1·25

1984. Corals (2nd series). New designs and Nos. 785/9 surch. Multicoloured.

966	1c. Type **208**	30	10
967	2c. "Millepora alcicornis"	30	10
968	3c. "Distichopora violacea"	40	10
969	5c. "Ptilosarcus gurneyi"	45	10
970	10c. "Lobophyllia bemprichii"	50	10
971	12c. "Sarcophyton digitatum"	60	15
972	14c. "Pavona praetorta"	60	15
973	18c. "Junceella gemmacea"	70	20
974	20c. "Stylaster"	70	20
975	24c. "Stylophora pistillata"	70	20
976	30c. "Palauastrea ramosa"	1·00	25
977	36c. "Melithaea albitincta"	1·25	30
978	40c. "Stylaster echinatus"	1·25	30
979	42c. "Fungia fungites"	1·25	35
980	48c. "Gonipora"	1·25	35
981	50c. "Melithaea squamata"	1·75	45
982	52c. "Bellonella indica"	1·75	60
983	55c. "Plerogyra sinuosa"	1·75	65
984	60c. "Tubastraea"	1·90	70
985	70c. "Heliofungia actiniformis"	2·00	85
986	85c. "Caulastraea echinulata"	2·25	1·00
987	96c. "Porites andrewsi"	2·50	1·10
988	$1.10 "Pectinia alcicornis"	2·50	1·40
989	$1.20 "Dendrophyllia gracilis"	2·50	1·50
990	$3.60 on $2 "Gonipora" (55×35 mm)	5·50	4·00
991	$4.20 on $3 "Heliofungia actiniformis" (55×35 mm)	6·00	5·00
992	$5 on $4 "Stylophora pistillata" (55×35 mm)	6·50	5·50
993	$7.20 on $6 "Stylaster echinatus" (55×35 mm)	8·50	8·50
994	$9.60 on $10 "Melithaea albitincta" (55×35 mm)	10·00	10·00

1984. Olympic Gold Medal Winners. Nos. 963/5 optd.

995	72c. Berlin, 1936 (optd **Equestrian Team Dressage Germany**)	60	65
996	96c. Rome, 1960 (optd **Decathlon Daley Thompson Great Britain**)	80	85
997	$1.20 Los Angeles, 1930 (optd **Four Gold Medals Carl Lewis U.S.A.**)	1·00	1·10

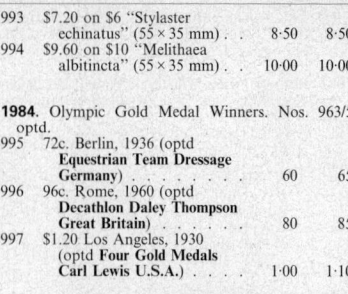

211 Captain Cook's Cottage, Melbourne

1984. "Ausipex" International Stamp Exhibition, Melbourne. Multicoloured.

998	36c. Type **211**	1·75	1·25
999	48c. H.M.S. "Endeavour" careened for Repairs" (Sydney Parkinson)	3·00	2·25
1000	60c. "Cook's landing at Botany Bay" (E. Phillips Fox)	3·25	3·00
1001	$2 "Captain James Cook" (John Webber)	4·00	4·00

1984. Birth of Prince Henry. Nos. 812 and 833/6 variously optd or surch also (No. 1007).

1003	$1.25 Optd **Commemorating-15 Sept. 1984** (No. 833)	1·75	1·10
1004	$1.25 Optd **Birth H.R.H. Prince Henry** (No. 834)	1·75	1·10
1005	$2.50 Optd **Commemorating-15 Sept. 1984** (No. 835)	2·50	2·00
1006	$2.50 Optd **Birth H.R.H. Prince Henry** (No. 836)	2·50	2·00
1007	$3 on $1 Optd **Royal Birth Prince Henry 15 Sept. 1984** (No. 812)	4·50	4·00

213 "Virgin on Throne with Child" (Giovanni Bellini)

214 Downy Woodpecker

1984. Christmas. Multicoloured.

1008	36c. Type **213**	1·25	40
1009	48c. "Virgin and Child" (anonymous, 15th century)	1·40	60
1010	60c. "Virgin and Child with Saints" (Alvise Vivarini)	1·50	80
1011	96c. "Virgin and Child with Angels" (H. Memling)	1·75	1·60
1012	$1.20 "Adoration of Magi" (G. Tiepolo)	2·00	2·00

1985. Birth Bicentenary of John J. Audubon (ornithologist). Designs showing original paintings. Multicoloured.

1015	30c. Type **214**	2·50	1·25
1016	55c. Black-throated blue warbler	2·75	1·75
1017	65c. Yellow-throated warbler	3·00	2·25
1018	75c. Chestnut-sided warbler	3·25	2·75
1019	95c. Dickcissel	3·25	3·00
1020	$1.15 White-crowned sparrow	3·25	3·50

215 "The Kingston Flyer" (New Zealand)

1985. Famous Trains. Multicoloured.

1022	20c. Type **215**	40	50
1023	55c. Class 625 locomotive (Italy)	55	85
1024	65c. Gotthard electric locomotive (Switzerland)	60	90
1025	75c. Union Pacific diesel locomotive No. 6900 (U.S.A.)	75	1·10
1026	95c. Canadian National "Super Continental" type diesel locomotive (Canada)	75	1·25
1027	$1.15 TGV express train (France)	80	1·50
1028	$2.20 "The Flying Scotsman" (Great Britain)	85	2·50
1029	$3.40 "Orient Express"	90	3·75

No. 1023 is inscribed "640" in error.

216 "Helena Fourment" (Peter Paul Rubens)

217 "Lady Elizabeth 1908" (Mabel Hankey)

1985. International Youth Year. Multicoloured.

1030	55c. Type **216**	3·00	2·50
1031	65c. "Vigee-Lebrun and Daughter" (E. Vigee-Lebrun)	3·25	3·00
1032	75c. "On the Terrace" (Renoir)	3·50	3·25
1033	$1.30 "Young Mother Sewing" (M. Cassatt)	4·50	6·50

1985. Life and Times of Queen Elizabeth the Queen Mother. Designs showing paintings. Multicoloured.

1035	65c. Type **217**	40	50
1036	75c. "Duchess of York, 1923" (Savely Sorine)	45	60
1037	$1.15 "Duchess of York, 1925" (Philip de Laszlo)	55	85
1038	$2.80 "Queen Elizabeth, 1938" (Sir Gerald Kelly)	1·40	2·25

218 Albert Henry (Prime Minister, 1965–78)

219 Golf

1985. 20th Anniv of Self-government. Mult.

1040	30c. Type **218**	80	60
1041	50c. Sir Thomas Davis (Prime Minister, 1978–April 1983 and from November 1983)	1·25	1·25
1042	65c. Geoffrey Henry (Prime Minister, April–November 1983)	1·50	1·75

1985. South Pacific Mini Games, Rarotonga. Multicoloured.

1044	55c. Type **219**	4·00	3·50
1045	65c. Rugby	4·00	4·00
1046	75c. Tennis	5·50	6·00

220 Sea Horse, Gearwheel and Leaves

221 "Madonna of the Magnificat"

1985. Pacific Conference, Rarotonga.

1048 **220**	55c. black, gold and red	1·10	65
1049 –	65c. black, gold and violet	1·25	80
1050 –	75c. black, gold and green	1·40	1·10

No. 1048 shows the South Pacific Bureau for Economic Co-operation logo and is inscribed "S.P.E.C. Meeting, 30 July–1 August 1985, Rarotonga". No. 1049 also shows the S.P.E.C. logo, but is inscribed "South Pacific Forum, 4–6 August 1985, Rarotonga". No. 1050 shows the Pacific Islands Conference logo and the inscription "Pacific Islands Conference, 7–10 August 1985, Rarotonga".

1985. Christmas. Virgin and Child Paintings by Botticelli. Multicoloured.

1052	55c. Type **221**	2·00	1·00
1053	65c. "Madonna with Pomegranate"	2·25	1·10
1054	75c. "Madonna and Child with Six Angels"	2·50	1·40
1055	95c. "Madonna and Child with St. John"	2·75	1·75

222 "The Eve of the Deluge" (John Martin)

223 Queen Elizabeth II

1986. Appearance of Halley's Comet. Paintings. Multicoloured.

1058	55c. Type **222**	1·25	1·25
1059	65c. "Lot and his Daughters" (Lucas van Leyden)	1·40	1·40
1060	75c. "Auspicious Comet" (from treatise c. 1857)	1·50	1·50
1061	$1.25 "Events following Charles I" (Herman Saftleven)	2·25	2·25
1062	$2 "Ossian receiving Napoleonic Officers" (Anne Louis Girodet-Trioson)	3·00	3·00

1986. 60th Birthday of Queen Elizabeth II. Designs showing formal portraits.

1065 **223**	95c. multicoloured	1·10	1·50
1066 –	$1.25 multicoloured	1·40	1·75
1067 –	$1.50 multicoloured	1·50	2·00

224 U.S.A. 1847 Franklin 5c. Stamp and H.M.S. "Resolution" at Rarotonga

1986. "Ameripex '86" International Exhibition, Chicago. Multicoloured.

1069	$1 Type **224**	5·00	3·75
1070	$1.50 Chicago	3·50	4·25
1071	$2 1975 definitive $2, Benjamin Franklin and H.M.S. "Resolution"	6·00	5·50

225 Head of Statue of Liberty

226 Miss Sarah Ferguson

1986. Centenary of Statue of Liberty. Multicoloured.

1072	$1 Type **225**	75	85
1073	$1.25 Hand and torch of Statue	90	1·10
1074	$2.75 Statue of Liberty	2·00	2·50

1986. Royal Wedding. Multicoloured.

1075	$1 Type **226**	1·25	1·25
1076	$2 Prince Andrew	2·00	2·50
1077	$3 Prince Andrew and Miss Sarah Ferguson (57×31 mm)	2·50	3·50

228 "Holy Family with St. John the Baptist and St. Elizabeth"

1986. Christmas. Paintings by Rubens. Mult.
1080 55c. Type **228** . . . . . . 1·75 1·00
1081 $1.30 "Virgin with the Garland" . . . . . 2·75 2·75
1082 $2.75 "Adoration of the Magi" (detail) . . . 5·50 6·00

1986. Visit of Pope John Paul II to South Pacific. Nos. 1080/2 surch **FIRST PAPAL VISIT TO SOUTH PACIFIC POPE JOHN PAUL II NOV 21-24 1986.**
1085 55c.+10c. Type **228** . . . . 2·75 2·00
1086 $1.30+10c. "Virgin with the Garland" . . . . 3·50 2·50
1087 $2.75+10c. "Adoration of the Magi" (detail) . . . . 6·00 3·75

1987. Various stamps surch. (a) On Nos. 741/56, 761/76 and 787/8.
1090 10c. on 15c. "Distichopora violacea" 20 20
1091 10c. on 15c. "Stylaster" . . 20 20
1092 10c. on 15c. "Gonipora" . . 20 20
1093 10c. on 15c. "Caulastraea echinulata" 20 20
1094 10c. on 25c. "Lobophyllia bemprichii" . . . 20 20
1095 10c. on 25c. "Palauastrea ramosa" 20 20
1096 10c. on 25c. "Bellonella indica" 20 20
1097 10c. on 25c. "Pectinia alcicornis" . . . 20 20
1098 18c. on 12c. "Millepora alcicornis" 25 25
1099 18c. on 12c. "Junceella gemmacea" . . . 25 25
1100 18c. on 12c. "Fungia fungites" 25 25
1101 18c. on 12c. "Heliofungia actiniformis" . . . 25 25
1102 18c. on 20c. "Ptilosarcus gurneyi" 25 25
1103 18c. on 20c. "Stylophora pistillata" 25 25
1104 18c. on 20c. "Melithaea squamata" 25 25
1105 18c. on 20c. "Porites andrewsi" . . . 25 25
1106 55c. on 35c. Type **184** . . . 40 45
1107 55c. on 35c. "Pavona praetorta" 40 45
1108 55c. on 35c. "Stylaster echinatus" . . . 40 45
1109 55c. on 35c. "Tubastraea" . . 40 45
1110 65c. on 50c. As No. 1098 . . 45 50
1111 65c. on 50c. As No. 1099 . . 45 50
1112 65c. on 50c. As No. 1100 . . 45 50
1113 65c. on 50c. As No. 1101 . . 45 50
1114 65c. on 60c. As No. 1090 . . 45 50
1115 65c. on 60c. As No. 1091 . . 45 50
1116 65c. on 60c. As No. 1092 . . 45 50
1117 65c. on 60c. As No. 1093 . . 45 50
1118 75c. on 70c. As No. 1102 . . 55 60
1119 75c. on 70c. As No. 1103 . . 55 60
1120 75c. on 70c. As No. 1104 . . 55 60
1121 75c. on 70c. As No. 1105 . . 55 60
1122 $6.40 on $4 "Stylophora pistillata" . . . . 4·50 4·75
1123 $7.20 on $6 "Stylaster echinatus" . . . . 5·00 5·25

(b) On Nos. 812/13.
1124 $9.40 on $1 Type **187** . . . 15·00 16·00
1125 $9.40 on $2 Prince Charles and Lady Diana Spencer 15·00 16·00

(c) On Nos. 835/6.
1126 $9.40 on $2.50 Princess of Wales (inscribed "21st Birthday") . . . . 15·00 16·00
1127 $9.40 on $2.50 As No. 1126, but inscribed "1 July 1982" . . . . 15·00 16·00

(d) On Nos. 966/8, 971/2, 975, 979/80, 982 and 987/9.
1128 5c. on 1c. Type **208** . . . 20 20
1129 5c. on 2c. "Millepora alcicornis" 20 20
1130 5c. on 3c. "Distichopora violacea" 20 20
1131 5c. on 12c. "Sarcophyton digitatum" 20 20
1132 5c. on 14c. "Pavona praetorta" 20 20
1133 18c. on 24c. "Stylophora pistillata" 25 25
1134 55c. on 52c. "Bellonella indica" 40 45
1135 65c. on 42c. "Fungia fungites" 45 50
1136 75c. on 48c. "Gonipora" . . 55 60
1137 95c. on 96c. "Porites andrewsi" 70 75
1138 95c. on $1.10 "Pectinia alcicornis" 70 75
1139 95c. on $1.20 "Dendrophyllia gracilis" . . . 70 75

(e) On Nos. 998/1001.
1140 $1.30 on 36c. Type **211** . . 2·00 2·00
1141 $1.30 on 48c. The "Endeavour" careened for Repairs" (Sydney Parkinson) . . . 2·00 2·00

1142 $1.30 on 60c. "Cook's landing at Botany Bay" (E. Phillips Fox) . . 2·00 2·00
1143 $1.30 on $2 "Captain James Cook" (John Webber) . . 2·00 2·00

(f) On Nos. 1065/7.
1144 **223** $2.30 on 95c. mult . . . 7·00 8·00
1145 – $2.80 on $1.25 mult . . . 7·00 8·00
1146 – $2.80 on $1.50 mult . . . 7·00 8·00

(g) On Nos. 1075/7.
1147 $2.80 on $1 Type **226** . . . 6·00 6·50
1148 $2.80 on $2 Prince Andrew 6·00 6·50
1149 $2.80 on $3 Prince Andrew and Miss Sarah Ferguson (57 × 31 mm) . . . . 6·00 6·50

1987. Various stamps surch.
1150 $2.80 on $2 "Gonipora" (No. 785) . . . . 3·00 3·25
1151 $5 on $3 "Heliofungia actiniformis" (No. 786) 5·00 5·50
1152 $9.40 on $10 "Melithaea albitincta" (No. 789) . . 8·00 9·00
1153 $9.40 on $1 Type **187** (No. 838) . . . . 8·00 9·00
1154 $9.40 on $1 Type **187** (No. 839) . . . . 8·00 9·00
1155 $9.40 on $2 Prince Charles and Lady Diana Spencer (No. 840) . . . . 8·00 9·00
1156 $9.40 on $2 Prince Charles and Lady Diana Spencer (No. 841) . . . . 8·00 9·00

1987. Hurricane Relief. Various stamps surch **HURRICANE RELIEF** and premium. (a) On Nos. 1035/8.
1158 65c.+50c. Type **217** . . . . 1·00 1·00
1159 75c.+50c. "Duchess of York, 1923" (Savely Sorine) . . . . 1·10 1·10
1160 $1.15+50c. "Duchess of York, 1925" (Philip de Laszlo) . . . . 1·40 1·50
1161 $2.80+50c. "Queen Elizabeth, 1938" (Sir Gerald Kelly) . . . 2·50 3·25

(b) On Nos. 1058/62.
1163 55c.+50c. Type **222** 85 85
1164 65c.+50c. "Lot and his Daughters" (Lucas van Leyden) 90 90
1165 75c.+50c. "Auspicious Comet" (from treatise c. 1587) . . . . 1·10 1·10
1166 $1.50+50c. "Events following Charles I" (Herman Saftleven) . . 1·40 1·50
1167 $2+50c. "Ossian receiving Napoleonic Officers" (Anne Louis Girodet-Trioson) . . . . 2·00 2·50

(c) On Nos. 1065/7.
1168 **223** 95c.+50c. mult . . . . 1·25 1·25
1169 – $1.25+50c. mult . . . . 1·50 1·50
1170 – $1.50+50c. mult . . . . 1·60 1·60

(d) On Nos. 1069/71.
1172 $1+50c. Type **224** . . . . 4·00 4·00
1173 $1.50+50c. Chicago . . . . 2·25 2·75
1174 $2+50c. 1975 definitive $2, Benjamin Franklin and H.M.S. "Resolution" . . 4·25 4·25

(e) On Nos. 1072/4.
1175 $1+50c. Type **225** . . . . 1·00 1·25
1176 $1.25+50c. Hand and torch of Statue . . . . . 1·25 1·50
1177 $2.75+50c. Statue of Liberty 2·25 3·00

(f) On Nos. 1075/7.
1178 $1+50c. Type **226** . . . . 1·25 1·25
1179 $2+50c. Prince Andrew . . 2·00 2·25
1180 $3+50c. Prince Andrew and Miss Sarah Ferguson (57 × 31 mm) . . . . 2·75 3·25

(g) On Nos. 1080/2.
1181 55c.+50c. Type **228** 85 85
1182 $1.30+50c. "Virgin with the Garland" . . . . 1·50 1·75
1183 $2.75+50c. "The Adoration of the Magi" (detail) . . . 2·50 3·00

(h) On Nos. 1122, 1134/7 and 1150/1.
1186 55c.+25c. on 52c. "Bellonella indica" . . . 80 80
1187 65c.+25c. on 42c. "Fungia fungites" 90 90
1188 75c.+25c. on 48c. "Gonipora" . . . . 1·00 1·00
1189 95c.+25c. on 96c. "Porites andrewsi" . . . 1·25 1·25
1190 $2.80+50c. on $2 "Gonipora" . . . . 3·50 3·50
1191 $5+50c. on $3 "Heliofungia actiniformis" . . . . 5·50 6·00
1192 $6.40+50c. on $4 "Stylophora pistillata" . . 7·00 8·00

1987. Royal Ruby Wedding. Nos. 484 and 787 optd **ROYAL WEDDING FORTIETH ANNIVERSARY.**
1193 $4 Queen Elizabeth II and sea shells . . . . 5·00 5·00
1194 $4 Queen Elizabeth II and "Stylophora pistillata" . . 5·00 5·00

233 "The Holy Family" (Rembrandt)

1987. Christmas. Different paintings of the Holy Family by Rembrandt.
1195 **233** $1.25 multicoloured . . . 2·50 2·25
1196 – $1.50 multicoloured . . . 3·00 2·50
1197 – $1.95 multicoloured . . . 4·50 4·50

234 Olympic Commemorative $50 Coin

1988. Olympic Games, Seoul. Multicoloured.
1200 $1.50 Type **234** . . . . . 3·75 2·50
1201 $1.50 Olympic torch and Seoul Olympic Park . . 3·75 2·50
1202 $1.50 Steffi Graf playing tennis and Olympic medal 3·75 2·50
Nos. 1200/2 were printed together, se-tenant, forming a composite design.

1988. Olympic Tennis Medal Winners, Seoul. Nos. 1200/2 optd.
1204 $1.50 Type **234** (optd **MILOSLAV MECIR CZECHOSLOVAKIA GOLD MEDAL WINNER MEN'S TENNIS**) . . . . 3·25 2·25
1205 $1.50 Olympic torch and Seoul Olympic Park (optd **TIM MAYOTTE UNITED STATES GABRIELA SABATINI ARGENTINA SILVER MEDAL WINNERS**) . . 3·25 2·25
1206 $1.50 Steffi Graf playing tennis and Olympic medal (optd **GOLD MEDAL WINNER STEFFI GRAF WEST GERMANY**) . . . 3·25 2·25

236 "Virgin and Child"

1988. Christmas.
1208 **236** 70c. multicoloured . . . 2·50 2·00
1209 – 85c. multicoloured . . . 2·75 2·25
1210 – 95c. multicoloured . . . 3·00 2·50
1211 – $1.25 multicoloured . . . 3·75 3·25
DESIGNS: 85c., 95c., $1.25, Various versions of the "Virgin and Child" by Durer.

237 "Apollo 11" leaving Earth

1989. 20th Anniv of First Manned Landing on Moon. Multicoloured.
1213 40c. Type **237** . . . . . 1·75 1·75
1214 40c. Lunar module over Moon . . . . . 1·75 1·75
1215 55c. Aldrin stepping onto Moon . . . . . 2·00 2·00
1216 55c. Astronaut on Moon . . 2·00 2·00
1217 65c. Working on lunar surface . . . . . 2·25 2·25
1218 65c. Conducting experiment 2·25 2·25
1219 75c. "Apollo 11" leaving Moon . . . . . 2·25 2·25
1220 75c. Splashdown in South Pacific . . . . . 2·25 2·25

238 Rarotonga Flycatcher

1989. Endangered Birds of the Cook Islands. Multicoloured.
1222 15c. Type **238** . . . . . 2·00 2·00
1223 20c. Pair of Rarotonga flycatchers . . . . 2·00 2·00
1224 65c. Pair of Rarotonga fruit doves . . . . . 2·75 2·75
1225 70c. Rarotonga fruit dove 2·75 2·75

239 Villagers

1989. Christmas. Details from "Adoration of the Magi" by Rubens. Multicoloured.
1227 70c. Type **239** . . . . . 1·40 1·40
1228 85c. Virgin Mary . . . . . 1·60 1·60
1229 95c. Christ Child . . . . . 1·75 2·00
1230 $1.50 Boy with gift . . . . 2·00 3·00

240 Reverend John Williams and L.M.S. Church

1990. Christianity in the Cook Islands. Multicoloured.
1232 70c. Type **240** 85 85
1233 85c. Mgr. Bernardine Castanie and Roman Catholic Church . . . 1·00 1·10
1234 95c. Elder Osborne Widstoe and Mormon Church . . . 1·10 1·40
1235 $1.60 Dr. J. E. Caldwell and Seventh Day Adventist Church . . . . . 1·90 2·25

241 "Woman writing a Letter" (Terborch)   243 Queen Elizabeth the Queen Mother

242 Sprinting

1990. 150th Anniv of the Penny Black. Designs showing paintings. Multicoloured.
1237 85c. Type **241** . . . . . 1·10 1·25
1238 $1.15 "George Gisze" (Holbein the Younger) . . 1·50 1·75

1239	$1.55 "Mrs. John Douglas" (Gainsborough)	1·90	2·25
1240	$1.85 "Portrait of a Gentleman" (Durer) . . .	2·25	2·50

1990. Olympic Games, Barcelona, and Winter Olympic Games, Albertville (1992) (1st issue). Multicoloured.

1242	$1.85 Type **242**	5·00	5·00
1243	$1.85 Cook Islands $50 commemorative coin . . .	5·00	5·00
1244	$1.85 Skiing	5·00	5·00

See also Nos. 1304/9.

1990. 90th Birthday of Queen Elizabeth the Queen Mother.

1246	**243** $1.85 multicoloured . .	5·00	4·75

244 "Adoration of the Magi" (Memling)

1990. Christmas. Religious Paintings. Mult.

1248	70c. Type **244**	1·75	1·60
1249	85c. "Holy Family" (Lotto)	1·90	1·75
1250	95c. "Madonna and Child with Saints John and Catherine" (Titian) . . .	2·25	2·00
1251	$1.50 "Holy Family" (Titian)	3·75	5·00

246 Columbus (engraving by Theodoro de Bry)

249 Red-breasted Wrasse

1991. 500th Anniv (1992) of Discovery of America by Columbus (1st issue).

1254	**246** $1 multicoloured . . .	2·75	2·75

See also No. 1302.

1991. 65th Birthday of Queen Elizabeth II. No. 789 optd **65TH BIRTHDAY**.

1255	$10 "Melithaea albitincta"	13·00	14·00

1991. Christmas. Religious Paintings. Mult.

1256	70c. Type **248**	2·00	1·75
1257	85c. "The Birth of the Virgin" (B. Murillo) . . .	2·25	2·00
1258	$1.15 "Adoration of the Shepherds" (Rembrandt)	2·75	2·75
1259	$1.50 "Adoration of the Shepherds" (L. le Nain)	4·00	5·00

1992. Reef Life (1st series). Multicoloured with white borders.

1261	5c. Type **249**	50	50
1262	10c. Blue sea star	50	50
1263	15c. Bicoloured angelfish ("Black and gold angelfish")	55	55
1264	20c. Spotted pebble crab .	70	70
1265	25c. Black-tipped grouper ("Black-tipped cod") . . .	70	70
1266	30c. Spanish dancer . . .	70	70
1267	50c. Regal angelfish . . .	90	90
1268	80c. Big-scaled soldierfish ("Squirrel fish")	1·25	1·25
1269	85c. Red pencil sea urchin .	3·00	2·75
1270	90c. Red-spotted rainbowfish	3·75	2·75
1271	$1 Cheek-lined wrasse . .	3·75	2·75
1272	$2 Long-nosed butterflyfish	3·75	3·25
1273	$3 Red-spotted rainbowfish	2·50	3·75
1274	$5 Blue sea-star	3·75	6·00
1275	$7 "Pygoplites diacanthus"	8·50	12·00
1276	$10 Spotted pebble crab .	10·00	13·00
1277	$15 Red pencil sea urchin	14·00	18·00

The 25, 50c., $1 and $2 include a silhouette of the Queen's head.

For designs in a larger size, 40 × 30 mm, and with brown borders, see Nos. 1342/52.

250 Tiger

1992. Endangered Wildlife. Multicoloured.

1279	$1.15 Type **250**	1·25	1·25
1280	$1.15 Indian elephant . . .	1·25	1·25
1281	$1.15 Brown bear	1·25	1·25
1282	$1.15 Black rhinoceros . .	1·25	1·25
1283	$1.15 Chimpanzee	1·25	1·25
1284	$1.15 Argali	1·25	1·25
1285	$1.15 Heaviside's dolphin	1·25	1·25
1286	$1.15 Eagle owl	1·25	1·25
1287	$1.15 Bee hummingbird . .	1·25	1·25
1288	$1.15 Puma	1·25	1·25
1289	$1.15 European otter . . .	1·25	1·25
1290	$1.15 Red kangaroo . . .	1·25	1·25
1291	$1.15 Jackass penguin . .	1·25	1·25
1292	$1.15 Asian lion	1·25	1·25
1293	$1.15 Peregrine falcon . .	1·25	1·25
1294	$1.15 Persian fallow deer .	1·25	1·25
1295	$1.15 Key deer	1·25	1·25
1296	$1.15 Alpine ibex	1·25	1·25
1297	$1.15 Mandrill	1·25	1·25
1298	$1.15 Gorilla	1·25	1·25
1299	$1.15 "Vanessa atalanta" (butterfly)	1·25	1·25
1300	$1.15 Takin	1·25	1·25
1301	$1.15 Ring-tailed lemur . .	1·25	1·25

251 Columbus and Landing in New World

1992. 500th Anniv of Discovery of America by Columbus (2nd issue).

1302	**251** $6 multicoloured	6·50	7·50

252 Football and $50 Commemorative Coin

1992. Olympic Games, Barcelona (2nd issue). Multicoloured.

1304	$1.75 Type **252**	2·50	2·50
1305	$1.75 Olympic gold medal	2·50	2·50
1306	$1.75 Basketball and $10 coin	2·50	2·50
1307	$2.25 Running	3·50	3·50
1308	$2.25 $10 and $50 coins .	3·50	3·50
1309	$2.25 Cycling	3·50	3·50

253 Festival Poster

255 "Worship of Shepherds" (Parmigianino)

1992. 6th Festival of Pacific Arts, Rarotonga. Multicoloured.

1311	80c. Type **253**	1·50	1·50
1312	85c. Seated Tangaroa carving	1·50	1·50
1313	$1 Seated Tangaroa carving (different)	1·60	1·60
1314	$1.75 Standing Tangaroa carving	2·50	3·25

1992. Royal Visit by Prince Edward. Nos. 1311/14 optd **ROYAL VISIT**.

1315	80c. Type **253**	1·75	1·75
1316	85c. Seated Tangaroa carving	1·75	1·75
1317	$1 Seated Tangaroa carving (different)	1·90	1·90
1318	$1.75 Standing Tangaroa carving	3·50	4·00

1992. Christmas. Religious Paintings by Parmigianino. Multicoloured.

1319	70c. Type **255**	1·00	1·00

1992. Endangered Wildlife. (continued — see top)

1320	85c. "Virgin with Long Neck"	1·25	1·25
1321	$1.15 "Virgin with Rose" .	1·50	1·75
1322	$1.90 "St. Margaret's Virgin"	2·75	3·75

256 Queen in Garter Robes

258 "Virgin with Child" (Filippo Lippi)

257 Coronation Ceremony

1992. 40th Anniv of Queen Elizabeth II's Accession. Multicoloured.

1324	80c. Type **256**	1·75	1·50
1325	$1.15 Queen at Trooping the Colour	2·00	2·00
1326	$1.50 Queen in evening dress	2·75	3·00
1327	$1.95 Queen with bouquet	3·00	3·50

1993. 40th Anniv of Coronation. Multicoloured.

1328	$1 Type **257**	2·50	1·75
1329	$2 Coronation photograph by Cecil Beaton . . .	3·75	3·75
1330	$3 Royal family on balcony	5·50	5·00

1993. Christmas. Religious Paintings. Mult.

1331	70c. Type **258**	80	80
1332	85c. "Bargellini Madonna" (Lodovico Carracci) . . .	95	95
1333	$1.15 "Virgin of the Curtain" (Rafael Sanzio)	1·40	1·60
1334	$2.50 "Holy Family" (Agnolo Bronzino) . . .	3·25	3·75
1335	$4 "Saint Zachary Virgin" (Parmigianino) (32 × 47 mm)	4·00	5·00

259 Skiing, Flags and Ice Skating (½-size illustration)

1994. Winter Olympic Games, Lillehammer.

1336	**259** $5 multicoloured . . .	7·50	8·00

260 Cup on Logo with German and Argentinian Players

1994. World Cup Football Championship, U.S.A.

1337	**260** $4.50 multicoloured . .	6·00	7·00

261 Neil Armstrong taking First Step on Moon

1994. 25th Anniv of First Manned Moon Landing. Multicoloured.

1338	$2.25 Type **261**	3·75	3·75
1339	$2.25 Astronaut on Moon and view of Earth . . .	3·75	3·75
1340	$2.25 Astronaut and flag . .	3·75	3·75
1341	$2.25 Astronaut with reflection in helmet visor	3·75	3·75

1994. Reef Life (2nd series). As Nos. 1261 and 1263/71, but each 40 × 30 mm and with brown borders.

1342	5c. Type **249**	50	50
1344	15c. Bicoloured angelfish . .	60	60
1345	20c. Spotted pebble crab .	65	65
1346	25c. Black-tipped grouper .	70	70
1347	30c. Spanish dancer . . .	70	70
1348	50c. Regal angelfish . . .	85	85
1349	80c. Big-scaled soldierfish .	1·10	1·10
1350	85c. Red pencil sea urchin .	1·10	1·10
1351	90c. Red-spotted rainbowfish	1·25	1·25
1352	$1 Cheek-lined wrasse . .	1·40	1·40

262 Actors in Outrigger Canoe

1994. Release of "The Return of Tommy Tricker" (film shot in Cook Islands). Scenes from film. Multicoloured.

1359	85c. Type **262**	1·10	1·25
1360	85c. Male and female dancers	1·10	1·25
1361	85c. European couple on beach	1·10	1·25
1362	85c. Aerial view of island	1·10	1·25
1363	85c. Two female dancers .	1·10	1·25
1364	85c. Cook Islands couple on beach	1·10	1·25
1364a	90c. Type **262**	65	80
1364b	90c. As No. 1360	65	80
1364c	90c. As No. 1361	65	80
1364d	90c. As No. 1362	65	80
1364e	90c. As No. 1363	65	80
1364f	90c. As No. 1364	65	80

263 "The Virgin and Child" (Morales)

1994. Christmas. Religious Paintings. Mult.

1365	85c. Type **263**	1·50	1·60
1366	85c. "Adoration of the Kings" (Gerard David) . .	1·50	1·60
1367	85c. "Adoration of the Kings" (Foppa)	1·50	1·60
1368	85c. "The Madonna and Child with St. Joseph and Infant Baptist" (Baroccio)	1·50	1·60
1369	$1 "Madonna with Iris" (Durer)	1·50	1·60
1370	$1 "Adoration of the Shepherds" (Le Nain) . .	1·50	1·60
1371	$1 "The Virgin and Child" (school of Leonardo) . . .	1·50	1·60
1372	$1 "The Mystic Nativity" (Botticelli)	1·50	1·60

264 Pirates ("Treasure Island")

1994. Death Centenary of Robert Louis Stevenson (author). Multicoloured.

1373	$1.50 Type **264**	2·50	2·50
1374	$1.50 Duel ("David Balfour")	2·50	2·50
1375	$1.50 Mr. Hyde, ("Dr. Jekyll and Mr. Hyde") . .	2·50	2·50
1376	$1.50 Rowing boat and sailing ship ("Kidnapped")	2·50	2·50

265 U.N. and National Flags with Peace Doves

1995. 50th Anniv of United Nations.

1377	**265** $4.75 multicoloured . . .	4·75	6·50

266 Queen Elizabeth the Queen Mother and Coat of Arms

1995. 95th Birthday of Queen Elizabeth the Queen Mother.
1378 **266** $5 multicoloured . . . . 8·50 8·00

267 German Delegation signing Unconditional Surrender at Rheims

1995. 50th Anniv of End of Second World War. Multicoloured.
1379 $3.50 Type **267** . . . . . . 7·00 7·00
1380 $3.50 Japanese delegation on U.S.S. "Missouri", Tokyo Bay . . . . . . 7·00 7·00

1995. 50th Anniv of F.A.O. As T **265**. Mult.
1381 $4.50 F.A.O. and U.N. emblems . . . . 4·75 6·50

268 Green Turtle

1995. Year of the Sea Turtle. Multicoloured.
1382 85c. Type **268** . . . . . 1·75 1·60
1383 $1 Hawksbill turtle . . . . 2·00 1·75
1384 $1.75 Green turtle on beach 3·00 3·25
1385 $2.25 Young hawksbill turtles hatching . . . . . 3·75 4·00

269 Emblem and Throwing the Discus

1996. Olympic Games, Atlanta. Multicoloured.
1386 85c. Type **269** . . . . . . 1·50 1·50
1387 $1 Athlete with Olympic Torch . . . . 1·75 1·75
1388 $1.50 Running . . . . . . 2·50 2·50
1389 $1.85 Gymnastics . . . . . 2·75 2·75
1390 $2.10 Ancient archery . . . 3·00 3·00
1391 $2.50 Throwing the javelin 3·00 3·00

270 Queen Elizabeth II

1996. 70th Birthday of Queen Elizabeth II. Multicoloured.
1392 $1.90 Type **270** . . . . . 2·75 2·75
1393 $2.25 Wearing tiara . . . . 3·25 3·25
1394 $2.75 In Garter robes . . . 3·50 3·50

1997. 28th South Pacific Forum. Nos. 1364a/f optd **28th South Pacific Forum** (Nos. 1396, 1399/1400) or **12–22 September 1997** (Nos. 1397/8 and 1401). Multicoloured.
1396 90c. Type **262** . . . . . . 1·00 1·25
1397 90c. As No. 1360 . . . . . 1·00 1·25
1398 90c. As No. 1361 . . . . . 1·00 1·25
1399 90c. As No. 1362 . . . . . 1·00 1·25
1400 90c. As No. 1363 . . . . . 1·00 1·25
1401 90c. As No. 1364 . . . . . 1·00 1·25

272 "Lampides boeticus" (female)

1997. Butterflies. Multicoloured.
1402 5c. Type **272** 10 10
1403 10c. "Vanessa atalanta" . . 10 10
1404 15c. "Lampides boeticus" (male) 10 10
1405 20c. "Papilio godeffroyi" . . 10 15
1406 25c. "Danaus hamata" . . . 15 20
1407 30c. "Xois sesara" 15 20
1408 50c. "Vagrans egista" . . . 30 35
1409 70c. "Parthenos sylvia" . . 40 45
1410 80c. "Hyblaea sanguinea" 45 50
1411 85c. "Melanitis leda" . . . 50 55
1412 90c. "Ascalapha odorata" 50 55
1413 $1 "Precis villida" 55 60
1414 $1.50 "Parthenos sylvia" . . 85 90
1415 $2 "Lampides boeticus" (female) . . . . 1·10 1·25
1416 $3 "Precis villida" . . . . . 1·75 1·90
1417 $4 "Melanitis leda" . . . . 2·25 2·40
1418 $5 "Vagrans egista" . . . . 2·75 3·00
1419 $7 "Hyblaea sanguinea" . . 4·00 4·25
1420 $10 "Vanessa atalanta" . . 6·00 6·25
1421 $15 "Papilio godeffroyi" . . 8·50 8·75

The $1 includes an outline portrait of Queen Elizabeth II. Nos. 1414/21 are larger, 41 × 25 mm, with the Queen's portrait included on the $4 to $15.

273 Queen Elizabeth and Prince Philip

1997. Golden Wedding of Queen Elizabeth and Prince Philip.
1424 **273** $2 multicoloured . . . . 2·00 2·25

274 Diana, Princess of Wales

277 Lady Elizabeth Bowes-Lyon

1998. Diana, Princess of Wales Commemoration.
1426 **274** $1.15 multicoloured . . 1·10 1·25

1999. New Millennium. Nos. 1311/14 optd **KIA ORANA THIRD MILLENNIUM**.
1429 80c. Type **253** 65 65
1430 85c. Seated Tangaroa carving 70 70
1431 $1 Seated Tangaroa carving (different) 80 80
1432 $1.75 Standing Tangaroa carving . . . . 1·40 1·75

2000. Queen Elizabeth the Queen Mother's 100th Birthday.
1433 **277** $4.50 brown and blue . . 3·25 3·25
1434 – $4.50 brown and blue . . 3·25 3·25
1435 – $4.50 multicoloured . . 3·25 3·25
1436 – $4.50 multicoloured . . 3·25 3·25

DESIGNS: 1434, Lady Elizabeth Bowes-Lyon as young woman; 1435, Queen Mother wearing green outfit; 1436, Queen Mother wearing pearl earrings and necklace.

278 Ancient Greek Runner on Urn

2000. Olympic Games, Sydney. Multicoloured.
1438 $1.75 Type **278** . . . . . 1·40 1·50
1439 $1.75 Modern runner . . . . 1·40 1·50
1440 $1.75 Ancient Greek archer 1·40 1·50
1441 $1.75 Modern archer . . . 1·40 1·50

2001. Suwarrow Wildlife Sanctuary. Nos. 1279/90 surch **80c SUWARROW SANCTUARY**.
1443 80c. on $1.15 Heavisides's dolphin 75 80
1444 80c. on $1.15 Eagle owl . . 75 80
1445 80c. on $1.15 Bee hummingbird 75 80
1446 80c. on $1.15 Puma 75 80
1447 80c. on $1.15 European otter 75 80
1448 80c. on $1.15 Red kangaroo 75 80
1449 90c. on $1.15 Type **250** . . 75 80
1450 90c. on $1.15 Indian elephant 75 80
1451 90c. on $1.15 Brown bear 75 80
1452 90c. on $1.15 Black rhinoceros 75 80
1453 90c. on $1.15 Chimpanzee 75 80
1454 90c. on $1.15 Argali 75 80

OFFICIAL STAMPS

1975. Nos. 228, etc, optd **O.H.M.S.** or surch also.
O 1 1c. multicoloured . . . . .
O 2 2c. multicoloured . . . . .
O 3 3c. multicoloured . . . . .
O 4 4c. multicoloured . . . . .
O 5 5c. on 2½c. multicoloured
O 6 8c. multicoloured . . . . .
O 7 10c. on 6c. multicoloured
O 8 18c. on 20c. multicoloured
O 9 25c. on 9c. multicoloured
O 10 30c. on 15c. multicoloured
O 11 50c. multicoloured . . . .
O 12 $1 multicoloured . . . . .
O 13 $2 multicoloured . . . . .
O 14 $4 multicoloured . . . . .
O 15 $6 multicoloured . . . . .
O1/15 Set of 15 . . . . † 8·00

These stamps were only sold to the public cancelled-to-order and not in unused condition.

1978. Nos. 466/7, 474, 478/81, 484/5, 542 and 568/9 optd **O.H.M.S.** or surch also.
O16 – 1c. mult (No. 467) . . . 60 10
O17 **141** 2c. on ½c. multicoloured 60 10
O18 – 5c. on ½c. multicoloured 60 10
O19 – 10c. on 8c. mult (No. 474) 65 10
O20 – 15c. on 50c. mult (No. 480) 90 10
O21 – 18c. on 60c. mult (No. 481) 90 15
O22 – 25c. mult (No. 478) . . . 1·00 20
O23 – 30c. mult (No. 479) . . . 1·00 25
O24 – 35c. on 60c. mult (No. 481) . . . . . . 1·25 30
O25 – 50c. mult (No. 480) . . . 1·75 35
O26 – 60c. mult (No. 481) . . . 2·00 45
O27 – $1 mult (No. 568) . . . 4·50 65
O28 – $1 mult (No. 569) . . . 4·50 65
O29 – $2 mult (No. 542) . . . 7·00 2·25
O30 – $4 mult (No. 484) . . . 13·00 2·25
O31 – $6 mult (No. 485) . . . 13·00 3·50

1985. Nos. 786/8, 862/5, 969/74, 976, 978, 981, 984/6 and 988/9 optd **O.H.M.S.** or surch also.
O32 5c. "Ptilosarcus gurneyi" . . 50 50
O33 10c. "Lobophyllia bemprichii" 50 50
O34 12c. "Sarcophyton digitatum" . . . . 3·25 60
O35 14c. "Pavona praetorta" . . 3·25 60
O36 18c. "Junceella gemmacea" 3·25 60
O37 20c. "Stylaster" 60 50
O38 30c. "Palauastrea ramosa" 60 50
O39 40c. "Stylaster echinatus" . 60 50
O40 50c. "Melithaea squamata" 4·00 70
O41 55c. on 85c. "Caulastraea echinulata" 70 50
O42 60c. "Tubastraea" 70 60
O43 70c. "Heliofungia actiniformis" . . . . . . 4·50 85
O46 75c. on 60c. Type **197** . . . 3·00 1·00
O47 75c. on 60c. Rarotonga oranges . . . . 3·00 1·00
O48 75c. on 60c. Rarotonga Airport . . . . 3·00 1·00
O49 75c. on 60c. Prime Minister Sir Thomas Davis . . . 3·00 1·00
O44 $1.10 "Pectinia alcicornis" 1·10 90
O45 $2 on $1.20 "Dendrophyllia gracilis" . . . . 2·00 1·75
O50 $5 on $3 "Heliofungia actiniformis" . . . . . . 10·00 4·75
O51 $9 on $4 "Stylophora pistillata" . . . . 8·00 8·25
O52 $14 on $6 "Stylaster echinatus" . . . . 12·50 13·00
O53 $18 on $10 "Melithaea albitincta" . . . . 17·00 17·00

1995. Nos. 1261/6 optd **O.H.M.S.**
O54 5c. Type **249** 10 10
O55 10c. Blue sea star 10 10
O56 15c. Bicoloured angelfish . . 10 10
O57 20c. Spotted pebble crab . . 10 15
O58 25c. Black-tipped grouper . . 15 20
O59 30c. Spanish dancer 15 20
O60 50c. Regal angelfish 30 35
O61 80c. Big-scaled soldierfish . . 45 50
O62 85c. Red pencil sea urchin 50 55
O63 90c. Red-spotted rainbowfish 50 55
O64 $1 Cheek-lined wrasse . . . 55 60
O65 $2 Long-nosed butterflyfish 1·10 1·25
O66 $3 Red-spotted rainbowfish 1·75 1·90
O67 $5 Blue sea star . . . . . . 2·75 3·00
O68 $7 "Pygoplites diacanthus" 4·00 4·25
O69 $10 Spotted pebble crab . . 6·00 6·25

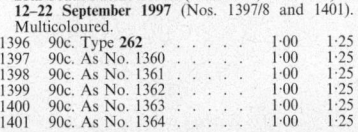

COSTA RICA Pt. 15

A republic of Central America. Independent since 1821.

1863. 8 reales = 1 peso.
1881. 100 centavos = 1 peso.
1901. 100 centimos = 1 colon.

1

8 General P. Fernandez

14 Pres. Soto

1863.
1 **1** ½r. blue 50 35
2 2r. red 55 85
4 4r. green . . . . 6·00 6·00
5 1p. orange . . . . 12·00 12·00

1881. Surch.
6 **1** 1c. on ½r. blue . . . . . . 1·10 4·50
8 2c. on ½r. blue . . . . . . 90 2·10
9 5c. on ½r. blue . . . . . . 2·75 7·25

1882. Surch **U.P.U.** and value.
10 **1** 5c. on ½r. blue . . . . . . 30·00 30·00
11 10c. on 2r. red . . . . . . 30·00 30·00
12 20c. on 4r. green . . . . . 90·00 90·00

1883.
13 **8** 1c. green 40 25
14 2c. red 40 30
15 5c. violet . . . . 7·25 25
16 10c. orange . . . . 21·00 2·75
17 40c. blue 45 55

1887.
18 **14** 5c. violet . . . . 3·25 25
19 10c. orange 90 50

1887. Fiscal stamps similar to T **8** and **14** optd **CORREOS**.
20 1c. red . . . . 1·50 65
21 5c. brown . . . . 1·50 45

17 Pres. Soto

19

1889. Various frames.
22 **17** 1c. brown 25 25
23 2c. green 20 20
24 5c. orange 40 25
25 10c. lake 20 20
26 20c. green 20 20
27 50c. red 45 80
28 1p. blue . . . . 65 1·25
29 2p. violet . . . . 6·00 7·00
30 5p. olive . . . . 15·00 18·00
31 10p. black . . . . 38·00 35·00

1892. Various frames.
32 **19** 1c. blue 20 20
33 2c. orange 20 20
34a 5c. mauve 20 20
35 10c. green 50 25
36 20c. red . . . . 6·00 25
37 50c. blue . . . . 3·00 2·00
38 1p. green on yellow 55 80
39 2p. red on grey . . . . . . 1·50 50
40 5p. blue on blue . . . . . 1·25 50
41a 10p. brown on buff . . . . 4·25 2·40

29 Juan Santamaria

31 Puerto Limon

1901. Various designs dated "1900".
42 **29** 1c. black and green 40 10
43 – 2c. black and red 25 15
52 – 4c. black and purple . . . . 1·90 75
44 **31** 5c. black and blue 35 15
53 – 6c. black and olive . . . . 4·50 2·40
45 – 10c. black and brown . . . 1·00 15
46 – 20c. black and lake . . . . 2·75 15
54 – 25c. brown and lilac . . . . 8·75 20
47 – 50c. blue and red . . . . . 2·40 70
48 – 1col. black and olive . . . . 38·00 7·50
49 – 2col. black and red . . . . 6·50 1·75
50 – 5col. black and brown . . . 17·00 1·75
51 – 10col. red and green . . . . 13·50 1·40

DESIGNS—VERT: 2c. Juan Mora F; 4c. Jose M. Canas; 6c. Julian Volio; 10c. Braulio (wrongly inscr "BRANLIO") Carrillo; 25c. Eusebio Figueroa; 50c. Jose M. Castro; 1col. Puente de Birris; 2col. Juan Rafael Mora; 5col. Jesus Jimenez. HORIZ: 20c. National Theatre; 10col. Arms.

1905. No. 46 surch **UN CENTIMO** in ornamental frame.
55 1c. on 20c. black and lake . . 50 50

43 Juan Santamaria

44 Juan Mora

1907. Dated "1907".

57	**43**	1c. blue and brown	50	20
58	**44**	2c. black and green	45	20
69	–	4c. blue and red	3·00	65
60	–	5c. blue and orange	35	20
71	–	10c. black and blue	4·25	10
72	–	20c. black and olive	4·75	2·40
63	–	25c. slate and lavender	1·10	35
74	–	50c. blue and red	17·00	4·25
75	–	1col. black and brown	8·25	4·25
76	–	2col. green and red	42·00	16·00

PORTRAITS: 4c. Jose M. Canas. 5c. Mauro Fernandez. 10c. Braulio Carrillo. 20c. Julian Volio. 25c. Eusebio Figueroa. 50c. Jose M. Castro. 1col. Jesus Jimenez. 2col. Juan Rafael Mora.

53 Juan Santamaria

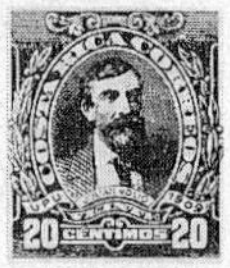

54 Julian Volio

1910. Various frames.

77	**53**	1c. brown	10	10
78	–	2c. green (Juan Mora F.)	20	10
79	–	4c. red (Jose M. Canas)	20	10
80	–	5c. orange (Mauro Fernandez)	20	10
81	–	10c. blue (B. Carrillo)	10	10
82	**54**	20c. olive	20	10
83	–	25c. purple (Eusebio Figueroa)	4·25	50
84	–	1col. brown (Jesus Jimenez)	40	25

1911. Optd **1911** between stars.

85	**29**	1c. black and green	50	35
86	**43**	1c. blue and brown	35	35
88	**44**	2c. black and green	35	35

1911. Optd **Habilitado 1911**.

93	4c. black and purple (No. 52)	1·00	10
90	5c. blue and orange (No. 60)	1·00	10
91	10c. black and blue (No. 71)	3·00	2·75

59 Liner "Antilles"

62

1911. Surch **Correos Un centimo** or **Correos 5 centimos**.

94	**59**	1c. on 10c. blue	30	15
96		1c. on 25c. violet	30	15
97		1c. on 50c. brown	55	45
98		1c. on 1c. brown	55	45
99		1c. on 5c. red	90	65
100		1c. on 10c. brown	1·10	95
101		5c. on 5c. orange	55	20

1912. Surch **Correos Dos centimos 2**.

102	**62**	2c. on 5c. brown	8·75	2·40
109		2c. on 10c. blue	£140	60·00
104		2c. on 50c. red	5·00	5·00
105		2c. on 1c. brown	22·00	3·00
112		2c. on 2c. red	2·50	90
107		2c. on 5c. green	8·75	2·40
108		2c. on 10col. purple	11·00	3·25

67 Plantation and Administration Building

1921. Centenary of Coffee Cultivation.

115	**67**	5c. black and blue	1·00	85

68 Simon Bolivar

69

1921.

116	**68**	15c. violet	25	15

1921. Cent of Independence of Central America.

117	**69**	5c. violet	25	35

70 Juan Mora and Julio Acosta

1921. Centenary of Independence.

118	**70**	2c. black and orange	50	50
119		3c. black and green	50	50
120		6c. black and red	65	55
121		15c. black and blue	1·75	1·75
122		30c. black and brown	2·75	2·75

1922. Coffee Publicity. Nos. 77/81 and 116 optd with sack inscr "CAFE DE COSTA RICA".

123	**53**	1c. brown	10	10
124	–	2c. green	15	10
125	–	4c. red	15	15
126	–	5c. orange	15	15
127	–	10c. blue	30	25
128	**68**	15c. violet	75	70

1922. Optd **CORREOS 1922**.

129	**69**	5c. violet	40	25

1922. Surch with red cross and **5c.**

130	5c.+5c. orange (No. 80)	50	25

1923. Optd **COMPRE UD. CAFE DE COSTA RICA** in circular frame.

131	5c. orange (No. 80)	25	15

77 Jesus Jimenez (statesman)

81 Coffee-growing

80 National Monument

1923. Birth Centenary of J. Jimenez.

132	**77**	2c. brown	15	15
133		4c. green	15	15
134		5c. blue	35	15
135		20c. red	20	20
136		1col. violet	35	35

1923.

137	**80**	1c. purple	10	10
138	**81**	2c. yellow	20	15
139	–	4c. green	40	35
140	–	5c. blue	70	10
141	–	5c. green	20	10
142	–	10c. brown	85	15
143	–	10c. red	25	10
144	–	12c. red	7·00	1·75
145	–	20c. blue	3·00	60
146	–	40c. orange	2·75	90
147	–	1col. olive	75	40

All the above are inscr "U.P.U. 1923." except the 10c. and 12c. which are inscr "1921 EN COMMEMORACION DEL PRIMER CONGRESO POSTAL", etc.

DESIGNS—HORIZ: 5c. P.O., San Jose; 10c. Columbus and Isabella I; 12c. "Santa Maria"; 20c. Columbus landing at Cariari; 40c. Map of Costa Rica. VERT: 4c. Banana-growing; 1col. M. Gutierrez.

85 Don R. A. Maldonado y Velasco

86 Map of Guanacaste

1924.

148	**85**	2c. green	15	10

For 3c. green see No. 211 and for other portraits as T **85** see Nos. 308/12.

1924. Cent of Province of Nicoya (Guanacaste).

149	**86**	1c. red	35	20
150		2c. purple	35	20
151		5c. green	35	20
152		10c. orange	1·25	50
153	–	15c. blue	40	45
154	–	20c. grey	65	45
155	–	25c. brown	90	75

DESIGN: 15c., 20c., 25c. Church at Nicoya.

88 Discus Thrower

93 Arms and Curtiss "Jenny"

1925. Inscr "JUEGOS OLIMPICOS". Imperf or perf.

156	**88**	5c. green	2·00	2·40
157	–	10c. red	2·00	2·40
158	–	20c. blue	4·00	3·50

DESIGNS—VERT: 10c. Trophy. HORIZ: 20c. Parthenon.

1926. Surch with values in ornamental designs.

159	3c. on 5c. (No. 140)	20	15
160	6c. on 10c. (No. 142)	35	25
161	30c. on 40c. (No. 146)	50	40
162	45c. on 1col. (No. 147)	55	50

1926. Surch with value between bars.

163	10c. on 12c. red (No. 144)	2·25	45

1926. Air.

164	**93**	20c. blue	1·25	40

94 Heredia Normal School

1926. Dated "1926".

165	–	3c. blue	15	15
166	–	6c. brown	25	20
167	**94**	30c. orange	35	25
168	–	45c. violet	90	50

DESIGNS: 3c. St. Louis College, Cartago; 6c. Chapui Asylum, San Jose; 45c. Ruins of Ujarras.

1928. Lindbergh Good Will Tour of Central America. Surch with aeroplane, **LINDBERGH ENERO 1928** and new value.

169	10c. on 12c. red (No. 144)	13·00	8·50

1928. Surch **5 5**.

170	**68**	5c. on 15c. violet	15	10

1929. Surch **CORREOS** and value.

171	**62**	5c. on 2c. red	1·00	35
173		13c. on 40c. green	1·25	40

98 Post Office

103 Juan Rafael Mora

1930. Types of 1923 reduced in size and dated "1929" as T **98**.

174	–	1c. purple (as No. 137)	10	10
175	**98**	5c. green	10	10
176	–	10c. red (as No. 143)	35	10

1930. Air. No. O178 surch **CORREO 1930 AEREO**, Bleriot XI airplane and new value.

177	O **95**	8c. on 1col.	50	40
178		20c. on 1col.	70	50
179		40c. on 1col.	1·40	1·00
180		1col. on 1col.	2·00	1·40

1930. Air. Optd **CORREO AEREO** (No. 181) or **Correo Aereo** (others) or surch also.

182	**62**	5c. on 10c. brown	90	25
181	–	10c. red (No. 143)	45	15
183	**62**	20c. on 50c. blue	1·25	25
184		40c. on 50c. blue	1·25	50
185		1col. orange	2·75	80

1931.

186	**103**	13c. red	25	15

1931. Air. Fiscal stamps (Arms design) inscr "TIMBRE 1929" (or "1930", 3col.), surch **Habilitado 1931 Correo Aereo** and new value.

190	2col. on 2col. green	16·00	16·00
191	3col. on 5col. brown	16·00	16·00
192	5col. on 10col. black	16·00	16·00

1932. Air. Telegraph stamp optd with wings inscr **CORREO CR AEREO**.

193	**62**	40c. green	3·50	80

106

1932. 1st National Philatelic Exhibition.

194	**106**	3c. orange	15	15
195		5c. green	25	25
196		10c. red	25	25
197		20c. blue	35	35

See also Nos. 231/4.

107 Ryan Brougham over La Sabana Airport, San Jose

1934. Air.

198	**107**	5c. green	15	10
507		5c. deep blue	10	10
508		5c. pale blue	10	10
199		10c. red	15	10
509		10c. green	10	10
510		10c. turquoise	10	10
200		15c. brown	30	10
511		15c. red	10	10
201		20c. blue	45	10
202		25c. orange	55	15
512		35c. violet	35	10
203		40c. brown	55	10
204		50c. black	40	15
205		60c. yellow	75	25
206		75c. violet	1·10	40
207	–	1col. red	85	10
208	–	2col. blue	90	35
209	–	5col. black	2·40	2·40
210	–	10col. brown	4·00	4·00

DESIGN: 1, 2, 5, 10col. Allegory of the Air Mail.

1934.

211	**85**	3c. green	10	10

109 Nurse at Altar

111 Our Lady of the Angels

1935. Costa Rican Red Cross Jubilee.

212	**109**	10c. red	35	15

1935. 300th Anniv of Apparition of Our Lady of the Angels.

213	–	5c. green	15	10
214	**111**	10c. red	35	15
215	–	30c. orange	50	25
216	–	45c. violet	65	40
217	**111**	50c. black	1·10	45

DESIGNS: 5c., 30c. Aerial view of Cartago; 45c. Allegory of the Apparition.

112 Cocos Island

1936.

218	**112**	4c. brown	25	10
219		8c. violet	30	15
220		25c. orange	35	15
221		35c. brown	50	15
222		40c. brown	40	25
223		50c. yellow	40	35
224		2col. green	4·75	3·75
225		5col. green	12·00	7·25

113 Cocos Island and Fleet of Columbus

1936.

226	**113**	5c. green	85	20
227		10c. red	1·10	20

114 Airplane over Mt. Poas

1937. Air. 1st Annual Fair.

228	114	1c. black	10	10
229		2c. brown	10	10
230		3c. violet	10	10

1937. 2nd National Philatelic Exhibition. As T **106**, but inscr "DICIEMBRE 1937".

231	106	2c. purple	15	15
232		3c. black	15	15
233		5c. green	15	15
234		10c. orange	15	15

115 Tunny

116 Native and Donkey carrying Bananas

117 Puntarenas

1937. National Exhibition, San Jose (1st Issue).

235	115	2c. black (postage)	20	15
236	116	5c. green	25	15
237	–	10c. red	35	20
238	117	2c. black (air)	10	10
239		5c. green	10	10
240		20c. blue	30	25
241		1col.40 brown	1·75	1·75

DESIGN—As Type **116**: 10c. Coffee gathering.

118 Purple Guaria Orchid "Carrleya skinneri"

119 National Bank

1938. National Exhibition, San Jose (2nd Issue).

242	118	1c. violet & grn (postage)	15	10
243		3c. brown	15	10
244	119	1c. violet (air)	10	10
245		3c. red	10	10
246		10c. red	15	10
247		75c. brown	90	90

DESIGN—As Type **118**: 3c. Cocoa-bean.

1938. No. 145 optd **1938**.

248	20c. blue	35	15

121 La Sabana Airport

1940. Air. Opening of San Jose Airport.

249	121	5c. green	10	10
250		10c. red	15	10
251		25c. blue	15	15
252		35c. brown	30	30
253		60c. orange	45	45
254		85c. violet	60	50
255		2col.35 green	3·25	3·25

1940. No. 168 variously surch **15 CENTIMOS** in ornamental frame.

256	15c. on 45c. violet	25	20

There are five distinct varieties of this surcharge.

1940. Pan-American Health Day. Unissued stamps prepared for the 8th Pan-American Child Welfare Congress optd **DIA PANAMERICANO DE LA SALUD 2. DICIEMBRE 1940**. (a) Postage. Allegorical design.

261	5c. green	20	10
262	10c. red	25	15
263	20c. blue	50	20
264	40c. brown	85	70
265	55c. orange	1·40	60

(b) Air. View of Duran Sanatorium.

266	10c. red	15	10
267	15c. violet	15	15
268	25c. blue	30	25
269	35c. brown	45	45
270	60c. green	35	35
271	75c. olive	75	85
272	1col.35 orange	3·25	3·25
273	5col. brown	14·00	14·00
274	10col. mauve	27·00	27·00

1940. Air. Pan-American Aviation Day. Surch **AERO Aviacion Panamericana Dic. 17 1940** and value.

275	15c. on 50c. yellow	50	50
276	30c. on 50c. yellow	50	50

1941. Surch **15 CENTIMOS 15**.

277	112	15c. on 25c. orange	25	20
278		15c. on 35c. brown	25	20
279		15c. on 40c. brown	25	20
280		15c. on 2col. green	25	20
281		15c. on 5col. green	40	35

131 Stadium and Flag

132 Football Match

1941. Central American and Caribbean Football Championship.

282	131	5c. green (postage)	45	25
283		10c. orange	40	25
284		15c. red	55	25
285		25c. blue	60	25
286		40c. brown	1·90	75
287		50c. violet	2·40	90
288		75c. orange	4·75	1·90
289		1col. red	7·75	3·75
290	132	15c. red (air)	45	15
291		30c. blue	50	25
292		40c. brown	50	40
293		50c. violet	65	45
294		60c. green	85	50
295		75c. yellow	1·40	75
296		1col. mauve	2·40	2·40
297		1col.40 red	5·00	5·00
298		2col. green	9·50	9·50
299		5col. black	21·00	21·00

1941. Air. Costa Rica–Panama Boundary Treaty. Optd **Mayo 1941 Tratado Limitrofe Costa Rica – Panama** or surch also.

300	107	5c. on 20c. blue	20	15
301		15c. on 20c. blue	25	20
302		40c. on 75c. violet	40	25
303	–	65c. on 1col. red (No. 207)	40	30
304	–	1col.40 on 2col. blue (No. 208)	1·90	1·90
305	–	5col. black (No. 209)	6·50	6·50
306	–	10col. brown (No. 210)	7·50	7·50

1941. As Type **85** but with new portraits.

308	–	3c. orange	10	10
309	–	3c. purple	10	10
310	–	3c. red	10	10
310a	–	3c. blue	10	10
311	–	5c. violet	10	10
312	–	5c. black	10	10

PORTRAITS: 3c. (Nos. 308/10) C. G. Viquez. 3c. (No. 310a) Mgr. B. A. Thiel. 5c. J. J. Rodriguez.

136 New Decree and Restored University

1941. Restoration of National University.

313	–	5c. green (postage)	25	10
314	136	10c. orange	30	10
315	–	15c. red	40	10
316	136	25c. blue	60	25
317	–	50c. brown	1·50	75
318	136	15c. red (air)	25	15
319	–	30c. blue	40	15
320	136	40c. orange	45	35
321	–	60c. blue	55	50
322	136	1col. violet	2·00	1·60
323	–	2col. black	5·00	3·75
324	136	5col. purple	16·00	13·00

DESIGN—(Nos. 313, 315, 317, 319, 321 and 323): The original Decree and University.

1941. Surch.

325	5c. on 6c. brn (No. 166)	15	15
326	15c. on 20c. blue (No. 248)	25	15

139 "V", Torch and Flags

140 Francisco Morazan

1942. War Effort.

327	139	5c. red	20	10
328		5c. orange	20	10
329		5c. green	20	10
330		5c. blue	20	10
331		5c. violet	20	10

1942. Portraits and dates.

332	A	1c. lilac (postage)	10	10
333	B	2c. black	10	10
334	C	3c. blue	10	10
335	D	5c. turquoise	10	10
336		5c. green	10	10
337	140	15c. red	10	10
338	E	25c. blue	20	15
339	F	50c. violet	1·25	50
340	G	1col. black	2·00	1·00
341	H	2col. orange	2·40	1·25
341a	I	5c. brown (air)	10	10
342	A	10c. red	10	10
342a		10c. olive	10	10
342b	J	15c. violet	10	10
343	K	25c. blue	15	10
344	L	30c. brown	15	10
345	D	40c. blue	25	10
346		40c. red	25	15
347	140	45c. purple	35	25
348	M	45c. black	20	15
349	E	50c. green	90	20
350		50c. orange	20	20
351	N	55c. purple	25	20
352	F	60c. blue	45	15
353		60c. green	20	15
354	G	65c. red	45	25
355		65c. blue	25	20
356	O	75c. green	40	25
357	H	85c. orange	55	35
358		85c. violet	65	45
359	P	1col. black	65	30
360		1col. red	50	20
361	Q	1col.05 sepia	60	40
362	R	1col.15 brown	90	85
363		1col.15 green	1·25	85
364	B	1col.40 violet	1·40	1·25
365		1col.40 yellow	85	75
366	C	2col. black	2·10	85
367		2col. olive	65	35

PORTRAITS: A, J. Mora Fernandez. B, B. Carranza. C, T. Guardia. D, M. Aguilar. E, J. M. Alfaro. F, F. M. Oreamuno. G, J. M. Castro. H, J. R. Mora. I, S. Lara. J, C. Duran. K, A. Esquivel. L, V. Herrera. M, J. R. de Gallegos. N, P. Fernandez. O, B. Soto. P, J. M. Montealegre. Q, B. Carrillo. R, J. Jimenez.

1943. Air. Optd **Legislacion Social 15 Setiembre 1943**.

368	5col. black (No. 209)	3·25	2·75
369	10col. brown (No. 210)	5·75	4·50

142 San Ramon

143 Allegory of Flight

1944. Centenary of San Ramon.

370	142	5c. green (postage)	10	10
371		10c. orange	15	10
372		15c. red	20	10
373		40c. grey	55	50
374		50c. blue	90	45
375	143	10c. orange (air)	15	10
376		15c. red	20	15
377		40c. blue	35	25
378		45c. red	40	35
379		60c. green	30	25
380		1col. brown	65	50
381		1col.40 grey	3·75	3·00
382		5col. violet	9·50	9·00
383		10col. black	27·00	24·00

1944. Ratification of Costa Rica and Panama Boundary Treaty. Optd **La entrevista ... 1944**.

384	139	5c. orange	10	10
385		5c. green	10	10
386		5c. blue	10	10
387		5c. violet	10	10

1944. Air. No. 207 optd **1944**.

388	1col. red	45	40

1945. Air. Official Air stamps of 1934 optd **1945** in oblong network frame.

389	107	5c. green	40	35
390		10c. red	40	35
391		15c. brown	40	35
392		20c. blue	40	40
393		25c. orange	40	40
394		40c. brown	40	40
395		50c. black	40	40
396		60c. yellow	55	40
397		75c. violet	45	40
398	–	1col. red (No. O220)	45	40
399	–	2col. blue (No. O221)	3·00	2·75
400	–	5col. black (No. O222)	3·75	3·25
401	–	10col. brown (No. O223)	5·50	5·00

1945. Air stamps. Telegraph stamps as Type **62** optd **CORREO AEREO 1945** and bar.

402	62	40c. green	80	45
403		50c. blue	1·00	45
404		1col. orange	2·40	75

148 Mauro Fernandez

149 Coffee Gathering

1945. Birth Centenary of Fernandez.

405	148	20c. green	15	10

1945.

406	149	5c. black and green	10	10
407		10c. black and orange	15	10
408		20c. black and red	20	15

150 Florence Nightingale and Nurse Cavell

1945. Air. 60th Anniv of National Red Cross Society.

409	150	1col. black	50	35

1946. Air. Central American and Caribbean Football Championship. As Type **132**, but inscribed "FEBRERO 1946".

410	132	25c. green	45	40
411		30c. orange	45	40
412		55c. blue	55	40

1946. Surch **15 15**.

413	148	15c. on 20c. green	15	10

152 San Juan de Dios Hospital

153 Ascension Esquivel

1946. Air. Centenary of San Juan de Dios Hospital.

414	152	5c. black and green	10	10
415		10c. black and brown	10	10
416		15c. black and red	10	10
417		25c. black and blue	15	15
418		30c. black and orange	25	20
419		40c. black and olive	15	15
420		50c. black and violet	25	25
421		60c. black and green	50	45
422		75c. black and brown	40	35
423		1col. black and blue	50	25
424		2col. black and brown	55	60

425		3col. black and purple	1·40	1·40
426		5col. black and yellow	1·75	1·75

1947. Air. Former Presidents.

427		– 2col. black and blue	65	50
428	153	3col. black and red	1·00	65
429		– 5col. black and green	1·50	1·00
430		– 10col. black and orange	3·00	1·90

PORTRAITS: 2col. Rafael Iglesias. 5col. Cleto Gonzalez Viquez. 10col. Ricardo Jimenez.

1947. No. O228 optd CORREOS 1947.

431	57	5c. green	50	10

1947. Air. Nos. 410/2 surch Habilitado para C 0.15 Decreto No. 16 de 28 abril de 1947.

432	132	15c. on 25c. green	55	45
433		15c. on 30c. orange	55	45
434		15c. on 55c. blue	55	45

156 Columbus at Cariari   158 Franklin D. Roosevelt

1947. Air.

435	156	25c. black and green	65	15
436		30c. black and blue	65	15
437		40c. black and orange	85	20
438		45c. black and violet	1·10	35
439		50c. black and red	1·25	35
440		65c. black and brown	3·00	90

1947. Air. Stamps of 1942 surch C0.15.

441	E	15c. on 50c. orange	15	15
442	F	15c. on 60c. green	15	15
443	O	15c. on 75c. green	15	15
444	P	15c. on 1col. red	20	20
445	Q	15c. on 1col.5 sepia	15	15

1947.

446	158	5c. green (postage)	10	10
447		10c. red	10	10
448		15c. blue	15	15
449		25c. orange	15	15
450		30c. red	35	25
451		15c. green (air)	10	10
452		30c. red	15	10
453		45c. brown	25	25
454		65c. orange	25	25
455		75c. blue	35	25
456		1col. green	50	45
457		2col. black	75	60
458		5col. red	1·50	1·50

159 Miguel de Cervantes Saavedra

1947. 400th Birth Anniv of Cervantes.

459	159	30c. blue	20	10
460		55c. red	35	25

160 Steam Locomotive "Maria Cecilia"

1947. Air. 50th Anniv of Pacific Electric Railway.

461	160	35c. black and green	4·75	1·50

161 National Theatre   162 Rafael Iglesias

1948. Air. 50th Anniv of National Theatre.

462	161	15c. black and blue	15	10
463		20c. black and red	15	15
464	162	35c. black and green	25	20
465	161	45c. black and violet	35	25
466		50c. black and red	35	25
467		75c. black and purple	45	45
468		1col. black and green	85	65
469		2col. black and lake	1·25	90

470	162	5col. black and yellow	2·10	2·00
471		10col. black and blue	4·75	3·00

1948. Air. Surch HABILITADO PARA C 0.35.

472	156	35c. on 40c. blk & orge	60	30

1949. Air. 125th Anniv of Annexation of Guanacaste. Nos. 361, 409, 363 and 365 variously surch 1824-1949 125 Aniversario de la Anexion Guanacaste and value.

473	Q	35c. on 1col. 5 sepia	15	15
474	150	50c. on 1col. black	25	15
475	R	55c. on 1col.15 green	45	35
476		55c. on 1col.40 yellow	45	35

165 Globe and Dove

1950. Air. 75th Anniv of U.P.U.

477	165	15c. red	15	10
478		25c. blue	15	10
479		1col. green	35	15

166 Battle of El Tejar, Cartago

167 Capture of Limon

1950. Air. Inscr "GUERRA DE LIBERACION NACIONAL 1948".

480	166	15c. black and red	15	10
481	167	20c. black and green	20	15
482		– 25c. black and blue	25	15
483		– 35c. black and brown	25	15
484		– 55c. black and violet	55	25
485		– 75c. black and orange	55	35
486		– 80c. black and grey	55	50
487		– 1col. black and orange	75	55

DESIGNS—VERT: 80c., 1col. Dr. C. L. Valverde. HORIZ: 25c. La Lucha Ranch; 35c. Trench of San Isidro Battalion; 55c., 75c. Observation post.

169 Bull   170 Queen Isabella and Caravels

1950. Air. National Agriculture and Industries Fair. Centres in black.

488	169	1c. green	10	10
489	A	2c. blue	10	10
490	B	3c. brown	10	10
491	C	5c. blue	10	10
492	169	10c. green	10	10
493	A	30c. violet	30	10
494	D	45c. orange	25	15
495	C	50c. grey	35	10
496	B	65c. blue	45	25
497	D	80c. red	45	30
498	169	2col. orange	1·25	1·00
499	A	3col. blue	3·75	2·40
500	C	5col. red	4·00	3·75
501	D	10col. red	4·00	3·75

DESIGNS—VERT: A, Fishing; B, Pineapple; C, Bananas; D, Coffee.

1952. Air. 500th Anniv of Isabella the Catholic.

502	170	15c. red	30	10
503		20c. orange	35	20
504		25c. blue	60	10
505		55c. green	1·25	50
506		2col. violet	3·00	1·00

1953. Air. Surch 15 15 within ornaments.

513	158	15c. on 30c. red	15	10
514		15c. on 45c. brown	15	10
515		15c. on 65c. orange	15	10

1953. Air. Surch HABILITADO PARA CINCO CENTIMOS 1953.

515a	155	5c. on 30c. blk & blue	1·60	1·25
516		5c. on 40c. blk & orge	20	15

517		5c. on 45c. blk & vio	20	15
518		5c. on 65c. blk & brn	50	35

173

1953. Fiscal stamps surch as in T 173.

519	173	5c. on 10c. green	10	10

174 "Vegetable Oil"   (175)

1954. Air. National Industries. Centres in black.

520		5c. red (Type 174)	10	10
520a		5c. blue (Type 174)	15	10
521		10c. indigo (Pottery)	10	10
521a		10c. blue (Pottery)	15	10
522		15c. green (Sugar)	10	10
522a		15c. yellow (Sugar)	15	10
523		20c. violet (Soap)	10	10
524		25c. lake (Timber)	10	10
525		30c. lilac (Matches)	30	20
526		35c. purple (Textiles)	15	10
527		40c. black (Leather)	25	15
528		45c. green (Tobacco)	50	25
529		50c. purple (Confectionery)	35	10
530		55c. yellow (Canning)	25	10
531		60c. brown (General industries)	60	35
532		65c. red (Metals)	45	50
533		75c. violet (Pharmaceutics)	65	45
533a		75c. red (as No. 533)	25	15
533b		80c. violet (as No. 533)	45	40
534		1col. turq (Paper)	35	20
535		2col. mauve (Rubber)	55	55
536		3col. green (Aircraft)	90	55
537		5col. black (Marble)	1·40	45
538		10col. yellow (Beer)	4·00	3·00

1955. Fiscal stamps optd for postal use as in T 175.

539	175	5c. on 2c. green	10	10
540		15c. on 2c. green	15	10

176 Rotary Emblem over Central America   177 Map of Costa Rica

1956. Air. 50th Anniv Rotary International.

542	176	10c. green	10	10
543		– 25c. blue	15	10
544		– 40c. brown	35	25
545		– 45c. red	25	20
546		– 60c. purple	25	20
547		– 2col. orange	45	45

DESIGNS: 25c. Emblem, hand and boy; 40c., 2col. Emblem and hospital; 45c. Emblem, leaves and Central America; 60c. Emblem and lighthouse.

1957. Air. Centenary of War of 1856–67.

548	177	5c. blue	25	10
549		– 10c. green	10	10
550		– 15c. orange	10	10
551		– 20c. brown	15	10
552		– 25c. blue	15	10
553		– 30c. violet	20	15
554		– 35c. red	20	15
555		– 40c. black	20	15
556		– 45c. red	25	15
557		– 50c. blue	25	15
558		– 55c. ochre	40	15
559		– 60c. red	30	25
560		– 65c. red	35	25
561		– 70c. yellow	45	30
562		– 75c. green	40	25
563		– 80c. sepia	45	20
564		– 1col. black	55	35

DESIGNS: 10c. Map of Guanacaste; 15c. Wartime inn; 20c. Santa Rosa house; 25c. Gen. D. J. M. Quiros; 30c. Old Presidential Palace; 35c. Minister D. J. B. Calvo; 40c. Dr. Luis Molina; 45c. Gen. D. J. J. Mora; 50c. Gen. D. J. M. Canas; 55c. Juan Santamaria Monument; 60c. National Monument; 65c. A. Vallerriestra; 70c. Pres. R. Castilla Marquesado of Peru; 75c. San Carlos Fortress; 80c. Vice-President D. F. M. Oreamuno of Costa Rica; 1col. Pres. D. J. R. Mora of Costa Rica.

1958. Obligatory Tax. Christmas. Nos. 489 and 521a surch SELLO DE NAVIDAD PRO - CIUDAD DE LOS NINOS 5 5.

565	A	on 2c. black & blue	10	10
566		– 5c. on 10c. black & blue	25	10

179 Pres. Gonzalez Viquez   180 Pres. R. J. Oreamuno and Electric Locomotive No. 31

1959. Air. Birth Centenaries of Presidents Gonzalez (1958) and Oreamuno (1959).

567	179	5c. blue and pink	10	10
568		– 10c. slate and red	10	10
569		– 15c. black and slate	10	10
570		– 20c. brown and red	1·00	25
571		– 35c. blue and purple	15	15
572		– 55c. violet and brown	25	20
573		– 80c. blue	40	35
574	180	1col. lake and orange	3·50	45
575		– 2col. lake and black	60	45

DESIGNS—As Type 179: 10c. Pres. Oreamuno. As Type 180: Pres. Gonzalez and: 15c. Highway bridge; 55c. Water pipe-line; 80c. National Library. Pres. Oreamuno and: 20c. Puntarenas Quay; 35c. Post Office, San Jose. 2col. Both presidents and open book inscr "PROBIDAD" ("Honesty").

181 Father Flanagan   182 Goal Attack

1959. Obligatory Tax. Christmas. Inscr "SELLO DE NAVIDAD".

576	181	5c. green	20	10
577		– 5c. mauve	20	10
578		– 5c. olive	20	10
579		– 5c. black	20	10

PAINTINGS: No. 577, "Girl with braids" (after Modigliani). No. 578, "Boy with a clubfoot" (after Ribera). No. 579, "The boy blowing on charcoal" (after "El Greco").

1960. Air. 3rd Pan-American Football Games.

580	182	10c. blue	10	10
581		– 25c. blue	15	10
582		– 35c. red	15	15
583		– 50c. brown	20	15
584		– 85c. turquoise	40	50
585		– 5col. purple	1·25	1·25

DESIGNS: 25c. Player heading ball; 35c. Defender tackling forward; 50c. Referee bouncing ball; 85c. Goalkeeper seizing ball; 5col. Player kicking high ball.

183 "Uprooted Tree"   184 Prof. J. A. Facio

1960. Air. World Refugee Year.

586	183	35c. blue and yellow	20	15
587		85c. black and pink	40	45

1960. Birth Centenary of Professor Justo A. Facio.

588	184	10c. red	10	10

185 "OEA" and Banner

1960. Air. 6th and 7th Chancellors' Reunion Conference, Organization of American States, San Jose. Multicoloured.

589	25c. Type 185		15	10
590	35c. "OEA" within oval chains		35	40
591	55c. Clasped hands and chains		50	40
592	5col. Flags in form of flying bird		1·90	1·75
593	10col. "OEA" on map of Costa Rica, and flags		3·00	2·40

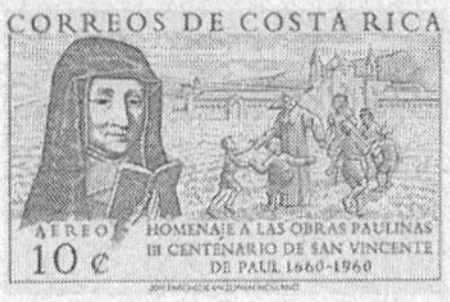

186 St. Louise de Marillac, Sister of Charity and Children

1960. Air. 300th Death Anniv of St. Vincent de Paul.
594 **186** 10c. green 10 10
595 – 25c. lake 10 10
596 – 50c. blue 25 15
597 – 1col. bistre 40 35
598 – 5col. sepia . . . . 1·25 95
DESIGNS—HORIZ: St. Vincent de Paul, and: 25c. Two-storey building; 1c. Modern building; 50c. As Type **186**, but scene shows Sister at bedside. VERT: 5col. Stained-glass window picturing St. Vincent de Paul with children.

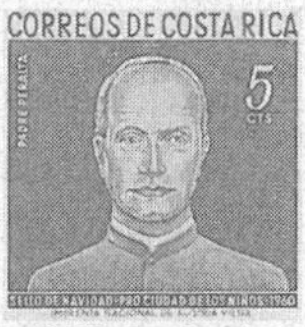

187 Father Peralta

1960. Obligatory Tax. Christmas. Inscr "SELLO DE NAVIDAD".
599 **187** 5c. brown 35 10
600 – 5c. orange 35 10
601 – 5c. red 35 10
602 – 5c. blue 35 10
DESIGNS: No. 600, "Girl" (after Renoir); No. 601, "The Drinkers" (after Velasquez); No. 602, "Children Singing" (sculpture, after Zuniga).

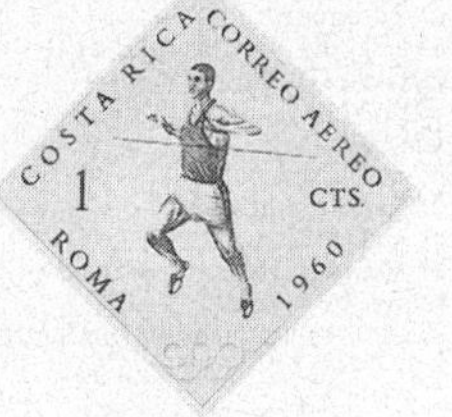

188 Running

1960. Air. Olympics Game, Rome. Centres and inscriptions in black.
603 1c. yellow (T **188**) 10 10
604 2c. blue (Diving) 10 10
605 3c. red (Cycling) 10 10
606 4c. yellow (Weightlifting) . . 10 10
607 5c. green (Tennis) 10 10
608 10c. red (Boxing) 10 10
609 25c. turquoise (Football) . . 10 10
610 85c. mauve (Basketball) . . . 55 45
611 1col. grey (Baseball) 65 55
612 10col. lavender (Pistol-shooting) . . . . 5·50 4·50

1961. Air. 15th World Amateur Baseball Championships. No. 533a optd **XV Campeonato Mundial de Beisbol de Aficionados** or surch also.
613 25c. on 75c. black and red 20 10
614 75c. black and red 55 25

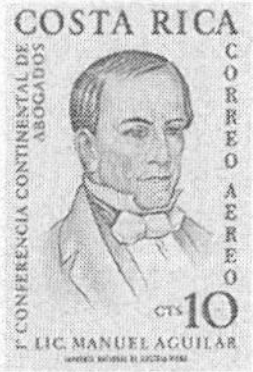

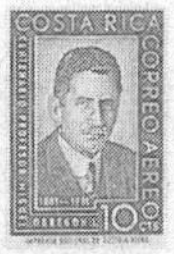

190 M. Aguilar **191** Prof. M. Obregon

1961. Air. 1st Continental Lawyers' Conference.
615 **190** 10c. blue 10 10
616 – 10c. purple 10 10
617 – 25c. violet 15 10
618 – 25c. sepia 15 10
PORTRAITS: No. 616, A. Brenes. No. 617, A. Gutierrez. No. 618, V. Herrera.
See also Nos. 628/31.

1961. Air. Birth Centenary of Obregon.
619 **191** 10c. turquoise 10 10

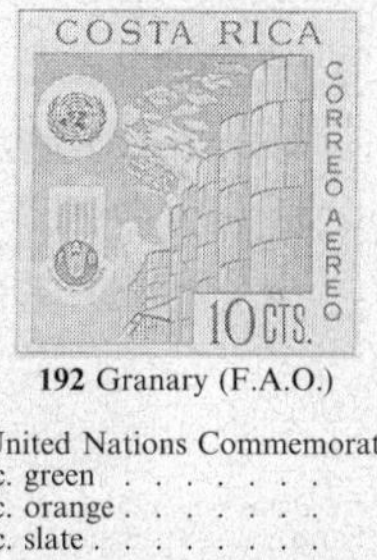

192 Granary (F.A.O.)

1961. Air. United Nations Commemoration.
620 **192** 10c. green 10 10
621 – 20c. orange 15 15
622 – 25c. slate 20 15
623 – 30c. blue 20 15
624 – 35c. red 50 25
625 – 45c. violet 35 20
626 – 85c. blue 40 30
627 – 10col. black . . . . . 3·00 2·40
DESIGNS: 20c. "Medical Care" (W.H.O.); 25c. Globe and workers (I.L.O.); 30c. Globe and communications satellite "Correo 1B" (I.T.U.); 35c. Compass and rocket (W.M.O.); 45c. "The Thinker" (statue) and open book (U.N.E.S.C.O.); 85c. Douglas DC-6 airliner and globe (I.C.A.O.); 10col. "Spiderman" on girder (International Bank).

1961. Air. 9th Central American Medical Congress. As T **190** but inscr "NOVENO CONGRESO MEDICO", etc.
628 10c. violet 10 10
629 10c. turquoise 10 10
630 25c. sepia 15 10
631 25c. purple 15 10
PORTRAITS: No. 628, Dr. E. J. Roman. No. 629, Dr. J. M. S. Alfaro. No. 630, Dr. A. S. Llorente. No. 631, Dr. J. J. U. Giralt.

1961. Air. Children's City Christmas issue. No. 522 surch **SELLO DE NAVIDAD PRO-CIUDAD DE LOS NINOS 5 5**.
632 5c. on 15c. black and green 15 10

1962. Air. Surch in figures.
633 10c. on 15c. black and green (No. 522) 10 10
634 25c. on 15c. black and green (No. 522) 10 10
635 35c. on 50c. black and purple (No. 529) 20 15
636 85c. on 80c. blue (No. 573) 55 45

1962. Air. 2nd Central American Philatelic Convention. Optd **II CONVENCION FILATELICA CENTROAMERICANA SETIEMBRE 1962**.
637 30c. blue (No. 623) 45 35
638 2col. red and black (No. 575) 85 65

1962. Air. No. 522 surch **C 0.10**.
639 10c. on 15c. black & green 10 10

1962. Air. Fiscal stamps as T **175** optd **CORREO AEREO** and surch with new value for postal use.
640 25c. on 2c. green 10 10
641 35c. on 2c. green 15 10
642 45c. on 2c. green 25 20
643 85c. on 2c. green 45 35

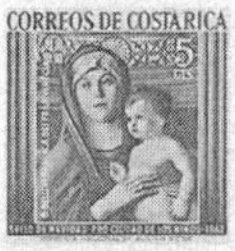

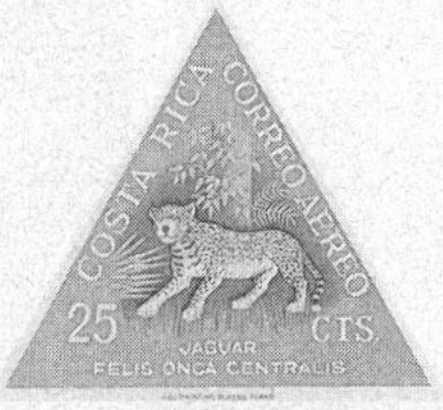

198 "Virgin and Child" (after Bellini) **199** Jaguar

1962. Obligatory Tax. Christmas.
644 **198** 5c. sepia 40 10
645 A 5c. green 40 10
646 B 5c. blue 40 10
647 C 5c. red 40 10
DESIGNS: A, "Angel with Violin" (after Mellozo); B, Mgr. Ruben Odio; C, "Child's Head" (after Rubens).
See also Nos. 674/7.

1963. Air.
648 – 5c. brown and olive . . . 10 10
649 – 10c. blue and orange . . 10 10
650 **199** 25c. yellow and blue . . . 20 10
651 – 30c. brown and green . . 35 30
652 – 35c. brown and bistre . . 65 30
653 – 40c. blue and green . . 70 45
654 – 85c. black and green . . 1·10 70
655 – 5col. brown and green . . 5·75 4·75
ANIMALS (As Type **199**): 5c. Paca. 10c. Bairds tapir. 30c. Ocelot. 35c. White-tailed deer. 40c. American manatee. 85c. White-throated capuchin. 5col. White-lipped peccary.

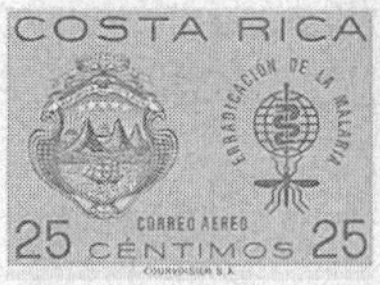

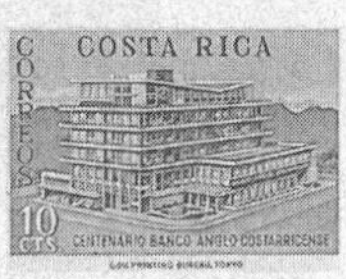

200 Arms and Campaign Emblem **202** Anglo-Costa Rican Bank

1963. Air. Malaria Eradication.
656 **200** 25c. red 10 10
657 35c. brown 15 15
658 45c. blue 25 20
659 85c. green 45 35
660 1col. blue 55 45

1963. Obligatory Tax Fund for Children's Village. Nos. 644/7 surch **1963 10 CENTIMOS**.
661 **198** 10c. on 5c. sepia 15 15
662 A 10c. on 5c. green 15 15
663 B 10c. on 5c. blue 15 15
664 C 10c. on 5c. red 15 15

1963. Anglo-Costa Rican Bank Centenary.
665 **202** 10c. blue 10 10

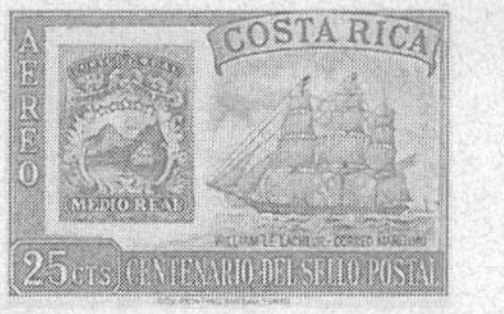

203 ½ real Stamp of 1863 and Sail Merchantman "William le Lacheur"

1963. Air. Stamp Centenary.
666 **203** 25c. blue and purple . . . 50 15
667 – 2col. orange and grey . . 1·25 85
668 – 3col. green and ochre . . 2·00 1·50
669 – 10col. brown and green 9·00 4·00
DESIGNS: 2col. 2 reales stamp of 1863 and Postmaster-General R. B. Carrillo; 3col. 4 reales stamp of 1863 and mounted postman and pack-mule of 1839; 10col. 1 peso stamp of 1863 and mule-drawn mail van.

1963. Unissued animal designs as T **199**. Surch.
670 10c. on 1c. brown and green 15 10
671 25c. on 2c. sepia and brown 20 10
672 35c. on 3c. brown and green 25 15
673 85c. on 4c. brown and lake 55 25
ANIMALS: 1c. Tamandua. 2c. Grey fox. 3c. Nine-banded armadillo. 4c. Giant anteater.

1963. Obligatory Tax. Christmas. As Nos. 644/7 but inscr "1963" and new colours.
674 **198** 5c. blue 20 10
675 A 5c. red 20 10
676 B 5c. black 20 10
677 C 5c. sepia 20 10

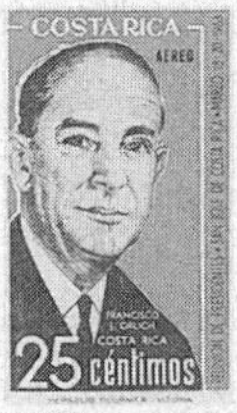

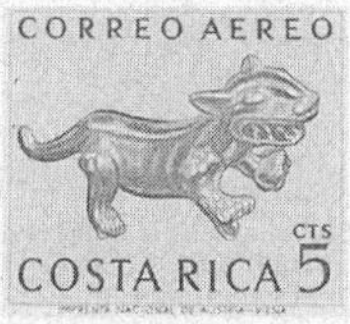

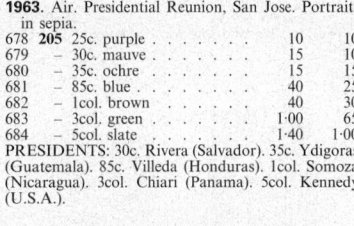

205 Pres. Orlich (Costa Rica) **206** Puma (clay statuette)

1963. Air. Presidential Reunion, San Jose. Portraits in sepia.
678 **205** 25c. purple 10 10
679 – 30c. mauve 15 10
680 – 35c. ochre 15 15
681 – 85c. blue 40 25
682 – 1col. brown 40 30
683 – 3col. green . . . . . . 1·00 65
684 – 5col. slate . . . . . . 1·40 1·00
PRESIDENTS: 30c. Rivera (Salvador). 35c. Ydigoras (Guatemala). 85c. Villeda (Honduras). 1col. Somoza (Nicaragua). 3col. Chiari (Panama). 5col. Kennedy (U.S.A.).

1963. Air. Archaeological Discoveries.
685 **206** 5c. turquoise and green 10 10
686 – 10c. turquoise and yellow 10 10
687 – 25c. sepia and red . . . 10 10
688 – 30c. turquoise and buff 10 10
689 – 35c. green and salmon . . 15 10
690 – 45c. brown and blue . . 15 10
691 – 50c. brown and blue . . 15 10
692 – 55c. brown and green . . 20 10
693 – 75c. brown and buff . . 20 15
694 – 85c. brown and yellow . . 55 35
695 – 90c. brown and yellow . . 45 35
696 – 1col. brown and blue . . 40 25
697 – 2col. turquoise & yellow 70 45
698 – 3col. brown and green . . 1·25 80
699 – 5col. brown & yellow . . 1·25 75
700 – 10col. green and mauve 2·00 1·90
DESIGNS—HORIZ: 10c. Ceremonial stool; 1col. Twin beakers; 2col. Alligator. VERT: 25c. Man (statuette); 30c. Dancer; 35c. Vase; 45c. Deity; 50c. Frog; 55c. "Eagle" bell; 75c. Multi-limbed deity; 85c. Kneeling effigy; 90c. "Bird" jug; 3col. Twin-tailed lizard; 5col. Child; 10col. Stone effigy of woman.

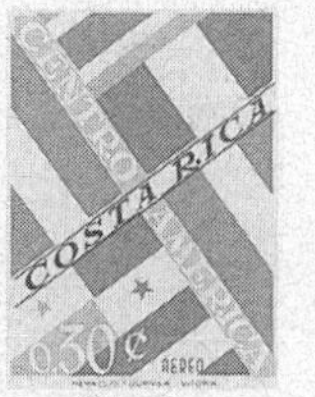

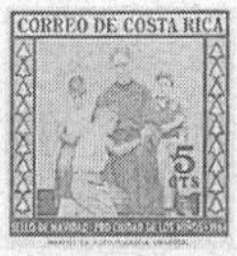

207 Flags **210** Mgr. R. Odio and Children

1964. Air. "Centro America".
701 **207** 30c. multicoloured 35 25

1964. Air. Surch.
702 – 5c. on 30c. (No. 688) . . 10 10
703 **207** 15c. on 30c. 10 10
704 – 15c. on 85c. (No. 694) . . 10 10
See Nos. 745/9.

1964. Paris Postal Conf. No. 695 surch **C 0.15 CONFERENCIA POSTAL DE PARIS - 1864**.
705 15c. on 90c. brn & yellow . . 10 10

1964. Obligatory Tax. Christmas. Inscr "SELLO DE NAVIDAD", etc.
706 **210** 5c. brown 15 10
707 A 5c. blue 15 10
708 B 5c. purple 15 10
709 C 5c. green 15 10
DESIGNS: A, Teacher and child; B, Children at play; C, Children in class.

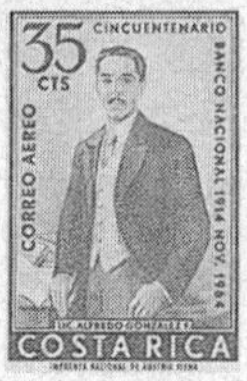

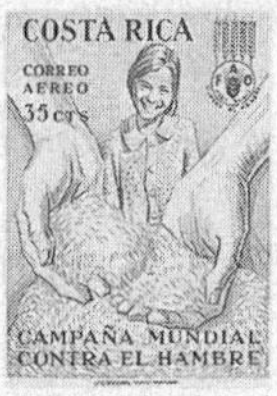

211 A. Gonzalez F. **213** Handfuls of Grain

1965. Air. 50th Anniv of National Bank.
710 **211** 35c. green 10 10

1965. Air. 75th Anniv of Chapui Hospital. No. 697 surch **75 ANIVERSARIO ASILO CHAPUI 1890–1965**.
711 2col. turquoise and yellow . . 60 45

1965. Air. Freedom from Hunger.
712 – 15c. black, grey & brown 10 10
713 **213** 35c. black and buff . . . 15 10
714 – 50c. green and blue . . . 20 15
715 – 1col. silver, black & green 35 20
DESIGNS—HORIZ: 15c. Map and grain silo; 1col. Douglas DC-8 airliner over map. VERT: 50c. Children and population graph.

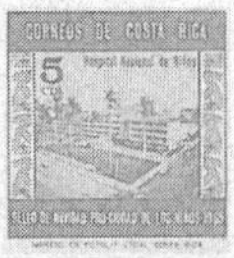

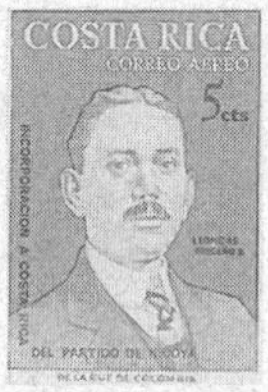

214 National Children's Hospital **215** L. Briceno B.

1965. Christmas Charity. Obligatory Tax. Inscr "SELLO DE NAVIDAD", etc.
716 **214** 5c. green 15 10
717 A 5c. brown 15 10
718 B 5c. red 15 10
719 C 5c. blue 15 10
DESIGNS—As Type **214**: A, Father Casiano; B, Poinsettia. DIAMOND: C, Father Christmas with children.

1965. Air. Incorporation of Nicoya District.
720 **215** 5c. slate, black & brown 10 10
721 – 10c. slate and blue . . . 10 10
722 – 15c. slate and bistre . . . 10 10
723 – 35c. slate and blue . . . 10 10
724 – 50c. violet and grey . . . 15 10
725 – 1col. slate and ochre . . . 40 25
DESIGNS: 10c. Nicoya Church; 15c. Incorporation scroll; 35c. Map of Guanacaste Province; 50c. Provincial dance; 1col. Guanacaste map and produce.

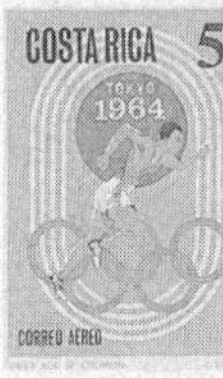

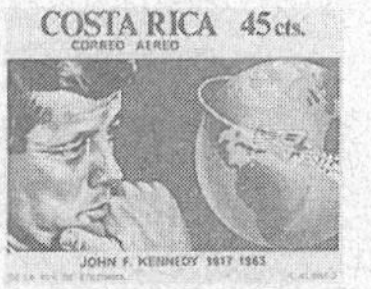

216 Running **217** Pres. John F. Kennedy and "Mercury" Space Capsule encircling Globe

1965. Air. Olympic Games (1964). Mult.
726 5c. Type **216** 10 10
727 10c. Cycling 10 10
728 40c. Judo 15 10
729 65c. Handball 25 15
730 80c. Football 35 20
731 1col. Olympic torches 45 25

1965. Air. 2nd Death Anniv of Pres. Kennedy. Multicoloured.
732 45c. Type **217** 15 15
733 55c. Kennedy in San Jose Cathedral (vert) 25 15
734 85c. President with son (vert) 35 25
735 1col. Facade of White House, Washington (vert) 35 30

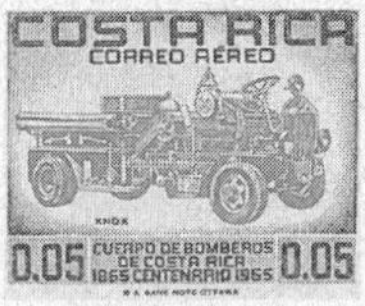

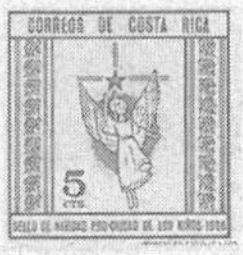

218 Fire Engine **219** Angel

1966. Air. Centenary of Fire Brigade.
736 **218** 5c. red and black 10 10
737 – 10c. red and yellow . . . 10 10
738 – 15c. black and red . . . 10 10
739 – 35c. yellow and black . . 40 10
740 – 50c. red and blue 75 10
DESIGNS—VERT: 10c. Fire engine of 1866; 15c.

Firemen with hoses; 35c. Brigade badge; 50c. Emblem of Central American Fire Brigades Confederation.

1966. Obligatory Tax. Christmas. Inscr "SELLO DE NAVIDAD", etc.

741	219	5c. blue	15	10
742	–	5c. red (Trinkets)	15	10
743	–	5c. green (Church)	15	10
744	–	5c. brown (Reindeer)	15	10

1966. Air. (a) Surch with new value.

745	–	15c. on 30c. (No. 688)	10	10
746	–	15c. on 45c. (No. 690)	10	10
747	–	35c. on 75c. (No. 693)	15	10
748	–	35c. on 55c. (No. 733)	15	10
749	–	50c. on 85c. (No. 734)	25	15

(b) Revenue stamps (as T **175**) surch **CORREOS DE COSTA RICA AEREO** and value.

750	15c. on 5c. blue	10	10
751	35c. on 10c. red	15	10
752	50c. on 20c. red	25	15

221 Central Bank, San Jose

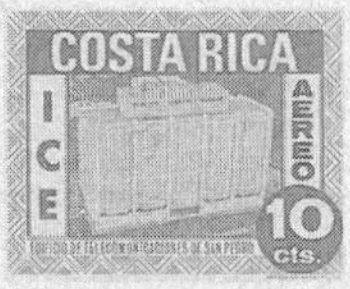
222 Telecommunications Building, San Pedro

1967. Obligatory Tax. Social Plan for Postal Workers.

753	10c. blue	10	10

DESIGN—as Type **221** (34×26 mm.): 10c. Post Office, San Jose.

1967. Air. 50th Anniv of Central Bank.

754	221	5c. green	10	10
755		15c. brown	10	10
756		35c. red	15	10

1967. Air. Costa Rican Electrical Industry.

757	–	5c. black	10	10
758	222	10c. mauve	10	10
759	–	15c. orange	10	10
760	–	25c. blue	10	10
761	–	35c. green	15	10
762	–	50c. brown	25	15

DESIGNS—VERT: 5c. Electric pylons; 15c. Central Telephone Exchange, San Jose. HORIZ: 25c. La Garita Dam; 35c. Rio Macho Reservoir; 50c. Cachi Dam.

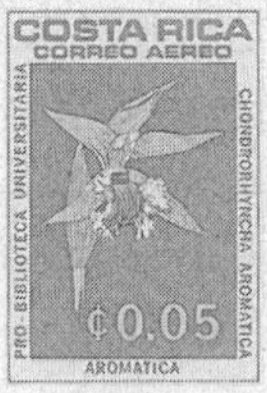
223 "Chondrorhyncha aromatica"

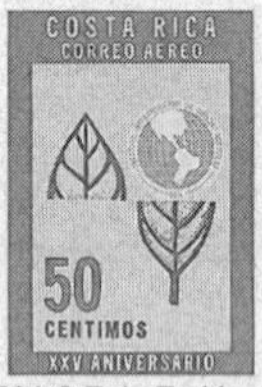
224 O.E.A. Emblem and Split Leaf

1967. Air. University Library. Orchids. Mult.

763	5c. Type **223**	10	10
764	10c. "Miltonia endresii"	10	10
765	15c. "Stanhopea cirrhata"	10	10
766	25c. "Trichopilia suavis"	15	10
767	35c. "Odontoglossum schlieperianum"	20	15
768	50c. "Cattleya skinneri"	25	15
769	1col. "Cattleya dowiana"	45	35
770	2col. "Odontoglossum chiriquense"	1·00	40

1967. Air. 25th Anniv of Inter-American Institute of Agricultural Science.

771	224	50c. ultramarine & blue	15	10

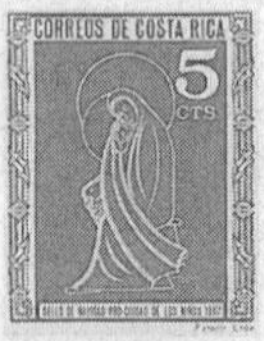
225 Madonna and Child

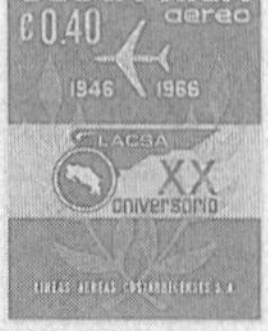
226 LACSA Emblem

1967. Obligatory Tax. Christmas.

772	225	5c. green	10	10
773		5c. mauve	10	10
774		5c. blue	10	10
775		5c. turquoise	10	10

1967. Air. 20th Anniv (1966) of LACSA (Costa Rican Airlines). Multicoloured.

776	40c. Type **226**	10	10
777	45c. LACSA emblem and jetliner (horiz)	15	10
778	50c. Wheel and emblem	15	15

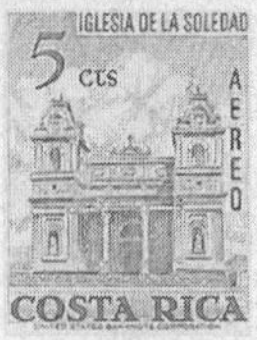
227 Church of Solitude

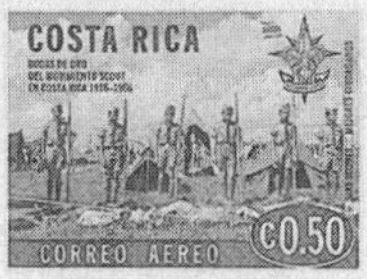
228 Scouts in Camp

1967. Air. Churches and Cathedrals (1st series).

779	227	5c. green	10	10
780	–	10c. blue	10	10
781	–	15c. purple	10	10
782	–	25c. ochre	10	10
783	–	30c. brown	10	10
784	–	35c. blue	10	10
785	–	40c. orange	10	10
786	–	45c. green	10	10
787	–	50c. olive	15	10
788	–	55c. brown	15	10
789	–	65c. mauve	15	15
790	–	75c. sepia	20	15
791	–	80c. yellow	25	20
792	–	85c. purple	1·10	20
793	–	90c. green	1·10	25
794	–	1col. slate	25	25
795	–	2col. green	75	90
796	–	3col. orange	2·10	1·25
797	–	5col. blue	2·00	1·50
798	–	10col. red	2·50	2·00

DESIGNS: 10c. Santo Domingo Basilica, Heredia; 15c. Tilaran Cathedral; 25c. Alajuela Cathedral; 30c. Church of Mercy; 35c. Our Lady of the Angels Basilica; 40c. San Rafael Church, Heredia; 45c. Ruins, Ujarras; 50c. Ruins of Parish Church, Cartago; 55c. San Jose Cathedral; 65c. Parish Church, Puntarenas; 75c. Orosi Church; 80c. Cathedral of San Isidro the General; 85c. San Ramon Church; 90c. Church of the Forsaken; 1col. Coronado Church; 2col. Church of St. Teresita; 3col. Parish Church, Heredia; 5col. Carmelite Church; 10col. Limon Cathedral.

See also Nos. 918/33.

1968. Air. Golden Jubilee (1966) of Scout Movement in Costa Rica. Multicoloured.

799	15c. Scout on traffic control	10	10
800	25c. Scouts tending campfire	15	10
801	35c. Scout badge and flags	20	15
802	50c. Type **228**	25	15
803	65c. First scout troop on parade (1916)	35	20

The 15c., 25c. and 35c. are vert designs.

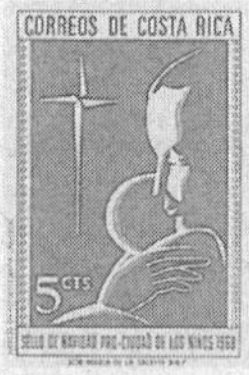
229 "Madonna and Child"

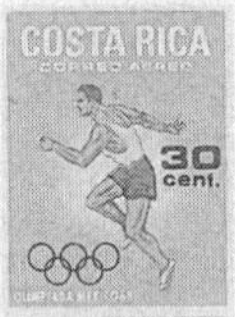
230 Running

1968. Christmas Charity. Obligatory Tax.

805	229	5c. black	10	10
806		5c. purple	10	10
807		5c. brown	10	10
808		5c. red	10	10

1969. Air. Olympic Games, Mexico. Mult.

809	30c. Type **230**	10	10
810	40c. Woman breasting tape	15	10
811	55c. Boxing	25	15
812	65c. Cycling	30	15
813	75c. Weightlifting	30	15
814	1col. High-diving	35	25
815	3col. Rifle-shooting	90	55

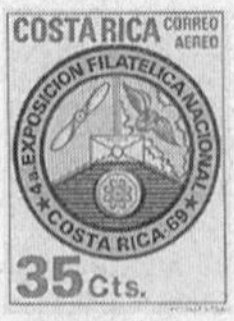
231 Exhibition Emblem

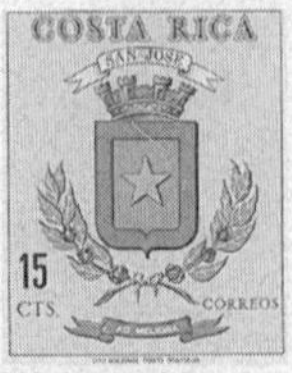
232 Arms of San Jose

1969. Air. "Costa Rica 69" Philatelic Exn.

816	231	35c. multicoloured	10	10
817		40c. multicoloured	15	10
818		50c. multicoloured	15	10
819		2col. multicoloured	1·10	40

1969. Coats of Arms. Multicoloured.

820	15c. Type **232**	10	10
821	35c. Cartago	10	10
822	50c. Heredia	15	10
823	55c. Alajuela	15	15
824	65c. Guanacaste	25	15
825	1col. Puntarenas	60	15
826	2col. Limon	70	35

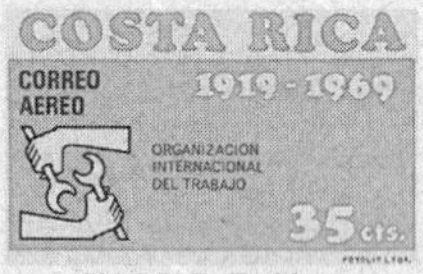
233 I.L.O. Emblem

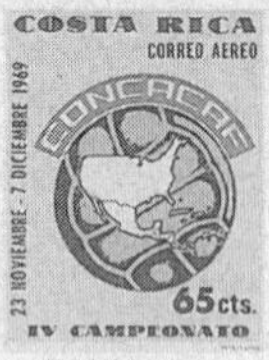
234 Map on Football

1969. Air. 50th Anniv of I.L.O.

827	233	35c. turquoise and black	15	10
828		50c. red and black	20	10

1969. Air. 4th CONCACAF Football Championships. Multicoloured.

829	65c. Type **234**	20	15
830	75c. Goalmouth melee	20	15
831	85c. Players with ball	25	15
832	1col. Two players with ball	30	20

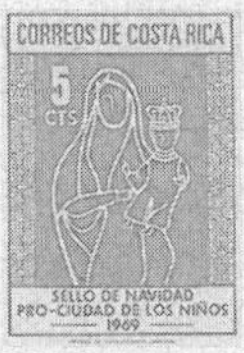
235 Madonna and Child

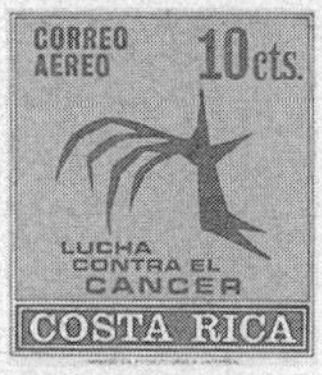
236 Stylized Crab

1969. Christmas. Charity. Obligatory Tax.

833	235	5c. turquoise	10	10
834		5c. lake	10	10
835		5c. blue	10	10
836		5c. orange	10	10

1970. Air. 10th Inter-American Cancer Congress, San Jose.

837	236	10c. black and mauve	10	10
838		15c. black and yellow	10	10
839		50c. black and orange	15	10
840		1col.10 black and green	30	15

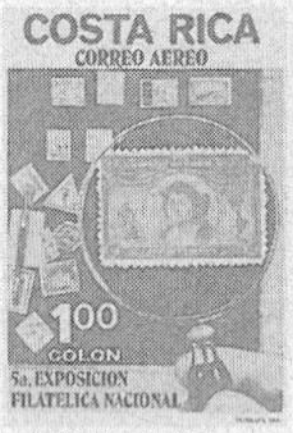
238 Costa Rican stamps and Magnifier

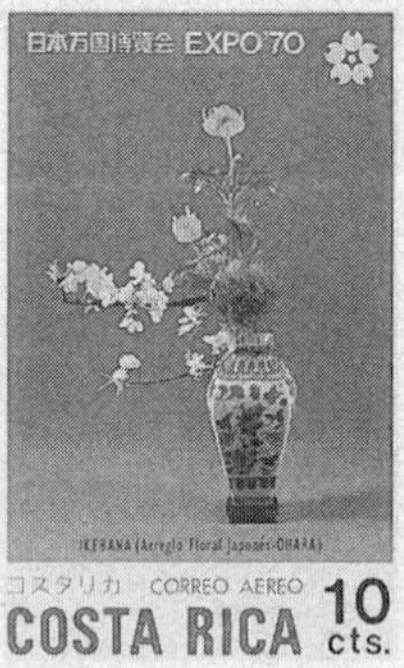
239 Japanese Vase and Flowers

1970. Air. "Costa Rica 70" Philatelic Exhibition.

843	238	1col. red and blue	55	20
844		2col. mauve and blue	1·10	45

1970. Air. Expo 70. Multicoloured.

845	10c. Type **239**	10	10
846	15c. Ornamental cart (horiz)	10	10
847	35c. Sun tower (horiz)	15	10
848	40c. Tea-ceremony (horiz)	15	10
849	45c. Coffee-picking	15	10
850	55c. View of Earth from Moon	15	10

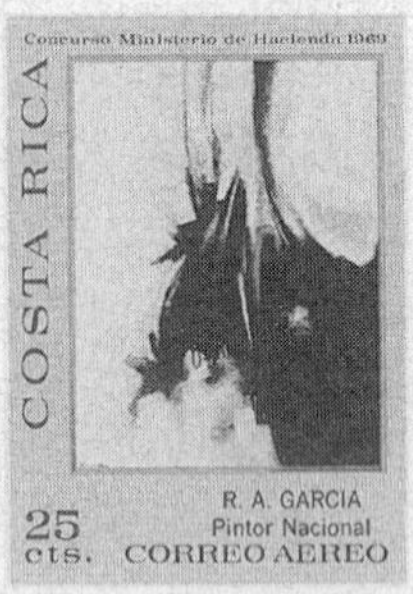
240 "Irazu" (R. A. Garcia)

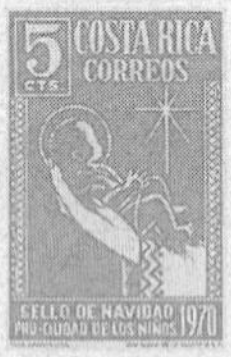
241 "Holy Child"

1970. Air. Costa Rican Paintings. Mult.

851	25c. Type **240**	30	10
852	45c. "Escazu Valley" (M. Bertheau)	30	10
853	80c. "Estuary Landscape" (T. Quiros)	65	15
854	1col. "The Other Face" (C. Valverde)	45	15
855	2col.50 "Madonna" (L. Daell) (vert)	1·25	60

1970. Christmas Charity. Obligatory Tax.

856	241	5c. mauve	10	10
857		5c. brown	10	10
858		5c. olive	10	10
859		5c. violet	10	10

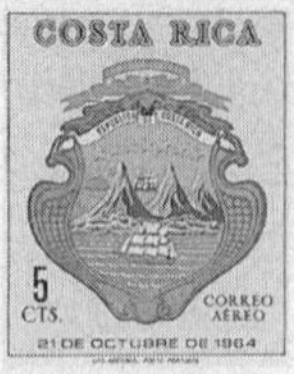
242 Costa Rican Arms of 21 October 1964

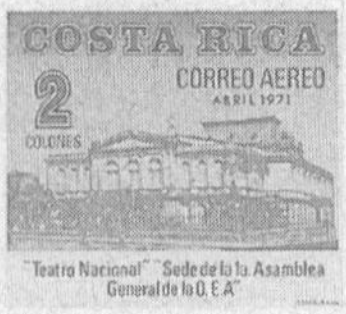
243 National Theatre, San Jose

1971. Air. Various Costa Rican Coats of Arms (with dates). Multicoloured.

860	5c. Type **242**	10	10
861	10c. 27 November 1906	10	10
862	15c. 29 September 1848	10	10
863	25c. 21 April 1840	10	10
864	35c. 22 November 1824	10	10
865	50c. 2 November 1824	10	10
866	1col. 6 March 1824	15	10
867	2col. 10 May 1823	60	20

1971. Air. O.E.A. General Assembly. San Jose.

868	243	2col. purple	35	25

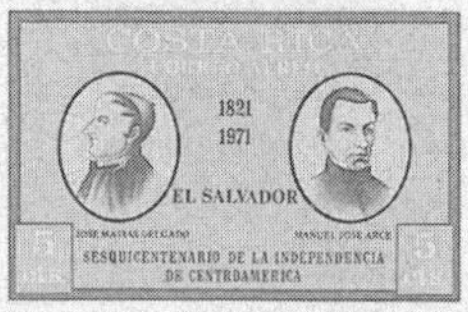
244 J. M. Delgado and M. J. Arce (Salvador)

1971. Air. 150th Anniv of Central American Independence. Multicoloured.

869	5c. Type **244**	10	10
870	10c. M. Larreinaga and M. A. de la Cerda (Nicaragua)	10	10
871	15c. J. C. del Valle and D. de Herrera (Honduras)	10	10
872	35c. P. Alvarado and F. del Castillo (Costa Rica)	10	10
873	50c. A. Larrazabal and P. Molina (Guatemala)	10	10
874	1col. O.D.E.C.A. flag (vert)	15	10
875	2col. O.D.E.C.A. emblem (vert)	35	25

O.D.E.C.A. = Organization of Central American States.

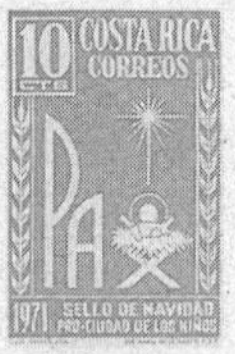
245 Cradle on "PAX"

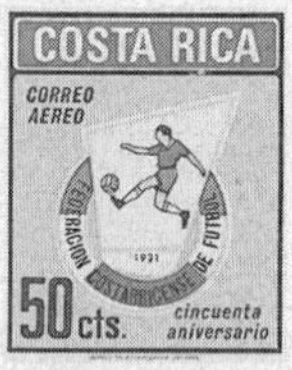
246 Federation Emblem

1971. Christmas Charity. Obligatory Tax.

876	245	10c. orange	10	10
877		10c. brown	10	10
878		10c. green	10	10
879		10c. blue	10	10

1971. Air. 50th Anniv of Costa Rican Football Federation.

880	246	50c. multicoloured	10	10
881		60c. multicoloured	10	10

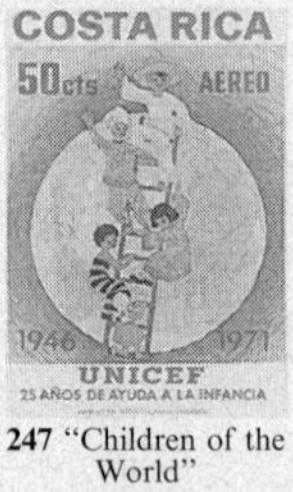
247 "Children of the World"

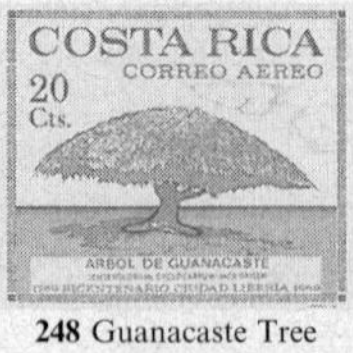
248 Guanacaste Tree

1972. Air. 25th Anniv of U.N.I.C.E.F.

882	247	50c. multicoloured	10	10
883		1col.10 multicoloured	20	15

1972. Air. Bicentenary of Liberia City. Mult.

884	20c. Type **248**	10	10
885	40c. Hermitage, Liberia	10	10
886	55c. Mayan petroglyphs	10	10
887	60c. Clay head (vert)	15	10

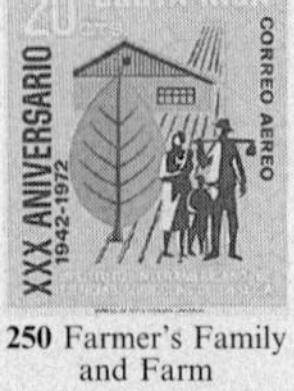
250 Farmer's Family and Farm

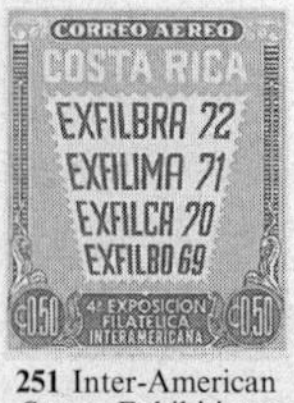

251 Inter-American Stamp Exhibitions

1972. Air. 30th Anniv of O.E.A. Institute of Agricultural Sciences (IICA).

892	**250**	20c. multicoloured	10	10
893	–	45c. multicoloured	10	10
894	–	50c. yellow, green & blk	10	10
895	–	10col. multicoloured	1·10	60

DESIGNS—HORIZ: 45c. Cattle. VERT: 50c. Tree-planting; 10col. Agricultural worker and map.

1972. Air. "Exfilbra 72" Stamp Exhibition.

896	**251**	50c. brown and orange	10	10
897		2col. violet and blue	35	25

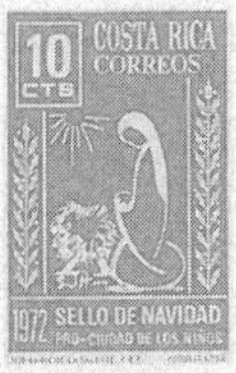

252 Madonna and Child

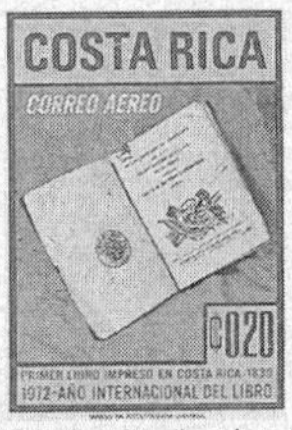

253 First Book printed in Costa Rica

1972. Christmas Charity. Obligatory Tax.

898	**252**	10c. red	10	10
899		10c. lilac	10	10
900		10c. blue	10	10
901		10c. green	10	10

1972. Air. International Book Year. Mult.

902		20c. Type **253**	10	10
903		50c. National Library, San Jose (horiz)	10	10
904		75c. Type **253**	15	10
905		5col. As 50c.	60	45

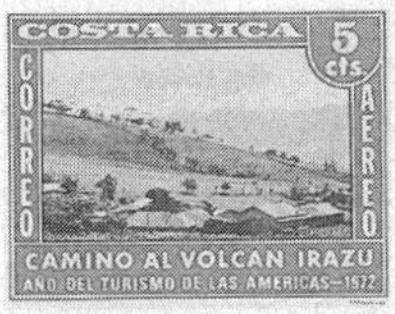

254 View near Irazu

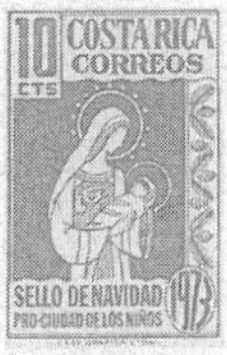

255 Madonna and Child

1972. Air. American Tourist Year. Mult.

906		5c. Type **254**	10	10
907		15c. Entrance to Culebra Bay	10	10
908		20c. Type **254**	10	10
909		25c. As 15c.	10	10
910		40c. Manuel Antonio Beach	10	10
911		45c. Costa Rican Tourist Institute emblem	10	10
912		50c. Lindora Lake	10	10
913		60c. Post Office Building, San Jose (vert)	15	10
914		80c. As 40c.	15	15
915		90c. As 45c.	15	15
916		1col. As 50c.	15	15
917		2col. As 60c.	35	25

1973. Air. Churches and Cathedrals (2nd series). As Nos. 779/94 but colours changed.

918	**227**	5c. grey	10	10
919	–	10c. green	10	10
920	–	15c. orange	10	10
921	–	25c. brown	10	10
922	–	30c. purple	10	10
923	–	35c. violet	15	10
924	–	40c. green	15	10
925	–	45c. brown	15	10
926	–	50c. red	10	10
927	–	55c. blue	10	10
928	–	65c. black	15	10
929	–	75c. red	15	10
930	–	80c. green	15	10
931	–	85c. lilac	15	15
932	–	90c. red	15	15
933	–	1col. blue	15	15

1973. Obligatory Tax. Christmas Charity.

934	**255**	10c. red	10	10
935		10c. purple	10	10
936		10c. black	10	10
937		10c. brown	10	10

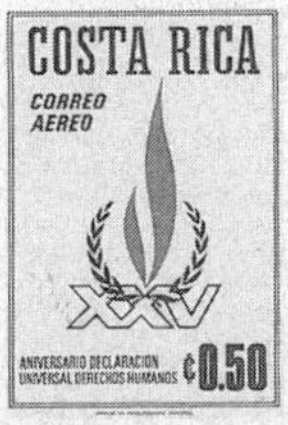

256 Flame Emblem

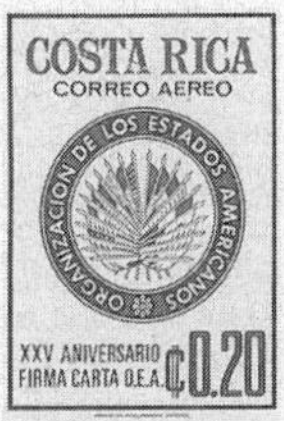

257 O.E.A. Emblem

1973. Air. 25th Anniv of Declaration of Human Rights.

938	**256**	50c. red and blue	10	10

1973. Air. 25th Anniv of Organization of American States.

939	**257**	20c. red and blue	10	10

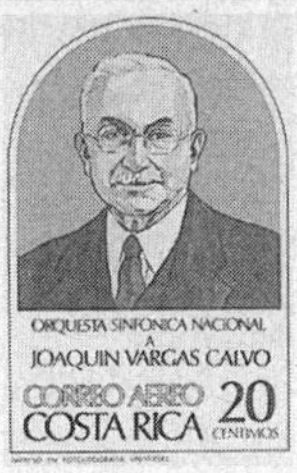

258 J. Vargas Calvo

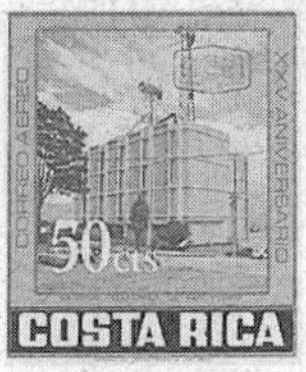

260 Telephone Centre, San Pedro

1974. Air. Costa Rican Composers. Mult.

940		20c. Type **258**	10	10
941		20c. Alejandro Monestel	10	10
942		20c. Julio Mata	10	10
943		60c. Julio Fonseca	15	10
944		2col. Rafael Chaves	35	25
945		5col. Manuel Gutierrez	85	70

1974. Air. Fiscal stamps as Type **175** (but without surcharge) optd **HABILITADO PARA CORREO AEREO**.

946		50c. brown	10	10
947		1col. violet	15	10
948		2col. orange	35	20
949		5col. green	85	70

1974. Air. 25th Anniv of Costa Rican Electrical Institute. Multicoloured.

950		50c. Type **260**	10	10
951		65c. Control Room, Rio Macho (horiz)	15	10
952		85c. Power house, Rio Macho	15	15
953		1col.25 Cachi Dam, Rio Macho (horiz)	20	15
954		2col. Institute H.Q. building	35	20

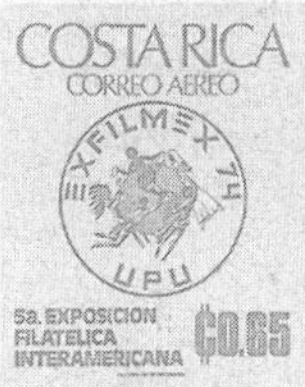

261 "Exfilmex" Emblem

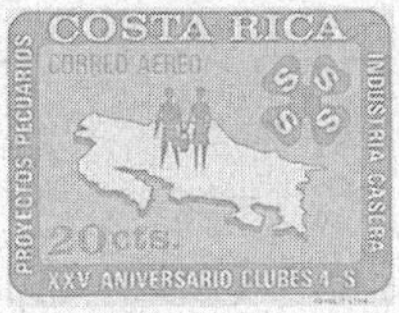

262 Couple on Map

1974. Air. "Exfilmex" Stamp Exhibition, Mexico City.

955	**261**	65c. green	15	10
956		3col. pink	50	35

1974. Air. 25th Anniv of 4-S Clubs.

957	**262**	20c. emerald and green	10	10
958	–	50c. multicoloured	10	10

DESIGN. 50c. Young agricultural workers.

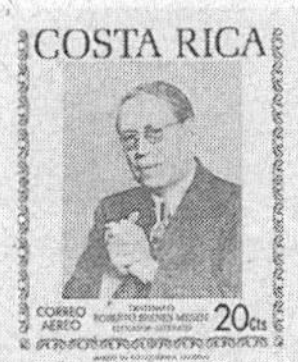

263 Brenes Mesen

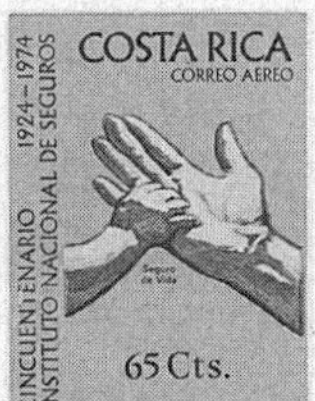

264 Child's and Adult's Hands

1974. Air. Birth Centenary of Roberto Brenes Mesen (educator).

959	**263**	20c. black and brown	10	10
960	–	85c. black and red	15	15
961	–	5col. brown and black	85	70

DESIGNS—VERT: 85c. Brenes Mesen's "Poems of Love and Death". HORIZ: 5col. Brenes Mesen's hands.

1974. Air. 50th Anniv of Costa Rican Insurance Institute.

962	–	20c. multicoloured	10	10
963	–	50c. multicoloured	10	10
964	**264**	65c. multicoloured	10	15
965	–	85c. multicoloured	15	15
966	–	1col.25 black and gold	20	15
967	–	2col. multicoloured	35	20
968	–	2col.50 multicoloured	45	35
969	–	20col. multicoloured	2·50	2·40

DESIGNS—HORIZ: 20c. R. Jimenez Oreamuno and T. Soley Guell (founders); 50c. Spade ("Harvest Insurance"). VERT: 85c. Paper boat within hand ("Marine Insurance"); 1col.25, Institute emblem; 2col. Arm in brace ("Workers' Rehabilitation"); 2col.50, Hand holding spanner ("Risks at Work"); 20col. House in protective hands ("Fire Insurance").

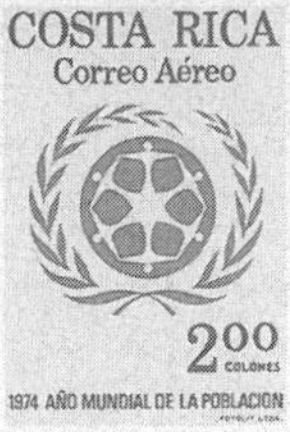

265 W.P.Y. Emblem

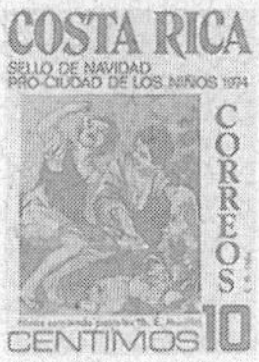

266 "Boys eating Cakes" (Murillo)

1974. Air. World Population Year.

970	**265**	2col. red and blue	35	20

1974. Obligatory Tax. Christmas.

971	**266**	10c. red	10	10
972	–	10c. purple	10	10
973	–	10c. black	10	10
974	–	10c. blue	10	10

DESIGNS: No. 972, "The Beautiful Gardener" (Raphael); No. 973, "Maternity" (J. R. Bonilla); No. 974, "The Prayer" (J. Reynolds).

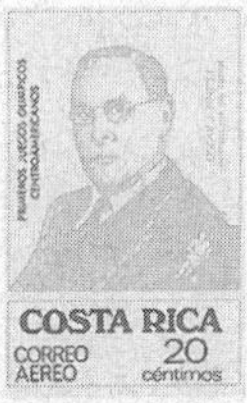

267 Oscar J. Pinto (football pioneer)

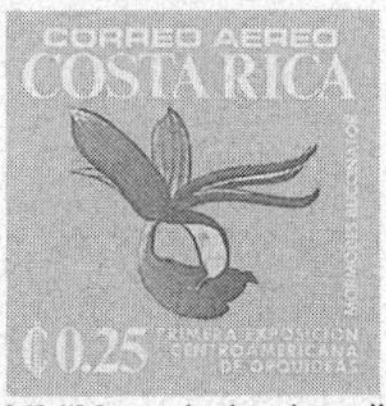

268 "Mormodes buccinator"

1974. Air. 1st Central American Olympic Games, Guatemala (1973). Each grey and blue.

975		20c. Type **267**	10	10
976		50c. D. A. Montes de Oca (shooting champion)	10	10
977		1col. Eduardo Garnier (promoter of athletics)	15	10

1975. Air. 1st Central American Orchids Exhibition. Multicoloured.

978		25c. Type **268**	10	10
979		25c. "Gongora claviodora"	10	10
980		25c. "Masdevallia ephippium"	10	10
981		25c. "Encyclia spondiadum"	10	10
982		65c. "Lycaste skinneri alba"	40	10
983		65c. "Peristeria elata"	40	10
984		65c. "Miltonia roezelii"	40	10
985		65c. "Brassavola digbyana"	40	10
986		80c. "Epidendrum mirabile"	50	15
987		80c. "Barkeria lindleyana"	50	15
988		80c. "Cattleya skinneri"	50	15
989		80c. "Sobralia macrantha splendens"	50	15
990		1col.40 "Lycaste cruenta"	65	15
991		1col.40 "Oncidium obryzatum"	65	15
992		1col.40 "Gongora armeniaca"	65	15
993		1col.40 "Sievekingia suavis"	65	15
994		1col.75 "Hexisea imbricata"	65	20
995		2col.15 "Warcewiczella discolor"	65	20
996		2col.50 "Oncidium kramerianum"	90	35
997		3col.25 "Cattleya dowiana"	1·25	40

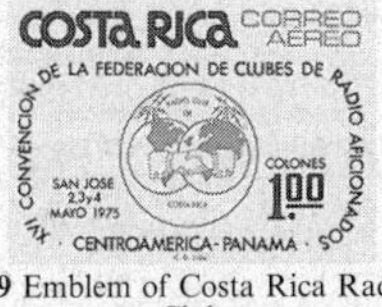

269 Emblem of Costa Rica Radio Club

1975. Air. 16th Convention of Radio Amateurs Federation of Central America and Panama, San Jose.

998	**269**	1col. purple and black	15	10
999	–	1col.10 red and blue	20	15
1000	–	2col. blue and black	35	20

DESIGNS—VERT: 1col.10, Federation emblem within "V" of Flags. HORIZ: 2col. Federation emblem.

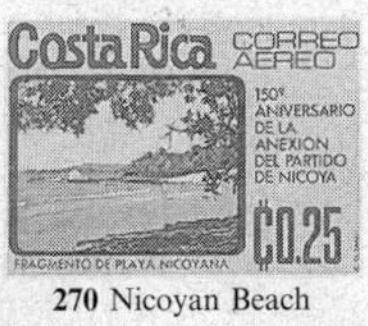

270 Nicoyan Beach

1975. Air. 150th Anniv of Annexation of Nicoya. Multicoloured.

1001		25c. Type **270**	10	10
1002		75c. Cattle-drive	15	15
1003		1col. Colonial church	15	15
1004		3col. Savannah riders (vert)	50	40

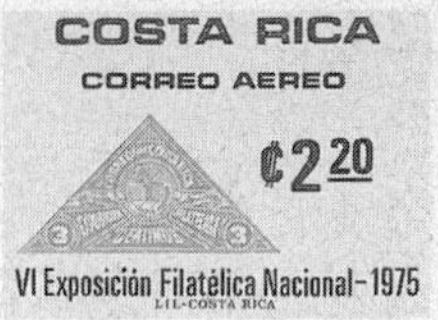

271 3c. Philatelic Exhibition Stamp of 1932

1975. Air. 6th National Philatelic Exhibition, San Jose.

1005	**271**	2col.20 orange & black	40	35
1006	–	2col.20 green and black	40	35
1007	–	2col.20 red and black	40	35
1008	–	2col.20 blue and black	40	35

DESIGNS: Stamps of 1932. No. 1006, 5c. stamp; No. 1007, 10c. stamp; No. 1008, 20c. stamp.

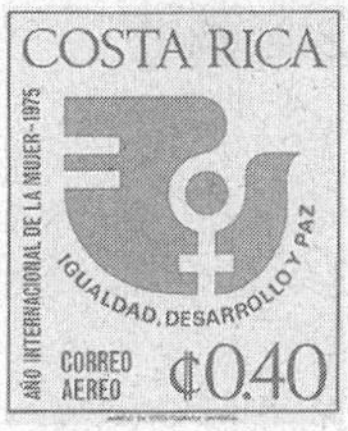

272 I.W.Y. Emblem

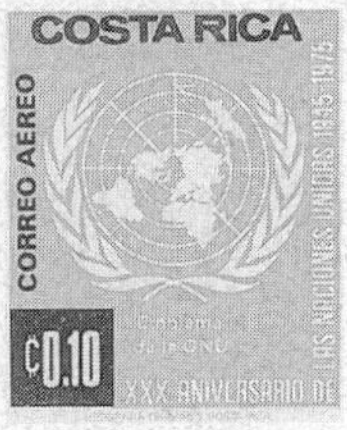

273 U.N. Emblem

1975. Air. International Women's Year.

1009	**272**	40c. red and blue	10	10
1010		1col.25 blue and black	20	15

1975. Air. 30th Anniv of United Nations.

1011	**273**	10c. blue and black	10	10
1012	–	60c. multicoloured	10	10
1013	–	1col.20 multicoloured	20	15

DESIGNS—HORIZ: 60c. General Assembly. VERT: 1col.20, U.N. Headquarters, New York.

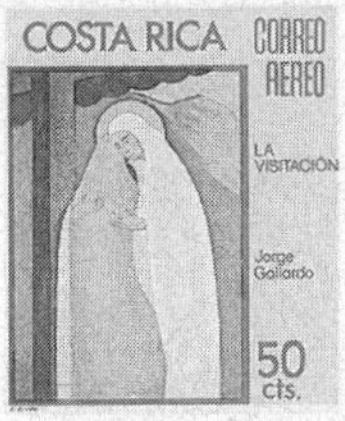

274 "The Visitation"

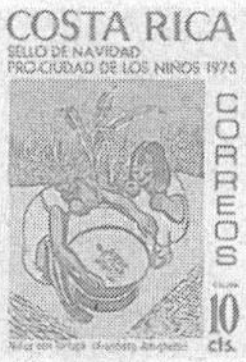

275 "Children with Tortoise" (F. Amighetti)

1975. Air. "The Christmas Tradition". Paintings by Jorge Gallardo. Multicoloured.

1014		50c. Type **274**	10	10
1015		1col. "The Nativity and the Comet"	15	10
1016		5col. "St. Joseph in his workshop"	60	45

1975. Obligatory Tax. Christmas. Children's Village. Multicoloured.

1017	**275**	10c. brown	10	10
1018	–	10c. purple	10	10
1019	–	10c. grey	10	10
1020	–	10c. blue	10	10

DESIGNS: No. 1018, "The Virgin of the Carnation" (Da Vinci); No. 1019, "Happy Dreams" (child in bed—Sonia Romero); No. 1020, "Child with Pigeon" (Picasso).

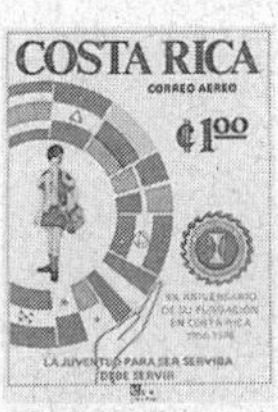

276 Schoolboy and Flags

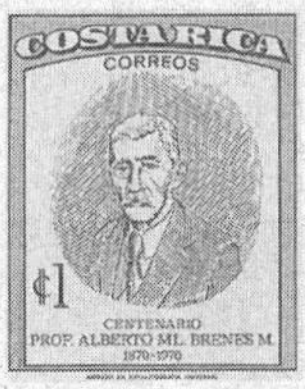

277 Prof. A. M. Brenes Mora

1976. Air. 20th Anniv of "20–30" Youth Clubs in Costa Rica.

1021	**276**	1col. multicoloured	15	10

1976. Birth Centenary (1970) of Professor A. M. Brenes Mora (botanist).

1022	**277**	1col. violet (postage)	15	15
1023	–	5c. multicoloured (air)	10	10
1024	–	30c. multicoloured	10	10
1025	–	55c. multicoloured	10	10
1026	–	2col. multicoloured	35	20
1027	–	10col. multicoloured	1·10	85

DESIGNS: 5c. "Quercus brenesii"; 30c. "Maxillaria albertii"; 55c. "Calathea brenesii"; 2col. "Brenesia costaricensis"; 10col. "Philodendron brenesii".

No. 1023 is wrongly inscribed "brenessi".

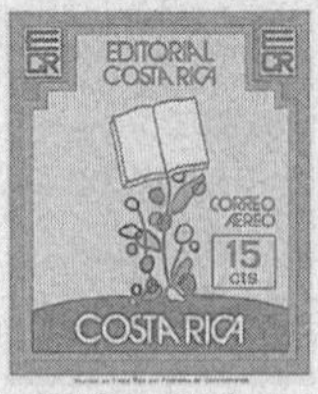

278 Open Book as "Flower"

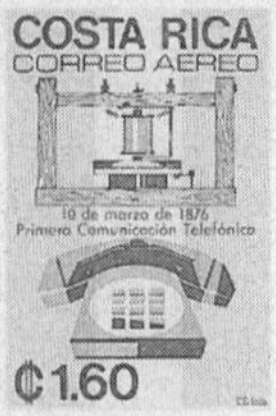

281 Early and Modern Telephones

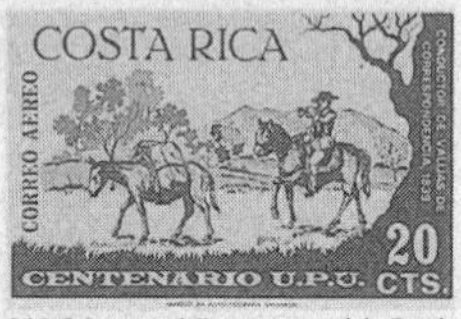

280 Mounted Postman with Pack Mule

1976. Air. Costa Rican Literature. Mult.

1028	15c. Type **278**	10	10
1029	1col.10 Reader with "T.V. eye"	15	15
1030	5col. Book and flag (horiz)	55	45

1976. Centenary (1974) of U.P.U.

1032	**280** 20c. black and yellow	10	10
1033	– 50c. multicoloured	10	10
1034	– 65c. multicoloured	15	10
1035	– 85c. multicoloured	15	15
1036	– 2col. black and blue	35	25

DESIGNS—HORIZ: 50c., 5c. U.P.U. stamp of 1882; 65c., 10c. U.P.U. stamp of 1882; 85c., 20c. U.P.U. stamp of 1882. VERT: 2col. U.P.U. Monument, Berne.

1976. Telephone Centenary.

1037	**281** 1col.60 black and blue	25	20
1038	– 2col. black, brown & grn	35	20
1039	– 5col. black and yellow	55	45

DESIGNS: 2col. Costa Rica's first telephone; 5col. Alexander Graham Bell.

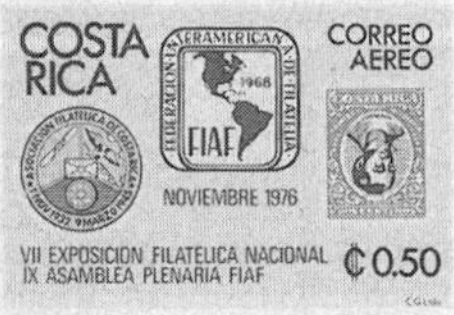

282 Emblems and Costa Rica 2c. Stamp of 1901 with Centre Inverted

1976. Air. 7th National Philatelic Exhibition.

1040	**282** 50c. multicoloured	10	10
1041	1col. multicoloured	15	10
1042	2col. multicoloured	35	20

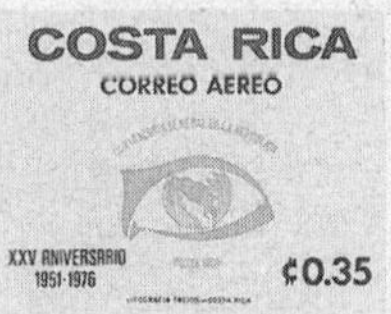

283 Emblem of Comptroller General

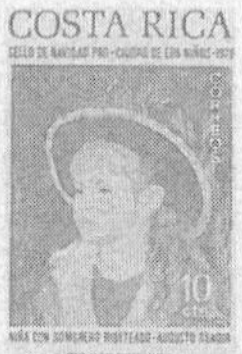

284 "Girl in Wide-brimmed Hat" (Renoir)

1976. Air. 25th Anniv of Comptroller General.

1044	**283** 35c. blue and black	10	10
1045	– 2col. black, brown & bl	35	20

DESIGN—VERT: 2col. Amadeo Quiros Blanco (1st Comptroller).

1976. Obligatory Tax. Christmas.

1046	**284** 10c. lake	10	10
1047	– 10c. purple	10	10
1048	– 10c. slate	10	10
1049	– 10c. blue	10	10

DESIGNS: No 1047, "Virgin and Child" (Hans Memling); No. 1048, "Meditation" (Floria Pinto de Herrero); No. 1049, "Gaston de Mezerville" (Lolita Zeller de Peralta).

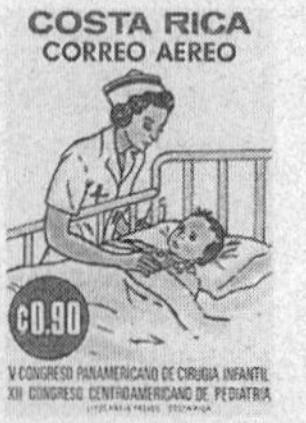

285 Nurse tending Child

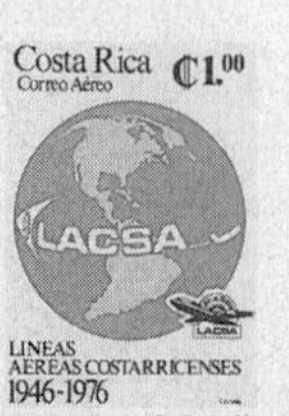

286 "L.A.C.S.A." encircling Globe

1976. Air. 5th Pan-American Children's Surgery Congress. Multicoloured.

1050	90c. Type **285**	15	15
1051	1col.10 National Children's Hospital (horiz)	20	15

1976. Air. 30th Anniv of LACSA Airline. Mult.

1052	1col. Type **286**	20	10
1053	1col.20 Route-map of LACSA services	25	15
1054	3col. LACSA emblem and Costa Rican flag	65	45

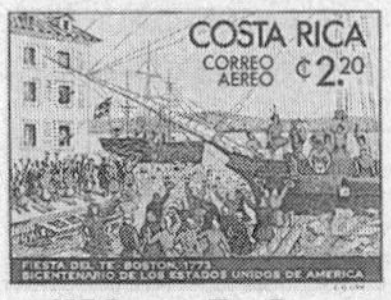

287 Boston Tea Party

1976. Air. Bicent of American Revolution. Mult.

1055	2col.20 Type **287**	70	25
1056	5col. Declaration of Independence	55	45
1057	10col. Ringing the Independence Bell (vert)	1·10	85

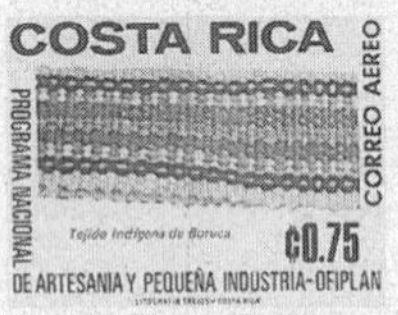

288 Boruca Textile

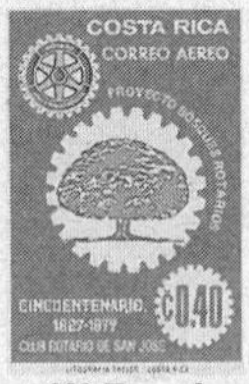

289 Tree of Guanacaste

1977. Air. National Handicrafts Project. Mult.

1058	75c. Type **288**	15	10
1059	1col.50 Decorative handicraft in wood	25	15

1977. Air. 50th Anniv of Rotary Club, San Jose.

1060	**289** 40c. green, blue and yellow	10	10
1061	– 50c. black, blue and yellow	10	10
1062	– 60c. black, blue and yellow	10	10
1063	– 3col. multicoloured	50	40
1064	– 10col. black, blue and yellow	1·25	85

DESIGNS—VERT: 50c. Felipe J. Alvarado (founder); 10col. Paul Harris, founder of Rotary International. HORIZ: 60c. Dr. Blanco Cervantes Hospital; 3col. Map of Costa Rica.

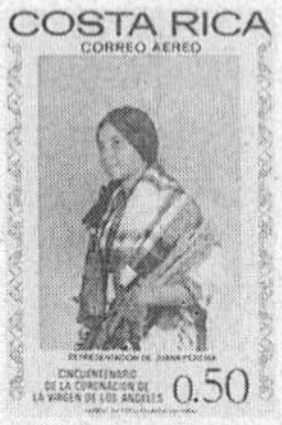

290 Juana Pereira

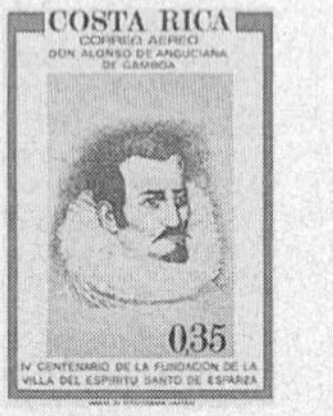

291 Alonso de Anguciana de Gamboa

1977. Air. 50th Anniv of Coronation of Our Lady of the Angels (Patron Saint of Costa Rica).

1065	50c. Type **290**	10	10
1066	1col. First church of Our Lady of the Angels (horiz)	15	10
1067	1col.10 Our Lady of the Angels	20	15
1068	1col.25 Our Lady's crown	25	15

1977. Air. 400th Anniv of Foundation of Esparza.

1069	**291** 35c. purple, mve & blk	10	10
1070	– 75c. brown, red & black	15	10
1071	– 1col. dp bl, bl & blk	15	10
1072	– 2col. green and black	35	25

DESIGNS: 75c. Church of Esparza; 1col. Our Lady of Candelaria, Patron Saint of Esparza; 2col. Diego de Artieda y Chirino.

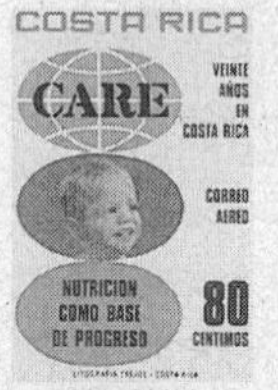

292 Child

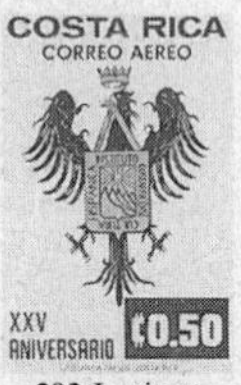

293 Institute Emblem

1977. Air. 20 Years of "CARE" in Costa Rica. Multicoloured.

1073	80c. Type **292**	15	10
1074	1col. Soya beans (horiz)	15	10

1977. Air. 25th Anniv of Hispanic Cultural Institute of Costa Rica. Multicoloured.

1075	50c. Type **293**	10	10
1076	1col.40 First map of the Americas, 1540 (40 × 30 mm)	25	20

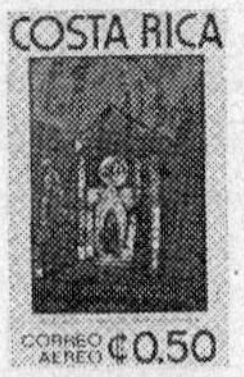

294 "Our Lady of Mercy Church" (R. Ulloa)

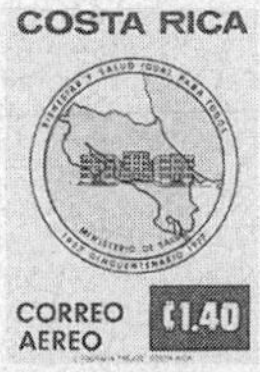

295 Health Ministry on Map

1977. Air. Mystical Paintings. Multicoloured.

1077	50c. Type **294**	10	10
1078	1col. "Christ" (F. Pinto de Herrero)	15	10
1079	5col. "St. Francis and the Birds" (L. Gonzalez de Saenz)	55	45

1977. Air. 50th Anniv of Health Ministry.

1080	**295** 1col.40 multicoloured	25	20

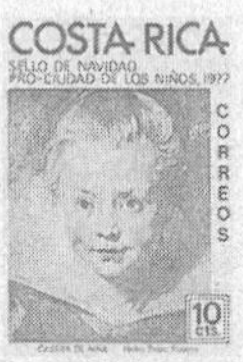

296 "Child's Head" (Rubens)

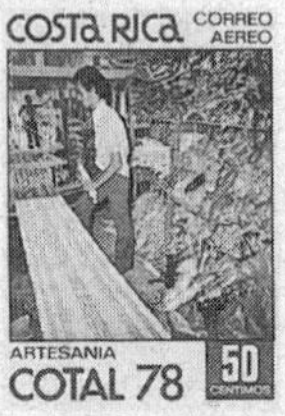

297 Weaving

1977. Obligatory Tax. Christmas.

1081	**296** 10c. red	10	10
1082	– 10c. blue	10	10
1083	– 10c. green	10	10
1084	– 10c. purple	10	10

DESIGNS: No. 1082, "Tenderness" (Cristina Fournier); No. 1083, "Abstraction" (Amparo Cruz); No. 1084, "Mariano Goya" (Francisco de Goya).

1978. Air. 21st Congress of Confederation of Latin American Tourist Organizations. Multicoloured.

1085	50c. Type **297**	10	10
1086	1col. Picnic	15	15
1087	2col. Beach scene	35	20
1088	5col. Fruit market	55	45
1089	10col. Lake scene	1·25	85

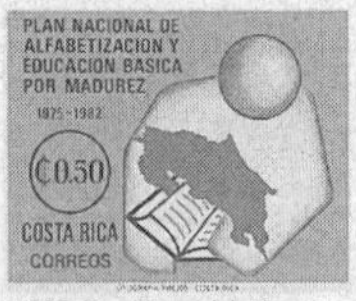

298 Reader with Book

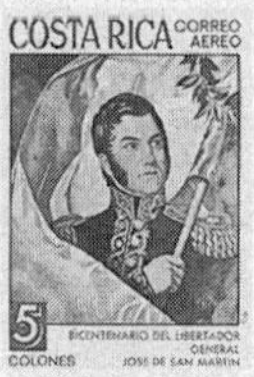

299 Jose de San Martin

1978. National Literacy Campaign.

1090	**298** 50c. blue, black & orge	10	10

1978. Air. Birth Bicent of Jose de San Martin.

1091	**299** 5col. multicoloured	60	40

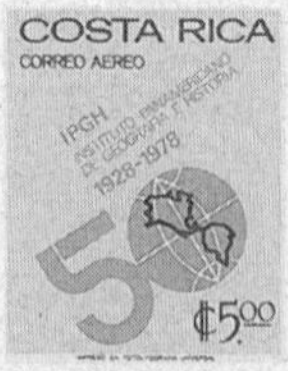

300 Globe

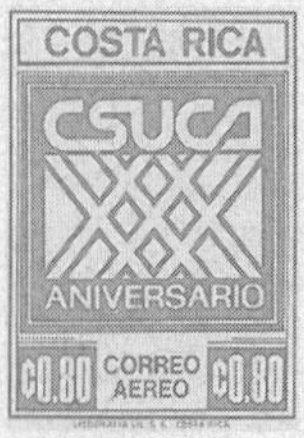

301 "XXX"

1978. Air. 50th Anniv of Pan-American Institute of Geography and History.

1092	**300** 5col. blue, gold & lt blue	50	60

1978. Air. 30th Anniv of Central American University Confederation.

1093	**301** 80c. blue	15	10

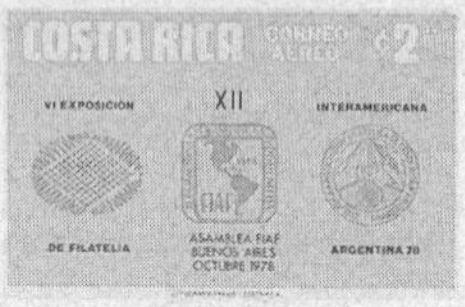

302 Emblems

1978. Air. 6th Inter-American Philatelic Exn, Buenos Aires.

1094	**302** 2col. turq, gold & blk	35	25

1978. Air. 50th Anniv of 1st PanAm Flight in Costa Rica. Nos. 994/6 optd **"50 Aniversario del primer vuelo de PAN AM en Costa Rica 1928 – 1978"**.

1095	1col.75 "Hexisea imbricata"	25	20
1096	2col.15 "Warcewiczella discolor"	35	25
1097	2col.50 "Oncidium kramerianum"	40	30

1978. Air. 50th Anniv of Lindbergh's Visit to Costa Rica. Nos. 994/6 optd **"50 Aniversario de la visita de Lindbergh a Costa Rica 1928 – 1978"**.

1098	1col.75 "Hexisea imbricata"	30	20
1099	2col.15 "Warcewiczella discolor"	35	25
1100	2col.50 "Oncidium kramerianum"	40	30

1978. Air. Carlos Maria Ulloa Hospital Centenary. Nos. 964 and 968 surch **"Centenario del Asilo Carlos Maria Ulloa 1878 – 1978"** and new value.

1101	50c. on 65c. multicoloured	10	10
1102	2col. on 2col.50 mult	35	25

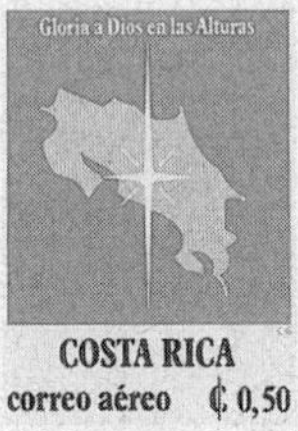

306 Star over Map of Costa Rica

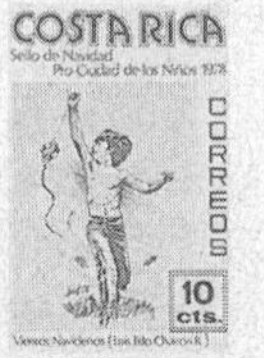

308 "Christmas Winds" (L. F. Chacon)

1978. Air. Christmas.

1103	**306** 50c. blue and black	10	10
1104	1col. mauve and black	15	15
1105	5col. red and black	55	55

1978. Air. Nos. 982/5 and 995/6 surch.

1106	50c. on 65c. "Lycaste skinneri alba"	10	10
1107	50c. on 65c. "Peristeria elata"	10	10
1108	50c. on 65c. "Miltonia roezelii"	10	10
1109	50c. on 65c. "Brassavola digbyana"	10	10
1110	1col.20 on 2col.15 "Warcewiczella discolor"	20	15
1111	2col. on 2col.50 "Oncidium kramerianum"	35	25

1978. Obligatory Tax. Christmas. Children's Village.

1112	**308** 10c. slate	10	10
1113	10c. red	10	10
1114	– 10c. mauve	10	10
1115	– 10c. blue	10	10

DESIGN: Nos. 1114/15, "Girl playing with Kite" (sculpture by Nester Zeledon).

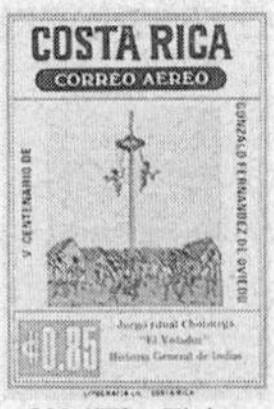

309 "The Flying Men", Chorotega Ritual

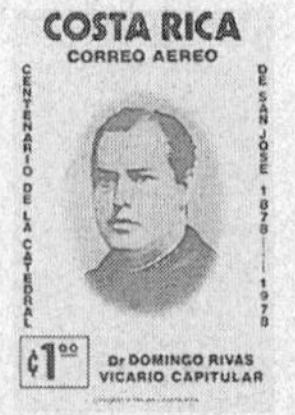

310 Domingo Rivas

1978. Air. 500th Anniv of Gonzalo Fernandez de Oviedo (first chronicler of Spanish Indies).

1116	**309** 85c. multicoloured	15	10
1117	– 1col.20 blue and black	20	15
1118	– 10col. multicoloured	1·25	75

DESIGNS—HORIZ: 1col.20, Oviedo giving his "History of Indies" to Duke of Calabria. VERT: 10col. Lord of Oviedo's coat of arms.

1978. Air. Centenary of San Jose Cathedral.

1119	**310** 1col. blue and black	15	15
1120	– 20col. multicoloured	2·10	2·00

DESIGN: 20c. San Jose Cathedral.

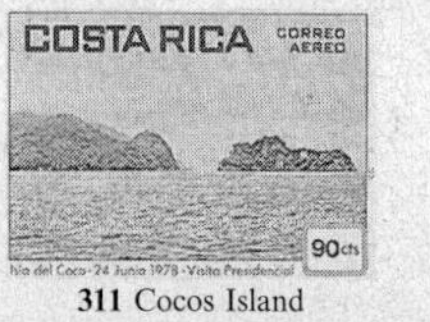

311 Cocos Island

1979. Air. Presidential Visit to Cocos Island. Mult.

1121	90c. Type **311**	15	10
1122	2col.10 Cocos Island (different)	35	25
1123	3col. Cocos Island (different)	50	35
1124	5col. Moon over Cocos Island (vert)	55	60
1125	10col. Commemorative plaque and people with flag (vert)	1·00	75

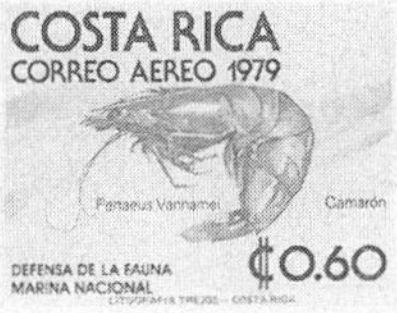

312 Shrimp

1979. Air. Conservation of Marine Fauna. Multicoloured.

1127	60c. Type **312**	10	10
1128	85c. Mahogany snapper	15	10
1129	1col.80 Yellow corvina	40	20
1130	3col. Lobster	50	35
1131	10col. Frigate mackerel	1·50	75

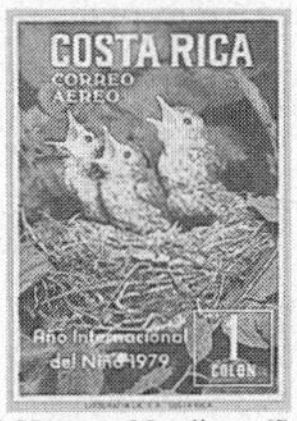

313 Hungry Nestlings (Song Thrushes)

1979. Air. International Year of the Child.

1132 **313**	1col. multicoloured	75	45
1133	2col. multicoloured	2·10	90
1134	20col. multicoloured	10·50	4·75

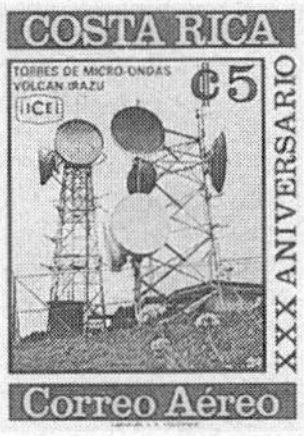

315 Microwave Transmitters

1979. Air. 30th Anniv of Costa Rican Electricity Institute. Multicoloured.

1136	1col. Arenal Dam	20	15
1137	5col. Type **315**	60	65

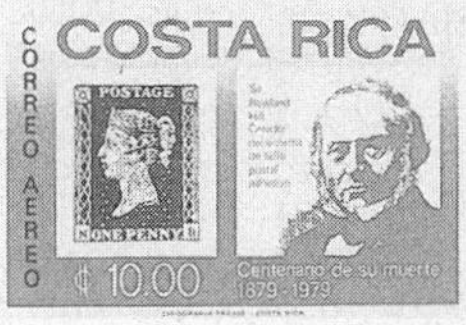

316 Sir Rowland Hill and Penny Black

1979. Air. Death Centenary of Sir Rowland Hill.

1138	– 5col. mauve and blue	55	45
1139 **316**	10col. blue and black	90	65

DESIGN: 5col. Sir Rowland Hill and first Costa Rican stamp.

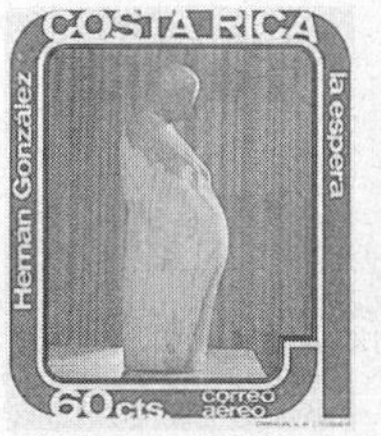

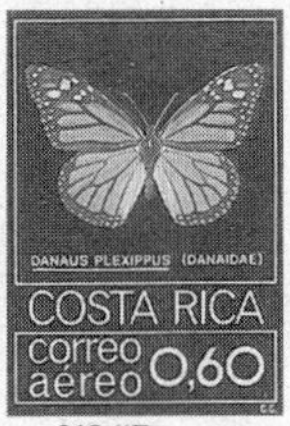

317 "Waiting" (Hernan Gonzalez) **318** "Danaus plexippus"

1979. Air. National Sculpture Competition. Multicoloured.

1140	60c. Type **317**	10	10
1141	1col. "The Heroes of Misery" (Juan Ramon Bonilla)	20	15
1142	2col.10 "Bullocks" (Victor M. Bermudez) (horiz)	30	25
1143	5col. "Chlorite Head" (Juan Rafael Chacon)	65	65
1144	20col. "Motherhood" (Francisco Zuniga)	2·50	2·10

1979. Air. Butterflies. Multicoloured.

1145	60c. Type **318**	15	10
1146	1col. "Phoebis philea"	35	15
1147	1col.80 "Rothschildia sp."	45	35
1148	2col.10 "Prepona omphale"	50	35
1149	2col.60 "Marpesia marcella"	70	55
1150	4col.05 "Morpho cypris"	95	75

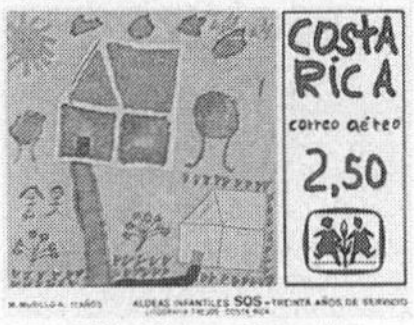

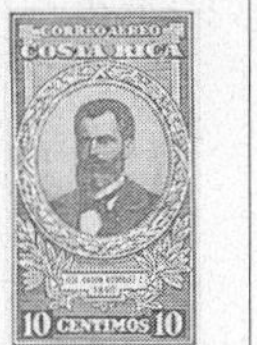

319 "Green House" (M. Murillo) **320** Jose Joaquin Rodriguez Zeledon

1979. Air. 30th Anniv of S.O.S. Children's Villages. Children's Paintings. Multicoloured.

1151	2col.50 Type **319**	45	30
1152	5col. "Four houses" (L. Varela)	60	65
1153	5col.50 "Blue house" (M. Perez)	65	70

1979. Air. Costa Rican Presidents (1st series).

1154 **320**	10c. blue	10	10
1155	– 60c. purple	10	10
1156	– 85c. red	15	10
1157	– 1col. orange	20	10
1158	– 2col. brown	35	25

DESIGNS: 60c. Rafael Iglesias Castro; 85c. Ascension Esquivel Ibarra; 1col. Cleto Gonzalez Viquez; 2col. Ricardo Jimenez Oreamuno.

See also Nos. 1180/4 and 1256/60.

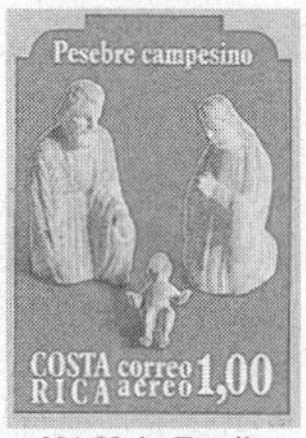

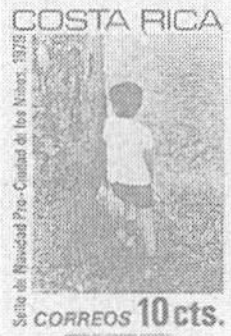

321 Holy Family **322** Boy leaning on Tree

1979. Air. Christmas.

1159 **321**	1col. multicoloured	20	15
1160	1col.60 multicoloured	30	20

1979. Obligatory Tax. Christmas. Children's Village.

1161 **322**	10c. blue	10	10
1162	10c. orange	10	10
1163	10c. mauve	10	10
1164	10c. green	10	10

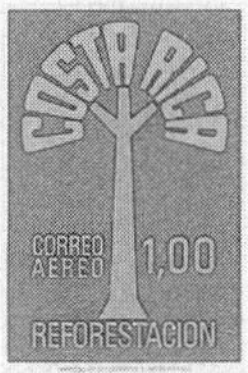

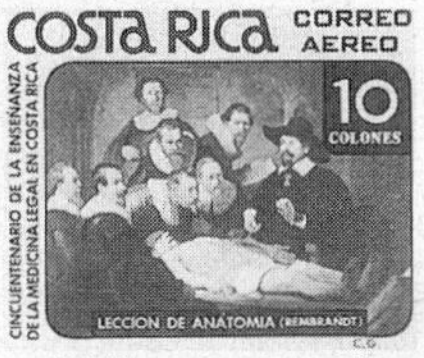

323 Tree **324** "Anatomy Lesson" (Rembrandt)

1980. Air. Reafforestation.

1165 **323**	1col. brown, blue & grn	20	15
1166	3col.40 brown, ol & grn	35	45

1980. Air. 50th Anniv of Legal Medical Teaching in Costa Rica.

1167 **324**	10col. multicoloured	90	90

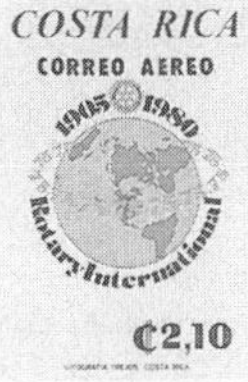

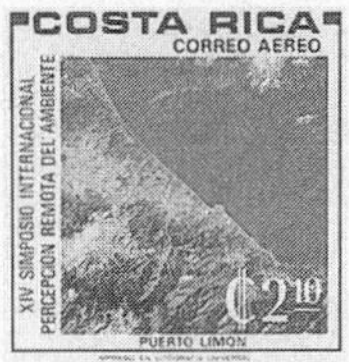

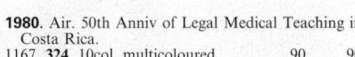

325 Rotary Anniversary Emblem **326** Puerto Limon

1980. 75th Anniv of Rotary International.

1168 **325**	2col.10 green, yellow and black	35	25
1169	5col. multicoloured	50	40

1980. Air. 14th International Symposium on Remote Sensing of the Environment. Multicoloured.

1170	2col.10 Type **326**	35	25
1171	5col. Gulf of Nicoya, Guanacaste	50	40

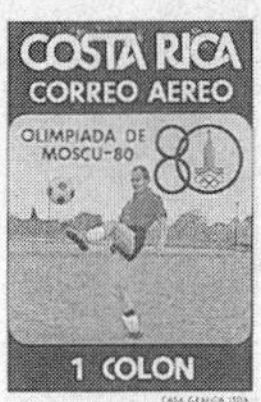

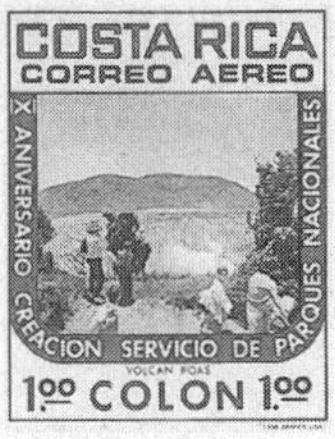

327 Football **328** Poas Volcano

1980. Air. Olympic Games, Moscow. Mult.

1172	1col. Type **327**	20	15
1173	3col. Cycling	30	40
1174	4col.05 Baseball	40	30
1175	20col. Swimming	1·50	2·00

1980. Air. 10th Anniv of National Parks Service.

1176	1col. Type **328**	20	15
1177	2col.50 Beach at Cahuita	45	30

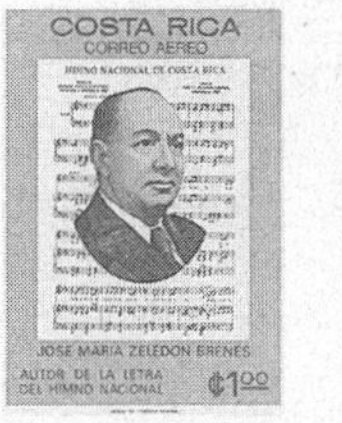

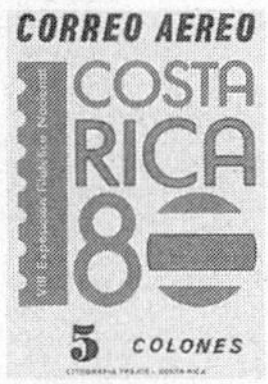

329 Jose Maria Zeledon Brenes (lyric writer) **330** Exhibition Emblem

1980. Air. National Anthem. Multicoloured.

1178	1col. Type **329**	20	15
1179	10col. Manuel Maria Gutierrez (composer)	90	90

1980. Air. Costa Rican Presidents (2nd series). As T **320**.

1180	1col. red	20	15
1181	1col.60 turquoise	30	20
1182	1col.80 brown	30	20
1183	2col.10 green	35	25
1184	3col. lilac	55	40

DESIGNS: 1col. Alfredo Gonzalez; 1col.60, Federico Tinoco; 1col.80, Francisco Aguilar; 2col.10, Julio Acosta; 3col. Leon Cortes.

1980. Air. 8th National Stamp Exhibition.

1185 **330**	5col. multicoloured	90	65
1186	20col. multicoloured	2·40	2·00

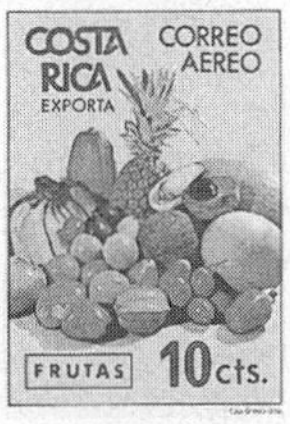

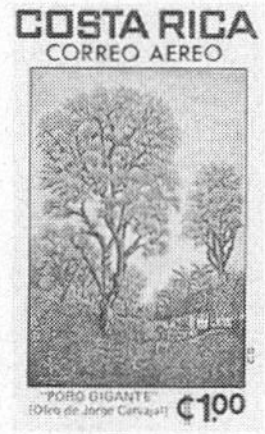

331 Fruit **332** "Giant Poro" (Jorge Carvajal)

1980. Air. Costa Rican Produce. Mult.

1187	10c. Type **331**	10	10
1188	60c. Chocolate	10	10
1189	1col. Coffee	20	15
1190	2col.10 Bananas	35	25
1191	3col.40 Flowers	35	45
1192	5col. Cane sugar	60	15

1980. Air. Paintings. Multicoloured.

1193	1col. Type **332**	20	15
1194	2col.10 "Secret Look" (Rolando Cubero)	35	25
1195	2col.45 "Consuelo" (Fernando Carballo) (31 × 32 mm)	45	30
1196	3col. "Volcano" (Lola Fernandez)	30	40
1197	4col.05 "Hearing Mass" (Francisco Amighetti)	40	30

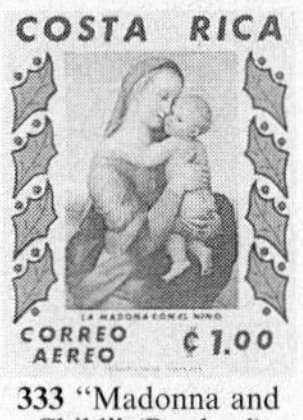

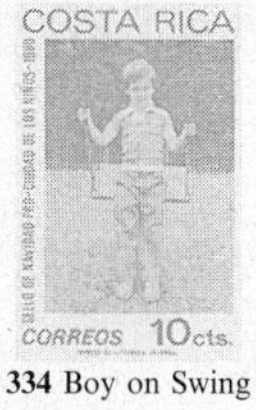

333 "Madonna and Child" (Raphael) **334** Boy on Swing

1980. Air. Christmas. Multicoloured.

1198	1col. Type **333**	20	15
1199	10col. "Madonna, Jesus and St. John" (Raphael)	90	90

1980. Obligatory Tax. Christmas. Children's Village.

1200 **334**	10c. red	10	10
1201	10c. yellow	10	10
1202	10c. blue	10	10
1203	10c. green	10	10

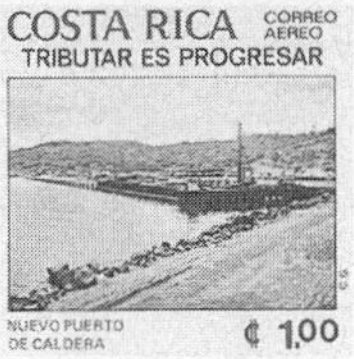

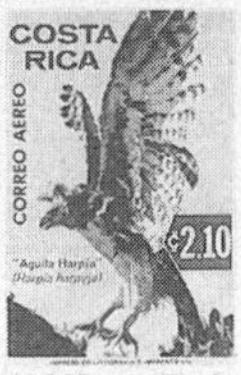

335 New Harbour, Caldera **336** Harpy Eagle

1980. Air. "Paying your Taxes Means Progress". Multicoloured.

1204	1col. Type **335**	20	15
1205	1col.30 Juan Santamaria International Airport (32 × 25 mm)	30	15
1206	2col.10 River Frio railway bridge	5·75	1·25
1207	2col.60 Highway to Colon City (25 × 32 mm)	45	35
1208	5col. Regional postal centre, Huetar	50	40

1980. Air. Fauna. Multicoloured.

1209	2col.10 Type **336**	1·90	55
1210	2col.50 Scarlet macaw	2·50	60
1211	3col. Puma	55	40
1212	5col.50 Black-handed spider monkey	1·00	1·75

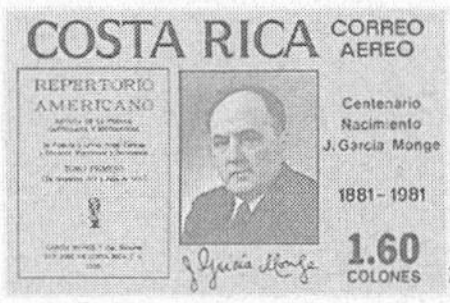

337 Monge and Magazine "Repertorio Americano"

1980. Air. Birth Centenary of Joaquin Garcia Monge.

1213 **337**	1col.60 blue, yell & red	30	20
1214	3col. blue, lt bl & red	30	40

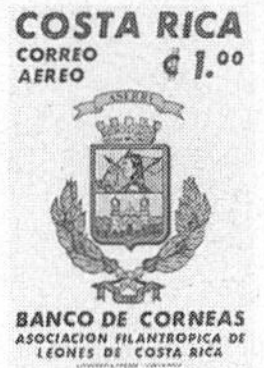

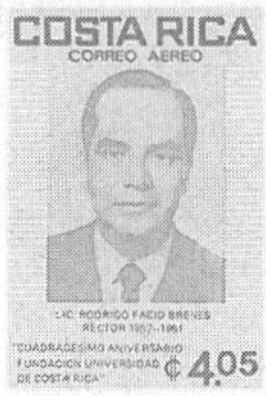

338 Arms of Aserri **339** Rodrigo Facio Brenes (rector)

1981. Air. Cornea Bank.

1215 **338**	1col. multicoloured	20	15
1216	1col.80 multicoloured	30	25
1217	5col. blue	50	40

DESIGNS: 1col.80, Eye; 5col. Abelardo Rojas (founder).

1981. Air. 40th Anniv of University of Costa Rica and 20th Anniv of Medical School.

1218	– 5c. multicoloured	10	10
1219	– 10c. multicoloured	10	10
1220	– 50c. multicoloured	10	10
1221	– 1col.30 multicoloured	10	10
1222	– 3col.40 multicoloured	25	20
1223 **339**	4col.05 grn, bl & dp bl	30	20

DESIGNS: HORIZ: 5c. Medical-surgical clinic; 10c. Physiology lesson; 50c. Medical School and Dr. Antonia Pena Chavarria (first Dean); 1col.30, School of Music and Fine Arts; 3col.40, Carlos Monge Alfaro Library.

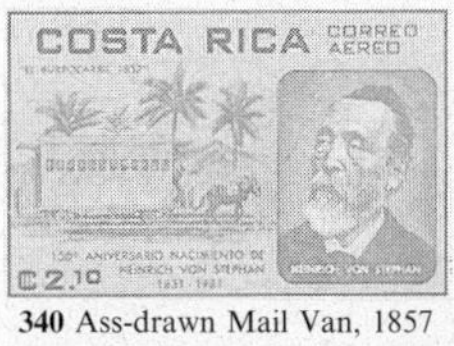

340 Ass-drawn Mail Van, 1857

1981. Air. 150th Birth Anniv of Heinrich von Stephan (founder of U.P.U.).

1224	– 1col. lt blue, grn & bl	20	15
1225 **340**	2col.10 yell, red & brn	4·75	2·50
1226	– 10col. grey, mve & grn	1·75	1·25

DESIGNS: 1col. Mail carried by mule, 1839; 10col. Carrying mail to Sarapiqui, 1858.

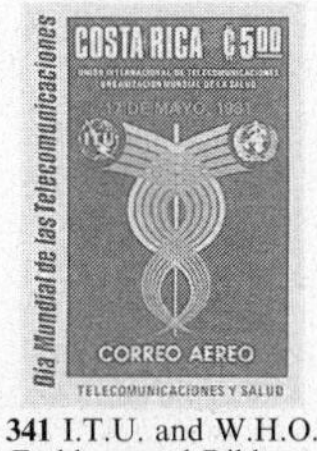

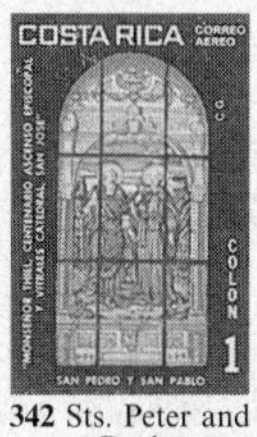

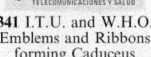

341 I.T.U. and W.H.O. Emblems and Ribbons forming Caduceus **342** Sts. Peter and Paul

1981. Air. World Telecommunications Day.

1227	341	5col. blue and black . .	50	40
1228		25col. multicoloured . .	2·40	1·75

1981. Air. Centenary of Consecration of Bernardo August Thiel as Bishop of San Jose. Mult.

1229		1col. Type 342	10	10
1230		1col. St. Vincent de Paul . .	10	10
1231		1col. Death of St. Joseph . .	10	10
1232		1col. Archangel St. Michael	10	10
1233		1col. Holy Family	10	10
1234		2col. Bishop Thiel	15	10

343 Juan Santamaria (national hero)   **344** Potter

1981. Air. Homage to the Province of Alajuela. Multicoloured.

1235	1col. Type 343 (150th birth anniv)	10	10
1236	1col.45 Alajuela Cathedral	20	15

1981. Air. Banco Popular and the Development of the Community. Multicoloured.

1237	15c. Type 344	10	10
1238	1col.60 Building construction	15	10
1239	1col.80 Farming	15	10
1240	2col.50 Fishermen . . .	30	15
1241	3col. Nurse and patient . .	25	15
1242	5col. Rural guard	45	30

345 Leon Fernandez Bonilla (founder)   **346** Disabled Person in Wheelchair holding Scales of Justice

1981. Air. National Archives. Multicoloured.

1243	1col.40 Type 345	15	10
1244	2col. Arms of National Archives	15	15
1245	3col. University of Santo Tomas (horiz) . . .	25	15
1246	3col.50 Model of new archives' building (horiz)	30	25

1981. Air. International Year of Disabled Persons.

1247	– 1col. multicoloured . . .	10	10
1248	**346** 2col.60 deep orange, orange and black . .	25	25
1249	– 10col. multicoloured . .	60	40

DESIGNS—VERT: 1col. Steps and disabled person in wheelchair. HORIZ: 10col. Healthy person helping disabled towards the sun.

347 F.A.O. Emblem   **348** Boy in Pedal-car

1981. Air. World Food Day.

1250	**347**	5col. multicoloured . . .	45	30
1251		10col. multicoloured . .	60	55

1981. Obligatory Tax. Christmas. Children's Village.

1252	**348**	10c. red	10	10
1253		10c. orange	10	10
1254		10c. blue	10	10
1255		10c. green	10	10

1981. Air. Costa Rican Presidents (3rd series) As T 320.

1256	1col. red	10	10
1257	2col. orange	15	15
1258	3col. green	25	15
1259	5col. blue	20	30
1260	10col. blue	45	55

DESIGNS: 1c. Rafael Angel Calderon Guardia; 2col. Teodoro Picado Milchalski; 3col. Jose Figueres Ferrer; 5col. Otilio Ulate Blanco; 10col. Mario Echandi Jimenez.

349 Arms of Bar Association

1982. Air. Centenary of Bar Association.

1261	**349**	1col. blue and black . .	10	10
1262		– 2col. multicoloured . .	15	10
1263		– 20col. green and black	90	45

DESIGNS—VERT: 2col. Eusebio Figueroa (first president of Association). HORIZ: 20col. Bar Association building.

350 Housing

1982. Air. Costa-Rican Progress. Mult.

1264		95col. Type 350	10	10
1265		1col.15 Farmers' fairs . . .	10	10
1266		1col.45 Grade and high schools	15	10
1267		1col.65 National plan for drinking water	15	10
1268		1col.80 Rural health . . .	15	10
1269		2col.10 Playgrounds . . .	20	10
1270		2col.35 National Theatre Square	20	10
1271		2col.60 Dish aerial (International and national telephone system)	20	15
1272		3col. Electric railway to Atlantic coast	3·25	1·00
1273		4col.05 Irrigation at Guanacaste	35	15

351 Fountain, Central Park   **352** Saint's Stone

1982. Air. Bicentenary of Alajuela. Mult.

1274	5col. Type 351	20	20
1275	10col. Juan Santamaria Historical and Cultural Museum (horiz)	40	10
1276	15col. Christ of Esquipulas Church	60	20
1277	20col. Mgr. Estevan Lorenzo de Tristan . .	80	45
1278	25col. Padre Juan Manuel Lopez del Corral . . .	1·00	60

1982. Air. 50th Anniv of Perez Zeledon County. Multicoloured.

1279	10c. Type 352	10	10
1280	50c. Monument to Mothers	10	10
1281	1col. Pedro Perez Zeledon	10	10
1282	1col.25 San Isidro Labrador Church	10	10
1283	3col.50 Municipal building (horiz)	30	15
1284	4col.25 County arms . . .	35	15

1982. Air. Nos. 1070 and 1207 surch.

1285	3col. on 75c. red and black	25	15
1286	5col. on 2col.60 mult . . .	45	20

1982. Air. 9th National Stamp Exhibition. Nos. 1005/8 surch **IX EXPOSICION FILATELICA - 1982** and new value.

1287	**271**	8col.40 on 2col.20 orange and black . . .	35	35
1288		– 8col.40 on 2col.20 green and black	35	35
1289		– 8col.40 on 2col.20 red and black	35	35
1290		– 8col.40 on 2col.20 blue and black	35	35
1291	**271**	9col.70 on 2col.20 orange and black . . .	45	45
1292		– 9col.70 on 2col.20 green and black	45	45
1293		– 9col.70 on 2col.20 red and black	45	45
1294		– 9col.70 on 2col.20 blue and black	45	45

355 Dr Robert Koch and Cross of Lorraine   **356** Student at Lathe

1982. Air. Centenary of Discovery of Tubercle Bacillus.

1295		– 1col.50 red and black . .	15	10
1296	**355**	3col. grey and black . .	25	15
1297		– 3col.30 multicoloured . .	30	15

DESIGNS: 1col.50, Koch and anti-T.B. Campaign emblem; 3col.30, Koch and Ministry of Public Health Building, San Jose.

1982. Obligatory Tax. Christmas. Children's Village.

1298	**356**	10c. red	10	10
1299		10c. grey	10	10
1300		10c. violet	10	10
1301		10c. blue	10	10

357 Blood Donors Association Emblem   **358** Migration Committee Emblem

1982. Air. 7th Pan-American Blood Donors Congress. Multicoloured.

1302	**357**	30col. multicoloured . . .	90	75
1303		– 50col. red, blue & black	1·50	75

DESIGN: 50col. Congress emblem.

1982. Air. 30th Anniv of Intergovernmental Migration Committee.

1304	**358**	8col.40 lt blue, bl & blk	35	20
1305		– 9col.70 blue and black	45	20
1306		– 11col.70 mult	55	25
1307		– 13col.05 bl, blk & grey	55	30

DESIGNS—HORIZ: 11col.70, Emblem and handshake; 13col.05, Emblem within double-headed arrow. VERT: 9col.70, Emblem.

359 "St. Francis" (El Greco)   **360** Pope John Paul II

1983. Air. 800th Birth Anniv (1982) of St. Francis of Assisi.

1308	**359**	4col.80 brown, blk & bl	20	10
1309		– 7col.40 brn, blk & grey	30	10

DESIGN: 7col.40, Portrait of Francis by unknown artist.

1983. Air. Papal Visit.

1310	**360**	5col. brown, yell & bl . .	25	10
1311		10col. brown, grn & bl	50	20
1312		15col. brown, mve & bl	1·00	30

361 W.C.Y. Emblem   **362** Egg

1983. World Communications Year.

1313	**361**	10c. multicoloured . . .	10	10
1314		50c. multicoloured . . .	10	10
1315		1col. multicoloured . . .	50	20

1983. 1st World Conference on Human Rights, Alajuela (1982).

1316	**362**	20col. grey and black . .	1·00	40

363 U.P.U. Monument, Berne, and 1883 2c. Stamp

1983. Centenary of U.P.U. Membership.

1317	**363**	3col. yellow, red & blk	45	10
1318		– 10col. yellow, bl & blk	90	20

DESIGN: 10col. Central Post Office, San Jose, and 1883 40c. stamp.

364 "Alliance Building, San Jose" (Cristina Fournier)   **365** Bolivar (after Francisco Zuniga)

1983. Centenary of French Alliance (French language-teaching association).

1319	**364**	12col. multicoloured . .	55	25

1983. Air. Birth Bicentenary of Simon Bolivar.

1320	**365**	10col. multicoloured . .	50	20

1983. Nos. 1308/9 surch.

1321	10c. on 4col.80 brown, black and blue	10	10
1321a	50c. on 4col.80 brown, black and blue	10	10
1322	1col.50 on 7col.40 brown, black and grey	15	10
1323	3col. on 7col.40 brown, black and grey	20	10

367 Repairing Wheelchair   **368** Three Kings

1988. Obligatory Tax. Christmas. Children's Village.

1324	**367**	10c. red	10	10
1325		10c. orange	10	10
1326		10c. blue	10	10
1327		10c. green	10	10

1983. Christmas. Multicoloured.

1328	1col.50 Type 368	15	10
1329	1col.50 Holy Family and Shepherds	15	10
1330	1col.50 People bearing gifts	15	10

Nos. 1328/30 were printed together, se-tenant, forming a composite design.

369 Fisherman   **370** Resplendent Quetzal ("Quetzal")

1983. Fisheries Development.

1331	**369**	8col.50 multicoloured . .	60	15

1984. Birds. Multicoloured.

1332	**370**	10c. Type 370	45	25
1333		50c. Red-legged honey-creeper ("Mielero Patirrojo") (horiz) . .	45	25
1334		1col. Clay-coloured thrush ("Mirlo Pardo") (horiz)	50	25
1335		1col.50 Blue-crowned motmot ("Momotode Diadema Azul")	60	25
1336		3col. Green violetear ("Colibri orejivioloceo verde")	1·25	45
1337		10col. Blue and white swallow ("Golondirina Azul y Blanca") (horiz)	3·75	75

371 Jose Joaquin Mora

1984. 1856 Campaign Heroes. Multicoloured.

1339	**371**	50c. Type 371	10	10

1340		1col.50 Pancha Carrasco	10	10
1341		3col. Juan Santamaria (horiz)	10	10
1342		8col.50 Juan Rafael Mora Porras	35	30

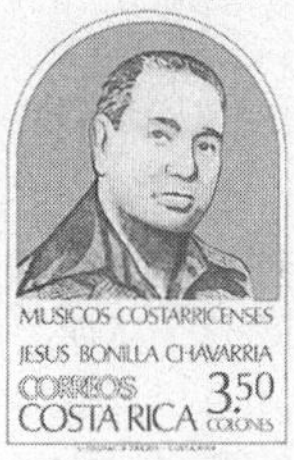

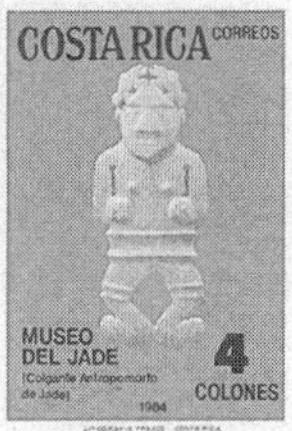

372 Jesus Bonilla Chavarria

373 Necklace Bead

1984. Musicians.

1343	**372**	3col. 50 violet and black	15	10
1344	–	5col. red and black	20	15
1345	–	12col. green and black	15	10
1346	–	13col. yellow and black	20	10

DESIGNS: 5col. Benjamin Gutierrez; 12col. Pilar Jimenez; 13col. Jose Daniel Zuniga.

1984. Jade Museum Artifacts. Multicoloured.

1347		4col. Type **373**	15	10
1348		7col. Seated figure	25	20
1349		10col. Ceramic dish (horiz)	35	30

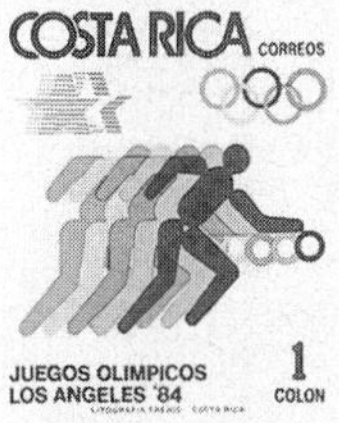

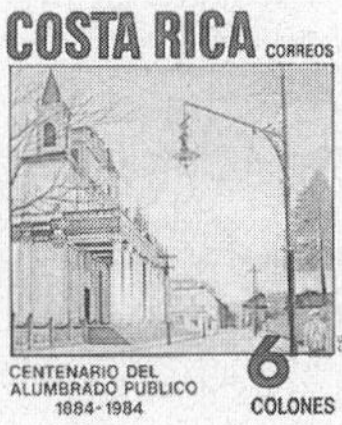

374 Basketball Players

375 Street Scene

1984. Olympic Games, Los Angeles. Mult.

1350		1col. Type **374**	10	10
1351		8col. Swimming	10	10
1352		11col. Cycling	15	10
1353		14col. Running	20	10
1354		20col. Boxing	25	10
1355		30col. Football	35	10

1984. Centenary of Public Street Lighting.

1356	**375**	6col. multicoloured	20	15

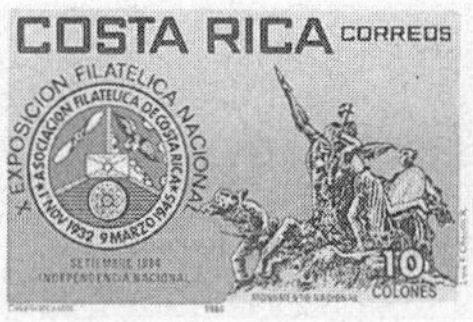

376 Emblem and National Independence Monument

1984. 10th National Philatelic Exhibition. Mult.

1357		10col. Type **376**	35	30
1358		10col. Emblem and Juan Mora Fernandez statue	35	30

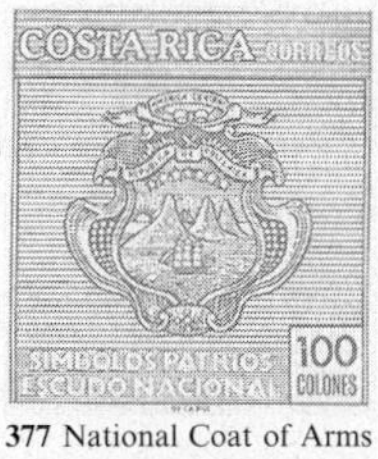

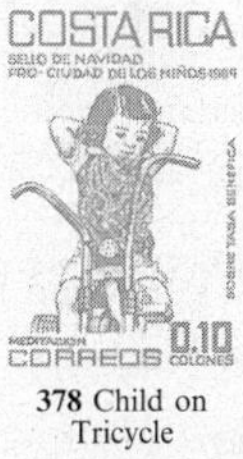

377 National Coat of Arms

378 Child on Tricycle

1984.

1360	**377**	100col. blue	2·40	1·90
1361		100col. yellow	2·40	1·90

1984. Obligatory Tax. Christmas. Children's Village.

1362	**378**	10c. violet	10	10

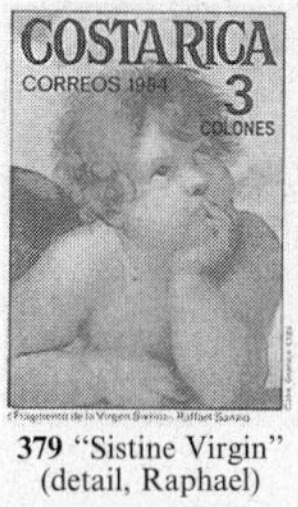

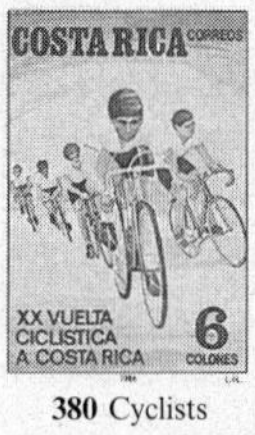

379 "Sistine Virgin" (detail, Raphael)

380 Cyclists

1984. Christmas. Multicoloured.

1363		3col. Type **379**	10	10
1364		3col. "Sistine Virgin" (detail) (different)	10	10

1984. 20th Costa Rica Cycle Race.

1365	**380**	6col. multicoloured	15	15

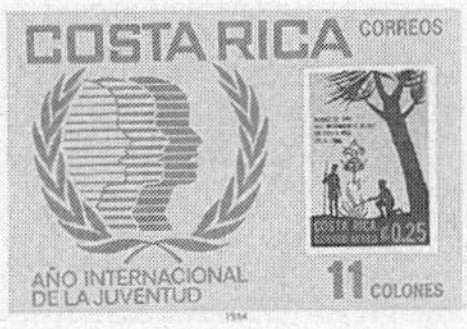

381 Emblem and 1968 Scouting Jubilee Stamp

1985. International Youth Year.

1366	**381**	11col. multicoloured	25	20

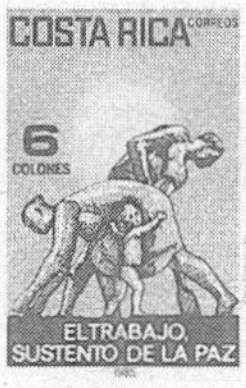

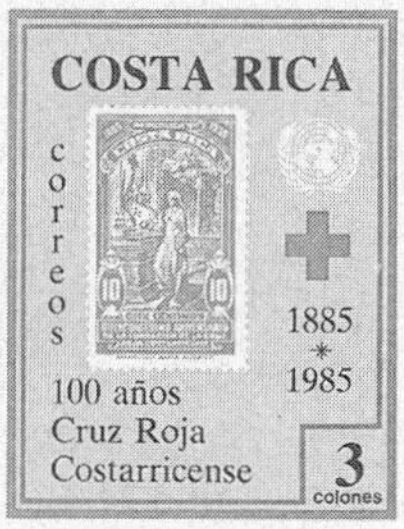

382 Workers' Monument (Francisco Zuniga)

383 U.N. Emblem and 1935 Red Cross Jubilee Stamp

1985. "National Values".

1367	**382**	6col. mauve and black	15	15
1368	–	11col. yell, blk & bl	25	20
1369	–	13col. multicoloured	35	30
1370	–	30col. multicoloured	70	70

DESIGNS—As T **382**. 11col. First printing press (Freedom of speech); 13col. Dove, flag and globe (Neutrality); 65 × 35 mm—30col. Nos. 1367/9.

1985. Centenary of Costa Rican Red Cross.

1371	**383**	3col. red, brown & blk	10	10
1372	–	5col. black, red and grey	15	10

DESIGN: 5col. U.N. Emblem and 1946 Red Cross Society stamp.

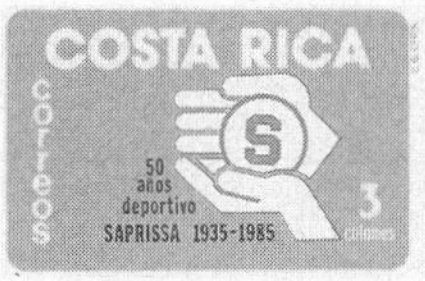

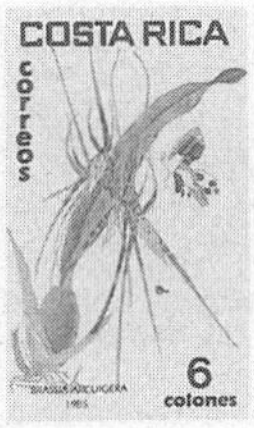

384 Hands holding "S"

385 "Brassia arcuigera"

1985. 50th Anniv of Saprissa Football Club.

1373	**384**	3col. mauve and green	10	10
1374	–	3col. black and mauve	10	10
1375	–	6col. mauve, brn & grn	15	15

DESIGNS: As T **384**—Hands holding football; 34 × 26 mm—6col. Ricardo Saprissa and Saprissa Stadium.

1985. Orchids. Multicoloured.

1376		6col. Type **385**	10	10
1377		6col. "Encyclia peraltensis"	10	10
1378		6col. "Maxillaria especie"	10	10
1379		13col. "Oncidium turialbae"	30	25
1380		13col. "Trichopilia marginata"	30	25
1381		13col. "Stanhopea ecornuta"	30	25

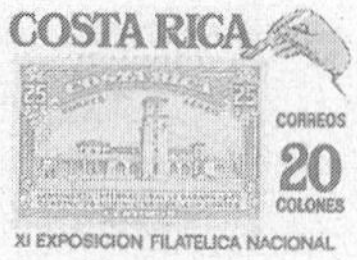

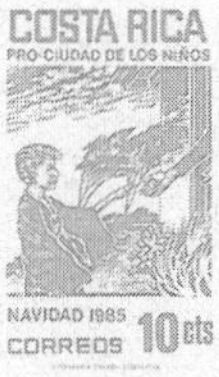

386 1940 25c. Stamp and Hand holding Tweezers

387 Hands reaching out to Child

1985. 11th National Stamp Exhibition.

1382	**386**	20col. bl, ultram & pink	50	45

1985. Obligatory Tax. Christmas. Children's Village.

1383	**387**	10c. brown	10	10

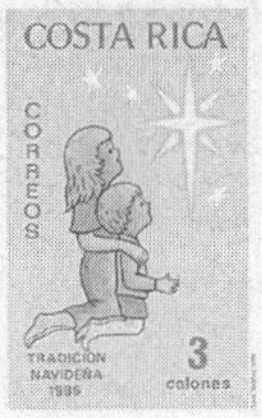

388 Children looking at Star

1985. Christmas.

1384	**388**	3col. multicoloured	10	10

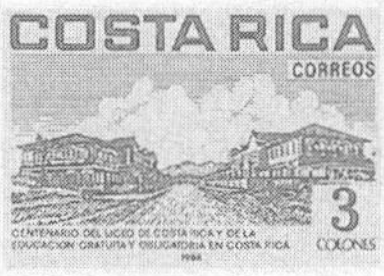

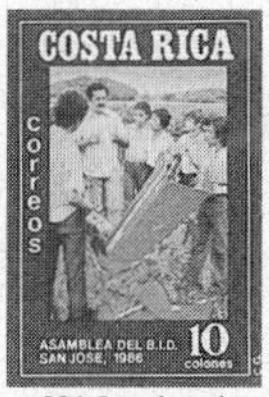

390 Costa Rica Lyceum

391 Land and Cattle College Project

1986. Centenary of Free Compulsory Education.

1390	**390**	3col. brown & lt brown	10	10
1391		30col. brown and pink	60	20

DESIGN: 30col. Mauro Fernandez Acuna (education Minister).

1986. 27th Annual Inter-American Development Bank Assembly, San Jose. Multicoloured.

1392		10col. Type **391**	20	15
1393		10col. Bank emblem	20	15
1394		10col. Cape Blanco fisherman	40	15

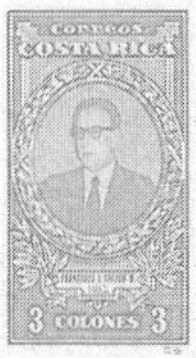

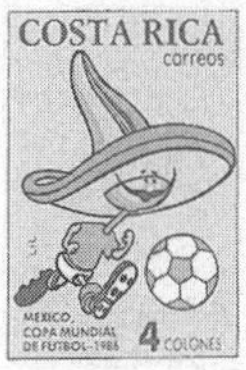

392 Francisco J. Orlich Bolmarcich

393 Pique (mascot)

1986. Former Presidents of Costa Rica.

1395	**392**	3col. green	10	10
1396	–	3col. green	10	10
1397	–	3col. green	10	10
1398	–	3col. green	10	10
1399	–	3col. green	10	10
1400	–	6col. brown	15	10
1401	–	6col. brown	15	10
1402	–	6col. brown	15	10
1403	–	6col. brown	15	10
1404	–	6col. brown	15	10
1405	–	10col. orange	20	15
1406	–	10col. orange	20	15
1407	–	10col. orange	20	15
1408	–	10col. orange	20	15
1409	–	10col. orange	20	15
1410	–	11col. grey	20	15
1411	–	11col. grey	20	15
1412	–	11col. grey	20	15
1413	–	11col. grey	20	15
1414	–	11col. grey	20	15
1415	–	13col. brown	25	20
1416	–	13col. brown	25	20
1417	–	13col. brown	25	20
1418	–	13col. brown	25	20
1419	–	13col. brown	25	20

DESIGNS: Nos. 1395, 1400, 1405, 1410, 1415, Type **392**; 1396, 1401, 1406, 1411, 1416, Jose Joaquin Trejos Fernandez; 1397, 1402, 1407, 1412, 1417, Daniel Oduber Quiros; 1398, 1403, 1408, 1413, 1418, Rodrigo Carazo Odio; 1399, 1404, 1409, 1414, 1419, Luis Alberto Monge Alvarez.

1986. World Cup Football Championship. Mexico.

1420	**393**	1col. multicoloured	10	10
1421	–	1col. multicoloured	10	10
1422	–	4col. multicoloured	10	10
1423	–	6col. pur, brn & black	15	10
1424	–	11col. pur, red & blk	20	15

DESIGNS:—VERT: No. 1420, 1422, Type **393**. HORIZ: No. 1421, 1423, Footballs and players; 1424, Footballs and players (different).

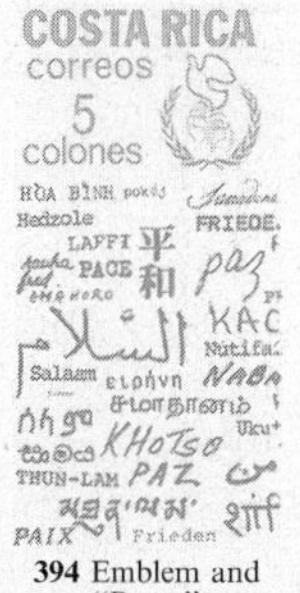

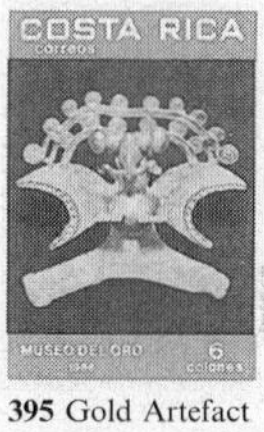

394 Emblem and "Peace"

395 Gold Artefact

1986. International Peace Year. Each bearing the Year emblem and "Peace" in various languages (first language given in brackets).

1425	**394**	5col. blue and brown (Hoa Binh)	10	10
1426	–	5col. blue and brown (Vrede)	10	10
1427	–	5col. blue and brown (Pace)	10	10

1986. Exhibits in Gold Museum. Mult.

1428		6col. Type **395**	15	10
1429		6col. Figure with three-lobed base	15	10
1430		6col. Frog	15	10
1431		6col. Centipede	15	10
1432		6col. Two monkeys in sun	15	10
1433		13col. Figure with dragon-head arms	25	10
1434		13col. Two monkeys	25	10
1435		13col. Animal-shaped figure	25	10
1436		13col. Sun with ball pendant	25	10
1437		13col. Figure within frame	25	10

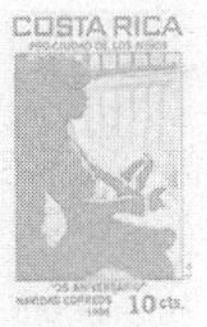

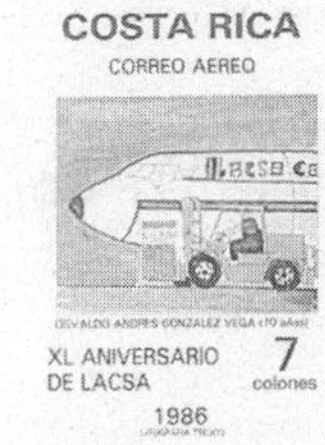

396 Child

397 Fork-lift Truck and Airplane (Osvaldo Andres Gonzalez Vega)

1986. Obligatory Tax. Christmas. Children's Village.

1438	**396**	10c. brown	10	10

1986. Air. 40th Anniv of LACSA (national airline). Children's Drawings. Multicoloured.

1439		1col. Airplane flying over house and van (Adriana Elias Hidalgo)	10	10
1440		7col. Type **397**	15	15
1441		16col. Airplane, letters and photographs (David Valverde Rodiguez)	30	25

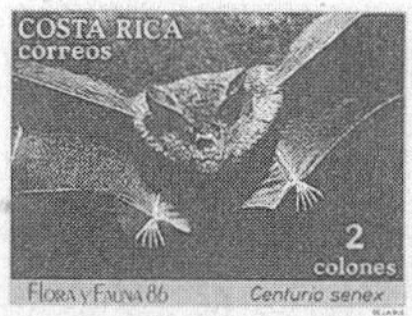

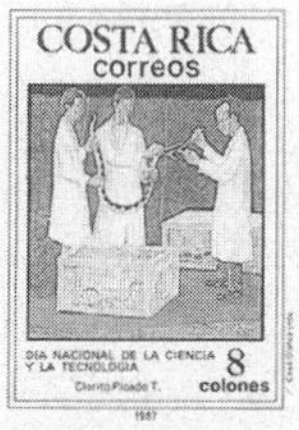

398 Lattice-winged Bat

399 Extracting Snake's Venom (detail of mural, Francisco Amighetti)

1986. Flora and Fauna. Bats and Frogs. Multicoloured.

1442		2col. Type **398**	10	10
1443		3col. Common long-tongued bat	10	10
1444		4col. White bat	10	10
1445		5col. Group of white bats	10	10
1446		6col. "Agalychnis callidryas" (frog)	15	10
1447		10col. "Dendrobates pumilio" (frog)	20	15
1448		11col. "Hyla ebraccata" (frog)	20	15
1449		20col. "Phyllobates lugubris" (frog)	40	35

1987. National Science and Technology Day.

1451	**399**	8col. multicoloured	20	15

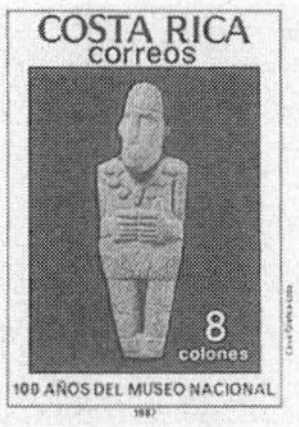

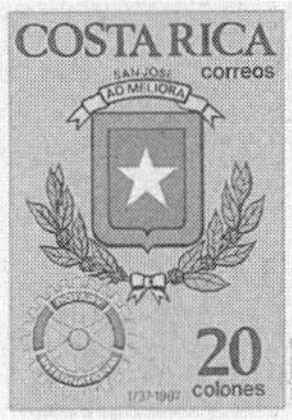

400 Statuette

401 Arms of San Jose Province

1987. Centenary of National Museum. Pre-Colombian Art. Multicoloured.

1452		8col. Type **400**	20	15
1453		8col. Jug in form of human figure	20	15
1454		8col. Vase in form of human figure	20	15
1455		8col. Stone jar	20	15
1456		8col. Pot with human-type legs and arms	20	15
1457		15col. Bowl (horiz)	30	25

1458	15col. Carving of animal defeating human (horiz)	30	25
1459	15col. Flask (horiz)	30	25

1987. 250th Anniv of San Jose.

1460	**401**	20col. multicoloured . . .	30	25
1461	–	20col. red, black & bl . .	30	25
1462	–	20col. red, black & bl . .	30	25

DESIGNS: Nos. 1461, Donkey cart in cobbled street; 1462, View down street.

402 16th-century Map of Audiencia, Guatemala

1987. Columbus Day.

1463	**402**	30col. brown and yellow	70	40

403 Map by Bartholomew Columbus, 1503

404 Cross and Doves

1987. 500th Anniv (1992) of Discovery of America by Columbus (1st issue). Each brown and yellow.

1464		4col. Type **403**	10	10
1465		4col. 16th-century map of Costa Rica	10	10

See also Nos. 1480, 1496, 1521 and 1538/40.

1987. Obligatory Tax. Christmas, Children's Village.

1466	**404**	10c. blue and brown . . .	10	10

405 "Village Scene" (Fausto Pacheco)

406 Pres. Arias and National Flag

1987. International Year of Shelter for the Homeless.

1467	**405**	1col. multicoloured . . .	10	10

1987. Award of Nobel Peace Prize to Pres. Oscar Arias Sanchez.

1468	**406**	10col. multicoloured . . .	15	15

407 Green Turtle

408 Anniversary Emblem

1988. 17th Annual General Assembly of International Union for Nature Conservation. Multicoloured.

1469		5col. Type **407**	10	10
1470		5col. Golden toad on leaf	10	10
1471		5col. Emperor (butterfly) . .	15	10

1988. 125th Anniv of Red Cross.

1472	**408**	30col. red and blue . . .	45	40

409 Man with Pen and Radio (Adult Education)

410 Symbols of Bank Activities

1988. Costa Rica–Liechtenstein Cultural Co-operation.

1473	**409**	18col. red, brown & grn	30	25
1474	–	20col. multicoloured	30	25

DESIGN: 20col. Headphones on books (radio broadcasts).

1988. 125th Anniv of Anglo–Costa Rican Bank.

1475	**410**	3col. blue, red & yellow	10	10

411 Games Emblem

412 Roman Macava and Curtiss Robin

1988. Olympic Games, Seoul. Multicoloured.

1476		25col. Type **411** . . .	40	35
1477		25col. Games mascot . . .	40	35

1988. Airmail Pioneers.

1478	**412**	10col. multicoloured . .	25	15

413 School Courtyard

414 Amerindian Necklace

1988. Centenary of Girls' High School.

1479	**413**	10col. brown & yellow	15	10

1988. 500th Anniv (1992) of Discovery of America by Columbus (2nd issue).

1480	**414**	4col. multicoloured . . .	10	10

415 Dengo and College

416 Former Observation Tower

1988. Birth Centenary of Omar Dengo (Director of Heredia Teachers' College).

1481	**415**	10col. brown, grey & bl	15	10

1988. Cent of National Meteorological Institute.

1482	**416**	2col. multicoloured . . .	10	10

417 "Eschweilera costarricensis"

418 Map of France and Costa Rican National Monument

1989. Flowers. Multicoloured.

1483		5col. Type **417**	10	10
1484		10col. "Heliconia wagneriana"	15	10
1485		15col. "Heliconia lophocarpa"	20	15
1486		20col. "Aechmea magdalenae"	30	25
1487		25col. "Psammisia ramiflora"	35	30
1488		30col. Passion flower . . .	45	40

1989. Bicentenary of French Revolution.

1489	**418**	30col. black, blue & red	45	40

419 Sugar Mill

420 Corn Grinder

1989. 151st Anniv of Grecia County.

1490	**419**	10col. multicoloured . . .	15	10

1989. America. Pre-Columbian Artefacts. Mult.

1491		50col. Type **420**	75	20
1492		100col. Granite sphere, 1500 A.D.	1·50	40

422 Orchid

423 Dr. Henri Pittier (first Director)

1989. "100 Years of Democracy" Presidents' Summit.

1493	**422**	10col. multicoloured . .	15	10

1989. Centenary of National Geographical Institute.

1494	**423**	18col. multicoloured . .	20	15

424 Teacher and Children

425 Pre-Columbian Gold Frog and Spanish Coin

1989. Obligatory Tax. Christmas. Children's Village.

1495	**424**	1col. blue, green & black	10	10

1989. 500th Anniv (1992) of Discovery of America by Columbus (3rd issue).

1496	**425**	4col. multicoloured . . .	10	10

426 "Exporting Coffee" (painting in theatre by Jose Villa)

427 Football in Cube

1990. Centenary of National Theatre.

1497	**426**	5col. multicoloured . . .	10	10

1990. World Cup Football Championship, Italy.

1498	**427**	5col. multicoloured . . .	10	10

428 "50 U"

1990. 50th Anniv of University of Costa Rica.

1499	**428**	18col. multicoloured . .	15	10

429 "Education Democracy Peace"

431 Painting by Juan Ramirez

1990. Patriotic Symbols.

1500	**429**	100col. blue and black	90	30
1501	–	200col. multicoloured . .	1·90	65
1502	–	500col. multicoloured . .	4·75	1·60

DESIGNS: 200col. Map of Costa Rica in national colours; 500col. State arms.

1991. Air. No. 1491 optd **LEY 7097 CORREO AEREO.**

1503	**420**	50col. multicoloured . . .	45	15

1990. Costa Rican Coffee.

1504	**431**	50col. multicoloured . . .	45	15

432 Penny Black

433 Heredia Hospital

1990. 150th Anniv of the Penny Black.

1505	**432**	50col. black and blue . .	45	15

1990. Hospital Centenaries.

1506	**433**	50col. blue, orge & grn	45	15
1507	–	100col. orange, bl & grn	90	30

DESIGN: 100col. National Psychiatric Hospital.

434 Yellow-bark Tree ("Tabebuia ochracea")

436 "Banana Picker" (Alleardo Villa, Ceiling of Grand Staircase)

1990. America. The Natural World. Mult.

1508		18col. Scarlet macaw ("Ara macao")	65	15
1509		18col. Buffon's macaw ("Ara ambigua")	65	15
1510		24col. Carao tree ("Cassia grandis")	20	10
1511		24col. Type **434**	20	10

1990. Obligatory Tax. Children's Village. No. 1490 optd **LEY 7157 PRO-CIUDAD DE LOS NINOS 1990.**

1512	**419**	10col. multicoloured . .	10	10

1991. Air. Paintings in National Theatre.

1516	**436**	30col. multicoloured . .	30	10

437 Costa Rica and Panama Flags and Seals

439 Route of First Voyage on Stone Globe

1991. 50th Anniv of Costa Rica–Panama Boundary Treaty.

1517	**437**	10col. multicoloured . .	10	10
1518	–	10col. black and blue . .	10	10
1519	–	10col. blue, brown & blk	10	10

DESIGNS: No. 1518. Presidents meeting: 1519, Map.

1991. Air. "Exfilcori '91" National Stamp Exhibition. No. 1501 optd **Aereo EXFILCORI '91.**

1520		200col. multicoloured . .	1·75	60

1991. 500th Anniv (1992) of Discovery of America by Columbus (4th issue).

1521	**439**	4col. red, black and blue	10	10

1991. Air. Centenary of Basketball. No. 1474 optd **CENTENARIO DEL BALONCESTO CORREO AEREO.**

1522		20col. multicoloured	20	10

1991. Nos. 1482 and 1342 surch.

1523	**416**	1col. on 2col. mult . . .	10	10
1524	–	3col. on 8col.50 mult . . .	10	10

443 Dr. Rafael Angel Calderon Guardia Hospital

444 Child praying

1991. Air. 50th Anniv of Social Security Administration.

1525	**443**	15col. multicoloured . . .	15	10

1991. Obligatory Tax. Christmas. Children's Village.

1526	**444**	10col. blue	10	10

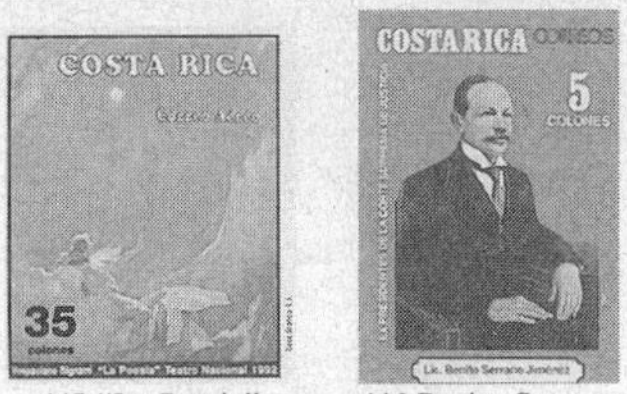

445 "La Poesia" (Vespaciano Bignami)
446 Benito Serrano Jimenez

1992. Air. Paintings in National Theatre.
1527 **445** 35col. multicoloured . . 30 10

1992. Former Presidents of Supreme Court of Justice. Multicoloured.
1528 5col. Type **446** 10 10
1529 5col. Luis Davila Solera . . 10 10
1530 5col. Fernando Baudrit Solera 10 10
1531 5col. Alejandro Alvarado Garcia 10 10

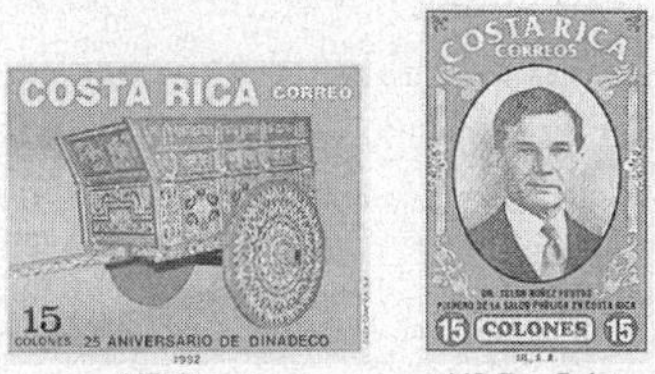

447 Oxcart
448 Dr. Solon Nunez Frutos (public health pioneer)

1992. 25th Anniv of National Directorate of Community Development.
1532 **447** 15col. multicoloured . . 15 10

1992.
1533 **448** 15col. black and red . . 15 10

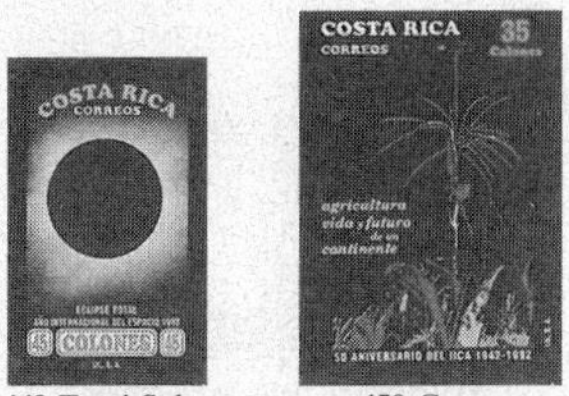

449 Total Solar Eclipse
450 Crops

1992. International Space Year. Mult.
1534 45col. Type **449** 65 25
1535 45col. Post office building and total eclipse 65 25
1536 45col. Partial eclipse 65 25

1992. 50th Anniv of Inter-American Institute for Agricultural Co-operation.
1537 **450** 35col. multicoloured . . 30 10

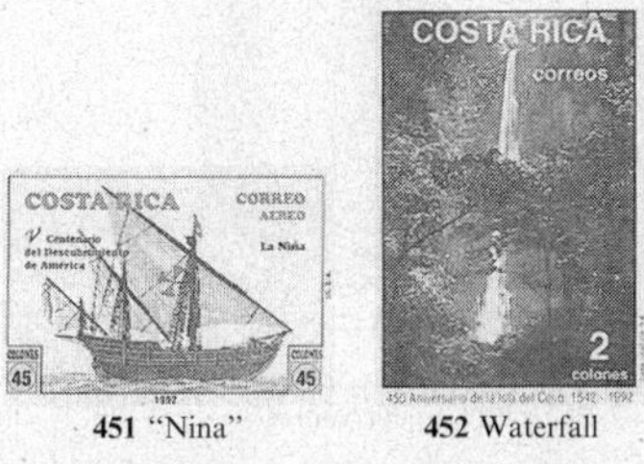

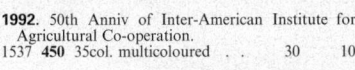

451 "Nina"
452 Waterfall

1992. Air. 500th Anniv of Discovery of America by Columbus (5th issue). Multicoloured.
1538 45col. Type **451** 40 15
1539 45col. "Santa Maria" . . . 40 15
1540 45col. "Pinta" 40 15

1992. 450th Anniv of Discovery of Coco Island. Multicoloured.
1541 2col. Type **452** 10 10
1542 15col. View of cliffs from sea 15 10

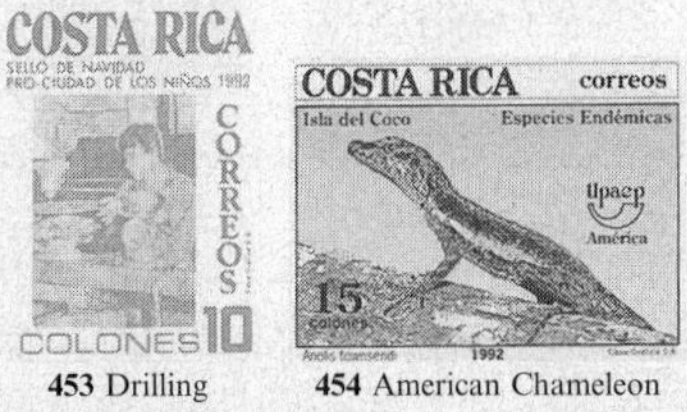

453 Drilling
454 American Chameleon

1992. Obligatory Tax. Christmas. Children's Village.
1543 **453** 10col. red 10 10

1992. America. Coco Island Fauna. Mult.
1544 15col. Type **454** 15 10
1545 35col. Cocos finch . . . . . 2·10 45

1992. Centenary of Limon. No. 1500 optd **CENTENARIO DE LIMON**.
1546 **429** 100col. blue and black 90 30

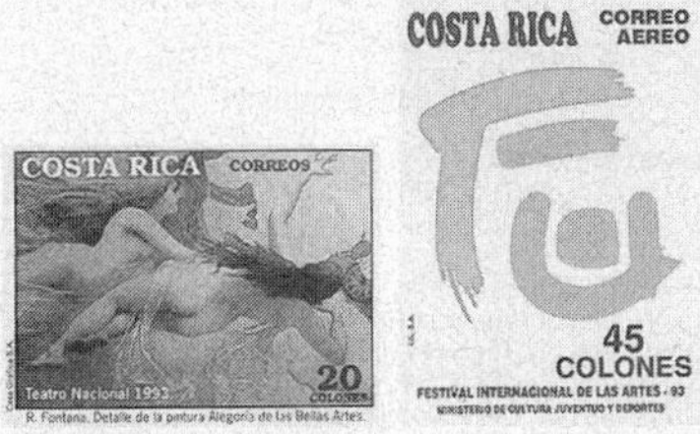

456 "Allegory of the Fine Arts" (detail, R. Fontana)
457 Emblem

1993. Paintings in National Theatre.
1547 **456** 20col. multicoloured . . 20 10

1993. Air. International Arts Festival.
1548 **457** 45col. multicoloured . . 40 15

1993. No. 1494 surch.
1549 **423** 5col. on 18col. mult . . 10 10

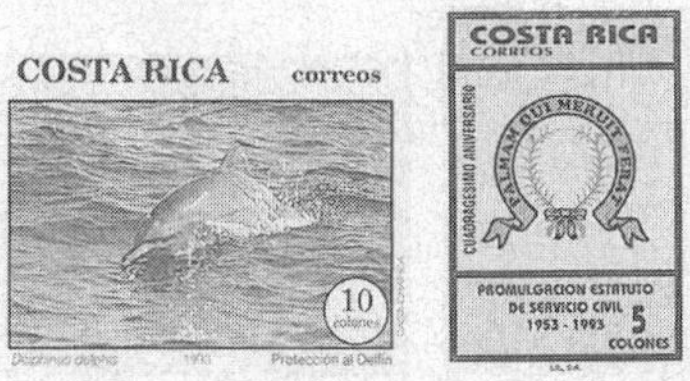

459 Common Dolphin
460 Emblem

1993. Dolphins. Multicoloured.
1550 10col. Type **459** 10 10
1551 20col. Striped dolphins . . . 20 10

1993. 40th Anniv of Civil Service Statute.
1552 **460** 5col. multicoloured . . . 10 10

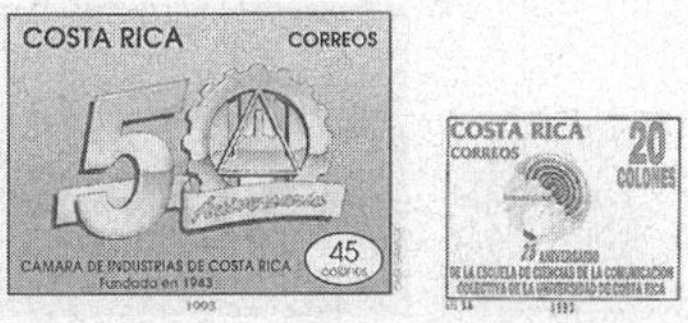

461 Anniversary Emblem
462 Communication Zone

1993. 50th Anniv of Chamber of Industry.
1553 **461** 45col. multicoloured . . 35 15

1993. 25th Anniv of University of Costa Rica School of Communication and Sciences.
1554 **462** 20col. black, red & blue 15 10

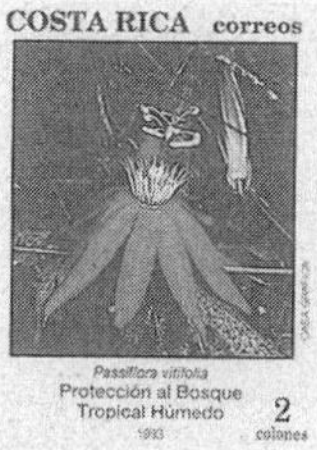

463 "Passiflora vitifolia"

1993. Tropical Rainforest Flora. Mult.
1555 2col. Type **463** 10 10
1556 35col. "Gurania megistantha" 25 10

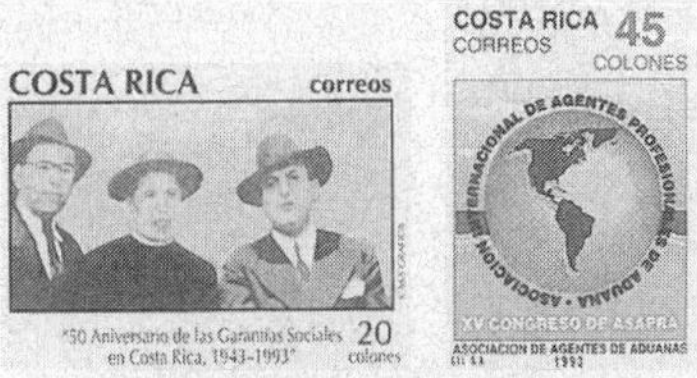

464 Campaigners
465 Association Emblem

1993. 50th Anniv of Guaranteed Social Rights.
1557 **464** 20col. multicoloured . . 15 ·10

1993. 15th International Customs Officers' Associations Congress.
1558 **465** 45col. multicoloured . . 35 15

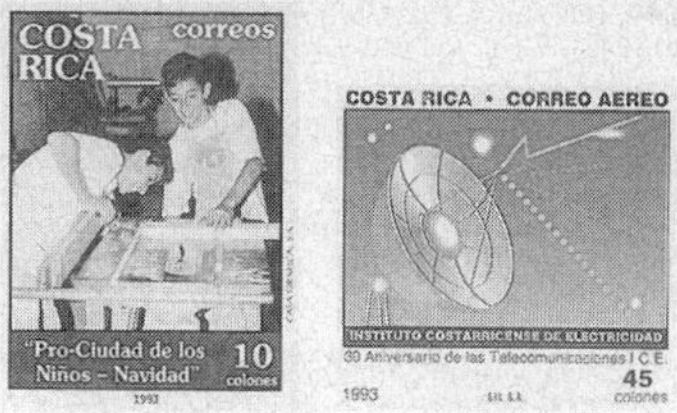

466 Carpentry
467 Dish Aerial

1993. Obligatory Tax. Christmas. Children's Village.
1559 **466** 10col. multicoloured . . 10 10

1993. Air. 30th Anniv of Costa Rican Electrical Institute's Responsibility for Development of Telecommunications.
1560 **467** 45col. multicoloured . . 35 15

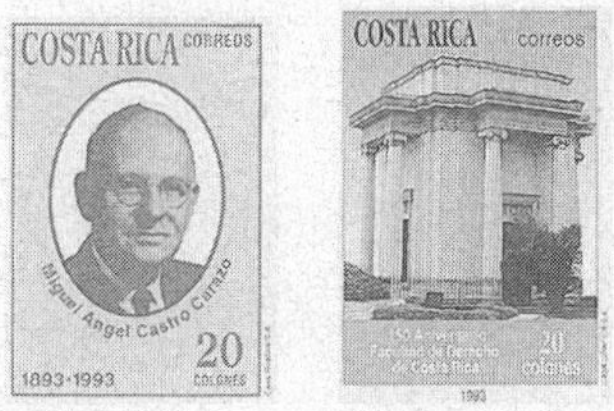

468 Prof. Castro
469 Assembly Hall

1993. Birth Centenary of Miguel Angel Castro Carazo (founder of Commercial School).
1561 **468** 20col. red and blue . . . 15 10

1993. 150th Anniv of Costa Rica University Faculty of Law.
1562 **469** 20col. multicoloured . . 15 10

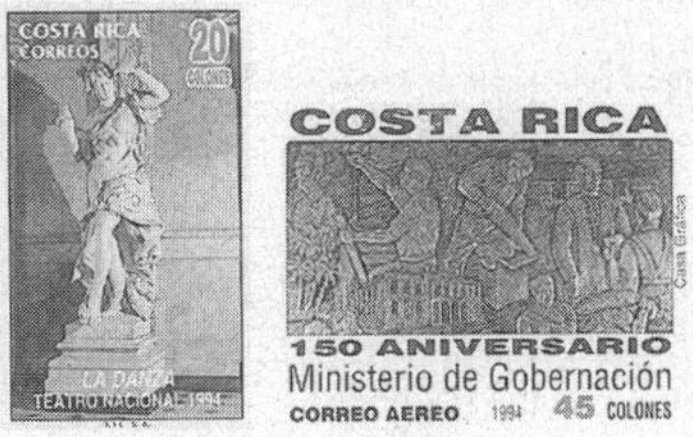

470 "The Dancer" (Adriatico Froli)
471 Mural (Luis Feron)

1994. National Theatre.
1563 **470** 20col. multicoloured . . 15 10

1994. Air. 150th Anniv of Ministry of Government and Police.
1564 **471** 45col. multicoloured . . 35 15

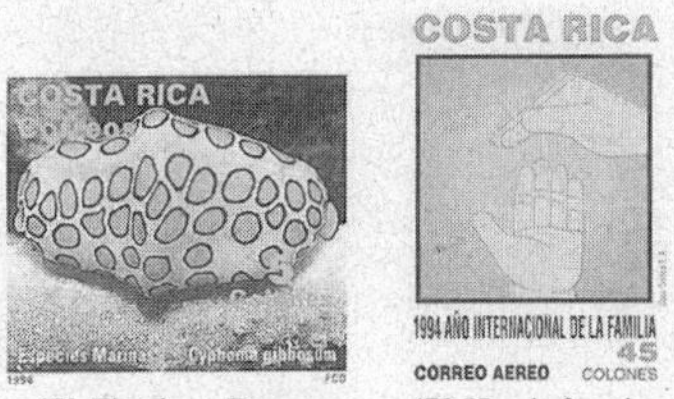

472 Flamingo Tongue
473 Hands forming Shelter

1994. Marine Animals. Multicoloured.
1565 5col. Type **472** 10 10
1566 10col. "Ophioderma rubicundum" 10 10
1567 15col. Black-barred soldierfish 10 10
1568 20col. King angelfish . . . 15 10
1569 35col. Creole-fish 25 10
1570 45col. "Tubastraea coccinea" 35 15
1571 50col. "Acanthaster planci" 40 15
1572 55col. "Ocypode sp." . . . 45 15
1573 70col. Speckled balloon-fish 55 20

1994. Air. International Year of the Family.
1575 **473** 45col. multicoloured . . 35 15

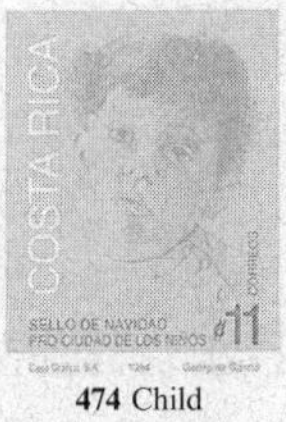

474 Child

1994. Obligatory Tax. Christmas. Children's Village.
1576 **474** 11col. green and lilac . . 10 10

475 Courier

1994. America. Postal Transport. Details of an illustration from "Album de Figueroa". Each orange, light orange and blue.
1577 20col. Type **475** 15 10
1578 20col. Rear of pack ox . . . 15 10

Nos. 1577/8 were issued together in se-tenant pairs with intervening label, each strip forming a composite design.

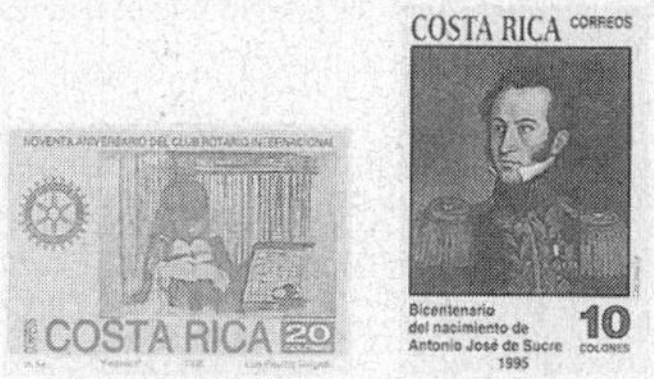

476 "Federico" (Luis Delgado)
477 Antonio Jose de Sucre (President of Bolivia. 1826–28)

1995. 90th Anniv of Rotary International.
1579 **476** 20col. multicoloured . . 15 10

1995. Anniversaries. Multicoloured.
1580 10col. Type **477** (birth bicentenary) 15 10
1581 30col. Jose Marti (poet and Cuban revolutionary) (death centenary) 20 10

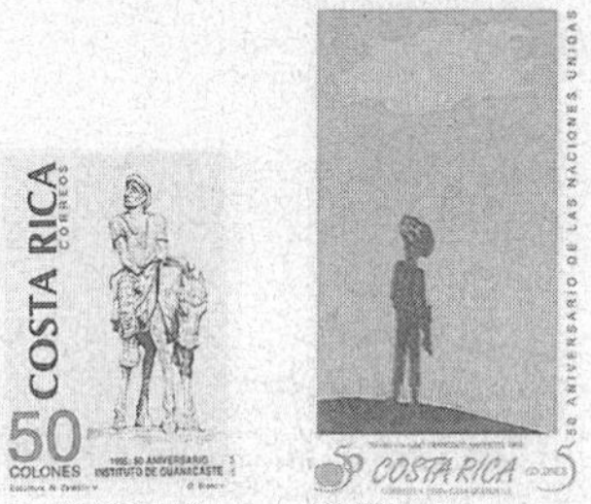

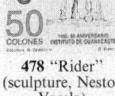

478 "Rider" (sculpture, Nestor Varela)
480 "The Boy and the Cloud" (Francisco Amighetti)

1995. 50th Anniv of Guanacaste Institute.
1582 **478** 50col. green, blk & gold 35 15

1995. No. 1561 surch **5**.
1583 **468** 5col. on 20col. red & bl 10 10

1995. 50th Anniv of U.N.O.
1584 **480** 5col. multicoloured . . . 10 10

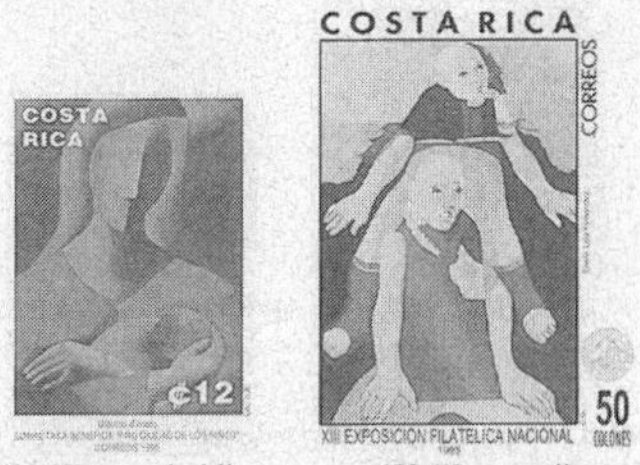

481 Woman holding Baby
482 "January"

1995. Obligatory Tax. Christmas. Children's Village.
1585 **481** 12col. multicoloured . . 10 10

1995. 13th National Stamp Exn. Seasonal paintings by Lola Fernandez. Multicoloured.
1587 50col. Type **482** 35 15
1588 50col. "November" 35 15

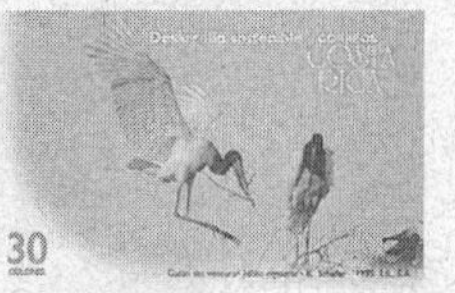

483 Jabiru

1995. America. Environmental Protection. Multicoloured. Rouletted.
1589 30col. Type **483** 20 10
1590 40col. Coastline 25 10
1591 40col. Woodland and lake 25 10
1592 50col. Leaf-cutting ant . . . 35 15

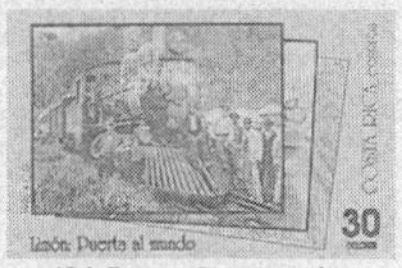

484 Steam Locomotive

1996. Postcards from Limon. Multicoloured.
1594 30col. Type **484** 30 15
1595 30col. Freighter at quay . . 50 15
1596 30col. View of Port Moin 15 10
1597 30col. "Fruitsellers" (Diego Villalobos) 15 10
1598 30col. "Calypso" (Jorge Esquivel) 15 10

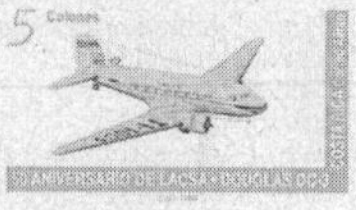
485 Douglas DC-3

1996. Air. 50th Anniv of LACSA (national airline). Multicoloured.
1599 5col. Type **485** 10 10
1600 10col. Curtiss C-46 Commando 10 10
1601 20col. Beechcraft 10 10
1602 30col. Douglas DC-6B . . . 15 10
1603 35col. B.A.C. One Eleven 20 10
1604 40col. Convair CV 440 Metropolitan 25 10
1605 45col. Lockheed L.188 Electra 25 10
1606 50col. Boeing 727-200 . . . 30 10
1607 55col. Douglas DC-8 . . . 30 10
1608 60col. Airbus Industrie A320 35 15

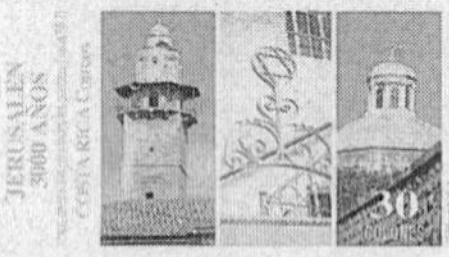

486 Mosque, Synagogue and Christian Church

1996. 3000th Anniv of Jerusalem.
1609 **486** 30col. multicoloured . . 15 10

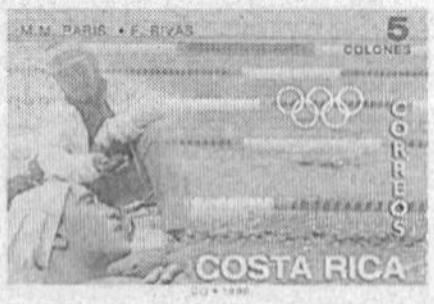

487 Maria del Milagro Paris and Francisco Rivas

1996. Olympic Games, Atlanta. Costa Rican Swimmers. Multicoloured.
1610 5col. Type **487** 10 10
1611 5col. Sylvia Poll and Federico Yglesias 10 10
1612 5col. Claudia Poll and Alfredo Cruz 10 10
Nos. 1610/12 were issued together, se-tenant, forming a composite design of a swimming pool.

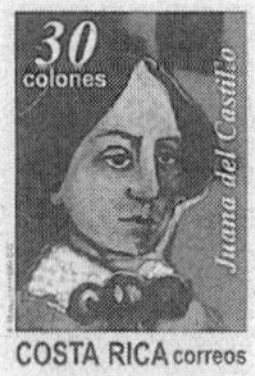

488 Juana del Castillo (wife of Jose Maria Castro)

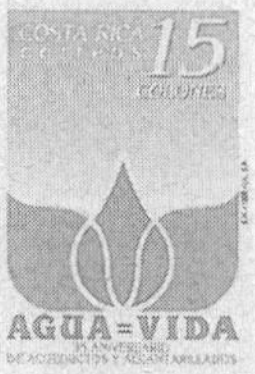

489 Water Droplet and Leaves

1996. 175th Anniv of Independence. Mult.
1613 30col. Type **488** 15 10
1614 30col. Juan Mora (President, 1849–59) 15 10
1615 30col. Jose Maria Castro (President, 1847–49 and 1866–68) 15 10
1616 30col. Pacifica Fernandez (wife of Juan Mora) . . . 15 10

1996. "Water is Life". 35th Anniv of Aqueducts and Sewers.
1617 **489** 15col. multicoloured . . 10 10

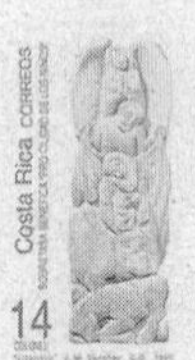

490 "Christmas Carol" (J. M. Sanchez)

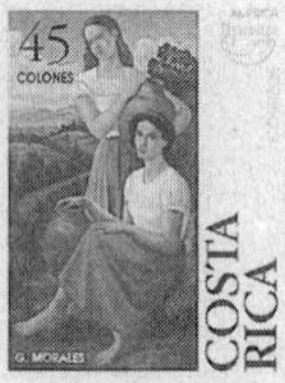

491 "Countrywomen" (Gonzalo Morales)

1996. Obligatory Tax. Christmas. Children's Village.
1618 **490** 14col. red and yellow . . 10 10

1996. America. Traditional Costumes. Mult.
1619 45col. Type **491** 20 10
1620 45col. "Lemon Black" (Manuel de la Cruz Gonzalez) (horiz) 20 10

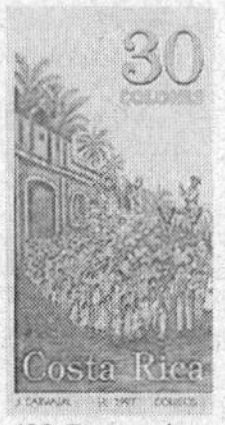

492 Procession passing Palm-topped Wall

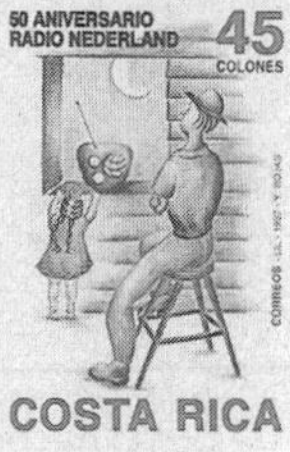

494 Child and Man listening to Radio

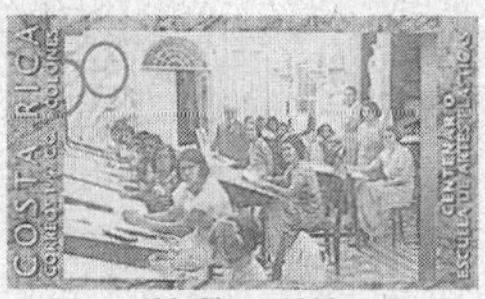

493 Class, 1930s

1997. Entrance of the Saints, San Ramon. Details of a painting by Jorge Carvajal. Multicoloured.
1621 30col. Type **492** 15 10
1622 30col. Church on hill behind procession 15 10
1623 30col. Procession passing beneath tree 15 10
Nos. 1621/3 were issued together, se-tenant, forming a composite design of the painting.

1997. Centenary of School of Fine Arts.
1624 **493** 50col. multicoloured . . 25 10

1997. 50th Anniv of Radio Nederland.
1625 **494** 45col. multicoloured . . 20 10

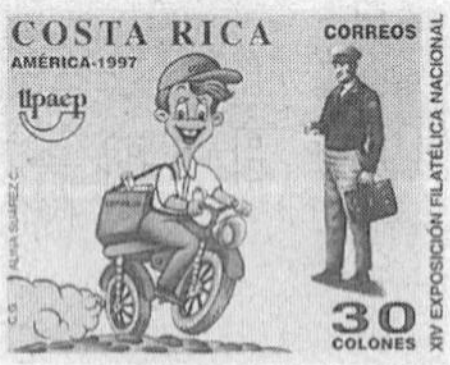

495 Postmen

1997. America. The Postman. 14th National Stamp Exhibition.
1626 **495** 30col. multicoloured . . 15 10

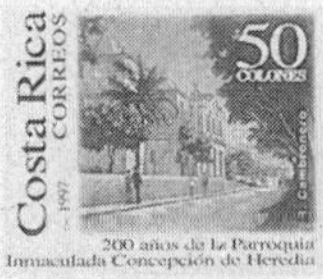

496 Church (Roberto Cambronero)

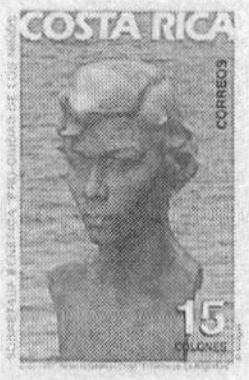

497 Antonio Obando Chan (bust, Olger Villegas)

1997. Bicentenary of Church of the Immaculate Conception, Heredia.
1627 **496** 50col. multicoloured . . 25 10

1997. Obligatory Tax. Christmas. Children's Village.
1628 **497** 15col. multicoloured . . 10 10

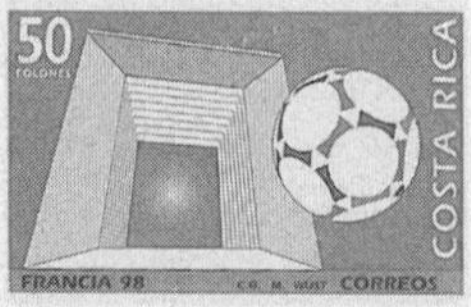

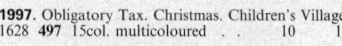

498 Arche de la Defense and Ball

1998. World Cup Football Championship, France.
1629 **498** 50col. black, blue & red 25 10

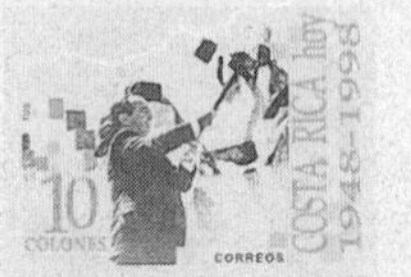

499 Figueres demolishing Fort Bellavista's Walls

1998. 50th Anniv of Second Republic. Mult.
1630 10col. Type **499** 10 10
1631 30col. Pres. Jose Figueres 15 10
1632 45col. Type **499** 20 10
1633 50col. Sledgehammer destroying wall 25 10

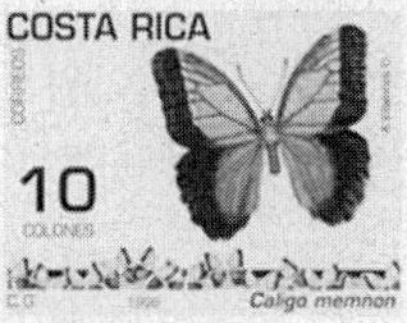

500 "Caligo memnon"

1998. Butterflies. Multicoloured.
1635 10col. Type **500** 10 10
1636 15col. Emperor 10 10
1637 20col. Orange swallowtail 10 10
1638 30col. Malachite 10 10
1639 35col. Great southern white 15 10
1640 40col. "Parides iphidamas" 15 10
1641 45col. "Smyrna blonfildia" 20 10
1642 50col. "Callicore pitheas" 20 10
1643 55col. Orion 20 10
1644 60col. Monarch 25 10

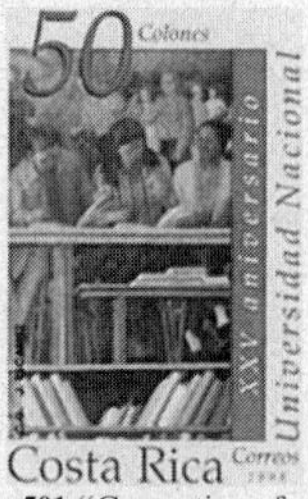

501 "Generation of Knowledge" (Julio Escamez)

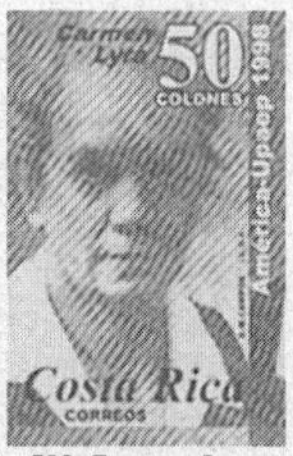

502 Carmen Lyra (writer)

1998. 25th Anniv of National University, Heredia.
1645 **501** 50col. multicoloured . . 20 10

1998. America. Famous Women.
1646 **502** 50col. orange, brown and ochre 20 10

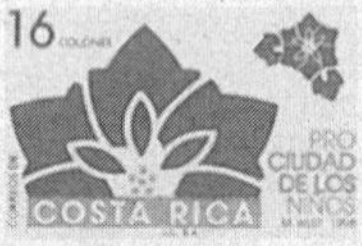

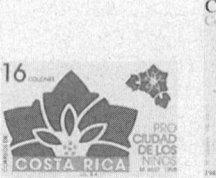

503 Poinsettias

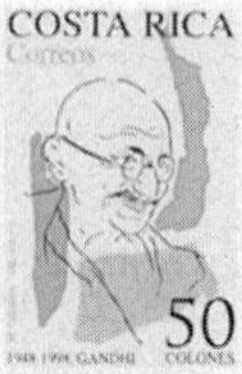

504 Gandhi

1998. Obligatory Tax. Christmas. Children's Village. Multicoloured (except No. 1649).
1647 16col. Poinsetta (gold background) 10 10
1648 16col. Type **503** 10 10
1649 16col. Berries on branch (green, black and red) . . 10 10

1998. 50th Death Anniv of Mahatma Gandhi.
1650 **504** 50col. multicoloured . . 20 10

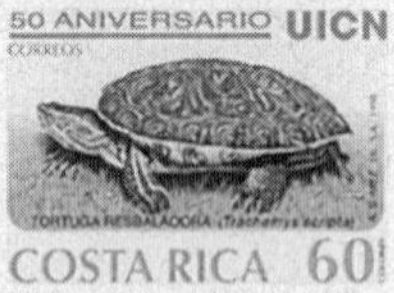

505 South American Red-lined Turtle

1998. 50th Anniv of International Nature Protection Union. Turtles. Multicoloured.
1651 60col. Type **505** 25 10
1652 70col. Mexican red turtle ("Rhinoclemmys pulcherrima") 30 10
1653 70col. Snapping turtle ("Chelydra serpentina") 30 10

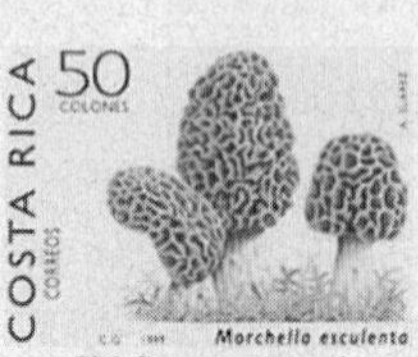

506 Common Morel

1999. Fungi. Mulicoloured.
1654 50col. Type **506** 20 10
1655 50col. Cep (*Boletus edulis*) 20 10

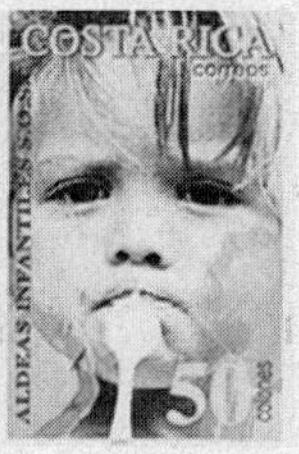

507 Boy

1999. 50th Anniv of S.O.S. Children's Villages.
1656 **507** 50col. multicoloured . . 50 10

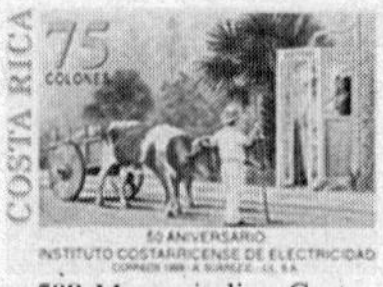

508 Man minding Cart outside Telephone Box

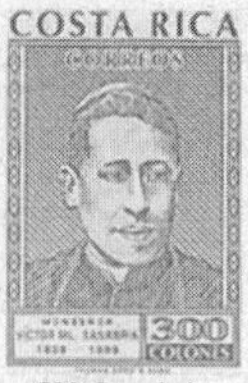

509 Sanabria Martinez

1999. 50th Anniv of National Electricity Corporation.
1657 **508** 75col. multicoloured . . 35 15

1999. Birth Centenary of Victor Sanabria Martinez (Archbishop of San Jose).
1658 **509** 300col. violet . . . . . 1·40 50

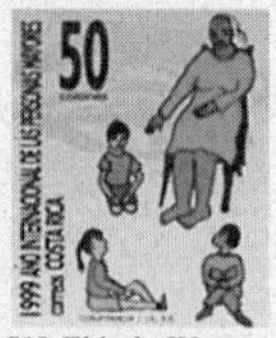

510 Elderly Woman with Children (poster, Fernando Francia)

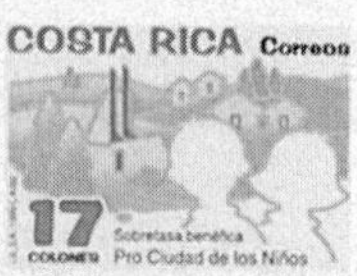

512 Village and Children

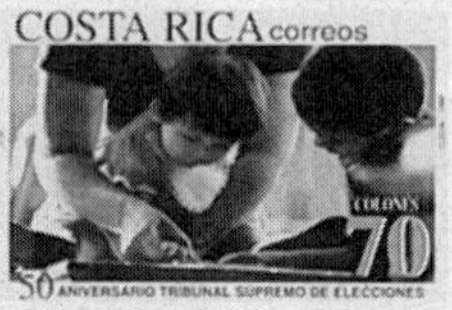

511 Woman helping Children

1999. International Year of the Elderly.
1659 **510** 50col. multicoloured . . 20 10

1999. 50th Anniv of Supreme Elections Tribunal.
1660 **511** 70col. multicoloured . . 30 10

1999. Obligatory Tax. Christmas. Children's Village.
1661 **512** 17col. multicoloured . . 10 10

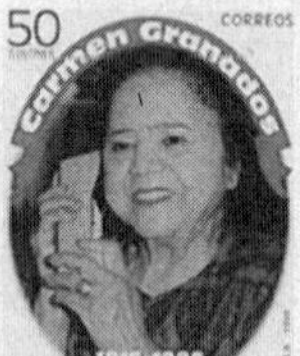

513 Granados

1999. Carmen Granados Death Commemoration.
1662 **513** 50col. multicoloured . . 20 10

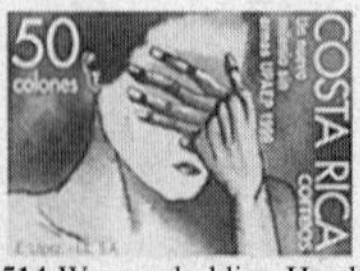

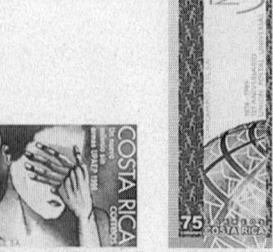

514 Woman holding Head

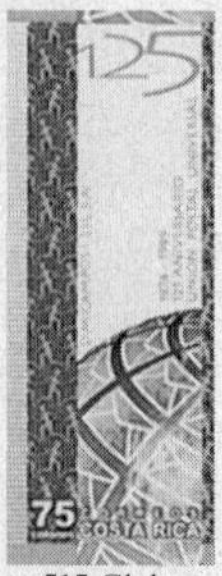

515 Globe

1999. America. A New Millennium without Arms. Multicoloured.
1663 50col. Type **514** 20 10
1664 70col. Man 30 10

1999. 125th Anniv of Universal Postal Union.
1665 **515** 75col. multicoloured . . 35 15

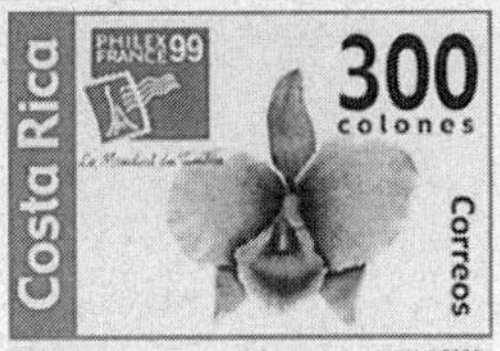

516 Orchid

1999. "Philexfrance 99" International Stamp Exhibition, Paris. Multicoloured

1666	300col. Type **516**	1·40	50
1667	300col. Orchid and Eiffel Tower	1·40	50

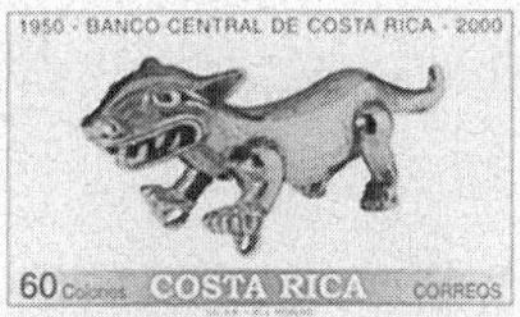

517 Jaguar

2000. 50th Anniv of Central Bank of Costa Rica. Multicoloured.

1668	60col. Type **517**	25	10
1669	60col. Scorpion	25	10
1670	60col. Bat	25	10
1671	60col. Crab	25	10
1672	60col. Dragon	25	10
1673	90col. Obverse and reverse of ½-escudo gold coin, 1825	40	15
1674	90col. Obverse and reverse of ½-unze gold coin, 1850	40	15
1675	90col. Obverse and reverse of ¼-peso silver coin, 1850	40	15
1676	90col. Obverse and reverse of 20 pesos gold coin, 1873	40	15
1677	90col. Obverse and reverse of 1-colon coin, 1900	40	15

EXPRESS DELIVERY STAMPS

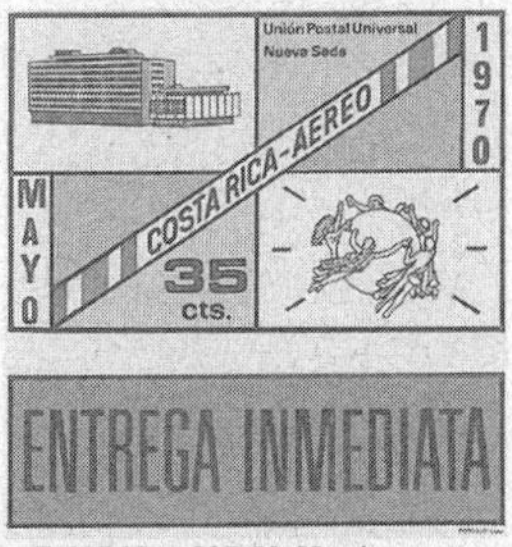

E **237** New U.P.U. Headquarters Building and Emblem

1970. Air. New U.P.U. Headquarters Building.

E841 E **237**	35c. multicoloured	15	10
E842	60c. multicoloured	20	10

In Type E **237** "ENTREGA INMEDIATA" is in the form of a perforated tab.

No. E842 has the same main design, but the tab is inscr "EXPRES".

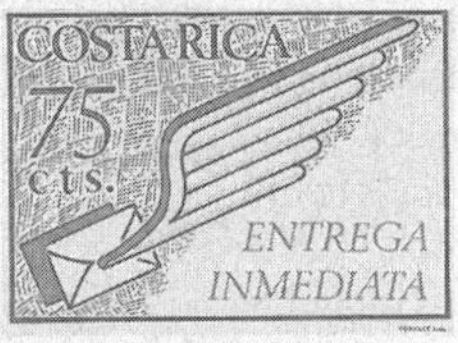

E **249** Winged Letter

1972.

E888 E **249**	75c. brown & red	15	15
E889	75c. green & red	15	15
E890	75c. mauve & red	15	15
E891	1col.50 blue & red	45	25

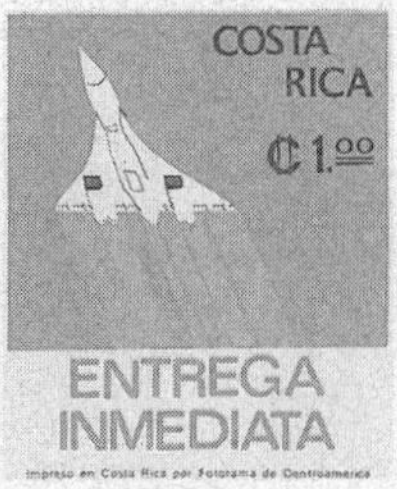

E **279** Concorde

1976.

E1031 E **279**	1col. multicoloured	25	15
E1135 –	2col. multicoloured	50	30
E1136 –	2col. multicoloured	50	30
E1137 –	4col. multicoloured	55	25

Nos. E1135/7 is as Type E **279**, but inscribed "EXPRESS".

OFFICIAL STAMPS

Various issues optd **OFICIAL** except where otherwise stated.

1883. Stamps of 1883.

O35 **8**	1c. green	45	45
O36	2c. red	40	40
O22	5c. violet	2·75	2·75
O37	10c. orange	3·50	3·50
O38	40c. blue	2·50	2·10

1887. Stamps of 1887.

O39 **14**	5c. violet	1·60	1·60
O40	10c. orange	40	40

1889. Stamps of 1889.

O41 **17**	1c. brown	25	20
O42	2c. blue	25	20
O43	5c. orange	25	20
O44	10c. lake	25	20
O45	20c. green	25	20
O46	50c. red	60	60

1892. Stamps of 1892.

O47 **19**	1c. blue	25	20
O48	2c. orange	25	20
O49	5c. mauve	25	20
O50	10c. green	60	60
O51	20c. red	25	20
O52	50c. blue	60	50

1901. Stamps of 1901 (Nos. 42/48).

O53	1c. black and green	35	35
O54	2c. black and red	35	35
O61	4c. black and purple	1·25	1·25
O55	5c. black and blue	35	35
O62	6c. black and olive	1·25	1·25
O56	10c. black and brown	60	60
O57	20c. black and lake	80	80
O63	25c. brown and lilac	5·25	3·25
O58	50c. blue and red	1·75	1·75
O59	1col. black and olive	55·00	32·00

1903. Stamp of 1901 optd **PROVISORIO OFICIAL**.

O60	2c. black & red (No. 43)	2·00	2·00

1908. Stamps of 1907 (Nos. 57/76).

O77	1c. blue and brown	10	10
O78	2c. black and green	10	10
O79	4c. blue and red	10	10
O80	5c. blue and orange	15	15
O81	10c. black and blue	85	85
O82	25c. slate and lavender	15	15
O83	50c. blue and red	25	25
O84	1col. black and brown	45	45

1917. Stamps of 1910 optd **OFICIAL 15-VI-1917**.

O115	5c. orange (No. 80)	20	20
O116	10c. blue (No. 81)	15	15

1920. No. 82 surch **OFICIAL 15 CENTIMOS**.

O117	15c. on 20c. olive	35	35

1921. Official stamps of 1908 optd **1921–22** or surch also.

O123	4c. blue & red (No.O79)	30	30
O124	6c. on 1c. blue & brown (No. O77)	35	35
O125	20c. on 25c. slate and lavender (No. O82)	35	35
O126	50c. blue & red (No. O83)	1·50	1·50
O127	1col. black & brn (No. O84)	3·00	3·00

1921. No. O115 surch **10 CTS.**

O128	10c. on 5c. orange	35	25

1923. Stamps of 1923.

O137 **77**	2c. brown	20	20
O138	4c. green	10	10
O139	5c. blue	20	20
O140	20c. red	15	15
O141	1col. violet	25	25

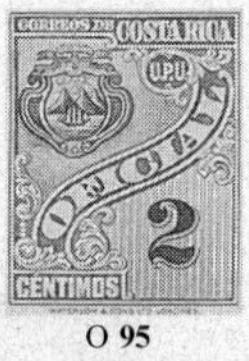

O **95**

1926.

O169 O **95**	2c. black and blue	10	10
O231	2c. black and lilac	10	10
O170	3c. black and red	10	10
O232	3c. black and brown	10	10
O171	4c. black and blue	10	10
O233	4c. black and red	10	10
O172	5c. black and green	10	10
O173	6c. black and yellow	10	10
O235	8c. black and brown	10	10
O174	10c. black and red	10	10
O175	20c. black and green	10	10
O237	20c. black and blue	10	10
O176	30c. black and orange	10	10
O238	40c. black and orange	15	15
O177	45c. black and brown	15	15
O239	55c. black and lilac	25	25
O178	1col. black and lilac	20	20
O240	1col. black and brown	20	20
O241	2col. black and blue	40	40
O242	5col. black & yellow	1·50	1·50
O243	10col. blue and black	9·50	9·50

1934. Air. Air stamps of 1934.

O211 **107**	5c. green	25	25
O212	10c. red	25	25
O213	15c. brown	40	40
O214	20c. blue	60	60
O215	25c. orange	60	60
O216	40c. brown	70	70
O217	50c. black	70	70
O218	60c. yellow	80	80
O219	75c. violet	80	80
O220 –	1col. red	1·25	1·25
O221 –	2col. blue	3·50	3·50
O222 –	5col. black	6·50	6·50
O223 –	10col. brown	7·50	7·50

1936. Stamps of 1936.

O228 **113**	5c. green	20	10
O229	10c. red	20	10

POSTAGE DUE STAMPS

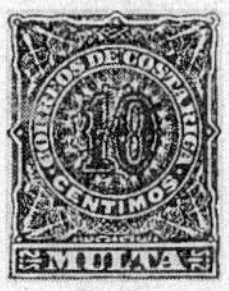

D **42**

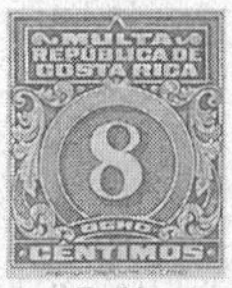

D **64**

1903.

D55 D **42**	5c. blue	4·50	90
D56	10c. brown	4·50	70
D57	15c. green	1·90	1·60
D58	20c. red	2·10	1·60
D59	25c. blue	2·75	1·60
D60	30c. brown	4·25	2·50
D61	40c. olive	4·25	2·50
D62	50c. red	4·25	2·10

1915.

D115 D **64**	2c. orange	10	10
D116	4c. blue	10	10
D117	8c. green	35	35
D118	10c. violet	15	15
D119	20c. brown	15	15

CRETE Pt. 3

Former Turkish island in the E. Mediterranean under the joint protection of Gt. Britain, France, Italy and Russia from 1898 to 1908, when the island was united to Greece. This was recognized by Turkey in 1913. Greek stamps now used.

100 lepta = 1 drachma.

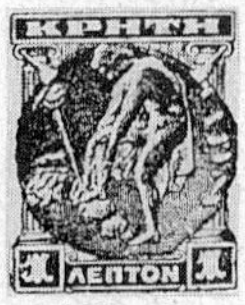

1 Hermes

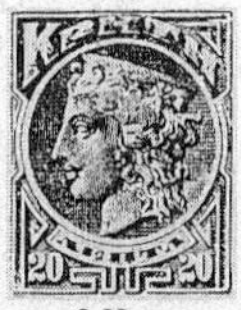

2 Hera

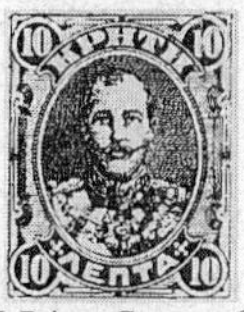

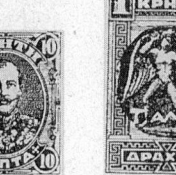

3 Prince George of Greece

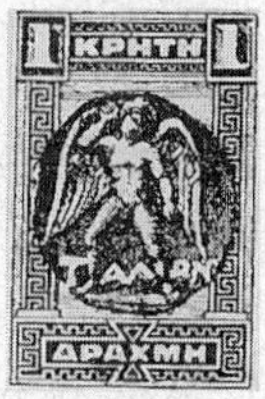

4 Talos

1900.

1 **1**	1l. brown	40	25
12	1l. yellow	50	45
2 **2**	5l. green	75	25
3 **3**	10l. red	1·50	25
4 **2**	20l. red	4·00	70
13	20l. orange	3·00	60
15 **3**	25l. blue	5·75	40
14 **1**	50l. blue	7·50	8·00
16	50l. lilac	19·00	11·00
17 **4**	1d. violet	19·00	13·00
18 –	2d. brown	5·75	4·00
19 –	5d. black and green	5·75	5·25

DESIGNS (as Type **4**): 2d. Minos; 5d. St. George and Dragon.

ΠΡΟΣΩΡΙΝΟΝ

(7) ("Provisional")

1900. Optd as T **7**.

5 **3**	25l. blue	1·00	50
6 **1**	50l. lilac	1·00	75
7 **4**	1d. violet	9·25	7·50
8 –	2d. brown (No. 18)	17·00	14·50
9 –	5d. black & green (No. 19)	55·00	60·00

1904. Surch **5** twice.

20 **2**	5 on 20l. orange	3·00	75

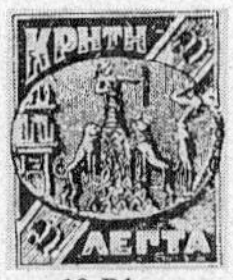

10 Rhea

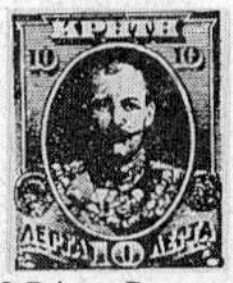

12 Prince George of Greece

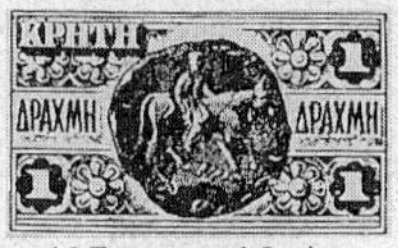

16 Europa and Jupiter

1905.

21 **10**	2l. lilac	1·25	25
22 –	5l. green	2·75	25
23 **12**	10l. red	3·00	35
24 –	20l. green	3·00	50
25 –	25l. blue	3·75	60
26 –	50l. brown	4·00	3·75
27 **16**	1d. sepia and red	38·00	35·00
28 –	3d. black and orange	24·00	22·00
29 –	5d. black and olive	14·00	10·00

DESIGNS—As Type **10**: 5l. Europa; 20l. Miletus; 25l. Triton; 50l. Ariadne. As Type **16**: 3d. Minos ruins. 44 × 28½ mm: 5d. Mt. Ida.

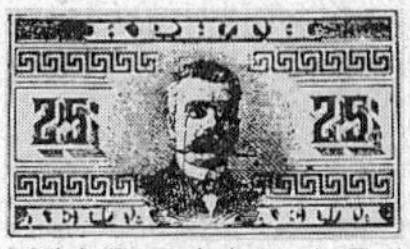

19 High Commissioner A. T. A. Zaimis

1907. Various designs.

30 **19**	25l. black and blue	25·00	50
31 –	1d. black and green	6·50	5·00

DESIGN—HORIZ: (larger): 1d. Landing of Prince George of Greece at Suda.

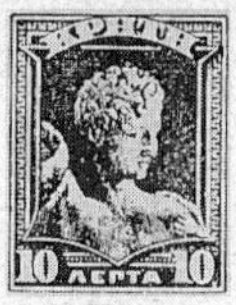

21 Hermes

ΕΛΛΑΣ

(22) ("Greece")

1908. Optd as T **22** in various sizes and styles.

32 **1**	1l. brown	40	30
33 **10**	2l. lilac	45	30
34 –	5l. green (No. 22)	50	30
35 **3**	10l. red	60	40
36 **21**	10l. red	1·75	50
37 –	20l. green (No. 24)	3·50	50
38 **19**	25l. black and blue	7·00	1·25
63 –	25l. blue (No. 25)	2·25	40
39 –	50l. brown (No. 26)	7·25	2·25
40 **16**	1d. sepia and red	38·00	38·00
52 –	1d. black & grn (No. 31)	3·25	1·75
41 –	2d. brown (No. 18)	7·00	7·00
42 –	3d. black & orge (No. 28)	20·00	20·00
43 –	5d. black & olive (No. 29)	18·00	18·00

1909. Optd with T **7** and **22** or surch with new value also.

44 **1**	1l. yellow (No. 12)	1·00	1·00
45 D **8**	1l. red (No. D10)	1·25	1·25
46	2 on 20l. red (No. D73)	1·25	1·25
47	2 on 20l. red (No. D13)	1·25	1·25
48 **2**	5 on 20l. red (No. 4)	65·00	65·00
49	5 on 20l. orange (No. 13)	1·25	1·25

OFFICIAL STAMPS

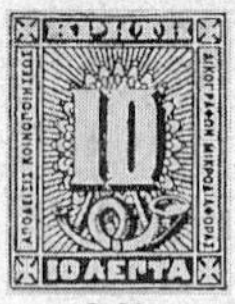

O **21**

1908.

O32 O **21**	10l. red	13·00	1·00
O33	30l. blue	25·00	1·00

In the 30l. the central figures are in an oval frame.

1908. Optd with T **22**.

O44 O **21**	10l. red	12·50	1·00
O45	30l. blue	22·00	1·00

POSTAGE DUE STAMPS

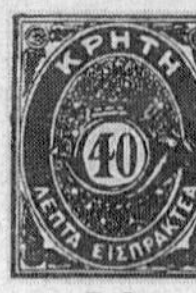

D 8

1901.

D10	D 8	1l. red	30	30
D11		5l. red	50	30
D12		10l. red	75	35
D13		20l. red	1·40	75
D14		40l. red	8·25	7·50
D15		50l. red	8·25	7·50
D16		1d. red	8·50	7·50
D17		2d. red	8·50	7·50

1901. Surch "1 drachma" in Greek characters.

D18	D 8	1d. on 1d. red	6·25	5·50

1908. Optd with T **22**.

D70	D 8	1l. red	30	25
D45		5l. red	70	50
D72		10l. red	50	50
D47		20l. red	2·00	1·25
D74		40l. red	6·50	6·75
D75		50l. red	6·75	6·75
D76		1d. red	12·50	12·50
D51		1d. on 1d. red (No. D18)	6·75	6·75
D52		2d. red	12·50	12·50

REVOLUTIONARY ASSEMBLY, 1905

In March, a revolt in favour of union with Greece began, organized by Venizelos with headquarters at Theriso, South of Canea. The revolt collapsed in November 1905.

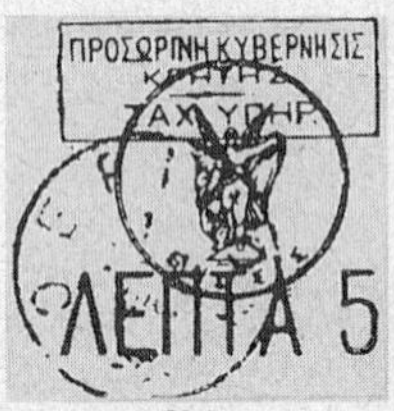

V 1

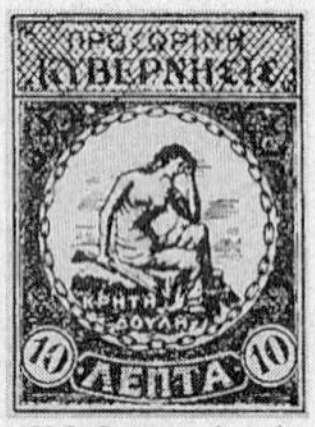

V 2 Crete enslaved

1905. Imperf.

V1	V 1	5l. red and green	10·00	4·50
V2		10l. green and red	10·00	4·50
V3		20l. blue and red	10·00	4·50
V4		50l. green and violet	10·00	4·50
V5		1d. red and blue	10·00	4·50

1905.

V 6	V 2	5l. orange	50	50
V 7		10l. grey	50	50
V 8		20l. mauve	60	60
V 9		50l. blue	75	75
V10	–	1d. violet and red	4·50	4·50
V11	–	2d. brown and green	5·00	5·00

DESIGN: 1, 2d. King George of Greece.

CROATIA Pt. 3

Part of Hungary until 1918 when it became part of Yugoslavia. In 1941 it was proclaimed an independent state but in 1945 it became a constituent republic of the Federal People's Republic of Yugoslavia.

In 1991 Croatia became independent.

April 1941. 100 paras = 1 dinar.
Sept 1941. 100 banicas = 1 kuna.
1991. 100 paras = 1 dinar.
1994. 100 lipa = 1 kuna.

NEZAVISNA
DRŽAVA
HRVATSKA
IIIII
(1)

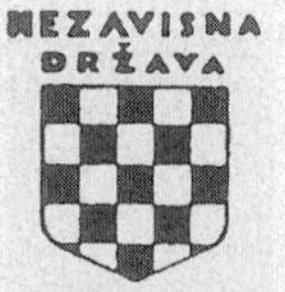

(2)

1941. Stamps of Yugoslavia optd as T **1** ("Independent Croat State").

1	99	50p. orange	1·00	2·25
2		1d. green	1·00	2·25
3		1d.50 red	1·00	1·00
4		2d. mauve	1·00	1·75
5		3d. brown	2·50	4·50
6		4d. blue	2·50	5·00
7		5d. blue	2·50	5·00
8		5d.50 violet	2·50	5·50

1941. Stamps of Yugoslavia optd as T **2**.

9	99	25p. black	20	30
10		50p. orange	20	30
11		1d. green	20	30
12		1d.50 red	20	30
13		2d. pink	20	60
14		3d. brown	20	90
15		4d. blue	25	1·00
16		5d. blue	40	1·00
17		5d.50 violet	40	1·25
18		6d. blue	50	1·75
19		8d. brown	80	2·00
20		12d. violet	90	2·50
21		16d. purple	1·00	3·00
22		20d. blue	1·25	3·50
23		30d. pink	2·00	5·50

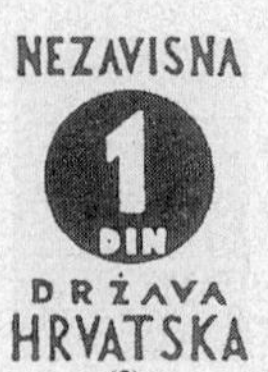

(3)

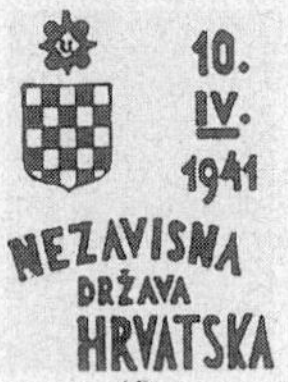

(4)

1941. Stamps of Yugoslavia surch as T **3**.

24	99	1d. on 3d. brown	15	40
25		2d. on 4d. blue	15	40

1941. Founding of Croatian Army. Nos. 414/26 of Yugoslavia optd with T **4**.

25a	99	25p. black		
25b		50p. orange		
25c		1d. green		
25d		1d.50 red		
25e		2d. pink		
25f		3d. brown		
25g		4d. blue		
25h		5d. blue		
25i		5d.50 violet		
25j		6d. blue		
25k		8d. brown		
25l		12d. violet		
25m		16d. purple		
25n		20d. blue		
25o		30d. pink		
		Set of 15	£150	£375

Sold at double face value.

1941. Stamps of Yugoslavia optd as T **2** but without shield.

26	109	1d.50+1d.50 black	5·00	10·00
27	–	4d.+3d. brown (No. 457)	5·00	10·00

1941. Postage Due stamps of Yugoslavia optd **NEZAVISNA DRZAVA HRVATSKA FRANCO**.

28	D 56	50p. violet	20	30
29		2d. blue	30	60
30		5d. orange	30	60
31		10d. brown	35	90

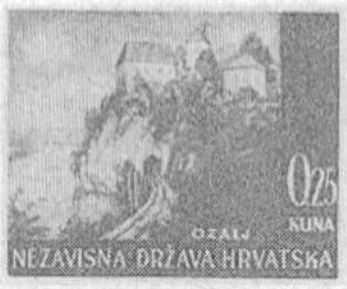

7 Mt. Ozalj

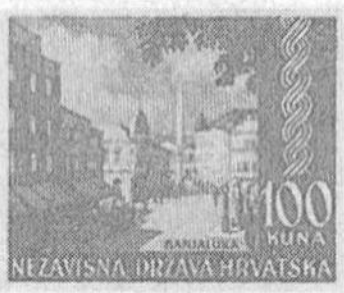

8 Banja Luka

1941.

32	7	25b. red	25	25
33	–	50b. green	10	10
34	–	75b. olive	10	10
35	–	1k. green	10	10
36	–	1k.50 green	10	10
37	–	2k. red	10	10
38	–	3k. red	10	10
39	–	4k. blue	10	10
40	–	5k. black	75	75
41	–	5k. blue	10	10
42	–	6k. olive	10	10
43	–	7k. orange	10	10
44	–	8k. brown	10	10
45	–	10k. violet	40	30
46	–	12k. brown	50	50
47	–	20k. brown	40	30
48	–	30k. brown	55	50
49	–	50k. green	1·00	1·00
50	8	100k. violet	1·60	2·25

DESIGNS: 50b. Waterfall at Jajce; 75b. Varazdin; 1k. Mt. Velebit; 1k.50, Zelenjak; 2k. Zagreb Cathedral; 3k. Church at Osijek; 4k. River Drina; 5k. (No. 40), Konjic Bridge; 5k. (No. 41), Modern building at Zemun; 6k. Dubrovnik; 7k. R. Save in Slavonia; 8k. Mosque at Sarajevo; 10k. Lake Plitvice; 12k. Klis Fortress near Split; 20k. Hvar; 30k. Harvesting in Syrmia; 50k. Senj.

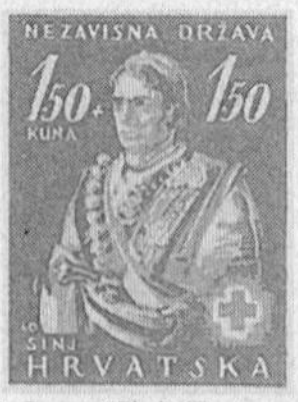

9 Croat (Sinj) Costume

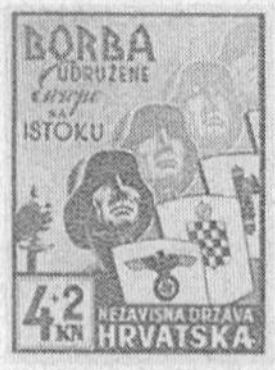

10 Emblems of Germany, Croatia and Italy

1941. Red Cross.

51	9	1k.50+1k.50 blue	35	60
52	–	2k.+2k. brown	35	70
53	–	5k.+4k. red	85	1·75

COSTUMES: 2k. Travnik. 4k. Turopolje.

1941. Eastern Volunteer Fund.

54	10	4k.+2k. blue	1·00	2·75

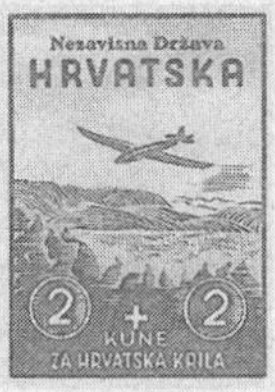

11 Glider

(**12**)

1942. Aviation Fund. Glider in flight as T **11**.

55	11	2k.+2k. brown (vert)	40	60
56	–	2k.50+2k.50 green	60	1·00
57	–	3 k+3k. red (vert)	75	1·25
58	–	4k.+4k. blue	85	1·90

DESIGNS—HORIZ: 2k.50, Glider (different); 4k. Seaplane glider. VERT: 3k. Boy with model glider.

1942. 1st Anniv of Croat Independence. Optd with T **12**.

59		2k. brown (as No. 37)	15	35
60		5k. red (as No. 40)	25	70
61		10k. green (as No. 45)	40	1·00

1942. Banja Luka Philatelic Exhibition. Inscr "F.I." in top right corner.

62	8	100k. violet	1·40	3·75

1942. Surch **0.25kn** and bar.

63		0.25k. on 2k. red (No. 37)	20	50

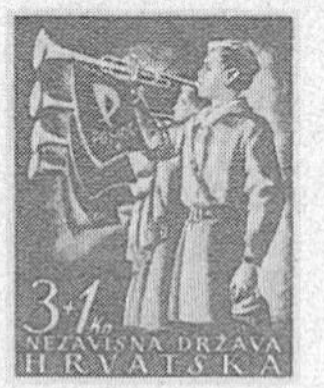

14 Trumpeters

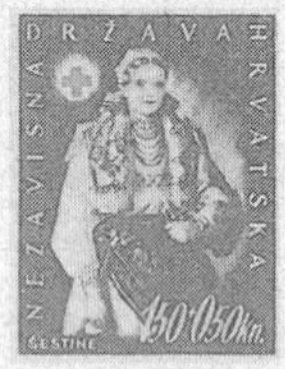

15 Sestine (Croatia)

1942. National Relief Fund.

64	14	3k.+1k. red	40	1·00
65	–	4k.+2k. brown	60	1·10
66	–	5k.+5k. blue	80	1·90

DESIGNS—HORIZ: 4k. Procession beneath triumphal archways. VERT: 5k. Mother and child.

1942. Red Cross Fund. Peasant girls in provincial costumes.

67	15	1k.50+50b. brown	60	1·25
68	–	3k.+1k. violet	60	1·25
69	–	4k.+2k. blue	80	1·75
70	–	10k.+5k. bistre	1·00	2·10
71	15	13k.+6k. red	2·00	4·50

COSTUMES: 3k. Slavonia. 4k. Bosnia. 10k. Dalmatia.

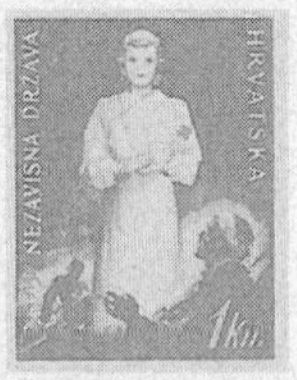

15a Red Cross Sister

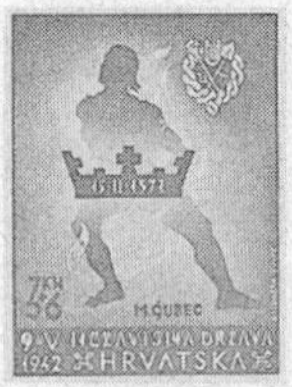

16 M. Gubec

1942. Charity Tax. Red Cross Fund. Cross in red.

71a	15a	1k. green	20	60

1942. Croat ("Ustascha") Youth Fund.

72	16	3k.+6k. red	25	70
73	–	4k.+7k. brown	25	70

PORTRAIT: 4k. A. Starcevic.

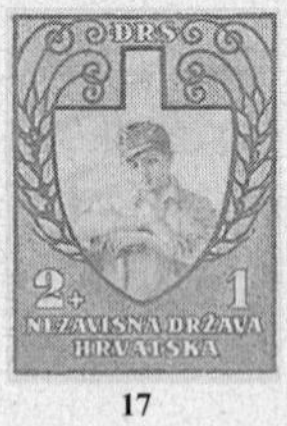

17

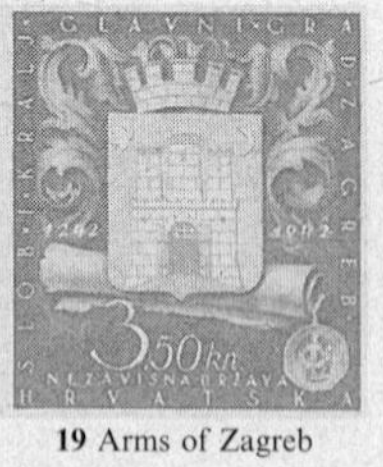

19 Arms of Zagreb

1943. Labour Front. Vert designs showing workers as T **17**.

74	17	2k.+1k. brown and olive	1·50	3·25
75	–	3k.+3k. brown & purple	1·50	3·25
76	–	7k.+4k. brown & grey	1·50	3·25

1943. 7th Centenary of Foundation of Zagreb.

77	19	3k.50 (+ 6k.50) blue	1·10	3·75

1943. Pictorial designs as T **8**, but with views surrounded by frame line.

78		3k.50 brown	35	40
79		12k.50 black	35	70

DESIGNS: 3k.50, Trakoscan Castle; 12k.50, Veliki Tabor.

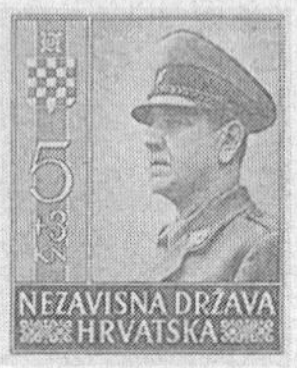

21 A. Pavelic

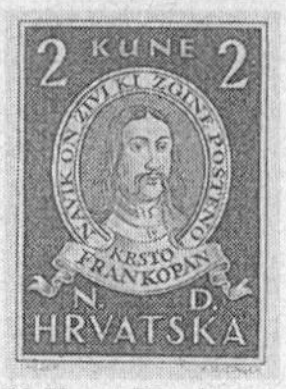

22 Krsto Frankopan

1943. Croat ("Ustascha") Youth Fund.

80	21	5k.+3k. red	15	65
81		7k.+5k. green	15	65

1943. Famous Croats.

82	–	1k. blue	15	30
83	22	2k. olive	15	30
84	–	3k.50 red	15	50

PORTRAITS: 1k. Katarina Zrinska. 3k.50, Peter Zrinski.

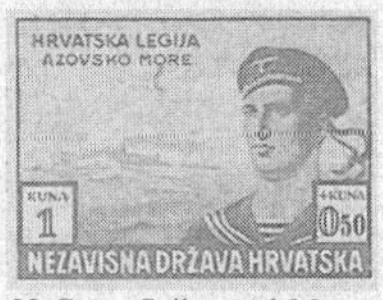

23 Croat Sailor and Motor Torpedo Boats

1943. Croat Legion Relief Fund.

85	23	1k.+50b. green	10	25
86	–	2k.+1k. red	10	25
87	–	3k.50+1k.50 blue	10	25
88	–	9k.+4k.50 brown	10	25

DESIGNS: 2k. Pilot and Heinkel bomber; 3k.50, Infantrymen; 9k. Mechanized column.

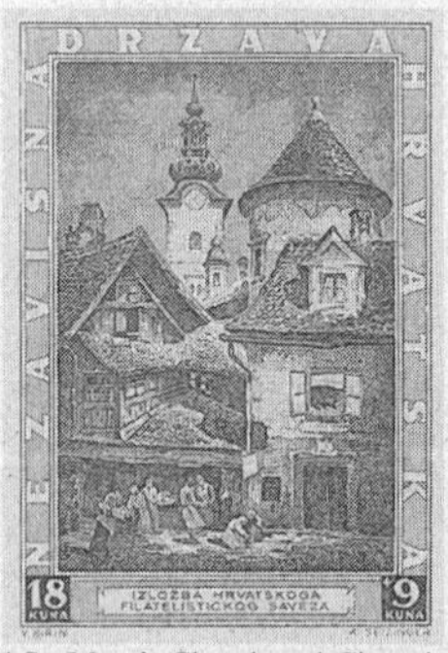

24 St. Mary's Church and Cistercian Monastery, 1650

1943. Philatelic Exhibition, Zagreb.

89	24	18k.+9k. blue	1·40	4·00

1943. Return of Sibenik to Croatia. Optd **HRVATSKO MORE 8, IX. 1943.**

90	24	18k.+9k. blue	3·25	9·00

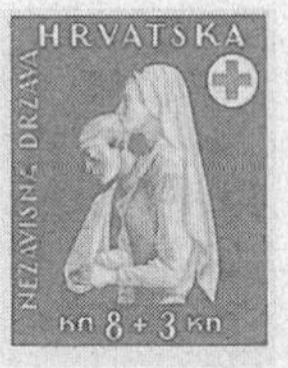

26 Nurse and Patient

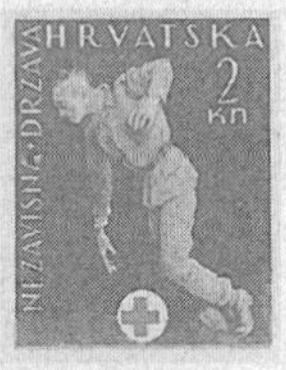

26a

1943. Red Cross Fund.

91	–	1k.+50b. blue	20	50
92	–	2k.+1k. red	20	50
93	–	3k.50+1k.50 blue	20	50
94	26	8k.+3k. brown	20	50
95		9k.+4k. green	20	50
96	–	10k.+5k. violet	30	75
97	26	12k.+6k. blue	30	90
98	–	12k.50+6k. brown	50	1·25
99	26	18k.+8k. orange	75	1·90
100		32k.+12k. grey	1·25	2·75

DESIGN: 1k., 2k., 3k.50, 10k., 12k.50, Mother and children.

1943. Charity Tax. Red Cross Fund. Cross in red.

100a	26a	2k. blue	20	50

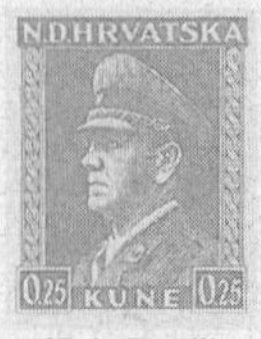

27 A. Pavelic

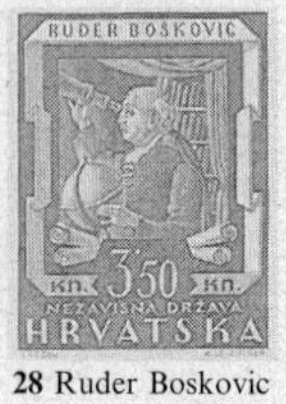

28 Ruder Boskovic

1943.

101	27	25b. red	10	15
105		50b. blue	10	15
102		75b. green	10	15
106		1k. green	10	15
107		1k.50 violet	10	15
108		2k. red	10	15

109	3k. red		10	15
110	3k.50 blue		10	15
111	4k. purple		10	15
103	5k. blue		10	15
112	8k. brown		10	15
113	9k. red		10	15
114	10k. purple		10	15
115	12k. brown		10	15
116	12k.50 black		10	15
117	18k. brown		10	15
104	32k. brown		10	15
118	50k. green		10	15
119	70k. orange		30	60
120	100k. violet		70	1·40

The design of the 25b., 75b., 5k., and 32k. is 20½ × 26 mm, the rest are 22 × 28 mm.

1943. Honouring Ruđer Boskovic (astronomer).

121	28	3k.50 red	15	35
122		12k.50 purple	30	50

29 Posthorn   30 St. Sebastian

1944. Postal and Railway Employees' Relief Fund.

123	29	7k.+3k.50 brn, red & bis	20	40
124		16k.+8k. blue	20	50
125		24k.+12k. red	30	70
126		32k.+16k. black & red	65	1·10

DESIGNS—VERT: 16k. Dove, airplane and globe; 24k. Mercury. HORIZ: 32k. Winged wheel.

1944. War Invalids' Relief Fund.

127	30	7k.+3k.50 mauve & red	20	50
128		16k.+8k. green	25	70
129		24k.+12k. yell, brn & red	25	70
130		32k.+16k. blue	45	1·10

DESIGNS—HORIZ: 16k. Blind man and cripple; 32k. Death of Peter Svacic, 1094. VERT: 24k. Mediaeval statuette.

31 The Legion in Action   32 Jure-Ritter Francetic

1944. Croat Youth Fund. No. 134 perf, others imperf.

131	31	3k.50+1k.50 brown	10	15
132		12k.50+6k.50 blue	10	15
134	32	12k.50+287k.50 black	3·50	11·50
133		18k.+9k. brown	10	15

DESIGN: No. 132, Sentries on the Drina.

33

1944. Labour Front. Inscr "D.R.S.".

135	33	3k.50+1k. red	10	20
136		12k.50+6k. brown	40	65
137		18k.+9k. blue	15	35
138		32k.+16k. green	15	35

DESIGNS: 12k.50, Digging; 18k. Instruction; 32k. "On Parade".

34 Bombed Home   35 War Victim

1944. Charity Tax. War Victims.

138b	34	1k. green	10	15
138c	35	2k. red	10	15
138d		5k. green	10	15
138e		10k. blue	15	35
138f		20k. brown	40	85

36   37 Storm Division Soldiers

1944. Red Cross. Cross in red.

139	36	2k.+1k. green	10	30
140		3k.50+1k.50 red	15	40
141		12k.50+6k. blue	20	50

1945. Creation of Croatian Storm Division on 9th October 1944.

142	37	50k.+50k. red and grey	42·00	£100
143		70k.+70k. sepia & grey	42·00	£100
144		100k.+100k. bl & grey	42·00	£100

DESIGNS: 70k. Storm Division soldiers in action; 100k. Divisional emblem.

38   39

1945. Postal Employees' Fund.

145	38	3k.50+1k.50 grey	10	20
146		12k.50+6k. purple	10	30
147		24k.+12k. green	15	35
148		50k.+25k. purple	20	60

DESIGNS: 12k.50, Telegraph linesman; 24k. Telephone switchboard; 50k. The postman calls.

1945. Labour Day.

149	39	3k.50 brown	20	1·25

40 Interior of Zagreb Cathedral   41 Statue of the Virgin and Shrine

1991. Obligatory Tax. Workers' Fund. Mass for Croatia. Perf or imperf.

150	40	1d.20 gold and black	40	40

1991. Obligatory Tax. Workers' Fund. 700th Anniv of Shrine of the Virgin, Trsat. Perf or imperf.

151	41	1d.70 multicoloured	50	50

42 State Arms   43 Members of Parliament

1991. Obligatory Tax. Workers' Fund. Rally in Ban Jelacic Square, Zagreb. Perf or imperf.

152	42	2d.20 multicoloured	50	50

See also No. 170.

1991. Obligatory Tax. Workers' Fund. First Multiparty Session of Croatian Parliament, 30 May 1990. Perf or imperf.

153	43	2d.20 multicoloured	50	50

44 Sud Aviation Caravelle Jetliner over Zagreb Cathedral and Dubrovnik   45 Anti-tuberculosis Emblem

1991. Air.

154	44	1d. blue, black and red	30	30
155		2d. multicoloured	30	30
156		3d. multicoloured	30	30

DESIGNS: 2d. Bell tower and ruins of Diocletian's Palace, Split; 3d. Sud Aviation Caravelle jetliner over Zagreb Cathedral and Pula amphitheatre.

1991. Obligatory Tax. Anti-tuberculosis Week.

157	45	2d.20 red and blue	30	30

46 Ban Jelacic Statue   48 First Article of Constitution in Croatian

1991. Obligatory Tax. Workers' Fund. Re-erection of Ban Josip Jelacic Equestrian Statue, Zagreb. Perf or imperf.

158	46	2d.20 multicoloured	50	50

1991. No. 150 surch 4⁰⁰ HPT and posthorn.

159	40	4d. on 1d.20 gold & blk	35	35

1991. Obligatory Tax. Workers' Fund. 1st Anniv of New Constitution. Multicoloured. Perf or imperf.

160		2d.20 Type 48	30	30
161		2d.20 Text in English	80	80
162		2d.20 Text in French	80	80
163		2d.20 Text in German	80	80
164		2d.20 Text in Russian	80	80
165		2d.20 Text in Spanish	80	80

49 Book of Croatian Independence   50 17th-century Crib Figures, Kosljun Monastery, Krk

1991. Recognition of Independence.

166	49	30d. multicoloured	1·10	1·10

1991. Christmas.

167	50	4d. multicoloured	60	60

51 "VUKOVAR" and Barbed Wire   52 Ban Josip Jelacic

1992. Obligatory Tax. Vukovar Refugees' Fund.

168	51	2d.20 brown and black	40	40

1992. No. 151 surch 2⁰⁰ HPT and posthorn.

169	41	20d. on 1d.70 mult	3·00	3·00

1992. As No. 152, but redrawn with new value and "HPT" emblem replacing obligatory tax inscr at foot.

170	42	10d. multicoloured	30	30

1992. Obligatory Tax. Famous Croatians. Multicoloured.

171		4d.+2d. Type 52	35	35
172		4d.+2d. Dr. Ante Starcevic (founder of Party of the Right)	30	30
173		7d.+3d. Stjepan Radic (founder of Croation Peasant Party)	30	30

53 Olympic Rings   54 Osijek Cathedral on Paper Dart

1992. Winter Olympic Games, Albertville, France.

174	53	30d. multicoloured	80	80

1992. Air.

175	54	4d. multicoloured	25	20

55 Knin   56 Statue of King Tomislav, Zagreb

1992. Croatian Towns (1st series).

176	55	6d. multicoloured	15	15
177		7d. multicoloured	15	15
178		20d. blue, red and yellow	75	75
179		30d. multicoloured	40	40
180		45d. multicoloured	75	75
181		50d. multicoloured	75	75
182		300d. multicoloured	2·50	2·50

DESIGNS: 7d. Von Eltz Castle, Lukovar; 20d. St. Francis's Church, Ilok; 30d. Dr. Ante Starcevic Street, Gospic; 45d. Rector's Palace, Dubrovnik; 50d. St. Jakov's Cathedral, Sibenik; 300d. Sokak houses, Beli Manastir.

See also Nos. 208/14, 382/7, 523/4, 636 and 639.

1992.

183	56	10d. green	20	20

57 Red Cross Emblems on Globe   58 Map of Croatia on Red Cross

1992. Obligatory Tax. Red Cross Week.

184	57	3d. red and black	20	20

1992. Obligatory Tax. Solidarity Week.

185	58	3d. red and black	20	20

59 Central Railway Station, Zagreb

1992. Centenary of Zagreb Central Railway Station.

186	59	30d. multicoloured	35	35

60 Society Imprint   61 Bishop Josip Strossmayer (patron) and Academy Building

1992. 150th Anniv of Matica Hrvatska (Croatian language society).

187	60	20d. gold and red	25	25

1992. 125th Anniv of Croatian Academy of Sciences and Arts.

188	61	30d. multicoloured	35	35

62 Olympic Rings on Computer Pattern

1992. Olympic Games, Barcelona. Mult.

189		40d. Type 62	35	35
190		105d. Rings and symbolic sports	65	65

63 Bellflowers   64 Blue Rock Thrush

1992. Flowers. Multicoloured.
191	30d. Type 63		25	25
192	85d. Degenia (vert)		50	50

1992. Environmental Protection. Mult.
193	40d. Type 64		25	25
194	75d. Red-spot snake		50	50

65 15th-century Carrack, Dubrovnik
66 "Madonna of Bistrica"

1992. Europa. 500th Anniv of Discovery of America by Columbus (1st issue).
195	65	30d. multicoloured	30	30
196	–	75d. black and red	75	75

DESIGN: 75d. "Indian Horseman" (bronze statue in Chicago by Ivan Mestrovic).
See also Nos. 198/9.

1992. Obligatory Tax. Fund for National Shrine to Madonna of Bistrica.
197	66	5d. gold and blue	20	20

1992. Europa. 500th Anniv of Discovery of America by Columbus (2nd issue). As Nos. 195/6, but new face values and with additional C.E.P.T. posthorns emblem.
198	65	60d. multicoloured	50	50
199	–	130d. black, red and gold (as No. 196)	1·10	1·10

67 Red Cross
69 Dove and Coat of Arms

68 "25"

1992. Obligatory Tax. Anti-tuberculosis Week.
200	67	5d. red and black	20	20

1992. Croatian Language Anniversaries. Mult.
201	40d. Type 68 (25th anniv of Croatian Language Declaration)		25	25
202	130d. "100" (centenary of Croatian "Orthography" by Dr. I. Broz)		45	45

1992. 750th Anniv of Grant of Royal City Charter to Samobor.
203	69	90d. multicoloured	35	35

70 Remains of Altar Screen from Uzdolje Church
71 St. George and the Dragon

1992. 1100th Anniv of Duke Mucimir's Donation (judgement in ecclesiastical dispute).
204	70	60d. multicoloured	25	25

1992. Obligatory Tax. Croatian Anti-cancer League.
205	71	15d. multicoloured	20	20

See also No. 255.

72 Seal of King Bela IV

1992. 750th Anniv of Zagreb's Charter from King Bela IV.
206	72	180d. multicoloured	50	50

73 "Croatian Christmas" (Ljubo Babic)

1992. Christmas.
207	73	80d. multicoloured	25	25

74 Former Town Hall, Vinkovci
75 Lorkovic

1992. Croatian Towns (2nd series). Mult.
208	100d. Type 74		25	20
209	200d. Castle, Pazin (vert)		35	30
210	500d. Jelacic Square, Slavonski Brod		80	75
211	1000d. Town Hall, Jelacic Square, Varazdin		1·25	1·00
212	2000d. Zorin cultural centre, Karlovac		1·40	1·25
213	5000d. St. Donat's Church and St. Stosija's Cathedral belltower, Zadar (vert)		1·60	1·50
214	10000d. Pirovo peninsula and Franciscan monastery, Vis		3·00	2·75

1992. Death Centenary of Blaz Lorkovic (political economist).
218	75	250d. multicoloured	50	50

76 Coiled National Colours
77 Bunic-Vucic

1992. 150th Anniv of "Kolo" (literary Magazine).
219	76	300d. multicoloured	60	60

1992. 400th Birth Anniv of Ivan Bunic-Vucic (poet).
220	77	350d. multicoloured	65	65

78 Ljudevit Gaj Square, Krapina

1993. 800th Anniv of Krapina.
221	78	300d. multicoloured	60	60

79 Tesla

1993. 50th Death Anniv of Nikola Tesla (physicist).
222	79	250d. multicoloured	50	50

80 Quinquerez ("self-portrait")

1993. Death Cent of Ferdo Quiquerez (painter).
223	80	100d. multicoloured	25	25

81 Red Deer

1993. Animals of the Kapacki Rit Swamp. Multicoloured.
224	500d. Type 81		70	70
225	550d. White-tailed sea eagle		80	80

82 Sulentic ("self-portrait")

1993. Birth Centenary of Zlatko Sulentic (painter).
226	82	350d. multicoloured	45	45

83 Kursalon, Lipik

1993. Centenary of Lipik Spa.
227	83	400d. multicoloured	45	45

84 Kovacic (statue, Vojin Bakic)

1993. 50th Death Anniv of Ivan Goran Kovacic (writer).
228	84	200d. multicoloured	30	30

85 Minceta Fortress, Dubrovnik

1993. 59th P.E.N. Literary Congress, Dubrovnik.
229	85	800d. multicoloured	1·00	1·00

86 Ivan Kakaljevic (writer)
87 Mask and Split Theatre

1993. 150th Anniv of First Speech in Croatian Language made to Croatian Parliament.
230	86	500d. multicoloured	45	45

1993. Centenary of Split Theatre.
231	87	600d. multicoloured	45	45

88 Boy and Ruined House
89 Pag in 16th Century

1993. Obligatory Tax. Red Cross Week.
232	88	80d. black and red	20	20

1993. 550th Anniv of Refoundation of Pag.
233	89	800d. multicoloured	60	60

90 Dove
91 Girl at Window

1993. 1st Anniv of Croatia's Membership of U.N.
234	90	500d. multicoloured	40	40

1993. Obligatory Tax. Solidarity Week.
235	91	100d. black and red	20	20

92 "In the Cafe" (Ivo Dulcic)

1993. Europa. Contemporary Art. Mult.
236	700d. Type 92		40	40
237	1000d. "The Waiting Room" (Miljenko Stancic)		60	60
238	1100d. "Two Figures" (Ljubo Ivancic)		80	80

93 "Homodukt" (Milivoj Bijelic)

1993. 45th Art Biennial, Venice. Mult.
239	250d. Type 93		25	25
240	600d. "Snails" (Ivo Dekovic)		45	45
241	1000d. "Esa carta de mi flor" (Zeljko Kipke)		70	70

94 Symbolic Running Track

1993. 12th Mediterranean Games, Roussillon (Languedoc), France.
242	94	700d. multicoloured	45	45

95 "Slavonian Oaks"

1993. 150th Birth Anniv of Adolf Waldinger (painter).
243	95	300d. multicoloured	25	25

96 Battle of Krbava, 1493

1993. Anniversaries of Famous Battles. 16th-century engravings.
244	800d. Type 96		50	50
245	1300d. Battle of Sisak, 1593		90	90

97 Krleza (after Marija Ujevic)

1993. Birth Centenary of Miroslav Krleza (writer).
246 **97** 400d. multicoloured . . . 30 30

98 Cardinal Stepinac

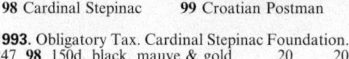

99 Croatian Postman

1993. Obligatory Tax. Cardinal Stepinac Foundation.
247 **98** 150d. black, mauve & gold 20 20

1993. 1st Anniv of Croatia's Membership of Universal Postal Union.
248 **99** 1800d. multicoloured . . . 85 85

100 Paljetak

1993. Birth Centenary of Vlaho Paljetak (singer-songwriter).
249 **100** 500d. multicoloured . . . 30 30

101 Peter Zrinski and Krsto Frankopan

1993. Obligatory Tax. Zrinski-Frankopan Foundation.
250 **101** 200d. blue and grey . . . 20 20

102 "Freedom of Croatia" (central motif of 1918 stamp)

1993. Stamp Day.
251 **102** 600d. multicoloured . . . 30 30

103 Red Cross

1993. Obligatory Tax. Anti-tuberculosis Week.
252 **103** 300d. green, black & red 20 20

104 Antonio Magini's Map of Istria, 1620

105 Smiciklas

1993. 50th Anniv of Incorporation of Istria, Rijeka and Zadar into Croatia.
253 **104** 2200d. multicoloured . . 80 80

1993. 150th Birth Anniv of Tadija Smiciklas (historian).
254 **105** 800d. black, gold and red 30 30

1993. Obligatory Tax. Croatian Anti-cancer League.
255 **71** 400d. multicoloured . . 20 20

106 Allegory of Birth of Croatian History on Shores of the Adriatic

1993. Centenary of National Archaeological Museum, Split.
256 **106** 1000d. multicoloured . . 40 40

107 Girl In Heart

108 Croatian and French Flags and Soldiers

1993. Obligatory Tax. Save Croatian Children Fund.
257 **107** 400d. red, blue and black 20 20

1993. 50th Anniv of Uprising of 13th Pioneer Battalion, Villefranche-de-Rouergue, France.
258 **108** 3000d. multicoloured . . 95 95

109 Tomic

110 Astronomical Diagram

1993. 150th Birth Anniv of Josip Eugen Tomic (writer).
259 **109** 900d. brown, green & red 30 30

1993. 850th Anniv of Publication of "De Essentiis" by Herman Dalmatin.
260 **110** 1000d. multicoloured . . 30 30

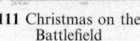

111 Christmas on the Battlefield

112 Skiers

1993. Christmas. Multicoloured.
261 1000d. Type **111** 35 35
262 4000d. "Nativity" (fresco, St. Mary's Church, Dvigrad) 1·40 1·40

1993. Cent of Competitive Skiing in Croatia.
263 **112** 1000d. multicoloured . . 35 35

113 Decorations and Badge

1993. 125th Anniv of Croatian Militia.
264 **113** 1100d. multicoloured . . 35 35

114 Printing Press

1994. 500th Anniv of Printing of First Croatian Book (a Glagolitic missal), Senj.
265 **114** 2200d. brown and red . . 70 70

115 Skier

1994. Winter Olympic Games, Lillehammer, Norway.
266 **115** 4000d. multicoloured . . 1·10 1·10

116 Iguanodon

117 Masthead

1994. Croatian Dinosaur Fossils from West Istria. Multicoloured.
267 2400d. Type **116** 60 60
268 4000d. Iguanodon, skeleton and map . . . . 1·00 1·00
Nos. 267/8 were issued together, se-tenant, forming a composite design.

1994. 150th Anniv of "Zora Dalmatinska" (literary periodical).
269 **117** 800d. multicoloured . . . 30 30

118 University, Emperor Leopold I's Seal and Vice-chancellor's Chain

119 Wolf

1994. 325th Anniv of Croatian University, Zagreb.
270 **118** 2200d. multicoloured . . 70 70

1994. Planet Earth Day.
271 **119** 3800d. multicoloured . . 1·25 1·25

120 Safety Signs and Worker wearing Protective Clothing

121 Globe and Map

1994. 75th Anniv of I.L.O. and 50th Anniv of Philadelphia Declaration (social charter).
272 **120** 1000d. multicoloured . . 40 40

1994. Obligatory Tax. Red Cross Week.
273 **121** 500d. black, stone & red 20 20

122 Flying Man (17th-century idea by Faust Vrancic)

123 Red Cross

1994. Europa. Inventions. Multicoloured.
274 3800d. Type **122** . . . . 1·25 1·25
275 4000d. Quill and pencil writing surname (technical pencil by Slavoljub Penkala, 1906) (32 × 23 mm) . . . . . 1·25 1·25

1994. Obligatory Tax. Solidarity Week.
276 **123** 50l. red, black and grey 20 20

124 Croatian Iris

125 Petrovic

1994. Flowers. Multicoloured.
277 2k.40 Type **124** 75 75
278 4k. Meadow saffron . . . 1·25 1·25

1994. 1st Death Anniv of Drazen Petrovic (basketball player).
279 **125** 1k. multicoloured . . . 35 35

126 Plitvice Lakes

1994. 150th Anniv of Tourism in Croatia. Multicoloured.
280 80l. Type **126** 20 20
281 1k. River Krka 25 25
282 1k.10 Kornati Islands 40 40
283 2k.20 Kopacki Trscak ornithological reserve . . . 70 70
284 2k.40 Opatija Riviera . . . 80 80
285 3k.80 Brijuni Islands . . . 1·25 1·25
286 4k. Trakoscan Castle, Zagorje . . . . 1·40 1·40

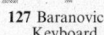

127 Baranovic at Keyboard

128 Monstrance

1994. Musical Anniversaries.
287 **127** 1k. multicoloured 35 35
288 – 2k.20 silver, black & red 65 65
289 – 2k.40 multicoloured . . 80 80
DESIGNS—VERT: 1k. Type **127** (birth centenary of Kresimir Baranovic (composer and conductor/director of Croatian National Theatre Opera, Zagreb, 1915–40)); 2k.20, Vatroslav Lisinski (composer, 175th birth anniv). HORIZ: 2k.40, Score and harp player (350th anniv of Pauline song-book).

1994. Obligatory Tax. Ludbreg Shrine.
290 **128** 50l. multicoloured . . . 20 20

129 Men dressed in Croatian and American Colours

130 Mother and Children

1994. Centenary of Croatian Brotherhood in U.S.A.
291 **129** 2k.20 multicoloured . . 70 60

1994. Obligatory Tax. Save Croatian Children Fund.
292 **130** 50l. multicoloured 20 20

131 Family

132 St. George and the Dragon

1994. International Year of the Family.
293   131   80l. multicoloured   30   30

1994. Obligatory Tax. Croatian Anti-Cancer League.
294   132   50l. multicoloured   20   20

133 Pope John Paul II and his Arms

134 Franjo Bucar (Committee member, 1920–46)

1994. Papal Visit.
295   133   1k. multicoloured   35   35

1994. Cent of International Olympic Committee.
296   134   1k. multicoloured   40   40

135 Red Cross on Leaf

136 The Little Prince (book character)

1994. Obligatory Tax. Anti-tuberculosis Week.
297   135   50l. red, green & black   20   20

1994. 50th Death Anniv of Antoine de Saint-Exupery (writer).
298   136   3k.80 multicoloured . . .   1·00   1·00

137 "Resurrection" (lunette, Gati, Omis)

1994. 13th International Convention on Christian Archaeology, Split and Porec.
299   137   4k. multicoloured . . . .   1·10   1·10

138 "Still Life with Fruits and Basket" (Marino Tartaglia)

1994. Paintings. Multicoloured.
300   2k.40 Type **138**   60   60
301   3k.80 "In the Park" (Milan Steiner)   95   95
302   4k. "Self-portrait" (Vilko Gecan) . . . .   1·25   1·25

139 Plan of Fortress

1994. Obligatory Tax. 750th Anniv of Slavonski Brod.
303   139   50l. yellow, black & red   20   20

140 I.O.C. Centenary Emblem and Flame

1994. Obligatory Tax. National Olympic Committee. Designs incorporating either the National Olympic Committee emblem or the International Olympic Committee centenary emblem.
304   50l. Type **140**   20   20
305   50l. As T **140** but with National Olympic Committee emblem   20   20
306   50l. Tennis and national emblem (vert)   20   20
307   50l. Football and centenary emblem (vert)   20   20
308   50l. As No. 306 but with centenary emblem (vert) . .   20   20
309   50l. As No. 307 but with national emblem (vert) . .   20   20
310   50l. Basketball and centenary emblem (vert)   20   20
311   50l. Handball and national emblem (vert)   20   20
312   50l. As No. 310 but with national emblem (vert) . .   20   20
313   50l. As No. 311 but with centenary emblem (vert) . .   20   20
314   50l. Kayaks and national emblem (vert)   20   20
315   50l. Water polo and centenary emblem (vert) . .   20   20
316   50l. As No. 314 but with centenary emblem (vert) . .   20   20
317   50l. As No. 315 but with national emblem (vert) . .   20   20
318   50l. Running and centenary emblem (vert)   20   20
319   50l. Gymnastics and national emblem (vert)   20   20
320   50l. As No. 318 but with national emblem (vert) . .   20   20
321   50l. As No. 319 but with centenary emblem (vert) . .   20   20

141 Cover of "Gazophylacium"

142 St. Mark's Church and Gas Lamp

1994. 400th Birth Anniv of Ivan Belostenec (lexicographer).
322   141   2k.20 multicoloured . . .   70   70

1994. 900th Annivs of Zagreb (323/5) and Zagreb Bishopric (326). Multicoloured.
323   1k. Type **142**   30   30
324   1k. Street scene from early film, Maxi Cat (cartoon character) and left side of Zagreb Exchange   30   30
325   1k. Right side of Zagreb Exchange, S. Penkala's biplane and Cibona building   30   30
326   4k. 15th-century bishop's crosier and 17th-century view of Zagreb by Valvasor . . . . .   1·00   1·00
Nos. 323/6 were issued together, se-tenant, forming a composite design.

143 "Epiphany" (relief, Vrhovac Church)

1994. Christmas.
328   143   1k. multicoloured   35   30

144 "Translation of the Holy House" (Giovanni Battista Tiepolo)

145 Modern Tie

1994. 700th Anniv of St. Mary's Sanctuary, Loreto.
329   144   4k. multicoloured . . . .   1·10   1·10

1995. Ties. Multicoloured.
330   1k.10 Type **145**   25   25
331   3k.80 English dandy, 1810 . .   80   80
332   4k. Croatian soldier, 1630 . .   85   85

146 St. Catherine's Church and Monastery, Zagreb, and Jesuit

1995. Monasteries. Multicoloured.
334   1k. Type **146** (350th anniv)   20   20
335   2k.40 St. Paul's Monastery, Visovac, and Franciscan monk (550th anniv) . . .   50   50

147 Istrian Short-haired Hunting Dog

1995. Dogs. Multicoloured.
336   2k.20 Type **147**   50   50
337   2k.40 Posavinian hunting dog   50   50
338   3k.80 Istrian wire-haired hunting dog . . . . .   1·00   1·00

148 Rowing

1995. Obligatory Tax. National Olympic Committee. Multicoloured.
339   50l. Type **148**   15   15
340   50l. Petanque   15   15
341   50l. Monument to Drazen Petrovic, Olympic Park, Lausanne   15   15
342   50l. Tennis   15   15
343   50l. Basketball   15   15

149 Reconstruction of Emperor Diocletian's Palace

1995. 1700th Anniv of Split. Multicoloured.
344   1k. Type **149**   20   20
345   2k.20 "Split Harbour" (Emanuel Vidovic)   40   40
346   4k. View of city and bust of Marko Marulic (Ivan Mestrovic)   80   80

150 Player

151 Woman's Head

1995. World Handball Championship, Iceland.
348   150   4k. multicoloured   80   80

1995. Obligatory Tax. Red Cross Week.
349   151   50l. black and red   15   15

152 Storm Clouds and Clear Sky

1995. Europa. Peace and Freedom. Mult.
350   2k.40 Type **152**   50   50
351   4k. Angel (detail of sculpture, Francesco Robba)   80   80

153 Shadow behind Cross

1995. 150th Anniv of July Riots (352) and 50th Anniv of Croatian Surrender at Bleiburg (353). Multicoloured.
352   1k.10 Type **153**   25   25
353   3k.80 Sunrise behind cross . .   80   80

154 Arms and Hand holding Rose

155 Hands

1995. Independence Day.
354   154   1k.10 multicoloured . . .   25   25

1995. Obligatory Tax. Solidarity Week.
355   155   50l. multicoloured   15   15

156 "Installation" (detail) (Martina Kramer)

1995. 46th Art Biennale, Venice. Work by Croatian artists. Multicoloured.
356   2k.20 Type **156**   45   45
357   2k.40 "Paracelsus Paraduchamps" (Mirk Zrinscak) (vert)   50   50
358   4k. "Shadows/136" (Goran Petercol)   80   80

157 "St. Antony" (detail of polyptych by Ljubo Babic, St. Antony's Sanctuary, Zagreb)

1995. 800th Birth Anniv of St. Antony of Padua.
359   157   1k. multicoloured   20   20

158 Loggerhead Turtle

1995. Animals. Multicoloured.
360   2k.40 Type **158**   60   60
361   4k. Bottle-nosed dolphin . .   90   90

159 Osijek Cathedral

160 "Croatian Pieta"

1995. Obligatory Tax. Restoration of Sts. Peter and Paul's Cathedral, Osijek.
362   159   65l. multicoloured   15   15

1995. Obligatory Tax. "Holy Mother of Freedom" War Memorial.
363   160   65l. on 50l. blk, red & bl   70   70
364   – 65l. black, red and blue   15   15
365   – 65l. blue and yellow . .   15   15
DESIGN: 65l. Projected memorial church.
Nos. 364/5 were not issued without surcharge.

161 Town and Fortress

1995. Liberation of Knin.
366 **161** 1k.30 multicoloured . . . 30 30

162 Electric Power Plant

1995. Centenary of Jaruga Hydro-electric Power Station, River Krka.
367 **162** 3k.60 multicoloured . . . 75 75

163 Postman

1995. Stamp Day.
368 **163** 1k.30 multicoloured . . . 30 30

165 Suppe and Heroine of "The Fair Galatea" (operetta)

1995. Death Centenary of Franz von Suppe (composer).
370 **165** 6k.50 multicoloured . . . 1·40 1·40

166 Petrinja Fortress (after Valvasor) and Cavalrymen
167 Ivo Tijardovic

1995. 400th Anniv of Habsburg Capture of Petrinja.
371 **166** 2k.20 multicoloured . . . 45 45

1995. Composers' Anniversaries. Mult.
372 1k.20 Type **167** (birth centenary) 25 25
373 1k.40 Lovro von Matacic (10th death) 30 30
374 6k.50 Jakov Gotovac (birth centenary) . . . . 1·40 1·40

168 Herman Bolle (architect, 150th birth)

1995. Anniversaries. Multicoloured.
375 1k.30 Type **168** 30 30
376 2k.40 Izidor Krsnjavi (artist and art administrator, 150th birth) 50 50
377 3k.60 Gala curtain by Vlaho Bukovac (cent of National Theatre) 75 75

169 Children in Nest
170 Left-hand Detail of Curtain

1995. Obligatory Tax. Save Croatian Children Fund.
378 **169** 65l. multicoloured 15 15

1995. Obligatory Tax. Centenary of National Theatre, Zagreb. Details of gala curtain by Vlaho Bukovac. Multicoloured.
379 65l. Type **170** 15 15
380 65l. Central detail 15 15
381 65l. Right-hand detail 15 15
Nos. 379/81 were issued together, se-tenant, forming a composite design.

171 Zagrebacka Street, Bjelovar

1995. Croatian Towns (3rd series). Mult.
382 1k. Type **171** 20 20
383 1k.30 St. Peter and St. Paul's Cathedral, Osijek (vert) . . 30 30
384 1k.40 Castle, Cakovec (vert) . . 30 30
385 2k.20 Rovinj 45 45
386 2k.40 Korcula 50 50
387 3k.60 Town Hall, Zupanja . . 75 75

172 "50"

1996. 50th Anniversaries. Multicoloured.
395 3k.60 Type **172** (U.N.O.) . . . 75 75
396 3k.60 "5" and "FAO" within biscuit forming "50" (F.A.O.) 75 75

173 Spiro Brusina (zoologist)
174 Birds flying through Sky

1995. Anniversaries. Multicoloured.
397 1k. Type **173** (150th birth) . . 20 20
398 2k.20 Bogoslav Sulek (philologist, death cent) . . 45 45
399 6k.50 Faust Vrancic's "Dictionary of Five European Languages" (400th anniv of publication) . . . . 1·40 1·40

1995. Obligatory Tax. Anti-drugs Campaign.
400 **174** 65l. multicoloured 15 15

175 Breast Screening
176 Hands reading Braille

1995. Obligatory Tax. Croatian Anti-cancer League. Breast Screening Campaign.
401 **175** 65l. multicoloured 15 15

1995. Centenary of Institute for Blind Children, Zagreb.
402 **176** 1k.20 red, yellow & black . . 25 25

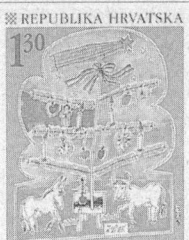

177 Animals under Christmas Tree

1995. Christmas.
403 **177** 1k.30 multicoloured 30 30

178 Polo, Animals in Boat and Court of Kublai Khan

1995. 700th Anniv of Marco Polo's Return from China.
404 **178** 3k.60 multicoloured . . . 75 75

179 Hrvatska Kostajnica
180 Lectionary of Bernardin of Split, 1495 (first printed book using Cakavian dialect)

1995. Liberated Towns. Multicoloured.
405 20l. Type **179** 10 10
406 30l. Slunj 10 10
407 50l. Gracac 10 10
408 1k.20 Drnis (vert) 25 25
409 6k.50 Glina . . . . 1·40 1·40
410 10k. Obrovac (vert) . . . . . 2·00 2·00

1995. Incunabula. Multicoloured.
420 1k.40 Type **180** 30 30
421 3k.60 Callipers and last page of "Spovid Opcena" (manual for confessors), 1496 (first book printed in Croatia) 75 75

 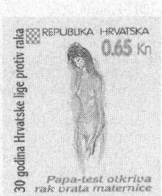

181 Crucifix
182 Breast Cancer Campaign

1996. Events and Anniversaries. Mult.
422 1k.30 St. Marko Krizevcanin (detail of mosaic (Ante Starcevic), St. Marko's Church, Zagreb) (canonization) 30 30
423 1k.30 Type **181** (700th anniv of veneration of miraculous crucifix, St. Guido's Church, Rijeka) 30 30
424 1k.30 Ivan Merz (teacher and Catholic youth worker, birth centenary) 30 30

1996. Obligatory Tax. 30th Anniv of Anti-cancer League.
425 **182** 65l. multicoloured 15 15

183 Eugen Kvaternik (125th anniv of Rakovica Uprising)
184 Madonna and Child and Church

1996. Anniversaries. Multicoloured.
426 1k.20 Type **183** 25 25
427 1k.40 Ante Starcevic (founder of Part of the Right, death centenary) (vert) 30 30

428 2k.20 Stjepan Radic (founder of Croatian Peasant Party) (125th birth anniv and 75th anniv of Peasant Republic constitution) (vert) . . . 45 45
429 3k.60 Collage (75th anniv of Labin Republic) (vert) . . . 75 75

1996. Obligatory Tax. St. Mary of Bistrica Sanctuary.
430 **184** 65l. multicoloured 15 15

185 Julije Domac (founder) and Culture

1996. Centenary of Pharmacology Institute, University of Zagreb.
431 **185** 6k.50 multicoloured . . . . 1·40 1·40

186 Score
187 Cvijeta Zuzoric (beauty)

1996. Music Anniversaries. Multicoloured.
432 2k.20 Type **186** (400th birth anniv of Vinko Jelic, composer) 45 45
433 2k.20 "O" over musical bars (150th anniv of "Love and Malice" (first Croatian opera) by Vatroslav Lisinski) 45 45
434 2k.20 Josip Slavenski (composer, birth cent) . . . 45 45
435 2k.20 "Lijepa nasa domovino" (birth bicent of Antun Mihanovic and 175th birth anniv of Josip Runjanin (composers of National Anthem)) 45 45

1996. Europa. Famous Women. Mult.
436 2k.20 Type **187** 45 45
437 3k.60 Ivana Brlic-Mazuranic (writer) 75 75

188 Olympic Rings
189 Nikola Subic Zrinski of Sziget (Ban of Croatia)

1996. Obligatory Tax. National Olympic Committee.
438 **188** 65l. multicoloured 15 15

1996. 16th and 17th-century Members of Zrinski and Frankopan Families. Multicoloured.
439 1k.30 Type **189** 30 30
440 1k.40 Nikola Zrinski (Ban of Croatia) 30 30
441 2k.20 Petar Zrinski (Ban of Croatia) 45 45
442 2k.40 Katarina Zrinski (wife of Petar and sister of Fran Krsto Frankopan) 50 50
443 3k.60 Fran Krsto Frankopan (writer and revolutionary) . . 75 75

 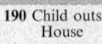 

190 Child outside House
191 Soldier carrying Child

1996. Obligatory Tax. Red Cross Fund.
445 **190** 65l. black and red 15 15

1996. 5th Anniv of National Guard.
446 **191** 1k.30 multicoloured . . . 30 30

192 Istrian Bluebell

193 Child with Red Cross Parcel

1996. Flowers. Multicoloured.
447	2k.40 Type **192**		45	45
448	3k.60 Dubrovnik corn-flower		75	75

1996. Obligatory Tax. Solidarity Week.
449	**193** 65l. black and red		15	15

194 Football

1996. European Football Championship, England.
450	**194** 2k.20 black and red . . .		45	45

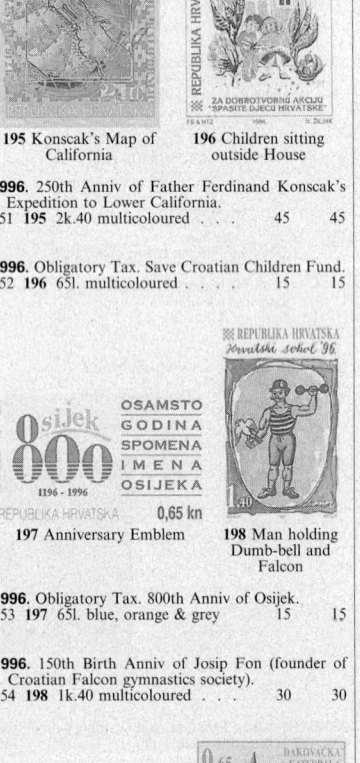

195 Konscak's Map of California

196 Children sitting outside House

1996. 250th Anniv of Father Ferdinand Konscak's Expedition to Lower California.
451	**195** 2k.40 multicoloured . . .		45	45

1996. Obligatory Tax. Save Croatian Children Fund.
452	**196** 65l. multicoloured		15	15

197 Anniversary Emblem

198 Man holding Dumb-bell and Falcon

1996. Obligatory Tax. 800th Anniv of Osijek.
453	**197** 65l. blue, orange & grey		15	15

1996. 150th Birth Anniv of Josip Fon (founder of Croatian Falcon gymnastics society).
454	**198** 1k.40 multicoloured . . .		30	30

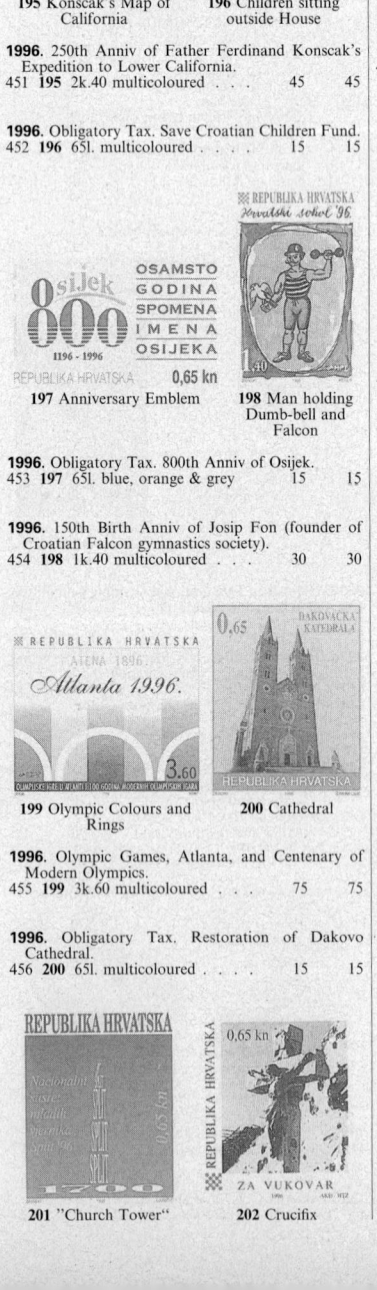

199 Olympic Colours and Rings

200 Cathedral

1996. Olympic Games, Atlanta, and Centenary of Modern Olympics.
455	**199** 3k.60 multicoloured . . .		75	75

1996. Obligatory Tax. Restoration of Dakovo Cathedral.
456	**200** 65l. multicoloured		15	15

201 "Church Tower"

202 Crucifix

1996. Obligatory Tax. 1700th Anniv of Split.
457	**201** 65l. ultramarine and blue		15	15

1996. Obligatory Tax. Vukovar.
458	**202** 65l. multicoloured		15	15

203 Lighted Candle, Shell and Lilies

204 Tweezers holding Stamp

1996. Obligatory Tax. Anti-drugs Campaign.
459	**203** 65l. multicoloured		15	15

1996. Stamp Day. 5th Anniv of Issue of First Postage Stamp by Independent Croatia.
460	**204** 1k.30 multicoloured . . .		30	30

205 Mountains

206 St. Elias's Chapel, Zumberak

1996. Obligatory Tax. Anti-tuberculosis Week.
461	**205** 65l. multicoloured		15	15

1996. 700th Anniv of First Written Reference to Zumberak.
462	**206** 2k.20 multicoloured . . .		45	45

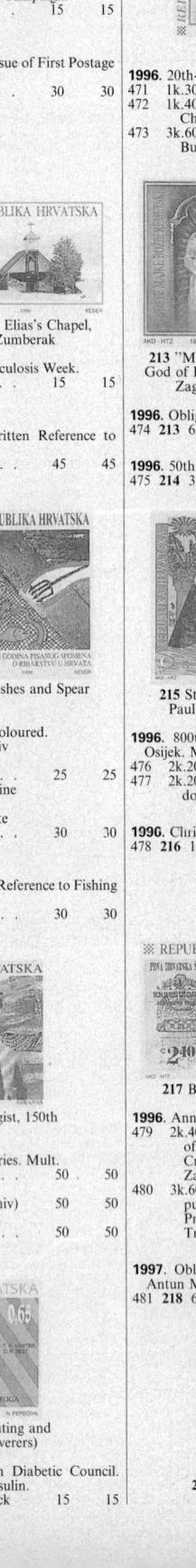

207 Illuminated Page

208 Fishes and Spear

1996. Early Middle Ages. Multicoloured.
463	1k.20 Type **207** (900th anniv of "Vekenega's Book of Gospels")		25	25
464	1k.40 Gottschalk (Benedictine abbot) (1150th anniv of Gottschalk's visit to Duke of Trpimir)		30	30

1996. Millenary of First Written Reference to Fishing in Croatia.
465	**208** 1k.30 multicoloured . . .		30	30

209 Gjuro Pilar (geologist, 150th anniv)

1996. Scientists' Birth Anniversaries. Mult.
466	2k.40 Type **209**		50	50
467	2k.40 Frane Bulic (archaeologist, 150th anniv)		50	50
468	2k.40 Ante Sercer (otolaryngologist, cent)		50	50

210 Sir Frederick Banting and Charles Best (discoverers)

1996. Obligatory Tax. Croatian Diabetic Council. 75th Anniv of Discovery of Insulin.
469	**210** 65l. gold, yellow & black		15	15

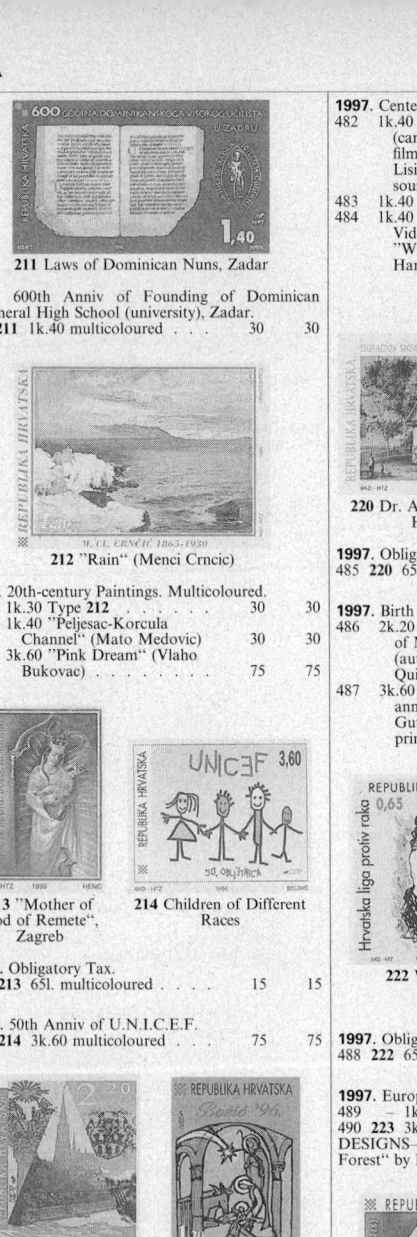

211 Laws of Dominican Nuns, Zadar

1996. 600th Anniv of Founding of Dominican General High School (university), Zadar.
470	**211** 1k.40 multicoloured . . .		30	30

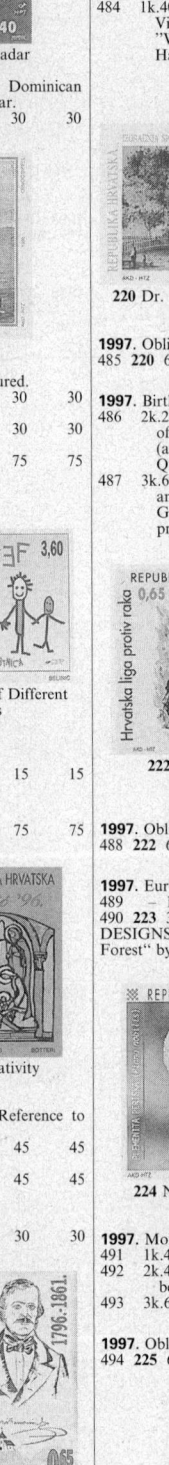

212 "Rain" (Menci Crncic)

1996. 20th-century Paintings. Multicoloured.
471	1k.30 Type **212**		30	30
472	1k.40 "Peljesac-Korcula Channel" (Mato Medovic)		30	30
473	3k.60 "Pink Dream" (Vlaho Bukovac)		75	75

213 "Mother of God of Remete", Zagreb

214 Children of Different Races

1996. Obligatory Tax.
474	**213** 65l. multicoloured . . .		15	15

1996. 50th Anniv of U.N.I.C.E.F.
475	**214** 3k.60 multicoloured . . .		75	75

215 Sts. Peter's and Paul's Cathedral

216 Nativity

1996. 800th Anniv of First Written Reference to Osijek. Multicoloured.
476	2k.20 Type **215**		45	45
477	2k.20 Riverbank and view down street		45	45

1996. Christmas.
478	**216** 1k.30 multicoloured . . .		30	30

217 Bond and Bank

218 Mihanovic

1996. Anniversaries. Multicoloured.
479	2k.40 Type **217** (150th anniv of founding of First Croatian Savings Bank, Zagreb)		50	50
480	3k.60 Frontispiece (bicent of publication of "The Principles of the Corn Trade" by Josip Sipus)		75	75

1997. Obligatory Tax. Birth Bicentenary (1996) of Antun Mihanovic.
481	**218** 65l. multicoloured		15	15

219 "Professor Baltazar" (Zagreb School of Animated Film)

1997. Centenary of Croatian Films. Mult.
482	1k.40 Oktavijan Miletic (cameraman and director) filming "Vatroslav Lisinski" (first Croatian sound film), 1944		30	30
483	1k.40 Type **219**		30	30
484	1k.40 Mirjana Bohanev-Vidovic and Relja Basic in "Who Sings Means No Harm", 1970		30	30

220 Dr. Ante Starcevic's House

221 Don Quixote and Windmill

1997. Obligatory Tax.
485	**220** 65l. multicoloured		15	15

1997. Birth Anniversaries. Multicoloured.
486	2k.20 Type **221** (450th anniv of Miguel de Cervantes (author of "Don Quixote"))		45	45
487	3k.60 Metal type (600th anniv of Johannes Gutenberg (inventor of printing)) (horiz)		75	75

222 Woman

223 "Big Joseph" by Vladimir Nazor (illus. Sasa Santel)

1997. Obligatory Tax. Croatian Anti-cancer League.
488	**222** 65l. multicoloured		15	15

1997. Europa. Tales and Legends.
489	– 1k.30 multicoloured . . .		30	30
490	**223** 3k.60 red, black & gold		75	75

DESIGNS—HORIZ: 1k.30, Elves from "Stribor's Forest" by Ivana Brlic-Mazuranic (illus. Cvijeta Job).

224 Noble Pen Shell

225 Comforting Hand

1997. Molluscs and Insects. Multicoloured.
491	1k.40 Type **224**		30	30
492	2k.40 "Radziella styx" (cave beetle)		50	50
493	3k.60 Giant tun		75	75

1997. Obligatory Tax. Red Cross Week.
494	**225** 65l. multicoloured		15	15

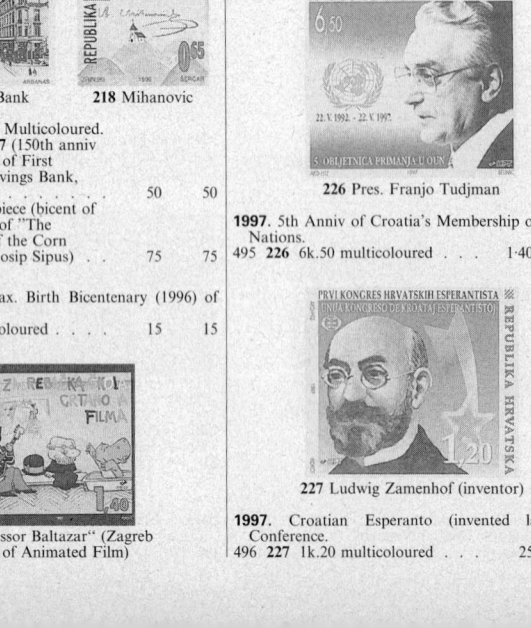

226 Pres. Franjo Tudjman

1997. 5th Anniv of Croatia's Membership of United Nations.
495	**226** 6k.50 multicoloured . . .		1·40	1·40

227 Ludwig Zamenhof (inventor)

1997. Croatian Esperanto (invented language) Conference.
496	**227** 1k.20 multicoloured		25	25

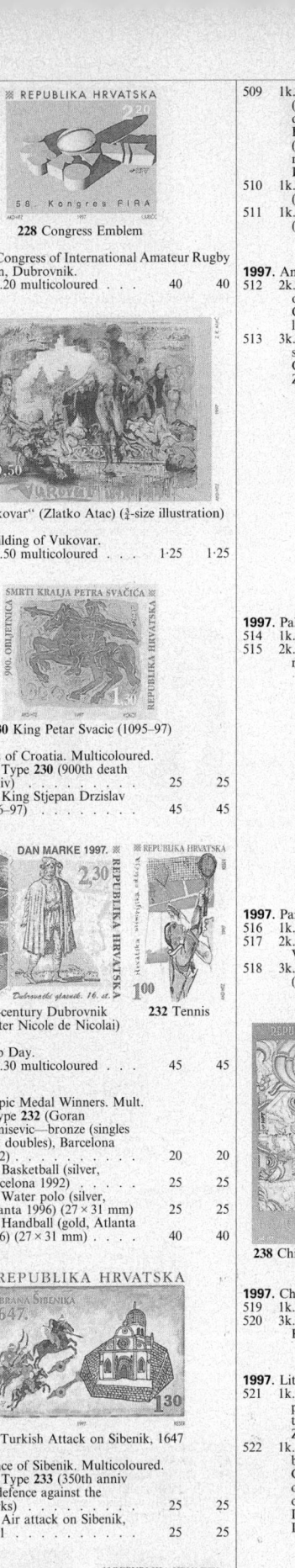

228 Congress Emblem

1997. 58th Congress of International Amateur Rugby Federation, Dubrovnik.
497 **228** 2k.20 multicoloured . . . 40 40

229 "Vukovar" (Zlatko Atac) (¾-size illustration)

1997. Rebuilding of Vukovar.
498 **229** 6k.50 multicoloured . . . 1·25 1·25

230 King Petar Svacic (1095–97)

1997. Kings of Croatia. Multicoloured.
499 1k.30 Type **230** (900th death anniv) . . . 25 25
500 2k.40 King Stjepan Drzislav (996–97) . . . 45 45

231 16th-century Dubrovnik Courier (after Nicole de Nicolai) **232** Tennis

1997. Stamp Day.
501 **231** 2k.30 multicoloured . . . 45 45

1997. Olympic Medal Winners. Mult.
502 1k. Type **232** (Goran Ivanisevic—bronze (singles and doubles), Barcelona 1992) . . . 20 20
503 1k.20 Basketball (silver, Barcelona 1992) . . . 25 25
504 1k.40 Water polo (silver, Atlanta 1996) (27 × 31 mm) . . . 25 25
505 2k.20 Handball (gold, Atlanta 1996) (27 × 31 mm) . . . 40 40

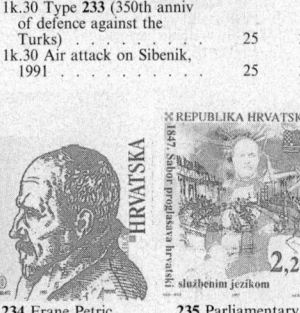

233 Turkish Attack on Sibenik, 1647

1997. Defence of Sibenik. Multicoloured.
506 1k.30 Type **233** (350th anniv of defence against the Turks) . . . 25 25
507 1k.30 Air attack on Sibenik, 1991 . . . 25 25

234 Frane Petric (philosopher) **235** Parliamentary Session (after Ivan Zasche) and Ivan Kukuljevic (politician)

1997. Anniversaries. Multicoloured.
508 1k.40 Type **234** (400th death anniv) . . . 25 25

509 1k.40 "Madonna and Child" (detail from the polyptich of St. Michael in Franciscan Church, Cavtat) (500th anniv of first recorded work of Vicko Lovrin (artist)) 25 25
510 1k.40 Frano Krsinic (sculptor, birth cent) . . . 25 25
511 1k.40 Dubravko Dujsin (actor, 50th death anniv) 25 25

1997. Anniversaries. Multicoloured.
512 2k.20 Type **235** (150th anniv of promulgation of Croatian as official language) 40 40
513 3k.60 Zagreb and elevation of school (centenary of Croatian Grammar School, Zadar) 70 70

236 Primordial Elephant

1997. Palaeontological Finds. Multicoloured.
514 1k.40 Type **236** 25 25
515 2k.40 Fossil of "Viviparus novskaensis" (periwinkle) 45 45

237 "Painter in the Pond" (Nikola Masic)

1997. Paintings. Multicoloured.
516 1k.30 Type **237** 25 25
517 2k.20 "Angelus" (Emanuel Vidovic) 40 40
518 3k.60 "Tree in the Snow" (Slava Raskaj) 70 70

238 Child Jesus in the Stable **239** "Electra" by Sophocles

1997. Christmas. Multicoloured.
519 1k.30 Type **238** 25 25
520 3k.60 "Birth of Jesus" (Isidor Krsnjavi) (33 × 59 mm) . . . 70 70

1997. Literary Anniversaries. Multicoloured.
521 1k. Type **239** (400th anniv of publication of collected translations by Dominko Zlataric) 20 20
522 1k.20 Closed book (300th birth anniv of Filip Grabovac and 250th anniv of publication of his "Best of Folk Speech and the Illyric or Croatian Language") 25 25

240 Ilok **241** Score and Varazdin (Baroque Evenings)

1998. Croatian Towns (4th series).
523 240 5k. violet, brown & red 95 95
524 – 10k. brown, violet & red 2·00 2·00
DESIGN: 10k. Dubrovnik.

1998. Europa. National Festivals. Mult.
531 1k.45 Type **241** 30 30
532 4k. Dubrovnik (Summer Festival) 75 75

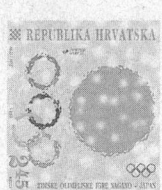

242 Olympic Rings and Japanese Red Sun

1998. Winter Olympic Games, Nagano, Japan.
533 **242** 2k.45 multicoloured . . . 45 45

243 Jelacics Flag and Battle near Moor (lithograph)

1998. Historical Events of 1848. Mult.
534 1k.60 Type **243** 30 30
535 1k.60 "Croatian Assembly in Session" (Dragutin Weingartner) 30 30
536 4k. Ban Josip Jelacic (after Ivan Zasche) (21 × 31 mm) 75 75

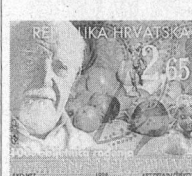

244 Mimara **245** Caesar's Mushroom

1998. Birth Centenary of Ante Topic Mimara (art collector).
537 **244** 2k.65 multicoloured . . . 50 50

1998. Fungi. Multicoloured.
538 1k.30 Type **245** 25 25
539 1k.30 Saffron milk cup ("Lactarius deliciosus") . . 25 25
540 7k.20 "Morchella conica" . . 1·40 1·40

246 Stepinac **247** Magnifying Glass over Fingerprint and Dubrovnik

1998. Birth Centenary of Cardinal Alojzije Stepinac (Archbishop of Zagreb).
541 **246** 1k.50 multicoloured . . . 30 30

1998. 27th European Regional Conference of Interpol, Dubrovnik.
542 **247** 2k.45 multicoloured . . . 50 50

249 Football

1998. World Cup Football Championship, France.
544 **249** 4k. multicoloured 75 75

250 Title Page of "Slavonic Fairy"

1998. Writers' Anniversaries. Multicoloured.
545 1k.20 Type **250** (450th birth anniv of Juraj Barakovic (poet)) 25 25
546 1k.50 Milan Begovic (50th death anniv) 30 30
547 1k.60 Mate Balota (birth centenary) 30 30
548 2k.45 Antun Gustav Matos (125th birth anniv) . . . 50 50
549 2k.65 Matija Antun Relkovic (death bicentenary) . . . 50 50
550 4k. Antun Branko Simic (birth centenary) . . . 75 75

251 Text on Water

1998. 19th Danube Countries Conference, Osijek.
551 **251** 1k.80 multicoloured 35 35

252 Betlheim

1998. Birth Centenary of Dr. Stjepan Betlheim (psychoanalyst).
552 **252** 1k.50 multicoloured . . . 30 30

254 Liburnian Sewn Boat (1st century B.C.)

1998. Croatian Ships. Multicoloured.
554 1k.20 Type **254** 25 25
555 1k.50 Condura (11th–12th centuries) 30 30
556 1k.60 Ragusan (Dubrovnik) carrack (16th century) . . 30 30
557 1k.80 Istrian bracera . . . 35 35
558 2k.45 River Neretva sailing barge 50 50
559 2k.65 Barque 50 50
560 4k. "Vila Velebita" (sail/ steam cadet ship) . . . 75 75
561 7k.20 "Amorela" (car ferry) 1·40 1·40
562 20k. "King Petar Kresimir IV" (missile corvette) . . . 3·75 3·75

255 Mail Coach and Posthorn

1998. Stamp Day. 150th Anniv of Creation of Croatian Supreme Postal Administration.
563 **255** 1k.50 multicoloured 30 30

256 Font and Cathedral

1998. 700th Anniv of Sibenik Bishopric and Proclamation of Sibenik as a Free Borough.
564 **256** 4k. multicoloured 75 75

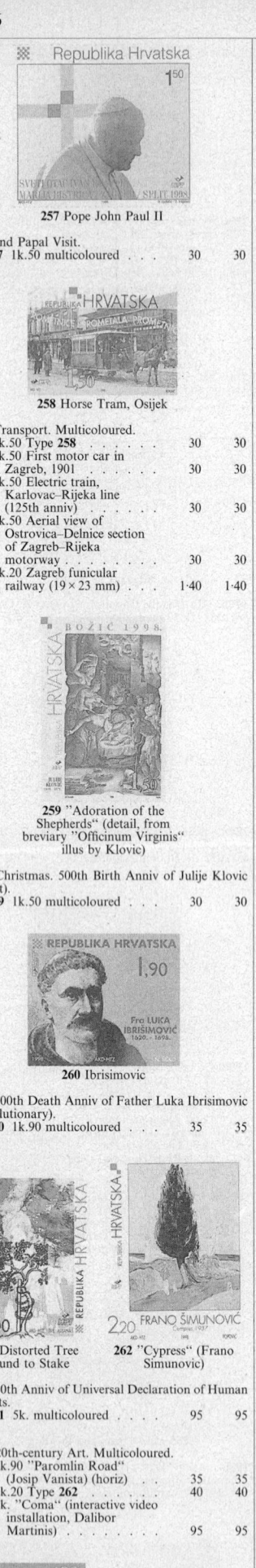

257 Pope John Paul II

1998. 2nd Papal Visit.
565 257 1k.50 multicoloured . . . 30 30

258 Horse Tram, Osijek

1998. Transport. Multicoloured.
566 1k.50 Type **258** 30 30
567 1k.50 First motor car in
Zagreb, 1901 . . . . . . 30 30
568 1k.50 Electric train,
Karlovac–Rijeka line
(125th anniv) 30 30
569 1k.50 Aerial view of
Ostrovica–Delnice section
of Zagreb–Rijeka
motorway 30 30
570 7k.20 Zagreb funicular
railway (19 × 23 mm) . . . 1·40 1·40

259 "Adoration of the
Shepherds" (detail, from
breviary "Officinum Virginis"
illus by Klovic)

1998. Christmas. 500th Birth Anniv of Julije Klovic
(artist).
571 259 1k.50 multicoloured . . . 30 30

260 Ibrisimovic

1998. 300th Death Anniv of Father Luka Ibrisimovic
(revolutionary).
572 260 1k.90 multicoloured . . . 35 35

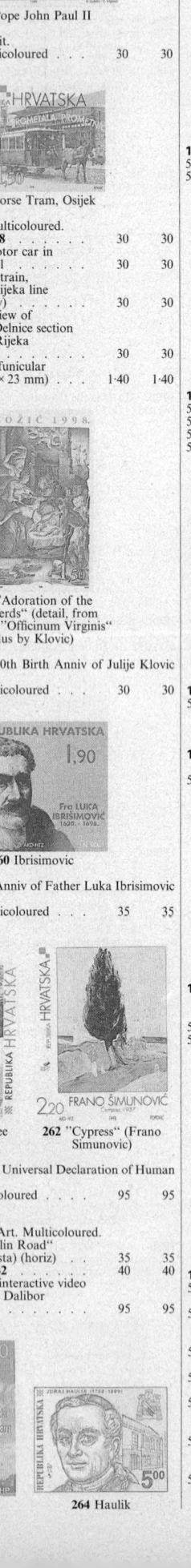

261 Distorted Tree
bound to Stake

262 "Cypress" (Frano
Simunovic)

1998. 50th Anniv of Universal Declaration of Human
Rights.
573 261 5k. multicoloured . . . 95 95

1998. 20th-century Art. Multicoloured.
574 1k.90 "Paromlin Road"
(Josip Vanista) (horiz) . . 35 35
575 2k.20 Type **262** 40 40
576 5k. "Coma" (interactive video
installation, Dalibor
Martinis) 95 95

263 Flags

264 Haulik

1999. Zagreb Fair.
577 263 1k.80 multicoloured . . . 35 35

1999. 130th Death Anniv of Cardinal Juraj Haulik
(first Archbishop of Zagreb).
578 264 5k. multicoloured . . . 95 95

265 Mljet Island National Park

1999. Europa. Parks and Gardens. Multicoloured.
579 1k.80 Type **265** 30 30
580 5k. River Lonja Basin Nature
Park 85 85

266 Viper

1999. The Orsini's Viper. Multicoloured.
581 2k.20 Type **266** 35 35
582 2k.20 Viper on alert . . . 35 35
583 2k.20 Two vipers 35 35
584 2k.20 Viper's head 35 35

267 Anniversary Emblem

268 Orlando's
Pillar with Mask

1999. 50th Anniv of Council of Europe.
585 267 2k.80 multicoloured . . . 45 45

1999. 19th Foundation of European Carnival Cities
Convention, Dubrovnik.
586 268 2k.30 multicoloured . . . 40 40

269 1 Kreutzer Coin, 1849

1999. 150th Anniv of Minting of Jelacic Kreutzer
(587) and Fifth Anniv of Croatian Kuna (588).
Multicoloured.
587 2k.30 Type **269** 40 40
588 5k. One kuna coin 85 85

270 Vladimir Nazor (writer)

1999. Anniversaries. Multicoloured.
589 1k.80 Type **270** (50th death
anniv) 30 30
590 2k.30 Ferdo Livadic
(composer, birth
bicentenary) 40 40
591 2k.50 Ivan Rendic (sculptor,
150th birth anniv) . . . 45 45
592 2k.80 Milan Lenuci (urban
planner, 150th birth anniv) 45 45
593 3k.50 Vjekoslav Klaic
(historian, 150th birth
anniv) 60 60
594 4k. Emilij Laszowski
(historian, 50th death
anniv) 70 70
595 5k. Antun Kanizlic (religious
writer and poet, 300th
birth anniv) 85 85

271 Basilica and Mosaics of Bishop
Euphrasius, St. Maurus and Fish

1999. Euphrasian Basilica, Porec.
596 271 4k. multicoloured 70 70

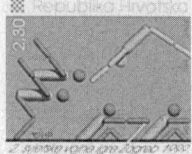

272 Swimming, Diving and
Rowing

1999. 2nd World Military Gamzes, Zagreb.
597 272 2k.30 multicoloured . . . 40 40

273 Reconstruction of Woman,
Skull Fragments and Stone
Tools

1999. Centenary of Discovery of Remains of Early
Man in Krapina. Multicoloured.
598 1k.80 Type **273** 30 30
599 4k. Dragutin Gorjanovic-
Kramberger
(palaeontologist and
discoverer of remains) and
bone fragments 70 70
Nos. 598/9 were issued together, se-tenant, forming
a composite design.

274 U.P.U. Emblem and Clouds

1999. World Post Day. 125th Anniv of Universal
Postal Union.
600 274 2k.30 multicoloured . . . 40 40

275 Lace, "Jesus expelling the
Merchants from the Temple"
(detail of fresco, Ivan Ranger),
and Angel, St. Mary's Church

1999. 600th Anniv of Founding of Paulist Monastery
of the Blessed Virgin Mary in Lepoglava.
Multicoloured.
601 5k. Type **275** 85 85
602 5k. Altar angel and facade of
St. Mary's Church . . . 85 85
603 5k. St. Elizabeth (statue),
detail of choir gallery and
lace 85 85

276 Josip Jelacic, Ban of
Croatia (after C. Lanzelli)

1999. 150th Anniv of Composing of the Jelacic
March by Johann Strauss, the Elder.
604 276 3k.50 multicoloured . . . 60 60

277 Cloud and Chemical Symbol for
Ozone

1999. World Ozone Layer Protection Day.
605 277 5k. multicoloured 85 85

278 Pazin Grammar School

1999. School Anniversaries. Multicoloured.
606 2k.30 Type **278** (centenary) 40 40
607 3k.50 Pozega Grammar
School (300th anniv) . . . 60 60

279 Hebrang

280 "Madonna of the Rose-
garden" (Blaz Jurjev of
Trogir)

1999. Birth Cent of Andrija Hebrang (politician).
608 279 1k.80 multicoloured . . . 30 10

1999. "Croats—Christianity, Culture, Art"
Exhibition, Vatican City.
609 280 5k. multicoloured 85 85

281 "Nativity for my
Children" (plaster relief, Mila
Wood)

1999. Christmas.
610 281 2k.30 multicoloured . . . 35 35

282 "Winter Landscape" (Gabrijel
Jurkic)

1999. Modern Art. Multicoloured.
611 2k.30 Type **282** 35 35
612 3k.50 "Klek" (Oton
Postruznik) 55 55
613 5k. "Stone Table" (Ignjat
Job) (vert) 75 75

283 Tudjman

284 Angel

1999. Death Commem of President Franjo Tudjman.
614 283 2k.30 black and red . . . 35 35
615 5k. blue, black and red . . . 75 75

2000. Holy Year 2000.
616 284 2k.30 multicoloured . . . 35 35

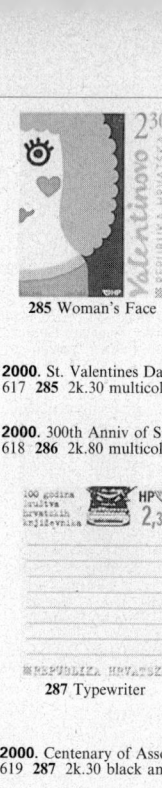

285 Woman's Face

286 Latin Text, Building and Archbishop Stjepan Cosmi (founder)

2000. St. Valentines Day.
617 285 2k.30 multicoloured . . .   35   35

2000. 300th Anniv of Split Grammar School.
618 286 2k.80 multicoloured . . .   40   40

287 Typewriter

288 "The Lamentation" (Andrija Medulic)

2000. Centenary of Association of Croatian Writers.
619 287 2k.30 black and red . . .   35   35

2000. Anniversaries. Multicoloured.
620   1k.80 Type 288 (artist, 500th birth anniv)   30   30
621   2k.30 Matija Petar Katancic (poet, 250th birth anniv)   35   35
622   2k.80 Marija Ruzicka-Strozzi (actress, 150th birth anniv)   40   40
623   3k.50 Statue of Marko Marulic (writer, 550th birth anniv)   55   55
624   5k. "Madonna with the Child and Saints" (Blaz Jurjev Trogiranin) (artist, 550th death anniv) (47 × 25 mm) . . .   75   75

289 Map of Croatia and European Union Stars

2000. Europa. 50th Anniv of Schuman Plan (proposal for pooling the coal and steel industries of France and West Germany). Multicoloured.
625   2k.30 Type 289   35   35
626   5k. "Building Europe" (vert) . . .   75   75

290 Flag

2000. 10th Anniv of Independence.
627 290 2k.30 multicoloured . . .   35   35

292 *Micromeria croatica*

2000. Flowers. Multicoloured.
629   3k.50 Type 292 . . .   55   55
630   5k. *Geranium dalmaticum* . .   75   75

293 Statute and Postcard of Kastav

2000. 600th Anniv of the Kastav Statute.
631 293 1k.80 multicoloured . . .   30   30

294 Blanusa Gospel and "2000"

2000. World Mathematics Year.
632 294 3k.50 multicoloured . . .   55   55

295 Angels (fresco), St. George's Church, Purga

2000. 300th Birth Anniv of Ivan Ranger (artist).
633 295 1k.80 multicoloured . . .   30   30

297 Latin Text

2000. 800th Birth Anniv of Toma, Archdeacon of Split.
635 297 3k.50 black, silver and blue   55   55

298 Vis

2000. Croatian Towns (5th series).
636   – 2k.30 multicoloured . . .   40   40
639 298 3k.50 multicoloured . . .   60   60
DESIGN: 2k.30, Makarska.

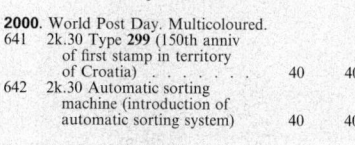

299 Austrian Empire 1850 9k. Stamp and Postmark

2000. World Post Day. Multicoloured.
641   2k.30 Type 299 (150th anniv of first stamp in territory of Croatia) . . .   40   40
642   2k.30 Automatic sorting machine (introduction of automatic sorting system) . . .   40   40

300 Basketball, Football, Handball, Water-polo and Tennis Balls

2000. Olympic Games, Sydney.
643 300 5k. multicoloured   85   85

301 "Nativity" (relief, Church of the Blessed Virgin Mary, Ogulin)

2000. Christmas.
644 301 2k.30 multicoloured . . .   40   40

302 "Korcula" (Vladimir Varlaj)

2000. Paintings. Multicoloured.
645   1k.80 Type 302   30   30
646   2k.30 "Brusnik" (Duro Tiljak)   40   40
647   5k. "Boats" (Ante Kastelancic)   85   85

303 White Dove, Ship and Village

2001. New Millennium.
648 303 2k.30 multicoloured . . .   40   40

305 Scene from *Radmio and Ljubmir* (poem)

2001. 500th Death Anniv of Dzore Drzic (playwright).
650 305 2k.80 multicoloured . . .   45   45

306 Black Rider (comic strip character)

2001. Birth Centenary of Andrija Maurovic (comic strip illustrator).
651 306 5k. multicoloured   85   85

307 Goran Ivanisevic

2001. Croatian Sporting Victories. Multicoloured.
652   2k.50 Type 307 (Wimbledon Men's Champion) . . .   40   40
653   2k.80 Janica Kostelic (Alpine Skiing World Cup Women's Champion) . . .   45   45

308 Olive Tree, Kastel Stafilic

2001.
654 308 1k.80 multicoloured . . .   30   30

309 Water (green splash to left)

2001. Europa. Water Resources. Multicoloured.
655   3k.50 Type 309   60   60
656   5k. Water (blue splash to right)   85   85
Nos. 655/6 were issued together, se-tenant, forming a composite design.

310 Poster (Mikele Janko)

2001. World No Smoking Day.
657 310 2k.50 multicoloured . . .   40   40

311 Apollo (*Parnassius apollo*)

2001. Butterflies. Multicoloured.
658   2k.50 Type 311   40   40
659   2k.80 Scarce large blue (*Maculinea teleius*)   45   45
660   5k. False ringlet (*Coenonympha oedippus*) . .   85   85

312 Vukovar

2001.
661 312 2k.80 multicoloured . . .   45   45

314 Mouths

2001. World Esperanto Congress, Zagreb.
663 314 5k. multicoloured   85   85

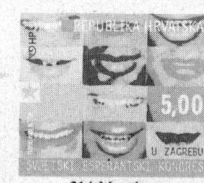

315 Woman and Wall

2001. 50th Anniv of United Nations Commissioner for Refugees (No. 664) and I.O.M. International Organization for Migration (No. 665). Mult.
664   1k.80 Type 315   30   30
665   5k. Refugees and 50IOM . . .   85   85

316 Perforated Blocks of Colour

2001. Stamp Day.
666 316 2k.50 multicoloured . . .   40   40

OFFICIAL STAMPS

O 11

O 12

1942.

O55	O 11	25b. red	10	10
O56		50b. grey	10	10
O57		75b. green	10	10
O58		1k. brown	10	10
O59		2k. blue	10	10
O60		3k. red	10	10
O61		3k.50 red	10	10
O62		4k. purple	10	10
O63		5k. blue	20	40
O64		6k. violet	10	10
O65		10k. green	10	10
O66		12k. red	15	30
O67		12k.50 orange	10	10
O68		20k. blue	20	40
O69	O 12	30k. grey and brown	15	30
O70		40k. grey and violet	15	30
O71		50k. grey and red	50	1·00
O72		100k. salmon & black	50	1·00

POSTAGE DUE STAMPS

1941. Nos. D259/63 of Yugoslavia optd **NEZAVISNA DRZAVA HRVATSKA** in three lines above a chequered shield.

D26	D 10	50p. violet	20	40
D27		1d. red	20	40
D28		2d. blue	6·00	12·50
D29		5d. orange	65	1·25
D30		10d. brown	3·00	8·00

D 9

D 15

1941.

D51	D 9	50b. red	15	45
D52		1k. red	15	45
D53		2k. red	20	60
D54		5k. red	35	90
D55		10k. red	50	1·25

1942.

D67	D 15	50b. olive and blue	15	30
D68		1k. olive and blue	15	35
D69		2k. olive and blue	15	35
D76		4k. olive and blue	10	20
D70		5k. olive and blue	20	40
D78		6k. olive and blue	10	55
D79		10k. blue and indigo	15	50
D80		15k. blue and indigo	15	50
D72		20k. blue and indigo	80	1·60

SERBIAN POSTS IN CROATIA

100 paras = 1 dinar.

REPUBLIC OF SRPSKA KRAJINA

Following Croatia's declaration of independence from Yugoslavia on 30 May 1991 fighting broke out between Serb inhabitants, backed by units of the Yugoslav Federal Army, and Croatian forces. By January 1992, when a ceasefire sponsored by the United Nations and the European Community became effective, the Croatian Serbs and their allies controlled 30% of the country organized into the districts of the Krajina, Western Slavonia and Eastern Slavonia. These were declared peace-keeping zones under United Nations supervision and the Yugoslav Army withdrew. In 1993 the Serbs proclaimed the Republic of Srpska Krajina, covering all three areas, and elections for a separate president and parliament were held in January 1994.

K 1 Stag, Kopacevo Marsh

K 3 Coat of Arms

1993.

K1	K 1	200d. green and yellow	25	25
K2	–	500d. black and red	65	65
K3	–	1000d. green and yellow	1·40	1·40
K4	–	1000d. green and yellow	1·40	1·40
K5	–	2000d. black and red	3·00	3·00

DESIGNS: No. K2, Krka Monastery; K3, Town walls, Knin; K4, Ruined house, Vukovar; K5, Coat of arms.

For 100000d. in same design as No. K2 see No. K12.

1993. Issued at Knin. Nos. 2594/5 of Yugoslavia surch.

K6	5000d. on 3d. black and red	65	65
K7	10000d. on 2d. blue and red	65	65

1993.

K8	K 3	A blue and red	45	45

No. K8 was sold at the internal letter rate.

K 4 Citadel, Knin

A
(K 5)

K 6 Helmet and Swords

1993.

K 9	K 4	5000d. green and red	10	10
K10	–	10000d. green and red	15	15
K11	–	50000d. blue and red	75	75
K12	–	100000d. blue and red	1·50	1·50

DESIGNS: 10000d. Heron, Kopacevo Marsh; 50000d. Icon and church, Vukovar; 100000d. Krka Monastery.

Currency Reform

1993. No. K8 surch with Type K 5 (Cyrillic letter "D").

K13	K 3	"D" on A blue and red	40	40

No. K13 was sold at the new internal letter rate.

1993. Nos. K9/12 surch with Type K 5 (Cyrillic letter "D").

K14	K 4	"D" on 5000d. grn & red	45	45
K15	–	"D" on 10000d. green and red	85	85
K16	–	"D" on 50000d. blue and red	2·50	2·50
K17	–	"D" on 100000d. bl & red	8·50	8·50

1993.

K18	K 6	R blue	1·10	1·10

No. K18 was sold at the internal registered letter rate.

K 7 St. Simeon

1994. Serb Culture and Tradition. Mult.

K19	50p. Type K 7	80	80
K20	80p. Krajina coat of arms (vert)	1·25	1·25
K21	1d. "The Vucedol Dove" (carving) (vert)	1·75	1·75

K 8 Cup-and-saucer

K 9 Krka Monastery

1994. Climbing Plants. Multicoloured.

K22	30p. Type K 8	60	60
K23	40p. "Dipladenia"	85	85
K24	60p. Black-eyed Susan	1·25	1·25
K25	70p. Climbing rose	1·50	1·50

1994.

K26	K 9	5p. red	10	10
K27	–	10p. brown	20	20
K28	–	20p. green	40	40
K29	–	50p. red	55	55
K30	–	60p. violet	70	70
K31	–	1d. blue	2·25	2·25

DESIGNS: 10p. Carin; 20p. Vukovar; 50p. Monument, Batina; 60p. Ilok; 1d. Lake, Plitvice.

K 10 "The Flower of Life" (memorial to Jasenovac Concentration Camp victims)

K 11 "A" over Mosaic

1995. 50th Anniv of End of Second World War.

K32	K 10	60p. multicoloured	1·40	1·40

1995.

K33	K 11	A red	30	30

No. K33 was sold at the internal letter rate.

K 12 Krcic Waterfall, Knin

1995.

K34	K 12	10p. blue	10	10
K35	–	20p. ochre	10	10
K36	–	40p. red	20	20
K37	–	2d. blue	1·10	1·10
K38	–	5d. brown	2·75	2·75

DESIGNS: 20p. Benkovac; 40p. Citadel, Knin; 2d. Petrinja; 5d. Pakrac.

In May 1995 the Croatian army occupied Western Slavonia and in August 1995 the Krajina and these areas were reincorporated into the Republic of Croatia. The only surviving part of the Serbian territories, Eastern Slavonia, was, by agreement, placed under temporary United Nations administration in November 1995 and was subsequently called Sremsko Baranjska Oblast (Srem and Baranya Region).

SREMSKO BARANJSKA OBLAST

K 13 Common Cormorant ("Phalocrocorax carbo"), Kopacevo Marsh

1995. Protected Species. Multicoloured.

K39	80p. Type K 13	90	90
K40	80p. Chamois, Lika	90	90

K 14 St. Dimitriev's Church, Dalj

K 15 Vukovar Marina, River Danube

1995. Churches (1st series).

K41	K 14	5p. green	10	10
K42	–	10p. red	15	15
K43	–	30p. mauve	35	35
K44	–	50p. brown	80	80
K45	–	1d. blue	1·10	1·10

DESIGNS: 10p. St. Peter and St. Paul's Church, Bolman; 30p. St. Nicholas's Church, Mirkovci; 50p. St. Nicholas's Church, Tenja; 1d. St. Nicholas's Church, Vukovar.

See also Nos. K48/53.

1996. River Danube Co-operation.

K46	K 15	1d. multicoloured	1·50	1·50

K 16 The Worker's Hall, Vukovar

K 17 Archangel Church, Darda

1996.

K47	K 16	A red	30	30

No. K47 was sold at the internal letter rate.

1996. Churches (2nd series).

K48	K 17	10p. brown	10	10
K49	–	50p. violet	10	10
K50	–	1d. green	15	15
K51	–	2d. green	45	45
K52	–	5d. blue	1·90	1·90
K53	–	10d. blue	3·75	3·75

DESIGNS: 50p. St. George's Church, Knezevo; 1 d St. Nicholas's Church, Jagodnjak; 2d. Archangel Gabriel's Church, Brsadin; 5d. St. Stephen's Church, Borovo Selo; 10d. St. Nicholas's Church, Pacetin.

K 18 Nikola Tesla

K 19 Milica Stojadinovic-Srpkinja (1830–78) (poetess)

1996. 140th Birth Anniv of Nikola Tesla (inventor).

K54	K 18	1d.50 multicoloured	1·50	1·50

1996. Europa, Famous Women, Mult.

K55	1d.50 Type K 19	2·50	2·50
K56	1d.50 Mileva Marie-Einstein (1875–1948) (mathematician)	2·50	2·50

K 20 Jasna Sekaric (Olympic gold medal winner)

K 21 Milutin Milankovic

1996. Centenary of Modern Olympic Games.

K57	K 20	1d.50 multicoloured	1·25	1·25

1996. Milutin Milankovic (geophysicist) Commemoration (1879–1958).

K58	K 21	1d.50 multicoloured	1·25	1·25

K 22 "Madonna and Child" (icon)

K 23 Pigeon

1996. Christmas.

K59	K 22	1d.50 multicoloured	1·25	1·25

1997. Domestic Pets. Multicoloured.

K60	1d. Type K 23	50	50
K61	1d. Budgerigar	50	50
K62	1d. Cat	50	50
K63	1d. Black labrador	50	50

1997. No. K18 surch or optd (No. K67) with crosses obliterating former name.

K64	K 6	10p. on R blue	10	10
K65		20p. on R blue	10	10
K66		30p. on R blue	15	15
K67		R (90p.) blue	40	40
K68		1d. on R blue	30	30
K69		1d.50 on R blue	60	60
K70		2d. on R blue	80	80
K71		5d. on R blue	1·50	1·50
K72		10d. on R blue	3·75	3·75
K73		20d. on R blue	9·00	9·00

K 25 St. Peter and St. Paul's Cathedral, Orolik

K 26 Prince Marko and The Turks

1997. Restoration of Orthodox Church, Ilok.

K74	K 25	50p.+50p. blue	35	35
K75	–	60p.+50p. mauve	35	35
K76	–	1d.20+50p. red	55	55

DESIGNS: 60p. St. George's Church, Tovarnik; 1d.20, Church, Negoslavci.

1997. Europa. Tales and Legends. Mult.

K77		1d. Type K **26**	70	70
K78		1d. Emperor Trajan	70	70

The postal administration of the Srem and Baranya Region was reincorporated into that of the Republic of Croatia on 19 May 1997. Eastern Slavonia was returned to Croatian control on 15 January 1998.

CUBA Pt. 15

An island in the W. Indies, ceded by Spain to the United States in 1898. A republic under U.S. protection until 1901 when the island became independent. The issues to 1871, except Nos. 13, 14, 19, 20/7, 32, 44 and 48, were for Puerto Rico also.

1855. 8 reales plata fuerte (strong silver reales) = 1 peso.
1866. 100 centimos = 1 escudo.
1871. 100 centimos = 1 peseta.
1881. 100 milesimas = 100 centavos = 1 peso.
1898. 100 cents = 1 U.S. dollar.
1899. 100 centavos = 1 peso.

SPANISH COLONY

1

5

1855. Imperf.

6	**1**	½r. green	5·00	50
9		½r. blue	2·50	50
10		1r. green	2·40	50
11a		2r. red	9·25	2·75

Nos. 10/11 optd **HABILITADO POR LA NACION** were issues of Philippines (Nos. 44/5).

1855. No. 11a surch **Y** ¼.

12	**1**	Y¼ on 2r. red	£160	55·00

1862. Imperf.

13	**5**	¼r. black on buff	9·50	11·50

6

7

1864. Imperf.

14	**6**	¼r. black on buff	11·50	16·00
15		½r. green	3·00	50
16		½r. green on pink	9·00	1·50
17		1r. blue on brown	2·50	55
18b		2r. red	15·00	4·50

1866. Dated "1866". Imperf.

19	**7**	5c. mauve	21·00	27·00
20		10c. blue	2·75	60
21		20c. green	1·25	60
22		40c. pink	7·00	5·50

1866. No. 14 optd **66**. Imperf.

23	**6**	¼r. black on buff	42·00	55·00

1867. Dated "1867". Perf.

24	**7**	5c. mauve	32·00	15·00
25		10c. blue	16·00	60
26		20c. green	11·00	60
27		40c. pink	11·00	12·00

9

11

1868. Dated "1868".

28	**9**	5c. lilac	11·00	9·00
29		10c. blue	2·50	1·00
30		20c. green	4·50	2·25
31		40c. pink	11·00	5·25

1868. Nos. 28/31 optd **HABILITADO POR LA NACION**.

36	**9**	5c. lilac	42·00	27·00
37		10c. blue	42·00	27·00
38		20c. green	42·00	27·00
39		40c. pink	42·00	27·00

1869. Dated "1869".

32	**9**	5c. pink	17·00	8·50
33		10c. brown	2·50	1·25
34		20c. orange	4·00	1·90
35		40c. lilac	24·00	8·00

1869. Nos. 32/5 optd **HABILITADO POR LA NACION**.

40	**9**	5c. pink	95·00	32·00
41		10c. brown	40·00	25·00
42		20c. orange	35·00	25·00
43		40c. lilac	50·00	25·00

1870.

44	**11**	5c. blue	£120	55·00
45		10c. green	1·50	50
46		20c. brown	1·50	50
47		40c. pink	£120	28·00

12

13

1871. Dated "1871".

48	**12**	12c. lilac	10·00	8·00
49		25c. blue	1·60	60
50		50c. green	1·60	60
51		1p. brown	23·00	5·50

1873.

52	**13**	12½c. green	16·00	9·00
53		25c. grey	1·50	50
54		50c. brown	85	50
55		1p. brown	£200	28·00

1874. Dated "1874".

56	**12**	12½c. brown	6·50	6·00
57		25c. blue	45	40
58		50c. lilac	55	40
59		1p. red	£100	50·00

14

15

1875.

60	**14**	12½c. mauve	60	85
61		25c. blue	30	15
62		50c. green	30	15
63		1p. brown	6·00	3·25

1876. Inscr "ULTRAMAR 1876".

64	**15**	12½c. green	1·40	1·50
65a		25c. lilac	45	25
66		50c. blue	45	25
67		1p. black	5·75	2·75

1877. Inscr "CUBA 1877".

68	**15**	10c. green	17·00	
69		12½c. lilac	4·50	3·00
70		25c. green	30	10
71		50c. black	30	10
72		1p. brown	22·00	8·75

1878. Inscr "CUBA 1878".

73	**15**	5c. blue	25	20
74		10c. black	45·00	
75a		12½c. bistre	2·40	1·75
76a		25c. green	15	10
77		50c. green	15	10
78		1p. red	6·00	3·75

1879. Inscr "CUBA 1879".

79	**15**	5c. black	35	25
80		10c. orange	70·00	30·00
81		12½c. pink	35	25
82		25c. blue	35	25
83		50c. grey	35	25
84		1p. bistre	11·00	7·25

1880. "Alfonso XII" key-type inscr "CUBA 1880".

85	X	5c. green	25	10
86		10c. red	50·00	
87		12½c. lilac	25	10
88		25c. lilac	25	10
89		50c. brown	25	10
90		1p. brown	3·00	1·90

1881. "Alfonso XII" key-type inscr "CUBA 1881".

91	X	1c. green	25	10
92		2c. pink	26·00	
93a		2½c. bistre	50	10
94		5c. lilac	25	10
95		10c. brown	25	10
96		20c. brown	3·25	3·25

1882. "Alfonso XII" key-type inscr "CUBA".

97	X	1c. green	35	15
98		2c. pink	1·40	15
118		2½c. brown	20	10
119		2½c. mauve	65	45
100		5c. lilac	1·40	20
123		5c. grey	1·75	25
101		10c. brown	30	10
126		10c. blue	85	55
121		20c. brown	11·00	1·90
122		20c. lilac	11·00	2·75

1883. 1882 issue optd or surch with fancy pattern.

103	X	5c. lilac	1·50	80
106		5 on 5c. lilac	1·00	65
104		10c. brown	4·00	3·75
107		10 on 10c. brown	1·60	1·00
105		20c. brown	65·00	29·00
111		20 on 20c. brown	16·00	11·50

The surcharges exist in four different patterns.

1890. "Baby" key-type inscr "ISLA DE CUBA".

135	Y	1c. brown	8·75	5·50
147		1c. grey	5·00	2·75
159		1c. blue	2·10	30
169		1c. purple	65	20
136		2c. blue	4·75	1·75
148		2c. brown	95	35
160		2c. pink	21·00	4·25
170		2c. red	5·50	15
137		2½c. green	6·50	3·50
149		2½c. orange	29·00	8·00
161		2½c. mauve	1·90	20
171		2½c. pink	40	15
138		5c. grey	50	55
150		5c. green	60	35
172		5c. blue	30	15
139		10c. brown	1·90	70
151		10c. pink	1·25	35
173		10c. green	1·50	15
140		20c. purple	50	45
152		20c. blue	6·50	6·50
162		20c. brown	16·00	8·50
174		20c. lilac	9·50	4·25
175		40c. brown	19·00	10·00
176		80c. brown	32·00	15·00

1898. "Curly Head" key-type inscr "CUBA 1898 Y 99".

183	Z	1m. brown	20	15
184		2m. brown	20	15
185		3m. brown	20	15
186		4m. brown	2·50	1·25
187		5m. brown	15	15
188		1c. purple	15	15
189		2c. green	15	15
190		3c. brown	15	15
191		4c. orange	6·00	2·00
192		5c. pink	55	15
193		6c. blue	20	15
194		8c. brown	50	20
195		10c. red	65	20
196		15c. grey	2·50	20
197		20c. purple	30	10
198		40c. mauve	1·60	15
199		60c. black	1·75	15
200		80c. brown	8·00	6·00
201		1p. green	8·00	6·00
202		2p. blue	16·00	6·00

OFFICIAL STAMPS

1860. As Nos. O50/3 of Spain but without full points after "OFICIAL" and "ONZAS" or "LIBRA". Imperf.

O12		½o. black on yellow	–	30·00
O13		1o. black on pink	–	30·00
O14		4o. black on green	–	£170
O15		1l. black on blue	–	£350

The face values of Nos. O12/15 are expressed in onzas (ounces) or libra (pound), referring to the maximum weight for which each value could prepay postage.

PRINTED MATTER STAMPS

All Printed Matter stamps are key-types inscribed "CUBA IMPRESOS".

1888. "Alfonso XII".

P129	X	½m. black	15	10
P130		1m. black	15	10
P131		2m. black	15	10
P132		3m. black	70	40
P133		4m. black	1·10	70
P134		8m. black	5·50	2·40

1890. "Baby".

P141	Y	½m. brown	45	35
P142		1m. brown	45	35
P143		2m. brown	75	50
P144		3m. brown	75	50
P145		4m. brown	6·25	3·50
P146		8m. brown	6·25	3·50

1892. "Baby".

P153	Y	½m. lilac	10	10
P154		1m. lilac	10	10
P155		2m. lilac	20	10
P156		3m. lilac	1·50	50
P157		4m. lilac	3·50	3·00
P158		8m. lilac	6·00	4·25

1894. "Baby".

P163	Y	½m. pink	15	10
P164		1m. pink	40	10
P165		2m. pink	40	10
P166		3m. pink	1·40	60
P167		4m. pink	2·50	70
P168		8m. pink	5·25	3·00

1896. "Baby".

P177	Y	½m. green	15	10
P178		1m. green	15	10
P179		2m. green	15	10
P180		3m. green	1·50	50
P181		4m. green	3·50	3·00
P182		8m. green	6·00	4·25

UNITED STATES ADMINISTRATION

1899. Stamps of United States of 1894 surch **CUBA** and value.

246		1c. on 1c. green (No. 283)	4·00	35
247		2c. on 2c. red (No. 270)	4·25	30
248		2½c. on 2c. red (No. 270)	2·50	40
249		3c. on 3c. violet (No. 271)	7·50	1·40
250		5c. on 5c. blue (No. 286)	8·00	1·25
251		10c. on 10c. brown (No. 289)	15·00	5·00

29 Statue of Columbus

1899.

307	**29**	1c. green	1·10	10
308	–	2c. red	1·10	10
303	–	3c. purple	2·00	15
304	–	5c. blue	3·25	45
310	–	10c. brown	2·25	35

DESIGNS: 2c. Palms; 3c. Statue of "La India" (Woman); 5c. Liner "Umbria" (Commerce); 10c. Ploughing Sugar Plantation.

POSTAGE DUE STAMPS

1899. Postage Due stamps of United States of 1894 surch **CUBA** and value.

D253	D **87**	1c. on 1c. red	35·00	4·00
D254		2c. on 2c. red	35·00	4·00
D255		5c. on 5c. red	35·00	4·00
D256		10c. on 10c. red	21·00	1·90

SPECIAL DELIVERY STAMP

1899. No. E283 of United States surch **CUBA. 10 c. de PESO.**

E252	E **46**	10c. on 10c. blue	£100	80·00

INDEPENDENT REPUBLIC

1902. Surch **UN CENTAVO HABILITADO OCTUBRE 1902** and figure **1**.

306		1c. on 3c. purple (No. 303)	1·75	40

36 Major-General Antonio Maceo

37 B. Maso

1907.

311	**36**	50c. black and slate	1·10	40
318		50c. black and violet	1·10	40

1910.

312	**37**	1c. violet and green	55	15
320		1c. green	85	10
313	–	2c. green and red	1·10	10
321	–	2c. red	85	10
314	–	3c. blue and violet	55	20
315	–	5c. green and blue	10·00	75
322	–	5c. blue	2·00	10
316	–	8c. violet and olive	55	20
323	–	8c. black and olive	2·00	35
317	–	10c. blue and sepia	4·50	25
319	–	1p. black and slate	6·50	3·00
324	–	1p. black	4·00	1·10

PORTRAITS: 2c. M. Gomez. 3c. J. Sanguily. 5c. I. Agramonte. 8c. C. Garcia. 10c. Mayia. 1p. C. Roloff.

40 Map of W. Indies

43 Gertrudis Gomez de Avellaneda

1914.

325	**40**	1c. green	40	15
326		2c. red	40	15
328		3c. violet	2·00	25
329		5c. blue	2·25	15
330		8c. olive	2·25	65
331		10c. brown	3·75	70
332		10c. olive	3·25	70
333		50c. orange	28·00	9·00
334		$1 slate	40·00	17·00

1914. Birth Centenary of Gertrudis Gomez de Avellaneda (poetess).

335	**43**	5c. blue	8·00	3·00

44 Jose Marti

47

1917.

336	**44**	1c. green	65	10
337	–	2c. red (Gomez)	65	10
338	–	3c. violet (La Luz)	65	10
339	–	5c. blue (Garcia)	65	10
349a	–	8c. brown (Agramonte)	2·75	20
341	–	10c. brown (Palma)	1·60	10
342	–	20c. green (Saco)	5·00	45

343 – 50c. red (Maceo) . . . . . 8·00 45
344 – 1p. black (Cespedes) . . . 8·00 45

1927. 25th Anniv of Republic.
352 **47** 25c. violet . . . . . 8·50 3·25

48 PN 9 Flying Boat over Havana Harbour

1927. Air.
353 **48** 5c. blue . . . . 3·25 1·40

49 T. Estrada Palma

1928. 6th Pan-American Conference.
354 **49** 1c. green 25 15
355 – 2c. red 25 15
356 – 5c. blue 55 25
357 – 8c. brown . . . . . . 3·75 1·50
358 – 10c. brown 55 45
359 – 13c. orange . . . . . 1·10 50
360 – 20c. olive . . . . . . 1·40 60
361 – 30c. purple . . . . . 4·50 1·25
362 – 50c. red . . . . 4·50 1·75
363 – 1p. black . . . . . . 9·00 5·00
DESIGNS: 2c. Gen. G. Machado; 5c. El Morro, Havana; 8c. Railway Station, Havana; 10c. President's Palace; 13c. Tobacco plantation; 20c. Treasury Secretariat; 30c. Sugar Mill; 50c. Havana Cathedral; 1p. Galician Immigrants' Centre, Havana.

1928. Air. Lindbergh Commemoration. Optd **LINDBERGH FEBRERO 1928.**
364 **48** 5c. red . . . . 4·00 1·60

51 The Capitol, Havana **52** Hurdler

1929. Inauguration of Capitol.
365 **51** 1c. green 25 20
366 – 2c. red 30 35
367 – 5c. blue 40 30
368 – 10c. brown 75 35
369 – 20c. purple . . . . . 3·25 1·40

1930. 2nd Central American Games, Havana.
370 **52** 1c. green 55 35
371 – 2c. red 55 40
372 – 5c. blue 85 40
373 – 10c. brown . . . . . 1·40 85
374 – 20c. purple . . . . . 9·00 3·00

1930. Air. Surch **CORREO AEREO NACIONAL** and value.
375 **47** 10c. on 25c. violet . . . . 2·75 1·10

54 Fokker Super Trimotor over Beach

1931. Air.
376 **54** 5c. green 20 10
377 – 8c. red . . . . 2·25 60
378 – 10c. blue 25 10
379 – 15c. red 60 25
380 – 20c. brown 65 10
381 – 30c. purple . . . . . 1·10 25
382 – 40c. orange . . . . . 2·75 45
383 – 50c. green . . . . . 3·00 50
384 – 1p. black . . . . . . 5·75 1·75

55 Ford "Tin Goose" over Forest

1931. Air.
385 **55** 5c. purple 20 10
386 – 10c. black 25 10
387 – 20c. red . . . . . . 1·25 35
388 – 20c. pink . . . . . . 2·25 70
389 – 50c. blue . . . . . . 3·75 1·00
390 – 50c. turquoise . . . 2·75 90

56 Mangos of Baragua **57** Battle of Mal Tiempo

1933. 35th Anniv of War of Independence.
391 **56** 3c. brown 80 20
392 **57** 5c. blue 60 30
393 – 10c. green . . . . . 1·60 30
394 – 13c. red . . . . . . 1·90 90
395 – 20c. black . . . . . 4·00 3·25
DESIGNS—HORIZ: 10c. Battle of Coliseo; 13c. Maceo, Gomez and Zayas. VERT: 20c. Campaign Monument.

1933. Establishment of Revolutionary Govt. Stamps of 1917 optd **GOBIERNO REVOLUCIONARIO 4-9-1933** or surch also.
396 **44** 1c. green 85 30
397 – 2c. on 3c. vio (No. 338) . . 85 30

59 Dr. Carlos J. Finlay **61** Map of Caribbean

1934. 101st Birth Anniv of C. J. Finlay ("yellow-fever" researcher).
398 **59** 2c. red . . . . 1·10 35
399 – 5c. blue . . . . 2·00 45

1935. Air. Havana–Miami "Air Train". Surch **PRIMER TREN AEREO INTERNACIONAL. 1935 O'Meara y du Pont + 10 cts.** Imperf or perf.
400 **54** 10c.+10c. red . . . . . 4·25 4·25

1936. Free Port of Matanzas. Inscr as in T **61.** Perf or imperf (same prices).
401 **61** 1c. green (postage) 20 15
402 – 2c. red 30 15
403 – 4c. purple . . . . . 1·25 20
404 – 5c. blue . . . . . . 1·50 35
405 – 8c. brown . . . . . 1·40 55
406 – 10c. green . . . . . 1·40 55
407 – 20c. brown . . . . . 2·75 2·25
408 – 50c. slate . . . . . 7·00 3·25
409 – 5c. violet (air) 40 20
410 – 10c. orange . . . . . 1·00 20
411 – 20c. green . . . . . 2·75 80
412 – 50c. black . . . . . 10·50 4·00
DESIGNS—POSTAGE: 2c. Matanzas Bay and Free Zone; 4c. "Rex" (liner) in Mantanzas Bay; 5c. Ships in the Free Zone; 8c. Bellamar Caves; 10c. Yumuri Valley; 20c. Yumuri River; 50c. Sailing ship and steamer. AIR: 5c. Aerial panorama; 10c. Airship "Macon" over Concord Bridge; 20c. Airplane "Cuatro Vientos" over Matanzas; 50c. San Severino Fortress.

63 President J. M. Gomez **64** Gen. J. M. Gomez Monument

1936. Inauguration of Gomez Monument.
413 **63** 1c. green . . . . . . 1·60 45
414 **64** 2c. red . . . . 2·10 65

65 "Peace and Labour"

66 Maximo Gomez Monument

1936. Inaug of Maximo Gomez Monument.
415 **65** 1c. green (postage) 30 15
416 **66** 2c. red 30 15
417 – 4c. purple 55 15
418 – 5c. blue . . . . . . 2·75 70

419 – 8c. olive . . . . . . 4·00 1·10
420 – 5c. violet (air) . . . . 2·25 1·40
421 – 10c. brown . . . . . 4·00 2·00
DESIGNS—VERT: 4c. Flaming torch; 8c. Dove of Peace. HORIZ: 5c. (No. 418) Army of Liberation; 5c. (No. 420) Lightning; 10c. "Flying Wing".

68 Caravel and Sugar Cane

1937. 400th Anniv of Cane Sugar Industry.
422 – 1c. green . . . . . . 1·10 45
423 – 2c. red 80 20
424 **68** 5c. blue . . . . 2·50 40
DESIGNS (each with caravel in upper triangle). HORIZ: 2c. Early sugar mill; 5c. Modern sugar mill.

69 Mountain View (Bolivia) **70** Camilo Henriquez (Chile)

1937. American Writers and Artists Assn.
424a – 1c. green (postage) . . . 55 55
424b **69** 1c. green 55 55
424c – 2c. red 55 55
424d – 2c. red 55 55
424e **70** 3c. violet 85 85
424f – 3c. violet 85 85
424g – 4c. brown 85 85
424h – 4c. brown . . . . . 1·75 1·75
424i – 5c. blue . . . . . . 1·10 1·10
424j – 5c. blue . . . . . . 1·10 1·10
424k – 8c. green . . . . . 3·25 3·25
424l – 8c. green . . . . . 1·40 1·40
424m – 10c. brown . . . . 1·75 1·75
424n – 10c. brown . . . . 1·75 1·75
424o – 25c. lilac . . . . . 35·00 18·00
424p – 5c. red (air) . . . . 3·75 3·25
424q – 5c. red . . . . . . 3·75 3·25
424r – 10c. blue . . . . . 3·75 3·25
424s – 10c. blue . . . . . 3·75 3·25
424t – 20c. green . . . . 6·00 5·50
424u – 20c. green . . . . 6·00 5·50
DESIGNS—POSTAGE: No. 424a, Arms of the Republic (Argentina); No. 424c, Arms (Brazil); No. 424f, Gen. F. de Paula Santander (Colombia); No. 424g, Autograph of Jose Marti (Cuba); No. 424j, Juan Montalvo (Ecuador); No. 424k, Abraham Lincoln (U.S.A.); No. 424l, Quetzal and scroll (Guatemala); No. 424m, Arms (Haiti); No. 424n, Francisco Morazan (Honduras); No. 424r, Inca gate, Cuzco (Peru); No. 424s, Atlacatl (Indian warrior) (El Salvador); No. 424t, Simon Bolivar (Venezuela); No. 424u, Jose Rodo (Uruguay). HORIZ: No. 424d, River bushes (Canada); No. 424h, National Monument (Costa Rica); No. 424i, Columbus Lighthouse (Dominican Republic); No. 424o, Ships of Columbus; No. 424p, Arch (Panama); No. 424q, Carlos Lopez (Paraguay).

1937. Centenary of Cuban Railway. Surch **1837-1937 PRIMER CENTENARIO FERROCARRIL EN CUBA** and value either side of an early engine and coach.
425 **47** 10c. on 25c. violet . . . . 5·50 1·00

1938. Air. 25th Anniv of D. Rosillo's Overseas Flight from Key West to Havana. Optd **1913 1938 ROSILLO Key West-Habana.**
426 **48** 5c. orange . . . . . . 3·75 1·75

74 Pierre and Marie Curie **75** Allegory of Child Care

1938. International Anti-cancer Fund. 40th Anniv of Discovery of Radium.
427 **74** 2c.+1c. red . . . . . 2·50 95
428 – 5c.+1c. blue . . . . . 2·50 95

1938. Obligatory Tax. Anti-T.B. Fund.
429 **75** 1c. green 30 20

76 Native and Cigar **80** Calixto Garcia

1939. Havana Tobacco Industry.
430 **76** 1c. green 20 10
431 – 2c. red 45 10
432 – 5c. blue . . . . . . 1·00 15
DESIGNS: 2c. Cigar, globe and wreath of leaves; 5c. Tobacco plant and box of cigars.

1939. Air. Experimental Rocket Post. Optd **EXPERIMENTO DEL COHETE Postal ANO DE 1939.**
433 **55** 10c. green . . . . . . 35·00 5·50

1939. Birth Centenary of Gen. Calixto Garcia. Perf or imperf.
434 **80** 2c. red 55 20
435 – 5c. blue . . . . . . 1·10 45
DESIGN: 5c. Garcia on horseback.

82 Nurse and Child **83** Gonzalo de Quesada and Union Flags **84** Rotarian Symbol, Flag and Tobacco Plant

1939. Obligatory Tax. Anti-T.B.
436 **82** 1c. red 30 10

1940. 50th Anniv of Pan-American Union.
437 **83** 2c. red . . . . 1·10 55

1940. Rotary International Convention.
438 **84** 2c. red . . . . 1·75 80

85 Lions, Emblem, Flag and Palms **86** Dr. Gutierrez

1940. Lions International Convention, Havana.
439 **85** 2c. red . . . . 1·75 80

1940. Centenary of Publication of First Cuban Medical Review.
440 **86** 2c. red 85 55
441 – 5c. blue . . . . . . 1·40 55

87 Sir Rowland Hill and G.B. 1d. of 1840 and Cuba Issues of 1855 and 1899

1940. Air. Centenary of 1st Adhesive Postage Stamps.
443 **87** 10c. brown . . . . . 4·50 2·50

88 "Health" protecting Children **89** Heredia and Niagara Falls

1940. Obligatory Tax. Children's Hospital and Anti-T.B. Funds.
445 **88** 1c. blue 20 10

1940. Air. Death Centenary of J. M. Heredia y Campuzano (poet).
446 – 5c. green . . . . . . 2·25 1·10
447 **89** 10c. grey . . . . . . 2·75 1·40
DESIGN: 5c. Heredia and palms.

90 General Moncada and Sword **91** Moncada riding into Battle

1941. Birth Centenary of H. Moncada.
448 **90** 3c. brown . . . . . . 1·00 50
449 **91** 5c. blue . . . . . . 1·00 50

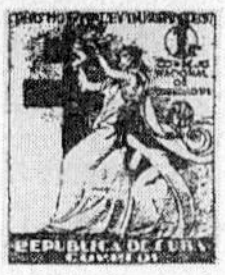
92 Mother and Child

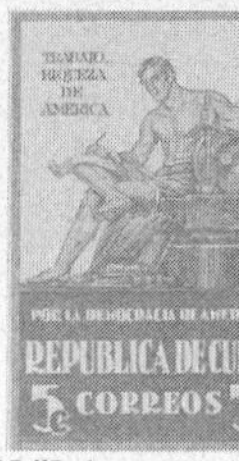
95 "Labour, Wealth of America"

1941. Obligatory Tax. Anti-T.B.
450 **92** 1c. brown 20 10

1942. American Democracy. Imperf or perf.
451 – 1c. green 25 10
452 – 3c. brown 35 15
453 **95** 5c. blue 55 20
454 – 10c. mauve . . . . 1·40 65
455 – 13c. red . . . . 2·00 85
DESIGNS: 1c. Western Hemisphere; 3c. Cuban Arms and portraits of Maceo, Bolivar, Juarez and Lincoln; 10c. Tree of Fraternity, Havana; 13c. Statue of Liberty.

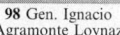

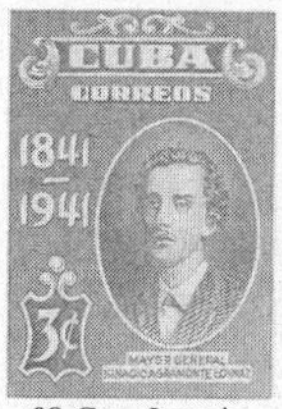
98 Gen. Ignacio Agramonte Loynaz

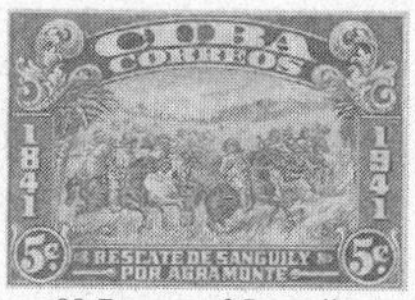
99 Rescue of Sanguily

1942. Birth Centenary of Gen. I. A. Loynaz.
456 **98** 3c. brown 75 40
457 **99** 5c. blue . . . . 1·50 55

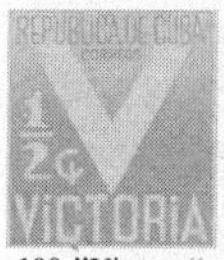
100 "Victory"

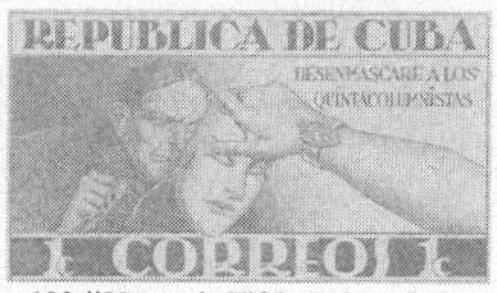
102 "Unmask Fifth Columnists"

1942. Obligatory Tax. Red Cross Fund.
458 **100** ½c. orange 20 10
459 ½c. grey 20 10

1942. Obligatory Tax. Anti-T.B. Fund. Optd **1942.**
460 **92** 1c. red 30 10

1943. Anti-Fifth Column.
461 **102** 1c. green 25 15
462 – 3c. red 45 15
463 – 5c. blue 45 20
464 – 10c. brown . . . . 1·75 70
465 – 13c. purple . . . . 2·25 1·10
DESIGNS—HORIZ: (45 × 25 mm.) 5c. Woman in snake's coils ("The Fifth Column is like the Serpent — destroy it"); 10c. Men demolishing column with battering-ram ("Fulfil your patriotic duty by destroying the Fifth Column"). As Type **102**. 13c. Woman with monster "Don't be afraid of the Fifth Column. Attack it". VERT: Girl with finger to lips "Be Careful! The Fifth Column is spying on you".

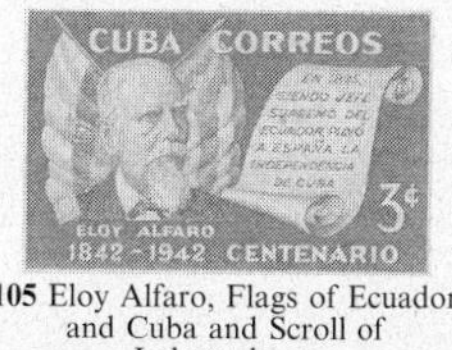
105 Eloy Alfaro, Flags of Ecuador and Cuba and Scroll of Independence

1943. Birth Centenary of E. Alfaro (former President of Ecuador).
466 **105** 3c. green . . . . 1·25 55

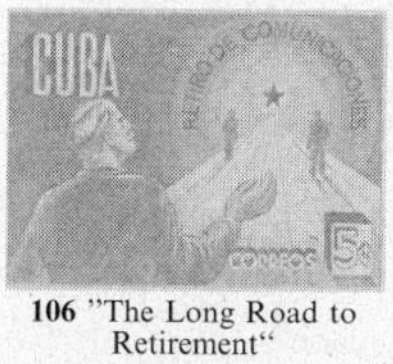
106 "The Long Road to Retirement"

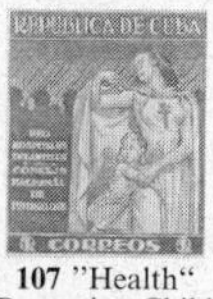
107 "Health" Protecting Child

1943. Postal Employees' Retirement Fund.
467 **106** 1c. green 65 35
470 3c. red 55 35
471 5c. blue 90 35

1943. Obligatory Tax. Anti-tuberculosis.
473 **107** 1c. brown 20 10

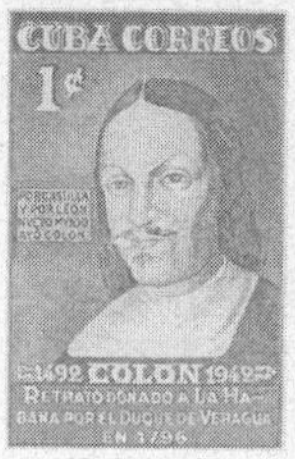
108 Columbus

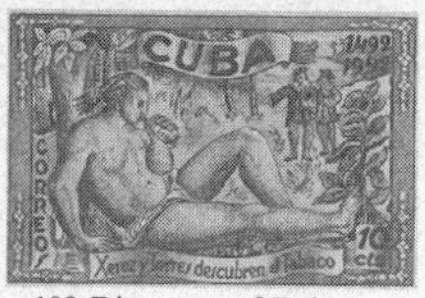
109 Discovery of Tobacco

1944. 450th Anniv of Discovery of America.
474 **108** 1c. green (postage) . . . 20 15
475 – 3c. brown 30 15
476 – 5c. blue 40 20
477 **109** 10c. violet . . . . 2·25 65
478 – 13c. red . . . . 6·50 1·25
479 – 5c. olive (air) . . . . . . 1·50 35
480 – 10c. grey . . . . 1·75 65
DESIGNS—VERT: 3c. Bartolome de las Casas; 5c. (No. 476), Statue of Columbus. HORIZ: 5c. (No. 479) Mountains of Gibara; 10c. (No. 480), Columbus Lighthouse; 13c. Columbus at Pinar del Rio.

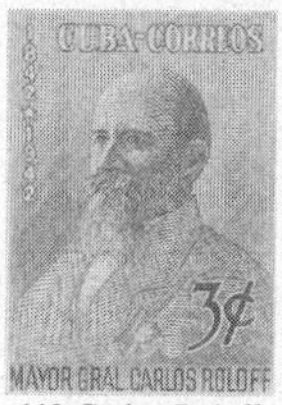
110 Carlos Roloff

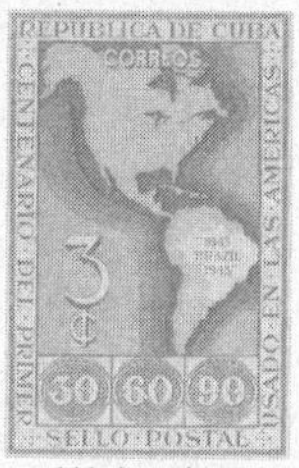
111 American Continents and Brazilian "Bull's Eyes" stamps

1944. Birth Centenary of Major-Gen. Roloff.
481 **110** 3c. violet 95 30

1944. Cent of 1st American Postage stamps.
482 **111** 3c. brown . . . . 1·75 55

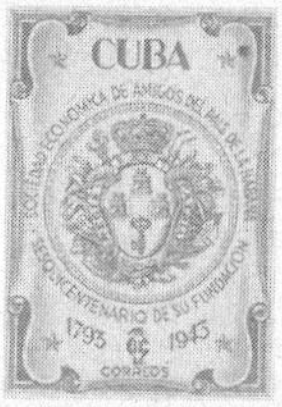
112 Society Seal

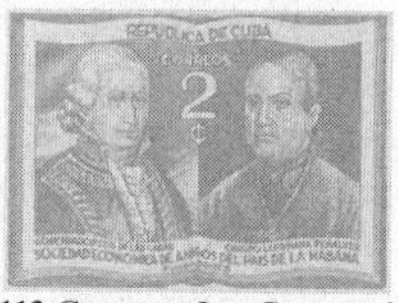
113 Governor Las Casas and Bishop Penalver

1945. 150th Anniv of Economic Society of Friends of Havana.
483 **112** 1c. green 35 15
484 **113** 2c. red 65 30

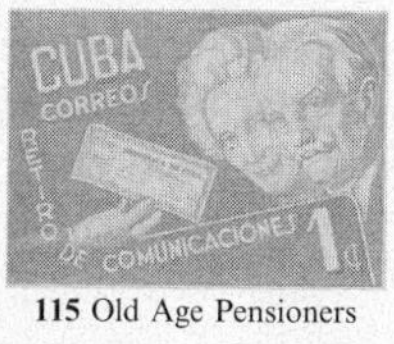
115 Old Age Pensioners

1945. Postal Employees' Retirement Fund.
485 **115** 1c. green 20 10
487 2c. red 40 15
489 5c. blue 75 30

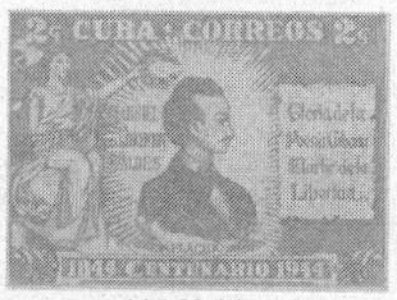
116 Valdes

1946. Death Centenary of Gabriel de la Concepcion Valdes (poet).
491 **116** 2c. red 85 45

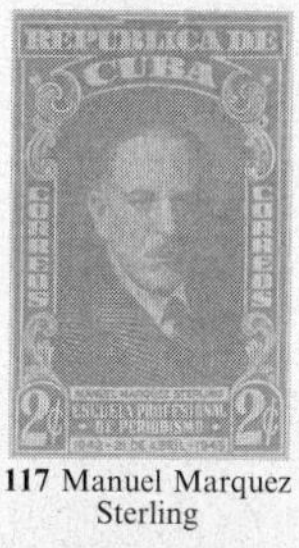
117 Manuel Marquez Sterling

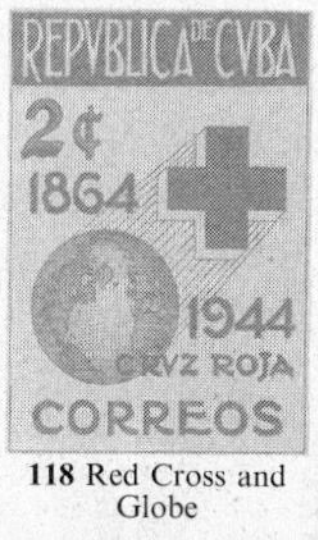
118 Red Cross and Globe

1946. Founding of "Manuel Marquez Sterling" Professional School of Journalism.
492 **117** 2c. red 85 45

1946. 80th Anniv of International Red Cross.
493 **118** 2c. red 90 45

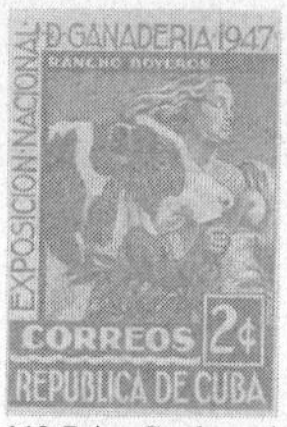
119 Prize Cattle and Dairymaid

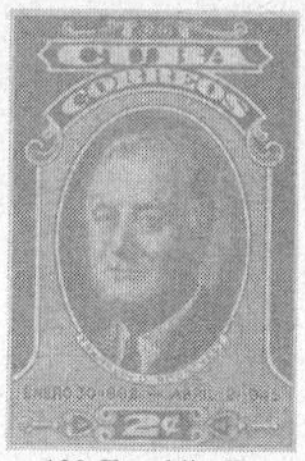
120 Franklin D. Roosevelt

1947. National Cattle Show.
494 **119** 2c. red . . . . 1·10 35

1947. 2nd Death Anniv of Pres. Roosevelt.
495 **120** 2c. red . . . . 1·25 35

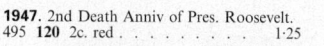

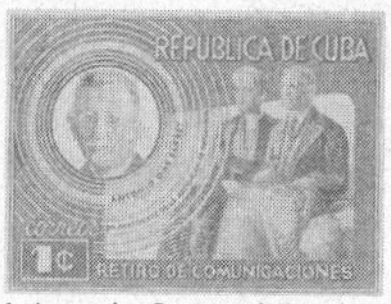
121 Antonio Oms and Pensioners

1947. Postal Employees' Retirement Fund.
496 **121** 1c. green 15 15
497 2c. red 25 15
498 5c. blue 75 30

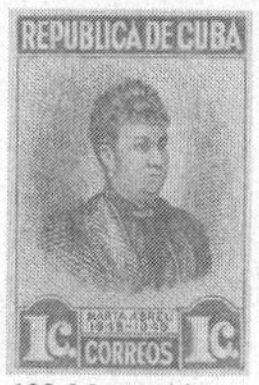
122 Marta Abreu

1947. Birth Centenary of M. Abreu (philanthropist).
499 **122** 1c. green 30 15
500 – 2c. red 45 20
501 – 5c. blue 65 30
502 – 10c. violet . . . . 1·40 65
DESIGNS: 2c. Allegory of Charity; 5c. Monument; 10c. Allegory of Patriotism.

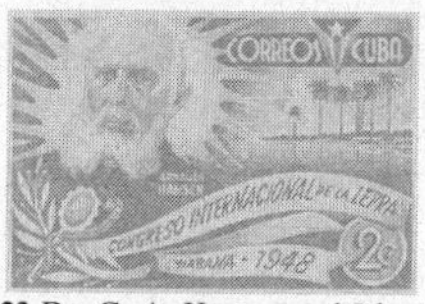
123 Dr. G. A. Hansen and Isle of Pines

1948. Int Leprosy Relief Congress, Havana.
503 **123** 2c. red 90 40

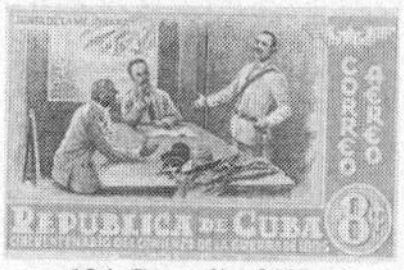
124 Council of War

1948. Air. 50th Anniv of War of Independence.
504 **124** 8c. black and yellow . . . 1·90 85

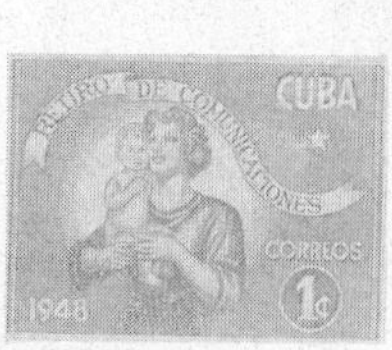
125 Woman and Child

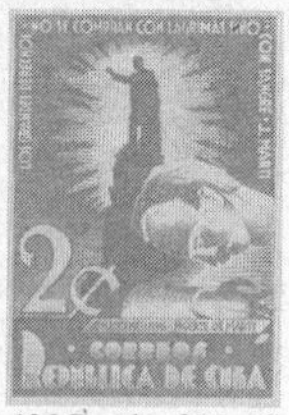
126 Death of Marti

1948. Postal Employees' Retirement Fund.
506 **125** 1c. green 30 15
507 2c. red 30 15
508 5c. blue 75 30

1948. 50th Death Anniv of Jose Marti.
509 **126** 2c. red 35 20
510 – 5c. blue . . . . 1·10 35
DESIGN: 5c. Marti disembarking at Playitas.

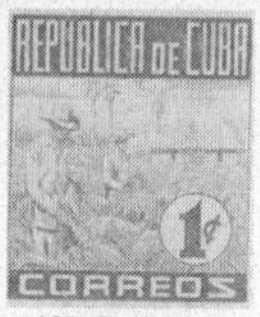
127 Gathering Tobacco

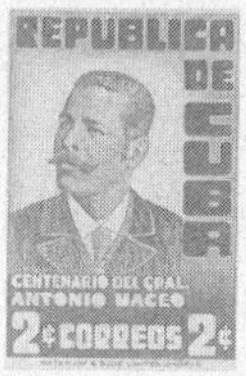
129 Antonio Maceo

1948. Havana Tobacco Industry.
511 **127** 1c. green 15 10
512 – 2c. red 20 10
513 – 5c. blue 35 15
DESIGNS: 2c. Girl with box of cigars and flag; 5c. Cigar and shield.
This set comes again redrawn with smaller designs of 21 × 25 mm.

1948. Birth Centenary of Gen. Maceo.
514 – 1c. green 10 10
515 **129** 2c. red 15 10
516 – 5c. blue 25 15
517 – 8c. brown and black . . . 35 30
518 – 10c. green and brown . . 45 20
519 – 20c. blue and red . . . . 1·75 75
520 – 50c. blue and red . . . . 3·00 2·00
521 – 1p. violet and black . . . 6·00 2·75
DESIGNS—VERT: 1c. Equestrian statue of Maceo; 5c. Mausoleum at El Cacahual. HORIZ: 8c. Maceo and raised swords; 10c. Maceo leading charge; 20c. Maceo at Peralejo; 50c. Declaration at Baragua; 1p. Death of Maceo at San Pedro.

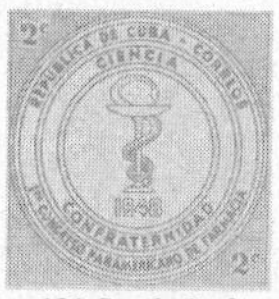
131 Symbol of Medicine

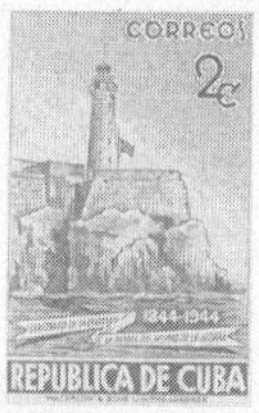
132 Morro Castle and Lighthouse

1948. 1st Pan-American Pharmaceutical Congress.
522 **131** 2c. red 95 40

1949. Centenary of El Morro Lighthouse.
523 **132** 2c. red . . . . 1·25 50

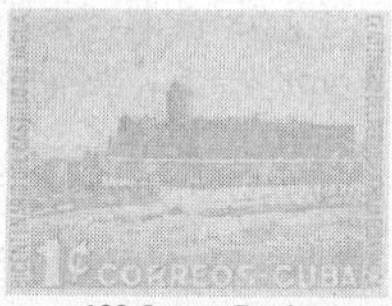
133 Jagua Castle

1949. Centenary of Newspaper "Hoja Economica" and Bicentenary of Jagua Fortress.
524 **133** 1c. green 40 20
525 2c. red 65 35

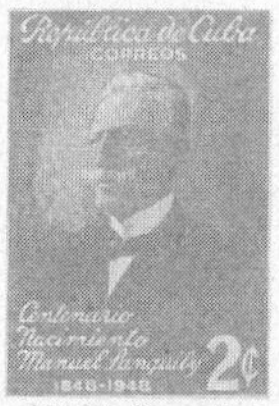
134 M. Sanguily

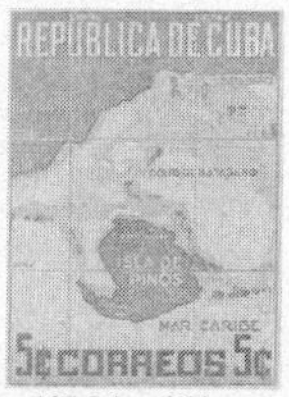
135 Isle of Pines

1949. Birth Centenary of Manuel Sanguily y Garritte (poet).
526 **134** 2c. red 35 20
527 5c. blue 90 35

1949. 20th Anniv of Return of Isle of Pines to Cuba.
528 **135** 5c. blue 95 35

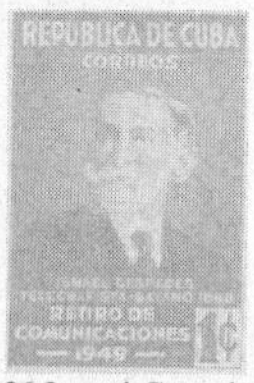
136 Ismael Cespedes

137 Woman and Child

1949. Postal Employees' Retirement Fund.
529 **136** 1c. green 25 15
530 2c. red 25 15
531 5c. blue 75 30

1949. Obligatory Tax. Anti-tuberculosis.
532 **137** 1c. blue 25 10
547 1c. red 25 10
No. 547 is dated "1950".

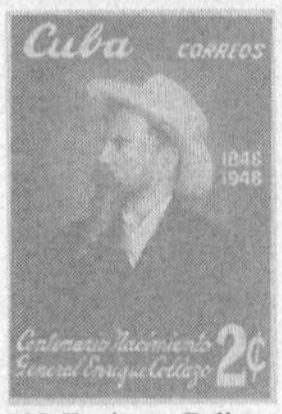
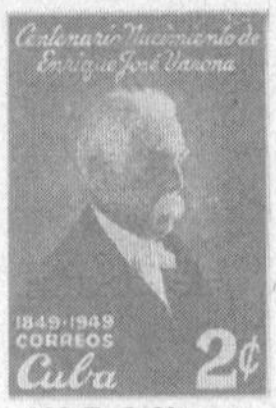

138 Enrique Collazo **139** E. J. Varona

1950. Birth Centenary of Gen. Collazo.
533 **138** 2c. red 30 15
534 5c. blue 90 35

1950. Birth Centenary of Varona (writer).
535 **139** 2c. red 35 20
536 5c. blue 90 35

1950. National Bank Opening. No. 512 optd **BANCO NACIONAL DE CUBA INAUGURACION 27 ABRIL 1950.**
540 2c. red 90 35

1950. 75th Anniv of U.P.U. Optd **U.P.U. 1874 1949.**
541 **127** 1c. green 35 15
542 – 2c. pink (As No. 512) 40 25
543 – 5c. blue (As No. 513) 95 35

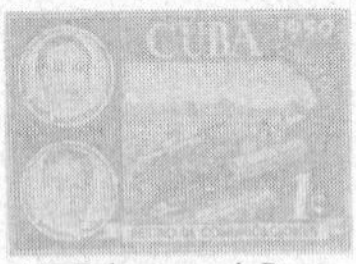
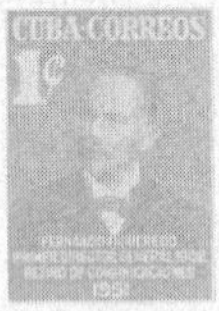

142 Balanzategui, Pausa and Railway Crash **143** F. Figueredo

1950. Postal Employees' Retirement Fund.
544 **142** 1c. green 2·50 1·10
545 2c. red 2·50 1·10
546 5c. blue 7·00 2·25

1951. Postal Employees' Retirement Fund.
548 **143** 1c. green 55 20
549 2c. red 55 20
550 5c. blue 90 35

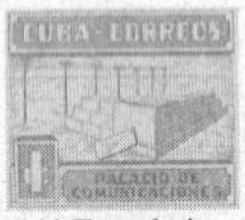
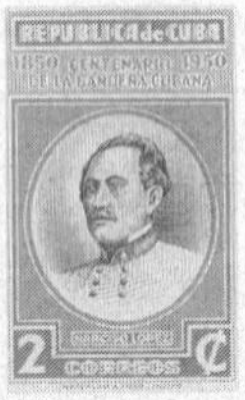

144 Foundation Stone **145** Narciso Lopez

1951. Obligatory Tax. P.O. Rebuilding Fund.
551 **144** 1c. violet 25 10

1951. Centenary of Cuban Flag.
552 – 1c. red, bl & grn (postage) 30 15
553 **145** 2c. black and red 50 25
554 – 5c. red and blue 1·10 50
555 – 10c. red, blue and violet 2·00 70

556 – 5c. red, blue & olive (air) 1·40 45
557 – 8c. red, blue and brown 1·75 65
558 – 25c. red, blue and black 2·25 1·10
DESIGNS—VERT: 1c. Miguel Teurbe Tolon; 5c. (No. 554) Emilia Teurbe Tolon; 8c. Raising the flag; 10c. Flag; 25c. Flag and El Morro lighthouse. HORIZ: 5c. (No. 556) Lopez landing at Cardenas.

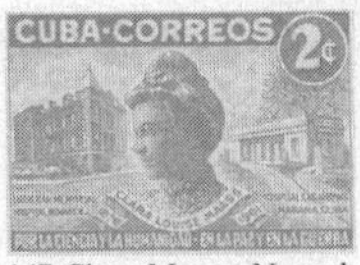

147 Clara Maass, Newark Memorial and Las Animas, Havana, Hospitals

1951. 50th Death Anniv of Clara Maass (nurse).
559 **147** 2c. red 1·00 40

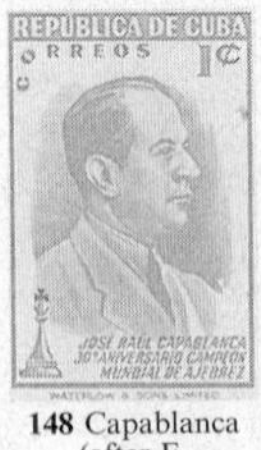
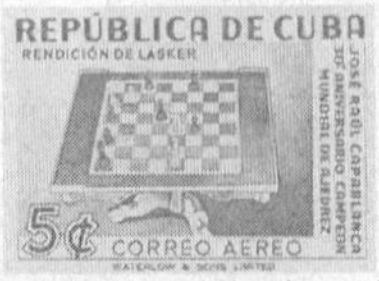

148 Capablanca (after E. Valderrama) **149** Chessboard showing end of Capablanca v. Lasker

1951. 30th Anniv of Jose Capablanca's Victory in World Chess Championship.
562 **148** 1c. orge & grn (postage) 1·75 45
563 – 2c. brown and red 2·25 85
564 E **150** 5c. blue and black 5·50 1·75
565 **149** 5c. yellow & green (air) 2·75 85
566 – 8c. purple and blue 4·00 1·10
567 **148** 25c. sepia & brown 7·00 1·90
DESIGN—VERT: 2c., 8c. Capablanca playing chess.

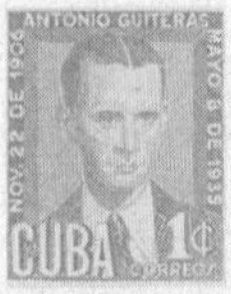
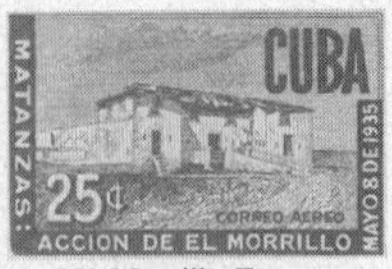

151 Dr. A. Guiteras Holmes **152** Morrillo Fortress

1951. 16th Death Anniv of Dr. A. Guiteras Holmes in skirmish at Morrillo.
568 **151** 1c. green (postage) 45 15
569 – 2c. red 65 30
570 **152** 5c. blue 1·40 50

571 **151** 5c. mauve (air) 1·60 1·10
572 – 8c. green 2·25 1·60
573 **152** 25c. black 4·00 2·75
DESIGN—HORIZ: 2c., 8c. Guiteras framing social laws.

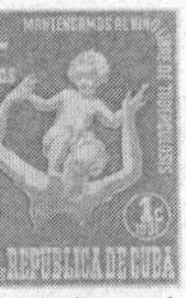
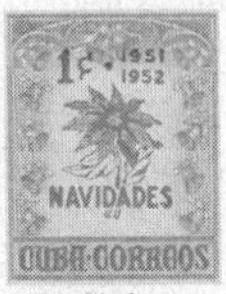

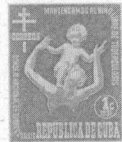

153 Mother and Child **154** Christmas Emblems

1951. Obligatory Tax. Anti-tuberculosis.
575 **153** 1c. brown 20 10
576 1c. red 20 10
577 1c. green 20 10
578 1c. blue 20 10

1951. Christmas Greetings.
579 **154** 1c. red and green 2·00 55
580 2c. green and red 2·50 65

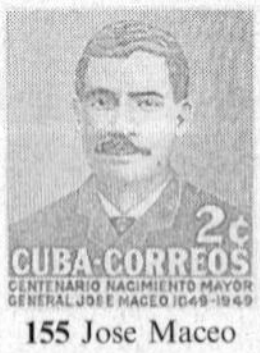
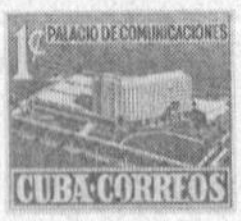
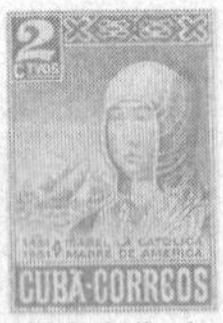

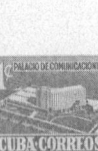

155 Jose Maceo **156** General Post Office **157** Isabella the Catholic

1952. Birth Centenary of Gen. Maceo.
581 **155** 2c. brown 50 15
582 5c. blue 90 35

1952. Obligatory Tax. P.O. Rebuilding Fund.
583 **156** 1c. blue 20 10
584 1c. red 55 15

1952. 5th Birth Centenary of Isabella the Catholic.
585 **157** 2c. red (postage) 3·00 75
586 25c. purple (air) 5·25 1·25

1952. As No. 549 surch with new value. (a) Postage.
588 **143** 10c. on 2c. brown 1·25 40

(b) Air. Optd **AEREO** in addition.
589 **143** 5c. on 2c. brown 45 20
590 8c. on 2c. brown 65 20
591 10c. on 2c. brown 1·10 20
592 25c. on 2c. brown 1·10 45
593 50c. on 2c. brown 3·75 1·40
594 1p. on 2c. brown 5·50 2·75

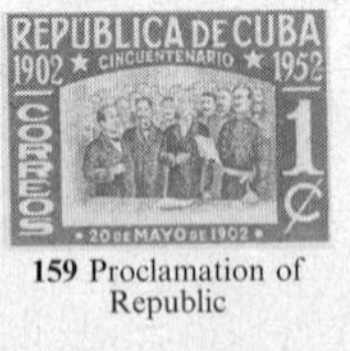
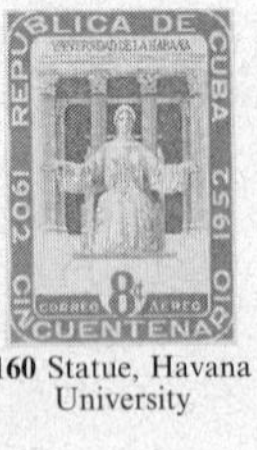

159 Proclamation of Republic **160** Statue, Havana University

1952. 50th Anniv of Republic.
595 **159** 1c. black & grn (postage) 20 15
596 – 2c. black and red 30 15
597 – 5c. black and blue 40 15
598 – 8c. black and brown 55 15
599 – 20c. black and olive 1·40 50
600 – 50c. black and orange 2·75 90

601 – 5c. green & violet (air) 55 25
602 **160** 8c. green and red 55 35
603 – 10c. green and blue 1·40 55
604 – 25c. green and purple 1·75 85
DESIGNS—HORIZ:–POSTAGE: 2c. Estrada Palma and Estevez Romero; 5c. Barnet, Finlay, Guiteras and Nunez; 8c. The Capitol; 20c. Map showing central highway; 50c. Sugar factory. AIR: 5c. Rural school; 10c. Presidential Palace; 25c. Banknote.

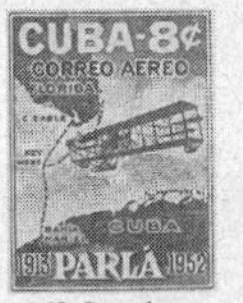
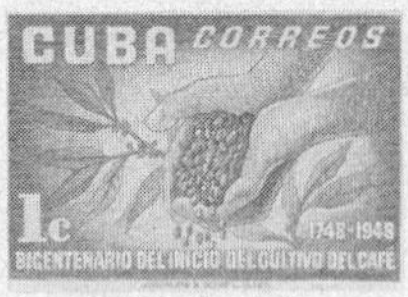

162 Seaplane and Route of Flight **164** Coffee Beans

1952. Air. 39th Anniv of Florida–Cuba flight by A. Parla.
605 **162** 8c. black 1·25 30
606 – 25c. blue 2·75 85
DESIGN—HORIZ: 25c. Agustin Parla Orduna and Curtiss A-1 seaplane.

1952. Bicentenary of Coffee Cultivation.
608 **164** 1c. green 35 15
609 – 2c. red 55 30
610 – 5c. green and blue 95 35
DESIGNS: 2c. Plantation worker and map; 5c. Coffee plantation.

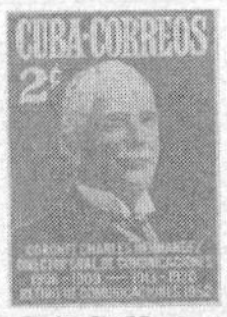

165 Col. C. Hernandez

1952. Postal Employees' Retirement Fund.
611 **165** 1c. green (postage) 20 15
612 2c. red 40 15
613 5c. blue 40 15
614 8c. black 1·00 35
615 10c. red 1·10 40
616 20c. brown 4·00 2·75

617 5c. orange (air) 25 10
618 8c. green 45 10
619 10c. brown 50 15
620 15c. green 55 20
621 20c. turquoise 55 30
622 25c. red 85 40
623 30c. violet 1·75 40
624 45c. mauve 1·90 1·40
625 50c. blue 1·60 85
626 1p. yellow 5·00 2·50

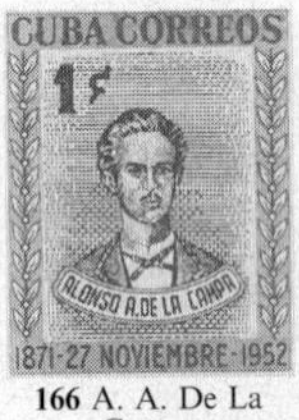
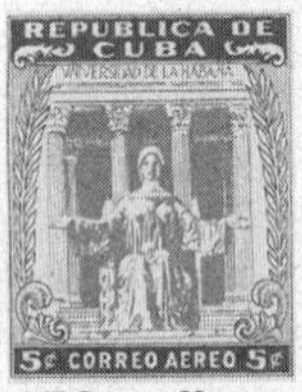

166 A. A. De La Campa **167** Statue, Havana University

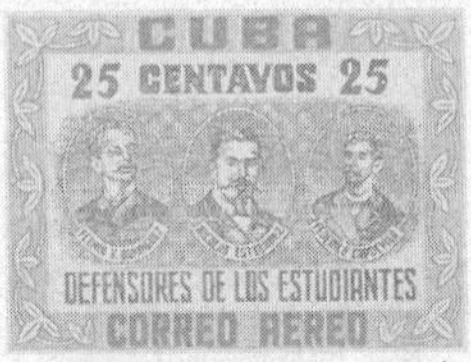

168 Dominguez, Estebanez and Capdevila (defence lawyers)

1952. 81st Anniv of Execution of Eight Rebel Medical Students.
627 **166** 1c. black & grn (postage) 15 10
628 – 2c. black and red 30 15
629 – 3c. black and violet 35 15
630 – 5c. black and blue 35 15
631 – 8c. black and sepia 65 35
632 – 10c. black and brown 75 30
633 – 13c. black and purple 1·90 45
634 – 20c. black and olive 2·25 65

635 **167** 5c. blue and indigo (air) 85 35
636 **168** 25c. green and orange 2·25 80
PORTRAITS: 2c. C. A. de la Torre. 3c. A. Bermudez. 5c. E. G. Toledo. 8c. A. Laborde. 10c. J. De M. Medina. 13c. P. Rodriguez. 20c. C. Verdugo.

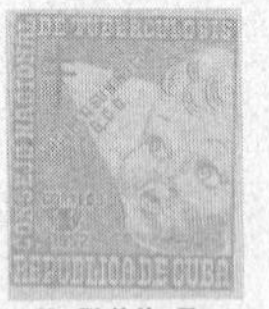
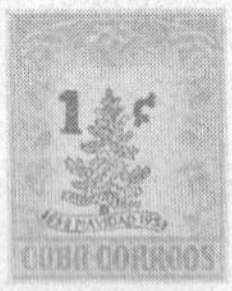

169 Child's Face **170** Christmas Tree

1952. Obligatory Tax. Anti- tuberculosis.
637 **169** 1c. orange 25 10
638 1c. red 25 10
639 1c. green 25 10
640 1c. blue 25 10

1952. Christmas.
641 **170** 1c. red and green 2·75 1·75
642 3c. green and violet 2·75 1·75

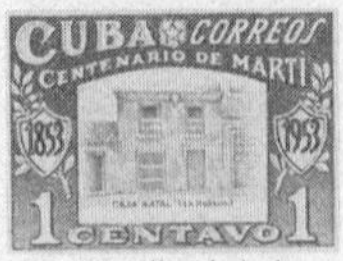
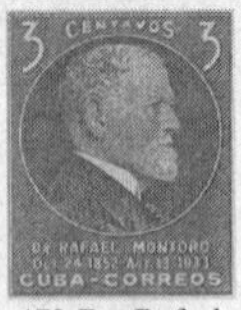

171 Marti's Birthplace **172** Dr. Rafael Montoro

1953. Birth Centenary of Jose Marti.
643 **171** 1c. brn & grn (postage) 15 10
644 – 1c. brown and green 15 10
645 – 3c. brown and violet 25 15
646 – 3c. brown and violet 25 15
647 – 5c. brown and blue 35 15
648 – 5c. brown and blue 35 15
649 – 10c. black and brown 90 30
650 – 10c. black and brown 75 30
651 – 13c. brown and green 1·60 55
652 – 13c. brown and green 1·60 55

653 – 5c. black & red (air) 25 15
654 – 5c. black and red 25 15
655 – 8c. black and green 30 15
656 – 8c. black and green 30 15
657 – 10c. red and blue 40 15
658 – 10c. blue and red 40 15
659 – 15c. black and violet 50 25
660 – 15c. black and violet 50 25
661 – 25c. red and brown 1·75 60
662 – 25c. red and brown 1·75 60
663 – 50c. blue and yellow 2·75 1·00
DESIGNS—HORIZ: No. 644, Marti before Council of War; No. 645, Prison wall; No. 647, "El Abra" ranch; No. 652, First edition of "Patria"; No. 656, House of Maximo Gomez, Montecristi; No. 658, Marti as an orator; No. 663, "Fragua Martiana" (modern building). VERT: No. 646, Marti in prison; No. 648, Allegory of Marti's poems; No. 649, Marti and Bolivar Statue, Caracas; No. 650, Marti writing; No. 651, Revolutionaries' meeting-place; No. 653, Marti in Kingston, Jamaica; No. 654, Marti in Ibor City; No. 655, Manifesto of Montecristi; No. 657, Marti's portrait; No. 659, Marti's first tomb; No. 660, Obelisk at Des Rios; No. 661, Monument in Havana; No. 662, Marti's present tomb.

1953. Birth Centenary of Montoro (statesman).
664 **172** 3c. purple 1·00 45

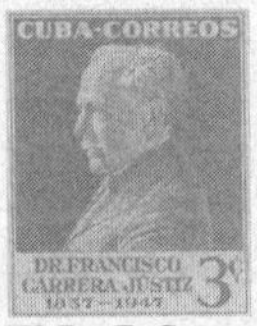
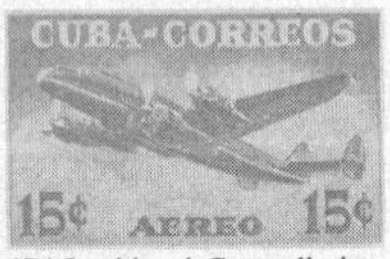

173 Dr. F. Carrera Justiz **174** Lockheed Constellation

1953.
665 **173** 3c. red 1·00 45

1953. Air.
666 **174** 8c. brown 55 25
667 15c. red 1·10 60
668 – 2p. brown and green 11·00 4·50
670 – 2p. myrtle and blue 11·00 4·50
669 – 5p. brown and blue 22·00 7·50
671 – 5p. myrtle and red 19·00 9·50
DESIGN: Nos. 668/71, Constellation facing right.

1953. No. 512 surch.
672 3c. on 2c. red 55 30

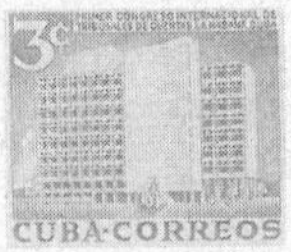
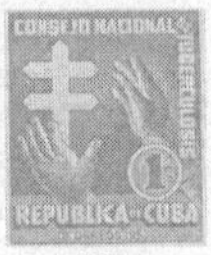

176 Congress Building **177**

1953. 1st Int Accountancy Congress, Havana.
673 **176** 3c. blue (postage) 70 35
674 – 8c. red (air) 1·60 55
675 – 25c. green 2·50 85
DESIGNS: 8c. Congress building and "Cuba"; 25c. Aerial view of building and airplane.

1953. Obligatory Tax. Anti-T.B.
676 **177** 1c. red 20 10

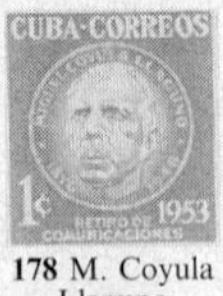
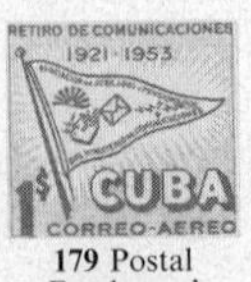

178 M. Coyula Llaguno **179** Postal Employees' Retirement Association Flag

1954. Postal Employees' Retirement Fund. Inscr "1953".
677 **178** 1c. green (postage) 30 10
678 – 3c. red 30 10
679 **179** 5c. blue 55 15
680 – 8c. red 1·10 45
681 – 10c. sepia 2·25 65

682 – 5c. blue (air) 55 25
683 – 8c. purple 65 25
684 – 10c. orange 1·00 25
685 **179** 1p. grey 3·50 2·00
PORTRAITS—VERT: Nos. 678, 680, F.L.C.

Hensell; Nos. 681, 683, A. G. Rojas; No. 684, G. H. Saez. HORIZ: No. 682, M. C. Llaguno.

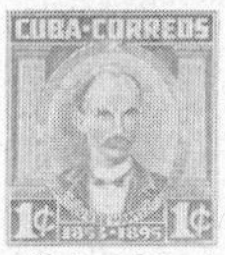

180 Jose Marti

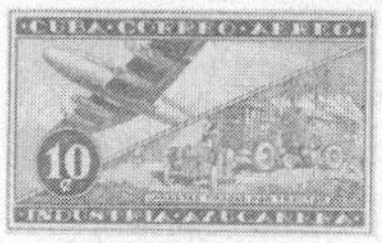

181 Hauling Sugar

1954. Portraits. Roul. (No. 1180a/b) or perf. (others).

686	180	1c. green	15	10
990		1c. red	35	15
1680		1c. blue	10	10
687	–	2c. red (Gomez)	10	10
991	–	2c. olive (Gomez)	45	15
1681	–	2c. green (Gomez)	15	10
688	–	3c. violet (de la Luz Caballero)	10	10
1180a	–	3c. orange (Caballero)	25	15
689	–	4c. mauve (Aldama)	10	10
690	–	5c. blue (Garcia)	15	10
691	–	8c. lake (Agramonte)	15	10
692	–	10c. sepia (Palma)	20	10
693	–	13c. red (Finlay)	30	10
1180b	–	13c. brown (Finlay)	95	25
694	–	14c. grey (Sanchez)	55	15
695	–	20c. olive (Saco)	1·40	35
1682	–	20c. violet (Saco)	1·40	20
696	–	50c. ochre (Maceo)	2·00	40
697	–	1p. orange (Cespedes)	3·00	40

1954. Air. Sugar Industry.

698	–	5c. green	35	10
699	–	8c. brown	85	35
700	181	10c. green	85	35
701	–	15c. brown	1·75	50
702	–	20c. blue	80	10
703	–	25c. red	65	30
704a	–	30c. purple	1·90	75
705	–	40c. blue	3·25	65
706	–	45c. violet	3·00	65
707	–	50c. blue	3·00	65
708	–	1p. blue	7·25	1·25

DESIGNS—VERT: 5c. Sugar cane; 1p. A. Reinoso. HORIZ: 8c. Sugar harvesting; 15c. Train load of sugar cane; 20c. Modern sugar factory; 25c. Evaporators; 30c. Stacking sugar in sacks; 40c. Loading sugar on ship; 45c. Oxen hauling cane; 50c. Primitive sugar factory.

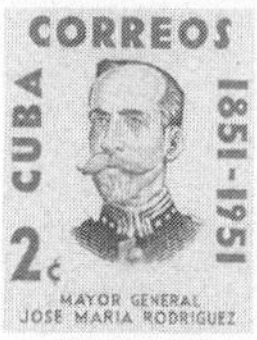

182 Jose M. Rodriguez

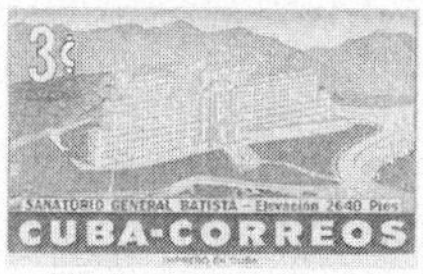

183 View of Sanatorium

1954. Birth Centenary of Rodriguez.

709	182	2c. sepia and lake	45	25
710	–	5c. sepia and blue	90	45

DESIGN: 5c. Rodriguez on horseback.

1954. General Batista Sanatorium.

711	183	3c. blue (postage)	90	40
712		9c. green (air)	1·75	65

184

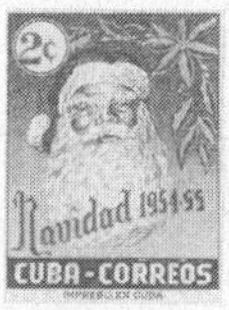

185 Father Christmas

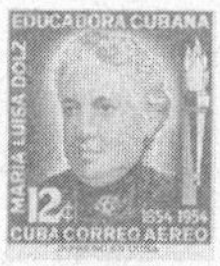

186 Maria Luisa Dolz

1954. Obligatory Tax. Anti-T.B.

713	184	1c. red	20	10
714		1c. green	20	10
715		1c. blue	20	10
716		1c. violet	20	10

1954. Christmas Greetings.

717	185	2c. green and red	3·00	1·40
718		4c. red and green	3·00	1·40

1954. Birth Centenary of Maria Dolz (educationist).

719	186	4c. blue (postage)	95	35
720		12c. mauve (air)	1·75	75

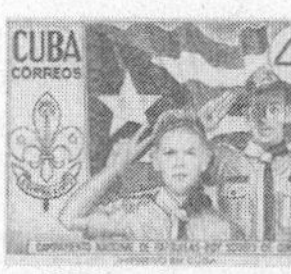

187 Boy Scouts and Cuban Flag

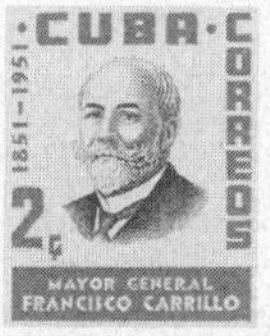

189 Major-Gen. F. Carrillo

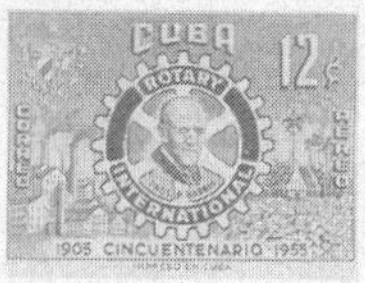

188 P. P. Harris and Rotary Emblem

1954. 3rd National Scout Camp.

721	187	4c. green	95	40

1955. 50th Anniv of Rotary International.

722	188	4c. blue (postage)	95	55
723		12c. red (air)	1·75	65

1955. Birth Centenary of Carrillo.

724	189	2c. blue and red	45	20
725	–	5c. sepia and blue	75	35

DESIGN: 5c. Half-length portrait.

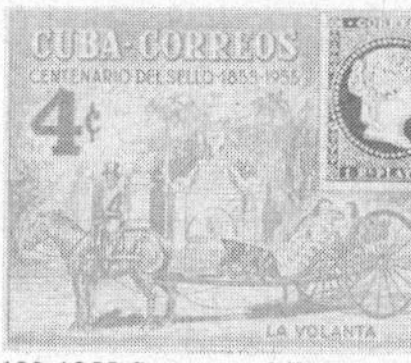

190 1855 Stamp and "La Volanta"

1955. Centenary of First Cuban Postage Stamps and 50th Anniv of First Republican Stamps.

726	–	2c. blue & pur (postage)	35	10
727	190	4c. green and buff	55	35
728	–	10c. red and blue	3·50	65
729	–	14c. orange and green	3·25	1·40
730	–	8c. green & blue (air)	55	20
731	–	12c. red and green	65	20
732	–	24c. blue and red	2·25	55
733	–	30c. brown & orange	1·75	85

DESIGNS (a) With 1855 stamp: 2c. Old Square and Convent of St. Francis; 10c. Havana in 19th century; 14c. Captain-General's residence and Plaza de Armas; (b) With 1855 and 1905 stamps: 8c. Palace of Fine Arts; 12c. Plaza de la Fraternidad; 24c. Aerial view of Havana; 30c. Plaza de la Republica.

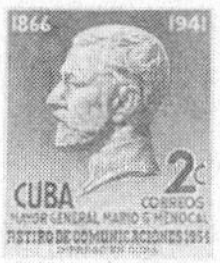

191 Maj.-Gen. Menocal

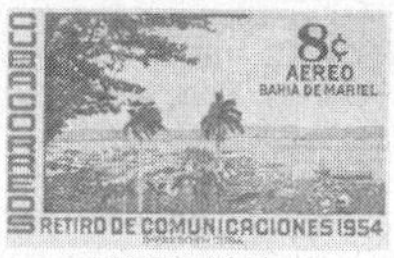

192 Mariel Bay

1955. Postal Employees' Retirement Fund.

734	191	2c. green (postage)	45	10
735	–	4c. mauve	55	25
736	–	10c. blue	95	35
737	–	14c. grey	2·25	85
738	192	8c. green and red (air)	55	25
739	–	12c. blue and brown	1·10	55
740	–	1p. ochre and green	3·00	1·75

DESIGNS—As Type 191: HORIZ: 4c. Gen. E. Nunez; 14c. Dr. A. de Bustamante. VERT: 10c. J. Gomez. As Type 192: HORIZ: 12c. Varadero Beach; 1p. Vinales Valley.

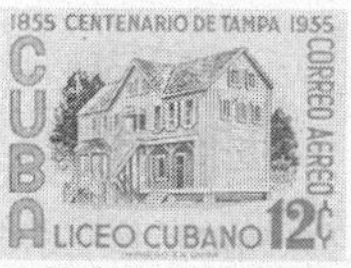

193 Cuban Academy

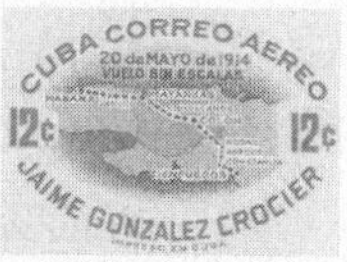

194 Route of 1914 Flight

1955. Air. Centenary of Tampa, Florida.

741	193	12c. brown and red	1·60	65

1955. Air. 35th Death Anniv of Crocier (aviator).

742	194	12c. green and red	85	35
743	–	30c. mauve and green	1·60	65

DESIGN: 30c. Crocier in aircraft cockpit.

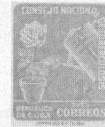

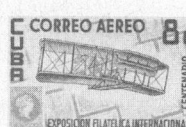

195

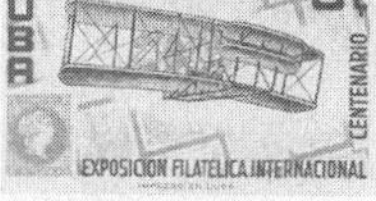

196 Wright Flyer 1

1955. Obligatory Tax. Anti-T.B.

744	195	1c. orange	30	15
745		1c. yellow	30	15
746		1c. blue	30	15
747		1c. mauve	30	15

1955. Air. Int Philatelic Exhibition, Havana.

748	196	8c. black, red and blue	1·25	55
749	–	12c. black, green and red	1·40	55
750	–	24c. black, violet & red	1·60	85
751	–	30c. black, blue & orange	3·50	1·90
752	–	50c. black olive & orange	5·50	2·25

DESIGNS: 12c. Lindbergh's airplane "Spirit of St. Louis"; 24c. Airship "Graf Zeppelin"; 30c. Lockheed Super Constellation airplane; 50c. Convair Delta Dagger airplane.

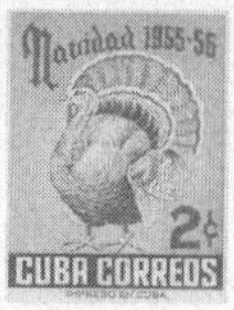

197 Turkey

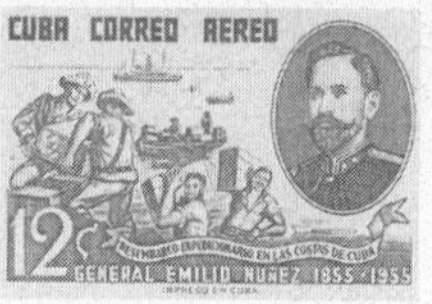

198 Expedition Disembarking

1955. Christmas Greetings.

754	197	2c. green and red	3·00	1·40
755		4c. lake and green	3·00	1·40

1955. Birth Centenary of General Nunez.

756	–	4c. lake (postage)	90	35
757	–	8c. blue and red (air)	1·75	45
758	198	12c. green and brown	1·75	65

DESIGNS—VERT: (22½ × 32½ mm.): 4c. Portrait of Nunez. HORIZ: As Type 198: 8c. "Three Friends" (tug).

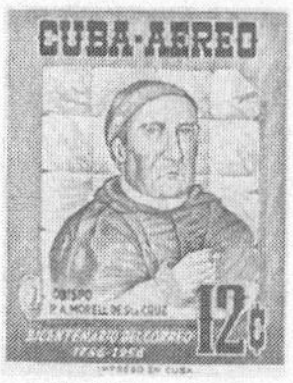

199 Bishop P. A. Morell de Santa Cruz

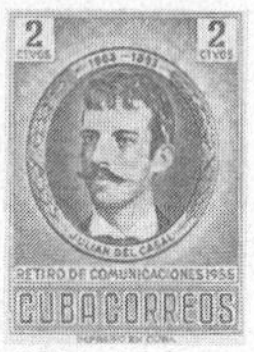

200 J. del Casal

1956. Bicentenary of Cuban Postal Service.

759	–	4c. blue & brn (postage)	90	40
760	199	12c. green & brown (air)	1·60	40

PORTRAIT: 4c. F. C. de la Vega.

1956. Postal Employees' Retirement Fund.

761	200	2c. black & grn (postage)	20	15
762	–	4c. black and mauve	55	20
763	–	10c. black and blue	90	35
764	–	14c. black and violet	1·90	75
765	–	8c. black & brown (air)	55	30
766	–	12c. black and ochre	85	35
767	–	30c. black and blue	1·60	55

PORTRAITS: 4c. Luisa Perez de Zambrana. 8c. Gen. J. Sanguily. 10c. J. Clemente Zenea. 12c. Gen. J. M. Aguirre. 14c. J. J. Palma. 30c. Col. E. Fonts Sterling.

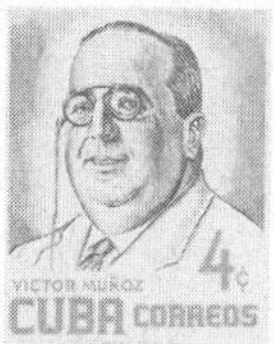

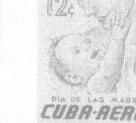

201 Victor Munoz

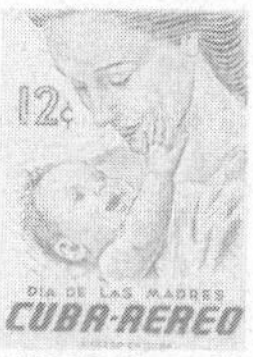

202 Mother and Baby

1956. Munoz Commemoration.

768	201	4c. brown and green	90	40

1956. Air. Mothers' Day.

769	202	12c. blue and red	1·75	40

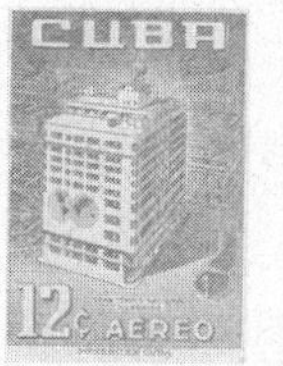

203 Aerial View of Temple

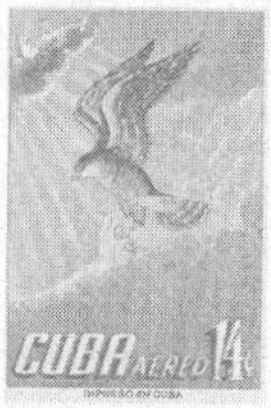

204 Gundlach's Hawk

1956. Masonic Grand Lodge of Cuba Temple, Havana.

770	–	4c. blue (postage)	95	40
771	203	12c. green (air)	1·75	45

DESIGN: 4c. Ground level view of Temple.

1956. Air. Birds.

772	–	8c. blue	1·40	25
773	–	12c. grey	9·00	25
783	–	12c. green	3·25	70
774	204	14c. olive	2·10	30
775	–	19c. brown	2·10	60
776	–	24c. mauve	2·10	70
777	–	29c. green	3·00	70
778	–	30c. brown	3·25	1·00
779	–	50c. slate	6·00	1·25
780	–	1p. red	13·00	2·75
784	–	1p. blue	6·50	5·25
781	–	2p. purple	22·00	5·00
785	–	2p. red	19·00	13·00
782	–	5p. red	55·00	9·50
786	–	5p. purple	42·00	32·00

DESIGNS—HORIZ: 8c. Wood duck; 12c. (2) Plain pigeon; 29c. Goosander; 30c. Northern bobwhite; 2p. (2) Northern jacana. VERT: 19c. Herring gull; 24c. American white pelican; 50c. Great blue heron; 1p. (2) Common caracara; 5p. (2) Ivory-billed woodpecker.

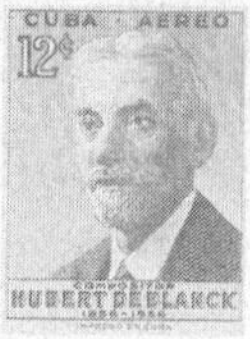

205 H. de Blanck

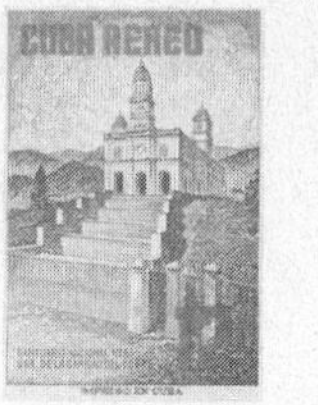

207 Church of Our Lady of Charity

1956. Air. Birth Centenary of H. De Blanck (composer).

787	205	12c. blue	1·60	45

1956. Air. Inaug of Philatelic Club of Cuba Building. No. 776 but colour changed and surch **Inauguracion Edificio Club Filatelico de la Republica de Cuba Julio 13 de 1956** and value.

788	–	8c. on 24c. orange	1·75	80

1956. Inscr "NTRA. SRA. DE LA CARIDAD", etc.

789	–	4c. blue & yell (postage)	95	40
790	207	12c. green & red (air)	1·90	55

DESIGN: 4c. Our Lady of Charity over landscape.

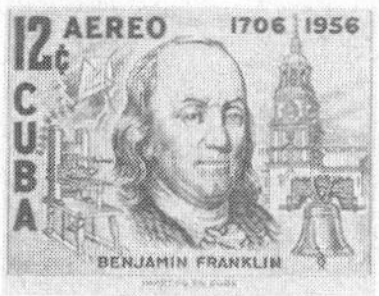

208

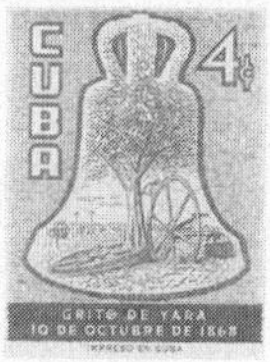

209

1956. Air. 250th Birth Anniv of Benjamin Franklin.

792	208	12c. brown	1·75	40

1956. "Grito de Yara" (War of Independence). Commem.

793	209	4c. sepia and green	95	35

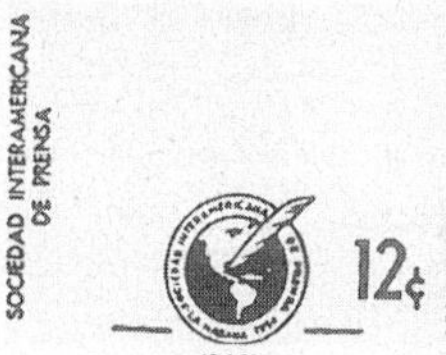

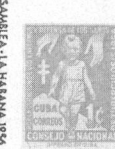

(210)

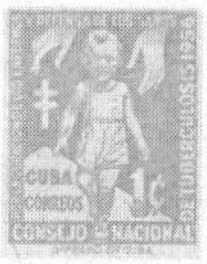

211

1956. Air. 12th Inter-American Press Assn. Meeting. As No. 781 but colour changed and surch with T 210.

794	–	12c. on 2p. grey	1·75	80

1956. Obligatory Tax. Anti-T.B.

795	211	1c. red	20	10
796		1c. green	20	10
797		1c. blue	20	10
798		1c. brown	20	10

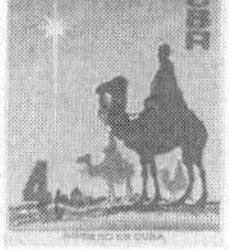

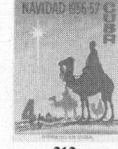

212

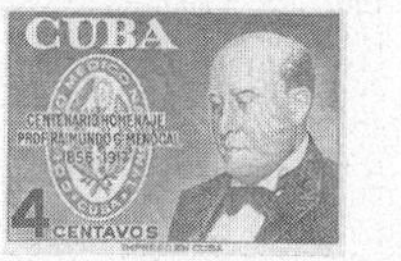

213 Prof. R. G. Menocal

1956. Christmas Greetings.

799	212	2c. red and green	3·00	1·40
800		4c. green and red	3·00	1·40

1956. Birth Centenary of Prof. R. G. Menocal.

801	213	4c. brown	90	35

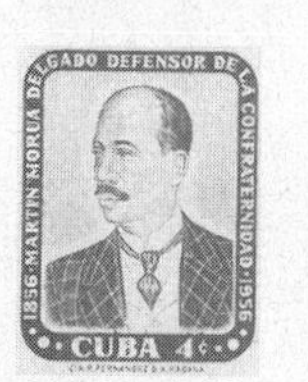

214a Martin M. Delgado

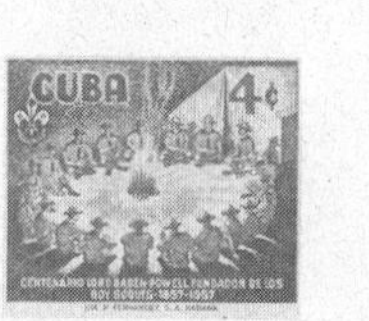

215 Scouts around Camp Fire

1957. Birth Centenary of Delgado (patriot).

802	214a	4c. green	90	40

1957. Birth Centenary of Lord Baden-Powell.

803	215	4c. green & red (postage)	1·10	45
804	–	12c. slate (air)	1·75	85

DESIGN—VERT: 12c. Lord Baden-Powell.

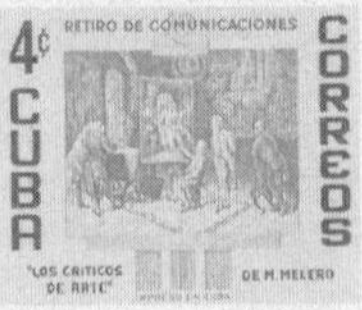

216 "The Art Critics" (Melero)

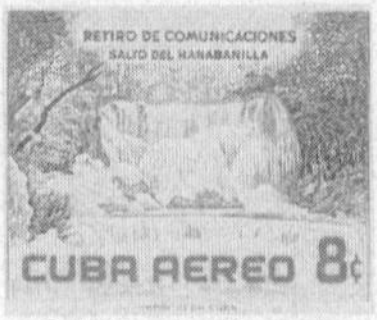

217 Hanabanilla Falls

1957. Postal Employees' Retirement Fund.

805	–	2c. green & brn (postage)	35	15
806	**216**	4c. red and brown	65	25
807	–	10c. olive and brown	95	35
808	–	14c. blue and brown	1·10	40
809	**217**	8c. blue and red (air)	40	15
810	–	12c. green and red	1·60	30
811	–	30c. olive and violet	1·75	50

DESIGNS—HORIZ: As Type **216** (Paintings): 2c. "The Blind" (Vega); 10c. "Carriage in the Storm" (Menocal); 14c. "The Convalescent" (Romanach); As Type **217**: 12c. Sierra de Cubitas; 30c. Puerto Boniato.

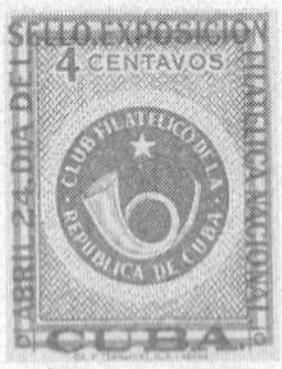

218 Posthorn Emblem of Cuban Philatelic Society

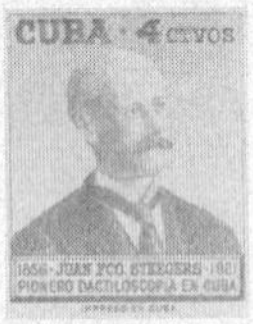

219 Juan F. Steegers

1957. Stamp Day. Cuban Philatelic Exn.

812	**218**	4c. bl, brn & red (postage)	90	35
813	–	12c. brn, yell & grn (air)	1·40	50

DESIGN: 12c. Philatelic Society Building, Havana.

1957. Birth Centenary of Steegers (fingerprint pioneer).

814	**219**	4c. blue (postage)	90	35
815	–	12c. brown (air)	1·40	45

DESIGN: 12c. Thumbprint.

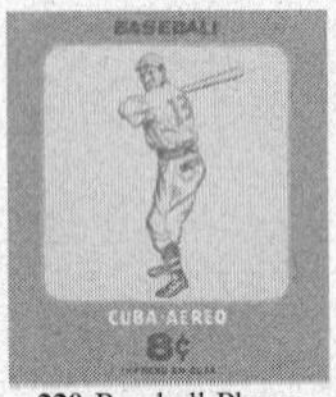

220 Baseball Player

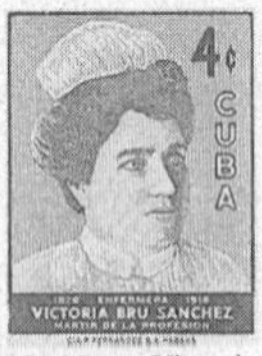

221 Nurse Victoria Bru Sanchez

1957. Air. Youth Recreation. Centres in brown.

816	**220**	8c. green on green	85	30
817	–	12c. lilac on lavender	1·10	55
818	–	24c. blue on blue	1·75	85
819	–	30c. flesh on orange	2·25	1·40

DESIGNS—12c. Ballet dancer; 24c. Diver; 30c. Boxers.

1957. Nurse Victoria Bru Sanchez Commem.

820	**221**	4c. blue	90	35

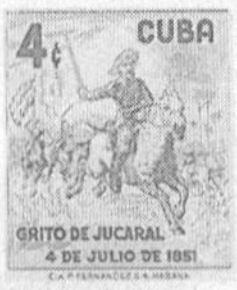

222 J. de Aguero leading Patriots

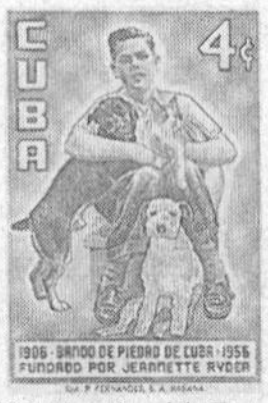

223 Youth with Dogs and Cat

1957. Joaquin de Aguero (patriot) Commem.

821	**222**	4c. green (postage)	90	35
822	–	12c. blue (portrait) (air)	1·40	50

1957. 50th Anniv of Band of Charity (for prevention of cruelty to animals).

823	**223**	4c. green (postage)	90	55
824	–	12c. brown (air)	1·40	40

DESIGN: 12c. Jeanette Ryder (founder).

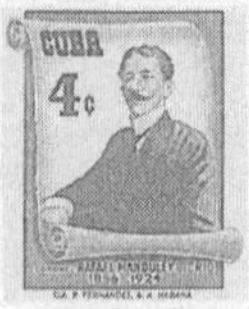

224 Col. R. Manduley del Rio (patriot)

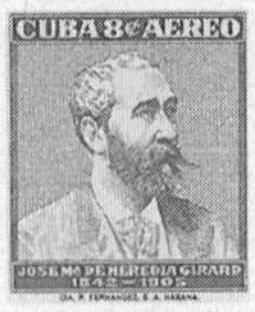

225 J. M. Heredia y Girard

1957. Col. R. Manduley del Rio. Commem.

825	**224**	4c. green	2·25	1·40

1957. Air. J. M. Heredia y Girard (poet). Commem.

826	**225**	8c. violet	95	35

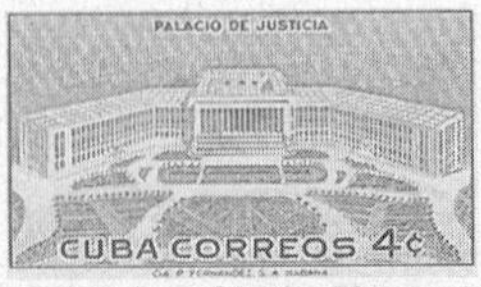

226 Palace of Justice, Havana

1957. Inauguration of Palace of Justice.

827	**226**	4c. grey (postage)	90	35
828		12c. green (air)	1·40	40

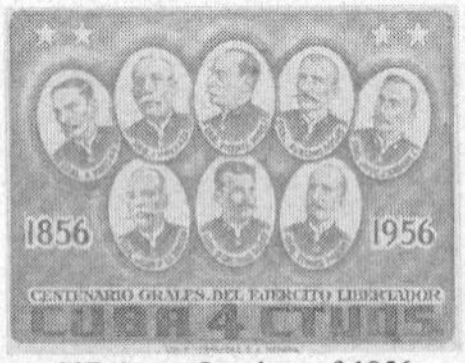

227 Army Leaders of 1856

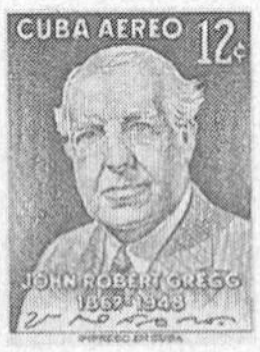

228 J. R. Gregg

1957. Centenary of Cuban Army of Liberation.

829	**227**	4c. brown and green	65	35
830		4c. brown and blue	65	35
831		4c. brown and pink	65	35
832		4c. brown and yellow	65	35
833		4c. brown and lilac	65	35

1957. Air. J. R. Gregg (shorthand pioneer) Commem.

834	**228**	12c. green	1·40	40

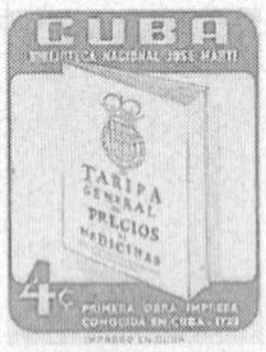

229 Cuba's First Publication, 1723

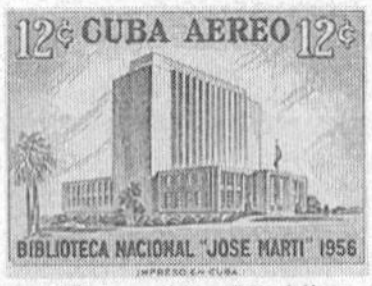

230 Jose Marti Public Library

1957. "Jose Marti" Public Library. Inscr "BIBLIOTECA NACIONAL".

835	**229**	4c. slate (postage)	90	35
836	–	8c. blue (air)	40	20
837	**230**	12c. sepia	1·25	40

DESIGN—VERT: As Type **230**: 8c. D. F. Caneda, first Director.

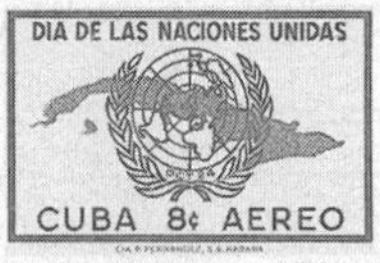

231 U.N. Emblem and Map of Cuba

1957. Air. U.N. Day.

838	**231**	8c. brown and green	65	30
839		12c. green and red	1·25	35
840		30c. mauve and blue	2·50	80

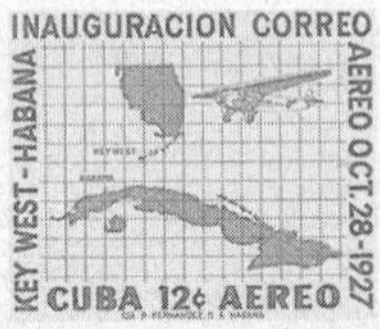

232 Fokker Trimotor "General New" and Map

1957. Air. 30th Anniv of Inaug of Air Mail Services between Havana and Key West, Florida.

841	**232**	12c. blue and purple	1·75	45

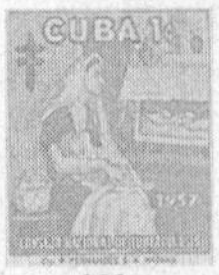

233

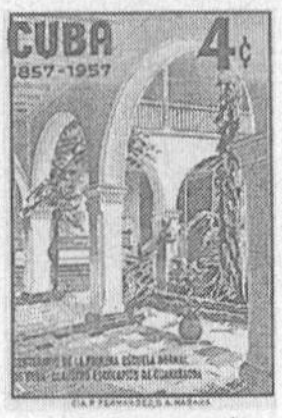

235 Courtyard

1957. Obligatory Tax. Anti-tuberculosis.

842	**233**	1c. red	30	10
843		1c. green	30	10
844		1c. blue	30	10
845		1c. grey	30	10

1957. Centenary of 1st Cuban Teachers' Training College.

846	**235**	4c. brn & grn (postage)	90	35
847	–	12c. buff and blue (air)	95	35
848	–	30c. sepia and red	1·60	45

DESIGNS—VERT: 12c. School facade. HORIZ: 30c. General view of school.

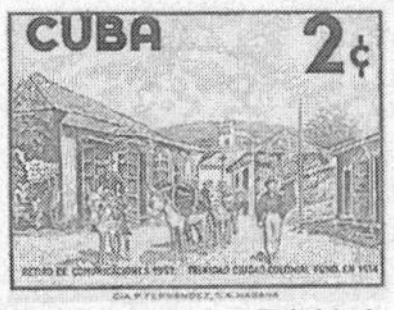

236 Street Scene, Trinidad

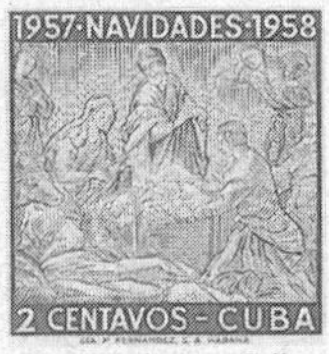

237 Christmas Crib

1957. Postal Employees' Retirement Fund.

849	**236**	2c. brown & bl (postage)	20	10
850	–	4c. green and brown	45	15
851	–	10c. sepia and red	70	30
852	–	14c. green and red	1·10	25
853	–	8c. black and red (air)	45	20
854	–	12c. black and brown	95	35
855	–	30c. brown and grey	1·75	45

DESIGNS—VERT: 4c. Sentry-box on old wall of Havana; 10c. Calle Padre Pico (street), Santiago de Cuba; 12c. Sancti Spiritus Church; 14c. Church and street scene, Camaguey. HORIZ: 8c. "El Viso" Fort, El Caney; 30c. Concordia Bridge, Matanzas.

1957. Christmas. Multicoloured centres.

856	**237**	2c. sepia	2·25	1·10
857		4c. black	2·25	1·10

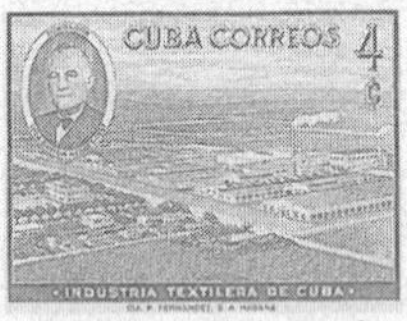

239 Dayton Hedges and Textile Factories

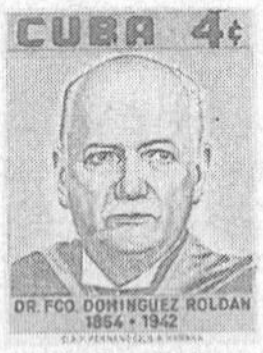

240 Dr. F. D. Roldan

1958. Dayton Hedges (founder of Cuban Textile Industry) Commemoration.

858	**239**	4c. blue (postage)	1·40	65
859		8c. green (air)	1·40	65

1958. Dr. Francisco D. Roldan (physiotherapy pioneer) Commemoration.

861	**240**	4c. green	95	35

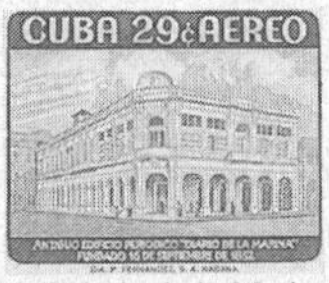

241 "Diario de la Marina" Building

1958. 125th Anniv of "Diario de la Marina" Newspaper.

862	–	4c. olive (postage)	95	35
863	**241**	29c. black (air)	1·75	85

PORTRAIT—VERT: 4c. J. I. Rivero y Alonso (journalist).

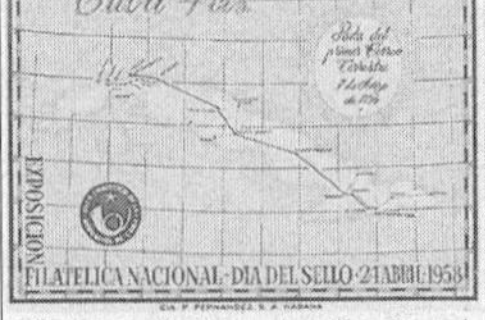

242 Map of Cuba showing Postal Routes of 1756

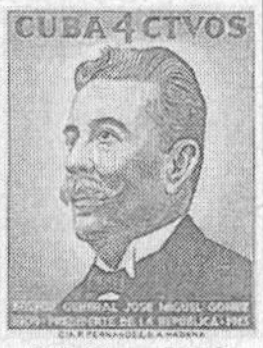

243 Gen. J. M. Gomez

1958. Stamp Day and National Philatelic Exhibition, Havana. Inscr as in T **242**.

864	**242**	4c. myrtle, buff and blue (postage)	95	40
865	–	29c. indigo, buff and blue (air)	1·90	85

DESIGN: 29c. Ocean map showing sea-post routes of 1765.

1958. Birth Centenary of Gen. J. M. Gomez.

866	**243**	4c. blue (postage)	90	35
867	–	12c. myrtle (air)	1·25	50

DESIGN: 12c. Gomez at Arroyo Blanco.

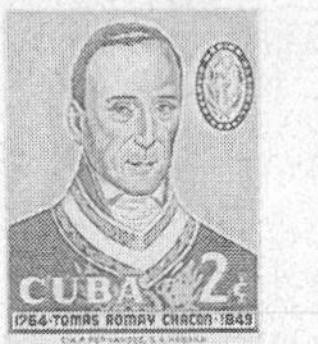

244 Dr. T. Romay Chacon

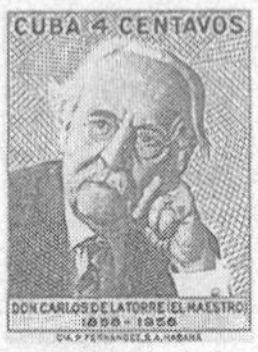

245 Dr. C. de la Torre

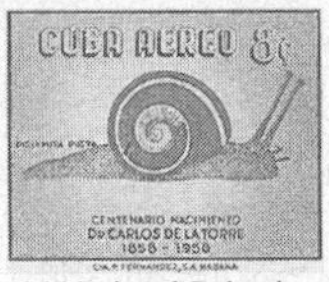

246 Painted Polymita

1958. Famous Cubans. Portraits as T **244**. (a) Doctors. With emblem of medicine.

868	2c. brown and green	45	15
869	4c. black and green	45	15
870	10c. red and green	45	15
871	14c. blue and green	65	15

(b) Lawyers. With emblem of law.

872	2c. sepia and red	50	15
873	4c. black and red	50	15
874	10c. green and red	50	15
875	14c. blue and red	55	20

(c) Composers. With lyre emblem of music.

876	2c. brown and blue	40	15
877	4c. purple and blue	40	15
878	10c. green and blue	55	15
879	14c. red and blue	60	15

PORTRAITS—Doctors: 2c. Type **244**. 4c. A. A. Aballi. 10c. F. G. del Valle. 14c. V. A. de Castro. Lawyers: 2c. J. M. G. Montes. 4c. J. A. G. Lanuza. 10c. J. B. H. Barreiro. 14c. P. G. Llorente. Composers: 2c. N. R. Espadero. 4c. I. Cervantes. 10c. J. White. 14c. B. de Salas.

1958. Birth Cent of De la Torre (archaeologist).

880	**245**	4c. blue (postage)	95	35
881	**246**	8c. red, yellow & blk (air)	2·25	85
882	–	12c. sepia on green	3·25	1·40
883	–	30c. green on pink	5·00	2·00

DESIGNS—As Type **246**: 12c. "Megalocnus rodens"; 30c. "Perisphinctes spinatus" (ammonite).

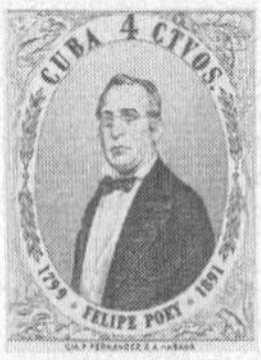

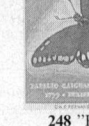

247 Felipe Poey (naturalist)

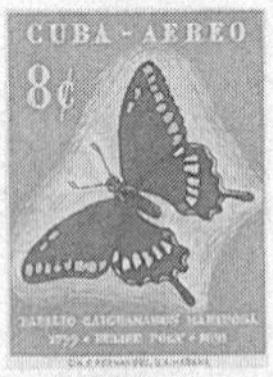

248 "Papilio caiguanabus" (butterfly)

1958. Poey Commemoration. Designs as T **247/8** inscr "1799–FELIPE POEY–1891".

884	–	2c. blk & lav (postage)	40	15
885	**247**	4c. sepia	95	35
886	**248**	8c. multicoloured (air)	1·75	35
887	–	12c. orange, black & grn	2·00	45
888	–	14c. multicoloured	2·50	45
889	–	19c. multicoloured	3·25	55
890	–	24c. multicoloured	3·25	1·00
891	–	29c. blue, brown & black	5·50	2·25
892	–	30c. brown, green & blk	8·50	3·25

DESIGNS—VERT: 2c. Cover of Poey's book; 12c. "Teria gundlachia"; 14c. "Teria ebriola"; 19c. "Nathalis felicia" (all butterflies). HORIZ: 24c. Tobacco fish; 29c. Butter hamlet; 30c. Tattler sea bass (all fishes).

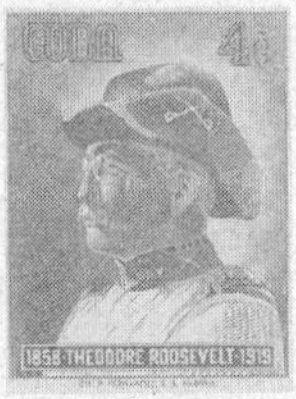

249 Theodore Roosevelt

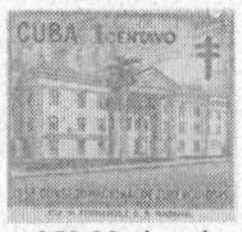

250 National Tuberculosis Hospital

1958. Birth Centenary of Roosevelt.

893	**249**	4c. green (postage)	95	35
894	–	12c. sepia (air)	1·40	50

DESIGN—HORIZ: 12c. Roosevelt leading Rough Riders at San Juan 1898.

1958. Obligatory Tax. Anti-T.B.

895	**250**	1c. brown	20	10
896		1c. green	20	10

897 1c. red 20 10
898 1c. grey 20 10

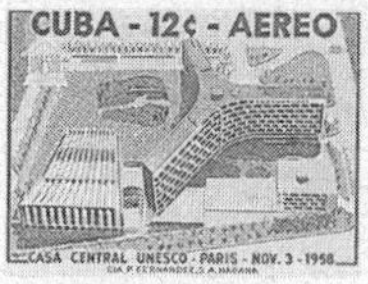

251 U.N.E.S.C.O. Headquarters, Paris

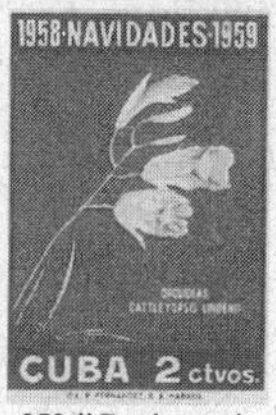

252 "Cattleyopsis lindenii" (orchid)

1958. Air. Inaug of U.N.E.S.C.O. Headquarters.
899 **251** 12c. green . . . . 1·25 45
900 – 30c. blue . . . . 1·60 65
DESIGN: 30c. Facade composed of letters "UNESCO" and map of Cuba.

1958. Christmas. Orchids. Multicoloured.
901 2c. Type **252** . . . . 2·50 1·10
902 4c. "Oncidium guibertianum" 2·50 1·10

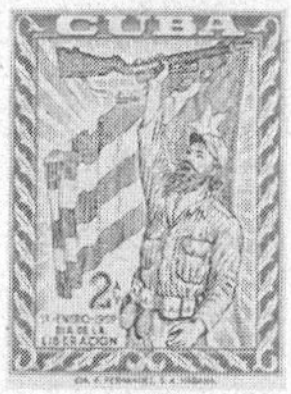

253 "The Revolutionary"

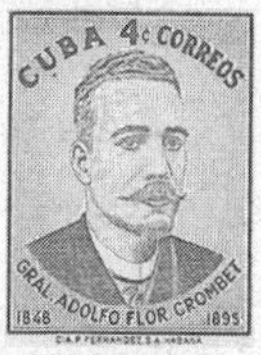

254 Gen. A. F. Crombet

1959. Liberation Day.
903 **253** 2c. black and red 65 25

1959. Gen. Crombet Commemoration.
904 **254** 4c. myrtle 90 35

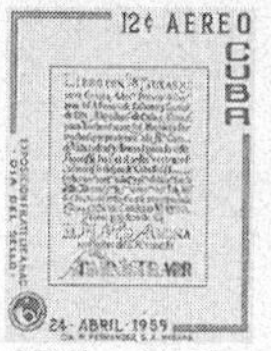

255 Postal Notice of 1765

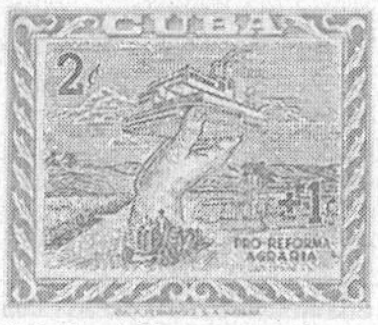

256 Hand Supporting Sugar Factory

1959. Air. Stamp Day and National Philatelic Exhibition, Havana.
905 **255** 12c. sepia and blue . . . 1·10 35
906 – 30c. blue and sepia . . . 1·40 65
DESIGN: 30c. Administrative postal book of St. Cristobal, Havana, 1765.

1959. Agricultural Reform.
907 **256** 2c.+1c. blue and red (postage) 65 20
908 – 12c.+3c. green and red (air) . . . . 1·40 45
DESIGN (42×30 mm.): 12c. Farm workers and factory plant.

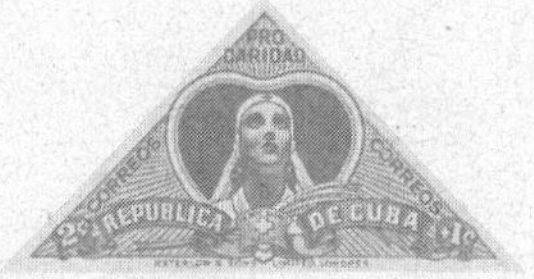

257 Red Cross Nurse

1959. "For Charity".
909 **257** 2c.+1c. red 35 25

1959. Air. American Society of Travel Agents Convention, Havana. No. 780 (colour changed) surch **CONVENCION ASTA OCTUBRE 17 1959 12c.** and bar.
910 12c. on 1p. green . . . . . . 1·90 1·00

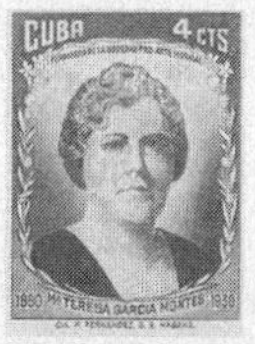

259 Teresa Garcia Montes (founder)

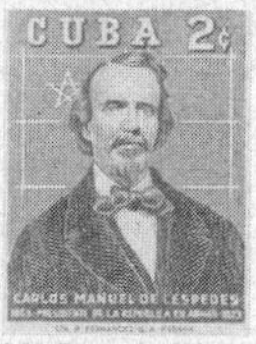

260 Pres. C. M. de Cespedes

1959. Musical Arts Society Festival, Havana.
911 **259** 4c. brown (postage) . . . 90 35
912 – 12c. green (air) . . . . . 1·40 55
DESIGN—HORIZ: 12c. Society Headquarters, Havana.

1959. Cuban Presidents.
913 2c. slate (Type **260**) 35 15
914 2c. green (Betancourt) . . . 35 15
915 2c. violet (Calvar) 35 15
916 2c. brown (Maso) 35 15
917 4c. red (Spotorno) 65 20
918 4c. brown (Palma) 65 20
919 4c. black (F. J. de Cespedes) 65 20
920 4c. violet (Garcia) 65 20

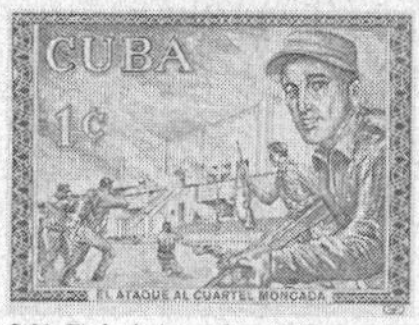

261 Rebel Attack at Moncada Barracks

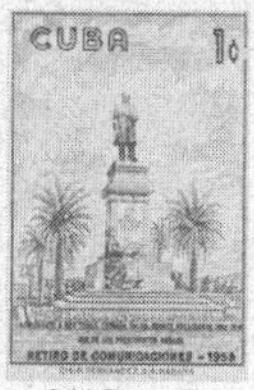

264 Pres. T. Estrada Palma Monument

1960. 1st Anniv of Cuban Revolution.
921 **261** 1c. grn, red & bl (postage) 15 10
922 – 2c. green, sepia and blue 1·25 15
923 – 10c. green, red and blue 1·40 55
924 – 12c. green, purple & blue 1·90 65
925 – 8c. green, red & bl (air) 2·50 50
926 – 12c. green, purple & brn 1·40 35
927 – 29c. red, black & green 1·75 70
DESIGNS: 2c. Rebels disembarking from "Granma"; 8c. Battle of Santa Clara; 10c. Battle of the Uvero; 12c. postage, "The Invasion" (Rebel and map of Cuba); 12c. air, Rebel Army entering Havana; 29c. Passing on propaganda ("Clandestine activities in the towns").

1960. Surch **HABILITADO PARA** and value (No. 932 without **PARA**).
928 **256** 2c. on 2c.+1c. blue and red (postage) 90 20
929 – 2c. on 4c. mve (No. 689) 65 35
930 – 2c. on 5c. blue (690) . . . 65 35
931 – 2c. on 13c. red (693) . . . 65 35
932 – 10c. on 20c. olive (342) 1·10 45
933 – 12c. on 12c.+3c. green and red (908) (air) . . . 1·40 55

1960. Surch in figures.
934 – 1c. on 4c. (No. 869) (postage) 40 15
935 – 1c. on 4c. (No. 873) . . . 40 15
936 – 1c. on 4c. (No. 877) . . . 40 15
937 **245** 1c. on 4c. blue 40 15
938 1c. on 4c. (No. 902) . . . 45 25
939 **254** 1c. on 4c. myrtle 40 15
940 **260** 1c. on 4c. brown 40 15
941 – 2c. on 14c. (No. 694) . . 80 15
942 **54** 12c. on 40c. orge (air) . . 1·40 50
943 – 12c. on 45c. (No. 706) . . 1·40 50

1960. Postal Employees' Retirement Fund.
944 **264** 1c. brn & blue (postage) 15 10
945 – 2c. green and red 35 10
946 – 10c. brown and red . . . 65 25
947 – 12c. green and violet . . . 1·10 45
948 – 8c. grey and red (air) . . 55 15
949 – 12c. blue and red . . . . 1·40 35
950 – 30c. violet and red . . . 1·75 50
MONUMENTS—VERT: 2c. "Mambi Victorioso"; 8c. Marti; 10c. Marta Abreu; 12c. (No. 947) Agramonte; 12c. (No. 949) Heroes of Cacarajicara. HORIZ: 30c. Dr. C. de la Torriente.

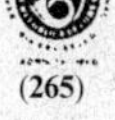

(265)

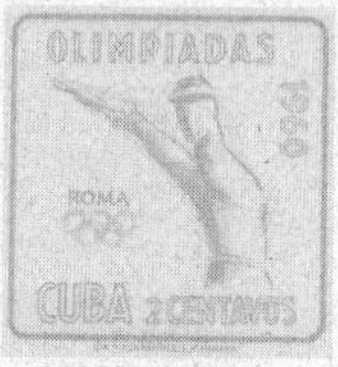

266 Pistol-shooting

1960. Air. Stamp Day and National Philatelic Exn, Havana. Nos. 772/3 in new colours optd with T **265**.
951 8c. yellow 55 35
952 12c. red . . . . 1·50 50

1960. Olympic Games.
954 – 1c. vio (Sailing) (postage) 45 20
955 **266** 2c. orange . . . . 1·00 35
956 – 8c. blue (Boxing) (air) . . 85 30
957 – 12c. red (Running) . . . 1·40 55

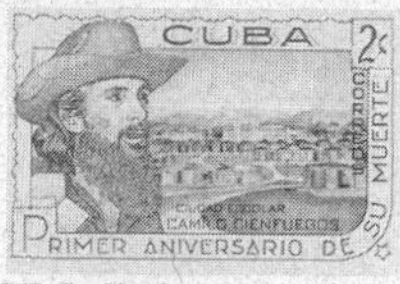

267 C. Cienfuegos and View of Escolar

1960. 1st Death Anniv of Cienfuegos (revolutionary leader). Centre multicoloured.
959 **267** 2c. sepia . . . . 1·00 15

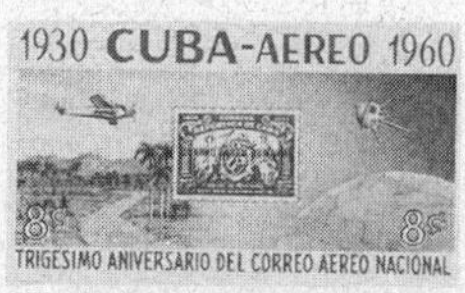

268 Air Stamp of 1930, Ford "Tin Goose" Airplane and "Sputnik"

1960. Air. 80th Anniv of National Airmail Service. Centre multicoloured.
960 **268** 8c. violet . . . . 3·25 1·40

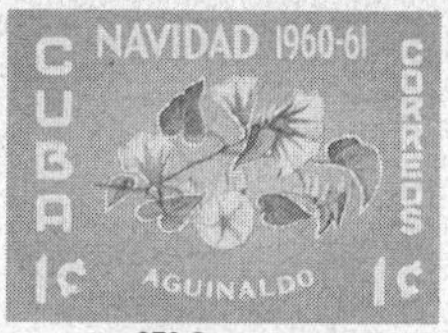

270 Ipomoea

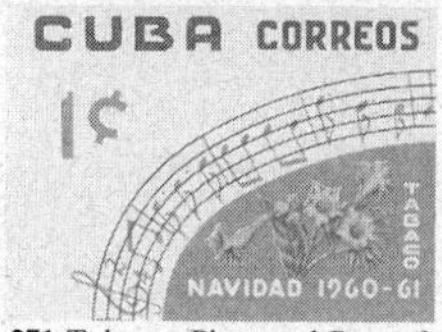

271 Tobacco Plant and Bars of "Christmas Hymn"

1960. Christmas. Inscr "NAVIDAD 1960–61".
(a) T **270**.
961 1c. multicoloured 55 55
962 2c. multicoloured 75 75
963 10c. multicoloured . . . . . 1·50 1·50

(b) As T **271**.
964a/d 1c. multicoloured . . . . 1·75 1·40
965a/d 2c. multicoloured . . . . 2·75 2·50
966a/d 10c. multicoloured . . . . 5·00 4·75
DESIGNS: As T **271** (same for each value) a, T **271**. b, Mariposa. c, Lignum-vitae. d, Coffee plant.
Prices are for single stamps.

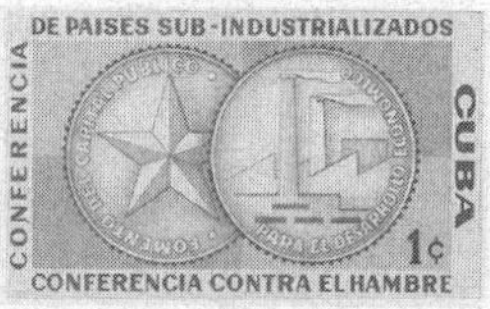

272

1960. Sub-industrialized Countries Conference.
967 **272** 1c. black, yellow and red (postage) 15 10
968 – 2c. multicoloured 15 10
969 – 6c. red, black and cream 1·10 40
970 – 8c. multicoloured (air) . . 40 15
971 – 12c. multicoloured . . . . 1·10 15
972 – 30c. red and grey . . . . 1·40 50
973 – 50c. multicoloured . . . . 1·75 60
DESIGNS—HORIZ: 2c. Graph and symbols; 6c. Cogwheels; 12c. Workers holding lever; 30c. Maps. VERT: 8c. Hand holding machete; 50c. Upraised hand.

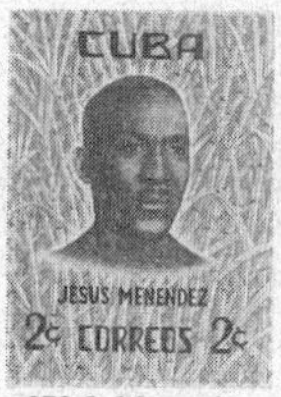

273 J. Menendez

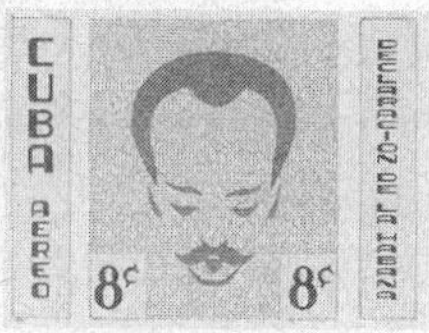

274 Jose Marti and "Declaration of Havana"

1961. Jesus Menendez Commemoration.
974 **273** 2c. sepia and green . . . 85 25

1961. Air. Declaration of Havana.
975 **274** 8c. red, black and yellow 75 65
976 12c. violet, black & buff 1·25 1·00
977 30c. brown, black & blue 3·00 2·75
The above were issued with part of background text of the declaration in English, French and Spanish. Prices the same for each language.

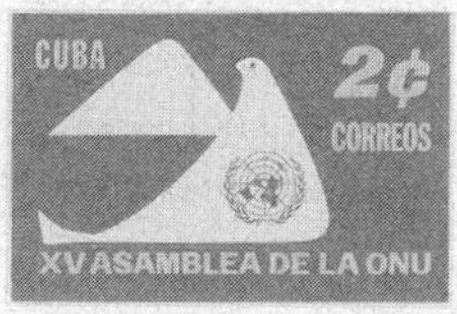

275 U.N. Emblem within Dove of Peace

1961. 15th Anniv of U.N.O.
979 **275** 2c. brn & grn (postage) 25 10
980 10c. green and purple . . 1·00 45
982 8c. red and yellow (air) 45 20
983 12c. blue and orange . . 1·10 40

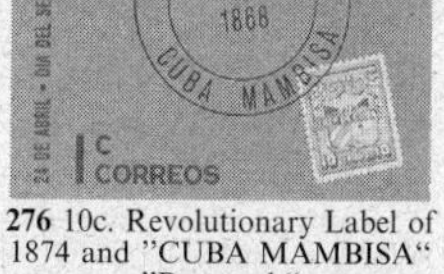

276 10c. Revolutionary Label of 1874 and "CUBA MAMBISA" "Postmark"

1961. Stamp Day. Inscr "24 DE ABRIL DIA DEL SELLO".
985 **276** 1c. red, green and black 15 10
986 – 2c. orange, slate & black 30 15
987 – 10c. turq, red & black . . 1·25 45
DESIGNS: 2c., 50c. stamp of 1907 and "CUBA REPUBLICANA" "postmark"; 10c., 2c. stamp of 1959 and "CUBA REVOLUCIONARIA" "postmark".

1961. May Day. Optd **PRIMERO DE MAYO 1961 ESTAMOS VENCIENDO**.
988 **273** 2c. sepia and green . . . 1·00 20

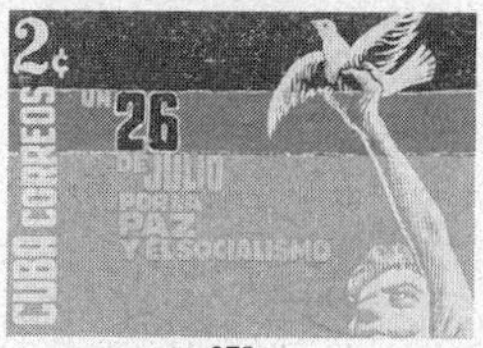

278

1961. "For Peace and Socialism".
989 **278** 2c. multicoloured . . . . 1·00 20
No. 989 is lightly printed on back with pattern of wavy lines and multiple inscr "CORREOS CUBA" in buff.

1961. Air. Surch **HABILITADO PARA 8 cts.**
992 **174** 8c. on 15c. red 50 30
993 **54** 8c. on 20c. brown 50 30

1961. 1st Official Philatelic Exhibition. No. 987 optd **primera exposicion filatelica oficial oct. 7-17, 1961.**
994 10c. turq, red and black . . . 1·00 35

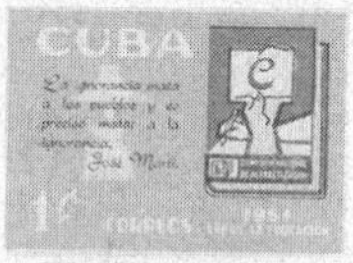

281 Book and Lamp

1961. Education Year.
995 **281** 1c. red, black and green 10 10
996 2c. red, black and blue . . 15 10
997 10c. red, black and violet 60 20
998 12c. red, black & orange 1·10 45
The 2, 10 and 12c. show the letters "U", "B" and "A" on the book forming the word "CUBA".

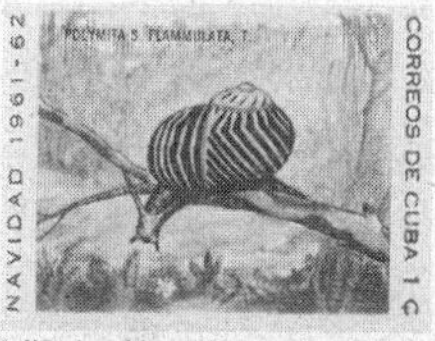

282 "Polymita sulfurosa flammulata"

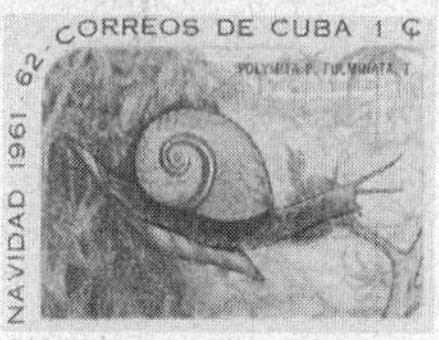

283 "Polymita picta fulminata"

1961. Christmas. Inscr "NAVIDAD 1961–62". Multicoloured. (a) Various designs as T **282**.
999 1c. Type **282** 30 15
1000 2c. Cuban grassquit (vert) 2·50 50
1001 10c. "Othreis toddi" (horiz) 1·75 70

(b) Various designs as T **283**.
1002a/d 1c. Snails (horiz) 30 15
1003a/d 2c. Birds (vert) . . . . . 2·50 50
1004a/d 10c. Butterflies (horiz) . . 1·75 70
DESIGNS: No. 1002a, Type **283**; 1002b, "Polymita p. nigrofasciata"; 1002c, "Polymita p. fuscolimbata"; 1002d, "Polymita p. roseolimbata"; 1003a, Cuban macaw; 1003b, Cuban trogon; 1003c, Bee hummingbird; 1003d, Ivory-billed woodpecker; 1004a, "Uranidia boisduvalii"; 1004b, "Phoebis avellaneda"; 1004c, "Phaloe cubana"; 1004d, "Papoilio gundlacchianus".
Prices are for single stamps.

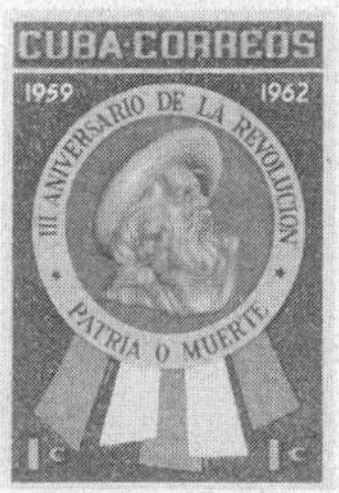

284 Castro Emblem

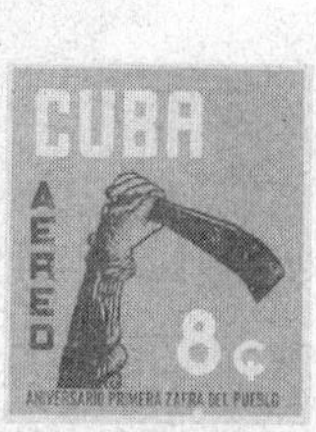

285 Hand with Machete

1962. 3rd Anniv of Cuban Revolution. Emblem in yellow, red, grey and blue. Colours of background and inscriptions given.
1005 **284** 1c. grn & pink (postage) 45 25
1006 2c. black and orange . . 95 30

1007 8c. brown & blue (air) . . . 45 20
1008 12c. ochre and green . . 1·10 35
1009 30c. violet and yellow . . 1·40 1·10

1962. Air. 1st Anniv of Socialist Republic's First Sugar Harvest.
1010 **285** 8c. sepia and red 50 15
1011 12c. black and lilac . . . 1·10 40

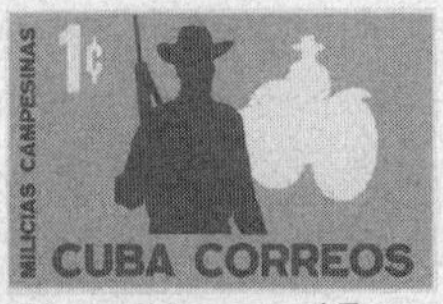

286 Armed Peasant and Tractor

1962. National Militia.
1012 **286** 1c. black and green . . . 20 10
1013 – 2c. black and blue . . . 35 20
1014 – 10c. black and orange 1·10 35
DESIGNS: 2c. Armed worker and welder; 10c. Armed woman and sewing-machinist.

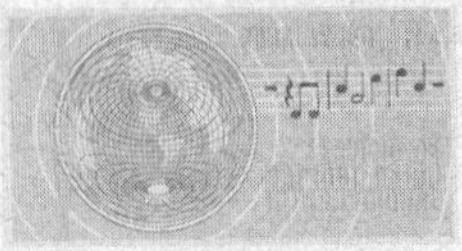

287 Globe and Music Emblem

1962. Air. International Radio Service. Inscr and aerial yellow; musical notation black; lines on globe brown, background colours given.
1015 **287** 8c. grey 55 20
1016 12c. blue . . . . 1·10 35
1017 30c. green . . . . 1·60 85
1018 1p. lilac . . . . 3·25 2·25

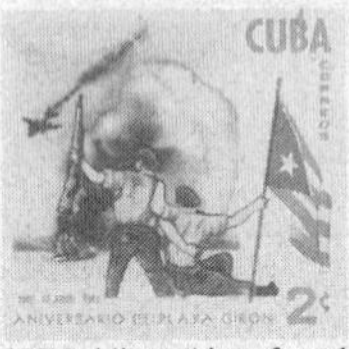

288 Soldiers, Aircraft and Burning Ship

1962. 1st Anniv of "Playa Giron" (Sea Invasion Attempt of Cuban Exiles).
1019 **288** 2c. multicoloured 40 10
1020 3c. multicoloured 40 10
1021 10c. multicoloured . . . 1·75 50

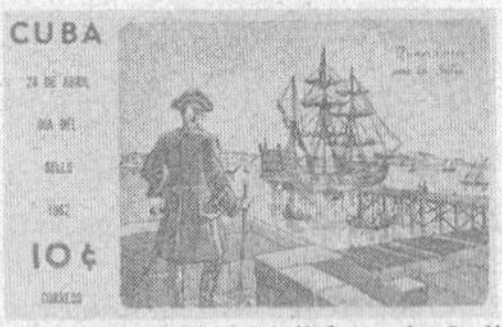

289 Arrival of First Mail from the Indies

1962. Stamp Day.
1022 **289** 10c. black and red on cream . . . . 3·00 60

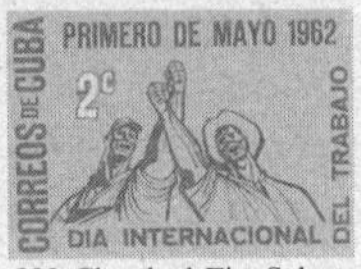

290 Clenched Fist Salute

1962. Labour Day.
1023 **290** 2c. black on buff 20 10
1024 3c. black on red 35 20
1025 10c. black on blue . . . 1·10 45

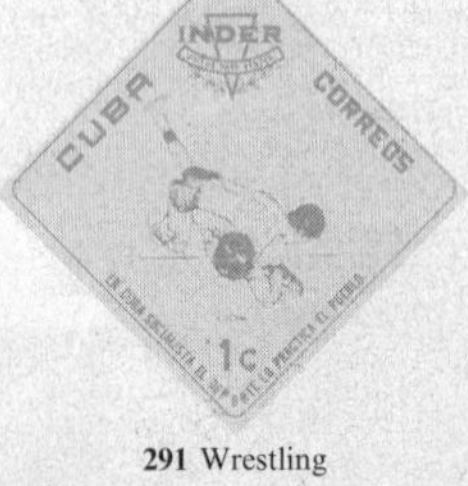

291 Wrestling

1962. National Sports Institute (I.N.D.E.R.) Commemoration. As T **291**. On cream paper.
1026a/e 1c. brown and red . . . 20 10
1027a/e 2c. red and green 20 15
1028a/e 3c. blue and red . . . . 1·00 15
1029a/e 9c. purple and blue . . . 40 15
1030a/e 10c. orange and purple . . 45 20
1031a/e 13c. black and red . . . 50 30
DESIGNS: No. 1026a, Type **291**; 1026b, Weight-lifting; 1026c, Gymnastics; 1026d, Judo; 1026e, Throwing the discus; 1027a, Archery; 1027b, Roller skating; 1027c, Show jumping; 1027d, Ninepin bowling; 1027e, Cycling; 1028a, Rowing (coxed four); 1028b, Speed boat; 1028c, Swimming; 1028d, Kayak; 1028e, Yachting; 1029a, Football; 1029b, Tennis; 1029c, Baseball; 1029d, Basketball; 1029e, Volleyball; 1030a, Underwater fishing; 1030b, Shooting; 1030c, Model airplane flying; 1030d, Water polo; 1030e, Boxing; 1031a, Pelota; 1031b, Sports stadium; 1031c, Jai alai; 1031d, Chess; 1031e, Fencing.
Prices are for single stamps.

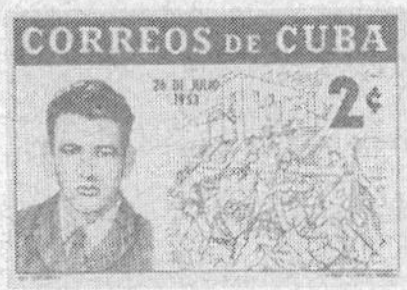

292 A. Santamaria and Soldiers

1962. 9th Anniv of "Rebel Day".
1032 **292** 2c. lake and blue 35 25
1033 – 3c. blue and lake 65 35
DESIGN: 3c. Santamaria and children.

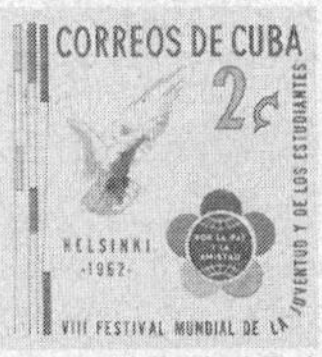

293 Dove and Festival Emblem

1962. World Youth Festival, Helsinki.
1034 **293** 2c. multicoloured 45 20
1035 – 3c. multicoloured 65 30
DESIGN: 3c. As Type **293** but with "clasped hands" instead of dove.

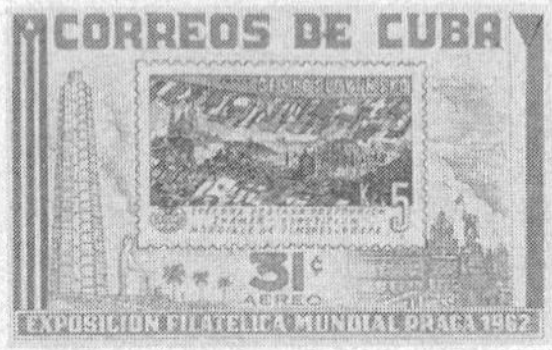

294 Czech 5k. "Praga 1962" stamp of 1961

1962. Air. International Stamp Exn, Prague.
1037 **294** 31c. multicoloured . . . 2·50 1·00

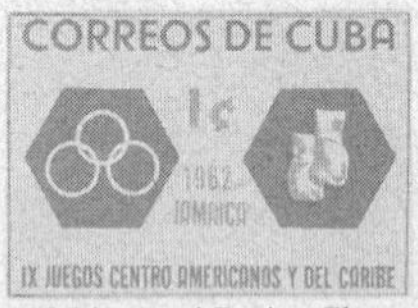

295 Rings and Boxing Gloves

1962. 9th Central American and Caribbean Games, Jamaica.
1039 **295** 1c. ochre and red . . . 10 10
1040 – 2c. ochre and blue . . . 15 10
1041 – 3c. ochre and purple . . 15 10
1042 – 13c. ochre and green . . 1·00 55
DESIGNS: Rings and: 2c. Tennis rackets; 3c. Baseball bats; 13c. Rapiers and mask.

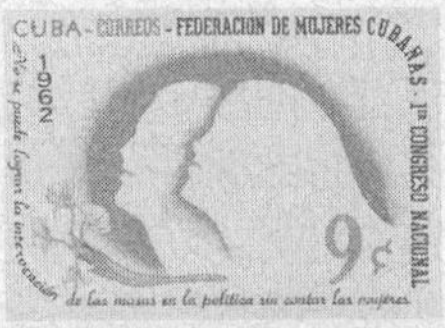

296 "Cuban Women"

1962. 1st Cuban Women's Federation National Congress.
1043 **296** 9c. red, green and black 45 20
1044 – 13c. black, blue & green 1·25 50
DESIGN—VERT: 13c. Mother and child, and Globe.

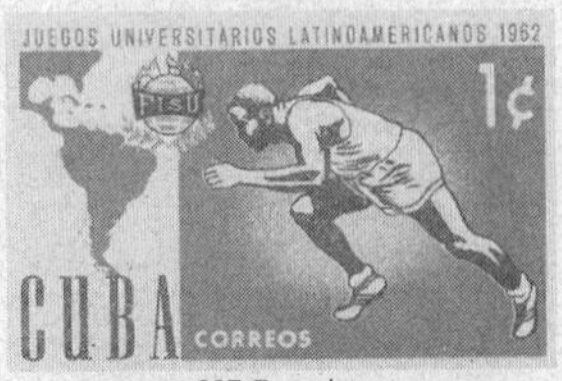

297 Running

1962. 1st Latin-American University Games. Multicoloured.
1045 1c. Type **297** 20 10
1046 2c. Baseball 20 10
1047 3c. Netball 45 20
1048 13c. Globe . . . . 1·10 45

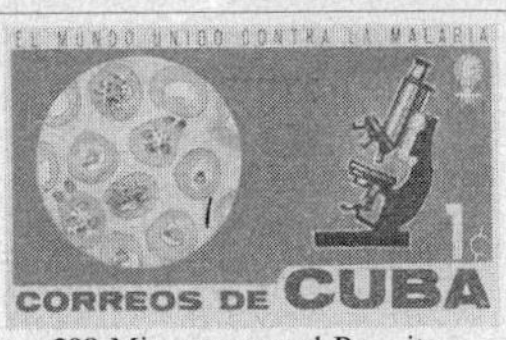

298 Microscope and Parasites

1962. Malaria Eradication. Mult.
1049 1c. Type **298** 30 20
1050 2c. Mosquito and pool . . . 30 20
1051 3c. Cinchona plant and formulae 95 30

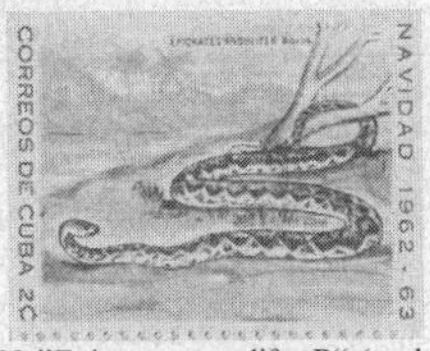

299 "Epicrates angulifer B" (snake)

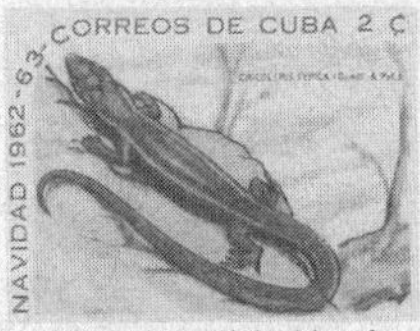

300 Cuban Night Lizard

1962. Christmas. Inscr "NAVIDAD 1962–63". Multicoloured. (a) Various designs as T **299**.
1052 2c. Type **299** 35 15
1053 3c. "Cubispa turquino" (vert) 50 45
1054 10c. Jamacian long-tongued bat . . . . 2·00 1·00
(b) Various designs as T **300**.
1055a/d 2c. Reptiles 35 15
1056a/d 3c. Insects (vert) 50 45
1057a/d 10c. Mammals . . . . . 2·00 1·00
DESIGNS: No. 1055a, Type **300**; 1055b, Knight anole; 1055c, Wright's ground boa; 1055d, Cuban ground iguana; 1056a, "Chrysis superba"; 1056b, "Essosthutha roberto"; 1056c, "Hortensia conciliata"; 1056d, "Lachnopus argus"; 1057a, Desmarest's hutia; 1057b, Prehensile-tailed hutia; 1057c, Cuban solenodon; 1057d, Desmarest's hutia (white race).
Prices are for single stamps.

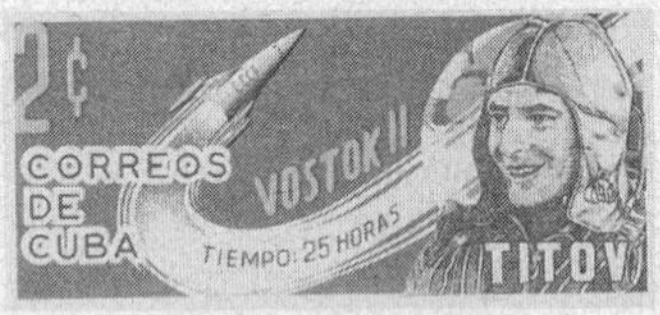

301 Titov and "Vostok 2"

1963. Cosmic Flights (1st issue).
1058 – 1c. blue, red and yellow 20 10
1059 **301** 2c. green, purple & yell 35 20
1060 – 3c. violet, red & yellow 35 20
DESIGNS: 1c. Gagarin and "Vostok 1"; 3c. Nikolaev, Popovich and "Vostoks 3 and 4".
See also Nos. 1133/4.

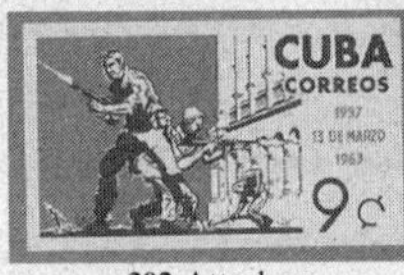

302 Attackers

1963. 6th Anniv of Attack on Presidential Palace.
1061 **302** 9c. black and red 55 15
1062 – 13c. purple and blue . . 65 35
1063 – 30c. green and red . . . 1·60 65
DESIGNS: 13c. Rodriguez, C. Servia, Machado and Westbrook; 30c. J. Echeverria and M. Mora.

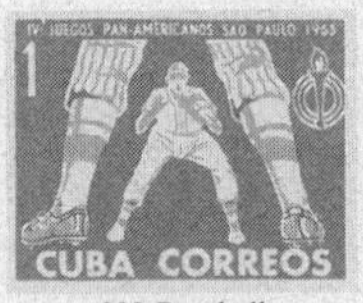

303 Baseball

1963. 4th Pan-American Games, Sao Paulo.
1064 **303** 1c. green 45 20
1065 – 13c. red (Boxing) . . . . 1·40 40

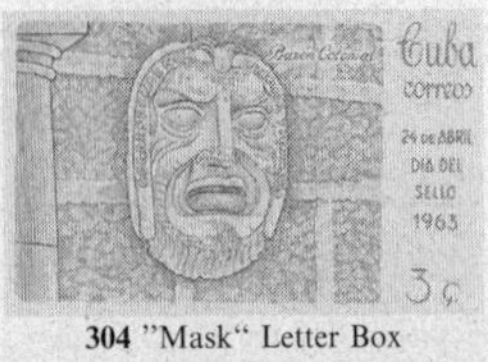

304 "Mask" Letter Box

1963. Stamp Day.
1066 **304** 3c. black and brown . . 45 20
1067 – 10c. black and violet . . 1·10 45
DESIGN: 10c. 19th-century Post Office, Cathedral Place, Havana.

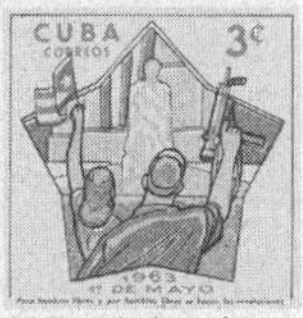

305 Revolutionaries and Statue

1963. Labour Day. Multicoloured.
1068 3c. Type **305** 30 10
1069 13c. Celebrating Labour Day . . . . 1·00 45

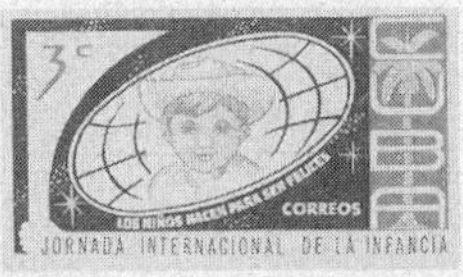

306 Child

1963. Children's Week.
1070 **306** 3c. brown and blue . . . 30 15
1071 30c. red and blue . . . . 1·40 65

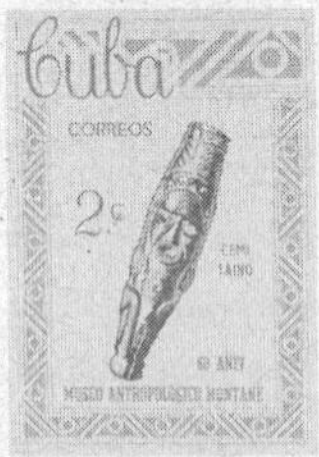

307 Ritual Effigy **308** "Breaking chains of old regime"

1963. 60th Anniv of Montane Anthropological Museum.
1072 **307** 2c. brown and salmon 45 15
1073 – 3c. purple and blue . . . 45 15
1074 – 9c. grey and red 75 40
DESIGNS—HORIZ: 3c. Carved chair; VERT: 9c. Statuette.

1963. 10th Anniv of "Rebel Day".
1075 **308** 1c. black and pink . . . 15 10
1076 – 2c. purple and lt blue . . 15 10
1077 – 3c. sepia and lilac . . . 15 10
1078 – 7c. purple and green . . 15 10
1079 – 9c. purple and yellow . . 40 20
1080 – 10c. green and ochre . . 1·00 35
1081 – 13c. blue and buff . . . 1·40 60
DESIGNS: 2c. Palace attack; 3c. "The Insurrection"; 7c. "Strike of April 9th" (defence of radio station); 9c. "Triumph of the Revolution" (upraised flag and weapons); 10c. "Agrarian Reform and Nationalization" (artisan and peasant); 13c. "Victory of Giron" (soldiers in battle).

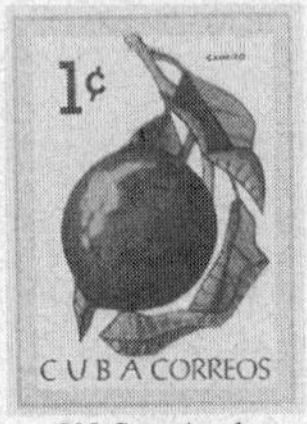

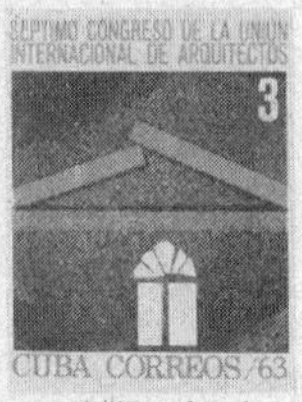

309 Star Apple **310** "Roof and Window"

1963. Cuban Fruits. Multicoloured.
1082 1c. Type **309** 15 10
1083 2c. Chiromoya 15 10
1084 3c. Cashew nut 20 15
1085 10c. Custard apple 95 35
1086 13c. Mango . . . . 1·40 1·00

1963. 7th Int Architects Union Congress, Havana.
1087 3c. multicoloured 25 10
1088 3c. multicoloured 25 10
1089 3c. black, blue and bistre . . 25 10
1090 3c. multicoloured 25 10
1091 13c. multicoloured 90 45
1092 13c. multicoloured 90 45
1093 13c. red, olive and black . . 90 45
1094 13c. multicoloured 90 45
DESIGNS—VERT: No. 1087, Type **310**; Nos. 1090/2, Symbols of building construction as Type **310**. HORIZ: Nos. 1089/90 and 1093, Sketches of urban buildings; No. 1094, as Type **310** (girders and outline of house).

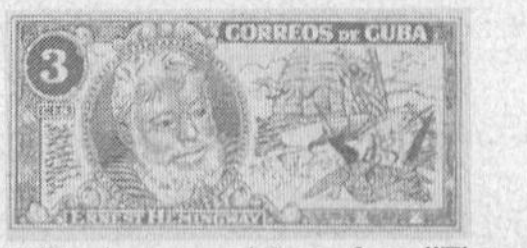

311 Hemingway and Scene from "The Old Man and the Sea"

1963. Ernest Hemingway Commemoration.

1095	311	3c. brown and blue	20	10
1096	–	9c. turquoise and mauve	45	20
1097	–	13c. black and green	1·25	55

DESIGNS—Hemingway and: 9c. Scene from "For Whom the Bell Tolls"; 13c. Residence at San Francisco de Paula, near Havana.

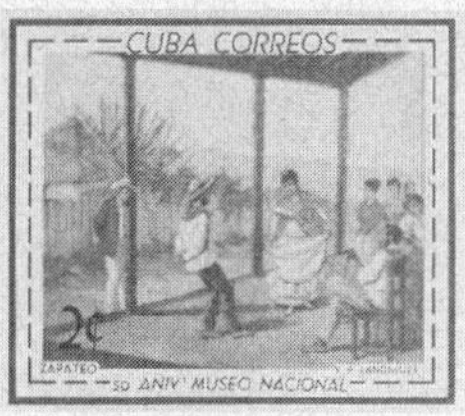

312 "Zapateo" (dance) after V. P. de Landaluze

1964. 50th Anniv of National Museum.

1098	312	2c. multicoloured	20	10
1099	–	3c. multicoloured	50	15
1100	–	9c. multicoloured	75	40
1101	–	13c. black and violet	1·25	75

DESIGNS—VERT: (32 × 42½ mm.): 3c. "The Rape of the Mulattos" (after C. Enriquez); 9c. Greek amphora; 13c. "Dilecta Mea" (bust, after J. A. Houdon).

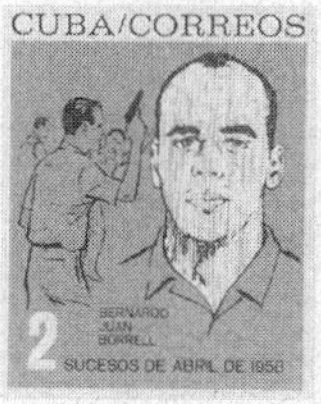

313 B. J. Borrell (revolutionary)

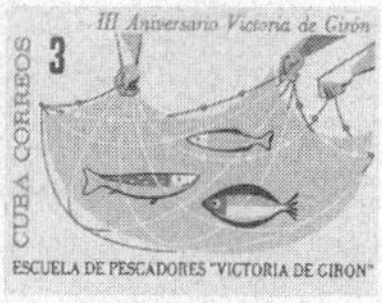

314 Fish in Net

1964. 5th Anniv of Revolution.

1102	313	2c. black, orange & grn	20	10
1103	–	3c. black, orange & red	30	15
1104	–	10c. black, orange & pur	55	25
1105	–	13c. black, orange & bl	1·10	50

PORTRAITS: 3c. M. Salado. 10c. O. Lucero. 13c. S. Gonzalez (revolutionaries).

1964. 3rd Anniv of Giron Victory.

1106	314	3c. multicoloured	20	10
1107	–	10c. black, grey & bistre	40	25
1108	–	13c. slate, black & orge	1·10	45

DESIGNS—HORIZ: 10c. Victory Monument. VERT: 13c. Fallen eagle.

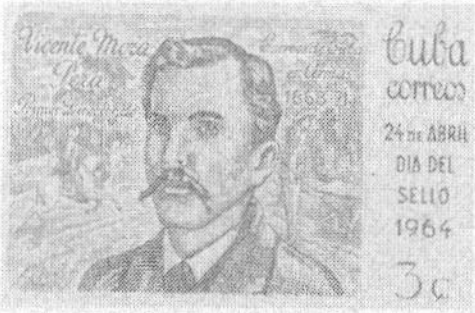

315 V. M. Pera (1st Director of Military Posts, 1868–71)

1964. Stamp Day.

1109	315	3c. blue and brown	35	15
1110	–	13c. green and lilac	1·25	45

DESIGN: 13c. Cuba's first (10c.) military stamp.

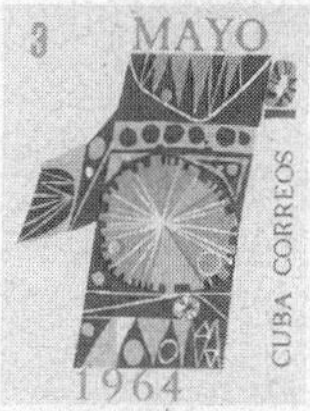

316 Symbolic "1"

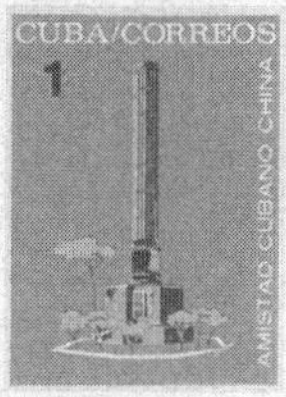

317 Chinese Monument, Havana

1964. Labour Day.

1111	316	3c. multicoloured	20	15
1112	–	13c. multicoloured	85	45

DESIGN: 13c. As Type **316** but different symbols within "1".

1964. Cuban–Chinese Friendship.

1113	317	1c. multicoloured	15	10
1114	–	2c. red, olive and black	25	10
1115	–	3c. multicoloured	40	15

DESIGNS—HORIZ: 2c. Cuban and Chinese. VERT: 3c. Flags of Cuba and China.

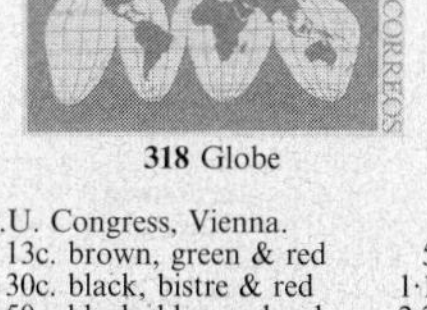

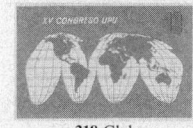

318 Globe

1964. U.P.U. Congress, Vienna.

1116	318	13c. brown, green & red	55	20
1117	–	30c. black, bistre & red	1·10	45
1118	–	50c. black, blue and red	2·25	75

DESIGNS: 30c. H. von Stephan (founder of U.P.U.); 50c. U.P.U. Monument, Berne.

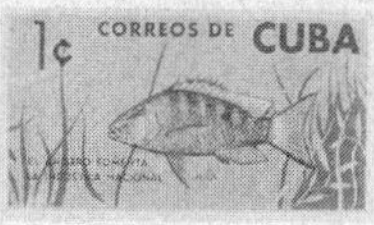

319 Mutton Snapper

1964. Popular Savings Movement. Mult.

1119	1c. Type **319**	25	10
1120	2c. Cow	25	10
1121	13c. Poultry	1·25	45

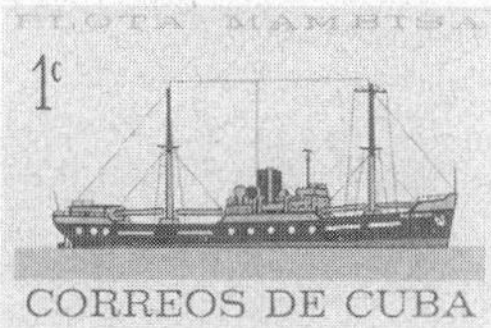

320 "Rio Jibacoa"

1964. Cuban Merchant Fleet. Multicoloured.

1122	1c. Type **320**	25	10
1123	2c. "Camilo Cienfuegos"	35	10
1124	3c. "Sierra Maestra"	55	10
1125	9c. "Bahia de Siguanea"	1·40	40
1126	10c. "Oriente"	3·50	75

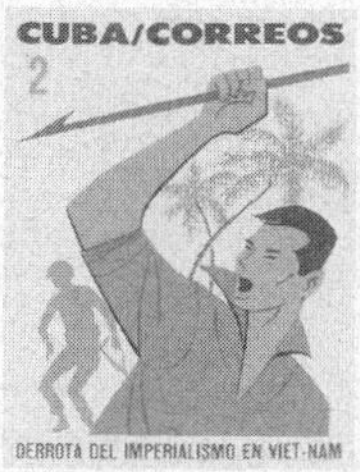

321 Vietnamese Fighter

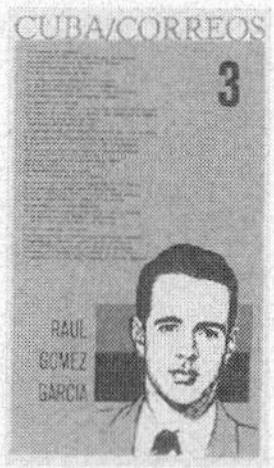

322 Raul Gomez Garcia and Poem

1964. "Unification of Vietnam" Campaign. Mult.

1127	2c. Type **321**	15	10
1128	3c. Vietnamese shaking hands across map	20	15
1129	10c. Hand and mechanical ploughing	45	20
1130	13c. Vietnamese, Cuban and flags	1·10	45

1964. 11th Anniv of "Rebel Day".

1131	322	3c. black, red and ochre	20	10
1132	–	13c. multicoloured	90	40

DESIGN: 13c. Inscr "LA HISTORIA ME ABSOLVERA" (Castro's book).

1964. Cosmic Flights (2nd issue). As T **301**.

1133	9c. yellow, violet and red	75	40
1134	13c. yellow, red and green	1·40	55

DESIGNS: 9c. "Vostok-5" and Bykovksy; 13c. "Vostok-6" and Tereshkova.

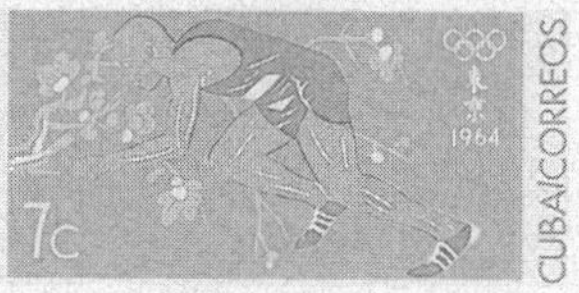

323 Start of Race

1964. Olympic Games, Tokyo.

1135	–	1c. yellow, blue and purple	20	10
1136	–	2c. multicoloured	20	10
1137	–	3c. brown, black & red	20	10
1138	323	7c. violet, blue and orange	40	15
1139	–	10c. yellow, purple & bl	85	40
1140	–	13c. multicoloured	1·50	65

DESIGNS—VERT: 1c. Gymnastics; 2c. Rowing; 3c. Boxing. HORIZ: 10c. Fencing; 13c. Games symbols.

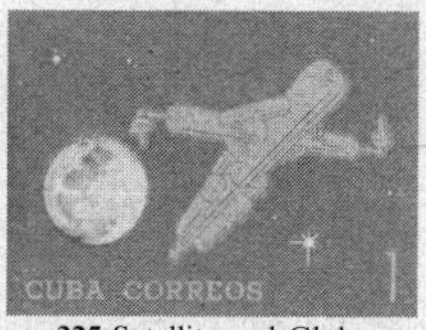

325 Satellite and Globe

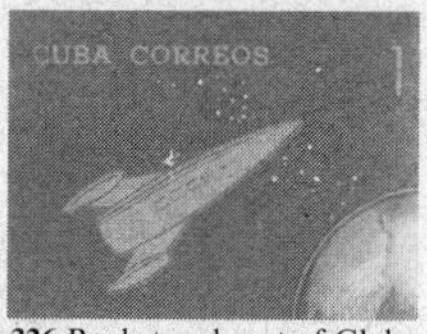

326 Rocket and part of Globe

1964. Cuban Postal Rocket Experiment. 25th Anniv Various rockets and satellites. (a) Horiz. designs as T **325**.

1141	325	1c. multicoloured	15	10
1142	–	2c. multicoloured	35	15
1143	–	3c. multicoloured	45	25
1144	–	9c. multicoloured	1·25	45
1145	–	13c. multicoloured	1·75	1·00

(b) Horiz. designs as T **326**.

1146	–	1c. multicoloured	15	10
1147	–	2c. multicoloured	35	15
1148	–	3c. multicoloured	45	25
1149	–	9c. multicoloured	1·25	45
1150	–	13c. multicoloured	1·75	1·00

(c) Larger 44 × 28 mm.

1151	–	50c. green and black	2·50	1·60

DESIGN: 50c. Cuban Rocket Post 10c. Stamp of 1939.

Nos. 1141 and 1146, 1142 and 1147, 1143 and 1148, 1144 and 1149, 1145 and 1150 were printed together in five sheets of 25, each comprising four stamps as Type **325** plus five se-tenant stamp-size labels inscribed overall "1939 COHETE POSTAL CUBANO 25 ANIVERSARIO 1964" forming a centre cross and four blocks of four different stamps as Type **326** in each corner. The four-stamp design incorporates different subjects, which together form a composite design around a globe.

Prices are for single stamps.

1964. 1st Three-Manned Space Flight. As No. 1151 but colours changed. Optd **VOSJOD-1 octubre 12 1964 PRIMERA TRIPULACION DEL ESPACIO** and large rocket.

1153	50c. green and brown	2·75	1·10

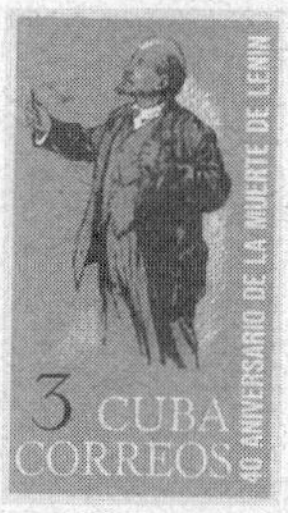

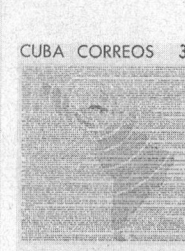

328 Lenin addressing Meeting

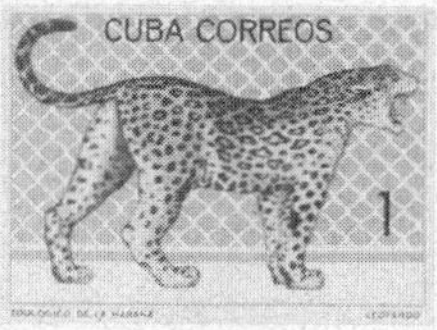

329 Leopard

1964. 40th Death Anniv of Lenin.

1154	328	3c. black and orange	20	10
1155	–	13c. red and violet	45	25
1156	–	30c. black and blue	1·00	55

DESIGNS—HORIZ: 13c. Lenin mausoleum. VERT: 30c. Lenin and hammer and sickle emblem.

1964. Havana Zoo Animals. Multicoloured.

1157	1c. Type **329**	10	10
1158	2c. Indian elephant (vert)	10	10
1159	3c. Red deer (vert)	15	10
1160	4c. Eastern grey kangaroo	20	10
1161	5c. Lions	25	10
1162	6c. Eland	25	10
1163	7c. Common zebra	25	15
1164	8c. Striped hyena	45	15
1165	9c. Tiger	45	15
1166	10c. Guanaco	50	15
1167	13c. Chimpanzees	50	15
1168	20c. Collared Peccary	70	20
1169	30c. Common racoon (vert)	1·00	50
1170	40c. Hippopotamus	2·10	85
1171	50c. Brazilian tapir	2·75	1·10
1172	60c. Dromedary (vert)	3·00	1·50
1173	70c. American Bison	3·00	1·50
1174	80c. Asiatic black bear (vert)	3·75	1·90
1175	90c. Water buffalo	3·75	2·40
1176	1p. Roe deer at Zoo Entrance	4·75	2·40

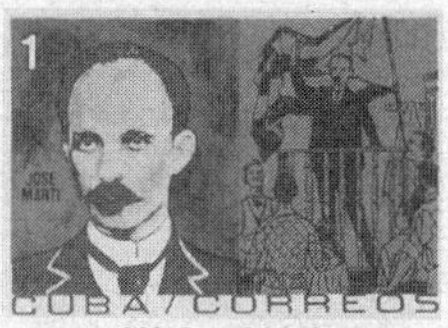

330 Jose Marti

1964. "Liberators of Independence". Multicoloured. Each showing portraits and campaigning scenes.

1177	1c. Type **330**	15	10
1178	2c. A. Maceo	20	15
1179	3c. M. Gomez	45	25
1180	13c. C. Garcia	1·00	55

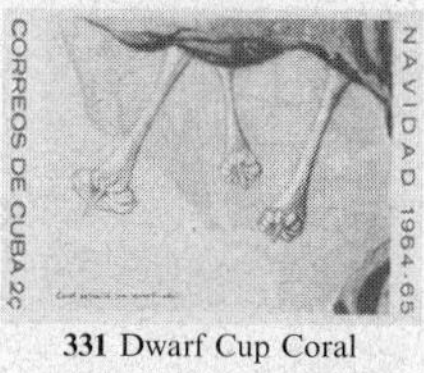

331 Dwarf Cup Coral

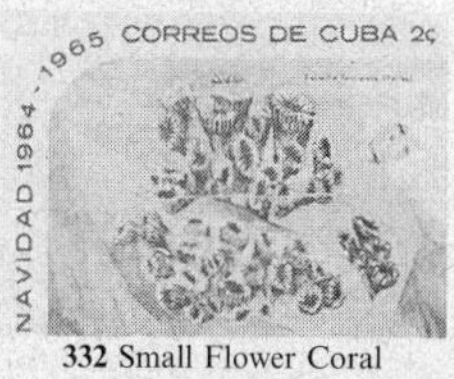

332 Small Flower Coral

1964. Christmas. Inscr "NAVIDAD 1964–65". Multicoloured. (a) As T **331**.

1181	2c. Type **331**	35	25
1182	3c. Sea anemone	65	35
1183	10c. Stone lily	1·00	65

(b) As T **332**.

1184a/d	2c. Coral	35	25
1185a/d	3c. Jellyfish	65	35
1186a/d	10c. Sea stars and urchins	1·00	65

DESIGNS: No. 1184a, Type **332**; 1184b, Elkhorn coral; 1184c, Dense moosehorn coral; 1184d, Yellow brain coral; 1185a, Portuguese man-of-war; 1185b, Moon jellyfish; 1185c, Thimble jellyfish; 1185d, Upside-down jellyfish; 1186a, Big-spined sea-urchin; 1186b, Edible sea urchin; 1186c, Caribbean brittle star; 1186d, Reticulated sea star.

Prices are for single stamps.

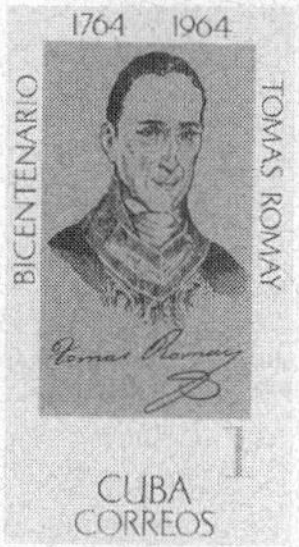

333 Dr. Tomas Romay

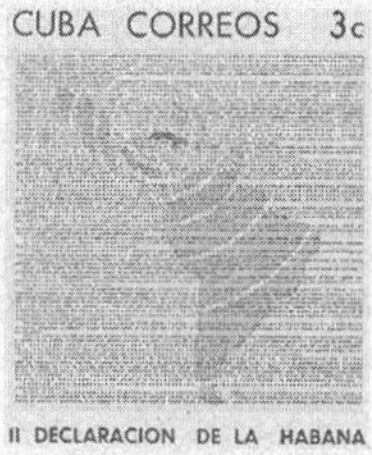

334 Map of Latin America and Part of Declaration

1964. Birth Bicentenary of Dr. Tomas Romay (scientist).

1187	333	1c. black and bistre	20	10
1188	–	2c. sepia and brown	20	10
1189	–	3c. brown and bistre	30	15
1190	–	10c. black and bistre	1·00	40

DESIGNS—VERT: 2c. First vaccination against smallpox. HORIZ: 3c. Dr. Romay and extract from his treatise on the vaccine; 10c. Dr. Romay's statue.

1964. 2nd Declaration of Havana. Mult.

1191	3c. Type **334**	45	30
1192	13c. Map of Cuba and native receiving revolutionary message	1·75	90

The two stamps have the declaration superimposed in tiny print across each horiz. row of five stamps, thus requiring strips of five to show the complete declaration.

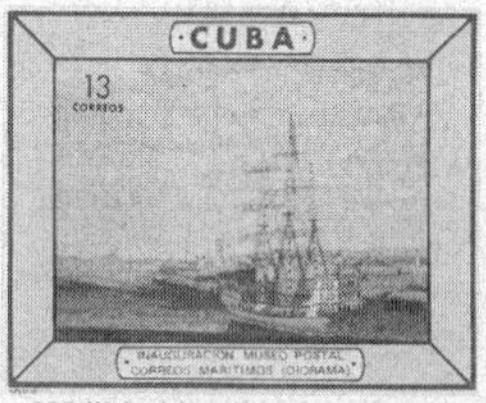

335 "Maritime Post" (diorama)

1965. Inauguration of Cuban Postal Museum. Mult.

1193	13c. Type **335**	2·75	65
1194	30c. "Insurgent Post" (diorama)	1·90	1·00

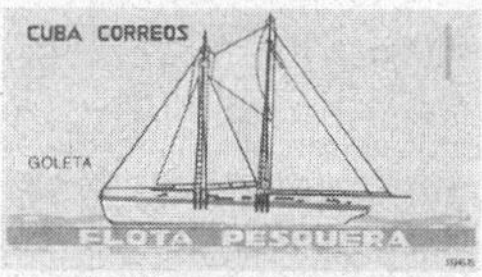

336 "Sondero" (schooner)

1965. Cuban Fishing Fleet. Multicoloured. Fishing crafts.

1196	1c. Type **336**	15	10
1197	2c. "Omicron"	25	10
1198	3c. "Victoria"	35	15
1199	9c. "Cardenas"	55	25
1200	10c. "Sigma"	2·10	50
1201	13c. "Lambda"	3·25	80

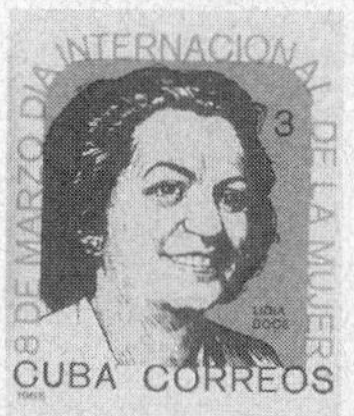

337 Lydia Doce

1965. International Women's Day. Multicoloured.

1202	3c. Type **337**	55	25
1203	13c. Clara Zetkin	85	45

338 Jose Antonio Echeverria University City

1965. "Technical Revolution". Inscr "REVOLUCION TECNICA".
1204 338 3c. black, brown and chestnut 25 15
1205 – 13c. multicoloured . . . . 1·10 45
DESIGN: 13c. Scientific symbols.

339 Leonov

1965. "Voskhod 2", Space flight.
1206 339 30c. brown and blue . . 1·40 55
1207 – 50c. blue and magenta . 2·75 1·10
DESIGN: 50c. Beliaiev, Leonov and "Voskhod 2".

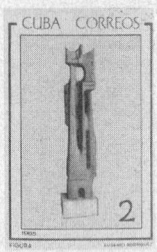

340 "Figure" (after E. Rodrigues)
341 Lincoln Statue, Washington

1965. National Museum Treasures. Mult.
1208 2c. Type 340 (27 × 42 mm) 30 10
1209 3c. "Landscape with sunflowers" (V. Manuel) (31 × 42 mm) . . 30 15
1210 10c. "Abstract" (W. Lam) (42 × 31 mm) . . 80 30
1211 13c. "Children" (E. Ponce) (39 × 33½ mm) . . . . . 1·40 55

1965. Death Centenary of Abraham Lincoln.
1212 – 1c. brown, grey and yellow 10 10
1213 – 2c. ultramarine & blue . . 25 10
1214 341 3c. black, red and blue . . 55 30
1215 – 13c. black, orange & bl . 1·10 50
DESIGNS—HORIZ: 1c. Cabin at Hodgenville, Kentucky (Lincoln's birthplace); 2c. Lincoln Monument, Washington. VERT: 13c. Abraham Lincoln.

342 18th-century Mail Ship and Old Postmarks (bicent of Maritime Mail)

1965. Stamp Day.
1216 342 3c. bistre and red . . 1·50 20
1217 – 13c. red, black and blue . 1·40 45
DESIGN: 13c. Cuban; 10c. "Air Train" stamp of 1935 and glider train over Capitol, Havana.

343 Sun and Earth's Magnetic Pole

1965. International Quiet Sun Year. Multicoloured.
1218 1c. Type 343 . . . . 20 10
1219 2c. I.Q.S.Y. emblem (vert) 20 10
1220 3c. Earth's magnetic fields 35 10
1221 6c. Solar rays 40 15
1222 30c. Effect of solar rays on various atmospheric layers 1·40 40
1223 50c. Effect of solar rays on satellite orbits . . . 1·90 95
Nos. 1221/3 are larger, 47 × 20 mm. or 20 × 47 mm. (30c.).

344 Telecommunications Station

1965. Centenary of I.T.U. Multicoloured.
1225 1c. Type 344 . . . . . 15 10
1226 2c. Satellite (vert) . . . 15 10
1227 3c. "Telstar" 20 10
1228 10c. "Telstar" and receiving station (vert) 65 20
1229 30c. I.T.U. emblem . . . . 1·75 65

345 Festival Emblem and Flags

1965. World Youth and Students Festival. Multicoloured.
1230 13c. Type 345 . . . . . . 75 35
1231 30c. Soldiers of three races and flags . . . . 1·60 45

346 M. Perez (pioneer balloonist), Balloon and Satellite

1965. Matias Perez Commemoration.
1232 346 3c. black and red . . . . 1·10 85
1233 – 13c. black and blue . . 1·40 85
DESIGN: 13c. As Type 346, but with rockets in place of satellite.

347 Rose (Europe)

1965. Flowers of the World. Multicoloured.
1234 1c. Type 347 . . . . 15 10
1235 2c. Chrysanthemum (Asia) . 15 10
1236 3c. Strelitzia (Africa) . . 20 10
1237 4c. Dahlia (N. America) . . 20 10
1238 5c. Orchid (S. America) . . 55 15
1239 13c. "Grevillea banksii" (Oceania) . . . . . 1·75 75
1240 30c. "Brunfelsia nitida" (Cuba) . . . . 2·25 1·40

348 Swimming

1965. First National Games.
1241 348 1c. multicoloured 15 10
1242 – 2c. multicoloured . . . 20 10
1243 – 3c. black, red and grey 45 20
1244 – 30c. black, red and grey 1·50 55
SPORTS: 2c. Basketball. 3c. Gymnastics. 30c. Hurdling.

349 Anti-tank gun

1965. Museum of the Revolution. Mult.
1245 1c. Type 349 . . . . . 10 10
1246 2c. Tank 10 10
1247 3c. Bazooka 20 10
1248 10c. Rebel Uniform . . . 55 20
1249 13c. Launch "Granma" and compass . . . . . 1·60 40

350 C. J. Finlay

351 "Anetia numidia" (butterfly)

1965. 50th Death Anniv of Carlos J. Finlay (malaria researcher).
1250 – 1c. black, green & blue 10 10
1251 – 2c. brown, ochre and black 15 10
1252 350 3c. brown and black . . . 15 10
1253 – 7c. black and lilac . . 20 10
1254 – 9c. bronze and black . . 40 20
1255 – 10c. black and blue . . 85 25
1256 – 13c. multicoloured . . 1·25 55
DESIGNS—HORIZ: 1c. Finlay's signature. VERT: 2c. Yellow fever mosquito; 7c. Finlay's microscope; 9c. Dr. C. Delgado; 10c. Finlay's monument; 13c. Finlay demonstrating his theories, after painting by Valderrama.

1965. Cuban Butterflies. Multicoloured.
1257 2c. Type 351 . . . . . 40 15
1258 2c. "Carathis gortynoides" 40 15
1259 2c. "Hymenitis cubana" . . 40 15
1260 2c. "Eubaphe heros" . . 40 15
1261 2c. "Dismorphia cubana" . 40 15
1262 3c. "Siderone nemesis" . . . 50 25
1263 3c. "Syntomidopsis variegata" 50 25
1264 3c. "Ctenuchidia virgo" . . 50 25
1265 3c. "Lycorea ceres" . . 50 25
1266 3c. "Eubaphe disparilis" . . 50 25
1267 13c. "Anetia cubana" . . 2·00 75
1268 13c. "Prepona antimache" . 2·00 75
1269 13c. "Sylepta reginalis" . . 2·00 75
1270 13c. "Chlosyne perezi" . . 2·00 75
1271 13c. "Anaea clytemnestra" 2·00 75

352 20c. Coin of 1962

1965. 50th Anniv of Cuban Coinage. Mult.
1273 1c. Type 352 . . . . 10 10
1274 2c. 1p. coin of 1934 . . 10 10
1275 3c. 40c. coin of 1962 . . 15 15
1276 8c. 1p. coin of 1915 . . 30 15
1277 10c. 1p. coin of 1953 . . 75 35
1278 13c. 20p. coin of 1915 . . . 1·10 40

353 Oranges

1965. Tropical Fruits. Multicoloured.
1279 1c. Type 353 . . . . . 10 10
1280 2c. Custard-apples 10 10
1281 3c. Papayas 15 15
1282 4c. Bananas 20 10
1283 10c. Avocado pears . . . 30 15
1284 13c. Pineapples 55 50
1285 20c. Guavas . . . . 1·40 50
1286 50c. Mameys . . . . 2·75 85

354 Northern Oriole
355 Painted Bunting

1965. Christmas. Vert. designs showing bird life.
(a) As T 354. Multicoloured.
1287 3c. Type 354 . . . . 2·50 1·60
1288 5c. Scarlet tanager . . . 3·00 2·10
1289 13c. Indigo bunting . . . 6·75 3·75
(b) As T 355.
1290a/d 3c. multicoloured . . . 2·50 1·60
1291a/d 5c. multicoloured . . . 3·00 2·10
1292a/d 13c. multicoloured . . . 6·75 3·75
DESIGNS: No. 1290a, Type 355; 1290b, American redstart; 1290c, Blackburnian warbler; 1290d, Rose-breasted grosbeak; 1291a, Yellow-throated warbler; 1291b, Blue-winged warbler; 1291c, Prothonotary warbler; 1291d, Blue-winged warbler; 1292a, Blue-winged teal; 1292b, Wood duck; 1292c, Common shoveler; 1292d, Black-crowned night heron.
Prices are for single stamps.

356 Hurdling

1965. 7th Anniv of International Athletics, Havana. Multicoloured.
1293 1c. Type 356 . . . . . 15 10
1294 2c. Throwing the discus . . 15 10
1295 3c. Putting the shot . . . 35 10
1296 7c. Throwing the javelin . . 35 20
1297 9c. High-jumping 45 25
1298 10c. Throwing the hammer . 95 40
1299 13c. Running . . . . 1·25 60

357 Sharksucker

1965. National Aquarium. Multicoloured.
1300 1c. Type 357 . . . . 20 10
1301 2c. Skipjack/Bonito tuna . . 20 10
1302 3c. Sergeant major . . . 40 10
1303 4c. Sailfish 45 10
1304 5c. Nassau grouper . . 45 10
1305 10c. Mutton snapper . . . 60 20
1306 13c. Yellow-tailed snapper . 2·00 60
1307 30c. Squirrelfish . . . . . 3·25 90

358 A. Voisin, Cuban and French Flags

1965. 1st Death Anniv of Prof. Andre Voisin (scientist).
1308 358 3c. multicoloured 40 20
1309 – 13c. multicoloured . . 1·10 40
DESIGN: 13c. Similar to Type 358 but with microscope and plant in place of cattle.

359 Skoda Omnibus

1965. Cuban Transport. Multicoloured.
1310 1c. Type 359 . . . . . 10 10
1311 2c. Ikarus omnibus . . . 10 10
1312 3c. Leyland omnibus . . 15 10
1313 4c. Russian-built Type TEM-4 diesel locomotive . . . . 2·25 45
1314 7c. French-built BB. 69,000 diesel locomotive . . . 2·25 45
1315 10c. Tug "R.D.A." . . . 1·00 25
1316 13c. Freighter "13 de Marzo" . . . . 1·60 45
1317 20c. Ilyushin IL-18 airliner . 1·75 65

360 Infantry Column

1966. 7th Anniv of Revolution. Mult.
1318 1c. Type 360 . . . . 20 10
1319 2c. Soldier and tank . . 20 10
1320 3c. Sailor and torpedo-boat 45 10
1321 10c. MiG-21 jet fighter . . 1·00 30
1322 13c. Rocket missile . . . 1·25 25
SIZES—As Type 360: 2c., 3c. HORIZ: (38½ × 23¼ mm): 10c. 13c.

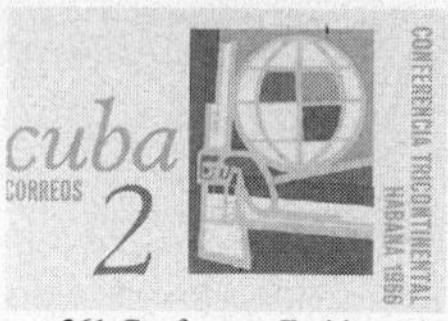

361 Conference Emblem

1966. Tricontinental Conference, Havana.
1323 **361** 2c. multicoloured 15 10
1324 – 3c. multicoloured 20 10
1325 – 13c. multicoloured . . . 95 40
DESIGNS: 3c., 13c. As Type **361** but re-arranged.

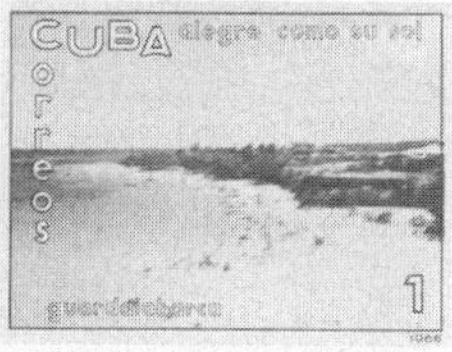

362 Guardalabarca Beach

1966. Tourism. Multicoloured.
1326 1c. Type **362** 10 10
1327 2c. La Gran Piedra (mountain resort) 15 10
1328 3c. Guama, Las Villas (country scene) 35 15
1329 13c. Waterfall, Soroa (vert) 1·40 40

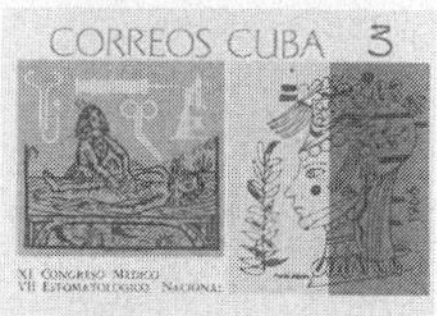

363 Congress Emblem and "Treating Patient" (old engraving)

1966. Medical and Stomachal Congresses, Havana. Multicoloured.
1330 3c. Type **363** 25 10
1331 13c. Congress emblem and children receiving treatment . . . . 1·10 40

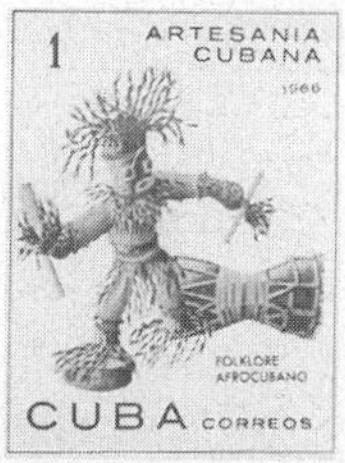

364 Afro-Cuban Doll

1966. Cuban Handicrafts. Multicoloured.
1332 1c. Type **364** 10 10
1333 2c. Sombreros 10 10
1334 3c. Vase 10 10
1335 7c. Gourd lampshades . . . 15 10
1336 9c. Rare-wood lampstand 35 15
1337 10c. "Horn" shark (horiz) 55 25
1338 13c. Painted polymita shell necklace and earrings (horiz) . . . . 1·10 45

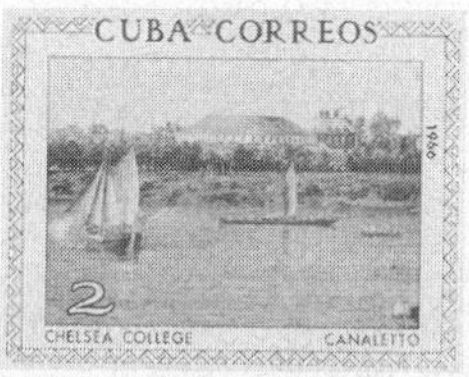

365 "Chelsea College" (after Canaletto)

1966. National Museum Exhibits. Inscr "1966". Multicoloured.
1339 1c. Ming Dynasty vase (vert) 10 10
1340 2c. Type **365** 40 10
1341 3c. "Portrait of a Young Girl" (after Goya) (vert) 35 20
1342 13c. Portrait of Fayum (vert) . . . . 1·40 45

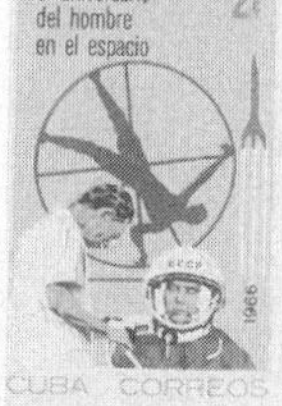

366 Cosmonauts in Training

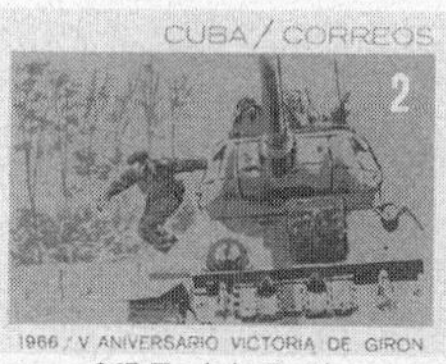

367 Tank in Battle

1966. 5th Anniv of 1st Manned Space Flight. Multicoloured.
1343 1c. Tsiolkovsky and diagram 10 10
1344 2c. Type **366** 10 10
1345 3c. Gagarin, rocket and globe 20 10
1346 7c. Nikolaev and Popovich 35 10
1347 9c. Tereshkova and Bykovsky 45 20
1348 10c. Komarov, Feoktistov and Yegorov 55 25
1349 13c. Leonov in space . . . 1·10 45
Nos. 1343, 1345 and 1347/9 are horiz.

1966. 5th Anniv of Giron Victory.
1350 **367** 2c. black, green and bistre 10 10
1351 – 3c. black, blue and red 40 10
1352 – 9c. black, brown & grey 20 10
1353 – 10c. black, blue and green 70 15
1354 – 13c. black, brown and blue . . . . 1·40 50
DESIGNS: 3c. "Houston" (freighter) sinking; 9c. Disabled tank and poster-hoarding; 10c. Young soldier; 13c. Operations map.

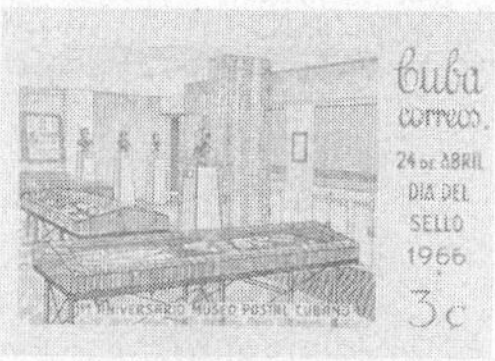

368 Interior of Postal Museum (1st Anniv)

1966. Stamp Day.
1355 **368** 3c. green and red 45 10
1356 – 13c. brown, black & red 1·40 45
DESIGN: 13c. Stamp collector and Cuban 2c. stamp of 1959.

369 Bouquet and Anvil

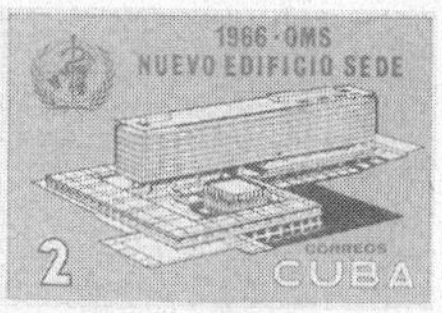

370 W.H.O. Building

1966. Labour Day. Multicoloured.
1357 2c. Type **369** 15 10
1358 3c. Bouquet and Machete 15 10
1359 10c. Bouquet and Hammer 45 20
1360 13c. Bouquet and parts of globe and cogwheel . . . 1·10 60

1966. Inaug of W.H.O. Headquarters, Geneva.
1361 **370** 2c. black, green & yell 15 10
1362 – 3c. black, blue and yellow 35 10
1363 13c. black, yellow and blue . . . . 1·10 45
DESIGNS (W.H.O. Building on): 3c. Flag; 13c. Emblem.

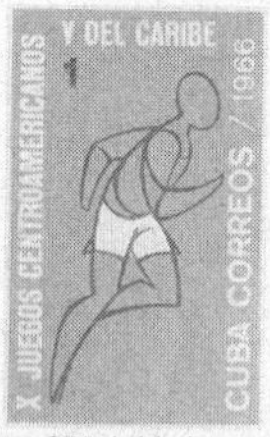

371 Athletics

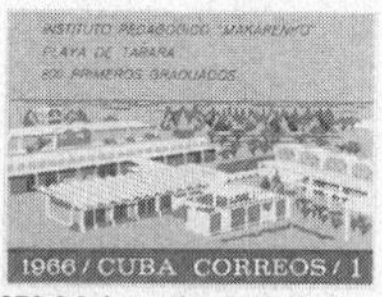

372 Makarenko Pedagogical Institute

1966. 10th Central American and Caribbean Games.
1364 **371** 1c. sepia and green . . . 10 10
1365 – 2c. sepia and orange . . 10 10
1366 – 3c. brown and yellow . . 10 10
1367 – 7c. blue and mauve . . . 15 10
1368 – 9c. black and blue . . . 30 15
1369 – 10c. black and brown . . 55 15
1370 – 13c. blue and red . . . . 1·25 40
DESIGNS—HORIZ: 2c. Rifle-shooting. VERT: 3c. Baseball; 7c. Volleyball; 9c. Football; 10c. Boxing; 13c. Basketball.

1966. Educational Development.
1371 **372** 1c. black and green . . . 10 10
1372 – 2c. black, ochre & yellow 10 10
1373 – 3c. black, ultram & bl 15 10
1374 – 10c. black, brown & grn 35 20
1375 – 13c. multicoloured . . . 95 40
DESIGNS: 2c. Alphabetization Museum; 3c. Lamp (5th anniv of National Alphabetization Campaign); 10c. Open-air class; 13c. "Farmers' and Workers' Education".

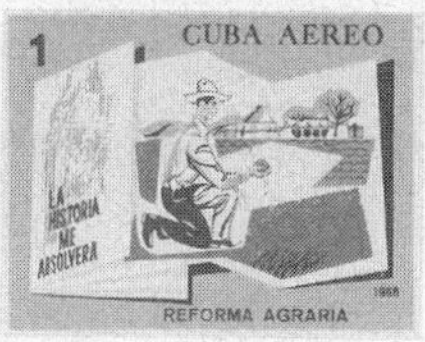

373 "Agrarian Reform"

1966. Air. "Conquests of the Revolution". Multicoloured.
1376 1c. Type **373** 15 10
1377 2c. "Industrialisation" . . . 15 10
1378 3c. "Urban Reform" . . . 20 10
1379 7c. "Eradication of Unemployment" 20 10
1380 9c. "Education" 40 15
1381 10c. "Public Health" . . . 85 15
1382 13c. Paragraph from Castro's book, "La Historia me Absolvera" 1·10 30

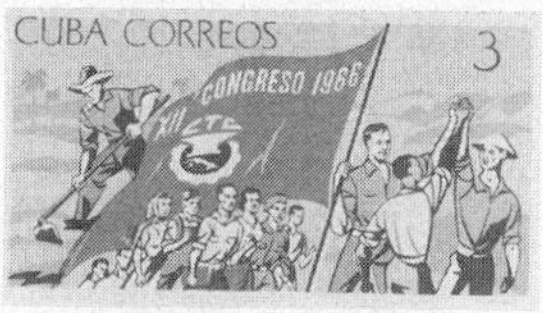

374 Workers with Flag

1966. 12th Revolutionary Workers' Union Congress, Havana.
1383 **374** 3c. multicoloured 55 20

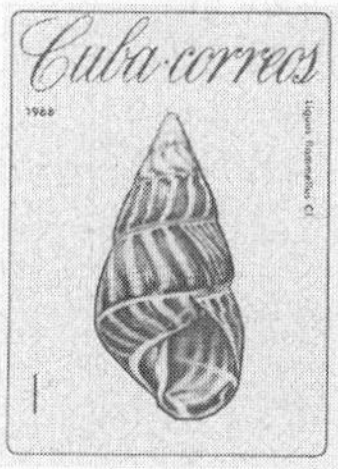

375 Flamed Cuban Liguus

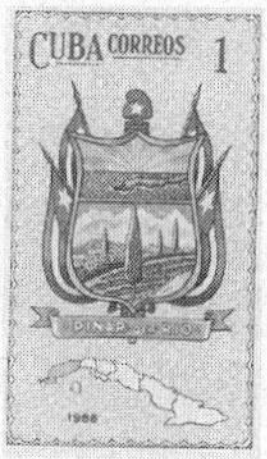

377 Arms of Pinar del Rio

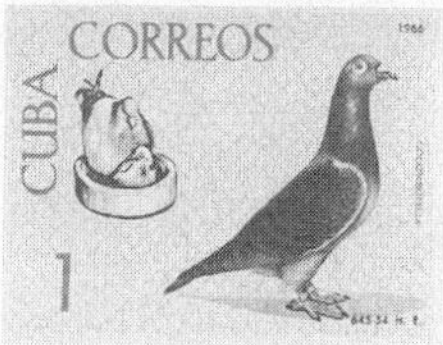

376 Pigeon and Breeding Pen

1966. Cuban Shells. Multicoloured.
1384 1c. Type **375** 20 10
1385 2c. Measled cowrie 25 15
1386 3c. West Indian fighting conch 35 15
1387 7c. Rough American scallops 40 20
1388 9c. Crenate liguus 50 20
1389 10c. Atlantic trumpet triton 80 30
1390 13c. Archer's Cuban liguus 1·90 55

1966. Pigeon-breeding. Multicoloured.
1391 1c. Type **376** 20 10
1392 2c. Pigeon and time-clock 20 10
1393 3c. Pigeon and pigeon-loft 20 15
1394 7c. Pigeon and breeder tending pigeon-loft . . . 35 20
1395 9c. Pigeon and pigeon-yard 35 25
1396 10c. Pigeon and breeder placing message in capsule 1·10 35
1397 13c. Pigeons in flight over map of Cuba (44½ × 28 mm) . . . . . 1·75 60

1966. National and Provincial Arms. Mult.
1398 1c. Type **377** 10 10
1399 2c. Arms of Havana 10 10
1400 3c. Arms of Matanzas . . . 15 10
1401 4c. Arms of Las Villas . . . 20 10
1402 5c. Arms of Camaguey . . . 30 15
1403 9c. Arms of Oriente 45 30
1404 13c. National Arms (26 × 44 mm) . . . . . . 1·00 40

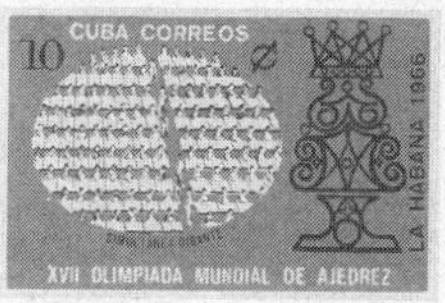

378 "Queen" and Simultaneous Games

1966. 17th Chess Olympiad, Havana.
1405 – 1c. black and green . . . 10 10
1406 – 2c. black and blue . . . 10 10
1407 – 3c. black and red 20 10
1408 – 9c. black and ochre . . . 35 20
1409 **378** 10c. black and mauve . . 85 30
1410 – 13c. black, blue & turq 1·10 65
DESIGNS—VERT: 1c. "Pawn"; 2c. "Rook"; 3c. "Knight"; 9c. "Bishop". HORIZ: 13c. Olympiad Emblem and "King".

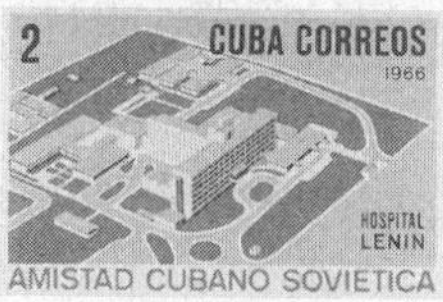

380 Lenin Hospital

1966. Cuban–Soviet Friendship. Mult.
1412 2c. Type **380** 15 10
1413 3c. World map and "Havana" (tanker) . . . 40 10
1414 10c. Cuban and Soviet technicians 60 20
1415 13c. Cuban fruit-pickers and Soviet tractor technicians 1·10 55

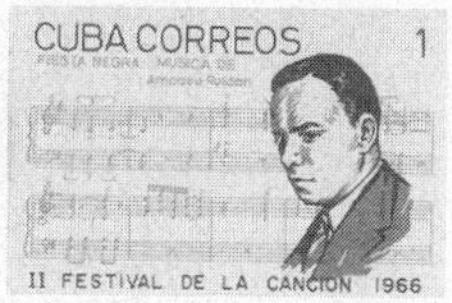

381 A. Roldan and Music of "Fiesta Negra"

1966. Song Festival.
1416 **381** 1c. brown, black & grn 10 10
1417 – 2c. brown, black & mve 10 10
1418 – 3c. brown, black & blue 25 10
1419 – 7c. brown, black & vio 40 10
1420 – 9c. brown, black & yell 40 20
1421 – 10c. brn, blk & orge . 1·25 30
1422 – 13c. brown, black & bl 1·75 60
CUBAN COMPOSERS AND WORKS: 2c. E. S. de Fuentes and "Tu" (habanera, Cuban dance). 3c. M. Simons and "El Manisero". 7c. J. Anckermann and "El arroyo que murmura". 9c. A. G. Caturla and "Pastoral Lullaby". 10c. E. Grenet and "Ay Mama Ines". 13c. E. Lecuona and "La Comparsa" (dance).

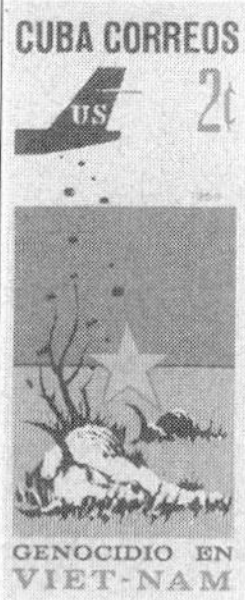

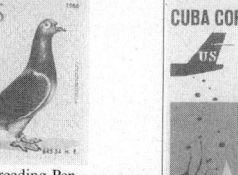

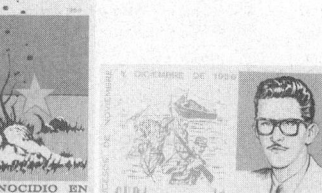

382 Bacteriological Warfare

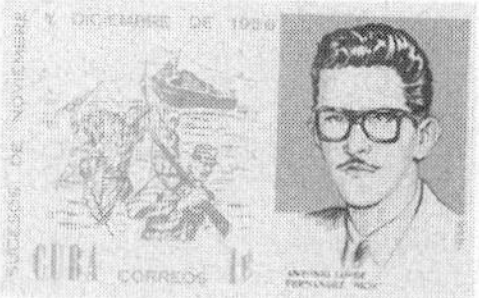

383 A. L. Fernandez ("Nico") and Beach Landing

1966. "Genocide in Viet-Nam". Mult.
1423 2c. Type **382** 10 10
1424 3c. Gas warfare 20 10
1425 13c. "Conventional" bombing . . . . 1·10 45

1966. 10th Anniv of 1956 Revolutionary Successes. Portrait in black and brown.
1426 **383** 1c. brown and green . . 10 10
1427 – 2c. brown and purple . . 10 10
1428 – 3c. brown and purple . . 15 10
1429 – 7c. brown and blue . . . 20 15
1430 – 9c. brown and turquoise 35 15
1431 – 10c. brown and olive . . 1·25 35
1432 – 13c. brown and orange 1·10 55
HEROES AND SCENES: 2c. C. Gonzalez and beach landing. 3c. J. Tey and street fighting. 7c. T. Aloma and street fighting. 9c. O. Parellada and street fighting. 10c. J. M. Marquez and beach landing. 13c. F. Pais and trial scene.

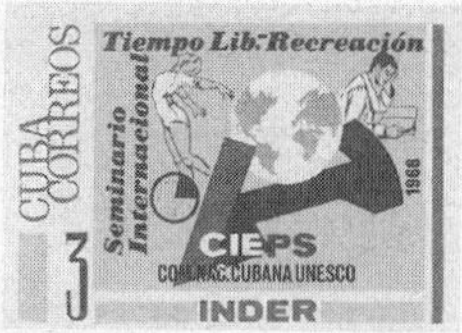

384 Globe and Recreational Activities

1966. International Leisure Time and Recreation Seminar. Multicoloured.
1433 3c. Type **384** 15 10
1434 9c. Clock, eye and world map 85 20
1435 13c. Seminar poster . . . . 1·10 45

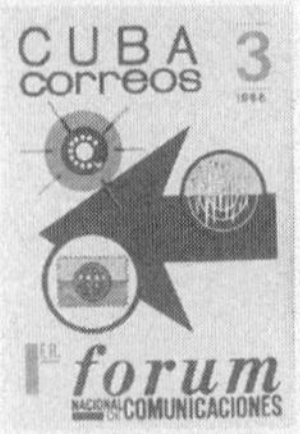

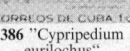

385 Arrow and Telecommunications Symbols

1966. 1st National Telecommunications Forum. Multicoloured.
1436 3c. Type **385** 20 10
1437 10c. Target and satellites . . 85 20
1438 13c. Shell and satellites (28½ × 36 mm) . . . . . 1·25 45

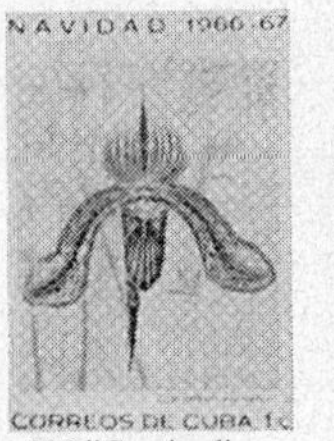

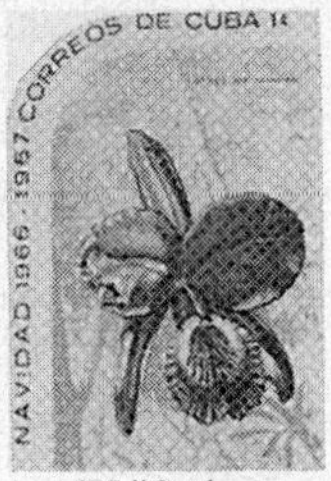

386 "Cypripedium eurilochus" **387** "Cattleya speciosissima"

1966. Christmas. Orchids. Multicoloured.
(a) As T **386**.
1440 1c. Type **386** 30 15
1441 3c. "Cypripedium hookerae volunteanum 45 25
1442 13c. "Cypripedium stonei" 1·75 95
(b) As T **387**.
1443a/d 1c. multicoloured 30 15
1444a/d 3c. multicoloured 45 25
1445a/d 13c. multicoloured . . . 1·75 95
DESIGNS: No. 1443a, Type **387**; 1443b, "Cattleya mendelli"; 1443c, "Cattleya trianae"; 1443d, "Cattleya labiata"; 1444a, "Cypripedium morganiae"; 1444b, "Cattleya" "Countess of Derby"; 1444c, "Cattleya gigas"; 1444d, "Cypripedium stonei"; 1445a, "Cattleya mendelli" "Countess of Montrose"; 1445b, "Oncidium macranthum"; 1445c, "Cattleya aurea"; 1445d, "Laelia anceps".
Prices are for single stamps.

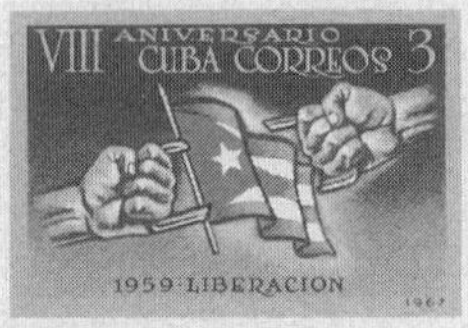

388 Flag and Hands ("1959—Liberation")

1966. 8th Anniv of Revolution. Mult.
1446 3c. Type **388** 15 10
1447 3c. Clenched fist ("1960—Agrarian Reform") . . . 15 10
1448 3c. Hands holding pencil ("1961—Education") . . 15 10
1449 3c. Hand protecting plant ("1965—Agriculture") . . 15 10
1450 13c. Head of Rodin's statue, "The Thinker", and arrows ("1962—Planning") 90 35
1451 13c. Hands moving lever ("1963—Organization") 90 35
1452 13c. Hand holding plant within cogwheel ("1964—Economy") 90 35
1453 13c. Hand holding rifle-butt, and part of globe ("1966—Solidarity") . . . 90 35
Nos. 1450/3 are vert.

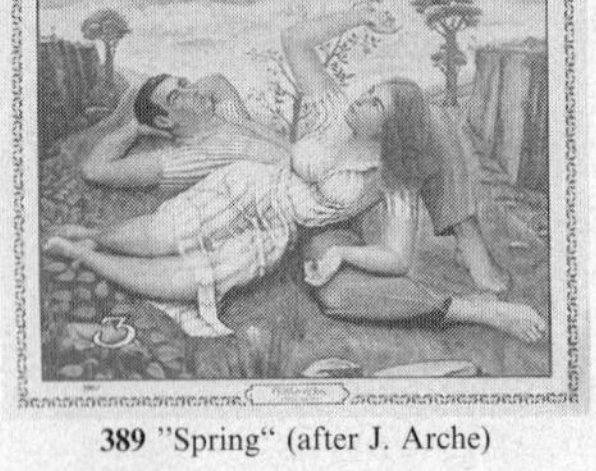

389 "Spring" (after J. Arche)

1967. National Museum Exhibits. Paintings (1st series). Multicoloured.
1454 1c. "Coffee-pot" (A. A. Leon) 30 10
1455 2c. "Peasants" (E. Abela) 40 10
1456 3c. Type **389** 60 15
1457 13c. "Still Life" (Amelia Pelaez) . . . . 1·50 75
1458 30c. "Landscape" (G. Escalante) . . . . 3·75 1·40
The 1, 2 and 13c. are vert.
See also Nos. 1648/54, 1785/91, 1871/7, 1900/6, 2005/11, 2048/54, 2104/9, 2180/5, 2260/5, 2346/51, 2430/5, 2530/5, 2620/5, 2685/90, 2816/21, 3218/23 and 3229/34.

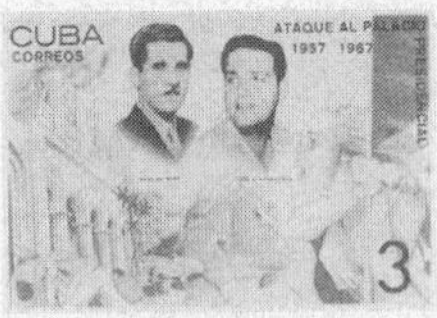

390 Menelao Mora, Jose A. Echeverria and Attack on Presidential Palace

1967. National Events of 13 March 1957.
1459 **390** 3c. green and black . . . 15 10
1460 – 13c. brown and black . . 1·50 50
1461 – 30c. blue and black . . . 1·40 55
DESIGNS (36½ × 24½ mm.): 13c. Calixto Sanchez and "Corynthia" landing; 30c. Dionisio San Roman and Cienfuegos revolt.

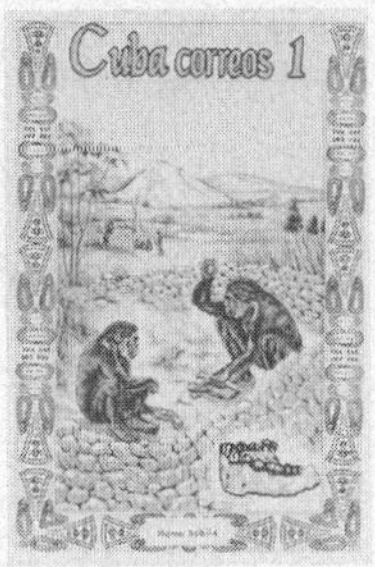

391 "Homo habilis"

1967. "Prehistoric Man". Multicoloured.
1462 1c. Type **391** 10 10
1463 2c. "Australopithecus" . . . 15 10
1464 3c. "Pithecanthropus erectus" 15 10
1465 4c. Peking man 20 15
1466 5c. Neanderthal man . . . 30 20
1467 13c. Cro-Magnon man carving ivory tusk . . . . 1·00 45
1468 20c. Cro-Magnon man painting on wall of cave 2·00 65

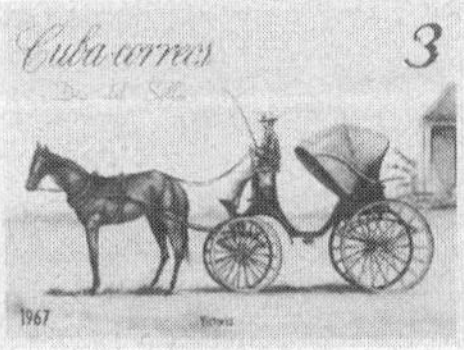

392 Victoria

1967. Stamp Day. Carriages. Multicoloured.
1469 3c. Type **392** 20 15
1470 9c. Volanta 95 30
1471 13c. Quitrin . . . . 1·40 55

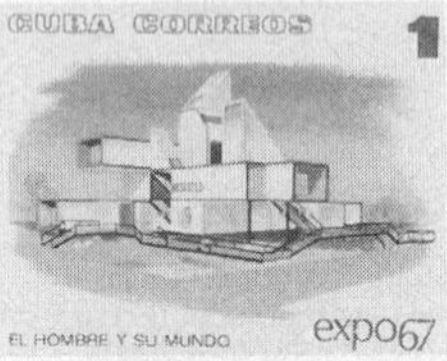

393 Cuban Pavilion

1967. "Expo 67", Montreal.
1472 **393** 1c. multicoloured 20 10
1473 – 2c. multicoloured 20 10
1474 – 3c. multicoloured 25 10
1475 – 13c. multicoloured . . . 1·25 55
1476 – 20c. multicoloured . . . 1·50 60
DESIGNS: 2c. Bathysphere, satellite and met. balloon ("Man as Explorer"); 3c. Ancient rock-drawing and tablet ("Man as Creator"); 13c. Tractor, ear of wheat and electronic console ("Man as Producer"); 20c. Olympic athletes ("Man in the Community").

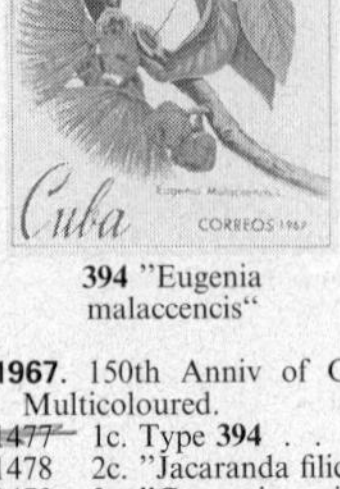

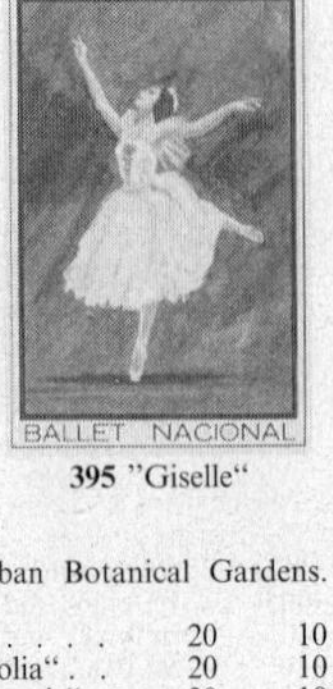

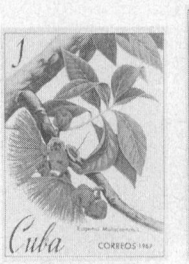

394 "Eugenia malaccencis" **395** "Giselle"

1967. 150th Anniv of Cuban Botanical Gardens. Multicoloured.
1477 1c. Type **394** 20 10
1478 2c. "Jacaranda filicifolia" . . 20 10
1479 3c. "Coroupita guianensis" 30 10
1480 4c. "Spathodea campanulata" 30 10
1481 5c. "Cassia fistula" 40 15
1482 13c. "Plumieria alba" . . . 1·25 65
1483 20c. "Erythrina poeppigiana" . . . . . . 2·00 75

1967. Int Ballet Festival, Havana. Mult.
1484 1c. Type **395** 30 10
1485 2c. "Swan Lake" 30 10
1486 3c. "Don Quixote" 35 10
1487 4c. "Calaucan" 75 15
1488 13c. "Swan Lake" (different) 1·60 60
1489 20c. "Nutcracker" . . . . . 2·25 1·00

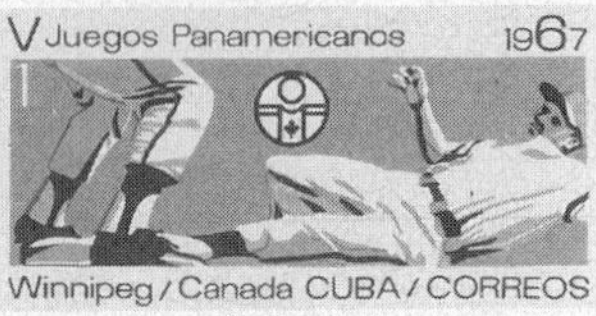

396 Baseball

1967. 5th Pan-American Games, Winnipeg. Mult.
1490 1c. Type **396** 15 10
1491 2c. Swimming 15 10
1492 3c. Basketball (vert) 30 10
1493 4c. Gymnastics (vert) . . . 30 10
1494 5c. Water-polo (vert) . . . 40 15
1495 13c. Weight-lifting . . . . . 1·25 35
1496 20c. Hurling the javelin . . 2·25 65

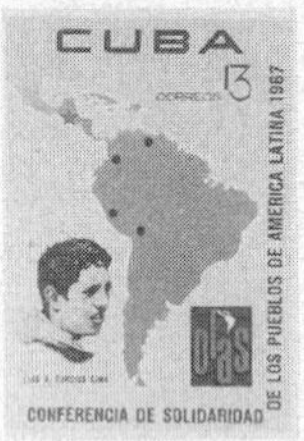

397 L. A. Turcios Lima, Map and OLAS Emblem

1967. 1st Conference of Latin-American Solidarity Organization (OLAS), Havana.
1497 13c. black, red and blue . . 95 40
1498 13c. black, red and brown 95 40
1499 13c. black, red and lilac . . 95 40
1500 13c. black, red and green . . 95 40
DESIGNS: No. 1497, Type **397**; No. 1498, Fabricio Ojidia; No. 1499, L. de La Puente Uceda; No. 1500, Camilo Torres; Martyrs of Guatemala, Venezuela, Peru and Colombia respectively. Each with map and OLAS emblem.

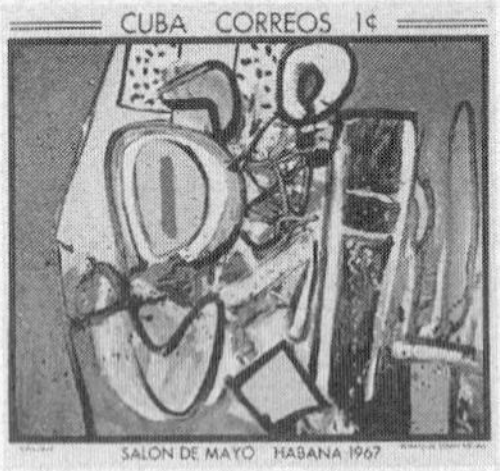

398 "Portrait of Sonny Rollins" (Alan Davie)

1967. "Contemporary Art" (Havana Exn from the Paris "Salon de Mayo"). Various designs showing modern paintings. Sizes given in millimetres. Multicoloured.
1501 1c. Type **398** 20 20
1502 1c. "Twelve Selenites" (F. Labisse) (39 × 41) . . 20 20
1503 1c. "Night of the Drinker" (F. Hundertwasser) (53 × 41) 20 20
1504 1c. "Figure" (Mariano) (48 × 41) 20 20
1505 1c. "All-Souls" (W. Lam) (45 × 41) 20 20
1506 2c. "Darkness and Cracks" (A. Tapies) (37 × 54) . . 30 20
1507 2c. "Bathers" (G. Singier) (37 × 54) 30 20
1508 2c. "Torso of a Muse" (J. Arp) (37 × 46) 30 20
1509 2c. "Figure" (M. W. Svanberg) (57 × 54) . . . 30 20
1510 2c. "Oppenheimer's Information" (Erro) (37 × 41) 30 20
1511 3c. "Where Cardinals are Born" (Max Ernst) (37 × 52) 50 30
1512 3c. "Havana Landscape" (Portocarrero) (37 × 41) 50 30
1513 3c. "EG 12" (V. Vasarely) (37 × 42) 50 30
1514 3c. "Frisco" (A. Calder) (37 × 50) 50 30
1515 3c. "The Man with the Pipe" (Picasso) (37 × 52) 50 30
1516 4c. "Abstract Composition" (S. Poliakoff) (36 × 50) . . 60 40
1517 4c. "Painting" (Bram van Velde) (36 × 68) 60 40
1518 4c. "Sower of Fires" (detail, Matta) (36 × 47) 60 40
1519 4c. "The Art of Living" (R. Magritte) (36 × 50) . . 60 40
1520 4c. "Poem" (J. Miro) (36 × 56) 60 40
1521 13c. "Young Tigers" (J. Messagier) (50 × 33) . . 1·25 60
1522 13c. "Painting" (Vieira da Silva) (50 × 36) . . . . . 1·25 60
1523 13c. "Live Cobra" (P. Alechinsky) (50 × 35) 1·25 60
1524 13c. "Stalingrad" (detail, A. Jorn) (50 × 46) . . . . . 1·25 60
1525 30c. "Warriors" (E. Pignon) (55 × 32) . . . . 6·00 2·50

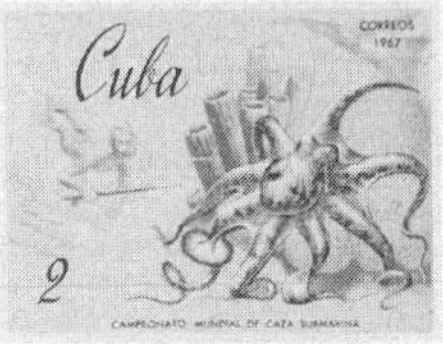

399 Common Octopus

1967. World Underwater Fishing Championships. Multicoloured.
1527 1c. Green moray 20 10
1528 2c. Type **399** 20 10
1529 3c. Great barracuda 20 10
1530 4c. Bull shark 40 10
1531 5c. Spotted Jewfish 75 30
1532 13c. Chupare stingray . . . 1·75 75
1533 20c. Green turtle . . . . . 2·75 85

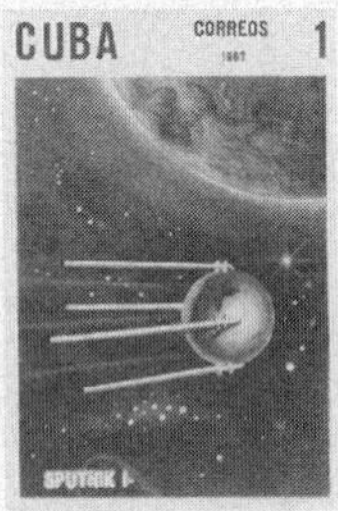

400 "Sputnik 1"

1967. Soviet Space Achievements. Mult.
1534 1c. Type **400** 10 10
1535 2c. "Lunik 3" 10 10
1536 3c. "Venusik" 15 10
1537 4c. "Cosmos" 20 10
1538 5c. "Mars 1" 30 15
1539 9c. "Electron 1, 2" 40 20
1540 10c. "Luna 9" 55 35
1541 13c. "Luna 10" . . . . . . 1·25 50

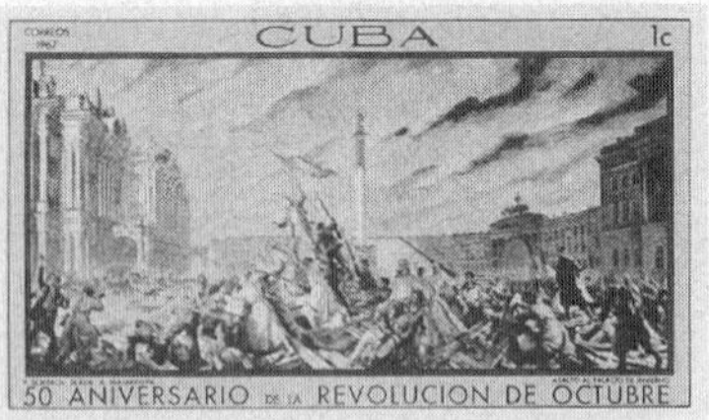

401 "Storming the Winter Palace" (from painting by Sokolov, Skalia and Miasnikova)

1967. 50th Anniv of October Revolution. Paintings. Multicoloured.
1543 1c. Type **401** 20 10
1544 2c. "Lenin addressing 2nd Soviet Congress" (Serov) (48 × 36) 20 10
1545 3c. "Lenin in the year 1919" (Nalbandian) (35 × 37) . 30 10
1546 4c. "Lenin explaining the GOELRO Map" (Schmatko) (48 × 36) . . . 30 15
1547 5c. "Dawn of the Five-Year Plan" construction work (Romas) (50 × 36) . . . . 1·75 50
1548 13c. "Kusnetzkroi steel Furnace No. 1" (Kotov) (36 × 51) . . . . 1·25 50
1549 30c. "Victory Jubilation" (Krivonogov) (50 × 36) . . 1·75 75

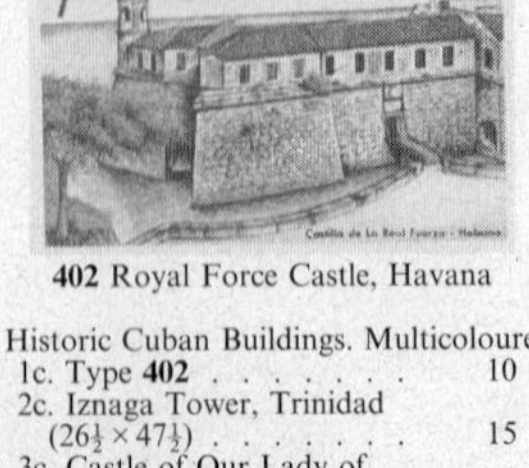

402 Royal Force Castle, Havana

1967. Historic Cuban Buildings. Multicoloured.
1550 1c. Type **402** 10 10
1551 2c. Iznaga Tower, Trinidad (26½ × 47½) 15 10
1552 3c. Castle of Our Lady of the Angels, Cienfuegos (41½ × 29) 20 10
1553 4c. Church of St. Francis of Paula, Havana (41½ × 29) 20 10
1554 13c. Convent of St. Francis, Havana (39 × 13) . . . . 1·10 45
1555 30c. Morro Castle, Santiago de Cuba (43 × 26) . . . . 1·75 75

403 Ostrich   404 Golden Pheasant

1967. Christmas. Birds of Havana Zoo. Mult.
(a) As T **403**.

1556	1c. Type **403**	65	70
1557	3c. Hyacinth macaw	1·25	1·10
1558	13c. Greater flamingoes	3·00	90

(b) As T **404**.

1559a/d	1c. multicoloured	65	70
1560a/d	3c. multicoloured	1·25	1·10
1561a/d	13c. multicoloured	3·00	1·90

DESIGNS: No. 1559a, Type **404**; 1559b, White stork; 1559c, Crowned crane; 1559d, Emu; 1560a, Grey parrot; 1560b, Chattering lory; 1560c, Keel-billed toucan; 1560d, Sulphur-crested cockatoo; 1561a, American white pelican, 1561b, Egyptian goose; 1561c, Mandarin; 1561d, Black swan.
Prices are for single stamps.

405 "Che" Guevara

1968. Major Ernesto "Che" Guevara Commem.

1562	**405** 13c. black and red	1·75	50

406 Man and Tree ("Problems of Artistic Creation, Scientific and Technical Work")

1968. Cultural Congress, Havana. Mult.

1563	3c. Chainbreaker cradling flame ("Culture and Independence") (vert)	10	10
1564	3c. Hand with spanner and rifle ("Integral Formation of Man") (vert)	10	10
1565	13c. Demographic emblems ("Intellectual Responsibility") (vert)	85	30
1566	13c. Hand with communications emblems ("Culture and Mass-Communications Media") (vert)	90	35
1567	30c. Type **406**	1·25	65

407 Canaries

1968. Canary-breeding.

1568	**407** 1c. multicoloured	10	10
1569	– 2c. multicoloured	10	10
1570	– 3c. multicoloured	10	10
1571	– 4c. multicoloured	15	10
1572	– 5c. multicoloured	30	15
1573	– 13c. multicoloured	1·40	55
1574	– 20c. multicoloured	1·60	50

DESIGNS: Canaries and breeding cycle—mating, eggs, incubation and rearing young.

408 "The Village Postman" (after J. Harris)

1968. Stamp Day. Multicoloured.

1575	13c. Type **408**	1·10	35
1576	30c. "The Philatelist" (after G. Sciltian)	1·60	50

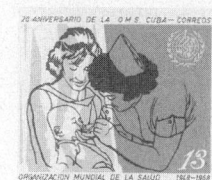

409 Nurse tending Child ("Anti-Polio Campaign")

1968. 20th Anniv of W.H.O.

1577	**409** 13c. black, red and olive	1·10	40
1578	– 30c. black, blue & olive	1·40	55

DESIGN: 30c. Two doctors ("Hospital Services").

410 "Children"

1968. International Children's Day.

1579	**410** 3c. multicoloured	55	20

411 "Cuatro Vientos" and Route Map

1968. 35th Anniv of Seville–Camaguey Flight by Barberan and Collar. Multicoloured.

1580	13c. Type **411**	1·40	30
1581	30c. Captain M. Barberan and Lieut. J. Collar	1·40	40

412 "Canned Fish"

1968. Cuban Food Products. Multicoloured.

1582	1c. Type **412**	10	10
1583	2c. "Milk Products"	15	10
1584	3c. "Poultry and Eggs"	25	20
1585	13c. "Cuban Rum"	1·40	35
1586	20c. "Canned Shell-fish"	1·60	50

413 Siboney Farmhouse

1968. 15th Anniv of Attack on Moncada Barracks. Multicoloured.

1587	3c. Type **413**	10	10
1588	13c. Map of Santiago de Cuba and assault route	1·00	40
1589	30c. Students and school buildings (on site of Moncada Barracks)	1·60	55

414 Committee Members and Emblem

1968. 8th Anniv of Revolutionary Defence Committee.

1590	**414** 3c. multicoloured	55	15

415 Che Guevara and Rifleman

1968. Day of the Guerrillas.

1591	**415** 1c. black, green & gold	10	10
1592	– 3c. black, brown & gold	10	10
1593	– 9c. multicoloured	30	10
1594	– 10c. black, green and gold	60	15
1595	– 13c. black, pink & gold	1·10	45

DESIGNS—"Che" Guevara and: 3c. Machine-gunners; 9c. Riflemen; 10c. Soldiers cheering; 13c. Map of Caribbean and South America.

416 C. M. de Cespedes and Broken Wheel

1968. Centenary of Cuban War of Independence. Multicoloured.

1596	1c. Type **416**	10	10
1597	1c. E. Betances and horsemen	10	10
1598	1c. I. Agramonte and monument	10	10
1599	1c. A. Maceo and "The Protest"	10	10
1600	1c. J. Marti & patriots	10	10
1601	3c. M. Gomez and "Invasion"	10	10
1602	3c. J. A. Mella and declaration	10	10
1603	3c. A. Guiteras and monument	10	10
1604	3c. A. Santamaria and riflemen	10	10
1605	3c. F. Pais & graffiti	10	10
1606	9c. J. Echeverria and students	50	15
1607	13c. C. Cienfuegos and rebels	1·25	45
1608	30c. "Che" Guevara and Castro addressing meeting	1·50	70

418 Parade of Athletes, Olympic Flag and Flame

1968. Olympic Games, Mexico. Multicoloured.

1610	1c. Type **418**	10	10
1611	2c. Basketball (vert)	10	10
1612	3c. Throwing the hammer (vert)	10	10
1613	4c. Boxing	15	10
1614	5c. Water-polo	20	10
1615	13c. Pistol-shooting	1·10	40
1616	30c. Calendar-stone (32½ × 50 mm)	1·60	55

419 Crop-spraying

1968. Civil Activities of Cuban Armed Forces. Multicoloured.

1618	3c. Type **419**	10	10
1619	9c. "Che Guevara" Brigade	40	10
1620	10c. Road-building Brigade	60	20
1621	13c. Agricultural Brigade	1·25	50

420 "Manrique de Lara's Family" (J.-B. Vermay)

1968. 150th Anniv of San Alejandro Painting School. Multicoloured.

1622	1c. Type **420**	20	10
1623	2c. "Seascape" (L. Romanach) (48 × 37)	30	10
1624	3c. "Wild Cane" (A. Rodriguez) (40 × 48)	30	10
1625	4c. "Self-portrait" (M. Melero) (40 × 50)	30	15
1626	5c. "The Lottery List" (J. J. Tejada) (48 × 37)	60	30
1627	13c. "Portrait of Nina" (A. Menocal) (40 × 50)	1·40	50
1628	30c. "Landscape" (E. S. Chartrand) (54 × 37)	2·25	75

421 Cuban Flag and Rifles   423 Mariana Grajales, Rose and Statue

1969. 10th Anniv of "The Triumph of the Rebellion".

1630	**421** 13c. multicoloured	1·10	40

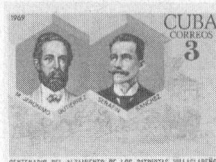

422 Gutierrez and Sanchez

1969. Cent of Villaclarenos Patriots Rebellion.

1631	**422** 3c. multicoloured	55	20

1969. Cuban Women's Day.

1632	**423** 3c. multicoloured	55	20

424 Cuban Pioneers

1969. Cuban Pioneers and Young Communist Unions. Multicoloured.

1633	3c. Type **424**	20	15
1634	13c. Young Communists	1·00	50

425 Guaimaro Assembly

1969. Centenary of Guaimaro Assembly.
1635 **425** 3c. brown and sepia . . . 55 20

426 "The Postman" (J. C. Cazin)

1969. Cuban Stamp Day. Multicoloured.
1636 13c. Type **426** . . . . . . 1·10 45
1637 30c. "Portrait of a Young
Man" (George Romney)
(36 × 44 mm) . . . . . . 1·75 65

427 Agrarian Law, Headquarters,
Eviction of Family, and Tractor

1969. 10th Anniv of Agrarian Reform.
1638 **427** 13c. multicoloured . . . 1·10 45

428 Hermit Crab in West Indian Chank

1969. Crustaceans. Multicoloured.
1639 1c. Type **428** 15 10
1640 2c. Spiny shrimp 15 10
1641 3c. Spiny lobster 15 10
1642 4c. Blue crab 15 15
1643 5c. Land crab 40 15
1644 13c. Freshwater prawn . . 1·75 40
1645 30c. Pebble crab . . . . 3·00 60

429 Factory and Peasants

1969. 50th Anniv of I.L.O. Mult.
1646 3c. Type **429** 20 15
1647 13c. Worker breaking chain 1·10 45

430 "Flowers" (R. Milian)

1969. National Museum Paintings (2nd series).
Multicoloured.
1648 1c. Type **430** 10 10
1649 2c. "The Annunciation"
(A. Eiriz) 10 10
1650 3c. "Factory" (M. Pogolotti) 75 15
1651 4c. "Territorial Waters"
(L. M. Pedro) 40 10
1652 5c. "Miss Sarah Gale"
(John Hoppner) . . . 40 10
1653 13c. "Two Women wearing
Mantillas" (I. Zuloaga) 1·25 45
1654 30c. "Virgin and Child"
(F. Zurbaran) . . . . 1·75 55
SIZES—HORIZ: 2c. As No. 1648. VERT: 3c. As
No. 1648. 4c. 40 × 44 mm; 5c. and 30c. 40 × 46 mm;
13c. 38 × 42 mm.

431 Television Cameras and Emblem

1969. Cuban Radiodiffusion Institute. Mult.
1655 3c. Type **431** 20 15
1656 13c. Broadcasting tower and
"Globe" . . . . . . 1·10 50
1657 1p. TV Reception diagram 2·50 1·10

432 Flamefish

1969. Cuban Pisciculture. Multicoloured.
1658 1c. Type **432** 15 10
1659 2c. Spanish hogfish . . . 15 10
1660 3c. Yellow-tailed damselfish 25 10
1661 4c. Royal gramma 25 10
1662 5c. Blue chromis 35 10
1663 13c. Black-barred soldierfish 2·10 40
1664 30c. Man-of-war fish (vert) 2·75 65

433 "Cuban Film Library"

1969. 10th Anniv of Cuban Cinema Industry.
Multicoloured.
1665 1c. Type **433** 10 10
1666 3c. "Documentaries" . . . 15 10
1667 13c. "Cartoons" . . . . 1·10 50
1668 30c. "Full-length Features" 1·75 60

434 "Napoleon in Milan". (A. Appiani
(the Elder))

1969. Paintings in Napoleonic Museum, Havana.
Multicoloured.
1669 1c. Type **434** 20 10
1670 2c. "Hortensia de
Beauharnais" (F. Gerard) 25 10
1671 3c. "Napoleon-First Consul"
(J. B. Regnault) . . . 25 10
1672 4c. "Elisa Bonaparte"
(R. Lefevre) 30 10
1673 5c. "Napoleon planning the
Coronation" (J. G.
Vibert) 50 25
1674 13c. "Corporal of
Cuirassiers"
(J. Meissonier) . . . 1·75 55
1675 30c. "Napoleon Bonaparte"
(R. Lefevre) . . . . 2·50 65
SIZES—VERT: 2c. 42½ × 55 mm; 3c. 46 × 56½ mm;
4c., 13c., 44 × 63 mm; 30c. 45½ × 60 mm. HORIZ: 5c.
64 × 47 mm.

435 Baseball Players

1969. Cuba's Victory in World Amateur Baseball
Championships, Dominican Republic.
1676 13c. multicoloured . . . 1·25 50

436 Von Humboldt, Book and American Eel

1969. Birth Bicentenary of Alexander von Humboldt.
Multicoloured.
1677 3c. Type **436** 25 10
1678 13c. Night monkey . . . 1·75 75
1679 30c. Andean condors . . . 3·75 1·00

437 Ancient Egyptians in Combat

1969. World Fencing Championships, Havana.
Multicoloured.
1683 1c. Type **437** 20 10
1684 2c. Roman Gladiators . . . 20 10
1685 3c. Norman and Viking . . 20 10
1686 4c. Medieval tournament . 25 10
1687 5c. French musketeers . . 30 10
1688 13c. Japanese samurai . . 1·25 35
1689 30c. Mounted Cubans, War
of Independence . . . 1·75 60

438 Militiaman

1969. 10th Anniv of National Revolutionary Militias.
1691 **438** 3c. multicoloured 55 20

439 Major Cienfuegos and Wreath on
Sea

1969. 10th Anniv of Disappearance of Major Camilo
Cienfuego.
1692 **439** 13c. multicoloured . . . 1·10 50

440 Strawberries and Grapes

1969. Agriculture and Livestock Projects.
Multicoloured.
1693 1c. Type **440** 10 10
1694 1c. Onion and asparagus . . 10 10
1695 1c. Rice 10 10
1696 1c. Bananas 10 10
1697 3c. Pineapple (vert) . . . 20 10
1698 3c. Tobacco plant (vert) . . 20 10
1699 3c. Citrus fruits (vert) . . 20 10
1700 3c. Coffee (vert) 20 10
1701 3c. Rabbits (vert) 20 10
1702 3c. Pigs (vert) 25 10
1703 13c. Sugar-cane . . . . 1·40 55
1704 30c. Bull . . . . . . 1·75 65

441 Stadium and Map of Cuba (2nd
National Games)

1969. Sporting Events of 1969. Multicoloured.
1705 1c. Type **441** 10 10

1706 2c. Throwing the discus (9th
Anniv Games) . . . 10 10
1707 3c. Running (Barrientos
commemoration) (vert) . 10 10
1708 10c. Basketball (2nd
Olympic Trial Games)
(vert) 20 10
1709 13c. Cycling (6th Cycle
Race) (vert) . . . . 1·50 55
1710 30c. Chessmen and Globe
(7th Capablanca Int.
Chess Tournament,
Havana) (vert) . . . 2·00 85

442 "Plumbago
capensis"　　443 "Petrea volubilis"

1969. Christmas. Flowers. (a) As T **442**. Mult.
1711 1c. Type **442** 25 10
1712 3c. "Turnera ulmifolia" . . 55 20
1713 13c. "Delonix regia" . . . 1·25 75

(b) As T **443**.
1714a/d 1c. multicoloured . . . 25 10
1715a/d 3c. multicoloured . . . 55 20
1716a/d 13c. multicoloured . . . 1·25 75
DESIGNS: No. 1714a, Type **443**; 1714b, "Clitoria
ternatea"; 1714c, "Duranta repens"; 1714d, "Ruellia
tuberosa"; 1715a, "Thevetia peruviana"; 1715b,
"Hibiscus elatus"; 1715c, "Allamanda cathartica";
1715d, "Cosmos sulphureus"; 1716a, "Nerium
oleander" (wrongly inscr "Neriun"); 1716b, "Cordia
sebestena"; 1716c, "Lochnera rosea"; 1716d,
"Jatropha integerrima".
Prices are for single stamps.

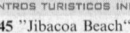
444 River Snake

1969. Swamp Fauna. Multicoloured.
1717 1c. Type **444** 10 10
1718 2c. Banana frog 10 10
1719 3c. Giant tropical gar (fish) 10 10
1720 4c. Dwarf hutia (vert) . . 15 20
1721 5c. Alligator 15 10
1722 13c. Cuban Amazon (vert) . 3·50 60
1723 30c. Red-winged blackbird
(vert) . . . . . . 4·50 1·00

445 "Jibacoa Beach"　446 Yamagua
(J. Hernandez)

1970. Tourism. Multicoloured.
1724 1c. Type **445** 10 10
1725 3c. "Trinidad City" . . . 10 10
1726 13c. Santiago de Cuba . . 1·25 55
1727 30c. Vinales Valley . . . 1·75 65

1970. Medicinal Plants. Multicoloured.
1728 1c. Type **446** 10 10
1729 3c. Albahaca Morada . . . 10 10
1730 10c. Curbana 25 10
1731 13c. Romerillo . . . . 1·25 55
1732 30c. Marilope . . . . . 1·60 65
1733 50c. Aguedita . . . . . 2·25 80

447 Weightlifting

1970. 11th Central American and Caribbean Games.
Multicoloured.
1734 1c. Type **447** 10 10

1735	3c. Boxing	10	10
1736	10c. Gymnastics	15	10
1737	13c. Athletics	1·10	40
1738	30c. Fencing	1·60	60

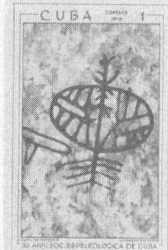

HACIA EL MEJOR DISFRUTE DE LA VIDA

448 "Enjoyment of Life"

1970. "EXPO 70" World Fair, Osaka, Japan. Multicoloured.

1740	1c. Type **448**	10	10
1741	2c. "Uses of nature" (vert)	10	10
1742	3c. "Better Living Standards"	20	10
1743	13c. "International Co-operation" (vert)	1·25	35
1744	30c. Cuban Pavilion	1·75	55

449 Oval Pictograph, Ambrosio Cave

1970. 30th Anniv of Cuban Speleological Society.

1745	**449** 1c. red and brown	10	10
1746	– 2c. black and brown	10	10
1747	– 3c. black and brown	10	10
1748	– 4c. black and brown	10	10
1749	– 5c. black, red and brown	15	10
1750	– 13c. black and brown	1·10	50
1751	– 30c. red and brown	2·25	55

DESIGNS—HORIZ: (42 × 32½ mm): 2c. Cave 1, Punta del Este, Isle of Pines; 5c. As 2c. (different); 30c. Stylized fish, Cave 2, Punta del Este. VERT: 3c. Stylized mask, Pichardo Cave, Sierra de Cubitas; 4c. Conical complex, Ambrosio Cave, Varadero; 13c. Human face, Garcia Robiou Cave, Catalina de Guines.

450 J. D. Blino, Balloon and Spacecraft

1970. Aviation Pioneers. Multicoloured.

1752	3c. Type **450**	50	10
1753	13c. A. Theodore, balloon and satellite	1·75	45

451 "Lenin in Kazan" (O. Vishniakov) (½-size illustration)

1970. Birth Centenary of Lenin. Paintings. Mult.

1754	1c. Type **451**	10	10
1755	2c. "Lenin's Youth" (Prager)	10	10
1756	3c. "The 2nd Socialist Party Congress" (Vinogradov)	10	10
1757	4c. "The First Manifesto" (Golubkov)	15	10
1758	5c. "The First Day of Soviet Power" (Babasiuk)	15	10
1759	13c. "Lenin in the Smolny Institute" (Sokolov)	1·25	45
1760	30c. "Autumn in Gorky" (Varlamov)	1·75	55

SIZES: 4, 5c. As Type **451**: 2, 3, 13, 30c. 70 × 34 mm.

CUBA CORREOS 1970 DIA del SELLO

452 "The Letter" (J. Archer)

1970. Cuban Stamp Day. Paintings. Mult.

1762	13c. Type **452**	1·10	45
1763	30c. "Portrait of a Cadet" (anonymous) (35 × 49 mm)	1·40	55

CUBA CORREOS

453 Da Vinci's Anatomical Drawing, Earth and Moon

1970. World Telecommunications Day.

1764	453 30c. multicoloured	1·40	55

454 Vietnamese Fisherman

1970. 80th Birthday of Ho Chi Minh (North Vietnamese leader). Multicoloured.

1765	1c. Type **454**	10	10
1766	3c. Cultivating rice-fields	20	10
1767	3c. Two Vietnamese children	20	10
1768	3c. Children entering air-raid shelter	20	10
1769	3c. Camouflaged machine-shop	25	10
1770	3c. Rice harvest	25	10
1771	13c. Pres. Ho Chi Minh	1·10	50

SIZES: Nos. 1766/7, 33 × 44½ mm. Nos. 1768, 1770, 33½ × 46 mm. No. 1769, 35 × 42 mm. No. 1771, 34½ × 39½ mm.

455 Tobacco Plantation and "Eden" Cigar band

1970. "Cuban Cigar Industry". Multicoloured.

1772	3c. Type **455**	10	10
1773	13c. 19th century cigar factory and "El Mambi" band	95	50
1774	30c. Packing cigars (19th-century) and "Gran Pena" band	1·50	70

ZAFRA DE LOS 10 MILLONES 1970

TANDEM AUTOMATICO

456 Cane crushing Machinery

1970. Cuban Sugar Harvest Target. "Over 10 million Tons". Multicoloured.

1775	1c. Type **456**	10	10
1776	2c. Sowing and crop-spraying	10	10
1777	3c. Cutting sugar-cane	10	10
1778	10c. Ox-cart and diesel-electric locomotive	3·00	30
1779	13c. Modern cane cutting machine	1·00	20
1780	30c. Cane-cutters and globe (vert)	1·40	50
1781	1p. Sugar warehouse	2·75	1·25

457 P. Figueredo and National Anthem (original version)

1970. Death Centenary of Pedro Figueredo (composer of National Anthem). Multicoloured.

1782	3c. Type **457**	20	10
1783	20c. 18 98 version of anthem	1·10	40

CUBA CORREOS 3

458 Cuban Girl, Flag and Federation Badge

1970. 10th Anniv of Cuban Women's Federation.

1784	458 3c. multicoloured	50	35

CUBA

459 "Peasant Militia" (S. C. Moreno)

1970. National Museum Paintings (3rd series). Multicoloured.

1785	1c. Type **459**	10	10
1786	2c. "Washerwoman" (A. Fernandez)	10	10
1787	3c. "Puerta del Sol, Madrid" (L. P. Alcazar)	10	10
1788	4c. "Fishermen's Wives" (J. Sorolla)	10	10
1789	5c. "Portrait of a Lady" (T. de Keyser)	15	10
1790	13c. "Mrs. Edward Foster" (Lawrence)	1·25	45
1791	30c. "Tropical Gipsy" (V. M. Garcia)	1·75	65

SIZES—HORIZ: 2c., 3c. 46 × 42 mm. SQUARE. 4c. 41 × 41 mm. VERT: 5c., 13c., 30c. 39 × 46 mm.

460 Crowd in Jose Marti Square, Havana (½-size illustration)

1970. 10th Anniv of Havana Declaration.

1792	460 3c. blue, red & black	15	10

CUBA 3

X Aniversario de los CDR

461 C. D. R. Emblem

1970. 10th Anniv of Revolution Defence Committees.

1793	461 3c. multicoloured	40	15

39 CONFERENCIA DE LA A.T.A.C. 1970
CUBA CORREOS
SO₂ 30

462 Laboratory, Emblem and Microscope

1970. 39th A.T.A.C. (Sugar Technicians Assn) Conference.

1794	462 30c. multicoloured	1·50	50

CUBA GUINEA FAUNA SILVESTRE

463 Helmeted Guineafowl

1970. Wildlife. Multicoloured.

1795	1c. Type **463**	90	30
1796	2c. Black-billed whistling duck	1·00	30
1797	3c. Common pheasant	1·25	30
1798	4c. Mourning dove	1·40	30
1799	5c. Northern bobwhite	1·50	40
1800	13c. Wild boar	1·50	70
1801	30c. White-tailed deer	2·50	1·00

Cuba correos 1970 1 FOLKLORE

464 "Black Magic Parade" (M. Puente)

1970. Afro-Cuban Folklore Paintings. Mult.

1802	1c. Type **464**	10	10
1803	3c. "Zapateo Hat Dance" (V. L. Landaluze)	10	10
1804	10c. "Los Hoyos Conga Dance" (D. Ravenet)	50	40
1805	13c. "Climax of the Rumba" (E. Abela)	1·25	55

SIZES—HORIZ: 10c. 45 × 44 mm. VERT: 3, 13c. 37 × 49 mm.

CUBA CORREOS 1970 3 SEMANA DEL TRANSITO

465 Common Zebra on Road Crossing

1970. Road Safety Week. Multicoloured.

1806	3c. Type **465**	35	15
1807	9c. Prudence the Bear on point duty	55	15

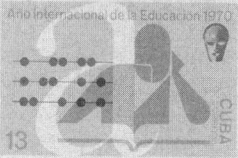

Año Internacional de la Educación 1970 13 CUBA

466 Letter "a" and Abacus

1970. International Education Year. Mult.

1808	13c. Type **466**	1·10	20
1809	30c. Microscope and cow	1·40	45

NAVIDAD 1970/71 CORREOS DE CUBA 1c
CORREOS DE CUBA 1c

467 Cuban Blackbird   **468** Cuban Pygmy Owl

1970. Christmas. Birds. Multicoloured. (a) As T **467**.

1810	1c. Type **467**	75	30
1811	3c. Oriente warbler	1·75	40
1812	13c. Zapata sparrow	3·25	1·00

(b) As T **468**.

1813a/d	1c. multicoloured	75	30
1814a/d	3c. multicoloured	1·75	40
1815a/d	13c. multicoloured	3·25	1·00

DESIGNS: No. 1813a, Type **468**; 1813b, Cuban tody; 1813c, Cuban green woodpecker; 1813d, Zapata wren; 1814a, Cuban solitaire; 1814b, Blue-grey gnatcatcher; 1814c, Cuban vireo; 1814d, Yellow-headed warbler; 1815a, Hook-billed kite; 1815b, Gundlach's hawk; 1815c, Blue-headed quail dove; 1815d, Cuban conure. Prices are for single stamps.

469 School Badge and Cadet Colour-party

1970. "Camilo Cienfuegos" Military School.
1816 **469** 3c. multicoloured 40 20

470 "Reporter" with Pen

1971. 7th Journalists International Organization Congress, Havana.
1817 **470** 13c. multicoloured . . . 95 35

471 Lockheed 8A Sirius

1971. 35th Anniv of Camaguey–Seville Flight by Menendez Pelaez. Multicoloured.
1818 13c. Type **471** . . . . . . 1·40 20
1819 30c. Lieut. Menendez Pelaez and map . . . . 1·75 50

472 Meteorological Class   **473** Games Emblem

1971. World Meteorological Day. Multicoloured.
1820 1c. Type **472** 10 10
1821 3c. Hurricane map (40 × 36 mm) 10 10
1822 8c. Meteorological equipment 55 20
1823 30c. Weather radar systems (horiz) . . . . 2·50 80

1971. 6th Pan-American Games, Cali, Colombia. Multicoloured.
1824 1c. Type **473** 10 10
1825 2c. Athletics 10 10
1826 3c. Rifle-shooting (horiz) . . 10 10
1827 4c. Gymnastics 10 10
1828 5c. Boxing 10 10
1829 13c. Water-polo (horiz) . . 1·10 25
1830 30c. Baseball (horiz) . . . . 1·50 40

474 Paris Porcelain, 19th-century   **475** Mother and Child

1971. Porcelain and Mosaics in Metropolitan Museum, Havana. Multicoloured.
1831 1c. Type **474** 10 10
1832 3c. Mexican pottery bowl, 17th-century 10 10
1833 10c. 19th-century Paris porcelain (similar to T **474**) 20 10
1834 13c. "Colosseum" Italian mosaic, 19th-century . . 1·10 20

1835 20c. 17th-century Mexican pottery dish (similar to 3c.) . . . . 1·10 45
1836 30c. "St. Peter's Square" (Italian mosaic 19th-cent.) 1·40 50
SIZES—VERT: 3c. 46 × 54 mm. 10c. as Type **474**. 20c. 43 × 49 mm. HORIZ: 13c., 30c. 50 × 33 mm.

1971. 10th Anniv of Cuban Infant Centres.
1837 **475** 3c. multicoloured 35 10

476 Cosmonaut in Training

1971. 10th Anniv of First Manned Space Flight. Multicoloured.
1838 1c. Type **476** 10 10
1839 2c. Speedometer test . . . 10 10
1840 3c. Medical examination . . . 10 10
1841 4c. Acceleration tower . . . 10 10
1842 5c. Pressurisation test . . . 10 10
1843 13c. Cosmonaut in gravity chamber . . . . . . 1·00 25
1844 30c. Crew in flight simulator 1·25 55

477 Cuban and Burning Ship

1971. 10th Anniv of Giron Victory.
1846 **477** 13c. multicoloured . . . 1·50 40

478 Sailing Packet "Windsor Castle" attacked by French Privateer Brig "Jeune Richard" (1807)

1971. Stamp Day. Multicoloured.
1847 13c. Type **478** . . . . . . 1·75 60
1848 30c. Mail steamer "Orinoco", 1851 . . . . . 2·50 80

479 Transmitter and Hemispheres

1971. 10th Anniv of Cuban International Broadcasting Services.
1849 **479** 3c. multicoloured 20 10
1850 50c. multicoloured . . . . 2·10 60

480 "Cattleya skinnerii"

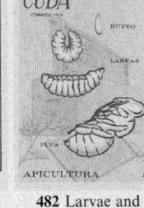

482 Larvae and Pupae

481 Loynaz del Castillo and "Invasion Hymn"

1971. Tropical Orchids (1st series). Mult.
1851 1c. Type **480** 10 10
1852 2c. "Vanda hibrida" 10 10
1853 3c. "Cypripedium callossum" 15 10
1854 4c. "Cypripedium glaucophyllum" 20 10
1855 5c. "Vanda tricolor" 20 10
1856 13c. "Cypripedium mowgh" 1·50 30
1857 30c. "Cypripedium solum" 2·25 55
See also Nos. 1908/14 and 2012/18.

1971. Birth Centenary of Enrique Loynaz del Castillo (composer).
1858 **481** 3c. multicoloured 40 20

1971. Apiculture. Multicoloured.
1859 1c. Type **482** 15 10
1860 3c. Working bee 15 10
1861 9c. Drone 30 10
1862 13c. Defending the hive . . 1·60 25
1863 30c. Queen bee . . . . . . 2·25 55

483 "The Ship" (Lydia Rivera)

1971. Exhibition of Children's Drawings. Havana. Multicoloured.
1864 1c. Type **483** 10 10
1865 3c. "Little Train" (Yuri Ruiz) 45 15
1866 9c. "Sugar-cane Cutter" (Horacio Carracedo) . . . 10 10
1867 10c. "Return of Cuban Fisherman" (Angela Munoz and Lazaro Hernandez) 25 15
1868 13c. "The Zoo" (Victoria Castillo) 85 25
1869 20c. "House and Garden" (Elsa Garcia) . . . . 1·40 45
1870 30c. "Landscape" (Orestes Rodriguez) (vert) . . . 1·60 65
SIZES: 9c., 13c. 45 × 35 mm. 10c. 45 × 38 mm. 20c. 47 × 42 mm. 30c. 39 × 49 mm.

1971. National Museum Paintings (4th series). As T **459**. Multicoloured.
1871 1c. "St. Catherine of Alexandria" (Zurbaran) 10 10
1872 2c. "The Cart" (F. Americo) (horiz) 10 10
1873 3c. "St. Christopher and the Child" (J. Bassano) . . . 10 10
1874 4c. "Little Devil" (R. Portocarrero) . . . 10 10
1875 5c. "Portrait of a Lady" (N. Maes) 10 10
1876 13c. "Phoenix" (R. Martinez) . . . . . 1·00 30
1877 30c. "Sir William Pitt" (Gainsborough) . . . 1·40 50
SIZES: 1, 3c. 30 × 56 mm. 2c. 48 × 37 mm. 4, 5c. 37 × 49 mm. 13, 30c. 39 × 49 mm.

485 Bonefish

1971. Sport Fishing. Multicoloured.
1878 1c. Type **485** 15 10
1879 2c. Great amberjack . . . 15 10
1880 3c. Large-mouthed black bass 15 10
1881 4c. Dolphin (fish) 20 10
1882 5c. Atlantic tarpon . . . 25 15
1883 13c. Wahoo . . . . . 1·40 40
1884 30c. Blue marlin . . . . . 2·40 65

486 Ball within "C"

1971. World Amateur Baseball Championships. Multicoloured.
1885 3c. Type **486** 15 10
1886 1p. Hand holding globe within "C" . . . . . . 2·75 1·10

487 "Dr. F. Valdes Dominguez" (artist unknown)

1971. Centenary of Medical Students' Execution. Multicoloured.
1887 3c. Type **487** 20 10
1888 13c. "Students Execution" (M. Mesa) (62 × 47 mm) 90 30
1889 30c. "Captain Federico Capdevila" (unknown artist) . . . . 1·40 40

488 American Kestrel

1971. Death Centenary of Ramon de la Sagra (naturalist). Cuban Birds. Multicoloured.
1890 1c. Type **488** 55 25
1891 2c. Cuban pygmy owl . . . 55 25
1892 3c. Cuban trogon 75 25
1893 4c. Great lizard cuckoo . . 90 30
1894 5c. Fernandina's flicker . . 1·10 40
1895 13c. Stripe-headed tanager (horiz) . . . . 2·10 70
1896 30c. Red-legged thrush (horiz) . . . . 3·75 1·40
1897 50c. Cuban emerald and ruby-throated hummingbirds (56 × 30 mm) . . . . 7·00 2·10

489 Baseball Player and Global Emblem

1971. Cuba's Victory in World Amateur Baseball.
1898 **489** 13c. multicoloured . . . 1·00 45

490 "Children of the World"

1971. 25th Anniv of U.N.I.C.E.F.
1899 **490** 13c. multicoloured . . . 1·10 45

1972. National Museum Paintings (5th series). As T **459**. Multicoloured.
1900 1c. "The Reception of
Ambassadors"
(V. Carpaccio) 10 10
1901 2c. "Senora Malpica"
(G. Collazo) 10 10
1902 3c. "La Chorrera Fortress
(E. Chartrand) 10 10
1903 4c. "Creole Landscape"
(C. Enriquez) 10 10
1904 5c. "Sir William Lemon"
(G. Romney) 10 10
1905 13c. "La Tajona Beach"
(H. Cleenewek) . . . . 1·25 30
1906 30c. "Valencia Beach"
(J. Sorolla y Bastida) . . 2·25 70
SIZES: 1c., 3c. 51 × 33 mm. 2c. 28 × 53 mm. 4c., 5c. 36 × 44 mm. 13c., 30c. 43 × 34 mm.

492 "Capitol" Stamp of 1929 (now Natural History Museum)

1972. 10th Anniv of Academy of Sciences.
1907 **492** 13c. purple and yellow 95 40

1972. Tropical Orchids (2nd series). As T **480**. Multicoloured.
1908 1c. "Brasso Cattleya
sindorossiana" 25 10
1909 2c. "Cypripedium doraeus" 25 10
1910 3c. "Cypripedium exul" . . 25 10
1911 4c. "Cypripedium
rosydawn" 25 10
1912 5c. "Cypripedium
champolliom" 25 10
1913 13c. "Cypripedium
bucolique" . . . . . . 1·75 75
1914 30c. "Cypripedium
sullanum" . . . . . . 2·50 90

493 "Eduardo Agramonte" (F. Martinez)

1972. Death Centenary of Dr. E. Agramonte (surgeon and patriot).
1915 **493** 3c. multicoloured 30 15

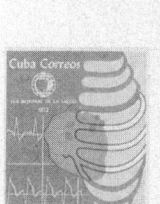 
494 Human Heart and Thorax   496 "Vincente Mora Pera" (Postmaster General, War of Independence) (R. Loy)

495 "Sputnik 1"

1972. World Health Day.
1916 **494** 13c. multicoloured . . . 95 40

1972. "History of Space". Multicoloured.
1917 1c. Type **495** 10 10
1918 2c. "Vostok 1" 10 10
1919 3c. Valentina Tereshkova in
capsule 20 10
1920 4c. A. Leonov in space . . 25 10
1921 5c. "Lunokhod 1" moon
Vehicle 25 10

1922 13c. Linking of "Soyuz"
capsules . . . . . 1·25 35
1923 30c. Dobrovolsky, Volkov
and Pataiev, victims of
"Soyuz 11" disaster . . 1·50 45

1972. Stamp Day. Multicoloured.
1924 13c. Type **496** 85 40
1925 30c. Mambi Mailcover of
1897 (48 × 39 mm) . . 1·40 45

497 Cuban Workers   498 Jose Marti and Ho Chi Minh

1972. Labour Day.
1926 **497** 3c. multicoloured 40 20

1972. 3rd Symposium on Indo-China War. Multicoloured.
1927 3c. Type **498** 20 10
1928 13c. Bombed house
(38 × 29 mm) 80 30
1929 30c. Symposium emblem . . 95 45

1972. Paintings from the Metropolitan Museum, Havana (6th series). As T **430**. Multicoloured.
1930 1c. "Salvador del Muro" (J.
del Rio) 10 10
1931 2c. "Louis de las Casas" (J.
del Rio) 10 10
1932 3c. "Christopher Columbus"
(anonymous) 20 10
1933 4c. "Tomas Gamba"
(V. Escobar) 25 10
1934 5c. "Maria Galarraga"
(V. Escobar) 25 10
1935 13c. "Isabella II of Spain"
(F. Madrazo) . . . . . 1·25 35
1936 30c. "Carlos III of Spain"
(M. Melero) . . . . . 1·50 50
SIZES—VERT: (35 × 44 mm) 1930/34. (34 × 52 mm) 1935/6.

500 Children in Boat

1972. Children's Song Competition.
1937 **500** 3c. multicoloured 50 20

501 Ilyushin Il-18, Map and Flags

1972. Air. 1st Anniv of Havana–Santiago de Chile Air Service.
1938 **501** 25c. multicoloured . . . 1·40 55

502 Tarpan

1972. Thoroughbred Horses. Multicoloured.
1939 1c. Type **502** 10 10
1940 2c. Kertag 10 10
1941 3c. Creole 10 10
1942 4c. Andalusian 10 10
1943 5c. Arab 10 10
1944 13c. Quarter-horse . . . . 2·00 50
1945 30c. Pursang . . . . . . 2·50 75

503 Frank Pais

1972. 15th Death Anniv of Frank Pais.
1946 **503** 13c. multicoloured . . . 85 40

504 Athlete and Emblem

1972. Olympic Games, Munich.
1947 **504** 1c. orange and brown . . 10 10
1948 – 2c. purple, blue & orge 10 10
1949 – 3c. green, yellow & blk 10 10
1950 – 4c. bl, yell & brn . . 10 10
1951 – 5c. red, black & yellow 10 10
1952 – 13c. lilac, green & blue 1·10 35
1953 – 30c. blue, red and green 1·40 50
DESIGNS—HORIZ: 2c. "M" and boxing; 3c. "U" and weightlifting; 4c. "N" and fencing; 5c. "I" and rifle-shooting; 13c. "C" and running; 30c. "H" and basketball.

505 "Landscape with Tree-trunks" (D. Ramos)

1972. International Hydrological Decade. Mult.
1955 1c. Type **505** 10 10
1956 3c. "Cyclone" (T. Lorenzo) 15 10
1957 8c. "Vineyards" (D. Ramos) 35 10
1958 30c. "Forest and Stream"
(A. R. Morey) (vert) . . 1·10 45

506 "Papilio thoas oviedo"

1972. Butterflies from the Gundlach Collection. Multicoloured.
1959 1c. Type **506** 10 10
1960 2c. "Papilio devilliers" . . 15 10
1961 3c. "Papilio polixenes
polixenes" 15 10
1962 4c. "Papilio androgeus
epidaurus" 15 10
1963 5c. "Papilio cayguanabus' 25 10
1964 13c. "Papilio andraemon
hernandezi" . . . . . 2·75 60
1965 30c. "Papilio celadon" . . 3·50 80

507 "In La Mancha" (A. Fernandez)

1972. 425th Birth Anniv of Cervantes. Paintings by A. Fernandez. Multicoloured.
1966 3c. Type **507** 10 10
1967 13c. "Battle with the Wine
Skins" (horiz) . . . . 1·25 35
1968 30c. "Don Quixote of La
Mancha" . . . . . . 1·50 40

508 E. "Che" Guevara and Map of Bolivia

1972. 5th Anniv of Guerrillas' Day. Mult.
1970 3c. Type **508** 10 10
1971 13c. T. "Tania" Bunke and
map of Bolivia . . . . 1·25 35
1972 30c. G. "Inti" Peredo and
map of Bolivia . . . . 1·50 40

509 "Abwe" (shakers)

1972. Traditional Musical Instruments. Mult.
1973 3c. Type **509** 10 10
1974 13c. "Bonko enchemiya"
(drum) . . . . 1·25 35
1975 30c. "Iya" (drum) . . . . 1·50 40

510 Cuban 2c. Stamp of 1951

1972. National Philatelic Exhibition, Matanzas. Multicoloured.
1976 13c. Type **510** . . . . 1·25 35
1977 30c. Cuban 25c. airmail
stamp of 1951 . . . . 1·75 45

511 Viking Longship

1972. Maritime History. Ships Through the Ages. Multicoloured.
1978 1c. Type **511** 15 10
1979 2c. Caravel (vert) 15 10
1980 3c. Galley 15 10
1981 4c. Galleon (vert) 20 10
1982 5c. Clipper 20 10
1983 13c. Steam packet . . . . 1·50 55
1984 30c. Atomic ice-breaker
"Lenin" and Adelie
penguins (55 × 29 mm) . 5·50 1·50

512 Lion of St. Mark

1972. U.N.E.S.C.O. "Save Venice" Campaign. Multicoloured.
1985 3c. Type **512** 10 10
1986 13c. Bridge of Sighs (vert) 85 35
1987 30c. St. Mark's Cathedral 1·10 65

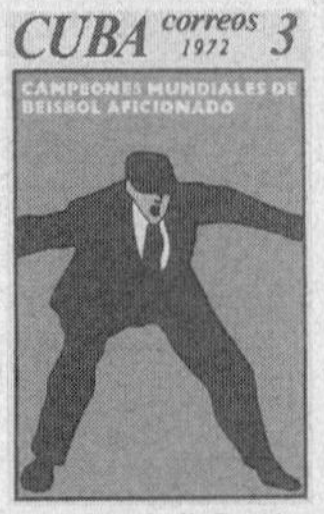

513 Baseball Coach (poster)

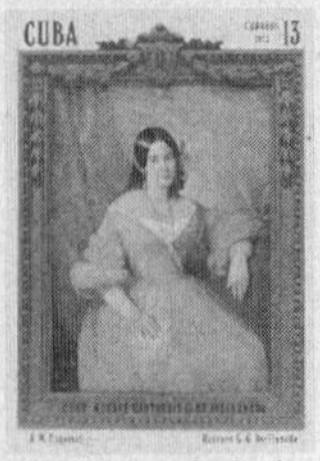

516 "Gertrude G. de Avellaneda" (A. Esquivel)

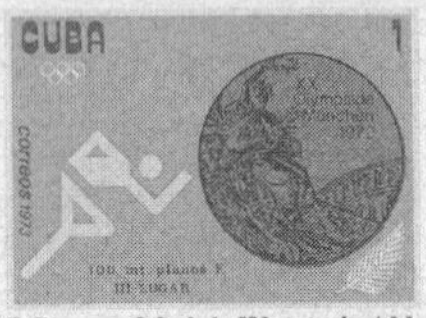

515 Bronze Medal, Women's 100 m

1972. "Cuba, World Amateur Baseball Champions of 1972".

1988	**513**	3c. violet and orange	50	10

1972. Sports events of 1972.

1989	–	1c. multicoloured	10	10
1990	–	2c. multicoloured	10	10
1991	**513**	3c. black, orange & grn	10	10
1992	–	4c. red, black and blue	10	10
1993	–	5c. orge, bl & lt bl	10	10
1994	–	13c. multicoloured	1·10	45
1995	–	30c. vio, blk & bl	1·40	65

DESIGNS AND EVENTS: 1c. Various sports (10th National Schoolchildren's Games); 2c. Pole vaulting (Barrientos Memorial Athletics); 3c. As Type **513**, but inscr changed to read "XI serie nacional de beisbol aficionado" and colours changed (11th National Amateur Baseball Series); 4c. Wrestling (Cerro Pelado International Wrestling Championships); 5c. Foil (Central American and Caribbean Fencing Tournament); 13c. Boxing (Giraldo Cordova Boxing Tournament); 30c. Fishes (Ernest Hemingway National Marlin Fishing Contest).

1972. Cuban Successes in Olympic Games, Munich. Multicoloured.

1996	1c. Type **515**	10	10
1997	2c. Bronze (women's 4 × 100 m relay)	10	10
1998	3c. Gold (boxing, 54 kg)	10	10
1999	4c. Silver (boxing, 81 kg)	10	10
2000	5c. Bronze (boxing, 51 kg)	10	10
2001	13c. Gold (boxing, 67 kg)	1·25	45
2002	30c. Gold (boxing, 81 kg) and Silver Cup (boxing Teofilo Stevenons)	1·50	65

1973. Death Centenary of Gertrude Gomez de Avellaneda (poetess).

2004	**516**	13c. multicoloured	95	40

1973. National Museum Paintings (6th series). As T **459**. Multicoloured.

2005	1c. "Bathers in the Lagoon" (C. Enriquez) (vert)	10	10
2006	2c. "Still Life" (W. C. Heda) (vert)	10	10
2007	3c. "Scene of Gallantry" (V. de Landaluse) (vert)	10	10
2008	4c. "Return at Evening" (C. Troyon) (vert)	10	10
2009	5c. "Elizabetta Mascagni" (F. X. Fabre) (vert)	10	10
2010	13c. "The Picador" (E. de Lucas Padilla)	1·25	45
2011	30c. "In the Garden" (J. A. Morell) (vert)	1·50	65

1973. Tropical Orchids (3rd series). As Type **480**. Multicoloured.

2012	1c. "Dendrobium" (hybrid)	10	10
2013	2c. "Cypripedium exul. O' Brien"	10	10
2014	3c. "Vanda miss. Joaquin"	10	10
2015	4c. "Phalaenopsis schilleriana Reichb"	10	10
2016	5c. "Vanda gilbert tribulet"	10	10
2017	13c. "Dendrobium" (hybrid) (different)	1·25	45
2018	30c. "Arachnis catherine"	1·50	65

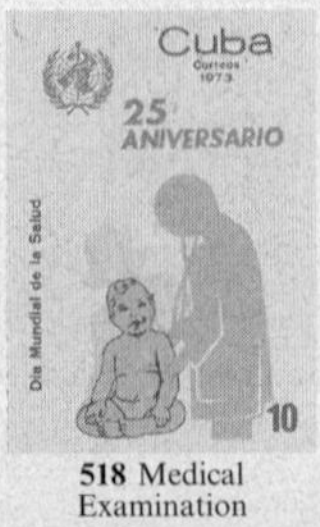

518 Medical Examination

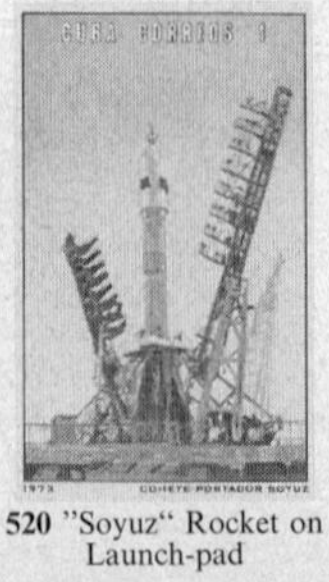

520 "Soyuz" Rocket on Launch-pad

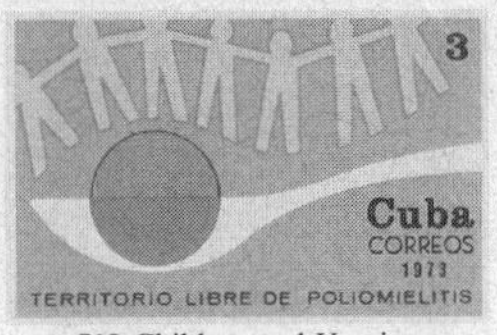

519 Children and Vaccine

1973. 25th Anniv of W.H.O.

2019	**518**	10c. multicoloured	55	25

1973. Freedom from Polio Campaign.

2020	**519**	3c. multicoloured	35	20

1973. Cosmonautics Day. Russian Space Exploration. Multicoloured.

2021	1c. Type **520**	25	10
2022	2c. "Luna 1" in moon orbit (horiz)	25	10
2023	3c. "Luna 16" leaving moon	25	10
2024	4c. "Venus 7" probe (horiz)	25	10
2025	5c. "Molniya 1" communications satellite	25	10
2026	13c. "Mars 3" probe (horiz)	2·00	55
2027	30c. Research ship "Kosmonavt Yury Gargarin" (horiz)	2·75	65

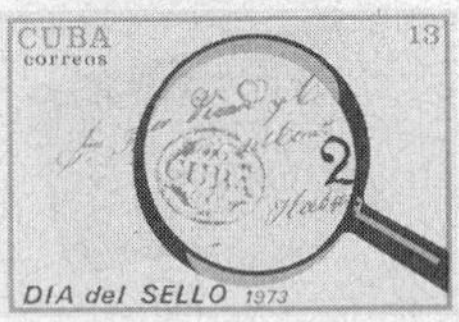

521 Santiago de Cuba Postmark, 1839

1973. Stamp Day. Multicoloured.

2028	13c. Type **521**	95	35
2029	30c. "Havana" postmark, 1760	1·10	40

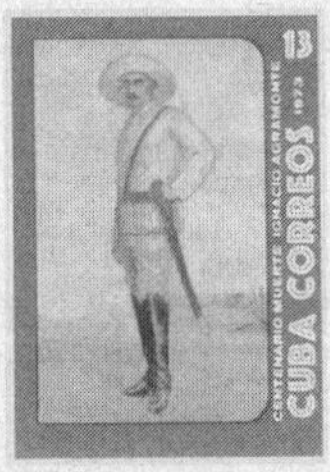

522 "Ignacio Agramonte" (A. Espinosa)

1973. Death Centenary of Maj.-Gen. Ignacio Agramonte.

2030	**522**	13c. multicoloured	75	35

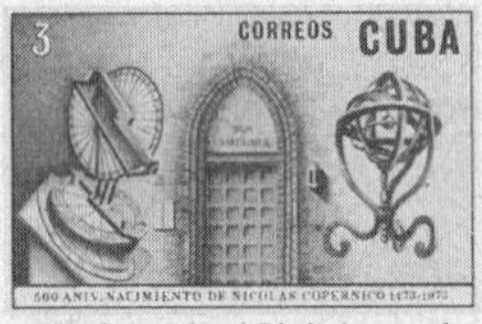

523 Copernicus' Birthplace and Instruments

1973. 500th Birth Anniv of Copernicus. Mult.

2031	3c. Type **523**	10	10
2032	13c. Copernicus and "spaceship"	1·00	35
2033	30c. "De Revolutionibus Orbium Celestium" and Frombork Tower	1·75	45

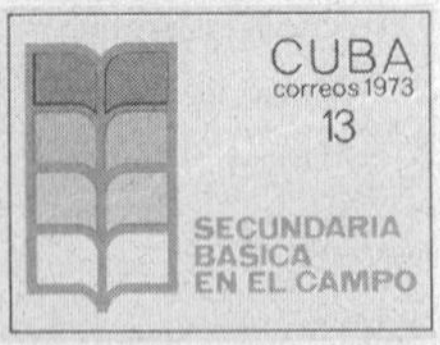

524 Emblem of Basic Schools

1973. Educational Development.

2035	**524**	13c. multicoloured	75	20

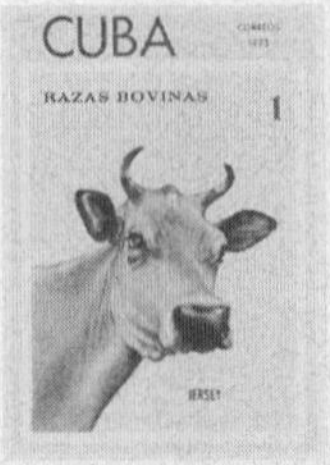

525 Jersey Breed

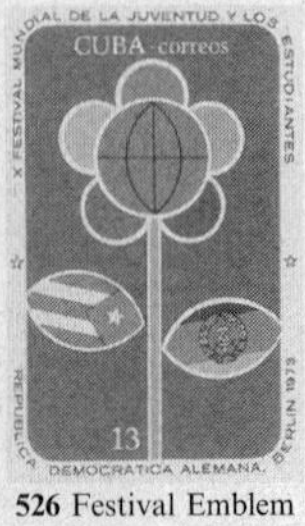

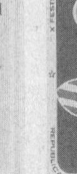

526 Festival Emblem

1973. Cattle Breeds. Multicoloured.

2036	1c. Type **525**	10	10
2037	2c. Charolais	10	10
2038	3c. Creole	10	10
2039	4c. Swiss	10	10
2040	5c. Holstein	10	10
2041	13c. St. Gertrude's	1·00	20
2042	30c. Brahman Cebu	1·60	40

1973. 10th World Youth and Students' Festival, East Berlin.

2043	**526**	13c. multicoloured	75	20

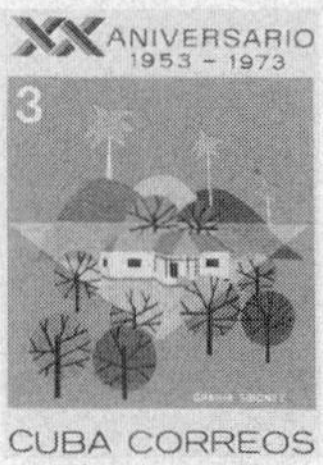

527 Siboney Farmhouse

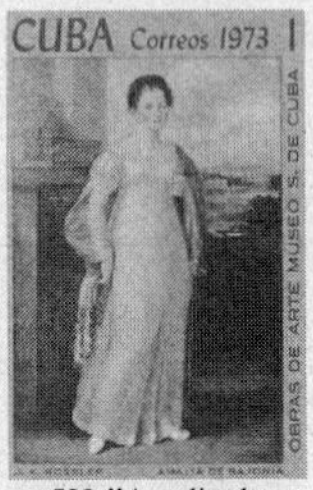

529 "Amalia de Sajonia" (J. K. Rossler)

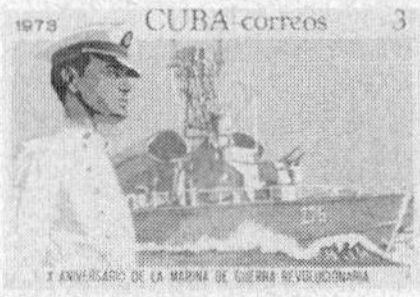

528 Midshipman and Destroyer

1973. 20th Anniv of Revolution. Mult.

2044	3c. Type **527**	20	15
2045	13c. Moncada Barracks	75	25
2046	30c. Revolution Square, Havana	1·10	40

1973. 10th Anniv of Revolutionary Navy.

2047	**528**	3c. multicoloured	60	20

1973. National Museum Paintings (7th series). Multicoloured.

2048	1c. Type **529**	10	10
2049	2c. "Interior" (M. Vicens) (horiz)	10	10
2050	3c. "Margaret of Austria" (J. Pantoja de la Cruz)	10	10
2051	4c. "Syndic of the City Hall" (anon)	10	10
2052	5c. "View of Santiago de Cuba" (J. H. Giro) (horiz)	10	10
2053	13c. "The Catalan" (J. J. Tejada)	1·10	60
2054	30c. "Guayo Alley" (J. J. Tejada)	1·50	85

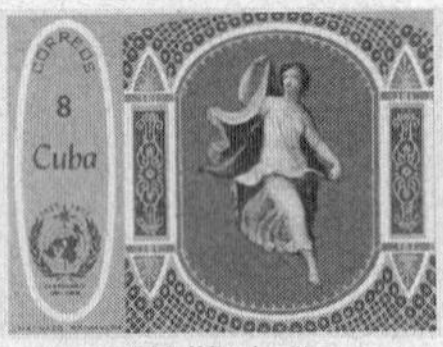

530 "Spring"

1973. Centenary of World Meteorological Organization. Paintings by J. Madrazo. Mult.

2055	8c. Type **530**	30	10
2056	8c. "Summer"	30	10
2057	8c. "Autumn"	30	10
2058	8c. "Winter"	30	10

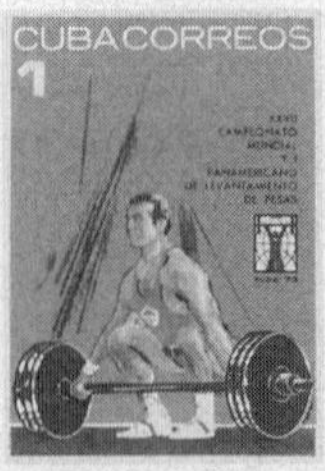

531 Weightlifting

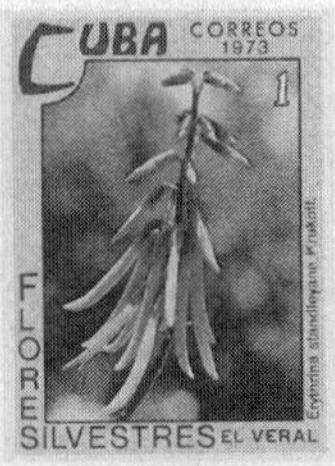

532 "Erythrina standleyana"

1973. 27th Pan-American World Weightlifting Championships, Havana. Designs showing various stages of weightlifting exercise.

2059	**531**	1c. multicoloured	10	10
2060	–	2c. multicoloured	20	10
2061	–	3c. multicoloured	20	10
2062	–	4c. multicoloured	20	10
2063	–	5c. multicoloured	20	10
2064	–	13c. multicoloured	1·25	80
2065	–	30c. multicoloured	2·50	1·50

1973. Wild Flowers (1st series). Mult.

2066	1c. Type **532**	10	10
2067	2c. "Lantana camara"	10	10
2068	3c. "Canavalia maritima"	10	10
2069	4c. "Dichromena colorata"	10	10
2070	5c. "Borrichia arborescens"	10	10
2071	13c. "Anguria pedata"	85	45
2072	30c. "Cordia sebestena"	1·40	65

See also Nos. 2152/6.

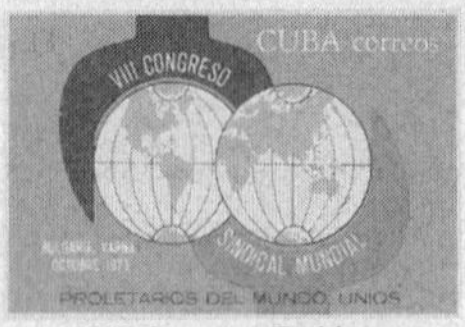

533 Congress Emblem

1973. 8th World Trade Union Congress, Varna, Bulgaria.

2073	**533**	13c. multicoloured	70	25

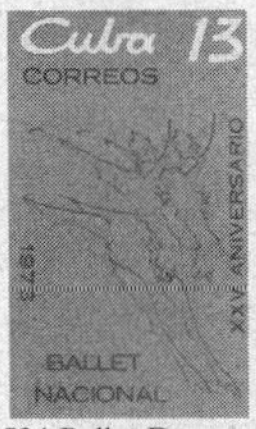

534 Ballet Dancers

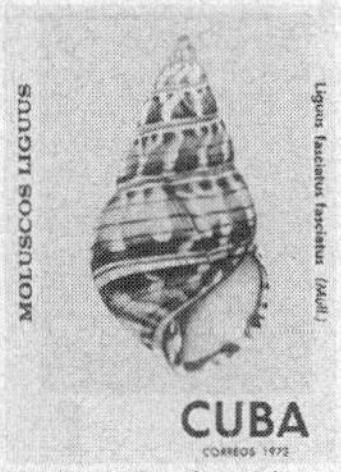

535 True Fasciate Liguus

1973. 25th Anniv of Cuban National Ballet.

2074	**534**	13c. lt blue, bl & gold	70	25

1973. Shells. Multicoloured

2075	1c. Type **535**	20	10
2076	2c. Guitart's liguus	20	10
2077	3c. Wharton's Cuban liguus	20	10
2078	4c. Angela's Cuban liguus	30	10
2079	5c. Yellow-banded liguus	30	10
2080	13c. "Liguus blainianus"	2·00	85
2081	30c. Ribbon liguus	2·25	1·10

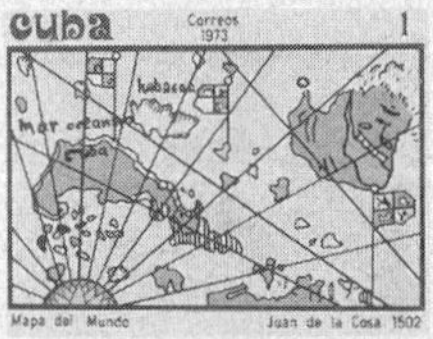

536 Juan de la Cosa's Map, 1502

1973. Maps of Cuba. Multicoloured.

2082	1c. Type **536**	10	10
2083	3c. Ortelius's map, 1572	10	10
2084	13c. Bellini's map, 1762	80	20
2085	40c. Cartographic survey map, 1973	1·10	50

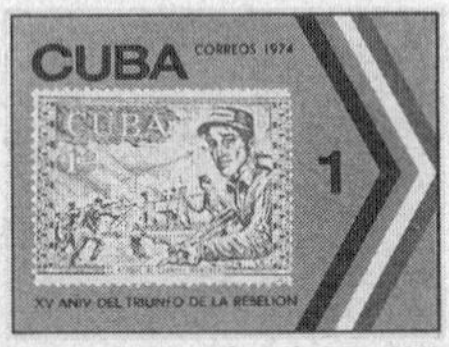

537 1c. Stamp of 1960 (No. 921)

1974. 15th Anniv of Revolution. Revolution stamps of 1960. Multicoloured.

2086	1c. Type **537**	10	10
2087	3c. 2c. stamp	20	10
2088	13c. 8c. air stamp	1·00	60
2089	40c. 12c. air stamp	1·25	75

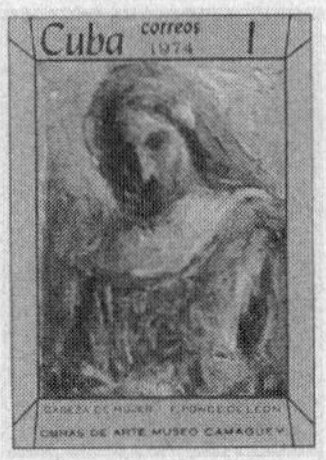

538 "Head of a Woman" (F. Ponce de Leon)

1974. Paintings in Camaguey Museum. Mult.

2090	1c. Type **538**	10	10
2091	3c. "Mexican Children" (J. Arche)	10	10
2092	8c. "Portrait of a Young Woman" (A. Menocal)	20	10
2093	10c. "Mulatto Woman with Coconut" (L. Romanach)	55	20
2094	13c. "Head of Old Man" (J. Arburu)	85	30

539 A. Cabral   **540** "Lenin" (after J. V. Kosmin)

1974. 1st Death Anniv of Amilcar Cabral (Guinea-Bissau guerilla leader).
2095 **539** 13c. multicoloured . . . 70 20

1974. 50th Anniv of Lenin's Death.
2096 **540** 30c. multicoloured . . . 1·10 45

541 Games Emblem   **542** "C. M. de Cespedes" (after F. Martinez)

1974. 12th Central American and Caribbean Games, Santo Domingo. Multicoloured.
2097 1c. Type **541** . . . 20 10
2098 2c. Throwing the javelin . . 20 10
2199 3c. Boxing 20 10
2100 4c. Baseball player (horiz) . . 20 10
2101 13c. Handball player (horiz) . 1·50 75
2102 30c. Volleyball (horiz) . . 2·00 1·00

1974. Death Centenary of Carlos M. de Cespedes (patriot).
2103 **542** 13c. multicoloured . . . 70 15

543 "Portrait of a Man" (J. B. Vermay)   **544** "Comecon" Headquarters Building, Moscow

1974. National Museum Paintings (8th series). Multicoloured.
2104 1c. Type **543** . . . 10 10
2105 2c. "Nodriza" (C. A. Van Loo) 10 10
2106 3c. "Cattle by a River" (R. Morey) (46 × 32 mm) . 10 10
2107 4c. "Village Landscape" (R. Morey) (46 × 32 mm) . 10 10
2108 13c. "Faun and Bacchus" (Rubens) 80 40
2109 30c. "Playing Patience" (R. Madrazo) . . . . . 1·25 75

1974. 25th Anniv of Council for Mutual Economic Aid.
2110 **544** 30c. multicoloured . . . 1·00 45

545 Jose Marti and Lenin

1974. Visit of Leonid Brezhnev (General Secretary of Soviet Communist Party). Multicoloured.
2111 13c. Type **545** . . . 65 25
2112 30c. Brezhnev with Castro . 1·00 45

546 "Martian Crater"

1974. Cosmonautics Day. Science Fiction paintings by Sokolov. Multicoloured.
2113 1c. Type **546** 10 10
2114 2c. "Fiery Labyrinth" . . . 10 10

2115 3c. "Amber Wave" 10 10
2116 4c. "Space Navigators" . . 15 10
2117 13c. "Planet in the Nebula" . 1·00 50
2118 30c. "The World of the Two Suns" . . . . 1·75 1·00
See also Nos. 2196/201.

547 Cuban Letter of 1874

1974. Centenary of U.P.U.
2119 **547** 30c. multicoloured . . . 1·00 45

1974. Stamp Day. Postal Markings of Pre-Stamp Exhibition. As T **521.** Multicoloured.
2120 1c. "Havana" postmark . . 10 10
2121 3c. "Matanzas" postmark . 15 10
2122 13c. "Trinidad" postmark . . 75 15
2123 20c. "Guana Vacoa" postmark . . . . . . 1·10 20

548 Congress Emblem

1974. 18th Sports' Congress of "Friendly Armies".
2124 **548** 3c. multicoloured . . . 40 10

549 "Eumaeus atala atala" (butterfly)

1974. 175th Birth Anniv of Felipe Poey (naturalist). Multicoloured.
2125 1c. Type **549** . . . 20 10
2126 2c. "Pineria terebra" (shell) . 10 10
2127 3c. Reef butterflyfish . . . 10 10
2128 4c. "Eurema dina dina" (butterfly) 50 10
2129 13c. "Hemitrochus fuscolabiata" (shell) . . . 2·00 1·00
2130 30c. Bicoloured damsel-fish . 2·50 1·25

550 A. Mompo and 'Cello

1974. 50th Anniv of Havana Philharmonic Orchestra. Leading Personalities. Multicoloured.
2132 1c. Type **550** . . . 10 10
2133 3c. C. P. Sentenat and piano . 20 10
2134 5c. P. Mercado and trumpet . 25 10
2135 10c. P. Sanjuan and emblem . 75 40
2136 13c. R. Ondina and flute . . 1·00 60

551 "Heliconia humilis"   **552** Boxers and Global Emblem

1974. Garden Flowers. Multicoloured.
2137 1c. Type **551** . . . 10 10
2138 2c. "Anthurium andraeanum" 10 10
2139 3c. "Canna generalis" . . . 10 10
2140 4c. "Alpinia purpurata" . . 20 10
2141 13c. "Gladiolus grandiflorus" . . . . . 1·10 10
2142 30c. "Amomum capitatum" . 2·75 45

1974. World Amateur Boxing Championships.
2143 **552** 1c. multicoloured . . . 15 10
2144 – 2c. multicoloured . . . 20 10
2145 – 13c. multicoloured . . . 75 20
DESIGNS: 3c., 13c. Stages of Boxing matches similar to Type **552.**

553 Mauritius Dodo ("Dodo")   **555** "Suriana maritima"

554 Salvador Allende

1974. Extinct Birds. Multicoloured.
2146 1c. Type **553** . . . 50 25
2147 3c. Cuban macaw ("Ara de Cuba") 50 25
2148 8c. Passenger pigeon ("Paloma Migratoria") . . 1·10 40
2149 10c. Moa . . . . 3·50 70
2150 13c. Great auk ("Gran Alca") . . . . 4·50 1·00

1974. 1st Death Anniv of Pres. Allende of Chile.
2151 **554** 13c. multicoloured . . . 65 30

1974. Wild Flowers. (2nd series). Mult.
2152 1c. Type **555** . . . 10 10
2153 3c. "Cassia ligustrina" . . . 10 10
2154 8c. "Flaveria linearis" . . . 20 15
2155 10c. "Stachytarpheta jamaicensis" . . . . . 1·10 20
2156 13c. "Bacopa monnieri" . . 2·00 60

556 Flying Model Airplane   **557** Indians playing Ball

1974. 10th Anniv of Civil Aeronautical Institute. Multicoloured.
2157 1c. Type **556** 20 10
2158 3c. Parachutist 20 10
2159 8c. Glider in flight (horiz) . 30 10
2160 10c. Antonov An-2 biplane spraying crops (horiz) . 1·00 60
2161 13c. Ilyushin Il-62M in flight (horiz) . . . . 1·60 90

1974. History of Baseball in Cuba. Mult.
2162 1c. Type **557** 10 10
2163 3c. Players of 1874 (First official game) 10 10
2164 8c. Emilio Sabourin 15 10
2165 10c. Modern players 50 30
2166 13c. Latin-American Stadium, Havana . . . 1·00 50
Nos. 2165/6 are horiz, 44 × 27 mm.

558 Stamp, Cachet and Horseman

1974. Cent of "Mambi" Revolutionary Stamp.
2167 **558** 13c. multicoloured . . . 85 20

559 Comecon Headquarters Building, Moscow and Emblem

1974. 16th Socialist Countries' Customs Conference.
2168 **559** 30c. blue and gold . . . 1·00 35

560 Maj. Camilo Cienfuegos (revolutionary)

1974. 15th Anniv of Disappearance of Cienfuegos.
2169 **560** 3c. multicoloured . . . 35 10

561 Miner's Helmet

1974. 8th World Mining Congress.
2170 **561** 13c. multicoloured . . . 1·00 20

562 Oil Refinery

1974. 15th Anniv of Cuban Petroleum Institute.
2171 **562** 3c. multicoloured . . . 50 10

563 Earth Station

1974. Inauguration of "Inter-Sputnik" Satellite Earth Station. Multicoloured.
2172 3c. Type **563** 10 10
2173 13c. Satellite and aerial . . 55 10
2174 1p. Satellite and flags . . . 1·50 65

564 Emblems and Magnifying Glass

1974. 10th Anniv of Cuban Philatelic Federation.
2175 **564** 30c. multicoloured . . . 1·10 40

566 F. Joliot-Curie (1st president) (Picasso)

1974. 25th Anniv of World Peace Congress.
2177 **566** 30c. multicoloured . . . 1·10 40

567 R. M. Villena

1974. 75th Birth Anniv of Ruben Martinez Villena (revolutionary).
2178 **567** 3c. red and yellow . . . 30 10

569 "The Word" (M. Pogolotti)

1975. National Museum Paintings (9th series). Multicoloured.

2180	1c. Type 569	10	10
2181	2c. "The Silk-Cotton Tree" (H. Cleenewerk)	10	10
2182	3c. "Landscape" (G. Collazo)	10	10
2183	5c. "Still Life" (F. Peralta)	15	10
2184	13c. "Maria Wilson" (F. Martinez) (vert)	70	20
2185	30c. "The Couple" (M. Fortunay)	1·10	40

570 Bouquet and Woman's Head

1975. International Woman's Year.

2186	570 13c. multicoloured	65	20

571 Skipjack Tuna and Fishing-boat

1975. Cuban Fishing Industry. Mult.

2187	1c. Type 571	15	10
2188	2c. Blue-finned tunny	15	10
2189	3c. Nassau grouper	15	10
2190	8c. Silver hake	15	15
2191	13c. Prawn	1·00	60
2192	30c. Lobster	2·25	1·00

572 Nickel

1975. Cuban Minerals. Multicoloured.

2193	3c. Type 572	50	20
2194	13c. Copper	1·00	60
2195	30c. Chromium	1·50	75

1975. Cosmonautics Day. Science Fiction paintings. As T **546.** Multicoloured.

2196	1c. "Cosmodrome"	20	10
2197	2c. "Exploration craft" (vert)	25	10
2198	3c. "Earth eclipsing the Sun"	25	10
2199	5c. "On the Threshold"	30	10
2200	13c. "Astronauts on Mars"	1·00	50
2201	30c. "Astronauts' view of Earth"	1·50	75

573 Letter and "Correos" Postmark

1975. Stamp Day. Multicoloured.

2202	3c. Type 573	10	10
2203	13c. Letter and steamship postmark	65	15
2204	30c. Letter and "N.A." postmark	1·00	30

574 Hoisting Red Flag over Reichstag, Berlin

1975. 30th Anniv of "Victory over Fascism".

2205	574 30c. multicoloured	1·00	30

575 Sevres Vase

1975. National Museum Treasures. Mult.

2206	1c. Type 575	10	10
2207	2c. Meissen "Shepherdess and Dancers"	20	10
2208	3c. Chinese Porcelain Dish—"Lady with Parasol" (horiz)	20	10
2209	5c. Chinese Bamboo Screen—"The Phoenix"	30	10
2210	13c. "Allegory of Music" (F. Boucher)	1·00	50
2211	30c. "Portrait of a Lady" (L. Toque)	1·10	60

576 Coloured Balls and Globe "Man"

1975. International Children's Day.

2213	576 3c. multicoloured	20	10

577 Cuban Vireo

1975. Birds (1st series). Multicoloured.

2214	1c. Type 577	30	15
2215	2c. Cuban screech owl	30	15
2216	3c. Cuban conure	30	15
2217	5c. Blue-headed quail dove	50	15
2218	13c. Hook-billed kite	2·75	50
2219	30c. Zapata rail	3·00	85

See also Nos. 2301/6.

578 View of Centre

1973. 10th Anniv of National Scientific Investigation Centre.

2220	578 13c. multicoloured	65	15

579 Commission Emblem and Drainage Equipment

1975. Int Commission on Irrigation and Drainage.

2221	579 13c. multicoloured	65	15

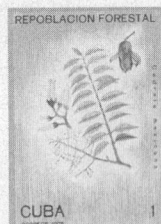 

580 "Cedrea mexicana"   581 Women cultivating Young Plants

1975. Reafforestation. Multicoloured.

2222	1c. Type 580	10	10
2223	3c. "Swietonia mahagoni"	25	10
2224	5c. "Calophyllum brasiliense"	30	10
2225	13c. "Hibiscus tiliaceus"	75	40
2226	30c. "Pinus caribaea"	1·10	70

1975. 15th Anniv of Cuban Women's Federation.

2227	581 3c. multicoloured	25	10

582 Conference Emblem and Broken Chains   583 Baseball

1975. International Conference on the Independence of Puerto Rico.

2228	582 13c. multicoloured	50	15

1975. 7th Pan-American Games, Mexico. Mult.

2229	1c. Type 583	20	10
2230	3c. Boxing	25	10
2231	5c. Handball	25	10
2232	13c. High jumping	75	40
2233	30c. Weightlifting	1·00	50

584 Emblem and Crowd

1975. 15th Anniv of Revolutionary Defence Committees.

2235	584 3c. multicoloured	20	10

585 Institute Emblem

1975. 15th Anniv of Cuban "Friendship Amongst the Peoples" Institute.

2236	585 3c. multicoloured	15	10

586 Silver 1 Peso Coin, 1913

1975. 15th Anniv of Nationalization of Bank of Cuba. Multicoloured.

2237	13c. Type 586	70	25
2238	13c. 1 peso banknote, 1934	70	25
2239	13c. 1 peso banknote, 1946	70	25
2240	13c. 1 peso banknote, 1964	70	25
2241	13c. 1 peso banknote, 1973	70	25

587 "La Junta", Cuba's first locomotive, 1837

1975. "Evolution of Railways". Multicoloured.

2242	1c. Type 587	15	10
2243	3c. Steam locomotive "M. M. Prieto", 1920	20	10
2244	5c. Russian-built Type TEM-4 diesel locomotive	20	10
2245	13c. Hungarian-built Type DVM-9 diesel locomotive	1·50	20
2246	30c. Russian-built Type M-62K diesel locomotive	1·75	35

588 Bobbins and Flag

1975. Textile Industry.

2247	588 13c. multicoloured	55	15

589 Sheep and Diagram

1975. Development of Veterinary Medicine. Animals and Disease Cycles. Multicoloured.

2248	1c. Type 589	10	10
2249	2c. Dog	10	10
2250	3c. Cockerel	20	10
2251	5c. Horse	20	10
2252	13c. Pig	1·00	50
2253	30c. Ox	1·50	75

590 Manuel Ascunce Domenech   592 Communists with Flags inside Figure "1"

1975. Manuel Domenech Educational Detachment.

2254	590 3c. multicoloured	20	10

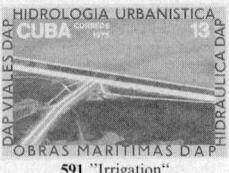

591 "Irrigation"

1975. Agriculture and Water-supply.

2255	591 13c. multicoloured	65	15

1976. 1st Cuban Communist Party Congress. Multicoloured.

2256	3c. Type 592	10	10
2257	13c. Workers with banner (horiz)	60	15
2258	30c. Jose Marti and Cuban leaders (horiz)	75	30

593 Pre-natal Exercises

1976. 8th Latin-American Obstetrics and Gynaecology Congress, Havana.

2259	593 3c. multicoloured	25	10

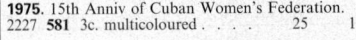

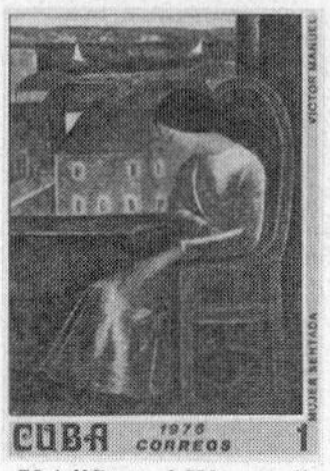

594 "Seated Woman" (V. Manuel)

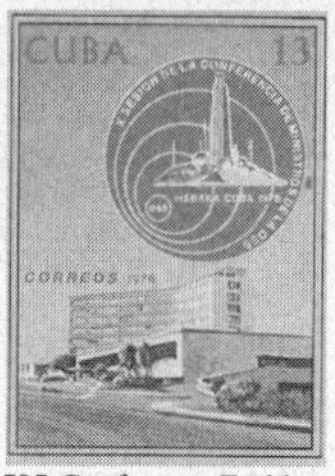

595 Conference Emblem and Building

1976. National Museum Paintings (10th series). Multicoloured.
2260 1c. Type **594** 20 10
2261 2c. "Garden" (S. Rusinol) (horiz) 20 10
2262 3c. "Guadalquivir River" (M. Barron y Carrillo) (horiz) 40 10
2263 5c. "Self-portrait" (Jan Steen) 25 10
2264 13c. "Portrait of Woman" (L. M. van Loo) 85 40
2265 30c. "La Chula" (J. A. Morell) (27 × 44 mm) . . 90 50

1976. Socialist Communications Ministers' Conference, Havana.
2266 **595** 13c. multicoloured . . . 65 15

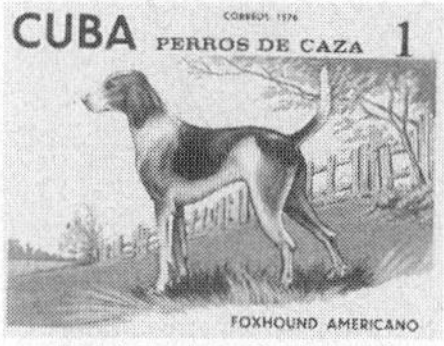

596 American Foxhound

1976. Hunting Dogs. Multicoloured.
2267 1c. Type **596** 20 10
2268 2c. Labrador retriever . . . 20 10
2269 3c. Borzoi 20 10
2270 5c. Irish setter 20 10
2271 13c. Pointer . . . . 1·25 75
2272 30c. Cocker Spaniel . . . . 1·75 1·10

597 Flags, Arms and Anthem

1976. Socialist Constitution, 1976.
2273 **597** 13c. multicoloured . . . 75 20

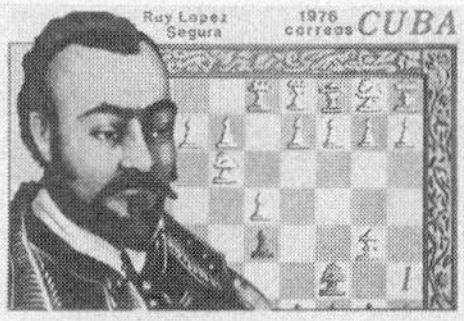

598 Ruy Lopez Segura

1976. History of Chess. Multicoloured.
2274 1c. Type **598** 20 10
2275 2c. Francois Philidor . . . 20 10
2276 3c. Wilhelm Steinitz 20 10
2277 13c. Emanuel Lasker . . . 85 40
2278 30c. Jose Raul Capablanca 1·00 50

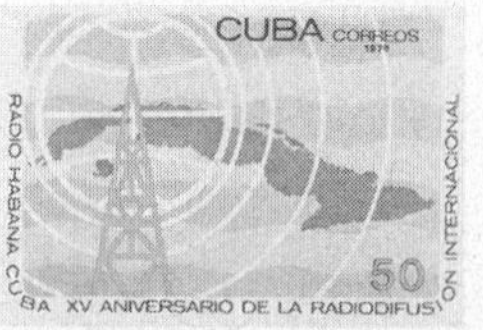

599 Radio Aerial and Map

1976. 15th Anniv of Cuban International Broadcasting Services.
2279 **599** 50c. multicoloured . . . 1·00 50

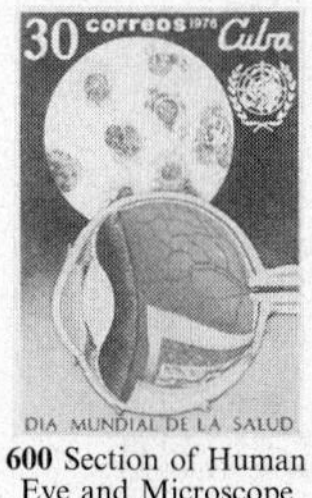

600 Section of Human Eye and Microscope Slide

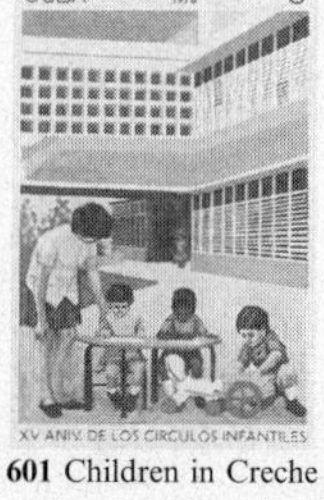

601 Children in Creche

1976. World Health Day.
2280 **600** 30c. multicoloured . . . 75 30

1976. 15th Anniv of Infant Welfare Centres.
2281 **601** 3c. multicoloured 25 10

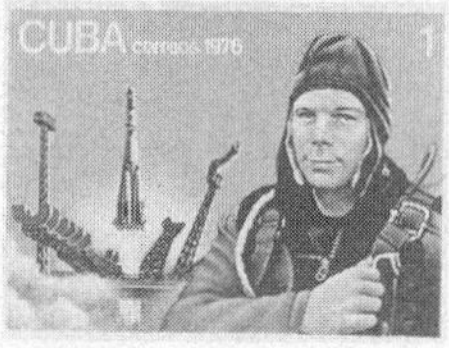

602 Y. Gagarin in Space-suit

1976. 15th Anniv of First Manned Space Flight. Multicoloured.
2282 1c. Type **602** 10 10
2283 2c. V. Tereshkova and rockets 25 10
2284 3c. Cosmonaut on "space walk" (vert) 10 10
2285 5c. Spacecraft and Moon (vert) 15 10
2286 13c. Spacecraft in manoeuvre (vert) 75 40
2287 30c. Space link 90 50

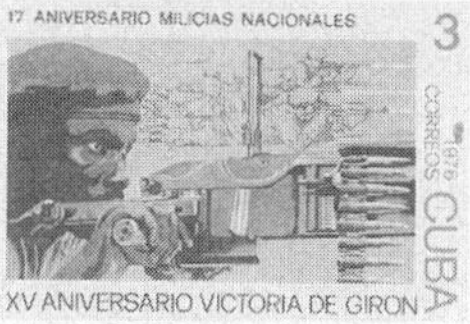

603 Cuban Machine-gunner

1976. 15th Anniv of Giron Victory. Mult.
2288 3c. Type **603** 10 10
2289 13c. Cuban pilot and Lockheed F-80 Shooting Star fighter attacking ship 70 15
2290 30c. Cuban soldier wielding rifle (vert) 85 35

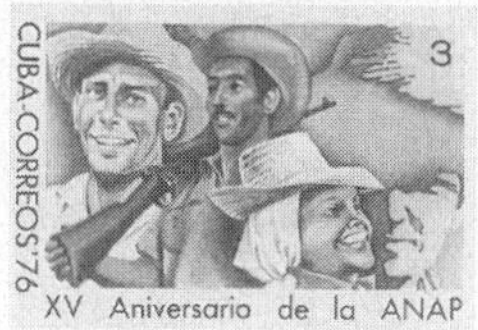

604 Heads of Farmers

1976. 15th Anniv of National Association of Small Farmers (ANAP).
2291 **604** 3c. multicoloured 20 10

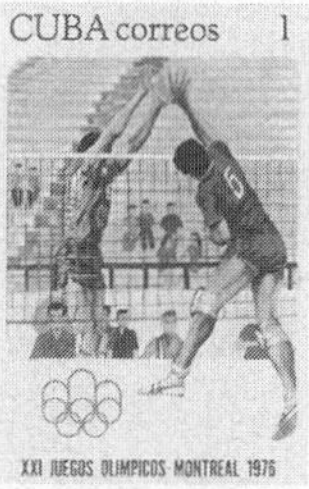

605 Volleyball

1976. Olympic Games, Montreal. Mult.
2292 1c. Type **605** 20 10
2293 2c. Basketball 20 10
2294 3c. Long-jumping 20 10
2295 4c. Boxing 20 10
2296 5c. Weightlifting 20 10
2297 13c. Judo 80 50
2298 30c. Swimming . . . . . . 1·50 1·00

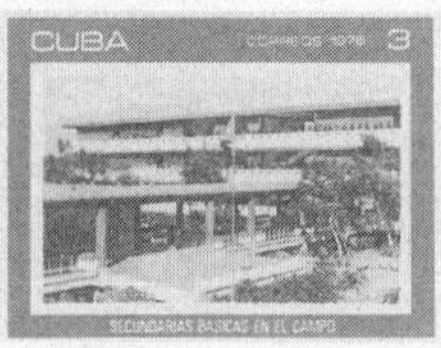

606 Modern Secondary School

1976. Rural Secondary Schools.
2300 **606** 3c. black and red 20 10

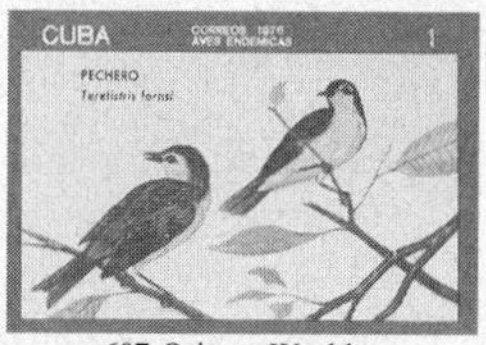

607 Oriente Warbler

1976. Birds (2nd series). Multicoloured.
2301 1c. Type **607** 40 15
2302 2c. Cuban pygmy owl . . . 40 15
2303 3c. Fernandina's flicker . . 40 15
2304 5c. Cuban tody 75 30
2305 13c. Gundlach's hawk . . . 1·50 40
2306 30c. Cuban trogon . . . . 3·50 1·00

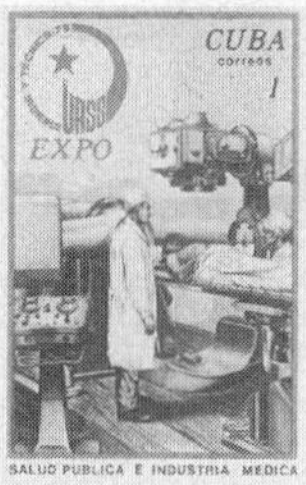

608 Medical Treatment

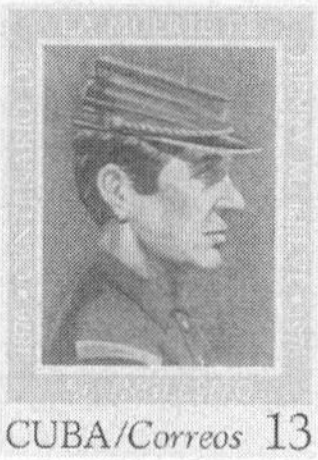

609 "El Inglesito"

1976. "Expo", Havana. Soviet Science and Technology. Multicoloured.
2307 1c. Type **608** 10 10
2308 3c. Child and deer ("Environmental Protection") 10 10
2309 10c. Cosmonauts on launch pad ("Cosmos Investigation") 25 10
2310 30c. Tupolev Tu-144 airplane ("Soviet Transport") (horiz) . . . 1·25 35

1976. Death Cent of Henry M. Reeve (patriot).
2311 **609** 13c. multicoloured . . . 35 15

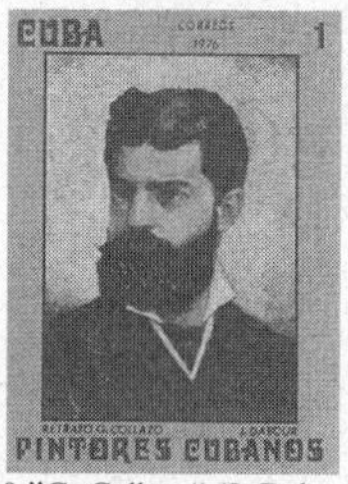

610 "G. Collazo" (J. Dabour)

1976. Cuban Paintings. Multicoloured.
2312 1c. Type **610** 10 10
2313 2c. "The Art Lovers" (G. Collazo) (horiz) . . . 10 10
2314 3c. "The Patio" (G. Collazo) 10 10
2315 5c. "Cocotero" (G. Collazo) 10 10
2316 13c. "New York Studio" (G. Collazo) (horiz) . . . 60 40
2317 30c. "Emelinz Collazo" (G. Collazo) (horiz) . . . 1·25 75

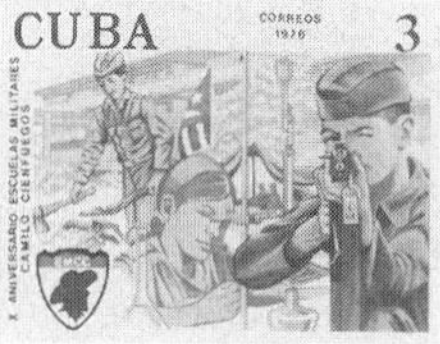

611 School Activities

1976. 10th Anniv of "Camilo Cienfuegos" Military School.
2318 **611** 3c. multicoloured 15 10

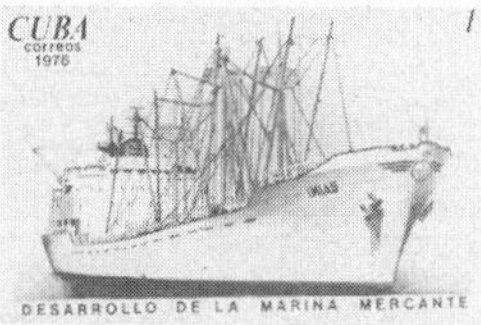

612 "Imias" (freighter)

1976. Development of Cuban Merchant Marine. Multicoloured.
2319 1c. Type **612** 25 10
2320 2c. "Comandante Camilo Cienfuegos" (freighter) . . 25 10
2321 3c. "Comandante Pinares" (cargo liner) 25 10
2322 5c. "Vietnam Heroico" (cargo liner) 40 10
2323 13c. "Presidente Allende" (ore carrier) . . . . . . 1·10 35
2324 30c. "XIII Congreso" (bulk carrier) . . . . 2·25 60

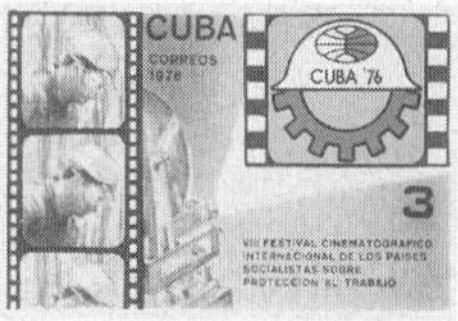

613 Emblem and part of Cine Film

1976. 8th International Cinematographic Festival of Socialist Countries, Havana.
2325 **613** 3c. multicoloured 15 10

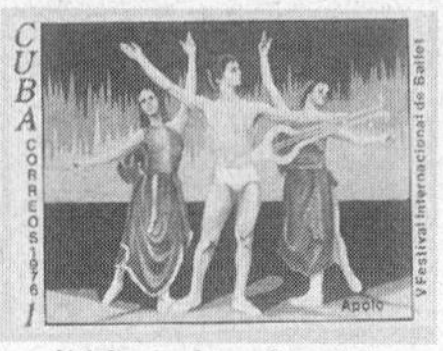

614 Scene from "Apollo"

1976. 5th International Ballet Festival, Havana. Multicoloured.
2326 1c. Type **614** 10 10
2327 2c. "The River and the Forest" (vert) 20 10
2328 3c. "Giselle" 25 10
2329 5c. "Oedipus Rex" (vert) . . 30 10
2330 13c. "Carmen" (vert) . . . 70 45
2331 30c. "Vital Song" (vert) . . 1·25 1·00

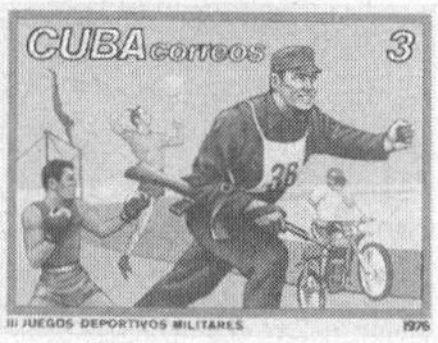

615 Soldier and Sportsmen

1976. 3rd Military Games.
2332 **615** 3c. multicoloured 30 10

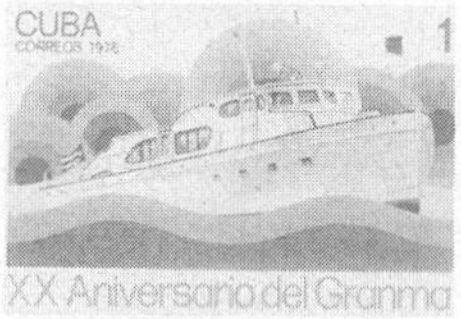

616 "Granma"

1976. 20th Anniv of "Granma" Landings.
2333 **616** 1c. multicoloured 10 10
2334 – 3c. multicoloured 10 10
2335 – 13c. multicoloured . . . 45 10
2336 – 30c. multicoloured . . . 75 35
DESIGNS: 3c. to 30c. Different scenes showing guerrillas.

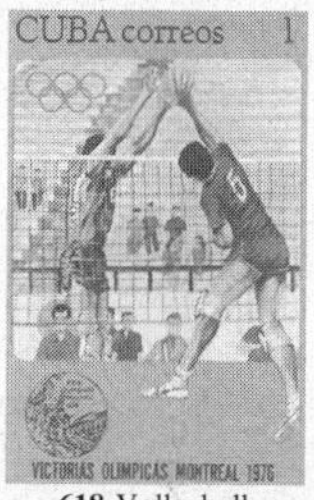

618 Volleyball

1976. Cuban Victories in Montreal Olympic Games. Multicoloured.
2338 1c. Type **618** 10 10
2339 2c. Hurdling 10 10
2340 3c. Running 10 10
2341 8c. Boxing 15 10
2342 13c. Winning race 70 35
2343 30c. Judo . . . . 1·10 70

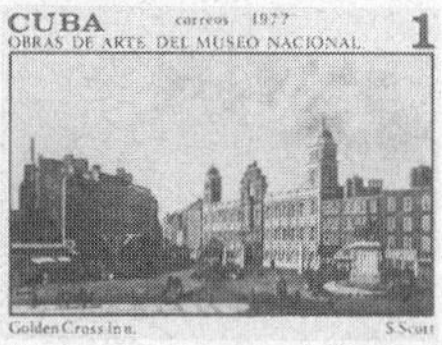

619 "Golden Cross Inn" (S. Scott)

1977. National Museum Paintings (11th series). Multicoloured.
2345 1c. Type **619** 10 10
2346 3c. "Portrait of a Man" (J. Verspronck) (vert) . . 10 10
2347 5c. "Venetian Landscape" (F. Guardi) 20 10
2348 10c. "Valley Corner" (H. Cleenewerck) (vert) . 15 10
2349 13c. "F. Xaviera Paula" (anon) (vert) 70 15
2350 30c. "F. de Medici" (C. Allori) (vert) . . . . 1·00 35
The vert designs are slightly larger, 27 × 43 mm.

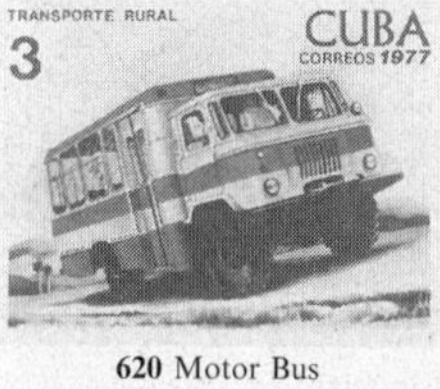

620 Motor Bus

1977. Rural Transport.
2351 **620** 3c. multicoloured 40 10

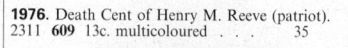

621 Map of Cuba

1977. Constitution of Popular Government.
2352 **621** 13c. multicoloured . . . 35 15

622 Cuban Green Woodpecker

1977. Cuban Birds. Multicoloured.
2353 1c. Type **622** 35 20
2354 4c. Cuban grassquit . . . 45 20
2355 10c. Cuban blackbird . . . 80 25
2356 13c. Zapata wren . . . 1·10 25
2357 30c. Bee hummingbird . . 2·25 55

623 Mechanical Scoop and Emblem

1977. Air. 6th Latin-American and Caribbean Sugar
Exporters Meeting, Havana.
2358 **623** 13c. multicoloured . . . 40 15

624 Fire-mouthed Cichlid

1997. Fish in Lenin Park Aquarium, Havana.
Multicoloured.
2359 1c. Type **624** 10 10
2360 3c. Tiger barb 10 10
2361 5c. Koi carp 15 10
2362 10c. Siamese fightingfish . . 20 10
2363 13c. Freshwater angelfish
(vert) 75 20
2364 30c. Buenos Aires tetra . . 1·50 40

625 "Sputnik 1" and East German Stamp

1977. 20th Anniv of 1st Artificial Satellite.
Multicoloured.
2365 1c. Type **625** 10 10
2366 3c. "Luna 16" and
Hungarian stamp . . . 20 10
2367 5c. "Cosmos" and North
Korean stamp . . . 25 10
2368 10c. "Sputnik 3" and Polish
stamp 40 25
2369 13c. Earth, Moon and
Yugoslav stamp . . . 85 50
2370 30c. Earth, Moon and
Cuban stamp . . . . 1·10 75

626 Antonio Maria Romeu

1977. Cuban Musicians. Multicoloured.
2372 3c. Type **626** (postage) . . 30 15
2373 13c. Jorge Ankerman (air) . 70 30

627 "Hibiscus rosa sinensis"

1977. Birth Centenary of Dr. Juan Tomas Roig
(botanist). Cuban Flowers. Multicoloured.
2374 1c. Type **627** (postage) . . . 10 10
2375 2c. "Nerium oleander" . . . 10 10
2376 5c. "Allamanda cathartica" . . 20 10
2377 10c. "Pelargonium zonale" . . 35 10
2378 13c. "Caesalpinia
pulcherrima" (air) 60 40
2379 30c. "Catharanthus roseus" . . 1·10 80

628 Horse-drawn Fire Engine

1977. Fire Prevention Week, Multicoloured.
2381 1c. Type **628** 10 10
2382 2c. Horse-drawn fire engine
(different) 10 10
2383 6c. Early motor fire pump . . 10 10
2384 10c. Modern motor fire
pump 25 10
2385 13c. Turntable-ladder . . . 50 30
2386 30c. Heavy rescue vehicle . . 1·10 80

629 20th Anniversary Medal

1977. National Decorations.
2387 **629** 1c. mult (postage) . . . 10 10
2388 – 3c. multicoloured 15 10
2389 – 13c. multicoloured (air) . . 35 10
2390 – 30c. multicoloured . . . 65 30
DESIGNS: 3c. to 30c. Various medals and ribbons.

630 "Portrait of **631** Boxing
Mary"

1977. Painting by Jorge Arche. Mult.
2391 1c. Type **630** (postage) . . . 10 10
2392 3c. "Jose Marti" 10 10
2393 5c. "Portrait of Aristides" . . 10 10
2394 10c. "Bathers" (horiz) . . . 25 10
2395 13c. "My Wife and I" (air) . . 30 10
2396 30c. "The Game of
Dominoes" (horiz) . . . 65 30

1977. Military Spartakiad. Multicoloured.
2398 1c. Type **631** (postage) . . . 10 10
2399 3c. Volleyball 10 10
2400 5c. Parachuting 10 10
2401 10c. Running 20 10
2402 13c. Grenade-throwing (air) . . 30 10
2403 30c. Rifle-shooting (horiz) . . 65 30

632 Che Guevara

1977. Air. 10th Anniv of Guerrilla Heroes Day.
2404 **632** 13c. multicoloured . . . 40 10

633 Curtiss A-1 Seaplane and Parla
Stamp of 1952

1977. 50th Anniv of Cuban Air Mail. Mult.
2405 1c. Type **633** (postage) . . . 10 10
2406 2c. Ford 5-AT trimotor
airplane and Havana–Key
West cachet 20 10
2407 5c. Flying boat "American
Clipper" and first flight
cachet 25 10
2408 10c. Douglas DC-4 and
Havana–Madrid cachet . . 40 30
2409 13c. Lockheed Super
Constellation and
Havana–Mexico cachet . . 60 40
2410 30c. Ilyushin Il-18 and
Havana–Prague cachet . . 1·00 60

634 Cruiser "Aurora"

1977. 60th Anniv of Russian Revolution.
2411 **634** 3c. black, red and gold . . 25 10
2412 – 13c. black, red and gold . . 50 25
2413 – 30c. gold, red and black . . 1·00 70
DESIGNS: 13c. Lenin and flags; 30c. Hammer and
sickle with scenes of technology.

636 Cat

1977. Felines in Havana Zoo. Multicoloured.
2415 1c. Type **636** (postage) . . . 20 10
2416 2c. Leopard (black race) . . 20 10
2417 8c. Puma 25 10
2418 10c. Leopard 90 50
2419 13c. Tiger (air) . . . . 1·00 60
2420 30c. Lion . . . . . 1·40 1·00

637 Cienfuegos Uprising

1977. 20th Anniv of Martyrs of the Revolution.
Multicoloured.
2421 13c. Type **637** (postage) . . . 20 10
2422 20c. Attack on the
Presidential Palace . . . 45 15
2423 13c. Landing from the
"Corynthia" (air) 65 35

638 Clinic, Havana

1977. 75th Anniv of Pan-American Health
Organization.
2424 **638** 13c. multicoloured . . . 10 10

639 Map of Cuba and Units of
Measurement

1977. International System of Measurement.
2425 **639** 3c. multicoloured 10 10

640 University Building and Coat of
Arms

1978. 250th Anniv of Havana University.
Multicoloured.
2426 3c. Type **640** (postage) . . . 10 10
2427 13c. University building and
crossed sabres (air) . . . 30 10
2428 30c. Student crowd and
statue 50 30

641 "Jose Marti" **642** "Seated Woman"
(A. Menocal) (R. Madrazo)

1978. Air. 125th Anniv of Jose Marti (patriot).
2429 **641** 13c. multicoloured . . . 30 10

1978. National Museum Paintings (12th series).
Multicoloured.
2430 1c. Type **642** (postage) . . . 10 10
2431 4c. "Girl" (J. Sorolla) . . . 10 10
2432 6c. "Landscape with
Figures" (J. Pilliment)
(horiz) 20 10
2433 10c. "The Cow" (E. Abela)
(horiz) 35 10
2434 13c. "El Guadalquivir"
(M. Barron) (horiz) (air) . . 75 50
2435 30c. "H. E. Ridley" (J. J.
Masqueries) 75 50

643 Patrol Boat, Frontier
Guard and Dog

1978. 15th Anniv of Frontier Troops.
2436 **643** 13c. multicoloured . . . 1·00 15

644 Cuban Solitaire

1978. Cuban Birds. Multicoloured.

2437	1c. Type **644** (postage)	60	25
2438	4c. Cuban gnatcatcher	60	30
2439	10c. Oriente warbler	1·60	40
2440	13c. Zapata sparrow (air)	2·10	70
2441	30c. Cuban macaw and ivory-billed woodpecker (vert)	3·00	1·10

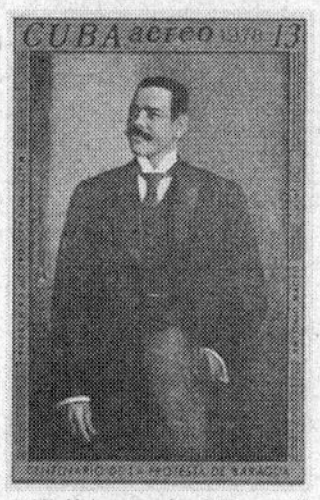

645 "Antonio Maceo" (A. Melero)

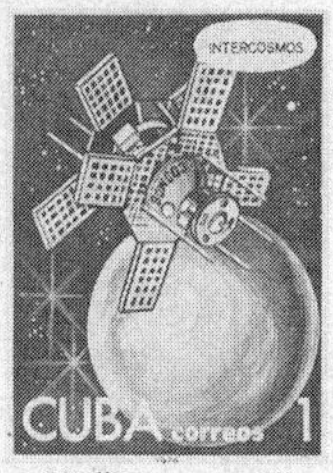

646 "Intercosmos" Satellite

1978. Air. Centenary of Baragua Protest.

2442	**645**	13c. multicoloured	30	10

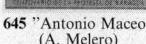

1978. Cosmonautics Day. Multicoloured.

2443	1c. Type **646** (postage)	10	10
2444	2c. "Luna 24" (horiz)	10	10
2445	5c. "Venus 9"	15	10
2446	10c. "Cosmos" (horiz)	15	10
2447	13c. "Venus 10" (horiz) (air)	30	10
2448	30c. "Lunokhod 2" (36 × 46 mm)	55	30

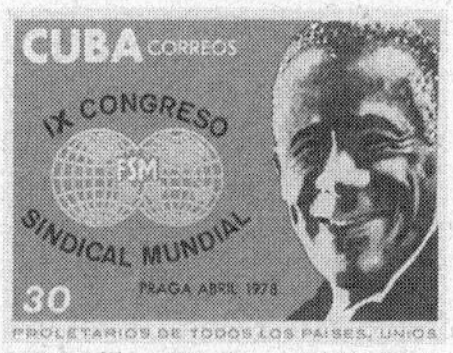

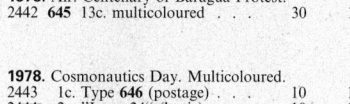

647 Smiling Worker and Emblem

1978. 9th World Federation of Trade Unions Congress, Prague.

2449	**647**	30c. red and black	45	25

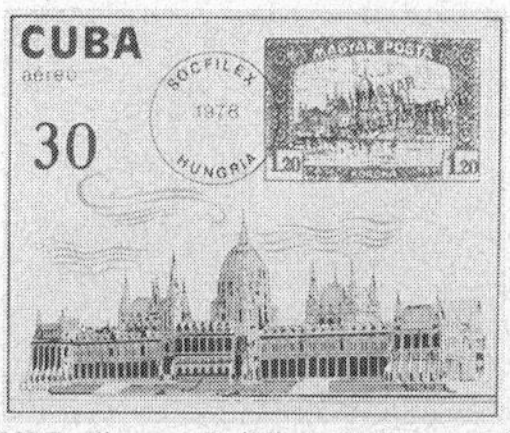

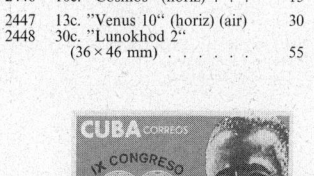

648 Parliament Building, Budapest and 1919 Hungarian Stamp

1978. Air "Socifilex" Stamp Exhibition, Budapest.

2450	**648**	30c. multicoloured	55	30

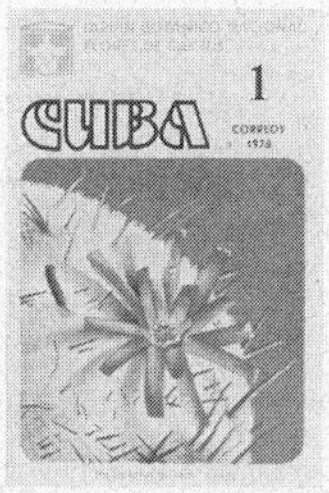

649 "Melocactus guitarti"

1978. Cactus Flowers. Multicoloured.

2451	1c. Type **649** (postage)	10	10
2452	4c. "Leptocereus wrightii"	10	10
2453	6c. "Opuntia militaris"	10	10
2454	10c. "Cylindropuntia hystrix"	30	10
2455	13c. "Rhodocactus cubensis" (air)	50	30
2456	30c. "Harrisia taetra"	85	50

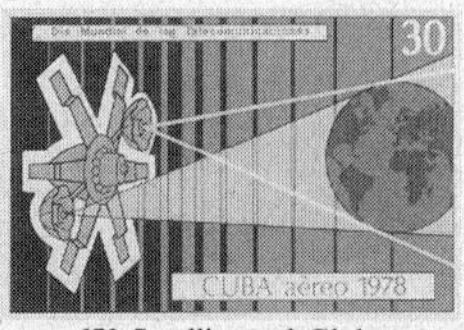

650 Satellite and Globe

1978. Air. World Telecommunications Day.

2457	**650**	30c. multicoloured	55	30

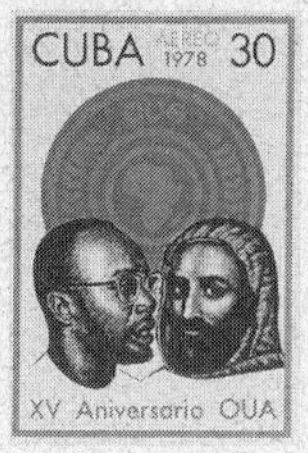

651 Africans and O.A.U. Emblem

1978. Air. 15th Anniv of Organization of African Unity.

2458	**651**	30c. multicoloured	50	30

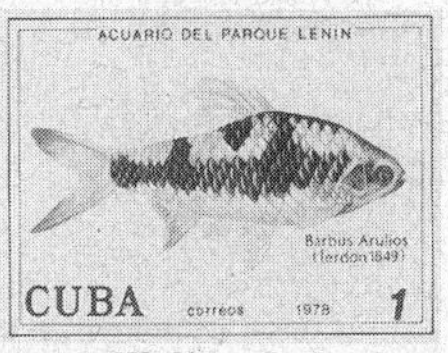

653 Clown Barb

1978. Fish in Lenin Park Aquarium, Havana. Multicoloured.

2460	1c. Type **653** (postage)	10	10
2461	4c. Flame tetra	25	10
2462	6c. Guppy	30	10
2463	10c. Dwarf gourami	35	20
2464	13c. Veil-tailed goldfish (air)	70	40
2465	30c. Brown discus	1·00	70

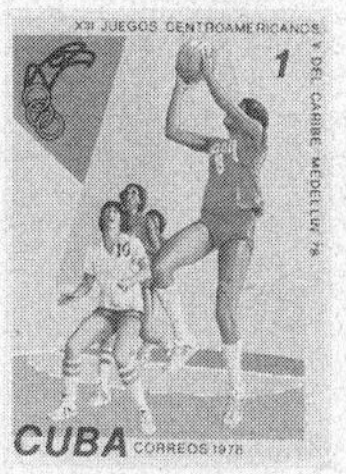

654 Basketball

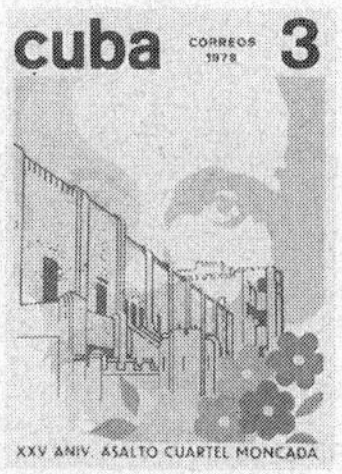

655 Moncada Fortress

1978. 13th Central American and Caribbean Games. Multicoloured.

2466	1c. Type **654** (postage)	10	10
2467	3c. Boxing	10	10
2468	5c. Weightlifting	10	10
2469	10c. Fencing (horiz)	25	10
2470	13c. Volleyball (air)	50	35
2471	30c. Running	75	45

1978. 25th Anniv of Attack on Moncada Fortress. Multicoloured.

2472	3c. Type **655** (postage)	10	10
2473	13c. Soldiers with rifles (air)	25	10
2474	30c. Dove and flags	50	25

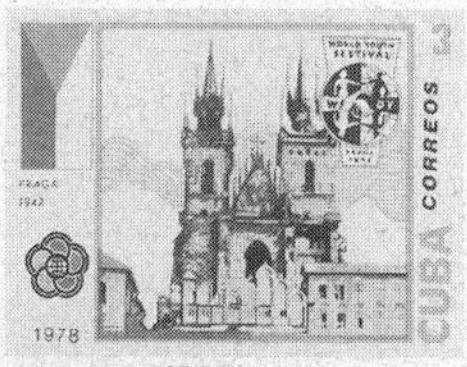

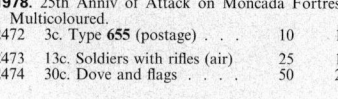

656 Prague

1978. 11th World Youth and Students' Festival, Havana. Multicoloured.

2475	3c. Type **656** (postage)	10	10
2476	3c. Budapest	10	10
2477	3c. Berlin	10	10
2478	3c. Bucharest	10	10
2479	3c. Warsaw	10	10
2480	13c. Moscow (air)	25	15
2481	13c. Vienna	25	15
2482	13c. Helsinki	25	15
2483	13c. Sofia	25	15
2484	13c. Berlin	25	15
2485	30c. Havana (46 × 36 mm)	55	25

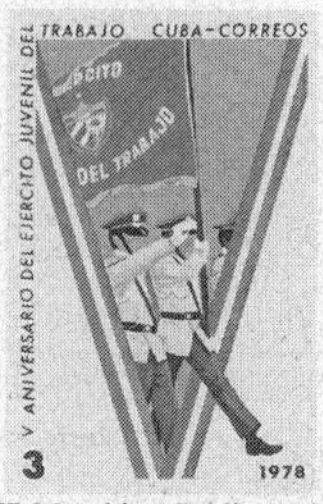

657 Marching Soldiers with Flag

1978. 5th Anniv of Young Workers Army.

2486	**657**	3c. multicoloured	10	10

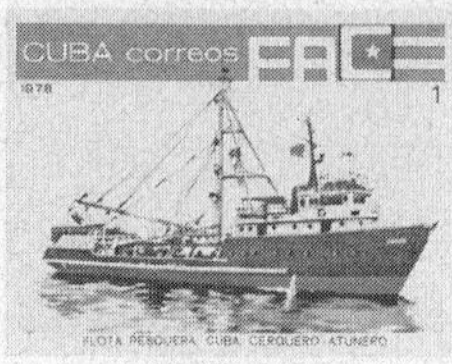

658 "Pargo"

1978. Fishing Fleet. Multicoloured.

2487	1c. Type **658** (postage)	15	10
2488	2c. Fish-processing ship	15	10
2489	5c. Shrimp fishing boat	15	10
2490	10c. Stern trawler	35	15
2491	13c. "Mar Carbide" (air)	60	20
2492	30c. Refrigeration and processing ship	1·10	40

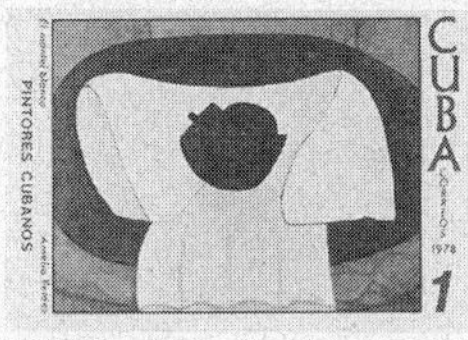

660 "The White Coat" (Pelaez del Casal)

1978. Painting by Amelia Pelaez del Casal. Multicoloured.

2494	1c. Type **660** (postage)	10	10
2495	3c. "Still Life with Flowers"	10	10
2496	6c. "Women"	20	10
2497	10c. "Fish"	30	10
2498	13c. "Flowering Almond" (air)	40	30
2499	30c. "Still Life in Blue"	80	50

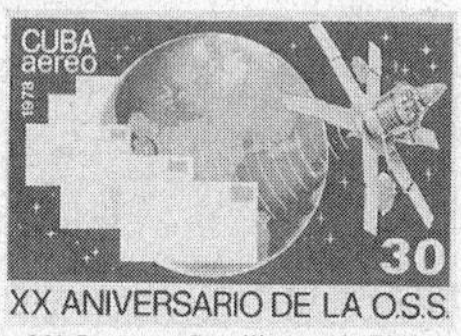

661 Letters, Satellite and Globe

1978. Air 20th Anniv of Organization for Communication Co-operation between Socialist Countries.

2501	**661**	30c. multicoloured	50	30

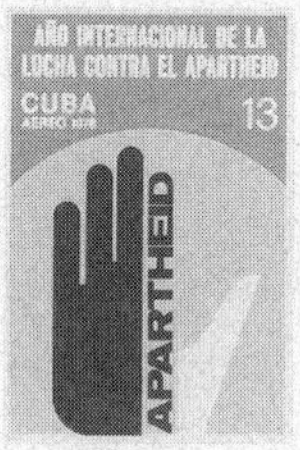

663 Hand

1978. Air. International Anti-Apartheid Year.

2503	**663**	13c. black, pink & mve	1·10	1·10

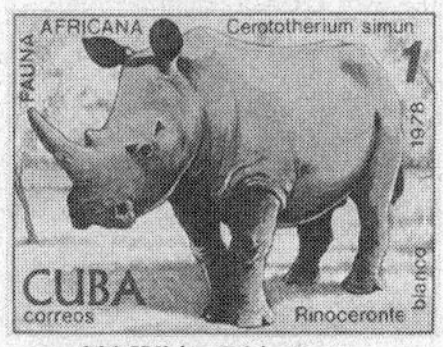

664 White Rhinoceros

1978. Animals in Havana Zoo. Multicoloured.

2504	1c. Type **664** (postage)	20	10
2505	4c. Okapi (vert)	20	10
2506	6c. Mandrill	20	10
2507	10c. Giraffe (vert)	40	25
2508	13c. Cheetah (air)	75	50
2509	30c. African elephant (vert)	1·25	75

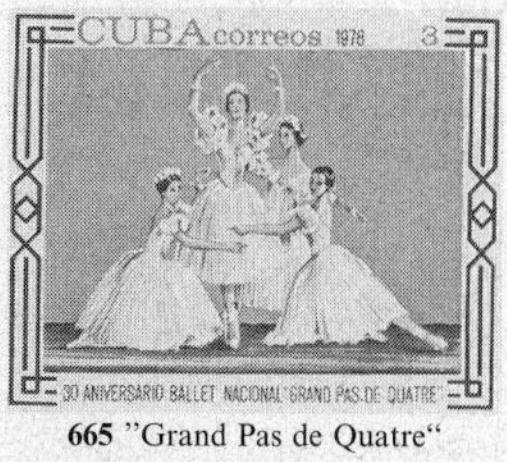

665 "Grand Pas de Quatre"

1978. 30th Anniv of National Ballet Company. Multicoloured.

2510	3c. Type **665** (postage)	20	10
2511	13c. "Giselle" (air)	35	15
2512	30c. "Genesis"	75	60

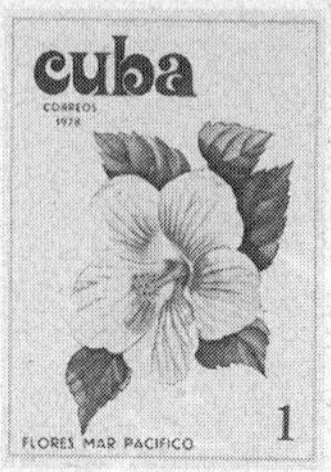

666 Hibiscus

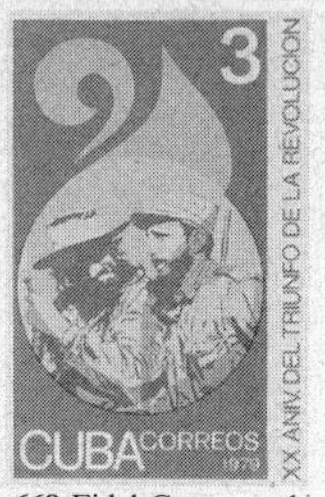

668 Fidel Castro and Soldier

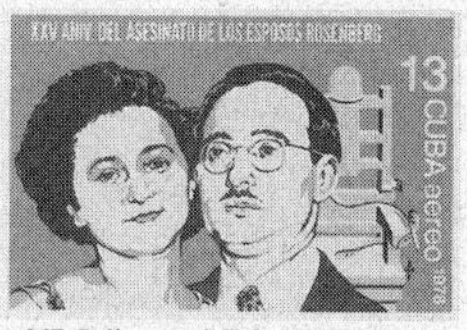

667 Julius and Ethel Rosenberg

1978. Pacific Flowers.

2513	**666**	1c. mult (postage)	10	10
2514	–	4c. multicoloured	10	10
2515	–	6c. multicoloured	20	10
2516	–	10c. multicoloured	35	20
2517	–	13c. mult (air)	50	30
2518	–	30c. multicoloured	85	50

DESIGNS: 4c. to 30c. Different flowers.

1978. Air. 25th Death Anniv of Julius and Ethel Rosenberg (American Communists).

2519	**667**	13c. multicoloured	25	10

1979. 20th Anniv of Revolution. Mult.

2520	3c. Type **668**	10	10
2521	13c. Symbols of industry	30	15
2522	1p. Flag, flame and globe	1·75	95

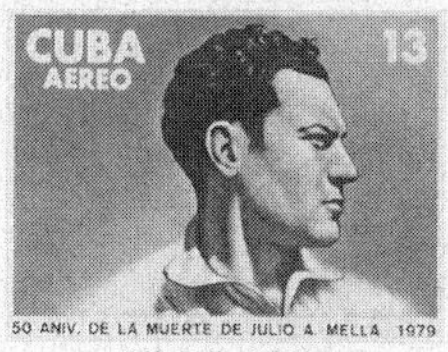

669 Julio Mella

1979. 50th Death Anniv of J. A. Mella.

2523	**669**	13c. multicoloured	20	10

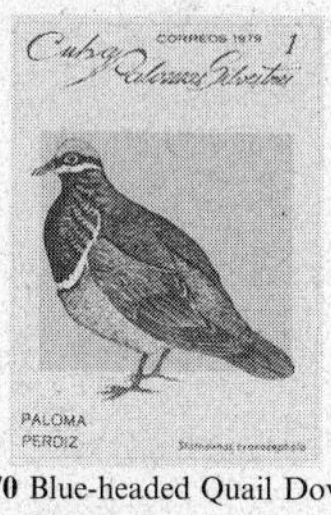

670 Blue-headed Quail Dove

1979. Doves and Pigeons. Multicoloured.

2524	1c. Type **670**	45	15
2525	3c. Key West quail dove	50	15
2526	7c. Grey-faced quail dove	50	15
2527	8c. Ruddy quail dove	60	15
2528	13c. White-crowned pigeon	1·25	40
2529	30c. Plain pigeon	2·25	1·25

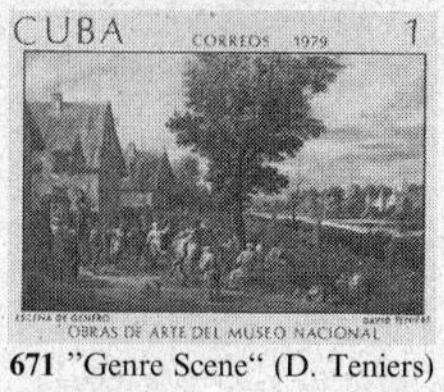

671 "Genre Scene" (D. Teniers)

1979. National Museum Paintings (13th series). Multicoloured.

2530	1c. Type **671**	10	10
2531	3c. "Arrival of Spanish Troops" (J. Meissonier)	15	10
2532	6c. "A Joyful Gathering" (Sir David Wilkie)	15	10
2533	10c. "Capea" (E. de Lucas Padilla)	25	10
2534	13c. "Teatime" (R. Madrazo) (vert)	35	25
2535	30c. "Peasant in front of a Tavern" (Adriaen van Ostade)	75	40

672 "Nymphaea capensis"   **673** "20" Flag and Film Frames

1979. Aquatic Flowers. Multicoloured.

2536	3c. Type **672**	20	10
2537	10c. "Nymphaea ampla"	25	10
2538	13c. "Nymphaea coerulea"	35	15
2539	30c. "Nymphaea rubra"	75	25

1979. 20th Anniv of Cuban Cinema.

2540	**673** 3c. multicoloured	10	10

674 Rocket Launch

1979. Cosmonautics Day. Multicoloured.

2541	1c. Type **674**	10	10
2542	4c. "Soyuz"	10	10
2543	6c. "Salyut"	10	10
2544	10c. "Soyuz" and "Salyut" link-up	25	10
2545	13c. "Soyuz" and "Salyut"	40	10
2546	30c. Parachute and capsule	75	30

675 Hands and Globe

1979. 6th Non-Aligned Countries Summit Conference. Multicoloured.

2548	3c. Type **675**	10	10
2549	13c. "6" ("Against Colonialism")	20	10
2550	30c. Joined coin and globe ("A New Economic Order")	50	30

676 Cuna Indian Tapestry, Panama

1979. 20th Anniv of "House of the Americas" Museum.

2551	**676** 13c. multicoloured	20	10

677 Farmer holding Title Deed

1979. 20th Anniv of Agrarian Reform.

2552	**677** 3c. multicoloured	10	10

679 "Eulepidotis rectimargo"

1979. Cuban Nocturnal Butterflies. Mult.

2554	1c. Type **679**	10	10
2555	4c. "Othreis materna"	10	10
2556	6c. "Noropsis hieroglyphica"	25	10
2557	10c. "Heterochroma sp."	25	10
2558	13c. "Melanchroia regnatrix"	75	50
2559	30c. "Attera gemmata"	1·50	1·00

680 Children's Heads

1979. Air. International Year of the Child.

2560	**680** 13c. multicoloured	20	10

681 "Avenue du Maine, Paris"

1979. 10th Death Anniv of Victor Manuel Garcia (painter). Multicoloured.

2561	1c. Type **681**	10	10
2562	3c. "Portrait of Enmita"	10	10
2563	6c. "Rio San Juan, Matanzas"	20	10
2564	10c. "Landscape with Woman carrying Hay"	20	10
2565	13c. "Still-life with Vase"	30	10
2566	30c. "Street by Night"	60	30

682 Clenched Fists, Dove and Bombs

1979. 30th Anniv of World Peace Council.

2568	**682** 30c. multicoloured	55	25

683 Lighthouse and Fireworks

1979. Air. "Carifesta 79" Festival, Havana.

2569	**683** 13c. multicoloured	50	10

684 Wrestling

1979. Pre-Olympics, Moscow 1980. Mult.

2570	1c. Type **684**	10	10
2571	4c. Boxing	10	10
2572	6c. Volleyball	20	10
2573	10c. Rifle-shooting	20	10
2574	13c. Weightlifting	35	10
2575	30c. High jump	75	25

685 "Rosa eglanteria"   **686** Council Emblem

1979. Roses. Multicoloured.

2576	1c. Type **685**	20	10
2577	2c. "Rosa centifolia anemonoides"	20	10
2578	3c. "Rosa indica vulgaris"	20	10
2579	5c. "Rosa eglanteria var. punicea"	20	10
2580	10c. "Rosa sulfurea"	20	10
2581	13c. "Rosa muscosa alba"	40	10
2582	20c. "Rosa gallica purpurea velutina, Parva"	70	20

1979. 30th Anniv of Council of Mutual Economic Aid.

2583	**686** 13c. multicoloured	20	15

687 Games Emblem and Activities

1979. Air. "Universiada 79" 10th World University Games, Mexico City.

2584	**687** 13c. green, gold & turq	25	15

688 Conventions Palace

1979. Air. 6th Non-Aligned Countries Summit Conference, Havana.

2585	**688** 50c. multicoloured	80	60

689 Sir Rowland Hill and Casket containing Freedom of the City of London

1979. Air. Death Centenary of Sir Rowland Hill.

2586	**689** 30c. multicoloured	75	20

690 Ford 5-AT Trimotor

1979. 50th Anniv of Cuban Airlines. Mult.

2587	1c. Type **690**	10	10
2588	2c. Sikorsky S-38 flying boat	10	10
2589	3c. Douglas DC-3	30	10
2590	4c. Ilyushin Il-18	30	20
2591	13c. Yakovlev Yak-40	85	50
2592	40c. Ilyushin Il-62M	1·75	90

691 Rumanian "New Constitution" Stamp of 1948

1979. Air. "Socfilex 79" Stamp Exhibition, Bucharest.

2593	**691** 30c. multicoloured	50	30

692 Camilo Cienfuegos

1979. 20th Anniv of Disappearance of Camilo Cienfuegos (revolutionary).

2594	**692** 3c. multicoloured	15	10

693 Alvaro Reinoso and Sugar Cane

1979. 15th Anniv of Sugar Cane Institute and 150th Birth Anniv of Alvaro Reinoso.

2595	**693** 13c. multicoloured	30	15

694 Chimpanzees

1979. Young Zoo Animals. Multicoloured.

2596	1c. Type **694**	10	10
2597	2c. Leopards	10	10
2598	3c. Fallow deer	15	10
2599	4c. Lions	20	10
2600	5c. Brown bears	25	10
2601	13c. Eurasian red squirrels	50	25
2602	30c. Giant pandas	1·00	50
2603	50c. Tigers	1·50	75

695 Ground Receiving Station

1979. Air. 50th Anniv of International Radio Consultative Committee.

2604	**695** 30c. multicoloured	50	20

696 "Rhina oblita"

1980. Insects. Multicoloured.

2605	1c. Type **696**	10	10
2606	5c. "Odontocera josemartii" (vert)	10	10
2607	6c. "Pinthocoelium columbinum"	10	10
2608	10c. "Calosoma splendida" (vert)	30	10
2609	13c. "Homophileurus cubanus" (vert)	60	30
2610	30c. "Heterops dimidiata" (vert)	1·00	40

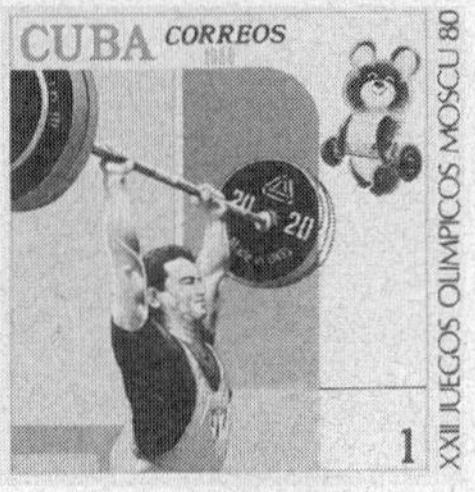

697 Weightlifting

1980. Olympic Games, Moscow. Multicoloured.

2611	1c. Type **697**	10	10
2612	2c. Shooting	10	10
2613	5c. Javelin	15	10
2614	6c. Wrestling	15	10
2615	8c. Judo	25	10
2616	10c. Running	25	10
2617	13c. Boxing	40	10
2618	30c. Volleyball	80	35

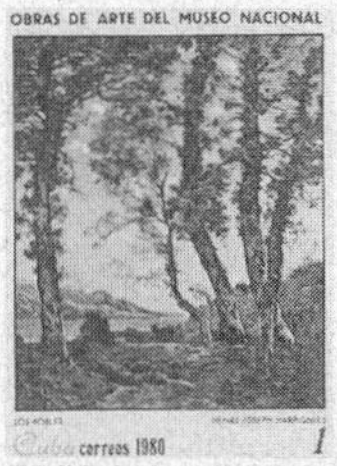

698 "Oak Trees" (Henry Joseph Harpignies)

1980. National Museum Paintings (14th series). Multicoloured.

2620	1c. Type **698**	10	10
2621	4c. "Family Reunion" (Willem van Mieris) (horiz)	10	10
2622	6c. "Poultry" (Melchior de Hondecoeter)	10	10
2623	9c. "Innocence" (Williams A. Bouguereau)	15	10
2624	13c. "Venetian Scene II" (Michele Marieschi) (horiz)	50	10
2625	30c. "Spanish Country-women" (Joaquin Dominguez Bequer)	75	35

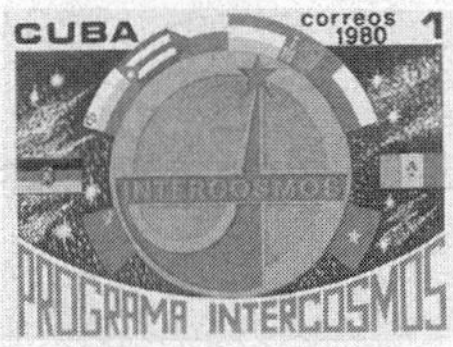

700 Intercosmos Emblem

1980. Intercosmos Programme. Mult.

2627	1c. Type **700**	10	10
2628	4c. Satellite and globe (Physics)	10	10
2629	6c. Satellite and dish aerial (Communications)	10	10
2630	10c. Satellite, grid lines and map (Meteorology)	15	10
2631	13c. Staff of Aesculapius, rocket and satellites (Biology and Medicine)	25	10
2632	30c. Surveying Satellite	50	35

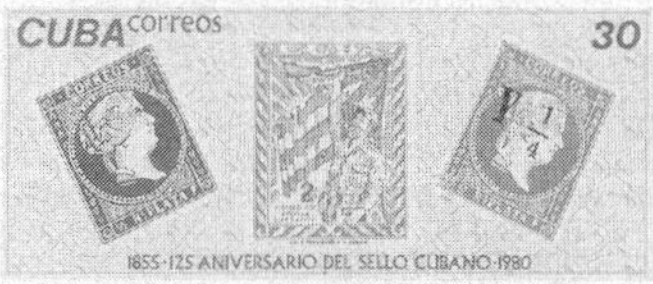

701 Cuban Stamps of 1955 and 1959 (⅔-size illustration)

1980. 125th Anniv of Cuban Stamps.

2633 **701**	30c. blue, red & lt blue	55	30

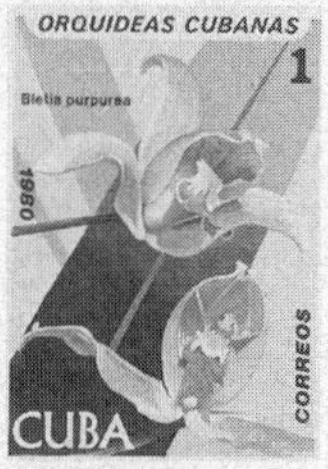

702 "Bletia purpurea"

1980. Orchids. Multicoloured.

2634	1c. Type **702**	10	10
2635	4c. "Oncidium leiboldii"	10	10
2636	6c. "Epidendrum cochieatum"	20	10
2637	10c. "Cattleyopsis lindenii"	25	10
2638	13c. "Encyclia fucata"	40	25
2639	30c. "Encyclia phoenicea"	1·00	50

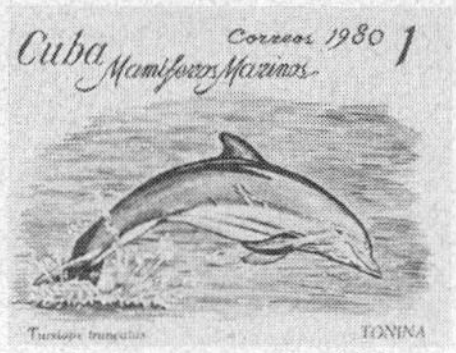

703 Bottle-nosed Dolphin

1980. Marine Mammals. Multicoloured.

2640	1c. Type **703**	25	10
2641	3c. Humpback whale (vert)	25	10
2642	13c. Cuvier's beaked whale	60	40
2643	30c. Caribbean monk seal	1·50	80

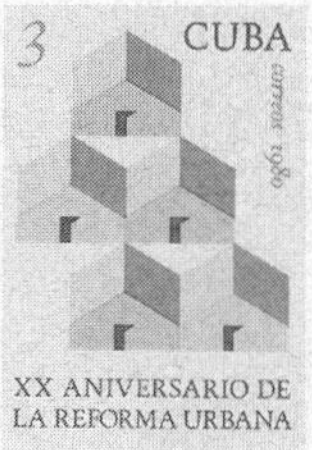

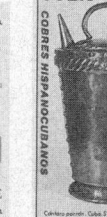

704 Houses

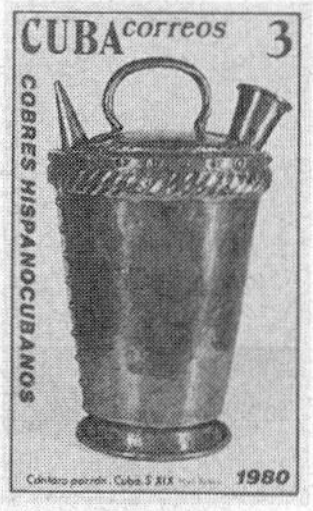

705 Pitcher

1980. "Moncada" Programme. Mult.

2644	3c. Type **704**	10	10
2645	13c. Refinery	20	10

ANNIVERSARIES: 3c. Urban Reform (20th Anniv). 13c. Foreign industry (20th Anniv).

1980. Copper Handicrafts. Multicoloured.

2646	3c. Type **705**	10	10
2647	13c. Wine container (38 × 26 mm)	20	15
2648	30c. Two handled pitcher	50	30

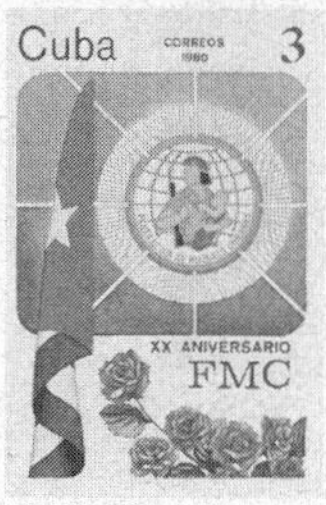

706 Emblem, Flag and Roses

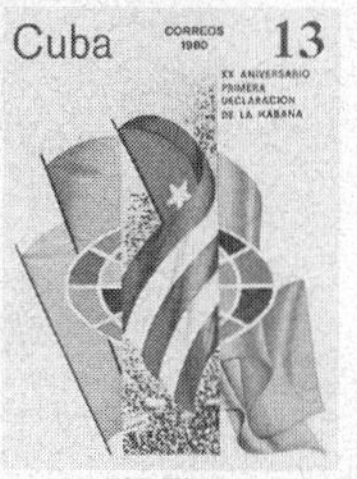

708 Flags

1980. 20th Anniv of Cuban Women's Federation.

2649 **706**	3c. multicoloured	10	10

1980. 20th Anniv of 1st Havana Declaration.

2651 **708**	13c. multicoloured	20	15

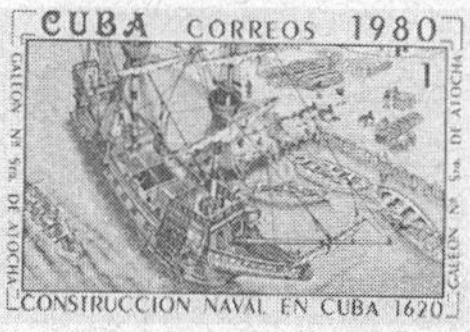

709 Building Galleon "Nuesta Sra. de Atocha", 1620

1980. Cuban Shipbuilding. Multicoloured.

2652	1c. Type **709**	15	10
2653	3c. Building ship of the line "El Rayo", 1749	15	10
2654	7c. Building ship of the line "Santisima Trinidad", 1769	15	10
2655	10c. "Santisima Trinidad" at sea, 1805 (vert)	50	30
2656	13c. Building steamships "Colon" and "Congreso", 1851	1·00	60
2657	30c. Cardenas and Chullima shipyards	1·50	1·00

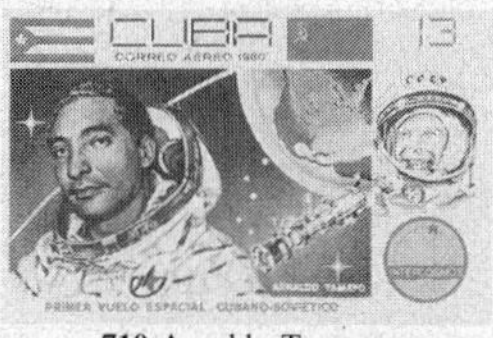

710 Arnaldo Tamayo

1980. Air. 1st Cuban–Soviet Space Flight.

2658 **710**	13c. multicoloured	30	15
2659	30c. multicoloured	55	30

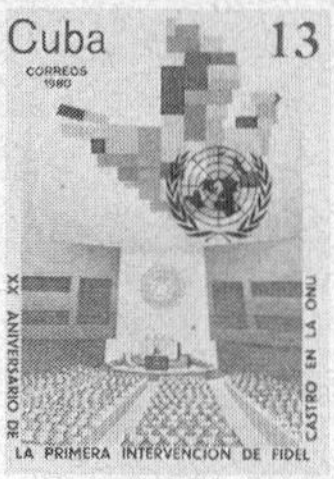

711 U.N. General Assembly

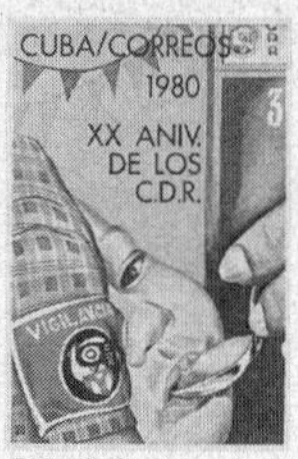

712 Child being Fed

1980. 20th Anniv of Fidel Castro's First Speech at the United Nations.

2660 **711**	13c. multicoloured	20	10

1980. 20th Anniv of Revolution's Defence Committees.

2661 **712**	3c. multicoloured	15	10

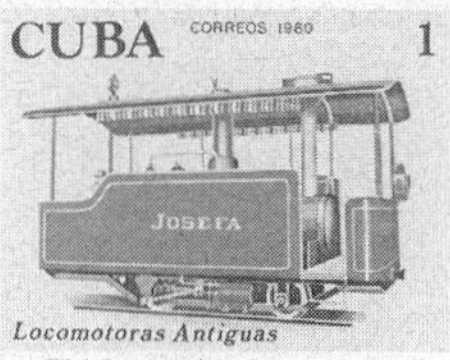

714 Inspection Locomotive

1980. Early Locomotives. Multicoloured.

2663	1c. Type **714**	20	10
2664	2c. Inspection locomotive, Chaparra Sugar Company	20	10
2665	7c. Fireless locomotive, San Francisco Sugar Mill	30	10
2666	10c. Saddle-tank locomotive, Australia Estate	40	10
2667	13c. Steam locomotive	70	10
2668	30c. Oil-fired locomotive, 1909, Smith Comas Estate	1·75	60

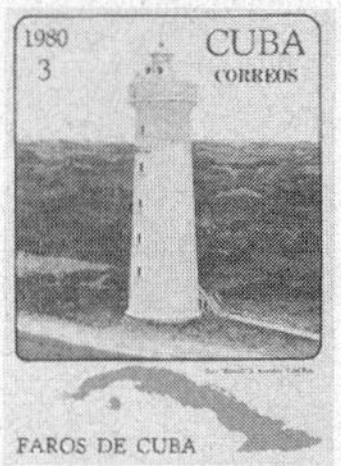

715 "Roncali" Lighthouse, San Antonio

1980. Lighthouses (1st series). Multicoloured.

2669	3c. Type **715**	20	10
2670	13c. Jagua, Cienfuegos	35	20
2671	30c. Punta Maisi, Guantanamo	80	70

See also Nos. 2746/8, 2859/61 and 2920/2.

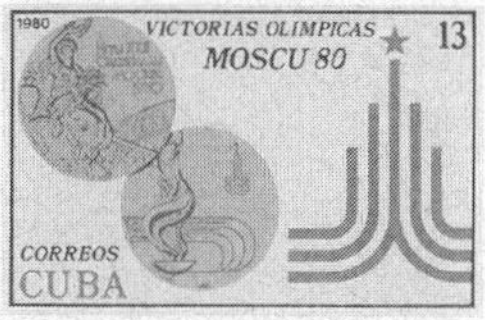

716 Bronze Medal

1980. Cuban Olympic Medal Winners. Mult.

2672	13c. Type **716**	20	15
2673	30c. Silver medal	60	20
2674	50c. Gold medal	1·00	50

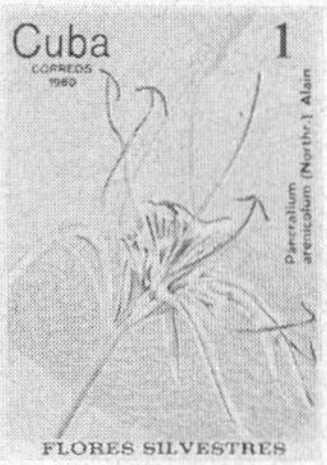

717 "Pancratium arenicolum"

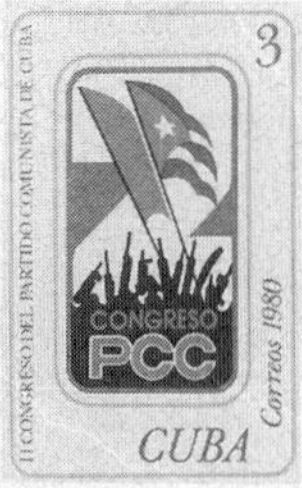

719 Congress Emblem

1980. Forest Flowers. Multicoloured.

2675	1c. Type **717**	10	10
2676	4c. "Urechites lutea"	15	10
2677	6c. "Solanum elaegnifolium"	20	10
2678	10c. "Hamelia patens"	25	10
2679	13c. "Morinda royoc"	35	10
2680	30c. "Centrosema virginianum"	85	25

1980. 2nd Communist Party Congress. Mult.

2682	3c. Type **719**	10	10
2683	13c. Dish aerial and factories (Industry)	20	10
2684	30c. Gymnast, reader and elderly man resting (Recreation)	45	20

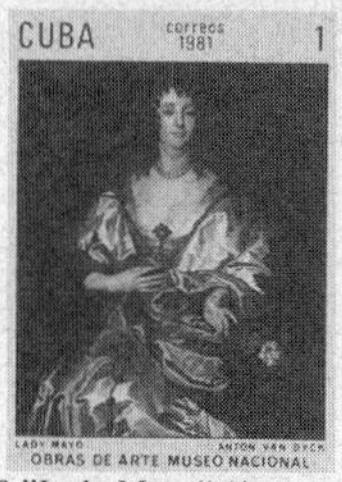

720 "Lady Mayo" (Anton van Dyck)

1981. National Museum Paintings (15th series). Multicoloured.

2685	1c. Type **720**	10	10
2686	6c. "La Hilandera" (Giovanni B. Piazzeta)	10	10
2687	10c. "Daniel Collyer" (Francis Cotes)	15	10
2688	13c. "Gardens of Palma de Mallorca" (Santiago Rusinol) (horiz)	20	15
2689	20c. "Landscape with Road and Houses" (Frederick W. Watts) (horiz)	30	15
2690	50c. "Landscape with Sheep" (Jean F. Millet) (horiz)	90	50

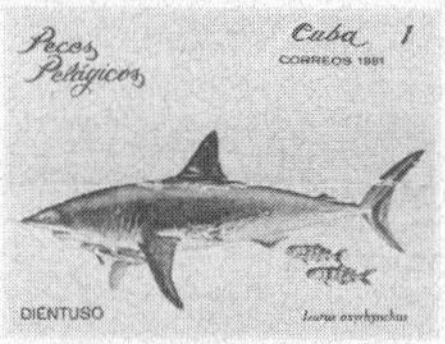

721 Short-finned Mako

1981. Fishes. Multicoloured.

2691	1c. Type **721**	15	10
2692	3c. Opah	15	10
2693	10c. Sailfish	20	15
2694	13c. Oceanic sunfish (vert)	1·50	35
2695	30c. Dolphin and flying-fish	75	30
2696	50c. White marlin	1·40	75

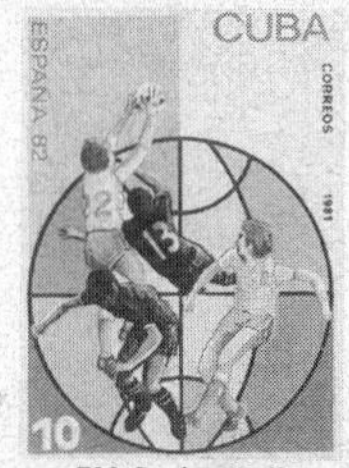

722 Saving Ball

1981. World Cup Football Championship, Spain (1982). (1st issue). Multicoloured.

2697	1c. Diving for ball (horiz)	10	10
2698	2c. Passing ball (horiz)	10	10
2699	3c. Running with ball (horiz)	10	10
2700	10c. Type **722**	25	10
2701	13c. Heading ball	50	10
2702	50c. Tackle (horiz)	1·25	50

See also Nos. 2775/81.

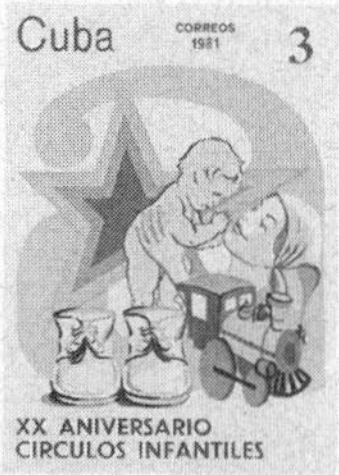

723 Mother, Child, Boots and Toy Train

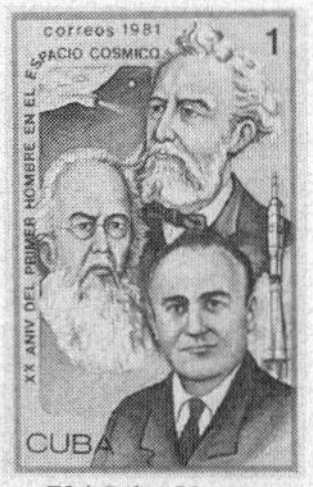

724 Jules Verne, Konstantin Tsiolkovsky and Sergei Korolev

1981. 20th Anniv of Kindergartens.

2704 **723**	3c. multicoloured	1·50	10

1981. 20th Anniv of First Man in Space. Mult.

2705	1c. Type **724**	10	10
2706	2c. Yuri Gagarin (first man in space) (horiz)	10	10
2707	3c. Valentina Tereshkova (first woman in space) (horiz)	10	10
2708	5c. Aleksandr Leonov (first space walker) (horiz)	10	10
2709	13c. Crew of "Voskhod I" (horiz)	20	10
2710	30c. Ryumen and Popov (horiz)	50	30
2711	50c. Tamayo and Romanenko (crew of Soviet–Cuban flight)	90	40

725 Jet Fighters and Rocket

1981. 20th Anniv of Defeat of Invasion Attempt by Cuban Exiles. Multicoloured.

2712	3c. Type **725** (Defence and Air Force Day)		10	10
2713	13c. Hand waving machine-pistol (Victory at Giron)		20	15
2714	30c. Book and flags (Proclamation of Revolution's socialist character) (horiz)		45	30

726 Reynold Garcia Garcia (leader of attack), Barracks and Children

1981. 25th Anniv of Attack on Goicuria Barracks.
2715 **726** 3c. multicoloured 15 10

727 Tractor and Women planting Crops

1981. 20th Anniv of National Association of Small Farmers.
2716 **727** 3c. multicoloured 15 10

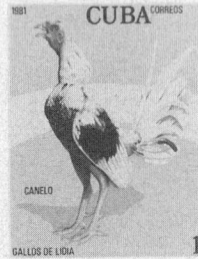

729 Canelo

1981. Fighting Cocks. Multicoloured.

2718	1c. Type **729**		10	10
2719	3c. Cenizo (horiz)		10	10
2720	7c. Blanco		15	10
2721	13c. Pinto		15	10
2722	30c. Giro (horiz)		50	30
2723	50c. Jabao		95	50

730 Anniversary Emblem   **733** "House in the Country" (Maria Cardidad de la O)

732 Tram

1981. 20th Anniv of Ministry of the Interior.
2724 **730** 13c. multicoloured ... 15 10

1981. Horse-drawn Vehicles. Multicoloured.

2726	1c. Type **732**		30	10
2727	4c. Village bus		10	10
2728	9c. Brake		15	10

2729	13c. Landau		15	10
2730	30c. Phaeton		60	30
2731	50c. Hearse		1·10	50

1981. International Year of Disabled People.
2732 **733** 30c. multicoloured ... 55 30

734 Sandinista Guerrilla and Map of Nicaragua

1981. 20th Anniv of Sandinista National Liberation Front.
2733 **734** 13c. multicoloured ... 20 15

735 Gymnasts

1981. 20th Anniv of State Organizations. Mult.

2734	3c. Type **735** (National Sports and Physical Recreation Institute)		10	10
2735	13c. "RHC", radio waves and map (Radio Havana)		15	10
2736	30c. Arrows ("Mincex" Foreign Trade Ministry)		55	30

736 Carlos J. Finlay, Mosquito and Theory

1981. Centenary of Biological Vectors Theory.
2737 **736** 13c. multicoloured ... 20 15

737 Arms of Non-aligned Countries, Manacled Hands and Hands releasing Dove

1981. 20th Anniv of Non-aligned Countries Movement.
2738 **737** 50c. multicoloured ... 90 50

738 White Horse

1981. Horses. Multicoloured.

2739	1c. Type **738**		10	10
2740	3c. Brown horse		10	10
2741	8c. Bucking white horse		15	10
2742	13c. Horse being broken-in		15	10
2743	30c. Black horse		75	40
2744	50c. Herd of horses (horiz)		1·25	70

1981. Lighthouses (2nd series). As T **715**. Mult.

2746	3c. Piedras del Norte		30	10
2747	13c. Punta Lucrecia		40	20
2748	40c. Guano del Este		1·25	60

740 "Flor de Cuba Sugar Mill"

1981. 80th Anniv of Jose Marti National Library. Lithographs by Eduardo Laplante. Multicoloured.

2749	3c. Type **740**		10	10
2750	13c. "El Progreso Sugar Mill"		25	10
2751	30c. "Santa Teresa Sugar Mill"		70	30

741 Pablo Picasso and Cuban Stamp

1981. Birth Centenary of Pablo Picasso (artist).
2752 **741** 30c. multicoloured ... 75 35

743 "Napoleon in Coronation Regalia" (Anon.)

1981. 20th Anniv of Napoleonic Museum. Mult.

2754	1c. Type **743**		10	10
2755	3c. "Napoleon with Landscape" (J. H. Vernet) (horiz)		10	10
2756	10c. "Bonaparte in Egypt" (Eduard Detaille)		15	10
2757	13c. "Napoleon on Horseback" (Hippolyte Bellange) (horiz)		15	10
2758	30c. "Napoleon in Normandy" (Bellange) (horiz)		60	30
2759	50c. "Death of Napoleon" (Anon)		1·10	45

744 Revolutionaries   **745** Cuban Emerald ("Zun-Zun")

1981. 25th Anniversaries. Multicoloured.

2760	3c. Type **744** (30th November insurrection)		10	10
2761	20c. Soldier (Revolutionary Armed Forces)		20	10
2762	1p. Launch "Granma" (disembarkation of revolutionary forces)		2·25	1·00

1981. Fauna.

2763	**745** 1c. blue		75	15
2764	– 2c. green		1·10	25
2765	– 5c. brown		15	15
2766	– 20c. red		50	15
2767	– 35c. lilac		1·00	20
2768	– 40c. grey		80	35

DESIGNS: 2c. Cuban conure ("Catey"); 5c. Desmarest's hutia; 20c. Cuban solenodon; 35c. American manatee; 40c. Crocodile.

746 Ortiz (after Jorge Arche y Silva)   **747** Conrado Benitez

1981. Birth Centenary of Fernando Ortiz (folklorist). Multicoloured.

2769	3c. Type **746**		10	10
2770	10c. Idol (pendant)		15	10
2771	30c. Arara drum		55	25
2772	50c. Thunder god (Chango carving)		90	45

1981. 20th Anniv of Literacy Campaign. Mult.

2773	5c. Type **747**		15	10
2774	5c. Manuel Ascunce		15	10

748 Goalkeeper   **749** Lazaro Pena (trade union delegate)

1982. World Cup Football Championship, Spain (2nd issue). Multicoloured.

2775	1c. Type **748**		10	10
2776	2c. Footballers		10	10
2777	5c. Heading ball		10	10
2778	10c. Kicking ball		15	10
2779	20c. Running for ball (horiz)		35	15
2780	40c. Tackle (horiz)		60	40
2781	50c. Shooting for goal		85	60

1982. 10th World Trade Unions' Congress, Havana.
2783 **749** 30c. multicoloured ... 50 30

750 "Euptoieta hegesia hegesia"

1982. Butterflies. Multicoloured.

2784	1c. Type **750**		10	10
2785	4c. "Metamorpha stelenes insularis"		10	10
2786	5c. "Helicantus charithanius ramsdeni"		10	10
2787	20c. "Phoebis avellaneda"		75	25
2788	30c. "Hamadryas ferox diasia"		1·25	45
2789	50c. "Marpesia eleuchea eleuchea"		2·10	75

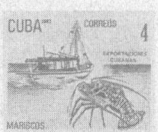

751 Lobster

1982. Exports.

2790	– 3c. green		10	10
2791	**751** 4c. red		30	10
2792	– 6c. blue		15	10
2793	– 7c. orange		15	10
2794	– 8c. lilac		15	10
2795	– 9c. grey		15	10
2796	– 10c. lilac		20	10
2797	– 30c. brown		30	15
2798	– 50c. red		85	25
2799	– 1p. brown		1·60	80

DESIGNS—HORIZ: 3c. Sugar; 6c. Tinned fruit; 7c. Agricultural machinery; 8c. Nickel. VERT: 9c. Rum; 10c. Coffee; 30c. Citrus fruit; 50c. Cigars; 1p. Cement.

752 "Greenland" (cottage tulip)

1982. Tulips. Multicoloured.
2800	1c. Type 752	20	10
2801	3c. "Mariette" (Lily-flowered tulip)	20	10
2802	8c. "Ringo" (triumph)	25	10
2903	20c. "Black Tulip" (Darwin)	50	25
2804	30c. "Jewel of Spring" (Darwin hybrid)	80	40
2805	50c. "Orange Parrot" (parrot tulip)	1·40	70

753 Youth Activities

1982. 20th Anniv of Communist Youth Union.
2806	753 5c. multicoloured	15	10

754 "Mars" Satellite

1982. Cosmonautics Day. Second United Nations Conference on Exploration and Peaceful Uses of Outer Space. Multicoloured.
2807	1c. Type 754	10	10
2808	3c. "Venera" satellite	10	10
2809	6c. "Salyut–Soyuz" link-up	10	10
2810	20c. "Lunokhod" moon vehicle	15	10
2811	30c. "Venera" with heatshield	50	20
2812	50c. "Kosmos" satellite	85	40

755 Letter from British Postal Agency, Havana, to Vera Cruz

1982. Stamp Day. Multicoloured.
2813	20c. Type 755	50	15
2814	30c. Letter from French postal agency, Havana, to Tampico, Mexico	75	20

756 Map of Cuba and Wave Pattern

757 "Portrait of Young Woman" (Jean Greuze)

1982. 20th Anniv of Cuban Broadcasting and Television Institute.
2815	756 30c. multicoloured	50	20

1982. National Museum Paintings (16th series). Multicoloured.
2816	1c. Type 757	10	10
2817	3c. "Procession in Brittany" (Jules Breton) (46 × 36 mm)	10	10
2818	9c. "Landscape" (Jean Piliment) (horiz)	40	10
2819	20c. "Towards Evening" (William Bourgueran)	30	15

2820	30c. "Tiger" (Delacroix) (horiz)	50	20
2821	40c. "The Chair" (Wilfredo Lam)	60	30

759 Hurdling and 1930 Sports Stamp

1982. "Deporfilex '82" Stamp and Coin Exhibition, Havana.
2823	759 20c. multicoloured	40	20

760 Tortoise

1982. Reptiles. Multicoloured.
2824	1c. Type 760	10	10
2825	2c. Snake	10	10
2826	3c. Cuban crocodile	25	10
2827	20c. Iguana	70	40
2828	30c. Lizard	1·00	60
2829	50c. Snake	1·50	1·00

761 Georgi Dimitrov

763 Baseball

762 Dr. Robert Koch and Bacillus

1982. Birth Centenary of Georgi Dimitrov (Bulgarian statesman).
2830	761 30c. multicoloured	55	20

1982. Centenary of Discovery of Tubercle Bacillus.
2831	762 20c. multicoloured	40	20

1982. 14th Central American and Caribbean Games, Havana. Multicoloured.
2832	1c. Type 763	10	10
2833	2c. Boxing	20	10
2834	10c. Water polo	25	10
2835	20c. Javelin	50	35
2836	35c. Weightlifting	1·00	60
2837	50c. Volleyball	1·00	70

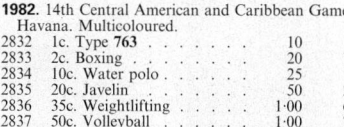
764 "Eichornia crassipes"

1982. 20th Anniv of Hydraulic Development Plan.
2838	5c. Type 764	15	10
2839	20c. "Nymphaea alba"	35	15

766 Hand holding Gun

1982. Namibia Day.
2841	766 50c. multicoloured	80	35

767 Goal

768 "Devil" (V. P. Landaluse)

1982. World Cup Football Championship Finalists. Multicoloured.
2842	5c. Type 767	15	10
2843	20c. Heading ball	35	20
2844	30c. Tackle	50	25
2845	50c. Saving goal	85	45

1982. 20th Anniv of National Folk Ensemble. Multicoloured.
2846	20c. Type 768	40	20
2847	30c. "Epiphany festival" (V.P. Landaluze) (horiz)	55	30

769 Prehistoric Owl

1982. Prehistoric Animals. Multicoloured.
2848	1c. Type 769	75	35
2849	5c. "Crocodylus rhombifer" (horiz)	20	10
2850	7c. Prehistoric eagle	3·00	45
2851	20c. "Geocapromys colombianus" (horiz)	50	25
2852	35c. "Megalocnus rodens"	90	50
2853	50c. "Nesophontes micrus" (horiz)	1·00	60

770 Che Guevara

1982. 15th Death Anniv of "Che" Guevara (guerrilla fighter).
2854	770 20c. multicoloured	40	20

771 Christopher Columbus, "Santa Maria" and Map of Cuba

1982. 490th Anniv of Discovery of America by Columbus. Multicoloured.
2855	5c. Type 771	95	35
2856	20c. "Santa Maria" (vert)	85	30
2857	35c. Caravel "Pinta" (vert)	1·40	65
2858	50c. Caravel "Nina" (vert)	1·75	80

1982. Lighthouses (3rd series). As T 715. Multicoloured.
2859	5c. Cayo Jutias	30	10
2860	20c. Cayo Paredon Grande	75	15
2861	30c. Morro, Santiago de Cuba	1·00	30

772 George Washington (anonymous painting)

1982. 250th Birth Anniv of George Washington. Multicoloured.
2862	5c. Type 772	15	10
2863	20c. Portrait of Washington by Daniel Huntington	40	15

774 Steam Locomotive (1917) and Boating Lake

1982. 10th Anniv of Lenin Park, Havana.
2865	774 5c. multicoloured	20	10

775 Capablanca as Child and Chess King

1982. 40th Death Anniv of Jose Capablanca (chess player). Multicoloured.
2866	5c. Type 775	15	10
2867	20c. Capablanca and rook	40	15
2868	30c. Capablanca and knight	55	30
2869	50c. Capablanca and queen	85	45

776 Lenin, Marx, Russian Arms and Kremlin Tower

1982. 60th Anniv of U.S.S.R.
2870	776 30c. multicoloured	55	30

777 Methods of Communications

1983. World Communications Year (1st issue).
2871	777 20c. multicoloured	40	15

See also Nos. 2929/33.

778 Birthplace and Birth Centenary Stamp

1983. 130th Birth Anniv of Jose Marti (writer).
2872	778 5c. multicoloured	15	10

779 Throwing the Javelin   780 "Che" Guevara and Radio Waves

1983. Olympic Games, Los Angeles (1984). Multicoloured.
2873	1c. Type 779	10	10
2874	5c. Volleyball	15	10
2875	6c. Basketball	15	10
2876	20c. Weightlifting	40	15

| 2877 | 30c. Wrestling | . . . . . | 55 | 30 |
| 2878 | 50c. Boxing | . . . . . . | 85 | 45 |

1983. 25th Anniv of Radio Rebelde.
| 2880 | **780** | 20c. multicoloured | . . . | 40 | 15 |

781 Karl Marx

1983. Death Centenary of Karl Marx.
| 2881 | **781** | 30c. multicoloured | . . . | 55 | 30 |

782 Charles's Hydrogen Balloon   **783** "Vostok 1"

1983. Bicentenary of Manned Flight. Mult.
2882	1c. Type **782**		10	10
2883	3c. Montgolfier balloon		10	10
2884	5c. Montgolfier balloon "Le Gustave"		15	10
2885	7c. Eugene Godard's quintuple "acrobatic" balloon		20	10
2886	30c. Montgolfier unmanned balloon		1·10	55
2887	50c. Charles Green's balloon "Royal Vauxhall"		1·10	55

1983. Cosmonautics Day. Multicoloured.
2889	1c. Type **783**		10	10
2890	4c. French "D1" satellite		10	10
2891	5c. "Mars 2"		15	10
2892	20c. "Soyuz"		40	15
2893	30c. Meteorological satellite		55	30
2894	50c. Intercosmos programme		85	45

784 Letter sent by First International Airmail Service

1983. Stamp Day. Multicoloured.
| 2895 | 20c. Type **784** | | 50 | 15 |
| 2896 | 30c. Letter sent by first Atlantic airmail service | | 75 | 30 |

786 Jose Rafael de las Heras

1983. Birth Bicentenary of Simon Bolivar. Mult.
| 2898 | 5c. Type **786** | | 15 | 10 |
| 2899 | 20c. Simon Bolivar | | 40 | 15 |

787 J. L. Tasende, Abel Santamaria and B. L. Santa Coloma

1983. 30th Anniv of Attack on Moncada Fortress. Multicoloured.
2900	5c. Jose Marti and fortress (horiz.)		15	10
2901	20c. Type **787**		40	15
2902	30c. Symbol of Castro's book "History Will Absolve Me"		55	30

789 Weightlifting

1983. 9th Pan-American Games, Caracas. Mult.
2904	1c. Type **789**		15	10
2905	2c. Volleyball		20	10
2906	3c. Baseball		20	10
2907	20c. High jump		50	30
2908	30c. Basketball		75	40
2909	40c. Boxing		1·00	60

790 "Harbour" (Claude Vernet)

1983. Centenary of French Alliance (French language-teaching association). Multicoloured.
| 2910 | **790** | 30c. multicoloured | . . . | 1·25 | 45 |

791 Salvador Allende and burning Presidential Palace

1983. 10th Death Anniv of Salvador Allende (President of Chile).
| 2911 | **791** | 20c. multicoloured | . . . | 40 | 15 |

792 Regional Peasants Committee

1983. 25th Anniv of Peasants in Arms Congress.
| 2912 | **792** | 5c. multicoloured | . . . | 10 | 10 |

793 "Portrait of a Young Man"

1983. 500th Birth Anniv of Raphael. Mult.
2913	1c. "Girl with Veil"		10	10
2914	2c. "The Cardinal"		10	10
2915	5c. "Francesco M. della Rovere"		20	10
2916	20c. Type **793**		60	40
2917	30c. "Magdalena Doni"		75	50
2918	50c. "La Fornarina"		1·10	70

794 Quality Seal and Exports

1983. State Quality Seal.
| 2919 | **794** | 5c. multicoloured | . . . . | 15 | 10 |

1983. Lighthouses (4th series). As T **715**. Multicoloured.
2920	5c. Carapachibey, Isle of Youth		20	10
2921	20c. Cadiz Bay		60	35
2922	75c. Punta Gobernadora		75	45

795 Hawksbill Turtle

1983. Turtles. Multicoloured.
2923	1c. Type **795**		20	10
2924	2c. "Lepidochelys kempi"		25	10
2925	5c. "Chrysemys decusata"		25	10
2926	20c. Loggerhead turtle		70	30
2927	30c. Green turtle		85	40
2928	50c. "Dermochelys coriacea"		1·40	1·00

796 Bell's Gallow Frame and Modern Telephones

1983. World Communications Year (2nd issue). Multicoloured.
2929	1c. Type **796**		10	10
2930	5c. Telegram and airmail envelopes and U.P.U. emblem		10	10
2931	10c. Satellite and antenna		25	10
2932	20c. Telecommunications satellite and dish aerial		40	15
2933	30c. Television and Radio Commemorative plaque and tower block		55	30

797 Cuban Stamps of 1933 and 1965

1983. 150th Birth Anniv of Carlos J. Finlay (malaria researcher).
| 2934 | **797** | 20c. multicoloured | . . . | 50 | 15 |

798 "Jatropha angustifolia"   **799** Tobacco Flowers

1983. Flora and Fauna. Multicoloured. (a) Flowers.
2935	5c. Type **798**		10	10
2936	5c. "Cochlospermum vitifolium"		10	10
2937	5c. "Tabebuia lepidota"		10	10
2938	5c. "Kalmiella ericoides"		10	10
2939	5c. "Jatropha integerrima"		10	10
2940	5c. "Melocactus actinacanthus"		10	10
2941	5c. "Cordia sebestana"		10	10
2942	5c. "Tabernaemontana apoda"		10	10
2943	5c. "Lantana camera"		10	10
2944	5c. "Cordia gerascanthus"		10	10
2945	5c. "Opuntia dillenii"		10	10
2946	5c. "Euphorbia podocarpifolia"		10	10
2947	5c. "Dinema cubincola"		10	10
2948	5c. "Guaiacum officinale"		10	10
2949	5c. "Magnolia cubensis"		10	10

(b) Birds.
2950	5c. Bee hummingbird		60	15
2951	5c. Northern mockingbird		60	15
2952	5c. Cuban tody		60	15
2953	5c. Cuban Amazon		60	15
2954	5c. Zapata wren		60	15
2955	5c. Brown pelican		1·00	20
2956	5c. Great red-bellied woodpecker		60	15
2957	5c. Red-legged thrush		60	15
2958	5c. Cuban conure		60	15
2959	5c. Eastern meadowlark		60	15
2960	5c. Cuban grassquit		60	15
2961	5c. White-tailed tropic bird		60	15
2962	5c. Cuban solitaire		60	15
2963	5c. Great lizard cuckoo		60	15
2964	5c. Cuban gnatcatcher		60	15

1983. Flowers.
2966	**799**	60c. green		1·00	55
2967	–	70c. red		1·10	65
2968	–	80c. blue		1·25	75
2969	–	90c. violet		1·40	85
DESIGNS: 70c. Lily; 80c. Mariposa; 90c. Orchid.

800 Flag and Plan of El Jigue Battlefield

1983. 25th Anniv of Revolution (1st issue). Multicoloured.
| 2970 | 5c. Type **800** | | 10 | 10 |
| 2971 | 20c. Flag and railway tracks at Santa Clara | | 2·50 | 75 |

801 Flag and Revolutionaries

1983. 25th Anniv of Revolution (2nd issue). Multicoloured.
2972	20c. Type **801**		35	15
2973	20c. "25" and star		35	15
2974	20c. Workers and Cuban Communist Party emblem		35	15

802 Lazaro Gonzalez, CTC Emblem and 15th Congress Flag

1984. 45th Anniv of Revolutionary Workers' Union.
| 2975 | **802** | 5c. multicoloured | . . . . | 10 | 10 |

803 "Ixias balice balice"

1984. Butterflies. Multicoloured.
2976	1c. Type **803**		10	10
2977	2c. "Phoebis avellaneda avellaneda"		10	10
2978	3c. "Anthocaris sara sara"		10	10
2979	5c. "Victorina superba superba"		20	10
2980	20c. "Heliconius cydno cydnides"		70	10
2981	30c. "Parides gundlachianus calzadillae"		1·25	45
2982	50c. "Catagramma sorana sorana"		2·00	70

804 Clocktower and Russian Stamps of 1924–25

1984. 60th Death Anniv of Lenin.
| 2983 | **804** | 30c. multicoloured | . . . | 50 | 25 |

805 Risso's Dolphin

1984. Whales and Dolphins. Multicoloured.
2984	1c. Type **805**	10	10
2985	2c. Common dolphin	10	10
2986	5c. Sperm whale (horiz)	20	10
2987	6c. Spotted dolphin	20	10
2988	10c. False killer whale (horiz)	50	30
2989	30c. Bottle-nosed dolphin	1·00	70
2990	50c. Humpback whale (horiz)	1·50	1·00

806 Sandino and Crowd holding Banner

1984. 50th Death Anniv of Augusto C. Sandino.
2991 **806** 20c. multicoloured . . . 35 15

807 Red Cross Flag and Stamp of 1946

1984. 75th Anniv of Cuban Red Cross.
2992 **807** 30c. multicoloured . . . 80 70

808 Scene from Cartoon Film

1984. 25th Anniv of Cuban Cinema.
2993 **808** 20c. multicoloured . . . 55 50

809 "Brownea grandiceps"

1984. Caribbean Flowers. Multicoloured.
2994	1c. Type **809**	10	10
2995	2c. "Couroupita guianensis"	10	10
2996	5c. "Triplaris surinamensis"	15	10
2997	20c. "Amherstia nobilis"	55	50
2998	30c. "Plumieria alba"	80	70
2999	50c. "Delonix regia"	1·40	1·25

810 "Electron 1"

1984. Cosmonautics Day. Multicoloured.
3000	2c. Type **810**	10	10
3001	3c. "Electron 2"	10	10
3002	5c. "Intercosmos 1"	15	10
3003	10c. "Mars 5"	30	15
3004	30c. "Soyuz 1"	80	70
3005	50c. Soviet-Bulgarian space flight, 1979	1·40	1·25

811 Mexican Mail Runner

1984. Stamp Day. Multicoloured.
3007	20c. Type **811**	55	50
3008	30c. Egyptian boatman	80	70

Nos. 3007/8 show details of mural by R. R. Radillo in Havana Stamp Museum.
See also Nos. 3097/8, 3170/1, 3336/7 and 3619/20.

813 Basketball

1984. Pre-Olympics.
3010 **813** 20c. multicoloured . . . 55 50

814 Pink Roses   **816** Saver and Pile of Coins

815 Workers in Field

1984. Mothers' Day. Multicoloured.
3011	20c. Type **814**	55	50
3012	20c. Red roses	55	50

1984. 25th Anniv of Land Reform Act.
3013 **815** 5c. multicoloured . . . 15 10

1984. 1st Anniv of People's Saving Bank.
3014 **816** 5c. multicoloured . . . 15 10

817 Locomotive

1984. Locomotives. Multicoloured.
3015	1c. Type **817**	15	10
3016	4c. Locomotive No. 73	20	10
3017	5c. Locomotive (different)	25	10
3018	10c. Locomotive (different)	40	10
3019	30c. Locomotive No. 350	95	30
3020	50c. Locomotive No. 495	1·90	55

819 Baron de Coubertin and Runner with Olympic Flame

1984. 90th Anniv of Int Olympic Committee.
3022 **819** 30c. multicoloured . . . 80 70

820 Baby with Toy Dog

1984. Children's Day.
3023 **820** 5c. multicoloured . . . 15 10

821 Wrestling   **822** Emilio Roig de Leuchsenring

1984. Olympic Games, Los Angeles. Mult.
3024	1c. Type **821**	10	10
3025	3c. Throwing the discus	10	10
3026	5c. Volleyball	15	10
3027	20c. Boxing	55	50
3028	30c. Basketball	80	70
3029	50c. Weightlifting	1·40	1·25

1984. 20th Death Anniv of Emilio Roig de Leuchsenring.
3031 **822** 5c. multicoloured . . . 15 10

824 Cow in Pasture

1984. Cattle. Multicoloured.
3033	2c. Type **824**	10	10
3034	3c. Cuban Carib	10	10
3035	5c. Charolaise (vert)	10	10
3036	30c. Cuban Cebu (vert)	75	40
3037	50c. White-udder cow	1·00	70

825 Men's Volleyball

1984. Friendship Tournament. Mult.
3038	3c. Type **825**	10	10
3039	5c. Women's volleyball	10	10
3040	8c. Water polo	30	10
3041	30c. Boxing	60	40

826 Polymita

1984. Cuban Wildlife. Multicoloured.
3042	1c. Type **826**	10	10
3043	2c. Cuban solenodon	10	10
3044	3c. "Alsophis cantherigerus" (snake)	10	10
3045	4c. "Osteopilus septentrionalis" (frog)	10	10
3046	5c. Bee hummingbirds	45	15
3047	10c. Bushy-tailed hutia	65	25
3048	30c. Cuban tody	2·75	1·10
3049	50c. Peach-faced lovebird	4·50	1·40

827 King Ferdinand and Queen Isabella

1984. "Espamer '85" International Stamp Exhibition, Havana. Multicoloured.
3050	5c. Type **827**	10	10
3051	20c. Columbus departing from Palos de Moguer	1·00	45
3052	30c. "Santa Maria", "Pinta" and "Nina"	1·40	65
3053	50c. Columbus arriving in America	75	70

829 Flag and Soldier

1984. 25th Anniv of National Militia.
3055 **829** 5c. multicoloured . . . 10 10

830 Camilo Cienfuegos

1984. 25th Anniv of Disappearance of Camilo Cienfuegos (revolutionary).
3056 **830** 5c. multicoloured . . . 10 10

831 Mother breast-feeding Baby

1984. Infant Survival Campaign.
3057 **831** 5c. multicoloured . . . 10 10

832 Morgan, 1909

1984. Cars, Multicoloured.
3058	1c. Type **832**	10	10
3059	2c. Austin, 1922	10	10
3060	5c. Dion-Bouton, 1903	10	10
3061	20c. "T" Ford, 1908	30	25
3062	30c. Karl Benz, 1885	70	40
3063	50c. Karl Benz, 1910	1·10	70

833 18th-century Letters and Museum Emblem

1985. 20th Anniv of Cuban Postal Museum.
3064 **833** 20c. multicoloured . . . 30 25

834 Celia Sanchez (after E. Escobedo)

1985. 5th Death Anniv of Celia Sanchez (revolutionary).
3065 **834** 5c. multicoloured 10 10

835 Pigeon

1985. "Porto-1985" International Pigeon Exhibition, Oporto, Portugal.
3066 **835** 20c. multicoloured . . . 30 25

836 Chile (1962)

1985. World Cup Football Championship, Mexico (1986) (1st issue). Multicoloured.
3067 1c. Type **836** 10 10
3068 2c. England (1966) 10 10
3069 3c. Mexico (1970) 10 10
3070 4c. West Germany (1974) . . 10 10
3071 5c. Argentina (1978) . . . 10 10
3072 30c. Spain (1982) 45 40
3073 50c. Sweden (1958) 75 70
See also Nos. 3135/40.

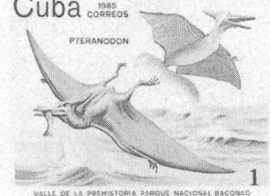

837 Pteranodon

1985. Baconao Valley National Park. Prehistoric Animals (1st series). Multicoloured.
3075 1c. Type **837** 10 10
3076 2c. Brontosaurus 10 10
3077 4c. Iguanodontus 20 15
3078 5c. Estegosaurus 20 15
3079 8c. Monoclonius 25 20
3080 30c. Corythosaurus . . . . 1·25 80
3081 50c. Tyrannosaurus . . . . 1·25 1·00
See also Nos. 3264/9.

838 Uruguay 1911 and Argentina 1921 Congress Stamps and Emblem (⅓-size illustration)

1985. 13th Postal Union of the Americas and Spain Congress, Havana.
3082 **838** 20c. multicoloured . . . 1·75 50

839 Indians playing Football

1985. "Espamer '85" International Stamp Exhibition, Havana. Multicoloured.
3083 1c. Type **839** 10 10
3084 2c. Indian sitting by fire . . 10 10
3085 5c. Fishing with nets and spears 30 10

3086 20c. Making pottery 30 25
3087 30c. Hunting with spears . . 45 40
3088 50c. Decorating canoe and paddle . . . . 1·90 1·10

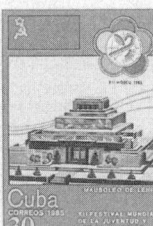

840 Spaceship circling Moon

1985. Cosmonautics Day. Multicoloured.
3090 2c. Type **840** 10 10
3091 3c. Spaceships 10 10
3092 10c. Cosmonauts meeting in space 15 15
3093 13c. Cosmonauts soldering in space 20 15
3094 20c. "Vostok II" and Earth . 30 25
3095 50c. "Lunayod I" crossing moon crater 75 70

841 Lenin's Tomb / 842 Peonies

1985. 12th World Youth and Students' Festival, Moscow.
3096 **841** 30c. multicoloured . . . 45 40

1985. Stamp Day. As T **811.** Multicoloured.
3097 20c. Roman soldier and chariot 30 25
3098 30c. Medieval nobleman and monks 45 40

1985. Mothers' Day. Multicoloured.
3099 1c. Type **842** 10 10
3100 4c. Carnations 15 10
3101 5c. Dahlias 20 10
3102 13c. Roses 30 15
3103 20c. Roses (different) . . . 50 25
3104 50c. Tulips . . . . 1·00 70

843 Guiteras and Aponte

1985. 50th Death Anniv of Antonio Guiteras and Carlos Aponte (revolutionaries).
3105 **843** 5c. multicoloured 10 10

844 Star, "40" and Soldier with Flag

1985. 40th Anniv of End of Second World War.
3106 **844** 5c. multicoloured 10 10
3107 — 20c. multicoloured . . . 30 25
3108 — 30c. red, yellow & violet . 45 40
DESIGNS: 20c. "40" and Soviet Memorial, Berlin-Treptow; 30c. Dove within "40".

846 Daimler, 1885

1985. Centenary of the Motor Cycle. Multicoloured.
3110 2c. Type **846** 10 10
3111 5c. Kayser tricycle, 1910 . . 20 10
3112 10c. Fanomovil, 1925 . . . . 25 15
3113 30c. Mars "A 20", 1926 . . . 75 50
3114 50c. Simson "BSW", 1936 . . 1·10 85

847 La Plata and Hermanos Ameijeiras Hospitals

1985. Development of Health Care since the Revolution.
3115 **847** 5c. multicoloured 10 10

848 Flowers and Soldier with Gun

1985. 25th Anniv of Federation of Cuban Women.
3116 **848** 5c. multicoloured 10 10

849 Athletes and Emblem

1985. World University Games, Kobe, Japan.
3117 **849** 50c. multicoloured . . . 90 85

850 Crowd, Flags and Statue

1985. 25th Anniv of First Havana Declaration.
3118 **850** 5c. multicoloured 10 10

852 Emblem in "25"

1985. 25th Anniv of Committees for Defence of the Revolution.
3120 **852** 5c. multicoloured 10 10

853 Cherub Angelfish

1985. Fishes. Multicoloured.
3121 1c. Type **853** 20 15
3122 3c. Rock beauty 20 15
3123 5c. Four-eyed butterflyfish . 20 15
3124 10c. Reef butterflyfish . . . 35 30
3125 20c. Spot-finned butterflyfish 85 60
3126 50c. Queen angelfish . . . . 2·10 1·75

854 Cuban and Party Flags and Central Committee Building

856 U.N. Building, New York, and Emblem

1985. 20th Anniv of Cuban Communist Party and Third Party Congress.
3127 **854** 5c. multicoloured 10 10

1985. 40th Anniv of U.N.O.
3129 **856** 20c. multicoloured . . . 35 30

857 Old Square and Arms

1985. U.N.E.S.C.O. World Heritage. Old Havana. Multicoloured.
3130 2c. Type **857** 10 10
3131 5c. Real Fuerza Castle . . . 10 10
3132 20c. Havana Cathedral . . . 35 30
3133 30c. Captain General's Palace 55 50
3134 50c. El Templete 90 85

858 Footballers / 860 Ministry Emblem

859 Red Flags and Emblem

1986. World Cup Football Championship, Mexico (2nd issue).
3135 **858** 1c. multicoloured 10 10
3136 — 4c. multicoloured 10 10
3137 — 5c. multicoloured 10 10
3138 — 10c. multicoloured 15 10
3139 — 30c. multicoloured 55 45
3140 — 50c. multicoloured 90 85
DESIGNS: 4c. to 50c. Various footballing scenes.

1986. 3rd Cuban Communist Party Congress, Havana. Multicoloured.
3142 5c. Type **859** 10 10
3143 20c. Red and national flags . 35 30

1986. 25th Anniv of Ministry of Interior Trade.
3144 **860** 5c. multicoloured 10 10

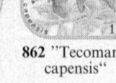

861 People practising Sports / 862 "Tecomaria capensis"

1986. 25th Anniv of National Sports Institute.
3145 **861** 5c. multicoloured 10 10

1986. Exotic Flowers. Multicoloured.
3146 1c. Type **862** 10 10
3147 3c. "Michelia champaca" . . 15 10
3148 5c. "Thunbergia grandiflora" 20 10
3149 8c. "Dendrobium phalaenopsis" 25 10
3150 30c. "Allamanda violacea" . . 75 50
3151 50c. "Rhodocactus bleo" . . 1·10 85

863 Gundlach and Red-winged Blackbird

1986. 90th Death Anniv of Juan C. Gundlach (ornithologist). Multicoloured.
3152 1c. Type **863** 40 20
3153 3c. Olive-capped warbler . . 40 20
3154 7c. La Sagra's flycatcher . . 70 50
3155 9c. Yellow warbler 90 60
3156 30c. Grey-faced quail dove . 3·50 2·50
3157 50c. Common flicker . . . . 5·50 4·00

864 Pioneers and "25" 865 Gomez and Statue

1986. 25th Anniv of Jose Marti Pioneers.
3158 864 5c. multicoloured 10 10

1986. 150th Birth Anniv of Maximo Gomez.
3159 865 20c. multicoloured 35 30

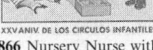

866 Nursery Nurse with Children   867 "Vostok" and Korolev (designer)

1986. 25th Anniv of Children's Day Care Centres.
3160 866 5c. multicoloured 10 10

1986. 25th Anniv of First Man in Space. Multicoloured.
3161 1c. Type 867 . . . . . . 10 10
3162 2c. Yuri Gargarin (first man in space) and "Vostok" 10 10
3163 5c. Valentina Tereshkova (first woman in space) and "Vostok" 10 10
3164 20c. "Salyut" space station 30 25
3165 30c. Capsule descending with parachute 35 30
3166 50c. "Soyuz" rocket on launch pad 90 85

868 National Flag and 1981 Stamp   869 Reels as National Flag and Globe and Tape forming "25"

1986. 25th Anniv of Socialist State (1959) and Victory at Giron. Multicoloured.
3168 5c. Type 868 . . . . 10 10
3169 20c. Flags and arms 30 25

1986. Stamp Day. As T 811 showing details of mural by R. R. Radillo in Havana Stamp Museum. Multicoloured.
3170 20c. Early mail coach . . . 30 25
3171 30c. Express rider 35 30

1986. 25th Anniv of Radio Havana Cuba.
3172 869 5c. multicoloured . . . 10 10

870 "Stourbridge Lion", U.S.A., 1829

1986. "Expo '86" World's Fair, Vancouver. Railway Locomotives. Multicoloured.
3173 1c. Type 870 . . . . 15 10
3174 4c. "Rocket", Great Britain, 1829 15 10
3175 5c. First Russian locomotive, 1845 15 10
3176 8c. Marc Seguin's locomotive, France, 1830 25 20
3177 30c. First Canadian locomotive, 1836 70 20
3178 50c. Steam locomotive, Belgium Grand Central Railway, 1872 1·90 35

871 Hand holding Machete and Farmer ploughing and driving Tractor

1986. 25th Anniv of National Association of Small Farmers.
3180 871 5c. multicoloured 10 10

872 Dove and Arms on Coin

1986. International Peace Year.
3181 872 30c. multicoloured . . . 35 30

873 Emblem

1986. 25th Anniv of Ministry of the Interior.
3182 873 5c. multicoloured 10 10

874 King

1986. 18th Death Anniv of Martin Luther King (human rights campaigner).
3183 874 20c. multicoloured . . . 30 25

875 Bonifacio Byrne

1986. 50th Death Anniv of Bonifacio Byrne (poet).
3184 875 5c. multicoloured 10 10

876 Dove, Pen Nib and Paint Brush   877 Sandino and Pres. Ortega of Nicaragua

1986. 25th Anniv of National Union of Cuban Writers and Artists.
3185 876 5c. multicoloured 10 10

1986. 25th Anniv of Sandinista Movement of Nicaragua.
3186 877 20c. multicoloured . . . 30 25

878 Tanker, Tupolev Tu-154 and Lorry

1986. 25th Anniv of Ministry of Transport.
3187 878 5c. multicoloured 30 15

879 Sportsmen and Emblem   882 "Cattleya hardyana"

881 Map

1986. 5th Central American and Caribbean University Games, Havana.
3188 879 20c. multicoloured . . . 35 30

1986. 25th Anniv of Non-Aligned Countries Movement.
3190 881 50c. multicoloured . . . 80 75

1986. Orchids. Multicoloured.
3191 1c. Type 882 . . . . . . 10 10
3192 4c. "Brassolaeliocattleya" "Horizon Flight" 15 10
3193 5c. "Phalaenopsis" "Margit Moses" 20 15
3194 10c. "Laeliocattleya" "Prism Palette" 25 20
3195 30c. "Phalaenopsis violacea" 75 60
3196 50c. "Disa uniflora" . . . . 1·00 90

883 Mayan House and Jade Statue (Belize)

1986. Latin American History. Pre-Columbian Culture (1st series). Multicoloured.
3197 1c. Type 883 . . . . 10 10
3198 1c. Inca vessel and Gateway of the Sun, Tiahuanacu (Bolivia) 10 10
3199 1c. Spain 1930 1p. stamp of Columbus and 500th anniv of Columbus's discovery of America emblem 10 10
3200 1c. Diaguitan duck-shaped pitcher and ruins, Pucara de Quitor (Chile) 10 10
3201 1c. Archaeological park, San Augustin and Quimbayan statuette (Columbia) 10 10
3202 5c. Moler memorial and Chorotega decorated earthenware statue (Costa Rica) 10 10
3203 5c. Tabaco idol and typical aboriginal houses (Cuba) 10 10
3204 5c. Spain 1930 40c. stamp of Martin Pinzon and anniversary emblem 10 10
3205 5c. Typical houses and animal shaped seat (Dominica) 10 10
3206 5c. Tolita statue and Ingapirca fort (Ecuador) 10 10
3207 10c. Maya vase and Tikal temple (Guatemala) 15 15
3208 10c. Copan ruins and Maya idol (Honduras) 15 15
3209 10c. Spain 1930 30c. stamp of Vincent Pinzon and anniversary emblem 15 15
3210 10c. Chichen-Itza temple and Zapoteca urn (Mexico) 15 15
3211 10c. Punta de Zapote idols and Ometepe ceramic (Nicaragua) 15 15
3212 20c. Tonosi ceramic and Barrile monolithic sculptures (Panama) 35 30
3213 20c. Machu Picchu ruin and Inca figure (Peru) 35 30
3214 20c. Spain 1930 10p. stamp of Columbus and Pinzon brothers and anniversary emblem 35 30
3215 20c. Typical aboriginal dwellings and triangular stone carving (Puerto Rico) 35 30
3216 20c. Santa Ana female figure and Santo Domingo cave (Venezuela) 35 30
See also Nos. 3276/95, 3371/90, 3458/77, 3563/82, 3666/85 and 3769/88.

884 Medal and Soldier with Rifle

1986. 50th Anniv of Formation International Brigades in Spain.
3217 884 30c. multicoloured . . . 50 45

885 "Two Children" (Gutierrez de la Vega)

1986. National Museum Paintings (17th series). Multicoloured.
3218 2c. Type 885 . . . . 10 10
3219 4c. "Sed" (Jean-Gorges Vibert) (horiz) 10 10
3220 6c. "Virgin and Child" (Niccolo Abbate) 20 10
3221 10c. "Bullfight" (Eugenio de Lucas Velazquez) (horiz) 25 15
3222 30c. "The Five Senses" (Anon) (horiz) 75 45
3223 50c. "Meeting at Thomops Castle" (Jean Louis Ernest) (horiz) 1·00 75

886 People and "Granma"

1986. 30th Annivs of "Granma" Landings (5c.) and Revolutionary Armed Forces (20c.). Multicoloured.
3224 5c. Type 886 . . . . 10 10
3225 20c. Soldier, rifle and flag 35 30

887 Scholars and "Che" Guevara

1986. 25th Anniv of Scholarship Programme.
3226 887 5c. multicoloured 10 10

888 Man learning to write and Sanmarti   890 "Gitana" (Joaquin Sorolla)

889 Map and Revolutionaries

1986. 25th Anniv of Literacy Campaign.
3227 888 5c. multicoloured 10 10

1987. 30th Anniv of Attack on La Plata Garrison.
3228 889 5c. multicoloured 10 10

1987. National Museum Paintings (18th series). Multicoloured.
3229 3c. Type 890 . . . . . . 10 10
3230 5c. "Sir Walter Scott" (Sir John W. Gordon) 20 10
3231 10c. "Farm Meadows" (Alfred de Breanski) (horiz) 25 15

3232	20c. "Still Life" (Isaac van Duynen) (horiz)	35	30
3233	30c. "Landscape with Figures" (Francesco Zuccarelli) (horiz)	60	45
3234	40c. "Waffle Seller" (Ignacio Zuloaga)	75	60

891 Palace, Delivery Van and Echeverria

1987. 30th Anniv of Attack on Presidential Palace.

3235	891	5c. multicoloured	10	10

892 Lazarus Ludwig Zamenhof (inventor) and Russia 1927 14k. Stamp

1987. Centenary of Esperanto (invented language).

3236	892	30c. multicoloured . . .	50	45

894 Badge and Slogan

1987. 25th Anniv and 5th Congress of Youth Communist League.

3238	894	5c. multicoloured	10	10

895 "Intercosmos I" Satellite　　897 Dahlias

896 Cover with Postal Fiscal Stamp, 1890

1987. Cosmonautics Day. 20th Anniv of Intercosmos Programme. Multicoloured.

3239	3c. Type 895	10	10
3240	5c. "Intercosmos II"	10	10
3241	10c. "TD"	15	15
3242	20c. "Cosmos 93"	35	30
3243	30c. "Molniya"	50	45
3244	50c. "Vostok 3"	80	75

1987. Stamp Day. Multicoloured.

3246	30c. Type 896	75	60
3247	50c. Cover with bisect, 1869	1·00	80

1987. Mothers' Day. Multicoloured.

3265	Type 897	10	10
	roses	20	10
	ses in basket	25	15
	rative dahlias	35	20
	dahlias	75	45
	s (different) . . .	1·00	25

898 Fractured Femur Immobilised in Frame　　899 Emblem

1987. "Orthopedia '87" Portuguese and Spanish Speaking Countries' Orthopedists Meeting, Havana.

3254	898	5c. multicoloured	10	10

1987. 25th Anniv of Cuban Broadcasting and Television Institute.

3255	899	5c. multicoloured	10	10

900 Battle Monument, Sierra Maestra Mountains

1987. 30th Anniv of Battle of El Uvero.

3256	900	5c. multicoloured	10	10

901 Messenger with Pack Llamas and 1868 Stamp (Bolivia)

1987. "Capex '87" International Stamp Exhibition, Toronto. 19th-century Mail Carriers as depicted on cigarette cards. Multicoloured.

3257	3c. Type 901	10	10
3258	5c. Postman and motor car and 1900 stamp (France)	10	10
3259	10c. Messenger on elephant and 1883 stamp (Siam) . .	15	15
3260	20c. Messenger on camel and 1879 stamp (Egypt)	35	30
3261	30c. Mail troika and stamp (Russia)	50	45
3262	50c. Messenger on horseback and stamp (Indo-China)	80	75

902 Model of Prehistoric Animal

1987. Prehistoric Valley, Baconao National Park (2nd series). Designs showing various exhibits. Multicoloured.

3264	902	3c. multicoloured	10	10
3265		5c. multicoloured	20	10
3266		10c. multicoloured	25	15
3267		20c. multicoloured	55	30
3268		35c. multicoloured	75	50
3269		40c. multicoloured	90	60

903 Pais and Rafael Maria Mendive Popular University Buildings

1987. 30th Death Anniv of Frank Pais (teacher and student leader).

3270	903	5c. multicoloured	10	10

904 Flags and Sportsmen

1987. 10th Pan-American Games, Indianapolis.

3271	904	50c. multicoloured . . .	1·00	75

905 Memorial

1987. 30th Anniv of Cienfuegos Uprising.

3272	905	5c. multicoloured	10	10

908 Coins and 1868 Independence War Centenary 30c. Stamp

1987. 20th Anniv of Heroic Guerilla Fighters Day.

3275	908	50c. multicoloured . . .	1·00	90

909 Tehuelche Man and Red-crowned Ant-tanager (Argentina)

1987. Latin American History (2nd series). Multicoloured.

3276	1c. Type 909	20	20
3277	1c. Red-billed toucan and Tibirica man (Brazil)	20	20
3278	1c. Spain 1930 5c. stamp of La Rabida Monastery and 500th anniv of Columbus's discovery of America emblem	10	10
3279	1c. Andean condor and Lautaro man (Chile) . . .	20	20
3280	1c. Calarca man and hoatzin (Colombia)	20	20
3281	5c. Cuban trogon and Hatuey man (Cuba) . . .	45	20
3282	5c. Scaly-breasted ground dove and Enriquillo man (Dominican Republic) .	45	20
3283	5c. Spain 1930 30c. stamp of departure from Palos and anniversary emblem . .	10	10
3284	5c. Toucan barbet and Ruminahui man (Ecuador)	45	20
3285	5c. Resplendent quetzal and Tecum Uman man (Guatemala)	45	20
3286	10c. Anacaona woman and limpkin (Haiti) . . .	75	20
3287	10c. Lempira man and slaty flowerpiercer (Honduras)	75	20
3288	10c. Spain 1930 10p. Columbus stamp and anniversary emblem . . .	15	10
3289	10c. Northern royal flycatcher and Cuauhtemoc woman (Mexico)	75	20
3290	10c. Painted redstart and Nicarao man (Nicaragua)	75	20
3291	20c. Andean cock of the rock and Atahualpa man (Peru)	1·25	30
3292	20c. Atlactl man and red-tailed hawk (El Salvador)	1·25	50
3293	20c. Spain 1930 10p. stamp of arrival in America and anniversary emblem . .	35	50
3294	20c. Abayuba man and red-breasted plantcutter (Uruguay)	1·25	50
3295	20c. Guaycaypuro man and blue and yellow macaw (Venezuela)	1·25	50

910 1950 2c. Train Stamp

1987. 150th Anniv of Cuban Railway. Designs showing Cuban stamps.

3296	910	3c. red, brown & black	10	10
3297		5c. multicoloured . . .	10	10
3298		10c. multicoloured . . .	15	10
3299		20c. multicoloured . . .	35	25
3300		35c. multicoloured . . .	65	45
3301		40c. multicoloured . . .	75	55

DESIGNS: 5c. 1965 7c. "BB.69,000" diesel locomotive stamp; 10c. 1975 1c. French-built "La Junta" locomotive stamp; 20c. 1975 3c. M. M. Prieto locomotive stamp; 35c. 1980 10c. locomotive stamp; 40c. 1980 13c. locomotive stamp.

911 Satellites and Russia 1927 14k. Stamp

1987. 70th Anniv of Russian Revolution.

3303	911	30c. multicoloured . . .	50	45

912 "Landscape" (Domingo Ramos)

1988. 170th Anniv of San Alejandro Arts School, Havana. Multicoloured.

3304	1c. Type 912	10	10
3305	2c. "Portrait of Rodriguez Morey" (Eugenio Gonzalez Olivera)	10	10
3306	3c. "Landscape with Malangas and Palm Trees" (Valentin Sanz Carta)	15	10
3307	5c. "Ox-carts" (Eduardo Morales)	20	15
3308	10c. "Portrait of Elena Herrera" (Armando Menocal) (vert)	25	20
3309	30c. "The Rape of Dejanira" (Miguel Melero) (vert)	75	50
3310	50c. "The Card Player" (Leopoldo Romanach) .	1·00	85

913 "Boletus satanas"　　915 Mario Munoz Santiago Monument, de Cuba

914 Radio Operator, Satellite and Caribe Ground Station

1988. Poisonous Mushrooms. Multicoloured.

3311	1c. Type 913	10	10
3312	2c. "Amanita citrina" . . .	10	10
3313	3c. "Tylopilus felleus" . .	10	10
3314	5c. "Paxillus involutus" . .	20	10
3315	10c. "Inocybe patouillardii"	40	15

3316	30c. "Amanita muscaria"	1·00	40
3317	50c. "Hypholoma fasciculare"	1·60	70

1988. 30th Anniv of Radio Rebelde.
3318	**914** 5c. multicoloured	10	10

1988. 30th Anniv of Mario Munoz Third Front.
3319	**915** 5c. multicoloured	10	10

916 Frank Pais Memorial and Eternal Flame

917 Red Roses

1988. 30th Anniv of Frank Pais Second Eastern Front.
3320	**916** 5c. multicoloured	10	10

1988. Mothers' Day. Multicoloured.
3321	1c. Type **917**	10	10
3322	2c. Pale pink roses	10	10
3323	3c. Daisies	10	10
3324	5c. Dahlias	10	10
3325	13c. White roses	15	15
3326	35c. Carnations	50	45
3327	40c. Pink roses	60	55

918 "Gorizont" Satellite

1988. Cosmonautics Day. Multicoloured.
3328	2c. Type **918**	10	10
3329	3c. "Mir"–"Kvant" link	10	10
3330	4c. "Signo 3"	10	10
3331	5c. Mars space probe	10	10
3332	10c. "Phobos"	15	15
3333	30c. "Vega" space probe	45	40
3334	50c. Space craft	75	70

1988. Stamp Day. As T **811**. Details of mural by R. R. Radillo in Havana Stamp Museum. Mult.
3336	30c. Telegraphist and mail coach	45	40
3337	50c. Carrier pigeon	75	70

919 Storage Tanks, Products, Sugar Cane and Laboratory Equipment

1988. 25th Anniv of ICIDCA (Cuban Institute for Research on Sugarcane Byproducts).
3338	**919** 5c. multicoloured	10	10

920 Havana–Madrid, 1948

1988. Cubana Airlines Transatlantic Flights. Mult.
3339	2c. Type **920**	10	10
3340	4c. Havana–Prague, 1961	15	10
3341	5c. Havana–Berlin, 1972	20	15
3342	10c. Havana–Luanda, 1975	30	25
3343	30c. Havana–Paris, 1983	75	50
3344	50c. Havana–Moscow, 1987	1·25	90

922 Steam Train (½-size illustration)

1988. Postal Union of the Americas and Spain Colloquium on "America" Postage Stamps, Havana.
3346	**922** 20c. multicoloured	1·25	50

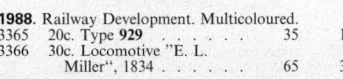

923 "Megasoma elephas"

1988. Beetles. Multicoloured.
3347	1c. Type **923**	10	10
3348	3c. "Platycoelia flavoscutellata" (vert)	20	10
3349	4c. "Plusiotis argenteola"	25	15
3350	5c. "Hetersoternus oberthuri"	30	20
3351	10c. "Odontotaenius zodiacus"	40	25
3352	35c. "Chrysophora chrysochlora" (vert)	90	75
3353	40c. "Phanaeus leander"	1·10	1·00

924 Chess Pieces

1988. Birth Centenary of Jose Capablanca (chess master). Multicoloured.
3354	30c. Type **924**	45	40
3355	40c. Juan Corzo, Capablanca and flags (1901 Cuban Championship) (horiz)	60	55
3356	50c. Emanuel Lasker and Capablanca (1921 World Championship) (horiz)	75	70
3357	1p. Checkmate in 1921 game with Lasker	1·50	1·25
3358	3p. "J. R. Capablanca" (E. Valderrama)	4·00	3·50
3359	5p. Chess pieces, flag, globe and Capablanca	6·00	5·50

925 Sun and Fortress

1988. 35th Anniv of Assault on Moncada Fortress.
3361	**925** 5c. red, yellow & black	10	10

927 Camilo Cienfuegos, and "Che" Guevara and Map

1988. 30th Anniv of Rebel Invasion Columns.
3363	**927** 5c. multicoloured	10	10

928 Emblem

1988. 30th Anniv of "Revista Internacional" (magazine).
3364	**928** 30c. multicoloured	45	40

929 Locomotive "Northumbrian", 1831

1988. Railway Development. Multicoloured.
3365	20c. Type **929**	35	15
3366	30c. Locomotive "E. L. Miller", 1834	65	30

3367	50c. "La Junta" (Cuba's first locomotive, 1840s)	1·40	55
3368	1p. Electric railcar	2·40	80
3369	2p. Russian-built M-62K diesel locomotive	4·50	1·90
3370	5p. Diesel railcar set	10·50	5·25

930 Arms and Jose de San Martin (Argentina)

1988. Latin-American History (3rd series). Mult.
3371	1c. Type **930**	10	10
3372	1c. Arms and M. A. Padilla (Bolivia)	10	10
3373	1c. 1944 10c. Discovery of America stamp	10	10
3374	1c. Arms and A. de Silva Xavier, "Tiradentes" (Brazil)	10	10
3375	1c. Arms and Bernardo O'Higgins (Chile)	10	10
3376	5c. A. Narino and arms (Colombia)	10	10
3377	5c. Arms and Jose Marti (Cuba)	10	10
3378	5c. 1944 13c. Discovery of America stamp	10	10
3379	5c. Arms and Juan Pablo Duarte (Dominican Republic)	10	10
3380	5c. Arms and Antonio Jose de Sucre (Ecuador)	10	10
3381	10c. Manuel Jose Arce and arms (El Salvador)	15	10
3382	10c. Arms and Jean Jacques Dessalines (Haiti)	15	10
3383	10c. 1944 5c. Discovery of America airmail stamp	15	10
3384	10c. Miguel Hidalgo and arms (Mexico)	15	10
3385	10c. Arms and J. Dolores Estrada (Nicaragua)	15	10
3386	20c. Jose E. Diaz and arms (Paraguay)	30	25
3387	20c. Arms and Francisco Bolognesi (Peru)	30	25
3388	20c. 1944 10c. Discovery of America airmail stamp	30	25
3389	20c. Arms and Jose Gervasio Artigas (Uruguay)	30	25
3390	20c. Simon Bolivar and arms (Venezuela)	30	25

931 Maces and Governor's Palace

1988. 20th Anniv of Havana Museum.
3391	**931** 5c. multicoloured	10	10

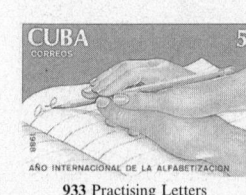

932 Ballerinas and Mute Swan

1988. 40th Anniv of National Ballet (3392) and 150th Anniv of Grand Theatre, Havana (3393). Multicoloured.
3392	5c. Type **932**	40	25
3393	5c. Theatre, 1838 and 1988	10	10

933 Practising Letters

1988. International Literacy Year.
3394	**933** 5c. multicoloured	10	10

---

934 Emblem

1988. 40th Anniv of Declaration of Human Rights.
3395	**934** 30c. multicoloured	50	45

935 Ernesto Che Guevara Plaza

1988. 30th Anniv of Battle of Santa Clara.
3396	**935** 30c. multicoloured	50	45

936 National Flag forming "30"

1989. 30th Anniv of Revolution.
3397	**936** 5c. multicoloured	10	10
3398	20c. multicoloured	30	25
3399	30c. gold, blue and red	50	45
3400	50c. gold, blue and red	80	75

937 "Pleurotus levis"

1989. Edible Mushrooms. Multicoloured.
3401	2c. Type **937**	10	10
3402	3c. "Pleurotus floridanus"	10	10
3403	5c. "Amanita caesarea"	15	10
3404	10c. "Lentinus cubensis" (horiz)	35	10
3405	40c. "Pleurotus ostreatus" (red)	1·25	60
3406	50c. "Pleurotus ostreatus" (brown)	1·40	75

939 1982 30c. Cuban Stamp

1989. 50th Anniv of Revolutionary Workers' Union.
3408	**939** 5c. multicoloured	10	10

940 "Metamorpho dido"

1989. Butterflies. Multicoloured.
3409	1c. Type **940**	10	10
3410	3c. "Callithea sapphira"	10	10
3411	5c. "Papilio zagreus"	20	10
3412	10c. "Mynes sestia"	30	15
3413	30c. "Papilio dardanus"	1·00	70
3414	50c. "Catagramma sorana"	1·75	1·2

941 Footballer　　**942** "30" and Arms

1989. World Cup Football Championship, Italy (1990).
3415	**941**	1c. multicoloured	10	10
3416		3c. multicoloured	15	10
3417		5c. multicoloured	20	15
3418		10c. multicoloured	25	20
3419		30c. multicoloured	70	60
3420		50c. multicoloured	1·00	90

DESIGNS: 3c to 50c. Various footballers.

1989. 30th Anniv of National Revolutionary Police.
3422	**942**	5c. multicoloured	10	10

943 "Zodiac" Rocket and 1934 Australian Cover

1989. Cosmonautics Day. Rocket Post (1st series). Multicoloured.
3423		1c. Type **943**	10	10
3424		3c. Rocket and cover from India to Poland, 1934	15	10
3425		5c. Rocket and 1934 English cover	20	15
3426		10c. "Icarus" rocket and 1935 Dutch cover	35	25
3427		40c. "La Douce France" rocket and 1935 French cover	85	75
3428		50c. Rocket and 1939 Cuban cover	1·00	90

See also Nos. 3516/21.

1989. Stamp Day. As T **811**. Details of mural by R. R. Radillo in Havana Stamp Museum. Mult.
3429		30c. Mail coach	50	45
3430		50c. 18th-century sailing packet	3·75	1·50

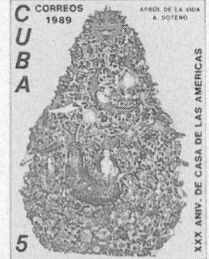

944 "Tree of Life" (A. Soteno)

1989. 30th Anniv of "House of the Americas" Museum, Havana.
3431	**944**	5c. multicoloured	10	10

946 Coded Envelope

1989. Post Codes.
3433	**946**	5c. multicoloured	10	10

...cco Flowers　　**948** Signing Decree

...Day. Perfumes and Flowers. Mult.
...7		10	10
		15	15
		20	20
		30	25

3438		30c. Jasmine	75	65
3439		50c. Orange-flower	1·10	1·00

1989. 30th Anniv of Agrarian Reform Law.
3440	**948**	5c. multicoloured	10	10

949 "40" and Headquarters Building, Moscow

1989. 40th Anniv of Council for Mutual Economic Aid.
3441	**949**	30c. multicoloured	50	45

950 Tower of Juche Idea, Pyongyang

1989. 13th World Youth and Students' Festival, Pyongyang.
3442	**950**	30c. multicoloured	50	45

952 Toco Toucan

1989. "Brasiliana '89" Stamp Exhibition. Rio de Janeiro. Birds. Multicoloured.
3444		1c. Type **952**	20	10
3445		3c. Chestnut-bellied heron	20	10
3446		5c. Scarlet ibis	30	10
3447		10c. White-winged trumpeter	50	15
3448		35c. Harpy eagle	1·90	70
3449		50c. Amazonian umbrellabird	2·40	1·10

953 "El Fenix" (galleon)

1989. Cuban Sailing Ships. Multicoloured.
3450		1c. Type **953**	10	10
3451		3c. "Triunfo" (ship of the line)	10	10
3452		5c. "El Rayo" (ship of the line)	10	10
3453		10c. "San Carlos" (ship of the line)	25	10
3454		30c. "San Jose" (ship of the line)	85	50
3455		50c. "San Genaro" (ship of the line)	1·40	85

954 Carved Stone and Men in Dugout Canoe

1989. America. Pre-Columbian Cultures. Mult.
3456		5c. Type **954**	10	10
3457		20c. Cave painters	30	25

955 Domingo F. Sarmiento and "Govenia utriculata" (Argentina)

1989. Latin American History (4th series). Multicoloured.
3458		1c. Type **955**	10	10
3459		1c. Machado de Assis and "Laelia grandis" (Brazil)	10	10
3460		1c. El Salvador 1892 1p. Columbus stamp	10	10
3461		1c. Jorge Isaacs and "Cattleya trianae" (Colombia)	10	10
3462		1c. Alejo Carpentier and "Cochleanthes discolor" (Cuba)	10	10
3463		5c. "Oxalis adenophylla" and Pablo Neruda (Chile)	10	10
3464		5c. Pedro H. Urena and "Epidendrum fragrans" (Dominican Republic)	10	10
3465		5c. El Salvador 1893 2p. City of Isabela stamp	10	10
3466		5c. Juan Montalvo and "Miltonia vexillaria" (Ecuador)	10	10
3467		5c. "Odontoglossum rossii" and Miguel A. Asturias (Guatemala)	10	10
3468		10c. "Laelia anceps" and Jose C. del Valle (Honduras)	15	10
3469		10c. "Laelia ancepes alba" and Alfonso Reyes (Mexico)	15	10
3470		10c. El Salvador 1893 5p. Columbus Statue stamp	15	10
3471		10c. "Brassavola acaulis" and Ruben Dario (Nicaragua)	15	10
3472		10c. Belisario Porras and "Pescatorea cerina" (Panama)	15	10
3473		20c. Ricardo Palma and "Coryanthes leucocorys" (Peru)	30	25
3474		20c. Eugenio Maria de Hostos and "Guzmania berteroniana" (Puerto Rico)	30	25
3475		20c. El Salvador 1893 10p. Departure from Palos stamp	30	25
3476		20c. "Cypella herbertii" and Jose E. Rodo (Uruguay)	30	25
3477		20c. "Cattleya mossiae" and Romulo Gallegos (Venezuela)	30	25

956 Cienfuegos and Flag

1989. 30th Anniv of Disappearance of Camilo Cienfuegos (revolutionary).
3478	**956**	5c. multicoloured	10	10

957 Church Tower

1989. 475th Anniv of Trinidad City.
3479	**957**	5c. multicoloured	10	10

958 "Outskirts of Niza" (E. Boudin)

1989. Paintings in National Museum. Mult.
3480		1c. "Family Scene" (Antoine Faivre)	10	10
3481		2c. "Flowers" (Emile J. H. Vernet)	10	10
3482		5c. "Judgement of Paris" (Charles Le Brun)	10	10
3483		20c. Type **958**	35	20
3484		30c. "Portrait of Sarah Bernhardt" (G. J. V. Clairin) (36 × 46 mm)	40	35
3485		50c. "Fishermen in Harbour" (C. J. Vernet)	90	60

959 Archery

1989. 11th Pan-American Games, Havana (1st issue). Multicoloured.
3486		5c. Type **959**	20	10
3487		5c. Shooting	20	10
3488		5c. Fencing	20	10
3489		5c. Cycling	20	10
3490		5c. Water polo	20	10
3491		20c. Lawn tennis (vert)	30	40
3492		30c. Swimming (vert)	80	60
3493		35c. Diving (vert)	80	70
3494		40c. Hockey	1·10	85
3495		50c. Basketball (vert)	1·25	1·00

See also Nos. 3584/93 and 3621/30.

960 Front Page

1989. Centenary of "Golden Age" (children's magazine compiled by Jose Marti).
3496	**960**	5c. blue, black and red	10	10

961 "Almendares" (paddle-steamer)

1990. 25th Anniv of Postal Museum. Mult.
3497		5c. Type **961**	15	10
3498		30c. Mail train	3·25	1·25

962 Cave Painters (½-size illustration)

1990. 50th Anniv of Speleological Society.
3499	**962**	30c. multicoloured	40	35

963 Player No. 11 and Colosseum 964 Baseball

1990. World Cup Football Championship, Italy. Multicoloured.

3500	5c. Type **963**	20	10
3501	5c. Player No. 10	20	10
3502	5c. Player No. 8	20	10
3503	10c. Goalkeeper	25	10
3504	30c. Player No. 11 and arch	60	55
3505	50c. Player	85	80

1990. Olympic Games, Barcelona (1992) (1st issue). Multicoloured.

3507	1c. Type **964**	10	10
3508	4c. Running	10	10
3509	5c. Basketball	10	10
3510	10c. Volleyball	25	10
3511	30c. Wrestling (horiz) . . .	75	50
3512	50c. Boxing	1·10	85

See also Nos. 3604/9 and 3692/7.

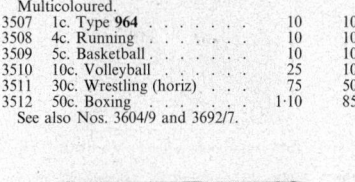

965 Tower of Babel, Dove and Globe

1990. 75th Esperanto Congress, Havana.

3514	**965** 30c. multicoloured . . .	40	35

1990. Cosmonautics Day. Rocket Post (2nd series). As T **943**. Multicoloured.

3516	1c. 1932 Austrian Cover and "U12" rocket	10	10
3517	2c. 1933 German cover, rocket and liner	10	10
3518	3c. 1934 Netherlands cover, "NRB" rocket and windmill	10	10
3519	10c. 1935 Belgian cover and rocket	15	10
3520	30c. 1935 Yugoslavian cover and "JUG1" rocket . . .	40	35
3521	50c. 1936 U.S.A. cover and rocket	65	60

1990. Stamp Day. As T **811**. Showing details of mural by R. R. Radillo in Havana Stamp Museum. Multicoloured.

3522	30c. Russian-built Type TEM-4 diesel locomotive leaving station	2·75	90
3523	50c. De Havilland Comet 1 airplane	65	60

967 Flag and Globe

1990. Centenary of Labour Day.

3524	**967** 5c. multicoloured	10	10

969 Hill and Penny Black

1990. 150th Anniv of the Penny Black. Mult.

3526	2c. Type **969**	10	10
3527	3c. Twopenny blue	10	10
3528	5c. G.B. 1855 4d. stamp . . .	10	10
3529	10c. G.B. 1847 1s. embossed stamp	15	10
3530	30c. G.B. paid hand-stamp	60	50
3531	50c. Twopenny blues on cover to Malta	85	80

970 Celia Sanchez (after O. Yanes)

1990. 70th Birth Anniv of Celia Sanchez Manduley (revolutionary).

3532	**970** 5c. multicoloured	10	10

971 Flags and Ho Chi Minh

1990. Birth Centenary of Ho Chi Minh (Vietnamese leader).

3533	**971** 50c. multicoloured . . .	65	60

972 Hogfish and Sample Analysis

1990. 25th Anniv of Oceanology Institute. Mult.

3534	5c. Type **972**	15	10
3535	30c. "Arrecife coralino" and research vessel	80	35
3536	50c. Lobster and diver collecting samples . . .	65	60

973 "Banara minutiflora" 974 Windsurfing

1990. 5th Latin American Botanical Congress. Multicoloured.

3537	3c. Type **973**	10	10
3538	5c. "Oplonia nannophylla"	20	15
3539	10c. "Jacquinia brunnescens"	25	20
3540	30c. "Rondeletia brachycarpa"	70	60
3541	50c. "Rondeletia odorata"	1·00	65

1990. Tourist Sports. Multicoloured.

3542	5c. Type **974**	20	15
3543	10c. Underwater fishing (horiz)	25	20
3544	30c. Sea fishing (horiz) . .	70	60
3545	40c. Shooting	75	65

975 "The Flute of Pan" (detail)

1990. Paintings by A. G. Menocal in National Museum. Multicoloured.

3546	5c. Type **975**	20	20
3547	20c. "Shepherd"	40	30
3548	50c. "Ganymede"	1·00	75
3549	1p. "Venus Anadiomena"	2·25	1·25

976 Great Crested Grebe

1990. "New Zealand 90" International Stamp Exhibition, Auckland. Birds. Multicoloured.

3551	2c. Type **976**	15	10
3552	3c. Weka rail	15	10
3553	5c. Kea	15	10
3554	10c. Bush wren	45	15
3555	30c. Parson bird	1·25	55
3556	50c. Tui	2·10	1·00

977 Lighthouse

1990. 8th U.N.O. Congress on Crime Prevention and Treatment of Delinquents.

3558	**977** 50c. red, blue and silver	65	60

978 Caravel and Shoreline

1990. America. The Natural World. Mult.

3559	5c. Type **978**	25	20
3560	20c. Christopher Columbus and native village . . .	75	60

979 Cameraman

1990. 40th Anniv of Cuban Television.

3561	**979** 5c. multicoloured	10	10

980 Steam Locomotive No. 1712 and Havana Railway Station

1990. 30th Anniv of Nationalization of Railways.

3562	**980** 50c. multicoloured . . .	1·50	1·10

981 Flag and Couple (Argentina)

1990. Latin-American History (5th series). Multicoloured.

3563	1c. Type **981**	10	10
3564	1c. Flag and couple (Bolivia)	10	10
3565	1c. Argentina 1892 5c. Discovery of America stamp	10	10
3566	1c. Flag and couple (Colombia)	10	10
3567	1c. Flag and couple (Costa Rica)	10	10
3568	5c. Flag and couple (Cuba)	10	10
3569	5c. Flag and couple (Chile)	10	10
3570	5c. Dominican Republic 1900 2c. Columbus stamp	10	10
3571	5c. Flag and couple (Ecuador)	10	10
3572	5c. Flag and couple (El Salvador)	10	10

3573	10c. Flag and couple (Guatemala)	15	10
3574	10c. Flag and couple (Mexico)	15	10
3575	10c. Puerto Rico 1893 3c. Discovery of America stamp	25	10
3576	10c. Flag and couple (Nicaragua)	15	10
3577	10c. Flag and couple (Panama)	15	10
3578	20c. Flag and couple (Paraguay)	30	20
3579	20c. Flag and couple (Peru)	30	20
3580	20c. El Salvador 1894 10p. Columbus stamp . . .	30	20
3581	20c. Flag and couple (Puerto Rico)	30	20
3582	20c. Flag and couple (Venezuela)	30	20

982 Player 983 Boxing

1990. 11th World Pelota Championship.

3583	**982** 30c. multicoloured . . .	45	30

1990. 11th Pan-American Games, Havana (1991) (2nd issue). As T **959**. Multicoloured.

3584	5c. Kayaking	20	10
3585	5c. Rowing	20	10
3586	5c. Yachting	30	10
3587	5c. Judo	20	10
3588	5c. Show jumping	20	10
3589	10c. Table tennis	25	20
3590	20c. Gymnastics (vert) . . .	45	30
3591	30c. Baseball (vert) . . .	65	45
3592	35c. Basketball (vert) . . .	80	45
3593	50c. Football (vert) . . .	1·25	70

1990. 16th Central American and Caribbean Games, Mexico. Multicoloured.

3594	5c. Type **983**	10	10
3595	30c. Baseball	45	30
3596	50c. Volleyball	80	45

984 "Chioides marmorosa" 986 Long Jumping

1991. Butterflies. Multicoloured.

3597	2c. Type **984**	20	10
3598	3c. "Composia fidelissima"	20	10
3599	5c. "Danaus plexippus" .	20	10
3600	10c. "Hypolimnas misippus"	40	30
3601	30c. "Hypna iphigenia" .	1·00	70
3602	50c. "Hemiargus ammon"	1·60	1·00

985 Guerra Aguiar and 1966 3c. Stamp

1991. 1st Death Anniv of Jose Guerra Aguiar (founder of Cuban Postal Museum).

3603	**985** 5c. multicoloured	10	10

1991. Olympic Games, Barcelona (1992) (2nd issue). Multicoloured.

3604	1c. Type **986**	10	10
3605	2c. Throwing the javelin .	15	10
3606	3c. Hockey	20	15
3607	5c. Weightlifting	25	20
3608	40c. Cycling	1·00	70
3609	50c. Gymnastics	1·25	80

987 Yuri Gagarin and "Vostok"

988 Statue and Flag

1991. 30th Anniv of First Man in Space. Mult.
3611	5c. Type 987	20	10
3612	10c. "Soyuz" and Y. Romanenko	25	20
3613	10c. "Salyut" space station and A. Tamayo	25	20
3614	30c. "Mir" space station (left half)	75	60
3615	30c. "Mir" space station (right half)	75	60
3616	50c. Launch of "Buran" space shuttle	1·25	1·00

Nos. 3612/13 and 3614/15 respectively were issued together, se-tenant, forming composite designs.

1991. 30th Anniversaries. Multicoloured.
3617	5c. Type 988 (proclamation of Socialism)	10	10
3618	50c. Playa Giron (invasion attempt by Cuban exiles)	1·25	55

1991. Stamp Day. Designs as T 811 showing details of mural by R. R. Radillo in Havana Stamp Museum. Multicoloured.
3619	30c. Rocket (vert)	75	60
3620	50c. Dish aerial	1·25	1·00

1991. 11th Pan-American Games, Havana (3rd series). As T 959. Multicoloured.
3621	5c. Volleyball (vert)	10	10
3622	5c. Synchronized swimming (vert)	10	10
3623	5c. Weightlifting (vert)	10	10
3624	5c. Baseball (vert)	10	10
3625	5c. Gymnastics (vert)	10	10
3626	10c. Ten-pin bowling	30	20
3627	20c. Boxing (vert)	60	40
3628	30c. Running	85	60
3629	35c. Wrestling	1·00	70
3630	50c. Judo	1·40	1·10

989 Simon Bolivar and Map

1991. 165th Anniv of Panama Congress.
3631	989	50c. multicoloured	80	45

990 Dirigible Balloon Design and Jean-Baptiste Meusnier

1991. "Espamer '91" Iberia–Latin America Stamp Exhibition, Buenos Aires. Airships. Mult.
3632	5c. Type 990	20	10
3633	10c. First steam-powered dirigible airship and Henri Giffard	30	20
3634	20c. Paul Hanlein and first airship with gas-powered motor	50	30
3635	30c. "Deutschland" (first airship with petrol motor) and Karl Wolfert	80	60
3636	50c. David Schwarz and first rigid aluminium airship	1·25	75
3637	1p. Ferdinand von Zeppelin and airship "Graf Zeppelin"	2·00	1·25

No. 3637 is inscr "Hindenburg".

992 Cayo Largo

1991. Tourism. Multicoloured.
3645	20c. Type 992	75	25
3646	20c. Varadero	60	50
3647	30c. San Carlos de la Cabana Fortress (horiz)	70	60
3648	30c. Castillo de los Tres Reyes del Morro (horiz)	70	60

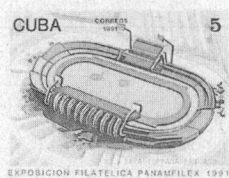
993 Stadium

1991. "Panamfilex 1991" Pan-American Stamp Exhibition. Multicoloured.
3649	5c. Type 993	20	10
3650	20c. Baragua swimming-pool complex	50	40
3651	30c. Ramon Fonst hall	85	50
3652	50c. Reynaldo Paseiro cycle-track	1·40	1·00

994 "Kataoka Dengoemon Takafusa" (Utagawa Kuniyoshi)

1991. "Phila Nippon '91" International Stamp Exhibition, Tokyo. Multicoloured.
3654	5c. Type 994	20	10
3655	10c. "Night Walk" (Hosoda Eishi)	30	20
3656	20c. "Courtesans" (Torii Kiyonaga)	50	35
3657	30c. "Conversation" (Kitagawa Utamaro)	70	60
3658	50c. "Inari-bashi Bridge" (Ando Hiroshige)	1·75	1·25
3659	1p. "On the Terrace" (Torii Kiyonaga)	2·25	1·50

996 Statue of Jose Marti

1991. 4th Cuban Communist Party Congress.
3661	996	5c. multicoloured	10	10
3662	–	50c. black, blue and red	80	45

DESIGN: 50c. Party emblem.

997 Christopher Columbus and Pinzon Brothers

1991. America. Voyages of Discovery. Mult.
3663	5c. Type 997	10	10
3664	20c. "Santa Maria", "Nina" and "Pinta"	60	20

998 Marti (after F. Martinez)

1991. Centenary of Publication of "The Simple Verses" by Jose Marti.
3665	998	50c. multicoloured	80	45

999 Julian Aguirre and Charango (Argentina)

1991. Latin-American History (6th series). Music. Multicoloured.
3666	1c. Type 999	10	10
3667	1c. Eduardo Caba and antara (pipes) (Bolivia)	10	10
3668	1c. Chile 1853 10c. stamp	10	10
3669	1c. Heitor Villalobos and trumpet with gourd resonator (Brazil)	10	10
3670	1c. Guillermo Uribe-Holguin and cununo macho (drum) (Colombia)	10	10
3671	5c. Claves (sticks) and Miguel Failde (Cuba)	20	10
3672	5c. Enrique Soro and Araucanian kultrum (Chile)	20	10
3673	5c. Chile 1903 10c. on 30c. stamp	20	10
3674	5c. Rondador (xylophone) and Segundo L. Moreno (Ecuador)	20	10
3675	5c. Marimba and Ricardo Castillo (Guatemala)	20	10
3676	10c. Vihuela and Carlos Chavez (Mexico)	30	25
3677	10c. Luis A. Delgadillo and maracas (Nicaragua)	30	25
3678	10c. Chile 1906 2c. stamp	30	25
3679	10c. Alfredo de Saint-Malo and mejorana (Panama)	30	25
3680	10c. Jose Asuncion Flores and harp (Paraguay)	30	25
3681	20c. Daniel Alomia and quena (flute) (Peru)	50	30
3682	20c. Cuatro (guitar) and Juan Morell y Campos (Puerto Rico)	50	30
3683	20c. Chile 1905 10c. stamp	50	30
3684	20c. Eduardo Fabini and tamboril (drums) (Uruguay)	50	30
3685	20c. Cuatro (guitar) and Juan V. Lecuna (Venezuela)	50	30

1000 Mascot

1991. 1st Jose Marti Pioneers Congress.
3686	1000	5p. multicoloured	10	10

1001 Toussaint L'Ouverture (revolutionary leader)

1991. Bicentenary of Haitian Revolution.
3687	1001	50c. multicoloured	80	45

1002 "35", Stars and Soldier

1991. 35th Anniversaries. Multicoloured.
3688	5c. Type 1002 (Revolutionary Armed Forces)	10	10
3689	50c. Launch "Granma" (disembarkation of revolutionary forces) (vert)	1·25	60

1003 Agramonte (after F. Martinez)

1991. 150th Birth Anniv of Ignacio Agramonte (poet).
3690	1003	5c. multicoloured	10	10

1005 Table Tennis and Plan of Montjuic Complex

1992. Olympic Games, Barcelona (3rd issue). Mult.
3692	3c. Type 1005	20	10
3693	5c. Handball and Vall d'Hebron complex	25	20
3694	10c. Shooting and Badalona complex	30	25
3695	20c. Long jumping and Montjuic complex (vert)	60	50
3696	35c. Judo and Diagonal complex	1·00	75
3697	50c. Fencing and Montjuic complex	1·40	1·00

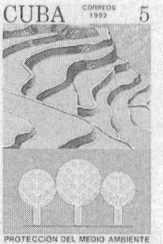
1006 Flooded Terraces and Dead Trees

1992. Environmental Protection. Mult.
3699	5c. Type 1006	10	10
3700	20c. Whale and dead fish in polluted sea	45	20
3701	35c. Satellite picture of ozone levels over Antarctica and gas mask in polluted air	60	30
3702	40c. Rainbows, globe, doves and nuclear explosion	70	40

1007 Blue Angelfish

1992. Fishes. Multicoloured.
3703	5c. Type 1007	15	10
3704	10c. Jackknife-fish	25	15
3705	20c. Blue tang	60	25
3706	30c. Sergeant-major	85	45
3707	50c. Yellow-tailed damselfish	1·50	65

1008 Boxer

1992. Dogs. Multicoloured.
3708	5c. Type **1008**	20	10
3709	10c. Great dane	25	20
3710	20c. German shepherd	60	40
3711	30c. Short-haired, long-haired and wire-haired dachshunds	1·00	70
3712	35c. Dobermann	1·25	90
3713	40c. Fox terrier	1·40	1·00
3714	50c. Poodle	1·50	1·10

1009 Badge

1992. 30th Anniv and Sixth Congress of Youth Communist League.
3716	**1009** 5c. multicoloured	10	10

1010 Jose Marti

1992. Centenary of Cuban Revolutionary Party.
3717	**1010** 5c. multicoloured	10	10
3718	50c. multicoloured	85	50

1011 Columbus Sighting Land

1992. America. 500th Anniv of Discovery of America by Columbus. Multicoloured.
3719	5c. Type **1011**	25	20
3720	20c. Columbus landing at San Salvador	75	50

1012 Alhambra, Sierra Nevada

1992. "Granada 92" International Philatelic Exhibition. Designs showing views of the Alhambra. Multicoloured.
3721	5c. Type **1012**	20	10
3722	10c. Sunset	30	20
3723	20c. Doorway and arches	60	40
3724	30c. Courtyard of the Lions	80	50
3725	35c. Bedroom	90	70
3726	50c. View of Albaicin from balcony	1·25	1·00

1013 Facade and Plate

1992. 50th Anniv of La Bodeguita del Medio (restaurant).
3727	**1013** 50c. multicoloured	85	50

1014 "Cattleya hibrida"

1992. 40th Anniv of Soroa Orchid Garden. Mult.
3728	3c. Type **1014**	20	10
3729	5c. "Phalaenopsis sp."	20	10
3730	10c. "Cattleyopsis lindenii"	30	20
3731	30c. "Bletia purpurea"	1·00	75
3732	35c. "Oncidium luridum"	1·25	1·00
3733	40c. "Vanda hibrida"	1·50	1·25

1015 Hummingbird

1992. The Bee Hummingbird. Multicoloured.
3734	5c. Type **1015**	30	15
3735	10c. Perched on twig	40	20
3736	20c. Perched on twig with flowers	90	25
3737	30c. Hovering over flower	1·40	40

1016 Guardalavaca Beach

1992. Tourism. Multicoloured.
3738	10c. Type **1016**	20	10
3739	20c. Hotel Bucanero	45	25
3740	30c. View of Havana	70	35
3741	50c. Varadero beach	1·10	65

1017 Eligio Sardinas

1992. "Olymphilex '92" International Olympic Stamps Exhibition, Barcelona. Designs showing Cuban sportsmen. Multicoloured.
3742	5c. Type **1017**	30	10
3743	35c. Ramon Fonst (fencer)	1·00	75
3744	40c. Sergio "Pipian" Martinez (cyclist)	1·10	85
3745	50c. Martin Dihigo (baseball player)	1·40	1·00

1019 Alvarez Cabral

1992. "Genova '92" International Thematic Stamp Exhibition. Explorers and their ships. Multicoloured.
3747	5c. Type **1019**	10	10
3748	10c. Alonso Pinzon	20	10
3749	20c. Alonso de Ojeda	45	25
3750	30c. Amerigo Vespucci	65	35
3751	35c. Henry the Navigator	75	40
3752	40c. Bartolomeu Dias	90	45

1020 High Jumping

1992. 6th World Athletics Cup, Havana. Mult.
3754	5c. Type **1020**	30	10
3755	20c. Throwing the javelin	60	40
3756	30c. Throwing the hammer	1·00	70
3757	40c. Long jumping (vert)	1·10	80
3758	50c. Hurdling (vert)	1·50	90

1021 Men's High Jump (Gold) and Women's Discus (Gold)

1992. Cuban Olympic Games Medal Winners. Multicoloured.
3760	5c. Type **1021**	40	20
3761	5c. Men's 4 × 400 m relay (silver) and men's discus (bronze)	40	20
3762	5c. Men's 4 × 100 m relay and women's high jump and 800 m (bronze)	40	20
3763	20c. Baseball (gold)	75	60
3764	20c. Boxing (7 gold and 2 silver)	75	60
3765	20c. Women's volleyball (gold)	75	60
3766	50c. Men's judo (bronze) and women's judo (gold, silver and 2 bronze)	1·50	1·00
3767	50c. Greco-roman (gold and 2 bronze) and freestyle (gold and bronze) wrestling	1·50	1·00
3768	50c. Fencing (silver, bronze) and weightlifting (silver)	1·50	1·00

1022 Christopher Columbus and Queen Isabella the Catholic

1992. Latin-American History (7th series). Multicoloured.
3769	1c. Type **1022**	10	10
3770	1c. Columbus at Rabida Monastery	10	10
3771	1c. Columbus presenting plans to King Ferdinand and Queen Isabella	10	10
3772	1c. Columbus before Salamanca Council	10	10
3773	1c. Departure from Palos	10	10
3774	5c. Fleet stopping off at Canary Islands	20	10
3775	5c. Columbus reassuring crew	20	10
3776	5c. Sighting of land	20	10
3777	5c. Columbus landing	20	10
3778	5c. Columbus's encounter with Amerindians	20	10
3779	10c. "Santa Maria" grounded off Hispaniola	30	20
3780	10c. Arrival of "Nina" at Palos	30	20
3781	10c. Columbus's procession through Barcelona	30	20
3782	10c. Columbus before King and Queen	30	20
3783	10c. Departure from Cadiz on second voyage	30	20
3784	20c. King and Queen welcoming Columbus	30	20
3785	20c. Fleet leaving on third voyage	55	60
3786	20c. Columbus's deportation in chains from Hispaniola	55	60
3787	20c. Fleet embarking on fourth voyage	55	60
3788	20c. Death of Columbus at Valladolid	55	60

1023 Chacon

1024 Sanctuary of Our Lady of Charity, Cobre

1992. Birth Centenary of Jose Maria Chacon y Calvo (historian).
3789	**1023** 30c. multicoloured	50	30

1992. Churches. Multicoloured.
3790	5c. Type **1024**	20	10
3791	20c. St. Mary's Church, Rosario	60	50
3792	30c. Church of the Holy Spirit, Havana	80	60
3793	50c. Guardian of the Holy Angel Church, Pena Pobre, Havana	1·25	90

1025 Diagram of Engine and Truck

1993. Development of Diesel Engine. Each showing an engine at a different stage of cycle. Multicoloured.
3794	5c. Type **1025**	10	10
3795	10c. Motor car	15	10
3796	30c. Tug	75	30
3797	40c. Diesel locomotive	2·50	1·25
3798	50c. Tractor	1·00	80

1026 Player

1993. Davis Cup Men's Team Tennis Championship. Designs showing tennis players. Multicoloured.
3800	5c. Type **1026**	25	20
3801	20c. Double-handed backhand	50	35
3802	30c. Serve	85	50
3803	35c. Stretched forehand (horiz)	90	70
3804	40c. Returning drop shot (horiz)	1·10	80

1027 Pedro Emilio Roux

1993. Scientists. Multicoloured.
3806	3c. Type **1027** (bacteriologist)	10	10
3807	5c. Carlos Finlay (biologist)	20	15
3808	10c. Ivan Petrovich Pavlov (physiologist)	30	20
3809	20c. Louis Pasteur (chemist)	60	40
3810	30c. Santiago Ramon y Cajal (histologist)	85	55
3811	35c. Sigmund Freud (psychiatrist)	1·00	70
3812	40c. Wilhelm Roentgen (physicist)	1·10	80
3813	50c. Joseph Lister (surgeon)	1·50	1·10

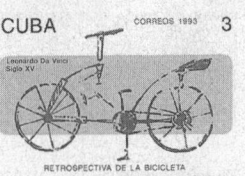

1028 Bicycle Design by Leonardo da Vinci

1993. Bicycles. Multicoloured.
3815	3c. Type **1028**	10	10
3816	5c. Draisiana hobby-horse	10	10

3817	10c. Michaux boneshaker	20	10
3818	20c. Starley penny-farthing	50	40
3819	30c. Lawson "Safety" bicycle	65	50
3820	35c. Modern bicycle	75	60

1029 "Valencian Fishwives"

1993. Paintings by Joaquin Sorolla in the National Museum. Multicoloured.

3821	3c. "Child eating Melon" (vert)	10	10
3822	5c. Type **1029**	10	10
3823	10c. "Regatta"	20	10
3824	20c. "Peasant Girl"	35	20
3825	40c. "Summertime"	70	40
3826	50c. "By the Sea"	90	50

1030 "Four Winds" and Statue of Barberan and Collar

1993. 60th Anniv of Seville (Spain)–Camaguey (Cuba) Flight by Mariano Barberan and Joaquin Collar.

3827	**1030** 30c. multicoloured	40	20

1031 Northern Jacana

1993. "Brasiliana '93" International Stamp Exhibition, Rio de Janeiro. Water Birds. Multicoloured.

3828	3c. Type **1031**	15	15
3829	5c. Great blue heron (27 × 44 mm)	15	15
3830	10c. Black-necked stilt	35	20
3831	20c. Black-crowned night heron	60	35
3832	30c. Sandhill crane (27 × 44 mm)	90	50
3833	50c. Limpkin	1·50	80

1032 Fidel Castro and Text

1993. Anniversaries. Multicoloured.

3834	5c. Type **1032** (40th anniv of publication of "History Will Absolve Me")	10	10
3835	5c. Jose Marti (140th birth anniv) and Rafael M. Mendive (vert)	10	10
3836	5c. Carlos M. de Cespedes and broken wheel (125th anniv of Yara Proclamation)	10	10
3837	5c. Moncada Barracks (40th anniv of attack on barracks)	10	10

1033 "Sedum allantoides" **1034 Devillier's Swallowtail**

1993. Cienfuegos Botanical Garden. Mult.

3838	3c. Type **1033**	10	10
3839	5c. "Heliconia caribaea"	20	10
3840	10c. "Anthurium andraeanum"	35	25
3841	20c. "Pseudobombax ellipticum"	55	40

3842	35c. "Ixora coccinea"	90	65
3843	50c. "Callistemon specious"	1·50	1·00

1993. "Bangkok 1993" International Stamp Exhibition. Butterflies. Multicoloured.

3844	3c. Type **1034**	20	10
3845	5c. Giant brimstone	25	15
3846	20c. Great southern white	60	40
3847	30c. Buckeye	85	50
3848	35c. White peacock	1·10	75
3849	50c. African monarch	1·50	1·10

1035 Greater Flamingo **1036 Simon Bolivar**

1993. America. Endangered Animals. Mult.

3850	5c. Type **1035**	50	30
3851	50c. Roseate spoonbill	75	60

1993. Latin-American Integration. Mult.

3852	50c. Type **1036**	70	50
3853	50c. Jose Marti	70	50
3854	50c. Benito Juarez	70	50
3855	50c. Che Guevara	70	50

Nos. 3852/5 were issued together, se-tenant, forming a composite design.

1037 Swimming

1993. 17th Central American and Caribbean Games, Ponce, Puerto Rico. Multicoloured.

3856	5c. Type **1037**	10	10
3857	10c. Pole vaulting	30	20
3858	20c. Boxing	50	40
3859	35c. Gymnastics (parallel bars) (vert)	75	55
3860	50c. Baseball (vert)	90	70

1038 Grajales **1039 Tchaikovsky**

1993. Death Centenary of Mariana Grajales.

3862	**1038** 5c. multicoloured	10	10

1993. Death Centenary of Pyotr Tchaikovsky (composer). Multicoloured.

3863	5c. Type **1039**	50	10
3864	20c. Ballerina in "Swan Lake"	50	35
3865	30c. Statue of Tchaikovsky	80	50
3866	50c. Tchaikovsky Museum (horiz)	1·40	1·00

1040 Flag, Dove and Broken Chains **1041 Players Challenging for Ball**

1994. 35th Anniv of Revolution.

3867	**1040** 5c. multicoloured	10	10

1994. World Cup Football Championship, U.S.A.

3868	**1041** 5c. multicoloured	20	10
3869	– 20c. multicoloured	35	20
3870	– 30c. multicoloured	50	30
3871	– 35c. multicoloured	70	45
3872	– 40c. multicoloured	75	60
3873	– 50c. multicoloured	1·00	80

DESIGNS: 20c. to 50c. Various footballing scenes.

1042 Blue Persian

1994. Cats. Multicoloured.

3875	5c. Type **1042**	10	10
3876	10c. Havana	20	15
3877	20c. Maine coon	60	40
3878	30c. British blue shorthair	90	60
3879	35c. Black and white bicolour Persian	1·10	80
3880	50c. Golden Persian	1·50	1·00

1043 Sage

1994. Medicinal Plants. Multicoloured.

3882	5c. Type **1043**	25	15
3883	10c. Aloe	25	15
3884	20c. Sunflower	75	60
3885	30c. False chamomile	1·00	80
3886	40c. Pot marigold	1·50	1·00
3887	50c. Large-leaved lime	1·75	1·25

1044 London Public Transport, 1860

1994. Carriages. Multicoloured.

3888	5c. Type **1044**	20	10
3889	10c. Coach of King Fernando VII and Maria Luisa of Spain	25	20
3890	30c. French Louis XV style coach	80	50
3891	35c. Queen Isabel II of Spain's gala-day coach	1·00	80
3892	40c. Empress Catherine II of Russia's summer carriage	1·10	1·00
3893	50c. Havana cab (68 × 27 mm)	1·40	1·10

1045 Caribbean Edible Oyster

1994. Aquaculture. Multicoloured.

3894	5c. Type **1045**	30	20
3895	20c. "Cardisoma guanhumi" (crab)	50	40
3896	30c. Red-breasted tilapia	90	70
3897	35c. "Hippospongia lachne" (sponge)	90	70
3898	40c. "Panulirus argus" (crustacean)	1·00	80
3899	50c. Common carp	1·60	1·10

1046 Ancient Greek Athletes and Olympic Flag

1994. Centenary of International Olympic Committee. Multicoloured.

3900	5c. Type **1046**	40	20
3901	30c. Olympic flag and world map in Olympic colours	1·00	75
3902	50c. Olympic flag and flame	1·75	1·25

1047 Michael Faraday (discoverer of electricity)

1994. Scientists. Multicoloured.

3903	5c. Type **1047**	20	10
3904	10c. Marie Sklodowska-Curie (co-discoverer of radium)	20	15
3905	20c. Pierre Curie (co-discoverer of radium)	50	35
3906	30c. Albert Einstein (formulated Theory of Relativity)	75	50
3907	40c. Max Planck (physicist)	1·00	75
3908	50c. Otto Hahn (chemist)	1·25	1·00

1048 "Opuntia dillenii"

1994. Cacti. Multicoloured.

3909	5c. Type **1048**	30	20
3910	10c. "Opuntia millspaughii" (vert)	35	25
3911	30c. "Leptocereus santamarinae"	1·00	70
3912	35c. "Pereskia marcanoi"	1·25	85
3913	40c. "Dendrocereus nudiflorus" (vert)	1·50	1·00
3914	50c. "Pilocereus robinii"	1·75	1·10

1050 Rough Collies

1994. Dogs. Multicoloured.

3916	5c. Type **1050**	25	15
3917	20c. American cocker spaniels	60	40
3918	30c. Dalmatians	90	60
3919	40c. Afghan hounds	1·25	90
3920	50c. English cocker spaniels	1·50	1·10

1051 "Carpilius corallinus" (crab)

1994. Cayo Largo. Multicoloured.

3921	15c. Type **1051**	50	35
3922	65c. Shore and Cayman Islands ground iguana (vert)	2·00	1·40
3923	75c. House and brown pelican	1·90	1·10
3924	1p. Fence and common green turtle	2·75	1·90

1052 Cienfuegos

1994. 35th Anniv of Disappearance of Camilo Cienfuegos (revolutionary).

3925	**1052** 15c. multicoloured	50	25

1053 Yellow-edged Grouper

1994. Caribbean Animals. Multicoloured.

3926	10c. Type **1053**	50	20
3927	15c. Spotted eagle ray (vert)	60	30
3928	15c. Sailfish	60	30
3929	15c. Greater flamingoes (vert)	45	25
3930	65c. Bottle-nosed dolphin	1·75	1·00
3931	65c. Brown pelican (vert)	1·50	1·00

1054 Douglas DC-3

1994. 50th Anniv of I.C.A.O.

3932	**1054** 65c. multicoloured . . .	1·50	70

1055 Bronze Statues of Deer

1994. 55th Anniv of Havana Zoo. Mult.

3933	15c. Type **1055**	50	30
3934	65c. Green-winged macaw	1·50	1·00
3935	75c. Eurasian goldfinch . .	1·90	1·25

1056 Boy with Stockbook

1994. 30th Anniv of Cuban Philatelic Federation.

3936	**1056** 15c. multicoloured . .	40	10

1057 Anole

1994. Reptiles. Multicoloured.

3937	15c. Type **1057**	45	20
3938	65c. Dwarf gecko	1·90	1·00
3939	75c. Curly-tailed lizard . .	2·00	1·00
3940	85c. Dwarf gecko (different)	2·25	1·10
3941	90c. Anole	2·50	1·25
3942	1p. Dwarf gecko (different)	3·00	1·40

1058 Cover and Spanish Mail Packet (18th-century sea mail)

1059 Cover of ″Postal History of Cuba″ by Jose Guerra Aguiar

1994. America. Postal Transport. Mult.

3943	15c. Type **1058**	40	20
3944	65c. Cover and messenger on horseback (19th-century rebel post) (horiz)	1·60	1·10

1995. 30th Anniv of Postal Museum.

3945	**1059** 15c. multicoloured . .	50	20

1060 Jose Marti and Flag

1995. Centenary of War of Independence.

3946	**1060** 15c. multicoloured . . .	20	10

1061 Boxing

1063 1855 Cuba and Puerto Rico ½r. Stamp

1995. 12th Pan-American Games, Mar del Plata, Argentina. Multicoloured.

3947	10c. Type **1061**	40	20
3948	15c. Weightlifting	55	30
3949	65c. Volleyball	2·50	1·00
3950	75c. Wrestling (horiz) . . .	2·50	1·00
3951	85c. Baseball (horiz) . . .	3·00	1·50
3952	90c. High jumping (horiz) .	3·00	1·50

1995. 50th Anniv of F.A.O.

3953	**1062** 75c. multicoloured . . .	1·25	50

1995. Postal Anniversaries.

3954	**1063** 15c. blue and black . .	30	10
3955	— 65c. multicoloured . .	1·25	1·00

DESIGNS: 15c. Type **1063** (140th anniv of first Cuban postage stamp); 65c. Colonial-style letterbox and letter (140th anniv of domestic postal service).

1064 Queen Angelfish

1995. 35th Anniv of National Aquarium. Mult.

3956	10c. Type **1064**	40	30
3957	15c. Shy hamlet	60	30
3958	65c. Porkfish	2·25	1·00
3959	75c. Red-spotted hawk-fish	2·50	1·10
3960	85c. French angelfish . . .	3·50	1·50
3961	90c. Blue tang	3·50	1·75

1065 Portrait of Marti and Death Scene

1995. Death Centenary of Jose Marti (revolutionary). Multicoloured.

3962	15c. Type **1065**	20	10
3963	65c. Marti and Maximo Gomez in boat . . .	85	50
3964	75c. Marti and Montecristi Declaration	95	55
3965	85c. Marti, Antonio Maceo and Gomez	1·10	65
3966	90c. Mausoleum and casket (vert)	1·10	65

1066 Maceo

1995. Centenary of Battle of Peralejo and 150th Birth Anniv of Antonio Maceo (revolutionary).

3967	**1066** 15c. multicoloured . . .	20	10

1067 Gulf Fritillary

1995. Butterflies. Multicoloured.

3968	10c. Type **1067**	15	10
3969	15c. ″Eunica tatila″	20	10
3970	65c. ″Melete salacia″ . . .	85	50
3971	75c. Cuban clearwing . .	95	55
3972	85c. Palmira sulphur . . .	1·10	65
3973	90c. Cloudless sulphur . .	1·10	65

1068 Supermarine Spitfire (Great Britain)

1995. 2nd World War Combat Planes. Mult.

3974	10c. Type **1068**	15	10
3975	15c. Ilyushin Il-2 (Russia) .	20	10
3976	65c. Curtiss P-40 (United States)	85	50
3977	75c. Messerschmitt ME-109 (Germany)	95	55
3978	85c. Morane Saulnier 406 (France)	1·10	65

1069 Lecuona

1070 Horse in Stable

1995. Birth Cent of Ernesto Lecuona (composer).

3979	**1069** 15c. multicoloured . . .	20	10

1995. ″Singapore '95″ International Stamp Exhibition. Arab Horses. Multicoloured.

3980	10c. Type **1070**	15	10
3981	15c. Two greys (horiz) . . .	20	10
3982	65c. Tethered horse . . .	85	50
3983	75c. Horse in field . . .	95	55
3984	85c. Mare and foal	1·10	65
3985	90c. Grey galloping in field	1·10	65

1072 Wrestling

1995. Olympic Games, Atlanta (1996) (1st issue). Multicoloured.

3987	10c. Type **1072**	15	10
3988	15c. Weightlifting	20	10
3989	65c. Volleyball	85	50
3990	75c. Running	95	55
3991	85c. Baseball	1·10	65
3992	90c. Judo	1·10	65

See also Nos. 4044/8.

1073 Acana Factory

1995. 400th Anniv of Sugar Production in Cuba. Paintings by Eduardo Laplante. Multicoloured.

3994	15c. Type **1073**	1·50	25
3995	65c. Manaca factory	85	50

1074 Flag and Anniversary Emblem

1995. 50th Anniv of U.N.O.

3996	**1074** 65c. multicoloured . . .	85	60

1075 Lion

1076 St. Clare of Assisi's Convent

1995. Animals from Havana Zoological Gardens. Multicoloured.

3997	10c. Type **1075**	15	10
3998	15c. Grevy's zebra (horiz) .	20	10
3999	65c. Orang-utan	85	50
4000	75c. Indian elephant (horiz)	95	55
4001	85c. Eurasian red squirrel (horiz)	1·10	65
4002	90c. Common racoon (horiz)	1·10	65

1995. 50th Anniv of U.N.E.S.C.O. World Heritage Sites. Multicoloured.

4003	65c. Type **1076**	85	50
4004	75c. St. Francis of Assisi's Monastery church	95	55

1077 ″Bletia patula″

1078 Greta Garbo

1995. Orchids. Multicoloured.

4005	40c. Type **1077**	50	30
4006	45c. ″Galeandra beyrichii″ .	60	35
4007	50c. ″Vanilla dilloniana″ . .	65	35
4008	65c. ″Macradenia lutescens″	85	50
4009	75c. ″Oncidium luridum″ .	95	55
4010	85c. ″Ionopsis utricularioides″	1·10	65

1995. Centenary of Motion Pictures. Designs showing film stars (except No. 4015). Mult.

4011	15c. Type **1078**	20	10
4012	15c. Marlene Dietrich . . .	20	10
4013	15c. Marilyn Monroe . . .	20	10
4014	15c. Charlie Chaplin . . .	20	10
4015	15c. Lumiere Brothers (inventors of cine camera)	20	10
4016	15c. Vittorio de Sica . . .	20	10
4017	15c. Humphrey Bogart . . .	20	10
4018	15c. Rita Montaner . . .	20	10
4019	15c. Cantinflas	20	10

1080 West Indian Red-bellied Woodpecker

1995. America. Environmental Protection. Mult.

4021	15c. Type **1080**	20	10
4022	65c. Cuban tody	80	45

1081 Alfonso Goulet and Francisco Crombet Ballon

1995. Death Centenaries of Generals killed during War of Independence (1st issue). Mult.

4023	15c. Type **1081**	20	10
4024	15c. Jesus Calvar, Jose Guillermo Moncada and Tomas Jordan	20	10
4025	15c. Francisco Borrero and Francisco Inchaustegui	20	10

Nos. 4023/5 were issued together, se-tenant, forming a composite design of the national flag behind the portraits.

See also Nos. 4089/91 and 4162/3.

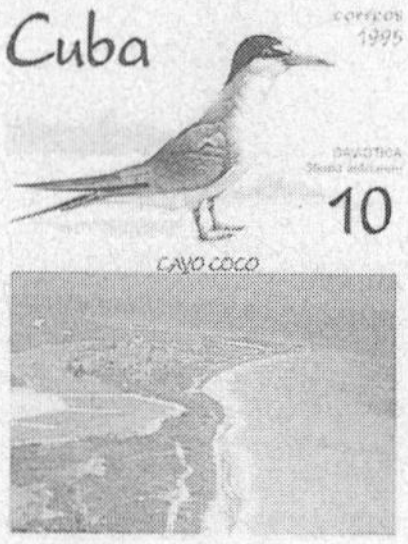

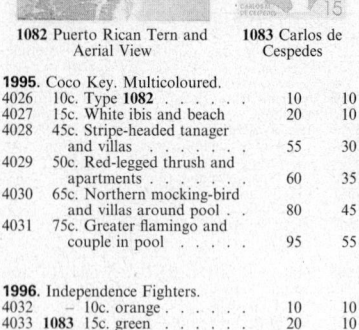

1082 Puerto Rican Tern and Aerial View

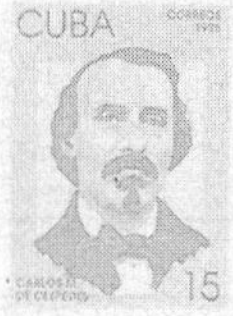

1083 Carlos de Cespedes

1995. Coco Key. Multicoloured.

4026	10c. Type **1082**	10	10
4027	15c. White ibis and beach	20	10
4028	45c. Stripe-headed tanager and villas	55	30
4029	50c. Red-legged thrush and apartments	60	35
4030	65c. Northern mocking-bird and villas around pool	80	45
4031	75c. Greater flamingo and couple in pool	95	55

1996. Independence Fighters.

4032	–	10c. orange	10	10
4033	**1083**	15c. green	20	10
4034	–	65c. blue	80	45
4035	–	75c. red	95	55
4036	–	85c. green	1·00	60
4037	–	90c. brown	1·10	65
4040	–	1p.05 mauve	1·25	75
4041	–	2p.05 brown	2·50	1·50
4042	–	3p. brown	3·75	2·25

DESIGNS: 10c. Serafin Sanchez; 65c. Jose Marti; 75c. Antonio Maceo; 85c. Juan Gualberto Gomez; 90c. Quintin Bandera; 1p.05, Ignacio Agramonte; 2p.05, Maximo Gomez; 3p. Calixto Garcia.

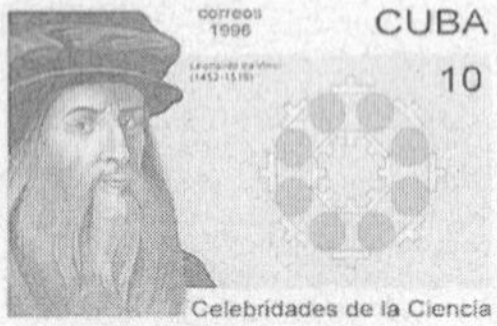

1084 Leonardo da Vinci

1996. Scientists. Multicoloured.

4046	10c. Type **1084**	10	10
4047	15c. Mikhail Lomonosov (aerodromic machines)	30	10
4048	65c. James Watt (steam engine)	1·10	60
4049	75c. Guglielmo Marconi (first radio transmitter)	1·25	75
4050	85c. Charles Darwin (theory of evolution)	1·50	85

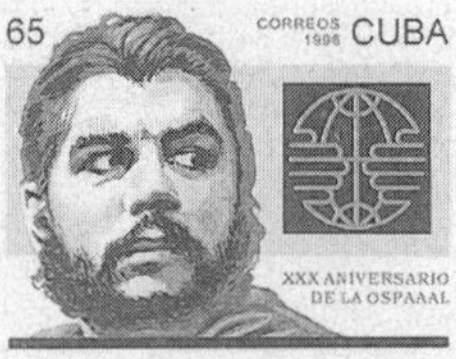

1085 "Che" Guevara and Emblem

1996. 30th Anniv of Organization of Solidarity of Peoples of Africa, Asia and Latin America.

4051	**1085** 65c. multicoloured	80	45

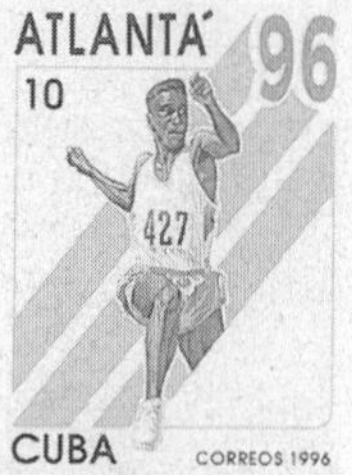

1086 Athletics

1996. Olympic Games, Atlanta (2nd issue). Multicoloured.

4052	10c. Type **1086**	10	10
4053	15c. Weightlifting	20	10
4054	65c. Judo	80	45
4055	75c. Wrestling (horiz)	95	55
4056	85c. Boxing (horiz)	1·10	65

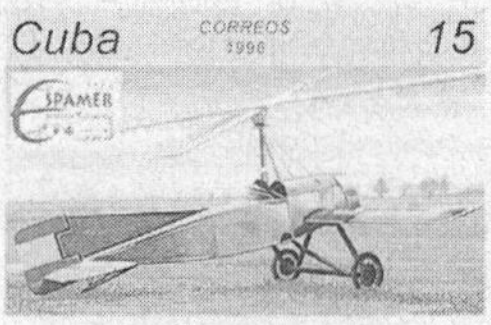

1087 Cierva C.4 Autogyro

1996. "Espamer" Spanish–Latin American and "Aviation and Space" Stamp Exhibitions, Seville, Spain. Multicoloured.

4058	15c. Type **1087**	20	10
4059	65c.35 2-L airplane	80	45
4060	75c. C-201 Alcotan airplane	95	55
4061	85c. CASA C-212 Aviocar	1·10	65

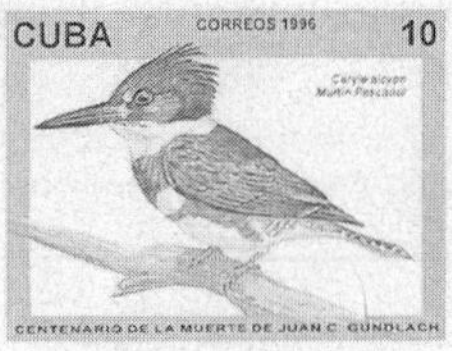

1088 Belted Kingfisher

1996. Death Centenary of Juan Gundlach (ornithologist). Birds. Multicoloured.

4063	10c. Type **1088**	10	10
4064	15c. American redstart	20	10
4065	65c. Yellowthroat	80	45
4066	75c. Painted bunting	95	55
4067	85c. Cedar waxwing	1·10	65

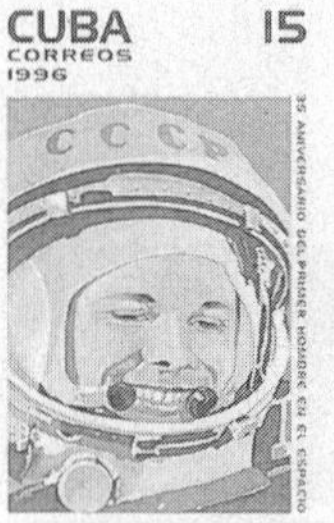

1089 Yuri Gagarin (cosmonaut)

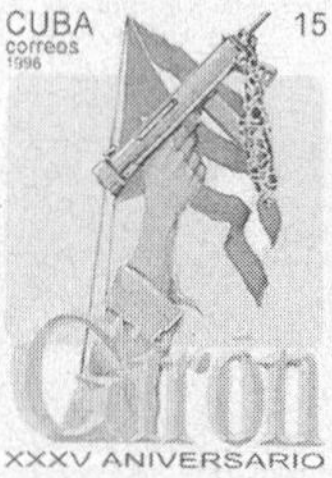

1090 National Flag and Hand holding Gun

1996. 35th Anniv of First Man in Space. Mult.

4069	15c. Type **1089**	20	10
4070	65c. Globes and "Vostok I" (spaceship) (horiz)	80	45

1996. 35th Anniversaries. Multicoloured.

4071	15c. Type **1090** (victory at Giron)	20	10
4072	65c. Flags and "35" (Declaration of Socialist character of the Revolution)	80	45

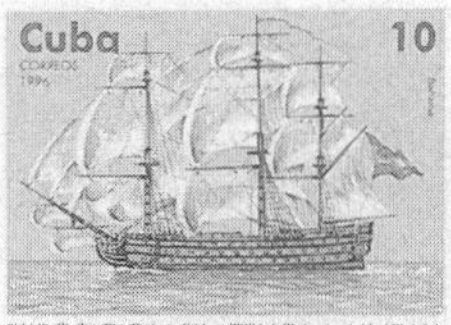

1091 "Bahama"

1996. "CAPEX'96" International Stamp Exhibition, Toronto, Canada. 18th-century Ships of the Line built in Cuban Yards. Multicoloured.

4073	10c. Type **1091**	10	10
4074	15c. "Santissima Trinidad"	20	10
4075	65c. "Principe de Asturias"	80	45
4076	75c. "San Pedro de Alcantara"	95	55
4077	85c. "Santa Ana"	1·10	65

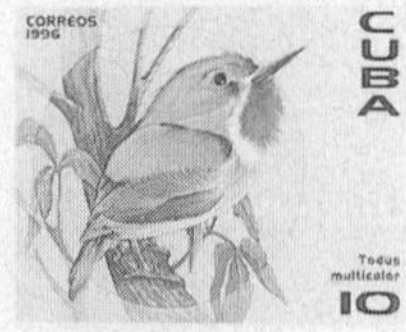

1092 Cuban Tody

1996. Caribbean Animals. Multicoloured.

4079	10c. Type **1092**	10	10
4080	15c. Purple-throated carib ("Eulampis jugularis")	20	10
4081	15c. Wood duck ("Aix sponsa")	20	10
4082	15c. Spot-finned butterflyfish	20	10
4083	65c. "Popilio cresphontes" (butterfly)	80	45
4084	65c. Indigo hamlet	80	45

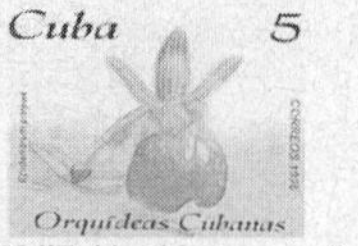

1093 "Epidendrum porpax"

1996. Orchids. Multicoloured.

4085	5c. Type **1093**	10	10
4086	10c. "Cyrtopodlium punctatum"	15	10
4087	15c. "Polyrrhiza lindeni"	20	10

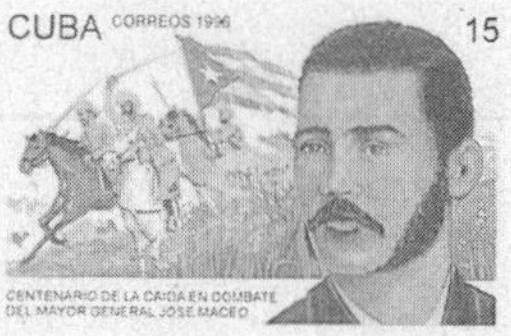

1094 Charging into Battle and Maceo

1996. Death Cent of General Jose Maceo.

4088	**1094** 15c. multicoloured	20	10

1996. Death Centenaries of Generals killed during War of Independence (2nd issue). As T **1081**. Multicoloured.

4089	15c. Esteban Tamayo and Angel Guerra	20	10
4090	15c. Juan Fernandez Ruz, Jose Maria Aguirre and Serafin Sanchez	20	10
4091	15c. Juan Bruno Zayas and Pedro Vargas Sotomayor	20	10

Nos. 4089/91 were issued together, se-tenant, forming a composite design.

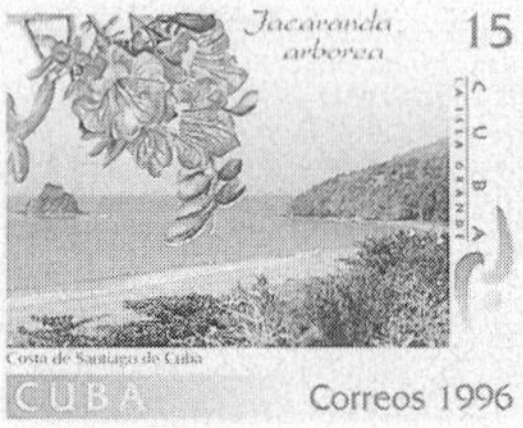

1095 "Jacaranda arborea" and Coast, Santiago de Cuba

1996. Tourism and Flowers. Multicoloured.

4092	15c. Type **1095**	20	10
4093	65c. "Begonia bissei" and San Pedro de la Roca Fort	1·25	45
4094	75c. "Byrsonima crassifolia" and Baconao Park, Santiago de Cuba (vert)	95	55
4095	85c. "Pereskia zinniiflora" and Sanctuary, Cobre (vert)	1·10	65

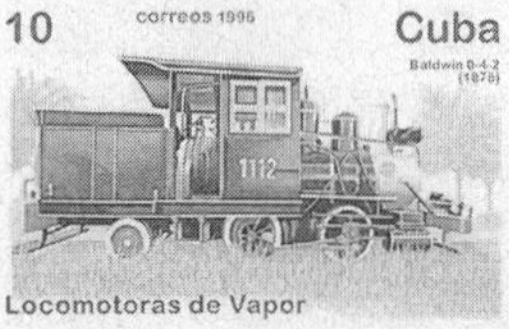

1096 Baldwin Locomotive No. 1112, 1878

1996. Steam Railway Locomotives. Mult.

4096	10c. Type **1096**	10	10
4097	15c. American locomotive No. 1302, 1904	20	10
4098	65c. Baldwin locomotive No. 1535, 1906	80	45
4099	75c. Rogers locomotive, 1914	95	55
4100	90c. Baldwin locomotive, 1920	1·25	75

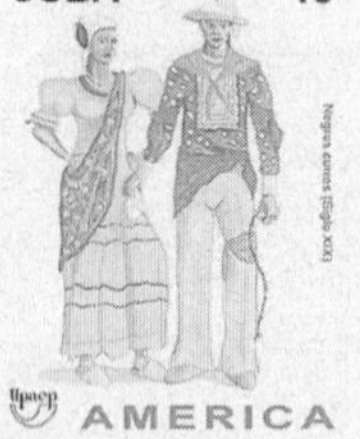

1097 Free Negroes, 19th-century

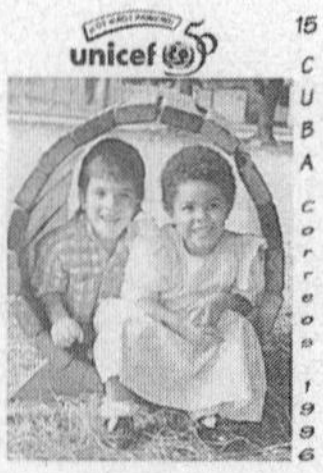

1098 Children

1996. America. Costumes. Multicoloured.

4101	15c. Type **1097**	20	10
4102	65c. Guayabera couple, 20th-century	80	45

1996. 50th Anniv of U.N.I.C.E.F.

4103	**1098** 15c. multicoloured	20	10

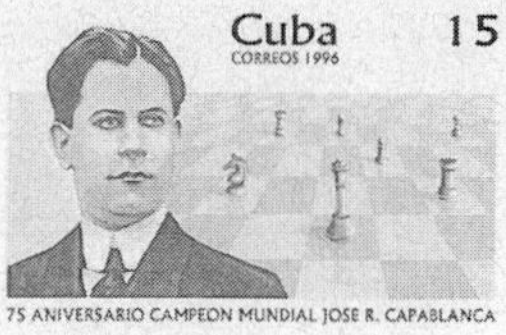

1099 Capablanca and Pieces

1996. 75th Anniv of Jose Raul Capablanca's First World Championship Victory. Mult.

4104	15c. Type **1099**	20	10
4105	65c. Capablanca and tournament	80	45
4106	75c. Globe on king and Capablanca	95	55
4107	85c. Capablanca as boy playing chess	1·00	60
4108	90c. Capablanca playing in tournament	1·25	75

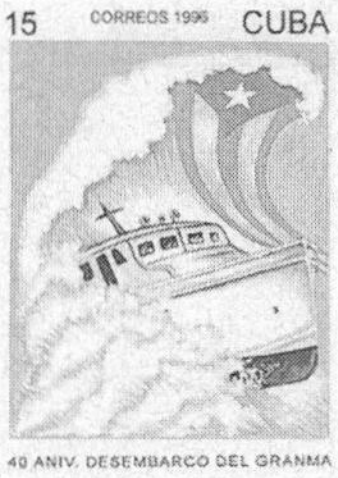

1100 Flag and "Granma"

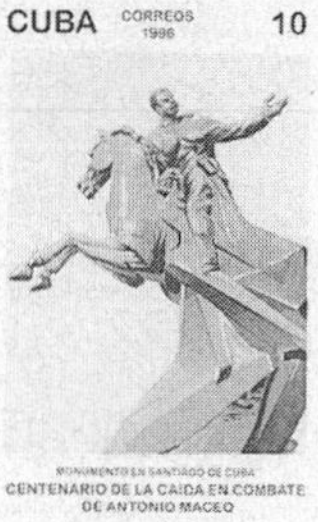

1101 Monument, Santiago de Cuba

1996. 40th Anniversaries of "Granma" Landings (15c.) and Revolutionary Armed Forces (65c.). Multicoloured.

4109	15c. Type **1100**	30	10
4110	65c. "40", flag and soldier with rifle	1·25	75

1996. Death Centenary of General Antonio Maceo. Multicoloured.

4111	10c. Type **1101**	10	10
4112	15c. Maceo	25	15
4113	15c. Memorial of Maceo's disembarkation, Duaba (horiz)	25	15
4114	65c. "Fall of Antonio Maceo" (detail, A. Menocal) (horiz)	1·25	75
4115	75c. Maceo, Panchito Gomez Toro and monument, San Pedro (horiz)	1·50	90

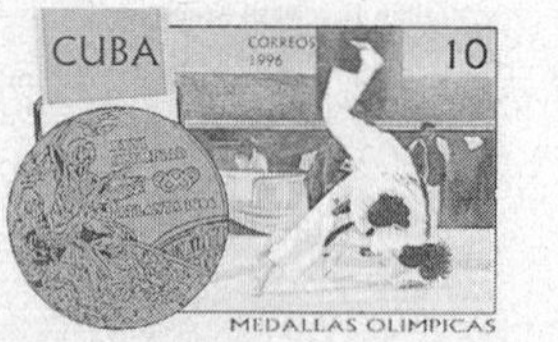

1102 Women's Judo and Gold Medal (Driulis Gonzalez)

1996. Cuban Medal Winners at Olympic Games, Atlanta. Multicoloured.

4116	10c. Type **1102**	15	10
4117	10c. Freestyle wrestling and bronze medal	15	10
4118	15c. Weightlifting and gold medal (Pablo Lara)	25	15
4119	15c. Greco-Roman wrestling and gold medal (Feliberto Aguilera)	25	15
4120	15c. Fencing and silver medal	25	15
4121	15c. Swimming and silver medal	25	15
4122	65c. Women's volleyball and gold medal	1·25	75
4123	65c. Boxing and gold medal (Maikro Romero, Hector Vinent, Ariel Hernandez and Felix Savon)	1·25	75
4124	65c. Women's running and silver medal	1·25	75
4125	65c. Baseball and gold medal	1·25	75

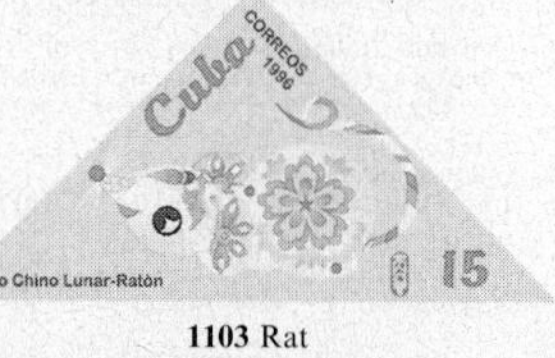

1103 Rat

1996. Chinese New Year. Year of the Rat.

4126	**1103** 15c. multicoloured	40	20

1104 Minho Douro, Portugal

1996. "Espamer '98" Spanish–Latin American Stamp Exhibition, Havana. Railway Locomotives. Multicoloured.

4127	15c. Type **1104**	25	15
4128	65c. Vulcan Iron Works, Brazil	1·25	75
4129	65c. Baldwin, Dominican Republic	1·25	75
4130	65c. Alco, Panama	1·25	75
4131	65c. Baldwin, Puerto Rico	1·25	75
4132	65c. Slaughter Gruning Co, Spain	1·25	75
4133	75c. Yorkshire Engine Co, Argentine Republic . . .	1·40	80
4134	75c. Porter, Chile	1·40	80
4135	75c. Locomotive, Paraguay	1·40	80
4136	75c. Locomotive No. 12, Mexico	1·40	80

1105 Seal-point Siamese   **1107** Dromedary

Centenario del Cine Cubano
1106 "Romance del Palmar", 1938

1997. "Hong Kong '97" International Stamp Exhibition. Cats. Multicoloured.

4138	10c. Type **1105**	10	10
4139	15c. Burmese	25	15
4140	15c. Japanese bobtail (horiz)	25	15
4141	65c. Singapura (horiz) . . .	1·25	75
4142	75c. Korat (horiz)	1·40	80

1997. Centenary of Cuban Films. Mult.

4144	15c. Type **1106**	25	15
4145	65c. "Memorias del Subdesarrollo", 1968 (vert)	1·25	75

1997. Zoo Animals. Multicoloured.

4146	10c. Type **1107**	20	10
4147	15c. White rhinoceros . . .	40	15
4148	15c. Giant panda	40	15
4149	75c. Orang-utan	1·75	1·10
4150	90c. European bison	2·00	1·25

1108 Ox

1997. Chinese New Year. Year of the Ox.

4151	**1108** 15c. multicoloured . .	60	20

1109 Menelao Mora and Palace

1997. 40th Anniv of Attack on Presidential Palace.

4152	**1109** 15c. multicoloured . . .	25	15

COPA MUNDIAL DE FUTBOL. FRANCIA '98
1110 Players

1997. World Cup Football Championship, France (1998).

4153	**1110** 10c. multicoloured . . .	20	10
4154	– 15c. multicoloured (red face value)	40	15
4155	– 15c. multicoloured (mauve face value)	40	15
4156	– 65c. multicoloured . . .	1·60	1·00
4157	– 75c. multicoloured . . .	1·75	1·10

DESIGNS: 15c. to 75c. Footballers (different).

1111 Youths with Flags and Emblem

1997. 35th Anniv of Communist Youth Union.

4159	**1111** 15c. multicoloured . . .	25	15

1112 "Caledonia"

1997. Stamp Day. Postal Services. Mult.

4160	15c. Type **1112** (170th anniv of maritime service) . .	45	15
4161	65c. Fokker F.10A Super Trimotor airplane (70th anniv of international airmail)	1·25	75

1113 Adolfo del Castillo and Enrique del Junco Cruz-Munoz

1997. Death Centenaries of Generals killed during War of Independence (3rd issue).

4162	15c. Type **1113**	25	15
4163	15c. Alberto Rodriguez Acosta and Mariano Sanchez Vaillant	25	15

Nos. 4162/3 were issued together, se-tenant, forming a composite design.

Mariposas Cubanas
1114 Black-bordered Orange

1997. Butterflies. Multicoloured.

4164	10c. Type **1114**	20	10
4165	15c. Bush sulphur ("Eurema dina")	40	15
4166	15c. Zebra ("Colobura dirce")	40	15
4167	65c. Red admiral	1·50	1·00
4168	85c. "Kricogonia castalia" .	1·75	1·00

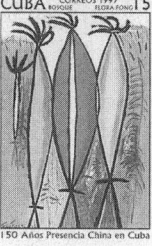

1115 Luperon   **1116** Royal Palms

1997. Death Cent of Gen Gregorio Luperon.

4169	**1115** 65c. multicoloured . . .	1·25	75

1997. 150th Anniv of Chinese Presence in Cuba.

4170	**1116** 15c. multicoloured . . .	80	35

1117 National Flag and United Nations Emblem

1997. 50th Anniv of Cuban United Nations Association.

4171	**1117** 65c. multicoloured . . .	1·50	75

1118 Rainbow and Dove holding Olive Branch

1997. 14th World Youth and Students Festival, Cuba. Multicoloured.

4172	10c. Type **1118**	15	10
4173	15c. "Alma Mater" (statue)	25	15
4174	15c. Children on play apparatus (vert)	25	15
4175	65c. Che Guevara	1·25	75
4176	75c. Statue and tower . . .	1·40	80

1119 Pharos of Alexandria

1997. Seven Wonders of the Ancient World. Mult.

4177	10c. Type **1119**	25	10
4178	15c. Egyptian pyramids . .	25	15
4179	15c. Hanging Gardens of Babylon	25	15
4180	15c. Colossus of Rhodes . .	30	15
4181	65c. Mausoleum of Halicarnassus	1·25	75
4182	65c. Statue of Zeus at Olympia	1·25	75
4183	75c. Temple of Artemis at Ephesus	1·40	80

1120 Pais and Testamonial of Fidel Castro

1997. 40th Death Anniv of Frank Pais (revolutionary).

4184	**1120** 15c. multicoloured . . .	25	15

1121 Mahatma Gandhi, Indian Flag and State Arms   **1122** Saffron Finch ("Sicalis flaveola")

1997. 50th Anniv of Indian Independence.

4185	**1121** 15c. multicoloured . . .	25	15

1997. Birds of the Caribbean. Multicoloured.

4186	15c. Type **1122**	25	15
4187	15c. Red-headed barbet ("Eubucco bourcierii") . .	25	15
4188	15c. Cuban Amazon ("Amazona leucocephala")	25	15
4189	15c. Blue-crowned trogon ("Trogon curucui") . . .	25	15
4190	65c. Blue-throated goldentail ("Hylocharis eliciae") . .	1·25	75
4191	65c. Yellow-crowned Amazon ("Amazona ochrocephala")	1·25	75
4192	75c. Goldfinch	1·40	80

1123 Franz Liszt and Memorial Stone commemorating his first Concert when Aged Nine

1997. Composers. Multicoloured.

4193	10c. Type **1123**	30	15
4194	15c. Johann Sebastian Bach and original manuscript score of Sonata in G minor for violin	35	20
4195	15c. Frederic Chopin and birthplace, Zelazowa Wola, Poland	35	20
4196	15c. Ludwig van Beethoven and Karntnerther Theatre where he presented the Ninth Symphony Mass in D major	35	20
4197	65c. Ignacio Cervantes and detail of score of "La Solitaria" (dance) . . .	1·25	75
4198	75c. Wolfgang Amadeus Mozart and detail of score of first attempt at choral composition . . .	1·40	80

1124 Cuban Solitaire and Valle de Vinales

1997. Tourism. Multicoloured.

4199	10c. Type **1124**	30	15
4200	15c. Cuban crow and Cape Jutia	35	20
4201	65c. Olive-caped warbler and Soroa Falls (vert) . .	1·25	75
4202	75c. Giant kingbird and San Juan River (vert)	1·40	80

1125 "Hibiscus elatus" ("Majagua")

1997. Caribbean Flowers. Multicoloured.

4203	15c. Type **1125**	35	20
4204	15c. Rose periwinkle ("Vicaria")	35	20
4205	15c. Geiger tree ("Vomitel")	35	20
4206	15c. Bur marigold ("Romerillo")	35	20
4207	65c. Minnie root ("Salta perico")	1·25	75
4208	75c. Marilope	1·40	80

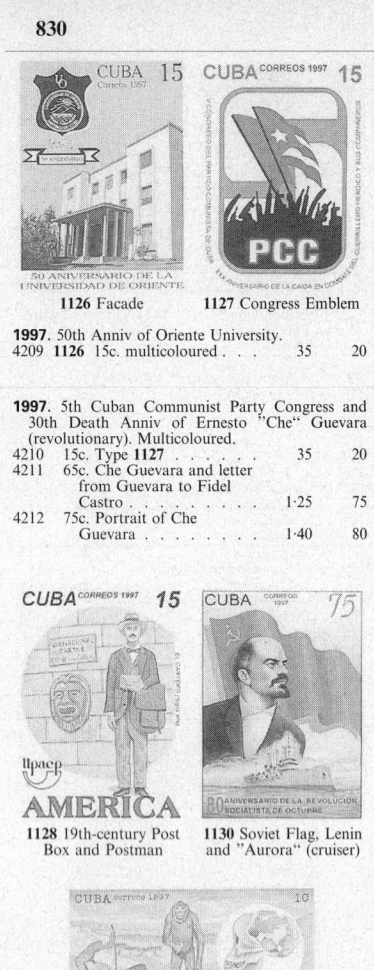

1126 Facade   **1127** Congress Emblem

1997. 50th Anniv of Oriente University.
4209	**1126**	15c. multicoloured	. . .	35	20

1997. 5th Cuban Communist Party Congress and 30th Death Anniv of Ernesto "Che" Guevara (revolutionary). Multicoloured.
4210	15c. Type **1127**	35	20
4211	65c. Che Guevara and letter from Guevara to Fidel Castro	1·25	75
4212	75c. Portrait of Che Guevara	1·40	80

1128 19th-century Post Box and Postman   **1130** Soviet Flag, Lenin and "Aurora" (cruiser)

1129 Australopithecus, South Africa

1997. America. The Postman. Multicoloured.
4213	15c. Type **1128**	35	20
4214	65c. 20th-century post boxes and postman	1·25	75

1997. Prehistoric Man. Multicoloured.
4215	10c. Type **1129**	30	15
4216	15c. Pithecanthropus, Java	35	20
4217	15c. Sinanthropus, China	35	20
4218	15c. Neanderthal man	35	20
4219	65c. Cro-Magnon man	1·25	75
4220	75c. Oberkassel man, Germany	1·40	80

1997. 80th Anniv of Russian Revolution.
4221	**1130**	75c. multicoloured	. . .	2·40	80

1131 "John Bull", 1831

1997. Railway Locomotives. Multicoloured.
4222	10c. Type **1131**	20	10
4223	15c. Baldwin steam locomotive, 1910–13	30	15
4224	15c. Locomotive "Old Ironsides", 1832, U.S.A.	30	15
4225	65c. Russian-built Type TEM-4.1 diesel locomotive, 1970	1·25	75
4226	75c. Russian-built Type TE-114k diesel locomotive, 1975	1·40	80

No. 4222 is inscribed "1830".

1132 National Flag and Capitol, Havana

1997. 50th Anniv of U.N. Conference on Trade and Employment, Havana.
4227	**1132**	65c. multicoloured	. . .	1·25	75

1133 Garcia and 1970 30c. Stamp

1997. Birth Centenary of Victor Manuel Garcia (painter).
4228	**1133**	15c. multicoloured	. . .	35	20

1134 Havana Cathedral and Pope John Paul II

1998. Papal Visit. Multicoloured.
4229	65c. Type **1134**	1·25	75
4230	75c. Our Lady of Charity Cathedral (vert)	1·40	80

1135 Menendez   **1136** Players

1998. 50th Death Anniv of Jesus Menendez (labour leader).
4232	**1135**	15c. multicoloured	. . .	35	20

1998. World Cup Football Championship, France. Multicoloured.
4233	10c. Type **1136**	30	15
4234	15c. Player in purple shirt lying on ground and player in red and white stripes	40	30
4235	15c. Player in yellow and black strip	50	40
4236	65c. Player in blue shirt tackling player in red and white strip (horiz)	1·50	1·00
4237	65c. Player in red and blue strip fending off player in light blue strip (horiz)	1·50	1·00

1137 Isabel Rubio Diaz   **1138** Revee

1998. Death Centenary of Captain Isabel Rubio Diaz (founder of mobile military hospital during War of Independence).
4239	**1137**	15c. multicoloured	. . .	35	20

1998. Death Centenary of Brigadier General Vidal Ducasse Revee (revolutionary).
4240	**1138**	15c. multicoloured	. . .	35	20

1139 Radio Operator and Che Guevara

1998. Communicators' Day. 40th Anniv of Radio Rebelde.
4241	**1139**	15c. multicoloured	. . .	35	20

1140 Shand Mason & Co Horse-drawn Fire Engine, 1901 (Havana)

1998. Fire Engines. Multicoloured.
4242	10c. Type **1140**	30	15
4243	15c. Horse-drawn personnel and equipment vehicle, 1905 (Havana Municipal Service)	50	20
4244	15c. American–French Fire Engine Co vehicle, 1921 (Guanabacoa)	50	20
4245	65c. Chevrolet 6400 fire engine, 1952 (used throughout Cuba)	1·50	75
4246	75c. American–French–Foamite Co fire engine, 1956 (Havana)	1·75	80

1141 Monument and Antonio Maceo (revolutionary)

1998. 120th Anniv of Baragua Protest (against slavery).
4247	**1141**	15c. multicoloured	. . .	35	20

1142 Flags, Soldiers and Tank   **1143** Tiger

1998. 10th Anniv of Victory of Angolan Government and Cuban Forces in Defence of Cuito Cuanavale, Angola.
4248	**1142**	15c. multicoloured	. . .	35	20

1998. Chinese New Year. Year of the Tiger.
4249	**1143**	15c. multicoloured	. . .	75	40

1144 Chihuahua ("Tatiana Vasti de Nino Angelo")

1998. Champion Dogs. Multicoloured.
4250	10c. Type **1144**	30	15
4251	15c. Beagle ("Danco")	40	20
4252	15c. Mexican naked hound ("Xolot del Mictlan")	40	20
4253	65c. German spaniel ("D'Milican Nalut Aiwa")	1·40	80
4254	75c. Chow-chow ("Yoki II")	1·50	90

1145 Ancestor of Chimpanzee

1998. Evolution of the Chimpanzee. Multicoloured.
4255	10c. Type **1145**	30	15
4256	15c. Head and skull of "Pan troglodytes blumenbach"	40	20
4257	15c. Chimpanzee and hand and foot	40	20

4258	65c. Mother with infant and new-born chimp	1·40	80
4259	75c. On branch and distribution map	1·50	90

1147 Skate

1998. Deep Sea Fishes. Multicoloured.
4261	15c. Type **1147**	40	20
4262	15c. Gulper ("Eurypharynx pelecanoides")	40	20
4263	65c. "Caulophryne" sp.	1·50	80
4264	75c. Sloan's viperfish	1·60	95

1148 Garcia Lorca

1998. Birth Cent of Federico Garcia Lorca (poet).
4265	**1148**	75c. multicoloured	. . .	1·60	95

1149 Crab   **1150** Diana, Princess of Wales

1998. International Year of the Ocean. Mult.
4266	65c. Type **1149**	1·40	80
4267	65c. Fishes	1·40	80

1998. Diana, Princess of Wales Commemoration. Multicoloured.
4268	10c. Type **1150**	30	15
4269	10c. Wearing patterned dress	30	15
4270	10c. Wearing yellow and pink jacket	30	15
4271	15c. Wearing checked jacket	40	20
4272	15c. Wearing red jacket	40	30
4273	65c. Wearing white jacket	1·40	80
4274	75c. Wearing purple jacket	1·50	90

1151 Abel Santamaria

1998. 45th Anniv of Attack on Moncada Barracks. Multicoloured.
4275	15c. Type **1151**	40	30
4276	65c. Jose Marti	1·40	80

1152 The Crystal Palace, London (Great Exhbition, 1851)

1998. "Expo 2000" World's Fair, Hanover, Germany.
4277	**1152**	15c. multicoloured	. . .	40	20
4278	–	15c. multicoloured	. . .	40	20
4279	–	15c. multicoloured	. . .	40	20
4280	–	15c. black, red & yellow	. . .	40	20
4281	–	65c. multicoloured	. . .	1·40	80
4282	–	75c. multicoloured	. . .	1·50	90

DESIGNS:—HORIZ: No. 4277, Type **1152**; 4278, Atomium, Brussels (International Exhibition, 1958); 4280, Map and flag of Germany; 4282, Twipsy (mascot) on globe and fireworks. VERT: No. 4279, Twipsy; 4281, Eiffel Tower, Paris (Exhibition, 1889).

1153 Baseball

1998. 18th Central American and Caribbean Games, Maracaibo, Venezuela.
4283 **1153** 15c. multicoloured . . .   30   15

1154 Kim Il Sung and Pyongyang Landmarks

1998. 50th Anniv of Korean People's Democratic Republic (North Korea).
4284 **1154** 75c. multicoloured . . .   1·50   90

1155 Japanese Bust

1998. Cent of First Japanese Immigrant to Cuba.
4285 **1155** 75c. multicoloured . . .   1·50   90

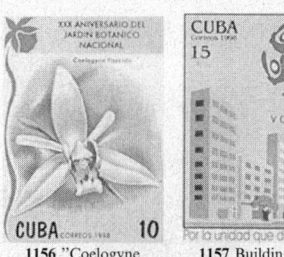

1156 "Coelogyne   **1157** Buildings and
flaccida"   Emblem

1998. 30th Anniv of National Botanical Garden. Orchids. Multicoloured.
4286 10c. Type **1156**   40   20
4287 15c. "Dendrobium
       fimbriatum"   40   20
4288 15c. Bamboo orchid
       ("Arundina graminifolia") .   40   20
4289 65c. "Bletia patula" . . . .   1·40   80
4290 65c. Nun's orchid ("Phaius
       tankervilliaea") . . . . .   1·40   80

1998. 5th Congress of Revolution Defence Committees.
4291 **1157** 15c. multicoloured . . .   30   15

1158 Knight Anole and Archway, Gibara

1998. World Tourism Day. Views of Holguin. Multicoloured.
4292 10c. Type **1158**   30   15
4293 15c. Water lizard, Mirador
       de Mayabe   40   20
4294 65c. Water chameleon,
       Guardalavaca Beach
       (horiz) . . . .   1·40   80
4295 75c. Stone lizard, Pinares de
       Mayari (horiz) . . . . .   1·50   90

1159 Bernarda Toro   **1160** Two Conures
(Manana)

1998. America. Famous Women. Independence Activists. Multicoloured.
4296 65c. Type **1159** . . . . . .   1·40   80
4297 75c. Maria Cabrales . . . .   1·50   90

1998. The Cuban Conure. Multicoloured.
4298 10c. Type **1160**   30   15
4299 15c. Head of conure   40   20
4300 65c. Conure on branch . . .   1·40   80
4301 75c. Conure and leaves . . .   1·50   90

1161 "Swan Lake"

1998. 50th Anniv of Cuban National Ballet.
4302 **1161** 15c. blue   40   20
4303 —   65c. multicoloured . . .   1·40   80
DESIGN: 65c. "Giselle".

1162 Apartment Building on O'Farrill and Goicuria Streets, Havana, and Victims

1998. 40th Death Anniv of Rogelia Perea, Angel Ameijeiras and Pedro Gutierrez (revolutionaries).
4304 **1162** 15c. multicoloured . . .   30   15

1163 Capt. Braulio Coroneaux (revolutionary) and Tank

1998. 40th Anniv of Battle of Guisa.
4305 **1163** 15c. multicoloured . . .   30   15

1164 Family holding   **1165** Garca Iniguez
Hands and United
Nations Emblem

1998. 50th Anniv of Universal Declaration of Human Rights.
4306 **1164** 65c. multicoloured . . .   1·40   80

1998. Death Centenary of Major-General Calixto Garca Iniguez (independence fighter).
4307 **1165** 65c. multicoloured . . .   1·40   80

1166 Varela and San Carlos Seminary, Havana

1998. 145th Death Anniv of Felix Varela (philosopher and Vicar-General of New York).
4308 **1166** 75c. multicoloured . . .   1·50   90

1167 Carlos Manuel de Cespedes

1998. Cent of Cuban War of Independence. Mult.
4309 15c. Type **1167**   40   20
4310 15c. Ignacio Agramonte
       Loynaz   40   20
4311 15c. Maximo Gomez Baez . .   40   20
4312 15c. Jose Maceo Grajales . .   40   20
4313 15c. Salvador Cisneros
       Betancourt   40   20
4314 15c. Calixto Garcia Iniguez .   40   20
4315 15c. Adolfo Flor Crombet . .   40   20
4316 15c. Serafin Sanchez
       Valdivia   40   20
4317 65c. Jose Marti Perez . . .   1·40   80
4318 75c. Antonio Maceo
       Grajales . . . . . .   1·50   90

1168 Revolutionaries and Map

1998. 40th Anniv of Capture of Palma Soriano by Revolutionaries.
4319 **1168** 15c. multicoloured . . .   30   15

1169 "Granma" Landings

1999. 40th Anniv of Revolution. Multicoloured.
4320 65c. Type **1169** . . . . . .   1·40   80
4321 65c. Camilo Cienfuegos and
       Fidel Castro . . . . .   1·40   80
4322 65c. Castro and white doves   1·40   80

1170 Police Car and Motor Cycle

1999. 40th Anniv of National Revolutionary Police.
4323 **1170** 15c. multicoloured . . .   30   15

1171 Workers' Rally   **1172** Rabbit

1999. 60th Anniv of Revolutionary Workers' Union.
4324 **1171** 15c. multicoloured . . .   30   15

1999. Chinese New Year. Year of the Rabbit.
4325 **1172** 75c. multicoloured . . .   1·40   80

1173 Lenin

1999. 75th Death Anniv of Vladimir Ilich Lenin (Russian statesman).
4326 **1173** 75c. multicoloured . . .   1·40   80

1174 Ornithosuchus

1999. Prehistoric Animals. Multicoloured.
4327 10c. Type **1174**   30   15
4328 15c. Bactrosaurus   40   20
4329 15c. Saltopus   40   20
4330 65c. Protosuchus . . . . .   1·40   80
4331 75c. Mussaurus . . . . . .   1·50   90

1175 Damaso Perez Prado

1999. Cuban Musicians. Multicoloured.
4332 5c. Type **1175**   15   10
4333 15c. Benny More   40   20
4334 15c. Chano Pozo   40   20
4335 35c. Miguelito Valdes . . .   70   40
4336 65c. Bola de Nieve . . . .   1·40   80
4337 75c. Rita Montaner . . . .   1·50   90

1176 Bolivar   **1177** Emblem

1999. Centenary of Simon Bolivar's Visit to Cuba. Multicoloured.
4338 65c. Type **1176** . . . . .   1·40   80
4339 65c. Simon Bolivar House
       and statue, Havana . . .   1·40   80

1999. 40th Anniv of State Security Department of the Ministry of the Interior.
4340 **1177** 65c. multicoloured . . .   1·40   80

1179 Postal Rocket

1999. Stamp Day.
4342 15c. Type **1179** (60th anniv)   40   20
4343 65c. Rider on horse (130th
       anniv of rebel postal
       service) . . . . . .   1·40   80

1180 Painting by Roberto Matta

1999. 40th Anniv of House of the Americas (cultural organization).
4344 **1180** 65c. multicoloured . . .   1·40   80

1182 Castro drafting Reform Law

1999. 40th Anniv of Agrarian Reform Law.
4346 **1182** 65c. multicoloured . . . . 1·40 80

1183 Royal Gramma

1999. Birth Bicentenary of Felipe Poey (naturalist). Fishes. Multicoloured.
4347 5c. Type **1183** 15 10
4348 15c. Peppermint basslet . . 40 20
4349 65c. Golden hamlet ("Hypoplectrus gummigutta") . . . . 1·40 80
4350 65c. Dusky damselfish ("Stegastes dorsopunicans") . . . . 1·40 80

1185 Baseball

1999. 13th Pan-American Games, Winnipeg, Canada. Multicoloured.
4353 15c. Type **1185** 40 20
4354 65c. Volleyball (vert) . . . . 1·40 80
4355 75c. Boxing . . . . 1·50 90

1186 "Victory of Wioming" (Gao Hong)

1999. 50th Anniv of People's Republic of China. Paintings. Multicoloured.
4356 5c. Type **1186** 15 10
4357 15c. "Nanchang Revolt" (Cai Lang) 40 20
4358 40c. "Red Army crossing Marsh" (Gao Quan) . . . 75 40
4359 65c. "Occupation of Presidential Palace" (Cheng Yifei and Wei Jingahan) . . . . . 1·40 80
4360 75c. "Founding of the Republic Ceremony" (Dong Xiwen) . . . . . 1·50 90

1187 "Morning Glory" (Qi Baishi)

1999. "China 1999" International Stamp Exhibition, Peking. Chinese Paintings. Multicoloured.
4361 5c. Type **1187** 15 10
4362 5c. "Three Galloping Horses" (Xu Beihong) . . 15 10
4363 15c. "Hunan Woman" (Fu Baoshi) 40 20
4364 15c. "Village of Luxun" (Wu Guanzhong) . . . 40 20
4365 15c. "Crossing" (Huangzhou) 40 20
4366 40c. "Pine Tree" (He Xiangning) 75 40
4367 65c. "Sleeping Woman" (Jin Shangyi) . . . . 1·40 80
4368 75c. "Poetic Scene in Xun Yang" (Chen Yifei) . . . 1·50 90

1188 Heinrich von Stephan (founder) and Emblem

1999. 125th Anniv of Universal Postal Union.
4369 **1188** 75c. multicoloured . . . . 1·50 90

1189 Havana Fortress and *Antia numidia*

1999. World Tourism Day. Butterflies and Views of Havana. Multicoloured.
4370 10c. Type **1189** 10 10
4371 15c. Cathedral and black swallowtail 30 20
4372 65c. St. Francis of Assisi Convent and flambeau . . 1·40 80
4373 75c. National Senate and *Eueides cleobaea* . . . . 1·50 90

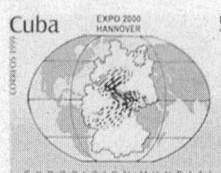

1190 Map of Germany on Globe

1999. "EXPO 2000" World's Fair, Hanover. Mult.
4374 5c. Type **1190** 10 10
4375 15c. Twipsy (mascot) (vert) . 30 20
4376 15c. Exhibition site, Philadelphia, 1876 . . . . 30 20
4377 15c. Exhibition site, Osaka, 1970 . . . . 30 20
4378 65c. Exhibition site, Hanover . . . . . 1·40 80
4379 75c. Exhibition site, Montreal, 1967 . . . . . 1·50 90

1191 Fokker F.27 Friendship

1999. 70th Anniv of Cuban Airlines. Multicoloured.
4380 15c. Type **1191** 30 20
4381 15c. Douglas DC-10 . . . . 30 20
4382 65c. Airbus Industrie A320 . 1·40 80
4383 75c. Douglas DC-3 . . . . 1·50 90

1192 Atomic Cloud and Pigeon

1194 Cienfuegos

1193 MINFAR Headquarters

1999. America. A New Millennium without Arms. Multicoloured.
4384 15c. Type **1192** 30 20
4385 65c. Globe and dove . . . . 1·40 80

1999. 40th Anniversaries. Multicoloured.
4386 15c. Type **1193** (Ministry of Revolutionary Armed Forces) 30 20
4387 65c. Militia members (National Revolutionary Militia) . . . . . . 1·40 80

1999. 40th Anniv of Disappearance of Major Camilo Cienfuegos (revolutionary).
4388 **1194** 15c. multicoloured . . . 30 20

1195 Vieja Plaza

1999. 9th Latin American Summit of Heads of State and Government, Havana. Multicoloured.
4389 65c. Type **1195** . . . . . 1·40 80
4390 75c. San Francisco de Asis Plaza . . . . 1·50 90

1197 Hemingway and Fisherman

1999. Birth Cent of Ernest Hemingway (writer).
4393 **1197** 65c. multicoloured . . . . 1·40 80

1198 Villena

1999. Birth Centenary of Ruben Martinez Villena (revolutionary).
4394 **1198** 15c. multicoloured 30 20

1199 Romay Chacon

1999. 150th Death Anniv of Tomas Romay Chacon (scientist).
4395 **1199** 65c. multicoloured . . . 1·40 80

1200 Dragon

2000. Chinese New Year. "Year of the Dragon".
4396 **1200** 15c. multicoloured . . . 30 20

1201 "Hot Rumba"

2000. Paintings by Concepcion Ferrant. Mult.
4397 10c. Type **1201** 15 10
4398 15c. "Cachumba" 30 20
4399 65c. "House of the babalao" . 1·40 80
4400 75c. "Tata Cunengue" . . . 1·50 90

1202 *Helcyra superba*

2000. "BANGKOK 2000" International Stamp Exhibition. Butterflies. Multicoloured.
4401 10c. Type **1202** 15 10
4402 15c. *Pantaporia punctata* . . 30 20
4403 15c. *Neptis themis* 30 20
4404 65c. *Curetis acuta* . . . . 1·40 80
4405 75c. *Chrysozephyrus ataxus* . 1·50 90

1203 World Map

2000. Group of 77 South Summit, Havana.
4406 **1203** 75c. multicoloured . . . . 1·50 90

1204 Lenin

2000. 130th Birth Anniv of Vladimir Ilich Lenin.
4407 **1204** 75c. multicoloured . . . . 1·50 90

1205 Cuba and Puerto Rico 1855 1r. Stamp

2000. Stamp Day. Multicoloured.
4408 65c. Type **1205** (145th anniv of first Cuba and Puerto Rico stamp) . . . . 1·40 80
4409 90c. Jaime Gonzalez Crocier (airmail pioneer), airplane and cover (70th anniv of the airmail service) . . . . 1·75 1·10

1206 Commander Guevara and Map

2000. 35th Anniv of Visit of "Che" Guevara (guerrilla fighter) to Congo.
4410 **1206** 65c. multicoloured . . . . 1·40 80

1207 Captain San Luis

2000. 60th Birth Anniv of Eliseo Reyes Rodriguez ("Captain San Luis").
4411 **1207** 65c. multicoloured . . . 1·40 80

1208 Baldwin Locomotive, 1882

2000. "Stamp Show 2000" International Stamp Exhibition, London. Steam Locomotives. Mult.
4412	5c. Type **1208**		10	10
4413	10c. Baldwin locomotive, 1895		15	10
4414	15c. Baldwin locomotive, 1912		30	20
4415	65c. Alco locomotive, 1919		1·40	80
4416	75c. Alco locomotive, 1925		1·50	90

1209 Henri Giffard and Steam-powered Dirigible Airship

2000. "WIPA 2000" International Stamp Exhibition, Vienna. Airship Development. Multicoloured.
4418	10c. Type **1209**		10	10
4419	15c. Albert and Gaston Tissander and airship (vert)		20	10
4420	50c. Charles Renard, Arthur Krebs and *La France* (airship)		70	40
4421	65c. Pierre and Paul Lebaudy and airship		90	50
4422	75c. August von Perseval and airship		1·10	65

1210 Emblem

2000. 2nd World Meeting of "Friendship and Solidarity with Cuba", Havana.
4424 **1210** 65c. multicoloured . . . 90 50

1211 Caballero

2000. Birth Bicentenary of Jose de la Luz y Caballero (educator).
4425 **1211** 65c. multicoloured . . . 90 50

1212 Music Score, Roldan and Violin

2000. Birth Centenary of Amadeo Roldan (musician and conductor).
4426 **1212** 65c. multicoloured . . . 90 50

1213 Mother holding Child ("Child of El Senor Don Pomposo")

2000. *The Golden Age* (children's magazine by Jose Marti). Designs illustrating stories featured in the magazines. Multicoloured.
4427	5c. Type **1213**		10	10
4428	10c. Child with doll ("The Black Doll")		15	10
4429	15c. Child reading ("Mischevious Child")		20	10
4430	50c. "The Nightingale" (Hans Christian Andersen)		70	40
4431	65c. Frontispiece		90	50
4432	75c. "The Enchanted Prawn" (Edourd R. L. Laboulaye)		1·10	65

1214 Members' Flags

2000. 20th Anniv of Latin American Association for Integration (A.L.A.D.I.).
4434 **1214** 65c. multicoloured . . . 90 50

1216 Running

2000. Olympic Games, Sydney. Multicoloured.
4436	5c. Type **1216**		10	10
4437	15c. Football		20	10
4438	65c. Baseball		90	50
4439	75c. Cycling		1·10	65

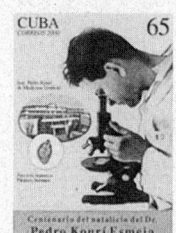

1217 Esmeja using Microscope

2000. Birth Centenary of Dr. Pedro Kouri Esmeja (tropical disease and parasitology pioneer).
4440 **1217** 65c. multicoloured . . . 90 50

1218 Women and Flag

2000. 40th Anniv of Federation of Cuban Women.
4441 **1218** 15c. multicoloured . . . 20 10

1219 18th-century Sailing Packet

2000. "Espana 2000" World Stamp Exhibition, Madrid. Multicoloured.
4442	10c. Type **1219**		15	10
4443	15c. Statue, La Cibeles Plaza, Madrid and Spain 1850 6c. stamp		20	10
4444	15c. Crystal Palace, Madrid (venue) and 1850 cover		20	10
4445	65c. Palace of Communications, Madrid and set of Spain 1850 stamps		90	50
4446	75c. Galician Centre, Havana with Cuba and Puerto Rica 1855 ½r. stamp		1·10	65

1220 Senen Casas Reguerio Railway Station, Santiago de Cuba

2000. 20th Congress of Pan-American Railways.
4448 **1220** 65c. multicoloured . . . 90 50

EXPRESS MAIL STAMPS

E 34

1900. As Type E **34**, but inscr "immediata".
E306 E **34** 10c. orange . . . . . 32·00 8·50

1902. Inscr "inmediata".
E307 E **34** 10c. orange . . . . . 2·00 1·00

E 39 J. B. Zayas

1910.
E320 E **39** 10c. blue and orange 4·00 1·40

E 41 Bleriot XI and Morro Castle

1914.
E352 E **41** 10c. blue . . . . . . 6·00 1·40

E 62 Mercury

1936. Free Port of Matanzas. Inscr as T **61**. Perf or imperf (same prices).
E409	E **62** 10c. purple (express)		3·50	3·50
E413	– 15c. blue (air express)		12·00	2·00
DESIGN: 15c. Maya Lighthouse.

E 67 "Triumph of the Revolution"

1936. Maximo Gomez Monument.
E422 E **67** 10c. orange . . . . . 3·75 2·75

E 71 Temple of Quetzalcoatl (Mexico)

1937. American Writers and Artists Association.
E424v	E **71** 10c. orange		3·75	2·75
E424w	– 10c. orange		3·75	2·75
DESIGN: No. 424w, Ruben Dario (Nicaragua).

E 114

1945.
E485 E **114** 10c. brown . . . . . 4·25 60

E 146 Government House, Cardenas

1951. Centenary of Cuban Flag.
E559 E **146** 10c. red, blue & orge 2·75 95

E 150 Capablanca Club, Havana

1951. 30th Anniv of Jose Capablanca's Victory in World Chess Championship.
E568 E **150** 10c. purple & green 5·50 2·25

1952. As No. 549 surch 10c E. ESPECIAL.
E595 **143** 10c. on 2c. brown . . . 1·25 40

E 161 National Anthem and Arms

E 176 Roseate Tern

1952. 50th Anniv of Republic.
E605 E **161** 10c. blue & orange . . 2·75 1·10

1952. Postal Employees' Retirement Fund. Inscr "ENTREGA ESPECIAL".
E627 **165** 10c. olive . . . . 1·75 85

1953.
E673 E **176** 10c. blue . . . . . . 4·00 2·00

1954. Postal Employees' Retirement Fund. Portrait of G. H. Saez as No. 684, inscr "ENTREGA ESPECIAL".
E686 10c. olive . . . . 1·90 95

1955. Postal Employees' Retirement Fund. Vert portrait (F. Varela) as T **191**, inscr "ENTREGA ESPECIAL".
E741 10c. lake . . . . 2·00 95

1956. Postal Employees' Retirement Fund. Vert portrait (J. J. Milanes) as T **200**, inscr "ENTREGA ESPECIAL".
E768 10c. black and red . . . . 1·90 95

1957. Postal Employees' Retirement Fund. As T **216** but inscr "ENTREGA ESPECIAL".
E812 10c. turquoise & brown . . 1·75 85
PAINTING: 10c. "Yesterday" (Cabrera).

1957. Postal Employees' Retirement Fund. As T **236** but inscr "ENTREGA ESPECIAL".
E856 10c. violet and brown . . . 1·75 85
DESIGN—HORIZ: 10c. Statue of Gen. A. Maceo, Independence Park, Pinar del Rio.

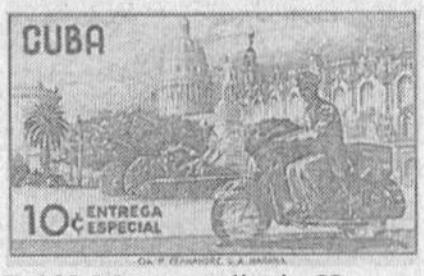

E 238 Motor-cyclist in Havana

1958.

E858	E 238	10c. blue	1·40	65
E954		10c. violet	1·40	65
E955		10c. orange	1·40	65
E859		20c. green	1·40	65

1958. Poey Commem. As Nos. 890/2 but inscr "ENTREGA ESPECIAL".

E893	10c. multicoloured	5·50	2·75
E894	20c. red, blue and black	8·50	5·50

DESIGNS—HORIZ: Fish: 10c. Black-finned snapper; 20c. Spotted mosquitofish.

1960. Surch **HABILITADO ENTREGA ESPECIAL 10c.**

E961	**55**	10c. on 20c. pink	1·10	35
E962		10c. on 50c. turquoise	1·10	35

1962. Stamp Day. As T **289** but inscr "ENTREGA ESPECIAL".

E1023	10c. brown & bl on yell	6·50	1·25

DESIGN: 10c. 18th-century sailing packet.

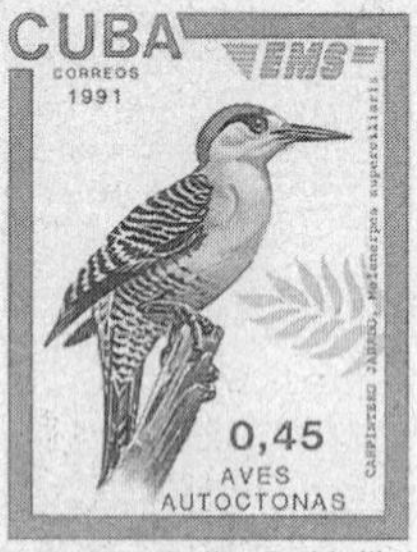

E 991 West Indian Red-bellied Woodpecker

1991. Birds. Multicoloured.

E3638	45c. Type E **991**	80	45
E3639	50c. Cuban solitaire	80	45
E3640	2p. Cuban trogon	3·00	2·00
E3641	4p. Cuban grassquit	6·00	4·00
E3642	5p. Ivory-billed woodpecker	7·00	5·00
E3643	10p. Cuban amazon (horiz)	15·00	10·00
E3644	16p.45 Bee hummingbird (horiz)	25·00	20·00

POSTAGE DUE STAMPS

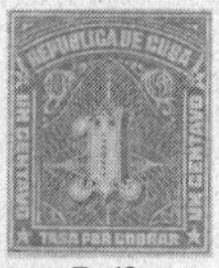

D 42

1914.

D335	D **42**	1c. red	1·25	65
D337		2c. red	1·25	65
D340		5c. red	2·75	1·10

CUNDINAMARCA Pt. 20

One of the states of the Granadine Confederation. A Department of Colombia from 1886, now uses Colombian stamps.

100 centavos = 1 peso.

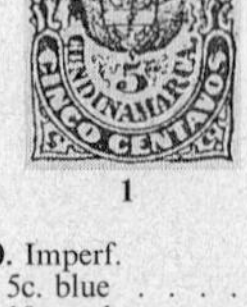

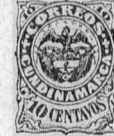

1

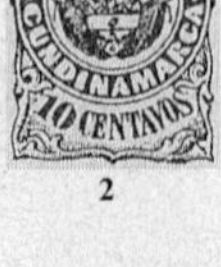

2

1870. Imperf.

1	**1**	5c. blue	2·75	2·75
2	**2**	10c. red	10·00	10·00

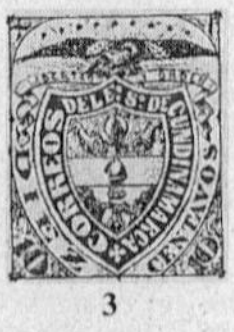

3

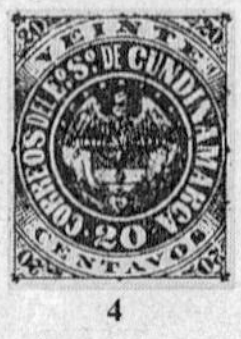

4

1877. Imperf.

5	**3**	10c. red	1·25	1·25
6	**4**	20c. green	2·25	2·25
7	–	50c. mauve	3·00	3·00
8a	–	1p. brown	5·00	5·00

The 50c. and 1p. are in larger Arms designs.

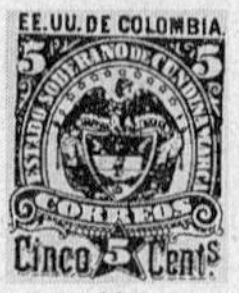

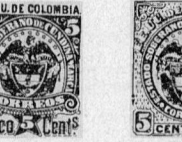

11

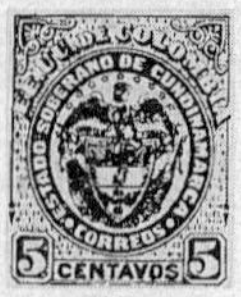

13

1884. Imperf.

14	**11**	5c. blue	50	60

1885. Imperf.

17	**13**	5c. blue	30	30
18		10c. red	1·50	1·50
19		10c. red on lilac	90	90
20		20c. green	1·25	1·25
21		50c. mauve	1·75	1·75
22		1p. brown	2·00	2·00

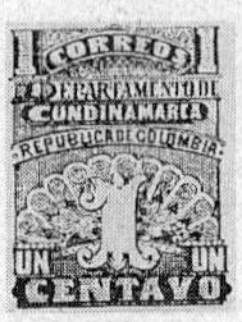

14

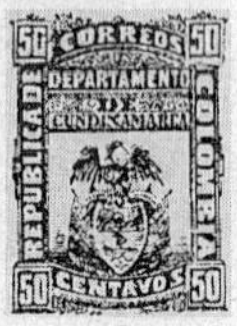

15

1904. Imperf or perf. Various frames.

23	**14**	1c. orange	15	15
24		2c. blue	15	15
35		2c. grey	45	45
25	**15**	3c. red	20	20
26		5c. green	20	20
27		10c. brown	20	20
28		15c. pink	25	25
29		20c. blue on green	20	20
32		20c. blue	40	40
42		40c. blue	30	30
30		50c. mauve	25	25
31		1p. green	25	25

The illustrations show the main type. The frames and position of the arms in Type **15** differ for each value.

REGISTRATION STAMP

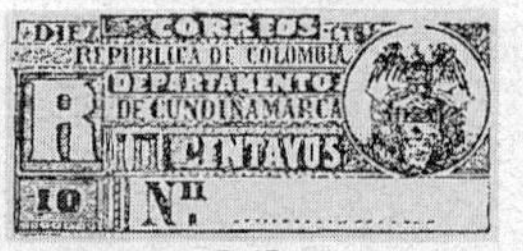

R 17

1904. Imperf or perf.

R46	R **17**	10c. brown	75	75

CURACAO Pt. 4

A Netherlands colony consisting of two groups of islands in the Caribbean Sea, N. of Venezuela. Later part of Netherlands Antilles.

100 cents = 1 gulden.

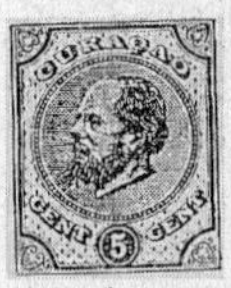

1

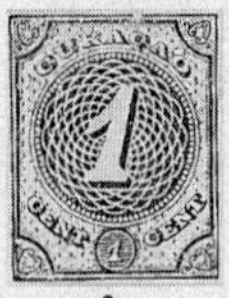

2

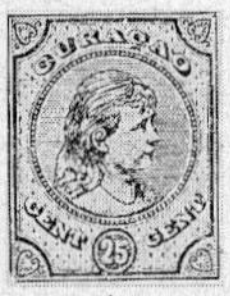

4

1873.

13	**1**	2½c. green	3·25	7·00
7		3c. bistre	55·00	£120
14		5c. red	8·50	8·50
33		10c. blue	60·00	13·00
34		12½c. yellow	£110	42·00
22		15c. brown	20·00	13·00
23		25c. brown	45·00	6·00
24		30c. grey	30·00	38·00
17		50c. lilac	1·25	2·25
26		60c. bistre	38·00	15·00
35		1g.50 indigo and blue	£120	75·00
12a		2g.50 mauve and bistre	28·00	24·00

1889.

37	**2**	1c. grey	55	75
38		2c. mauve	40	95
39		2½c. green	3·50	1·50
40a		3c. brown	4·50	3·75
41		5c. red	20·00	1·00

1891. Surch **25 CENT.**

42	**1**	25c. on 30c. grey	13·00	13·00

1892.

43	**4**	10c. blue	85	85
44		12½c. green	24·00	5·00
45		15c. red	2·00	2·25
46		25c. brown	90·00	4·50
47		30c. grey	2·00	6·50

1895. Surch **2½ cent** (No. 48) or **2½ CENT** (No. 50).

48	**1**	2½c. on 10c. blue	10·00	6·00
50		2½c. on 30c. grey	£120	4·00

1899. 1898 stamps of Netherlands surch **CURACAO** and value.

51	**12**	12½c. on 12½c. blue	23·00	6·00
52		25c. on 25c. blue and red	85	85
53	**13**	1g.50 on 2½g. lilac	13·00	19·00

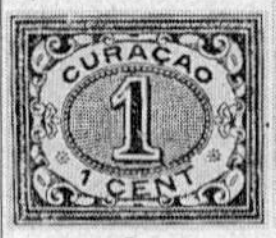

9

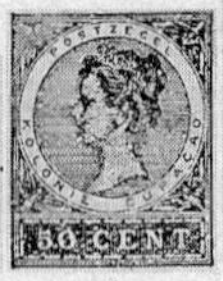

10

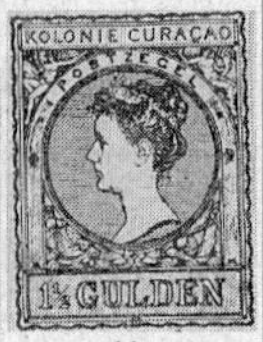

11

1903.

54	**9**	1c. olive	1·00	50
55a		2c. brown	11·00	2·75
56		2½c. green	3·25	25
57		3c. orange	6·50	4·00
58		5c. red	5·50	25
59		7½c. grey	26·00	4·50
60	**10**	10c. slate	10·00	2·50
61		12½c. blue	1·00	20
62		15c. brown	13·00	9·00
63		22½c. olive and brown	13·00	7·00
64		25c. violet	13·00	1·75
65		30c. brown	32·00	12·00
66		50c. brown	26·00	7·50
67	**11**	1½g. brown	35·00	25·00
68		2½g. blue	35·00	25·00

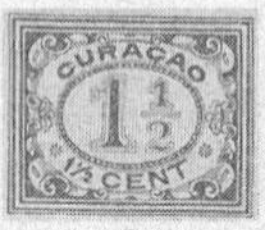

12

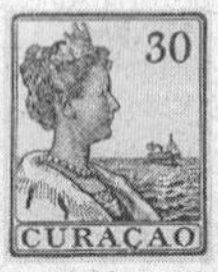

13

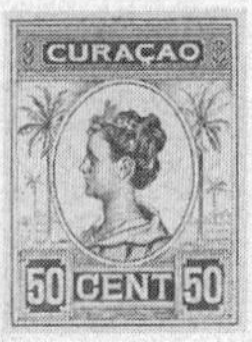

14

1915.

69	**12**	½c. lilac	40	70
70		1c. olive	20	15
71		1½c. blue	15	10
72		2c. brown	1·25	1·10
73		2½c. green	1·00	15
74		3c. yellow	1·25	1·25
75		3c. green	2·00	2·00
76		5c. red	1·40	10
77		5c. green	2·50	2·00
78		5c. mauve	1·10	15
79c	**12**	7½c. bistre	1·10	15
80	**13**	10c. red	13·00	2·50
81	**12**	10c. lilac	3·50	3·75
82		10c. red	4·50	1·25
83	**13**	12½c. blue	1·50	45
84		12½c. red	1·40	1·50
85		15c. olive	40	65
86		15c. blue	2·75	2·25
87		20c. blue	6·00	2·50
88		20c. olive	1·60	2·25
89		22½c. orange	1·25	2·25
90		25c. mauve	2·75	85
91		30c. slate	2·75	65
92		35c. slate and orange	2·75	3·50
93a	**14**	50c. green	2·25	20
94		1½g. violet	11·00	11·00
95		2½g. red	20·00	20·00

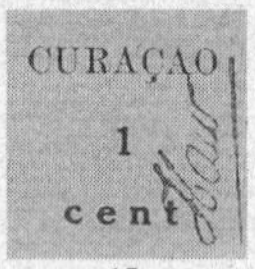

15

1918.

96	**15**	1c. black on buff	7·00	3·50

1919. Surch **5 CENT.**

97	**13**	5c. on 12½c. blue	3·50	2·00

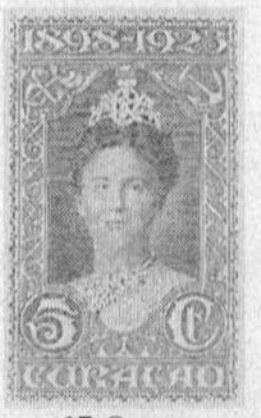

17 Queen Wilhelmina

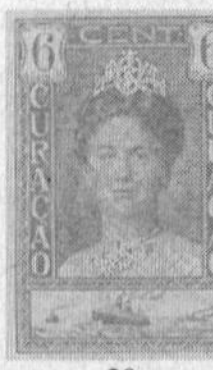

20

1923. Queen's Silver Jubilee.

98	**17**	5c. green	55	1·75
99		7½c. green	1·10	1·40
100		10c. red	1·10	1·75
101		20c. grey	1·75	2·75
102		1g. purple	30·00	17·00
103		2g.50 black	60·00	£180
104		5g. brown	80·00	£200

1927. Unissued Marine Insurance stamps, as Type M **22** of Netherlands, inscr "CURACAO", surch **FRANKEERZEGEL** and value.

105	3c. on 15c. green	20	35
106	10c. on 60c. red	20	30
107	12½c. on 75c. brown	25	30
108	15c. on 1g.50 blue	3·00	2·50
109	25c. on 2g.25 brown	7·00	6·50
110	30c. on 4½g. black	13·00	12·00
111	50c. on 7½g. red	7·50	7·50

1928.

112	**20**	6c. orange	1·40	25
113		7½c. orange	55	50
114		10c. red	1·40	45
115		12½c. brown	1·40	1·25
116		15c. blue	1·40	35
117		20c. blue	5·50	65
118		21c. green	8·50	11·00
119		25c. purple	3·25	1·60
120		27½c. black	11·00	14·00
121		30c. green	5·50	65
122		35c. black	1·75	2·25

1929. Air. Surch **LUCHTPOST** and value.

123	**13**	50c. on 12½c. red	11·00	12·00
124		1g. on 20c. blue	11·00	12·00
125		2g. on 15c. olive	38·00	45·00

1929. Surch **6 ct.** and bars.

126	**20**	6c. on 7½c. orange	1·10	85

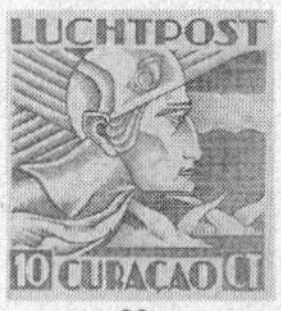

23

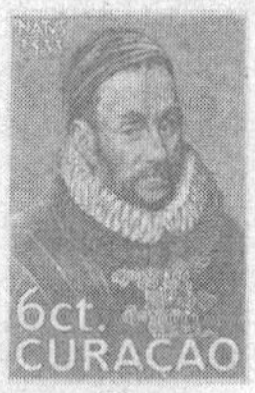

24a

1931. Air.

126a	**23**	10c. green	15	10
126b		15c. slate	25	15
127		20c. red	75	15
127a		25c. olive	45	40
127b		30c. yellow	30	20
128		35c. blue	75	70
129		40c. green	55	20
130		45c. orange	2·00	2·00
130a		50c. red	40	55
131		60c. purple	55	25
132		70c. black	6·00	2·00
133		1g.40 brown	3·75	5·00
134		2g.80 bistre	4·25	5·50

1931. Surch.

134a	**12**	1½ on 2½c. green	3·00	3·00
135		2½ on 3c. green	1·00	1·00

1933. 400th Birth Anniv of William I of Orange.

136	**24a**	6c. orange	1·25	1·00

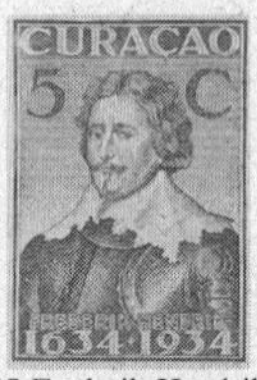

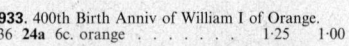

25 Frederik Hendrik

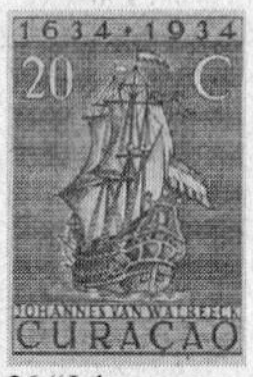

26 "Johannes van Walbeeck"

1934. 300th Anniv of Dutch Colonization. Inscr "1634 1934".

137	–	1c. black	1·00	1·50
138	–	1½c. mauve	75	30
139	–	2c. orange	1·00	1·50
140	**25**	2½c. green	85	1·50
141		5c. brown	85	95
142		6c. blue	75	25
143	–	10c. red	2·25	85
144	–	12½c. brown	6·00	5·50
145	–	15c. blue	1·75	90
146	**26**	20c. black	4·00	2·25
147		21c. brown	13·00	19·00
148		25c. green	12·00	12·00
149	–	27½c. purple	14·00	18·00
150	–	30c. red	11·00	4·25
151	–	50c. yellow	11·00	7·50
152	–	1g.50 blue	50·00	60·00
153	–	2g.50 green	60·00	55·00

PORTRAITS: 1c. to 2c. Willem Usselinx. 10c. to 15c. Jacob Binckes. 27½c. to 50c. Cornelis Evertsen, the younger. 1g.50, 2g.50, Louis Brion.

1934. Air. Surch **10 CT.**

154	**23**	10c. on 20c. red	20·00	17·00

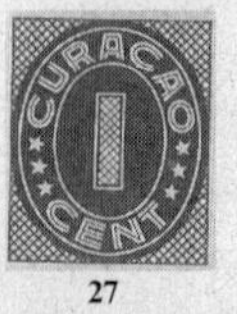

27

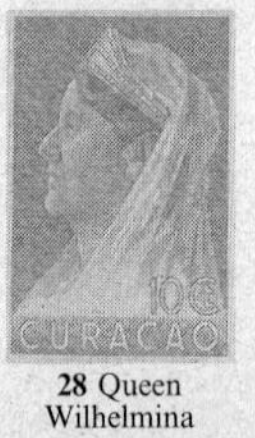

28 Queen Wilhelmina

1936.

155	27	1c. brown	20	15
156		1½c. blue	20	10
157		2c. orange	25	25
158		2½c. green	20	20
159		5c. red	20	10

1936.

160	28	6c. purple	50	10
161		10c. red	1·00	15
162		12½c. green	1·50	70
163		15c. blue	1·10	35
164		20c. orange	1·10	55
165		21c. black	2·25	2·50
166		25c. red	1·50	80
167		27½c. brown	2·50	2·75
168		30c. bistre	60	15
169		50c. green	3·00	20
170		1g.50 brown	22·00	15·00
171a		2g.50 red	12·00	7·50

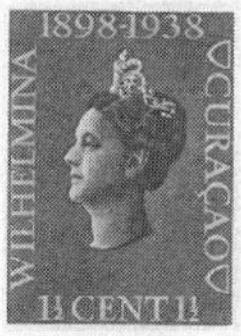

29 Queen Wilhelmina

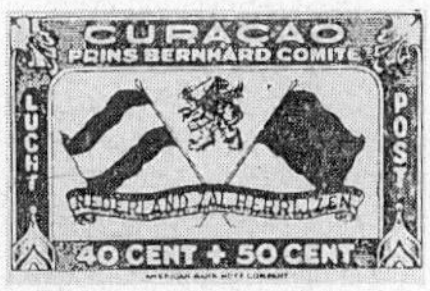

30 Dutch Flags and Arms

1938. 40th Anniv of Coronation.

172	29	1½c. violet	15	20
173		6c. red	70	65
174		15c. blue	1·25	95

1941. Air. Prince Bernhard Fund to equip Dutch Forces. Centres in red, blue and orange.

175	30	10c.+10c. red	2·75	3·25
176		15c.+25c. blue	14·00	14·00
177		20c.+25c. brown	14·00	18·00
178		25c.+25c. violet	14·00	18·00
179		30c.+50c. orange	14·00	18·00
180		35c.+50c. green	14·00	18·00
181		40c.+50c. brown	14·00	18·00
182		50c.+1g. blue	14·00	18·00

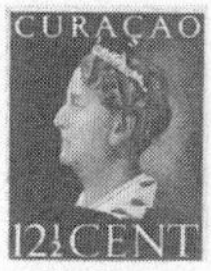

31 Queen Wilhelmina

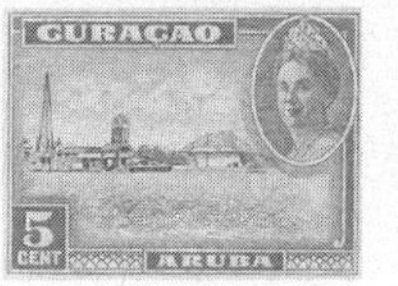

33 Aruba

1941.

248	31	6c. violet	1·40	2·00
184a		10c. red	1·00	85
185		12½c. green	1·50	55
251		15c. blue	1·40	2·00
187		20c. orange	30	45
188		21c. grey	1·40	1·60
254		25c. red	20	15
255		27½c. brown	1·40	1·40
256		30c. bistre	1·75	75
257		50c. green	2·00	15
192		50c. green (21 × 26 mm)	10·00	20
193		1½g. brown (21 × 26 mm)	12·00	90
194		2½g. purple (21 × 26 mm)	11·00	1·00

See also Nos. 258/61.

1942.

195	–	1c. brown and violet	10	10
196	–	1½c. green and blue	15	15
197	–	2c. brown and black	40	35
198	–	2½c. yellow and green	20	20
199	33	5c. black and red	85	15
200	–	6c. blue and purple	60	65

DESIGNS—HORIZ: 1c. Bonaire. 2c. Saba. 2½c. St. Maarten. 6c. Curacao. VERT: 1½c. St. Eustatius.

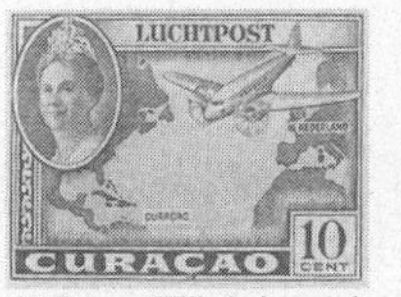

34 Queen Wilhelmina and Douglas DC-2 over Atlantic Ocean

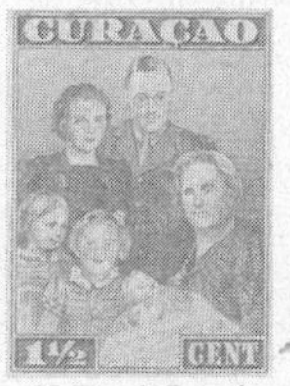

35 Dutch Royal Family

1942. Air.

201	34	10c. blue and green	15	10
202	–	15c. green and red	20	15
203	–	20c. green and brown	25	15
204	–	25c. brown and blue	15	20
205	–	30c. violet and red	30	30
206	34	35c. green and violet	45	30
207	–	40c. brown and green	55	40
208	–	45c. black and red	35	20
209	–	50c. black and violet	75	15
210	–	60c. blue and brown	75	60
211	34	70c. blue and brown	1·00	60
212	–	1g.40 green and blue	4·50	1·25
213	–	2g.80 blue & ultramarine	6·50	2·50
214	–	5g. green and purple	12·00	11·00
215	–	10g. brown and green	17·00	17·00

DESIGNS: 15, 40c., 1g.40, Fokker airplane "Zilvermeeuw" over coast. 20, 45c., 2g.80, Map of Netherlands West Indies. 25, 50c., 5g. Side view of Douglas DC-2 airplane. 30, 60c., 10g. Front view of Douglas DC-2 airplane.

1943. Birth of Princess Margriet.

216	35	1½c. orange	10	10
217		2½c. red	15	10
218		6c. black	70	55
219		10c. blue	70	80

1943. Air. Dutch Prisoners of War Relief Fund. Nos. 212/15 surch **Voor Krijgsgevangenen** and new value.

220		40c.+50c. on 1g.40 green & bl	3·75	4·50
221		45c.+50c. on 2g.80 blue & ult	3·50	4·25
222		50c.+75c. on 5g. green & pur	3·50	4·25
223		60c.+100c. on 10g. brn & grn	3·50	4·50

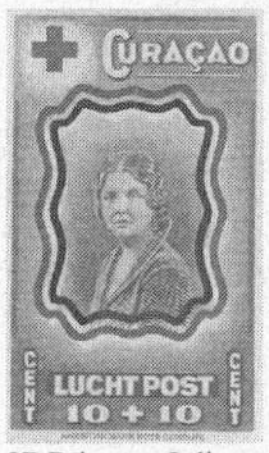

37 Princess Juliana

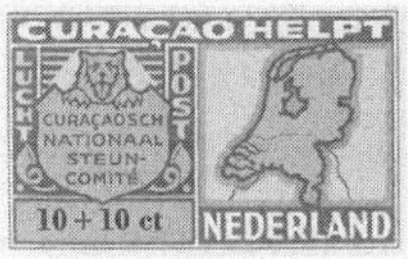

38 Map of Netherlands

1944. Air. Red Cross Fund. Cross in red; frame in red and blue.

224	37	10c.+10c. brown	1·50	1·75
225		15c.+25c. green	1·40	1·75
226		20c.+25c. black	1·40	1·75
227		25c.+25c. grey	1·40	1·75
228		30c.+50c. purple	1·40	1·75
229		35c.+50c. brown	1·40	1·75
230		40c.+50c. green	1·40	1·75
231		50c.+100c. violet	1·50	2·00

1946. Air. Netherlands Relief Fund. Value in black.

232	38	10c.+10c. orange & grey	1·00	1·25
233		15c.+25c. grey and red	1·25	1·25
234		20c.+25c. orange & grn	1·25	1·25
235		25c.+25c. grey & violet	1·25	1·25
236		30c.+50c. buff & green	1·25	1·50
237		35c.+50c. orange & red	1·25	1·50
238		40c.+75c. buff & blue	1·25	1·75
239		50c.+100c. buff & violet	1·25	1·75

1946. Air. National Relief Fund. As T **38** but showing map of Netherlands Indies and inscr "CURACAO HELPT ONZEOOST". Value in black.

240		10c.+10c. buff & violet	1·00	1·25
241		15c.+25c. buff & blue	1·25	1·25
242		20c.+25c. orange & red	1·25	1·25
243		25c.+25c. buff & green	1·25	1·25
244		30c.+50c. grey & violet	1·25	1·50
245		35c.+50c. orange & grn	1·25	1·50
246		40c.+75c. grey & red	1·25	1·75
247		50c.+100c. orange & grey	1·25	1·75

1947. Size 25 × 31½ mm.

258	31	1½g. brown	90	55
259		2½g. purple	23·00	5·00
260		5g. olive	95·00	£130
261		10g. orange	£120	£190

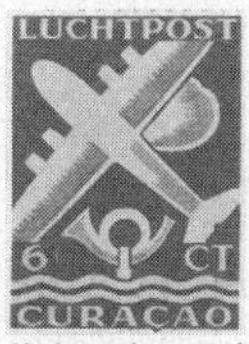

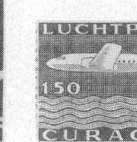

40 Aeroplane and Posthorn

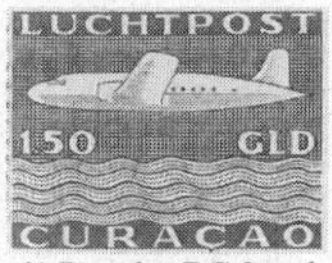

41 Douglas DC-2 and Waves

1947. Air.

262	40	6c. black	20	10
263		10c. red	20	15
264		12½c. purple	35	15
265		15c. blue	35	20
266		20c. green	50	25
267		25c. orange	50	15
268		30c. violet	75	30
269		35c. red	80	50
270		40c. green	75	50
271		45c. violet	90	75
272		50c. red	90	15
273		60c. blue	1·10	50
274		70c. brown	2·50	1·25
275	41	1g.50 black	1·40	50
276		2g.50 red	12·00	2·75
277		5g. green	22·00	6·00
278		7g.50 blue	70·00	65·00
279		10g. violet	50·00	12·00
280		15g. red	90·00	80·00
281		25g. brown	80·00	65·00

1947. Netherlands Indies Social Welfare Fund. Surch **NIWIN** and value.

282	28	1½c.+2½c. on 6c. purple	80	80
283		2½c.+5c. on 10c. red	80	80
284		5c.+7½c. on 15c. blue	80	80

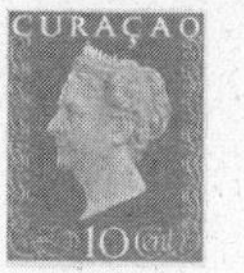

43

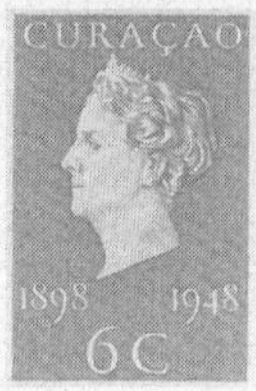

45 Queen Wilhelmina

1948. Portrait of Queen Wilhelmina.

285	43	6c. purple	1·00	1·25
286		10c. red	1·00	1·60
287		12½c. green	1·00	80
288		15c. blue	1·00	1·25
289		20c. orange	1·00	1·75
290		21c. black	1·00	1·75
291		25c. mauve	35	10
292		27½c. brown	18·00	17·00
293		30c. olive	15·00	80
294		50c. green	15·00	25
295		1g.50c. brn (21½ × 28½ mm)	24·00	4·50

1948. Golden Jubilee.

296	45	6c. orange	50	50
297		12½c. blue	50	50

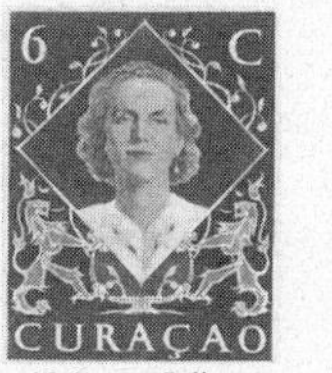

46 Queen Juliana

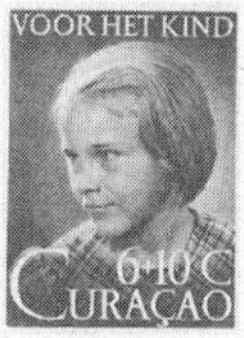

47

1948. Accession of Queen Juliana.

298	46	6c. red	45	45
299		12½c. green	45	45

1948. Child Welfare Fund. Inscr "VOOR HET KIND".

300	47	6c.+10c. brown	2·25	1·50
301	–	10c.+15c. red	2·25	1·50
302	–	12½c.+20c. green	2·25	1·60
303	47	15c.+25c. blue	2·25	1·75
304	–	20c.+30c. brown	2·25	1·75
305	–	25c.+35c. violet	2·25	2·00

DESIGNS—10, 20c. Native boy in straw hat. 12½, 25c. Curly-haired girl.

POSTAGE DUE STAMPS

For stamps as Nos. D42/61 and D96/105 in other colours see Postage Due stamps of Netherlands Indies and Surinam.

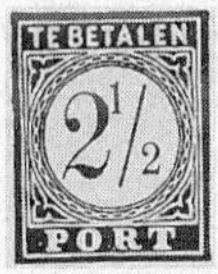

D 3

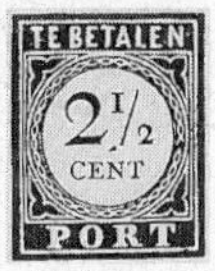

D 5

1889.

D42	D 3	2½c. black and green	1·60	2·25
D43		5c. black and green	1·00	1·00
D44		10c. black and green	20·00	17·00
D45		12½c. black and green	£275	£140
D46		15c. black and green	14·00	11·00
D47		20c. black and green	5·50	5·50
D48		25c. black and green	£130	£110
D49		30c. black and green	7·00	5·50
D50		40c. black and green	7·00	5·50
D51		50c. black and green	26·00	25·00

1892.

D52	D 5	2½c. black and green	20	15
D53		5c. black and green	45	30
D54		10c. black and green	1·00	25
D55		12½c. black and green	1·10	40
D56		15c. black and green	1·75	70
D57		20c. black and green	2·25	1·00
D58		25c. black and green	85	55
D59		30c. black and green	18·00	10·00
D60		40c. black and green	18·00	11·00
D61		50c. black and green	22·00	11·00

1915.

D 96	D 5	2½c. green	50	50
D 97		5c. green	50	50
D 98		10c. green	45	45
D 99		12½c. green	55	55
D100		15c. green	1·00	1·25
D101		20c. green	50	1·00
D102		25c. green	20	10
D103		30c. green	2·00	2·25
D104		40c. green	2·00	2·25
D105		50c. green	1·60	1·90

For later issues see **NETHERLANDS ANTILLES**.

CYPRUS Pt. 1

An island in the East Mediterranean. A British colony, which became a republic within the British Commonwealth in 1960.

1880. 12 pence = 1 shilling.
1881. 40 paras = 1 piastre; 180 piastres = 1 pound.
1955. 1000 mils = 1 pound.
1983. 100 cents = 1 pound.

1880. Stamps of Great Britain (Queen Victoria) optd **CYPRUS**.

1	7	½d. red	£100	£100
2	5	1d. red	9·50	29·00
3	41	2½d. mauve	2·25	7·50
4	–	4d. green (No. 153)	£120	£200
5	–	6d. grey (No. 161)	£500	£650
6	–	1s. green (No. 150)	£650	£450

1881. Stamps of Great Britain (Queen Victoria) surch with new values.

9	5	½d. on 1d. red	45·00	65·00
10		30 paras on 1d. red	£100	80·00

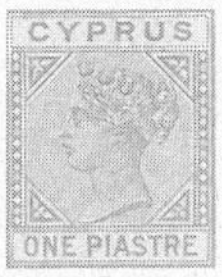

7

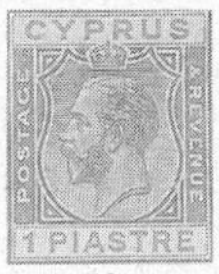

13

1881.

31	7	½pi. green	4·00	70
40		½pi. green and red	4·00	1·25
32		30pa. mauve	4·25	4·25
41		30pa. mauve and green	2·00	1·25
33		1pi. red	10·00	1·50
42		1pi. red and blue	5·00	1·25
34		2pi. blue	14·00	1·75
43		2pi. blue and purple	6·00	1·25
35a		4pi. olive	18·00	23·00
44		4pi. olive and purple	14·00	4·25
21		6pi. grey	42·00	17·00
45		6pi. brown and green	11·00	13·00
46		9pi. brown and red	15·00	16·00
22		12pi. brown	£170	35·00
47		12pi. brown and black	16·00	50·00
48		18pi. grey and brown	45·00	45·00
49		45pi. purple and blue	90·00	£130

1882. Surch.

25	7	½pi. on ½pi. green	£120	6·50
24		30pa. on 1pi. red	£1400	£100

1903. As T **7** but portrait of King Edward VII.

60		5pa. brown and black	1·00	70
61		10pa. orange and green	3·00	50
50		½pi. green and red	3·75	1·25
51		30pa. violet and green	6·00	2·75
64		1pi. red and blue	4·00	1·00
65		2pi. blue and purple	5·50	1·75
66		4pi. brown and purple	10·00	7·00
67		6pi. brown and green	12·00	14·00
68		9pi. brown and red	28·00	8·50
69		12pi. brown and black	23·00	35·00
70		18pi. black and brown	30·00	11·00
71		45pi. purple and blue	75·00	£140

1912. As T **7** but portrait of King George V.

74b		10pa. orange and green	2·25	1·25
86		10pa. grey and yellow	11·00	6·50
75		½pi. green and red	1·75	20
76		30pa. violet and green	2·50	60
88		30pa. green	7·00	40
77		1pi. red and blue	3·75	1·75
90		1pi. violet and red	3·00	4·00
91		1½pi. yellow and black	3·75	4·50
78		2pi. blue and purple	6·50	2·00
93		2pi. red and blue	9·00	22·00
94		2¾pi. blue and purple	7·00	9·00
79		4pi. olive and purple	4·25	4·50
80		6pi. brown and green	3·50	8·50
81		9pi. brown and red	23·00	26·00
82		12pi. brown and black	13·00	30·00
83		18pi. black and brown	24·00	28·00
84		45pi. purple and blue	70·00	£120
100		10s. green and red on yellow	£350	£700
101		£1 purple and black on red	£1000	£1600

1924.

103	13	¼pi. grey and brown	1·00	15
104		½pi. black	2·50	7·50
118		½pi. green	2·25	85
105		¾pi. green	2·25	90
119		¾pi. black	1·75	10
106		1pi. purple and brown	2·00	70
107		1½pi. orange and black	2·00	6·00
120		1½pi. red	2·50	30
108		2pi. red and green	2·25	11·00
121		2pi. yellow and black	5·50	2·75
122		2½pi. blue	2·75	30
109		2¾pi. blue and purple	3·25	2·75
110		4pi. olive and purple	3·25	2·25
111		4½pi. blk & orge on green	3·50	3·50
112		6pi. brown and green	3·75	5·50
113		9pi. brown and purple	6·00	4·25
114		12pi. brown and black	9·00	55·00
115		18pi. black and orange	20·00	5·00
116		45pi. purple and blue	35·00	38·00
117		90pi. grn & red on yellow	80·00	£170
102		£1 purple & black on red	£325	£650
117a		£5 black on yellow	£2750	£6000

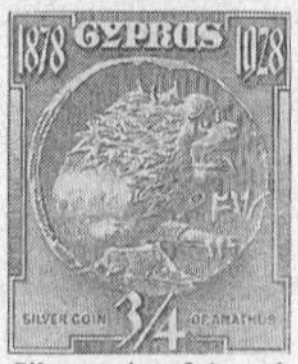

14 Silver coin of Amathus, 6th-century BC

1928. 50th Anniv of British Rule. Dated "1878 1928".
123 **14** ¾pi. violet . . . . 2·75 1·00
124 – 1pi. black and blue . . . . 3·00 1·50
125 – 1½pi. red . . . . 4·50 2·00
126 – 2½pi. blue . . . . 3·50 2·25
127 – 4pi. brown . . . . 5·00 6·00
128 – 6pi. blue . . . . 6·50 20·00
129 – 9pi. purple . . . . 7·50 11·00
130 – 18pi. black and brown . . 17·00 17·00
131 – 45pi. violet and blue . . . 35·00 45·00
132 – £1 blue and brown £200 £300
DESIGNS—VERT: 1pi. Philosopher Zeno; 2½pi. Discovery of body of St. Barnabas; 4pi. Cloister, Abbey of Bella Paise; 9pi. Tekke of Umm Haram; 18pi. Statue of Richard I, Westminster; 45pi. St. Nicholas Cathedral, Famagusta, (now Lala Mustafa Pasha Mosque); £1 King George V. HORIZ: 1½pi. Map of Cyprus; 6pi. Badge of Cyprus.

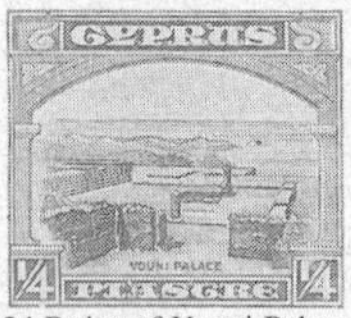

24 Ruins of Vouni Palace

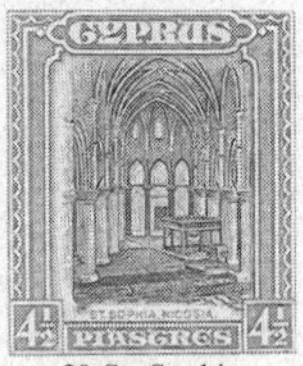

30 St. Sophia Cathedral, Nicosia (now Selimiye Mosque)

1934.
133 **24** ¼pi. blue and brown . . . 1·00 50
134 – ½pi. green . . . . 1·25 1·00
135 – ¾pi. black and violet . . . 1·00 10
136 – 1pi. black and brown . . . 1·00 80
137 – 1½pi. red . . . . 1·50 55
138 – 2½pi. blue . . . . 1·50 1·75
139 **30** 4½pi. black and red . . . . 3·00 3·50
140 – 6pi. black and blue . . . . 8·50 12·00
141 – 9pi. brown and violet . . . 6·50 4·25
142 – 18pi. black and green . . . 40·00 27·00
143 – 45pi. green and black . . . 65·00 48·00
DESIGNS—HORIZ: ½pi. Small Marble Forum, Salamis; ¾pi. Church of St. Barnabas and St. Hilarion, Peristerona; 1pi. Roman theatre, Soli; 1½pi. Kyrenia Harbour; 2½pi. Kolossi Castle; 45pi. Forest scene, Troodos. VERT: 6pi. Bayraktar Mosque, Nicosia; 9pi. Queen's Window, St. Hilarion Castle; 18pi. Buyuk Khan, Nicosia.
The ¼pi. to 2½pi. values have a medallion portrait of King George V.

1935. Silver Jubilee. As T **13** of Antigua.
144 ¾pi. blue and grey . . . . . 1·75 40
145 1½pi. blue and red . . . . . 3·50 2·50
146 2½pi. brown and blue . . . . 3·75 1·50
147 9pi. grey and purple . . . . 13·00 12·00

1937. Coronation. As T **2** of Aden.
148 ¾pi. grey 60 20
149 1½pi. red 90 80
150 2½pi. blue . . . . 2·00 1·25

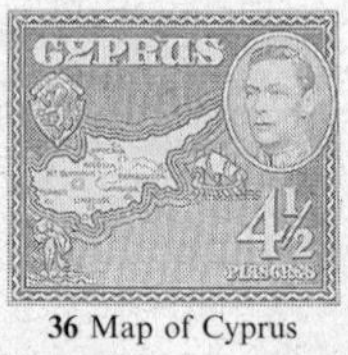

36 Map of Cyprus

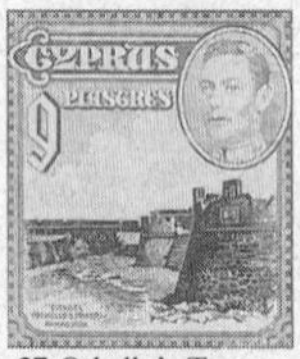

37 Othello's Tower, Famagusta

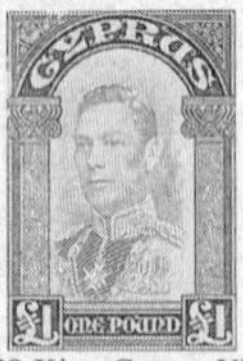

38 King George VI

1938.
151 – ¼pi. blue and brown . . 20 20
152 – ½pi. green 40 10
152a – ½pi. violet . . . . 2·25 20
153 – ¾pi. black and violet . . 14·00 40
154 – 1pi. orange 80 10
155 – 1½pi. red . . . . 5·50 1·50
155a – 1½pi. violet 50 30
155ab – 1½pi. green . . . . 2·75 40
155b – 2pi. black and red . . . 70 10
156 – 2½pi. blue . . . . 22·00 2·50
156a – 3pi. blue . . . . 1·25 15
156b – 4pi. blue . . . . 3·00 30
157 **36** 4½pi. grey 70 10
158 – 6pi. black and blue . . . 1·25 1·00
159 **37** 9pi. black and purple . . 2·25 20
160 – 18pi. black and olive . . 6·00 85
161 – 45pi. green and black . . 17·00 2·50
162 **38** 90pi. mauve and black 22·00 4·75
163 – £1 red and blue . . . . 48·00 23·00

DESIGNS: 2pi. Peristerona Church; 3pi., 4pi. Kolossi Castle. All other values except 4½pi., 9pi., 90pi. and £1 have designs as 1934 issue but portrait of King George VI.

1946. Victory. As T **9** of Aden.
164 1½pi. violet 15 10
165 3pi. blue 15 15

1948. Silver Wedding. As T **10/11** of Aden.
166 1½pi. violet 50 20
167 £1 blue . . . . 42·00 48·00

1949. U.P.U. As T **20/23** of Antigua.
168 1½pi. violet 40 70
169 2pi. red . . . . 1·50 1·50
170 3pi. blue . . . . 70 1·00
171 9pi. purple . . . . 1·50 1·25

1953. Coronation. As T **13** of Aden.
172 1½pi. black and green . . . . 1·00 10

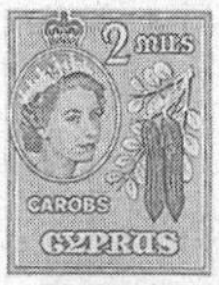

39 Carobs

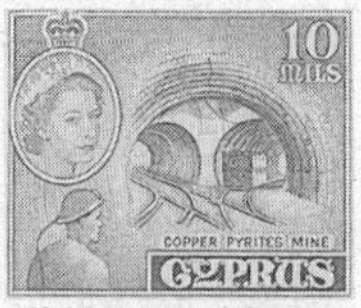

42 Mavrovouni Copper Pyrites Mine

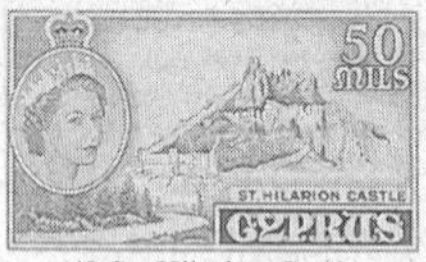

49 St. Hilarion Castle

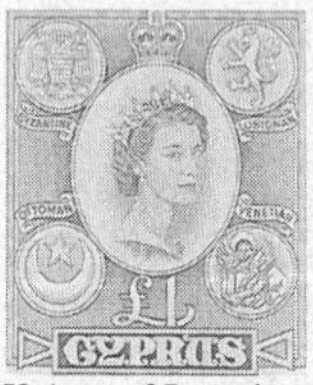

53 Arms of Byzantium, Lusignan, Ottoman Empire and Venice

1955.
173 **39** 2m. brown 10 40
174 – 3m. violet 10 15
175 – 5m. orange 70 10
176 **42** 10m. brown and green . . 1·00 10
177 – 15m. olive and blue . . . 2·50 45
178 – 20m. brown and blue . . . 1·00 15
179 – 25m. turquoise . . . . . 2·00 60
180 – 30m. black and lake . . . 1·50 10
181 – 35m. brown and turquoise 65 40
182 – 40m. green and brown . . 1·00 60
183 **49** 50m. blue and brown . . . 85 30
184 – 100m. mauve and green . . 12·00 60
185 – 250m. blue and brown . . 9·00 8·50
186 – 500m. slate and purple . . 26·00 11·00
187 **53** £1 lake and slate . . . . . 24·00 35·00
DESIGNS—As Type **39**: 3m. Grapes; 5m. Oranges. As Type **42**: 15m. Troodos Forest; 20m. Beach of Aphrodite; 25m. 5th-century B.C. coin of Paphos; 30m. Kyrenia; 35m. Harvest in Mesaoria; 40m. Famagusta harbour. As Type **49**: 100m. Hala Sultan Tekke; 250m. Kanakaria Church. As Type **53**: 500m. Coins of Salamis, Paphos, Citium and Idalium.

ΚΥΠΡΙΑΚΗ
ΔΗΜΟΚΡΑΤΙΑ
KIBRIS
CUMHURIYETI

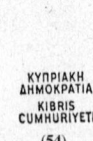

(**54**)

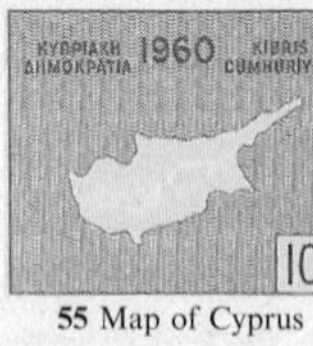

55 Map of Cyprus

1960. Nos. 173/87 optd as T **54** ("CYPRUS REPUBLIC" in Greek and Turkish).
188 **39** 2m. brown 20 75
189 – 3m. violet 20 15
190 – 5m. orange . . . . 1·00 10
191 **42** 10m. brown and green . . 80 10
192 – 15m. olive and blue . . . 75 10
193 – 20m. brown and blue . . . 50 1·25
194 – 25m. turquoise . . . . . 1·25 1·25
195 – 30m. black and lake . . . 1·75 10
196 – 35m. brown and turquoise 1·75 70
197 – 40m. green and brown . . 2·00 2·00
198 **49** 50m. blue and brown . . . 2·00 60
199 – 100m. mauve and green . . 9·00 60
200 – 250m. blue and brown . . 25·00 3·75
201 – 500m. slate and purple . . 40·00 17·00
202 **53** £1 lake and slate . . . . . 48·00 48·00

1960. Constitution of Republic.
203 **55** 10m. sepia and green . . . 30 10
204 30m. blue and brown . . . 65 10
205 100m. purple and slate . . 2·00 2·00

56 Doves

1962. Europa.
206 **56** 10m. purple and mauve . . 10 10
207 40m. blue and cobalt . . . 20 15
208 100m. emerald and green 20 20

57 Campaign Emblem

1962. Malaria Eradication.
209 **57** 10m. black and green . . . 15 15
210 30m. black and brown . . 30 15

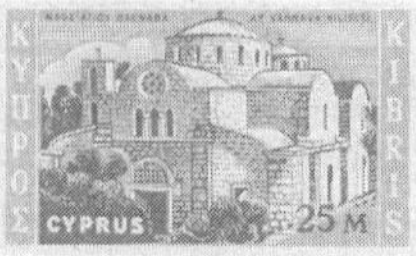

63 St. Barnabas's Church

1962.
211 – 3m. brown and orange . . 10 30
212 – 5m. purple and green . . . 10 10
213 – 10m. black and green . . . 15 10
214 – 15m. black and purple . . 30 15
215 **63** 25m. brown and chestnut 30 20
216 – 30m. blue and light blue 20 10
217 – 35m. green and blue . . . 35 10
218 – 40m. black and blue . . . 1·25 1·50
219 – 50m. bronze and bistre . . 50 10
220 – 100m. brown and bistre . . 3·50 30
221 – 250m. black and brown . . 8·50 2·25
222 – 500m. brown and green . . 15·00 8·00
223 – £1 bronze and grey . . . . 16·00 28·00
DESIGNS—VERT: 3m. Iron Age jug; 5m. Grapes; 10m. Bronze head of Apollo; 15m. Selimiye Mosque, Nicosia; 35m. Head of Aphrodite; 100m. Hala Sultan Tekke; 500m. Mouflon. HORIZ: 30m. Temple of Apollo Hylates; 40m. Skiing, Troodos; 50m. Salamis Gymnasium; 250m. Bella Paise Abbey; £1 St. Hilarion Castle.

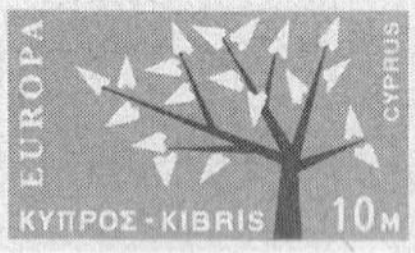

72 Europa "Tree"

1963. Europa.
224 **72** 10m. blue and black . . . 1·00 20
225 40m. red and black . . . . 5·00 2·00
226 150m. green and black . . 18·00 6·00

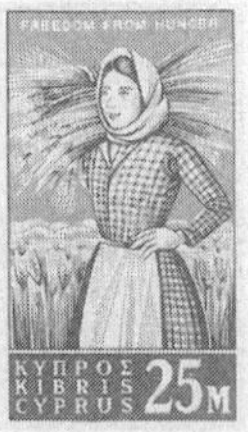

73 Harvester

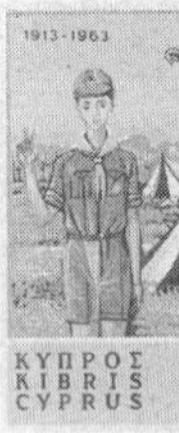

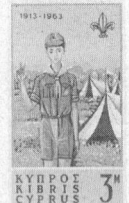

75 Wolf Cub in Camp

1963. Freedom from Hunger.
227 **73** 25c. ochre, sepia and blue 30 25
228 – 75m. grey, black and lake 1·75 1·00
DESIGN: 75m. Demeter, Goddess of Corn.

1963. 50th Anniv of Cyprus Scout Movement and 3rd Commonwealth Scout Conference, Platres. Multicoloured.
229 3m. Type **75** 10 20
230 20m. Sea Scout 35 10
231 150m. Scout with Mouflon 1·00 2·50

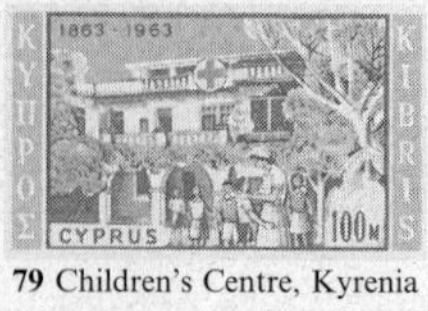

79 Children's Centre, Kyrenia

1963. Centenary of Red Cross. Multicoloured.
232 10m. Nurse tending child (vert) 50 15
233 100m. Type **79** . . . . 2·00 3·50

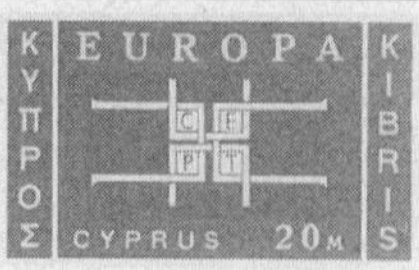

80 "Co-operation" (emblem)

1963. Europa.
234 **80** 20m. buff, blue and violet 1·75 40
235 30m. grey, yellow and blue 2·25 40
236 150m. buff, blue and brown . . . . 16·00 9·00

1964. U.N. Security Council's Cyprus Resolution, March 1964. Nos. 213 etc. optd with U.N. emblem and **1964**.
237 10m. black and green 15 10
238 30m. blue and light blue . . 15 10
239 40m. black and blue 15 20
240 50m. bronze and bistre . . . 15 10
241 100m. brown and bistre . . . 15 50

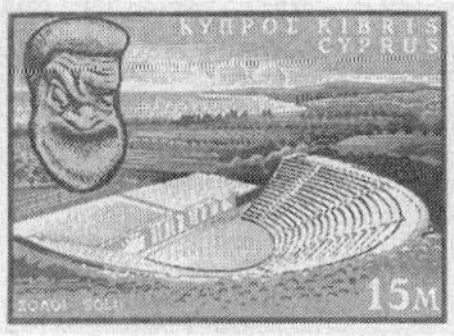

82 Soli Theatre

1964. 400th Birth Anniv of Shakespeare. Mult.
242 15m. Type **82** 40 15
243 35m. Curium Theatre 40 15
244 50m. Salamis Theatre 40 15
245 100m. Othello Tower, and scene from "Othello" . . . 1·00 2·25

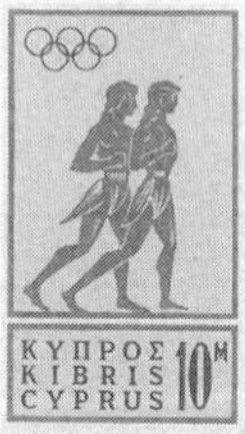

86 Running

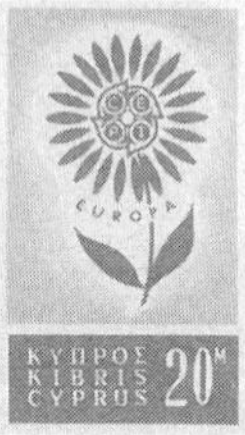

89 Europa "Flower"

1964. Olympic Games, Tokyo.
246 **86** 10m. brown, black & yell 10 10
247 – 25m. brown, black and slate 20 10
248 – 75m. brown, black and chest 35 65
DESIGNS—HORIZ: 25m. Boxing; 75m. Charioteers.

1964. Europa.
249 **89** 20m. brown and ochre . . 1·00 10
250 30m. ultramarine and blue 1·25 10
251 150m. olive and green . . 12·00 5·00

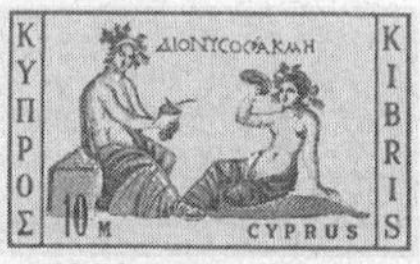

90 Dionysus and Acme

1964. Cyprus Wines. Multicoloured.
252 10m. Type **90** 25 10
253 40m. Silenus (satyr) . . . . 55 1·25
254 50m. Commandaria wine . . 55 10
255 100m. Wine factory . . . . 1·50 2·00
Nos. 253/4 are vert.

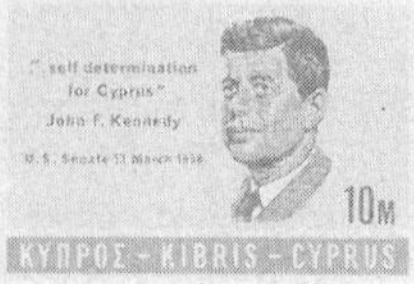

94 President Kennedy

1965. President Kennedy Commemoration.
256 **94** 10m. blue 10 10
257 40m. green 25 35
258 100m. red 30 35

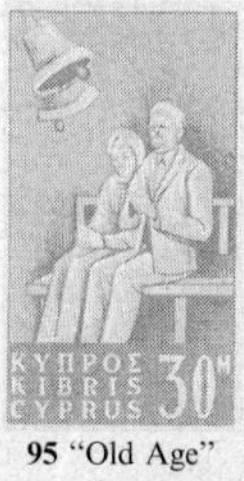

95 "Old Age"

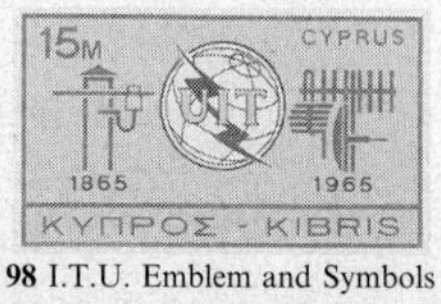

98 I.T.U. Emblem and Symbols

1965. Introduction of Social Insurance Law.

259	**95**	30m. drab and green . . .	15	10
260	–	45m. green, blue and ultramarine	20	10
261	–	75m. brown and flesh . .	1·25	2·50

DESIGNS—(As Type **95**): 45m. "Accident". LARGER (23 × 48 mm): 75m. "Maternity".

1965. Centenary of I.T.U.

262	**98**	15m. black, brown & yell	75	20
263	–	60m. black, grn & lt grn	6·00	2·75
264	–	75m. black, indigo & bl . .	6·50	4·75

99 I.C.Y. Emblem

1965. International Co-operation Year.

265	**99**	50m. brown and green . .	75	10
266	–	100m. purple and green . .	1·25	50

100 Europa "Sprig"

1965. Europa.

267	**100**	5m. black, brown & orge	25	10
268	–	45m. black, brown & grn	1·75	1·50
269	–	150m. black, brn & grey	4·50	3·75

1966. U.N. General Assembly's Cyprus Resolution. Nos. 211, 213, 216 and 221 optd **U.N. Resolution on Cyprus 18 Dec. 1965**.

270	3m. brown and orange . . .	10	30
271	10m. black and green . . .	10	10
272	30m. blue and light blue . .	10	15
273	250m. black and brown . . .	55	2·00

102 Discovery of St. Barnabas's Body

1966. 1900th Death Anniv of St. Barnabas.

274	**102**	15m. multicoloured	10	10
275	–	25m. drab, black and blue	15	10
276	–	100m. multicoloured . . .	45	2·00

DESIGNS—HORIZ: 25m. St. Barnabas's Chapel. VERT: 100m. St. Barnabas (icon).

1966. No. 211 surch **5M**.

278	5m. on 3m. brown & orange	10	10

107 General K. S. Thimayya and U.N. Emblem

1966. General Thimayya Commemoration.

279	**107** 50m. black and brown . .	30	10

108 Europa "Ship"   113 Silver Coin of Evagoras I

109 Stavrovouni Monastery

1966. Europa.

280	**108**	20m. green and blue . . .	25	10
281	–	30m. purple and blue . . .	25	10
282	–	150m. bistre and blue . .	1·50	3·00

1966. Multicoloured.

283	**109**	3m. Type **109**	40	10
284	–	5m. Church of St. James, Trikomo	10	10
285	–	10m. Zeno of Citium (marble bust)	15	10
286	–	15m. Minoan wine ship of 700 B.C. (painting) . .	15	10
287	–	20m. Type **113**	1·25	1·00
288	–	25m. Sleeping Eros (marble statue)	30	10
289	–	30m. St. Nicholas Cathedral, Famagusta	50	20
290	–	35m. Gold sceptre from Curium	50	30
291	–	40m. Silver dish from 7th century	70	30
292	–	50m. Silver coin of Alexander the Great	90	10
293	–	100m. Vase, 7th century B.C.	3·75	15
294	–	250m. Bronze ingot-stand .	1·00	40
295	–	500m. "The Rape of Ganymede" (mosaic) . . .	2·25	70
296	–	£1 Aphrodite (marble statue)	2·00	6·50

DESIGNS—VERT (As Type **109**): 5m. and 10m. HORIZ (As Type **113**): 15m., 25m. and 50m. VERT (As Type **113**): 30m., 35m., 40m. and 100m. Nos. 294/6 are as Type **113** but larger, 28 × 40 mm.

123 Power Station, Limassol   124 Cogwheels

1967. First Development Programme. Mult.

297	**123**	10m. Type **123**	10	10
298	–	15m. Arghaka-Maghounda Dam	15	10
299	–	35m. Troodos Highway . . .	20	10
300	–	50m. Hilton Hotel, Nicosia	20	10
301	–	100m. Famagusta Harbour	20	1·10

Nos. 298/301 are vert.

1967. Europa.

302	**124**	20m. olive, grn & lt grn	25	10
303	–	30m. violet, lilac and mauve	25	10
304	–	150m. sepia, brn chestnut	1·00	2·25

125 Throwing the Javelin

1967. Athletic Games, Nicosia. Multicoloured.

305	**125**	15m. Type **125**	20	10
306	–	35m. Running	35	35
307	–	100m. High-jumping	30	1·00

127 Ancient Monuments

1967. International Tourist Year. Multicoloured.

309	**127**	10m. Type **127**	10	10
310	–	40m. Famagusta Beach . . .	15	90
311	–	50m. Hawker Siddeley Comet-4 at Nicosia Airport	15	10
312	–	100m. Skier and youth hostel	20	95

128 Saint Andrew Mosaic   129 "The Crucifixion" (icon)

1967. Centenary of St Andrew's Monastery.

313	**128** 25m. multicoloured . . .	10	10

1967. Cyprus Art Exhibition, Paris.

314	**129** 50m. multicoloured . . .	10	10

130 The Three Magi   131 Human Rights Emblem over Stars

1967. 20th Anniv of U.N.E.S.C.O.

315	**130** 75m. multicoloured . . .	20	20

1968. Human Rights Year. Multicoloured.

316	**131**	50m. Type **131**	10	10
317	–	90m. Human Rights and U.N. emblems	30	70

134 Europa "Key"

1968. Europa.

319	**134**	20m. multicoloured . . .	15	10
320	–	30m. multicoloured . . .	15	10
321	–	150m. multicoloured . . .	35	2·25

135 U.N. Children's Fund Symbol and Boy drinking Milk

1968. 21st Anniv of U.N.I.C.E.F.

322	**135** 35m. brown, red and black	10	10

136 Aesculapius   137 Throwing the Discus

1968. 20th Anniv of W.H.O.

323	**136** 50m. black, green and olive	10	10

1968. Olympic Games, Mexico. Multicoloured.

324	**137**	10m. Type **137**	10	10
325	–	25m. Sprint finish	10	10
326	–	100m. Olympic Stadium (horiz)	20	1·25

138 I.L.O. Emblem   141 Europa Emblem

139 Mercator's Map of Cyprus, 1554

1969. 50th Anniv of I.L.O.

327	**138**	50m. brown and blue . .	15	10
328	–	90m. brown, black and grey	15	55

1969. 1st International Congress of Cypriot Studies.

329	**139**	50m. multicoloured . . .	20	30
330	–	50m. multicoloured . . .	20	10

DESIGN: 50m. Blaeu's map of Cyprus, 1635.

1969. Europa.

331	**141**	20m. multicoloured . . .	20	10
332	–	30m. multicoloured . . .	20	10
333	–	150m. multicoloured . . .	80	2·00

142 Northern Roller ("Roller")

1969. Birds of Cyprus. Multicoloured.

334	**142**	5m. Type **142**	40	15
335	–	15m. Audouin's gull	60	15
336	–	20m. Cyprus warbler . . .	60	15
337	–	30m. Jay ("Cyprus Jay") . .	60	15
338	–	40m. Hoopoe	65	30
339	–	90m. Eleonora's falcon . . .	1·50	5·00

Nos. 337/339 are vert.

143 "The Nativity" (12th-century wall painting)

1969. Christmas. Multicoloured.

340	**143**	20m. Type **143**	15	10
341	–	45m. "The Nativity" (14th-century wall painting) . . .	15	20

146 Mahatma Gandhi

1970. Birth Centenary of Mahatma Gandhi.

343	**146**	25m. blue, drab and black	15	10
344	–	75m. brown, drab and black	20	65

147 "Flaming Sun"

1970. Europa.

345	**147**	20m. brown, yell & orge	20	10
346	–	30m. blue, yellow & orge	20	10
347	–	150m. purple, yell & orge	80	2·50

148 Gladioli   149 I.E.Y. Emblem

1970. Nature Conservation Year. Multicoloured.

348	**148**	10m. Type **148**	10	10
349	–	50m. Poppies	15	10
350	–	90m. Giant fennel	50	1·40

1970. Anniversaries and Events.

351	**149**	5m. black and brown . .	10	10
352	–	15m. multicoloured . . .	10	10
353	–	75m. multicoloured . . .	15	75

DESIGNS AND EVENTS: 5m. International Education Year. HORIZ: 15m. Mosaic (50th General Assembly of International Vine and Wine Office); 75m. Globe, dove and U.N. emblem (25th anniv of United Nations).

152 Virgin and Child   153 Cotton Napkin

1970. Christmas. Wall-painting from Church of Panayia Podhythou, Galata. Multicoloured.

354	–	25m. Archangel (facing right)	15	20
355	**152**	25m. Type **152**	15	20

356	25m. Archangel (facing left)	15	20
357	75m. Virgin and Child between Archangels (42 × 30 mm)	15	30

1971. Multicoloured.

358	3m. Type **153**	30	35
359	5m. Saint George and Dragon (19th-century bas-relief)	10	10
360	10m. Woman in festival costume	15	35
361	15m. Archaic Bichrome Kylix (cup) (horiz)	20	10
362	20m. A pair of donors (Saint Mamas Church) . . .	35	65
363	25m. "The Creation" (6th-century mosaic) . . .	30	10
364	30m. Athena and horse-drawn chariot (4th-century B.C. terracotta) (horiz) . .	30	10
365	40m. Shepherd playing pipe (14th-century fresco) . .	1·00	1·00
366	50m. Hellenistic head (3rd-century B.C.) . . .	80	10
367	75m. "Angel" (mosaic detail), Kanakaria Church . .	1·75	1·00
368	90m. Mycenaean silver bowl (horiz)	2·00	2·00
369	250m. Moufflon (detail of 3rd-century mosaic) (horiz)	1·50	30
370	500m. Ladies and sacred tree (detail 6th-century amphora) (horiz) . .	80	40
371	£1 Horned god from Enkomi (12th-century bronze statue)	1·50	60

SIZES: 24 × 37 mm or 37 × 24 mm 10m. to 90m.; 41 × 28 mm or 28 × 41 mm 250m. to £1.

154 Europa Chain

1971. Europa.

372	**154**	20m. blue, ultram & blk	15	10
373		30m. green, myrtle & blk	15	10
374		150m. yellow, grn & blk	50	2·50

155 Archbishop Kyprianos

1971. 150th Anniv of Greek War of Independence. Multicoloured.

375	15m. Type **155**	10	10
376	30m. "Taking the Oath" (horiz)	10	10
377	100m. Bishop Germanos, flag and freedom-fighters . . .	20	50

156 Kyrenia Castle

1971. Tourism. Multicoloured.

378	15m. Type **156**	10	10
379	25m. Gourd on sunny beach (vert)	10	10
380	60m. Mountain scenery (vert)	20	60
381	100m. Church of Saint Evlalios, Lambousa . .	20	65

157 Madonna and Child in Stable
159 "Communications"

158 Heart

1971. Christmas. Multicoloured.

382	10m. Type **157**	10	10
383	50m. The Three Wise Men	15	35
384	100m. The Shepherds	20	35

1972. World Heart Month.

385	**158**	15m. multicoloured	10	10
386		50m. multicoloured	20	45

1972. Europa.

387	**159**	20m. orange, sepia & brn	25	15
388		30m. orange, ultram & bl	25	15
389		150m. orge, myrtle & grn	2·00	3·75

160 Archery

1972. Olympic Games, Munich. Multicoloured.

390	10m. Type **160**	25	10
391	40m. Wrestling	35	15
392	100m. Football	75	1·40

161 Stater of Marion
162 Bathing the Child Jesus

1972. Ancient Coins of Cyprus (1st series).

393	**161**	20m. blue, black and silver	20	10
394		30m. blue, black and silver	20	10
395		40m. brown, blk & silver	20	20
396		100m. pink, black and silver	60	1·00

COINS: 30m. Stater of Paphos; 40m. Stater of Lapithos; 100m. Stater of Idalion.
See also Nos. 486/9.

1972. Christmas. Detail of mural in Holy Cross Church, Agiasmati. Multicoloured.

397	10m. Type **162**	10	10
398	20m. The Magi	10	10
399	100m. The Nativity	15	30

163 Mount Olympus, Troodos

1973. 29th International Ski Federation Congress. Multicoloured.

401	20m. Type **163**	10	10
402	100m. Congress emblem . . .	25	35

164 Europa "Posthorn"

1973. Europa.

403	**164**	20m. multicoloured . . .	15	10
404		30m. multicoloured . . .	15	10
405		150m. multicoloured . . .	1·10	3·00

165 Archbishop's Palace, Nicosia

1973. Traditional Architecture. Multicoloured.

406	20m. Type **165**	10	10
407	30m. House of Hajigeorgajis Cornessios, Nicosia (vert)	10	10

408	50m. House at Gourri, 1850 (vert)	15	10
409	100m. House at Rizokarpaso, 1772	40	75

1973. No. 361 surch **20M**.

410	20m. on 15m. multicoloured	15	15

167 Scout Emblem
168 Archangel Gabriel

1973. Anniversaries and Events.

411	**167**	10m. green and brown	20	10
412		25m. blue and lilac . . .	20	10
413		35m. olive, stone and green	20	25
414		50m. blue and indigo . .	20	10
415		100m. brown and sepia	50	80

DESIGNS AND EVENTS—VERT: 10m. (60th anniv of Cyprus Boy Scouts); 50m. Airline emblem (25th anniv of Cyprus Airways); 100m. Interpol emblem (50th anniv of Interpol). HORIZ: 25m. Outlines of Cyprus and the E.E.C. (Association of Cyprus with "Common Market"); 35m. F.A.O. emblem (10th anniv of F.A.O.).

1973. Christmas. Murals from Araka Church. Multicoloured.

416	10m. Type **168**	10	10
417	20m. Madonna and Child . .	10	10
418	100m. Araka Church (horiz)	40	75

169 Grapes
170 "The Rape of Europa" (Silver Stater of Marion)

1974. Products of Cyprus. Multicoloured.

419	25m. Type **169**	10	15
420	50m. Grapefruit	20	60
421	50m. Oranges	20	60
422	50m. Lemons	20	60

1974. Europa.

423	**170**	10m. multicoloured . . .	15	10
424		40m. multicoloured . . .	35	30
425		150m. multicoloured . . .	1·10	2·75

171 Title Page of A. Kyprianos' "History of Cyprus" (1788)
174 "Refugees"

1974. 2nd International Congress of Cypriot Studies. Multicoloured.

426	10m. Type **171**	10	10
427	25m. Solon (philosopher) in mosaic (horiz) . .	15	10
428	100m. "Saint Neophytos" (wall painting) . .	60	75

1974. Obligatory Tax. Refugee Fund. No. 359 surch **REFUGEE FUND** in English, Greek and Turkish and **10M**.

430	10m. on 5m. multicoloured	10	10

1974. U.N. Security Council Resolution 353. Nos. 360, 365, 366 and 369 optd **SECURITY COUNCIL RESOLUTION 353 20 JULY 1974**.

431	10m. multicoloured	20	10
432	40m. multicoloured	25	50
433	50m. multicoloured	25	10
434	250m. multicoloured	60	2·75

1974. Obligatory Tax. Refugee Fund.

435	**174**	10m. black and grey . . .	10	10

175 "Virgin and Child between Two Angels", Stavros Church

1974. Christmas. Church Wall-paintings. Mult.

436	10m. Type **175**	10	10
437	50m. "Adoration of the Magi", Ayios Neophytos Monastery (vert) . . .	20	10
438	100m. "Flight into Egypt", Ayios Neophytos Monastery	25	45

176 Larnaca–Nicosia Mail-coach, 1878

1975. Anniversaries and Events.

439	**176**	20m. multicoloured . . .	25	10
440		30m. blue and orange . .	25	60
441	**176**	50m. multicoloured . . .	25	10
442		100m. multicoloured . . .	40	1·40

DESIGNS AND EVENTS—HORIZ: 20m., 50m. Centenary of Universal Postal Union. VERT: 30m. "Disabled Persons" (8th European Meeting of International Society for the Rehabilitation of Disabled Persons); 100m. Council flag (25th anniv of Council of Europe).

177 "The Distaff" (M. Kashalos)
178 Red Cross Flag over Map

1975. Europa. Multicoloured.

443	20m. Type **177**	25	40
444	30m. "Nature Morte" (C. Savva)	25	50
445	150m. "Virgin and Child of Liopetri" (G. P. Georghiou)	40	80

1975. Anniversaries and Events. Multicoloured.

446	25m. Type **178**	20	10
447	30m. Nurse and lamp (horiz)	20	10
448	75m. Woman's steatite idol (horiz)	20	90

EVENTS: 25m. 25th anniv of Red Cross; 30m. International Nurses' Day; 75m. International Women's Year.

179 Submarine Cable Links
181 Human-figured Vessel, 19th-century

1976. Telecommunications Achievements.

449	**179**	50m. multicoloured . . .	30	10
450		100m. yellow, vio & lilac	35	90

DESIGN—HORIZ: 100m. International subscriber dialling.

1976. Surch **10M**.

451	**153**	10m. on 3m. multicoloured	20	60

1976. Europa. Ceramics. Multicoloured.

452	20m. Type **181**	20	10
453	60m. Composite vessel, 2100–2000 B.C. . . .	50	80
454	100m. Byzantine goblet . .	90	1·75

182 Self-help Housing

1976. Economic Reactivation. Multicoloured.

455	10m. Type **182**	10	10
456	25m. Handicrafts	15	20

457 30m. Reafforestation 15 20
458 60m. Air communications 30 55

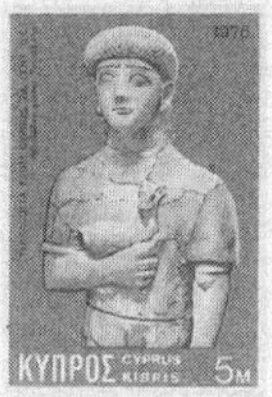

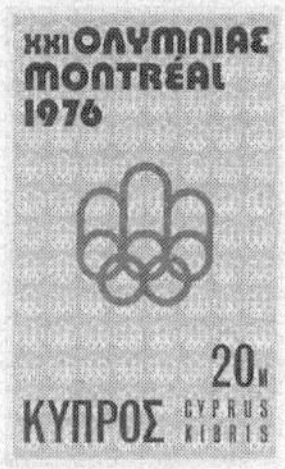

183 Terracotta Statue of Youth
184 Olympic Symbol

1976. Cypriot Treasures.
459 **183** 5m. multicoloured 10 60
460 – 10m. multicoloured 10 40
461 – 20m. red, yellow and black 20 40
462 – 25m. multicoloured 20 10
463 – 30m. multicoloured 20 10
464 – 40m. green, brown & blk 30 45
465 – 50m. lt brown, brn & blk 30 10
466 – 60m. multicoloured 30 20
467 – 100m. multicoloured 40 40
468 – 250m. blue, grey and black 50 1·50
469 – 500m. black, brown & grn 60 2·00
470 – £1 multicoloured 1·00 2·25
DESIGNS—VERT: 10m. Limestone head (23 × 34 mm); 20m. Gold necklace from Lambousa (24 × 37 mm); 25m. Terracotta warrior (24 × 37 mm); 30m. Statue of a priest of Aphrodite (24 × 37 mm); 250m. Silver dish from Lambousa (28 × 41 mm); 500m. Bronze stand (28 × 41 mm); £1 Statue of Artemis (28 × 41 mm). HORIZ: 40m. Bronze tablet (37 × 24 mm); 50m. Mycenaean crater (37 × 24 mm); 60m. Limestone sarcophagus (37 × 24 mm); 100m. Gold bracelet from Lambousa (As Type **183**).

1976. Olympic Games, Montreal.
471 **184** 20m. red, black and yellow 10 10
472 – 60m. multicoloured (horiz) 20 30
473 – 100m. multicoloured (horiz) 30 35
DESIGNS: 60m. and 100m. Olympic symbols (different).

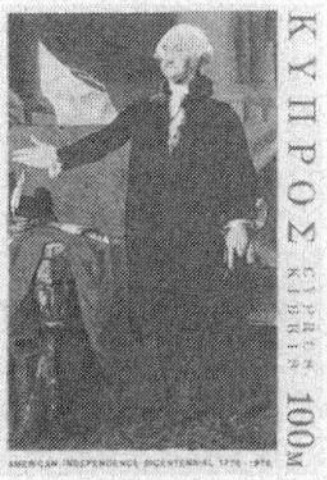

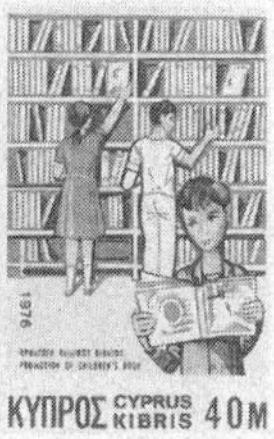

185 "George Washington" (G. Stuart)
186 Children in Library

1976. Bicentenary of American Revolution.
474 **185** 100m. multicoloured 40 30

1976. Anniversaries and Events.
475 **186** 40m. multicoloured 15 15
476 – 50m. brown and black 15 10
477 – 80m. multicoloured 30 60
DESIGNS AND EVENTS: 40m. Type **186** (Promotion of Children's books); 50m. Low-cost housing (HABITAT Conference, Vancouver); 80m. Eye protected by hands (World Health Day).

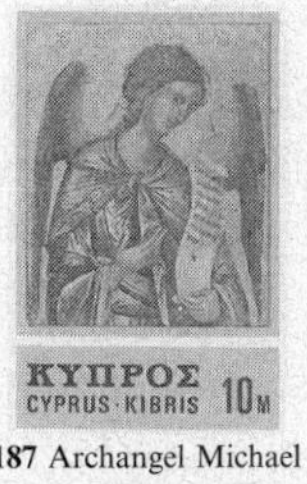

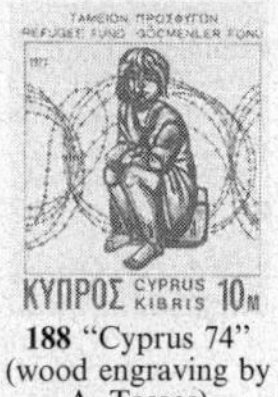

187 Archangel Michael
188 "Cyprus 74" (wood engraving by A. Tassos)

1976. Christmas. Multicoloured.
478 10m. Type **187** 10 10
479 15m. Archangel Gabriel 10 10
480 150m. The Nativity 45 80
Designs show icons from Ayios Neophytis Monastery.

1977. Refugee Fund.
481 **188** 10m. black 20 10
See also Nos. 634 and 892 (after No. 728).

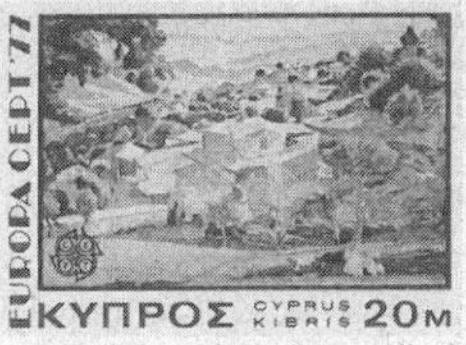

189 "View of Prodhromos" (A. Diamantis)

1977. Europa. Paintings. Multicoloured.
482 20m. Type **189** 20 10
483 60m. "Springtime at Monagroulli" (T. Kanthos) 30 55
484 120m. "Old Port, Limassol" (V. Ioannides) 60 1·75

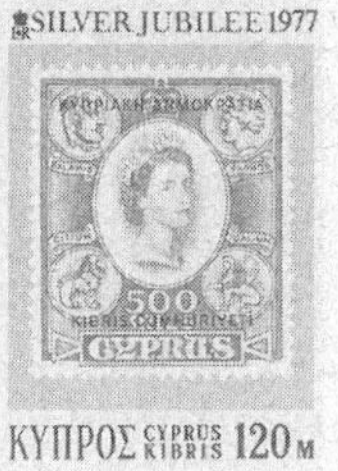

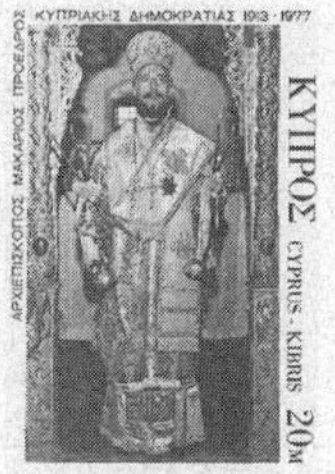

190 500m. Stamp of 1960
192 Archbishop Makarios in Ceremonial Robes

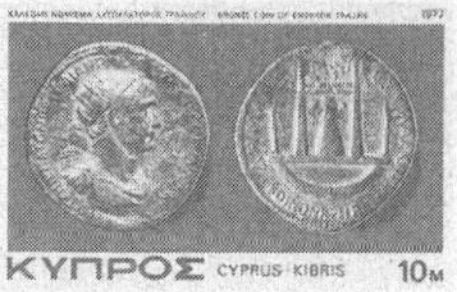

191 Bronze Coin of Emperor Trajan

1977. Silver Jubilee.
485 **190** 120m. multicoloured 30 30

1977. Ancient Coins of Cyprus (2nd series).
486 **191** 10m. black, gold and blue 15 10
487 – 40m. black, silver and blue 30 30
488 – 60m. black, silver & orge 35 35
489 – 100m. black, gold and green 50 95
DESIGNS: 40m. Silver tetradrachm of Demetrios Poliorcetes; 60m. Silver tetradrachm of Ptolemy VIII; 100m. Gold octadrachm of Arsinoe II.

1977. Death of Archbishop Makarios. Mult.
490 20m. Type **192** 15 10
491 60m. Archbishop in doorway 20 10
492 250m. Head and shoulders portrait 50 1·10

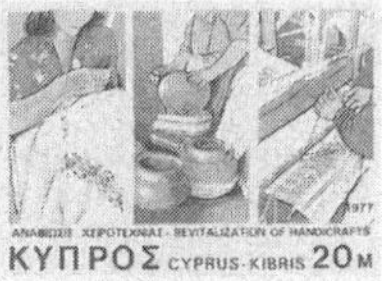

193 Embroidery, Pottery and Weaving

1977. Anniversaries and Events. Multicoloured.
493 20m. Type **193** 10 10
494 40m. Map of Mediterranean 15 20
495 60m. Gold medals 20 20
496 80m. Sputnik 20 85
DESIGNS COMMEMORATE: 20m. Revitalization of handicrafts; 40m. "Man and the Biosphere" Programme in the Mediterranean region; 60m. Gold medals won by Cypriot students in the Orleans Gymnasiade; 80m. 60th anniv of Russian Revolution.

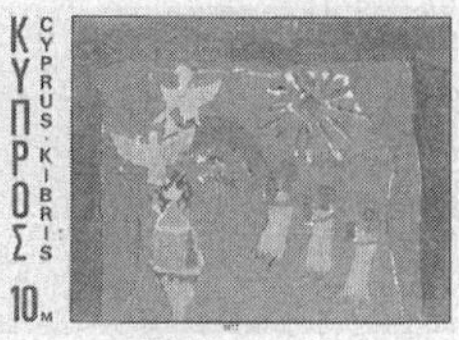

194 "Nativity"

1977. Christmas. Children's Paintings Mult.
497 10m. Type **194** 10 10
498 40m. "The Three Kings" 10 10
499 150m. "Flight into Egypt" 25 80

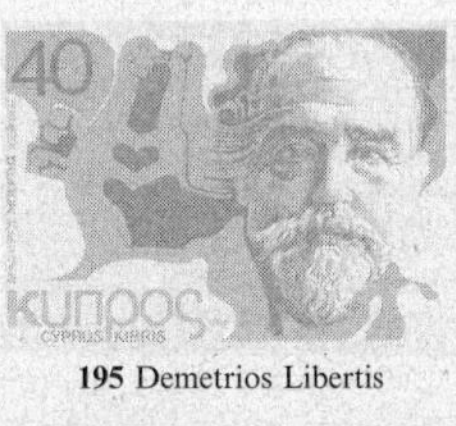

195 Demetrios Libertis

1978. Cypriot Poets.
500 **195** 40m. brown and bistre 10 10
501 – 150m. grey, black and red 30 80
DESIGN: 150m. Vasilis Michaelides.

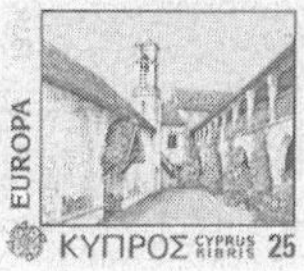

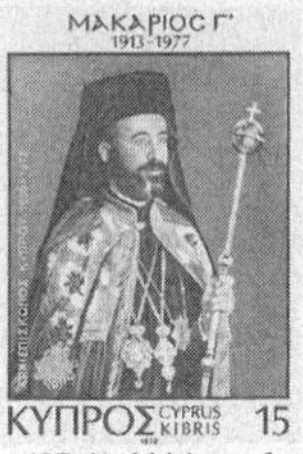

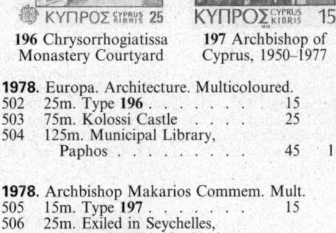

196 Chrysorrhogiatissa Monastery Courtyard
197 Archbishop of Cyprus, 1950–1977

1978. Europa. Architecture. Multicoloured.
502 25m. Type **196** 15 10
503 75m. Kolossi Castle 25 35
504 125m. Municipal Library, Paphos 45 1·50

1978. Archbishop Makarios Commem. Mult.
505 15m. Type **197** 15 20
506 25m. Exiled in Seychelles, 9 March 1956–28 March 1957 15 20
507 50m. President of the Republic 1960–1977 20 25
508 75m. "Soldier of Christ" 20 30
509 100m. "Fighter for Freedom" 25 35

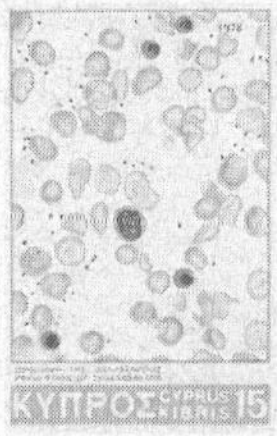

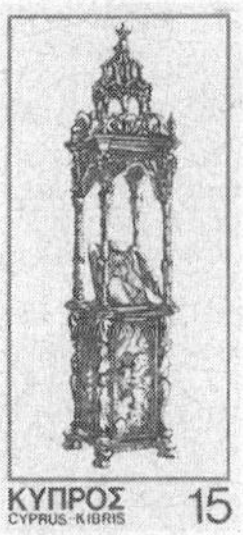

198 Affected Blood Corpuscles (Prevention of Thalassaemia)
199 Icon Stand

1978. Anniversaries and Events.
511 **198** 15m. multicoloured 10 10
512 – 35m. multicoloured 15 10
513 – 75m. black and grey 20 30
514 – 125m. multicoloured 35 80
DESIGNS—VERT: 35m. Aristotle (sculpture) (2300th death anniv). HORIZ: 75m. "Heads" (Human Rights); 125m. Wright brothers and Wright Flyer I (75th anniv of Powered Flight).

1978. Christmas.
515 **199** 15m. multicoloured 10 10
516 – 35m. multicoloured 15 10
517 – 150m. multicoloured 40 60
DESIGNS: 35m., 150m. Different icon stands.

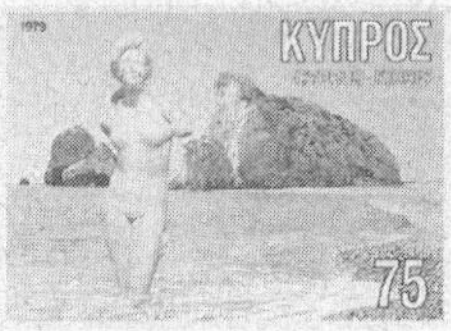

200 Aphrodite (statue from Soli)

1979. Goddess Aphrodite (1st issue). Multicoloured.
518 75m. Type **200** 25 10
519 125m. Aphrodite on shell (detail from Botticelli's "Birth of Venus") 35 25
See also Nos. 584/5.

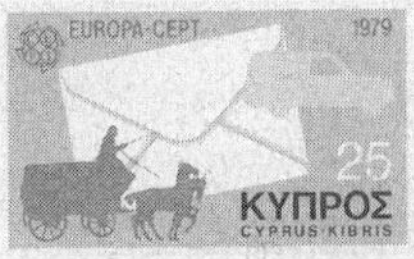

201 Van, Larnaca–Nicosia Mail-coach and Envelope

1979. Europa. Communications. Multicoloured.
520 25m. Type **201** 15 10
521 75m. Radar, satellite and early telephone 30 20
522 125m. Aircraft, ship and envelopes 65 1·10

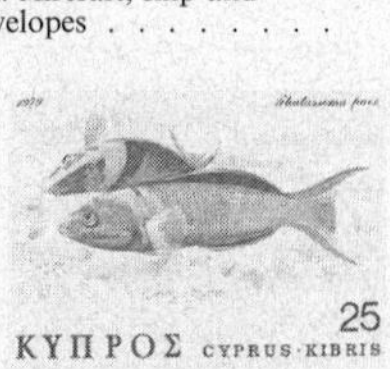

202 Peacock Wrasse

1979. Flora and Fauna. Multicoloured.
523 25m. Type **202** 15 10
524 50m. Black partridge (vert) 70 60
525 75m. Cedar (vert) 45 30
526 125m. Mule 50 1·25

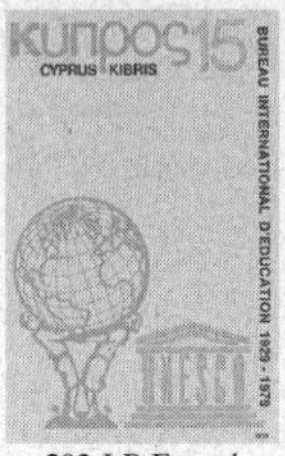

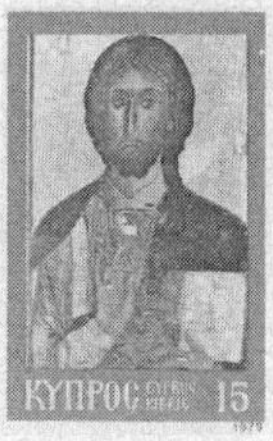

203 I.B.E. and U.N.E.S.C.O. Emblems
204 "Jesus" (from Church of the Virgin Mary of Arakas, Lagoudhera)

1979. Anniversaries and Events.
527 **203** 15m. multicoloured 10 10
528 – 25m. multicoloured 10 10
529 – 50m. black, brown and ochre 20 15
530 – 75m. multicoloured 25 10
531 – 100m. multicoloured 30 20
532 – 125m. multicoloured 30 75
DESIGNS AND COMMEMORATIONS—VERT: 15m. Type **203** (50th anniv of International Bureau of Education); 125m. Rotary International emblem and "75" (75th anniv). HORIZ: 25m. Graphic design of dove and stamp album (20th anniv of Cyprus Philatelic Society); 50m. Lord Kitchener and map of Cyprus (Cyprus Survey Centenary); 75m. Child's face (International Year of the Child); 100m. Graphic design of footballers (25th anniv of U.E.F.A. European Football Association).

1979. Christmas. Icons. Multicoloured.
533 15m. Type **204** 10 10
534 35m. "Nativity" (Church of St Nicholas, Famagusta District) (29 × 41 mm) 10 10
535 150m. "Holy Mary" (Church of the Virgin Mary of Arakas) 25 45

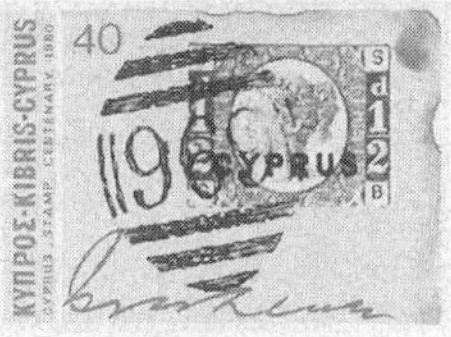

205 1880 ½d. Stamp with "969" (Nicosia) Postmark

1980. Centenary of Cyprus Stamps. Multicoloured.
536 40m. Type **205** 10 10
537 125m. 1880 2½d. stamp with "974" (Kyrenia) postmark 15 15
538 175m. 1880 1s. stamp with "942" (Larnaca) postmark 15 20

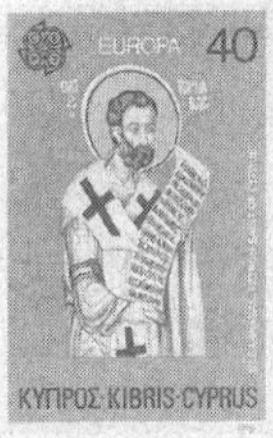

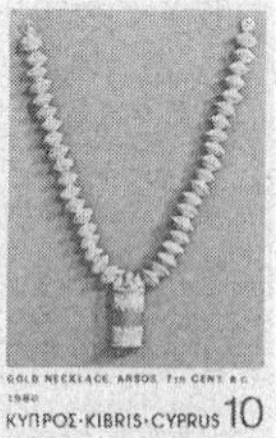

206 St. Barnabas (patron saint of Cyprus)
208 Gold Necklace, Arsos (7th-century B.C.)

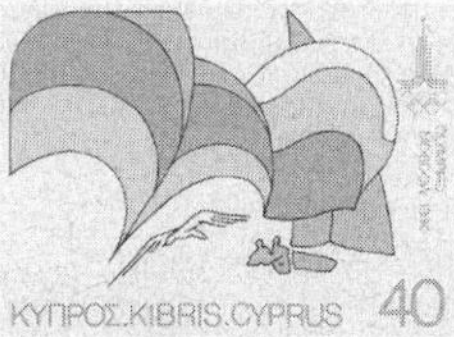

207 Sailing

1980. Europa. Personalities. Multicoloured.
540 40m. Type **206** 15 10
541 125m. Zeno of Citium (founder of Stoic philosophy) 30 20

1980. Olympic Games, Moscow. Multicoloured.
542 40m. Type **207** 10 10
543 125m. Swimming 20 20
544 200m. Gymnastics 25 25

1980. Archaeological Treasures.
545 **208** 10m. multicoloured 30 70
546 – 15m. multicoloured 30 70
547 – 25m. multicoloured 30 30
548 – 40m. multicoloured 40 65
549 – 50m. multicoloured 40 10
550 – 75m. multicoloured 90 1·25
551 – 100m. multicoloured 65 15
552 – 125m. multicoloured 65 60
553 – 150m. multicoloured 75 15
554 – 175m. multicoloured 75 1·00
555 – 200m. multicoloured 75 30
556 – 500m. multicoloured 75 1·25
557 – £1 multicoloured 1·00 1·25
558 – £2 multicoloured 1·75 2·00

DESIGNS—HORIZ: 15m. Bronze cow, Vouni Palace (5th-cent B.C.); 40m. Gold finger-ring, Enkomi (13th-cent B.C.); 500m. Stone bowl, Khirokitia (6th-millennium B.C.). VERT: 25m. Amphora, Salamis (6th-cent B.C.); 50m. Bronze cauldron, Salamis (8th-cent B.C.); 75m. Funerary stele, Marion (5th-cent B.C.). 100m. Jug (15–14th-cent B.C.); 125m. Warrior (terracotta) (6th–5th-cent B.C.); 150m. Lions attacking bull (bronze relief), Vouni Palace (5th-cent B.C.); 175m. Faience rhyton, Kition (13th-cent B.C.); 200m. Bronze statue of Ingot God, Enkomi (12th-cent B.C.); £1 Ivory plaque, Salamis (7th-cent B.C.); £2 "Leda and the Swan" (mosaic), Kouklia (3rd-cent A.D.).

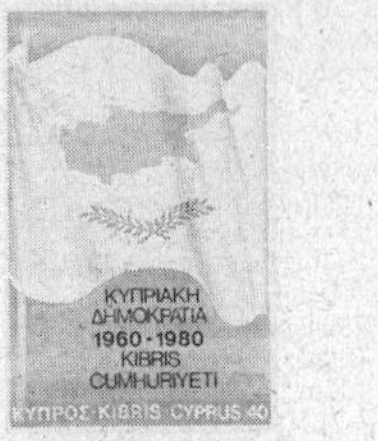

209 Cyprus Flag

1980. 20th Anniv of Republic of Cyprus. Multicoloured.
559 40m. Type **209** 10 10
560 125m. Signing Treaty of Establishment (41 × 29 mm) 20 15
561 175m. Archbishop Makarios 35 25

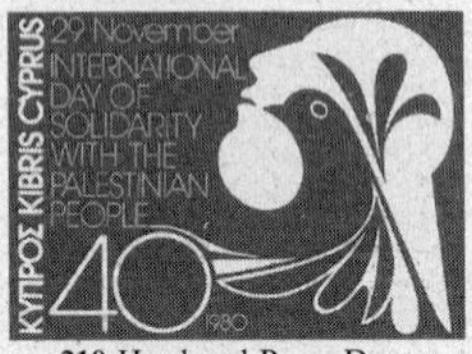

210 Head and Peace Dove

1980. International Day of Solidarity with Palestinian People.
562 **210** 40m. black and grey . . . 20 20
563 – 125m. black and grey . . 35 35
DESIGN: 125m. Head and dove with olive branch.

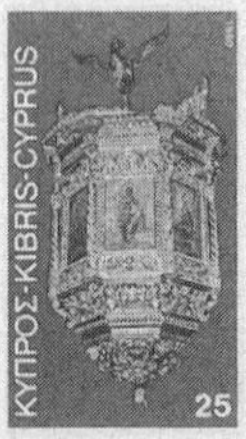

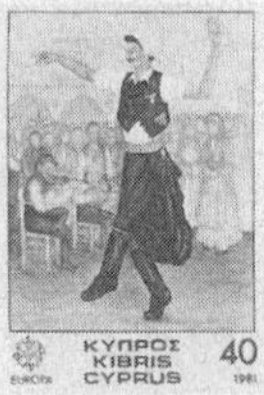

211 Pulpit, Tripiotis Church, Nicosia **212** Folk Dancing

1980. Christmas. Multicoloured.
564 25m. Type **211** 10 10
565 100m. Holy Doors, Panayia Church Paralimni 15 20
565 125m. Pulpit, Ayios Lazaros Church, Larnaca 15 20

1981. Europa. Folklore, showing folk-dancing from paintings by T. Photiades.
567 **212** 40m. multicoloured . . . 30 10
568 – 175m. multicoloured . . . 60 50

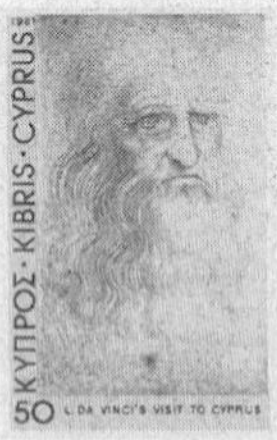

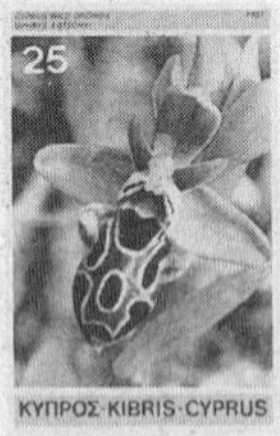

213 Self-portrait **214** "Ophrys kotschyi"

1981. 500th Anniv of Leonardo da Vinci's Visit. Multicoloured.
569 50m. Type **213** 40 10
570 125m. "The Last Supper" (50 × 25 mm) 70 40
571 175m. Cyprus lace and Milan Cathedral 95 60

1981. Cypriot Wild Orchids. Multicoloured.
572 25m. Type **214** 50 60
573 50m. "Orchis punctulata" . . 60 70
574 75m. "Ophrys argolica elegans" 70 80
575 150m. "Epipactis veratrifolia" 75 90

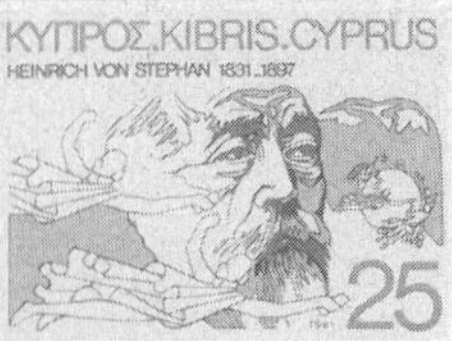

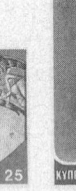

215 Heinrich von Stephan

1981. Anniversaries and Events.
576 **215** 25m. dp green, grn & bl 15 10
577 – 40m. multicoloured . . . 15 10
578 – 125m. black, red and green 30 25
579 – 150m. multicoloured . . . 35 30
580 – 200m. multicoloured . . . 40 35
DESIGNS AND COMMEMORATIONS: 25m. Type **137** (150th birth anniv of Heinrich von Stephan (founder of U.P.U.); 40m. Stylised man holding dish of food (World Food Day); 125m. Stylised hands (International Year for Disabled People); 150m. Stylised building and flower (European Campaign for Urban Renaissance); 200m. Prince Charles, Lady Diana Spencer and St. Paul's Cathedral (Royal Wedding).

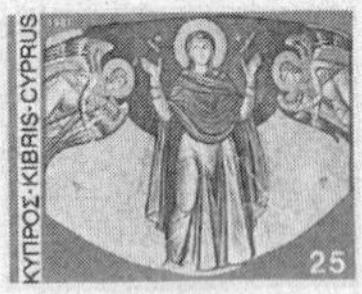

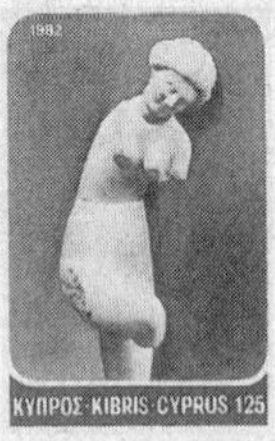

216 "The Lady of the Angels" (from Church of the Transfiguration of Christ, Palekhori) **217** "Louomene" (Aphrodite bathing) (statue, 250 B.C.)

1981. Christmas. Murals from Nicosia District Churches. Multicoloured.
581 25m. Type **216** 20 10
582 100m. "Christ Pantokrator" (Church of Madonna of Arakas, Lagoudera) (vert) 60 20
583 125m. "Baptism of Christ" (Church of Our Lady of Assinou, Nikitari) 70 30

1982. Aphrodite (Greek goddess of love and beauty) Commemoration (2nd issue). Mult.
584 125m. Type **217** 55 45
585 175m. "Anadyomene" (Aphordite emerging from the waters) (Titian) 70 65

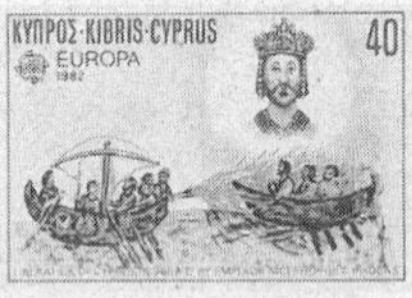

218 Naval Battle with Greek Fire, 985 A.D.

1982. Europa. Historic Events. Multicoloured.
586 40m. Type **218** 60 10
587 175m. Conversion of Roman Proconsul Sergius Paulus to Christianity, Paphos, 45 A.D. . . . . 1·00 2·50

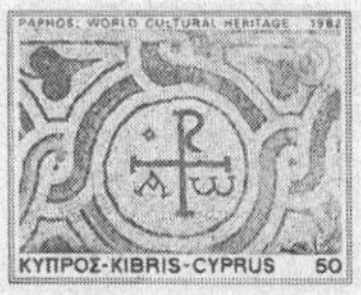

219 "XP" (monogram of Christ) (mosaic)

1982. World Cultural Heritage. Multicoloured.
588 50m. Type **219** 25 10
589 125m. Head of priest-king of Paphos (sculpture) (24 × 37 mm) 50 25
590 225m. Theseus (Greek god) (mosaic) 75 95

1982. No. 550 surch **100**.
591 100m. on 75m. Funerary stele, Marion (5th-century B.C.) 50 50

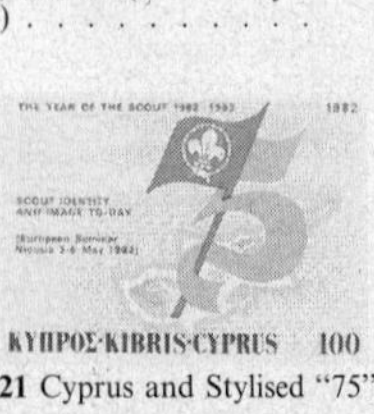

221 Cyprus and Stylised "75"

1982. 75th Anniv of Boy Scout Movement. Multicoloured.
592 100m. Type **221** 40 20
593 125m. Lord Baden-Powell . . 45 30
594 175m. Camp-site 55 55

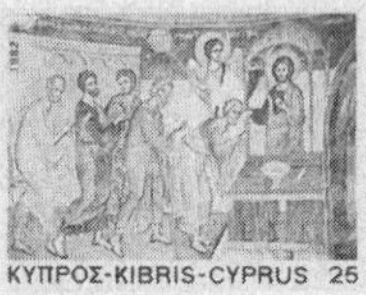

222 Holy Communion, The Bread

1982. Christmas.
595 **222** 25m. multicoloured . . . 10 10
596 – 100m. gold and black . . 30 15
597 – 250m. multicoloured . . . 70 1·00
DESIGN—VERT: 100m. Holy Chalice. HORIZ: 250m. Holy Communion, The Wine.

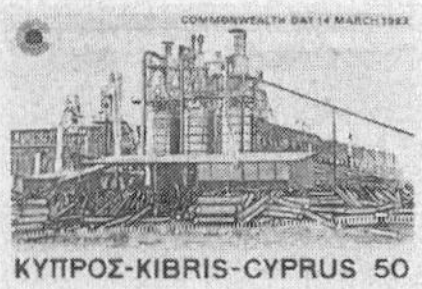

223 Cyprus Forest Industries' Sawmill

1983. Commonwealth Day. Multicoloured.
598 50m. Type **223** 10 10
599 125m. "Ikarios and the Discovery of Wine" (3rd-century mosaic) 20 25
600 150m. Folk-dancers, Commonwealth Film and Television Festival, 1980 25 35
601 175m. Royal Exhibition Building, Melbourne (Commonwealth Heads of Government Meeting, 1981) 25 40

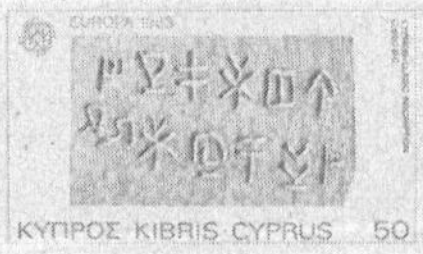

224 Cyprosyllabic Inscription (6th-century B.C.)

1983. Europa. Multicoloured.
602 50m. Type **224** 40 10
603 200m. Copper ore, ingot (Enkomi 1400–1250 B.C.) and bronze jug (2nd century A.D.) . . . . . . 1·10 2·40

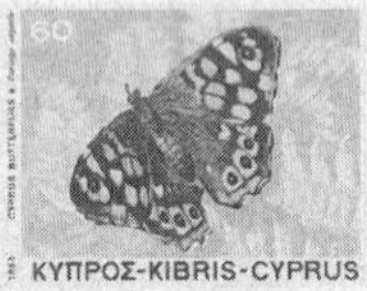

225 "Pararge aegeria"

1983. Butterflies. Multicoloured.
604 60m. Type **225** 25 20
605 130m. "Aricia agestis" . . . 45 25
606 250m. "Glaucopsyche melanops" . . . . 85 2·25

1983. Nos. 545/56 surch.
607 1c. on 10m. Type **208** 35 40
608 2c. on 15m. Bronze cow, Vouni Palace (5th-century B.C.) (horiz) 35 60
609 3c. on 25m. Amphora, Salamis (6th-century B.C.) 35 40
610 4c. on 40m. Gold finger-ring, Enkomi (13th-century B.C.) (horiz) 40 40
611 5c. on 50m. Bronze cauldron, Salamis (8th-century B.C.) 50 50
612 6c. on 75m. Funerary stele, Marion (5th-century B.C.) 50 50
613 10c. on 100m. Jug (15th–14th-century B.C.) 50 40
614 13c. on 125m. Warrior (Terracotta) (6–5th-cent B.C.) 50 50
615 15c. on 150m. Lions attacking bull (bronze relief), Vouni Palace (5th-century B.C.) (horiz) . . . 50 55
616 20c. on 200m. Bronze statue of Ingot God, Enkomi (12th-century B.C.) 50 65
617 25c. on 175m. Faience rhyton, Kition (13th-century B.C.) . . . . . . 55 1·10
618 50c. on 500m. Stone bowl, Khirokitia (6th-millenium B.C.) (horiz) . . . . 75 2·00

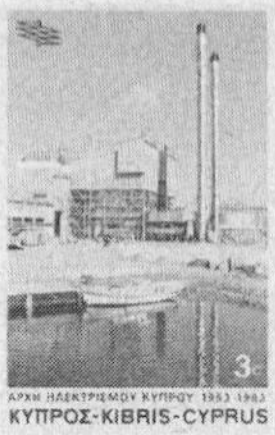

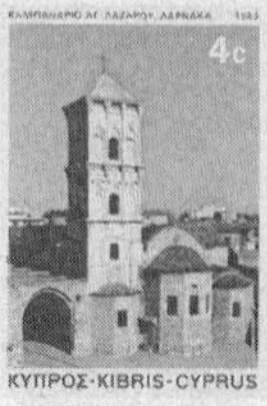

227 View of Power Station **228** St Lazaros Church, Larnaca

1983. Anniversaries and Events. Multicoloured.
619 3c. Type **227** 10 20
620 6c. W.C.Y. logo 15 15
621 13c. "Sol Olympia" (liner) and "Polys" (tanker) . . . 30 35
622 15c. Human Rights emblem and map of Europe . . . 30 25
623 20c. Nicos Kazantzakis . . . 30 75
624 25c. Makarios in church . . 35 75
COMMEMORATIONS: 3c. 30th anniv of Cyprus Electricity Authority; 6c. World Communications Year; 13c. 25th anniv of International Maritime Organization; 15c. 35th anniv of Universal Declaration of Human Rights; 20c. Birth centenary; 25c. 70th birth anniv.

1983. Christmas. Church Towers. Multicoloured.
625 4c. Type **228** 15 10
626 13c. St. Varvara Church, Kaimakli, Nicosia 40 35
627 20c. St. Ioannis Church, Larnaca . . . . 70 1·50

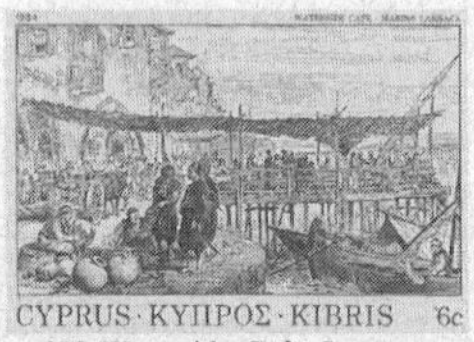

229 Waterside Cafe, Larnaca

1984. Old Engravings. Each brown and black.
628 6c. Type **229** 15 15
629 20c. Bazaar at Larnaca (39 × 25 mm) 40 85
630 30c. Famagusta Gate, Nicosia (39 × 25 mm) . . . . . . 65 1·50

230 C.E.P.T. 25th Anniversary Logo

1984. Europa.
632 **230** 6c. lt green, green & blk 40 10
633 15c. lt blue, blue & black 70 2·00

1984. Obligatory Tax. Refugee Fund. As T **188** but new value and dated "1984".
634 1c. black 10 10

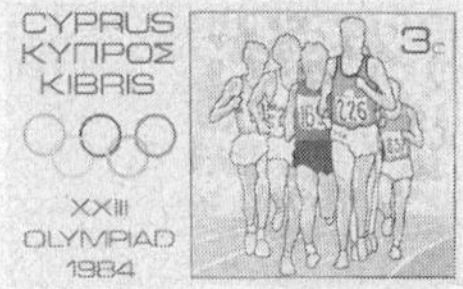

231 Running

1984. Olympic Games, Los Angeles. Multicoloured.
635 3c. Type **231** 15 10
636 4c. Olympic column 15 20
637 13c. Swimming 45 75
638 20c. Gymnastics . . . . . . 60 1·50

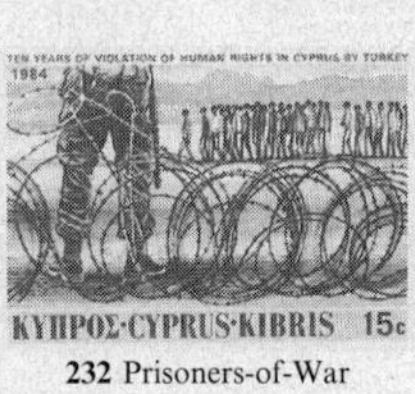

232 Prisoners-of-War

1984. 10th Anniv of Turkish Landings in Cyprus. Multicoloured.
639 15c. Type **232** 40 45
640 20c. Map and burning buildings 50 55

233 Open Stamp Album (25th Anniv of Cyprus Philatelic Society)

234 St. Mark (miniature from 11th-century Gospel)

1984. Anniversaries and Events. Multicoloured.
641 6c. Type **233** 30 20
642 10c. Football in motion (horiz) (50th anniv of Cyprus Football Association) 45 30
643 15c. "Dr. George Papanicolaou" (medical scientist) (birth centenary) 60 50
644 25c. Antique map of Cyprus and ikon (horiz) (International Symposia on Cartography and Medieval Paleography) . . . . . . 1·00 2·00

1984. Christmas. Illuminated Gospels. Mult.
645 4c. Type **234** 25 10
646 13c. Beginning of St. Mark's Gospel 45 50
647 20c. St. Luke (miniature from 11th-century Gospel) . . . 70 2·00

235 Autumn at Platania, Troodos Mountains

1985. Cyprus Scenes and Landscapes. Mult.
648 1c. Type **235** 20 40
649 2c. Ayia Napa Monastery . . 20 40
650 3c. Phini Village–panoramic view 20 30
651 4c. Kykko Monastery . . . 20 30
652 5c. Beach at Makronissos, Ayia Napa 20 20
653 6c. Village street, Omodhos (vert) 30 20
654 10c. Panoramic sea view . . 45 30
655 13c. Windsurfing 55 25
656 15c. Beach at Protaras . . . 65 25
657 20c. Forestry for development (vert) 80 50
658 25c. Sunrise at Protaras (vert) 1·00 1·00
659 30c. Village house, Pera . . 1·25 1·25
660 50c. Apollo Hylates Sanctuary, Curium . . . . 2·00 1·75
661 £1 Snow on Troodos Mountains (vert) . . . . 3·50 3·00
662 £5 Personification of Autumn, House of Dionyssos, Paphos (vert) 13·00 15·00

236 Clay Idols of Musicians (7/6th century B.C.)

1985. Europa. European Music Year. Mult.
663 6c. Type **236** 65 35
664 15c. Violin lute, flute and score from the "Cyprus Suite" . . . . 1·10 2·00

237 Cyprus Coat of Arms (25th Anniv of Republic)

238 "The Visit of the Madonna to Elizabeth" (Lambadistis Monastery, Kalopanayiotis)

1985. Anniversaries and Events.
665 **237** 4c. multicoloured . . . 15 15
666 – 6c. multicoloured . . . 15 15
667 – 13c. multicoloured . . . 40 1·00

668 – 15c. black, green and orange . . . . 1·00 1·25
669 – 20c. multicoloured . . . . 50 1·75
DESIGNS—HORIZ (43 × 30 mm): 6c. "Barn of Liopetri" (detail) (Pol. Georghiou) (30th anniv of EOKA Campaign); 13c. Three profiles (International Youth Year); 15c. Solon Michaelides (composer and conductor) (European Music Year). VERT— (as T **237**): 20c. U.N. Building, New York, and flags (40th anniv of United Nations Οδικα Οργάνιζατιον).

1985. Christmas. Frescoes from Cypriot Churches. Multicoloured.
670 4c. Type **238** 25 10
671 13c. "The Nativity" (Lambadistis Monastery, Kalopanayiotis) 60 65
672 20c. "Candlemas-day" (Asinou Church) . . . . 1·00 2·00

239 Figure from Hellenistic Spoon Handle

1986. New Archaeological Museum Fund. Multicoloured.
673 15c. Type **239** 60 45
674 20c. Pattern from early Ionian helmet and foot from statue 70 75
675 25c. Roman statue of Eros and Psyche 80 95
676 30c. Head of statue . . . . 1·00 1·10
No. 676 also commemorates the 50th anniv of the Department of Antiquities.

240 Cyprus Moufflon and Cedars

1986. Europa. Protection of Nature and the Environment. Multicoloured.
678 7c. Type **240** 35 30
679 17c. Greater flamingos ("Flamingos") at Larnaca Salt Lake . . . . . 1·40 2·50

241 Cat's-paw Scallop

1986. Sea Shells. Multicoloured.
680 5c. Type **241** 30 15
681 7c. Atlantic trumpet triton . 35 15
682 18c. Purple dye murex . . . 60 70
683 25c. Yellow cowrie . . . . 1·00 2·00

1986. Nos. 653 and 655 surch.
684 7c. on 6c. Village street, Omodhos (vert) 40 30
685 18c. on 13c. Windsurfing . . 1·10 70

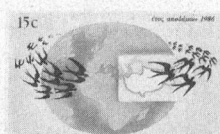

243 Globe Outline Map of Cyprus and Barn Swallows (Overseas Cypriots' Year)

1986. Anniversaries and Events. Multicoloured.
686 15c. Type **243** . . . . . . 1·00 45
687 18c. Halley's Comet over Cyprus beach (40 × 23 mm) 1·25 2·00
688 18c. Comet's tail over sea and Edmond Halley (40 × 23 mm) . . . . 1·25 2·00
Nos. 687/8 were printed together, se-tenant, forming a composite design.

244 Pedestrian Crossing

1986. Road Safety Campaign. Multicoloured.
689 5c. Type **244** 75 30
690 7c. Motor cycle crash helmet 80 30
691 18c. Hands fastening car seat belt . . . . 1·75 3·00

245 "The Nativity" (Church of Panayia tou Araka)

1986. Christmas. International Peace Year. Details of Nativity frescoes from Cypriot churches. Multicoloured.
692 5c. Type **245** 30 15
693 15c. Church of Panayia tou Moutoulla 80 30
694 17c. Church of St. Nicholas tis Steyis . . . . . 90 2·00

246 Church of Virgin Mary, Asinou

1987. Troodos Churches on the World Heritage List. Multicoloured.
695 15c. Type **246** . . . . . . 80 1·10
696 15c. Fresco of Virgin Mary, Moutoulla's Church . . . 80 1·10
697 15c. Church of Virgin Mary, Podithou . . . . . 80 1·10
698 15c. Fresco of Three Apostles, St. Ioannis Lampadistis Monastery . . 80 1·10
699 15c. Annunciation fresco, Church of the Holy Cross, Pelentriou . . . . . 80 1·10
700 15c. Fresco of Saints, Church of the Cross, Ayiasmati . . 80 1·10
701 15c. Fresco of Archangel Michael and Donor, Pedoula's Church of St. Michael . . . . . 80 1·10
702 15c. Church of St. Nicolaos, Steyis . . . . . . 80 1·10
703 15c. Fresco of Prophets, Church of Virgin Mary, Araka . . . . . . 80 1·10

247 Proposed Central Bank of Cyprus Building

1987. Europa. Modern Architecture.
704 **247** 7c. multicoloured 50 30
705 – 18c. black, grey and green 1·10 2·00
DESIGN: 18c. Headquarters complex, Cyprus Telecommunications Authority.

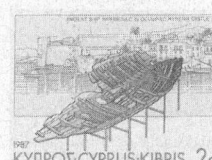

248 Remains of Ancient Ship and Kyrenia Castle

1987. Voyage of "Kyrenia II" (replica of ancient ship). Multicoloured.
706 2c. Type **248** 30 20
707 3c. "Kyrenia II" under construction, 1982–5 . . 40 90
708 5c. "Kyrenia II" at Paphos, 1986 . . . . . . 65 20
709 17c. "Kyrenia II" at New York, 1986 . . . . 1·60 90

249 Hands (from Michelangelo's "Creation") and Emblem

1987. Anniversaries and Events. Multicoloured.
710 7c. Type **249** (10th anniv of Blood Donation Co-ordinating Committee) . . 50 25
711 15c. Snail with flowered shell and countryside (European Contryside Campaign) . . 1·10 40
712 20c. Symbols of ocean bed and Earth's crust ("Troodos '87" Ophiolites and Oceanic Lithosphere Symposium) . . . . . 1·40 3·00

250 Nativity Crib

1987. Christmas. Traditional Customs. Mult.
713 5c. Type **250** 35 15
714 15c. Door knocker decorated with foliage . . . . 1·10 35
715 17c. Bowl of fruit and nuts . 1·25 2·00

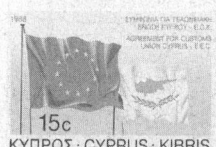

251 Flags of Cyprus and E.E.C.

1988. Cypriot–E.E.C. Customs Union. Mult.
716 15c. Type **251** . . . . . . 80 1·50
717 18c. Outline maps of Cyprus and E.E.C. countries . . . 80 80

252 Intelpost Telefax Terminal

1988. Europa. Transport and Communications. Multicoloured.
718 7c. Type **252** 65 85
719 7c. Car driver using mobile telephone 65 85
720 18c. Nose of Cyprus Airways airliner and greater flamingos . . . . . 2·25 2·75
721 18c. Boeing 739 airliner in flight and greater flamingos 2·25 2·75

253 Sailing

255 "Cyprus 74" (wood-engraving by A. Tassos)

1988. Olympic Games, Seoul. Multicoloured.
722 5c. Type **253** 30 20
723 7c. Athletes at start 35 40
724 10c. Shooting 40 70
725 20c. Judo . . . . . . 90 1·50

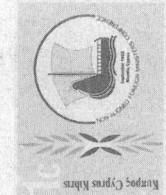

254 Conference Emblem

1988. Non-Aligned Foreign Ministers' Conference, Nicosia.
726 **254** 1c. black, blue and green . 10 10
727 – 10c. multicoloured . . . 45 70
728 – 50c. multicoloured . . . 2·25 2·50

DESIGNS: 10c. Emblem of Republic of Cyprus; 50c. Nehru, Tito, Nasser and Makarios.

1988. Obligatory Tax. Refugee Fund. Variously dated.
| 892 | 255 | 1c. black and grey .... | 10 | 10 |

1988. No. 651 surch 15c.
| 730 | 15c. on 4c. Kykko Monastery | 1·25 | 70 |

256 "Presentation of Christ at the Temple" (Church of Holy Cross tou Agiasmati)

257 Human Rights Logo

1988. Christmas. Designs showing frescoes from Cypriot churches. Multicoloured.
731	5c. Type 256	25	20
732	15c. "Virgin and Child" (St. John Lampadistis Monastery)	55	25
733	17c. "Adoration of the Magi" (St. John Lampadistis Monastery)	80	1·75

1988. 40th Anniv of Universal Declaration of Human Rights.
| 734 | 257 | 25c. lt blue, dp blue & bl | 90 | 1·25 |

258 Basketball

1989. 3rd Small European States' Games, Nicosia. Multicoloured.
735	1c. Type 258	10	15
736	5c. Javelin	20	15
737	15c. Wrestling	45	20
738	18c. Athletics	60	1·00

259 Lingri Stick Game

1989. Europa. Children's Games. Multicoloured.
740	7c. Type 259	90	1·25
741	7c. Ziziros	90	1·25
742	18c. Sitsia	1·00	1·40
743	18c. Leapfrog	1·00	1·40

260 "Universal Man"

1989. Bicentenary of the French Revolution.
| 744 | 260 | 18c. multicoloured ... | 60 | 60 |

261 Stylized Human Figures

262 Worker Bees tending Larvae

1989. Centenary of Interparliamentary Union (15c.) and 9th Non-Aligned Summit Conference, Belgrade (30c.). Multicoloured.
| 745 | 15c. Type 261 .... | 50 | 40 |
| 746 | 30c. Conference logo ... | 1·00 | 1·10 |

1989. Bee-keeping. Multicoloured.
748	3c. Type 262	20	25
749	10c. Bee on rock-rose flower	50	50
750	15c. Bee on lemon flower ...	75	50
751	18c. Queen and worker bees	85	1·25

263 Outstretched Hand and Profile (aid for Armenian earthquake victims)

264 Winter (detail from "Four Seasons")

1989. Anniversaries and Events. Multicoloured.
752	3c. Type 263	25	60
753	5c. Airmail envelope (Cyprus Philatelic Society F.I.P. membership)	40	10
754	7c. Crab symbol and daisy (European Cancer Year)	65	1·25
755	17c. Vegetables and fish (World Food Day)	1·00	1·25

1989. Roman Mosaics from Paphos. Multicoloured.
756	1c. Type 264	20	50
757	2c. Personification of Crete (32 × 24 mm)	25	50
758	3c. Centaur and Maenad (24 × 32 mm)	30	50
759	4c. Poseidon and Amymone (32 × 24 mm)	40	60
760	5c. Leda	40	20
761	7c. Apollon	45	25
762	10c. Hermes and Dionysos (24 × 32 mm)	55	30
763	15c. Cassiopeia	90	45
764	18c. Orpheus (32 × 24 mm)	1·00	50
765	20c. Nymphs (24 × 32 mm)	1·25	75
766	25c. Amazon (24 × 32 mm)	1·25	80
767	40c. Doris (32 × 24 mm) .	2·00	1·50
768	50c. Heracles and the Lion (39 × 27 mm)	2·00	1·50
769	£1 Apollon and Daphne (39 × 27 mm)	3·25	3·00
770	£3 Cupid (39 × 27 mm) .	8·50	8·50

265 Hands and Open Book (International Literacy Year)

1990. Anniversaries and Events. Multicoloured.
771	15c. Type 265	55	50
772	17c. Dove and profiles (83rd Inter-Parliamentary Conference, Nicosia) ...	65	90
773	18c. Lions International emblem (Lions Europa Forum, Limassol)	75	90

266 District Post Office, Paphos

1990. Europa. Post Office Buildings. Mult.
| 774 | 7c. Type 266 .... | 1·00 | 25 |
| 775 | 18c. City Centre Post Office, Limassol .... | 1·25 | 2·25 |

267 Symbolic Lips (25th anniv of Hotel and Catering Institute)

1990. European Tourism Year. Multicoloured.
776	5c. Type 267	25	25
777	7c. Bell tower, St. Lazarus Church (1100th anniv) ...	30	25
778	15c. Butterflies and woman	1·50	45
779	18c. Birds and man	2·00	3·50

268 Sun (wood carving)

269 "Chionodoxa lochiae"

1990. 30th Anniv of Republic. Multicoloured.
| 780 | 15c. Type 268 .... | 55 | 45 |

781	17c. Bulls (pottery design) .	65	60
782	18c. Fishes (pottery design)	75	70
783	40c. Tree and birds (wood carving)	2·00	3·25

1990. Endangered Wild Flowers. Book illustrations by Elektra Megaw. Multicoloured.
785	2c. Type 269	40	80
786	3c. "Pancratium maritimum"	40	80
787	5c. "Paeonia mascula" ...	60	20
788	7c. "Cyclamen cyprium" ..	65	25
789	15c. "Tulipa cypria"	1·25	30
790	18c. "Crocus cyprius" ...	1·40	3·00

270 "Nativity"

271 Archangel

1990. Christmas. 16th-century Icons. Mult.
791	5c. Type 270	35	20
792	15c. "Virgin Hodegetria" ..	1·00	30
793	17c. "Nativity" (different) ..	1·25	2·75

1991. 6th-century Mosaics from Kanakaria Church. Multicoloured.
794	5c. Type 271	20	15
795	15c. Christ Child	75	20
796	17c. St. James	1·50	1·50
797	18c. St. Matthew	1·00	1·75

272 "Ulysses" Spacecraft

1991. Europa. Europa in Space. Multicoloured.
| 798 | 7c. Type 272 .... | 75 | 20 |
| 799 | 18c. "Giotto" and Halley's Comet .... | 1·50 | 2·50 |

273 Young Cyprus Wheatear

1991. Cyprus Wheatear. Multicoloured.
800	5c. Type 273	60	40
801	7c. Adult bird in autumn plumage	65	40
802	15c. Adult male in breeding plumage	1·00	50
803	30c. Adult female in breeding plumage	1·50	2·75

274 Mother and Child with Tents

1991. 40th Anniv of U.N. Commission for Refugees. Each deep brown, brown and silver.
804	5c. Type 274	25	15
805	15c. Three pairs of legs ...	90	65
806	18c. Three children	1·10	2·00

275 The Nativity

276 Swimming

1991. Christmas. Multicoloured.
808	5c. Type 275	25	15
809	15c. Saint Basil	60	40
810	17c. Baptism of Jesus ...	90	1·75

1992. Olympic Games, Barcelona. Multicoloured.
811	10c. Type 276	60	35
812	20c. Long jump	1·00	70
813	30c. Running	1·40	1·40
814	35c. Discus	1·60	2·50

277 World Map and Emblem ("EXPO '92" Worlds Fair, Seville)

1992. Anniversaries and Events. Multicoloured.
815	20c. Type 277	1·00	80
816	25c. European map and football (10th under-16 European Football Championship) ...	1·40	95
817	30c. Symbols of learning (inauguration of University of Cyprus)	1·40	2·75

278 Compass Rose and Map of Voyage

1992. Europa. 500th Anniv of Discovery of America by Columbus. Multicoloured.
818	10c. Type 278	90	1·25
819	10c. "Departure from Palos" (R. Balaga)	90	1·25
820	30c. Fleet of Columbus ...	1·40	1·75
821	30c. Christopher Columbus	1·40	1·75

Nos. 818/19 and 820/1 were each issued together, se-tenant, forming composite designs.

279 "Chamaeleo chamaeleon"

1992. Reptiles. Multicoloured.
822	7c. Type 279	55	30
823	10c. "Lacerta laevis troodica" (lizard)	75	45
824	15c. "Mauremys caspica" (turtle)	90	80
825	20c. "Coluber cypriensis" (snake)	1·00	2·00

280 Minoan Wine Ship of 7th Century B.C. and Modern Tanker

1992. 7th International Maritime and Shipping Conference, Nicosia.
| 826 | 280 | 50c. multicoloured .... | 2·75 | 2·75 |

281 "Visitation of the Virgin Mary to Elizabeth", Church of the Holy Cross, Pelendri

282 School Building and Laurel Wreath

1992. Christmas. Church Fresco Paintings. Mult.
827	7c. Type 281	40	25
828	15c. "Virgin and Child Enthroned", Church of Panayia tou Araka	75	65
829	20c. "Virgin and Child", Ayios Nicolaos tis Stegis Church	1·10	1·90

1993. Centenary of Pancyprian Gymnasium (secondary school).
| 830 | 282 | 10c. multicoloured .... | 60 | 50 |

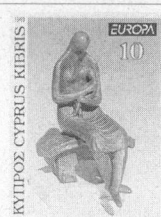

283 "Motherhood" (bronze sculpture, Nicos Dymiotis)

1993. Europa. Comtemporary Art. Multicoloured.
831 10c. Type **283** 50 40
832 30c. "Motherhood" (painting, Christoforos Savva) (horiz) 1·25 2·00

284 Women Athletes (13th European Cup for Women)

1993. Anniversaries and Events. Multicoloured.
833 7c. Type **284** 40 30
834 10c. Scout symbols (80th anniv of Scouting in Cyprus) (vert) . . . 55 40
835 20c. Water-skier, dolphin and gull (Moufflon Encouragement Cup) (inscr "Mufflon") . . . . 10·00 10·00
835a 20c. Water-skier, dolphin and seabird (inscr "Moufflon") 95 95
836 25c. Archbishop Makarios III and monastery (80th birth anniv) . . . . . 1·40 2·00

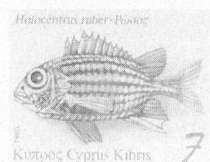

285 Red Squirrelfish

1993. Fishes. Multicoloured.
837 7c. Type **285** 40 25
838 15c. Red scorpionfish . . . 65 55
839 20c. Painted comber 75 85
840 30c. Grey triggerfish . . . . 1·40 2·25

286 Conference Emblem

1993. 12th Commonwealth Summit Conference.
841 **286** 35c. brown and ochre . 1·60 1·90
842 40c. brown and ochre . . 1·90 2·40

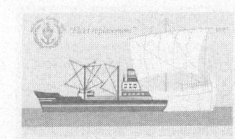

287 Ancient Sailing Ship and Modern Coaster

1993. "Maritime Cyprus '93" International Shipping Conference, Nicosia.
843 **287** 25c. multicoloured . . . . 1·40 1·40

288 Cross from Stavrouvouni Monastery
290 Symbols of Disability (Persons with Special Needs Campaign)

289 Copper Smelting

1993. Christmas. Church Crosses. Multicoloured.
844 7c. Type **288** 30 25
845 20c. Cross from Lefkara . . 75 75
846 25c. Cross from Pedoulas (horiz) . . . . . . 1·00 2·00

1994. Europa. Discoveries. Ancient Copper Industry. Multicoloured.
847 10c. Type **289** 50 35
848 30c. Ingot, ancient ship and map of Cyprus . . . . 1·25 2·00

1994. Anniversaries and Events. Multicoloured.
849 7c. Type **290** 40 25
850 15c. Olympic rings in flame (Centenary of International Olympic Committee) . . 65 55
851 20c. Peace doves (World Gymnasiade, Nicosia) . . 80 80
852 25c. Adults and unborn baby in tulip (International Year of the Family) . . . . 1·10 2·00

291 Houses, Soldier and Family

1994. 20th Anniv of Turkish Landings in Cyprus. Multicoloured.
853 10c. Type **291** 50 40
854 50c. Soldier and ancient columns . . . . . . 2·00 3·00

292 Black Pine

1994. Trees. Multicoloured.
855 7c. Type **292** 30 25
856 15c. Cyprus cedar 55 55
857 20c. Golden oak 70 80
858 30c. Strawberry tree . . . . 1·10 2·00

293 Airliner, Route Map and Emblem

1994. 50th Anniv of I.C.A.O.
859 **293** 30c. multicoloured . . . . 1·50 1·75

294 "Virgin Mary" (detail) (Philip Goul)
295 Woman from Paphos wearing Foustani

1994. Christmas. Church Paintings. Multicoloured.
860 7c. Type **294** 40 25
861 20c. "The Nativity" (detail) (Byzantine) . . . . 1·00 70
862 25c. "Archangel Michael" (detail) (Goul) . . . . 1·25 2·25

1994. Traditional Costumes. Multicoloured.
863 1c. Type **295** 20 40
864 2c. Bride from Karpass . . . 30 40
865 3c. Woman from Paphos wearing sayia 35 40
866 5c. Woman from Messaoria wearing foustani . . . 40 50
867 7c. Bridegroom 45 20
868 10c. Shepherd from Messaoria 55 40
869 15c. Woman from Nicosia in festive costume 90 40

870 20c. Woman from Karpass wearing festive sayia . . 1·00 50
871 25c. Woman from Pitsillia . . . 1·25 60
872 30c. Woman from Karpass wearing festive doupletti 1·40 70
873 35c. Countryman . . . . . 1·40 1·00
874 40c. Man from Messaoria in festive costume . . . . 1·50 1·50
875 50c. Townsman . . . . . 1·75 1·75
876 £1 Townswoman wearing festive sarka . . . . . 2·75 2·75

296 "Hearth Room" Excavation, Alassa, and Frieze
297 Statue of Liberty, Nicosia (left detail)

1995. 3rd International Congress of Cypriot Studies, Nicosia. Multicoloured.
877 20c. Type **296** 75 75
878 30c. Hypostyle hall, Kalavasos, and Mycenaean amphora . . . . . . 1·00 1·75

1995. 40th Anniv of Start of E.O.K.A. Campaign. Different details of the statue. Multicoloured.
880 20c. Type **297** . . . . . . 90 1·10
881 20c. Centre detail (face value at top right) . . . . 90 1·10
882 20c. Right detail (face value at bottom right) . . . . 90 1·10
Nos. 880/2 were printed together, se-tenant, forming a composite design.

298 Nazi Heads on Peace Dove over Map of Europe
299 Symbolic Figure holding Healthy Food

1995. Europa. Peace and Freedom. Multicoloured.
883 10c. Type **298** 75 35
884 30c. Concentration camp prisoner and peace dove 1·75 2·50

1995. Healthy Living. Multicoloured.
885 7c. Type **299** 25 25
886 10c. "AIDS" and patients (horiz) 50 50
887 15c. Drug addict (horiz) . . . 55 55
888 20c. Smoker and barbed wire 75 1·00

300 European Union Flag and European Culture Month Logo

1995. European Culture Month and "Europhilex '95" International Stamp Exhibition, Nicosia. Each blue, yellow and stone.
889 20c. Type **300** 55 60
890 25c. Map of Europe and Cypriot church . . . . 70 1·10

301 Peace Dove with Flags of Cyprus and United Nations

1995. Anniversaries and Events. Multicoloured.
893 10c. Type **301** (50th anniv of United Nations) 30 35
894 15c. Hand pushing ball over net (cent of volleyball) (vert) 65 50
895 20c. Safety pin on leaf (European Nature Conservation Year) (vert) 75 70
896 25c. Clay pigeon contestant (World Clay Target Shooting Championship) 85 1·60

302 Reliquary from Kykko Monastery
303 Family (25th anniv of Pancyprian Organization of Large Families)

1995. Christmas.
897 **302** 7c. multicoloured 20 25
898 – 20c. multicoloured 60 60
899 – 25c. multicoloured . . . . 75 1·40
DESIGNS: 20, 25c. Different reliquaries of Virgin and Child from Kykko Monastery.

1996. Anniversaries and Events. Multicoloured.
900 10c. Type **303** 45 35
901 20c. Film camera (centenary of cinema) 75 70
902 35c. Silhouette of parent and child in globe (50th anniv of U.N.I.C.E.F.) . . . . 1·40 1·60
903 40c. "13" and Commonwealth emblem (13th Conference of Commonwealth Speakers and Presiding Officers) . . . 1·50 2·50

304 Maria Synglitiki
306 Watermill

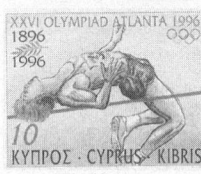

305 High Jump

1996. Europa. Famous Women. Multicoloured.
904 10c. Type **304** 40 30
905 30c. Queen Caterina Cornaro 1·00 1·75

1996. Centennial Olympic Games, Atlanta. Multicoloured.
906 10c. Type **305** 50 30
907 20c. Javelin 85 65
908 25c. Wrestling . . . . . 95 1·00
909 30c. Swimming . . . . . 1·25 2·00

1996. Mills. Multicoloured.
910 10c. Type **306** 50 40
911 15c. Olivemill 65 50
912 20c. Windmill 80 90
913 25c. Handmill . . . . . 90 1·50

307 Icon of Our Lady of Iberia, Moscow

1996. Cyprus–Russia Joint Issue. Orthodox Religion. Multicoloured.
914 30c. Type **307** . . . . . . 1·40 1·60
915 30c. Stavrovouni Monastery, Cyprus . . . . . 1·40 1·60
916 30c. Icon of St. Nicholas, Cyprus . . . . . 1·40 1·60
917 30c. Voskresenskie Gate, Moscow . . . . . 1·40 1·60

308 "The Nativity" (detail)

1996. Christmas. Religious Murals from Church of The Virgin of Asinou. Multicoloured.

918	7c. Type **308**		40	25
919	20c. "Virgin Mary between the Archangels Gabriel and Michael"		1·10	60
920	25c. "Christ bestowing Blessing" (vert)		1·50	2·25

309 Basketball

1997. Final of European Basketball Cup.

921	**309** 30c. multicoloured	1·75	1·75

310 "The Last Supper"

1997. Easter. Religious Frescoes from Monastery of St. John Lambadestis. Multicoloured.

922	15c. Type **310**	50	50
923	25c. "The Crucifixion" . . .	75	1·25

311 Kori Kourelleni and Prince

1997. Europa. Tales and Legends. Multicoloured.

924	15c. Type **311**	50	40
925	30c. Digenis and Charon .	1·00	1·75

312 "Oedipoda miniata" (grasshopper)

1997. Insects. Multicoloured.

926	10c. Type **312**	40	30
927	15c. "Acherontia atropos" (hawk moth)	65	40
928	25c. "Daphnis nerii" (hawk moth)	1·10	1·10
929	35c. "Ascalaphus macaronius" (owl-fly) . . .	1·25	1·25

313 Archbishop Makarios III and Chapel

1997. 20th Death Anniv of Archbishop Makarios III.

930	**313** 15c. multicoloured	75	50

314 The Nativity

1997. Christmas. Byzantine Frescos from the Monastery of St. John Lambadestis. Mult.

931	10c. Type **314**	35	40
932	25c. Three Kings following the star	1·25	70
933	30c. Flight into Egypt . .	1·40	2·25

315 Green Jasper

1998. Minerals. Multicoloured.

934	10c. Type **315**	40	30
935	15c. Iron pyrite	60	45
936	25c. Gypsum	80	80
937	30c. Chalcedony	1·00	1·60

316 Players competing for Ball

1998. World Cup Football Championship, France.

938	**316** 35c. multicoloured	1·60	1·40

317 Cataclysmos Festival, Larnaca

1998. Europa. Festivals. Multicoloured.

939	15c. Type **317**	75	40
940	30c. House of Representatives, Nicosia (Declaration of Independence)	1·25	2·00

318 Mouflon Family Group

319 Flames and Globe Emblem

1998. Endangered Species. Cyprus Mouflon. Mult.

941	25c. Type **318**	1·00	1·25
942	25c. Mouflon herd	1·00	1·25
943	25c. Head of ram	1·00	1·25
944	25c. Ram on guard . . .	1·00	1·25

1998. 50th Anniv of Universal Declaration of Human Rights.

959	**319** 50c. multicoloured	1·25	1·60

320 World "Stamp" and Magnifying Glass

1998. World Stamp Day.

960	**320** 30c. multicoloured	1·10	1·25

321 "The Annunciation"

322 "Pleurotus eryngii"

1998. Christmas. Multicoloured.

961	10c. Type **321**	35	20
962	25c. "The Nativity" . . .	80	65
963	30c. "The Baptism of Christ"	1·00	1·75

1999. Mushrooms of Cyprus. Multicoloured.

965	10c. Type **322**	30	30
966	15c. "Lactarius deliciosus"	60	40
967	25c. "Sparassis crispa" . .	90	90
968	30c. "Morchella elata" . .	1·00	1·60

323 Pair of Moufflons at Tripylos Reserve

1999. Europa. Parks and Gardens. Multicoloured.

969	15c. Type **323**	45	40
970	30c. Turtles on beach at Lara Reserve	80	1·00

324 Council of Europe Building, Emblem and Flags

1999. 50th Anniv of Council of Europe.

971	**324** 30c. multicoloured	90	1·25

325 Temple of Hylates Apollo, Kourion

329 Angel

326 Paper Aeroplane Letters and U.P.U. Emblem

1999. Cyprus–Greece Joint Issue. 4000 Years of Greek Culture. Multicoloured.

972	25c. Type **325**	75	85
973	25c. Mycenaean pot depicting warriors	75	85
974	25c. Mycenaean crater depicting horse	75	85
975	25c. Temple of Apollo, Delphi	75	85

1999. 125th Anniv of Universal Postal Union. Multicoloured.

976	15c. Type **326**	45	40
977	35c. "125" and U.P.U. emblem	90	1·10

1999. Christmas. Multicoloured.

980	10c. Type **329**	30	10
981	25c. The Three Kings . . .	70	60
982	30c. Madonna and child .	1·00	1·50

331 Necklace, 4500–4000 B.C.

332 "Building Europe"

2000. Jewellery. Multicoloured.

984	10c. Type **331**	20	25
985	15c. Gold earrings, 3rd-cent B.C.	35	40
986	20c. Gold earring from Lampousa, 6th–7th-cent .	45	50
987	25c. Brooch, 19th-cent . . .	55	60
988	30c. Gold cross, 6th–7th-cent	65	70
989	35c. Necklace, 18th–19th-cent	75	80
990	40c. Gold earring, 19th-cent	85	90
991	50c. Spiral hair ring, 5th–4th-cent B.C.	1·10	1·25
992	75c. Gold-plated silver plaques from Gialia, 700–600 B.C. (horiz)	1·60	1·75
993	£1 Gold frontlet from Egkomi, 14th–13th-cent B.C. (horiz)	2·25	2·40
994	£2 Gold necklace from Egkomi, 13th-cent B.C. (horiz)	4·25	4·50
995	£3 Buckles, 19th-cent (horiz)	6·50	6·75

2000. Europa.

996	**332** 30c. multicoloured	90	90

333 "50", Cross and Map of Cyprus

2000. 50th Anniv of Red Cross in Cyprus.

997	**333** 15c. multicoloured	70	50

334 Flame, Map of Cyprus and Broken Chain

335 Weather Balloon, Map and Satellite

2000. 45th Anniv of Struggle for Independence.

998	**334** 15c. multicoloured	60	50

2000. 50th Anniv of World Meteorological Organization.

999	**335** 30c. multicoloured	1·00	1·10

336 Monastery of Antifontis, Kalograia

337 Council of Europe Emblem

2000. Greek Orthodox Churches in Northern Cyprus.

1000	**336** 10c. brown and red . .		40	25
1001	– 15c. dp green & green		55	35
1002	– 25c. dp violet & violet		80	70
1003	– 30c. red and grey . .		90	1·10

DESIGNS—VERT: 15c. Church of St. Themonianos, Lysi. HORIZ: 25c. Church of Panagia Kanakaria, Lytrhagkomi; 30c. Church of Avgasida Monastery, Milia.

2000. 50th Anniv of European Convention of Human Rights

1004	**337** 30c. multicoloured	90	1·00

338 Archery

339 "The Annunciation"

2000. Olympic Games, Sydney. Multicoloured.

1005	10c. Type **338**	40	25
1006	15c. Gymnastics	55	35
1007	25c. Diving	80	70
1008	35c. Trampolining	95	1·25

2000. Christmas. Gold Gospel Covers. Multicoloured.

1009	10c. Type **339**	30	25
1010	25c. "The Nativity" . . .	65	55
1011	30c. "The Baptism of Christ"	80	1·00

340 "25" and Commonwealth Symbol

2001. 25th Anniv of Commonwealth Day.

1012	**340** 30c. multicoloured	75	80

341 Silhouette, Dove and Barbed Wire

2001. 50th Anniv of United Nations High Commissioner for Refugees.
1013 **341** 30c. multicoloured . . . 75 80

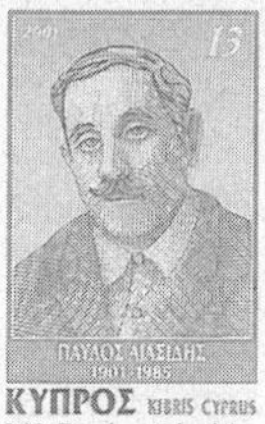
342 Pavlos Liasides

2001. Birth Centenary of Pavlos Liasides (poet).
1014 **342** 13c. chocolate, ochre & brown 35 35

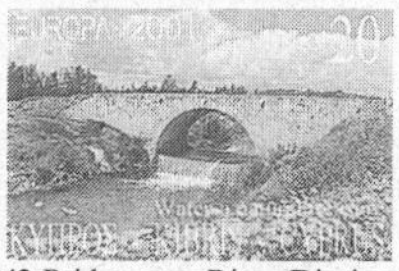
343 Bridge over River Diarizos

2001. Europa. Cypriot Rivers. Multicoloured.
1015 20c. Type **343** 45 50
1016 30c. Mountain torrent, River Akaki 65 70

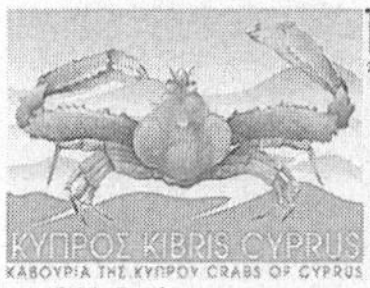
344 *Pathenope massena*

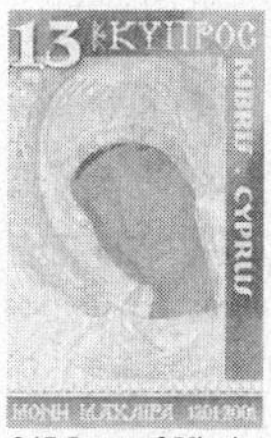
345 Icon of Virgin Mary

2001. Crabs. Multicoloured.
1017 13c. Type **344** 15 20
1018 20c. *Calappa granulata* . . . 45 50
1019 25c. *Ocypode cursor* 55 60
1020 30c. *Pagurus bernhardus* . . 65 70

2001. Christmas. 800th Anniv of Macheras Monastery. Multicoloured.
1021 13c. Type **345** 15 20
1022 25c. Macheras Monastery 55 60
1023 30c. Ornate gold crucifix . . 65 70

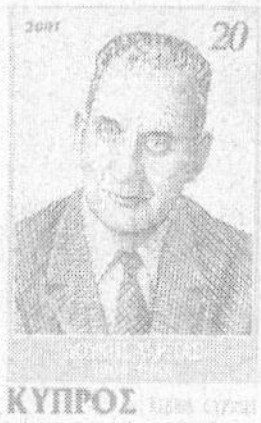
346 Loukis Akritas

2001. Loukis Akritas (writer) Commemoration.
1024 **346** 20c. green and brown . . 45 50

TURKISH CYPRIOT POSTS

After the inter-communal clashes during December 1963, a separate postal service was established on 6 January 1964, between some of the Turkish Cypriot areas, using handstamps inscribed "KIBRIS TURK POSTALARI". During 1964, however, an agreement was reached between representatives of the two communities for the restoration of postal services. This agreement to which the United Nations representatives were a party, was ratified in November 1966 by the Republic's Council of Ministers. Under the scheme postal servcies were provided for the Turkish Cypriot communities in Famagusta, Limassol, Lefka and Nicosia, staffed by Turkish Cypriot employees of the Cypriot Department of Posts.

On 8 April 1970, 5m. and 15m. locally produced labels, originally designated "Social Aid Stamps", were issued by the Turkish Cypriot community and these can be found on commercial covers. These local stamps are outside the scope of this catalogue.

On 29 October 1973 Nos. 1/7 were placed on sale, but were again used only on mail between the Turkish Cypriot areas.

Following the intervention by the Republic of Turkey in July 1974 these stamps replaced issues of the Republic of Cyprus in that part of the island, north and east of the Attila Line, controlled by the Autonomous Turkish Cypriot Administration.

1974. 1000 mils = 1 pound.
1978. 100 kurus = 1 lira.

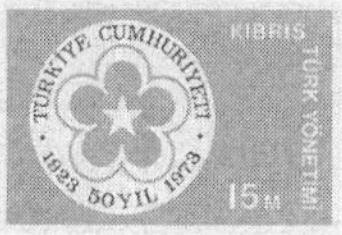
1 50th Anniversary Emblem

1974. 50th Anniv of Republic of Turkey.
1 – 3m. multicoloured . . . . . . 30·00 30·00
2 – 5m. multicoloured 60 40
3 – 10m. multicoloured 50 20
4 **1** 15m. red and black . . . . . 2·50 1·50
5 – 20m. multicoloured 70 20
6 – 50m. multicoloured . . . . . 2·00 1·50
7 – 70m. multicoloured . . . . . 16·00 16·00
DESIGNS—VERT: 3m. Woman sentry; 10m. Man and woman with Turkish flags; 20m. Ataturk statue, Kyrenia Gate, Nicosia; 50m. "The Fallen". HORIZ: 5m. Military parade, Nicosia; 70m. Turkish flag and map of Cyprus.

1975. Proclamation of the Turkish Federated State of Cyprus. Nos. 3 and 5 surch **KIBRIS TURK FEDERE DEVLETI 13.2.1975** and value.
8 30m. on 20m. multicoloured . . 75 1·00
9 100m. on 10m. multicoloured 1·25 2·00

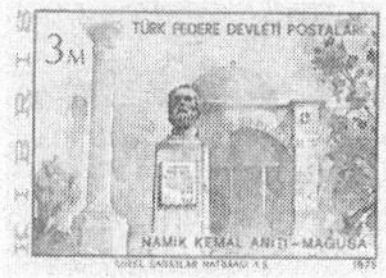
3 Namik Kemal's Bust, Famagusta

1975. Multicoloured.
10 3m. Type **3** 15 40
11 10m. Ataturk Statue, Nicosia 15 10
12 15m. St. Hilarion Castle . . . 25 20
13 20m. Ataturk Square, Nicosia 35 20
14 25m. Famagusta Beach . . . 35 30
15 30m. Kyrenia Harbour 45 10
16 50m. Lala Mustafa Pasha Mosque, Famagusta (vert) 50 10
17 100m. Interior, Kyrenia Castle 80 90
18 250m. Castle walls, Kyrenia 1·00 2·25
19 500m. Othello Tower, Famagusta (vert) . . . . . 1·50 4·50
See also Nos. 36/8.

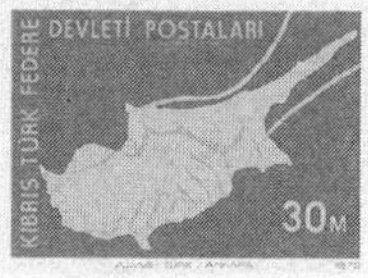
4 Map of Cyprus

1975. "Peace in Cyprus". Multicoloured.
20 30m. Type **4** 20 15
21 50m. Map, laurel and broken chain 25 20
22 150m. Map and laurel-sprig on globe (vert) . . . . 65 1·00

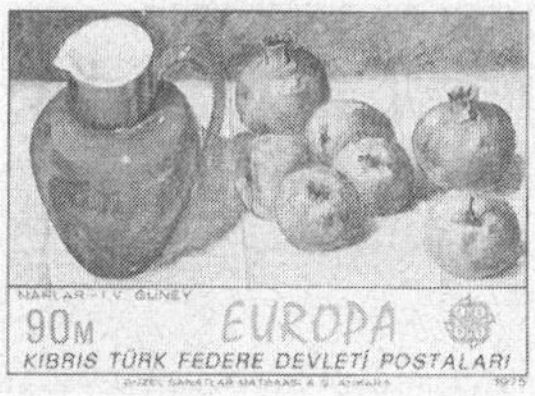
5 "Pomegranates" (I. V. Guney)

1975. Europa. Paintings. Multicoloured.
23 90m. Type **5** 70 70
24 100m. "Harvest Time" (F. Direkoglu) 80 70

1976. Nos. 16/17 surch.
25 10m. on 50m. multicoloured 35 70
26 30m. on 100m. multicoloured 35 80

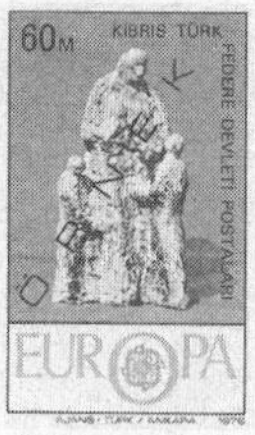
7 "Expectation" (ceramic statuette)

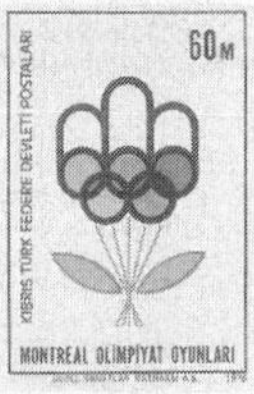
9 Olympic Symbol "Flower"

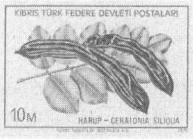

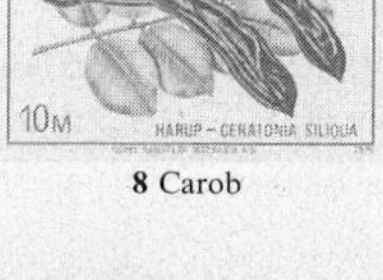
8 Carob

1976. Europa. Multicoloured.
27 60m. Type **7** 40 80
28 120m. "Man in Meditation" 60 1·25

1976. Export Products. Fruits. Multicoloured.
29 10m. Type **8** 20 10
30 25m. Mandarin 25 10
31 40m. Strawberry 30 25
32 60m. Orange 40 65
33 80m. Lemon . . . . 45 1·75

1976. Olympic Games, Montreal. Multicoloured.
34 60m. Type **9** 25 20
35 100m. Olympic symbol and doves 35 25

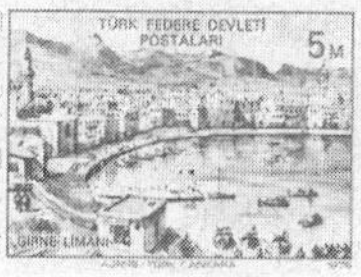
10 Kyrenia Harbour

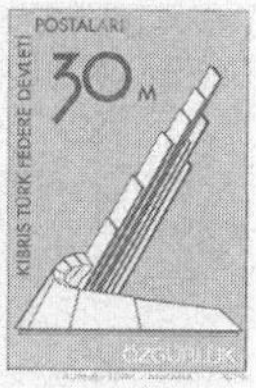
11 Liberation Monument, Karaeglanoglu (Ay Georghios)

1976. Multicoloured.
36 5m. Type **10** 40 15
37 15m. St. Hilarion Castle . . . 40 15
38 20m. Ataturk Square, Nicosia 40 15

1976. Liberation Monument.
47 **11** 30m. blue, pink and black 15 20
48 – 150m. red, pink and black 35 45
DESIGN: 150m. Liberation Monument (different view).

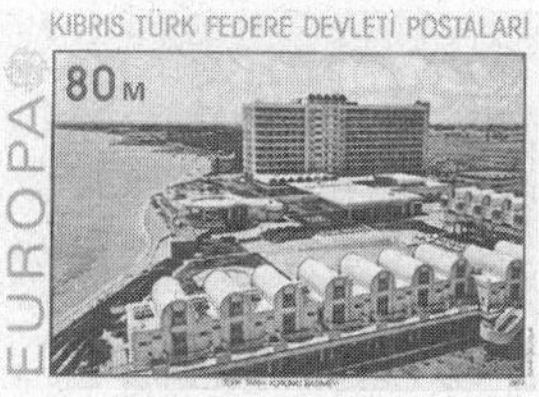
12 Hotel, Salamis Bay

1977. Europa. Multicoloured.
49 80m. Type **12** 65 80
50 100m. Kyrenia Port 75 80

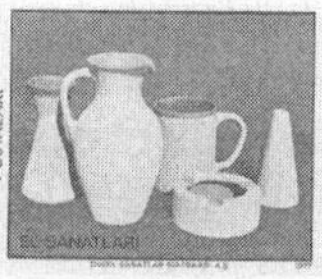
13 Pottery

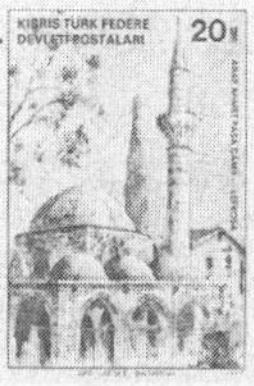
14 Arap Ahmet Pasha Mosque, Nicosia

1977. Handicrafts. Multicoloured.
51 15m. Type **13** 10 10
52 30m. Pottery (vert) 10 10
53 125m. Basketware 30 50

1977. Turkish Buildings in Cyprus. Multicoloured.
54 20m. Type **14** 10 10
55 40m. Paphos Castle (horiz) . . 10 10
56 70m. Bekir Pasha aqueduct (horiz) 15 20
57 80m. Sultan Mahmut library (horiz) 15 25

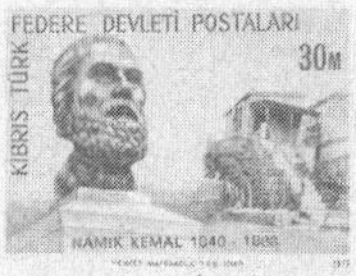
15 Namik Kemal (bust) and House, Famagusta

1977. Namik Kemal (patriotic poet). Multicoloured.
58 30m. Type **15** 15 15
59 140m. Namik Kemal (portrait) (vert) 35 60

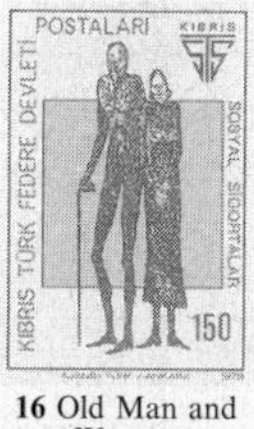
16 Old Man and Woman

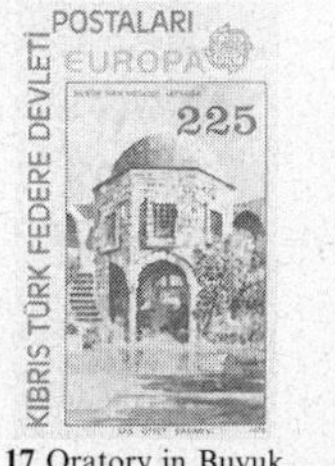
17 Oratory in Buyuk Han, Nicosia

1978. Social Security.
60 **16** 150k. black, yellow and blue 10 10
61 – 275k. black, orange and green 15 15
62 – 375k. black, blue and orange 25 20
DESIGNS: 275k. Injured man with crutch; 375k. Woman with family.

1978. Europa. Multicoloured.
63 225k. Type **17** 30 30
64 450k. Cistern in Selimiye Mosque, Nicosia 60 70

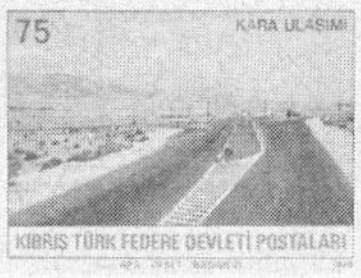
18 Motorway Junction

1978. Communications. Multicoloured.
65 75k. Type **18** 15 10
66 100k. Hydrofoil 15 10
67 650k. Boeing 720 at Ercan Airport 50 35

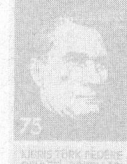

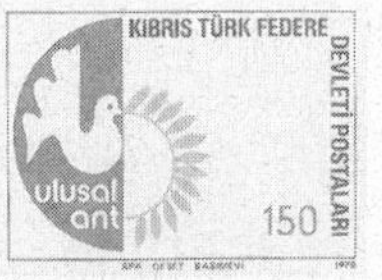
19 Dove with Laurel Branch

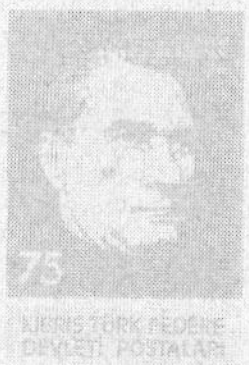
20 Kemal Ataturk

1978. National Oath.
68 **19** 150k. yellow, violet and black 10 10
69 – 225k. black, red and yellow 10 10
70 – 725k. black, blue and yellow 20 20
DESIGNS—VERT: 225k. "Taking the Oath". HORIZ: 725k. Symbolic dove.

1978. Ataturk Commemoration.
71 **20** 75k. turquoise & dp turq . . 10 10
72 450k. pink and brown . . . 15 15
73 650k. blue and light blue . . 20 25

1979. Nos. 30/3 surch.
74 50k. on 25k. Mandarin . . . 10 10
75 1l. on 40m. Strawberry 15 10
76 3l. on 60m. Orange 15 10
77 5l. on 80m. Lemon 35 15

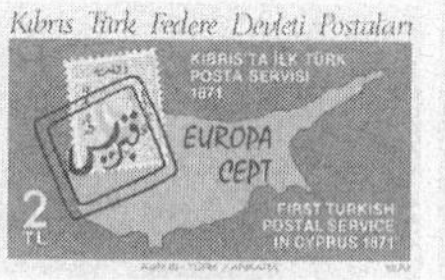
23 Postage Stamp and Map of Cyprus

24 Microwave Antenna

1979. Europa. Communications. Multicoloured.
79 2l. Type **23** 10 10
80 3l. Postage stamps, building and map 10 10
81 8l. Telephones, Earth and satellite 20 30

1979. 50th Anniv of International Consultative Radio Committee.
82 **24** 2l. multicoloured 20 10
83 5l. multicoloured 20 10
84 6l. multicoloured 25 15

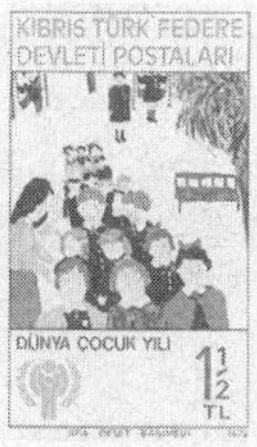
25 School Children

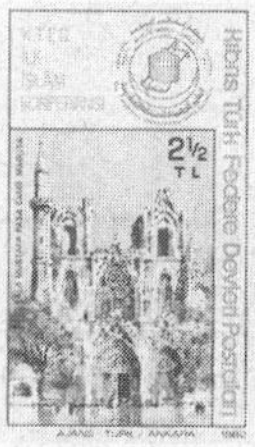
26 Lala Mustafa Pasha Mosque, Magusa

1979. International Year of the Child. Mult.
85 1½l. Type **25** 25 15
86 4½l. Children and globe (horiz) 40 20
87 6l. College children 60 20

1980. Islamic Commemorations. Multicoloured.
88 2½l. Type **26** 10 10
89 10l. Arap Ahmet Pasha Mosque, Lefkosa 30 15
90 20l. Mecca and Medina . . . 50 20
COMMEMORATIONS: 2½l. 1st Islamic Conference in Turkish Cyprus; 10l. General Assembly of World Islam Congress; 20l. Moslem Year 1400 AH.

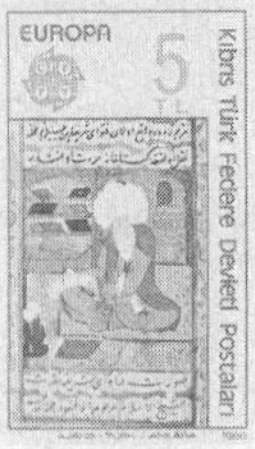

27 Ebu-Su'ud Efendi (philosopher)

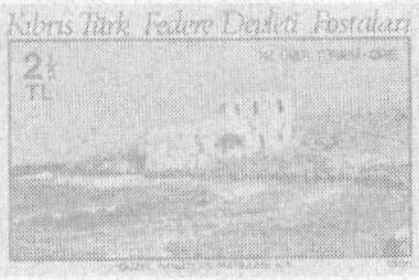

28 Omer's Shrine, Kyrenia

1980. Europa. Personalities. Multicoloured.
91 5l. Type **27** 20 10
92 30l. Sultan Selim II 70 40

1980. Ancient Monuments.
93 **28** 2½l. blue and stone 10 10
94 – 3½l. green and pink 10 10
95 – 5l. brown on green 15 10
96 – 10l. mauve and green . . . 20 10
97 – 20l. blue and yellow 35 25
DESIGNS: 3½l. Entrance gate, Famagusta; 5l. Funerary monuments (16th-century), Famagusta; 10l. Bella Paisc Abbey, Kyrenia; 20l. Selimiye Mosque, Nicosia.

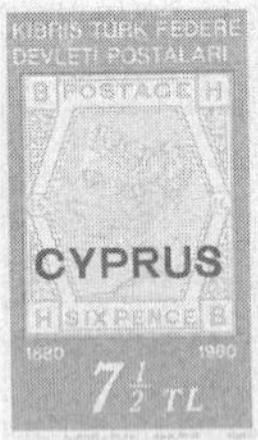

29 Cyprus 1880 6d. Stamp

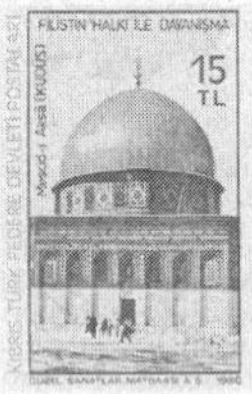

30 Dome of the Rock

1980. Cyprus Stamp Centenary.
98 **29** 7½l. black, brown and green 20 10
99 – 15l. brown, dp blue & bl 25 10
100 – 50l. black, red and grey . . 65 55
DESIGNS—HORIZ: 15l. Cyprus 1960 Constitution of the Republic 30m. commemorative stamp. VERT: 50l. Social Aid local, 1970.

1980. Palestinian Solidarity. Multicoloured.
101 15l. Type **30** 30 15
102 35l. Dome of the Rock (horiz) 70 30

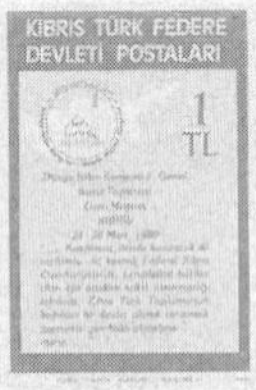

31 Extract from World Muslim Congress Statement in Turkish

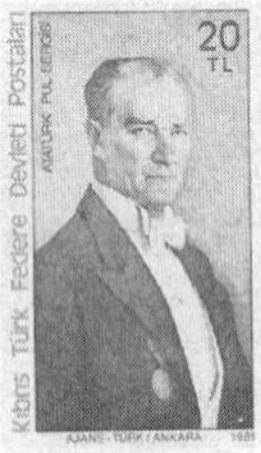

32 "Ataturk" (F. Duran)

1981. Day of Solidarity with Islamic Countries.
103 **31** 1l. buff, red and brown . . 15 55
104 – 35l. light green, black green 55 85
DESIGN: 35l. Extract in English.

1981. Ataturk Stamp Exhibition, Lefkosa.
105 **32** 10l. multicoloured 25 35

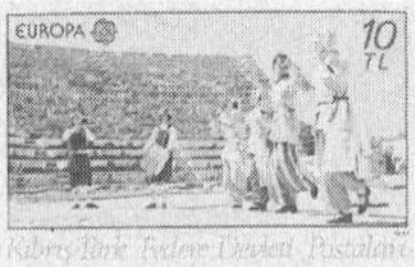

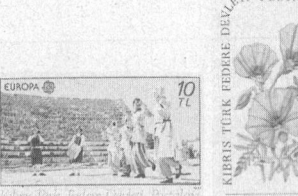

33 Folk-dancing

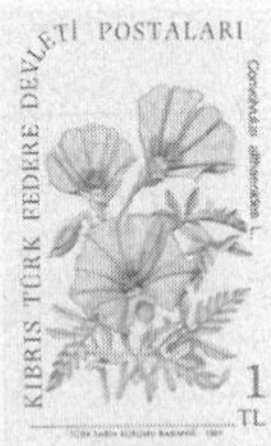

35 Wild Convolvulus

1981. Europa. Folklore. Multicoloured.
106 10l. Type **33** 40 15
107 30l. Folk-dancing (different) 60 35

1981. Flowers. Multicoloured.
109 1l. Type **35** 10 10
110 5l. Persian cyclamen (horiz) 10 10
111 10l. Spring mandrake (horiz) 10 10
112 25l. Corn poppy 15 10
113 30l. Wild arum (horiz) . . . 15 10
114 50l. Sage-leaved rock rose . . 20 20
115 100l. "Cistus salviaefolius L." 30 30
116 150l. Giant fennel (horiz) . . 50 90

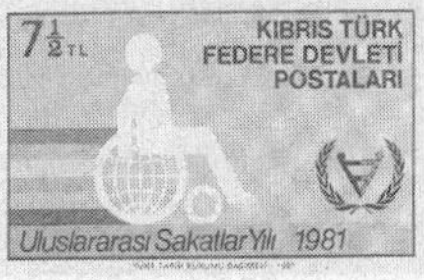

36 Stylised Disabled Person in Wheelchair

1981. Commemorations. Multicoloured.
117 7½l. Type **36** 25 35
118 10l. Heads of people of different races, peace dove and barbed wire (vert) . . 35 55
119 20l. People of different races reaching out from globe, with dishes (vert) 50 85
COMMEMORATIONS: 7½l. International Year for Disabled Persons; 10l. Anti-Apartheid publicity; 20l. World Food Day.

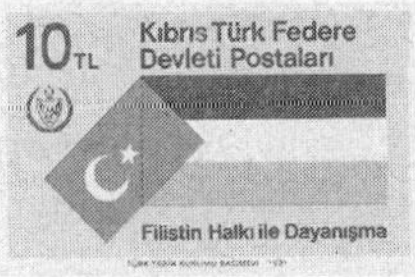

37 Turkish Cypriot and Palestinian Flags

1981. Palestinian Solidarity.
120 **37** 10l. multicoloured 30 40

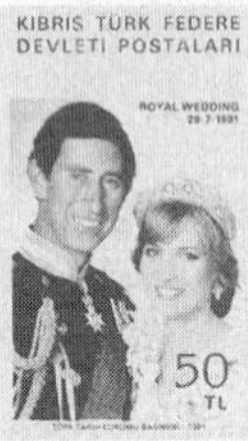

38 Prince Charles and Lady Diana Spencer

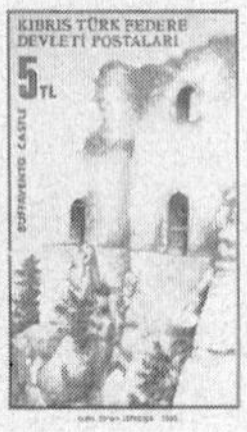

40 Buffavento Castle

1981. Royal Wedding.
121 **38** 50l. multicoloured . . . . 1·00 85

1982. Tourism. Multicoloured.
123 5l. Type **40** 10 10
124 10l. Windsurfing 15 10
125 15l. Kantara Castle 25 15
126 30l. Shipwreck (300 B.C.) . . 60 40
Nos. 124/6 are horiz.

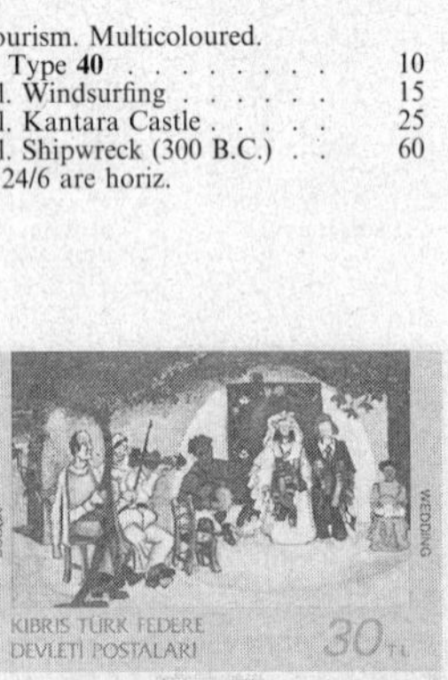

41 "Wedding" (A. Orek)

1982. Paintings (1st series). Multicoloured.
127 30l. Type **41** 15 30
128 50l. "Carob Pickers" (O. Nazim Selenge) (vert) 30 70
See also Nos. 132/3, 157/8, 176/7, 185/6, 208/9, 225/7, 248/50, 284/5, 315/16, 328/9, 369/70 and 436/7.

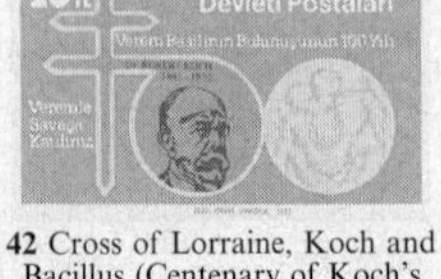

42 Cross of Lorraine, Koch and Bacillus (Centenary of Koch's Discovery of Tubercle Bacillus)

1982. Anniversairies and Events. Multicoloured.
129 10l. Type **42** . . . . 1·00 40
130 30l. Spectrum on football pitch (World Cup Football Championships, Spain) . . 1·75 1·10
131 70l. "75" and Lord Baden-Powell (75th Anniv of Boy Scout movement and 125th birth anniv) (vert) . . . . 2·25 4·00

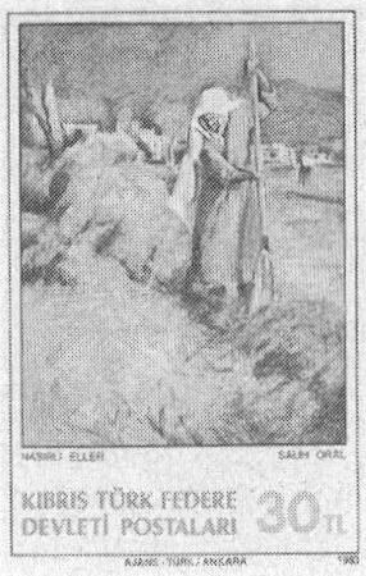

43 "Calloused Hands" (Salih Oral)

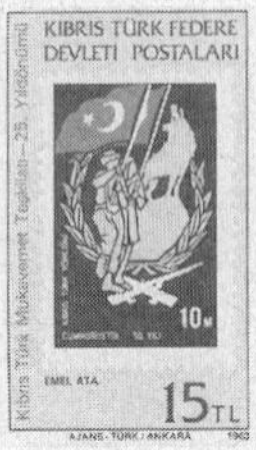

45 First Turkish Cypriot 10m. Stamp

1983. Paintings (2nd series). Multicoloured.
132 30l. Type **43** . . . . 75 1·40
133 35l. "Malya–Limassol Bus" (Emin Cizenel) . . . . . 75 1·40

1983. Anniversaries and Events. Multicoloured.
135 15l. Type **45** 70 50
136 20l. "Turkish Achievements in Cyprus" (horiz) 70 60
137 25l. "Liberation Fighters" . . 80 80
138 30l. Dish aerial and telegraph pole (horiz) . . . . . . 95 1·25
139 50l. Dove and envelopes (horiz) . . . . 2·25 3·25
EVENTS: 15, 20, 25l. T.M.T. (25th anniv of Turkish Cypriot Resistance Organization); 30, 50l. World Communications Year.

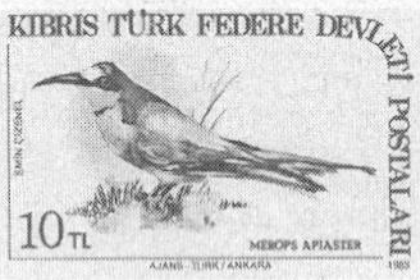

46 European Bee Eater

1983. Birds of Cyprus. Multicoloured.
140 10l. Type **46** . . . . 80 1·25
141 15l. Eurasian goldfinch . . . 1·00 1·25
142 50l. European robin . . . . 1·25 1·50
143 65l. Golden oriole . . . . . 1·40 1·50

1983. Establishment of Republic. Nos. 109, 111/12 and 116 optd **Kuzey Kibris Turk Cumhuriyeti 15.11.1983**, or surch also.
144 10l. Spring mandrake 20 15
145 15l. on 1l. Type **35** 30 15
146 25l. Corn poppy 40 25
147 150l. Giant fennel . . . . . 2·25 3·25

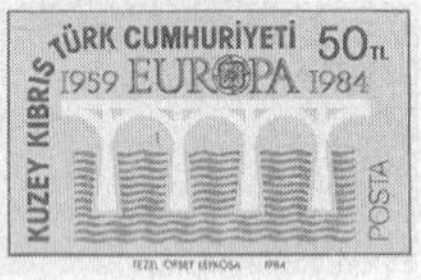

48 C.E.P.T. 25th Anniversary Logo

1984. Europa.
148 **48** 50l. yellow, brown and black . . . . 2·25 3·00
149 100l. lt blue, blue & black 2·25 3·00

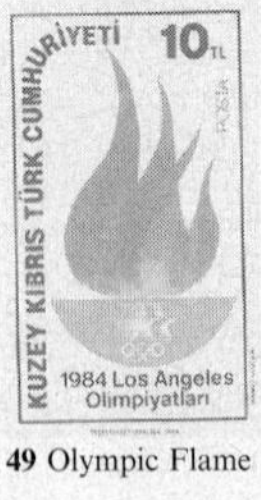

49 Olympic Flame

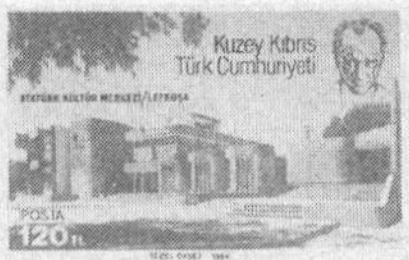

50 Ataturk Cultural Centre

1984. Olympic Games, Los Angeles. Multicoloured.
150 10l. Type **49** 15 10
151 20l. Olympic events within rings (horiz) 35 25
152 70l. Martial arts event (horiz) 60 1·75

1984. Opening of Ataturk Cultural Centre, Lefkosa.
153 **50** 120l. stone, black and brown . . . . 1·25 1·75

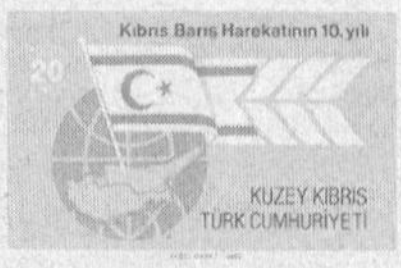

52 Turkish Cypriot Flag and Map

1984. 10th Anniv of Turkish Landings in Cyprus. Multicoloured.
154 20l. Type **52** 50 25
155 70l. Turkish Cypriot flag within book . . . . 1·00 2·00

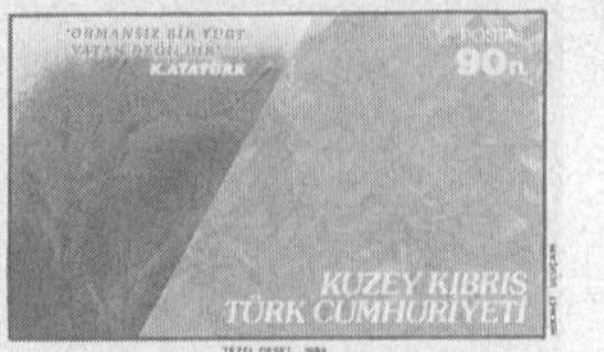

53 Burnt and Replanted Forests

1984. World Forestry Resources.
156 **53** 90l. multicoloured . . . . 1·25 1·75

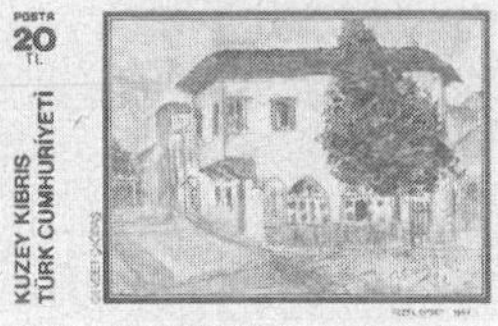

54 "Old Turkish Houses, Nicosia" (Cevdet Cagdas)

1984. Paintings (3rd series). Multicoloured.
157 20l. Type **54** 50 40
158 70l. "Scenery" (Olga Rauf) 1·10 2·00
See also Nos. 176/7, 185/6, 208/9, 225/7, 248/50, 284/5, 315/16, 328/9 and 369/70.

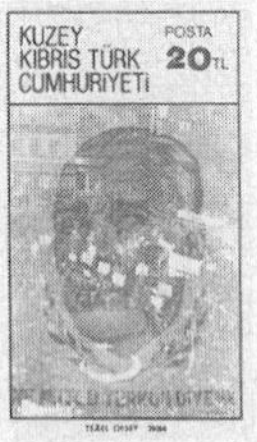

55 Kemal Ataturk, Flag and Crowd

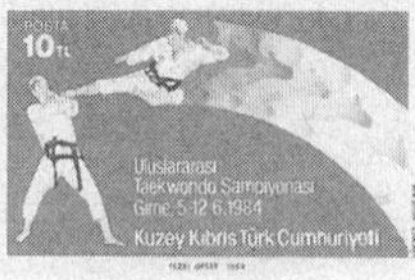

56 Taekwondo Bout

1984. 1st Anniv of Turkish Republic of Northern Cyprus. Multicoloured.
159 20l. Type **55** 50 40
160 70l. Legislative Assembly voting for Republic (horiz) 1·10 2·00

1984. Int Taekwondo Championship, Girne.
161 **56** 10l. black, brown and grey 40 25
162 – 70l. multicoloured . . . . 1·60 2·50
DESIGN: 70l. Emblem and flags of competing nations.

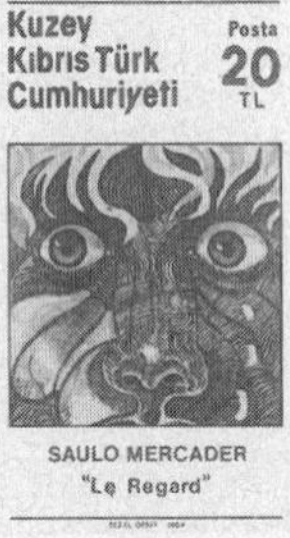

57 "Le Regard"

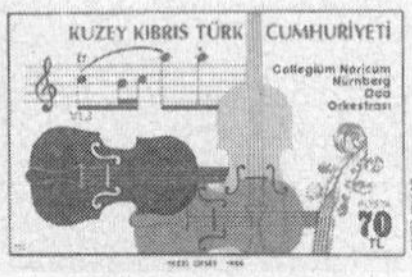

58 Musical Instruments and Music

1984. Exhibition by Saulo Mercader (artist). Multicoloured.
163 20l. Type **57** 30 25
164 70l. "L'equilibre de L'esprit" (horiz) . . . . 1·10 2·25

1984. Visit of Nurnberg Chamber Orchestra.
165 **58** 70l. multicoloured . . . . 1·50 2·25

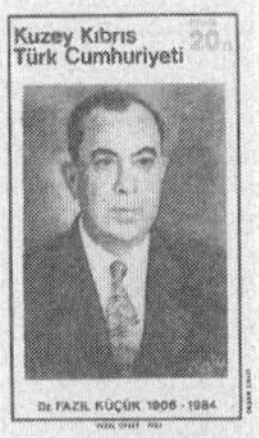

59 Dr. Fazil Kucuk (politician)

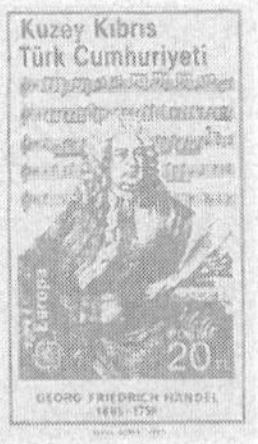

61 George Frederick Handel

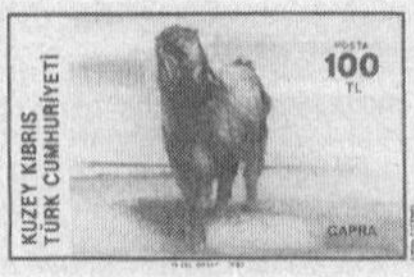

60 Goat

1985. 1st Death Anniv of Dr. Fazil Kucuk (politician). Multicoloured.
166	20l. Type **59**		30	30
167	70l. Dr. Fazil Kucuk reading newspaper		95	2·00

1985. Domestic Animals. Multicoloured.
168	100l. Type **60**		55	30
169	200l. Cow and calf		90	80
170	300l. Ram		1·25	2·00
171	500l. Donkey		2·00	3·25

1985. Europa. Composers.
172	**61**	20l. purple, green & lt grn	2·00	2·50
173	–	20l. purple, brown and pink	2·00	2·50
174	–	100l. purple, blue & lt blue	2·50	3·00
175	–	100l. purple, brn & lt brn	2·50	3·00

DESIGNS: No. 173, Giuseppe Domenico Scarlatti; 174, Johann Sebastian Bach; 175, Buhurizade Mustafa Itri Efendi.

1985. Paintings (4th series). As T **54**. Mult.
176	20l. "Village Life" (Ali Atakan)		60	50
177	50l. "Woman carrying Water" (Ismet V. Guney))		1·40	2·50

62 Heads of Three Youths

1985. International Youth Year. Multicoloured.
178	20l. Type **62**		75	40
179	100l. Dove and globe		3·50	4·00

63 Parachutist (Aviation League)

65 Karagoz Show Puppets

1985. Anniversaries and Events.
180	**63**	20l. multicoloured		1·50	45
181	–	50l. black, brown and blue		1·75	1·25
182	–	100l. brown		1·75	2·75
183	–	100l. multicoloured . . .		1·75	2·75
184	–	100l. multicoloured . . .		2·00	2·75

DESIGNS—VERT: No. 181, Louis Pasteur (Centenary of Discovery of Rabies vaccine); 182, Ismet Inonu (Turkish statesman) (birth centenary (1984)). HORIZ: 183, "40" in figures and symbolic flower (40th anniv of United Nations Organization); 184, Patient receiving blood transfusion (Prevention of Thalassaemia).

1986. Paintings (5th series). As T **54**. Mult.
185	20l. "House with Arches" (Gonen Atakol) . . .		50	30
186	100l. "Ataturk Square" (Yalkin Muhtaroglu) . . .		1·75	1·75

1986. Karagoz Folk Puppets.
188	**65**	100l. multicoloured		2·25	2·50

66 Old Bronze Age Composite Pottery

1986. Archaeological Artefacts. Cultural Links with Anatolia. Multicoloured.
189	10l. Type **66**		55	20
190	20l. Late Bronze Age bird jug (vert)		95	30
191	50l. Neolithic earthenware pot		1·75	2·00
192	100l. Roman statue of Artemis (vert)		2·25	3·50

67 Soldiers, Defence Force Badge and Ataturk (10th anniv of Defence Forces)

69 Prince Andrew and Miss Sarah Ferguson

68 Guzelyurt Dam and Power Station

1986. Anniversaries and Events. Multicoloured.
193	20l. Type **67**		80	30
194	50l. Woman and two children (40th anniv of F.A.O.) . .		1·40	1·40
195	100l. Football and world map (World Cup Football Championship, Mexico) (horiz)		2·75	3·50
196	100l. Orbit of Halley's Comet and "Giotto" space probe (horiz)		2·75	3·50

1986. Modern Development (1st series). Mult.
197	20l. Type **68**		1·25	30
198	50l. Low cost housing project, Lefkosa . . .		1·40	1·40
199	100l. Kyrenia Airport . . .		3·25	4·25
See also Nos. 223/4 and 258/63.

1986. 60th Birthday of Queen Elizabeth II and Royal Wedding. Multicoloured.
200	100l. Queen Elizabeth II . .		2·00	2·50
201	100l. Type **69**		2·00	2·50

70 Locomotive No. 11 and Trakhoni Station

1986. Cyprus Railway. Multicoloured.
202	50l. Type **70**		3·50	2·75
203	100l. Locomotive No. 1 . . .		4·00	4·25

1987. Nos. 94, 96/7 and 113 optd **Kuzey Kibris Turk Cumhuriyeti** or surch as (No. 205).
204	10l. mauve and green . . .		50	70
205	15l. on 3½l. green and pink		50	70
206	20l. blue and yellow . . .		55	75
207	30l. multicoloured		70	1·10

1987. Paintings (6th series). As T **54**. Mult.
208	50l. "Shepherd" (Feridun Isiman)		1·25	1·25
209	125l. "Pear Woman" (Mehmet Uluhan)		1·75	3·00

72 Modern House (architect A. Vural Behaeddin)

1987. Europa. Modern Architecture. Multicoloured.
210	50l. Type **72**		1·00	30
211	200l. Modern house (architect Necdet Turgay)		1·75	3·25

73 Kneeling Folk Dancer

74 Regimental Colour (1st anniv of Infantry Regiment)

1987. Folk Dancers. Multicoloured.
212	20l. Type **73**		60	20
213	50l. Standing male dancer . .		90	40
214	200l. Standing female dancer .		2·00	1·75
215	1000l. Woman's headdress . .		4·75	6·50

1987. Anniversaries and Events. Multicoloured.
216	50l. Type **74**		1·50	85
217	50l. President Denktash and Turgut Ozal (1st anniv of Turkish Prime Minister's visit) (horiz)		1·50	85
218	200l. Emblem and Crescent (5th Islamic Summit Conference, Kuwait) . . .		2·75	3·75
219	200l. Emblem and laurel leaves (Membership of Pharmaceutical Federation) (horiz)		2·75	3·75

75 Ahmet Belig Pasha (Egyptian judge)

76 Tourist Hotel, Girne

1987. Turkish Cypriot Personalities.
220	**75**	50l. brown and yellow . .		65	40
221	–	50l. multicoloured		65	40
222	–	125l. multicoloured		1·50	3·00

DESIGNS: 50l. (No. 221) Mehmet Emin Pasha (Ottoman Grand Vizier); 125l. Mehmet Kamil Pasha (Ottoman Grand Vizier).

1987. Modern Development (2nd series). Mult.
223	150l. Type **68**		1·50	1·50
224	200l. Dogu Akdeniz University		1·75	2·25

1988. Paintings (7th series). As T **54**. Mult.
225	20l. "Woman making Pastry" (Ayhan Mentes) (vert) .		50	20
226	50l. "Chair Weaver" (Osman Guvenir)		75	75
227	150l. "Woman weaving a Rug" (Zekai Yesiladali) (vert)		1·75	3·25

77 "Piyale Pasha" (tug)

1988. Europa. Transport and Communications. Multicoloured.
228	200l. Type **77**		2·00	75
229	500l. Dish aerial and antenna tower, Selvilitepe (vert) . .		2·75	4·50
No. 229 also commemorates the 25th anniv of Bayrak Radio and Television Corporation.

78 Lefkosa

79 Bulent Ecevit

1988. Tourism. Multicoloured.
230	150l. Type **78**		80	80
231	200l. Gazi-Magusa		90	1·00
232	300l. Girne		1·50	2·00

1988. Turkish Prime Ministers. Multicoloured.
233	50l. Type **79**		60	85
234	50l. Bulent Ulusu		60	85
235	50l. Turgut Ozal		60	85

80 Red Crescent Members on Exercise

1988. Civil Defence.
236	**80**	150l. multicoloured		1·25	1·50

81 Hodori the Tiger (Games mascot) and Fireworks

1988. Olympic Games, Seoul. Multicoloured.
237	50l. Type **81**		80	1·00
238	250l. Athletics		1·00	1·25
239	400l. Shot and running track with letters spelling "SEOUL"		1·50	2·00

82 Sedat Simavi (journalist)

85 Girl with Doll

1988. Anniversaries and Events.
240	**82**	50l. green		25	25
241	–	100l. multicoloured		50	45
242	–	300l. multicoloured		70	1·00
243	–	400l. multicoloured		1·50	1·75
244	–	400l. multicoloured		1·00	1·75
245	–	600l. multicoloured		1·50	1·75

DESIGNS—HORIZ: No. 241, Stylised figures around table and flags of participating countries (International Girne Conferences); 244, Presidents Gorbachev and Reagan signing treaty (Summit Meeting). VERT: No. 242, Cogwheels as flowers (North Cyprus Industrial Fair); 243, Globe (125th anniv of International Red Cross); 245, "Medical Services" (40th anniv of W.H.O.).

1989. Paintings (8th series). As T **54**. Mult.
248	150l. "Dervis Pasa Mansion, Lefkosa" (Inci Kansu) . .		90	60
249	400l. "Gamblers' Inn, Lefkosa" (Osman Guvenir)		1·75	2·25
250	600l. "Mosque, Paphos" (Hikmet Ulucam) (vert) . .		2·50	3·00

1989. Europa. Children's Games. Multicoloured.
251	600l. Type **85**		1·75	1·25
252	1000l. Boy with kite		2·00	3·50

86 Meeting of Presidents Vassiliou and Denktash

1989. Cyprus Peace Summit, Geneva, 1988.
253	**86**	500l. red and black		1·25	1·25

87 Chukar Partridge

1989. Wildlife. Multcoloured.
254	100l. Type **87**		65	25
255	200l. Cyprus hare		70	35
256	700l. Black partridge		2·50	2·00
257	2000l. Red fox		3·00	4·00

88 Road Construction

1989. Modern Development (3rd series). Mult.
258	100l. Type **88**		15	15
259	150l. Laying water pipeline (vert)		20	20
260	200l. Seedling trees (vert) . .		30	30
261	450l. Modern telephone exchange (vert) . . .		75	1·00
262	650l. Steam turbine power station (vert)		1·00	1·75
263	700l. Irrigation reservoir . .		1·25	1·75

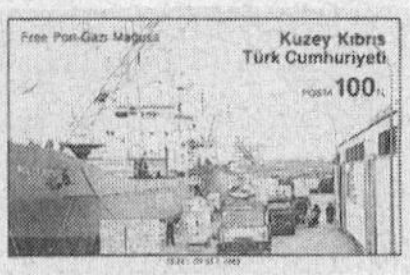

89 Unloading "Polly Pioneer" (freighter) at Quayside (15th anniv of Gazi Magusa Free Port)

1989. Anniversaries.
264 **89** 100l. multicoloured 60 20
265 – 450l. black, blue and red 80 80
266 – 500l. black, yellow and grey 80 80
267 – 600l. black, red and blue 1·75 2·00
268 – 1000l. multicoloured . . . 3·00 4·00
DESIGNS—VERT (26×47 mm): 450l. Airmail letter and stylized bird (25th anniv of Turkish Cypriot postal service). HORIZ (as T **89**): 500l. Newspaper and printing press (centenary of "Saded" newspaper); 600l. Statue of Aphrodite, lifebelt and seabird (30th anniv of International Maritime Organization); 1000l. Soldiers (25th anniv of Turkish Cypriot resistance).

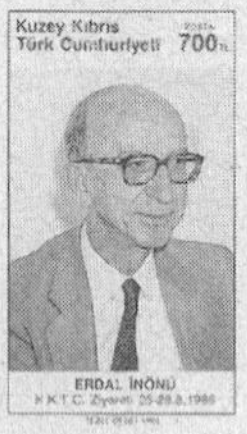

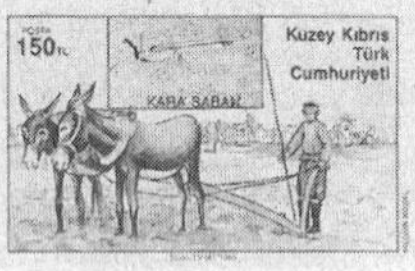

90 Erdal Inonu **91** Mule-drawn Plough

1989. Visit of Professor Erdal Inonu (Turkish politician).
269 **90** 700l. multicoloured 50 70

1989. Traditional Agricultural Implements. Mult.
270 150l. Type **91** 15 20
271 450l. Ox-drawn threshing sledge 50 70
272 550l. Olive press (vert) . . . 60 85

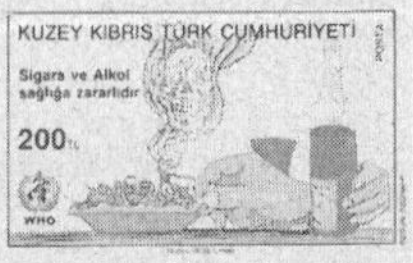

92 Smoking Ashtray and Drinks

1990. World Health Day. Multicoloured.
273 200l. Type **92** 75 40
274 700l. Smoking cigarette and heart . . . . 1·75 2·50

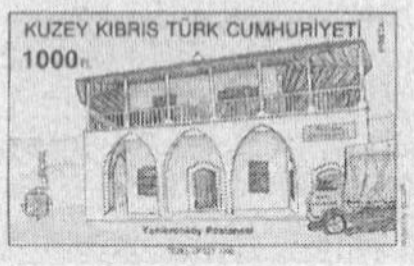

93 Yenierenkoy Post Office

1990. Europa. Post Office Buildings. Mult.
275 1000l. Type **93** . . . . 1·40 75
276 1500l. Ataturk Meydani Post Office . . . . 1·90 3·00

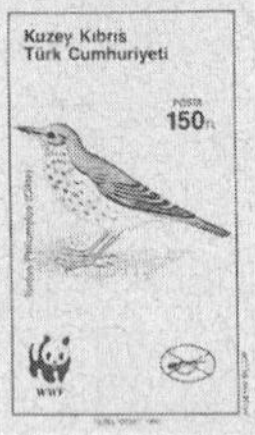

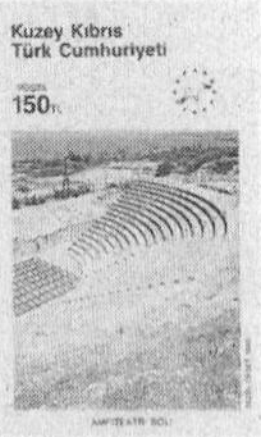

94 Song Thrush **96** Amphitheatre, Soli

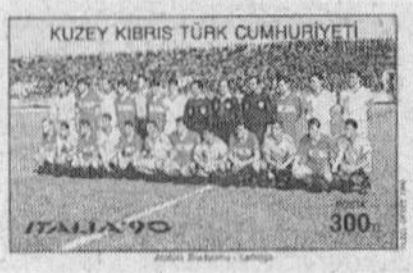

95 Two Football Teams

1990. World Environment Day. Birds. Mult.
278 150l. Type **94** . . . . 1·75 65
279 300l. Blackcap . . . . 2·50 90
280 900l. Black redstart . . . . . 4·00 3·25
281 1000l. Chiff-chaff . . . . . 4·00 3·25

1990. World Cup Football Championship, Italy. Mult.
282 300l. Type **95** 75 50
283 1000l. Championship symbol, globe and ball . . . . . . 2·50 3·25

1990. Paintings (9th series). As T **54**. Multicoloured.
284 300l. "Abstract" (Filiz Ankacc) 25 25
285 1000l. Wooden sculpture (S. Tekman) (vert) . . . . 85 1·50

1990. Tourism. Multicoloured.
286 150l. Type **96** 40 20
287 1000l. Swan mosaic, Soli . . 1·75 2·50

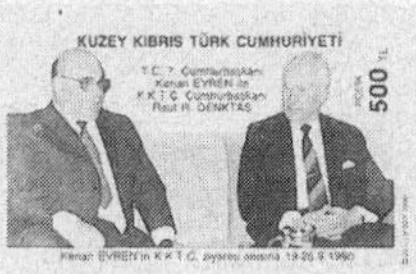

97 Kenan Evren and Rauf Denktas

1990. Visit of President Kenan Evren of Turkey.
288 **97** 500l. multicoloured . . . . 1·00 1·00

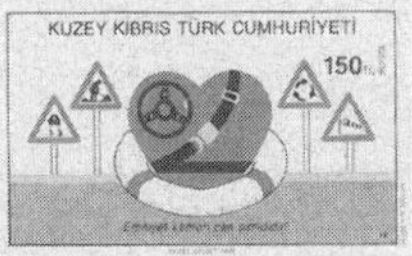

98 Road Signs and Heart wearing Seat Belt

1990. Traffic Safety Campaign. Multicoloured.
289 150l. Type **98** 65 30
290 300l. Road signs, speeding car and spots of blood . . 90 50
291 1000l. Traffic lights and road signs . . . . 2·75 3·50

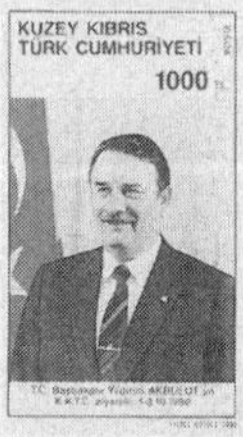

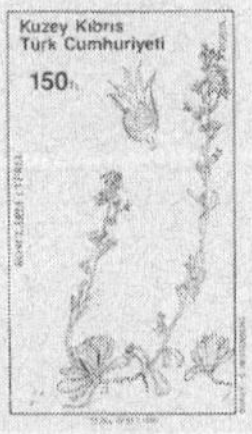

99 Yildirim Akbulut **100** "Rosularia cypria"

1990. Visit of Turkish Prime Minister Yildrim Akbulut.
292 **99** 1000l. multicoloured . . . 1·10 1·10

1990. Plants. Multicoloured.
293 150l. Type **100** 45 20
294 200l. "Silene fraudratrix" . . 55 30
295 300l. "Scutellaria sibthorpii" 65 35
296 600l. "Sedum lampusae" . . 95 85
297 1000l. "Onosma caespitosum" 1·10 1·50
298 1500l. "Arabis cypria" . . . 1·60 2·75

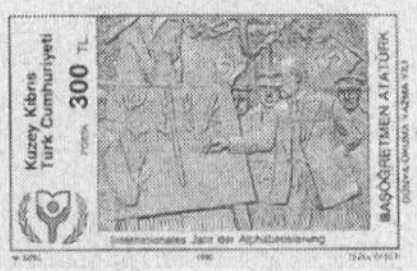

101 Kemal Ataturk at Easel (wood carving)

1990. International Literacy Year. Multicoloured.
299 300l. Type **101** 65 35
300 750l. Globe, letters and books 1·75 2·25

1991. Nos. 189, 212 and 293 surch.
301 **66** 250l. on 10l. multicoloured 70 70
302 **73** 250l. on 20l. multicoloured 70 70
303 **100** 500l. on 150l. multicoloured . . . . . 1·00 1·00

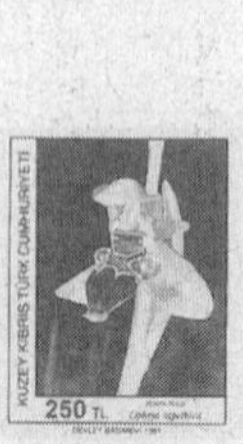

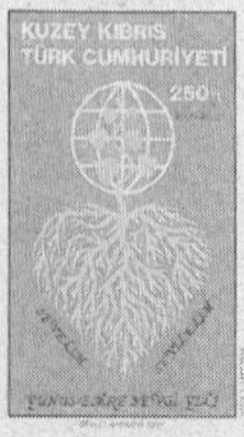

103 "Ophrys lapethica" **106** Symbolic Roots (Year of Love to Yunus Emre)

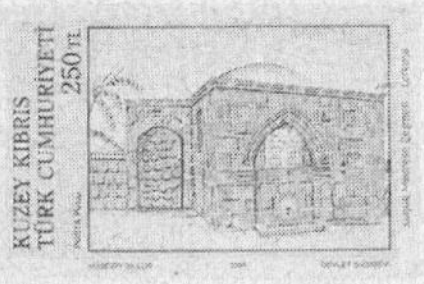

105 Kucuk Medrese Fountain, Lefkosa

1991. Orchids (1st series). Multicoloured.
304 250l. Type **103** . . . . 1·25 60
305 500l. "Ophrys kotschyi" . . . 2·25 2·75
See also Nos. 311/14.

1991. Fountains. Multicoloured.
307 250l. Type **105** 35 15
308 500l. Cafer Pasa fountain, Magusa 55 30
309 1500l. Sarayonu Square fountain, Lefkosa . . . . 1·10 1·25
310 5000l. Arabahmet Mosque fountain, Lefkosa . . . . 3·00 4·00

1991. Orchids (2nd series). As T **103**. Mult.
311 100l. "Serapias levantina" . . 65 20
312 500l. "Dactylorhiza romana" 1·50 50
313 2000l. "Orchis simia" . . . . 3·00 3·25
314 3000l. "Orchis sancta" . . . 3·25 4·00

1991. Paintings (10th series). As T **54**. Mult.
315 250l. "Hindiler" (S. Cizel) (vert) . . . . 1·25 50
316 500l. "Dusme" (A. Mene) (vert) . . . . 1·75 2·00

1991. Anniversaries and Events.
317 **106** 250l. yellow, black and mauve 25 25
318 – 500l. multicoloured . . . 45 60
319 – 500l. multicoloured . . . 45 60
320 – 1500l. multicoloured . . 2·50 3·50
DESIGNS—VERT: No. 318, Mustafa Cagatay commemoration; 319, University building (5th anniv of Eastern Mediterranean University). HORIZ: No. 320, Mozart (death bicentenary).

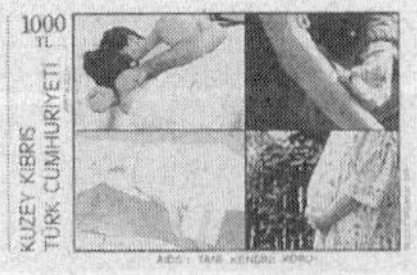

107 Four Sources of Infection

1991. "AIDS" Day.
321 **107** 1000l. multicoloured . . . 2·00 1·75

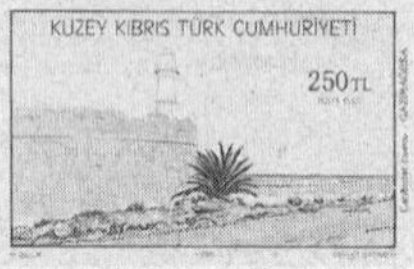

108 Lighthouse, Gazimagusa

1991. Lighthouses. Multicoloured.
322 250l. Type **108** . . . . 1·40 45
323 500l. Ancient lighthouses, Girne harbour . . . . . . 1·75 1·10
324 1500l. Modern lighthouse, Girne harbour . . . . . . 3·50 4·25

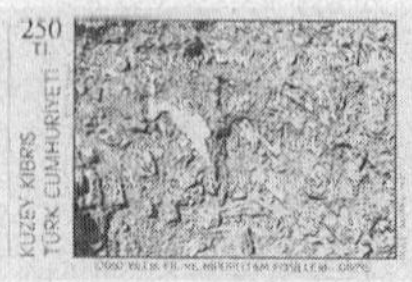

109 Elephant and Hippopotamus Fossils, Karaoglanoglu

1991. Tourism (1st series). Multicoloured.
325 250l. Type **109** . . . . 1·25 40
326 500l. Roman fish ponds, Lambusa . . . . 1·40 65
327 1500l. Roman remains, Lambusa . . . . 2·25 3·25
See also Nos. 330/3 and 351/2.

1992. Paintings (11th series). As T **54**, but 31×49 mm. Multicoloured.
328 500l. "Ebru" (A. Kandulu) 50 20
329 3500l. "Street in Lefkosa" (I. Tatar) . . . . 2·50 3·50

1992. Tourism (2nd series). As T **109**. Mult.
330 500l. Bugday Camii, Gazimagusa 50 50
331 500l. Clay pigeon shooting 50 50
332 1000l. Salamis Bay Hotel, Gazimagusa 85 90
333 1500l. Casino, Girne (vert) 1·75 2·50

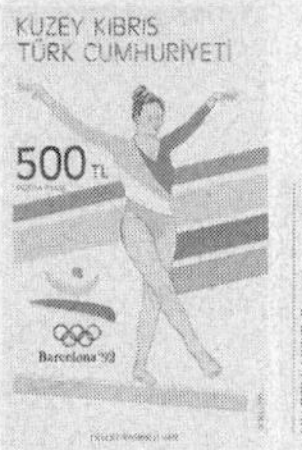

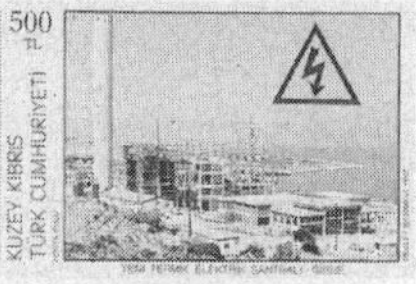

112 Gymnastics **113** New Generating Station, Girne

1992. Olympic Games, Barcelona. Multicoloured.
336 500l. Type **112** 70 90
337 500l. Tennis 70 90
338 1000l. High jumping (horiz) 80 1·00
339 1500l. Cycling (horiz) . . . . 2·25 2·50

1992. Anniversaries and Events (1st series). Multicoloured.
340 500l. Type **113** 30 30
341 500l. Symbol of Housing Association (15th anniv) 30 30
342 1500l. Domestic animals and birds (30th anniv of Veterinary Service) . . . . 2·50 2·75
343 1500l. Cat (International Federation of Cat Societies Conference) . . . . 2·50 2·75

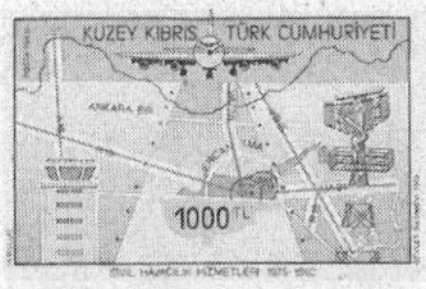

114 Airliner over Runway

1992. Anniversaries and Events (2nd series). Multicoloured.
344 1000l. Type **114** (17th anniv of civil aviation) . . . . . 1·40 1·40
345 1000l. Meteorological instruments and weather (18th anniv of Meteorological Service) . . 1·40 1·40
346 1200l. Surveying equipment and map (14th anniv of Survey Department) . . . 1·75 2·25

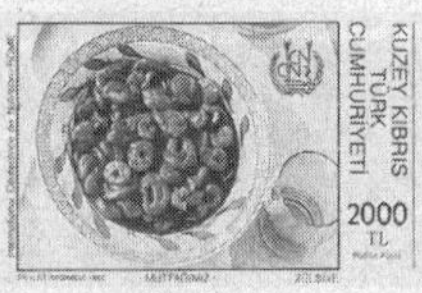

115 Zubiye

1992. International Conference on Nutrition, Rome. Turkish Cypriot Cuisine. Multicoloured.
347 2000l. Type **115** . . . . . . 90 1·00
348 2500l. Cicek Dolmasi . . . . 1·00 1·10
349 3000l. Tatar Boregi . . . . . 1·25 1·40
350 4000l. Seftali Kebabi . . . . 1·50 1·75

1993. Tourism (3rd series). As T **109**. Mult.
351 500l. St. Barnabas Church and Monastery, Salamis . . 30 15
352 10000l. Ancient pot . . . . . 3·25 4·00

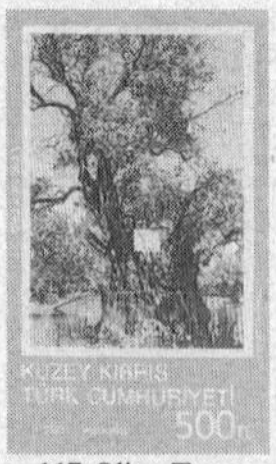

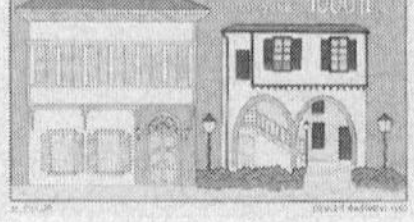

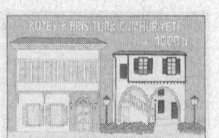

117 Olive Tree, Girne **118** Traditional Houses

1993. Ancient Trees. Multicoloured.
354 500l. Type **117** 20 15
355 1000l. River red gum, Kyrenia Gate, Lefkosa . . 30 25
356 3000l. Oriental plane, Lapta 80 1·25
357 4000l. Calabrian pine, Cinarli 90 1·60

1993. Arabahmet District Conservation Project, Lefkosa. Multicoloured.
358 1000l. Type **118** 85 40
359 3000l. Arabahmet street . . . 1·90 2·50

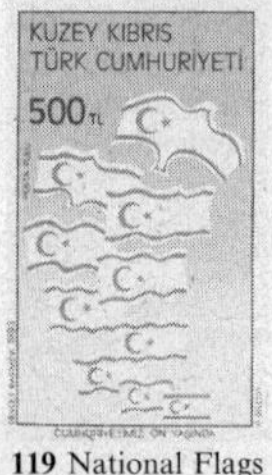

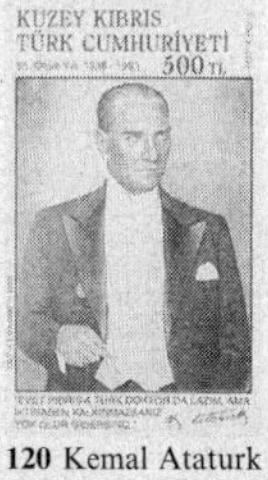

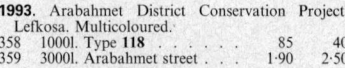

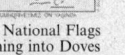

119 National Flags turning into Doves **120** Kemal Ataturk

1993. 10th Anniv of Proclamation of Turkish Republic of Northern Cyprus.
360 **119** 500l. red, black and blue . . . 20 20
361 – 500l. red and blue 20 20
362 – 1000l. red, black and blue . . 30 30
363 – 5000l. multicoloured . . . . 1·40 2·25
DESIGNS—HORIZ: No. 361, National flag forming figure "10"; No. 362, Dove carrying national flag; No. 363, Map of Cyprus and figure "10" wreath.

1993. Anniversaries. Multicoloured.
364 500l. Type **120** (55th death anniv) 20 20
365 500l. Stage and emblem (30th anniv of Turkish Cypriot theatre) (horiz) 20 20
366 1500l. Branch badges (35th anniv of T.M.T. organization) (horiz) 40 50
367 2000l. World map and computer (20th anniv of Turkish Cypriot news agency) (horiz) 70 80
368 5000l. Ballet dancers and Caykovski'nin (death centenary) (horiz) . . . . 2·50 3·00

121 "Soyle Falci" (Goral Ozkan)

1994. Art (12th series). Multicoloured.
369 1000l. Type **121** 20 20
370 6500l. "IV. Hareket" (sculpture) (Senol Ozdevrim) . . . . . . 1·10 1·60
See also Nos. 436/7.

122 Dr. Kucuk and Memorial

1994. 10th Death Anniv of Dr. Fazil Kucuk (politician).
371 **122** 1500l. multicoloured . . . 60 70

124 Peace Doves and Letters over Pillar Box   **125** World Cup Trophy

1994. 30th Anniv of Turkish Cypriot Postal Service.
373 **124** 50000l. multicoloured . . . 3·00 4·50

1994. World Cup Football Championship, U.S.A. Multicoloured.
374 2500l. Type **125** 50 25
375 10000l. Footballs on map of U.S.A. (horiz) . . . . . 1·75 2·50

126 Peace Emblem

1994. 20th Anniv of Turkish Landings in Cyprus.
376 **126** 2500l. yellow, green and black 40 30
377 – 5000l. multicoloured . . . 60 60
378 – 7000l. multicoloured . . . 80 1·00
379 – 8500l. multicoloured . . . 1·10 1·50
DESIGNS—HORIZ: 5000l. Memorial; 7000l. Sculpture; 8500l. Peace doves forming map of Cyprus and flame.

127 Cyprus 1934 4½ pi. Stamp and Karpas Postmark

1994. Postal Centenary. Multicoloured.
380 1500l. Type **127** 25 20
381 2500l. Turkish Cypriot Posts 1979 Europa 2l. and Gazimagusa postmark . . . 35 30
382 5000l. Cyprus 1938 6pi. and Bey Keuy postmark . . . 60 70
383 7000l. Cyprus 1955 100m. and Aloa postmark . . . 80 1·10
384 8500l. Cyprus 1938 18pi. and Pyla postmark . . . . . 1·00 1·50

128 Trumpet Triton

1994. Sea Shells. Multicoloured.
385 2500l. Type **128** 45 30
386 12500l. Mole cowrie . . . . 1·25 1·75
387 12500l. Giant tun . . . . . 1·25 1·75

1994. Nos. 280, 295, 315 and 317 surch.
388 1500l. on 250l. Type **106** . . 15 10
389 2000l. on 900l. Black redstart . 1·25 60
390 2500l. on 250l. "Hindiler" (Sizel) 30 30
391 3500l. on 300l. "Scutellaria sibthorpii" . . . . . . 1·25 1·25

130 Donkeys on Mountain

1995. European Conservation Year. Multicoloured.
392 2000l. Type **130** 30 20
393 3500l. Coastline 30 30
394 15000l. Donkeys in field . . . 1·50 2·50

132 Sini Katmeri

1995. Turkish Cypriot Cuisine. Multicoloured.
396 3500l. Type **132** 20 20
397 10000l. Kolokas musakka and bullez kizartma 55 65
398 14000l. Enginar dolmasi . . . 90 1·60

133 "Papilio machaon"

1995. Butterflies. Multicoloured.
399 3500l. Type **133** 30 15
400 4500l. "Charaxes jasius" . . . 35 20
401 15000l. "Cynthia cardui" . . . 1·00 1·40
402 30000l. "Vanessa atalanta" . . 1·75 2·50

134 Forest

1995. Obligatory Tax. Forest Regeneration Fund.
403 **134** 1000l. green and black . . 1·50 20

135 Beach, Girne

1995. Tourism. Multicoloured.
404 3500l. Type **135** 30 20
405 7500l. Sail boards 50 45

406 15000l. Ruins of Salamis (vert) . . . . 1·00 1·25
407 20000l. St. George's Cathedral, Gazimagusa (vert) . . . . 1·00 1·25

136 Suleyman Demirel and Rauf Denktas

1995. Visit of President Suleyman Demirel of Turkey.
408 **136** 5000l. multicoloured . . . 40 40

137 Stamp Printing Press   **138** Kultegin Epitaph and Sculpture

1995. Anniversaries.
409 **137** 3000l. multicoloured . . . 40 40
410 – 3000l. multicoloured . . . 40 40
411 – 5000l. multicoloured . . . 70 70
412 – 22000l. ultram, bl & blk . . 1·00 1·40
413 – 30000l. multicoloured . . . 1·40 1·90
414 – 30000l. multicoloured . . . 1·40 1·90
DESIGNS—HORIZ: No. 409, Type **137** (20th anniv of State Printing Works); 410, Map of Turkey (75th anniv of Turkish National Assembly); 411, Louis Pasteur (chemist) and microscope (death centenary); 412, United Nations anniversary emblem (50th anniv); 413, Guglielmo Marconi (radio pioneer) and dial (centenary of first radio transmissions). VERT: No. 414, Stars and reel of film (centenary of cinema).

1995. Centenary of Deciphering of Orhon Epitaphs. Multicoloured.
415 5000l. Type **138** 60 40
416 10000l. Epitaph and tombstone . . . . . . 1·00 1·40

139 "Bosnia" (sculpture)   **140** Striped Red Mullet

1996. Support for Moslems in Bosnia and Herzegovina.
417 **139** 10000l. multicoloured . . 1·00 1·25

1996. Fishes. Multicoloured.
418 6000l. Type **140** 65 30
419 10000l. Peacock wrasse . . . 85 45
420 28000l. Common two-banded seabream . . . . . . 1·50 1·75
421 40000l. Dusky grouper . . . 2·00 2·50

141 Palm Trees   **142** Beria Remzi Ozoran

1996. Tourism. Multicoloured.
422 100000l. Type **141** 50 30
423 150000l. Pomegranate 75 55
424 250000l. Ruins of Bella Paise Abbey (horiz) . . . . 1·25 1·25
425 500000l. Traditional dancers (horiz) . . . . . . 2·25 2·75

1996. Europa. Famous Women. Multicoloured.
426 150000l. Type **142** 60 25
427 500000l. Kadriye Hulusi Hacibulgur . . . . . . 1·50 2·25

145 Symbolic Footballs

1996. European Football Championship, England. Multicoloured.
430 150000l. Type **145** 80 65
431 350000l. Football and flags of participating nations . . . 1·60 2·00

146 Houses on Fire (Auxiliary Fire Service)   **147** "Amanita phalloides"

1996. Anniversaries and Events. Multicoloured.
432 100000l. Type **146** 30 30
433 200000l. Colour party (20th anniv of Defence Forces) (vert) 40 40
434 500000l. Children by lake (Nasreddin-Hoca Year) . . 85 85
435 750000l. Flowers (Children's Rights) . . . . . . 1·25 1·75

1997. Arts (13th series). As T **121**. Multicoloured.
436 25000l. "City" (Lebibe Sonuc) (horiz) 75 50
437 700000l. "Woman opening Letter" (Ruzen Atakan) (horiz) . . . . . . 1·75 2·50

1997. Fungi. Multicoloured.
438 150000l. Type **147** 40 30
439 25000l. "Morchella esculenta" 55 50
440 25000l. "Pleurotus eryngii" . . 55 50
441 700000l. "Amanita muscaria" . 1·25 2·00

148 Flag on Hillside   **150** Prime Minister Necmettin Erbakan of Turkey

149 Mother and Children playing Leapfrog

1997. Besparmak Mountains Flag Sculpture.
442 **148** 600000l. multicoloured . . 1·00 1·25

1997. Europa. Tales and Legends. Multicoloured.
443 25000l. Type **149** 75 30
444 70000l. Apple tree and well . . 1·75 2·50

1997. Visit of the President and the Prime Minister of Turkey.
445 15000l. Type **150** 30 20
446 80000l. President Suleyman Demirel of Turkey (horiz) . 1·25 2·00

151 Golden Eagle   **152** Coin of Sultan Abdulaziz, 1861–76

1997. Birds of Prey. Multicoloured.
447 400000l. Type **151** 70 70
448 400000l. Eleonora's falcon . . 70 70
449 750000l. Common kestrel . . . 1·25 1·50
450 1000000l. Honey buzzard . . . 1·40 1·75

1997. Rare Coins. Multicoloured.
451 25000l. Type **152** 25 20

452	400001.	Coin of Sultan Mahmud II, 1808–39	35	30
453	750001.	Coin of Sultan Selim II, 1566–74	55	85
454	1000001.	Coin of Sultan Mehmed V, 1909–18	80	1·25

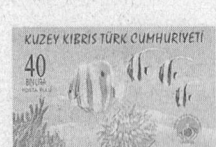

153 Open Book and Emblem

1997. Anniversaries.

455	**153**	250001. multicoloured	45	20
456	–	400001. multicoloured	55	30
457	–	1000001. black, red and stone	1·25	1·40
458	–	1500001. multicoloured	1·75	2·25

DESIGNS—HORIZ: 250001. Type **153** (centenary of Turkish Cypriot Scouts); 400001. Guides working in field (90th anniv of Turkish Cypriot Guides); 1500001. Rudolph Diesel and first oil engine (centenary of the diesel engine). VERT: 1000001. Couple and symbols (AIDS prevention campaign).

154 Ahmet and Ismet Sevki

1998. Ahmet and Ismet Sevki (photographers) Commemoration. Multicoloured.

459		400001. Type **154**	35	25
460		1050001. Ahmet Sevki (vert)	1·40	2·00

155 "Agrion splendens" (dragonfly)   **156** Wooden Double Door

1998. Useful Insects. Multicoloured.

461		400001. Type **155**	45	25
462		650001. "Ascalaphus macaronius" (owl-fly)	60	40
463		1250001. "Podalonia hirsuta"	1·25	1·50
464		1500001. "Rhyssa persuasoria"	1·50	1·90

1998. Old Doors.

465	**156**	1150001. multicoloured	1·25	1·40
466	–	1400001. multicoloured	1·25	1·40

DESIGN: 1400001. Different door.

157 Legislative Assembly Building (Republic Establishment Festival)

1998. Europa. Festivals. Multicoloured.

467		400001. Type **157**	50	25
468		1500001. Globe, flags and map (Int Children's Folk Dance Festival) (vert)	1·75	2·00

158 Marine Life

1998. International Year of the Ocean.

469	**158**	400001. multicoloured	60	40
470	–	900001. multicoloured	1·25	1·50

DESIGN: 900001. Different underwater scene.

159 Prime Minister Mesut Yilmaz of Turkey

1998. Prime Minister Yilmaz's Visit to Northern Cyprus.

471	**159**	750001. multicoloured	1·25	1·25

160 Pres. Suleyman Demirel of Turkey   **162** Deputy Prime Minister Bulent Ecevit

161 Victorious French Team

1998. President Demirel's "Water for Peace" Project.

472		750001. Type **160**	75	50
473		1750001. Turkish and Turkish Cypriot leaders with inflatable water tank (horiz)	1·75	2·25

1998. World Cup Football Championship, France. Multicoloured.

474		750001. Type **161**	75	50
475		1750001. World Cup trophy (vert)	1·75	2·25

1998. Visit of the Deputy Prime Minister of Turkey.

476	**162**	200000l. multicoloured	1·50	1·75

163 Itinerant Tinsmiths

1998. Local Crafts. Multicoloured.

477		500001. Type **163**	25	25
478		750001. Basket weaver (vert)	45	35
479		1300001. Grinder sharpening knife (vert)	85	95
480		4000001. Wood carver	2·75	3·50

164 Stylised Satellite Dish   **165** Dr. Fazil Kucuk

1998. Anniversaries. Multicoloured (except No. 483).

481		500001. Type **164**	60	25
482		750001. Stylised birds and "15"	65	70
483		750001. "75" and Turkish flag (red, black and orange)	65	70
484		1750001. Scroll, "50" and quill pen (vert)	1·10	1·75

ANNIVERSARIES: No. 481, 35th anniv of Bayrak Radio and Television; 482, 15th anniv of Turkish Republic of Northern Cyprus; 483, 75th anniv of Turkish Republic; 484, 50th anniv of Universal Declaration of Human Rights.

1999. 15th Death Anniv of Dr. Fazil Kucuk (politician).

486	**165**	750001. multicoloured	70	70

167 "Malpolon monspessulanus insignitus" (Montepellier)

1999. Snakes. Multicoloured.

488		500001. Type **167**	40	25
489		750001. "Hierophis jugularis"	60	35
490		1950001. "Vipera lebetina lebetina" (levantine viper)	1·25	1·50
491		2200001. "Natrix natrix" (grass snake)	1·25	1·50

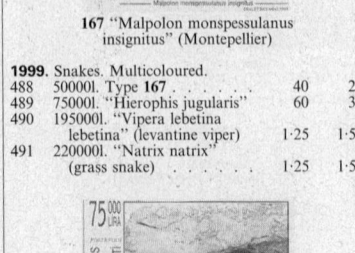

168 Entrance to Cave

1999. Europa. Parks and Gardens. Incirli Cave. Multicoloured.

492		750001. Type **168**	60	25
493		2000001. Limestone rocks inside cave (vert)	1·40	1·75

169 Peace Dove and Map of Cyprus

1999. 25th Anniv of Turkish Landings in Cyprus. Multicoloured.

494		1500001. Type **169**	1·00	1·00
495		2500001. Peace dove, map of Cyprus and sun	1·25	1·50

170 Air Mail Envelope and Labels

1999. Anniversaries and Events. Multicoloured.

496		750001. Type **170** (35th anniv of Turkish Cypriot Posts)	30	20
497		2250001. "125" and U.P.U. emblem (125th anniv of U.P.U.)	75	80
498		2500001. Total eclipse of the Sun, August 1999	95	1·25

171 Turkish Gateway, Limassol

1999. Destruction of Turkish Buildings in Southern Cyprus. Each light brown and brown.

499		750001. Type **171**	30	25
500		1500001. Mosque, Evdim	55	40
501		2100001. Bayraktar Mosque, Lefkosa	70	60
502		10000001. Kebir Mosque, Baf (vert)	3·50	4·25

172 Mobile Phone

2000. New Millennium. Technology.

503	**172**	750001. black, green and blue	25	20
504	–	1500001. black and blue	40	25
505	–	2750001. multicoloured	70	90
506	–	3000001. multicoloured	85	1·10

DESIGNS: 1500001. "Hosgeldin 2000"; 2750001. Computer and "internet" in squares; 3000001. Satellite over Earth.

173 Beach Scene

2000. Holidays. Multicoloured.

507		3000001. Type **173**	80	1·00
508		3400001. Deck-chair on sea-shore	80	1·00

175 Bellapais Abbey   **176** Pres. Ahmet Sezer of Turkey

2000. 4th International Bellapais Music Festival. Multicoloured.

510		1500001. Type **175**	40	40
511		3500001. Emblem (vert)	85	1·10

2000. Visit of President Ahmet Sezer of Turkey.

512	**176**	1500001. multicoloured	50	50

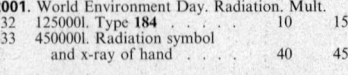

177 Olympic Torch and Rings   **179** Grasshopper on Cactus

2000. Olympic Games, Sydney. Multicoloured.

513		1250001. Type **177**	35	35
514		2000001. Runner (horiz)	65	75

2000. No. 418 surch **50000 LIRA POSTA PULU.**

515		500001. on 60001. Type **140**	15	10

2000. Nature. Insects and Flowers. Multicoloured.

516		1250001. Type **179**	10	15
517		2000001. Butterfly on flower	20	25
518		2750001. Bee on flower	25	30
519		6000001. Snail on flower	60	65

180 Traditional Kerchief

2000. Traditional Handicrafts. Kerchiefs.

520	**180**	1250001. multicoloured	30	30
521	–	2000001. multicoloured	50	45
522	–	2650001. multicoloured	70	80
523	–	3500001. multicoloured	80	90

DESIGNS: 2000001. to 3500001. Different kerchiefs.

181 Lusignan House, Lefkosa

2001. Restoration of Historic Buildings. Mult.

524		1250001. Type **181**	10	15
525		2000001. The Eaved House, Lefkosa	20	25

182 "Cuprum Kuprum Bakir Madeni" (Inci Kansu)

2001. Modern Art. Multicoloured.

526		1250001. Type **182**	10	15
527		2000001. "Varolus" (Emel Samioglu)	20	25
528		3500001. "Ask Kuslara Ucar" (Ozden Selenge) (vert)	35	40
529		4000001. "Suyun Yolculugu" (Ayhatun Atesin)	40	45

183 Degirmenlik Reservoir   **184** Atomic Symbol and X-ray

2001. Europa. Water Resources. Multicoloured.

530		2000001. Type **183**	20	25
531		5000001. The Waters of Sinar	50	55

2001. World Environment Day. Radiation. Mult.

532		1250001. Type **184**	10	15
533		4500001. Radiation symbol and x-ray of hand	40	45

185 Ottoman Policeman, 1885   **186** MG TF Sports Car, 1954

2001. Turkish Cypriot Police Uniforms. Multicoloured.
534 1250000l. Type **185** 10 15
535 2000000l. Colonial policeman, 1933 20 25
536 5000000l. Mounted policeman, 1934 50 55
537 7500000l. Policewoman, 1983 75 80

2001. Classic Cars. Multicoloured.
538 1750000l. Type **186** 15 20
539 3000000l. Vauxhall 14, 1948 30 35
540 4750000l. Bentley, 1922 45 50
541 6000000l. Jaguar XK 120, 1955 60 65

CYRENAICA Pt. 8

Part of the former Italian colony of Libya, N. Africa. Allied Occupation, 1942–49. Independent Administration, 1949–52. Then part of independent Libya.

Stamps optd **BENGASI** formerly listed here will be found under Italian P.O.s in the Turkish Empire, Nos. 169/70.

100 centesimi = 1 lira.

Stamps of Italy optd **CIRENAICA**.

1923. Tercent of Propagation of the Faith.
1 **66** 20c. orange and green 2·00 6·00
2 30c. orange and red 2·00 6·00
3 50c. orange and violet 2·00 6·00
4 1l. orange and blue 2·00 6·00

1923. Fascist March on Rome stamps.
5 **77** 10c. green 1·40 6·00
6 30c. violet 1·40 6·00
7 50c. red 1·40 6·00
8 **74** 1l. blue 1·40 6·00
9 2l. brown 1·40 6·00
10 **75** 5l. black and blue 1·40 7·50

1924. Manzoni stamps (Nos. 155/60).
11 **77** 10c. black and purple 75 12·00
12 – 15c. black and green 75 12·00
13 – 30c. black 75 13·00
14 – 50c. black and brown 75 12·00
15 – 1l. black and blue 18·00 90·00
16 – 5l. black and purple £250 £1000

1925. Holy Year stamps.
17 – 20c.+10c. brown & green 1·00 4·25
18 **81** 30c.+15c. brown & choc 1·00 4·25
19 – 50c.+25c. brown & violet 1·00 4·25
20 – 60c.+30c. brown and red 1·00 4·25
21 – 1l.+50c. purple and blue 1·00 4·25
22 – 5l.+2l.50 purple and red 1·00 4·25

1925. Royal Jubilee stamps.
23 **82** 60c. red 25 2·75
24 1l. blue 35 2·75
24a 1l.25 blue 60 8·50

1926. St. Francis of Assisi stamps.
25 **83** 20c. green 1·00 4·25
26 – 40c. violet 1·00 4·25
27 – 60c. red 1·00 4·25
28 – 1l.25 blue 1·00 4·25
29 – 5l.+2l.50 olive (as No. 196) 2·00 5·50

ISTITUTO·COLONIALE·ITALIANO
POSTE
CIRENAICA
6

POSTE CIRENAICA
SOCIETA AFRICANA D'ITALIA
8

1926. Colonial Propaganda.
30 **6** 5c.+5c. brown 20 2·25
31 10c.+5c. olive 20 2·25
32 20c.+5c. green 20 2·25
33 40c.+5c. red 20 2·25
34 60c.+5c. orange 20 2·25
35 1l.+5c. blue 20 2·25

1927. 1st National Defence stamps of Italy optd **CIRENAICA**.
36 **89** 40+20c. black & brown 1·00 4·25
37 – 60+30c. brown and red 1·00 4·25
38 – 1l.25+60c. black & blue 1·00 4·25
39 – 5l.+2l.50 black & green 1·50 6·50

1927. Volta Centenary stamps of Italy optd **Cirenaica**.
40 **90** 20c. violet 3·00 10·00
41 50c. orange 3·00 7·00
42 1l.25 blue 4·00 10·00

1928. 45th Anniv of Italian–African Society.
43 **8** 20c.+5c. green 75 4·00
44 30c.+5c. red 75 4·00
45 50c.+10c. violet 75 4·00
46 1l.25+20c. blue 75 4·00

Stamps of Italy optd **CIRENAICA**. Colours changed in some instances.

1929. 2nd National Defence stamps.
47 **89** 30c.+10c. black & red 1·40 4·75
48 50c.+20c. grey & lilac 1·40 4·75
49 1l.25+50c. blue & brown 1·75 6·00
50 – 5l.+2l. black & green 1·75 6·00

1929. Montecassino stamps (No. 57 optd **Cirenaica**).
51 **104** 20c. green 1·75 4·25
52 – 25c. red 1·75 4·25
53 – 50c.+10c. red 1·75 8·50
54 – 75c.+15c. brown 1·75 8·50
55 **104** 1l.25+25c. purple 3·25 8·50
56 – 5l.+1l. blue 3·25 8·50
57 – 10l.+2l. brown 3·25 10·00

1930. Marriage of Prince Humbert and Princess Marie Jose stamps.
58 **109** 20c. green 40 1·90
59 50c.+10c. red 35 2·50
60 1l.25+25c. red 35 6·00

1930. Ferrucci stamps (optd **Cirenaica**).
61 **114** 20c. violet 50 1·60
62 – 25c. green 50 1·60
63 – 50c. black 50 1·60
64 – 1l.25 blue 50 1·60
65 – 5l.+2l. red 1·75 2·75

1930. 3rd National Defence stamps.
66 **89** 30c.+10c. turq & grn 5·00 15·00
67 – 50c.+10c. purple & green 5·00 15·00
68 – 1l.25+30c. lt brown & brn 5·00 20·00
69 – 5l.+1l.50 green and blue 14·00 50·00

ISTITUTO AGRICOLO COLONIALE ITALIANO 1904-1929
POSTE
CIRENAICA
13

LIRE
1
POSTA AEREA
CIRENAICA
17 Columns of Leptis

1930. 25th Anniv (1929) of Italian Colonial Agricultural Institute.
70 **13** 50c.+20c. brown 1·00 5·00
71 1l.25+20c. blue 1·00 5·00
72 1l.75+20c. green 1·00 5·00
73 2l.55+50c. violet 1·75 7·00
74 5l.+1l. red 1·75 10·00

1930. Virgil Bimillenary stamps optd **CIRENAICA**.
75 **118** 15c. violet 40 1·40
76 – 20c. brown 40 1·40
77 – 25c. green 40 1·40
78 – 30c. brown 40 1·40
79 – 50c. purple 40 1·40
80 – 75c. red 40 1·40
81 – 1l.25 blue 40 1·40
82 – 5l.+1l.50 purple 2·00 10·00
83 – 10l.+2l.50 brown 2·00 10·00

1931. St. Anthony of Padua stamps optd **Cirenaica** (75c., 5l.) or **CIRENAICA** (others).
84 **121** 20c. brown 55 2·50
85 – 25c. green 55 2·50
86 – 30c. brown 55 2·50
87 – 50c. purple 55 1·40
88 – 75c. grey (as No. 308) 55 2·50
89 – 1l.25 blue 55 4·00
90 – 5l.+2l.50 brn (as No. 310) 2·00 18·00

1932. Air stamps of Tripolitania optd **Cirenaica**.
91 **18** 50c. red 30 10
92 60c. orange 1·60 8·50
93 80c. purple 1·60 8·50

1932. Air stamps of Tripolitania of 1931 optd **CIRENAICA** and bars.
94 **18** 50c. red 50 20
95 80c. purple 2·00 11·00

1932. Air.
96 – 50c. violet 1·25 10
97 – 75c. red 2·00 5·00
98 – 80c. blue 2·00 5·00
99 **17** 1l. black 50 10
100 2l. green 85 2·50
101 5l. red 1·40 5·50
DESIGN—VERT: 50c. to 80c. Arab on Camel.

POSTA AEREA
LIRE 3
CROCIERA ZEPPELIN
1933 CIRENAICA A.XI
18 "Graf Zeppelin"

1933. Air. "Graf Zeppelin". Inscr "CROCIERA ZEPPELIN".
102 **18** 3l. brown 5·00 35·00
103 – 5l. violet 5·00 35·00
104 – 10l. green 5·00 55·00
105 – 12l. blue 5·00 85·00
106 **18** 15l. red 5·00 70·00
107 – 20l. black 5·00 £100
DESIGNS: 5l., 12l. "Graf Zeppelin" and Roman galley; 10l., 20l. "Graf Zeppelin" and giant archer.

CIRENAICA POSTA AEREA
CROCIERA NORD ATLANTICA
19 Air Squadron

1933. Air. Balbo Transatlantic Mass Formation Flight by Savoia Marchetti S-55X Flying Boats.
108 **19** 19l.75 blue and green 10·00 £225
109 44l.75 blue and red 10·00 £225

1934. Air. Rome–Buenos Aires Flight. T **17** (new colours) optd with Savoia Marchetti S-71 airplane and **1934-XII PRIMO VOLO DIRETTO ROMA = BUENOS-AYRES TRIMOTORE "LOMBARDI-MAZZOTTI"** or surch also.
110 **17** 2l. on 5l. brown 1·50 28·00
111 3l. on 5l. green 1·50 28·00
112 5l. brown 1·50 28·00
113 10l. on 5l. pink 1·50 28·00

CIRENAICA
RR. POSTE COLONIALI ITALIANE
CENT. 5
II^ MOSTRA INTERNAZIONALE D'ARTE COLONIALE NAPOLI A. XII-1934
21 Arab Horseman

1934. 2nd International Colonial Exn, Naples.
114 **21** 5c. brn & grn (postage) 1·50 7·50
115 10c. black and brown 1·50 7·50
116 20c. blue and red 1·50 7·50
117 50c. brown and violet 1·50 7·50
118 60c. blue and brown 1·50 7·50
119 1l.25 green and blue 1·50 7·50
120 – 25c. orange & blue (air) 1·50 7·50
121 – 50c. blue and green 1·50 7·50
122 – 75c. orange and brown 1·50 7·50
123 – 80c. green and brown 1·50 7·50
124 – 1l. green and red 1·50 7·50
125 – 2l. brown and blue 1·50 7·50
DESIGNS: 25 to 75c. Arrival of Caproni Ca 101 mail plane; 80c. to 2l. Caproni Ca 101 mail plane and Venus of Cyrene.

CIRENAICA
RR. POSTE COLONIALI
POSTA AEREA
ROMA MOGADISCIO
Cent. 25
22

1934. Air. Rome–Mogadiscio Flight.
126 **22** 25c.+10c. green 2·00 5·00
127 50c.+10c. brown 2·00 5·00
128 75c.+15c. red 2·00 5·00
129 80c.+15c. black 2·00 5·00
130 1l.+20c. brown 2·00 5·00
131 2l.+20c. blue 2·00 5·00
132 3l.+25c. violet 16·00 40·00
133 5l.+25c. orange 16·00 40·00
134 10l.+30c. purple 16·00 40·00
135 25l.+2l. green 16·00 40·00

OFFICIAL AIR STAMP

1934. Optd **SERVIZIO DI STATO** and crown.
O136 **22** 25l.+2l. red £1400 £850

For stamps of British Occupation see under British Occupation of Italian Colonies.

CZECHOSLOVAK ARMY IN SIBERIA Pt. 5

During the War of 1914–18 many Czech and Slovak soldiers in the Austro-Hungarian armies surrendered to the Russian Army. After the war many of these formed an army in Siberia and fought the Bolshevists. They issued stamps for their own postal service and these were also sold to the public on the Siberian Railway.

100 kopeks = 1 rouble.

1 Church in Irkutsk

VOJENSKÁ POŠTA
ČESKOSLOVENSKÉ VOJSKO NA RUSI
1
3 Sentry

1919. Imperf.
1 **1** 25k. red 17·00 12·50
2 – 50k. green 17·00 32·00
3 **3** 1r. red 32·00 25·00
DESIGN: 50k. Armoured train "Orlik".

1920. Perf.
4 **1** 25k. red 14·00 10·00
5 – 50k. green (as No. 2) 14·00 10·00
6 **3** 1r. brown 21·00 19·00

4 Lion of Bohemia

1919.
7 **4** (25k.) red and blue 1·75

1920. No. 7 optd **1920**.
8 **4** (25k.) red and blue 8·00

1920. No. 8 surch.
9 **4** 2(k.) red and blue 35·00
10 3(k.) red and blue 35·00
11 5(k.) red and blue 35·00
12 10(k.) red and blue 35·00
13 15(k.) red and blue 35·00
14 25(k.) red and blue 35·00
15 35(k.) red and blue 35·00
16 50(k.) red and blue 35·00
17 1r. red and blue 35·00

CZECHOSLOVAKIA Pt. 5

Formed in 1918 by the Czechs of Bohemia and Moravia and the Slovaks of northern Hungary (both part of Austro-Hungarian Empire). Occupied by Germany in 1939 (see note after No. 393c); independence restored 1945.

On 31 December 1992 the Czech and Slovak Federative Republic was dissolved, the two constituent republics becoming independent as the Czech Republic and Slovakia.

100 haleru = 1 koruna.

POŠTA ČESKÝCH SKAUTŮ
20 20
VE SLUŽBÁCH NÁRODNÍ VLÁDY
1

10
2 Hradcany, Prague

1918. Roul.
1 **1** 10h. blue 13·50 12·00
2 20h. red 13·50 12·00

1918. (a) Imperf.
4 **2** 3h. mauve 10 10
9 30h. olive 25 10
10 40h. orange 25 10
12 100h. brown 65 10
14 400h. violet 1·40 10

(b) Imperf or perf.
5 **2** 5h. green 10 10
6 10h. red 10 10
7 20h. green 10 10
8 25h. blue 10 10
13 200h. blue 1·10 10

POŠTA
ČESKO-SLOVENSKÁ
1
3

1919. Imperf or perf.
3 **3** 1h. brown 10 10
38 5h. green 10 10
39 10h. green 10 10
40 15h. red 10 10
41 20h. red 10 10
28 25h. purple 10 10
49 30h. mauve 35 10
11 50h. purple 25 10
30 50h. blue 25 10
50 60h. orange 25 10
32 75h. green 65 10
33 80h. green 1·10 10
34 120h. black 1·10 45
35 300h. green 3·50 45
36 500h. brown 2·10 40
37 1000h. purple 11·50 80

6

7

1919. 1st Anniv of Independence and Czechoslovak Legion Commemoration.

61	6	15h. green	10	10
62		25h. brown	10	10
63		50h. blue	10	10
64	7	75h. grey	10	10
65		100h. brown	10	10
66		120h. violet on yellow	10	10

1919. Charity. Stamps of Austria optd **POSTA CESKOSLOVENSKA 1919**. A. Postage stamp issue of 1916.

67	49	3h. violet	10	40
68		5h. green	10	40
69		6h. orange	50	65
70		10h. purple	60	1·00
71		12h. blue	60	70
72	60	15h. red	10	10
73		20h. green	10	10
75		25h. blue	10	25
76		30h. violet	10	25
77	51	40h. green	10	25
78		50h. green	10	25
79		60h. blue	10	25
80		80h. brown	10	25
81		90h. purple	45	45
82		1k. red on yellow	35	40
83aa	52	2k. blue	1·40	2·10
85aa		3k. red	6·00	7·00
87 a		4k. green	14·00	14·00
89 a		10k. violet	£325	£170

B. Air stamps of 1918 optd **FLUGPOST** or surch also.

91	52	1k.50 on 2k. mauve	£150	£120
92		2k.50 on 3k. yellow	£150	£130
93		4k. grey	£600	£500

C. Newspaper stamp of 1908. Imperf.

94	N 43	10h. red	£1500	£1500

D. Newspaper stamps of 1916. Imperf.

95	N 53	2h. brown	10	10
96		4h. green	25	35
97		6h. blue	25	30
98		10h. orange	3·50	4·25
99		30h. red	1·75	1·60

E. Express Newspaper stamps of 1916.

100	N 54	2h. red on yellow	29·00	25·00
101		5h. green on yellow	£1400	£1100

F. Express Newspaper stamps of 1917.

102	N 61	2h. red on yellow	10	15
103		5h. green on yellow	10	10

G. Postage Due stamps of 1908.

104	D 44	2h. red	£5250	£3000
105		4h. red	28·00	25·00
106		6h. red	11·00	7·75
108		14h. red	55·00	40·00
109		25h. red	35·00	30·00
110		30h. red	£350	£250
111		50h. red	£1100	£800

H. Postage Due stamps of 1916.

112	D 55	5h. red	10	10
113		10h. red	15	20
114		15h. red	15	20
115		20h. red	1·90	2·40
116		25h. red	1·10	1·50
117		30h. red	45	80
118		40h. red	1·10	1·50
119		50h. red	£550	£275
120	D 56	1k. blue	10·50	7·00
121		5k. blue	45·00	35·00
122		10k. blue	£425	£225

I. Postage Due stamps of 1916 (optd **PORTO** or surch **15** also).

123	36	1h. black	27·00	22·00
124	–	15h. on 2h. violet	£130	70·00

J. Postage Due stamps of 1917 (surch **PORTO** and value).

125	50	10h. on 24h. blue	70·00	80·00
126		15h. on 36h. violet	45	60
127		20h. on 54h. orange	70·00	80·00
128		50h. on 42h. brown	50	65

1919. Various stamps of Hungary optd **POSTA CESKOSLOVENSKA 1919**. A. Postage stamp issue of 1900 ("Turul" type).

129	7	1f. grey	£2250	£1300
130		2f. yellow	4·00	5·25
131		3f. orange	50·00	40·00
132		6f. olive	4·75	5·25
133		50f. lake on blue	60	60
134		60f. green on red	50·00	38·00
135		70f. brown on green	£2750	£1250

B. Postage stamp issue of 1916 ("Harvester" and "Parliament" types).

136	18	2f. brown (No. 245)	10	10
137		3f. red	10	10
138		5f. green	10	10
139		6f. blue	50	60
140		10f. red (No. 250)	1·10	1·10
141		10f. red (No. 243)	£400	£250
142		15f. purple (No. 251)	10	20
143		15f. purple (No. 244)	£200	£180
144		20f. brown	8·00	9·00
145		25f. blue	60	60
146		35f. brown	8·00	10·50
147		40f. green	2·10	1·75
148	19	50f. purple	45	65
149		75f. green	50	50
150		80f. green	1·10	1·10
151		1k. red	1·25	1·25
152		2k. brown	7·75	10·50
153		3k. grey and violet	38·00	60·00
154		5k. lt brown & brown	£130	75·00
155		10k. mauve and brown	£1600	£900

C. Postage stamp issue of 1918 ("Charles" and "Zita" types).

156	27	10f. red	10	10
157		20f. brown	25	30
158		25f. blue	1·75	1·10
159	28	40f. green	3·00	2·25
160		50f. purple	45·00	28·00

D. War Charity stamps of 1916.

161	20	10+2f. red	35	60
162	–	15+2f. lilac (No. 265)	50	90
163	22	40+2f. red	6·75	3·75

E. Postage stamps of 1919 ("Harvester" type inscr "MAGYAR POSTA").

164	30	10f. red (No. 305)	8·75	7·00
165		20f. brown	£6500	£6500

F. Newspaper stamp of 1900.

166	N 9	2f. orange (No. N136)	10	30

G. Express Letter stamp of 1916.

167	E 18	2f. olive & red (No. E245)	10	30

H. Postage Due stamps of 1903 with figures in black.

170	D 9	1f. green (No. D170)	£1400	£700
173		2f. green	£900	£425
174		5f. green	£1800	£900
168		12f. green	£5500	£3250
172		50f. green	£325	£130

I. Postage Due stamps of 1915 with figures in red.

176	D 9	1f. green (No. D190)	£160	£100
177		2f. green	70	50
178		5f. green	10·50	14·00
179		6f. green	1·75	1·75
180		10f. green	35	45
181		12f. green	2·10	2·40
182		15f. green	6·00	6·50
183		20f. green	80	1·25
184		30f. green	35·00	38·00

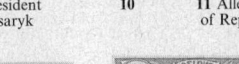

9 President Masaryk

10

11 Allegories of Republic

12 Hussite

13

1920.

185	9	125h. blue	70	25
186		500h. black	3·00	2·00
187		1,000h. brown	5·25	4·25

1920.

188	10	5h. blue	10	10
189		5h. violet	10	10
190		10h. green	10	10
191		10h. olive	10	10
192		15h. brown	10	10
196	11	20h. red	10	10
193b	10	20h. orange	10	10
197	11	25h. brown	10	10
194a	10	25h. green	15	10
198	11	30h. purple	10	10
195	10	30h. purple	4·00	10
199	11	40h. brown	10	10
200		50h. red	10	10
201		50h. green	10	10
202		60h. blue	10	10
203	12	80h. violet	10	25
204		90h. sepia	35	70
205	13	100h. green	45	10
206	11	100h. brown	45	10
227	13	100h. red on yellow	2·00	10
207	11	150h. red	3·50	60
208		185h. orange	1·40	20
209	13	200h. purple	80	10
228		200h. blue on yellow	7·00	10
210	11	250h. green	2·75	40
211	13	300h. red	1·75	10
229		300h. purple on yellow	5·25	15
212		400h. brown	4·75	30
213		500h. green	6·00	50
214		600h. purple	7·75	30

1920. Air. Surch with airplane and value. Imperf or perf.

215	2	14k. on 200h. blue (No. 13)	18·00	20·00
216	3	24k. on 500h. brn (No. 36)	45·00	30·00
220		28k. on 1000h. pur (No. 37)	40·00	25·00

1920. Red Cross Fund. Surch with new value in emblem

221	2	40h.+20h. yellow	80	1·00
222	3	60h.+20h. green	80	1·00
223	9	125h.+25h. blue	2·25	2·50

1922. Surch with airplane and value.

224	13	50 on 100h. green	1·75	2·25
225		100 on 200h. purple	4·25	3·75
226		250 on 400h. brown	7·00	8·00

18 President Masaryk, after portrait by M. Savatimsky

20

23a

1923. 5th Anniv of Republic.

230	18	50h. (+50h.) green	1·00	60
231		100h. (+100h.) red	1·40	1·00
232		200h. (+200h.) blue	7·00	5·50
233		300h. (+300h.) brown	8·50	7·00

1925.

234	20	40h. orange	85	20
235		50h. green	1·75	10
236		60h. purple	1·90	10
237	18	1k. red	1·00	10
238		2k. blue	3·50	30
245		3k. brown	6·75	10
240		5k. green	1·75	30

The 1, 2 and 3k. (which with the 5k. differ slightly in design from the haleru values) come in various sizes, differing in some cases in the details of the designs.

1925. International Olympic Congress. Optd **CONGRES OLYMP. INTERNAT. PRAHA 1925.**

246	18	50h. (+50h.) green	6·00	10·00
247		100h. (+100h.) red	9·25	14·00
248		200h. (+200h.) blue	55·00	90·00

1926. 8th All-Sokol Display, Prague. Optd **VIII. SLET VSESOKOLSKY PRAHA 1926.**

249	18	50h. (+50h.) green	4·75	6·00
250		100h. (+100h.) red	4·75	6·00
251		200h. (+200h.) blue	23·00	21·00
252		300h. (+300h.) brown	35·00	45·00

1926.

254b	23a	50h. green	10	10
254c		60h. purple	60	10
254d		1k. red	25	10

25 Karluv Tyn Castle

26 Strahov

27 Pernstyn Castle

28 Orava Castle

30 Hradcany, Prague

1926. Perf or imperf × perf.

267	25	20h. red	25	10
268	27	30h. green	10	10
258	28	40h. brown	50	10
259	25	1k.20 purple	35	45
270	26	1k.20 purple	35	10
271	25	1k.50 red	35	15
272	27	2k. green	25	10
263	30	2k. blue	90	10
273	25	2k.50 blue	5·25	20
273a	–	2k.50 blue	35	15
273b	28	3k. brown	45	20
264a	30	3k. red	1·75	10
265	–	4k. purple	6·25	65
277	–	5k. green	8·75	1·10

DESIGNS—As T **25/28**: 2k.50 (No. 273a), Statue of St. Wenceslas, Prague. As T **30**: 4, 5k. Upper Tatra.

32 Hradek Castle

33 Pres. Masaryk

1928. 10th Anniv of Independence.

278	32	30h. black	10	10
279	–	40h. brown	10	10
280	–	50h. green	15	10
281	–	60h. red	15	20
282	–	1k. red	25	15
283	–	1k.20 purple	40	65
284	–	2k. blue	45	55
285	–	2k.50 blue	1·40	1·75
286	33	3k. sepia	1·10	1·25
287	–	5k. violet	1·40	2·25

DESIGNS—HORIZ: 40h. Town Hall, Levoca; 50h. Telephone Exchange, Prague; 60h. Village of Jasina; 1k. Hluboka Castle; 1k.20, Pilgrim's House, Velehrad; 2k.50, The Grand Tatra. VERT: 2k. Brno Cathedral; 5k. Town Hall, Prague.

34 National Arms

35 St. Wenceslas on Horseback

1929. Perf or imperf × perf.

287a	34	5h. blue	10	10
287b		10h. brown	10	10
288		20h. red	10	10
289		25h. green	10	10
290		30h. purple	10	10
291a		40h. brown	10	10

1929. Death Millenary of St. Wenceslas.

293	35	50h. green	15	10
294	–	60h. violet	30	10
295	–	2k. blue	75	35
296	–	3k. brown	1·10	25
297	–	5k. purple	3·50	2·50

DESIGNS: 2k. Foundation of St. Vitus's Church; 3k., 5k. Martyrdom of St. Wenceslas.

36 Brno Cathedral

1929.

298	36	3k. brown	1·10	10
299	–	4k. blue	4·00	60
300	–	5k. green	3·00	35
301	–	10k. violet	8·75	3·00

DESIGNS: 4k. Tatra Mountains; 5k. Town Hall, Prague; 10k. St. Nicholas Church, Prague.

38

39

1930.

302a	38	50h. green	10	10
303		60h. purple	50	10
304		1k. red	10	10

See also No. 373.

1930. 80th Birthday of President Masaryk.

305	39	2k. green	80	35
306		3k. red	1·25	35
307		5k. blue	3·25	2·40
308		10k. black	7·00	4·75

40 Fokker F.IXD

41 Smolik S.19

1930. Air.

394	40	30h. violet	10	10
309		50h. green	10	15
310		1k. red	25	30
311	41	2k. green	55	70
312		3k. purple	1·10	95
313	–	4k. blue	85	90
314	–	5k. brown	1·60	1·90
315	–	10k. blue	4·00	5·50
316	–	20k. violet	5·00	5·00

DESIGNS—As Type **41**: 4, 5k. Smolik S.19 with tree in foreground; 10, 20k. Fokker F.IXD over Prague.

43 Krumlov

44 Dr. Miroslav Tyrs

1932. Views.

317	–	3k.50 purple (Krivoklat)	1·40	80
318	–	4k. blue (Orlik)	1·60	60
319	43	5k. green	2·75	65

1932. Birth Centenary of Dr. Tyrs, founder of the "Sokol" Movement.

320	44	50h. green	30	10
321		1k. red	80	10
322	–	2k. blue	5·00	40
323	–	3k. brown	8·00	45

On the 2k. and 3k. the portrait faces left.

46 Dr. M. Tyrs

47 Church and Episcopal Palace, Nitra

1933.

324	**46**	60h. violet	10	10

1933. 1100th Anniv of Foundation of 1st Christian Church at Nitra.

325	**47**	50h. purple	30	10
326	–	1k. red (Church gateway)	3·25	25

49 Frederick Smetana

50 Consecrating Colours at Kiev

1934. 50th Death Anniv of Smetana.

327	**49**	50h. green	10	10

1934. 20th Anniv of Czechoslovak Foreign Legions.

328	**50**	50h. green	20	10
329	–	1k. red	25	10
330	–	2k. blue	1·75	30
331	–	3k. brown	2·25	30

DESIGNS—HORIZ: 1k. French battalion enrolling at Bayonne. VERT: 2k. Standard of the Russian Legion; 3k. French, Russian and Serbian legionaries.

52 Antonin Dvorak

53 "Where is my Fatherland?"

1934. 30th Death Anniv of Dvorak.

332	**52**	50h. green	10	10

1934. Centenary of Czech National Anthem.

333	**53**	1k. purple	35	15
334		2k. blue	90	40

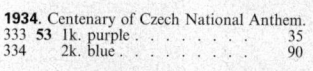

54 Autograph portrait of Pres. Masaryk

55

1935. 85th Birthday of President Masaryk.

335	**54**	50h. green	15	10
336		1k. red	30	10
337	**55**	2k. blue	1·00	35
338		3k. brown	2·10	55

See also No. 374.

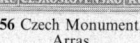

56 Czech Monument, Arras

57 Gen. M. R. Stefanik

1935. 20th Anniv of Battle of Arras.

339	**56**	1k. red	40	10
340		2k. blue	95	40

1935. 16th Death Anniv of Gen. Stefanik.

341	**57**	50h. green	10	10

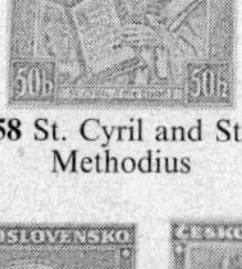

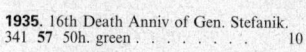

58 St. Cyril and St. Methodius

59 J. A. Komensky (Comenius)

60 Dr. Edward Benes

60a Gen. M. R. Stefanik

61 Pres. Masaryk

1935. Prague Catholic Congress.

342	**58**	50h. green	15	10
343		1k. red	25	10
344		2k. blue	1·10	45

1935.

345	**59**	40h. blue	10	10
346	**60**	50h. green	10	10
390	**60a**	50h. green	10	10
347		60h. violet	10	10
391		60h. blue	7·00	14·00
348	**61**	1k. purple	10	10
395		1k. purple	10	10

No. 390 differs from No. 341 in having an ornament in place of the word "HALERU".

No. 348 has "1 Kc" in value tablets, No. 395 "1 K".

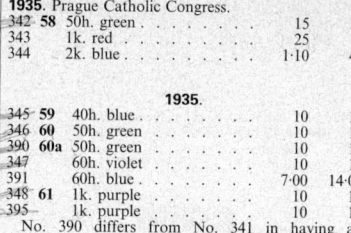

62 Symbolic of Infancy

63 K. H. Macha

1936. Child Welfare.

349	–	50h.+50h. green	20	35
350	**62**	1k.+50h. red	30	55
351	–	2k.+50h. blue	85	1·75

DESIGN: 50h., 2k. Grandfather, mother and child from centre of Type **62** (enlarged).

1936. Death Centenary of Macha (poet).

352	**63**	50h. green	10	10
353		1k. red	30	10

64 Banska Bystrica

65 Podebrady

1936.

354	–	1k.20 purple	10	10
355	**64**	1k.50 red	10	10
355a	–	1k.60 olive	10	10
356	–	2k. green	10	10
357	–	2k.50 blue	10	10
358	–	3k. brown	10	10
359	–	3k.50 violet	70	45
360	**65**	4k. violet	30	10
361	–	5k. green	30	10
362	–	10k. blue	55	45

DESIGNS—As Type **64**: 1k.20, Palanok Castle; 1k.60, St. Barbara's Church, Kutna Hora; 2k. Zvikov (Klingden Berg) Castle; 2k.50, Strecno Castle; 3k. Hruba Skala Castle (Cesky Raj); 3k.50, Slavkov Castle; 5k. Town Hall, Olomouc (23½ × 29½ mm). As Type **65**: 10k. Bratislava and Danube.

66 President Benes

1937.

363	**66**	50h. green	10	10

67 Mother and Child

68 "Lullaby"

1937. Child Welfare.

364	**67**	50h.+50h. green	30	35
365		1k.+50h. red	45	60
366	**68**	2k.+1k. blue	85	1·60

69 Czech Legionaries

70 Prague

1937. 20th Anniv of Battle of Zborov.

367	**69**	50h. green	15	10
368		1k. red	15	10

1937. 16th Anniv of Founding of Little Entente.

369	**70**	2k. green	45	15
370		2k.50 blue	70	50

71 J. E. Purkyne

73 Peregrine Falcon

1937. 150th Birth Anniv of J. E. Purkyne (physiologist).

371	**71**	50h. green	10	10
372		1k. red	15	10

1937. Mourning for Pres. Masaryk. As T **38** and **55**, but panels of T **55** dated "14.IX.1937".

373	**38**	50h. black	10	10
374	**55**	2k. black	25	10

1937. Labour Congress, Prague. Optd **B.I.T. 1937.**

375	**66**	50h. green	15	30
376	**64**	1k.50 red	15	30
377	–	2k. green (No. 356)	40	60

1938. 10th International Sokol Display, Prague.

378	**73**	50h. green	30	10
379		1k. red	30	10

74 Pres. Masaryk and Slovak Girl

75 Czech Legionaries at Bachmac

1938. Child Welfare and Birthday of Late President Masaryk.

380	**74**	50h.+50h. green	35	50
381	**74**	1k.+50h. red	45	65

1938. 20th Anniv of Battles in Russia, Italy and France. Inscr "1918 1938".

382	**75**	50h. green	20	10
383	–	50h. green	10	10
384	–	50h. green	10	10

DESIGNS: Czech Legionaries at Doss Alto (No. 383) and at Vouziers (No. 384).

76 J. Fugner

77 Armament Factories, Pilsen

1938. 10th Sokol Summer Games.

385	**76**	50h. green	10	10
386		1k. red	10	10
387		2k. blue	15	10

1938. Provincial Economic Council Meeting, Pilsen.

388	**77**	50h. green	10	10

78 St. Elizabeth's Cathedral, Kosice

79 "Peace"

1938. Kosice Cultural Exhibition.

389	**78**	50h. green	10	10

1938. 20th Anniv of Czech Republic.

392	**79**	2k. blue	15	10
393		3k. brown	35	10

1939. Inauguration of Slovak Parliament. No. 362 surcharged **Otvorenie slovenskeho snemu 18.1.1939** and **300 h** between bars.

393b		300h. on 10k. blue	60	3·00

No. 393b was only issued in Slovakia but was withdrawn prior to the establishment of the Slovak state. The used price is for cancelled to order stamps.

80 Jasina

1939. Inaug of Carpatho-Ukrainian Parliament.

393c	**80**	3k. blue	10·00	55·00

The used price is for cancelled-to-order.

From mid-1939 until 1945, Czechoslovakia was divided into the German Protectorate of Bohemia and Moravia and the independent state of Slovakia. Both these countries issued their own stamps. Germany had already occupied Sudetenland where a number of unauthorized local issues were made at Asch, Karlsbad, Konstantinsbad, Hiklasdorf, Reichenberg-Maffersdorf and Rumburg. Hungary occupied Carpatho-Ukraine and the stamps of Hungary were used there. In 1945, upon liberation, stamps of Czechoslovakia were once again issued.

81 Clasped Hands

82 Arms and Soldier

1945. Kosice Issue. Imperf.

396	**81**	1k.50 purple	1·75	2·00
397	**82**	2k. red	15	15
398		5k. green	1·40	1·60
399		6k. blue	30	35
400	**81**	9k. red	30	35
401		13k. brown	75	85
402		20k. blue	1·60	1·50

83 Arms and Linden Leaf

84 Linden Leaf and Buds

85 Linden Leaf and Flower

1945. Bratislava Issue. Imperf.

403	**83**	50h. green	10	10
404		1k. purple	10	10
405		1k.50 red	10	10
406		2k. blue	10	10
407		2k.40 red	30	20
408		3k. brown	10	10
409		4k. green	15	10
410		6k. violet	15	10
411		10k. brown	30	20

1945. Prague Issue.

412	**84**	10h. black	10	10
413		30h. brown	10	10
414		50h. green	10	10
415		60h. blue	10	10
416	**85**	60h. blue	10	10
417		80h. red	10	10
418		120h. red	10	10
419		300h. purple	10	10
420		500h. green	10	10

86 Pres. Masaryk

87 Staff Capt. Ridky

1945. Moscow Issue. Perf.

421	**86**	5h. violet	10	10
422		10h. yellow	10	10
423		20h. brown	10	10
424		50h. green	10	10
425		1k. red	10	10
426		2k. blue	10	10

1945. War Heroes.

427	**87**	5h. grey	10	10
428	–	10h. brown	10	10
429	–	20h. red	10	10
430	–	25h. red	10	10
431	–	30h. violet	15	10
432	–	40h. brown	10	10
433	–	50h. green	10	10
434	–	60h. violet	15	10
435	**87**	1k. red	10	10
436	–	1k.50 red	10	10
437	–	2k. blue	10	10
438	–	2k.50 violet	10	10
439	–	3k. brown	10	10
440	–	4k. mauve	10	10
441	–	5k. green	15	10
442	–	10k. blue	25	10

PORTRAITS: 10h., 1k.50, Dr. Novak. 20h., 2k. Capt. O. Jaros. 25h., 2k.50, Staff Capt. Zimprich. 30h., 3k. Lt. J. Kral. 40h., 4k. J. Gabcik (parachutist). 50h., 5k. Staff Capt. Vasatko. 60h., 10k. Fr. Adamek.

88 Allied Flags

89 Russian Soldier and Slovak Partisan

1945. 1st Anniv of Slovak Rising.

443	**88**	1k.50 red	10	10
444	–	2k. blue	10	10
445	**89**	4k. brown	20	20
446	–	4k.50 violet	20	20
447	–	5k. green	30	40

DESIGNS—VERT: 2k. Banska Bystrica. HORIZ: 4k.50, Sklabina; 5k. Strecno and partisan.

90 Pres. Masaryk **91** Pres. Benes **92**

1945.

452	–	30h. purple	10	10
448	**90**	50h. brown	10	10
453	**91**	60h. blue	15	10
449	–	80h. green	10	10
454	–	1k. orange	10	10
455	**90**	1k.20 red	15	10
456		1k.20 mauve	10	10
450	**91**	1k.60 green	15	10
457	–	2k.40 red	15	10
458	**91**	3k. purple	20	10
459	**90**	4k. blue	15	10
460		5k. green	20	10
461	**91**	7k. black	25	10
462	–	10k. blue	55	10
451	**90**	15k. purple	50	10
462a	–	20k. brown	85	10

PORTRAIT: 30h., 80h., 1k., 2k.40, 10k., 20k. Gen. M. R. Stefanik.

1945. Students' World Congress, Prague.

463	**92**	1k.50+1k.50 red	10	10
464		2k.50+2k.50 blue	20	20

93 J. S. Kozina Monument

94 St. George and Dragon

1945. Execution of Jan Stadky Kozina, 1695.

465	**93**	2k.40 red	15	10
466		4k. blue	20	25

1946. Victory.

467	**94**	2k.40+2k.60 red	15	15
468		4k.+6k. blue	20	15

94a Lockheed Constellation over Charles Bridge, Prague

1946. Air. 1st Prague–New York Flight.

468b	**94a**	24k. blue on buff	90	60

See also Nos. 475/6.

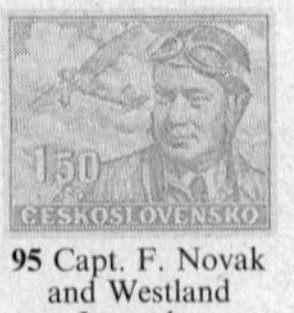

95 Capt. F. Novak and Westland Lysander

96 Lockheed Constellation over Bratislava

1946. Air.

469	**95**	1k.50 red	15	10
470		5k.50 blue	35	15
471		9k. purple	60	15
472	**96**	10k. green	50	30
473	**95**	16k. violet	80	40
474	**96**	20k. blue	80	65
475	**94a**	24k. red	1·00	65
476		50k. blue	2·00	1·25

97 K. H. Borovsky

98 Brno

1946. 90th Death Anniv of Borovsky (Independence advocate).

477	**97**	1k.20h. grey	10	15

1946.

478	**98**	2k.40 red	35	15
479	–	7k.40 violet (Hodonin) (horiz)	20	10

100 Emigrants

101 President Benes

1946. Repatriation Fund.

480	–	1k.60+1k.40 brown	60	65
481	**100**	2k.40+2k.60 red	20	25
482	–	4k.+4k. blue	35	35

DESIGNS: 1k.60, Emigrants' departure; 4k. Emigrants' return.

1946. Independence Day.

483	**101**	60h. blue	10	10
484		1k.60 green	10	10
485		3k. purple	10	10
486		8k. purple	20	10

102 Flag and Symbols of Transport, Industry, Agriculture and Learning

103 St. Adalbert

1947. "Two Year Plan".

487	**102**	1k.20 green	10	10
488		2k.40 red	10	10
489		4k. blue	55	20

1947. 950th Death Anniv of St. Adalbert (Bishop of Prague).

490	**103**	1k.60 black	45	35
491		2k.40 red	65	50
492		5k. green	1·00	40

104 "Grief"

105 Rekindling Flame of Remembrance

1947. 5th Anniv of Destruction of Lidice.

493	**104**	1k.20 black	30	20
494		1k.60 black	40	30
495	**105**	2k.40 mauve	50	30

106 Congress Emblem

107 Pres. Masaryk

1947. Youth Festival.

496	**106**	1k.20 purple	45	25
497		4k. grey	45	15

1947. 10th Death Anniv of Pres Masaryk.

498	**107**	1k.20 black on buff	15	15
499		4k. blue on cream	25	25

108 Stefan Moyses

109 "Freedom"

1947. 150th Birth Anniv of Stefan Moyses (Slavonic Society Organizer).

500	**108**	1k.20 purple	15	15
501		4k. blue	25	25

1947. 30th Anniv of Russian Revolution.

502	**109**	2k.40 red	25	15
503		4k. blue	40	15

110 Pres. Benes

1948.

504	**110**	1k.50 brown	10	10
505		2k. purple (19×23 mm)	10	10
506		5k. blue (19×23 mm)	15	10

111 "Athletes paying Homage to Republic"

115 Dr. J. Vanicek

1948. 11th Sokol Congress, Prague. (a) 1st issue.

507	**111**	1k.50 brown	10	10
508		3k. red	15	10
509		5k. blue	40	10

(b) 2nd issue. Inscr "XI. VSESOKOLSKY SLET V PRAZE 1948".

515	**115**	1k. green	10	10
516	–	1k.50 brown	15	10
517	–	2k. blue	15	10
518	**115**	3k. purple	20	10

PORTRAIT: 1k.50, 2k. Dr. J. Scheiner.

112 Charles IV

113 St. Wenceslas and Charles IV

1948. 600th Anniv of Charles IV University, Prague.

510	**112**	1k.50 brown on buff	10	10
511	**113**	2k. brown on buff	15	10
512		3k. red on buff	15	10
513	**112**	5k. blue on buff	20	15

114 Insurgents

117 Fr. Palacky and Dr. F. L. Rieger

1948. Centenary of Abolition of Serfdom.

514	**114**	1k.50 black	10	10

1948. Cent of Constituent Assembly at Kromeriz.

519	**117**	1k.50 violet on buff	10	10
520		3k. purple on buff	15	10

118 J. M. Hurban

119 President Benes

1948. Centenary of Slovak Insurrection.

521	**118**	1k.50 brown	10	10
522	–	3k. red (L. Stur)	10	10
523	–	5k. blue (M. Hodza)	25	20

1948. Death of President Benes.

524	**119**	8k. black	15	10

120 "Independence"

121 President Gottwald

1948. 30th Anniv of Independence.

525	**120**	1k.50 blue	15	10
526		3k. red	20	15

1948.

772	**121**	15h. green	40	10
773		20h. brown	50	10
526a		1k. green	10	10
774		1k. lilac	1·25	10
527		1k.50 brown	10	10
528b		3k. red	15	10
775		3k. black	90	10
529		5k. blue	25	10
530		20k. violet (23×30 mm)	60	10

See also No. 538.

122 Czech and Russian Workers

123 Girl and Birds

1948. 5th Anniv of Russian Alliance.

531	**122**	3k. red	10	10

1948. Child Welfare.

532	–	1k.50+1k. purple	30	10
533	–	2k.+1k. blue	15	10
534	**123**	3k.+1k. red	25	10

DESIGNS: 1k.50, Boy and birds; 2k. Mother and child.

124 V. I. Lenin

125 Pres. Gottwald Addressing Rally

1949. 25th Death Anniv of Lenin.

535	**124**	1k.50 purple	25	10
536		5k. blue	25	15

1949. 1st Anniv of Gottwald Government.

537	**125**	3k. brown	10	10

1949. As T **121** (23×30 mm) but inscr "UNOR 1948".

538	**121**	10k. green	35	15

126 P. O. Hviezdoslav

127 Mail Coach and Steam Train

1949. Poets.

539	**126**	50h. purple	10	10
540	–	80h. red	10	10
541	–	1k. green	10	10
542	–	2k. blue	30	10
543	–	4k. purple	30	10
544	–	8k. black	45	10

PORTRAITS: 80h. V. Vancura. 1k. J. Sverma. 2k. J. Fucik. 4k. J. Wolker. 8k. A. Jirasek.

1949. 75th Anniv of U.P.U.

545	**127**	3k. red	1·10	1·10
546	–	5k. blue	70	40
547	–	13k. green	1·75	35

DESIGNS: 5k. Mounted postman and mail van; 13k. Sailing ship and Douglas DC-2 airliner.

128 Girl Agricultural Worker

130 Industrial Worker

1949. 9th Meeting of Czechoslovak Communist Party.
548 **128** 1k.50 green 45 50
549 – 3k. red 25 25
550 **130** 5k. blue 45 50
DESIGN—HORIZ: 3k. Workers and flag.

131 F. Smetana and National Theatre, Prague

132 A. S. Pushkin

1949. 125th Birth Anniv of Smetanà (composer).
551 **131** 1k.50 green 15 10
552 5k. blue 60 20

1949. 150th Birth Anniv of A. S. Pushkin (poet).
553 **132** 2k. green 25 15

133 F. Chopin and Warsaw Conservatoire

134 Globe and Ribbon

1949. Death Centenary of Chopin (composer).
554 **133** 3k. red 45 20
555 8k. purple 45 45

1949. 50th Sample Fair, Prague.
556 **134** 1k.50 purple 25 25
557 5k. blue 75 75

135 Zvolen Castle

1949.
558 **135** 10k. lake 60 10

1949. Air. Nos. 469/76 surch.
559 **95** 1k. on 1k.50 red 15 10
560 3k. on 5k.50 blue 25 10
561 6k. on 9k. purple 40 10
562 7k.50 on 16k. violet . . . 50 20
563 **96** 8k. on 10k. green 50 55
564 12k.50 on 20k. blue . . . 90 45
565 **94a** 15k. on 24k. red . . . . 2·25 75
566 30k. on 50k. blue . . . . 1·75 75

137 Mediaeval Miners

138 Modern Miner

1949. 700th Anniv of Czechoslovak Mining Industry and 150th Anniv of Miners' Laws.
567 **137** 1k.50 violet 50 40
568 **138** 3k. red . . . . 5·25 1·90
569 – 5k. blue . . . . 4·00 1·50
DESIGN—HORIZ: 5k. Miner with cutting machine.

139 Carpenters

140 Dove and Buildings

1949. 2nd T.U.C., Prague. Inscr 1949".
570 **139** 1k. green . . . . 2·75 1·25
571 – 2k. purple (Mechanic) . . 1·75 45

1949. Red Cross Fund. Inscr "CS CERVENY KRIZ".
572 **140** 1k.50h.+50h. red . . . . 3·50 2·25
573 – 3k.+1k. red . . . . . . 3·50 2·25
DESIGN—VERT: 3k. Dove and globe.

141 Mother and Child

142 Joseph Stalin

1949. Child Welfare Fund. Inscr "DETEM 1949".
574 **141** 1k.50+50h. grey . . . . . 3·25 1·25
575 – 3k.+1k. red . . . . . . 4·75 2·00
DESIGN: 3k. Father and child.

1949. 70th Birth Anniv of Joseph Stalin.
576 **142** 1k.50 green on buff . . . 75 40
577 – 3k. purple on buff . . . . 4·00 1·50
PORTRAIT: 3k. Stalin facing left.

143 Skier

144 Efficiency Badge

1950. Tatra Cup Ski Championship.
578 **143** 1k.50 blue . . . . 2·75 1·00
579 **144** 3k. red and buff . . . . 2·75 1·00
580 **143** 5k. blue . . . . 1·90 90

145 V. Mayakovsky

146 Soviet Tank Driver and Hradcany, Prague

1950. 20th Death Anniv of Mayakovsky (poet).
581 **145** 1k.50 purple . . . . . . 2·10 1·10
582 3k. red . . . . 1·75 80

1950. 5th Anniv of Republic (1st issue).
583 **146** 1k.50 green 25 20
584 – 2k. purple 95 90
585 – 3k. red 20 10
586 – 5k. blue 40 15
DESIGNS: 2k. "Hero of Labour" medal; 3k. Workers and Town Hall; 5k. "The Kosice Programme" (part of text).

147 Factory and Workers

1950. 5th Anniv of Republic (2nd issue).
587 **147** 1k.50 green . . . . 1·40 75
588 – 2k. brown . . . . 1·75 65
589 – 3k. red 90 35
590 – 5k. blue 90 35
DESIGNS: 2k. Crane and Tatra Mts; 3k. Labourer and tractor; 5k. Three workers.

148 S. K. Neumann

1950. 75th Birth Anniv of S. K. Neumann (writer).
591 **148** 1k.50 blue 25 10
592 3k. purple . . . . 1·10 85

149 Bozena Nemcova

150 "Liberation of Colonial Nations"

1950. 130th Birth Anniv of Bozena Nemcova (authoress).
593 **149** 1k.50 blue . . . . 1·25 85
594 7k. purple 25 20

1950. 2nd International Students' World Congress, Prague. Inscr "II KONGRES MSS".
595 **150** 1k.50 green 15 10
596 – 2k. purple . . . . 1·50 95
597 – 3k. red 20 25
598 – 5k. blue 40 60
DESIGNS—HORIZ: 2k. Woman, globe and dove ("Fight for Peace"); 3k. Group of students ("Democratisation of Education"); 5k. Students and banner ("International Students, Solidarity").

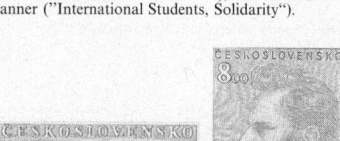

151 Miner, Soldier and Farmer

152 Z. Fibich

1950. Army Day.
599 **151** 1k.50 blue . . . . 90 1·00
600 – 3k. red 25 65
DESIGN: 3k. Czechoslovak and Russian soldiers.

1950. Birth Centenary of Fibich (composer).
601 **152** 3k. red . . . . 1·40 1·40
602 8k. green 25 15

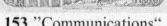

153 "Communications"

154 J. G. Tajovsky

1950. 1st Anniv of League of Postal, Telephone and Telegraph Employees.
603 **153** 1k.50 brown 25 15
604 3k. red 70 60

1950. 10th Death Anniv of J. Gregor Tajovsky (writer).
605 **154** 1k.50 brown 85 30
606 5k. blue 85 45

155 Reconstruction of Prague

1950. Philatelic Exhibition, Prague.
607 **155** 1k.50 blue 35 15
608 3k. red 60 55

156 Czech and Russian Workers

1950. Czechoslovak–Soviet Friendship.
609 **156** 1k.50 brown 55 25
610 5k. blue 75 50

157 Dove (after Picasso)

1951. Czechoslovak Peace Congress.
611 **157** 2k. blue . . . . 5·00 2·75
612 3k. red . . . . 3·00 1·60

158 Julius Fucik

159 Mechanical Hammer

1951. Peace Propaganda.
613 **158** 1k.50 grey 50 30
614 5k. blue . . . . 1·90 1·75

1951. Five Year Plan (heavy industry).
615 **159** 1k.50 black 10 10
616 – 3k. brown 15 10
617 **159** 4k. blue 65 45
DESIGN—HORIZ: 3k. Installing machinery.

160 Industrial Workers

161 Karlovy Vary

1951. International Women's Day.
618 **160** 1k.50 olive 25 10
619 – 3k. red . . . . 2·25 65
620 – 5k. blue 50 10
DESIGNS: 3k. Woman driving tractor; 5k. Korean woman and group.

1951. Air. Spas.
621 **161** 6k. green . . . . 2·25 75
622 – 10k. purple . . . . . . 2·25 95
623 – 15k. blue . . . . 5·50 75
624 – 20k. brown . . . . . . 7·00 2·25
DESIGNS—Ilyushin Il-12 airplane over: 10k. Piestany; 15k. Marianske Lazne; 20k. Silac.

162 Miners

163 Ploughing

1951. Mining Industry.
625 **162** 1k.50 black . . . . 1·00 75
626 3k. purple 10 15

1951. Agriculture.
627 **163** 1k.50 brown 50 80
628 – 2k. green (Woman and cows) . . . . 1·75 1·25

164 Tatra Mountains

165 Partisan and Soviet Soldier

1951. Recreation Centres. Inscr "ROH".
629 **164** 1k.50 green 20 10
630 – 2k. brown 95 80
631 – 3k. red 25 10
DESIGNS: 2k. Beskydy Mts; 3k. Krkonose Mts.

1951. 30th Anniv of Czechoslovak Communist Party. Inscr "30 LET" etc.
635 – 1k.50 grey 95 25
632 – 2k. brown 25 10
633 **165** 3k. red 30 10
636 – 5k. blue . . . . 1·90 95
634 – 8k. black 70 30
DESIGNS—HORIZ: 1k.50, 5k. Gottwald and Stalin; 8k. Marx, Engels, Lenin and Stalin. VERT: 2k. Factory militiaman.

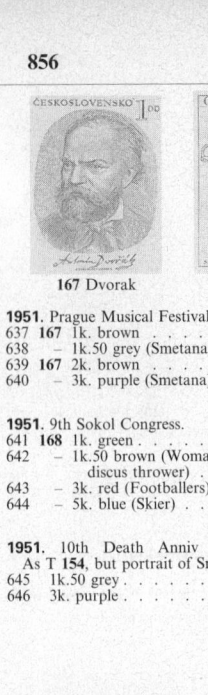

167 Dvorak

168 Gymnast

1951. Prague Musical Festival.

637	167	1k. brown	25	10
638	–	1k.50 grey (Smetana)	1·25	50
639	167	2k. brown	1·25	65
640	–	3k. purple (Smetana)	25	15

1951. 9th Sokol Congress.

641	168	1k. green	60	20
642	–	1k.50 brown (Woman discus thrower)	55	25
643	–	3k. red (Footballers)	1·25	25
644	–	5k. blue (Skier)	3·25	1·40

1951. 10th Death Anniv of Bohumir Smeral. As T **154**, but portrait of Smeral.

645	1k.50 grey	45	25
646	3k. purple	45	15

170 Scene from "Fall of Berlin"

172 A. Jirasek

173 "Fables and Fates" (M. Ales)

1951. International Film Festival, Karlovy Vary. Inscr "SE SOVETSKYM FILMEM", etc.

647	170	80h. red	35	20
648	–	1k.50 grey	35	20
649	170	4k. blue	1·10	85

DESIGN: 1k.50, Scene from "The Great Citizen".

1951. 30th Death Anniv of J. Hybes (politician). As T **154**, but portrait of Hybes.

650	1k.50 brown	10	10
651	2k. red	1·00	35

1951. Birth Centenary of Jirasek (author).

652	172	1k.50 black	40	10
653	173	3k. red	40	10
654	–	4k. black	40	10
655	172	5k. blue	1·90	1·10

DESIGN—As Type **173**: 4k. "The Region of Tabor" (M. Ales).

174 Miner and Pithead

176 Soldiers Parading

1951. Miner's Day.

656	174	1k.50 brown	15	10
657	–	3k. red (miners drilling)	15	10
658	174	5k. blue	1·25	95

1951. Army Day. Inscr "DEN CS ARMADY 1951".

659	176	80h. brown	25	15
660	–	1k. green	25	25
661	–	1k.50 black	40	25
662	–	3k. purple	45	25
663	–	5k. blue	1·60	60

DESIGNS—VERT: 1k. Gunner and field-gun; 1k.50, Pres. Gottwald; 3k. Tank driver and tank; 5k. Two pilots and aircraft.

178 Stalin and Gottwald

179 P. Jilemnicky

1951. Czechoslovak–Soviet Friendship.

664	178	1k.50 black	10	10
665	–	3k. red	15	10
666	178	4k. blue	1·25	50

DESIGN (23½ × 31 mm): 3k. Lenin, Stalin and Russian soldiers.

1951. 50th Birth Anniv of Jilemnicky (writer).

667	179	1k.50 purple	25	15
668		2k. blue	90	35

180 L. Zapotocky

181 J. Kollar

1952. Birth Centenary of Zapotocky (socialist pioneer).

669	180	1k.50 red	10	15
670		4k. black	1·10	35

1952. Death Centenary of Kollar (poet).

671	181	3k. red	10	10
672		5k. blue	1·10	50

182 Lenin Hall, Prague

183 Dr. E. Holub and Negro

1952. 40th Anniv of 6th All-Russian Party Conference.

673	182	1k.50 red	10	20
674		5k. blue	1·00	65

1952. 50th Death Anniv of Dr. Holub (explorer).

675	183	3k. red	40	25
676		5k. blue	1·90	1·50

184 Electric Welding

1952. Industrial Development.

677	184	1k.50 black	35	20
678	–	2k. brown	1·40	50
679	–	3k. red	15	10

DESIGNS: 2k. Foundry; 3k. Chemical plant.

185 Factory-worker and Farm-girl

186 Young Workers

1952. International Women's Day.

680	185	1k.50 blue on cream	1·00	40

1952. International Youth Week.

681	186	1k.50 blue	10	10
682	–	2k. green	15	10
683	186	3k. red	1·60	65

DESIGN: 2k. Three heads and globe.

187 O. Sevcik

188 J. A. Komensky (Comenius)

1952. Birth Centenary of Sevcik (musician).

684	187	2k. brown	70	45
685		3k. red	15	15

1952. 360th Birth Anniv of Komensky (educationist).

686	188	1k.50 brown	1·25	50
687		11k. blue	25	10

189 Anti-fascist

190 Woman and Children

1952. "Fighters Against Fascism" Day.

688	189	1k.50 brown	10	10
689		2k. blue	1·00	50

1952. Child Welfare.

690	190	2k. purple on cream	1·25	95
691		3k. red on cream	15	15

191 Combine Harvester

1952. Agriculture Day.

692	191	1k.50 blue	1·90	1·10
693		2k. brown	25	20
694	–	3k. red (Combine drill)	25	20

192 May Day Parade

1952. Labour Day.

695	192	3k. red	35	35
696		4k. brown	1·40	95

193 Russian Tank and Crowd

1952. 7th Anniv of Liberation.

697	193	1k.50 red	65	50
698		5k. blue	1·90	1·25

194 Boy Pioneer and Children

195 J. V. Myslbek

1952. International Children's Day.

699	194	1k.50 brown	10	10
700		2k. green	1·60	75
701	–	3k. red (Pioneers and teacher)	15	10

1952. 30th Death Anniv of Myslbek (sculptor).

702	195	1k.50 brown	10	10
703		2k. brown	1·25	1·10
704	–	8k. green	15	10

DESIGN: 8k. "Music" (statue).

196 Beethoven

197 "Rebirth of Lidice"

1952. International Music Festival, Prague. No. 706 inscr "PRAZSKE JARO 1952", etc.

705	196	1k.50 brown	30	25
706	–	3k. lake	30	25
707	196	5k. blue	1·60	90

DESIGN—HORIZ: 3k. The House of Artists.

1952. 10th Anniv of Destruction of Lidice.

708	197	1k.50 black	10	10
709		5k. blue	90	50

198 Jan Hus

199 Bethlehem Chapel, Prague

1952. Renovation of Bethlehem Chapel and 550th Anniv of Installation of Hus as Preacher.

710	198	1k.50 brown	10	10
711	199	3k. brown	10	10
712	198	5k. black	1·10	75

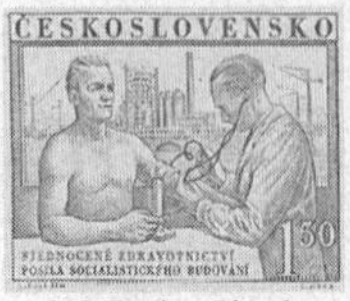

200 Testing Blood-pressure

201 Running

1952. National Health Service.

713	200	1k.50 brown	1·10	1·00
714	–	2k. violet	25	10
715	200	3k. red	30	10

DESIGN—HORIZ: 2k. Doctor examining baby.

1952. Physical Culture Propaganda.

716	201	1k.50 brown	70	35
717	–	2k. green (Canoeing)	2·00	90
718	–	3k. brown (Cycling)	50	35
719	–	4k. blue (Ice hockey)	3·25	2·25

202 F. L. Celakovsky

1952. Death Centenary of Celakovsky (poet).

720	202	1k.50 sepia	15	10
721		2k. green	1·60	85

203 M. Ales

204 Mining in 17th Century

1952. Birth Centenary of Mikulas Ales (painter) (1st issue).

722	203	1k.50 green	40	20
723		6k. brown	2·25	1·75

See also Nos. 737/8.

1952. Miner's Day.

724	204	1k. brown	1·25	75
725	–	1k.50 blue	10	10
726	–	2k. black	10	10
727	–	3k. brown	15	10

DESIGNS: 1k.50, Mining machinery; 2k. Petr Bezruc Mine, Ostrava; 3k. Mechanical excavator.

205 Jan Zizka

206 "Fraternization" (after Pokorny)

1952. Army Day.

728	205	1k.50 red	15	10
729	206	2k. brown	15	10
730	–	3k. red	15	10
731	205	4k. black	1·75	75

DESIGNS: 3k. Soldiers marching with flag.

207 R. Danube, Bratislava

208 Lenin, Stalin and Revolutionaries

1952. National Philatelic Exhibition, Bratislava.
732 **207** 1k.50 brown 10 10

1952. 35th Anniv of Russian Revolution.
733 **208** 2k. brown . . . . 1·25 60
734 — 3k. red 10 10

209 Nurses and Red Cross Flag   **211** Flags

210 Matej Louda z Chlumu (Hussite Warrior)

1952. 1st Czechoslovak Red Cross Conference.
735 **209** 2k. brown . . . . 1·25 55
736 — 3k. red 15 10

1952. Birth Centenary of Mikulas Ales (2nd issue).
737 **210** 2k. brown 25 10
738 — 3k. black 60 10
DESIGN: 3k. ''Trutnov'' (warrior fighting dragon).

1952. Peace Congress, Vienna.
739 **211** 3k. red 20 10
740 — 4k. blue . . . . 1·40 65

212 ''Dove of Peace'' (after Picasso)   **213** Smetana Museum, Prague

1953. 2nd Czechoslovak Peace Congress, Prague.
741 **212** 1k.50 sepia 10 10
742 — 4k. blue 55 30
DESIGN: 4k. Workman, woman and child (after Lev Haas).

1953. 75th Birth Anniv of Prof. Z. Nejedly (museum founder).
743 **213** 1k.50 brown 10 10
744 — 4k. black . . . . 1·40 60
DESIGN: 4k. Jirasek Museum, Prague.

214 Marching Soldiers   **215** M. Kukucin

1953. 5th Anniv of Communist Govt.
745 **214** 1k.50 blue 15 10
746 — 3k. red 15 10
747 — 8k. brown . . . . 1·90 85
DESIGNS—VERT: 3k. Pres. Gottwald addressing meeting. HORIZ: 8k. Stalin, Gottwald and crowd with banners.

1953. Czech Writers and Poets.
748 **215** 1k. grey 10 10
749 — 1k.50 brown 10 10
750 — 2k. lake 10 10
751 — 3k. brown 50 35
752 — 5k. blue . . . . 1·90 75
PORTRAITS—VERT: 1k.50, J. Vrchlicky. 2k. E. J. Erben. 3k. V. M. Kramerius. 5k. J. Dobrovsky.

216 Torch and Open Book   **217** Woman Revolutionary

1953. 10th Death Anniv of Vaclavek (writer).
753 **216** 1k. brown . . . . 1·50 50
754 — 3k. brown (Vaclavek) . . . 15 10

1953. International Women's Day.
755 **217** 1k.50 blue 15 10
756 **217** 2k. red . . . . 1·00 40
DESIGN—VERT: 1k.50, Mother and baby.

218 Stalin   **219** Pres. Gottwald

1953. Death of Stalin.
757 **218** 1k.50 black 35 15

1953. Death of President Gottwald.
758 **219** 1k.50 black 20 10
759 — 3k. black 20 10

220 Pecka, Zapotocky and Hybes

1953. 75th Anniv of 1st Czech Social Democratic Party Congress.
760 **220** 2k. brown 20 10

221 Cyclists

1953. 6th International Cycle Race.
761 **221** 3k. blue 60 30

222 1890 May Day Medal

223 Marching Crowds

1953. Labour Day.
762 **222** 1k. brown . . . . 1·75 90
763 — 1k.50 blue 10 10
764 **223** 3k. red 20 10
765 — 8k. green 25 15
DESIGNS—As Type 222: 1k.50, Lenin and Stalin; 8k. Marx and Engels.

224 Hydro-electric Barrage   **225** Seed-drills

1953.
766 **224** 1k.50 green . . . . 1·00 40
767 — 2k. blue 20 10
768 — 3k. brown 20 10
DESIGNS—VERT: 2k. Welder and blast furnaces, Kuncice, HORIZ: 3k. Gottwald Foundry, Kuncice.

1953.
769 **225** 1k.50 brown 20 10
770 — 7k. green (Combine harvester) . . . . . 1·60 1·75

226 President Zapotocky   **229**

1953.
776 **226** 30h. blue 75 10
780 **229** 30h. blue 40 10
777 **226** 60h. red 40 10
781 **229** 60h. pink 80 10

227 J. Slavik   **228** L. Janacek

1953. Prague Music Festival. (a) 120th Death Anniv of Slavik (violinist).
778 **227** 75h. blue 50 10
(b) 25th Death Anniv of Janacek (composer).
779 **228** 1k.60 brown . . . . 1·00 10

230 Charles Bridge, Prague

1953.
782a **230** 5k. grey . . . . 3·75 10

231 J. Fucik   **232** Book, Carnation and Laurels

1953. 10th Death Anniv of Julius Fucik (writer).
783 **231** 40h. black 20 10
784 **232** 60h. mauve 45 25

233 Miner and Banner   **234** Volley ball

1953. Miner's Day.
785 **233** 30h. black 20 10
786 — 60h. purple . . . . 1·25 50
DESIGN: 60h. Miners and colliery shafthead.

1953. Sports.
787 **234** 30h. red . . . . 2·10 1·40
788 — 40h. purple . . . . 3·75 70
789 — 60h. purple . . . . 3·75 70
DESIGNS—HORIZ: 40h. Motor cycling. VERT: 60h. Throwing the javelin.

235 Hussite Warrior   **236** ''Friendship'' (after T. Bartfay)

1953. Army Day.
790 **235** 30h. sepia 25 10
791 — 60h. red 30 10
792 — 1k. red . . . . 1·60 1·25
DESIGNS: 60h. Soldier presenting arms; 1k. Czechoslovak Red Army soldiers.

1953. Czechoslovak–Korean Friendship.
793 **236** 30h. sepia . . . . 2·50 1·10

237 Hradcany, Prague and Kremlin, Moscow

1953. Czechoslovak–Soviet Friendship: Inscr ''MESIC CESKOSLOVENSKO SOVETSKEHO'', etc.
794 **237** 30h. black . . . . 1·00 60
795 — 60h. brown . . . . 1·25 75
796 — 1k.20 blue . . . . 2·50 1·25
DESIGNS: 60h. Lomonosov University, Moscow; 1k.20, ''Stalingrad'' tug, Lenin Ship-Canal.

238 Ema Destinnova (Opera Singer)   **239** National Theatre, Prague

1953. 70th Anniv of National Theatre, Prague.
797 **238** 30h. black 95 80
798 **239** 60h. brown 25 10
799 — 2k. sepia . . . . 2·25 80
PORTRAIT—As Type 238: 2k. E. Vojan (actor).

240 J. Manes (painter)   **241** Vaclav Hollar (etcher)

1953.
800 **240** 60h. lake 25 10
801 — 1k.20 blue . . . . 1·40 95

1953. Inscr ''1607 1677''.
802 **241** 30h. black 25 10
803 — 1k.20 black . . . . 1·25 50
PORTRAIT: 1k.20, Hollar and engraving tools.

242 Leo Tolstoy   **243** Class 498.0 Steam Locomotive

1953. 125th Birth Anniv of Tolstoy (writer).
804 **242** 60h. green 15 10
805 — 1k. brown . . . . 1·40 40

1953.
806 **243** 60h. blue and brown . . . 65 25
807 — 1k. blue and brown . . . 1·60 90
DESIGN: 1k. Ilyushin Il-12 (30th anniv of Czech airmail services).

244 Lenin (after J. Lauda)

245 Lenin Museum, Prague

1954. 30th Death Anniv of Lenin.
808 **244** 30h. sepia 45 10
809 **245** 1k.40 brown . . . . 1·75 1·25

246 Gottwald Speaking   **247** Gottwald Mausoleum, Prague

248 Gottwald and Stalin (after relief by O. Spaniel)

1954. 25th Anniv of 5th Czechoslovak Communist Party Congress. Inscr "1929 1954".

810	246	60h. brown	. . . .	30	10
811		2k.40 lake	. . . .	3·75	1·40

DESIGN: 2k.40, Revolutionary and flag.

1954. 1st Anniv of Deaths of Stalin and Gottwald.

812	247	30h. sepia	. . . . . .	25	10
813	248	60h. blue	. . . . . .	30	10
814		1k.20h. lake	. . . . .	1·75	1·00

DESIGN—HORIZ: As Type 247: 1k.20h. Lenin-Stalin Mausoleum, Moscow.

249 Girl and Sheaf of Corn   **250** Athletics

1954.

815		15h. green	. . . . . .	20	10
816		25h. lilac	. . . . . .	25	10
817		40h. brown	. . . . . .	35	10
818		45h. blue	. . . . . .	35	10
819		50h. green	. . . . . .	25	10
820		75h. blue	. . . . . .	25	10
821		80h. brown	. . . . . .	25	10
822	249	1k. green	. . . . . .	50	10
823		1k.20 blue	. . . . . .	25	10
824		1k.60 black	. . . . . .	1·75	10
825		2k. brown	. . . . . .	1·50	10
826		2k.40 blue	. . . . . .	1·75	10
827		3k. red	. . . . . .	1·50	10

DESIGNS: 15h. Labourer; 20h. Nurse; 40h. Postwoman; 45h. Foundry worker; 50h. Soldier; 75h. Metal worker; 80h. Mill girl; 1k.20, Scientist; 1k.60, Miner; 2k. Doctor and baby; 2k.40 Engine-driver; 3k. Chemist.

1954. Sports.

828	250	30h. sepia	. . . . . .	2·25	90
829		80h. green	. . . . . .	6·50	3·50
830		1k. blue	. . . . . .	1·40	60

DESIGNS—HORIZ: 80h. Hiking. VERT: 1k. Girl diving.

251 Dvorak   **252** Prokop Divis (physicist)

1954. Czechoslovak Musicians. Inscr as in T 251.

831	251	30h. brown	. . . . . .	95	20
832		40h. red (Janacek)	. . . .	1·50	20
833		60h. blue (Smetana)	. . .	80	15

1954. Bicentenary of Invention of Lightning Conductor by Divis.

834	252	30h. black	. . . . . .	25	10
835		75h. brown	. . . . . .	1·25	40

253 Partisan   **254** A. P. Chekhov

1954. 10th Anniv of Slovak National Uprising. Inscr "1944–29. 8–1954".

836	253	30h. red	. . . . . .	20	10
837		1k.20 bl (Woman partisan)	. . . .	1·10	90

1954. 50th Death Anniv of Chekhov (playwright).

838	254	30h. green	. . . . . .	20	10
839		45h. brown	. . . . . .	1·25	50

255 Soldiers in Battle   **257** J. Neruda

256 Farm Workers in Cornfield

1954. Army Day. 2k. inscr "ARMADY 1954".

840	255	60h. green	. . . . . .	20	10
841		2k. brown	. . . . . .	1·10	1·00

DESIGN: 2k. Soldier carrying girl.

1954. Czechoslovak-Russian Friendship.

842	256	30h. brown	. . . . . .	15	10
843		60h. blue	. . . . . .	25	10
844		2k. salmon	. . . . . .	1·75	1·40

DESIGNS: 60h. Factory workers and machinery; 2k. Group of girl folk dancers.

1954. Czechoslovak Poets.

845	257	30h. blue	. . . . . .	50	15
846		60h. red	. . . . . .	1·50	40
847		1k.60 purple	. . . . . .	40	15

PORTRAITS—VERT: 60h. J. Jesensky. 1k.60 J. Wolker.

258 Ceske Budejovice

1954. Czechoslovak Architecture. Background in buff.

848		30h. black (Telc)	. . . .	90	10
849		60h. brown (Levoca)	. . .	45	10
850	258	3k. blue	. . . . . .	1·75	1·25

259 President Zapotocky   **260** "Spirit of the Games"

1954. 70th Birthday of Zapotocky.

851	259	30h. sepia	. . . . . .	45	10
852		60h. blue	. . . . . .	20	10

See also Nos. 1006/7.

1955. 1st National Spartacist Games (1st issue). Inscr as in T 260.

853	260	30h. red	. . . . . .	1·25	20
854		45h. black & blue (Skier)	. .	3·50	20

See also Nos. 880/2.

261 University Building

1955. 35th Anniv of Comenius University, Bratislava. Inscr as in T 261.

855	261	60h. green	. . . . . .	30	10
856		75h. brown	. . . . . .	1·75	55

DESIGN: 75h. Comenius Medal (after O. Spaniel).

262 Cesky Krumlov

1955. Air.

857	262	80h. green	. . . . . .	1·10	25
858		1k.55 sepia	. . . . . .	1·50	40
859		2k.35 blue	. . . . . .	1·50	15
860		2k.75 purple	. . . . . .	2·75	30
861		10k. blue	. . . . . .	5·25	1·10

DESIGNS: 1k.55, Olomouc; 2k.35, Banska Bystrica; 2k.75, Bratislava; 10k. Prague.

263 Skoda Motor Car   **264** Russian Tank-driver

1955. Czechoslovak Industries.

862	263	45h. green	. . . . . .	70	45
863		60h. blue	. . . . . .	15	10
864		75h. black	. . . . . .	25	10

DESIGNS: 60h. Shuttleless jet loom; 75h. Skoda Machine-tool.

1955. 10th Anniv of Liberation. Inscr as in T 264.

865		30h. blue	. . . . . .	25	10
866	264	35h. brown	. . . . . .	1·25	55

867		60h. red	. . . . . .	25	10
868		60h. black	. . . . . .	25	10

DESIGNS—VERT: 30h. Girl and Russian soldier; No. 867, Children and Russian soldier. HORIZ: No. 868, Stalin Monument, Prague.

265 Agricultural Workers   **266** "Music and Spring"

1955. 3rd Trades' Union Congress. Inscr as in T 265.

869		30h. blue	. . . . . .	15	10
870	265	45h. green	. . . . . .	1·25	45

DESIGN: 30h. Foundry worker.

1955. International Music Festival, Prague. Inscr as in T 266.

871	266	30h. indigo and blue	. . .	35	10
872		1k. blue and pink	. . .	1·25	1·00

DESIGN: 1k. "Music" playing a lyre.

267 A. S. Popov (60th anniv of radio discoveries)   **268** Folk Dancers

1955. Cultural Anniversaries. Portraits.

873		20h. brown	. . . . . .	20	10
874		30h. black	. . . . . .	20	10
875		40h. green	. . . . . .	75	10
876		60h. black	. . . . . .	50	10
877	267	75h. purple	. . . . . .	1·50	60
878		1k.40 black on yellow	. .	40	30
879		1k.60 blue	. . . . . .	40	20

PORTRAITS: 20h. Jakub Arbes (writer). 30h. Jan Stursa (sculptor). 40h. Elena Marothy-Soltesova (writer). 60h. Josef V. Sladek (poet). 1k.40 Jan Holly (poet). 1k.60 Pavel J. Safarik (philologist).

1955. 1st National Spartacist Games (2nd issue). Inscr as in T 268.

880		20h. blue	. . . . . .	80	40
881	268	60h. green	. . . . . .	25	10
882		1k.60 red	. . . . . .	85	20

DESIGNS: 20h. Girl athlete; 1k.60, Male athlete.

269 "Friendship"   **270** Ocova Woman, Slovakia

1955. 5th World Youth Festival, Warsaw.

883	269	60h. blue	. . . . . .	35	10

1955. National Costumes (1st series).

884	270	60h. sepia, rose and red		10·00	7·00
885		75h. sepia, orange & lake		5·75	4·25
886		1k.60 sepia, blue & orge		10·00	5·50
887		2k. sepia, yellow and red		10·00	5·50

DESIGNS: 75h. Detva man, Slovakia; 1k.60, Chodsko man, Bohemia; 2k. Hana woman, Moravia. See also Nos. 952/5 and 1008/11.

271 Swallowtail

1955. Animals and Insects.

888		20h. black and blue	. . .	55	15
889		30h. brown and red	. . .	55	10
890		35h. brown and buff	. .	1·10	20
891	271	1k.40 black and yellow	.	5·25	1·90
892		1k.50 black and green	. .	55	20

DESIGNS: 20h. Common carp; 30h. Stag beetle; 35h. Grey partridge; 1k.50, Brown hare.

272 Tabor

1955. Towns of Southern Bohemia.

893	272	30h. purple	. . . . . .	20	10
894		45h. red	. . . . . .	75	60
895		60h. green	. . . . . .	20	10

TOWNS: 45h. Prachatice, 60h. Jindrichuv Hradec.

273 Motor Cyclists and Trophy

1955. 30th Int Motor Cycle Six-Day Trial.

896	273	60h. purple	. . . . . .	2·25	40

274 Soldier and Family   **275** Hans Andersen

1955. Army Day. Inscr as in T 274.

897	274	30h. brown	. . . . . .	25	10
898		60h. grn (Tank attack)	. .	1·75	1·25

1955. Famous Writers. Vert portraits.

899	275	30h. red	. . . . . .	15	10
900		40h. blue (Schiller)	. .	2·10	90
901		60h. purple (Mickiewicz)		25	10
902		75h. blk (Walt Whitman)		50	10

276 Railway Viaduct

1955. Building Progress. Inscr "STAVBA SOCIALISMU".

903	276	20h. green	. . . . . .	25	20
904		30h. brown	. . . . . .	25	10
905		60h. blue	. . . . . .	25	10
906		1k.60 red	. . . . . .	45	10

DESIGNS: 30h. Train crossing viaduct; 60k. Train approaching tunnel; 1k.60, Housing project, Ostrava.

277 "Electricity"   **278** Karlovy Vary

1956. Five Year Plan. Inscr "1956–1960".

907	277	5h. brown	. . . . . .	20	10
908		10h. black	. . . . . .	20	10
909		25h. red	. . . . . .	20	10
910		30h. green	. . . . . .	20	10
911		60h. blue	. . . . . .	20	10

DESIGNS—HORIZ: 10h. "Mining"; 25h. "Building"; 30h. "Agriculture"; 60h. "Industry".

1956. Czechoslovak Spas (1st series).

912	278	30h. green	. . . . . .	1·10	25
913		45h. brown	. . . . . .	1·00	35
914		75h. purple	. . . . . .	5·00	3·25
915		1k.20 blue	. . . . . .	65	15

SPAS: 45h. Marianske Lazne; 75h. Piestany; 1k.20, Vysne Ruzbachy, Tatra Mountains.

279 Jewellery

280 "We serve our People" (after J. Cumpelik)

1956. Czechoslovak Products.
916 **279** 30h. green 25 10
917 – 45h. blue (Glassware) . . 4·75 3·00
918 – 60h. purple (Ceramics) . . 1·00 10
919 – 75h. black (Textiles) . . . 25 10

1956. Defence Exhibition.
920 **280** 30h. brown 35 10
921 – 60h. red 35 10
922 – 1k. blue . . . . 5·50 3·75
DESIGNS: 60h. Liberation Monument, Berlin; 1k. "Tank Soldier with Standard" (after T. Schor).

281 Cyclists

282 Discus Thrower, Hurdler and Runner

1956. Sports Events of 1956.
923 **281** 30h. green and blue . . . 2·75 20
924 – 45h. blue and red . . . . 1·10 20
925 – 60h. blue and buff . . . . 1·50 55
926 **282** 75h. brown and yellow . . 1·00 20
927 – 80h. purple & lavender . . 1·00 15
928 **282** 1k.20 green & orange . . 95 25
DESIGNS—As Type **281**. VERT: 30h. T **281** (9th International Cycle Race); 45h. Basketball players (5th European Women's Basketball Championship, Prague). HORIZ: 60h. Horsemen jumping (Pardubice Steeplechase); 80h. Runners (International Marathon, Kosice). T **282**: 75h., 1k.20, (16th Olympic Games, Melbourne).

283 Mozart

284

1956. Bicentenary of Birth of Mozart and Prague Music Festival. Centres in black.
929 **283** 30h. yellow . . . . . . 1·00 90
930 – 45h. green . . . . 14·50 12·00
931 – 60h. purple 55 10
932 – 1k. salmon . . . . 1·60 55
933 – 1k.40 blue . . . . 2·75 1·25
934 – 1k.60 lemon . . . . 1·00 15
DESIGNS: 45h. J. Myslivecek; 60h. J. Benda; 1k. "Bertramka" (Mozart's villa); 1k.40, Mr. and Mrs. Dushek; 1k.60, Nostic Theatre.

1956. 1st National Meeting of Home Guard.
935 **284** 60h. blue 85 15

285 J. K. Tyl

286 Naval Guard

1956. Czech Writers (1st issue).
936 – 20h. purple (Stur) 70 10
937 – 30h. blue (Sramek) 35 10

938 **285** 60h. black 25 10
939 – 1k.40 pur (Borovsky) . . 4·50 2·40
See also Nos. 956/9.

1956. Frontier Guards' Day.
940 **286** 30h. blue . . . . 1·25 45
941 – 60h. green 15 10
DESIGN: 60h. Military guard and watchdog.

287 Picking Grapes

1956. National Products.
942 **287** 30h. lake 25 10
943 – 35h. green 30 20
944 – 80h. blue 60 15
945 – 95h. brown . . . . 1·50 1·40
DESIGNS—VERT: 35h. Picking hops. HORIZ: 80h. Fishing; 95h. Logging.

288 "Kladno", 1855

1956. European Freight Services Timetable Conference. Railway engines.
946 – 10h. brown . . . . 1·25 10
947 **288** 30h. black 75 10
948 – 40h. green . . . . 3·50 20
949 – 45h. purple . . . . 19·00 9·50
950 – 60h. blue 75 10
951 – 1k. blue . . . . 1·25 20
DESIGNS—VERT: 10h. "Zbraslav", 1846. HORIZ: 40h. Class 534, 1945; 45h. Class 556.0, 1952; 60h. Class 477.0, 1955; 1k. Class E499.0 electric locomotive, 1954.

1956. National Costumes (2nd series). As T **270**.
952 30h. sepia, red and blue . . 2·25 75
953 1k.20 sepia, blue and red . . 2·25 15
954 1k.40 brown, yellow & red . 4·00 1·90
955 1k.60 sepia, green & red . . 2·50 40
DESIGNS: 30h. Slovacko woman; 1k.20, Blata woman; 1k.40, Cicmany woman, 1k.60, Novohradsko woman.

1957. Czech Writers (2nd issue). As T **285**. On buff paper.
956 15h. brown (Olbracht) . . . 30 10
957 20h. green (Toman) 30 10
958 30h. sepia (Salda) 30 10
959 1k.60 blue (Vansova) 50 10

289 Forestry Academy, Banska Stiavnica

1957. Towns and Monuments Anniversaries.
960 – 30h. blue 20 10
961 **289** 30h. purple 20 10
962 – 60h. red 40 10
963 – 60h. brown 40 10
964 – 60h. green 30 10
965 – 1k.25 black . . . . 3·25 1·50
DESIGNS: No. 960, Kolin; 962, Uherske Hradiste; 963, Charles Bridge; Prague; 964, Karlstejn Castle; 965, Moravska Trebova.

290 Girl Harvester

1957. 3rd Collective Farming Agricultural Congress, Prague.
966 **290** 30h. turquoise 70 10

291 Komensky's Mausoleum
292 J. A. Komensky (Comenius)

1957. 300th Anniv of Publication of Komensky's "Opera Didactica Omnia".
967 **291** 30h. brown 40 10
968 – 40h. green 40 10
969 **292** 60h. brown . . . . . . 1·90 1·25
970 – 60h. red 55 10
DESIGNS: As Type **291**: 40h. Komensky at work; 1k. Illustration from "Opera Didactica Omnia".

293 Racing Cyclists

1957. Sports Events of 1957.
971 **293** 30h. purple and blue . . 35 10
972 – 60h. green and bistre . . 1·60 1·50
973 – 60h. violet and brown . . 35 10
974 – 60h. purple and brown . . 35 10
975 – 60h. black and green . . 35 10
976 – 60h. black and blue . . 1·00 10
DESIGNS—HORIZ: Nos. 971/2 (10th Int Cycle Race); 973, Rescue squad (Mountain Rescue Service); 975, Archer (World Archery Championships, Prague). VERT: 974, Boxers (European Boxing Championships, Prague); 976, Motor Cyclists (32nd Int Motor Cycle Six-Day Trial).

294 J. B. Foerster

1957. Int Music Festival Jubilee. Musicians.
977 – 60h. violet (Stamic) . . . 25 10
978 – 60h. black (Laub) 25 10
979 – 60h. blue (Ondricek) . . . 25 10
980 **294** 60h. sepia 25 10
981 – 60h. brown (Novak) . . . 85 10
982 – 60h. turquoise (Suk) . . . 25 10

295 J. Bozek (founder)
296 Young Collector Blowing Posthorn

1957. 250th Anniv of Polytechnic Engineering Schools, Prague.
983 **295** 30h. black 15 10
984 – 60h. brown 30 10
985 – 1k. purple 30 15
986 – 1k.40 violet 45 15
DESIGNS—VERT: 60h. F. J. Gerstner; 1k. R. Skuhersky. HORIZ: 1k.40, Polytechnic Engineering Schools Building, Prague.

1957. Junior Philatelic Exn, Pardubice.
987 **296** 30h. orange and green . . 50 10
988 – 60h. blue and brown . . 2·00 1·25
DESIGN: 60h. Girl sending letter by pigeon.

297 "Rose of Friendship and Peace"

298 Karel Klic and Printing Press

1957. 15th Anniv of Destruction of Lidice.
989 – 30h. black 30 10
990 **297** 60h. red and black . . . 85 35
DESIGN: 30h. Veiled woman.

1957. Czech Inventors.
991 **298** 30h. black 15 10
992 – 60h. blue 30 10
DESIGN: 60h. Joseph Ressel and propeller.

299 Chamois

300 Marycka Magdonova

1957. Tatra National Park.
993 **299** 20h. black and green . . 65 45
994 – 30h. brown and blue . . 65 10
995 – 40h. blue and brown . . 1·25 30
996 – 60h. green and yellow . . 50 10
997 – 1k.25 black and ochre . . 1·25 1·25
DESIGNS—VERT: 30h. Brown bear. HORIZ: 40h. Gentian; 60h. Edelweiss; 1k.25 (49 × 29 mm), Tatra Mountains.

1957. 90th Birthday of Petr Bezruc (poet).
998 **300** 60h. black and red . . . 50 10

301 Worker with Banner

303 Television Tower and Aerials

302 Tupolev Tu-104A and Paris–Prague–Moscow Route

1957. 4th World T.U.C., Leipzig.
999 **301** 75h. red 50 15

1957. Air. Opening of Czechoslovak Airlines.
1000 **302** 75h. blue and red . . . 80 10
1001 – 2k.35 blue and yellow . . 95 10
DESIGN: 2k.35, "Prague–Cairo–Beirut–Damascus".

1957. Television Development.
1002 **303** 40h. blue and red . . . 20 10
1003 – 60h. brown and green . . 25 10
DESIGN: 60h. Family watching television.

304 Youth, Globe and Lenin

1957. 40th Anniv of Russian Revolution.
1004 **304** 30h. red 20 10
1005 – 60h. blue 40 10
DESIGN: 60h. Lenin, refinery and Russian emblem.

1957. Death of President Zapotocky. As T **259** but dated "19 XII 1884–13 XI 1957".
1006 30h. black 10 10
1007 60h. black 20 10

1957. National Costumes (3rd series). As T **270**.
1008 45h. sepia, red and blue . . 2·75 1·25
1009 75h. sepia, red and green . . 1·90 80
1010 1k.25 sepia, red & yellow . . 2·75 65
1011 1k.95 sepia, blue and red . . 3·25 2·10
DESIGNS—VERT: 45h. Pilsen woman; 75h. Slovacko man; 1k.25, Hana woman; 1k.95, Tesin woman.

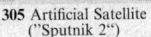

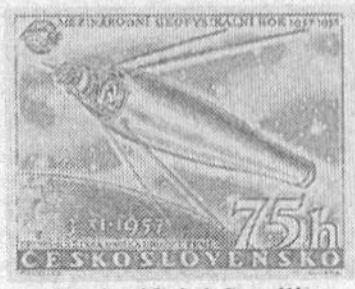
305 Artificial Satellite ("Sputnik 2")

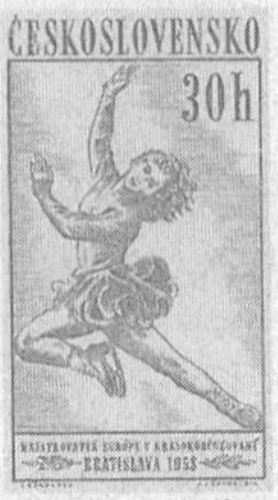
306 Figure Skating (European Championships, Bratislava)

1957. International Geophysical Year. Showing globe and dated "1957–1958".
1012 – 30h. brown . . . . . . 1·40 45
1013 – 45h. brown and blue . . 30 25
1014 **305** 75h. red and blue . . . 2·00 65
DESIGNS—HORIZ: 30h. Radio-telescope and observatory. VERT: 45h. Lomnicky Stit meteorological station.

1958. Sports Events of 1958.
1015 **306** 30h. purple 95 20
1016 – 40h. blue 30 20
1017 – 60h. brown 30 10
1018 – 80h. violet . . . . . . 1·40 70
1019 – 1k.60 green 50 15
EVENTS: 40h. Canoeing (World Canoeing Championships, Prague); 60h. Volleyball (European Volleyball Championships, Prague); 80h. Parachuting (4th World Parachute-jumping Championship, Bratislava); 1k.60, Football (World Cup Football Championship, Stockholm).

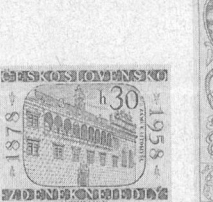

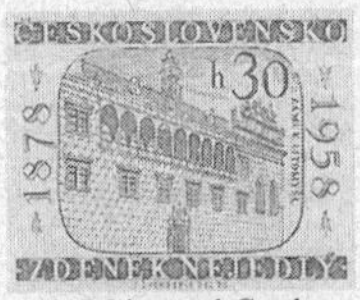
307 Litomysl Castle (birthplace of Nejedly)

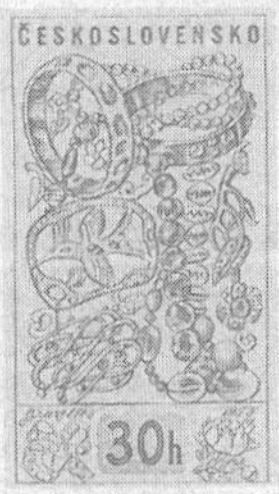
309 Jewellery

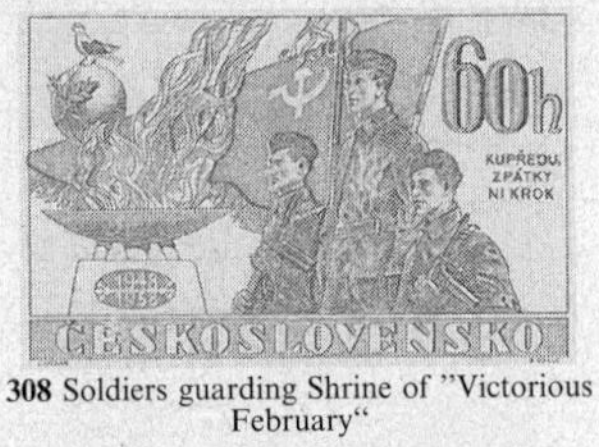
308 Soldiers guarding Shrine of "Victorious February"

1958. 80th Birthday of Nejedly (musician).
1020 **307** 30h. green 20 10
1021 – 60h. brown 20 10
DESIGN—HORIZ: 60h. Bethlehem Chapel, Prague.

1958. 10th Anniv of Communist Govt.
1022 – 30h. blue and yellow . . 30 10
1023 **308** 60h. brown and red . . 30 10
1024 – 1k.60 green and orange . 45 10
DESIGNS—VERT: 30h. Giant mine-excavator. HORIZ: 1k.60, Combine-harvester.

1958. Brussels International Exhibition. Inscr "Bruxelles 1958".
1025 **309** 30h. red and blue . . . 20 10
1026 – 45h. red and lilac . . . 40 10
1027 – 60h. violet and green . . 20 10
1028 – 75h. blue and orange . . 95 90
1029 – 1k.20 green and red . . 40 10
1030 – 1k.95 brown and blue . . 60 15
DESIGNS—VERT: 45h. Toy dolls; 60h. Draperies; 75h. Kaplan turbine; 1k.20, Glassware. HORIZ: (48½ × 29½ mm), 1k.95, Czech pavilion.

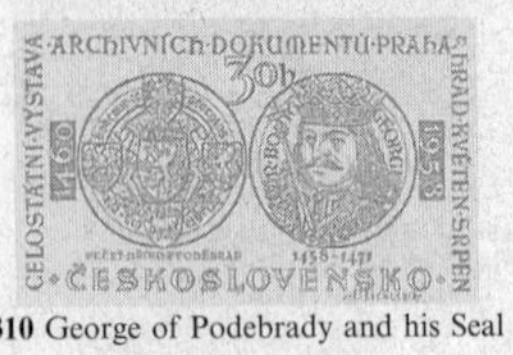
310 George of Podebrady and his Seal

1958. National Exhibition of Archive Documents. Inscr as in T **310**.
1031 **310** 30h. red 35 10
1032 – 60h. violet 30 10
DESIGN: 60h. Prague, 1628 (from engraving).

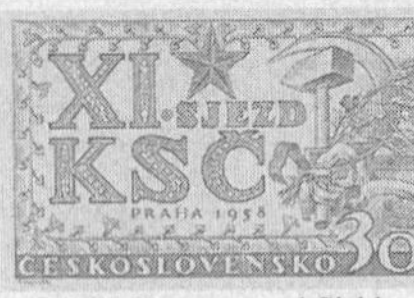
311 Hammer and Sickle

1958. 11th Czech Communist Party Congress and 15th Anniv of Czech–Soviet Friendship Treaty. 45h. inscr as in T **311** and 60h. inscr "15. VYROCI UZAVRENI".
1033 **311** 30h. red 20 10
1034 – 45h. green 20 10
1035 – 60h. blue 20 10
DESIGNS: 45h. Map of Czechoslovakia, with hammer and sickle; 60h. Atomic reactor, Rez (near Prague).

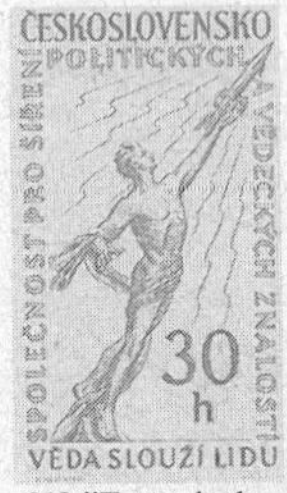
312 "Towards the Stars" (after sculpture by G. Postnikov)

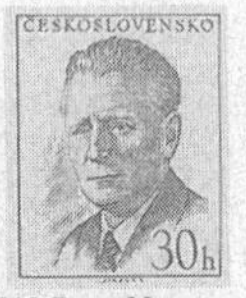
313 Pres. Novotny

1958. Cultural and Political Events. 45h. inscr "IV. KONGRES MEZINARODNI", etc, and 60h. inscr "I. SVETOVA ODBOROVA", etc.
1036 **312** 30h. red 70 40
1037 – 45h. purple 20 20
1038 – 60h. blue 20 10
DESIGNS—VERT: 45h. Three women of different races and globe (4th Int Democratic Women's Federation Congress, Vienna). HORIZ: 60h. Boy and girl with globes (1st World T.U. Conference of Working Youth, Prague). Type **312** represents the Society for the Dissemination of Cultural and Political Knowledge.

1958.
1039 **313** 30h. violet 45 10
1039a 30h. purple . . . . . . 3·50 1·10
1040 60h. red 45 10

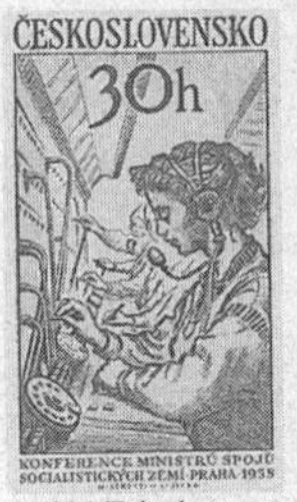
314 Telephone Operator

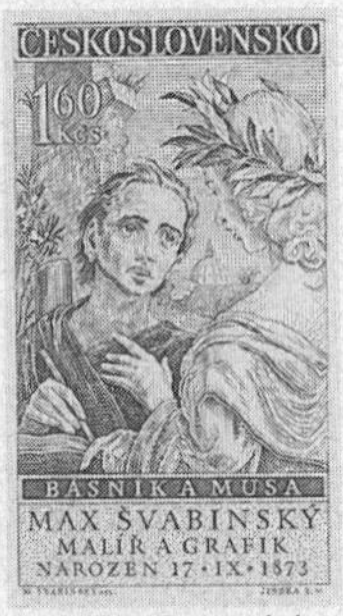
316 "The Poet and the Muse" (after Max Svabinsky)

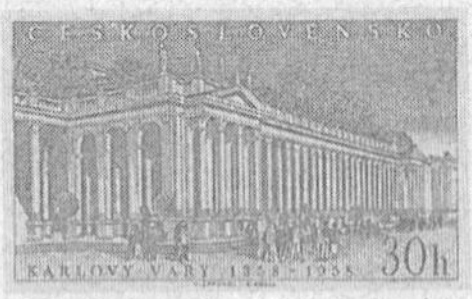
315 Karlovy Vary (600th Anniv)

1958. Communist Postal Conference, Prague. Inscr as in T **314**.
1041 **314** 30h. sepia and brown . . 30 10
1042 – 45h. black and green . . 30 30
DESIGN: 45h. Aerial mast.

1958. Czech Spas (2nd series).
1043 **315** 30h. lake 10 10
1044 – 40h. brown 10 10
1045 – 60h. green 15 10
1046 – 80h. sepia 25 10
1047 – 1k.20 blue 40 15
1048 – 1k.60 violet 95 75
SPAS: 40h. Podebrady; 60h. Marianske Lazne (150th Anniv); 80h. Luhacovice; 1k.20, Strbske Pleso; 1k.60, Trencianske.

1958. 85th Birthday of Dr. Max Svabinsky (artist).
1049 **316** 1k.60 black . . . . . . 3·25 80

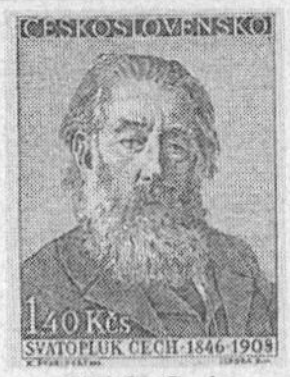
317 S. Cech

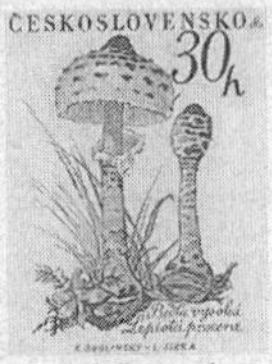
319 Parasol Mushroom

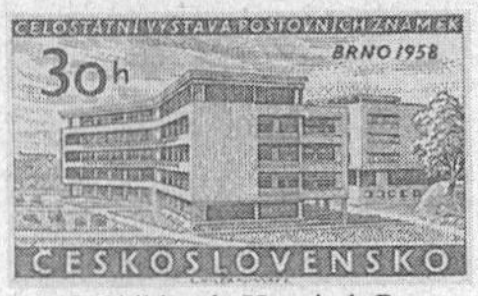
318 Children's Hospital, Brno

1958. Writers' Anniversaries.
1050 – 30h. red (Julius Fucik) 25 10
1051 – 45h. violet (Gustav K. Zechenter) . . . . . 1·25 45
1052 – 60h. blue (Karel Capek) 15 10
1053 **317** 1k.40 black 50 15

1958. National Stamp Exn, Brno. Inscr as in T **318**.
1054 **318** 30h. violet 20 10
1055 – 60h. red 20 10
1056 – 1k. sepia 45 10
1057 – 1k.60 myrtle . . . . . . 1·60 1·50
DESIGNS: 60h. New Town Hall, Brno; 1k. St. Thomas's Church, Red Army Square; 1k.60, (50 × 28½ mm), Brno view.

1958. Mushrooms.
1058 **319** 30h. buff, green & brown 40 15
1059 – 40h. buff, red & brown 45 15
1060 – 60h. red, buff and black 55 25
1061 – 1k.40 red, green & brn 70 35
1062 – 1k.60 red, green & blk 5·25 2·40
DESIGNS—VERT: 40h. Cep; 60h. Red cap; 1k.40, Fly agaric; 1k.60, Boot-lace fungus.

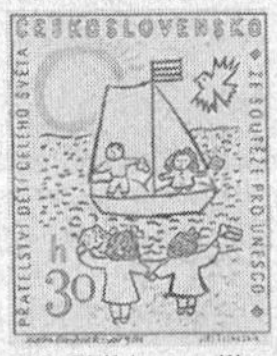
320 Children sailing

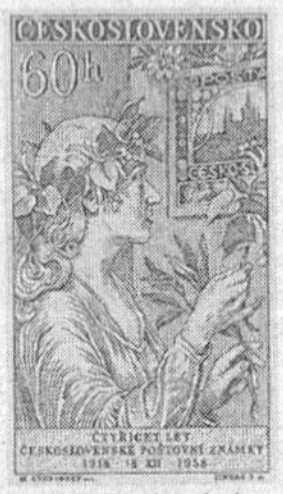
322 Garlanded Woman ("Republic") with First Czech Stamp

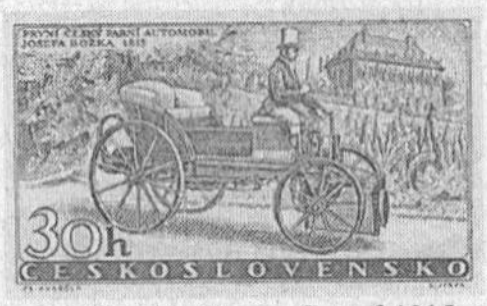
321 Bozek's Steam Car of 1815

1958. Inauguration of U.N.E.S.C.O. Headquarters Building, Paris. Inscr "ZE SOUTEZE PRO UNESCO".
1063 **320** 30h. red, yellow & blue 20 10
1064 – 45h. red and blue . . . 50 10
1065 – 60h. blue, yellow & brn 20 10
DESIGNS: 45h. Mother, child and bird; 60h. Child skier.

1958. Czech Motor Industry Commemoration.
1066 **321** 30h. violet and yellow 65 10
1067 – 45h. brown and green . . 50 10
1068 – 60h. green and orange 65 10
1069 – 80h. red and green . . . 50 10
1070 – 1k. brown and green . . 50 10
1071 – 1k.25 green & yellow . . 1·60 75
DESIGNS: 45h. "President" car of 1897; 60h. Skoda "450" car; 80h. Tatra "603" car; 1k. Skoda "706" motor coach; 1k.25, Tatra "III" and Praga "VS 3" motor trucks in Tibet.

1958. 40th Anniv of 1st Czech Postage Stamps.
1072 **322** 60h. blue 20 10

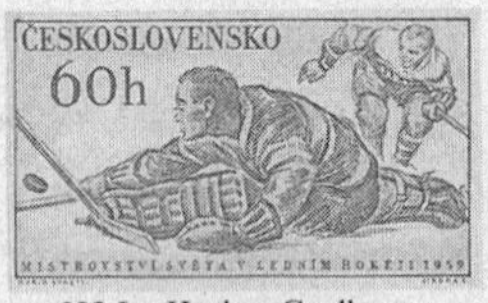
323 Ice Hockey Goalkeeper

1959. Sports Events of 1959.
1073 – 20h. brown and grey . . 30 10
1074 – 30h. brown & orange . . 30 10
1075 **323** 60h. blue and green . . 30 10
1076 – 1k. lake and yellow . . . 30 10
1077 – 1k.60 violet and blue . . 45 10
1078 – 2k. brown and blue . . . 1·60 1·40
DESIGNS: 20h. Ice hockey player (50th anniv of Czech Ice Hockey Association); 30h. Throwing the javelin; 60h. (Type **323**) World Ice Hockey Championships, 1959; 1k. Hurdling; 1k.60, Rowing; 2k. High jumping.

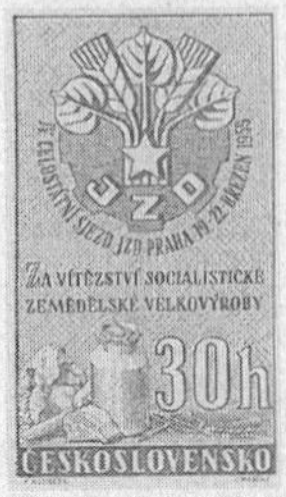
324 U.A.C. Emblem

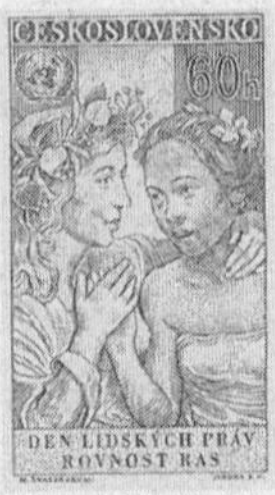
325 "Equal Rights"

1959. 4th National Unified Agricultural Co-operatives Congress, Prague.
1079 **324** 30h. lake and blue . . . 15 10
1080 – 60h. blue and yellow . . 30 10
DESIGN: 60h. Artisan shaking hand with farmer.

1959. 10th Anniv of Declaration of Human Rights.
1081 **325** 60h. green 15 10
1082 – 1k. sepia 25 10
1083 – 2k. blue . . . . . . 1·40 60
DESIGNS: 1k. "World Freedom" (girl with Dove of Peace); 2k. "Freedom for Colonial Peoples" (native woman with child).

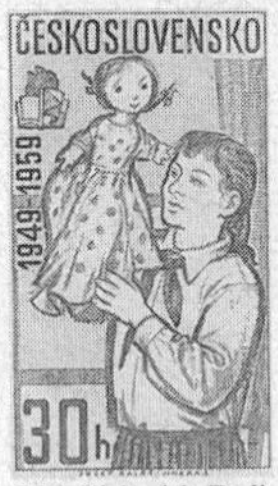
326 Girl with Doll

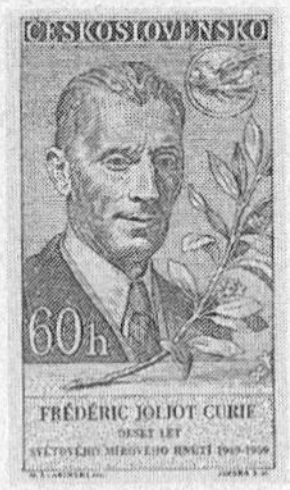
327 F. Joliot-Curie (scientist)

1959. 10th Anniv of Young Pioneers' Movement.
1084 **326** 30h. blue and yellow . . 30 10
1085 – 40h. black and blue . . 30 20
1086 – 60h. black and purple . . 30 10
1087 – 80h. brown and green . . 30 20
DESIGNS: 40h. Boy hiker; 60h. Young radio technician; 80h. Girl planting tree.

1959. 10th Anniv of Peace Movement.
1088 **327** 60h. purple . . . . . . 1·25 40

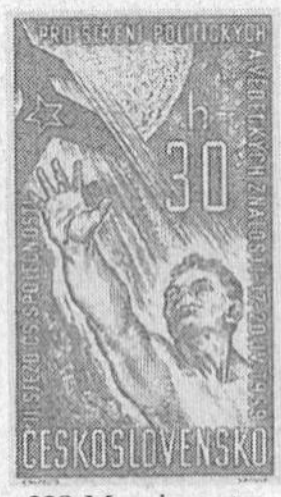
328 Man in outer space and Moon Rocket

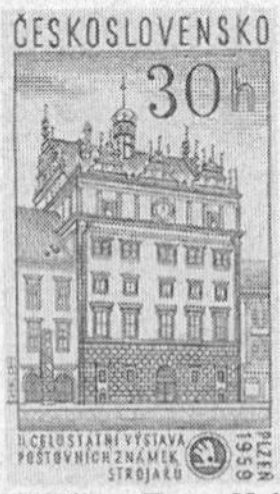
329 Pilsen Town Hall

1959. 2nd Czech Political and Cultural Knowledge Congress, Prague.
1089 **328** 30h. blue 85 25

1959. Centenary of Skoda Works and National Stamp Exhibition, Pilsen. Inscr "PLZEN 1959".
1090 **329** 30h. brown 15 10
1091 – 60h. violet and green . . 15 10
1092 – 1k. blue 25 15
1093 – 1k.60 black & yellow . . 1·25 1·10
DESIGNS: 60h. Part of steam turbine; 1k. St. Bartholomew's Church, Pilsen; 1k.60, Part of SR-1200 lathe.

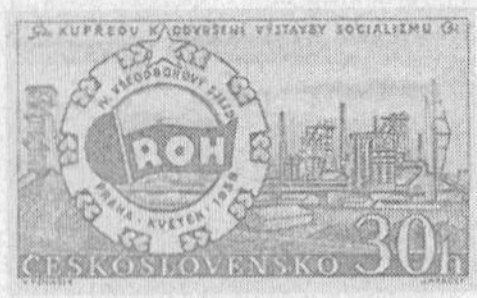
330 Congress Emblem and Industrial Plant

1959. 4th Trades Union Congress, Prague.
1094 **330** 30h. red and yellow . . 20 10
1095 – 60h. olive and blue . . . 20 10
DESIGN: 60h. Dam.

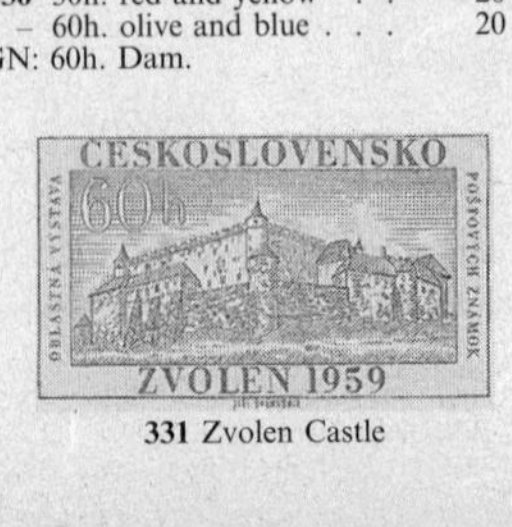
331 Zvolen Castle

1959. Slovak Stamp Exhibition, Zvolen.
1096 **331** 60h. olive and yellow . . 35 10

332 F. Benda (composer)

1959. Cultural Anniversaries.
1097 **332** 15h. blue 10 10
1098 – 30h. red 10 10
1099 – 40h. green 15 10
1100 – 60h. brown 15 10
1101 – 60h. black 25 10
1102 – 80h. violet 15 10
1103 – 1k. brown 15 10
1104 – 3k. brown 60 75
PORTRAITS: 30h. Vaclav Klicpera (dramatist); 40h. Aurel Stodola (engineer); 60h. (1100) Karel V. Rais (writer); 60h. (1101) Haydn (composer); 80h. Antonin Slavicek (painter); 1k. Petr Bezruc (poet). 3k. Charles Darwin (naturalist).

333 "Z" Pavilion

1959. Int Fair, Brno. Inscr "BRNO 6-20. IX. 1959".
1105 – 30h. purple & yellow . . 15 10
1106 – 60h. blue 15 10
1107 **333** 1k.60 blue & yellow . . 40 10
DESIGNS: 30h. View of Fair; 60h. Fair emblem and world map.

334 Revolutionary (after A. Holly)

1959. 15th Anniv of Slovak National Uprising and 40th Anniv of Republic. Inscr "1944 29.8.1959".
1108 **334** 30h. black & mauve . . 15 10
1109 – 60h. red 20 10
1110 – 1k.60 blue & yell . . 40 10
DESIGNS—VERT: 60h. Revolutionary with upraised rifle (after sculpture "Forward" by L. Snopka). HORIZ: 1k.60, Factory, sun and linden leaves.

335 Moon Rocket

1959. Landing of Russian Rocket on Moon.
1111 **335** 60h. red and blue . . 1·25 25

336 Lynx

1959. 10th Anniv of Tatra National Park. Inscr "1949 TATRANSKY NARODNY PARK 1959".
1112 – 30h. black and grey . . 65 10
1113 – 40h. brown & turquoise . 65 10
1114 **336** 60h. red & yellow . . 90 10
1115 – 1k. brown & blue . . 2·00 75
1116 – 1k.60 brown . . . . . 1·75 10
DESIGNS—HORIZ: 30h. Alpine marmots; 40h. European bison; 1k. Wolf; 1k.60, Red deer.

337 Stamp Printing Works, Peking

1959. 10th Anniv of Chinese People's Republic.
1117 **337** 30h. red and green . . . 25 10

338 Bleriot XI Monoplanes at First Czech Aviation School

1959. Air. 50th Anniv of 1st Flight by Jan Kaspar.
1118 **338** 1k. black and yellow . . 15 10
1119 – 1k.80 black & blue . . . 75 10
DESIGN: 1k.80, Jan Kaspar and Bleriot XI in flight.

339 Great Spotted Woodpecker

341 Exercises

1959. Birds.
1120 **339** 20h. multicoloured . . . 85 15
1121 – 30h. multicoloured . . . 85 15
1122 – 40h. multicoloured . . . 2·10 1·10
1123 – 60h. multicoloured . . . 85 15
1124 – 80h. multicoloured . . . 85 15
1125 – 1k. red, blue & black . . 85 15
1126 – 1k.20 brn, blue & blk . . 1·10 40
BIRDS: 30h. Blue tit; 40h. Eurasian nuthatch; 60h. Golden oriole; 80h. Eurasian goldfinch; 1k. Northern bullfinch; 1k.20, River kingfisher.

340 Tesla and Electrical Apparatus

1959. Radio Inventors.
1127 **340** 25h. black and red . . 1·10 25
1128 – 30h. black and brown . . 15 10
1129 – 35h. black and lilac . . 20 10
1130 – 60h. black and blue . . 25 10
1131 – 1k. black and green . . 20 10
1132 – 2k. black and bistre . . 80 90
INVENTORS (each with sketch of invention): 30h. Aleksandr Popov; 35h. Edouard Branly; 60h. Guglielmo Marconi; 1k. Heinrich Hertz; 2k. Edwin Armstrong.

1960. 2nd National Spartacist Games (1st issue). Inscr as in T **341**.
1133 **341** 30h. brown and red . . . 1·10 10
1134 – 60h. blue & light blue . . 45 20
1135 – 1k.60 brown & bistre . . 70 25
DESIGNS: 60h. Skiing; 1k.60, Basketball.
See also Nos. 1160/2.

342 Freighter "Lidice"

1960. Czech Ships.
1136 – 30h. green and red . . . 80 15
1137 – 60h. red and turquoise . . 25 10
1138 – 1k. violet and yellow . . 80 20
1139 **342** 1k.20 purple and green . 1·75 1·00
SHIPS: 30h. Dredger "Praha Liben"; 60h. Tug "Kharito Latjev"; 1k. River boat "Komarno".

343 Ice Hockey

1960. Winter Olympic Games. Inscr as in T **343**.
1140 **343** 60h. sepia and blue . . 40 25
1141 – 1k.80 black & green . . 3·50 2·10
DESIGN: 1k.80, Skating pair.
See also Nos. 1163/5.

1959. 10th Anniv of Chinese People's Republic.
1117 **337** 30h. red and green . . . 25 10

344 Trencin Castle   345 Lenin

1960. Czechoslovak Castles.
1142 5h. blue (Type **344**) 15 10
1143 10h. black (Bezdez) 15 10
1144 20h. orange (Kost) 25 10
1145 30h. green (Pernstejn) . . . 25 10
1146 40h. brn (Kremnica) 25 10
1146a 50h. black (Krivoklat) . . . 25 10
1147 60h. red (Karestejn) 45 10
1148 1k. purple (Smolenice) . . . 30 10
1149 1k.60 blue (Kokorin) 70 10

1960. 90th Birth Anniv of Lenin.
1150 **345** 60h. olive 85 30

346 Soldier and Child

1960. 15th Anniv of Liberation.
1151 **346** 30h. lake and blue . . . 30 10
1152 – 30h. green and lavender . 25 10
1153 – 30h. red and pink . . . 25 10
1154 – 60h. blue and buff . . . 25 10
1155 – 60h. purple and green . . 25 10
DESIGNS—VERT: No. 1152, Solider with liberated political prisoner; 1153, Child eating pastry. HORIZ: No. 1154, Welder; 1155, Tractor-driver.

347 Smelter

1960. Parliamentary Elections.
1156 **347** 30h. red and grey . . . 15 10
1157 – 60h. green and blue . . 20 10
DESIGN: 60h. Country woman and child.

348 Red Cross Woman with Dove

1960. 3rd Czechoslovak Red Cross Congress.
1158 **348** 30h. red and blue . . . 10 10

349 Fire-prevention Team with Hose

1960. 2nd Firemen's Union Congress.
1159 **349** 60h. blue and pink . . . 30 10

1960. 2nd National Spartacist Games (2nd issue). As T **341**.
1160 – 30h. red and green . . . 40 10
1161 – 60h. black and pink . . . 40 10
1162 – 1k. blue and orange . . . 60 15
DESIGNS: 30h. Ball exercises; 60h. Stick exercises; 1k. Girls with hoops.

1960. Olympic Games, Rome. As Type **343**.
1163 – 1k. black and orange . . 50 20
1164 1k.80 black and red . . . 1·25 25
1165 – 2k. black and blue . . . 2·00 85
DESIGNS: 1k. Sprinting; 1k.80, Gymnastics; 2k. Rowing.

350 Czech 10k. Stamp of 1936

1960. National Philatelic Exn, Bratislava (1st issue).
1166 – 60h. black and yellow . . 40 10
1167 **350** 1k. black and blue 90 10
DESIGN: 60h. Hand of philatelist holding stamp Type **350**.
See also Nos. 1183/4.

351 Stalin Mine, Ostrava-Hermanice   352 V. Cornelius of Vsehra (historian)

1960. 3rd Five Year Plan (1st issue).
1168 **351** 10h. black and green . . 20 10
1169 – 20h. lake and blue . . . 20 10
1170 – 30h. blue and red . . . 20 10
1171 – 40h. green and lilac . . . 20 10
1172 – 60h. blue and yellow . . 20 10
DESIGNS: 20h. Hodonin Power Station; 30h. Klement Gottwald Iron Works, Kuncice; 40h. Excavator; 60h. Naphtha refinery.
See also Nos. 1198/1200.

1960. Cultural Anniversaries.
1173 **352** 10h. black 20 10
1174 – 20h. brown 30 10
1175 – 30h. red 40 10
1176 – 40h. green 45 10
1177 – 60h. violet 50 10
PORTRAITS: 20h. K. M. Capek Chod (writer). 30h. Hana Kvapilova (actress); 40h. Oskar Nedbal (composer); 60h. Otakar Ostricil (composer).

353 Zlin Trener 6 flying upside-down

1960. 1st World Aviation Aerobatic Championships, Bratislava.
1178 **353** 60h. violet and blue . . 85 15

354 "New Constitution"

1960. Proclamation of New Constitution.
1179 **354** 30h. blue and red . . . 25 10

355 Worker with "Rude Pravo"

1960. Czechoslovak Press Day (30h.) and 40th Anniv of Newspaper "Rude Pravo".
1180 – 30h. blue and orange . . 10 10
1181 **355** 60h. red and blue . . . 20 10
DESIGN—HORIZ: (inscr "DEN TISKU"): 30h. Steel-workers with newspaper.

356 Globes

1960. 15th Anniv of W.F.T.U.
1182 **356** 30h. blue and bistre . . 25 10

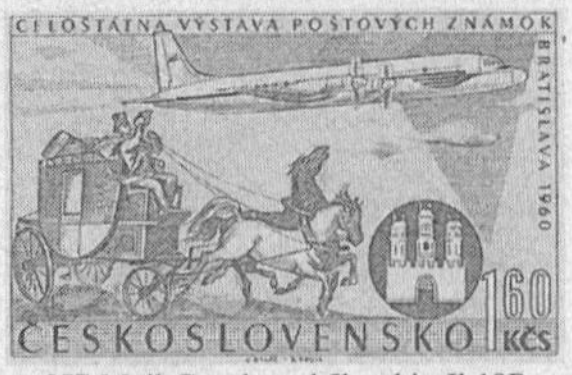

357 Mail Coach and Ilyushin Il-18B

1960. Air. National Philatelic Exhibition, Bratislava (2nd issue).
1183 357 1k.60 blue and grey . . 2·50 4·00
1184 – 2k.80 green & cream . . 4·00 1·60
DESIGN: 2k.80, MIL Mi-4 helicopter over Bratislava.

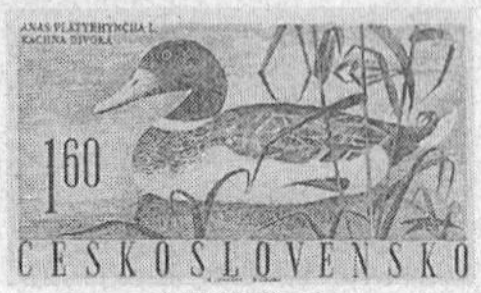

358 Mallard

1960. Water Birds.
1185 – 25h. black and blue . . 55 10
1186 – 30h. black and green . . 1·25 10
1187 – 40h. black and blue . . 80 15
1188 – 60h. black and pink . . 90 15
1189 – 1k. black and yellow . . 1·40 15
1190 358 1k.60 black and lilac . . 2·75 1·60
BIRDS—VERT: 25h. Black-crowned night heron; 30h. Great crested grebe; 40h. Northern lapwing; 60h. Grey heron. HORIZ: 1k. Greylag goose.

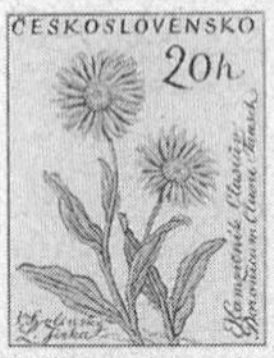

359 "Doronicum clusii tausch"

1960. Flowers. Inscr in black.
1191 359 20h. yellow, orge & grn 60 10
1192 – 30h. red and green . . . 80 15
1193 – 40h. yellow and green . . 80 15
1194 – 60h. pink and green . . 85 15
1195 – 1k. blue, violet & green 1·25 40
1196 – 2k. yellow, green & pur 3·00 1·50
FLOWERS: 30h. "Cyclamen europaeum L"; 40h. "Primula auricula L"; 60h. "Sempervivum mont L"; 1k. "Gentiana clusil perr, et song". 2k. "Pulsatilla slavica reuss".

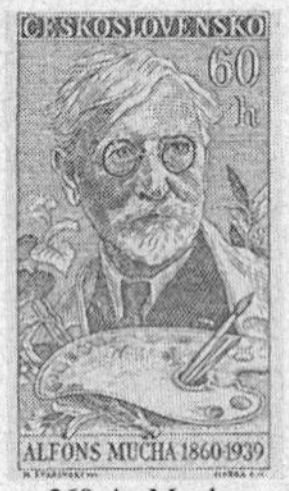

360 A. Mucha (painter and stamp designer)

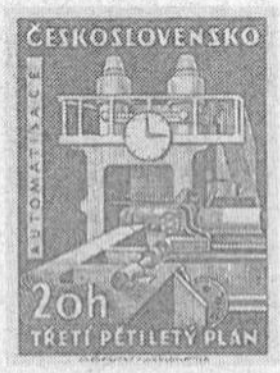

361 Automatic Machinery

1960. Stamp Day and Birth Centenary of Mucha.
1197 360 60h. blue 70 10

1961. 3rd Five Year Plan (2nd issue).
1198 361 20h. blue 10 10
1199 – 30h. red 15 10
1200 – 60h. green 15 10
DESIGNS: 30h. Turbo-generator and control desk; 60h. Excavator.

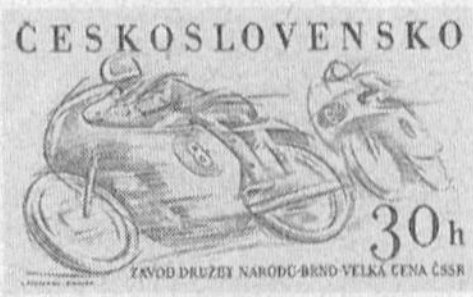

362 Motor Cyclists (Int Grand Prix, Brno)

1961. Sports Events of 1961.
1201 362 30h. blue and mauve . . 20 10
1202 – 30h. red and blue . . . 20 10
1203 – 40h. black and red . . . 35 10
1204 – 60h. purple and blue . . 35 10
1205 – 1k. blue and yellow . . . 35 10
1206 – 1k.20 green & salmon . . 35 10
1207 – 1k.60 brown and red . . 1·60 1·10
DESIGNS—VERT: 30h. (No. 1202), Athletes with banners (40th anniv of Czech Physical Culture); 60h. Figure skating (World Figure Skating Championships, Prague); 1k. Rugger (35th anniv of rugby football in Czechoslovakia); 1k.20, Football (60th anniv of football in Czechoslovakia); 1k.60, Running (65th anniv of Bechovice–Prague Marathon Race). HORIZ: 40h. Rowing (European Rowing Championships, Prague).

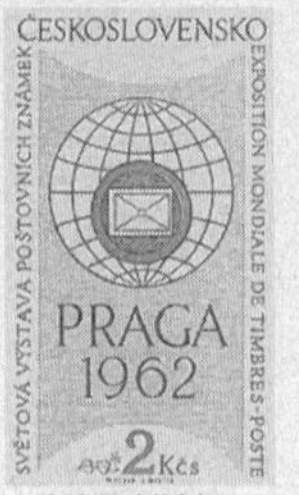

363 Exhibition Emblem

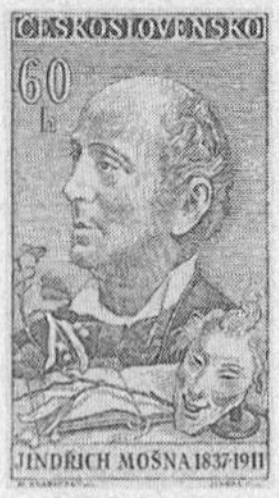

365 J. Mosna

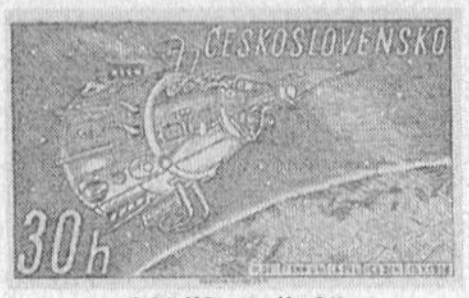

364 "Sputnik 3"

1961. "PRAGA 1962" Int Stamp Exn (1st issue).
1208 363 2k. red and blue . . . . 2·00 15
See also Nos. 1250/6, 1267/70, 1297/1300 and 1311/15.

1961. Space Research (1st series).
1209 – 20h. red and violet . . . 50 10
1210 364 30h. blue and buff . . . 50 10
1211 – 40h. red and green . . . 45 15
1212 – 60h. violet and yellow 30 10
1213 – 1k.60 blue and green . . 50 10
1214 – 2k. purple and blue . . . 1·50 1·10
DESIGNS—VERT: 20h. Launching cosmic rocket; 40h. Venus rocket. HORIZ: 60h. "Lunik 1"; 1k.60, "Lunik 3" and Moon; 2k. Cosmonaut (similar to T 366).
See also Nos. 1285/90 and 1349/54.

1961. Cultural Anniversaries.
1215 365 60h. green 25 10
1216 – 60h. black 30 10
1217 – 60h. blue 30 10
1218 – 60h. red 25 10
1219 – 60h. brown 25 10
PORTRAITS: No. 1216, J. Uprka (painter); 1217, P. O. Hviezdoslav (poet); 1218, A. Mrstik (writer); 1219, J. Hora (poet).

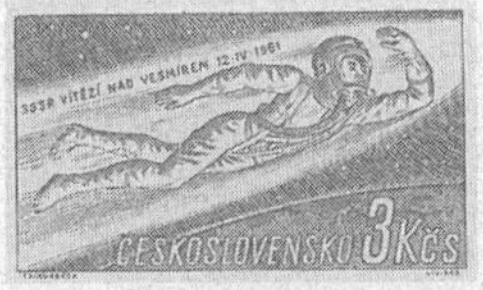

366 Man in Space

1961. World's 1st Manned Space Flight.
1220 366 60h. red and turquoise 55 10
1221 3k. blue and yellow . . . 2·00 50

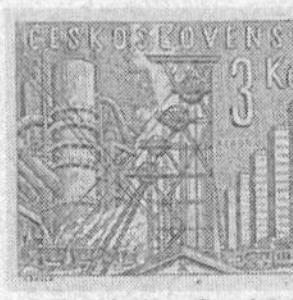

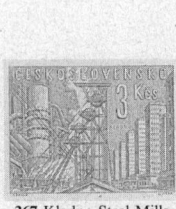

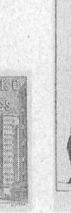

367 Kladno Steel Mills

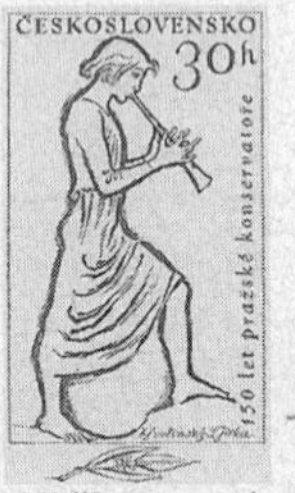

368 "Instrumental Music"

1961.
1222 367 3k. red 85 10

1961. 150th Anniv of Prague Conservatoire.
1223 368 30h. sepia 30 10
1224 – 30h. red 35 10
1225 – 60h. blue 30 10
DESIGNS: No. 1224, Dancer; 1225, Girl playing lyre.

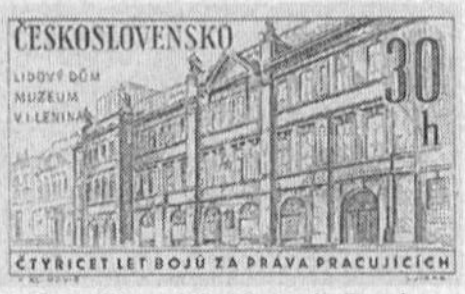

369 "People's House" (Lenin Museum), Prague

1961. 40th Anniv of Czech Communist Party.
1226 369 30h. brown 20 10
1227 – 30h. blue 20 10
1228 – 30h. violet 20 10
1229 – 60h. red 20 10
1230 – 60h. myrtle 20 10
1231 – 60h. red 20 10
DESIGNS—HORIZ: No. 1227, Gottwald's Museum, Prague. VERT: No. 1228, Workers in Wenceslas Square, Prague; 1229, Worker, star and factory plant; 1230, Woman wielding hammer and sickle; 1231, May Day procession, Wenceslas Square.

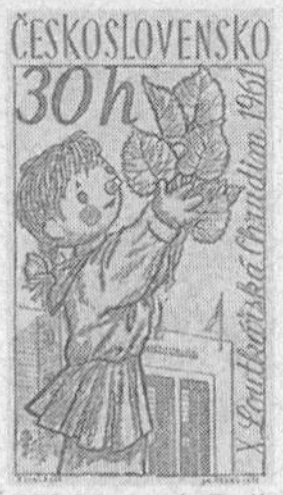

370 Manasek Doll

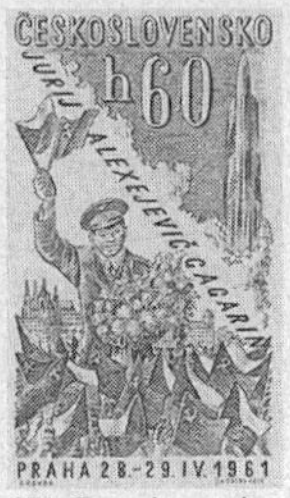

371 Gagarin waving Flags

1961. Czech Puppets.
1232 370 30h. red and yellow . . 20 10
1233 – 40h. sepia & turquoise 20 10
1234 – 60h. blue and salmon . . 20 10
1235 – 1k. green and blue . . . 20 10
1236 – 1k.60 red and blue . . . 1·25 45
PUPPETS: 40h. "Dr. Faustus and Caspar"; 60h. "Spejbl and Hurvinek"; 1k. Scene from "Difficulties with the Moon" (Askenazy); 1k.60, "Jasanek" of Brno.

1961. Yuri Gagarin's (first man in space) Visit to Prague.
1237 371 60h. black and red . . . 25 10
1238 – 1k.80 black and blue . . . 40 10
DESIGN: 1k.80, Yuri Gagarin in space helmet, rocket and dove.

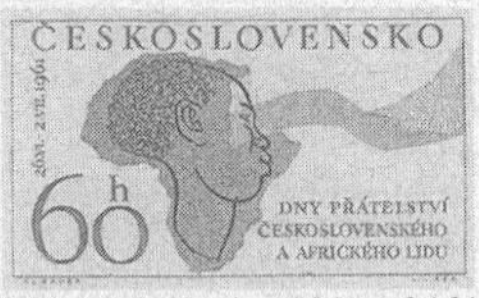

372 Woman's Head and Map of Africa

1961. Czecho-African Friendship.
1239 372 60h. red and blue . . . 25 10

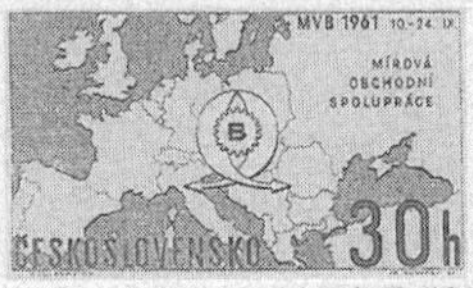

373 Map of Europe and Fair Emblem

1961. Int Trade Fair, Brno. Inscr "M.V.B. 1961".
1240 373 30h. blue and green . . 15 10
1241 – 60h. green & salmon . . 25 10
1242 – 1k. brown and blue . . . 25 10
DESIGNS—VERT: 60h. Horizontal drill. HORIZ: 1k. Scientific discussion group.

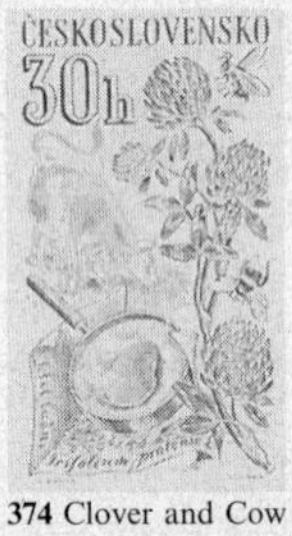

374 Clover and Cow

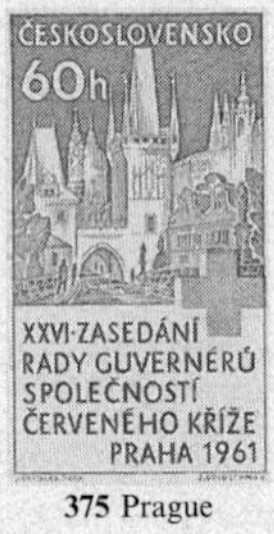

375 Prague

1961. Agricultural Produce.
1243 – 20h. purple and blue . . . 15 10
1244 374 30h. ochre and purple 15 10
1245 – 40h. orange and brown 15 10
1246 – 60h. bistre and green . . 20 10
1247 – 1k.40 brown & choc . . 40 10
1248 – 2k. blue and purple . . . 1·40 60
DESIGNS: 20h. Sugar beet, cup and saucer; 40h. Wheat and bread; 60h. Hops and beer; 1k.40, Maize and cattle; 2k. Potatoes and factory.

1961. 26th Session of Red Cross Societies League Governors' Council, Prague.
1249 375 60h. violet and red . . . 1·00 10

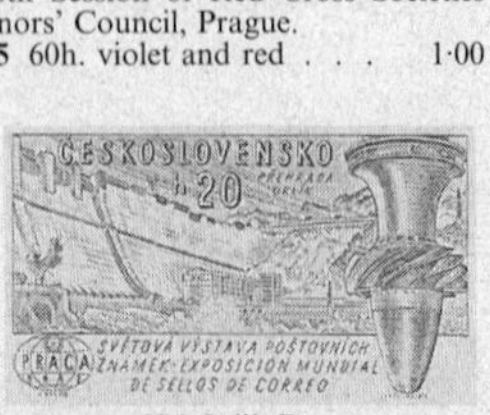

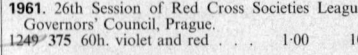

376 Orlik Dam

1961. "Praga 1962" International Stamp Exhibition (2nd and 3rd issues).
1250 376 20h. black and blue . . 80 15
1251 – 30h. blue and red . . . 45 10
1252 – 40h. blue and green . . 80 15
1253 – 60h. slate and bistre . . 80 15
1267 – 1k. purple and green . . 55 50
1254 – 1k.20 green and pink . . 95 50
1268 – 1k.60 brown and violet 95 70
1269 – 2k. black and orange . . 1·50 1·25
1255 – 3k. blue and yellow . . 1·75 50
1256 – 4k. violet and orange . . 2·40 1·25
1270 – 5k. multicoloured . . . 22·00 20·00
DESIGNS—As Type 376: 30h. Prague; 40h. Hluboka Castle from lake; 60h. Karlovy Vary; 1k. Pilsen; 1k.20, North Bohemian landscape; 1k.60, High Tatras; 2k. Iron-works, Ostrava-Kuncice; 3k. Brno; 4k. Bratislava. (50 × 29 mm): 5k. Prague and flags.

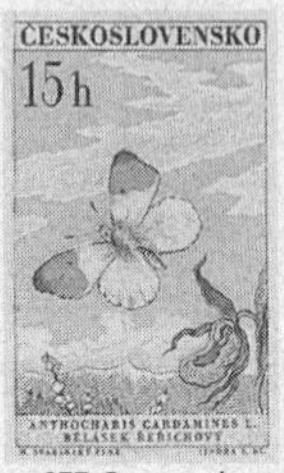

377 Orange-tip

1961. Butterflies and Moths. Multicoloured.
1257 15h. Type 377 . . . . . . 35 10
1258 20h. Southern festoon . . . 50 10
1259 30h. Apollo 90 20
1260 40h. Swallowtail 90 25
1261 60h. Peacock . . . . 1·10 25
1262 80h. Camberwell beauty . . 1·25 25
1263 1k. Clifden's nonpareil . . . 1·25 25
1264 1k.60 Red admiral . . . . 1·40 40
1265 2k. Brimstone . . . . . . 2·75 1·90

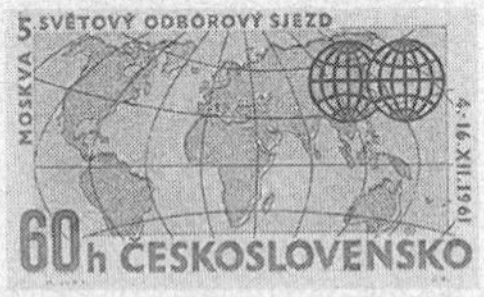

378 Congress Emblem and World Map

1961. 5th W.F.T.U. Congress, Moscow.
1266 378 60h. blue and red . . . 40 10

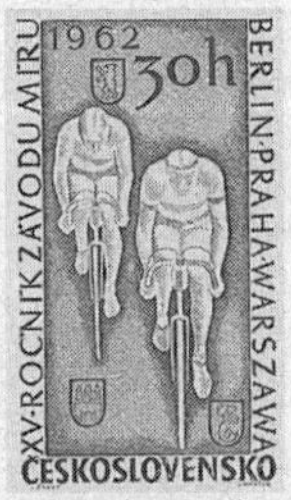

379 Racing Cyclists (Berlin–Prague–Warsaw Cycle Race)

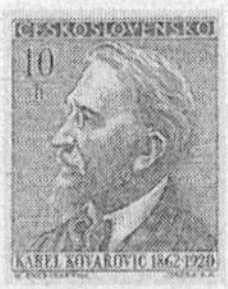

380 K. Kovarovic (composer, centenary of birth)

1962. Sports Events of 1962.
1271 379 30h. black and blue . . 25 10
1272 – 40h. black and yellow . . 20 10
1273 – 60h. grey and blue . . . 30 10
1274 – 1k. black and pink . . . 30 10
1275 – 1k.20 black and green 30 10
1276 – 1k.60 black and green 1·40 75
DESIGNS: 40h. Gymnastics (15th World Gymnastics Championships, Prague); 60h. Figure Skating (World Figure Skating Championships, Prague); 1k. Bowling (World Bowling Championships, Bratislava); 1k.20, Football (World Cup Football Championship, Chile); 1k.60, Throwing the discus (7th European Athletic Championships, Belgrade).
See also No. 1306.

1962. Cultural Celebrities and Anniversaries.
1277 380 10h. brown 10 10
1278 – 20h. blue 10 10
1279 – 30h. brown 10 10
1280 – 40h. purple 15 10
1281 – 60h. black 15 10
1282 – 1k.60 myrtle 40 10
1283 – 1k.80 blue 50 10
DESIGNS—As Type 380: 20h. F. Skroup (composer); 30h. Bozena Nemcova (writer); 60h. Rod of Aesculapius and Prague Castle (Czech Medical Association Cent); 1k.60, L. Celakovsky (founder, Czech Botanical Society). HORIZ: (41 × 22½ mm): 40h. F. Zaviska and K. Petr; 1k.80, M. Valouch and J. Hronec. (These two commemorate Czech Mathematics and Physics Union Cent).

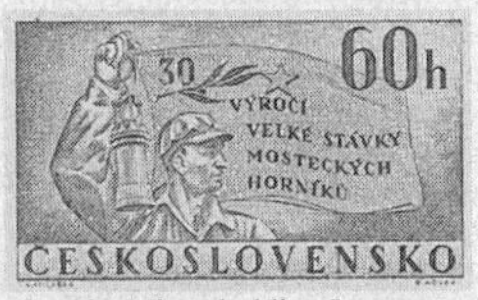

381 Miner holding Lamp

1962. 30th Anniv of Miners' Strike, Most.
1284 381 60h. blue and red . . . 25 10

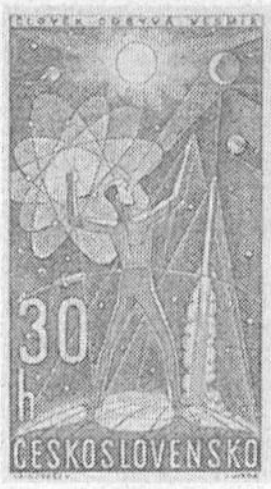
382 "Man Conquers Space"

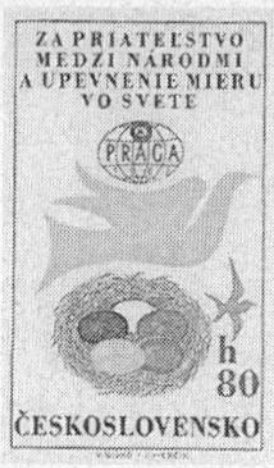
384 Dove and Nest

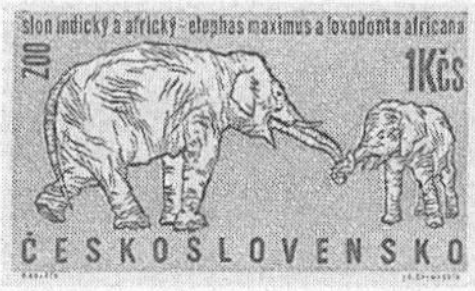
383 Indian and African Elephants

1962. Space Research (2nd series).
1285 **382** 30h. red and blue . . . 25 10
1286 – 40h. blue and orange . . 25 10
1287 – 60h. blue and pink . . . 25 10
1288 – 80h. purple and green . . 60 10
1289 – 1k. blue and yellow . . . 25 25
1290 – 1k.60 green and yellow 1·40 75
DESIGNS—VERT: 40h. Launching of Soviet rocket; 1k. Automatic station on Moon. HORIZ: 60h. "Vostok-II"; 80h. Multi-stage automatic rocket; 1k.60, Television satellite station.

1962. Animals of Prague Zoos.
1291 – 20h. black & turquoise 55 10
1292 – 30h. black and violet . . 55 10
1293 – 60h. black and yellow . . 65 10
1294 **383** 1k. black and green . . 95 10
1295 – 1k.40 black and mauve 1·00 25
1296 – 1k.60 black and brown 2·10 1·25
ANIMALS—VERT: 20h. Polar bear; 30h. Chimpanzee; 60h. Bactrian camel. HORIZ: 1k.40, Leopard; 1k.60, Wild horses.

1962. Air. "Praga 1962" International Stamp Exhibition (4th issue).
1297 **384** 80h. multicoloured . . . 50 25
1298 – 1k.40 red, blue & black 2·00 2·75
1299 – 2k.80 multicoloured . . 3·25 2·75
1300 – 4k.20 multicoloured . . 4·75 2·75
DESIGNS: 1k.40, Dove; 2k.80, Flower and bird; 4k.20, Plant and bird. All designs feature "Praga 62" emblem. The 80h. and 2k.80 are inscr in Slovakian and the others in Czech.

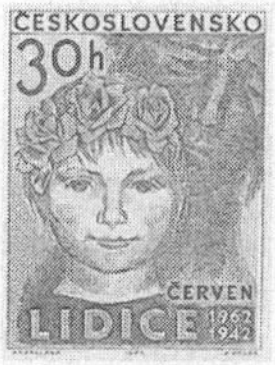
385 Girl of Lidice

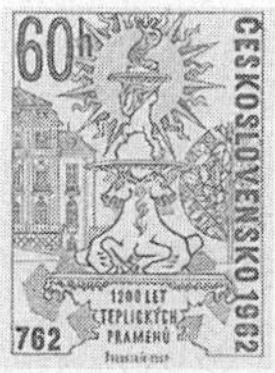
386 Klary's Fountain, Teplice

1962. 20th Anniv of Destruction of Lidice and Lezaky.
1301 **385** 30h. black and red . . . 35 10
1302 – 60h. black and blue . . . 35 10
DESIGN: 60h. Flowers and Lezaky ruins.

1962. 1200th Anniv of Discovery of Teplice Springs.
1303 **386** 60h. green and yellow . . 40 10

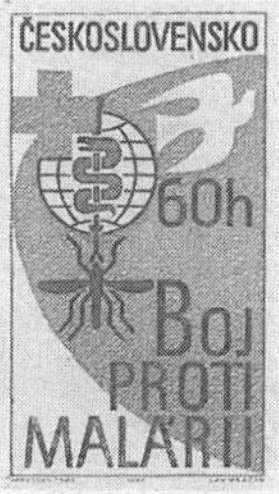
387 Campaign Emblem

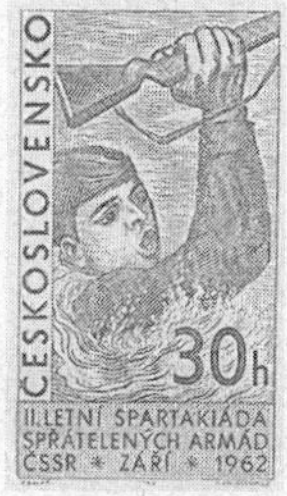
388 Swimmer with Rifle

1962. Malaria Eradication.
1304 **387** 60h. red and black . . . 15 10
1305 – 3k. blue and black . . . 1·25 60
DESIGN: 3k. Campaign emblem and dove (different).

1962. Czechoslovakia's Participation in World Cup Football Championship Final, Chile. As No. 1275 but inscr "CSSR VE FINALE" and new value.
1306 1k.60 green and yellow . . . 1·25 15

1962. 2nd Military Spartacist Games. Inscr as in T **388**.
1307 **388** 30h. myrtle and blue . . 15 10
1308 – 40h. violet and yellow 20 10
1309 – 60h. brown and green . . 25 10
1310 – 1k. blue and red . . . 30 10
DESIGNS: 40h. Soldier mounting obstacle; 60h. Footballer; 1k. Relay Race.

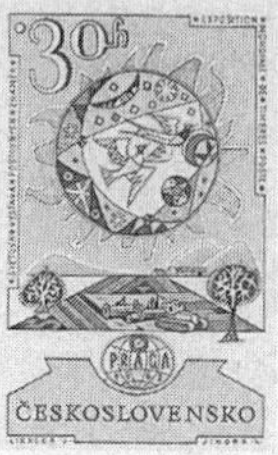
389 "Sun" and Field (Socialized Agriculture)

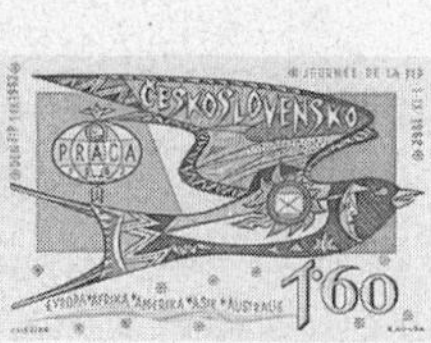
390 Swallow, "Praga 62" and Congress Emblems

1962. "Praga 1962" Int Stamp Exn (5th issue).
1311 **389** 30h. multicoloured . . . 3·00 1·25
1312 – 60h. multicoloured . . . 80 10
1313 – 80h. multicoloured . . . 3·50 2·00
1314 – 1k. multicoloured . . . 3·50 3·00
1315 – 1k.40 multicoloured . . 3·50 3·00
DESIGNS—VERT: 60h. Astronaut in "spaceship"; 1k.40, Children playing under "tree". HORIZ: 80h. Boy with flute, and peace doves; 1k. Workers of three races. All have "Praga 62" emblem.

1962. F.I.P. Day (Federation Internationale de Philatelie).
1316 **390** 1k.60 multicoloured . . 4·75 4·00

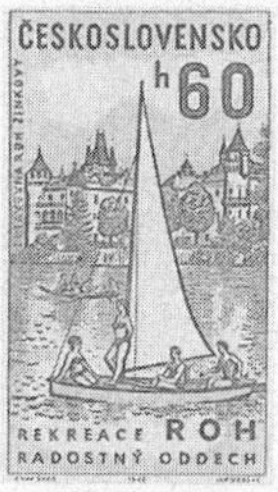
391 Zinkovy Sanatorium and Sailing Dinghy

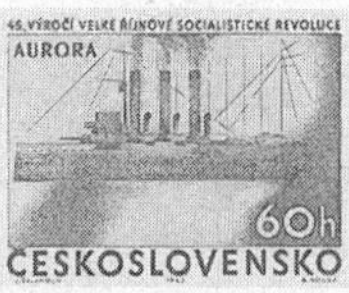
392 Cruiser "Aurora"

1962. Czech Workers' Social Facilities.
1317 – 30h. black and blue . . . 20 10
1318 **391** 60h. sepia and ochre . . 25 10
DESIGN—HORIZ: 30h. Children in day nursery, and factory.

1962. 45th Anniv of Russian Revolution.
1319 **392** 30h. sepia and blue . . . 10 10
1320 60h. black and pink . . 30 10

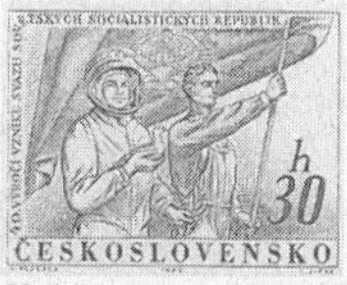
393 Astronaut and Worker

1962. 40th Anniv of U.S.S.R.
1321 **393** 30h. red and blue . . . 30 10
1322 – 60h. black and pink . . 35 10
DESIGN—VERT: 60h. Lenin.

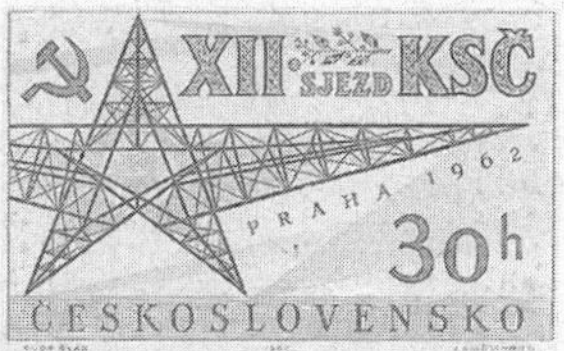
394 Crane ("Building Construction")

1962. 12th Czech Communist Party Congress, Prague
1323 **394** 30h. red and yellow . . 25 10
1324 – 40h. blue and yellow . . 25 10
1325 – 60h. black and pink . . 25 10
DESIGNS—VERT: 40h. Produce ("Agriculture"). HORIZ: 60h. Factory plants ("Industry").

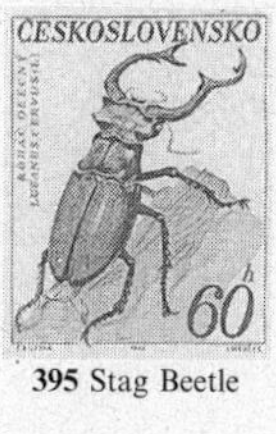
395 Stag Beetle

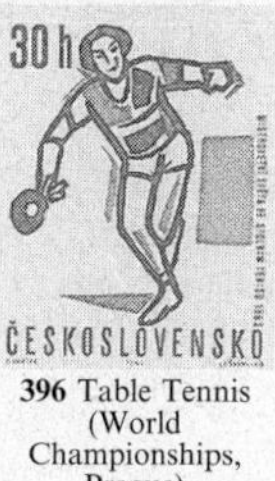
396 Table Tennis (World Championships, Prague)

1962. Beetles. Multicoloured.
1326 20h. Caterpillar-hunter (horiz) 25 10
1327 30h. Cardinal beetle (horiz) 25 10
1328 60h. Type **395** 25 10
1329 1k. Great dung beetle (horiz) 75 10
1330 1k.60 Alpine longhorn beetle 1·10 30
1331 2k. Blue ground beetle . . . 2·75 1·50

1963. Sports Events of 1963.
1332 **396** 30h. black and green . . 25 10
1333 – 60h. black and orange 25 10
1334 – 80h. black and blue . . 25 10
1335 – 1k. black and violet . . 30 10
1336 – 1k.20 black and brown 30 15
1337 – 1k.60 black and red . . 90 15
DESIGNS: 60h. Cycling (80th Anniv of Czech Cycling); 80h. Skiing (1st Czech Winter Games); 1k. Motor-cycle dirt track racing (15th Anniv of "Golden Helmet" Race, Pardubice); 1k.20, Weightlifting (World Championships, Prague); 1k.60, Hurdling (1st Czech Summer Games).

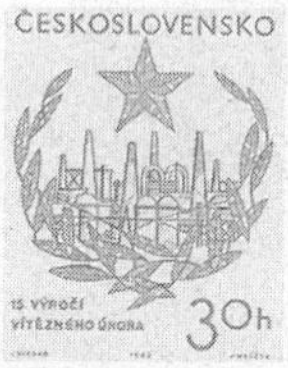
397 Industrial Plant

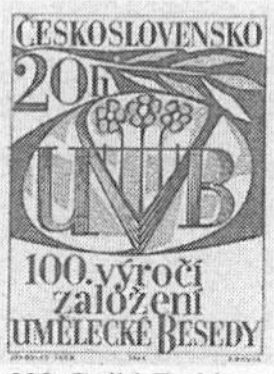
398 Guild Emblem

1963. 15th Anniv of "Victorious February" and 5th T.U. Congress.
1338 **397** 30h. red and blue . . . 15 10
1339 – 60h. red and black . . . 15 10
1340 – 60h. black and red . . . 15 10
DESIGNS—VERT: No. 1339, Sun and campfire. HORIZ: No. 1340, Industrial plant and annual "stepping stones".

1963. Cultural Anniversaries.
1341 **398** 20h. black and blue . . 10 10
1342 – 30h. red 10 10
1343 – 30h. red and blue . . . 10 10
1344 – 60h. black 15 10
1345 – 60h. purple and blue . . 15 10
1346 – 60h. myrtle 15 10
1347 – 1k.60 brown 45 15
DESIGNS—VERT: No. 1341 (Artist's Guild cent); 1342, E. Urx (journalist); 1343, J. Janosik (national hero); 1344, J. Palkovic (author); 1346, Woman with book, and children (cent of Slovak Cultural Society, Slovenska Matice); 1347, M. Svabinsky (artist, after self-portrait). HORIZ: 1345, Allegorical figure and National Theatre, Prague (80th anniv).

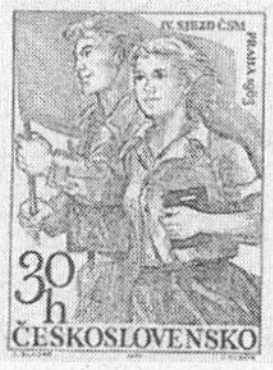
399 Young People

1963. 4th Czech Youth Federation Congress, Prague.
1348 **399** 30h. blue and red . . . 25 10

1963. Space Research (3rd series). As T **364** but inscr "1963" at foot.
1349 30h. purple, red & yellow 15 10
1350 50h. blue and turquoise . . 25 10
1351 60h. turquoise & yellow . . 25 10
1352 1k. black and brown . . . 55 10
1353 1k.60 sepia and green . . . 40 10
1354 2k. violet and yellow . . . 1·60 90
DESIGNS—HORIZ: 30h. Rocket circling Sun; 50h. Rockets and Sputniks leaving Earth; 60h. Spacecraft and Moon; 1k. "Mars 1" rocket and Mars; 1k.60, Rocket heading for Jupiter; 2k. Spacecraft returning from Saturn.

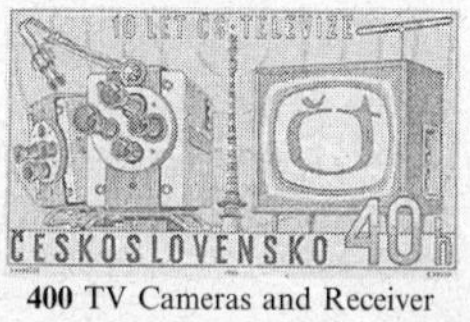
400 TV Cameras and Receiver

1963. 10th Anniv of Czech Television Service. Inscr as in T **400**.
1355 **400** 40h. blue and orange . . 20 10
1356 – 60h. red and blue . . . 20 10
DESIGN—VERT: 60h. TV transmitting aerial.

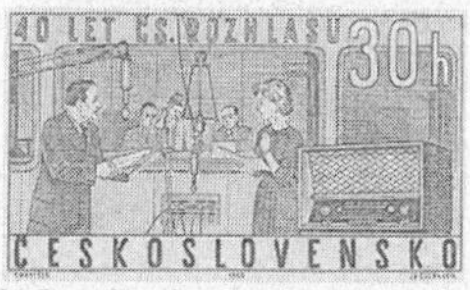
401 Broadcasting Studio and Receiver

1963. 40th Anniv of Czech Radio Service. Inscr as in T **401**.
1357 **401** 30h. purple and blue . . 15 10
1358 – 1k. purple & turquoise 25 10
DESIGN—VERT: 1k. Aerial mast, globe and doves.

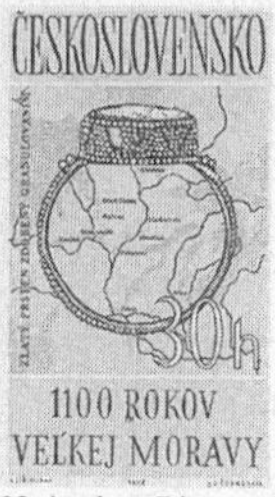
402 Ancient Ring and Moravian Settlements Map

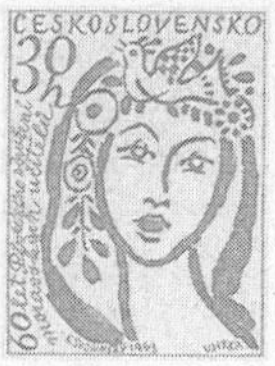
404 Singer

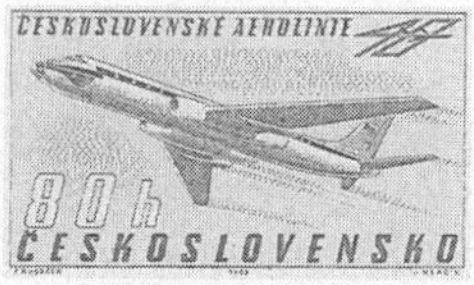
403 Tupolev Tu-104A

1963. 1100th Anniv of Moravian Empire.
1359 **402** 30h. black and green . . 20 10
1360 – 1k.60 black and yellow 40 10
DESIGN: 1k.60, Ancient silver plate showing falconer with hawk.

1963. 40th Anniv of Czech Airlines.
1361 **403** 80h. violet and blue . . 80 10
1362 – 1k.80 blue and green . . 1·50 40
DESIGN: 1k.80, Ilyushin Il-18B.

1963. 60th Anniv of Moravian Teachers' Singing Club.
1363 **404** 30h. red 30 10

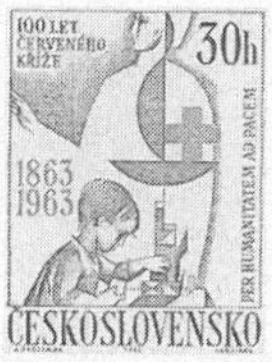
405 Nurse and Child

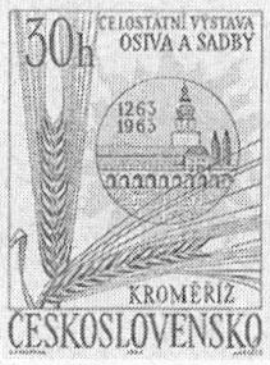
406 Wheatears and Kromeriz Castle

1963. Centenary of Red Cross.
1364 **405** 30h. blue and red . . . 30 10

1963. National Agricultural Exhibition.
1365 **406** 30h. green and yellow . . 30 10

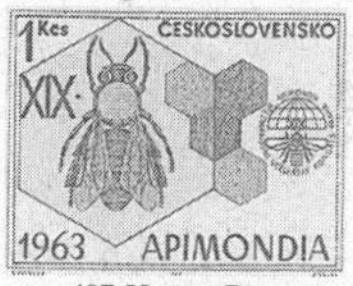
407 Honey Bee, Honeycomb and Congress Emblem

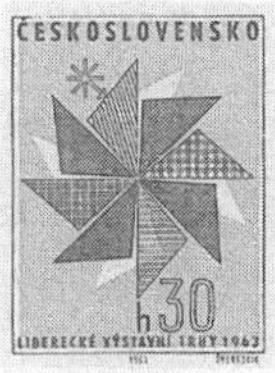
409 "Modern Fashion"

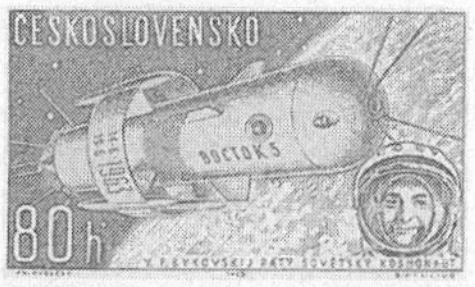
408 "Vostok 5" and Bykovsky

1963. 19th International Bee-keepers' Congress ("Apimondia '63").
1366 **407** 1k. brown and yellow . . 40 10

1963. 2nd "Team" Manned Space Flights.
1367 **408** 80h. pink and blue . . . 35 10
1368 – 2k.80 blue and purple . . 2·25 25
DESIGN: 2k.80, "Vostok 6" and Valentina Tereshkova.

1963. Liberec Consumer Goods Fair.
1369 **409** 30h. black and mauve 30 10

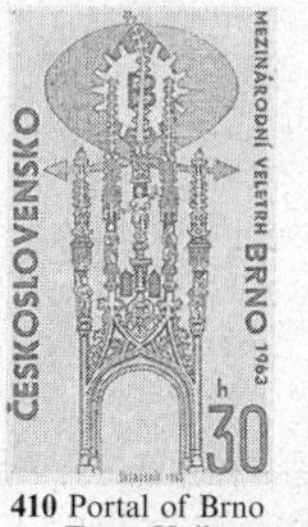
410 Portal of Brno Town Hall

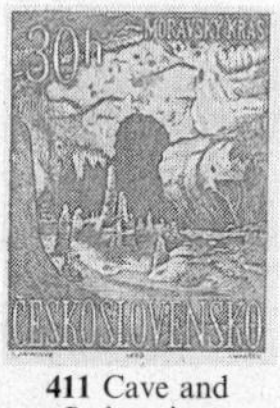
411 Cave and Stalagmites

1963. Brno International Fair.
1370 **410** 30h. purple and blue . . 20 10
1371 – 60h. blue and salmon . . 25 10
DESIGN: 60h. Tower of Brno Town Hall.

1963. Czech Scenery. (a) Moravia.
1372 **411** 30h. brown and blue . . 25 10
1373 – 80h. brown and pink . . 40 10
(b) Slovakia.
1374 – 30h. blue and green . . . 30 10
1375 – 60h. blue, green & yellow 30 10
DESIGNS: No. 1373, Macocha Chasm; 1374, Pool, Hornad Valley; 1375, Waterfall, Great Hawk Gorge.

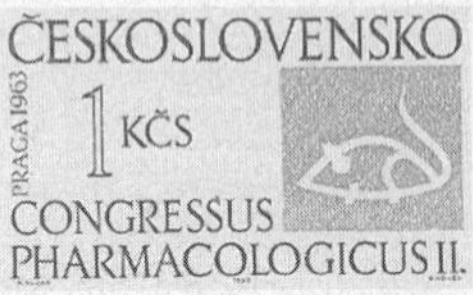

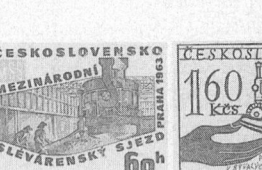

412 Mouse

1963. 2nd International Pharmacological Congress, Prague.
1376 **412** 1k. red and black . . . 40 10

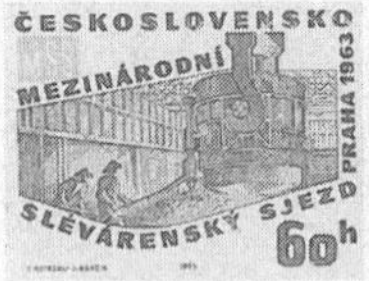

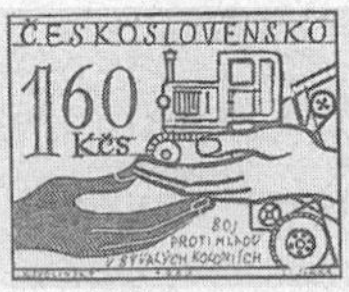

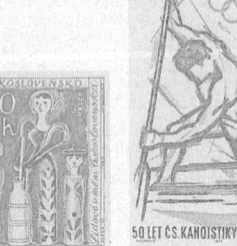

413 Blast Furnace **414** "Aid for Farmers Abroad"

1963. 30th International Foundry Congress, Prague.
1377 **413** 60h. black and blue . . 25 10

1963. Freedom from Hunger.
1378 **414** 1k.60 sepia 45 10

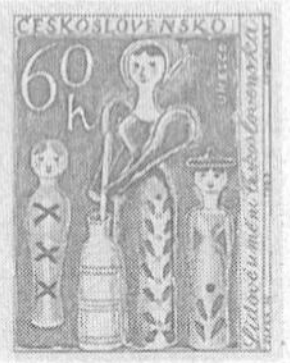

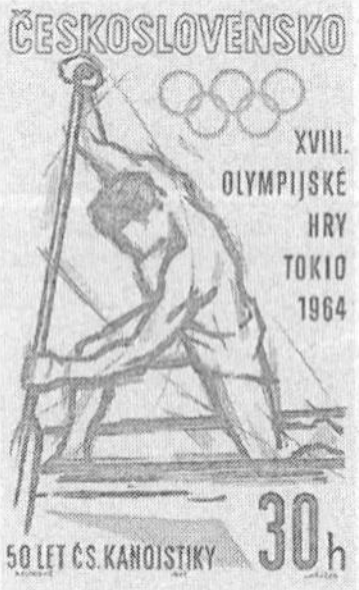

415 Dolls **416** Canoeing

1963. U.N.E.S.C.O. Folk Art. Multicoloured.
1379 60h. Type **415** 20 10
1380 80h. Rooster 25 10
1381 1k. Vase of flowers 35 20
1382 1k.20 Detail of glass-painting "Janosik and his Men" 35 10
1383 1k.60 Stag 35 10
1384 2k. Horseman . . . . 2·75 70

1963. Olympic Games, Tokyo, 1964, and 50th Anniv of Czech Canoeing (30h.).
1385 **416** 30h. blue and green . . 30 10
1386 – 40h. brown and blue . . 30 10
1387 – 60h. lake and yellow . . 25 10
1388 – 80h. violet and red . . . 30 15
1389 – 1k. blue and red 30 15
1390 – 1k.60 ultram & blue . . 1·50 75
DESIGNS: 40h. Volleyball; 60h. Wrestling; 80h. Basketball; 1k. Boxing; 1k.60, Gymnastics.

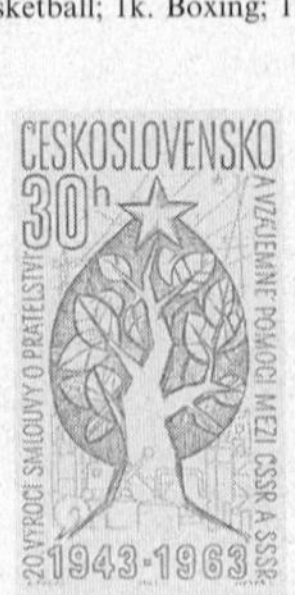

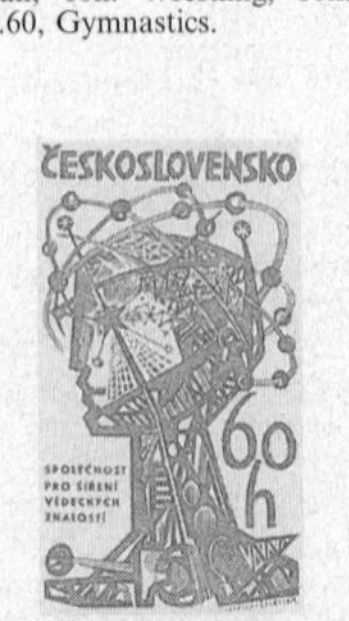

417 Linden Tree **418** "Human Reason and Technology."

1963. 20th Anniv of Czech–Soviet Treaty of Friendship.
1391 **417** 30h. brown and blue . . 15 10
1392 – 60h. red and green . . . 15 10
DESIGN: 60h. Hammer and sickle, and star.

1963. Technical and Scientific Knowledge Society Congress.
1393 **418** 60h. violet 35 10

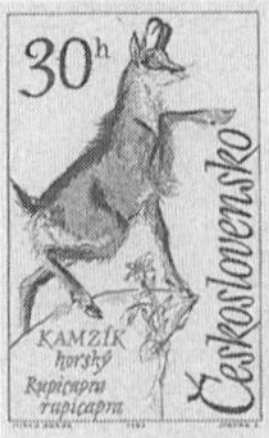

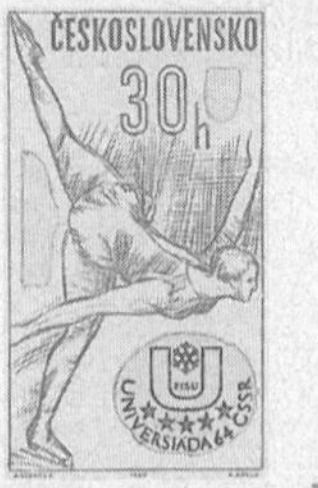

419 Chamois **420** Figure Skating

1963. Mountain Animals.
1394 **419** 30h. multicoloured . . . 65 20
1395 – 40h. multicoloured . . . 65 35
1396 – 60h. sepia, yellow & grn 1·00 25
1397 – 1k.20 multicoloured . . 1·00 20
1398 – 1k.60 multicoloured . . 1·40 35
1399 – 2k. brown, orge & grn 4·00 2·00
ANIMALS: 40h. Ibex; 60h. Mouflon; 1k.20, Roe deer; 1k.60, Fallow deer; 2k. Red deer.

1964. Sports Events of 1964.
1400 **420** 30h. violet and yellow 25 10
1401 – 80h. blue and orange . . 25 10
1402 – 1k. brown and lilac . . . 75 15
DESIGNS—VERT: 30h. Type **420** (Czech Students' Games); 1k. Handball (World Handball Championships). HORIZ: 80h. Cross-country skiing (Students' Games).

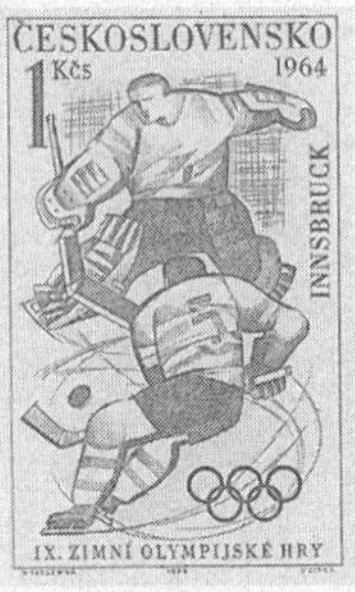

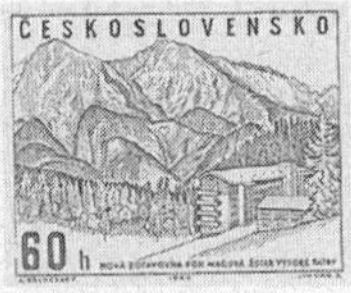

421 Ice Hockey **423** Magura Hotel, Zdiar, High Tatra

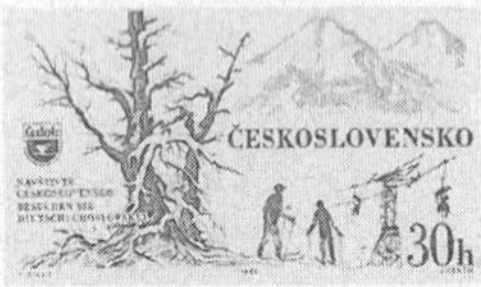

422 Belanske Tatra Mountains, Skiers and Tree

1964. Winter Olympic Games, Innsbruck.
1403 **421** 1k. purple and turquoise 75 40
1404 – 1k.80 green & lavender 1·00 60
1405 – 2k. blue and green . . . 2·50 2·40
DESIGNS—VERT: 1k.80, Tobogganing. HORIZ: 2k. Ski jumping.

1964. Tourist Issue.
1406 **422** 30h. purple and blue . . 20 10
1407 – 60h. blue and red . . . 30 10
1408 – 1k. brown and olive . . 55 10
1409 – 1k.80 green and orange 1·00 30
DESIGNS: 60h. Telc (Moravia) and motorcamp; 1k. Spis Castle (Slovakia) and angler; 1k.80, Cesky Krumlov (Bohemia) and sailing dinghies. Each design includes a tree.

1964. Trade Union Recreation Hotels.
1410 **423** 60h. green and yellow . . 20 10
1411 – 80h. blue and pink . . . 20 10
DESIGN: 80h. "Slovak Insurrection" Hotel, Lower Tatra.

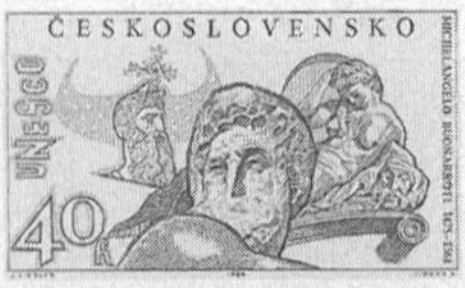

424 Statuary (after Michelangelo)

1964. U.N.E.S.C.O. Cultural Anniversaries.
1412 **424** 40h. black and green . . 20 10
1413 – 60h. black and red . . . 20 10
1414 – 1k. black and blue . . . 40 10
1415 – 1k.60 black and yellow 40 10
DESIGNS—HORIZ: 40h. Type **424** (400th death anniv of Michelangelo); 60h. Bottom, "Midsummer Night's Dream" (400th birth anniv of Shakespeare); 1k.60, King George of Podebrady (500th anniv of his mediation in Europe). VERT: 1k. Galileo Galilei (400th birth anniv).

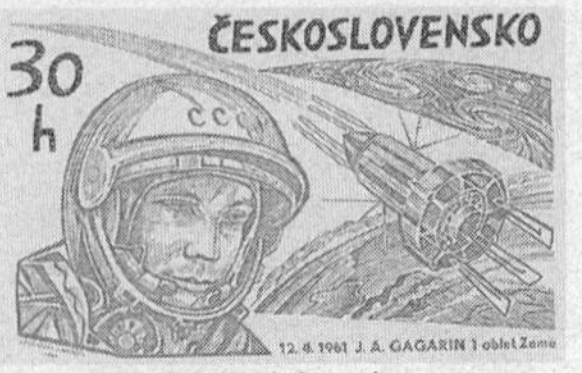

425 Yuri Gagarin

1964. "Space Exploration". On cream paper.
1416 **425** 30h. blue and black . . 50 25
1417 – 60h. red and green . . . 25 10
1418 – 80h. violet and lake . . 50 20
1419 – 1k. violet and blue . . . 75 25
1420 – 1k.20 bronze and red . . 50 25
1421 – 1k.40 turq & black . . . 1·10 65
1422 – 1k.60 turq & violet . . . 3·25 1·40
1423 – 2k. red and blue 75 30
ASTRONAUTS—HORIZ: 60h. Titov; 80h. Glenn; 1k.20, Popovich and Nikolaev. VERT: 1k. Carpenter; 1k.40, Schirra; 1k.60, Cooper; 2k. Tereshkova and Bykovsky.

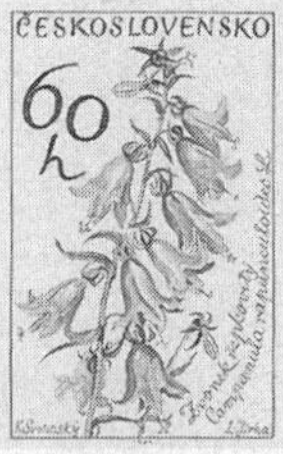

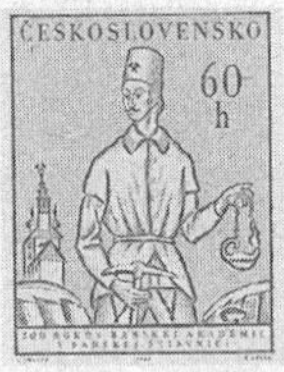

426 Campanula **427** Miner of 1764

1964. Wild Flowers.
1424 **426** 60h. purple, orge & grn 1·50 20
1425 – 80h. multicoloured . . . 1·50 20
1426 – 1k. blue, pink & green 1·50 40
1427 – 1k.20 multicoloured . . 60 25
1428 – 1k.60 violet & green . . 80 40
1429 – 2k. red, turq & violet . . 4·75 2·00
FLOWERS: 80h. Musk thistle; 1k. Chicory; 1k.20, Yellow iris; 1k.60, Marsh gentian; 2k. Common poppy.

1964. Czech Anniversaries.
1430 – 30h. black and yellow . . 25 10
1431 – 60h. red and blue . . . 50 10
1432 **427** 60h. sepia and green . . 25 10
DESIGNS—HORIZ: (30½ × 22½ mm): 30h. Silesian coat of arms (stylized) (150th Anniv of Silesian Museum, Opava). (41½ × 23 mm): 60h. (No. 1431), Skoda ASC-16 fire engine (Centenary of Voluntary Fire Brigades); 60h. (No. 1432), (Bicentenary of Banska Stiavnica Mining School).

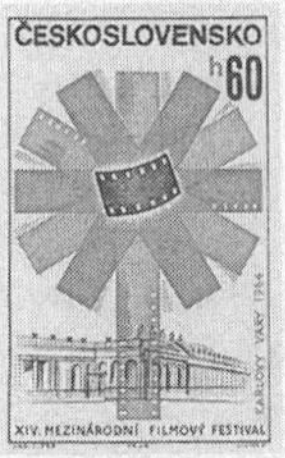

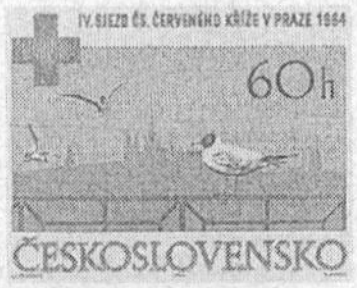

428 Cine-film "Flower" **429** Hradcany, Praque and Black-headed Gulls

1964. 14th Int Film Festival, Karlovy Vary.
1433 **428** 60h. black, blue & red 1·60 10

1964. 4th Czech Red Cross Congress, Prague.
1434 **429** 60h. violet and red . . . 45 10

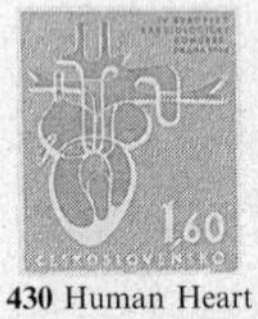

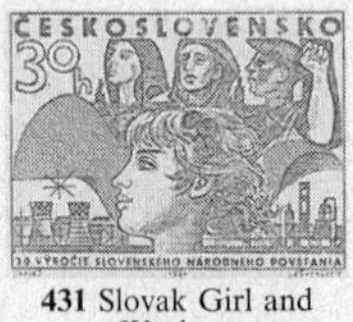

430 Human Heart **431** Slovak Girl and Workers

1964. 4th European Cardiological Congress, Prague.
1435 **430** 1k.60 red and blue . . . 95 10

1964. 20th Anniv of Slovak Rising and Dukla Battles.
1436 **431** 30h. red and brown . . 10 10
1437 – 60h. blue and red . . . 10 10
1438 – 60h. sepia and red . . 10 10
DESIGNS: No. 1437, Armed Slovaks; 1438, Soldiers in battle at Dukla Pass.

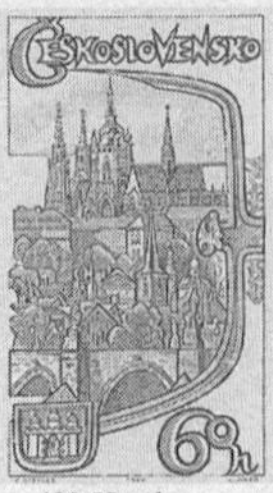

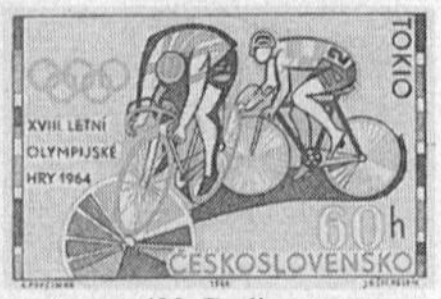

432 Hradcany, Prague **433** Cycling

1964. Millenary of Prague.
1439 **432** 60h. brown & mauve . . 40 10

1964. Olympic Games, Tokyo. Multicoloured.
1440 60h. Type **433** 40 10
1441 80h. Throwing the discus and pole vaulting (vert) 45 15
1442 1k. Football (vert) 45 15
1443 1k.20 Rowing (vert) 60 25
1444 1k.60 Swimming 95 30
1445 2k.80 Weightlifting . . . . 4·25 1·75

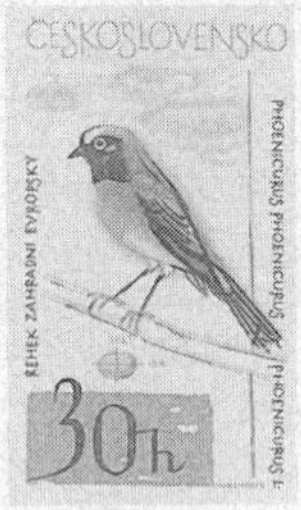

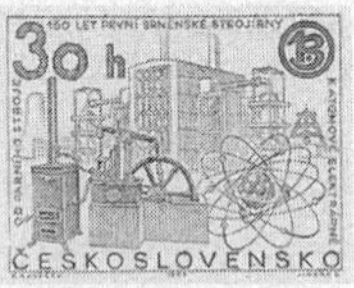

434 Common Redstart **435** Brno Engineering Works (150th Anniv)

1964. Birds. Multicoloured.
1446 30h. Type **434** 35 10
1447 60h. Green woodpecker . . 65 10
1448 80h. Hawfinch 95 20
1449 1k. Black woodpecker . . . 95 35
1450 1k.20 European robin . . . 95 45
1451 1k.60 Eurasian roller . . . 1·50 80

1964. Czech Engineering.
1452 **435** 30h. brown 10 10
1453 – 60h. green and salmon 25 10
DESIGN: 60h. Class T334.0 diesel-hydraulic shunter.

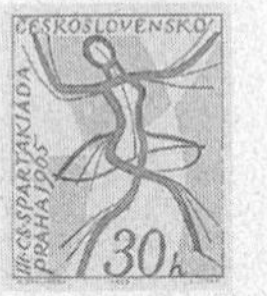

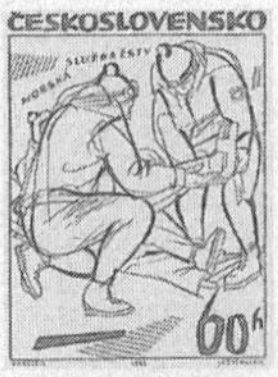

436 "Dancing Girl" **437** Mountain Rescue Service (10th Anniv)

1965. 3rd National Spartacist Games.
1454 **436** 30h. red and blue . . . 10 10
See also Nos. 1489/92.

1965. Sports Events of 1965.
1455 **437** 60h. violet and blue . . 20 10
1456 – 60h. lake and orange . . 20 10
1457 – 60h. green and red . . . 20 10
1458 – 60h. green and yellow . . 20 10
SPORTS: No. 1456, Exercising with hoop (1st World Artistic Gymnastics Championships, Prague); 1457, Cycling (World Indoor Cycling Championships, Prague); 1458, Hurdling (Czech University Championships, Brno).

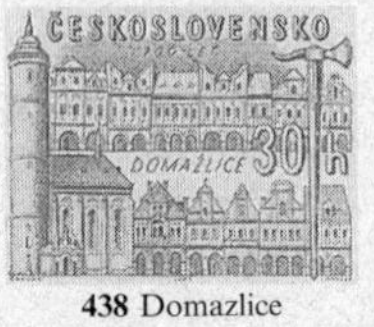

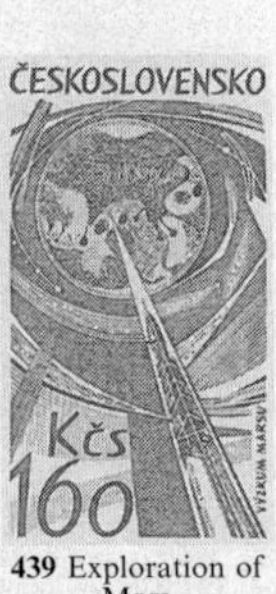

438 Domazlice **439** Exploration of Mars

1965. 700th Annivs of Six Czech Towns, and 20th Anniv of Terezin Concentration Camp (No. 1465).
1459 **438** 30h. violet and yellow . . 20 10
1460 – 30h. violet and blue . . 20 10
1461 – 30h. blue and olive . . . 20 10
1462 – 30h. sepia and olive . . 20 10
1463 – 30h. green and buff . . . 20 10
1464 – 30h. slate and drab . . . 20 10
1465 – 30h. red and black . . . 20 10
TOWNS: No. 1460, Beroun; 1461, Zatec; 1462, Policka; 1463, Lipnik and Becvou; 1464, Frydek-Mistek; 1465, Terezin concentration camp.

1965. Int Quiet Sun Years and Space Research.
1466 – 20h. purple and red . . 25 10
1467 – 30h. yellow and red . . 25 10

1468 – 60h. blue and yellow . . 25 10
1469 – 1k. violet & turquoise . . 50 10
1470 – 1k.40 slate and salmon 50 25
1471 **439** 1k.60 black and pink . . 50 25
1472 – 2k. blue & turquoise . . 1·40 1·50
DESIGNS—HORIZ: 20h. Maximum sun-spot activity; 30h. Minimum sun-spot activity ("Quiet Sun"); 60h. Moon exploration; 1k.40, Artificial satellite and space station; 2k. Soviet "Kosmos" and U.S. "Tiros" satellites. VERT: 1k. Space-ships rendezvous.

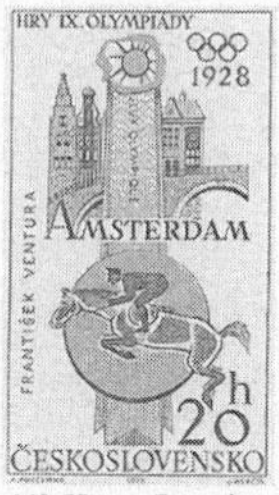

440 Horse Jumping (Amsterdam, 1928)

1965. Czechoslovakia's Olympic Victories.
1473 **440** 20h. brown and gold . . 20 10
1474 – 30h. violet and green . . 20 10
1475 – 60h. blue and gold . . . 20 10
1476 – 1k. brown and gold . . 40 20
1477 – 1k.40 green and gold . . 85 65
1478 – 1k.60 black and gold . . 85 65
1479 – 2k. red and gold 85 25
DESIGNS (each with city feature): 30h. Throwing the discus (Paris, 1900); 60h. Marathon (Helsinki, 1952); 1k. Weightlifting (Los Angeles, 1932); 1k.40, Gymnastics (Berlin, 1936); 1k.60, Rowing (Rome, 1960); 2k. Gymnastics (Tokyo, 1964).

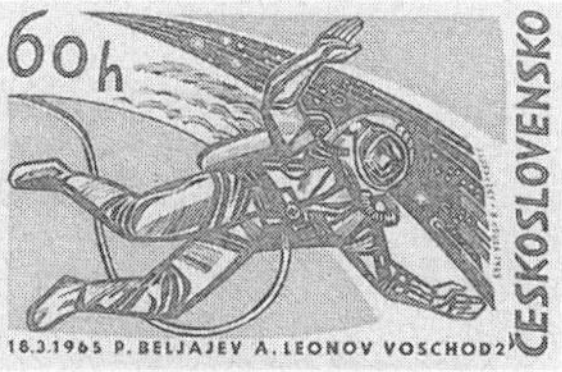

441 Leonov in Space

1965. Space Achievements.
1480 **441** 60h. purple and blue . . 15 20
1481 – 60h. blue and mauve . . 15 20
1482 – 3k. purple and blue . . . 1·40 1·10
1483 – 3k. blue and mauve . . 1·40 1·10
DESIGNS: No. 1481, Grissom, Young and "Gemini 3"; 1482, Leonov leaving spaceship "Voskhod 2"; 1483, "Gemini 3" on launching pad at Cape Kennedy.

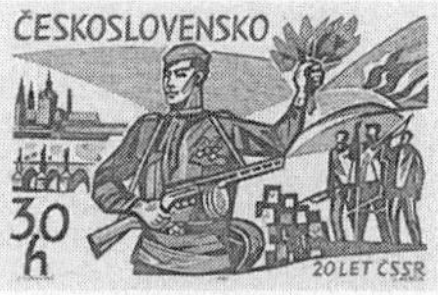

442 Soldier

1965. 20th Anniv of Liberation. Inscr "20 LET CSSR".
1484 **442** 30h. olive, black & red 20 10
1485 – 30h. violet, blue & red 20 10
1486 – 60h. black, red & blue 25 10
1487 – 1k. violet, brown & orge 50 15
1488 – 1k.60 multicoloured . . 80 45
DESIGNS: 30h. (No. 1485), Workers; 60h. Mechanic; 1k. Building worker; 1k.60, Peasant.

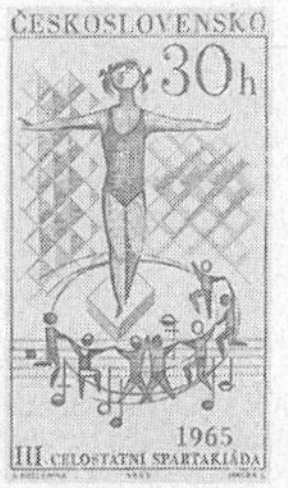

443 Children's Exercises

1965. 3rd National Spartacist Games.
1489 **443** 30h. blue and red . . . 15 10
1490 – 60h. brown and blue . . 20 10
1491 – 1k. blue and yellow . . 30 10
1492 – 1k.60 red and brown . . 35 30
DESIGNS: 60h. Young gymnasts; 1k. Women's exercises; 1k.60, Start of race.

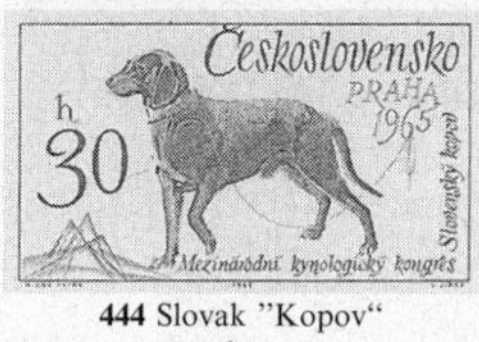

444 Slovak "Kopov"

1965. Canine Events.
1493 **444** 30h. black and red . . . 40 10
1494 – 40h. black & yellow . . 40 10
1495 – 60h. black and red . . . 50 10
1496 – 1k. black and red . . . 90 10
1497 – 1k.60 black & yellow . . 60 25
1498 – 2k. black and orange . . . 2·10 1·25
DOGS: 30h. Type **444**; 1k. Poodle (Int Dog-breeders' Congress, Prague); 40h. German sheepdog; 60h. Czech "fousek" (retriever), (both World Dog Exn, Brno); 1k.60, Czech terrier; 2k. Afghan hound (both Plenary Session of F.C.I.—Int Federation of Cynology, Prague).

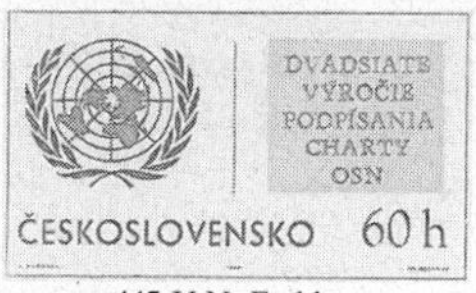

445 U.N. Emblem

1965. U.N. Commem and Int Co-operation Year.
1499 **445** 60h. brown & yellow . . 20 10
1500 – 1k. blue and turquoise 45 10
1501 – 1k.60 red and gold . . . 45 45
DESIGNS: 60h. T **445** (The inscr reads "Twentieth Anniversary of the signing of the U.N. Charter"); 1k. U.N. Headquarters ("20th Anniv of U.N."); 1k.60, I.C.Y. emblem.

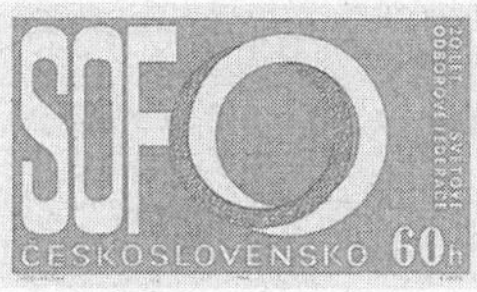

446 "SOF" and Linked Rings

1965. 20th Anniv of World Federation of Trade Unions.
1502 **446** 60h. red and blue . . . 35 10

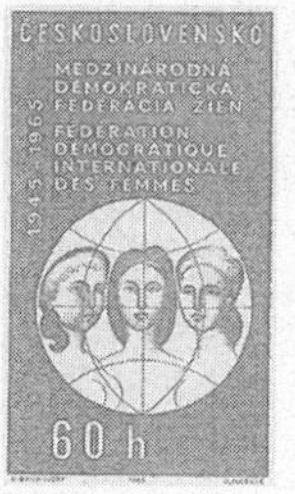

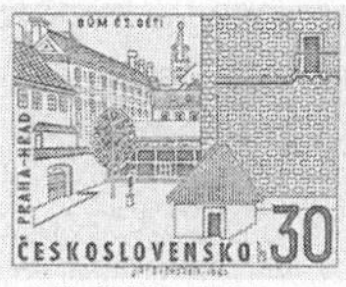

447 Women of Three Races **448** Children's House

1965. 20th Anniv of International Democratic Women's Federation.
1503 **447** 60h. blue 35 10

1965. Prague Castle (1st series). Inscr "PRAHA HRAD".
1504 **448** 30h. green 20 10
1505 – 60h. sepia 25 10
DESIGN—VERT: 60h. Mathias Gate.
See also Nos. 1572/3, 1656/7, 1740/1, 1827/8, 1892/3, 1959/60, 2037/8, 2103/4, 2163/4, 2253/4, 2305/6, 2337/8, 2404/5, 2466/7, 2543/4, 2599/2600, 2637/8, 2685/6, 2739/40, 2803/4, 2834/5, 2878/9, 2950/1, 2977/8 and 3026/7.

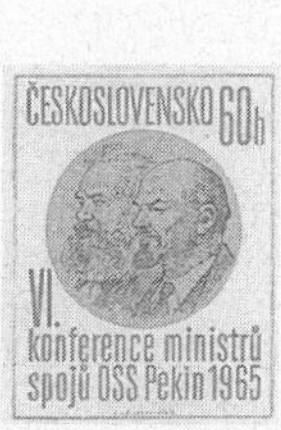

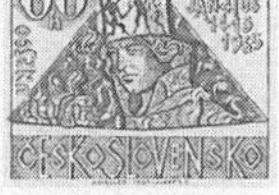

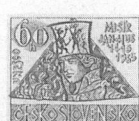

449 Marx and Lenin **450** Jan Hus

1965. 6th Organization of Socialist Countries' Postal Ministers Conference, Peking.
1506 **449** 60h. red and gold . . . 25 10

1965. Various Anniversaries and Events (1st issue).
1507 **450** 60h. black and red . . . 25 10
1508 – 60h. blue and red . . . 25 10
1509 – 60h. lilac and gold . . . 25 10
1510 – 1k. blue and orange . . 30 10
DESIGNS—VERT: No. 1507, T **450** (reformer, 550th death anniv); 1508, G. J. Mendel (publication cent in Brno of his study of heredity). HORIZ: (30½ × 23 mm): No. 1509, Jewellery emblems ("Jablonec 65" Jewellery Exn); 1510, Early telegraph and telecommunications satellite (I.T.U. cent).

1965. Various Anniversaries and Events (2nd issue).
1512 30h. black and green . . . 15 10
1513 30h. black and brown . . 15 10
1514 60h. black and red 20 10
1515 60h. brown on cream . . . 20 10
1516 1k. black and orange . . . 20 10
DESIGNS—As Type **450**. HORIZ: No. 1512, L. Stur (nationalist, 150th birth anniv); 1513, J. Navratil (painter, death cent). VERT: No. 1514, B. Martinu (composer, 75th birth anniv). LARGER—VERT: (23½ × 30½ mm): No. 1515, Allegoric figure (Academia Istropolitana, Bratislava, 500th anniv). HORIZ: (30 × 22½ mm): No. 1516, Emblem (IUPAC Macromolecular Symposium, Prague).

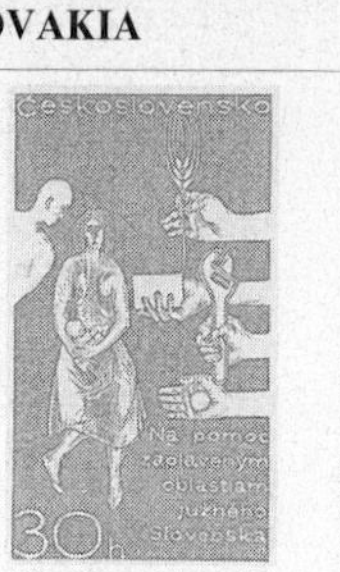

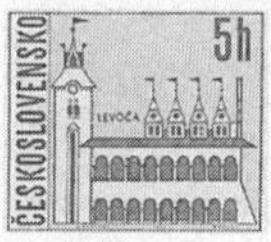

452 "Fourfold Aid" **454** Levoca

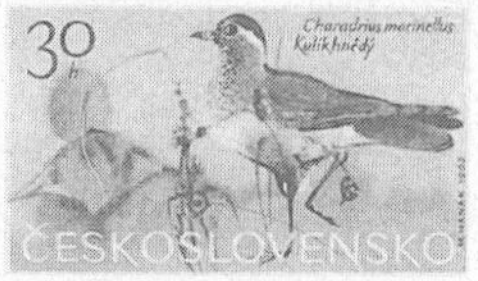

453 Dotterel

1965. Flood Relief.
1517 **452** 30h. blue 15 10
1518 – 2k. black and olive . . . 70 45
DESIGN—HORIZ: 2k. Rescue by boat.

1965. Mountain Birds. Multicoloured.
1519 30h. Type **453** 60 10
1520 60h. Wallcreeper (vert) . . . 60 10
1521 1k.20 Redpoll 65 30
1522 1k.40 Golden eagle (vert) . . 1·10 30
1523 1k.60 Ring ousel 95 40
1524 2k. Spotted nutcracker (vert) 2·10 1·60

1965. Czech Towns. (a) Size 23 × 19 mm.
1525 **454** 5h. black and yellow . . 10 10
1526 – 10h. blue and bistre . . 15 10
1527 – 20h. sepia and blue . . . 10 10
1528 – 30h. blue and green . . 15 10
1529 – 40h. sepia and blue . . . 15 10
1530 – 50h. black and buff . . . 20 10
1531 – 60h. red and blue . . . 25 10
1532 – 1k. violet and green . . 30 10

(b) Size 30½ × 23½ mm.
1533 – 1k.20 olive and blue . . . 25 10
1534 – 1k.60 blue and yellow . . . 45 10
1535 – 2k. bronze and green . . . 55 10
1536 – 3k. purple & yellow . . . 70 10
1537 – 5k. black and pink . . . . 1·25 10
TOWNS: 10h. Jindrichuv Hradec; 20h. Nitra; 30h. Kosice; 40h. Hradec Kralove; 50h. Telc; 60h. Ostrava; 1k. Olomouc; 1k.20, Ceske Budejovice; 1k.60, Cheb; 2k. Brno; 3k. Bratislava; 5k. Prague.

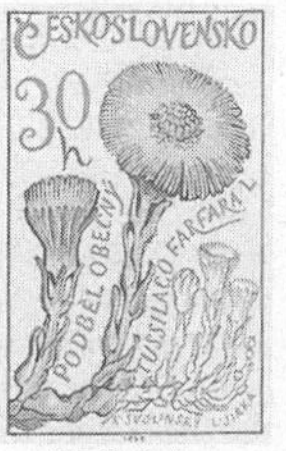

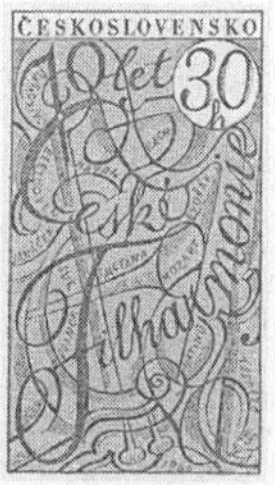

455 Coltsfoot **457** "Music"

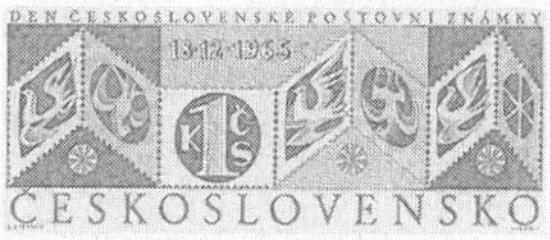

456 Panorama of "Stamps"

1965. Medicinal Plants. Multicoloured.
1538 30h. Type **455** 25 10
1539 60h. Meadow saffron . . . 45 10
1540 80h. Common poppy . . . 50 10
1541 1k. Foxglove 60 15
1542 1k.20 Arnica . . . . 1·00 25
1543 1k.60 Cornflower 75 35
1544 2k. Dog rose . . . . 3·00 1·50

1965. Stamp Day.
1545 **456** 1k. red and green . . . 3·75 3·50

1966. 70th Anniv of Czech Philharmonic Orchestra.
1546 **457** 30h. black and gold . . 50 25

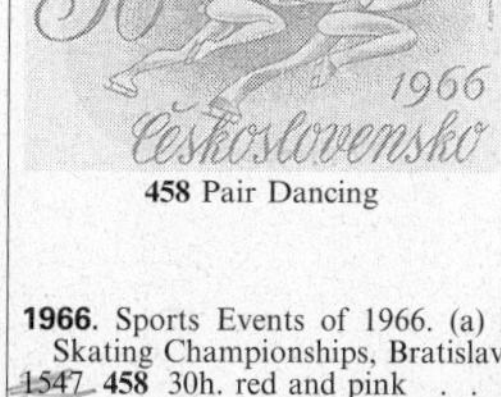

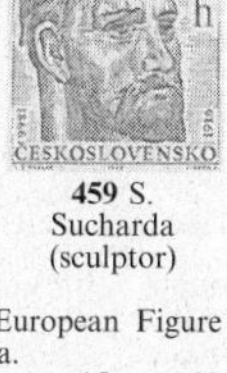

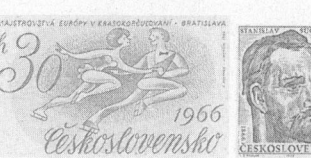

458 Pair Dancing **459** S. Sucharda (sculptor)

1966. Sports Events of 1966. (a) European Figure Skating Championships, Bratislava.
1547 **458** 30h. red and pink . . . 15 10
1548 – 60h. emerald and green 20 10
1549 – 1k.60 brown & yellow 40 10
1550 – 2k. blue and turquoise 2·50 45
DESIGNS: 60h. Male skater leaping; 1k.60, Female skater leaping; 2k. Pair-skaters taking bows.

(b) World Volleyball Championships, Prague.
1551 – 60h. red and buff 20 10
1552 – 1k. violet and blue 25 10
DESIGNS—VERT: 60h. Player leaping to ball; 1k. Player falling.

1966. Cultural Anniversaries.
1553 **459** 30h. green 10 10
1554 – 30h. blue 10 10
1555 – 60h. red 15 10
1556 – 60h. brown 15 10
PORTRAITS: No. 1553, Type **459** (birth centenary); 1554, Ignac J. Pesina (veterinary surgeon, birth bicentenary); 1555, Romain Rolland (writer, birth centenary); 1556, Donatello (sculptor, 500th death anniv).

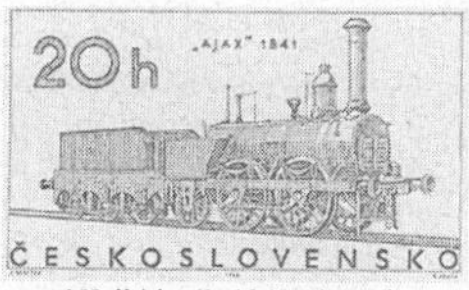

460 "Ajax", 1841, Austria

1966. Railway Locomotives.
1557 **460** 20h. brown on cream . . 50 10
1558 – 30h. violet on cream . . 50 10
1559 – 60h. purple on cream . . 50 15
1560 – 1k. blue on cream . . . 90 20
1561 – 1k.60 blue on cream . . 1·00 20
1562 – 2k. red on cream . . . . 4·00 1·60
LOCOMOTIVES: 30h. "Karlstejn", 1865; 60h. Class 423.0 steam locomotive, 1946; 1k. Class 498.0 steam locomotive, 1946; 1k.60, Class S699.0 electric locomotive, 1964; 2k. Class T699.0 diesel locomotive, 1964.

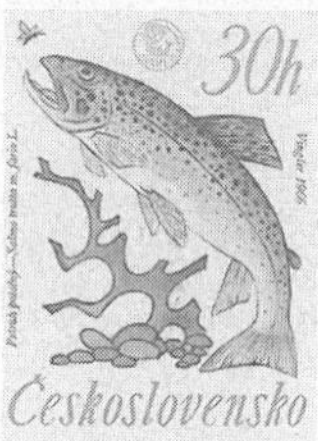

462 Brown Trout

1966. World Angling Championships, Svit. Mult.
1564 30h. Type **462** 30 10
1565 60h. Eurasian perch (horiz) 50 10
1566 1k. Common (Mirror) carp (horiz) 65 10
1567 1k.20 Northern pike (horiz) 65 20
1568 1k.40 European grayling (horiz) . . . . 1·00 30
1569 1k.60 European eel (horiz) 3·00 1·25

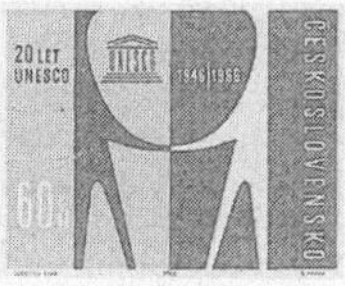

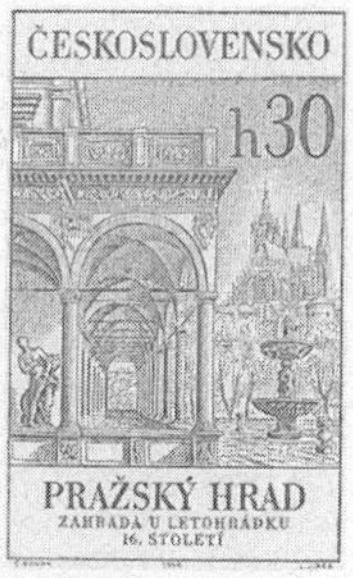

463 "Solidarity of Mankind" **465** Belvedere Palace

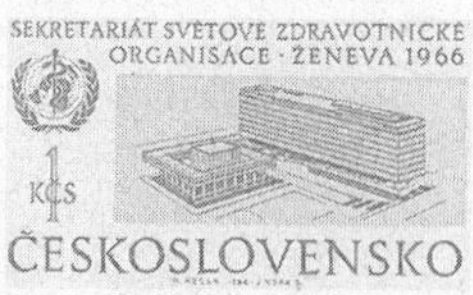

464 W.H.O. Building

1966. 20th Anniv of U.N.E.S.C.O.
1570 **463** 60h. black and yellow . . 25 10

1966. Inaug of W.H.O. Headquarters, Geneva.
1571 **464** 1k. ultramarine and blue 45 10

1966. Prague Castle (2nd series).
1572 **465** 30h. blue 20 10
1573 – 60h. black and yellow . . 35 15
DESIGN: 60h. Wood triptych, "Virgin and Child" (St. George's Church).
See also Nos. 1656/7 and 1740/1.

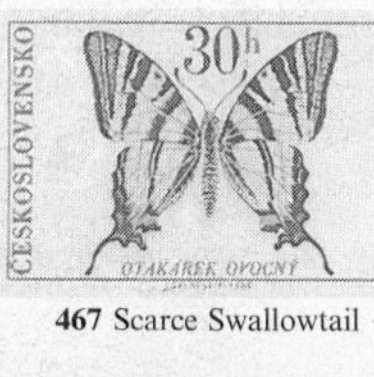

467 Scarce Swallowtail

1966. Butterflies and Moths. Multicoloured.
1575 30h. Type 467 . . . . . . 35 10
1576 60h. Moorland clouded
yellow 60 10
1577 80h. Lesser purple emperor 60 15
1578 1k. Apollo 60 25
1579 1k.20 Scarlet tiger moth . . 1·25 35
1580 2k. Cream-spot tiger moth 4·00 2·00

468 Flags

1966. 13th Czechoslovakian Communist Party
Congress.
1581 **468** 30h. red and blue . . . 15 10
1582 – 60h. red and blue . . . 15 10
1583 – 1k.60 red and blue . . 50 10
DESIGNS: 60h. Hammer and sickle; 1k.60, Girl.

469 Indian Village

1966. "North American Indians". Centenary of
Naprstek's Ethnographic Museum, Prague.
1584 **469** 20h. blue and orange . . 20 10
1585 – 30h. black and brown . . 20 10
1586 – 40h. sepia and blue . . 20 10
1587 – 60h. green and yellow . . 25 10
1588 – 1k. purple and green . . 35 10
1589 – 1k.20 blue and mauve . . 50 20
1590 – 1k.40 multicoloured . . 1·25 75
DESIGNS—VERT: 30h. Tomahawk; 40h. Haida
totem poles; 60h. Katchina, "good spirit" of Hopi
tribe; 1k.20, Dakote calumet (pipe of peace); 1k.40,
Dakota Indian chief. HORIZ: 1k. Hunting American
bison.

470 Atomic Symbol

1966. Centenary of Czech Chemical Society.
1591 **470** 60h. black and blue . . 35 10

471 "Guernica", after Picasso (½-size
illustration)

1966. 30th Anniv of International Brigade's War
Service in Spain.
1592 **471** 60h. black and blue . . 1·75 1·75

474 "Atomic Age" **475** Olympic Coin

1966. Jachymov (source of pitch-blende).
1598 **474** 60h. black and red . . . 35 10

1966. 70th Anniv of Olympic Committee.
1599 **475** 60h. black and gold . . 20 10
1600 – 1k. blue and red . . . 80 30
DESIGN: 1k. Olympic flame and rings.

476 Missile Carrier, Tank and
Mikoyan Gurevich MiG-21D Fighter

1966. Military Manoeuvres.
1601 **476** 60h. black and yellow . . 35 10

477 Moravian Silver **480** Eurasian badger
Thaler (reverse and
obverse)

479 First Space Rendezvous

1966. Brno Stamp Exhibition.
1602 **477** 30h. black and red . . 25 10
1603 – 60h. black and orange . . 25 10
1604 – 1k.60 black and green . . 70 30
DESIGNS—HORIZ: 60h. "Mercury"; 1k.60, Brno
buildings and crest.

1966. Space Research.
1606 **479** 20h. violet and green . . 20 10
1607 – 30h. green and orange . . 20 10
1608 – 60h. blue and mauve . . 20 10
1609 – 80h. purple and blue . . 20 10
1610 – 1k. black and violet . . 20 10
1611 – 1k.20 red and blue . . 1·90 60
DESIGNS: 30h. Satellite and "back" of Moon; 60h.
"Mariner 4" and first pictures of Mars; 80h. Satellite
making "soft" landing on Moon; 1k. Satellite, laser
beam and binary code; 1k.20, "Telstar", Earth and
tracking station.

1966. Game Animals. Multicoloured.
1612 **480** 30h. Type 480 . . . . . 20 10
1613 – 40h. Red deer (vert) . . . 25 10
1614 – 60h. Lynx 30 10
1615 – 80h. Brown hare 40 20
1616 – 1k. Red fox 50 25
1617 – 1k.20 Brown bear (vert) . . 50 30
1618 – 2k. Wild boar . . . . . 3·75 1·10

481 "Spring" (V. Hollar)

1966. Art (1st series).
1619 **481** 1k. black . . . . . . 5·25 2·25
1620 – 1k. multicoloured . . . 3·00 2·25
1621 – 1k. multicoloured . . . 3·25 2·75
1622 – 1k. multicoloured . . . 3·00 2·25
1623 – 1k. multicoloured . . . 26·00 20·00
PAINTINGS: No. 1620, "Mrs. F. Wussin"
(J. Kupecky); 1621, "Snowy Owl" (K. Purkyne); 1622,
"Bouquet" (V. Spale); 1623, "Recruit" (L. Fulla).

See also Nos. 1669, 1699/1703, 1747, 1753, 1756,
1790/4, 1835/8, 1861/5, 1914/18, 1999/2003, 2067/71,
2134/9, 2194/8, 2256/60, 2313/16, 2375/9, 2495/9,
2549/53, 2601/5, 2655/9, 2702/6, 2757/61, 2810/14,
2858/62, 2904/8, 2954/6, 3000/2, 3044/7, 3077/81 and
3107/9.

482 "Carrier Pigeon"

1966. Stamp Day.
1624 **482** 1k. blue and yellow . . . 1·10 85

483 "Youth" (5th Czech **484** Distressed
Youth Federation Family
Congress)

1967. Czech Congresses.
1625 **483** 30h. red and blue . . . 15 10
1626 – 30h. red and yellow . . . 15 10
DESIGN: No. 1626, Rose and T.U. emblem (6th
Trade Union Congress).

1967. "Peace for Viet-Nam".
1627 **484** 60h. black and salmon 25 10

485 Jihlava

1967. International Tourist Year.
1628 **485** 30h. purple 15 10
1629 – 40h. red 15 10
1630 – 1k.20 blue 40 25
1631 – 1k.60 black . . . . . 2·00 50
DESIGNS—As Type 485: 40h. Brno. (76 × 30 mm):
1k.20, Bratislava; 1k.60, Prague.

486 Black-tailed Godwit

1967. Water Birds. Multicoloured.
1632 30h. Type **486** 25 10
1633 40h. Common shoveler
(horiz) 35 15
1634 60h. Purple heron . . . 35 10
1635 80h. Penduline tit . . . 70 30
1636 1k. Pied avocet 70 30
1637 1k.40 Black stork . . . . 1·50 50
1638 1k.60 Tufted duck (horiz) . 2·75 2·25

487 Sun and Satellite

1967. Space Research.
1639 **487** 30h. red and yellow . . 15 10
1640 – 40h. blue and grey . . . 15 10
1641 – 60h. green and violet . . 25 10
1642 – 1k. blue and mauve . . 25 10
1643 – 1k.20 black and blue . . 40 25
1644 – 1k.60 lake and grey . . 1·75 45
DESIGNS: 40h. Space vehicles in orbit; 60h. "Man
on the Moon" and orientation systems; 1k.
"Exploration of the planets"; 1k.20, Lunar satellites;
1k.60, Lunar observatory and landscape.

488 Gothic Art (after painting by
Theodoric)

1967. World Fair, Montreal. Multicoloured.
1645 30h. Type **488** 15 10
1646 40h. Jena Codex—ancient
manuscript, "Burning of
John Hus) 15 10
1647 60h. Lead crystal glass . . . 20 10
1648 80h. "The Shepherdess and
the Chimney Sweep"
(Andersen's Fairy Tales),
after painting by J. Trnka 30 10
1649 1k. Atomic diagram
("Technical Progress") . . 35 25
1650 1k.20 Dolls by P. Rada
("Ceramics") . . . . . . 1·60 85

489 Bicycle Wheels and Dove

1967. Sports Events of 1967.
1652 **489** 60h. black and red . . . 20 10
1653 – 60h. black & turquoise 20 10
1654 – 60h. black and blue . . 20 10
1655 – 1k.60 black and violet . 1·50 60
DESIGNS—HORIZ: Type **489** (20th Warsaw–
Berlin–Prague Cycle Race): No. 1654, Canoeist in
kayak (5th World Canoeing Championships). VERT:
No. 1653, Basketball players (World Women's
Basketball Championships); 1655, Canoeist (10th
World Water-slalom Championships).

1967. Prague Castle (3rd series). As Type **465**.
1656 30h. lake 20 10
1657 60h. slate 45 10
DESIGNS: 30h. "Golden Street"; 60h. St. Wenceslas
Hall.

490 "PRAZSKE **491** Synagogue
1967" Curtain (detail)

1967. Prague Music Festival.
1659 **490** 60h. violet and green . . 25 10

1967. Jewish Culture.
1660 **491** 30h. red and blue . . 20 10
1661 – 60h. black and green . . 25 10
1662 – 1k. blue and mauve . . 35 10
1663 – 1k.20 red and brown . . 50 10
1664 – 1k.40 black and yellow . . 50 10
1665 – 1k.60 green and yellow . . 4·50 3·00
DESIGNS: 60h. Printers' imprint (1530); 1k. Mikulov
jug (1801); 1k.20, "Old-New" Synagogue, Prague
(1268); 1k.40, Jewish memorial candelabra, Pinkas
Synagogue (1536) (The memorial is for Czech victims
of Nazi persecution); 1k.60, David Gans' tombstone
(1613).

492 Lidice Rose **493** "Architecture"

1967. 25th Anniv of Destruction of Lidice.
1666 **492** 30h. black and red . . . 25 10

1967. 9th Int Architects' Union Congress, Prague.
1667 **493** 1k. black and gold . . . 35 10

494 Petr Bezruc

1967. Birth Centenary of Petr Bezruc (poet).
1668 **494** 60h. black and red . . . 25 10

1967. Publicity for "Praga 68" Stamp Exhibition. As
Type **481**. Multicoloured.
1669 2k. "Henri Rousseau" (self-
portrait) . . . . . . 2·40 1·40

1966. Cultural Anniversaries.
1593 **472** 30h. lilac 15 10
1594 – 60h. blue 20 10
1595 – 60h. green 20 10
1596 – 60h. brown 20 10
DESIGNS: Type **472** (21st anniv of liberation of
Bratislava); 1594, L. Stur (Slovak leader) and Devin
Castle; 1595, Nachod (700th anniv); 1596, Arms,
globe, books and view of Olomouc (400th anniv of
State Science Library).

1966. Brno International Fair.
1597 **473** 60h. black and red . . . 25 10

472 Pantheon, **473** Fair Emblem
Bratislava

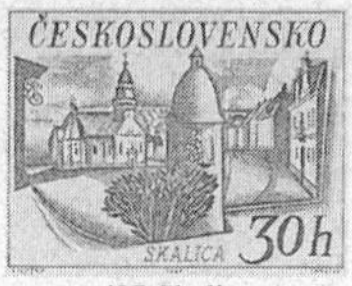

495 Skalica

1967. Czech Towns.
1670 **495** 30h. blue 20 10
1671 – 30h. lake (Presov) . . . 20 10
1672 – 30h. green (Pribram) . . 20 10

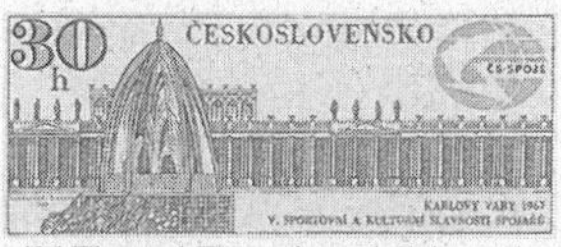

496 Thermal Fountain and Colonnade, Karlovy Vary

1967. Postal Employees' Games.
1673 **496** 30h. violet and gold . . 25 10

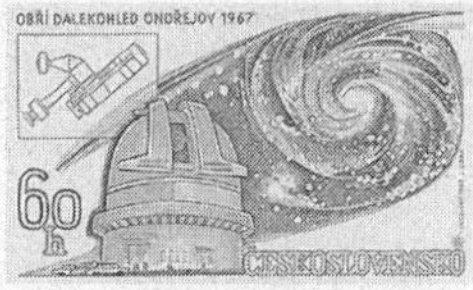

497 Ondrejov Observatory and Universe

1967. 13th Int Astronomic Union Congress, Prague.
1674 **497** 60h. silver, blue & purple 1·75 35

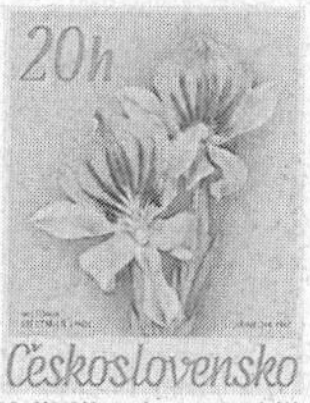

498 "Miltonia spectabilis"

1967. Botanical Garden Flowers. Multicoloured.
1675 20h. Type **498** 25 10
1676 30h. Cup and saucer plant 25 10
1677 40h. "Lycaste deppei" . . . 25 15
1678 60h. "Glottiphyllum davisii" 40 10
1679 1k. Painter's palette 60 20
1680 1k.20 "Rhodocactus bleo" 60 35
1681 1k.40 "Dendrobium phalaenopsis" . . . . . 2·40 55

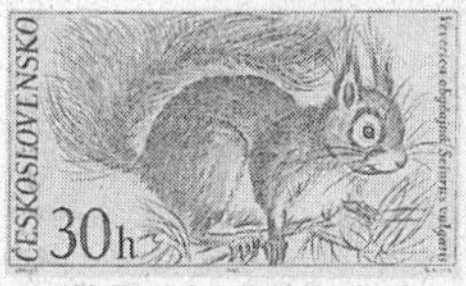

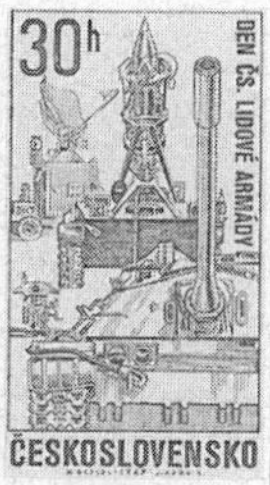

499 Eurasian Red Squirrel **500** Military Vehicles

1967. Fauna of Tatra National Park.
1682 **499** 30h. black, orge & yell 35 10
1683 – 60h. black and buff . . . 35 10
1684 – 1k. black and blue . . . 40 15
1685 – 1k.20 black, yell & grn 60 15
1686 – 1k.40 black, yell & pink 85 20
1687 – 1k.60 black, orge & yell 3·00 1·25
DESIGNS: 60h. Wild cat; 1k. Stoat; 1k.20, Hazel dormouse; 1k.40, West European hedgehog; 1k.60, Pine marten.

1967. Army Day.
1688 **500** 30h. green 25 10

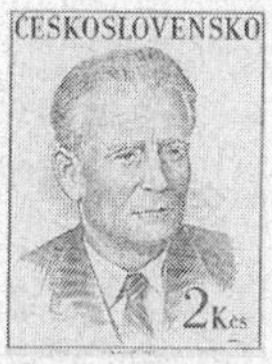

501 Prague Castle ("PRAGA 62") **503** Pres. Novotny

1967. Air. "PRAGA 1968" Int Stamp Exhbition (1st issue).
1689 **501** 30h. multicoloured . . . 15 10
1690 – 60h. multicoloured . . . 25 10
1691 – 1k. multicoloured . . . 25 15
1692 – 1k.40 multicoloured . . 35 20
1693 – 1k.60 multicoloured . . 35 30
1694 – 2k. multicoloured . . . 55 25
1695 – 5k. multicoloured . . . 2·50 2·25
DESIGNS (Sites of previous Int Stamp Exns): 60h. Selimiye Mosque, Edirne ("ISTANBUL 1963"); 1k. Notre Dame, Paris ("PHILATEC 1964"); 1k.40, Belvedere Palace, Vienna ("WIPA 1965"); 1k.60, Capitol, Washington ("SIPEX 1965"); 2k. Amsterdam ("AMPHILEX 1967"). (40 × 55 mm): 5k. Prague ("PRAGA 1968").
See also Nos. 1718/20, 1743/8, 1749/54 and 1756.

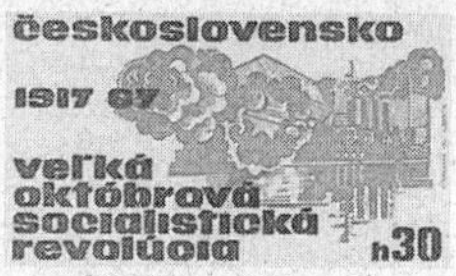

502 Cruiser "Aurora"

1967. 50th Anniv of October Revolution.
1696 **502** 30h. red and black . . . 10 10
1697 – 60h. red and black . . . 15 10
1698 – 1k. red and black . . . 15 10
DESIGNS—VERT: 60h. Hammer and sickle emblems; 1k. "Reaching hands".

1967. Art (2nd series). As T **481**. Multicoloured.
1699 60h. "Conjurer with Cards" (F. Tichy) 25 25
1700 80h. "Don Quixote" (C. Majernik) 25 25
1701 1k. "Promenade in the Park" (N. Grund) 55 55
1702 1k.20 "Self-Portrait" (P. J. Brandl) 55 55
1703 1k.60 "Epitaph to Jan of Jeren" (Czech master) . . 4·25 4·25
All in National Gallery, Prague.

1967.
1704 **503** 2k. green . . . . 1·10 10
1705 3k. brown . . . . 1·50 10

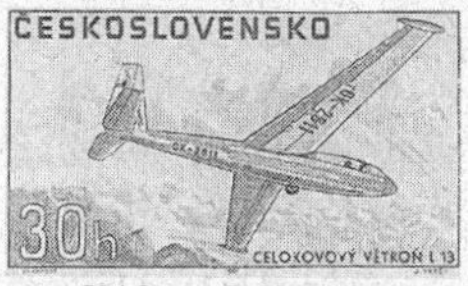

504 Letov L-13 Glider

1967. Czech Aircraft. Multicoloured.
1706 30h. Type **504** 15 10
1707 60h. Letov L-40 Meta-Sokol 20 10
1708 80h. Letov L-200 Morava 20 10
1709 1k. Letov Z-37 Cmelak crop-sprayer 45 10
1710 1k.60 Zlin Z-526 Trener Master 55 10
1711 2k. Aero L-29 Delfin jet trainer . . . . 1·75 75

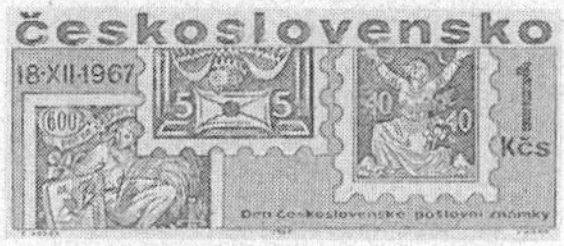

505 Czech Stamps of 1920

1967. Stamp Day.
1712 **505** 1k. lake and silver . . . 1·75 1·40

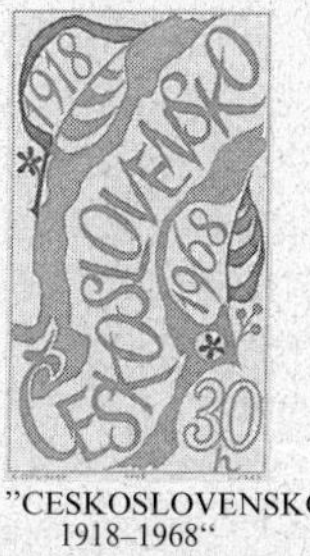

506 "CESKOSLOVENSKO 1918–1968"

1968. 50th Anniv of Republic (1st issue).
1713 **506** 30h. red, blue & ultram 70 25
See Nos. 1780/1.

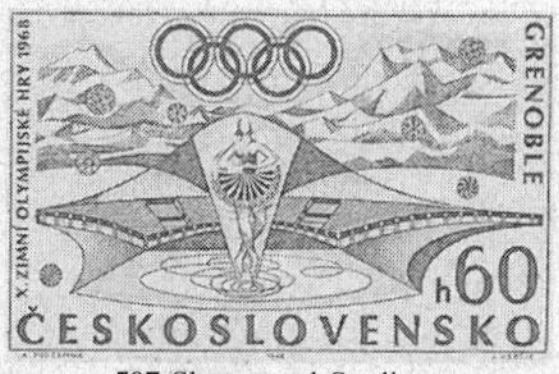

507 Skater and Stadium

1968. Winter Olympic Games, Grenoble.
1714 **507** 60h. black, yell & ochre 15 10
1715 – 1k. brown, bistre & blue 30 10
1716 – 1k.60 black, grn & lilac 55 10
1717 – 2k. black, blue & yellow 1·10 45
DESIGNS: 1k. Bobsleigh run; 1k.60, Ski jump; 2k. Ice hockey.

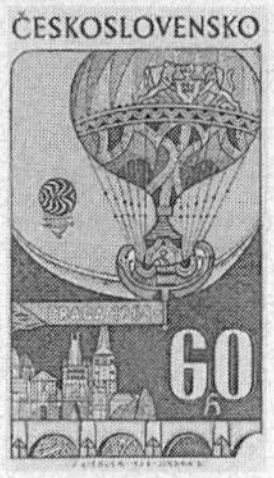

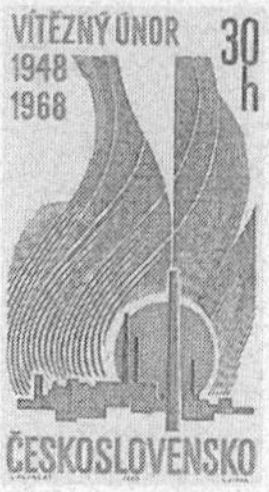

508 Charles Bridge, Prague, and Charles's Hydrogen Balloon **509** Industrial Scene and Red Sun

1968. Air. "PRAGA 1968" International Stamp Exhibition (2nd issue). Multicoloured.
1718 60h. Type **508** 40 15
1719 1k. Royal Summer-house, Belvedere, and William Henson's "Aerial Steam Carriage" 65 25
1720 2k. Prague Castle and airship 75 60

1968. 20th Anniv of "Victorious February".
1721 **509** 30h. red and blue . . . 10 10
1722 – 60h. red and blue . . . 15 10
DESIGN: 60h. Workers and banner.

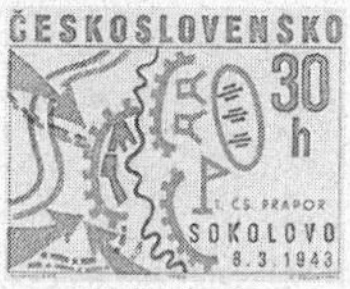

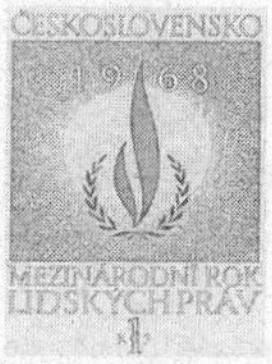

510 Battle Plan **511** Human Rights Emblem

1968. 25th Anniv of Sokolovo Battles.
1723 **510** 30h. red, blue & green 40 10

1968. Human Rights Year.
1724 **511** 1k. red . . . . 1·10 35

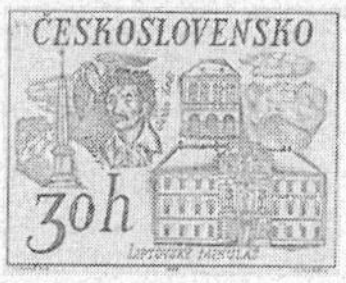

512 Liptovsky Mikulas (town) and Janko Kral (writer)

1968. Various Commemorations.
1725 **512** 30h. green 25 10
1726 – 30h. blue and orange . . 25 10
1727 – 30h. red and gold . . . 25 10
1728 – 30h. purple 25 10
1729 – 1k. multicoloured . . . 40 10
DESIGNS—VERT: No. 1726, Allegorical figure of woman (150th anniv of Prague National Museum); 1727, Girl's head (cent of Prague National Theatre); 1728, Karl Marx (150th anniv of birth); 1729, Diagrammatic skull (20th anniv of W.H.O.).

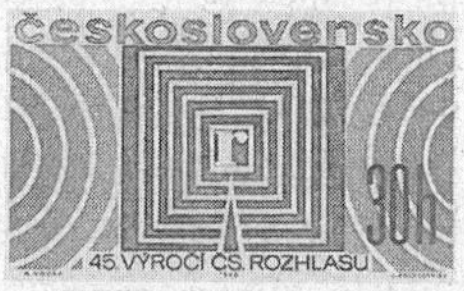

513 "Radio" (45th anniv)

1968. Czech Radio and Television Annivs.
1730 **513** 30h. black, red and blue 20 10
1731 – 30h. black, red and blue 20 10
DESIGN: No. 1731, "Television" (15th anniv).

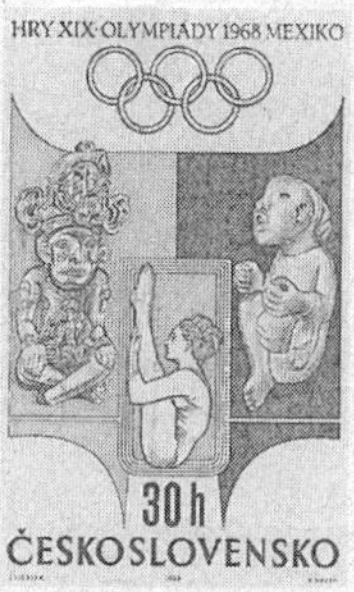

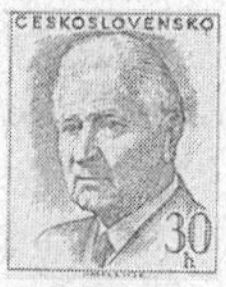

514 Athlete and Statuettes **515** Pres. Svoboda

1968. Olympic Games, Mexico. Multicoloured.
1732 30h. Type **514** 15 10
1733 40h. Runner and seated figure (Quetzalcoatl) . . . 20 10
1734 60h. Netball and ornaments 25 10
1735 1k. Altar and Olympic emblems 35 15
1736 1k.60 Football and ornaments 50 20
1737 2k. Prague Castle and key 1·75 70

1968.
1738 **515** 30h. blue 10 10
1738a 50h. green 10 10
1739 60h. red 20 10
1739a 1k. red 25 10

1968. Prague Castle (4th series). As Type **465**.
1740 30h. multicoloured 25 10
1741 60h. black, green & red . . 25 10
DESIGN: 30h. "Bretislav I" (from tomb in St. Vitus' Cathedral); 60h. Knocker on door of St. Wenceslas' Chapel.

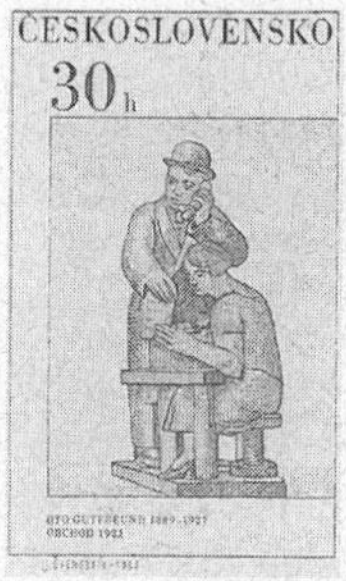

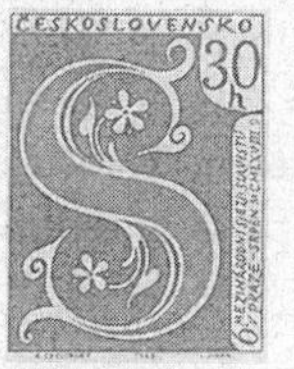

516 "Business" (sculpture by O. Gutfreund) **519** Symbolic "S"

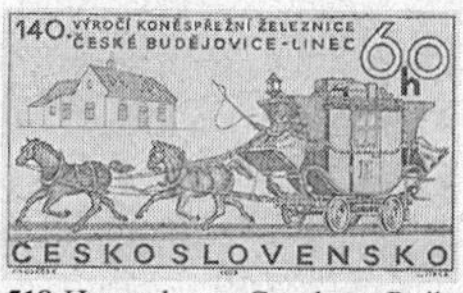

518 Horse-drawn Coach on Rails "Hannibal" (140th Anniv of Ceske–Budejovice–Linz Railway)

1968. "PRAGA 1968" Int Stamp Exn (3rd Issue). Multicoloured.
1743 30h. Type **516** 20 10
1744 40h. Broadcasting building, Prague 20 10
1745 60h. Parliament Building . . 20 15
1746 1k.40 "Prague" (Gobelin tapestry by Jan Bauch) . . 50 25
1747 2k. "The Cabaret Artiste" (painting by F. Kupka) (size 40 × 50 mm) . . . . 1·90 1·50
1748 3k. Presidential standard . . 50 45

1969. "PRAGA 1968" Int Stamp Exn (4th issue).
1749 30h. green, yellow & grey 20 10
1750 60h. violet, gold & green . . 20 10
1751 1k. indigo, pink and blue . . 30 15
1752 1k.60 multicoloured 55 25
1753 2k. multicoloured . . . . . 1·10 1·00
1754 3k. black, blue, pink & yell 1·25 35
DESIGNS—As Type **516**: 30h. St. George's Basilica, Prague Castle; 60h. Renaissance fountain; 1k. Dvorak's Museum; 1k.60, "Three Violins" insignia (18th-cent house); 3k. Prague emblem of 1475. As Type **481**: 2k. "Josefina" (painting by Josef Manes, National Gallery, Prague).

1968. "PRAGA 1968" (6th issue—F.I.P. Day). As T **481**.
1756 5k. multicoloured . . . . . 4·25 3·50
DESIGN: 5k. "Madonna of the Rosary" (detail from painting by Albrecht Durer in National Gallery, Prague).

1968. Railway Anniversaries.
1757 **518** 60h. multicoloured . . . 30 15
1758 – 1k. multicoloured . . . 80 25
DESIGN: 1k. Early steam locomotive "Johann Adolf" and modern electric locomotive (centenary of Ceske–Budejovice–Pilsen Railway).

1968. 6th Int Slavonic Congress, Prague.
1759 **519** 30h. red and blue . . . 50 10

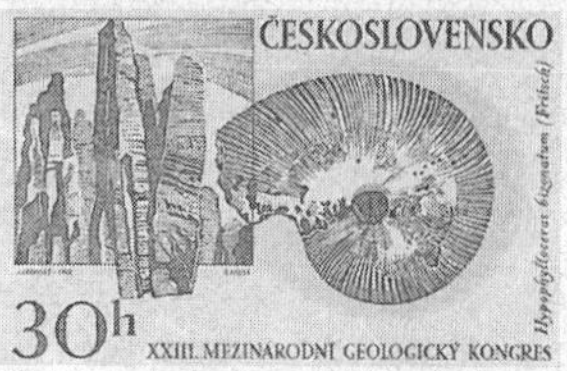

520 Adrspach Rocks and "Hypophylloceras bizonatum" (ammonite)

1968. 23rd Int Geological Congress, Prague.
1760 **520** 30h. black and yellow . . 20 10
1761 – 60h. black and mauve 20 10
1762 – 80h. black, pink & lav 30 10
1763 – 1k. black and blue . . . 40 10
1764 – 1k.60 black and yellow 1·50 60
DESIGNS: 60h. Basalt columns and fossilised frog; 80h. Bohemian "Paradise" and agate; 1k. Tatra landscape and "Chlamys gigas" shell; 1k.60, Barrandien (Bohemia) and limestone.

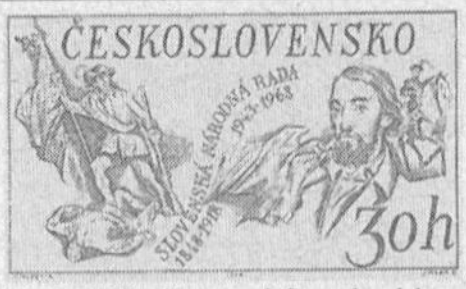

521 M. J. Hurban and Standard-bearer

1968. 120th Anniv of Slovak Insurrection and 25th Anniv of Slovak National Council.
1765 **521** 30h. blue 10 10
1766 – 60h. red 10 10
DESIGN: 60h. Partisans (120th anniv of Slovak Insurrection).

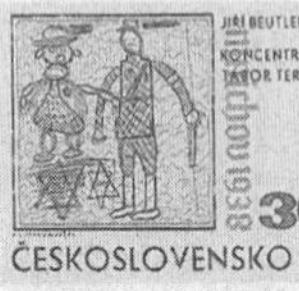

522 "Man and Child" (Jiri Beutler, aged 10)

1968. Munich Agreement. Drawings by children in Terezin concentration camp. Multicoloured.
1767 30h. Type **522** 20 10
1768 60h. "Butterflies" (Kitty Brunnerova, aged 11) . . 30 10
1769 1k. "The Window" (Jiri Schlessinger, aged 10) . . 45 10
The 1k. is larger (40 × 22 mm).

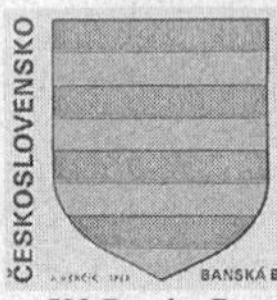

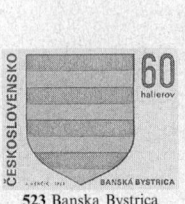

523 Banska Bystrica

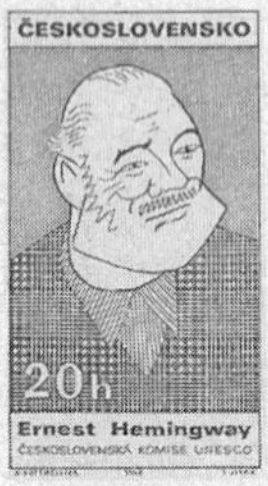

525 Ernest Hemingway

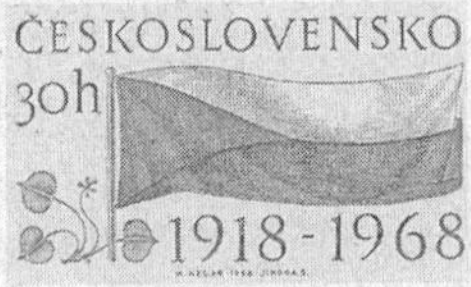

524 National Flag

1968. Arms of Czech Regional Capitals (1st series). Multicoloured.
1770 60h. Type **523** 20 10
1771 60h. Bratislava 20 10
1772 60h. Brno 20 10
1773 60h. Ceske Budejovice . . . 20 10
1774 60h. Hradec Kralove 20 10
1775 60h. Kosice 20 10
1776 60h. Ostrava 20 10
1777 60h. Pilsen 20 10
1778 60h. Usti nad Labem . . . 20 10
1779 1k. Prague (vert) 85 15
See also Nos. 1855/60, 1951/6, 2106/8 and 2214/15.

1968. 50th Anniv of Republic (2nd issue).
1780 **524** 30h. deep blue & blue 20 10
1781 – 60h. multicoloured . . . 20 10
DESIGN: 60h. Prague and Bratislava within outline "map".

1968. U.N.E.S.C.O. "Cultural Personalities of the 20th century in Caricature" (1st series).
1783 **525** 20h. black and red . . . 15 10
1784 – 30h. multicoloured . . . 15 10
1785 – 40h. red, black & lilac 15 10
1786 – 60h. black, green & bl 15 10
1787 – 1k. black, brn & yell . . 45 10
1788 – 1k.20 black, vio & red 50 20
1789 – 1k.40 black, brn & orge 1·40 55
PERSONALITIES: 30h. Karel Capek (dramatist); 40h. George Bernard Shaw; 60h. Maxim Gorky; 1k. Picasso; 1k.20, Taikan Yokoyama (painter); 1k.40, Charlie Chaplin.
See also Nos. 1829/34.

1968. Art (3rd series). As T **481**. Paintings in National Gallery, Prague. Multicoloured.
1790 60h. "Cleopatra II" (J. Zrzavy) 45 35
1791 80h. "The Black Lake" (J. Preisler) 60 40
1792 1k.20 "Giovanni Francisci as a Volunteer" (P. Bohun) . . . . . . 1·25 1·10
1793 1k.60 "Princess Hyacinth" (A. Mucha) 80 60
1794 3k. "Madonna and Child" (altar detail, Master Paul of Levoca) . . . . . . 3·50 3·25

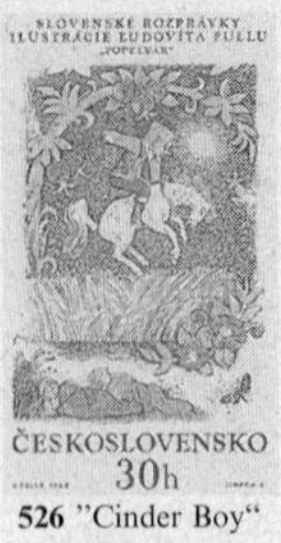

526 "Cinder Boy"

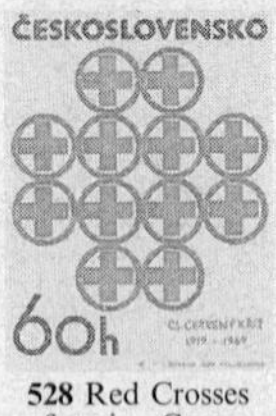

528 Red Crosses forming Cross

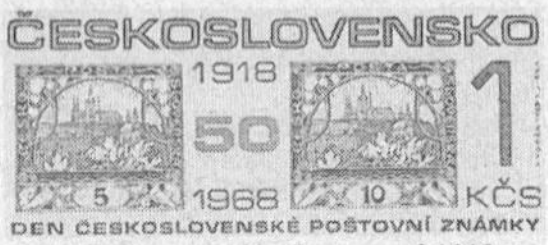

527 5h. and 10h. Stamps of 1918

1968. Slovak Fairy Tales. Multicoloured.
1795 30h. Type **526** 15 10
1796 60h. "The Proud Lady" . . 25 10
1797 80h. "The Knight who ruled the World" 30 10
1798 1k. "Good Day, Little Bench" 40 15
1799 1k.20 "The Enchanted Castle" 45 15
1800 1k.80 "The Miraculous Hunter" . . . . 2·10 55

1968. Stamp Day and 50th Anniv of 1st Czech Stamps.
1801 **527** 1k. gold and blue . . . 1·40 1·25

1969. 50th Anniv of Czech Red Cross and League of Red Cross Societies.
1802 **528** 60h. red, gold and sepia 25 10
1803 – 1k. red, blue and black 45 15
DESIGN: 1k. Red Cross symbols within heart-shaped "dove".

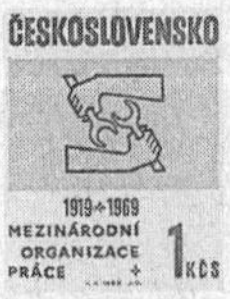

529 I.L.O. Emblem

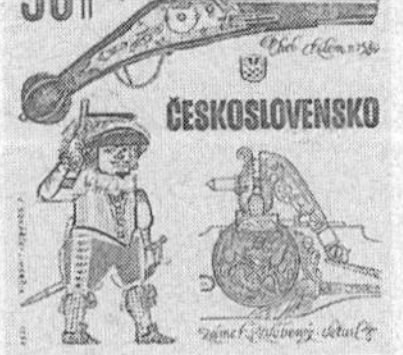

530 Wheel-lock Pistol, c. 1580

1969. 50th Anniv of Int Labour Organization.
1804 **529** 1k. black and grey . . . 25 10

1969. Early Pistols. Multicoloured.
1805 30h. Type **530** 15 10
1806 40h. Italian horse-pistol, c. 1600 . . . . 20 10
1807 60h. Kubik wheel-lock carbine, c. 1720 . . . . . 20 10
1808 1k. Flint-lock pistol, c. 1760 30 10
1809 1k.40 Lebeda duelling pistols, c. 1830 . . . . . 50 15
1810 1k.60 Derringer pistols, c. 1865 . . . . 1·60 35

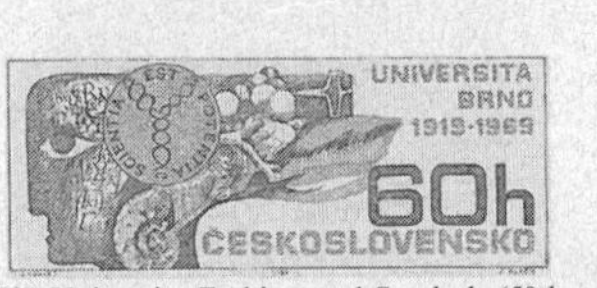

531 University Emblem and Symbols (50th Anniv of Brno University)

1969. Anniversaries.
1811 **531** 60h. black, blue & gold 20 10
1812 – 60h. blue 20 10
1813 – 60h. multicoloured . . . 20 10
1814 – 60h. black and red . . . 20 10
1815 – 60h. red, silver & blue 20 10
1816 – 60h. black and gold . . 20 10
DESIGNS and ANNIVERSARIES: No. 1812, Bratislava Castle, open book and head of woman (50th Anniv Comenius University, Bratislava); 1813, Harp and symbolic eagle (50th Anniv Brno Conservatoire); 1814, Theatrical allegory (50th Anniv Slovak National Theatre (1970); 1815, Arms and floral emblems (Slovak Republican Council, 50th Anniv); 1816, Grammar school and allegories of Learning (Zniev Grammar School. Cent).

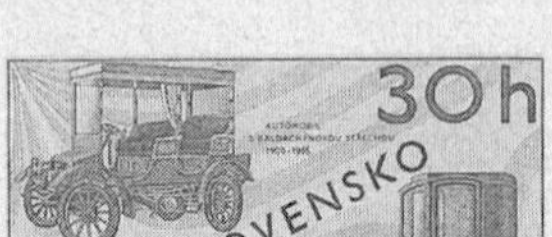

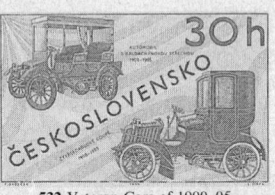

532 Veteran Cars of 1900–05

1969. Motor Vehicles. Multicoloured.
1817 30h. Type **532** 40 10
1818 1k.60 Veteran Cars of 1907 70 15
1819 1k.80 Prague Buses of 1907 and 1967 . . . . 1·75 95

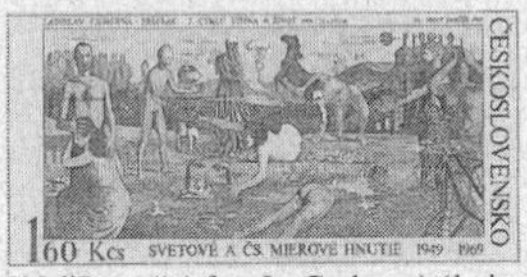

533 "Peace" (after L. Guderna) (½-size ilustration)

1969. 20th Anniv of Peace Movement.
1820 **533** 1k.60 multicoloured . . . 50 25

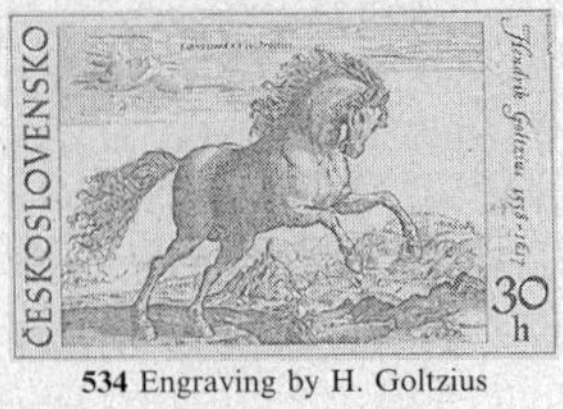

534 Engraving by H. Goltzius

1969. Horses. Works of Art.
1821 **534** 30h. sepia on cream . . 25 10
1822 – 80h. purple on cream . . 25 10
1823 – 1k.60 slate on cream . . 40 15
1824 – 1k.80 black on cream . . 40 25
1825 – 2k.40 mult on cream . . 2·50 70
DESIGNS—HORIZ: 80h. Engraving by M. Merian. VERT: 1k.60, Engraving by V. Hollar; 1k.80, Engraving by A. Durer; 2k.40, Painting by J. E. Ridinger.

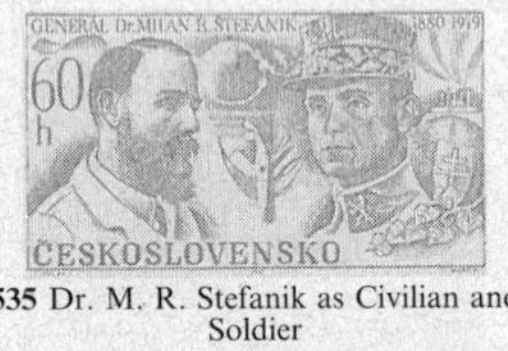

535 Dr. M. R. Stefanik as Civilian and Soldier

1969. 50th Death Anniv of General Stefanik.
1826 **535** 60h. red 35 10

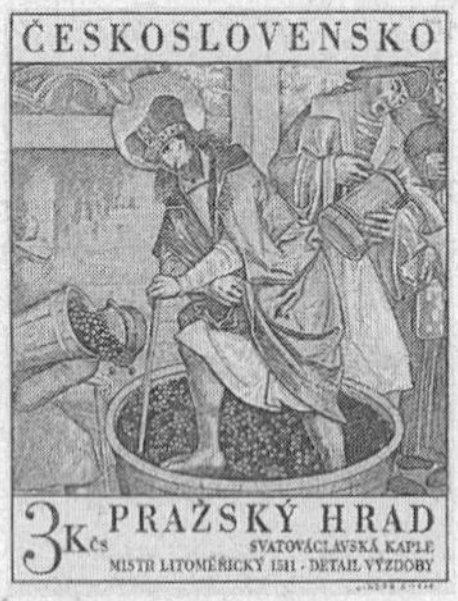

536 "St. Wenceslas" (mural detail, Master of Litomerice, 1511)

1969. Prague Castle (5th series). Multicoloured.
1827 3k. Type **536** . . . . . . 2·00 1·90
1828 3k. Coronation Banner of the Czech Estates, 1723 2·00 1·90
See also Nos. 1892/3, 1959/60, 2037/8, 2103/4, 2163/4, 2253/4, 2305/6, 2337/8, 2404/5, 2466/7, 2543/4, 2599/600 and 2637/8.

1969. U.N.E.S.C.O. "Cultural Personalities of the 20th Century in Caricature" (2nd series). Designs as Type **525**.
1829 30h. black, red and blue . . 10 10
1830 40h. black, violet & blue . . 15 10
1831 60h. black, red & yellow . . 15 10
1832 1k. multicoloured 30 10
1833 1k.80 black, blue & orge . . 40 10
1834 2k. black, yellow & green 1·90 75
DESIGNS: 30h. P. O. Hviezdoslav (poet); 40h. G. K. Chesterton (writer); 60h. V. Mayakovsky (poet); 1k. Henri Matisse (Painter); 1k.80, A. Hrdlicka (anthropologist); 2k. Franz Kafka (novelist).

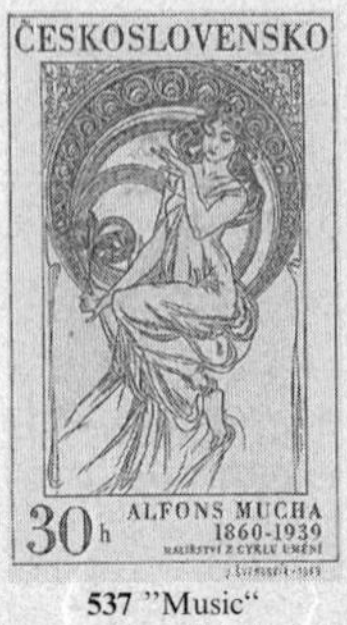

537 "Music"

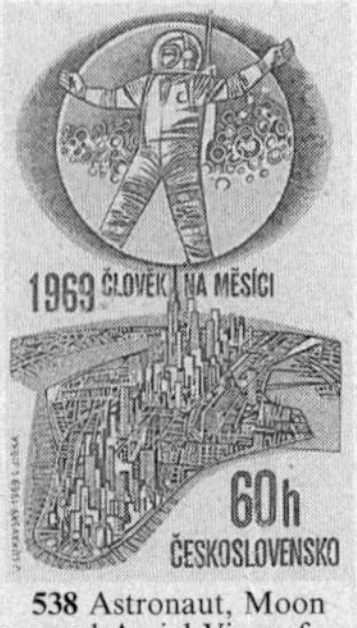

538 Astronaut, Moon and Aerial View of Manhattan

1969. "Woman and Art". Paintings by Alfons Mucha. Multicoloured.
1835 30h. Type **537** 25 10
1836 60h. "Painting" 30 10
1837 1k. "Dance" 45 10
1838 2k.40 "Ruby and Amethyst" (40 × 51 mm) . . . . . . 1·75 1·10

1969. Air. 1st Man on the Moon. Multicoloured.
1839 60h. Type **538** 20 10
1840 3k. "Eagle" module and aerial view of J. F. Kennedy Airport, New York . . . . 2·25 1·10

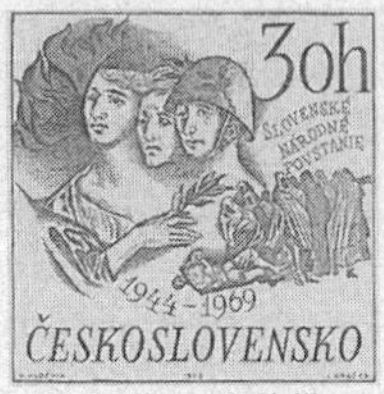

539 Soldier and Civilians

1969. 25th Anniv of Slovak Rising and Battle of Dukla.
1841 **539** 30h. bl & red on cream 10 10
1842 – 30h. grn & red on cream 10 10
DESIGN: No. 1842, General Svoboda and partisans.

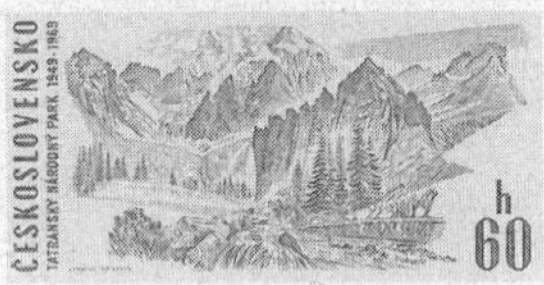

540 Ganek (½-size illustration)

1969. 20th Anniv of Tatra National Park.
1843 **540** 60h. purple 15 10
1844 – 60h. blue 15 10
1845 – 60h. green 15 10
1846 – 1k.60 multicoloured . . 1·75 50
1847 – 1k.60 multicoloured . . 45 15
1848 – 1k.60 multicoloured . . 45 15
DESIGNS: No. 1844, Mala Valley; 1845, Bielovodska Valley. (SMALLER 40 × 23 mm): 1846, Velka Valley and gentian; 1847, Mountain stream, Mala Valley and gentian; 1848, Krivan Peak and autumn crocus.

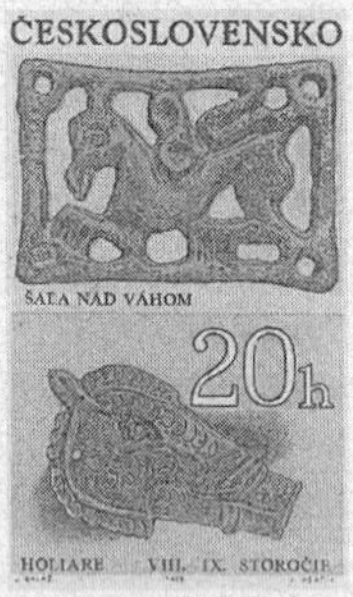

541 Bronze Belt Fittings (8th–9th century)

1969. Archaeological Discoveries in Bohemia and Slovakia. Multicoloured.
1849 20h. Type **541** 15 10
1850 30h. Decoration showing masks (6th–8th century) 15 10
1851 1k. Gold Earrings (8th–9th century) 25 10
1852 1k.80 Metal Crucifix (obverse and reverse) (9th century) 50 20
1853 2k. Gilt ornament with figure (9th century) . . . 1·75 50

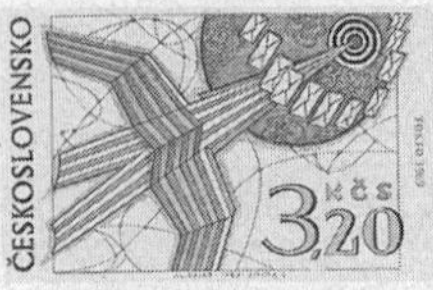

542 "Focal Point"—Tokyo

1969. 16th U.P.U. Congress, Tokyo.
1854 **542** 3k.20 multicoloured . . 1·60 1·00

1969. Arms of Czech Regional Capitals (2nd series). As T **523**. Multicoloured.
1855 50h. Bardejov 20 10
1856 50h. Hranice 20 10
1857 50h. Kezmarok 20 10
1858 50h. Krnov 20 10
1859 50h. Litomerice 20 10
1860 50h. Manetin 20 10

1969. Art (4th series). As T **481**. Multicoloured.
1861 60h. "Great Requiem" (F. Muzika) 55 45
1862 1k. "Resurrection" (Master of Trebon) 55 45
1863 1k.60 "Crucifixion" (V. Hloznik) 55 45
1864 1k.80 "Girl with Doll" (J. Bencur) 55 65
1865 2k.20 "St. Jerome" (Master Theodoric) . . . . . . 2·75 2·25

543 Emblem and "Stamps"

1969. Stamp Day.
1866 543 1k. purple, gold & blue 1·50 1·10

544 Ski Jumping

1970. World Skiing Championships, High Tatras. Multicoloured.
1867 50h. Type 544 . . . 20 10
1868 60h. Cross-country skiing 20 10
1869 1k. Ski jumper "taking off" 20 10
1870 1k.60 Woman skier . . . 1·10 30

545 J. A. Comenius (300th Death Anniv)

1970. U.N.E.S.C.O. Anniversaries of World Figures.
1871 545 40h. black 15 10
1872 – 40h. grey 25 10
1873 – 40h. brown 25 10
1874 – 40h. red 15 10
1875 – 40h. red 15 10
1876 – 40h. brown 15 10
DESIGNS: No. 1872, Ludwig van Beethoven (composer, birth bicent); 1873, Tosef Manes (artist, 150th birth anniv); 1874, Lenin (birth cent); 1875, Friedrich Engels (150th birth anniv); 1876, Maximilian Hell (astronomer, 250th birth anniv).

546 Bells

1970. World Fair, Osaka, Japan. "Expo 70". Multicoloured.
1877 50h. Type 546 . . . 15 10
1878 80h. Heavy Machinery . . . 25 10
1879 1k. Beehives (folk sculpture) 25 15
1880 1k.60 "Angels and Saints" (17th-century icon) . . . 45 35
1881 2k. "Orlik Castle, 1787" (F. K. Wolf) . . . 50 35
1882 3k. "Fujiyama" (Hokusai) 2·40 90
Nos. 1880/2 are larger, 51 × 37 mm.

547 Town Hall, Kosice   549 Lenin

548 "Autumn, 1955"

1970. 25th Anniv of Kosice Reforms.
1883 547 60h. blue, gold & red . . 35 10

1970. Paintings by Joseph Lada. Multicoloured.
1884 60h. Type 548 . . . 20 10
1885 1k. "The Magic Horse" . . . 40 10

1886 1k.80 "The Water Demon" 45 15
1887 2k.40 "Children in Winter, 1943" . . . 2·10 60
Nos. 1885/6 are vert.

1970. Birth Centenary of Lenin.
1888 549 30h. red and gold . . . 10 10
1889 – 60h. black and gold . . . 10 10
DESIGN: 60h. Lenin (bareheaded).

550 Prague Panorama and Hand giving "V" Sign

1970. 25th Anniv of Prague Rising and Liberation of Czechoslovakia.
1890 550 30h. purple, gold & blue 20 10
1891 – 30h. green, gold & red 20 10
DESIGN: No. 1891, Soviet tank entering Prague.

1970. Prague Castle. Art Treasures (6th series). As Type 536. Multicoloured.
1892 3k. "Hermes and Athena" (painting by B. Spranger) 1·90 1·75
1893 3k. "St. Vitus" (bust) 1·90 1·75

551 Compass and "World Capitals" (½-size illustration)

1970. 25th Anniv of United Nations.
1894 551 1k. multicoloured . . . 35 25

552 Thirty Years War Cannon and "Baron Munchausen"

1970. Historic Artillery. Multicoloured.
1895 30h. Type 552 . . . 15 10
1896 60h. Hussite bombard and St. Barbara . . . 15 10
1897 1k.20 Austro-Prussian War field-gun and Hradec Kralove . . . 45 10
1898 1k.80 Howitzer (1911) and Verne's "Colombiad" . . . 75 25
1899 2k.40 Mountain-gun (1915) and "Good Soldier Schweik" . . . 1·50 60

553 "Rude Pravo"   554 "Golden Sun", Bridge-tower, Prague

1970. 50th Anniv of "Rude Pravo" (newspaper).
1900 553 60h. red, drab & black 15 10

1970. Ancient Buildings and House-signs from Prague, Brno and Bratislava. Multicoloured.
1901 40h. Type 554 . . . 15 10
1902 60h. "Blue Lion" and Town Hall tower, Brno . . . 25 10
1903 1k. Gothic bolt and Town Hall tower, Bratislava . . . 25 10
1904 1k.40 Coat of arms and Michael Gate, Bratislava 1·90 30
1905 1k.60 "Moravian Eagle" and Town Hall gate, Brno 40 15
1906 1k.80 "Black Sun", "Green Frog" and bridge-tower, Prague . . . 60 15

555 World Cup Emblem and Flags

1970. World Cup Football Championship, Mexico. Multicoloured.
1907 20h. Type 555 . . . 10 10
1908 40h. Two players and badges of Germany and Uruguay 15 10
1909 60h. Two players and badges of England and Czechoslovakia 20 10
1910 1k. Three players and badges of Rumania and Czechoslovakia 30 10
1911 1k.20 Three players and badges of Brazil and Italy 50 10
1912 1k.80 Two players and badges of Brazil and Czechoslovakia . . . . 1·60 40

556 "S.S.M." and Flags   557 Dish Aerial

1970. 1st Congress of Czechoslovak Socialist Youth Federation.
1913 556 30h. multicoloured . . . 35 10

1970. Art (5th series). As T 481. Multicoloured.
1914 1k. "Mother and Child" (M. Galanda) 25 20
1915 1k.20 "The Bridesmaid" (K. Svolinsky) 50 40
1916 1k.40 "Walk by Night" (F. Hudecek) 50 40
1917 1k.80 "Banska Bystrica Market" (detail, D. Skutecky) 65 55
1918 2k.40 "Adoration of the Kings" (Vysehrad Codex) 2·10 2·40

1970. "Intercosmos". Space Research Programme. Multicoloured.
1919 20h. Type 557 . . . 10 10
1920 40h. Experimental satellite 15 10
1921 60h. Meteorological satellite 20 10
1922 1k. Astronaut ("medical research") . . . 25 10
1923 1k.20 Solar research . . . 30 10
1924 1k.60 Rocket on Launch-pad . . . 1·40 45

558 "Adam and Eve with Archangel Michael" (16th-century)

1970. Slovak Icons. Multicoloured.
1925 30h. Type 558 . . . 20 20
1926 1k. "Mandylon" (16th-century) (horiz) 30 30
1927 2k. "St. George slaying the Dragon" (18th-century) (horiz) 50 50
1928 2k.80 "St. Michael the Archangel" (18th-century) 2·40 2·25

559 Czech 5h. Stamps of 1920

1970. Stamp Day.
1929 559 1k. red, black & green 90 90

560 "Songs from the Walls" (frontispiece, K. Stika)   561 Saris Church

1971. Czechoslovak Graphic Art (1st series).
1930 560 40h. brown 15 10
1931 – 50h. multicoloured . . . 20 10
1932 – 60h. grey 20 10
1933 – 1k. grey 25 10
1934 – 1k.60 black & cream 45 10
1935 – 2k. multicoloured . . . 1·90 60
DESIGNS: 50h. "The Fruit Trader" (C. Bouda); 60h. "Moon searching for Lilies-of-the-valley" (J. Zrzavy); 1k. "At the End of the Town" (K. Sokol); 1k.60, "Summer" (V. Hollar); 2k. "Shepherd and Gamekeeper, Orava Castle" (P. Bohun). See also Nos. 2026/30, 2079/82, 2147/50 and 2202/5.

1971. Regional Buildings.
1936 – 50h. multicoloured . . . 10 10
1936a – 1k. black, red & blue 20 10
1937 561 1k.60 black, vio & grn 45 10
1938 – 2k. multicoloured . . . 55 10
1939 – 2k.40 multicoloured . . . 55 10
1940 – 3k. multicoloured . . . 70 10
1941 – 3k.60 multicoloured . . . 90 10
1942 – 5k. multicoloured . . . 1·10 10
1943 – 5k.40 multicoloured . . . 1·10 10
1944 – 6k. multicoloured . . . 1·40 10
1945 – 9k. multicoloured . . . 2·25 10
1946 – 10k. multicoloured . . . 1·75 10
1947 – 14k. multicoloured . . . 2·40 10
1948 – 20k. multicoloured . . . 3·00 50
DESIGNS: —HORIZ: 50h., 3k.60, Church, Chrudimsko; 2k.40, House, Jicinsko, 5k.40, Southern Bohemia baroque house, Posumavi; 10k. Wooden houses, Liptov; 14k. House and belfry, Valassko; 20k. Decorated house, Cicmany. (22 × 19 mm): 3k. Half-timbered house, Melnicko; 6k. Cottages, Orava; 9k. Cottage, Turnovsko. VERT: (19 × 22 mm): 1k. Ornamental roofs, Horacko; 2k. Bell-tower, Hornsek; 5k. Watch-tower, Nachodsko.

562 "The Paris Commune" (allegory) (½-size illustration)

1971. U.N.E.S.C.O. World Annivs. Multicoloured.
1949 1k. Type 562 . . . . . 30 20
1950 1k. "World Fight against Racial Discrimination" (allegory) 30 20

1971. Arms of Czech Regional Capitals (3rd series). As Type 523. Multicoloured.
1951 60h. Ceska Trebova . . . 15 10
1952 60h. Karlovy Vary . . . 15 10
1953 60h. Levoca 15 10
1954 60h. Trutnov 15 10
1955 60h. Uhersky Brod . . . 15 10
1956 60h. Zilina 15 10

563 Chorister   564 Lenin

1971. 50th Annivs. Multicoloured.
1957 30h. Type 563 (Slovak Teachers' Choir) 20 10
1958 30h. Edelweiss, ice-pick and mountain (Slovak Alpine Organisation) (19 × 48 mm) 20 10

1971. Prague Castle (7th series). Art Treasures. As Type 536. Multicoloured.
1959 3k. brown, buff and black 2·00 2·00
1960 3k. multicoloured . . . 2·00 2·00
DESIGNS: No. 1959, "Music" (16th-century wall painting); 1960, Head of 16th-century crozier.

1971. 50th Anniv of Czech Communist Party.
1961 30h. Type 564 . . . 10 10
1962 40h. Hammer and sickle emblems 10 10
1963 60h. Clenched fists 15 10
1964 1k. Emblem on pinnacle . . 20 10

565 "50" Star Emblem

1971. 14th Czech Communist Party Congress. Multicoloured.
1965 30h. Type 565 . . . 10 10
1966 60h. Clenched fist, worker and emblems (vert) . . . 15 10

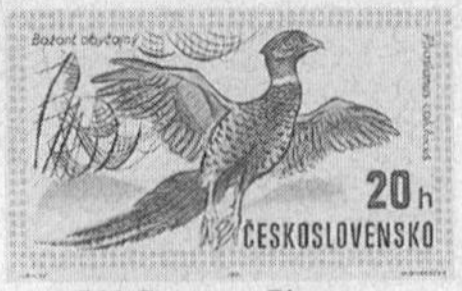
566 Common Pheasant

1971. World Hunting Exn, Budapest. Mult.
1967 20h. Type **566** 45 10
1968 60h. Rainbow trout 15 10
1969 80h. Mouflon 20 10
1970 1k. Chamois 20 10
1971 2k. Red deer 45 15
1972 2k.60 Wild boar . . . . . 2·75 75

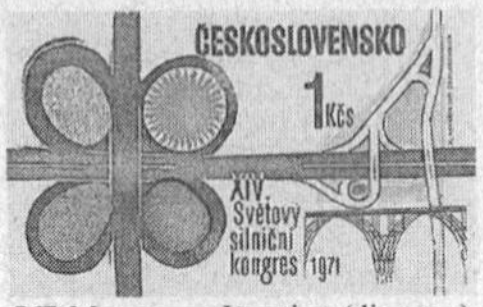
567 Motorway Junction (diagram)

1971. World Road Congress.
1973 **567** 1k. multicoloured . . . 25 10

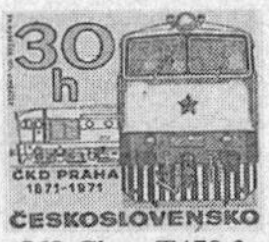
568 Class T478.3 Diesel Locomotive

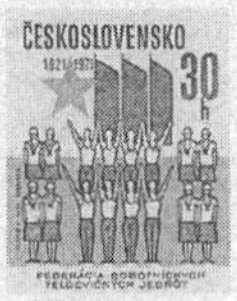
569 Gymnasts

1971. Cent of Prague C.K.D. Locomotive Works.
1974 **568** 30h. black, red & blue 10 10

1971. 50th Anniv of Proletarian Physical Federation.
1975 **569** 30h. multicoloured . . . 10 10

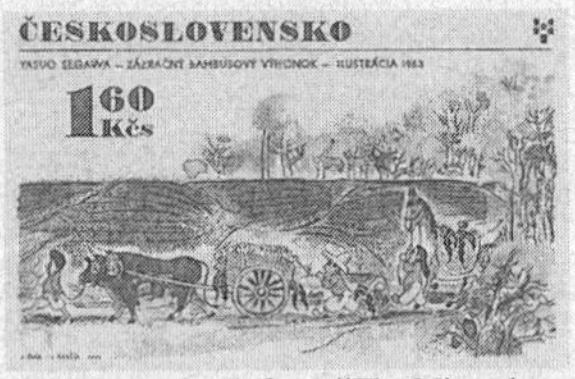
570 "Procession" (from "The Miraculous Bamboo Shoot" by K. Segawa)

1971. Biennial Exhibition of Book Illustrations for Children, Bratislava. Multicoloured.
1976 60h. "Princess" (Chinese Folk Tales, E. Bednarova) (vert) 20 10
1977 1k. "Tiger" (Animal Fairy Tales, Hanak) (vert) . . . 20 10
1978 1k.60 Type **570** 50 25

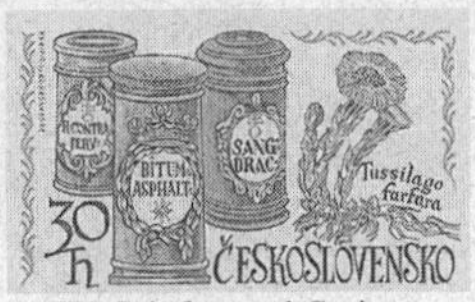
571 Coltsfoot and Canisters

1971. International Pharmaceutical Congress, Prague. Medicinal Plants and Historic Pharmaceutical Utensils. Multicoloured.
1979 30h. Type **571** 10 10
1980 60h. Dog rose and glass jars 15 10
1981 1k. Yellow pheasant's-eye and hand scales 25 10
1982 1k.20 Common valerian, pestle and mortar 40 15
1983 1k.80 Chicory and crucibles 55 15
1984 2k.40 Henbane and grinder 1·40 55

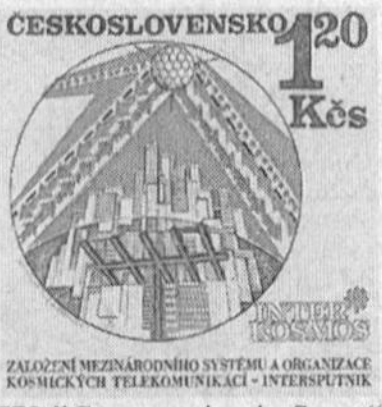
573 "Co-operation in Space"

1971. "Intersputnik" Day.
1997 **573** 1k.20 multicoloured . . 35 10

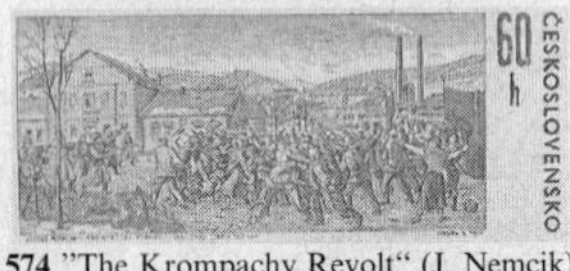
574 "The Krompachy Revolt" (J. Nemcik) (½-size illustration)

1971. 50th Anniv of The Krompachy Revolt.
1998 **574** 60h. multicoloured . . . 35 10

1971. Art (6th issue). As Type **481**. Multicoloured.
1999 1k. "Waiting" (I. Weiner-Kral) 40 35
2000 1k.20 "The Resurrection" (unknown 14th century artist) 40 35
2001 1k.40 "Woman with Jug" (M. Bazovsky) 50 45
2002 1k.80 "Woman in National Costume" (J. Manes) . . 65 60
2003 2k.40 "Festival of the Rosary" (Durer) . . . . 2·25 2·40

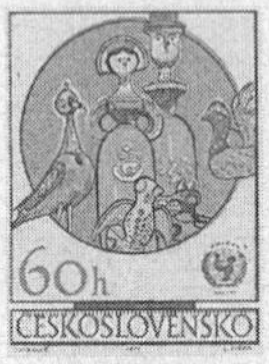
575 Wooden Dolls and Birds

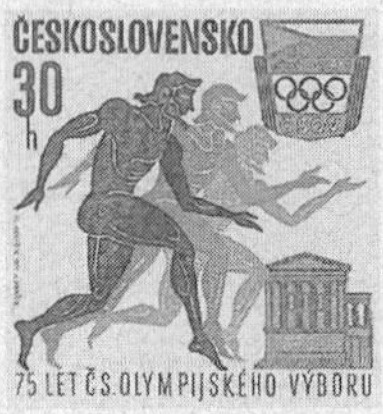
576 Ancient Greek Runners

1971. 25th Anniv of U.N.I.C.E.F. Czech and Slovak Folk Art. Multicoloured.
2004 60h. Type **575** (frame and U.N.I.C.E.F. emblem in bl) 15 10
2005 60h. Type **575** (frame and U.N.I.C.E.F. emblem in black) . . . . 2·50 1·40
2006 80h. Decorated handle . . . 20 10
2007 1k. Horse and rider 25 15
2008 1k.60 Shepherd 40 20
2009 2k. Easter eggs and rattle 55 25
2010 3k. Folk hero . . . . 2·40 65

1971. 75th Anniv of Czechoslovak Olympic Committee and 1972 Games at Sapporo and Munich. Multicoloured.
2011 30h. Type **576** 10 10
2012 40h. High Jumper 10 10
2013 1k.60 Skiers 50 10
2014 2k.60 Discus-throwers, ancient and modern . . . 1·75 75

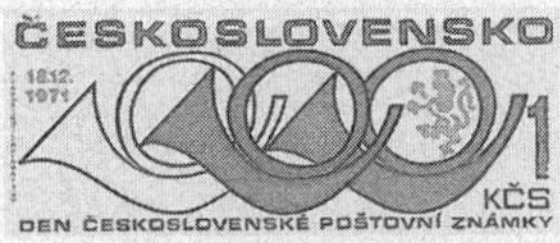
577 Posthorns

1971. Stamp Day.
2015 **577** 1k. multicoloured . . . 35 10

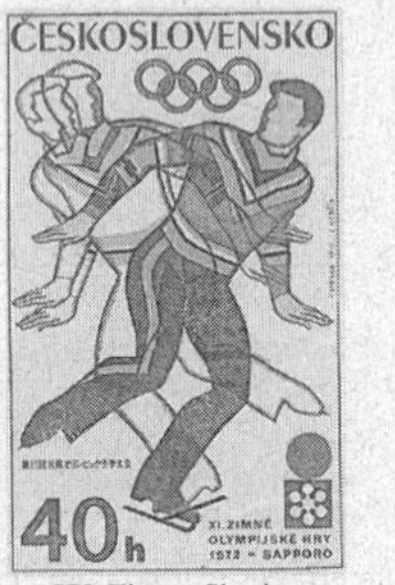
578 Figure Skating

1972. Winter Olympic Games, Sapporo, Japan. Multicoloured.
2016 40h. Type **578** 10 10
2017 50h. Skiing 15 10
2018 1k. Ice hockey 50 10
2019 1k.60 Bobsleighing . . . . 1·10 60

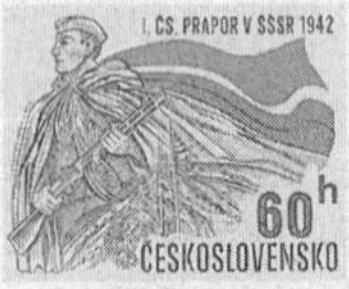
579 Sentry

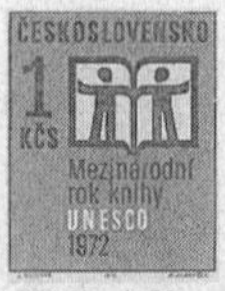
580 Book Year Emblem

1972. 30th Annivs.
2020 – 30h. black and brown . . 10 10
2021 – 30h. black, red & yellow 10 10
2022 **579** 60h. multicoloured . . . 20 10
2023 – 60h. black, red & yellow 20 10
ANNIVERSARIES: No. 2020, Child and barbed wire (Terezin Concentration Camp); 2021, Widow and buildings (Destruction of Lezaky); 2022, Type **579** (Czechoslovak Unit in Russian Army); 2023, Hand and ruined building (Destruction of Lidice).

1972. International Book Year.
2024 **580** 1k. black and red . . . 35 10

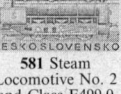

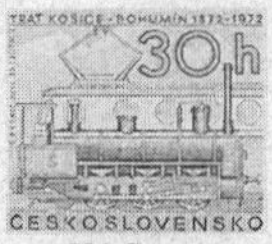
581 Steam Locomotive No. 2 and Class E499.0 Electric Locomotive

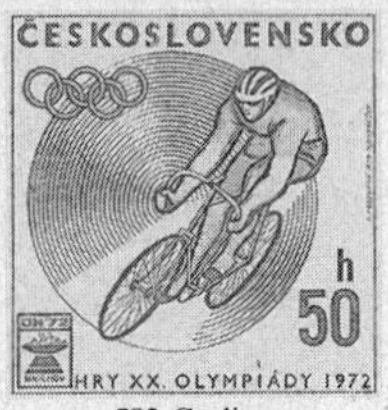
582 Cycling

1972. Centenary of Kosice–Bohumin Railway.
2025 **581** 30h. multicoloured . . . 35 10

1972. Czechoslovak Graphic Art (2nd series). As Type **560**. Multicoloured.
2026 40h. "Pasture" (V. Sedlacek) 10 10
2027 50h. "Dressage" (F. Tichy) 15 10
2028 60h. "Otakar Kubin" (V. Fiala) 20 15
2029 1k. "The Three Kings" (E. Zmetak) 30 25
2030 1k.60 "Toilet" (L. Fulla) . . 1·40 1·25

1972. Olympic Games, Munich. Multicoloured.
2031 50h. Type **582** 15 10
2032 1k.60 Diving 35 10
2033 1k.80 Kayak-canoeing . . . 40 20
2034 2k. Gymnastics . . . . . . 1·25 55

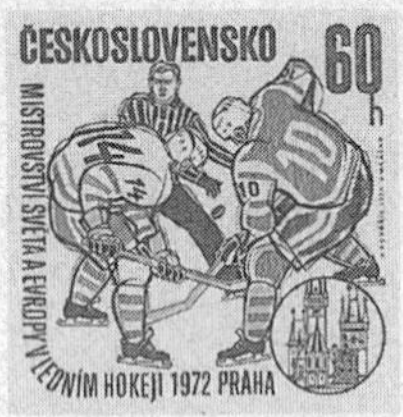
583 Players in Tackle

1972. World and European Ice Hockey Championships, Prague. Multicoloured.
2035 60h. Type **583** 30 10
2036 1k. Attacking goal 50 10

1972. Prague Castle (8th series). Roof Decorations. As T **536**. Multicoloured.
2037 3k. Bohemian Lion emblem (roof boss), Royal Palace 1·00 75
2038 3k. "Adam and Eve" (bracket), St. Vitus Cathedral . . . . 2·40 2·50

1972. Czech Victory in Ice Hockey Championships. Nos. 2035/6 optd.
2039 **583** 60h. multicoloured . . . 7·00 7·00
2040 – 1k. multicoloured . . . 7·00 7·00
OVERPRINTS: 60h. **CSSR MISTREM SVETA**. 1k. **CSSR MAJSTROM SVETA**.

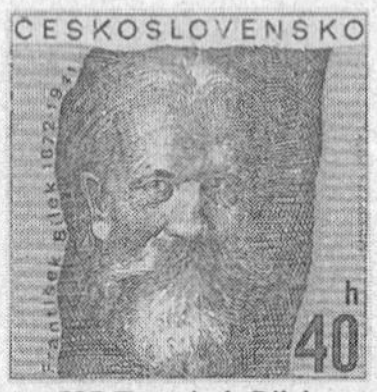
585 Frantisek Bilek (sculptor, birth centenary)

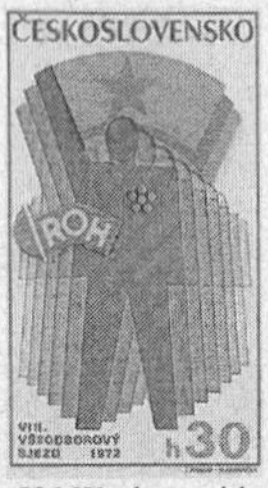
586 Workers with Banners

1972. Cultural Anniversaries.
2041 **585** 40h. multicoloured . . . 15 10
2042 – 40h. multicoloured . . . 15 10
2043 – 40h. green, yellow & blue 15 10
2044 – 40h. multicoloured . . . 15 10
2045 – 40h. violet, blue & green 15 10
2046 – 40h. green, brown & orge 15 10
DESIGNS: No. 2042, Antonin Hudecek (painter, birth cent); 2043, Janko Kral (poet, 150th birth anniv); 2044, Ludmila Podjavorinska (writer, birth cent); 2045, Andrej Sladkovic (painter, death cent); 2046, Jan Preisler (painter, birth cent).

1972. 8th Trade Union Congress, Prague.
2047 **586** 30h. violet, red & yellow 10 10

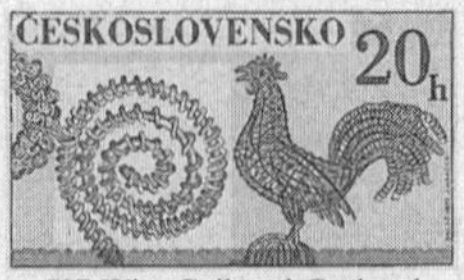
587 Wire Coil and Cockerel

1972. Slovak Wireworking. Multicoloured.
2048 20h. Type **587** 10 10
2049 60h. Aeroplane and rosette 15 10
2050 80h. Dragon and gilded ornament 20 10
2051 1k. Steam locomotive and pendant 60 10
2052 2k.60 Owl and tray 80 60

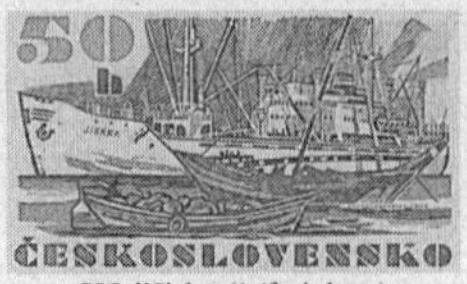
588 "Jiskra" (freighter)

1972. Czechoslovak Ocean-going Ships. Mult.
2053 50h. Type **588** 25 10
2054 60h. "Mir" (freighter) . . . 35 10
2055 80h. "Republika" (freighter) 40 10
2056 1k. "Kosice" (tanker) . . . 45 10
2057 1k.60 "Dukla" (freighter) 65 10
2058 2k. "Kladno" (freighter) . . 1·75 45
Nos. 2056/8 are size 49 × 30 mm.

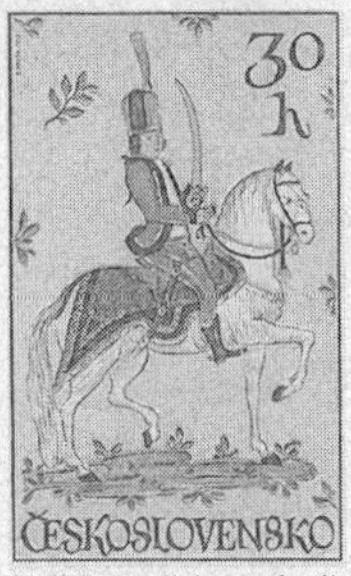
589 "Hussar" (ceramic tile)

1972. "Horsemanship". Ceramics and Glass. Multicoloured.
2059 30h. Type **589** 10 10
2060 60h. "Turkish Janissary" (enamel on glass) 15 10
2061 80h. "St. Martin" (painting on glass) 25 10
2062 1k.60 "St. George" (enamel on glass) 45 10
2063 1k.80 "Nobleman's Guard, Bohemia" (enamel on glass) 55 10
2064 2k.20 "Cavalryman, c. 1800" (ceramic tile) . . 1·60 60

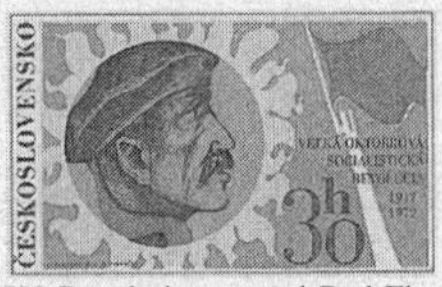
590 Revolutionary and Red Flag

1972. 55th Anniv of Russian October Revolution and 50th Anniv of U.S.S.R.
2065 **590** 30h. multicoloured . . . 10 10
2066 – 60h. red and gold . . . 15 10
DESIGN: 60h. Soviet star emblem.

1972. Art (7th issue). As T **481**.
2067 1k. multicoloured 70 50
2068 1k.20 multicoloured 95 55
2069 1k.40 brown and cream . . 95 65
2070 1k.80 multicoloured . . . . 1·00 95
2071 2k.40 multicoloured . . . . 2·10 2·40
DESIGNS: 1k. "Nosegay" (M. Svabinsky); 1k.20, "St. Ladislav fighting a Nomad" (14th century painter); 1k.40, "Lady with Fur Cap" (V. Hollar); 1k.80, "Midsummer Night's Dream" (J. Liesler); 2k.40, "Self-portrait" (P. Picasso).

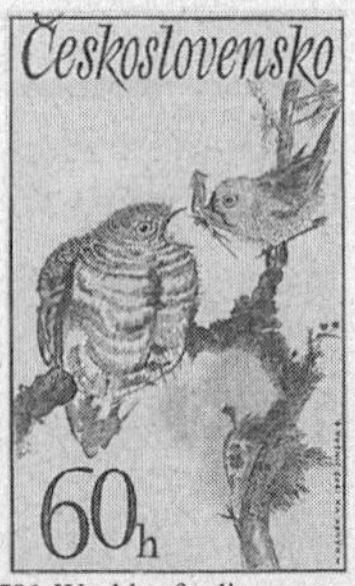
591 Warbler feeding young European Cuckoo

1972. Songbirds. Multicoloured.
2072 60h. Type **591** 35 15
2073 80h. European cuckoo . . . 45 15
2074 1k. Black-billed magpie . . 45 15
2075 1k.60 Northern bullfinch (30 × 23 mm) 60 20
2076 2k. Eurasian goldfinch (30 × 23 mm) . . . . . . 1·00 45
2077 3k. Song thrush (30 × 23 mm) . . . . . . 4·50 1·40

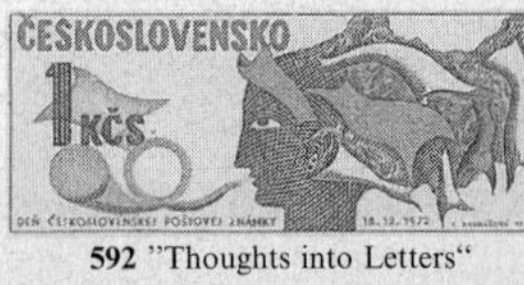
592 "Thoughts into Letters"

1972. Stamp Day.
2078 **592** 1k. black, gold & pur . . 45 45

1973. Czechoslovak Graphic Art (3rd series). As Type **560**. Multicoloured.
2079 30h. "Flowers in the Window" (J. Grus) . . . 10 10
2080 60h. "Quest for Happiness" (J. Balaz) 15 10
2081 1k.60 "Balloon" (K. Lhotak) 45 20
2082 1k.80 "Woman with Viola" (R. Wiesner) . . . . . . 1·50 35

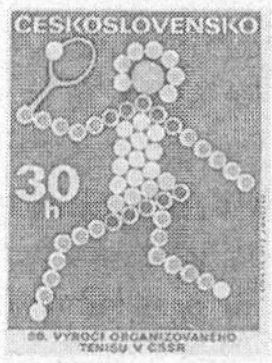
593 "Tennis Player"

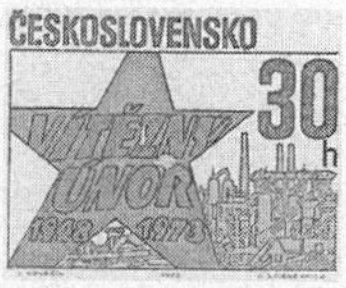
594 Red Star and Factory Buildings

1973. Sports Events. Multicoloured.
2083 30h. Type **593** 30 10
2084 60h. Figure skating 15 10
2085 1k. Spartakaid emblem . . . 30 10
EVENTS: 30h. 80th anniv of lawn tennis in Czechoslovakia; 60h. World Figure Skating Championships, Bratislava; 1k. 3rd Warsaw Pact Armies Summer Spartakiad.

1973. 25th Anniv of "Victorious February" and People's Militia (60h.).
2086 **594** 30h. multicoloured . . . 10 10
2087 – 60h. blue, red & gold . . 15 10
DESIGN: 60h. Militiaman and banners.

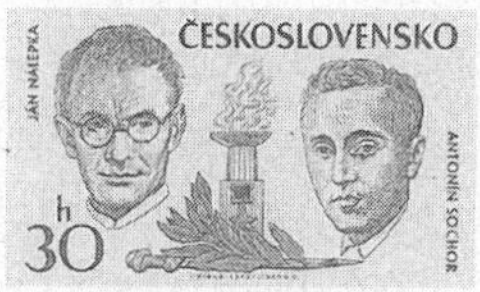
595 Jan Nalepka and Antonin Sochar

1973. Czechoslovak Martyrs during World War II.
2088 **595** 30h. black, red and gold on cream 10 10
2089 – 40h. black, red and green on cream 15 10
2090 – 60h. black, red and gold on cream 15 10
2091 – 80h. black, red and green on cream 15 10
2092 – 1k. black, pink and green on cream . . . 20 10
2093 – 1k.60 black, red and silver on cream . . . 1·25 60
DESIGNS: 40h. Evzen Rosicky and Mirko Nespor; 60h. Vlado Clementis and Karol Smidke; 80h. Jan Osoha and Josef Molak; 1k. Marie Kuderikova and Jozka Jaburkova; 1k.60, Vaclav Sinkule and Eduard Urx.

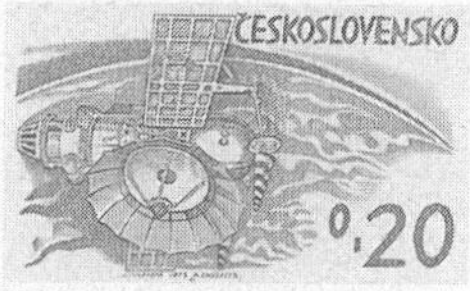
596 Russian "Venera" Space-probe

1973. Cosmonautics' Day. Multicoloured.
2094 20h. Type **596** 10 10
2095 30h. "Cosmos" satellite . . 10 10
2096 40h. "Lunokhod" on Moon 10 10
2097 3k. American astronauts Grissom, White and Chaffee . . . . 1·00 70
2098 3k.60 Russian cosmonaut Komarov, and crew of "Soyuz II" . . . . 1·10 1·40
2099 5k. Death of Yuri Gagarin (first cosmonaut) . . . . 4·25 4·00
Nos. 2094/6 are size 40 × 23 mm.

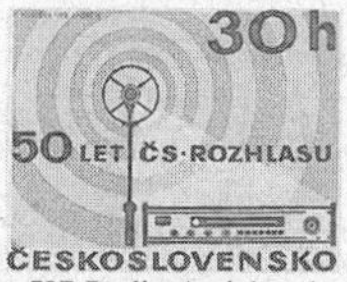
597 Radio Aerial and Receiver

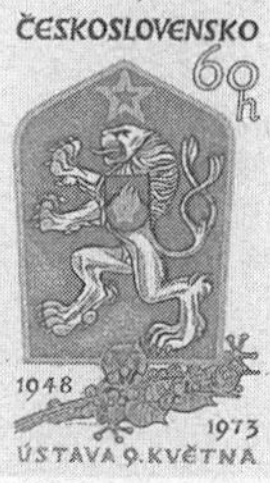
598 Czechoslovak Arms

1973. Telecommunications Annivs. Multicoloured.
2100 30h. Type **597** 10 10
2101 30h. T.V. colour chart . . . 10 10
2102 30h. Map and telephone . . 10 10
ANNIVERSARIES: No. 2100, 50th anniv of Czech broadcasting; 2101, 20th anniv of Czechoslovak television service; 2102, 20th anniv of nationwide telephone system.

1973. Prague Castle (9th series). As Type **536**. Multicoloured.
2103 3k. Gold seal of Charles IV 1·75 2·00
2104 3k. Rook showing Imperial Legate (from "The Game and Playe of Chesse" by William Caxton) 90 70

1973. 25th Anniv of May 9th Constitution.
2105 **598** 60h. multicoloured . . . 10 10

1973. Arms of Czech Regional Capitals (4th series). As T **523**.
2106 60h. multicoloured (Mikulov) 20 10
2107 60h. multicoloured (Smolenice) 20 10
2108 60h. black and gold (Zlutice) 20 10

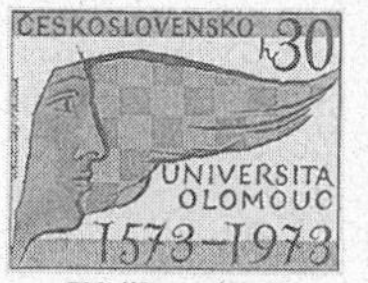
599 "Learning."

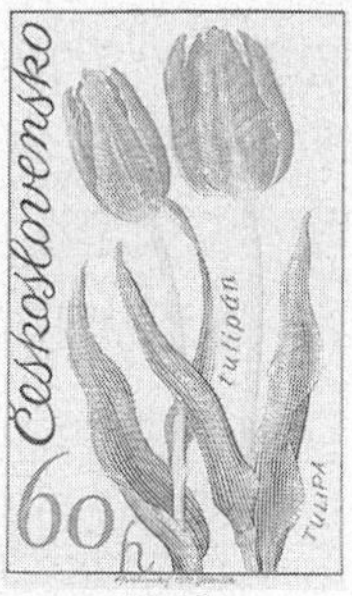
600 Tulip

1973. 400th Anniv of Olomouc University.
2109 **599** 30h. multicoloured . . . 10 10

1973. Olomouc Flower Show. Multicoloured.
2110 60h. Type **600** 95 65
2111 1k. Rose 75 30
2112 1k.60 Anthurium 35 15
2113 1k.80 Iris 40 20
2114 2k. Chrysanthemum . . . . 1·75 2·40
2115 3k.60 Boat orchid . . . . . 1·10 25
Nos. 2112/13 and 2115 are smaller, size 23 × 50 mm.

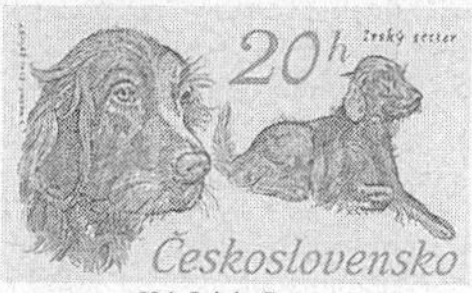
601 Irish Setter

1973. 50th Anniv of Czechoslovak Hunting Organization. Hunting Dogs. Multicoloured.
2116 20h. Type **601** 10 10
2117 30h. Czech whisker 10 10
2118 40h. Bavarian mountain bloodhound 10 10
2119 60h. German pointer . . . 15 10
2120 1k. Golden cocker spaniel 20 10
2121 1k.60 Dachshund . . . . . 2·00 75

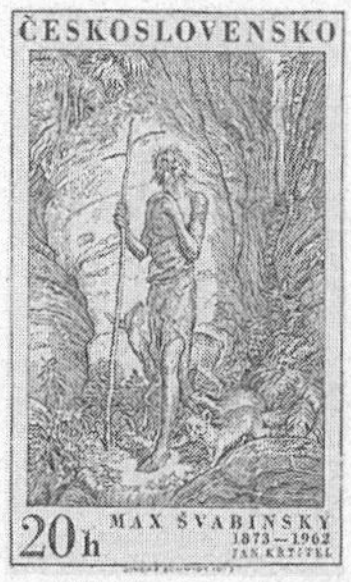
602 "St. John the Baptist" (M. Svabinsky)

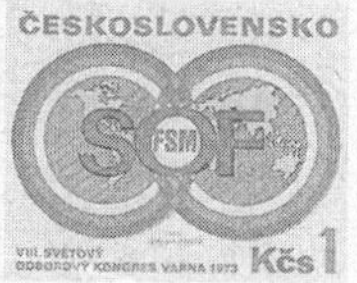
603 Congress Emblem

1973. Birth Centenary of Max Svabinsky (artist and designer).
2122 **602** 20h. black and green . . 10 10
2123 – 60h. black and yellow . . 20 10
2124 – 80h. black 25 25
2125 – 1k. green 25 25
2126 – 2k.60 multicoloured . . . 2·10 2·00
DESIGNS: 60h. "August Noon"; 80h. "Marriage of True Minds"; 1k. "Paradise Sonata 1"; 2k.60, "The Last Judgement" (stained glass window).

1973. 8th World Trade Union Congress, Varna, Bulgaria.
2127 **603** 1k. multicoloured . . . 10 10

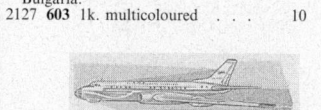

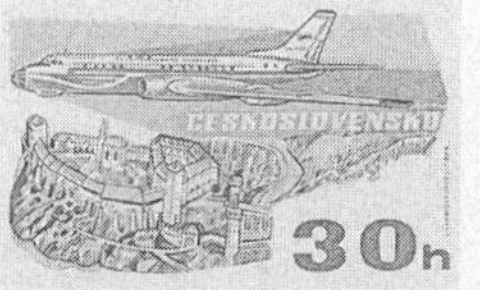
604 Tupolev Tu-104A over Bitov Castle

1973. 50th Anniv of Czechoslovak Airlines. Multicoloured.
2128 30h. Type **604** 10 10
2129 60h. Ilyushin Il-62 and Bezdez Castle 15 10
2130 1k.40 Tupolev Tu-134A and Orava Castle 40 10
2131 1k.90 Ilyushin Il-18 and Veveri Castle 55 20
2132 2k.40 Ilyushin Il-14P and Pernstejn Castle . . . . . 2·75 70
2133 3k.60 Tupolev Tu-154 and Trencin Castle 70 30

1973. Art (8th series). As Type **481**.
2134 1k. multicoloured . . . . . 1·75 1·75
2135 1k.20 multicoloured . . . . 1·75 1·75
2136 1k.80 black and buff 65 65
2137 2k. multicoloured 75 75
2138 2k.40 multicoloured 90 90
2139 3k.60 multicoloured . . . . 1·10 1·40
DESIGNS: 1k. "Boy from Martinique" (A. Pelc); 1k.20, "Fortitude" (M. Benka); 1k.80, Self-portrait (Rembrandt); 2k. "Pierrot" (B. Kubista); 2k.40, "Ilona Kubinyiova" (P. Bohun); 3k.60, Madonna and Child" (unknown artist, c. 1350).

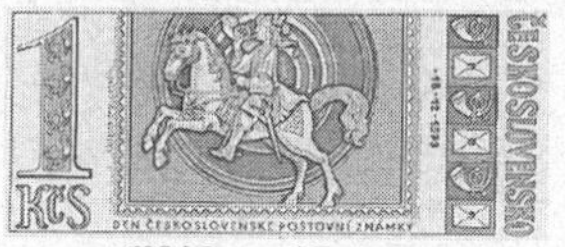
605 Mounted Postman

1973. Stamp Day.
2140 **605** 1k. multicoloured . . . 25 15

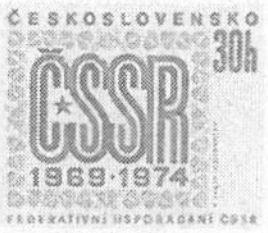
606 "CSSR 1969–1974"

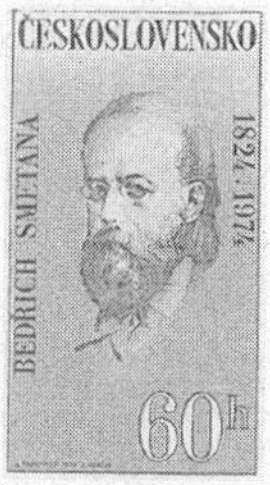
607 Bedrich Smetana (composer) (150th birth anniv)

1974. 5th Anniv of Federal Constitution.
2141 **606** 30h. red, blue and gold 10 10

1974. Celebrities' Birth Anniversaries.
2142 **607** 60h. multicoloured . . . 20 10
2143 – 60h. multicoloured . . . 20 10
2144 – 60h. brown, blue & red 20 10
DESIGNS AND ANNIVERSARIES: No. 2143, Josef Suk (composer, birth anniv); 2144, Pablo Neruda (Chilean poet, 70th birth anniv).

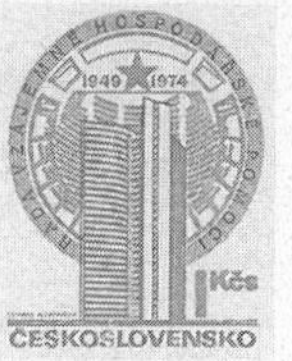
608 Council Building, Moscow

1974. 25th Anniv of Communist Bloc Council of Mutual Economic Assistance.
2145 **608** 1k. violet, red & gold . . 10 10

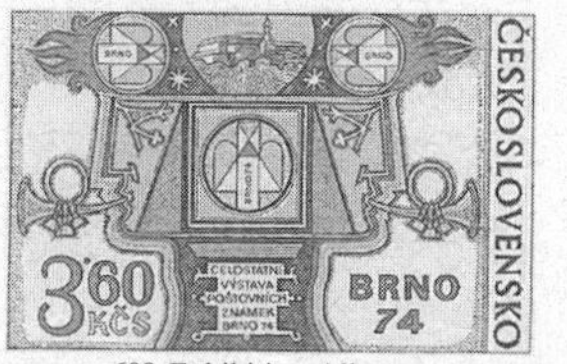
609 Exhibition Allegory

1974. "BRNO 74" National Stamp Exhibition (1st issue).
2146 **609** 3k.60 multicoloured . . 75 25

1974. Czechoslovak Graphic Art (4th series). As T **560**. Inscr "1974". Multicoloured.
2147 60h. "Tulips" (J. Broz) . . . 20 10
2148 1k. "Structures" (O. Dubay) 30 10
2149 1k.60 "Golden Sun-Glowing Day" (A. Zabransky) . . 55 15
2150 1k.80 "Artificial Flowers" (F. Gross) . . . . 1·50 45

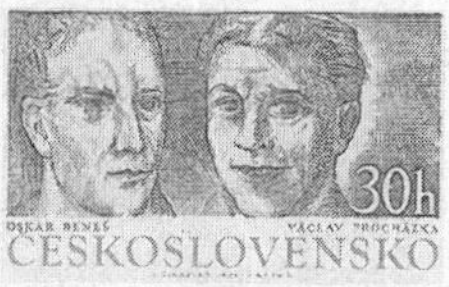
610 Oskar Benes and Vaclav Prochazka

1974. Czechoslovak Partisan Heroes. Mult.
2151 30h. Type **610** 10 10
2152 40h. Milos Uher and Anton Sedlacek 10 10
2153 60h. Jan Hajecek and Marie Sedlackova 15 10
2154 80h. Jan Sverma and Albin Grznar 20 10
2155 1k. Jaroslav Neliba and Alois Hovorka 30 10
2156 1k.60 Ladislav Exnar and Ludovit Kukorelli . . . . 1·50 25

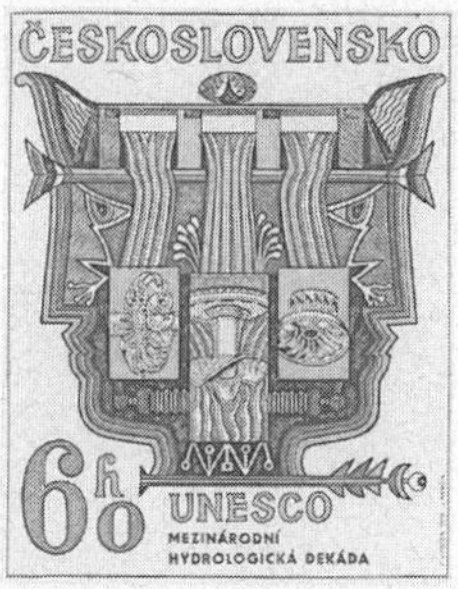
611 "Water—Source of Energy"

1974. International Hydrological Decade. Mult.
2157 60h. Type **611** 55 40
2158 1k. "Water for Agriculture" 55 40
2159 1k.20 "Study of the Oceans" 55 40
2160 1k.60 Decade emblem . . . 60 40
2161 2k. "Keeping water pure" 1·75 1·90

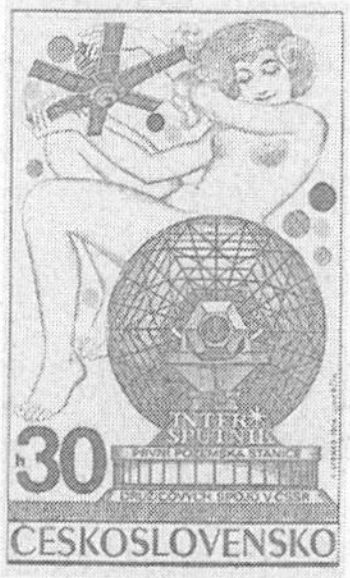
612 "Telecommunications"

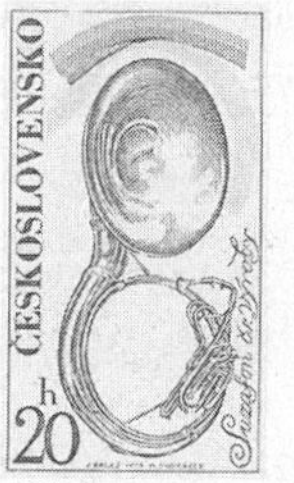
613 Sousaphone

1974. Inauguration of Czechoslovak Satellite Telecommunications Earth Station.
2162 **612** 30h. multicoloured . . . 25 10

1974. Prague Castle (10th series). As Type **536**. Multicoloured.
2163 3k. "Golden Cockerel", 17th-century enamel locket . . . . 1·75 1·90
2164 3k. Bohemian glass monstrance, 1840 . . . . 1·75 1·90

1974. Musical Instruments. Multicoloured.
2165 20h. Type **613** 15 10
2166 30h. Bagpipes 15 10
2167 40h. Benka violin 20 10
2168 1k. Sauer pyramid piano . . 30 15
2169 1k.60 Hulinsky tenor quinton . . . . 1·25 35

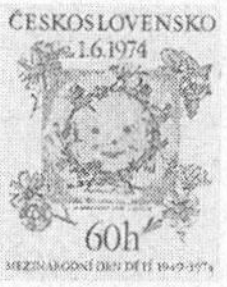
614 Child and Flowers (book illustration)

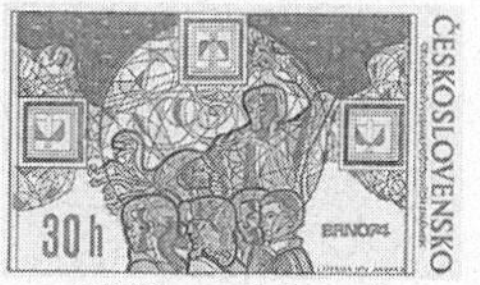
615 "Stamp Collectors"

1974. 25th International Children's Day.
2170 **614** 60h. multicoloured . . . 10 10

1974. "BRNO 74" National Stamp Exhibition (2nd issue). Multicoloured.
2171 30h. Type **615** 10 10
2172 6k. "Rocket Post" . . . . . 2·00 1·60

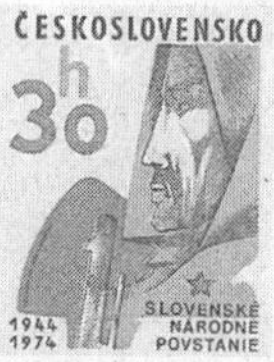
616 Slovak Partisan

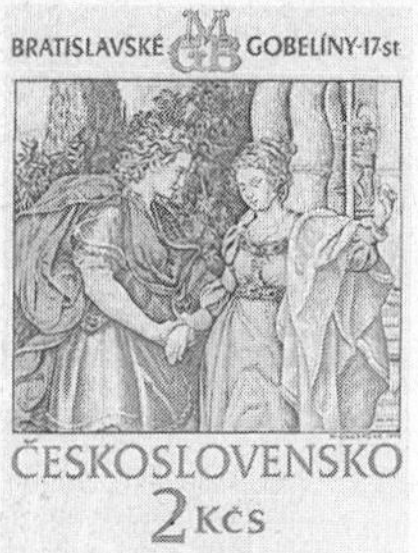
617 "Hero and Leander"

1974. Czechoslovak Anniversaries. Multicoloured.
2173 30h. Type **616** 10 10
2174 30h. Folk-dancer 10 10
2175 30h. Actress holding masks 10 10
EVENTS: No. 2173, 30th anniv of Slovak Uprising;

2174, 25th anniv of Slovak SLUK Folk Song and Dance Ensemble; 2175, 25th anniv of Bratislava Academy of Music and Dramatic Arts.

1974. Bratislava Tapestries. "Hero and Leander" (1st series). Multicoloured.
2176 2k. Type **617** . . . . 1·50 1·40
2177 2k.40 "Leander Swimming across the Hellespont" . . 1·50 1·75
See also Nos. 2227/8 and 2281/2.

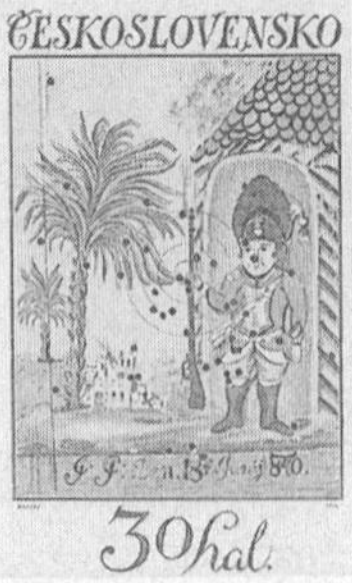
618 "Soldier on Guard"

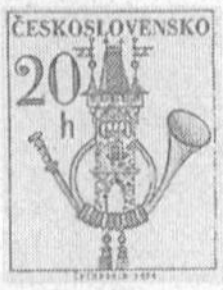
620 Posthorn and Old Town Bridge Tower, Prague

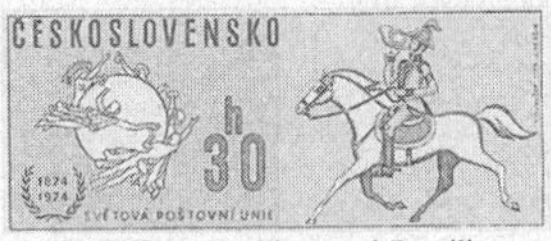
619 U.P.U. Emblem and Postilion

1974. Old Shooting Targets. Multicoloured.
2178 30h. Type **618** 15 10
2179 60h. "Pierrot and Owl", 1828 . . . . 20 15
2180 1k. "Diana awarding Marksman's Crown", 1832 . . . . 30 15
2181 1k.60 "Still Life with Guitar", 1839 . . . . . . 45 45
2182 2k.40 "Stag", 1834 . . . . 70 50
2183 3k. "Turk and Giraffe", 1831 . . . . 2·75 2·75

1974. Centenary of Universal Postal Union. Mult.
2184 30h. Type **619** 10 10
2185 40h. Early mail coach . . . 10 10
2186 60h. Early railway carriage 35 10
2187 80h. Modern mobile post office 25 10
2188 1k. Ilyushin Il-14 mail plane 60 10
2189 1k.60 Dish aerial, earth station . . . . 1·00 35

1974. Czechoslovak Postal Services.
2190 **620** 20h. multicoloured . . . 10 10
2191 – 30h. red, blue & brn . . 10 10
2192 – 40h. multicoloured . . . 15 10
2193 – 60h. orange, yell & bl . . 20 10
DESIGNS: 30h. P.T.T. emblem within letter; 40h. Postilion; 60h. P.T.T. emblem on dove's wing.
See also No. 2900.

1974. Art (9th series). As Type **481**. Multicoloured.
2194 1k. "Self-portrait" (L. Kuba) 80 70
2195 1k.20 "Frantisek Ondricek" (V. Brozik) 80 70
2196 1k.60 "Pitcher with Flowers" (O. Khubin) . . 80 70
2197 1k.80 "Woman with Pitcher" (J. Alexy) . . . 80 70
2198 2k.40 "Bacchanalia" (K. Skreta) . . . . 2·00 1·75

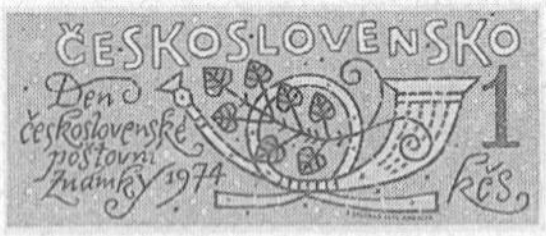
621 Stylized Posthorn

1974. Stamp Day.
2199 **621** 1k. multicoloured . . . 25 10

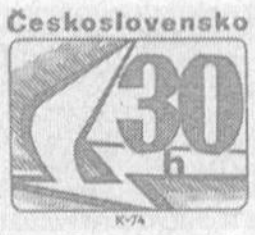
622 Winged Emblem

1975. Coil Stamps.
2200 **622** 30h. blue 10 10
2201 60h. red 15 10

1975. Czechoslovak Graphic Art (5th series). Engraved Hunting Scenes. As T **560**.
2202 60h. brown & cream 25 10
2203 1k. brown and cream . . . 30 20
2204 1k.60 brown & green . . . 45 25
2205 1k.80 brown & lt brown . . 1·75 50
DESIGNS: 60h. "Still Life with Hare" (V. Hollar); 1k. "The Lion and the Mouse" (V. Hollar); 1k.60, "Deer Hunt" (detail, P. Galle); 1k.80, "Grand Hunt" (detail, J. Callot).

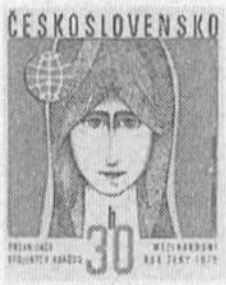
623 "Woman"

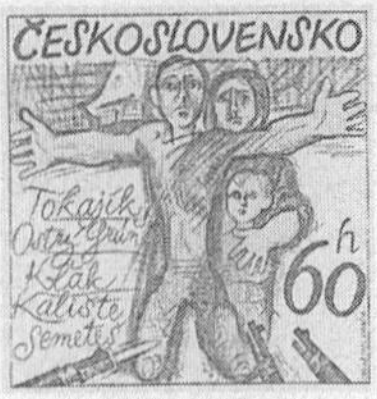
624 Village Family

1975. International Women's Year.
2206 **623** 30h. multicoloured . . . 10 10

1975. 30th Anniv of Razing of 14 Villages. Multicoloured.
2207 60h. Type **624** 20 10
2208 1k. Women and flames . . . 25 10
2209 1k.20 Villagers and flowers 35 10

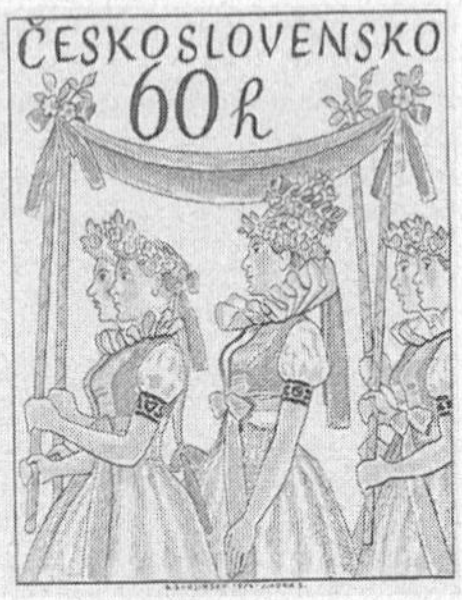
625 "Little Queens" (Moravia)

1975. Czechoslovak Folk Customs. Multicoloured.
2210 60h. Type **625** 60 60
2211 1k. Shrovetide parade, Slovakia 60 60
2212 1k.40 "Maid Dorothea" (play) 60 60
2213 2k. "Morena" effigy, Slovakia . . . . 1·40 1·40

1975. Arms of Czech Regional Capitals (5th series). As T **523**.
2214 60h. black, gold and red . . 20 10
2215 60h. multicoloured . . . 20 10
ARMS: No. 2214, Nymburk. 2215, Znojmo.

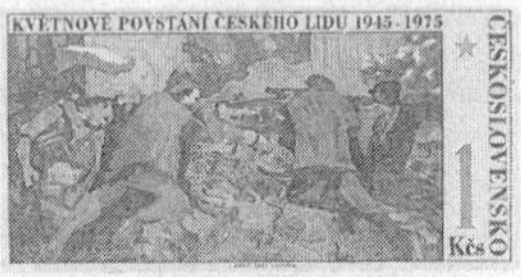
626 Partisans at Barricade (½-size illustration)

1975. Czechoslovak Anniversaries.
2216 **626** 1k. multicoloured . . . 30 15
2217 – 1k. sepia and cream . . 30 15
2218 – 1k. multicoloured . . . 30 15
DESIGNS and ANNIVERSARIES: No. 2216, Type **626** (30th anniv of Czech Rising); 2217, Liberation celebrations (30th anniv of Liberation by Soviet Army); 2218, Czech–Soviet fraternity (5th anniv of Czech–Soviet Treaty).

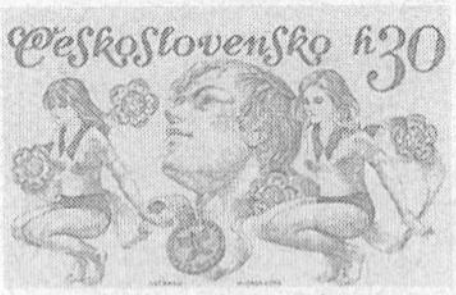
627 Youth Exercises

1975. National Spartacist Games.
2219 **627** 30h. purple, bl & pink 10 10
2220 – 60h. red, lilac & yellow 15 10
2221 – 1k. violet, red & yell . . 25 15
DESIGNS: 60h. Children's exercises; 1k. Adult exercises.

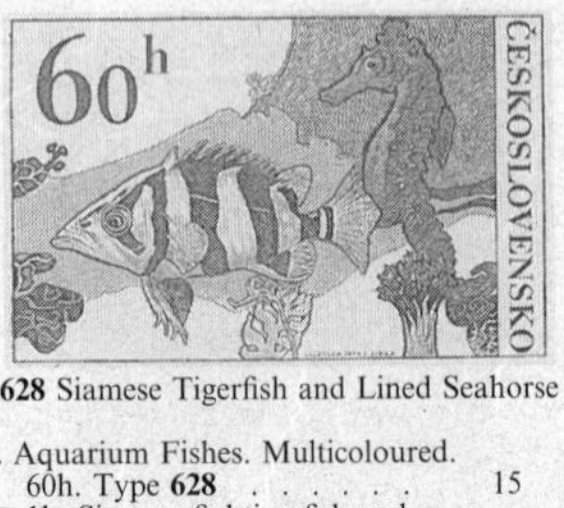

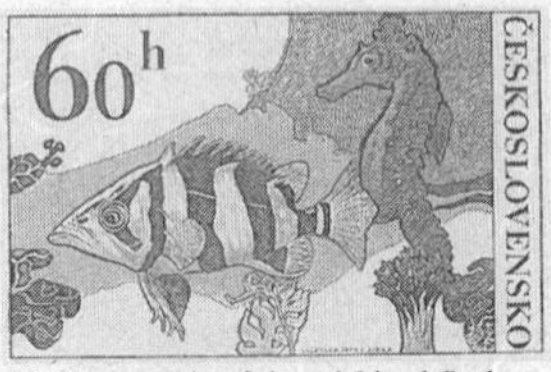
628 Siamese Tigerfish and Lined Seahorse

1975. Aquarium Fishes. Multicoloured.
2222 60h. Type **628** 15 10
2223 1k. Siamese fighting fish and freshwater angelfish . . . 30 10
2224 1k.20 Veil-tailed goldfish . . 60 15
2225 1k.60 Clown anemone-fish and butterflyfish 70 20
2226 2k. Yellow-banded angelfish, palette surgeonfish and semicircle angelfish . . . 3·25 60

1975. Bratislava Tapestries. "Hero and Leander" (2nd series). As T **617**. Multicoloured.
2227 3k. "Leander's Arrival" . . 90 70
2228 3k.60 "Hermione" . . . . . 2·25 2·25

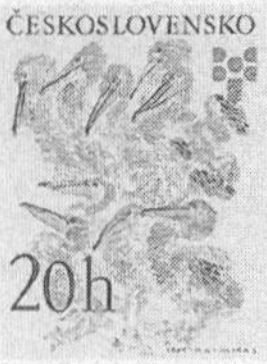
629 "Pelicans" (N. Charushin)

1975. Biennial Exhibition of Book Illustrations for Children, Bratislava. Multicoloured.
2229 20h. Type **629** 10 10
2230 30h. "Sleeping Hero" (L. Schwarz) 10 10
2231 40h. "Horseman" (V. Munteau) 15 10
2232 60h. "Peacock" (K. Ensikat) 20 10
2233 80h. "The Stone King" (R. Dubravec) 70 25

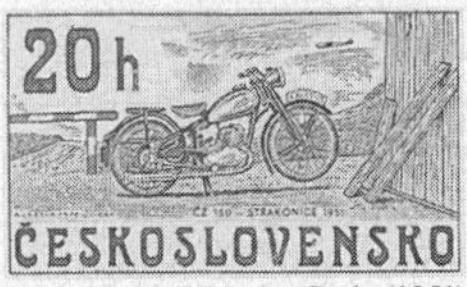
630 "CZ-150" Motor Cycle (1951)

1975. Czechoslovak Motor Cycles. Multicoloured.
2234 20h. Type **630** 15 10
2235 40h. "Jawa 250", 1945 . . . 20 10
2236 60h. "Jawa 175", 1935 . . . 25 10
2237 1k. Janatka "ITAR", 1921 30 15
2238 1k.20 Michi "Orion", 1903 45 20
2239 1k.80 Laurin and Klement, 1898 . . . . 1·60 45

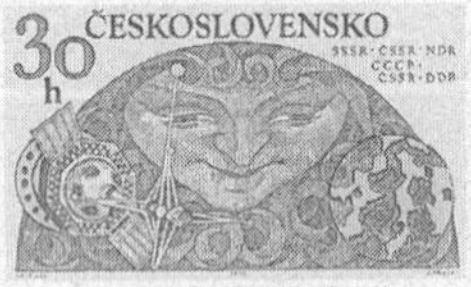
631 "Solar Radiation"

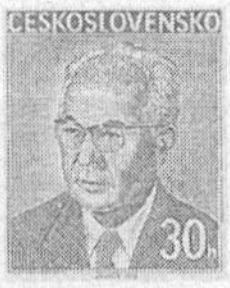
632 President Gustav Husak

1975. Co-operation in Space Research.
2240 **631** 30h. violet, yellow & red 15 10
2241 – 60h. red, lilac & yellow 20 10
2242 – 1k. purple, yell & blue 25 10
2243 – 2k. multicoloured . . . 55 10
2244 – 5k. multicoloured . . . 3·00 2·75
DESIGNS—HORIZ: 60h. "Auroa Borealis"; 1k. Cosmic radiation measurement; 2k. Copernicus and solar radiation. VERT (40 × 50 mm): 5k. "Apollo-soyuz" space link.

1975.
2245 **632** 30h. blue 10 10
2246 60h. red 15 10

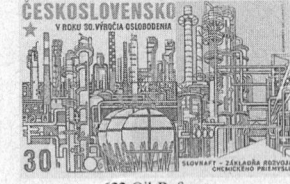

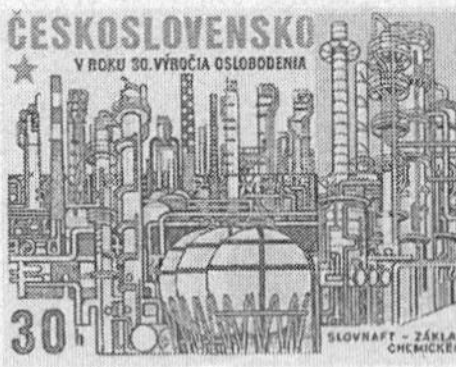
633 Oil Refinery

1975. 30th Anniv of Liberation. Multicoloured.
2247 30h. Type **633** 15 10
2248 60h. Atomic power complex 15 10
2249 1k. Underground Railway, Prague 45 10
2250 1k.20 Laying oil pipelines 35 15
2251 1k.40 Combine-harvesters and granary 30 20
2252 1k.60 Building construction 1·25 40

1975. Prague Castle. Art Treasures (11th series). As T **536**. Multicoloured.
2253 3k. Late 9th-century gold earring 95 85
2254 3k.60 Leather Bohemian Crown case, 1347 . . . . 1·90 1·90

1975. Art (10th series). As T **481**.
2256 1k. red, brown and black . . 75 60
2257 1k.40 multicoloured 75 60
2258 1k.80 multicoloured 75 60
2259 2k.40 multicoloured . . . . 1·10 1·25
2260 3k.40 multicoloured . . . . 1·75 1·75
PAINTINGS—VERT: 1k. "May" (Z. Sklenar); 1k.40, "Girl in National Costume" (E. Nevan); 2k.40, "Fire" (J. Capek); 3k.40, "Prague, 1828" (V. Morstadt). HORIZ: 1k.80, "Liberation of Prague" (A. Cermakova).

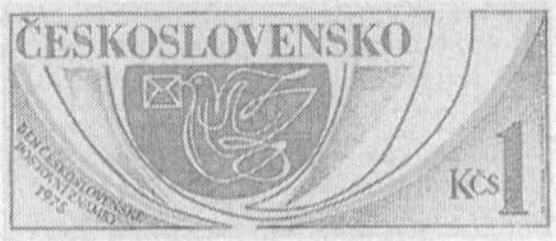
635 Posthorn Motif

1975. Stamp Day.
2261 **635** 1k. multicoloured . . . 35 25

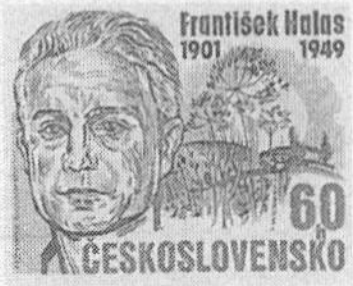
636 Frantisek Halas (poet)

1975. Celebrities' Anniversaries.
2262 **636** 60h. multicoloured . . . 15 10
2263 – 60h. multicoloured . . . 15 10
2264 – 60h. multicoloured . . . 30 10
2265 – 60h. blue, red & yellow 15 10
2266 – 60h. multicoloured . . . 15 10
DESIGNS AND ANNIVERSARIES—HORIZ: No. 2262, Type **636** (75th birth anniv); 2266, Ivan Krasko (poet, birth cent). VERT: No. 2263, Wilhelm Pieck (German statesman, birth cent); 2264, Frantisek Lexa (Egyptologist, birth cent); 2265, Jindrich Jindrich (ethnographer, birth cent).

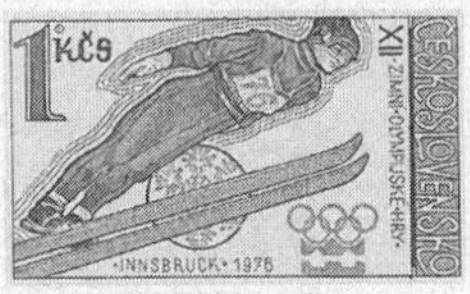
637 Ski Jumping

1976. Winter Olympic Games, Innsbruck. Mult.
2267 1k. Type **637** 20 10
2268 1k.40 Figure skating 30 15
2269 1k.60 Ice hockey . . . . . 1·40 35

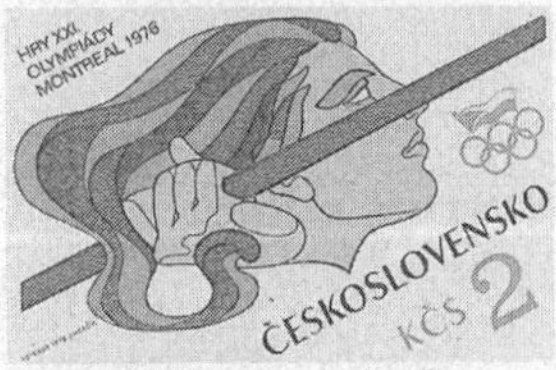
638 Throwing the Javelin

1976. Olympic Games, Montreal. Multicoloured.
2270 2k. Type **638** 45 25
2271 3k. Relay-racing 75 35
2272 3k.60 Putting the shot . . . 2·75 1·10

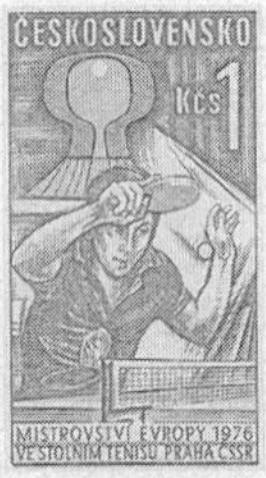
639 Table Tennis Player

1976. European Table Tennis Championships, Prague and 50th Anniv of Organized Table Tennis in Czechoslovakia.
2273 **639** 1k. multicoloured . . . 35 10

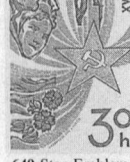

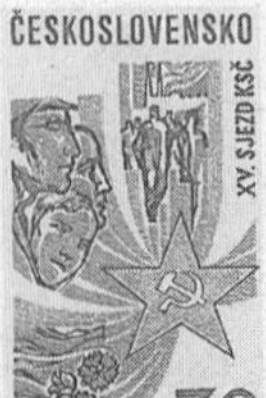
640 Star Emblem and Workers

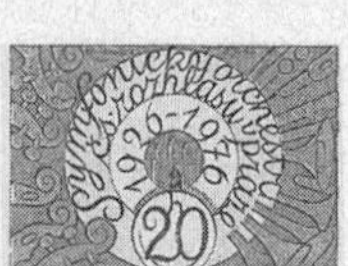
641 Microphone and Musical Instruments

1976. 15th Czechoslovak Communist Party Congress, Prague. Multicoloured.
2274 30h. Type **640** 10 10
2275 60h. Furnace and monolith 15 10

1976. Cultural Events and Anniversaries.
2276 **641** 20h. multicoloured . . . 10 10
2277 – 20h. multicoloured . . . 10 10
2278 – 20h. multicoloured . . . 10 10
2279 – 30h. multicoloured . . . 10 10
2280 – 30h. violet, red & blue 10 10
DESIGNS—HORIZ: No. 2276, Type **641** (50th anniv of Czechoslovak Radio Symphony Orchestra); 2278, Stage revellers (30th anniv of Nova Scena Theatre, Bratislava); 2279, Folk dancers, Wallachia (International Folk Song and Dance Festival,

Straznice). VERT: No. 2277, Ballerina, violin and mask (30th anniv of Prague Academy of Music and Dramatic Art); 2280, Film "profile" (20th Film Festival, Karlovy Vary).

1976. Bratislava Tapestries. "Hero and Leander" (3rd series). As T **617**. Multicoloured.
2281 3k. "Hero with Leander's body" . . . . 2·00 1·25
2282 3k.60 "Eros grieving" . . . 85 55

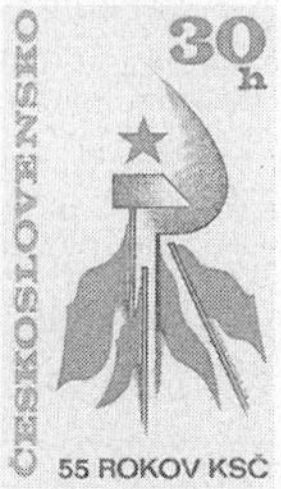

642 Hammer, Sickle and Red Flags

1976. 55th Anniv of Czechoslovak Communist Party.
2283 **642** 30h. blue, gold and red 15 10
2284 – 60h. multicoloured . . . 20 10
DESIGN: 60h. Hammer and Sickle on flag.

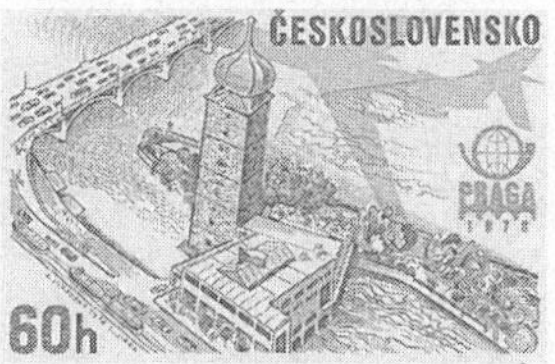

643 Manes Hall, Czechoslovakia Artists' Union

1976. Air. "PRAGA 78" International Stamp Exhibition (1st issue). Prague Architecture. Multicoloured.
2286 60h. Type **643** 35 10
2287 1k.60 Congress Hall, Julius Fucik Park 40 15
2288 2k. Powder Tower, Old Town (vert) 70 20
2289 2k.40 Charles Bridge and Old Bridge Tower 55 20
2290 4k. Old Town Square and Town Hall (vert) 85 35
2291 6k. Prague Castle and St. Vitus Cathedral (vert) . . 3·50 1·00
See also 2313/16, 2326/30, 2339/42, 2349/52, 2358/62, 2389/93, 2407/12, 2413/17 and 2420/3.

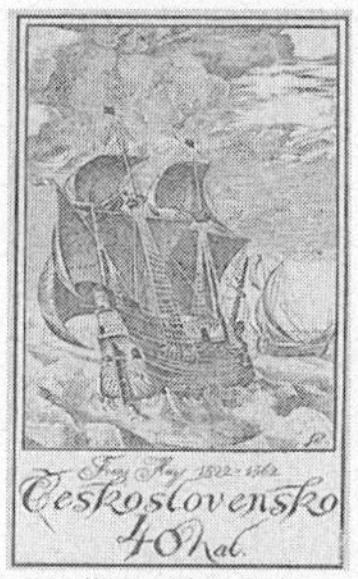

644 "Warship" (Frans Huys)

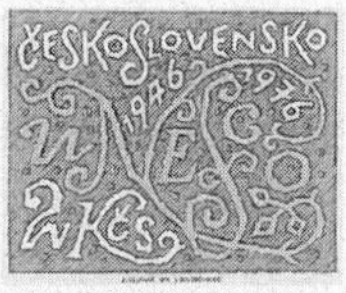

645 "UNESCO" Plant

1976. Ship Engravings.
2292 **644** 40h. blk, cream & drab 35 10
2293 – 60h. blk, cream & grey 35 10
2294 – 1k. black, cream & grn 55 10
2295 – 2k. black, cream & blue 1·25 45
DESIGNS: 60h. "Dutch Merchantman" (V. Hollar); 1k. "Ship at Anchor" (N. Zeeman); 2k. "Galleon under Full Sail" (F. Chereau).

1976. 30th Anniv of U.N.E.S.C.O.
2296 **645** 2k. multicoloured . . . 95 50

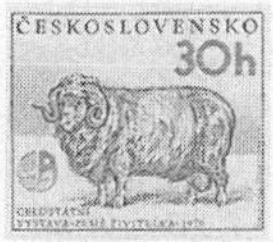

647 Merino Ram

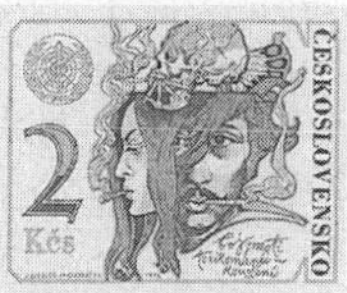

648 "Stop Smoking"

1976. "Bountiful Earth" Agricultural Exhibition, Ceske Budejovice. Multicoloured.
2298 30h. Type **647** 15 10
2299 40h. Berna-Hana Cow . . . 15 10
2300 1k.60 Kladruby stallion . . 45 10

1976. W.H.O. Campaign against Smoking.
2301 **648** 2k. multicoloured . . . 85 45

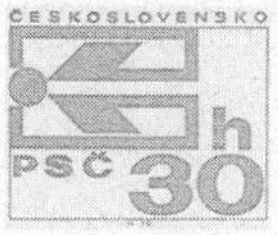

649 Postal Code Emblem

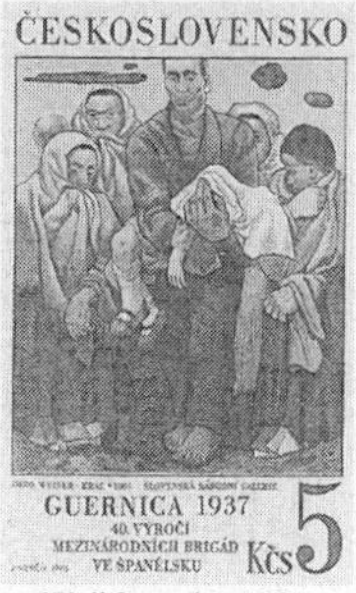

650 "Guernica 1937" (I. Weiner-Kral)

1976. Coil Stamps. Postal Code Campaign.
2302 **649** 30h. green 10 10
2303 – 60h. red 15 10
DESIGN: 60h. Postal map.

1976. 40th Anniv of International Brigades in Spanish Civil War.
2304 **650** 5k. multicoloured . . . 1·10 55

1976. Prague Castle. Art Treasures (12th series). As T **536**. Multicoloured.
2305 3k. "Prague Castle, 1572" (F. Hoogenberghe) . . . 2·00 2·00
2306 3k.60 "Satyrs" (relief from summer-house balustrade) 60 80

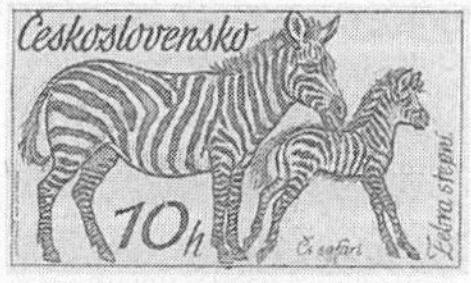

651 Common Zebra with Foal

1976. Dvurkralove Wildlife Park. Multicoloured.
2307 10h. Type **651** 15 10
2308 20h. African elephant, calf and cattle egret (vert) . . 50 15
2309 30h. Cheetah 15 10
2310 40h. Giraffe and calf (vert) 15 10
2311 60h. Black rhinoceros . . . 20 10
2312 3k. Bongo with offspring (vert) . . . . 2·00 70

1976. "PRAGA 1978" International Stamp Exhibition (2nd series). Art (11th series). As T **481**. Multicoloured.
2313 1k. "Flowers in Vase" (P. Matejka) 85 55
2314 1k.40 "Oleander Blossoms" (C. Bouda) . . . . 1·10 80
2315 2k. "Flowers in Vase" (J. Brueghel) . . . . . . 1·75 1·40
2316 3k.60 "Tulips and Narcissi" (J. R. Bys) 85 80

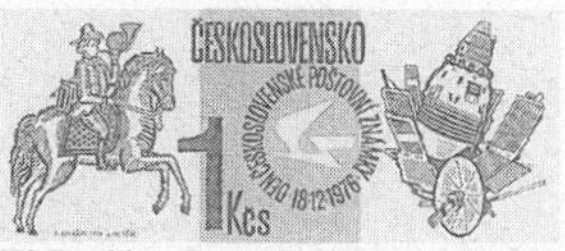

652 Postilion, Postal Emblem and Satellite

1976. Stamp Day.
2317 **652** 1k. blue, mauve & gold 25 10

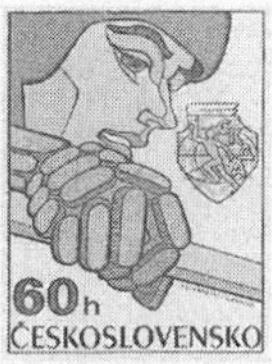

653 Ice Hockey

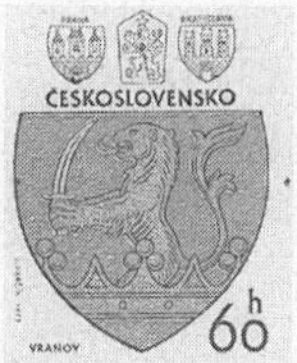

654 Arms of Vranov

1977. 6th Winter Spartakiad of Warsaw Pact Armies. Multicoloured.
2318 60h. Type **653** 25 10
2319 1k. Rifle shooting (Biathlon) 30 10
2320 1k.60 Ski jumping . . . . . 1·40 65
2321 2k. Slalom 50 30

1977. Coats of Arms of Czechoslovak Towns (1st series). Multicoloured.
2322 60h. Type **654** 15 10
2323 60h. Kralupy and Vltavou . 15 10
2324 60h. Jicin 15 10
2325 60h. Valasske Mezirici . . . 15 10
See also Nos. 2511/14, 2612/15, 2720/3, 2765/7, 2819/21 and 3017/20.

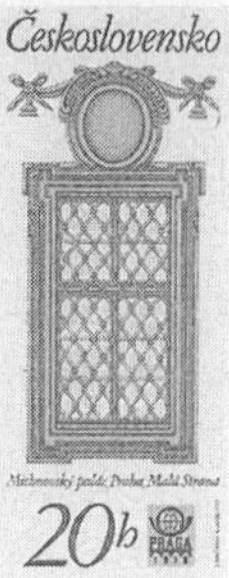

655 Window, Michna Palace

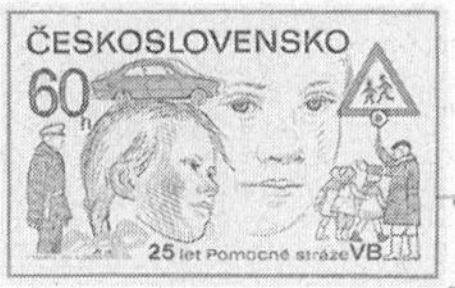

656 Children Crossing Road

1977. "PRAGA 78" International Stamp Exhibition (3rd issue). Historic Prague Windows. Multicoloured.
2326 20h. Type **655** 10 10
2327 30h. Michna Palace (different) 10 10
2328 40h. Thun Palace 10 10
2329 60h. Archbishop's Palace . . 15 10
2330 5k. Church of St. Nicholas 2·10 75

1977. 25th Anniv of Police Aides Corps.
2331 **656** 60h. multicoloured . . . 10 10

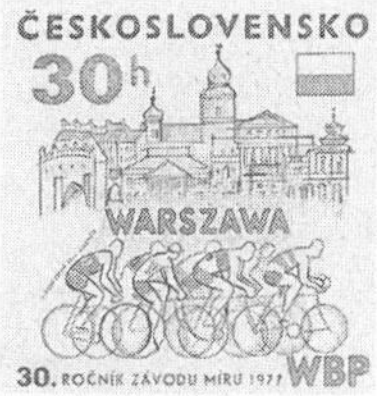

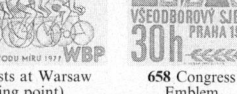

657 Cyclists at Warsaw (starting point)

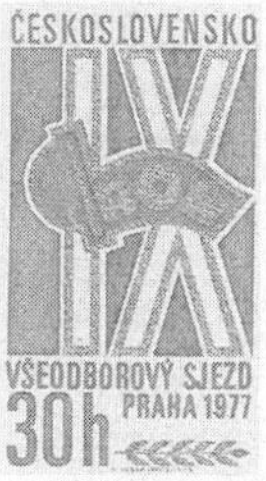

658 Congress Emblem

1977. 30th Anniv of Peace Cycle Race. Mult.
2332 30h. Type **657** 15 10
2333 60h. Cyclists at Berlin . . . 20 10
2334 1k. Cyclists at Prague (finishing point) 90 25
2335 1k.40 Cyclists and modern buildings 40 15

1977. 9th Trade Unions Congress.
2336 **658** 30h. gold, red & carmine 10 10

1977. Prague Castle (13th series). As T **536**.
2337 3k. multicoloured . . . . . 1·10 1·25
2338 3k.60 green, gold & black 1·90 1·50
DESIGNS: 3k. Onyx cup, 1350 (St. Vitus Cathedral); 3k.60, Bronze horse, 1619 (A. de Vries).

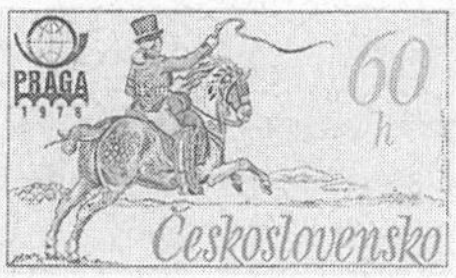

659 French Postal Rider, 19th-century

1977. "PRAGA 78" International Stamp Exhibition (4th issue). Multicoloured.
2339 60h. Type **659** 15 10
2340 1k. Austrian postal rider, 1838 . . . . 25 10
2341 2k. Austrian postal rider, c. 1770 . . . . 45 20
2342 3k.60 German postal rider, 1700 . . . . 2·00 85

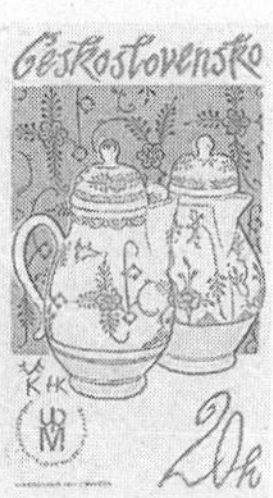

660 Coffee Pots

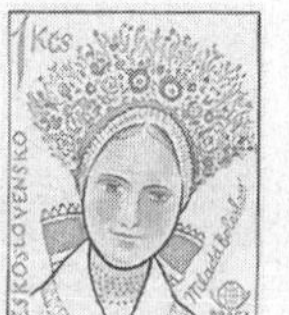

661 Mlada Boleslav Headdress

1977. Czechoslovak Porcelain.
2343 **660** 20h. multicoloured . . . 10 10
2344 – 30h. multicoloured . . . 10 10
2345 – 40h. multicoloured . . . 15 10
2346 – 60h. multicoloured . . . 20 10
2347 – 1k. blue, grn & violet . . 25 10
2348 – 3k. blue, gold and red 2·25 55
DESIGNS: 30h. Vase; 40h. Amphora; 60h. Jug, beaker, cup and saucer; 1k. Plate and candlestick; 3k. Coffee pot, cup and saucer.

1977. "PRAGA 78" International Stamp Exhibition (5th issue). Regional Headdresses. Multicoloured.
2349 1k. Type **661** 75 75
2350 1k.60 Vazek . . . . 3·50 3·50
2351 3k.60 Zavadka 75 75
2352 5k. Belkovice . . . . 1·25 1·25

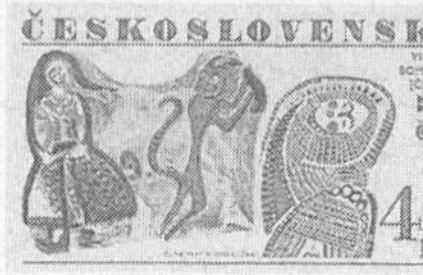

662 V. Bombova's Illustrations of "Janko Gondashik and the Golden Lady"

1977. 6th Biennial Exhibition of Children's Book Illustrators, Bratislava. Multicoloured.
2353 40h. Type **662** 10 10
2354 60h. "Tales of Amur" (G. Pavlishin) 15 10
2355 1k. "Almgist et Wiksel" (U. Lofgren) 25 10
2356 2k. "Alice in Wonderland" and "Through the Looking Glass" (Nicole Claveloux) 75 25
2357 3k. "Eventyr" (J. Trnka) . . 2·25 65

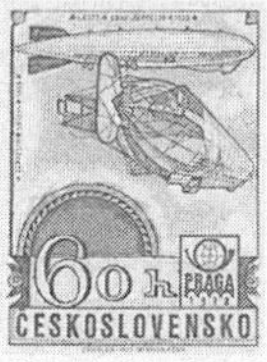

663 Airships LZ-5 and "Graf Zeppelin"

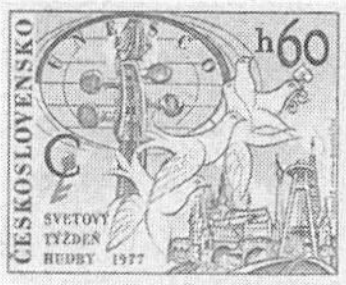

664 U.N.E.S.C.O. Emblem, Violin and Doves

1977. Air. "PRAGA 1978" International Stamp Exhibition (6th issue). Early Aviation. Mult.
2358 60h. Type **663** 15 10
2359 1k. Clement Ader's monoplane "Eole", Etrich Holubice and Dunne D-8 30 10
2360 1k.60 Jeffries and Blanchard balloon, 1785 . . . . . . 40 15
2361 2k. Lilienthal biplane glider, 1896 . . . . 50 20
2362 4k.40 Jan Kaspar's Bleriot XI over Prague . . . . . 3·50 90

1977. Congress of U.N.E.S.C.O. International Music Council.
2363 **664** 60h. multicoloured . . . 10 10

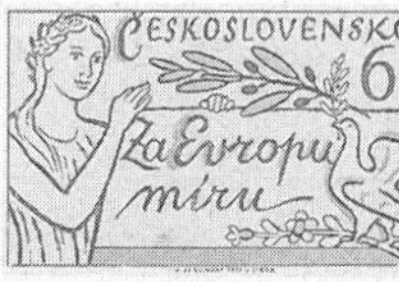

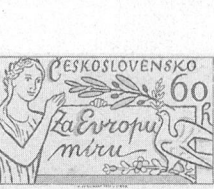

665 "Peace"

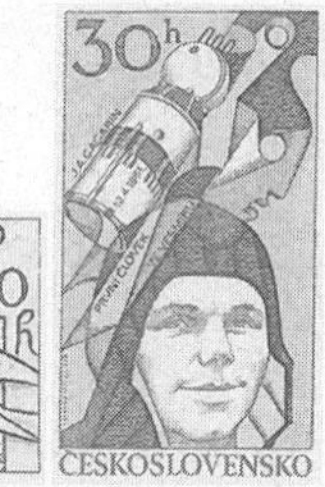

666 Yuri Gagarin

1977. European Co-operation for Peace. Mult.
2364 60h. Type **665** 15 10
2365 1k.60 "Co-operation" . . . 40 20
2366 2k.40 "Social Progress" . . 1·50 65

1977. Space Research. Multicoloured.
2367 20h. S. P. Koroliov (space technician, launch of first satellite) 10 10
2368 30h. Type **666** (first man in space) 10 10
2369 40h. Aleksei Leonov (first space walker) 10 10
2370 1k. Neil Armstrong (first man on the Moon) . . . 25 10
2371 1k.60 "Salyut" and "Skylab" space stations 1·25 35

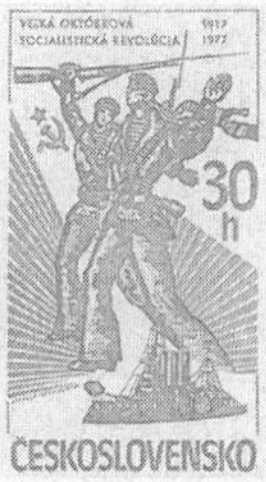

667 Revolutionaries and Cruiser "Aurora"

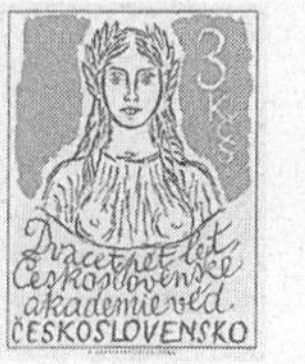

668 "Wisdom"

1977. 60th Anniv of Russian Revolution, and 55th Anniv of U.S.S.R. Multicoloured.
2372 30h. Type **667** 15 10
2373 30h. Russian woman, Kremlin, rocket and U.S.S.R. arms 15 10

1977. 25th Anniv of Czechoslovak Academy of Science.
2374 **668** 3k. multicoloured . . . 70 25

1977. Art (12th series). As Type **481**.
2375 2k. multicoloured 75 70
2376 2k.40 multicoloured . . . . 2·50 3·00
2377 2k.60 stone and black . . . 2·10 1·60

2378　3k. multicoloured .... 1·00　95
2379　5k. multicoloured .... 1·00　95
DESIGNS: 2k. "Fear" (J. Mudroch); 2k.40, "Portrait of Jan Francis" (P. M. Bohun); 2k.60, "Self Portrait" (V. Hollar); 3k. "Portrait of a Girl" (L. Cranach); 5k. "Cleopatra" (Rubens).

669 "Bratislava, 1574" (G. Hoefnagel)

1977. Historic Bratislava (1st series). Mult.
2380　3k. Type 669 ..... 1·90　2·00
2381　3k.60 Bratislava Arms, 1436　1·10　80
　See also Nos. 2402/3, 2500/1, 2545/6, 2582/3, 2642/3, 2698/9, 2736/7, 2793/4, 2842/3, 2898/9, 2952/3, 2997/8 and 3034/5.

670 Posthorn and Stamps

1977. Stamp Day.
2382　670 1k. multicoloured ... 25

671 Z. Nejedly　　674 Modern Coins
(historian)

672 Civilians greeting Armed Guards

1978. Cultural Anniversaries. Multicoloured.
2383　30h. Type 671 (birth cent)　10　10
2384　40h. Karl Marx (160th birth
　　　anniv) .... 10　10

1978. 30th Annivs of "Victorious February" and National Front. Multicoloured.
2385　1k. Type 672 .... 20　10
2386　1k. Intellectual, peasant
　　　woman and steel worker　20　10

1978. Soviet–Czechoslovak Space Flight. No. 2368 optd **SPOLECNY LET SSSR*CSSR**.
2387　30h. red .... 20　20
2388　3k.60 blue .... 4·00　4·50

1978. 650th Anniv of Kremnica Mint and "PRAGA 1978" International Stamp Exhibition (7th issue). Multicoloured.
2389　20h. Type 674 ..... 10　10
2390　40h. Culture medal, 1972
　　　(Jan Kulich) ..... 10　10
2391　1k.40 Charles University
　　　Medal, 1948 (O. Spaniel)　2·40　35
2392　3k. Ferdinand I medal, 1563
　　　(L. Richter) ...... 80　40
2393　5k. Gold florin of Charles
　　　Robert, 1335 .... 95　55

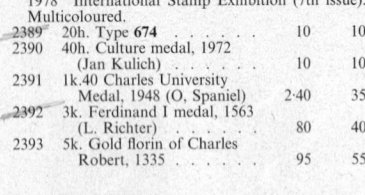

675 Tyre Marks and　676 Hands supporting
　　Ball　　　　　　　　Globe

1978. Road Safety.
2394　675 60h. multicoloured ... 10　10

1978. 9th World Federation of Trade Unions Congress, Prague.
2395　676 1k. multicoloured ... 20　10

677 Putting the Shot

1978. Sports.
2396　– 30h. multicoloured ... 15　10
2397　677 40h. multicoloured ... 15　10
2398　– 60h. multicoloured ... 70　20
2399　– 1k. multicoloured ... 35　10
2400　– 2k. yellow, blue & red　55　25
2401　– 3k.60 multicoloured ... 1·75　80
DESIGNS AND EVENTS—HORIZ: 70th anniv of bandy hockey: 30h. Three hockey players, World Ice Hockey Championships; 60h. Tackle in front of goal; 2k. Goalmouth scrimmage. VERT: European Athletics Championships, Prague: 1k. Pole vault; 3k.60, Running.

1978. Historic Bratislava (2nd series). As T 669.
2402　3k. green, violet and red　1·25　1·25
2403　3k.60 multicoloured ... 2·75　2·50
DESIGNS: 3k. "Bratislava" (Orest Dubay); 3k.60, "Fishpond Square, Bratislava" (Imro Weiner-Kral).

1978. Prague Castle (14th series). As T 536.
2404　3k. yellow, black & green　90　80
2405　3k.60 multicoloured ... 3·00　2·50
DESIGNS: 3k. Memorial to King Premysl Otakar II, St. Vitus Cathedral; 3k.60, Portrait of King Charles IV (Jan Ocka).

678 Ministry of Posts, Prague

1978. 14th COMECON Meeting, Prague.
2406　678 60h. multicoloured ... 10　10

679 Palacky Bridge

1978. "PRAGA 78" International Stamp Exhibition (8th issue). Prague Bridges. Multicoloured.
2407　20h. Type 679 ..... 10　10
2408　40h. Railway bridge ... 55　10
2409　1k. Bridge of 1st May ... 25　10
2410　2k. Manes Bridge ..... 45　20
2411　3k. Svatopluk Cech Bridge　55　35
2412　5k.40 Charles Bridge ... 3·50　1·10

680 St. Peter and other　681 Dancers
　　Apostles

1978. "PRAGA 78" International Stamp Exhibition (9th issue). Prague Town Hall Astronomical Clock. Multicoloured.
2413　40h. Type 680 ..... 15　10
2414　1k. Astronomical clock face　20　15
2415　2k. Centre of Manes's
　　　calendar .... 35　20
2416　3k. "September" (grape
　　　harvest) .... 2·00　75
2417　3k.60 "Libra" (sign of the
　　　Zodiac) .... 1·25　25

1978. 25th Vychodna Folklore Festival.
2419　681 30h. multicoloured ... 10　10

682 Gottwald Bridge

1978. "PRAGA 78" International Stamp Exhibition (10th issue). Modern Prague. Multicoloured.
2420　60h. Type 682 ...... 60　10
2421　1k. Powder Gate Tower and
　　　Kotva department store　25　10
2422　2k. Ministry of Posts ... 50　20
2423　6k. Prague Castle and flats　2·00　1·25

685 Fair Buildings　　686 "Postal
　　　　　　　　　　　Newspaper Service"
　　　　　　　　　　　(25th Anniv)

1978. 20th International Engineering Fair, Brno.
2426　685 30h. multicoloured ... 10　10

1978. Press, Broadcasting and Television Days.
2427　686 30h. green, blue & orge　10　10
2428　– 30h. multicoloured ... 10　10
2429　– 30h. multicoloured ... 10　10
DESIGNS: No. 2428, Microphone, newspapers, camera and Ministry of Information and Broadcasting; 2429, Television screen and Television Centre, Prague (25th anniv of Czechoslovak television).

687 Horses falling at Fence

1978. Pardubice Steeplechase. Multicoloured.
2430　10h. Type 687 ...... 10　10
2431　20h. Sulky racing ..... 10　10
2432　30h. Racing horses .... 15　10
2433　40h. Passing the winning
　　　post .... 15　10
2434　1k.60 Jumping a fence ... 40　20
2435　4k.40 Jockey leading a
　　　winning horse ..... 2·50　1·00

688 Woman holding Arms of
　　Czechoslovakia

1978. 60th Anniv of Independence.
2436　688 60h. multicoloured ... 10　10

689 "Still Life with Flowers"　690 Violinist and
　　(J. Bohdan)　　　　　　　Bass Player
　　　　　　　　　　　　　　　(J. Konyves)

1978. 30th Anniv of Slovak National Gallery, Bratislava. Multicoloured.
2437　2k.40 Type 689 ..... 75　60
2438　3k. "Dream in a Shepherd's
　　　Hut" (L. Fulla) (horiz)　75　75
2439　3k.60 "Apostle with Censer"
　　　(detail, Master of the Spis
　　　Chapter) .... 3·50　3·50

1978. Slovak Ceramics.
2440　690 20h. multicoloured ... 10　10
2441　– 30h. blue and violet ... 10　10

2442　– 40h. multicoloured ... 10　10
2443　– 1k. multicoloured ... 25　10
2444　– 1k.60 multicoloured ... 2·00　25
DESIGNS: 30h. Horseman (J. Franko); 40h. Man in Kilt (M. Polasko); 1k. Three girl singers (I. Bizmayer); 1k.60, Miner with axe (F. Kostka).

691 Alfons Mucha and design for 1918
Hradcany Stamp

1978. Stamp Day.
2445　691 1k. multicoloured ... 20　15

692 Council Building,
Moscow

1979. Anniversaries.
2446　– 30h. brown, grn & orge　10　10
2447　– 60h. multicoloured ... 15　10
2448　692 1k. multicoloured ... 20　10
DESIGNS—HORIZ: 30h. Girl's head and ears of wheat (30th anniv of Unified Agricultural Co-operatives); 60h. Czechoslovakians and doves (10th anniv of Czechoslovak Federation). VERT: 1k. Type 692 (30th anniv of Council of Economic Mutual Aid).

693 "Soyuz 28"

1979. 1st Anniv of Russian–Czech Space Flight. Multicoloured.
2449　30h. Type 693 ..... 15　10
2450　60h. A. Gubarev and V.
　　　Remek (vert) ..... 15　10
2451　1k.60 J. Romanenko and G.
　　　Grechko .... 45　10
2452　2k. "Salyut 6" space
　　　laboratory ...... 1·90　45
2453　4k. "Soyuz 28" touch down
　　　(vert) .... 85　45

694 "Campanula　　695 Stylized
　　alpina"　　　　　Satellite

1979. 25th Anniv of Mountain Rescue Service. Multicoloured.
2455　10h. Type 694 ..... 10　10
2456　20h. "Crocus scepusiensis"　10　10
2457　30h. "Dianthus glacialis"　10　10
2458　40h. Alpine hawkweed ... 15　10
2459a　3k. "Delphinium
　　　oxysepalum" ..... 1·25　50

1979. Anniversaries.
2460　695 10h. multicoloured ... 10　10
2461　– 20h. multicoloured ... 10　10
2462　– 20h. blue, orge & lt bl　10　10
2463　– 30h. blue, gold & red ... 10　10
2464　– 30h. red, blue & blk ... 10　10
2465　– 60h. multicoloured ... 15　10
DESIGNS AND EVENTS—HORIZ: No. 2460, Type 695 30th anniv of Telecommunications Research. 46 × 19 mm: (No. 2461), Artist and model (30th anniv of Academy of Fine Arts, Bratislava); 2462, Student and technological equipment (40th anniv of Slovak Technical University, Bratislava); 2463, Musical instruments and Bratislava Castle (50th anniv of Radio Symphony Orchestra, Bratislava); 2464, Pioneer's scarf and I.Y.C. emblem (30th anniv of Young Pioneer Organization and International Year of the Child); 2465, Adult and child with doves (30th anniv of Peace Movement).

1979. Prague Castle (15th series). As T 536. Multicoloured.
2466　3k. Burial crown of King
　　　Premysl Otakar II　2·25　2·25
2467　3k.60 Portrait of Miss B.
　　　Reitmayer (Karel
　　　Purkyne) ...... 1·10　1·00

696 Arms of Vlachovo Brezi

697 Healthy and Polluted Forests

1979. Animals in Heraldry. Multicoloured.
2468 30h. Type **696** 10 10
2469 60h. Jesenik (bear and eagle) 15 10
2470 1k.20 Vysoke Myto (St. George and the dragon) 30 10
2471 1k.80 Martin (St. Martin on horseback) . . . . . . 1·60 40
2472 2k. Zebrak (half bear, half lion) 40 10

1979. Man and the Biosphere. Multicoloured.
2473 60h. Type **697** 15 15
2474 1k.80 Clear and polluted water 45 30
2475 3k.60 Healthy and polluted urban environment . . . 2·50 90
2476 4k. Healthy and polluted pasture 90 35

698 Numeral and Printed Circuit

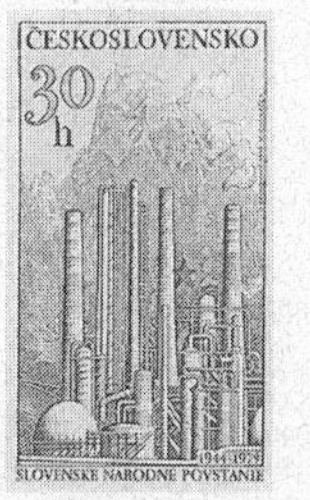
699 Industrial Complex

1979. Coil Stamps.
2477 – 50h. red 15 10
2478 **698** 1k. brown 20 10
2478a – 2k. green 50 25
2478b – 3k. purple 80 35
DESIGNS: Numeral and—50h. Dish aerial; 2k. Airplane; 3k. Punched tape.

1979. 35th Anniv of Slovak Uprising.
2479 **699** 30h. multicoloured . . . 10 10

700 Illustration by Janos Kass

1979. International Year of the Child and Biennial Exhibition of Children's Book Illustrations, Bratislava. Designs showing illustrations by artists named. Multicoloured.
2480 20h. Type **700** 10 10
2481 40h. Rumen Skorcev . . . 15 10
2482 60h. Karel Svolinsky . . . 15 10
2483 1k. Otto S. Svend 30 10
2484 3k. Tatyana Mavrina . . . 1·90 50

701 Modern Bicycles

1979. Historic Bicycles. Multicoloured.
2485 20h. Type **701** 15 10
2486 40h. Bicycles, 1910 . . . . 15 10
2487 60h. "Ordinary" and tricycle, 1886 . . . . . . 15 10
2488 2k. "Bone-shakers", 1870 50 20
2489 3k.60 Drais cycles, 1820 . . 2·75 75

702 Bracket Clock (Jan Kraus)

1979. Historic Clocks. Multicoloured.
2490 40h. Type **702** 10 10
2491 60h. Rococo clock 15 10
2492 80h. Classicist clock . . . . 1·75 35
2493 1k. Rococo porcelain clock (J. Kandler) 25 10
2494 2k. Urn-shaped clock (Dufaud) 50 20

1979. Art (13th series). As T **481**.
2495 1k.60 multicoloured 70 55
2496 2k. multicoloured 80 65
2497 3k. multicoloured . . . . . 1·10 85
2498 3k.60 multicoloured . . . . 3·00 2·75
2499 5k. yellow and black . . . . 90 1·10
DESIGNS: 1k.60, "Sunday by the River" (Alois Moravec); 2k. "Self-portrait" (Gustav Mally); 3k. "Self-portrait" (Ilja Jefimovic Repin); 3k.60, "Horseback Rider" (Jan Bauch); 5k. "Village Dancers" (Albrecht Durer).

1979. Historic Bratislava (3rd issue). As T **669**. Multicoloured.
2500 3k. "Bratislava, 1787" (L. Janscha) . . . . . . 1·10 95
2501 3k.60 "Bratislava, 1815" (after stone engraving by Wolf) . . . . 2·50 2·40

703 Postmarks, Charles Bridge and Prague Castle

1979. Stamp Day.
2502 **703** 1k. multicoloured 25 10

704 Skiing

1980. Winter Olympic Games, Lake Placid.
2503 **704** 1k. multicoloured . . . 25 10
2504 – 2k. red, pink & blue . . 1·60 40
2505 – 3k. multicoloured . . . 1·00 50
DESIGNS: 2k. Ice skating; 3k. Four-man bobsleigh.

705 Basketball

1980. Olympic Games, Moscow, Multicoloured.
2506 40h. Type **705** 15 10
2507 1k. Swimming 25 10
2508 2k. Hurdles . . . . 2·50 45
2509 3k.60 Fencing 90 35

706 Marathon

1980. 50th International Peace Marathon, Kosice.
2510 **706** 50h. multicoloured . . . 10 10

1980. Arms of Czech Towns (2nd series). As T **654**.
2511 50h. blue, black and gold 15 10
2512 50h. black and silver 15 10
2513 50h. multicoloured 15 10
2514 50h. gold, black and blue 15 10
DESIGNS: No. 2511, Bystrice nad Pernstejnem; 2512, Kunstat; 2513, Rozmital pod Tremsinem; 2514, Zlata Idka.

707 Bratislava Opera House and Bakovazena as King Lear

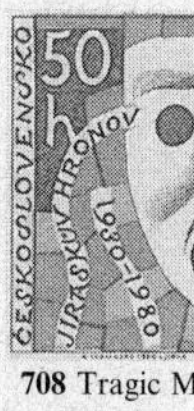
708 Tragic Mask

1980. 60th Anniv of Slovak National Theatre, Bratislava.
2515 **707** 1k. blue, yellow & orange 20 10

1980. 50th Anniv of Theatrical Review "Jiraskuv Hronov".
2516 **708** 50h. multicoloured . . . 10 10

709 Mouse in Space

710 Police Parade Banner

1980. "Intercosmos" Space Programme.
2517 **709** 50h. blue, black and red 15 10
2518 – 1k. multicoloured . . . 30 10
2519 – 1k.60 violet, blk & red 2·25 60
2520 – 4k. multicoloured . . . 1·00 35
2521 – 5k. blue, black & purple 1·50 45
DESIGNS—VERT: 1k. Weather map and satellite; 1k.60, "Inter-sputnik" T.V. transmission; 4k. Survey satellite and camera. HORIZ: 5k. Czech-built satellite station; 10k. "Intercosmos" emblem.

1980. 35th Anniv of National Police Corps.
2523 **710** 50h. gold, red & blue . . 10 10

711 Lenin

712 Flag, Flowers and Prague Buildings

1980. 110th Birth Anniv of Lenin and 160th Birth Anniv of Engels.
2524 **711** 1k. brown, red & grey 20 10
2525 – 1k. blue and brown . . . 20 10
DESIGN: No. 2525, Engels.

1980. Anniversaries. Multicoloured.
2526 50h. Type **712** 15 10
2527 1k. Child writing "Mir" (peace) 25 10
2528 1k. Czech and Soviet arms 25 10
2529 1k. Flowers, flags and dove 25 10
ANNIVERSARIES: No. 2526, 35th anniv of May uprising; 2527, 35th anniv of Liberation; 2528, 10th anniv of Czech–Soviet Treaty; 2529, 25th anniv of Warsaw Pact.

713 Gymnast

1980. National Spartakiad.
2530 – 50h. black, red & blue 10 10
2531 **713** 1k. multicoloured . . . 25 10
DESIGN: HORIZ:- 50h. Opening parade of athletes.

715 "Gerbera jamesonii"

716 "Chod Girl"

1980. Olomuc and Bratislava Flower Shows. Multicoloured.
2533 50h. Type **715** 15 15
2534 1k. "Aechmea fasciata" . . 1·75 35
2535 2k. Bird of paradise flower 35 25
2536 4k. Slipper orchid 85 45

1980. Graphic Cut-outs by Cornelia Nemeckova.
2537 **716** 50h. multicoloured . . . 15 10
2238 – 1k. mauve, brown & red 25 10
2539 – 2k. multicoloured . . . 45 20
2540 – 4k. multicoloured . . . 2·50 90
2541 – 5k. blue, mauve & lt bl 1·10 50
DESIGNS: 1k. "Punch with his dog"; 2k. "Dandy cat with Posy"; 4k. Lion and Moon ("Evening Contemplation"); 5k. Dancer and piper ("Wallachian Dance").

717 Map of Czechoslovakia and Family

718 Heads

1980. National Census.
2542 **717** 1k. multicoloured . . . 20 10

1980. Prague Castle (16th series). As T **536**. Multicoloured.
2543 3k. Gateway of Old Palace 2·50 2·50
2544 4k. Armorial lion . . . . . 1·10 75

1980. Historic Bratislava (4th issue). As T **669**. Multicoloured.
2545 3k. "View across the Danube" (J. Eder) . . . . 2·50 2·50
2546 4k. "The Old Royal Bridge" (J. A. Lantz) . . . . . . 1·10 75

1980. 10th Anniv of Socialist Youth Federation.
2547 **718** 50h. blue, orange & red 10 10

1980. Paintings (14th series). As T **481**.
2549 1k. buff, blue and brown . . 1·25 1·00
2550 2k. multicoloured . . . . . 2·00 2·10
2551 3k. red, brown and green . . 55 55
2552 4k. multicoloured 65 55
2553 5k. green, buff and black . . 85 80
DESIGNS—VERT: 1k. "Pavel Jozef Safarik" (Jozef B. Klemens); 2k. "Peasant Revolt" (mosaic, A. Podzemma); 3k. Bust of Saint from Lucivna Church; 5k. "Labour" (sculpture, Jan Stursa). HORIZ: 4k. "Waste Heaps" (Jan Zrzavy).

719 Carrier Pigeon

1980. Stamp Day.
2554 **719** 1k. black, red & blue . . 25 10

720 Five Year Plan Emblem

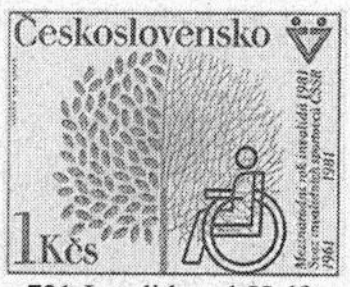
721 Invalid and Half-bare Tree

1981. 7th Five Year Plan.
2555 **720** 50h. multicoloured . . . 10 10

1981. International Year of Disabled Persons.
2556 **721** 1k. multicoloured . . . 25 10

722 Landau, 1800

723 Jan Sverma (partisan)

1981. Historic Coaches in Postal Museum.
2557 **722** 50h. yellow, black & red 20 10
2558 – 1k. yellow, black & grn 30 10
2559 – 3k.60 lt blue, blk & bl 2·00 40
2560 – 5k. stone, black & red 1·25 50
2561 – 7k. yellow, black & blue 1·50 65
DESIGNS: 1k. Mail coach, c. 1830–40; 3k.60, Postal sleigh, 1840; 5k. Mail coach and four horses, 1860; 7k. Coupe carriage, 1840.

1981. Celebrities' Anniversaries. Multicoloured.
2562 50h. Type **723** (80th birth anniv) 20 10
2563 50h. Mikulas Schneider-Trnavsky (composer) (birth cent) 30 10
2564 50h. Juraj Hronec (mathematician) (birth cent) 20 10
2565 50h. Josef Hlavka (architect) (150th birth anniv) . . . 20 10
2566 1k. Dimitri Shostakovich (composer) (75th birth anniv) 50 10
2567 1k. George Bernard Shaw (dramatist) (125th birth anniv) 50 10
2568 1k. Bernardo Bolzano (philosopher) (birth bicent) . . . . 1·25 30
2569 1k. Wolfgang Amadeus Mozart (composer) (225th birth anniv) 60 20

725 Party Member with Flag

1981. 60th Anniv of Czechoslovak Communist Party. Multicoloured.
2571 50h. Type **725** 10 15
2572 1k. Symbols of progress and hands holding flag 25 15
2573 4k. Party member holding flag bearing symbols of industry (vert) 75 40

726 Hammer and Sickle

1981. 16th Czechoslovak Communist Party Congress. Multicoloured.
2574 50h. Type **726** 10 10
2575 1k. "XVI" and Prague buildings 20 10

727 Fallow-plough **728** Man, Woman and Dove

1981. 90th Anniv of Agricultural Museum.
2577 **727** 1k. multicoloured . . . 25 10

1981. Elections to Representative Assemblies.
2578 **728** 50h. red, stone & blue 10 10

729 "Uran" (Tatra Mountains) and "Rudy Rijen" (Bohemia)

1981. Achievements of Socialist Construction (1st series). Multicoloured.
2579 80h. Type **729** (Trade Union recreational facilities) . . . 25 10
2580 1k. Prague–Brno–Bratislava expressway 30 15
2581 2k. Jaslovske Bohunice nuclear plant 50 20
See also Nos. 2644/6, 2695/7, 2753/5 and 2800/2.

1981. Historic Bratislava (5th issue). As T **669**. Multicoloured.
2582 3k. "Bratislava, 1760" (G. B. Probst) . . . . . 2·10 2·75
2583 4k. "Grassalkovichov Palace, 1815" (C. Bschor) 60 70

731 Puppets **732** Map

1981. 30th National Festival of Amateur Puppetry Ensembles, Chrudim.
2585 **731** 2k. multicoloured . . . 40 25

1981. National Defence. Multicoloured.
2586 40h. Type **732** (Defence of borders) 10 10
2587 50h. Emblem of Civil Defence Organization (30th Anniv) (vert) . . . 15 10
2588 1k. Emblem of Svazarm (Organization for Co-operation with Army, 30th anniv) (28 × 23 mm) 20 10

733 Edelweiss, Climbers and Lenin

1981. 25th International Youth Climb of Rysy Peaks.
2589 **733** 3k.60 multicoloured . . 85 40

734 Illustration by Albin Brunovsky **736** Skeletal Hand removing Cigarette

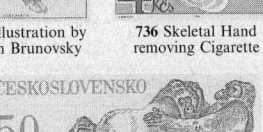

735 Gorilla Family

1981. Biennial Exhibition of Book Illustrations for Children, Bratislava. Multicoloured.
2590 50h. Type **734** 15 10
2591 1k. Adolf Born 30 10
2592 2k. Vive Tolli 60 25
2593 4k. Etienne Delessert 90 45
2594 10k. Suekichi Akaba . . . . 3·00 1·25

1981. 50th Anniv of Prague Zoo. Multicoloured.
2595 50h. Type **735** 30 10
2596 1k. Lion family 35 15
2597 7k. Przewalski's horses . . . 2·75 1·50

1981. Anti-smoking Campaign.
2598 **736** 4k. multicoloured . . . 1·75 80

1981. Prague Castle (17th series). As T **536**. Multicoloured.
2599 3k. Fragment of Pernstejn terracotta from Lobkovic Palace (16th century) . . 90 45
2600 4k. St. Vitus Cathedral (19th century engraving by J. Sembera and G. Dobler) 2·25 2·50

1981. Art (15th series). As T **481**.
2601 1k. multicoloured . . . . . 3·50 3·75
2602 2k. brown 60 65
2603 3k. multicoloured 80 85
2604 4k. multicoloured 90 80
2605 5k. multicoloured . . . . . 1·10 1·60
DESIGNS: 1k. "View of Prague from Petrin Hill" (V. Hollar); 2k. "Czech Academy of Arts and Sciences Medallion" (Otakar Spaniel); 3k. South Bohemian embroidery (Zdenek Sklenar); 4k. "Peonies" (A. M. Gerasimov); 5k. "Figure of a Woman Standing" (Picasso).

737 Eduard Karel (engraver)

1981. Stamp Day.
2606 **737** 1k. yellow, red and blue 25 15

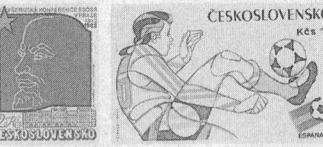

738 Lenin **739** Player kicking Ball

1982. 70th Anniv of 6th Russian Workers' Party Congress, Prague.
2607 **738** 2k. red, gold and blue 50 25

1982. World Cup Football Championship, Spain. Multicoloured.
2609 1k. Type **739** 20 15
2610 3k.60 Heading ball 75 40
2611 4k. Saving goal . . . . . . 2·50 65

740 Hrob **741** Conference Emblem

1982. Arms of Czech Towns (3rd series). Multicoloured.
2612 50h. Type **740** 15 10
2613 50h. Mlada Boleslav 15 10
2614 50h. Nove Mesto and Metuji 15 10
2615 50h. Trencin 15 10
See also Nos. 2720/3, 2765/7, 2819/21 and 3017/20.

1982. Tenth World Federation of Trade Unions Congress, Havana.
2616 **741** 1k. multicoloured . . . 25 10

742 Workers and Mine

1982. 50th Anniv of Great Strike at Most (coalminers' and general strike).
2617 **742** 1k. multicoloured . . . 25 10

743 Locomotives of 1922 and 1982

1982. 60th Anniv of International Railways Union.
2618 **743** 6k. multicoloured . . . 1·75 75

744 Worker with Flag **745** Georgi Dimitrov

1982. 10th Trade Unions Congress, Prague.
2619 **744** 1k. multicoloured . . . 25 10

1982. Birth Centenary of Georgi Dimitrov (Bulgarian statesman).
2620 **745** 50h. multicoloured . . . 10 10

747 "Euterpe" (Crispin de Passe) **749** Child's Head, Rose and Barbed Wire (Lidice)

1982. Engravings with a Music Theme.
2622 **747** 40h. black, gold & brown 15 10
2623 – 50h. black, gold & red 20 10
2624 – 1k. black, gold & brown 30 15
2625 – 2k. black, gold & blue 50 25
2626 – 3k. black, gold & green 2·40 75
DESIGNS: 50h. "The Sanguine Man" (Jacob de Gheyn); 1k. "The Crossing of the Red Sea" (Adriaen Collaert); 2k. "Wandering Musicians" (Rembrandt); 3k. "Beggar with Viol" (Jacques Callot).

1982. 40th Anniv of Destruction of Lidice and Lezaky. Multicoloured.
2628 1k. Type **749** 25 10
2629 1k. Hands and barbed wire (Lezaky) 25 10

750 Memorial and Statue of Jan Zizka

1982. 50th Anniv of National Memorial, Prague.
2630 **750** 1k. multicoloured . . . 25 10

752 Krivoklat Castle

1982. Castles. Multicoloured.
2632 50h. Type **752** 20 10
2633 1k. Interior and sculptures at Krivoklat Castle . . . 35 15
2634 2k. Nitra Castle 65 30
2635 3k. Archaeological finds from Nitra Castle . . . . 1·00 45

1982. Prague Castle (18th series). As T **536**.
2637 3k. brown and green . . . . 2·25 75
2638 4k. multicoloured . . . . . 1·10 1·00
DESIGNS: 3k. "St. George" (statue by George and Martin of Kluz, 1372); 4k. Tomb of Prince Vratislav I, Basilica of St. George.

753 Ferry "Kamzik" in Bratislava Harbour

1982. Danube Commission. Multicoloured.
2639 3k. Type **753** 80 30
2640 3k.60 "TR 100" tug at Budapest . . . . 1·00 40

1982. Historic Bratislava (6th issue). As T **669**.
2642 3k. black and red . . . . . 1·90 65
2643 4k. multicoloured . . . . . 2·10 1·25
DESIGNS: 3k. "View of Bratislava with Steamer"; 4k. "View of Bratislava with Bridge".

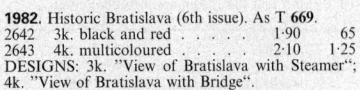

754 Agriculture

1982. Achievements of Socialist Construction (2nd series). Multicoloured.
2644 20h. Type **754** 10 10
2645 1k. Industry 35 10
2646 3k. Science and technology 90 45
See also Nos. 2695/7, 2753/5 and 2800/2.

755 "Scientific Research"

1982. 30th Anniv of Academy of Sciences.
2647 **755** 6k. multicoloured . . . 1·10 55

756 Couple with Flowers and Silhouette of Rider

1982. 65th Anniv of October Revolution and 60th Anniv of U.S.S.R. Multicoloured.
2648 50h. Type **756** 15 10
2649 1k. Cosmonauts and industrial complex 25 20

757 "Jaroslav Hasek" (writer) (Jose Malejovsky) **759** President Husak

758 Jaroslav Goldschmied (engraver) and Engraving Tools

1982. Sculptures. Multicoloured.
2650 1k. Type **757** 30 10
2651 2k. "Jan Zrzavy" (patriot) (Jan Simota) 55 20
2652 4k.40 "Leos Janacek" (composer) (Milos Axman) . . . . 1·10 50

2653	6k. "Martin Kukucin" (patriot) (Jan Kulich)	1·50	70
2654	7k. "Peaceful Work" (detail) (Rudolf Pribis)	3·00	1·50

1982. Art (16th series). As T **481**. Multicoloured.

2655	1k. "Revolution in Spain" (Josef Sima)	1·60	30
2656	2k. "Woman drying Herself" (Rudolf Kremlicka)	2·50	1·50
2657	3k. "The Girl Bride" (Dezider Milly)	1·50	1·10
2658	4k. "Oil Field Workers" (Jan Zelibsky)	1·50	1·75
2659	5k. "The Birds Lament" (Emil Filla)	1·75	1·90

1983. Stamp Day.

2660	**758** 1k. multicoloured	25	10

1983. 70th Birthday of President Husak.

2661	**759** 50h. blue	10	10

See also No. 2911.

763 Ski Flyer

760 Jaroslav Hasek (writer)   761 Armed Workers

1983. Celebrities' Anniversaries.

2662	**760** 50h. green, blue & red	15	10
2663	– 1k. brown, blue & red	25	10
2664	– 2k. multicoloured	45	20
2665	– 5k. black, blue & red	1·40	55

DESIGNS: Type **760** (birth centenary); 1k. Julius Fucik (journalist) (80th birth and 40th death annivs); 2k. Martin Luther (church reformist) (500th birth anniv); 5k. Johannes Brahms (composer) (150th birth anniv).

1983. Anniversaries. Multicoloured.

2666	50h. Type **761** (35th anniv of "Victorious February")	15	10
2667	1k. Family and agriculture and industrial landscapes (35th anniversary of National Front)	25	15

762 Radio Waves and Broadcasting Emblem   763 Ski Flyer

1983. Communications. Multicoloured.

2668	40h. Type **762** (60th anniv of Czech broadcasting)	15	10
2669	1k. Television emblem (30th anniv of Czech television)	20	10
2670	2k. W.C.Y. emblem and "1983" (World Communications Year) (40 × 23 mm)	45	25
2671	3k.60 Envelopes, Aero A-10 aircraft and mail vans (60th anniv of airmail and 75th anniv of mail transport by motor vehicles) (49 × 19 mm)	1·00	55

1983. 7th World Ski Flying Championships, Harrachov.

2672	**763** 1k. multicoloured	25	10

765 Emperor Moth and "Viola sudetica"

1983. Nature Protection. Multicoloured.

2674	50h. Type **765**	20	10
2675	1k. Water lilies and edible frogs	40	20
2676	2k. Red crossbill and cones	1·60	50
2677	3k.60 Grey herons	1·60	60
2678	5k. Lynx and "Gentiana asclepiadea"	1·50	50
2679	7k. Red deer	3·25	1·40

766 Ivan Stepanovich Kbnev

1983. Soviet Army Commanders. Multicoloured.

2680	50h. Type **766**	15	10
2681	1k. Andrei Ivanovich Yeremenko	25	15
2682	2k. Rodion Yakovlevich Malinovsky	55	25

767 Dove   768 "Rudolf II" (Adrian de Vries)

1983. World Peace and Life Congress, Prague.

2683	**767** 2k. multicoloured	45	45

1983. Prague Castle (19th series).

2685	**768** 4k. multicoloured	1·40	1·00
2686	– 5k. orange, blk & red	85	1·00

DESIGN: 5k. Kinetic relief with timepiece by Rudolf Svoboda.

769 Mounted Messenger (Oleg K. Zotov)

1983. 9th Biennial Exhibition of Book Illustration for Children.

2687	**769** 50h. multicoloured	15	10
2688	– 1k. multicoloured	25	10
2689	– 4k. multicoloured	95	45
2690	– 7k. red and black	1·40	55

DESIGNS: 1k. Boy looking from window at birds in tree (Zbigniew Rychlicki); 4k. "Hansel and Gretel" (Lisbeth Zwerger); 7k. Three young negroes (Antonio P. Domingues).

770 Ilyushin Il-62 and Globe

1983. World Communications Year and 60th Anniv of Czechoslovak Airlines.

2692	**770** 50h. red, purple & pink	15	10
2693	– 1k. purple, red & pink	30	10
2694	– 4k. purple, red & pink	1·75	85

DESIGNS—VERT: 1k. Ilyushin Il-62 and envelope. HORIZ: 4k. Ilyushin Il-62 and Aero A-14 biplane.

1983. Achievements of Socialist Construction (3rd series). As T **754**.

2695	50h. Surveyor	15	10
2696	1k. Refinery	30	10
2697	3k. Hospital and operating theatre	75	50

1983. Historic Bratislava (7th series). As T **669**.

2698	3k. green, red and black	1·50	70
2699	4k. multicoloured	1·50	70

DESIGNS: 3k. Sculptures by Viktor Tilgner; 4k. "Mirbachov Palace" (Julius Schubert).

771 National Theatre, Prague   772 "Soldier with Sword and Shield" (Hendrik Goltzius)

1983. Czechoslovak Theatre Year.

2700	**771** 50h. brown	15	10
2701	– 2k. green	60	25

DESIGN: 2k. National Theatre and Tyl Theatre, Prague.

1983. Art (17th series), showing works from the National Theatre, Prague. As Type **481**.

2702	1k. multicoloured	1·25	90
2703	2k. multicoloured	2·75	90
2704	3k. yellow, black and blue	1·00	60
2705	4k. multicoloured	1·00	60
2706	5k. multicoloured	1·00	60

DESIGNS: 1k. "Zalov" (lunette detail by Mikolas Ales); 2k. "Genius" (stage curtain detail, Vojtech Hynais); 3k. "Music" and "Lyrics" (ceiling drawings, Frantisek Zenisek); 4k. "Prague" (detail from

President's box, Vaclav Brozik); 5k. "Hradcany Castle (detail from President's box, Julius Marak).

1983. Period Costume from Old Engravings. Multicoloured.

2707	40h. Type **772**	15	10
2708	50h. "Warrior with Sword and Lance" (Jacob de Gheyn)	15	10
2709	1k. "Lady with Muff" (Jacques Callot)	30	10
2710	4k. "Lady with Flower" (Vaclav Hollar)	1·10	40
2711	5k. "Gentleman with Cane" (Antoine Watteau)	2·40	80

773 Karel Seizinger (stamp engraver)

1983. Stamp Day.

2712	**773** 1k. multicoloured	25	10

774 National Flag, with Bratislava and Prague Castles   775 Council Emblem

1984. 15th Anniv of Czechoslovak Federation.

2713	**774** 50h. multicoloured	10	10

1984. 35th Anniv of Council for Mutual Economic Aid.

2714	**775** 1k. multicoloured	20	10

776 Cross-country Skiing

1984. Winter Olympic Games, Sarajevo. Mult.

2715	2k. Type **776**	45	25
2716	3k. Ice hockey	65	35
2717	5k. Biathlon	1·40	65

777 Olympic Flag, Ancient Greek Athletes and Olympic Flame

1984. 90th Anniv of International Olympic Committee.

2719	**777** 7k. multicoloured	1·25	55

1984. Arms of Czech Towns (4th series). As T **740**. Multicoloured.

2720	50h. Turnov	30	10
2721	50h. Kutna Hora	30	10
2722	1k. Milevsko	45	15
2723	1k. Martin	45	15

778 "Soyuz" and Dish Aerials   779 Vendellin Opatrny

1984. "Interkosmos" International Space Flights. Multicoloured.

2724	50h. Type **778**	20	10
2725	1k. "Salyut"–"Soyuz" complex	35	15
2726	2k. Cross-section of orbital station	50	25
2727	4k. "Salyut" taking pictures of Earth's surface	70	60
2728	5k. "Soyuz" returning to Earth	95	70

1984. Anti-fascist Heroes.

2729	**779** 50h. black, red & blue	20	10
2730	– 1k. black, red & blue	30	20
2731	– 2k. black, red & blue	55	30
2732	– 4k. black, red & blue	1·10	50

DESIGNS: 1k. Ladislav Novomesky; 2k. Rudolf Jasiok; 4k. Jan Nalepka.

780 Musical Instruments   781 Telecommunications Building

1984. Music Year.

2733	**780** 50h. lt brown, gold & brn	20	10
2734	– 1k. multicoloured	30	10

DESIGN: 1k. Organ pipes.

1984. Central Telecommunications Building, Bratislava.

2735	**781** 2k. multicoloured	80	25

1984. Historic Bratislava (8th series). As T **669**. Multicoloured.

2736	3k. Arms of Vintners' Guild	1·10	80
2737	4k. Painting of 1827 Skating Festival	1·10	80

1984. Prague Castle (20th series). As T **768**. Multicoloured.

2739	3k. Weather cock, St. Vitus Cathedral	75	70
2740	4k. King David playing psaltery (initial from Roudnice Book of Psalms)	1·40	1·25

783 Jack of Spades (16th century)

1984. Playing Cards. Multicoloured.

2741	50h. Type **783**	20	10
2742	1k. Queen of Spades (17th century)	35	10
2743	2k. Nine of Hearts (18th century)	50	25
2744	3k. Jack of Clubs (18th century)	85	40
2745	5k. King of Hearts (19th century)	1·25	60

784 Family and Industrial Complex

1984. 40th Anniv of Slovak Uprising.

2746	**784** 50h. multicoloured	10	10

785 Soldiers with Banner

1984. 40th Anniv of Battle of Dukla Pass.

2747	**785** 2k. multicoloured	45	25

786 High Jumping

1984. Olympic Games, Los Angeles. Mult.

2748	2k. Type **786**	30	15
2749	2k. Cycling	50	25
2750	3k. Rowing	70	45
2751	5k. Weightlifting	1·10	60

1984. Achievements of Socialist Construction (4th series). As T **754**. Multicoloured.

2753	1k. Telephone handset and letters (Communications)	40	10
2754	2k. Containers on railway trucks and river barge (Transport)	75	30
2755	3k. Map of Transgas pipeline	65	45

1984. Art (18th series). As T **481**. Multicoloured.

2757	1k. "Milevsky River" (Karel Stehlik)	1·25	85
2758	2k. "Under the Trees" (Viktor Barvitius)	1·25	85

2759 3k. "Landscape with Flowers" (Zolo Palugyay) 1·25 85
2760 4k. Illustration of king from Vysehrad Codex 1·25 85
2761 5k. "Kokorin" (Antonin Manes) 1·25 85

787 Dove and Head of Girl
788 Zapotocky

1984. 45th Anniv of International Students Day.
2762 787 1k. multicoloured 20 10

1984. Birth Centenary of Antonin Zapotocky (politician).
2763 788 50h. multicoloured 10 10

789 Bohumil Heinz (engraver) and Hands engraving

1984. Stamp Day.
2764 789 1k. multicoloured 20 20

1985. Arms of Czech Towns (5th series). As T **740**. Multicoloured.
2765 50h. Kamyk nad Vltavou 30 10
2766 50h. Havirov 30 10
2767 50h. Trnava 30 10

790 "Art and Pleasure" (Jan Simota)
792 Helmet, Mail Shirt and Crossbow

1985. Centenary of Prague University of Applied Arts.
2768 790 3k. multicoloured 65 35

1985. 350th Anniv of Trnava University.
2769 791 2k. multicoloured 30 25

1985. Exhibits from Military Museum. Mult.
2770 50h. Type 792 15 10
2771 1k. Cross and star of Za vitezstvi order 30 10
2772 2k. Avia B-534 airplane and "Soyuz 28" (horiz) 70 35

791 View of Trnava

795 State Arms and Crowd
796 State Arms and Soldiers with National Flag

1985. 40th Anniv of Kosice Reforms.
2775 795 4k. multicoloured 70 35

1985. 40th Anniv of National Security Forces.
2776 796 50h. multicoloured 10 10

798 Emblem and Ice Hockey Players

1985. World and European Ice Hockey Championships, Prague.
2778 798 1k. multicoloured 25 10

799 Pieces on Chessboard
802 Tennis

1985. 80th Anniv of Czechoslovak Chess Organization.
2779 799 6k. multicoloured 1·25 75

800 Freedom Fighters and Prague

1985. Anniversaries. Multicoloured.
2780 1k. Type 800 (40th anniv of May uprising) 30 10
2781 1k. Workers shaking hands, flags and industrial motifs (15th anniv of Czechoslovak–Soviet Treaty) 30 10
2782 1k. Girl giving flowers to soldier, Prague Castle and tank (40th anniv of liberation) 30 10
2783 1k. Soldiers and industrial motifs (30th anniv of Warsaw Pact) 30 10

1985. Czechoslovak Victory in Ice Hockey Championships. No. 2778 optd **CSSR MISTREM SVETA**.
2784 798 1k. multicoloured 5·75 5·00

1985. National Spartakiad. Multicoloured.
2785 50h. Type 802 15 10
2786 1k. Gymnasts performing with ribbons (48 × 19 mm) 25 10

803 Study for "Fire" and "Republic" (Josef Capek)

1985. Anti-fascist Artists. Multicoloured.
2787 50h. Type 803 15 10
2788 2k. "Geneva Conference on Disarmament" and "Prophecy of Three Parrots" (Frantisek Bidlo) 45 25
2789 4k. "Unknown Conscript" and "The almost peaceful Dove" (Antonin Pelc) 65 40

805 Moscow Buildings and Young People holding Doves

1985. 12th World Youth and Students' Festival, Moscow.
2791 805 1k. multicoloured 25 10

806 Figures on Globe
807 Rocking Horse (Kveta Pacovska)

1985. 40th Anniv of World Federation of Trade Unions.
2792 806 50h. multicoloured 10 10

1985. Historic Bratislava (9th series). As T **669**.
2793 3k. lt brown, green & brown 70 70
2794 4k. black, green and red 1·00 1·00
DESIGNS: 3k. Tapestry (Elena Holeczyova); 4k. Pottery.

1985. 10th Biennial Exhibition of Book Illustrations for Children, Bratislava. Mult.
2795 1k. Type 807 20 10
2796 2k. Elves (Gennady Spirin) 35 15

2797 3k. Girl, butterfly and flowers (Kaarina Kaila) 60 40
2798 4k. Boy shaking hands with hedgehog (Erick Ingraham) 70 45

1985. Achievements of Socialist Construction (5th series). As T **754**. Multicoloured.
2800 50h. Mechanical excavator 10 10
2801 1k. Train and map of Prague underground railway 30 20
2802 2k. Modern textile spinning equipment 35 25

808 Gateway to First Courtyard
809 Jug (4th century)

1985. Prague Castle (21st series).
2803 808 2k. black, blue & red 50 30
2804 – 3k. multicoloured 1·10 40
DESIGN: 3k. East side of Castle.

1985. Centenary of Prague Arts and Crafts Museum. Glassware. Multicoloured.
2805 50h. Type 809 10 10
2806 1k. Venetian glass container (16th century) 20 10
2807 2k. Bohemian glass with hunting scene (18th century) 40 20
2808 4k. Bohemian vase (18th century) 70 40
2809 6k. Bohemian vase (c. 1900) 1·40 75

1985. Art (19th series). As T **481**. Multicoloured.
2810 1k. "Young Woman in Blue Dress" (Josef Ginovsky) 1·50 85
2811 2k. "Lenin on Charles Bridge" (Martin Sladky) 1·50 85
2812 3k. "Avenue of Poplars" (Vaclav Rabas) 1·50 85
2813 4k. "Beheading of St. Dorothea" (Hans Baldung Grien) 1·50 85
2814 5k. "Jasper Schade van Westrum" (Frans Hals) 1·50 85

810 Bohdan Roule (engraver) and Engraving Plate

1985. Stamp Day.
2815 810 1k. multicoloured 25 10

811 Peace Dove and Olive Twig

1986. International Peace Year. Multicoloured.
2816 811 1k. multicoloured 25 10

812 Victory Statue Prague
813 Zlin Z-50LS Airplane, Locomotive "Kladno" and Rock Drawing of Chariot

1986. 90th Anniv of Czech Philharmonic Orchestra.
2817 812 1k. black, brown & vio 25 10

1986. "Expo '86" International Transport and Communications Exhibition, Vancouver.
2818 813 4k. multicoloured 70 35

1986. Arms of Czech Towns (6th series). As T **740**. Multicoloured.
2819 50h. Vodnany 25 10
2820 50h. Zamberk 25 10
2821 50h. Myjava 25 10

814 Banner, Industry and Hammer and Sickle

1986. 17th Communist Party Congress, Prague. Multicoloured.
2822 50h. Type 814 10 10
2823 1k. Buildings, hammer and sickle and star 20 10

815 Couple, Banner and Star

1986. 65th Anniv of Czechoslovakian Communist Party. Multicoloured.
2824 50h. Type 815 10 10
2825 1k. Workers, banner and hammer and sickle 20 10

816 Map and Stylized Man

1986. National Front Election Programme.
2826 816 50h. multicoloured 10 10

817 Emblem and Crest on Film

1986. 25th Int Film Festival, Karlovy Vary.
2827 817 1k. multicoloured 25 10

818 Musical Instruments
819 Ilyushin Il-86 and Airspeed Envoy II

1986. 40th Anniv of Prague Spring Music Festival.
2828 818 1k. multicoloured 25 10

1986. 50th Anniv of Prague–Moscow Air Service.
2829 819 50h. multicoloured 10 10

820 Sports Pictograms

1986. 90th Anniv of Czechoslovak Olympic Committee.
2830 820 2k. multicoloured 40 30

821 Map and Goalkeeper

1986. World Cup Football Championship, Mexico.
2831 821 4k. multicoloured 75 50

822 Globe, Net and Ball

1986. Women's World Volleyball Championship, Prague.
2832 **822** 1k. multicoloured . . . 35 10

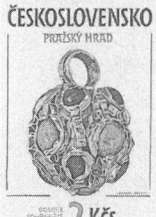

824 Funeral Pendant 825 Wooden Cock, Slovakia

1986. Prague Castle (22nd series).
2834 **824** 2k. multicoloured . . . 60 50
2835 – 3k. orange, brown & bl 70 60
DESIGN: 3k. "Allegory of Blossoms" (sculpture, Jaroslav Horejc).

1986. 40th Anniv of U.N.I.C.E.F. Toys. Mult.
2836 10h. Type **825** 10 10
2837 20h. Wooden soldier on
hobby horse, Bohemia . . 10 10
2838 1k. Rag doll, Slovakia . . . 15 10
2839 2k. Doll 35 10
2840 3k. Mechanical bus . . . 50 25

826 Registration Label and Mail Coach

1986. Centenary of Registration Label.
2841 **826** 4k. multicoloured . . . 65 35

1986. Historic Bratislava (10th series). As T **669.**
2842 3k. black, red and blue . . 55 50
2843 4k. black, red and green . 70 45
DESIGNS: 3k. Sigismund Gate, Bratislava Castle; 4k. "St. Margaret with a Lamb" (relief from Castle).

827 Eagle Owl

1986. Owls. Multicoloured.
2844 50h. Type **827** 25 10
2845 2k. Long-eared owl . . . 55 30
2846 3k. Tawny owl 55 40
2847 4k. Barn owl 70 50
2848 5k. Short-eared owl . . . 1·60 60

829 Type "Kt8" Articulated Tram and 1920s' Prague Tram

1986. Rail Vehicles. Multicoloured.
2850 50h. Type **829** 20 10
2851 1k. Series E 458.1 electric
shunting engine and 1882–
1913 steam locomotive . . 30 10
2852 3k. Series T 466.2 diesel
locomotive and 1900–24
steam locomotive . . . 70 25
2853 5k. Series M 152.0 railcar
and 1930–35 railbus . . 1·00 60

830 "The Circus Rider" (Jan Bauch)

1986. Circus and Variety Acts on Paintings. Multicoloured.
2854 1k. Type **830** . . . . . 1·25 25
2855 2k. "The Ventriloquist"
(Frantisek Tichy) . . . 1·60 50
2856 3k. "In the Circus" (Vincent
Hloznik) . . . . . . 1·50 60
2857 6k. "Clown" (Karel
Svolinsky) . . . . . . 1·75 1·10

1986. Art (20th series). As T **481.** Multicoloured.
2858 1k. "The Czech Lion, May
1918" (Vratislav H.
Brunner) . . . . . . 1·60 40
2859 2k. "Boy with Mandolin"
(Jozef Sturdik) . . . . 1·50 70
2860 3k. "The Metra Building"
(Frantisek Gross) . . . 85 80
2861 4k. "Maria Maximiliana of
Sternberk" (Karel Skreta) 85 1·10
2862 5k. "Adam and Eve" (Lucas
Cranach) . . . . . . 1·10 1·25

831 Brunner and Stamps of 1920

1986. Stamp Day. Birth Centenary of Vratislav Hugo Brunner (stamp designer).
2863 **831** 1k. multicoloured . . . 25 10

832 Bicyclists

1987. World Cross-country Cycling Championships, Mlada Boleslav.
2864 **832** 6k. multicoloured . . . 95 55

833 Pins and Ball

1987. 50th Anniv of Czechoslovakian Bowling Federation.
2865 **833** 2k. multicoloured . . . 35 25

834 Gold Stars of Heroes of C.S.S.R. and of Socialist Labour

1987. State Orders and Medals.
2866 **834** 50h. red, black & gold 10 10
2867 – 2k. multicoloured . . . 30 20
2868 – 3k. multicoloured . . . 55 40
2869 – 4k. multicoloured . . . 70 55
2870 – 5k. multicoloured . . . 90 55
DESIGNS: 2k. Order of Klement Gottwald; 3k. Order of the Republic; 4k. Order of Victorious February; 5k. Order of Labour.

835 Poplar Admiral

1987. Butterflies and Moths. Multicoloured.
2871 1k. Type **835** 20 10
2872 2k. Eyed hawk moth . . . 45 25
2873 3k. Large tiger moth . . . 75 40
2874 4k. Viennese emperor moth 1·00 50

836 Emblem

1987. Nuclear Power Industry.
2875 **836** 5k. multicoloured . . . 75 50

837 Emblem

1987. 11th Trades Union Congress, Prague.
2876 **837** 1k. multicoloured . . . 10 10

839 Stained Glass Window, St. Vitus's Cathedral (Frantisek Sequens)

1987. Prague Castle (23rd series). Multicoloured.
2878 2k. Type **839** 45 35
2879 3k. Arms (mural), New
Land Rolls Hall, Old
Royal Palace 75 55
See also Nos. 2950/1 and 2977/8.

840 Telephone, 1894

1987. "Praga 88" Int Stamp Exhibition (1st issue). Technical Monuments. Multicoloured.
2880 3k. Type **840** 40 35
2881 3k. Mail Van, 1924 . . . . 40 35
2882 4k. Tank locomotive
"Archduke Charles" 1907 85 35
2883 4k. Prague tram, 1900 . . 85 35
2884 5k. Steam roller, 1936 . . 85 60
See also Nos. 2900, 2923/6, 2929/32 2934/7 and 2940/3.

841 "When the Fighting Ended" (Pavel Simon) 843 Chickens in Kitchen (Asun Balzola)

842 Prague Town Hall Clock and Theory of Functions Diagram

1987. 45th Anniv of Destruction of Lidice and Lezaky. Multicoloured.
2885 1k. Type **841** 20 10
2886 1k. "The End of the Game"
(Ludmila Jirincova) . . . 20 10

1987. 125th Anniv of Union of Czech Mathematicians and Physicists. Multicoloured.
2887 50h. Type **842** 10 10
2888 50h. J. M. Petzval, C.
Strouhal and V. Iarnik . . 10 10
2889 50h. Trajectory of Brownian
motion and earth fold
diagram 10 10

1987. 11th Biennial Exhibition of Book Illustrations for Children, Bratislava. Designs showing illustrations by artists named. Multicoloured.
2890 50h. Type **843** 35 15
2891 1k. Cranes with egg at
railway points (Frederic
Clement) 45 20
2892 2k. Birds on nest (Elzbieta
Gaudasinska) 35 20
2893 4k. Couple looking over
rooftops (Marija Lucija
Stupica) 35 35

844 Barbed Wire, Flames and Menorah

1987. 40th Anniv of Terezin Memorial.
2895 **844** 50h. multicoloured . . . 10 10

845 "OSS" and Communications Equipment

1987. 30th Anniv of Organization of Socialist Countries' Postal Administrations.
2896 **845** 4k. multicoloured . . . 70 35

846 Purkyne and Microtome

1987. Birth Bicentenary of Jan Evangelista Purkyne (physiologist).
2897 **846** 7k. multicoloured . . . 1·25 65

1987. Historic Bratislava (11th series). As T **669.**
2898 3k. buff, black and blue . . 50 45
2899 4k. black and brown . . . 1·00 95
DESIGNS: 3k. Detail of projecting window by Vyzdoby; 4k. "View of Bratislava" (engraving, Hans Mayer).

848 Postilion 849 Symbols of Industry, Lenin and Red Flag

1987. "Praga '88" International Stamp Exhibition (2nd issue).
2900 **848** 1k. multicoloured . . . 25 10

1987. 70th Anniv of Russian Revolution (2901) and 65th Anniv of USSR (2902). Multicoloured.
2901 50h. Type **849** 10 10
2902 50h. Hammer and sickle . . . 10 10

1987. Art (21st series). As T **481.**
2904 1k. multicoloured 65 25
2905 2k. multicoloured 85 55
2906 3k. multicoloured . . . . . 1·25 85
2907 4k. black, blue and red . . 85 95
2908 5k. multicoloured . . . . . 1·25 1·10
DESIGNS: 1k. "Enclosure of Dreams" (Kamil Lhotak); 2k. "Tulips" (Ester Simerova-Martincekova); 3k. "Bohemian Landscape" (triptych, Josef Lada); 4k. "Accordion Player" (Josef Capek); 5k. "Self-portrait" (Jiri Trnka).

850 Obrovsky and Detail of 1919 Stamp

1987. Stamp Day. 105th Birth Anniv of Jakub Obrovsky (designer).
2909 **850** 1k. multicoloured . . . 10 10

851 "Czechoslovakia", Linden Tree and Arms

1988. 70th Anniv of Czechoslovakia.
2910 **851** 1k. multicoloured . . . 10 10

1988. 75th Birthday of President Husak.
2911 **759** 1k. brown and red . . . 10 10

852 Ski Jumping and Ice Hockey

1988. Olympic Games, Calgary and Seoul. Mult.
2912 50h. Type **852** 10 10
2913 1k. Basketball and football 15 10
2914 6k. Throwing the discus and
weightlifting 95 40

853 Red Flags and Klement Gottwald Monument, Pecky

1988. 40th Annivs of "Victorious February" (2915) and National Front (2916). Multicoloured.
2915 50h. Type **853** 10 10
2916 50h. Couple and detail of "Czech Constitution, 1961" (Vincent Hloznik) 10 10

854 Laurin and Klement Car, 1914

1988. Historic Motor Cars. Multicoloured.
2918 50h. Type **854** 10 10
2919 1k. Tatra "NW" type B, 1902 . . . . 15 10
2920 2k. Tatra "NW" type E, 1905 . . . . 35 15
2921 3k. Tatra "12 Normandie", 1929 . . . . 50 20
2922 4k. "Meteor", 1899 . . . . 70 40

855 Praga Post Office and Velka Javorina T.V. Transmitter

1988. "Praga '88" International Stamp Exhibition (3rd issue) and 70th Anniv of Postal Museum. Multicoloured.
2923 50h. Type **855** 10 10
2924 1k. Mlada Boleslav telecommunications centre and Carmelite Street post office, Prague 30 10
2925 2k. Prague 1 and Bratislava 56 post offices 40 20
2926 4k. Malta Square, Prague, and Prachatice post offices 85 40

856 Woman with Linden Leaves as Hair and Open Book

857 Strahov Monastery

1988. 125th Anniv of Slovak Cultural Society.
2928 **856** 50h. multicoloured . . . 10 10

1988. "Praga '88" International Stamp Exhibition (4th issue). National Literature Memorial, Strahov Monastery. Multicoloured.
2929 1k. Type **857** 15 10
2930 2k. Open book and celestial globe 35 15
2931 5k. Illuminated initial "B", scrolls and decorative binding 85 45
2932 7k. Astrological signs, Strahov, illuminated book and globe . . . . 1·60 95

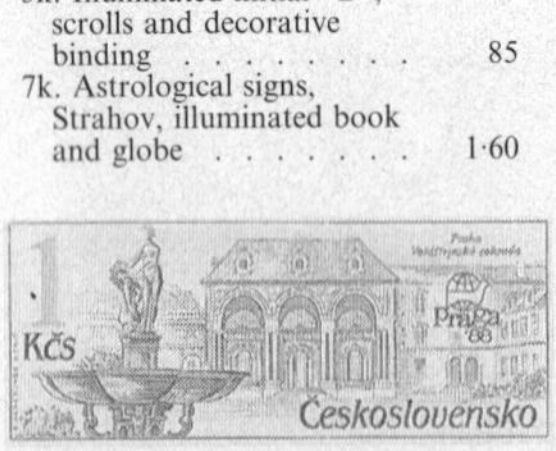

858 Waldstein Garden Fountain

1988. "Praga '88" International Stamp Exhibition (5th issue). Prague Fountains.
2934 **858** 1k. black, lilac & blue 15 10
2935 – 2k. multicoloured . . . 35 15
2936 – 3k. black, orange & lilac 55 30
2937 – 4k. black, orange & grn 65 50
DESIGNS: 2k. Old Town Square; 3k. Charles University; 4k. Courtyard, Prague Castle.

860 Trade Unions Central Recreation Centre

1988. "Praga '88" International Stamp Exhibition (6th issue). Present-day Prague. Multicoloured.
2941 50h. Type **860** 10 10
2942 1k. Koospol foreign trade company 20 10
2943 2k. Motol teaching hospital 40 15
2944 4k. Palace of Culture . . . 70 35

1988. Prague Castle (24th series). As T **839**. Multicoloured.
2950 2k. 17 th-century pottery jug 30 30
2951 3k. "St. Catherine" (Paolo Veronese) 50 50

1988. Historic Bratislava (12th series). As T **669**. Multicoloured.
2952 3k. Hlavne Square (detail of print by R. Alt-Sandman) 45 40
2953 4k. Ferdinand House . . . 55 50

1988. Art (22nd series). As T **481**.
2954 2k. multicoloured 40 40
2955 6k. brown, black and blue 1·25 1·25
2956 7k. multicoloured . . . . . 1·75 1·60
DESIGNS: 2k. "Field Workers carrying Sacks" (Martin Benka); 6k. "Woman watching Bird" (Vojtech Preissig); 7k. "Leopard attacking Horseman" (Eugene Delacroix).

865 Benda and Drawings

1988. Stamp Day. 106th Birth Anniv of Jaroslav Benda (stamp designer).
2957 **865** 1k. multicoloured . . . 10 10

866 Emblem

867 Globe and Truck

1989. 20th Anniv of Czechoslovak Federal Socialist Republic.
2958 **866** 50h. multicoloured . . . 10 10

1989. Paris–Dakar Rally. Multicoloured.
2959 50h. Type **867** 10 10
2960 1k. Globe and view of desert on truck side . . . 15 10
2961 2k. Globe and truck (different) 30 15
2962 4k. Route map, turban and truck 50 30

868 Taras G. Shevchenko

870 Dove and Pioneers

869 "Republika" (freighter)

1989. Birth Anniversaries.
2963 **868** 50h. multicoloured . . . 15 10
2964 – 50h. multicoloured . . . 15 10
2965 – 50h. brown and green . . 15 10
2966 – 50h. brown and green . . 15 10
2967 – 50h. black, brn & dp brn 15 10
2968 – 50h. multicoloured . . . 15 10
DESIGNS: No. 2963, Type **868** (Ukrainian poet and painter, 175th anniv); 2964, Modest Petrovich Musorgsky (composer, 150th anniv); 2965, Jan Botto (poet, 160th anniv); 2966, Jawaharlal Nehru (Indian statesman, cent); 2967, Jean Cocteau (writer and painter, centenary); 2968, Charlie Chaplin (actor, centenary).

1989. Shipping.
2969 **869** 50h. grey, red and blue 15 10
2970 – 1k. multicoloured . . . 20 10
2971 – 2k. multicoloured . . . 25 15
2972 – 3k. grey, red and blue 35 20
2973 – 4k. multicoloured . . . 45 35
2974 – 5k. multicoloured . . . 50 40
DESIGNS: 1k. "Pionyr" (trawler); 2k. "Brno" (tanker); 3k. "Trinec" (container ship); 4k. "Orlik" (container ship); 5k. "Vltava" (tanker) and communications equipment.

1989. 40th Anniv of Young Pioneer Organization.
2975 **870** 50h. multicoloured . . . 10 10

1989. Prague Castle (25th series). As T **839**.
2977 2k. brown, yellow and red 20 20
2978 3k. multicoloured 35 35
DESIGNS: 2k. King Kard of Bohemia (relief by Alexandra Colin from Archduke Ferdinand I's mausoleum); 3k. "Self-portrait" (V. V. Reiner).

872 White-tailed Sea Eagle

1989. Endangered Species.
2980 **872** 1k. multicoloured . . . 25 20

873 Fire-bellied Toads

1989. Endangered Amphibians. Multicoloured.
2981 2k. Type **873** 30 25
2982 3k. Yellow-bellied toad . . 45 30
2983 4k. Alpine newts 85 55
2984 5k. Carpathian newts . . . 1·10 65

874 Dancers

1989. 40th Anniv of Slovak Folk Art Collective.
2985 **874** 50h. multicoloured . . . 10 10

875 Horsemen and Mountains

1989. 45th Anniv of Slovak Rising.
2986 **875** 1k. multicoloured . . . 10 10

876 "Going Fishing" (Hannu Taina)

877 "Nolanea verna"

1989. 12th Biennial Exhibition of Book Illustrations for Children. Multicoloured.
2987 50h. Type **876** 10 10
2988 1k. "Donkey Rider" (Aleksandur Aleksov) . . 15 10
2989 2k. "Animal Dreams" (Jurgen Spohn Zapadny) 25 15
2990 4k. "Scarecrow" (Robert Brun) 45 30

1989. Poisonous Fungi.
2992 **877** 50h. brown, deep brown and green 10 10
2993 – 1k. multicoloured . . . 20 10
2994 – 2k. green and brown . . 35 20
2995 – 3k. brown, yellow & red 50 30
2996 – 5k. multicoloured . . . 70 60
DESIGNS: 1k. Death cap; 2k. Destroying angel; 3k. "Cortinarius orellanus"; 5k. "Galerina marginata".

1989. Historic Bratislava (13th series). As T **669**.
2997 3k. multicoloured 30 35
2998 4k. black, red and green . . 50 50
DESIGNS: 3k. Devin Fortress and flower; 4k. Devin Fortress and pitcher.

878 Jan Opletal (Nazi victim)

1989. 50th Anniv of International Students Day.
2999 **878** 1k. multicoloured . . . 10 10

1989. Art (24th series). As T **481**. Multicoloured.
3000 2k. "Nirvana" (Anton Jasusch) 25 25
3001 4k. "Dusk in the Town" (Jakub Schikaneder) (horiz) 50 45
3002 5k. "Bakers" (Pravoslav Kotik) (horiz) 80 80

879 Bearded Falcon Stamp, Pens and Bouda

1989. Stamp Day. 5th Death Anniv of Cyril Bouda (stamp designer).
3003 **879** 1k. brown, yellow & red 10 10

880 Practising Alphabet

881 Tomas Masaryk (first President)

1990. International Literacy Year.
3004 **880** 1k. multicoloured . . . 10 10

1990. Birth Anniversaries. Multicoloured.
3005 50h. Type **881** (140th anniv) 10 10
3006 50h. Karel Capek (writer, centenary) 10 10
3007 1k. Vladimir Ilyich Lenin (120th anniv) 15 10
3008 2k. Emile Zola (novelist, 150th anniv) 30 15
3009 3k. Jaroslav Heyrovsky (chemist, centenary) . . . 35 20
3010 10k. Bohuslav Martinu (composer, centenary) . . 1·10 85

882 Pres. Vaclav Havel

883 Players

1990.
3011 **882** 50h. ultram, bl & red . . 10 10

1990. Men's World Handball Championship.
3012 **883** 50h. multicoloured . . . 10 10

884 Snapdragon

885 Pope John Paul II

1990. Flowers. Multicoloured.
3013 50h. Type **884** 10 10
3014 1k. "Zinnia elegans" 15 10
3015 3k. Tiger flower 35 20
3016 5k. Madonna lily 60 45

1990. Arms of Czech Towns (7th series). As T **740**. Multicoloured.
3017 50h. Bytca 10 10
3018 50h. Podebrady 10 10
3019 50h. Sobeslav 10 10
3020 50h. Prostejov 10 10

1990. Papal Visit.
3021 **885** 1k. brown, yellow & red 10 10

886 Woman holding Flags

888 Footballers

1990. 45th Anniv of Liberation.
3022 886 1k. multicoloured . . . 10 10

1990. World Cup Football Championship, Italy.
3024 888 1k. multicoloured . . . 10 10

889 Victory Signs

1990. Free General Election.
3025 889 1k. multicoloured . . . 10 10

1990. Prague Castle (26th series). As T 824.
3026 2k. multicoloured 50 50
3027 3k. green, dp green & red 70 70
DESIGNS: 2k. Jewelled glove (from reliquary of St. George); 3k. Seal of King Premsyl Otakar II of Bohemia.

890 Map of Europe and Branch

1990. 15th Anniv of European Security and Co-operation Conference, Helsinki.
3028 890 7k. multicoloured . . . 80 55

891 Milada Horakova

1990. 40th Anniv of Execution of Milada Horakova.
3029 891 1k. multicoloured . . . 10 10

892 Poodles

1990. "Inter Canis" Dog Show, Brno. Mult.
3030 50h. Type 892 . . . . . 10 10
3031 1k. Afghan hound, Irish
wolfhound and greyhound 15 10
3032 4k. Czech terrier,
bloodhound and
Hanoverian bearhound 45 30
3033 7k. Cavalier King Charles,
cocker and American
cocker spaniels 70 50

1990. Historic Bratislava (14th series). As T 669.
3034 3k. black and red 40 40
3035 4k. multicoloured 60 60
DESIGNS: 3k. Coin; 4k. "M. R. Stefanik" (J. Mudroch).

893 Horses jumping

1990. Centenary of Pardubice Steeplechase. Mult.
3036 50h. Type 893 . . . . . 10 10
3037 4k. Horses galloping . . . 45 35

894 Alpine Marmot

1990. Mammals. Multicoloured.
3038 50h. Type 894 . . . . 10 10
3039 1k. Eurasian wild cat 10 10
3040 4k. Eurasian beaver . . . 40 35
3041 5k. Common long-eared bat 55 40

895 European Flag

1990. Helsinki Pact Civic Gathering, Prague.
3042 895 3k. blue, yellow & gold 35 30

896 Snow-covered Church

1990. Christmas.
3043 896 50h. multicoloured . . . 10 10

1990. Art (25th series). As T 481. Multicoloured.
3044 2k. multicoloured . . . 40 40
3045 3k. black, brown & blue . 50 50
3046 4k. multicoloured . . . 60 60
3047 5k. multicoloured . . . 70 70
DESIGNS—HORIZ: 2k. "Krucemburk" (Jan Zrzavy). VERT: 3k. "St. Agnes" (detail of sculpture, Josef Vaclav Myslbek); 4k. "Slovene in his Homeland" (detail, Alfons Mucha); 5k. "St. John the Baptist" (detail of sculpture, Auguste Rodin).

897 Karel Svolinsky (stamp designer) and "Czechoslovakia"

1990. Stamp Day.
3048 897 1k. purple, lilac & blue 10 10

898 Judo Throw   899 Svojsik

1991. European Judo Championships, Prague.
3049 898 1k. multicoloured . . . 10 10

1991. 80th Anniv of Czechoslovak Scout Movement and 115th Birth Anniv of A. B. Svojsik (founder).
3050 899 3k. multicoloured . . . 35 10

900 Jan Hus   901 Alois Senefelder
preaching

1991. Anniversaries.
3051 900 50h. brown, stone & red 10 10
3052 – 1k. multicoloured . . . 10 10
3053 – 5k. multicoloured . . . 60 30
DESIGNS AND EVENTS: 50h. Type 900 (600th anniv of Bethlehem Chapel, Prague); 40×23 mm: 1k. Estates Theatre, Prague (re-opening) and Mozart (death bicent); 49×20 mm: 5k. Paddle-steamer "Bohemia" (150th anniv of boat excursions in Bohemia).

1991. Birth Anniversaries.
3054 901 1k. green, brown & red 15 10
3055 – 1k. black, green & red 15 10
3056 – 1k. blue, mauve & red 15 10
3057 – 1k. violet, blue and red 15 10
3058 – 1k. brown, orange & red 15 10
DESIGNS: No. 3054, Type 901 (inventor of lithography, 220th anniv); 3055, Andrej Kmet (naturalist, 150th anniv); 3056, Jan Masaryk (politician, 105th anniv); 3057, Jaroslav Seifert (composer, 90th anniv); 3058, Antonin Dvorak (composer, 150th anniv).

902 "Magion II"   903 Exhibition
Satellite and Earth   Pavilion, 1891

1991. Europa. Europe in Space.
3059 902 6k. blue, black & red . . 70 45

1991. Cent of International Exhibition, Prague.
3060 903 1k. blue, grey & mauve 10 10

904 Chinstrap Penguins, Map and Flag

1991. 30th Anniv of Antarctic Treaty.
3061 904 8k. multicoloured . . . 90 55

905 Blatna Castle   906 Jan Palach

1991. Castles. Multicoloured.
3062 50h. Type 905 . . . . . 10 10
3063 1k. Bouzov 10 10
3064 3k. Kezmarok 35 20

1991. Jan Palach Scholarship.
3065 906 4k. black 35 30

907 Rip   908 "The Frog King"
              (Binette Schroeder)

1991. Beauty Spots.
3066 907 4k. red, blue & yellow 40 40
3067 – 4k. purple, green & blk 40 40
DESIGN: No. 3067, Krivan.

1991. 13th Biennial Exhibition of Book Illustrations for Children. Multicoloured.
3068 1k. Type 908 . . . . . 10 10
3069 2k. "Pinocchio" (Stasys
Eidrigevicius) 20 15

909 Hlinka   910 "Prague Jesus
                   Child" (Maria-Victoria
                   Church)

1991. 53rd Death Anniv of Father Andrej Hlinka (Slovak nationalist).
3070 909 10k. black . . . . . 1·25 60

1991. Prague and Bratislava. Multicoloured.
3071 3k. Type 910 . . . . . 45 45
3072 3k. St. Elisabeth's Church,
Bratislava 45 45

911 "Gagea   912 Boys in
bohemica"   Costume

1991. Nature Protection. Flowers. Multicoloured.
3073 1k. Type 911 . . . . . 10 10
3074 2k. "Aster alpinus" . . . 20 15
3075 5k. "Fritillaria meleagris" 50 40
3076 11k. "Daphne eneorum" . . 1·25 75

1991. Art (26th series). As T 481. Multicoloured.
3077 2k. "Family at Home" (Max
Ernst) 20 20
3078 3k. "Milenci" (Auguste
Renoir) 30 30
3079 4k. "Christ" (El Greco) . . 70 40

3080 5k. "Coincidence" (Ladislav
Guderna) 80 50
3081 7k. "Two Japanese Women"
(Utamaro) . . . . . 1·10 75

1991. Christmas.
3082 912 50h. multicoloured . . . 10 10

913 Martin Benka (stamp designer) and Slovakian 1939 Stamp

1991. Stamp Day.
3083 913 2k. red, black & orange 35 15

914 Biathlon   916 Player

1992. Winter Olympic Games, Albertville.
3084 914 1k. multicoloured . . . 10 10

1992. World Ice Hockey Championship, Prague and Bratislava.
3086 916 3k. multicoloured . . . 35 30

917 Traffic Lights

1992. Road Safety Campaign.
3087 917 2k. multicoloured . . . 25 10

918 Tower, Seville Cathedral

1992. "Expo '92" World's Fair, Seville.
3088 918 4k. multicoloured . . . 40 25

919 Amerindian, "Santa Maria" and Columbus

1992. Europa. 500th Anniv of Discovery of America by Columbus.
3089 919 22k. multicoloured . . . 2·50 1·90

920 J. Kubis and J. Gabcik

1992. Free Czechoslovak Forces in World War II. Multicoloured.
3090 1k. Type 920 (50th anniv of
assassination of Reinhard
Heydrich) 10 10
3091 2k. Spitfires (air battles over
England, 1939–45) . . . 20 10
3092 3k. Barbed wire and soldier
(Tobruk, 1941) 25 15
3093 6k. Soldiers (Dunkirk,
1944–45) 90 30

921 Tennis Player   922 Nurse's Hats and
                          Red Cross

1992. Olympic Games, Barcelona.
3094 **921** 2k. multicoloured . . . 35 10

1992. Red Cross.
3095 **922** 2k. multicoloured . . . 25 10

923 Player   **924** Crawling Cockchafer

1992. European Junior Table Tennis Championships, Topolcany.
3096 **923** 1k. multicoloured . . . 10 10

1992. Beetles. Multicoloured.
3097 1k. Type **924** 10 10
3098 2k. "Ergates faber" 20 15
3099 3k. "Meloe violaceus" . . . 25 20
3100 4k. "Dytiscus latissimus" . . 30 30

925 Troja Castle   **926** Double Head and Posthorns

1992.
3101 **925** 6k. multicoloured . . . 60 45
3102 – 7k. black and lilac . . . 70 60
3103 – 8k. multicoloured . . . 90 75
DESIGNS—VERT: 7k. "St. Martin" (sculpture, G. R. Donner), Bratislava Cathedral. HORIZ: 8k. Lednice Castle.

1992. Post Bank.
3104 **926** 20k. multicoloured . . . 1·75 80

927 Anton Bernolak and Georgius Fandly

1992. Bicentenary of Slovak Education Assn.
3105 **927** 5k. multicoloured . . . 50 20

928 Cesky Krumlov   **929** Organ

1992.
3106 **928** 3k. brown and red . . . 35 10

1992. Art (27th series). As T **481.**
3107 6k. black and brown 50 45
3108 7k. multicoloured 60 50
3109 8k. multicoloured . . . . . 1·00 95
DESIGNS—VERT: 6k. "The Old Raftsman" (Koloman Sokol); 8k. "Abandonned" (Toyen). HORIZ: 7k. "Still Life with Grapes" (Georges Braque).

1992. Christmas.
3110 **929** 2k. multicoloured . . . 10 10

930 Jindra Schmidt (engraver)

1992. Stamp Day.
3111 **930** 2k. multicoloured . . . 10 10

NEWSPAPER STAMPS

N 4   **N 67** Dove   **N 94** Messenger

1918. Imperf.
N24 N 4 2h. green 10 10
N25 5h. green 10 10
N26 6h. red 10 10
N27 10h. lilac 10 10
N28 20h. blue 10 10
N29 30h. brown 15 10
N30 50h. orange 15 10
N31 100h. brown 40 10

1925. Surch with new value and stars.
N249 N 4 5 on 2h. green 65 55
N250 5 on 6h. red 30 75

1926. Newspaper Express stamps optd **NOVINY** or surch also.
N251 E 4 5h. on 2h. pur on yell 10 10
N253 5h. green on yellow 45 45
N254 10h. brown on yellow 20 15

1934. Optd **O.T.**
N332 N 4 10h. lilac 10 10
N333 20h. brown 10 10
N334 30h. brown 15 15

1937. Imperf.
N364 N 67 2h. brown 10 10
N365 5h. blue 10 10
N366 7h. orange 10 10
N367 9h. green 10 10
N368 10h. lake 10 10
N369 12h. blue 10 10
N370 20h. green 10 10
N371 50h. brown 10 10
N372 1k. olive 10 10

1946. Imperf.
N467 N 94 5h. blue 10 10
N468 10h. red 10 10
N469 15h. green 10 10
N470 20h. green 10 10
N471 25h. purple 10 10
N472 30h. brown 10 10
N473 40h. red 10 10
N474 50h. brown 10 10
N475 1k. grey 10 10
N476 5k. blue 10 10

EXPRESS NEWSPAPER STAMPS

E 4

1918. Imperf. On yellow or white paper.
E24 E 4 2h. purple 10 10
E25 5h. green 10 10
E26 10h. brown 45 45

OFFICIAL STAMPS

O 92   **O 103**

1945.
O463 O 92 50h. green 10 10
O464 1k. blue 10 10
O465 1k.20 purple 15 10
O466 1k.50 red 10 10
O467 2k.50 blue 15 10
O468 5k. purple 25 30
O469 8k. red 35 45

1947.
O490 O 103 60h. red 10 10
O491 80h. olive 10 10
O492 1k. blue 10 10
O493 1k.20 purple 10 10
O494 2k.40 red 10 10
O495 4k. blue 15 10
O496 5k. purple 15 30
O497 7k.40 violet 20 30

PERSONAL DELIVERY STAMPS

P 66

1937. For Prepayment. "V" in each corner.
P363 P 66 50h. blue 20 40

1937. For Payment on Delivery. "D" in each corner.
P364 P 66 50h. red 20 40

P 95

1946.
P469 P 95 2k. blue 20 20

POSTAGE DUE STAMPS

D 4

1919. Imperf.
D24 D 4 5h. olive 10 10
D25 10h. olive 10 10
D26 15h. olive 10 10
D27 20h. olive 10 10
D28 25h. olive 10 10
D29 30h. olive 25 10
D30 40h. olive 25 25
D31 50h. olive 25 10
D32 100h. brown . . . . . 1·25 15
D33 250h. orange . . . . 6·00 95
D34 400h. red . . . . . 8·25 95
D35 500h. green . . . . 3·00 10
D36 1000h. violet . . . . 3·00 40
D37 2000h. blue . . . . . 16·00 75

1922. Postage stamps surch **DOPLATIT** and new value. Imperf or perf.
D229 2 10 on 3h. mauve 10 10
D224a 20 on 3h. mauve . . . 10 10
D230 30 on 3h. mauve . . . 10 10
D257 3 30 on 15h. red . . . 35 20
D231 2 40 on 3h. mauve . . . 10 10
D258 3 40 on 15h. red . . . 30 30
D225 50 on 75h. green . . . 25 25
D262 60 on 50h. purple . . . 3·00 1·50
D263 60 on 50h. blue . . . 3·50 1·90
D232 60 on 75h. green . . . 40 10
D226 60 on 80h. green . . . 20 10
D227 100 on 80h. green . . . 30 10
D233 100 on 120h. black . . . 90 10
D264 100 on 400h. violet . . . 55 10
D265 3 100 on 1000h. purple . . . 1·10 30
D228 2 200 on 400h. violet . . . 50 20

1924. Postage Due stamp surch.
D249 D 4 10 on 5h. olive 10 10
D250 20 on 5h. olive 10 10
D251 30 on 15h. olive 10 10
D252 40 on 15h. olive 10 10
D253 50 on 250h. orange . . . 65 10
D234 50 on 400h. red . . . 50 10
D254 60 on 250h. orange . . . 90 20
D235 60 on 400h. red . . . 2·10 60
D255 100 on 250h. orange . . 1·90 20
D236 100 on 400h. red . . . 1·25 20
D256 200 on 500h. green . . 3·00 1·75

1926. Postage stamps optd **DOPLATIT** or surch also.
D266 13 30 on 100h. green . . . 10 10
D279 11 40 on 185h. orange . . . 10 10
D267 13 40 on 200h. purple . . . 10 10
D268 40 on 300h. red . . . 1·10 25
D280 11 50 on 20h. red . . . 10 10
D281 50 on 150h. red . . . 25 10
D269 13 50 on 250h. green . . . 50 10
D282 11 60 on 25h. brown . . . 25 20
D283 60 on 40h. orange . . . 25 10
D270 13 60 on 400h. brown . . . 45 10
D278 11 100h. brown 50 10
D284 100 on 25h. brown . . . 35 10
D271 13 100 on 600h. purple . . . 1·75 35

D 34   **D 94**

1928.
D285 D 34 5h. red 10 10
D286 10h. red 10 10
D287 20h. red 10 10
D288 30h. red 10 10
D289 40h. red 10 10
D290 50h. red 10 10
D291 60h. red 10 10
D292 1k. blue 10 10
D293 2k. blue 35 10
D294 5k. blue 60 10
D295 10k. blue . . . . . . 1·25 10
D296 20k. blue . . . . . . 2·40 10

1946.
D467 D 94 10h. blue 10 10
D468 20h. blue 10 10
D469 50h. blue 15 10
D470 1k. red 30 10
D471 1k.20 red 35 10
D472 1k.50 red 40 10
D473 1k.60 red 45 10
D474 2k. red 55 10
D475 2k.40 red 60 10
D476 3k. red . . . . . . 1·00 10
D477 5k. red . . . . . . 1·50 10
D478 6k. red . . . . . . 2·10 10

D 257   **D 258**

1954.
D845 D 257 5h. green 10 10
D846 10h. green 10 10
D860 30h. green 10 10
D861 50h. green 15 10
D849 60h. green 15 10
D850 95h. green 35 10
D863 D 258 1k. violet 25 10
D864 1k.20 violet 30 10
D865 1k.50 violet 45 10
D854 1k.60 violet 40 10
D855 2k. violet 75 10
D866 3k. violet . . . . 1·25 30
D867 5k. violet . . . . 1·60 45

D 572 Stylized Plant

1971.
D1985 – 10h. pink and blue 10 10
D1986 – 20h. blue & purple 10 10
D1987 – 30h. pink & green 10 10
D1988 – 60h. green & pur 15 10
D1989 – 80h. blue & orange 20 10
D1990 – 1k. green & red 25 10
D1991 – 1k.20 orange & grn 30 10
D1992 – 2k. red and blue 55 30
D1993 – 3k. yellow & black 90 30
D1994 – 4k. blue & brown 1·10 45
D1995 D 572 5k.40 lilac and red 1·60 60
D1996 – 6k. yellow and red 1·90 75
DESIGNS: Various stylized plants as Type D **572.**

CZECH REPUBLIC   Pt. 5

Formerly part of Czechoslovakia, a federation dissolved on 31 December 1992 when the constituent republics became separate states.

100 haleru = 1 koruna.

1 State Arms

1993.
1 **1** 3k. multicoloured 20 20

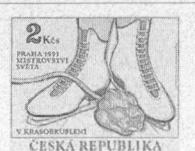

2 Skater's Boots and Tulip

3 Pres. Vaclav Havel

1993. Ice Skating Championships, Prague.
2 **2** 2k. multicoloured 15 10

1993.
3 **3** 2k. purple, blue & mauve . . 10 10
3a 3k.60 violet, mauve & blue 20 10

4 St. John and Charles Bridge, Prague

1993. 600th Death Anniv of St. John of Nepomuk (patron saint of Bohemia).
4 **4** 8k. multicoloured 80 45

5 "Hladovy Svaty I" (Mikulas Medek)

1993. Europa. Contemporary Art.
5 **5** 14k. multicoloured . . . . . . 7·50 2·40

6 Church of Sacred Heart, Prague

1993.
6 **6** 5k. multicoloured . . . . . . 1·50 45
See also No. 45.

7 Brevnov Monastery

1993. U.N.E.S.C.O. World Heritage Site. Millenary of Brevnov Monastry, Prague.
7 **7** 4k. multicoloured 35 20

8 Weightlifter

9 Town Hall Tower and Cathedral of St. Peter and St. Paul

1993. Junior Weightlifting Championships, Cheb.
8 **8** 6k. multicoloured 50 30

1993. 750th Anniv of Brno.
9 **9** 8k. multicoloured . . . . . . 1·75 65

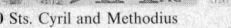

10 Sts. Cyril and Methodius

12 Ceske Budejovice

1993. 1130th Anniv of Arrival of Sts. Cyril and Methodius in Moravia.
10 **10** 8k. multicoloured 60 25

1993. Towns.
12 **12** 1k. brown and red 10 10
13 — 2k. red and blue 10 10
14 — 3k. blue and red 15 10
15 — 3k. blue and red 15 10
16 — 5k. green and brown 50 25
17 — 6k. green and yellow 50 20
18 — 7k. brown and green 55 20
20 — 8k. violet and yellow 40 30
21 — 10k. green and red 55 35
23 — 20k. red and blue . . . 1·10 70
26 — 50k. brown and green . . 3·00 1·60
DESIGNS—VERT: 2k. Usti nad Labem; 3k. (15) Brno; 5k. Pilsen; 6k. Slanyi; 7k. Antonin Dvorak Theatre, Ostrava; 8k. Olomouc; 10k. Hradec Kralove; 20k. Prague; 50k. Opava. HORIZ: 3k. (14) Cesky Krumlov (U.N.E.S.C.O. World Heritage Site).

13 Rower

14 August Sedlacek (historian, 150th anniv)

1993. World Rowing Championships, Racice.
27 **13** 3k. multicoloured 20 30

1993. Birth Anniversaries.
28 **14** 2k. buff, blue and green . . . 15 10
29 — 3k. buff, blue and violet . . 25 10
DESIGN: 3k. Eduard Cech (mathematician, centenary).

15 Pedunculate Oak

17 St. Nicholas

16 "Composition" (Joan Miro)

1993. Trees. Multicoloured.
30 5k. Type **15** 35 10
31 7k. Hornbeam 50 30
32 9k. Scots pine 75 45

1993. Art (1st series). Multicoloured.
33 11k. Type **16** . . . . 2·00 1·10
34 14k. "Green Corn Field with Cypress" (Vincent van Gogh) . . . . 3·25 1·40
See also Nos. 62/4, 116/18, 140/2, 174/6, 200/1, 221/2, 252/4, 282/4 and 312/14.

1993. Christmas.
35 **17** 2k. multicoloured 20 10

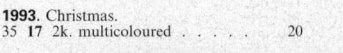

18 "Strahov Madonna"

1993. Christmas.
36 **18** 9k. multicoloured . . . . . 3·00 90

19 "Family"
(C. Littasy-Rollier)

20 Kubelik

1994. International Year of the Family.
37 **19** 2k. multicoloured 10 10

1994. 54th Death Anniv of Jan Kublik (composer and violinist).
38 **20** 3k. yellow and black 20 10

21 Voltaire (writer, 300th anniv)

1994. Birth Anniversaries.
39 **21** 2k. purple, grey & mauve 15 15
40 — 6k. black, blue and green . . 45 30
DESIGN: 6k. Georg Agricola (mineralogist, 500th anniv).

22 Athletes

23 Marco Polo and Fantasy Animal

1994. Winter Olympic Games, Lillehammer, Norway.
41 **22** 5k. multicoloured 35 30

1994. Europa. Discoveries. Marco Polo's Journeys to the Orient. Multicoloured.
42 14k. Type **23** . . . . 1·10 1·10
43 14k. Marco Polo and woman on fantasy animals . . . . 1·10 1·10

24 Benes

26 Crayon Figures

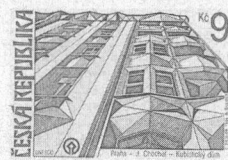

25 Cubist Flats by Josef Chochol, Prague

1994. 110th Birth Anniv of Edvard Benes (President of Czechoslovakia 1935–38 and 1945–48).
44 **24** 5k. violet and purple . . . 35 20

1994. U.N.E.S.C.O. World Heritage Sites. Mult.
45 8k. Market place, Telc . . . . 1·00 55
46 9k. Type **25** . . . . 1·25 70
No. 45 is similar to Type **6**.

1994. For Children.
47 **26** 2k. multicoloured 10 10

27 "Stegosaurus ungulatus"

1994. Prehistoric Animals. Multicoloured.
48 2k. Type **27** 20 15
49 3k. "Apatosaurus excelsus" . . 30 15
50 5k. "Tarbosaurus bataar" (vert) 50 15

28 Statue of Liberty holding Football

29 Flag of Prague Section

1994. World Cup Football Championship, U.S.A.
51 **28** 8k. multicoloured 75 45

1994. 12th Sokol (sports organization) Congress, Prague.
52 **29** 2k. multicoloured 10 10

30 Olympic Flag and Flame

1994. Centenary of Int Olympic Committee.
53 **30** 7k. multicoloured 60 35

31 Stylized Carrier Pigeons

1994. 120th Anniv of Universal Postal Union.
54 **31** 11k. multicoloured 90 50

32 Common Stonechat

33 NW, 1900

1994. Birds. Multicoloured.
55 3k. Type **32** 15 15
56 5k. Common rosefinch 25 15
57 14k. Bluethroat . . . . . . 1·10 75

1994. Racing Cars. Multicoloured.
58 2k. Type **33** 15 15
59 3k. L & K, 1908 . . . . . . 25 15
60 9k. Praga, 1912 . . . . . . 65 45

34 Angel

35 Emblem

1994. Christmas.
61 **34** 2k. multicoloured 10 10

1994. Art (2nd series). As T **16**.
62 7k. black and buff 45 50
63 10k. multicoloured . . . . . 90 1·00
64 14k. multicoloured . . . . . 1·50 1·10
DESIGNS—VERT: 7k. "The Old Man and the Woman" (Lucas van Leyden); 10k. "Moulin Rouge" (Henri de Toulouse-Lautrec); 14k. "Madonna of St. Vitus".

1995. 20th Anniv of World Tourism Organization.
65 **35** 8k. blue and red 65 45

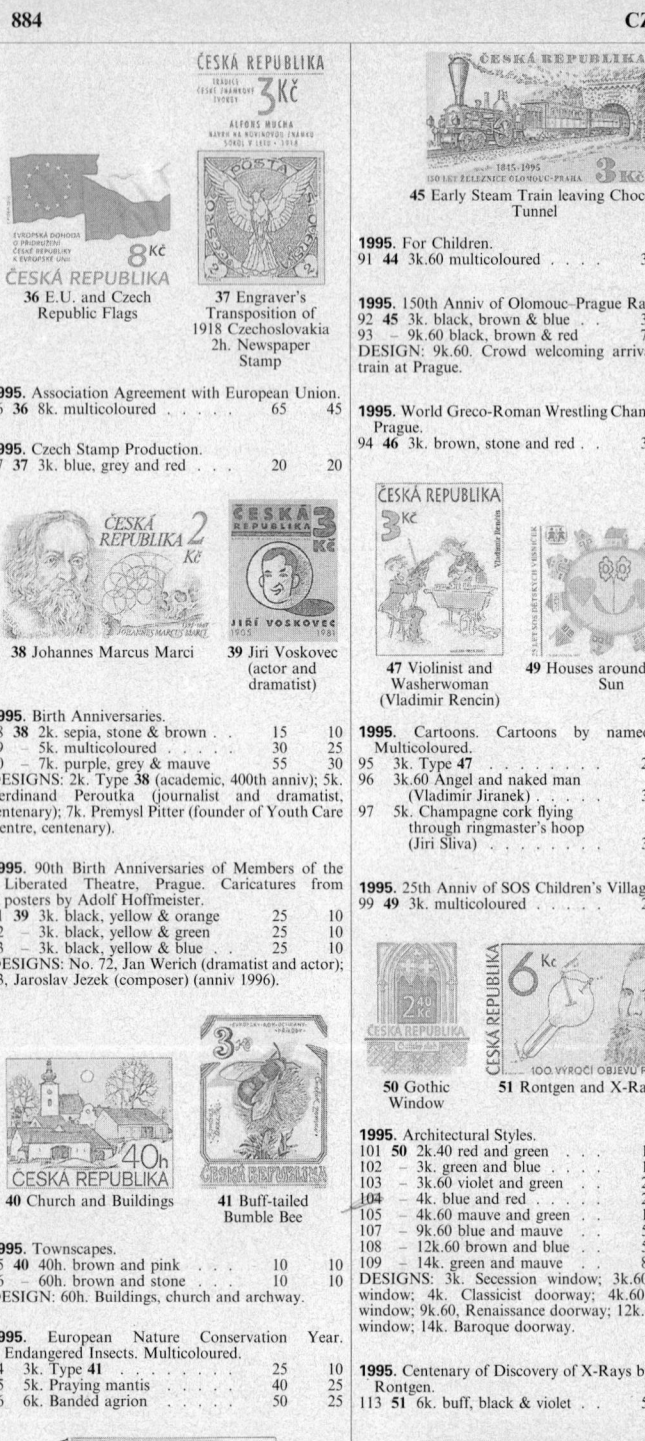

36 E.U. and Czech Republic Flags

37 Engraver's Transposition of 1918 Czechoslovakia 2h. Newspaper Stamp

1995. Association Agreement with European Union.
66   **36**   8k. multicoloured   65   45

1995. Czech Stamp Production.
67   **37**   3k. blue, grey and red . . .   20   20

38 Johannes Marcus Marci

39 Jiri Voskovec (actor and dramatist)

1995. Birth Anniversaries.
68   **38**   2k. sepia, stone & brown . .   15   10
69   —   5k. multicoloured   30   25
70   —   7k. purple, grey & mauve .   55   30
DESIGNS: 2k. Type **38** (academic, 400th anniv); 5k. Ferdinand Peroutka (journalist and dramatist, centenary); 7k. Premysl Pitter (founder of Youth Care Centre, centenary).

1995. 90th Birth Anniversaries of Members of the Liberated Theatre, Prague. Caricatures from posters by Adolf Hoffmeister.
71   **39**   3k. black, yellow & orange   25   10
72   —   3k. black, yellow & green   25   10
73   —   3k. black, yellow & blue .   25   10
DESIGNS: No. 72, Jan Werich (dramatist and actor); 73, Jaroslav Jezek (composer) (anniv 1996).

40 Church and Buildings

41 Buff-tailed Bumble Bee

1995. Townscapes.
75   **40**   40h. brown and pink . . .   10   10
76   —   60h. brown and stone . . .   10   10
DESIGN: 60h. Buildings, church and archway.

1995. European Nature Conservation Year. Endangered Insects. Multicoloured.
84   **41**   3k. Type **41**   25   10
85   —   5k. Praying mantis   40   25
86   —   6k. Banded agrion   50   25

42 Sandstone Arch, Labske Piskovce

1995. Rock Formations. Multicoloured.
87   8k. Stone Organ (basalt columns), Central Bohemia   70   55
88   9k. Type **42**   75   60

43 Rose and Women's Profiles

1995. Europa. Peace and Freedom. Multicoloured.
89   9k. Type **43**   80   35
90   14k. Butterfly, girl and profiles of ageing woman . . . .   1·10   65

44 Cat

46 Wrestlers

---

45 Early Steam Train leaving Chocen Tunnel

1995. For Children.
91   **44**   3k.60 multicoloured . . .   35   20

1995. 150th Anniv of Olomouc–Prague Railway.
92   **45**   3k. black, brown & blue . .   35   10
93   —   9k.60 black, brown & red   70   25
DESIGN: 9k.60. Crowd welcoming arrival of first train at Prague.

1995. World Greco-Roman Wrestling Championship, Prague.
94   **46**   3k. brown, stone and red . .   35   10

47 Violinist and Washerwoman (Vladimir Rencin)

49 Houses around smiling Sun

1995. Cartoons. Cartoons by named artists. Multicoloured.
95   3k. Type **47**   20   10
96   3k.60 Angel and naked man (Vladimir Jiranek)   30   15
97   5k. Champagne cork flying through ringmaster's hoop (Jiri Sliva)   35   20

1995. 25th Anniv of SOS Children's Villages.
99   **49**   3k. multicoloured   20   10

50 Gothic Window

51 Rontgen and X-Ray Tube

1995. Architectural Styles.
101   **50**   2k.40 red and green . . .   10   10
102   —   3k. green and blue   15   10
103   —   3k.60 violet and green . .   20   10
104   —   4k. blue and red   20   10
105   —   4k.60 mauve and green . .   15   10
107   —   9k.60 blue and mauve . .   50   45
108   —   12k.60 brown and blue . .   50   45
109   —   14k. green and mauve . .   85   60
DESIGNS: 3k. Secession window; 3k.60, Roman window; 4k. Classicist doorway; 4k.60, Rococo window; 9k.60, Renaissance doorway; 12k.60, Cubist window; 14k. Baroque doorway.

1995. Centenary of Discovery of X-Rays by Wilhelm Rontgen.
113   **51**   6k. buff, black & violet . .   50   20

52 Emblem

1995. 50th Anniv of U.N.O.
114   **52**   14k. multicoloured . . . .   1·25   60

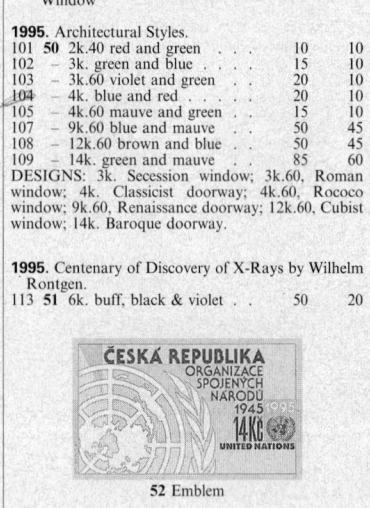

53 Christmas Tree

55 Stamp Design by Jaroslav Benda

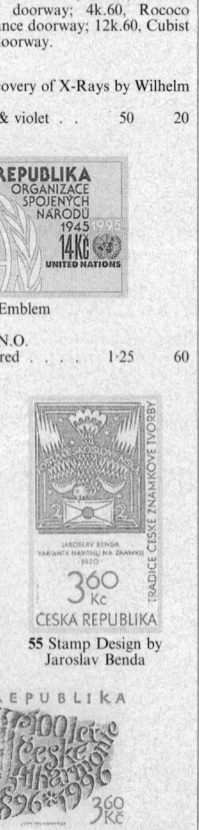

54 Allegory of Music

1995. Christmas.
115   **53**   3k. multicoloured   20   15

1995. Art (3rd series). As T **16**.
116   6k. black, blue and buff . . .   25   30
117   9k. multicoloured   40   45
118   14k. multicoloured   65   75
DESIGNS: 6k. "Parisienne" (Ludek Marold); 9k. "Bouquet" (J. K. Hirschely); 14k. "Portrait of the Sculptor Josef Malinsky" (Antonin Machek).

1996. Cent of Czech Philharmonic Orchestra.
119   **54**   3k.60 multicoloured . . .   30   25

1996. Tradition of Czech Stamp Production.
120   **55**   3k.60 multicoloured . . .   30   25

56 Mencikova and Chessmen

1996. 90th Birth Anniv of Vera Mencikova (chess champion).
121   **56**   6k. black, buff and red . .   30   20

57 Woman with Bowl of Easter Eggs

58 Sudek and Camera

1996. Easter.
122   **57**   3k. multicoloured   20   15

1996. Birth Cent of Josef Sudek (photographer).
123   **58**   9k.60 buff, black & grey . .   80   45

59 Jiri Guth-Jarkovsky (first President of National Olympic Committee) and Stadium

62 Ema Destinnova (singer)

60 Jan (John the Blind)

1996. Centenary of Modern Olympic Games.
124   **59**   9k.60 multicoloured . . .   80   45

1996. Bohemian Kings of the Luxembourg Dynasty.
125   **60**   14k. blue, grey & purple   1·10   90
126   —   14k. green, grey & purple   1·10   90
127   —   14k. green, grey & purple   1·10   90
128   —   14k. blue, grey & purple   1·10   90
DESIGNS: No. 126, Karel (Charles IV, Holy Roman Emperor); 127, Vaclav IV; 128, Sigismund.

1996. Europa. Famous Women.
130   **62**   8k. lilac, black & mauve   65   45

63 Entering Stage as Pierrot

64 Throwing the Javelin

1996. Birth Bicentenary of Jean Gaspard Deburau (mime actor).
131   **63**   12k. multicoloured   90   45

1996. Olympic Games, Atlanta.
132   **64**   3k. multicoloured   20   10

65 Boy and Girl on Cat

66 St. John of Nepomuk's Church, Zelena Hora

1996. For Children.
133   **65**   3k. multicoloured   20   10

1996. Tourist Sites. Multicoloured.
134   8k. Type **66** (U.N.E.S.C.O. World Heritage Site)   60   50
135   9k. Prague Loretto   70   55

67 Boy playing Flute and Flowers forming Butterfly

1996. 50th Anniv of U.N.I.C.E.F.
136   **67**   3k. multicoloured   20   10

68 Black Horse

1996. Kladruby Horses. Multicoloured.
137   3k. Type **68**   20   10
138   3k. White horse   20   10

1996. Art (4th series). As T **16**. Multicoloured.
140   9k. "Eden" (Josef Vachal) . .   60   60
141   11k. "Breakfast with Egg" (Georg Flegel) (vert)   80   75
142   20k. "Baroque Chair" (Endre Nemes) (vert) . . . . .   1·50   1·10

70 Brahe

1996. 450th Birth Anniv of Tycho Brahe (astronomer).
143   **70**   5k. multicoloured   35   25

71 Letov S-1

72 Nativity

1996. Biplanes. Multicoloured.
144   7k. Type **71**   50   25
145   8k. Aero A-11   60   30
146   10k. Avia BH-21   75   35

1996. Christmas.
147   **72**   3k. multicoloured   20   10

73 Czechoslovakia 1920 Stamp Design of V. Brunner

74 Easter Symbols

1997. Czech Stamp Production.
148 73 3k.60 blue and red 20 10

1997. Easter.
149 74 3k. multicoloured 20 10

75 Dog's-tooth Violet

76 Girl and Cats ("Congratulations")

1997. Endangered Plants. Multicoloured.
150 3k.60 Type 75 . . . . . . 20 10
151 4k. Bog arum 30 10
152 5k. Lady's slipper 30 10
153 8k. Dwarf bearded iris . . . 60 30

1997. Greetings Stamp.
154 76 4k. multicoloured 30 10

77 St. Adalbert

78 Prince Bruncvik, Neomenie and Lion

1997. Death Millenary of St. Adalbert (Bishop of Prague).
155 77 7k. lilac 50 30

1997. Europa. Tales and Legends. Multicoloured.
156 8k. Type 78 . . . . . . 60 45
157 8k. King Wenceslas IV watching Zito the Magician in cart pulled by cocks . . 60 45

79 Ark of the Torah, Old-New Synagogue (east side)

81 Rakosnicek (cartoon character) and Rowan Berries

1997. Jewish Monuments in Prague. Each black, blue and red.
158 8k. Type 79 . . . . . . 65 50
159 10k. Grave of Rabbi Loew (Chief Rabbi of Prague), Old Jewish Cemetery . . 75 55

1997. For Children.
161 81 4k.60 multicoloured . . . 35 10

82 Krizik and Arc Lamp

1997. 150th Birth Anniv of Frantisek Krizik (electrical engineer).
162 82 6k. pink, blue and red . . 45 15

83 Swimmer

1997. European Swimming and Diving Championships, Prague.
163 83 11k. black, buff & blue . 75 30

84 Mrs. Muller and Svejk in Wheelchair

1997. 110th Anniv of "Fortunes of the Good Soldier Svejk" (novel by Jaroslav Hasek). Illustrations by Josef Lada. Multicoloured.
164 4k. Type 84 . . . . . . 35 15
165 4k.60 Lt. Lukas and Col. Kraus von Zillergut with stolen dog 35 15
166 6k. Svejk smoking pipe . . . 45 25

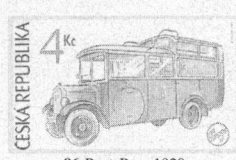

85 Prague Castle

1997. "Praga 1998" International Stamp Exhibition. Multicoloured.
167 15k. Type 85 . . . . . . 95 55
168 15k. View of Prague Old Town 95 55

86 Post Bus, 1928

1997. Historic Service Vehicles. Multicoloured.
170 4k. Type 86 . . . . . . 30 10
171 4k.60 Skoda Sentinel lorry, 1924 . . . . 30 10
172 8k. Tatra fire engine, 1933 . 60 25

87 Carp, Candle, Fir, Apple and Nut

88 Olympic Rings and Ice Hockey Puck

1997. Christmas.
173 87 4k. multicoloured 30 10

1997. Art (5th series). As T 16.
174 7k. multicoloured 30 30
175 12k. green and black . . . 85 65
176 16k. multicoloured . . . . 1·00 1·00
DESIGNS—HORIZ: 7k. "Landscape with Chateau in Chantilly" (Antonin Chittussi). VERT: 12k. "The Prophets came out of the Desert" (Frantisek Bilek); 16k. "Parisian Second-hand Booksellers" (T. F. Simon).

1998. Winter Olympic Games, Nagano, Japan.
177 88 7k. multicoloured 45 25

89 Jakub Obvrovsky's 1920 Design

90 Pres. Vaclav Havel

1998. Czech Stamp Production.
178 89 12k.60 brown and green . 90 45

1998.
179 90 4k.60 green and red . . 35 10
179a 5k.40 blue and brown . . 40 10

91 Cupid and Heart

92 Slalom

1998. St. Valentine's Day.
180 91 4k. multicoloured 30 10

1998. World Skibob Championships, Spindleruv Mlyn.
181 92 8k. multicoloured 60 25

94 Chick in Egg Shell

1998. Easter.
183 94 4k. multicoloured 30 10

95 Observatory Building and Telescope Dome

1998. Centenary of Ondrejov Observatory.
184 95 4k.60 yellow, black & red 35 30

98 Grey Partridge

99 Book and Copyright Symbol

1998. Endangered Species. Multicoloured.
187 4k.60 Type 98 . . . . . 35 30
188 4k.60 Black grouse ("Lyrurus tetrix") 35 30
189 8k. White deer ("Cervus elphus") 50 45
190 8k. Elk ("Alces alces") . . 50 45

1998. World Book and Copyright Day.
191 99 10k. multicoloured . . . 75 30

100 The King's Ride, Moravia

1998. Europa. National Festivals. Multicoloured.
192 11k. Type 100 . . . . . 70 35
193 15k. Carnival masks . . . 95 45

101 Devil Musicians

102 Frantisek Kmoch (composer)

1998. For Children. Multicoloured.
194 4k. Type 101 . . . . . 25 10
195 4k.60 Water sprite riding catfish 30 10

1998. Anniversaries. Multicoloured.
196 4k. Type 102 (150th birth anniv) 25 10
197 4k.60 Frantisek Palacky (historian, birth bicent) . 35 30
198 6k. Rafael Kubelik (conductor, 2nd death anniv) 40 30

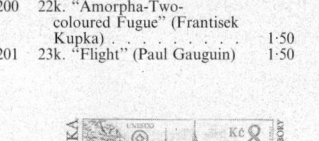

103 Prague Barricades, June 1848

1998. 150th Anniv of 1848 Revolutions.
199 103 15k. multicoloured . . . 1·00 60

1998. Art (6th series). As T 16. Multicoloured.
200 22k. "Amorpha-Two-coloured Fugue" (Frantisek Kupka) . . . . . . 1·50 1·10
201 23k. "Flight" (Paul Gauguin) 1·50 1·25

104 St. Barbara's Cathedral, Kutna Hora

1998. World Heritage Sites. Multicoloured.
202 8k. Type 104 . . . . . 60 50
203 11k. Chateau Valtice . . . 90 80

105 Soldiers with Flags

106 Capricorn

1998. 80th Anniv of Founding of Czechoslovak Republic. Paintings by Vojtech Preissig. Mult.
204 4k.60 Type 105 . . . . . 20 20
205 5k. Soldiers marching . . . 20 20
206 12k.60 Flags in Mala Street, Prague 50 50

1998. Signs of the Zodiac.
206a — 40h green, brown & blk 10 10
207 106 1k. yellow, red and black 10 10
208 — 2k. black, lilac and blue 10 10
209 — 5k. red, black and yellow 30 15
210 — 5k.40 green, black & brn 30 15
211 — 8k. red, black & purple 50 25
212 — 9k. green, black & orge 60 30
213 — 10k. yellow, blue & black 70 20
214 — 12k. orange, blue & black 80 50
217 — 20k. violet, black & brn 1·40 70
DESIGNS: 40h. Pisces; 2k. Virgo; 5k. Taurus; 5k.40; Scorpio; 8k. Cancer; 9k. Libra; 10k. Aquarius; 12k. Leo; 20k. Sagittarius.

107 People following Star

1998. Christmas. Multicoloured.
219 4k. Type 107 . . . . . 25 10
220 6k. Angel with trumpet over village (vert) 45 30

1998. Art (7th series). As T 16. Multicoloured.
221 15k. Section of "The Greater Cycle" (Jan Preisler) . . . 1·10 60
222 16k. "Spinner" (Josef Navratil) (vert) . . . . 1·25 65

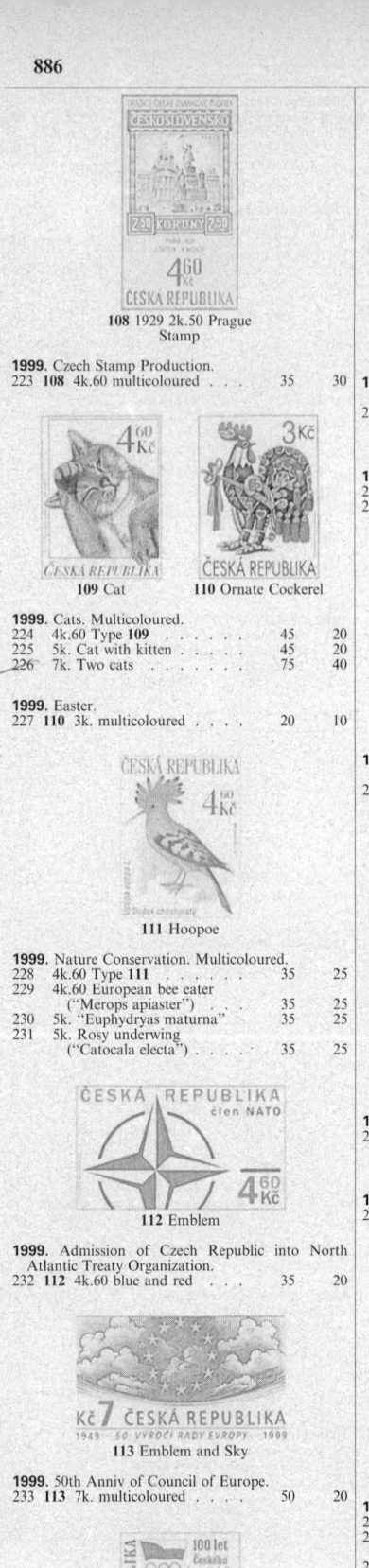

108 1929 2k.50 Prague Stamp

1999. Czech Stamp Production.
223 **108** 4k.60 multicoloured . . . 35 30

109 Cat   **110** Ornate Cockerel

1999. Cats. Multicoloured.
224   4k.60 Type **109** 45 20
225   5k. Cat with kitten 45 20
226   7k. Two cats 75 40

1999. Easter.
227 **110** 3k. multicoloured 20 10

111 Hoopoe

1999. Nature Conservation. Multicoloured.
228   4k.60 Type **111** 35 25
229   4k.60 European bee eater
     ("Merops apiaster") . . 35 25
230   5k. "Euphydryas maturna" . 35 25
231   5k. Rosy underwing
     ("Catocala electa") 35 25

112 Emblem

1999. Admission of Czech Republic into North Atlantic Treaty Organization.
232 **112** 4k.60 blue and red . . . 35 20

113 Emblem and Sky

1999. 50th Anniv of Council of Europe.
233 **113** 7k. multicoloured 50 20

114 Josef Rossler-Orovsky (co-founder)

1999. Centenary of Czech Olympic Committee.
234 **114** 9k. multicoloured 65 30

115 Sumava National Park

1999. Europa. Parks and Gardens. Multicoloured.
235   11k. Type **115** 80 50
236   17k. Podyji National Park . . 1·10 70

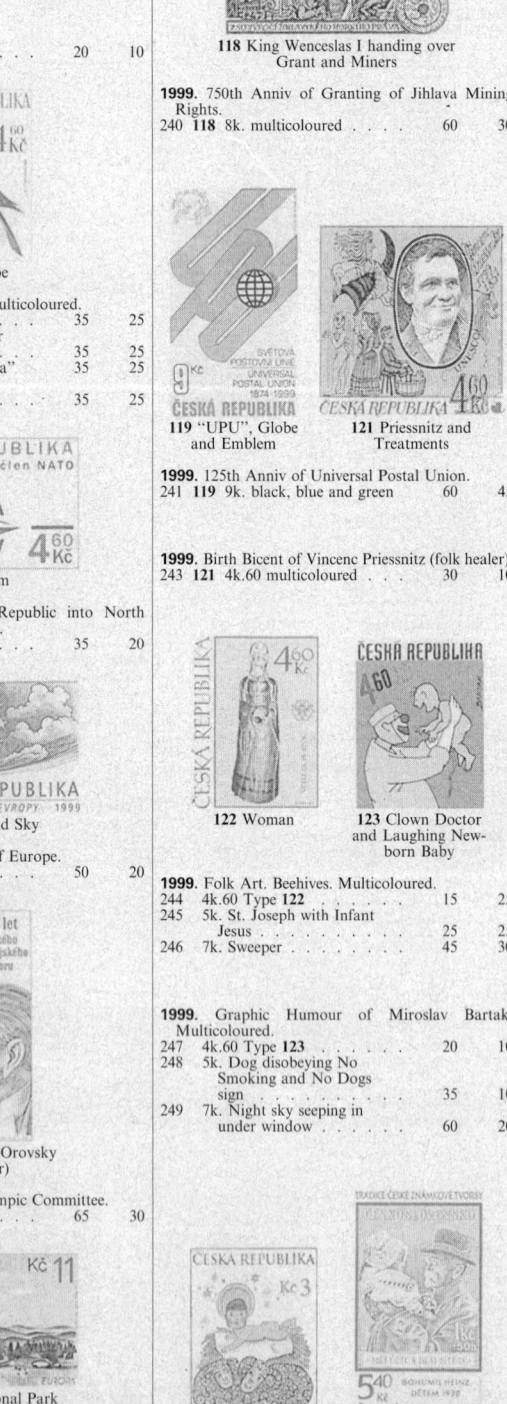

116 "Ferda the Ant, Pytlik the Beetle and The Proud Ladybird"

117 Chain Bridge, Stadlec

1999. For Children. Birth Centenary of Ondrej Sekora (children's writer).
237 **116** 4k.60 multicoloured . . . 30 15

1999. Bridges. Multicoloured.
238   8k. Type **117** 60 35
239   11k. Wooden bridge, Cernvir
     (horiz) 80 50

118 King Wenceslas I handing over Grant and Miners

1999. 750th Anniv of Granting of Jihlava Mining Rights.
240 **118** 8k. multicoloured 60 30

119 "UPU", Globe and Emblem   **121** Priessnitz and Treatments

1999. 125th Anniv of Universal Postal Union.
241 **119** 9k. black, blue and green 60 45

1999. Birth Bicent of Vincenc Priessnitz (folk healer).
243 **121** 4k.60 multicoloured . . . 30 10

122 Woman   **123** Clown Doctor and Laughing Newborn Baby

1999. Folk Art. Beehives. Multicoloured.
244   4k.60 Type **122** 15 25
245   5k. St. Joseph with Infant
     Jesus 25 25
246   7k. Sweeper 45 30

1999. Graphic Humour of Miroslav Bartak. Multicoloured.
247   4k.60 Type **123** 20 10
248   5k. Dog disobeying No
     Smoking and No Dogs
     sign 35 10
249   7k. Night sky seeping in
     under window 60 20

125 Baby Jesus with Sheep and Lamb

127 Czechoslovakia 1938 1k.+50h. Child Welfare Stamp

1999. Christmas.
251 **125** 3k. multicoloured 20 10

1999. Art (8th series). As T **16**. Multicoloured.
252   13k. "Red Orchid" (Jindrich
     Styrsky) (vert) 85 65
253   17k. "Landscape with
     Marsh" (Julius Marak)
     (vert) . . . . 1·10 90
254   26k. "Monument" (Frantisek
     Hudecek) (vert) . . . . . 1·60 1·25

2000. Czech Stamp Production.
257 **127** 5k.40 multicoloured . . . 35 20

128 Kutna Hora Coat of Arms and 14th-century Miners

130 Animal-shaped Cake and Painted Eggs

2000. 700th Anniv of Granting of Royal Mining Rights to Kutn Hora.
258 **128** 5k. multicoloured 20 15

2000. Easter.
260 **130** 5k. multicoloured 20 15

132 Vitezslav Nezval (poet) (centenary)   **134** "Building Europe"

2000. Birth Anniversaries.
262 **132** 5k. blue, lilac and violet   20 15
263   – 8k. mauve, red and violet   30 20
DESIGN: 8k. Gustav Mahler (composer, 140th anniv).

2000. Europa.
265 **134** 9k. multicoloured 35 25

135 Alarm Clock and Bird   **137** Geastrum pouzarii

136 Fermat's Great Theorem

2000. International Children's Day.
266 **135** 5k.40 multicoloured 20 15

2000. World Mathematics Year.
267 **136** 7k. multicoloured 45 30

2000. Endangered Fungi. Multicoloured.
268   5k. Type **137** 15 10
269   5k. Devil's boletus (Boletus
     satanas) 15 10
270   5k.40 Verpa bohemica . . . 20 15
271   5k.40 Morchella pragensis . 20 15

138 Old Town Bridge Tower

2000. Historic Buildings. Multicoloured.
272   9k. Type **138** 30 30
273   11k. St. Nicolas's Church . . 40 30
274   13k. Municipal Hall 45 35

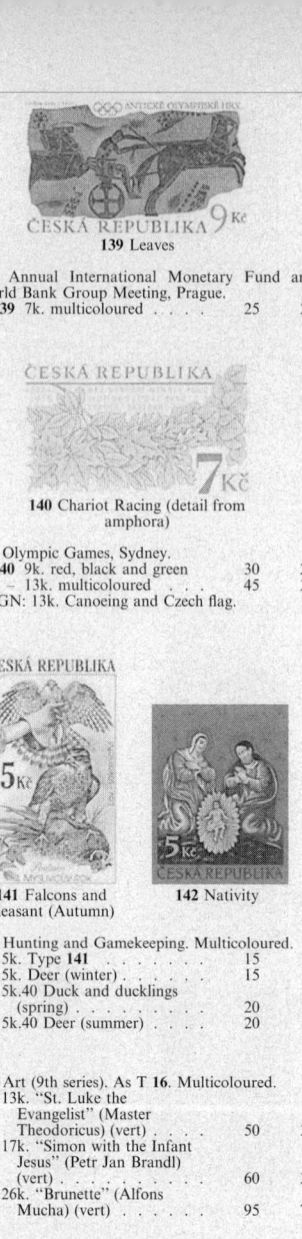

139 Leaves

2000. Annual International Monetary Fund and World Bank Group Meeting, Prague.
275 **139** 7k. multicoloured 25 20

140 Chariot Racing (detail from amphora)

2000. Olympic Games, Sydney.
276 **140** 9k. red, black and green   30 25
277   – 13k. multicoloured 45 35
DESIGN: 13k. Canoeing and Czech flag.

141 Falcons and Pheasant (Autumn)   **142** Nativity

2000. Hunting and Gamekeeping. Multicoloured.
278   5k. Type **141** 15 10
279   5k. Deer (winter) 15 10
280   5k.40 Duck and ducklings
     (spring) 20 10
281   5k.40 Deer (summer) 20 10

2000. Art (9th series). As T **16**. Multicoloured.
282   13k. "St. Luke the
     Evangelist" (Master
     Theodoricus) (vert) . . 50 30
283   17k. "Simon with the Infant
     Jesus" (Petr Jan Brandl)
     (vert) 60 35
284   26k. "Brunette" (Alfons
     Mucha) (vert) 95 75

2000. Christmas.
285 **142** 5k. multicoloured 15 10

143 Cat   **144** Czechoslovakia 1951 5c. Stamp

2000. Old and New Millennia. Multicoloured.
286   9k. Type **143** 35 20
287   9k. Magician pulling rabbit
     from hat 35 20

2001. Czech Stamp Production. 150th Birth Anniv of Alois Jirasek (writer).
288 **144** 5k.40 multicoloured . . . 20 10

145 Jan Amos Komensky (Comenius) (philosopher)   **146** Cockerel and Woman

2001.
289 **145** 9k. black, red and brown   35 20

2001. Easter.
290 **146** 5k.40 multicoloured 20 15

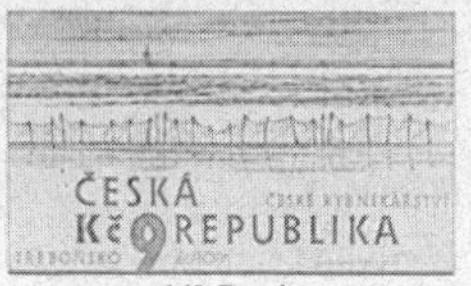

149 Pond

2001. Europa. Water Resources.
293 **149** 9k. lilac and black 35 20

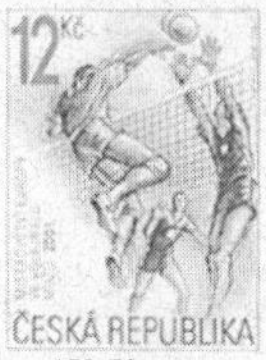

150 Players

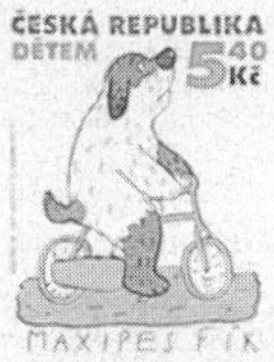

151 Maxipes Fik riding Bicycle

2001. Men's European Volleyball Championship, Ostrava.
294 **150** 12k. multicoloured . . . 45 25

2001. International Children's Day. *Vecernicek* (cartoon created by Rudolf Cechura).
295 **151** 5k.40 multicoloured . . . 20 10

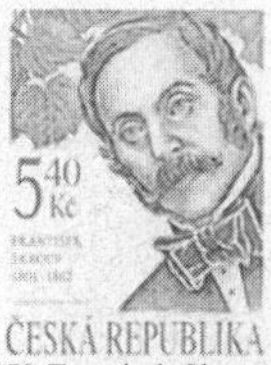

152 Frantisek Skroup (composer)

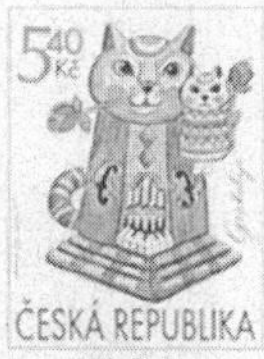

153 Cats

2001. Birth Anniversaries. Multicoloured.
296 5k.40 Type **152** (bicentenary) 20 10
297 16k. Frantisek Halas (poet, centenary) 65 35

2001. Greetings Stamp. "Congratulations".
298 **153** 5k.40 multicoloured . . . 20 10

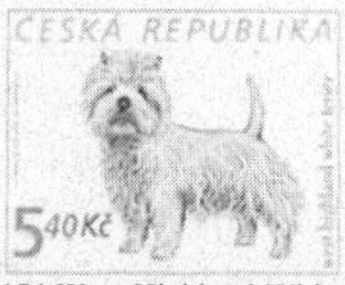

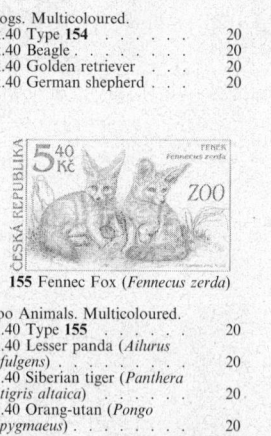

154 West Highland White Terrier

2001. Dogs. Multicoloured.
299 5k.40 Type **154** 20 10
300 5k.40 Beagle 20 10
301 5k.40 Golden retriever . . . 20 10
302 5k.40 German shepherd . . . 20 10

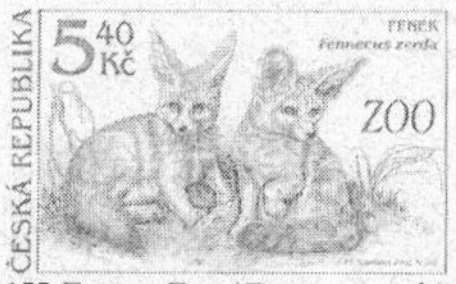

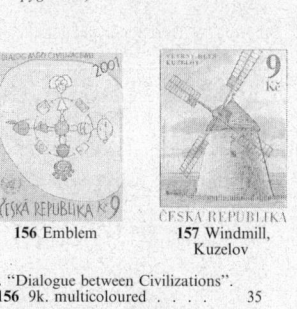

155 Fennec Fox (*Fennecus zerda*)

2001. Zoo Animals. Multicoloured.
303 5k.40 Type **155** 20 10
304 5k.40 Lesser panda (*Ailurus fulgens*) 20 10
305 5k.40 Siberian tiger (*Panthera tigris altaica*) 20 10
306 5k.40 Orang-utan (*Pongo pygmaeus*) 20 10

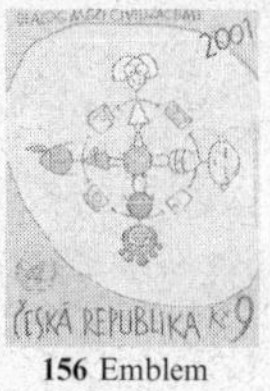

156 Emblem

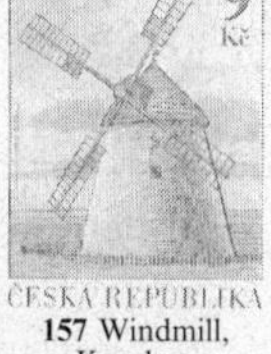

157 Windmill, Kuzelov

2001. "Dialogue between Civilizations".
307 **156** 9k. multicoloured 35 20

2001. Mills. Multicoloured.
308 9k. Type **157** 35 20
309 14k.40 Water mill, Strehom 55 30

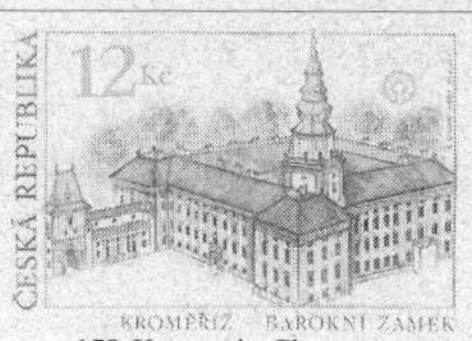

158 Kromeriz Chateau

2001. U.N.E.S.C.O. World Heritage Sites. Mult.
310 12k. Type **158** 45 25
311 14k. Holasovice village . . . 60 35

2001. Art (10th series). As T **16**.
312 12k. black, buff and blue . . 45 25
313 17k. multicoloured 65 40
314 26k. multicoloured . . . . . 1·00 60
DESIGNS—VERT: 12k. "The Annunciation of the Virgin Mary" (Michael Jindrich Rentz); 17k. "Sans-Souci Bar in Nimes" (Cyril Bouda); 26k. "The Goose Keeper" (Vaclav Brozik).

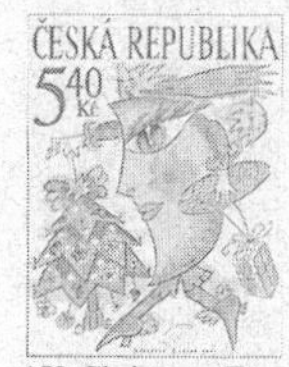

159 Christmas Tree and Half Moon carrying Gifts

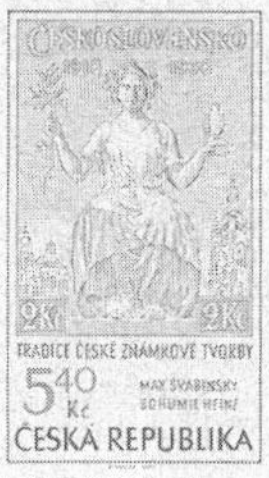

160 1938 2k. Stamp

2001. Christmas.
315 **159** 5k.40 multicoloured . . . 20 15

2002. 40th Death Anniv of Max Svabinsky (stamp designer).
316 **160** 5k.40 multicoloured . . . 20 15

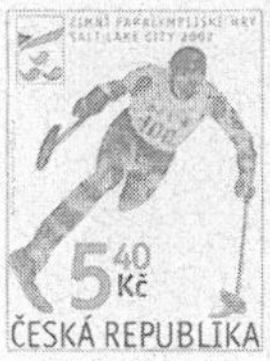

161 Skier

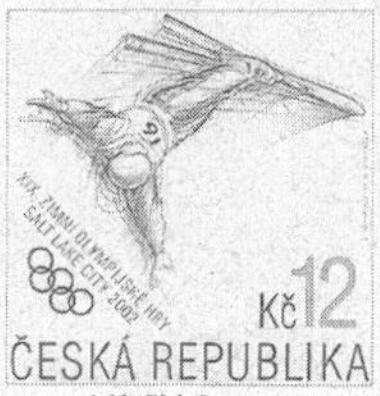

162 Ski Jumper

2002. Winter Paralympic Games, Salt Lake City, U.S.A.
317 **161** 5k.40 multicoloured . . . 20 15

2002. Winter Olympic Games, Salt Lake City, U.S.A.
318 **162** 12k. multicoloured . . . 45 25

DAHOMEY Pt. 6; Pt. 12

A French colony on the W. Coast of Africa, incorporated in French West Africa in 1944. In 1958 it became an autonomous republic within the French Community, and in 1960 was proclaimed fully independent. The area used the issues of French West Africa from 1944 until 1960.

100 centimes = 1 franc.

1899. "Tablet" key-type inscr "DAHOMEY ET DEPENDANCES".
1 D 1c. black and red on blue . . 85 90
2 2c. brown & blue on buff . . 60 70
3 4c. brown & blue on grey . . 1·40 1·50
4 5c. green and red . . . . . 2·75 1·10
5 10c. red and blue . . . . . 3·25 2·50
6 15c. grey and red . . . . . 4·00 1·75
7 20c. red & blue on green . . 9·00 14·50
8 25c. black & red on pink . . 6·75 3·50
9 25c. blue and red . . . . . 6·75 11·50
10 30c. brown & bl on drab . . 13·50 17·00
11 40c. red & blue on yellow . 9·00 8·75
12 50c. brown & red on blue . 10·00 21·00
13 50c. brown & blue on blue 32·00 17·00
14 75c. brown & red on orge . 65·00 50·00
15 1f. green and red . . . . . 32·00 32·00
16 2f. violet and red on pink . . 80·00 85·00
17 5f. mauve & blue on blue . . 85·00 90·00

1906. "Faidherbe", "Palms" and "Balay" key-types inscr "DAHOMEY".
18 I 1c. grey and red . . . . . . 1·40 85
19 2c. brown and red . . . . . 1·40 65
20 4c. brown & red on blue . . 1·90 1·25
21 5c. green and red . . . . . 4·75 50
22 10c. pink and blue . . . . . 19·00 55
23 J 20c. black & red on blue . . 9·50 9·00
24 25c. blue and red . . . . . 6·00 6·25
25 30c. brown & red on pink 12·50 13·00
26 35c. black & red on yellow 45·00 5·00
27 45c. brown & red on green 16·00 17·00
28 50c. violet and red . . . . . 11·50 16·00
29 75c. green & red on orange 16·00 19·00
30 K 1f. black and red on blue . . 23·00 32·00
31 2f. blue and red on pink . . 90·00 85·00
32 5f. red & blue on yellow . . £100 £110

1912. Surch in figures.
33 05 on 2c. brown & blue on buff . . . . 85 1·25
34 05 on 4c. brown & blue on grey . . . . 95 1·40
35 05 on 15c. grey and red . . . 1·10 2·00
36 05 on 20c. red & blue on green . . . . 80 2·25
37 05 on 25c. blue and red . . . 1·25 3·00
38 05 on 30c. brown & bl on drab . . . . 95 1·75
39 10c. on 40c. red & bl on yellow . . . . 85 1·00
40 10c. on 50c. brn & bl on blue 1·10 2·75
40a 10c. on 50c. brn & red on blue £850 £900
41 10c. on 75c. brown and red on orange . . . . 4·50 8·00

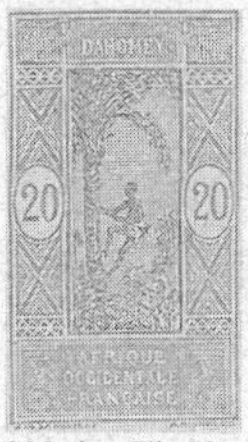

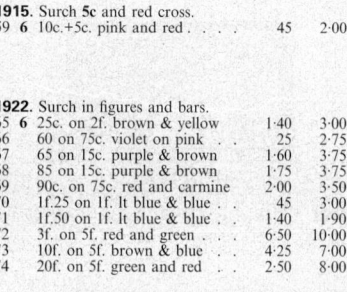

6 Native Climbing Palm

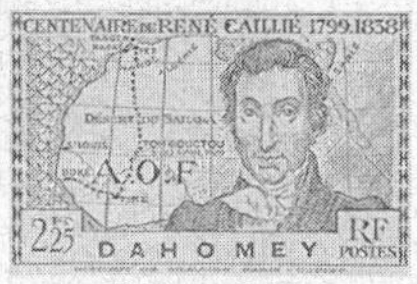

11 Rene Caillie

1913.
42 **6** 1c. black and violet 10 15
43 2c. pink and brown 10 20
44 4c. brown and black 10 45
45 5c. green and light green . . 1·40 70
60 5c. violet and purple 15 45
46 10c. pink and red . . . . . 1·75 55
61 10c. green and lt green . . . 75 1·25
75 10c. green and red 10 10
47 15c. purple and brown . . . 20 25
48 20c. brown and grey . . . . 60 1·10
76 20c. green . . . . 15 1·40
77 20c. black and mauve . . . 15 60
49 25c. blue & ultramarine . . 2·50 1·60
62 25c. orange and purple . . . 20 20
50 30c. violet and brown . . . 3·00 4·00
63 30c. carmine and red . . . 95 4·00
78 30c. violet and yellow . . . 60 50
79 30c. green and olive 50 75
51 35c. black and brown . . . 1·10 1·75
80 35c. green and turquoise . . 85 3·25
52 40c. orange and black . . . 65 70
53 45c. blue and grey . . . . . 70 2·50
54 50c. brown & chocolate . . 4·50 6·50
64 50c. blue & ultramarine . . 20 2·25
81 50c. blue and red 20 20
82 55c. brown and green . . . 50 2·50
83 60c. violet on pink . . . . 1·75 2·75
84 65c. green and brown . . . 25 95
55 75c. violet and blue 35 55
85 80c. blue and brown . . . . 50 3·00
86 85c. pink and blue . . . . . 50 2·75
87 90c. red and carmine . . . 75 1·90
87a 90c. red and brown . . . . 1·40 3·25
56 1f. black and green . . . . 65 1·00
88 1f. light blue and blue . . . 1·25 1·00
89 1f. red and brown 50 45
90 1f. red and light red . . . . 2·00 2·75
91 1f.10 brown and violet . . . 3·25 4·50
92 1f.25 brown and blue . . . 17·00 18·00
93 1f.50 light blue and blue . . 2·50 2·00
94 1f.75 orange and brown . . 3·75 3·50
94a 1f.75 ultramarine & blue . . 60 2·00
57 2f. brown and yellow . . . 1·00 65
95 3f. mauve on pink . . . . . 3·00 3·00
58 5f. blue and violet . . . . . 2·50 3·50

1915. Surch **5c** and red cross.
59 **6** 10c.+5c. pink and red . . . . 45 2·00

1922. Surch in figures and bars.
65 **6** 25c. on 2f. brown & yellow 1·40 3·00
66 60 on 75c. violet on pink . . 25 2·75
67 65 on 15c. purple & brown 1·60 3·75
68 85 on 15c. purple & brown 1·75 3·75
69 90c. on 75c. red and carmine 2·00 3·50
70 1f.25 on 1f. lt blue & blue . . 45 3·00
71 1f.50 on 1f. lt blue & blue . . 1·40 1·90
72 3f. on 5f. red and green . . . 6·50 10·00
73 10f. on 5f. brown & blue . . 4·25 7·00
74 20f. on 5f. green and red . . 2·50 8·00

1931. "Colonial Exhibition" key-types inscr "DAHOMEY".
96 E 40c. green . . . . 5·00 7·50
97 F 50c. mauve . . . . 5·25 7·25
98 G 90c. red . . . . 5·50 6·75
99 H 1f.50 blue . . . . 5·50 7·00

1937. Paris Int Exn. As Nos. 110/15 of Cameroun.
100 20c. violet . . . . 1·25 3·25
101 30c. green . . . . 1·00 3·00
102 40c. red . . . . 65 3·25
103 50c. brown . . . . 1·00 2·00
104 90c. red . . . . 70 2·25
105 1f.50 blue . . . . 60 1·60

1938. Int Anti-cancer Fund. As T **19** of Cameroun.
106 1f.75+50c. blue . . . . . . 5·00 15·00

1939. Death Centenary of R. Caillie (explorer).
107 **11** 90c. orange . . . . 40 2·00
108 2f. violet . . . . 95 3·25
109 2f.25 blue . . . . 1·25 3·50

1939. New York World's Fair. As T **20** of Cameroun.
110 1f.25 red . . . . 1·90 3·00
111 2f.25 blue . . . . 2·00 2·25

1939. 150th Anniv of French Revolution. As T **25** of Cameroun.
112 45c.+25c. green . . . . . . 4·25 11·00
113 70c.+30c. brown . . . . . . 5·25 11·00
114 90c.+35c. orange . . . . . . 4·50 11·00
115 1f.25+1f. red . . . . 4·50 11·00
116 2f.25+2f. blue . . . . 4·25 11·00

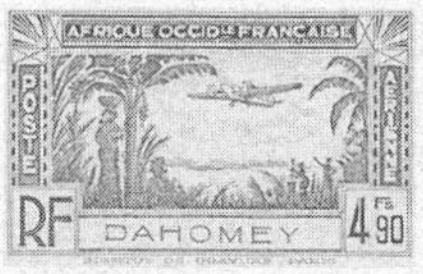

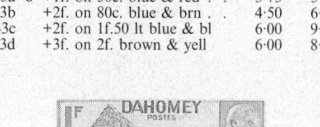

12 African Landscape

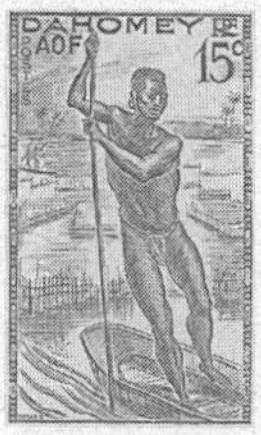

13 Native Poling Canoe

1940. Air.
117 **12** 1f.90 blue . . . . 1·25 2·50
118 2f.90 red . . . . 1·25 3·00
119 4f.50 green . . . . 1·40 2·75
120 4f.90 olive . . . . 1·10 2·75
121 6f.90 orange . . . . 90 3·25

1941.
122 **13** 2c. red . . . . 15 1·25
123 3c. blue . . . . 15 2·50
124 5c. violet . . . . 95 2·75
125 10c. green . . . . 25 2·50
126 15c. black . . . . 15 2·25
127 – 20c. brown . . . . 1·10 2·75
128 – 30c. violet . . . . 45 2·75
129 – 40c. red . . . . 55 2·75
130 – 50c. green . . . . 95 2·75
131 – 60c. black . . . . 65 2·75
132 – 70c. mauve . . . . 1·75 3·25
133 – 80c. black . . . . 1·10 2·75
134 – 1f. violet 30 35
135 – 1f.30 violet . . . . 1·00 3·25
136 – 1f.40 green . . . . 1·75 3·25
137 – 1f.50 red . . . . 1·25 3·00
138 – 2f. orange . . . . 95 3·50
139 – 2f.50 blue . . . . 1·90 3·25
140 – 3f. red . . . . 55 2·75
141 – 5f. green . . . . 60 2·25
142 – 10f. brown . . . . 70 4·00
143 – 20f. black . . . . 1·00 4·50
DESIGNS—HORIZ: 20c. to 70c. Village on piles. VERT: 80c. to 2f. Sailing pirogue on Lake Nokoue; 2f.50 to 20f. Dahomey warrior.

1941. National Defence Fund. Surch **SECOURS NATIONAL** and value.
143a **6** +1f. on 50c. blue & red . . 3·75 5·50
143b +2f. on 80c. blue & brn . . 4·50 6·25
143c +2f. on 1f.50 lt blue & bl 6·00 9·25
143d +3f. on 2f. brown & yell 6·00 8·25

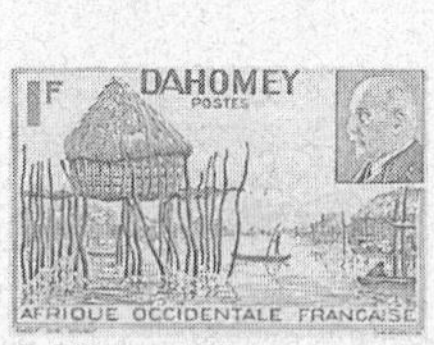

14b Village on Piles and Marshal Petain

1942. Marshal Petain Issue.
143e **14b** 1f. green . . . . 40 2·75
143f 2f.50 blue . . . . 25 3·00

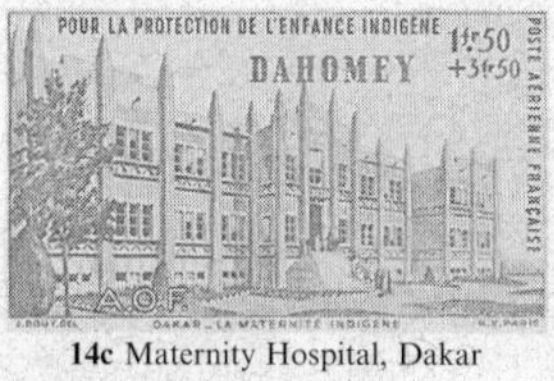

14c Maternity Hospital, Dakar

1942. Air. Colonial Child Welfare Fund.
143g **14c** 1f.50+3f.50 green . . . . 20 2·50
143h – 2f.+6f. brown . . . . . 20 2·50
143i – 3f.+9f. red . . . . 90 2·50
DESIGNS: 2f. Dispensary, Mopti. (48½ × 27 mm): 3f. "Child welfare".

14d "Vocation" **14e** Camel Caravan

1942. Air. "Imperial Fortnight".
143j **14d** 1f.20+1f.80 blue & red   1·10   2·50

1942. Air.
143k **14e** 50f. blue and green . . .   3·75   4·75

15 Ganvie Village

1960.
144 **15** 25f. brn, red & bl (postage)   75   25
145 – 100f. brown, ochre & bl
             (air) . . . .   3·25   2·25
146 – 500f. red, bistre & green   12·00   4·25
DESIGNS: 100f. Somba fort; 500f. Royal Court,
Abomey.

1960. 10th Anniv of African Technical Co-operation
Commission. As T **62** of Cameroun.
147   5f. blue and purple . . . . .   1·60   2·00

16 Conseil de   **17** Prime Minister
l'Entente Emblem   Maga

1960. 1st Anniv of Conseil de l'Entente.
148 **16** 25f. multicoloured . . . .   1·75   1·90

1960. Independence Proclamation.
149 **17** 85f. purple and sepia . . .   90   55

18 Weaver

1961. Artisans.
150 **18** 1f. purple and orange . .   10   10
151 – 2f. chocolate and brown . .   10   10
152 – 3f. orange and green . . .   10   10
153 – 4f. lake and bistre   15   15
154 **18** 6f. red and lilac   15   15
155 – 10f. myrtle and blue   25   20
156 – 15f. violet and purple . . .   35   25
157 – 20f. turquoise and blue . .   45   30
DESIGNS—VERT: 2f., 10f. Wood-carver. HORIZ:
3f., 15f. Fisherman casting net; 4f., 20f. Potter.

1961. 1st Anniv of Independence. No. 149 surch
100 F President de la Republique.
158 **17** 100f. on 85f. pur & sepia   1·50   1·50

20 Doves and U.N.   **22** Wrecked Car and Fort
Emblem

1961. 1st Anniv of Admission into U.N.O.
159 **20** 5f. multicoloured (postage)   25   20
160 – 60f. multicoloured   75   60
161 – 200f. multicoloured (air)   2·50   1·90

1961. Abidjan Games. Optd **JEUX SPORTIFS
D'ABIDJAN 24 AU 31 DECEMBRE 1961.**
162 **15** 25f. brown, red and blue   45   30

1962. Air. Foundation of "Air Afrique" Airline.
As T **69** of Cameroun.
163   25f. blue, brown & black . .   45   35

1962. Malaria Eradication. As T **70** of Cameroun.
164   25f.+5f. brown   45   45

1962. 1st Anniv of Portuguese Evacuation from Fort
Ouidah.
165 **22** 30f. multicoloured   45   25
166 – 60f. multicoloured   70   40

1962. 1st Anniv of Union of African and Malagasy
States. As No. 328 of Cameroun.
167 **72** 30f. multicoloured   50   35

23 Map, Nurses and Patients

1962. Red Cross.
168 **23** 5f. red, blue and purple . .   15   15
169 – 20f. red, blue and green . .   30   25
170 – 25f. red, blue and sepia . .   40   30
171 – 30f. red, blue and brown   45   40

24 Peuhl Herd-boy   **25** Boxing

1963. Dahomey Tribes.
172 A 2f. violet and blue   10   10
173 B 3f. black and blue   10   10
174 **24** 5f. green, brown & black   15   10
175 C 15f. brown, chest & turq   25   15
176 D 20f. black, red & green . .   40   20
177 E 25f. turquoise, brown & bl   40   15
178 D 30f. brown, mauve & red   45   30
179 E 40f. blue, brown, & green   55   25
180 C 50f. brown, black & green   65   30
181 **24** 60f. orange, red & purple   70   45
182 B 65f. brown and red   90   50
183 A 85f. brown and blue . . .   1·50   75
DESIGNS—VERT: A, Ganvie girl in pirogue; B,
Bariba chief of Nikki; C, Ouidah witch-doctor and
python; D, Nessoukoue witch-doctors of Abomey.
HORIZ: E, Dahomey girl.

1963. Freedom from Hunger. As T **76** of Cameroun.
184   25f.+5f. red, brown & green   50   50

1963. Dakar Games.
185 **25** 50c. black and green . . .   10   10
186 – 1f. black, bistre & brown   10   10
187 – 2f. brown, blue & bronze   10   10
188 – 5f. black, green & brown   15   10
189 **25** 15f. purple and violet . . .   25   20
190 – 20f. black, green & red . .   40   30
DESIGNS—HORIZ: 1f., 20f. Football. VERT: 2f.,
5f. Running.

27 U.A.M. Palace

1963. Air. Meeting of Heads of State of African and
Malagasy Union.
191 **27** 250f. multicoloured . . . .   3·00   1·75

28 Presidential Palace, Cotonou

1963. 3rd Anniv of Independence.
192 **28** 25f. multicoloured   35   25

1963. Air. African and Malagasy Posts and
Telecommunications Union. As T **18** of Central
African Republic.
193   25f. red, buff, brown & blue   40   25

29 Boeing 707 Airliner

1963. Air.
194 **29** 100f. bistre, green & violet   1·75   60
195 – 200f. violet, brown & grn   3·00   1·60
196 – 300f. purple, grn and blue   4·25   2·25
197 – 500f. purple, brown & blue   7·75   3·25
DESIGNS: 200f. Aerial views of Boeing 707; 300f.
Cotonou Airport; 500f. Boeing 707 in flight.

30 Toussaint   **31** Flame on U.N.
L'Ouverture   Emblem

1963. 150th Death Anniv of Toussaint L'Ouverture
(Haitian statesman).
198 **30** 25f. multicoloured   35   20
199 – 30f. multicoloured   40   25
200 – 100f. multicoloured . . . .   1·10   65

1963. 15th Anniv of Declaration of Human Rights.
Multicoloured. Background colours given.
201 **31** 4f. blue   10   10
202 – 6f. brown   15   15
203 – 25f. green   35   25

32 Sacred Boat of Isis, Philae

1964. Air. Nubian Monuments Preservation.
204 **32** 25f. brown and violet . . .   80   50

33 Somba Dance (Taneka
Coco)

1964. Native Dances.
205 **33** 2f. black, red and green . .   10   10
206 – 3f. red, green and blue . .   10   10
207 – 10f. black, red & violet . .   20   15
208 – 15f. sepia, lake & green . .   25   15
209 – 25f. blue, brown and orge   40   25
210 – 30f. red, orange & brown   45   30
DANCES—HORIZ: 3f. Nago (Pobe-Ketou). 15f.
Nago (Ouidah). 30f. Nessou houessi (Abomey).
VERT: 10f. Baton (Paysbariba). 25f. Sakpatassi
(Abomey).

1964. Olympic Games, Tokyo.
211 **34** 60f. green and brown . .   65   50
212 – 85f. purple and blue . . .   1·25   75
DESIGN: 85f. Cycling.

1964. French, African and Malagasy Co-operation.
As T **88** of Cameroun.
213   25f. brown, violet & orange   40   25

35 Mother and Child   **36** Satellite and Sun

1964. 18th Anniv of U.N.I.C.E.F.
214 **35** 20f. black, green & red . .   35   25
215 – 25f. black, blue & red . . .   40   25
DESIGN: 25f. Mother and child (different).

1964. International Quiet Sun Year.
216 **36** 25f. green and yellow . .   45   20
217 – 100f. yellow and purple . . .   1·25   65
DESIGN: 100f. Another satellite and Sun.

37 "Weather"

1965. Air. World Meteorological Day.
218 **37** 50f. multicoloured   65   45

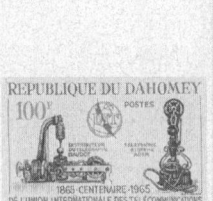

38 Rug Pattern

1965. Abomey Rug-weaving. Multicoloured.
219   20f. Bull, tree, etc. (vert) . .   30   25
220   25f. Witch-doctor, etc. (vert)   45   30
221   50f. Type **38**   70   35
222   85f. Ship, tree, etc . . . . .   1·25   70

39 Baudot's Telegraph and   **40** Sir Winston
Ader's Telephone   Churchill

1965. Centenary of I.T.U.
223 **39** 100f. black, purple & orge   1·40   1·00

1965. Air. Churchill Commemoration.
224 **40** 100f. multicoloured . . . .   1·40   1·10

41 Heads of Three Races within I.C.Y.
Emblem

1965. Air. International Co-operation Year.
225 **41** 25f. lake, green & violet . .   35   20
226 – 85f. lake, green & blue . .   80   55

42 Lincoln

1965. Air. Death Centenary of Abraham Lincoln.
227 **42** 100f. multicoloured . . . .   1·25   95

43 Cotonou Port

1965. Inaug of Cotonou Port. Multicoloured.
228 25f. Type 43 . . . . 65 25
229 100f. Cotonou Port . . 1·60 85
  The two stamps joined together form a complete design and were issued se-tenant in the sheets.

44 Spanish Mackerel   45 Independence Monument

1965. Fishes.
230 44 10f. black, turquoise & bl 40 25
231 – 25f. orange, grey & blue 55 40
232 – 30f. blue and turquoise 1·00 50
233 – 50f. grey, orange & blue 1·40 80
FISHES: 25f. Sama seabream. 30f. Sailfish. 50f. Tripletail.

1965. 2nd Anniv of 28th October Revolution.
234 45 25f. red, grey and black . . 35 20
235 – 30f. red, blue and black . . 40 25

1965. No. 177 surch 1f.
236 1f. on 25f. turq, brn & bl . 15 10

47 Arms and Pres. Kennedy

1965. Air. 2nd Death Anniv of Pres. Kennedy.
237 47 100f. brown and green . . 1·50 1·00

48 Dr. Schweitzer and Hospital Scene

1966. Air. Schweitzer Commemoration.
238 48 100f. multicoloured . . 1·50 90

49 Porto-Novo Cathedral   50 Beads, Bangles and Anklets

1966. Dahomey Cathedrals.
239 49 30f. purple, blue & green 30 20
240 – 50f. brown, blue & purple 50 30
241 – 70f. purple, blue & green 80 50
DESIGNS—VERT: 50f. Ouidah Church (old Pro-Cathedral). HORIZ: 70f. Cotonou Cathedral.

1966. World Festival of Negro Arts, Dakar.
242 50 15f. purple and black . . . 25 15
243 – 30f. red, purple & blue . . 35 25
244 – 50f. blue and brown . . . 60 40
245 – 70f. lake and black . . . . 1·10 65
DESIGNS: 50f. Building construction; 50f. Craftsman; 70f. Religious carvings.

1966. 5th Anniv of France–Dahomey Treaty. Nos. 228/9 surch **ACCORD DE COOPÉRATION FRANCE - DAHOMEY 5e Anniversaire - 24 Avril 1996.**
246 43 15f. on 25f. mult 35 25
247 – 15f. on 100f. mult 35 25

52 W.H.O. Building and Emblem

1966. Inaug of W.H.O. Headquarters, Geneva.
248 52 30f. multicoloured (post) 40 30
249 – 100f. multicoloured (air) 1·40 1·00
DESIGN (48 × 27 mm): 100f. W.H.O. building (different view) and emblem.

53 African Pygmy Goose   54 Industrial Emblems

1966. Air. Birds. Multicoloured.
250 50f. Type 53 . . . . 2·50 95
251 100f. Fiery-breasted bush shrike 3·50 1·40
252 500f. Iris glossy starling . . . 17·00 9·25
  See also Nos. 271/2.

1966. Air. "Europafrique".
253 54 100f. multicoloured . . . . 1·50 85

55 Pope Paul and St. Peter's

1966. Air. Pope Paul's Visit to U.N.
254 55 50f. red, brown & green . . 55 35
255 – 70f. red, green and blue . . 85 45
256 – 100f. purple and blue . . . 1·25 85
DESIGNS—HORIZ: 70f. Pope Paul and New York. VERT: (36 × 48 mm); 100f. Pope Paul and U.N. General Assembly.

1966. Air. Inauguration of DC-8F Air Services. As T 54 of Central African Republic.
258 30f. grey, black and purple 50 30

56 Scout signalling with flags

1966. Scouting.
259 56 5f. red, ochre and brown 10 10
260 – 10f. mauve, green & black 15 10
261 – 30f. orange, red & violet 35 25
262 – 50f. brown, green & blue 70 40
DESIGNS—VERT: 10f. Tent-pole and banners; 30f. Scouts, camp-fire and map. HORIZ: 50f. Constructing bridge.

57 Scientific Emblem

1966. Air. 20th Anniv of U.N.E.S.C.O.
264 57 30f. blue & purple 35 25
265 – 45f. lake and green 50 40
266 – 100f. blue, lake & black . . 1·25 80
DESIGNS—VERT: 45f. Cultural Emblem; HORIZ: 100f. Educational emblem.

58 "The Nativity" (15th-cent. Beaune Tapestry)

1966. Air. Christmas. Multicoloured.
268 50f. Type 58 . . . . . . 10·25 3·00
269 100f. "The Adoration of the Shepherds" (after Jose Ribera) 10·25 4·50
270 200f. "Madonna and Child" (after A. Baldovinetti) 19·00 6·75
  See also Nos. 311/14, 348/51, 384/7 and 423/6.

59 African Broad-billed Roller   60 "Clappertonia ficifolia"

1967. Air. Birds. Multicoloured.
271 200f. Type 59 . . . . . . 9·50 3·75
272 250f. African Emerald cuckoo 12·50 5·25

1967. Flowers. Multicoloured.
273 1f. Type 60 . . . . 10 10
274 3f. "Hewittia sublobata" . . 15 10
275 5f. "Clitoria ternatea" . . 20 15
276 10f. "Nymphaea micrantha" 35 15
277 5f. "Commelina forskalaei" 35 25
278 30f. "Eremomastax speciosa" 75 35

1967. Nos. 182/3 surch.
279 30f. on 65f. brown & red . . 40 30
280 30f. on 85f. brown & blue . . 40 30

62 Bird bearing Lions Emblem   63 "Ingres" (self-portrait)

1967. 50th Anniv of Lions International.
281 62 100f. blue, green & violet 1·50 80

1967. Air. Death Centenary of Ingres (painter). Multicoloured.
282 100f. Type 63 . . . . . . 2·10 1·25
283 100f. "Oedipus and the Sphinx" (after Ingres) . . . 2·10 1·25
  See also Nos. 388/90, 429/30, 431/2 and 486/7.

64 "Suzanne" (barque)

1967. Air. French Sailing ships. Multicoloured.
284 30f. Type 64 . . . . 90 35
285 45f. "Esmeralda" (schooner) (vert) . . . . 1·25 55
286 80f. "Marie Alice" (schooner) (vert) . . . . 2·10 75
287 100f. "Antonin" (barque) . . 2·50 1·10

1967. Air. 50th Birth Anniv of Pres. Kennedy. Nos. 227 and 237 surch **29 MAI 1967 50e Anniversaire de la naissance de John F. Kennedy.**
288 42 125f. on 100f. mult . . . 1·75 90
289 47 125f. on 100f. brn & grn . 1·75 90

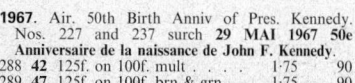

66 "Man in the City" Pavilion

1967. World Fair, Montreal.
290 66 30f. brn & grn (postage) . 40 20
291 – 70f. red and green 90 50
292 – 100f. blue & brown (air) . 1·10 65
DESIGNS—HORIZ: 70f. "New Africa" pavilions. VERT: (27 × 48 mm): 100f. "Man Examines the Universe".

67 Dr. Konrad Adenauer (from painting by O. Kokoschka)   68 "Economic Association"

1967. Air. Dr. Adenauer Commemoration.
294 67 70f. multicoloured . . . . 1·10 90

1967. Europafrique.
296 68 30f. multicoloured 35 25
297 – 45f. multicoloured 50 25

69 Scouts Climbing

1967. World Scout Jamboree, Idaho.
298 69 30f. ind, brn & bl (postage) 35 15
299 – 70f. purple, green & blue 90 55
300 – 100f. pur, grn & bl (air) . . 1·10 65
DESIGNS—HORIZ: 70f. Scouts with canoe. VERT: (27 × 48 mm): 100f. Jamboree emblem, rope and map.

1967. Air. Riccione Stamp Exhibition. No. 270 surch **RICCIONE 12-29 Aout 1967** and value.
302 150f. on 200f. mult . . . . . 2·10 1·50

71 Rhone at Grenoble

1967. Winter Olympic Games, Grenoble.
303 71 30f. blue, brown & green 40 25
304 – 45f. blue, green & brown 60 40
305 – 100f. purple, green & blue 1·40 90
DESIGNS—VERT: 45f. View of Grenoble. HORIZ: 100f. Rhone Bridge, Grenoble, and Pierre de Coubertin.

1967. Air. 5th Anniv of U.A.M.P.T. As T 123 of Cameroun.
307 100f. green, red & purple . . 1·10 90

72 Currency Tokens   73 Pres. de Gaulle

1967. 5th Anniv of West African Monetary Union.
308 72 30f. black, red & green . . 40 30

1967. Air. "Homage to General de Gaulle". President Soglo of Dahomey's visit to Paris.
309 73 100f. multicoloured . . . . 2·10 1·40

74 "The Adoration" (Master of St. Sebastian)

1967. Air. Christmas. Religious paintings. Mult.
311 30f. "Virgin and Child"
  (M. Grunewald) (vert) . . 40 35
312 50f. Type **74** 80 45
313 100f. "The Adoration of the
  Magi" (Ulrich Apt the
  Elder) (vert) . . . . . 1·40 90
314 200f. "The Annunciation"
  (M. Grunewald) (vert) . . 3·00 1·40

75 Venus de Milo and   **76** African Buffalo
  "Mariner 5"

1968. Air. "Exploration of the Planet Venus".
  Multicoloured.
315 30f. Type **75** . . . . . . 1·00 55
316 70f. Venus de Milo and
  "Venus 4" . . . . . . 1·00 55

1968. Fauna (1st series). Multicoloured.
318 15f. Type **76** 25 15
319 30f. Lion 45 25
320 45f. Kob 80 40
321 70f. Crocodile . . . . . 1·25 45
322 100f. Hippopotamus . . . . 2·25 1·10
  See also Nos. 353/7.

77 W.H.O. Emblem

1968. 20th Anniv of W.H.O.
323 **77** 30f. brown, blue & ultram 40 30
324 70f. multicoloured . . . . 3·75 1·25

78 Gutenberg   **79** Dr. Martin Luther
  Memorial, Strasbourg   King

1968. Air. 500th Death Anniv of Johann Gutenberg.
325 **78** 45f. green and orange . . . 60 35
326 – 100f. deep blue & blue . . 1·40 85
DESIGNS: 100f. Gutenberg statue, Mainz, and
printing-press.

1968. Air. Martin Luther King Commemoration.
328 – 30f. black, brown & yellow 50 30
329 – 55f. multicoloured . . . 80 45
330 **79** 100f. multicoloured . . 1·25 80
DESIGNS: 55f. Dr. King receiving Nobel Peace Prize.
LARGER (25 × 46 mm): 30f. Inscription "We must
meet hate with creative love" (also in French and
German).

80 Schuman

1968. Air. 5th Anniv of Europafrique.
332 **80** 30f. multicoloured 40 25
333 – 45f. purple, olive & orge 55 35
334 – 70f. multicoloured 90 40
DESIGNS: 45f. De Gasperi; 70f. Dr. Adenauer.

81 "Battle of Montebello" (Philippoteaux)

1968. Air. Red Cross. Paintings. Multicoloured.
335 30f. Type **81** 50 35
336 45f. "2nd Zouaves at
  Magenta" (Riballier) . . 65 45
337 70f. "Battle of Magenta"
  (Charpentier) . . . . . 1·25 80
338 100f. "Battle of Solferino"
  (Charpentier) . . . . . 1·75 1·00

82 Mail Van

1968. Air. Rural Mail Service. Multicoloured.
339 30f. Type **82** 35 25
340 45f. Rural Post Office and
  mail van 45 30
341 55f. Collecting mail at riverside 60 35
342 70f. Loading mail on train 3·75 1·25

83 Aztec Stadium

1968. Air. Olympic Games, Mexico.
343 **83** 30f. green and purple . . . 40 25
344 – 45f. lake and blue 65 35
345 – 70f. brown and green . . . 1·00 55
346 – 150f. brown and red . . . 1·90 1·10
DESIGNS—VERT: 45f. "Pelota-player" (Aztec
figure); 70f. "Uxpanapan wrestler" (Aztec figure).
HORIZ: 150f. Olympic Stadium.

1968. Air. Christmas. Paintings by Foujita. As T **74**.
  Multicoloured.
348 30f. "The Nativity" (horiz) 55 40
349 70f. "The Visitation" . . . 1·10 55
350 100f. "Virgin and Child" . . 1·40 95
351 200f. "Baptism of Christ" . . 2·75 1·90

1968. Air. "Philexafrique" Stamp Exhibition,
Abidjan (Ivory Coast, 1969). As T **137** of
Cameroun. Multicoloured.
352 100f. "Diderot" (L. M.
  Vanloo) . . . . 1·75 1·75

84 Warthog

1969. Fauna (2nd series). Multicoloured.
353 5f. Type **84** 15 10
354 30f. Leopard 50 25
355 60f. Spotted hyena . . . . 1·00 45
356 75f. Olive baboon . . . . 1·40 55
357 90f. Hartebeest . . . . . 2·00 90

1969. Air. "Philexafrique" Stamp Exn, Abidjan,
Ivory Coast (2nd issue). As T **138** of Cameroun.
358 50f. violet, sepia and blue . 1·10 1·10
DESIGN: 50f. Cotonou harbour and stamp of 1941.

85 Heads and Globe

1969. 50th Anniv of I.L.O.
359 **85** 30f. multicoloured 40 25
360 – 70f. multicoloured 95 55

86 "The Virgin of the Scales"
  (C. da Sesto-Da Vinci School)

1969. Air. Leonardo da Vinci Commem. Mult.
361 100f. Type **86** . . . . . . 1·40 75
362 100f. "The Virgin of the
  Rocks" (Da Vinci) . . . . 1·40 75

87 "General Bonaparte" (J. L.
  David)

1969. Air. Birth Bicentenary of Napoleon Bonaparte.
  Multicoloured.
363 30f. Type **87** . . . . . . 1·10 1·00
364 60f. "Napoleon I in 1809"
  (Lefevre) . . . . . . 2·00 1·25
365 75f. "Napoleon at the Battle
  of Eylau" (Gros) (horiz) 2·50 1·75
366 200f. "General Bonaparte at
  Arcola" (Gros) . . . . . 5·50 3·25

88 Arms of Dahomey

1969.
367 **88** 5f. multicoloured (postage) 15 15
368 – 30f. multicoloured 45 30
369 – 50f. multicoloured (air) . . 45 25

89 "Apollo 8" over Moon

1969. Air. Moon flight of "Apollo 8". Embossed on
gold foil.
370 **89** 1,000f. gold . . . . 15·00

1969. Air. 1st Man on the Moon (1st issue). Nos. 315/
6 surch **ALUNISSAGE APOLLO XI JUILLET
1969**, lunar module and value.
371 **75** 125f. on 70f. (No. 315) . 1·75 1·40
372 – 125f. on 70f. (No. 316) . . 1·75 1·40

91 Bank Emblem and   **93** Dahomey Rotary
  Cornucopia   Emblem

92 Kenaf Plant and Mill, Bohicon

1969. 5th Anniv of African Development Bank.
373 **91** 30f. multicoloured 50 40

1969. "Europafrique". Multicoloured.
374 30f. Type **92** (postage) . . 40 25
375 45f. Cotton plant & mill,
  Parakou 50 30
376 100f. Coconut and palm-oil
  plant, Cotonou (air) . . . 1·10 70

1969. Air. Rotary International Organization.
378 **93** 50f. multicoloured 65 40

1969. Air. No. 250 surch.
379 **53** 10f. on 50f. multicoloured 50 20

95 Sakpata Dance   **96** F. D. Roosevelt

1969. Dahomey Dances. Multicoloured.
380 10f. Type **95** (postage) . . . 30 25
381 30f. Guelede dance 40 30
382 45f. Sato dance 50 35
383 70f. Teke dance (air) 80 45

1969. Air. Christmas. Paintings. As T **58**. Mult.
384 30f. "The Annunciation"
  (Van der Stockt) 40 30
385 45f. "The Nativity" (15th-
  cent. Swabian School) . . 60 40
386 110f. "Virgin and Child"
  (Masters of the Gold
  Brocade) . . . . . . 1·60 1·00
387 200f. "The Adoration of the
  Magi" (Antwerp School,
  c. 1530) . . . . 2·50 1·90

1969. Air. Old Masters. As T **63**. Multicoloured.
388 100f. "The Painter's Studio"
  (G. Courbet) . . . . . 1·40 90
389 100f. "Self-portrait with Gold
  Chain" (Rembrandt) . . . 1·40 90
390 150f. "Hendrickje Stoffels"
  (Rembrandt) . . . . . 2·10 1·25

1970. Air. 25th Death Anniv of Franklin D.
  Roosevelt.
391 **96** 100f. black, green & bl . . . 1·25 55

97 Rocket and Men   **98** "U.N. in War and Peace"
  on Moon

1970. Air. 1st Man on Moon (2nd issue).
392 **97** 30f. multicoloured 40 25
  The 50, 70, 110f. values were only issued in
  miniature sheet form.

1970. 25th Anniv of U.N.
394 **98** 30f. indigo, blue & red . . 40 25
395 – 40f. green, blue & brown . . 50 30

99 Walt Whitman and African Village

1970. Air. 150th Birth Anniv. of Walt Whitman (American poet).
396 **99** 100f. brown, blue & grn . . . 1·25 50

1970. Air. Space Flight of "Apollo 13". No. 392 surch **40F APOLLO 13 SOLIDARITE SPATIALE INTERNATIONALE.**
397 **97** 40f. on 30f. multicoloured 75 75

101 Footballers and Globe

1970. Air. World Cup Football Championship, Mexico. Multicoloured.
398 40f. Type **101** 50 40
399 50f. Goalkeeper saving goal 60 45
400 200f. Player kicking ball . . 2·50 1·10

1970. 10th Anniv. (1969) of Aerial Navigation Security Agency for Africa and Madagascar (A.S.E.C.N.A.). As T **150** of Cameroun.
401 40f. red and purple 60 25

103 Mt. Fuji and "EXPO" Emblem   **104** "La Justice" and "La Concorde" (French warships)

1970. World Fair "EXPO 70", Osaka, Japan. Multicoloured.
402 5f. Type **103** (postage) . . 45 20
403 70f. Dahomey Pavilion (air) 70 45
404 120f. Mt. Fuji and temple . . 1·25 65

1970. 300th Anniv of Ardres Embassy to Louis XIV of France.
405 **104** 40f. brown, blue & green 1·00 35
406 – 50f. red, brown & green 60 35
407 – 70f. brown, slate & bistre 90 50
408 – 200f. brown, blue & red 2·50 1·10
DESIGNS: 50f. Matheo Lopes; 70f. King Alkemy of Ardres; 200f. Louis XIV of France.

1970. Air. Brazil's Victory in World Cup Football Championship. No. 400 surch **BRESIL–ITALIE 4 – 1** and value.
409 100f. on 200f. multicoloured 1·40 70

106 Mercury   **107** Order of Independence

1970. Air. Europafrique.
410 **106** 40f. multicoloured 50 35
411 70f. multicoloured 80 45

1970. 10th Anniv of Independence.
412 **107** 30f. multicoloured . . . 25 15
413 40f. multicoloured . . . 40 20

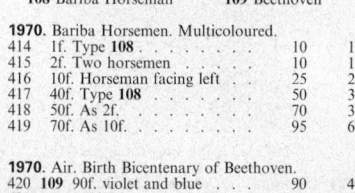

108 Bariba Horseman   **109** Beethoven

1970. Bariba Horsemen. Multicoloured.
414 1f. Type **108** 10 10
415 2f. Two horsemen 10 10
416 10f. Horseman facing left . . 25 20
417 40f. Type **108** 50 30
418 50f. As 2f. 70 35
419 70f. As 10f. 95 60

1970. Air. Birth Bicentenary of Beethoven.
420 **109** 90f. violet and blue . . 90 40
421 110f. brown and green . . 1·00 55

110 Emblems of Learning   **111** "The Annunciation"

1970. Air. Laying of Foundation Stone, Calavi University.
422 **110** 100f. multicoloured . . . . 1·00 50

1970. Air. Christmas. Miniatures of the Rhenish School c. 1340. Multicoloured.
423 40f. Type **111** 40 25
424 70f. "The Nativity" 70 45
425 110f. "The Adoration of the Magi" . . . . . . 1·60 90
426 200f. "The Presentation in the Temple" . . . . . 2·50 1·60

112 De Gaulle and Arc de Triomphe

1971. Air. 1st Death Anniv of Gen. Charles de Gaulle. Multicoloured.
427 40f. Type **112** 55 45
428 500f. De Gaulle and Notre Dame, Paris . . . . 5·00 2·50

1971. Air. 250th Death Anniv of Watteau. Paintings. As T **63**. Multicoloured.
429 100f. "The Dandy" . . . . . 1·75 1·10
430 100f. "Girl with Lute" . . . 1·75 1·10

1971. Air. 500th Birth Anniv of Durer. As T **63**. Multicoloured.
431 100f. Self-portrait, 1498 . . . 1·40 90
432 200f. Self-portrait, 1500 . . . 2·75 1·60

113 Hands supporting Heart   **114** "The Twins" (wood-carving) and Lottery Ticket

1971. Racial Equality Year.
433 **113** 40f. red, brn & green . . 40 25
434 – 100f. red, blue & green . . 95 50
DESIGN—HORIZ: 100f. "Heart" on Globe.

1971. 4th Anniv of National Lottery.
435 **114** 35f. multicoloured 35 15
436 40f. multicoloured 40 25

115 Kepler, Earth and Planets

1971. Air. 400th Birth Anniv of Johannes Kepler (astronomer).
437 **115** 40f. black, pur and blue 55 40
438 – 200f. green, red & blue 2·25 1·25
DESIGN: 200f. Kepler, globe, satellite and rocket.

116 Boeing 747 Airliner linking Europe and Africa

1971. Air. Europafrique.
439 **116** 50f. orge, blue & black . . 75 45
440 100f. multicoloured . . . . 2·25 80
DESIGN: 100f. "General Mangin" (liner) and maps of Europe and Africa.

117 Cockerel and Drum (King Ganyehoussou)

1971. Emblems of Dahomey Kings. Multicoloured.
441 25f. Leg, saw and hatchet (Agoliagbo) 25 15
442 35f. Type **117** 40 25
443 40f. Fish and egg (Behanzin) (vert) 40 25
444 100f. Cow, tree and birds (Guezo) (vert) . . . . . . 1·00 45
445 135f. Fish and hoe (Ouegbadja) . . . . . 1·75 90
446 140f. Lion and sickle (Glele) 1·60 90

1971. Air. 10th Anniv of U.A.M.P.T. As T **184** of Cameroun. Multicoloured.
447 100f. U.A.M.P.T. H.Q., Brazzaville and Arms of Dahomey . . . . 1·00 50

119 "Adoration of the Shepherds" (Master of the Hausbuch)

1971. Air. Christmas. Paintings. Multicoloured.
448 40f. Type **119** 60 35
449 70f. "Adoration of the Magi" (Holbein) 95 45
450 100f. "Flight into Egypt" (Van Dyck) (horiz) . . . 1·25 60
451 200f. "Birth of Christ" (Durer) (horiz) . . . . . 2·50 1·40

120 "Prince Balthazar" (Velazquez)

1971. Air. 25th Anniv of U.N.I.C.E.F. Paintings of Children. Multicoloured.
452 40f. Type **120** 65 40
453 100f. "The Maids of Honour" (detail, Velazquez) . . . . . 1·40 65

1972. No. 395 surch in figures.
454 **98** 35f. on 40f. green, bl & brn 40 25

122 Cross-country Skiing   **123** Scout taking Oath

1972. Winter Olympic Games, Sapporo, Japan.
455 **122** 35f. purple, brown and green (postage) 50 30
456 – 150f. purple, blue and brown (air) . . . . 1·75 90
DESIGN: 150f. Ski-jumping.

1972. Air. International Scout Seminar, Cotonou. Multicoloured.
457 35f. Type **123** 25 20
458 40f. Scout playing "xylophone" 40 25
459 100f. Scouts working on the land (26 × 47 mm) . . . . 1·00 55

124 Friedrich Naumann and Institute Building

1972. Air. Laying of Foundation Stone for National Workers Education Institute. Multicoloured.
461 100f. Type **124** 90 50
462 250f. Pres. Heuss of West Germany and Institute . . 25 1·10

125 Stork with Serpent

1972. Air. U.N.E.S.C.O. "Save Venice" Campaign. Mosaics in St. Mark's Basilica. Multicoloured.
463 35f. Type **125** 55 35
464 40f. Cockerels carrying fox 65 45
465 65f. Noah releasing dove . . 1·10 80

126 Exhibition Emblem and Dancers

1972. Air. 12th International Philatelic Exhibition, Naples.
466 **126** 100f. multicoloured . . . 95 50

127 Running   **129** Brahms, and Clara Schumann at Piano

128 Louis Bleriot and Bleriot XI

1972. Air. Olympic Games, Munich.

467	127	20f. brown, grn & blue . .	30	20
468		— 85f. brown, blue & green	85	45
469		— 150f. brown, blue & grn	1·75	80

DESIGNS: 85f. High-jumping; 150f. Putting the shot.

1972. Air. Birth Centenary of Louis Bleriot (pioneer airman).

| 471 | 128 | 100f. blue, violet & red | 1·75 | 90 |

1972. 75th Death Anniv of Johannes Brahms (composer).

| 472 | | — 30f. black, brn & violet | 40 | 25 |
| 473 | 129 | 65f. black, violet & lake | 70 | 45 |

DESIGN—VERT: Brahms and opening bars of "Soir d'Ete".

130 "The Hare and the Tortoise"

1972. Fables of Jean de La Fontaine.

474	130	10f. grey, blue & lake . .	25	15
475		— 35f. blue, lake & purple	40	25
476		— 40f. indigo, blue & purple	55	35

DESIGNS—VERT: 35f. "The Fox and the Stork". HORIZ: 40f. "The Cat, the Weasel and the Little Rabbit".

131 "Adam" (Cranach)

1972. Air. 500th Birth Anniv of Lucas Cranach (painter). Multicoloured.

| 477 | | 150f. Type 131 . . . . . . | 1·75 | 1·00 |
| 478 | | 200f. "Eve" (Cranach) . . . | 2·50 | 1·40 |

132 Africans and 500f. Coin

1972. 10th Anniv of West African Monetary Union.

| 479 | 132 | 40f. brown, grey & yell | 65 | 20 |

133 "Pauline Borghese" (Canova)

1972. Air. 150th Death Anniv of Antonio Canova.

| 480 | 133 | 250f. multicoloured . . . . | 2·75 | 1·40 |

1972. Air. Olympic Medal Winners. Nos. 467/9 optd as listed below.

481	127	20f. brown, blue & grn . .	30	20
482		— 85f. brown, blue & green	85	40
483		— 150f. brown, blue & grn	1·75	85

OVERPRINTS: 20f. **5.000m. – 10.000m. VIREN 2 MEDAILLES D'OR.** 85f. **HAUTEUR DAMES MEYFARTH MEDAILLE D'OR.** 150f. **POIDS KOMAR MEDAILLE D'OR.**

135 Pasteur and Apparatus

1972. Air. 150th Birth Anniv of Louis Pasteur (scientist).

| 485 | 135 | 100f. pur, violet & grn . . | 1·00 | 50 |

1972. Air. Paintings by G. de la Tour. As T **63**. Multicoloured.

| 486 | | 35f. "Hurdy-gurdy Player" (vert) | 40 | 30 |
| 487 | | 150f. "The New-born Child" | 1·75 | 1·10 |

136 "The Annunciation" (School of Agnolo Gaddi)

1972. Air. Christmas. Religious Paintings. Mult.

488		35f. Type 136	35	20
489		125f. "The Nativity" (Simone dei Crocifissi)	1·00	50
490		140f. "The Adoration of the Shepherds" (P. di Giovanni)	1·50	80
491		250f. "Adoration of the Magi" (Giotto)	2·25	1·25

137 Dr. Hansen, Microscope and Bacillus   139 Arms of Dahomey

138 Statue and Basilica, Lisieux

1973. Centenary of Identification of Leprosy Bacillus by Hansen.

| 492 | 137 | 35f. brown, purple & blue | 30 | 25 |
| 493 | | — 85f. brown, orange & grn | 65 | 50 |

DESIGN: 85f. Dr. Gerhard Armauer Hansen.

1973. Air. Birth Centenary of St. Theresa of Lisieux. Multicoloured.

| 494 | | 40f. Type 138 . . . . . . | 45 | 30 |
| 495 | | 100f. St. Theresa of Lisieux (vert) . . . . | 1·20 | 65 |

1973.

496	139	5f. multicoloured	10	10
497		35f. multicoloured	25	15
498		40f. multicoloured	30	15

140 Scouts in Pirogue

1973. Air. 24th World Scouting Congress, Nairobi, Kenya.

499	140	15f. purple, green & blue	35	15
500		— 20f. blue and brown . .	25	20
501		— 40f. blue, green & brown	40	25

DESIGNS—VERT: 20f. Lord Baden-Powell. HORIZ: 40f. Bridge-building.

141 Interpol Badge and "Communications"   142 "Education in Nutrition"

1973. 50th Anniv of International Criminal Police Organization (Interpol).

| 503 | | — 35f. brown, green & red | 30 | 20 |
| 504 | 141 | 50f. green, brown & red | 45 | 30 |

DESIGN—HORIZ: 35f. Interpol emblem and web.

1973. 25th Anniv of World Health Organization. Multicoloured.

| 505 | | 35f. Type 142 . . . . | 30 | 20 |
| 506 | | 100f. Pre-natal examination | 80 | 45 |

1973. Pan-African Drought Relief. No. 321 surch **SECHERESSE SOLIDARITE AFRICAINE** and value.

| 507 | | 100f. on 70f. multicoloured | 1·00 | 55 |

144 Copernicus, "Venera" and "Mariner" Probes and Plane of Solar System

1973. Air. 500th Birth Anniv of Copernicus.

| 508 | 144 | 65f. black, purple & yell | 85 | 45 |
| 509 | | — 125f. green, blue & purple | 1·40 | 70 |

DESIGN—VERT: 125f. Copernicus.

1973. U.A.M.P.T. As T **216** of Cameroun.

| 510 | | 100f. violet, red & black . . | 80 | 40 |

1973. Air. African Fortnight, Brussels. As T **217** of Cameroun.

| 511 | | 100f. black, green & blue . . | 70 | 40 |

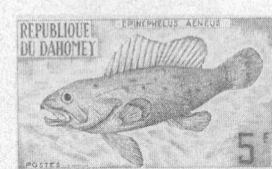

145 White Grouper

1973. Fishes.

512	145	5f. dp blue and blue . . .	25	20
513		— 15f. black and blue . . .	40	20
514		— 35f. lt brn, brn & grn . .	90	40

DESIGNS: 15f. African spadefish; 35f. Blue-pointed porgy.

148 W.M.O. Emblem and World Weather Map

1973. Air. Centenary of I.M.O./W.M.O.

| 515 | 148 | 100f. brown and green . . | 95 | 10 |

1973. Air. Europafrique.

| 516 | 149 | 35f. blue, green & yell . . | 35 | 20 |
| 517 | | — 40f. brown, ultram & bl | 40 | 25 |

DESIGN: 40f. Europafrique, plant and cogwheels.

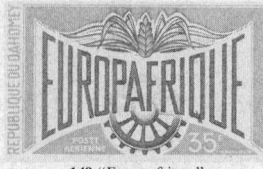

149 "Europafrique"

150 President John F. Kennedy   152 Chameleon

151 Footballers

1973. Air. 10th Death Anniv of President Kennedy.

| 518 | 150 | 200f. grn, violet & grn . . | 1·90 | 1·40 |

1973. Air. World Football Championship Cup.

520	151	35f. green, brn & bistre	35	20
521		— 40f. brown, blue & orange	40	25
522		— 100f. green, brown & blue	65	45

DESIGNS: 40f., 100f. Football scenes similar to Type **151**.

1973. 1st Anniv of 26th October Revolution. Multicoloured.

| 523 | | 35f. Type 152 . . . . | 35 | 20 |
| 524 | | 40f. Arms of Dahomey (vert) | 35 | 25 |

153 "The Annunciation" (Dirk Bouts)   155 "The Elephant, the Chicken and the Dog"

1973. Air. Christmas. Multicoloured.

525		35f. Type 153	40	30
526		100f. "The Nativity" (Giotto)	70	50
527		150f. "The Adoration of the Magi" (Botticelli)	1·40	80
528		200f. "The Adoration of the Shepherds" (Bassano) (horiz)	1·75	1·25

1974. Air. "Skylab". No. 515 surch **OPERATION SKYLAB 1973-1974** and value.

| 529 | 148 | 200f. on 100f. brn & grn | 1·50 | 95 |

1974. Dahomey Folk Tales. Multicoloured.

530	155	5f. Type 155	15	10
531		10f. "The Sparrowhawk and the Dog"	20	10
532		25f. "The Windy Tree" (horiz)	30	20
533		40f. "The Eagle, the Snake and the Chicken" (horiz)	40	20

156 Snow Crystal and Skiers

1974. Air. 50th Anniv of Winter Olympic Games.

| 534 | 156 | 100f. blue, brn and vio . . | 95 | 65 |

157 Alsatian

1974. Breeds of Dogs. Multicoloured.

535		40f. Type 157	35	25
536		50f. Boxer	40	25
537		100f. Saluki	80	50

158 Map of Member Countries

1974. 15th Anniv of Council of Accord.

| 538 | 158 | 40f. multicoloured . . . . | 35 | 15 |

159 Lenin (50th Death Anniv)

1974. Air. Celebrities' Anniversaries.
539 **159** 50f. purple and red . . . 50 30
540 – 125f. brn & green . . . 1·10 65
541 – 150f. blue & purple . . . 1·60 1·10
DESIGNS AND ANNIVERSARIES: 125f. Marie
Curie (40th death anniv); 150f. Sir Winston Churchill
(birth cent).

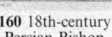

160 18th-century   161 Beethoven and
Persian Bishop   opening bars of the
                     "Moonlight" Sonata

1974. Air. 21st Chess Olympiad, Nice. Mult.
542 50f. Type **160** 55 35
543 200f. 19th-century Siamese
        queen . . . . 1·75 1·10

1974. Air. Famous Composers.
544 **161** 150f. red and black . . . 1·25 80
545 – 150f. red and black . . . 1·25 80
DESIGN: No. 545, Chopin.

162 Earth seen through Astronaut's
Legs

1974. Air. 5th Anniv of 1st Manned Moon Landing.
546 **162** 150f. brn, blue & red . . 1·40 85

Sets commemorating the World Cup, U.P.U.
Centenary, Treaty of Berne, Space Exploration and
West Germany's World Cup Victory appeared in
1974. Their status is uncertain.

1974. Air. 11th Pan-Arab Scout Jamboree, Batroun,
Lebanon. Nos. 499/500 surch **XIe JAMBOREE
PANARABE DE BATROUN – LIBAN** and value.
547 **140** 100f. on 15f. purple, green
        and blue 65 45
548 – 140f. on 20f. bl & brn . . 1·25 65

1974. Air. West Germany's Victory in World Cup
Football Championships. Nos. 521/2 surch **R F A
2 HOLLANDE 1** and value.
549 100f. on 40f. brn, bl & orge 65 45
550 150f. on 100f. grn, brn & bl 1·00 80

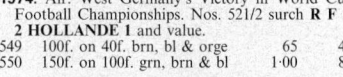

165 U.P.U. Emblem and Globe

1974. Air. Centenary of U.P.U.
551 **165** 35f. violet and red . . . 35 30
552 – 65f. blue and red . . . 1·25 60
553 – 125f. green, blue & lt bl 2·75 1·00
554 – 200f. blue, yellow & brn 1·75 1·25
DESIGNS: 65f. Concorde in flight over African
village; 125f. French mobile post office, circa 1860;
200f. Drummer and mail van.

166 "Lion of Belfort"

1974. Air. 70th Death Anniv of F. Bartholdi
(sculptor).
555 **166** 100f. brown . . . . . 1·25 65

1974. Air. 30th Death Anniv of Philippe de
Champaigne (painter). As T **153**. Mult.
556 250f. "Young Girl with
        Falcon" . . . . 2·25 1·40

167 Locomotive No. 3.1102, 1911, France

1974. Steam Locomotives.
557 **167** 35f. multicoloured . . . 80 35
558 – 40f. grey, black & red . 1·00 45
559 – 100f. multicoloured . . . 2·50 85
560 – 200f. multicoloured . . . 4·25 1·90
DESIGNS: 40f. Goods locomotive, 1877; 100f.
Crampton Type 210 locomotive, 1849; 200f.
Stephenson locomotive "Aigle", 1846, France.

168 Rhamphorhynchus

1974. Air. Prehistoric Animals. Multicoloured.
561 **168** 35f. Type **168** 35 20
562 150f. Stegosaurus . . . . 1·00 70
563 200f. Tyrannosaurus . . . 1·50 95

169 Globe, Notes and Savings
Bank

1974. World Savings Day.
564 **169** 35f. brown, myrtle & grn 35 25

170 Europafrique Emblem on Globe

1974. Air. Europafrique.
565 **170** 250f. multicoloured . . . 1·90 1·40

1974. Air. Christmas. Paintings by Old Masters.
As T **153**. Multicoloured.
566 35f. "The Annunciation"
        (Schongauer) 30 20
567 40f. "The Nativity"
        (Schongauer) 35 25
568 100f. "The Virgin of the Rose
        Bush" (Schongauer) . . 80 45
569 250f. "The Virgin, Infant
        Jesus and St. John the
        Baptist" (Botticelli) . . . 2·25 1·40

171 "Apollo" and "Soyuz"
Spacecraft

1975. Air. "Apollo–Soyuz" Space Link. Mult.
570 **171** 35f. Type **171** 35 25
571 200f. Rocket launch and flags
        of Russia and U.S.A. . . . 1·60 90
572 500f. "Apollo" and "Soyuz"
        docked together . . . . 3·50 2·25

172 Dompago Dance,   173 Flags on Map of
Hissi   Africa

1975. Dahomey Dances and Folklore. Mult.
573 10f. Type **172** 20 15
574 25f. Fetish dance, Vaudou-
        Tchinan 30 15
575 40f. Bamboo dance,
        Agbehoun 40 30
576 100f. Somba dance, Sandoua
        (horiz) 75 50

1975. "Close Co-operation with Nigeria".
Multicoloured.
577 65f. Type **173** 40 30
578 100f. Arrows linking maps of
        Dahomey and Nigeria
        (horiz) 65 40

174 Community Emblem and Pylons

1975. Benin Electricity Community. Mult.
579 40f. Type **174** 35 25
580 150f. Emblem and pylon
        (vert) . . . . 1·10 65
C.E.B. = "Communaute Electrique du Benin".

175 Head of Ceres

1975. Air. "Arphila 75" International Stamp
Exhibition, Paris.
581 **175** 100f. purple, ind & blue 90 55

176 Rays of Light and   178 Dr. Schweitzer
Map

1975. "New Dahomey Society".
582 **176** 35f. multicoloured 30 20

1975. Air. "Apollo–Soyuz" Space Test Project.
Nos. 570/1 surch **RENCONTRE APOLLO-
SOYOUZ 17 Juil. 1975** and value.
583 **171** 100f. on 35f. mult 65 45
584 – 300f. on 200f. mult . . . 2·00 1·10

1975. Birth Centenary of Dr. Albert Schweitzer.
585 **178** 200f. olive, brown &
        green . . . . 1·75 90

179 "The Holy Family"   180 Woman and
(Michelangelo)   I.W.Y. Emblem

1975. Air. Europafrique.
586 **179** 300f. multicoloured . . . 1·90 1·25

1975. International Women's Year.
587 **180** 50f. blue and violet . . . 35 25
588 – 150f. orange, brn & grn 1·10 65
DESIGN: 150f. I.W.Y. emblem within ring of
bangles.

181 Continental Infantry   183 "Allamanda
                            cathartica"

182 Diving

1975. Air. Bicent of American Revolution.
589 **181** 75f. lilac, red & green . . 55 35
590 – 135f. brown, pur & bl . . 95 70
591 – 300f. brown, red & blue 2·00 1·40
592 – 500f. brown, red & grn 3·50 1·75
DESIGNS: 135f. "Spirit of '76"; 300f. Artillery
battery; 500f. Cavalry.

1975. Air. Olympic Games, Montreal.
593 **182** 40f. brown, bl and vio . . 35 25
594 – 250f. brown, grn & red 1·60 1·10
DESIGN: 250f. Football.

1975. Flowers. Multicoloured.
595 10f. Type **183** 15 10
596 35f. "Ixora coccinea" . . . 30 15
597 45f. "Hibiscus rosa-sinensis" 45 30
598 60f. "Phaemeria magnifica" 55 40

184 "The Nativity" (Van Leyden)

1975. Air. Christmas. Multicoloured.
599 40f. Type **184** 35 25
600 85f. "Adoration of the Magi"
        (Rubens) (vert) 55 45
601 140f. "Adoration of the
        Shepherds" (Le Brun) . . . 1·00 65
602 300f. "The Virgin of the Blue
        Diadem" (Raphael) (vert) . 2·00 1·50

For later issues see **BENIN**.

PARCEL POST STAMPS

1967. Surch **COLIS POSTAUX** and value.
P271 **18** 5f. on 1f. (postage) . . . 10 10
P272 – 10f. on 2f. (No. 151) . . 25 25
P273 **18** 20f. on 6f. 30 30
P274 – 25f. on 3f. (No. 152) . . 40 40
P275 – 30f. on 4f. (No. 153) . . 45 45
P276 – 50f. on 10f. (No. 155) . . 70 70
P277 – 100f. on 20f. (No. 157) . 1·50 1·50
P278 – 200f. on 200f. (No. 195)
        (air) . . . . 3·00 2·25
P279 **29** 300f. on 100f. . . . . 3·50 3·00
P280 – 500f. on 300f. (No. 196) . 6·50 4·50
P281 – 1000f. on 500f. (No. 197) 14·00 11·00
P282 – 500f. on 100f. (No. 145) 55·00 55·00

POSTAGE DUE STAMPS

1906. "Natives" key-type inscr "DAHOMEY" in
blue (10, 30c.) or red (others).
D33 L 5c. green . . . . 1·75 1·50
D34 – 10c. red . . . . 3·00 2·75
D35 – 15c. blue on blue . . . 4·00 3·00
D36 – 20c. black on yellow . . 3·00 7·00
D37 – 30c. red on cream . . . 3·25 8·00
D38 – 50c. violet . . . . . . 8·50 25·00
D39 – 60c. black on buff . . . 6·50 21·00
D40 – 1f. black on pink . . . 30·00 55·00

1914. "Figure" key-type inscr "DAHOMEY".
D59 M 5c. green . . . . 10 2·25

D60		10c. red	15	2·00
D61		15c. grey	40	2·00
D62		20c. brown	40	2·75
D63		30c. blue	1·00	3·00
D64		50c. black	75	3·75
D65		60c. orange	1·25	2·25
D66		1f. violet	1·75	3·25

1927. Surch in figures.

D96	M	2f. on 1f. mauve	1·75	1·75
D97		3f. on 1f. brown	2·50	4·50

D 14 Native Head

D 26 Panther attacking African

1941.

D143	D 14	5c. black	1·10	2·75
D144		10c. red	20	2·75
D145		15c. blue	10	2·00
D146		20c. green	35	2·75
D147		30c. orange	1·25	3·00
D148		50c. brown	1·90	3·25
D149		60c. green	1·90	3·50
D150		1f. red	2·25	3·50
D151		2f. yellow	2·75	3·25
D152		3f. purple	2·75	4·25

1963.

D191	D 26	1f. red and green	10	10
D192		2f. green & brown	10	10
D193		5f. blue and orange	10	10
D194		10f. black and purple	25	25
D195		20f. orange & blue	30	30

D 72 Pirogue

1967.

D308	D 72	1f. plum, blue & brn	10	10
D309	A	1f. brown, bl & plum	10	10
D310	B	3f. green, orge & brn	10	10
D311	C	3f. brown, orge & grn	10	10
D312	D	5f. purple, blue & brn	15	15
D313	E	5f. brown, blue & pur	35	20
D314	F	10f. green, vio & brn	30	30
D315	G	10f. brown, grn & vio	30	30
D316	H	30f. violet, red & bl	50	50
D317	I	30f. blue, red & vio	50	50

DESIGNS: A, Heliograph; B, Old morse receiver; C, Postman on cycle; D, Old telephone; E, Renault ABH diesel railcar; F, Citroen "2-CV" mail van; G, Radio station; H, Douglas DC-8-10/50CF airliner; I, "Early Bird" satellite.

DANISH WEST INDIES Pt. 11

A group of islands in the West Indies formerly belonging to Denmark and purchased in 1917 by the United States, whose stamps they now use. Now known as the United States Virgin Islands.

1855. 100 cents = 1 dollar.
1905. 100 bit = 1 franc.

1

2

5

1855. Imperf.

4	1	3c. red	29·00	48·00

1872. Perf.

6	1	3c. red	60·00	£150
7		4c. blue	£150	£300

1873.

31	2	1c. red and green	8·75	13·00
32		3c. red and blue	7·25	9·50
33		4c. blue and brown	8·00	7·50
19		5c. brown and green	19·00	12·00
21		7c. yellow and purple	21·00	70·00
25		10c. brown and blue	19·00	22·00
27		12c. green and purple	29·00	£100
28		14c. green and lilac	£450	£800
29		50c. lilac	£100	£180

1887. Handstamped **1 CENT**.

37	2	1c. on 7c. yellow & purple	45·00	£140

1895. Surch **10 CENTS 1895**.

38	2	10c. on 50c. lilac	26·00	48·00

1900.

39	5	1c. green	2·40	2·40
40		2c. red	6·25	18·00
41		5c. blue	12·50	18·00
42		8c. brown	22·00	40·00

1902. Surch **2** (or **8**) **CENTS 1902**.

43	2	2c. on 3c. red and blue	6·50	17·00
47		8c. on 10c. brown & blue	8·00	8·25

1905. Surch **5 BIT 1905**.

48	2	5b. on 4c. blue & brown	12·00	38·00
49	5	5b. on 5c. blue	10·00	29·00
50		5b. on 8c. brown	10·00	30·00

10 King Christian IX

11 Charlotte Amalie Harbour and Training ship "Ingolf"

1905.

51	10	5b. green	3·75	3·00
52		10b. red	3·75	3·00
53		20b. blue and green	7·50	6·50
54		25b. blue	7·50	7·50
55		40b. grey and red	7·50	6·00
56		50b. grey and yellow	7·50	8·25
57	11	1f. blue and green	16·00	26·00
58		2f. brown and red	26·00	38·00
59		5f. brown and yellow	55·00	£180

14 King Frederik VIII

15 King Christian X

1907.

60	14	5b. green	2·25	1·10
61		10b. red	2·25	1·00
62		15b. brown and violet	3·75	3·75
63		20b. blue and green	22·00	18·00
64		25b. blue	2·25	1·90
65		30b. black and red	40·00	38·00
66		40b. grey and red	5·50	4·50
67		50b. brown and yellow	5·25	7·00

1915.

68	15	5b. green	4·25	4·00
69		10b. red	4·25	42·00
70		15b. brown and lilac	4·25	42·00
71		20b. blue and green	4·25	42·00
72		25b. blue	4·25	10·00
73		30b. black and red	4·25	55·00
74		40b. grey and red	4·25	55·00
75		50b. brown and yellow	4·25	55·00

POSTAGE DUE STAMPS

D 6

D 12

1902.

D43	D 6	1c. blue	4·75	13·50
D44		4c. blue	9·00	19·00
D45		6c. blue	17·00	40·00
D46		10c. blue	16·00	45·00

1905.

D60	D 12	5b. grey and red	4·00	5·00
D61		20b. grey and red	5·75	12·00
D62		30b. grey and red	5·25	12·00
D63		50b. grey and red	5·00	26·00

DANZIG Pt. 7

A Baltic seaport, from 1920–1939 (with the surrounding district) a free state under the protection of the League of Nations. Later incorporated in Germany. Now part of Poland.

1920. 100 pfennige = 1 mark.
1923. 100 pfennige = 1 Danzig gulden.

Stamps of Germany inscr "DEUTSCHES REICH" optd or surch.

1920. Optd **Danzig** horiz.

1	10	5pf. green	30	30
2		10pf. red	30	30
3	24	15pf. brown	30	30
4	10	20pf. blue	30	40
5		30pf. black & orge on buff	30	30
6		40pf. red	30	30
7		50pf. black & pur on buff	35	30
8	12	1m. red	60	80
9		1m.25 green	40	50
10		1m.50 brown	70	70
11	13	2m. blue	1·90	4·75
12		2m.50 red	1·90	4·75
13	14	3m. black	4·75	10·00
14	10	4m. red and black	5·50	6·00
15a	15	5m. red and black	2·10	2·40

1920. Surch **Danzig** horiz and large figures of value.

16	10	5 on 30pf. black and orange on buff	20	20
17		10 on 20pf. blue	20	20
18		25 on 30pf. black and orange on buff	20	20
19		60 on 30pf. black and orange on buff	50	50
20		80 on 30pf. black and orange on buff	50	60

1920. Optd **Danzig** diagonally and bar.

21	24	2pf. grey	£130	£180
22		2½pf. grey	£150	£325
23	10	3pf. brown	7·25	13·00
24		5pf. green	30	30
25	24	7½pf. orange	38·00	50·00
26	10	10pf. red	2·75	6·00
27	24	15pf. violet	50	50
28	10	20pf. blue	50	50
29		25pf. blk & red on yell	50	50
30		30pf. blk & orge on buff	42·00	70·00
31		40pf. black and red	1·75	2·10
32		50pf. blk & pur on buff	£140	£275
32a		60pf. mauve	£1100	£2250
33		75pf. black and green	50	60
34		80pf. blk & red on pink	2·10	3·50
34a	12	1m. red	£950	£1400

1920. Optd **DANZIG** three times in semicircle.

34b	13	2m. blue	£1000	£2000

1920. No. 5 of Danzig surch **MARK 1 MARK** and Types of Germany with burelage added surch with new value and **DANZIG** (36/37), **Danzig** (38, 40f) or **DANZIG** and flag (40e).

35 A	10	1m. on 30pf. black and orange on buff	70	1·25
36 A		1¼m. on 3pf. brown	70	1·25
37 A	24	2m. on 35pf. brown	70	1·25
38 A		3m. on 7½pf. orange	70	1·25
39 A		5m. on 2pf. grey	70	1·25
40AF		10m. on 7½pf. orange	1·25	2·00

1920. Air. No. 6 of Danzig surch with airplane or wings and value.

41	10	40 on 40pf. red	1·25	2·25
42		60 on 40pf. red	1·40	2·50
43		1m. on 40pf. red	1·25	3·00

13 Hanse Kogge

1921. Constitution of 1920.

44	13	5pf. purple and brown	30	30
45		10pf. violet and orange	35	30
46		25pf. red and green	50	60
55		40pf. red	65	90
48		80pf. blue	40	50
49	–	1m. grey and red	1·75	1·75
50	–	2m. green and blue	5·50	4·50
51	–	3m. green and black	1·75	2·00
52	–	5m. red and grey	1·75	1·50
53	–	10m. brown and green	2·10	3·50

The mark values are as Type **13**, but larger.

15

16 Sabaltnig PIII over Danzig

1921. Air.

57	15	40pf. green	25	40
58		60pf. purple	25	40
59		1m. red	25	40
60		2m. brown	25	40
116	16	5m. violet	40	70
117		10m. green	40	70
118		20m. brown	40	70
119	15	25m. blue	35	50
120	16	50m. orange	35	50
121		100m. red	35	50
122		250m. brown	35	50
123		500m. red	30	65

Nos. 120 to 123 are similar to Type **16**, but larger.

1921. No. 33 of Danzig surch **60** and bars.

63	10	60 on 75pf. black & green	55	70

18

19

1921.

64	18	5pf. orange	25	25
65		10pf. brown	25	25
66		15pf. green	25	25
67		20pf. grey	25	25
68		25pf. green	25	25
69		30pf. red and blue	25	25
70		40pf. red and green	25	25
71		50pf. red and green	25	25
72		60pf. red	35	35
73		75pf. purple	25	25
74		80pf. red and black	30	50
75		80pf. green	25	25
76		1m. red and orange	30	50
77		1.20m. blue	1·25	1·50
78		1.25m. red and purple	25	25
79		1.50m. grey	25	45
80		2m. red and grey	2·10	3·50
81		2m. red	25	25
82		2.40m. red and brown	70	1·50
83		3m. red and purple	6·50	6·50
84		3m. red	25	40
106		4m. blue	25	40
86		5m. green	25	35
87		6m. red	25	35
88		8m. blue	35	70
89		10m. orange	25	25
90		20m. brown	35	35
110		40m. blue	25	40
111		80m. red	25	40

1921. Rouletted.

91	19	5m. green, black and red	90	1·75
91b		9m. orange and red	2·40	6·50
92		10m. blue, black and red	90	1·75
93		20m. black and red	90	1·75

20

21

1921. Tuberculosis Week.

93a	20	30pf.(+30pf.) grn & orge	40	70
93b		60pf.(+60pf.) red & yell	1·00	1·00
93c		1.20m.(+1.20m.) bl & orge (25 × 29½ mm)	1·50	1·50

1922.

94b	21	50m. red and gold	1·50	3·25
95a		100m. red and green	2·50	5·00

1922. Surch in figures.

96	18	6 on 3m. red	30	50
97		8 on 4m. blue	30	70
98		20 on 8m. blue	30	50

25

26

1923.

99	25	50m. red and blue	25	40
136		50m. blue	20	45
100		100m. red and green	25	40
137		100m. green	20	45
101		150m. red and purple	25	40
138		200m. orange	20	45
102	26	250m. red and purple	30	40
103		500m. red and grey	30	40
104		1000m. pink and brown	30	40
105		5000m. pink and silver	1·10	5·00
139		10000m. red and orange	40	45
140		20000m. red and blue	40	85
141		50000m. red and green	40	85

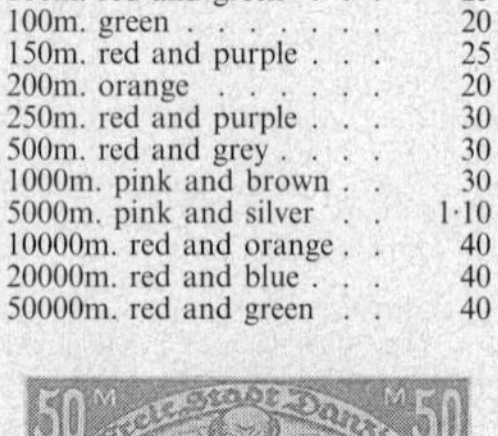

28

1923. Poor People's Fund.

123b	28	50+20m. red	25	55
123c		100+30m. purple	25	55

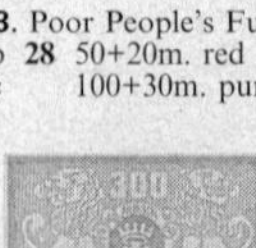

29

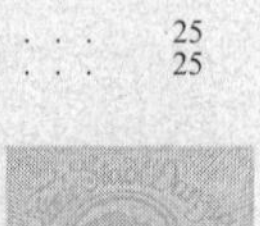

35 Etrich/Rumpler Taube

1923.

124	29	250m. red and purple	20	40
125		300m. red and green	20	40
126		500m. red and grey	20	40
127		1000m. brown	20	35
128		1000m. red and brown	20	40
129		3000m. red and violet	20	40
130		5000m. pink	20	35
131		20000m. blue	20	35
132		50000m. green	20	35
133		100000m. blue	20	35
134		250000m. purple	20	35
135		500000m. grey	20	35

1923. Surch with figure of value and **Tausend** (T) or **Million** or **Millionen** (M).

142	25	40T. on 200m. orange	70	1·90
143		100T. on 200m. orange	70	1·90
144		250T. on 200m. orange	5·50	10·00

145 400T. on 100m. green 40 40
146 29 500T. on 50000m. green 40 40
147 1M. on 10000m. orange 3·25 5·25
148 1M. on 10000m. red 25 40
149 2M. on 10000m. red 25 40
150 3M. on 10000m. red 25 40
151 5M. on 10000m. red 25 40
152 10M. on 10000m. lavender 40 60
158 26 10M. on 1000000m. orge 50 50
153 29 20M. on 10000m. lavender 40 60
154 25M. on 10000m. lavender 25 60
155 40M. on 10000m. lavender 25 60
156 50M. on 10000m. lavender 25 60
159 100M. on 10000m. lav 25 60
160 300M. on 10000m. lav 25 60
161 500M. on 10000m. lav 25 60

1923. Surch **100000** and bar.
157 26 100000 on 20000m. red and blue 90 6·25

1923. Air.
162a 35 250,000m. red 35 95
163a 500,000m. red 30 95

1923. Surch in **Millionen**.
164a 35 2m. on 100,000m. red 30 95
165a 5m. on 50,000m. red 35 95

1923. Surch with new currency, **Pfennige** or **Gulden**.
166 25 5pf. on 50m. red 40 40
167 10pf. on 50m. red 40 40
168 20pf. on 100m. red 40 40
169 25pf. on 50m. red 2·75 8·25
170 30pf. on 50m. red 2·25 1·90
171 40pf. on 100m. red 1·90 1·90
172 50pf. on 100m. red 1·90 2·40
173 75pf. on 100m. red 5·25 13·00
174 26 1g. on 1000000m. red 3·50 5·00
175 2g. on 1000000m. red 6·00 13·00
176 3g. on 1000000m. red 17·00 55·00
177 5g. on 1000000m. red 20·00 60·00

39

40 Etrich/Rumpler Taube

1924.
177b 39 3pf. brown 1·10 1·40
268 5pf. orange 70 1·10
178e 7pf. green 1·10 2·10
178f 8pf. green 1·50 4·75
270 10pf. green 70 1·10
180 15pf. grey 11·50 4·25
180b 15pf. red 7·50 90
181 20pf. red and carmine 10·00 60
182 20pf. grey 1·50 1·50
183 25pf. red and grey 17·00 3·00
272 25pf. red 1·75 6·50
185 30pf. red and green 8·50 70
186 30pf. purple 1·50 3·50
186a 35pf. blue 2·10 1·40
187 40pf. blue and indigo 7·75 85
188 40pf. red and brown 4·50 9·50
189 40pf. blue 1·75 3·50
274 50pf. red and blue 1·75 6·00
190b 55pf. red and purple 4·25 11·50
191 60pf. red and green 4·50 13·00
192 70pf. red and green 2·00 4·25
193 75pf. red and purple 8·00 8·00
194 80pf. red and brown 2·00 5·50

1924. Air.
195 40 10pf. red 17·00 3·50
196 20pf. mauve 1·75 1·10
197 40pf. brown 3·50 1·75
198 1g. green 3·00 1·75
199 – 2½g. purple (22 × 40 mm) 17·00 26·00

42 Oliva

44 Fountain of Neptune

1924.
200 42 1g. black and green 17·00 40·00
275 1g. black and orange 3·50 12·00
201 – 2g. black and purple 35·00 95·00
206 – 2g. black and red 3·25 5·50
202 – 3g. black and blue 3·50 5·00
203 – 5g. black and lake 3·50 6·50
204 – 10g. black and brown 17·00 80·00
DESIGNS—HORIZ: 2g. Krantor and River Mottlau; 3g. Zoppot. VERT: 5g. St. Mary's Church; 10g. Town Hall and Langemarkt.

1929. Int Philatelic Exhibition. Various frames.
207 44 10pf.(+10pf.) blk & grn 1·75 2·10
208 15pf.(+15pf.) blk & red 1·75 2·10
209 25pf.(+25pf.) blk & bl 6·50 6·50

1930. 10th Anniv of Constitution of Free City of Danzig. Optd **1920 15. November 1930.**
210 39 5pf. orange 2·10 3·50
211 10pf. green 2·75 4·25
212 15pf. red 4·75 9·50
213 20pf. red and carmine 2·40 5·00
214 25pf. red and grey 3·00 9·50
215 30pf. red and green 6·00 23·00
216 35pf. blue 26·00 70·00
217 40pf. blue and indigo 8·50 35·00
218 50pf. red and blue 26·00 70·00
219 75pf. red and purple 26·00 70·00
220 42 1g. black and orange 26·00 70·00

1932. Danzig Int Air Post Exn ("Luposta"). Nos. 200/4 surch **Luftpost-Ausstellung 1932** and value.
221 42 10pf.+10pf. on 1g. black and green 6·50 19·00
222 – 15pf.+15pf. on 2g. black and purple 6·50 19·00
223 – 20pf.+20pf. on 3g. black and blue 6·50 19·00
224 – 25pf.+25pf. on 5g. black and lake 6·50 19·00
225 – 30pf.+30pf. on 10g. black and brown 6·50 19·00

1934. "Winter Relief Work" Charity. Surch **5 W.H.W.**in Gothic characters.
226 39 5pf.+5pf. orange 6·50 17·00
227 10pf.+5pf. green 20·00 42·00
228 15pf.+5pf. red 13·50 29·00

1934. Surch.
229 39 6pf. on 7pf. green 70 1·75
230a 8pf. on 7pf. green 1·00 1·75
231 30pf. on 35pf. blue 9·50 19·00

50 Junkers F-13

51

1935. Air.
233 50 10pf. red 1·00 70
234 15pf. yellow 1·00 1·00
235 25pf. green 1·00 1·75
236 50pf. blue 6·00 8·50
237 51 1g. purple 2·75 8·50

52 Stockturm, 1346

54 Brosen War Memorial

1935. Winter Relief Fund.
238 52 5pf.+5pf. orange 60 1·50
239 – 10pf.+5pf. green 85 2·00
240 – 15pf.+10pf. red 1·75 3·25
DESIGNS—HORIZ: 10pf. Lege Tor. VERT: 15pf. Georgshalle, 1487.

1936. 125th Anniv of Brosen. Inscr "125 JAHRE OSTEEBAD BROSEN".
241 – 10pf. green 60 60
242 – 25pf. red 85 2·00
243 54 40pf. blue 1·00 4·00
DESIGNS—HORIZ: 10pf. Brosen Beach; 25pf. Zoppot end of Brosen Beach.

55 Frauentor and Observatory

56 D(anziger) L(uftschutz) B(und)

57a Danziger Dorf, Magdeburg

1936. Winter Relief Fund.
244 – 10pf.+5pf. blue 1·00 2·75
245 55 15pf.+5pf. green 1·00 4·25
246 – 25pf.+10pf. red 1·75 5·50
247 – 40pf.+20pf. brn & red 2·40 8·50
248 – 50pf.+20pf. blue 4·25 13·00
DESIGNS—VERT: 10pf. Milchkannenturm; 25pf. Krantor. HORIZ: 40pf. Langgartertor; 50pf. Hohestor.

1937. Air Defence League.
249 56 10pf. blue 40 1·10
250 15pf. purple 1·50 1·75

1937. Foundation of Danzig Community, Magdeburg.
253 57a 25pf. (+25pf.) red 2·40 4·50
254 – 40pf. (+40pf.) red & bl 2·40 4·50
DESIGN—HORIZ: 40pf. Village and Arms of Danzig and Magdeburg.

58 Madonna and Child

59 Schopenhauer

1937. Winter Relief Fund. Statues.
255 58 5pf.+5pf. violet 2·10 5·00
256 – 10pf.+5pf. brown 2·10 5·00
257 – 15pf.+5pf. orange & blue 2·10 5·00
258 – 25pf.+10pf. green & blue 2·75 6·00
259 – 40pf.+25pf. blue & red 4·75 13·00
DESIGNS: 10pf. Mercury; 15pf. The "Golden Knight"; 25pf. Fountain of Neptune; 40pf. St. George and Dragon.

1938. 150th Birth Anniv of Schopenhauer (philosopher). Portraits inscr as in T **59**.
260 – 15pf. blue (as old man) 1·40 1·90
261 – 25pf. brown (as youth) 2·75 7·00
262 59 40pf. red 1·40 3·75

60 Yacht "Peter von Danzig" (1936)

61 Teutonic Knights

1938. Winter Relief Fund. Ships.
276 60 5pf.+5pf. green 90 1·50
277 – 10pf.+5pf. brown 1·40 2·40
278 – 15pf.+10pf. olive 1·50 2·40
279 – 25pf.+10pf. blue 2·00 3·00
280 – 40pf.+15pf. purple 2·40 6·00
DESIGNS: 10pf. Dredger "Fu Shing"; 15pf. Liner "Columbus"; 25pf. Liner "Hansestadt Danzig"; 40pf. Sailing ship "Peter von Danzig" (1472).

1939. 125th Anniv of Prussian Annexation. Historical designs.
281 61 5pf. green 40 1·75
282 – 10pf. brown 70 2·10
283 – 15pf. blue 70 2·10
284 – 25pf. purple 1·00 3·50
DESIGNS: 10pf. Danzig–Swedish treaty of neutrality, 1630; 15pf. Danzig united to Prussia, 2.1.1814; 25pf. Stephen Batori's defeat at Weichselmunde, 1577.

62 Gregor Mendel

1939. Anti-cancer Campaign.
285 62 10pf. brown 40 70
286 – 15pf. black (Koch) 40 1·50
287 – 25pf. green (Rontgen) 70 2·10

OFFICIAL STAMPS

1921. Stamps of Danzig optd **D M.**
O 94 18 5f. orange 30 25
O 95 10pf. brown 30 25
O 96 15pf. green 30 25
O 97 20pf. grey 25 20
O 98 25pf. green 25 20
O 99 30pf. red and blue 55 55
O100 40pf. red and green 30 25
O101 50pf. red and green 30 25
O102 60pf. red 25 25
O103 75pf. purple 25 40
O104 80pf. red and black 70 70
O105 80pf. green 25 70
O106 1m. orange 30 30
O107 1m.20 blue 1·00 1·50
O108 1m.25 red and purple 25 70
O109 1m.50 grey 25 40
O110 2m. red and grey 13·00 8·50
O111 2m. red 25 95
O112 2m.40 red and brown 1·10 1·75
O113 3m. red and purple 8·50 9·00
O114 3m. red 25 40
O122 4m. blue 30 40
O116 5m. green 25 40
O117 6m. red 25 40
O118 10m. orange 25 40
O119 20m. brown 25 25

1922. Stamps of Danzig optd **D M.**
O120a 19 5m. green, black and red (No. 91) 3·25 5·50
O126a 25 50m. red and blue 20 40
O142 50m. blue 20 40
O127a 100m. red and green 20 40
O143 100m. green 20 40
O144 200m. orange 20 30
O145 29 300m. red and green 30 40
O146 500m. red and grey 20 40
O147 100m. red and brown 20 65

1922. No. 96 optd **D M.**
O121 18 6 on 3m. red 25 65

1924. Optd **Dienst-marke**.
O195 39 5pf. orange 2·40 6·50
O196 10pf. green 2·40 5·00
O197 15pf. grey 2·40 2·75
O198 15pf. red 14·50 8·00
O199 20pf. red and carmine 2·00 1·75
O200 25pf. red and black 14·00 20·00
O201 30pf. red and green 2·40 2·40
O202 35f. blue 35·00 42·00
O203 40pf. blue and indigo 5·00 6·50
O204 50pf. red and blue 14·50 26·00
O205 75pf. red and purple 29·00 85·00

POSTAGE DUE STAMPS

D 20

D 39

1921. Value in "pfennig" (figures only).
D 94 D 20 10pf. purple 30 60
D 95 20pf. purple 30 40
D 96 40pf. purple 30 40
D 97 60pf. purple 30 40
D 98 75pf. purple 30 40
D 99 80pf. purple 30 40
D112 100pf. purple 40 30
D100 120pf. purple 30 40
D101 200pf. purple 70 90
D102 240pf. purple 30 90
D114 300pf. purple 40 70
D115 400pf. purple 40 70
D116 500pf. purple 40 70
D117 800pf. purple 75 90

Value in "marks" ("M" after figure).
D118a D 20 10m. purple 40 70
D119a 20m. purple 40 70
D120a 50m. purple 40 70
D121 100m. purple 40 90
D122 500m. purple 40 90

1923. Surch with figures and bar.
D162 D 20 1000 on 100m. pur £130 £300
D163 5000 on 50m. purple 40 75
D164 10000 on 20m. pur 40 75
D165 50000 on 500m. pur 40 75
D166 100000 on 20m. pur 70 1·10

1924.
D178 D 39 5pf. blue and black 70 1·10
D179 10pf. blue and black 70 70
D180 15pf. blue and black 40 70
D181 20pf. blue and black 1·10 1·75
D182 30pf. blue and black 6·50 1·75
D183 40pf. blue and black 1·25 2·75
D184 50pf. blue and black 1·75 2·75
D185 60pf. blue and black 9·50 14·50
D186 100pf. blue and black 13·00 8·00
D187 3g. blue and red 6·00 40·00

1932. Surch in figures over bar.
D226 D 39 5 on 40pf. blue & blk 2·10 5·50
D227 10 on 60pf. bl & blk 26·00 9·50
D228 20 on 100pf. bl & blk 2·00 6·00

DEDEAGATZ Pt. 6

Former French Post Office, closed in August 1914. Dedeagatz was part of Turkey to 1913, then a Bulgarian town.

25 centimes = 1 piastre.

1893. Stamps of France optd **Dedeagh** or surch also in figures and words.
59 10 5c. green 5·50 10·50
60 10c. black on lilac 18·50 16·50
62a 15c. blue 24·00 21·00
63 1pi. on 25c. black on red 26·00 20·00
64 2pi. on 50c. red 55·00 38·00
65 4pi. on 1f. olive 60·00 55·00
66 8pi. on 2f. brn on blue 60·00 55·00

1902. "Blanc", "Mouchon" and "Merson" key-types inscr "DEDEAGH". Some surch in figures and words.
67a A 5c. green 2·25 2·75
68 B 10c. red 55 1·50
70 15c. orange 2·50 3·00
71 1pi. on 25c. blue 3·25 3·50
72 C 2pi. on 50c. brown & lav 4·00 7·25
73 4pi. on 1f. red and green 13·00 12·50
74 8pi. on 2f. lilac & yellow 18·00 22·00

DENMARK Pt. 11

A kingdom in N. Europe, on a peninsula between the Baltic and the North Sea.

1851. 96 rigsbank skilling = 1 rigsdaler.
1875. 100 ore = 1 krone.

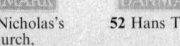

1

2

4

1851. Imperf.

3	**1**	2r.b.s. blue	£2250	£750
4	**2**	4r.b.s. brown	£500	26·00

1854. Dotted background. Brown burelage. Imperf.

8	**4**	2sk. blue	60·00	38·00
9b		4sk. orange	£225	7·00
12		8sk. green	£275	50·00
13		16sk. lilac	£475	£120

5

7

8

1858. Background of wavy lines. Brown burelage. Imperf.

15	**5**	4sk. brown	65·00	6·00
18		8sk. green	£700	70·00

1863. Brown burelage. Roul

20	**5**	4sk. brown	70·00	11·00
21	**4**	16sk. mauve	£1100	£500

1864. Perf.

22	**7**	2sk. blue	65·00	30·00
25		3sk. mauve	85·00	50·00
28		4sk. red	38·00	6·25
29		8sk. bistre	£275	90·00
30a		16sk. green	£400	85·00

1870. Value in "skilling".

39	**8**	2sk. blue and grey	42·00	19·00
42		3sk. purple and grey	60·00	60·00
44		4sk. red and grey	60·00	7·00
46		8sk. brown and grey	£200	55·00
48		16sk. green and grey	£225	£110
37		48sk. lilac and brown	£400	£170

1875. As T **8**, but value in "ore".

80	**8**	3ore grey and blue	1·90	2·75
81		4ore blue and grey	3·75	20
56		5ore blue and red	20·00	50·00
82		8ore red and grey	3·50	20
83		12ore purple and grey	4·00	2·00
84		16ore brown and grey	9·00	2·50
72		20ore grey and red	75·00	19·00
85		25ore green and grey	6·50	3·00
86		50ore purple and brown	19·00	12·00
87		100ore orange and grey	19·00	8·00

10

14 King Christian IX

15

1882.

96	**10**	1ore orange	40	40
97		5ore green	2·25	10
98		10ore red	2·25	10
99		15ore mauve	8·00	60
100		20ore blue	13·00	2·50
101		24ore brown	6·00	2·00

1904. No. 82 and 101 surch.

102	**8**	4ore on 8ore red & grey	1·90	2·50
103	**10**	15ore on 24ore brown	2·75	3·00

1904.

119	**14**	5ore green	2·50	10
104		10ore red	8·00	10
105		20ore blue	12·00	1·10
106		25ore brown	16·00	2·25
107		50ore lilac	45·00	40·00
108		100ore brown	7·00	25·00

1905. Solid background.

173	**15**	1ore orange	20	20
174		2ore red	1·75	20
175		3ore grey	3·00	20
176		4ore blue	4·50	20
177		5ore brown	50	10
178		5ore green	1·60	10
179		7ore green	2·10	2·00
180		7ore violet	9·00	2·25
181		8ore grey	3·25	1·50
114		10ore pink	4·00	10
182		10ore green	65	10
183		10ore brown	1·75	15
184		12ore lilac	14·00	3·50
115		15ore mauve	23·00	70
116		20ore blue	23·00	60

For stamps with lined background but without rts, see Nos. 265/76k.

17 King Frederik VIII

20 G.P.O., Copenhagen

1907.

121	**17**	5ore green	85	10
122		10ore red	1·75	10
124		20ore blue	9·00	40
125		25ore brown	16·00	45
127		35ore orange	2·50	2·10
128		50ore purple	17·00	3·00
130		100ore brown	65·00	2·00

1912. (a) Nos. 84 and 72 surch **35 ORE**.

131	**8**	35ore on 16ore brn & grey	7·00	25·00
132		35ore on 20ore grey and red	13·00	35·00

(b) No. O98 surch **35 ORE FRIMAERKE**.

133	**O 9**	35ore on 32ore green	13·00	40·00

1912.

134	**20**	5k. red	£200	75·00

21 King Christian X

22

1913.

135	**21**	5ore green	90	10
136		7ore orange	2·10	75
137		8ore grey	5·25	2·50
138		10ore red	95	10
139		12ore grey	3·25	5·50
141a		15ore mauve	1·75	10
142		20ore blue	10·00	20
143		20ore brown	55	10
144		20ore red	85	10
145		25ore brown	10·00	20
146		25ore black and brown	42·00	2·50
147		25ore red	1·50	60
148		25ore green	1·50	30
149		27ore black and red	17·00	26·00
150		30ore black and green	21·00	1·25
151		30ore orange	1·75	1·10
152		30ore blue	80	25
153		35ore yellow	17·00	1·60
154		35ore black and yellow	3·25	3·25
155		40ore black and violet	13·00	2·25
156		40ore blue	2·25	65
157		40ore yellow	1·10	65
158		50ore purple	22·00	1·40
159		50ore black and purple	38·00	80
160a		50ore grey	8·25	10
161		60ore blue and brown	38·00	3·25
162		60ore blue	7·50	50
163		70ore green and brown	22·00	1·50
164		80ore green	23·00	7·00
165		90ore red and brown	8·50	2·00
166	**22**	1k. brown	65·00	65
167	**21**	1k. blue and brown	48·00	2·00
168	**22**	2k. black	£100	3·25
169	**21**	2k. purple and grey	32·00	8·75
170	**22**	5k. violet	8·00	5·00
171	**21**	5k. brown and mauve	2·75	3·50
172		10k. green and red	£200	23·00

1915. (a) No. O94 surch **DANMARK 80 ORE POSTFRIM.**

186	**O 9**	80ore on 8ore red	25·00	60·00

(b) No. 83 surch **80 ORE**.

187	**8**	80ore on 12ore pur & grey	18·00	70·00

1918. Newspaper stamps surch **POSTFRIM. ORE 27 ORE DANMARK**.

197	**N 18**	27ore on 1ore green	2·00	6·50
198		27ore on 5ore blue	4·00	15·00
199		27ore on 7ore red	2·00	5·75
200		27ore on 8ore green	3·25	7·50
201		27ore on 10ore lilac	2·10	6·00
202		27ore on 20ore green	3·00	7·00
203		27ore on 29ore orge	2·10	5·50
204		27ore on 38ore orge	14·00	48·00
205		27ore on 41ore brn	4·50	24·00
194		27ore on 68ore brn	3·25	17·00
206		27ore on 1k. pur & grn	2·00	5·50
195		27ore on 5k. grn & pk	3·25	11·00
196		27ore on 10k. bl & stone	4·00	15·00

1919. No. 135 surch **2 ORE**.

207	**21**	2ore on 5ore green	£1200	£250

27 Castle of Kronborg, Elsinore

29 Roskilde Cathedral

1920. Recovery of Northern Schleswig.

208	**27**	10ore red	2·25	20
209		10ore green	5·00	30
210	–	20ore slate	1·75	20
211	**29**	40ore brown	10·00	2·75
212		40ore blue	32·00	4·00

DESIGN—HORIZ: 20ore Sonderborg Castle.

1921. Nos. 136 and 139 surch **8 8**.

217	**21**	8 on 7ore orange	1·90	2·00
213		8 on 12ore green	2·00	4·75

1921. Red Cross. Nos. 209/10 surch with figure of value between red crosses.

214	**27**	10ore+5ore green	10·50	26·00
215	–	20ore+10ore grey	13·50	35·00

1921. No. 175 surch **8**.

216	**15**	8 on 3ore grey	1·90	2·00

33 Christian IV

34 Christian X

35

1924. 300th Anniv of Danish Post. A. Head facing to left.

218A	**33**	10ore green	4·25	3·25
221A	**34**	10ore green	4·25	3·25
219A	**33**	15ore mauve	4·25	3·25
222A	**34**	15ore mauve	4·25	3·25
220A	**33**	20ore brown	4·25	3·25
223A	**34**	20ore brown	4·25	3·25

B. Head facing to right.

218B	**33**	10ore green	4·25	3·25
221B	**34**	10ore green	4·25	3·25
219B	**33**	15ore mauve	4·25	3·25
222B	**34**	15ore mauve	4·25	3·25
220B	**33**	20ore brown	4·25	3·25
223B	**34**	20ore brown	4·25	3·25

1925. Air.

224	**35**	10ore green	13·50	20·00
225		15ore lilac	38·00	38·00
226		25ore red	24·00	35·00
227		50ore grey	70·00	£120
228		1k. brown	65·00	£120

1926. Surch **20 20**.

229	**21**	20 on 30ore orange	2·75	6·00
230		20 on 40ore blue	3·25	7·25

38

39

40 Caravel

1926. 75th Anniv of First Danish stamps.

231	**38**	10ore olive	50	10
232	**39**	20ore red	75	10
233		30ore blue	3·00	65

1926. Various stamps surch.

234	**15**	7 on 8ore grey	1·10	2·50
235	**21**	7 on 20ore red	35	80
236		7 on 27ore black & red	2·40	6·00
237		12 on 15ore lilac	1·40	3·00

1926. Official stamps surch **DANMARK 7 ORE POSTFRIM.**

238	**O 9**	7ore on 1ore orange	1·90	6·00
239		7ore on 3ore grey	7·25	13·00
240		7ore on 4ore blue	1·75	6·50
241		7ore on 5ore green	22·00	65·00
242		7ore on 10ore green	1·75	6·00
243		7ore on 15ore lilac	1·75	6·00
244		7ore on 20ore blue	8·25	32·00

1927. Solid background.

246	**40**	15ore red	3·25	10
247		20ore grey	7·50	65
248		25ore blue	55	10
249		30ore yellow	75	10
250		35ore red	14·00	55
251		40ore green	12·00	10

For stamps with lined background see Nos. 277b, etc.

41

42 King Christian X

43 Numeral

1929. Danish Cancer Research Fund.

252	**41**	10ore (+5ore) green	2·50	3·50
253		15ore (+5ore) red	3·50	5·50
254		25ore (+5ore) blue	13·00	22·00

1930. 60th Birthday of King Christian X.

255	**42**	5ore green	1·25	10
256		7ore violet	4·75	1·90
257		8ore grey	15·00	12·00
258		10ore brown	2·40	10
259		15ore red	7·00	10
260		20ore grey	14·00	3·25
261		25ore blue	4·75	55
262		30ore yellow	5·00	1·00
263		35ore red	6·50	1·90
264		40ore green	6·25	60

1933. Lined background.

265	**43**	1ore green	10	10
266		2ore red	10	10
267		4ore blue	25	25
268		5ore green	50	10
268c		5ore purple	15	10
268d		5ore orange	10	10
268e		6ore orange	10	10
269		7ore violet	75	20
269a		7ore green	55	35
269b		7ore brown	20	10
270		8ore grey	10	15
270a		8ore green	10	10
271		10ore orange	5·00	10
271b		10ore brown	3·00	15
271c		10ore violet	20	15
271d		10ore green	10	10
272		12ore green	15	10
272a		15ore green	15	10
272c		20ore blue	10	10
272e		25ore green	10	10
272f		25ore blue	10	10
273		30ore green	10	10
273a		30ore orange	10	10
273c		40ore orange	10	10
273d		40ore purple	10	10
274		50ore brown	10	10
274d		60ore green	25	25
274e		60ore grey	30	50
275		70ore red	35	10
275a		70ore green	15	10
275d		80ore green	10	10
275e		80ore brown	20	25
276		100ore green	35	10
276a		100ore blue	20	10
276b		125ore brown	30	15
276c		150ore green	35	10
276ca		150ore violet	35	10
276d		200ore green	35	10
276e		230ore green	50	20
276f		250ore green	55	30
276g		270ore green	70	40
276h		300ore green	70	25
276i		325ore green	60	25
276j		350ore green	50	30
276k		375ore green	75	60

45 King Christian X

47 Fokker FVIIa over Copenhagen

49 Hans Andersen

1933. T **40** with lined background.

277b	**40**	15ore red	1·50	15
277de		15ore green	3·75	10
278a		20ore grey	2·50	10
278b		20ore red	40	10
279		25ore blue	48·00	14·50
279b		25ore brown	40	20
280a		30ore orange	35	10
280b		30ore blue	1·40	25
281		35ore violet	55	35
282		40ore green	7·00	25
282b		40ore blue	70	10
283	**45**	50ore grey	80	10
283a		60ore green	1·90	10
283b		75ore blue	10	20
284		1k. brown	3·25	10
284a		2k. red	3·75	55
284b		5k. violet	7·50	1·90

1934. Nos. 279 and 280a surch.

285	**40**	4 on 25ore blue	30	20
286		10 on 30ore orange	1·50	1·75

1934. Air.

287	**47**	10ore orange	50	90
288		15ore red	1·90	3·25
289		20ore green	2·10	4·00
290		50ore green	2·10	4·00
291		1k. brown	7·00	12·00

1935. Centenary of Hans Andersen's Fairy Tales.

292	–	5ore green	2·75	10
293	**49**	7ore violet	1·25	1·50
294	–	10ore orange	3·75	10
295	**49**	15ore red	8·50	10
296		20ore grey	8·25	65
297		30ore blue	1·50	20

DESIGNS: 5ore "The Ugly Duckling"; 10ore "The Little Mermaid".

51 St. Nicholas's Church, Copenhagen

52 Hans Tausen

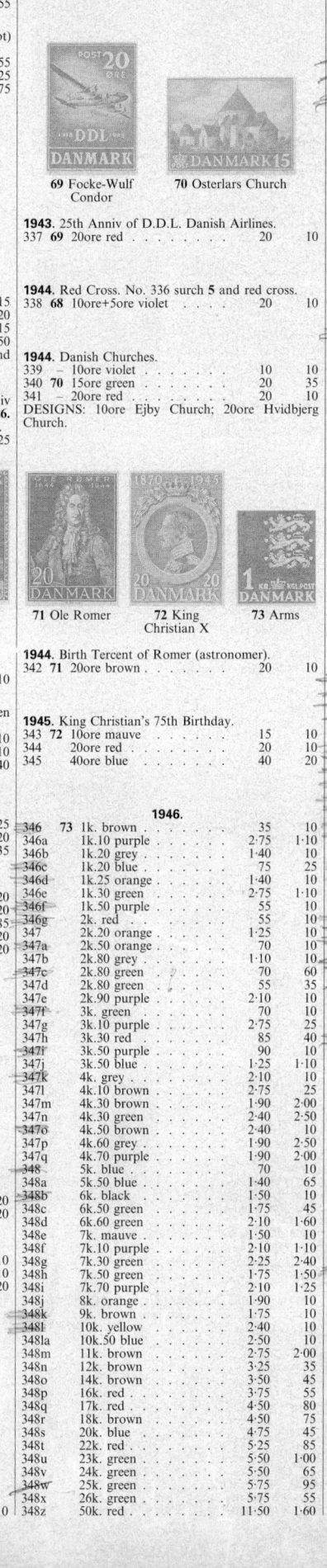

53 Ribe Cathedral   54 Dybbol Mill

1936. 400th Anniv of Reformation.
298 51 5ore green . . . . 1·00 10
299 — 7ore mauve . . . . 1·00 1·90
300 52 10ore brown . . . . . . 1·40 10
301 — 15ore red . . . . 2·10 10
302 53 30ore blue . . . . 9·00 55

1937. H. P. Hanssen (North Schleswig patriot)
Memorial Fund.
303 54 5ore+5ore green 35 55
304 — 10ore+5ore brown . . . 1·90 3·25
305 — 15ore+5ore red . . . . . 1·90 3·75

56 King Christian X

1937. Silver Jubilee of King Christian X.
306 — 5ore green 95 15
307 56 10ore brown 85 20
308 — 15ore red 85 15
309 56 30ore blue . . . . 10·50 1·50
DESIGNS—HORIZ: 5ore Marselisborg Castle and
"Rita" (King's yacht); 15ore Amalienborg Castle.

1937. Copenhagen Philatelic Club's 50th Anniv
Stamp Exhibition. No. 271b optd **K.P.K. 17.-26.
SEPT. 19 37** (="Kobenhavns Philatelist Klub").
310 43 10ore brown . . . . . . 85 1·25

58 Emancipation Monument   59 B. Thorvaldsen   61 Queen Alexandrine

1938. 150th Anniv of Abolition of Villeinage.
311 58 15ore red 35 10

1938. Centenary of Return of Sculptor Thorvaldsen
to Denmark.
312 59 5ore purple 15 10
313 — 10ore violet 20 10
314 59 30ore blue . . . . 1·10 40
DESIGN: 10ore Statue of Jason.

1939. Red Cross Charity. Cross in red.
314a 61 5ore+3ore purple . . . 20 25
315 — 10ore+5ore violet . . . 25 20
316 — 15ore+5ore red 25 35

1940. Stamps of 1933 (lined background) surch.
317 43 6 on 7ore green 20 20
318 — 6 on 8ore grey 20 20
319a 40 15 on 40ore green . . 25 85
320 — 20 on 15ore red 50 20
321 — 40 on 30ore blue 45 20

65 Queen Ingrid (when Princess) and Princess Margrethe   66 Bering's Ship "Sv. Pyotr"

1941. Child Welfare.
322 65 10ore+5ore violet 20 20
323 — 20ore+5ore red 20 20

1941. Death Bicent of Vitus Bering (explorer).
324 66 10ore violet 20 10
325 — 20ore brown 45 10
326 — 40ore green 30 10

67 King Christian X   68 Round Tower of Trinity Church

1942.
327 67 10ore violet 20 10

328 — 15ore green 20 10
329 — 20ore red 20 10
330 — 25ore brown 25 20
331 — 30ore orange 20 10
332 — 35ore purple 20 20
333 — 40ore blue 20 10
333a — 45ore olive 20 10
334 — 50ore grey 25 10
335 — 60ore green 25 10
335a — 75ore blue 25 25

1942. Tercentenary of the Round Tower.
336 68 10ore violet 20 10

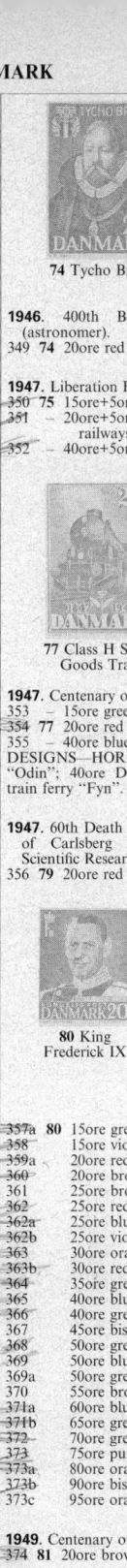

69 Focke-Wulf Condor   70 Osterlars Church

1943. 25th Anniv of D.D.L. Danish Airlines.
337 69 20ore red 20 10

1944. Red Cross. No. 336 surch **5** and red cross.
338 68 10ore+5ore violet . . . 20 10

1944. Danish Churches.
339 — 10ore violet 10 10
340 70 15ore green 20 35
341 — 20ore red 20 10
DESIGNS: 10ore Ejby Church; 20ore Hvidbjerg
Church.

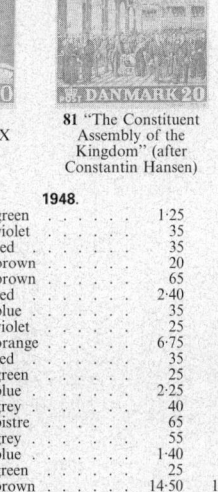

71 Ole Romer   72 King Christian X   73 Arms

1944. Birth Tercent of Romer (astronomer).
342 71 20ore brown 20 10

1945. King Christian's 75th Birthday.
343 72 10ore mauve 15 10
344 — 20ore red 20 10
345 — 40ore blue 40 20

1946.
346 73 1k. brown 35 10
346a — 1k.10 purple . . . . . . 2·75 1·10
346b — 1k.20 grey . . . . 1·40 10
346c — 1k.20 blue 75 25
346d — 1k.25 orange . . . . . . 1·40 10
346e — 1k.30 green . . . . 2·75 1·10
346f — 1k.50 purple 55 10
346g — 2k. red 55 10
347 — 2k.20 orange . . . . . . 1·25 10
347a — 2k.50 orange 70 10
347b — 2k.80 grey . . . . 1·10 10
347c — 2k.80 green 70 60
347d — 2k.80 green 55 35
347e — 2k.90 purple . . . . . . 2·10 10
347f — 3k. green 70 10
347g — 3k.10 purple . . . . . . 2·75 25
347h — 3k.30 red 85 40
347i — 3k.50 purple 90 10
347j — 3k.50 blue . . . . 1·25 1·10
347k — 4k. grey . . . . 2·10 10
347l — 4k.10 brown . . . . . . 2·75 25
347m — 4k.30 brown . . . . . . 1·90 2·00
347n — 4k.30 green . . . . 2·40 2·50
347o — 4k.50 brown . . . . . . 2·40 10
347p — 4k.60 grey . . . . 1·90 2·50
347q — 4k.70 purple . . . . . . 1·90 2·00
348 — 5k. blue 70 10
348a — 5k.50 blue . . . . 1·40 65
348b — 6k. black . . . . 1·50 10
348c — 6k.50 green . . . . 1·75 45
348d — 6k.60 green . . . . 2·10 1·60
348e — 7k. mauve . . . . 1·50 10
348f — 7k.10 purple . . . . . . 2·10 10
348g — 7k.30 green . . . . 2·25 2·40
348h — 7k.50 purple . . . . . . 1·75 1·50
348i — 7k.70 purple . . . . . . 2·10 1·25
348j — 8k. orange . . . . 1·90 10
348k — 9k. brown . . . . 1·75 10
348l — 10k. yellow . . . . 2·40 10
348la — 10k.50 blue . . . . . . 2·50 10
348m — 11k. brown . . . . . . 2·75 2·00
348n — 12k. brown . . . . 3·25 35
348o — 14k. brown . . . . 3·50 45
348p — 16k. red . . . . 3·75 55
348q — 17k. red . . . . 4·50 80
348r — 18k. brown . . . . 4·50 55
348s — 20k. blue . . . . 4·75 45
348t — 22k. red . . . . 5·25 85
348u — 23k. green . . . . 5·50 1·00
348v — 24k. green . . . . 5·50 65
348w — 25k. green . . . . 5·75 95
348x — 26k. green . . . . 5·75 55
348z — 50k. red . . . . 11·50 1·60

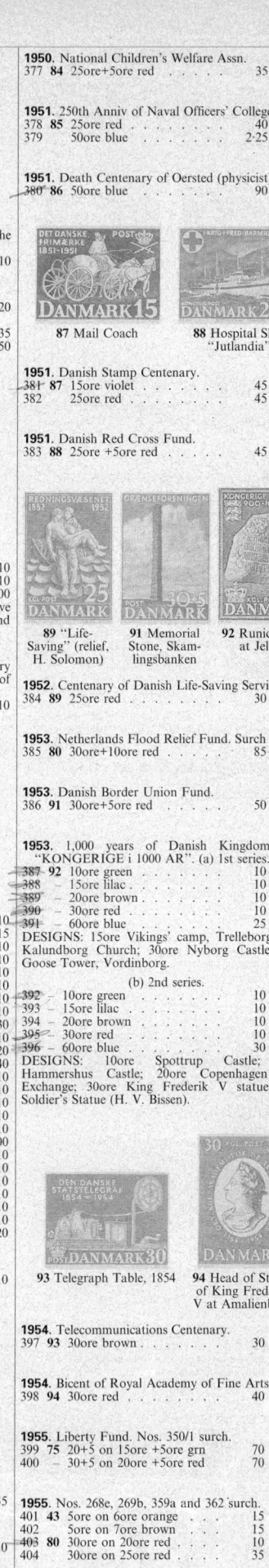

74 Tycho Brahe   75 Symbols of Freedom

1946. 400th Birth Anniv of Tycho Brahe
(astronomer).
349 74 20ore red 20 10

1947. Liberation Fund.
350 75 15ore+5ore green 15 20
351 — 20ore+5ore red (Bombed
railways) 50 35
352 — 40ore+5ore blue (Flag) . 35 50

77 Class H Steam Goods Train   79 I. C. Jacobsen

1947. Centenary of Danish Railways.
353 — 15ore green 25 10
354 77 20ore red 35 10
355 — 40ore blue . . . . 1·75 10
DESIGNS—HORIZ: 15ore First Danish locomotive
"Odin"; 40ore Diesel-electric train "Lyntog" and
train ferry "Fyn".

1947. 60th Death Anniv of Jacobsen and Centenary
of Carlsberg Foundation for Promotion of
Scientific Research.
356 79 20ore red 20 10

80 King Frederick IX   81 "The Constituent Assembly of the Kingdom" (after Constantin Hansen)

1948.
357a 80 15ore green . . . . . . 1·25 10
358 — 15ore violet 35 15
359a — 20ore red 35 10
360 — 20ore brown 20 10
361 — 25ore brown 65 10
362 — 25ore red . . . . 2·40 10
362a — 25ore blue 35 10
362b — 25ore violet 25 10
363 — 30ore orange . . . . . . 6·75 30
363b — 30ore red 35 10
364 — 35ore green 25 20
365 — 40ore blue . . . . 2·25 40
366 — 40ore grey 40 10
367 — 45ore bistre 65 10
368 — 50ore grey 55 10
369 — 50ore blue . . . . 1·40 10
369a — 50ore green 25 10
370 — 55ore brown . . . . 14·50 1·00
371a — 60ore blue 35 10
371b — 65ore grey 35 10
372 — 70ore green . . . . 1·25 10
373 — 75ore purple 55 10
373a — 80ore orange 35 10
373b — 90ore bistre . . . . . . 1·40 10
373c — 95ore orange 35 10

1949. Centenary of Danish Constitution.
374 81 20ore brown 25 10

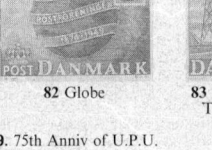

82 Globe   83 Kalundborg Transmitter

1949. 75th Anniv of U.P.U.
375 82 40ore blue 35 35

1950. 25th Anniv of State Broadcasting.
376 83 20ore brown 25 10

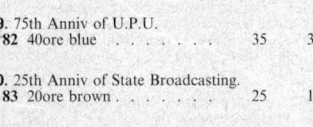

84 Princess Anne-Marie   85 "Fredericus Quartus" (warship)   86 H. C. Oersted (after C. A. Jensen)

1950. National Children's Welfare Assn.
377 84 25ore+5ore red 35 40

1951. 250th Anniv of Naval Officers' College.
378 85 25ore red 40 20
379 — 50ore blue . . . . 2·25 60

1951. Death Centenary of Oersted (physicist).
380 86 50ore blue 90 40

87 Mail Coach   88 Hospital Ship "Jutlandia"

1951. Danish Stamp Centenary.
381 87 15ore violet 45 10
382 — 25ore red 45 10

1951. Danish Red Cross Fund.
383 88 25ore +5ore red 45 45

89 "Life-Saving" (relief, H. Solomon)   91 Memorial Stone, Skamlingsbanken   92 Runic Stone at Jelling

1952. Centenary of Danish Life-Saving Service.
384 89 25ore red 30 20

1953. Netherlands Flood Relief Fund. Surch **NL+10.**
385 80 30ore+10ore red 85 85

1953. Danish Border Union Fund.
386 91 30ore+5ore red 50 75

1953. 1,000 years of Danish Kingdom. Inscr
"KONGERIGE i 1000 AR". (a) 1st series.
387 92 10ore green 10 10
388 — 15ore lilac 10 10
389 — 20ore brown 10 10
390 — 30ore red 10 10
391 — 60ore blue 25 10
DESIGNS: 15ore Vikings' camp, Trelleborg; 20ore
Kalundborg Church; 30ore Nyborg Castle; 60ore
Goose Tower, Vordinborg.

(b) 2nd series.
392 — 10ore green 10 10
393 — 15ore lilac 10 10
394 — 20ore brown 10 10
395 — 30ore red 10 10
396 — 60ore blue 30 10
DESIGNS: 10ore Spottrup Castle; 15ore
Hammershus Castle; 20ore Copenhagen Stock
Exchange; 30ore King Frederik V statue; 60ore
Soldier's Statue (H. V. Bissen).

93 Telegraph Table, 1854   94 Head of Statue of King Frederik V at Amalienborg

1954. Telecommunications Centenary.
397 93 30ore brown 30 20

1954. Bicent of Royal Academy of Fine Arts.
398 94 30ore red 40 20

1955. Liberty Fund. Nos. 350/1 surch.
399 75 20+5 on 15ore +5ore grn 70 70
400 — 30+5 on 20ore +5ore red 70 70

1955. Nos. 268e, 269b, 359a and 362 surch.
401 43 5ore on 6ore orange . . 15 10
402 — 5ore on 7ore brown . . . 15 10
403 80 30ore on 20ore red . . . 10 10
404 — 30ore on 25ore red . . . 35 10

98 S. Kierkegaard (philosopher)   99 Ellehammer's Aircraft

1955. Death Centenary of Kierkegaard.
405 **98** 30ore red 20 10

1956. 50th Anniv of 1st Flight by J. C. H. Ellehammer.
406 **99** 30ore red 30 10

100 Whooper Swans **102** National Museum

1956. Northern Countries' Day.
407 **100** 30ore red 90 10
408   60ore blue 85 50

1957. Danish Red Cross Hungarian Relief Fund. No. 373c surch **Ungarns-hjaelpen 30 + 5.**
409 **80** 30ore+5ore on 95ore orange 50 40

1957. 150th Anniv of National Museum.
410 **102** 30ore red 40 10
411   60ore blue 50 40
DESIGN: 50ore "Sun-God's Chariot" (bronze age model).

103 Harvester **105** King Frederik IX **106** Margrethe Schanne in "La Sylphide"

1958. Centenary of Danish Royal Veterinary and Agricultural College.
412 **103** 30ore red 20 10

1959. Greenland Fund. No. 363b surch **Gronlands-fonden + 10.**
413 **80** 30ore+10ore red 60 60
The Greenland Fund was devoted to the relatives of the crew and passengers of the "Hans Hedtoft", the Greenland vessel lost at sea on 30 January 1959.

1959. 60th Birthday of King Frederik IX.
414 **105** 30ore red 10 10
415   35ore purple 20 20
416   60ore blue 20 20

1959. Danish Ballet and Music Festival, 1959.
417 **106** 35ore purple 10 10
See also Nos. 445 and 467.

107 **109** Sowing Machine

1959. Centenary of Red Cross.
418 **107** 30ore+5ore red 40 45
419   60ore+5ore red & blue . . 55 60

1960. World Refugee Year. Surch 30 **Verdensflygtninge-aret 1959-60** and uprooted tree.
420 **80** 30ore on 15ore violet . . . 10 10

1960. 1st Danish Food Fair.
421 **109** 12ore green 10 10
422 – 30ore red 10 10
423 – 60ore blue 35 35
DESIGNS: 30ore Combine-harvester; 60ore Plough.

110 King Frederik and Queen Ingrid **111** Ancient Bascule Light

1960. Royal Silver Wedding.
424 **110** 30ore red 30 10
425   60ore blue 40 40

1960. 400th Anniv of Danish Lighthouse Service.
111 30ore red 20 10

112 N. Finsen **113** Mother and Child

1960. Birth Cent of Niels R. Finsen (physician).
427 **112** 30ore red 30 10

1960. W.H.O. 10th European Regional Committee Meeting.
428 **113** 60ore blue 35 35

113a Conference Emblem **114** Queen Ingrid

1960. Europa.
429 **113a** 60ore blue 35 35

1960. 25th Year of Queen Ingrid's Service in Girl Guides.
430 **114** 30ore+10ore red 60 60

115 Douglas DC-8 **116** Coastal Scene

1961. 10th Anniv of Scandinavian Airlines System (SAS).
431 **115** 60ore blue . . . . . . 1·25 25

1961. 50th Anniv of Society for Preservation of Danish National Amenities.
432 **116** 30ore red 20 10

117 King Frederik IX **118** Borkop Watermill **119** African Mother and Child

1961.
433 **117** 20ore brown 20 10
434   25ore brown 20 10
435   30ore red 20 10
436   35ore green 35 35
437   35ore red 20 10
438   40ore grey 55 10
438a   40ore brown 20 10
439   50ore turquoise 20 10
439a   50ore red 30 10
439b   50ore brown 30 10
440   60ore blue 35 10
440a   60ore red 30 20
441   70ore green 55 20
442   80ore orange 70 10
442a   80ore blue 25 30
442b   80ore green 35 10
443   90ore olive . . . . 2·50 25
443a   90ore blue 35 20
444   95ore purple 55 60

1962. Danish Ballet and Music Festival, 1962. As T 106 but inscr "15-31 MAJ".
445   60ore blue 20 10

1962. "Dansk Fredning" (Preservation of Danish Natural Amenities and Ancient Monuments) and Centenary of Abolition of Mill Monopolies.
446 **118** 10ore brown 10 10

1962. Aid for Under-developed Countries.
447 **119** 30ore+10ore red 60 60

120 "Selandia"

1962. 50th Anniv of Freighter "Selandia".
448 **120** 60ore blue 90 60

121 "Tivoli"

1962. 150th Birth Anniv of George Carstensen (founder of Tivoli Pleasure Gardens, Copenhagen).
449 **121** 35ore purple 20 10

122 Cliffs, Island of Mon **123** Wheat

1962. "Dansk Fredning" (Preservation of Danish Natural Amenities and Ancient Monuments).
450 **122** 20ore brown 10 20

1963. Freedom from Hunger.
451 **123** 35ore red 20 10

124 Rail and Sea Symbols **125** 19th-century Mail Transport

1963. Opening of Denmark–Germany Railway ("Bird-flight Line").
452 **124** 15ore green 10 10

1963. Centenary of Paris Postal Conference.
453 **125** 60ore blue 30 35

126 Hands **127** Prof. Niels Bohr

1963. Danish Cripples Foundation Fund.
454 **126** 35ore+10ore red 70 55

1963. 50th Anniv of Bohr's Atomic Theory.
455 **127** 35ore red 25 10
456   60ore blue 35 35

128 Ancient Bridge, Immervad **129** "Going to School" (child's slate)

1964. Danish Border Union Fund.
457 **128** 35ore+10ore red 40 40

1964. 150th Anniv of Institution of Primary Schools.
458 **129** 35ore brown 20 25

130 Princesses Margrethe, Benedikte and Anne-Marie **131** "Exploration of the Sea"

1964. Danish Red Cross Fund.
459 **130** 35ore+10ore red 35 40
460   60ore+10ore blue & red . . 55 60

1964. International Council for the Exploration of the Sea Conference, Copenhagen.
461 **131** 60ore blue 25 25

132 Danish Stamp "Watermarks, Perforations and Varieties" **133** Landscape, R. Karup

1964. 25th Anniv of Stamp Day.
462 **132** 35ore pink 20 10

1964. "Dansk Fredning" (Preservation of Danish Natural Amenities and Ancient Monuments).
463 **133** 25ore brown 10 10

134 Office Equipment **135** Morse Key, Teleprinter Tape and I.T.U. Emblem

1965. Centenary of 1st Commercial School.
464 **134** 15ore green 10 10

1965. Centenary of I.T.U.
465 **135** 80ore blue 40 10

136 C. Nielsen **137** Child in Meadow

1965. Birth Centenary of Carl Nielsen (composer).
466 **136** 50ore red 20 10

1965. Danish Ballet and Music Festival, 1965. As T 106 but inscr "15-31 MAJ".
467   50ore red 20 10

1965. Child Welfare.
468 **137** 50ore+10ore red 40 40

138 Bogo Windmill **139** Titles of International Red Cross Organizations

1965. "Dansk Fredning" (Preservation of Danish Natural Amenities and Ancient Monuments).
469 **138** 40ore brown 10 10

1966. Danish Red Cross Fund.
470 **139** 50ore+10ore red 35 35
471   80ore+10ore bl & red . . 55 55

140 Heathland **141** C. Kold

1966. Centenary of Danish Heath Society.
472 **140** 25ore green 10 10

1966. 150th Birth Anniv of Christen Kold (educationist).
473 **141** 50ore red 10 10

142 Almshouses, Copenhagen **143** Trees at Bregentved

1966. "Dansk Fredning" (Preservation of Danish Natural Amenities and Ancient Monuments).
474 **142** 50ore red 15 10
475 **143** 80ore blue 40 20

144 G. Jensen **145** Fund Emblem

1966. Birth Cent of Georg Jensen (silversmith).
476 144 80ore blue 40 25

1966. "Refugee 66" Fund.
477 145 40ore+10ore brown 35 45
478 – 50ore+10ore red 35 45
479 – 80ore+10ore blue 70 80

146 Barrow in Jutland   **147** Musical Instruments

1966. "Dansk Fredning" (Preservation of Danish Natural Amenities and Ancient Monuments).
480 146 1k.50 green 40 10

1967. Cent of Royal Danish Academy of Music.
481 147 50ore red 20 10

148 Cogwheels   **149** Old City and Windmill

1967. European Free Trade Assn.
482 148 80ore blue 40 20

1967. 800th Anniv of Copenhagen.
483 149 25ore green 10 10
484 – 40ore brown 20 10
485 – 50ore brown 30 10
486 – 80ore blue 60 40
DESIGNS: 40ore Old bank and ship's masts; 50ore Church steeple and burgher's house; 80ore Building construction.

150 Princess Margrethe and Prince Henri de Monpezat   **151** H. C. Sonne

1967. Royal Wedding.
487 150 50ore red 20 10

1967. 150th Anniv of Hans Sonne (founder of Danish Co-operative Movement).
488 151 60ore red 20 10

152 "Rose"   **153** Porpoise and Cross-anchor

1967. The Salvation Army.
489 152 60ore+10ore red 35 40

1967. Centenary of Danish Seamen's Church in Foreign Ports.
490 153 90ore blue 35 25

154 Esbjerg Harbour   **155** Koldinghus Castle

1968. Cent of Esbjerg Harbour Construction Act.
491 154 30ore green 20 10

1968. 700th Anniv of Koldinghus Castle.
492 155 60ore red 20 10

156 "The Children in the Round Tower" (Greenlandic legend)   **157** Shipbuilding

1968. Greenlandic Child Welfare.
493 156 60ore+10ore red 40 45

1968. Danish Industries.
494 157 30ore green 10 10
495 – 50ore brown 10 10
496 – 60ore red 10 10
497 – 90ore blue 55 55
INDUSTRIES: 50ore Chemicals, 60ore Electric power, 90ore Engineering.

158 "The Sower"   **159** Viking Ships (from old Swedish coin)

1969. Bicentenary of Danish Royal Agricultural Society.
498 158 30ore green 10 10

1969. 50th Anniv of Northern Countries' Union.
499 159 60ore red 35 10
500 – 90ore blue 80 90

160 King Frederik IX   **161** Colonnade

1969. King Frederik's 70th Birthday.
501 160 50ore brown 30 30
502 – 60ore red 30 30

1969. Europa.
503 161 90ore blue 50 45

162 Kronborg Castle   **163** Fall of Danish Flag

1969. 50th Anniv of "Danes Living Abroad" Association.
504 162 50ore brown 10 10

1969. 750th Anniv of "Danish Flag Falling from Heaven".
505 163 60ore red, blue & black 20 10

164 M. A. Nexo   **165** Niels Stensen (geologist)

1969. Birth Cent of Martin Andersen Nexo (poet).
506 164 80ore green 35 10

1969. 300th Anniv of Stensen's "On Solid Bodies".
507 165 1k. sepia 35 10

166 "Abstract"   **167** Symbolic "P"

1969. "Non-figurative" stamp.
508 166 60ore red, rose and blue 20 10

1969. Birth Cent of Valdemar Poulsen (inventor).
509 167 30ore green 20 10

168 Princess Margrethe, Prince Henri and Prince Frederik (baby)   **169** "Postgiro"

1969. Danish Red Cross.
510 168 50ore+10ore brn & red 35 35
511 – 60ore+10ore brn & red 35 35

1970. 50th Anniv of Danish Postal Giro Service.
512 169 60ore and orange 10 10

170 School Safety Patrol   **171** Child appealing for Help

1970. Road Safety.
513 170 50ore brown 10 10

1970. 25th Anniv of Save the Children Fund.
514 171 60ore+10ore red 40 45

172 Candle in Window   **173** Red Deer in Park

1970. 25th Anniv of Liberation.
515 172 50ore black, yellow & bl 30 10

1970. 300th Anniv of Jaegersborg Deer Park.
516 173 60ore brown, red & grn 30 10

174 Ship's Figurehead ("Elephanten")   **175** "The Reunion"

1970. 300th Anniv of "Royal Majesty's Model Chamber" (Danish Naval Museum).
517 174 30ore multicoloured . . . 10 10

1970. 50th Anniv of North Schleswig's Reunion with Denmark.
518 175 60ore violet, yellow & grn 30 10

176 Electromagnetic Apparatus

1970. 150th Anniv of Oersted's Discovery of Electromagnetism.
519 176 80ore green 30 10

177 Bronze-age Ship (from engraving on razor)

1970. Danish Shipping.
520 177 30ore purple and brown 20 10
521 – 50ore brn and purple . . 20 10
522 – 60ore brown and green 20 10
523 – 90ore blue and green . . 55 65
DESIGNS: 50ore Viking shipbuilders (Bayeux Tapestry); 60ore "Emanuel" (schooner); 90ore "A. P. Moller" (tanker).

178 Strands of Rope   **179** B. Thorvaldsen from self-portrait

1970. 25th Anniv of United Nations.
524 178 90ore red, green & blue 60 60

1970. Birth Bicentenary of Bertel Thorvaldsen (sculptor).
525 179 2k. blue 55 40

180 Mathilde Fibiger (suffragette)   **181** Refugees

1971. Centenary of Danish Women's Association ("Kvindesamfund").
526 180 80ore green 35 10

1971. Aid for Refugees.
527 181 50ore brown 10 10
528 – 60ore red 10 10

182 Danish Child   **183** Hans Egede

1971. National Children's Welfare Association.
529 182 60ore+10ore red 40 45

1971. 25th Anniv of Hans Egede's Arrival in Greenland.
530 183 1k. brown 35 10

184 Swimming   **185** Georg Brandes

1971. Sports.
531 184 30ore green and blue . . 10 10
532 – 50ore dp brown & brown 10 10
533 – 60ore yellow, blue & grey 35 10
534 – 90ore violet, green & bl 55 45
DESIGNS: 50ore Hurdling; 60ore Football; 90ore Yachting.

1971. Centenary of First Lectures by Georg Brandes (writer).
535 185 90ore blue 35 25

186 Beet Harvester

1972. Centenary of Danish Sugar Production.
536 186 80ore green 35 10

187 Meteorological Symbols

1972. Cent of Danish Meteorological Office.
537 187 1k.20 brown, blue & pur 50 45

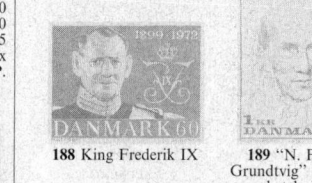
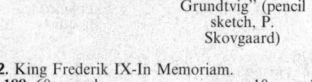

188 King Frederik IX   **189** "N. F. S. Grundtvig (pencil sketch, P. Skovgaard)

1972. King Frederik IX-In Memoriam.
538 188 60ore red 10 10

1972. Death Centenary of N. F. S. Grundtvig (poet and clergyman).
539 189 1k. brown 35 35

190 Locomotive "Odin", Ship and Passengers

191 Rebild Hills

1972. 125th Anniv of Danish State Railways.
540 **190** 70ore red 20 10

1972. Nature Protection.
541 **191** 1k. green, brown & blue 30 10

192 Marsh Marigold

193 "The Tinker" (from Holberg's satire)

1972. Centenary of "Vanforehjemmet" (Home for the Disabled).
542 **192** 70ore+10ore yellow & bl 50 55

1972. 250th Anniv of Theatre in Denmark and of Holberg's Comedies.
543 **193** 70ore red 10 10

194 W.H.O. Building, Copenhagen

195 Little Belt Bridge

1972. Inauguration of World Health Organization Building, Copenhagen.
544 **194** 2k. black, blue and red 55 40

1972. Danish Construction Projects.
545 **195** 40ore green 10 10
546 – 60ore brown 20 10
547 – 70ore red 20 10
548 – 90ore green 35 35
DESIGNS: 60ore Hanstholm port; 70ore Limfjord Tunnel; 90ore Knudshoved port.

196 House, Aeroskobing

197 Johannes Jensen

1972. Danish Architecture.
549 **196** 40ore black, brown & red 10 10
550 – 60ore blue, green & brn 10 10
551 – 70ore brown, red & verm 20 10
552 – 1k.20 grn, brn & dp brn 70 60
DESIGNS—28 × 21 mm: 60ore Farmhouse, East Bornholm; 37 × 21 mm: 1k.20, Farmhouse, Hvide Sande; 21 × 37 mm: 70ore House, Christanshavn.

1973. Birth Cent of Johannes Jensen (writer).
553 **197** 90ore green 35 10

198 Cogwheels and Guardrails

199 P. C. Abildgaard (founder)

1973. Centenary of 1st Danish Factory Act.
554 **198** 50ore brown 20 10

73. Bicentenary of Royal Veterinary College, hristianshavn.
199 1k. blue 35 35

200 "Rhododendron impeditum"

201 Nordic House, Reykjavik

1973. Cent of Jutland Horticultural Society.
556 **200** 60ore violet, green & brn 35 10
557 – 70ore pink, green & red 35 10
DESIGN: 70ore "Queen of Denmark" rose.

1973. Nordic Countries' Postal Co-operation.
558 **201** 70ore multicoloured . . . 30 10
559 1k. multicoloured 95 80

202 Stella Nova and Sextant

203 "St. Mark the Evangelist" (Book of Dalby)

1973. 400th Anniv of Tycho Brahe's "De Nove Stella" (book on astronomy).
560 **202** 2k. blue 50 25

1973. 300th Anniv of Royal Library.
561 **203** 1k.20 multicoloured . . . 55 40

204 Heimaey Eruption

205 "Devil and Scandalmongers" (Fanefjord Church)

1973. Aid for Victims of Heimaey Eruption, Iceland.
562 **204** 70ore+20ore red and blue 35 45

1973. Church Frescoes. Each red, turquoise and yellow on cream.
563 70ore Type **205** 80 30
564 70ore "Queen Esther and King Xerxes" (Tirsted Church) 80 30
565 70ore "The Harvest Miracle" (Jetsmark Church) . . . 1·00 30
566 70ore "The Crowning with Thorns" (Biersted Church) 85 30
567 70ore "Creation of Eve" (Fanefjord Church) 85 30

206 Drop of Blood and Donors

207 Queen Margrethe

1974. Blood Donors Campaign.
568 **206** 90ore red and violet . . . 35 20

1974.
569 **207** 60ore brown 35 35
570 60ore orange 30 30
571 70ore red 20 10
572 70ore brown 20 10
573 80ore green 35 10
574 80ore brown 35 10
575 90ore purple 35 10
576 90ore red 35 10
577 90ore olive 35 20
577a 90ore grey . . . . . 1·25 1·50
578 100ore blue 35 10
579 100ore grey 35 10
580 100ore red 35 10
580a 100ore brown 35 10
580b 110ore orange 50 35
580c 110ore brown 55 25
581 120ore grey 40 35
581b 120ore red 40 10
582 130ore blue 90 90
582a 130ore red 35 10
582b 130ore brown 35 25
582c 140ore orange 40 70
582d 150ore blue 45 55
582e 150ore red 40 45
582f 160ore blue 55 55
582g 160ore red 60 40
582h 180ore green 55 20
582i 180ore blue 40 45
582j 200ore blue 55 60
582k 210ore grey 75 90
582l 230ore green 70 65
582m 250ore green 55 45

208 Theatre Facade

209 Hverringe

1974. Centenary of Tivoli Pantomime Theatre, Copenhagen.
583 **208** 100ore blue 35 10

1974. Provincial Series.
584 **209** 50ore multicoloured . . . 20 10
585 – 60ore grn, dp grn & mve 35 35
586 – 70ore multicoloured . . . 35 40
587 – 90ore multicoloured . . . 35 10
588 – 120ore grn, red & orge . . 35 40
DESIGNS—HORIZ: 60ore Carl Nielsen's birthplace, Norre Lyndelse; 70ore Hans Christian Andersen's birthplace, Odense; 1k.20, Hindsholm. VERT: 90ore Hessselagergaard.

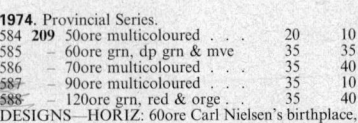

210 Orienteering

211 "Iris spuria"

1974. World Orienteering Championships.
589 **210** 70ore brown and blue . . 40 40
590 – 80ore blue and brown . . 20 10
DESIGN: 80ore Compass.

1974. Cent of Botanical Gardens, Copenhagen.
591 **211** 90ore blue, green & brn 35 10
592 – 120ore red, green and blue 50 40
DESIGN: 120ore "Dactylorhiza purpurella" (orchid).

212 Mail-carriers of 1624 and 1780

213 Pigeon with Letter

1974. 350th Anniv of Danish Post Office.
593 **212** 70ore bistre and purple 35 40
594 – 90ore green and purple 40 10
DESIGN: 90ore Johan Colding's postal balloon (1808) H.M.S. "Edgar" and H.M.S. "Dictator".

1974. Centenary of U.P.U.
595 **213** 120ore blue 40 20

215 Radio Equipment of 1925

216 Queen Margrethe and I.W.Y. Emblem

1975. 50th Anniv of Danish Broadcasting.
597 **215** 90ore pink 35 10

1975. International Women's Year.
598 **216** 90ore+20ore red 55 60

217 Floral Decorated Plate

218 Moravian Brethren Church Christiansfeld

1975. Danish Porcelain.
599 **217** 50ore green 10 10
600 – 90ore red 35 10
601 – 130ore blue 55 65
DESIGNS: 90ore Floral decorated tureen; 130ore Floral decorated vase and tea-caddy.

1975. European Architectural Heritage Year.
602 **218** 70ore brown 35 40
603 – 120ore green 40 40
604 – 150ore blue 35 20
DESIGNS—HORIZ: 120ore Farmhouse, Lejre. VERT: 150ore Anna Queenstraede (street), Helsingore.

219 "Numskull Jack" (V. Pedersen)

220 Watchman's Square, Aabenraa

1975. 170th Birth Anniv of Hans Christian Andersen.
605 **219** 70ore grey and brown . . 40 50
606 – 90ore brown and red . . 40 10
607 – 130ore brown and blue 95 1·00
DESIGNS: 90ore Hans Andersen (from photograph by G. E. Hansen); 130ore "The Marshking's Daughter" (L. Frolich).

1975. Provincial series. South Jutland.
608 **220** 70ore multicoloured . . . 30 35
609 – 90ore brown, red & blue 30 10
610 – 100ore multicoloured . . 35 20
611 – 120ore blue, black & grn 40 35
DESIGNS—VERT: 90ore, Haderslev Cathedral. HORIZ: 100ore, Mogeltonder Polder; 120ore, Estuary of Vidaaen at Hojer floodgates.

221 River Kingfisher

1975. Danish Endangered Animals.
612 **221** 50ore blue 30 25
613 – 70ore brown 30 35
614 – 90ore brown 30 10
615 – 130ore blue 70 75
616 – 200ore black 40 10
DESIGNS: 70ore West European hedgehog; 90ore Cats; 130ore Pied avocets; 200ore European otter.
The 90ore also commemorates the centenary of the Danish Society for the Prevention of Cruelty to Animals.

222 Viking Longship

1976. Bicentenary of American Revolution.
618 **222** 70ore+20ore brown . . . 50 40
619 – 90ore+20ore red 50 40
620 – 100ore+20ore green . . . 50 40
621 – 130ore+20ore blue . . . 50 40
DESIGNS: 90ore Freighter "Thingvalla"; 100ore Liner "Frederik VIII"; 130ore Cadet full-rigged ship "Danmark".

223 "Humanity"

224 Old Copenhagen

1976. Centenary of Danish Red Cross.
622 **223** 100ore+20ore black and red 40 40
623 130ore+20ore black, red and blue 55 55

1976. Provincial Series. Copenhagen.
624 **224** 60ore multicoloured . . . 20 20
625 – 80ore multicoloured . . . 20 20
626 – 100ore red & vermilion 40 20
627 – 130ore grn, dp brn & brn 75 80
DESIGNS—VERT: 80ore View from the Round Tower; 100ore Interior of the Central Railway Station. HORIZ: 130ore Harbour buildings.

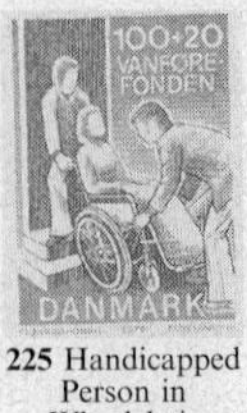

225 Handicapped Person in Wheelchair

226 Mail Coach Driver (detail from "A String of Horses outside an Inn" (O. Bache))

1976. Danish Foundation for the Disabled.
628 **225** 100ore+20ore black and red 40 40

1976. "Hafnia 76" Stamp Exhibition.
629 **226** 130ore multicoloured . . 70 65

227 Prof. Emil Hansen
228 Moulding Glass

1976. Centenary of Carlsberg Foundation.
631 227 100ore red 35 10

1976. Danish Glass Industry.
632 228 60ore green 20 25
633 – 80ore brown 35 10
634 – 130ore blue 55 60
635 – 150ore red 35 10
DESIGNS: 80ore Removing glass from pipe; 130ore Cutting glass; 150ore Blowing glass.

229 Five Water Lilies
230 "Give Way"

1977. Northern Countries Co-operation in Nature Conservation and Environment Protection.
636 229 100ore multicoloured . . 30 10
637 130ore multicoloured . . 70 1·00

1977. Road Safety.
638 230 100ore brown 35 10

231 Mother and Child
232 Allinge

1977. 25th Anniv of Danish Society for the Mentally Handicapped.
639 231 100ore+20ore green, blue and brown 50 45

1977. Europa.
640 232 1k. brown 40 10
641 – 1k.30 blue . . . . 2·40 2·00
DESIGN: 1k.30, Farm near Ringsted.

233 Kongeaen
234 Hammers and Horseshoes

1977. Provincial Series. South Jutland.
642 233 60ore green and blue . . 70 65
643 – 90ore multicoloured . . 40 35
644 – 150ore multicoloured . . 40 35
645 – 200ore grn, pur & emer 50 40
DESIGNS: 90ore Skallingen; 150ore Torskind; 200ore Jelling.

1977. Danish Crafts.
646 234 80ore brown 20 10
647 – 1k. red 20 10
648 – 1k.30 blue 40 40
DESIGNS: 1k. Chisel, square and plane; 1k.30, Trowel, ceiling brush and folding rule.

235 Globe Flower
236 Handball Player and Emblem

1977. Endangered Flora.
649 235 1k. green, yellow & brn 35 10
650 – 1k.50 green, ol & brn . . 70 60
DESIGN: 1k.50, "Cnidium dubium".

1978. Men's Handball World Championship.
651 236 1k.20 red 40 20

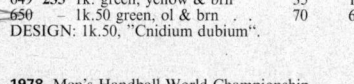

237 Christian IV on Horseback
238 Jens Bang's House, Aalborg

1978. Centenary of National History Museum, Frederiksborg.
652 237 1k.20 brown 35 10
653 – 1k.80 black 50 30
DESIGN: 1k.80, North-west aspect of Frederiksborg Castle.

1978. Europa.
654 238 1k.20 brown 40 10
655 – 1k.50 blue and dp blue 75 65
DESIGN: 1k.50, Plan and front elevation of Frederiksborg Castle, Copenhagen.

239 Kongenshus Memorial Park
240 Boats in Harbour

1978. Provincial Series. Central Jutland.
656 239 70ore multicoloured . . . 30 35
657 – 1k.20 multicoloured . . . 35 10
658 – 1k.50 multicoloured . . . 70 65
659 – 1k.80 blue, brn & grn . . 40 45
DESIGNS: 1k.20, Post office, Aarhus Old Town; 1k.50, Lignite fields, Soby; 1k.80, Church wall, Stadil Church.

1978. Fishing Industry.
660 240 70ore green 35 35
661 – 1k. brown 35 35
662 – 1k.80 black 50 35
663 – 2k.50 brown 70 35
DESIGNS: 1k. Eel traps; 1k.80, Fishing boats on the slipway; 2k.50, Drying ground.

241 Campaign Emblem

1978. 50th Anniv of Danish Cancer Campaign.
664 241 120ore+20ore red 55 55

242 Common Morel
243 Early and Modern Telephones

1978. Mushrooms.
665 242 1k. brown 40 40
666 – 1k.20 red 40 10
DESIGN: 1k.20, Satan's mushroom.

1979. Centenary of Danish Telephone System.
667 243 1k.20 red 35 10

244 Child
245 University Seal

1979. International Year of the Child.
668 244 1k.20+20ore red & brn . . 50 55

1979. 500th Anniv of Copenhagen University.
669 245 1k.30 red 35 10
670 – 1k.60 black 40 40
DESIGN: 1k.60, Pentagram representing the five faculties.

246 Letter Mail Cariole
247 Pendant

1979. Europa.
671 246 1k.30 red 60 10
672 – 1k.60 blue 95 60
DESIGN: 1k.60, Morse key and sounder.

1979. Viking "Gripping Beast" Decorations.
673 247 1k.10 brown 30 10
674 – 2k. green 55 30
DESIGN: 2k. Key.

248 Mols Bjerge
249 Silhouette of Oehlenschlager

1979. Provincial Series. North Jutland.
675 248 80ore green, ultram & brown 30 30
676 – 90ore multicoloured . . . 90 1·00
677 – 200ore grn, orge & red . . 50 20
678 – 280ore slate, sepia & brn 60 60
DESIGNS. 90ore Orslev Kloster; 200ore Trans; 280ore Bovbjerg.

1979. Birth Bicentenary of Adam Oehlenschlager (poet).
679 249 1k.30 red 35 20

250 Music, Violin and Dancers (birth cent of Jacob Gade (composer))
251 Royal Mail Guards' Office, Copenhagen (drawing, Peter Klaestrup)

1979. Anniversaries.
680 250 1k.10 brown 35 35
681 – 1k.60 blue 40 40
DESIGN: 1k.60, Dancer at bar (death centenary of August Bournonville (ballet master)).

1980. Bicentenary of National Postal Service.
682 251 1k.30 red 35 20

252 Stylised Wheelchair
253 Karen Blixen (writer)

1980. 25th Anniv of Foundation for the Disabled.
683 252 130ore+20ore red 50 50

1980. Europa.
684 253 1k.30 red 35 10
685 – 1k.60 blue 60 55
DESIGN: 1k.60, August Krogh (physiologist).

254 Symbols of Employment, Health and Education
255 Lindholme Hoje

1980. U.N. Decade for Women World Conference.
686 254 1k.60 blue 55 35

1980. Provincial Series. Jutland North of Limfjorden. Multicoloured.
687 80ore Type 255 . . . . . . 30 35
688 110ore Skagen lighthouse (vert) 35 35
689 200ore Borglum 50 20
690 280ore Fishing boats at Vorupor . . . . 90 1·00

256 Silver Pitcher, c. 1641

1980. Nordic Countries Postal Co-operation.
691 256 1k.30 black and red . . . 35 10
692 – 1k.80 blue & dp blue . . 70 75
DESIGN: 1k.80, Bishop's bowl.

257 Earliest Danish Coin, Hedeby (c. 800)

1980. Coins from the Royal Collection.
693 257 1k.30 red and brown . . 35 30
694 – 1k.40 olive and green . . 70 65
695 – 1k.80 blue and grey . . . 70 65
DESIGNS: 1k.40, Silver coin of Valdemar the Great and Bishop Absalon (1152–82); 1k.80, Christian VII gold current ducat (1781).

258 Lace Pattern
259 Children Playing in Yard

1980. Lace Patterns. Various designs showing lace.
696 258 1k.10 brown 35 35
697 – 1k.30 red 35 10
698 – 2k. green 50 10

1981. National Children's Welfare Association.
699 259 1k.60+20ore red 55 55

260 Original Houses, 1631
261 Tilting at a Barrel (Shrovetide custom)

1981. 350th Anniv of Nyboder (Naval Barracks), Copenhagen.
700 260 1k.30 red and yellow . . 55 55
701 – 1k.60 red and yellow . . 40 10
DESIGN: 1k.60, 18th-century terraced houses.

1981. Europa.
702 261 1k.60 red 50 25
703 – 2k. blue 70 40
DESIGN: 2k. Midsummer bonfire.

262 Soro
263 Rigensgade District, Copenhagen

1981. Provincial Series. Zealand and Surrounding Islands.
704 262 100ore blue and brown 35 35
705 – 150ore black and green 35 35
706 – 160ore brown and green 40 10
707 – 200ore multicoloured . . 55 55
708 – 230ore blue and brown 60 45
DESIGNS: 150ore N. F. S. Grundtvig's childhood home, Udby; 160ore Kaj Munk's childhood home, Opager; 200ore Gronsund; 230ore Bornholm.

1981. European Urban Renaissance Year.
709 263 1k.60 red 40 10

264 Decaying Tree
265 Ellehammer at Lindholm, 1906

1981. International Year for Disabled Persons.
710 264 2k.+20ore blue 70 75

1981. History of Aviation.
711 265 1k. green and black . . . 35 40
712 – 1k.30 brown & dp brn . . 50 40
713 – 1k.60 vermilion & red . . 35 10
714 – 2k.30 blue & dp blue . . 1·50 40
DESIGNS: 1k.30, A. T. Botved's Fokker biplane "R-1" (Copenhagen–Tokyo, 1926); 1k.60, Hojriis Hillig's Bellanca Special "Liberty" (U.S.A.–Denmark, 1931); 2k.30. Douglas DC-7C "Seven Seas" (first Polar flight, 1957).

266 Queen Margrethe II
267 Revenue Cutter "Argus"

1982.
715 266 1k.60 red 50 10
716 1k.60 green . . . . . . 95 1·75
717 1k.80 brown 50 40
718 2k. red 50 10
719 2k.20 green 75 80
720 2k.30 violet 50 45

721 2k.50 red . . . . 1·25 10
722 2k.70 blue 55 40
723 2k.70 red 60 10
724 2k.80 red 55 20
725 3k. violet 55 10
726 3k. red 70 10
727 3k.20 violet 75 45
727a 3k.20 red 90 10
728 3k.30. black 80 45
729 3k.40 green . . . . . . 1·40 1·25
730 3k.50 blue 85 35
730a 3k.50 purple 90 45
730b 3k.50 red 70 10
731 3k.50 blue 85 35
732 3k.75 green 85 60
733 3k.80 blue 95 35
734 3k.80 purple . . . . . 2·25 2·00
735 4k.10 blue . . . . . . 1·40 60
736 4k.20 violet . . . . . . 3·75 65
737 4k.40 blue . . . . . . 4·00 1·00
738 4k.50 purple 95 90
739 4k.75 blue 95 35

1982. 350th Anniv Customs Service.
740 267 1k.60 red 40 10

268 Skater
269 Villein (Abolition of adscription, 1788)

1982. World Figure Skating Championships, Copenhagen.
741 268 2k. blue 55 35

1982. Europa.
742 269 2k. brown 70 10
743 — 2k.70 blue 90 60
DESIGN: 2k.70, Procession of women (Enfranchisement of women, 1915).

270 Distorted Plant
271 Dairy Farm at Hjedding and Butter Churn

1982. 25th Anniv of Danish Multiple Sclerosis Society.
744 270 2k.+40ore red . . . . . 90 1·00

1982. Centenary of Co-operative Dairy Farming.
745 271 1k.80 brown 55 45

272 Hand holding Quill Pen
273 Blicher (after J. V. Gertner)

1982. 400th Anniv of Record Office.
746 272 2k.70 green 75 40

1982. Birth Bicent of Steen Steensen Blicher (poet).
747 273 2k. red 55 10

274 Odense Printing Press, 1482
275 Petersen and the Number Men

1982. 500th Anniv of Printing in Denmark.
748 274 1k.80 brown 55 45

1982. Birth Centenary of Robert Storm Petersen (cartoonist).
749 275 1k.50 red and blue . . . 40 35
750 — 2k. green and red 55 35
DESIGN—HORIZ: 2k. Peter and Ping with dog.

276 Library Seal

1982. 500th Anniv University Library.
751 276 2k.70 brown and black . . . 75 35

277 "Interglobal Communications"
278 Nurse tending Patient

1983. World Communications Year.
752 277 2k. orange, red & blue . . . 55 10

1983. Red Cross.
753 278 2k.+40ore blue & red . . . 95 1·00

279 Clown and Girl with Balloon
280 Lene Koppen

1983. 400th Anniv of Dyrehavsbakken Amusement Park.
754 279 2k. multicoloured 55 10

1983. World Badminton Championships.
755 280 2k.70 blue 75 35

281 Burin and Engraving of lore Numeral Stamp
282 Egeskov Castle

1983. 50th Anniv of Danish Recess-printed Stamps.
756 281 2k.50 red 55 20

1983. Nordic Countries Postal Co-operation. "Visit the North".
757 282 2k.50 dp brown & brn . . . 60 20
758 — 3k.50 dp blue & blue . . . 90 45
DESIGN: 3k.50, Troldkirken long barrow, North Jutland.

283 Kildeskovshallen Recreation Centre, Copenhagen
284 Weights and Measures

1983. Europa.
759 283 2k.50 red and brown . . . 75 10
760 — 3k.50 dp blue & blue . . . 1·00 45
DESIGN: 3k.50, Sallingsund Bridge.

1983. 300th Anniv of Weights and Measures Ordinance.
761 284 2k.50 red 55 10

285 Title Page of Law
286 Crashed Car and Hand with Eye (Police)

1983. 300th Anniv of King Christian V's Danish Law (code of laws for Norway).
762 285 5k. dp brown & brown . . . 1·25 55

1983. Life-saving Services.
763 286 1k. brown 30 20
764 — 2k.50 red 55 35
765 — 3k.50 blue 55 35
DESIGNS: 2k.50 Ladder, stretcher and fire-hose (ambulance and fire services); 3k.50 Lifebelt and lifeboat (sea-rescue services).

287 Family Group

288 Grundtvig (after Constantin Hansen)

1983. The Elderly in Society.
766 287 2k. green 55 45
767 — 2k.50 red 60 10
DESIGN: 2k.50 Elderly people in train.

1983. Birth Bicentenary of Nicolai Frederik Severin Grundtvig (writer).
768 288 2k.50 brown 60 20

289 Perspective Painting

1983. Birth Bicentenary of Christoffer Wilhelm Eckersberg (painter).
769 289 2k.50 red 60 10

290 Spade and Sapling
291 Billiards

1984. Plant a Tree Campaign.
770 290 2k.70 yellow, red and green 70 20

1984. World Billiards Championships.
771 291 3k.70 green 95 35

292 Athletes
293 Compass Rose

1984. Olympic Games, Los Angeles.
772 292 2k.70+40ore mult . . . . 1·00 1·25

1984. Bicentenary of Hydrographic Department (2k.30) and 300th Anniv of Pilotage Service (2k.70).
773 293 2k.30 green 60 55
774 — 2k.70 red 75 10
DESIGN: 2k.70, Pilot boat.

294 Parliament Emblem
295 Girl Guides

1984. 2nd Direct Elections to European Parliament.
775 294 2k.70 yellow and blue . . . 70 10

1984. Scout Movement.
776 295 2k.70 multicoloured . . . 70 10

296 Bridge
297 Anchor (memorial to Danish Sailors)

1984. Europa. 25th Anniv of European Post and Telecommunications Conference.
777 296 2k.70 red 90 10
778 — 3k.70 blue . . . . . . 1·25 85

1984. 40th Anniv of Normandy Invasion.
779 297 2k.70 purple 70 20

298 Prince Henrik

299 Old Danish Inn

1984. 50th Birthday of Prince Henrik.
780 298 2k.70 brown 75 10

1984.
781 299 3k. multicoloured 80 70

300 Shoal of Fish (research)

1984. Danish Fisheries and Shipping.
782 300 2k.30 blue and green . . . 90 85
783 — 2k.70 blue and red . . . 70 20
784 — 3k.30 blue and violet . . . 95 85
785 — 3k.70 blue & ultramarine . . . 95 80
DESIGNS: 2k.70, Ships (sea transport); 3k.30, "Bettina" (deep sea fishing boat); 3k.70, Deck of trawler "Jonna Tornby".

301 Heart and Cardiograph

302 Bird with Letter

1984. Heart Foundation.
786 301 2k.70+40ore red . . . . 1·10 1·25

1984.
787 302 1k. multicoloured 35 20

303 "Holberg meeting Officer and Dandy" (Wilhelm Marstrand)
304 Woman and Sabbath Candles

1984. 300th Birth Anniv of Ludvig Holberg (historian and playwright).
788 303 2k.70 black, stone & red . . . 75 10

1984. 300th Anniv of Jewish Community.
789 304 3k.70 multicoloured . . . 95 80

305 "Ymer sucking Milk from the Cow Odhumble" (Nicolai Abildgaard)

1984. Paintings. Multicoloured.
790 5k. "Carnival in Rome" (Christoffer Wilhelm Eckersberg) (horiz) . . . . 1·90 1·75
791 10k. Type 305 . . . . 3·25 2·75

306 Gothersgade Reformed Church, Copenhagen

1985. 300th Anniv of French and German Reformed Church in Denmark.
792 306 2k.80 red 70 10

307 Flags and Border

1985. 30th Anniv of Copenhagen–Bonn Declarations.
793 307 2k.80 multicoloured . . . 85 30

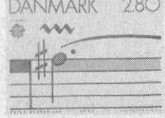

308 Flag, Girl and Boy
310 Music Score

1985. International Youth Year.
794 **308** 3k.80 multicoloured . . . 95 60

1985. Europa. Music Year.
796 **310** 2k.80 yell, red & verm . . 85 30
797 – 3k.80 black, bl & grn . . 1·25 85
DESIGN: 3k.80, Music score (different).

311 Flames and Houses
312 Queen Ingrid and "Chrysanthemum frutescens" "Sofieri"

1985. 40th Anniv of Liberation.
798 **311** 2k.80+50ore mult . . . . 1·00 1·10
The surtax was for the benefit of Resistance veterans.

1985. 50th Anniv of Queen Ingrid's Arrival in Denmark.
799 **312** 2k.80 multicoloured . . . 70 20

313 Faro Bridges
314 St. Canute and Lund Cathedral

1985. Inauguration of Faro Bridges.
800 **313** 2k.80 multicoloured . . . 70 15

1985. 900th Anniv of St. Canute's Deed of Gift to Lund.
801 **314** 2k.80 black and red . . . 70 20
802 – 3k. black and red . . . 1·10 95
DESIGN: 3k. St. Canute and Helsingborg.

315 Gymnastics
316 Woman Cyclist

1985. Sports. Multicoloured.
803 2k.80 Type **315** 75 10
804 3k.80 Canoeing 95 55
805 6k. Cycling . . . . 1·25 95

1985. United Nations Women's Decade.
806 **316** 3k.80 multicoloured . . . 95 65

317 Kronborg Castle
318 Dove and U.N. Emblem

1985. 400th Anniv of Kronborg Castle, Elsinore.
807 **317** 2k.80 multicoloured . . . 70 10

1985. 40th Anniv of U.N.O.
808 **318** 3k.80 multicoloured . . . 95 60

319 Niels and Margrethe Bohr
320 Tapestry (detail) by Caroline Ebbesen

1985. Birth Centenary of Niels Bohr (nuclear physicist).
809 **319** 2k.80 multicoloured . . . 90 80

1985. 25th Anniv of National Society for Welfare of the Mentally Ill.
810 **320** 2k.80+40ore mult . . . 95 1·00

321 "D" in Sign Language
322 Stern of Boat

1985. 50th Anniv of Danish Association of the Deaf.
811 **321** 2k.80 brown & black . . 70 20

1985.
812 **322** 2k.80 multicoloured . . . 75 20

323 "Head"

1985.
813 **323** 3k.80 multicoloured . . . 1·75 1·75

1985.
324 Leaves and Barbed Wire

1986. 25th Anniv of Amnesty International.
814 **324** 2k.80 multicoloured . . . 70 10

325 Girl with Bird
326 Reichhardt as Papageno in "The Magic Flute"

1986.
815 **325** 2k.80 multicoloured . . . 90 75

1986. 1st Death Anniv of Poul Reichhardt (actor).
816 **326** 2k.80+50ore mult . . . 95 1·00

328 Hands reading Braille
329 Bands of Colour

1986. 75th Anniv of Danish Society for the Blind.
818 **328** 2k.80+50ore red, brown and black 95 95

1986. 50th Anniv of Danish Arthritis Association.
819 **329** 2k.80+50ore mult . . . 95 95

330 Changing the Guard at Barracks

1986. Bicentenary of Royal Danish Life Guards Barracks, Rosenborg.
820 **330** 2k.80 multicoloured . . . 70 20

331 Academy and Arms
332 Hands reaching out

1986. 400th Anniv of Soro Academy.
821 **331** 2k.80 multicoloured . . . 70 10

1986. International Peace Year.
822 **332** 3k.80 multicoloured . . . 1·00 55

333 Prince Frederik
334 Station

1986. 18th Birthday of Crown Prince Frederik.
823 **333** 2k.80 black and red . . . 95 20

1986. Inaug of Hoje Tastrup Railway Station.
824 **334** 2k.80 black, bl & red . . 85 10

335 Aalborg
336 Common Raven

1986. Nordic Countries Postal Co-operation. Twinned Towns.
825 **335** 2k.80 black 75 20
826 – 2k.80 blue and red . . 95 45
DESIGN: 3k.80, Thisted.

1986. Birds. Multicoloured.
827 2k.80 Type **336** . . . . 1·10 80
828 2k.80 Common starling ("Sturnus vulgaris") . . 1·10 80
829 2k.80 Mute swan ("Cygnus olor") . . . . . . 1·10 80
830 2k.80 Northern lapwing ("Vanellus vanellus") . . . 1·10 80
831 2k.80 Eurasian skylark ("Alauda arvensis") . . . 1·10 80

337 Post Box, Wires and Telephone
338 Sports Pictograms

1986. 19th International Postal Telegraph and Telephone Congress, Copenhagen.
832 **337** 2k.80 multicoloured . . . 80 10

1986. 125th Anniv of Danish Rifle, Gymnastics and Sports Clubs.
833 **338** 2k.80 multicoloured . . . 80 10

339 Roadsweeper
341 Man fleeing

1986. Europa.
834 **339** 2k.80 red 95 10
835 – 3k.80 blue . . . . . . 1·25 75
DESIGN: 3k.80, Refuse truck.

1986. Aid for Refugees.
837 **341** 2k.80 blue, brown & blk . . 70 20

342 Cupid
343 Lutheran Communion Service in Thorslunde Church

1986. Bicentenary of First Performance of "The Whims of Cupid and the Ballet Master" by V. Galeotti and J. Lolle.
838 **342** 3k.80 multicoloured . . . 90 55

1986. 450th Anniv of Reformation.
839 **343** 6k.50 multicoloured . . . 1·90 80

344 Graph of Danish Economic Growth and Unemployment Rate
345 Abstract

1986. 25th Anniv of Organization of Economic Co-operation and Development.
840 **344** 3k.80 multicoloured . . . 1·25 1·00

1987.
841 **345** 2k.80 multicoloured . . . 85 10

346 Price Label through Magnifying Glass
347 Fresco

1987. 40th Anniv of Danish Consumer Council.
842 **346** 2k.80 black and red . . . 85 10

1987. Ribe Cathedral. Multicoloured.
843 3k. Type **347** 85 50
844 3k.80 Stained glass window (detail) . . . . . . 1·25 85
845 6k.50 Mosaic (detail) . . . . 1·90 1·50

348 Cog and Oscillating Waves
349 Gentofte Central Library

1987. 50th Anniv of Danish Academy of Technical Sciences.
846 **348** 2k.50 black and red . . . 70 80

1987. Europa. Architecture.
847 **349** 2k.80 red 85 30
848 – 3k.80 blue . . . . 1·25 85
DESIGN—HORIZ: 3k.80, Hoje Tastrup Senior School.

350 Ball and Ribbons
351 Pigs

1987. 8th Gymnaestrada (World Gymnastics Show), Herning.
849 **350** 2k.80 multicoloured . . . 80 10

1987. Centenary of First Co-operative Bacon Factory, Horsens.
850 **351** 3k.80 multicoloured . . . 1·00 85

352 1912 5k. Stamp, Steam Locomotive and Mail Wagon

1987. "Hafnia 87" International Stamp Exhibition, Copenhagen.
851 **352** 280ore multicoloured . . . 85 80

353 Single Scull
354 Abstract

1987. World Rowing Championships, Bagsvaerd Lake.
853 353 3k.80 indigo and blue ... 95 45

1987.
854 354 2k.80 multicoloured ... 80 10

355 Waves

1987. 25th Anniv of Danish Epileptics Association.
855 355 2k.80+50ore blue, red and green ... 1·10 1·10

356 Rask   357 Association Badge

1987. Birth Bicentenary of Rasmus Kristjan Rask (philologist).
856 356 2k.80 red and brown ... 80 10

1987. 125th Anniv of Clerical Association for Home Mission in Denmark.
857 357 3k. brown ... 80 30

358 Lions supporting Monogram

1988. 400th Anniv of Accession of King Christian IV.
858 358 3k. gold and blue ... 80 20
859 – 4k.10 multicoloured ... 1·10 50
DESIGN: 4k.10, Portrait of Christian IV by P. Isaacsz.

359 Worm and Artefacts   360 St. Canute's Church

1988. 400th Birth Anniv of Ole Worm (antiquarian).
860 359 7k.10 brown ... 1·90 1·90

1988. Millenary of Odense.
861 360 3k. brown, black & green ... 80 10

361 African Mother and Child   362 Sirens, Workers and Emblem

1988. Danish Church Aid.
862 361 3k.+50ore mult ... 1·10 1·00

1988. 50th Anniv of Civil Defence Administration.
863 362 2k.70 blue and orange ... 75 55

363 Blood Circulation of Heart   364 Postwoman on Bicycle

1988. 40th Anniv of W.H.O.
864 363 4k.10 red, blue and black ... 1·00 60

1988. Europa. Transport and Communications. Multicoloured.
865 3k. Type 364 ... 75 10
866 4k.10 Mobile telephone ... 1·10 60

365 "King Christian VII riding past Liberty Monument" (C. W. Eckersberg)   366 "Men of Industry" (detail, P. S. Kroyer)

1988. Bicentenary of Abolition of Villeinage.
867 365 3k.20 multicoloured ... 85 55

1988. 150th Anniv of Federation of Danish Industries.
868 366 3k. multicoloured ... 80 30

367 Speedway Riders   368 Glass Mosaic (Niels Winkel)

1988. World Speedway Championships.
869 367 4k.10 multicoloured ... 1·00 45

1988. Centenary of Danish Metalworkers' Union.
870 368 3k. multicoloured ... 80 20

369 College

1988. Bicent of Tonder Teacher Training College.
871 369 3k. brown ... 80 10

370 "Tribute to Leon Degand" (Robert Jacobsen)

1988. Franco-Danish Cultural Co-operation.
872 370 4k.10 red and black ... 1·50 1·60

371 Emblem   372 Lumby Windmill

1988. 5th Anniv of National Council for the Unmarried Mother and Her Child.
873 371 3k.+50ore red ... 1·10 1·00

1988. Mills.
874 372 3k. black, red & orange ... 80 10
875 – 7k.10 black, ultramarine and blue ... 1·90 1·60
DESIGN: 7k.10, Veistrup water mill.

373 "Bathing Boys 1902" (Peter Hansen)

1988. Paintings. Multicoloured.
876 4k.10 Type 373 ... 1·50 1·60
877 10k. "Hill at Overkoerby. Winter 1917" (Fritz Syberg) ... 3·00 3·25

374 "The Little Mermaid" (statue, Edvard Eriksen), Copenhagen   375 Army Members in Public House

1989. Centenary of Danish Tourist Association.
878 374 3k.20 green ... 80 10

1989. 102nd Anniv of Salvation Army in Denmark.
879 375 3k.20+50ore mult ... 1·25 1·10

376 Footballer   377 Emblem

1989. Centenary of Danish Football Association.
880 376 3k.20 red, blk & lt red ... 85 10

1989. 40th Anniv of N.A.T.O.
881 377 4k.40 bl, cobalt & gold ... 1·25 70

378 "Valby Woman"   379 "Parliament Flag"

1989. Nordic Countries' Postal Co-operation. Traditional Costumes. Engravings by Christoffer Wilhelm Eckersberg. Multicoloured.
882 3k.20 Type 378 ... 80 20
883 4k.40 "Pork Butcher" ... 1·25 70

1989. 3rd Direct Elections to European Parliament.
884 379 3k. blue and yellow ... 90 90

380 Lego Bricks   381 Tractor, 1917

1989. Europa. Children's Toys. Multicoloured.
885 3k.20 Type 380 ... 80 10
886 4k.40 Wooden guardsmen by Kay Bojesen ... 1·25 65

1989. Centenary of Danish Agricultural Museum.
887 381 3k.20 red ... 80 10

382 Diagram of Folketing (Parliament) Chamber

1989. Centenary of Interparliamentary Union.
888 382 3k.40 red and black ... 1·40 1·25

383 Chart and Boat Identity Number

1989. Centenary of Danish Fishery and Marine Research Institute.
889 383 3k.20 multicoloured ... 80 20

384 "Ingemann" (after J. V. Gertner)   385 Scene from "They Caught the Ferry" (50th anniv of Danish Government Film Office)

1989. Birth Bicentenary of Bernhard Severin Ingemann (poet)
890 384 7k.70 green ... 1·90 1·00

1989. Danish Film Industry.
891 385 3k. blue, black & orge ... 80 50
892 – 3k.20 pink, blk & orge ... 80 20
893 – 4k.40 brown, blk & orge ... 1·10 60
DESIGNS: 3k.20, Scene from "The Golden Smile" (birth cent of Bodil Ipsen, actress); 4k.40, Carl Th. Dreyer (director, birth cent).

386 Stamps

1989. 50th Stamp Day.
894 386 3k.20 salmon, orge & brn ... 60 20

387 "Part of Northern Citadel Bridge" (Christen Kobke)

1989. Paintings. Multicoloured.
895 4k.40 Type 387 ... 1·50 1·60
896 10k. "A Little Girl, Elise Kobke, with Cup" (Constantin Hansen) ... 2·50 3·00

388 Silver Coffee Pot (Axel Johannes Kroyer, 1726)   389 Andrew Mitchell's Steam Engine

1990. Centenary of Museum of Decorative Art, Copenhagen.
897 388 3k.50 black and blue ... 90 20

1990. Bicent of Denmark's First Steam Engine.
898 389 8k.25 brown ... 1·90 1·00

390 Queen Margrethe II   391 Royal Monogram over Door of Haderslev Post Office

1990.
910 390 3k.50 red ... 70 10
911 3k.75 green ... 1·10 1·25
912 3k.75 red ... 85 10
913 4k. brown ... 95 70
914 4k.50 violet ... 1·10 1·10
915 4k.75 blue ... 1·10 40
916 4k.75 violet ... 1·10 85
917 5k. blue ... 95 85
918 5k.25 black ... 95 65
919 5k.50 green ... 95 85

1990. Europa. Post Office Buildings.
930 391 3k.50 yellow, red & blk ... 1·25 10
931 – 4k.75 multicoloured ... 1·60 55
DESIGN: 4k.75, Odense Post Office.

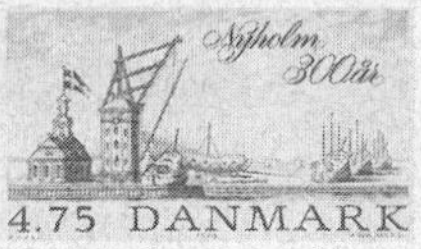

392 Main Guardhouse, Rigging Crane and Ships (after C. O. Willars)

1990. 300th Anniv of Nyholm.
932 **392** 4k.75 black . . . . 1·10 55

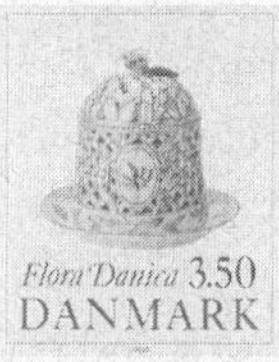

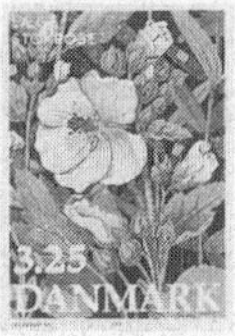

393 Covered Ice Dish **394** Marsh Mallow

1990. Bicentenary of Flora Danica Banquet Service. Multicoloured.
933 3k.50 Type **393** . . . . . . 95 1·00
934 3k.50 Sauce boat . . . . . . 95 1·00
935 3k.50 Lidded ice pot . . . . 95 1·00
936 3k.50 Serving dish . . . . . 95 1·00

1990. Endangered Flowers. Multicoloured.
937 3k.25 Type **394** 85 85
938 3k.50 Red helleborine . . . . 1·40 20
939 3k.75 Purple orchis . . . . . 1·10 80
940 4k.75 Lady's slipper . . . . 1·10 55

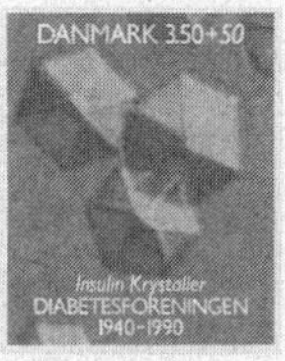

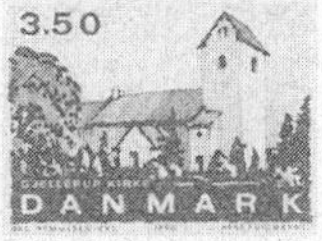

395 Insulin Crystals **396** Gjellerup Church

1990. 50th Anniv of Danish Diabetes Association.
941 **395** 3k.50+50ore mult . . . . 1·50 1·60

1990. Jutland Churches. Each brown.
942 3k.50 Type **396** 95 20
943 4k.75 Veng Church . . . . . 1·00 50
944 8k.25 Bredsten Church (vert) 2·40 1·25

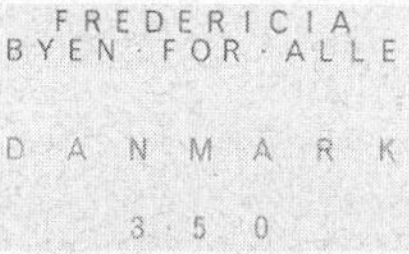

397 Slogan and Braille

1990. Fredericia: "Town for Everybody" (access for the handicapped project).
945 **397** 3k.50 red and black . . . 95 40

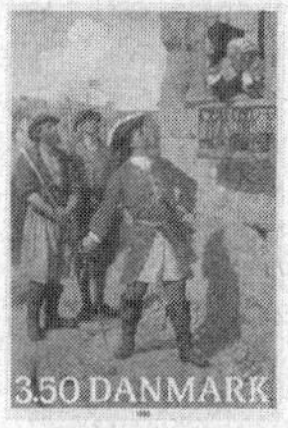

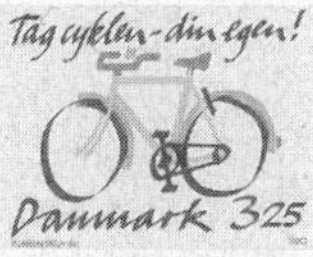

398 "Tordenskiold and Karlsten's Commandant" (Otto Bache) **399** Bicycle (Bicycle stealing)

1990. 300th Birth Anniv of Admiral Tordenskiold (Peter Wessel).
946 **398** 3k.50 multicoloured . . . 1·00 30

1990. Campaigns.
947 **399** 3k.25 multicoloured . . . 95 70
948 – 3k.50 black, bl & mve . . 1·00 30
DESIGN: 3k.50, Glass and car (Drunken driving).

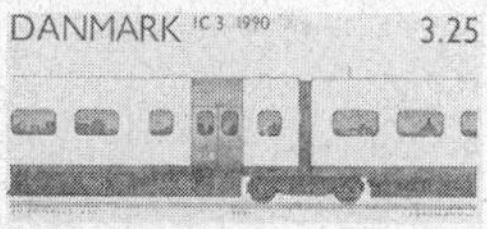

400 IC3 Diesel Passenger Train, 1990

1991. Railway Locomotives.
949 **400** 3k.25 blue, red & green 95 1·00
950 – 3k.50 black and red . . . 90 40
951 – 3k.75 brown & dp brn . . 95 80
952 – 4k.75 black and red . . . 1·10 60
DESIGNS: 3k.50, Class A steam locomotive, 1882; 3k.75, Class MY diesel-electric locomotive, 1954; 4k.75, Class P steam locomotive, 1907.

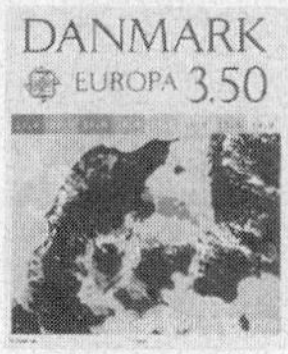

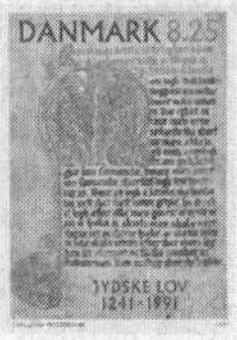

401 Satellite Picture of Denmark's Water Temperatures **402** First Page of 1280s Manuscript

1991. Europa. Europe in Space. Mult.
953 3k.50 Type **401** 95 25
954 4k.75 Denmark's land temperatures . . . . . . 1·10 65

1991. 750th Anniv of Jutland Law.
955 **402** 8k.25 multicoloured . . . 2·00 1·60

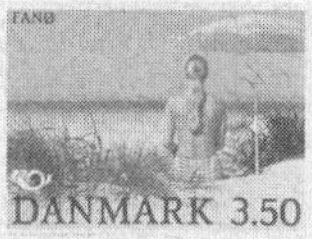

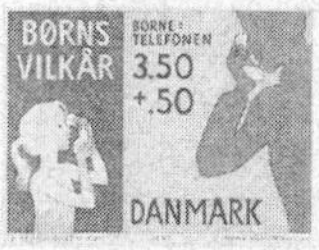

403 Fano **404** Child using Emergency Helpline

1991. Nordic Countries' Postal Co-operation. Tourism. Multicoloured.
956 3k.50 Type **403** 95 20
957 4k.75 Christianso . . . . . 1·10 35

1991. 15th Anniv of Living Conditions of Children (child welfare organization).
958 **404** 3k.50+50ore blue . . . . 1·25 1·25

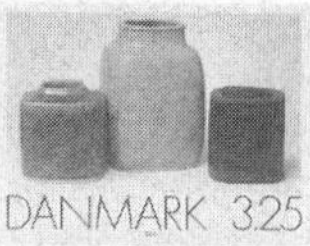

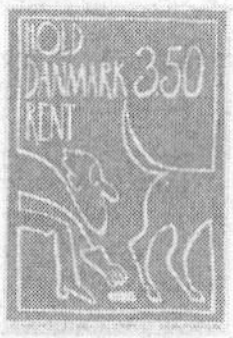

405 Stoneware Vessels (Christian Poulsen) **406** Man cleaning up after Dog

1991. Danish Design. Multicoloured.
959 3k.25 Type **405** 80 60
960 3k.50 Chair, 1949 (Hans Wegner) (vert) 90 30
961 4k.75 Silver cutlery, 1938 (Kay Bojesen) (vert) . . . 1·10 65
962 8k.25 "PH5" lamp, 1958 (Poul Henningsen) . . . . 2·10 1·75

1991. "Keep Denmark Clean".
963 **406** 3k.50 red 85 20
964 – 4k.75 blue . . . . 1·10 80
DESIGN: 4k.75, Woman putting litter into bin.

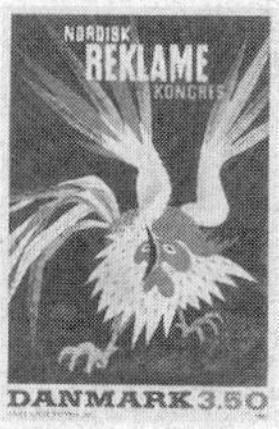

407 Nordic Advertising Congress 1947 (Arne Ungermann)

1991. Posters. Multicoloured.
965 3k.50 Type **407** 90 35
966 4k.50 Poster Exhibition, Copenhagen Zoo, 1907 (Valdemar Andersen) . . . 1·60 1·60
967 4k.75 D.D.L. (Danish Airlines, 1945) (Ib Andersen) . . . . 1·10 70
968 12k. Casino's "The Sinner", 1925 (Sven Brasch) . . . . 2·75 2·25

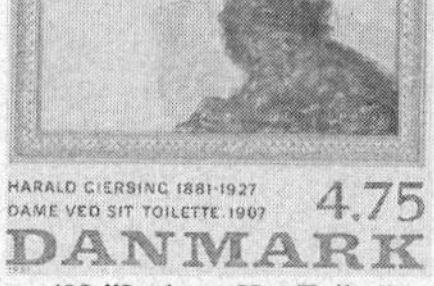

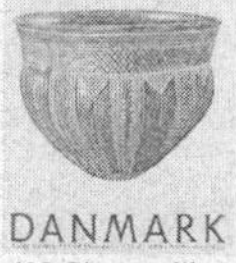

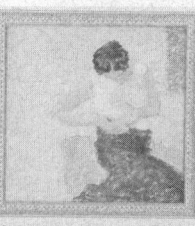

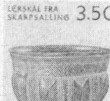

408 "Lady at Her Toilet" (Harald Giersing) **409** Skarpsalling Earthenware Bowl

1991. Paintings. Multicoloured.
969 4k.75 Type **408** . . . . . . 1·25 1·60
970 14k. "Road through Wood" (Edvard Weie) . . . . . . 3·75 3·50

1992. Re-opening of National Museum, Copenhagen. Exhibits from Prehistoric Denmark Collection.
971 **409** 3k.50 brown and lilac . . 90 30
972 – 4k.50 green and blue . . 1·40 1·25
973 – 4k.75 black & brown . . 1·10 70
974 – 8k.25 purple & green . . 2·00 1·75
DESIGNS: 4k.50, Grevensvaenge bronze figure of dancer; 4k.75, Bottom plate of Gundestrup Cauldron; 8k.25, Hindsgavl flint knife.

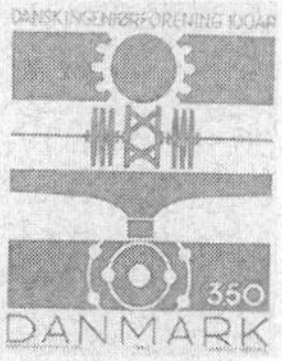

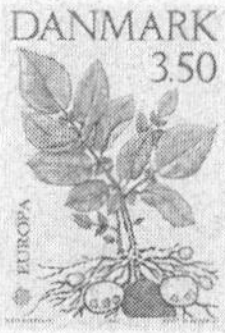

410 Aspects of Engineering **412** Potato Plant

1992. Centenary of Danish Society of Chemical, Civil, Electrical and Mechanical Engineers.
975 **410** 3k.50 red 90 25

1992. Europa. 500th Anniv of Discovery of America by Columbus.
977 **412** 3k.50 green & brown . . 95 25
978 – 4k.75 green & yellow . . 1·25 1·10
DESIGN: 4k.75, Head of maize.

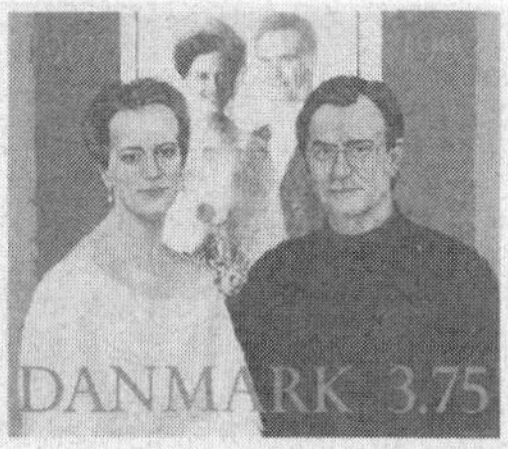

413 Royal Couple in 1992 and in Official Wedding Photograph

1992. Silver Wedding of Queen Margrethe and Prince Henrik.
979 **413** 3k.75 multicoloured . . . 95 70

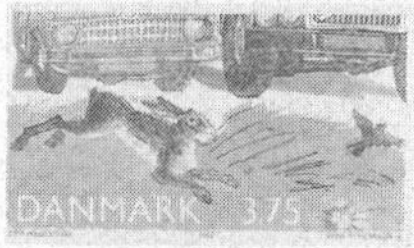

414 Hare, Eurasian Sky Lark and Cars

1992. Environmental Protection. Multicoloured.
980 3k.75 Type **414** 90 20
981 5k. Atlantic herrings and sea pollution . . . . . . 1·25 55
982 8k.75 Felled trees and saplings (vert) . . . . . 2·10 1·10

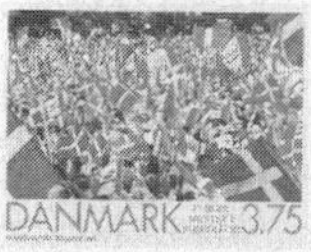

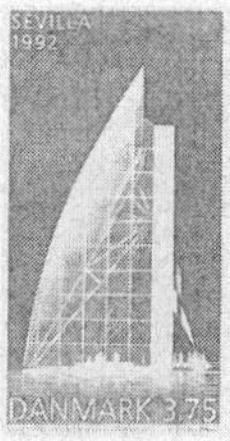

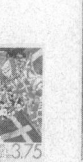

415 Celebrating Crowd **416** Danish Pavilion

1992. Denmark, European Football Champion.
983 **415** 3k.75 multicoloured . . . 95 25

1992. "Expo '92" World's Fair, Seville.
984 **416** 3k.75 blue 90 25

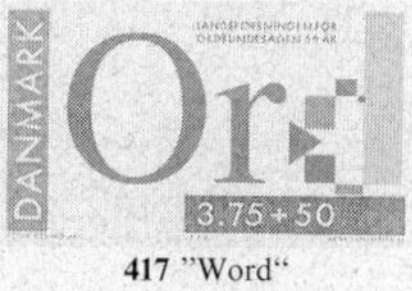

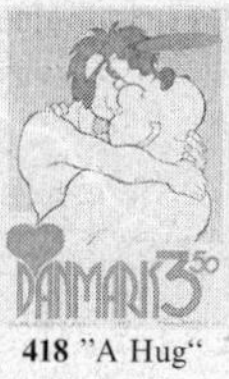

417 "Word" **418** "A Hug"

1992. 50th Anniv of Danish Dyslexia Association.
985 **417** 3k.75+50ore mult . . . . 1·25 1·25

1992. Danish Cartoon Characters.
986 **418** 3k.50 purple, red & gold 95 65
987 – 3k.75 violet and red . . . 95 20
988 – 4k.75 black and red . . . 1·25 1·25
989 – 5k. blue and red . . . . 1·25 45
DESIGNS: 3k.75, "Love Letter"; 4k.75, "Domestic Triangle"; 5k. "The Poet and his Little Wife".

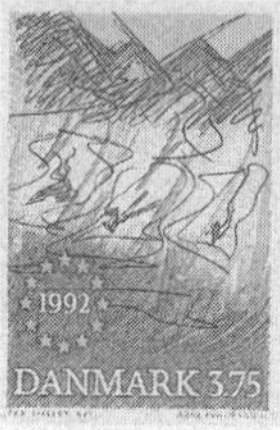

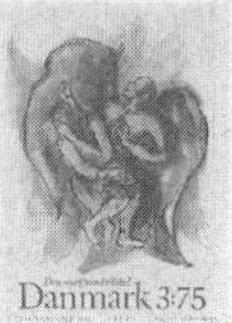

419 Abstract **420** "Jacob's Fight with the Angel" (bible illustration by Bodil Kaalund)

1992. European Single Market.
990 **419** 3k.75 blue and yellow . . 90 40

1992. Publication of New Danish Bible.
991 **420** 3k.75 multicoloured . . . 90 20

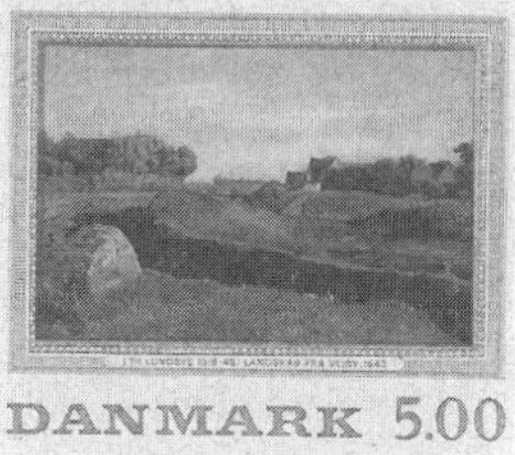

421 "Landscape from Vejby, 1843" (Johan Thomas Lundbye)

1992. Paintings. Multicoloured.
992 5k. Type **421** . . . . 1·40 1·25
993 10k. "Motif from Halleby Brook, 1847" (Peter Christian Skovgaard) . . . 2·50 2·50

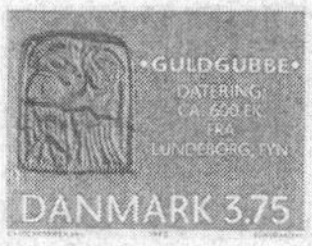

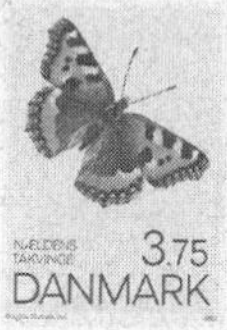

422 Funen Guldgubber **423** Small Tortoiseshell

1993. Danish Treasure Trove. Guldgubber (anthropomorphic gold foil figures). Mult.
994 3k.75 Type **422** 90 20
995 5k. Bornholm guldgubber (vert) . . . . 1·25 45

1993. Butterflies. Multicoloured.
996 3k.75 Type **423** 90 20
997 5k. Large blue . . . . . . 1·25 45
998 8k.75 Marsh fritillary . . . . 2·40 1·90
999 12k. Red admiral . . . . . 2·75 2·40

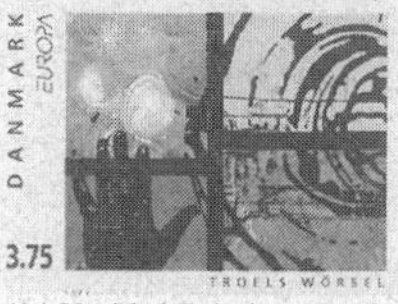

424 Untitled Painting (Troels Worsel)

1993. Europa. Contemporary Art. Mult.
1000 3k.75 Type **424** 85 40
1001 5k. "The 7 Corners of the Earth" (Stig Brogger) (vert) . . . . 1·40 65

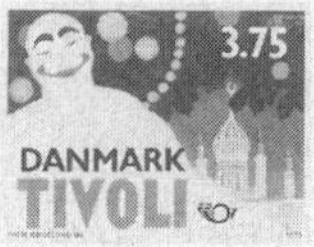

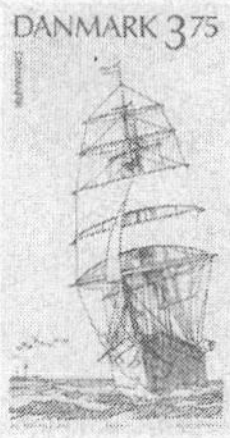

425 "Pierrot" (Thor Bogelund, 1947) **426** "Danmark"

1993. Nordic Countries' Postal Co-operation. Tourism. Publicity posters for Tivoli Gardens, Copenhagen. Multicoloured.
1002 3k.75 Type **425** 85 20
1003 5k. Child holding balloons (Wilhelm Freddie, 1987) (vert) . . . . 1·40 60

1993. Training Ships. Multicoloured.
1004 3k.75 Type **426** 90 20
1005 4k.75 "Jens Krogh" (25×30 mm) . . . . . . 1·25 1·25
1006 5k. "Georg Stage" . . . . . 1·40 65
1007 9k.50 "Marilyn Anne" (36×26 mm) . . . . . . 2·40 2·50

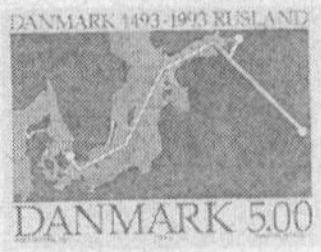

427 Map

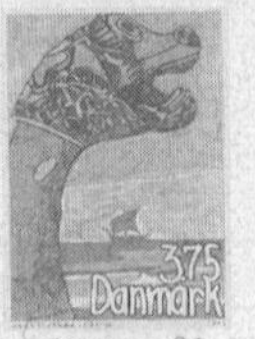

428 Prow of Viking Ship

1993. Inauguration of Denmark–Russia Submarine Cable and 500th Anniv of Friendship Treaty.
1008 **427** 5k. green . . . . 1·25 55

1993. Children's Stamp Design Competition.
1009 **428** 3k.75 multicoloured . . 95 20

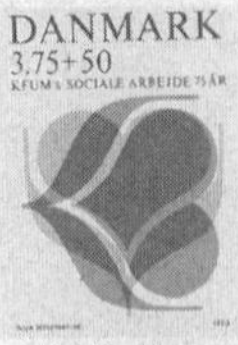

429 Emblem

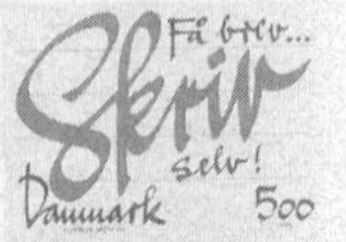

430 "If you want a Letter...Write one Yourself"

1993. 75th Anniv of Social Work of Young Men's Christian Association.
1010 **429** 3k.75+50ore green, red and black . . . . . . 1·40 1·10

1993. Letter-writing Campaign.
1011 **430** 5k. ultram, bl & blk . . 1·40 60

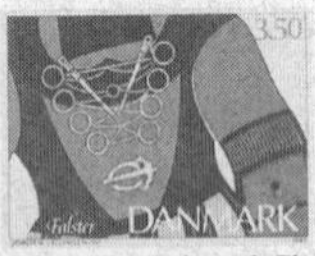

431 Silver Brooch and Chain, North Falster

1993. Traditional Jewellery. Multicoloured.
1012 3k.50 Type **431** 90 65
1013 3k.75 Gilt-silver brooch with owner's monogram, Amager 95 20
1014 5k. Silver buttons and brooches, Laeso . . . . . 1·40 45
1015 8k.75 Silver buttons, Romo 2·10 1·60

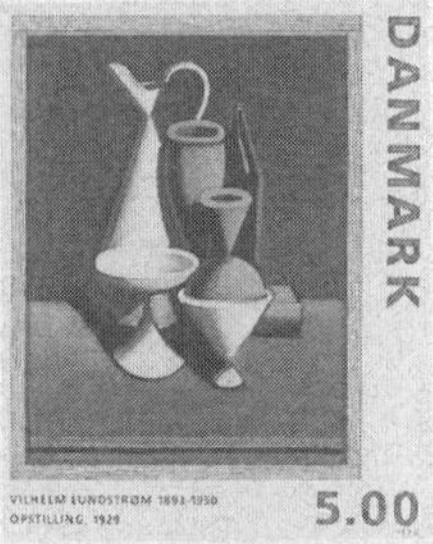

432 "Assemblage" (Vilhelm Lundstrom)

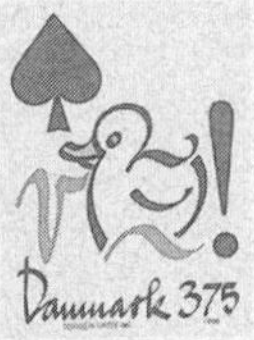

433 Duck

1993. Paintings. Multicoloured.
1016 5k. Type **432** . . . . 1·40 1·40
1017 15k. "Composition" (Franciska Clausen) . . . 3·50 3·25

1994. Save Water and Energy Campaign.
1018 **433** 3k.75 multicoloured . . 90 20
1019 – 5k. green, red & black 1·10 40
DESIGN: 5k. Spade (in Danish "spar" = save) and "CO2".

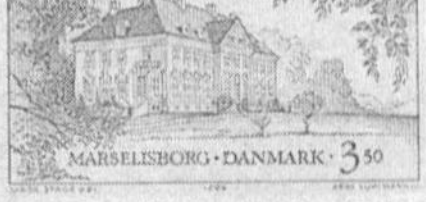

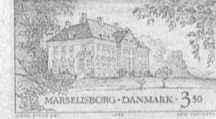

434 Marselisborg Castle, Aarhus

1994. Royal Residences.
1020 **434** 3k.50 dp brn, grn & brn 90 65
1021 – 3k.75 multicoloured . . 90 20
1022 – 5k. grn, dp brn & brn 1·25 55
1023 – 8k.75 dp brn, grn & brn 2·00 1·60
DESIGNS: 3k.75, Amalienborg Castle, Copenhagen; 5k. Fredensborg Castle, North Zealand; 8k.75, Graasten Castle, South Jutland.

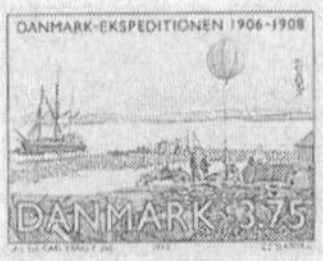

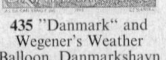

435 "Danmark" and Wegener's Weather Balloon, Danmarkshavn

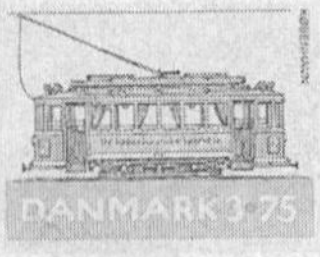

436 Copenhagen Tram No. 2, 1911

1994. Europa. Discoveries. "Danmark" Expedition to North-East Greenland, 1906–08.
1024 **435** 3k.75 purple 90 20
1025 – 5k. black . . . . 1·25 55
DESIGN: 5k. Johan Peter Koch and theodolite.

1994. Trams. Multicoloured.
1026 3k.75 Type **436** 90 20
1027 4k.75 Aarhus tram, 1928 . . 1·10 1·25
1028 5k. Odense tram, 1911 (vert) 1·25 65
1029 12k. Copenhagen horse tram "Honen", 1880 (37 × 21 mm) . . . . . . 2·75 3·00

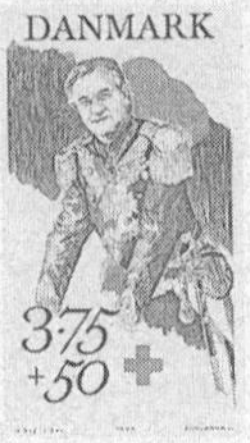

437 Prince Henrik

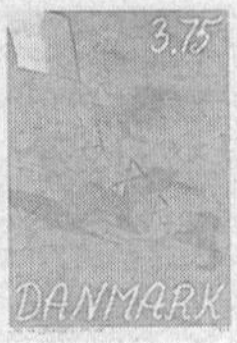

438 Kite

1994. Danish Red Cross Fund. 60th Birthday of Prince Henrik, the Prince Consort.
1030 **437** 3k.75+50ore mult . . . 1·10 1·10

1994. Children's Stamp Design Competition.
1031 **438** 3k.75 multicoloured . . 90 20

439 Emblem

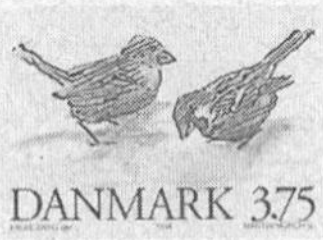

440 House Sparrows

1994. 75th Anniv of I.L.O.
1032 **439** 5k. multicoloured . . . 1·25 30

1994. Protected Animals. Multicoloured.
1033 3k.75 Type **440** 90 20
1034 4k.75 Badger . . . . 1·10 1·10
1035 5k. Red squirrel (vert) . . . 1·25 60
1036 9k.50 Pair of black grouse 2·40 2·10
1037 12k. Black grass snake (36 × 26 mm) . . . . . . 3·00 3·00

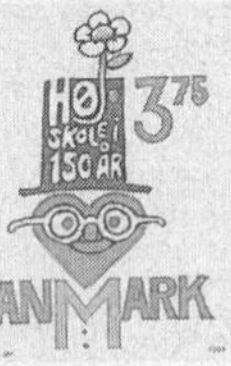

441 Teacher

1994. 150th Anniv of Folk High Schools.
1038 **441** 3k.75 multicoloured . . 90 20

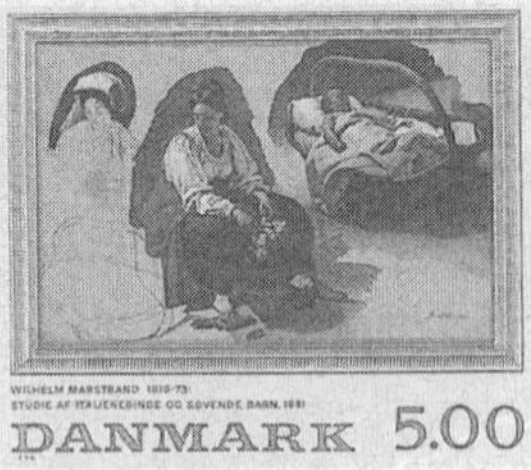

442 Study for "Italian Woman with Sleeping Child" (Wilhelm Marstrand)

1994. Paintings. Multicoloured.
1039 5k. Type **442** . . . . 1·25 1·25
1040 15k. "Interior from Amaliegade with the Artist's Brothers" (Wilhelm Bendz) . . . . 3·25 3·50

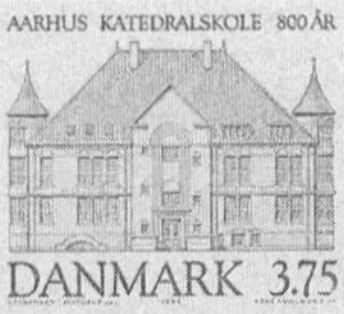

443 The Red Building (architect's drawing, Hack Kampmann)

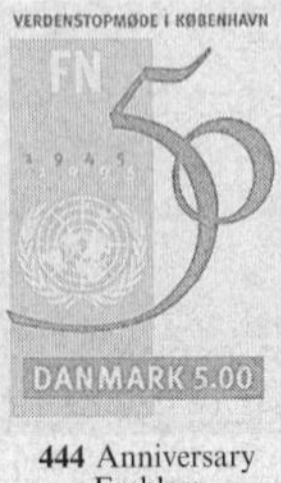

444 Anniversary Emblem

1995. 800th Anniv of Aarhus Cathedral School.
1041 **443** 3k.75 multicoloured . . 90 20

1995. 50th Anniv of United Nations Organization. U.N. World Summit for Social Development, Copenhagen.
1042 **444** 5k. multicoloured . . . 1·10 45

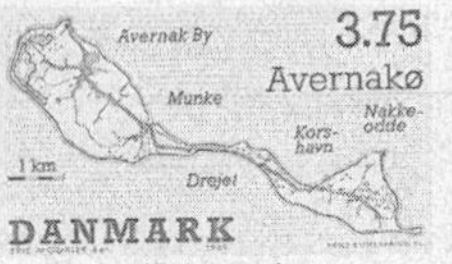

445 Avernako

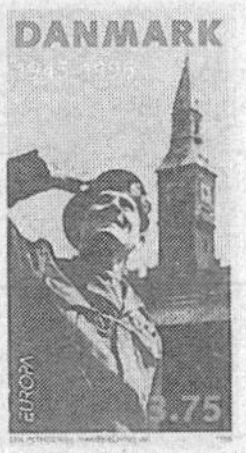

446 Field-Marshal Montgomery and Copenhagen Town Hall

1995. Danish Islands. Each brown, blue and red.
1043 3k.75 Type **445** 90 20
1044 4k.75 Fejo . . . . 1·10 90
1045 5k. Fur . . . . 1·25 55
1046 9k.50 Endelave . . . . . . 2·25 1·75

1995. Europa. Peace and Freedom. Mult.
1047 3k.75 Type **446** 95 20
1048 5k. White coaches (repatriation of Danes from German concentration camps) (horiz) . . . . 1·40 55
1049 8k.75 Dropping of supplies from Allied aircraft (horiz) . . . . 2·10 1·40
1050 12k. Jews escaping by boat to Sweden (horiz) . . . . 2·75 1·75

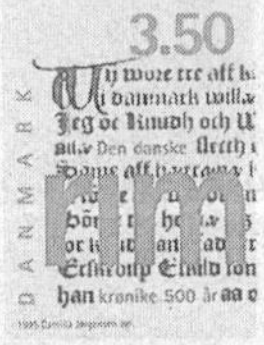

447 Detail of Page

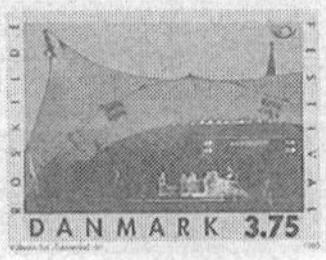

448 Stage

1995. 500th Anniv of "The Rhymed Chronicle" by Friar Niels (first book printed in Danish).
1051 **447** 3k.50 multicoloured . . 90 55

1995. Nordic Countries' Postal Co-operation. Music Festivals. Multicoloured.
1052 3k.75 Type **448** (25th anniv of Roskilde Festival) . . 90 20
1053 5k. Violinist (21st anniv of Tonder Festival) (20 × 38 mm) . . . . . . 1·25 40

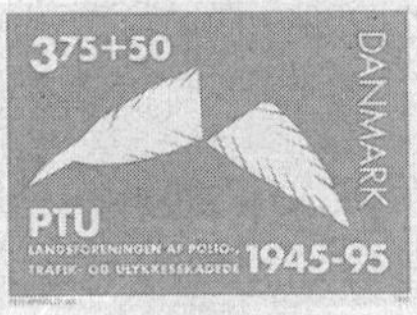

449 Broken Feather

1995. 50th Anniv of National Society of Polio and Accident Victims.
1054 **449** 3k.75+50ore red . . . . 1·10 1·25

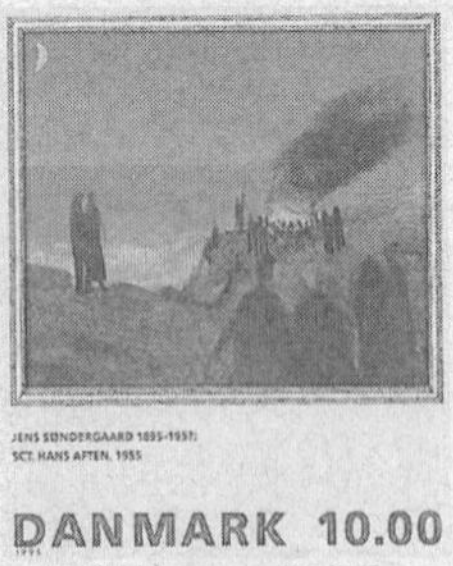

450 "Midsummer Eve" (Jens Sondergaard)

1995. Paintings. Multicoloured.
1055 10k. Type **450** . . . . . . 2·40 2·25
1056 15k. "Landscape at Gudhjem" (Niels Lergaard) . . . . 3·75 3·50

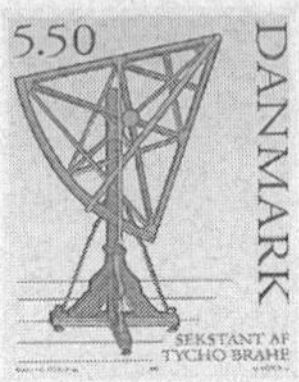

451 Sextant

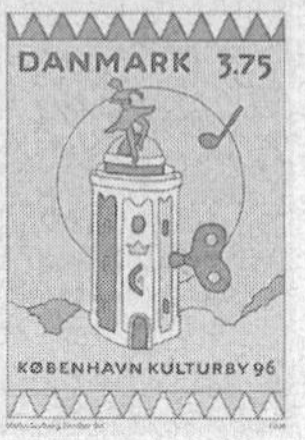

453 The Round Tower

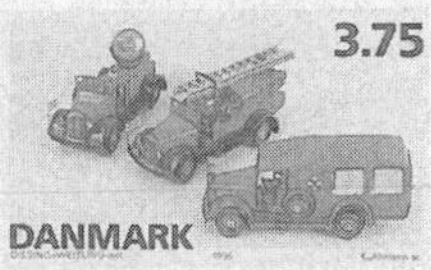

452 TEKNO Model Vehicles

1995. 450th Birth Anniv of Tycho Brahe (astronomer). Multicoloured.
1057 3k.75 Uraniborg (Palace Observatory) 90 25
1058 5k.50 Type **451** . . . . . . 1·25 1·10

1995. Danish Toys. Multicoloured.
1059 3k.75 Type **452** 90 20
1060 5k. Edna (celluloid doll), Kirstine (china doll) and Holstebro teddy bear . . 1·25 60
1061 8k.75 Toy bin-plate locomotives and rolling stock . . . . 2·10 1·50
1062 12k. Glud & Marstrand horse-drawn fire engine and carriage . . . . . . 2·75 2·50

1996. Copenhagen, European Cultural Capital. Multicoloured.
1063 3k.75 Type **453** 90 20
1064 5k. Christiansborg . . . . . 1·10 45
1065 8k.75 Dome of Marble Church as hot-air balloon 2·10 1·50
1066 12k. "The Little Mermaid" on stage . . . . 2·75 2·75

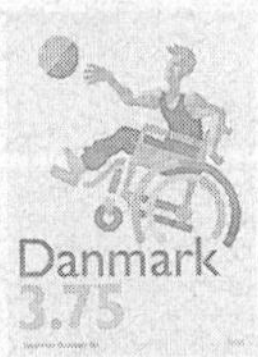

454 Disabled Basketball Player

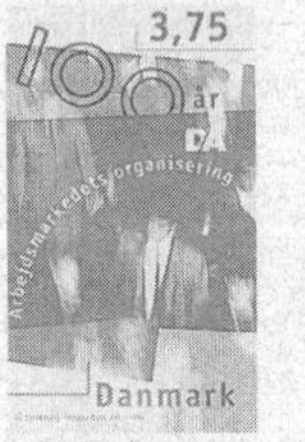

455 Businessmen

1996. Sport. Multicoloured.
1067 3k.75 Type **454** 90 20
1068 4k.75 Swimming . . . . . 1·10 90
1069 5k. Yachting . . . . 1·25 45
1070 9k.50 Cycling . . . . 2·25 2·00

1996. Cent of Danish Employers' Confederation.
1071 **455** 3k.75 multicoloured . . 90 20

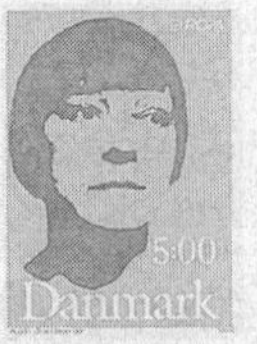

456 Asta Nielsen (actress)

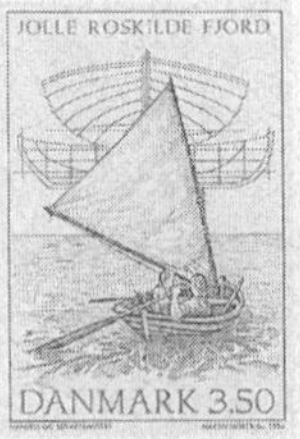

457 Roskilde Fjord Boat

1996. Europa. Famous Women.
1072 – 3k.75 brown & dp brn 90 20
1073 **456** 5k. grey and blue . . . 1·10 45
DESIGN: 3k.75, Karin Blixen (writer).

1996. Wooden Sailing Boats.
1074 **457** 3k.50 brn, bl & red . . . 90 80
1075 – 3k.75 lilac, grn & red . . 90 20
1076 – 12k.25 blk, brn & red . . 2·75 3·00
DESIGNS—As T **457**: 12k.25, South Funen Archipelago smack; 20 × 38 mm: 3k.75, Limfjorden skiff.

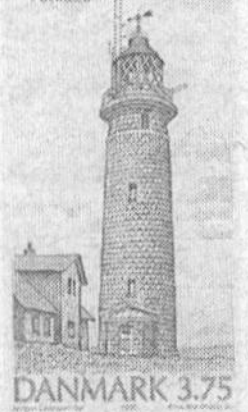

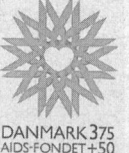

458 Fornaes

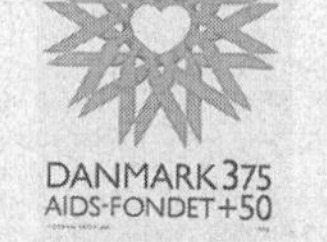

459 Ribbons forming Hearts within Star

1996. Lighthouses. Multicoloured.
1077 3k.75 Type **458** 90 20
1078 5k. Blavandshuk . . . . . . 1·10 40
1079 5k.25 Bovbjerg . . . . . . 1·25 1·60
1080 8k.75 Mon . . . . 2·10 1·25

1996. AIDS Foundation.
1081 **459** 3k.75+50ore red & blk 1·00 1·10

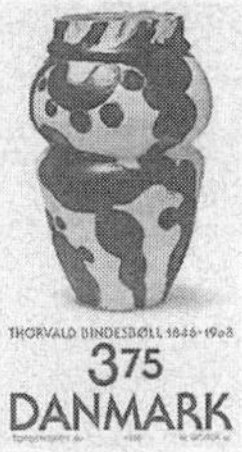

460 Vase

1996. 150th Birth Anniv of Thorvald Bindesboll (ceramic artist). Multicoloured.
1082 3k.75 Type **460** 90 20
1083 4k. Portfolio cover 95 80

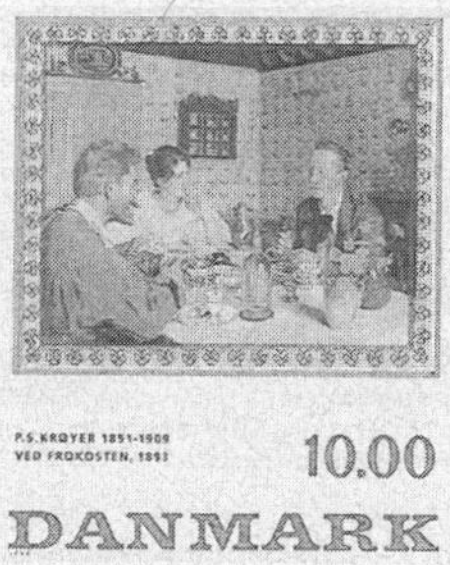

461 "At Lunch" (Peder Kroyer)

1996. Paintings. Multicoloured.
1084 10k. Type **461** . . . . . . 2·40 2·40
1085 15k. "Girl with Sunflowers" (Michael Ancher) . . . . 3·25 3·25

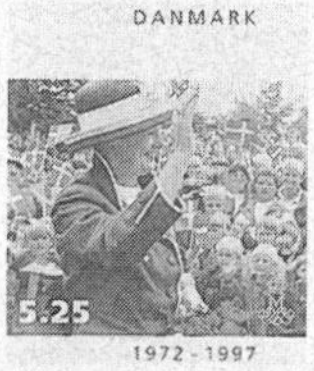

462 Queen Margrethe waving to Children

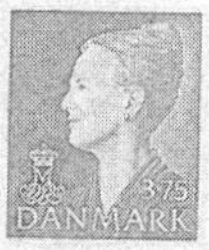

463 Queen Margrethe

1997. Silver Jubilee of Queen Margrethe. Mult.
1086 3k.50 Queen Margrethe and Prince Henrik 90 55
1087 3k.75 Queen Margrethe and Crown Prince Frederik . . 90 20
1088 4k. Queen Margrethe at desk 95 70
1089 5k.25 Type **462** . . . . . . 1·25 1·00

1997.
1092 **463** 3k.75 red 90 10
1093 4k. green . . . . 1·50 1·10
1094 4k. red 85 10
1095 4k.25 brown 85 50
1096 4k.50 blue . . . . . . 1·00 75
1097 4k.75 brown . . . . . . 1·00 90
1098 5k. violet . . . . . . 1·00 35
1099 5k.25 blue . . . . . . 1·00 65
1100 5k.50 red . . . . . . 1·25 1·10
1101 5k.75 blue . . . . . . 1·00 60
1104 6k.75 green . . . . . . 1·40 1·40

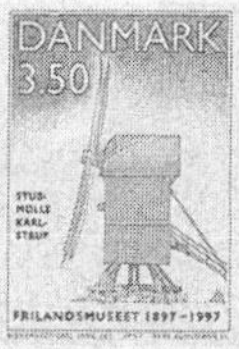

464 Karlstrup Post Mill, Zealand

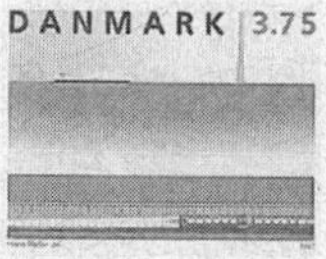

465 The East Tunnel

1997. Centenary of Open Air Museum, Lyngby. Construction Drawings by B. Ehrhardt.
1111 **464** 3k.50 brown & purple 90 45
1112 – 3k.75 lilac and green . . 90 20
1113 – 5k. green and lilac . . . 1·10 40
1114 – 8k.75 green & brown . . 2·75 1·90
DESIGNS: 3k.75, Ellested water mill, Funen; 5k. Fjellerup Manor Barn, Djursland; 8k.75, Toftum farm, Romo.

1997. Inauguration of Railway Section of the Great Belt Link. Multicoloured.
1115 3k.75 Type **465** 90 20
1116 4k.75 The West Bridge . . . 1·10 80

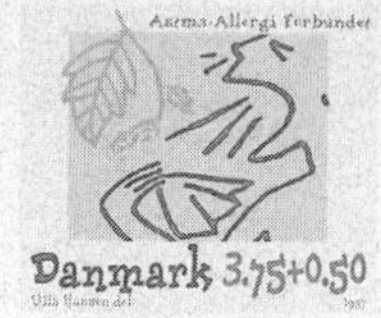

466 Sneezing

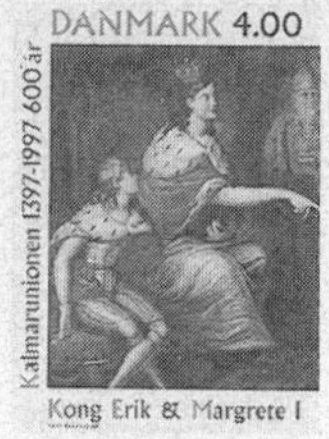

468 King Erik and Queen Margrete I

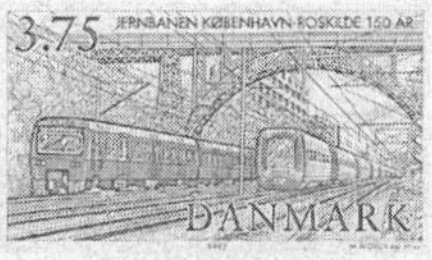

467 Electric Trains under New Carlsberg Bridge

1997. Asthma Allergy Association.
1117 **466** 3k.75+50ore mult . . . 1·10 1·10

1997. 150th Anniv of Copenhagen–Roskilde Railway. Multicoloured.
1118 3k.75 Type **467** 90 20
1119 8k.75 Steam train under original Carlsberg bridge (after H. Holm) . . . . . 2·00 1·10

1997. 600th Anniv of Kalmar Union (of Denmark, Norway and Sweden). Multicoloured.
1120 4k. Type **468** . . . . 1·00 85
1121 4k. The Three Graces . . . 1·00 85
Nos. 1120/1 were issued, se-tenant, forming a composite design of a painting by an unknown artist.

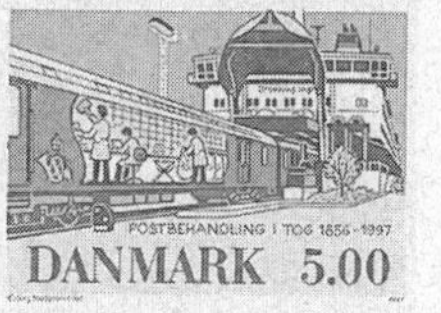

469 Post Office Cars on Great Belt Ferry

1997. Closure of Travelling Post Offices.
1122 **469** 5k. multicoloured . . . 1·10 45

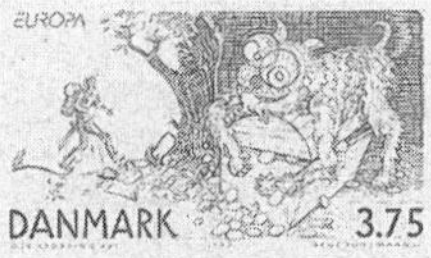

470 "The Tinder-box"

1997. Europa. Tales and Legends by Hans Christian Andersen.
1123 **470** 3k.75 dp brn & brn . . 90 35
1124 – 5k.25 red, dp grn & grn 1·25 85
DESIGN: 5k.25, "Thumbelina".

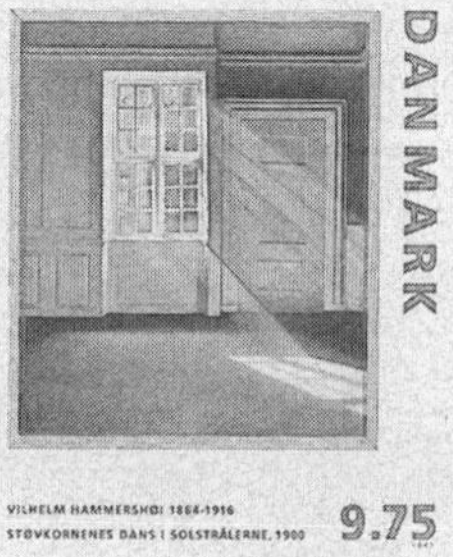

471 "Dust dancing in the Sun" (Vilheim Hammershoi)

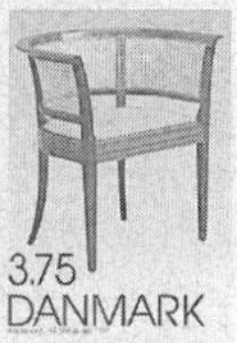

472 Faaborg Chair (Kaare Klint)

1997. Paintings. Multicoloured.
1125 9k.75 Type **471** . . . . . . 2·25 2·40
1126 13k. "Woman Mountaineer" (Jens Willumsen) . . . . 2·75 3·00

1997. Danish Design. Multicoloured.
1127 3k.75 Type **472** 90 25
1128 4k. Margrethe bowls (Sigvard Bernadotte and Acton Bjorn) 90 65
1129 5k. The Ant chairs (Arne Jacobsen) (horiz) . . . . 1·25 40
1130 12k.25 Silver bowl (Georg Jensen) . . . . 2·75 2·75

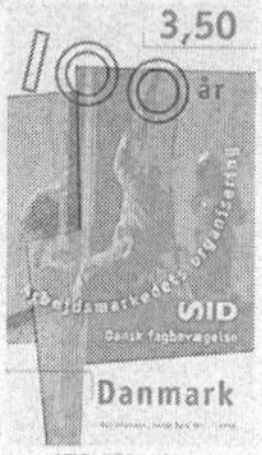

473 Workers

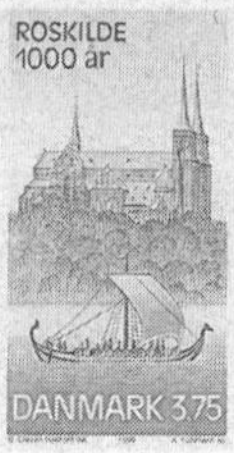

474 Roskilde Cathedral and Viking Longship

1998. Centenary of Danish Confederation of Trade Unions. Multicoloured.
1131 3k.50 Type **473** (General Workers' Union in Denmark) 90 60
1132 3k.75 Crowd at meeting (Danish Confederation of Trade Unions) 90 20
1133 4k.75 Nurse (Danish Nurses' Organization) . . . . . . 1·10 85
1134 5k. Woman using telephone (Union of Commercial and Clerical Employees in Denmark) . . . . 1·10 40

1998. Millenary of Roskilde.
1135 **474** 3k.75 multicoloured . . 90 25

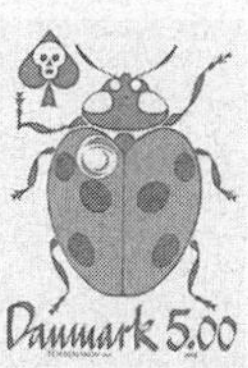

475 Seven-spotted Ladybird

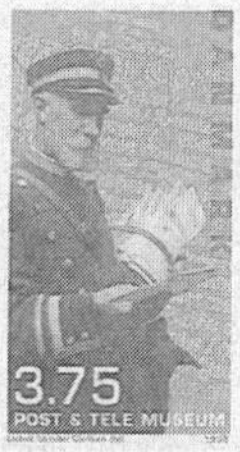

476 Postman, 1922

1998. Environmental Issues. Gardening Without Chemicals.
1136 **475** 5k. red and black . . . 1·10 25

1998. Post and Tele Museum, Copenhagen. Mult.
1137 3k.75 Type **476** 90 25
1138 4k.50 Morse operator, 1910 95 90
1139 5k.50 Telephonist, 1910 . . 1·25 1·00
1140 8k.75 Postman, 1998 . . . . 2·00 1·75

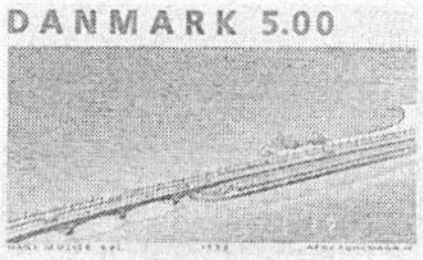

477 The West Bridge

1998. Inauguration of Road Section of the Great Belt Link. Each blue, black and red.
1141 5k. Type **477** . . . . . . 1·10 60
1142 5k. The East Bridge . . . . 1·10 60

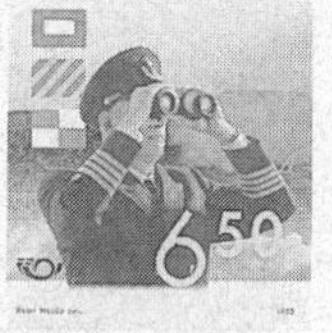

478 Harbour Master

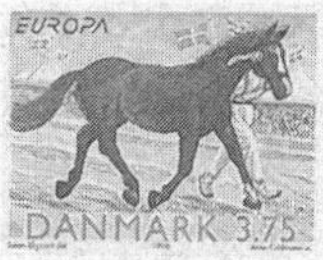

479 Horse (Agriculture Show)

1998. Nordic Countries' Postal Co-operation. Shipping. Multicoloured.
1143 6k.50 Type **478** . . . . . . 1·40 1·00
1144 6k.50 Sextant and radar image of Copenhagen harbour . . . . 1·40 1·00
Nos. 1143/4 were issued together, se-tenant, forming a composite design.

1998. Europa. National Festivals. Mult.
1146 3k.75 Type **479** 90 25
1147 4k.50 Aarhus Festival Week 95 85

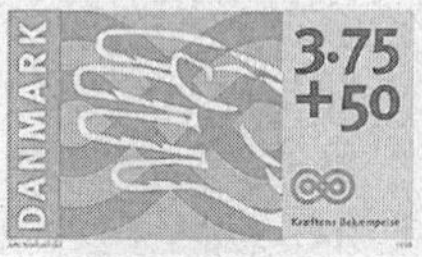

480 Reaching Hand

1998. Anti-cancer Campaign.
1148 **480** 3k.75+50ore red, orange and black . . . . . . 1·00 1·00

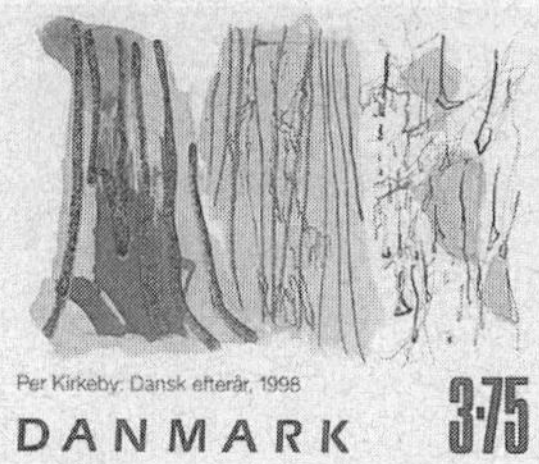

481 "Danish Autumn" (Per Kirkeby)

1998. Philatelic Creations. Multicoloured.
1149 3k.75 Type **481** 90 70
1150 5k. "Alpha" (Mogens Andersen) (vert) . . . . 1·10 95
1151 8k.75 "Imagery" (Ejler Bille) (vert) . . . . 2·00 1·90
1152 19k. "Celestial Horse" (Carl-Henning Pedersen) 4·00 3·75

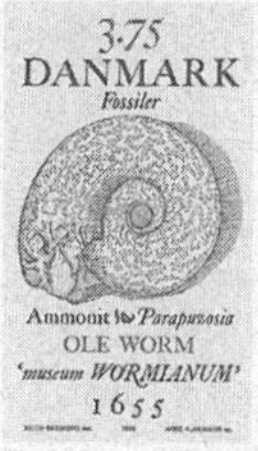

482 Ammonite (from "Museum Wormianum" by Ole Worm)

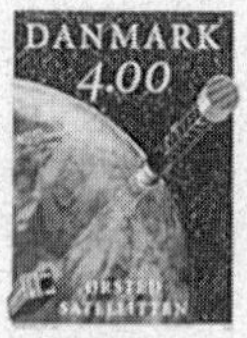

483 Satellite and Earth

1998. Fossils. Designs reproducing engravings from geological works. Each black and red on cream.
1153 3k.75 Type **482** 90 25
1154 4k.50 Shark's teeth (from "De Solido" by Niels Stensen) . . . . 1·10 95
1155 5k.50 Sea urchin (from "Stevens Klint" by Soren Abildgaard) . . . . . . 1·25 1·10
1156 15k. Pleurotomariida (from "Den Danske Atlas" by Erich Pontoppidan) . . . 3·25 2·50

1999. Launch of "Orsted" Satellite (Danish research satellite).
1158 **483** 4k. multicoloured . . . 1·00 20

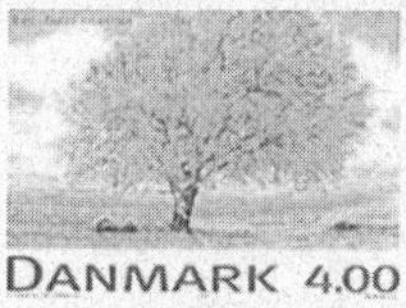

484 Beech

1999. Deciduous Trees. Multicoloured.
1159 4k. Type **484** 95 35
1160 5k. Ash (vert) . . . . 1·25 85
1161 5k.25 Small-leaved lime (vert) . . . . 1·25 60
1162 9k.25 Pendunculate oak . . 2·10 1·75

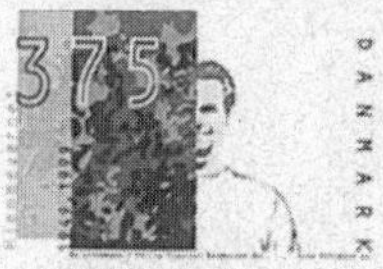

485 Home Guard

1999. 50th Anniv of Home Guard.
1163 **485** 3k.75 multicoloured . . 90 70

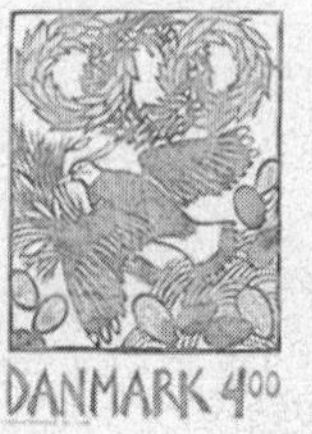

486 Lapwing and Eggs

1999. Harbingers of Spring. Multicoloured.
1164 4k. Type **486** 90 25
1165 5k.25 Greylag goose with chicks . . . . 1·25 65

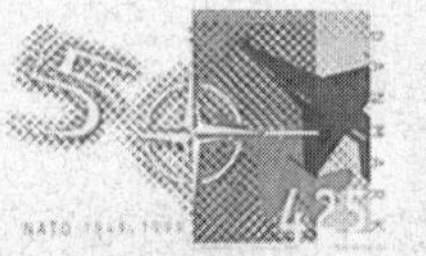
487 Emblem and Jet Fighters

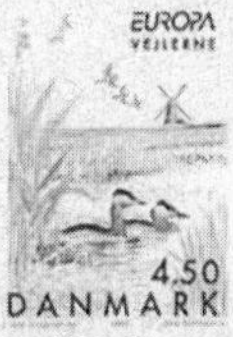

488 Vejlerne

1999. 50th Anniv of North Atlantic Treaty Organization.

1167	487	4k.25 multicoloured . . .	1·10	90

1999. Europa. Parks and Gardens. Multicoloured.

1168		4k.50 Type **488**	1·10	90
1169		5k.50 Langli Island	1·25	1·10

489 Anniversary Emblem   490 "g" and Paragraph Sign

1999. 50th Anniv of Council of Europe.

1170	489	9k.75 blue	2·10	1·90

1999. 150th Anniv of Danish Constitution.

1171	490	4k. red and black . . .	95	20

491 Kjeld Petersen and Dirch Passer

1999. 150th Anniv of Danish Revue.

1172	491	4k. red	1·10	25
1173	–	4k.50 black	1·10	90
1174	–	5k.25 blue	1·25	80
1175	–	6k.75 mauve	1·40	1·40

DESIGNS—4k.50, Osvald Helmuth; 5k.25, Preben Kaas and Jorgen Ryg; 6k.75, Liva Weel.

492 Emblem   493 The "Black Diamond"

1999. Alzheimer's Disease Association.

1176	492	4k.+50ore. red and blue	1·10	1·10

1999. Inauguration of Royal Library Extension, Copenhagen.

1177	493	8k.75 black	2·00	2·00

494 "Four Colours" (Thomas Kluge)

1999. Paintings. Multicoloured.

1178		9k.25 Type **494**	2·10	2·00
1179		16k. "Boy" (Lise Malinovsky)	3·75	3·75

495 Barn Swallows   496 Hearts

1999. Migratory Birds. Multicoloured.

1180		4k. Type **495**	1·00	65
1181		5k.25 Greylag geese with goslings	1·10	90
1182		5k.50 Eiders	1·10	1·10
1183		12k.25 Arctic tern feeding chick	2·50	2·50

1999. New Millennium. Multicoloured.

1185		4k. Type **496**	80	25
1186		4k. Horizontal wavy lines	80	25

497 Johan Henrik Deuntzer (Prime Minister) on Front Page of *Aftenposten* (newspaper)   498 Queen Margrethe II (Pia Schutzmann)

2000. The Twentieth Century (1st series).

1187	497	4k. black and cream . .	80	25
1188	–	4k.50 multicoloured . .	90	1·00
1189	–	5k.25 multicoloured . .	1·10	50
1190	–	5k.75 multicoloured . .	1·40	1·25

DESIGNS—4k. Type **497** (Venstre (workers') party victory in election, 1901); 4k.50, Caricature of Frederik Borgbjerg (party member, Alfred Schmidt) (first Social Democrat Lord Mayor in Denmark, 1903); 5k.25, Asta Nielson and Poul Reumert (actors) in scene from *The Abyss* (film), 1910; 5k.75, Telephone advertising poster, 1914.

See also Nos. 1207/10, 1212/15 and 1221/4.

2000. 60th Birthday of Queen Margrethe II.

1191	498	4k. black and red . . .	80	25
1192	–	5k.25 black and blue . .	1·00	50

499 Queen Margrethe II

2000.

1194	499	4k. red	70	10
1195		4k.25 blue	75	90
1196		4k.50 red	80	1·00
1196a		4k.75 brown	80	1·00
1197		5k. green	85	1·00
1198		5k.25 blue	90	40
1199		5k.50 violet	1·00	50
1200		5k.75 green	1·25	90
1201		6k. brown	1·25	90
1201a		6k.50 green	1·10	1·00
1202		6k.75 red	1·00	60
1203		7k. purple	1·25	70

500 Map of Oresund Region

2000. Inauguration of Oresund Link (Denmark–Sweden road and rail system).

1205	500	4k.50 blue, white & blk	80	1·00
1206	–	4k.50 blue, green & blk	80	1·00

DESIGN: No. 1206, Oresund Bridge.

501 Suffragette on Front Page of *Politiken* (newspaper)   502 "Building Europe"

2000. The Twentieth Century (2nd series).

1207	501	4k. red, blk & cream . .	70	25
1208	–	5k. multicoloured . . .	85	1·00
1209	–	5k.50 multicoloured . .	95	1·25
1210	–	6k.75 multicoloured . .	1·40	1·50

DESIGNS—4k. Type **501** (women's suffrage, 1915); 5k. Caricature of Thorvald Stauning (Prime Minister 1924–26 and 1929–42) (Herluf Jensenius) (The Kanslergade Agreement (economic and social reforms)), 1933; 5k.50, Poster for *The Wheel of Fortune* (film), 1927; 6k.75, Front page of *Radio Weekly Review* (magazine), 1925.

2000. Europa.

1211	502	9k.75 multicoloured . .	1·75	1·75

503 Front Page of *Kristeligt Dagblad* (newspaper), 5 May 1945   504 Linked Hands

2000. The Twentieth Century (3rd series).

1212	503	4k. black and cream . .	70	25
1213	–	5k.75 multicoloured . .	1·00	1·25
1214	–	6k.75 multicoloured . .	1·40	1·40
1215	–	12k.25 multicoloured . .	2·50	2·40

DESIGNS—4k. Type **503** (Liberation of Denmark); 5k.75, Caricature of Princess Margrethe (Herlif Jenserius) (adoption of new constitution, 1953); 6k.75, Ib Schonberg and Hvid Moller (actors) in a scene from *Cafe Paradise* (film), 1950; 12k.25, Front cover of brochure for Danish Arena televisions, 1957.

2000. Cerebral Palsy Association.

1216	504	4k.+50ore blue and red	1·00	1·00

505 Lockheed C-130 Hercules Transport Plane

2000. 50th Anniv of Royal Danish Air Force.

1217	505	9k.75 black and red . .	2·00	2·00

506 "Pegasus" (Kurt Trampedach)

2000. Paintings. Multicoloured.

1219		4k. Type **506**	70	90
1220		5k.25 "Untitled" (Nina Sten-Knudsen)	4·25	1·10

507 Front Page of *Berlingske Tidende* (newspaper), 3 October 1972

2000. The Twentieth Century (4th series).

1221	507	4k. red, blk & cream . .	70	10
1222	–	4k.50 multicoloured . .	75	45
1223	–	5k.25 blk, red & cream .	90	55
1224	–	5k.50 multicoloured . .	95	55

DESIGNS: 4k. Type **507** (referendum on entry to European Economic Community); 4k.50, Caricature from *Blaeksprutten* (magazine), 1969 (The Youth Revolt); 5k.25, Poster for *The Olsen Gang* (film, 1968); 5k.50, Web page (development of the internet).

508 Kite

2001. 40th Anniv of Amnesty International.

1225	508	4k.+50 ore blk & red . . .	75	75

509 Palm House

2001. 400th Anniv of Copenhagen University Botanical Gardens. Multicoloured.

1226		4k. Type **509**	70	10
1227		6k. Lake (28 × 21 mm) . . .	1·00	60
1228		12k.25 Giant lily-pad (28 × 21 mm)	2·10	1·25

510 "a", Text and Flowers

2001. Reading. Danish Children's Book "ABC" (first reader) by Halfdan Rasmussen. Multicoloured.

1229		4k. Type **510**	70	10
1230		7k. "Z" and text	1·10	70

511 Martinus William Ferslew (designer and engraver)   512 Hands catching Water

2001. 150th Anniv of First Danish Stamp. Each black, red and brown.

1231		4k. Type **511**	70	10
1232		5k.50 Andreas Thiele (printer)	90	55
1233		6k. Frantz Christopher von Jessen (Copenhagen postmaster)	1·00	60
1234		10k.25 Magrius Otto Sophus (Postmaster-General) . .	1·75	1·00

2001. Europa. Water Resources. Multicoloured.

1235		4k.50 Type **512**	75	10
1236		9k.75 Woman in shower . .	1·60	1·00

513 Skateboarder

2001. Youth Culture. Multicoloured.

1237		4k. Type **513**	70	10
1238		5k.50 Couple kissing	90	55
1239		6k. Mixing records	1·00	60
1240		10k.25 Pierced tongue . . .	1·75	1·00

514 "Missus" (Jorn Larsen)

2001. Paintings.

1242	514	18k. black and red . . .	3·00	1·75
1243	–	22k. multicoloured . . .	3·75	2·25

DESIGN: 22k. "Postbillede" (Henning Damgaard-Sorensen).

515 Queen Margrethe II with 1984 Prince Henrik and 1994 Marselisborg Castle Stamps   517 Rasmus Klump (Vilhelm Hansen)

516 *Bukken-Bruse*

2001. HAFNIA '01 International Stamp Exhibition, Copenhagen. Multicoloured.
1244 4k. Type **515** ... 70 10
1245 4k.50 King Frederik IX with 1985 Queen Ingrid and 1994 Graasten Castle stamps ... 75 10
1246 5k.50 King Christian X with 1994 Amalienborg Castle and 1939 Queen Alexandrine stamps ... 90 55
1247 7k. King Christian IX with 1994 Fredensborg Castle and 1907 King Frederik VIII stamps ... 1·10 70

2001. Ferries.
1249 **516** 3k.75 black, green and emerald ... 60 10
1250 – 4k. black, brown and green ... 70 10
1251 – 4k.25 black, green and blue ... 75 10
1252 – 6k. grey, black and red 1·00 60
DESIGNS: 4k. *Ouro*; 4k.25, *Hjarno*; 6k. *Barsofargen*.

2002. Danish Cartoons. Multicoloured.
1253 4k. Type **517** ... 70 10
1254 5k.50 Valhalla (Peter Madsen) ... 90 55
1255 6k.50 Jungo and Rita (Flemming Quist Moller) 1·10 65
1256 10k.50 Cirkleen (Hanne and Jannik Hastrup) ... 1·60 95

MILITARY FRANK STAMPS

1917. Nos. 135 and 138 optd **S F** (= "Soldater Frimaerke").
M188 **21** 5ore green ... 8·50 20·00
M189 10ore red ... 7·00 16·00

NEWSPAPER STAMPS

N 18

1901.
N185 N 18 1ore green ... 10·00 1·25
N186 5ore blue ... 23·00 6·50
N133 7ore red ... 14·00 1·10
N188 8ore green ... 27·00 1·60
N189 10ore lilac ... 35·00 1·60
N135 20ore green ... 23·00 1·00
N191 29ore orange ... 42·00 2·50
N136 38ore green ... 35·00 1·00
N193 41ore brown ... 48·00 2·25
N137 68ore brown ... 80·00 24·00
N138 1k. purple & green . 23·00 1·60
N139 5k. green and pink . . £140 20·00
N140 10k. blue and stone . . £160 17·00

OFFICIAL STAMPS

O 9

1871. Value in "skilling".
O51a O 9 2sk. blue ... £160 70·00
O52 4sk. red ... 60·00 11·00
O53 16sk. green ... £375 £170

1875. Value in "ore".
O185 O 9 1ore orange ... 55 85
O100 3ore lilac ... 2·10 3·25
O186 3ore grey ... 2·10 5·25
O101 4ore blue ... 1·60 1·60
O188 5ore green ... 1·00 40
O189 5ore brown ... 1·90 12·50
O 94 8ore red ... 10·00 1·60
O104 10ore red ... 2·75 1·40
O191 10ore green ... 1·25 2·25
O192 20ore lilac ... 8·00 21·00
O193 20ore blue ... 14·50 7·50
O 98 32ore green ... 19·00 18·00

PARCEL POST STAMPS

1919. Various types optd **POSTFAERGE.**
P208 **21** 10ore red ... 35·00 42·00
P209 **15** 10ore green ... 16·00 9·00
P210 10ore brown ... 12·50 5·75
P211 **21** 30ore lilac ... 10·00 17·00
P212 30ore orange ... 11·00 18·00
P213 30ore blue ... 2·25 3·50
P214 50ore black & purple . £150 £200
P215a 50ore grey ... 21·00 9·50
P216 **22** 1k. brown ... 90·00 £110
P217 **21** 1k. blue and brown . 29·00 25·00

P218 5k. brown & mauve ... 1·10 1·25
P219 10k. green and red ... 38·00 60·00

1927. Stamps of 1927 (solid background) optd **POSTFAERGE.**
P252 **40** 15ore red ... 10·00 7·50
P253 30ore yellow ... 8·50 10·00
P254 40ore green ... 17·00 8·00

1936. Stamps of 1933 (lined background) optd **POSTFAERGE.**
P491 **43** 5ore purple ... 40 35
P299 10ore orange ... 14·00 13·00
P300 10ore brown ... 75 1·10
P301 10ore violet ... 20 25
P302 10ore green ... 35 20
P303a **40** 15ore red ... 40 85
P304 30ore blue ... 4·00 2·75
P305 30ore orange ... 20 60
P306 40ore green ... 2·75 3·25
P307 40ore blue ... 20 60
P308 **45** 50ore grey ... 55 90
P309 1k. brown ... 50 65

1945. Stamps of 1942 optd **POSTFAERGE.**
P346 **67** 30ore orange ... 1·40 1·10
P347 40ore blue ... 80 90
P348 50ore grey ... 95 80

1949. Stamps of 1946 and 1948 optd **POSTFAERGE.**
P376 **80** 30ore orange ... 2·75 1·10
P377 30ore red ... 1·00 1·00
P378 40ore blue ... 2·10 1·10
P379 40ore grey ... 1·00 1·00
P380 50ore grey ... 12·00 2·25
P381 50ore green ... 1·10 1·00
P382 70ore green ... 95 1·00
P383 **73** 1k. brown ... 1·00 85
P384 1k.25 orange ... 4·50 5·25
P495 2k. red ... 1·40 1·90
P496 5k. blue ... 3·50 4·25

1967. Optd **POSTFAERGE.**
P488 **117** 40ore brown ... 55 60
P492 50ore brown ... 25 40
P489 80ore blue ... 55 70
P493 90ore blue ... 55 85

1975. Optd **POSTFAERGE.**
P597 **207** 100ore blue ... 70 1·10

POSTAGE DUE STAMPS

1921. Stamps of 1905 and 1913 optd **PORTO.**
D214 **15** 1ore orange ... 1·50 1·50
D215 **21** 5ore green ... 4·50 1·75
D216 7ore orange ... 2·25 1·75
D217 10ore red ... 17·00 7·00
D218 20ore blue ... 10·50 5·50
D219 25ore black and brown 20·00 3·25
D220 50ore black & purple . 6·50 3·00

D 32

1921. Solid background.
D221 D 32 1ore orange ... 55 80
D222 4ore blue ... 2·75 2·00
D223 5ore brown ... 2·50 85
D224 5ore green ... 2·10 65
D225 7ore green ... 11·00 13·00
D226 7ore violet ... 24·00 26·00
D227 10ore green ... 2·50 60
D228 10ore brown ... 1·60 60
D229 20ore blue ... 1·10 65
D230 20ore grey ... 2·00 1·40
D231 25ore red ... 3·75 1·10
D232 25ore lilac ... 2·10 1·75
D233 25ore blue ... 3·75 2·25
D234 1k. blue ... 50·00 5·50
D235 1k. blue and brown . . 6·00 3·50
D236 5k. violet ... 12·00 5·50

For stamps with lined background see Nos. D285/97.

1921. Military Frank stamp optd **PORTO.**
D237 **21** 10ore red (No. M189) . . 8·00 7·75

1934. Lined background.
D285 D 32 1ore green ... 10 10
D286 2ore red ... 10 10
D287 5ore green ... 10 10
D288 6ore green ... 45 20
D289 8ore mauve ... 1·40 1·75
D290 10ore orange ... 10 10
D291 12ore blue ... 40 40
D292 15ore violet ... 45 20
D293 20ore grey ... 40 10
D294 25ore blue ... 40 10
D295 30ore green ... 40 10
D296 40ore purple ... 55 45
D297 1k. brown ... 55 10

1934. Surch **PORTO 15.**
D298 **15** 15 on 12ore lilac ... 3·75 3·25

SPECIAL FEE STAMPS

1923. No. D227 optd **GEBYR GEBYR.**
S218 D 32 10ore green ... 11·50 2·50

S 36

1926. Solid background.
S229 S 36 5ore green ... 10·50 90
S230 10ore brown ... 6·00 80

1934. Lined background.
S285 S 36 5ore green ... 10 10
S286 10ore orange ... 10 10

DHAR   Pt. 1

A state of Central India. Now uses Indian stamps.

4 pice = 1 anna.

1   2

1897. Imperf.
1 1 ½pice black on red ... 2·25 2·75
3 ¼a. black on orange ... 2·25 3·25
4 ¼a. black on mauve ... 3·50 4·25
5 1a. black on green ... 7·00 12·00
6 2a. black on yellow ... 24·00 38·00

1898. Perf.
7b 2 ½a. red ... 2·75 5·50
8 1a. purple ... 3·00 6·00
10 2a. green ... 5·50 20·00

DIEGO-SUAREZ   Pt. 6

A port in N. Madagascar. A separate colony till 1896, when it was incorporated with Madagascar.

100 centimes = 1 franc.

1890. Stamps of French Colonies (Type J Commerce), surch **15** sideways.
1 J 15 on 1c. black on blue ... £170 70·00
2 15 on 5c. green ... £450 70·00
3 15 on 10c. black on lilac . . £180 55·00
4 15 on 20c. red on green . . £450 70·00
5 15 on 25c. black on red ... 85·00 21·00

2   3

1890. Various designs.
6 2 1c. black ... £350 85·00
7 5c. black ... £325 75·00
8 15c. black ... 85·00 32·00
9 25c. black ... £110 35·00

1891.
10 3 5c. black ... £120 70·00

1891. Stamps of French Colonies. (Type J Commerce) surch **1891 DIEGO-SUAREZ 5 c.**
13 J 5c. on 10c. black on lilac . £160 80·00
14 5c. on 20c. red on green . . £140 65·00

1892. Stamps of French Colonies (Type J Commerce) optd **DIEGO-SUAREZ.**
15 J 1c. black on blue ... 24·00 12·50
16 2c. brown on buff ... 28·00 13·50
17 4c. brown on grey ... 28·00 22·00
18 5c. green on green ... 85·00 55·00
19 10c. black on lilac ... 23·00 23·00
20 15c. blue on blue ... 18·00 12·50
21 20c. red on green ... 26·00 21·00
22 25c. black on pink ... 16·00 13·50
23 30c. brown on drab ... £850 £600
24 35c. black on orange . . £850 £600
25 75c. red on pink ... 65·00 26·00
26 1f. green ... 60·00 40·00

1892. "Tablet" key-type inscr "DIEGO-SUAREZ ET DEPENDANCES".
38 D 1c. black ... 1·75 3·75
39 2c. brown on buff ... 2·25 1·25
40 4c. brown on grey ... 85 4·00
41 5c. green on green ... 1·60 4·75
42 10c. black on lilac ... 5·75 6·50
43 15c. blue ... 4·25 11·00
44 20c. red on green ... 8·75 10·00
45 25c. black on pink ... 6·50 8·75
46 30c. brown on drab ... 9·00 22·00
47 40c. red on yellow ... 15·00 13·50

48 50c. red on pink ... 19·00 13·00
49 75c. brown on yellow . . 42·00 26·00
50 1f. green ... 60·00 55·00

1894. "Tablet" key-type inscr "DIEGO-SUAREZ".
51 D 1c. black on yellow ... 50 2·75
52 2c. brown on buff ... 1·25 3·50
53 4c. brown on grey ... 1·75 3·50
54 5c. green on green ... 2·25 5·25
55 10c. black on lilac ... 5·75 6·25
56 15c. blue ... 3·50 5·50
57 20c. red on green ... 8·00 14·50
58 25c. black on pink ... 4·25 4·00
59 30c. brown on drab ... 9·00 6·25
60 40c. red on yellow ... 7·75 5·00
61 50c. red on pink ... 6·00 8·00
62 75c. brown on yellow . . 2·75 6·00
63 1f. green ... 8·25 12·00

POSTAGE DUE STAMPS

D 4

1891.
D11 D 4 5c. violet ... 65·00 24·00
D12 50c. black on yellow . . 65·00 35·00

1892. Postage Due stamps of French Colonies overprinted **DIEGO-SUAREZ.**
D27 D 4 1c. black ... £100 50·00
D29 2c. black ... £110 45·00
D30 4c. black ... £110 50·00
D31 5c. black ... £110 60·00
D32 10c. black ... 27·00 25·00
D33 15c. black ... 27·00 27·00
D34 20c. black ... £160 £110
D35 30c. black ... 90·00 60·00
D36 60c. black ... £850 £600
D37 1f. brown ... £1600 £850

DJIBOUTI   Pt. 6

A port in French Somaliland S. of the Red Sea, later capital of French Territory of the Afars and the Issas.

100 centimes = 1 franc.

1893. "Tablet" key-type stamp of Obock optd **DJ.**
83 D 5c. green & red on green . . £110 £120

1894. Same type surch in figures and **DJIBOUTI.**
85 D 25 on 2c. brn & bl on buff £275 £180
86 50 on 1c. blk & red on blue £325 £225

1894. Triangular stamp of Obock optd **DJIBOUTI** or surch **1** also.
87 5 1f. on 5f. red ... £600 £400
88 5f. red ... £1400 £1100

12 Djibouti (The apparent perforation is part of the design.)

13 "Pingouin" (French gunboat)

14 Crossing the Desert

1894. Imperf.
89 12 1c. red and black ... 1·10 1·25
90 2c. black and red ... 45 45
91 4c. blue and brown ... 3·00 1·90
92 5c. red and green ... 2·25 1·60
93 5c. green ... 2·50 3·50
94 – 10c. green and brown . . 3·75 1·00
95 – 15c. green and lilac ... 3·25 1·75

96	– 25c. blue and red	5·00	2·00
97	– 30c. red and brown . . .	3·75	3·75
98	– 40c. blue and yellow . .	55·00	60·00
99	– 50c. red and blue	18·00	12·00
100	– 75c. orange and mauve .	35·00	29·00
101	– 1f. black and olive . . .	21·00	21·00
102	– 2f. red and brown . . .	85·00	70·00
103	**13** 5f. blue and red	£190	£120
104	**14** 25f. blue and red	£850	£850
105	– 50f. red and blue	£650	£650

DESIGNS— As Type **12**: 10 to 75c. Different views of Djibouti; 1, 2f. Port of Djibouti.

1899. As last, surch.

108	– 0.05 on 75c. orge & mve	55·00	32·00
109	– 0.10 on 1f. blk & olive .	70·00	60·00
106	**12** 0.40 on 4c. blue & brown	£2750	£900
110	– 0.40 on 2f. red & brown	£550	£350
111	**13** 0.75 on 5f. blue and red . .	£450	£375

1902. Rectangular stamp of Obock surch **0.05**.

107	**6** 0.05 on 75c. lilac & orange	£1200	£900

1902. Triangular stamps of Obock surch.

112	**7** 5c. on 25f. blue and brown	55·00	60·00
113	– 10c. on 50f. green & red . .	75·00	60·00

1902. Nos. 98/9 surch.

114	5c. on 40c. blue and yellow	2·25	2·00
115	10c. on 50c. red and blue .	15·00	20·00

1902. Stamps of Obock surch **DJIBOUTI** and value.

120	**6** 5c. on 30c. yellow & grn . .	5·50	12·50
116	– 10c. on 25c. black & blue .	4·50	7·75
118	**7** 10c. on 2f. orange & lilac .	35·00	50·00
119	– 10c. on 10f. lake and red . .	30·00	30·00

For later issues see **FRENCH SOMALI COAST, FRENCH TERRITORY OF THE AFARS AND THE ISSAS** and **DJIBOUTI REPUBLIC**.

DJIBOUTI REPUBLIC   Pt. 12

Formerly French Territory of the Afars and the Issas.

112 Map and Flag   115 Head Rest

1977. Independence. Multicoloured.

685	45f. Type **112**	1·50	80
686	65f. Map of Djibouti (horiz)	2·25	95

1977. Various stamps of the French Territory of the Afars and the Issas optd **REPUBLIQUE DE DJIBOUTI** or surch also. (a) Sea Shells.

687	**81** 1f. on 4f. mult	20	20
688	– 2f. on 5f. brown, mauve and violet (629) . . .	20	20
689	– 20f. brown & grn (633) . .	55	55
690	– 30f. brn, pur & grn (634) .	65	65
691	– 40f. brown & grn (635) . .	90	90
692	– 45f. brn, grn & bl (636) . .	1·00	1·00
693	– 60f. black & brn (638) . . .	1·40	1·40
694	– 70f. brn, bl & blk (639) . .	1·90	1·90

(b) Flora and Fauna.

695	**103** 5f. on 20f. multicoloured .	20	20
696	**106** 45f. multicoloured	90	90
697	– 50f. multicoloured (675) .	1·40	1·40
698	**107** 70f. multicoloured	1·60	1·60
699	– 100f. multicoloured (653) .	2·50	2·50
700	– 150f. multicoloured (676) .	3·00	3·00
701	– 300f. multicoloured (654) .	7·50	7·50

(c) Buildings.

702	**99** 8f. grey, red & bl (postage)	30	30
703	**109** 500f. mult (air)	9·75	8·25

(d) Celebrities.

704	**111** 55f. red, grey & grn (air)	1·40	1·10
705	– 75f. red, brn & grn (682) .	2·50	2·50

706	**104** 200f. blue, green and orange (postage) . .	3·75	3·75

(e) Sport.

707	**108** 200f. multicoloured	4·50	4·50

1977. Local Art. Multicoloured.

708	10f. Type **115**	20	10
709	20f. Water cask (vert) . . .	45	15
710	25f. Washing jar (vert) . . .	65	20

116 Ostrich   117 "Glossodoris"

1977. Birds. Multicoloured.

711	90f. Type **116**	2·75	1·00
712	100f. Vitelline masked weaver	3·75	1·75

1977. Sea Life. Multicoloured.

713	45f. Type **117**	1·00	90
714	70f. Turtle	1·10	45
715	80f. Catalufa	1·60	65

118 Map, Dove and U.N. Emblem

1977. Air. Admission to the United Nations.

716	**118** 300f. multicoloured . . .	4·50	2·75

119 Crabs "Uca lactea"

1977. Fauna. Multicoloured.

717	15f. Type **119**	45	15
718	50f. Klipspringer	1·25	40
719	150f. Dolphin (fish)	3·25	2·00

120 President Hassan Gouled Aptidon and Flag

1978.

720	**120** 65f. multicoloured . . .	90	45

121 Marcel Brochet MB 101

1978. Air. Djibouti Aero Club. Multicoloured.

721	60f. Type **121**	95	60
722	85f. De Havilland Tiger Moth	1·25	80
723	200f. Morane Saulnier Rallye Commodore	2·75	1·60

122 "Charaxes hansali"

123 "Head of an Old Man"

1978. Butterflies. Multicoloured.

724	5f. Type **122**	10	10
725	20f. "Colias electo"	55	20

726	25f. "Acraea chilo"	80	40
727	150f. "Junonia hierta" . . .	3·00	1·50

1978. Air. 400th Birth Anniv of Rubens. Mult.

728	50f. Type **123**	85	35
729	500f. "The Hippopotamus Hunt" (detail)	8·00	3·25

124 Necklace   125 Player with Cup

1978. Native Handicrafts. Multicoloured.

730	45f. Type **124**	85	40
731	55f. Necklace	1·10	45

1978. Air. World Cup Football Championship, Argentina. Multicoloured.

732	100f. Type **125**	1·40	45
733	300f. World Cup, footballer and map of Argentina . .	4·25	1·25

126 "Bougainvillea glabra"

1978. Flowers. Multicoloured.

734	15f. Type **126**	40	10
735	35f. "Hibiscus schizopetalus"	70	20
736	250f. "Caesalpinia pulcherrima"	4·50	85

1978. Air. Argentina's Victory in World Cup Football Championship. Nos. 722/3 optd.

737	100f. Type **125**	1·60	45
738	300f. World Cup, footballer and map of Argentina . .	4·50	1·50

OVERPRINTS: 100f. **ARGENTINE CHAMPION 1978**; 300f. **ARGENTINE HOLLANDE 3–1**.

128 "The Hare" (Albrecht Durer)

1978. Air. Paintings. Multicoloured.

739	100f. "Tahitian Women" (Paul Gauguin) (horiz) . .	1·90	55
740	250f. Type **128**	4·75	1·90

129 Knobbed Triton

1978. Sea Shells. Multicoloured

741	10f. Type **129**	75	35
742	80f. Trumpet triton	2·50	90

130 Copper-banded Butterflyfish   131 Dove and U.P.U. Emblem

1978. Fishes. Multicoloured.

743	8f. Type **130**	40	15
744	30f. Yellow tang	85	25
745	40f. Harlequin sweetlips . . .	1·60	45

1978. Air. "Philexafrique" Exhibition, Libreville, Gabon (1st issue) and Int. Stamp Fair, Essen, W. Germany. As T **237** of Benin. Multicoloured.

746	90f. Jay and Brunswick 1852 3sqr. stamp	1·90	1·40
747	90f. African spoonbill and Djibouti 1977 optd 300f. stamp	1·90	1·40

1978. Air. Centenary of Paris U.P.U. Congress.

748	**131** 200f. green, brn & turq	2·75	1·40

132 Alsthom BB 1201 Diesel Locomotive

1979. Djibouti–Addis Ababa Railway. Mult.

749	40f. Type **132**	90	40
750	55f. Pacific locomotive No. 231	80	30
751	60f. Steam locomotive No. 130	1·00	35
752	75f. Alsthom CC 2001 diesel-electric locomotive . .	1·40	60

133 Children learning to Count

1979. International Year of the Child. Multicoloured.

753	20f. Type **133**	35	10
754	200f. Mother and child . . .	3·00	1·25

134 De Havilland Twin Otter over Crater

1979. Ardoukoba Volcano. Multicoloured.

755	30f. Sud Aviation Alouette II helicopter over crater . .	65	40
756	90f. Type **134**	1·90	70

135 Sir Rowland Hill and 300f. Stamp, 1977

1979. Death Centenary of Sir Rowland Hill. Multicoloured.

757	25f. Type **135**	35	10
758	100f. Letters with 1894 50f. and 1977 45f. stamps . .	2·25	60
759	150f. Loading mail on ship .	2·25	80

136 Junkers Ju 52/3m and Dewoitine D-338 Trimotor

1979. Air. 75th Anniv of Powered Flight. Multicoloured.
760 140f. Type **136** . . . . 2·25 95
761 250f. Potez 63-11 bomber and
   Supermarine Spitfire
   Mk. VII . . . . 3·25 1·90
762 500f. Concorde and Sikorsky
   S-40 flying boat "American
   Clipper" . . . . 7·25 3·25

137 Djibouti, Local Woman and Namaqua Dove

1979. "Philexafrique 2" Exhibition, Gabon (2nd issue). Multicoloured.
763 55f. Type **137** . . . . 2·25 1·40
764 80f. U.P.U. emblem, map,
   Douglas DC-8-60 "Super
   Sixty", Alsthom diesel-
   electric train and postal
   runner . . . . 2·75 1·25

138 "Opuntia"

1979. Flowers. Multicoloured.
765 2f. Type **138** 10 10
766 8f. "Solanacea" (horiz) . . . 20 10
767 15f. "Trichodesma" (horiz) . . 35 10
768 45f. "Acacia etbaica" (horiz) . 65 15
769 50f. "Thunbergia alata" . . . 90 15

139 "The Washerwoman"

1979. Air. Death Centenary of Honore Daumier (painter).
770 **139** 500f. multicoloured . . . 8·25 2·75

140 Basketball

1979. Pre-Olympic Year. Multicoloured.
771 70f. Type **140** . . . . . . 1·10 30
772 120f. Running . . . . 1·60 55
773 300f. Football . . . . 2·75 85

141 Bull-mouth Helmet

1979. Shells. Multicoloured.
774 10f. Type **141** 20 15
775 40f. Arthritic spider conch . . 1·00 20
776 300f. Ventral harp . . . . . 5·50 1·60

142 Winter Sports Equipment and Mosque

1980. Air. Winter Olympic Games, Lake Placid.
777 **142** 150f. multicoloured . . . 2·25 65

143 Lions Club Banner and Steam Locomotive

1980. Djibouti Clubs. Multicoloured.
778 90f. Rotary Club banner and
   Morane Saulnier MS 892
   (75th anniv of Rotary
   International) . . . . . . 1·75 70
779 100f. Type **143** . . . . . . 2·50 50

144 "Colotis danae"   **147** Basketball

145 Boeing 737

1980. Butterflies. Multicoloured.
780 5f. Type **144** 20 20
781 55f. "Danaus chrysippus" . . 1·00 65

1980. Air. Foundation of "Air Djibouti".
782 **145** 400f. multicoloured . . . 6·00 2·25

1980. Air. Winter Olympic Games. No. 777 surch with names of Medal Winners.
783 **142** 80f. on 150f. . . . . . . 1·10 45
784 200f. on 150f. . . . . . . 2·75 1·25
OVERPRINTS: 80f. **A.M. MOSER-PROEL AUTRICHE DESCENT DAMES MEDAILLE D'OR.** 200f. **HEIDEN USA 5 MEDAILLES D'OR PATINAGE DE VITESSE.**

1980. Olympic Games, Moscow. Multicoloured.
785 60f. Type **147** 90 20
786 120f. Football . . . . 1·60 45
787 250f. Running . . . . 3·00 1·00

148 "Apollo XI" Moon Landing

1980. Air. Conquest of Space. Multicoloured.
788 200f. Type **148** . . . . . . 2·75 65
789 300f. "Apollo-Soyuz" link-up . 4·50 1·00

149 Samisch v Romanovsky Game, Moscow, 1925

1980. Founding of International Chess Federation, 1924. Multicoloured.
790 20f. Type **149** 70 15
791 75f. "Royal Chess Party"
   (15th-century Italian book
   illustration) . . . . 1·90 40

150 Satellite and Earth Station

1980. Air. Inauguration of Satellite Earth Station.
792 **150** 500f. multicoloured . . . 7·25 1·90

151 Sieve Cowrie

1980. Shells. Multicoloured.
793 15f. Type **151** 50 20
794 85f. Chambered nautilus . . . 1·90 65

152 Sir Alexander Fleming and Penicillin

1980. Anniversaries. Multicoloured.
795 20f. Type **152** 50 20
796 130f. Jules Verne and space
   capsules . . . . 2·25 65
ANNIVERSARIES: 20f. Discovery of penicillin, 25th anniv. 130f. Jules Verne, 75th death anniv.

153 "Graf Zeppelin" and Sphinx

1980. Air. 80th Anniv of First Zeppelin Flight. Multicoloured.
797 100f. Type **153** . . . . . . 2·00 60
798 150f. Ferdinand von Zeppelin . 2·50 90

154 Capt. Cook and H.M.S. "Endeavour"

1980. Death Bicentenary (1979) of Captain James Cook. Multicoloured.
799 55f. Type **154** 90 80
800 90f. Cook's ships and map of
   voyages . . . . 1·60 1·10

155 "Voyager" and Saturn

1980. Air. Space Exploration. Multicoloured.
801 **155** 250f. multicoloured . . . 4·00 1·10

156 Saving a Goal

1981. Air. World Cup Football Eliminators. Multicoloured.
802 80f. Type **156** . . . . 1·10 35
803 200f. Tackle . . . . 2·75 80

157 Transport   **158** Yuri Gagarin and "Vostok 1"

1981. Air European–African Economic Convention.
804 **157** 100f. multicoloured . . . 3·00 90

1981. Air. Space Anniversaries and Events. Multicoloured.
805 75f. Type **158** (20th anniv of
   first man in space) . . . . 1·10 35
806 120f. "Viking" exploration of
   Mars (horiz) . . . . . . 1·60 50
807 150f. Alan Shepard and
   "Freedom 7" (20th anniv
   of first American in space) . 2·25 65

159 Arabian Angelfish

1981. Djibouti Tropical Aquarium. Mult.
808 25f. Type **159** 60 15
809 55f. Moorish idol . . . . . 1·40 35
810 70f. Golden trevally . . . . 1·60 90

160 Caduceus, Satellite and Rocket

1981. World Telecommunications Day.
811 **160** 140f. multicoloured . . . 1·90 55

161 German 231 and American RC4 Diesel Locomotives

1981. Locomotives. Multicoloured.
812 40f. Type **161** 85 30
813 55f. George Stephenson,
   "Rocket" (1829) and
   Djibouti locomotive . . . . 1·25 40
814 65f. French TGV and
   Japanese "Hikari" high
   speed trains . . . . . . 1·75 40

162 Antenna on Globe and Morse Key

1981. Djibouti Amateur Radio Club.
815 **162** 250f. multicoloured . . . 3·50   1·10

163 Prince Charles and Lady Diana Spencer

1981. Royal Wedding. Multicoloured.
816 180f. Type **163** . . . . 2·75   85
817 200f. Prince Charles and Lady Diana in wedding dress . . . . 3·00   1·10

164 Admiral Nelson and H.M.S. "Victory"

1981. Admiral Nelson Commemoration. Mult.
818 100f. Type **164** . . . . 1·60   1·00
819 175f. Nelson and stern view of H.M.S. "Victory" . . . . 2·75   1·50

165 Tree Hyrax and Scout tending Camp-fire

1981. 28th World Scouting Congress, Dakar, and Fourth Panafrican Scouting Conference, Abidjan. Multicoloured.
820 60f. Type **165** . . . . 1·25   40
821 105f. Scouts saluting, map reading and greater kudu   1·60   50

166 "Football Players" (Picasso)

1981. Air. Paintings. Multicoloured.
822 300f. Type **166** . . . . 5·00   1·40
823 400f. "Portrait of a Man in a Turban" (Rembrandt) . . . 5·50   1·90

167 Launch   **168** 19th-century Chinese Pawn and Knight

1981. Air. Space Shuttle. Multicoloured.
824 90f. Type **167** . . . . 1·40   45
825 120f. Space Shuttle landing   1·75   65

1981. Chess Pieces. Multicoloured.
826 50f. 13th-century Swedish pawn and queen (horiz) . . 1·10   35
827 130f. Type **168** . . . . 2·25   80

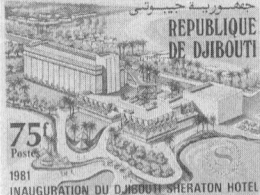

169 Aerial View

1981. Inauguration of Djibouti Sheraton Hotel.
828 **169** 75f. multicoloured . . . . 1·10   40

1981. 2nd Flight of Space Shuttle "Columbia". Nos. 824/5 optd.
829 90f. Type **167** . . . . 1·40   55
830 120f. Space Shuttle landing   1·75   85
OPTS: 90f. **COLUMBIA 2eme VOL SPATIAL 12 NOVEMBRE 1981.** 120f. **JOE ENGLE et RICHARD TRULY 2eme VOL SPATIAL—12 Nov. 1981.**

171 "Clitoria ternatea"

1981. Flowers. Multicoloured.
831 10f. Type **171** 20   10
832 30f. "Acacia mellifera" (horiz) 45   15
833 35f. "Punica granatum" (horiz) 70   20
834 45f. Malvacee 85   20

1981. World Chess Championship, Merano (1st issue). Nos. 826/7 optd.
835 50f. multicoloured 95   35
836 130f. multicoloured . . . . . 2·25   80
OPTS: 50f. **Octobre-Novembre 1981 ANATOLI KARPOV VICTOR KORTCHNOI MERANO (ITALIE).** 130f. **ANATOLI KARPOV Champion du Monde 1981.**
See also Nos. 843/4.

173 Saving Goal

1982. Air. World Cup Football Championship, Spain. Multicoloured.
837 110f. Type **173** . . . . 1·60   55
838 220f. Footballers . . . . . . 3·25   1·10

174 John H. Glenn   **175** Dr. Robert Koch, Bacillus and Microscope

1982. Air. Space Anniversaries. Mult.
839 40f. "Luna 9" (15th anniv of first unmanned moon landing) 55   20
840 60f. Type **174** (20th anniv of flight) 90   35
841 180f. "Viking 1" (5th anniv of first Mars landing) (horiz) . . . . 2·40   85

1982. Centenary of Robert Koch's Discovery of Tubercle Bacillus.
842 **175** 305f. multicoloured . . . . 4·75   1·60

176 14th-century German Bishop and 18th-century Marie de Medici Bishop   **177** Princess of Wales

1982. World Chess Championship, Merano (2nd issue). Multicoloured.
843 125f. Type **176** . . . . 2·50   75
844 175f. Late 19th-century queen and pawn from Nuremberg   3·00   95

1982. Air. 21st Birthday of Princess of Wales. Multicoloured.
845 120f. Type **177** . . . . 1·60   85
846 180f. Princess of Wales (different) . . . . 2·50   1·00

178 I.Y.C. Stamp, Collector, Greater Flamingoes and Emblems

1982. "Philexfrance" International Stamp Exhibition, Paris. Multicoloured.
847 80f. Type **178** . . . . 2·50   1·25
848 140f. Rowland Hill stamp Exhibition Centre and U.P.U. emblem . . . . . . 2·25   95

179 Microwave Antenna   **180** Mosque, Medina

1982. World Telecommunications Day.
849 **179** 150f. multicoloured . . . 2·25   90

1982. Air. 1350th Death Anniv of Mohammed.
850 **180** 500f. multicoloured . . . 6·75   2·50

181 Lord Baden-Powell

1982. Air. 125th Birth Anniv of Lord Baden-Powell. Multicoloured.
851 95f. Type **181** . . . . 1·25   55
852 200f. Saluting Scout and camp . . . . 2·75   1·10

182 Bus and Jeep

1982. Transport. Multicoloured.
853 20f. Type **182** 35   15
854 25f. Ferry and dhow 65   35
855 55f. Boeing 727-100 airliner and Alsthom Series BB 500 diesel locomotive and train   3·75   55

1982. Air. World Cup Football Championship winners. Nos. 837/8 optd.
856 110f. Type **173** . . . . 1·60   65
857 220f. Footballers . . . . . . 3·00   1·40

OPTS: 110f. **ITALIE RFA 3-1 POLOGNE FRANCE 3-2.** 220f. **ITALIE RFA 3-1 2 RFA 3 POLOGNE.**

1982. Air. Birth of Prince William of Wales. Nos. 845/6 optd.
858 120f. Type **177** . . . . 1·60   85
859 180f. Princess of Wales (different) . . . . 2·50   1·10
OPTS: 120f. **21 JUIN 1982 WILLIAM-ARTHUR-PHILIPPE-LOUIS PRINCE DES GALLES.** 180f. **21ST JUNE 1982 WILLIAM-ARTHUR-PHILIP-LOUIS PRINCE OF WALES.**

185 Satellite, Dish Aerial and Conference

1982. Air. Second U.N. Conference on the Exploration and Peaceful Uses of Outer Space, Vienna.
860 **185** 350f. multicoloured . . . 5·00   1·60

186 Franklin D. Roosevelt   **187** Red Sea Cowrie

1982. Air. 250th Birth Anniv of George Washington and Birth Centenary of Franklin D. Roosevelt. Multicoloured.
861 115f. Type **186** . . . . 1·60   55
862 250f. George Washington . . 3·25   1·10

1982. Shells. Multicoloured.
863 10f. Type **187** 25   15
864 15f. Sumatran cone 40   20
865 25f. Lovely cowrie 55   25
866 30f. Engraved cone 75   40
867 70f. Heavy bonnet . . . . . 1·75   75
868 150f. Burnt cowrie . . . . . 3·50   1·25

188 Dove perched on Gun   **189** Montgolfier's Balloon, 1783

1982. Palestinian Solidarity Day.
869 **188** 40f. multicoloured . . . 55   25

1983. Air. Bicentenary of Manned Flight. Mult.
870 35f. Type **189** 60   25
871 45f. Henri Giffard's balloon "Le Grand Ballon Captif", 1878 90   45
872 120f. Balloon "Double Eagle II", 1978 . . . . 2·25   1·10

190 Volleyball   **192** Martin Luther King

191 Bloch 220 Gascogne

1983. Air. Olympic Games, Los Angeles (1984). Multicoloured.
873	75f. Type **190**	1·10	45
874	125f. Wind-surfing	2·25	1·25

1983. Air. 50th Anniv of Air France. Mult.
875	25f. Type **191**	40	25
876	100f. Douglas DC-4	1·40	1·00
877	175f. Boeing 747-200	2·50	1·25

1983. Flowers. As T **171**. Multicoloured.
878	5f. Ipomoea	10	10
879	50f. Moringa (horiz)	85	35
880	55f. Cotton flower	1·00	40

1983. Air. Celebrities. Multicoloured.
881	180f. Type **192** (15th death anniv)	2·25	90
882	250f. Alfred Nobel (150th birth anniv)	3·25	1·40

193 W.C.Y. Emblem   194 Yacht and Rotary Club Emblem

1983. World Communications Year.
883	**193** 500f. multicoloured	6·75	2·75

1983. Air. International Club Meetings. Mult.
884	90f. Type **194**	2·00	1·50
885	150f. Minaret and Lions Club emblem	2·00	90

195 Renault, 1904

1983. Air. Early Motor Cars. Multicoloured.
886	60f. Type **195**	1·25	40
887	80f. Mercedes Knight, 1910 (vert)	1·90	50
888	100f. Lorraine-Dietrich, 1912	2·25	80

197 "Vostok VI"

1983. Air. Conquest of Space. Multicoloured.
890	120f. Type **197**	1·60	65
891	200f. "Explorer I"	2·75	1·10

198 Development Projects

1983. Donors Conference.
892	**198** 75f. multicoloured	1·10	55

199 Red Sea Marginella

1983. Shells. Multicoloured.
893	15f. Type **199**	40	15
894	30f. Jickeli's cone	85	25
895	55f. MacAndrew's cowrie	1·40	60
896	80f. Cuvier's cone	1·90	75
897	100f. Tapestry turban	2·10	1·00

200 "Colotis chrysonome"

1984. Butterflies.
898	5f. Type **200**	10	10
899	20f. "Colias erate"	25	20
900	30f. "Junonia orithyia"	45	30
901	75f. "Acraea doubledayi"	1·40	90
902	110f. "Byblia ilithya"	1·75	1·40

201 Speed Skating

1984. Air. Winter Olympic Games, Sarajevo. Mult.
903	70f. Type **201**	1·10	40
904	130f. Ice dancing	1·90	70

203 Microlight

1984. Air. Microlight Aircraft. Multicoloured.
906	65f. Type **203**	1·00	80
907	85f. Powered hang-glider "Jules"	1·25	1·00
908	100f. Microlight (different)	1·50	1·25

1984. Air. Winter Olympic Games Medal Winners. Nos. 903/4 optd.
909	70f. **1000 METRES HOMMES OR: BOUCHER (CANADA) ARGENT: KHLEBNIKOV (URSS) BRONZE: ENGELSTADT (NORV.)**	1·10	55
910	130f. **DANSE OR: TORVILL-DEAN (G.B.) ARGENT: BESTEMIANOVA-BUKIN (URSS) BRONZE: KLIMOVA-PONOMARENKO (URSS)**	1·90	85

205 "Marguerite Matisse with Cat"

1984. Air. 30th Death Anniv of Matisse and Birth Centenary of Modigliani. Multicoloured.
911	150f. Type **205**	2·50	90
912	200f. "Mario Varvogli" (Modigliani)	3·50	1·40

206 Randa

1984. Landscapes. Multicoloured.
913	2f. Type **206**	10	10
914	8f. Ali Sabieh	10	10
915	10f. Lake Assal	15	10
916	15f. Tadjoura	20	10
917	40f. Alaili Dada (vert)	55	20
918	45f. Lake Abbe	60	25
919	55f. Obock	1·50	85
920	125f. Presidential Palace	3·00	1·60

207 Marathon

1984. Air. Olympic Games, Los Angeles. Mult.
921	50f. Type **207**	65	30
922	60f. High jump	85	35
923	80f. Swimming	1·10	45

208 Battle of Solferino

1984. Air. 125th Anniv of Battle of Solferino and 120th Anniv of Red Cross.
924	**208** 300f. multicoloured	4·50	1·60

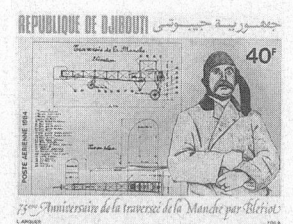

209 Bleriot and Diagram of Bleriot XI

1984. Air. 75th Anniv of Louis Bleriot's Cross-Channel Flight. Multicoloured.
925	40f. Type **209**	65	50
926	75f. Bleriot and Bleriot XI and Britten Norman Islander aircraft	1·10	90
927	90f. Bleriot and Boeing 727 airliner	1·25	1·10

210 Marathon

212 Men on Moon, Telescope and Planets

211 U.S.A. Attack-pumper Fire Engine

1984. Membership of International Olympic Committee.
928	**210** 45f. multicoloured	65	30

1984. Fire Fighting. Multicoloured.
929	25f. Type **211**	70	20
930	95f. French P.P.M. rescue crane	2·10	65
931	100f. Canadair CL-215 fire-fighting amphibian	2·25	1·25

1984. Air. 375th Anniv of Galileo's Telescope. Multicoloured.
932	120f. Type **212**	1·60	65
933	180f. Galileo, telescope and planets	2·50	1·00

213 Football Teams (Europa Cup)

1984. Air. European Football Championship and Olympic Games, Los Angeles. Multicoloured.
934	80f. Type **213**	1·25	55
935	80f. Football teams (Olympic Games)	1·25	55

214 Motor Carriage, 1886

1984. 150th Birth Anniv of Gottlieb Daimler (automobile designer). Multicoloured.
936	35f. Type **214**	55	20
937	65f. Cannstatt-Daimler cabriolet, 1896	1·00	35
938	90f. Daimler "Phoenix", 1900	1·50	55

215 Pierre Curie

1985. Pierre and Marie Curie (physicists). Mult.
939	150f. Type **215** (150th birth anniv)	2·25	85
940	150f. Marie Curie (50th death anniv)	2·25	85

216 White-throated Bee Eater

1985. Birth Bicentenary of John J. Audubon. Multicoloured.
941	5f. Type **216**	25	15
942	15f. Chestnut-bellied sand-grouse	1·10	45
943	20f. Yellow-breasted barbet	1·25	50
944	25f. European roller	1·50	55

217 Dr. Hansen, Bacilli, Lepers and Lions Emblem   218 Globe and Pictograms

1985. Air. International Organizations. Mult.
946   50f. Type **217** (World
     Leprosy Day)   80   40
947   60f. Rotary International
     emblem and pieces on
     chessboard . . . .   1·40   65

1985. International Youth Year.
948 **218** 10f. multicoloured   80   25
949   30f. multicoloured . . . .   2·25   50
950   40f. multicoloured . . . .   3·00   90

219 Steam Locomotive No. 29, Addis
Ababa–Djibouti Railway

1985. Railway Locomotives. Multicoloured.
951   55f. Type **219** . . . . .   1·50   65
952   75f. "Adler", 1835 (150th
     anniv of German railways)   2·25   85

220 Planting Sapling   **221** Victor Hugo
(novelist)

1985. Foundation of Djibouti Scouting Association.
Multicoloured.
953   35f. Type **220**   65   30
954   65f. Childcare . . . .   1·40   45

1985. Writers. Multicoloured.
955   80f. Type **221** . . . . . .   1·10   50
956   100f. Arthur Rimbaud (poet)   1·40   60

222 Dish Aerials, Off-shore Oil Rigs and
Building

1985. Air. "Philexafrique" Stamp Exhibition, Lome
(1st issue). Multicoloured.
957   80f. Type **222** . . . . . .   2·25   1·50
958   80f. Carpenter, girl at
     microscope and man at
     visual display unit . . . .   1·60   1·10
See also Nos. 969/70.

1985. Shells. As T **199**. Multicoloured.
959   10f. Twin-blotch cowrie . . .   25   15
960   15f. Thrush cowrie   35   20
961   30f. Vice-Admiral cowrie . .   95   25
962   40f. Giraffe cone . . . . . .   1·10   55
963   55f. Terebra cone . . . . .   1·75   75

223 Team Winners on Rostrum

1985. 1st Marathon World Cup, Hiroshima.
Multicoloured.
964   75f. Type **223** . . . . . .   1·00   45
965   100f. Finishing line and
     officials . . . .   1·50   65

224 Launch of "Ariane"

1985. Air. Telecommunications Development. Mult.
966   50f. International
     Transmission Centre . . .   65   30
967   90f. Type **224** . . . . . .   1·25   50
968   120f. "Arabsat" satellite . . .   1·60   65

225 Windsurfing and Tennis

1985. Air. "Philexafrique" Stamp Exhibition, Lome,
Togo (2nd issue). Multicoloured.
969   100f. Type **225** . . . . .   2·00   1·25
970   100f. Construction of
     Tadjoura road . . . . . .   1·60   1·10

226 Edmond Halley, Bayeux Tapestry and
Comet

1986. Appearance of Halley's Comet. Multicoloured.
971   85f. Type **226** . . . . . .   1·10   45
972   90f. Solar system, comet
     trajectory and space probes
     "Giotto" and "Vega 1" . .   1·40   55

227 Footballers

1986. Air. World Cup Football Championship,
Mexico. Multicoloured.
973   75f. Type **227** . . . . . .   1·00   45
974   100f. Players and stadium . .   1·40   65

228 Runners on Shore

1986. "ISERST" Solar Energy Project. Mult.
975   50f. Type **228**   65   30
976   150f. "ISERST" building . .   2·00   85

229 "Santa Maria"

1986. Historic Ships of Columbus, 1492.
Multicoloured.
977   60f. Type **229** . . . . . .   1·90   1·25
978   90f. "Nina" and "Pinta" . .   2·50   2·00

230 Statue of Liberty, Eiffel Tower and
French and U.S. Flags

1986. Air. Centenary of Statue of Liberty.
979 **230** 250f. multicoloured . . . .   3·25   1·40

231 Rainbow Runner

1986. Red Sea Fish. Multicoloured.
980   20f. Type **231**   80   50
981   25f. Sehel's grey mullet . .   1·00   50
982   55f. Blubber-lipped snapper   2·40   1·25

232 People's Palace

1986. Public Buildings. Multicoloured.
983   105f. Type **232** . . . . .   1·40   55
984   115f. Ministry of the Interior,
     Posts and
     Telecommunications . . .   1·60   65

233 Transmission Building and Keyboard

1986. Inauguration of Sea-Me-We Submarine
Communications Cable.
985 **233** 100f. multicoloured . . .   1·40   65

1986. Air. World Cup Football Championship
Winners. Nos. 973/4 optd. Multicoloured.
987   75f. **FRANCE-BELGIQUE**
     4–2 . . . .   1·00   65
988   100f. **3–2 ARGENTINA-RFA**   1·40   90

235 Javanese Bishop, Knight
and Queen

1986. Air. World Chess Championship, London and
Leningrad. Multicoloured.
989   80f. Type **235** . . . . . .   1·40   65
990   120f. German rook, pawn
     and king . . . .   2·25   1·00

1986. 5th Anniv of Inaug of Djibouti Sheraton Hotel.
No. 828 surch **5e ANNIVERSAIRE**.
991 **169** 55f. on 75f. mult   90   55

237 Gagarin and Space Capsule

1986. Air. 25th Anniv of First Man in Space and 20th
Anniv of "Gemini 8"–"Agena" Link-up.
Multicoloured.
992   150f. Type **237** . . . . .   2·25   65
993   200f. "Gemini 8" and
     "Agena" craft over Earth   3·00   1·00

238 Amiot 370

1987. Air. Flight Anniversaries and Events.
Multicoloured.
994   55f. Type **238** (45th anniv of
     first Istres-Djibouti flight)   90   60
995   80f. "Spirit of St Louis" and
     Charles Lindbergh (60th
     anniv of first solo flight
     across North Atlantic) . .   1·10   95
996   120f. Dick Rutan, Jeana
     Yeager and "Voyager"
     (first non-stop flight
     around the world) . . . .   1·75   1·25

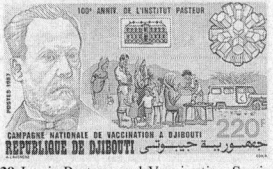

239 Louis Pasteur and Vaccination Session

1987. Centenary of Pasteur Institute. National
Vaccination Campaign in Djibouti.
997 **239** 220f. multicoloured . . .   3·25   1·10

241 "Macrolepiota   **242** Hare
imbricata"

1987. Fungi. Multicoloured.
999   35f. Type **241** . . . . . .   1·25   65
1000   50f. "Lentinus squarrosulus"   2·00   95
1001   95f. "Terfezia boudieri" . .   3·50   1·50

1987. Wild Animals. Multicoloured.
1002   5f. Type **242**   10   10
1003   30f. Young dromedary with
     mother   45   20
1004   140f. Cheetah . . . .   2·25   80

243 President Hassan Gouled
Aptidon, Map, Flag and Crest

1987. Air. 10th Anniv of Independence.
1005 **243** 250f. multicoloured . . .   3·25   1·40

244 Pierre de Coubertin (founder of
modern Games) and Athlete lighting Flame

1987. Olympic Games, Calgary and Seoul (1st issue)
(1988). Multicoloured.
1006   85f. Type **244** . . . . . .   1·10   45
1007   135f. Ski-jumper . . . . . .   1·60   65
1008   140f. Runners and
     spectators . . . .   1·90   80
See also No. 1021.

245 "Telstar" Satellite

1987. Air. Telecommunications Anniversaries. Multicoloured.
1009   190f. Type 245 (25th anniv)   2·50   90
1010   250f. Samuel Morse and morse key (150th anniv of morse telegraph)   .   .   .   3·25   1·40

246 Djibouti Creek and Quay, 1887

1987. Air. Centenary of Djibouti City.
1011   246   100f. agate and stone   .   .   .   2·00   1·40
1012   –   150f. multicoloured   .   .   .   2·25   80
DESIGN: 150f. Aerial view of Djibouti, 1987.

247 Comb   249 Anniversary Emblem

1988. Traditional Djibouti Art. Multicoloured.
1014   30f. Type 247   45   20
1015   70f. Water pitcher   95   45

1988. Air. 125th Anniv of Red Cross.
1017   249   300f. multicoloured   .   .   .   4·25   1·60

250 Rabat and Footballers

1988. 16th African Nations Cup Football Championship, Morocco.
1018   250   55f. multicoloured   .   .   .   85   35

251 Ski Jumping   252 Doctor examining Child

1988. Winter Olympic Games, Calgary.
1019   251   45f. multicoloured   .   .   .   65   30

1988. U.N.I.C.E.F. "Universal Vaccinations by 1990" Campaign.
1020   252   125f. multicoloured   .   .   .   1·75   65

253 Runners and Stadium

1988. Air. Olympic Games, Seoul (2nd issue).
1021   253   105f. multicoloured   .   .   .   1·40   55

1988. Air. Paris–Djibouti–St. Denis (Reunion) Roland Garros Air Race. No. 994 surch **PARIS-DJIBOUTI-ST DENIS LA REUNION RALLYE ROLAND GARROS 70 F.**
1022   238   70f. on 55f. mult   .   .   .   .   1·25   65

255 Animals at Water Trough

1988. Anti-drought Campaign.
1023   255   50f. multicoloured   .   .   .   85   35

256 Djibouti Post Offices of 1890 and 1977

1988. Air. World Post Day.
1024   256   1000f. multicoloured   .   .   13·50   4·00

257 Combine Harvester, Tractor and Ploughman with Camel

1988. 10th Anniv of International Agricultural Development Fund.
1025   257   135f. multicoloured   .   .   .   1·75   65

258 De Havilland Tiger Moth, 1948, and Socata Tobago, 1988

1988. 40th Anniv of Michel Lafoux Air Club.
1026   258   145f. multicoloured   .   .   .   2·00   95

1988. 1st Djibouti Olympic Medal Winner. No. 1021 optd **AHMED SALAH 1re MEDAILLE OLYMPIQUE.**
1027   253   105f. multicoloured   .   .   .   1·40   90

260 "Lobophyllia costata"

1989. Underwater Animals. Multicoloured.
1028   90f. Type 260   .   .   .   .   .   1·40   35
1029   160f. Giant spider conch   .   .   3·25   1·40

261 "Colotis protomedia"

1989.
1030   261   70f. multicoloured   .   .   .   90   60

1989. Nos. 849 and 913 surch **70f.**
1031   206   70f. on 2f. mult   .   .   .   95   45
1032   179   70f. on 150f. mult   .   .   .   95   45

263 Dancers   264 Pale-bellied Francolin ("Francolin de Djibouti")

1989. Folklore. Multicoloured.
1033   30f. Type 263   40   20
1034   70f. Dancers with parasol   .   .   1·00   45

1989.
1035   264   35f. multicoloured   .   .   .   75   35

265 Arrows and Dish Aerials

1989. Air. World Telecommunications Day.
1036   265   150f. multicoloured   .   .   .   1·90   65

266 "Calotropis procera"

1989.
1037   266   25f. multicoloured   .   .   .   35   15

267 Emblem, Declaration and People

1989. Air. "Philexfrance 89" International Stamp Exhibition, Paris, and Bicentenary of Declaration of Rights of Man.
1038   267   120f. multicoloured   .   .   .   1·60   65

268 Emblem and State Arms   270 Child going to School

269 Collecting Salt

1989. Cent of Interparliamentary Union.
1039   268   70f. multicoloured   .   .   .   95   35

1989. Air. Lake Assal.
1040   269   300f. multicoloured   .   .   4·00   1·10

1989. International Literacy Year.
1041   270   145f. multicoloured   .   .   .   1·90   65

271 Tourka Maddw Cave Painting

1989.
1042   271   5f. multicoloured   10   10

272 Traditional Ornaments

1989.
1043   272   55f. multicoloured   .   .   .   80   35

1990. Nos. 914 and 916/17 surch.
1044   30f. on 8f. multicoloured   .   .   40   15
1045   50f. on 40f. mult   .   .   .   65   30
1046   120f. on 15f. mult   .   .   .   1·60   45

274 Water-storage Drums and Arid Landscape

1990. Anti-drought Campaign.
1047   274   120f. multicoloured   .   .   .   1·60   55

275 Basketry

1990. Traditional Crafts. Multicoloured.
1048   30f. Type 275   40   20
1049   70f. Jewellery (vert)   95   35

275a Blue-spotted Stingray

1990. Multicoloured, colour of face-value box given.
1049b   275a   70f. yellow   .   .   .   .   .
1049c   –   100f. green   .   .   .   .   .   .

276 "Commiphora sp." 277 Footballers

1990.
1050 276 30f. multicoloured . . . 45 30

1990. World Cup Football Championship, Italy.
1051 277 100f. multicoloured . . . 1·40 55

278 Athlete 279 Queue of Patients

1990. Djibouti 20 km Race.
1052 278 55f. multicoloured . . . 80 35

1990. Vaccination Campaign.
1053 279 300f. multicoloured . . . 3·25 1·40

280 De Gaulle 281 Technology in Developed Countries

1990. Birth Centenary of Charles de Gaulle (French statesman).
1054 280 200f. multicoloured . . . 2·50 1·25

1990. United Nations Conference on Less Developed Countries.
1055 281 45f. multicoloured . . . 60 35

282 Mammoth and Fossilized Remains 283 Hamadryas Baboon

1990.
1056 282 90f. multicoloured . . . 1·40 65

1990.
1057 283 50f. multicoloured . . . 65 35

284 Emblem and Map 285 "Acropora"

1991. African Tourism Year.
1058 284 115f. multicoloured . . . 1·50 85

1991. Corals. Multicoloured.
1059 40f. Type 285 . . . . . 55 35
1060 45f. "Seriatopora hytrise" . . 65 35

286 Pink-backed Pelican

1991. Birds. Multicoloured.
1061 10f. Type 286 . . . . . 35 15
1062 15f. Western reef heron . . 50 25
1063 20f. Goliath heron (horiz) . 75 30
1064 25f. White spoonbill (horiz) 90 40

287 Osprey

1991.
1065 287 200f. multicoloured . . . 4·00 2·50

288 Traditional Game

1991.
1066 288 250f. multicoloured . . . 3·25 1·40

289 Diesel Locomotive

1991. Djibouti–Ethiopia Railway (1st issue).
1067 289 85f. multicoloured . . . 2·25 75
See also No. 1076.

290 Hands holding Earth above Polluted Sea

1991. World Environment Day.
1068 290 110f. multicoloured . . . 1·50 55

291 Windsurfers and Islets

1991. "Philexafrique" Stamp Exhibition.
1069 291 120f. multicoloured . . . 90 45

292 Handball 293 Harvesting Crops

1991. Olympic Games, Barcelona (1992) (1st issue).
1070 292 175f. multicoloured . . . 1·40 70
See also No. 1079.

1991. World Food Day.
1071 293 105f. multicoloured . . . 80 40

294 Route-map, Woman using Telephone and Cable-laying Ship

1991. Inauguration of Marseilles–Djibouti–Singapore Submarine Cable.
1072 294 130f. multicoloured . . . 1·50 70

295 Columbus and Ships

1991. 500th Anniv (1992) of Discovery of America by Columbus (1st issue).
1073 295 145f. multicoloured . . . 1·60 80
See also No. 1080.

296 Rimbaud, Ship and Serpent

1991. Death Centenary of Arthur Rimbaud (poet). Multicoloured.
1074 90f. Type 296 . . . . . 1·10 50
1075 150f. Rimbaud, camel train and map . . . . . . 1·10 55

297 Camel Driver and Diesel Train

1992. Djibouti–Ethiopia Railway (2nd issue).
1076 297 70f. multicoloured . . . 1·50 45

298 Boys Playing Game

1992. Traditional Games.
1078 298 100f. multicoloured . . . 80 40

299 Athlete and Globe 301 Crushing Grain

1992. Olympic Games, Barcelona (2nd issue).
1079 299 80f. multicoloured . . . 60 30

1992. 500th Anniv of Discovery of America by Columbus (2nd issue).
1080 300 125f. multicoloured . . . 1·40 65

1992. Traditional Methods of Preparing Food. Multicoloured.
1081 30f. Type 301 . . . . . 25 10
1082 70f. Winnowing 55 25

300 Caravel crossing Atlantic

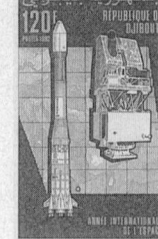

302 Players, Map of Africa and Final Result 303 "Ariane" Rocket and Satellite

1992. 18th African Nations Cup Football Championship, Senegal.
1083 302 15f. multicoloured . . . 10 10

1992. International Space Year. Multicoloured.
1084 120f. Type 303 . . . . . 90 45
1085 135f. Satellite and astronaut (horiz) . . . . 1·00 50

304 Salt's Dik-dik

1992.
1086 304 5f. multicoloured 10 10

305 Loggerhead Turtle

1992.
1087 305 200f. multicoloured . . . 1·50 75

306 Preparing Mofo

1992. Mofo. Multicoloured.
1088 45f. Type 306 . . . . .
1089 75f. Cooking mofo . . . . .

307 Nomadic Girl

1993. Traditional Costumes. Multicoloured.
1090 70f. Type 307 . . . . . 55 25
1091 120f. Nomadic girl with headband 90 45

308 White-eyed Gull ("Geoland a Iris Blanc")

1993.
1092 308 300f. multicoloured . . . 3·50 1·40

309 Amin Salman Mosque

1993.
1093 309 500f. multicoloured . . .

310 Headrest

1993. Crafts. Multicoloured.
1094 100f. Type 310
1095 125f. Flask . . . .

311 Savanna Monkey

1993.
1096 311 150f. multicoloured . . .

312 Flags of Member Countries

1993. 30th Anniv of Organization of African Unity.
1097 312 200f. multicoloured . . .

313 Woman carrying   314 Plants and
Water on Back   Spacecraft

1993. Water Carriers. Multicoloured.
1098 30f. Type 313 . . . .
1099 50f. Man carrying water on
yoke

1993. Space.
1100 314 90f. multicoloured . . .

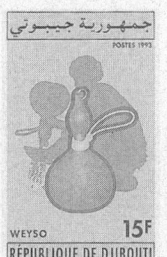 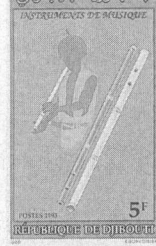

315 Water Jar   316 Pipes

1993. Utensils. Multicoloured.
1101 15f. Type 315   10   10
1102 20f. Hangol (agricultural
tool)   15   10

1103 25f. Comb   20   10
1104 30f. Water-skin   25   10

1993. Musical Instruments. Multicoloured.
1105 5f. Type 316   10   10
1106 10f. Hand-held drum and
lines of women   10   10

318 Runners and   319 Mother with
Route Map   Children

1994. Djibouti 20 km Race.
1108 318 50f. multicoloured . . .   40   20

1994. U.N.I.C.E.F. Breast-feeding Campaign.
Multicoloured.
1109 40f. Type 319   30   15
1110 45f. Woman breast-feeding
baby   35   15

320 Stadium

1994. Hassan Gouled Aptidon Stadium.
1111 320 70f. multicoloured . . .   55   25

321 Spinner Dolphins

1994.
1112 321 120f. multicoloured . . .

322 Houses encircling Globe

1994. World Housing Day.
1113 322 30f. multicoloured . . .

323 White-bellied Bustards

1994.
1114 323 10f. multicoloured . . .

324 Trophy, Globe and Players

1994. World Cup Football Championship, U.S.A.
1115 324 200f. multicoloured . . .

325 Nomadic Man

1994. Traditional Costumes. Multicoloured.
1116 100f. Type 325 . . . . . .
1117 150f. Town dress . . . . . .

326 Golden Jackals

1994.
1118 326 400f. multicoloured . . .

327 Walkers

1994. World Walking Day.
1119 327 75f. multicoloured . . .

328 Book Rests   329 Traditional
Dancers

1994. Traditional Crafts.
1120 328 55f. multicoloured . . .

1994. Folklore.
1121 329 35f. multicoloured . . .

330 Camel, Ostrich   331 U.N. Flag tied
and Net   around Cracked
Globe

1995. Centenary of Volleyball.
1122 330 70f. multicoloured . . .

1995. 50th Anniv of U.N.O.
1123 331 120f. multicoloured . . .

332 Drawing Water from Well

1995. Drought Relief Campaign.
1124 332 100f. multicoloured . . .

333 Greater Flamingo

1995. Birds. Multicoloured.
1125 30f. Type 333 . . . . . .
1126 50f. Sacred ibis . . . . . .

334 Camel Rider

1995. Telecommunications Day.
1127 334 125f. multicoloured . . .

335 Spotted Hyena

1995.
1128 335 200f. multicoloured . . .

336 Council held under Tree   337 Nomads

1995.
1129 336 150f. multicoloured . . .

1995. Nomadic Life.
1130 337 45f. multicoloured . . .

338 Palm Tree, Map and
Emblem

1995. 50th Anniv of F.A.O.
1131 338 250f. multicoloured . . .

339 Development Project and   340 Traditional
Emblem   Costume

1995. 30th Anniv of African Development Bank.
1132 339 300f. multicoloured . . .

1995.
1133 340 90f. multicoloured . . .

341 Trophy on Map   342 Leopard
and Football

1996. Africa Cup Football Championship.
1134 341 70f. multicoloured . . .

1996. Wildlife. Multicoloured.
1135 70f. Type 342 . . . . . .
1136 120f. Ostrich (vert) . . . .

343 Woman wearing   344 Olympic Flag
Amber Necklace

1996. Traditional Crafts.
1137 343 30f. multicoloured . . .

1996. Olympic Games, Atlanta.
1138 344 105f. multicoloured . . .

345 "Commicarpus grandiflorus"   346 Women's Rite

1996.
1139 **345** 350f. multicoloured . . .

1996. Folklore.
1140 **346** 95f. multicoloured . . .

347 The Lion and the Three Bullocks

1996. Stories and Legends.
1141 **347** 95f. multicoloured . . .

348 Children with Flags

1996. National Children's Day.
1142 **348** 130f. multicoloured . . .

349 Fox and Tortoise   350 Mother and Child

1997. Stories and Legends. The Tortoise and the Fox. Multicoloured.
1143 60f. Type **349** . . . .
1144 60f. Fox running away from tortoise . . . .
1145 60f. Tortoise winning race

1997. 50th Anniv of U.N.I.C.E.F. Multicoloured.
1146 80f. Type **350** . . . .
1147 90f. Arms cradling globe of children . . . .

351 Dancers   352 Using Necklace as Pendulum

1997. Folklore.
1148 **351** 70f. multicoloured . . .

1997. Local Fortune Telling. Multicoloured.
1149 200f. Type **352** . . . . .
1150 300f. Using pebbles . . . .

353 Woman weaving Basket   355 Arta Post Office

354 Writing Board

1997. Women's Day.
1151 **353** 250f. multicoloured . . .

1997. Traditional Implements. Multicoloured.
1152 30f. Type **354** . . . .
1153 400f. Bowl and spoon (vert)

1997. 20th Anniv of Independence. Multicoloured.
1154 30f. Type **355** . . . .
1155 100f. Telecommunications station . . . .
1156 120f. Undersea cable, route map and cable ship (horiz) . . . .

356 Goats in Tree

1997.
1157 **356** 120f. multicoloured . . .

357 Diana, Princess of Wales

1998. Diana, Princess of Wales Commemoration.
1158 **357** 125f. multicoloured . . . 95 45
1159 130f. multicoloured . . . 1·00 50
1160 150f. multicoloured . . . 1·25 60

358 Paradise Tanager

1998. International Year of the Ocean. Mult.
1161 75c. Type **358** . . . . . .
1162 75c. Red-eyed tree frog ("Agalychnis callidryas")
1163 75c. Common dolphin ("Delphinus delphis") and humpback whale ("Megaptera novaeangliae") . . . . .
1164 75c. Savanna monkey ("Cercopithecus aethiops") . . . .
1165 75c. Great hammerhead ("Sphyrna mokarran") and yellow-lipped sea snakes ("Laticaudia colubrina") . . . .
1166 75c. Long-horned cowfish ("Lactoria cornuta") and common dolphin ("Delphinus delphis") . .
1167 75c. Common dolphins ("Delphinus delphis") . .
1168 75c. Striped mimic blenny ("Aspidontus taeniatus") and foxface ("Lovulpinus") . . . . .
1169 75c. Big-fin reef squid ("Sepioteuthis lessoniana)
1170 75c. Ornate butterflyfish ("Chaetodon ornatissimus) and blue shark ("Prionace glauca")
1171 75c. Hermit crab ("Eupagurus bernherdus")
1172 75c. Common octopus ("Octopus vulgaris") . . .

Nos. 1161/72 were issued together, se-tenant, forming a composite design.

359 Gandhi   360 Vase

1998. 50th Death Anniv of Mahatma Gandhi (Indian patriot).
1173 **359** 250f. multicoloured . . .

1998. Traditional Art.
1174 **360** 30f. multicoloured . . .

361 Woman carrying Basket on Back and Road-crossing Officer

1998. Women's Rights and International Peace.
1175 **361** 70f. multicoloured . . .

362 Water Pump and Donkey carrying Water Containers

1998. World Water Day.
1176 **362** 45f. multicoloured . . .

363 Football, Trophy and Eiffel Tower   364 Octopus

1998. World Cup Football Championship, France.
1177 **363** 200f. multicoloured . . .

1998. Marine Life. Multicoloured.
1178 20f. Type **364** . . . .
1179 25f. Shark (horiz) . . . . .

365 Catmint and Cats   366 Globe using Mobile Phone and Computer

1998.
1180 **365** 120f. multicoloured . . .

1998. World Telecommunications Day.
1181 **366** 150f. multicoloured . . .

367 National Bank   368 Flags of Member States and Emblem

1998. Public Buildings.
1182 **367** 100f. multicoloured . . .

1998. Inter-Governmental Authority on Development.
1183 **368** 85f. multicoloured . . .

369 Boys playing Goos

1998. Traditional Games.
1184 **369** 110f. multicoloured . . .

370 Fishing Harbour

1998. Public Buildings.
1185 **370** 100f. multicoloured . . .

371 Seabirds and Maskali Island

1998. Tourist Sites.
1186 **371** 500f. multicoloured . . .

372 Mother Teresa

1998. Mother Teresa (founder of Missionaries of Charity) Commemoration.
1187 **372** 130f. multicoloured . . . 90 45

POSTAGE DUE STAMP

D 248 Milking Bowl

1988. Traditional Djibouti Art.
D1016 D **248** 60f. multicoloured 90 65

DODECANESE ISLANDS Pt. 8

A group of islands off the coast of Asia Minor occupied by Italy in May 1912 and ceded to her by Turkey in 1920. The islands concerned are now known as Kalimnos, Kasos, Kos, Khalki, Leros, Lipsoi, Nisiros, Patmos, Tilos (Piskopi), Rhodes (Rodos), Karpathos, Simi and Astipalaia. Castelrosso came under the same administration in 1921.

In 1944 the Dodecanese Islands were occupied by British forces (see **BRITISH OCCUPATION OF ITALIAN COLONIES**). In 1947 they were transferred to Greek administration, since when Greek stamps have been used.

A. ITALIAN OCCUPATION

100 centesimi = 1 lira.

1912. Stamps of Italy optd **EGEO**.
1 **39** 25c. blue . . . . 27·00 14·50
2 – 50c. violet . . . . 27·00 14·50

1912. Stamps of Italy optd, or surch also, for the individual islands (all in capitals on Nos. 6 and 10, in upper and lower case on others). A. Calimno

3A	**31**	2c. brown	4·25	3·75
4A	**37**	5c. green	1·25	3·75
5A		10c. red	40	3·75
6A	**41**	15c. grey	17·00	7·00
7A	**37**	15c. grey	2·25	23·00
8A	**41**	20c. on 15c. grey	8·75	13·50
10A		20c. orange	2·40	23·00
11A	**39**	25c. blue	3·75	3·75
12A		40c. brown	40	3·75
13A		50c. violet	40	6·75

B. Caso

3B	**31**	2c. brown	4·25	3·75
4B	**37**	5c. green	1·40	3·75
5B		10c. red	40	3·75
6B	**41**	15c. grey	20·00	7·00
7B	**37**	15c. grey	2·25	23·00
8B	**41**	20c. on 15c. grey	60	11·00
10B		20c. orange	2·00	20·00
11B	**39**	25c. blue	40	3·75
12B		40c. brown	40	3·75
13B		50c. violet	40	6·75

C. Cos

3C	**31**	2c. brown	4·25	3·75
4C	**37**	5c. green	35·00	3·75
5C		10c. red	1·75	3·75
6C	**41**	15c. grey	20·00	7·00
7C	**37**	15c. grey	2·25	27·00
8C	**41**	20c. on 15c. grey	9·00	16·00
10C		20c. orange	1·75	20·00
11C	**39**	25c. blue	16·00	3·75

12C 40c. brown . . . . 40 3·75
13C 50c. violet . . . . 40 6·75

D. Karki

3D **31** 2c. brown . . . . 4·25 3·75
4D **37** 5c. green . . . . 1·40 3·75
5D 10c. red . . . . 40 3·75
6D **41** 15c. grey . . . . 20·00 7·00
7D **37** 15c. grey . . . . 2·25 23·00
8D **41** 20c. on 15c. grey . . . . 1·00 12·50
10D 20c. orange . . . . 2·40 21·00
11D **39** 25c. blue . . . . 40 3·75
12D 40c. brown . . . . 40 3·75
13D 50c. violet . . . . 40 6·75

E. Lerso

3E **31** 2c. brown . . . . 4·25 3·75
4E **37** 5c. green . . . . 2·75 3·75
5E 10c. red . . . . 65 3·75
6E **41** 15c. grey . . . . 30·00 7·00
7E **37** 15c. grey . . . . 2·25 21·00
8E **41** 20c. on 15c. grey . . . . 7·00 14·00
10E 20c. orange . . . . 26·00 70·00
11E **39** 25c. blue . . . . 17·00 3·75
12E 40c. brown . . . . 1·90 3·75
13E 50c. violet . . . . 40 6·75

F. Lipso

3F **31** 2c. brown . . . . 4·25 3·75
4F **37** 5c. green . . . . 1·60 3·75
5F 10c. red . . . . 75 3·75
6F **41** 15c. grey . . . . 20·00 7·00
7F **37** 15c. grey . . . . 2·25 21·00
8F **41** 20c. on 15c. grey . . . . 65 13·50
10F 20c. orange . . . . 2·25 23·00
11F **39** 25c. blue . . . . 1·10 3·75
12F 40c. brown . . . . 75 3·75
13F 50c. violet . . . . 40 6·75

G. Nisiros

3G **31** 2c. brown . . . . 4·25 3·75
4G **37** 5c. green . . . . 1·25 3·75
5G 10c. red . . . . 40 3·75
6G **41** 15c. grey . . . . 18·00 7·00
7G **37** 15c. grey . . . . 12·00 22·00
8G **41** 20c. on 15c. grey . . . . 70 13·50
10G 20c. orange . . . . 48·00 50·00
11G **39** 25c. blue . . . . 1·10 3·75
12G 40c. brown . . . . 40 3·75
13G 50c. violet . . . . 2·00 6·75

H. Patmos

3H **31** 2c. brown . . . . 4·25 3·75
4H **37** 5c. green . . . . 1·40 3·75
5H 10c. red . . . . 1·25 3·75
6H **41** 15c. grey . . . . 18·00 7·00
7H **37** 15c. grey . . . . 2·25 23·00
8H **41** 20c. on 15c. grey . . . . 8·25 16·00
10H 20c. orange . . . . 35·00 70·00
11H **39** 25c. blue . . . . 50 3·75
12H 40c. brown . . . . 1·75 3·75
13H 50c. violet . . . . 40 3·75

I. Piscopi

3I **31** 2c. brown . . . . 4·25 3·75
4I **37** 5c. green . . . . 1·40 3·75
5I 10c. red . . . . 40 3·75
6I **41** 15c. grey . . . . 20·00 7·00
7I **37** 15c. grey . . . . 7·75 23·00
8I **41** 20c. on 15c. grey . . . . 70 13·50
10I 20c. orange . . . . 24·00 32·00
11I **39** 25c. blue . . . . 40 3·75
12I 40c. brown . . . . 40 3·75
13I 50c. violet . . . . 40 6·75

J. Rodi

3J **31** 2c. brown . . . . 40 3·75
4J **37** 5c. green . . . . 1·25 3·75
5J 10c. red . . . . 40 3·75
6J **41** 15c. grey . . . . 22·00 7·00
7J **37** 15c. grey . . . . 70·00 32·00
8J **41** 20c. on 15c. grey . . . . 65·00 70·00
10J 20c. orange . . . . 3·50 8·75
11J **39** 25c. blue . . . . 1·25 3·75
12J 40c. brown . . . . 1·60 3·75
13J 50c. violet . . . . 40 3·75

K. Scarpanto

3K **31** 2c. brown . . . . 4·25 3·75
4K **37** 5c. green . . . . 1·25 3·75
5K 10c. red . . . . 40 3·75
6K **41** 15c. grey . . . . 17·00 7·00
7K **37** 15c. grey . . . . 8·25 18·00
8K **41** 20c. on 15c. grey . . . . 70 14·00
10K 20c. orange . . . . 24·00 24·00
11K **39** 25c. blue . . . . 4·00 3·75
12K 40c. brown . . . . 40 3·75
13K 50c. violet . . . . 1·10 6·75

L. Simi

3L **31** 2c. brown . . . . 4·25 3·75
4L **37** 5c. green . . . . 10·00 3·75
5L 10c. red . . . . 40 3·75
6L **41** 15c. grey . . . . 25·00 7·00
7L **37** 15c. grey . . . . 65·00 32·00
8L **41** 20c. on 15c. grey . . . . 5·50 12·00
10L 20c. orange . . . . 32·00 20·00
11L **39** 25c. blue . . . . 1·25 3·75
12L 40c. brown . . . . 40 3·75
13L 50c. violet . . . . 40 6·75

M. Stampalia

3M **31** 2c. brown . . . . 4·25 3·75
4M **37** 5c. green . . . . 40 3·75
5M 10c. red . . . . 40 3·75
6M **41** 15c. grey . . . . 20·00 7·00
7M **37** 15c. grey . . . . 5·50 18·00
8M **41** 20c. on 15c. grey . . . . 60 10·00
10M 20c. orange . . . . 23·00 25·00
11M **39** 25c. blue . . . . 50 3·75
12M 40c. brown . . . . 1·75 3·75
13M 50c. violet . . . . 60 6·75

1916. Optd **Rodi**.
14 **33** 20c. orange . . . . 1·60 3·75
15 **39** 85c. brown . . . . 38·00 55·00
16 **34** 1l. brown & green . . . . . 2·50

1 Rhodian Windmill

2 Knight kneeling before the Holy City

1929. King of Italy's Visit.
17 **1** 5c. purple 65 15
18 – 10c. brown 65 15
19 – 20c. red 65 15
20 – 25c. green 65 15
21 **2** 30c. blue 65 15
22 – 50c. brown 65 15
23 – 1l.25 blue 65 15
24 **2** 5l. purple 65 80
25 10l. green . . . . 1·40 1·60
DESIGNS—As Type **1**: 10c. Galley of Knights of St. John; 20c., 25c. Knight defending Christianity; 50c., 1l.25, Knight's tomb.

1930. 21st Hydrological Congress. Nos. 17/25 optd **XXI Congresso Idrologico**.
26 5c. purple . . . . 3·50 6·25
27 10c. brown . . . . 3·50 6·25
28 20c. red . . . . 4·50 6·00
29 25c. green . . . . 5·50 6·00
30 30c. blue . . . . 4·00 6·25
31 50c. brown . . . . £350 26·00
32 1l.25 blue . . . . £250 40·00
33 5l. purple £110 £150
34 10l. green £110 £170

1930. Ferrucci issue of Italy (colours changed) optd for each individual island, in capitals. A. CALINO; B. CASO; C. COO; D. CALCHI; E. LERO; F. LISSO; G. NISIRO; H. PATMO; I. PISCOPI; J. RODI; K. SCARPANTO; L. SIMI; M. STAMPALIA.
35 **114** 20c. violet . . . . 1·60 3·25
36 – 25c. green . . . . 1·60 3·25
37 – 50c. black . . . . 1·60 3·25
38 – 1l.25 blue . . . . 1·60 3·25
39 – 5l.+2l. red . . . . 2·40 8·00
Same prices for each of the 13 islands.

1930. Air. Ferrucci air stamps of Italy (colours changed) optd **ISOLE ITALIANE DELL'EGEO**.
40 **117** 50c. purple . . . . 4·75 9·50
41 1l. blue . . . . 4·75 9·50
42 5l.+2l. red . . . . 11·00 28·00

1930. Virgil stamps of Italy optd **ISOLE ITALIANE DELL'EGEO**.
43 – 15c. violet (postage) . . . 85 5·00
44 – 20c. brown . . . . 85 5·00
45 – 25c. green . . . . 85 2·25
46 – 30c. brown . . . . 85 2·25
47 – 50c. purple . . . . 85 2·25
48 – 75c. red . . . . 85 5·00
49 – 1l.25 blue . . . . 85 7·75
50 – 5l+1l.50 purple . . . . . 2·40 15·00
51 – 10l.+2l.50 brown . . . . 2·40 15·00
52 **119** 50c. green (air) . . . . . 1·50 10·50
53 1l. red . . . . 1·50 12·00
54 7l.70+1l.30 brown . . . . 2·50 17·00
55 9l.+2l. grey . . . . . . 2·50 23·00

1931. Italian Eucharistic Congress. Nos. 17/25 optd **1931 CONGRESSO EUCARISTICO ITALIANO**.
56 5c. red . . . . 2·50 4·75
57 10c. brown . . . . 2·50 4·75
58 20c. red . . . . 2·50 8·25
59 25c. green . . . . 2·50 9·00
60 30c. blue . . . . 2·50 9·00
61 50c. brown . . . . 27·00 18·00
62 1l.25 blue . . . . 22·00 35·00

1932. St. Antony of Padua stamps of Italy optd **ISOLE ITALIANE DELL'EGEO**.
63 **121** 20c. purple . . . . 13·00 8·50
64 – 25c. green . . . . 13·00 8·50
65 – 30c. brown . . . . 13·00 9·75
66 – 50c. purple . . . . 13·00 7·75
67 – 75c. red . . . . 13·00 11·50
68 – 1l.25 blue . . . . 13·00 14·50
69 – 5l.+2l.50 orange . . . . 13·00 45·00

1932. Dante stamps of Italy optd **ISOLE ITALIANE DELL'EGEO**.
70 – 10c. green (postage) . . . 75 1·90
71 – 15c. violet . . . . 75 1·90
72 – 20c. brown . . . . 75 1·90
73 – 25c. green . . . . 75 1·90
74 – 30c. red . . . . 75 1·90
75 – 50c. purple . . . . 75 1·25
76 – 75c. red . . . . 75 2·40
77 – 1l.25 blue . . . . 75 1·90
78 – 1l.75 sepia . . . . 90 2·50
79 – 2l.75 red . . . . 90 2·50
80 – 5l.+2l. violet . . . . . . 1·25 8·25
81 **124** 10l.+2l.50 brown . . . . 1·25 12·00
82 **125** 50c. red (air) . . . . . . 85 2·00
83 – 1l. green . . . . 85 2·00
84 – 3l. purple . . . . 85 2·50
85 – 5l. red . . . . 85 2·50
86 **125** 7l.70+2l. sepia . . . . . 1·25 6·00
87 – 10l.+2l.50 blue . . . . . 1·25 8·00
88 **127** 100l. olive and blue . . . 13·00 55·00
No. 88 is inscribed instead of optd.

1932. Garibaldi issue of Italy (colours changed) optd for each individual island in capital letters. A. CALINO; B. CASO; C. COO; D. CARCHI; E. LERO; F. LIBO; G. NISIRO; H. PATMO; I. PISCOPI; J. RODI; K. SCARPANTO; L. SIMI; M. STAMPALIA.
89 – 10c. sepia . . . . 4·75 8·75
90 **128** 20c. brown . . . . 4·75 8·75
91 – 25c. green . . . . 4·75 8·75
92 **128** 30c. black . . . . 4·75 8·75
93 – 50c. lilac . . . . 4·75 8·75
94 – 75c. red . . . . 4·75 8·75
95 – 1l.25 blue . . . . 4·75 8·75
96 – 1l.75+25c. sepia . . . . . 4·75 8·75
97 – 2l.55+50c. red . . . . . . 4·75 8·75
98 – 5l.+1l. violet . . . . . . 4·75 8·75
Same prices for each of the 13 islands.

1932. Air. Garibaldi air stamps of Italy optd **ISOLE ITALIANE DELL'EGEO**.
99 **130** 50c. green . . . . 24·00 42·00
100 – 80c. red . . . . 24·00 42·00
101 **130** 1l.+25c. blue . . . . . . 24·00 42·00
102 – 2l.+50c. brown . . . . . 24·00 42·00
103 – 5l.+1l. black . . . . . . 24·00 42·00

8

1932. 20th Anniv of Italian Occupation of Dodecanese Islands.
106 **8** 5c. red, black and green . . 3·00 7·00
107 10c. red, black and blue . . 3·00 4·00
108 20c. red, black and yellow 3·00 4·00
109 25c. red, black and violet . . 3·00 4·00
110 30c. red, black and red . . . 3·00 4·00
111 – 50c. red, black and blue . . 3·00 4·00
112 – 1l.25 red, purple & blue . . 3·00 9·50
113 – 5l. red and blue . . . . . 10·00 27·00
114 – 10l. red, green and blue . . 25·00 48·00
115 – 25l. red, brown and blue . . £250 £500
DESIGN—VERT: 50c. to 25l. Arms on map of Rhodes.

10 Airship "Graf Zeppelin"

11 Wing from Arms of Francesco Sans

1933. Air. "Graf Zeppelin".
116 **10** 3l. brown . . . . 30·00 60·00
117 5l. purple . . . . 27·00 70·00
118 10l. green . . . . 27·00 £130
119 12l. blue . . . . 27·00 £140
120 15l. red . . . . 27·00 £140
121 20l. black . . . . 27·00 £140

1933. Air. Balbo Mass Formation Flight issue of Italy optd **ISOLE ITALIANE DELL'EGEO**.
122 **135** 5l.25+19l.75 red, green and blue . . . . . . 23·00 50·00
123 **136** 5l.25+44l.75 red, green and blue . . . . . . 23·00 55·00

1934. Air.
124 **11** 50c. black and yellow . . . 20 20
125 80c. black and red . . . . 2·75 2·50
126 1l. black and green . . . . 1·60 30
127 5l. black and mauve . . . 5·00 6·50

1934. World Football Championship stamps of Italy (some colours changed) optd **ISOLE ITALIANE DELL'EGEO**.
128 **142** 20c. red (postage) . . . . 38·00 35·00
129 – 25c. green . . . . 38·00 35·00
130 – 50c. violet . . . . £130 19·00
131 – 1l.25 blue . . . . 38·00 60·00
132 – 5l.+2l.50 blue . . . . . . 38·00 £150
133 – 50c. brown (air) . . . . . 4·00 21·00
134 – 75c. red . . . . 4·00 21·00
135 – 5l.+2l.50 orange . . . . . 12·00 45·00
136 – 10l.+5l. green . . . . . . 12·00 60·00

1934. Military Medal Centenary stamps of Italy (some colours changed) optd **ISOLE ITALIANE DELL'EGEO**.
157 **146** 10c. grey (postage) . . . 28·00 35·00
158 – 15c. brown . . . . 28·00 35·00
159 – 20c. orange . . . . 28·00 35·00
160 – 25c. green . . . . 28·00 35·00
161 – 30c. red . . . . 28·00 35·00
162 – 50c. green . . . . 28·00 35·00
163 – 75c. red . . . . 28·00 35·00
164 – 1l.25 blue . . . . 28·00 35·00
165 – 1l.75+1l. violet . . . . . 18·00 35·00
166 – 2l.55+2l. red . . . . . . 18·00 35·00
167 – 2l.75+2l. brown . . . . . 18·00 35·00
168 – 25c. green (air) . . . . . 32·00 42·00
169 – 50c. grey . . . . 32·00 42·00
170 – 75c. red . . . . 32·00 42·00
171 – 80c. brown . . . . 32·00 42·00
172 – 1l.+50c. green . . . . . . 27·00 42·00
173 – 2l.+1l. blue . . . . 27·00 42·00
174 – 3l.+2l. violet . . . . . . 27·00 42·00

16

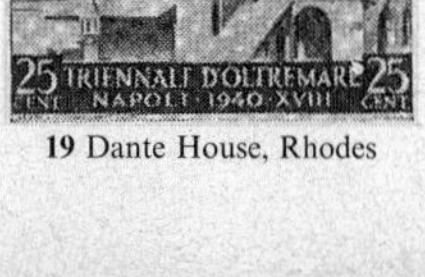

19 Dante House, Rhodes

1935. Holy Year.
177 **16** 5c. orange . . . . 6·50 9·50
178 10c. brown . . . . 6·50 9·50
179 20c. red . . . . 6·50 9·50
180 25c. green . . . . 6·50 9·50
181 30c. purple . . . . 6·50 9·50
182 50c. brown . . . . 6·50 9·50
183 1l.25 blue . . . . 6·50 9·50

1938. Augustus the Great stamps of Italy (colours changed) optd **ISOLE ITALIANE DELL'EGEO**.
186 **163** 10c. brown (postage) . . 1·75 2·40
187 – 15c. violet . . . . 1·75 2·40
188 – 20c. brown . . . . 1·75 2·40
189 – 25c. green . . . . 1·75 2·40
190 – 30c. purple . . . . 1·75 2·40
191 – 50c. green . . . . 1·75 4·25
192 – 75c. red . . . . 1·75 4·25
193 – 1l.25 blue . . . . 1·75 4·25
194 – 1l.75+1l. orange . . . . . 2·50 8·75
195 – 2l.55+2l. brown . . . . . 2·50 8·75
196 – 25c. violet (air) . . . . . 1·75 2·75
197 – 50c. green . . . . 1·75 2·75
198 – 80c. blue . . . . 1·75 6·00
199 – 1l.+1l. purple . . . . . . 3·00 9·75
200 **164** 5l.+1l. red . . . . 4·00 21·00

1938. Giotto stamps of Italy optd **ITALIANE ISOLE DELL'EGEO**.
201 1l.25 blue (No. 527) . . . . 90 1·60
202 2l.75+2l. brown (530) . . . . 1·00 6·25

1940. Colonial Exhibition. Inscr as in T **19**.
203 – 5c. brown (postage) . . . 35 40
204 – 10c. orange 35 40
205 **19** 25c. green 50 75
206 – 50c. violet 50 75
207 – 75c. red . . . . 50 1·40
208 **19** 1l.25 blue . . . . 50 1·50
209 – 2l.+75c. red . . . . 50 8·25
DESIGNS—VERT: 5c., 50c. Roman Wolf statue; 10c., 75c., 2l. Crown and Maltese Cross.

210 50c. brown (air) . . . . . . 1·00 1·50
211 1l. violet . . . . 1·00 1·50
212 2l.+75c. blue . . . . 1·00 3·00
213 5l.+2l.50 brown . . . . . 1·00 5·00
DESIGNS—HORIZ: Savoia Marchetti S.M.75 airplane over: 50c., 2l. statues, Rhodes Harbour; 1, 5l. Government House, Rhodes.

1943. Aegean Relief Fund. Nos. 17/25 surch **PRO ASSISTENZA EGEO** and value.
214 **1** 5c.+5c. purple 50 50
215 – 10c.+10c. brown 50 50
216 – 20c.+20c. red 50 50
217 – 25c.+25c. green 50 50
218 **2** 30c.+30c. blue 75 65
219 – 50c.+50c. brown . . . . . 1·00 1·25
220 – 1l.25+1l.25 blue . . . . . 2·00 1·60
221 **2** 5l.+5l. purple . . . . . . 55·00 50·00

1944. War Victims' Relief. Nos. 17/20 and 22/23 surch **PRO SINISTRATI DI GUERRA**, value and stag symbol.
224 **1** 5c.+3l. purple . . . . . . 1·00 1·75
225 – 10c.+3l. brown . . . . . . 1·00 1·75
226 – 20c.+3l. red . . . . 1·00 1·75
227 – 25c.+3l. green . . . . . . 1·00 1·75
228 – 50c.+3l. brown . . . . . . 1·00 1·75
229 – 1l.25+5l. blue . . . . . . 18·00 20·00

1944. Air. War Victims Relief. Surch **PRO SINISTRATI DI GUERRA** and value.
232 **11** 50c.+2l. blk & yellow . . . 6·25 3·25
233 80c.+2l. black and red . . 7·75 4·75
234 1l.+2l. black & green . . . 10·00 5·00
235 5l.+2l. black & mauve . . 48·00 48·00

1945. Red Cross Fund. Nos. 24/5 surch **FEBBRAIO 1945 + 10** and Cross.
236 +10l. on 5l. purple . . . . . 5·00 8·25
237 +10l. on 10l. green . . . . . 5·00 8·25

EXPRESS STAMPS

1932. Air. Garibaldi Air Express stamps of Italy optd **ISOLE ITALIANE DELL'EGEO**.
E104 **E 3** 2l.25+1l. red & blue . . 30·00 50·00
E105 4l.50+1l.50 grey and yellow . . . . 30·00 50·00

1934. Air. As Nos. E442/3 of Italy, but colours changed, optd **ISOLE ITALIANE DELL'EGEO**.
E175 2l.+1l.25 blue . . . . . . 26·00 45·00
E176 4l.50+2l. green . . . . . . 26·00 45·00

E 17

1935.
E184 **E 17** 1l.25 green . . . . . . 1·40 1·00
E185 2l.50 orange . . . . . . 2·10 2·25

1943. Aegean Relief Fund. Surch **PRO ASSISTENZA EGEO** and value.
E222 **E 17** 1l.25+1l.25 green . . . 26·00 18·00
E223 2l.50+2l.50 orge . . . 35·00 20·00

1944. Nos. 19/20 surch **ESPRESSO** and value.
E230 1l.25 on 25c. green . . . . 50 1·10
E231 2l.50 on 50c. red . . . . . 50 1·10

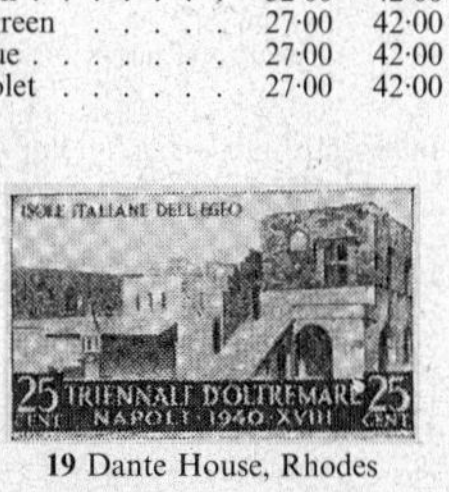

PARCEL POST STAMPS

P 12

1934.

P137	P 12	5c. orange	1·00	1·25
P138		10c. red	1·00	1·25
P139		20c. green	1·00	1·25
P140		25c. violet	1·00	1·25
P141		50c. blue	1·00	1·25
P142		60c. black	1·00	1·25
P143	–	1l. orange	1·00	1·25
P144	–	2l. red	1·00	1·25
P145	–	3l. green	1·00	1·25
P146	–	4l. violet	1·00	1·25
P147	–	10l. blue	1·00	1·25

DESIGN: 1l. to 10l. Left half: Stag as in Type E **17**; Right half: Castle.

POSTAGE DUE STAMPS

D **14** Badge of the Knights of St. John

D **15** Immortelle

1934.

D148	D 14	5c. orange	70	95
D149		10c. red	70	95
D150		20c. green	70	50
D151		30c. violet	70	75
D152		40c. blue	70	1·75
D153	D 15	50c. orange	70	50
D154		60c. red	70	2·75
D155		1l. green	70	2·75
D156		2l. violet	70	1·75

B. GREEK MILITARY ADMINISTRATION

100 lepta = 1 drachma.

1947. Stamps of Greece optd with characters as in Type G **1**.

G1	–	10d. on 2000d. blue (No. 623)	50	45
G3	89	50d. on 1d. grn (No. 642)	80	80
G4		250d. on 3d. brn (No. 643)	80	80

Σ. Δ. Δ.

(G 1)

1947. Stamps of Greece surch as Type G **1**.

G 5	–	20d. on 500d. brown (No. 582)	70	70
G 6	–	30d. on 5d. green (No. 574)	70	70
G 7	106	50d. on 2d. brown	60	60
G 8	–	250d. on 10d. brown (No. 510)	55	55
G 9	–	400d. on 15d. green (No. 511)	80	80
G10	–	1000d. on 200d. blue (No. 581)	90	90

DOMINICA Pt. 1

Until 31 December 1939 one of the Leeward Islands, but then transferred to the Windward Islands. Used Leeward Island stamps concurrently with Dominican issues from 1903 to above date.

1874. 12 pence = 1 shilling;
20 shillings = 1 pound.
1949. 100 cents = 1 West Indian dollar.

1

1874.

13	1	½d. yellow	2·50	10·00
20		½d. green	1·50	5·50
5		1d. lilac	5·00	2·00
22a		1d. red	2·75	6·00
15		2½d. brown	£140	2·00
23		2½d. blue	3·75	5·00
7		4d. blue	£110	2·50
24		4d. grey	2·75	4·00
8		6d. green	£150	20·00
25		6d. orange	7·00	40·00
9		1s. mauve	£120	48·00

1882. No. 5 bisected and surch with a small ½.

10	1	½(d.) on half 1d. lilac	£160	38·00

1882. No. 5 bisected and surch with large ½.

11	1	½(d.) on half 1d. lilac	28·00	15·00

1883. No. 5 bisected and surch **HALF PENNY** vert.

12	1	½d. on half 1d. lilac	60·00	20·00

1886. Nos. 8 and 9 surch in words and bar.

17	1	½d. on 6d. green	4·25	3·50
18		1d. on 6d. green	£20000	£10000
19		1d. on 1s. mauve	14·00	16·00

9 "Roseau from the Sea" (Lt. Caddy)

10

1903.

37	9	½d. green	3·50	3·25
38		1d. grey and red	2·00	40
29		2d. green and brown	2·50	4·50
30		2½d. grey and blue	5·00	4·00
31		3d. purple and black	8·00	3·25
32		6d. grey and brown	4·50	18·00
43		1s. mauve and green	3·75	55·00
34		2s. black and purple	26·00	29·00
45		2s.6d. green and orange	22·00	60·00
46	10	5s. black and brown	60·00	60·00

1908.

48bw	9	1d. red	1·00	50
64		1½d. orange	3·00	11·00
65		2d. grey	2·75	3·25
66		2½d. blue	2·00	8·50
51		3d. purple on yellow	3·00	4·25
52a		6d. purple	3·50	18·00
53		1s. black on green	3·00	2·75
53b		2s. purple and blue on blue	25·00	85·00
70		2s.6d. black and red on blue	32·00	85·00

1914. As T **10**, but portrait of King George V.

54		5s. red and green on yellow	55·00	80·00

1916. No. 37 surch **WAR TAX ONE HALFPENNY**.

55	9	½d. on ½d. green	60	75

1918. Optd **WAR TAX**.

57	9	½d. green	15	50
58		3d. purple on yellow	1·25	4·00

1919. Surch **WAR TAX 1½D.**

59	9	1½d. on 2½d. orange	15	55

1920. Surch **1½D.**

60	9	1½d. on 2½d. orange	2·50	4·50

16

1923.

71	16	½d. black and green	1·75	60
72		1d. black and violet	2·00	1·75
73		1d. black and red	9·00	1·00
74		1½d. black and red	2·75	65
75		1½d. black and brown	9·00	70
76		2d. black and grey	1·75	50
77		2½d. black and yellow	1·50	9·00
78		2½d. black and blue	4·25	2·00
79		3d. black and blue	1·50	12·00
80		3d. black and red on yellow	1·50	1·00
81		4d. black and brown	2·50	5·50
82		6d. black and mauve	3·50	7·00
83		1s. black on green	2·25	2·75
84		2s. black and blue on blue	10·00	17·00
85		2s.6d. black and red on blue	18·00	19·00
86		3s. black and purple on yellow	3·25	12·00
87		4s. black and red on green	11·00	20·00
90		5s. black and green on yellow	9·00	50·00
91		£1 black and purple on red	£225	£350

1935. Silver Jubilee. As T **13** of Antigua.

92		1d. blue and red	75	20
93		1½d. blue and grey	1·50	75
94		2½d. brown and blue	1·50	2·50
95		1s. grey and purple	1·50	3·50

1937. Coronation. As T **2** of Aden.

96		1d. red	40	10
97		1½d. brown	40	10
98		2½d. blue	60	1·25

17 Fresh Water Lake

21 King George VI

1938.

99	17	½d. brown and green	10	15
100	–	1d. black and red	20	20
101	–	1½d. green and purple	30	70
102	–	2d. red and black	50	1·25
103a	–	2½d. purple and blue	20	1·25
104	–	3d. olive and brown	30	50
104a	–	3½d. blue and mauve	2·00	1·75
105	17	6d. green and violet	1·75	1·50
105a		7d. green and brown	1·75	1·50
106	–	1s. violet and olive	2·75	1·50
106a	–	2s. grey and purple	5·50	8·00
107	17	2s.6d. black and red	12·00	4·75
108	–	5s. blue and brown	7·50	8·00
108a	–	10s. black and orange	12·00	15·00

DESIGNS—As Type **17**: 1d., 3d., 2s., 5s. Layou River; 1½d., 2½d., 3½d. Picking Limes; 2d., 1s., 10s. Boiling Lake.

1940.

109a	21	½d. brown	10	10

1946. Victory. As T **9** of Aden.

110		1d. red	20	10
111		3½d. blue	20	10

1948. Silver Wedding. As T **10/11** of Aden.

112		1d. red	15	10
113		10s. brown	9·50	23·00

1949. U.P.U. As T **20/23** of Antigua.

114		5c. blue	15	15
115		6c. brown	1·00	2·00
116		12c. purple	45	1·00
117		24c. olive	30	30

1951. Inauguration of B.W.I. University College. As T **24/25** of Antigua.

118		3c. green and violet	50	70
119		12c. green and red	75	30

23 Drying Cocoa

40 Seashore at Rosalie

1951. New Currency.

120	–	½c. brown	10	30
121	23	1c. black and red	10	30
122	–	2c. brown and green	10	30
123	–	3c. green and purple	15	1·25
124	–	4c. orange and sepia	40	1·40
125	–	5c. black and red	85	30
126	–	6c. olive and brown	90	30
127	–	8c. green and blue	80	70
128	–	12c. black and green	60	1·25
129	–	14c. blue and purple	95	1·25
130	–	24c. purple and red	75	30
131	–	48c. green and orange	3·50	7·50
132	–	60c. red and black	3·50	5·50
133	–	$1.20 green and black	4·25	6·00
134	–	$2.40 orange and black	23·00	35·00

DESIGNS: ½c. As Type **21**, but with portrait as Type **23**. HORIZ (as Type **23**): 2c., 60c. Carib baskets; 3c., 48c. Lime plantation; 4c. Picking oranges; 5c. Bananas; 6c. Botanical Gardens; 8c. Drying vanilla beans; 12c., $1.20, Fresh Water Lake; 14c. Layou River, 24c. Boiling Lake. VERT: $2.40, Pickling oranges.

1951. New Constitution. Stamps of 1951 optd **NEW CONSTITUTION 1951**.

135		3c. green and violet	15	70
136		5c. black and red	15	80
137		8c. green and blue	15	15
138		14c. blue and violet	35	20

1953. Coronation. As T **13** of Aden.

139		2c. black and green	20	10

1954. As Nos 120/34 but with portrait of Queen Elizabeth II.

140		½c. brown	10	30
141		1c. black and red	10	10
142		2c. brown and green	55	1·25
143		3c. green and purple	1·25	30
144		3c. black and red	3·25	2·25
145		4c. orange and brown	20	10
146		5c. black and red	1·25	50
147		5c. blue and brown	10·00	1·00
148		6c. green and brown	40	10
149		8c. green and blue	80	10
150		10c. green and brown	5·00	2·25
151		12c. black and green	50	10
152		14c. blue and purple	30	10
153		24c. purple and red	40	10
154		48c. green and orange	1·60	7·00
155		48c. brown and violet	1·25	80
156		60c. red and black	1·00	1·00
157		$1.20 green and black	16·00	7·00
158		$2.40 orange and black	16·00	14·00

DESIGNS (New)—HORIZ: Nos. 144, 155, Mat making; 147, Canoe making; 150, Bananas.

1958. British Caribbean Federation. As T **25** of Antigua.

159		3c. green	40	10
160		6c. blue	60	1·25
161		12c. red	70	15

1963.

162	40	1c. green, blue and sepia	10	85
163	–	2c. blue	30	30
164	–	3c. brown and blue	1·00	1·00
165	–	4c. green, sepia and violet	10	10
166	–	5c. mauve	30	20
167	–	6c. green, bistre and violet	10	45
168	–	8c. green, sepia and black	30	20
169	–	10c. sepia and pink	10	10
170	–	12c. green, blue and sepia	70	10
171	–	14c. multicoloured	70	10
204	–	15c. yellow, green and brown	70	10
173	–	24c. multicoloured	8·50	20
174	–	48c. green, blue and black	75	50
175	–	60c. orange, green and black	1·00	70
176	–	$1.20 multicoloured	6·50	1·00
177	–	$2.40 blue, turq & brn	3·25	2·50
178	–	$4.80 green, blue and brown	9·00	20·00

DESIGNS—VERT: 2c., 5c. Queen Elizabeth II (after Annigoni); 14c. Traditional costume; 24c. Imperial amazon ("Sisserou Parrot"); $2.40, Trafalgar Falls; $4.80, Coconut palm. HORIZ: 3c. Sailing canoe; 4c. Sulphur springs; 6c. Road making; 8c. Dug-out canoe; 10c. Crapaud (frog); 12c. Scott's Head; 15c. Bananas; 48c. Goodwill; 60c. Cocoa tree; $1.20, Coat of Arms.

1963. Freedom from Hunger. As T **28** of Aden.

179		15c. violet	15	10

1963. Centenary of Red Cross. As T **33** of Antigua.

180		5c. red and black	20	40
181		15c. red and blue	40	60

1964. 400th Birth Anniv of Shakespeare. As T **34** of Antigua.

182		15c. purple	20	10

1965. Centenary of I.T.U. As T **36** of Antigua.

183		2c. green and blue	10	10
184		48c. turquoise and grey	45	20

1965. I.C.Y. As T **37** of Antigua.

185		1c. purple and turquoise	10	20
186		15c. green and lavender	35	10

1966. Churchill Commemoration. As T **38** of Antigua.

187		1c. blue	10	75
188		5c. green	15	10
189		15c. brown	30	10
190		24c. violet	40	20

1966. Royal Visit. As T **39** of Antigua.

191		5c. black and blue	75	30
192		15c. black and mauve	1·00	30

1966. World Cup Football Championship. As T **40** of Antigua.

193		5c. multicoloured	25	15
194		24c. multicoloured	85	15

1966. Inauguration of W.H.O. Headquarters, Geneva. As T **41** of Antigua.

195		5c. black, green and blue	15	15
196		24c. black, purple and ochre	30	15

1966. 20th Anniv of U.N.E.S.C.O. As T **54/6** of Antigua.

197		5c. red, yellow and orange	20	15
198		15c. yellow, violet and olive	50	10
199		24c. black, purple and orange	60	15

56 Children of Three Races

1967. National Day. Multicoloured.

205		5c. Type **56**	10	10
206		10c. The "Santa Maria" and motto	40	15
207		15c. Hands holding motto ribbon	15	15
208		24c. Belaire dancing	15	20

57 John F. Kennedy

1968. Human Rights Year. Multicoloured.

209		1c. Type **57**	10	10
210		10c. Cecil E. A. Rawle	10	10
211		12c. Pope John XXIII	50	15

212	48c. Florence Nightingale	20	25
213	60c. Albert Schweitzer	20	25

1968. Associated Statehood. Nos. 162 etc, optd **ASSOCIATED STATEHOOD.**

214	1c. green, blue and sepia	10	10
215	2c. blue	10	10
216	3c. brown and blue	10	10
217	4c. green, sepia and violet	10	10
218	5c. mauve	10	10
219	6c. green, bistre and violet	10	10
220	8c. green, sepia and black	10	10
221	10c. sepia and pink	55	10
222	12c. green, blue and brown	10	10
224	14c. multicoloured	10	10
225	15c. yellow, green and brown	10	10
226	24c. multicoloured	3·75	10
227	48c. green, blue and black	55	1·50
228	60c. orange, green and black	90	1·00
229	$1.20 multicoloured	1·00	3·00
230	$2.40 blue, turquoise and brown	1·00	2·50
231	$4.80 green, blue and brown	1·25	5·50

1968. National Day. Nos. 162/4, 171 and 176 optd **NATIONAL DAY 3 NOVEMBER 1968.**

232	1c. green, blue and sepia	10	10
233	2c. blue	10	10
234	3c. brown and blue	10	10
235	14c. multicoloured	10	10
236	$1.20 multicoloured	55	40

60 Forward shooting at Goal

1968. Olympic Games, Mexico. Multicoloured.

237	1c. Type **60**	10	10
238	1c. Goalkeeper attempting to save ball	10	10
239	5c. Swimmers preparing to dive	10	10
240	5c. Swimmers diving	10	10
241	48c. Javelin-throwing	15	15
242	48c. Hurdling	15	15
243	60c. Basketball	90	25
244	60c. Basketball players	90	25

61 "The Small Cowper Madonna" (Raphael)

62 "Venus and Adonis" (Rubens)

1968. Christmas.

245	**61** 5c. multicoloured	10	10

1969. 20th Anniv of World Health Organization.

246	**62** 5c. multicoloured	20	10
247	– 15c. multicoloured	30	10
248	– 24c. multicoloured	30	10
249	– 50c. multicoloured	50	40

DESIGNS: 15c. "The Death of Socrates" (J.-L. David); 24c. "Christ and the Pilgrims of Emmaus" (Velasquez); 50c. "Pilate washing his Hands" (Rembrandt).

66 Picking Oranges

71 "Spinning" (J. Millet)

1969. Tourism. Multicoloured.

250	10c. Type **66**	15	10
251	10c. Woman, child and ocean scene	15	10
252	12c. Fort Yeoung Hotel	50	10
253	12c. Red-necked amazon	50	10
254	24c. Calypso band	30	10
255	24c. Women dancing	30	15

256	48c. Underwater life	30	25
257	48c. Skin-diver and turtle	30	25

1969. 1st Anniv of C.A.R.I.F.T.A. (Caribbean Free Trade Area). Multicoloured.

258	5c. Type **67**	10	10
259	8c. Hawker Siddeley H.S.748 aircraft, emblem and island	30	20
260	12c. Chart of Caribbean Sea and emblem	30	25
261	24c. Steamship unloading, tug and emblem	40	25

1969. 50th Anniv of International Labour Organization. Multicoloured.

262	15c. Type **71**	10	10
263	30c. "Threshing" (J. Millet)	15	15
264	38c. "Flax-pulling" (J. Millet)	15	15

72 Mahatma Gandhi weaving and Clock Tower, Westminster

1969. Birth Cent of Mahatma Gandhi. Mult.

265	6c. Type **72**	25	10
266	38c. Gandhi, Nehru and Mausoleum	40	15
267	$1.20 Gandhi and Taj Mahal	45	90

All stamps are incorrectly inscribed "Ghandi".

75 "Saint Joseph"

1969. National Day. Multicoloured.

268	6c. Type **75**	10	10
269	8c. "Saint John"	10	10
270	12c. "Saint Peter"	10	10
271	60c. "Saint Paul"	30	50

79 Queen Elizabeth II

99 "Virgin and Child with St. John" (Perugino)

80 Purple-throated Carib ("Humming Bird") and Flower

1969. Centres multicoloured; colours of "D" given.

272a	**79** ½c. black and silver	30	1·50
273	**80** 1c. black and yellow	30	1·75
274	– 2c. black and yellow	15	10
275a	– 3c. black and yellow	2·50	1·50
276a	– 4c. black and yellow	2·50	1·50
277a	– 5c. black and yellow	2·00	1·50
278a	– 6c. black and brown	2·50	2·75
279	– 8c. black and brown	20	10
280	– 10c. black and yellow	20	10
281	– 12c. black and yellow	20	10
282	– 15c. black and blue	20	10
283	– 25c. black and red	30	10
284a	– 30c. black and olive	1·50	70
285	– 38c. black and purple	8·00	1·75
286	– 50c. black and brown	50	45
287	– 60c. black and yellow	55	1·50
288	– $1.20 black and yellow	1·00	1·75
289	– $2.40 black and gold	1·00	4·00
290	– $4.80 black and gold	1·25	7·00

DESIGNS—HORIZ (As Type **80**): 2c. Poinsettia; 3c. Redneck pigeon ("Ramier"); 4c. Imperial amazon ("Sisserou"); 5c. "Battus polydamas" (butterfly); 6c. "Dryas julia" (butterfly); 8c. Shipping bananas; 10c. Portsmouth Harbour; 12c. Copra processing plant; 15c. Straw workers; 25c. Timber plant; 30c. Pumice mine; 38c. Grammar school and playing fields; 50c. Roseau Cathedral. (38 × 26½ mm); 60c. Government Headquarters. (40 × 27 mm); $1.20, Melville Hall

airport. (39½ × 26 mm): $2.40, Coat of arms. VERT: (26 × 39 mm): $4.80, As Type **79**, but larger.

1969. Christmas. Paintings. Multicoloured.

291	6c. "Virgin and Child with St. John" (Lippi)	10	10
292	10c. "Holy Family with Lamb" (Raphael)	10	10
293	15c. Type **99**	10	10
294	$1.20 "Madonna of the Rose Hedge" (Botticelli)	35	40

101 Astronaut's First Step onto the Moon

1970. Moon Landing. Multicoloured.

296	½c. Type **101**	10	10
297	5c. Scientific experiment on the Moon and flag	15	10
298	8c. Astronauts collecting rocks	15	10
299	30c. Module over Moon	30	15
300	50c. Moon plague	40	25
301	60c. Astronauts	40	30

107 Giant Green Turtle

1970. Flora and Fauna. Multicoloured.

303	6c. Type **107**	50	20
304	24c. Atlantic flyingfish	60	45
305	38c. Anthurium lily	70	65
306	60c. Imperial and red-necked amazons	3·25	5·50

108 18th-century National Costume

1970. National Day. Multicoloured.

308	5c. Type **108**	10	10
309	8c. Carib basketry	10	10
310	$1 Flag and chart of Dominica	30	40

109 Scrooge and Marley's Ghost

1970. Christmas and Death Centenary of Charles Dickens. Scenes from "A Christmas Carol". Multicoloured.

312	2c. Type **109**	10	10
313	15c. "Fezziwig's Ball"	20	10
314	30c. Scrooge and his Nephew's Party	20	10
315	$1.20 Scrooge and the Ghost of Christmas Present	65	90

110 "The Doctor" (Sir Luke Fildes)

1970. Centenary of British Red Cross. Multicoloured.

317	8c. Type **110**	10	10
318	10c. Hands and Red Cross	10	10
319	15c. Flag of Dominica and Red Cross emblem	15	10
320	50c. "The Sick Child" (E. Munch)	50	45

111 Marigot School

1971. International Education Year. Multicoloured.

322	5c. Type **111**	10	10
323	8c. Goodwill Junior High School	10	10
324	14c. University of West Indies (Jamaica)	10	10
325	$1 Trinity College, Cambridge	35	30

112 Waterfall

1971. Tourism. Multicoloured.

327	5c. Type **112**	15	10
328	10c. Boat-building	15	10
329	30c. Sailing	25	10
330	50c. Yacht and motor launch	40	30

113 U.N.I.C.E.F. Symbol in "D"

1971. 25th Anniv of U.N.I.C.E.F.

332	**113** 5c. violet, black and gold	10	10
333	10c. yellow, blk & gold	10	10
334	38c. green, blk & gold	10	10
335	$1.20 orange, blk & gold	30	45

114 German Boy Scout

1971. World Scout Jamboree, Asagiri, Japan. Various designs showing Boy Scouts from the nations listed. Multicoloured.

337	20c. Type **114**	15	15
338	24c. Great Britain	20	15
339	30c. Japan	25	20
340	$1 Dominica	50	2·00

115 Groine at Portsmouth

1971. National Day. Multicoloured.

342	8c. Type **115**	10	10
343	15c. Carnival scene	10	10
344	20c. Carifta Queen (vert)	10	10
345	50c. Rock of Atkinson (vert)	20	25

116 Eight Reals Piece, 1761

1972. Coins.

347	**116** 10c. black, silver and violet	10	10
348	– 30c. black, silver and green	15	15
349	– 35c. black, silver and blue	15	20
350	– 50c. black, silver and red	25	1·75

DESIGNS—HORIZ: 30c. Eleven and three bitt pieces, 1798. VERT: 35c. Two reals and two bitt pieces, 1770; 50c. Mocos, pieces-of-eight and eight reals-eleven bitts piece, 1798.

117 Common Opossum

1972. U.N. Conference on the Human Enviroment, Stockholm. Multicoloured.
352	½c. Type **117**	10	10
353	35c. Brazilian agouti (rodent)	30	15
354	60c. Orchid	2·00	50
355	$1.20 Hibiscus	1·25	1·60

118 Sprinter

1972. Olympic Games, Munich. Multicoloured.
357	30c. Type **118**	10	10
358	35c. Hurdler	15	15
359	58c. Hammer-thrower (vert)	20	20
360	72c. Long-jumper (vert)	40	40

119 General Post Office

1972. National Day. Multicoloured.
362	10c. Type **119**	10	10
363	20c. Morne Diablotin	10	10
364	30c. Rodney's Rock	15	15

1972. Royal Silver Wedding. As T **52** of Ascension, but with Bananas and Imperial Parrot in background.
366	5c. green	20	10
367	$1 green	60	40

121 "The Adoration of the Shepherds" (Caravaggio) **122** Launching of Weather Satellite

1972. Christmas. Multicoloured.
368	8c. Type **121**	10	10
369	14c. "The Myosotis Virgin" (Rubens)	10	10
370	30c. "Madonna and Child with St Francesca Romana" (Gentileschi)	15	10
371	$1 "Adoration of the Kings" (Mostaert)	50	90

1973. Centenary of I.M.O./W.M.O. Multicoloured.
373	½c. Type **122**	10	10
374	1c. Nimbus satellite	10	10
375	2c. Radiosonde balloon	10	10
376	30c. Radarscope (horiz)	15	15
377	35c. Diagram of pressure zones (horiz)	20	20
378	50c. Hurricane shown by satellite (horiz)	30	35
379	$1 Computer weather-map (horiz)	60	65

123 Going to Hospital

1973. 25th Anniv of W.H.O. Multicoloured.
381	½c. Type **123**	10	10
382	1c. Maternity care	10	10
383	2c. Smallpox inoculation	10	10
384	30c. Emergency service	30	15
385	35c. Waiting for the doctor	30	15
386	50c. Medical examination	30	25
387	$1 Travelling doctor	40	60

124 Cyrique Crab

1973. Flora and Fauna. Multicoloured.
389	½c. Type **124**	10	10
390	22c. Blue land-crab	30	10
391	25c. Bread fruit	30	15
392	$1.20 Sunflower	55	2·00

125 Princess Anne and Captain Mark Phillips

1973. Royal Wedding.
394	**125** 25c. multicoloured	10	10
395	– $2 multicoloured	30	30

DESIGN: $2 As Type **125**, but with different frame.

126 "Adoration of the Kings" (Brueghel)

1973. Christmas. Religious Paintings. Multicoloured.
397	½c. Type **126**	10	10
398	1c. "Adoration of the Magi" (Botticelli)	10	10
399	2c. "Adoration of the Magi" (Durer)	10	10
400	12c. "Mystic Nativity" (Botticelli)	20	10
401	22c. "Adoration of the Magi" (Rubens)	25	10
402	35c. "The Nativity" (Durer)	25	10
403	$1 "Adoration of the Shepherds" (Giorgione)	60	55

127 Carib Basket-weaving

1973. National Day. Multicoloured.
405	5c. Type **127**	10	10
406	10c. Staircase of the Snake	10	10
407	50c. Miss Caribbean Queen	15	15
408	60c. Miss Carifta Queen	15	15
409	$1 Dance group	25	30

Nos. 407/8 are vert.

128 University Centre, Dominica

1973. 25th Anniv of West Indies University. Multicoloured.
411	12c. Type **128**	10	10
412	30c. Graduation ceremony	10	10
413	$1 University coat of arms	25	35

129 Dominica 1d. Stamp of 1874 and Map

1974. Stamp Centenary. Multicoloured.
415	½c. Type **129**	10	10
416	1c. 6d. stamp of 1874 and posthorn	10	10
417	2c. 1d. stamp of 1874 and arms	10	10
418	10c. Type **129**	20	10

419	50c. As 1c.	40	30
420	$1.20 As 2c.	50	70

130 Footballer and Flag of Brazil

1974. World Cup Football Championship, West Germany. Multicoloured.
422	½c. Type **130**	10	10
423	1c. West Germany	10	10
424	2c. Italy	10	10
425	30c. Scotland	50	10
426	40c. Sweden	50	10
427	50c. Netherlands	55	35
428	$1 Yugoslavia	90	90

131 Indian Hole

1974. National Day. Multicoloured.
430	10c. Type **131**	10	10
431	40c. Teachers' Training College	10	10
432	$1 Bay Oil distillery plant, Petite Savanne	50	45

132 Churchill with "Colonist"

1974. Birth Centenary of Sir Winston Churchill. Multicoloured.
434	½c. Type **132**	10	10
435	1c. Churchill and Eisenhower	10	10
436	2c. Churchill and Roosevelt	10	10
437	20c. Churchill and troops on assault-course	15	10
438	45c. Painting at Marrakesh	20	10
439	$2 Giving the "V" sign	50	1·00

133 Mailboats "Orinoco" (1851) and "Geesthaven" (1974)

1974. Centenary of U.P.U. Multicoloured.
441	10c. Type **133**	20	10
442	$2 De Haviland D.H.4 (1918) and Boeing 747-100 (1974)	80	1·00

134 "The Virgin and Child" (Tiso)

1974. Christmas. Multicoloured.
444	½c. Type **134**	10	10
445	1c. "Madonna and Child with Saints" (Costa)	10	10
446	2c. "The Nativity" (school of Rimini, 14th-century)	10	10
447	10c. "The Rest on the Flight into Egypt" (Romanelli)	20	10
448	25c. "The Adoration of the Shepherds" (da Sermoneta)	35	10
449	45c. "The Nativity" (Guido Reni)	45	10
450	$1 "The Adoration of the Magi" (Caselli)	65	40

135 Queen Triggerfish

1975. Fishes. Multicoloured.
452	½c. Type **135**	10	10
453	1c. Porkfish	10	10
454	2c. Sailfish	10	10
455	3c. Swordfish	10	10
456	20c. Great barracuda	75	50
457	$2 Nassau grouper	1·75	2·75

136 "Myscelia antholia"

1975. Dominican Butterflies. Multicoloured.
459	½c. Type **136**	10	40
460	1c. "Lycorea ceres"	10	40
461	2c. "Anaea marthesia" ("Siderone nemesis")	15	40
462	6c. "Battus polydamas"	50	55
463	30c. "Anartia lytrea"	1·00	70
464	40c. "Morpho peleides"	1·00	75
465	$2 "Dryas julia"	1·40	7·50

137 "Yare" (cargo liner)

1975. "Ships tied to Dominica's History". Mult.
467	½c. Type **137**	20	35
468	1c. "Thames II" (liner), 1890	20	35
469	2c. "Lady Nelson" (cargo liner)	20	35
470	20c. "Lady Rodney" (cargo liner)	60	35
471	45c. "Statesman" (freighter)	80	55
472	50c. "Geestcape" (freighter)	80	80
473	$2 "Geeststar" (freighter)	1·50	4·50

138 "Women in Agriculture"

1975. International Women's Year. Multicoloured.
475	10c. Type **138**	10	10
476	$2 "Women in Industry and Commerce"	40	60

139 Miss Caribbean Queen, 1975   **140** "Virgin and Child" (Mantegna)

1975. National Day. Multicoloured.
477	5c. Type **139**	10	10
478	10c. Public library (horiz)	10	10
479	30c. Citrus factory (horiz)	10	10
480	$1 National Day Trophy	25	50

1975. Christmas. "Virgin and Child" paintings by artists named. Multicoloured.
482	½c. Type **140**	10	10
483	1c. Fra Filippo Lippi	10	10
484	2c. Bellini	10	10
485	10c. Botticelli	15	10
486	25c. Bellini	25	10
487	45c. Correggio	30	10
488	$1 Durer	55	50

141 Hibiscus

1975. Multicoloured.

490	½c. Type **141**	10	50
491	1c. African tulip	15	50
492	2c. Castor-oil tree	15	50
493	3c. White cedar flower	15	50
494	4c. Egg plant	15	50
495	5c. Needlefish ("Gare")	20	50
496	6c. Ochro	20	60
497	8c. Zenaida dove ("Mountain Dove")	2·50	60
498	10c. Screw pine	20	15
499	20c. Mango longue	30	15
500	25c. Crayfish	35	15
501	30c. Common opossum	90	80
502	40c. Bay leaf groves	90	80
503	50c. Tomatoes	40	50
504	$1 Lime factory	55	65
505	$2 Rum distillery	1·00	3·50
506	$5 Bay Oil distillery	1·25	5·00
507	$10 Queen Elizabeth II (vert)	1·75	15·00

Nos. 502/7 are larger, 28 × 44 mm ($10) or 44 × 28 (others).

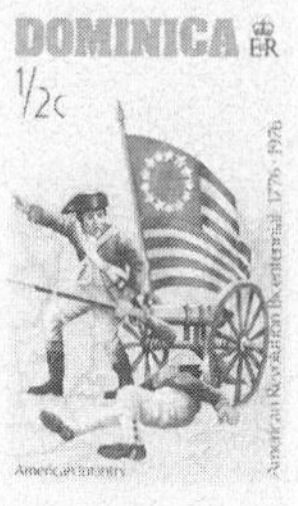
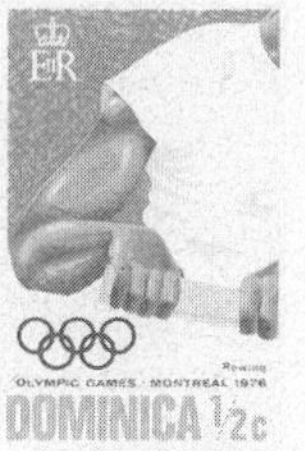

142 American Infantry **143** Rowing

1976. Bicentenary of American Revolution. Mult.

508	½c. Type **142**	10	10
509	1c. British three-decker, 1782	10	10
510	2c. George Washington	10	10
511	45c. British sailors	30	10
512	75c. British ensign	40	40
513	$2 Admiral Hood	60	1·25

1976. Olympic Games, Montreal. Multicoloured.

515	½c. Type **143**	10	10
516	1c. Shot putting	10	10
517	2c. Swimming	10	10
518	40c. Relay	15	10
519	45c. Gymnastics	15	10
520	60c. Sailing	20	20
521	$2 Archery	55	80

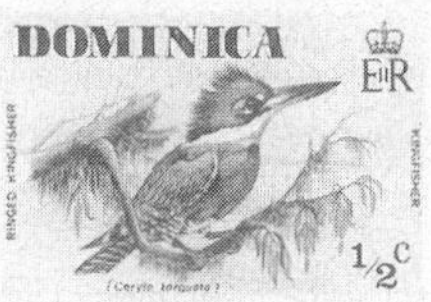

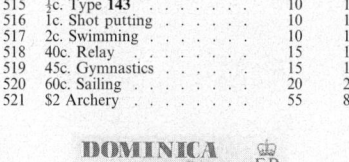

144 Ringed Kingfisher

1976. Wild Birds. Multicoloured.

523	½c. Type **144**	10	50
524	1c. Mourning dove	15	50
525	2c. Green-backed heron ("Green Heron")	15	50
526	15c. Blue-winged hawk (vert)	75	35
527	30c. Blue-headed hummingbird (vert)	1·00	55
528	45c. Bananaquit (vert)	1·10	60
529	$2 Imperial amazon ("Imperial Parrot") (vert)	2·25	12·00

1976. West Indian Victory in World Cricket Cup. As Nos. 559/60 of Barbados.

531	15c. Map of the Caribbean	75	1·25
532	25c. Prudential Cup	75	1·75

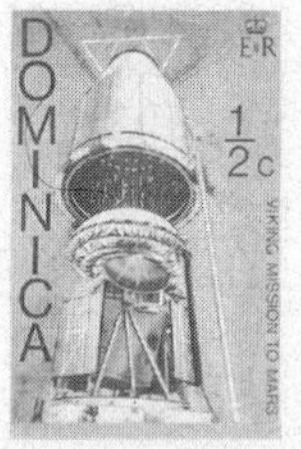
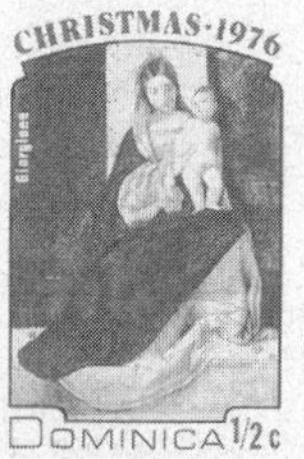

145 Viking Spacecraft System **146** "Virgin and Child with Saints Anthony of Padua and Roch" (Giorgione)

1976. Viking Space Mission. Multicoloured.

533	½c. Type **145**	10	10
534	1c. Landing pad (horiz)	10	10
535	2c. Titan IIID and Centaur DII	10	10
536	3c. Orbiter and lander capsule	10	10
537	45c. Capsule, parachute unopened	20	15
538	75c. Capsule, parachute opened	30	50
539	$1 Lander descending (horiz)	35	60
540	$2 Space vehicle on Mars (horiz)	50	1·60

1976. Christmas. "Virgin and Child" paintings by artists named. Multicoloured.

542	½c. Type **146**	10	10
543	1c. Bellini	10	10
544	2c. Mantegna	10	10
545	6c. Mantegna (different)	10	10
546	25c. Memling	15	10
547	45c. Correggio	20	10
548	$3 Raphael	1·00	1·00

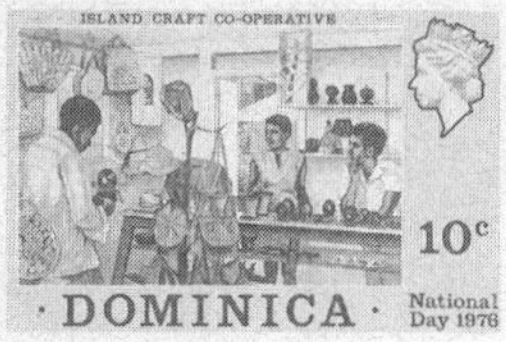

147 Island Craft Co-operative

1976. National Day. Multicoloured.

550	10c. Type **147**	10	10
551	50c. Harvesting bananas	15	10
552	$1 Boxing plant	30	35

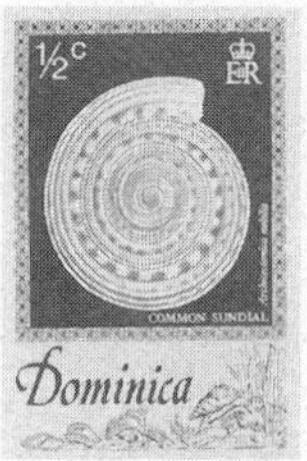
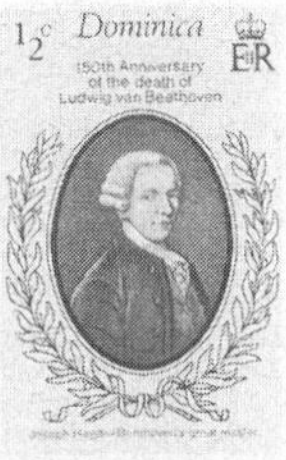

148 American Giant Sundial **150** Joseph Haydn

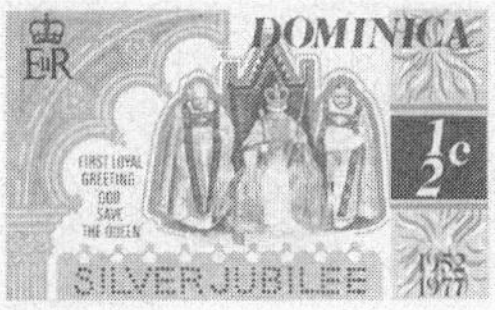

149 The Queen Crowned and Enthroned

1976. Shells. Multicoloured.

554	½c. Type **148**	10	10
555	1c. Flame helmet	10	10
556	2c. Mouse cone	10	10
557	20c. Caribbean vase	35	10
558	40c. West Indian fighting conch	55	25
559	50c. Short coral shell	55	25
560	$3 Apple murex	2·00	3·25

1977. Silver Jubilee. Multicoloured.

562	½c. Type **149**	10	10
563	1c. Imperial State Crown	10	10
564	45c. The Queen and Princess Anne	15	10
565	$2 Coronation Ring	25	30
566	$2.50 Ampulla and Spoon	30	40

1977. 150th Death Anniv of Ludwig van Beethoven. Multicoloured.

568	½c. Type **150**	10	10
569	1c. Scene from "Fidelio"	10	10
570	2c. Maria Casentini (dancer)	10	10
571	15c. Beethoven and pastoral scene	30	10
572	30c. "Wellington's Victory"	30	10
573	40c. Henriette Sontag (singer)	30	10
574	$2 The young Beethoven	75	2·00

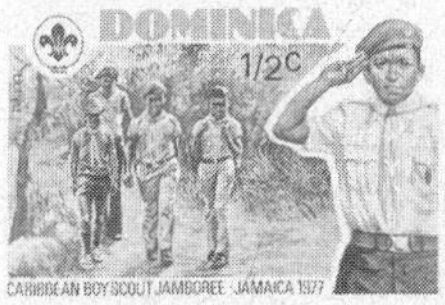

151 Hiking

1977. Caribbean Scout Jamboree, Jamaica. Mult.

576	½c. Type **151**	10	10
577	1c. First-aid	10	10
578	2c. Camping	10	10
579	45c. Rock climbing	25	15
580	50c. Canoeing	30	20
581	$3 Sailing	1·40	1·75

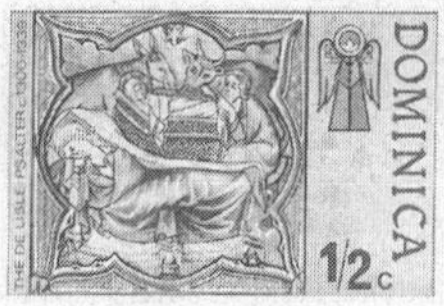

152 Holy Family

1977. Christmas. Multicoloured.

583	½c. Type **152**	10	10
584	1c. Angel and Shepherds	10	10
585	2c. Holy Baptism	10	10
586	6c. Flight into Egypt	15	10
587	15c. Three Kings with gifts	15	10
588	45c. Holy Family in the Temple	30	10
589	$3 Flight into Egypt (different)	80	1·10

1977. Royal Visit. Nos. 562/66 optd **ROYAL VISIT W.I. 1977.**

591	½c. Type **149**	10	10
592	1c. Imperial State Crown	10	10
593	45c. The Queen and Princess Anne	15	10
594a	$2 Coronation Ring	30	30
595a	$2.50 Ampulla and Spoon	35	35

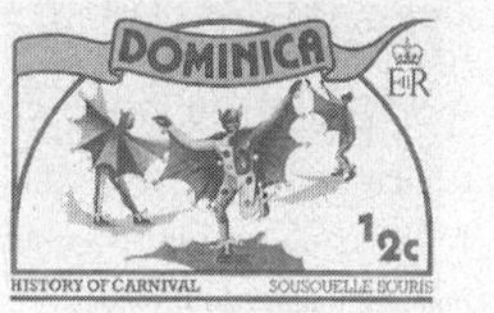

154 "Sousouelle Souris"

1978. "History of Carnival". Multicoloured.

597	½c. Type **154**	10	10
598	1c. Sensay costume	10	10
599	2c. Street musicians	10	10
600	45c. Douiette band	15	10
601	50c. Pappy Show wedding	15	10
602	$2 Masquerade band	45	60

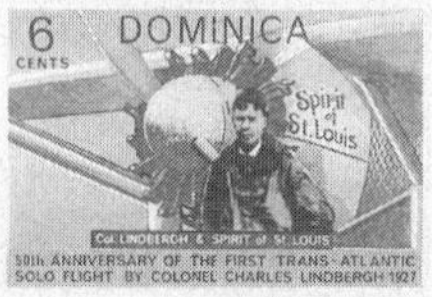

155 Colonel Charles Lindbergh and "Spirit of St. Louis"

1978. Aviation Anniversaries. Multicoloured.

604	6c. Type **155**	20	40
605	10c. "Spirit of St. Louis", New York, 20 May 1927	25	10
606	15c. Lindbergh and map of Atlantic	35	10
607	20c. Lindbergh reaches Paris, 21 May 1927	45	10
608	40c. Airship LZ-1, Lake Constance, 1900	55	20
609	60c. Count F. von Zeppelin and Airship LZ-2, 1906	65	30
610	$3 Airship "Graf Zeppelin", 1928	1·40	2·00

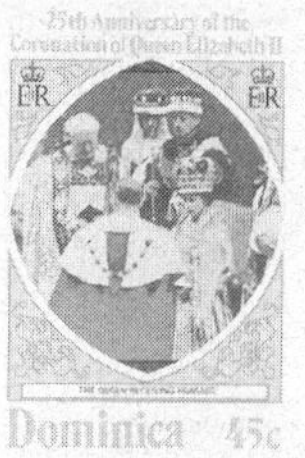
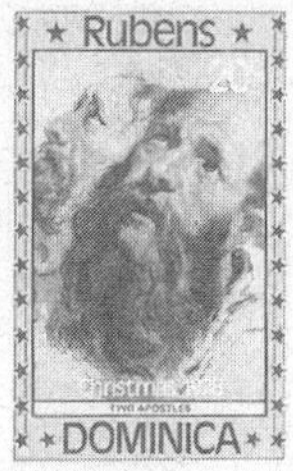

156 Queen receiving Homage **158** "Two Apostles"

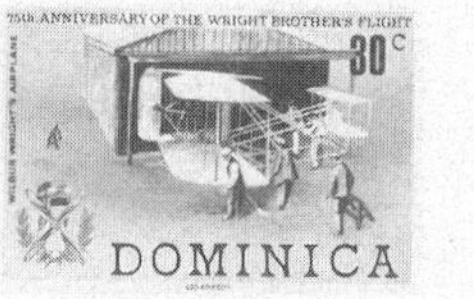

157 Wright Flyer III

1978. 25th Anniv of Coronation. Multicoloured.

612	45c. Type **156**	15	10
613	$2 Balcony scene	30	30
614	$2.50 Queen and Prince Philip	40	40

1978. 75th Anniv of First Powered Flight. Mult.

616	30c. Type **157**	15	15
617	40c. Wright Type A, 1908	20	20
618	60c. Wright Flyer I	25	25
619	$2 Wright Flyer I (different)	85	85

1978. Christmas. Paintings by Rubens. Mult.

621	20c. Type **158**	10	10
622	45c. "Descent from the Cross"	15	10
623	50c. "St Ildefonso receiving the Chasuble"	15	10
624	$3 "Assumption of the Virgin"	35	80

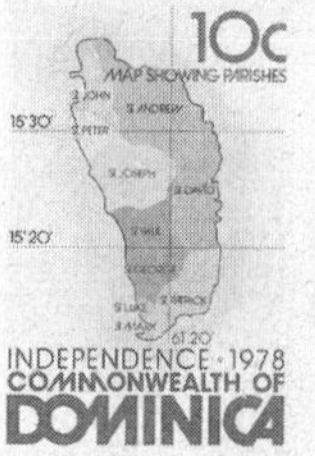
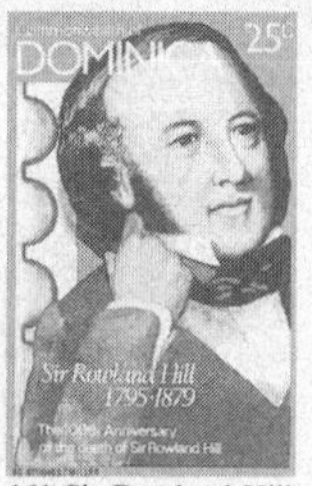

159 Map showing Parishes **161** Sir Rowland Hill

1978. Independence. Multicoloured.

626	10c. Type **159**	45	15
627	25c. "Sabinea carinalis" (national flower)	50	15
628	45c. New National flag	55	15
629	50c. Coat of arms	55	30
630	$2 Prime Minister Patrick John	70	2·25

1978. Nos. 490/507 optd **INDEPENDENCE 3rd NOVEMBER 1978.**

632	½c. Type **57**	40	10
633	1c. African tulip	45	10
634	2c. Castor-oil tree	45	10
635	3c. White cedar flower	50	15
636	4c. Egg plant	50	15
637	5c. Needlefish ("Gare")	50	15
638	6c. Ochro	50	15
639	8c. Zenaida dove	2·50	20
640	10c. Screw pine	50	15
641	20c. Mango longue	60	15
642	25c. Crayfish	70	20
643	30c. Common opossum	70	20
644	40c. Bay leaf groves	70	25
645	50c. Tomatoes	80	30
646	$1 Lime factory	80	65
647	$2 Rum distillery	1·00	1·00
648	$5 Bay Oil distillery	1·25	2·25
649	$10 Queen Elizabeth II	1·75	4·50

1979. Death Centenary of Sir Rowland Hill. Multicoloured.

650	25c. Type **161**	10	10
651	45c. G.B. 1840 Twopenny Blue	15	10
652	50c. Dominica 1874 1d. stamp	15	10
653	$2 Maltese Cross handstamps	35	65

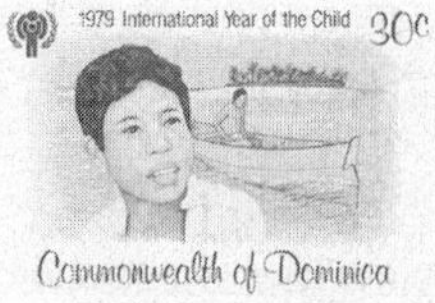

162 Children and Canoe

1979. International Year of the Child. Multicoloured.

655	30c. Type **162**	25	15
656	40c. Children with bananas	25	15
657	50c. Children playing cricket	1·25	80
658	$3 Child feeding rabbits	1·75	2·00

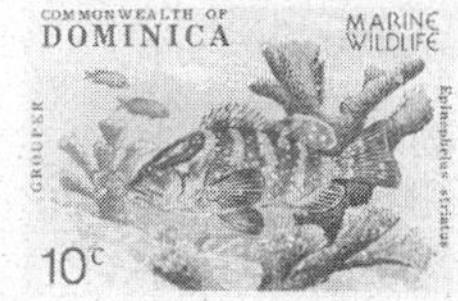

163 Nassau Grouper

1979. Marine Wildlife. Multicoloured.

660	10c. Type **163**	40	15
661	30c. Striped dolphin	70	35
662	50c. White-tailed tropic-bird	2·25	65
663	60c. Brown pelican	2·25	1·50
664	$1 Long-finned pilot whale	2·50	1·75
665	$2 Brown booby	3·00	4·50

No. 661 is inscr "SPOTTED DOLPHIN" in error.

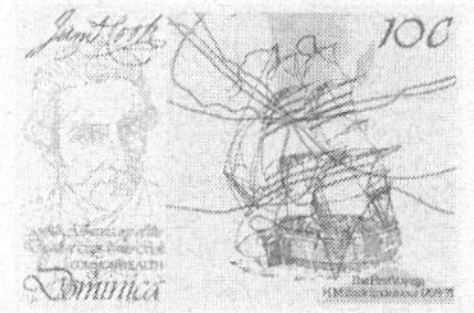

164 H.M.S. "Endeavour"

1979. Death Bicent of Captain Cook. Mult.

667	10c. Type **164**	65	30
668	50c. H.M.S. "Resolution" (Second Voyage)	1·10	1·00
669	60c. H.M.S. "Discovery" (Third Voyage)	1·25	1·50
670	$2 Detail of Cook's chart of New Zealand, 1770	1·60	2·50

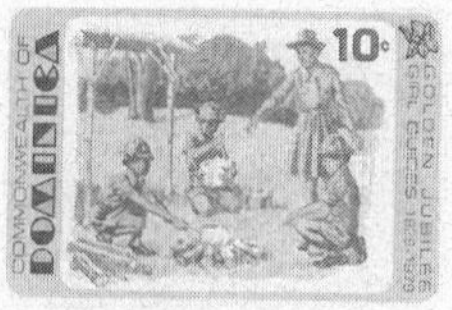

165 Cooking at Campfire

1979. 50th Anniv of Girl Guide Movement in Dominica. Multicoloured.

672	10c. Type **165**	20	10
673	20c. Pitching emergency rain tent	25	10
674	50c. Raising Dominican flag	35	10
675	$2.50 Singing and dancing to accordion	90	80

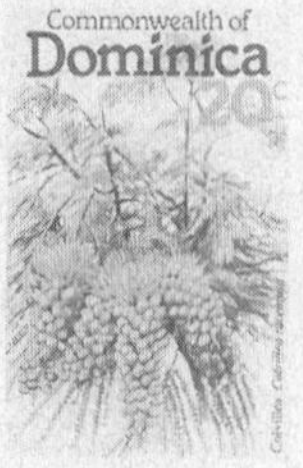

166 Colvillea

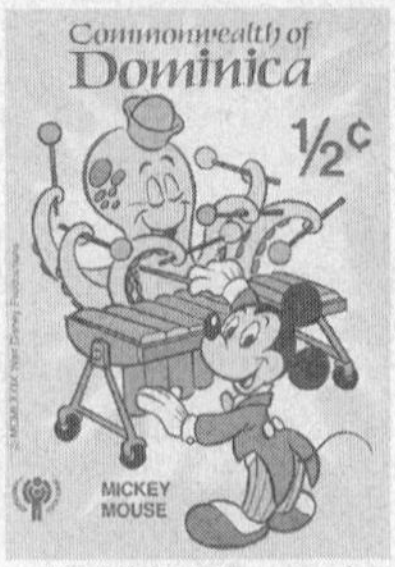

169 Mickey Mouse and Octopus playing Xylophone

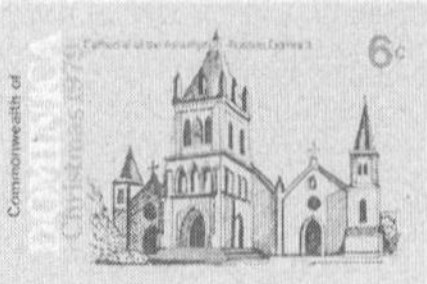

167 Cathedral of the Assumption, Roseau

1979. Flowering Trees. Multicoloured.

677	20c. Type **166**	15	10
678	40c. "Lignum vitae"	20	15
679	60c. Dwarf poinciana	25	15
680	$2 Fern tree	50	75

1979. Christmas. Cathedrals. Multicoloured.

682	6c. Type **167**	10	10
683	45c. St. Paul's, London (vert)	15	10
684	60c. St. Peter's, Rome	15	10
685	$3 Notre Dame, Paris (vert)	55	60

1979. Hurricane Relief. Nos. 495, 502 and 506/7 optd **HURRICANE RELIEF**.

687	5c. Gare	10	10
688	40c. Bay leaf groves	10	10
689	$5 Bay Oil distillery	1·00	1·25
690	$10 Queen Elizabeth II	1·25	1·75

1979. International Year of the Child. Walt Disney Cartoon Characters. Multicoloured.

691	½c. Type **169**	10	10
692	1c. Goofy playing guitar on rocking-horse	10	10
693	2c. Mickey Mouse playing violin and Goofy on bagpipes	10	10
694	3c. Donald Duck playing drum with a pneumatic drill	10	10
695	4c. Minnie Mouse playing saxophone	10	10
696	5c. Goofy one-man band	10	10
697	10c. Horace Horsecollar blowing Dale from french horn	10	10
698	$2 Huey, Dewey and Louie playing bass	1·50	2·00
699	$2.50 Donald Duck at piano and Huey playing trumpet	1·50	2·25

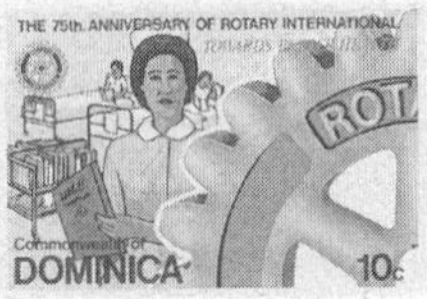

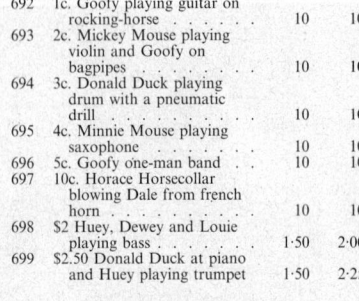

170 Hospital Ward

1980. 75th Anniv of Rotary International. Mult.

701	10c. Type **170**	10	10
702	20c. Electro-cardiogram	15	10
703	40c. Mental hospital site	20	15
704	$2.50 Paul Harris (founder)	55	90

1980. "London 1980" International Stamp Exhibition. Otpd **LONDON 1980**.

706 **161**	25c. multicoloured	25	10
707 –	45c. multicoloured	30	15
708 –	50c. brown, blue and red	30	15
709 –	$2 brown, red and yellow	80	60

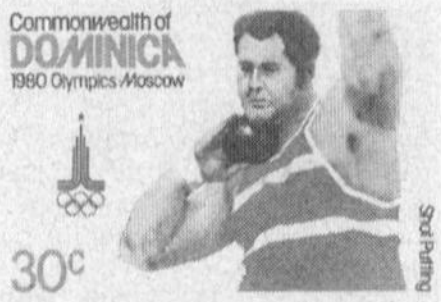

171 Shot Putting

1980. Olympic Games, Moscow. Multicoloured.

710	30c. Type **171**	15	10
711	40c. Basketball	60	15
712	60c. Swimming	35	20
713	$2 Gymnastics	60	65

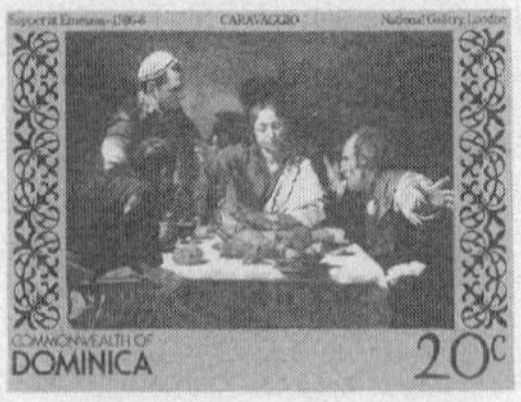

172 "Supper at Emmaus" (Caravaggio)

1980. Famous Paintings. Multicoloured.

715	20c. Type **172**	20	10
716	25c. "Portrait of Charles I Hunting" (Van Dyck) (vert)	20	10
717	30c. "The Maids of Honour" (Velasquez) (vert)	25	10
718	45c. "The Rape of the Sabine Women" (Poussin)	25	10
719	$1 "Embarkation for Cythera" (Watteau)	35	35
720	$5 "Girl before a Mirror" (Picasso) (vert)	1·00	1·50

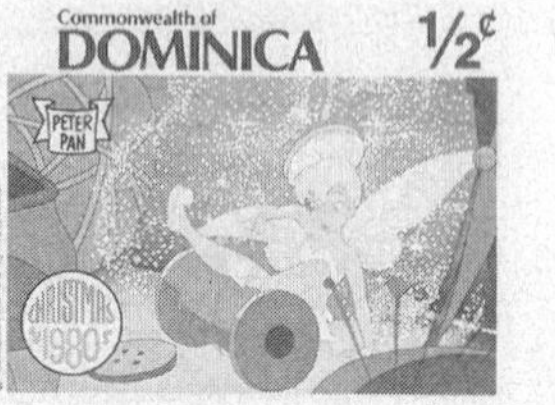

173 Scene from "Peter Pan"

1980. Christmas. Scenes from "Peter Pan". Multicoloured.

722	½c. Type **173** (Tinker Bell)	10	10
723	1c. Wendy sewing back Peter's shadow	10	10
724	2c. Peter introduces the mermaids	10	10
725	3c. Wendy and Peter with lost boys	10	10
726	4c. Captain Hook, Pirate Smee and Tiger Lily	10	10
727	5c. Peter with Tiger Lily and her father	10	10
728	10c. Captain Hook captures Peter and Wendy	10	10
729	$2 Peter fights Captain Hook	2·25	1·50
730	$2.50 Captain Hook in crocodile's jaws	2·25	1·75

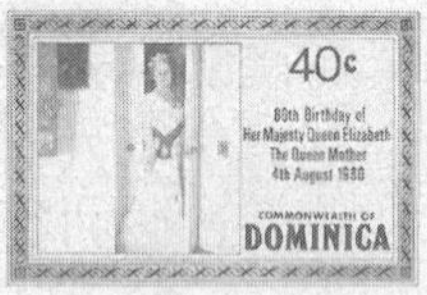

174 Queen Elizabeth the Queen Mother in Doorway

1980. 80th Birthday of the Queen Mother.

732a **174**	40c. multicoloured	15	15
733a	$2.50 multicoloured	45	60

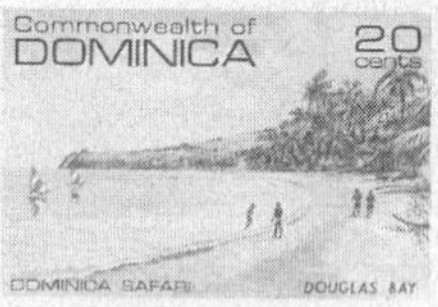

175 Douglas Bay

1981. "Dominica Safari". Multicoloured.

735	20c. Type **175**	10	10
736	30c. Valley of Desolation	10	10
737	40c. Emerald Pool (vert)	10	10
738	$3 Indian River (vert)	75	1·10

1981. Walt Disney's Cartoon Character, Pluto. As T **169**. Multicoloured.

740	$2 Pluto and Fifi	80	1·50

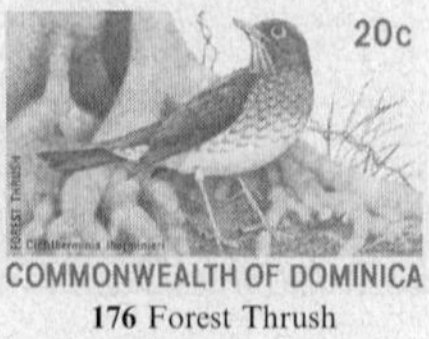

176 Forest Thrush

1981. Birds. Multicoloured.

742	20c. Type **176**	55	30
743	30c. Wied's crested flycatcher	65	35
744	40c. Blue-hooded euphonia	75	45
745	$5 Lesser Antillean pewee	3·50	4·75

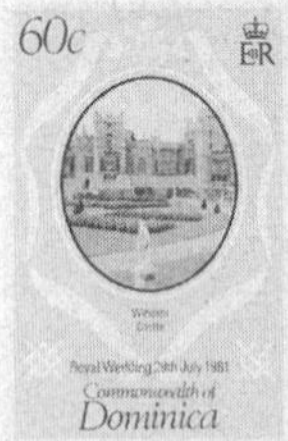

177 Windsor Castle

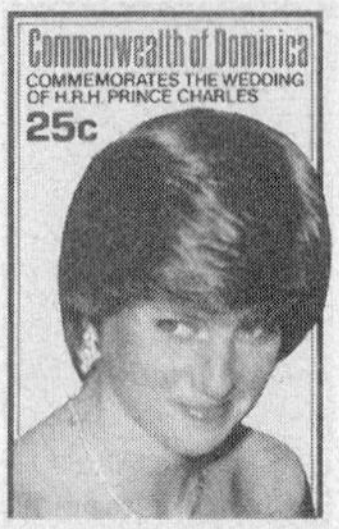

178 Lady Diana Spencer

1981. Royal Wedding. Multicoloured.

747	40c. Prince Charles and Lady Diana Spencer	10	10
748	60c. Type **177**	15	15
749a	$4 Prince Charles flying helicopter	30	50

1981. Royal Wedding. Multicoloured.

751	25c. Type **178**	20	35
752	$2 Prince Charles	50	1·00
753	$5 Prince Charles and Lady Diana Spencer	1·75	2·50

1981. Christmas. Scenes from Walt Disney's cartoon film "Santa's Workshop". As T **169**.

754	½c. multicoloured	10	10
755	1c. multicoloured	10	10
756	2c. multicoloured	10	10
757	3c. multicoloured	10	10
758	4c. multicoloured	15	10
759	5c. multicoloured	15	10
760	10c. multicoloured	20	10
761	45c. multicoloured	1·50	30
762	$5 multicoloured	4·25	5·50

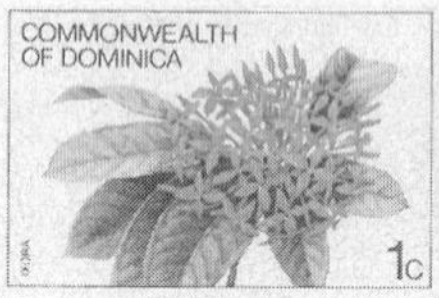

179 Ixora

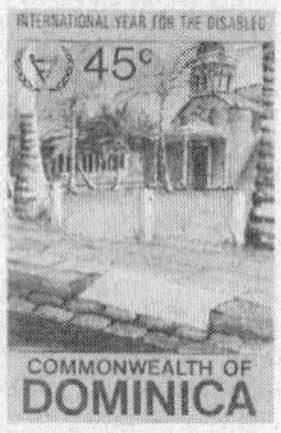

180 Curb Slope for Wheelchairs

1981. Plant Life. Multicoloured.

764A	1c. Type **179**	10	50
765A	2c. Flamboyant	10	50
766A	4c. Poinsettia	15	40
767A	5c. Bois caribe (national flower of Dominica)	15	20
768A	8c. Annatto or roucou	20	20
769A	10c. Passion fruit	30	10
770A	15c. Breadfruit or yampain	55	15
771A	20c. Allamanda or buttercup	40	15
772A	25c. Cashew nut	40	15
773A	35c. Soursop or couassol	45	30
774A	40c. Bougainvillea	45	30
775A	45c. Anthurium	50	35
776A	60c. Cacao or cocoa	1·25	70
777A	90c. Pawpaw tree or papay	70	1·00
778A	$1 Coconut palm	1·50	1·00
779A	$2 Coffee tree or cafe	1·00	2·75
780B	$5 Heliconia or lobster claw	3·25	5·50
781A	$10 Banana fig	2·25	11·00

Nos. 769, 770, 776, 778, 780 and 781 come with or without imprint date.

1981. International Year for Disabled People. Multicoloured.

782	45c. Type **180**	40	15
783	60c. Bus with invalid step	50	20
784	75c. Motor car controls adapted for handicapped	60	30
785	$4 Bus with wheelchair ramp	1·00	2·50

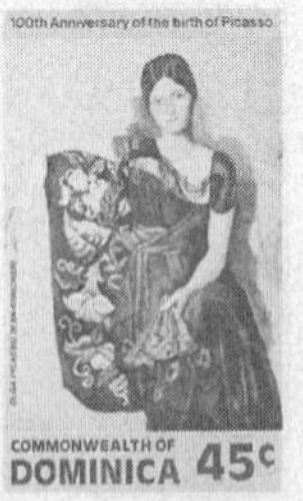

181 "Olga Picasso in an Armchair"

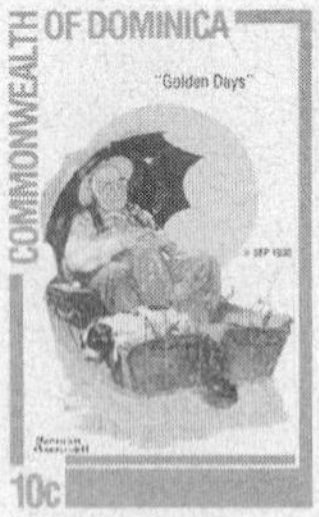

182 "Gone Fishing"

1981. Birth Centenary of Picasso. Multicoloured.

787	45c. Type **181**	35	15
788	60c. "Bathers"	40	15
789	75c. "Woman in Spanish Costume"	40	25
790	$4 "Detail of Dog and Cock"	1·00	2·25

1982. World Cup Football Championship, Spain. Walt Disney Cartoon Characters. As T **169**. Mult.

792	½c. Goofy chasing ball with butterfly net	10	10
793	1c. Donald Duck with ball in beak	10	10
794	2c. Goofy as goalkeeper	10	10
795	3c. Goofy looking for ball	10	10
796	4c. Goofy as park attendant puncturing ball with litter spike	10	10
797	5c. Pete and Donald Duck playing	10	10
798	10c. Donald Duck after kicking rock instead of ball	15	10
799	60c. Donald Duck feeling effects of a hard game and Daisy Duck dusting ball	1·50	1·25
800	$5 Goofy hiding ball under his jersey from Mickey Mouse	5·50	6·50

1982. Norman Rockwell (painter) Commemoration. Multicoloured.

802	10c. Type **182**	10	10
803	25c. "Breakfast"	20	10
804	45c. "The Marbles Champ"	30	30
805	$1 "Speeding Along"	55	65

No. 802 is inscribed "Golden Days" and No. 803 "The Morning News".

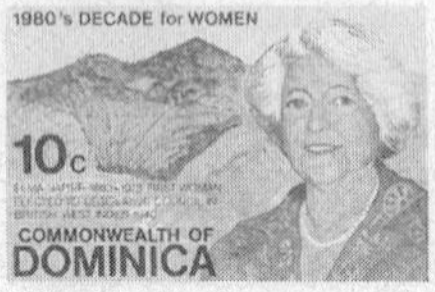

183 Elma Napier (first woman elected to B.W.I. Legislative Council)

1982. Decade for Women. Multicoloured.

806	10c. Type **183**	10	10
807	45c. Margaret Mead (anthropologist)	30	30
808	$1 Mabel (Cissy) Caudeiron (folk song composer and historian)	55	55
809	$4 Eleanor Roosevelt	2·25	2·25

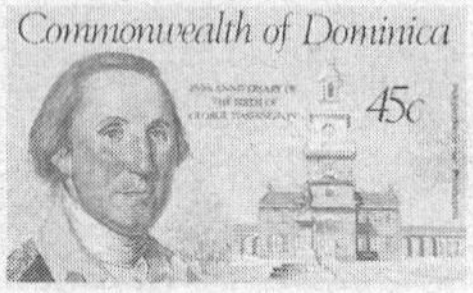

184 George Washington and Independence Hall, Philadelphia

1982. 250th Birth Anniv of George Washington and Birth Centenary of Franklin D. Roosevelt. Multicoloured.

811	45c. Type **184**	25	25
812	60c. Franklin D. Roosevelt and Capitol, Washington D.C.	30	35
813	90c. Washington at Yorktown (detail "The Surrender of Cornwallis" by Trumbull)	40	55
814	$2 Construction of dam (from W. Groppers' mural commemorating Roosevelt's) "New Deal"	70	1·60

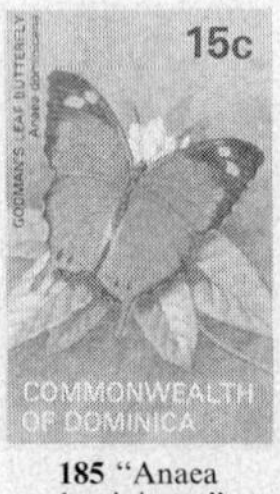

185 "Anaea dominicana"

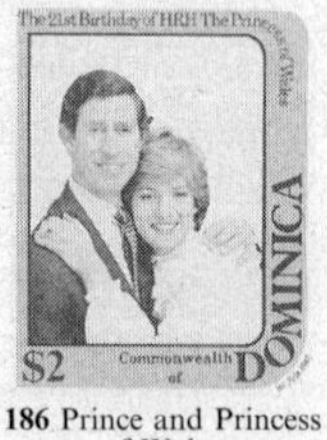

186 Prince and Princess of Wales

1982. Butterflies. Multicoloured.

816	15c. Type **185**	1·50	35
817	45c. "Heliconius charithonia"	2·50	65
818	60c. "Hypolimnas misippus"	2·75	1·75
819	$3 "Biblis hyperia"	5·50	6·00

1982. 21st Birthday of Princess of Wales. Multicoloured.

821	45c. Buckingham Palace	20	10
822	$2 Type **186**	50	70
823	$4 Princess of Wales	1·10	1·25

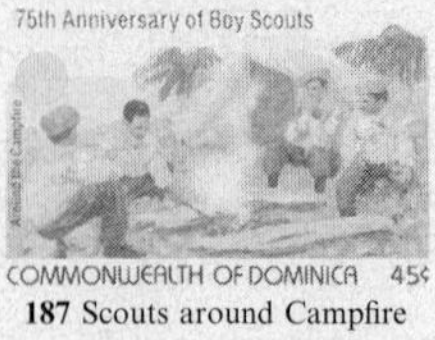

187 Scouts around Campfire

1982. 75th Anniv of Boy Scouts Movement. Mult.

825	45c. Type **187**	1·25	50
826	60c. Temperature study, Valley of Desolation	1·75	1·25

827	75c. Learning about native birds	2·25	1·50
828	$3 Canoe trip along Indian River	4·25	5·50

1982. Birth of Prince William of Wales. Nos. 821/3 optd **ROYAL BABY 21.6.82.**

830	45c. Buckingham Palace	30	30
831	$2 Type **186**	80	1·10
832	$4 Princess of Wales	1·40	1·90

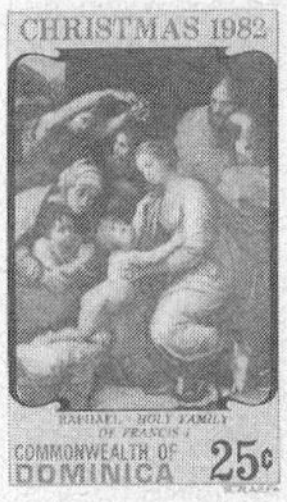

188 "Holy Family of Francis I"

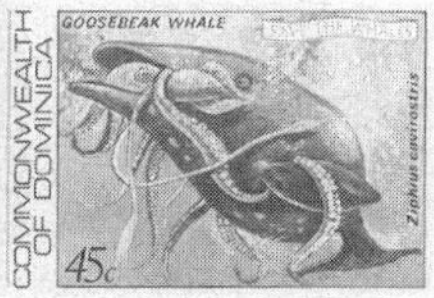

189 Cuvier's Beaked Whale

1982. Christmas. Raphael Paintings. Multicoloured.

834	25c. Type **188**	15	10
835	30c. "Holy Family of the Pearl"	15	10
836	90c. "Canigiani Holy Family"	30	35
837	$4 "Holy Family of the Oak Tree"	1·25	1·50

1983. Save the Whales. Multicoloured.

839	45c. Type **189**	2·00	65
840	60c. Humpback whale	2·25	1·75
841	75c. Black right whale	2·25	2·25
842	$3 Melon-headed whale	4·50	6·50

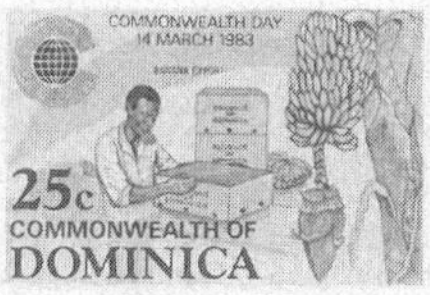

190 Banana Export

1983. Commonwealth Day. Multicoloured.

844	25c. Type **190**	15	15
845	30c. Road building	15	20
846	90c. Community nursing	30	45
847	$3 Tourism-handicrafts	75	1·50

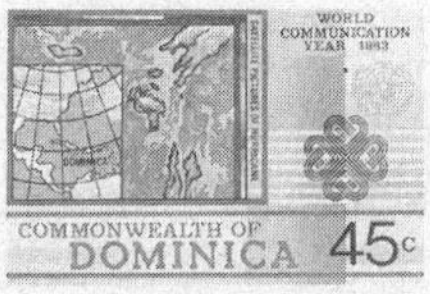

191 Map and Satellite Picture of Hurricane

1983. World Communications Year. Multicoloured.

848	45c. Type **191**	20	25
849	60c. Aircraft-to-ship transmission	25	35
850	90c. Satellite communications	30	45
851	$2 Shortwave radio	75	1·00

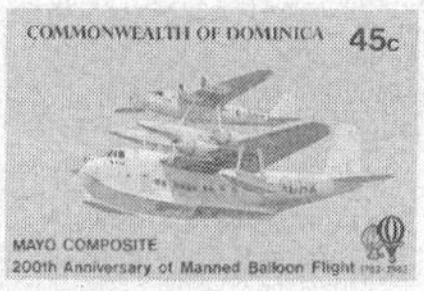

192 Short-Mayo Composite

1983. Bicentenary of Manned Flight. Mult.

853	45c. Type **192**	50	30
854	60c. Macchi M.39 Schneider Trophy seaplane	60	65
855	90c. Fairey Swordfish torpedo bomber	70	1·50
856	$4 Airship LZ-3	1·25	4·75

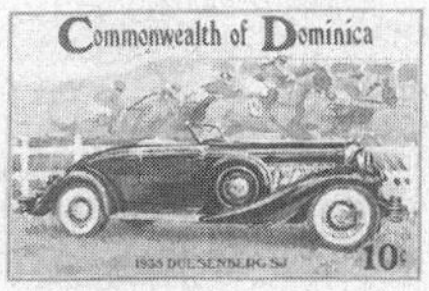

193 Duesenberg "SJ", 1935

1983. Classic Motor Cars. Multicoloured.

858	10c. Type **193**	25	15
859	45c. Studebaker "Avanti", 1962	35	25
860	60c. Cord "812"	40	35
861	75c. MG "TC", 1945	45	50
862	90c. Camaro "350 SS", 1967	50	60
863	$3 Porsch "356", 1948	1·00	1·60

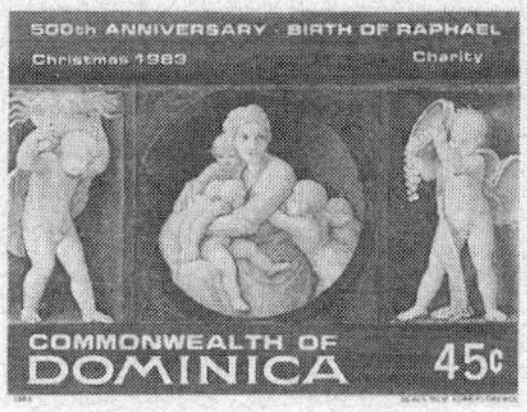

194 "Charity"

1983. Christmas. 500th Birth Anniv of Raphael. Multicoloured.

865	45c. Type **194**	30	30
866	60c. "Hope"	30	30
867	90c. "Faith"	40	60
868	$4 "The Cardinal Virtues"	1·00	3·25

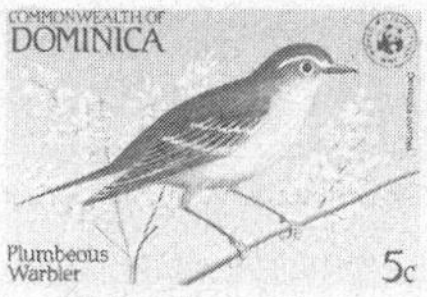

195 Plumbeous Warbler

1984. Birds. Multicoloured.

870	5c. Type **195**	2·25	1·10
871	45c. Imperial amazon ("Imperial Parrot")	4·50	75
872	60c. Blue-headed hummingbird	5·00	3·25
873	90c. Red-necked amazon ("Red-necked Parrot")	6·00	6·00

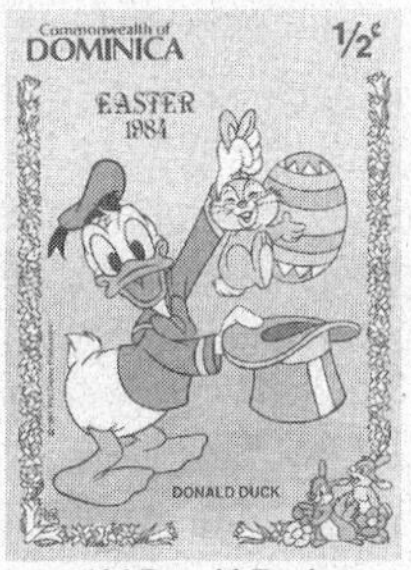

196 Donald Duck

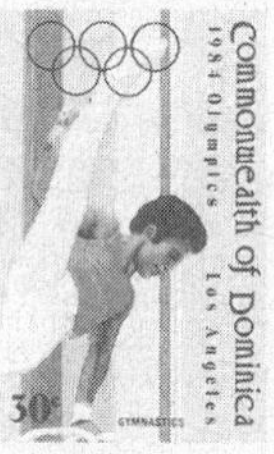

197 Gymnastics

1984. Easter. Multicoloured.

875	½c. Type **196**	10	10
876	1c. Mickey Mouse	10	10
877	2c. Tortoise and Hare	10	10
878	3c. Brer Rabbit and Brer Bear	10	10
879	4c. Donald Duck (different)	10	10
880	5c. White Rabbit	10	10
881	10c. Thumper	10	10
882	$2 Pluto	3·25	2·75
883	$4 Pluto (different)	4·50	4·00

1984. Olympic Games, Los Angeles. Multicoloured.

885	30c. Type **197**	20	25
886	45c. Javelin-throwing	30	35
887	60c. High diving	40	45
888	$4 Fencing	2·00	2·50

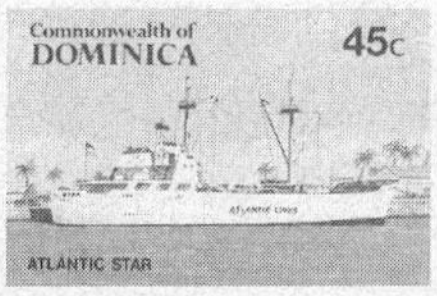

198 "Atlantic Star"

1984. Shipping. Multicoloured.

890	45c. Type **198**	1·75	75
891	60c. "Atlantic" (liner)	2·00	1·25
892	90c. Carib fishing boat	2·50	2·50
893	$4 "Norway" (liner)	6·00	8·50

1984. U.P.U. Congress, Hamburg. Nos. 769 and 780 optd **19th UPU CONGRESS HAMBURG.**

895	10c. Passion fruit	10	10
896	$5 Heliconia or lobster claw	2·75	3·75

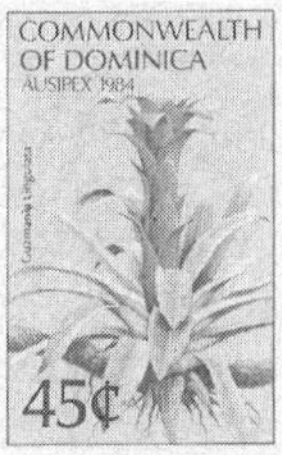

200 "Guzmania lingulata"

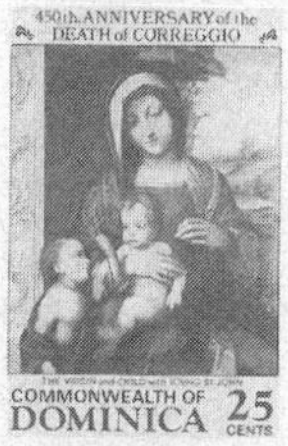

201 "The Virgin and Child with Young St. John" (Correggio)

1984. "Ausipex" International Stamp Exhibition, Melbourne. Bromeliads. Multicoloured.

897	45c. Type **200**	30	35
898	60c. "Pitcairnia angustifolia"	40	55
899	75c. "Tillandsia fasciculata"	50	75
900	$3 "Aechmea smithiorum"	2·00	3·25

1984. 450th Death Anniv of Correggio (painter). Multicoloured.

902	25c. Type **201**	30	20
903	60c. "Christ bids Farewell to the Virgin Mary"	40	40
904	90c. "Do not Touch Me"	50	80
905	$4 "The Mystical Marriage of St Catherine"	80	3·25

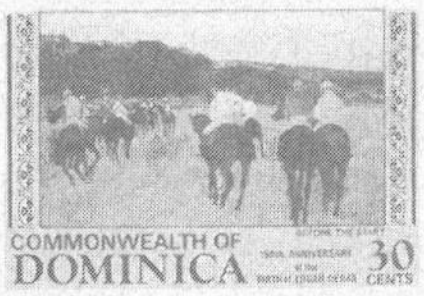

202 "Before the Start" (Edgar Degas)

1984. 150th Birth Anniv of Edgar Degas (painter). Multicoloured.

907	30c. Type **202**	30	25
908	45c. "Race on the Racecourse"	35	35
909	$1 "Jockeys at the Flagpole"	55	1·10
910	$3 "Racehorses at Longchamp"	80	3·50

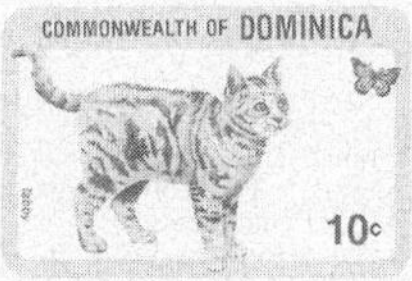

203 Tabby

1984. Cats. Multicoloured.

912	10c. Type **203**	20	15
913	15c. Calico shorthair	25	15
914	20c. Siamese	35	15
915	25c. Manx	40	20
916	45c. Abyssinian	65	30
917	60c. Tortoise-shell longhair	80	65
918	$1 Cornish rex	1·00	1·00
919	$2 Persian	1·25	3·00
920	$3 Himalayan	1·50	4·00
921	$5 Burmese	2·00	7·00

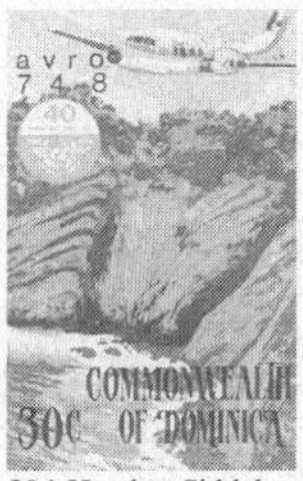

204 Hawker Siddeley H.S.748

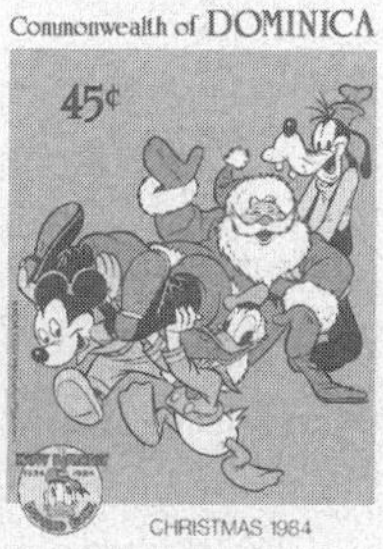

205 Donald Duck, Mickey Mouse and Goofy with Father Christmas

1984. 40th Anniv of International Civil Aviation Organisation. Multicoloured.

923	30c. Type **204**	1·00	35
924	60c. De Havilland Twin Otter 100	1·75	50
925	$1 Britten Norman Islander	2·00	1·60
926	$3 De Havilland Twin Otter 100 (different)	3·00	5·50

1984. Christmas. Walt Disney Cartoon Characters. Multicoloured.

928	45c. Type **205**	1·25	30
929	60c. Donald Duck as Father Christmas with toy train	1·50	70
930	90c. Donald Duck as Father Christmas in sleigh	2·00	1·75
931	$2 Donald Duck and nephews in sledge	3·25	3·75
932	$4 Donald Duck in snow with Christmas tree	4·25	5·50

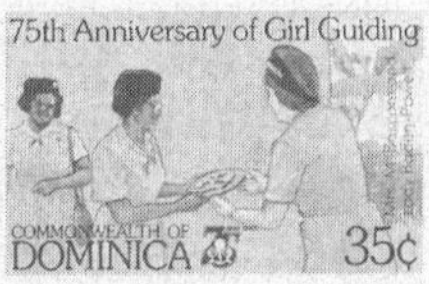

206 Mrs. M. Bascom presenting Trefoil to Chief Guide Lady Baden-Powell

1985. 75th Anniv of Girl Guide Movement. Mult.

934	35c. Type **206**	60	30
935	45c. Lady Baden-Powell inspecting Dominican brownies	80	35
936	60c. Lady Baden-Powell with Mrs. M. Bascom and Mrs. A. Robinson (guide leaders)	1·00	65
937	$3 Lord and Lady Baden-Powell (vert)	2·50	3·50

1985. Birth Bicentenary of John J Audubon (ornithologist) (1st issue). As T **198** of Antigua. Multicoloured.

939	45c. Clapper rail ("King Rail")	1·10	30
940	$1 Black and white warbler (vert)	2·00	1·25
941	$2 Broad-winged hawk (vert)	2·75	2·75
942	$3 Ring-necked duck	3·50	3·25

See also Nos. 1013/16.

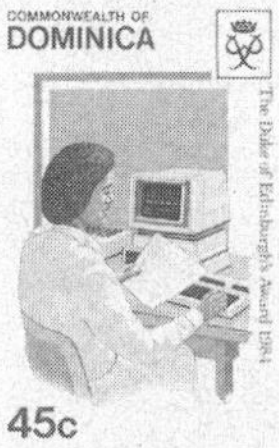

207 Student with Computer

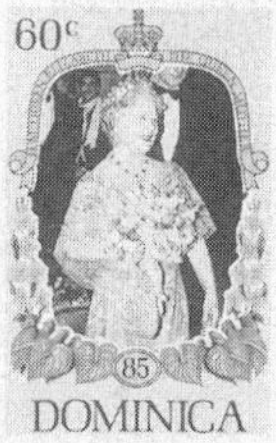

208 The Queen Mother visiting Sadlers Wells Opera

1985. Duke of Edinburgh's Award Scheme. Multicoloured.

944	45c. Type **207**	40	30
945	60c. Assisting doctor in hospital	1·25	40
946	90c. Two youths hiking	1·40	80
947	$4 Family jogging	3·25	5·00

1985. Life and Times of Queen Elizabeth the Queen Mother. Multicoloured.

949	60c. Type **208**	1·25	50
950	$1 Fishing in Scotland	1·25	60
951	$3 On her 84th birthday	2·25	2·75

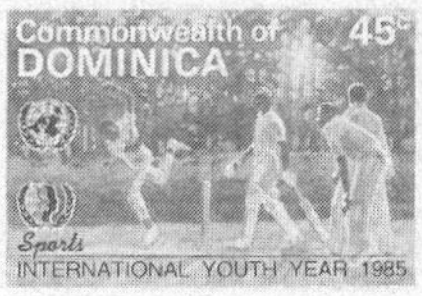

209 Cricket Match ("Sports")

1985. International Youth Year. Multicoloured.

953	45c. Type **209**	3·50	1·50
954	60c. Bird-watching ("Environmental Study")	3·75	2·25
955	$1 Stamp collecting ("Education")	4·00	3·25
956	$3 Boating ("Leisure")	5·50	7·50

1985. 300th Birth Anniv of Johann Sebastian Bach (composer). As T **206** of Antigua. Multicoloured.

958	45c. Cornet	1·50	40
959	60c. Coiled trumpet	1·75	60
960	$1 Piccolo	2·25	1·00
961	$3 Violoncello piccolo	4·00	3·50

1985. Royal Visit. As T **207** of Antigua. Mult.

963	60c. Flags of Great Britain and Dominica	75	50
964	$1 Queen Elizabeth II (vert)	75	1·25
965	$4 Royal Yacht "Britannia"	1·75	5·50

1985. 150th Birth Anniv of Mark Twain (author). As T **118** of Anguilla showing Walt Disney cartoon characters in scenes from "Tom Sawyer". Multicoloured.

967	20c. "The glorius white-washer"	75	30
968	60c. "Aunt Polly's home dentistry"	1·50	75
969	$1 "Aunt Polly's pain killer"	2·00	1·25
970	$1.50 Mickey Mouse balancing on fence	2·50	3·00
971	$2 "Lost in the cave with Becky"	2·75	3·50

1985. Birth Bicentenaries of Grimm Brothers (folklorists). Designs as T **119** of Anguilla showing Walt Disney cartoon characters in scenes from "Little Red Cap". Multicoloured.

973	10c. Little Red Cap (Daisy Duck) meeting the Wolf	30	20
974	45c. The Wolf at the door	85	30
975	90c. The Wolf in Grandmother's bed	1·75	1·75
976	$1 The Wolf lunging at Little Red Cap	2·00	1·75
977	$3 The Woodsman (Donald Duck) chasing the Wolf	3·75	5·00

1985. 40th Anniv of United Nations Organization. Designs as T **208** of Antigua showing United Nations (New York) stamps. Multicoloured.

979	45c. Lord Baden-Powell and 1984 International Youth Year 35c.	70	50
980	$2 Maimonides (physician) and 1966 W.H.O. Building 11c.	1·50	3·25
981	$3 Sir Rowland Hill (postal reformer) and 1976 25th anniv of U.N. Postal Administration 13c.	1·50	3·50

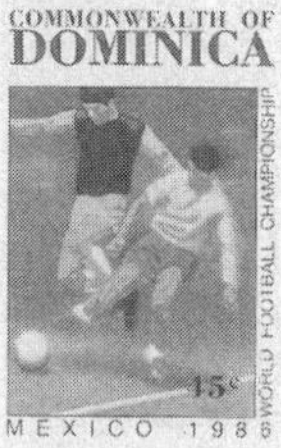

210 Two Players competing for Ball

1986. World Cup Football Championship, Mexico. Multicoloured.
983 45c. Type **210** . . . . 1·75 40
984 60c. Player heading ball . . . 2·00 1·50
985 $1 Two players competing for ball (different) . . . . . . 2·25 1·75
986 $3 Player with ball . . . . . 4·50 6·00

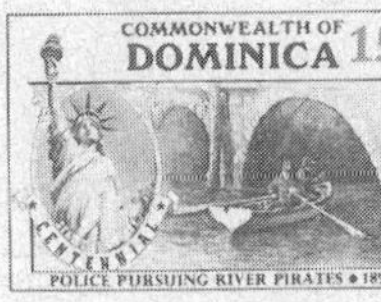

211 Police in Rowing Boat pursuing River Pirates, 1890

1986. Centenary of Statue of Liberty. Mult.
988 15c. Type **211** . . . . 1·75 65
989 25c. Police patrol launch, 1986 . . . . 2·25 85
990 45c. Hoboken Ferry Terminal c. 1890 . . . . 2·25 85
991 $4 Holland Tunnel entrance and staff, 1986 . . . . . . 4·75 6·50

1986. Appearance of Halley's Comet (1st issue). As T **123** of Anguilla. Multicoloured.
993 5c. Nasir al Din al Tusi (Persian astronomer) and Jantal Mantar Observatory, Delhi 20 20
994 10c. Bell XS-1 Rocket Plane breaking sound barrier for first time, 1947 . . . . . . 25 25
995 45c. Halley's Comet of 1531 (from "Astronomicum Caesareum", 1540) 65 30
996 $4 Mark Twain and quotation, 1910 . . . . . 3·25 4·00
See also Nos. 1032/5.

1986. 60th Birthday of Queen Elizabeth II. As T **125** of Anguilla. Multicoloured.
998 2c. Wedding photograph, 1947 . . . . 10 15
999 $1 Queen meeting Pope John Paul II, 1982 . . . 70 80
1000 $4 Queen on Royal Visit, 1971 . . . . 2·00 3·00

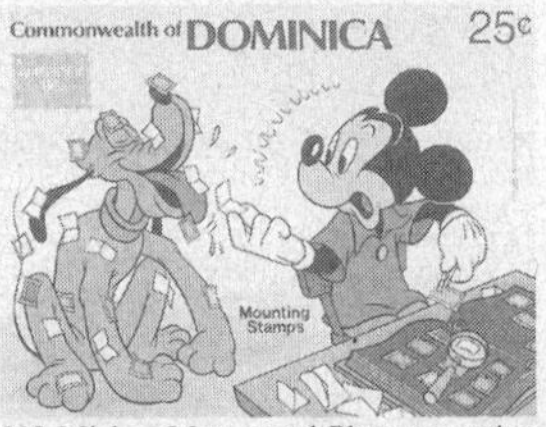

212 Mickey Mouse and Pluto mounting Stamps in Album

1986. "Ameripex" International Stamp Exhibition, Chicago. Showing Walt Disney cartoon characters. Multicoloured.
1002 25c. Type **212** 60 40
1003 45c. Donald Duck examining stamp under magnifying glass 80 65
1004 60c. Chip n' Dale soaking and drying stamps . . . . 1·10 1·50
1005 $4 Donald Duck as scoutmaster awarding merit badges to Nephews 3·50 6·00

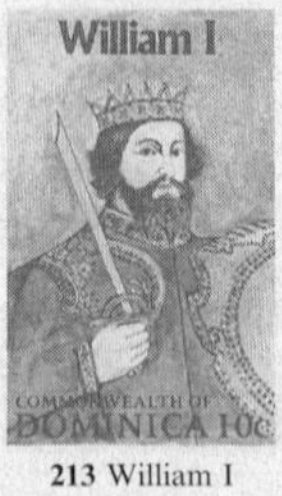

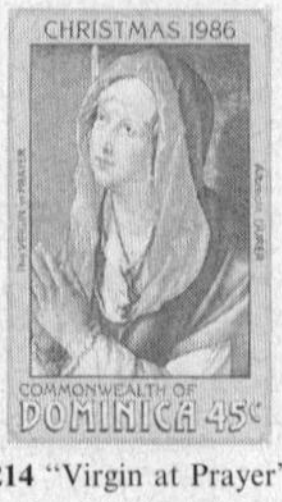

213 William I **214** "Virgin at Prayer"

1986. 500th Anniv (1985) of Succession of House of Tudor to English Throne. Multicoloured.
1007 10c. Type **213** 40 40
1008 40c. Richard II 80 80
1009 50c. Henry VIII 90 90
1010 $1 Charles II . . . . 1·00 1·75
1011 $2 Queen Anne . . . . . . 1·50 3·00
1012 $4 Queen Victoria . . . . . 2·00 4·50

1986. Birth Bicentenary (1985) of John J. Audubon (ornithologist) (2nd issue). As T **198** of Antigua showing original paintings. Multicoloured.
1013 25c. Black-throated diver . . 1·50 50
1014 60c. Great blue heron (vert) 2·00 1·50
1015 90c. Yellow-crowned night heron (vert) . . . . . . 2·00 2·25
1016 $4 Common shoveler ("Shoveler Duck") . . . 4·50 6·50

1986. Royal Wedding. As T **213** of Antigua. Multicoloured.
1018 45c. Prince Andrew and Miss Sarah Ferguson . . 35 30
1019 50c. Prince Andrew 45 45
1020 $4 Prince Andrew climbing aboard aircraft . . . . . 2·00 3·00

1986. World Cup Football Championship Winners, Mexico. Nos. 983/6 optd **WINNERS Argentina 3 W. Germany 2**.
1022 45c. Type **210** . . . . . . 1·50 55
1023 60c. Player heading ball . . 1·75 1·50
1024 $1 Two players competing for ball . . . . 2·25 2·50
1025 $3 Player with ball . . . . 5·00 7·00

1986. Christmas. Paintings by Durer. Multicoloured.
1027 45c. Type **214** . . . . . . 1·00 35
1028 60c. "Madonna and Child" 1·50 1·25
1029 $1 "Madonna of the Pear" 2·00 2·25
1030 $3 "Madonna and Child with St. Anne" . . . . . 5·50 8·50

1986. Appearance of Halley's Comet (2nd issue). Nos. 993/6 optd as T **218** of Antigua.
1032 5c. Nasir al Din al Tusi (Persian astronomer) and Jantal Mantar Observatory, Delhi . . . 15 15
1033 10c. Bell XS-1 Rocket Plane breaking sound barrier for first time, 1947 . . . . . 20 15
1034 45c. Halley's Comet of 1531 (from "Astronomicum Caesareum", 1540) . . . 55 30
1035 $4 Mark Twain and quotation, 1910 . . . . . 2·50 3·50

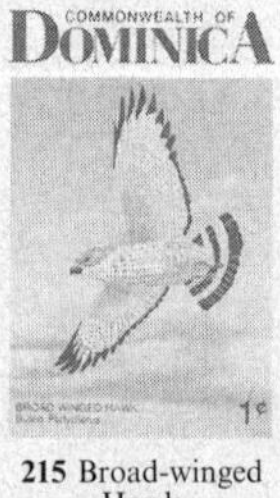

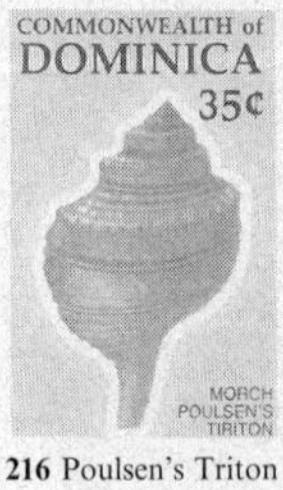

215 Broad-winged Hawk **216** Poulsen's Triton

1987. Birds of Dominica. Multicoloured.
1037 1c. Type **215** 20 40
1038 2c. Ruddy quail dove . . . 20 40
1039 5c. Red-necked pigeon . . . 30 40
1040 10c. Green-backed heron ("Green Heron") 30 15
1041 15c. Moorhen ("Common Gallinule") 40 20
1042 20c. Ringed kingfisher . . . 40 20
1043 25c. Brown pelican 40 20
1044 35c. White-tailed tropic bird 40 30
1045 45c. Red-legged thrush . . . 50 30
1046 60c. Purple-throated carib 65 45
1047 90c. Magnificent frigate bird 70 70
1048 $1 Brown trembler ("Trembler") 80 80
1049 $2 Black-capped petrel . . . 1·25 4·00
1050 $5 Barn owl . . . . 3·00 5·00
1051 $10 Imperial amazon ("Imperial Parrot") . . . 5·00 9·50

1987. America's Cup Yachting Championships. As T **222** of Antigua. Multicoloured.
1052 45c. "Reliance", 1903 . . . 60 30
1053 60c. "Freedom", 1980 . . . 70 55
1054 $1 "Mischief", 1881 . . . . 80 90
1055 $3 "Australia", 1977 . . . . 1·25 3·00

1987. Birth Centenary of Marc Chagall (artist). As T **225** of Antigua. Multicoloured.
1057 25c. "Artist and His Model" 20 10
1058 35c. "Midsummer Night's Dream" 25 20
1059 45c. "Joseph the Shepherd" 30 25
1060 60c. "The Cellist" 35 30
1061 90c. "Woman with Pigs" . . 50 45
1062 $1 "The Blue Circus" . . . 55 50
1063 $3 "For Vava" . . . . . . 1·25 1·60
1064 $4 "The Rider" . . . . . . 1·50 1·60

1987. Sea Shells.
1066 **216** 35c. multicoloured . . . 20 20
1067 – 45c. violet, black and red 25 25
1068 – 60c. multicoloured . . . 30 40
1069 – $5 multicoloured . . . . 2·40 4·25
DESIGNS: 45c. Elongate janthina; 60c. Banded tulip; $5 Deltoid rock shell.
No. 1066 is inscribed "TIRITON" in error.

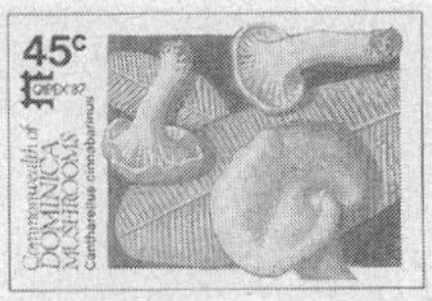

217 "Cantharellus cinnabarinus"

1987. "Capex '87" International Stamp Exhibition, Toronto. Mushrooms of Dominica. Multicoloured.
1071 45c. Type **217** . . . . . . 1·50 50
1072 60c. "Boletellus cubensis" 2·00 1·25
1073 $2 "Eccilia cystiophorus" 4·25 4·50
1074 $3 "Xerocomus guadelupae" 4·50 5·00

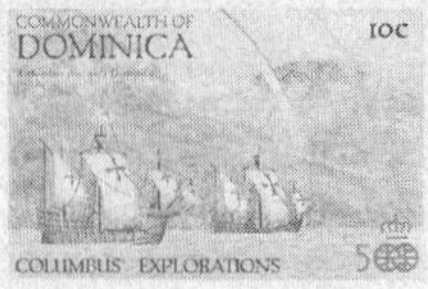

218 Discovery of Dominica, 1493

1987. 500th Anniv (1992) of Discovery of America by Columbus (1st issue). Multicoloured.
1076 10c. Type **218** 40 25
1077 15c. Caribs greeting Columbus's fleet 50 30
1078 45c. Claiming the New World for Spain 65 35
1079 60c. Wreck of "Santa Maria" 80 60
1080 90c. Fleet leaving Spain . . 1·00 1·00
1081 $1 Sighting the New World 1·10 1·25
1082 $3 Trading with Indians . . 2·25 3·00
1083 $5 Building settlement . . . 3·25 4·00
See also Nos. 1221/5, 1355/62, 1406/13, 1547/53 and 1612/13.

1987. Milestones of Transportation. As T **226** of Antigua. Multicoloured.
1085 10c. H.M.S. "Warrior" (first ironclad warship, 1860) 50 50
1086 15c. "MAGLEV-MLU 001" (fastest train), 1979 . . . 60 60
1087 25c. "Flying Cloud" (fastest clipper passage New York–San Francisco) (vert) 70 70
1088 35c. First elevated railway, New York, 1868 (vert) . . 80 80
1089 45c. Peter Cooper's locomotive "Tom Thumb" (first U.S. passenger locomotive), 1829 . . . . 80 80
1090 60c. "Spray" (Slocum's solo, circumnavigation), 1895–98 (vert) 90 90
1091 90c. "Sea-Land Commerce" (fastest Pacific passage), 1973 (vert) . . . . . . 1·25 1·25
1092 $1 First cable cars, San Francisco, 1873 . . . . 1·40 1·40
1093 $3 "Orient Express", 1883 3·00 3·25
1094 $4 "Clermont" (first commercial paddle-steamer), 1807 . . . . . 3·25 3·50

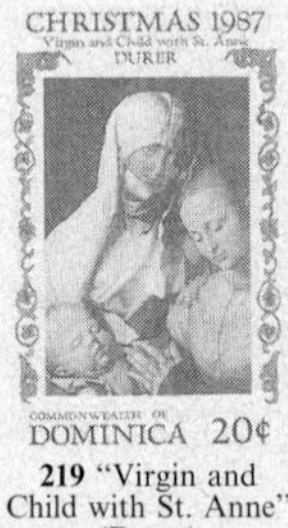

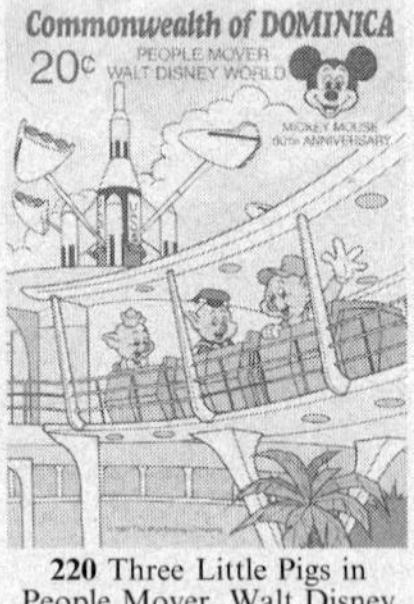

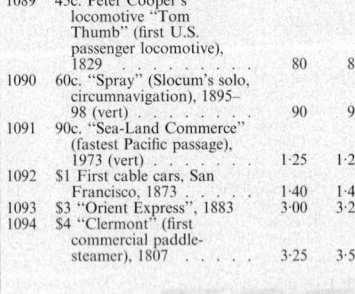

219 "Virgin and Child with St. Anne" (Durer) **220** Three Little Pigs in People Mover, Walt Disney World

1987. Christmas. Religious Paintings. Mult.
1095 20c. Type **219** 30 15
1096 25c. "Virgin and Child" (Murillo) 30 15
1097 $2 "Madonna and Child" (Foppa) . . . . 1·50 2·25
1098 $4 "Madonna and Child" (Da Verona) . . . . . . 2·75 4·25

1987. 60th Anniv of Mickey Mouse (Walt Disney cartoon character). Cartoon characters in trains. Multicoloured.
1100 20c. Type **220** 45 35
1101 25c. Goofy driving horse tram, Disneyland 45 35
1102 45c. Donald Duck in "Roger E. Broggie", Walt Disney World 75 65
1103 60c. Goofy, Mickey Mouse, Donald Duck and Chip 'n Dale aboard "Big Thunder Mountain" train, Disneyland 85 75
1104 90c. Mickey Mouse in "Walter E. Disney", Disneyland . . . . 1·40 1·25
1105 $1 Mickey and Minnie Mouse, Goofy, Donald and Daisy Duck in monorail, Walt Disney World . . . . 1·50 1·40
1106 $3 Dumbo flying over "Casey Jr" . . . . 3·25 3·75
1107 $4 Daisy Duck and Minnie Mouse in "Lilly Belle", Walt Disney World . . . 3·75 4·50

1988. Royal Ruby Wedding. As T **234** of Antigua.
1109 45c. multicoloured 70 30
1110 60c. brown, black and green 80 50
1111 $1 multicoloured . . . . . 1·00 1·00
1112 $3 multicoloured . . . . . 2·00 3·75
DESIGNS: 45c. Wedding portrait with attendants, 1947; 60c. Princess Elizabeth with Prince Charles, c. 1950; $1 Princess Elizabeth and Prince Philip with Prince Charles and Princess Anne, 1950; $3 Queen Elizabeth.

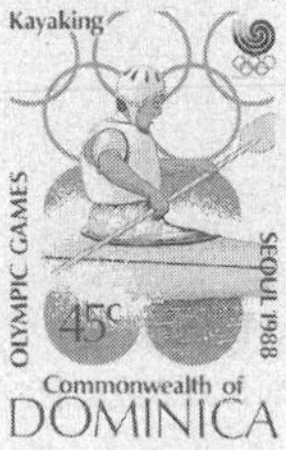

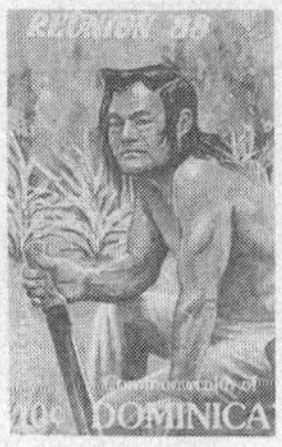

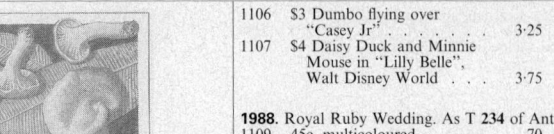

221 Kayak Canoeing **222** Carib Indian

1988. Olympic Games, Seoul. Multicoloured.
1114 45c. Type **221** 60 25
1115 60c. Taekwon-do 80 60
1116 $1 High diving . . . . . . 85 1·00
1117 $3 Gymnastics on bars . . . 1·75 3·75

1988. "Reunion '88" Tourism Programme. Mult.
1119 10c. Type **222** 10 10
1120 25c. Mountainous interior (horiz) 10 15
1121 35c. Indian River 10 15
1122 60c. Belaire dancer and tourists 15 30
1123 90c. Boiling Lake 20 60
1124 $3 Coral reef (horiz) . . . . 60 2·00

1988. Stamp Exhibitions. Nos. 1092/3 optd.
1126 $1 First cable cars, San Francisco, 1873 (optd **FINLANDIA 88**, Helsinki) . . . . 1·00 75
1127 $3 "Orient Express", 1883 (optd **INDEPENDENCE 40**, Israel) . . . . 2·50 2·75

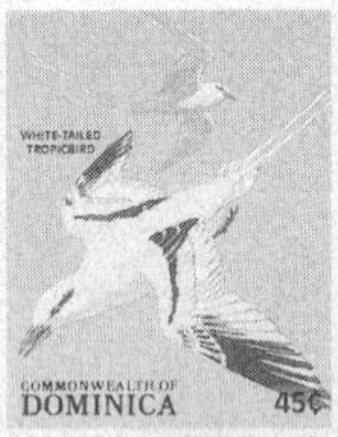

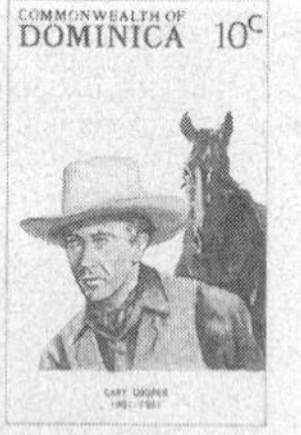

223 White-tailed Tropic Bird **225** Gary Cooper

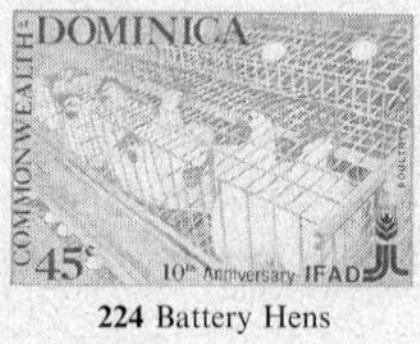

224 Battery Hens

1988. Dominica Rain Forest Flora and Fauna. Multicoloured.
1129 45c. Type **223** 50 50
1130 45c. Blue-hooded euphonia ("Blue-throated Euphonia") 50 50
1131 45c. Smooth-billed ani . . . 50 50
1132 45c. Scaly-breasted thrasher 50 50
1133 45c. Purple-throated carib 50 50
1134 45c. "Marpesia petreus" and "Strymon maesites" (butterflies) 50 50
1135 45c. Brown trembler ("Trembler") 50 50
1136 45c. Imperial amazon ("Imperial Parrot") . . . 50 50
1137 45c. Mangrove cuckoo . . . 50 50
1138 45c. "Dynastes hercules" (beetle) 50 50
1139 45c. "Historis odius" (butterfly) 50 50
1140 45c. Red-necked amazon ("Red-necked Parrot") . . 50 50
1141 45c. Tillandsia (plant) . . . 50 50
1142 45c. Bananaquit and "Polystacha luteola" (plant) 50 50
1143 45c. False chameleon . . . 50 50
1144 45c. Iguana 50 50
1145 45c. "Hypolimnas misippus" (butterfly) 50 50
1146 45c. Green-throated carib 50 50
1147 45c. Heliconia (plant) . . . 50 50
1148 45c. Agouti 50 50
Nos. 1129/48 were printed together, se-tenant, forming a composite design.

1988. 10th Anniv of International Fund for Agricultural Development. Multicoloured.
1149 45c. Type **224** 50 30

No.			Unused	Used
1150	60c.	Pig	70	65
1151	90c.	Cattle	95	1·25
1152	$3	Black belly sheep	2·25	4·00

1988. Entertainers. Multicoloured.

1154	10c.	Type **225**	10	10
1155	35c.	Josephine Baker	15	20
1156	45c.	Maurice Chevalier	20	25
1157	60c.	James Cagney	25	30
1158	$1	Clark Gable	45	50
1159	$2	Louis Armstrong	85	90
1160	$3	Liberace	1·25	1·40
1161	$4	Spencer Tracy	1·75	2·00

1988. Flowering Trees. As T 242 of Antigua. Multicoloured.

1163	15c.	Sapodilla	10	10
1164	20c.	Tangerine	10	10
1165	25c.	Avocado pear	10	10
1166	45c.	Amherstia	20	25
1167	90c.	Lipstick tree	40	55
1168	$1	Cannonball tree	45	55
1169	$3	Saman	1·25	1·75
1170	$4	Pineapple	1·60	2·00

1988. 500th Birth Anniv of Titian (artist). As T 238 of Antigua. Multicoloured.

1172	25c.	"Jacopo Strada"	15	15
1173	35c.	"Titian's Daughter Lavinia"	20	15
1174	45c.	"Andrea Navagero"	20	15
1175	60c.	"Judith with Head of Holofernes"	25	15
1176	$1	"Emilia di Spilimbergo"	40	50
1177	$2	"Martyrdom of St. Lawrence"	70	1·25
1178	$3	"Salome"	1·00	2·00
1179	$4	"St. John the Baptist"	1·25	2·25

226 Imperial Amazon   227 President and Mrs. Kennedy

1988. 10th Anniv of Independence. Multicoloured.

1181	20c.	Type **226**	1·50	40
1182	45c.	Dominica 1874 1d. stamp and landscape (horiz)	90	30
1183	$2	1978 Independence 10c. stamp and landscape (horiz)	1·50	2·75
1184	$3	Carib wood (national flower)	1·75	3·25

1988. 25th Death Anniv of John F. Kennedy (American statesman). Multicoloured.

1186	20c.	Type **227**	10	10
1187	25c.	Kennedy sailing	10	10
1188	$2	Outside Hyannis Port house	80	1·50
1189	$4	Speaking in Berlin (vert)	1·60	2·50

228 Donald Duck's Nephews decorating Christmas Tree

1988. Christmas. "Mickey's Christmas Mall". Walt Disney Cartoon Characters. Multicoloured.

1191	60c.	Type **228**	55	65
1192	60c.	Daisy Duck outside clothes shop	55	65
1193	60c.	Winnie the Pooh in shop window	55	65
1194	60c.	Goofy with parcels	55	65
1195	60c.	Donald Duck as Father Christmas	55	65
1196	60c.	Mickey Mouse contributing to collection	55	65
1197	60c.	Minnie Mouse	55	65
1198	60c.	Chip n' Dale with peanut	55	65

Nos. 1191/8 were printed together, se-tenant, forming a composite design.

229 Raoul Wallenberg (diplomat) and Swedish Flag

1988. 40th Anniv of Universal Declaration of Human Rights.

1200	**229**	$3 multicoloured	2·00	2·50

230 Greater Amberjack

1988. Game Fishes. Multicoloured.

1202	10c.	Type **230**	20	15
1203	15c.	Blue marlin	20	15
1204	35c.	Cobia	35	30
1205	45c.	Dolphin (fish)	45	30
1206	60c.	Cero	60	55
1207	90c.	Mahogany snapper	85	95
1208	$3	Yellow-finned tuna	2·50	3·25
1209	$4	Rainbow parrotfish	3·00	3·75

231 Leatherback Turtle

1988. Insects and Reptiles. Multicoloured.

1211	10c.	Type **231**	45	35
1212	25c.	"Danaus plexippus" (butterfly)	1·25	75
1213	60c.	Green anole (lizard)	1·60	1·25
1214	$3	"Mantis religiosa" (mantid)	4·00	6·50

1989. Olympic Medal Winners, Seoul. Nos. 1114/17 optd.

1216	45c.	Type **221** (optd **Men's C-1, 500m O. Heukrodt DDR**)	20	25
1217	60c.	Taekwon-do (optd **Women's Flyweight N. Y. Choo S. Korea**)	25	35
1218	$1	High diving (optd **Women's Platform Y. Xu China**)	40	60
1219	$3	Gymnastics on bars (optd **V. Artemov USSR**)	1·25	2·25

1989. 500th Anniv (1992) of Discovery of America by Columbus (2nd issue). Pre-Columbian Carib Society. As T 247 of Antigua but horiz. Mult.

1221	20c.	Carib canoe	20	20
1222	35c.	Hunting with bows and arrows	30	20
1223	$1	Dugout canoe making	70	90
1224	$3	Shield contest	1·75	3·00

233 Map of Dominica, 1766   235 "Oncidium pusillum"

234 "Papilio homerus"

1989. "Philexfrance '89" International Stamp Exhibition, Paris. Multicoloured.

1226	10c.	Type **233**	45	30
1227	35c.	French coin of 1653 (horiz)	65	40
1228	$1	French warship, 1720 (horiz)	1·40	1·25
1229	$4	Coffee plant (horiz)	2·00	3·25

1989. Japanese Art. Paintings by Taikan. As T 250 of Antigua but vert. Multicoloured.

1231	10c.	"Lao-tzu" (detail)	10	10
1232	20c.	"Red Maple Leaves" (panels 1 and 2)	10	10
1233	45c.	"King Wen Hui learns a Lesson from his Cook" (detail)	20	25
1234	60c.	"Red Maple Leaves" (panels 3 and 4)	25	35
1235	$1	"Wild Flowers" (detail)	45	50
1236	$2	"Red Maple Leaves" (panels 5 and 6)	85	1·10
1237	$3	"Red Maple Leaves" (panels 7 and 8)	1·00	1·60
1238	$4	"Indian Ceremony of Floating Lamps on the River" (detail)	1·25	2·00

1989. Butterflies. Multicoloured.

1255	10c.	Type **234**	40	30
1256	15c.	"Morpho peleides"	45	30
1257	25c.	"Dryas julia"	65	30
1258	35c.	"Parides gundlachianus"	70	30
1259	60c.	"Danaus plexippus"	1·00	75
1260	$1	"Agraulis vanillae"	1·25	1·25
1261	$3	"Phoebis avellaneda"	2·75	3·25
1262	$5	"Papilio andraemon"	3·75	5·00

1989. Orchids. Multicoloured.

1264	10c.	Type **235**	35	30
1265	35c.	"Epidendrum cochleata"	70	30
1266	45c.	"Epidendrum ciliare"	75	40
1267	60c.	"Cyrtopodium andersonii"	1·00	80
1268	$1	"Habenaria pauciflora"	1·25	1·25
1269	$2	"Maxillaria alba"	2·00	2·25
1270	$3	"Selenipedium palmifolium"	2·50	2·75
1271	$4	"Brassavola cucullata"	3·25	3·75

236 "Apollo 11" Command Module in Lunar Orbit

1989. 20th Anniv of First Manned Landing on Moon. Multicoloured.

1273	10c.	Type **236**	30	30
1274	60c.	Neil Armstrong leaving lunar module	70	70
1275	$2	Edwin Aldrin at Sea of Tranquility	1·60	2·00
1276	$3	Astronauts Armstrong and Aldrin with U.S. flag	2·00	2·50

237 Brazil v Italy Final, 1970

1989. World Cup Football Championship, Italy (1st issue). Multicoloured.

1278	$1	Type **237**	1·75	2·00
1279	$1	England v West Germany, 1966	1·75	2·00
1280	$1	West Germany v Holland, 1974	1·75	2·00
1281	$1	Italy v West Germany, 1982	1·75	2·00

Nos. 1278/81 were printed together, se-tenant, forming a composite central design of a football surrounded by flags of competing nations.

See also Nos. 1383/6.

238 George Washington and Inauguration, 1789

1989. "World Stamp Expo '89" International Stamp Exhibition, Washington. Bicentenary of U.S. Presidency. Multicoloured.

1283	60c.	Type **238**	75	75
1284	60c.	John Adams and Presidential Mansion, 1800	75	75
1285	60c.	Thomas Jefferson, Graff House, Philadelphia and Declaration of Independence	75	75
1286	60c.	James Madison and U.S.S. "Constitution" defeating H.M.S. "Guerriere", 1812	75	75
1287	60c.	James Monroe and freed slaves landing in Liberia	75	75
1288	60c.	John Quincy Adams and barge on Erie Canal	75	75
1289	60c.	Millard Fillmore and Perry's fleet off Japan	75	75
1290	60c.	Franklin Pierce, Jefferson Davis and San Xavier Mission, Tucson	75	75
1291	60c.	James Buchanan, "Buffalo Bill" Cody carrying mail and Wells Fargo Pony Express stamp	75	75
1292	60c.	Abraham Lincoln and U.P.U. Monument, Berne	75	75
1293	60c.	Andrew Johnson, polar bear and Mount McKinley, Alaska	75	75
1294	60c.	Ulysses S. Grant and Golden Spike Ceremony, 1869	75	75
1295	60c.	Theodore Roosevelt and steam shovel excavating Panama Canal	75	75
1296	60c.	William H. Taft and Admiral Peary at North Pole	75	75
1297	60c.	Woodrow Wilson and Curtis "Jenny" on first scheduled airmail flight, 1918	75	75
1298	60c.	Warren G. Harding and airship U.S.S. "Shenandoah" at Lakehurst	75	75
1299	60c.	Calvin Coolidge and Lindbergh's "Spirit of St Louis" on trans-Atlantic flight	75	75
1300	60c.	Mount Rushmore National Monument	75	75
1301	60c.	Lyndon B. Johnson and Earth from Moon as seen by "Apollo 8" crew	75	75
1302	60c.	Richard Nixon and visit to Great Wall of China	75	75
1303	60c.	Gerald Ford and "Gorch Fock" (German cadet barque) at Bicentenary of Revolution celebrations	75	75
1304	60c.	Jimmy Carter and President Sadat of Egypt with Prime Minister Begin of Israel	75	75
1305	60c.	Ronald Reagan and space shuttle "Columbia"	75	75
1306	60c.	George Bush and Grumman TBF Avenger (fighter-bomber)	75	75

1989. Mickey Mouse in Hollywood (Walt Disney cartoon character). As T 267 of Antigua. Mult.

1308	20c.	Mickey Mouse reading script	40	40
1309	35c.	Mickey Mouse giving interview	55	55
1310	45c.	Mickey and Minnie Mouse with newspaper and magazines	65	65
1311	60c.	Mickey Mouse signing autographs	75	75
1312	$1	Trapped in dressing room	1·25	1·25
1313	$2	Mickey and Minnie Mouse with Pluto in limousine	2·00	2·50
1314	$3	Arriving at Awards ceremony	2·25	2·75
1315	$4	Mickey Mouse accepting award	2·40	2·75

1989. Christmas. Paintings by Botticelli. As T 259 of Antigua. Multicoloured.

1317	20c.	"Madonna in Glory with Seraphim"	40	30
1318	25c.	"The Annunciation"	40	30
1319	35c.	"Madonna of the Pomegranate"	55	40
1320	45c.	"Madonna of the Rosegarden"	65	45
1321	60c.	"Madonna of the Book"	80	60
1322	$1	"Madonna under a Baldachin"	1·00	90
1323	$4	"Madonna and Child with Angels"	3·00	4·50
1324	$5	"Bardi Madonna"	3·50	4·75

240 Lady Olave Baden-Powell and Agatha Robinson (Guide leaders)   241 Jawaharal Nehru

1989. 60th Anniv of Girl Guides in Dominica.

1326	**240**	60c. multicoloured	1·00	1·00

1989. Birth Centenary of Jawaharal Nehru (Indian statesman).

1328	**241**	60c. multicoloured	1·50	1·25

242 Cocoa Damselfish

1990. Tropical Fishes. Multicoloured.

1330	45c.	Type **242**	45	50
1331	45c.	Stinging jellyfish	45	50
1332	45c.	Dolphin (fish)	45	50
1333	45c.	Atlantic spadefish and queen angelfish	45	50
1334	45c.	French angelfish	45	50
1335	45c.	Blue-striped grunt	45	50
1336	45c.	Porkfish	45	50
1337	45c.	Great hammerhead	45	50

1338 45c. Atlantic spadefish . . . 45 50
1339 45c. Great barracuda . . . 45 50
1340 45c. Southern stingray . . . 45 50
1341 45c. Black grunt 45 50
1342 45c. Spot-finned butterflyfish 45 50
1343 45c. Dog snapper 45 50
1344 45c. Band-tailed puffer . . . 45 50
1345 45c. Four-eyed butterfly fish 45 50
1346 45c. Lane snapper 45 50
1347 45c. Green moray 45 50
Nos. 1330/47 were printed together, se-tenant, forming a composite design.

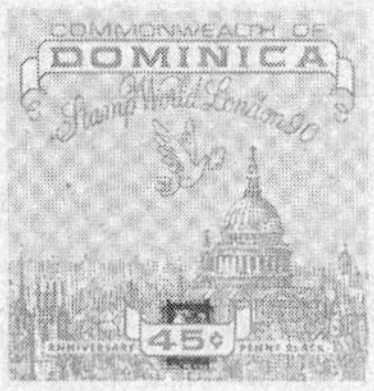

243 St. Paul's Cathedral, London, c. 1840

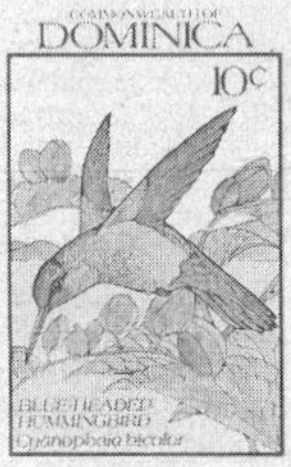

244 Blue-headed Hummingbird

1990. 150th Anniv of the Penny Black and "Stamp World London 90" International Stamp Exhibition.
1348 **243** 45c. green and black . . 50 25
1349 – 50c. blue and black . . . 55 35
1350 – 60c. blue and black . . . 65 45
1351 – 90c. green and black . . 85 85
1352 – $3 blue and black . . 2·25 3·00
1353 – $4 blue and black . . . 2·75 3·50
DESIGNS: 50c. British Post Office "accelerator" carriage, 1830; 60c. St. Paul's and City of London; 90c. Travelling post office, 1838; $3 "Hen and chickens" delivery cycle, 1883; $4 London skyline.

1990. 500th Anniv (1992) of Discovery of America by Columbus (3rd issue). New World Natural History—Seashells. As T **260** of Antigua. Mult.
1355 10c. Reticulated cowrie-helmet 30 30
1356 20c. West Indian chank . . 40 40
1357 35c. West Indian fighting conch 50 35
1358 60c. True tulip 75 60
1359 $1 Sunrise tellin . . . . . . 1·00 1·00
1360 $2 Crown cone . . . . . . 1·75 2·75
1361 $3 Common dove shell . . . 2·50 3·50
1362 $4 Common or Atlantic fig shell . . . . 2·75 3·50

1990. Birds. Multicoloured.
1364 10c. Type **244** 35 35
1365 20c. Black-capped petrel . . 45 45
1366 45c. Red-necked amazon ("Red-necked Parrot") . . 65 40
1367 60c. Black swift 80 70
1368 $1 Troupial . . . . 1·25 1·25
1369 $2 Common noddy ("Brown Noddy") . . . . 2·00 2·50
1370 $4 Lesser Antillean pewee 3·25 3·50
1371 $5 Little blue heron . . . . 3·75 4·25

1990. 90th Birthday of Queen Elizabeth the Queen Mother. As T **266** of Antigua.
1373 20c. multicoloured 20 15
1374 45c. multicoloured 35 25
1375 60c. multicoloured 60 60
1376 $3 multicoloured . . . . . 2·25 3·00
DESIGNS: 20c. to $3, Recent photographs of Queen Mother.

1990. Olympic Games, Barcelona (1992) (1st issue). As T **268** of Antigua. Multicoloured.
1378 45c. Tennis . . . . 1·25 40
1379 60c. Fencing . . . . 1·25 50
1380 $2 Swimming . . . . 2·00 3·25
1381 $3 Yachting . . . . 2·50 3·75
See also Nos. 1603/11.

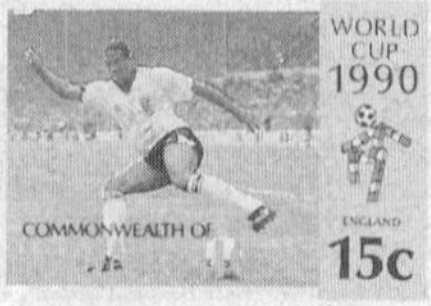

245 Barnes, England

1990. World Cup Football Championship, Italy (2nd issue). Multicoloured.
1383 15c. Type **245** 40 30
1384 45c. Romario, Brazil . . . 70 30
1385 60c. Franz Beckenbauer, West Germany manager 85 70
1386 $4 Lindenberger, Austria . . 3·25 5·00

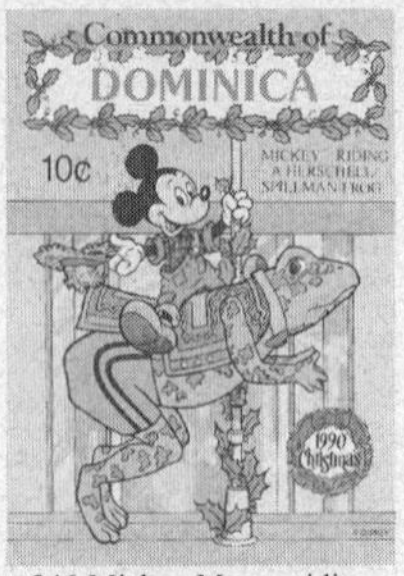

246 Mickey Mouse riding Herschell-Spillman Frog

1990. Christmas. Walt Disney cartoon characters and American carousel animals. Multicoloured.
1388 10c. Type **246** 30 20
1389 15c. Huey, Dewy and Louie on Allan Herschell elephant 35 25
1390 25c. Donald Duck on Allan Herschell polar bear . . . 45 30
1391 45c. Goofy on Dentzel goat 70 30
1392 $1 Donald Duck on Zalar giraffe . . . . 1·00 1·00
1393 $2 Daisy Duck on Herschell-Spillman stork 1·75 2·50
1394 $4 Goofy on Dentzel lion 3·00 4·00
1395 $5 Daisy Duck on Stein and Goldstein palomino stander . . . . 3·50 4·25

1991. Cog Railways. As T **275** of Antigua. Mult.
1397 10c. Steam locomotive, Glion-Roches De Naye rack railway, 1890 . . . . 45 30
1398 35c. Electric railcar, Mt. Pilatus rack railway . . . 65 30
1399 45c. Schynige Platte rack railway train 75 30
1400 60c. Steam train on Bugnli Viaduct, Furka–Oberalp rack railway (vert) . . . . 1·00 55
1401 $1 Jungfrau rack railway train, 1910 . . . . 1·25 1·00
1402 $2 Testing Pike's Peak railcar, Switzerland, 1983 1·75 1·90
1403 $4 Brienz–Rothorn railway locomotive, 1991 . . . . 2·50 2·75
1404 $5 Steam locomotive, Arth-Rigi, 1890 . . . . 2·50 2·75

1991. 500th Anniv (1992) of Discovery of America by Columbus (4th issue). History of Exploration. As T **277** of Antigua. Multicoloured.
1406 10c. Gil Eannes sailing south of Cape Bojador, 1433–34 . . . . 25 25
1407 25c. Alfonso Baldaya sailing south to Cape Blanc, 1436 35 35
1408 45c. Bartolomeu Dias in Table Bay, 1487 . . . . 45 35
1409 60c. Vasco da Gama on voyage to India, 1497–99 55 50
1410 $1 Vallarte the Dane off African coast 75 90
1411 $2 Aloisio Cadamosto in Cape Verde Islands, 1456–58 . . . . 1·40 2·00
1412 $4 Diogo Gomes on River Gambia, 1457 . . . . . 2·75 3·75
1413 $5 Diogo Cao off African coast, 1482–85 . . . . . 3·25 4·00

1991. "Phila Nippon '91" International Stamp Exhibition, Tokyo. As T **279** of Antigua. Mult.
1415 10c. Donald Duck as Shogun's guard (horiz) . . 40 20
1416 15c. Mickey Mouse as Kabuki actor (horiz) . . . 50 25
1417 25c. Minnie and Mickey Mouse as bride and groom (horiz) 60 25
1418 45c. Daisy Duck as geisha 75 25
1419 $1 Mickey Mouse in Sokutai court dress . . . 1·25 90
1420 $2 Goofy as Mino farmer 1·75 2·25
1421 $4 Pete as Shogun . . . . . 3·00 3·50
1422 $5 Donald Duck as Samurai (horiz) . . . . 3·25 3·75

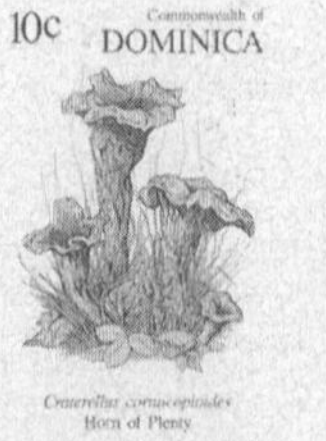

247 "Craterellus cornucopioides"

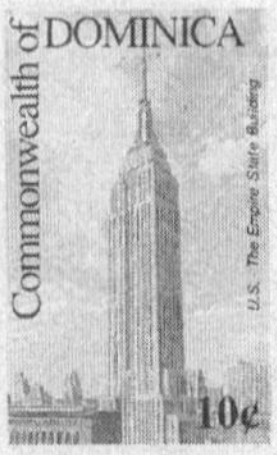

248 Empire State Building, New York

1991. Fungi. Multicoloured.
1424 10c. Type **247** 25 25
1425 15c. "Coprinus comatus" . . 50 25
1426 45c. "Morchella esculenta" 50 25
1427 60c. "Cantharellus cibarius" 60 30
1428 $1 "Lepista nuda" 80 70
1429 $2 "Suillus luteus" . . . . 1·40 1·75
1430 $4 "Russula emetica" . . . 2·25 2·75
1431 $5 "Armillaria mellea" . . . 2·25 2·75

1991. 65th Birthday of Queen Elizabeth II. As T **280** of Antigua. Multicoloured.
1433 10c. Queen and Prince William on Buckingham Palace Balcony, 1990 . . 30 20
1434 60c. The Queen at Westminster Abbey, 1988 75 50
1435 $2 The Queen and Prince Philip in Italy, 1990 . . . 1·60 2·00
1436 $5 The Queen at Ascot, 1986 . . . . 2·50 3·00

1991. 10th Wedding Anniv of Prince and Princess of Wales. As T **280** of Antigua. Multicoloured.
1438 15c. Prince and Princess of Wales in West Germany, 1987 . . . . 75 25
1439 40c. Separate photographs of Prince, Princess and sons . . . . 1·25 25
1440 $1 Separate photographs of Prince William and Prince Henry . . . . 1·25 95
1441 $4 Prince Charles at Caister and Princess Diana in Thailand . . . . 4·00 4·50

1991. Death Centenary (1990) of Vincent van Gogh (artist). As T **278** of Antigua. Multicoloured.
1443 10c. "Thatched Cottages" (horiz) 40 30
1444 25c. "The House of Pere Eloi" (horiz) 55 30
1445 45c. "The Midday Siesta" (horiz) 70 30
1446 60c. "Portrait of a Young Peasant" 90 35
1447 $1 "Still Life: Vase with Irises against Yellow Background" . . . . . . 1·25 85
1448 $2 "Still Life: Vase with Irises" (horiz) . . . . . . 1·75 1·90
1449 $4 "Blossoming Almond Tree" (horiz) . . . . . . 2·50 2·75
1450 $5 "Irises" (horiz) . . . . . 2·50 2·75

1991. International Literacy Year (1990). Scenes from Disney cartoon film "The Little Mermaid". As T **269** of Antigua. Multicoloured.
1452 10c. Ariel, Flounder and Sebastian (horiz) 30 25
1453 25c. King Triton (horiz) . . 45 30
1454 45c. Sebastian playing drums (horiz) 60 30
1455 60c. Flotsam and Jetsam taunting Ariel (horiz) . . 85 55
1456 $1 Scuttle, Flounder and Ariel with pipe (horiz) . . 1·25 1·00
1457 $2 Ariel and Flounder discovering book (horiz) 2·00 2·00
1458 $4 Prince Eric and crew (horiz) . . . . 3·25 3·50
1459 $5 Ursula the Sea Witch (horiz) . . . . 3·50 4·00

1991. World Landmarks. Multicoloured.
1461 10c. Type **248** 40 30
1462 25c. Kremlin, Moscow (horiz) 40 30
1463 45c. Buckingham Palace, London (horiz) 60 30
1464 60c. Eiffel Tower, Paris . . 75 60
1465 $1 Taj Mahal, Agra (horiz) 2·50 1·50
1466 $2 Opera House, Sydney (horiz) . . . . 3·25 3·00
1467 $4 Colosseum, Rome (horiz) 3·50 4·00
1468 $5 Pyramids, Giza (horiz) 4·00 4·50

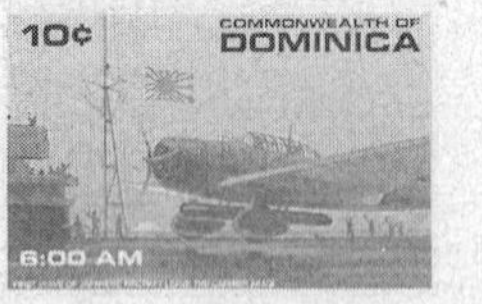

249 Japanese Aircraft leaving Carrier "Akagi"

1991. 50th Anniv of Japanese Attack on Pearl Harbor. Multicoloured.
1470 10c. Type **249** 25 25
1471 15c. U.S.S. "Ward" (destroyer) and Consolidated Catalina flying boat attacking midget submarine 30 25
1472 45c. Second wave of Mitsubishi A6M Zero-Sen aircraft leaving carriers . . 50 25
1473 60c. Japanese Mitsubishi M6M Zero-Sen aircraft attacking Kaneche naval airfield 60 30
1474 $1 U.S.S. "Breeze", "Medusa" and "Curtiss" (destroyers) sinking midget submarine 80 70
1475 $2 U.S.S. "Nevada" (battleship) under attack 1·40 1·50
1476 $4 U.S.S. "Arizona" (battleship) sinking . . . 2·25 2·50
1477 $5 Mitsubishi A6M Zero-Sen aircraft . . . . 2·25 2·50

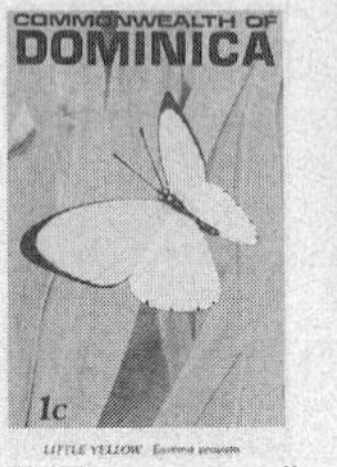

250 "Eurema venusta"

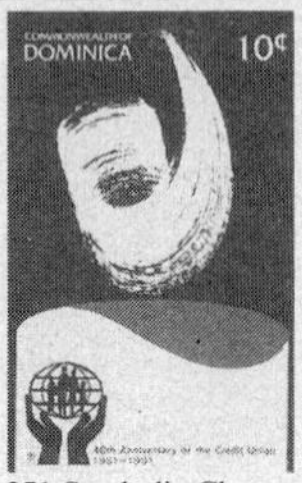

251 Symbolic Cheque

1991. Butterflies. Multicoloured.
1479 1c. Type **250** 30 60
1480 2c. "Agraulis vanillae" . . 30 60
1481 5c. "Danaus plexippus" . . 40 60
1482 10c. "Biblis hyperia" . . . 40 15
1483 15c. "Dryas julia" 50 15
1484 20c. "Phoebis agarithe" . . 50 20
1485 25c. "Junonia genoveva" . . 50 20
1486 35c. "Battus polydamas" . . 60 30
1487 45c. "Leptotes cassius" . . 60 30
1487a 55c. "Ascia monuste" . . . 75 55
1488 60c. "Anaea dominicana" . . 70 35
1488a 65c. "Hemiargus hanno" . . 75 55
1489 90c. "Hypolimnas misippus" 80 55
1490 $1 "Urbanus proteus" . . . 80 60
1490a $1.20 "Historis odius" . . 1·00 1·50
1491 $2 "Phoebis sennae" . . . 1·50 2·00
1492 $5 "Cynthia cardui" ("Vanessa cardui") . . . 2·50 4·00
1493 $10 "Marpesia petreus" . . 4·75 6·50
1494 $20 "Anartia jatrophae" . . 9·50 12·00

1991. Birth Centenary (1990) of Charles De Gaulle (French statesman). As T **283** of Antigua.
1495 45c. brown . . . . 1·50 75
DESIGN—VERT: 45c. De Gaulle in uniform.

1992. 40th Anniv of Credit Union Bank.
1497 **251** 10c. grey and black . . . 30 20
1498 – 60c. multicoloured . . . 95 80
DESIGN—HORIZ: 60c. Credit Union symbol.

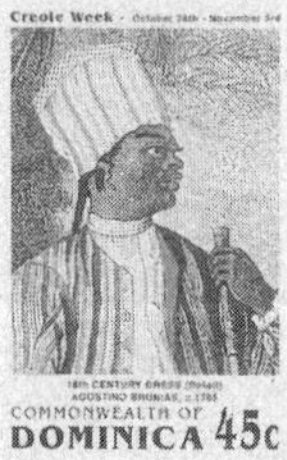

252 "18th-Century Creole Dress" (detail) (Agostino Brunias)

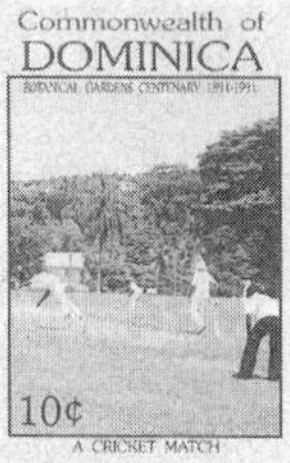

254 Cricket Match

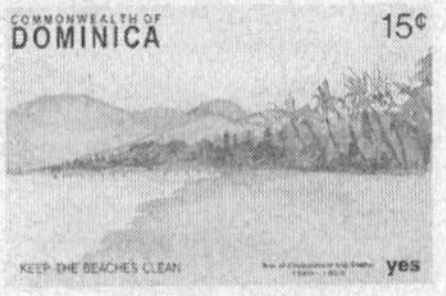

253 Island Beach

1991. Creole Week. Multicoloured.
1499 45c. Type **252** 60 25
1500 60c. Jing Ping band 80 60
1501 $1 Creole dancers . . . . . 1·10 1·60

1991. Year of Environment and Shelter. Mult.
1503 15c. Type **253** 15 15
1504 60c. Imperial amazon . . . 2·25 1·25

1991. Christmas. Religious Paintings by Jan van Eyck. As T **287** of Antigua. Multicoloured.
1506 10c. "Virgin Enthroned with Child" (detail) 50 30
1507 20c. "Madonna at the Fountain" 60 30
1508 35c. "Virgin in a Church" 70 30
1509 45c. "Madonna with Canon van der Paele" 80 30
1510 60c. "Madonna with Canon van der Paele" (detail) . . 1·25 60
1511 $1 "Madonna in an Interior" . . . . 1·50 1·00
1512 $3 "The Annunciation" . . 2·75 3·75
1513 $5 "The Annunciation" (different) . . . . 3·75 6·00

1992. 40th Anniv of Queen Elizabeth II's Accession. As T **288** of Antigua. Multicoloured.
1515 10c. Coastline 10 10
1516 15c. Mountains overlooking small village 10 10
1517 $1 River estuary 55 60
1518 $5 Waterfall . . . . 3·00 3·50

1992. Centenary (1991) of Botanical Gardens. Multicoloured.
1520 10c. Type **254** . . . . . . 1·00 60
1521 15c. Scenic entrance 40 20
1522 45c. Traveller's tree 40 25
1523 60c. Bamboo House 55 30
1524 $1 The Old Pavilion 80 70
1525 $2 "Ficus benjamina" . . . 1·40 2·00

1526 $4 Cricket match (different) 3·75 3·50
1527 $5 Thirty-five Steps . . . . 3·00 3·50

1992. Easter. Religious Paintings. As T **291** of Antigua. Multicoloured.
1529 10c. "The Supper at Emmaus" (Van Honthorst) 20 20
1530 15c. "Christ before Caiaphas" (Van Honthorst) (vert) 25 25
1531 45c. "The Taking of Christ" (De Boulogne) 40 30
1532 60c. "Pilate washing his Hands" (Preti) (vert) . . . 55 45
1533 $1 "The Last Supper" (detail) (Master of the Church of S. Francisco d'Evora) 75 75
1534 $2 "The Three Marys at the Tomb" (detail) (Bouguereau) (vert) . . . 1·50 2·00
1535 $3 "Denial of St. Peter" (Terbrugghen) . . . . . 1·75 2·50
1536 $5 "Doubting Thomas" (Strozzi) . . . . 2·75 3·75

1992. "Granada '92" International Stamp Exhibition, Spain. Art of Diego Rodriguez Velasquez. As T **292** of Antigua. Mult.
1538 10c. "Pope Innocent X" (detail) 15 10
1539 15c. "The Forge of Vulcan" (detail) 20 10
1540 45c. "The Forge of Vulcan" (different detail) 40 25
1541 60c. "Queen Mariana of Austria" (detail) 50 30
1542 $1 "Pablo de Valladolid" . . 80 70
1543 $2 "Sebastian de Morra" . . 1·25 1·60
1544 $3 "King Felipe IV" (detail) 1·60 2·25
1545 $4 "King Felipe IV" . . . . 1·75 2·40

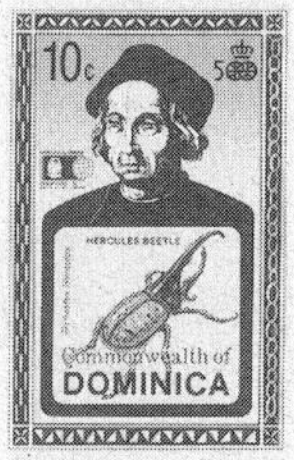

255 Columbus and "Dynastes hercules" (beetle)

1992. 500th Anniv of Discovery of America by Columbus (5th issue). World Columbian Stamp "Expo '92", Chicago. Multicoloured.
1547 10c. Type **255** 40 25
1548 25c. Columbus and "Leptodactylus fallax" (frog) 75 25
1549 75c. Columbus and red-necked amazon (bird) . . 1·75 90
1550 $2 Columbus and "Ameiva fuscata" (lizard) . . . . . 2·00 2·25
1551 $4 Columbus and royal gramma (fish) . . . . . . 2·50 3·25
1552 $5 Columbus and "Rosa sinensis" (flower) . . . . 2·50 3·25

1992. "Genova '92" International Thematic Stamp Exhibition. Hummingbirds. As T **295** of Antigua. Multicoloured.
1554 10c. Female purple-throated carib 40 25
1555 15c. Female rufous-breasted hermit 40 25
1556 45c. Male Puerto Rican emerald 65 30
1557 60c. Female Antillean mango 80 45
1558 $1 Male green-throated carib . . . . 1·25 85
1559 $2 Male blue-headed hummingbird . . . . . . 1·75 2·00
1560 $4 Female eastern streamertail . . . . . . 2·50 2·75
1561 $5 Female Antillean crested hummingbird . . . . . . 2·75 3·00

1992. Prehistoric Animals. As T **290** of Antigua, but horiz. Multicoloured.
1563 10c. Head of Camptosaurus 40 25
1564 15c. Edmontosaurus 45 25
1565 25c. Corythosaurus 55 25
1566 60c. Stegosaurus 90 30
1567 $1 Torosaurus . . . . . . 1·25 70
1568 $3 Euoplocephalus . . . . 2·00 2·25
1569 $4 Tyrannosaurus . . . . . 2·25 2·50
1570 $5 Parasaurolophus . . . . 2·50 2·75

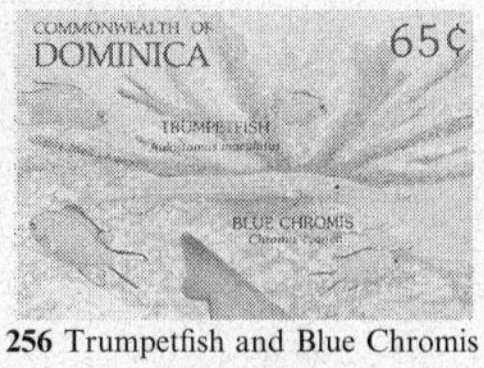

256 Trumpetfish and Blue Chromis

1992. Marine Life. Multicoloured.
1572/1601 65c. × 30. As Type **256** 12·00 13·00

1992. Olympic Games, Barcelona (2nd issue). As T **268** of Antigua. Multicoloured.
1603 10c. Archery 30 25
1604 15c. Two-man canoeing . . 35 25
1605 25c. Men's 110 m hurdles 40 25
1606 60c. Men's high jump . . . 70 30
1607 $1 Greco-Roman wrestling 1·00 65
1608 $2 Men's gymnastics—rings 1·50 2·00
1609 $4 Men's gymnastics—parallel bars . . . . . . 2·75 3·25
1610 $5 Equestrian dressage . . . 3·50 3·50

1992. 500th Anniv of Discovery of America by Columbus (6th issue). Organization of East Caribbean States. As Nos. 1670/1 of Antigua. Multicoloured.
1612 $1 Columbus meeting Amerindians 65 65
1613 $2 Ships approaching island 1·10 1·25

1992. Hummel Figurines. As T **302** of Antigua. Multicoloured.
1614 20c. Angel playing violin . . 20 15
1615 25c. Angel playing recorder 20 15
1616 55c. Angel playing lute . . . 40 30
1617 65c. Seated angel playing trumpet 50 35
1618 90c. Angel on cloud with lantern 65 65
1619 $1 Angel with candle . . . 70 70
1620 $1.20 Flying angel with Christmas tree . . . . . 80 1·10
1621 $6 Angel on cloud with candle . . . . 3·25 4·50

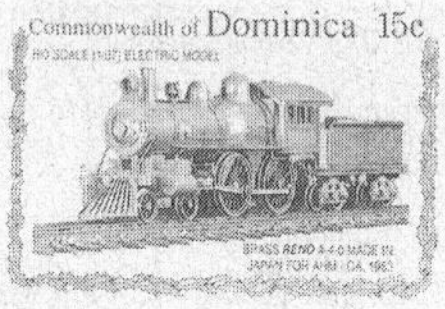

257 Brass "Reno" Locomotive, Japan (1963)

1992. Toy Trains from Far Eastern Manufacturers. Multicoloured.
1623 15c. Type **257** 35 25
1624 25c. Union Pacific "Golden Classic" locomotive, China (1992) 45 25
1625 55c. L.M.S. third class brake carriage, Hong Kong (1970s) 65 30
1626 65c. Brass Wabash locomotive, Japan (1958) 75 35
1627 75c. Pennsylvania "Duplex" type locomotive, Korea (1991) 85 75
1628 $1 Streamlined locomotive, Japan (post 1945) 90 80
1629 $3 Japanese National Railways Class "C62" locomotive, Japan (1960) 2·00 2·25
1630 $5 Tinplate friction driven trains, Japan (1960s) . . . 2·50 3·00

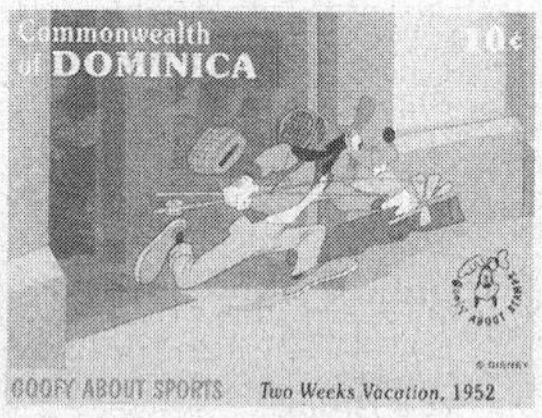

258 Goofy in "Two Weeks Vacation", 1952

1992. 60th Anniv of Goofy (Disney cartoon character). Designs showing sports from cartoon films. Multicoloured.
1632 10c. Type **258** 55 20
1633 15c. "Aquamania", 1961 . . 65 20
1634 25c. "Goofy Gymnastics", 1949 . . . . 75 20
1635 45c. "How to Ride a Horse", 1941 . . . . . . 1·00 25
1636 $1 "Foul Hunting", 1947 . . 1·50 75
1637 $2 "For Whom the Bulls Toil", 1953 . . . . 2·25 2·50
1638 $4 "Tennis Racquet", 1949 3·00 3·50
1639 $5 "Double Dribble", 1946 3·00 3·50

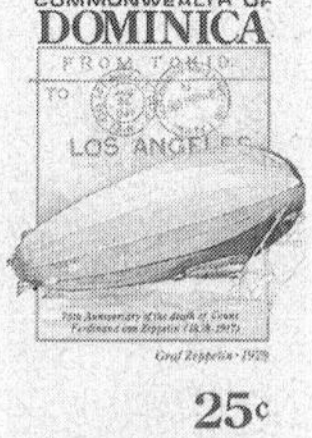

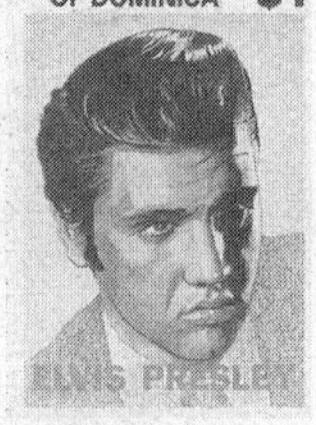

259 "Graf Zeppelin", 1929

260 Elvis Presley

1992. Anniversaries and Events. Multicoloured.
1641 25c. Type **259** 50 30
1642 45c. Elderly man on bike . . 40 30
1643 45c. Elderly man with seedling 40 30
1644 45c. Elderly man and young boy fishing 40 30
1645 90c. Space Shuttle "Atlantis" 80 60
1646 90c. Konrad Adenauer (German statesman) . . . 60 60
1647 $1.20 Sir Thomas Lipton and "Shamrock N" (yacht) . . . . 1·25 1·25
1648 $1.20 Snowy egret (bird) . . 1·25 1·25
1649 $1.20 Wolfgang Amadeus Mozart . . . . 1·75 1·25
1650 $2 Pulling fishing net ashore 1·50 1·75
1651 $3 Helen Keller (lecturer) . . 2·00 2·25
1652 $4 Eland (antelope) . . . . 3·00 3·00
1653 $4 Map of Allied Zones of Occupation, Germany, 1949 . . . . 3·00 3·00
1654 $4 Earth resources satellite 3·00 3·00
1655 $5 Count von Zeppelin . . 3·25 3·25

ANNIVERSARIES AND EVENTS: Nos. 1641, 1655, 75th death anniv of Count Ferdinand von Zeppelin; 1642/4, International Day of the Elderly; 1645, 1654, International Space Year; 1646, 1653, 25th death anniv of Konrad Adenauer; 1647, Americas Cup Yachting Championship; 1648, 1652, Earth Summit '92, Rio; 1649, Death bicent of Mozart; 1650, International Conference on Nutrition, Rome; 1651, 75th anniv of International Association of Lions Clubs.

1993. Bicentenary of the Louvre, Paris. As T **305** of Antigua. Multicoloured.
1657 $1 "Madonna and Child with St. Catherine and a Rabbit" (left detail) (Titian) 70 70
1658 $1 "Madonna and Child with St. Catherine and a Rabbit" (right detail) (Titian) 70 70
1659 $1 "Woman at her Toilet" (Titian) 70 70
1660 $1 "The Supper at Emmaus" (left detail) (Titian) 70 70
1661 $1 "The Supper at Emmaus" (right detail) (Titian) 70 70
1662 $1 "The Pastoral Concert" (Titian) 70 70
1663 $1 "An Allegory, perhaps of Marriage" (detail) (Titian) 70 70
1664 $1 "An Allegory, perhaps of Marriage" (different detail) (Titian) 70 70

1993. 15th Death Anniv of Elvis Presley (singer). Multicoloured.
1666 $1 Type **260** 90 80
1667 $1 Elvis with guitar 90 80
1668 $1 Elvis with microphone . . 90 80

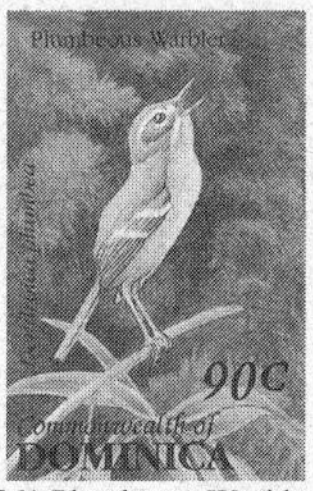

261 Plumbeous Warbler

1993. Birds. Multicoloured.
1669 90c. Type **261** . . . . . . 1·00 1·00
1670 90c. Black swift . . . . . . 1·00 1·00
1671 90c. Blue-hooded euphonia 1·00 1·00
1672 90c. Rufous-throated solitaire . . . . 1·00 1·00
1673 90c. Ringed kingfisher . . . 1·00 1·00
1674 90c. Blue-headed hummingbird . . . . . . 1·00 1·00
1675 90c. Bananaquit . . . . . 1·00 1·00
1676 90c. Brown trembler ("Trembler") . . . . . . 1·00 1·00
1677 90c. Forest thrush . . . . . 1·00 1·00
1678 90c. Purple-throated carib 1·00 1·00
1679 90c. Ruddy quail dove . . . 1·00 1·00
1680 90c. Least bittern . . . . . 1·00 1·00

Nos. 1669/80 were printed together, se-tenant, forming a composite design.

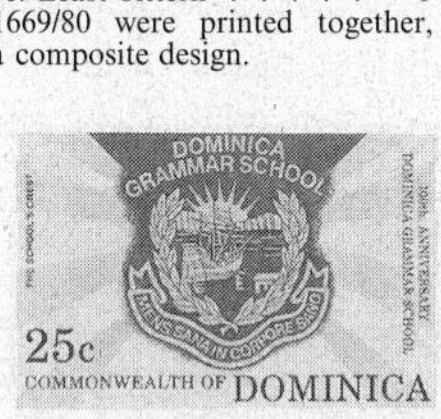

262 School Crest

1993. Cent of Dominica Grammar School. Mult.
1682 25c. Type **262** 20 15
1683 30c. V. Archer (first West Indian headmaster) . . . 25 20
1684 65c. Hubert Charles (first Dominican headmaster) 45 50
1685 90c. Present school buildings 65 80

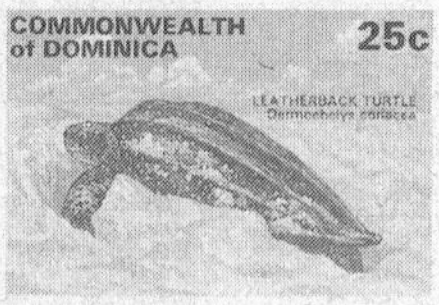

263 Leatherback Turtle on Beach

1993. Turtles. Multicoloured.
1686 25c. Type **263** 50 15
1687 55c. Hawksbill turtle swimming 70 40
1688 65c. Atlantic ridley turtle . . 80 50
1689 90c. Green turtle laying eggs 1·00 70
1690 $1 Green turtle swimming 1·00 70
1691 $2 Hawksbill turtle swimming (different) . . . 1·50 2·00
1692 $4 Loggerhead turtle . . . 2·25 2·75
1693 $5 Leatherback turtle swimming . . . . 2·25 2·75

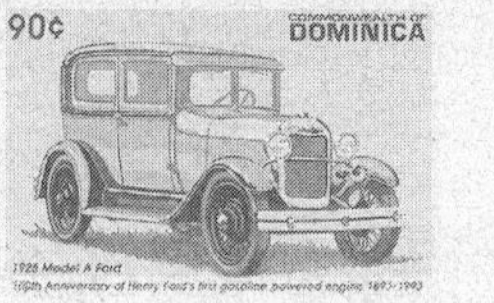

264 Ford "Model A", 1928

1993. Centenaries of Henry Ford's First Petrol Engine (90c., $5) and Karl Benz's First Four-wheeled Car (others). Multicoloured.
1695 90c. Type **264** 65 45
1696 $1.20 Mercedes Benz car winning Swiss Grand Prix, 1936 . . . . 85 55
1697 $4 Mercedes Benz car winning German Grand Prix, 1935 . . . . 2·25 2·75
1698 $5 Ford "Model T", 1915 2·25 2·75

1993. 40th Anniv of Coronation. As T **307** of Antigua.
1700 20c. multicoloured 60 75
1701 25c. brown and black . . . 60 75
1702 65c. multicoloured . . . . . 85 1·00
1703 $5 multicoloured . . . . . 4·25 4·50

DESIGNS: 20c. Queen Elizabeth II at Coronation (photograph by Cecil Beaton); 25c. Queen wearing King Edward's Crown during Coronation ceremony; 65c. Coronation coach; $5 Queen and Queen Mother in carriage.

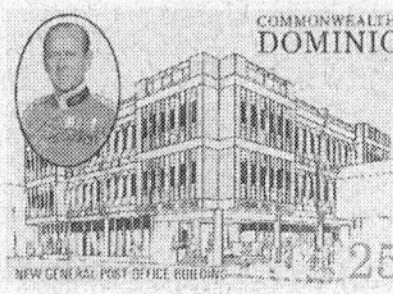

265 New G.P.O. and Duke of Edinburgh

1993. Anniversaries and Events. Each brown, deep brown and black (Nos. 1707, 1717) or multicoloured (others).
1705 25c. Type **265** 30 25
1706 25c. "Bather with Beach Ball" (Picasso) (vert) . . . 30 25
1707 65c. Willy Brandt and Pres. Eisenhower, 1959 . . . . 35 35
1708 90c. As Type **265** but portrait of Queen Elizabeth II 60 45
1709 90c. "Portrait of Leo Stein" (Picasso) (vert) 60 45
1710 90c. Monika Holzner (Germany) (speed skating) (vert) 60 45
1711 90c. "Self-portrait" (Marian Szczyrbula) (vert) 60 45
1712 90c. Prince Naruhito and engagement photographs 60 45
1713 $1.20 16th-century telescope (vert) 85 70
1714 $3 "Bruno Jasienski" (Tytus Czyzewski) (vert) . . . . 1·75 2·25
1715 $3 Modern observatory (vert) . . . . 2·00 2·25
1716 $4 Ray Leblanc and Tim Sweeney (U.S.A.) (ice hockey) (vert) . . . . . 2·50 2·75
1717 $5 "Wilhelm Unde" (Picasso) (vert) . . . . . 2·25 2·75
1718 $5 Willy Brandt and N. K. Winston at World's Fair, 1964 . . . . 2·25 2·75
1719 $5 Masako Owada and engagement photographs 2·25 2·75
1720 $5 Pres. Clinton and wife applauding . . . . 2·25 2·75

ANNIVERSARIES AND EVENTS: Nos. 1705, 1708, Opening of New General Post Office Building; 1706, 1709, 1717, 20th death anniv of Picasso (artist); 1707, 1718, 80th birth anniv of Willy Brandt (German politician); 1710, 1716, Winter Olympic Games '94, Lillehammer; 1711, 1714, "Polska '93" International Stamp Exhibition, Poznan; 1712, 1719, Marriage of Crown Prince Naruhito of Japan; 1713, 1715, 450th death anniv of Copernicus (astronomer); 1720, Inauguration of U.S. President William Clinton.

No. 1714 is inscribed "Tyrus" in error.

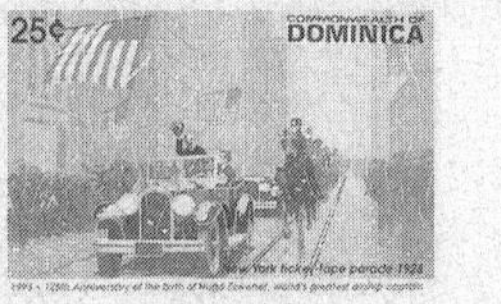

266 Hugo Eckener in New York Parade, 1928

1993. Aviation Anniversaries. Multicoloured.
1722 25c. Type **266** 70 30
1723 55c. English Electric Lightning F.2 (fighter) . . 1·25 40
1724 65c. Airship "Graf Zeppelin" over Egypt, 1929 . . . . 1·25 55
1725 $1 Boeing 314A (flying boat) on transatlantic mail flight . . . . 1·40 85

1726 $2 Astronaut carrying mail to the Moon . . . . . . 2·00 2·25
1727 $4 Airship "Viktoria Luise" over Kiel harbour, 1912 3·00 3·50
1728 $5 Supermarine Spitfire (vert) . . . . 3·00 3·50

ANNIVERSARIES: Nos. 1722, 1724, 1727, 125th birth anniv of Hugo Eckener (airship commander); 1723, 1728, 75th anniv of Royal Air Force; 1725/6, Bicentenary of first airmail flight.

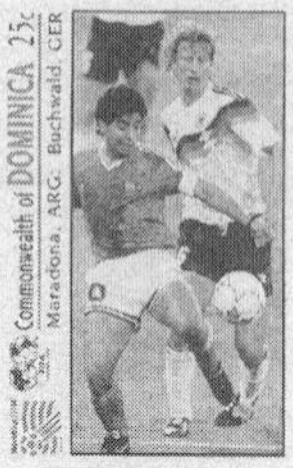

267 Maradona (Argentina) and Buchwald (Germany)

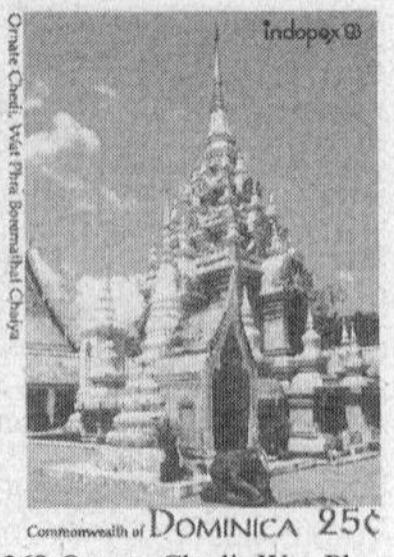

268 Ornate Chedi, Wat Phra Boromathat Chaiya

1993. World Cup Football Championship, U.S.A. (1994) (1st issue). Multicoloured.

1730 25c. Type **267** 60 20
1731 55c. Ruud Gullit (Netherlands) 85 40
1732 65c. Chavarria (Costa Rica) and Bliss (U.S.A.) 85 45
1733 90c. Diego Maradona (Argentina) . . . . 1·25 75
1734 90c. Leonel Alvares (Colombia) . . . . 1·25 75
1735 $1 Altobelli (Italy) and Yong-hwang (South Korea) . . . . 1·25 80
1736 $2 Stopyra (France) . . . . 2·00 2·25
1737 $5 Renquin (Belgium) and Yaremtchuk (Russia) . . 3·00 4·00

See also Nos. 1849/55.

1993. Asian International Stamp Exhibitions. Multicoloured. (a) "Indopex '93", Surabaya, Indonesia.

1739 25c. Type **268** 30 30
1740 55c. Temple ruins, Sukhothai 50 30
1741 90c. Prasat Hin Phimai, Thailand 70 45
1742 $1.65 Arjuna and Prabu Gilling Wesi puppets . . 1·00 1·00
1743 $1.65 Loro Blonyo puppet 1·00 1·00
1744 $1.65 Yogyanese puppets . . 1·00 1·00
1745 $1.65 Wayang gedog puppet, Ng Setro . . . . 1·00 1·00
1746 $1.65 Wayang golek puppet 1·00 1·00
1747 $1.65 Wayang gedog puppet, Raden Damar Wulan . . . . 1·00 1·00
1748 $5 Main sanctuary, Prasat Phanom Rung, Thailand 2·25 2·50

(b) "Taipei '93", Taiwan.

1750 25c. Aw Boon Haw Gardens, Causeway Bay 30 30
1751 65c. Observation building, Kenting Park 50 30
1752 90c. Tzu-en pagoda on lakeshore, Taiwan 70 45
1753 $1.65 Chang E kite . . . . . 1·00 1·00
1754 $1.65 Red Phoenix and Rising Sun kite . . . . . 1·00 1·00
1755 $1.65 Heavenly Judge kite 1·00 1·00
1756 $1.65 Monkey King kite . . 1·00 1·00
1757 $1.65 Goddess of Luo River kite . . . . 1·00 1·00
1758 $1.65 Heavenly Maiden kite 1·00 1·00
1759 $5 Villa, Lantau Island . . 2·25 2·50

(c) "Bangkok '93", Thailand.

1761 25c. Tugu Monument, Java 30 30
1762 55c. Candi Cangkuang mon, West Java 50 30
1763 90c. Merus, Pura Taman Ayun, Mengwi 70 45
1764 $1.65 Hun Lek puppets of Rama and Sita . . . . . 1·00 1·00
1765 $1.65 Burmese puppet . . . 1·00 1·00
1766 $1.65 Burmese puppets . . . 1·00 1·00
1767 $1.65 Demon puppet at Wat Phra Kaew . . . . 1·00 1·00
1768 $1.65 Hun Lek puppet performing Khun Chang 1·00 1·00
1769 $1.65 Hun Lek puppets performing Ramakien . . 1·00 1·00
1770 $5 Stone mosaic, Ceto . . 2·25 2·50

No. 1753 is inscribed "Chang E Rising Up th the Moon" in error.

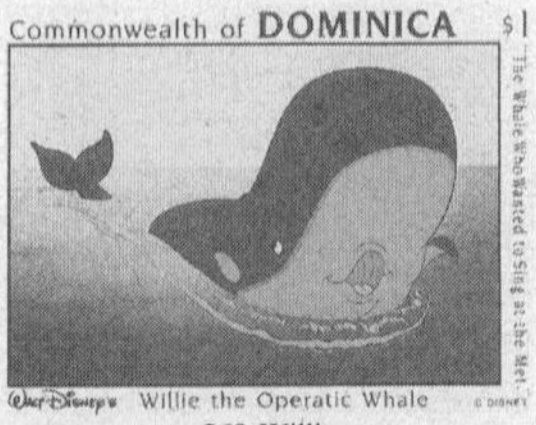

269 Willie

1993. "Willie the Operatic Whale". Scenes from Walt Disney's cartoon film. Multicoloured.

1772 $1 Type **269** . . . . . . 1·00 1·00
1773 $1 Willie's pelican friend . . 1·00 1·00
1774 $1 Willie singing to seals . . 1·00 1·00
1775 $1 Willie singing "Lucia" 1·00 1·00
1776 $1 Willie in "Pagliacci" . . 1·00 1·00
1777 $1 Willie as Mephistopheles 1·00 1·00
1778 $1 Tetti Tatti searching for Willie . . . . 1·00 1·00
1779 $1 Whalers listening to Willie . . . . 1·00 1·00
1780 $1 Tetti Tatti with harpoon gun . . . . 1·00 1·00

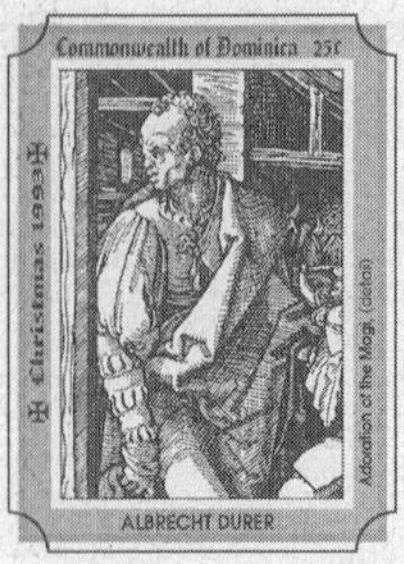

270 "Adoration of the Magi" (detail) (Durer)

1993. Christmas. Religious Paintings. Each black, yellow and red (Nos. 1782/5) or multicoloured (others).

1782 25c. Type **270** 35 20
1783 55c. "Adoration of the Magi" (different detail) (Durer) 55 30
1784 65c. "Adoration of the Magi" (different detail) (Durer) 65 35
1785 90c. "Adoration of the Magi" (different detail) (Durer) 80 65
1786 90c. "Madonna of Foligno" (detail) (Raphael) 80 65
1787 $1 "Madonna of Foligno" (different detail) (Raphael) 90 70
1788 $3 "Madonna of Foligno" (different detail) (Raphael) 2·00 3·00
1789 $5 "Madonna of Foligno" (different detail) (Raphael) 2·75 4·00

1994. "Hong Kong '94" International Stamp Exhibition (1st issue). As T **317** of Antigua. Multicoloured.

1791 65c. Hong Kong 1988 Peak Tramway 50c. stamp and skyscrapers 75 90
1792 65c. Dominica 1991 Cog Railways $5 stamp and Hong Kong Peak tram . . 75 90

Nos. 1791/2 were printed together, se-tenant, forming a composite design.

See also Nos. 1793/8.

1994. "Hong Kong '94" International Stamp Exhibition (2nd issue). Tang Dynasty Jade. As T **318** of Antigua, but vert. Multicoloured.

1793 65c. Horse 55 60
1794 65c. Cup with handle . . . 55 60
1795 65c. Vase with birthday peaches 55 60
1796 65c. Vase 55 60
1797 65c. Fu Dog with puppy . . 55 60
1798 65c. Drinking cup 55 60

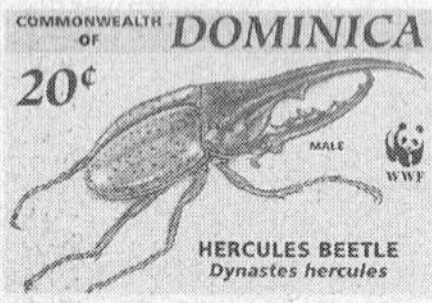

271 Male "Dynastes hercules" (beetle)

1994. Endangered Species. Birds and Insects. Multicoloured.

1799 20c. Type **271** 20 15
1800 25c. Male "Dynastes hercules" (different) . . . 20 15
1801 65c. Male "Dynastes hercules" (different) . . . 45 35
1802 90c. Female "Dynastes hercules" 60 55
1803 $1 Imperial Amazon ("Imperial Parrot") . . . 90 75
1804 $2 "Marpesia petreus" (butterfly) . . . . 1·50 2·00
1805 $3 "Hypolimnus misippus" (butterfly) . . . . . . 2·00 2·50
1806 $5 Purple-throated carib . . 2·75 3·50

Nos. 1803/7 do not carry the W.W.F. Panda emblem.

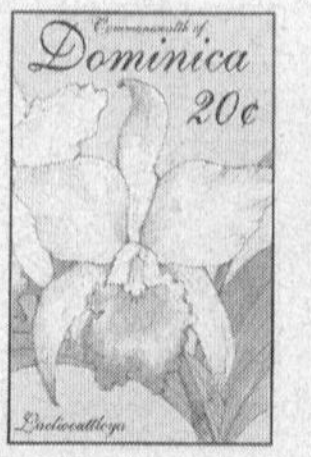

272 "Laelio-cattleya"

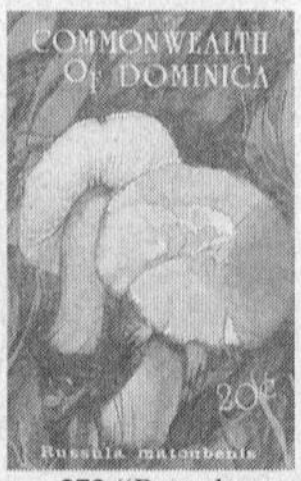

273 "Russula matoubenis"

1994. Orchids. Multicoloured.

1808 20c. Type **272** 35 15
1809 25c. "Sophrolaelio cattleya" 35 15
1810 65c. "Odontocidium" . . . 70 45
1811 90c. "Laelio-cattleya" (different) 90 75
1812 $1 "Cattleya" . . . . 1·00 75
1813 $2 "Odontocidium" (different) . . . . 1·50 2·00
1814 $3 "Epiphronitis" . . . . . 2·00 2·75
1815 $4 "Oncidium" . . . . . . 2·00 2·75

1994. Fungi. Multicoloured.

1817 20c. Type **273** 40 25
1818 25c. "Leptonia caeruleocapitata" 40 25
1819 65c. "Inocybe littoralis" . . 60 35
1820 90c. "Russula hygrophytica" 70 55
1821 $1 "Pyrrhoglossum lilaceipes" 80 70
1822 $2 "Hygrocybe konradii" 1·25 1·75
1823 $3 "Inopilus magnificus" . . 1·75 2·25
1824 $5 "Boletellus cubensis" . . 2·25 2·75

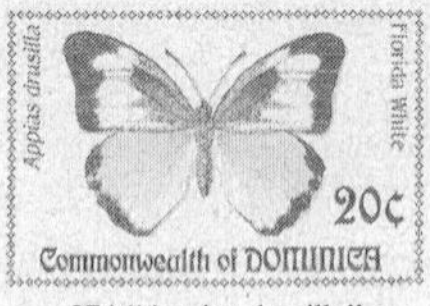

274 "Appias drusilla"

1994. Butterflies. Multicoloured.

1826 20c. Type **274** 35 15
1827 25c. "Didonis biblis" . . . 35 15
1828 55c. "Eurema daira" . . . 70 45
1829 65c. "Hypolimnas misippus" 75 45
1830 $1 "Phoebis agarithe" . . . 1·00 75
1831 $2 "Marpesia petreus" . . . 1·50 2·00
1832 $3 "Libytheana fulvescens" 1·75 2·75
1833 $5 "Precis evarete" . . . . 2·50 3·50

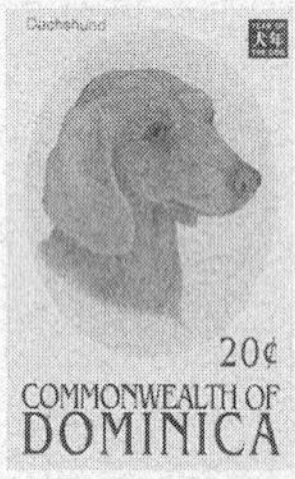

275 Dachshund

1994. Chinese New Year ("Year of the Dog"). Multicoloured.

1835 20c. Type **275** 30 25
1836 25c. Beagle 30 25
1837 55c. Greyhound 50 30
1838 90c. Jack Russell terrier . . 70 55
1839 $1 Pekingese 80 70
1840 $2 Wire fox terrier . . . . 1·25 1·50
1841 $4 English toy spaniel . . . 2·25 2·75
1842 $5 Irish setter . . . . 2·25 2·75

1994. Royal Visit. Nos. 1700/4 optd **ROYAL VISIT FEBRUARY 19, 1994.**

1844 20c. multicoloured 75 85
1845 25c. brown and black . . . 75 85
1846 65c. multicoloured . . . . . 1·25 1·40
1847 $5 multicoloured . . . . . 3·25 3·75

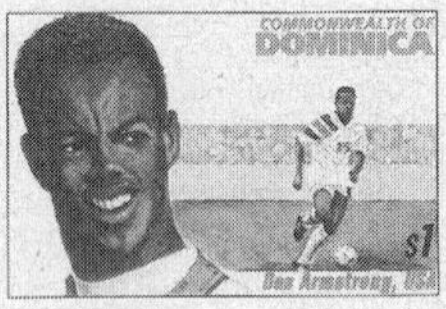

277 Des Armstrong (U.S.A.)

1994. World Cup Football Championship, U.S.A. (2nd issue). Multicoloured.

1849 25c. Jefferey Edmund (Dominica) 50 25
1850 $1 Type **277** 75 80
1851 $1 Dennis Bergkamp (Netherlands) 75 80
1852 $1 Roberto Baggio (Italy) 75 80
1853 $1 Rai (Brazil) 75 80
1854 $1 Cafu (Brazil) 75 80
1855 $1 Marco van Basten (Netherlands) 75 80

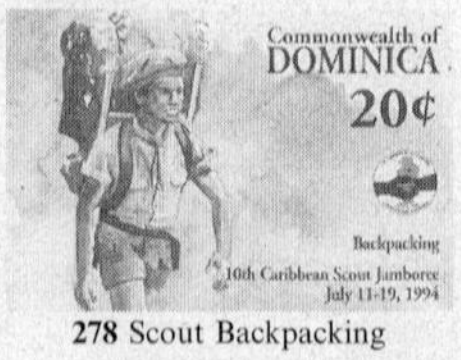

278 Scout Backpacking

1994. 10th Caribbean Scout Jamboree. Multicoloured.

1857 20c. Type **278** 35 15
1858 25c. Cooking over campfire 35 15
1859 55c. Erecting tent 60 30
1860 65c. Serving soup 70 45
1861 $1 Corps of drums . . . . 1·00 75
1862 $2 Planting tree . . . . . . 1·50 2·00
1863 $4 Sailing dinghy . . . . . 2·25 2·75
1864 $5 Saluting . . . . 2·25 2·75

1994. 25th Anniv of First Manned Moon Landing. As T **326** of Antigua. Multicoloured.

1866 $1 Crew of "Apollo 14" . . 70 80
1867 $1 "Apollo 14" mission logo 70 80
1868 $1 Lunar module "Antares" on Moon 70 80
1869 $1 Crew of "Apollo 15" . . 70 80
1870 $1 "Apollo 15" mission logo 70 80
1871 $1 Lunar crater on Mt. Hadley 70 80

1994. Centenary of International Olympic Committee. Gold Medal Winners. As T **327** of Antigua. Multicoloured.

1873 55c. Ulrike Meyfarth (Germany) (high jump), 1984 . . . . 50 40
1874 $1.45 Dieter Baumann (Germany) (5000 m), 1992 1·25 1·50

1994. Centenary (1995) of First English Cricket Tour to the West Indies. As T **329** of Antigua. Multicoloured.

1876 55c. David Gower (England) (vert) 40 30
1877 90c. Curtly Ambrose (West Indies) and Wisden Trophy 60 60
1878 $1 Graham Gooch (England) (vert) 70 80

1994. 50th Anniv of D-Day. As T **331** of Antigua. Multicoloured.

1880 65c. American Waco gliders 60 45
1881 $2 British Horsa glider . . . 1·25 1·40
1882 $3 British glider and troops attacking Pegasus Bridge 1·50 1·75

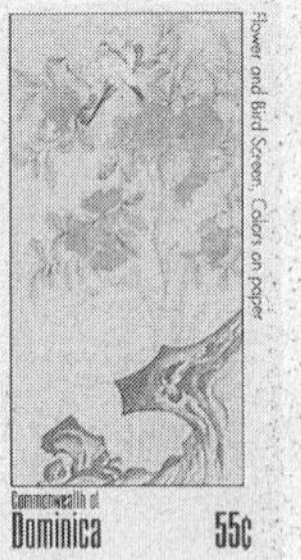

279 Pink Bird and Red Flowers Screen Painting

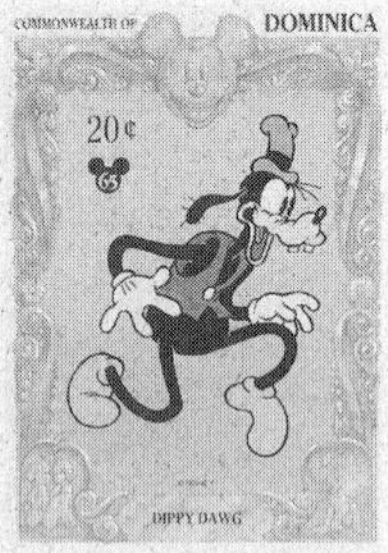

280 Dippy Dawg

1994. "Philakorea '94" International Stamp Exhibition, Seoul. Multicoloured.

1884 55c. Type **279** 25 30
1885 55c. Bird with yellow, pink and red flowers 25 30
1886 55c. Pair of birds and yellow flowers 25 30
1887 55c. Chickens and flowers 25 30
1888 55c. Pair of birds and pink flowers 25 30
1889 55c. Ducks and flowers . . 25 30
1890 55c. Blue bird and red flowers 25 30
1891 55c. Common pheasant and flowers 25 30
1892 55c. Stork and flowers . . . 25 30
1893 55c. Deer and flowers . . . 25 30
1894 65c. P'alsang-jon Hall (38 × 24 mm) 30 35
1895 90c. Popchu-sa Temple (38 × 24 mm) 35 40
1896 $2 Uhwajong Pavillion (38 × 24 mm) 85 90

1994. 65th Anniv (1993) of Mickey Mouse. Walt Disney Cartoon Characters. Multicoloured.

1898 20c. Type **280** 45 20
1899 25c. Clarabelle Cow 45 20
1900 55c. Horace Horsecollar . . 70 35
1901 65c. Mortimer Mouse . . . 80 45
1902 $1 Joe Piper . . . . 1·25 85
1903 $3 Mr. Casey . . . . 2·25 2·50
1904 $4 Chief O'Hara . . . . . 2·50 3·00
1905 $5 Mickey and The Blot . . 2·50 3·00

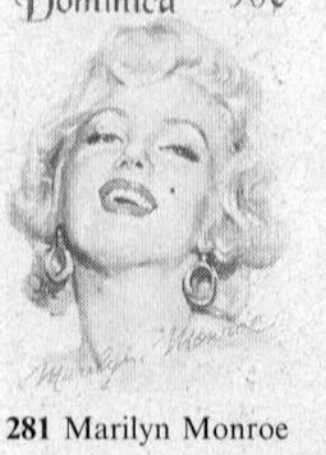

281 Marilyn Monroe

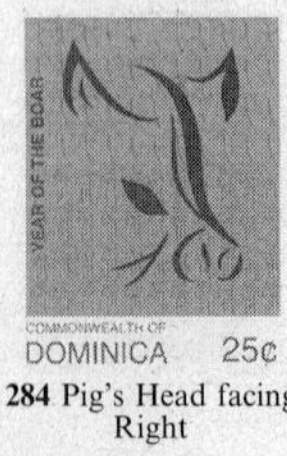

284 Pig's Head facing Right

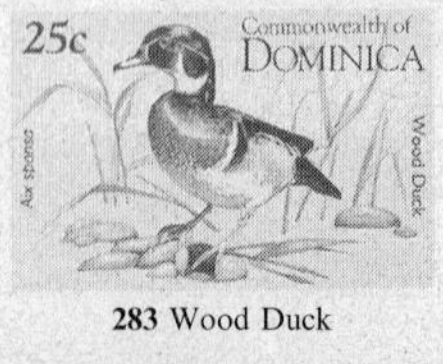

283 Wood Duck

1994. Entertainers. Multicoloured.
1907 20c. Sonia Lloyd (folk singer) 20 20
1908 25c. Ophelia Marie (singer) 20 20
1909 55c. Edney Francis (accordion player) 40 30
1910 65c. Norman Letang (saxophonist) 50 35
1911 90c. Edie Andre (steel-band player) 60 45
1912 90c. Type **281** 85 85
1913 90c. Marilyn Monroe wearing necklace 85 85
1914 90c. In yellow frilled dress 85 85
1915 90c. In purple dress 85 85
1916 90c. Looking over left shoulder 85 85
1917 90c. Laughing 85 85
1918 90c. In red dress 85 85
1919 90c. Wearing gold cluster earrings 85 85
1920 90c. In yellow dress 85 85
No. 1907 is inscribed "Llyod" in error.

1994. Christmas. Religious Paintings. As T **336** of Antigua. Multicoloured.
1922 20c. "Madonna and Child" (Luis de Morales) 25 10
1923 25c. "Madonna and Child with Yarn Winder" (De Morales) 25 10
1924 55c. "Our Lady of the Rosary" (detail) (Zurbaran) 40 30
1925 65c. "Dream of the Patrician" (detail) (Murillo) 50 55
1926 90c. "Madonna of Charity" (El Greco) 70 45
1927 $1 "The Annunciation" (Zurbaran) 75 50
1928 $2 "Mystical Marriage of St. Catherine" (Jusepe de Ribera) . . . . 1·25 2·00
1929 $3 "The Holy Family with St. Bruno and Other Saints" (detail) (De Ribera) . . . . 1·50 2·50

1994. First Recipients of Order of the Caribbean Community. As Nos. 2046/8 of Antigua. Mult.
1931 25c. Sir Shridath Ramphal 20 10
1932 65c. William Demas 50 50
1933 90c. Derek Walcott 70 80

1995. 18th World Scout Jamboree, Netherlands. Nos. 1860 and 1863/4 optd **18th World Scout Jamboree Mondial, Holland, May 6, 1995**.
1934 65c. Serving soup 60 35
1935 $4 Sailing dinghy . . . . . 2·25 2·75
1936 $5 Saluting . . . . 2·25 2·75

1995. Water Birds. Multicoloured.
1938 25c. Type **283** 60 30
1939 55c. Mallard 70 40
1940 65c. Blue-winged teal . . . 75 55
1941 65c. Cattle egret (vert) . . . 75 80
1942 65c. Snow goose (vert) . . . 75 80
1943 65c. Peregrine falcon (vert) 75 80
1944 65c. Barn owl (vert) 75 80
1945 65c. Black-crowned night heron (vert) 75 80
1946 65c. Common grackle (vert) 75 80
1947 65c. Brown pelican (vert) . . 75 80
1948 65c. Great egret (vert) . . . 75 80
1949 65c. Ruby-throated hummingbird (vert) . . . 75 80
1950 65c. Laughing gull (vert) . . 75 80
1951 65c. Greater flamingo (vert) 75 80
1952 65c. Moorhen ("Common Morehen") (vert) 75 80
1953 $5 Red-eared conure ("Blood eared parakeet") 2·75 3·50
Nos. 1941/5 were printed together, se-tenant, forming a composite design.
No. 1946 is inscribed "Common Gralkle" in error.

1995. Chinese New Year ("Year of the Pig"). Multicoloured.
1955 25c. Type **284** 40 40
1956 65c. Pig facing to the front 45 45
1957 $1 Pig facing left 50 50

1995. 50th Anniv of End of Second World War in Europe. As T **340** of Antigua. Multicoloured.
1960 $2 German Panther tank in the Ardennes . . . . . . 1·25 1·25
1961 $2 American fighter-bomber 1·25 1·25
1962 $2 American mechanized column crossing the Rhine 1·25 1·25
1963 $2 Messerschmitt Me 163B Komet and Allied bombers . . . . 1·25 1·25
1964 $2 V2 rocket on launcher 1·25 1·25
1965 $2 German U-boat surrendering . . . . . . 1·25 1·25
1966 $2 Heavy artillery in action 1·25 1·25
1967 $2 Soviet infantry in Berlin 1·25 1·25

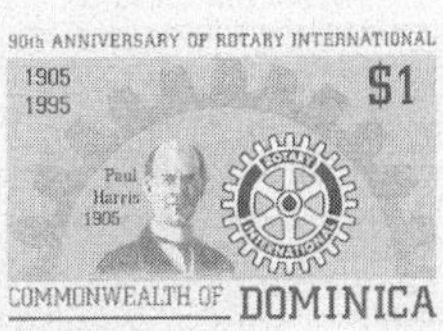

285 Paul Harris (founder) and Emblem

1995. 90th Anniv of Rotary International.
1969 **285** $1 brown, purple & blk 75 75

1995. 50th Anniv of End of Second World War in the Pacific. As T **340** of Antigua. Multicoloured.
1971 $2 Mitsubishi A6M Zero-Sen torpedo-bomber . . . 1·25 1·25
1972 $2 Aichi D3A "Val" dive bomber . . . . 1·25 1·25
1973 $2 Nakajima B5N "Kate" bomber . . . . 1·25 1·25
1974 $2 "Zuikaku" (Japanese aircraft carrier) . . . . . 1·25 1·25
1975 $2 "Akagi" (Japanese aircraft carrier) . . . . . 1·25 1·25
1976 $2 "Ryuho" (Japanese aircraft carrier) . . . . . 1·25 1·25

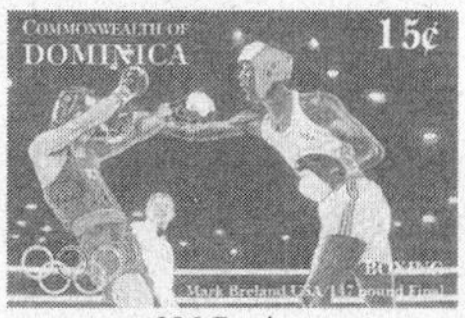

286 Boxing

1995. Olympic Games, Atlanta (1996). (1st Issue). Multicoloured.
1978 15c. Type **286** 30 25
1979 20c. Wrestling 35 25
1980 25c. Judo 45 25
1981 55c. Fencing 50 30
1982 65c. Swimming 60 35
1983 $1 Gymnastics (vert) 80 70
1984 $2 Cycling (vert) . . . . . 2·00 1·75
1985 $5 Volleyball . . . . 2·75 3·25
See also Nos. 2122/45 and 2213.

1995. 50th Anniv of United Nations. As T **341** of Antigua. Multicoloured.
1987 65c. Signatures and U.S. delegate 40 45
1988 $1 U.S. delegate 55 60
1989 $2 Governor Stassen (U.S. delegate) . . . . 85 1·25
Nos. 1987/9 were printed together, se-tenant, forming a composite design.

1995. 95th Birthday of Queen Elizabeth the Queen Mother. As T **344** of Antigua.
1993 $1.65 brown, lt brown & blk 90 1·10
1994 $1.65 multicoloured . . . . 90 1·10
1995 $1.65 multicoloured . . . . 90 1·10
1996 $1.65 multicoloured . . . . 90 1·10
DESIGNS: No. 1993, Queen Elizabeth the Queen Mother (pastel drawing); 1994, Holding bouquet of flowers; 1995, At desk (oil painting); 1996, Wearing blue dress.

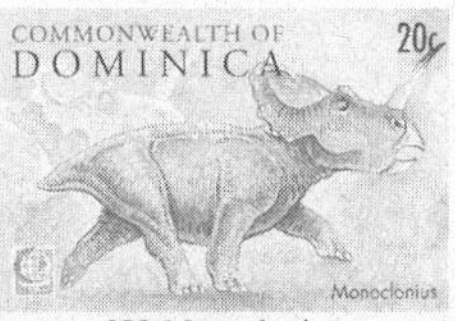

288 Monoclonius

1995. "Singapore '95" International Stamp Exhibition. Prehistoric Animals. Multicoloured.
1998 20c. Type **288** 30 25
1999 25c. Euoplocephalus 30 25
2000 55c. Head of coelophysis . . 40 30
2001 65c. Head of compsognathus 50 35
2002 90c. Dimorphodon 60 60
2003 90c. Ramphorynchus . . . 60 60
2004 90c. Head of giant alligator 60 60
2005 90c. Pentaceratops 60 60
2006 $1 Ceratosaurus (vert) . . . 65 65
2007 $1 Comptosaurus (vert) . . 65 65
2008 $1 Stegosaur (vert) 65 65
2009 $1 Camarasaurs (vert) . . . 65 65
2010 $1 Baronyx (vert) 65 65
2011 $1 Dilophosaurus (vert) . . 65 65
2012 $1 Dromaeosaurids (vert) 65 65
2013 $1 Deinonychus (vert) . . . 65 65
2014 $1 Dinicthys (terror fish) (vert) 65 65
2015 $1 Head of carcharodon (Giant-toothed shark) (vert) 65 65
2016 $1 Nautiloid (vert) 65 65
2017 $1 Trilobite (vert) 65 65
Nos. 2002/5 and 2006/17 were respectively printed together, se-tenant, forming composite designs.
Nos. 2002/5 do not carry the "Singapore '95" exhibition logo.

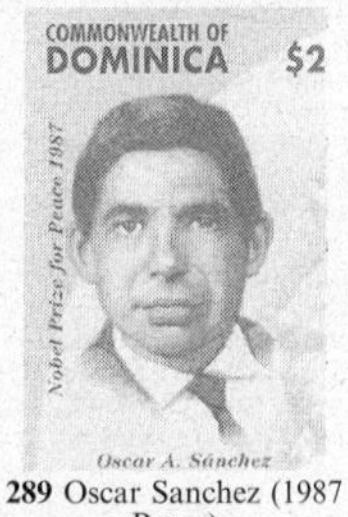

289 Oscar Sanchez (1987 Peace)

1995. Centenary of Nobel Prize Trust Fund. Mult.
2019 $2 Type **289** . . . . 1·25 1·25
2020 $2 Ernst Chain (1945 Medicine) . . . . 1·25 1·25
2021 $2 Aage Bohr (1975 Physics) 1·25 1·25
2022 $2 Jaroslav Seifert (1984 Literature) . . . . 1·25 1·25
2023 $2 Joseph Murray (1990 Medicine) . . . . 1·25 1·25
2024 $2 Jaroslav Heyrovsky (1959 Chemistry) . . . . 1·25 1·25
2025 $2 Adolf von Baeyer (1905 Chemistry) . . . . 1·25 1·25
2026 $2 Eduard Buchner (1907 Chemistry) . . . . 1·25 1·25
2027 $2 Carl Bosch (1931 Chemistry) . . . . 1·25 1·25
2028 $2 Otto Hahn (1944 Chemistry) . . . . 1·25 1·25
2029 $2 Otto Diels (1950 Chemistry) . . . . 1·25 1·25
2030 $2 Kurt Alder (1950 Chemistry) . . . . 1·25 1·25

1995. Christmas. Religious Paintings. As T **357** of Antigua. Multicoloured.
2032 20c. "Madonna and Child with St. John" (Pontormo) 25 20
2033 25c. "The Immaculate Conception" (Murillo) . . 25 20
2034 55c. "The Adoration of the Magi" (Filippino Lippi) 45 30
2035 65c. "Rest on the Flight into Egypt" (Van Dyck) . . . 55 35
2036 90c. "The Holy Family" (Van Dyck) 75 50
2037 $5 "The Annunciation" (Van Eyck) . . . . 2·75 3·75

1995. Centenary (1992) of Sierra Club (environmental protection society). Endangered Species. As T **320** of Antigua. Multicoloured.
2039 $1 Florida panther 50 50
2040 $1 Manatee 50 50
2041 $1 Sockeye salmon 50 50
2042 $1 Key deer facing left . . . 50 50
2043 $1 Key deer doe 50 50
2044 $1 Key deer stag 50 50
2045 $1 Wallaby with young in pouch 50 50
2046 $1 Wallaby feeding young 50 50
2047 $1 Wallaby and young feeding 50 50
2048 $1 Florida panther showing teeth (horiz) 50 50
2049 $1 Head of Florida panther (horiz) 50 50
2050 $1 Manatee (horiz) 50 50
2051 $1 Pair of manatees (horiz) 50 50
2052 $1 Pair of sockeye salmon (horiz) 50 50
2053 $1 Sockeye salmon spawning (horiz) 50 50
2054 $1 Pair of southern sea otters (horiz) 50 50
2055 $1 Southern sea otter with front paws together (horiz) 50 50
2056 $1 Southern sea otter with front paws apart (horiz) 50 50

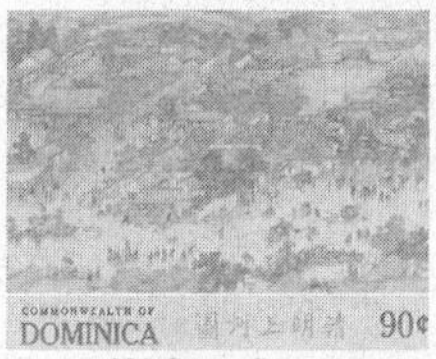

290 Street Scene

1995. "A City of Cathay" (Chinese scroll painting). Multicoloured.
2057 90c. Type **290** 55 60
2058 90c. Street scene and city wall 55 60
2059 90c. City gate and bridge . . 55 60
2060 90c. Landing stage and junk 55 60
2061 90c. River bridge 55 60
2062 90c. Moored junks 55 60
2063 90c. Two rafts on river . . 55 60
2064 90c. Two junks on river . . 55 60
2065 90c. Roadside tea house . . 55 60
2066 90c. Wedding party on the road 55 60

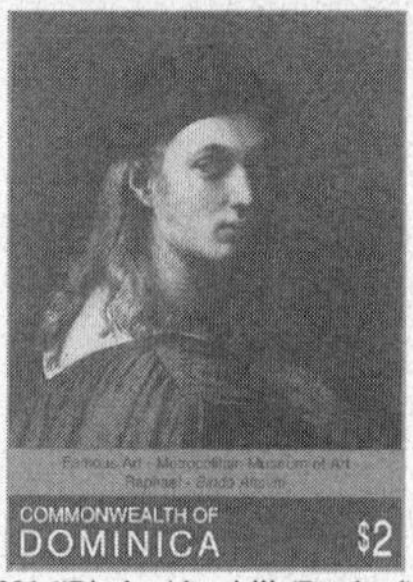

291 "Bindo Altoviti" (Raphael)

1995. Paintings by Raphael. Multicoloured.
2068 $2 Type **291** . . . . 1·40 1·40
2069 $2 "Pope Leo with Nephews" . . . . 1·40 1·40
2070 $2 "Agony in the Garden" 1·40 1·40

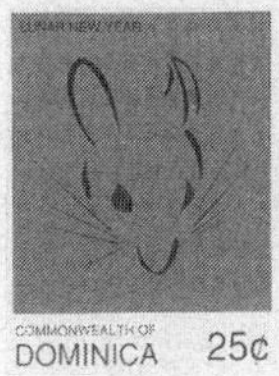

292 Rat

1996. Chinese New Year ("Year of the Rat").
2072 **292** 25c. black, violet and brown 15 20
2073 – 65c. black, red and green 35 40
2074 – $1 black, mauve and blue 50 55
DESIGNS: 65c., $1, Rats and Chinese symbols (different).

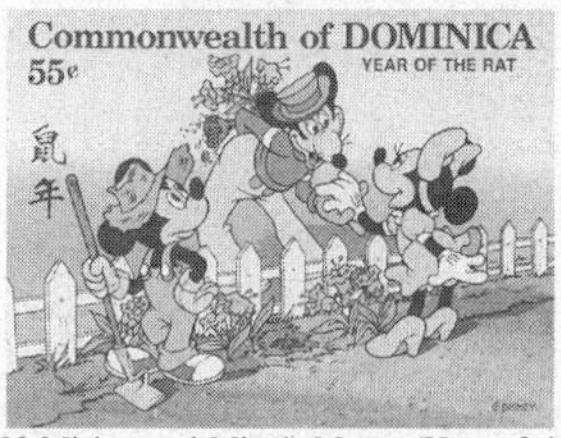

293 Mickey and Minnie Mouse (Year of the Rat)

1996. Chinese Lunar Calendar. Walt Disney Cartoon Characters. Multicoloured.
2077 55c. Type **293** 60 65
2078 55c. Casey Jones (Year of the Ox) 60 65
2079 55c. Tigger, Pooh and Piglet (Year of the Tiger) . . . 60 65
2080 55c. White Rabbit (Year of the Rabbit) 60 65
2081 55c. Dragon playing flute (Year of the Dragon) . . 60 65
2082 55c. Snake looking in mirror (Year of the Snake) . . . 60 65
2083 55c. Horace Horsecollar and Clarabelle Cow (Year of the Horse) 60 65
2084 55c. Black Lamb and blue birds (Year of the Ram) 60 65
2085 55c. King Louis reading book (Year of the Monkey) 60 65
2086 55c. Cock playing lute (Year of the Cock) 60 65
2087 55c. Mickey and Pluto (Year of the Dog) 60 65
2088 55c. Pig building bridge (Year of the Pig) 60 65

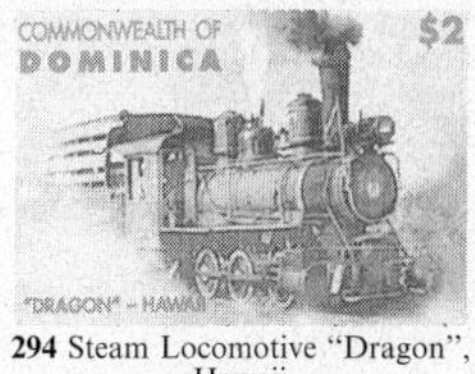

294 Steam Locomotive "Dragon", Hawaii

1996. Trains of the World. Multicoloured.
2090 $2 Type **294** . . . . 1·00 1·10
2091 $2 Class 685 steam locomotive "Regina", Italy . . . . 1·00 1·10
2092 $2 Class 745 steam locomotive, Calazo to Padua line, Italy . . . . 1·00 1·10
2093 $2 Mogul steam locomotive, Philippines . . . . 1·00 1·10
2094 $2 Class 23 and 24 steam locomotives, Germany . . 1·00 1·10
2095 $2 Class BB-15000 electric locomotive "Stanislaus", France . . . . 1·00 1·10
2096 $2 Class "Black Five" steam locomotive, Scotland . . 1·00 1·10
2097 $2 Diesel-electric locomotive, France . . . . 1·00 1·10
2098 $2 LNER class A4 steam locomotive "Sir Nigel Gresley", England . . . . 1·00 1·10
2099 $2 Class 9600 steam locomotive, Japan . . . . 1·00 1·10
2100 $2 "Peloponnese Express" train, Greece . . . . . . 1·00 1·10
2101 $2 Porter type steam locomotive, Hawaii . . . . . 1·00 1·10
2102 $2 Steam locomotive "Holand", Norway . . . 1·00 1·10
2103 $2 Class 220 diesel-hydraulic locomotive, Germany . . 1·00 1·10
2104 $2 Steam locomotive, India 1·00 1·10
2105 $2 East African Railways Class 29 steam locomotive 1·00 1·10
2106 $2 Electric trains, Russia . . 1·00 1·10
2107 $2 Steam locomotive, Austria . . . . 1·00 1·10

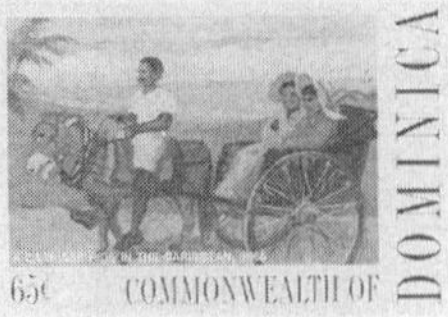

295 Horse-drawn Gig, 1965

1996. Traditional Island Transport. Multicoloured.

2109	65c. Type **295**	70	35
2110	90c. Early automobile, 1910	85	55
2111	$2 Lorry, 1950	1·50	1·75
2112	$3 Bus, 1955	1·75	2·25

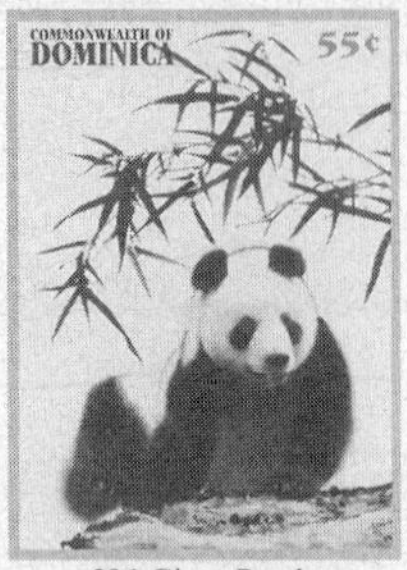

296 Giant Panda

1996. "CHINA '96" 9th Asian International Stamp Exhibition, Peking. Giant Pandas. Multicoloured.

2113	55c. Type **296**	30	35
2114	55c. Panda on rock	30	35
2115	55c. Panda eating bamboo shoots	30	35
2116	55c. Panda on all fours	30	35

1996. 70th Birthday of Queen Elizabeth II. As T **364** of Antigua. Multicoloured.

2118	$2 As Type **364** of Antigua	1·00	1·10
2119	$2 Queen in robes of Order of St. Michael and St. George	1·00	1·10
2120	$2 Queen in blue dress with floral brooch	1·00	1·10

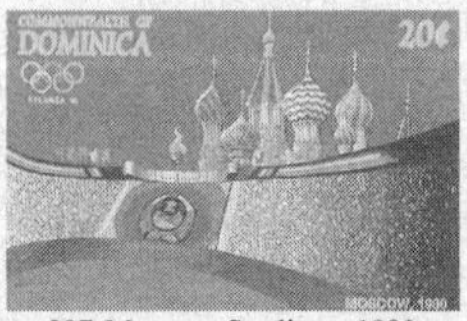

297 Moscow Stadium, 1980

1996. Olympic Games, Atlanta (2nd issue). Multicoloured.

2122	20c. Type **297**	10	15
2123	25c. Hermine Joseph (running) (vert)	15	20
2124	55c. Zimbabwe women's hockey team, 1980	30	35
2125	90c. Jerome Romain (long jump) (vert)	45	50
2126	90c. Sammy Lee (diving), 1948 and 1952 (vert)	45	50
2127	90c. Bruce Jenner (decathalon), 1976 (vert)	45	50
2128	90c. Olga Korbut (gymnastics), 1972 (vert)	45	50
2129	90c. Steffi Graff (tennis), 1988 (vert)	45	50
2130	90c. Florence Griffith-Joyner (track and field), 1988 (vert)	45	50
2131	90c. Mark Spitz (swimming), 1968 and 1972 (vert)	45	50
2132	90c. Li Ning (gymnastics), 1984 (vert)	45	50
2133	90c. Erika Salumae (cycling), 1988 (vert)	45	50
2134	90c. Abebe Bikila (marathon), 1960 and 1964 (vert)	45	50
2135	90c. Ulrike Meyfarth (high jump), 1972 and 1984 (vert)	45	50
2136	90c. Pat McCormick (diving), 1952 and 1956 (vert)	45	50
2137	90c. Takeichi Nishi (equestrian), 1932 (vert)	45	50
2138	90c. Peter Farkas (Greco-Roman wrestling), 1992 (vert)	45	50
2139	90c. Carl Lewis (track and field), 1984, 1988 and 1992 (vert)	45	50
2140	90c. Agnes Keleti (gymnastics), 1952 and 1956 (vert)	45	50
2141	90c. Yasuhiro Yamashita (judo), 1984 (vert)	45	50
2142	90c. John Kelly (single sculls), 1920 (vert)	45	50
2143	90c. Naim Suleymanoglu (weightlifting), 1988 and 1992 (vert)	45	50
2144	$1 Polo (vert)	50	55
2145	$2 Greg Louganis (diving), 1976, 1984 and 1988	1·00	1·10

Nos. 2126/34 and 2135/43 respectively were printed together, se-tenant, the backgrounds forming composite designs.

1996. 50th Anniv of U.N.I.C.E.F. As T **366** of Antigua. Multicoloured.

2147	20c. Child and globe (horiz)	10	15
2148	55c. Child with syringe and stethoscope (horiz)	30	35
2149	$5 Doctor and child (horiz)	2·50	2·75

1996. Centenary of Radio. Entertainers. As T **368** of Antigua. Multicoloured.

2153	90c. Artie Shaw	45	50
2154	$1 Benny Goodman	50	55
2155	$2 Duke Ellington	1·00	1·10
2156	$4 Harry James	2·00	2·10

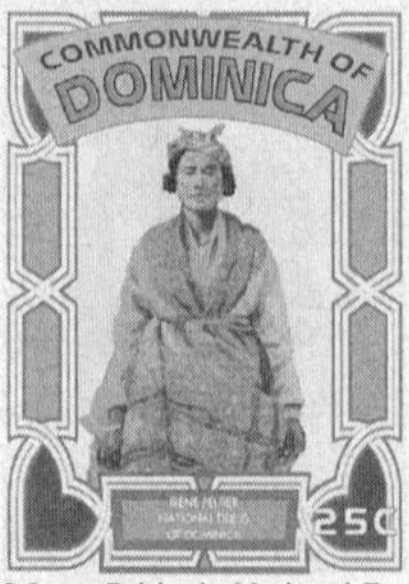

298 Irene Peltier in National Dress

1996. Local Entertainers. Multicoloured.

2158	25c. Type **298**	15	20
2159	55c. Rupert Bartley (steel-band player)	30	35
2160	65c. Rosemary Cools-Lartigue (pianist)	35	40
2161	90c. Celestine 'Orion' Theophile (singer)	45	50
2162	$1 Cecil Bellot (band master)	50	55

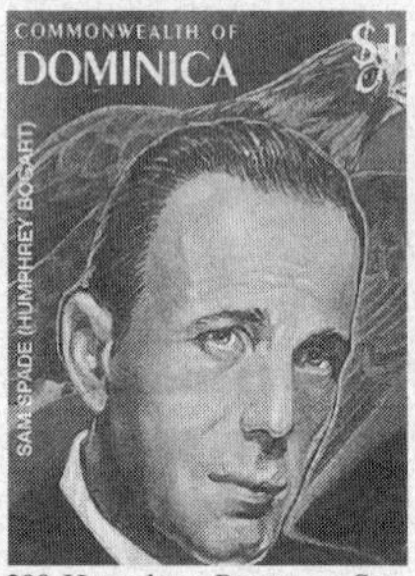

299 Humphrey Bogart as Sam Spade

1996. Centenary of Cinema. Screen Detectives. Multicoloured.

2163	$1 Type **299**	50	55
2164	$1 Sean Connery as James Bond	50	55
2165	$1 Warren Beatty as Dick Tracy	50	55
2166	$1 Basil Rathbone as Sherlock Holmes	50	55
2167	$1 William Powell as the Thin Man	50	55
2168	$1 Sidney Toler as Charlie Chan	50	55
2169	$1 Peter Sellers as Inspector Clouseau	50	55
2170	$1 Robert Mitchum as Philip Marlowe	50	55
2171	$1 Peter Ustinov as Hercule Poirot	50	55

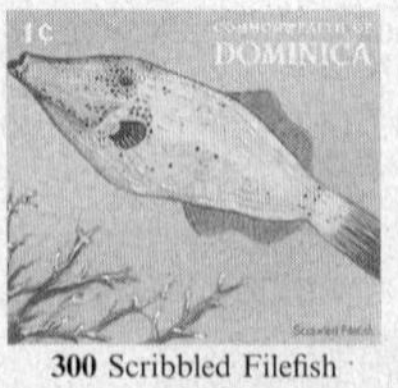

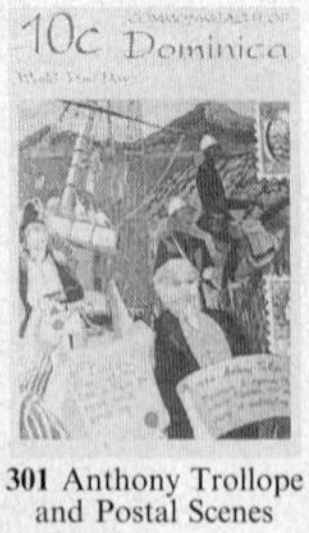

300 Scribbled Filefish **301** Anthony Trollope and Postal Scenes

1996. Fishes. Multicoloured.

2173	1c. Type **300**	10	10
2174	2c. Lionfish	10	10
2175	5c. Porcupinefish	10	10
2176	10c. Powder-blue surgeon fish	10	10
2177	15c. Red hind	10	15
2178	20c. Golden butterflyfish	10	15
2179	25c. Copper-banded butterflyfish	15	20
2180	35c. Pennant coralfish	20	25
2181	45c. Spotted drum	25	30
2182	55c. Blue-girdled angelfish	30	35
2183	60c. Scorpionfish	30	35
2184	65c. Harlequin sweetlips	35	40
2185	90c. Flame angelfish	45	50
2186	$1 Queen triggerfish	50	55
2187	$1.20 Spotlight parrotfish	60	65
2188	$1.45 Black durgon	75	80
2189	$2 Glass-eyed snapper	1·00	1·10
2190	$5 Balloonfish	2·50	2·75
2191	$10 Creole wrasse	5·00	5·25
2192	$20 Sea bass	10·00	10·50

For these designs size 24×21 mm, see Nos. 2374/91.

1996. World Post Day. Multicoloured.

2193	10c. Type **301**	10	10
2194	25c. Anthony Trollope and Dominican postmen	15	20
2195	55c. "Yare" (mail streamer)	30	35
2196	65c. Rural post office	35	40
2197	90c. Postmen carrying mail	45	50
2198	$1 Grumman Goose (seaplane) and 1958 Caribbean Federation 12c. stamp	50	55
2199	$2 Old and new post offices and 1978 Independence 10c. stamp	1·00	1·10

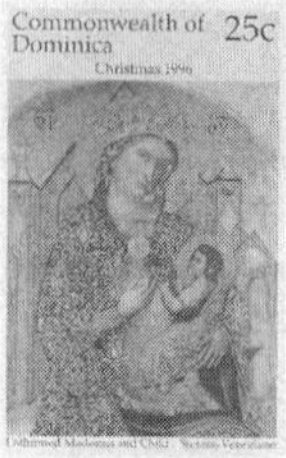

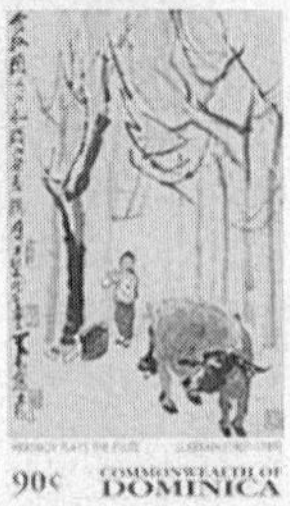

302 "Enthroned Madonna and Child" (S. Veneziano) **303** "Herdboy playing the Flute" (Li Keran)

1996. Christmas. Religious Paintings. Mult.

2201	25c. Type **302**	15	20
2202	55c. "Noli Me Tangere" (Fra Angelico)	30	35
2203	65c. "Madonna and Child Enthroned" (Angelico)	35	40
2204	90c. "Madonna of Corneto Tarquinia" (F. Lippi)	45	50
2205	$2 "The Annunciation" and "The Adoration of the Magi" (School of Angelico)	1·00	1·10
2206	$5 "Madonna and Child of the Shade" (Angelico)	2·50	2·75

1997. Lunar New Year ("Year of the Ox"). Paintings by Li Keran. Multicoloured.

2208	90c. Type **303**	45	50
2209	90c. "Playing Cricket in the Autumn"	45	50
2210	90c. "Listening to the Summer Cicada"	45	50
2211	90c. "Grazing in the Spring"	45	50

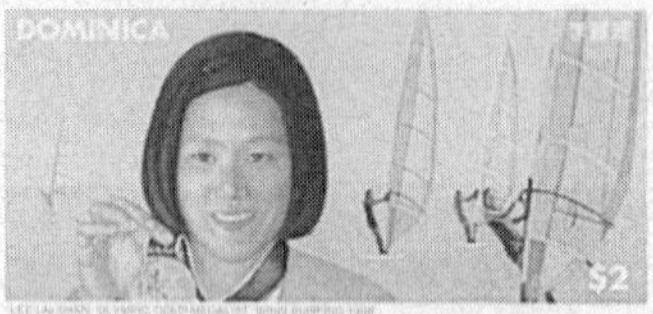

304 Lee Lai-shan (Gold Medal – Windsurfing, 1996)

1997. Olympic Games, Atlanta (3rd issue).

2213	**304** $2 multicoloured	1·00	1·10

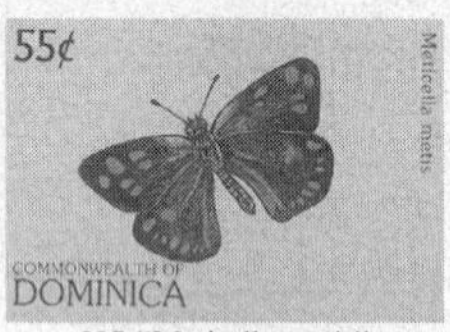

305 "Meticella metis"

1997. Butterflies. Multicoloured.

2215	55c. Type **305**	30	35
2216	55c. "Coeliades forestan"	30	35
2217	55c. "Papilio dardanus"	30	35
2218	55c. "Mylothris chloris"	30	35
2219	55c. "Poecilmitis thysbe"	30	35
2220	55c. "Myrina silenus"	30	35
2221	55c. "Bematistes aganice"	30	35
2222	55c. "Euphaedra neophron"	30	35
2223	55c. "Precis hierta"	30	35
2224	90c. "Coeliadas forestan" (vert)	45	50
2225	90c. "Spialia spio" (vert)	45	50
2226	90c. "Belenois aurota" (vert)	45	50
2227	90c. "Dingana bowkom" (vert)	45	50
2228	90c. "Charaxes jasius" (vert)	45	50
2229	90c. "Catacroptera cloanthe" (vert)	45	50
2230	90c. "Colias electo" (vert)	45	50
2231	90c. "Junonia archesia" (vert)	45	50

No. 2230 is inscribed "Collas electo" in error.

Nos. 2215/23 and 2224/31 respectively were printed together, se-tenant, with the backgrounds forming a composite design.

1997. 50th Anniv of U.N.E.S.C.O. As T **374** of Antigua. Multicoloured.

2233	55c. Temple roof, China	30	35
2234	65c. The Palace of Diocletian, Split, Croatia	35	40
2235	90c. St. Mary's Cathedral, Hildesheim, Germany	45	50
2236	$1 The Monastery of Rossanou, Mount Athos, Greece	50	55
2237	$1 Carved face, Copan, Honduras (vert)	50	55
2238	$1 Cuzco Cathedral, Peru (vert)	50	55
2239	$1 Church, Olinda, Brazil (vert)	50	55
2240	$1 Canaima National Park, Venezuela (vert)	50	55
2241	$1 Galapagos Islands National Park, Ecuador (vert)	50	55
2242	$1 Church ruins, La Santisima Jesuit Missions, Paraguay (vert)	50	55
2243	$1 San Lorenzo Fortress, Panama (vert)	50	55
2244	$1 Fortress, National Park, Haiti (vert)	50	55
2245	$2 Scandola Nature Reserve, France	1·00	1·10
2246	$4 Church of San Antao, Portugal	2·00	2·10

No. 2234 is inscr "DICELECIAN" in error.

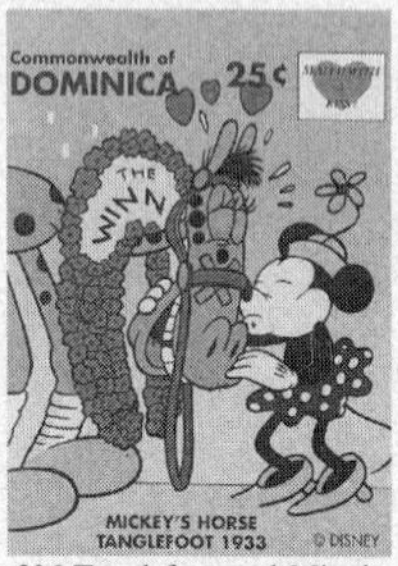

306 Tanglefoot and Minnie

1997. Disney Sweethearts. Multicoloured.

2248	25c. Type **306**	35	20
2249	35c. Mickey and Minnie kissing on ship's wheel	45	20
2250	55c. Pluto and kitten	60	30
2251	65c. Clarabelle Cow kissing Horace Horsecollar	60	35
2252	90c. Elmer Elephant and tiger	75	55
2253	$1 Minnie kissing Mickey in period costume	80	70
2254	$2 Donald Duck and nephew	1·40	1·60
2255	$4 Dog kissing Pluto	2·00	2·75

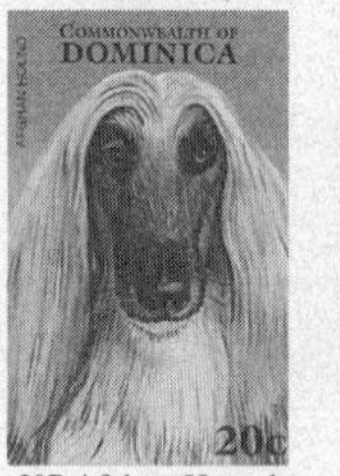

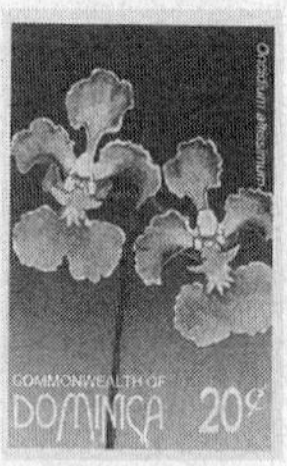

307 Afghan Hound **308** "Oncidium altissimum"

1997. Cats and Dogs. Multicoloured.

2257	20c. Type **307**	10	15
2258	25c. Cream Burmese	15	20
2259	55c. Cocker spaniel	30	35
2260	65c. Smooth fox terrier	35	40
2261	90c. West highland white terrier	45	50
2262	90c. St. Bernard puppies	45	50
2263	90c. Boy with grand basset	45	50
2264	90c. Rough collie	45	50
2265	90c. Golden retriever	45	50
2266	90c. Golden retriever, Tibetan spaniel and smooth fox terrier	45	50
2267	90c. Smooth fox terrier	45	50
2268	$1 Snowshoe	50	55
2269	$2 Sorrell Abyssinian	1·00	1·10
2270	$2 British bicolour shorthair	1·00	1·10
2271	$2 Maine coon and Somali kittens	1·00	1·10
2272	$2 Maine coon kitten	1·00	1·10
2273	$2 Lynx point Siamese	1·00	1·10
2274	$2 Blue Burmese kitten and white Persian	1·00	1·10
2275	$2 Persian kitten	1·00	1·10
2276	$5 Torbie Persian	2·50	2·75

Nos. 2262/7 and 2270/5 respectively were printed together, se-tenant, with the backgrounds forming composite designs.

1997. Orchids of the Caribbean. Multicoloured.

2278	20c. Type **308**	10	15
2279	25c. "Oncidium papilio"	15	20
2280	55c. "Epidendrum fragrans"	30	35
2281	65c. "Oncidium lanceanum"	35	40
2282	90c. "Campylocentrum micranthum'	45	50
2283	$1 "Brassavola cucculata" (horiz)	50	55
2284	$1 "Epidendrum ibaguense" (horiz)	50	55
2285	$1 "Ionopsis utricularioides" (horiz)	50	55
2286	$1 "Rodriguezia lanceolata" (horiz)	50	55
2287	$1 "Oncidium cebolleta" (horiz)	50	55

DOMINICA 933

2288 $1 "Epidendrum ciliare" (horiz) 50 55
2289 $4 "Pogonia rosea" . . . . 2·00 2·10
Nos. 2283/8 were printed together, se-tenant, with the backgrounds forming a composite design.

1997. 10th Anniv of Chernobyl Nuclear Disaster. As T **376** of Antigua. Multicoloured.
2292 $2 As Type **376** of Antigua 1·00 1·10
2293 $2 As Type **376** of Antigua but inscribed "CHABAD'S CHILDREN OF CHERNOBYL" at foot 1·00 1·10

1997. 50th Death Anniv of Paul Harris (founder of Rotary International). As T **377** of Antigua. Multicoloured.
2294 $2 Paul Harris and irrigation project, Honduras . . . . 1·00 1·10

1997. Golden Wedding of Queen Elizabeth and Prince Philip. As T **378** of Antigua. Multicoloured.
2296 $1 Queen Elizabeth II . . . 50 55
2297 $1 Royal Coat of Arms . . 50 55
2298 $1 Queen Elizabeth and Prince Philip in shirt sleeves 50 55
2299 $1 Queen Elizabeth and Prince Philip in naval uniform 50 55
2300 $1 Buckingham Palace . . . 50 55
2301 $1 Prince Philip 50 55

1997. "Pacific '97" International Stamp Exhibition, San Francisco. Death Centenary of Heinrich von Stephan (founder of the U.P.U.). As T **379** of Antigua.
2303 $2 violet . . . . 1·00 1·10
2304 $2 brown . . . . 1·00 1·10
2305 $2 brown . . . . 1·00 1·10
DESIGNS: No. 2303, Kaiser Wilhelm II and Heinrich von Stephan; 2304, Heinrich von Stephan and Mercury; 2305, Early Japanese postal messenger.

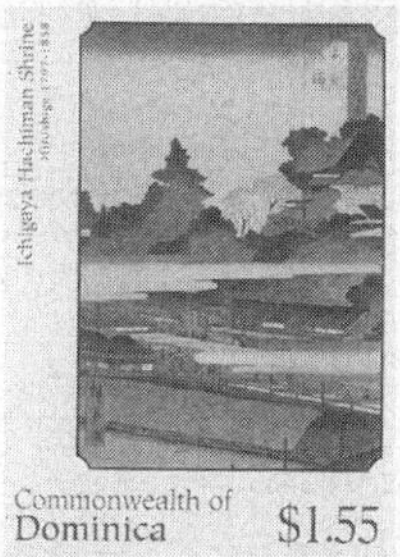
Ichigaya Hachiman Shrine
Commonwealth of Dominica $1.55
310 "Ichigaya Hachiman Shrine"

1997. Birth Centenary of Hiroshige (Japanese painter). "One Hundred Famous Views of Edo". Multicoloured.
2307 $1.55 Type **310** 80 85
2308 $1.55 "Blossoms on the Tama River Embankment" 80 85
2309 $1.55 "Kumano Junisha Shrine, Tsunohazu" . . . 80 85
2310 $1.55 "Benkei Moat from Soto-Sakurada to Kojimachi" 80 85
2311 $1.55 "Kinokuni Hill and View of Akasak Tameike" 80 85
2312 $1.55 "Naito Shinjuku, Yotsuya" 80 85

1997. 175th Anniv of Brothers Grimm's Third Collection of Fairy Tales. The Goose Girl. As T **380** of Antigua. Multicoloured.
2314 $2 Goose girl with horse . . 1·00 1·10
2315 $2 Geese in front of castle 1·00 1·10
2316 $2 Goose girl . . . . 1·00 1·10

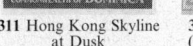

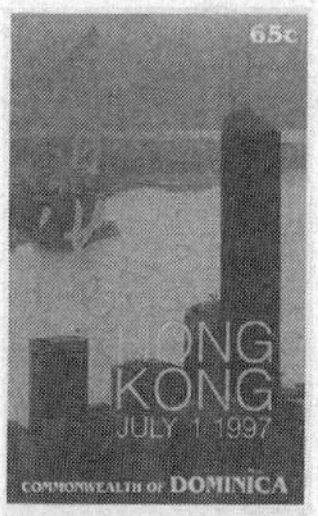
65c
HONG KONG
JULY 1 1997
COMMONWEALTH OF DOMINICA
311 Hong Kong Skyline at Dusk

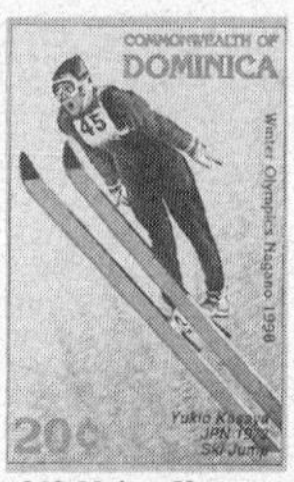
COMMONWEALTH OF
DOMINICA
20¢
312 Yukto Kasaya (Japan) (ski jump), 1972

1997. Return of Hong Kong to China. Multicoloured.
2318 65c. Type **311** 35 40
2319 90c. Type **311** 45 50
2320 $1 Type **311** 50 55
2321 $1 Hong Kong at night . . 50 55
2322 $1.45 Hong Kong by day 75 80
2323 $2 Hong Kong at night (different) . . . . 1·00 1·10
2324 $3 Type **311** . . . . . . 1·50 1·60

1997. Winter Olympic Games, Nagano, Japan (1998). Multicoloured.
2325 20c. Type **312** 10 15
2326 25c. Jens Weissflog (Germany) (ski jump), 1994 . . . . 15 20
2327 55c. Anton Maier (Norway) (100 m men's speed skating), 1968 . . . . . 30 35
2328 55c. Ljubov Egorova (Russia) (women's 5 km cross-country skiing), 1994 30 35
2329 65c. Swedish ice hockey, 1994 . . . . 35 40
2330 90c. Bernhard Glass (Germany) (men's single luge), 1980 . . . . 45 50
2331 $1 Type **312** 50 55
2332 $1 As No. 2326 . . . . . . 50 55
2333 $1 As No. 2327 . . . . . . 50 55
2334 $1 Christa Rethenburger (Germany) (women's 100 m speed skating), 1988 . . . . 50 55
2335 $4 Frank-Peter Roetsch (Germany) (men's biathlon), 1988 . . . . . 2·00 2·10

1997. World Cup Football Championship, France (1998). As T **383** of Antigua. Multicoloured (except Nos. 2343/4, 2348, 2350, 2353/4).
2337 20c. Klinsmann, Germany (vert) 10 15
2338 55c. Bergkamp, Holland (vert) 30 35
2339 65c. Ravanelli, Italy (vert) 35 40
2340 65c. Wembley Stadium, England 35 40
2341 65c. Bernabeu Stadium, Spain 35 40
2342 65c. Maracana Stadium, Brazil 35 40
2343 65c. Stadio Torino, Italy (black) 35 40
2344 65c. Centenary Stadium, Uruguay (black) 35 40
2345 65c. Olympiastadion, Germany 35 40
2346 65c. Rose Bowl, U.S.A. . . 35 40
2347 65c. Azteca Stadium, Mexico 35 40
2348 65c. Meazza, Italy (black) 35 40
2349 65c. Matthaus, Germany . . 35 40
2350 65c. Walter, West Germany (black) 35 40
2351 65c. Maradona, Argentina 35 40
2352 65c. Beckenbaur, Germany 35 40
2353 65c. Moore, England (black) 35 40
2354 65c. Dunga, Brazil (black) 35 40
2355 65c. Zoff, Italy 35 40
2356 90c. Klinkladze, Georgia . . 45 50
2357 $2 Shearer, England (vert) 1·00 1·10
2358 $4 Dani, Portugal (vert) . . 2·00 2·10

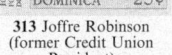

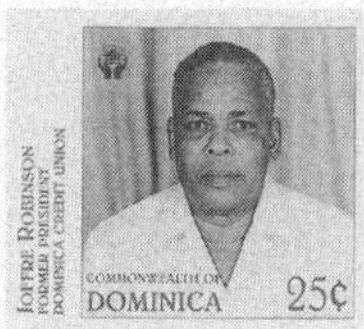
JOFFRE ROBINSON
FORMER PRESIDENT
DOMINICA CREDIT UNION
COMMONWEALTH OF
DOMINICA 25¢
313 Joffre Robinson (former Credit Union President)

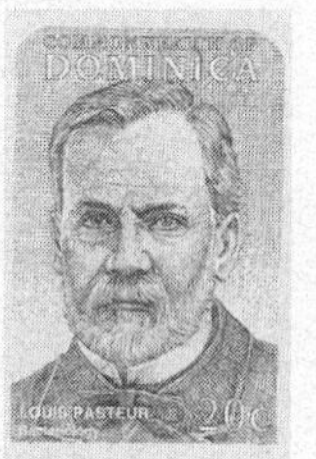
DOMINICA
LOUIS PASTEUR
20¢
314 Louis Pasteur

1997. 40th Anniv of Co-operative Credit Union League.
2360 **313** 25c. blue and black . . . 15 20
2361 – 55c. green and black . . 30 35
2362 – 65c. purple and black . . 35 40
2363 – 90c. multicoloured . . . 45 50
DESIGNS—As T **313**: 55c. Sister Alicia (founder); 65c. Lorrel Bruce (first Credit Union President). 30 × 60 mm: $5 Sister Alicia, Joffre Robinson and Lorrel Bruce.

1997. Medical Pioneers.
2365 **314** 20c. brown 10 15
2366 – 25c. pink and red . . . 15 20
2367 – 55c. violet 30 35
2368 – 65c. red and brown . . . 35 40
2369 – 90c. yellow and olive . . 45 50
2370 – $1 blue and ultramarine 50 55
2371 – $2 black . . . . 1·00 1·10
2372 – $3 red and brown . . . 1·50 1·60
DESIGNS: 25c. Christiaan Barnard (first heart transplant); 55c. Sir Alexander Fleming (discovery of penicillin); 65c. Camillo Golgi (neurologist); 90c. Jonas Salk (discovery of polio vaccine); $1 Har Gobind Khorana (genetics); $2 Elizabeth Black (first woman doctor); $3 Sir Frank MacFarlane Burnet (immunologist).

1997. Fishes. As Nos. 2175/92, but smaller, 24 × 21mm.
2374 5c. Porcupinefish 10 10
2375 10c. Powder-blue surgeonfish 10 10
2376 15c. Red hind 10 15
2377 20c. Golden butterflyfish . . 10 15
2378 25c. Copper-banded butterflyfish 15 20
2379 35c. Pennant coralfish . . . 20 25
2380 45c. Spotted drum 25 30
2381 55c. Blue-girdled angelfish 30 35
2382 60c. Scorpionfish 30 35
2383 65c. Harlequin sweetlips . . 35 40
2384 90c. Flame angelfish 45 50
2385 $1 Queen triggerfish 50 55
2386 $1.20 Spotlight parrotfish 60 65
2387 $1.45 Black durgon 75 80
2388 $2 Glass-eyed snapper . . . 1·00 1·10
2389 $5 Balloonfish . . . . . . 2·50 2·75
2390 $10 Creole wrasse . . . . . 5·00 5·25
2391 $20 Seabass . . . . 10·00 10·50

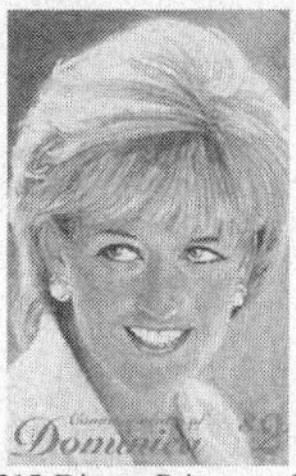
Dominica
315 Diana, Princess of Wales

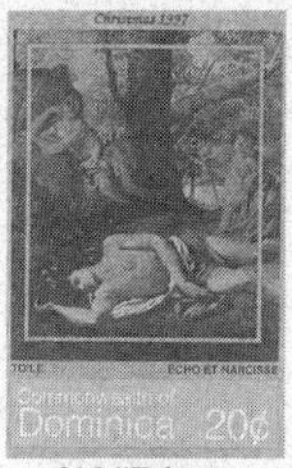
Christmas 1997
TOILE ECHO ET NARCISSE
Commonwealth of
Dominica 20¢
316 "Echo et Narcisse" (Toile)

1997. Diana, Princess of Wales Commemoration. Multicoloured.
2392 $2 Type **315** . . . . 1·00 1·10
2393 $2 Wearing diamond-drop earrings . . . . 1·00 1·10
2394 $2 Resting head on hand . . 1·00 1·10
2395 $2 Wearing tiara . . . . . 1·00 1·10

1997. Christmas. Paintings.
2397 20c. Type **316** 10 15
2398 55c. "The Archangel Raphael leaving the Family of Tobias" (Rembrandt) 30 35
2399 65c. "Seated Nymphs with Flute" (Francois Boucher) 35 40
2400 90c. "Angel" (Rembrandt) 45 50
2401 $2 "Dispute" (Raphael) . . 1·00 1·10
2402 $4 "Holy Trinity" (Raphael) 2·00 2·10

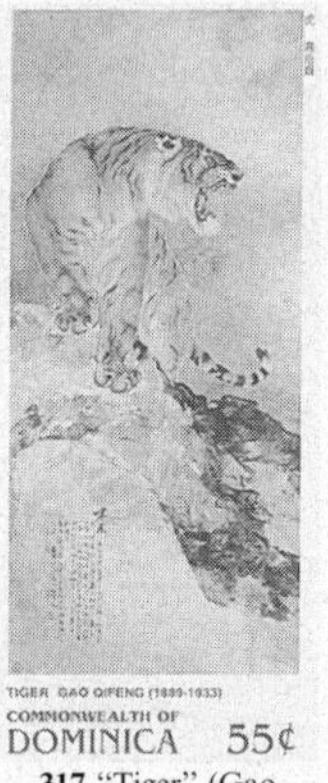
TIGER GAO QIFENG (1889-1933)
COMMONWEALTH OF
DOMINICA 55¢
317 "Tiger" (Gao Qifeng)

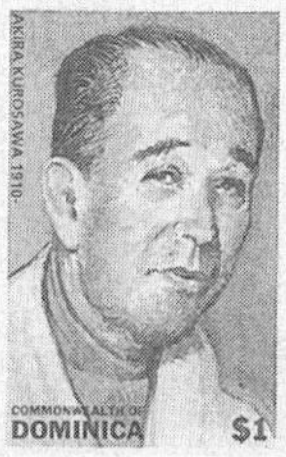
AKIRA KUROSAWA 1910-
DOMINICA $1
318 Akira Kurosawa

1998. Chinese New Year ("Year of the Tiger"). Multicoloured.
2404 55c. Type **317** 30 35
2405 65c. "Tiger" (Zhao Shao'ang) 35 40
2406 90c. "Tiger" (Gao Jianfu) 45 50
2407 $1.20 "Tiger" (different) (Gao Jianfu) 60 65

1998. Millennium Series. Famous People of the Twentieth Century. Multicoloured (except Nos. 2410 and 2413/14). (a) Japanese Cinema Stars.
2409 $1 Type **318** 50 55
2410 $1 "Rashomon" directed by Kursawa (56 × 42 mm) . . 50 55
2411 $1 Toshiro Mifune in "Seven Samurai" (black and grey) (56 × 42 mm) 50 55
2412 $1 Toshiro Mifune 50 55
2413 $1 Yasujiro Ozu 50 55
2414 $1 "Late Spring" directed by Ozu (black and grey) (56 × 42 mm) 50 55
2415 $1 Sessue Hayakawa in "Bridge on the River Kwai" (brown, deep brown and black) (56 × 42 mm) 50 55
2416 $1 Sessue Hayakawa 50 55

(b) Sporting Record Holders. Multicoloured.
2418 $1 Jesse Owens (winner of four Olympic gold medals, Berlin, 1936) 50 55
2419 $1 Owens competing at Berlin (56 × 42 mm) . . . 50 55
2420 $1 Isaac Berger competing (56 × 42 mm) 50 55
2421 $1 Isaac Berger (weightlifter) 50 55
2422 $1 Boris Becker (Wimbledon champion) 50 55
2423 $1 Boris Becker on court (56 × 42 mm) 50 55
2424 $1 Ashe with Wimbledon trophy (56 × 42 mm) . . . 50 55
2425 $1 Arthur Ashe (1st African-American Wimbledon singles champion, 1975) 50 55

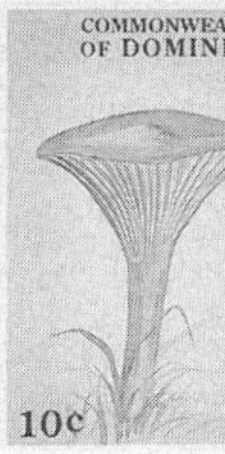
COMMONWEALTH
OF DOMINICA
Omphalotus illudens
10¢
319 "Omphalotus illudens"

1998. Fungi of the World. Multicoloured.
2427 10c. Type **319** 10 10
2428 15c. "Inocybe fastigiata" . . 10 15
2429 20c. "Marasmius plicatulus" 10 15
2430 50c. "Mycena lilacifolia" . . 25 30
2431 55c. "Armillaria straminea" and "Calastrina argiolus" (butterfly) 30 35
2432 90c. "Tricholomopsis rutilans" and "Melitaea didyma" (butterfly) . . . 45 50
2433 $1 "Lepiota naucina" . . . 50 55
2434 $1 "Cortinarius violaceus" 50 55
2435 $1 "Boletus aereus" 50 55
2436 $1 "Tricholoma aurantium" 50 55
2437 $1 "Lepiota procera" . . . 50 55
2438 $1 "Clitocybe geotropa" . . 50 55
2439 $1 "Lepiota acutesquamosa" 50 55
2440 $1 "Tricholoma saponaceum" 50 55
2441 $1 "Lycoperdon gemmatum" 50 55
2442 $1 "Boletus ornatipes" . . . 50 55
2443 $1 "Russula xerampelina" 50 55
2444 $1 "Cortinarius collinitus" 50 55
2445 $1 "Agaricus meleagris" . . 50 55
2446 $1 "Coprinus comatus" . . 50 55
2447 $1 "Amanita caesarea" . . 50 55
2448 $1 "Amanita brunnescens" 50 55
2449 $1 "Amanita muscaria" . . 50 55
2450 $1 "Morchella esculenta" . . 50 55
Nos. 2433/41 and 2442/50 respectively were printed together, se-tenant, with the backgrounds forming composite designs.

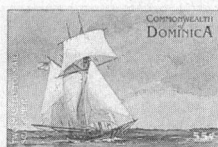

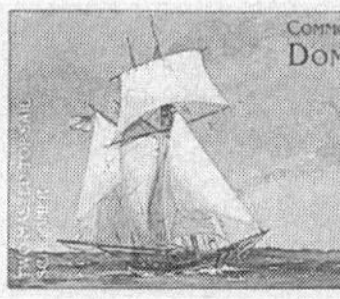
COMMONWEALTH
DOMINICA
320 Topsail Schooner

1998. History of Sailing Ships. Multicoloured.
2452 55c. Type **320** 30 35
2453 55c. "Golden Hind" (Drake) 30 35
2454 55c. "Moshulu" (barque) . . 30 35
2455 55c. "Bluenose" (schooner) 30 35
2456 55c. Roman merchant ship 30 35
2457 55c. "Gazela Primiero" (barquentine) 30 35
2458 65c. Greek war galley . . . 35 40
2459 90c. Egyptian felucca . . . 45 50
2460 $1 Viking longship 50 55
2461 $2 Chinese junk . . . . . . 1·00 1·10
No. 2457 is inscribed "GAZELA PRIMERIRO", and both Nos. 2458/9 "EGPYTIAN FELUCCA", all in error.

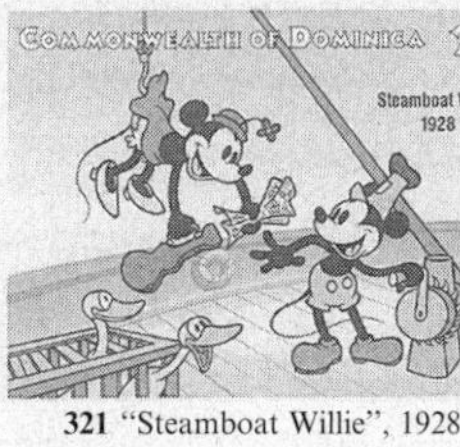
COMMONWEALTH OF DOMINICA 25¢
Steamboat Willie
1928
321 "Steamboat Willie", 1928

1998. 70th Anniv of Mickey and Minnie Mouse. Multicoloured.
2463 25c. Type **321** 70 75
2464 55c. "The Brave Little Tailor", 1938 . . . . . 85 90
2465 65c. "Nifty Nineties", 1941 90 95
2466 90c. "Mickey Mouse Club", 1955 . . . . 1·10 1·25
2467 $1 Mickey and Minnie at opening of Walt Disney World, 1971 . . . . . . 1·10 1·25
2468 $1.45 "Mousercise Mickey and Minnie", 1980 . . . 1·25 1·40
2469 $5 "Runaway Brain", 1995 (97 × 110 mm) . . . . . 2·50 2·75

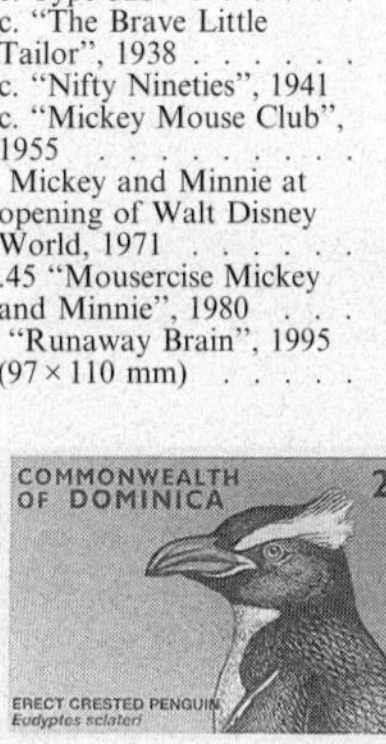
COMMONWEALTH
OF DOMINICA 25¢
ERECT CRESTED PENGUIN
Eudyptes sclateri
322 Big-crested Penguin ("Erect Crested Penguin")

1998. Sea Birds. Multicoloured.
2471 25c. Type **322** 15 20
2472 65c. Humboldt penguin . . 35 40
2473 90c. Knot 45 50
2474 90c. Crested tern 45 50
2475 90c. Franklin's gull 45 50

2476 90c. Australian pelican . . . 45 50
2477 90c. Fairy prion 45 50
2478 90c. Andean gull 45 50
2479 90c. Blue-eyed cormorant ("Imperial Shag") 45 50
2480 90c. Grey phalarope ("Red Phalarope") 45 50
2481 90c. Hooded grebe 45 50
2482 90c. Least auklet 45 50
2483 90c. Little grebe 45 50
2484 90c. Pintado petrel ("Cape Petrel") 45 50
2485 90c. Slavonian grebe ("Horned Grebe") 45 50
2486 $1 Audubon's shearwater 50 55

Nos. 2474/85 were printed together, se-tenant, with the backgrounds forming a composite design.

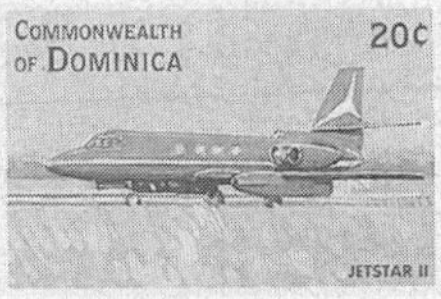

323 Jetstar II

1998. Modern Aircraft. Multicoloured.

2488 20c. Type **323** 10 15
2489 25c. AN 225 . . . . 15 20
2490 55c. L.I.A.T. Dash-8 . . . 30 35
2491 65c. Cardinal Airlines, Beech-99 . . . . 35 40
2492 90c. American Airlines Eagle 45 50
2493 $1 SR 71 "Blackbird" spy plane 50 55
2494 $1 Stealth Bomber 50 55
2495 $1 Northrop YF23 . . . . 50 55
2496 $1 F-14A Tomcat 50 55
2497 $1 F-15 Eagle S 50 55
2498 $1 MiG 29 Fulcrum 50 55
2499 $1 Europa X5 . . . . . . 50 55
2500 $1 Camion 50 55
2501 $1 E 400 . . . . 50 55
2502 $1 CL-215 C-GKDN amphibian 50 55
2503 $1 Piper Jet 50 55
2504 $1 Beech Hawker 50 55
2505 $1 Lockheed YF22 . . . . 50 55
2506 $1 Piper Seneca V 50 55
2507 $1 CL-215 amphibian . . . 50 55
2508 $1 Vantase 50 55
2509 $2 Itansa HFB 320 . . . . 1·00 1·10

1998. 50th Anniv of Organization of American States. As T **399** of Antigua. Multicoloured.

2511 $1 Stylised Americas 50 55

1998. 25th Death Anniv of Pablo Picasso (painter). As T **400** of Antigua. Multicoloured.

2512 90c. "The Painter and his Model" 45 50
2513 $1 "The Crucifixion" . . . 50 55
2514 $2 "Nude with Raised Arms" (vert) . . . . . . 1·00 1·10

1998. Birth Centenary of Enzo Ferrari (car manufacturer). As T **401** of Antigua. Mult.

2516 55c. 365 GT 2+2 . . . . . 60 40
2517 90c. Boano/Ellena 250 GT 80 80
2518 $1 375 MM coupe 90 90

1998. 19th World Scout Jamboree, Chile. As T **402** of Antigua. Multicoloured.

2520 65c. Scout saluting 35 40
2521 $1 Scout handshake 50 55
2522 $2 International scout flag 1·00 1·10

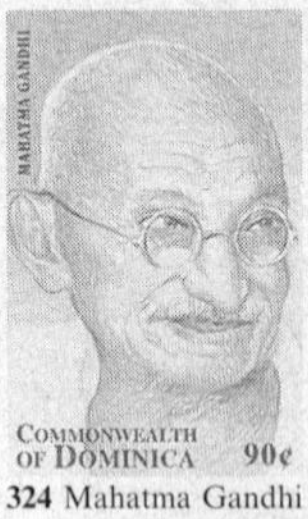

324 Mahatma Gandhi

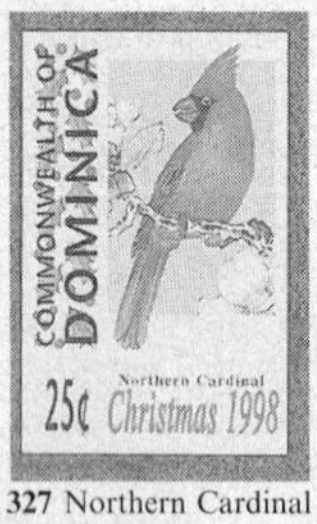

327 Northern Cardinal

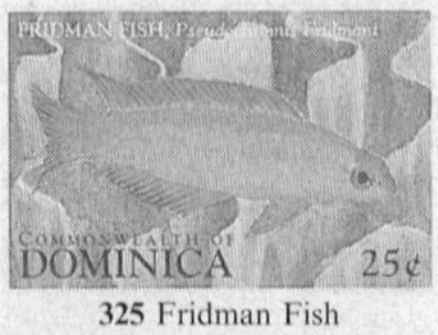

325 Fridman Fish

1998. 50th Death Anniv of Mahatma Gandhi. Multicoloured.

2524 **324** 90c. multicoloured . . . 45 50

1998. 80th Anniv of Royal Air Force. As T **404** of Antigua. Multicoloured.

2526 $2 H.S. 801 Nimrod MR2P (reconnaissance) . . . . . 1·00 1·10
2527 $2 Lockheed C-130 Hercules (transport) . . . . 1·00 1·10
2528 $2 Panavia Tornado GR1 1·00 1·10
2529 $2 Lockheed C-130 Hercules landing . . . . 1·00 1·10

No. 2529 is inscribed "Panavia Tornado GR1" in error.

1998. International Year of the Ocean. Multicoloured.

2531 25c. Type **325** 15 20
2532 55c. Hydrocoral 30 35
2533 65c. Feather-star 35 40
2534 90c. Royal angelfish 45 50
2535 $1 Monk seal 50 55
2536 $1 Galapagos penguin . . . 50 55
2537 $1 Manta ray 50 55
2538 $1 Hawksbill turtle 50 55
2539 $1 Moorish idols 50 55
2540 $1 Nautilius 50 55
2541 $1 Giant clam 50 55
2542 $1 Tubeworms 50 55
2543 $1 Nudibranch 50 55
2544 $1 Spotted dolphins 50 55
2545 $1 Atlantic sailfish 50 55
2546 $1 Sailfin flying fish 50 55
2547 $1 Fairy basslet 50 55
2548 $1 Atlantic spadefish . . . 50 55
2549 $1 Leatherback turtle . . . 50 55
2550 $1 Blue tang 50 55
2551 $1 Coral-banded shrimp . . 50 55
2552 $1 Rock beauty 50 55

Nos. 2535/43 and 2544/52 respectively were printed together, se-tenant, with the backgrounds forming composite designs.

1998. Save the Turtles Campaign. Nos. 1686/7, 1689/90 and 1692 optd **Save the Turtles**.

2554 25c. Type **263** 15 20
2555 55c. Hawksbill turtle swimming 30 35
2556 90c. Green turtle laying eggs 45 50
2557 $1 Green turtle swimming 50 55
2558 $4 Loggerhead turtle . . . 2·00 2·10

1998. Christmas. Birds. Multicoloured.

2559 25c. Type **327** 15 20
2560 55c. Eastern bluebird . . . 30 35
2561 65c. Carolina wren 35 40
2562 90c. Blue jay 45 50
2563 $1 Evening grosbeak 50 55
2564 $2 Bohemian waxwing . . . 1·00 1·10

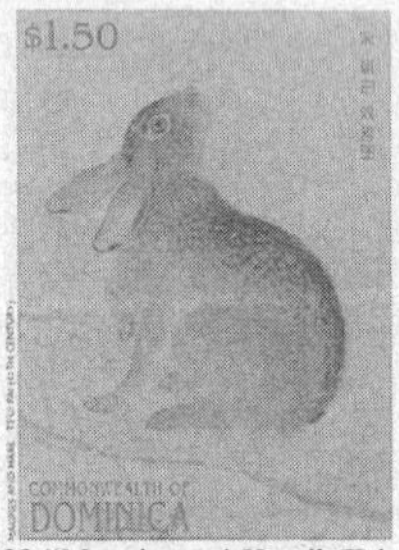

328 "Magpies and Hare" (Ts'ui Pai)

1999. Chinese New Year ("Year of the Rabbit").

2566 **328** $1.50 multicoloured . . 80 85

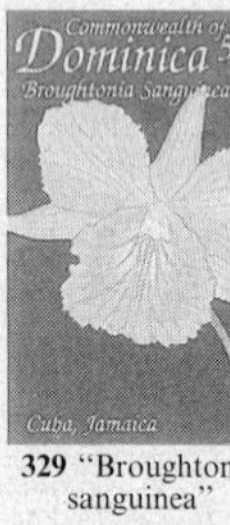

329 "Broughtonia sanguinea"

1999. Orchids of the Caribbean. Multicoloured.

2567 55c. Type **329** 30 35
2568 65c. "Cattleyonia Keith Roth" "Roma" 35 40
2569 90c. "Comparettia falcata" 45 50
2570 $1 "Dracula erythiochaete" 50 55
2571 $1 "Lycasle aromatica" . . 50 55
2572 $1 "Masdevallia marguerile" 50 55
2573 $1 "Encyclia marlae" . . . 50 55
2574 $1 "Laelia gouldiana" . . . 50 55
2575 $1 "Huntleya meleagris" . . 50 55
2576 $1 "Galeandria baueri" . . 50 55
2577 $1 "Lycale deppei" 50 55
2578 $1 "Anguloa clowesii" . . . 50 55
2579 $1 "Lemboglossum cervantesii" 50 55
2580 $1 "Oncidium cebolleta" . . 50 55
2581 $1 "Millonia" 50 55
2582 $1 "Pescatorea lehmannll" 50 55
2583 $1 "Sophronitis coccinea" 50 55
2584 $1 "Pescatorea cerina" . . . 50 55
2585 $1 "Encyclia vitellina" . . . 50 55
2586 $2 "Cochleanthes discolor" 50 55

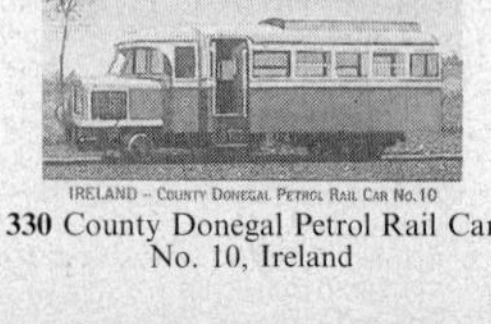

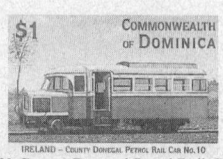

330 County Donegal Petrol Rail Car No. 10, Ireland

1999. "Australia '99" International Stamp Exhibition, Melbourne. Diesel and Electric Trains. Multicoloured.

2588 $1 Type **330** 50 55
2589 $1 Canadian Pacific rail car, Canada 50 55
2590 $1 Class WDM locomotive, India 50 55
2591 $1 Bi-polar locomotive, No. E-2, U.S.A. 50 55
2592 $1 Class X locomotive, Australia 50 55
2593 $1 Class "Beijing" locomotive, China 50 55
2594 $1 Class E428 locomotive, Italy 50 55
2595 $1 Class 581 twelve-car train, Japan 50 55
2596 $1 Class 103.1 locomotive, West Germany 50 55
2597 $1 Class 24 Trans-Pennine train, Great Britain . . . 50 55
2598 $1 Amtrak Class GG1, No. 902, U.S.A. 50 55
2599 $1 Class LRC train, Canada 50 55
2600 $1 Class EW train, New Zealand 50 55
2601 $1 Class SS1 Shao-Shani, China 50 55
2602 $1 Gulf, Mobile and Ohio train, U.S.A. 50 55
2603 $1 Class 9100 locomotive, France 50 55

No. 2589 is inscribed "USA - RDC Single Rail Car" in error.

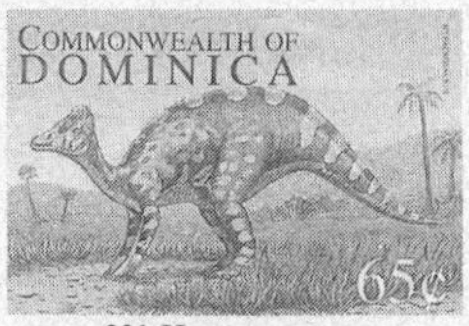

331 Hypacrosaurus

1999. Prehistoric Animals. Multicoloured.

2605 25c. Tyrannosaurus (vert) 15 20
2606 65c. Type **331** 35 40
2607 90c. Sauropelta 45 50
2608 $1 Barosaurus 50 55
2609 $1 Rhamphorhynchus . . . 50 55
2610 $1 Apatosaurus 50 55
2611 $1 Archaeopteryx 50 55
2612 $1 Diplodocus 50 55
2613 $1 Ceratosaurus 50 55
2614 $1 Stegosaurus 50 55
2615 $1 Elaphrosaurus 50 55
2616 $1 Vulcanodon 50 55
2617 $1 Psittacosaurus 50 55
2618 $1 Pteranodon 50 55
2619 $1 Ichythyornis 50 55
2620 $1 Spinosaurus 50 55
2621 $1 Parasaurolophus 50 55
2622 $1 Ornithomimus 50 55
2623 $1 Anatosaurus 50 55
2624 $1 Triceratops 50 55
2625 $1 Baryonx 50 55
2626 $2 Zalambdalestes 50 55

Nos. 2608/16 and 2617/25 respectively were each printed together, se-tenant, with the backgrounds forming composite designs.

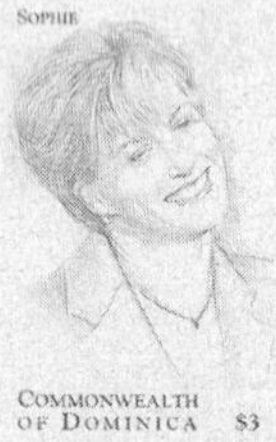

332 Miss Sophie Rhys-Jones

1999. Royal Wedding.

2628 **332** $3 blue and black . . . 1·50 1·60
2629 – $3 multicoloured . . . . 1·50 1·60
2630 – $3 blue and black . . . 1·50 1·60

DESIGNS: No. 2629, Miss Sophie Rhys-Jones and Prince Edward; 2630, Prince Edward.

1999. "iBRA '99" International Stamp Exhibition, Nuremberg. As T **416** of Antigua. Multicoloured.

2632 65c. "Eendracht" (Dirk Hartog) with Cameroons Expeditionary Force 1915 2d. and 3d. surcharges . . 35 40
2633 90c. "Eendracht" with Kamerun 1900 10pf. and 25pf. stamps 45 50
2634 $1 Early German railway locomotive with Kamerun 1900 5m. stamp 50 55
2635 $2 Early German railway locomotive with Kamerun 1890 overprinted 50pf. stamp . . . . 1·00 1·10

1999. 150th Death Anniv of Katsushika Hokusai (Japanese artist). As T **417** of Antigua, but vert. Multicoloured.

2637 $2 "Pilgrims at Kirifuri Waterfall" . . . . 1·00 1·10
2638 $2 "Kakura-Sato" (rats pulling on rope) . . . . . 1·00 1·10
2639 $2 "Travellers on the Bridge by Ono Waterfall" . . . 1·00 1·10
2640 $2 "Fast Cargo Boat battling the Waves" . . . 1·00 1·10
2641 $2 "Kakura-Sato" (rats with barrels) . . . . 1·00 1·10
2642 $2 "Buufinfinh and Weeping Cherry" . . . . 1·00 1·10
2643 $2 "Cuckoo and Azalea" . . 1·00 1·10
2644 $2 "Soldiers" (with lamp) 1·00 1·10
2645 $2 "Lovers in the Snow" . . 1·00 1·10
2646 $2 "Ghost of Koheiji" . . . 1·00 1·10
2647 $2 "Soldiers" (with hand on hip) . . . . 1·00 1·10
2648 $2 "Chinese Poet in Snow" 1·00 1·10

1999. 10th Anniv of United Nations Rights of the Child Convention. As T **419** of Antigua. Multicoloured.

2650 $3 Small girl (vert) . . . . 1·50 1·60
2651 $3 Small boy (vert) . . . . 1·50 1·60
2652 $3 Small boy and girl (vert) 1·50 1·60

Nos. 2650/2 were printed together, se-tenant, forming a composite design which continues onto the sheet margins.

1999. 250th Birth Anniv of Johann von Goethe (German writer). As T **421** of Antigua.

2655 $2 multicoloured . . . . . 1·00 1·10
2656 $2 blue, purple and black 1·00 1·10
2657 $2 multicoloured . . . . . 1·00 1·10

DESIGNS: No. 2655, Faust and astrological sign; 2656, Von Goethe and Von Schiller; 2657, Faust tempted by Mephistopheles.

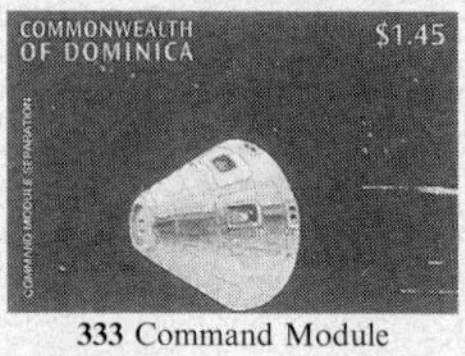

333 Command Module

1999. 30th Anniv of First Manned Landing on Moon. Multicoloured.

2659 $1.45 Type **333** 75 80
2660 $1.45 Service module . . . 75 80
2661 $1.45 Booster separation . . 75 80
2662 $1.45 Lunar and command modules 75 80
2663 $1.45 Tracking telescope . . 75 80
2664 $1.45 Goldstone radio telescope 75 80

1999. "Queen Elizabeth the Queen Mother's Century". As T **444** of Antigua.

2666 $2 black and gold . . . . . 1·00 1·10
2667 $2 black and gold . . . . . 1·00 1·10
2668 $2 multicoloured . . . . . 1·00 1·10
2669 $2 multicoloured . . . . . 1·00 1·10

DESIGNS: No. 2666, Queen Elizabeth, 1939; 2667, Queen Mother in Australia, 1958; 2668, Queen Mother in blue hat and coat, 1982; 2669, Queen Mother laughing, 1982.

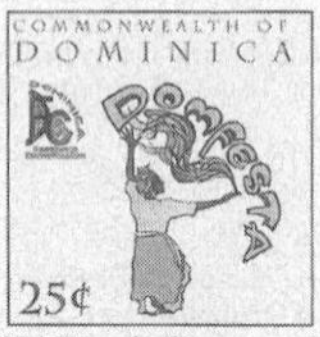

334 Female Dancer and "DOMFESTA"

1999. 21st Anniv of Dominica Festivals Commission. Multicoloured.

2671 25c. Type **334** 15 20
2672 55c. "21st BIRTHDAY" logo 30 35
2673 65c. Carnival Development Committee emblem . . . 35 40
2674 90c. World Creole music emblem 45 50

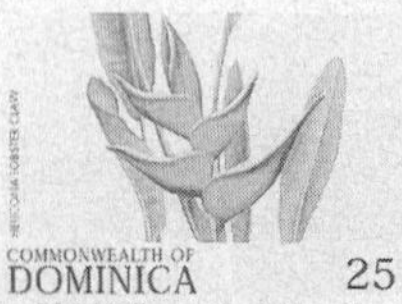

336 Helicona Lobster Claw

1999. Flora and Fauna. Multicoloured.

2677 25c. Type **336** 15 20
2678 65c. Broad-winged hawk . . 35 40
2679 90c. White-throated sparrow 45 50
2680 90c. Blue-winged teal . . . 45 50
2681 90c. Racoon 45 50
2682 90c. Alfalfa butterfly 45 50
2683 90c. Foot bridge 45 50
2684 90c. Whitetail deer 45 50
2685 90c. Grey squirrel 45 50
2686 90c. Banded-purple butterfly 45 50
2687 90c. Snowdrops 45 50
2688 90c. Bullfrog 45 50
2689 90c. Mushrooms 45 50
2690 90c. Large-blotched ensatina 45 50
2691 $1 Anthurium 50 55
2692 $1.55 Blue-headed hummingbird 80 85
2693 $2 Bananaquit . . . . . . 1·00 1·10
2694 $4 Agouti . . . . 2·00 2·10

Nos. 2679/90 were printed together, se-tenant, with the backgrounds forming a composite design.

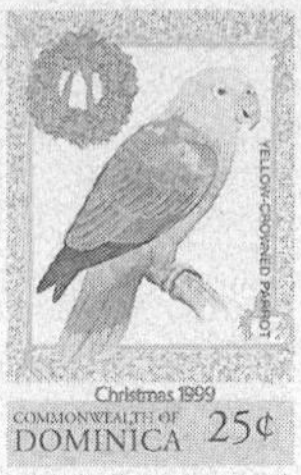

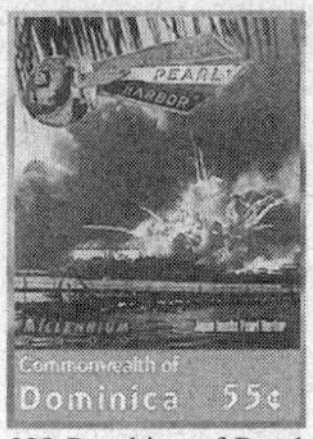

337 Yellow-crowned Parrot

338 Bombing of Pearl Harbor, 1941

1999. Christmas. Birds. Multicoloured.

2696 25c. Type **337** 15 20
2697 55c. Red bishop 30 35
2698 65c. Troupial 35 40
2699 90c. Puerto Rican woodpecker 45 50
2700 $2 Mangrove cuckoo . . . 1·00 1·10
2701 $3 American robin . . . . 1·50 1·60

No. 2699 is inscribed "PUERTO RECAN WOODPECKER".

1999. New Millennium. People and Events of Thirteenth Century (1200–50). As T **445** of Antigua. Multicoloured.

2703 55c. Leonardo Fibonacci (mathematician, 1202) . . 30 35
2704 55c. St. Francis of Assisi (founder of Franciscan Order, 1207) 30 35
2705 55c. Mongol horsemen (Conquest of China, 1211) 30 35
2706 55c. Children with banner (Children's Crusade, 1212) 30 35
2707 55c. King John signing Magna Carta, 1215 . . . 30 35
2708 55c. University class (foundation of Salamanca University, 1218) 30 35
2709 55c. Snorre Sturlusson (author of the "Edda", 1222) 30 35
2710 55c. Ma Yuan (Chinese painter) in garden (died 1224) 30 35
2711 55c. Genghis Khan (Mongol Emperor) (died 1227) . . 30 35
2712 55c. Student and Buddha (establishment of Zen Buddhism in Japan, 1227) 30 35
2713 55c. Galleys (The Sixth Crusade, 1228) 30 35
2714 55c. Seals (Lubeck–Hamburg Treaty, 1230) 30 35
2715 55c. Cardinal and angel (Holy Inquisition, 1231) 30 35
2716 55c. Palace interior (conquest of Cordoba, 1236) 30 35
2717 55c. San Marino (town founded, 1243) 30 35
2718 55c. Maimonides (Jewish philosopher) (died 1204) (59 × 39 mm) 30 35
2719 55c. Notre Dame Cathedral, Paris (completed 1250) . . 30 35

1999. New Millennium. People and Events of Twentieth Century (1940–49). Multicoloured.

2720 55c. Type **338** 30 35
2721 55c. Sir Winston Churchill (British Prime Minister, 1940) 30 35
2722 55c. Children in front of set (start of television broadcasting in U.S.A., 1940) 30 35
2723 55c. Anne Frank (Holocaust, 1942) 30 35
2724 55c. Troops wading ashore (D-Day, 1944) 30 35
2725 55c. Churchill, Roosevelt and Stalin (Yalta Conference, 1945) 30 35
2726 55c. U.N. Headquarters, New York (United Nations Organization, 1945) 30 35
2727 55c. American G.I. and concentration camp (Surrender of Germany, 1945) 30 35
2728 55c. Hoisting the Red Flag on the Reichstag (Fall of Berlin, 1945) 30 35
2729 55c. "Eniac" (first operational computer, 1946) 30 35
2730 55c. Indian with flag (Independence of India, 1947) 30 35
2731 55c. Early transistor, 1947 30 35
2732 55c. Mahatma Gandhi assassinated, 1948 . . . . 30 35
2733 55c. Israelis with flag (Establishment of Israel, 1948) 30 35
2734 55c. Aircraft and children (Berlin Airlift, 1948) . . 30 35
2735 55c. Atomic bomb test, New Mexico, 1948 (59 × 39 mm) 30 35
2736 55c. Great Wall of China (People's Republic established, 1949) 30 35

No. 2732 is inscribed "Ghandi" in error.

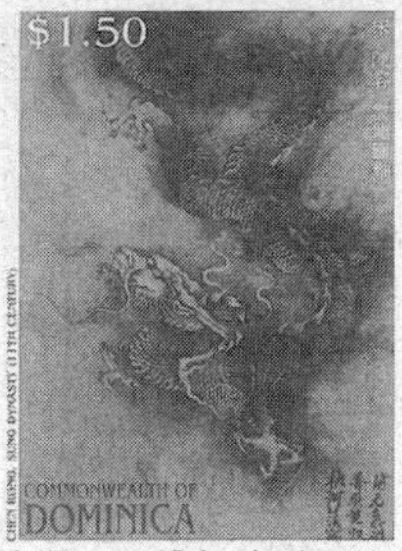

339 "Dragon flying in the Mist" (Chen Rong)

2000. Chinese New Year ("Year of the Dragon").

2737 **339** $1.50 multicoloured . . 80 85

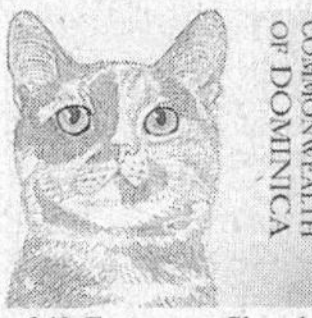

340 European Shorthair

2000. Cats and Dogs of the World. Multicoloured.

2739 $1 Type **340** 50 55
2740 $1 Devon rex 50 55
2741 $1 Chartreux 50 50
2742 $1 Bengal 50 55
2743 $1 American wirehair . . . 50 55
2744 $1 Siberian 50 55
2745 $1 Burmese 50 55
2746 $1 American shorthair . . . 50 55
2747 $1 Asian longhair 50 55
2748 $1 Burmilla 50 55
2749 $1 Snowshoe 50 55
2750 $1 Pekeface Persian 50 55
2751 $1 Himalayan Persian . . . 50 55
2752 $1 Japanese bobtail 50 55
2753 $1 Seychelles longhair . . . 50 55
2754 $1 Exotic shorthair 50 55
2755 $1 Jack Russell puppy (vert) 50 55
2756 $1 Shar pei puppies (vert) 50 55
2757 $1 Basset hound puppy (vert) 50 55
2758 $1 Boxer puppies (vert) . . 50 55
2759 $1 Wire-haired terrier (cross) puppy (vert) 50 55
2760 $1 Golden retriever puppies (vert) 50 55

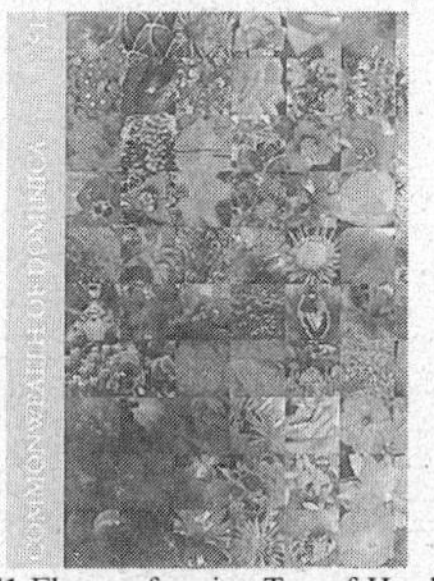

341 Flowers forming Top of Head

2000. Faces of the Millennium: Diana, Princess of Wales. Designs showing collage of miniature flower photographs. Multicoloured.

2762 $1 Type **341** (face value at left) 50 55
2763 $1 Top of head (face value at right) 50 55
2764 $1 Ear (face value at left) 50 55
2765 $1 Eye and temple (face value at right) 50 55
2766 $1 Cheek (face value at left) 50 50
2767 $1 Cheek (face value at right) 50 55
2768 $1 Blue background (face value at left) 50 55
2769 $1 Chin (face value at right) 50 55

Nos. 2762/9 were printed together, se-tenant, in sheetlets of 8 with the stamps arranged in two vertical columns separated by a gutter also containing miniature photographs. When viewed as a whole, the sheetlet forms a portrait of Diana, Princess of Wales.

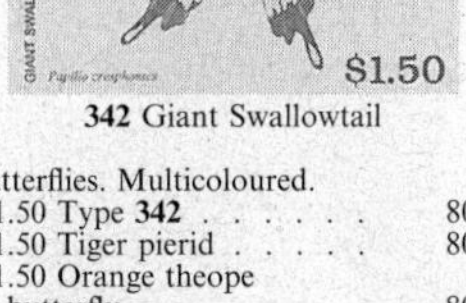

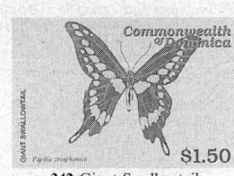

342 Giant Swallowtail

2000. Butterflies. Multicoloured.

2770 $1.50 Type **342** 80 85
2771 $1.50 Tiger pierid 80 85
2772 $1.50 Orange theope butterfly 80 85
2773 $1.50 White peacock 80 85
2774 $1.50 Blue tharops 80 85
2775 $1.50 Mosaic 80 85
2776 $1.50 Banded king shoemaker 80 85
2777 $1.50 Figure-of-eight butterfly 80 85
2778 $1.50 Grecian shoemaker . . 80 85
2779 $1.50 Blue night butterfly 80 85
2780 $1.50 Monarch 80 85
2781 $1.50 Common morpho . . 80 85
2782 $1.50 Orange-barred sulphur 80 85
2783 $1.50 Clorinde 80 85
2784 $1.50 Small flambeau . . . 80 85
2785 $1.50 Small lace-wing . . . 80 85
2786 $1.50 Polydamas swallowtail 80 85
2787 $1.50 The atala 80 85

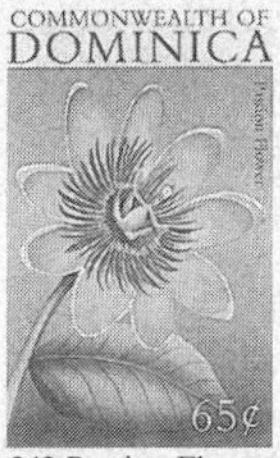

343 Passion Flower

2000. Flowers. Multicoloured. (a) Size 28 × 42 mm.

2789 65c. Type **343** 35 40
2790 90c. Spray orchid 45 50
2791 $1 Peach angels trumpet . . 50 55
2792 $4 Allamanda . . . . . . 2·00 2·10

(b) Size 32 × 48 mm.

2793 $1.65 Bird of paradise . . . 85 90
2794 $1.65 Lobster claw heliconia 85 90
2795 $1.65 Candle bush 85 90
2796 $1.65 Flor de San Miguel 85 90
2797 $1.65 Hibiscus 85 90
2798 $1.65 Oleander 85 90
2799 $1.65 Anthurium 85 90
2800 $1.65 Fire ginger 85 90
2801 $1.65 Shrimp plant 85 90
2802 $1.65 Sky vine thumbergia 85 90
2803 $1.65 Ceriman 85 90
2804 $1.65 Morning glory 85 90

Nos. 2793/8 and 2799/804 were each printed together, se-tenant, with the backgrounds forming composite designs.

2000. 400th Birth Anniv of Sir Anthony Van Dyck (Flemish painter). As T **429** of Antigua. Multicoloured.

2806 $1.65 "The Ages of Man" (horiz) 85 90
2807 $1.65 "Portrait of a Girl as Ermina accompanied by Cupid" (horiz) 85 90
2808 $1.65 "Cupid and Psyche" (horiz) 85 90
2809 $1.65 "Vertumnus and Pomona" (horiz) 85 90
2810 $1.65 "The Continence of Scipio" (horiz) 85 90
2811 $1.65 "Diana and Endymion surprised by a Satyr" (horiz) 85 90
2812 $1.65 "Ladies-in-Waiting" (horiz) 85 90
2813 $1.65 "Thomas Wentworth, Earl of Strafford, with Sir Philip Mainwaring" (horiz) 85 90
2814 $1.65 "Dorothy Rivers Savage, Viscountess Andover, and her sister Lady Elizabeth Thimbleby" (horiz) . . . 85 90
2815 $1.65 "Mountjoy Blount, Earl of Newport, and Lord George Goring with a Page" (horiz) 85 90
2816 $1.65 "Thomas Killigrew and an Unidentified Man" (horiz) 85 90
2817 $1.65 "Elizabeth Villiers, Lady Dalkeith, and Cecilia Killigrew" (horiz) 85 90
2818 $1.65 "Lady Jane Goodwin (Mrs. Arthur)" 85 90
2819 $1.65 "Philip Herbert, Earl of Pembroke" 85 90
2820 $1.65 "Philip, Lord Wharton" 85 90
2821 $1.65 "Sir Thomas Hammer" 85 90
2822 $1.65 "Olivia Porter" . . . 85 90
2823 $1.65 "Sir Thomas Chaloner" 85 90

No. 2813 is inscribed "Wenthworth" in error.

2000. 18th Birthday of Prince William. As T **433** of Antigua. Multicoloured.

2825 $1.65 In skiing gear 85 90
2826 $1.65 In red jumper 85 90
2827 $1.65 Holding order of service 85 90
2828 $1.65 Prince William laughing 85 90

2000. "EXPO 2000" World Stamp Exhibition, Anaheim. Space Satellites. As T **434** of Antigua. Multicoloured.

2830 $1.65 "Essa 8" 85 90
2831 $1.65 "Echo 1" 85 90
2832 $1.65 "Topex Poseidon" . . 85 90
2833 $1.65 "Diademe" 85 90
2834 $1.65 "Early Bird" 85 90
2835 $1.65 "Molyna" 85 90
2836 $1.65 "Explorer 14" 85 90
2837 $1.65 "Luna 16" 85 90
2838 $1.65 "Copernicus" 85 90
2839 $1.65 "Explorer 16" 85 90
2840 $1.65 "Luna 10" 85 90
2841 $1.65 "Arybhattan" 85 90

Nos. 2830/5 and 2836/41 were printed together, se-tenant, with the backgrounds forming composite designs.

2000. 25th Anniv of "Apollo–Soyuz" Joint Project. As T **435** of Antigua. Multicoloured.

2843 $3 Saturn 1B ("Apollo" launch vehicle) . . . . . 1·50 1·60
2844 $3 "Apollo 18" command module . . . . 1·50 1·60
2845 $3 Donald Slayton ("Apollo 18" crew) . . . . 1·50 1·60

No. 2843 is inscribed "Vechicle" in error.

2000. 50th Anniv of Berlin Film Festival. As T **436** of Antigua. Multicoloured.

2847 $1.65 Satyajit Ray (director of Ashani Sanket) 85 90
2848 $1.65 *Mahanagar*, 1964 . . 85 90
2849 $1.65 *La Tulipe*, 1952 . . . 85 90
2850 $1.65 *Le Salaire de la Peur*, 1953 . . . . 85 90
2851 $1.65 *Les Cousins*, 1959 . . 85 90
2852 $1.65 *Hon Dansade en Sommar*, 1952 . . . . . 85 90

2000. 175th Anniv of Stockton and Darlington Line (first public railway). As T **437** of Antigua. Multicoloued.

2854 $3 George Stephenson and *Locomotion No. 1*, 1875 1·50 1·60
2855 $3 John B. Jervis's *Brother Jonathan*, 1832 . . . . . 1·50 1·60

No. 2855 is inscribed "Jonathon" in error.

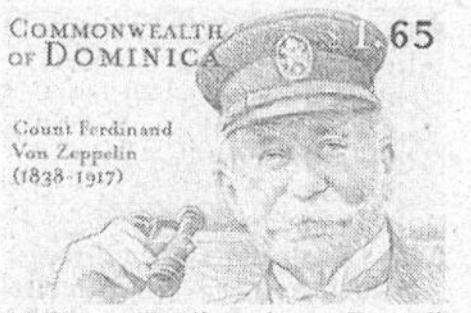

344 Count Ferdinand von Zeppelin

2000. Centenary of First Zeppelin Flight. Mult.

2858 $1.65 Type **344** 85 90
2859 $1.65 LZ-1 at Lake Constance, 1900 . . . . 85 90
2860 $1.65 LZ-10 *Schwaben*, over flock of sheep, 1911 . . . 85 90
2861 $1.65 LZ-6 and LZ-7 *Deutschland* in hangar, Friedrichshafen 85 90
2862 $1.65 LZ-4 at Luneville, 1913 . . . . 85 90
2863 $1.65 LZ-11 *Viktoria-Luise* over Kiel Harbour . . . 85 90

No. 2861 is inscribed "Friedrichshrfed" in error.

2000. Olympic Games, Sydney. As T **441** of Antigua. Multicoloured.

2865 $2 Jesse Owens (athletics), Berlin (1936) . . . . . 1·00 1·10
2866 $2 Pole-vaulting . . . . . . 1·00 1·10
2867 $2 Lenin Stadium, Moscow (1980) and U.S.S.R. flag 1·00 1·10
2868 $2 Ancient Greek discus-thrower . . . . 1·00 1·10

2000. West Indies Cricket Tour and 100th Test Match at Lord's. As T **442** of Antigua. Multicoloured.

2869 $4 Norbert Phillip . . . . . 2·00 2·10

No. 2869 is inscribed "Phillp" in error.

2000. 80th Birthday of Pope John Paul II. As T **341** ,showing collage of miniature religious photographs. Multicoloured.

2871 $1 Top of head (face value at left) 50 55
2872 $1 Top of head (face value at right) 50 55
2873 $1 Ear (face value at left) 50 55
2874 $1 Forehead (face value at right) 50 55
2875 $1 Neck (face value at left) 50 55
2876 $1 Cheek (face value at right) 50 55
2877 $1 Shoulder (face value at left) 50 55
2878 $1 Hands (face value at right) 50 55

Nos. 2871/8 were printed together, se-tenant, in sheetlets of 8 with the stamps arranged in two vertical columns separated by a gutter also containing miniature photographs. When viewed as a whole, the sheetlet forms a portrait of Pope John Paul.

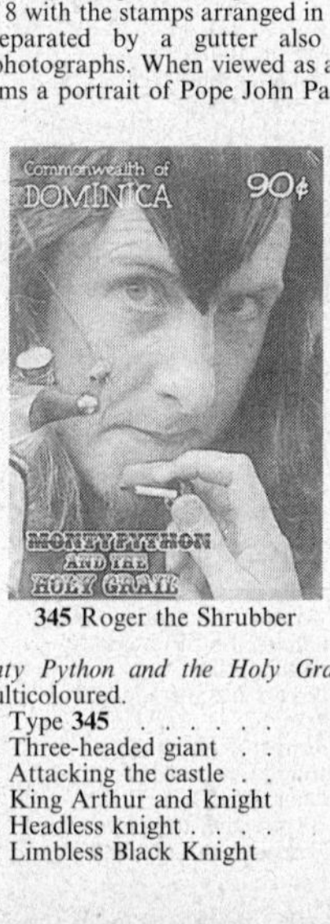

345 Roger the Shrubber

2000. *Monty Python and the Holy Grail* (comedy film). Multicoloured.

2879 90c. Type **345** 45 50
2880 90c. Three-headed giant . . . 45 50
2881 90c. Attacking the castle . . 45 50
2882 90c. King Arthur and knight 45 50
2883 90c. Headless knight 45 50
2884 90c. Limbless Black Knight 45 50

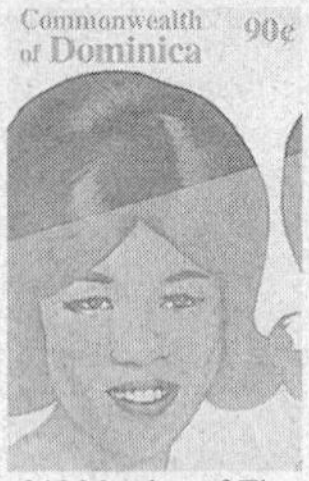

346 Member of The Crystals

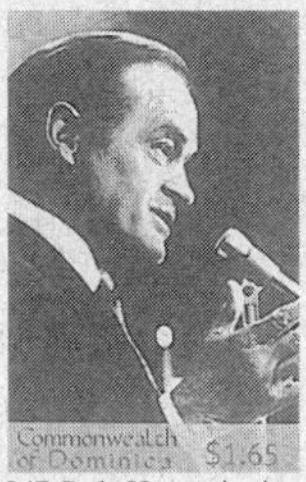

347 Bob Hope singing

2000. Famous Girl Pop Groups. The Crystals. Mult.

2885 90c. Type **346** 45 50
2886 90c. Group member with long hair (blue background in top right corner) 45 50
2887 90c. Group member with long hair (yellow background in top right corner) 45 50
2888 90c. Group member with short hair 45 50

Nos. 2885/8 were printed together, se-tenant, forming a composite design.

2000. Bob Hope (American entertainer).

2889 **347** $1.65 black, blue and lilac 85 90
2890 – $1.65 multicoloured . . 85 90
2891 – $1.65 black, blue and lilac 85 90
2892 – $1.65 multicoloured . . 85 90
2893 – $1.65 black, blue and lilac 85 90
2894 – $1.65 multicoloured . . 85 90

DESIGNS: No. 2890, Entertaining troops; 2891, As English comic character; 2892, In 50th birthday cake; 2893, Making radio broadcast; 2894, With Man in the Moon.

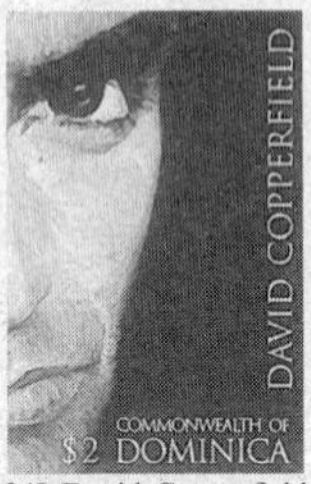

348 David Copperfield

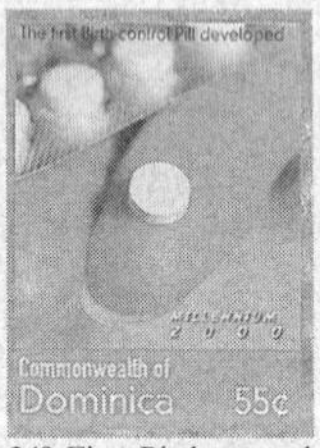

349 First Birth-control Pill, 1961

2000. David Copperfield (conjurer).

2895 **348** $2 multicoloured . . . . 1·00 1·10

2000. Monarchs of the Millennium. As T **447** of Antigua.

2896 $1.65 multicoloured 85 90
2897 $1.65 black, stone and brown 85 90
2898 $1.65 multicoloured 85 90
2899 $1.65 black, stone and brown 85 90
2900 $1.65 multicoloured 85 90
2901 $1.65 black, stone and brown 85 90

DESIGNS: No. 2896, King Edward IV of England; 2897, Tsar Peter the Great of Russia; 2898, King Henry VI of England; 2899, King Henry III of England; 2900, King Richard III of England; 2901, King Edward I of England.

2000. Popes of the Millennium. As T **447** of Antigua. Each black, yellow and green.

2903 $1.65 Clement X 85 90
2904 $1.65 Innocent X 85 90
2905 $1.65 Nicholas V 85 90
2906 $1.65 Martin V 85 90
2907 $1.65 Julius III 85 90
2908 $1.65 Innocent XII 85 90

2000. Christmas and Holy Year. As T **452** of Antigua. Multicoloured.

2910 25c. Angel in blue robe . . 15 20
2911 65c. Young angel 35 40
2912 90c. Angel with drapery . . 45 50
2913 $1.90 As 25c. . . . . 95 1·00
2914 $1.90 As 65c. . . . . 95 1·00
2915 $1.90 As 90c. . . . . 95 1·00
2916 $1.90 As $5 . . . . 95 1·00
2917 $5 Head and shoulders of angel . . . . 2·50 2·75

2000. New Millennium. People and Events of the Fourteenth Century (1350–1400). As T **445** of Antigua. Multicoloured.

2919 65c. Couple with hawk (Minnesangers in Germany, 1350) 35 40
2920 65c. Acamapitzin, first King of the Aztecs, 1352 . . . 35 40
2921 65c. Rat (end of Black Death, 1353) 35 40
2922 65c. Giotto's *Campanile* (completed by Francesco Talenti, 1355) 35 40
2923 65c. First French franc, 1360 . . . . 35 40
2924 65c. Emperor Hung-wu (foundation of Ming Dynasty, 1360) 35 40
2925 65c. Tamerlane (foundation of Timurid Empire, 1369) 35 40
2926 65c. "Triumph of Death" (Francis Traini), 1370 . . 35 40
2927 65c. Robin Hood (first appearance in English legends, 1375) 35 40
2928 65c. "The Knight" (The Canterbury Tales by Geoffrey Chaucer, 1387) 35 40
2929 65c. Mounted samurai (disputed succession in Japan, 1392) 35 40
2930 65c. Refugees (Jews expelled from France, 1394) . . . 35 40
2931 65c. Temple of the Golden Pavilion, Kyoto (constructed, 1394) . . . 35 40
2932 65c. Carving, Strasbourg Cathedral (completed, 1399) 35 40
2933 65c. Alhambra Palace, Granada (completed, 1390) (60 × 40 mm) . . . 35 40
2934 65c. Ife Bronzes produced in Nigeria, 1400 . . . . . . 35 40

No. 2929 is inscribed "SUDDESSION" in error.

2000. New Millennium. Two Thousand Years of Chinese Paintings. As T **446** of Antigua. Mult.

2935 55c. "Eight Prize Steeds" (Guiseppe Castiglione) . . 30 35
2936 55c. "Oleanders" (Wu Hsi Tsai) 30 35
2937 55c. "Mynah and Autumn Flowers" (Chang Hsiung) 30 35
2938 55c. "Hen and Chicks beneath Chrysanthemums," (Chu Ch'ao) 30 35
2939 55c. "Long Living Pine and Crane" (Xugu) 30 35
2940 55c. "Flowers and Fruits" (Chu Lien) 30 35
2941 55c. "Lotus and Willow" (Pu Hua) 30 35
2942 55c. "Kuan-Yin" (Ch'ien Hui-an) 30 35
2943 55c. "Human Figures" (Jen Hsun) 30 35
2944 55c. "Han-Shan and Shih-Te" (Ren Yi) 30 35
2945 55c. "Landscape and Human Figure" (Jen Yu) 30 35
2946 55c. "Poetic Thoughts while Walking with a Staff" (Wangchen) 30 35
2947 55c. "Peony" (Chen Heng-ko) 30 35
2948 55c. "Plum and Orchid" (Wu Chang-shih) 30 35
2949 55c. "Monkey" (Kao Chi-feng) 30 35
2950 55c. "Grapes and Locust" (Chi Pai-shih); and "Galloping Horse" (Xu Beihong) (60 × 40 mm) . . 30 35
2951 55c. "The Beauty" (Lin Fengmian) 30 35

No. 2937 is inscribed "YNAH" and No. 2948 "ORCHIS", both in error.

2000. New Millennium. People and Events of Twentieth Century (1960–69). Multicoloured.

2952 55c. Type **349** 30 35
2953 55c. Yuri Gagarin (first man in Space), 1961 . . . . . 30 35
2954 55c. Fans with The Beatles tickets, 1962 . . . . . . 30 35
2955 55c. Funeral of President John F. Kennedy, 1963 30 35
2956 55c. Martin Luther King's "I Have a Dream" speech, 1963 . . . . . . 30 35
2957 55c. Betty Friedan (author of *The Feminist Mystique*), 1963 . . . . 30 35
2958 55c. Duke of Edinburgh and Jomo Kenyatta (independence of Kenya), 1963 . . . . 30 35
2959 55c. Anti-smoking poster, 1964 . . . . 30 35
2960 55c. Civil Rights demonstrators (U.S. Civil Rights Act), 1964 . . . . 30 35
2961 55c. Troops outside Saigon (U.S. involvement in Vietnam), 1965 . . . . . 30 35
2962 55c. Ernesto "Che" Guevara (Cuban revolutionary) killed in Peru, 1965 . . . 30 35
2963 55c. Dr. Christiaan Barnard (first heart transplant operation), 1967 . . . . 30 35
2964 55c. General Moshe Dayan addressing Arabs ("Six-Day" War), 1967 . . . . 30 35
2965 55c. Death of Ho Chi Minh (North Vietnamese leader), 1969 . . . . . . 30 35
2966 55c. Neil Armstrong on the Moon, 1969 . . . . . . 30 35
2967 55c. Couple at Berlin Wall, 1961 (60 × 40 mm). . . . 30 35
2968 55c. Woodstock Festival, 1969 . . . . 30 35

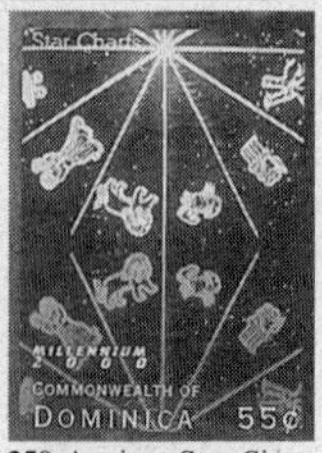

350 Ancient Star Signs

2000. New Millennium. Inventions. Multicoloured.

2969 55c. Type **350** 30 35
2970 55c. Precision tools 30 35
2971 55c. Astral chart 30 35
2972 55c. Growth of medicine . . 30 35
2973 55c. Exchange of medical information 30 35
2974 55c. Monastic chapterhouse 30 35
2975 55c. Water alarm clock . . 30 35
2976 55c. Weighted clock 30 35
2977 55c. Spring-loaded miniature clock movement 30 35
2978 55c. Glass blowing 30 35
2979 55c. Early screws 30 35
2980 55c. Wood lathe 30 35
2981 55c. Ship building 30 25
2982 55c. Interchangeable rifle parts 30 35
2983 55c. Study of movement . . 30 35
2984 55c. The Industrial Revolution (60 × 40 mm) 30 35
2985 55c. Concept of efficiency 30 35

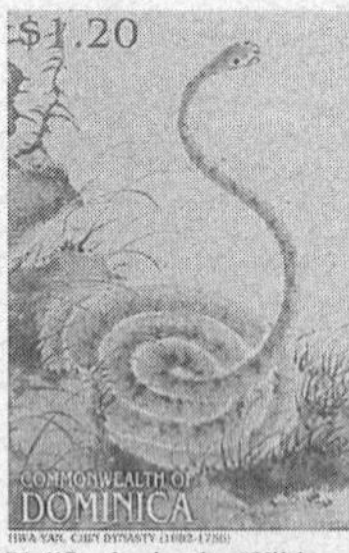

351 "Snake in the Wilderness" (Hwa Yan)

2001. Chinese New Year. "Year of the Snake".

2986 **351** $1.20 multicoloured . . 60 65

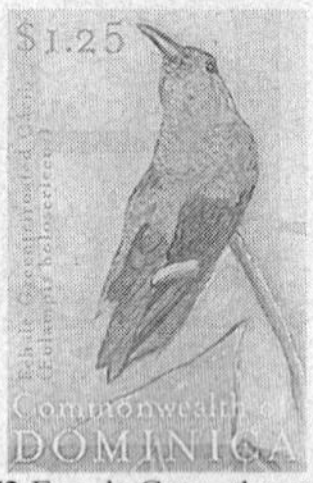

352 Female Green-throated Carib

2001. Hummingbirds. Multicoloured.

2987 $1.25 Type **352** 65 70
2988 $1.25 Male bee hummingbird ("Mellisuga helenae") 65 70
2989 $1.25 Male bee hummingbird ("Russelia eqoisetiformis") 65 70
2990 $1.25 Female bahama woodstar 65 70
2991 $1.25 Antillean mango . . . 65 70
2992 $1.25 Female blue-headed hummingbird 65 70
2993 $1.65 Male streamertail . . 85 90
2994 $1.65 Purple-throated carib 85 90
2995 $1.65 Vervain hummingbird 85 90
2996 $1.65 Bahama woodstar . . 85 90
2997 $1.65 Puerto Rican emerald 85 90
2998 $1.65 Antillean crested hummingbird 85 90

Nos. 2987/92 and 2993/8 were each printed together, se-tenant, with the backgrounds forming composite designs.

No. 2987 is inscribed "Fehale Greentriroated Carib", No. 2990 "Tenale", No. 2994 "Triroated" and No. 2998 "Cresteo", all in error.

No. 2989 carries the inscription "Russelia eqoisetiformis". This should read "Russelia equisetiformis", and refers to the plant (commonly known as a Firecracker Plant) at the bottom of the stamp, not the hummingbird.

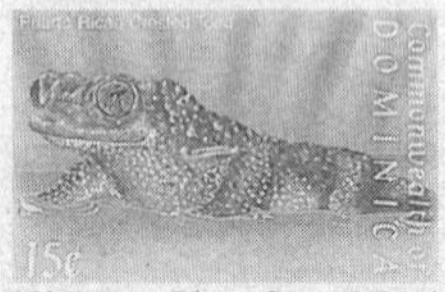

353 Puerto Rican Crested Toad

2001. Caribbean and Latin-American Fauna. Mult.

3000 15c. Type **353** 10 10
3001 20c. Axolotl 10 15
3002 $1.45 St. Vincent parrot . . 75 80
3003 $1.45 Indigo macaw 75 80
3004 $1.45 Cock of the rock . . . 75 80
3005 $1.45 Cuban solenodon . . 75 80
3006 $1.45 Cuban hutia 75 80
3007 $1.45 Chinchilla 75 80
3008 $1.45 South American flamingo 75 80
3009 $1.45 Golden conure . . . 75 80
3010 $1.45 Ocelot 75 80
3011 $1.45 Giant armadillo . . . 75 80
3012 $1.45 Margay 75 80
3013 $1.45 Maned wolf 75 80
3014 $1.90 Panamanian golden frog . . . . 95 1·00
3015 $2.20 Manatee . . . . . . 1·10 1·25

Nos. 3002/7 and 3008/13 were each printed together, se-tenant, with the backgrounds forming composite designs.

2001. Characters from "Pokemon" (children's cartoon series). As T **454** of Antigua. Multicoloured.

3017 $1.65 "Butterfree No. 12" 85 90
3018 $1.65 "Bulbasaur No. 01" 85 90
3019 $1.65 "Caterpie No. 10" . . 85 90
3020 $1.65 "Charmander No. 04" 85 90
3021 $1.65 "Squirtle No. 07" . . 85 90
3022 $1.65 "Pidgeotto No. 17" 85 90

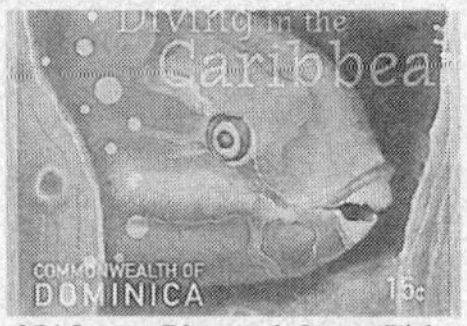

354 Large Blue and Green Fish

2001. Diving in the Caribbean. Depicting marine life. Multicoloured.

3024 15c. Type **354** 10 10
3025 65c. Ray 35 40
3026 90c. Octopus 45 50
3027 $2 Shark . . . . 1·00 1·10
3028 $2 Starfish . . . . 1·00 1·10
3029 $2 Seahorse . . . . 1·00 1·10
3030 $2 Pink anemonefish . . . . 1·00 1·10
3031 $2 Crab . . . . 1·00 1·10
3032 $2 Moray eel . . . . 1·00 1·10
3033 $3 Pink anemonefish . . . . 1·50 1·60

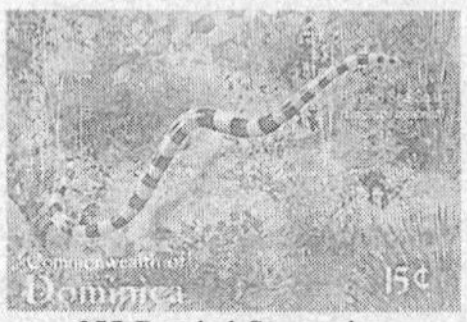

355 Banded Sea-snake

2001. Caribbean Marine Life. Multicoloured.

3035 15c. Type **355** 10 10
3036 25c. Soldierfish 15 10
3037 55c. False moorish idol ("Banner Fish") 30 35
3038 90c. Crown of Thorns starfish 45 50
3039 $1.65 Red sponge and shoal of anthias 85 90
3040 $1.65 Undulate triggerfish ("Orange-Striped Trigger Fish") 85 90
3041 $1.65 Coral hind ("Coral Grouper") and soft tree coral 85 90
3042 $1.65 Peacock fan-worms and Gorgonian sea fan . . 85 90
3043 $1.65 Sweetlips and sea fan 85 90
3044 $1.65 Giant clam and golden cup coral 85 90
3045 $1.65 White-tipped reef shark, lionfish and sergeant majors 85 90
3046 $1.65 Blue-striped snappers 85 90
3047 $1.65 Great hammerhead shark, stovepipe sponge and pink vase sponge . . 85 90
3048 $1.65 Hawaiian monk seal and bluetube coral . . . 85 90
3049 $1.65 False clown anemonefish ("Common Clown Fish"), chilka seahorse and red feather star coral 85 90
3050 $1.65 Bat starfish and brown octopus 85 90

Nos. 3039/44 and 3045/50 were each printed together, se-tenant, with the backgrounds forming composite designs.

No. 3045 is inscribed "Sargent" and 3049 "Cconn", both in error.

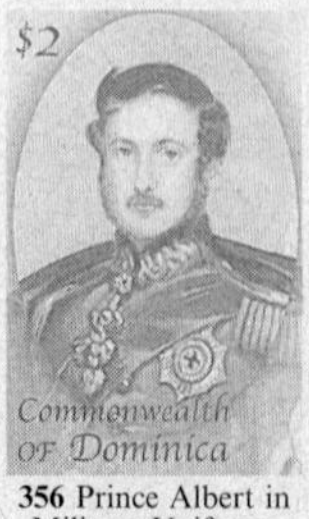

356 Prince Albert in Military Uniform

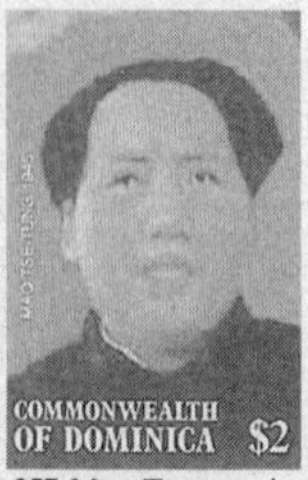

357 Mao Tse-tung in 1945

2001. Death Centenary of Queen Victoria. Multicoloured.

3052 $2 Type **356** . . . . . . 1·00 1·10
3053 $2 Young Queen Victoria wearing crown . . . . . 1·00 1·10

3054 $2 Young Queen Victoria wearing tiara . . . . . . 1·00 1·10
3055 $2 Prince Albert in evening dress . . . . 1·00 1·10

2001. 25th Death Anniv of Mao Tse-tung (Chinese leader). Portraits. Multicoloured.
3057 $2 Type **357** . . . . 1·00 1·10
3058 $2 Mao in 1926 . . . . . . 1·00 1·10
3059 $2 Mao in 1949 . . . . . . 1·00 1·10

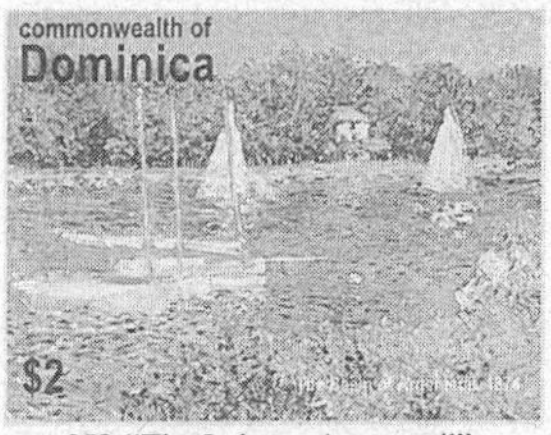

358 "The Lake at Argenteuil"

2001. 75th Death Anniv of Claude-Oscar Monet (French painter). Multicoloured.
3061 $2 Type **358** . . . . 1·00 1·10
3062 $2 "Bridge at Argenteuil" 1·00 1·10
3063 $2 "Railway bridge at Argenteuil" . . . . . . 1·00 1·10
3064 $2 "Seine bridge at Argenteuil" . . . . . . 1·00 1·10

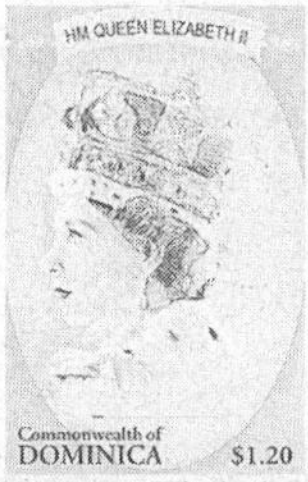

359 Queen Elizabeth at Coronation

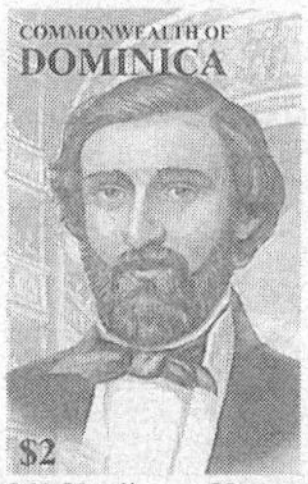

360 Verdi as a Young Man

2001. 75th Birthday of Queen Elizabeth II. Multicoloured.
3066 $1.20 Type **359** 60 65
3067 $1.20 Queen Elizabeth wearing yellow hat . . . 60 65
3068 $1.20 Bare-headed portrait after Annigoni 60 65
3069 $1.20 Queen Elizabeth wearing fur hat 60 65
3070 $1.20 With Prince Andrew as a baby 60 65
3071 $1.20 Wearing white hat and pearl necklace 60 65

2001. Death Centenary of Giuseppe Verdi (Italian composer). Multicoloured.
3073 $2 Type **360** . . . . 1·00 1·10
3074 $2 "Lady Macbeth" . . . . 1·00 1·10
3075 $2 Orchestra . . . . 1·00 1·10
3076 $2 Score for Verdi's *Macbeth* (opera) . . . . 1·00 1·10

Nos. 3073/6 were printed together, se-tenant, with the backgrounds forming a composite design.

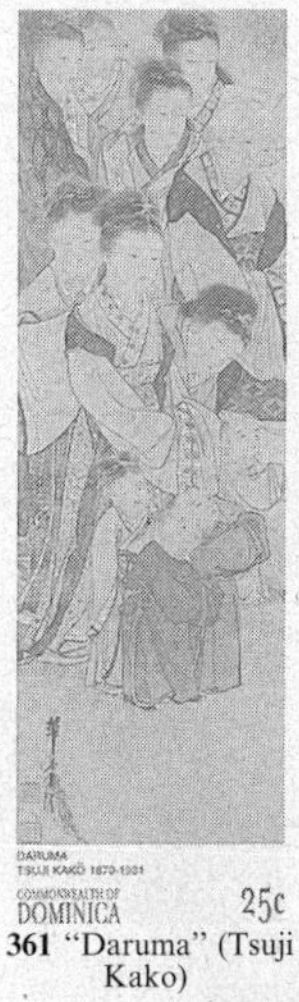

361 "Daruma" (Tsuji Kako)

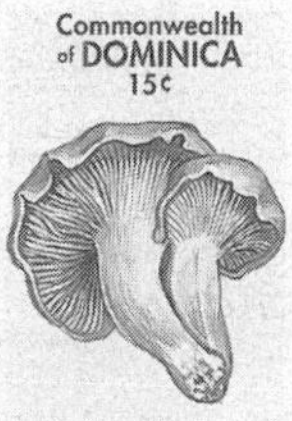

363 *Cantharellus cibarius*

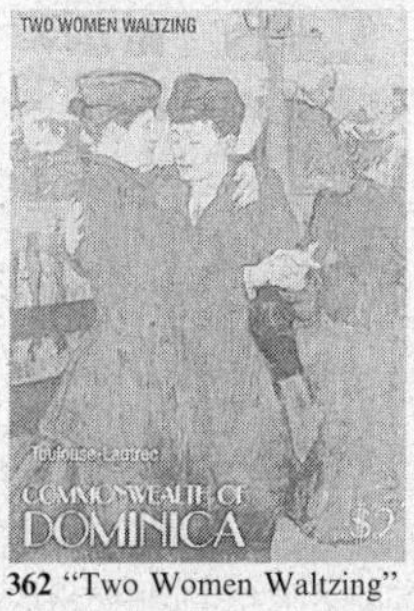

362 "Two Women Waltzing"

2001. "Philanippon '01" International Stamp Exhibition, Tokyo. Japanese Paintings. Multicoloured.
3078 25c. Type **361** 15 20
3079 55c. "Village by Bamboo Grove" (Takeuchi Seiho) 30 35
3080 65c. "Mountain Village in Spring" (Suzuki Hyakunen) 35 40
3081 90c. "Gentleman amusing Himself" (Domoto Insho) 45 50
3082 $1 "Calmness of Spring Light" (Takeuchi Seiho) 50 55
3083 $1.65 "Thatched Cottages in Willows" (Tsuji Kako) . . 85 90
3084 $1.65 "Joy in the Garden" (Tsuji Kako) 85 90
3085 $1.65 "Azalea and Butterfly" (Kikuchi Hobun) 85 90
3086 $1.65 "Pine Grove" (Tsuji Kako) 85 90
3087 $1.65 "Woodcutters talking in an Autumn Valley" (Kubota Beisen) 85 90
3088 $1.65 "Waterfowl in Snow" (Tsuji Kako) 85 90
3089 $1.65 "Heron and Willow" (Tsuji Kako) 85 90
3090 $1.65 "Crow and Cherry Blossoms" (Kikuchi Hobun) 85 90
3091 $1.65 "Chrysanthemum Immortal" (Yamamoto Shunkyo) 85 90
3092 $1.65 "Cranes of Immortality" (Tsuji Kako) 85 90
3093 $2 "Su's Embankment on a Spring Morning" (Tomioka Tessai) . . . . 1·00 1·10

2001. Death Centenary of Henri de Toulouse-Lautrec (French painter). Multicoloured.
3095 $2 Type **362** . . . . 1·00 1·10
3096 $2 "The Medical Inspection" . . . . 1·00 1·10
3097 $2 "Two Girlfriends" . . . 1·00 1·10
3098 $2 "Woman pulling up her Stockings" . . . . 1·00 1·10

2001. Fungi of the World. Multicoloured.
3100 15c. Type **363** 10 10
3101 25c. *Hygrocybe pratensis* . . 15 20
3102 55c. *Leccinum aurantiacum* 25 30
3103 90c. *Caesar's amanita* (horiz) 45 50
3104 90c. *Agaricus augustus* (horiz) 45 50
3105 90c. *Clitocybe nuda* (horiz) 45 50
3106 90c. *Hygrocybe plavescens* (horiz) 45 50
3107 90c. *Stropharia kaufmanii* (horiz) 45 50
3108 90c. *Hygrophorus speciosus* (horiz) 45 50
3109 $2 *Marasmiellus candidus* . . 1·00 1·10
3110 $2 *Calostoma cinnabarina* . . 1·00 1·10
3111 $2 *Cantharellus infundibuliformis* . . . . 1·00 1·10
3112 $2 *Hygrocybe punicea* . . . 1·00 1·10
3113 $2 *Dictyophora indusiata* . . 1·00 1·10
3114 $2 *Agrocybe praecox* . . . 1·00 1·10
3115 $3 *Mycena haematopus* . . . 1·50 1·60

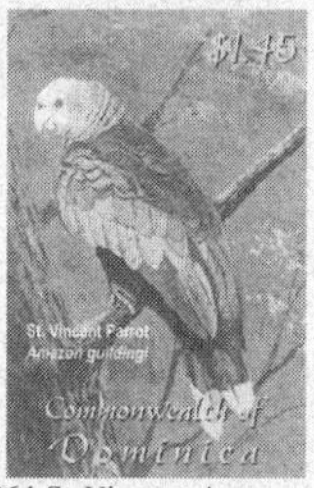

364 St Vincent Amazon

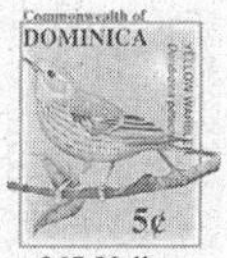

365 Yellow Warbler

2001. Caribbean Fauna. Multicoloured.
3117 $1.45 Type **364** 75 80
3118 $1.45 Painted bunting . . . 75 80
3119 $1.45 Jamaican giant anole 75 80
3120 $1.45 White-fronted capuchin monkey 75 80
3121 $1.45 Strand racerunner . . 75 80
3122 $1.45 Agouti 75 80
3123 $2 Cook's tree boa . . . . 1·00 1·10
3124 $2 Tamandua . . . . 1·00 1·10
3125 $2 Common iguana . . . . 1·00 1·10
3126 $2 Solenodon . . . . 1·00 1·10

2001. Birds. Multicoloured.
3128 5c. Type **365** 10 10
3129 10c. Palm chat 10 10
3130 15c. Snowy cotinga 10 10
3131 20c. Blue-grey gnatcatcher 10 10
3132 25c. Belted kingfisher . . . 15 20
3133 55c. Red-legged thrush . . 30 35
3134 65c. Bananaquit 35 40
3135 90c. Yellow-bellied sapsucker 45 50
3136 $1 White-tailed tropicbird 50 55
3137 $1.45 Ruby-throated hummingbird 75 80
3138 $1.90 Painted bunting . . . 95 1·00
3139 $2 Great Frigate bird . . 1·00 1·10
3140 $5 Brown trembler . . . . 2·50 2·75
3141 $10 Red-footed booby . . . 5·00 5·25
3142 $20 Sooty tern . . . . . . 10·00 10·50

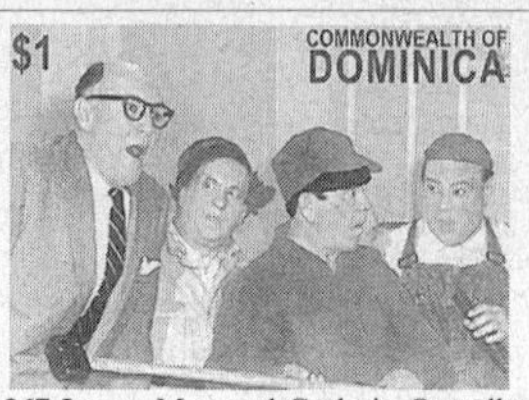

367 Larry, Moe and Curly in Overalls

2001. Scenes from *The Three Stooge* (American T.V. comedy series). Multicoloured.
3144 $1 Type **367** 50 55
3145 $1 Larry, Moe and Curly with woman in floral dress 50 55
3146 $1 Larry, Moe and Curly under table 50 55
3147 $1 Larry, Moe and Curly attacking singer in red dress 50 55
3148 $1 Larry, Moe and Curly with pony in cot 50 55
3149 $1 Larry in naval uniform, being arrested 50 55
3150 $1 Larry in evening dress (face value at top left) . . 50 55
3151 $1 Curly in green shirt . . . 50 55
3152 $1 Moe in evening dress (face value at top right) 50 55

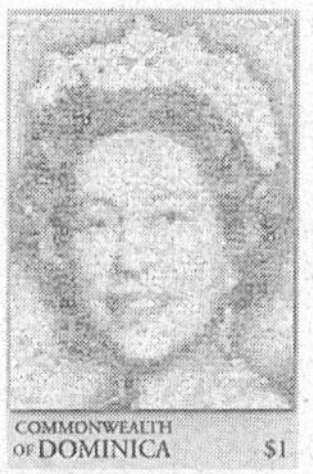

368 Queen Elizabeth II

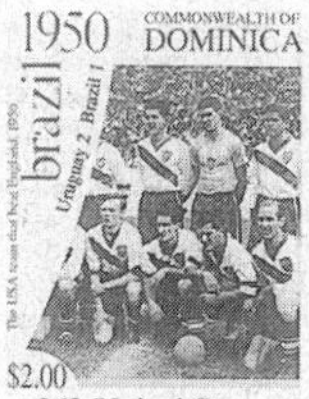

369 United States Team, Brazil, 1950

2001. Golden Jubilee.
3154 **368** $1 Multicoloured 50 55

No. 3154 was printed in sheetlets of 8, containing two vertical rows of four, separated by a large illustrated central gutter. Both the stamp and the illustration on the central gutter are made up of a collage of miniature flower photographs.

2001. World Cup Football Championship, Japan and Korea (2002). Multicoloured.
3155 $2 Type **369** . . . . 1·00 1·10
3156 $2 Publicity poster, Switzerland, 1954 . . . . 1·00 1·10
3157 $2 Publicity poster, Sweden, 1958 . . . . 1·00 1·10
3158 $2 Zozimo (Brazil), Chile, 1962 . . . . 1·00 1·10
3159 $2 Gordon Banks (England), England, 1966 1·00 1·10
3160 $2 Pele (Brazil), Mexico, 1970 . . . . 1·00 1·10
3161 $2 Daniel Passarella (Argentina), Argentina, 1978 . . . . 1·00 1·10
3162 $2 Paolo Rossi (Italy), Spain, 1982 . . . . . . 1·00 1·10
3163 $2 Diego Maradona (Argentina), Mexico, 1986 1·00 1·10
3164 $2 Publicity poster, Italy, 1990 . . . . 1·00 1·10
3165 $2 Seo Jungulon (South Korea), U.S.A., 1994 . . 1·00 1·10
3166 $2 Jürgen Klinsmann (Germany), France, 1998 1·00 1·10

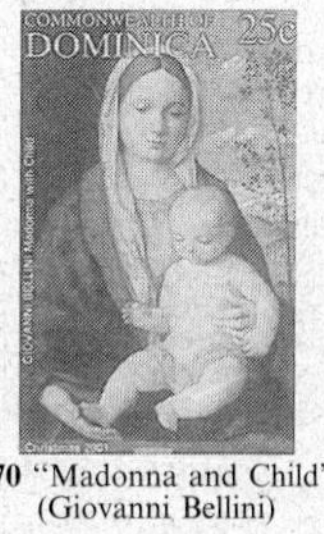

370 "Madonna and Child" (Giovanni Bellini)

2001. Christmas. Paintings by Giovanni Bellini. Multicoloured.
3168 25c. Type **370** 15 20
3169 65c. "Madonna with Child" 35 40
3170 90c. "Baptism of Christ" . . 45 50
3171 $1.20 "Madonna with Child" (different) 60 65
3172 $4 "Madonna with Child" (different) . . . . 2·00 2·10

2002. Golden Jubilee (2nd issue). As T **473** of Antigua. Multicoloured.
3174 $2 Queen Elizabeth in blue hat and coat . . . . . . 1·00 1·10
3175 $2 Queen Elizabeth presenting Prince Philip with polo trophy . . . . 1·00 1·10
3176 $2 Queen Elizabeth in evening dress . . . . . . 1·00 1·10
3177 $2 Queen Elizabeth in pink hat and coat . . . . . . 1·00 1·10

2002. "United We Stand". Support for Victims of 11 September 2001 Terrorist Attacks. As T **474** of Antigua.
3179 $2 U. S. Flag as Statue of Liberty and Dominica flag 1·00 1·10

APPENDIX

The following stamps have either been issued in excess of postal needs, or have not been made available to the public in reasonable quantities at face value.

1978.

History of Aviation. $16 × 30, each embossed on gold foil.

DOMINICAN REPUBLIC Pt. 15

The Eastern portion of the island of Hispaniola in the W. Indies finally became independent of Spain in 1865.

1865. 8 reales = 1 peso.
1880. 100 centavos = 1 peso.
1883. 100 centimos = 1 franco.
1885. 100 centavos = 1 peso.

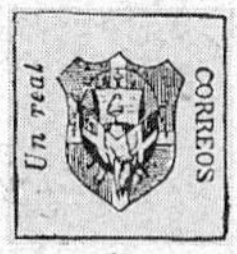

1

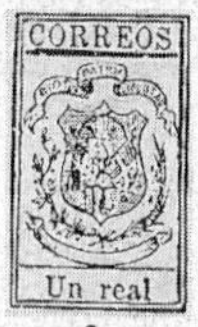

3

1865. Imperf.
1 **1** ½r. black on red £225 £200
3 ½r. black on green £350 £350
2 1r. black on green £600 £550
4 1r. black on yellow £1100 £950

1865. Imperf.
5 **3** ½r. black on buff £125 £100
7 ½r. black on red . . . . . 40·00 40·00
12 ½r. black on grey £120 £120
18 ½r. black and blue on red . . 50·00 30·00
19 ½r. black on yellow . . . . 25·00 25·00
20 1r. black on green . . . . . 50·00 50·00
9 1r. black on blue . . . . . 35·00 35·00
15 1r. black on flesh £100 £100
21 1r. black on lilac £200 £200

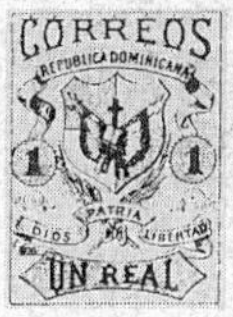

4

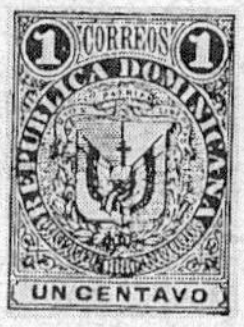

5

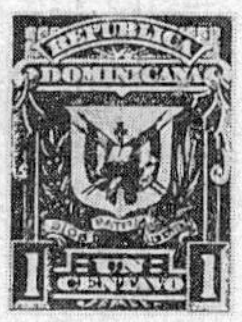
15

1879. Perf.
22 **4** ½r. violet . . . . 1·50 1·50
24 1r. red . . . . 1·50 1·50

1880. Rouletted.
35 **5** 1c. green 60 60
36 2c. red 60 60
28 5c. blue 85 70
38 10c. pink 60 60
39 20c. bistre 70 70
40 25c. mauve . . . . 1·25 1·00
32 50c. orange . . . . 1·50 1·10
33 75c. blue . . . . 3·25 3·25
34 1p. gold . . . . 4·00 4·00

1883. Surch.
44 **5** 5c. on 1c. green . . . . . 1·10 1·00
73 10c. on 2c. red . . . . . . 2·00 2·00
46 25c. on 5c. blue . . . . . 4·00 3·50
47 50c. on 10c. pink . . . . . 12·00 6·00
58 1f. on 20c. bistre . . . . . 7·00 7·00
51 1f.25 on 25c. mauve . . . 11·00 11·00
52 2f.50 on 50c. orange . . . 14·00 14·00
53 3f.75 on 75c. blue . . . . 16·00 16·00
64 5f. on 1p. gold . . . . . . 50·00 50·00

1885. Figures in lower corners only.
77 **15** 1c. green 30 15
78 2c. red 30 15
79 5c. blue 50 20
80 10c. orange 80 30
81 20c. brown 85 50
82 50c. violet . . . . 4·50 3·00
83 1p. red . . . . 10·00 10·00
84 2p. brown . . . . 12·00 10·00

1895. As T **15** but figures in four corners.
85 1c. green 60 30
86 2c. red 60 30
87 5c. blue 70 30
88 10c. orange 75 30

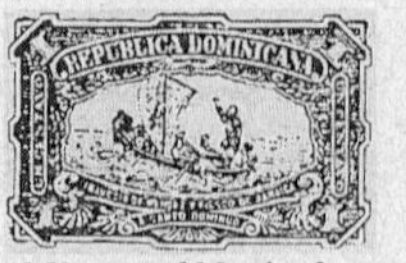
18 Voyage of Mendez from Jamaica to Santo Domingo

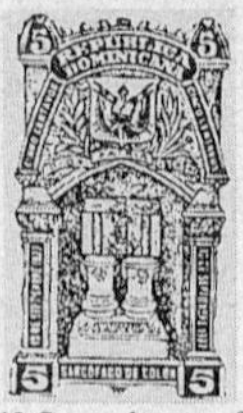
19 Sarcophagus of Columbus

1899. Columbus Mausoleum Fund.

98	**19**	½c. black	1·00	1·00
99	–	½c. black	1·00	1·00
89	**18**	1c. purple	4·50	3·50
90		1c. green	1·00	40
91	–	2c. red	50	50
92	**19**	5c. blue	75	55
93	–	10c. orange	2·00	1·00
94	–	20c. brown	4·00	4·00
95	–	50c. green	4·00	4·00
96	–	1p. black on blue	12·00	10·00
97	–	2p. brown on cream	25·00	25·00

DESIGNS—AS TYPE **18**: ½c. (No. 99), 1p. Columbus at Salamanca Assembly; 2c. Enriquillo's Rebellion; 20c. Toscanelli replying to Columbus; 50c. Las Casas defending Indians. As Type **19**: 10c. Hispaniola guarding remains of Columbus; 2p. Columbus Mausoleum, Santo Domingo Cathedral.

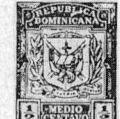

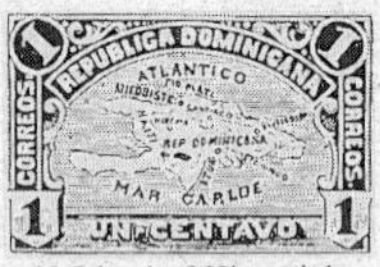
20 Island of Hispaniola

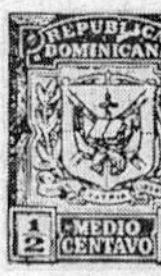
21

1900.

100	**20**	½c. blue	45	40
101		½c. red	45	40
102		1c. olive	45	35
103		2c. green	45	35
104		5c. brown	45	35
105		10c. orange	35	35
106		20c. purple	1·50	1·50
107		50c. black	1·40	1·25
108		1p. brown	1·40	1·25

1901.

109	**21**	½c. lilac and red	25	25
110		1c. lilac and olive	35	20
111		2c. lilac and green	35	20
112		5c. lilac and brown	35	25
113		10c. lilac and orange	75	30
114		20c. lilac and brown	1·50	80
115		50c. lilac and black	4·50	2·50
116		1p. lilac and brown	9·50	7·00

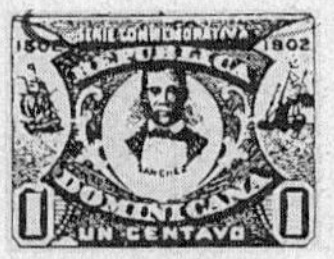
24 Sanchez

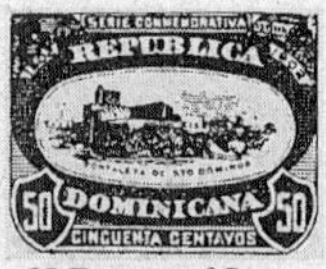
25 Fortress of Santo Domingo

1902. 400th Anniv of Santo Domingo.

125	**24**	1c. black & green	25	25
126		2c. black & red (Duarte)	25	25
127		5c. blk & blue (Duarte)	25	25
128		10c. blk & orge (Sanchez)	25	25
129		12c. blk & violet (Mella)	25	25
130		20c. black & red (Mella)	25	25
131	**25**	50c. black and brown	1·60	1·75

1904. Surch with new value.

132	**21**	2c. on 50c. lilac & black	5·50	4·25
133		2c. on 1p. lilac & brown	7·50	4·50
134		5c. on 50c. lilac & black	2·00	1·60
135		5c. on 1p. lilac and brown	3·00	2·40
136		10c. on 50c. lilac & black	4·75	4·00
137		10c. on 1p. lilac & brown	4·75	4·00

1904. Official stamps optd **16 de Agosto 1904** or surch **1 1** also.

138	O **23**	1c. on 20c. blk & yell	3·25	2·75
139		2c. black and red	5·00	3·00
140		5c. black and blue	3·00	2·25
141		10c. black and green	4·75	3·25

1904. Postage Due stamps optd **REPUBLICA DOMINICANA CENTAVOS CORREOS** or surch 1 also.

142	D **22**	1c. on 2c. sepia	1·75	85
143		1c. on 4c. sepia	70	50
145		2c. sepia	70	35

1905. Surch **1905** and new value.

146	**15**	2c. on 20c. brown	5·00	4·00
147		5c. on 20c. brown	2·25	1·40
148		10c. on 20c. brown	5·00	4·00

1905.

149	**21**	½c. orange and black	1·00	55
150		1c. blue and black	1·25	50
151		2c. mauve and black	1·25	40
152		5c. red and black	1·50	70
153		10c. green and black	2·75	1·40
154		20c. olive and black	8·50	4·75
155		50c. brown and black	27·00	15·00
156		1p. grey and black	£150	£150

1906. Postage Due stamps surch **REPUBLICA DOMINICANA.** and new value.

157	D **22**	1c. on 4c. sepia	70	40
158		1c. on 10c. sepia	85	40
159		2c. on 5c. sepia	85	40

1907.

168	**21**	½c. black and green	55	15
169		1c. black and red	55	15
170		2c. black and brown	55	15
171		5c. black and blue	60	20
164		10c. black and purple	85	35
165		20c. black and olive	4·75	2·40
166		50c. black and brown	4·75	4·00
167		1p. black and violet	12·00	6·50

1911. No. O178 optd **HABILITADO. 1911**.

182	O **23**	2c. black and red	1·00	50

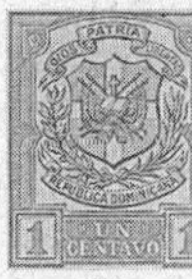
34

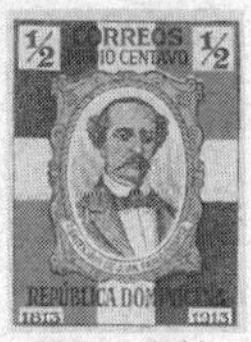
35 Jaun Pablo Duarte

1911.

183	**34**	½c. black and orange	25	15
184		1c. black and green	25	10
185		2c. black and red	25	10
186		5c. black and blue	50	15
187		10c. black and purple	1·00	40
188		20c. black and olive	5·50	3·25
189		50c. black and brown	2·40	2·00
190		1p. black and violet	4·00	2·40

For stamps in other colours see Nos. 235/8 and for stamps in similar type see No. 240/6.

1914. Birth Centenary of Duarte. Background in red, white and blue.

195	**35**	½c. black and orange	45	35
196		1c. black and green	45	35
197		2c. black and red	45	35
198		5c. black and grey	55	40
199		10c. black and mauve	85	50
200		20c. black and olive	2·00	1·40
201		50c. black and brown	2·75	2·40
202		1p. black and lilac	4·00	3·00

1915. Nos. O177/181 optd **Habilitado 1915** or surch **MEDIO CENTAVO** also.

203	O **23**	½c. on 20c. blk & yell	50	35
204		1c. black and green	70	25
205		2c. black and red	70	35
206		5c. black and blue	85	35
207		10c. black and green	2·00	1·60
208		20c. black and yellow	6·50	5·50

1915. Optd **1915**.

209	**34**	½c. black and mauve	55	15
210		1c. black and brown	55	10
211		2c. black and olive	2·00	25
213		5c. black and red	2·00	25
214		10c. black and blue	2·00	35
215		20c. black and red	5·50	1·25
216		50c. black and green	6·00	2·75
217		1p. black and orange	12·00	5·50

1916. Optd **1916**.

218	**34**	½c. black and mauve	70	10
219		1c. black and green	1·40	10

1917. Optd **1917**.

220	**34**	½c. black and mauve	1·00	25
221		1c. black and green	1·00	10
222		2c. black and olive	85	10
223		5c. black and red	7·50	70

1919. Optd **1919**.

224	**34**	2c. black and olive	4·00	10

1920. Optd **1920**.

225	**34**	½c. black and mauve	45	20
226		1c. black and green	45	10
227		2c. black and olive	45	10
228		5c. black and red	4·75	45
229		10c. black and blue	2·75	20
230		20c. black and red	4·75	45
231		50c. black and green	40·00	10·00

1921. Optd **1921**.

233	**34**	1c. black and green	1·25	25
234		2c. black and olive	2·40	30

1922.

235	**34**	½c. black and red	25	10
236		1c. green	70	10
237		2c. red	1·00	10
238		5c. blue	2·00	25

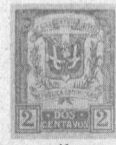

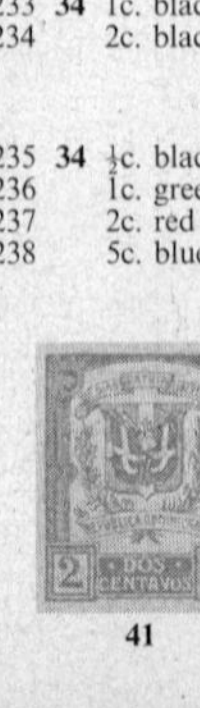
41

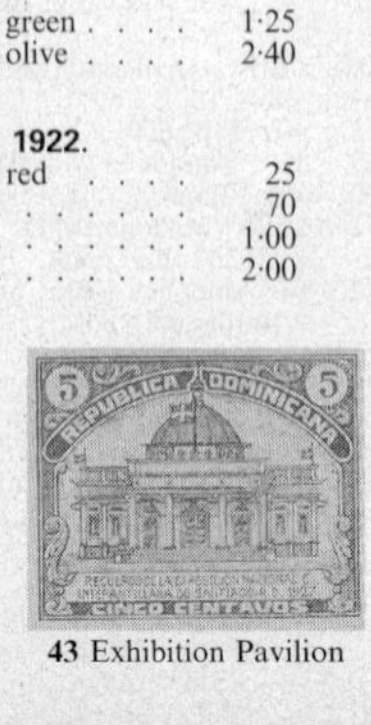
43 Exhibition Pavilion

1924. Straight top to shield.

240	**41**	1c. green	40	10
241		2c. red	55	10
242		5c. blue	55	10
243		10c. black and blue	6·50	1·40
245		50c. black and green	35·00	2·00
246		1p. black and orange	12·00	8·50

1927. National and West Indian Exn, Santiago.

248	**43**	2c. red	70	45
249		5c. blue	85	45

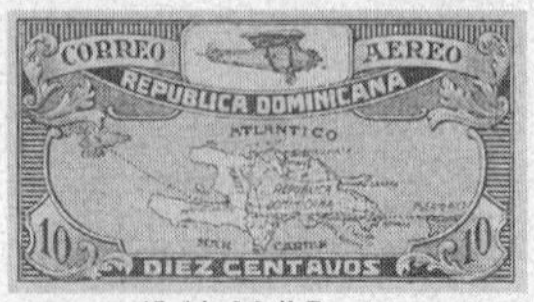
45 Air Mail Routes

1928. Air.

256	**45**	10c. deep blue	5·75	3·00
280		10c. pale blue	1·90	75
271		10c. yellow	4·00	3·00
272		15c. red	7·75	4·00
281		15c. turquoise	4·00	1·10
273		20c. green	3·75	60
282		20c. brown	4·50	55
274		30c. violet	7·75	4·50
283		30c. brown	7·25	1·75

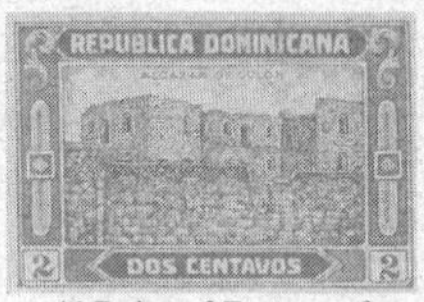
46 Ruins of Fortress of Columbus

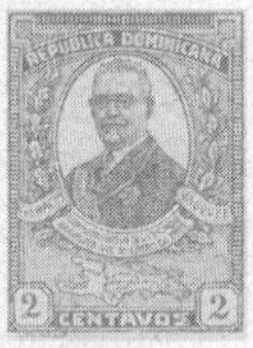
47 Horacio Vasquez

1928.

258	**46**	½c. red	45	25
259		1c. green	40	10
260		2c. red	40	10
261		5c. blue	1·00	25
262		10c. blue	1·00	25
263		20c. red	1·50	40
264		50c. green	8·50	4·75
265		1p. yellow	15·00	10·00

1929. Frontier Agreement with Haiti.

266	**47**	½c. red	40	20
267		1c. green	40	15
268		2c. red	45	15
269		5c. blue	85	25
270		10c. blue	3·00	55

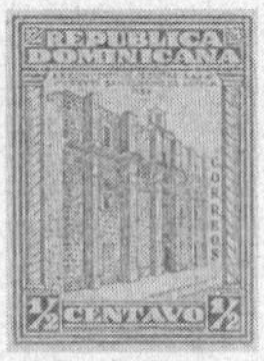
48 Jesuit Convent of San Ignacio de Loyola

49 After the Hurricane

1930.

275	**48**	½c. brown	50	40
276		1c. green	45	10
277		2c. red	45	10
278		5c. blue	1·25	35
279		10c. blue	2·40	85

1930. Hurricane Relief.

284	–	1c. green and red	15	35
285	–	2c. red	20	25
286	**49**	5c. blue and red	35	50
287		10c. yellow and red	40	70

DESIGN: 1c., 2c. Riverside.

1931. Air. Hurricane Relief. Surch with airplane, **HABILITADO PARA CORREO AEREO** and premium. Imperf or perf.

288	**49**	5c.+5c. blue and red	6·50	6·50
289		5c.+5c. black and red	15·00	15·00
290		10c.+10c. yellow & red	5·00	6·50
291		10c.+10c. black & red	15·00	15·00

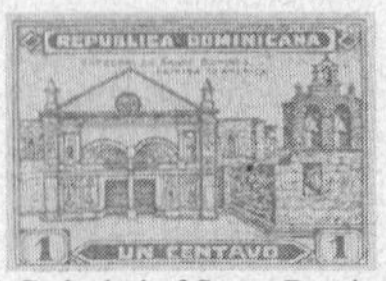
52 Cathedral of Santo Domingo

1931.

294	**52**	1c. green	50	15
295		2c. red	50	15
296		3c. purple	55	10
297		7c. blue	1·40	20
298		8c. brown	2·40	70
299		10c. blue	3·00	85

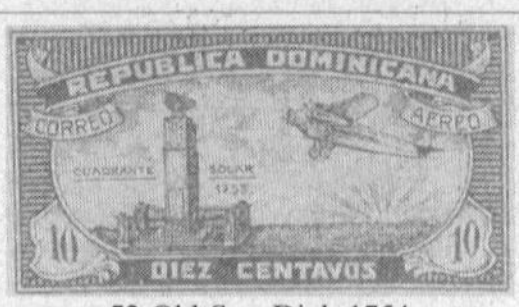
53 Old Sun Dial, 1754

1931. Air.

300	**53**	10c. red	5·00	60
301		10c. blue	2·00	55
302		10c. green	8·00	2·75
303		15c. mauve	3·75	55
304		20c. blue	7·25	1·60
306		30c. green	3·25	40
307		50c. brown	4·75	80
308		1p. orange	13·00	2·75

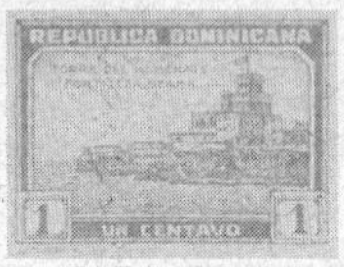
54 Fort Ozama

1932.

309	**54**	1c. green	50	40
310		1c. green	25	10
311		3c. violet	35	10

No. 310 is inscribed "CORREOS".

1932. Red Cross stamps inscr "CRUZ ROJA DOMINICANA", with cross in red and optd **HABILITADO Dic. 20-1932 En. 5-1933 CORREOS** or surch also.

312		1c. green	20	15
313		3c. on 2c. violet	30	15
314		5c. blue	70	60
315		7c. on 10c. blue	1·10	85

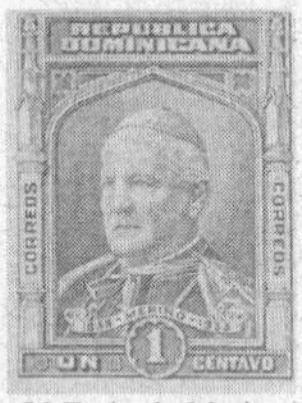
56 F. A. de Merino

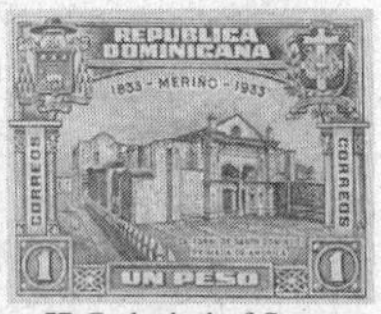
57 Cathedral of Santo Domingo

1933. Birth Centenary of F. A. de Merino.

316	–	½c. violet	25	15
317	**56**	1c. green	25	15
318	–	2c. red	70	55
319	**56**	3c. violet	35	15
320	–	5c. blue	45	20
321	–	7c. blue	90	35
322	–	8c. green	1·25	70
323	**56**	10c. orange	1·00	25
324	–	20c. red	2·25	1·40
325	**57**	50c. olive	9·00	5·50
326		1p. sepia	22·00	13·00

DESIGNS—VERT: ½c., 5c., 8c. Merino's Tomb; 2c., 7c., 20c. Merino in uniform.

1933. Portraits as T **56**.

327		1c. black and green	50	25
328		3c. black and violet	55	15
329		7c. black and blue	1·60	55

DESIGNS: 1c., 7c. Pres. Trujillo in uniform; 3c. Pres. Trujillo in evening dress.

1933. Air. Optd **CORREO AEREO INTERNO**.

330	**52**	2c. red	40	30

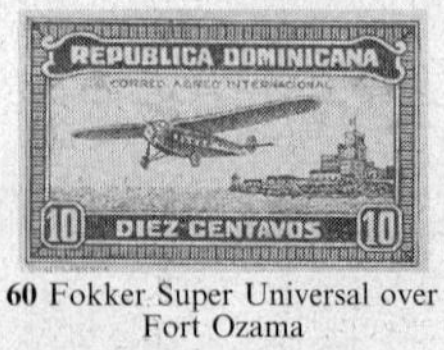
60 Fokker Super Universal over Fort Ozama

1933. Air.

331	**60**	10c. blue	3·50	50

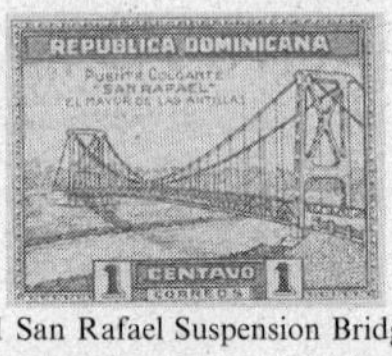
61 San Rafael Suspension Bridge

1934.

332	**61**	½c. mauve	55	25
333		1c. green	80	15
334		3c. violet	1·25	10

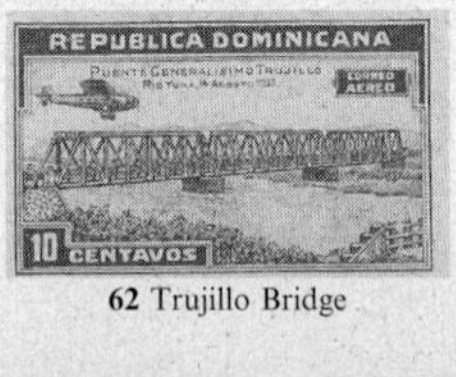
62 Trujillo Bridge

1934. (a) Postage. As T **62** but without airplane and inscr "CORREOS".

335	–	½c. brown	50	15
336	–	1c. green	80	10
337	–	3c. violet	1·00	10

(b) Air.

338	**62**	10c. blue	3·25	50

64 National Palace

1935. For obligatory use on mail addressed to the President.

346	**64**	25c. orange	2·00	15

1935. Opening of Ramfis Bridge. As T **62** but view of Ramfis Suspension Bridge.

347	1c. green	45	10
348	3c. brown	45	10
349	5c. purple	1·00	50
350	10c. pink	2·00	1·00

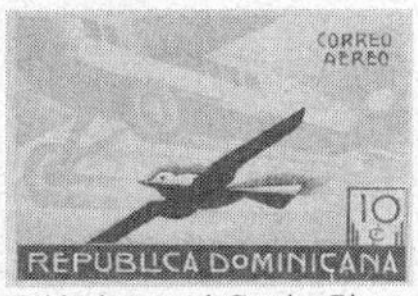

66 Airplane and Carrier Pigeon

1935. Air.

351	**66**	10c. light blue and blue	2·50	45

67 President Trujillo

1935. Frontier Agreement.

352	**67**	3c. brown and yellow	30	15
353	–	5c. brown and orange	35	10
354	–	7c. brown and blue	55	10
355	–	10c. brown and purple	85	10

RECTANGULAR DESIGNS: Portrait as Type **67**. Red, white and blue ribbons in side panels on 7c. or diagonally across 5c. and 10c.

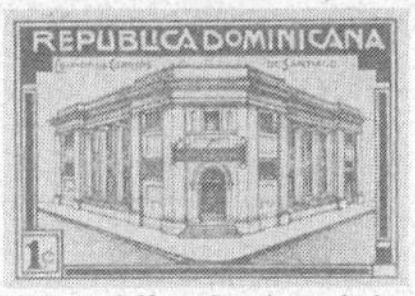

69 Post Office, Santiago de los Caballeros

1936.

356	**69**	½c. violet	30	20
357		1c. green	30	10

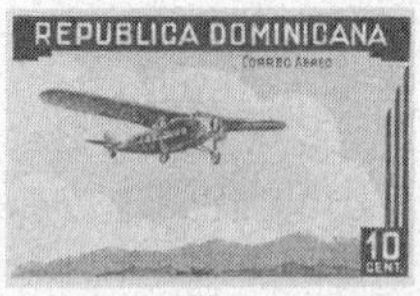

70

1936. Air.

358	**70**	10c. blue	2·75	45

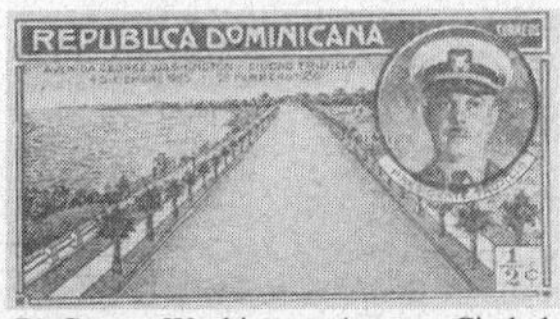

71 George Washington Avenue, Ciudad Trujillo

1936. Dedication of George Washington Avenue.

359	**71**	½c. brown	35	25
360		2c. brown and red	60	20
361		3c. brown and yellow	60	15
362		7c. brown and blue	85	50

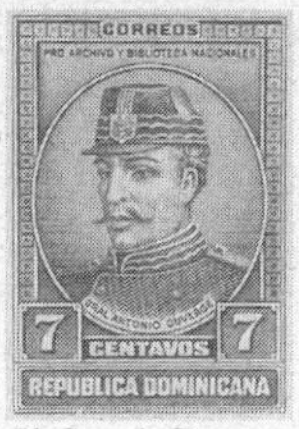

72 Gen. A. Duverge

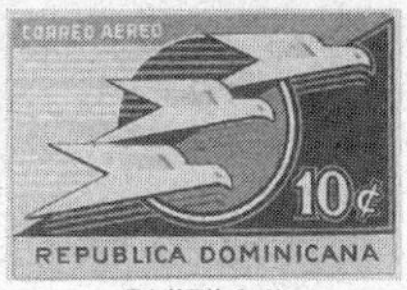

74 "Flight"

1936. National Archives and Library Fund. Inscr "PRO ARCHIVO Y BIBLIOTECA NACIONALES".

363	–	½c. lilac	25	15
364	–	1c. green	20	10
365	–	2c. red	20	10
366	–	3c. violet	25	10
367	–	5c. blue	40	25
368	**72**	7c. blue	70	50
369	–	10c. orange	85	30
370	–	20c. olive	3·25	1·90
371	–	25c. purple	3·25	2·00
372	–	30c. red	5·00	2·75
373	–	50c. brown	6·00	2·75
374	–	1p. black	15·00	12·00
375	–	2p. brown	40·00	35·00

DESIGNS—As Type **72**: ½c. J. N. de Caceres; 1c. Gen. G. Luperon; 2c. E. Tejera; 3c. Pres. Trujillo; 5c. Jose Reyes; 10c. Felix M. Del Monte; 25c. F. J. Peynado; 30c. Salome Urena; 50c. Gen. Jose Ma. Cabral; 1p. Manuel Js. Galvan; 2p. Gaston F. Deligne. TRIANGULAR: 20c. National Library.

1936. Air.

376	**74**	10c. blue	2·10	35

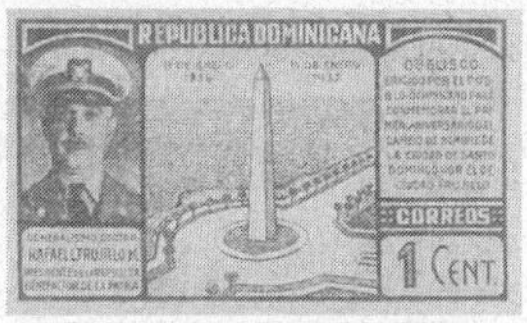

75 Obelisk in Ciudad Trujillo

1937. 1st Anniv of Naming of Ciudad Trujillo (formerly Santo Domingo).

377	**75**	1c. green	20	10
378		3c. violet	40	10
379		7c. blue	1·25	60

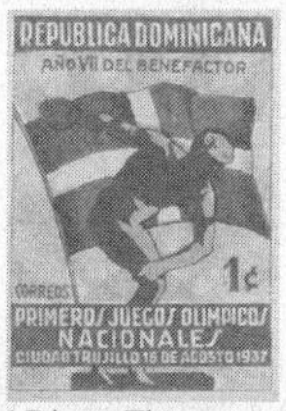

76 Discus Thrower and National Flag

1937. 1st National Olympic Games, Ciudad Trujillo. Flag blue, white and red.

380	**76**	1c. green	6·50	70
381		3c. violet	8·50	50
382		7c. blue	15·00	2·75

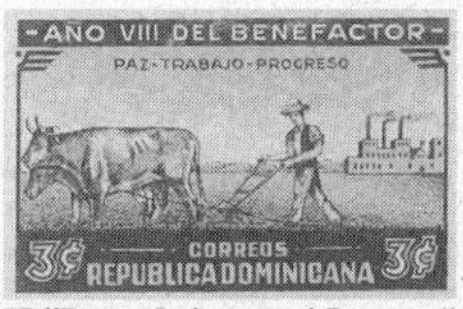

77 "Peace, Labour and Progress"

1937. 8th Year of Trujillo Presidency.

383	**77**	3c. violet	35	10

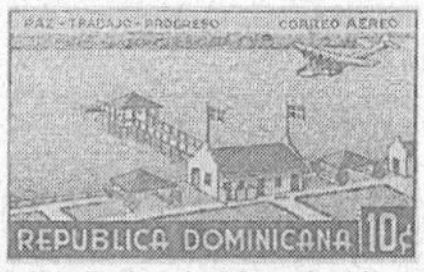

78 San Pedro de Macoris Airport

1937. Air.

384	**78**	10c. green	1·25	10

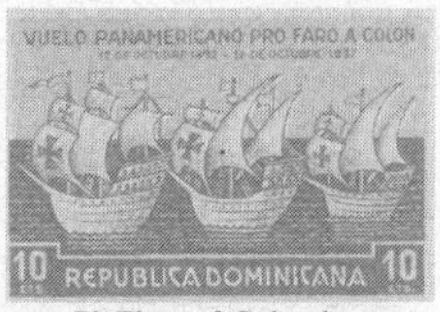

79 Fleet of Columbus

1937. Air. Pan-American Goodwill Flight.

385	**79**	10c. red	3·75	1·25
386	A	15c. violet	1·75	70
387	B	20c. blue	1·75	70
388	A	25c. purple	2·50	85
389	B	30c. green	2·25	70
390	A	50c. brown	4·25	1·00
391	B	75c. olive	11·00	11·00
392	**79**	1p. red	12·00	2·75

DESIGNS—A, Junkers F-13 aircraft in Goodwill Flight; B, Junkers F-13 aircraft over Columbus Lighthouse.

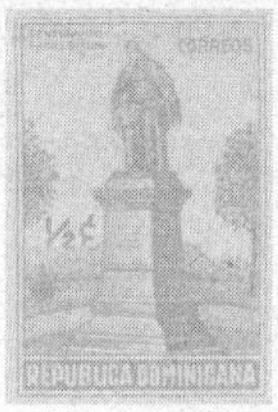

83 Father Billini

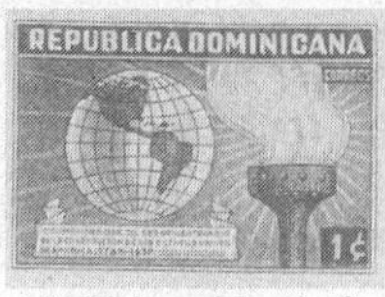

84 Globe and Torch of Liberty

1938. Birth Centenary of Father Billini.

396	**83**	½c. orange	15	10
397		5c. violet	45	15

1938. 150th Anniv of U.S. Constitution.

398	**84**	1c. green	30	10
399		3c. violet	45	10
400		10c. orange	85	20

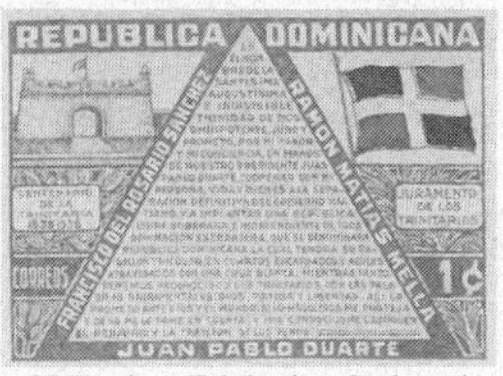

85 Bastion, Trinitarian Oath and National Flag

1938. Centenary of Trinitarian Rebellion.

401	**85**	1c. green	40	20
402		3c. violet	50	15
403		10c. orange	1·00	45

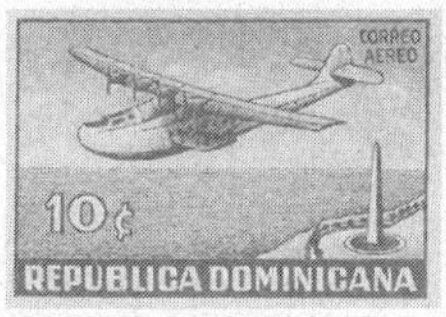

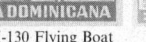

86 Martin M-130 Flying Boat over Obelisk

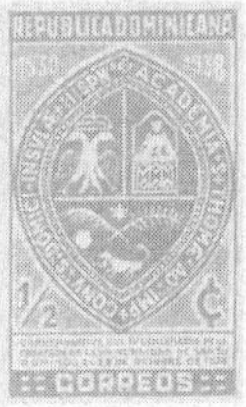

87 Arms of University

1938. Air.

404	**86**	10c. green	1·40	15

1938. 400th Anniv of Santo Domingo University.

405	**87**	½c. orange	25	15
406		1c. green	35	10
407		3c. violet	40	10
408		7c. blue	85	40

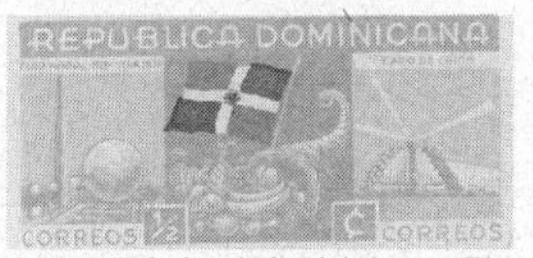

89 N.Y. Fair Symbol, Lighthouse, Flag and Cornucopia

1939. New York World's Fair. (a) Postage. Flag in blue, white and red.

418	**89**	½c. orange	35	15
419		1c. green	40	15
420		3c. violet	40	15
421		10c. yellow	1·25	45

(b) Air. Flag, etc, replaced by airplane.

422	10c. green	1·50	55

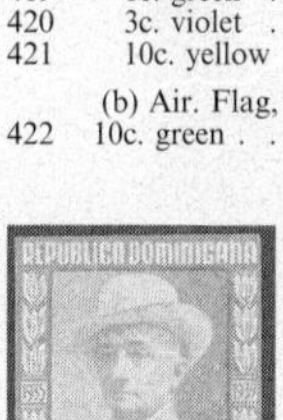

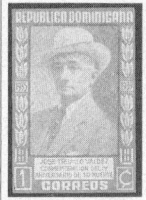

90 Jose Trujillo Valdez

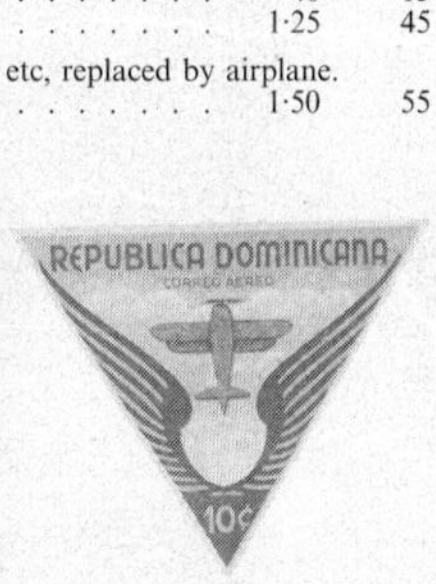

91

1939. 4th Death Anniv of Jose Trujillo Valdez. Black borders.

423	**90**	½c. grey	25	15
424		1c. green	35	10
425		3c. brown	40	10
426		7c. blue	85	50
427		10c. violet	1·50	40

1939. Air.

428	**91**	10c. green	1·40	20

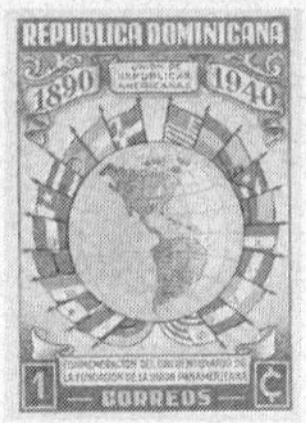

92 Western Hemisphere and Union Flags

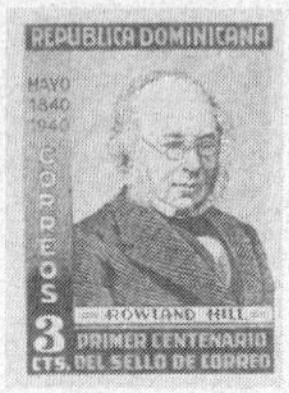

93 Sir Rowland Hill

1940. 50th Anniv of Pan-American Union. Flags in national colours.

429	**92**	1c. green	25	10
430		2c. red	35	15
431		3c. violet	55	10
432		10c. orange	1·10	20
433		1p. brown	15·00	10·00

1940. Centenary of 1st Adhesive Postage Stamps.

434	**93**	3c. mauve	6·50	40
435		7c. blue	12·00	1·50

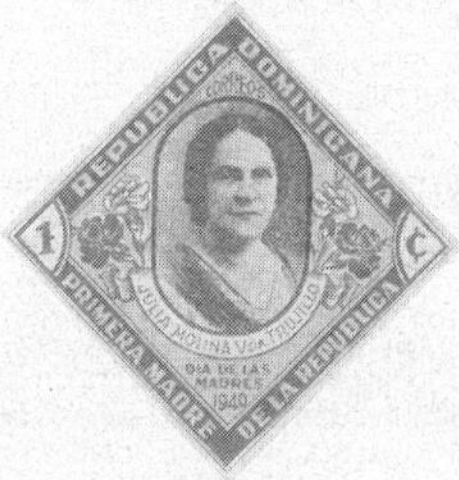

94 Julia Molina de Trujillo

1940. Mothers' Day.

436	**94**	1c. green	30	10
437		2c. red	40	10
438		3c. orange	50	10
439		7c. blue	1·25	45

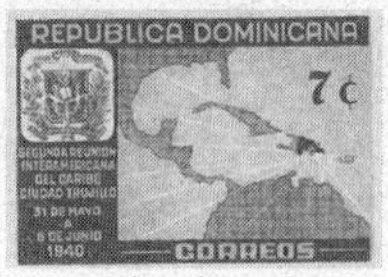

95 Central America and Arms of Dominican Republic

1940. 2nd Caribbean Conference, Trujillo City.

440	**95**	3c. red	40	10
441		7c. blue	85	15
442		1p. green	8·50	4·25

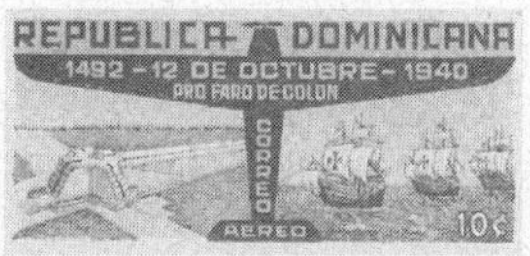

96 Lighthouse, Aeroplane and Caravels

1940. Air. Discovery of America and Columbus Memorial Lighthouse. Inscr "PRO FARO DE COLON".

443	**96**	10c. blue	1·40	50
444	–	15c. brown	80	70
445	–	20c. red	80	70
446	–	25c. mauve	80	35
447	–	50c. green	4·00	1·60

DESIGNS: 15c. Columbus and lighthouse; 20c. Lighthouse; 25c. Columbus; 50c. Caravel and wings.

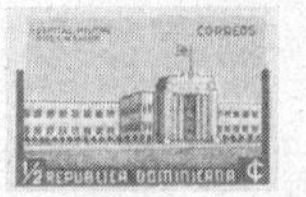

99 Marion Military Hospital

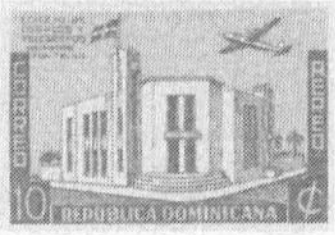

100 Post Office, San Cristobal

1940.

457	**99**	½c. brown	25	20

1941. Air.

458	**100**	10c. mauve	65	15

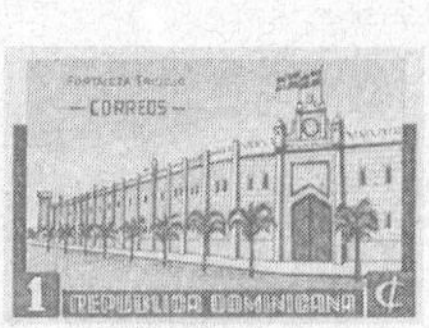

101 Trujillo Fortress

1941.

460	**101**	1c. green	15	10
461	–	2c. red	15	10
462	–	10c. brown	55	10

DESIGN—VERT: 2, 10c. Statue of Columbus, Ciudad Trujillo.

103 Sanchez, Duarte, Mella and Trujillo

1941. Trujillo-Hull Treaty.

463	103	3c. mauve	25	10
464		4c. red	30	10
465		13c. blue	70	20
466		15c. brown	2·00	85
467		17c. blue	2·00	90
468		1p. orange	7·50	3·25
469		2p. grey	15·00	7·50

104 Bastion of 27 February

1941.

470	104	5c. blue	55	20

105 Rural School, Torch of Knowledge and Pres. Trujillo

1941. Popular Education Campaign.

471	105	$\frac{1}{2}$c. brown	20	10
472		1c. green	25	10

106 Globe and Winged Envelope

1941. Air.

473	106	10c. brown	55	10
474		75c. orange	3·25	2·00

107 National Reserve Bank

1942.

475	107	5c. brown	40	10
476		17c. blue	1·00	40

108 Symbolic of Communications

109 Our Lady of Highest Grace

1942. 8th Anniv of Postal and Telegraph Services Day.

477	108	3c. multicoloured	4·00	1·00
478		15c. multicoloured	8·00	4·00

1942. 20th Anniv of Our Lady of Highest Grace.

479	109	$\frac{1}{2}$c. grey	85	10
480		1c. green	1·60	10
481		3c. mauve	7·50	10
482		5c. purple	2·40	10
483		10c. red	6·50	25
484		15c. blue	7·50	35

111 Banana Tree

112 Cows

1942.

494	111	3c. green and brown	45	10
495		4c. black and red	50	20
496	112	5c. brown and blue	45	10
497		15c. green and purple	85	35

113 Party Emblems and Votes

1943. Re-election of Gen. Trujillo to Presidency.

498	113	3c. orange	40	10
499		4c. red	50	15
500		13c. purple	1·10	20
501		1p. blue	5·00	1·90

114 Trujillo Market

1943.

502	114	2c. brown	15	10

115 Douglas DC-3

1943. Air.

503	115	10c. mauve	50	10
504		20c. blue	55	15
505		25c. olive	6·75	2·75

116 Bastion of 27 February

117 Monument and Dates

1944. Centenary of Independence. (a) Postage. Flag in blue and red.

506	116	$\frac{1}{2}$c. ochre	10	10
507		1c. green	10	10
508		2c. red	15	10
509		3c. purple	15	10
510		5c. orange	20	10
511		7c. blue	25	10
512		10c. brown	40	30
513		20c. olive	70	45
514		50c. blue	2·00	1·40

(b) Air. Flag in grey, blue and red.

515	117	10c. multicoloured	40	10
516		20c. multicoloured	50	15
517		1p. multicoloured	2·40	1·60

118 Dr. Martos Sanatorium

1944. Tuberculosis Relief Fund.

518	118	1c. blue and red	15	10

119 Nurse and Battlefield

1944. 80th Anniv of International Red Cross.

519	119	1c. green, red and yellow	15	10
520		2c. brown, red and yellow	35	10
521		3c. blue, red and yellow	35	10
522		10c. red and yellow	70	15

120 Communications Building, Ciudad Trujillo

1944. Air.

523	120	9c. blue and green	25	10
524		13c. red and brown	35	10
525		25c. red and orange	50	10
526		30c. blue and black	1·10	80

121 Municipal Building, San Cristobal

122 Emblem of Communications

1945. Centenary of 1st Constitution of Dominican Republic.

527	121	$\frac{1}{2}$c. blue	10	10
528		1c. green	10	10
529		2c. orange	10	10
530		3c. brown	15	10
531		10c. blue	45	15

1945. Centres in blue and red.

532	122	3c. orange (postage)	15	10
533		20c. green	80	20
534		50c. blue	1·60	60
535		7c. green (air)	20	25
536		12c. orange	25	15
537		13c. blue	30	15
538		25c. brown	60	20

124 Flags and National Anthem

125 Law Courts, Ciudad Trujillo

1946. Air. National Anthem.

540	124	10c. red	45	40
541		15c. blue	1·00	70
542		20c. brown	1·25	70
543		35c. orange	1·40	70
544	–	1p. green	13·00	10·00

DESIGN: 1p. As Type **124**, but horiz.

1946.

545	125	3c. brown and buff	20	10

126 Caribbean Air Routes

1946. 450th Anniv of Santo Domingo.

546	126	10c. mult (postage)	40	15
547		10c. multicoloured (air)	35	15
548		13c. multicoloured	55	15

127 Jimenoa Waterfall

128 Nurse and Child

1947. Centres multicoloured, frame colours given.

549	127	1c. green (postage)	15	10
550		2c. red	15	10
551		3c. blue	15	10
552		13c. purple	45	25
553		20c. brown	1·00	25
554		50c. yellow	1·90	1·00
555		18c. blue (air)	50	50
556		23c. red	70	55
557		50c. violet	1·00	45
558		75c. brown	1·40	1·00

1947. Obligatory Tax. Tuberculosis Relief Fund.

559	128	1c. blue and red	15	10

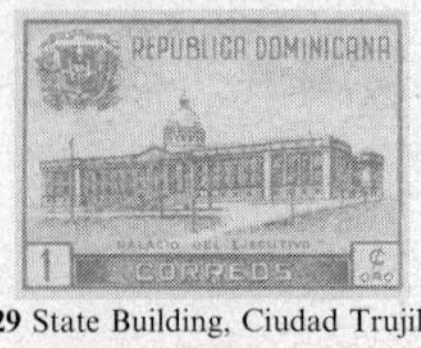
129 State Building, Ciudad Trujillo

1948.

560	129	1c. green (postage)	10	10
561		3c. blue	15	10
562		37c. brown (air)	1·00	70
563		1p. orange	2·75	1·60

130 Ruins of San Francisco Church, Ciudad Trujillo

131 El Santo Socorro Sanatorium

1949.

564	130	1c. green (postage)	10	10
565		3c. blue	15	10
566		7c. olive (air)	15	10
567		10c. brown	15	10
568		15c. red	50	25
569		20c. green	70	45

1949. Tuberculosis Relief Fund.

570	131	1c. blue and red	15	10

132 General Pedro Santana

133 Monument

1949. Centenary of Battle of Las Carreras.

571	132	3c. blue (postage)	15	10
572	133	10c. red (air)	25	10

134 Bird and Globe

136 Hotel Jimani

135 Youth Holding Banner

138 Ruins of Church and Hospital of St. Nicholas of Bari

1949. 75th Anniv of U.P.U.

573	134	1c. brown and green	15	10
574		2c. brown and yellow	15	10
575		5c. brown and blue	20	10
576		7c. brown and blue	45	15

1950. Tuberculosis Relief Fund.

584	135	1c. blue and red	20	10

1950. Various Hotels.

585	136	$\frac{1}{2}$c. brown (postage)	10	10
586	–	1c. green (Hamaca)	10	10
587	–	2c. orange (Hamaca)	10	10
588	–	5c. blue (Montana)	20	10
589	–	15c. orge (San Cristobal)	45	10
590	–	20c. lilac (Maguana)	85	15
591	136	$1 yellow and brown	3·25	1·40
592	–	12c. bl (Montana) (air)	25	10
593	–	37c. red (San Cristobal)	1·90	1·50

1950. 13th Pan-American Sanitary Congress. Inscr as T **138**.

595	138	2c. brown & green (postage)	20	10
596	–	5c. brown and blue	25	10
597	–	12c. orange & brn (air)	55	10

DESIGNS—VERT: 5c. Medical school; 12c. Map and aeroplane.

139 "Suffer Little Children to Come Unto Me"

148

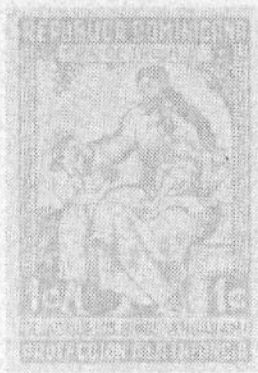

148a **148b**

1950. Child Welfare. (a) Child at left with light hair.
598 **139** 1c. blue 25 10

(b) Child at left with dark hair.
599 **139** 1c. blue 85 15

(c) Child at left with dark hair.
626 **148** 1c. blue 20 10

(d) Child at left with light hair.
627 **148a** 1c. blue 15 10

(e) Dark hair, smaller figures and square value tablet.
628 **148b** 1c. blue 15 10
There are two versions of No. 628, differing in size.
See also Nos. 835 and 907.

140 Isabella the Catholic

1951. 500th Birth Anniv of Isabella the Catholic.
600 **140** 5c. brown and blue . . . 25 10

141 Santiago Tuberculosis Sanatorium

1952. Tuberculosis Relief Fund.
601 **141** 1c. blue and red 15 10

142 Dr. S. B. Gautier Hospital

1952.
602 **142** 1c. green (postage) . . . 10 10
603 2c. red 15 10
604 5c. blue 25 10

605 23c. blue (air) 55 55
606 29c. red . . . . 1·40 1·00

143 Columbus Lighthouse and Flags **144**

1953. 460th Anniv of Columbus's Discovery of Santo Domingo. (a) Postage.
607 **143** 2c. green 15 10
608 5c. blue 20 10
609 10c. red 35 20

(b) Air. Similar design inscr "S./S.A.S./XMY", etc.
610 12c. brown 35 15
611 14c. blue 35 20
612 20c. sepia 65 40
613 23c. purple 70 45
614 25c. blue 70 45
615 29c. green 90 45
616 1p. brown . . . . 3·25 2·00
DESIGN: Nos. 610/16, Douglas DC-6 airplane over Columbus Lighthouse.

1953. Anti-cancer Fund. No. 619 has "1 c" larger with line through "c" and no stop. No. 620 is as 619 but with smaller "c".
618 **144** 1c. red 20 10
619 1c. red 35 10
620 1c. red 15 10
See also Nos. 1029/30, 1066/7, 1171a, 1196a, 1237a, 1270a and 1338a.

145 T.B. Children's Dispensary

1953. Obligatory Tax. Tuberculosis Relief Fund.
621 **145** 1c. blue and red 15 10
There are two versions of this design.

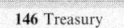

146 Treasury **149** Jose Marti

150 Monument to Trujillo Peace **147** Rio Haina Sugar Factory

1953.
622 **146** ½c. brown 10 10
623 2c. blue 10 10
624 **147** 5c. brown and blue . . . 15 10
625 **146** 15c. orange 50 15

1953. Birth Cent of Marti (Cuban revolutionary).
629 **149** 10c. sepia and blue . . . 30 15

1954.
630 **150** 2c. green 10 10
631 7c. blue 15 10
632 20c. orange 55 10
There are two versions of No. 631.

151 **152** Rotary Emblem

1954. Air. Marian Year.
633 **151** 8c. purple 15 10
634 11c. blue 25 10
635 33c. orange 70 45

1955. 50th Anniv of Rotary International.
636 **152** 7c. blue (postage) 30 10

637 11c. red (air) 25 15

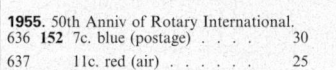

153 **154** Pres. R. Trujillo

1955. Obligatory Tax. Tuberculosis Relief Fund.
638 **153** 1c. black, red & yellow 15 10

1955. 25th Year of Trujillo Era.
639 **154** 2c. red (postage) 10 10
640 – 4c. green 15 10
641 – 7c. blue 15 10
642 – 10c. brown 35 15

643 – 11c. red, yell & bl (air) . . 30 10
644 – 25c. purple 45 25
645 – 33c. brown 70 40
DESIGNS: 4c. Pres. R. Trujillo in civilian clothes; 7c. Equestrian statue; 10c. Allegory of Prosperity; 11c. National flags; 25c. Gen. Hector B. Trujillo in evening clothes; 33c. Gen. Hector B. Trujillo in uniform.

156 Angelita Trujillo

1955. Child Welfare.
654 **156** 1c. violet 15 10

157 Angelita Trujillo **158** Gen. R. Trujillo

1955. Peace and Brotherhood Fair, Ciudad Trujillo.
656 **158** 7c. purple (postage) . . . 25 10
657 10c. green 35 15
655 **157** 10c. blue and ultramarine 35 15

658 **158** 11c. red (air) 25 10

159 "B.C.G." = "Bacillus" Calmette-Guerin **160** Punta Caucedo Airport

1956. Obligatory Tax. Tuberculosis Relief Fund.
659 **159** 1c. multicoloured 15 10

1956. 3rd Caribbean Region Aerial Navigation Conference.
660 **160** 1c. brown (postage) . . . 10 10
661 2c. orange 20 10

662 11c. blue (air) 35 10

161 Cedar Tree **162** Fanny Blankers-Koen and Dutch Flag

1956. Re-afforestation. Inscr "REPOBLACION FORESTAL".
664 **161** 5c. green, brown and red (postage) 20 10
665 – 6c. green and purple . . . 25 10

666 – 13c. green & orge (air) . . 35 10
DESIGNS: 6c. Pine tree; 13c. Mahogany tree.

1957. Olympic Games (1st issue). Famous Athletes. Flags in national colours.
667 **162** 1c. mult (postage) 10 10
668 – 2c. sepia, purple & blue . . 10 10
669 – 3c. purple and red 15 15
670 – 5c. orange, pur & blue . . 25 15
671 – 7c. green and purple . . . 35 25

673 – 11c. blue and red (air) . . 20 20
674 – 16c. red and green 30 30
675 – 17c. black and purple . . . 40 40
DESIGNS—(each with national flag of athlete): 2c. Jesse Owens; 3c. Kee Chung Sohn; 5c. Lord Burghley; 7c. Bob Mathias; 11c. Paavo Nurmi; 16c. Ugo Frigerio; 17c. Mildred Didrickson.
See also Nos. 689/96, 713/21, 748/56 and 784/91.

163 Horse's Head and Globe **165**

1957. 2nd Int Livestock Fair, Ciudad Trujillo.
677 **163** 7c. blue, brown & red . . 25 10

1957. Hungarian Refugees Fund. Nos. 667/75 surch with red cross in circle surrounded by **ASISTENCIA REFUGIADOS HUNGAROS 1957** and **+2c.**
678 **162** 1c.+2c. (postage) 10 10
679 – 2c.+2c. 10 10
680 – 3c.+2c. 10 10
681 – 5c.+2c. 15 15
682 – 7c.+2c. 25 25

684 – 11c.+2c. (air) 40 40
685 – 16c.+2c. 40 40
686 – 17c.+2c. . . . . 1·50 1·50

1957. Obligatory Tax. Tuberculosis Relief Fund.
688 **165** 1c. multicoloured 15 10

166 Chris Brasher and Union Jack (steeplechase)

1957. Olympic Games (2nd issue). Winning Athletes. Inscr "MELBOURNE 1956". Flags in national colours.
689 – 1c. brown & bl (postage) 10 10
690 – 2c. red and blue 10 10
691 – 3c. blue 10 10
692 – 5c. olive and blue 15 10
693 – 7c. red and blue 25 15

694 – 11c. green & blue (air) . . 20 20
695 **166** 16c. purple and blue . . . 25 25
696 – 17c. sepia and green . . . 30 30
DESIGNS—(each with national flag of athlete): 1c. Lars Hall (Sweden, pentathlon); 2c. Betty Cuthbert (Australia, 100 and 200 m); 3c. Egil Danielson (Norway, javelin-throwing); 5c. Alain Mimoum (France, marathon); 7c. Norman Read (New Zealand, 50 km walk); 11c. Robert Morrow (U.S.A.; 100 and 200 m); 17c. A. Ferreira da Silva (Brazil; hop, step and jump).

1957. 50th Anniv of Boy Scout Movement, and Birth Cent of Lord Baden-Powell. Nos 689/96 surch **CENTENARIO LORD BADEN-POWELL, 1857-1957 +2c.** surrounding Scout badge.
699 1c.+2c. brn & bl (postage) . . 15 15
700 2c.+2c. red and blue 20 15
701 3c.+2c. blue 25 25
702 5c.+2c. olive and blue . . . 35 25
703 7c.+2c. red and blue 40 30

704 11c.+2c. grn & blue (air) . . 40 35
705 16c.+2c. purple and blue . . 50 50
706 17c.+2c. sepia and green . . 55 55

168 Mahogany Flower

1957.
709 **168** 2c. red and green 10 10
710 4c. red and mauve 10 10
711 7c. green and blue 25 10
712 25c. orange and brown . . 55 25

169 Gerald Ouellette and Canadian Flag (rifle-shooting)

1957. Olympic Games (3rd issue). More winning athletes. Flags in national colours.
713 **169** 1c. brown (postage) . . . 10 10
714 – 2c. sepia 10 10
715 – 3c. violet 10 10
716 – 5c. orange 15 15
717 – 7c. slate 20 20

719 – 11c. blue (air) 20 15
720 – 16c. red 30 30
721 – 17c. purple 35 35
DESIGNS—(each with national flag of athlete): 2c. Ron Delaney (Ireland 1500 m); 3c. Tenley Albright (U.S.A., figure-skating); 5c. J. Capilla (Mexico, high-diving); 7c. Ercole Baldini (Italy, cycle-racing); 11c. Hans Winkler (Germany, horse-jumping); 16c. Alfred Oerter (U.S.A., discus-throwing); 17c. Shirley Strickland (Australia; 80 m hurdles). The designs of

Nos. 714, 716 and 720 are arranged with the long side of the triangular format uppermost.

170

171 Cervantes, Open Book, Marker and Globe

1958. Tuberculosis Relief Fund.
723	170	1c. red and claret	10	10

See also No. 763.

1958. 4th Latin-American Book Fair.
724	171	4c. green	10	10
725		7c. mauve	15	10
726		10c. bistre	25	10

1958. U.N. Relief and Works Agency for Palestine Refugees. Nos. 713/21 surch. A. For Jewish Refugees. Star of David and **REFUGIADOS**.
727		1c.+2c. brown (postage) . . .	15	15
728		2c.+2c. brown	20	20
729		3c.+2c. violet	20	20
730		5c.+2c. orange	25	25
731		7c.+2c. blue	35	35
732		11c.+2c. blue (air)	25	25
733		16c.+2c. red	35	35
734		17c.+2c. purple	40	40

B. For Arab Refugees. Red Crescent and **REFUGIADOS**.
735		1c.+2c. brown (postage) . . .	15	15
736		2c.+2c. brown	20	20
737		3c.+2c. violet	20	20
738		5c.+2c. orange	25	25
739		7c.+2c. blue	35	35
740		11c.+2c. blue (air)	25	25
741		16c.+2c. red	35	35
742		17c.+2c. purple	40	40

172 Gen. R. Trujillo   **173** "Rhadames" (freighter) and Arms of Republic

1958. 25th Anniv of Gen Trujillo's designation as "Benefactor of the Country".
743	172	2c. mauve and yellow . . .	10	10
744		4c. green and yellow . . .	10	10
745		7c. sepia and yellow . . .	15	10

1958. Merchant Marine Day.
747	173	7c. blue	1·25	30

174 Gillian Sheen and   **175** Union Jack (fencing)

176 Dominican Republic Pavilion

1958. Olympic Games (4th issue). More winning athletes. Flags in national colours.
748	174	1c. slate, blue and red (postage)	10	10
749		– 2c. brown and blue . . .	10	10
750		– 3c. multicoloured . . .	15	15
751		– 5c. multicoloured . . .	20	20
752		– 7c. multicoloured . . .	25	25
754		– 11c. sepia, olive and blue (air)	25	25
755		– 16c. blue, orge & grn . .	30	30
756		– 17c. blue, yell and red . .	1·00	50

DESIGNS (each with national flag of athlete)—VERT: 2c. Milton Campbell (U.S.A., decathlon). HORIZ: 3c. Shozo Sasahara (Japan, featherweight wrestling); 5c. Madeleine Berthod (Switzerland, skiing); 7c. Murray Rose (Australia, 400 m and 1,500 m free-style); 11c. Charles Jenkins and Thomas

Courtney (U.S.A., 400 m and 800 m, and 1,600 m relay); 16c. Indian team in play (India, hockey); 17c. Swedish dinghies (Sweden, sailing).

1958. Inauguration of U.N.E.S.C.O. Headquarters Building, Paris.
758	175	7c. blue and red	15	10

1958. Brussels International Exhibition.
759	176	7c. green (postage) . . .	20	15
760		9c. grey (air)	20	15
761		25c. violet	50	30

1959. Obligatory Tax. Tuberculosis Relief Fund. As T 170 but inscr "1959".
763	170	1c. red and lake	15	10

1959. I.G.Y. Nos. 748/56 surch with globe and **ANO GEOFISICO INTERNACIONAL 1957-1958 +2c.**
764		1c.+2c. (postage)	25	25
765		2c.+2c.	30	30
766		3c.+2c.	35	35
767		5c.+2c.	40	40
768		7c.+2c.	45	45
770		11c.+2c. (air)	50	50
771		16c.+2c.	70	70
772		17c.+2c.	1·00	1·00

178 Leonidas R.   **179** Gen. Trujillo before Trujillo (Team   National Shrine Captain)

1959. Jamaica–Dominican Republic Polo Match, Trujillo City. Inscr as in T **178**.
774	178	2c. violet (postage)	15	10
775		– 7c. brown	30	15
776		– 10c. green	35	25
777		– 11c. orange (air)	30	25

DESIGNS—HORIZ: 7c. Jamaican team; 10c. Dominican Republic team's captain on horseback; 11c. Dominican Republic team.

1959. 29th Year of Trujillo Era.
778	179	9c. multicoloured	20	10

180 Gen. Trujillo and Cornucopia

1959. National Census of 1960. Centres in black, red and blue. Frame colours given.
780	180	1c. pale blue	15	10
781		9c. green	30	15
782		13c. orange	35	25

181 Trujillo Stadium

1959. 3rd Pan-American Games, Chicago.
783	181	9c. black and green . . .	35	20

1959. 3rd Pan-American Games, Chicago. Nos. 667/71 and 673/5, surch **III JUEGOS DEPORTIVOS PANAMERICANOS + 2** and runner.
784	162	1c.+2c. mult (postage) . . .	15	15
785		– 3c.+2c. multicoloured . .	15	15
786		– 3c.+2c. pur & red . . .	15	15
787		– 5c.+2c. multicoloured . .	15	15
788		– 7c.+2c. multicoloured . .	20	20
789		– 11c.+2c. blue, red and orange (air)	20	20
790		– 16c.+2c. red, green and carmine	30	30
791		– 17c.+2c. multicoloured . .	30	30

182 Emperor Charles V   **183** Rhadames Bridge

1959. 4th Death Centenary of Emperor Charles V.
792	182	5c. mauve	15	10
793		9c. blue	15	10

1959. Opening of Rhadames Bridge.
794		1c. black and green . . .	10	10
795	183	2c. black and blue . . .	15	10
796		2c. black and red . . .	15	10
797	183	5c. brown and bistre . . .	20	15

DESIGN—Nos. 794, 796, Close-up view of Rhadames Bridge.

184 Douglas DC-4 Airliner, "San Cristobal"

1960. Air. Dominican Civil Aviation.
798	184	13c. multicoloured	45	15

185

1960. Obligatory Tax. Tuberculosis Relief Fund.
779	185	1c. red, blue and cream	20	15

186 Sosua Refugee Colony

1960. World Refugee Year. Inscr "ANO MUNDIAL DE LOS REFUGIADOS". Centres in black.
800	186	5c. green & brn (postage)	10	10
801		9c. blue, purple & red . .	20	10
802		13c. green, brn & orge . .	25	15
803		– 10c. green, mauve and purple (air)	35	30
804		– 13c. green and grey . . .	45	35

DESIGN: Nos. 802/803, Refugee children.

1960. World Refugee Year Fund. Nos. 800/4 surch **+5** with **c** below.
805	186	5c.+5c. green and brown (postage)	15	15
806		9c.+5c. bl, pur & red . .	20	20
807		13c.+5c. green, brown and orange	40	40
808		– 10c.+5c. green, mauve and purple (air) . .	25	25
809		– 13c.+5c. green & grey . .	30	30

188 General Post Office, Ciudad Trujillo

1960.
811	188	2c. black and blue . . .	10	10

189 Cattle in Street

1960. Agricultural and Industrial Fair, San Juan de la Maguana.
812	189	9c. black and red . . .	25	15

190 Gholam Takhti (Iran,   **192** lightweight wrestling)

1960. Olympic Games, 1960. More Winning Athletes of Olympic Games, Melbourne, 1956. Flags in national colours.
813	190	1c. black, grn & red (posta)	10	10
814		– 2c. brown, turq & orge	10	10
815		– 3c. blue and red . . .	10	10
816		– 5c. brown and blue . .	15	15
817		– 7c. brn, blue & green . .	15	15
819		– 11c. brown, grey & bl (air)	20	20
820		– 16c. green, brown & red	25	25
821		– 17c. ochre, blue & black	30	30

DESIGNS (each with national flag of athlete): 2c. Mauru Furukawa (Japan, 200 m breast-stroke swimming); 3c. Mildred McDaniel (U.S.A., high jump); 5c. Terence Spinks (spelt "Terrence" on stamp) (Great Britain, featherweight boxing); 7c. Carlo Pavesi (Italy, fencing); 11c. Pat McCormick (U.S.A., high diving); 16c. Mithat Bayrack (Turkey, Greco-Roman welterweight wrestling); 17c. Ursula Happe (Germany, women's 200 m breaststroke swimming).

1961. Surch **HABILITADO PARA** and value.
823		– 2c. on 1c. black and green (No. 794)	15	10
824	168	9c. on 4c. red & mauve	45	10
825		9c. on 7c. green & blue	45	15
826	146	36c. on ½c. brown . . .	1·50	70
827	127	1p. on 50c. yellow	3·25	1·90

1961. Obligatory Tax. Tuberculosis Relief Fund.
828	192	1c. red and blue	10	10

See also No. 876.

193 Madame Trujillo and Houses

1961. Welfare Fund.
829	193	1c. red	20	10

194   **195** Coffee Plant and Cocoa Beans

1961.
830	194	1c. brown	10	10
831		2c. myrtle	10	10
832		4c. purple	40	35
833		5c. blue	25	10
834		9c. orange	30	20

1961. Obligatory Tax. Child Welfare. As Nos. 627/8 but with "ERA DE TRUJILLO" omitted. (a) Size 23½ × 32 mm.
835	148a	1c. blue	15	10

(b) Size 21¾ × 32 mm.
907	148b	1c. blue	15	10

1961.
836	195	1c. green (postage) . . .	10	10
837		2c. brown	10	10
838		4c. violet	10	10
839		5c. blue	10	10
840		9c. grey	25	10
841		13c. red (air)	25	25
842		33c. yellow	55	55

1961. 15th Anniv of U.N.E.S.C.O. Nos. 813/21 surch **XV ANIVERSARIO DE LA UNESCO +2c.**
843		1c.+2c. (postage) . . .	10	10
844		2c.+2c.	10	10
845		3c.+2c.	10	10
846		5c.+2c.	15	15
847		7c.+2c.	15	15
849		11c.+2c. (air)	25	25
850		16c.+2c.	35	35
851		17c.+2c.	35	35

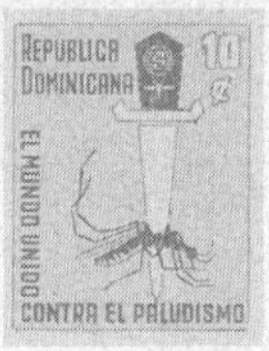

197 Mosquito and Dagger

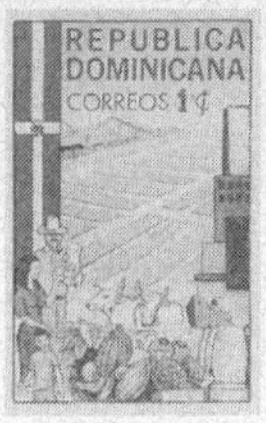

198 Plantation

1962. Malaria Eradication.

853 **197** 10c. mauve (postage) 15 10
854 10c.+2c. mauve 20 15
855 20c. sepia 35 30
856 20c.+2c. sepia 35 25
857 25c. green 45 55
858 13c. red (air) 25 20
859 13c.+2c. red 25 25
860 33c. orange 50 50
861 33c.+2c. orange 60 60

1962. Farming and Industrial Development. Flag in red and blue.

863 **198** 1c. green and blue 10 10
864 2c. red and blue 10 10
865 3c. brown and blue 10 10
866 5c. blue 15 10
867 15c. orange and blue 25 15

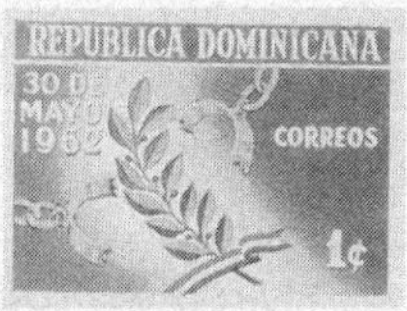

199 Laurel Sprig and Broken Link

1962. 1st Anniv of Assassination of Pres. Trujillo.

868 **199** 1c. mult (postage) 10 10
869 – 9c. red, blue and ochre 25 15
870 – 20c. red, blue & turq 45 25
871 – 1p. red, blue & violet 2·75 1·60
873 **199** 13c. multicoloured (air) 25 20
874 – 50c. red, blue & mauve 1·00 70

DESIGNS—VERT: 9c., 1p. "Justice" on map. HORIZ: 20c., 50c. Flag and flaming torch.

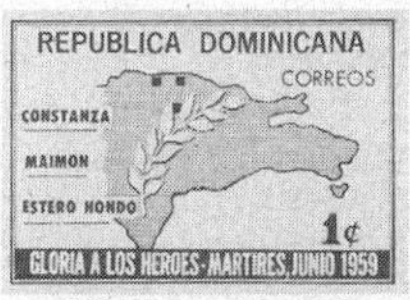

200 Map and Laurel

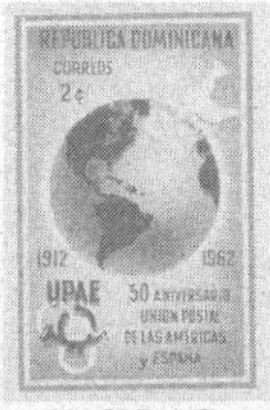

201 U.P.A.E. Emblem

1962. Martyrs of June 1959 Revolution.

875 **200** 1c. black 25 15

1962. Tuberculosis Relief Fund. As No. 828 but inscr "1962".

876 **192** 1c. red and blue 10 10

1962. 50th Anniv of Postal Union of the Americas and Spain.

877 **201** 2c. red (postage) 10 10
878 9c. orange 25 15
879 14c. turquoise 25 20
880 13c. blue (air) 35 20
881 22c. brown 45 40

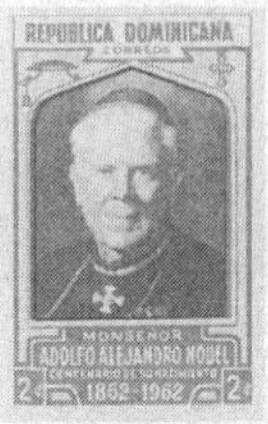

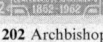

202 Archbishop Nouel

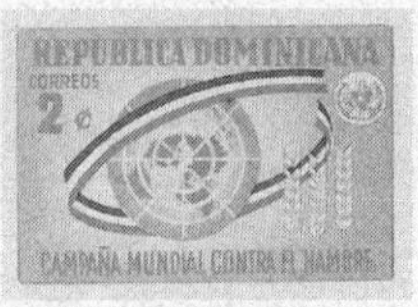

203 Globe, Riband and Campaign Emblem

1962. Birth Cent of Archbishop Adolfo Nouel.

882 **202** 2c. myrtle & green (postage) 10 10
883 9c. brown and orange 25 15
884 13c. purple and brown 30 20
885 – 12c. blue (air) 35 20
886 – 25c. violet 50 40

DESIGN: Air stamps as Type **202** but different frame.

1963. Freedom from Hunger. Riband in red and blue.

888 **203** 2c. green 10 10
891 2c.+1c. green 10 10
889 5c. mauve 15 10
892 5c.+2c. mauve 20 20
890 9c. orange 25 15
893 9c.+2c. orange 20 20

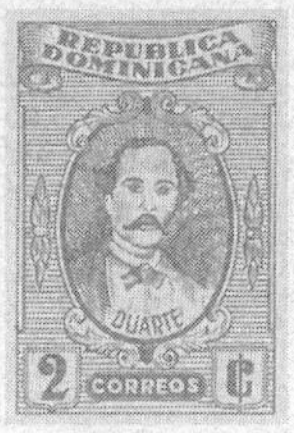

204 Duarte

1963. 120th Anniv of Separation from Haiti.

895 **204** 2c. blue (postage) 10 10
896 – 7c. green (Sanchez) 15 15
897 – 9c. purple (Mella) 15 15
898 – 15c. salmon (air) 20 15

DESIGN—HORIZ: 15c. Sanchez, Duarte and Mella.

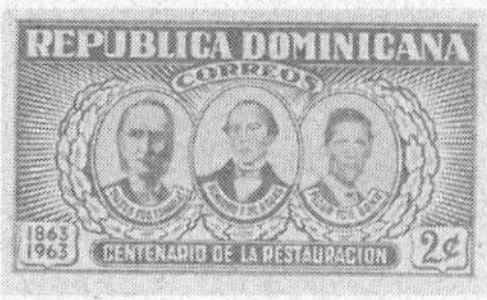

205 Espaillat, de Rojas and Bono

1963. "Centenary of the Restoration".

899 **205** 2c. green 10 10
900 – 4c. red 10 10
901 – 5c. brown 10 10
902 – 9c. blue 15 15

DESIGNS: 4c. Rodriguez, Cabrera and Moncion; 5c. Capotillo Monument; 9c. Polanco, Luperon and Salcedo.

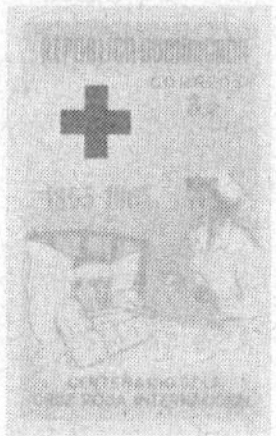

206 Nurse tending Patient

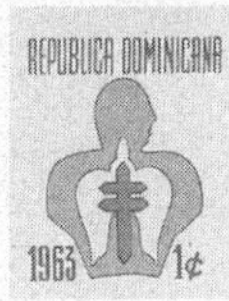

207

1963. Centenary of Red Cross. Cross in red.

904 **206** 3c. grey (postage) 10 10
905 6c. green 15 10
906 – 10c. grey (air) 25 20

DESIGN—HORIZ: 10c. Map of continents bordering Atlantic.

1963. Obligatory Tax. T.B. Relief Fund.

908 **207** 1c. red and blue 15 10

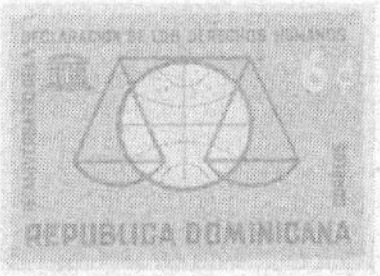

208 Scales of Justice and Globe

1963. 15th Anniv of Declaration of Human Rights.

911 **208** 6c. red (postage) 15 10
912 50c. green 80 55
913 7c. brown (air) 20 15
914 10c. blue 25 15

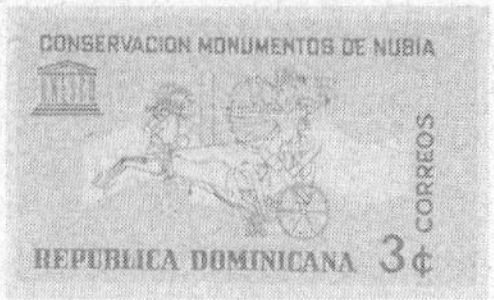

209 Rameses II in War Chariot, Abu Simbel

1964. Nubian Monuments Preservation. Designs as T **209**, also surch **2c** in circle.

915 **209** 3c. red (postage) 10 10
916 3c.+2c. red 15 15
917 – 6c. blue 15 10
918 – 6c.+2c. blue 15 15
919 **209** 9c. brown 20 15
920 9c.+2c. brown 25 25
921 – 10c. violet (air) 25 20
922 – 10c.+2c. violet 25 20
923 – 13c. yellow 25 20
924 – 13c.+2c. yellow 25 25

DESIGNS—HORIZ: 6c. Heads of Rameses II. VERT: 10c., 13c. As Type **209**.

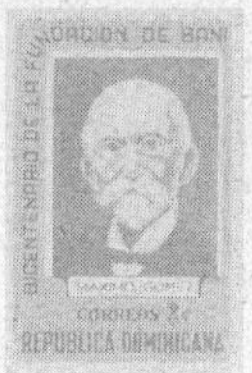

211 M. Gomez (founder)

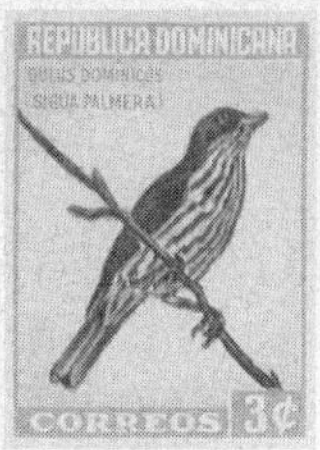

212 Palm Chat

1964. Bicentenary of Bani Foundation.

925 **211** 2c. blue & light blue 10 10
926 6c. purple and brown 15 10

1964. Dominican Birds. Multicoloured.

927 1c. Narrow-billed tody (postage) 1·75 15
928 2c. Hispaniolan emerald 1·75 15
929 3c. Type **212** 1·75 15
930 6c. Hispaniolan amazon 2·10 15
931 6c. Hispaniolan trogons 2·50 15
932 10c. Hispaniolan woodpecker (air) 3·75 20

The 1c., 2c. and 6c. (No. 931) are smaller (26 × 37½ mm); the 10c. is horiz (43½ × 27½ mm).

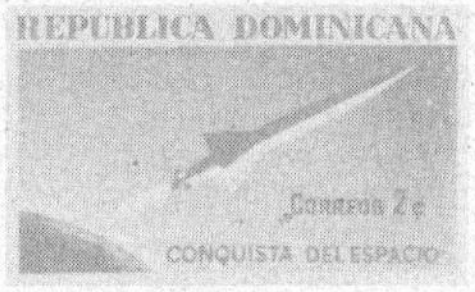

213 Rocket

1964. "Conquest of Space".

933 – 1c. blue (postage) 10 10
934 **213** 2c. green 10 10
935 – 3c. blue 15 10
936 **213** 6c. blue 25 15
937 **213** 7c. green (air) 25 25
938 – 10c. blue 35 70

DESIGNS—VERT: 1c. Rocket launching. HORIZ: 3c., 10c. Capsule in orbit.

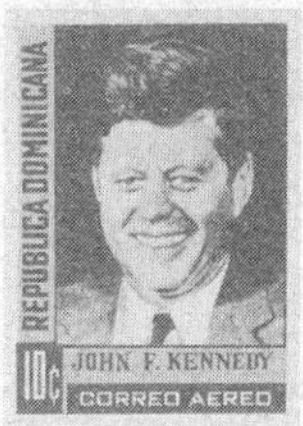

214 Pres. Kennedy

1964. Air. Pres. Kennedy Commemoration.

940 **214** 10c. brown and buff 35 25

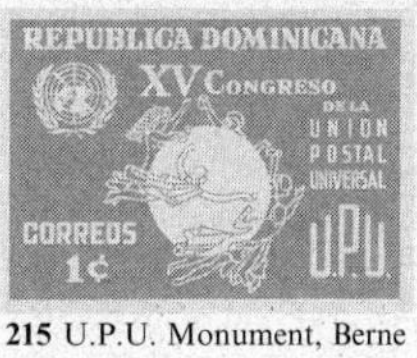

215 U.P.U. Monument, Berne

1964. 15th U.P.U. Congress, Vienna.

941 **215** 1c. red (postage) 10 10
942 4c. green 15 10
943 5c. orange 15 10
944 7c. blue (air) 15 10

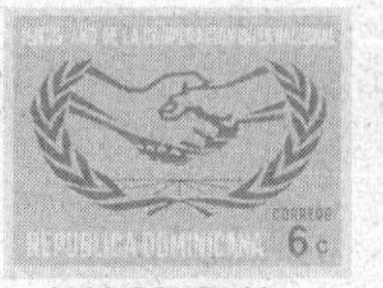

216 I.C.Y. Emblem

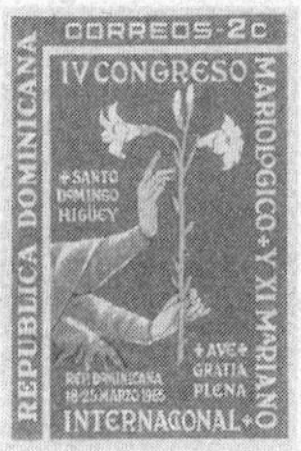

217 Hands and Lily

1965. International Co-operation Year.

945 **216** 2c. blue and light-blue (postage) 10 10
946 3c. green and emerald 10 10
947 6c. red and pink 15 10
948 10c. violet & lilac (air) 25 20

1965. 4th Mariological and 11th Int Marian Congresses. Multicoloured.

949 2c. Type **217** (postage) 10 10
950 6c. Virgin of the Altagracia 35 25
951 10c. Douglas DC-8 airliner over Basilica of Virgin of Altagracia (39½ × 31½ mm) (air) 30 15

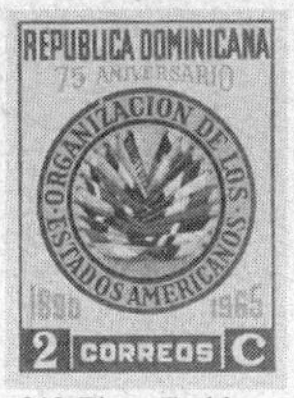

218 Flags Emblem

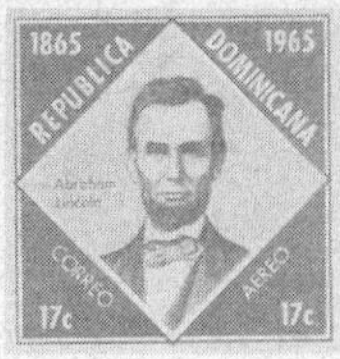

219 Lincoln

1965. 75th Anniv of Organization of American States.

952 **218** 2c. multicoloured 10 10
953 6c. multicoloured 15 10

1965. Air. Death Centenary of Abraham Lincoln.

954 **219** 17c. grey and blue 35 25

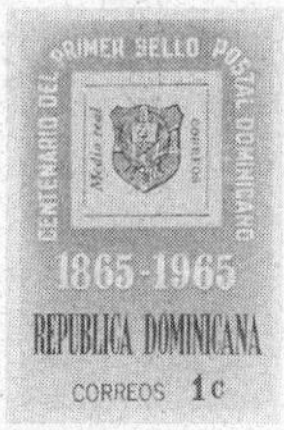

220 ½r. Stamp of 1865

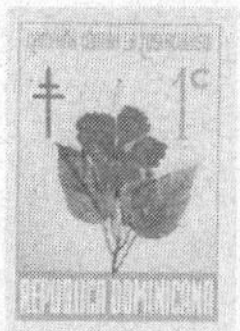

221 Hibiscus

1965. Stamp Centenary.

955 **220** 1c. multicoloured (post) 10 10
956 2c. multicoloured 10 10
957 6c. multicoloured 15 10
958 – 7c. multicoloured (air) 25 20
959 – 10c. multicoloured 25 25

DESIGN: 7c., 10c. As Type **220**, but showing 1r. stamp of 1865.

1966. Obligatory Tax. Tuberculosis Relief Fund.

963 **221** 1c. red and green 15 10
999 – 1c. mauve, lilac & red 10 10
1015 – 1c. multicoloured 10 10
1016 – 1c. multicoloured 10 10
1017 – 1c. multicoloured 10 10

DESIGN (21½ × 30 mm): No. 999, Orchid. (20 × 28 mm): No. 1015, Dogbane; 1016, Violets; 1017, "Eeanthus capitatus".

222 I.T.U. Emblem and Symbols

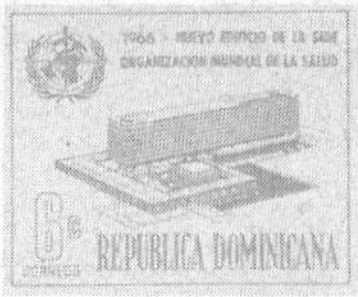

223 W.H.O. Building

1966. Air. Centenary (1965) of I.T.U.

964 **222** 28c. red and pink 55 40
965 45c. green and emerald 55 70

1965. Inaug of W.H.O. Headquarters, Geneva.

966 **223** 6c. blue 15 10
967 10c. purple 20 15

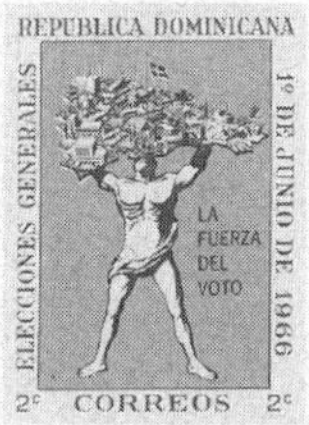

224 Man supporting "Republic"

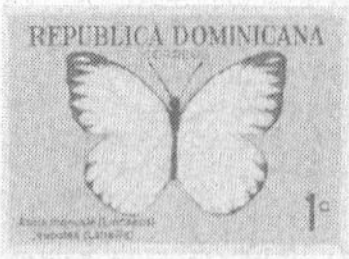

225 "Ascia monuste"

1966. General Elections.

968 **224** 2c. black and green 10 10
969 6c. black and red 15 10

1966. Butterflies. Multicoloured.

970 1c. Type **225** (postage) 10 10
971 2c. "Heliconius charitonius" 10 10
972 3c. "Phoebis sennae sennae" 15 15
973 6c. "Anteos clorinde clorinde" 25 25
974 8c. "Siderone hemesis" 35 35
975 10c. "Eurema gundlachia" (air) 45 25
976 50c. "Clothilda pantherata pantherata" 2·10 1·00
977 75c. "Papilio androgeus epidaurus" 3·00 1·50

Nos. 975/7 are larger, 35 × 24½ mm.

1966. Hurricane Inez Relief. Nos. 970/77 surch **PRO DAMNIFICADOS CICLON INES** and value.

978 **225** 1c.+2c. mult (postage) 15 10
979 – 2c.+2c. multicoloured 15 10
980 – 3c.+2c. multicoloured 15 10
981 – 6c.+4c. multicoloured 30 25
982 – 8c.+4c. multicoloured 40 30
983 – 10c.+5c. mult (air) 40 35
984 – 50c.+10c. mult 1·40 1·40
985 – 75c.+10c. mult 1·75 1·75

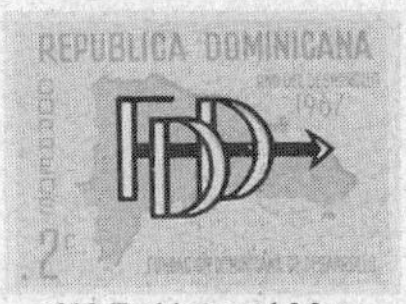

227 National Shrine
228 Emblem and Map

1967. (a) Postage.
986 **227** 1c. blue 10 10
987 2c. red 10 10
988 3c. green 10 10
989 4c. grey 10 10
990 5c. yellow 10 10
991 6c. orange 10 10

(b) Air. Size 20½ × 25 mm.
992 **227** 7c. olive 15 10
993 10c. lilac 15 15
994 20c. brown 30 25

1967. Development Year. Emblem and map in black and blue.
996 **228** 2c. orange and yellow 10 10
997 6c. orange 15 10
998 10c. green 25 15

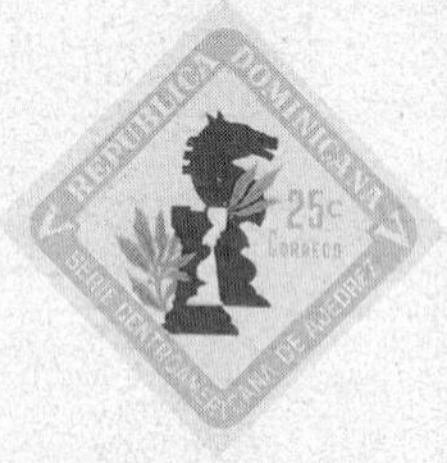
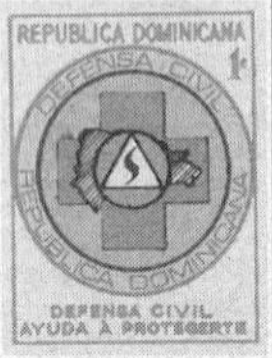

229 Rook and Knight
230 Civil Defence Emblem

1967. 5th Central American Chess Championship, Santo Domingo.
1000 **229** 25c. mult (postage) 55 40
1001 – 10c. black & grn (air) 35 25
DESIGN: 10c. Bishop and pawn.

1967. Obligatory Tax. Civil Defence Fund.
1003 **230** 1c. multicoloured 15 15

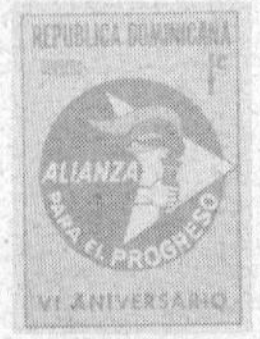
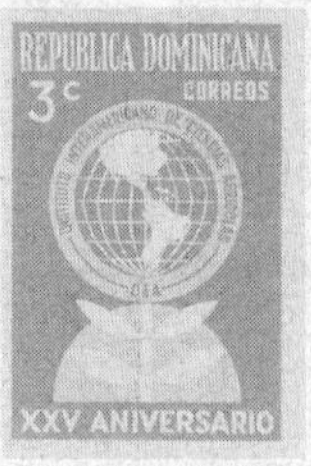

231 Alliance Emblem
232 Institute Emblem

1967. 6th Anniv of "Alliance for Progress".
1004 **231** 1c. green (postage) 10 10
1005 8c. grey (air) 15 10
1006 10c. blue 20 15

1967. 25th Anniv of Inter-American Agricultural Institute.
1007 **232** 3c. green (postage) 10 10
1008 6c. pink 15 10
1009 – 12c. mult (air) 20 15
DESIGN: 12c. Emblem and cornucopia.

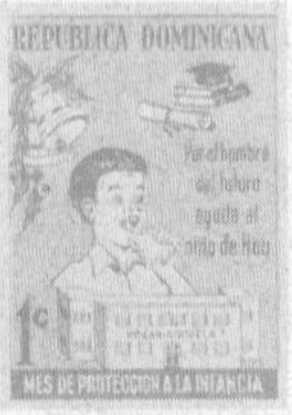
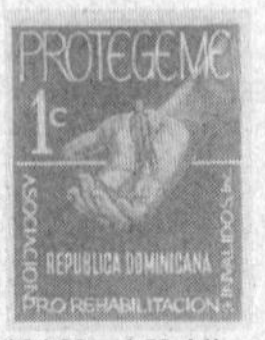

233 Child and Children's Home
234 Hand Holding Invalid

1967. Obligatory Tax. Child Welfare.
1010 **233** 1c. red 25 10
1010a 1c. orange 15 10
1011 1c. violet 10 10
1011a 1c. brown 15 10
1037 1c. green 10 10
See also No. 1278a.

1968. Obligatory Tax. Rehabilitation of the Handicapped.
1012 **234** 1c. yellow and green 10 10
1013 1c. blue 10 10
1014 1c. bright purple 10 10
1015 1c. brown 10 10

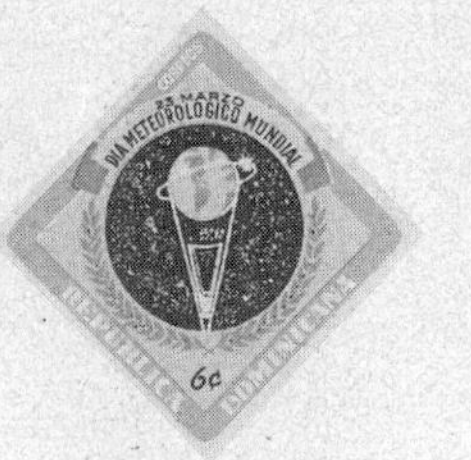

236 W.M.O. Emblem

1968. World Meteorological Day.
1019 **236** 6c. mult (postage) 20 15
1020 10c. multicoloured (air) 25 20
1021 15c. multicoloured 35 25

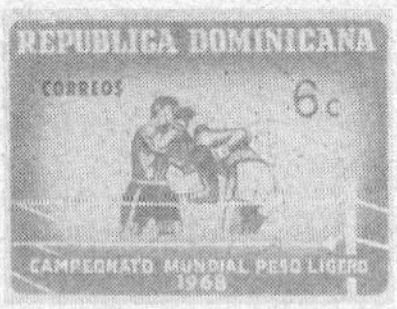
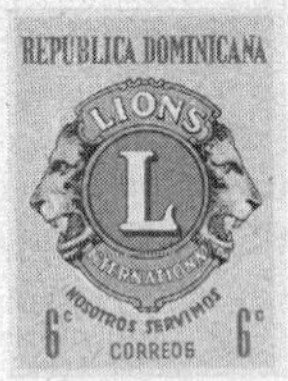

237 Ortiz v. Cruz
238 "Lions" Emblem

1968. World Lightweight Boxing Championship. Designs showing similar scenes of the contest.
1024 **237** 6c. pur & red (postage) 15 15
1025 – 7c. green & yellow (air) 15 10
1026 – 10c. blue and brown 25 15

1968. Lions International.
1027 **238** 6c. mult (postage) 15 10
1028 10c. multicoloured (air) 25 15

1968. Obligatory Tax. Anti-cancer Fund.
1029 **144** 1c. green 10 10
1030 1c. orange 10 10

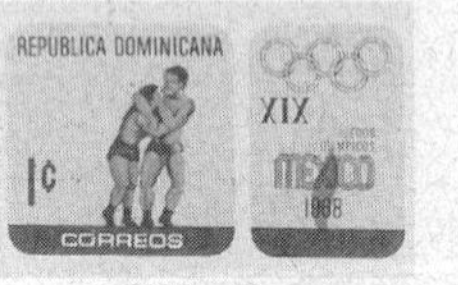

239 Wrestling

1968. Olympic Games, Mexico. Multicoloured.
1031 1c. Type **239** (postage) 10 10
1032 6c. Running 15 10
1033 25c. Boxing 70 35
1034 10c. Weightlifting (air) 25 25
1035 33c. Pistol-shooting 80 70

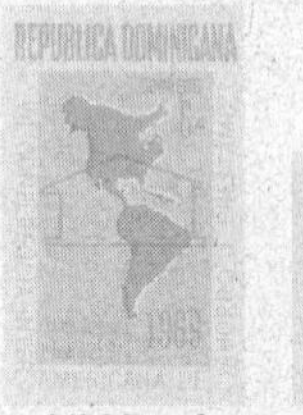
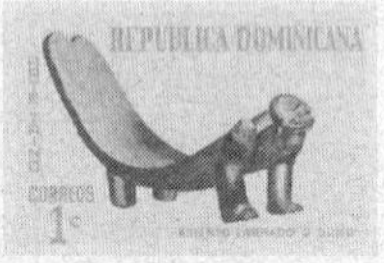

240 Map of Americas and House
241 Carved Stool

1969. 7th Inter-American Savings and Loans Congress, Santo Domingo. Multicoloured.
1038 6c. Type **240** (postage) 15 10
1039 10c. Latin-American flags (air) 25 15

1969. Taino Art. Multicoloured.
1040 1c. Type **241** (postage) 10 10
1041 2c. Female idol (vert) 10 10
1042 3c. Three-cornered footstone 10 10
1043 4c. Stone axe (vert) 15 10
1044 5c. Clay pot 15 15
1045 7c. Spatula and carved handles (vert) (air) 25 10
1046 10c. Breast-shaped vessel 35 25
1047 20c. Figured vase (vert) 35 75

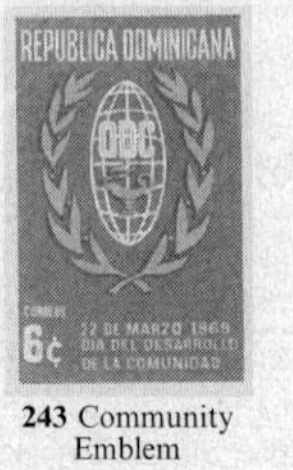

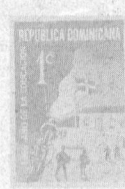

242 School Playground and Torch
243 Community Emblem

1969. Obligatory Tax. Education Year.
1048 **242** 1c. blue 10 10

1969. Community Development Day.
1049 **243** 6c. gold and green 15 10

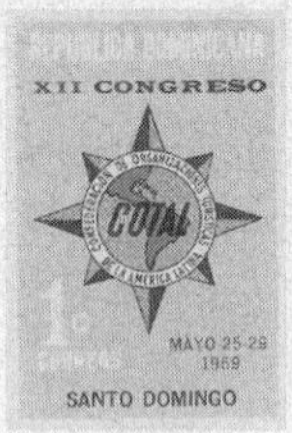
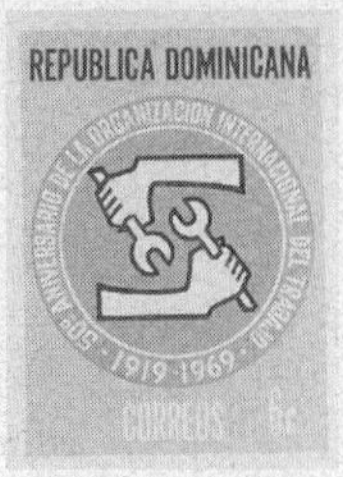

244 C.O.T.A.L. Emblem
245 I.L.O. Emblem

1969. 12th C.O.T.A.L. (Confederation of Latin American Tourist Organizations) Congress, Santo Domingo.
1050 **244** 1c. blue, red and light blue (postage) 10 10
1051 – 2c. lt green & green 10 10
1052 – 6c. red 15 10
1053 – 10c. brown (air) 30 10
DESIGNS—VERT: 2c. Boy with flags. HORIZ: (39 × 31 mm): 6c. C.O.T.A.L. Building and emblem; 10c. "Airport of the Americas", Santo Domingo.

1969. 50th Anniv of I.L.O.
1054 **245** 6c. blk & turq (postage) 25 10
1055 10c. black and red (air) 15 15

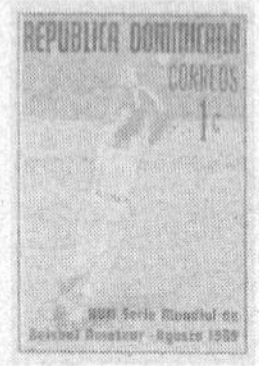
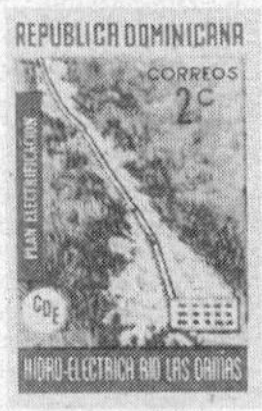

246 Taking a Catch
247 Las Damas Hydro-electric Scheme

1969. World Baseball Championships, Santo Domingo.
1056 **246** 1c. grey and green (postage) 10 10
1057 – 2c. green 10 10
1058 – 3c. brown and violet 10 10
1059 – 7c. orange and purple (air) 20 15
1060 – 10c. red 25 15
1061 – 1p. brown and blue 2·00 1·40
DESIGNS—VERT: 3c. Making for base; 10c. Player making strike. HORIZ: (43 × 30½ mm): 2c. Cibao Stadium; 7c. Tetelo Vargas Stadium; 1p. Quisqueya Stadium.

1969. National Electrification Plan.
1062 **247** 2c. mult (postage) 10 10
1063 – 3c. multicoloured 10 10
1064 – 6c. purple 15 10
1065 – 10c. red (air) 20 10
DESIGNS—HORIZ: 3c. Las Damas Dam; 6c. Arroyo Hondo substation; 10c. Haina River power station.

1969. Obligatory Tax. Anti-cancer Fund. T **144** re-drawn in larger format and inscriptions.
1066 **144** 1c. purple 10 10
1067 1c. green 15 10

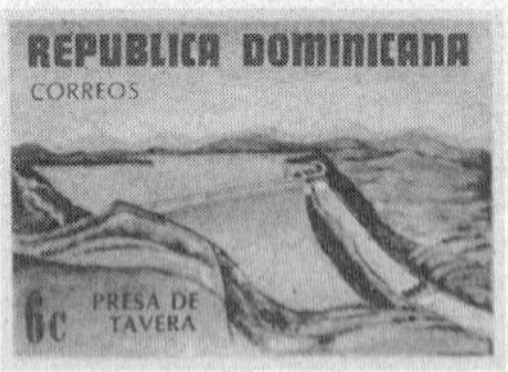

248 Tavera Dam

1969. Completion of Dam Projects. Mult.
1068 6c. Type **248** (postage) 15 10
1069 10c. Valdesia Dam (air) 20 10

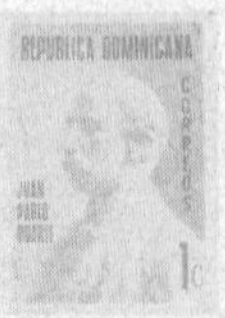
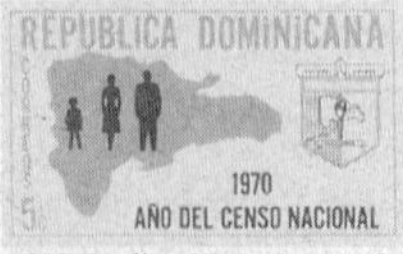

249 Juan Pablo Duarte
250 Outline Map, Arms of Census Office and Family

1970. Juan Pablo Duarte (patriot) Commem.
1070 **249** 1c. green (postage) 10 10
1071 2c. red 10 10
1072 3c. purple 10 10
1073 6c. blue 15 10
1074 10c. brown (air) 20 15

1970. National Census.
1075 **250** 5c. blk & grn (postage) 10 10
1076 – 6c. ultram and blue 15 10
1077 – 10c. multicoloured (air) 25 15
DESIGNS: 6c. Arms and quotation; 10c. Arms and buildings.

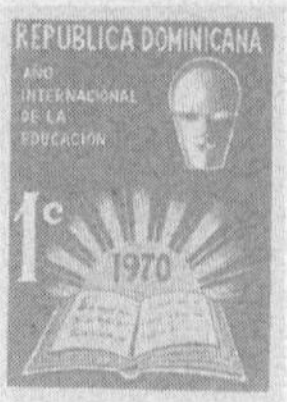
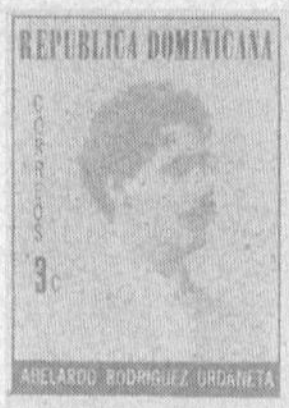

251 Open Book and Emblem
252 Abelardo Urdaneta

1970. Obligatory Tax. Int Education Year.
1078 **251** 1c. purple 10 10

1970. Birth Cent of A. R. Urdaneta (sculptor).
1079 **252** 3c. blue (postage) 10 10
1080 – 6c. green 15 10
1081 – 10c. blue (air) 20 15
DESIGNS—HORIZ: (39½ × 27 mm): 6c. "One of Many" (sculpture). VERT: (25 × 39 mm): 10c. Prisoner (statue).

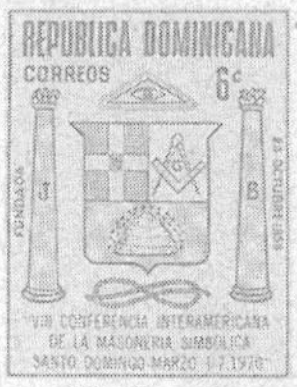
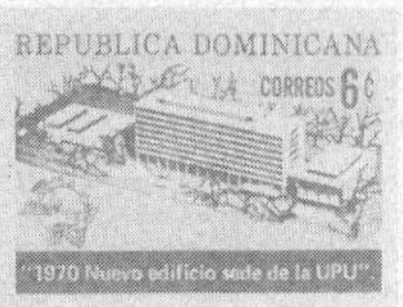

253 Masonic Symbols
255 New U.P.U. Building

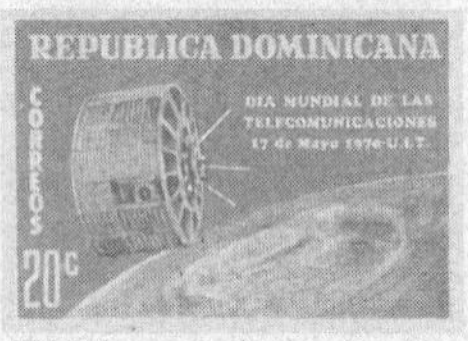

254 Telecommunications Satellite

1970. 8th Inter-American Masonic Conference, Santo Domingo.
1082 **253** 6c. green (postage) 15 10
1083 10c. brown (air) 20 10

1970. World Telecommunications Day.
1084 **254** 20c. grey & grn (postage) 50 30
1085 7c. grey and blue (air) 15 10

1970. New U.P.U. Headquarters Building, Berne.
1086 **255** 6c. brn & grey (postage) 15 10
1087 10c. brown & yell (air) 15 10

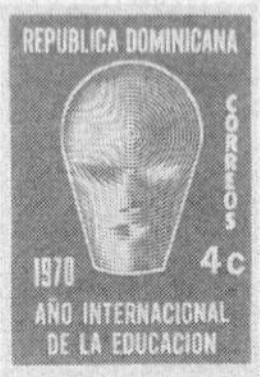
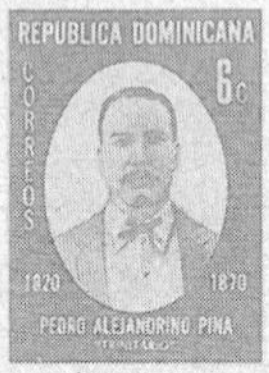

256 I.E.Y. Emblem
257 Pedro Alejandrino Pina

1970. International Education Year.
1088 **256** 4c. purple (postage) 10 10
1089 15c. mauve (air) 20 15

1970. 150th Birth Anniv and Death Centenary of Pedro A. Pina (writer).
1090 **257** 6c. black & brown 15 10

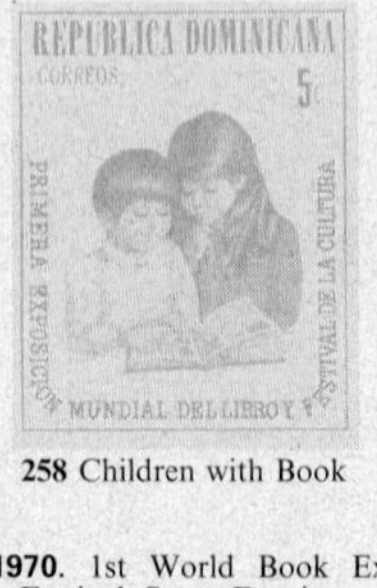
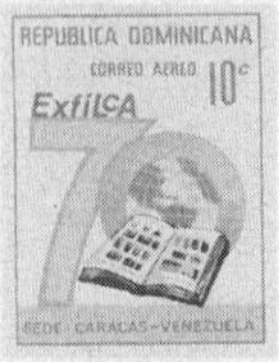

258 Children with Book
259 Emblem and Stamp Album

1970. 1st World Book Exhibition, and Cultural Festival, Santo Domingo.
1091 **258** 5c. green (postage) 10 10
1092 – 7c. multicoloured (air) 15 10
1093 – 10c. multicoloured 20 15
DESIGNS: 7c. Dancers; 10c. U.N. emblem within "wheel".

1970. Air. "EXFILICA 70" Inter-American Philatelic Exhibition, Caracas, Venezuela.
1094 **259** 10c. multicoloured 20 15

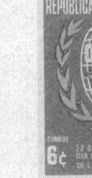

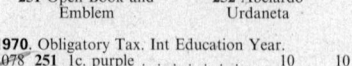

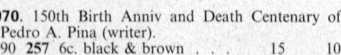

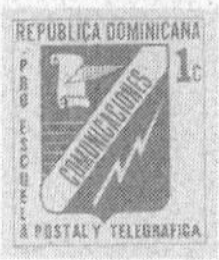

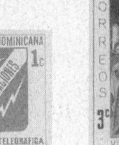

260 Communications Emblems

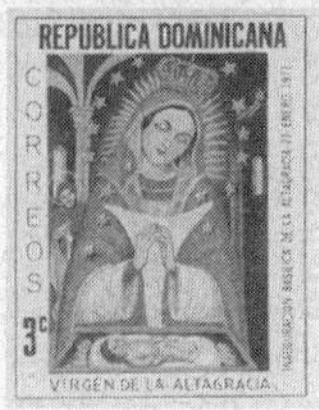

261 Virgin of Altagracia

1971. Obligatory Tax. Postal and Telecommunications School. (a) Size 18 × 20½ mm.
1095 **260** 1c. blue and red (white background) 15 10

(b) Size 19 × 22 mm.
1095a **260** 1c. blue and red (red background) 15 10
1095b 1c. blue, red and green 15 10
1095c 1c. blue, red and yellow 15 10
1095d 1c. blue, red and mauve 15 10
1095e 1c. blue, red and light blue 10 10
1096 1c. blue and red (blue background) 10 10

1971. Inauguration of Our Lady of Altagracia Basilica. Multicoloured.
1097 3c. Type **261** (postage) . . . 10 10
1098 17c. Basilica (22½ × 36 mm) (air) 35 25

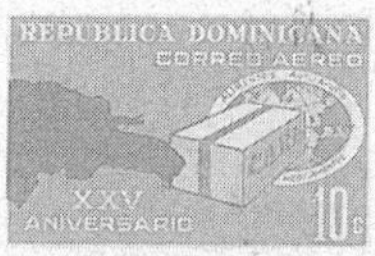

262 Parcel, Emblem and Map

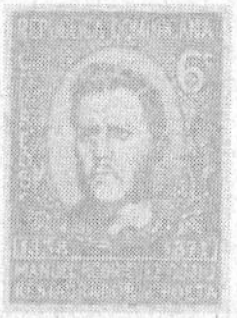
263 Manuel Objio

1971. Air. 25th Anniv of C.A.R.E. (Cooperative for American Relief Everywhere).
1099 **262** 10c. green and blue . . . 15 15

1971. Death Cent of Manuel Rodriguez Objio (poet).
1100 **263** 6c. blue 15 10

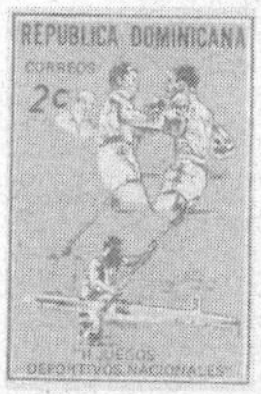

264 Boxing and Canoeing

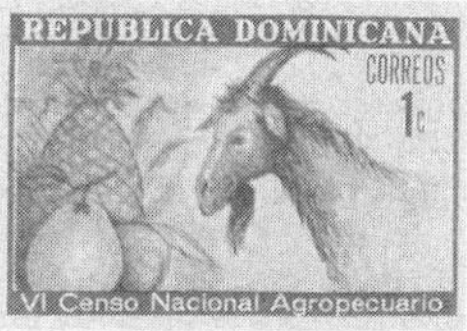

265 Goat and Fruit

1971. 2nd National Games.
1101 **264** 2c. brown and orange (postage) 10 10
1102 – 5c. brown and green . . 15 10
1103 – 7c. purple & grey (air) 15 10
DESIGNS: 5c. Basketball; 7c. Volleyball.

1971. 6th National Agricultural Census. Mult.
1104 1c. Type **265** (postage) . . . 10 10
1105 2c. Cow and goose 10 10
1106 3c. Cocoa pods and horse 10 10
1107 6c. Bananas, coffee beans and pig 15 10
1108 25c. Cockerel and grain (air) 40 30

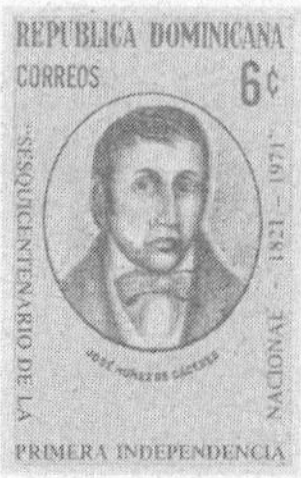

266 Jose Nunez de Caceres

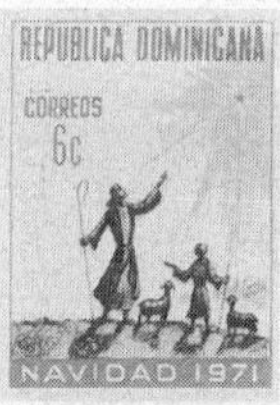

267 Shepherds and Star

1971. 150th Anniv of 1st Declaration of Independence.
1109 **266** 6c. blue, violet and light blue (postage) 15 10
1110 – 10c. bl, red & yell (air) 25 20
DESIGN: 10c. Flag of the Santo Domingo–Colombia Union.

1971. Christmas.
1111 **267** 6c. brn, yell & bl (post) 15 10
1112 – 10c. red, blk & yell (air) 15 15
DESIGN: 10c. Spanish bell of 1493.

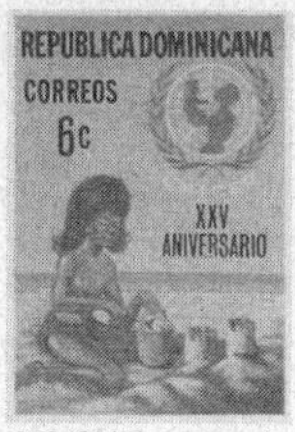

268 Child on Beach

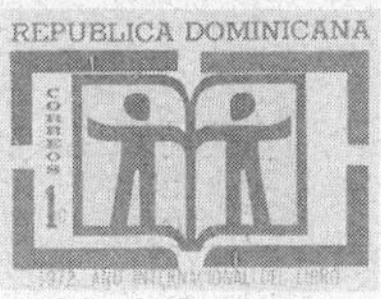

269 Book Year Emblem

1971. 25th Anniv of U.N.I.C.E.F.
1113 **268** 6c. mult (postage) . . . 15 10
1114 15c. multicoloured (air) 25 20

1971. International Book Year.
1115 **269** 1c. green, red and blue (postage) 10 10
1116 2c. brown, red and blue 10 10
1117 12c. purple, red and blue (air) 20 15

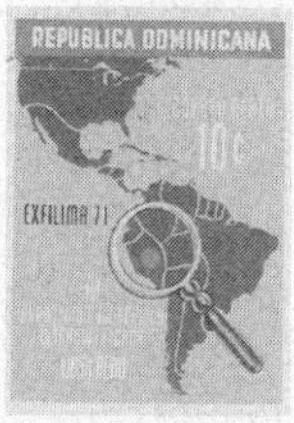

270 Magnifier on Map

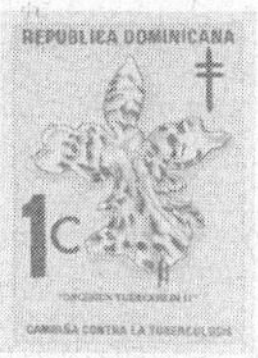

271 Orchid

1972. Air. "Exfilima 71" Inter American Philatelic Exhibition, Lima, Peru.
1118 **270** 10c. multicoloured . . . 25 15

1972. Obligatory Tax. Tuberculosis Relief Fund.
1119 **271** 1c. multicoloured 10 10

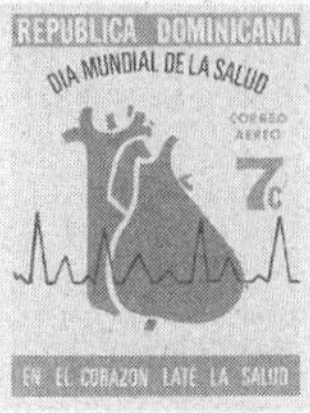

272 Heart Emblem

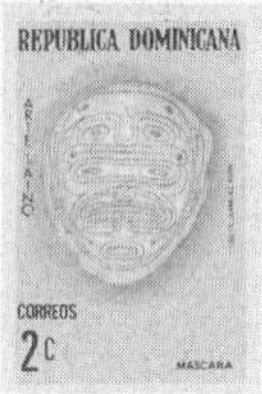

273 Mask

1972. Air. World Health Day.
1120 **272** 7c. multicoloured 15 10

1972. Taino Arts and Crafts. Multicoloured.
1121 2c. Type **273** (postage) . . . 10 10
1122 4c. Spoon and amulet . . . 10 10
1123 6c. Nasal aspirator (horiz) 10 10
1124 8c. Ritual vase (horiz) (air) 15 10
1125 10c. Atlantic trumpet triton (horiz) 30 10
1126 25c. Ritual spatulas 45 25

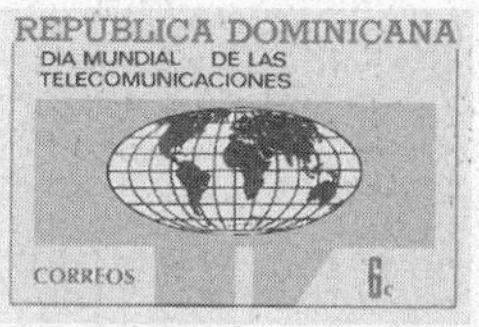

274 Globe

1972. World Telecommunications Day.
1127 **274** 6c. mult (postage) . . . 15 10
1128 21c. multicoloured (air) 35 20

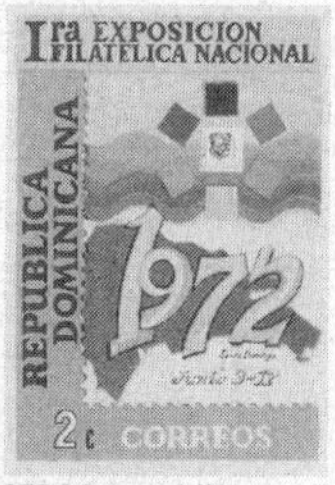

275 Map and "Stamps"

1972. 1st National Stamp Exn, Santo Domingo.
1129 **275** 2c. mult (postage) . . . 10 10
1130 33c. mult (air) 60 35

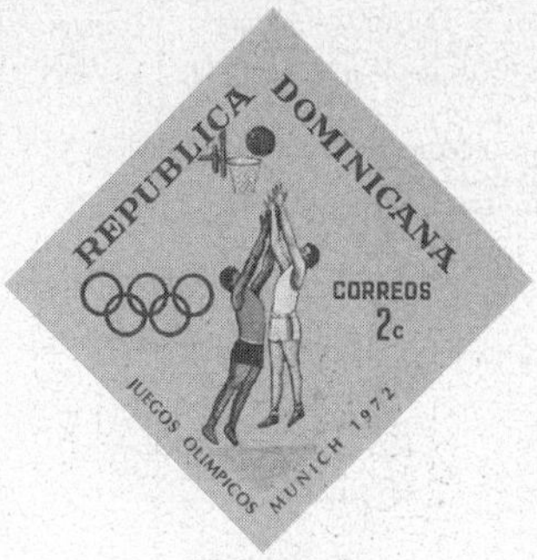

276 Basketball

1972. Olympic Games, Munich. Mult.
1131 2c. Type **276** (postage) . . . 10 10
1132 33c. Running (air) 70 40

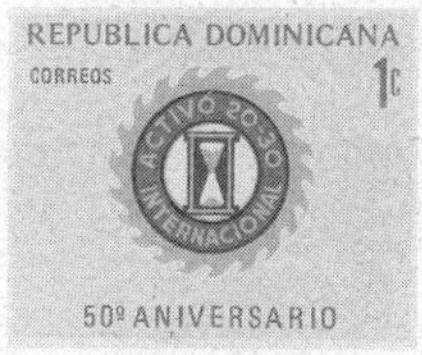

277 Club Badge

1972. 50th Anniv of Int Activo 20–30 Club.
1133 **277** 1c. mult (postage) . . . 10 10
1134 20c. mult (air) 35 20

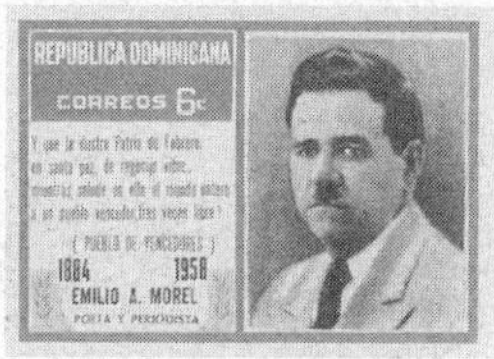

278 Emilio Morel and Quotation

1972. Morel (poet and journalist). Commem.
1135 **278** 6c. mult (postage) . . . 15 10
1136 10c. mult (air) 15 10

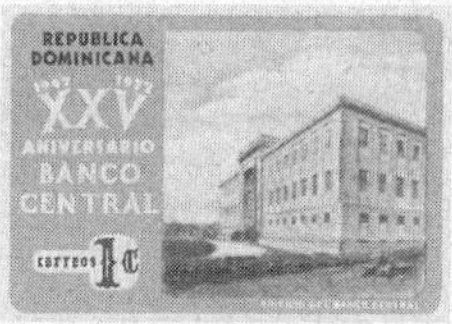

279 Bank Building

1972. 25th Anniv of Central Bank. Mult.
1137 1c. Type **279** 10 10
1138 5c. One-peso banknote . . . 10 10
1139 25c. 1947 50c. coin and mint 40 25

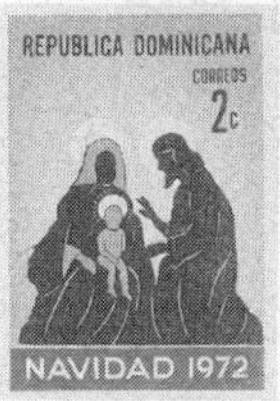

280 Nativity Scene

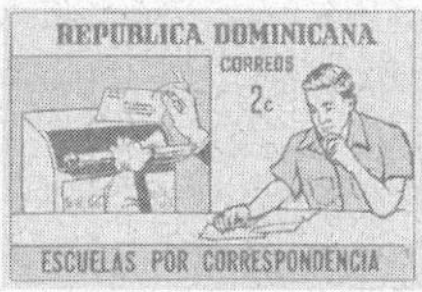

281 Student and Letter-box

1972. Christmas. Multicoloured.
1140 2c. Type **280** (postage) . . . 10 10
1141 6c. Poinsettia (horiz) 15 10
1142 10c. "La Navidad" Fort, 1492 (horiz) (air) 15 10

1972. Publicity for Correspondence Schools.
1143 **281** 2c. red and pink 10 10
1144 6c. blue and light blue 15 10
1145 10c. green and yellow . . 20 10

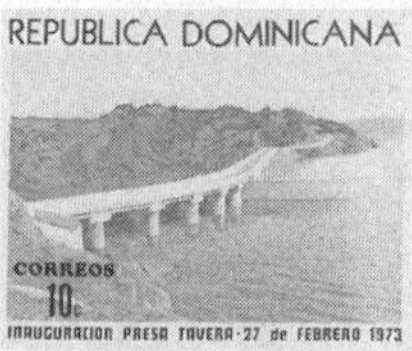

282 View of Dam

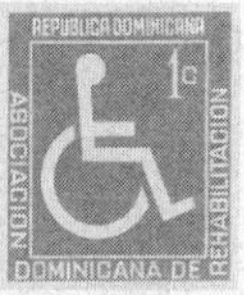

283 Invalid in Wheel-chair

1973. Inauguration of Tavera Dam.
1146 **282** 10c. multicoloured . . . 20 10

1973. Obligatory Tax. Rehabilitation of the Handicapped.
1147 **283** 1c. green 10 10

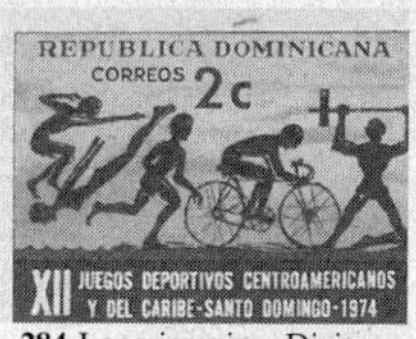

284 Long-jumping, Diving, Running, Cycling and Weightlifting

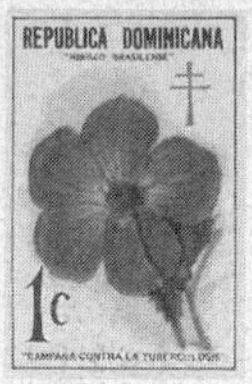

285 Hibiscus

1973. 12th Central American and Caribbean Games, Santo Domingo. Multicoloured.
1148 2c. Type **284** (postage) . . . 10 10
1149 2c. Boxing, football, wrestling and shooting . . 10 10
1150 2c. Fencing, tennis, high-jumping and sprinting . . 10 10
1151 2c. Putting the shot, throwing the javelin and show-jumping 10 10
1152 25c. Type **284** 55 25
1153 25c. As No. 1149 . . . . . 55 25
1154 25c. As No. 1150 . . . . . 55 25
1155 25c. As No. 1151 . . . . . 55 25
1156 8c. Type **284** (air) 15 10
1157 8c. As No. 1149 . . . . . 15 10
1158 8c. As No. 1150 . . . . . 15 10
1159 8c. As No. 1151 . . . . . 15 10
1160 10c. Type **284** 25 15
1161 10c. As No. 1149 . . . . . 25 15
1162 10c. As No. 1150 . . . . . 25 15
1163 10c. As No. 1151 . . . . . 25 15

1973. Obligatory Tax. Tuberculosis Relief Fund.
1164 **285** 1c. multicoloured 10 10

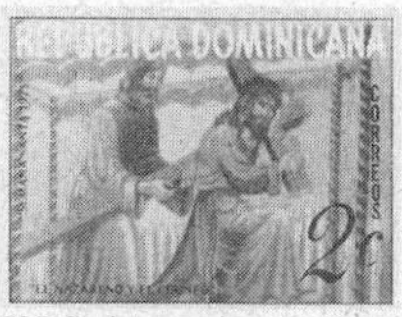

286 Christ carrying the Cross

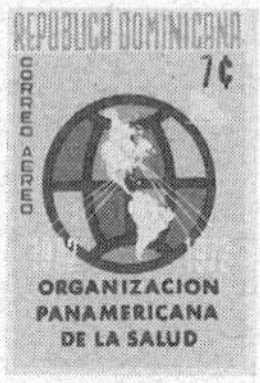

287 Global Emblem

1973. Easter. Multicoloured.
1165 2c. Type **286** (postage) . . . 10 10
1166 6c. Belfry, Church of Our Lady of Carmen (vert) . . 15 10
1167 10c. Belfry, Chapel of Our Lady of Succour (vert) (air) 20 10

1973. Air. 70th Anniv of Pan-American Health Organization.
1168 **287** 7c. multicoloured 15 10

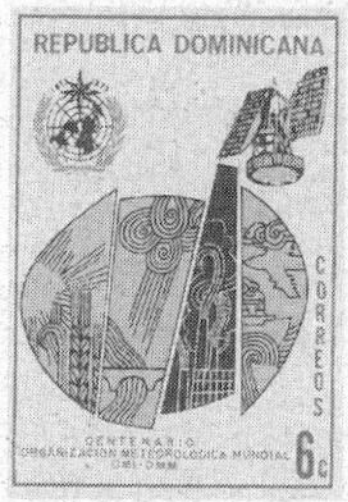

288 Weather Zones

1973. Cent of World Meteorological Organization.
1169 **288** 6c. mult (postage) . . . 15 10
1170 7c. multicoloured (air) 15 10

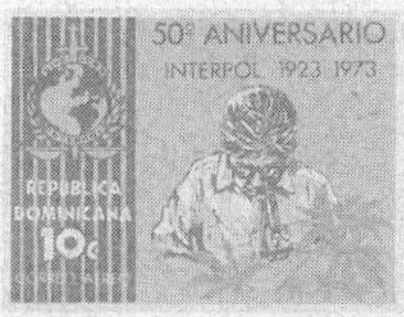

289 Forensic Scientist

1973. Air. 50th Anniv of International Criminal Police Organization (Interpol).
1171 **289** 10c. blue, green and light blue 20 15

1973. Obligatory Tax. Anti-cancer Fund. As T **144** but dated "1973".
1171a **144** 1c. olive 15 10
See also Nos. 1270a and 1338a.

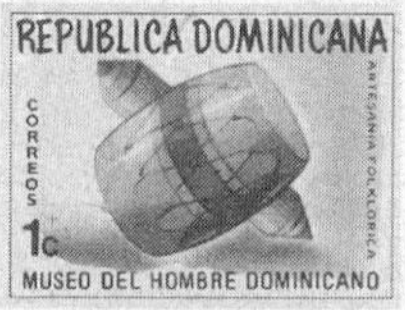

290 Maguey Drum

1973. Opening of Museum of Dominican Man, Santo Domingo. Multicoloured.

1172	1c. Type **290** (postage) . . .	10	10
1173	2c. Amber carvings	10	10
1174	4c. Cibao mask (vert)	10	10
1175	6c. Pottery (vert)	15	10
1176	7c. Model ship in mosaic (vert) (air)	15	10
1177	10c. Maracas rattles	20	15

291 Nativity Scene

1973. Christmas. Multicoloured.

1178	2c. Type **291** (postage) . . .	10	10
1179	6c. "Prayer" (stained-glass window) (vert)	15	10
1180	10c. Angels beside crib (air)	20	15

292 Scout Badge

1973. 50th Anniv of Dominican Boy Scouts. Multicoloured.

1181	1c. Type **292** (postage) . . .	10	10
1182	5c. Scouts and flag	10	10
1183	21c. Scouts cooking, and Lord Baden Powell (air)	40	30

No. 1182 is smaller, size 26 × 36 mm.

293 Stadium and Basketball Players

294 Belfry, Santo Domingo Cathedral

1974. 12th Central American and Caribbean Games, Santo Domingo. Multicoloured.

1184	2c. Type **293** (postage) . . .	10	10
1185	6c. Arena and cyclist	15	10
1186	10c. Swimming pool and diver (air)	20	15
1187	25c. Stadium, soccer players and discus-thrower	50	35

1974. Obligatory Tax. Rehabilitation of the Handicapped. As T **283** but larger, 22 × 27 mm.

1187a	**283** 1c. blue	15	15

1974. Holy Week.

1188	**294** 2c. mult (postage) . . .	10	10
1189	– 6c. purple, green & ol . .	15	10
1190	– 10c. multicoloured	20	15

DESIGN—VERT: 6c. "Sorrowful Mother" (D. Bouts). HORIZ: 10c. "The Last Supper" (R. M. Budi).

295 Francisco del Rosario Sanchez Bridge

1974. Dominican Bridges. Multicoloured.

1191	6c. Type **295** (postage) . . .	15	10
1192	10c. Iliguamo Bridge (air)	20	15

296 Emblem and Patient

1974. Anti-diabetes Campaign. Mult.

1193	4c. Type **296** (postage) . . .	10	10
1194	5c. Emblem and pancreas	10	10

1195	7c. Emblem and Kidney (air)	15	10
1196	33c. Emblem, eye and heart	70	45

1974. Obligatory Tax. Anti-cancer Fund. As T **144** but dated "1974".

1196a	**144** 1c. orange	15	10

297 Steam Train

1974. Centenary of Universal Postal Union. Mult.

1197	2c. Type **297** (postage) . . .	45	55
1198	6c. Stage-coach	15	10
1199	7c. "Eider" mail steamer (air)	60	15
1200	33c. Boeing 727-200 of Dominicana Airways . . .	95	30

298 Emblems of World Amateur Golf Council and of Dominican Golf Association

1974. World Amateur Golf Championships.

1202	**298** 2c. black and yellow (postage)	10	10
1203	– 6c. multicoloured	10	10
1204	– 10c. multicoloured (air)	25	15
1205	– 20c. multicoloured	45	30

DESIGNS—VERT: 6c. Golfers teeing-off. HORIZ: 10c. Council emblem and golfers; 20c. Dominican Golf Association emblem, golfer and hand with ball and tee.

299 Christmas Decorations

301 Dr. Defillo

1974. Christmas. Multicoloured.

1206	2c. Type **299** (postage) . . .	10	10
1207	6c. Virgin and Child	15	10
1208	10c. Hand holding dove (horiz) (air)	20	15

1974. 10th Anniv of World Food Programme. Multicoloured.

1209	2c. Type **300** (postage) . . .	10	10
1210	3c. Avocado pears	10	10
1211	5c. Coconuts	10	10
1212	10c. Bee, hive and cask of honey (air)	20	15

1975. Birth Centenary of Dr. Fernando Defillo (medical scientist).

1213	**301** 1c. brown	10	10
1214	6c. green	15	10

1975. Obligatory Tax. Rehabilitation of the Handicapped. As T **283** but dated "1975".

1214a	**283** 1c. brown	15	10

300 Tomatoes

302 "I am the Resurrection and the Life"

303 Spanish 6c. Stamp of 1850

1975. Holy Week. Multicoloured.

1215	2c. Type **302** (postage) . . .	10	10
1216	6c. Bell tower, Nuestra Senora del Rosario convent	15	10
1217	10c. Catholic emblems (air)	20	15

1975. Obligatory Tax. Tuberculosis Relief Fund. As T **221** but dated "1975".

1217a	**221** 1c. multicoloured . . .	15	10

DESIGN: 1c. "Catteeyopsis rosea".

1975. Air. "Espana 75" International Stamp Exhibition, Madrid.

1218	**303** 12c. black, red & yell . .	25	15

304 Hands supporting "Agriculture" and Industry

305 Earth Station

1975. 16th Meeting of Industrial Development Bank Governors, Santo Domingo.

1219	**304** 6c. mult (postage) . . .	15	10
1220	10c. mult (air)	20	15

1975. Opening of Satellite Earth Station. Multicoloured.

1221	5c. Type **305** (postage) . . .	10	10
1222	15c. Hemispheres and satellites (horiz) (air) . . .	30	20

306 "Apollo" Spacecraft with Docking Tunnel

307 Father Castellanos

1975. "Apollo–Soyuz" Space Link. Mult.

1223	1c. Type **306** (postage) . . .	10	10
1224	4c. "Soyuz" spacecraft	10	10
1225	2p. Docking manoeuvre (air)	3·25	2·00

The 2p. is larger, 42 × 28 mm.

1975. Birth Cent of Father Rafael C. Castellanos.

1226	**307** 6c. brown and buff . . .	15	10

308 Women encircling I.W.Y. Emblem

1975. International Women's Year.

1227	**308** 3c. multicoloured . . .	10	10

309 Guacanagarix

310 Basketball

1975. Indian Chiefs. Multicoloured.

1228	1c. Type **309** (postage) . . .	10	10
1229	2c. Guarionex	10	10
1230	3c. Caonabo	10	10
1231	4c. Bohechio	10	10
1232	5c. Cayacoa	10	10
1233	6c. Anacaona	15	10
1234	9c. Hatuey	20	15
1235	7c. Mayobanex (air)	15	10
1236	8c. Cotubanama with Juan de Esquivel	15	10
1237	10c. Enriquillo and wife, Mencia	20	15

1975. Obligatory Tax. Anti-cancer Fund. As T **144** but dated "1975".

1237a	**144** 1c. violet	15	10

1975. 7th Pan-American Games, Mexico City. Multicoloured.

1238	2c. Type **310** (postage) . . .	10	10
1239	6c. Baseball	15	10

1240	7c. Volleyball (horiz) (air)	15	15
1241	10c. Weightlifting (horiz) . .	25	15

311 Carol-singers

1975. Christmas. Multicoloured.

1242	2c. Type **311** (postage) . . .	10	10
1243	6c. "Dominican" Nativity	15	10
1244	10c. Dove and Peace message (air)	20	15

312 Pearl Sergeant Major ("Abudefdul marginatus")

1976. Fishes. Multicoloured.

1245	10c. Type **312**	35	25
1246	10c. Puddingwife ("Halichoeres radiata")	35	25
1247	10c. Squirrelfish ("Holocentrus ascensionis")	35	25
1248	10c. Queen angelfish ("Angelochthys ciliaris")	35	25
1249	10c. Aya snapper ("Lutianus aya")	35	25

313 Valdesia Dam

1976. Air. Inauguration of Valdesia Dam.

1250	**313** 10c. multicoloured . . .	15	15

1976. Obligatory Tax. Rehabilitation of the Disabled. As T **283** but dated "1976".

1250a	**283** 1c. blue	15	10

314 Orchid

1976. Obligatory Tax. Tuberculosis Relief Fund.

1251	**314** 1c. multicoloured	10	10

315 "Magdalene" (E. Godoy)

316 Schooner "Separacion Dominicana"

1976. Holy Week. Multicoloured.

1252	2c. Type **315** (postage) . . .	10	10
1253	6c. "The Ascension" (V. Priego)	10	10
1254	10c. "Mount Calvary" (E. Castillo) (air)	20	15

1976. Navy Day.

1255	**316** 20c. multicoloured . . .	1·75	40

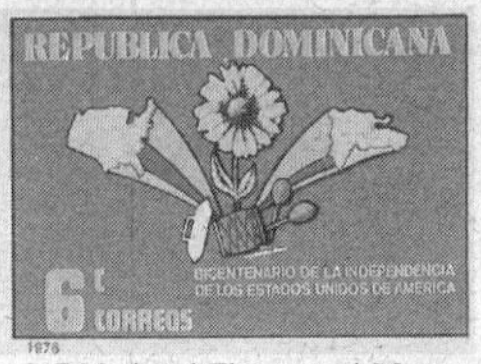

317 National Flower and Maps

1976. Bicentenary of American Revolution, and "Interphil '76" Int Stamp Exn, Philadelphia.
1256 **317** 6c. mult (postage) . . . 15 10
1257 – 9c. multicoloured 20 10
1258 – 10c. multicoloured (air) 50 15
1259 – 75c. black and orange 1·50 1·00
DESIGNS—HORIZ: 9c. Maps within cogwheels; 10c. Maps within hands. VERT: 75c. George Washington and Philadelphia buildings.

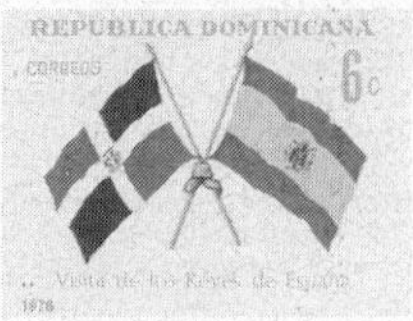

318 Flags of Spain and Dominican Republic

1976. Visit of King and Queen of Spain. Multicoloured.
1260 6c. Type **318** (postage) . . . 35 10
1261 21c. King Juan Carlos I and Queen Sophia (air) . . . 1·00 35

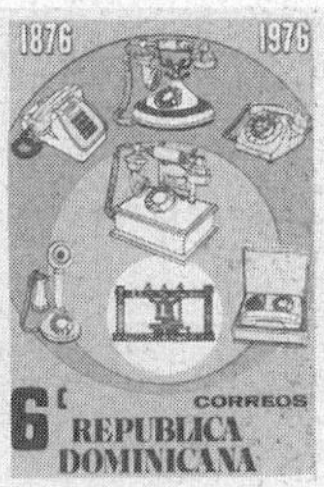

319 Various Telephones

1976. Telephone Centenary. Multicoloured.
1262 6c. Type **319** (postage) . . . 15 10
1263 10c. A. Graham Bell (horiz) (air) 20 15

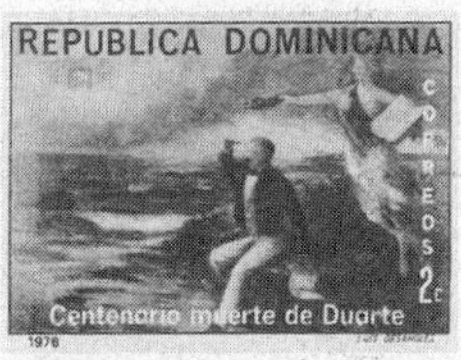

320 "Duarte's Vision" (L. Desangles)

1976. Death Centenary of Juan Duarte (patriot). Multicoloured.
1264 2c. Type **320** (postage) . . . 10 10
1265 6c. "Juan Duarte" (R. Mejia) (vert) 15 10
1266 10c. Text of Duarte's Declaration (vert) (air) . . 20 15
1267 33c. "Duarte Sailing to Exile" (E. Godoy) 70 45

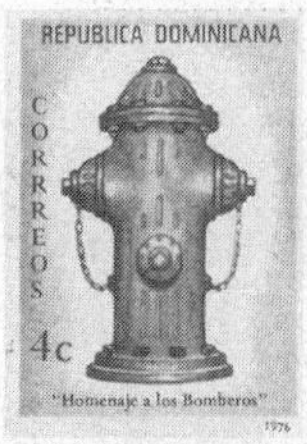

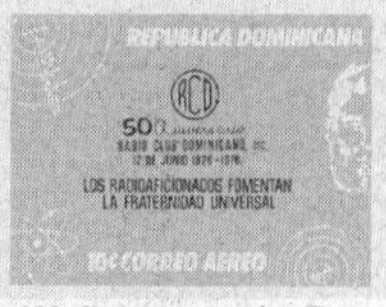

321 Fire Hydrant **322** Commemorative Text and Emblem

1976. Dominican Fire Service. Multicoloured.
1268 4c. Type **321** (postage) . . . 10 10
1269 6c. Fire Service emblem . . 15 10
1270 10c. Fire engine (horiz) (air) 20 15

1976. Obligatory Tax. Anti-cancer Fund. As T **144** but dated "1976".
1270a **144** 1c. green 15 10

1976. 50th Anniv of Dominican Radio Club.
1271 **322** 6c. black & red (postage) 15 10
1272 10c. black & blue (air) 20 15

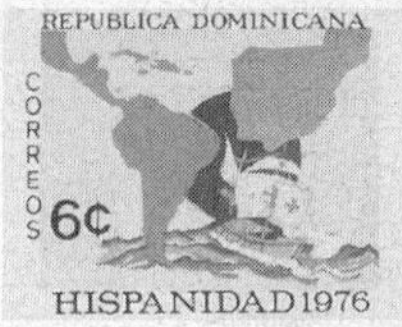

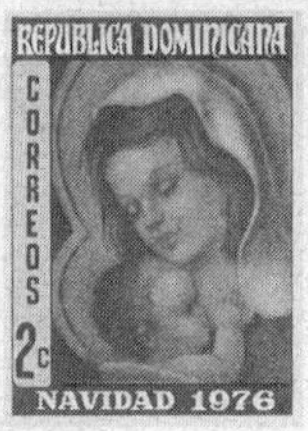

323 Map and Caravel **325** Virgin and Child

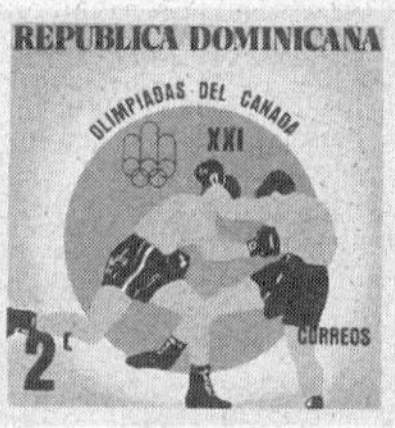

324 Boxing

1976. "Hispanidad 1976". Multicoloured.
1273 6c. Type **323** (postage) . . . 60 15
1274 21c. Heads of Spaniard and Dominicans (air) 45 30

1976. Olympic Games, Montreal. Mult.
1275 2c. Type **324** (postage) . . . 10 10
1276 3c. Weightlifting 10 10
1277 10c. Running (air) 20 15
1278 25c. Basketball 50 35

1976. Obligatory Tax. Child Welfare. As T **233** but dated "1976".
1278a **233** 1c. mauve 15 10

1976. Christmas. Multicoloured.
1279 2c. Type **325** (postage) . . . 10 10
1280 6c. The Three Kings (22 × 32 mm) 15 10
1281 10c. Angel with bells (22 × 32 mm) (air) 20 15

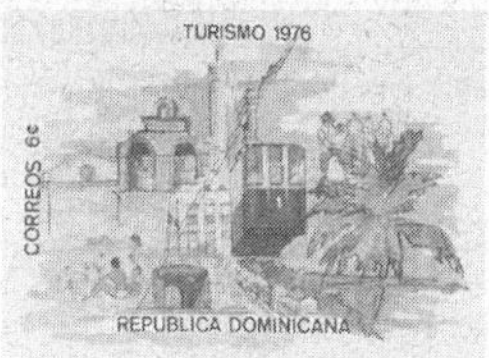

326 Cable-car and Beach Scenes

1977. Tourism. Multicoloured.
1282 6c. Type **326** (postage) . . . 15 10
1283 10c. Tourist activities (air) 20 15
1284 12c. Fishing and hotel . . . 25 15
1285 25c. Horse-riding and waterfall 50 35
No. 1283 measures 36 × 36 mm, No. 1284 35 × 26 mm and No. 1285 26 × 35 mm.

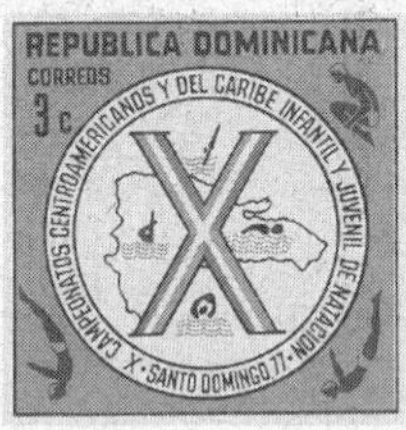

327 Championships Emblem

1977. 10th Central American and Caribbean Children's Swimming Championships, Santo Domingo.
1286 **327** 3c. mult (postage) . . . 10 10
1287 5c. multicoloured 10 10
1288 10c. multicoloured (air) 20 15
1289 25c. multicoloured . . . 30 35

1977. Obligatory Tax. Rehabilitation of the Disabled. As T **283** but dated "1977".
1289a **283** 1c. blue 15 10

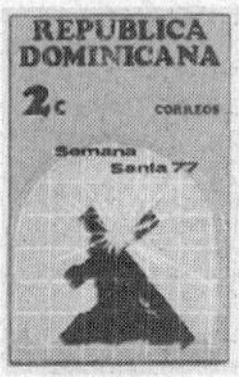

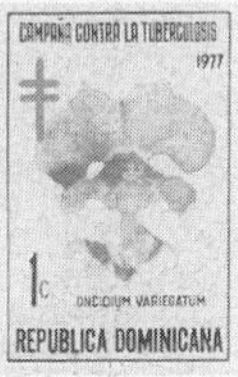

328 Allegory of Holy Week **329** "Oncidium variegatum" (orchid)

1977. Holy Week.
1290 **328** 2c. mult (postage) . . . 10 10
1291 – 6c. black and mauve . . 10 10
1292 – 10c. blk, red & bl (air) 20 10

DESIGNS: 6c. Christ crowned with thorns; 10c. Church and book.

1977. Obligatory Tax. Tuberculosis Relief Fund.
1293 **329** 1c. multicoloured 10 10

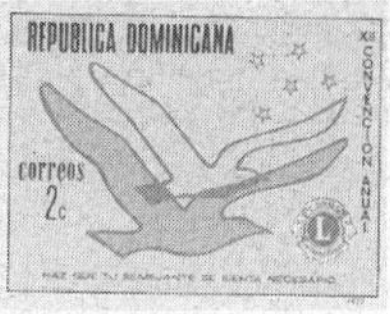

330 Gulls in Flight

1977. 12th Annual Lions Clubs Convention, Santo Domingo.
1294 **330** 2c. mult (postage) . . . 10 10
1295 6c. multicoloured 15 10
1296 7c. multicoloured (air) 15 10

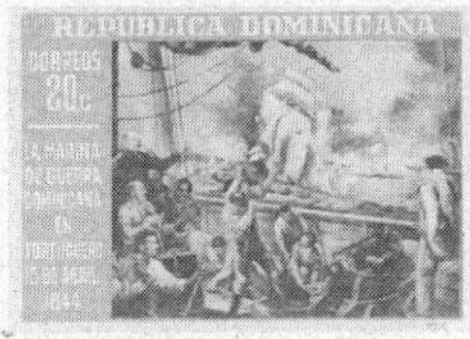

331 "Battle of Tortuguero" (G. Fernandez)

1977. Navy Day.
1297 **331** 20c. multicoloured . . . 90 30

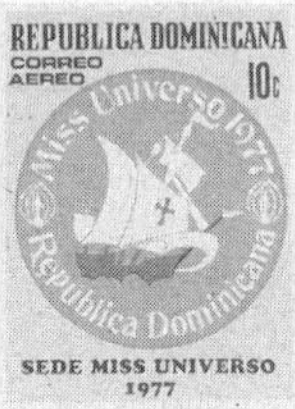

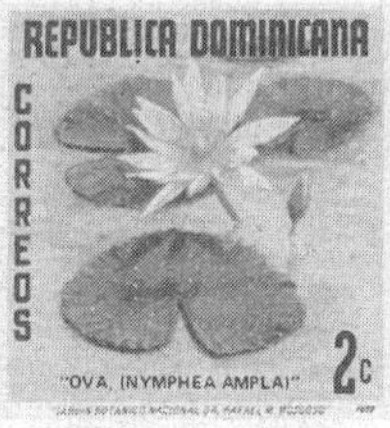

332 "Miss Universe" Emblem **333** "Nymphaea ampla" ("Nymphea" on stamp)

1977. Air. "Miss Universe" Competition.
1298 **332** 10c. multicoloured . . . 20 15

1977. Dominican Flora. Plants in the Dr. Rafael M. Moscoso National Botanical Gardens. Mult.
1299 2c. Type **333** (postage) . . . 10 10
1300 4c. "Broughtonia domingensis" 10 10
1301 6c. "Cordia sebestena" . . . 15 10
1302 7c. "Melocatus lemairei" (cactus) (air) 15 10
1303 33c. "Coccothrinax argentea" (tree) 70 45

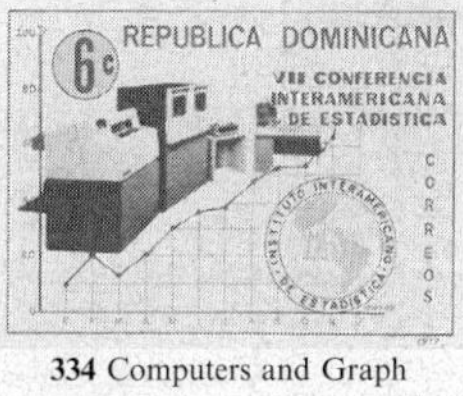

334 Computers and Graph

1977. Seventh Inter-American Statistic Conference. Multicoloured.
1304 6c. Type **334** (postage) . . . 15 10
1305 28c. Factories and graph (27 × 37 mm) (air) 55 35

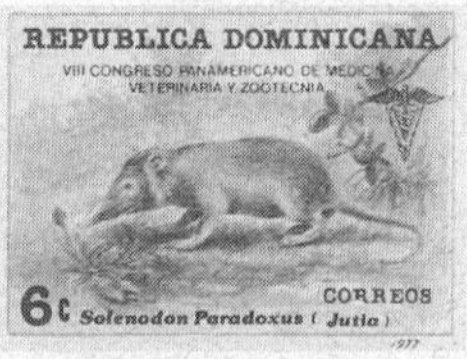

335 Haitian Solenodon

1977. 8th Inter-American Veterinary Congress. Multicoloured.
1306 6c. Type **335** (postage) . . . 15 10
1307 20c. Iguana 40 25
1308 10c. "Red Roman" stud bull (air) 20 15
1309 25c. Greater Flamingo (vert) 3·00 45

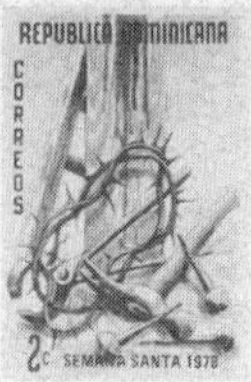

336 Main Gateway of Casa del Cordon **337** Tools and Crown of Thorns at Foot of Cross

1978. "Hispanidad 1977". Multicoloured.
1310 6c. Type **336** (postage) . . . 15 10
1311 21c. Gothic-style window, Casa del Tostado (28 × 41 mm) (air) 45 30

1978. Holy Week.
1312 **337** 2c. mult (postage) . . . 10 10
1313 – 6c. green 15 10
1314 – 7c. multicoloured (air) 15 10
1315 – 10c. multicoloured . . . 20 15
DESIGNS—(22 × 33 mm): 6c. Christ wearing Crown of Thorns. (27 × 37 mm): 7c. Facade of Santo Domingo Cathedral; 10c. Facade of Dominican Convent.

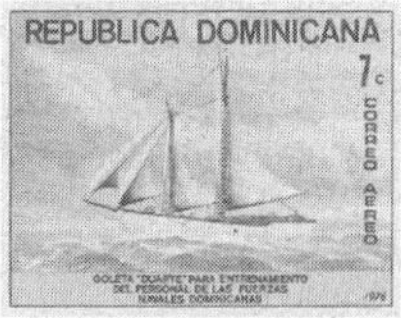

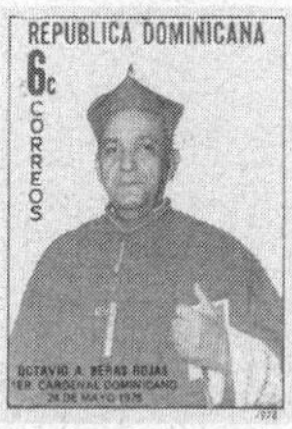

338 Schooner "Duarte" **339** Cardinal Octavio A. Beras Rojas

1978. Air. Navy Day.
1316 **338** 7c. multicoloured 75 15

1978. Consecration of First Cardinal from Dominican Republic.
1317 **339** 6c. mult (postage) . . . 15 10
1318 10c. multicoloured (air) 20 15

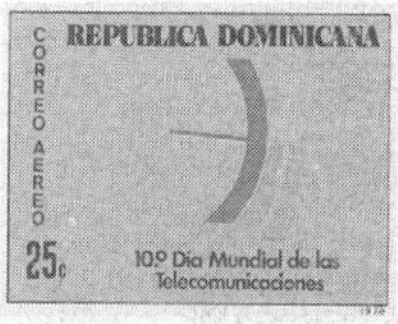

340 Microwave Antenna

1978. Air. 10th World Telecommunications Day.
1319 **340** 25c. multicoloured . . . 50 35

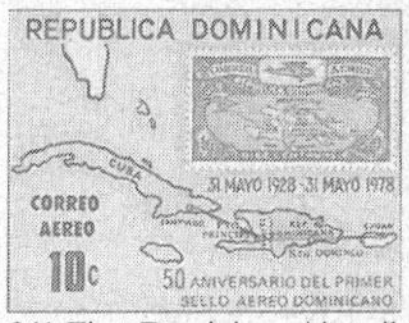

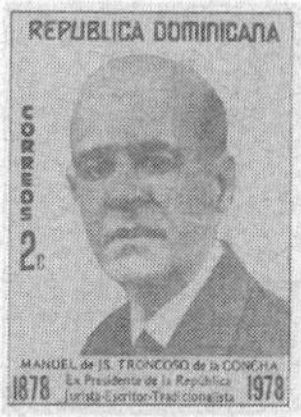

341 First Dominican Airmail Stamp and Map of First Airmail Service **342** Pres. Manuel de Troncoso

1978. Air. 50th Anniv of First Dominican Airmail Stamp.
1320 **341** 10c. multicoloured . . . 20 15

1978. Birth Centenary of President Troncoso.
1321 **342** 2c. brown, mauve & blk 10 10
1322 6c. brown, grey & black 15 10

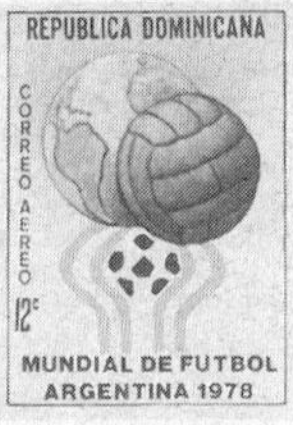

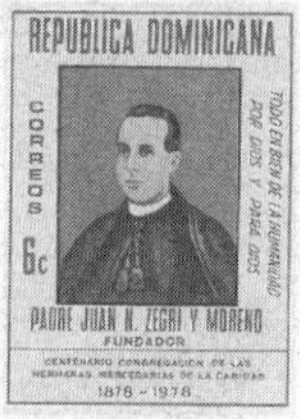

343 Globe, Football and Emblem **344** Father Juan N. Zegri y Moreno (founder)

1978. Air. World Cup Football Championship, Argentina. Multicoloured.
1323	12c. Type **343**	25	15
1324	33c. Emblem and map on football pitch	75	45

1978. Centenary of Merciful Sisters of Charity. Multicoloured.
1325	6c. Type **344** (postage)	15	10
1326	21c. Symbol of the Order (air)	40	30

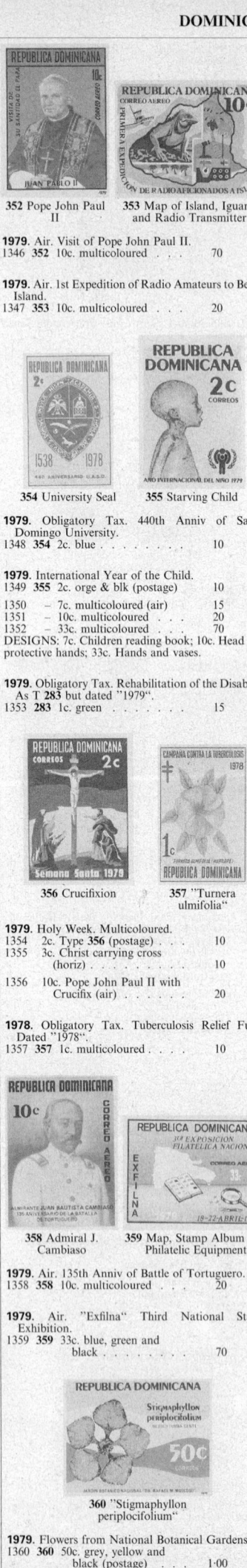

345 Boxing

1978. 13th Central American and Caribbean Games, Medellin, Colombia. Multicoloured.
1327	2c. Type **345** (postage)	10	10
1328	6c. Weightlifting	15	10
1329	7c. Baseball (vert) (air)	15	10
1330	10c. Football (vert)	20	15

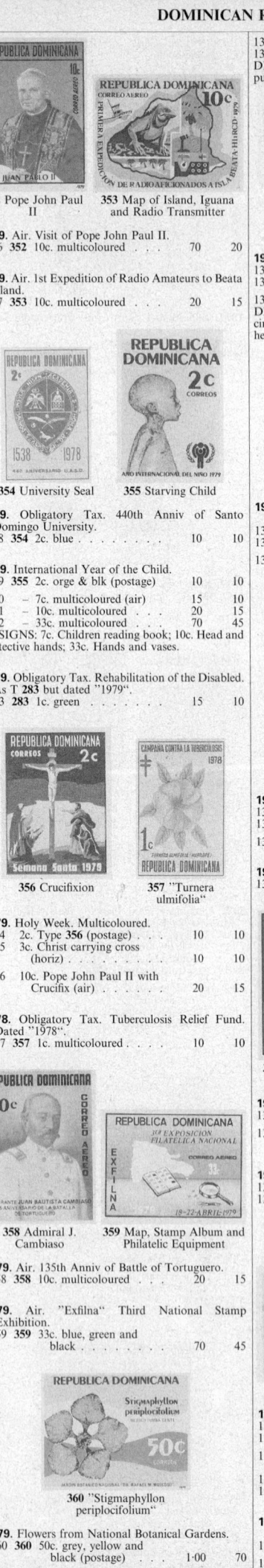

346 Douglas DC-6, Boeing 707 and Wright Flyer I   **347** Sun over Landscape

1978. Air. 75th Anniv of First Powered Flight.
1331	**346** 7c. multicoloured	15	15
1332	– 10c. brown, yellow & red	35	15
1333	– 13c. blue & dp blue	45	20
1334	– 45c. multicoloured	1·25	75

DESIGNS: 10c. Wright brothers and Wright Glider No. I; 13c. Diagram of airflow over wing; 45c. Wright Flyer I and world map.

1978. Tourism. Multicoloured.
1335	2c. Type **347** (postage)	10	10
1336	6c. Sun over beach	15	10
1337	7c. Sun and musical instruments (air)	15	10
1338	10c. Sun over Santo Domingo	20	15

1978. Obligatory Tax. Anti-cancer Fund. As T **144** but dated "1977".
1338a	**144** 1c. purple	15	10

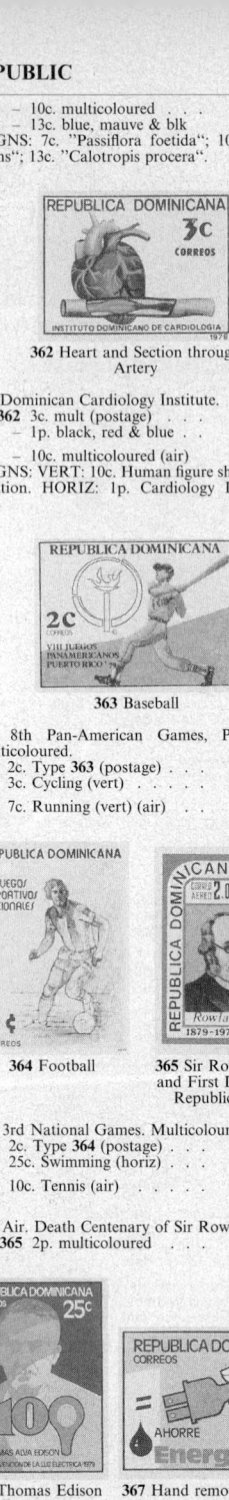

348 Galleons   **349** Flags of Dominican Republic and United Nations

1978. "Hispanidad 1978". Multicoloured.
1339	2c. Type **348** (postage)	10	10
1340	21c. Figures holding hands in front of globe (air)	45	25

1978. Air. 33rd Anniv of United Nations.
1341	**349** 33c. multicoloured	70	25

350 Mother and Child   **351** Dove, Lamp and Poinsettia

1978. Obligatory Tax. Child Welfare.
1342	**350** 1c. green	10	10

1978. Christmas. Multicoloured.
1343	2c. Type **351** (postage)	10	10
1344	6c. Dominican family and star	15	10
1345	10c. Statue of the Virgin (air)	20	15

No. 1345 is vert, 22 × 33 mm.

352 Pope John Paul II   **353** Map of Island, Iguana and Radio Transmitter

1979. Air. Visit of Pope John Paul II.
1346	**352** 10c. multicoloured	70	20

1979. Air. 1st Expedition of Radio Amateurs to Beata Island.
1347	**353** 10c. multicoloured	20	15

354 University Seal   **355** Starving Child

1979. Obligatory Tax. 440th Anniv of Santo Domingo University.
1348	**354** 2c. blue	10	10

1979. International Year of the Child.
1349	**355** 2c. orge & blk (postage)	10	10
1350	– 7c. multicoloured (air)	15	10
1351	– 10c. multicoloured	20	15
1352	– 33c. multicoloured	70	45

DESIGNS: 7c. Children reading book; 10c. Head and protective hands; 33c. Hands and vases.

1979. Obligatory Tax. Rehabilitation of the Disabled. As T **283** but dated "1979".
1353	**283** 1c. green	15	10

356 Crucifixion   **357** "Turnera ulmifolia"

1979. Holy Week. Multicoloured.
1354	2c. Type **356** (postage)	10	10
1355	3c. Christ carrying cross (horiz)	10	10
1356	10c. Pope John Paul II with Crucifix (air)	20	15

1978. Obligatory Tax. Tuberculosis Relief Fund. Dated "1978".
1357	**357** 1c. multicoloured	10	10

358 Admiral J. Cambiaso   **359** Map, Stamp Album and Philatelic Equipment

1979. Air. 135th Anniv of Battle of Tortuguero.
1358	**358** 10c. multicoloured	20	15

1979. Air. "Exfilna" Third National Stamp Exhibition.
1359	**359** 33c. blue, green and black	70	45

360 "Stigmaphyllon periplocifolium"

1979. Flowers from National Botanical Gardens.
1360	**360** 50c. grey, yellow and black (postage)	1·00	70
1361	– 7c. multicoloured (air)	15	10

362 Heart and Section through Artery

1979. Dominican Cardiology Institute.
1364	**362** 3c. mult (postage)	10	10
1365	– 1p. black, red & blue	2·00	1·40
1366	– 10c. multicoloured (air)	20	15

DESIGNS: VERT: 10c. Human figure showing blood circulation. HORIZ: 1p. Cardiology Institute and heart.

363 Baseball

1979. 8th Pan-American Games, Puerto Rico. Multicoloured.
1367	2c. Type **363** (postage)	10	10
1368	3c. Cycling (vert)	10	10
1369	7c. Running (vert) (air)	15	10

364 Football   **365** Sir Rowland Hill and First Dominican Republic Stamp

1979. 3rd National Games. Multicoloured.
1370	2c. Type **364** (postage)	10	10
1371	25c. Swimming (horiz)	55	35
1372	10c. Tennis (air)	20	15

1979. Air. Death Centenary of Sir Rowland Hill.
1373	**365** 2p. multicoloured	4·25	1·10

366 Thomas Edison (inventor)   **367** Hand removing Electric Plug

1979. Centenary of Electric Light-bulb. Mult.
1374	25c. Type **366** (postage)	55	30
1375	10c. "100" forming lightbulb (horiz) (air)	20	15

1979. "Save Energy". Multicoloured.
1376	2c. Type **367** (postage)	10	10
1377	6c. Car being refuelled	15	10

368 Hispaniolan Conure   **369** Lions Emblem

1979. Birds. Multicoloured.
1378	2c. Type **368** (postage)	1·00	25
1379	6c. Hispaniolan trogon	1·10	25
1380	7c. Black-crowned palm tanager (air)	1·60	35
1381	10c. Chat-tanager	2·40	35
1382	45c. Black-cowled oriole	7·00	1·25

1979. 15th Anniv of Dominican Republic Lions Club. Multicoloured.
1383	20c. Type **369** (postage)	45	20
1384	10c. Melvin Jones (founder) (air)	20	10

371 Holy Family   **372** Christ carrying Cross

1979. Christmas. Multicoloured.
1386	2c. Type **371** (postage)	10	10
1387	10c. Three Kings (air)	20	15

1980. Holy Week.
1388	**372** 3c. black, red and lilac (postage)	10	10
1389	– 7c. blk, red & yell (air)	15	10
1390	– 10c. black, red & bistre	20	15

DESIGNS: 7c. Crucifixion; 10c. Resurrection.

1980. Obligatory Tax. Rehabilitation of the Disabled. As T **283** but dated "1980".
1391	**283** 1c. olive and green	10	10

374 Navy Crest   **376** Cocoa Harvest

375 "Stamp"

1980. Air. Navy Day.
1392	**374** 21c. multicoloured	45	30

1980. Air. 25th Anniv of Dominican Philatelic Society.
1393	**375** 10c. multicoloured	20	15

1980. Agricultural Year. Multicoloured.
1394	1c. Type **376**	10	10
1395	2c. Coffee	10	10
1396	3c. Plantain	10	10
1397	4c. Sugar cane	10	10
1398	5c. Maize	10	10

377 Cotuf Gold Mine, Pueblo Viejob   **379** "Tourism"

1980. Nationalization of Gold Mines. Mult.
1399	6c. Type **377** (postage)	15	10
1400	10c. Drag line mining (air)	20	15
1401	33c. General view of location of gold mines	70	45

378 Blind Man's Buff

1980. Children's Games. Multicoloured.
1402	3c. Type **378**	10	10
1403	4c. Marbles	10	10
1404	5c. Spinning top	10	10
1405	15c. Hopscotch	15	10

1980. Air. World Tourism Conference, Manila, Philippines. Multicoloured.
1406	10c. Type **379**	20	15
1407	33c. Conference emblem	70	45

380 Cuban Iguana

1980. Animals. Multicoloured.
1408 20c. Type **380** (postage) . . . 45 30
1409 7c. American crocodile (air) 15 10
1410 10c. Hispaniolan hutia . . . 25 15
1411 25c. American manatee . . . 65 35
1412 45c. Hawksbill turtle 95 60

381 "El Merengue" (Jaime Colson)

1980. Paintings. Multicoloured.
1413 3c. Type **381** (postage) . . . 10 10
1414 50c. "The Mirror"
(G. H. Ortega) . . . . . 1·10 70
1415 10c. "Genesis de un Ganga"
(Paul Guidicelli) (air) 20 15
1416 17c. "The Countryman"
(Yoryi Morel) 35 25

1980. Obligatory Tax. Anti-cancer Fund. As T **144**
but dated "1980".
1417 **144** 1c. blue and violet . . . 10 10

383 Map of Catalina Island   384 Rotary Emblem
on Globe

1980. Air. Visit of Radio Amateurs to Catalina
Island.
1418 **383** 7c. green, blue & black 15 10

1980. Air. 75th Anniv of Rotary International.
Multicoloured.
1419 10c. Type **384** 20 15
1420 33c. Rotary emblem in "75" 70 45

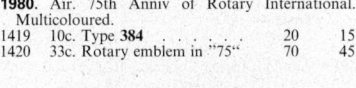

385 Carrier Pigeons with Letters

1980. Centenary of U.P.U. Membership. Mult.
1421 33c. Type **385** 70 45
1422 45c. Row of stylized pigeons
and letter 95 60
1423 50c. Carrier pigeon with
letter and letter . . . . 1·10 70

1980. Obligatory tax. Child Welfare. As T **350** but
dated "1980".
1425 **350** 1c. blue 10 10

386 The Three Kings   387 Arms of Salcedo

1980. Christmas. Multicoloured.
1426 3c. Type **386** (postage) . . . 10 10
1427 6c. Carol singers 15 10
1428 10c. The Holy Family (air) 20 15

1981. Centenary of Salcedo Province. Mult.
1429 6c. Type **387** (postage) . . . 15 10
1430 10c. Arms and map of
Salcedo (air) 20 15

388 Juan Pablo Duarte   389 Industrial Symbols

1981. Juan Pablo Duarte (patriot). Commemoration.
1431 **388** 2c. brown and ochre . . 10 10

1981. Air. Chemical Engineering Seminar.
1432 **389** 10c. multicoloured . . . 20 15
1433 – 33c. gold and black 70 45
DESIGN: 33c. Emblem of Dominican College of
Engineering and Architecture (CODIA).

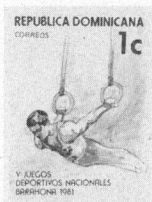 

390 Gymnastics   391 Mother Mazzarello

1981. Fifth National Games (1st issue). Mult.
1434 1c. Type **390** (postage) . . . 10 10
1435 2c. Running 10 10
1436 5c. Pole-vaulting 10 10
1437 6c. Boxing 15 10
1438 10c. Baseball (air) 20 15
See also Nos. 1463/4.

1981. Death Centenary of Mother Mazarello
(founder of Daughters of Mary).
1439 **391** 6c. brown and black 15 10

392 Admiral Juan   393 Radio Waves
Alejandro Acosta

1981. Air. 137th Anniv of Battle of Tortuguero.
1440 **392** 10c. multicoloured . . . 20 15

1981. Obligatory Tax. Tuberculosis Relief Fund.
Dated "1981".
1441 **357** 1c. multicoloured . . . 10 10

1981. Air. World Telecommunications Day.
1442 **393** 10c. multicoloured . . . 15 15

394 Pedro Henriquez   395 Forest
Urena

1981. 35th Death Anniv of Pedro Henriquez Urena.
1443 **394** 6c. pale grey and grey 15 10

1981. Forest Conservation. Multicoloured.
1444 2c. Type **395** 10 10
1445 6c. Forest river 15 10

396 Heinrich von   397 "Disabled People"
Stephan

1981. Air. 150th Birth Anniv of Heinrich von Stephan
(founder of U.P.U.).
1446 **396** 33c. brown and yellow 70 45

1981. Air. International Year of Disabled Persons.
Multicoloured.
1447 7c. Type **397** 15 10
1448 33c. Cobbler in wheelchair 70 45

398 Exhibition Emblem

1981. Air. "Expuridom '81" International Stamp
Exhibition, Santo Domingo.
1149 **398** 7c. black, blue and red 15 10

399 Target

1981. Air. 2nd World Air Gun Shooting
Championship. Multicoloured.
1450 10c. Type **399** 20 15
1451 15c. Stylized riflemen . . . 30 20
1452 25c. Stylized pistol shooters 55 55

400 Family and House

1981. National Census. Multicoloured.
1453 3c. Type **400** 10 10
1454 6c. Farmer with cow and
agricultural produce . . . 15 10

1981. Obligatory Tax. Anti-cancer Fund. As T **144**
but dated "1981".
1455 **144** 1c. blue and deep blue 10 10

401 Fruit

1981. Air. World Food Day. Multicoloured.
1456 10c. Type **401** 20 15
1457 50c. Fish, eggs and
vegetables . . . . . . 1·10 70

402 Gem Stones and   403 Javelin-throwing
Jewellery

1981. Air. Exports. Multicoloured.
1458 7c. Type **402** 15 10
1459 10c. Handicrafts 20 15
1460 11c. Fruit 25 15
1461 17c. Cocoa, coffee, tobacco
and sugar 35 25

1981. Obligatory Tax. Child Welfare. As T **350** but
dated "1981".
1462 **350** 1c. green 10 10

1981. Air. 5th National Games, Barahona (2nd
issue). Multicoloured.
1463 10c. Type **403** 20 15
1464 50c. Cycling . . . . . . 1·10 70

404 "Encyclia cochleata"

1981. Air. Orchids. Multicoloured.
1465 7c. Type **404** 10 15
1466 10c. "Broughtonia
domingensis" 15 20
1467 25c. "Encyclia truncata" . . 55 35
1468 65c. "Elleanthus capitatus" 1·60 1·10

405 Bells   406 Juan Pablo Duarte

1981. Christmas. Multicoloured.
1469 2c. Type **405** (postage) . . . 10 10
1470 3c. Holly 10 10
1471 10c. Dove and moon (air) 20 15

1982. Juan Pablo Duarte (patriot) Commemoration.
1472 **406** 2c. light blue and blue 10 10

407 Citizens arriving at Polling
Station

1982. National Elections. Multicoloured.
1473 2c. Type **407** 10 10
1474 3c. Entering polling booth
(vert) 10 10
1475 6c. Casting vote 15 10

408 American Air Forces Co-
operation Emblem

1982. Air. 22nd American Air Force's Commanders
Conference, Buenos Aires.
1476 **408** 10c. multicoloured . . . 20 15

409 Naval Cadet Parade

1982. Air. Battle of Tortuguero Commem.
1477 **409** 10c. multicoloured . . . 20 15

410 Tackling   411 Lord Baden-Powell
(statue)

1982. Air. World Cup Football Championship, Spain. Multicoloured.

1478	10c. Type **410**	20	15
1479	21c. Dribbling	45	30
1480	33c. Heading ball into goal	70	45

1982. Air. 75th Anniv of Boy Scout Movement. Multicoloured.

1481	10c. Type **411**	20	15
1482	15c. Scouting emblems (horiz)	30	20
1483	25c. Baden-Powell and scout at camp fire	55	35

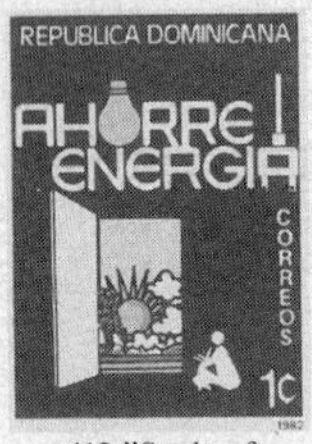

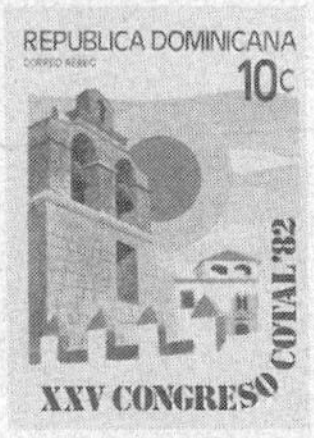

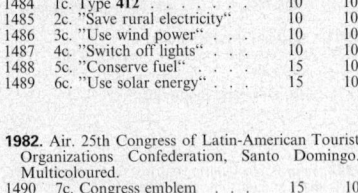

412 "Study of Daylight" **413** Cathedral and House

1982. Energy Conservation. Multicoloured.

1484	1c. Type **412**	10	10
1485	2c. "Save rural electricity"	10	10
1486	3c. "Use wind power"	10	10
1487	4c. "Switch off lights"	10	10
1488	5c. "Conserve fuel"	15	10
1489	6c. "Use solar energy"	15	10

1982. Air. 25th Congress of Latin-American Tourist Organizations Confederation, Santo Domingo. Multicoloured.

1490	7c. Congress emblem	15	10
1491	10c. Type **413**	20	15
1492	33c. Dancers and beach scene	70	45

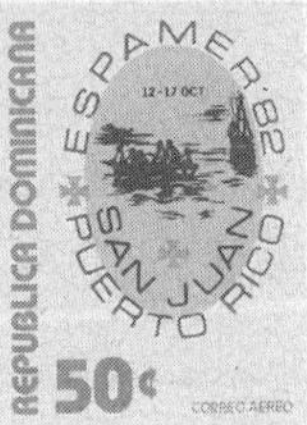

414 Exhibition Emblem

1982. Air. "Espamer '82" Stamp Exhibition, Puerto Rico. Multicoloured.

1493	7c. Stamp bearing map of Puerto Rico (horiz)	15	10
1494	13c. Stylized postage stamps (horiz)	30	20
1495	50c. Type **414**	1·10	70

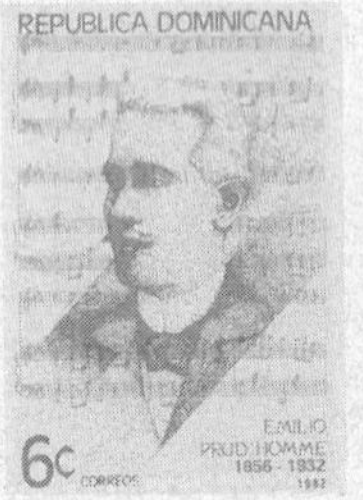

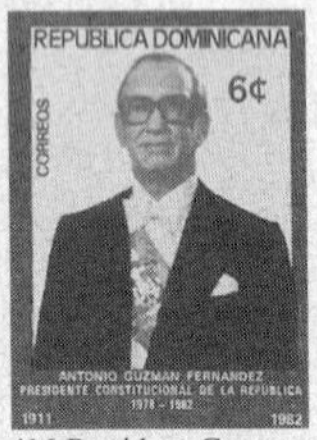

415 Emilio Prud'Homme and Score of Dominican National Anthem **416** President Guzman

1982. 50th Death Anniv of Emilio Prud'Homme (composer).

1496	**415** 6c. multicoloured	15	10

1982. President Antonio Guzman Commemoration.

1497	**416** 6c. multicoloured	15	10

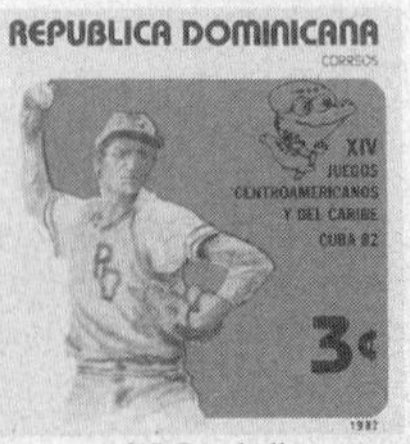

417 Baseball

1982. Central American and Caribbean Games, Cuba. Multicoloured.

1498	3c. Type **417** (postage)	10	10
1499	10c. Basketball (air)	20	15
1500	13c. Boxing	30	20
1501	25c. Gymnastics	55	30

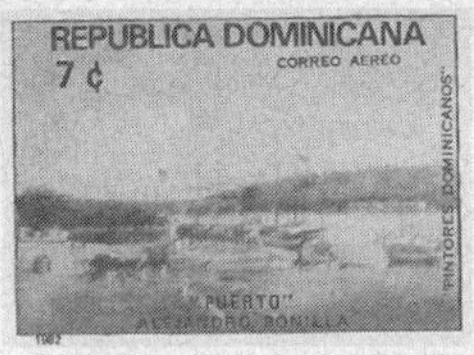

418 "Harbour" (Alejandro Bonilla)

1982. Air. Paintings. Multicoloured.

1502	7c. Type **418**	15	10
1503	10c. "Portrait of a Woman" (Leopoldo Navarro)	20	15
1504	45c. "Portrait of Amelia Francasci" (Luis Desangles)	95	65
1505	2p. "Portrait" (Abelardo Rodriguez Urdaneta)	4·25	2·75

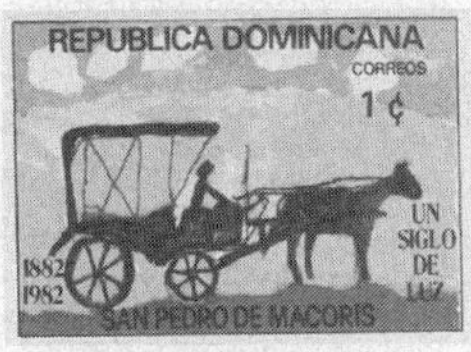

419 Horse-drawn Carriage

1982. Centenary of San Pedro de Macoris Province. Multicoloured.

1506	1c. Type **419** (postage)	10	10
1507	2c. Stained-glass window, San Pedro Apostle Church (25 × 34½ mm)	10	10
1508	5c. Centenary emblem	15	10
1509	7c. View of San Pedro de Macoris City (air)	45	20

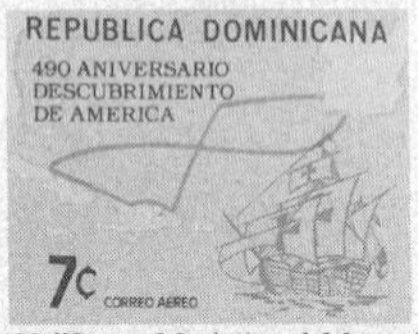

420 "Santa Maria" and Map of Voyage

1982. Air. 490th Anniv of Discovery of America by Columbus. Multicoloured.

1510	7c. Type **420**	1·00	30
1511	10c. "Santa Maria"	1·25	35
1512	21c. Statue of Columbus, Santo Domingo	45	30

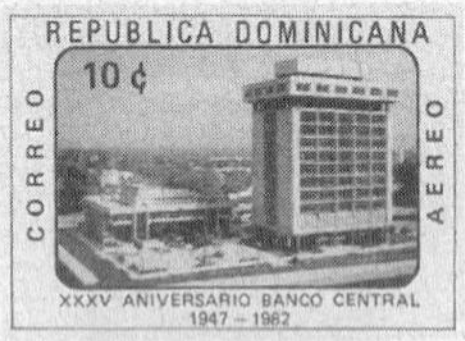

421 Central Bank

1982. 35th Anniv of Central Bank.

1513	**421** 10c. multicoloured	20	15

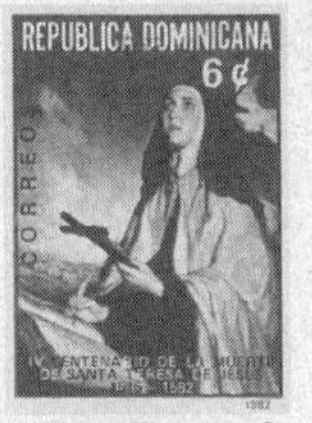

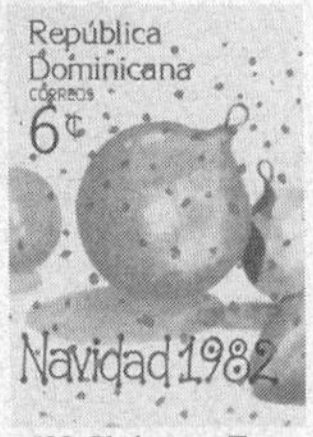

422 St. Theresa of Avila **423** Christmas Tree Decorations

1982. 400th Death Anniv of St. Theresa of Avila.

1514	**422** 6c. multicoloured	15	10

1982. Christmas. Multicoloured.

1515	6c. Type **423** (postage)	10	10
1516	10c. Tree decorations (different) (air)	20	15

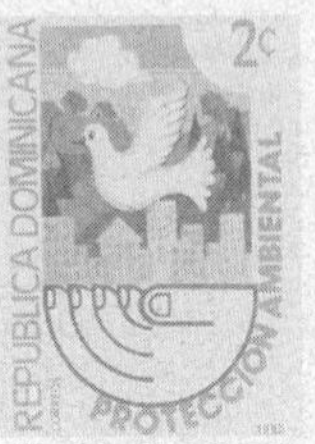

424 Hand holding Rural and Urban Environments

1982. Environmental Protection. Mult.

1517	2c. Type **424**	10	10
1518	3c. Hand holding river in the country	10	10
1519	6c. Hand holding forest	10	10
1520	20c. Hand holding swimming fish	35	25

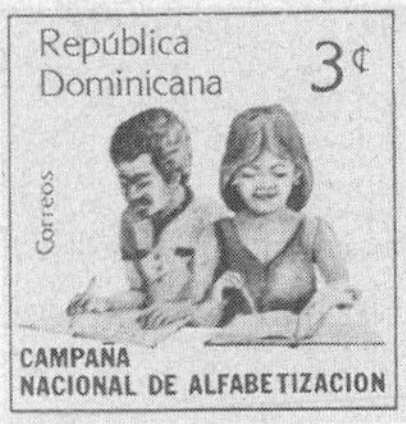

425 Adults writing

1983. National Literacy Campaign. Mult.

1521	2c. Girl and boy writing on blackboard	10	10
1522	3c. Type **425**	10	10
1523	6c. Children, rainbow and pencil	10	10

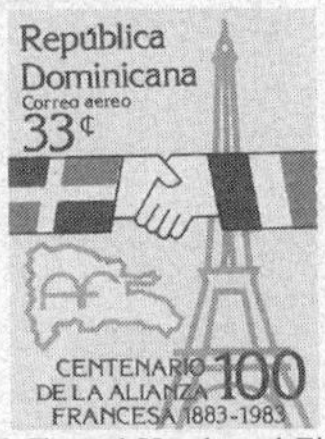

426 Clasped Hands and Eiffel Tower

1983. Air. Centenary of French Alliance (French language-teaching association).

1524	**426** 33c. multicoloured	50	30

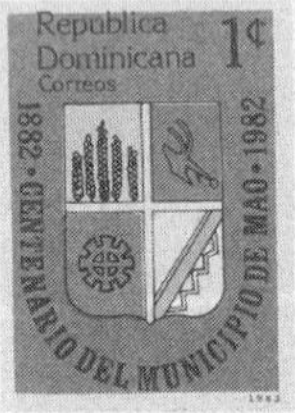

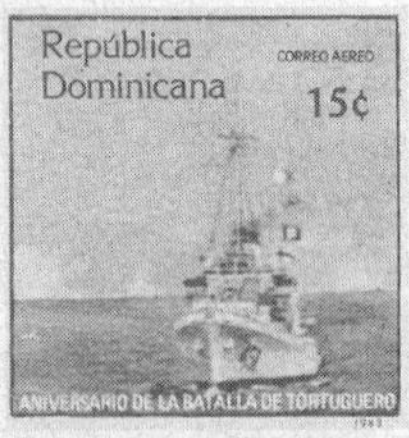

427 Arms of Mao City Council **428** Frigate "Mella"

1983. Centenary of Mao City Council. Mult.

1525	1c. Type **427**	10	10
1526	5c. Centenary monument	10	10

1983. Air. Battle of Tortuguero. Commemoration.

1527	**428** 15c. multicoloured	1·50	40

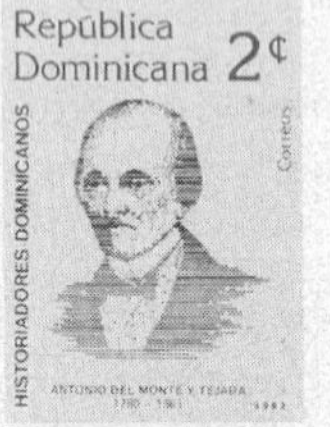

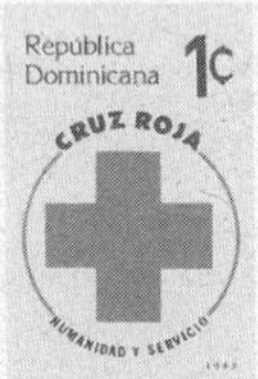

429 Antonio del Monte y Tejada **430** Red Cross

1983. Dominican Historians.

1528	**429** 2c. red & brn (postage)	10	10
1529	– 3c. pink and brown	10	10
1530	– 5c. blue and brown	15	10
1531	– 6c. lt brown & brown	15	10
1532	– 7c. pink & brown (air)	15	10
1533	– 10c. grey and brown	20	15

DESIGNS: 3c. Manuel Ubaldo Gomez; 5c. Emiliano Tejera; 6c. Bernardo Pichardo; 7c. Americo Lugo; 10c. Jose Gabriel Garcia.

1983. Obligatory Tax. Red Cross.

1534	**430** 1c. red, gold & black	10	10

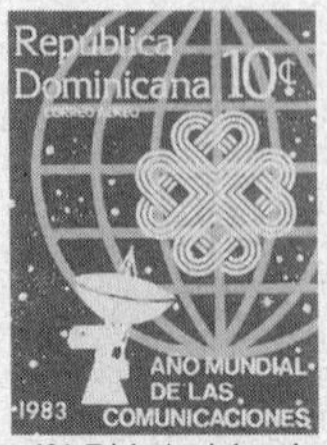

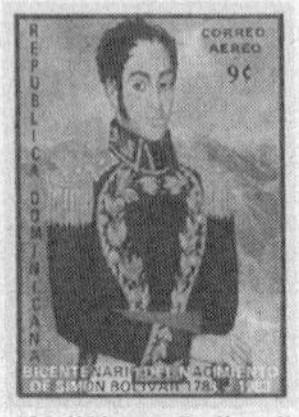

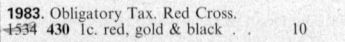

431 Dish Aerial and W.C.Y. Emblem **432** "Simon Bolivar" (Plutarco Andujar)

1983. Air. World Communications Year.

1535	**431** 10c. light blue & blue	20	15

1983. Air. Birth Bicentenary of Simon Bolivar.

1536	**432** 9c. multicoloured	15	10

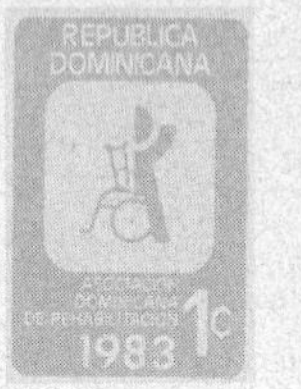

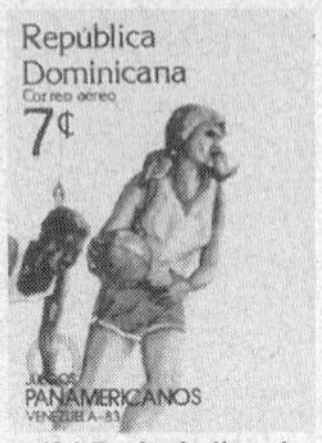

433 Pictogram of Rehabilitation **434** Basketball and Gymnastics

1983. Obligatory Tax. Rehabilitation of the Disabled.

1537	**433** 1c. blue	10	10

1983. Air. Pan-American Games, Venezuela. Multicoloured.

1538	7c. Type **434**	15	10
1539	10c. Boxing and pole vaulting	20	15
1540	15c. Baseball, weightlifting and cycling	25	15

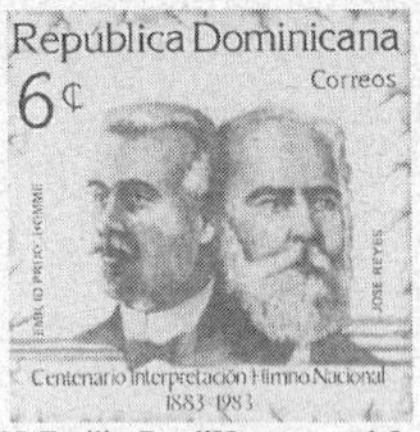

435 Emilio Prud'Homme and Jose Reyes (composers)

1983. Cent of Dominican National Anthem.

1541	**435** 6c. multicoloured	10	10

1983. Obligatory Tax. Anti-cancer Fund. As T **144** but dated "1983".

1542	**144** 1c. turquoise & green	10	10

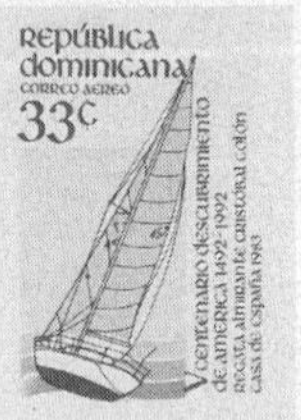

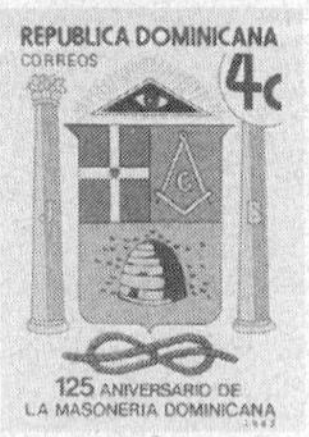

436 "Sotavento" (winner of 1982 regatta) **437** Arms

1983. Air. Christopher Columbus Regatta and 500th Anniv (1992) of Discovery of America by Columbus (1st issue).

1543	– 10c. stone, brn & blk	1·00	45
1544	– 21c. multicoloured	1·25	60
1545	**436** 33c. multicoloured	1·90	65

DESIGNS—HORIZ: 10c. Old map of Greater Antilles; 21c. Christopher Columbus Regatta trophy.

See also Nos. 1583/5, 1617/20, 1649/52, 1683/6, 1717/20, 1754/7, 1777/80, 1791/4 and 1805/8.

1983. 125th Anniv of Dominican Freemasons.

1547	**437** 4c. multicoloured	10	10

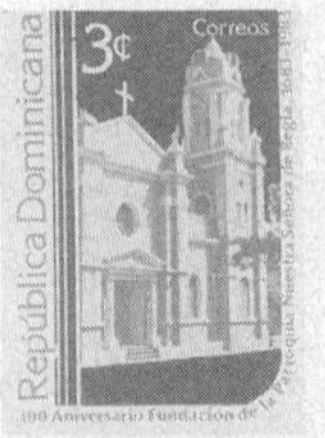

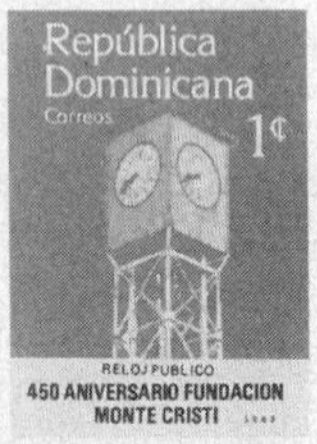

438 Our Lady of Regla Church **439** Clocktower

1983. 300th Anniv of Our Lady of Regla Church.

1548	**438** 3c. deep blue & blue	10	10
1549	– 6c. red and deep red	10	10

DESIGN: 6c. Statue of Our Lady of Regla.

1983. 450th Anniv of Monte Cristi Province.

1550	**439** 1c. green and black	10	10
1551	– 2c. multicoloured	10	10
1552	– 5c. grey	10	10
1553	– 7c. grey and blue	15	10

DESIGNS—VERT: 2c. Provincial coat of arms. HORIZ: 5c. Wooden building in which independence of Cuba was signed; 7c. Men digging out salt crystals.

1983. Obligatory Tax. Child Welfare. As T **350** but dated "1983".

1554	**350** 1c. green	10	10

440 Commission Emblem

1983. Air. 10th Anniv of Latin American Civil Aviation Commission.
1555 **440** 10c. blue 15 10

441 Baseball, Boxing and Cycling   **442** Bells and Christmas Tree Decorations

1983. 6th National Games, San Pedro de Macoris. Multicoloured.
1556 6c. Type **441** (postage) . . . 10 10
1557 10c. Weightlifting, running and swimming (air) . . . 15 10

1983. Air. Christmas.
1558 **442** 10c. multicoloured . . . 15 10

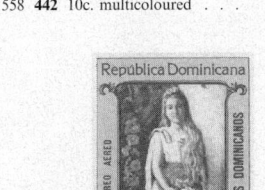

443 "Portrait of a Girl" (Adriana Billini)

1983. Air. Paintings. Multicoloured.
1559 10c. "The Litter" (Juan Bautista Gomez) (horiz) 15 10
1560 15c. "The Meeting between Maximo Gomez and Jose Marti at Guayubin" (Enrique Garcia Godoy) (horiz) 20 15
1561 21c. "St. Francis" (Angel Perdomo) 30 20
1562 33c. Type **443** 45 30

444 Monument to Heroes of Capotillo

1983. 120th Anniv of Restoration of the Republic.
1563 **444** 1c. purple and blue . . . 10 10

445 Man holding Dominican Flag and Rifle

1983. 67th Anniv of Battle of Barranquita.
1564 **445** 5c. multicoloured 10 10

446 Matias Ramon Mella and Dominican Flag

1984. 140th Anniv of Independence. Mult.
1565 6c. Type **446** 10 10
1566 25c. Puerta de la Misericordia and Mella's rifle 15 15

Dr. Heriberto Pieter (1884-1972) Médico-Humanista-Filántropo Centenario de su Nacimiento

447 Dr. Heriberto Pieter

1984. Birth Centenary of Dr. Heriberto Pieter.
1567 **447** 3c. multicoloured 10 10

448 Jose Maria Imbert, Fernando Valerio, Cannon and National Flag

1984. 140th Anniv of Battle of Santiago.
1568 **448** 7c. multicoloured 10 10

449 Coastguard Patrol Boat

1984. 140th Anniv of Battle of Tortuguero.
1569 **449** 10c. multicoloured . . . 1·00 20

450 Monument to the Heroes of June 1959

1984. 25th Anniv of Expedition to Constanza, Maimon and Estero Hondo.
1570 **450** 6c. multicoloured 10 10

451 Salome Urena

1984. Birth Centenary of Pedro Henriquez Urena (poet).
1571 **451** 7c. pink and brown . . . 10 10
1572 − 10c. yellow and brown 10 10
1573 − 22c. yellow and brown 15 15
DESIGNS: 10c. Lines from poem "Mi Pedro"; 22c. Pedro H. Urena.

452 Running

1984. Olympic Games, Los Angeles. Each in blue, red and black.
1574 1p. Type **452** 55 50
1575 1p. Weightlifting 55 50
1576 1p. Boxing 55 50
1577 1p. Baseball 55 50

453 Stygian Owl   **455** Pope John Paul II

454 Christopher Columbus landing in Hispaniola

1984. Protection of Wildlife. Multicoloured.
1578 10c. Type **453** . . . . 1·50 30
1579 15c. Greater flamingo . . . 2·00 40
1580 25c. White-lipped peccary 15 10
1581 35c. Haitian solenodon . . . 25 20

1984. 500th Anniv (1992) of Discovery of America by Columbus (2nd issue).
1582 **454** 10c. multicoloured 10 10
1583 − 35c. multicoloured . . . 25 20
1584 − 65c. brown, yell & blk 40 35
1585 − 1p. multicoloured . . . 55 50
DESIGNS: 35c. Destruction of Fort La Navidad; 65c. First mass in America; 1p. Battle of Santo Cerro.

1984. Papal Visit to Santo Domingo. 500th Anniv of Christianity in the New World. Multicoloured.
1586 75c. Type **455** 45 40
1587 75c. Pope in priest's attire and map 45 40
1588 75c. Globe and Pope in ceremonial attire . . . 45 40
1589 75c. Bishop's crosier 45 40

456 Gomez on Horseback

1984. 150th Birth Anniv (1986) of Maximo Gomez (leader of Cuban Revolution). Multicoloured.
1590 10c. Type **456** 10 10
1591 20c. Maximo Gomez 15 10

457 "Navidad 1984"

1984. Christmas.
1592 **457** 5c. mauve, blue and gold 10 10
1593 − 10c. blue, gold & mauve 10 10
DESIGN: 10c. "Navidad 1984" (different).

458 "The Sacrifice of the Kid" (Eligio Pichardo)

1984. Art. Multicoloured.
1594 5c. Type **458** 10 10
1595 10c. "Pumpkin Sellers" (statuette, Gaspar Mario Cruz) (vert) 10 10
1596 25c. "The Market" (Celeste Woss y Gil) 15 15
1597 50c. "Horses in a Storm" (Dario Suro) 30 25

459 Old Church, Higuey

1985. Our Lady of Altagracia's Day. Mult.
1598 5c. Type **459** 10 10
1599 10c. "Our Lady of Altagracia" (1514 painting) 15 10
1600 25c. Basilica of Our Lady of Altagracia, Higuey . . . 35 30

460 Sanchez, Durate and Mella

1985. 141st Anniv of Independence.
1601 **460** 5c. multicoloured 10 10
1602 − 10c. multicoloured . . . 15 10
1603 − 25c. multicoloured . . . 35 30

461 Gen. Antonia Duverge

1985. 141st Anniv of Azua Battle.
1604 **461** 10c. cream, red & brown 15 10

462 Santo Domingo Lighthouse, 1853   **463** Flags and Emblem

1985. 141st Anniv of Battle of Tortuguero.
1605 **462** 25c. multicoloured 35 30

1985. 25th Anniv of American Airforces Co-operation System.
1606 **463** 35c. multicoloured 50 45

464 Carlos Maria Rojas (first Governor)   **465** Table Tennis Player

1985. Centenary of Espaillat Province.
1607 **464** 10c. multicoloured . . . 10 10

1985. "MOCA 85" (Seventh National Games). Multicoloured.
1608 5c. Type **465** 10 10
1609 10c. Walking race 10 10

466 Young People of Different Races

1985. International Youth Year. Mult.
1610 5c. Type **466** 10 10
1611 25c. The Haitises 15 10
1612 35c. Mt. Duarte summit . . . 20 15
1613 2p. Mt. Duarte 90 85

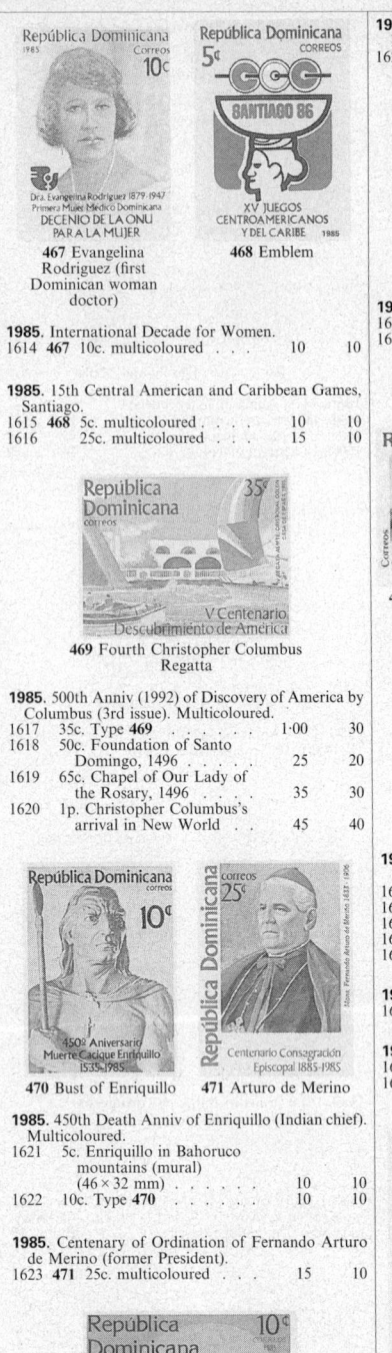

467 Evangelina Rodriguez (first Dominican woman doctor)

468 Emblem

1985. International Decade for Women.
1614 467 10c. multicoloured . . . 10 10

1985. 15th Central American and Caribbean Games, Santiago.
1615 468 5c. multicoloured . . . 10 10
1616 — 25c. multicoloured . . . 15 10

469 Fourth Christopher Columbus Regatta

1985. 500th Anniv (1992) of Discovery of America by Columbus (3rd issue). Multicoloured.
1617 35c. Type 469 . . . . . 1·00 30
1618 50c. Foundation of Santo Domingo, 1496 . . . 25 20
1619 65c. Chapel of Our Lady of the Rosary, 1496 . . . 35 30
1620 1p. Christopher Columbus's arrival in New World . . 45 40

470 Bust of Enriquillo

471 Arturo de Merino

1985. 450th Death Anniv of Enriquillo (Indian chief). Multicoloured.
1621 5c. Enriquillo in Bahoruco mountains (mural) (46 × 32 mm) 10 10
1622 10c. Type 470 . . . . . 10 10

1985. Centenary of Ordination of Fernando Arturo de Merino (former President).
1623 471 25c. multicoloured . . 15 10

472 Fruit, Candle and Holly

1985. Christmas.
1624 472 10c. multicoloured . . . 15 10
1625 — 25c. multicoloured . . . 15 10

473 Haina Harbour

1985. 25th Anniv of Inter-American Development Bank. Multicoloured.
1626 10c. Type 473 . . . . 55 15
1627 25c. Map and ratio diagram of development activities 15 10
1628 1p. Tavera-Bao-Lopez hydro-electric complex . . 45 40

474 Mirabal Sisters

1985. 25th Death Anniv of Minerva, Patria and Maria Mirabal.
1629 474 10c. multicoloured . . . 10 10

475 Tomb of Duarte, Sanchez and Mella

1986. National Independence Day.
1630 475 5c. multicoloured . . . 10 10
1631 — 10c. multicoloured . . . 10 10

476 St. Michael's Church

478 Voters, Ballot Box and Map

1986. Holy Week. Santo Domingo Churches. Multicoloured.
1632 5c. Type 476 . . . . 10 10
1633 5c. St. Andrew's Church . . 10 10
1634 10c. St. Lazarus's Church . . 10 10
1635 10c. St. Charles's Church . . 10 10
1636 10c. St. Barbara's Church . . 10 10

477 "Leonor" (schooner) and Dominican Navy Founders

1986. Navy Day.
1637 477 10c. multicoloured . . . 80 20

1986. National Elections. Multicoloured.
1638 5c. Type 478 . . . . 10 10
1639 10c. Hand dropping voting slip into ballot box . . . 30 10

479 Emblem

480 Weightlifting

1986. Creation of "Inposdom" (Dominican Postal Institute).
1640 479 10c. blue, red and gold 10 10
1641 — 25c. blue, red and silver 15 10
1642 — 50c. blue, red and black 25 20

1986. 15th Central American and Caribbean Games, Santiago. Multicoloured.
1643 10c. Type 480 . . . . 10 10
1644 25c. Gymnast on rings . . . 15 10
1645 35c. Diving 20 15
1646 50c. Show-jumping . . . 25 20

481 Ercilia Pepin

482 Fifth Christopher Columbus Regatta

1986. Writers' Birth Centenaries. Each brown and silver.
1647 5c. Type 481 . . . . . 10 10
1648 10c. Ramon Emilio Jiminez and Victor Garrido . . . 10 10

1986. 500th Anniv (1992) of Discovery of America by Columbus (4th issue). Multicoloured.
1649 25c. Type 482 . . . . . 30 10
1650 50c. Foundation of Isabela city 25 20

1651 65c. Spanish soldiers 35 30
1652 1p. Columbus before King of Spain 45 40

483 Goalkeeper saving Ball

484 Maize

1986. World Cup Football Championship, Mexico. Multicoloured.
1654 50c. Type 483 . . . . . 25 20
1655 75c. Footballer and ball . . . 40 35

1986. 2nd Caribbean Pharmacopoeia Seminar. Medicinal Plants. Multicoloured.
1656 5c. Type 484 . . . . . 10 10
1657 10c. Arnotto 10 10
1658 25c. "Momordica charantia" 15 10
1659 50c. Custard-apple 25 20

485 Town with Christmas Tree

1986. Christmas. Multicoloured.
1660 5c. Type 485 . . . . . 15 10
1661 25c. Village 15 10

486 Gomez on Horseback

488 Emblem

1986. 150th Birth Anniv of Maximo Gomez.
1662 486 10c. black and mauve . . 10 10
1663 — 25c. black and brown . . 15 10
DESIGN: 25c. Head of Gomez.

1987. 16th Pan-American Ophthalmology Congress, Santo Domingo.
1676 488 50c. red, blue & black . . 20 15

489 "Ascension of Jesus Christ" (stained glass window), St. John Bosco Church)

490 "Sorghum bicolor"

1987. Ascension Day.
1677 489 35c. multicoloured . . . 10 10

1987. Edible Plants. Multicoloured.
1678 5c. Type 490 . . . . . 10 10
1679 25c. "Maranta arundinacea" 10 10
1680 65c. "Calathea allouia" . . 20 15
1681 1p. "Voandzeia subterranea" 35 30

491 Emblem and People on Map

1987. 25th Anniv of Club Activo 20–30 in Dominican Republic.
1682 491 35c. multicoloured . . . 10 10

492 Sixth Christopher Columbus Regatta

1987. 500th Anniv (1992) of Discovery of America by Columbus (5th issue). Multicoloured.
1683 50c. Type 492 . . . . . 10 10
1684 75c. Columbus writing diary 15 10
1685 1p. Foundation of city of Santiago 20 15
1686 1p.50 Columbus and Bobadilla 30 25

493 Games Emblem

494 Jose Antonio Hungria

1987. 50th Anniv of La Vega Province Games.
1688 493 40c. multicoloured . . . 10 10

1987. Writers' Birth Anniversaries.
1689 494 10c. brown & lt brown 10 10
1690 — 25c. dp green & green 10 10
DESIGN: 25c. Joaquin Sergio Inchaustegui.

495 Baseball

496 Statue

1987. 8th National Games, San Cristobal. Multicoloured.
1691 5c. Type 495 . . . . . 10 10
1692 10c. Boxing 10 10
1693 50c. Karate 10 10

1987. 150th Birth Anniv of Fr. Francisco Xavier Billini.
1694 496 10c. deep blue and blue 10 10
1695 — 25c. green and olive . . 10 10
1696 — 75c. brown and pink . . 15 10
DESIGNS: 25c. Fr. Billini; 75c. Ana Hernandez de Billini (mother).

497 Maj. Frank Feliz and Airplane

1987. 50th Anniv of Pan-American Flight for Columbus Lighthouse Fund.
1697 497 25c. multicoloured . . . 20 10

498 Spit-roasting Pig

1987. Christmas. Multicoloured.
1699 10c. Type 498 . . . . . 10 10
1700 50c. Passengers disembarking from airplane 20 10

499 "Bromelia pinguin"

1988. Flowers. Multicoloured.
1701 50c. Type 499 . . . . . 10 10

1702	50c. "Tillandsia compacta"		
	(vert)	10	10
1703	50c. "Tillandsia fasciculata"	10	10
1704	50c. "Tillandsia hotteana"		
	(vert)	10	10

500 St. John Bosco

1988. Death Centenary of St. John Bosco (founder of Salesian Brothers). Multicoloured.

| 1705 | 10c. Type **500** | 10 | 10 |
| 1706 | 70c. Stained glass window | 15 | 10 |

501 Rainbow, Doves and Cloud

1988. 25th Anniv of Dominican Rehabilitation Association.

| 1707 | **501** 20c. multicoloured . . . | 10 | 10 |

502 Perdomo   **503** Emblem

1988. Birth Centenary of Dr. Manuel Emilio Perdomo.

| 1708 | **502** 20c. brown and flesh . . | 10 | 10 |

1988. 25th Anniv of Dominican College of Engineering and Architecture (CODIA).

| 1709 | **503** 20c. multicoloured . . . | 10 | 10 |

504 Church and Madonna and Child   **505** Flags and Juan Pablo Duarte (Dominican patriot)

1988. Centenary of Parish Church of Our Lady of the Carmelites, Duverge.

| 1710 | **504** 50c. multicoloured . . . | 10 | 10 |

1988. Mexican Independence Day. Mult.

1711	50c. Type **505**	10	10
1712	50c. Flags and Miguel		
	Hidalgo (Mexican patriot)	10	10

506 Athletics   **507** Seventh Christopher Columbus Regatta

1988. Olympic Games, Seoul. Multicoloured.

1713	50c. Type **506**	10	10
1714	70c. Table tennis	15	10
1715	1p. Judo	20	15
1716	1p.50 "Ying Yang symbol		
	and Balls" (Tete Marella)		
	(horiz)	30	25

1988. 500th Anniv of Discovery of America by Columbus (6th issue). Multicoloured.

1717	50c. Type **507**	10	10
1718	70c. Building fort at La		
	Vega Real, 1494	15	10
1719	1p.50 Bonao Fort	30	25
1720	2p. Nicolas de Ovando		
	(Governor of Hispaniola)	40	35

508 Duarte, Mella and Sanchez   **509** Parchment, Knife and Pestle and Mortar

1988. 150th Anniv of Trinitarian Rebellion.

1722	**508** 10c. silver, red and blue	10	10
1723	– 1p. multicoloured . . .	20	15
1724	– 5p. multicoloured . . .	95	90

DESIGNS: 1p. Plaza La Trinitaria; 5p. Plaza de la Independencia.

1988. 13th Pan-American and 16th Central American Congresses of Pharmacy and Biochemistry.

| 1725 | **509** 1p. multicoloured . . . | 20 | 15 |

510 "Doni Tondo" (Michelangelo)   **511** Emblem

1988. Christmas. Multicoloured.

| 1726 | 10c. Type **510** . . . . . | 10 | 10 |
| 1727 | 20c. Stained glass window | 10 | 10 |

1988. 50th Anniv of Dominican Municipal Association.

| 1728 | **511** 20c. multicoloured . . . | 10 | 10 |

512 Ana Teresa Paradas

1988. 28th Death Anniv of Ana Teresa Paradas (lawyer).

| 1729 | **512** 20c. red . . . . | 10 | 10 |

513 Birds

1989. Bicentenary of French Revolution.

| 1730 | **513** 3p. red, blue and black | 30 | 25 |

516 Battle Scene

1989. 145th Anniv of Battle of Tortuguero.

| 1737 | **516** 40c. multicoloured . . . | 70 | 25 |

517 Drug Addict

1989. Anti-drugs Campaign.

1738	**517** 10c. multicoloured . . .	10	10
1739	20c. multicoloured . . .	10	10
1740	50c. multicoloured . . .	10	10
1741	70c. multicoloured . . .	10	10
1742	1p. multicoloured . . .	10	10
1743	1p.50 multicoloured . . .	15	10
1744	2p. multicoloured . . .	20	15
1745	5p. multicoloured . . .	50	45
1746	10p. multicoloured . . .	1·00	95

518 Breast-feeding Baby   **519** Eugenio Maria de Hostos

1989. Mothers' Day.

| 1747 | **518** 20c. multicoloured . . . | 10 | 10 |

1989. 150th Birth Anniversaries. Mult.

| 1748 | 20c. Type **519** . . . . . | 10 | 10 |
| 1749 | 20c. Gen. Gregorio Luperon | 10 | 10 |

520 Baseball

1989. 50th Anniv of Baseball Minor League.

| 1750 | **520** 1p. multicoloured . . . | 10 | 10 |

521 Map and Human Organs

1989. 7th Latin American Diabetes Association Congress.

| 1751 | **521** 1p. multicoloured . . . | 10 | 10 |

522 Cohoba Artefact and Ritual Dance

1989. America. Pre-Columbian Culture. Mult.

1752	20c. Type **522**	10	10
1753	1p. Taina vessel, pounding		
	instrument and Indians		
	preparing manioc cake . .	10	10

523 Eighth Christopher Columbus Regatta   **524** Dead and Living Leaves

1989. 500th Anniv (1992) of Discovery of America by Columbus (7th issue). Multicoloured.

1754	50c. Type **523**	10	10
1755	70c. Brother Pedro de		
	Cordoba preaching to		
	Indians (horiz)	10	10
1756	1p. Columbus dividing		
	Indian lands (horiz) . . .	10	10
1757	3p. Brother Antonio		
	Montesinos giving sermon		
	(horiz)	30	25

1989. National Reafforestation Campaign. Mult.

1758	10c. Type **524**	10	10
1759	20c. Forest	10	10
1760	50c. Forest and lake . . .	10	10
1761	1p. Living tree and avenue		
	of dead trees	10	10

525 Map and Cyclist   **526** Mary and Body of Jesus

1990. 9th National Games, La Vega. Mult.

1762	10c. Type **525**	10	10
1763	20c. Map and runner . . .	10	10
1764	50c. Map and handball		
	player	10	10

1990. Holy Week. Multicoloured.

| 1765 | 20c. Type **526** . . . . . | 10 | 10 |
| 1766 | 50c. Jesus carrying cross . . | 10 | 10 |

527 Cogwheel and Workers

1990. International Labour Day.

| 1767 | **527** 1p. multicoloured . . . | 10 | 10 |

528 Avenida Mexico

1990. Urban Development. Multicoloured.

1768	10c. Type **528**	10	10
1769	20c. Avenida Nunez de		
	Caceres road tunnel . . .	10	10
1770	50c. National Library . . .	10	10
1771	1p. V Centenario Motorway	10	10

529 Penny Black   **530** "Ruins of St. Nicholas's Church, Bari"

1990. 150th Anniv of the Penny Black. Mult.

| 1772 | **529** 1p. multicoloured . . . | 10 | 10 |

1990. Children's Drawings. Multicoloured.

| 1774 | 50c. Type **530** . . . . . | 10 | 10 |
| 1775 | 50c. "House, Tostado" . . . | 10 | 10 |

531 Members' Flags   **532** Yachts (Ninth Christopher Columbus Regatta)

1990. Centenary of Organization of American States.

| 1776 | **531** 2p. multicoloured . . . | 20 | 15 |

1990. 500th Anniv (1992) of Discovery of America by Columbus (8th issue). Multicoloured.

1777	50c. Type **532**	40	10
1778	1p. Confrontation between		
	natives and sailors (horiz)	10	10
1779	2p. Meeting of Columbus		
	and Guacanagari (horiz)	20	15
1780	5p. Caonabo imprisoned by		
	Columbus (horiz)	45	30

533 Amerindians in Canoe

534 Perez Rancier

1990. America. Multicoloured.
1781 50c. Type **533** 30 10
1782 3p. Amerindian in hammock 25 15

1991. Birth Centenary of Dr. Tomas Eudoro Perez Rancier (physician).
1783 **534** 2p. black and yellow . . 20 10

535 First Official Mass in America

536 Boxing

1991. Spanish America. Multicoloured.
1784 50c. Type **535** 10 10
1785 1p. Arms (first religious orders) 10 10
1786 3p. Map of Hispaniola (first European settlement) (horiz) 30 20
1787 4p. Christopher Columbus (first viceroy and governor) 45 30

1991. 11th Pan-American Games, Havana. Multicoloured.
1788 30c. Type **536** 10 10
1789 50c. Cycling 10 10
1790 1p. Putting the shot 10 10

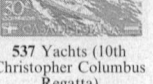

537 Yachts (10th Christopher Columbus Regatta)

538 Eye and Hands

1991. 500th Anniv (1992) of Discovery of America by Columbus (9th issue). Multicoloured.
1791 30c. Type **537** 10 10
1792 50c. Meeting of three cultures (horiz) 10 10
1793 3p. Columbus and Doctor Alvarez Chanco (horiz) 30 20
1794 4p. Enriquillo's war (horiz) 45 30

1991. Cornea Bank.
1795 **538** 3p. black and red . . . 30 20

539 "Santa Maria"

540 Meeting Emblem

1991. America. Voyages of Discovery. Mult.
1796 1p. Type **539** 20 15
1797 3p. Columbus and fleet . . 40 25

1992. 33rd Annual Meeting of Governors of Inter-American Development Bank, Santo Domingo.
1798 **540** 1p. multicoloured . . . 10 10

541 Valentin Salinero (founder)

542 Flags of Cuba, Dominican Republic and Puerto Rica, and Magnifying Glass

1992. Centenary (1991) of Order of the Apostles.
1799 **541** 1p. brown, black & blue 10 10

1992. "Espanola 92" Stamp Exhibition.
1800 **542** 3p. black, violet & red 30 20

543 First Monastery in Americas

1992. Ruins. Multicoloured.
1801 50c. Type **543** 10 10
1802 3p. First hospital in Americas 30 20

544 La Vega Cathedral and Pope

545 Yacht (11th Christopher Columbus Regatta)

1992. Visit of Pope John Paul II. Mult.
1803 50c. Type **544** 10 10
1804 3p. Santo Domingo Cathedral and Pope . . . 30 20

1992. 500th Anniv of Discovery of America by Columbus (10th issue). Multicoloured.
1805 50c. Type **545** 10 10
1806 1p. Amerindian women preparing food and Columbus (horiz) 10 10
1807 2p. Amerindians demonstrating use of tobacco to Columbus (horiz) 20 10
1808 3p. Amerindian woman and Columbus by maize field (horiz) 30 20

546 Columbus Lighthouse

547 Convention Emblem

1992.
1809 **546** 30c. multicoloured . . . 10 10
1810 1p. multicoloured . . . 10 10

1992. 23rd Pan-American Round Table Convention, Santo Domingo.
1812 **547** 1p. brown, cream & red 10 10

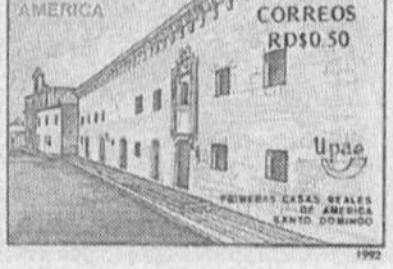

548 First Royal Palace in Americas, Santo Domingo

549 Torch Bearer

1992. America. Multicoloured.
1813 50c. Type **548** 10 10
1814 3p. First Vice-regal residence in Americas, Colon . . . 30 20

1992. 10th National Games, San Juan.
1815 **549** 30c. multicoloured . . . 10 10
1816 – 1p. multicoloured . . . 10 10
1817 – 4p. black and blue . . . 40 25
DESIGNS: 1p. Emblem of Secretary of State for Sports Education and Recreation; 4p. Judo.

550 Emblem

551 Ema Balaguer

1993. 7th Population and Housing Census.
1818 **550** 50c. blue, black & pink 10 10
1819 1p. blue, black & brown 10 10
1820 3p. blue, black & grey 30 20
1821 4p. blue, black & green 40 25

1993. Ema Balaguer (humanitarian worker) Commemoration.
1822 **551** 30c. multicoloured . . . 10 10
1823 50c. multicoloured . . . 10 10
1824 1p. multicoloured . . . 10 10

552 Emblem and Stylized Figures

1993. 50th Anniv of Santo Domingo Rotary Club. Multicoloured.
1825 30c. Type **552** 10 10
1826 1p. National flags and rotary emblem 10 10

553 Institute

1993. Inauguration of New Dominican Postal Institute Building.
1827 **553** 1p. multicoloured . . . 10 10
1828 3p. multicoloured . . . 30 20
1829 4p. multicoloured . . . 40 25
1830 5p. multicoloured . . . 50 30
1831 10p. multicoloured . . . 95 60

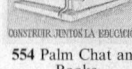

554 Palm Chat and Books

556 Chest (first university)

555 Racketball

1993. Ten Year Education Plan.
1833 **554** 1p.50 multicoloured . . 1·40 1·40

1993. 17th Central American and Caribbean Games, Ponce (Puerto Rico). Multicoloured.
1834 50c. Type **555** 10 10
1835 4p. Swimming 40 25

1993. American Firsts in Hispaniola (1st series). Multicoloured.
1836 50c. Type **556** 10 10
1837 3p. First arms conferred on American city 30 20
See also Nos. 1840 and 1882/3.

557 Hispaniolan Conure

1993. America. Endangered Animals. Mult.
1838 1p. Type **557** . . . . 1·25 95
1839 3p. Rhinoceros iguana . . . 30 20

558 Cross and Eucharist (500th anniv of first Mass)

1994. American Firsts in Hispaniola (2nd series).
1840 **558** 2p. multicoloured . . . 20 10

559 State Flag, 1946 15c. and 1944 3c. Stamps

1994. 5th National Stamp Exhibition.
1841 **559** 3p. multicoloured . . . 30 20

560 Signing of Independence Treaty (left-hand detail)

1994. 150th Anniv of Independence. Mult.
1842 2p. Type **560** 20 10
1843 2p. Signing of Independence Treaty (right-hand detail) 20 10
1844 2p. State flag 20 10
1845 2p. Soldier with young woman 20 10
1846 2p. Boy helping woman make flag 20 10
1847 3p. Revolutionaries (back view of left-hand man) . . 30 20
1848 3p. Revolutionaries (window behind men) 30 20
1849 3p. State arms 30 20
1850 3p. Revolutionaries (all turned away from door) 30 20
1851 3p. Revolutionaries with flag 30 20
Stamps of the same value were issued together, se-tenant, Nos. 1842/3, 1845/6, 1847/8 and 1850/1 forming composite designs.

561 Solenodon on Dead Wood

1994. The Haitian Solenodon. Multicoloured.
1853 1p. Type **561** 10 10
1854 1p. Solenodon amongst leaves 10 10
1855 1p. Solenodon on stony ground 10 10
1856 1p. Solenodon eating insect 10 10

562 Fusiliers behind Barricade (19 March)

563 Ballot Boxes

1994. 150th Anniversaries of Battles of 19 and 30 March. Multicoloured.
1857 2p. Type **562** 20 10
1858 2p. Battle at fort (30 March) . 20 10

1994. National Elections.
1859 **563** 2p. multicoloured 20 10

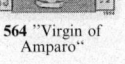

564 "Virgin of Amparo"   **565** Goalkeeper

1994. 150th Anniv of Naval Battle of Puerto Tortuguero.
1860 **564** 3p. multicoloured . . . 30 20

1994. World Cup Football Championship, U.S.A. Multicoloured.
1861 4p. Type **565** 40 25
1862 6p. Players contesting possession of ball . . . 60 40

566 Figures in Houses

1994. Ema Balguer Children's City.
1863 **566** 1p. mauve and brown . . 10 10

567 1866 Medio Real Stamp and Cancellation

1994. Stamp Day.
1864 **567** 5p. red, black & yellow . . . 45 30

568 Postal Carrier on Horseback   **571** Writing Desk and Constitution

1994. America. Postal Vehicles. Multicoloured.
1865 2p. Type **568** 20 10
1866 6p. Schooner 50 35

1994. 150th Anniv of First Constitution of Dominican Republic.
1876 **571** 3p. multicoloured 25 15

572 Flight into Egypt

1994. Christmas. International Year of the Family. Multicoloured.
1877 2p. Type **572** 20 10
1878 3p. Family 25 15

573 Ruins of St. Francis's Monastery

1994. 500th Anniv of Concepcion de la Vega.
1879 **573** 3p. multicoloured 25 15

574 Wall of La Isabela Church

1994. 500th Anniv of First Church in Dominican Republic. Multicoloured.
1880 3p. Type **574** 25 15
1881 3p. Temple of the Americas 25 15
Nos. 1880/1 were issued together, se-tenant, forming a composite design.

1994. American Firsts in Hispaniola (3rd series). As T **556**. Multicoloured.
1882 2p. First coins, 1505 . . . . . 20 10
1883 5p. Antonio Montesino (first plea for justice (in Advent sermon), 1511) 45 30

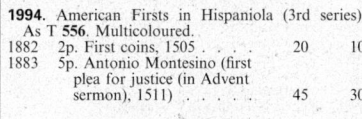

575 "Hypsirhynchus ferox"

1994. National Natural History Museum. Snakes. Multicoloured.
1884 2p. Type **575** 20 10
1885 2p. "Antillophis parvifrons" . 20 10
1886 2p. "Uromacer catesbyi" . . . 20 10
1887 2p. Bahama boa ("Epicrates striatus") 20 10
Nos. 1884/5 and 1886/7 respectively were issued together, se-tenant, each pair forming a composite design of a tree and the snakes.

576 Taekwondo

1995. Pan-American Games, Mar del Plata, Argentine Republic.
1888 **576** 4p. blue, red & black . . 35 20
1889 – 13p. green, black & yell . 1·25 80
DESIGN: 13p. Tennis.

577 Allegory of Dominican Agriculture

1995. 50th Anniv of F.A.O.
1890 **577** 4p. multicoloured . . . 35 20

578 Jose Marti, Maximo Gomez and Monte Cristi Clock Tower   **579** Emblem

1995. Centenaries.
1891 **578** 2p. brown, pink & black . 20 10
1892 – 3p. pink, black & blue . . 25 15
1893 – 4p. black and pink . . . 35 20
DESIGNS: 3p. Jose Marti on Cuban national flag

(death centenary); 4p. Gomez and Marti signing Monte Cristi manifesto.

1995. "Centrobasket" Basketball Championship, Santo Domingo.
1894 **579** 3p. blue, red & black . . . 25 15

580 "Pimenta ozua"   **581** San Souci Port

1995. Medicinal Plants. Multicoloured.
1895 2p. Type **580** 20 10
1896 2p. "Melocactus communis" . . 20 10
1897 3p. "Smilax sp." 25 15
1898 3p. "Zamia sp." 25 15

1995. Tourism. Multicoloured.
1899 2p. Type **581** 35 20
1900 5p. Barahona airport . . . 45 30
1901 6p. G. Luperon airport . . . 55 35
1902 13p. Las Americas airport . 1·25 80

582 Ruins of Jacagua Church

1995. 500th Anniv of Santiago de los Caballeros.
1903 **582** 3p. multicoloured 25 15

583 Sei Whale ("Balaenoptera borealis")

1995. Natural History Museum. Whales. Mult.
1904 3p. Type **583** 25 15
1905 3p. Humpback whales ("Megaptera novaeangliae") 25 15
1906 3p. Sperm whales ("Physeter macrocephalus") . . . 25 15
1907 3p. Cuvier's beaked whales ("Ziphius cavirostris") . . 25 15

584 Rafael Colon   **585** Cancelled 1880 2c. Stamp

1995. Singers. Multicoloured.
1908 2p. Type **584** 20 10
1909 3p. Casandra Damiron . . . 25 15

1995. Stamp Day.
1910 **585** 4p. multicoloured . . . 35 20

586 Player   **587** Anniversary Emblem

1995. Centenary of Volleyball.
1911 **586** 6p. multicoloured . . . 55 35

1995. 50th Anniv of U.N.O.
1913 **587** 2p. blue and gold . . . 20 10
1914 – 6p. multicoloured . . . 55 35
DESIGN—33 × 55 mm: 6p. Allegorical design.

588 Allegory   **589** Columbus Lighthouse

1995. 4th World Conference on Women, Peking.
1915 **588** 2p. multicoloured . . . 20 10

1995.
1916 **589** 10p. ultram, blue & blk . 90 60
1994 10p. green and silver . . 85 55
2025 10p. mauve and silver . . 75 50
2089 10p. yellow and black . . 75 50

590 Enriquillo Lake   **591** Antonio Mesa (tenor)

1995. America. Environmental Protection. Mult.
1917 2p. Type **590** 20 10
1918 6p. Mangrove plantation . . 55 35

1995. Singers. Each red and brown.
1919 2p. Type **591** 20 10
1920 2p. Susano Polanco (tenor) . 20 10
1921 2p. Julieta Otero (soprano) . 20 10

592 Cathedral

1995. Centenary of Santiago Cathedral.
1922 **592** 3p. multicoloured . . . 25 15

593 Corsair Fighter

1995. 50th Anniv of Dominican Air Force (1st issue). Multicoloured.
1923 2p. Type **593** 20 10
1924 2p. Stearman Pt-17 Kaydett bomber 20 10
1925 2p. North American T-6 Texan trainer 20 10
1926 2p. Consolidated PBY-5A Catalina amphibian . . . 20 10
1927 2p. Bristol Beaufighter fighter 20 10
1928 2p. De Havilland Mosquito bomber 20 10
1929 2p. Lockheed P-38 Lightning fighter 20 10
1930 2p. North American P-51 Mustang fighter 20 10
1931 2p. Boeing B-17 Flying Fortress bomber 20 10
1932 2p. Republic P-47 Thunderbolt fighter . . . 20 10
1933 2p. De Havilland Vampire jet fighter 20 10
1934 2p. Curtiss C-46 Commander 20 10
1935 2p. Boeing B-26 Invader . . 20 10
1936 2p. Douglas C-47 Skytrain transport 20 10
1937 2p. T-28D Trojan 20 10
1938 2p. T-33A Silverstar . . . 20 10
1939 2p. Cessna T-41D 20 10
1940 2p. T-34 Mentor 20 10
1941 2p. Cessna O-2A 20 10
1942 2p. Cessna A-37B Dragonfly fighter 20 10
See also Nos. 1958/63, 2026/31 and 2040/4.

594 Brito

596 Children

595 Yachts

1996. 50th Death Anniv of Eduardo Brito (singer).
1943 594 1p. multicoloured . . . 10   10
1944 – 2p. multicoloured . . . 20   10
1945 – 3p. black and pink . . . 25   15
DESIGNS—55 × 35 mm: 2p. Brito playing maracas.
As T 594: 3p. Brito (different).

1996. Hispaniola Cup Yachting Championship.
1946 595 5p. multicoloured . . . 45   30

1996. 50th Anniv of U.N.I.C.E.F.
1947 596 2p. black and green . . . 20   10
1948 – 4p. black and green . . . 35   20
DESIGN—4p. As T 596 but motif reversed.

597 Arturo Pallerano, Freddy Gaton and Rafael Herrera

1996. National Journalists' Day.
1949 597 5p. multicoloured . . . 45   30

598 Emblem, Astronaut and Biplane

1996. "Espamer" Spanish–Latin American and "Aviation and Space" Stamp Exhibitions, Seville, Spain.
1950 598 15p. multicoloured . . . 1·40   90

599 Judo

1996. Olympic Games, Atlanta. Each black, blue and red.
1951 599 5p. Type 599 45   30
1952 – 15p. Torchbearer . . . . . 1·40   90

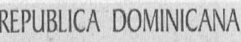

600 Greek 1896 2l. Olympic Stamp

1996. Centenary of Modern Olympic Games.
1953 600 6p. green, red & black . . 55   35
1954 – 15p. multicoloured . . . 1·40   90
DESIGN: 15p. Dominican Republic 1937 7c. Olympic stamp.

601 "Girl at Postbox"

1996. "The Post is your Friend". Winning Entries in Children's Stamp Design Competition. Mult.
1955 3p. Type 601 20   10
1956 3p. Representations of world post 20   10
1957 3p. Postal carrier on horseback delivering letter (vert) 20   10

602 Sikorsky S-55

1996. 50th Anniv of Air Force (2nd issue). Helicopters. Multicoloured.
1958 3p. Type 602 20   10
1959 3p. Sud Aviation Alouette II   20   10
1960 3p. Sud Aviation Alouette III 20   10
1961 3p. OH-6A Cayuse 20   10
1962 3p. Bell 205 A-1 20   10
1963 3p. Aerospatiale SA.365 Dauphin 2 20   10

603 Workers and Children

604 Man

1996. United Nations Decade against Drug Trafficking.
1964 603 15p. multicoloured . . . 1·40   90

1996. America. Costumes. Multicoloured.
1965 2p. Type 604 15   10
1966 6p. Woman 50   30

605 Stylized Dinghy

1996. 26th International "Sunfish" Dinghy Sailing Championships. Multicoloured.
1967 6p. Type 605 50   30
1968 10p. Sailor in dinghy (horiz) 85   55

606 1905 1p. Stamp

1996. Stamp Day.
1969 606 5p. stone and black . . . 40   25

607 Ridgway's Hawk ("Buteo ridgwayi")

608 Mirabal Sisters

1996. Birds. Multicoloured.
1970 2p. Type 607 15   10

1971 2p. Hispaniolan conure ("Aratinga chloroptera") 15   10
1972 2p. Hispaniolan amazon ("Amazona ventralis") . . 15   10
1973 2p. Rufous-breasted cuckoo ("Hyetornis rufigularis") 15   10
1974 2p. Lizard cuckoo ("Saurothera longirostris") 15   10
1975 2p. Least pauraque ("Siphonorhis brewsteri") 15   10
1976 2p. Hispaniolan emerald ("Chlorostilbon swainsonii") 15   10
1977 2p. Narrow-billed tody ("Todus angustirostris") 15   10
1978 2p. Broad-billed tody ("Todus subulatus") . . 15   10
1979 2p. Hispaniolan trogon ("Temnotrogon roseigaster) 15   10
1980 2p. Antillean piculet ("Nesoctites micromegas") 15   10
1981 2p. Hispaniolan wood- pecker ("Melanerpes striatus") 15   10
1982 2p. La Selle thrush ("Turdus swalesi") 15   10
1983 2p. Antillean siskin ("Carduelis dominicensis") 15   10
1984 2p. Palm chat ("Dulus dominicus") 15   10
1985 2p. Green-tailed ground warbler ("Microligea palustris") 15   10
1986 2p. Flat-billed vireo ("Vireo nanus") 15   10
1987 2p. White-winged ground warbler ("Xenoligea montana") 15   10
1988 2p. La Selle thrush ("Turdus swalesi dodae") 15   10
1989 2p. Chat-tanager ("Calyptophilus frugivorus tertius") . . 15   10
1990 2p. White-necked crow ("Corvus leucognaphalus") . . . 15   10
1991 2p. Chat-tanager ("Calyptophilus frugivorus neibae") . . 15   10

1996. International Day of No Violence against Women.
1992 608 5p. multicoloured . . . 40   25
1993 – 10p. multicoloured . . . 85   55

609 Leatherback Turtles ("Dermochelys coriacea")

1996. Turtles. Multicoloured.
1995 5p. Type 609 40   25
1996 5p. Loggerhead turtles ("Caretta caretta") . . 40   25
1997 5p. Indian Ocean green turtles ("Chelonia mydas") 40   25
1998 5p. Hawksbill turtles ("Eretmochelys imbricata") 40   25
Nos. 1995/8 were issued together, se-tenant, forming a composite design.

610 Youths leaping for Sun

611 Flag and Lyrics by Emilio Prudhomne

1997. National Youth Day.
1999 610 3p. multicoloured . . . 25   15

1997. National Anthem. Each black, blue and red.
2000 2p. Type 611 15   10
2001 3p. Flag and score by Jose Reyes 25   15

612 Salome Urena

613 Comet, Palm Tree and House

1997. Death Cent of Salome Urena (educationist).
2002 612 3p. multicoloured . . . 25   15

1997. Hale-Bopp Comet.
2003 613 5p. multicoloured . . . 40   25

614 Mascot with Torch and Emblem

1997. 11th National Games. Multicoloured.
2005 2p. Type 614 15   10
2006 3p. Mascot with baseball bat (26 × 36 mm) 25   15
2007 5p. Athlete breasting tape (36 × 26 mm) 40   25

615 Von Stephan

616 Blood Vessel

1997. Death Centenary of Heinrich von Stephan (founder of U.P.U).
2008 615 10p. violet, blk & red . . . 85   55

1997. 15th International Haemostasis and Thrombosis Congress.
2010 616 10p. multicoloured . . . 85   55

617 Helmet, Flowers and Epaulettes

618 Emblem

1997. Death Cent of General Gregorio Luperon.
2011 617 3p. multicoloured . . . 25   15

1997. 80th Anniv of Spanish House in Santo Domingo.
2012 618 5p. multicoloured . . . 40   25

619 First Minting

1997. Centenary of the Peso.
2013 619 2p. multicoloured . . . 15   10

620 Icon

1997. 75th Anniv of Coronation of "Our Lady of Altagracia" (icon). Multicoloured.
2014 3p. Type 620 25   15
2015 5p. Icon and church . . . 40   25

621 Dog attacking Postman on Motor Cycle

1997. America. The Postman. Multicoloured.
2016 2p. Type 621 . . . . . . 15 10
2017 6p. Dog attacking postman
delivering letter
(35½ × 37 mm) 45 30

622 Weeping Child, Mother Teresa
and Man on Donkey

1997. Int Fight against Poverty Day.
2018 **622** 5p. multicoloured . . . 40 25

623 1936 and 1899 2p. stamps

1997. Stamp Day.
2019 **623** 5p. brown and black . . 40 25

624 Buildings

1997. 50th Anniv of Central Bank.
2020 **624** 10p. multicoloured . . . 75 50

625 "Erophyllus bombifrons"

1997. Bats. Multicoloured.
2021 5p. Type 625 . . . . . 40 25
2022 5p. Cuban fruit-eating bat
("Brachyphylla nana") . . 40 25
2023 5p. Kerr's mastiff bat
("Molossus molossus") . . 40 25
2024 5p. Red bat ("Lasiurus
borealis") 40 25

626 Air Force Badge

1997. 50th Anniv of Air Force (3rd issue). Division
Badges, Multicoloured.
2026 3p. Type 626 . . . . . 25 15
2027 3p. Air Command North . . 25 15
2028 3p. Air Command 25 15
2029 3p. Rescue 25 15
2030 3p. Maintenance Command 25 15
2031 3p. Combat Squadron . . 25 15

627 Facade

1997. 50th Anniv of National Palace.
2032 **627** 10p. multicoloured . . . 75 50

628 Painting

1998. 1st Regional Symposium on Influence of Pre-
Columbian Culture on Contemporary Caribbean
Art.
2033 **628** 6p. multicoloured . . . 45 30

629 Emblem 630 Open Book

1998. 75th Anniv of American Chamber of
Commerce of Dominican Republic.
2034 **629** 10p. blue, red and gold 75 50

1998. 25th Anniv of National Book Fair and First
International Book Fair, Santo Domingo.
2035 **630** 3p. blue, red and black 25 15
2036 – 5p. blue, red and black 40 25
DESIGN—40 × 40 mm: 5p. Book Fair emblem.

631 Emblem

1998. 50th Anniv of Organization of American
States. Multicoloured.
2037 5p. Type 631 . . . . . . 40 25
2038 5p. As Type 631 but inscr
for the 50th anniv of
signing of the
Organization charter . . 40 25

632 Olive Branches, Menorah and
Star of David

1998. 50th Anniv of State of Israel.
2039 **632** 10p. ultram, bl & mve 75 50

633 General Frank Felix Miranda

1998. 50th Anniv of Air Force (4th issue). Mult.
2040 3p. Type 633 . . . . . . 25 15
2041 3p. Curtiss-Wright R-19 . . 25 15
2042 3p. Coronel Ernesto Tejeda
(portrait at right) 25 15
2043 3p. As No. 2042, but
portrait at left 25 15
2044 3p. As Type 633, but
portrait at right 25 15

634 Sundial

1998. 500th Anniv of Santo Domingo. Mult.
2045 2p. Type 634 . . . . . . 15 10

2046 3p. St. Lazarus's Church
and Hospital (horiz) . . . 25 15
2047 4p. First cathedral in the
Americas (horiz) 30 20
2048 5p. Fortress (horiz) 40 25
2049 6p. Tower of Honour
(horiz) 45 30
2050 10p. St. Nicholas of Bari's
Church and Hospital . . 75 50

635 Theatre

1998. 25th Anniv of National Theatre.
2051 **635** 10p. multicoloured . . . 75 50

636 Latin Inscription

1998. 44th Anniv of Latin Union.
2052 **636** 10p. gold, grey & black 75 50

637 Cocoa Beans and Route Map of
First American–Europe Shipment,
1502

1998. 25th Anniv of Int Cocoa Organization.
2053 **637** 10p. multicoloured . . . 75 50

638 Nino Ferrua (stamp
designer)

1998. Stamp Day.
2054 **638** 5p. multicoloured . . . 40 25

639 Pope John Paul II venerating
Portrait of Virgin Mary

1998. 20th Anniv of Pontificate of Pope John Paul II.
Multicoloured.
2055 5p. Type 639 . . . . 40 25
2056 10p. Pope John Paul II . . 75 50

640 Bay Rum

1998. Medicinal Plants. Multicoloured.
2057 3p. Type 640 . . . . . 20 10
2058 3p. "Pimenta haitiensis" . . 20 10
2059 3p. "Cymbopogon citratus" 20 10
2060 3p. Seville orange ("Citrus
aurantium") 20 10

641 Juana Saltitopa (Independence
fighter)

1998. America. Famous Women. Multicoloured.
2061 2p. Type 641 . . . . . 15 10
2062 6p. Anacaona (Indian chief) 45 30

642 Earth and 643 Statue of
Emblem Columbus

1998. International Year of the Ocean.
2063 **642** 5p. multicoloured . . . 35 25

1998. "Expofila 98" Stamp Exhibition, Santo
Domingo. 500th Anniv of Santo Domingo.
2064 **643** 5p. multicoloured . . . 35 25

644 Fernando Valerio

1998. Military Heroes. Each brown and green.
2065 3p. Type 644 . . . . . 20 10
2066 3p. Benito Moncion . . . 20 10
2067 3p. Jose Maria Cabral . . 20 10
2068 3p. Antonio Duverge . . . 20 10
2069 3p. Gregorio Luperon . . 20 10
2070 3p. Jose Salcedo 20 10
2071 3p. Fco. Salcedo 20 10
2072 3p. Gaspar Polanco . . . 20 10
2073 3p. Santiago Rodriguez . . 20 10
2074 3p. Admiral Juan Cambiaso 20 10
2075 3p. Jose Puello 20 10
2076 3p. Jose Imbert 20 10
2077 3p. Admiral Juan Acosta . . 20 10
2078 3p. Marcos Adon 20 10
2079 3p. Matias Mella 20 10
2080 3p. Francisco Sanchez . . 20 10
2081 3p. Juan Pablo Duarte . . 20 10
2082 3p. Olegario Tenares . . . 20 10
2083 3p. General Pedro Santana 20 10
2084 3p. Juan Sanchez Ramirez 20 10

645 Banknotes

1998. 150th Anniv of Paper Money.
2085 **645** 10p. multicoloured . . . 75 50

646 Spit-roasting Pig

1998. Christmas. Multicoloured.
2086 2p. Type 646 . . . . . 15 10
2087 5p. Three Wise Men on
camels 35 25

647 Couple and Human Rights Emblem

1998. 50th Anniv of Universal Declaration of Human Rights.
2088 647 10p. multicoloured . . . 75 50

648 Vega's Lyria

1998. Shells. Multicoloured.
2090 5p. Type **648** 35 25
2091 5p. Queen conch
      ("Strombus gigas") . . . 35 25
2092 5p. West Indian top shell
      ("Cittarium pica") . . . 35 25
2093 5p. Bleeding tooth ("Nerita
      peloronta") 35 25

649 Hernandez

1998. Birth Bicentenary of Gaspar Hernandez (priest and Independence fighter).
2094 649 3p. multicoloured . . . 20 10

650 Earth

1999. 10th National Congress, First International Postgraduate Lectures and 25th Anniv of Dominican Society for Endocrinology and Nutrition.
2095 650 10p. multicoloured . . . 75 50

652 Cigar and Tobacco Leaf

1999. Exports. Multicoloured.
2097 6p. Type **652** 45 30
2098 10p. Woman sewing
      (textiles) (vert) 75 50

653 Magnifying Glass over Map of Dominican Republic

1999. 155th Anniv of Office of Comptroller-General.
2099 653 2p. multicoloured . . . 15 10

654 Bosch, "The Seagull" (poem) and Main Tower, Santo Domingo

---

1999. Contemporary Writers. 90th Birthday of Pres. Juan Bosch (poet). Multicoloured.
2100 2p. Type **654** 15 10
2101 10p. Portrait of Bosch (vert) 75 50

655 "Pseudophoenix   657 Baseball
ekmanii"

656 Gen. Juan Pablo Duarte
(revolutionary)

1999. Flowers and their Fruit. Multicoloured.
2102 5p. Type **655** 35 25
2103 5p. "Murtigia colabura" . . 35 25
2104 5p. "Pouteria dominguensis" 35 25
2105 5p. "Rubus dominguensis" 35 25

1999.
2106 656 3p. multicoloured . . . 20 15

1999. 13th Pan-American Games, Winnipeg, Canada. Multicoloured.
2107 5p. Type **657** 35 25
2108 6p. Weightlifting 45 30

658 Tomas Bobadilla y Briones

1999. Leaders of the Dominican Republic. Mult.
2109 3p. Type **658** 20 15
2110 3p. Pedro Santana
      (President, 1844–48, 1853–
      56 and 1859–61) 20 15
2111 3p. Manuel Jimenez
      (President, 1848–49) . . . 20 15
2112 3p. Buenaventura Baez
      (President, 1849–53, 1856–
      58, 1865–66, 1868–74 and
      1876–78) 20 15
2113 3p. Manuel de Regla Motta
      (President, June–October
      1856) 20 15
2114 3p. Jose Desiderio Valverde
      (President, 1858–59) . . . 20 15
2115 3p. Jose Antonio Salcedo . . 20 15
2116 3p. Gaspar Polanco 20 15

659 "St. Christopher"

1999. Jose Vela Zanetti (Spanish artist) Commemoration. Multicoloured
2117 2p. Type **659** 15 10
2118 3p. "Bride and Groom" . . . 20 15
2119 5p. "Burial of Christ"
      (horiz) 35 20
2120 6p. "Cock-fighting" 45 30
2121 10p. "Self-portrait" 75 50

660 "Strataegus quadrifoveatus"

1999. Insects. Multicoloured.
2122 5p. Type **660** 35 20
2123 5p. "Anetia jaegeri"
      (butterfly) 35 20
2124 5p. "Polyancistroydes
      tettigonidae" 35 20
2125 5p. Stick insect ("Phasmidae
      aploppus") 35 20

661 Emblem and Cross-
section of Skin

1999. 50th Anniv of Dominican Dermatological Society.
2126 661 3p. multicoloured . . . 20 15

662 Maternity Clinic, Santo Domingo

1999. 900th Anniv of Sovereign Military Order of Malta. Multicoloured.
2127 2p. Type **662** 15 10
2128 10p. Maltese Cross and
      anniversary emblem
      (36½ × 38 mm) 75 50

663 Children   664 Man

1999. 50th Anniv of S.O.S. Children's Villages.
2129 663 10p. multicoloured . . . 85 55

1999. International Year of the Elderly.
2130 664 2p. black and blue . . . 20 10
2131 – 5p. black and red . . . 45 30
DESIGN: 5p. Woman.

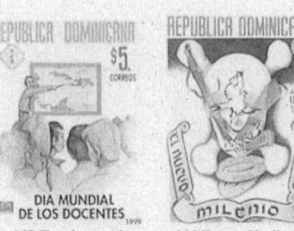

665 Teacher and   666 Dove, Skull and
Students   Crossbones, Gun,
                       Emblem and Mines

1999. Teachers' Day.
2132 665 5p. multicoloured . . . 45 30

1999. America. A New Millennium without Arms. Multicoloured.
2133 2p. Type **666** 20 10
2134 6p. Atomic cloud and
      emblem 50 30

667 Luis F. Thomen   669 Map of Caribbean
(philatelist and author)   and Whale

668 Globe and Forests

1999. Stamp Day.
2135 667 5p. drab, black and
      green 45 30

1999. New Millennium. Multicoloured.
2136 3p. Type **668** 25 10
2137 5p. Astronaut, satellite,
      computer and man 45 30

1999. 2nd Summit of African, Caribbean and Pacific Heads of State. Multicoloured.
2138 5p. Type **669** 45 30
2139 6p. Moai Statues; Easter
      Island 50 30
2140 10p. Map of Africa and lion 85 55

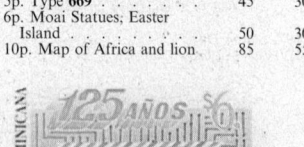

670 Means of Communication

1999. 125th Anniv of Universal Postal Union.
2141 670 6p. multicoloured . . . 50 30

671 Globe and "50"

1999. 50th Anniv of Union of Latin American Universities.
2143 671 6p. multicoloured . . . 50 30

1999. As No. 1916 but colours changed.
2144 589 10p. brown and silver . . 85 55

672 Juan Garcia (trumpeter)

1999. Classical Musicians.
2145 672 5p. blue and black 45 30
2146 – 5p. mauve and black . . . 45 30
2147 – 5p. green and black . . . 45 30
DESIGNS: 2146, Manuel Simo (saxophonist); 2147, Jose Ravelo (clarinettist).

673 Santiago and Cotui
Banknotes

1999. Centenary of Banknotes. Multicoloured.
2148 2p. Type **673** 20 10

2149 2p. San Francisco de
Macoris and La Vega
banknotes 20 10
2150 2p. San Cristobal and
Samana banknotes . . . 20 10
2151 2p. Santo Domingo and San
Pedro de Macoris
banknotes (horiz) 20 10
2152 2p. Puerto Plata and Moca
banknotes (horiz) 20 10

674 Emblem

1999. 75th Anniv of Spanish Chamber of Trade and
Industry.
2154 **674** 10p. multicoloured . . . 85 55

675 Emblem

2000. 25th Anniv of Anti-Drugs Campaign.
2155 **675** 5p. multicoloured . . . 45 30

676 Institute Facade

2000. Duartiano Institute.
2156 **676** 2p. multicoloured . . . 20 10

677 Child's Head and Emblem

2000. Prevention of Child Abuse Programme.
2157 **677** 2p. multicoloured . . . 20 10

678 Flag and San Judas Tadeo
(statue)

2000. National Police Force. Multicoloured.
2158 2p. Type **678** 20 10
2159 5p. Flag and Police emblem
(37 × 28 mm) 45 30

679 Institute Building and
Emblem

2000. 25th Anniv of Industry and Technology
Institute.
2160 **679** 2p. multicoloured . . . 20 10

---

680 Emblem

2000. 50th Anniv of Independence.
2161 **680** 3p. multicoloured . . . 25 10

681 Baseball Glove and Ball

2000. 12th National Youth Games, La Romana.
Multicoloured.
2162 2p. Type **681** 20 15
2163 3p. Boxing gloves 25 15
2164 5p. Emblem and mascot
(35 × 36 mm) 45 30

682 Violinist (Dario Suro)   **683** Building, Scales of
Justice and Hand
posting Ballot Paper

2000. Art. Multicoloured.
2165 5p. Type **682** 45 30
2166 10p. Portrait of man
(Theodore Chasseriau) . . 85 55

2000. Presidential Elections.
2167 **683** 2p. multicoloured . . . 20 15

684 Enrique de Marchena Dujarric
(pianist)

2000. Classical Musicians. Each black, orange and
brown.
2168 5p. Type **684** 45 30
2169 5p. Julio Alberto Hernandez
Camejo (pianist) 45 30
2170 5p. Ramon Diaz (flautist) . . 45 30

685 Emblem

2000. "EXPO 2000" World's Fair, Hanover.
Multicoloured.
2171 5p. Type **685** 45 30
2172 10p. Emblem 85 55

EXPRESS DELIVERY STAMPS

E 40 Biplane

1920.
E232 E **40** 10c. blue . . . . . . 5·50 1·00

E 42

1925. Inscr "ENTREGA ESPECIAL".
E247 E **42** 10c. blue . . . . . . 10·00 2·00

1927. Inscr "EXPRESO".
E250 E **42** 10c. brown . . . . . 5·00 1·00
E459 10c. green . . . . . . 2·00 70

E 123

1945.
E539 E **123** 10c. blue, red & carm 45 20

E 137 Shield, Hand and Letter

1950.
E594 E **137** 10c. red, grn & blue 45 20

E 161

1956.
E663 E **161** 25c. green 70 30

E 228 Pigeon and Letter

1967.
E995 E **228** 25c. blue 65 25

E 345 Globe, and   **E 370** Motorcycle
Pigeon carrying Letter   Messenger and Airplane

1978.
E1330 E **345** 25c. multicoloured 55 30

1979.
E1385 E **370** 25c. ultram, bl & red 55 35

E 514 Motor Cyclist

1989. Special Delivery.
E1731 E **514** 1p. multicoloured . . 10 10

E 651 Postman

1999.
E2096 E **651** 8p. multicoloured . . 60 30

OFFICIAL STAMPS

O **23** Bastion of   O **44** Columbus
27 Febuary   Lighthouse

1902.
O121 O **23** 2c. black and red . . 25 15
O122 5c. black and blue . . 40 15
O123 10c. black and green 45 20
O124 20c. black and yellow 55 35

1910. As Type O **23**, but inscr "27 DE FEBRERO
1844" and "10 DE AGOSTO 1865" at sides.
O177 O **23** 1c. black and green . 15 15
O178 2c. black and red . . 15 15
O179 5c. black and blue . . 25 20
O180 10c. black and green 55 40
O181 20c. black and yellow 1·00 55

1928.
O251 O **44** 1c. green 10 10
O252 2c. red 10 10
O253 5c. blue 15 15
O254 10c. blue 25 25
O255 20c. yellow 35 35

1931. Air. Optd **CORREO AEREO.**
O292 O **44** 10c. blue . . . . . . 12·00 10·00
O293 20c. yellow . . . . . 12·00 10·00

O **82** Columbus Lighthouse

1937. White letters and figures.
O393 O **82** 3c. violet 25 10
O394 7c. blue 35 25
O395 10c. yellow 45 35

O **88** Columbus Lighthouse

1939. Coloured letters and figures.
O409 O **88** 1c. green 10 10
O410 2c. red 10 10
O411 3c. violet 10 10
O412 5c. blue 25 15
O414 7c. blue 55 15
O415 10c. orange 40 15
O416 20c. brown . . . . . 1·00 25
O577 50c. mauve . . . . . 1·25 70
O417 50c. red . . . . . . 2·00 85
No. O417 has smaller figures of value than No.
O577.

1950. Values inscr "CENTAVOS ORO".
O578 O **88** 5c. blue 15 10
O581 7c. blue 15 10
O579 10c. yellow 35 15
O582 20c. brown 35 25
O583 50c. purple 85 55

POSTAGE DUE STAMPS

D **22**   D **110**

1901.
D117 D **22** 2c. sepia 40 10
D118 4c. sepia 50 15
D119 5c. sepia . . . . . . 1·00 20
D175 6c. sepia . . . . . . 1·40 50
D120 10c. sepia . . . . . . 1·60 20

1913.
D239 D **22** 1c. olive 40 35
D191 2c. olive 35 20
D192 4c. olive 40 15
D193 6c. olive 50 15
D194 10c. olive 70 30

1942. Size 20½ × 25½ mm.
D485 D **110** 1c. red 15 10
D486 2c. blue 15 10
D487 2c. blue 70 50
D488 4c. green 15 15
D489 6c. brown and buff . 20 10

D490		8c. orange & yellow	25	20
D491		10c. mauve and pink	35	30

1966. Size 21 × 25½ mm. Inscr larger and in white.

D492	D 110	1c. red	70	70
D493		2c. blue	70	70
D494		4c. green	1·75	1·75

REGISTRATION STAMPS

1935. De Merino stamps of 1933 surch **PRIMA VALORES DECLARADOS SERVICIO INTERIOR** and value in figures and words.

R339	–	8c. on ½c. (No. 316)	1·40	1·00
R340	–	8c. on 7c. blue	35	15
R342	56	15c. on 10c. orange	35	15
R343	–	30c. on 8c. green	1·40	50
R344	–	45c. on 20c. red	2·00	70
R345	57	70c. on 50c. olive	4·75	1·00

R 97 National Coat of Arms

R 98 National Coat of Arms

1940.

R448	R 97	8c. black and red	45	20
R449		15c. black & orange	85	30
R450		30c. black and green	1·40	15
R451		70c. black & purple	3·25	1·00

1944. Redrawn. Larger figures of value and "c" as in Type R 98.

R452	R 98	45c. black and blue	1·60	35
R453		70c. black and green	2·00	30

1953.

R454	R 98	8c. black and red	45	20
R455		10c. black and red	50	15
R456		15c. black & orange	9·50	2·40

R 155

R 221

1955. Redrawn. Arms and "c" smaller.

R646	R 155	10c. black and red	35	10
R647		10c. black and lilac	70	25
R648		15c. black & orange	1·40	1·10
R649		20c. black & orange	60	35
R650		20c. black and red	70	45
R651		30c. black and green	90	20
R652a		40c. black and green	1·25	55
R653		45c. black and blue	2·50	1·10
R654		60c. black & yellow	1·60	1·10
R655		70c. black & brown	2·50	1·40

1963. Redrawn as Type R 97.

R909		10c. black and orange	40	25
R910		20c. black and orange	55	45

1965.

R961	R 221	10c. black & lilac	35	20
R962		40c. black & yellow	1·40	85

R 282a

R 487

1973.

R1335	R 282a	10c. black & violet	35	15
R1148		20c. black & orge	70	55
R1149		40c. black & green	85	45
R1150		70c. black and blue	1·60	1·10

1986. Redrawn with figures of value and "c" smaller. Inscribed "PRIMA DE VALORES DECLARADOS". Arms in black.

R1664	R 487	20c. mauve	10	10
R1665		60c. orange	20	15
R1666		1p. blue	35	30
R1667		1p.25 pink	40	35
R1668		1p.50 red	50	45
R1669		3p. green	1·00	95
R1670		3p.50 bistre	1·25	1·10
R1671		4p. yellow	1·40	1·25
R1672		4p.50 green	1·50	1·40
R1673		5p. brown	1·75	1·50
R1674		6p. grey	2·00	1·75
R1675		6p.50 blue	2·25	2·00

R 515

1989. Inscr "PRIMA VALORES DECLARADOS". Arms in black.

R1732	R 515	20c. purple	10	10
R1733		60c. orange	10	10
R1734		1p. blue	10	10
R1735		1p.25 pink	15	10
R1736		1p.50 red	15	15

R 569

R 570

1994. Arms in black.

R1867	R 569	50c. mauve	10	10
R1868	R 570	1p. blue	10	10
R1869		1p.50 red	15	10
R1870		2p. pink	20	10
R1871		3p. blue	25	15
R1872		5p. yellow	45	30
R1873		6p. green	55	35
R1874		8p. green	70	45
R1875		10p. silver	90	60

DUBAI Pt. 19

One of the Trucial States in the Persian Gulf. Formerly used the stamps of Muscat. British control of the postal services ceased in 1963.

On 2 December 1971, Dubai and six other Gulf Sheikhdoms formed the State of the United Arab Emirates. U.A.E. issues commenced in 1973.

1963. 100 naye paise = 1 rupee.
1966. 100 dirhams = 1 riyal.

IMPERF STAMPS. Some of the following issues exist imperf from limited printings.

1 Hermit Crab

2 Shaikh Rashid bin Said

1963.

1	1	1n.p. red & blue (postage)	10	10
2	A	2n.p. brown and blue	10	10
3	B	3n.p. sepia and green	10	10
4	C	4n.p. orange and purple	10	10
5	D	5n.p. black and violet	15	10
6	E	10n.p. black and brown	15	15
7	1	15n.p. red and drab	20	15
8	A	20n.p. orange and red	30	20
9	B	25n.p. brown and green	30	20
10	C	30n.p. red and grey	30	25
11	D	35n.p. deep blue and lilac	40	25
12	E	50n.p. sepia and orange	65	35
13	F	1r. salmon and blue	1·40	60
14	G	2r. brown and bistre	3·00	1·40
15	H	3r. black and red	6·00	3·00
16	1	5r. brown and turquoise	10·00	4·75
17	2	10r. black, turq & purple	22·00	10·00
18	J	20n.p. blue & brown (air)	25	15
19	K	25n.p. purple and yellow	1·60	30
20	J	30n.p. black and red	40	15
21	K	40n.p. purple and brown	2·10	45
22	J	50n.p. red and green	75	25
23	K	60n.p. black and brown	2·00	1·00
24	J	75n.p. green and violet	3·25	60
25	K	1r. brown and yellow	5·75	90

DESIGNS (Postage)—HORIZ: A, Common cuttlefish; B, Edible snail; C, Crab; D, Turban sea urchin; E, Radish murex; F, Mosque; G, Buildings; H, Ancient wall and tower; I, Dubai view. (Air)—HORIZ: J, Peregrine falcon in flight over bridge. VERT: K, Peregrine falcon.

3 Dhows

4 Mosquito

1963. Centenary of Red Cross.

26	3	1n.p. bl, yell & red (postage)	25	25
27	–	2n.p. brown, yellow & red	25	25
28	–	3n.p. brown, orange & red	25	25
29	–	4n.p. brown, red & green	30	25
30	3	20n.p. brn, yell & red (air)	70	40
31	–	30n.p. blue, orange & red	75	50
32	–	40n.p. black, yellow & red	95	95
33	–	50n.p. violet, red & turq	2·75	1·25

DESIGNS: 2, 30n.p. First aid field post; 3, 40n.p. Camel train; 4, 50n.p. March moth.

1963. Malaria Eradication.

34	4	1n.p. brown & red (postage)	10	10
35		1n.p. brown and green	10	10
36		1n.p. red and blue	10	10
37	–	2n.p. blue and red	10	10
38	–	2n.p. red and brown	10	10
39	–	3n.p. blue and brown	10	10
40	4	30n.p. green & purple (air)	25	15
41	–	40n.p. grey and red	35	25
42	–	70n.p. yellow and purple	70	40

DESIGNS: 2, 40n.p. Mosquito and snake emblem; 3, 70n.p. Mosquitoes and swamp.

5 Ears of Wheat

7 Scout Gymnastics

6 U.S. Seal and Pres. Kennedy

1963. Air. Freedom from Hunger.

43	5	30n.p. brown and violet	25	10
44	–	40n.p. olive and red	35	15
45	–	70n.p. orange and green	70	65
46	–	1r. blue and brown	95	50

DESIGNS: 40n.p. Palm and campaign emblem; 70n.p. Emblem within hands; 1r. Woman bearing basket of fruit.

1964. Air. Pres. Kennedy Memorial Issue.

47	6	75n.p. black & green on grn	75	50
48		1r. black & brown on buff	1·10	75
49		1¼r. black & red on grey	1·60	95

1964. World Scout Jamboree, Marathon (1963).

50	7	1n.p. bistre & brown (postage)	10	10
51	–	2n.p. brown and red	10	10
52	–	3n.p. brown and blue	10	10
53	–	4n.p. blue and mauve	10	10
54	–	5n.p. turquoise and blue	10	10
55	7	20n.p. brown & green (air)	25	15
56	–	30n.p. brown and violet	35	20
57	–	40n.p. green and blue	55	25
58	–	70n.p. grey and green	70	40
59	–	1r. red and blue	1·25	65

DESIGNS: 2, 30n.p. Bugler; 3, 40n.p. Wolf cubs; 4, 70n.p. Scouts on parade; 5n.p., 1r. Scouts with standard.

1964. Nos. 27/8 surch.

59b		20n.p. on 2n.p. brown, yellow and red	18·00	
59c		30n.p. on 3n.p. brown, orange and red	18·00	

8 Spacecraft

1964. Air. "Honouring Astronauts". Multicoloured.

60		1n.p. "Atlas" rocket (vert)	10	10
61		2n.p. "Mercury" capsule (vert)	10	10
62		3n.p. Type 8	10	10
63		4n.p. Two spacecraft	10	10
64		5n.p. As No. 60	10	10
65		1r. As No. 61	65	45
66		1½r. Type 8	95	60
67		2r. As No. 63	1·60	95

9 Globe, New York and Dubai Harbours

1964. New York World's Fair.

68	9	1n.p. red & blue (postage)	25	10
69	–	2n.p. blue, red and mauve	10	10
70	9	3n.p. green and brown	25	10
71	–	4n.p. red, green & turquoise	10	10
72	9	5n.p. violet, olive & green	25	10
73	–	10n.p. black, brown & red	10	10
74	–	75n.p. black, grn & bl (air)	90	45
75	–	2r. ochre, turquoise & brn	1·75	90
76	–	3r. orange, turquoise & green	2·25	1·25

DESIGNS: 2, 4, 10n.p. New York skyline and Dubai hotel; 75n.p., 2, 3r. Statue of Liberty, New York, and "Rigorous" (tug), Dubai.

10 Flame of Freedom and Scales of Justice

1964. Air. 15th Anniv of Human Rights Declaration. Flame in red.

77	10	35n.p. brown and blue	25	10
78		50n.p. green and blue	45	25
79		1r. black and turquoise	85	40
80		3r. ultramarine and blue	2·25	90

11 Shaikh Rashid bin Said and View of Dubai

1964.

81	11	10n.p. olive, red & brown (postage)	20	10
82	A	20n.p. brown, red & green	35	10
83	11	30n.p. black, red & blue	35	15
84	A	40n.p. blue, red & cerise	45	25
85	B	1r. olive, red & brn (air)	1·00	45
86	C	2r. brown, red & green	2·25	95
87	B	3r. black, red and blue	3·50	1·60
88	C	5r. blue, red and cerise	5·50	3·75

SCENES: A, Waterfront; B, Waterside buildings; C, Harbour.

1964. Air. Winter Olympic Games, Innsbruck. Nos. 55/9 optd with Olympic Rings, Games Emblem and **INNSBRUCK 1964**.

89	7	20n.p. brown and green	40	40
90	–	30n.p. brown and violet	55	50
91	–	40n.p. green and blue	75	65
92	–	70n.p. grey and green	1·10	1·00
93	–	1r. red and blue	2·25	1·75

1964. Air. 48th Birth Anniv of Pres. Kennedy. Optd **MAY 29** (late President's birthday).

94	6	75n.p. blk & grn on grn	1·25	1·25
95		1r. black & brown on buff	2·25	1·90
96		1¼r. black and red on grey	2·75	2·50

1964. Air. Anti-T.B. Campaign. Optd **ANTI TUBERCULOSE** in English and Arabic, and Cross of Lorraine. Perf or roul.

101	3	20n.p. brown, yell & red	3·25	3·25
102	–	30n.p. blue, orange & red	3·25	3·25
103	–	40n.p. black, yellow & red	3·25	3·25
104	–	50n.p. violet, red & turq	3·25	3·25

15 Gymnastics

1964. Olympic Games, Tokyo.

105	15	1n.p. brown and olive	10	10
106	–	2n.p. sepia & turquoise	10	10
107	–	3n.p. blue and brown	10	10
108	–	4n.p. violet and yellow	10	10
109	–	5n.p. ochre and slate	10	10
110	–	10n.p. blue and buff	15	15
111	–	20n.p. olive and red	25	15
112	–	30n.p. blue and yellow	50	25
113	–	40n.p. green and buff	85	50
114	–	1r. purple and blue	2·25	1·25

DESIGNS: 2n.p. to 1r. Various gymnastic exercises as Type **12**, each with portrait of Ruler.

1964. Air. 19th Anniv of U.N. Nos. 43/6 optd **UNO 19th ANNIVERSARY** in English and Arabic.

115	5	30n.p. brown and violet	65	40
116	–	40n.p. olive and red	1·25	80
117	–	70n.p. orange and green	1·75	1·25
118	–	1r. blue and brown	3·00	1·90

17 Shaikh Rashid and Shaikh Ahmad of Qatar

1964. "Educational Progress". Portraits in black; torch orange.

119	17	5n.p. purple (postage)	15	10
120		10n.p. red	15	10
121		15n.p. blue	20	10
122	–	20n.p. olive	25	15
123	–	30n.p. red (air)	90	45
124	–	40n.p. brown	2·00	75
125	–	50n.p. blue	2·75	90
126	–	1r. green	3·75	1·50

DESIGNS: 20, 30, 40n.p. Shaikh Rashid and Shaikh Abdullah of Kuwait; 50n.p., 1r. Shaikh Rashid and Pres. Nasser of Egypt.

1964. Air. Outer Space Achievements, 1964. Optd **OUTER SPACE ACHIEVEMENTS 1964** in English and Arabic, **RANGER 7** and space capsule motif.

127	1r. multicoloured (No. 65)	2·50	2·50
128	1½r. multicoloured (No. 66)	2·50	2·50
129	2r. multicoloured (No. 67)	2·50	2·50

19 Globe and Rockets

1964. Space Achievements. Unissued stamps surch as T **19**. Multicoloured.

130	10n.p. on 75n.p. "Man on Moon" (25 × 78 mm)	2·50	2·50
131	20n.p. on 1r.50 Type **19**	3·25	3·25
132	30n.p. on 2r. "Universe" (25 × 78 mm)	3·25	3·25

1964. Air. 1st Death Anniv of Pres. J. Kennedy. As No. 47 with colours changed, optd **22 NOVEMBER**.

133	6	75n.p. black and green	8·50	6·25

21 Telephone Handset

1966. Opening of Dubai Automatic Telephone Exchange.

134	21	10n.p. brn & grn (postage)	10	10
135		15n.p. red and plum	20	10
136		25n.p. green and blue	25	10
137	–	40n.p. blue & grn (air)	35	20
138	–	60n.p. orange and sepia	80	35
139	–	75n.p. violet and black	90	55
140	–	2r. green and red	3·25	2·10

DESIGN: Nos. 137/40, As Type **21** but showing telephone dial.

22 Sir Winston Churchill and Catafalque

1966. Churchill Commemoration. (a) Postage.

142	22	1r. black and violet	40	30
143		1r.50 black and olive	65	30
144		3r. black and blue	1·50	1·10
145		4r. black and red	2·50	1·90

(b) Air. Nos. 142/5 optd **AIR MAIL** in English and Arabic and with black borders.

147	22	1r. black and violet	40	30
148		1r.50 black and olive	65	50
149		3r. black and blue	1·50	1·10
150		4r. black and red	2·50	1·90

23 Ruler's Palace **24** Bridge

1966.

152	23	5n.p. brown and blue	10	10
153		10n.p. black and orange	10	10
154		15n.p. blue and brown	15	10
155	A	20n.p. blue and brown	20	15
156		25n.p. red and blue	20	15
157	B	35n.p. violet and green	30	20
158		40n.p. turquoise & blue	45	25
159	24	60n.p. green and red	60	25
160		1r. ultramarine and blue	95	50
161	C	1r.25 brown and black	1·25	85
162	D	1r.50 purple and green	2·10	1·10
163		3r. brown and violet	4·00	2·10
164	E	5r. red	6·75	5·25
165		10r. blue	15·00	11·00

DESIGNS—HORIZ: (28 × 21 mm): A, Waterfront, Dubai; B, Bridge and dhow. As Type **24**: C, Minaret (Ruler's portrait on right); D, Fort Dubai. VERT: (32½ × 42½ mm): E, Shaikh Rashid bin Said.

25 Oil Rig **26** "Tasman" (oil rig)

1966. Air. Oil Exploration. (a) "Land" series as T **25**.

166	–	5n.p. black and lilac	20	10
167	–	15n.p. black and bistre	35	15
168	–	25n.p. black and blue	55	30
169	–	35n.p. black and red	70	35
170	–	50n.p. black and brown	1·00	50
171	25	70n.p. black and red	2·25	1·10

DESIGNS—HORIZ: 5n.p. Map of Dubai; 15n.p. Surveying; 25n.p. Dubai Petroleum Company building; 35n.p. Oil drilling. VERT: 50n.p. Surveying with level.

(b) "Sea" series as T **26**.

173	26	10n.p. purple and blue	20	10
174	–	20n.p. mauve and green	30	10
175	26	30n.p. brown and green	55	20
176	–	40n.p. lilac and agate	55	15
177	26	50n.p. blue and olive	85	20
178	–	60n.p. blue and violet	95	35
179	26	75n.p. green and brown	1·50	50
180	–	1r. green and blue	1·75	70

DESIGN: 20, 40, 60n.p. and 1r. Ocean well-head.

27 Rulers of Gulf Arab States (⅔-size illustration)

1966. Gulf Arab States Summit Conference.

182	27	35p. multicoloured	85	50
183		60p. multicoloured	2·25	1·40
184		150p. multicoloured	4·50	3·50

28 Jules Rimet Cup

1966. World Cup Football Championship. Multicoloured.

185	40d. Type **28**	35	15
186	60d. Various football scenes	45	25
187	1r. Various football scenes	70	35
188	1r.25 Various football scenes	90	45
189	3r. Wembley Stadium, London	1·40	1·10

1966. England's World Cup Victory. Nos. 185/9 optd **ENGLAND WINNERS**.

191	28	40d. multicoloured	35	15
192	–	60d. multicoloured	45	25
193	–	1r. multicoloured	70	35
194	–	1r.25 multicoloured	90	45
195	–	3r. multicoloured	1·40	1·10

29 Rulers of Dubai and Kuwait, and I.C.Y. Emblem

1966. International Co-operation Year (1965). Currency expressed in rupees.

197	29	1r. brown and green	1·00	50
198	A	1r. green and brown	1·00	50
199	B	1r. blue and violet	1·00	50
200	C	1r. blue and violet	1·00	50
201	D	1r. turquoise and red	1·00	50
202	E	1r. turquoise and red	1·00	50
203	F	1r. violet and blue	1·00	50
204	G	1r. violet and blue	1·00	50
205	H	1r. red and turquoise	1·00	50
206	I	1r. red and turquoise	1·00	50

HEADS OF STATE and POLITICAL LEADERS (Ruler of Dubai and): A, Pres. John F. Kennedy. B, Prime Minister Harold Wilson; C, Pres. Helou of the Lebanon; D, Pres. De Gaulle; E, Pres. Nasser; F, Pope Paul VI; G, Ruler of Bahrain; H, Pres. Lyndon Johnson; I, Ruler of Qatar.

30 "Gemini" Capsules manoeuvring

1966. "Gemini" Space Rendezvous. Mult.

208	35d. Type **30**	40	15
209	40d. "Gemini" capsules linked	40	15
210	60d. "Gemini" capsules separating	50	25
211	1r. Schirra and Stafford in "Gemini 6"	90	40
212	1r.25 "Gemini" orbits	1·25	65
213	3r. Borman and Lovell in "Gemini 7"	2·00	1·25

1967. Nos. 197/206 surch **Riyal** in English and Arabic and bars.

215	29	1r. on 1r.	1·10	65
216	A	1r. on 1r.	1·10	65
217	B	1r. on 1r.	1·10	65
218	C	1r. on 1r.	1·10	65
219	D	1r. on 1r.	1·10	65
220	E	1r. on 1r.	1·10	65
221	F	1r. on 1r.	1·10	65
222	G	1r. on 1r.	1·10	65
223	H	1r. on 1r.	1·10	65
224	I	1r. on 1r.	1·10	65

1967. Gemini Flight Success. Nos. 208/13 optd **SUCCESSFUL END OF GEMINI FLIGHT**.

226	30	35d. multicoloured	45	20
227	–	40d. multicoloured	45	20
228	–	60d. multicoloured	50	25
229	–	1r. multicoloured	90	40
230	–	1r.25 multicoloured	1·25	65
231	–	3r. multicoloured	2·00	1·25

1967. Nos. 152/61, 163/5 with currency names changed by overprinting in English and Arabic (except Nos. 244/5 which have the currency name in Arabic only).

233	23	5d. on 5n.p.	20	10
234		10d. on 10n.p.	20	10
235		15d. on 15n.p.	30	15
236	A	20d. on 20n.p.	45	20
237		25d. on 25n.p.	50	20
238	B	35d. on 35n.p.	60	20
239		40d. on 40n.p.	80	25
240	24	60d. on 60n.p.	1·25	30
241		1r. on 1r.	1·90	45
242	C	1r.25 on 1r.25	3·50	90
243	D	3r. on 3r.	6·00	2·50
244	E	5r. on 5r.	11·00	5·00
245		10r. on 10r.	17·00	10·00

37 "The Moving Finger writes..."

1967. Rubaiyat of Omar Khayyam. Mult.

246	60d. Type **37**	1·10	40
247	60d. "Here with a Loaf of Bread..."	1·10	40
248	60d. "So, while the Vessels..."	1·10	40
249	60d. "Myself when young..."	1·10	40
250	60d. "One Moment in Annihilation's Waste..."	1·10	40
251	60d. "And strange to tell..."	1·10	40

38 "The Straw Hat" (Rubens)

1967. Paintings. Multicoloured.

253	1r. Type **38**	1·60	40
254	1r. "Thomas, Earl of Arundel" (Rubens)	1·60	40
255	1r. "A peasant boy leaning on a sill" (Murillo)	1·60	40

See also Nos. 273/5.

39 Ruler and Lanner Falcon **40** "Bayan" (dhow)

1967.

257	39	5d. red and orange	60	30
258		10d. sepia and green	60	25
259		20d. purple and blue	75	25
260		35d. turquoise & mauve	1·00	35
261		60d. blue and green	2·00	55
262		1r. green and purple	2·75	1·10
263	40	1r.25 purple and blue	2·75	55
264		3r. purple and blue	3·25	1·60
265		5r. violet and green	6·75	3·25
266		10r. green and mauve	10·00	6·00

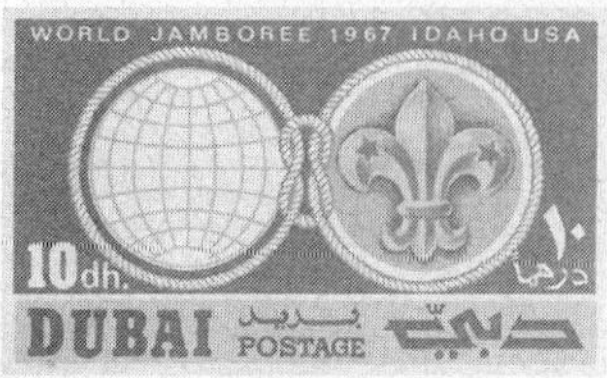

41 Globe and Scout Badge

1967. World Scout Jamboree, Idaho. Mult.

267	10d. Type **41**	35	15
268	20d. Dubai scout and dromedaries	70	20
269	35d. Bugler	90	25
270	60d. Jamboree emblem and U.S. flags	1·60	30
271	1r. Lord Baden-Powell	2·25	60
272	1r.25 Idaho on U.S. Map	3·00	1·25

1967. Goya's Paintings in National Gallery, London. As T **38**. Multicoloured.

273	1r. "Dr. Peral"	1·60	45
274	1r. "Dona Isabel Cobos de Porcel"	1·60	45
275	1r. "Duke of Wellington"	1·60	45

42 Kaiser-i-Hind ("Teinopalpus imperialis")

1968. Butterflies and Moths. Multicoloured.

277	60d. Type **42**	1·60	25
278	60d. "Erasmia pulchella"	1·60	25
279	60d. Gaudy baron ("Euthalia indica")	1·60	25
280	60d. Atlas moth ("Attacus atlas")	1·60	25
281	60d. "Dysphania militaris"	1·60	25
282	60d. "Neochera butleri"	1·60	25
283	60d. African monarch ("Danaus chrysippus")	1·60	25
284	60d. Chestnut tiger ("Danaus tytia")	1·60	25

43 "Madonna and Child" (Ferruzi)

1968. Arab Mothers' Day. Multicoloured.
285	60d. "Games in the Park" (Zandomeneghi)	40	25
286	1r. Type **43**	65	35
287	1r.25 "Mrs Cockburn and Children" (Reynolds) (wrongly inscr "Cookburn")	1·25	60
288	3r. "Self-portrait with Daughter" (Vigee-Lebrun)	1·90	1·10

44 "Althea rosea"

1968. Flowers. Multicoloured.
289	60d. Type **44**	1·60	25
290	60d. "Geranium lancastriense"	1·60	25
291	60d. "Catharanthus roseus"	1·60	25
292	60d. "Convolvulus minor"	1·60	25
293	60d. "Opuntia"	1·60	25
294	60d. "Gaillardia aristata"	1·60	25
295	60d. "Heliopsis"	1·60	25
296	60d. "Centaurea moschata"	1·60	25

45 Running

1968. Olympic Games, Mexico. Multicoloured.
297	15d. Type **45**	70	10
298	20d. Swimming	75	10
299	25d. Boxing	1·25	15
300	3d. Water-polo	1·40	20
301	40d. High jump	1·75	20
302	60d. Gymnastics	2·50	30
303	1r. Football	3·50	40
304	1r.25 Fencing	4·75	50

46 "Young Girl with Kitten" (Perronneau)

1968. Children's Day. Multicoloured.
306	60d. "Two Boys with Mastiff" (Goya)	50	15
307	1r. Type **46**	80	30
308	1r.25 "Soap Bubbles" (Manet)	1·25	35
309	3r. "The Fluyder Boys" (Lawrence)	2·00	60

47 Common Pheasant

1968. Arabian Gulf Birds. Multicoloured.
310	60d. Type **47**	1·90	20
311	60d. Red-collared dove ("Turtle Dove")	1·90	20
312	60d. Western red-footed falcon ("Red-footed flaca")	1·90	20
313	60d. European bee eater ("Bee-eater")	1·90	20
314	60d. Hoopoe	1·90	20
315	60d. Great egret ("Common Egret")	1·90	20
316	60d. Little terns	1·90	20
317	60d. Lesser black-backed gulls	1·90	20

48 "Bamora" (freighter), 1914

1969. 60th Anniv of Dubai Postal Service. Multicoloured.
318	25d. Type **48**	30	10
319	35d. De Havilland D.H.66 Hercules airplane, 1930	40	10
320	60d. "Sirdhana" (liner), 1947	80	20
321	1r. Armstrong Whitworth Atalanta airplane, 1938	80	45
322	1r.25 "Chandpara" (freighter), 1949	1·25	60
323	3r. Short Sunderland flying boat, 1943	1·50	80

49 "Madonna and Child" (Bartolome Murillo)

1969. Arab Mothers' Day. Multicoloured.
325	60d. Type **49**	60	20
326	1r. "Madonna with Rose" (Francesco Mozzola (Parmigianino))	1·10	30
327	1r.25 "Mother and Children" (Peter Paul Rubens)	1·50	60
328	3r. "Campori Madonna" (Antonio Correggio)	3·50	90
No. 326 wrongly inscribed "Mazzuoli".

50 Porkfish

1969. Fishes. Multicoloured.
329	60d. Type **50**	1·25	25
330	60d. Greasy ("Spotted") grouper	1·25	25
331	60d. Diamond fingerfish ("Moonfish")	1·25	25
332	60d. Striped sweetlips	1·25	25
333	60d. Blue-ringed angelfish ("Blue angel")	1·25	25
334	60d. Roundel ("Texas") skate	1·25	25
335	60d. Black-backed ("Striped") butterflyfish	1·25	25
336	60d. Emperor ("Imperial") angelfish	1·25	25

51 Burton, Doughty, Burckhardt, Thesiger and Map

1969. Explorers of Arabia.
337	51	25d. brown and green	70	20
338		60d. blue and brown	1·25	35
339		1r. green and blue	2·50	50
340		1r.25 black and red	3·25	1·25

52 Underwater Storage Tank Construction

1969. Oil Industry. Multicoloured.
341	5d. Type **52**	20	15
342	20d. Floating-out storage tank	45	15
343	35d. Underwater tank in operation	85	45
344	60d. Ruler, oil rig and monument	1·75	60
345	1r. Fateh marine oilfield	2·40	90

53 Astronauts on Moon

1969. 1st Man on the Moon. Multicoloured.
346	60d. Type **53** (postage)	50	25
347	1r. Astronaut and ladder	65	25
348	1r.25 Astronauts planting U.S. flag on Moon (air)	85	35
No. 348 is horiz, size 62 × 38 mm.

54 "Weather Reporter" launching Radio-Sonde and Handley Page Hastings Weather Reconnaissance Airplane

1970. World Meteorological Day. Mult.
349	60d. Type **54**	45	15
350	1r. Kew-type radio-sonde and dish aerial	65	30
351	1r.25 "Tiros" satellite and rocket	80	40
352	3r. "Ariel" satellite and rocket	1·50	90

55 New Headquarters Building

1970. New U.P.U. Headquarters Building, Berne. Multicoloured.
353	5d. Type **55**	25	10
354	60d. U.P.U. Monument, Berne	1·00	25

56 Charles Dickens

1970. Death Cent of Charles Dickens. Mult.
355	60d. Type **56**	35	15
356	1r. Signature, quill and London sky-line (horiz)	70	35
357	1r.25 Dickens and Victorian street	90	70
358	3r. Dickens and books (horiz)	1·75	1·40

57 "The Graham Children" (Hogarth)

1970. Children's Day. Multicoloured.
359	35d. Type **57**	25	10
360	60d. "Caroline Murat and Children" (Gerard) (vert)	55	20
361	1r. "Napoleon as Uncle" (Ducis)	1·00	40

58 Shaikh Rashid

1970. Multicoloured.
362	5d. Type **58**	15	15
363	10d. Dhow building (horiz)	25	10
364	20d. Al Maktum Bridge (horiz)	45	15
365	35d. Great Mosque	50	10
366	60d. Dubai National Bank (horiz)	85	15
367	1r. International airport (horiz)	1·75	25
368	1r.25 Harbour project (horiz)	2·50	65
369	3r. Hospital (horiz)	3·50	1·40
370	5r. Trade school (horiz)	5·25	2·75
371	10r. Television and "Intelsat 4"	9·00	5·00
The riyal values are larger, 40 × 25 or 25 × 40 mm.

59 Terminal Building and Control Tower

1971. Opening of Dubai International Airport. Multicoloured.
372	1r. Type **59**	1·90	1·25
373	1r.25 Airport entrance	2·40	1·50

60 Telecommunications Map and Satellites

1971. Outer Space Telecommunications Congress, Paris. Multicoloured.
374	60d. Type **60** (postage)	40	15
375	1r. Rocket and "Intelsat 4" (air)	55	30
376	5r. Eiffel Tower and Goonhilly aerial	2·00	1·75

61 Scout Badge, Fan and Map   **62** Albrecht Durer

1971. 13th World Scout Jamboree, Asagiri (Japan). Multicoloured.
377	60d. Type **61**	35	15
378	1r. Canoeing	60	30
379	1r.25 Rock-climbing	75	55
380	3r. Scouts around camp-fire (horiz)	1·50	1·25

1971. Famous People (1st issue). Mult.
381	60d. Type **62** (postage)	25	10
382	1r. Sir Isaac Newton (air)	65	30
383	1r.25 Avicenna	90	45
384	3r. Voltaire	1·40	75
See also Nos. 388/91.

63 Boy in Meadow

1971. 25th Anniv of U.N.I.C.E.F. Mult.

385	60d. Type **63** (postage)	25	15
386	5r. Children with toys (horiz)	1·75	75
387	1r. Mother and children (air)	35	15

1972. Famous People (2nd issue). As T **62**. Multicoloured.

388	10d. Leonardo da Vinci (postage)	10	10
389	35d. Beethoven	30	15
390	75d. Khalil Gibran (poet) (air)	30	20
391	5r. Charles de Gaulle	2·75	2·00

65 Nurse supervising children

1972. Air. World Health Day. Multicoloured.

392	75d. Type **65**	70	20
393	1r.25 Doctor treating baby (horiz)	1·50	70

67 Gymnastics

1972. Olympic Games, Munich. Multicoloured.

399	35d. Type **67** (postage)	25	10
400	40d. Fencing	45	10
401	65d. Hockey	65	20
402	75d. Water-polo (air)	90	25
403	1r. Horse-jumping	1·10	35
404	1r.25 Athletics	1·50	60

POSTAGE DUE STAMPS

1963. Designs as T **1** but inscr "DUE".

D26	L	1n.p. red and grey	20	20
D27	M	2n.p. blue and bistre	20	20
D28	N	3n.p. green and red	20	20
D29	L	4n.p. red and green	20	20
D30	M	5n.p. black and red	20	20
D31	N	10n.p. violet and olive	25	25
D32	L	15n.p. red and blue	85	55
D33	M	25n.p. green & brown	1·90	1·40
D34	N	35n.p. orange and blue	4·25	2·75

DESIGNS—HORIZ: L, Common European cockle; M, Common blue mussel; N, Portuguese oyster.

D **66** Shaikh Rashid

1972.

D394	D **66**	5d. grey, blue & brn	55	60
D395		10d. brn, ochre & bl	80	90
D396		20d. brn, red and blue	1·50	1·60
D397		30d. violet, lilac & blk	2·00	2·25
D398		50d. brn, ochre & pur	4·25	4·50

DUNGARPUR Pt. 1

A state of Rajasthan. Now uses Indian stamps.

12 pies = 1 anna; 16 annas = 1 rupee.

1 State Arms

2 Maharawal Lakshman Singh

1933.

1	**1**	¼a. yellow	–	£150
2		¼a. red	–	£425
3		¼a. brown	–	£275
4		1a. blue	–	£120
5		1a. red	–	£1400
6		1a.3p. mauve	–	£180
7		2a. green	–	£250
8		4a. red	–	£450

1932. T **2** (various frames).

9	**2**	¼a. orange	£750	60·00
10		½a. red	£200	45·00
11		1a. blue	£200	35·00
12		1a.3p. mauve	£750	£170
13		1¼a. violet	£800	£170
14		2a. green	£950	£325
15		4a. brown	£750	£140

DUTTIA (DATIA) Pt. 1

A state of Central India. Now uses Indian stamps.

12 pies = 1 anna; 16 annas = 1 rupee.

2 (½a.) Ganesh

3 (4a.) Ganesh

1894?. Imperf.

1	**2**	½a. black on green	£7000
2a		2a. blue on yellow	£2250

Nos. 1/2a are as Type **2**, but have rosettes in lower corners.

1896. Imperf.

4	**3**	¼a. black on orange	£3000
5		½a. black on green	£3500
6		2a. black on yellow	£1900
7		4a. black on red	£1300

Stamps of Type **3** come with the circular handstamp as shown on Type **2**. Examples of Nos. 4/5 without handstamp are worth slightly less than the prices quoted.

1896. Imperf.

8b	**2**	½a. black on green	18·00	£180
3		1a. red	£2250	£2500
9		1a. black	70·00	£200
10		2a. black on yellow	24·00	£190
11		4a. black on red	20·00	£160

4 (½a.)

5 (¼a.)

1897. Imperf.

12	**4**	½a. black on green	70·00	£400
13		1a. black	£140	
14		2a. black on yellow	80·00	
15		4a. black on red	75·00	

1899. Imperf, roul or perf.

16c	**5**	¼a. red	3·75	15·00
38		¼a. blue	2·75	10·00
37		¼a. black	4·00	19·00
17		½a. black on green	2·50	15·00
30		½a. green	5·50	20·00
35		½a. blue	3·25	14·00
39		½a. pink	3·00	15·00
18		1a. black	2·75	15·00
31		1a. purple	5·00	22·00
36		1a. pink	3·00	16·00
19b		2a. black on yellow	2·50	17·00
32		2a. brown	13·00	26·00
33		2a. lilac	5·00	25·00
20		4a. black on red	3·00	16·00
34		4a. brown	75·00	

INDEX

Notes

Notes